...K & VANS

& TRUCKS

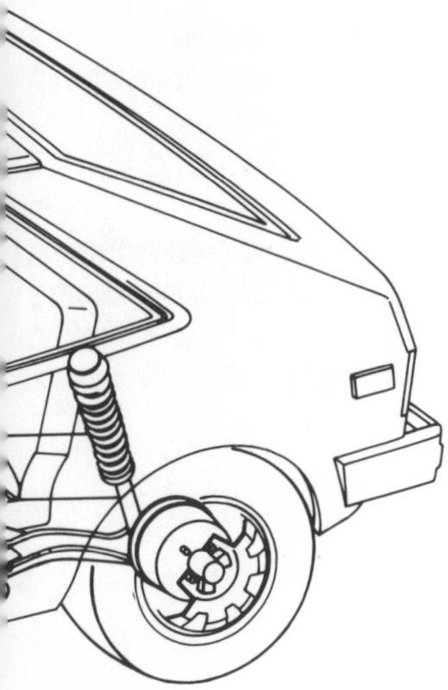

PREFACE

This is the 1986 edition of Mitchell Information Services Transmission Service and Repair Manual. This book, like the many Mitchell publications which have preceded it, represents our commitment to professionalism. in the automotive service market.

The automotive industry advances every year, and Mitchell Information Services pledges to advance and improve its products as we maintain the quality and usefulness of all Mitchell publications.

We cordially acknowledge the good will and mutual goals that exist in the automotive business, and it is in this spirit that we thank the automotive manufacturers, distributors, dealers and the entire automotive industry for their fine cooperation and assistance which have made this publication possible.

MITCHELL®

1986 EDITION TRANSMISSION SERVICE & REPAIR

DOMESTIC CARS, LIGHT TRUCKS & VANS

IMPORTED CARS & TRUCKS

MANUALS FOR THE AUTOMOTIVE PROFESSIONAL

Published By:
MITCHELL INFORMATION SERVICES, INC.
A Cordura Company
P.O. BOX 26260
SAN DIEGO, CA 92126

ISBN 0-8470-1203-4

MITCHELL®
information services inc.
a Cordura Company

PUBLISHER
Barry A. Norton, President

SALES
James E. Lown, Vice President

PRODUCT DEVELOPMENT & PLANNING
Dennis L. Bailey, Director

EDITORIAL
Vice President
Editor-in-Chief
Kenneth A. Young

Managing Editor
Daniel M. Kelley

Assistant Managing Editors
Daryl F. Visser
Thomas G. Meyer

Art Director
Eloise S. Stiverson

Detroit Editors
Lynn D. Meeker
Andy Henry

Coordinating Editors
Daniel D. Fleming
David L. Skora
Eddie Santangelo

ACKNOWLEDGEMENT

Mitchell Information Services, Inc. thanks the domestic and import automobile and light truck manufacturers, distributors, and dealers for their generous cooperation and assistance which makes this manual possible.

Technical Editors
Thomas L. Landis
Chuck Ackerman
David R. Costantino
Ramiro Gutierrez
Chuck Vedra
Roger Leftridge
William B. Disch
Ronald E. Garrett
Donald T. Pellettera
Lorenzo Cuevas
Tom L. Hall
Ed Donohue
James A. Wafford
Eric L. Lewis
Richard H. King
Scott Olsen

Electrical Quality Control
Matthew Krimple
Electrical Editors
Leonard McVicker
Santiago Llano
Mike Debreceni

PUBLISHED BY

MITCHELL INFORMATION SERVICES, INC.
9889 Willow Creek Road
P.O. Box 26260
San Diego, California 92126-0260

a division of
CORDURA PUBLICATIONS, INC.
Richard J. Harrington, President
John Opelt, Senior Vice President of Finance & Administration
Peter B. Jones, Vice President of Business Development
Robert W. Ladd, Vice President of Manufacturing

For Subscription Information:
CALL TOLL FREE 800-854-7030. In California CALL TOLL FREE 800-421-0159. Or WRITE: P.O. Box 26260, San Diego, CA 92126-0260

ISBN 0-8470-1203-4 LITHO IN U.S.A.

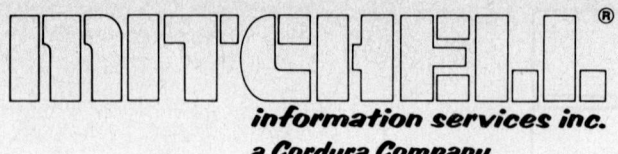

Tool Applications

ALL MANUFACTURERS

DESCRIPTION

Tool applications used in this manual are noted in the text of all articles where applicable. These tools are usually specific tools that must be used to perform a specific function in Removal, Installation, Overhaul or Testing of a component.

For example; "Using Spline Adapter (J-28513) and Holding Wrench (J-28514), tighten pinion nut until end play is taken up." Although other tools could possibly be substituted, the tool references in text are those that are recommended by the vehicle manufacturer. These tools should be used whenever possible. In cases where a non-specific tool is called for, no tool number will be given.

For example; "Place bearing insert in rod and install guides on rod bolts. Compress piston rings using ring compressor." Since just about any ring compressor that works and does not damage the components can be used, no specific tool number will be called out.

The following descriptions show an example of the reference in text, the maker of the tools recommended by the manufacturer and the tool maker address. Further information on tools and local suppliers of the tools can be obtained from the tool maker. It is also possible, for example, that a Kent-Moore tool may be cross-referenced to another tool maker. In this case it is imperative that the tools be exactly the same in design, or the specific function of the tool may not be able to be performed.

CHRYSLER CORP.

Chrysler Corp. tool applications called out in this manual will appear as follows: "Assemble pinion locating spacer (SP-6030) over body of main tool (SP-5385). Install shaft locating sleeve (L-4507), washer (C-4656) and compression nut (SP-533)."

The prefixes "C," "L" and "SP" mean that the tools are manufactured by Miller Special Tools. The number after the letter prefix is the basic tool part number. Any letters or numbers after the basic part number designate either a revised tool number or that the tool is part of a set.

CHRYSLER CORP. TOOL MANUFACTURER

Miller Special Tools
Division of Utica Tool Co., Inc.
32615 Park Lane
Garden City, Mich. 48135
Telephone (313) 522-6717

FORD

Ford tool applications called out in this manual will appear as follows: "Remove pinion bearing with slide hammer (T50T-100A with attachment T58L-101-A). Remove bearing with puller (T81P-3504-S, T58L-101-A and T81P-3504-T)."

Ford tools are manufactured by Owatonna Tools. The prefix used with Ford tool numbers means that the tools are essential tools. The number after the prefix is the basic tool part number. Any letters or numbers after the basic part number designate either a revised tool number or that the tool is part of a set.

FORD TOOL MANUFACTURER

Owatonna Tool Co. Inc.
Owatonna, Minn. 55060
Telephone (507) 455-2626
Telex 29-0876

GENERAL MOTORS

General Motors tool applications called out in this manual will appear as follows; "Install pivot pin remover (J-21854-1) and remove pins. Using pin punch (J-22635), drive out lever pin."

The "J" in front of the first set of numbers means that it is a Kent-Moore tool. The second set of numbers is the basic tool part number. Part numbers with no additional characters after the basic part number means that the tool listed is a complete tool. The last number means that it is either part of a set (-2,-3 etc.), or a revised tool number (-02,-03, or -B,-C etc,).

GENERAL MOTORS TOOL MANUFACTURER

Kent-Moore Tool Division
29784 Little Mack
Roseville, Mich., 48066-2298
Telephone (313) 774-9500
Telex 23-5377

JEEP

Jeep tool applications called out in this manual will appear as follows: "Use bearing remover (J-21473-1) and extension (J-21054-1) to drive out bearing." The "J" in front of the first set of numbers means that it is a Kent-Moore tool. The second set of numbers is the basic tool part number. Part numbers with no additional characters after the basic part number means that the tool listed is a complete tool. The last number means that it is either part of a set (-2,-3 etc.), or a revised tool number (-02,-03, or -B,-C etc,).

JEEP TOOL MANUFACTURER

Kent-Moore Tool Division
29784 Little Mack
Roseville, Mich., 48066-2298
Telephone (313) 774-9500
Telex 23-5377

1986 Light Truck Model Identification

In this manual, Light Truck models will be referred to by the manufacturer's model and/or series designation. When a specific model does not have a designated model or series designation, it will be referred to by model name.

NOTE: **When General Motors is referred to within this manual (rather than Chevrolet or GMC), the Chevrolet numerical vehicle series designations will be abbreviated for common reference to both Chevrolet and GMC models. The GMC counterpart models will be identified as follows: 10 = 1500 (except S15); 20 = 2500; 30 = 3500.**

CHEVROLET

MODEL IDENTIFICATION

Model	Description
C10	[1] 1/2 Ton Conventional Cab 2WD
C20	[1] 3/4 Ton Conventional Cab 2WD
C30	1 Ton Conventional Cab 2WD
K10	[1] 1/2 Ton Conventional Cab 4WD & Blazer
K20	[1] 3/4 Ton Conventional Cab 4WD
K30	1 Ton Conventional Cab 4WD
G10	1/2 Ton Van
G20	3/4 Ton Van
G30	[2] 1 Ton Van
M	Astro Panel & Passenger Van
P20	3/4 Ton Parcel Delivery Van
P30 (42)	1 Ton Parcel Delivery Van
S10	1/2 Ton Conventional Cab 2WD & Blazer
T10	1/2 Ton Conventional Cab 4WD & Blazer

[1] – Includes Suburban models.
[2] – Includes Front Section and Hi-Cube models.

DODGE

MODEL IDENTIFICATION

Model	Description
AD150	Ramcharger 2WD
AW150	Ramcharger 4WD
B150	1/2 Ton Van/Wagon
B250	3/4 Ton Van/Wagon
B350	1 Ton Van/Wagon
D100	Light Duty 1/2 Ton Conventional Cab 2WD
D150	Heavy Duty 1/2 Ton Conventional Cab 2WD
D250	3/4 Ton Conventional Cab 2WD
D350	1 Ton Conventional Cab 2WD
K	Caravan & Mini Ram Van
W100	Light Duty 1/2 Ton Conventional Cab 4WD
W150	Heavy Duty 1/2 Ton Conventional Cab 4WD
W250	3/4 Ton Conventional Cab 4WD
W350	1 Ton Conventional Cab 4WD

FORD

MODEL IDENTIFICATION

Model	Description
Aerostar	Trim-Sized Panel & Passenger Van
Bronco	Full-Sized Family 4WD Wagon
Bronco II	Trim-Sized Family 4WD Wagon
E150	1/2 Ton Van
E250	3/4 Ton Van

FORD (Cont.)

MODEL IDENTIFICATION

Model	Description
E350	[1] 1 Ton Van
F150	1/2 Ton Conventional Cab 2WD & 4WD
F250	3/4 Ton Conventional Cab 2WD & 4WD
F350	1 Ton Conventional Cab 2WD & 4WD
Ranger	1/2 Ton Conventional Cab 2WD & 4WD

[1] – Includes Front Section models.

GMC

MODEL IDENTIFICATION

Model	Description
C1500	[1] 1/2 Ton Conventional Cab 2WD
C2500	[1] 3/4 Ton Conventional Cab 2WD
C3500	1 Ton Conventional Cab 2WD
K1500	[1] 1/2 Ton Conventional Cab 4WD & Blazer
K2500	[1] 3/4 Ton Conventional Cab 4WD
K3500	1 Ton Conventional Cab 4WD
G1500	1/2 Ton Van
G2500	3/4 Ton Van
G3500	[2] 1 Ton Van
M	Safari Panel & Passenger Van
P2500	3/4 Ton Parcel Delivery Van
P3500 (42)	1 Ton Parcel Delivery Van
S15	1/2 Ton Conventional Cab 2WD & Blazer
T15	1/2 Ton Conventional Cab 4WD & Blazer

[1] – Includes Suburban models.
[2] – Includes Front Section and Hi-Cube models.

JEEP

MODEL IDENTIFICATION

Model	Description
Cherokee (73)	Cherokee 2WD (2-Door)
Cherokee (74)	Cherokee 2WD (4-Door)
Cherokee (77)	Cherokee 4WD (2-Door)
Cherokee (78)	Cherokee 4WD (4-Door)
CJ7 (87)	94" Wheelbase Utility Vehicle 4WD
Comanche (65)	Pickup 2WD (2-Door)
Comanche (66)	Pickup 4WD (2-Door)
Grand Wagoneer (15)	Heavy Duty Fam. Wagon 4WD
J10 (25)	119" Wheelbase 1/2 Ton Conv. Cab 4WD
J10 (26)	131" Wheelbase 1/2 Ton Conv. Cab 4WD
J20 (27)	3/4 Ton Conventional Cab 4WD
Wagoneer (75)	Wagoneer 4WD (4-Door)
Wrangler (81)	
1987	Open Door Vehicle 4WD

PLYMOUTH

MODEL IDENTIFICATION

Model	Description
H	Voyager

1986 DOMESTIC GENERAL INDEX

The first step in using these pages is to locate the listed components that you require information on. Go down the list under the specific component heading to the model or transmission type of the vehicle you are working on. On the right-hand side of the column is the number of the article you require.

1986 Domestic General Index

A

1986 Domestic General Index

N

S

1986 Domestic General Index

SECTION 1

DOMESTIC GENERAL SERVICING

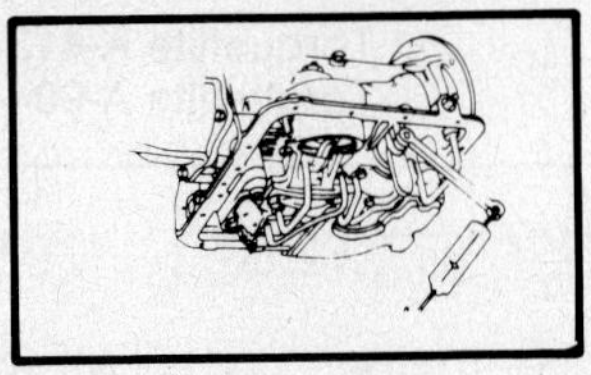

TRANSMISSION APPLICATIONS — Page

TRANSMISSION OIL PAN IDENTIFICATION

AUTOMATIC TRANSMISSION SERVICING

AUTOMATIC TRANSMISSION REMOVAL

AUTOMATIC TRANSAMISSION REMOVAL (Cont.) — Page

AUTOMATIC TRANSMISSION TROUBLE SHOOTING

MANUAL TRANSMISSION SERVICING

MANUAL TRANSMISSION REMOVAL

MANUAL TRANSMISSION TROUBLE SHOOTING

GENERAL SERVICING

NOTE: ALSO SEE GENERAL INDEX.

Transmission Application

AUTOMATIC TRANSMISSIONS – DOMESTIC CARS

MANUFACTURER & MODEL	TRANSMISSION MODEL
AMERICAN MOTORS	
Alliance & Encore – 1.4L & 1.7L	Renault MB1 (Transaxle)
Eagle – 4.2L	Torque-Command 998
CHRYSLER CORP.	
Aries, Caravelle, Charger, Daytona, Executive, Lancer, Laser, LeBaron, LeBaron GTS, New Yorker, Omni, Reliant, Turismo & 600 – 2.2L & 2.5L	Torqueflite A-413 (Transaxle)
Diplomat, Fifth Avenue & Gran Fury Salon – 5.2L	Torqueflite A-904-LA
FORD MOTOR CO.	
Lynx – 1.6L Escort & Lynx – 1.9L Tempo & Topaz – 2.3L	Ford Motor Co. 3-Speed ATX (Transaxle)
Capri, Cougar, Marquis, Mustang & Thunderbird – 2.3L	Ford Motor Co. C-3
Sable & Taurus – 2.5L	Ford Motor Co. 3-Speed ATX (Transaxle)
Sable & Taurus – 3.0L	Ford Motor Co. 4-Speed AXOD (Transaxle)
Capri, Cougar, LTD, Marquis, Mustang & Thunderbird – 3.8L	Ford Motor Co. C-5 Ford Motor Co. 4-Speed Automatic Overdrive
Capri, Crown Victoria, Continental, Grand Marquis, Lincoln Town Car, Mark VII & Mustang – 5.0L & 5.8L	Ford Motor Co. 4-Speed Automatic Overdrive
GENERAL MOTORS	
BUICK – Skyhawk – 1.8L, 2.0L & 2.8L Century – 2.5L & 2.8L Skylark & Somerset – 2.5L & 3.0L CADILLAC – Cimarron – 2.0L & 2.8L CHEVROLET – Cavalier – 2.0L & 2.8L & Celebrity – 2.5L & 2.8L OLDSMOBILE – Calais – 2.5L & 3.0L, Ciera – 2.5L & 2.8L, Firenza – 1.8L, 2.0L & 2.8L PONTIAC – Fiero – 2.5L & 2.8L, Grand Am – 2.5L & 3.0L, Sunbird – 1.8L & 6000 – 2.5L & 2.8L	Turbo Hydra-Matic 125C (Transaxle)
CHEVROLET – Chevette – 1.6L PONTIAC – 1000 – 1.6L	Turbo Hydra-Matic 180C
BUICK – Regal – 3.8L CHEVROLET – Caballero & El Camino – 4.3L & 5.0L Caprice – 4.3L & 5.0L & Monte Carlo – 3.8L, 4.3L & 5.0L OLDSMOBILE – Cutlass – 3.8L PONTIAC – Bonneville & Grand Prix – 3.8L & 4.3L Parisienne – 4.3L	Turbo Hydra-Matic 200C
BUICK – LeSabre & Electra Estate Wagon – 5.0L Regal – 3.8L & 5.0L CADILLAC – Fleetwood Brougham – 5.0L CHEVROLET – Caballero & El Camino – 4.3L & 5.0L Caprice & Monte Carlo – 4.3L & 5.0L OLDSMOBILE – Custom Cruiser & Cutlass Supreme – 5.0L PONTIAC – Bonneville & Grand Prix – 3.8L, 4.3L & 5.0L & Parisienne – 4.3L & 5.0L	Turbo Hydra-Matic 200-4R

Transmission Application

AUTOMATIC TRANSMISSIONS – DOMESTIC CARS (Cont.)

MANUFACTURER & MODEL	TRANSMISSION MODEL
GENERAL MOTORS (Cont.) BUICK – Century – 2.8L & 3.8L, Electra – 3.8L, LaSabre & Riviera – 3.0L & 3.8L CADILLAC – DeVille – 4.1L, Eldorado – 3.8L & 4.1L, Fleetwood & Seville – 4.1L CHEVROLET – Celebrity – 2.8L OLDSMOBILE – Ciera – 2.8L & 3.8L, Delta 88 – 3.0L & 3.8L, Ninety-Eight & Toronado – 3.8L PONTIAC – 6000 – 2.8L	Turbo Hydra-Matic 440-T4 (Transaxle)
CHEVROLET – Caballero & El Camino – 4.3L & 5.0L Camaro – 2.5L, 2.8L & 5.0L Caprice – 4.3L & 5.0L Corvette – 5.7L Monte Carlo – 4.3L & 5.0L PONTIAC – Bonneville – 4.3L & 5.0L, Firebird – 2.5L, 2.8L & 5.0L, Grand Prix – 4.3L & 5.0L, Parisienne – 4.3L & 5.0L	Turbo Hydra-Matic 700-R4
CHEVROLET – Nova – 1.6L	Toyota A131L (3-Speed Transaxle)

Transmission Applications

MANUAL TRANSMISSIONS – DOMESTIC CARS

MANUFACTURER & MODEL	TRANSMISSION MODEL
AMERICAN MOTORS	
Alliance & Encore	Renault JB0, JB1 or JB3 (Transaxle)
Eagle	Borg-Warner T4 4-Speed or T5 5-Speed
CHRYSLER CORP.	
Aries, Charger, Daytona, Horizon, Lancer, Laser, LeBaron, LeBaron GTS, New Yorker, Omni, Reliant, Turismo & 600	A-460 4-Speed or A-525 5-Speed (Transaxle)
FORD MOTOR CO.	
Escort, Lynx, Tempo & Topaz	Ford MTX 4-Speed or 5-Speed (Transaxle)
Capri & Mustang – 2.3L OHC	85 ET 4-Speed
Capri, Cougar, Mustang & Thunderbird	T5-OD (5-Speed Overdrive)
GENERAL MOTORS	
BUICK – Skyhawk, Skylark & Somerset CHEVROLET – Cavalier & Celebrity OLDSMOBILE – Calais & Firenza PONTIAC – Fiero – 2.5L & 2.8L, Grand Am & Sunbird – 1.8L	GM 76 MM 4-Speed or 5-Speed (Transaxle)
CHEVROLET – Chevette – 1.8L (Diesel)	Isuzu 69.5 MM 5-Speed
CHEVROLET – Chevette – 1.6L (Gas) PONTIAC – 1000 – 1.6L (Gas)	GM 70 MM 4-Speed
CHEVROLET – Camaro – 2.5L & 5.0L, Chevette – 1.6L (Gas) PONTIAC – Firebird – 2.5L & 2.8L, 1000 – 1.6L (Gas)	GM 77 MM 5-Speed
CHEVROLET – Corvette – 5.7L	GM 83 MM 4-Speed W/Auto. Overdrive
CHEVROLET – Nova – 1.6L	Toyota C51 5-Speed (Transaxle)

Transmission Applications

AUTOMATIC TRANSMISSIONS – LIGHT TRUCKS

MANUFACTURER & MODEL	TRANSMISSION MODEL
CHRYSLER CORP. Ram Van/Wagon, 2WD/4WD Pickup, 4WD Ramcharger	Chrysler Corp. Loadflite A-727
Ram Van/Wagon, 2WD/4WD Pickup	Chrysler Corp. Loadflite A-904T
Ram Van/Wagon, 2WD/4WD Pickup, 2WD/4WD Ramcharger	Chrysler Corp. Loadflite A-999
Caravan, Mini Ram Van, Voyager – 2.2L	Chrysler Corp. Torqueflite A-413
Caravan, Mini Ram Van, Voyager – 2.6L	Chrysler Corp. Torqueflite A-470
FORD Aerostar, 2WD/4WD Ranger, Bronco II	Ford A4LD Automatic Overdrive
Bronco, E-150/250 Van, 2WD/4WD F-150/250 Pickup	Ford AOD Automatic Overdrive
F-150/350 Pickup (4.9L, 5.0L)	Ford C-5
Bronco, E-150/350 Van, 2WD/4WD F-150/350 Pickup	Ford C-6
GENERAL MOTORS "C" Series, "G" Series, "K" Series	Turbo Hydra-Matic 350C
"C" Series, "G" Series, "K" Series, "P" Series	Turbo Hydra-Matic 400
Astro/Safari Van, "C" Series, "G" Series, "K" Series, "S" Series	Turbo Hydra-Matic 700-R4
JEEP CJ7, J10 Pickup, Grand Wagoneer	Chrysler Corp. Loadflite 999
J10/20 Pickup, Grand Wagoneer	Chrysler Corp. Loadflite 727
Cherokee, Comanche, Wagoneer	Chrysler Corp. Loadflite 904

Transmission Applications

MANUAL TRANSMISSIONS – LIGHT TRUCKS

MANUFACTURER & MODEL	TRANSMISSION MODEL
CHRYSLER CORP. 2WD/4WD Pickups, Ramcharger	New Process 435 4-Speed
Ram Van/Wagon, 1/2 Ton 2WD Pickup	Overdrive 4-Speed
Caravan, Voyager, Mini Ram Van – 2.2L	Chrysler A-460 4-Speed
Caravan, Voyager, Mini Ram Van – 2.6L	Chrysler A-525 5-Speed (Close Ratio)
FORD Aerostar – 2.3L, 2.8L, 3.0L	Mazda 5-Speed
Bronco II – 2.3L & 2.9L, Ranger – 2.0L, 2.3L (Gas), 3.0L 2WD & 4WD 4WD 2WD 2.3L (Diesel)	 Mazda 5-Speed Mitsubishi 5-Speed Mazda 5-Speed
E-150/350 Van, F-150 Pickup	Ford 3.03 3-Speed Ford 4-Speed (SROD) Overdrive
Bronco, E-150/350 Van, F-150/350 Pickup	New Process 435 4-Speed
Bronco, E-150/350, F-150/350 Pickup	Warner T-18 4-Speed
Bronco, F-150/250 2WD Pickup, F-150 4WD Pickup	Ford Top Shifter (TOD) 4-Speed Overdrive
F-250/350 Pickup (6.9L Diesel & 7.5 Gas)	Warner T-19B/19D 4-Speed
GENERAL MOTORS Astro/Safari Van "S" Series	 GM 76 MM 4-Speed GM 77 MM 4-Speed
"S" Series	GM 77.5 MM 4-Speed
Astro/Safari Van, "S" Series	GM 77 MM 5-Speed
"C" Series, "G" Series, "K" Series, "P" Series	Muncie 76 MM 3-Speed
"C" Series, "G" Series, "K" Series, "P" Series	New Process 89 MM 4-Speed Overdrive
"C" Series, "G" Series, "K" Series, "P" Series	GM 117 MM 4-Speed
JEEP CJ7	Borg-Warner T4 4-Speed
CJ7	Borg-Warner T5 5-Speed Overdrive
J10 Pickup, Grand Wagoneer (Fleet)	Tremec T176 4-Speed
Cherokee, Comanche, Wagoneer	Aisin AX4 4-Speed
Cherokee, Comanche, Wagoneer	Aisin AX5 5-Speed Overdrive

OIL PAN GASKET IDENTIFICATION

Fig. 1: AMC (Renault) MB1

Fig. 2: AMC/Jeep 904 & 998 and Chrysler Corp. A-904 & A-999

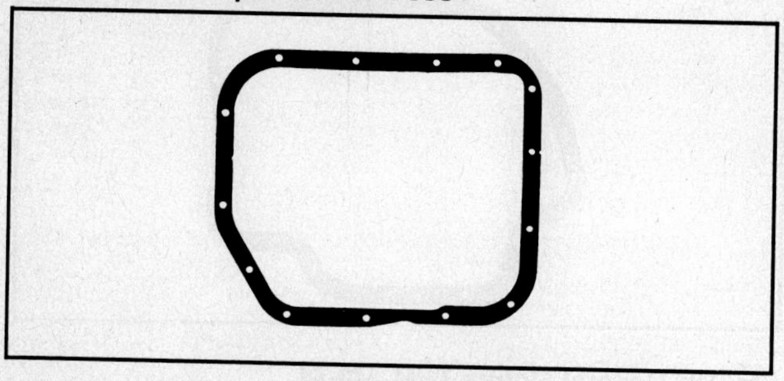

Fig. 3: Chrysler Corp. A-413 & A-470

Fig. 4: Chrysler Corp. & Jeep A-727

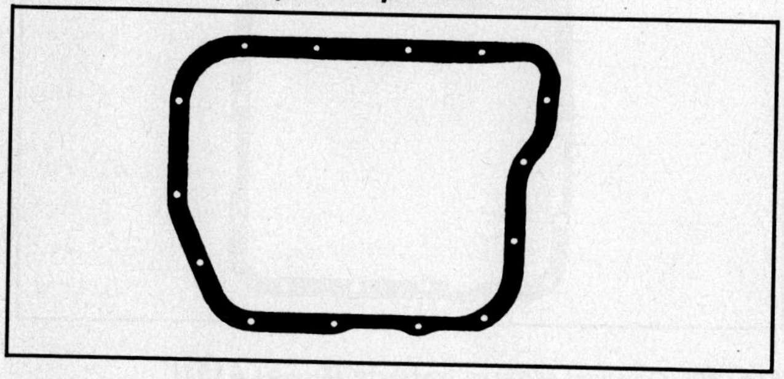

Fig. 5: Ford Motor Co. A4LD

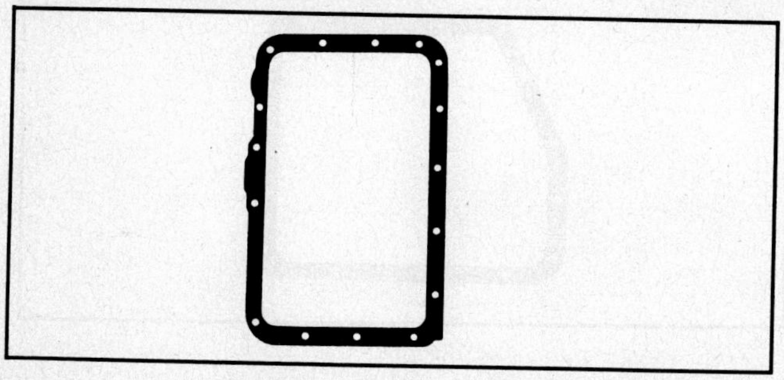

Fig. 6: Ford Motor Co. AOT

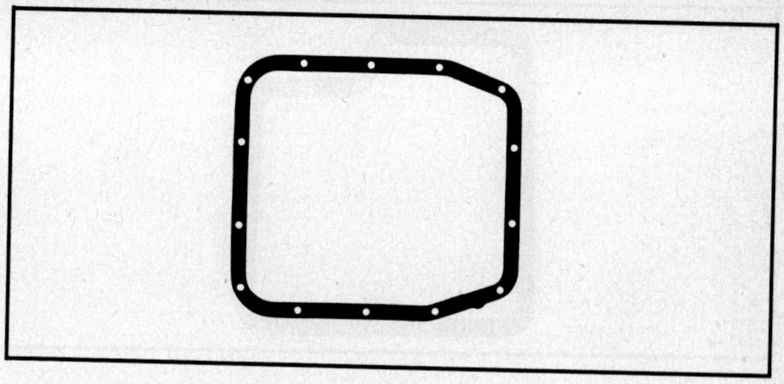

Fig. 7: Ford Motor Co. ATX

Fig. 8: Ford Motor Co. AXOD

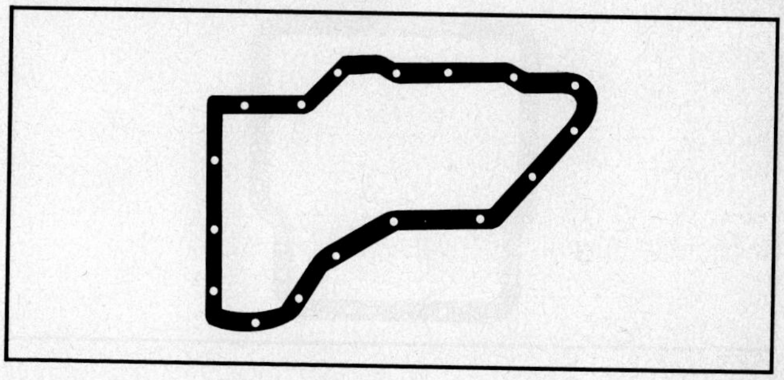

Fig. 9: Ford Motor Co. C-3

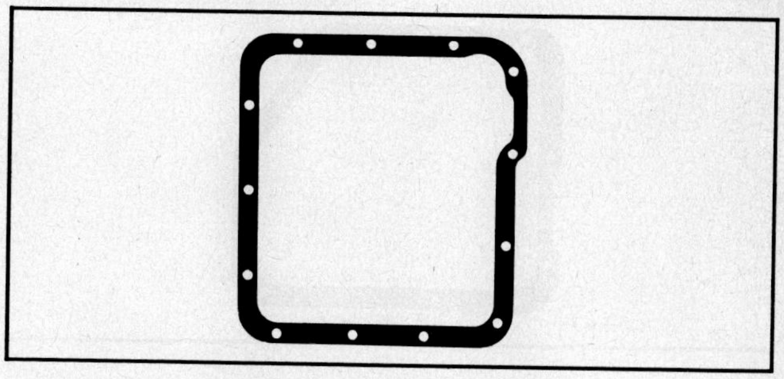

Fig. 10: Ford Motor Co. C-5

Automatic Transmissions

OIL PAN GASKET IDENTIFICATION (Cont.)

***Fig. 11:* Ford Motor Co. C-6**

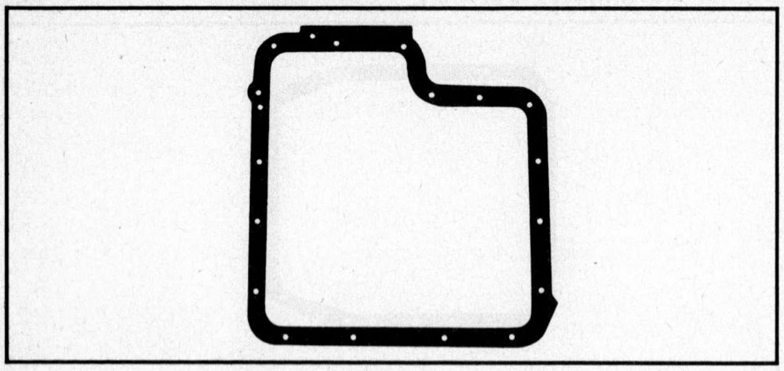

***Fig. 12:* General Motors THM 125C**

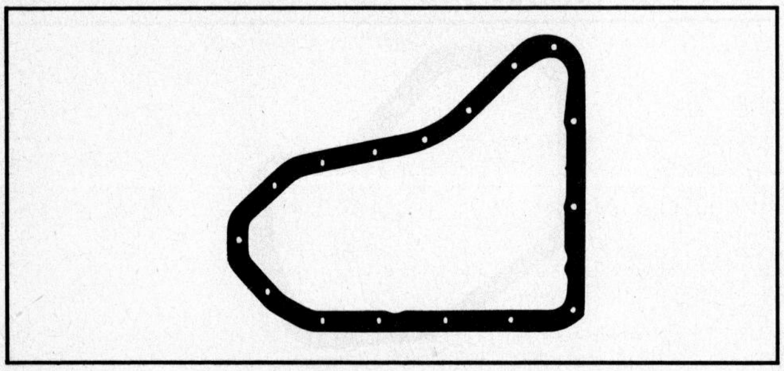

***Fig. 13:* General Motors THM 180C**

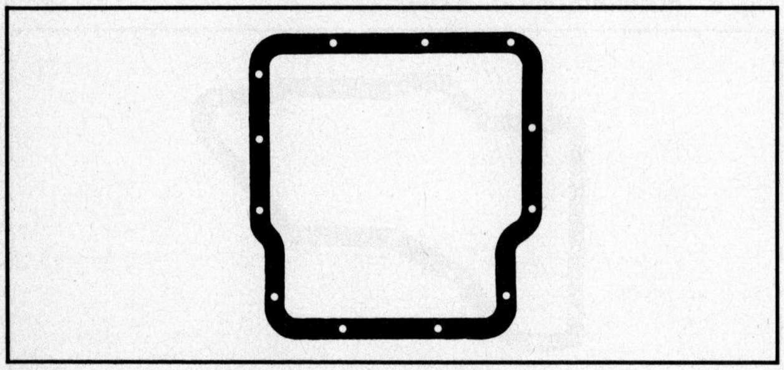

***Fig. 14:* General Motors THM 200C**

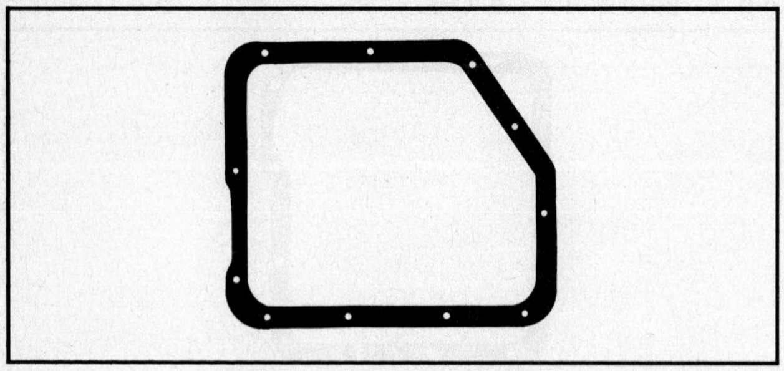

***Fig. 15:* General Motors THM 200-4R**

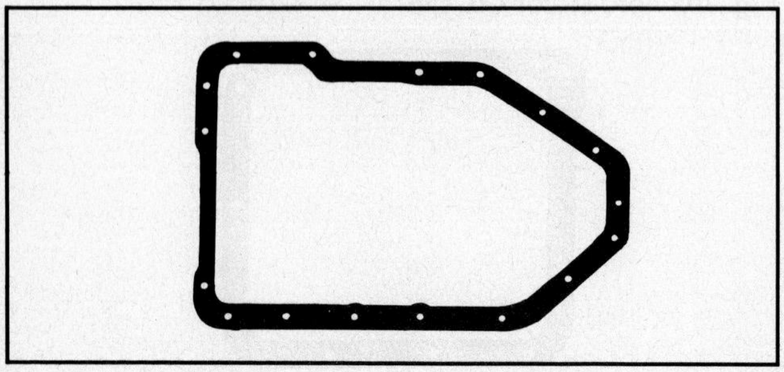

***Fig. 16:* General Motors THM 350C**

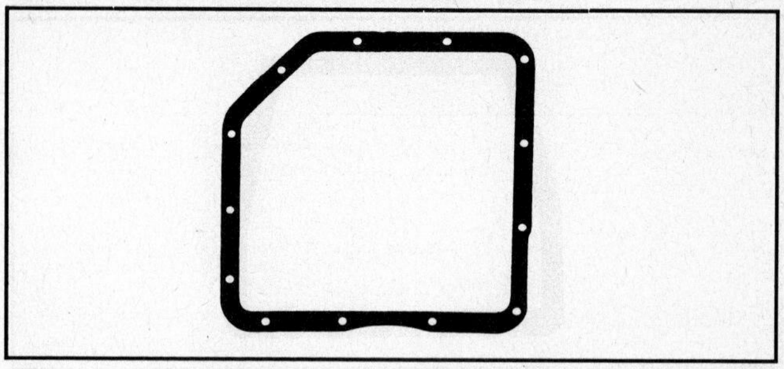

***Fig. 17:* General Motors THM 400**

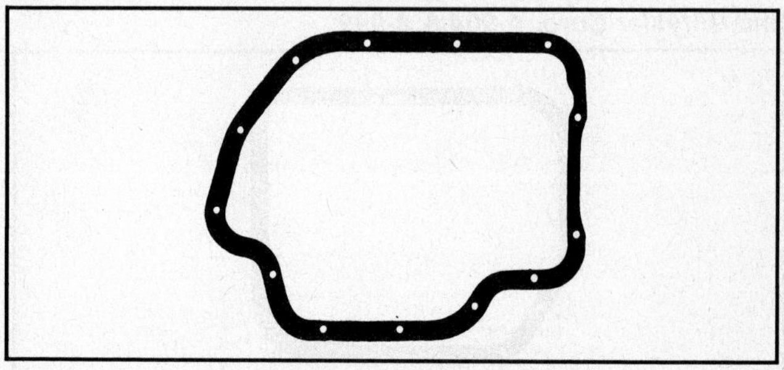

***Fig. 18:* General Motors THM 440-T4**

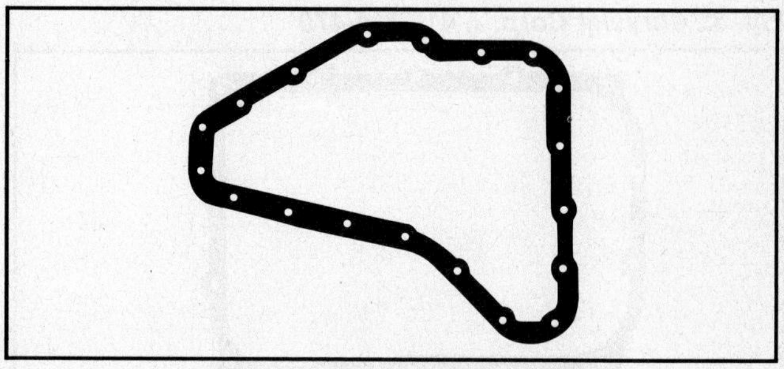

***Fig. 19:* General Motors THM 700-R4**

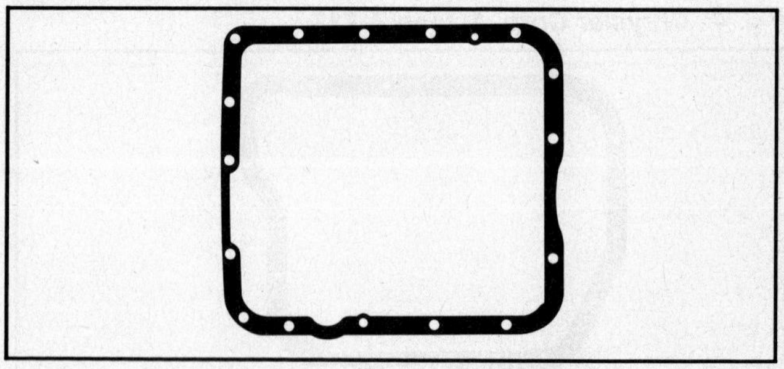

***Fig. 20:* General Motors Imports (Nova) A131L**

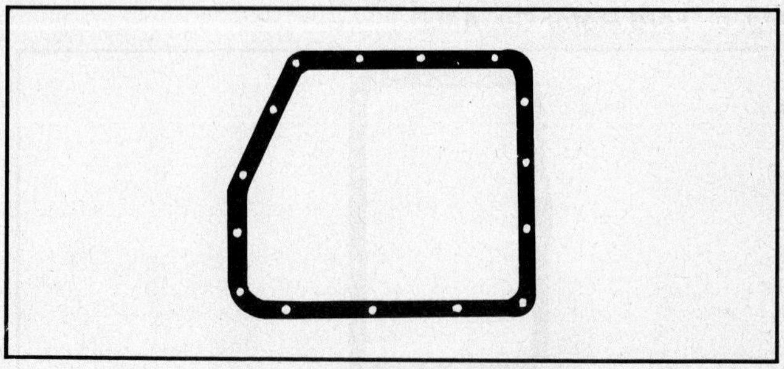

AMERICAN MOTORS

LUBRICATION

SERVICE INTERVALS

On Alliance and Encore models, transaxle fluid and filter should be changed at 24 month or 30,000 mile intervals. On Eagle models, transmission fluid and filter should be changed at 30,000 mile intervals.

CHECKING FLUID LEVEL

Alliance & Encore

Ensure transaxle is at normal operating temperature with engine at curb idle. With vehicle on a level surface and parking brake applied, check fluid level in Park. Fluid level should be between the "FULL" and "ADD" marks on the dipstick.

NOTE: **It takes only 1/2 pint (.25L) of fluid to raise the level from the "ADD" mark to the "FULL" mark on the dipstick.**

Eagle

Ensure transmission is at normal operating temperature with engine at curb idle. With vehicle on a level surface with parking brake applied, check fluid level in Neutral. Fluid level should be between "FULL" and "ADD 1 PINT" marks on dipstick. DO NOT overfill. Fully reseat dipstick.

RECOMMENDED FLUID

All Models

Use only fluid of the type labeled Dexron Type II automatic transmission fluid.

FLUID CAPACITY

NOTE: **Transmission and converter assembly capacities given below are approximate. Correct fluid level should be determined by the mark on dipstick. Converter is a welded assembly and is not serviceable. Replacement is recommended if contaminated.**

TRANSMISSION REFILL CAPACITIES

Application	Quantity
Alliance & Encore	
Model MB1 Transaxle	3.7 qts. (3.5L)
Eagle	
Model 998	[1] 8.5 qts. (8.1L)

[1] – Including torque converter.

DRAINING & REFILLING

Alliance & Encore

1) Remove drain plug on bottom of transaxle oil pan, and drain fluid. Remove transaxle mount bolt. Raise transaxle assembly to gain clearance for oil pan removal.

2) Remove oil pan bolts and oil pan. Remove oil filter and seal. Install new oil filter and seal. Clean oil pan, and install with new gasket. Lower transaxle, install transaxle mount bolt, and tighten.

3) Pour 3.7 quarts (3.5L) of fluid into transaxle. Start engine and allow to idle for a few minutes. Ensure engine is at curb idle and vehicle is on a level surface. With parking brake applied, move shift selector through all positions, ending in Park.

4) Add sufficient fluid to bring level to "ADD" mark on dipstick. Recheck fluid level after transaxle has reached normal operating temperature.

Eagle

1) Loosen oil pan bolts and tap pan to break loose, allowing fluid to drain. Remove oil pan bolts and oil pan. Remove oil filter mounting bolts and remove filter. Clean oil pan. Install new oil filter. Install oil pan with new gasket.

2) Pour 6 quarts (5.7L) of fluid into transmission. Start engine and allow to idle for at least 2 minutes. Ensure engine is at curb idle, and vehicle is on a level surface. With parking brake applied, move shift selector lever through all positions, ending in Neutral.

3) Add sufficient fluid to bring level to "ADD 1 PINT" mark. Recheck fluid level after transmission has reached normal operating temperature.

4) Level should then be between "FULL" mark and the "ADD 1 PINT" mark on dipstick. Fully reseat dipstick.

ADJUSTMENTS

KICKDOWN BAND (FRONT)

NOTE: **Kickdown band adjusting screw is located on left side of transmission case above throttle linkage lever.**

Eagle

1) Mark drive shaft and axle yoke for reassembly reference. Disconnect shaft and move aside. Loosen adjusting screw lock nut and back off nut 5 turns. Ensure screw turns freely in case.

2) Tighten screw to 36 INCH lbs. (4 N.m), if torque wrench, adapter tool, and 5/16" square socket are used. If not, tighten screw to 72 INCH lbs. (8 N.m). Back off adjusting screw 3 turns. Hold screw in this position and tighten lock nut to 35 ft. lbs. (47 N.m).

LOW-REVERSE BAND (REAR)

NOTE: **Low-Reverse band adjusting screw is located on rear servo lever. Transmission oil pan must be removed to provide access to band adjusting screw.**

Eagle

1) Drain transmission fluid and remove oil pan. Remove band adjusting screw lock nut. Tighten screw to 72 INCH lbs. (8 N.m). Back off screw 4 turns.

2) Install and tighten lock nut to 35 ft. lbs. (47 N.m). Install oil pan with new gasket, tighten bolts to 150 INCH lbs. (17 N.m). Fill transmission with fluid.

AMERICAN MOTORS (Cont.)

Fig. 1: View of Transmission Showing Location of Low-Reverse Band (REAR) Adjusting Screw

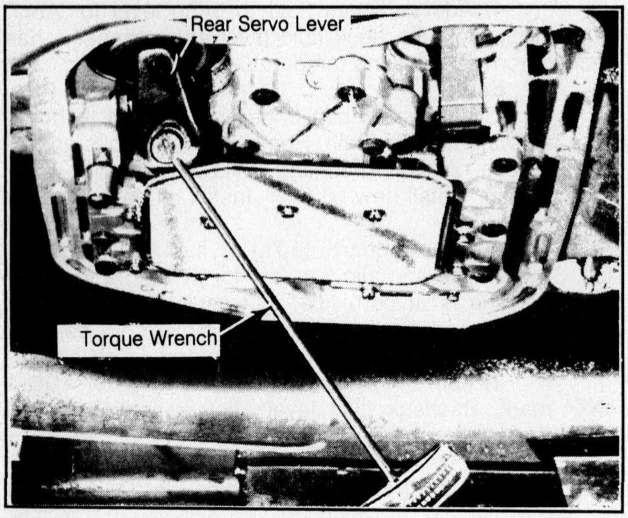

Oil pan must be removed to provide access to adjusting screw.

Fig. 2: View of Throttle Position Potentiometer Showing Testing and Adjustment Locations

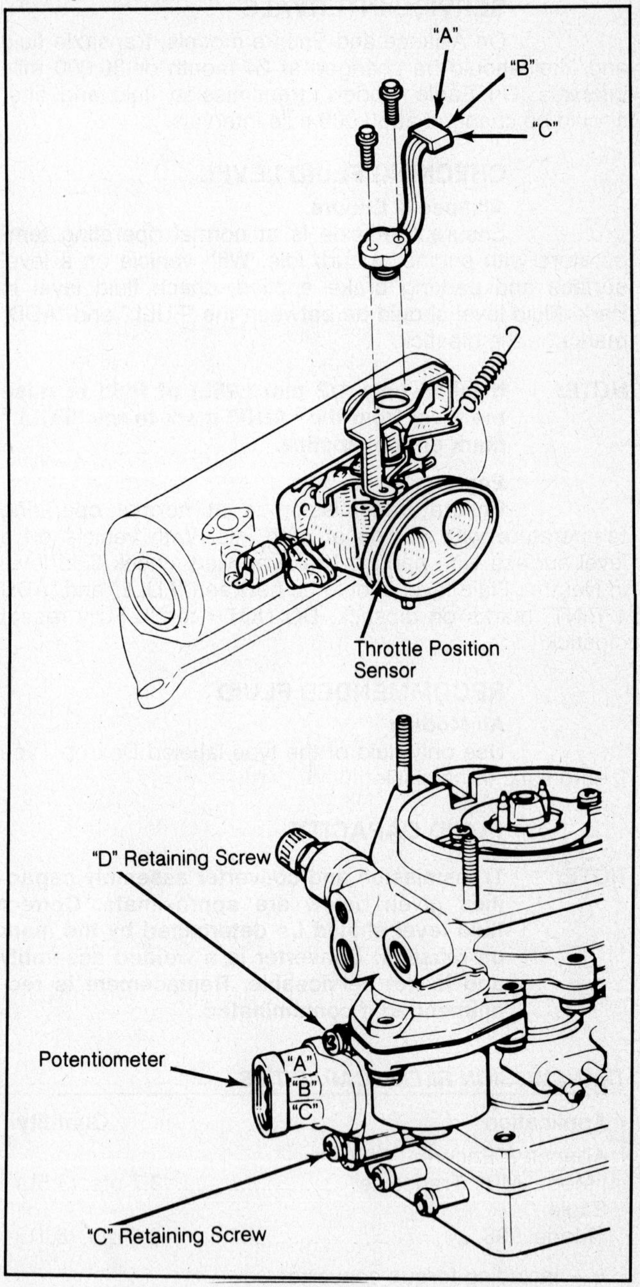

Rough adjustment done by "C" retaining screw, and fine adjustment done by "D" retaining screw.

THROTTLE POSITION POTENTIOMETER

Alliance & Encore

1) Remove air filter assembly. Turn ignition on. Using a digital volt-ohmmeter, insert negative lead into terminal "C" of potentiometer. *See Fig. 2.*

2) DO NOT disconnect connector. Insert voltmeter lead in rear of connector, and push-in to contact terminal. Insert positive lead into terminal "B" of throttle position sensor.

3) Move throttle plate to wide open throttle position. Be sure throttle contacts stop. Note the exact voltmeter reading. It should be about 4.3 volts. This is the input voltage.

4) Remove positive lead from terminal "B", and insert in terminal "A" of throttle position sensor. Open throttle plate to wide open throttle position. Note the exact voltmeter reading. This is the output voltage.

5) Adjust potentiometer so that output voltage is 4% ± 0.5% of input voltage. For rough adjustment, loosen bottom potentiometer "C" retaining screw and pivot potentiometer on adjustment slot. For fine adjustment, loosen top "D" retaining screw and pivot potentiometer.

TRANSMISSION THROTTLE ROD

Eagle

1) Disconnect throttle control rod spring. Block choke plate open and release fast idle cam. Raise vehicle and use spring to hold transmission throttle valve control lever forward against stop. *See Fig. 3.*

2) Loosen both retaining bolts on throttle control adjusting link. DO NOT remove spring clip and nylon washer. Hold transmission throttle lever forward against stop. Push on end of link to eliminate lash.

3) Pull clamp rearward so bolt in rod bottoms in rear of slot in rod. Tighten clamp to adjusting link.

4) Pull control rod rearward so bolt in rod bottoms in front of slot in rod. Tighten rear retaining bolt. Install throttle control rod spring on control rod.

SHIFT LINKAGE

Alliance & Encore

1) Place gear selector in Park. Raise and support vehicle. Loosen adjustment yoke nuts, and slide yoke and cable forward to remove slack in cable.

2) Tighten yoke nuts. Lower vehicle and ensure all 6 gear positions are available. Check that vehicle starts in Park position.

Eagle

1) Loosen rod trunnion setscrews. Place gearshift lever in Park position. Move valve body lever rearward into park detent.

AMERICAN MOTORS (Cont.)

Fig. 3: Eagle Throttle Rod Adjustment

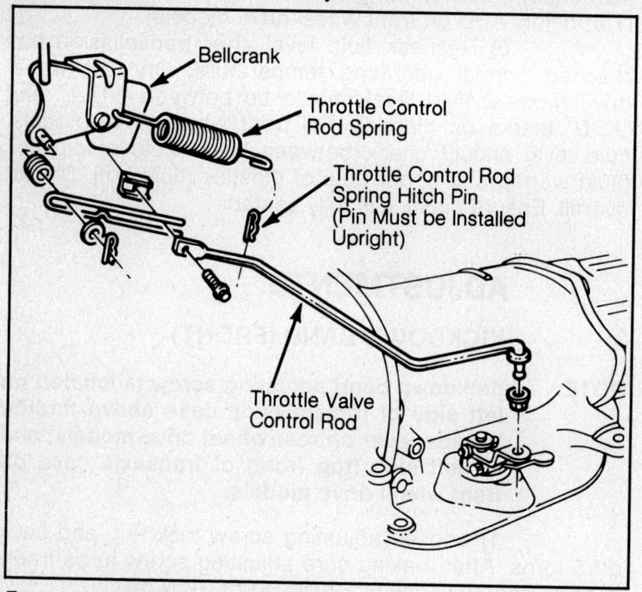

Ensure choke plate is fully open, and fast idle cam is released.

2) Check for positive engagement by attempting to rotate driveshaft. Adjust shift rod trunnion to eliminate lash, and to obtain free pin fit in bellcrank arm. Tighten trunnion setscrews.

NEUTRAL START & BACK-UP LIGHT SWITCH

Alliance & Encore

The neutral start and back-up light switch is not adjustable and is incorporated in a multifunction switch. The multifunction switch is located on transaxle.

Eagle

1) Center terminal of 3-terminal neutral start and back-up light switch provides ground for starter solenoid circuit through selector lever in "P" or "N" positions only.

2) To test, remove wiring connector from switch and check for continuity between center pin of switch and case. Continuity should exist only when transmission is in "P" or "N" position.

NOTE: **Check shift linkage adjustment before replacing a switch which tests bad.**

3) To replace, unscrew switch from case (some fluid will escape). Move selector lever to "P" and "N" positions. Check that switch operating fingers are centered in switch opening in case.

4) Install switch with new seal into case, and tighten. Check transmission fluid level. Back-up light switch circuit is through the 2 outside terminals of switch.

5) Continuity between the 2 terminals should exist only when selector lever is in "R" position. No continuity should exist from either terminal to case.

Fig. 4: Installed View of Neutral Start and Back-Up Light Switch

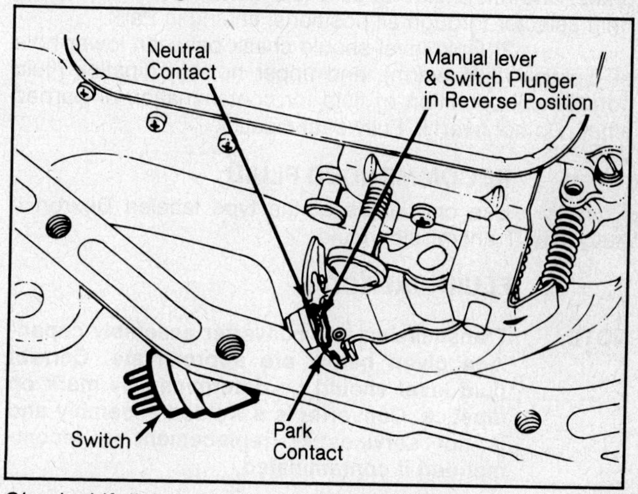

Check shift linkage adjustment before replacing a switch which tests bad.

Automatic Transmission Servicing

CHRYSLER CORP.

LUBRICATION

SERVICE INTERVALS

Check fluid level every 6 months. Draining, refilling and band adjustments are not required under normal driving conditions. Under heavy duty (severe service) conditions, change fluid, replace filter, and adjust bands every 15,000 miles.

CHECKING FLUID LEVELS

RWD Models

1) With vehicle on level ground, apply parking brake. Start engine and run at curb idle. Shift gear selector through all positions, ending in Neutral.

2) Fluid level should be between "ADD" and "FULL" marks on dipstick. Check condition of fluid for contamination.

FWD Models

1) With vehicle on level ground, apply parking brake, and run engine at curb idle for at least 60 seconds. Shift selector through all positions, ending in Park.

2) Fluid level should check between lower hole of dipstick (fluid warm), and upper hole of dipstick (fluid hot). Check condition of fluid for contamination or burned smell. Do not overfill. Fully seat dipstick.

RECOMMENDED FLUID

Use only fluids of the type labeled Dexron II Automatic Transmission Fluid.

FLUID CAPACITY

NOTE: **Transmission and converter assembly capacities given below are approximate. Correct fluid level should be determined by mark on dipstick. Converter is a welded assembly and is not serviceable, replacement is recommended if contaminated.**

TRANSMISSION REFILL CAPACITIES

Application	Quantity
A-904-LA (Lock-Up)	[1] 17.1 pts. (8.1L)
A-413 & A-470	[2] 17.8 pts. (8.4L)

[1] – Add .5 pts. (.2L) for non-lock-up converter.
[2] – Add 1.4 pts. (.7L) for fleet models.

DRAINING AND REFILLING

1) Loosen oil pan bolts at one corner. Tap pan to break it loose, allowing fluid to drain. Remove pan bolts and remove pan. Adjust rear band on rear wheel drive models, if required.

2) Install a new filter and gasket (if equipped) on bottom of valve body and tighten screws. Clean pan.

3) On rear wheel drive models, install pan with new gasket. Make sure round magnet is over boss in right front corner of oil pan. On front wheel drive models, install new pan, using RTV to form gasket.

4) On all models, add 4 quarts (3.8L) of transmission fluid. Start engine and allow to idle for at least 2 minutes (1 minute on front wheel drive models).

5) With engine at curb idle and parking brake applied, move shift selector lever through all positions, ending in "N" position ("P" on front wheel drive models). Add enough fluid to bring level to "ADD" mark on dipstick (1/8" below ADD on front wheel drive models).

6) Recheck fluid level after transmission has reached normal operating temperature. On rear wheel drive models, fluid level should be between "FULL" and "ADD" marks on dipstick. On front wheel drive models, fluid level should check between lower hole of dipstick (fluid warm), and upper hole of dipstick (fluid hot). Do not overfill. Ensure dipstick is fully seated.

ADJUSTMENTS

KICKDOWN BAND (FRONT)

NOTE: **Kickdown band adjusting screw is located on left side of transmission case above throttle linkage lever on rear wheel drive models, and on left side (top front) of transaxle case on front wheel drive models.**

1) Loosen adjusting screw lock nut, and back off 5 turns. After making sure adjusting screw turns freely in case, tighten screw to 72 INCH Lbs. (8 N.m).

2) Back off screw 2 1/2 turns. Hold adjusting screw in this position and tighten lock nut.

KICKDOWN BAND ADJUSTMENT

Application	Back Off Screw
All Models	2 1/2 Turns

LOW-REVERSE BAND (REAR)

NOTE: **Low-Reverse band adjusting screw is located on rear servo lever. Transmission oil pan must be removed to provide access to band adjusting screw.**

Fig. 1: Low-Reverse Band Adjustment (Rear) Screw Location

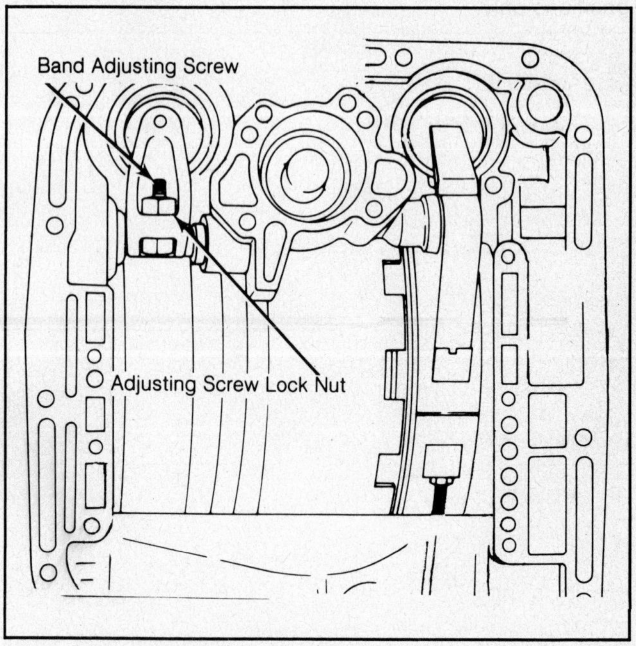

CHRYSLER CORP. (Cont.)

1) Drain transmission and remove oil pan. Loosen band adjusting screw lock nut about 5 turns. Ensure adjusting screw turns freely in case. On rear wheel drive models, tighten screw to 72 INCH Lbs. (8 N.m). On front wheel drive models, tighten adjusting screw to 41 INCH lbs. (4.6 N.m).

2) On all models, back off adjusting screw specified number of turns given in Low-Reverse Band Adjustment table. Hold in this position and tighten lock nut. Install oil pan and fill transmission with fluid.

LOW-REVERSE BAND ADJUSTMENT

Application	Back Off Screw
A-904-LA	4 Turns
A-413 & A-470	3 1/2 Turns

TRANSMISSION THROTTLE ROD

RWD Models

1) Make sure carburetor is not on fast idle cam (disconnect choke if necessary). Raise vehicle on hoist to make adjustment at transmission throttle lever. Loosen adjustment swivel lock screw. Swivel must be free to slide along flat end of throttle rod so that preload spring action is not restricted.

2) Hold transmission lever firmly forward against its internal stop, and tighten swivel lock screw. This completes throttle rod adjustment, as linkage backlash was automatically removed by the preload spring.

3) To check linkage freedom of operation, move throttle rod rearward, and release slowly. Ensure it returns to full forward position.

Fig. 2: Throttle Rod Adjustment Linkage For All RWD Models

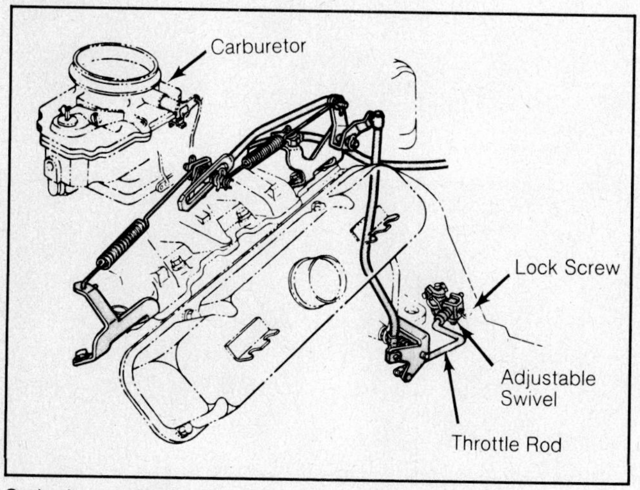

Swivel must be free to slide on throttle rod for proper adjustment.

TRANSMISSION THROTTLE CABLE

FWD Models

1) Make sure carburetor is not on fast idle cam (disconnect choke if necessary). Loosen adjustment bracket lock screw. Bracket must be free to slide on its slot for proper adjustment.

2) Slide bracket to left (toward engine) to limit of its travel. Release bracket and move throttle lever fully to right, against its internal stop. Tighten adjusting bracket

Fig. 3: Typical Throttle Adjustment For FWD Models

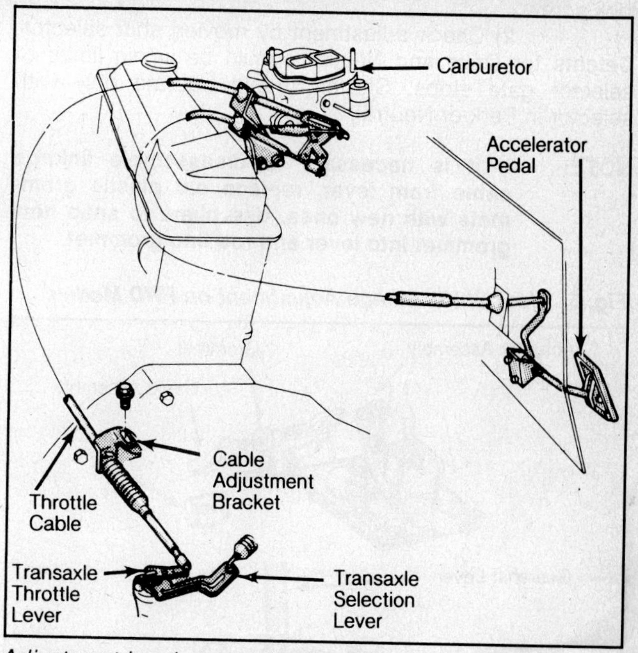

Adjustment bracket must be free to slide for correct adjustment.

lock screw. This completes adjustment, as backlash was automatically removed.

3) To check linkage freedom of operation, move transaxle throttle lever forward and slowly release. Ensure it returns to full rear position.

SHIFT LINKAGE

Column Shift (RWD Models)

1) Place shift selector in "P" position. Loosen adjustable swivel lock screw, making sure swivel block is free to turn on shift rod. Move shift lever on transmission

Fig. 4: Column Shift Linkage Adjustment on RWD Models

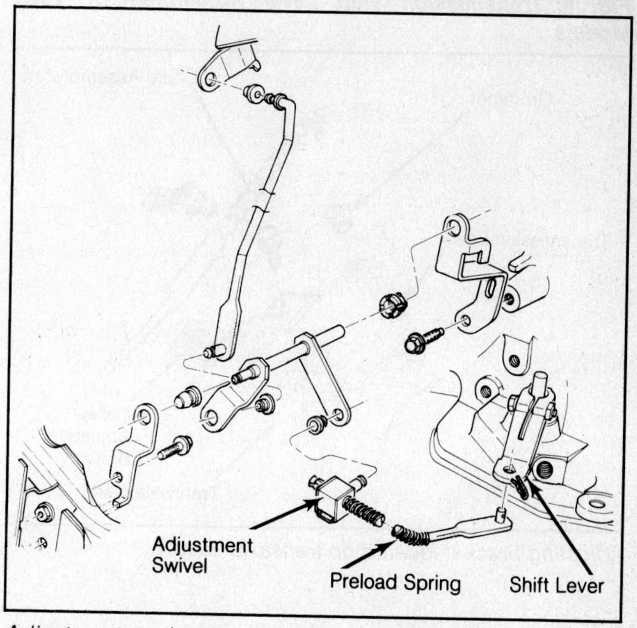

Adjustment made with shift lever in "P" Position.

CHRYSLER CORP. (Cont.)

all the way to rear detent position (Park). Tighten swivel lock screw.

2) Check adjustment by moving shift selector. Detents for Drive and Neutral should be within limits of selector gate stops. Starter should operate only with selector in Park or Neutral.

NOTE: **If it is necessary to disassemble linkage cable from lever, replace old plastic grommets with new ones. Use pliers to snap new grommet into lever and rod into grommet.**

Fig. 5: Floor Shift Linkage Adjustment on FWD Models

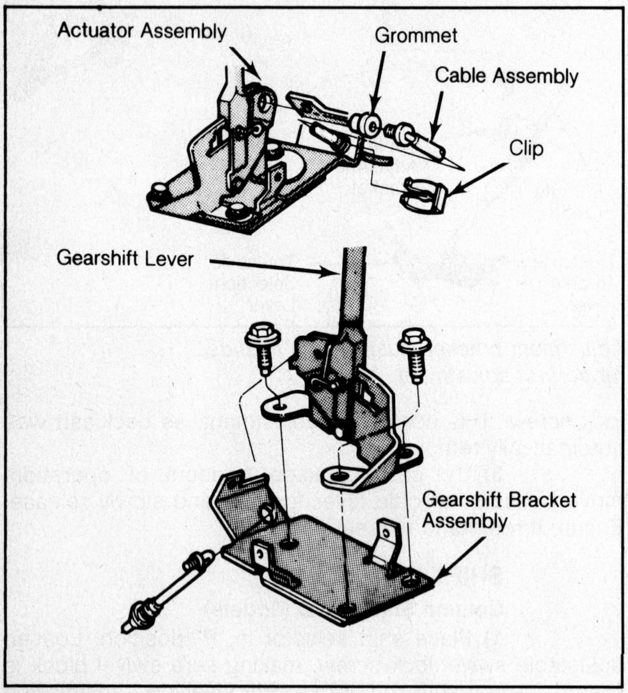

Replace grommet if linkage is disconnected.

Fig. 6: Transmission Shift Lever Adjustment on FWD Models

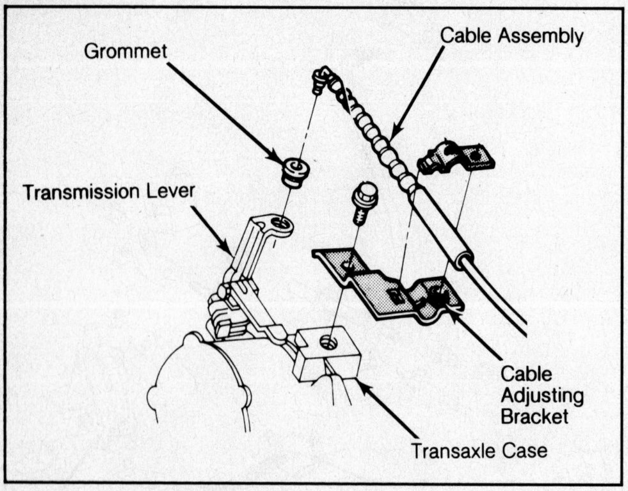

Adjusting bracket located on transaxle case.

Console or Column Shift (FWD Models)

Place shift selector in "P" position. Loosen lock bolt on cable adjusting bracket on transaxle. Move shift lever on transaxle all the way to rear detent (Park) and hold. Tighten lock bolt.

NOTE: **If it is necessary to disassemble linkage cable from lever, replace old plastic grommets with new ones. Use pliers to snap new grommet into lever and rod into grommet.**

NEUTRAL SAFETY SWITCH

1) Center terminal of the 3 terminal neutral starting and back-up light switch provides ground for starter solenoid circuit through shift selector lever in Park or Neutral positions only.

2) To test, remove wiring connector from switch and check for continuity between center pin of switch and case. Continuity should exist only when transmission is in Park or Neutral.

NOTE: **Check shift linkage adjustment before replacing a switch that tests bad.**

3) To replace, unscrew switch from case (some fluid will escape). Move shift selector lever to Park, and then to Neutral position. Check to see that switch operating fingers are centered in switch opening in case.

4) Install switch with new seal into case and tighten. Check transmission fluid level. The back-up light switch circuit is through the 2 outside terminals of the switch.

5) Continuity should exist between the two terminals only when transmission is in reverse. No continuity should exist from either terminal to case.

FORD MOTOR CO.

LUBRICATION

SERVICE INTERVALS

Check fluid level at every engine oil change. Fluid, filter changes and band adjustments are not required under normal operation. Under heavy duty (severe service), change fluid every 30 months or 30,000 miles. Adjust bands when fluid is changed.

CHECKING FLUID LEVEL

1) With transmission at normal operating temperature, place vehicle on level ground. Apply parking brake, and run engine at curb idle. Shift selector through all positions, ending in Park.

2) With transmission at normal operating temperature, fluid level should be between "ADD" and "DON'T ADD" or "MAX" marks on dipstick. If transmission is at room temperature, fluid level should be between middle and top holes on dipstick.

3) If fluid level is correct at room temperature, it will be between "ADD" and "DON'T ADD" or "MAX" marks on dipstick when normal operating temperature is reached. Do not overfill. Check condition of fluid for contamination or burned smell. Fully reseat dipstick.

RECOMMENDED FLUID

C-3 transmissions use Dexron II automatic transmission fluid (Ford XT-2-QDX). The AOD, AXOD, ATX and C-5 (except with 12" torque converter) transmissions use Ford automatic transmission fluid Type H (or equivalent Ford ESP-M2C166-H). C-5 with 12" torque converter require Ford XT-4-H transmission fluid (Ford ESP-M2C166-A).

FLUID CAPACITY

NOTE: **Transmission and converter assembly capacities given below are approximate, and correct fluid level should be determined by mark on dipstick, rather than by amount added.**

TRANSMISSION REFILL CAPACITIES

Application	[1] Quantity
AOD	12.3 qts. (11.6L)
ATX	8.3 qts. (7.9L)
AXOD	10.4 (13.3)
C-3	8.0 qts. (7.6L)
C-5	11.0 qts. (10.4L)

[1] – Includes oil cooler (if equipped).

DRAINING & REFILLING

1) To drain torque converter on AOD transmission, remove lower engine dust cover. Rotate torque converter until drain plug is accessible. Remove plug and allow to drain. Flush cooler lines completely. This procedure must be done before any other operation.

2) On "pan-filled" C-5 transmissions, disconnect fluid filler tube from transmission pan to drain fluid. Remove oil pan.

3) On all other models, loosen oil pan attaching bolts to drain fluid. Remove oil pan. On all except AOD transmissions, remove and clean filter screen. Reinstall filter screen using a new gasket. On AOD transmissions, discard used filter and gasket. Install new filter and gasket. On all models, clean oil pan, and install pan with new gasket.

4) On "pan-filled" C-5 transmissions, connect fluid filler tube to oil pan and tighten fitting. On all models, pour 3 quarts (2.8L) of fluid through filler tube. Check fluid level.

ADJUSTMENTS

INTERMEDIATE BAND (FRONT)

C-3

1) Remove downshift rod from transmission downshift lever. Clean all dirt from band adjusting screw area. Remove and discard lock nut. Install a new lock nut on band adjusting screw.

2) Tighten band adjusting screw to 10 ft. lbs. (14 N.m). Back off screw EXACTLY 2 turns. Hold adjusting screw in this position and tighten lock nut to 35-45 ft. lbs. (48-61 N.m). Connect downshift rod to downshift lever.

Fig. 1: Location of Front Band Adjusting Screw on C-3 Transmission

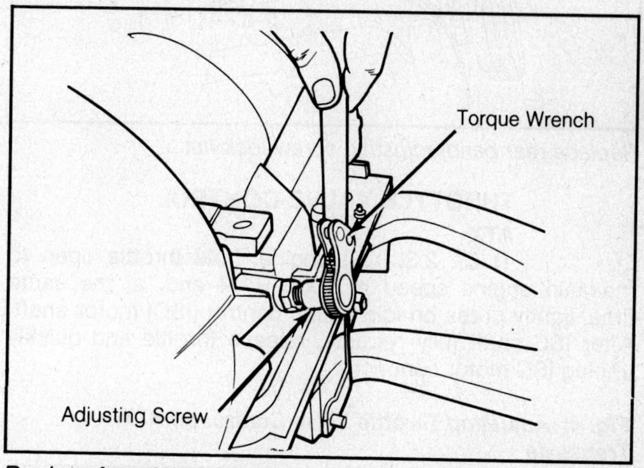

Replace front band adjusting screw lock nut.

C-5

1) Clean all dirt from band adjusting screw area. Remove and discard adjusting screw lock nut. Install a new lock nut on adjusting screw, leaving lock nut loose.

2) Tighten band adjusting screw to 10 ft. lbs. (14 N.m). Back off adjusting screw EXACTLY 4 1/4 turns. Hold adjusting screw in this position and tighten lock nut to 40 ft. lbs. (54 N.m).

Fig. 2: Location of Front Band Adjusting Screw on C-5 Transmission

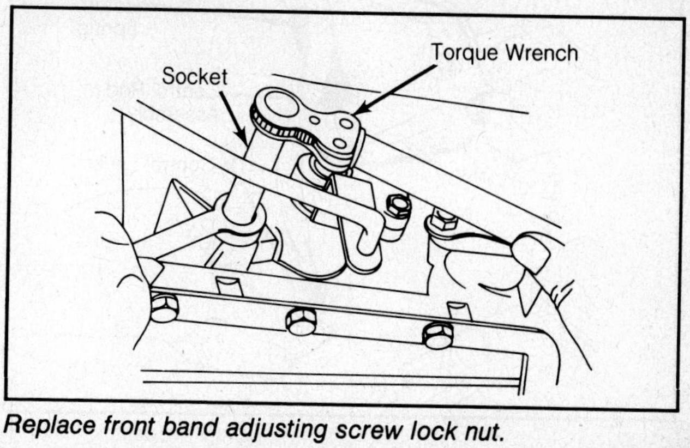

Replace front band adjusting screw lock nut.

FORD MOTOR CO. (Cont.)

LOW-REVERSE BAND (REAR)

C-5

1) Clean all dirt from band adjusting screw area. Remove and discard adjusting screw lock nut. Install a new adjusting screw lock nut, leaving nut loose.

2) Tighten band adjusting screw to 10 ft. lbs. (14 N.m). Back off screw EXACTLY 3 turns. Hold adjusting screw in this position and tighten lock nut to 40 ft. lbs. (54 N.m).

Fig. 3: Location of Rear Band Adjusting Screw on C-5 Transmission

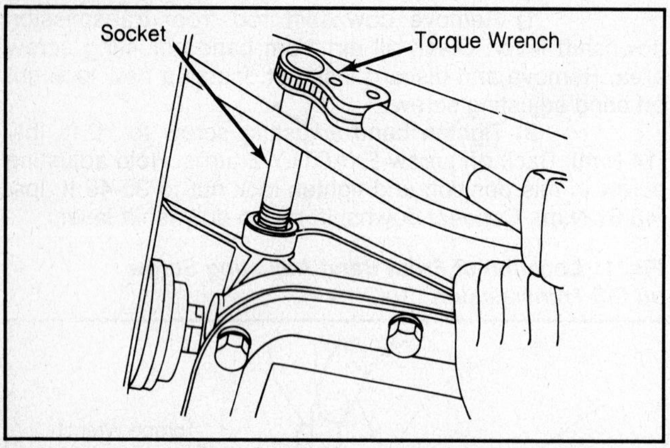

Replace rear band adjusting screw lock nut.

THROTTLE VALVE CONTROL

ATX

1) On 2.3L CFI engine, hold throttle open to maintain engine speed at 1000 RPM and, at the same time, lightly press on idle speed control (ISC) motor shaft. After ISC shaft fully retracts, release throttle and quickly unplug ISC motor connector.

Fig. 4: Adjusting Throttle Valve Control on ATX Transaxle

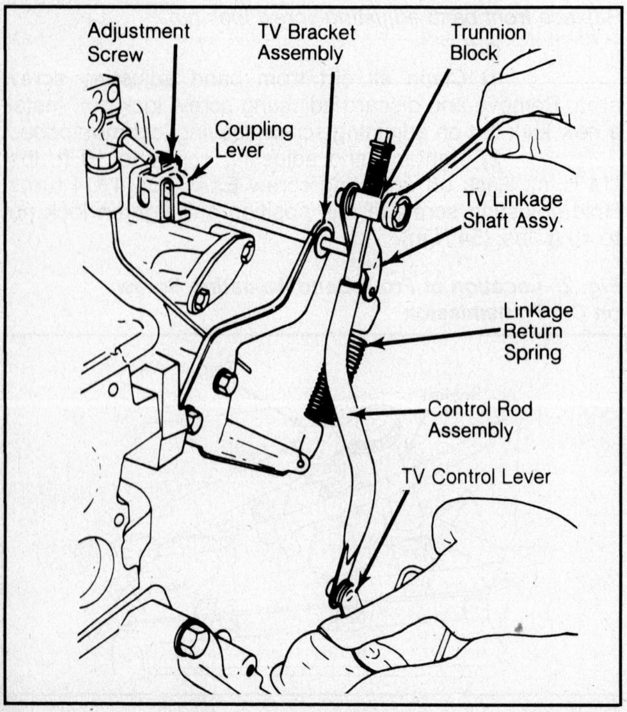

2) On all other engines, engine must be at normal operating temperature (choke fully open) and transaxle in Park. Curb idle speed must be set to specification.

3) On all engines, loosen bolt on sliding trunnion block at least 1 turn. Make sure that block can slide freely on rod. *See Fig. 4*.

4) Rotate transaxle T.V. control lever upward with finger, using a force of about 1 pound to ensure that it is against internal idle stop. Hold T.V. control and tighten trunnion block bolt.

Automatic Overdrive Transmission (AOD)

1) Engine must be at normal operating temperature. On models without Idle Speed Control (ISC), throttle lever must be resting on idle stop or throttle solenoid positioner stop. On all models, place transmission selector lever in Neutral and set parking brake.

2) On vehicles with ISC, locate the self test connector and self test input connector in engine compartment. *See Fig. 5*. Connect a jumper wire between the self test input connector and the signal return ground terminal.

Fig. 5: Location of Self Test Connectors

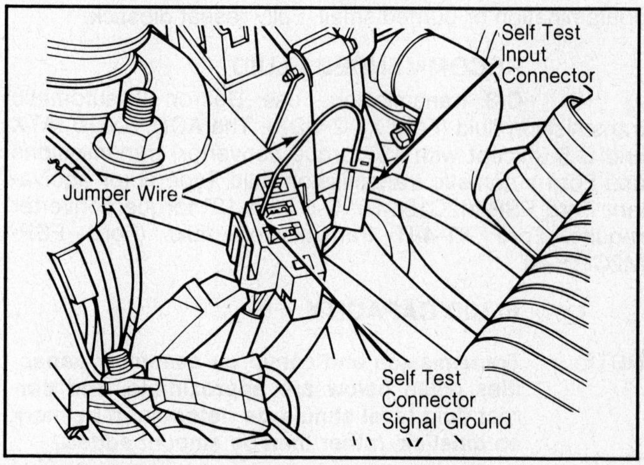

Use jumper wire to return ISC to idle position.

3) Turn ignition key to "RUN" position. DO NOT start engine. Wait 10 seconds to allow ISC plunger to fully retract. Turn ignition key off. Remove jumper wire and air cleaner.

4) On all vehicles, back out linkage adjusting screw counterclockwise until screw end is flush with lever face. Turn adjusting screw clockwise to obtain .005" (.12 mm) clearance between end of screw and throttle lever.

5) Open and close throttle to eliminate friction and recheck clearance. DO NOT apply any load on levers while checking. Turn adjusting screw clockwise 3 full turns.

6) If screw travel is limited, 1 turn minimum is permitted, however 3 turns are preferred. If idle speed requires adjustment of more than 50 RPM, turn adjustment screw on linkage lever.

NOTE: **If adjustment of linkage lever screw is not possible, adjustment of the T.V. control rod at transmission is required. This adjustment is also required when a new T.V. control rod is installed.**

AOD Throttle Valve (T.V.) Control Rod

1) Engine must be at normal operating temperature. On models without Idle Speed Control (ISC), throttle

FORD MOTOR CO. (Cont.)

lever must be resting on idle stop or throttle solenoid positioner stop. On vehicles equipped with ISC, retract the ISC plunger as previously described. On all models, place transmission selector lever in Neutral and set parking brake.

2) Set linkage lever adjustment screw about mid-range. Raise vehicle and allow exhaust system to cool. Loosen bolt on T.V. control rod trunnion block at transmission lever. Ensure that trunnion block is free to slide on rod.

3) Push upward on lower end of T.V. rod (at transmission) to ensure that carburetor linkage is held firmly against throttle lever. Control rod should stay in position when released.

4) Firmly hold T.V. control lever on transmission upward against internal stop and tighten trunnion block bolt in position. Lower vehicle. On models without ISC, check that throttle lever resting on idle stop or throttle solenoid positioner stop. On models with ISC, plug in ISC motor electrical connector.

AXOD Transaxle

1) Ensure T.V. cable eye is connected to throttle control lever link. Ensure cable boot is attached to chain cover.

2) With T.V. cable mounted in engine bracket, ensure threaded shank is fully retracted. *See Fig. 6.* To retract shank, hold spring rest and wriggle top of thread shank while pressing shank toward spring.

Fig. 6: Adjusting AXOD T.V. Cable

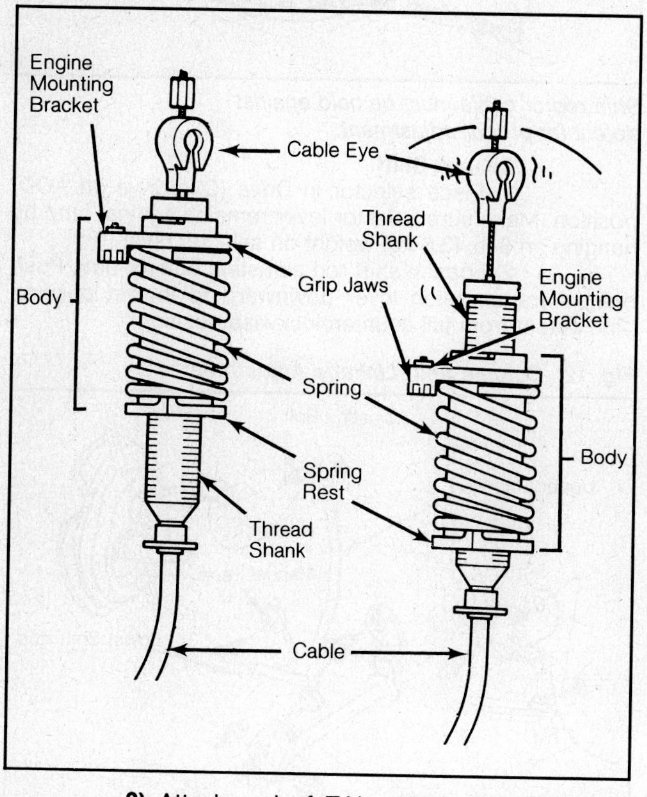

3) Attach end of T.V. cable to throttle body. Rotate throttle lever to WOT position and release. Threaded shank must show movement or "ratchet" out of grip jaws. If no movement is observed, inspect T.V. cable system for broken or disconnected components and repeat procedure.

C-3 & C-5 Transmissions

1) Hold carburetor or throttle body at wide open throttle position. Hold throttle valve control rod downward with 6 lbs. (2.7 kg) against "through detent" stop.

2) Turn kickdown screw to obtain .010-.080" (.25-2.0 mm) clearance between screw and throttle arm.

3) Return to idle. Tighten adjusting screw lock nut, or install kickdown retracting spring, as equipped. Return throttle and kickdown rod to normal position.

Fig. 7: Transmission Kickdown Linkage Adjustment on 2.3L Non-Turbo Engine

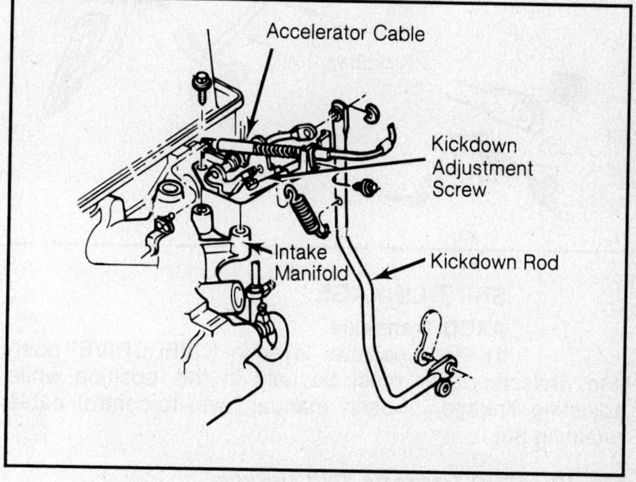

2.3L EFI Turbo & C3 Transmission

1) Ensure cable and kickdown return spring are installed at transmission kickdown lever. Remove clip in cable adjuster located at accelerator bracket fitting.

2) Rotate carburetor throttle lever to wide open throttle position. While holding throttle at wide open throttle, install clip in kickdown cable adjuster.

Fig. 8: Transmission Kickdown Linkage Adjustment on 2.3L Turbo Engine

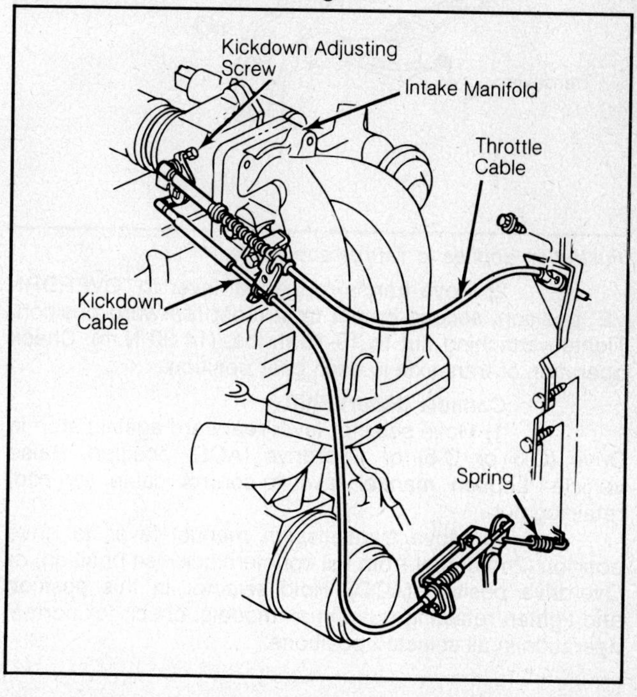

FORD MOTOR CO. (Cont.)

Fig. 9: Transmission Kickdown Linkage Adjustment on 3.8L Engine

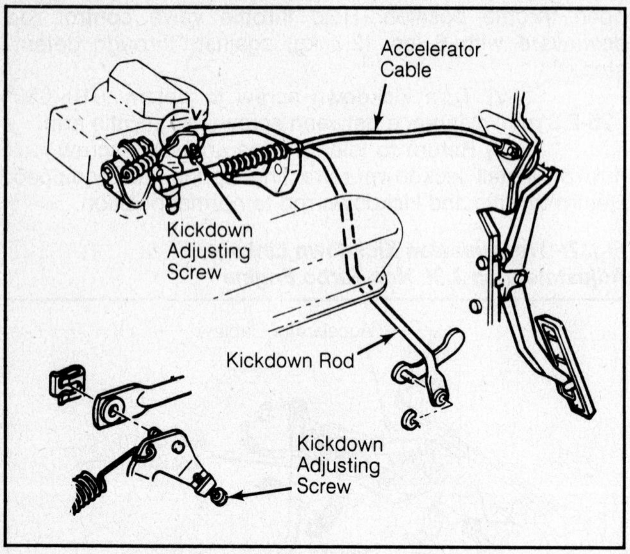

SHIFT LINKAGE

AXOD Transaxle

1) Place selector lever in "OVERDRIVE" position. Selector lever must be held in this position while adjusting linkage. Loosen manual lever-to-control cable retaining nut.

Fig. 10: AXOD Transaxle Shift Linkage

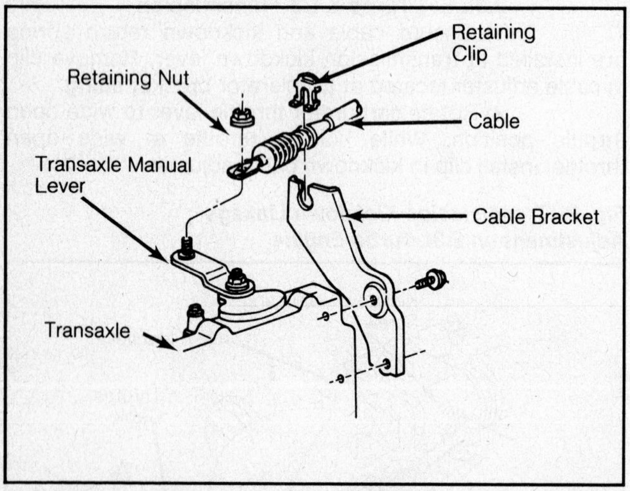

Illustration applies to Taurus and Sable.

2) Move transaxle manual lever to "OVERDRIVE" position, second detent from most rearward position. Tighten attaching nut to 10-15 ft. lbs. (14-20 N.m). Check operation of transaxle in each gear position.

Console (Floor) Shift

1) Move selector lever rearward against stop in Drive (C-3 or C-5) or Overdrive (AOD) position. Raise vehicle. Loosen manual lever-to-control cable (or rod) retaining nut.

2) Move transmission manual lever to drive position (2nd detent from full counterclockwise position) or Overdrive position (AOD). Hold selector in this position and tighten retaining nut. On all models, check for normal operation in all selected positions.

Fig. 11: Console (Floor) Shift Linkage Adjustment

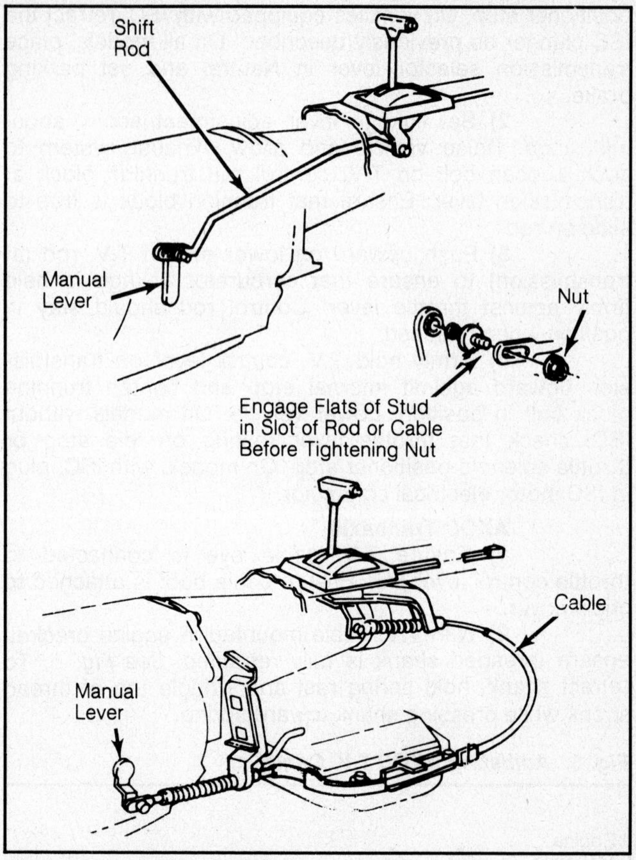

Shift rod or cable must be held against detent for proper adjustment.

Column Shift

1) Place selector in Drive (Overdrive on AOD) position. Make sure selector lever remains against stop by hanging an 8 lb. (3.6 kg) weight on selector lever.

2) Loosen shift rod adjusting bolt (or nut). Push manual transmission lever downward to lowest position (2nd detent from full counterclockwise position).

Fig. 12: Column Shift Linkage Adjustment

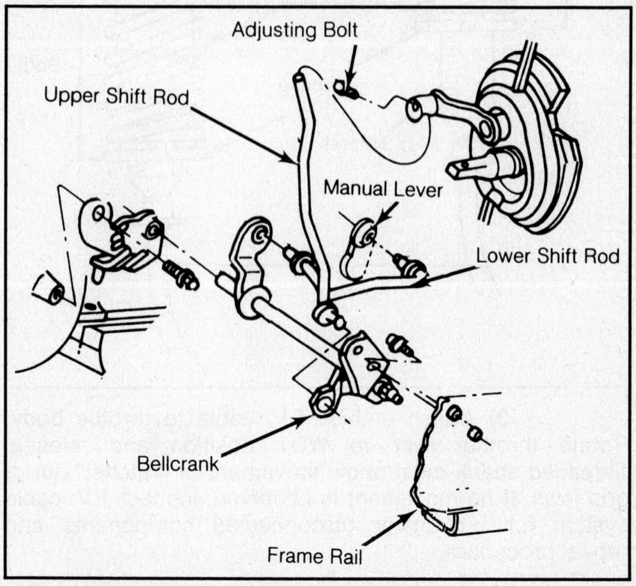

Crown Victoria, Grand Marquis and Lincoln with AOT.

FORD MOTOR CO. (Cont.)

3) Ensure the slotted rod end has flats aligned with flats on mounting stud, if equipped. Ensure selector lever has not moved from Drive (C-3 and C-5) or Overdrive (AOD) position. Tighten bolt (or nut) and check operation in all selector detent positions.

Fig. 13: Column Shift Linkage Adjustment

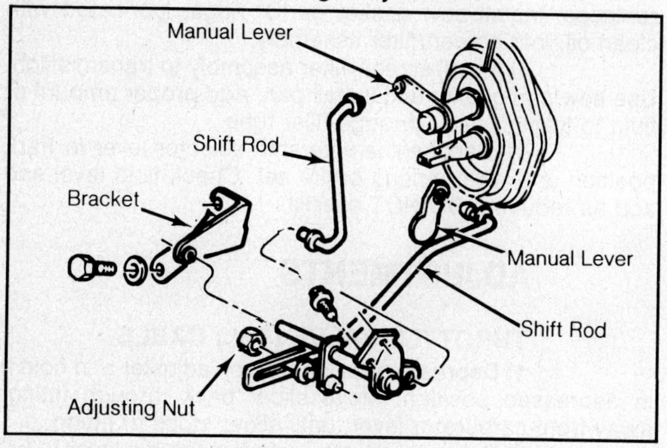

Cougar, LTD, Marquis and Thunderbird with C-3 and C-5 transmission.

Fig. 14: Column Shift Linkage Adjustment

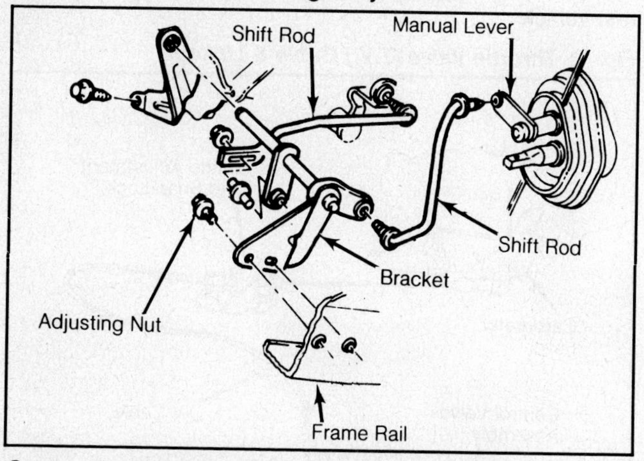

Cougar, Continental and Thunderbird with AOT.

NEUTRAL SAFETY SWITCH

Column Shift

1) Vehicles equipped with an automatic transmission and a column shift do not use a neutral start switch.

2) The ignition switch mechanism in steering column is designed so that ignition switch may be turned to start position only when selector lever is in Neutral or Park positions.

3) Switch is blocked from start position in all other selector lever positions.

Floor Shift (Transmission Mounted Switch)

1) With transmission shift linkage properly adjusted, loosen the 2 switch attaching bolts.

2) Place transmission manual lever in Neutral position, then rotate switch and insert a gauge pin (No. 43 drill shank) into gauge pin holes of switch.

3) Gauge pin must be inserted to a full 15/32" into the 3 holes of the switch. Tighten switch attaching bolts and remove gauge pin.

4) Check operation of switch. Engine should start in Neutral and Park positions only.

Fig. 15: Transmission Mounted Neutral Safety Switch

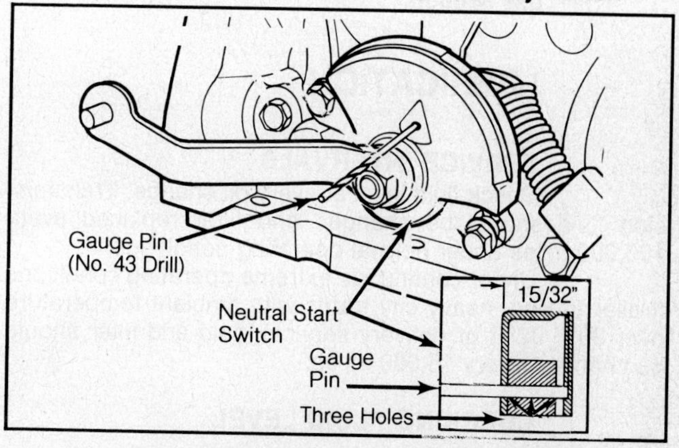

Floor Shift (Console Mounted Switch)

1) With transmission shift linkage adjusted and engine off, place selector lever in Neutral position. Remove selector lever handle, dial housing, and pointer back-up shield.

2) Loosen the 2 screws securing neutral start switch to selector lever housing. Place selector lever in Park position and hold it against the forward stop.

3) Move neutral switch rearward to end of its travel. Hold switch in rearward position and tighten the 2 attaching screws. Check operation of switch. Engine should start in Neutral and Park positions only.

REMOVAL & INSTALLATION

GROMMET

Shift linkage systems use an oil impregnated plastic grommet to connect various rods and levers. A new grommet must be installed each time any rod is disconnected from a grommet-type connector.

Transmission On Bench

1) For removal and installation with transmission out of vehicle, Remover/Replacer (Ford T67P-7341-A) is required to install grommet into shift lever and to install shift linkage rod into grommet.

2) Remove grommet as follows: Place lower jaw of tool between shift lever and shift rod. Position stop pin against end of shift rod and force rod out of grommet. Remove grommet by cutting off the large shoulder with a sharp knife.

3) Before installing new grommet, adjust stop pin to 1/2" and coat outside of grommet with lubricant. Place grommet on stop pin and force into lever hole.

4) Turn grommet several times to ensure proper seating. Squeeze rod into bushing until stop washer seats against grommet.

Transmission In Vehicle

1) Disconnect linkage from grommet. Position Grommet Replacer (T84P-7341-A). Rotate screw in tool until grommet is forced out of lever.

2) Adjust stop on Grommet Replacer (T84P-7341-A) to 1/2". Coat outside of grommet with lubricant. Position grommet on lever.

3) Use replacer tool to force grommet into position. Ensure grommet is fully seated in lever. Connect linkage.

GENERAL MOTORS – BUICK, CHEVROLET, OLDSMOBILE & PONTIAC

NOTE: **For information on Chevrolet Nova, see GENERAL MOTORS - CHEVROLET NOVA in this section.**

LUBRICATION

SERVICE INTERVALS

Check fluid level at every oil change. Transmission fluid should be changed and filter replaced every 100,000 miles under normal operating conditions.

Under continuous extreme operating conditions (trailer towing, heavy city traffic with ambient temperature over 90°F/32°C or delivery service), fluid and filter should be changed every 15,000 miles.

CHECKING FLUID LEVEL

CAUTION: **Do not overfill. One pint of fluid will raise level from "ADD 1 PT. OR .5L" to "FULL HOT" mark on dipstick with a hot transmission.**

1) Warm transmission to normal operating temperature by at least 15 miles of highway driving. With engine at curb idle, move selector lever through all ranges, ending in Park.

2) Remove dipstick. Wipe dipstick clean and reinstall. Remove again and inspect level. Fluid level should check between "ADD 1 PT. OR .5L" and "FULL HOT" marks on dipstick.

CAUTION: **If vehicle has been operated for an extended period of time at high speed, in city traffic in hot weather, or if vehicle has been pulling a trailer, an accurate fluid level cannot be determined until fluid has cooled down (about 30 minutes after vehicle has been parked).**

RECOMMENDED FLUID

Use only Dexron II or equivalent automatic transmission fluid.

FLUID CAPACITY

NOTE: **Quantities listed are approximate. Correct fluid level should be determined by mark on dipstick rather than by amount added.**

TRANSMISSION REFILL CAPACITIES

Application	Refill Quantity	Total Quantity
THM 125C	8 pts. (3.8L)	12 pts. (5.7L)
THM 180C	6 pts. (2.8L)	10 pts. (4.7L)
THM 200C	7 pts. (3.3L)	19 pts. (9.0L)
THM 200-4R	7 pts. (3.3L)	22 pts. (10.4L)
THM 440-T4	6 pts. (2.8L)	10 pts. (4.7L)
THM 700-R4	10 pts. (4.7L)	23 pts. (10.9L)

DRAINING & REFILLING

1) With vehicle raised and drain pan placed under transmission, remove front and side transmission oil pan bolts. Loosen rear pan bolts about 4 turns each.

2) Carefully pry pan loose with screwdriver, allowing fluid to drain. Remove remaining bolts and oil pan with gasket. Remove screen/filter-to-valve body bolts and remove screen/filter with gasket.

3) Thoroughly clean pan and screen with solvent and dry with compressed air. Paper type filters should be replaced. Install new gasket or "O" rings, lubricated with clean oil, into screen/filter assembly.

4) Install screen/filter assembly to transmission. Use new pan gasket and install pan. Add proper amount of fluid to transmission through filler tube.

5) Start engine with shift selector lever in Park position and with parking brake set. Check fluid level and add as required. DO NOT overfill.

ADJUSTMENTS

THROTTLE VALVE (T.V.) CABLE

1) Depress metal lock tab on adjuster and hold it in depressed position. Move slider back through fitting, away from carburetor lever, until slider stops at fitting.

2) Release lock tab and open throttle lever to full throttle stop to automatically adjust slider to correct setting. Release throttle lever. *See Figs. 1 and 2.*

3) Check cable for sticking and binding. Road test vehicle.

Fig. 1: Throttle Valve (T.V.) Cable & Linkage

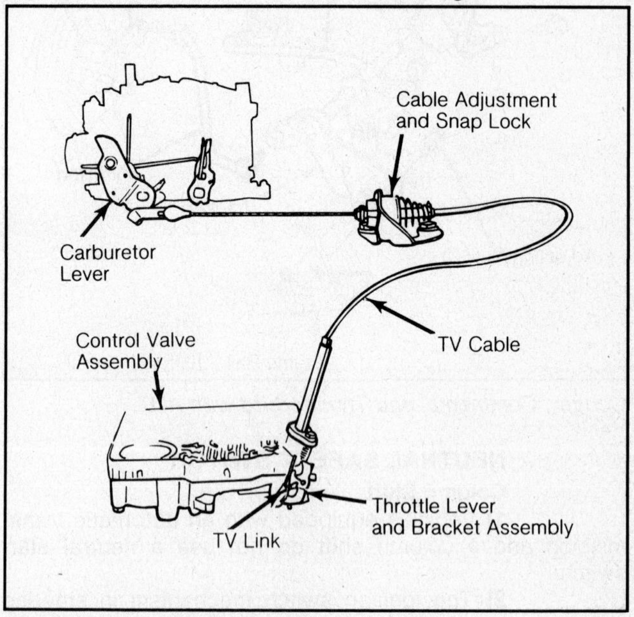

Fig. 2: Self-Adjusting Throttle Valve Cable

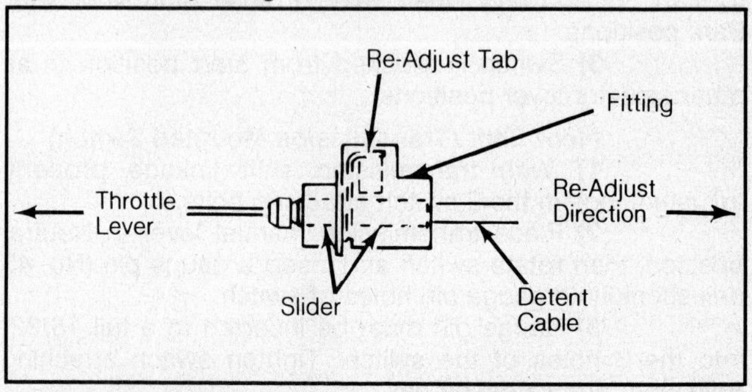

Press tab to move slider in correct direction.

GENERAL MOTORS – BUICK, CHEVROLET, OLDSMOBILE & PONTIAC (Cont.)

4) If delayed or only full throttle shifts occur, proceed as follows: remove transmission oil pan and inspect throttle lever and bracket assembly.

5) Ensure T.V. exhaust valve lifter rod is not distorted and binding in control valve assembly or spacer plate. T.V. exhaust check ball must move up and down as lifer does. Lifter spring must hold lifter rod up against bottom of control valve assembly. Ensure correct throttle lever-to-cable link is used.

SHIFT LINKAGE

1) Linkage should be adjusted so that engine cannot be started in any position except "P" or "N". If linkage is improperly adjusted, an internal leak could occur causing a clutch and/or band failure.

2) With selector lever in "P" position, parking pawl should engage rear/reaction internal gear lugs or output ring gear lugs. Pointer on indicator quadrant should line up properly with range indicators in all ranges.

Column Shift (Rod Type, RWD Models)

1) Position steering column shift lever in Neutral gate notch. Loosen swivel clamp lock screw and place transmission lever in Neutral.

2) Hold swivel clamp against equalizer lever. Tighten clamp screw without applying tension on either equalizer lever or selector rod. *See Fig. 3.*

Fig. 3: Rod Type Column Shift Linkage

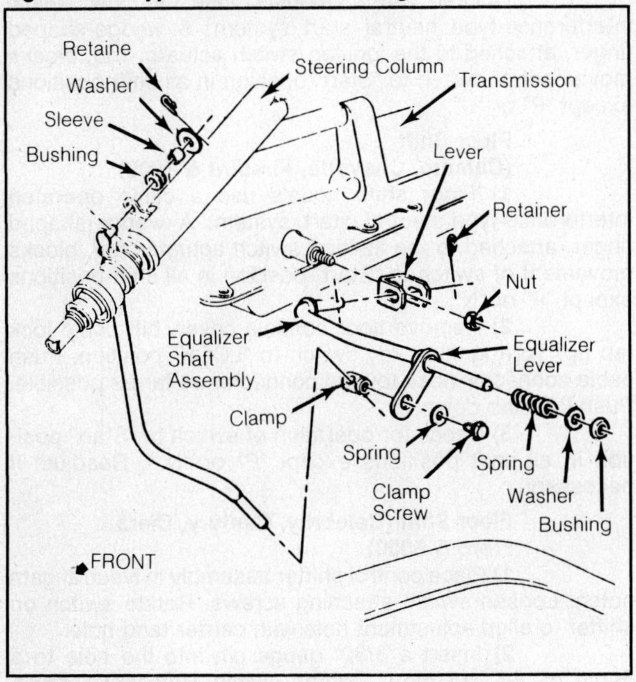

Ensure there is no tension on either equalizer lever or selector rod.

Floor Shift (RWD Models)

1) Disconnect shifter link from shifter assembly and place shifter assembly in Neutral notch of detent plate. *See Fig. 4.*

2) Place transmission lever in Neutral position by moving clockwise to maximum detent position, then back (counterclockwise) 2 detents to Neutral. Adjust link until hole and pin line up. Install shim and retainer.

Fig. 4: Floor Shift Linkage (Chevette & 1000)

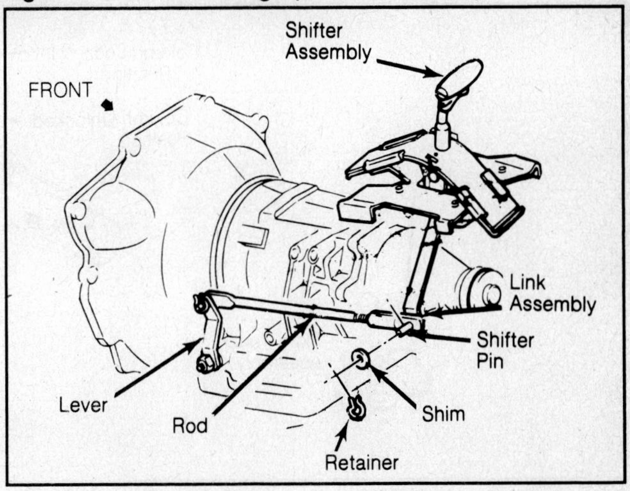

Chevette & 1000 shown; others are similar.

Floor Shift (FWD Models)

1) Place shift lever in Neutral position. Place transaxle lever in Neutral notch. Loosely assemble nut to pin through transaxle lever with transaxle cable assembled to pin.

2) Assemble steering column shift lever pin and transaxle control cable bracket. Tighten nut. Lever must be held out of Park when tightening nut.

Fig. 5: Typical Floor Shift Linkage (FWD Models)

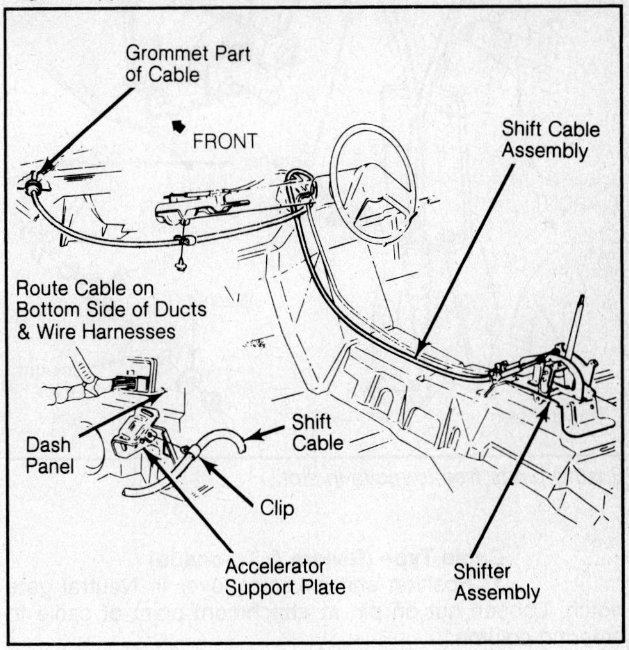

Cable Type (FWD Models Exc. Riviera & Toronado)

1) Position shift selector lever and transaxle lever in Neutral position. Loosely assemble pin and nut through transaxle lever with transaxle cable assembled to pin.

2) Assemble steering column shift lever pin and transaxle control cable bracket. Tighten nut (lever must be held out of Park when tightening nut).

GENERAL MOTORS – BUICK, CHEVROLET, OLDSMOBILE & PONTIAC (Cont.)

Fig. 6: Floor Shift Column Lock (Corvette)

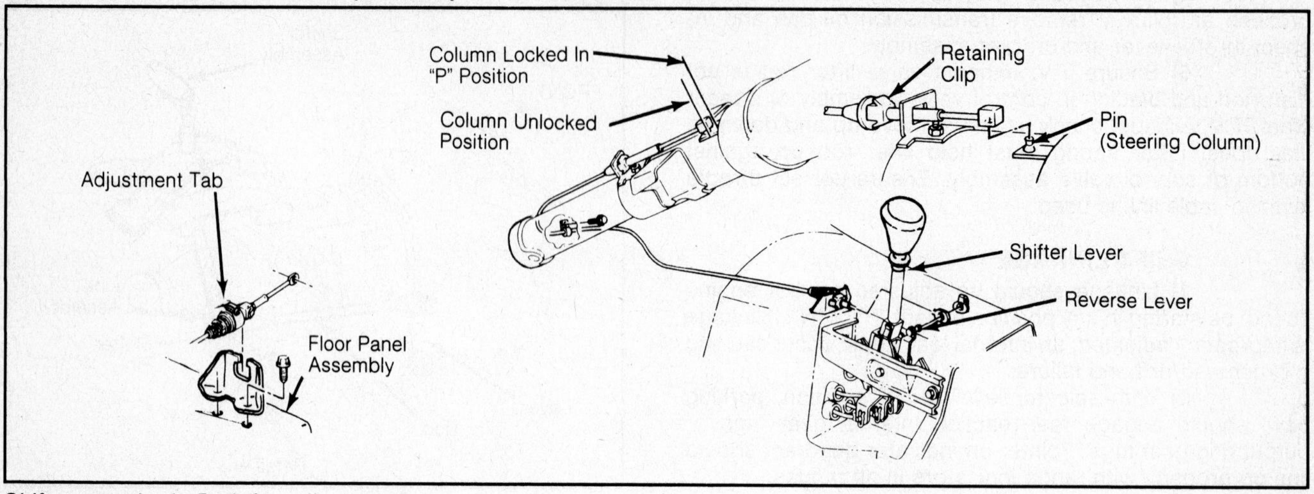

Shifter must be in Park for adjustment.

Fig. 7: Cable Type Adjustment (FWD Models)

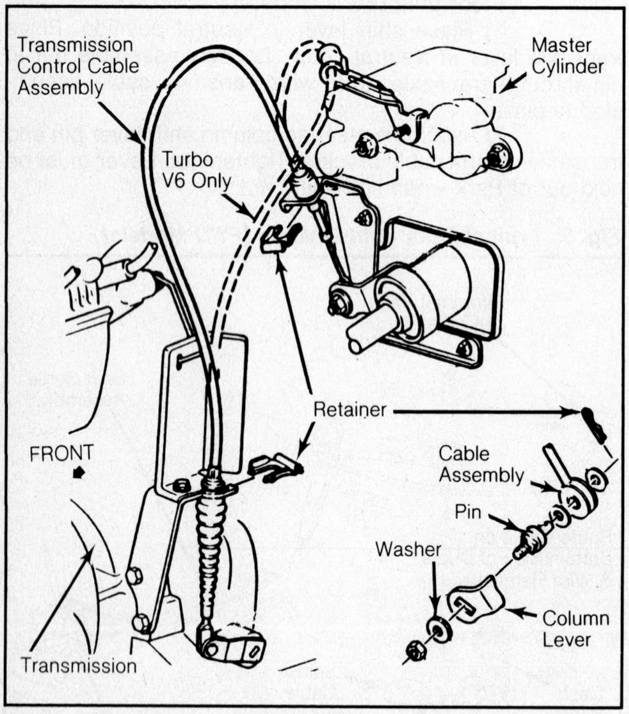

Ensure pin is free to move in slot.

Cable Type (Riviera & Toronado)

1) Position shift selector lever in Neutral gate notch. Loosen nut on pin at attachment point of cable to steering column.

2) Move transaxle lever to Neutral position and ensure that pin is free to move in slot. Tighten pin without applying tension on cable or lever.

Floor Shift Column Lock (Corvette)

1) Place steering column lock lever in locked position. Place selector lever in Park position. Release cable retainer at column lever lock pin.

2) Apply tension to the shifter rearward on the park stop. Pull cable adjustment tab up. Reinstall cable retainer at column lock pin. Push cable adjustment tab down.

NEUTRAL SAFETY SWITCH

Column Shift Models

Column shift models use a mechanical interference-type neutral start system. A wedge-shaped finger, attached to the ignition switch actuator rod, blocks movement of switch to "Start" position in all shift positions except "P" or "N".

Floor Shift (Camaro, Chevette, Firebird & 1000)

1) Floor shift models use a cable operated interference-type neutral start system. A wedge-shaped finger, attached to the ignition switch actuator rod, blocks movement of switch to "Start" position in all shift positions except "P" or "N".

2) Remove floor console cover. Lift cable lock tab up. Turn ignition key switch to "LOCK" position. Push cable connector nose toward connector as far as possible. Push lock tab down.

3) Check for operation of switch to "Start" position in all shift positions except "P" or "N ". Readjust if necessary.

Floor Shift (Celebrity, Century, Ciera, Fiero & 6000)

1) Place control shifter assembly in Neutral gate notch. Loosen switch attaching screws. Rotate switch on shifter to align adjustment hole with carrier tang hole.

2) Insert a 3/32" gauge pin into the hole to a depth of .60" (15 mm). Tighten switch attaching screws. Remove gauge pin.

TORQUE CONVERTER CLUTCH BRAKE SWITCH

The torque converter clutch brake switch must be adjusted to prevent vehicle stalling at idle. Ensure brake pedal is fully released. Adjust plunger to just touch brake pedal lever.

GENERAL MOTORS – BUICK, CHEVROLET, OLDSMOBILE & PONTIAC (Cont.)

Fig. 8: Floor Shift Column Lock (Corvette)

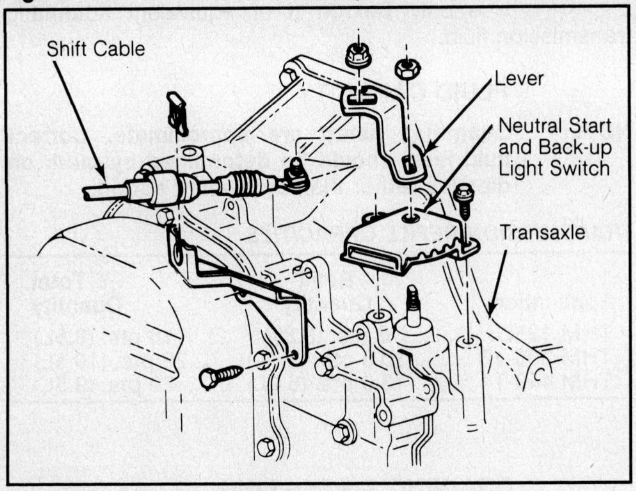

All other models are located at base of shifter.

Automatic Transmission Servicing

GENERAL MOTORS – CADILLAC

LUBRICATION

SERVICE INTERVALS

Check fluid level at every oil change. Transmission fluid should be changed and filter replaced every 100,000 miles under normal operating conditions.

Under continuous extreme operating conditions (trailer towing, heavy city traffic with ambient temperature over 90°F/32°C or delivery service), fluid and filter should be changed every 15,000 miles.

CHECKING FLUID LEVEL

CAUTION: **Do not overfill. One pint of fluid will raise level from "ADD 1 PT. OR .5L" to "FULL HOT" mark on dipstick with a hot transmission.**

1) Warm transmission to normal operating temperature by at least 15 miles of highway driving. With engine at curb idle, move selector lever through all ranges, ending in Park.

2) Remove dipstick. Wipe dipstick clean and reinstall. Remove again and inspect level. Fluid level should check between "ADD 1 PT. OR .5L" and "FULL HOT" marks on dipstick.

CAUTION: **If vehicle has been operated for an extended period of time at high speed, in city traffic in hot weather, or if vehicle has been pulling a trailer, an accurate fluid level cannot be determined until fluid has cooled down (about 30 minutes after vehicle has been parked).**

RECOMMENDED FLUID

Use only Dexron II or equivalent automatic transmission fluid.

FLUID CAPACITY

NOTE: **Quantities listed are approximate. Correct fluid level should be determined by mark on dipstick rather than by amount added.**

TRANSMISSION REFILL CAPACITIES

Application	Refill Quantity	Total Quantity
THM 125C	8 pts. (3.8L)	18 pts. (8.5L)
THM 200-4R	10.6 pts. (5.0L)	22 pts. (10.4L)
THM 440-T4	13.0 pts. (6.2L)	20 pts. (9.5L)

DRAINING & REFILLING

Oil Pans Installed With RTV Sealant

1) If oil pan is installed with RTV sealant, a modified oil pan bolt must be used to remove pan. Modify an old pan bolt by grinding down a section of the shank, just below head of bolt, to 3/16" diameter. *See Fig. 1.*

2) With vehicle raised and drain pan placed under transmission, remove all oil pan bolts, except "A" and "B". Remove bolt "A" and install modified oil pan bolt. Loosen bolt "B" 4 turns. *See Fig. 1.*

3) DO NOT pry pan loose, as damage to pan flange or case will occur. Using a rubber mallet, strike oil pan corner. *See Fig. 1.* Remove modified oil pan bolt and

Fig. 1: Removal of Oil Pan Bolts on Transmissions Using RTV Sealant Instead of A Gasket

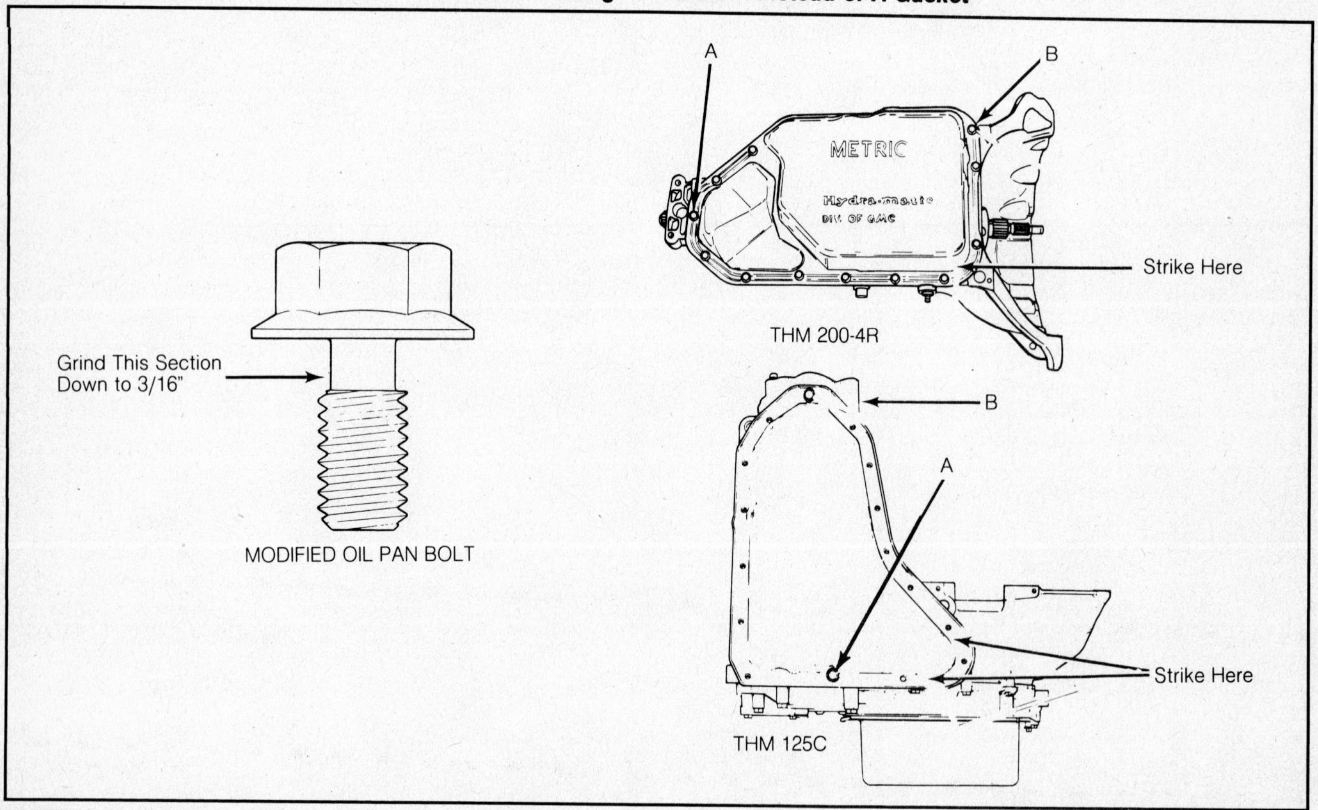

Modified oil pan bolt must be used to remove oil pan.

allow fluid to drain. Remove screen/filter-to-valve body bolts and remove screen/filter with gasket.

4) Thoroughly clean pan and remove excess RTV sealant. Install new gasket or "O" rings lubricated with clean oil into new screen/filter assembly and install screen/filter assembly to transmission.

5) Apply 1/16" bead of RTV sealant on oil pan flange, and install pan while RTV is still wet. Lower vehicle and add proper amount of fluid to transmission through filler tube. Start engine in Park position with parking brake set.

6) With engine idling, move selector lever through all positions, ending in Park. Check fluid level and add as required. DO NOT overfill. See CHECKING FLUID LEVEL.

Oil Pans Installed With Gasket

1) With vehicle raised and drain pan placed under transmission, remove front and side oil pan bolts. On THM 440-T4, loosen rear oil pan bolts about 4 turns and carefully pry oil pan loose with screwdriver. Allow fluid to drain. Remove remaining oil pan bolts and pan with gasket attached.

2) On all other models, strike oil pan corner opposite remaining bolt with a rubber mallet. Remove remaining bolt and allow fluid to drain.

3) On all models, remove screen/filter-to-valve body bolts and remove screen/filter with gasket. Thoroughly clean pan with solvent and dry with compressed air. Install new gasket or "O" rings lubricated with clean oil into new screen/filter assembly. Install screen/filter assembly on transmission.

4) Using new oil pan gasket, install oil pan. Lower vehicle and add proper amount of fluid to transmission through filler tube. Start engine in Park position with parking brake applied.

5) With engine idling, move selector lever through all positions, ending in Park. Check fluid level and add as required. DO NOT overfill. See CHECKING FLUID LEVEL.

ADJUSTMENTS

THROTTLE VALVE CABLE

This system not only controls downshift, but also controls line pressure, shift points, shift feel, part throttle downshifts and detent downshifts.

Self-Adjusting Type T.V. Cable

1) Depress lock tab and move slider back through fitting away from throttle body or pump lever until slider stops against fitting.

2) Release lock tab and open throttle to full throttle stop position to automatically adjust T.V. cable. Release throttle.

Fig. 2: Self-Adjusting Throttle Valve Cable

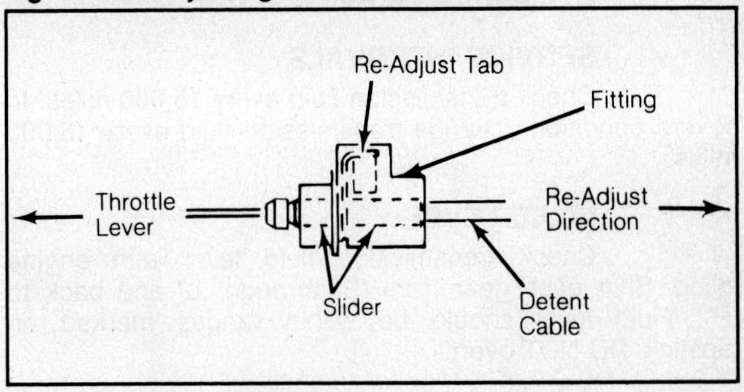

Press tab to move slider in correct direction.

SHIFT LINKAGE

1) Linkage should be adjusted so that engine cannot be started in any position except "P" or "N". If linkage is improperly adjusted, an internal leak could occur causing a clutch and/or band failure.

2) With selector lever in "P" position, parking pawl should engage rear/reaction internal gear lugs or output ring gear lugs. Pointer on indicator quadrant should line up properly with range indicators in all ranges.

NEUTRAL SAFETY SWITCH

Column Shift Models

Column shift models use a mechanical interference type neutral start system. A wedge-shaped finger, attached to the ignition switch actuator rod, blocks movement of switch to "START" position in all shift positions except "N" or "P".

TORQUE (OR VISCOUS) CONVERTER CLUTCH BRAKE SWITCH

The torque (or viscous) converter clutch brake switch must be adjusted to prevent vehicle stalling at idle. Ensure brake pedal is fully released. Adjust plunger to just touch brake pedal lever.

VISCOUS CONVERTER CLUTCH THERMISTOR SWITCH

The THM 440-T4 is equipped with a thermistor switch that senses the temperature of the transaxle fluid. This information is sent to the ECM for Viscous Converter Clutch (VCC) operation. The ECM will engage the VCC when fluid temperature is 200°F (93°C) or less, provided all other conditions have been met. If fluid temperature is higher than this, ECM will not allow VCC engagement until vehicle speed is about 36 MPH.

GENERAL MOTORS – CHEVROLET NOVA

LUBRICATION

SERVICE INTERVALS

Check transmission fluid every 15,000 miles. In severe conditions change transmission fluid every 15,000 miles.

FLUID LEVEL

Check transmission fluid level with engine idling. Shift each gear from "P" through "L" and back to "P". Fluid level should be within ranges marked on dipstick. DO NOT overfill.

RECOMMENDED FLUID

The A131L transaxle uses Dexron II automatic transmission fluid.

FLUID CAPACITY

TRANSMISSION REFILL CAPACITIES

Application	Refill Quantity	Dry Fill Quantity
Nova (FWD)	2.4 qts. (2.3L)	5.8 qts. (5.5L)

DRAINING & REFILLING

Automatic Transaxle

1) Remove drain plug in pan in drain pan. Reinstall plug securely.

2) With engine off, add new fluid through dipstick tube. Start engine and shift into all gear positions.

3) With engine idling, check fluid level with transaxle in "Park" position. Add fluid up to "COOL" level on dipstick.

Differential

Remove drain plug in differential carrier cover and drain fluid. Reinstall drian plug securely. Remove filler plug in side of carrier cover. Add new fluid (Dexron II) until it begins to run out of filler hole.

ADJUSTMENTS

FLOOR SHIFTER LINKAGE

1) Loosen swivel nut on shift lever at transaxle. *See Fig. 1*. Push manual lever fully toward right side of vehicle.

2) Return lever 2 notches to "Neutral" position. Set shift lever in "N" range. While holding lever lightly toward "R" range side, tighten swivel nut.

THROTTLE CABLE

1) Depress accelerator pedal to floor and ensure throttle valve opens fully. If not, adjust accelerator link.

Fig. 1: Adjusting Transaxle Control Cable

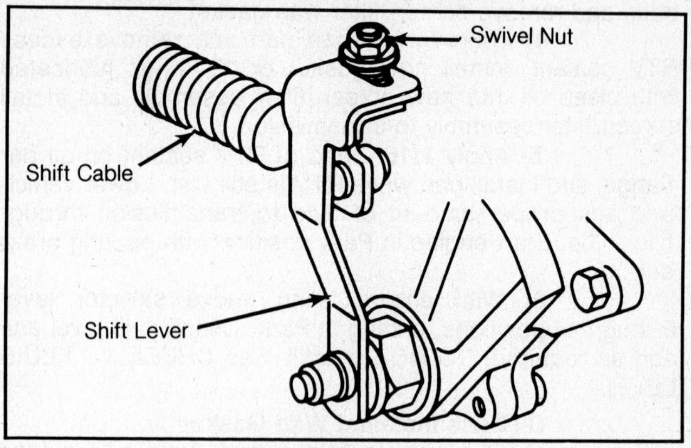

2) Fully depress accelerator. Loosen throttle cable adjusting nuts. *See Fig. 2*.

3) Adjust cable housing so distance between end of boot and stopper on cable is 0-.04" (0-1 mm). Tighten adjusting nuts. Recheck adjustment.

Fig. 2: Adjusting Throttle Cable

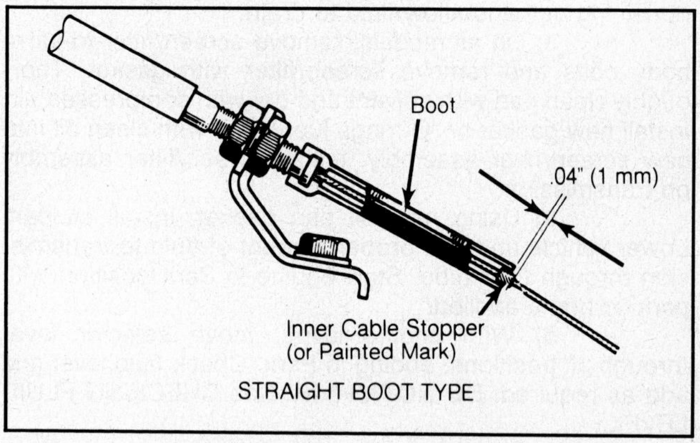

NEUTRAL SAFETY SWITCH

1) Loosen neutral safety switch bolts at transaxle. Set shift selector lever in "N" range. Disconnect switch connector. *See Fig. 3*.

2) Connect an ohmmeter between terminals and adjust switch to the point where there is continuity between terminals. Tighten screws and plug in switch connector.

Fig. 3: Neutral Safety Switch Adjustment

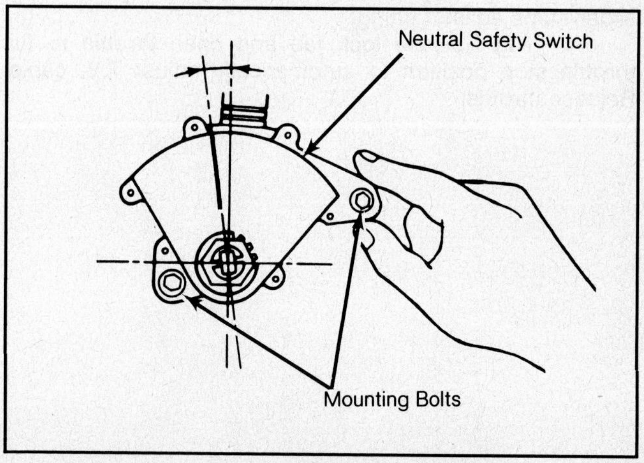

CHRYSLER CORP. FWD LIGHT TRUCKS

LUBRICATION

SERVICE INTERVALS

Light duty service requires transmission servicing (fluid drained and refilled, bands adjusted) every 37,500 miles. Under normal heavy duty conditions, service transmission every 24,000 miles. Vehicles subjected to severe heavy duty conditions should have transmission serviced every 12,000 miles.

CHECKING FLUID LEVEL

1) Check fluid level with vehicle parked on level surface, engine idling at normal operating temperature and parking brake applied. Move selector lever through all gear ranges, ending in "P" or "N".

2) Fluid level should be between "ADD" and "OK" marks on dipstick. Check condition of fluid for contamination or burned smell.

RECOMMENDED FLUID

Use only Dexron II type automatic transmission fluid.

FLUID CAPACITY

NOTE: Use capacities listed in table as a guide. Correct fluid level should always be determined by marks on dipstick.

TRANSMISSION REFILL CAPACITIES

Application	Refill Quantity	Dry Fill Quantity
A-413/A-470	4 qts. (3.8L)	19.0 qts. (8.6)

DRAINING & REFILLING

1) Loosen oil pan bolts. Tap lightly at one corner to break loose and allow fluid to drain. Remove pan. Install new filter on bottom of valve body and tighten retaining screws. Clean oil pan. Clean magnet (if used), and place over boss in right front corner of pan. Install pan with new gasket.

2) Refill transmission. Start engine and allow to run at idle for at least 2 minutes. With engine at curb idle and parking brake applied, move shift selector lever through all ranges, ending in "P" or "N". Add fluid up to "ADD" mark on dipstick. Do not overfill. Recheck fluid level when transmission reaches normal operating temperature.

ADJUSTMENT

KICKDOWN (FRONT) BAND

1) Locate kickdown band adjusting screw at left side (top front) of transmission case. Loosen adjusting screw lock nut and back off 5 turns. Ensure adjusting screw turns freely in case.

2) Using Wrench (C-3380-A) with Adapter (C-3705), tighten adjusting screw to 48 INCH lbs. (5 N.m). If adapter is not used, tighten adjusting screw to 72 INCH lbs. (8 N.m).

3) Back off front adjusting screw. See KICKDOWN BAND ADJUSTMENT table. Hold adjusting screw and tighten lock nut to 35 ft. lbs. (47 N.m).

KICKDOWN BAND ADJUSTMENT

Application	Back Off Screw
A-413/A-470	2 1/2 Turns

LOW-REVERSE (REAR) BAND

1) Drain transaxle fluid and remove oil pan. Apply 30 psi (2.1 kg/cm²) air pressure to low-reverse servo and measure gap between band ends. If less than .080" (2.0 mm), band is excessively worn and should be replaced.

2) To adjust band, loosen lock nut approximately 5 turns and tighten adjusting screw to 44 INCH lbs. (5 N.m). Back off adjusting screw. See LOW-REVERSE BAND ADJUSTMENT table. Hold screw in position and tighten lock nut.

LOW-REVERSE BAND ADJUSTMENT

Application	Back Off Screw
A-413/A-470	3 1/2 Turns

THROTTLE CONTROL CABLE

1) Ensure carburetor is not on fast idle cam (disconnect choke if necessary). Loosen adjustment bracket lock screw. Ensure bracket slides freely along full length of adjustment. *See Fig. 1.*

2) Slide bracket to the left (toward engine) to the limit of its travel. Release bracket and move throttle lever fully to the right against its internal stop and tighten lock screw. This completes adjustment. Cable backlash is automatically removed.

3) To check cable freedom of operation, move transaxle throttle lever forward and slowly release. Ensure cable returns to full rear position.

Fig. 1: Throttle Cable Adjustment

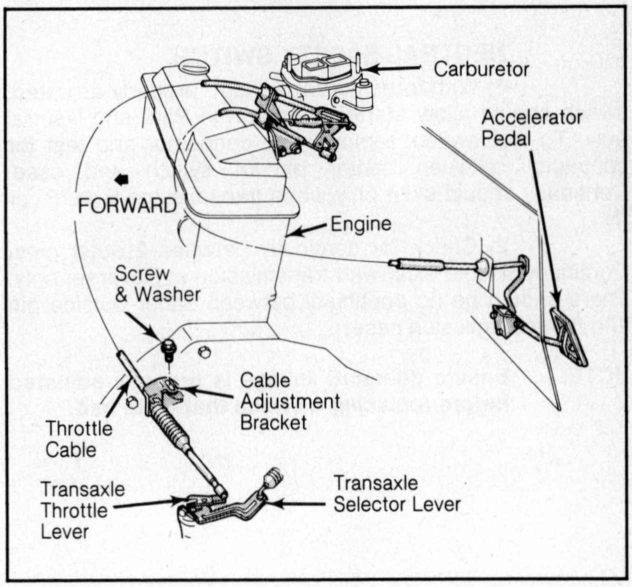

GEARSHIFT LINKAGE

Place shift selector in "P" position. Loosen lock screw on cable adjusting bracket on transaxle. Move shift lever on transaxle all the way to rear detent (Park) position and hold. Tighten lock screw.

CHRYSLER CORP. FWD LIGHT TRUCKS (Cont.)

Fig. 2: Gearshift Linkage Adjustment

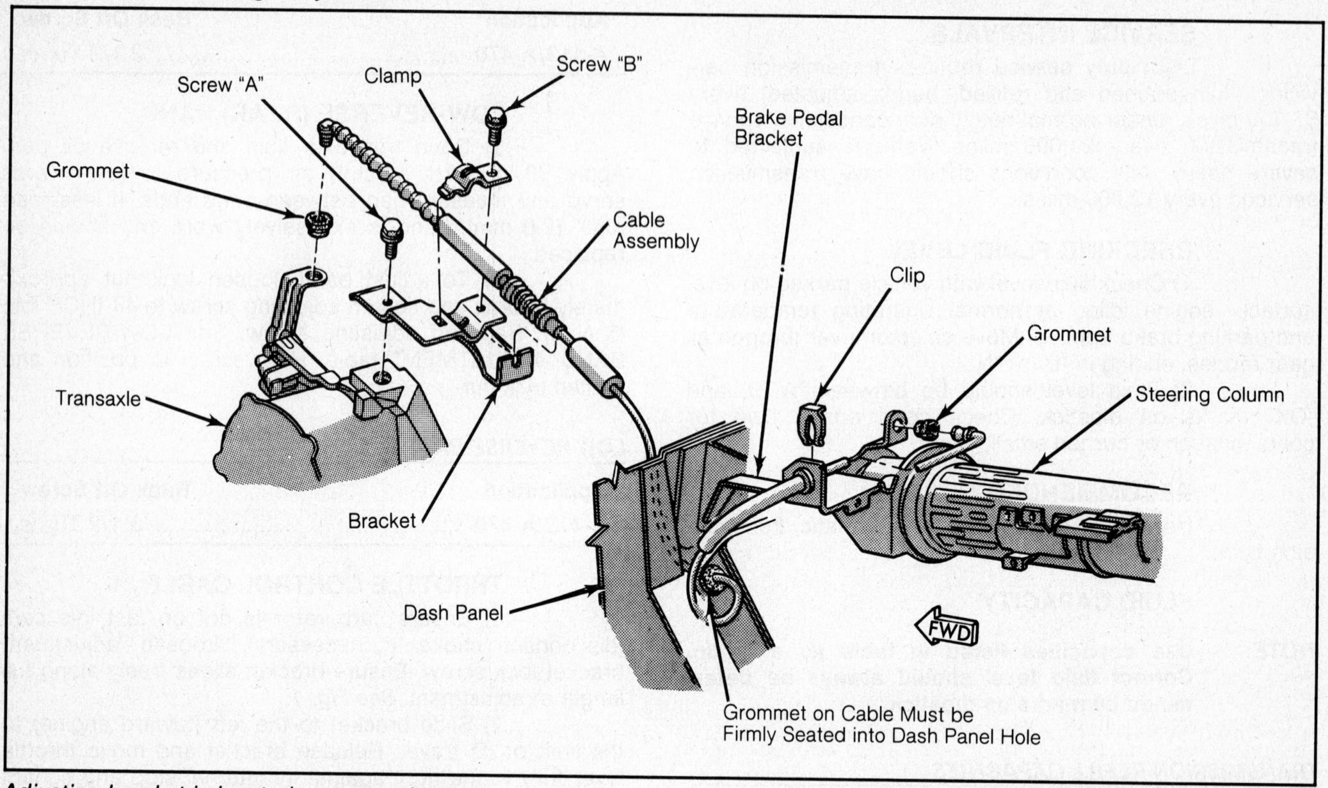

Adjusting bracket is located on transaxle case.

NOTE: If linkage cable is disconnected from transmission lever for any reason, always use a new plastic grommet when reassembling linkage.

NEUTRAL SAFETY SWITCH

1) With transmission linkage properly adjusted, switch should allow starter operation in Park and Neutral only. To test switch, remove wire connector and test for continuity between center pin of switch and case. Continuity should exist only when transmission is in "P" or "N".

2) Check for continuity between 2 outer pins. Continuity should exist with transmission in Reverse, only. There should be no continuity between either outside pin and the transmission case.

NOTE: Ensure gearshift linkage is properly adjusted before replacing a switch that tests bad.

3) To replace, remove switch from case and allow fluid to drain. Move selector lever to Park and Neutral positions and check that switch operating fingers are centered in switch opening. Install new switch and seal. Retest switch for continuity and add transmission fluid.

Fig. 3: Back-Up Light/Neutral Safety Switch

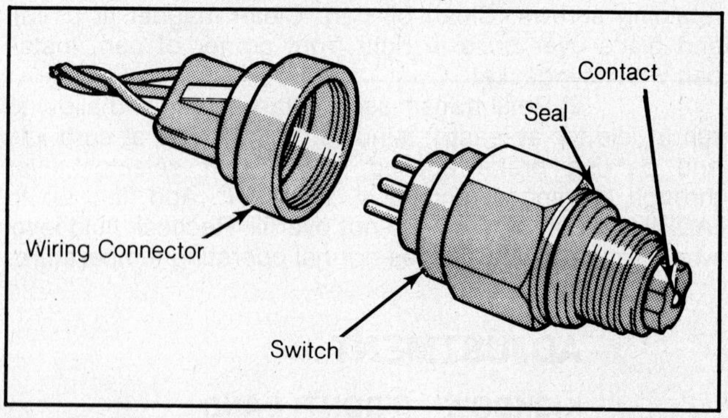

When installing new switch, tighten to 24 ft. lbs. (33 N.m).

CHRYSLER CORP. RWD LIGHT TRUCKS

LUBRICATION

SERVICE INTERVALS

Light duty service requires transmission servicing (fluid drained and refilled, bands adjusted) every 37,500 miles. Under normal heavy duty conditions, service transmission every 24,000 miles. Vehicles subjected to severe heavy duty conditions should have transmission serviced every 12,000 miles.

CHECKING FLUID LEVEL

1) Check fluid level with vehicle parked on level surface, engine idling at normal operating temperature and parking brake applied. Move selector lever through all gear ranges, ending in "P" or "N".

2) Fluid level should be between "FULL" and "ADD" marks on dipstick. Check condition of fluid for contamination or burned smell. NEVER overfill automatictransmissions.

RECOMMENDED FLUID

Use only Dexron II type automatic transmission fluid.

FLUID CAPACITY

NOTE: **Use capacities listed in table as a guide. Correct fluid level should always be determined by marks on dipstick. Capacities listed include torque converter.**

TRANSMISSION REFILL CAPACITIES [1]

Application	Quantity
A-727	
Lock-Up Converter	8.3 qts. (7.9L)
Non Lock-Up Converter	8.5 qts. (8.1L)
A-904T/A-999	8.5 qts. (8.1L)

[1] - Includes torque converter.

DRAINING & REFILLING

1) Loosen oil pan bolts. Tap lightly at one corner to break loose and allow fluid to drain. Remove pan. Install new filter on bottom of valve body and tighten retaining screws. Clean oil pan. Ensure magnet (if used) is over boss in right front corner of pan. Install pan with new gasket.

2) Refill transmission with 4 quarts (3.8L) of fluid. Start engine and allow to run at idle for at least 2 minutes. With engine at curb idle and parking brake applied, move shift selector lever through all ranges, ending in "P" or "N". Add fluid up to "ADD" mark on dipstick. DO NOT overfill. Recheck fluid level when transmission reaches normal operating temperature.

ADJUSTMENT

KICKDOWN (FRONT) BAND

1) Locate kickdown band adjusting screw at left side of transmission case, near throttle lever shaft. *See Fig. 1.* Loosen adjusting screw lock nut and back off 5 turns. Ensure adjusting screw turns freely in case.

2) Using Wrench (C-3380-A) with Adapter (C-3705), tighten adjusting screw to 48 INCH lbs. (5 N.m). If adapter is not used, tighten adjusting screw to 72 INCH lbs. (8 N.m).

3) Back off front adjusting screw. See KICKDOWN BAND ADJUSTMENT table. Hold adjusting screw in position and tighten lock nut to 35 ft. lbs. (47 N.m).

KICKDOWN BAND ADJUSTMENT

Application	Back Off Screw
All Models	2 1/2 Turns

Fig. 1: Adjusting Kickdown Band

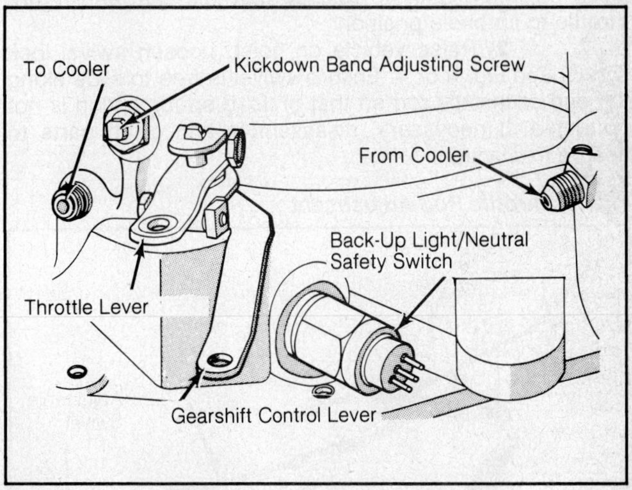

With band properly adjusted, tighten lock nut to 35 ft. lbs. (47 N.m).

LOW-REVERSE (REAR) BAND

1) Drain transmission and remove oil pan. Locate low-reverse band adjusting screw on rear servo lever. *See Fig. 2.* Loosen adjusting screw lock nut and back off about 5 turns. Ensure screw turns freely in lever. Using Wrench (C-3380-A), tighten adjusting screw to 72 INCH lbs. (8 N.m).

2) Back off rear adjusting screw. See LOW-REVERSE BAND ADJUSTMENT table. Hold adjusting screw in position and tighten lock nut to 35 ft. lbs. (47 N.m). Clean oil pan, install new gasket with pan and fill transmission with fluid.

Fig. 2: Low-Reverse Band Adjusting Screw Location

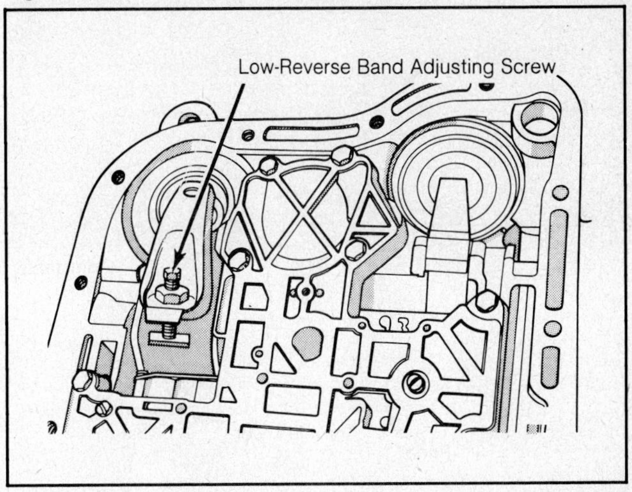

Adjust band and tighten lock nut to 35 ft. lbs. (47 N.m).

CHRYSLER CORP. RWD LIGHT TRUCKS (Cont.)

LOW-REVERSE BAND ADJUSTMENT

Application	Back Off Screw
A-904T/A-999	4 Turns
A-727	2 Turns

TRANSMISSION THROTTLE ROD

1) With engine at normal operating temperature and carburetor off fast idle cam, check and adjust idle speed as needed. Turn off engine and disconnect choke at carburetor or block choke valve in full open position. Open throttle slightly to release fast idle cam and return throttle to curb idle position.

2) Raise vehicle on hoist. Loosen swivel lock screw. *See Fig. 3 or 4.* Ensure swivel is free to slide along flat end of throttle rod so that preload spring action is not restricted. If necessary, disassemble and clean parts to assure free action.

Fig. 3: Throttle Rod Adjustment

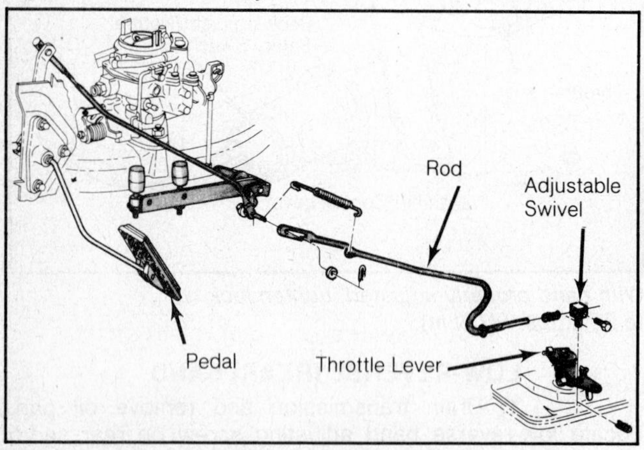

Linkage for vehicles with 6-cylinder engine.

3) Hold transmission lever firmly forward against internal stop and tighten swivel lock screw. Adjustment is complete. Linkage backlash is automatically removed by preload spring.

4) Lower vehicle and reconnect choke. To test linkage, move throttle rod rearward and slowly release it to confirm full forward return.

Fig. 4: Throttle Rod Adjustment

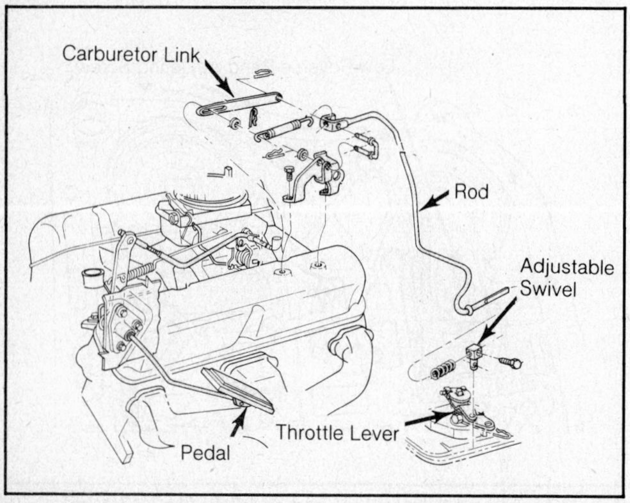

Linkage is for vehicles with V8 engines.

GEARSHIFT LINKAGE

1) With column shift lever in "P" position, loosen adjustable swivel lock screw. *See Fig. 5.* Ensure swivel is free to move on shift rod. Disassemble and clean components if required.

2) Move shift lever on transmission to full rear detent (Park) position and tighten swivel lock screw. When linkage is properly adjusted, detent positions for Neutral and Drive will be within limits of shift lever gate stops and engine will start only in "P" or "N".

Fig. 5: Column Shift Linkage Adjustment

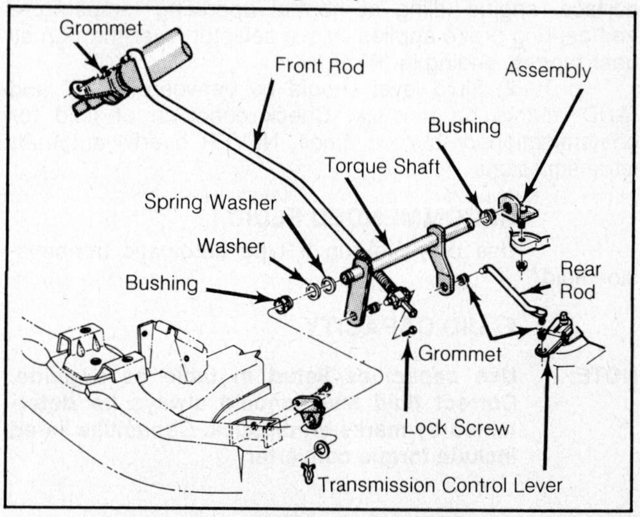

NEUTRAL SAFETY SWITCH

1) With transmission linkage properly adjusted, switch should allow starter operation in Park and Neutral only. To test switch, remove wire connector and test for continuity between center pin of switch and case. Continuity should exist only with transmission in "P" or "N".

2) Check for continuity between 2 outer pins. Continuity should exist with transmission in reverse, only. There should be no continuity between either outside pin or transmission case.

NOTE: **Ensure gearshift linkage is properly adjusted before replacing a switch that tests bad.**

3) To replace, remove switch from case and allow fluid to drain. Move selector lever to "P" and "N" positions and check that switch operating fingers are centered in switch opening. Install new switch and seal. Retest switch for continuity and add transmission fluid.

Fig. 6: Back-Up Light/Neutral Safety Switch

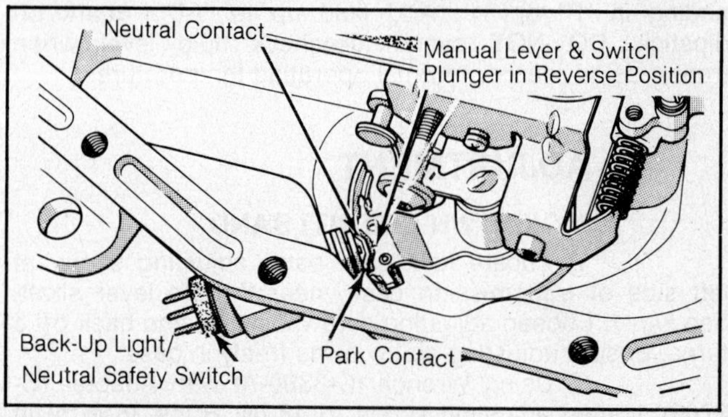

When installing new switch, tighten to 24 ft. lbs. (33 N.m).

FORD LIGHT TRUCKS

LUBRICATION

SERVICE INTERVALS

Vehicles used in normal service do not require regularly scheduled maintenance. Fluid level should be checked whenever underhood maintenance is performed, or if leakage is detected. Clutch bands on A4LD, C-5 and C-6 should be adjusted when quality of shifts deteriorates or otherwise indicates improper band adjustment.

On vehicles used for fleet service or those operated under severe conditions (such as police, taxi or towing), regular transmission fluid changes are required every 30,000 miles.

CHECKING FLUID LEVEL

1) Check fluid level with vehicle parked on level surface, engine and transmission at normal operating temperatures and engine idling. Apply parking brake and move transmission selector lever through all ranges, ending in "P".

2) Fluid level should check between "ADD" and "DON'T ADD" marks on dipstick (in crosshatched area). Add fluid through filler tube as needed. DO NOT overfill.

RECOMMENDED FLUID

On C-5 transmissions, use fluid which meets Ford specification ESP-M2C166-H or type H fluid. On A4LD, AOD and C-6 transmissions, use Dexron II or equivalent.

FLUID CAPACITY

NOTE: Fluid capacities listed are approximate. Always determine correct fluid level by mark on dipstick rather than by amount of fluid added.

TRANSMISSION REFILL CAPACITIES

Application	Capacity
AOD Transmission	12.3 qts. (11.6L)
A4LD Transmission	9.5 qts. (9.0L)
C-5 Transmission	
All Except Bronco II & Ranger	11.0 qts. (10.4L)
2WD Ranger	7.5 qts. (7.1L)
Bronco II & 4WD Ranger	8.0 qts. (7.5L)
C-6 Transmission	
2WD Models	11.8 qts. (11.2L)
4WD Models	13.5 qts. (12.8L)

DRAINING & REFILLING

1) On C-5 transmissions, disconnect fluid filler tube from oil pan to drain fluid. On all other transmissions, loosen oil pan bolts and tap pan to break gasket seal. Allow fluid to drain. Remove oil pan bolts and oil pan.

2) On C-5 transmissions, remove and clean filter screen. Reinstall filter screen using a new gasket. On all other transmissions, discard used filter and gasket. Install new filter and gasket. On all transmissions, clean pan and install with new gasket. On C-5 transmissions, install filler tube.

CAUTION: On AOD transmissions, do not attempt to reuse oil filter after soaking filter in solvent. Filter material may disintegrate.

3) On all transmissions, add 3 quarts transmission fluid. Check fluid level as previously described. When filling a dry transmission and converter, refer to TRANSMISSION REFILL CAPACITIES. Recheck fluid level when transmission is at normal operating temperature. Do not overfill.

Fig. 1: Adjusting Intermediate or Overdrive Band (A4LD, C-3 & C-5)

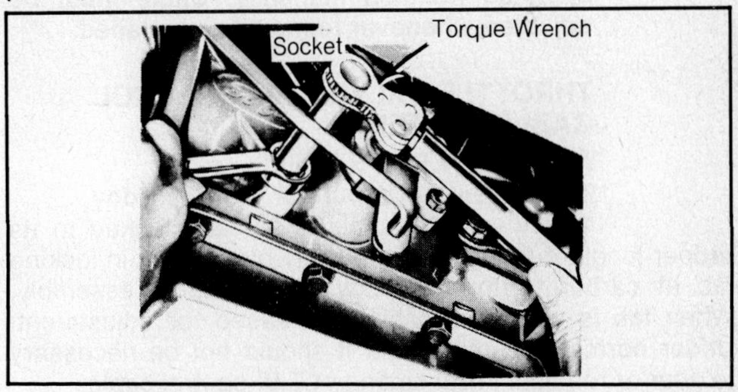

Ford C-5 shown; all others are similar.

ADJUSTMENT

INTERMEDIATE (FRONT) OR OVERDRIVE BAND

1) Clean dirt from band adjusting screw area. Remove and discard band adjusting screw lock nut. Install new lock nut.

2) Tighten adjusting screw to 120 INCH lbs. (14 N.m). *See Fig. 1.* Back off screw exact number of turns. See INTERMEDIATE (FRONT) OR OVERDRIVE BAND ADJUSTMENT table. Hold adjusting screw in position and tighten new lock nut to 40 ft. lbs. (56 N.m).

INTERMEDIATE OR OVERDRIVE BAND ADJUSTMENT

Application	Back Off Screw
A4LD	2 Turns
C-5	4 1/4 Turns
C-6	1 1/2 Turns

LOW-REVERSE (REAR) BAND

A4LD & C-5 Only

1) Clean all dirt from band adjusting screw area. Remove and discard band adjusting screw lock nut. Install new lock nut on adjusting screw.

2) Tighten screw to 120 INCH lbs. (14 N.m). Back off 2 full turns (A4LD) or 3 full turns (C-5). Hold screw in position and tighten lock nut to 40 ft. lbs. (54 N.m).

Fig. 2: Adjusting Low-Reverse Band (A4LD & C-5)

Install new nut before performing band adjustment.

FORD LIGHT TRUCKS (Cont).

KICKDOWN CONTROL CABLE

NOTE: **Kickdown control cable self-adjusts .5-1.5" (13-38 mm) after installation by depressing accelerator pedal to floor. No adjustment is required, but cable must be locked in the adjusted position manually. Cable must be adjusted whenever removed or replaced.**

THROTTLE VALVE (T.V.) CONTROL CABLE SYSTEM

AOD Only (4.9L & 5.0L EFI)

Adjustment at Carburetor/Throttle Body

1) T.V. control cable is set and locked to its proper length during initial assembly by pushing in locking tab at carburetor/throttle body end of cable assembly. When tab is unlocked, cable is released for adjustment. Under normal circumstances, it should not be necessary to alter or readjust initial setting of T.V. control cable.

2) On 4.9L engine, Idle Speed Control (ISC) plunger automatically extends when engine is shut off and moves throttle lever to fast idle in preparation for next engine start. The ISC plunger must first be retracted.

3) In engine compartment (near right fender-well), locate self-test connectors. *See Fig. 4.* Connect a jumper wire between single wire connector and ground (Signal Return) of self-test connector. *See Fig. 3.*

Fig. 3: Connecting Ground on Self-Test Connector

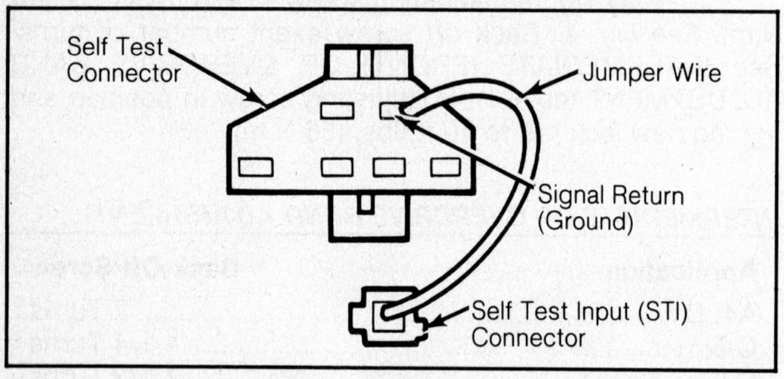

4) Turn ignition switch to "RUN" position, but do not start engine. ISC plunger will retract. Wait 10 seconds until plunger is fully retracted. Turn key off. Disconnect ISC harness connection. Remove jumper wire and air cleaner.

5) On 4.9L and 5.0L EFI engines, set parking brake and put selector in "N". Ensure throttle lever is resting against idle stop. Verify cable routing is free of sharp bends or pressure points and cable operates freely. Unlock locking tab at carburetor/throttle body end by pushing up from below and prying up rest of way to free cable.

6) Install a retention spring with about 10 lbs. (4.5 kg) force to hold T.V. control lever to hold it in idle position (to rear of travel). If necessary, use two throttle return springs to hold T.V. lever back. Attach spring(s) to transmission T.V. lever and hook rear of spring to transmission case.

7) On 4.9L engines, rotate fast idle cam on carburetor so throttle lever is at its idle stop. Carburetor throttle lever must be in anti-diesel idle position.

8) Verify take-up spring (carburetor/throttle body end of cable) properly tensions cable. If spring is loose or bottomed out, check for bent cable brackets. Push down on locking key until flush. Remove retension

Fig. 4: Location of Self-Test Connectors

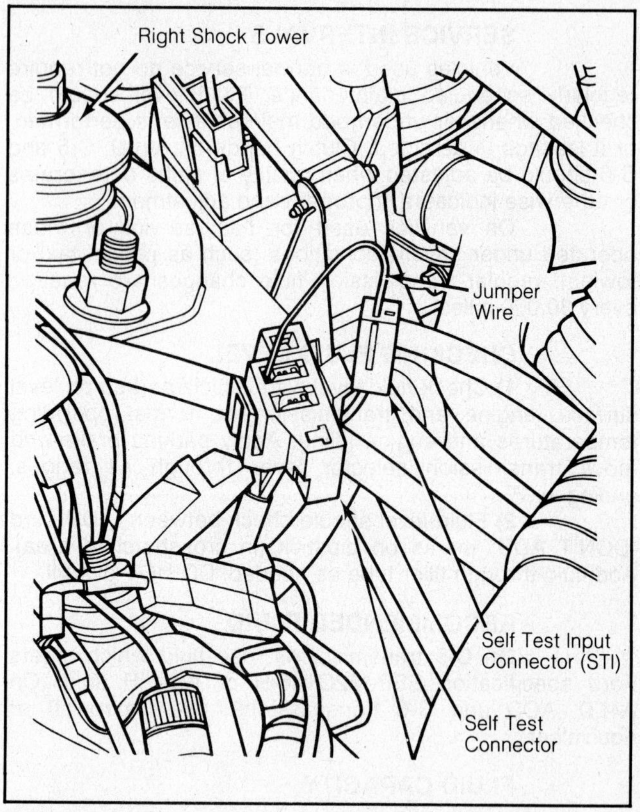

Note location of jumper wire.

sping(s) from transmission T.V. lever. On 4.9L engine, reconnect ISC motor.

VACUUM REGULATOR VALVE (VRV)

All models equipped with the 6.9L V8 diesel engine and automatic transmission include a VRV. Mounted on the left side of the fuel injection pump, it provides a vacuum signal to the transmission to control shift points. Signal strength is determined by a VRV.

Checking VRV Operation

1) Disconnect vacuum connector from VRV. Remove throttle cable from injection pump throttle lever (on right side of pump). Disconnect throttle return spring.

2) Attach one end of return spring over throttle lever ball stud. Install other end of spring over throttle cable support bracket. Insert .515" (13 mm) Gauge Block (T83T-7B200-AH) between pump boss and wide-open throttle stop screw. Spring will hold throttle lever against gauge block during vacuum check and VRV adjustment.

3) Attach vacuum pump to "VAC" (upper) port of VRV. Attach vacuum gauge to "TRANS" (lower) port. Apply and maintain 20 in. Hg of vacuum. Vacuum gauge should indicate 6-8 in. Hg of vacuum. If not, VRV requires adjustment.

Adjusting VRV

1) Loosen mounting screws (2) attaching VRV to fuel injection pump. With vacuum pump, gauge, gauge block and return spring in position (as during checking procedure), maintain 20 in. Hg of vacuum with pump. Rotate VRV until vacuum gauge reads 7 in. Hg of vacuum. Tighten mounting screws.

2) If correct vacuum reading cannot be obtained by adjusting VRV, it must be replaced. If correct

FORD LIGHT TRUCKS (Cont.)

reading is obtained, remove gauge block, and connect throttle return spring. Ensure pump lever returns to idle position.

3) Apply 20 in. Hg of vacuum with vacuum pump and check gauge reading. If vacuum gauge reads less than 13 in. Hg, replace VRV. Remove vacuum pump and gauge and re-connect vacuum connector to VRV. Connect throttle cable.

GEARSHIFT LINKAGE

NOTE: **Adjustment of manual shift linkage/cable is critical. Ensure "D" or (Overdrive) detent in transmission corresponds exactly with stop in console.**

All Except Aerostar, Bronco II & Ranger

1) Move selector lever rearward against stop in "D" position. On models with column mounted shift levers, hold lever against stop by hanging an 8 lb. (3.6 kg) weight from selector lever.

2) Loosen manual lever-to-control cable (or rod) retaining nut. Move transmission manual lever to drive position (second detent from rear). Hold selector against rear of "D" position and tighten retaining nut. Check for normal operation in all selected positions.

Aerostar

1) From inside vehicle, place gearshift lever in "Overdrive" position. From under vehicle, loosen adjustment screw on shift cable and remove end fitting from manual lever ball stud.

2) Position manual lever in "Overdrive" position by moving lever all the way rearward, then moving it 3 detents forward. Connect cable end fitting to manual lever.

NOTE: **Excessive arm pressure can move shifter to "D" position. Apply pressure only until resisitance of detent nib is felt.**

3) Tighten adjusting screw to 45-60 INCH lbs. (5-7 N.m). After adjustment, check for "P" position engagement. Control lever must move to right when engaged in "P" detent.

4) Check control lever corresponds in all detent positions with engine running to ensure correct detent/transmission action.

Bronco II & Ranger

1) With engine off and parking brake applied, place shift lever in "D". Loosen trunnion bolt. Move shift lever at transmission all the way to the rear, then forward 4 steps. This places lever in "D" position.

2) Apply light forward pressure on shift control lever (at transmission) and tighten trunnion bolt to 18-31 ft. lbs. (13-23 N.m). Move lever through all positions making sure transmission is at full detent in each position.

NEUTRAL SAFETY SWITCH

NOTE: **AOD and A4LD switches are not adjustable. If necessary, use Neutral Start Switch Socket (T74P-77247-A) to replace switch. If any other socket is used, damage to switch may occur.**

1) With transmission shift linkage properly adjusted, loosen the 2 switch attaching bolts. *See Fig. 5.*

Fig. 5: Location of Neutral Safety Switch

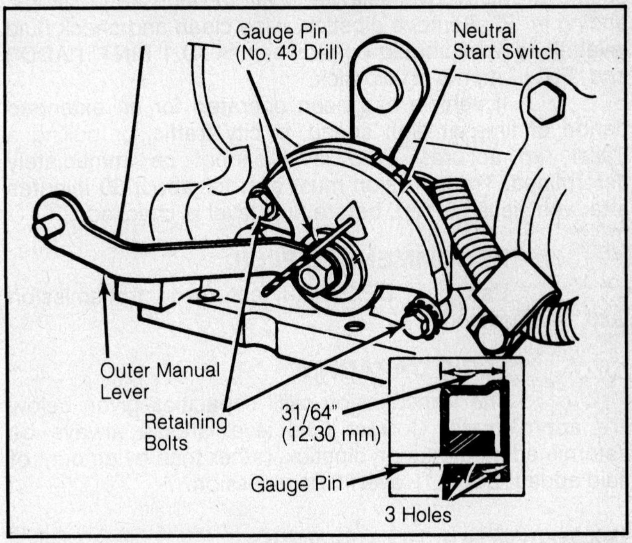

Note location of No. 43 drill bit.

2) Place transmission manual lever in neutral position. Rotate switch and insert a gauge pin (No. 43 drill bit) into gauge pin hole of switch.

3) Gauge pin must be inserted completely through all 3 holes of switch. Tighten switch attaching bolts and remove gauge pin. Check operation of switch. Engine should start in "N" or "P" positions, only.

GENERAL MOTORS LIGHT TRUCKS

LUBRICATION

SERVICE INTERVALS

Check transmission fluid level at each engine oil change. Change transmission fluid and filter at 100,000 mile intervals on vehicles in normal use. If vehicle is used in severe service conditions (commercial use, trailer pulling, constant stop and go city traffic), change fluid and filter every 15,000 miles.

CHECKING FLUID LEVEL

NOTE: One pint of fluid will raise level from "ADD 1 PT." ("ADD") mark to "FULL" mark on dipstick in a hot transmission. Do not overfill.

With vehicle parked on a level surface and engine at idle, move selector lever through all positions, ending in "P". Remove dipstick, wipe clean and check fluid level. Fluid level should be between "ADD 1 PINT" ("ADD") and "FULL" marks on dipstick.

If vehicle has been operated for an extended period of time at high speed, in city traffic, or pulling a trailer, an accurate fluid level cannot be immediately determined. Transmission must cool for about 30 minutes after vehicle is parked, before fluid level is checked.

RECOMMENDED FLUID

Use only DEXRON-II automatic transmission fluid, or equivalent.

FLUID CAPACITY

The transmission refill capacities given below are approximate. Correct fluid level should always be determined by marks on dipstick, rather than by amount of fluid added. DO NOT overfill transmission.

TRANSMISSION REFILL CAPACITIES

Application	Refill Quantity	Dry Fill Quantity
THM 350C	3.2 qts. (3.0L)	10 qts. (9.5L)
THM 400	4.5 qts. (4.3L)	11 qts. (10.4L)
THM 700-R4	5.0 qts. (4.8L)	11.5 qts. (11L)

DRAINING & REFILLING

Loosen transmission oil pan bolts. Pry pan loose with a large screwdriver and allow fluid to drain. Remove oil pan, gasket and filter or filter screen. Replace paper element filter (if used). Clean filter screen and pan with solvent and blow dry with compressed air. Install oil pan with new gasket. Add fluid to proper mark on dipstick.

ADJUSTMENT

DETENT (DOWNSHIFT) OR THROTTLE VALVE (T.V.) CABLE

Diesel Engines

1) Remove cruise control rod (if equipped). Disconnect detent cable terminal from throttle assembly. Loosen lock nut on pump rod and back off several turns. Rotate throttle lever assembly (at valve body) to full open position and hold.

2) Lengthen pump rod until injection pump lever contacts full throttle stop. Release throttle lever and tighten pump rod lock nut.

Fig. 1: Detent/TV Cable Adjustment Components

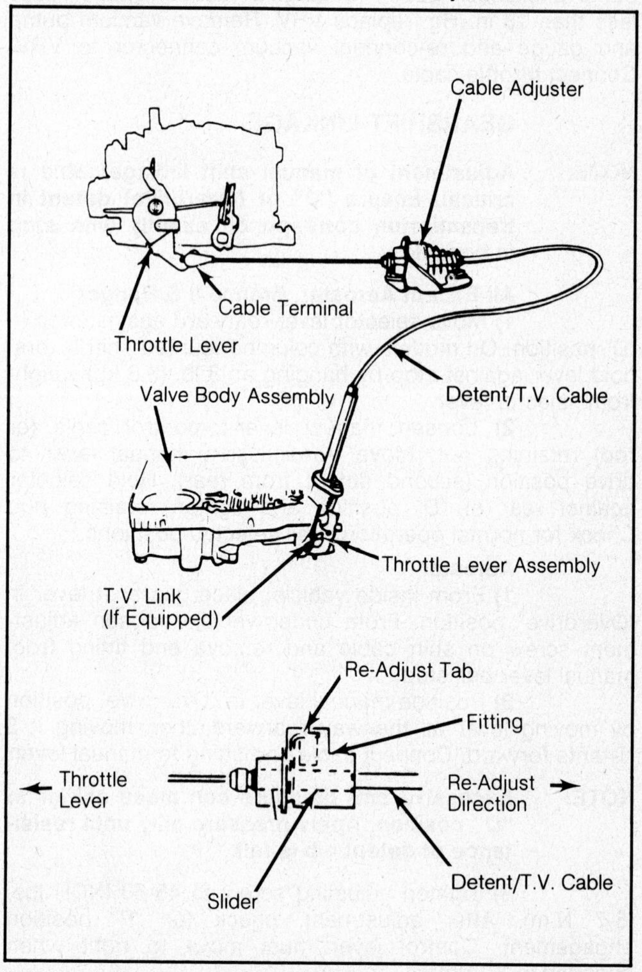

T.V. cable is used only on 700-R4 transmissions, All other models use detent cable.

3) Remove pump rod from lever assembly. Reconnect detent cable terminal to throttle assembly. Depress and hold metal adjusting tab on cable adjuster. Move slider through fitting, away from throttle lever, until slider stops against fitting. Release tab.

4) Rotate lever assembly to full throttle position and release. Reconnect pump rod. If equipped with cruise control, reconnect rod and adjust servo throttle rod to minimum slack with engine off. Install clip in free hole nearest to bellcrank and within servo bail.

Gasoline Engines

Depress metal lock tab on adjuster and hold. Move slider back through fitting away from carburetor lever until slider stops at fitting. Release lock tab and open carburetor lever to full throttle stop. This automatically adjusts slider to correct setting.

DETENT (DOWNSHIFT) SWITCH

THM 400 Only

With engine off, push detent switch plunger as far forward as possible. This presets switch for adjustment. Depress accelerator pedal to wide open position.

GENERAL MOTORS (Cont.)

Switch will self adjust. Operation of detent switch circuit can be checked by connecting a test lamp across switch terminals.

TRANSMISSION VACUUM REGULATOR VALVE

With Electrical Control

1) Loosely assemble throttle position switch to fuel injection pump with throttle lever in closed position. Attach an ohmmeter across terminals IGN (Pink wire) and EGR (Yellow wire).

2) Insert "switch-closed" .624" (15.8 mm) Gauge Bar for Emission Label Code YJH or .646" (16.4 mm) Gauge Bar (J-33043) for all other models, between gauge boss on pump and wide open stop screw on throttle shaft. Rotate and hold throttle lever against gauge block.

3) Rotate throttle switch clockwise (facing throttle switch) until continuity occurs (high meter reading) across terminals. Hold switch body at this position and tighten mounting bolts to 4-5 ft. lbs. (5-7 N.m).

NOTE: Switch point must be set only while rotating switch body in clockwise direction.

4) Release throttle lever and allow it to return to idle position. Remove "switch-closed" gauge bar and insert "switch-open" .646" (16.4 mm) Gauge Bar (J-33043) for Emission Label Code (YJH) or .668" (16.9 mm) Gauge Bar for all other models. If no continuity exists, switch is set properly. If continuity exists, switch must be reset or replaced.

With Vacuum Regulator Valve (VRV)

1) Loosen VRV-to-injection pump bolts enough to allow for regulator valve rotation. Attach vacuum pump to bottom vacuum port of valve (vacuum gauge to top port).

2) Insert .646" (16.4 mm) Gauge Bar (J-33043) between gauge boss on injection pump and wide open stop screw on throttle lever. Rotate throttle shaft against bar.

3) Apply 18-21 in. Hg to VRV. Slowly rotate VRV body clockwise (facing valve) until vacuum gauge reads 7-9 in. Hg. Hold valve body in this position and tighten mounting screws.

NOTE: Valve MUST be set while rotating in a clockwise direction.

4) Check adjustment by allowing throttle shaft to return to idle position, then rotate shaft back against gauge bar. If vacuum gauge reading is not 7-9 in. Hg, re-adjust valve.

SHIFT LINKAGE

"C", "K" & "G" Models

1) Ensure shift tube and lever assembly are free in steering column. Disconnect shift lever rod from swivel at lower column lever. Move transmission lever clockwise to stop, then counterclockwise 2 detents. This is neutral position. Place selector lever in "N". Locate position using mechanical stops, NOT indicator pointer.

2) Slide swivel and clamp onto shift lever rod. Install grommets, washers and nut (as needed) but do not tighten nut. Hold lower column lever against neutral stop on park side. Tighten swivel nut to 20 ft. lbs. (27 N.m).

Astro, Safari & "S" Models

1) Ensure shift tube and lever are free in steering column. To adjust linkage, remove screw and spring washer from swivel. Turn transmission lever clockwise to stop, then counterclockwise 2 detents. This is neutral position.

2) Place selector lever in "N". Locate proper position using mechanical stops, NOT indicator pointer. Hold swivel against shift lever. Install spring washer and screw and tighten finger tight. Avoid applying force in either direction (along shift rod or lever) while tightening screw to 20 ft. lbs. (27 N.m).

NEUTRAL SAFETY SWITCH

With Column Mounted Switch

1) Place gearshift selector lever in neutral position and loosen switch attaching screws. Rotate switch on column until a .095" (2.5 mm) gauge pin can be inserted into switch gauge hole to a depth of .4" (10 mm).

2) Tighten switch attaching screws and remove gauge pin. Check for engine starting in neutral and park only.

With Trans. Mounted Switch

1) Raise and support vehicle and loosen switch mounting bolts. Align hole in switch lever with hole in switch assembly. Insert a .095" (2.5 mm) gauge pin through switch holes to hold switch in neutral position.

2) With selector lever on transmission in neutral detent position, tighten switch mounting bolts and remove gauge pin. Lower vehicle and check operation of switch.

JEEP

LUBRICATION

SERVICE INTERVALS

Check fluid level and condition of fluid at each engine oil change. Under normal, light duty operating conditions, change fluid, replace filter and adjust bands every 2 yrs. or 25,000 miles. Under heavy duty service, change fluid, replace filter and adjust bands every 12 months or 12,500 miles.

CHECKING FLUID LEVEL

Park vehicle on a level surface and apply parking brake. With engine idling at normal operating temperature, move transmission selector lever through all gears, ending in "N". Check fluid level. Fluid level should be between "FULL" and "ADD ONE PINT" mark on dipstick. Add fluid as needed. DO NOT overfill.

RECOMMENDED FLUID

Use only Dexron II automatic transmission fluid.

FLUID CAPACITY

NOTE: **Transmission and converter capacities are approximate. Fluid level should always be determined by reading on dipstick, rather than amount of fluid added.**

TRANSMISSION REFILL CAPACITIES

Application	Capacity Quantity
All Models	
Including Converter	8.5 qts. (8.0L)
Without Converter	4.3 qts. (4.0L)

DRAINING & REFILLING

1) Loosen oil pan bolts, tap pan to break it loose and allow fluid to drain. Remove pan. Install new filter on bottom of valve body and tighten retaining screws. Install new "O" ring on fluid pick-up pipe (if needed). Clean oil pan and install with new gasket.

2) Refill transmission with fluid. Start engine and allow to run at curb idle for a few minutes. With vehicle on level surface, engine idling and parking brake applied, move shift selector lever through all gear ranges, ending in "N". Add fluid up to "ADD ONE PINT" mark on dipstick.

3) Recheck fluid level when transmission reaches normal operating temperature. Fluid should be between "ADD ONE PINT" and "FULL" marks on dipstick. Transmission must NOT be overfilled.

ADJUSTMENT

KICKDOWN (FRONT) BAND

1) Locate kickdown band adjusting screw on left side of case (near throttle lever shaft). Loosen adjusting screw lock nut and back off approximately 5 turns. Ensure adjusting screw turns freely in case.

2) Using Adapter (J-24063) and 5/16" square socket, tighten screw to 36 INCH lbs. (4 N.m). If adapter is not used, tighten screw to 72 INCH lbs. (8 N.m). Back off adjusting screw. See KICKDOWN (FRONT) BAND ADJUSTMENT table. Hold adjusting screw in position and tighten lock nut to 35 ft. lbs. (48 N.m).

KICKDOWN (FRONT) BAND ADJUSTMENT

Application	[1] Back Off Screw
All Models	2 1/2 Turns

[1] – Tighten screw to 72 INCH lbs. (8 N.m) and back off indicated number of turns.

Fig. 1: Kickdown Band Adjusting Screw Location

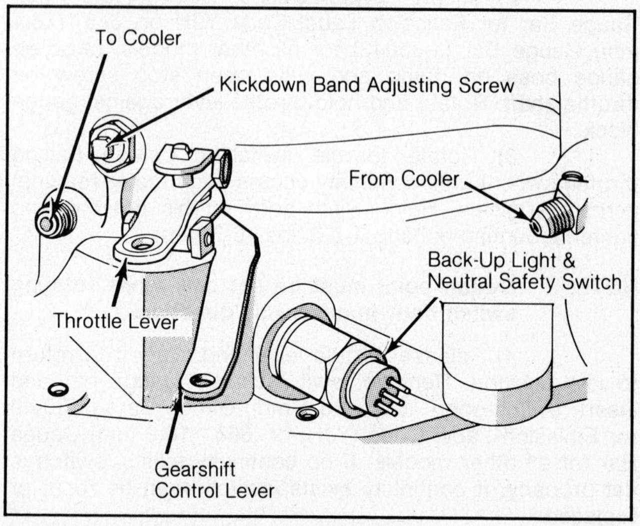

Tighten screw to 72 INCH lbs. (8 N.m), back off 2 1/2 turns and tighten lock nut.

LOW-REVERSE (REAR) BAND

1) Raise vehicle, drain transmission fluid and remove oil pan. Locate adjusting screw on rear servo lever. Loosen adjusting screw lock nut and back off about 5 turns.

2) Tighten screw to 41 INCH lbs. (4.6 N.m) and back off indicated number of turns. See LOW-REVERSE (REAR) BAND ADJUSTMENT table. Hold adjusting screw in position and tighten lock nut to 35 ft. lbs. (48 N.m). Install oil pan and fill transmission with fluid.

Fig. 2: Adjusting Low-Reverse Band

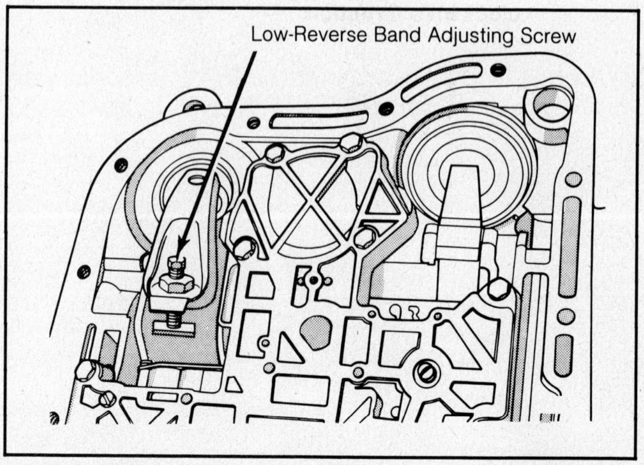

Band should be adjusted whenever oil pan is removed.

JEEP (Cont.)

TRANSMISSION THROTTLE CABLE/LINKAGE

NOTE: **A special Idle Speed Actuator (ISA) Exerciser Box Tool is required to initially set ISA motor and adjust transmission throttle linkage on 4-Cylinder models with gas engines.**

4-Cylinder Models with Gasoline Engine

1) Raise vehicle. Using a spring, hook one end on throttle control lever and other end on torque converter housing. Lower vehicle.

2) Disconnect the ISA motor and connect Exerciser Box to ISA. Adjustment light should turn off and ready light should turn on. Press retrack button. Wait until ISA adjusts, ready light goes off and adjust light goes on.

3) Loosen bolt on throttle control link. Pull on link end to eliminate lash. Tighten adjusting bolt. Press extend button on Exerciser Box. When ISA ratches, release button and disconnect Exerciser Box. Connect ISA wiring and remove spring from throttle control lever. Install and reconnect any parts removed and/or disconnected.

4-Cylinder Models with Diesel Engine

NOTE: **The throttle cable used on diesel engines is not adjustable. If shifting problems related to throttle cable or damage to throttle cable occurs, a Replacement Throttle Cable (9853 001 796) and Special Gauge Tool (J-35514) are available from the manufacturer.**

6-Cylinder Models with 904 Transmission

1) Remove air cleaner. Hold throttle control lever rearward against its stop. Block choke plate open and set carburetor linkage completely off fast idle cam.

2) Unlock throttle control cable by lifting "T" shaped adjuster clamp with small screwdriver. Move cable outer sheath forward to remove any cable load on throttle cable bellcrank.

3) Adjust cable by moving cable and sheath rearward until there is no lash between cable and throttle linkage. Lock cable by pressing "T" shaped clamp downward until clamp snaps into place. Install and reconnect any parts removed and/or disconnected.

6-Cyl. Models with 727 Transmission

1) Disconnect throttle control rod spring. Use spring to hold transmission throttle control lever forward, against stop. Block choke open and release fast idle cam.

2) On carburetors equipped wih throttle operated solenoid valve, turn key to "ON" position to energize solenoid. Open throttle halfway to allow solenoid to lock. Return throttle to idle position.

3) Loosen retaining bolt on throttle control adjusting link. DO NOT remove spring clip or nylon washer. Pull on end of link to eliminate lash. Tighten link retaining bolt. Reconnect throttle control rod spring.

6-Cyl. Models with 999 Transmission

1) Disconnect throttle control rod spring. Use spring to hold adjusting link in forward position, against nylon washer. Block choke open and release fast idle cam.

2) Raise vehicle. Loosen both retaining bolts on adjusting link clamp. DO NOT remove spring clip or nylon washer. Use a spare spring to hold transmission throttle lever against forward stop.

3) Push adjusting link to eliminate lash and pull clamp to rear so that bolt in rod bottoms in rear of slot in rod. Tighten forward clamp retaining bolt.

4) Pull throttle control rod to the rear so that bolt in rod bottoms in front of slot and tighten rear retaining bolt. Remove spare spring. Lower vehicle and reconnect throttle control rod spring.

V8 Models

1) Disconnect throttle control rod spring. Use spring to hold transmission throttle valve control lever against forward stop. Block choke open and release fast idle cam.

2) On carburetors equipped with throttle operated solenoid valve, turn key to "ON" position to energize solenoid. Open throttle halfway to allow solenoid to lock. Return throttle to idle position.

3) Loosen retaining bolt on throttle control rod adjusting link. Remove spring clip and slide nylon washer to rear of link. Push on end of link to eliminate lash and tighten retaining bolt. Install nylon washer and spring clip. Reconnect throttle control rod spring.

SHIFT LINKAGE

1) Loosen shift rod trunnion jam nuts at transmission lever. Remove shift rod-to-bellcrank lock pin. Disengage trunnion and shift rod. Place selector lever in "P" position and lock steering column. Move transmission shift lever to full rear Park position.

2) Adjust shift rod trunnion to obtain free pin fit in bellcrank arm. Tighten jam nuts. On vehicles with shift lever on column, make sure linkage lash is eliminated by pulling down on shift rod and pushing up on outer bellcrank when tightening jam nuts.

3) Check steering column lock for ease of operation. Ensure engine starts in "N" or "P" only. If starter engages in any drive gear, or does not work in "N" or "P", check for proper shift linkage adjustment or faulty neutral safety switch.

NEUTRAL SAFETY SWITCH

1) Switch combines functions of neutral safety switch and back-up light switch. With transmission linkage properly adjusted, switch should allow starter operation in "P" and "N" only.

2) To test switch, remove wire connector and test for continuity between center pin of switch and case. Continuity should only exist when transmission is in "P" or "N".

3) Check for continuity between 2 outer pins. Continuity should exist with transmission in "R" only. There should be no continuity between either outer pin and transmission case. If any of these conditions are not met, the switch should be replaced.

4) To replace switch, unscrew from case. Move selector lever to "P" and "N" positions and check that switch operating fingers are centered in switch opening. Install switch and new seal in case. Check fluid level and add as needed.

Automatic Transmission Removal

AMERICAN MOTORS

REMOVAL & INSTALLATION

TORQUE-COMMAND 998

Removal

NOTE: Transmission and converter must be removed as an assembly to prevent damage to drive plate, pump bushing and oil seal.

1) Open hood. Disconnect fan shroud (if equipped). Disconnect transmission filler tube at upper bracket. Place transmission in Neutral. Raise vehicle on a hoist.

NOTE: Hood must remain open during transmission removal to prevent damage to hood and air cleaner when rear crossmember is removed.

2) Mark propeller shafts and yokes for installation reference. Remove propeller shafts and skid plate. Disconnect exhaust pipe from manifold and move it aside to provide working clearance.

3) Remove converter housing inspection cover. Remove transmission filler tube. Remove starter and stiffening braces.

4) Remove speedometer adapter and cable assembly. Plug adapter bore in case. Disconnect gearshift and throttle linkage. If equipped with column shift, remove linkage, and bellcrank bracket-to-converter housing bolt. Disconnect neutral safety switch wires.

5) Mark converter drive plate and converter for installation reference. Remove converter-to-drive plate attaching bolts.

NOTE: Use a ratchet and socket on crankshaft front pulley bolt to rotate crankshaft and drive plate for access to converter attaching bolts.

6) Support transmission and transfer case with a transmission jack. Retain transmission on jack with safety chain. Lower transmission slightly and disconnect oil cooler lines at transmission.

7) Remove rear support cushion-to-rear support cushion bracket (attached to extension housing). Remove crossmember. Remove engine-to-transmission attaching bolts.

8) Move transmission, transfer case and converter rearward to clear crankshaft. Hold converter in place and lower transmission assembly until converter housing clears engine.

Installation

1) Insert Pump Alignment (J-24033) into pump. Engage pump rotor, rotate tool until drilled hole is vertical. Remove tool. Rotate converter until pump drive slots are vertical and carefully install converter into pump.

2) Using a transmission jack, raise assembly and align converter with drive plate (aligning marks made during removal). Move transmission forward, carefully aligning bell housing pilot holes with dowels in engine.

3) Install 2 lower bell housing attaching bolts and pull housing up snug. Install remaining bolts and tighten all bell housing bolts. To complete installation, reverse removal procedures.

MB 1 TRANSAXLE

Removal

NOTE: Engine and transaxle must be removed as an assembly.

1) Disconnect negative battery cable. Drain transaxle and engine oil. Drain cooling system from bottom of the radiator and from cylinder block.

2) Remove air cleaner assembly. Remove radiator. Disconnect wire harness connectors attached to engine assembly. Disconnect vacuum hoses that would interfere with engine removal. Disconnect the ground cable from transaxle.

3) Disconnect accelerator cable. Remove exhaust pipe clamp from exhaust manifold. Remove heater hoses and set aside. Disconnect power brake booster vacuum hose.

4) Remove the 2 selector lever bracket retaining bolts and spacers, and remove gear shift selector lever assembly. Disconnect automatic transaxle cooler hoses.

5) Remove front wheels. Using Extractor (T.Av.476), remove the tie rod end ball joints. Remove brake calipers and suspend from vehicle body using a piece of wire.

6) Remove the axle shaft on the left side by removing the 3 bolts attaching the boot plate. Remove shock absorber bottom mounting bolts. Tilt the stub axle assembly to release the drive shaft. Use care to avoid damaging the boot at the wheel end.

7) Remove the axle shaft on the right side by removing the roll pins holding the axle shaft-to-sun wheel. Remove the shock absorber bottom mounting bolts and withdraw the axle shaft. Do not damage the boot at the wheel end.

8) Using a engine hoist, support engine/transaxle assembly. Remove the front and rear engine and transaxle mounting nuts. Carefully lift engine/transaxle assembly from vehicle.

Installation

To install reverse removal procedure, and note the following: Fill the engine and transaxle oil sumps to the correct fluid level. See AUTOMATIC TRANSMISSION SERVICING in this section. Fill and purge cooling system. Use new bolts when installing exhaust pipe clamp.

TIGHTENING SPECIFICATIONS

Application	Ft. Lbs. (N.m)
Torque Command 998	
Converter-to-Flywheel	22 (30)
Rear Mount-to-Transmission	30 (41)
Transmission-to-Engine	30 (41)
MB 1 Transaxle	
Engine Mount	25 (35)
Exhaust Flange Bolts	20-26 (29-35)
Tie Rod End	25 (35)
Transaxle-to-Engine	31 (42)

CHRYSLER CORP. DOMESTIC CARS

REMOVAL & INSTALLATION

TORQUEFLITE (RWD MODELS)

Removal

1) Disconnect negative battery cable. Remove engine to transmission struts (if equipped). Remove cooler lines at transmission. Remove cooler line bracket, starter motor and torque converter cover. Loosen oil pan bolts, tap pan to break it loose allowing fluid to drain. Reinstall pan.

NOTE: Some models require that exhaust system be dropped for clearance.

2) Mark converter and drive plate for installation reference. Using a socket wrench on crankshaft vibration damper bolt, rotate engine clockwise to position converter attaching bolts for removal. Mark propeller shaft and yoke for installation reference. Remove propeller shaft.

3) Disconnect electrical leads. Disconnect gearshift rod, torque shaft assembly and throttle rod lever from left side of transmission. Remove linkage at bellcrank (if so equipped) from transmission.

4) Remove oil filler tube and speedometer cable. Support rear of engine with safety stand. Raise transmission slightly to relieve load on mounts. Remove bolts securing transmission mount-to-crossmember and crossmember-to-frame. Remove crossmember.

5) Remove converter housing-to-engine attaching bolts. Pull transmission assembly back and remove from under vehicle.

NOTE: Attach a small "C" clamp to edge of converter housing to hold torque converter in place during transmission removal.

Installation

CAUTION: Flush the oil cooler and cooler lines before replacing transmission.

1) To install, reverse removal procedures and note the following: To install the converter, rotate pump rotors with Pump Alignment (C-3756) until 2 small holes in handle are vertical.

2) Hold converter hub slots vertical to fully engage pump inner rotor lugs. Slide converter over input shaft and reaction shaft. Ensure surface of converter front cover lug is at least 1/2" below front edge of transmission when converter is installed.

3) Attach a small "C" clamp to converter housing. Inspect converter drive plate for distortion or cracks and replace if necessary. Coat converter hub hole in crankshaft with multi-purpose grease.

NOTE: When drive plate replacement is necessary, ensure both transmission dowel pins are in engine block.

4) Place transmission and converter assembly on a jack. Rotate converter so mark on converter (made during removal) will align with mark on drive plate. Offset holes in drive plate are located next to 1/8" hole in inner circle of plate. A stamped "O" identifies offset hole in converter.

5) Place transmission in position rear of engine. Install and tighten all bolts. Adjust shift and throttle linkage. Refill transmission with DEXRON II automatic transmission fluid.

6) To complete installation, reverse removal procedures. Tighten bolts holding struts-to-transmission (if equipped) before tightening strut-to-engine bolts.

All FWD MODELS (A-413 Transaxle)

Removal

1) Disconnect negative battery cable. Disconnect throttle linkage and shift linkage from transaxle. Remove upper and lower oil cooling lines. Install engine support fixture. Remove upper bell housing bolts. Remove hub cotter pin and castle nut. Raise vehicle on a hoist.

2) Remove front wheels. Remove left splash shield. Remove speedometer cable from housing. Disconnect sway bar and remove pinch bolts at lower control arm ball joint. Pry control arm down to remove ball joint. Remove drive axles from hub.

3) Remove drive axles from transaxle and from vehicle. Remove torque converter dust cover. Mark torque converter and flexplate and remove flexplate bolts. Remove access plug (in right shield) to rotate engine. Remove neutral safety switch connector.

4) Remove engine mount bracket from front crossmember. Remove front mount through-bolt and bell housing bolts. Position a jack under transaxle. Remove left engine mount. Remove starter and remaining bell housing bolts. Lower transaxle on jack. Pry engine for clearance and remove transaxle from vehicle.

Installation

To install, reverse removal procedures. Adjust throttle and shift linkage as necessary. Fill transaxle and differential sumps to correct level when installation is completed. Road test vehicle. See AUTOMATIC TRANSMISSION SERVICING in this section.

TIGHTENING SPECIFICATIONS

Application	Ft. Lbs. (N.m)
Torqueflite	
Converter-to-Flywheel	22 (30)
Rear Mount-to-Transmission	30 (41)
Transmission-to-Engine	30 (41)
A-413 Torqueflite	
Ball Joint Bolt	50 (68)
Converter-to-Flywheel	40 (54)
Mount-to-Transaxle	40 (54)
Transaxle-to-Engine	70 (95)

FORD MOTOR CO. DOMESTIC CARS

REMOVAL & INSTALLATION

AUTOMATIC OVERDRIVE & C-3

Removal

1) Raise and support vehicle. Drain transmission oil. Remove converter drain plug access cover and adapter plate bolts from lower end of converter housing. Remove the 4 flexplate nuts. Turn engine to gain access to nuts.

CAUTION: On belt driven overhead camshaft engines, NEVER turn engine backwards.

2) Remove converter drain plug and allow fluid in converter to drain. After all fluid has drained, reinstall drain plug and tighten.

3) Mark position of yokes and remove propeller shaft and install a seal remover tool in extension housing. Disconnect speedometer cable. Disconnect shift rod and downshift rod at transmission.

4) Remove starter bolts and place starter out of the way. Disconnect neutral safety switch wires and vacuum line. Position jack under transmission and raise it slightly.

5) Remove crossmember. Remove inlet pipe steady rest from inlet pipe and rear engine support. Disconnect muffler inlet pipe at exhaust manifold and secure it out of way. Lower transmission jack and place a screw jack under front of engine to gain access to the 2 upper converter housing-to-engine bolts.

6) Disconnect oil cooling lines at transmission and plug all openings. Remove lower converter housing-to-engine attaching bolts. Remove transmission filler tube. Secure transmission to jack with a safety chain. Remove the 2 upper converter housing-to-engine bolts. Slide transmission to the rear and remove it from vehicle.

Installation

1) Ensure torque converter drain plug is tight. Position converter to transmission making sure the converter hub is fully engaged in pump gear.

2) With converter installed, place transmission on a jack and secure with safety chain. Align converter drive studs and drain plug with holes in flywheel.

3) With transmission mounted on jack, move converter and transmission assembly forward into position. Install the 2 upper converter housing-to-engine attaching bolts and tighten.

CAUTION: Do not allow transmission to get into a nosed down position. This may cause converter to move forward and disengage from pump gear. Converter must rest squarely against flywheel.

4) To complete installation, reverse removal procedure and note the following: Fill transmission with fluid to proper level. See AUTOMATIC TRANSMISSION SERVICING in this section. Adjust manual and downshift linkage as required.

C-5

Removal

1) Disconnect negative battery cable. If equipped with a 3.8L engine, remove air cleaner and disconnect thermactor air tube to catalytic converter check valve. Remove fan shroud. On 3.8L engines, remove 2 bolts from top of bell housing.

2) Raise vehicle on a hoist and drain transmission. Mark position of yokes and remove drive shaft. Remove muffler inlet pipe, header pipe and catalytic converter. Remove speedometer cable from housing. Remove electrical wiring and kick down rod.

3) Disconnect shifter linkage. Remove torque converter cover and remove flexplate bolts. Remove starter motor. Loosen nuts on rear crossmember. Support transmission with a jack and remove bolts from rear crossmember. Lower transmission and remove oil cooling lines.

4) Remove converter housing to engine bolts. Disengage transmission from engine and lower transmission from vehicle.

Installation

To install, reverse removal procedure and note the following: Adjust manual and downshift linkage. Fill transmission with fluid to proper level. See AUTOMATIC TRANSMISSION SERVICING in this section.

CAUTION: The converter must rest squarely against flywheel. This indicates that converter pilot is not binding in engine crankshaft.

ATX TRANSAXLE

Removal (Escort, EXP & Lynx)

1) Disconnect negative battery cable. Remove bolts attaching managed air valve-to-valve body cover. Disconnect wiring from neutral safety switch. Disconnect throttle valve linkage and manual lever cable.

2) Remove the 2 upper transaxle-to-engine attaching bolts. Raise and support vehicle. Remove control arm-to-steering knuckle attaching bolt and nut (at both ball joints). Using a pry bar, carefully separate control arms from steering knuckles.

CAUTION: Use care not to damage ball joint boot. Pry bar must not contact lower arm.

3) Remove bolts attaching stablizer bar brackets to frame. Remove stabilizer bar-to-control arm attaching nut and washer. Pull bar out of control arms.

4) Remove bolts attaching brake hose routing clips to suspension strut brackets. Disconnect tie rod ends from steering knuckles. Pry axle shaft out of right side of transaxle and position shaft on transaxle housing.

5) Insert a driver into right side differential side gear. Drive left axle shaft from differential side gear. Pull axle shaft from transaxle and support out of way. Install Plugs (T81P-1177-B) into differential seals to prevent spline misalignment.

6) Remove starter support bracket, disconnect starter cable and remove starter. Remove transaxle support bracket. Remove dust cover from torque converter housing. Remove flexplate nuts.

7) Remove nuts attaching left front insulator to body bracket, bracket-to-body bolts and remove bracket. Remove left rear insulator bracket attaching nut.

8) Disconnect oil cooling lines at transaxle. Remove manual lever bracket to transaxle case. Position transmission jack under transaxle and remove the 4 remaining transaxle-to-engine attaching bolts.

9) Insert a screwdriver between flexplate and torque converter. Carefully move transaxle and converter away from engine. When converter studs are clear of flywheel, lower transaxle slightly (2-3"). Disconnect speedometer cable and lower transaxle from vehicle.

FORD MOTOR CO. DOMESTIC CARS (Cont.)

NOTE: If transaxle contacts body before converter studs clear flex-plate, remove left front insulator.

Installation

1) To install, reverse removal procedure, and note the following: Prior to installing axle shaft, replace snap ring on CV joint stub shaft.

2) To install axle shaft, carefully align splines on shaft with differential splines. Push CV joint until snap ring is felt to seat in groove in side gear.

3) Attach lower ball joint to steering knuckle, taking care not to damage or cut ball joint boot. Install new service pinch bolt, and install new nut.

4) Fill transaxle with fluid to proper level. See AUTOMATIC TRANSMISSION SERVICING in this section.

Removal (Tempo & Topaz)

NOTE: Engine/Transaxle are removed as assembly.

1) Mark hinges for reinstallation. Remove hood. Disconnect negative battery cable. Remove air cleaner assembly. Drain cooling system. Remove upper and lower radiator hoses. If equipped, disconnect transmission oil cooling lines at hoses below radiator.

2) Remove coil assembly. Disconnect cooling fan. Remove radiator fan assembly. Remove radiator. Discharge A/C system and disconnect hoses at compressor. Disconnect all electrical and vacuum lines.

3) Disconnect T.V. linkage. Disconnect accelerator linkage, fuel lines at engine and thermactor discharge hose at pump.

4) If equipped, disconnect power steering hoses at pump. Remove hose bracket at cylinder head. Attach engine support tool to lifting eye. Raise vehicle.

5) Remove starter cable, catalytic converter hose, exhaust pipe bracket bolt at oil pan and exhaust pipe-to-manifold. Remove exhaust system and set aside. Disconnect speedometer cable at transaxle.

6) Disconnect heater hoses at engine. Remove water pump inlet tube and clamps. Disconnect control arms at body. Remove stabilizer bar brackets. Remove axle shaft assemblies and install alignment plugs in differential side gears.

7) Disconnect manual shift cable clip and remove manual shift linkage bracket. Remove left-hand rear insulator mount bracket. Remove left-hand front insulator-to-transaxle mount bolts. Lower vehicle. Attach engine hoist to lifting eyes. Remove engine support tool.

CAUTION: Do not allow front wheels to touch floor.

8) Remove right-hand insulator intermediate bracket from engine bracket and insulator. Lower engine/transaxle assembly to floor.

Installation

1) To install, reverse removal procedure, and note the following: Prior to installing axle shaft, replace snap ring on CV joint stub shaft.

2) To install axle shaft, carefully align splines on shaft with differential splines. Push CV joint until snap ring is felt to seat in groove in side gear.

3) Attach lower ball joint to steering knuckle, taking care not to damage or cut ball joint boot. Install new service pinch bolt, and install new nut.

4) Fill transaxle with fluid to proper level. See AUTOMATIC TRANSMISSION SERVICING in this section.

AXOD TRANSAXLE

Removal (Sable & Taurus)

1) Remove negative battery cable and air cleaner assembly. Remove shifter cable and bracket from transaxle. Disconnect neutral safety switch and bulkhead connector from rear of transaxle.

2) Remove T.V. cable from throttle body and transaxle. Remove through bolt from left motor mount strut. Remove bolts from top of bell housing-to-transaxle. Attach Engine Support (D79P-6000-B) and raise engine to take pressure off engine mounts.

3) Raise vehicle on hoist. Remove wheels and lower ball joints. Remove lower control arms. Remove sway bar link-to-body bolts. Remove steering rack-to-subframe bolts.

4) Remove all subframe-to-engine mount bolts. Disconnect O_2 sensor lead. Remove exhaust system section under subframe and transaxle. Support subframe. Remove remaining subframe-to-body bolts and lower subframe.

5) Position a transaxle jack under transaxle. Remove speedometer or vehicle speed sensor. Remove transaxle-to-engine supports and transaxle mount. Remove starter and dust cover.

6) Remove 4 flexplate-to-torque converter nuts. Disconnect transaxle cooler lines. Using Slide Hammer (D79P-100-A), CV Joint Puller (T86P-3514-A1) and Extension (T86P-3514-A2), pull CV joints from transaxle.

7) Remove remaining transaxle-to-engine bolts. Separate transaxle and lower out from under vehicle.

Installation

To install, reverse removal procedure and note the following: Adjust T.V. cable and shift linkage. Fill transmission with fluid to proper level. See AUTOMATIC TRANSMISSION SERVICING in this section.

TIGHTENING SPECIFICATIONS

Application	Ft. Lbs. (N.m)
C-3, C-5 & AOD	
Bell Housing-to-Engine	
3.8L & 5.0L	28-38 (38-52)
2.3L & AOD	40-50 (54-68)
Converter Drain Plug	8-23 (11-31)
Converter-to-Flywheel	
C-3	27-49 (37-67)
AOD & C-5	20-34 (27-46)
Oil Cooler Line	7-10 (10-14)
ATX & AXOD	
Ball Joint Bolt	36-44 (50-60)
Converter-to-Flywheel	23-39 (31-53)
Oil Pan-to-Transaxle	30-39 (41-53)
Starter	30-40 (40-54)
Transaxle Mount	25-33 (34-45)
Transaxle-to-Engine	25-33 (34-45)

Automatic Transmission Removal

GENERAL MOTORS DOMESTIC CARS

REMOVAL & INSTALLATION

A131L (TRANSAXLE)

Removal (Nova)

1) Remove negative battery cable, air cleaner and speedometer cable at transaxle. Remove neutral start switch. Disconnect thermostat housing and ground cable.

2) Remove T.V. cable from carburetor lever. Remove top mount to bracket bolt and 2 upper transaxle to engine bolts. Support engine with overhead support tool.

3) Raise vehicle on a hoist and drain transmission. Remove left wheel and splash shield. Remove right and center splash shields. Remove center support beam. Remove shift cable, starter motor, wiring connectors and oil cooling lines. Plug cooling line openings.

4) Remove torque converter cover. Mark the flexplate and torque converter to aid in reassembly. Remove flexplate bolts. Separate both lower control arms at ball joints. Pull both axle shafts at transaxle.

5) Support transaxle with a jack. Remove remaining transaxle mount. Remove remaining transaxle to engine bolts. Move transaxle back and lower from vehicle.

Installation

1) Reverse removal procedure and note the following: Install torque converter. Ensure weld nuts on converter are at least 25/32" below front edge of transaxle.

2) Install the White torque converter bolt. Install the 5 remaining Yellow bolts. Hand start all 6 bolts and then tighten. Adjust shift linkage and T.V. cable as necessary. Fill transaxle to proper level with fluid. See AUTOMATIC TRANSMISSION SERVICING in this section.

THM 180-C, THM 200C, THM 200-4R & THM 700-R4 (TRANSMISSIONS)

Removal (RWD Models)

1) Disconnect negative battery cable. Remove air cleaner, T.V. cable at its upper end, and oil dipstick and tube. Raise vehicle on a hoist. Mark position of yokes and remove drive shaft.

NOTE: **On Corvette models, remove complete exhaust system and driveline beam. On Camaro and Firebird, remove torque arm from rear suspension. On Cadillac, remove header pipe at exhaust manifold, catalytic converter and fuel line-to-transmission bracket.**

2) Remove floor reinforcement (if used). Remove speedometer cable. Remove shifter linkage and electrical connectors. Remove flexplate cover. Mark flexplate and torque converter and remove bolts.

3) Remove catalytic converter support bracket. Remove transmission support. Lower transmission to gain access to oil cooling lines and T.V. cable attachments.

4) Support engine with a screw jack and remove transmission to engine bolts. Pull transmission back. Install Torque Converter Holder (J-21366) and lower transmission from vehicle.

Installation

1) To install transmission, reverse removal procedures noting the following: Observe marks made during disassembly and line-up in original positions.

2) Ensure weld nuts on torque converter are flush with flexplate. Test torque converter for freedom of rotation. Tighten flexplate bolts finger tight, then tighten to specifications.

THM 125-C & 440-T4 (TRANSAXLES)

Removal (Celebrity, Century, Ciera & 6000)

NOTE: **Anytime the cradle assembly is removed or lowered from vehicle, the rack and pinion steering assembly must be properly disconnected from the cradle. The rack and pinion steering assembly must then be supported in a manner in which it is not allowed to "hang" by the intermediate shaft. Failure to do so will result in damage to the intermediate shaft.**

1) Disconnect negative battery cable. Remove air cleaner, wiring and cable routing clips and straps. Remove bolt securing T.V. cable to transaxle. Install Engine Support (J-28467). Raise vehicle on a hoist. Drain transaxle fluid. Remove strut shock bracket bolts and oil cooling lines from transaxle.

2) Remove transaxle to engine bolts leaving bolt near starter loosely installed. Remove speedometer cable at upper and lower couplings. Remove shifter linkage retaining clip, washer and bracket from transaxle.

3) Remove front and left sections of cradle. Position Axle Shaft Remover (J-33008) and Slide Hammer (J-2619-01) behind axle shaft cones and pull cones away from transaxle. Pull left axle shaft out of transaxle and plug bore to minimize fluid leakage.

4) Rotate strut so axle shaft is out of way. Remove starter motor and converter shields. Mark torque converter and remove flexplate bolts. Remove 2 transaxle extension bolts from engine-to-transaxle. Remove rear transaxle mount bracket. (It may be necessary to raise transaxle).

5) Support transaxle with a jack. Remove 2 braces to right end of transaxle boots. Remove remaining transaxle to engine bolt (located near starter). Slide transaxle from engine, toward driver's side. Lower transaxle from vehicle.

Removal (Calais, Cavalier, Cimarron, Firenza, Grand Am, Somerset, Skyhawk, Skylark & Sunbird)

1) Disconnect negative battery cable. Remove air cleaner and T.V. cables from carburetor and transaxle. Remove airflow meter and intake duct (if equipped). Remove shift linkage and wiring routing clips and straps.

2) Remove dipstick tube and install Engine Holding Fixture (J-28467). On Cavalier, Cimarron, Firenza, Skyhawk and Sunbird, insert a 1/4" x 2" bolt in hole at front right motor mount to maintain driveline alignment. Remove nut securing wiring harness to transaxle.

3) Remove wiring connectors from transaxle. Disconnect shifter linkage. Remove top 2 transaxle to engine bolts and left upper transaxle bracket and mount. Remove rubber hose from transaxle to vent pipe. Remove remaining upper engine to transaxle bolts.

4) Raise vehicle on a hoist. Remove front wheels. Drain transaxle. Remove shift linkage bracket from transaxle. Remove lower ball joints from control arms. Remove and support axles. Remove transaxle mounting strut. Remove left stabilizer bar link pin bolt and left stabilizer bar frame bushing clamp nuts.

5) Remove left frame support assembly. Remove header pipe at exhaust manifold (if equipped with 1.8L). Remove speedometer cable and starter motor. Remove torque converter cover. Mark position of flexplate and torque converter. Remove flexplate bolts. Remove oil cooling lines. Remove transaxle to engine support bracket.

GENERAL MOTORS DOMESTIC CARS (Cont.)

Position jack under transaxle. Remove remaining engine to transaxle bolts. Slide transaxle from engine and lower from vehicle.

Removal (Delta 88, DeVille, Eldorado, Electra Fleetwood, LeSabre, Riviera, Seville, Toronado & 98)

1) Remove hood and disconnect negative battery cable. On DeVille, Eldorado, Fleetwood and Seville, remove air cleaner, air injection crossover pipe, air management valve and exhaust crossover pipe. On all others, remove airflow meter.

2) Remove T.V. cable at transaxle, shift linkage and vacuum modulator line. Remove neutral start, cruise control and vehicle speed sensor wiring. Remove upper transaxle mounting bolts.

3) Install Engine Support (J-28467) and raise engine to unload engine mounts. On Eldorado, Toronado and Seville, remove driveline damper and engine mount. On all vehicles, raise on a hoist and remove front wheels.

4) Remove both lower ball joints from steering knuckle. Install Axle Boot Protectors (J-34754). Using Drive Axle Remover (J-33008), remove both drive axles from transaxle. Tie drive axles out of way.

NOTE: **If necessary, raise left side of engine 2" to remove left engine mount and left cradle attaching bolts. Ensure engine is lowered back to original position.**

5) Remove stabilizer linkage at left side. Remove left splash shield, vacuum pump (if equipped), and all wiring and hoses. Remove all transaxle to cradle, and engine to left cradle assembly mounting bolts. Support left cradle assembly. Remove right and left cradle attaching bolts and remove left cradle assembly.

6) Remove oil cooler lines and converter dust cover. Position jack under transaxle. Remove torque converter bolts. Remove remaining transaxle mounting bolts and remove from vehicle.

NOTE: **Locate 1 bolt connecting transaxle to engine installed from the opposite direction. On some models, a 3 FOOT socket extension placed through the right wheelhousing will help remove this bolt.**

Installation (All Models)

To install, reverse removal procedure and note the following: As transaxle is being installed, guide right axle shaft into transaxle. Adjust T.V. and shift cables. Refill transaxle to proper fluid level. See AUTOMATIC TRANSMISSION SERVICING in this section.

THM 125C (TRANSAXLE)

Removal (Fiero)

1) Remove air cleaner and negative battery cable. Remove ground strap, shift cable and T.V. cable at transaxle. Remove electrical connectors. Remove upper transaxle bolts. Install Engine Support Fixture (J-28467).

NOTE: **Remove neutral start switch connector in a straight horizontal movement. DO NOT rock or tip connector when removing.**

2) Raise vehicle. Remove rear wheels. Remove both axle shafts. See DRIVE AXLE removal and installation procedures in DRIVE AXLES section. Remove catalytic converter heat shield. Remove header pipe at manifold. Remove cradle nuts-to-engine and transaxle. Support cradle. Remove remaining nuts and lower cradle out of way.

3) Remove oil cooling lines. Remove starter shield and starter. Mark position of flex-plate and torque converter. Remove flexplate nuts. Position jack under transaxle. Remove lower transaxle-to-engine bolts. Lower transaxle from vehicle.

Installation

Reverse removal procedure and note the following: Adjust T.V. and shift cables. Refill transaxle to proper level with fluid. See AUTOMATIC TRANSMISSION SERVICING in this section.

NOTE: **In the following table, the letter "J" refers to Cavalier, Cimarron, Firenza, Skyhawk and Sunbird. The letter "N" refers to Calais, Grand Am, Somerset and Skylark.**

TIGHTENING SPECIFICATION

Application	Ft. Lbs. (N.m)
A131L	
Center Support-to-Body	29 (39)
Mount-to-Center Support	29 (39)
Torque Converter-to-Flexplate	13 (18)
Transaxle-to-Engine (10 mm)	35 (47)
Transaxle-to-Engine (12 mm)	47 (64)
THM 180C, 200C, 200-4R & 700-R4	
Converter Housing-to-Engine	35 (47)
Torque Converter-to-Flexplate	35 (47)
Transmission-to-Mount	35 (47)
THM 125C (Fiero)	
Engine Mount-to-Cradle	40 (54)
Front Cradle-to-Body	67 (90)
Rear Cradle-to-Body	76 (103)
Torque Converter-to-Flexplate	35 (47)
Transaxle-to-Engine	55 (75)
Transaxle Mount-to-Cradle	
Front	36 (48)
Rear	18 (24)
THM 125C & 440-T4 (Except Fiero)	
Converter Housing-to-Engine	55 (75)
Cooler Lines	16 (22)
Front Cradle Assembly	
"J" & "N" Bodies	65 (88)
All Others	74 (100)
Torque Converter-to-Flexplate	
"J" & "N" Bodies	35 (47)
All Others	46 (63)
Transaxle-to-Mount Nuts	40 (54)

Automatic Transmission Removal

CHRYSLER CORP. FWD LIGHT TRUCKS

TRANSAXLE

ALL MODELS

NOTE: **Transaxle removal does not require engine removal.**

NOTE: **Transaxle and torque converter must be removed as an assembly; other wise, the torque converter drive plate, pump bushing or oil seal may be damaged. The drive plate will not support a load; therefore, none of the weight of the transaxle should be allowed to rest on the plate during removal.**

Removal

1) Disconnect battery negative cable. Disconnect throttle linkage and shift linkage from transaxle. Remove upper and lower oil cooler hoses. Support engine using an engine support fixture. Remove bell housing upper bolts. Remove hub castle lock, nut and cotter pin.

2) Raise vehicle and remove front wheels. Remove wheel hub nut and driveshafts. Remove left splash shield. Remove speedometer adapter, cable and pinion as an assembly. Disconnect sway bar. Remove both lower ball joint-to-steering knuckle bolts.

3) Pry lower ball joint from steering knuckle. Remove both driveshafts. Remove dust cover, mark torque converter and drive plate, and remove torque converter mounting bolts. Remove access plug in right splash shield to rotate engine crankshaft.

4) Remove neutral safety switch connector. Remove engine mount bracket from front crossmember. Remove front mount insulator through-bolt and bell housing bolts. Position transmission jack under transaxle. Remove left engine mount. Remove starter and lower bell housing bolts.

5) Slowly lower transaxle. It may be necessary to pry at engine to provide for clearance.

Installation

To install, reverse removal procedure. Be sure to adjust gearshift and throttle cables. Refill transaxle with Dexron II type automatic transmission fluid.

TIGHTENING SPECIFICATIONS

Application	Ft. Lbs. (N.m)
Flex Plate-to-Crankshaft	
A-413	65 (88)
A-470	100 (136)
Flex Plate-to-Torque Converter	40 (54)
Transaxle-to-Cylinder Block	70 (95)
Starter-to-Transaxle Bell Housing	40 (54)
Manual Cable-to-Transaxle Case	21 (28)
Front Motor Mount	40 (54)
Left Motor Mount	40 (54)
	INCH lbs.
Bell Housing Cover	108 (12)
Lower Bell Housing Cover	108 (12)
Manual Control Lever	108 (12)
Throttle Cable-to-Transaxle Case	108 (12)
Throttle Lever-to-Transaxle Shaft	108 (12)
Speedometer-to-Extension	60 (7)

CHRYSLER CORP. RWD LIGHT TRUCKS

TRANSFER CASE

MODEL NP-205

NOTE: **Safety goggles should be worn at all times when working on the transfer case.**

Removal

1) Raise vehicle and drain transfer case. Replace plug. Disconnect speedometer cable. Remove skid plate, crossmember and strut rods as needed. Disconnect propeller shafts and wire out of way. DO NOT allow propeller shafts to hang free, as damage to universal joints may result.

2) Disconnect shift lever rod from shift rail link. Support transfer case and remove transfer case-to-transmission adapter bolts. Move transfer case to rear until input shaft clears adapter. Lower transfer case from vehicle.

Installation

To install transfer case, reverse removal procedure. Ensure that all attaching bolts are tight. Fill transfer case with lubricant.

MODEL NP-208

Removal

1) Raise vehicle, remove plug and drain transfer case. Mark front and rear output shaft yokes and propeller shafts for reassembly reference. Disconnect speedometer cable and indicator switch wires.

2) Disconnect shift lever link from operating lever. Support transfer case with transmission jack and remove crossmember. Disconnect front and rear propeller shafts at yokes and wire to frame.

3) If necessary, disconnect parking brake cable guide from pivot on right frame rail. Remove bolts attaching exhaust pipe support bracket to transfer case. Remove transfer case-to-transmission bolts.

4) Move assembly to the rear until clear of output shaft. Lower transfer case from vehicle. Remove all gasket material from rear of the transmission adapter housing.

Installation

Install new transmission-to-transfer case gasket with sealer on both sides. Align transfer case with transmission. Rotate transfer case output shaft until transmission output shaft engages transfer case input shaft. Move transfer case until case seats flush against transmission. Install transfer case attaching bolts. Reverse removal procedures to complete installation.

TRANSMISSION

ALL MODELS

NOTE: **Transmission and converter must be removed and installed as an assembly to prevent damage to converter drive plate, front pump bushing, and oil seal. DO NOT allow weight of transmission to rest on plate during removal or installation.**

CHRYSLER CORP. RWD LIGHT TRUCKS (Cont.)

Removal

1) Remove transfer case from 4WD vehicles. Disconnect negative battery cable. Disconnect lower exhaust system as needed for removal clearance. Remove engine-to-transmission struts (if equipped). Disconnect cooler lines at transmision. Remove starter, cooler line bracket and converter access cover.

2) Loosen oil pan bolts. Tap pan to break loose and allow fluid to drain. Reinstall pan. Rotate crankshaft clockwise with socket on vibration damper bolt to gain access to converter-to-drive plate bolts. Remove bolts. Mark propeller shaft for reassembly reference and remove from vehicle.

NOTE: Crankshaft flange bolt circle, inner and outer circle of holes in drive plate and tapped holes in converter all have one hole offset so parts can only be installed in original position.

3) Disconnect wiring connector from back-up light/neutral safety switch. Disconnect gearshift rod and torque shaft assembly from transmission. Disconnect transmission throttle rod from lever. Remove linkage bellcrank assembly, if equipped. Remove oil filler tube. Disconnect speedometer cable.

4) Install an engine support fixture under rear of engine. Raise transmission with service jack to relieve load on supports. Remove bolts securing crossmember to transmission and frame, then remove crossmember. Remove all converter housing-to-engine attaching bolts.

5) Carefully work transmission and converter assembly rearward off engine block dowel pins, disengaging converter hub from end of crankshaft. Attach a small "C" clamp on edge of converter housing to hold converter in place while transmission is being removed. Lower transmission and remove from vehicle.

Installation

1) Before installing converter, rotate front pump rotors with Alignment Tool (C3881) until 2 small holes in tool handle are vertical. Slide torque converter over input and reaction shafts, making sure converter hub slots are vertical, and fully engage pump inner rotor lugs.

2) Test for full engagement by placing a straightedge across face of transmission case. Surface of converter front cover lug should be at least 1/2" to rear of straightedge when converter is fully engaged. Attach a small "C" clamp to edge of converter housing to hold converter in place while installing transmission.

3) Inspect converter drive plate for distortion or cracks and replace if necessary. Install drive plate and tighten bolts to 55 ft. lbs. (75 N.m).

4) Coat converter hub hole in crankshaft with multipurpose grease. Place transmission assembly on jack and position under vehicle. Make sure marks on converter and drive plate (made during removal) are aligned.

5) Carefully work transmission assembly into position over dowels. Install all converter housing-to-engine retaining bolts. Tighten bolts to 30 ft. lbs. (41 N.m).

Installation

To install, reverse removal procedure. Adjust shift and throttle linkages and fill transmission with fluid. On 4WD models, install transfer case.

TIGHTENING SPECIFICATIONS

Application	Ft. Lbs. (N.m)
Converter Housing-to-Engine	30 (41)
Cooler Line Fitting	15 (20)
Drain & Fill Plugs	
NP-205 Transfer Case	30 (41)
NP-208 Transfer Case	18 (24)
Oil Pan Bolts	13 (18)
Torque Converter-to-Drive Plate Bolts	22 (30)
Transfer Case-to-Transmission	40 (54)

FORD LIGHT TRUCKS

TRANSFER CASE

NP-208 (BRONCO, F-150 & F-250)

Removal

1) Raise and support vehicle. Remove drain plug and drain fluid from transfer case. Replace plug. Disconnect 4WD indicator switch connector at transfer case. Disconnect speedometer driven gear from transfer case rear bearing retainer.

2) Remove transmission shift lever-to-transfer case retaining nut. Remove skid plate from frame. Support transfer case with transmission jack. Disconnect front and rear propeller shafts from transfer case output shaft yokes and wire out of way. DO NOT allow shafts to hang free as damage to universal joints may result.

3) Remove transfer case-to-transmission adapter bolts. Remove gasket between transfer case and adapter and lower transfer case out of vehicle.

Installation

To install transfer case, reverse removal procedures. Fill case with 7 pints (3.3 liters) of Dexron II type automatic transmission fluid.

BORG-WARNER 1345 (F-150 & F-350)

Removal

1) Raise vehicle. Remove drain plug and drain fluid from transfer case. Replace plug. Disconnect 4WD indicator switch connector at transfer case. If equipped, remove skid plate.

2) Disconnect front and rear propeller shafts from transfer case output shaft yokes, and wire out of way. DO NOT allow shafts to hang free as damage to universal joints may result.

3) Disconnect speedometer driven gear from rear bearing retainer. Remove retaining clips and shift rod from transfer case control and transfer case shift levers. Disconnect vent hose from case.

4) Remove heat shield. Support transfer case with transmission jack, remove transfer case-to-transmission adapter bolts and slide transfer case off of transmission output shaft (towards rear). Lower transfer case out of vehicle and remove gasket from between transfer case and adapter.

FORD LIGHT TRUCKS (Cont.)

Installation

Reverse removal procedures to install transfer case. Fill case with 6.5 pints (3.1 liters) of Dexron II type automatic transmission fluid.

BORG-WARNER 1350 (BRONCO II & RANGER)

Removal

1) Raise vehicle. Remove skid plate (if equipped). Remove drain plug and drain fluid from case. Replace plug. Disconnect 4WD indicator switch connector at transfer case. Disconnect front propeller shaft from front axle. Loosen front shaft boot clamp and slide out propeller shaft and boot as an assembly.

2) Disconnect rear propeller shaft from transfer case. Disconnect speedometer driven gear from transfer case rear cover. Disconnect vent hose from control lever.

3) Loosen or remove large and small bolts (one each) retaining shifter to extension housing. Pull on control lever until bushing slides off transfer case shift lever pin. Unscrew shift lever from control lever, as needed.

4) Remove heat shield from transfer case. Support transfer case with jack and remove transfer case-to-transmission extension housing bolts (5). Slide transfer case to the rear and off of transmission output shaft. Lower case from vehicle. Remove gasket from between transfer case and extension housing.

Installation

Reverse removal procedures to install transfer case, noting the following:

1) When installing shift lever assembly, tighten large bolt first, then small bolt.

2) When installing vent assembly, White marking on hose should be positioned in notch in shifter with upper end of hose 2 inches above top of shifter, inside of shift lever boot.

3) Before installing front propeller shaft into transfer case, lubricate female splines of transfer case input shaft with multipurpose grease.

4) Fill transfer case to bottom of fill plug hole with Dexron-II automatic transmission fluid.

TRANSMISSION

C-3 (RANGER 2WD)

Removal

1) Disconnect battery negative cable. Raise vehicle. Loosen transmission pan bolts. Tap edge of pan to break seal and allow fluid to drain. Reinstall pan after fluid has drained. Remove converter drain plug access cover. Remove adapter plate bolts from lower end of converter housing.

2) Remove converter-to-flex plate attaching nuts and converter drain plug. Allow fluid to drain from converter, then reinstall and tighten drain plug. Mark propeller shaft for reassembly. Disconnect shaft at rear axle and slide out of transmission.

3) Remove speedometer cable from extension housing. Disconnect shift rod at manual lever and downshift rod at downshift lever. Remove starter-to-converter housing bolts and position starter out of way. DO NOT allow starter to hang by cables.

4) Disconnect neutral start switch connector from switch. Remove vacuum line from vacuum modulator. Raise slightly and support transmission with transmission jack. Remove rear mount-to-crossmember bolts.

5) Remove crossmember-to-frame side support bolts and remove crossmember insulator, support and damper. Lower jack under transmission and allow transmission to hang. Position a second jack at front of engine and raise enough to gain access to 2 top converter housing-to-engine bolts. DO NOT remove bolts at this time.

6) Disconnect transmission cooler lines and plug connections. Remove lower converter housing-to-engine bolts. Remove transmission filler tube. Raise transmission jack up to transmission and secure transmission to jack with safety chain.

7) Remove top 2 converter housing-to-engine bolts. Move transmission rearward and remove from vehicle.

Installation

To install, reverse removal procedures. Ensure full converter engagement in transmission before installing transmission. During installation, keep transmission in a "nose-up" position at all times to prevent disengagement of the torque converter and pump gear.

C-5 (F-150)

Removal

1) Disconnect battery negative cable. On 4WD vehicles, remove filler tube bracket bolt from valve cover bracket. On all models, raise and support vehicle. Drain transmission fluid and replace pan. Remove converter drain plug access cover. On 2WD models, remove adapter plate bolts from lower end of converter housing.

2) On all models, remove converter-to-flex plate attaching nuts and converter drain plug. Allow fluid to drain from converter, then reinstall and tighten drain plug. On 2WD models, mark propeller shaft for reassembly. Disconnect shaft at rear axle and slide out of transmission.

3) On all models, disconnect battery cable from starter motor and remove starter. Disconnect neutral start switch wires at connector. Remove rear mount-to-crossmember nuts and 2 crossmember-to-frame bolts. Remove right and left gussets. On 4WD vehicles, remove 2 rear insulator-to-extension housing bolts.

4) On all models, disconnect throttle valve (T.V.) linkage rod from transmission T.V. lever. Disconnect manual rod from manual lever at transmission. On 4WD models, disconnect downshift and manual linkage rods from levers on transmission. Remove vacuum hose from diaphragm unit. Remove vacuum line from retaining clip.

5) On all models, remove 2 bellcrank housing-to-converter housing bolts. Remove transfer case (4WD models). Raise transmission enough to allow removal of crossmember. Remove rear mount from crossmember, then remove crossmember.

6) Lower transmission as needed to disconnect oil cooler lines. Disconnect cooler lines. Disconnect speedometer cable from extension housing. On 2WD models, remove transmission filler tube-to-engine bolt and lift filler tube out of transmission.

7) On all models, secure transmission to jack with safety chain. Remove converter housing-to-engine bolts. Carefully remove transmission and converter assembly from vehicle.

FORD LIGHT TRUCKS (Cont.)

Installation

1) To install transmission, reverse removal procedures. Ensure that converter is fully engaged with pump gear before installation.

2) When installing filler tube, install a new "O" ring on bottom of tube. On 2WD models, when installing damper assembly over engine rear support studs.

3) Ensure that the painted surface of the damper is facing forward when installed in vehicle. Before installing rear propeller shaft, apply a small amount of multi-purpose grease to splines of yoke.

C-6 ("E" SERIES)

Removal

1) Remove engine compartment cover and disconnnect electrical leads at plug connector. Remove flex hose from air cleaner heat tube (V8 models only), then remove upper converter housing-to-engine attaching bolts. Remove fluid filler tube-to-engine bolt.

2) Raise vehicle, drain transmission pan and remove converter drain plug access cover. Remove converter-to-flex plate attaching nuts and converter drain plug. Drain fluid and replace drain plug.

3) Disconnect propeller shaft. Remove filler tube. Disconnect starter cable and remove starter. Position an engine support bar to side rail and oil pan flanges. Disconnect oil cooler lines and vacuum lines from transmission.

4) Remove speedometer driven gear from extension housing and manual and downshift linkage rods from transmission control levers. Support transmission with transmission jack and secure with safety chain.

5) Remove bolts and nuts securing rear mount to crossmember and bolts retaining crossmember to side rails. Remove 2 support inserts, and raise transmission with jack. Remove transmission crossmember. Remove remaining converter housing-to-engine bolts. Lower transmission out of vehicle.

Installation

1) To install, reverse removal procedures. Ensure that converter is fully engaged with pump gear during installation.

2) Always use a new "O" ring on the end of the fluid filler tube. When installation is complete, fill transmission with Dexron II type automatic transmission fluid.

C-6 (BRONCO & "F" SERIES)

Removal

1) Disconnect negative cable from battery. Remove 2 upper converter housing-to-engine bolts. Raise vehicle, drain transmission pan and remove converter drain plug access cover.

2) Remove converter-to-flex plate attaching nuts and converter drain plug. Allow fluid to drain, then reinstall and tighten converter drain plug. On 2WD models, disconnect propeller shaft at rear axle and slide shaft out of transmission.

3) On all models, disconnect speedometer cable from extension housing. Disconnect downshift and manual linkage rods from levers at transmission. Disconnect oil cooler lines from transmission.

4) Remove vacuum line from vacuum unit. Remove retaining clip from vacuum line. Disconnect starter cable from starter and remove starter. On 4WD models, remove transfer case. See TRANSFER CASE in this article.

5) On all models, remove 2 rear crossmember-to-frame attaching bolts. Remove 2 rear support-to-extension housing attaching bolts and 6 bolts securing second crossmember to frame side rails.

6) Raise transmission with a transmission jack and remove both crossmembers. Secure transmission to the jack with safety chain. Remove remaining converter housing-to-engine attaching bolts. Move transmission away from engine, lower the jack and remove converter and transmission assembly from vehicle.

Installation

Install, reverse removal procedure. Ensure that torque converter is fully engaged in transmission before and during installation. When installing fluid filler tube, always use a new "O" ring on end of tube. When installation is complete, fill transmission with Dexron II type automatic transmission fluid.

AUTOMATIC OVERDRIVE (E-150/250, F-150/250 & BRONCO) A4LD (AEROSTAR, 2WD/4WD RANGER & BRONCO II)

Removal

1) Disconnect negative battery cable. Raise vehicle and drain transmission fluid. Remove converter drain plug access cover. Remove converter-to-flex plate attaching nuts and torque converter drain plug. Drain converter, then reinstall and tighten converter drain plug.

2) Disconnect propeller shaft from rear axle and remove shaft from transmission. Disconnect starter cable and remove starter. Disconnect neutral start switch wires at connector.

3) Remove rear mount-to-crossmember bolts and crossmember-to-frame bolts. Remove bolts securing engine rear support to extension housing. Disconnect TV linkage rod and manual rod from transmission levers.

4) Remove 2 bellcrank bracket-to-converter housing bolts. Raise transmission with jack and remove crossmember. Lower transmission enough to remove oil cooler lines.

5) Disconnect speedometer cable from extension housing. Remove bolt securing filler tube to engine and remove filler tube. Secure transmission to jack with safety chain. Remove converter housing-to-engine bolts. Move transmission to rear and down to remove from vehicle.

Installation

1) To install, reverse removal procedure. Ensure that converter is fully seated in transmission before and during installation procedure.

2) Install new "O" ring on end of fluid filler tube before installing tube. When installation is complete, fill transmission with Dexron II type automatic transmission fluid.

FORD LIGHT TRUCKS (Cont.)

TIGHTENING SPECIFICATIONS

Application	Ft. Lbs. (N.m)
Converter Housing-to-Engine	
C-3	28-38 (38-51)
C-5	
Bronco II, Ranger	28-38 (38-51)
All Others	40-50 (55-67)
C-6	
Gasoline Engines	40-50 (55-67)
Diesel Engines	50-65 (67-87)
AOT	40-50 (55-67)
A4LD	28-38 (38-51)
Converter-to-Flex Plate	
C-3	27-50 (37-67)
All Others	20-30 (28-40)

TIGHTENING SPECIFICATIONS (Cont.)

Application	Ft. Lbs. (N.m)
Starter Mounting Bolts	
Bronco II & Ranger	15-20 (20-28)
All Other Models	
Gasoline Engine	40-50 (55-67)
Diesel Engine	50-65 (67-87)
Control Lever-to-Transfer Case (Bronco II & Ranger)	
Large Bolt	70-90 (95-112)
Small Bolt	30-42 (40-57)

GENERAL MOTORS LIGHT TRUCKS

TRANSFER CASE

NP-205 (30 SERIES)

Removal

1) Raise and support vehicle on hoist. Drain transfer case. Disconnect speedometer cable. Remove skid plate and crossmember supports as necessary. Disconnect rear drive shaft from transfer case and tie up away from work area.

2) Disconnect front drive shaft from transfer case and tie up shaft away from work area. Disconnect shift lever rod from shift rail link. Support transfer case and remove bolts attaching transfer case to transmission adapter.

3) Move transfer case to rear until input shaft clears adapter and lower assembly from vehicle.

Installation

To install, reverse removal procedure.

NP-207 ("S" SERIES)

Removal

1) With transfer case shift lever in "4H" position, disconnect negative battery cable. Raise vehicle and remove skid plate. Drain transfer case. Mark front and rear output shaft yokes and propeller shafts for reassembly reference and remove shafts.

2) Disconnect speedometer cable and vacuum harness from transfer case. Remove shift lever from case. Remove catalytic converter hanger bolts at converter. Raise transmission and transfer case assembly with jack and remove transmission mount bolts. Remove mount.

3) Lower complete assembly. Support transfer case alone and remove transmission-to-transfer case bolts. Remove shift lever bracket from transfer case adapter in order to reach upper left attaching bolt.

4) Separate transfer case from transmission adapter and remove from vehicle.

Installation

To install, reverse removal procedure. Always use a new gasket between the transfer case and adapter.

NP-208 (10 & 20 SERIES)

Removal

1) Place transfer case in "4H". Raise vehicle. Drain lubricant from transfer case. Remove cotter pin from shift lever swivel. Mark transfer case front and rear output shaft yokes and propeller shafts for assembly alignment reference.

2) Disconnect speedometer cable and indicator switch wires. Disconnect front drive shaft at transfer case yoke. Disconnect parking brake cable guide from pivot located on right frame rail, if necessary. Remove engine strut rod from transfer case.

3) Place support under transfer case and remove transfer case-to-transmission adapter bolts. Move transfer case assembly rearward until free of transmission output shaft and remove assembly. Remove all gasket material from rear of transmission adapter housing.

Installation

To install, reverse removal procedure.

TRANSMISSIONS

ALL MODELS (EXC. ASTRO/SAFARI VAN, "S" & "K" SERIES)

Removal

1) Disconnect negative battery cable. Remove air cleaner and disconnect T.V. or detent cable at carburetor. Remove dipstick and filler tube support bracket bolt. Raise and support vehicle. Mark propeller shaft for reassembly reference and remove from vehicle.

2) Disconnect speedometer cable and shift linkage and all electrical leads from transmission. Remove transmission support brackets (if present) and flywheel inspection cover.

3) Mark flex plate and torque converter for reassembly in same position and remove torque converter-to-flex plate bolts. Disconnect catalytic converter support bracket (if equipped).

4) Remove transmission rear mount bolts. Support transmission with jack and raise slightly. Remove transmission support-to-frame bolts and insulators. Remove support.

5) Lower transmission enough to remove oil cooler lines and TV or detent cable from transmission. Disconnect lines and cable. Support engine with jack and remove transmission-to-engine bolts.

6) Disconnect transmission assembly from engine. Install Torque Converter Retainer (J-21366) and remove transmission from vehicle.

Installation

To install, reverse removal procedure. Before installing flex plate-to-converter bolts, make certain that the weld nuts on converter are flush with the flex plate and the converter rotates freely by hand in this position. Finger tighten all 3 bolts before tightening to specifications.

ASTRO/SAFARI VAN

Removal

1) Open hood and disconnect negative cable at battery. Remove engine cover. Disconnect T.V. cable at its upper end. Raise vehicle. Remove propeller shaft. Disconnect speedometer cable at transmission. Disconnect shift linkage at transmission.

2) Disconnect all electrical leads at transmission and any clips that retain leads to transmission case. Remove transmission support brace attaching bolts at converter. Disconnect exhaust crossover pipe from exhaust manifolds.

3) Remove converter cover and mark flywheel and torque converter to maintain original balance. Remove torque converter to flywheel bolts and/or nuts. Position a transmission jack under transmission and raise it slightly.

4) Remove transmission crossmember to mount bolts and crossmember to frame bolts (and insulator if used). Slide crossmember rearward and remove from vehicle. Lower transmission to gain access to oil cooler lines and T.V. Cable attachments. Disconnect oil cooler lines and T.V. cable. Cap all openings.

5) Support engine with a suitable tool and remove transmission to engine bolts. Disconnect transmission assembly, being careful not to damage any cables, lines or linkage. Install Torque Converter Holder (J-21366) and remove transmission from vehicle.

Installation

To install, reverse removal procedure.

"K" SERIES

Removal

1) Disconnect negative battery cable. Remove air cleaner and disconnect T.V. or detent cable at carburetor. Remove transfer case shift lever knob and boot. Raise and support vehicle.

2) Mark propeller shafts for reassembly reference and remove from vehicle. Disconnect speedometer cable, shift linkage and all electrical leads from transmission and transfer case. Disconnect transfer case shift linkage.

3) Remove transmission support strut rods and flywheel inspection cover. Mark flex plate and converter for reassembly reference. Remove torque converter-to-flex plate retaining bolts.

4) Disconnect transmission oil cooler lines from transmission. Using a transmission jack, support transmission and transfer case. Remove transfer case-to-frame bracket bolts. Remove mount bolts and transmission crossmember.

5) Remove transmission/transfer case assembly mounting bolts and remove assembly from vehicle. Separate transmission from transfer case.

Installation

To install, reverse removal procedure. Before installing flex plate-to-converter bolts, make certain that the weld nuts on converter are flush with the flex plate and the converter rotates freely by hand in this position. Then, hand start all 3 bolts and tighten finger tight before tightening to specifications.

"S" SERIES

NOTE: **On 4WD models, refer to Transfer Case removal procedures to remove transfer case.**

Removal

1) Disconnect negative battery cable. Remove air cleaner and isconnect T.V. cable at carburetor. On models with 1.9L 4-cylinder engine, remove upper starter retaining nut. On all models, raise and support vehicle.

2) Mark propeller shaft for reassembly reference and remove shaft. Disconnect speedometer cable, shift linkage and all electrical leads from transmission. On 4WD models, remove brake line to crossmember clips and remove crossmember.

3) Remove transmission support brace bolts and converter cover (if equipped). Remove exhaust crossover pipe and converter attaching bolts. Remove crossover and converter as an assembly.

4) Remove flywheel inspection plate and mark flex plate and torque converter-to-flex plate bolts. Disconnect catalytic converter support bracket.

5) Place a jack under transmission and raise slightly. Remove transmission support-to-frame bolts and insulators. Remove left body mounting bolts and loosen radiator support mount bolt.

6) Raise cab on left side as needed to remove upper transmission-to-engine bolts. Support cab with wood block between body and frame. Slide transmission support towards rear and lower transmission enough to remove oil cooler lines and T.V. cable. Disconnect lines and cable.

7) Support engine with jack and remove remaining transmission-to-engine bolts. Slide transmission away from engine and install Torque Converter Retainer (J-21366) to prevent converter damage during removal. Remove transmission.

Installation

To install, reverse removal procedure. Before installing flex plate-to-converter bolts, make certain that the weld nuts on converter are flush with the flex plate and the converter rotates freely by hand in this position. Finger tighten all 3 bolts before tightening to specifications.

TIGHTENING SPECIFICATIONS

Application	Ft. Lbs. (N.m)
Transmission-to-Engine Bolts	
"S" Series	25 (34)
All Others	35 (47)
Converter-to-Flex Plate	
"S" Series	35 (47)
All Others	35 (47)
Transmission Mount-to-Crossmember Bolts	
"S" Series	25 (34)
All Others	35 (47)
Transmission-to-Mount Bolts	
"S" Series	35 (47)
All Others	35 (47)
Crossmember-to-Frame Bolts	
"S" Series	25 (34)
All Others	35 (47)
Transfer Case-to-Adapter Bolts	
"S" Series	20-25 (27-34)
All Others	25 (34)
Transmission-to-Adapter Bolts	25 (34)

Automatic Transmission Removal

JEEP

TRANSFER CASE

MODEL NP-207

Removal

1) Shift transfer case into "4H" position. Raise and support vehicle. Drain lubricant from transfer case. Mark rear axle yoke and drive shaft for installation reference. Remove rear drive shaft. Disconnect speedometer cable, vacuum hoses and vent hose from transfer case.

2) Raise transmission and transfer case and remove transmission crossmember attaching bolts. Remove crossmember and lower transmission and transfer case. Mark transfer case front output shaft flange and drive shaft for installation reference.

3) Disconnect front drive shaft from transfer case. Disconnect shift lever linkage rod at transfer case. Remove shift lever bracket bolts. Support transfer case and remove transfer case attaching bolts. Remove transfer case assembly.

Installation

To intall, reverse removal procedure.

MODEL NP-208

Removal

1) Raise vehicle. Drain lubricant from transfer case. Disconnect speedometer cable and indicator switch wires and disconnect transfer case shift lever link at operating lever. Place a safety stand under transmission and remove the rear transmission crossmember.

2) Mark transfer case front and rear output shaft yokes and drive shafts for assembly alignment reference. Disconnect front and rear drive shafts at transfer case yokes. Secure shafts to frame rails with wire. Disconnect parking brake cable guide from pivot located on right frame rail, if necessary.

3) Remove bolts attaching exhaust pipe support bracket-to-transfer case (if necessary). Remove transfer case-to-transmission bolts. Move transfer case assembly rearward until free of transmission output shaft and remove assembly. Remove all gasket material from rear of transmission adapter housing.

Installation

To install, reverse removal procedure.

MODEL NP-229

Removal

1) Raise and support vehicle. Drain lubricant from transfer case. Disconnect speedometer cable and vent hose. Disconnect transfer case shift lever link at operating lever. Place a safety stand under transmission and remove rear transmission crossmember.

2) Mark transfer case front and rear output shafts at transfer case yokes and drive shafts for installation alignment reference. Disconnect front and rear drive shafts at transfer case yokes. Secure shafts. Disconnect shift motor vacuum hoses.

3) Disconnect transfer case shift linkage. Remove transfer case-to-transmission bolts. Move transfer case assembly rearward until clear of transmission output shaft and remove assembly. Remove all gasket material from rear of transmission adapter housing.

Installation

To install, reverse removal procedure.

MODEL NP-300

Removal

1) Remove floor covering (if equipped). Remove transmission access cover from floorpan. Raise vehicle and drain lubricant from transfer case. Position support stand under clutch housing to support engine and transmission and remove rear transmission crossmember.

2) Disconnect front and rear drive shafts at transfer case. Mark drive shaft yokes for assembly reference. Disconnect speedometer cable at transfer case. If necessary, disconnect parking brake cable at equalizer. Disconnect exhaust pipe support bracket at transfer case (if equipped). Remove bolts attaching transfer case to transmission and remove transfer case.

Installation

To install, reverse removal procedure.

TRANSMISSION

REMOVAL

1) Disconnect fan shroud and transmission fill tube upper bracket. Raise vehicle. Remove converter inspection cover and fill tube. Remove starter.

2) Mark drive shafts for reassembly. Disconnect shafts at transfer case and wire to frame rails. DO NOT allow shafts to hang free as damage to universal joints may result. On V8 models, disconnect exhaust pipes from exhaust manifolds. Drain transfer case lubricant. Disconnect speedometer cable from transmission.

3) Disconnect all shift and throttle linkages and wiring from transmission and transfer case. Mark converter drive plate and converter for reassembly and remove torque converter-to-drive plate bolts. Rotate crankshaft to gain access to bolts.

4) Support transmission/transfer case assembly with jack and secure with chain. Remove bolts and rear transmission crossmember. Lower transmission enough to disconnect cooler lines at transmission. Remove transmission-to-engine retaining bolts and slowly slide transmission assembly away from engine.

5) Hold converter in position while lowering transmission assembly from vehicle. Separate transmission from transfer case.

INSTALLATION

To install, reverse removal procedures. DO NOT tighten exhaust pipe attaching bolts until crossmember has been installed and transmission jack has been removed. Make sure all index marks made at removal are aligned. Tighten all bolts to specification and fill transmission and transfer case with fluid.

TIGHTENING SPECIFICATIONS

Application	Ft. Lbs. (N.m)
Cooler Line Nuts	25 (34)
Torque Converter-to-Drive Plate Bolts	22 (30)
Transfer Case-to-Transmission Bolts	40 (54)
Transmission-to-Engine Bolts	30 (41)

Automatic Transmissions

AMC EAGLE & JEEP TROUBLE SHOOTING

Every diagnosis of automatic transmission problems should begin with a check of the transmission fluid and linkage. Most of the following conditions can be caused by one or more of the following factors: (1) Incorrect fluid level, (2) Contaminated fluid, (3) Improperly adjusted linkage, or (4) Damaged or worn linkage.

CONDITION	POSSIBLE CAUSE	CORRECTION
Harsh Engagement of "R", "D", "2", "1"	Engine idle speed	Check setting and adjust
	Throttle linkage	Check for smooth travel; clean linkage pivot points as required, but do not lubricate them and then adjust
	Hydraulic pressure	Perform hydraulic pressure test; Repair hydraulic components as required; Check and correct throttle and line pressure settings
	Rear band	Check and adjust rear band
	Accumulator	Clean and inspect for broken seal rings, scratched bore or broken/collapsed spring; Check piston for cracks or evidence of it cocking in bore
	Valve body	Remove, disassemble, clean thoroughly and inspect valves and plugs for nicks, scratches, burrs and rounded edges on valve lands; Check bores for scratches, springs for collapsed coils, and all mating surfaces for nicks, burrs or warpage; Reassemble and install, tightening all screws to specification
	Front clutch	Clean and inspect all parts; Examine retainer and piston for scores and scratches; discs and plates for wear; return springs for collapsed coils; and seal rings for damage; vent check ball in retainer must operate freely
	Rear clutch	Inspect all rear clutch parts as outlined for front clutch
Slow to Engage "N", "R", "D", "2", "1"	Fluid level and condition	Fluid should be at "FULL" mark with engine at idle; replace fluid if "milky" and full of bubbles, or dark and smells burned
	Gearshift linkage	Check and adjust linkage
	Engine idle speed	Check setting and adjust
	Hydraulic pressure	Perform hydraulic pressure test; Repair hydraulic components as required; Check and correct throttle and line pressure settings
	Clogged oil filter	Inspect and replace filter
	Rear band	Check and adjust rear band
	Clutch and band operation	Remove valve body and perform air pressure test to apply clutches and bands to check operation
	Accumulator	Clean and inspect for broken seal rings, scratched bore or broken/collapsed spring; Check piston for cracks or evidence of it cocking in bore
	Valve body	Remove, disassemble, clean thoroughly and inspect valves and plugs for nicks, scratches, burrs and rounded edges on valve lands; Check bores for scratches, springs for collapsed coils, and all mating surfaces for nicks, burrs or warpage; Reassemble and install, tightening all screws to specification

Automatic Transmissions

AMC EAGLE & JEEP TROUBLE SHOOTING (Cont.)

CONDITION	POSSIBLE CAUSE	CORRECTION
Slow to Engage "N", "R", "D", "2", "1" (Cont.)	Oil pump	Clean pump and check all clearances; Inspect rotors for scoring and seal and bushings for wear; Inspect pump housing and reaction shaft support mating surfaces for flatness
	Front clutch	Clean and inspect all parts; Examine retainer and piston for scores and scratches; discs and plates for wear; return springs for collapsed coils; and seal rings for damage; vent check ball in retainer must operate freely
	Rear clutch	Inspect all rear clutch parts as outlined for front clutch
	Seal Rings	Inspect seal rings on reaction shaft support and governor support for wear, cracks or breakage; Inspect ring grooves on both support assemblies for nicks, burrs or distortion; Inspect bores in front clutch retainer and output shaft support for nicks, grooves, wear, cracks, or scratches
No Upshift, Stuck in Low Gear	Fluid level and condition	Fluid should be at "FULL" mark with engine at idle; replace fluid if "milky" and full of bubbles, or dark and smells burned
	Throttle linkage	Check for smooth travel; clean linkage pivot points as required, but do not lubricate them and then adjust
	Gearshift linkage	Check and adjust linkage
	Hydraulic pressure	Perform hydraulic pressure test; Repair hydraulic components as required; Check and correct throttle and line pressure settings
	Governor valve	Clean and inspect all parts; Check weights, shaft and valve for burrs, nicks, scores or binding; Check spring for collapsed or distorted coils and snap rings for distortion; Check filter for dirt and debris; Inspect body for cracks or warpage; Check torque on governor and output shaft support bolts
	Valve body	Remove, disassemble, clean thoroughly and inspect valves and plugs for nicks, scratches, burrs and rounded edges on valve lands; Check bores for scratches, springs for collapsed coils, and all mating surfaces for nicks, burrs or warpage; Reassemble and install, tightening all screws to specification
	Front band	Check and adjust front band
	Front servo and linkage	Inspect piston for wear, cracks and worn or broken seal rings; Check springs for collapsed or broken coils; Check servo bore for scratches, nicks or wear; Check lever, strut and band for damage; Check lever shaft for wear, looseness in case, or for leaking "O" ring
	Clutch and band operation	Remove valve body and perform air pressure test to apply clutches and bands to check operation

Automatic Transmissions

AMC EAGLE & JEEP TROUBLE SHOOTING (Cont.)

CONDITION	POSSIBLE CAUSE	CORRECTION
No Upshift, Stuck in Low Gear (Cont.)	Oil pump	Clean and check all clearances; Inspect rotors for scoring and seal and bushings for wear; Inspect housing and reaction shaft support mating surfaces for flatness
	Front clutch	Clean and inspect all parts; Examine retainer and piston for scores and scratches; discs and plates for wear; return springs for collapsed coils; and seal rings for damage; vent check ball in retainer must operate freely
No Low Gear, Moves in 2nd or 3rd Gear	Governor valve	Clean and inspect all parts; Check weights, shaft and valve for burrs, nicks, scores or binding; Check spring for collapsed or distorted coils and snap rings for distortion; Check filter for dirt and debris; Inspect body for cracks or warpage; Check torque on governor and output shaft support bolts
	Valve body	Remove, disassemble, clean thoroughly and inspect valves and plugs for nicks, scratches, burrs and rounded edges on valve lands; Check bores for scratches, springs for collapsed coils, and all mating surfaces for nicks, burrs or warpage; Reassemble and install, tightening all screws to specification
No Kickdown or Normal Downshift	Fluid level and condition	Fluid should be at "FULL" mark with engine at idle; replace fluid if "milky" and full of bubbles, or dark and smells burned
	Throttle linkage	Check for smooth travel; clean linkage pivot points as required, but do not lubricate them and then adjust
	Gearshift linkage	Check and adjust linkage
	Front band	Check and adjust front band
	Hydraulic pressure	Perform hydraulic pressure test; Repair hydraulic components as required; Check and correct throttle and line pressure settings
	Governor valve	Clean and inspect all parts; Check weights, shaft and valve for burrs, nicks, scores or binding; Check spring for collapsed or distorted coils and snap rings for distortion; Check filter for dirt and debris; Inspect body for cracks or warpage; Check torque on governor and output shaft support bolts
	Valve body	Remove, disassemble, clean thoroughly and inspect valves and plugs for nicks, scratches, burrs and rounded edges on valve lands; Check bores for scratches, springs for collapsed coils, and all mating surfaces for nicks, burrs or warpage; Reassemble and install, tightening all screws to specification
	Front servo and linkage	Inspect piston for wear, cracks and worn or broken seal rings; Check springs for collapsed or broken coils; Check servo bore for scratches, nicks or wear; Check lever, strut and band for damage; Check lever shaft for wear, looseness in case, or for leaking "O" ring
	Clutch and band operation	Remove valve body and perform air pressure test to apply clutches and bands to check operation

Automatic Transmissions

AMC EAGLE & JEEP TROUBLE SHOOTING (Cont.)

CONDITION	POSSIBLE CAUSE	CORRECTION
Delayed Erratic Shifts – Harsh at Times	Fluid level and condition	Fluid should be at "FULL" mark with engine at idle; replace fluid if "milky" and full of bubbles, or dark and smells burned
	Throttle linkage	Check for smooth travel; clean linkage pivot points as required, but do not lubricate them and then adjust
	Gearshift linkage	Check and adjust linkage
	Hydraulic pressure	Perform hydraulic pressure test; Repair hydraulic components as required; Check and correct throttle and line pressure settings
	Front band	Check and adjust front band
	Governor valve	Clean and inspect all parts; Check weights, shaft and valve for burrs, nicks, scores or binding; Check spring for collapsed or distorted coils and snap rings for distortion; Check filter for dirt and debris; Inspect body for cracks or warpage; Check torque on governor and output shaft support bolts
	Clogged oil filter	Inspect and replace filter
	Valve body	Remove, disassemble, clean thoroughly and inspect valves and plugs for nicks, scratches, burrs and rounded edges on valve lands; Check bores for scratches, springs for collapsed coils, and all mating surfaces for nicks, burrs or warpage; Reassemble and install, tightening all screws to specification
	Front servo and linkage	Inspect piston for wear, cracks and worn or broken seal rings; Check springs for collapsed or broken coils; Check servo bore for scratches, nicks or wear; Check lever, strut and band for damage; Check lever shaft for wear, looseness in case, or for leaking "O" ring
	Rear servo and linkage	Inspect piston for wear, cracks, worn or broken seal ring, or damaged seal; Check springs for collapsed or broken coils; Check servo bore for scratches, nicks or wear; Check lever and band for damage; Check lever shaft for wear or looseness in case
	Oil pump	Clean pump and check all clearances; Inspect rotors for scoring and seal and bushings for wear; Inspect pump housing and reaction shaft support mating surfaces for flatness
Slips in Forward Drive Ranges	Fluid level and condition	Fluid should be at "FULL" mark with engine at idle; replace fluid if "milky" and full of bubbles, or dark and smells burned
	Throttle linkage	Check for smooth travel; clean linkage pivot points as required, but do not lubricate them and then adjust
	Gearshift linkage	Check and adjust linkage
	Hydraulic pressure	Perform hydraulic pressure test; Repair hydraulic components as required; Check and correct throttle and line pressure settings
	Front band	Check and adjust front band

Automatic Transmissions

AMC EAGLE & JEEP TROUBLE SHOOTING (Cont.)

CONDITION	POSSIBLE CAUSE	CORRECTION
Slips in Forward Drive Ranges (Cont.)	Valve body	Remove, disassemble, clean thoroughly and inspect valves and plugs for nicks, scratches, burrs and rounded edges on valve lands; Check bores for scratches, springs for collapsed coils, and all mating surfaces for nicks, burrs or warpage; Reassemble and install, tightening all screws to specification
	Front servo and linkage	Inspect piston for wear, cracks and worn or broken seal rings; Check springs for collapsed or broken coils; Check servo bore for scratches, nicks or wear; Check lever, strut and band for damage; Check lever shaft for wear, looseness in case, or for leaking "O" ring
	Rear servo and linkage	Inspect piston for wear, cracks, worn or broken seal ring, or damaged seal; Check springs for collapsed or broken coils; Check servo bore for scratches, nicks or wear; Check lever and band for damage; Check lever shaft for wear or looseness in case
	Accumulator	Clean and inspect for broken seal rings, scratched bore or broken/collapsed spring; Check piston for cracks or evidence of it cocking in bore
	Clutch and band operation	Remove valve body and perform air pressure test to apply clutches and bands to check operation
	Oil pump	Clean pump and check all clearances; Inspect rotors for scoring and seal and bushings for wear; Inspect pump housing and reaction shaft support mating surfaces for flatness
	Front clutch	Clean and inspect all parts; Examine retainer and piston for scores and scratches; discs and plates for wear; return springs for collapsed coils; and seal rings for damage; vent check ball in retainer must operate freely
	Rear clutch	Inspect all rear clutch parts as outlined for front clutch
	Rear band	Inspect band for wear and for good bonding of lining to band; Inspect lining for burn marks, glazing, uneven wear patterns, flaking or if band grooves are worn away at any portion of band; Replace band if any of these conditions are present
	Seal Rings	Inspect seal rings on reaction shaft support and governor support for wear, cracks or breakage; Inspect ring grooves on both support assemblies for nicks, burrs or distortion; Inspect bores in front clutch retainer and output shaft support for nicks, grooves, wear, cracks, or scratches
Slips in Reverse Only	Fluid level and condition	Fluid should be at "FULL" mark with engine at idle; replace fluid if "milky" and full of bubbles, or dark and smells burned
	Gearshift linkage	Check and adjust linkage

AMC EAGLE & JEEP TROUBLE SHOOTING (Cont.)

CONDITION	POSSIBLE CAUSE	CORRECTION
Slips in Reverse Only (Cont.)	Hydraulic pressure	Perform hydraulic pressure test; Repair hydraulic components as required; Check and correct throttle and line pressure settings
	Front band	Check and adjust front band
	Valve body	Remove, disassemble, clean thoroughly and inspect valves and plugs for nicks, scratches, burrs and rounded edges on valve lands; Check bores for scratches, springs for collapsed coils, and all mating surfaces for nicks, burrs or warpage; Reassemble and install, tightening all screws to specification
	Rear servo and linkage	Inspect piston for wear, cracks, worn or broken seal ring, or damaged seal; Check springs for collapsed or broken coils; Check servo bore for scratches, nicks or wear; Check lever and band for damage; Check lever shaft for wear or looseness in case
	Clutch and band operation	Remove valve body and perform air pressure test to apply clutches and bands to check operation
	Oil pump	Clean pump and check all clearances; Inspect rotors for scoring and seal and bushings for wear; Inspect pump housing and reaction shaft support mating surfaces for flatness
	Front clutch	Clean and inspect all parts; Examine retainer and piston for scores and scratches; discs and plates for wear; return springs for collapsed coils; and seal rings for damage; vent check ball in retainer must operate freely
	Rear band	Inspect band for wear and for good bonding of lining to band; Inspect lining for burn marks, glazing, uneven wear patterns, flaking or if band grooves are worn away at any portion of band; Replace band if any of these conditions are present
Will Not Move in Forward or Reverse	Fluid level and condition	Fluid should be at "FULL" mark with engine at idle; replace fluid if "milky" and full of bubbles, or dark and smells burned
	Gearshift linkage	Check and adjust linkage
	Hydraulic pressure	Perform hydraulic pressure test; Repair hydraulic components as required; Check and correct throttle and line pressure settings
	Clogged oil filter	Inspect and replace filter
	Valve body	Remove, disassemble, clean thoroughly and inspect valves and plugs for nicks, scratches, burrs and rounded edges on valve lands; Check bores for scratches, springs for collapsed coils, and all mating surfaces for nicks, burrs or warpage; Reassemble and install, tightening all screws to specification
	Clutch and band operation	Remove valve body and perform air pressure test to apply clutches and bands to check operation

AMC EAGLE & JEEP TROUBLE SHOOTING (Cont.)

CONDITION	POSSIBLE CAUSE	CORRECTION
Will Not Move in Forward or Reverse (Cont.)	Converter drive plate	Check plate for flatness, cracks at mounting bolt holes, loose attaching bolts or damaged ring gear teeth; A broken drive plate may indicate engine-to-transmission misalignment caused by loose, missing or misaligned dowels
	Oil pump	Clean pump and check all clearances; Inspect rotors for scoring and seal and bushings for wear; Inspect pump housing and reaction shaft support mating surfaces for flatness
	Planetary gear set	Clean and inspect annulus gear, planet pinion carrier assembly and sun gear for worn thrust washers, damaged gear teeth and excessive pinion end clearance; Examine bushings in sun gear for excessive wear
Slips in Low Gear "D" Only, But Not in "1"	Overrunning clutch	Clean and inspect clutch parts for brinelled clutch rollers or cam, or improperly assembled rollers or springs; Check for collapsed springs and bent spring retainer tabs
Reverse Okay, Will Not Move Forward in "D", "2", "1"	Gearshift linkage	Check and adjust linkage
	Hydraulic pressure	Perform hydraulic pressure test; Repair hydraulic components as required; Check and correct throttle and line pressure settings
	Valve body	Remove, disassemble, clean thoroughly and inspect valves and plugs for nicks, scratches, burrs and rounded edges on valve lands; Check bores for scratches, springs for collapsed coils, and all mating surfaces for nicks, burrs or warpage; Reassemble and install, tightening all screws to specification
	Clutch and band operation	Remove valve body and perform air pressure test to apply clutches and bands to check operation
	Rear clutch	Inspect all rear clutch parts as outlined for front clutch
No Reverse	Gearshift linkage	Check and adjust linkage
	Hydraulic pressure	Perform hydraulic pressure test; Repair hydraulic components as required; Check and correct throttle and line pressure settings
	Front band	Check and adjust front band
	Rear servo and linkage	Inspect piston for wear, cracks, worn or broken seal ring, or damaged seal; Check springs for collapsed or broken coils; Check servo bore for scratches, nicks or wear; Check lever and band for damage; Check lever shaft for wear or looseness in case
	Clutch and band operation	Remove valve body and perform air pressure test to apply clutches and bands to check operation
	Front clutch	Clean and inspect all parts; Examine retainer and piston for scores and scratches; discs and plates for wear; return springs for collapsed coils; and seal rings for damage; vent check ball in retainer must operate freely

AMC EAGLE & JEEP TROUBLE SHOOTING (Cont.)

CONDITION	POSSIBLE CAUSE	CORRECTION
No Reverse (Cont.)	Rear band	Inspect band for wear and for good bonding of lining to band; Inspect lining for burn marks, glazing, uneven wear patterns, flaking or if band grooves are worn away at any portion of band; Replace band if any of these conditions are present
Moves in Neutral Position (Creeps)	Gearshift linkage	Check and adjust linkage
	Valve body	Remove, disassemble, clean thoroughly and inspect valves and plugs for nicks, scratches, burrs and rounded edges on valve lands; Check bores for scratches, springs for collapsed coils, and all mating surfaces for nicks, burrs or warpage; Reassemble and install, tightening all screws to specification
	Rear clutch	Inspect all rear clutch parts as outlined for front clutch
Drags or Locks Up	Hydraulic pressure	Perform hydraulic pressure test; Repair hydraulic components as required; Check and correct throttle and line pressure settings
	Front band	Check and adjust front band
	Front band	Check and adjust front band
	Park lock	Check condition of lock rod, lock rod ball, sprag reaction plug, governor support, and sprag shaft; Replace parts as required
	Valve body	Remove, disassemble, clean thoroughly and inspect valves and plugs for nicks, scratches, burrs and rounded edges on valve lands; Check bores for scratches, springs for collapsed coils, and all mating surfaces for nicks, burrs or warpage; Reassemble and install, tightening all screws to specification
	Front servo and linkage	Inspect piston for wear, cracks and worn or broken seal rings; Check springs for collapsed or broken coils; Check servo bore for scratches, nicks or wear; Check lever, strut and band for damage; Check lever shaft for wear, looseness in case, or for leaking "O" ring
	Rear servo and linkage	Inspect piston for wear, cracks, worn or broken seal ring, or damaged seal; Check springs for collapsed or broken coils; Check servo bore for scratches, nicks or wear; Check lever and band for damage; Check lever shaft for wear or looseness in case
	Accumulator	Clean and inspect for broken seal rings, scratched bore or broken/collapsed spring; Check piston for cracks or evidence of it cocking in bore
	Front clutch	Clean and inspect all parts; Examine retainer and piston for scores and scratches; discs and plates for wear; return springs for collapsed coils; and seal rings for damage; vent check ball in retainer must operate freely
	Rear clutch	Inspect all rear clutch parts as outlined for front clutch

Automatic Transmissions

AMC EAGLE & JEEP TROUBLE SHOOTING (Cont.)

CONDITION	POSSIBLE CAUSE	CORRECTION
Drags or Locks Up (Cont.)	Planetary gear set	Clean and inspect annulus gear, planet pinion carrier assembly and sun gear for worn thrust washers, damaged gear teeth and excessive pinion end clearance; Examine bushings in sun gear for excessive wear
	Rear band	Inspect band for wear and for good bonding of lining to band; Inspect lining for burn marks, glazing, uneven wear patterns, flaking or if band grooves are worn away at any portion of band; Replace band if any of these conditions are present
	Overrunning clutch	Clean and inspect clutch parts for brinelled clutch rollers or cam, or improperly assembled rollers or springs; Check for collapsed springs and bent spring retainer tabs
	TRANSMISSION NOISY	
Grating, Growling or Scraping Noise	Fluid level and condition	Fluid should be at "FULL" mark with engine at idle; replace fluid if "milky" and full of bubbles, or dark and smells burned
	Park lock	Check condition of lock rod, lock rod ball, sprag reaction plug, governor support, and sprag shaft; Replace parts as required
	Output shaft bearing, bushing, or seal	Remove extension housing, inspect parts, and replace parts as required
	Clogged oil filter	Inspect and replace filter
	Converter drive plate	Check plate for flatness, cracks at mounting bolt holes, loose attaching bolts or damaged ring gear teeth; A broken drive plate may indicate engine-to-transmission misalignment caused by loose, missing or misaligned dowels
	Oil pump	Clean pump and check all clearances; Inspect rotors for scoring and seal and bushings for wear; Inspect pump housing and reaction shaft support mating surfaces for flatness
	Front clutch	Clean and inspect all parts; Examine retainer and piston for scores and scratches; discs and plates for wear; return springs for collapsed coils; and seal rings for damage; vent check ball in retainer must operate freely
	Planetary gear set	Clean and inspect annulus gear, planet pinion carrier assembly and sun gear for worn thrust washers, damaged gear teeth and excessive pinion end clearance; Examine bushings in sun gear for excessive wear
	Overrunning clutch	Clean and inspect clutch parts for brinelled clutch rollers or cam, or improperly assembled rollers or springs; Check for collapsed springs and bent spring retainer tabs
	Torque Converter	If converter hub seal surface or drive slots are damaged or if converter contains foreign material, burned-oxidized fluid or debris, replace converter; Do not attempt to clean or flush converter
Buzzing Noise	Fluid level and condition	Fluid should be at "FULL" mark with engine at idle; replace fluid if "milky" and full of bubbles, or dark and smells burned

Automatic Transmissions

AMC EAGLE & JEEP TROUBLE SHOOTING (Cont.)

CONDITION	POSSIBLE CAUSE	CORRECTION
	TRANSMISSION NOISY (Cont.)	
Buzzing Noise (Cont.)	Governor valve	Clean and inspect all parts; Check weights, shaft and valve for burrs, nicks, scores or binding; Check spring for collapsed or distorted coils and snap rings for distortion; Check filter for dirt and debris; Inspect body for cracks or warpage; Check torque on governor and output shaft support bolts
	Valve body	Remove, disassemble, clean thoroughly and inspect valves and plugs for nicks, scratches, burrs and rounded edges on valve lands; Check bores for scratches, springs for collapsed coils, and all mating surfaces for nicks, burrs or warpage; Reassemble and install, tightening all screws to specification
	Clutch and band operation	Remove valve body and perform air pressure test to apply clutches and bands to check operation
	Oil pump	Clean pump and check all clearances; Inspect rotors for scoring and seal and bushings for wear; Inspect pump housing and reaction shaft support mating surfaces for flatness
	Torque Converter	If converter hub seal surface or drive slots are damaged or if converter contains foreign material, burned-oxidized fluid or debris, replace converter; Do not attempt to clean or flush converter
Oil Blows Out Filler Tube	Fluid level and condition	Fluid should be at "FULL" mark with engine at idle; replace fluid if "milky" and full of bubbles, or dark and smells burned
	Transmission Oil Cooler	Check lines and cooler for obstructions, or leaks (look for transmission fluid in radiator coolant, or milky-colored transmission fluid which indicates coolant in fluid)
	Clogged oil filter	Inspect and replace filter
	Valve body	Remove, disassemble, clean thoroughly and inspect valves and plugs for nicks, scratches, burrs and rounded edges on valve lands; Check bores for scratches, springs for collapsed coils, and all mating surfaces for nicks, burrs or warpage; Reassemble and install, tightening all screws to specification
	Oil pump	Clean pump and check all clearances; Inspect rotors for scoring and seal and bushings for wear; Inspect pump housing and reaction shaft support mating surfaces for flatness
	Transmission vent	Make sure vent is open and not obstructed
Transmission Overheats	Fluid level and condition	Fluid should be at "FULL" mark with engine at idle; replace fluid if "milky" and full of bubbles, or dark and smells burned
	Engine idle speed	Check setting and adjust
	Transmission Oil Cooler	Check lines and cooler for obstructions, or leaks (look for transmission fluid in radiator coolant, or milky-colored transmission fluid which indicates coolant in fluid)
	Front band	Check and adjust front band

Automatic Transmissions

AMC EAGLE & JEEP TROUBLE SHOOTING (Cont.)

CONDITION	POSSIBLE CAUSE	CORRECTION
	TRANSMISSION NOISY (Cont.)	
Transmission Overheats (Cont.)	Hydraulic pressure	Perform hydraulic pressure test; Repair hydraulic components as required; Check and correct throttle and line pressure settings
	Clogged oil filter	Inspect and replace filter
	Front band	Check and adjust front band
	Valve body	Remove, disassemble, clean thoroughly and inspect valves and plugs for nicks, scratches, burrs and rounded edges on valve lands; Check bores for scratches, springs for collapsed coils, and all mating surfaces for nicks, burrs or warpage; Reassemble and install, tightening all screws to specification
	Converter drive plate	Check plate for flatness, cracks at mounting bolt holes, loose attaching bolts or damaged ring gear teeth; A broken drive plate may indicate engine-to-transmission misalignment caused by loose, missing or misaligned dowels
Starter Will Not Operate in Neutral or Park	Gearshift linkage	Check and adjust linkage
	Neutral start switch	Check wires and connections; Test switch; See if valve body manual lever grounds switch in "P" and "N" positions; If not okay, check ground strip at valve body manual lever; If okay, check starting circuit
	Engine performance	Verify proper engine operation; Be sure compression meets specifications and that fuel and ignition systems are functioning properly
	Valve body	Remove, disassemble, clean thoroughly and inspect valves and plugs for nicks, scratches, burrs and rounded edges on valve lands; Check bores for scratches, springs for collapsed coils, and all mating surfaces for nicks, burrs or warpage; Reassemble and install, tightening all screws to specification
Sluggish Acceleration, Excessive Throttle Needed to Maintain Speed	Fluid level and condition	Fluid should be at "FULL" mark with engine at idle; replace fluid if "milky" and full of bubbles, or dark and smells burned
	Engine performance	Verify proper engine operation; Be sure compression meets specifications and that fuel and ignition systems are functioning properly
	Throttle linkage	Check for smooth travel; clean linkage pivot points as required, but do not lubricate them and then adjust
	Stall test	Perform stall test to check holding ability of converter and transmission clutches
	Hydraulic pressure	Perform hydraulic pressure test; Repair hydraulic components as required; Check and correct throttle and line pressure settings
	Torque Converter	If converter hub seal surface or drive slots are damaged or if converter contains foreign material, burned-oxidized fluid or debris, replace converter; Do not attempt to clean or flush converter

Automatic Transmissions

AMC EAGLE & JEEP TROUBLE SHOOTING (Cont.)

CONDITION	POSSIBLE CAUSE	CORRECTION
	TRANSMISSION NOISY (Cont.)	
Sluggish Acceleration, Excessive Throttle Needed to Maintain Speed (Cont.)	Rear clutch	Inspect all rear clutch parts as outlined for front clutch
	LOCK-UP CONVERTER DIAGNOSIS	
No Lock-Up	Faulty oil pump	Replace oil pump
	Sticking governor valve	Repair or replace as required
	Valve body malfunction Stuck switch valve Stuck lock-up valve Stuck fail-safe valve	Repair or replace valve body or its internal components as required
	Failed locking clutch	Replace torque converter
	Leaking turbine hub seal	Replace torque converter
	Faulty input shaft or seal ring	Repair or replace as required
Will Not Unlock	Sticking governor valve	Repair or replace as required
	Valve body malfunction Stuck switch valve Stuck lock-up valve Stuck fail-safe valve	Repair or replace valve body or its internal components as required
Stays Locked Up at Too Low a Speed in Direct	Sticking governor valve	Repair or replace as required
	Valve body malfunction Stuck switch valve Stuck lock-up valve Stuck fail-safe valve	Repair or replace valve body or its internal components as required
Locks Up or Drags in Low or Second	Faulty oil pump	Replace oil pump
	Valve body malfunction Stuck switch valve Stuck fail-safe valve	Repair or replace valve body or its internal components as required
Sluggish or Stalls in Reverse	Faulty oil pump	Replace oil pump
	Plugged cooler, cooler lines or fittings	Flush or replace cooler and flush lines and fittings
	Valve body malfunction Stuck switch valve Faulty input shaft or seal ring	Repair or replace valve body or its internal components as required
Loud Chatter During Lock-Up Engagement (Cold)	Faulty torque converter	Replace torque converter
	Failed locking clutch	Replace torque converter
	Leaking turbine hub seal	Replace torque converter
Vibration or Shudder During Lock-Up Engagement	Faulty oil pump	Repair or replace oil pump
	Valve body malfunction	Repair or replace valve body or its internal components as required
	Faulty torque converter	Replace torque converter
	Engine performance	Diagnose and tune engine
Vibration After Lock-Up Engagement	Faulty torque converter	Replace torque converter
	Exhaust system vibration	Align exhaust system
	Engine performance	Diagnose and tune engine

AMC EAGLE & JEEP TROUBLE SHOOTING (Cont.)

CONDITION	POSSIBLE CAUSE	CORRECTION
	LOCK-UP CONVERTER DIAGNOSIS (Cont.)	
Vibration After Lock-Up Engagement (Cont.)	Throttle linkage misadjusted	Check and adjust throttle linkage
Vibration When "Reved" in Neutral	Torque converter out of balance	Replace torque converter
Overheating: Oil Blows Out of Dipstick Tube or Pump Seal	Plugged cooler, cooler lines or fittings	Flush or replace cooler and flush lines and fittings
	Stuck switch valve	Repair switch valve in valve body or replace valve body
Shudder After Lock-Up Engagement	Faulty oil pump	Repair or replace oil pump
	Plugged cooler, cooler lines or fittings	Flush or replace cooler and flush lines and fittings
	Valve body malfunction	Repair or replace valve body or its internal components as required
	Faulty torque converter	Replace torque converter
	Faulty locking clutch	Replace torque converter
	Exhaust system vibration	Align exhaust system
	Engine performance	Diagnose and tune engine
	Throttle linkage misadjusted	Check and adjust throttle linkage

Automatic Transmissions

CHRYSLER CORP. TROUBLE SHOOTING

Every diagnosis of automatic transmission problems should begin with a check of the transmission fluid and linkage. Most of the following conditions can be caused by one or more of the following factors: (1) Incorrect fluid level, (2) Contaminated fluid, (3) Improperly adjusted linkage, or (4) Damaged or worn linkage.

CONDITION	POSSIBLE CAUSE	CORRECTION
Harsh Engagement From Neutral to "D"	Engine idle speed too high	Check setting and adjust
	Valve body malfunction or leakage	Check valve body operation and perform HYDRAULIC PRESSURE tests
	Hydraulic pressure too high	Check and adjust hydraulic pressure
	Worn or faulty rear clutch	Check and replace clutch
	Faulty lock-up clutch (except A413 & A470)	Check and replace lock-up clutch
	Engine performance (A413 & A470)	Perform engine diagnosis and tune-up
Harsh Engagement From Neutral to "R"	Engine idle speed too high	Check setting and adjust
	Valve body malfunction or leakage (except A413 & A470)	Check valve body operation and perform HYDRAULIC PRESSURE tests
	Hydraulic pressure too high	Check and adjust hydraulic pressure
	Worn or faulty front clutch	Check and replace front clutch
	Faulty lock-up clutch (except A413 & A470)	Check and replace lock-up clutch
	Low-Reverse band worn or misadjusted (A413 & A470)	Check and replace, or adjust Low-Reverse band
	Low-Reverse servo, band or linkage malfunction (A413 & A470)	Check servo, band and linkage for damage
	Engine performance (A413 & A470)	Perform engine diagnosis and tune-up
Delayed Engagement From Neutral to "D"	Hydraulic pressure too low	Check and adjust hydraulic pressure
	Valve body malfunction or leakage	Check valve body operation and perform HYDRAULIC PRESSURE tests
	Low fluid level	Check and replenish as required
	Incorrect gearshift linkage control adjustment	Check and adjust linkage, see GENERAL SERVICING
	Oil filter clogged	Clean and replace filter
	Faulty oil pump	Check and replace oil pump
	Worn or broken input shaft seal rings	Check and replace seal rings
	Air in transmission fluid	Check and replace fluid
	Engine idle speed too low	Check setting and adjust
	Worn or broken reaction shaft support seal rings (except A413 & A470)	Check and replace seal rings
	Worn or faulty rear clutch	Check and replace clutch
Delayed Engagement From Neutral to "R"	Low-Reverse servo, band or linkage malfunction	Check servo, band and linkage for damage
	Low-Reverse band misadjusted or worn out (A413 & A470)	Check and adjust, or replace, Low-Reverse band
	Hydraulic pressure too low	Check and adjust hydraulic pressure
	Valve body malfunction or leakage	Check valve body operation and perform HYDRAULIC PRESSURE tests
	Low fluid level	Check and replenish as required

CHRYSLER CORP. TROUBLE SHOOTING (Cont.)

CONDITION	POSSIBLE CAUSE	CORRECTION
Delayed Engagement From Neutral to "R" (Cont.)	Incorrect gearshift linkage control adjustment	Check and adjust linkage, see GENERAL SERVICING
	Oil filter clogged	Clean and replace filter
	Faulty oil pump	Check and replace oil pump
	Worn or broken input shaft seal rings	Check and replace seal rings
	Air in transmission fluid	Check and replace fluid
	Engine idle speed too low	Check setting and adjust
	Worn or broken reaction shaft support seal rings	Check and replace seal rings
	Worn or faulty front clutch	Check and replace clutch
Runaway Upshift	Hydraulic pressure too low	Check and adjust hydraulic pressure
	Valve body malfunction or leakage	Check valve body operation and perform HYDRAULIC PRESSURE tests
	Low fluid level	Check and replenish as required
	Oil filter clogged	Clean and replace filter
	Air in transmission fluid	Check and replace fluid
	Incorrect throttle linkage adjustment	Check and adjust linkage, see GENERAL SERVICING
	Kickdown servo band or linkage malfunction	Check and adjust band and/or linkage
	Worn or faulty front clutch	Check and replace clutch
	Worn or broken reaction shaft support seal rings	Check and replace seal rings
No Upshift	Hydraulic pressure too low	Check and adjust hydraulic pressure
	Valve body malfunction or leakage	Check valve body operation and perform HYDRAULIC PRESSURE tests
	Low fluid level	Check and replenish as required
	Incorrect gearshift linkage control adjustment	Check and adjust linkage, see GENERAL SERVICING
	Incorrect throttle linkage adjustment	Check and adjust linkage, see GENERAL SERVICING
	Governor support seal rings broken or worn (A413 & A470)	Check and replace support seal rings
	Worn or broken reaction shaft support seal rings	Check and replace seal rings
	Governor malfunction	Check and repair or replace governor
	Kickdown servo band or linkage malfunction	Check and adjust band and/or linkage
	Worn or faulty front clutch	Check and replace clutch
	Engine performance (A413 & A470)	Perform engine diagnosis and tune-up
3-2 Kickdown Runaway	Hydraulic pressure too low	Check and adjust hydraulic pressure
	Valve body malfunction or leakage	Check valve body operation and perform HYDRAULIC PRESSURE tests
	Low fluid level	Check and replenish as required
	Air in transmission fluid	Check and replace fluid
	Incorrect throttle linkage adjustment	Check and adjust linkage, see GENERAL SERVICING

CHRYSLER CORP. TROUBLE SHOOTING (Cont.)

CONDITION	POSSIBLE CAUSE	CORRECTION
3-2 Kickdown Runaway (Cont.)	Kickdown band out of adjustment	Check and adjust kickdown band
	Governor support seal rings broken or worn (A413 & A470)	Check and replace support seal rings
	Worn or broken reaction shaft support seal rings (except A413 & A470)	Check and replace seal rings
	Kickdown servo band or linkage malfunction	Check and adjust band and/or linkage
	Worn or faulty front clutch	Check and replace clutch
No Kickdown or Normal Downshift	Valve body malfunction or leakage	Check valve body operation and perform HYDRAULIC PRESSURE tests
	Incorrect throttle linkage adjustment	Check and adjust linkage, see GENERAL SERVICING
	Governor malfunction	Check and repair or replace governor
	Kickdown servo band or linkage malfunction	Check and adjust band and/or linkage
Shifts Erratic	Hydraulic pressure too low	Check and adjust hydraulic pressure
	Valve body malfunction or leakage	Check valve body operation and perform HYDRAULIC PRESSURE tests
	Low fluid level	Check and replenish as required
	Incorrect gearshift linkage control adjustment	Check and adjust linkage, see GENERAL SERVICING
	Oil filter clogged	Clean and replace filter
	Faulty oil pump	Check and replace oil pump
	Air in transmission fluid	Check and replace fluid
	Incorrect throttle linkage adjustment	Check and adjust linkage, see GENERAL SERVICING
	Governor support seal rings broken or worn	Check and replace support seal rings
	Worn or broken reaction shaft support seal rings	Check and replace seal rings
	Governor malfunction	Check and repair or replace governor
	Kickdown servo band or linkage malfunction	Check and adjust band and/or linkage
	Worn or faulty front clutch	Check and replace clutch
	Engine performance (A413 & A470)	Perform engine diagnosis and tune-up
Slips in Forward Drive Positions	Hydraulic pressure too low	Check and adjust hydraulic pressure
	Valve body malfunction or leakage	Check valve body operation and perform HYDRAULIC PRESSURE tests
	Low fluid level	Check and replenish as required
	Incorrect gearshift linkage control adjustment	Check and adjust linkage, see GENERAL SERVICING
	Oil filter clogged	Clean and replace filter
	Faulty oil pump	Check and replace oil pump
	Worn or broken input shaft seal rings	Check and replace seal rings
	Air in transmission fluid	Check and replace fluid

CHRYSLER CORP. TROUBLE SHOOTING (Cont.)

CONDITION	POSSIBLE CAUSE	CORRECTION
Slips in Forward Drive Positions (Cont.)	Incorrect throttle linkage adjustment	Check and adjust linkage, see GENERAL SERVICING
	Overrunning clutch not holding, or clutch is worn, broken, or seized	Check and replace overrunning clutch
	Worn or faulty rear clutch	Check and replace clutch
Slips in Reverse Only	Low-Reverse band worn or misadjusted	Check and replace, or adjust Low-Reverse band
	Hydraulic pressure too low	Check and adjust hydraulic pressure
	Valve body malfunction or leakage	Check valve body operation and perform HYDRAULIC PRESSURE tests
	Low-Reverse servo, band or linkage malfunction	Check servo, band and linkage for damage
	Low fluid level	Check and replenish as required
	Incorrect gearshift linkage control adjustment	Check and adjust linkage, see GENERAL SERVICING
	Faulty oil pump	Check and replace oil pump
	Air in transmission fluid	Check and replace fluid
	Worn or broken reaction shaft support seal rings	Check and replace seal rings
	Worn or faulty front clutch	Check and replace clutch
Slips in All Positions	Hydraulic pressure too low	Check and adjust hydraulic pressure
	Valve body malfunction or leakage	Check valve body operation and perform HYDRAULIC PRESSURE tests
	Low fluid level	Check and replenish as required
	Oil filter clogged	Clean and replace filter
	Faulty oil pump	Check and replace oil pump
	Worn or broken input shaft seal rings	Check and replace seal rings
	Air in transmission fluid	Check and replace fluid
No Drive in Any Position	Hydraulic pressure too low	Check and adjust hydraulic pressure
	Valve body malfunction or leakage	Check valve body operation and perform HYDRAULIC PRESSURE tests
	Low fluid level	Check and replenish as required
	Oil filter clogged	Clean and replace filter
	Faulty oil pump	Check and replace oil pump
	Planetary gear sets broken or seized	Check and replace gear sets
No Drive in Forward Drive Positions	Hydraulic pressure too low	Check and adjust hydraulic pressure
	Valve body malfunction or leakage	Check valve body operation and perform HYDRAULIC PRESSURE tests
	Low fluid level	Check and replenish as required
	Worn or broken input shaft seal rings	Check and replace seal rings
	Overrunning clutch not holding, or clutch is worn, broken, or seized	Check and replace overrunning clutch
	Worn or faulty rear clutch	Check and replace clutch
	Planetary gear sets broken or seized	Check and replace gear sets
No Drive in Reverse	Low-Reverse band worn or misadjusted	Check and replace, or adjust Low-Reverse band
	Hydraulic pressure too low	Check and adjust hydraulic pressure
	Valve body malfunction or leakage	Check valve body operation and perform HYDRAULIC PRESSURE tests

CHRYSLER CORP. TROUBLE SHOOTING (Cont.)

CONDITION	POSSIBLE CAUSE	CORRECTION
No Drive in Reverse (Cont.)	Low-Reverse servo, band or linkage malfunction	Check servo, band and linkage for damage
	Incorrect gearshift linkage control adjustment	Check and adjust linkage, see GENERAL SERVICING
	Worn or broken reaction shaft support seal rings	Check and replace seal rings
	Worn or faulty front or rear clutch	Check and replace defective clutch
	Planetary gear sets broken or seized	Check and replace gear sets
Drives in Neutral (Creeps)	Valve body malfunction or leakage	Check valve body operation and perform HYDRAULIC PRESSURE tests
	Incorrect gearshift linkage control adjustment	Check and adjust linkage, see GENERAL SERVICING
	Insufficient clutch plate clearance	Check and adjust clutch plate clearance
	Dragging, faulty, or worn rear clutch	Check and replace rear clutch
Drags or Locks-Up	Low-Reverse band worn or misadjusted	Check and replace, or adjust Low-Reverse band
	Kickdown band adjustment too tight	Check and adjust kickdown band adjustment
	Planetary gear sets broken or seized	Check and replace gear sets
	Overrunning clutch worn, broken, or seized	Check and replace overrunning clutch
	Stuck lock-up valve (except A413 & A470)	Check, clean and/or replace valve
	Faulty oil pump (except A413 & A470)	Check and replace oil pump
Slips in Reverse or Manual Low (except A413 & A470)	Low-Reverse band misadjusted	Check and adjust Low-Reverse band
	Oil filter clogged	Clean and replace filter
Harsh Upshift	Hydraulic pressure too high or too low	Check and adjust hydraulic pressure
	Incorrect throttle linkage adjustment	Check and adjust linkage, see GENERAL SERVICING
	Kickdown band out of adjustment	Check and adjust kickdown band
	Faulty lock-up clutch (except A413 & A470)	Check and replace lock-up clutch
	Engine performance (A413 & A470)	Perform engine diagnosis and tune-up
Delayed Upshift	Incorrect throttle linkage adjustment	Check and adjust linkage, see GENERAL SERVICING
	Kickdown band out of adjustment	Check and adjust kickdown band
	Governor support seal rings broken or worn	Check and replace support seal rings
	Worn or broken reaction shaft support seal rings	Check and replace seal rings
	Governor malfunction	Check and repair or replace governor
	Kickdown servo band or linkage malfunction	Check and adjust band and/or linkage
	Worn or faulty front clutch	Check and replace clutch
	Engine performance (A413 & A470)	Perform engine diagnosis and tune-up
	TRANSMISSION NOISY	
Grating, Growling or Scraping Noise	Low-Reverse band worn or misadjusted	Check and replace, or adjust Low-Reverse band
	Kickdown band adjustment too tight	Check and adjust kickdown band adjustment

Automatic Transmissions

CHRYSLER CORP. TROUBLE SHOOTING (Cont.)

CONDITION	POSSIBLE CAUSE	CORRECTION
	TRANSMISSION NOISY (Cont.)	
Grating, Growling or Scraping Noise (Cont.)	Drive shafts(s) bushing(s) damaged (A413 & A470)	Replace bushings
	Planetary gear sets broken or seized	Check and replace gear sets
	Overrunning clutch worn, broken, or seized	Check and replace overrunning clutch
	Output shaft bearing and/or bushing damaged (except A413 & A470)	Replace bearing and/or bushing
Buzzing Noise	Valve body malfunction or leakage	Check valve body operation and perform HYDRAULIC PRESSURE tests
	Low fluid level	Check and replenish as required
	Faulty oil pump	Check and replace oil pump
	Air in transmission fluid	Check and replace fluid
	Overrunning clutch inner race damaged	Check and replace overrunning clutch
Hard to Fill, Oil Blows Out Filler Tube	Oil filter clogged	Clean and replace filter
	Air in transmission fluid	Check and replace fluid
	Fluid level too high	Correct fluid level
	Transmission breather clogged (except A413 & A470)	Clean breather
Transmission Overheats	Stuck switch valve	Clean and replace valve
	Engine idle speed too high	Check setting and adjust
	Hydraulic pressure too low	Check and adjust hydraulic pressure
	Low fluid level	Check and replenish as required
	Incorrect gearshift linkage control adjustment	Check and adjust linkage, see GENERAL SERVICING
	Faulty oil pump	Check and replace oil pump
	Kickdown band adjustment too tight	Check and adjust kickdown band adjustment
	Insufficient clutch plate clearance	Check and adjust clutch plate clearance
	Faulty cooling system	Check for damaged or restricted cooling lines
	LOCK-UP CONVERTER DIAGNOSIS – EXCEPT A413 & A470	
No Lock-Up	Faulty oil pump	Check and replace oil pump
	Sticking governor valve	Clean and replace governor valve
	Valve body malfunction	Check valve body operation and perform HYDRAULIC PRESSURE tests
	Stuck switch valve	Clean and replace switch valve
	Stuck lock-up valve	Clean and replace lock-up valve
	Stuck fail-safe valve	Clean and replace fail-safe valve
	Faulty torque converter	
	Possible failed locking clutch	Replace torque converter
	Possible leaking turbine hub seal	Replace hub seal
	Faulty input shaft or seal ring	Check and replace input shaft or seal ring
Will Not Unlock	Sticking governor valve	Clean and replace governor valve
	Valve body malfunction	Check valve body operation and perform HYDRAULIC PRESSURE tests
	Stuck switch valve	Clean and replace switch valve

CHRYSLER CORP. TROUBLE SHOOTING (Cont.)

CONDITION	POSSIBLE CAUSE	CORRECTION
LOCK-UP CONVERTER DIAGNOSIS – EXCEPT A413 & A470 (Cont.)		
Will Not Unlock (Cont.)	Stuck lock-up valve	Clean and replace lock-up valve
	Stuck fail-safe valve	Clean and replace fail-safe valve
Stays Locked Up At Too Low a Speed in Direct	Sticking governor valve	Clean and replace governor valve
	Valve body malfunction	Check valve body operation and perform HYDRAULIC PRESSURE tests
	Stuck switch valve	Clean and replace switch valve
	Stuck lock-up valve	Clean and replace lock-up valve
	Stuck fail-safe valve	Clean and replace fail-safe valve
Locks-Up or Drags in Low or Second	Faulty oil pump	Check and replace oil pump
	Valve body malfunction	Check valve body operation and perform HYDRAULIC PRESSURE tests
	Stuck switch valve	Clean and replace switch valve
	Stuck fail-safe valve	Clean and replace fail-safe valve
Stalls or is Sluggish in Reverse	Faulty oil pump	Check and replace oil pump
	Plugged cooler, lines, or fittings	Check cooler, lines, and fittings for obstruction
	Valve body malfunction	Check valve body operation and perform HYDRAULIC PRESSURE tests
	Stuck switch valve	Clean and replace switch valve
	Faulty input shaft or seal ring	Check and replace input shaft or seal ring
Loud Chatter During Lock-Up Engagement (Cold)	Faulty torque converter	
	Possible failed locking clutch	Replace torque converter
	Possible leaking turbine hub seal	Replace hub seal
Vibration or Shudder During Lock-Up Engagement	Faulty oil pump	Check and replace oil pump
	Valve body malfunction	Check valve body operation and perform HYDRAULIC PRESSURE tests
	Faulty torque converter	Replace torque converter
	Engine performance	Diagnose and perform engine tune-up
Vibrations After Lock-Up Engagement	Faulty torque converter	Replace torque converter
	Misaligned exhaust system	Check and align exhaust system
	Engine performance	Diagnose and perform engine tune-up
	Throttle linkage misadjusted	Check and adjust throttle linkage, see GENERAL SERVICING
Shudder After Lock-Up Engagement	Faulty oil pump	Check and replace oil pump
	Plugged cooler, lines, or fittings	Check cooler, lines, and fittings for obstruction
	Valve body malfunction	Check valve body operation and perform HYDRAULIC PRESSURE tests
	Faulty torque converter	
	Possible failed locking clutch	Replace torque converter
	Engine performance	Diagnose and perform engine tune-up
	Misaligned exhaust system	Check and align exhaust system
	Throttle linkage misadjusted	Check and adjust throttle linkage, see GENERAL SERVICING

CHRYSLER CORP. TROUBLE SHOOTING (Cont.)

CONDITION	POSSIBLE CAUSE	CORRECTION
LOCK-UP CONVERTER DIAGNOSIS – EXCEPT A413 & A470 (Cont.)		
Vibration When "Reved" in Neutral	Faulty torque converter Converter out of balance	Replace torque converter
Overheating; Blowing Oil Out Dipstick or Pump Seal	Plugged cooler, lines, or fittings	Check cooler, lines, and fittings for obstruction
	Stuck switch valve	Clean and replace switch valve

FORD MOTOR CO. (EXC. ATX & AXOD) TROUBLE SHOOTING

Every diagnosis of automatic transmission problems should begin with a check of the transmission fluid and linkage. Most of the following conditions can be caused by one or more of the following factors: (1) Incorrect fluid level, (2) Contaminated fluid, (3) Improperly adjusted linkage, or (4) Damaged or worn linkage.

CONDITION	POSSIBLE CAUSE	CORRECTION
Slow Initial Engagement	Improper fluid level	Check fluid level; See GENERAL SERVICING
	Damaged or improperly adjusted linkage	Service or adjust linkage; See GENERAL SERVICING
	Contaminated fluid	Check fluid condition
	Improper clutch and band application, or low main control pressure	Perform CONTROL PRESSURE test
Rough Initial Engagement	Improper fluid level	Check fluid level; See GENERAL SERVICING
	Engine idle speed too high	Check and adjust idle speed
	Automatic choke on (warm temperatures)	Disengage choke
	Looseness in propeller shaft, "U" joints, or engine mounts	Service and repair, or replace components as required
	Improper clutch or band operation, or oil control pressure	Perform CONTROL PRESSURE test
	Sticking or dirty valve body	Clean, service or replace valve body
	Converter clutch not disengaging (A4LD)	Check converter clutch engagement and disengagement
Harsh Engagements – Warm Engine	Improper fluid level	Check fluid level; See GENERAL SERVICING
	T.V. linkage misadjusted (long), disconnected, sticking or damaged; disconnected return spring (A.O.T.)	Check and adjust, or repair T.V. linkage
	Curb idle speed too high	Check and adjust idle speed
	Valve body bolts loose or too tight	Tighten valve body bolts to specification
	Valve body dirty or contains sticking valves	Clean, inspect and repair, or replace valve body
No or Delayed Forward Engagement – Reverse OK	Improper fluid level	Check fluid level; See GENERAL SERVICING
	Manual linkage misadjusted or damaged	Check and adjust linkage or service as required
	Low main control pressure (leakage)	Perform CONTROL PRESSURE test and note results
	Forward clutch stator support seal rings leaking – No. 3 & No. 4 on A.O.T. (except A4LD)	Perform AIR PRESSURE test or visually inspect if forward clutch plates are burnt
	Forward clutch assembly burnt or damaged	Perform AIR PRESSURE test or visually inspect if forward clutch plates are burnt
	Forward clutch cylinder check ball leaking; leaking piston seal rings	Perform AIR PRESSURE test or visually inspect if forward clutch plates are burnt
	Valve body bolts loose or too tight	Tighten valve body bolts to specification
	Valve body dirty or contains sticking valves	Clean, inspect and repair or replace valve body
	Transmission filter plugged	Replace filter
	Pump damaged or leaking	Inspect pump gears; replace pump if required
No or Delayed Reverse Engagement – Forward OK	Improper fluid level	Check fluid level; See GENERAL SERVICING
	Manual linkage misadjusted or damaged	Check and adjust linkage, or service as required

FORD MOTOR CO. (EXC. ATX & AXOD) TROUBLE SHOOTING (Cont.)

CONDITION	POSSIBLE CAUSE	CORRECTION
No or Delayed Reverse Engagement – Forward OK (Cont.)	Low main control pressure in Reverse	Perform CONTROL PRESSURE test
	High reverse clutch or reverse clutch stator support seal rings leaking (No. 1 & No. 2 on A.O.T.)	Perform AIR PRESSURE test or visually inspect if reverse clutch plates are burnt
	Reverse clutch assembly burnt or worn	Perform AIR PRESSURE test or visually inspect if reverse clutch plates are burnt
	Reverse clutch piston check ball leaking; leaking piston seal rings	Perform AIR PRESSURE test or visually inspect if reverse clutch plates are burnt
	Valve body bolts loose or too tight	Tighten valve body bolts to specification
	Valve body dirty or contains sticking valves	Clean, inspect and repair or replace valve body
	Transmission filter plugged	Replace filter
	Pump damaged or leaking	Inspect pump gears; replace pump if required
	Intermediate servo piston seal cut or leaking (C5)	Check and replace piston seal
	Low-reverse servo piston seal cut or leaking (A4LD)	Perform AIR PRESSURE test; Check and replace piston seal; Check and replace low-reverse band
No or Delayed Reverse Engagement and/or No Engine Braking in Manual Low (1)	Improper fluid level	Check fluid level; See GENERAL SERVICING
	Manual linkage (T.V. linkage on A.O.T.) misadjusted or damaged	Check and adjust linkage or service as required
	Low-reverse band burnt or worn	Perform AIR PRESSURE test
	Low-reverse servo piston seal leaking	Perform AIR PRESSURE test or visually inspect if low-reverse band is burnt
	Band out of adjustment (C5)	Adjust reverse band
	Polished, glazed low-reverse band or drum (A4LD & C5)	Service or replace as required
	Planetary low one-way clutch damaged (except A4LD)	Replace low one-way clutch
	End play clearance too tight	Check and adjust transmission end play clearance
	Overdrive clutch, overdrive one-way clutch damaged (A4LD)	Check and replace if necessary
	Rear one-way clutch damaged (A4LD)	Replace rear one-way clutch
No Engine Braking in Manual 2nd	Intermediate band out of adjustment	Adjust intermediate band
	Improper clutch or band operation, or oil control pressure	Perform CONTROL PRESSURE test
	Intermediate servo leaking	Perform AIR PRESSURE test of intermediate servo to check for leakage; Service as required
	Intermediate one-way clutch damaged (except A4LD)	Replace clutch
	Polished or glazed band or drum	Service or replace as required
No Engine Braking in Manual 2nd (Cont.)	Overdrive clutch or overdrive one-way clutch damaged (A4LD)	Replace as required

FORD MOTOR CO. (EXC. ATX & AXOD) TROUBLE SHOOTING (Cont.)

CONDITION	POSSIBLE CAUSE	CORRECTION
Slips, Shudders or Chatters Upon Forward Engagement	Improper fluid level	Check fluid level; See GENERAL SERVICING
	T.V. linkage misadjusted or short (A.O.T.)	Adjust T.V. linkage
	Manual linkage misadjusted or damaged (except A.O.T.)	Check and adjust, or service as required
	Low main control pressure	Perform CONTROL PRESSURE test
	Valve body bolts loose or too tight	Tighten valve body bolts to specification
	Valve body dirty or contains sticking valves	Clean, inspect and repair or replace valve body
	Forward clutch piston check ball not seating or leaking	Replace forward clutch cylinder; Service transmission as required
	Forward clutch piston seal(s) cut or worn	Replace seal and service clutch as required
	Forward clutch stator support seal rings leaking – No. 3 & No. 4 on A.O.T. (except A4LD)	Perform AIR PRESSURE test or visually inspect if forward clutch plates are burnt
	Planetary low one-way clutch damaged (except A4LD)	Replace low one-way clutch
	Overdrive one-way clutch damaged (A4LD)	Repair or replace clutch
	Rear one-way clutch damaged (A4LD)	Determine cause of condition and service as required
Slips, Shudders or Chatters Upon Reverse Engagement	Improper fluid level	Check fluid level; See GENERAL SERVICING
	Low main control pressure in Reverse	Perform CONTROL PRESSURE test
	Low-reverse servo leaking	Perform AIR PRESSURE test; Visually inspect seal rings and piston bore
	Planetary low one-way clutch damaged (except A4LD)	Replace low one-way clutch
	Reverse clutch drum bushing damaged (except A4LD)	Determine cause of condition and service as required
	Reverse clutch stator support seal rings or ring grooves worn or damaged (except A4LD)	Determine cause of condition and service as required
	Reverse clutch piston seal cut or worn (except A4LD)	Determine cause of condition and service as required
	Overdrive and/or rear one-way clutch damaged (A4LD)	Determine cause of condition and service as required
	Overdrive and/or rear reverse-high clutch drum bushing damaged (A4LD)	Determine cause of condition and service as required
	Overdrive and/or rear reverse-high clutch center support seal rings or ring grooves worn or damaged (A4LD)	Determine cause of condition and service as required
	Overdrive and/or rear reverse-high clutch piston seals cut or worn	Determine cause of condition and service as required

FORD MOTOR CO. (EXC. ATX & AXOD) TROUBLE SHOOTING (Cont.)

CONDITION	POSSIBLE CAUSE	CORRECTION
Slips, Shudders or Chatters Upon Reverse Engagement (Cont.)	Low-reverse servo piston damaged or worn (A4LD)	Service as required
	Low-reverse band out of adjustment	Inspect and adjust low-reverse band on C5 and A4LD; Nonadjustable on all others, service as required
	Low-reverse servo piston, seals, or bores damaged (A4LD)	Perform AIR PRESSURE test
	Looseness in propeller shaft, "U" joints, or engine mounts	Service and repair or replace components as required
No Drive, Slips or Chatters in 1st Gear – All Other Gears OK (1st Gear in "D" or "OD" – A.O.T. & A4LD)	Worn or damaged planetary one-way clutch (rear one-way clutch on A4LD)	Service or replace clutch as required
No Drive, Slips or Chatters in 2nd Gear	Intermediate band out of adjustment (except A.O.T.)	Check and adjust intermediate band
	Intermediate friction clutch or one-way clutch worn or damaged (A.O.T.)	Service as required
	Intermediate clutch piston bleed hole blocked or not positioned at 12 o'clock (A.O.T.)	Clean and install bleed hole at 12 o'clock position
	Improper band or clutch application, or control pressure	Perform CONTROL PRESSURE test
	Damaged or worn intermediate servo piston seals and/or internal leaks (C3, C5 & C6)	Perform AIR PRESSURE test
	Damaged or worn intermediate servo piston and/or internal leaks (A4LD)	Perform AIR PRESSURE test
	Dirty or sticky valve body	Clean, service or replace valve body
	Polished, glazed intermediate band or drum (except A.O.T.)	Replace or service as required
Starts Up in 2nd or 3rd	Improper band or clutch application, or control pressure	Perform CONTROL PRESSURE test
	Intermediate clutch pack clearance too tight (A.O.T.)	Check and adjust clearance
	Damaged, worn, or sticking governor	Check governor and clean screen, or replace and service governor as required
	Valve body loose	Tighten valve body
	Dirty or sticky valve body	Clean, service or replace valve body
	Cross leaks between valve body and case mating surface	Service or replace valve body and/or case as required
Incorrect Shift Points	Improper fluid level	Check fluid level; See GENERAL SERVICING
	Vacuum line damaged, clogged, or leaks (except A.O.T.)	Perform VACUUM SUPPLY test
	Improper operation of EGR system (except A.O.T.)	Check and repair as required
	T.V. linkage out of adjustment (A.O.T.)	Check and adjust T.V. linkage
	Improper speedometer gear installed	Check and replace gear
	Improper band or clutch application, or control pressure	Perform CONTROL PRESSURE test

FORD MOTOR CO. (EXC. ATX & AXOD) TROUBLE SHOOTING (Cont.)

CONDITION	POSSIBLE CAUSE	CORRECTION
Incorrect Shift Points (Cont.)	Damaged or worn governor	Clean screen; Service or replace governor
	T.V. control rod or vacuum diaphragm bent, sticking, or leaks (C3, C5 & C6)	Replace as required
	Vacuum diaphragm bent, sticking or leaks (A4LD)	Service or replace as required
	Dirty or sticky valve body	Clean, service or replace valve body
	Vacuum regulator valve misadjusted or damaged (C6 with 6.9L Diesel engine)	Check adjustment and function; Adjust or replace
All Upshifts Harsh or Delayed, or No Upshifts	Improper fluid level	Check fluid level; See GENERAL SERVICING
	Throttle linkage disconnected, sticking, damaged or misadjusted (too long) or return spring disconnected (A.O.T.)	Check and adjust throttle linkage; Service as required
	Manual linkage misadjusted or damaged	Check and adjust linkage; Service as required
	Governor valve sticking	Perform GOVERNOR TEST; Service as required
	Main control pressure too high	Perform CONTROL PRESSURE test; Service as required
	T.V. control rod incorrect (C5)	Check and replace T.V. control rod
	Valve body bolts loose or too tight	Tighten valve body bolts to specification
	Valve body dirty or contains sticking valves	Clean, inspect and repair or replace valve body
	Vacuum leak to diaphragm unit (C3, C5 & A4LD)	Check and service vacuum lines to diaphragm unit; Perform VACUUM SUPPLY and DIAPHRAGM tests
	Vacuum diaphragm bent, sticking or leaks (C3, C5 & A4LD)	Check diaphragm unit and service as required
	Vacuum regulator valve misadjusted or damaged (C6 with 6.9L Diesel engine)	Check adjustment and function; Adjust or replace
All Upshifts Early or Mushy	Improper fluid level	Check fluid level; See GENERAL SERVICING
	T.V. throttle linkage sticking, damaged or misadjusted - too short (A.O.T.)	Check and adjust throttle linkage; Service as required
	Low main control pressure	Perform CONTROL PRESSURE test and note results
	Valve body bolts loose or too tight	Tighten valve body bolts to specification
	Valve body or throttle control valve sticking	Clean, inspect and repair or replace as required
	Governor valve sticking	Perform GOVERNOR TEST; Service as required
	T.V. control rod too short	Install correct T.V. control rod (except A4LD)
	Vacuum regulator valve misadjusted or damaged (C6 with 6.9L Diesel engine)	Check adjustment and function; Adjust or replace
	Kickdown linkage misadjusted, sticking, or damaged (A4LD)	Adjust linkage; Service as required
No 1-2 Upshift	Improper fluid level	Check fluid level; See GENERAL SERVICING
	T.V. throttle linkage disconnected, sticking, or misadjusted - too long (A.O.T.)	Check and adjust throttle linkage; Service as required

FORD MOTOR CO. (EXC. ATX & AXOD) TROUBLE SHOOTING (Cont.)

CONDITION	POSSIBLE CAUSE	CORRECTION
No 1-2 Upshift (Cont.)	Kickdown system damaged (A4LD)	Replace damaged parts
	Manual linkage misadjusted or damaged	Check and adjust, or service as required
	Low main control pressure to intermediate intermediate friction clutch (A.O.T.)	Perform CONTROL PRESSURE test and note results
	Governor valve sticking	Perform GOVERNOR TEST; Service as required
	Intermediate band out of adjustment (except A.O.T.)	Adjust intermediate band
	Vacuum leak to diaphragm unit (C3, C5 & A4LD)	Check and service vacuum lines to diaphragm unit
	Vacuum diaphragm bent, sticking or leaks (C3, C5 & A4LD)	Check diaphragm unit and service as required
	Valve body bolts loose or too tight	Tighten valve body bolts to specification
	Valve body dirty or contains sticking valves	Clean, inspect and repair or replace valve body
	Intermediate clutch band and/or servo assembly burnt	Perform AIR PRESSURE test
Rough, Harsh or Delayed 1-2 Upshift	Improper fluid level	Check fluid level; See GENERAL SERVICING
	Poor engine performance	Diagnose and tune engine
	T.V. linkage misadjusted (long) or damaged (A.O.T.)	Adjust linkage; Service as required
	Intermediate band out of adjustment (except A.O.T.)	Adjust intermediate band
	Main control pressure too high	Perform CONTROL PRESSURE test; Note results
	Governor valve sticking	Perform GOVERNOR TEST; Service as required
	Kickdown linkage misadjusted (A4LD)	Adjust linkage
	Damaged intermediate servo (C3, C5 & A4LD)	Perform AIR PRESSURE check of intermediate servo
	Engine vacuum leak (except A.O.T.)	Check engine vacuum lines and service as required; Check vacuum diaphragm unit and service as required; Perform VACUUM SUPPLY and DIAPHRAGM tests
	Valve body bolts loose or too tight	Tighten valve body bolts to specification
	Valve body dirty or contains sticking valves	Clean, inspect and repair or replace valve body
	Vacuum leak to diaphragm unit (C3, C5 & A4LD)	Check and service vacuum lines to diaphragm unit
	Vacuum diaphragm bent, sticking or leaks (C3, C5 & A4LD)	Check diaphragm unit and service as required
	Vacuum regulator valve misadjusted or damaged (C6 with 6.9L Diesel engine)	Check adjustment and function; Adjust or replace
Early, Mushy, Soft or Slipping 1-2 Upshift	Improper fluid level	Check fluid level; See GENERAL SERVICING
	Main regulator or throttle valve stuck (A4LD)	Service as required
	Incorrect engine performance	Diagnose and tune engine
	T.V. throttle linkage misadjusted (short), sticking, or damaged (A.O.T.)	Adjust linkage; Service as required

FORD MOTOR CO. (EXC. ATX & AXOD) TROUBLE SHOOTING (Cont.)

CONDITION	POSSIBLE CAUSE	CORRECTION
Early, Mushy, Soft or Slipping 1-2 Upshift (Cont.)	Intermediate band out of adjustment (except A.O.T.)	Adjust intermediate band
	Low main control pressure	Perform CONTROL PRESSURE test; Note results
	Valve body bolts loose or too tight	Tighten valve body bolts to specification
	Valve body dirty or contains sticking valves	Clean, inspect and repair or replace valve body
	Intermediate friction clutch burnt or worn (A.O.T.)	Determine cause of condition and service as required
	Governor valve sticking	Perform GOVERNOR TEST; Service as required
	Damaged intermediate servo or band	Perform AIR PRESSURE check; Service as required
	Polished, glazed intermediate band or drum (except A.O.T.)	Service or replace as required
	Vacuum regulator valve misadjusted or damaged (C6 with 6.9L Diesel engine)	Check adjustment and function; Adjust or replace
No 2-3 Upshift	Improper fluid level	Check fluid level; See GENERAL SERVICING
	T.V. throttle linkage misadjusted (long), sticking, or damaged (except A4LD)	Adjust linkage; Service as required
	Kickdown system damaged (A4LD)	Replace damaged parts
	Low main control pressure to direct clutch (except A4LD)	Perform CONTROL PRESSURE test; Note results
	Low main control pressure to reverse-high clutch (A4LD)	Perform CONTROL PRESSURE test; Note results
	Valve body bolts loose or too tight	Tighten valve body bolts to specification
	Valve body dirty or contains sticking valves	Clean, inspect and repair or replace valve body
	Direct clutch or reverse-high clutch assembly burnt or worn	Perform STALL test (except A4LD); Determine cause of condition and service as required
	Converter damper hub weld broken (A.O.T.)	Check converter damper hub weld; Replace torque converter if required
Harsh or Delayed 2-3 Upshift	Incorrect engine performance	Diagnose and tune engine
	Engine vacuum leak (except A.O.T.)	Check engine vacuum lines and service as required; Check vacuum diaphragm unit and service as required; Perform VACUUM SUPPLY and DIAPHRAGM tests
	T.V. throttle linkage misadjusted (long), sticking, or damaged (except A4LD)	Adjust linkage; Service as required
	2-3 accumulator piston apply passage plugged or omitted (A.O.T.)	Remove 2-3 accumulator piston and visually inspect, or AIR test to detect plugging or omission
	2-3 accumulator piston seals cut or worn (A.O.T.)	Determine cause of condition and replace seals; Service as required
	Damaged 2-3 accumulator (A.O.T.)	Service as required

FORD MOTOR CO. (EXC. ATX & AXOD) TROUBLE SHOOTING (Cont.)

CONDITION	POSSIBLE CAUSE	CORRECTION
Harsh or Delayed 2-3 Upshift (Cont.)	Damaged or worn intermediate servo release and high clutch piston check ball (C3, C5 & C6)	Perform AIR PRESSURE test of intermediate servo; Apply and release high clutch piston check ball; Service as required
	Valve body bolts loose or too tight	Tighten valve body bolts to specification
	Valve body dirty or contains sticking valves (2-3 capacity modulator valve on A.O.T.)	Clean, inspect and repair or replace valve body
	Vacuum diaphragm or T.V. control rod bent, sticking or leaking	Check diaphragm and rod; Service or replace as required
	Damaged or worn intermediate servo release and reverse-high clutch piston check ball (A4LD)	Perform AIR PRESSURE test of intermediate servo; Apply and release reverse-high clutch piston check ball; Service as required
	Throttle valve stuck (A4LD)	Service as required
	Vacuum regulator valve misadjusted or damaged (C6 with 6.9L Diesel engine)	Check adjustment and function; Adjust or replace
Soft, Early or Mushy 2-3 Upshift	T.V. throttle linkage misadjusted (short), sticking, or damaged (A.O.T.)	Adjust linkage; Service as required
	Kickdown system damaged (A4LD)	Replace damaged parts
	Valve body bolts loose or too tight	Tighten valve body bolts to specification
	Valve body dirty or contains sticking valves	Clean, inspect and repair or replace valve body
	Direct clutch or reverse-high clutch assembly burnt or worn (A.O.T.)	Perform STALL test; Determine cause of condition and service as required
	Vacuum diaphragm or T.V. control rod bent, sticking or leaking	Check diaphragm and rod; Service as required
	Vacuum regulator valve misadjusted or damaged (C6 with 6.9L Diesel engine)	Check adjustment and function; Adjust or replace
	Throttle valve stuck (A4LD)	Service as required
Erratic Shifts	Improper fluid level	Check fluid level; See GENERAL SERVICING
	Poor engine performance	Diagnose and tune engine
	T.V. linkage binding or sticking (A.O.T.)	Check linkage; Service as required
	Vacuum line damaged (A4LD)	Check engine vacuum lines and service as required
	Valve body bolts loose or too tight	Tighten valve body bolts to specification
	Valve body dirty or contains sticking valves	Clean, inspect and repair or replace valve body
	Governor valve sticking	Perform GOVERNOR TEST; Service as required
	Output shaft collector body seal rings damaged	Service as required
Shifts 1-3 in Drive or "OD" – A.O.T. & A4LD	Intermediate band out of adjustment (except A.O.T.)	Check and adjust intermediate band
	Intermediate friction clutch burnt or damaged (A.O.T.)	Determine cause of condition and service as required

FORD MOTOR CO. (EXC. ATX & AXOD) TROUBLE SHOOTING (Cont.)

CONDITION	POSSIBLE CAUSE	CORRECTION
Shifts 1-3 in Drive or "OD" – A.O.T. & A4LD (Cont.)	Intermediate one-way clutch damaged (A.O.T.)	Determine cause of condition and service as required
	Damaged intermediate servo and/or internal leaks (except A.O.T.)	Perform AIR PRESSURE test; Service front servo and/or internal leaks
	Improper band or clutch application, or control pressure	Perform CONTROL PRESSURE test
	Polished, glazed intermediate band or drum (except A.O.T.)	Replace or service as required
	Dirty or sticky valve body	Clean, service or replace valve body
	Governor valve sticking	Perform GOVERNOR TEST; Service as required
	Kickdown system damaged (A4LD)	Replace damaged parts
Engine Overspeeds on 2-3 Upshift	Linkage out of adjustment (except A4LD)	Service or adjust linkage
	Throttle linkage binding, damaged, misadjusted, or sticking (A.O.T.)	Check and adjust linkage; Service as required; Check vacuum regulator valve on C6 with 6.9L diesel engine
	Kickdown system damaged (A4LD)	Replace damaged parts
	Improper band or clutch application, or control pressure	Perform CONTROL PRESSURE test
	Damaged or worn high clutch (reverse-high clutch on A4LD) and/or intermediate servo	Perform AIR PRESSURE test; Service as required
	Intermediate servo piston seals cut or worn	Replace seal; Check for leaking
	Dirty or sticky valve body	Clean, service or replace valve body
	Throttle valve stuck (A4LD)	Service as required
	Vacuum diaphragm damaged (A4LD)	Replace vacuum diaphragm
	Torque converter damper or hub broken (A.O.T.)	Check converter damper hub weld; Replace torque converter if required
Engine Overspeeds on 3-2 Downshift (C3, C5 & A4LD)	Linkage out of adjustment	Service or adjust linkage
	Intermediate band out of adjustment	Check and adjust intermediate band
	Improper band or clutch application, and one-way clutch, or control pressure	Perform CONTROL PRESSURE test; Service clutch
	Damaged or worn intermediate servo	Perform AIR PRESSURE test; Service servo and/or seals
	Polished, glazed intermediate band or drum	Replace or service as required
	Dirty or sticky valve body	Clean, service or replace valve body
No 3-4 Upshift, Stays in 3rd – A.O.T. Only	T.V. throttle linkage misadjusted (long), bent or sticking	Adjust throttle linkage; Service as required; Bent, sticking or misadjusted T.V. throttle linkage will not properly synchronize with carburetor lever at time 3-4 shift should occur

FORD MOTOR CO. (EXC. ATX & AXOD) TROUBLE SHOOTING (Cont.)

CONDITION	POSSIBLE CAUSE	CORRECTION
No 3-4 Upshift, Stays in 3rd - A.O.T. Only (Cont.)	Direct clutch circuit leakage - Burnt plates will help confirm leakage in direct clutch circuit; Replacing plates without finding cause of problem will result in repeat occurrence	Perform DIRECT CLUTCH PRESSURE test; Check and tighten valve body bolts to specification to prevent leaks; Replace case if nicks or porosity are found in case passages or valve body-to-case mating surfaces; Perform CHECK BALL leak test to test direct clutch piston check ball for leaking, and replace piston if leakage is confirmed; Check and replace clutch piston inner and outer seal rings if leaking; Check No. 5 and No. 6 direct clutch output shaft seal rings for free movement on shaft and for metal shavings or burrs between seal and shaft, and replace as required; Check large seal rings (Nos. 7, 8, 9, 10) on output shaft for freedom of movement on shaft and for metal shavings, and replace as required; Inspect output shaft feed passages and cup plug for leakage and replace as required
	Dirty or sticky valve body	Clean valve body; Check for following sticking valves: Overdrive servo regulator valve, 3-4 shift valve, 3-4 T.V. modulator valve, orifice control valve and replace valve body if sticking valve cannot be freed
	Main control gasket distorted	Ensure gasket is not blocking an orifice; Replace if required
	Case warpage causing sticking valve	Reduce valve body bolt torque to minimum side of specification
	Governor leaking	Check last 2 large seal rings (Nos. 9, 10) for freedom of movement and metal shavings or burrs between seal and output shaft, and replace as required; Check seal ring bore at rear of case for scoring (light scoring is OK) and deep grooving, and replace case if required; Check governor-to-output shaft retaining ring for proper seating on output shaft, and service as required; Check fit of governor counterweight on output shaft, and replace counterweight if fit is loose
No 3-4 Upshift (A4LD Only)	Kickdown system damaged	Replace damaged parts
	Vacuum line damaged	Repair or replace as required
	Vacuum diaphragm damaged	Repair or replace as required
	Throttle valve stuck	Service as required
	Overdrive servo damaged or leaking	Check and replace overdrive piston seal if required
	Polished, glazed overdrive band or drum	Replace or service as required
	Dirty or sticky valve body	Clean, service or replace valve body
Harsh or Delayed 3-4 Upshift - A.O.T. Only	T.V. linkage misadjusted (long), bent or sticking	Check and adjust, or repair T.V. linkage
	T.V. return spring at carburetor (throttle body) not on T.V. lever	Replace spring
	Valve body bolts loose or too tight	Tighten valve body bolts to specification

FORD MOTOR CO. (EXC. ATX & AXOD) TROUBLE SHOOTING (Cont.)

CONDITION	POSSIBLE CAUSE	CORRECTION
Harsh or Delayed 3-4 Upshift – A.O.T. Only (Cont.)	Valve body dirty or contains sticking valves	Clean, inspect and repair, or replace valve body
	Incorrect engine performance	Diagnose and tune engine
	3-4 accumulator piston seals worn or cut	Determine cause of condition and service as required
	3-4 accumulator piston drain passage blocked	Determine cause of condition and service as required
Slips in 4th Gear (A.O.T. Only)	Overdrive circuit leaking or blocked passage – Burnt overdrive band will help confirm leakage in overdrive circuit; Replacing overdrive band without finding cause of problem will result in repeat occurrence	Check and tighten valve body bolts to specification; Check and replace servo cover "O" rings as required; Check and replace overdrive servo piston seal if found leaking; Check overdrive servo cover for cracks and porosity by covering with fluid and apply air to overdrive servo apply passage with Adapter (T80L-77030-B), replace cover if bubbles appear on overdrive servo cover
	Overdrive servo piston not applying overdrive band and/or band not applying	Overdrive servo case apply passage blocked; Perform AIR PRESSURE test and replace case if required
	Overdrive band mislocated	Service overdrive servo piston if not seated to band-end seat; Service overdrive band if not seated to anchor pin
	Converter damper plate and hub fracturing, weld or rivet fatigue, or damper springs broken	Using Adapter (T83L-7902-A), check converter damper and hub assembly weld, and replace converter if shaft turns more than 2° or if grinding noise is heard while applying 50 ft. lbs. (78 N.m) torque
	Direct drive shaft splines distorted	Check and replace direct drive shaft if splines on ends of shaft or spines in direct clutch cylinder are distorted
Slips in 4th Gear (A4LD Only)	Overdrive servo damaged or leaking	Check and replace overdrive piston seal if required
	Polished, glazed overdrive band or drum	Replace or service as required
Shift Hunting 3-4 and 4-3 (A.O.T. Only)	Poor engine performance, or EGR solenoid worn or damaged	Diagnose and tune engine; Replace EGR solenoid
	Throttle linkage misadjusted	Inspect and adjust throttle linkage
	Manual linkage misadjusted	Check and adjust or service as required
Rough Shudder 3-1 Shift at Closed Throttle in "D" – "OD" for A.O.T. & A4LD	Incorrect engine idle or engine performance	Diagnose and tune engine; Adjust idle speed
	Improper kickdown linkage adjustment (A4LD)	Service or adjust kickdown linkage

FORD MOTOR CO. (EXC. ATX & AXOD) TROUBLE SHOOTING (Cont.)

CONDITION	POSSIBLE CAUSE	CORRECTION
Rough Shudder 3-1 Shift at Closed Throttle in "D" – "OD" for A.O.T. & A4LD (Cont.)	Improper linkage adjustment (except A4LD)	Service or adjust linkage; Check vacuum regulator valve on C6 with 6.9L diesel engine
	Improper band or clutch application or control pressure	Perform CONTROL PRESSURE test
	Improper governor operation	Perform GOVERNOR test and service as required
	Dirty or sticky valve body	Clean, service or replace valve body
Rough or Mushy 4-2 or 3-1 Downshift (A.O.T.)	Incorrect engine performance	Diagnose and tune engine
	Improper throttle or manual linkage adjustment	Service or adjust linkage
	Improper application of intermediate friction and one-way clutch	Service as required
	Dirty or sticky valve body	Clean, service or replace valve body
No Forced Downshifts	Kickdown linkage (cable) out of adjustment (except A.O.T.)	Service or adjust linkage
	Damaged internal kickdown linkage (except A.O.T.)	Service internal linkage
	Damaged or misadjusted (short) throttle linkage (A.O.T.)	Inspect and adjust throttle linkage; Service as required
	Improper band or clutch application or control pressure	Perform CONTROL PRESSURE test
	Dirty or sticking governor	Check governor and clean screen, or replace and service governor as required
	Dirty or sticky valve body	Clean, service or replace valve body
High Shift Effort	Manual shift linkage misadjusted or damaged	Check and adjust, or service as required
	Inner manual lever nut loose	Tighten nut to specification
	Manual lever retainer pin damaged	Adjust linkage and install new pin
Transmission Overheats	Improper fluid level	Check fluid level; See GENERAL SERVICING
	Incorrect engine performance	Diagnose and tune engine
	Improper band or clutch application, or control pressure	Perform CONTROL PRESSURE test
	Restriction in cooler or lines	Check cooler and lines for obstruction and service as required
	Seized converter one-way clutch	Replace one-way clutch
	Dirty or sticky valve body	Clean, service or replace valve body
Transmission Leaks	Damaged or obstructed case breather vent	Check and service as required
	Leakage at gasket, seals, etc.	Remove all traces of lubricant on exposed surfaces; Check vent for obstruction and damage; Operate transmission at normal temperatures and perform FLUID LEAKAGE test; Service as required
Poor Vehicle Acceleration	Poor engine performance	Diagnose and tune engine
	Torque converter one-way clutch locked up	Replace torque converter

FORD MOTOR CO. (EXC. ATX & AXOD) TROUBLE SHOOTING (Cont.)

CONDITION	POSSIBLE CAUSE	CORRECTION
	TRANSMISSION NOISY	
Valve Resonance	Improper fluid level	Check fluid level; See GENERAL SERVICING
	Linkage out of adjustment	Adjust or service linkage
	Improper band or clutch application or control pressure	Perform CONTROL PRESSURE test
	Cooler lines grounding	Free cooler lines
	Dirty or sticky valve body	Clean, service or replace valve body
	Internal leakage or pump cavitation	Service pump as required
Other Than Valve Resonance	Linkage adjustment	Check and adjust, or replace linkage
	Improper fluid level	Check fluid level; See GENERAL SERVICING
	Contaminated fluid	Disassemble, clean and service transmission; Flush torque converter and cooler
	Faulty torque converter	Service or replace torque converter
	Faulty oil pump	Service or replace oil pump
	Faulty speedometer driven gear	Replace speedometer driven gear
	Worn or damaged extension housing bushing or seal	Service as required
	Faulty propeller shaft	Service as required
	Faulty planetary gear set	Service gear set as required
	Faulty one-way clutch	Service one-way clutch as required
	Loose converter-to-flywheel mounting bolts	Tighten bolts to specification
	TORQUE CONVERTER DIAGNOSIS - A4LD ONLY	
Converter Clutch Does Not Engage	Converter clutch solenoid not being energized electrically	Perform EEC-IV KEY ON-ENGINE OFF test
	Wires to solenoid shorted or open	Perform EEC-IV KEY ON-ENGINE OFF test
	Transmission case connector not seated	Perform EEC-IV KEY ON-ENGINE OFF test
	Open or short inside solenoid	Perform EEC-IV KEY ON-ENGINE OFF test
	Faulty engine coolant temperature sensor (CTS)	Perform EEC-IV KEY ON-ENGINE OFF test
	Faulty throttle position sensor (TPS)	Perform EEC-IV KEY ON-ENGINE OFF test
	Faulty manifold absolute pressure (MAP) sensor	Perform EEC-IV KEY ON-ENGINE OFF test
	Vacuum line disconnected from MAP sensor	Perform EEC-IV KEY ON-ENGINE OFF test
	Brake switch faulty	Perform EEC-IV ENGINE RUNNING test
	Faulty EEC-IV processor	Run diagnostic check on processor
	Converter clutch solenoid being energized electronically, but foreign material on solenoid valve preventing valve closure	Remove oil pan and valve body; Remove solenoid and check operation; Service as required
	Converter clutch shuttle valve stuck in unlocked position (against plug) or spring load too high	Remove valve body and check operation of shuttle valve; Remove any contamination; Spring load should be about 4 lbs. at .512" (1.8 kg at 13 mm)

FORD MOTOR CO. (EXC. ATX & AXOD) TROUBLE SHOOTING (Cont.)

CONDITION	POSSIBLE CAUSE	CORRECTION
	TORQUE CONVERTER DIAGNOSIS - A4LD ONLY (Cont.)	
Converter Clutch Does Not Engage (Cont.)	Converter clutch shift valve stuck in downshift position	Remove valve body and check operation of shift valve; Remove any contamination; Make sure valve moves freely
	Torque converter internal malfunction preventing lock-up piston application	Replace torque converter
Converter Clutch Always Engaged (Vehicle Moves Only With Engine at High RPM in "OD")	Converter clutch shift valve stuck in locked position	Remove valve body and check to ensure shift valve moves freely
	Converter clutch shuttle valve stuck in locked position	Remove valve body and check to ensure shuttle valve moves freely
	Lock-up piston in torque converter will not disengage	Replace torque converter
Converter Clutch Will Not Disengage on Coastdown	Faulty throttle position sensor (should unlock at closed throttle)	Perform EEC-IV KEY ON-ENGINE OFF test
	Converter clutch solenoid sticking	Remove valve body and check operation of solenoid; Replace if required

FORD MOTOR CO. ATX TROUBLE SHOOTING

Every diagnosis of automatic transaxle problems should begin with a check of the transmission fluid and linkage. Most of the following conditions can be caused by one or more of the following factors: (1) Incorrect fluid level, (2) Contaminated fluid, (3) Improperly adjusted linkage, or (4) Damaged or worn linkage.

CONDITION	POSSIBLE CAUSE	CORRECTION
Slow Initial Engagement	Improper fluid level	Check fluid level; See GENERAL SERVICING
	Damaged or improperly adjusted linkage	Service or adjust linkage; See GENERAL SERVICING
	Contaminated fluid	Check fluid condition
	Improper clutch and band application, or low main control pressure	Perform CONTROL PRESSURE test
	Dirty valve body	Clean, service or replace valve body
Rough Initial Engagement (Forward or Reverse)	Improper fluid level	Check fluid level; See GENERAL SERVICING
	Engine idle speed too high	Check and adjust idle speed
	Automatic choke on (warm temperatures)	Disengage choke
	Looseness in half-shafts, "CV" joints, or engine mounts	Service and repair, or replace components as required
	Improper clutch or band operation, or oil control pressure	Perform CONTROL PRESSURE test
	Sticking or dirty valve body	Clean, service or replace valve body
No Drive in Any Gear	Improper fluid level	Check fluid level; See GENERAL SERVICING
	Damaged or improperly adjusted manual linkage	Check and adjust; See GENERAL SERVICING
	Improper clutch or band operation, or oil control pressure	Perform CONTROL PRESSURE test
	Internal leakage	Check and service as required
	Valve body bolts loose or too tight	Tighten valve body bolts to specification
	Damaged or worn clutches or band	Perform AIR PRESSURE test; Service as required
	Valve body dirty or contains sticking valves	Clean, inspect and repair, or replace valve body
	Broken pump or turbine shaft	Service as required
No Forward Engagement – Reverse OK	Improper fluid level	Check fluid level; See GENERAL SERVICING
	Manual linkage misadjusted or damaged	Check and adjust linkage or service as required
	Improper one-way clutch, band application, or oil control pressure	Perform CONTROL PRESSURE test; Service as required

FORD MOTOR CO. ATX TROUBLE SHOOTING (Cont.)

CONDITION	POSSIBLE CAUSE	CORRECTION
No Forward Engagement – Reverse OK (Cont.)	Valve body bolts loose or too tight	Tighten valve body bolts to specification
	Valve body dirty or contains sticking valves	Clean, inspect and repair or replace valve body
	Damaged or worn band or servo	Perform AIR PRESSURE test; Service as required
Slips, Shudders or Chatters In Reverse – Forward OK	Improper fluid level	Check fluid level; See GENERAL SERVICING
	Manual linkage misadjusted or damaged	Check and adjust linkage or service as required
	Improper control pressure	Perform CONTROL PRESSURE test
	Valve body bolts loose or too tight	Tighten valve body bolts to specification
	Valve body dirty or contains sticking valves	Clean, inspect and repair or replace valve body
	Damaged or worn Reverse clutch	Perform AIR PRESSURE test; Service as required
Will Not Start in "N" or "P"	Neutral safety switch improperly adjusted	Check and adjust switch
	Neutral safety switch wire disconnected or damaged	Service as required
	Manual linkage misadjusted or damaged	Check and adjust linkage or service as required
Slips or Chatters in 1st	Improper fluid level	Check fluid level; See GENERAL SERVICING
	Damaged or worn band	Service or replace band
Slips or Chatters in 2nd	Improper fluid level	Check fluid level; See GENERAL SERVICING
	Internal leakage	Check and service as required
	Valve body dirty or contains sticking valves	Clean, inspect and repair, or replace valve body
	Improper clutch application	Perform CONTROL PRESSURE test; Service as required
	Intermediate friction clutch faulty	Service clutch
	Polished, glazed band or drum	Replace or service as required
Starts Up in 2nd or 3rd	Improper fluid level	Check fluid level; See GENERAL SERVICING
	Manual linkage misadjusted or damaged	Check and adjust linkage or service as required
	Governor valve stuck	Perform GOVERNOR CHECK; Service or replace governor
	Improper clutch or band operation, or oil control pressure	Perform CONTROL PRESSURE test
	Valve body bolts loose or too tight	Tighten valve body bolts to specification
	Valve body dirty or contains sticking valves	Clean, inspect and repair, or replace valve body
	Cross leaks between valve body and case mating surface	Replace valve body and/or case as required
Incorrect Shift Points	Improper fluid level	Check fluid level; See GENERAL SERVICING
	Damaged or worn governor	Clean screen; Service or replace governor
	Improper band or clutch application, or control pressure	Perform CONTROL PRESSURE test
	Dirty or sticky valve body	Clean, service or replace valve body
No Upshift in Any Speed in "D"	Improper fluid level	Check fluid level; See GENERAL SERVICING
	Damaged or worn governor	Service or replace governor; Clean screen
	Valve body dirty or contains sticking valves	Clean, inspect and repair or replace valve body

FORD MOTOR CO. ATX TROUBLE SHOOTING (Cont.)

CONDITION	POSSIBLE CAUSE	CORRECTION
No Upshift at Any Speed in "D" (Cont.)	Improper clutch or band operation, or oil control pressure	Perform CONTROL PRESSURE test
Shifts 1-3 in Drive	Dirty or sticking valve body	Clean, service or replace valve body
	Intermediate friction clutch burnt or damaged	Service as required
	Improper clutch application, or control pressure	Perform CONTROL PRESSURE test
Engine Overspeeds on 2-3 Upshift	Improper fluid level	Check fluid level; See GENERAL SERVICING
	Improper band or clutch application, or control pressure	Perform CONTROL PRESSURE test
	Damaged or worn direct clutch and/or servo	Perform AIR PRESSURE test; Service as required
	Dirty or sticking valve body	Clean, service or replace valve body
Early, Mushy, Soft or Slipping 1-2 Upshift	Improper fluid level	Check fluid level; See GENERAL SERVICING
	Improper intermediate clutch application, or oil control pressure	Perform CONTROL PRESSURE test
	Damaged intermediate clutch	Perform AIR PRESSURE test
	Valve body dirty or contains sticking valves	Clean, inspect and repair or replace valve body
Rough, Harsh or Delayed 1-2 Upshift	Improper fluid level	Check fluid level; See GENERAL SERVICING
	Incorrect engine performance	Diagnose and tune engine
	Improper intermediate clutch application, or oil control pressure	Perform CONTROL PRESSURE test
	Valve body dirty or contains sticking valves	Clean, inspect and repair or replace valve body
Rough 2-3 Shift (1-2 Shift OK)	Improper fluid level	Check fluid level; See GENERAL SERVICING
	Incorrect engine performance	Diagnose and tune engine
	Improper band release or direct clutch application, or oil control pressure	Perform CONTROL PRESSURE test
	Damaged or worn servo release and direct clutch piston check ball	Perform AIR PRESSURE test on servo apply and release, and direct clutch piston check ball; Service as required
	Dirty or sticking valve body	Clean, service or replace valve body
	Internal leakage or pump cavitation	Service pump as required
Rough 3-2 Shift at Closed Throttle in "D"	Improper fluid level	Check fluid level; See GENERAL SERVICING
	Incorrect engine idle or performance	Diagnose and tune engine
	Improper band or clutch application, or oil control pressure	Perform CONTROL PRESSURE test
	Improper governor operation	Perform GOVERNOR test; Service as required
	Dirty or sticking valve body	Clean, service or replace valve body

Automatic Transmissions

FORD MOTOR CO. ATX TROUBLE SHOOTING (Cont.)

CONDITION	POSSIBLE CAUSE	CORRECTION
No Forced Downshifts	Improper fluid level	Check fluid level; See GENERAL SERVICING
	Improper band or clutch application, or control pressure	Perform CONTROL PRESSURE test
	Damaged internal T.V. lever	Service internal lever
	Dirty or sticky valve body	Clean, service or replace valve body
	Dirty or sticking governor	Clean or replace governor
Engine Overspeeds on 3-2 or 3-1 Downshift (1-2 Shift OK)	Improper fluid level	Check fluid level; See GENERAL SERVICING
	Dirty or sticking valve body	Clean, service or replace valve body
	Band or clutch out of adjustment	Check and adjust servo rod travel
	Improper band or clutch application, or control pressure	Perform CONTROL PRESSURE test
	Damaged or worn servo	Perform AIR PRESSURE test; Service servo and/or seals
	Polished, glazed band or drum	Replace or service as required
No Engine Braking in Manual 1st	Improper fluid level	Check fluid level; See GENERAL SERVICING
	Manual linkage misadjusted or damaged	Check and adjust linkage or service as required
	Band or clutch out of adjustment	Check direct clutch and service as required; Check and adjust servo rod travel
	Improper control pressure	Perform CONTROL PRESSURE test
	Polished, glazed band or drum	Replace or service as required
	Dirty or sticking valve body	Clean, service or replace valve body
No Engine Braking in Manual 2nd	Improper fluid level	Check fluid level; See GENERAL SERVICING
	Manual linkage misadjusted or damaged	Check and adjust linkage or service as required
	Improper band or clutch application, or control pressure	Perform CONTROL PRESSURE test
	Leaking servo	Perform AIR PRESSURE test on servo to detect leaks; Service as required
	Polished, glazed band or drum	Replace or service as required
Transaxle Overheats	Excessive tow loads	Check owner's manual for restrictions
	Improper fluid level	Check fluid level; See GENERAL SERVICING
	Incorrect engine idle or performance	Diagnose and tune engine
	Improper band or clutch application, or control pressure	Perform CONTROL PRESSURE test
	Restriction in cooler or lines	Check cooler and lines for obstruction and service as required
	Seized converter one-way clutch	Replace torque converter
	Dirty or sticky valve body	Clean, service or replace valve body
Transaxle Leaks	Improper fluid level	Check fluid level; See GENERAL SERVICING
	Leakage at gasket, seals, etc.	Remove all traces of lubricant on exposed surfaces; Check vent for obstruction and damage; Operate transaxle at normal temperatures and perform FLUID LEAKAGE test; Service as required

Automatic Transmissions

FORD MOTOR CO. ATX TROUBLE SHOOTING (Cont.)

CONDITION	POSSIBLE CAUSE	CORRECTION
	TRANSAXLE NOISY	
Valve Resonance	Improper fluid level	Check fluid level; See GENERAL SERVICING
	Improper band or clutch application or control pressure	Perform CONTROL PRESSURE test
	Cooler lines grounding	Free cooler lines
	Dirty or sticking valve body	Clean, service or replace valve body
	Internal leakage or pump cavitation	Service pump as required
Other Than Valve Resonance	Linkage adjustment	Check and adjust, or replace linkage
	Improper fluid level	Check fluid level; See GENERAL SERVICING
	Contaminated fluid	Disassemble, clean and service transaxle; Flush torque converter and cooler
	Faulty speedometer driven gear	Replace speedometer driven gear
	Faulty half-shafts or "CV" joints	Service as required
	Faulty planetary gear set	Service gear set as required
	Faulty final drive gear set	Service gear set as required
	Loose converter-to-flywheel mounting bolts	Tighten bolts to specification

FORD MOTOR CO. AXOD TROUBLE SHOOTING

Every diagnosis of automatic transmission problems should begin with a check of the transmission fluid and linkage. Most of the following conditions can be caused by one or more of the following factors: (1) Incorrect fluid level, (2) Contaminated fluid, (3) Improperly adjusted linkage, or (4) Damaged or worn linkage.

CONDITION	POSSIBLE CAUSE	CORRECTION
No 1-2 Shift (1st Gear Only)	Governor assembly binding, damaged or leaking; Valve ball stuck or missing	Perform governor test; Service as required
	Intermediate clutch assembly damaged; Check ball stuck or missing	Determine source of contamination or damage; Service as required
	Direct-Intermediate clutch hub seals damaged, missing or holes blocked	Determine source of contamination or damage; Service as required
	Driven sprocket support seals damaged, missing or holes blocked	Determine source of contamination or damage; Service as required
	1-2 shift valve stuck, nicked or damaged	Determine source of contamination or damage; Service as required
	1-2 throttle delay valve stuck, nicked or damaged	Determine source of contamination or damage; Service as required
	1-2 accumulator capacity modulator valve stuck, nicked or damaged	Determine source of contamination or damage; Service as required
	No. 9 check ball missing	Replace check ball
	Valve body assembly bolts loose or too tight	Tighten bolts to specification
	Carrier damaged	Inspect welds; Service as required
	Intermediate clutch tap plug loose or missing	Service as required
1-2 Shift Feels Harsh or Soft	High or low oil pressure	Perform control pressure test; Service as required
	1-2 accumulator regulator valve stuck, nicked or damaged; Spring missing or damaged	Determine source of contamination or damage; Service as required
	1-2 accumulator modulator valve stuck, nicked or damaged; Spring missing or damaged	Determine source of contamination or damage; Service as required
	1-2 accumulator assembly piston stuck or damaged; Seals or springs damaged or missing	Determine source of contamination or damage; Service as required
No 2-3 Shift (1-2 Shift OK)	Governor assembly binding, damaged or leaking; Valve ball stuck or missing	Perform governor test; Service as required
	Low-Intermediate servo apply rod too long; Servo bore or piston damaged; Piston seals damaged or missing; Return spring or retaining clip broken or missing	Install correct apply rod; Determine source of contamination or damage; Service as required
	Direct clutch assembly damaged; Piston or seals damaged; Check ball stuck or missing	Determine source of contamination or damage; Service as required
	Direct-Intermediate clutch hub seals damaged or missing or holes blocked	Determine source of contamination or damage; Service as required

FORD MOTOR CO. AXOD TROUBLE SHOOTING (Cont.)

CONDITION	POSSIBLE CAUSE	CORRECTION
No 2-3 Shift (1-2 Shift OK) (Cont.)	Driven sprocket support seals damaged or missing or holes blocked	Determine source of contamination or damage; Service as required
	Direct one-way clutch cage/rollers/springs damaged; Rollers missing or misassembled on inner race	Disassemble and inspect; Service as required
	Valve body assembly bolts loose or too tight	Tighten to specification
	2-3 shift valve stuck, nicked or damaged	Determine source of contamination or damage; Service as required
	No. 4 check ball missing	Service as required
	Bypass solenoid not energized during WOT upshift	Refer to Electrical System Diagnosis in AXOD Service and Repair article
	Case servo release passage blocked	Determine source of blockage; Service as required
	Servo release tube leaking or improperly installed	Service as required
	Direct clutch pressure tap plug loose or missing	Service as required
2-3 Shift Feels Harsh or Soft	Low oil pressure	Perform control pressure test; Service as required
	Low-Intermediate servo apply rod length wrong; Piston, seal, springs, or rod damaged	Install correct apply rod; Determine source of damage; Service as required
	2-3 servo regulator valve stuck, nicked or damaged; Spring damaged	Determine source of contamination or damage; Service as required
	Backout valve stuck, nicked or damaged; Spring damaged	Determine source of contamination or damage; Service as required
No 3-4 Shift	Governor assembly binding, damaged or leaking	Perform governor test; Service as required
	Overdrive band assembly not holding	Perform air pressure test; Service as required
	Overdrive servo apply rod too long; Servo bore, piston, or seals damaged; Return spring or retaining clip missing or broken	Install correct apply rod. Determine source of contamination or damage; Service as required
	Forward clutch return springs or piston damaged	Determine source of damage; Service as required
	Front ring gear damaged	Determine source of damage; Service as required
	Valve body bolts loose or too tight	Tighten bolts to specification
	3-4 shift valve stuck, nicked or damaged; Spring damaged	Determine source of contamination or damage; Service as required
	3-4 modulator valve stuck, nicked or damaged; Spring missing	Determine source of contamination or damage; Service as required
	4-3 scheduling valve stuck, nicked or damaged; Spring missing	Determine source of contamination or damage; Service as required

FORD MOTOR CO. AXOD TROUBLE SHOOTING (Cont.)

CONDITION	POSSIBLE CAUSE	CORRECTION
3-4 Shift Feels Harsh or Soft	Oil pressure low or too high	Perform control pressure test
	3-4 accumulator piston stuck or damaged; piston seal or springs missing or damaged	Determine source of contamination or damage; Service as required
	No. 14 check ball missing	Replace check ball
4-3 Downshifts Harsh	Overdrive servo apply rod wrong length; Piston, seal or springs damaged or missing	Install correct apply rod; Determine source of contamination or damage; Service as required
3-2 Downshift Harsh	Low-intermediate servo apply rod length wrong; Piston, seal or springs damaged or missing	Install correct apply rod; Determine source of contamination or damage; Service as required
	3-2 control valve stuck, nicked or damaged	Determine source of contamination or damage; Service as required
	No. 5 check ball missing	Replace check ball
3-1, 2-1 Downshift Harsh	Low-intermediate servo apply rod length wrong; Piston, seal or springs damaged or missing	Install correct apply rod; Determine source of contamination or damage; Service as required
	No. 9 check ball missing (3-1 shift only)	Replace check ball
No Drive in Drive Range	Oil level low	Service as required
	Oil pressure too low	Perform control pressure test; Service as required
	Manual linkage misadjusted, disconnected or damaged; TV linkage missing	Service as required
	Oil pump assembly worn or damaged; Oil pump driveshaft damaged	Determine source of damage; Service as required
	Drive chain assembly damaged or broken	Determine source of damage; Service as required
	Drive sprocket shaft to converter turbine spline damaged	Determine source of damage; Service as required
	Driven sprocket shaft to direct-intermediate clutch hub damaged	Determine source of damage; Service as required
	Forward clutch assembly damaged; Seals missing or damaged; Check ball missing or damaged; Pistons damaged	Determine source of contamination or damage; Service as required
	Low one-way clutch improperly assembled or sprag is damaged	Determine source of damage; Service as required
	Front sun gear or shell damaged	Determine source of damage; Service as required
	Front or rear carrier pinions or lugs to rear ring gear damaged	Determine source of damage; Service as required
	Rear ring gear or lugs to forward carrier damaged	Determine source of damage; Service as required

Automatic Transmissions

FORD MOTOR CO. AXOD TROUBLE SHOOTING (Cont.)

CONDITION	POSSIBLE CAUSE	CORRECTION
No Drive in Drive Range (Cont.)	Low-intermediate band burned or broken	Determine source of damage; Service as required
	Low-intermediate servo apply rod too short; Piston, seal or rod damaged	Install correct rod; Determine source of contamination; Service as required
	Low-intermediate servo oil tubes damaged; Oil tube case bores damaged	Service as required
	Final drive or final drive sun gear shaft pinion or gears damaged	Determine source of damage; Service as required
	Output shaft splines damaged; Misassembled with axles	Determine source of damage; Service as required
	Halfshaft splines damaged or disengaged from transaxle	Service as required
No Reverse	Low oil pressure or low oil level	Perform control pressure test; Check oil level
	Manual linkage misadjusted, disconnected or damaged; TV linkage missing	Service as required
	Oil pump or oil pump driveshaft damaged	Determine source of damage; Service as required
	Drive chain assembly damaged or broken	Service as required
	Drive sprocket shaft to converter turbine spline damaged	Determine source of damage; Service as required
	Driven sprocket shaft to direct-intermediate clutch hub damaged	Determine source of damage; Service as required
	Reverse clutch burned or missing plates	Determine source of damage; Service as required
	Forward clutch damaged; Seals damaged or missing; Check ball damaged or missing; Burned or missing clutch plates	Disassemble and inspect clutch assembly; Service as required
	Low one-way clutch improperly assembled or sprag is damaged	Service as required
	Front and rear carrier pinions or lugs to rear ring gear damaged	Determine source of damage; Service as required
	Reverse apply tube leaking or improperly installed	Service as required
No Park Range	Damaged park mechanism; Actuating rod, parking pawl, park gear or return spring broken; Manual linkage misadjusted	Determine source of damage; Service as required
Harsh Neutral to Reverse or Harsh Neutral to Drive	Low-intermediate servo apply rod length wrong; Springs damaged or missing	Install correct apply rod; Determine source of contamination or damage; Service as required
	3-2 control valve stuck, nicked or damaged	Determine source of contamination; Service as required
	No. 5 check ball missing	Replace check ball

Automatic Transmissions

FORD MOTOR CO. AXOD TROUBLE SHOOTING (Cont.)

CONDITION	POSSIBLE CAUSE	CORRECTION
Harsh Neutral to Reverse or Harsh Neutral to Drive (Cont.)	Neutral-Drive accumulator piston stuck; Seal or springs damaged or missing	Determine source of contamination or damage; Service as required
	No. 1 check ball missing (Harsh Reverse)	Replace check ball
	Valve body separator plate thermal elements do not close when warm	Service as required
Transaxle Overheats	Excessive tow loads	Check owners manual for tow restrictions
	Improper fluid level	Check fluid level
	Incorrect engine idle or performance	Tune or adjust engine idle
	Improper clutch or band application, or oil pressure control system	Perform control pressure test
	Restriction in cooler or lines	Service as required
	Seized converter one-way clutch	Replace converter
	Dirty or sticking valve body	Clean, service or replace valve body
Transaxle Leaks	Improper fluid level	Check fluid level
	Side pan or bottom pan bolts loose; Gasket or pan rail damaged; Pan distorted	Service as required
	TV cable, fill tube or electrical bulkhead connector loose fit	Service as required
	Manual shaft seal damaged	Replace seal
	Governor cover or servo covers "O" ring seals damaged	Replace "O" ring
	Cooler fittings or pressure taps loose or have damaged threads	Service as required
	Cooler or converter seal leaking; Garter spring missing; Weld seam leaking	Service as required
	Halfshaft seals damaged or garter spring missing	Replace seal
	Speedometer cable or speed sensor "O" ring seal damaged	Replace "O" ring
Oil Venting or Foaming	Transaxle overfilled	Drain and fill to proper level
	Transmission fluid contaminated with antifreeze or engine overheating	Determine source of leak; Service as required
	Bi-metallic element stuck open	Replace element
	Oil filter "O" rings damaged	Replace "O" rings
High or Low Oil Pressure (Verify With Gauge)	Oil level low or too high	Drain or fill transaxle as necessary
	TV cable or linkage stuck or damaged	Service as required
	Pressure regulator valve or bore nicked or scored; Spring damaged	Determine source of damage; Service as required
	Pressure relief valve damaged; Spring or check ball missing	Service as required
	Oil pump slide stuck; Seals or vanes damaged; Driveshaft broken or damaged	Determine source of damage; Service as required
1-2 Shift Speed High or Low	Governor weights binding; Springs, gear or tube damaged; Seal missing or valve stuck	Perform governor test; Service as required

Automatic Transmissions

FORD MOTOR CO. AXOD TROUBLE SHOOTING (Cont.)

CONDITION	POSSIBLE CAUSE	CORRECTION
1-2 Shift Speed High or Low (Cont.)	TV control valve, TV plunger, TV line modulator valve or 1-2 throttle delay valve stuck, nicked or damaged; Springs missing or damaged	Determine source of contamination; Service as required
2-3 Shift Speed High or Low	Governor weights binding; Springs, gear or tube damaged; Seal missing or valve stuck	Perform governor test; Service as required
	TV cable damaged or disconnected	Service cable as required
	TV control valve, TV plunger, TV line modulator valve or 1-2 throttle delay valve stuck, nicked or damaged; Springs missing or damaged; Governor tube leaking	Determine source of contamination or damage; Service as required
3-4 Shift Speed High or Low	Governor weights binding; Springs, gear or tube damaged; Seal missing or valve stuck	Perform governor test; Service as required
	TV control valve, TV plunger, TV line modulator valve or 1-2 throttle delay valve stuck, nicked or damaged; Springs missing or damaged	Determine source of contamination or damage; Service as required
	TV cable damaged or disconnected	Service as required

GENERAL MOTORS CONVERTER CLUTCH TROUBLE SHOOTING

Every diagnosis of automatic transmission problems should begin with a check of the transmission fluid and linkage. Most of the following conditions can be caused by one or more of the following factors: (1) Incorrect fluid level, (2) Contaminated fluid, (3) Improperly adjusted linkage, or (4) Damaged or worn linkage. When diagnosing Converter Clutch problems, ensure engine and vacuum systems are in perfect operating order.

CONDITION	POSSIBLE CAUSE	CORRECTION
No Converter Clutch Apply	Problem in Electronic Control Module (if equipped with Computer Command Control)	Verify Electronic Control Module operation
	Electrical Problem	
	Voltage not reaching transmission	Ensure 12 volts reach transmission to engage solenoid
	Ground inside transmission	Ensure solenoid is not grounded inside case
	Defective connector, wiring harness, or solenoid	Check and repair or replace as required
	Defective pressure switch (if equipped)	Check and replace pressure switch as required
	3rd clutch switch inoperative (THM 440-T4)	Check and replace switch as required
	4th clutch switch inoperative (THM 440-T4)	Check and replace switch as required
	Valve Body Assembly	
	Sticking converter clutch apply valve	Clean, service and/or replace valve body as required
	Sticking converter clutch shift valve	Clean, service and/or replace valve body as required
	Sticking throttle valve	Clean, service and/or replace valve body as required
	No. 10 check ball missing (THM 440-T4)	Inspect valve body and service as required
	Oil Pump Assembly	
	Orifice plugged for converter signal oil in pump	Clean and inspect orifice for blockage
	Solenoid "O" ring damaged or missing	Check and replace "O" ring
	Oil pump wear plate or gasket mispositioned or damaged	Check and replace wear plate or gasket
	Improper torque on oil pump-to-converter housing bolts	Tighten bolts to specifications
	Turbine shaft seals damaged	Check and replace seals
	Orifice cup plug omitted from cooler in passage	Check and install plug
	Channel Plate (THM 440-T4)	Check and replace converter clutch blow-off check ball if not seated or if damaged; Check and replace torque converter clutch accumulator piston or seal if damaged
Converter Clutch Apply Rough, Slipping, or Shudders	Converter clutch pressure plate faulty	Check plate for damage and service as required
	Damaged or missing check ball in end of turbine shaft	Check and replace turbine shaft, if required
	Converter clutch regulator valve stuck	Clean, service and/or replace valve body as required
	Converter clutch accumulator piston or seal damaged	Check and service as required
	Channel plate spring damaged (THM 440-T4)	Replace channel plate
	Incorrect converter clutch blow-off spring installed (THM 440-T4)	Check and install correct spring

GENERAL MOTORS CONVERTER CLUTCH TROUBLE SHOOTING (Cont.)

CONDITION	POSSIBLE CAUSE	CORRECTION
Converter Clutch Apply Rough, Slipping, or Shudders (Cont.)	Channel plate seals damaged or missing	Check and service as required
	Turbine shaft seals damaged or missing (THM 440-T4)	Check and replace turbine shaft seals or shaft
Converter Clutch Does Not Release	Solenoid does not exhaust	Verify Electronic Control Module operation (vehicles with Computer Command Control)
	Converter clutch apply valve stuck	Clean, service and/or replace valve body as required
	Check damaged converter	Replace torque converter
	Cup plug missing from pump release passage	Check and replace plug or pump assembly
	Turbine shaft end seal damaged or missing	Check and replace end seal or turbine shaft as required
	Hole not drilled through turbine shaft	Replace turbine shaft

GENERAL MOTORS THM 125C TROUBLE SHOOTING

Every diagnosis of automatic transmission problems should begin with a check of the transmission fluid and linkage. Most of the following conditions can be caused by one or more of the following factors: (1) Incorrect fluid level, (2) Contaminated fluid, (3) Improperly adjusted linkage, or (4) Damaged or worn linkage.

CONDITION	POSSIBLE CAUSE	CORRECTION
Delayed, Full Throttle, or No Upshifts	Improper fluid level	Check fluid level; See GENERAL SERVICING
	Manual linkage out of adjustment	Check and adjust linkage; see GENERAL SERVICING
	T.V. cable out of adjustment, damaged or sticking	Check and adjust or service as required; see GENERAL SERVICING
	Governor	
	Cover worn	Replace cover or governor as required
	Thrust washer omitted	Check and install thrust washer
	Governor seal worn or cut	Check and replace seal or governor assembly
	Spring not seated	Service as required
	Weights binding	Service as required
	Check ball missing	Install check ball
	Intermediate Servo	
	Wrong apply pin installed	Check and replace apply pin
	Seals cut, damaged, or leaking	Replace seals as required
	Piston damaged	Replace piston or intermediate servo as required
	Porosity in case bore area	Check and replace case
	Piston or apply pin sticking	Clean and service as required

GENERAL MOTORS THM 125C TROUBLE SHOOTING (Cont.)

CONDITION	POSSIBLE CAUSE	CORRECTION
Delayed, Full Throttle, or No Upshifts (Cont.)	Valve Body	
	Contains sticking valves	Clean, inspect and replace valve body as required
	Spacer plate gaskets leaking or incorrectly installed	Check and replace gaskets
	Valve body-to-case spacer plate clearance misadjusted	Check and adjust clearance as required
	Restricted feed orifice to 1-2 and 2-3 valves, and Drive to governor	Clean and clear obstruction; Service as required
	Intermediate band burnt or worn	Replace transmission
	Porous case cover, undrilled holes or missing plugs	Check and replace as required
	Leaks in governor passages and/or pipe in case cover	Perform pressure test and replace as required
	Case or case cover 2nd oil passage leaking	Check and service as required
	Driven gear stripped	Replace driven gear
1-2 Shift Complaint	Improper fluid level	Check fluid level; See GENERAL SERVICING
	T.V. cable out of adjustment, damaged or sticking	Check and adjust or service as required; see GENERAL SERVICING
	Oil pressure too high or too low	Perform OIL PRESSURE test and service as required
	Intermediate Servo	
	Seals cut, damaged, or leaking	Replace seals as required
	Piston damaged	Replace piston or intermediate servo as required
	Porosity in case bore	Check and replace case
	Servo orifice bleed cup plug missing	Check and install plug
	Leak between servo apply pin and case	Clean and service as required
	Wrong intermediate apply pin installed	Check and replace apply pin
	Band apply pin binds in case	Clean and service as required
	Valve Body	
	Contains sticking valves	Clean, inspect and replace valve body as required
	T.V. plunger, shift T.V. valve, or 1-2 accumulator valve binding	Service and replace as required
	1-2 accumulator piston binding, spring broken or missing, piston seal damaged, or piston bore damaged	Service as required
	Spacer plate gaskets leaking or incorrectly installed	Check and replace gaskets
	Case or case cover 2nd or servo apply oil passages leaking	Check and service as required
	Case or case cover 1-2 accumulator oil passage leaking	Check and service as required
	Intermediate band burnt	Check cause of condition; Service transmission
	Case cover bolts improperly tightened	Tighten bolts to specification
2-3 Shift Complaint	Improper fluid level	Check fluid level; See GENERAL SERVICING
	T.V. cable out of adjustment, damaged or sticking	Check and adjust or service as required; see GENERAL SERVICING

Automatic Transmissions

GENERAL MOTORS THM 125C TROUBLE SHOOTING (Cont.)

CONDITION	POSSIBLE CAUSE	CORRECTION
2-3 Shift Complaint (Cont.)	Manual linkage out of adjustment	Check and adjust linkage; see GENERAL SERVICING
	Oil pressure too high or too low	Perform OIL PRESSURE test and service as required
	Direct Clutch	
	Feed orifice in spacer plate restricted	Clear obstruction; Service as required
	Direct clutch check ball or capsule leaking	Service as required
	Accumulator exhaust hole plugged or not drilled	Clear obstruction; Service as required
	Exhaust valve check ball No. 1 missing, out of place, or leaking	Check position and seal of check ball; Service as required
	Accumulator exhaust check valve not seating in case	Check cause of condition; Service as required
	Piston seals missing or damaged	Service as required
	Direct clutch piston or housing cracked or damaged	Service as required
	Direct clutch apply ring missing or incorrect	Service direct clutch assembly
	Incorrect number of clutch plates	Install correct number of clutch plates
	Porosity in direct clutch case cover passages or incorrect case cover gaskets	Check porosity and gasket installation; Service as required
	Intermediate Servo	
	Piston-to-case oil seal ring missing or damaged	Replace seal as required
	Piston or case servo bore damaged	Service and repair or replace as required
	Orifice plug missing from case in servo bore area	Check and install plug
	Valve Body	
	Throttle valve and plunger, or shift T.V. valve binding	Clean and service as required
	Spacer plate gaskets leaking or incorrectly installed	Check and replace gaskets
	Valve body-to-case spacer plate clearance misadjusted	Check and adjust clearance as required
	Case cover check ball No. 5 not seating	Clean and clear obstruction; Service as required
	Driven Sprocket	
	Support passages interconnected, leaking, or restricted	Check passages; Service as required
	Support oil seal rings damaged or missing	Check seal rings; Service as required
	Sleeve loose or out of position	Check and correctly install sleeve
No or Delayed 2-3 Upshift – 1-2 OK	Improper fluid level	Check fluid level; See GENERAL SERVICING
	T.V. cable out of adjustment, damaged or sticking	Check and adjust or service as required; see GENERAL SERVICING
	Manual linkage out of adjustment	Check and adjust linkage; see GENERAL SERVICING

GENERAL MOTORS THM 125C TROUBLE SHOOTING (Cont.)

CONDITION	POSSIBLE CAUSE	CORRECTION
No or Delayed 2-3 Upshift - 1-2 OK (Cont.)	Case cover bolts loose, or center gasket leaking	Tighten bolts to specification; Replace gasket
	Case no. 5 case check ball missing or improperly seated	Service as required
	Governor	
	Cover worn	Replace governor assembly
	Thrust washer missing	Install thrust washer
	Seal worn or cut	Replace seal or governor assembly
	Spring not seated	Clean and properly seat or replace spring
	Weights binding	Correct cause of condition; Service as required
	Driven gear stripped or loose	Service as required
	Intermediate Servo	
	Piston-to-case oil seal ring missing or damaged	Replace seal as required
	Piston or case servo bore damaged	Service and repair or replace as required
	Orifice bleed plug missing from case	Check and install plug
	Direct clutch accumulator cup plug (in case) leaking or missing	Check or replace cup plug
	Porosity in case bore area	Check and replace case
	Accumulator exhaust check valve not seating in case	Check cause of condition; Service as required
	Valve Body	
	Valve body and spacer plate 2-3 shift, 2-3 T.V., or shift T.V. valves sticking	Clean and service as required
	Governor feed to 2-3 valve or direct clutch feed orifices restricted	Clean and clear obstruction; Service as required
	Spacer plate or gaskets leaking or incorrectly installed	Check and replace gaskets or spacer plate
	Case cover check ball No. 5 not seating	Clean and clear obstruction; Service as required
	Case-to-governor shaft sleeve damaged or missing	Service sleeve as required
	Direct Clutch	
	Piston seals missing or damaged	Service as required
	Piston or housing cracked	Service as required
	Clutch plates damaged or missing	Replace clutch plates
	Backing plate snap ring not seated in groove	Install snap ring properly
	Check ball capsule damaged or leaking	Service as required
	Driven Sprocket	
	Support passages interconnected, leaking, or restricted	Check passages; Service as required
	Support oil seal rings damaged or missing	Check seal rings; Service as required
	Sleeve loose or out of position	Check and correctly install sleeve
Delay in Drive & Reverse	Improper line pressures	Perform LINE PRESSURE tests; Service as required
	Converter drainback (noted by 3-5 second delay in "D" and "R" with engine off for 1 hour or longer)	Check and replace converter
	Turbine shaft Teflon seals damaged	Replace turbine shaft or seals; Replace scarf-cut seals with solid seals

GENERAL MOTORS THM 125C TROUBLE SHOOTING (Cont.)

CONDITION	POSSIBLE CAUSE	CORRECTION
No Drive in "D" or Intermediate Range (Lo & Reverse OK)	Lo roller clutch not holding	Service as required
No Drive in Forward Gears (Reverse Ties Up)	Sleeve turned in driven sprocket support	Service as required
No Drive Forward or Reverse in Any Gear	Pulls Engine Down	
	Internal mechanical damage	Disassemble and inspect components; Service as required
	Differential broken up	Disassemble and inspect components; Service as required
	Link and/or sprocket faulty	Check link and sprocket assembly for obstruction and alignment; Service as required
	Acts Like Neutral	
	Improper fluid level	Check fluid level; See GENERAL SERVICING
	Converter-to-flex plate bolts	Ensure all bolts are present and properly tightened
	Improper line pressures	Perform LINE PRESSURE tests; Service as required
	Manual linkage not moving manual valve	Service internal and external linkage as required
	Input shaft broken away from forward clutch drum	Inspect and service as required
	Reaction carrier broken at lo roller clutch cam	Inspect and service as required
	Chain assembly broken	Inspect and replace chain assembly
	Pressure regulator valve sticking	Clean and inspect regulator valve
	Worn pump seals	Replace seals
	Clutch plates burnt or worn	Check and replace clutch plates
	Broken oil pump shaft	Inspect and replace oil pump
No Drive in "D" (Reverse, Lo & Intermediate OK)	Improper fluid level	Check fluid level; See GENERAL SERVICING
	Forward clutch feed in input shaft restricted (if problem occurs only with cold engine or at fast engine idle)	Inspect and service as required
	Leak between case cover and driven sprocket support passages (if problem acts like Neutral or slips)	Replace gaskets
No Drive in Any Forward Gear (Reverse OK)	Improper line pressures	Perform LINE PRESSURE tests; Service as required
	Manual linkage not moving manual valve	Service internal and external linkage as required
	Drive oil passage in driven sprocket support or driven sprocket support-to-case cover gasket restricted	Check and replace gasket
	Drive oil passage leak in case cover	Check and replace case cover
	Sleeve in driven sprocket support loose or mislocated	Replace sleeve or sprocket support
	Forward clutch burnt	Determine cause and replace clutch
	Valve body pipe in control valve pump assembly leaking or missing	Replace pump assembly

GENERAL MOTORS THM 125C TROUBLE SHOOTING (Cont.)

CONDITION	POSSIBLE CAUSE	CORRECTION
No Reverse (All Forward Gears OK)	Forward clutch will not release	Replace clutch plates if burnt; Replace piston seal ring; Clean exhaust check ball
	Improper line pressures	Perform LINE PRESSURE tests; Service as required
	Case-to-lo and reverse clutch housing cup plug assembly restricted or not fully seated	Replace plug assembly
	Lo and reverse clutch seals or piston leaks	Perform AIR PRESSURE test; Service as required
	Lo and reverse pipe "O" ring or washer damaged or missing	Replace "O" ring, washer of pipe as required
	Incorrect gasket for driven sprocket support height	Replace gasket
	Case cover leaking or damaged	Replace gasket or cover
	Plugged or missing lo 1st orifice in spacer plate	Clear obstruction or replace spacer plate
	Direct clutch or lo and reverse clutch burnt	Determine cause and replace clutch
Starts Up in 2nd, Misses 1st at Times	Governor springs distorted or out of place	Replace governor assembly
	Governor weights binding	Determine cause of condition and service as required
	1-2 shift valve or 1-2 throttle valve sticking in upshift position	Clean and inspect valve body; Service as required
Shifts 3-1 at High Speeds for Passing Gear (Detent Downshifts)	Governor faulty	Check and replace governor assembly
	Intermediate servo sticking	Clean and inspect servo; Service as required
	Direct clutch orifice controlled by No. 2 check ball restricted	Clear obstruction; Service as required
	1-2 accumulator piston missing, or seal leaking	Inspect and replace piston assembly
Slips, Chatters in 1st Gear	Improper fluid level	Check fluid level; See GENERAL SERVICING
	Improper line pressures	Perform LINE PRESSURE tests; Service as required
	T.V. cable out of adjustment, damaged or sticking	Check and adjust or service as required; see GENERAL SERVICING
	Restricted feed to forward clutch	Clear obstruction and service as required
	Forward clutch burnt	Determine cause of condition; Service as required
	Rough machine surface on driven sprocket support	Service as required
	Incorrect case cover gaskets	Install correct gaskets
Shifts 1-3	Intermediate servo sticking, leaking, or damaged	Service intermediate servo as required
	Accumulator exhaust check valve sticking, or not seating	Service check valve as required
	1-2 valve sticking in control valve pump assembly	Clean and service as required
	Spacer plate gaskets incorrectly installed	Replace gaskets

GENERAL MOTORS THM 125C TROUBLE SHOOTING (Cont.)

CONDITION	POSSIBLE CAUSE	CORRECTION
Shifts 1-3 (Cont.)	Governor feed to 1-2 valve in spacer plate blocked	Clean and clear obstruction; Replace spacer plate
	Spacer plate intermediate band apply feed orifice blocked	Clean and clear obstruction; Replace spacer plate
	Wrong spacer installed	Check and replace spacer plate
	Intermediate servo apply passage (2nd oil passage) in case or case cover blocked	Clean and clear obstruction; Replace case or case cover
	Intermediate band improperly installed, burnt or broken	Service intermediate band as required
No Full Throttle (Detent) Downshift 3-2	T.V. cable out of adjustment, damaged or sticking	Check and adjust or service as required; see GENERAL SERVICING
	Accelerator pedal and/or linkage will not open carburetor to wide open throttle	Service control linkage as required
	Control valve pump assembly shift T.V. valve or throttle valve binding	Clean and service as required
	Spacer plate holes plugged (gaskets mispositioned or damaged)	Check and replace gasket or spacer plate
No 2nd Gear	Servo oil seal ring missing or damage	Replace servo oil seal ring
	Intermediate band out of position, broken or burnt	Determine cause of condition; Service as required
	1-2 accumulator piston or pin damaged or missing	Replace accumulator piston assembly
No Overrun Braking in Lo (Reverse OK)	Manual linkage out of adjustment	Check and adjust manual linkage; See GENERAL SERVICING
	Lo-Reverse pipe or Lo-Reverse piston seals leaking	Service as required
	Lo blow-off valve assembly damaged	Service as required
	TRANSAXLE NOISY	
Park, Neutral & All Drive Ranges	Pump Cavitation	
	Improper fluid level	Check fluid level; See GENERAL SERVICING
	Damaged "O" ring seal	Replace seal
	Porosity in case intake area	Check for porosity; Service as required
	Water in oil	Determine cause; Service as required
	Drive Link Assembly	
	Rubbing on case	Inspect and service as required
	Pump or driven sprocket needle bearing improperly installed	Check installation; Service as required
	Converter	
	Loose converter-to-flex plate bolts	Tighten bolts to specification
	Cracked or broken flex plate	Check and replace flex plate
	Converter damaged	Replace converter

GENERAL MOTORS THM 125C TROUBLE SHOOTING (Cont.)

CONDITION	POSSIBLE CAUSE	CORRECTION
	TRANSAXLE NOISY (Cont.)	
During Acceleration – Any Gear	Transmission cooler lines grounded to underbody	Service as required
	Sprocket support needle bearings worn or damaged	Check installation; Service as required
	Drive link assembly worn or damaged	Replace drive link assembly
Squeal at Low Vehicle Speeds (Hot)	Speedometer driven gear shaft seal faulty or needs lubrication	Lubricate or replace shaft seal
	Speedometer adapter too long	Replace speedometer adapter
1st & Reverse Gears Only	Worn or damaged input gear set	Inspect and replace gear set
	Worn or damaged reaction gear set	Inspect and replace gear set
	Worn or damaged final drive gear set	Inspect and replace gear set
	Worn or damaged differential gear set	Inspect and replace gear set
	Worn or damaged planetary gear set	Inspect and replace gear set
2nd Gear Only	Worn or damaged input gear set	Inspect and replace gear set
	Worn or damaged final drive gear set	Inspect and replace gear set
	Worn or damaged differential gear set	Inspect and replace gear set
	Worn or damaged planetary gear set	Inspect and replace gear set
3rd Gear Only and/or on Turns	Worn or damaged final drive gear set	Inspect and replace gear set
	Worn or damaged differential gear set	Inspect and replace gear set
	Worn or damaged planetary gear set	Inspect and replace gear set

GENERAL MOTORS THM 180C TROUBLE SHOOTING

Every diagnosis of automatic transmission problems should begin with a check of the transmission fluid and linkage. Most of the following conditions can be caused by one or more of the following factors: (1) Incorrect fluid level, (2) Contaminated fluid, (3) Improperly adjusted linkage, or (4) Damaged or worn linkage.

CONDITION	POSSIBLE CAUSE	CORRECTION
No Drive in Any Drive Range	Improper fluid level	Check fluid level; See GENERAL SERVICING
	Blocked suction screen	Clean screen
	Manual valve linkage or inner transmission selector lever disconnected	Service as required
	Input shaft broken	Replace input shaft assembly
	Pressure regulator valve stuck open	Clean and service as required
	Oil pump faulty	Replace oil pump
Delayed Drive in Any Drive Range (Possible After Repeat Selector Movement)	Manual Valve Position Does Not Coincide With Valve Body Channels	
	Selector shaft retaining pin missing	Replace retaining pin
	Connecting rod to manual valve loose	Repair or replace rod
	Selector lever shaft nut loose	Tighten nut

Automatic Transmissions

GENERAL MOTORS THM 180C TROUBLE SHOOTING (Cont.)

CONDITION	POSSIBLE CAUSE	CORRECTION
No Drive After Shifting from "P" to "D", "L_2" or "L_1" (Inadequate Engine Acceleration	Parking Pawl Does Not Disengage	Service as required
Sudden Drive Only After Increase of Engine RPM	Band servo piston jamming	Determine cause and service as required
	Improper fluid level	Check fluid level; See GENERAL SERVICING
	Oil pump faulty	Replace oil pump
	Oil screen missing	Replace screen
	Sealing ball in valve body missing	Replace ball
Heavy Jerking When Starting	Incorrect oil pressure	Perform PRESSURE test; Service as required
	Wrong modulator valve	Inspect and install correct valve
	Pressure regulator valve stuck	Determine cause; Service as required
	Sealing ball in valve body missing	Replace ball
No Drive in "D" or "L_2" ("L_1" & "R" OK)	Input sprag faulty or installed backward	Check and properly install or replace sprag
No Drive in "D" or "L_2" & "L_1" ("R" OK)	Band worn, does not grip	Replace band
	Band servo piston jamming	Determine cause; Service as required
	Excessive leak in band servo	Service as required
	Parking pawl does not disengage	Service as required
No Drive in "R" (All Others OK)	Reverse clutch failure	Replace clutch assembly
Drives in Neutral	Inadequate selector lever linkage	Replace linkage
	Planetary gear set broken	Replace planetary gear set
	Improper band adjustment	Adjust band; See GENERAL SERVICING
No 1-2 Upshift in "D" and "L_2" (Transmission Remains in 1st)	Governor valves stuck	Clean and free valves; Service as required
	1-2 shift valve stuck in 1st gear position	Clean and free valve; Service as required
	Oil pump hub seal rings leaking	Replace seal rings or oil pump hub
	Leak in governor pressure circuit	Perform PRESSURE test; Service as required
	Governor screen blocked	Clear blockage
No 2-3 Upshift in "D" (Transmission Remains in 2nd)	2-3 shift valve stuck	Clean and free valve; Service as required
	Leak in governor pressure circuit	Perform PRESSURE test; Service as required
Upshifts in "D" & "L_2" Only at Full Throttle	Faulty vacuum modulator	Replace vacuum modulator
	Leak or block in modulator vacuum line	Determine cause and service as required
	Engine vacuum leaks	Service as required
	Detent valve or cable stuck	Service as required
Upshifts in "D" & "L_2" Only at Part Throttle (No Detent Position)	Detent pressure regulator valve stuck	Clean and free valve; Service as required
	Detent cable broken or misadjusted	Check and adjust, or replace cable
Drive Only in 1st Gear of "D" & "L_2" (Blocks in 2nd & "R")	"L_1" and "R" control valve stuck in "L_1" or "R"	Clean and free valves; Service as required

GENERAL MOTORS THM 180C TROUBLE SHOOTING (Cont.)

CONDITION	POSSIBLE CAUSE	CORRECTION
No Part Throttle 3-2 Downshift at Low Speeds	3-2 downshift control valve stuck	Clean and free valve; Service as required
No Forced Downshift	Detent cable broken or misadjusted	Check and adjust, or replace cable
	Detent pressure regulator valve stuck	Clean and free valve; Service as required
After Full Throttle Upshift, Transmission Shifts to Lower Gear When Foot Eases Off Accelerator Pedal	Detent valve stuck in open position	Clean and free valve; Service as required
	Detent cable stuck	Service as required
	Leak or block in modulator vacuum line	Determine cause and service as required
At Higher Speed, Transmission Shifts to Lower Gear	Selector lever shaft retaining pin in transmission dropped out	Replace pin
	Loose selector lever linkage to manual valve	Tighten or replace linkage
	Pressure loss at governor	Perform PRESSURE test; Service as required
Hard Disengagement of Lever From "P"	Steel guide bushing of parking pawl actuating rod missing	Check and replace guide bushing
	Manual selector valve stuck	Clean and free valve; Service as required
Slipping 1-2 Upshift (Engine Flares)	Improper fluid level	Check fluid level; See GENERAL SERVICING
	Valve body sealing ball dropped out	Replace sealing ball
	Second clutch piston seals leaking	Service as required
	Second clutch centrifugal ball stuck open	Clean and free ball; Service as required
	Second clutch piston cracked or broken	Replace piston assembly
	Second clutch plates worn	Replace plates
	Oil pump hub seal rings leaking	Replace seal rings or oil pump hub
Slipping 2-3 Upshift (Engine Flares)	Improper fluid level	Check fluid level; See GENERAL SERVICING
	Band adjustment loose	Adjust band
	Third clutch piston seals leaking	Service as required
	Third clutch centrifugal ball stuck open	Clean and free ball; Service as required
	Third clutch piston cracked or broken	Replace piston assembly
	Input shaft bearing worn	Replace input shaft bearing
	Valve body sealing ball dropped out	Replace sealing ball
Abrupt 1-2 Upshift	High oil pressure	Perform PRESSURE test; Service as required
	1-2 accumulator valve stuck	Clean and free valve; Service as required
	Broke second clutch spring cushion	Service as required
	Second gear ball valve missing	Replace valve
Abrupt 2-3 Upshift	High oil pressure	Perform PRESSURE test; Service as required
	Incorrect band adjustment	Check and adjust band
Abrupt 3-2 Detent Downshift at High Speed	High speed downshift valve stuck open	Clean and free valve; Service as required
	Incorrect band adjustment	Check and adjust band
Abrupt 3-2 Coast Downshift	Low speed downshift timing valve stuck open	Clean and free valve; Service as required

GENERAL MOTORS THM 180C TROUBLE SHOOTING (Cont.)

CONDITION	POSSIBLE CAUSE	CORRECTION
Flare on High Speed Forced Downshift	Low oil pressure	Perform PRESSURE test; Service as required
	Incorrect band adjustment	Check and adjust band
Flare on Low Speed Forced Downshift	Low oil pressure	Perform PRESSURE test; Service as required
	Incorrect band adjustment	Check and adjust band
	High speed downshift timing valve stuck closed	Clean and free valve; Service as required
	Sprag race does not grip on 3-1 downshifting	Determine cause of condition; Service as required
No Engine Braking in "L_1"	Selector lever linkage improperly adjusted	Adjust linkage
	Manual low control valve stuck	Clean and free valve; Service as required
No Engine Braking in "L_2"	Selector lever linkage improperly adjusted	Adjust linkage
No Park	Selector lever linkage improperly adjusted	Adjust linkage
	Parking lock actuator spring	Check and replace spring
	Parking pawl	Check and replace pawl
	Governor hub	Check and replace governor assembly
	TRANSMISSION NOISY	
Excessive Noise in All Drive Ranges	Too much backlash between sun gear and planetary gear	Check backlash; Service as required
	Lock plate on planetary carrier loose	Tighten or replace plate or planetary gear set
	Defective thrust bearing	Replace thrust bearing
	Bearing bushings worn	Replace bearing assembly
	Excessive transmission axial play	Determine cause of condition; Service as required
	Unhooked parking pawl spring contacts governor hub	Service as required
	Converter balancing weights loose	Replace converter
	Converter housing attaching bolt loose and contacting converter	Check for damage; Service as required
Screeching Noise When Starting	Converter failure	Determine cause of condition; Replace converter
Short Vibrating, Hissing Noise Shortly Before 1-2 Upshift	Dampening cushion of reverse clutch wearing into transmission case	Determine cause of condition; Service as required
Buzzing Noise	Clogged oil filter	Replace oil filter and gasket

GENERAL MOTORS THM 200C TROUBLE SHOOTING

Every diagnosis of automatic transmission problems should begin with a check of the transmission fluid and linkage. Most of the following conditions can be caused by one or more of the following factors: (1) Incorrect fluid level, (2) Contaminated fluid, (3) Improperly adjusted linkage, or (4) Damaged or worn linkage.

CONDITION	POSSIBLE CAUSE	CORRECTION
No Drive in "D"	Improper fluid level	Check fluid level; See GENERAL SERVICING
	Manual linkage misadjusted	Adjust linkage; See GENERAL SERVICING
	Low oil pressure	Perform PRESSURE test; Service as required
	Forward clutch	
	Does not apply	Check piston for cracks and/or damaged or missing seals
	Burnt clutch plates	Determine cause of condition; Service as required
	Snap ring out of groove	Check and correctly install
	Oil seal rings missing or damaged on turbine shaft	Check and replace seal rings or turbine shaft
	Leak in feed circuits	Clean and check circuits; Service as required
	Pump-to-case gasket mispositioned or damaged	Replace gasket
	Clutch housing check ball stuck or missing	Clean and free ball; Service as required
	Cup plug leaking or missing in rear of turbine shaft in clutch apply passage	Check and replace cup plug
	Wrong forward clutch piston assembly	Check and replace piston assembly
	Wrong number of clutch plates	Verify number of plates; Service as required
	Turbine shaft feed orifice plugged	Clean and clear obstruction; Service as required
	Roller Clutch	
	Springs missing	Replace roller clutch
	Rollers galled or missing	Service as required
1-2 Shift at Full Throttle Only	Throttle valve cable binding, unhooked, broken or misadjusted	Service as required
	Throttle lever and bracket assembly binding or unhooked	Service as required
	T.V. exhaust ball lifter or No. 5 ball binding, mispositioned, or unhooked (Allowing No. 5 ball to seat causes full T.V. pressure regardless of throttle valve position)	Service as required
	Throttle valve and plunger binding	Clean and free valve and plunger; Service as required
	Valve body assembly gaskets leaking, damaged, incorrectly installed	Service as required
1st Only, No 1-2 Upshift	Governor and Governor Feed Passages	
	Plugged governor oil feed orifice in spacer plate	Clear obstruction; Service as required
	Plugged governor oil-to-shift valve passage in spacer plate	Clear obstruction; Service as required
	Governor ball(s) missing	Replace governor assembly
	Inner governor cover "O" ring seal missing or leaking	Replace seal (If outer "O" ring seal leaks, leak will be present with no upshifts)
	Governor shaft seal missing or damaged	Replace seal
	Governor weights binding on pin	Replace governor

GENERAL MOTORS THM 200C TROUBLE SHOOTING (Cont.)

CONDITION	POSSIBLE CAUSE	CORRECTION
1st Only, No 1-2 Upshift (Cont.)	Case	
	Porosity in channels or undrilled 2nd speed feed holes	Service as required
	Excessive leakage between case bore and intermediate band apply ring	Service as required
	Intermediate band anchor pin missing or unhooked from band	Replace anchor pin
	Broken or missing band	Service as required
	Intermediate Servo Assembly	
	Servo-to-cover oil seal ring missing or damaged	Replace oil seal
	Porosity in cover or piston	Service as required
	Wrong intermediate band apply pin	Replace pin
	Incorrect usage of cover and pin	Service as required
	1-2 shift valve or 1-2 throttle valve in valve body stuck in downshift position	Clean and free valve; Service as required
1st & 2nd Only, No 2-3 Shift	Valve Body and Spacer Plate	
	2-3 shift valve or 2-3 throttle valve stuck in downshift position	Clean and free valve; Service as required
	Direct clutch feed orifice in spacer plate plugged	Clean and clear obstruction; Service as required
	Valve body gaskets leaking, damaged or incorrectly installed	Replace gasket
	Pump	
	Channels plugged or leaking	Clean and clear obstruction; Service as required
	Pump-to-case gasket mislocated	Replace gasket
	Rear oil seal ring leaking or missing	Replace oil seal ring
	Direct Clutch	
	Oil seals missing or damaged on piston	Replace oil seals
	Piston or housing cracked	Service as required
	Plates damaged or missing	Replace plates
	Backing plate snap ring out of groove	Install or replace snap ring
	Intermediate Servo Assembly	
	Servo-to-case oil seal ring broken or missing on piston	Replace intermediate servo piston
	Exhaust hole in case between piston seal rings plugged or undrilled	Service as required
	Porosity in case channels	Service as required

GENERAL MOTORS THM 200C TROUBLE SHOOTING (Cont.)

CONDITION	POSSIBLE CAUSE	CORRECTION
Drive in Neutral (Creeps)	Manual linkage misadjusted or disconnected	Adjust or service as required; See GENERAL SERVICING
	Forward clutch does not release	Determine cause of condition; Service as required
	Cross leakage in pump passages	Determine cause of condition; Service as required
	Cross leakage to forward clutch passages in case	Determine cause of condition; Service as required
No Drive or Slips in Reverse	Throttle valve cable binding or misadjusted	Adjust or service as required; See GENERAL SERVICING
	Manual linkage misadjusted	Adjust linkage; See GENERAL SERVICING
	Throttle valve binding	Clean and service as required
	Shift T.V. valve binding in valve body bore	Clean and service as required
	Reverse boost valve binding in valve body bore	Clean and service as required
	Low overrun clutch valve binding in valve body bore (Line pressure readings normal)	Clean and service as required
	Reverse clutch piston cracked, broken, or seals missing	Service as required
	Reverse clutch plates burnt	Determine cause of condition; Service as required
	Reverse clutch has wrong selective spacer ring	Inspect and determine correct spacer ring; Service as required
	Direct Clutch Passages	
	Porosity in case passages	Service as required
	Pump case-to-pump gasket faulty	Check gasket for correct positioning and damage; Replace gasket
	Pump channels leaking or restricted	Determine condition and service as required
	Pump cover oil seal rings faulty	Check for presence of rings and condition; Replace oil seal rings
	Piston or housing cracked	Replace piston or housing
	Piston seals cut or missing	Replace piston seals
	Housing check ball faulty	Inspect check ball for sticking, leaking, or missing; Service as required
	Plates burnt	Determine cause of condition; Service as required
	Incorrect piston	Inspect and replace piston, if required
	Spacer plate orifices plugged	Clean and clear obstruction; Service as required
	Intermediate servo-to-case oil seal ring cut or missing	Check and replace oil seal ring
Slipping 1-2 Shift	Improper fluid level	Check fluid level; See GENERAL SERVICING
	Spacer plate 2nd speed feed orifice partially blocked	Clean and clear obstruction; Service as required
	Spacer plate gaskets damaged or mispositioned	Replace spacer plate gaskets

Automatic Transmissions

GENERAL MOTORS THM 200C TROUBLE SHOOTING (Cont.)

CONDITION	POSSIBLE CAUSE	CORRECTION
Slipping 1-2 Shift (Cont.)	1-2 accumulator valve sticking in valve body	Clean valve; Service as required
	Weak or missing 1-2 accumulator valve spring	Replace valve and spring assembly
	1-2 accumulator piston seal leaking, spring broken or missing	Service as required
	Leak between 1-2 accumulator piston and pin	Determine cause and service as required
	Wrong intermediate band apply pin	Check and determine correct apply pin; Service as required
	Excessive leakage between intermediate band apply pin and case	Determine cause and service as required
	Porosity in intermediate servo piston	Service as required
	Intermediate servo assembly cover-to-servo oil seal ring damaged or missing	Replace oil seal ring
	Incorrect intermediate servo assembly cover and piston	Check and determine correct cover and piston; Service as required
	Throttle valve cable misadjusted	Adjust or service as required; See GENERAL SERVICING
	Throttle valve binding	Clean and service as required
	Shift T.V. valve binding in valve body bore	Clean and service as required
	Intermediate band worn or burnt	Determine cause of condition; Service as required
	Case porosity in 2nd clutch passages	Service as required
Rough 1-2 Shift	Throttle valve cable misadjusted or binding	Adjust or service as required; See GENERAL SERVICING
	Throttle valve binding	Clean and service as required
	Throttle valve plunger binding	Clean and service as required
	Shift T.V. valve binding	Clean and service as required
	1-2 accumulator valve binding	Clean valve; Service as required
	Wrong intermediate servo band apply pin	Check and determine correct apply pin; Service as required
	Intermediate servo piston-to-case oil seal ring damaged or missing	Replace oil seal ring
	1-2 accumulator oil ring damaged	Replace oil ring
	1-2 accumulator piston stuck	Clean and clear piston; Service as required
	1-2 accumulator spring broken or missing	Replace 1-2 accumulator
	1-2 accumulator bore damaged	Service as required
Slipping 2-3 Shift	Improper fluid level	Check fluid level; See GENERAL SERVICING
	Throttle valve cable misadjusted	Adjust as required; See GENERAL SERVICING
	Throttle valve binding	Clean and service as required
	Direct clutch orifice partially blocked in spacer plate	Clean and clear obstruction; Service as required
	Spacer plate gaskets damaged or mispositioned	Replace gaskets
	Intermediate servo-to-case oil seal ring damaged	Determine cause and service as required

GENERAL MOTORS THM 200C TROUBLE SHOOTING (Cont.)

CONDITION	POSSIBLE CAUSE	CORRECTION
Slipping 2-3 Shift (Cont.)	Direct Clutch Feed	
	Porosity in feed channels in case	Service as required
	Pump case-to-pump gasket faulty	Check gasket for correct positioning and damage; Replace gasket
	Pump channels leaking or restricted	Determine condition and service as required
	Pump cover oil seal rings faulty	Check for presence of rings and condition; Replace oil seal rings
	Piston or housing cracked	Replace piston or housing
	Piston seals cut or missing	Replace piston seals
	Plates burnt	Determine cause of condition; Service as required
Rough 2-3 Shift	Throttle valve cable misadjusted or binding	Adjust or service as required; See GENERAL SERVICING
	Throttle valve binding	Clean and service as required
	Throttle valve plunger binding	Clean and service as required
	Shift T.V. valve binding	Clean and service as required
	Exhaust hole undrilled or plugged between intermediate servo piston seals, not allowing piston to complete stroke	Service as required
	Direct clutch exhaust valve check ball No. 4 missing or mispositioned	Replace No. 4 check ball
No Engine Braking in "L2"	Intermediate boost valve binding in valve body	Clean and service as required
	Intermediate reverse check ball (No. 3 check ball) mispositioned or missing	Replace No. 3 check ball
	Shift T.V. check ball (No. 1 check ball) mispositioned or missing	Replace No. 1 check ball
	Intermediate servo assembly cover-to-servo oil seal ring damaged or missing	Replace oil seal ring
	Intermediate band off anchor pin	Service as required
	Intermediate band broken or burnt	Determine cause of condition; Service as required
No Engine Braking in "L1"	Low overrun clutch valve binding in valve body	Clean and service as required
	Low-Reverse clutch assembly worn or damaged	Service as required
No Engine Braking in "L1" With No Reverse	Piston seals broken or missing	Replace seals
	Porosity in piston or housing	Service as required
	Clutch housing snap ring out of case	Replace snap ring
	Cup plug or rubber seal missing or damaged between case and Low-Reverse clutch housing	Service as required
No Part Throttle Downshift	Throttle plunger bushing passages not open	Determine cause of condition; Service as required
	2-3 throttle valve bushing passages not open	Determine cause of condition; Service as required
	Valve body gaskets mispositioned or damaged	Replace valve body gaskets

GENERAL MOTORS THM 200C TROUBLE SHOOTING (Cont.)

CONDITION	POSSIBLE CAUSE	CORRECTION
No Part Throttle Downshift (Cont.)	Spacer plate hole plugged or undrilled	Service as required
	Throttle valve cable improperly set	Adjust or replace; See GENERAL SERVICING
	Shift T.V. valve binding	Clean and free valve; Service as required
	Throttle valve binding	Clean and free valve; Service as required
No Park	Manual linkage misadjusted	Adjust linkage; See GENERAL SERVICING
	Internal linkage parking pawl binding in case or broken	Service as required
	Internal linkage actuator rod or plunger damaged	Service as required
	Internal linkage parking bracket loose or damaged	Service as required
	Inside detent lever and pin assembly nut loose, or lever hole worn or damaged	Service as required
	Manual detent roller and spring assembly bolt loose holding roller assembly to valve body, or pin or roller damaged, mispositioned or missing	Service as required

GENERAL MOTORS THM 200-4R TROUBLE SHOOTING

Every diagnosis of automatic transmission problems should begin with a check of the transmission fluid and linkage. Most of the following conditions can be caused by one or more of the following factors: (1) Incorrect fluid level, (2) Contaminated fluid, (3) Improperly adjusted linkage, or (4) Damaged or worn linkage.

CONDITION	POSSIBLE CAUSE	CORRECTION
No Drive in "D"	Improper fluid level	Check fluid level; See GENERAL SERVICING
	Manual linkage out of adjustment	Check and adjust linkage; see GENERAL SERVICING
	Low oil pressure	
	Plugged or restricted oil filter	Replace oil filter
	Cut or missing oil filter "O" rings	Replace "O" rings or filter
	Pump pressure regulator stuck	Clean and free regulator; Service as required
	Pump rotor tangs damaged by converter	Determine cause of condition; Service as required
	Porosity in filter-to-pump intake bore	Service as required
	Overdrive unit springs missing in roller clutch	Replace roller clutch
	Overdrive unit rollers galled or missing	Replace roller clutch
	Forward Clutch	
	Does not apply – piston cracked; piston seals damaged or missing; clutch plates burnt; snap ring out of groove	Service as required
	Oil seal rings missing or damaged on turbine shaft; leak in feed circuits; pump-to-case gasket mispositioned or damaged	Service as required
	Clutch housing check ball stuck or missing	Replace check ball
	Cup plug leaking or missing in rear of forward clutch shaft in clutch apply passage	Replace cup plug

GENERAL MOTORS THM 200-4R TROUBLE SHOOTING (Cont.)

CONDITION	POSSIBLE CAUSE	CORRECTION
No Drive in "D" (Cont.)	Lo and Reverse roller clutch springs missing in roller clutch	Replace roller clutch
	Lo and Reverse roller clutch rollers galled or missing	Replace roller clutch
1-2 Shift at Full Throttle Only	Throttle valve cable binding, unhooked, broken, or misadjusted	Service as required; See GENERAL SERVICING
	Throttle lever and bracket assembly binding or unhooked	Service as required
	T.V. exhaust ball lifter binding, mispositioned, or unhooked (No. 5 check ball sealing causes full T.V. pressure regardless of throttle valve position)	Service as required
	Throttle valve and plunger binding	Clean and free valve and plunger; Service as required
	Valve body gaskets leaking, damaged, or mispositioned	Replace valve body gaskets
	Porosity in case assembly	Service as required
1st Only – No 1-2 Shift	Governor and Governor Feed Passages	
	Plugged governor oil feed orifice in spacer plate	Clean orifice of blockage
	Governor ball(s) missing	Replace governor assembly
	Governor shaft seal missing or damaged	Replace governor shaft seal
	Governor driven gear stripped	Replace governor assembly
	Governor weights binding on pin	Determine cause of condition; Service as required
	Governor driven gear not engaged with governor shaft	Service as required
	1-2 shift, Lo-1st/Detent, or 1-2 throttle valves stuck in downshift position in valve body	Service as required
	Spacer plate gaskets mispositioned	Replace spacer plate gaskets
	Porosity in case channels or undrilled 2nd oil feed hole in case	Service as required
	Excessive leakage between case bore and intermediate band apply rings	Service as required
	Intermediate band anchor pin missing or unhooked from band	Replace band anchor pin
	Broken or missing intermediate band	Replace intermediate band
	Intermediate servo cover oil seal ring missing	Replace oil seal ring
	Porosity in intermediate servo, cover, inner piston, or outer piston	Service as required
	Wrong intermediate band apply pin	Check and determine correct band apply pin; Service as required
	Incorrect usage of intermediate cover and piston	Check and determine correct cover and piston; Service as required
	1-2 accumulator housing bolts loose, housing face damaged, or damaged or missing accumulator plate	Service as required

GENERAL MOTORS THM 200-4R TROUBLE SHOOTING (Cont.)

CONDITION	POSSIBLE CAUSE	CORRECTION
1st & 2nd Only – No 2-3 Shift	Valve Body and Spacer Plate Assembly	
	2-3 shift or 2-3 throttle valves stuck in downshift position	Clean and free valves; Service as required
	Gaskets leaking, damaged or mispositioned	Replace gaskets
	Reverse/3rd check ball not seating, damaged or missing	Replace Reverse/3rd check ball
	Porosity in case channels	Service as required
	Center support direct clutch feed passage plugged or not drilled	Service as required
	Center support steel oil rings damaged	Replace center support
	Direct Clutch	
	Inner oil seal ring missing or damaged on piston	Replace oil seal or piston
	Center oil seal ring missing or damaged on direct clutch hub	Replace oil seal or clutch
	Check ball and/or retainer damaged or missing from piston	Replace direct clutch piston
	Piston or housing damaged or missing	Service as required
	Plates damaged or missing	Replace plates
	Backing plate snap ring out of groove	Install or replace snap ring
	Release spring guide mislocated	Replace release spring guide
	Intermediate Servo Assembly (3rd Clutch Accumulator Oil Passages)	
	Servo-to-case oil seal ring broken or missing on piston	Replace intermediate servo piston
	Intermediate servo and/or capsule missing or damaged	Replace intermediate servo assembly
	Exhaust hole in case between piston seal rings plugged or undrilled	Service as required
	Bleed orifice cup plug missing from intermediate servo pocket in case	Replace bleed orifice cup plug
No Drive or Slips in "R"	Throttle valve cable binding or misadjusted	Adjust or replace cable; See GENERAL SERVICING
	Manual linkage misadjusted	Adjust manual linkage; See GENERAL SERVICING
	Throttle valve binding	Clean and free valve; Service as required
	T.V. limit valve binding	Clean and free valve; Service as required
	Line bias valve binding	Clean and free valve; Service as required
	Reverse boost valve bind in pressure regulator bore	Clean and free valve; Service as required
	Reverse/3rd or Lo/Reverse check ball missing or spacer plate seat damaged	Replace check ball or spacer plate
	Reverse clutch piston cracked, or missing inner or outer seals	Replace Reverse clutch piston assembly
	Reverse clutch plates burnt	Determine cause of condition; Service as required
	Reverse clutch oil seal in case missing or damaged	Replace oil seal
	Reverse clutch missing clutch or wave plate	Service as required

Automatic Transmissions

GENERAL MOTORS THM 200-4R TROUBLE SHOOTING (Cont.)

CONDITION	POSSIBLE CAUSE	CORRECTION
No Drive or Slips in "R" (Cont.)	Center support attaching bolts loose or missing	Tighten or replace bolts
	Center support passages blocked or holes not drilled	Service as required
	Center support porosity	Replace center support
	Direct clutch piston or housing cracked	Replace piston or housing
	Direct clutch check ball in housing or piston missing or damaged	Replace check ball
	Direct clutch plates burnt	Determine cause of condition; Service as required
	Lo/Reverse overrun clutch orifice in spacer plate plugged	Clean and clear obstruction; Service as required
Drives in Neutral (Creeps)	Manual linkage misadjusted or disconnected	Service or adjust manual linkage; See GENERAL SERVICING
	Forward clutch does not release	Determine cause of condition; Service as required
	Foward clutch exhaust check ball sticking	Clean and free check ball; Service as required
	Forward clutch plates burnt	Determine cause of condition; Service as required
	Cross leakage in case to forward clutch passage	Determine cause of condition; Service as required
Slipping 1-2 Shift	Improper fluid level	Check fluid level; See GENERAL SERVICING
	Spacer plate gaskets damaged or mispositioned	Replace spacer plate gaskets
	Accumulator valve sticking in valve body, or weak or missing spring	Service as required
	1-2 accumulator piston seal leaking	Replace 1-2 accumulator piston assembly
	1-2 accumulator piston spring broken or missing	Replace accumulator piston assembly
	Leak between 1-2 accumulator piston and pin	Determine cause and service as required
	1-2 accumulator piston binding or piston bore damaged	Service as required
	Wrong intermediate band apply pin	Check and determine correct band apply pin; Service as required
	Excessive leakage between intermediate band apply pin and case	Determine cause and service as required
	Intermediate band apply pin feed hole not completely drilled	Service as required
	Porosity in intermediate servo piston	Service as required
	Leak between intermediate servo apply pin and case	Determine cause and service as required
	Throttle valve cable misadjusted	Adjust throttle valve cable; See GENERAL SERVICING
	Throttle valve binding	Clean and free valve; Service as required
	T.V. limit valve sticking	Clean and free valve; Service as required
	Line bias valve binding	Clean and free valve; Service as required
	Intermediate band worn or burnt	Determine cause of condition; Service as required
	Case porosity in 2nd clutch passage	Service as required

GENERAL MOTORS THM 200-4R TROUBLE SHOOTING (Cont.)

CONDITION	POSSIBLE CAUSE	CORRECTION
Rough 1-2 Shift	Throttle valve cable misadjusted or binding	Adjust or service throttle valve cable; See GENERAL SERVICING
	Throttle valve or T.V. plunger binding	Clean and free valve or plunger; Service as required
	T.V. limit valve binding	Clean and free valve; Service as required
	Accumulator valve binding	Clean and free valve; Service as required
	Line bias valve binding	Clean and free valve; Service as required
	Wrong intermediate servo apply pin	Check and determine correct apply pin; Service as required
	Intermediate servo-to-case oil seal ring damaged or missing	Replace oil seal ring
	Bleed orifice cup plug missing from intermediate servo pocket in case	Replace bleed orifice cup plug
	1-2 accumulator piston oil ring damaged	Replace 1-2 accumulator piston assembly
	1-2 accumulator piston spring broken or missing	Replace accumulator piston assembly
	1-2 accumulator piston bore damaged	Service as required
	1-2 shift check ball No. 8 missing or sticking	Service as required
Slipping 2-3 Shift	Improper fluid level	Check fluid level; See GENERAL SERVICING
	Throttle valve cable misadjusted	Adjust throttle valve cable; See GENERAL SERVICING
	Throttle valve binding	Clean and free valve; Service as required
	Spacer plate direct clutch orifice partially blocked	Clean and clear obstruction; Service as required
	Spacer plate gaskets damaged or mispositioned	Replace spacer plate gaskets
	Intermediate servo-to-case oil seal ring damaged or missing	Replace oil seal ring
	Intermediate servo piston or servo bore damaged	Service as required
	Bleed orifice cup plug missing from intermediate servo pocket in case	Replace bleed orifice cup plug
	Porosity in case in servo bore area	Service as required
	Direct Clutch Feed	
	Porosity in feed channels in case	Service as required
	Case-to-support bolts not tight	Tighten bolts to specifications
	Piston or housing cracked	Replace piston or housing
	Piston seals cut or missing	Replace piston seals
	Plates burnt	Determine cause of condition; Service as required
	Check ball in piston and/or housing missing, damaged or leaking	Replace check ball
	Check ball capsule damaged	Replace check ball capsule
	Release spring guide mislocated preventing check ball from seating	Replace release spring guide
	Center support channels cross feeding, leaking or restricted	Determine cause and service as required
	Center support oil seal rings damaged or missing	Replace support oil seal rings

Automatic Transmissions

GENERAL MOTORS THM 200-4R TROUBLE SHOOTING (Cont.)

CONDITION	POSSIBLE CAUSE	CORRECTION
Rough 2-3 Shift	Improper fluid level	Check fluid level; See GENERAL SERVICING
	Throttle valve cable misadjusted or binding	Adjust or service throttle valve cable; See GENERAL SERVICING
	Throttle valve or T.V. plunger binding	Clean and free valve or plunger; Service as required
	T.V. limit valve binding	Clean and free valve; Service as required
	Intermediate servo exhaust hole undrilled or plugged between servo piston seals, not allowing piston to complete stroke	Service as required
	3-2 exhaust check ball No. 4 missing or mispositioned	Replace No. 4 check ball
	3rd accumulator check ball No. 2 missing or mispositioned	Replace No. 2 check ball
Slipping 3-4 Shift	Improper fluid level	Check fluid level; See GENERAL SERVICING
	Spacer plate gaskets or spacer plate damaged or mispositioned	Replace spacer plate gaskets
	Valve body accumulator valve sticking	Clean and free valve; Service as required
	Weak or missing accumulator valve spring in valve body	Replace accumulator valve assembly
	3-4 accumulator piston stuck, bore damaged, or oil ring damaged	Service as required
	Center support porosity	Service as required
	Center support attaching bolts loose	Tighten bolts to specification
	4th clutch piston surface damaged	Determine cause of condition; Service as required
	4th clutch piston seals damaged	Determine cause of condition; Service as required
	Improper 4th clutch plate usage	Replace 4th clutch plates
	4th clutch plates burnt	Determine cause of condition; Service as required
	Case porosity	Service as required
	1-2 accumulator housing bolts loose	Tighten bolts to specification
	3-4 accumulator piston seal damaged	Determine cause of condition; Service as required
	3-4 accumulator leaking between piston and pin	Determine cause of condition; Service as required
	3-4 accumulator bore damaged	Determine cause of condition; Service as required
Rough 3-4 Shift	Throttle valve cable mispositioned or missing	Service or replace throttle valve cable
	Throttle valve plunger or valve binding	Clean and free valve; Service as required
	T.V. limit valve binding	Clean and free valve; Service as required
	3-4 accumulator piston stuck or bore damaged	Service as required
	4th clutch piston binding	Clean and free piston; Service as required
1st, 2nd & 3rd Only – No 3-4 Shift	3-4 shift valve or 3-4 throttle valve stuck in valve body	Clean and free valve; Service as required
	Orifice in spacer plate plugged	Clean and clear obstruction; Service as required

GENERAL MOTORS THM 200-4R TROUBLE SHOOTING (Cont.)

CONDITION	POSSIBLE CAUSE	CORRECTION
1st, 2nd & 3rd Only – No 3-4 Shift (Cont.)	Center support oil passages plugged or not drilled; attaching bolts loose or missing	Service as required
	Center support 4th clutch piston cracked or damaged, or piston seals damaged, missing or improperly assembled	Replace piston or piston seals
	Improper center support plate usage	Check and install proper support plate
	Overrun clutch plates or 4th clutch plates burnt	Determine cause of condition; Service as required
	Case porosity	Replace case
	Orifice cup plug missing in case 3-4 accumulator passage	Replace orifice cup plug
	Leakage between accumulator piston and pin in case	Determine cause and service as required
	3-4 accumulator bore damaged in case	Service as required
No Engine Braking in "L_1"	Valve Body and Spacer Plate	
	Manual linkage out of adjustment	Adjust linkage; See GENERAL SERVICING
	Spacer plate orifice D3 plugged	Clean and clear obstruction; Service as required
	Gaskets leaking, damaged or improperly installed	Replace gaskets
	D2 oil pipe leaking or out of position	Replace D2 oil pipe
	Lo overrun clutch valve binding	Clean and free valve; Service as required
	Lo-Reverse check ball (No. 10) or Lo-Detent check ball (No. 9) mispositioned or missing	Replace No. 9 or No. 10 check ball
	Lo-Reverse overrun clutch orifice in spacer plate plugged	Clean and clear obstruction; Service as required
	Part throttle D3 check ball (No. 3) mispositioned or missing	Replace No. 3 check ball
	Turbine Shaft and Overrun Clutch (Also Cause No "L_3" or "L_2")	
	D3 oil passage not drilled in turbine shaft or overrun clutch hub, or plugged in turbine shaft	Service as required
	Oil seals missing or damaged in clutch piston	Replace oil seals
	Clutch plates burnt	Determine cause of condition; Service as required
	Clutch backing plate snap ring out of groove	Replace snap ring
	Case porosity	Replace case
	Lo-Reverse Clutch Assembly (Also Cause No "R")	
	Piston seals broken or missing	Replace piston seals
	Clutch housing snap ring out of case	Replace snap ring
	Piston or housing cracked or porous	Replace piston or housing
	Cup plug or rubber seal missing or damaged between case and clutch housing	Replace cup plug or rubber seal
No Engine Braking in "L_2"	Valve Body and Spacer Plate	
	Manual linkage out of adjustment	Adjust linkage; See GENERAL SERVICING
	Gaskets leaking, damaged or improperly installed	Replace gaskets

GENERAL MOTORS THM 200-4R TROUBLE SHOOTING (Cont.)

CONDITION	POSSIBLE CAUSE	CORRECTION
No Engine Braking in "L_2" (Cont.)	Valve Body and Spacer Plate (Cont.)	
	D2 oil pipe leaking or out of position	Replace D2 oil pipe
	Spacer plate orifice D3 plugged	Clean and clear obstruction; Service as required
	Part throttle D3 check ball (No. 3) mispositioned or missing	Replace No. 3 check ball
	Case porosity	Replace case
	Intermediate servo cover-to-case oil seal ring missing or damaged	Replace cover-to-case oil seal ring
	Intermediate band off anchor pin, broken, or burnt	Determine cause of condition; Service as required
	Turbine Shaft and Overrun Clutch	
	D3 oil passage not drilled in turbine shaft or overrun clutch hub, or plugged in turbine shaft	Service as required
	Oil seals missing or damaged in clutch piston	Replace oil seals
	Clutch plates burnt	Determine cause of condition; Service as required
	Clutch backing plate snap ring out of groove	Replace snap ring
No Engine Braking in "L_3"	Valve Body and Spacer Plate	
	Manual linkage out of adjustment	Adjust linkage; See GENERAL SERVICING
	Spacer plate orifice D3 plugged	Clean and clear obstruction; Service as required
	Gaskets leaking, damaged or improperly installed	Replace gaskets
	Part throttle D3 check ball (No. 3) mispositioned or missing	Replace No. 3 check ball
	Turbine Shaft and Overrun Clutch	
	D3 oil passage not drilled in turbine shaft or overrun clutch hub, or plugged in turbine shaft	Service as required
	Oil seals missing or damaged in clutch piston	Replace oil seals
	Clutch plates burnt	Determine cause of condition; Service as required
	Clutch backing plate snap ring out of groove	Replace snap ring
No Park	Manual linkage out of adjustment	Adjust linkage; See GENERAL SERVICING
	Internal linkage binding, mispositioned, loose, or missing	Replace components as required
	Inside detent lever and pin assembly nut loose, or hole in lever worn or damaged	Tighten nut or replace lever
	Manual detent roller and spring assembly bolt loose holding roller assembly to valve body, or pin or roller damaged, mispositioned, or missing	Service as required
No Part Throttle Downshifts	Throttle valve or T.V. limit valve binding	Clean and free valve; Service as required
	Spacer plate hole plugged or undrilled	Service as required
	Valve body gaskets mispositioned or damaged	Replace valve body gaskets
	T.V. modulator downshift valve stuck	Clean and free valve; Service as required
	Throttle valve cable improperly set	Adjust cable; See GENERAL SERVICING

Automatic Transmissions

GENERAL MOTORS THM 200-4R TROUBLE SHOOTING (Cont.)

CONDITION	POSSIBLE CAUSE	CORRECTION
No Part Throttle 4-3 Downshift (Only Models With P.T. Passage in Throttle Plunger Bushing)	Throttle plunger bushing or 3-4 throttle valve bushing passages not open	Clean and clear obstruction; Service as required
	Part throttle D3 check ball (No. 3) mispositioned or missing	Replace No. 3 check ball
	Valve body gaskets mispositioned or damaged	Replace valve body gaskets
	Throttle valve cable improperly set	Adjust cable; See GENERAL SERVICING
	T.V. limit valve binding	Clean and free valve; Service as required

GENERAL MOTORS THM 350C TROUBLE SHOOTING

Every diagnosis of automatic transmission problems should begin with a check of the transmission fluid and linkage. Most of the following conditions can be caused by one or more of the following factors: (1) Incorrect fluid level, (2) Contaminated fluid, (3) Improperly adjusted linkage, or (4) Damaged or worn linkage.

CONDITION	POSSIBLE CAUSE	CORRECTION
No Drive in "D"	Improper fluid level	Check fluid level; See GENERAL SERVICING
	Manual linkage out of adjustment	Adjust linkage; See GENERAL SERVICING
	Low oil pressure	Perform OIL PRESSURE test
	Manual lever disconnected from inner lever in valve body	Service as required
	Forward Clutch Does not apply – piston cracked; piston seals damaged or missing; clutch plates burnt; snap ring out of groove	Service as required
	Clutch Plates Pump feed circuit to forward clutch oil seal rings missing or broken on pump cover, leak in feed circuits, pump-to-case gasket mispositioned or damaged, clutch drum check ball missing or stuck	Service as required
	Broken roller clutch assembly spring or damaged case	Replace roller clutch assembly
1-2 Shift, Full Throttle Only	Detent valve misadjusted, sticking or binding linkage	Service as required
	Vacuum leak	Repair engine vacuum lines or fittings
	Valve body gaskets leaking, damaged, or improperly positioned	Replace gaskets
	Detent valve train or 1-2 shift valve stuck in valve body	Clean and free valve; Service as required
	Case porosity	Replace case
1st Gear Only, No 1-2 Upshift	Governor Assembly Valve sticking	Clean and free valve; Service as required
	Drive gear loose damaged or worn (check for pin in case and length of pin showing; if gear is damaged, check output shaft drive gear for nicks or rough finish	Service as required

Automatic Transmissions

GENERAL MOTORS THM 350C TROUBLE SHOOTING (Cont.)

CONDITION	POSSIBLE CAUSE	CORRECTION
1st Gear Only, No 1-2 Upshift (Cont.)	Valve Body	
	1-2 shift valve train stuck closed	Clean and free valve; Service as required
	Governor feed channels blocked	Clean and clear obstruction; Service as required
	Gaskets leaking, damaged or improperly positioned	Replace gaskets
	Case porosity between channels	Replace case
	Case governor feed channels blocked or cross pressure leak (due to scored or worn governor bore)	Service as required
	Intermediate clutch piston seals missing, improperly sealed or cut	Replace piston seals
	Intermediate roller clutch spring broken or cage damaged	Replace intermediate roller clutch
1st & 2nd Only (No 2-3 Shift)	2-3 shift valve train stuck in valve body	Clean and free valve; Service as required
	Valve body gaskets leaking, damaged, or incorrectly positioned	Replace gaskets
	Direct clutch pump hub oil seal rings broken or missing	Replace oil seal rings
	Direct clutch piston seals missing, improperly assembled or cut, or piston check ball stuck or missing	Service as required
No "R", Or Slips In "R"	Improper fluid level	Check fluid level; See GENERAL SERVICING
	Manual linkage out of adjustment	Adjust linkage; See GENERAL SERVICING
	Incorrect oil pressure	
	Modulator valve stuck	Clean and free valve; Service as required
	Modulator and reverse boost valve stuck	Clean and free valve; Service as required
	Direct clutch pump hub oil seal rings broken or missing	Replace oil seal rings
	Direct clutch piston seals cut or missing	Replace piston seals
	Low/Reverse clutch piston seal cut or missing	Replace piston seal
	Valve body gaskets leaking, damaged, or incorrectly positioned	Replace gaskets
	2-3 shift valve stuck in upshift position in valve body (can also cause 1-3 upshift in "D")	Clean and free valve; Service as required
	1-2 shift valve stuck in upshift position in valve body (can also cause 1-3 upshift in "D")	Clean and free valve; Service as required
	Intermediate servo piston or pin stuck (applies intermediate overrun band)	Service as required
	Low/Reverse clutch piston out, or seal damaged or missing	Replace piston or seal
	Direct clutch outer seal damaged or missing, or plates burnt	Determine cause and service as required
	Forward clutch not releasing (also causes creeping in "N")	Determine cause and service as required
Drives In Neutral (Creeps)	Manual linkage out of adjustment	Adjust linkage; See GENERAL SERVICING
	Forward clutch not releasing (also causes no "R")	Determine cause and service as required

GENERAL MOTORS THM 350C TROUBLE SHOOTING (Cont.)

CONDITION	POSSIBLE CAUSE	CORRECTION
Slips in All Gears	Improper fluid level	Check fluid level; See GENERAL SERVICING
	Improper oil pressure	
	Inoperative vacuum modulator	Tighten fittings and clear obstructions in line
	Modulator valve stuck	Clean and free valve; Service as required
	Oil filter plugged or leaking	Replace filter
	Pressure regulator valve stuck	Clean and free valve; Service as required
	Pump-to case gasket damaged or improperly installed	Replace pump-to case gasket
	Forward clutch slipping due to cross leaks or porosity	Determine cause and service as required
Slipping 1-2 Shift	Improper fluid level	Check fluid level; See GENERAL SERVICING
	Improper oil pressure	
	Inoperative vacuum modulator	Tighten fittings and clear obstructions in line
	Modulator valve stuck	Clean and free valve; Service as required
	Pump pressure regulator valve faulty	Replace pressure regulator
	2-3 accumulator oil ring is damaged or missing	Replace oil ring
	1-2 accumulator oil ring is damaged or missing, or case bore damaged	Service as required
	Pump-to-case gasket damaged or mispositioned	Replace pump-to-case gasket
	Case porosity between channels	Replace case
	Intermediate clutch piston seals missing, improperly sealed or cut, or clutch plates burnt	Service as required
Rough 1-2 Shift	Improper oil pressure	
	Inoperative vacuum modulator	Tighten fittings and clear obstructions in line
	Modulator valve stuck	Clean and free valve; Service as required
	Regulator or boost valve stuck in valve body	Clean and free valve; Service as required
	Pump-to-case gasket damaged or mispositioned	Replace pump-to-case gasket
	Case porosity between channels	Replace case
	1-2 Accumulator Assembly	
	Oil rings damaged	Replace oil rings
	Piston stuck	Clean and free piston; Service as required
	Broken or missing spring	Replace spring
	Bore damaged	Service as required
	Restricted accumulator feed hole in valve body plate	Clear obstruction; Service as required
Slipping 2-3 Shift	Improper fluid level	Check fluid level; See GENERAL SERVICING
	Improper oil pressure	
	Inoperative vacuum modulator	Tighten fittings and clear obstructions in line
	Modulator valve stuck	Clean and free valve; Service as required
	Regulator or boost valve stuck in valve body	Clean and free valve; Service as required
	Pump-to-case gasket damaged or mispositioned	Replace pump-to-case gasket
	Case porosity between channels	Replace case
	Direct clutch piston seals or check ball leaking	Service as required

Automatic Transmissions

GENERAL MOTORS THM 350C TROUBLE SHOOTING (Cont.)

CONDITION	POSSIBLE CAUSE	CORRECTION
Rough 2-3 Shift	Improper Oil Pressure	
	Vacuum leak	Clean and service vacuum line
	Inoperative vacuum modulator	Tighten fittings and clear obstructions in line
	Modulator valve stuck	Clean and free valve; Service as required
	Regulator or boost valve stuck in valve body	Clean and free valve; Service as required
	2nd accumulator spring broken or missing	Replace spring
No Engine Braking In "L2"	Intermediate servo and/or 2-3 accumulator oil rings or bores leaking, or servo piston stuck	Service as required
	Intermediate overrun band broken or burnt	Determine cause and service as required
	Pressure regulator and/or boost valve stuck	Clean and free valve; Service as required
No Engine Braking In "L1"	Manual low control valve stuck	Clean and free valve; Service as required
	Intermediate overrun band broken or burnt	Determine cause and service as required
	Pressure regulator and/or boost valve stuck	Clean and free valve; Service as required
	Pressure regulator and/or boost valve stuck	Clean and free valve; Service as required
	Low/Reverse clutch piston inner seal damaged or missing	Replace piston inner seal
No Kickdown Shift	Vacuum modulator assembly, modulator valve or pressure regulator valve stuck or binding	Perform PRESSURE TEST; Service as required
	Detent valve and linkage sticking, disconnedted or broken	Service as required
	2-3 shift valve stuck	Clean and free valve; Service as required
No Detent Downshifts	2-3 shift valve stuck	Clean and free valve; Service as required
	Detent valve and linkage sticking, disconnedted or broken	Service as required
No "Park"	Manual linkage out of adjustment	Adjust linkage; See GENERAL SERVICING
	Internal linkage damaged, mispositioned, or misassembled	Clean or replace internal linkage as required
Locks Up in "L" (Usually When Hot)	Convertor pressure leaking into direct clutch through stator shaft	Check stator shaft postion; Service as required
	Direct clutch bore undersized, piston oversize, or feed hole missing small chamber	Service as required
2nd Only, or Slips in 2nd Only	Incorrect number of intermediate clutch plates or wrong intermediate clutch piston	Service as required
Locks Up in "R" (Usually When Hot)	Forward clutch bore undersized or piston oversize	Service as required
	Direct clutch feeding forward clutch through stator shaft	Check stator shaft postion; Service as required
Locks When Moving From "P" to "R"	Burrs on leading edge of parking pawl	Service parking pawl
"R" But No "D" When Cold	Pressure regulator bore or sleeve to tight	Service as required

GENERAL MOTORS THM 350C TROUBLE SHOOTING (Cont.)

CONDITION	POSSIBLE CAUSE	CORRECTION
Shifts Cold But Not Warm	Governor roll pin too short or missing	Replace roll pin
No "D" ("L1" OK)	Low/Reverse roller clutch installed backward	Install roller clutch correctly
No 1-2 Shift (1-3 Shift Normal, All Manual Shifts Normal)	Intermediate roller clutch not locking	Determine cause and service as required
Slow "R" Actuation When Cold	Improper fluid level	Check fluid level; See GENERAL SERVICING
Harsh 1-2 Shift	1-2 accumulator piston or spring faulty, or feed hole restricted in valve plate	Service as required
Slow "R" Actuation When Hot	Leaking valva body support plate	Determine cause and service as required
	Shift selector damaged or improperly assembled	Inspect shift selector components and service as required

GENERAL MOTORS THM 400 TROUBLE SHOOTING

Every diagnosis of automatic transmission problems should begin with a check of the transmission fluid and linkage. Most of the following conditions can be caused by one or more of the following factors: (1) Incorrect fluid level, (2) Contaminated fluid, (3) Improperly adjusted linkage, or (4) Damaged or worn linkage.

CONDITION	POSSIBLE CAUSE	CORRECTION
No or Delayed 1-2 Shift	Improper fluid level	Check fluid level; See GENERAL SERVICING
	Disconnect Electrical Plug From Transmission	
	Normal upshift	Check for short circuit and correct detent switch or wiring
	No upshift	Perform LINE PRESSURE test; Service as required
1-2 Shift Complaints	Improper fluid level	Check fluid level; See GENERAL SERVICING
	Poor engine performance	Check and tune engine
	Improper line pressure	Perform LINE PRESSURE test; Service as required
	Vacuum system leaking	Check vacuum lines and modulator; Service as required
2-3 Shift Complaints	Improper fluid level	Check fluid level; See GENERAL SERVICING
	Poor engine performance	Check and tune engine
Drives In Neutral (Creeps)	Manual linkage binding or out of adjustment	Adjust or service linkage; See GENERAL SERVICING
	Manual valve disconnected or end broken	Service as required
	Pressure leak into forward clutch apply passage	Check pump assembly and service as required
	Wrong forward clutch plate usage or burnt plates	Determine cause of condition; Service as required

GENERAL MOTORS THM 400 TROUBLE SHOOTING (Cont.)

CONDITION	POSSIBLE CAUSE	CORRECTION
Will Not Hold or Release Park	Manual linkage binding or out of adjustment	Adjust or service linkage; See GENERAL SERVICING
	Internal linkage damaged, mispositioned, or misassembled	Check and replace internal linkage components as required
No Engine Braking in "L1"	Lo-Reverse check ball mispositioned or missing, or case damaged at Lo-Reverse check ball area	Replace check ball or case
	Rear servo oil seal ring, bore or piston damaged	Service as required
	Rear Servo band apply pin too short or improperly assembled	Service as required
	Rear band broken, burnt, not engaged on anchor pins and/or servo pin	Determine cause of condition; Service as required
No Engine Braking in "L2"	Front servo and accumulator oil rings and/or bores leaking, or front servo piston cocked or stuck	Service as required
	Front band broken, burnt, not engaged on anchor pin and/or servo pin	Service as required
No or Slips in "R"	Improper fluid level	Check fluid level; See GENERAL SERVICING
	Manual linkage binding or out of adjustment	Adjust or service linkage; See GENERAL SERVICING
	Low Line Pressure (in "R")	Determine cause of condition; Service as required
	Normal Line Pressure (in "R")	
	2-3 valve train stuck open (also cause 1-3 shift in "D")	Clean and free valve; Service as required
	Cross channel leak or porosity in reverse feed passage in case or valve body	Determine cause and service as required
	Valve body gaskets leaking	Replace gaskets
	Rear servo piston seal ring damaged or missing	Replace servo piston seal ring
	Short rear servo band apply pin	Replace rear servo band apply pin
	Damaged rear servo piston or bore	Service as required
	Forward clutch does not release (also cause drive in "N")	Determine cause of condition; Service as required
	Direct clutch plate burnt	Determine cause of condition; Service as required
	Rear band broken, burnt, or apply pin or anchor pins not engaged	Determine cause of condition; Service as required
	Center support oil seal rings or grooves damaged or worn	Replace center support oil seal rings
1st & 2nd Only (No 2-3 Upshift)	Valve body gasket mispositioned or leaking, or 2-3 valve stuck	Service as required
	Direct clutch plates burnt	Determine cause of condition; Service as required
	Improper vacuum	Check engine vacuum lines and modulator; Service as required

GENERAL MOTORS THM 400 TROUBLE SHOOTING (Cont.)

CONDITION	POSSIBLE CAUSE	CORRECTION
No Drive in "D"	Improper fluid level	Check fluid level; See GENERAL SERVICING
	Manual linkage binding or out of adjustment	Adjust or service linkage; See GENERAL SERVICING
	Low Line Pressure (in "D")	Determine cause of condition; Service as required
	Normal Line Pressure (in "D")	
	Forward clutch feed passage not drilled or restricted in pump assembly	Service as required
	Forward clutch plates burnt	Determine cause of condition; Service as required
	Lo roller clutch damaged or installed backward	Service as required
No Detent Downshift	Place vehicle on lift. Turn ignition on (engine off). Disconnect electrical plug from transmission. Connect test light to "detent" terminal of disconnected wiring harness. Fully depress accelerator.	
	Light On	
	Detent solenoid inoperative, poor connections, shorted wire, open wire, valve stuck, or orifice plugged	Service as required
	Detent valve train stuck or binding in valve body	Clean and free valve; Service as required
	Light Off	
	Detent solenoid switch inproperly adjusted	Adjust detent solenoid switch; See GENERAL SERVICING
	Faulty switch, connections, fuse, or shorted wire	Service as required
	TRANSMISSION NOISY	
Park, Neutral & All Driving Ranges	Improper fluid level	Check fluid level; See GENERAL SERVICING
	Wrong, plugged, or restricted oil filter	Replace oil filter
	Pump intake pipe split, "O" ring damaged, or porosity in case intake pipe hose	Service as required
	Water in fluid	Determine cause of condition; service as required and replace fluid
	Porosity or voids at transmission case (pump face) intake port	Service as required
	Pump-to-case gasket mispositioned	Replace gasket
	Pump gears damaged, faulty, driving gear installed backward; cresent interference; pressure regulator cup plug damaged or missing; seal rings damaged or worn	Service as required
	Loose converter-to-flywheel bolts	Tighten bolts and check for damage; Service as required
1st, 3nd & "R" Only	Planetary gears or thrust bearings damaged	Thoroughly clean bearings and races; Inspect needle bearings and surfaces for pitting and roughness; Replace planetary gear set
	Planetary gear set front internal gear ring damaged	Replace planetary gear set

GENERAL MOTORS THM 400 TROUBLE SHOOTING (Cont.)

CONDITION	POSSIBLE CAUSE	CORRECTION
During Acceleration in Any Gear	Transmission cooling lines grounded to underbody	Service as required
	Broken or loose motor mounts	Replace motor mounts
Squeak at Low Speeds	Speedometer driven gear shaft seal faulty or needs lubrication	Service as required
	Extension housing oil seal faulty or needs lubrication	Service as required

GENERAL MOTORS THM 440-T4 TROUBLE SHOOTING

Every diagnosis of automatic transaxle problems should begin with a check of the transaxle fluid and linkage. Most of the following conditions can be caused by one or more of the following factors: (1) Incorrect fluid level, (2) Contaminated fluid, (3) Improperly adjusted linkage, or (4) Damaged or worn linkage.

CONDITION	POSSIBLE CAUSE	CORRECTION
No Drive in "D"	Improper fluid level	Check fluid level; See GENERAL SERVICING
	Manual linkage out of adjustment or disconnected	Adjust linkage; See GENERAL SERVICING
	Low oil pressure	Perform OIL PRESSURE test
	Torque converter stator roller clutch sluggish, or converter not bolted to flex plate	Service as required
	Oil pump drive shaft or pump damaged	Replace oil pump
	Input clutch/reverse check ball (No. 8 check ball) missing	Replace check ball
	Damaged drive link, sprocket or bearings	Service as required
	Input Clutch Assembly	
	Burnt or missing plates	Determine cause and service as required
	Damaged piston or seals	Replace piston assembly
	Housing check ball assembly worn or damaged	Replace check ball or assembly as necesssary
	Input shaft seals damaged or fluid passages blocked	Service as required
	Input sprag and sun gear assembly improperly assembled or sprag damaged	Service as required
	Input and reaction carrier pinions, internal gear, or sun gear damaged	Replace component(s) as necessary
	1-2 band assembly burnt	Determine cause and service as required
	1-2 servo piston or seal damaged or incorrect apply pin installed	Replace piston, seal and/or apply pin as required
	Leaking 1-2 servo oil pipes	Service as required
	Final drive assembly internally damaged	Replace component(s) as necessary
	Final drive sun gear shaft sides, gears, or pinion are internally damaged	Replace component(s) as necessary
	Parking pawl spring broken	Replace spring
	Output shaft damaged or improperly installed to axle	Service or repair as required

GENERAL MOTORS THM 440-T4 TROUBLE SHOOTING (Cont.)

CONDITION	POSSIBLE CAUSE	CORRECTION
1st Gear Only, No 1-2 Upshift	Governor weights binding, springs or gear damaged	Replace governor
	Accumulator & Pipes	
	Exhaust check balls missing or damaged	Replace check balls
	Cover or pipes leaking	Service as required
	No. 14 check ball missing	Replace check ball
	1-2 shift valve stuck in valve body	Clean and free valve; Service as required
	2nd clutch plates, piston or seals damaged or misassembled	Service as required
	Driven sprocket support oil seal rings damaged	Replace oil seal rings
	Reverse reaction drum splines damaged, or drum plates missing	Replace reaction drum assembly
Harsh Or Soft 1-2 Shift	Improper oil pressure	Perform PRESSURE test
	Accumulator cover bolts loose, or pistons, seals or springs damaged	Service as required
	Accumulator valve stuck in valve body	Clean and free valve; Service as required
	2nd clutch check ball (check ball No. 4) missing	Replace check ball
High Or Low 1-2 Shift Speed	T.V. cable disconnected or misadjusted	Service or adjust cable; See GENERAL SERVICING
	T.V. link or lever assembly bent or damaged	Replace link or lever assembly
	T.V. valve or plunger stuck or binding	Clean and free valve or plunger; Service as required
	Incorrect governor pressure	Determine cause and service as required
1st & 2nd Only (No 2-3 Shift)	Incorrect 1-2 servo apply pin	Replace apply pin
	Check ball missing from capsule in case	Replace check ball
	1-2 servo bore orifice cup plug missing	Replace cup plug
	2-3 shift valve train stuck in valve body	Clean and free valve; Service as required
	No. 6 check ball not seating	Determine cause and service as required
	Valve body bolts improperly tightened	Tighten bolts to specification
	Input seals damaged or oil passages blocked	Service as required
	3rd clutch plates burnt or piston seals or check ball assembly damaged	Service as required
	Damaged 3rd roller clutch cage, rollers out of cage, springs damaged, or roller clutch improperly assembled on input sun gear shaft	Service as required
	2-3 accumulator exhaust valve check ball (check ball No. 3) damaged or 2-3 accumulator feed check ball (check ball No. 3) damaged or not seating, or 2-3 accumulator valve stuck in valve body	Replace check ball; Clean and free valve; Service as required
Harsh Or Soft 2-3 Shift	Improper Oil Pressure	Perform PRESSURE test
	1-2 servo feed check ball (No. 7 check ball) mislocated	Replace check ball

GENERAL MOTORS THM 440-T4 TROUBLE SHOOTING (Cont.)

CONDITION	POSSIBLE CAUSE	CORRECTION
High Or Low 2-3 Shift Speed	T.V. cable disconnected or misadjusted	Service or adjust cable; See GENERAL SERVICING
	T.V. link or lever assembly bent or damaged	Replace link or lever assembly
	T.V. valve or plunger stuck or binding	Clean and free valve or plunger; Service as required
	Incorrect governor pressure	Determine cause and service as required
No 3-4 Shift	Governor weights binding, springs or gear damaged	Replace governor
	3-4 shift valve stuck in valve body	Clean and free valve; Service as required
	Burnt 4th clutch plates, piston or seals damaged, or plates or pistom mislocated	Service as required
	4th clutch shaft spline damaged	Replace 4th clutch shaft
Harsh Or Soft 3-4 Shift	Improper Oil Pressure	Perform PRESSURE test
	Accumulator cover bolts loose, or pistons, seals or springs damaged	Service as required
	4th clutch check ball (No. 1 check ball) mislocated	Replace check ball
High Or Low 3-4 Shift Speed	T.V. cable disconnected or misadjusted	Service or adjust cable; See GENERAL SERVICING
	T.V. link or lever assembly bent or damaged	Replace link or lever assembly
	T.V. valve or plunger stuck or binding	Clean and free valve or plunger; Service as required
	Incorrect governor pressure	Determine cause and service as required
Harsh 4-3 Downshift	4th clutch check ball (No. 1 check ball) missing	Replace check ball
Harsh 3-2 Downshift	1-2 servo control valve, 3-2 control valve or 3-2 coast valve stuck in valve body, or 1-2 servo feed check ball (No. 7 check ball) or 3rd clutch check ball (No. 2 check ball) missing	Clean and free valve; Service as required; Replace missing check ball(s)
	Damaged input clutch accumulator piston or seal in channel plate	Replace piston or seal
Harsh 2-1 Downshift	Reverse servo feed check ball (No. 4 check ball) missing	Replace check ball
No Drive In "R"	Low oil pressure	Perform OIL PRESSURE test
	Oil pump drive shaft or pump damaged	Replace oil pump
	Damaged drive link, sprocket or bearings	Service as required
	Reverse band burnt or damaged	Determine cause and service as required
	Input Clutch Assembly	
	Burnt or missing plates	Determine cause and service as required
	Damaged piston or seals	Replace piston assembly
	Housing check ball assembly worn or damaged	Replace check ball or assembly as necesssary
	Input shaft seals damaged or fluid passages blocked	Service as required
	Input sprag and sun gear assembly improperly assembled or sprag damaged	Service as required

Automatic Transmissions

GENERAL MOTORS THM 440-T4 TROUBLE SHOOTING (Cont.)

CONDITION	POSSIBLE CAUSE	CORRECTION
No Drive In "R" (Cont.)	Reverse servo piston or seal damaged, or wrong apply pin	Replace piston or pin as required
	Input and reaction carrier pinions, internal gear, or sun gear damaged	Replace component(s) as necessary
No Park	Final drive park pawl, spring or gear damaged	Replace component(s) as necessary
Harsh "N" To "R" (Or "N" To "D")	Reverse servo feed check ball (No. 4 check ball) missing (harsh "R")	Replace check ball
	1-2 servo feed check ball missing (harsh "D")	Replace check ball
	Spacer plate thermal elements do not close when warm	Determine cause and service as required
No Viscous Clutch Apply (If Equipped)	Verify proper computer command control operation; check for damaged thermistor or temperature switch	Service as required

GENERAL MOTORS THM 700-R4 TROUBLE SHOOTING

Every diagnosis of automatic transmission problems should begin with a check of the transmission fluid and linkage. Most of the following conditions can be caused by one or more of the following factors: (1) Incorrect fluid level, (2) Contaminated fluid, (3) Improperly adjusted linkage, or (4) Damaged or worn linkage.

CONDITION	POSSIBLE CAUSE	CORRECTION
1st Only, No Upshift	Governor Assembly	
	Valve sticking	Clean and free valve; Service as required
	Driven gear loose or damaged	Replace governor assembly
	Drive gear retaining pin missing	Replace retaining pin
	Nicks or burrs on output shaft, governor sleeve, or case bore	Service as required
	Improper support pin length	Replace support pin
	Governor weights or springs missing, damaged, or binding	Service as required
	1-2 shift valve sticking in valve body, or spacer plate or gaskets mispositioned or damaged	Service as required
	Case-to-valve body face not flat or damaged, or governor screen restricted or damaged	Service as required
	2-4 Servo Assembly	
	Restricted or blocked case passages	Clean and clear obstructions
	Nicks or burrs on servo pin or case pin bore	Service as required
	Missing or damaged piston or pin seals	Replace piston or seals
	4th servo piston installed backward	Replace servo piston
	2-4 band worn or damaged, or band anchor pin not engaged	Service as required

GENERAL MOTORS THM 700-R4 TROUBLE SHOOTING (Cont.)

CONDITION	POSSIBLE CAUSE	CORRECTION
Slips in 1st	Forward Clutch Assembly	
	Clutch plates worn	Replace clutch plates
	Piston porosity or damaged	Replace piston
	Piston seals missing or damaged	Replace piston seals
	Input housing-to-forward clutch housing "O" ring seal missing or damaged	Replace "O" ring seal
	Damaged housing	Replace housing
	Housing retainer and ball assembly not seating or damaged	Replace retainer and ball assembly
	Input housing and shaft assembly turbine shaft seals missing or damaged	Replace turbine shaft seals
	Accumulator valve stuck in valve body	Clean and free valve; Service as required
	Valve body face not flat, damaged lands, or interconnected passages	Replace valve body
	Spacer plate or gaskets incorrect, mispositioned, or damaged	Replace spacer plate or gaskets
	T.V. cable binding or broken	Service or replace as required
	1-2 Accumulator Piston Assembly	
	Porosity in piston or cover and pin assembly	Replace piston or cover and pin assembly
	Damaged piston ring grooves	Replace piston
	Piston seal missing or damaged	Replace piston seal
	Cover gasket missing or damaged	Replace cover gasket
	Broken accumulator spring	Replace spring
	Improper oil presure	Perform PRESSURE test; Service as required
High or Low 1-2 Shift Speeds	T.V. cable improperly adjusted, binding or broken	Adjust or service cable; See GENERAL SERVICING
	Governor Assembly	
	Valve sticking	Clean and free valve; Service as required
	Driven gear loose or damaged	Replace governor assembly
	Drive gear retaining pin missing	Replace retaining pin
	Nicks or burrs on output shaft, governor sleeve, or case bore	Service as required
	Improper support pin length	Replace support pin
	Governor weights or springs missing, damaged, or binding	Service as required
	Throttle lever and bracket assembly misassembled, binding or damaged, or T.V. link missing, binding or damaged	Service as required
	Valve body face not flat, T.V. exhaust check ball stuck, or T.V. plunger sticking	Service as required
	Oil pump assembly or case face not flat	Replace oil pump assembly or case
Slipping or Rough 1-2 Shift	Throttle lever and bracket assembly incorrectly installed or damaged, or T.V. cable broken or binding	Replace throttle lever and bracket assembly or T.V. cable
	Valve Body Assembly	
	Throttle valve sticking	Clean and free valve; Service as required
	T.V. bushing turned in bore	Replace bushing

GENERAL MOTORS THM 700-R4 TROUBLE SHOOTING (Cont.)

CONDITION	POSSIBLE CAUSE	CORRECTION
Slipping or Rough 1-2 Shift (Cont.)	Valve Body Assembly (Cont.)	
	1-2 shift valve train, line bias valve, accumulator valve or T.V. limit valve stuck	Clean and free valve; Service as required
	Gaskets or spacer plate incorrect, mispositioned or damaged	Replace gaskets or spacer plate
	Body face not flat	Replace valve body
	2-4 Servo Assembly	
	Apply pin too long or too short	Replace apply pin
	Servo seals or "O" ring seals missing or damaged	Replace servo seals or "O" ring seals
	Restricted or missing oil passages	Service as required
	Case servo bore damaged	Service as required
	2nd Accumulator	
	Porosity in 1-2 accumulator housing or piston	Replace piston or housing
	Piston seal or groove damaged	Replace piston
	Nicks or burrs in 1-2 accumulator housing	Service as required
	Missing or restricted oil passages	Replace accumulator
	Worn or mispositioned 2-4 band	Replace 2-4 band
	Oil pump assembly or case faces not flat	Replace oil pump or case
Slipping, Rough or No 2-3 Shift	Internal converter damage	Replace converter
	Governor Assembly	
	Valve stuck	Clean and free valve; Service as required
	Drive gear retaining pin missing or loose	Replace retaining pin
	Weights binding	Service as required
	Governor drive gear damaged	Replace drive gear
	Support pin in case too long or too short	Replace support pin
	Oil pump stator shaft sleeve scored or mislocated	Replace shaft sleeve
	Valve Body	
	2-3 valve train or accumulator valve stuck	Clean and free valve train; Service as required
	Spacer plate or gaskets incorrect, mispositioned or damaged	Replace spacer plate or gaskets
	Throttle valve or T.V. limit valve stuck	Clean and free valve; Service as required
	Input Housing Assembly	
	Forward or 3-4 clutch plates worn	Determine cause of condition; Service as required
	Excessive clutch plate travel	Determine cause and service as required
	Forward or 3-4 piston seals damaged	Replace piston seals
	Porosity in 3-4 clutch housing or piston, or 3-4 piston check ball stuck, damaged or not sealing	Replace 3-4 clutch housing, piston or piston check ball
	Restricted apply passages	Clean and clear obstructions; Service as required

GENERAL MOTORS THM 700-R4 TROUBLE SHOOTING (Cont.)

CONDITION	POSSIBLE CAUSE	CORRECTION
Slipping, Rough or No 2-3 Shift (Cont.)	Input Housing Assembly (Cont.)	
	Forward clutch piston or 3rd accumulator retainer and ball assembly not seating	Replace retainer and ball assembly
	Sealing balls loose or missing	Replace sealing balls
	2-4 servo pin seals or 2nd apply piston seals missing or damaged	Replace pin seals
Rough, Slipping or No 3-4 Shift	Governor	
	Weights binding	Service as required
	Valve sticking	Clean and free valve; Service as required
	Drive gear damaged, or retaining pin missing or loose	Replace drive gear or retaining pin
	Improper support pin length	Replace support pin
	Oil pump assembly faces not flat, or pump cover retainer and ball assembly omitted or damaged	Replace pump or cover retainer and ball assembly
	Valve Body Assembly	
	2-3 valve train, accumulator valve, throttle valve, T.V. limit valve, 1-2 shift valve or 3-2 control valve stuck	Clean and free valve; Service as required
	Manual valve link bent or damaged	Replace manual valve link
	Spacer plates or gaskets incorrect, mispositioned or damaged	Replace spacer plates or gaskets
	2-4 Servo Assembly	
	Incorrect band apply pin	Replace band apply pin
	Missing or damaged servo seals	Replace seals
	Porosity in pistons, cover or case	Service as required
	Plugged or missing orifice cup plug	Clean and clear obstruction or replace cup plug
	Case	
	3rd accumulator retainer and ball assembly leaking	Determine cause and service as required
	Porosity in 3-4 accumulator piston or bore	Replace piston or case
	3-4 accumulator piston seal or seal grooves damaged	Replace piston seal or piston
	Plugged or missing orifice cup plug	Clean and clear obstruction or replace cup plug
	Restricted oil passage	Clear obstruction; Service as required
	Input Housing Assembly	
	Forward or 3-4 clutch plates worn, or excessive plate travel	Determine cause of condition; Service as required
	Forward or 3-4 piston seals damaged	Replace piston seals
	Porosity in 3-4 clutch housing or piston	Replace 3-4 clutch housing or piston
	3-4 piston check ball or sealing balls stuck, damaged or not sealing	Replace check ball or sealing balls
	Restricted apply passages	Clean and clear obstructions; Service as required
	Forward clutch piston retainer and ball assembly not seating	Replace retainer and ball assembly
	2-4 band assembly worn or misassembled	Replace band assembly

Automatic Transmissions

GENERAL MOTORS THM 700-R4 TROUBLE SHOOTING (Cont.)

CONDITION	POSSIBLE CAUSE	CORRECTION
No or Slips in "R"	Input Housing Assembly	
	3-4 apply ring stuck in applied position	Clean and free ring; Service as required
	Forward clutch not releasing	Determine cause of condition; Service as required
	Turbine shaft seals missing or damaged	Replace turbine shaft seals
	Manual linkage out of adjustment	Adjust linkage; See GENERAL SERVICING
	Oil Pump Assembly	
	Retainer and ball assembly missing or damaged	Replace retainer and ball assembly
	Stator shaft seal rings or ring grooves damaged	Replace shaft or seal rings
	Stator shaft sleeve scored or damaged	Replace shaft sleeve
	Reverse boost valve stuck, damaged or misassembled	Clean and free, or replace valve
	Cup plug missing	Replace cup plug
	Restricted oil passage	Clean and clear obstructions; Service as required
	Faces not flat	Replace pump assembly
	Converter clutch apply valve stuck	Clean and free valve; Service as required
	Valve Body Assembly	
	2-3 shift valve stuck	Clean and free valve; Service as required
	Manual linkage out of adjustment	Adjust linkage; See GENERAL SERVICING
	Spacer plate and gaskets incorrect, mispositioned or damaged	Replace spacer plate or gaskets
	Reverse Input Clutch	
	Clutch plate worn	Determine cause of condition; Service as required
	Housing and drum assembly cracked at weld	Replace housing and drum assembly
	Clutch plate or return spring assembly retaining ring out of groove	Replace retaining ring
	Piston deformed or dished	Replace piston
	Seals damaged or missing	Replace seals
	Retainer and ball assembly not sealing	Replace retainer and ball assembly
	Restricted apply passage	Clean and clear obstructions; Service as required
	Lo-Reverse Clutch	
	Clutch plates worn or retaining ring mispositioned	Determine cause of worn plates; Replace retaining ring
	Porosity in piston	Replace piston
	Seals damaged	Replace seals
	Return spring assembly retaining ring mispositioned	Replace retaining ring
	Restricted apply passage	Clean and clear obstructions; Service as required
	Case porosity	Replace case
	Case cover plate improperly tightened, or gasket missing or damaged	Tighten bolts; Replace gasket

Automatic Transmissions

GENERAL MOTORS THM 700-R4 TROUBLE SHOOTING (Cont.)

CONDITION	POSSIBLE CAUSE	CORRECTION
No Part Throttle or Delayed Downshifts	External linkage not adjusted	Adjust linkage; See GENERAL SERVICING
	2-4 Servo Assembly	
	Apply pin seal damaged or missing	Replace apply pin seal
	Servo cover retaining ring missing or misassembled	Replace retaining ring
	4th apply piston damaged or misassembled	Replace 4th apply piston
	Inner housing damaged or misassembled	Replace inner housing
	Governor weights binding, or valve stuck	Service as required
	Valve Body Assembly	
	Throttle valve, 3-2 control valve or T.V. modulated downshift valve stuck	Clean and free valve; Service as required
	T.V. sleeve turned in bore	Replace T.V. sleeve
	4-3 sequence valve body channel blocked	Clean and clear channel of obstruction; Service as required
	No. 5 check ball missing	Replace No. 5 check ball
No Overrun Braking in "L_1", "L_2" or "L_3"	External linkage out of adjustment	Adjust linkage; Service as required
	Valve Body Assembly	
	4-3 sequence valve or throttle valve stuck	Clean and free valve; Service as required
	No. 3 check ball mispositioned	Replace No. 3 check ball
	Spacer plate and gaskets incorrect, damaged or mispositioned	Replace spacer plate or gaskets
	Input Clutch Assembly	
	Turbine shaft oil passages plugged or not drilled	Service as required
	Turbine shaft seal rings damaged	Replace shaft seal rings
	Turbine shaft sealing balls loose or missing	Replace sealing balls
	Porosity in forward or overrun clutch piston	Replace forward or overrun clutch piston
	Overrun piston seals damaged or missing	Replace piston seals
	Overrun piston check ball not sealing	Replace check ball
Drives in Neutral (Creeps)	Forward clutch not releasing	Determine cause of condition; Service as required
	Internal converter damage	Replace converter
	Converter clutch apply valve stuck in oil pump	Clean and free valve; Service as required
	Internal leakage in case, or face not flat	Replace case
Starts in 2nd in "D"	Governor support pin too long or missing, or valve stuck in governor assembly	Service as required
	Forward sprag clutch assembly installed backward	Replace sprag clutch assembly
No Park	Parking linkage binding, mispositioned, loose, or missing	Replace components as required

AMERICAN MOTORS

LUBRICATION

SERVICE INTERVALS

Check fluid level every 7500 miles. Drain and refill at every 30,000 mile service.

CHECKING FLUID LEVEL

Check lubricant level at filler plug hole on side of transmission. Lubricant should be level with bottom of filler plug hole. Add lubricant as necessary to bring to correct level.

RECOMMENDED FLUID

Use AMC SAE 85W-90 grade GL-5, or SAE 80 W grade GL-5 multipurpose gear lubricant.

CAUTION: DO NOT use gear lubricants containing lead, sulfur or chlorine compounds.

FLUID CAPACITY

TRANSMISSION REFILL CAPACITIES

Application	Quantity
4-Speed	
JB 0 Transaxle	6.8 pts. (3.2L)
5-Speed	
T5	4.5 pts. (2.1L)
JB 1 Transaxle	7.0 pts. (3.4L)
JB 3 Transaxle	7.0 pts. (3.4L)

ADJUSTMENTS

SHIFT ROD LINKAGE

Alliance & Encore

1) Shift transaxle into second gear. Raise vehicle. Wedge transaxle shift lever to prevent movement during adjustment. Loosen shift rod clamp bolt below shifter lever.

2) Lower vehicle. Remove shift lever boot. Place a .02" (.5 mm) feeler gauge between the reverse stop release holder and the left side gearshift lever housing.

3) Have an assistant hold shift lever against feeler gauge. Raise vehicle. Tighten shift rod clamp bolt. Rear edge of clamp should be positioned about .313" (8 mm) from end of shift rod. Check transaxle for proper gear engagement.

Fig. 1: Location of Transaxle Shift Lever

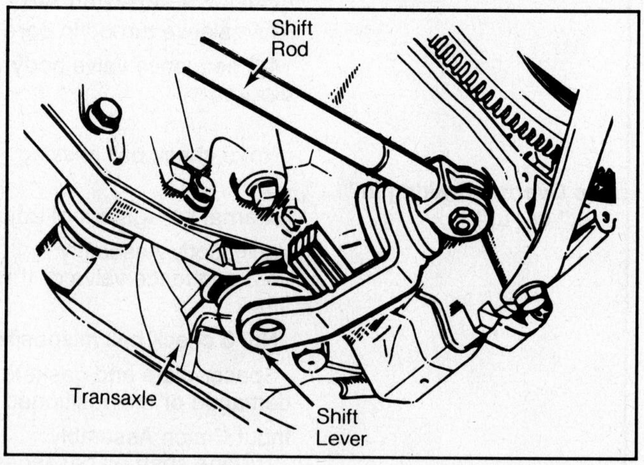

CHRYSLER CORP.

LUBRICATION

SERVICE INTERVALS

Check fluid level every 6 months. Drain and refill at 15,000 mile intervals.

CHECKING FLUID LEVEL

Check lubricant level at filler plug hole on top of transaxle. Lubricant should be level with bottom of filler plug hole. Add lubricant as necessary to bring to correct level.

RECOMMENDED FLUID

A-460 & A-525 Transaxles

Use Dexron II automatic transmission fluid.

FLUID CAPACITY

TRANSAXLE REFILL CAPACITIES

Application	Quantity
4-Speed	
A-460	4.0 pts. (1.8L)
5-Speed	
A-525	4.6 pts. (2.1L)

ADJUSTMENTS

SHIFT LINKAGE

Rod Operated Transaxles

1) Place transaxle in Neutral position. Working over left front fender, remove lock pin from transaxle selector shaft housing. Reverse lock pin (long end down) and insert into same threaded hole while pushing selector shaft into selector housing.

2) Raise vehicle on hoist. Loosen clamp bolt that secures gearshift tube to gear shift connector. Check to see that gearshift connector slides and turns freely in gearshift tube. *See Fig. 1.*

3) Position shifter mechanism connector assembly so isolator is contacting the upstanding flange, and rib on isolator is aligned fore and aft with the hole in the block-out bracket. Hold in this position while tightening clamp bolt on gearshift tube to 14 ft. lbs. (19 N.m). No significant force should be exerted on linkage during this operation.

4) Lower vehicle. Remove lock pin from selector shaft housing and reinstall lock pin upside down in selector shaft housing. Tighten lock pin. Check for shift into 1st and Reverse. Check for block-out into Reverse.

CHRYSLER CORP. (Cont.)

Fig. 1: Rod Operated Gearshift Linkage Adjustment

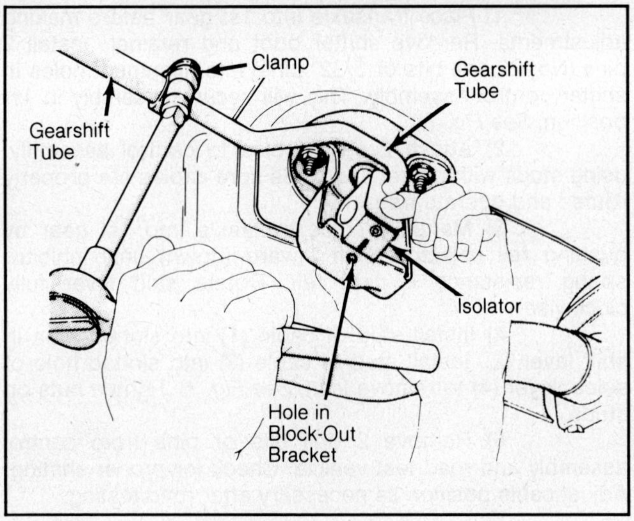

No significant force should be exerted on linkage during this operation.

Cable Operated Transaxle

1) Place transaxle in Neutral position. Working over left front fender, remove lock pin from transaxle selector shaft housing. Reverse lock pin (long end down) and insert into same threaded hole while pushing selector shaft into selector housing.

2) Remove gear shift knob, retaining nut and pull-up ring. Remove screws attaching center console and remove console. Fabricate 2 adjustment pins from 3/16" diameter rod. *See Fig. 2.* Install adjustment pins in gear shifter mechanism.

3) Loosen crossover and selector cable adjustment screws. Allow both cables to center themselves in the adjustment slot. Retighten cable adjustment set screws to 55 INCH. lbs. (6 N.m).

CAUTION: Proper torque on crossover and selector cable set screws is very important.

Fig. 2: Cable Operated Gearshift Linkage Adjustments

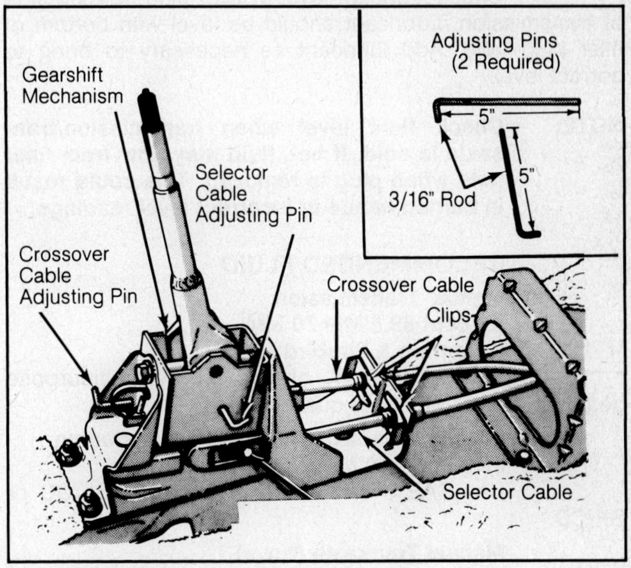

Inset shows adjustment pin fabrication.

FORD MOTOR CO.

LUBRICATION

SERVICE INTERVALS

Check fluid level at 15 month/15,000 mile intervals. Draining and refilling are not required, except at time of overhaul or service.

CHECKING FLUID LEVEL

Check lubricant level at filler plug hole on side of transmission. Lubricant should be level with bottom of filler plug hole. Add lubricant as necessary to bring to correct level.

RECOMMENDED FLUID

83ET Transmission

Use SAE 80 W, or SAE 90 W multipurpose gear lubricant of API GL-5 quality.

MTX Transaxle & T5O-D 5-Speed Transmission

Use Dexron II automatic transmission fluid.

FLUID CAPACITY

TRANSMISSION REFILL CAPACITIES

Application	Pints (L)
4-Speed	
MTX Transaxle	5.0 (2.5)
83ET	2.8 (1.3)
5-Speed	
MTX Transaxle	6.1 (2.9)
T5O-D 5-Speed Overdrive	5.6 (2.6)

ADJUSTMENTS

SHIFT LINKAGE

No in-service adjustment of shift linkage is necessary.

Manual Transmission Servicing

GENERAL MOTORS CORP.

LUBRICATION

SERVICE INTERVALS

Check fluid level at 3 month/3000 mile intervals. Draining and refilling is not required, except at time of overhaul or service.

CHECKING FLUID LEVEL

Check lubricant level at filler plug hole on side of transmission. Lubricant should be level with bottom of filler plug hole. Add lubricant as necessary to bring to correct level.

NOTE: Check fluid level when transmission/transaxle is cold. If hot, fluid may flow from filler hole when plug is removed. This could result in burned hands or incorrect level readings.

RECOMMENDED FLUID

Manual Transmission (Except 69.5 MM,70 MM & Camaro & Firebird 77MM)

Use SAE 80 W, or SAE 90 W multipurpose gear lubricant of API GL-5 quality.

Manual Transaxle Except Nova (Including 69.5 MM &70 MM Transmision)

Use SAE 5 W-30 W engine oil SF, SF/CC or SF/CD.

Manual Transaxle (Nova)

Use SAE 75W-90 or SAE 80W-90 GL-5 gear lubricant.

Manual Transmission (Corvette Overdrive Unit & Camaro & Firebird 77 MM)

Use Dexron II automatic transmission fluid.

FLUID CAPACITY

TRANSMISSION REFILL CAPACITIES

Application	Quantity
4-Speed	
70 MM	3.4 pts. (1.6L)
76 MM Transaxle	6.0 pts. (2.8L)
83 MM	2.0 pts. (1.0L)
5-Speed	
C51 Transaxle (Nova)	5.5 pts. (2.6L)
69.5 MM	3.3 pts. (1.5L)
76 MM Transaxle	6.0 pts. (2.8L)
77 MM	4.2 pts. (2.0L)
Overdrive	4.0 pts. (2.0L)

ADJUSTMENTS

SHIFT LINKAGE

69.5 MM, 70 MM 4-Speed & 77 MM 5-Speed

NOTE: Integral type shift linkage is used, therefore, no adjustment is necessary.

C51 5-Speed (Transaxle) Nova

NOTE: Shift cables are fixed length. No adjustment is provided.

76 MM 4-Speed (Transaxle)

1) Place transaxle into 1st gear before making adjustments. Remove shifter boot and retainer. Install 2 pins (No. 22 drill bits or 5/32" pins) into alignment holes in shifter control assembly. This will secure assembly in 1st position. *See Fig. 1.*

2) Attach 2 shift cables to control assembly, using studs with pin retainers. Be sure cables are properly routed and operate freely.

3) Manually place transaxle into 1st gear by pushing rail selector shaft inward (down) until inhibitor spring resistance is first felt. Rotate shift lever fully clockwise.

4) Install stud of cable (1) into slotted area in shift lever (2). Install stud of cable (3) into slotted hole of select lever (4) to remove lash. *See Fig. 1.* Tighten nuts on studs.

5) Remove 2 drill bits or pins from control assembly and road test vehicle. Check for proper shifting. Adjust cable position as necessary after road testing.

77 MM 5-Speed (Transaxle)

1) Disconnect negative battery cable and place transaxle in 3rd gear position. Remove locking pin at transaxle and reinstall tapered end down, locking transaxle in 3rd gear. *See Fig. 2.* Loosen shift cable attaching nuts at transaxle shift levers.

2) From inside vehicle, remove console trim plate, slide shifter boot up and remove console. Install a 5/32" drill bit (No. 22) in alignment hole in shifter assembly. Align slot in shifter lever with shifter plate and install 3/16" drill bit.

3) Tighten attaching nuts loosened in step **1)**. Remove both drill bits. Remove locking pin at transaxle and reinstall, tapered end up. Install console, shifter boot and trim plate. Reconnect negative ground cable.

4) Road test vehicle to ensure proper linkage adjustment. Readjust if necessary.

83 MM 4-Speed Overdrive (Corvette)

1) Disconnect negative battery cable. Remove left seat. If equipped with power seats, remove electrical leads. Remove shift knob, console cover and shifter cover. Loosen lock nuts at shift rod swivels. Place shift levers in Neutral at transmission. Rods should pass freely through swivels. *See Fig. 3.*

2) Move shift control lever into neutral detent and align control assembly levers. Insert alignment gauge pin into lever adjustment slot. Tighten lock nuts at shift rod swivels and remove locating gauge pin.

3) After adjustments have been made, the centerlines of shift levers must be aligned to each other to provide free crossover motion. Check transmission shift operation. Readjust as necessary. Reinstall interior in vehicle.

PARK LOCK CABLE

83 MM 4-Speed Overdrive (Corvette)

1) Disconnect negative battery cable. Remove left seat. If equipped with power seats, remove electrical leads. Remove shift knob, console cover and shifter cover.

GENERAL MOTORS CORP. (Cont.)

Fig. 1: Adjusting 4-Speed Transaxle Shift Cables

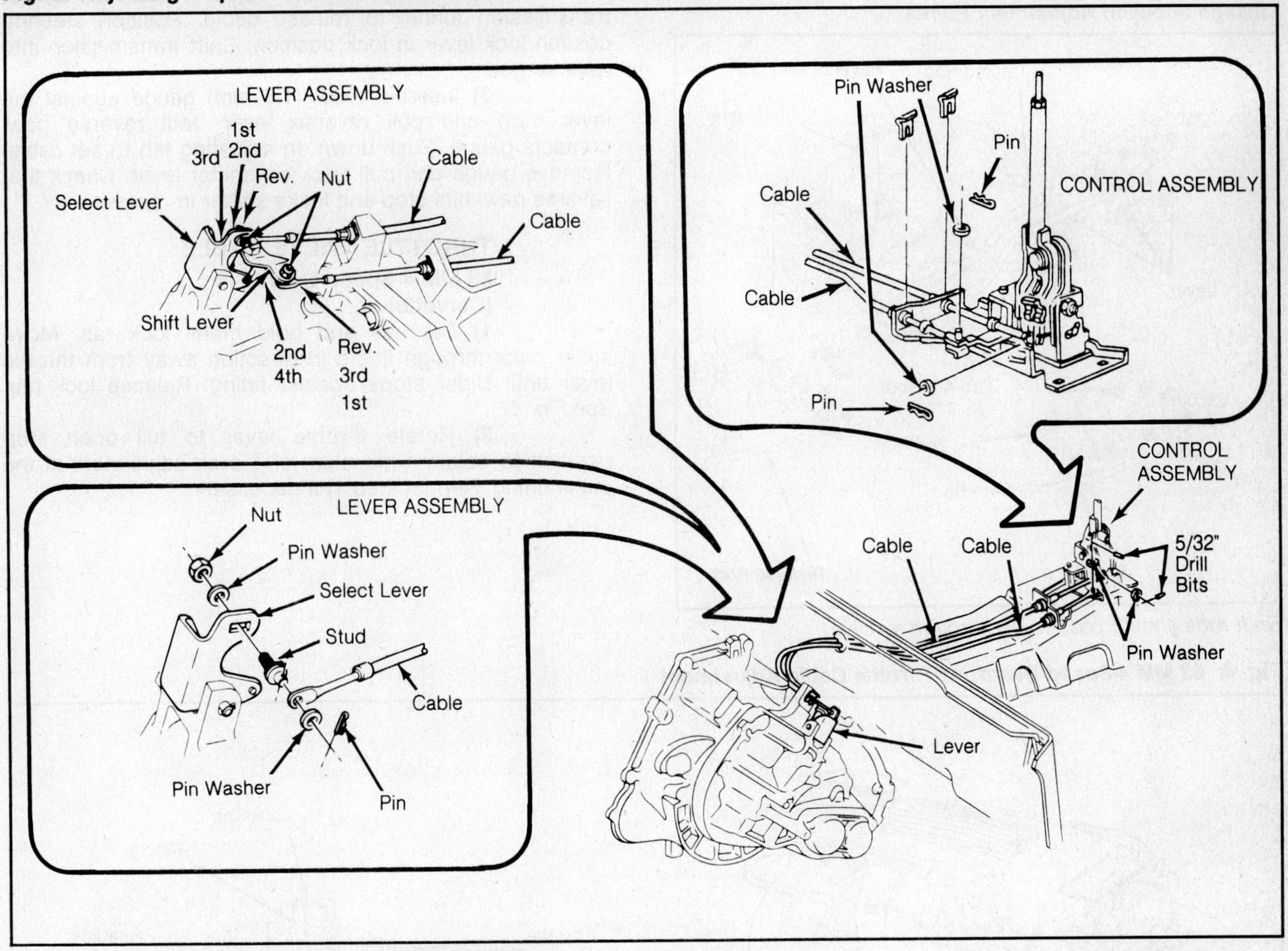

Place transaxle in 1st gear before making adjustment.

Fig. 2: Adjusting 5-Speed Transaxle Shift Cables

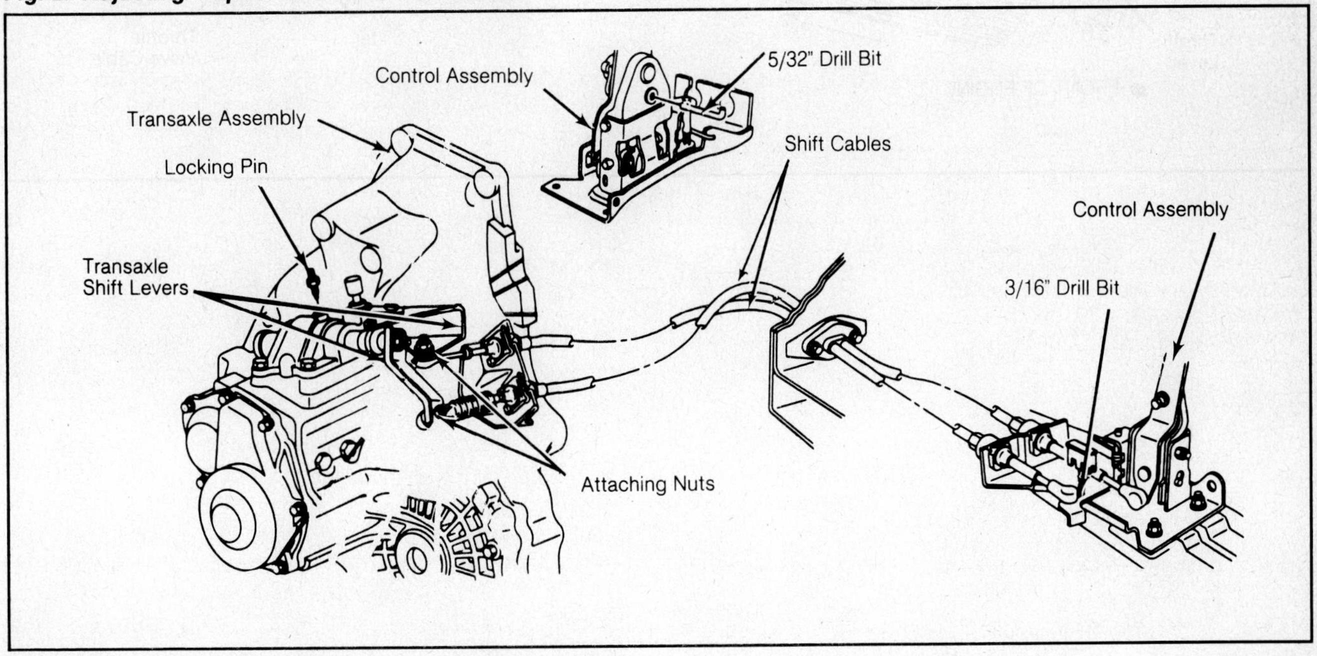

Adjustment is performed with transaxle in 3rd gear position.

GENERAL MOTORS CORP. (Cont.)

Fig. 3: View of 83 MM 4-Speed Overdrive Gearshift Linkage Showing Adjustment Points

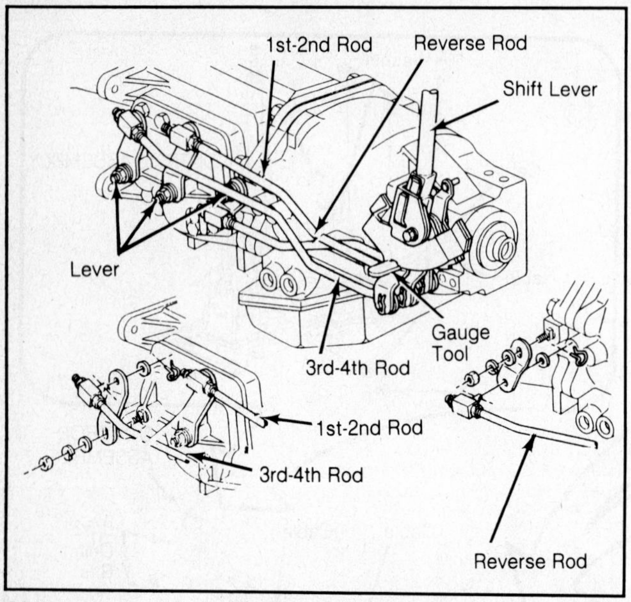

Shift rods should pass freely through swivels.

2) Lift up adjuster locking tab on top of transmission tunnel to release cable. Position steering column lock lever in lock position. Shift transmission into reverse gear.

3) Insert a .060" (1.5 mm) gauge against the lever stop and pull reverse lever until reverse pawl contacts gauge. Push down on adjusting tab to set cable. Remove gauge and pull back on shifter lever. Check that reverse pawl hits stop and locks shifter in reverse.

THROTTLE VALVE CABLE

83 MM 4-Speed Overdrive (Corvette)

1) Depress and hold metal lock tab. Move slider back through fitting in direction away from throttle lever until slider stops against fitting. Release lock tab. *See Fig. 4.*

2) Rotate throttle lever to full open stop position to obtain a minimum of 1 click adjustment at the cable fitting. Repeat step **1)** if necessary.

Fig. 4: 83 MM 4-Speed Overdrive Throttle Cable Adjustment

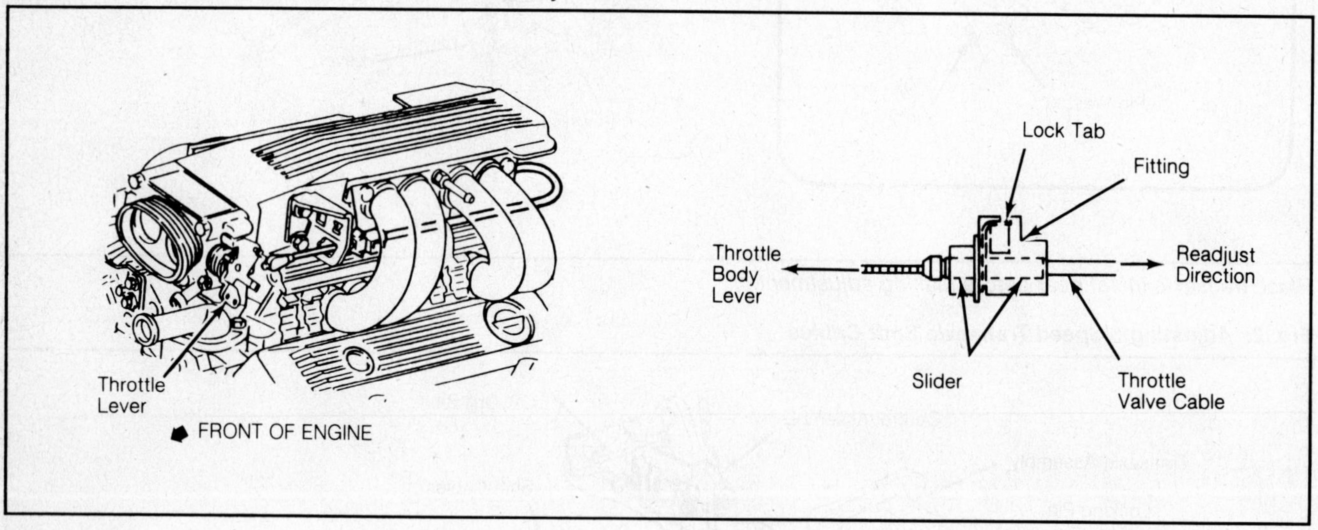

CHRYSLER CORP. FWD LIGHT TRUCKS

LUBRICATION

SERVICE INTERVALS

1) Under normal operating conditions, fluid installed at factory will give satisfactory lubrication for life of vehicle. Fluid changes are not necessary unless lubricant has been contaminated with water.

2) If vehicle is operated at sustained high speed during hot weather, above 90°F (32°C), transmission fluid should be changed and magnet (attached to inside of differential pan) cleaned every 15,000 miles.

Shift & Clutch Linkage

1) If linkage begins to squeak or grunt, pivot hole in adjuster and teeth of adjusting positioner should be lubricated with a thin film of multipurpose grease.

2) Gearshift control mechanism should be lubricated whenever high shift effort or noise (mechanism rattling) is apparent. A multipurpose grease is suitable for this application.

CHECKING FLUID LEVEL

Check lubricant level at filler plug hole on side of transmission. Lubricant should be level with bottom of filler plug hole. Add lubricant as needed to bring to correct level.

RECOMMENDED FLUID

FWD vehicles may be equipped with the A-460 or A-525 manual transaxles. If it becomes necessary to add fluid, use only fluids of the type labeled Dexron II automatic transmission fluid.

TRANSMISSION REFILL CAPACITIES

Application	Quantity
All Models [1]	2.1 qts. (2.0L)

[1] – Measure given is approximate.

ADJUSTMENT

SHIFT LINKAGE

1) Working over left front fender, remove lock pin from transaxle selector shaft housing. Reverse lock pin (long end down), and insert lock pin into same threaded hole while pushing selector shaft into selector housing. A hole in selector shaft will align with lock pin, allowing lock pin to be screwed into housing. This operation locks selector shaft in 1-2 position.

2) Remove gearshift knob, retaining nut, and pull-up ring. Remove boot from console. Install 2 cable adjusting pins. Torque selector cable adjusting screw to 55 INCH lbs. (6 N.m). Torque crossover cable adjusting screw to 55 INCH lbs. (6 N.m). *See Fig. 1.*

3) Install console boot, pull-up ring, retaining nut and gearshift knob. Remove lock pin from selector shaft housing and reinstall lock pin (so long end is up) in selector shaft housing. Tighten lock pin to 106 INCH lbs. (12 N.m). Check for shift into first and reverse. Check for blockout into reverse.

Fig. 1: Adjusting Gearshft Linkage

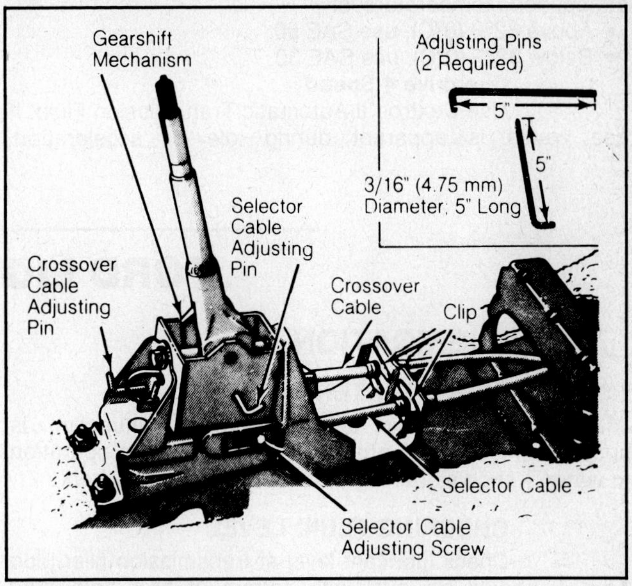

CHRYSLER CORP. RWD LIGHT TRUCKS

LUBRICATION

SERVICE INTERVALS

NOTE: **There are 2 light duty truck emission control standards classifications: Light Duty and Heavy Duty. Light Duty refers to vehicles up to 8500 lbs. GVW; Heavy Duty refers to vehicles over 8500 lbs. GVW.**

1) Check fluid level whenever vehicle is serviced. On vehicles used in normal service with heavy duty emissions, transmission should be drained and refilled every 36,000 miles.

2) On vehicles containing light duty emissions, transmission should be drained and refilled every 37,500 miles. On vehicles used under severe conditions, drain and refill transmission every 18,000 miles.

Shift Linkage

1) Gearshift control mechanism should be lubricated every 22,500 miles or every 2 years. Lubricate more frequently if shift effort or noise is apparent. The 4-speed gearshift linkage has a grease fitting located on left side of mechanism. Lubricate linkage from under vehicle.

2) Use a high pressure grease gun to lubricate linkage with multipurpose grease. Lubricate until grease is visible on operating levers.

CHRYSLER CORP. RWD LIGHT TRUCKS (Cont.)

CHECKING FLUID LEVEL

Check lubricant level at filler plug hole on side of transmission. Lubricant should be level with bottom of filler plug hole. Add lubricant as needed to bring to correct level.

RECOMMENDED FLUID

New Process 435 4-Speed

Either multipurpose gear lubricants meeting API specification GL-5 or engine oils labeled for API Service "SF" may be used.

If multipurpose gear lubricant is used and the minimum anticipated atmospheric temperature is:

- Above 90°F (32°C), use SAE 140.
- As low as -10°F (-23°C), use SAE 90.
- Below -10°F (-23°C), use SAE 80.

If engine oil is used and the minimum anticipated atmospheric temperature is:

- Above 32°F (0°C), use SAE 50.
- Below 32°F (0°C). use SAE 30.

Overdrive 4-Speed

Use Dextron II Automatic Transmission Fluid. If gear rattle is apparent during idle or acceleration, multipurpose gear lubricant SAE 90, SAE 75W, 75W-80, SAE 80W-90 or SAE 85W-90 may be used.

FLUID CAPACITY

TRANSMISSION REFILL CAPACITY

Application	Quanity
Overdrive 4-Speed	7.5 pts. (3.5L)
NP 435	7.0 pts. (3.5L)

ADJUSTMENTS

SHIFT LINKAGE

Overdrive 4-Speed

1) Install floor shift lever aligning tool to hold levers in neutral crossover position. *See Fig. 1.* Remove all rods from transmission shift levers and place levers in neutral detent positions.

2) Rotate shift rods until they are centered in transmission lever mounting holes, starting with 1st-2nd shift rod. Replace all washers and clips. Remove aligning tool and test shifting action.

FORD LIGHT TRUCKS

LUBRICATION

SERVICE INTERVALS

Check fluid level whenever malfunction is suspected, leakage is observed, or after vehicle operation in water. Periodic draining and refilling is not required.

CHECKING FLUID LEVEL

Check lubricant level at transmission filler plug hole. It should be level with bottom of filler hole. Add lubricant as needed.

RECOMMENDED FLUID

All transmissions except Warner T19B should use 80W multipurpose gear lubricant meeting Ford specification ESP-M2C83-C. Warner T19B transmissions use SAE 30 or SAE 50 engine oil, depending upon ambient air temperatures. If vehicle will be operated at temperatures below 0°F (-18°C), SAE 30 should be used. SAE 50 should be used if temperatures are consistently above 0°F (-18°C).

ADJUSTMENTS

SHIFT LINKAGE

Shift linkage may be adjusted only on the 3-speed and 4-speed overdrive transmissions. All other models use a internal shift linkage which cannot be adjusted.

3-Speed

1) Insert a 3/16" gauge pin through steering column shift levers and plastic spacer.

2) Loosen shift rod lock nuts at transmission shift levers. Place both shift levers in Neutral position. Tighten lock nuts and remove gauge pin. Check shift linkage operation for smoothness.

4-Speed Overdrive

1) Disconnect all 3 shift rods and insert a 1/4" diameter pin in alignment hole in shifter assembly. Align 1-2 (rear) and 3-4 (front) shift levers in Neutral position. Turn Reverse (middle) lever counterclockwise to theNeutral position.

2) Rotate transmission output shaft to ensure all levers are in Neutral. Turn reverse lever fully clockwise to Reverse position. This causes the interlock system to align 1-2 and 3-4 rails in precise Neutral positions. Install 1-2 and 3-4 shift rods on shift levers and tighten lock nuts.

3) Rotate reverse lever back to Neutral position. Install reverse shift rod and lock nut. Remove alignment pin and check for proper linkage operation.

FLUID CAPACITY

TRANSMISSION REFILL CAPACITY

Application	Quanity
Aerostar	
Mazda 5-Speed	4.0 pts. (1.7L)
Pickup, Van, Bronco	
Ford 3.03 3-Speed	3.5 pts. (1.6L)
Warner T-18 4-Speed	7.0 pts. (3.3L)
Warner T-19B 4-Speed	7.0 pts. (3.3L)
New Process 435 4-Speed	
With Extension	7.0 pts. (3.3L)
Without Extension	6.5 pts. (3.3L)
Ford Top Shifter (TOD)	
4-Speed Overdrive	4.5 pts. (2.1L)
Ford 4-Speed Overdrive	4.5 pts. (2.1L)
Bronco II, Ranger	
Mazda 5-Speed (2WD) or (4WD)	4.0 pts. (1.7L)
Mitsubishi 5-Speed (4WD)	3.0 pts. (1.4L)

GENERAL MOTORS LIGHT TRUCKS

LUBRICATION

SERVICE INTERVALS

NOTE: **There are 2 Light Duty truck emission control standards classifications: Light Duty and Heavy Duty. Light Duty refers to vehicles up to 8500 lbs. (GVW); Heavy Duty refers to vehicles over 8500 lbs. (GVW).**

On "S" models with 4-speed transmission, change transmission fluid after the first 7500 miles and at 30,000 mile intervals thereafter. On all other Light Duty vehicles, check transmission fluid every 12 months or 7500 miles. On Heavy Duty vehicles, check fluid level every 12 months or 6000 miles. Periodic draining and refilling is not required.

CHECKING FLUID LEVEL

Check lubricant level at transmission filler plug hole. Lubricant should be level with bottom of hole. Add as needed.

RECOMMENDED FLUID

All manual transmissions except 4-speed (89 MM), 5-speed (77 MM) and those in the "S" series, use SAE 80W, GL-5 or SAE 80W-90 GL-5 multipurpose gear lubricant. The 4-speed (89 MM), 5-speed (77 MM) and all "S" series vehicles with manual transmissions use Dexron II automatic transmission fluid.

FLUID CAPACITY

NOTE: **Capacities listed in the following chart are approximations only. Correct fluid level should be determined by level at filler plug hole, rather than by amount added.**

TRANSMISSION REFILL CAPACITIES

Application	Quanity
3-Speed (76 MM)	3.2 pts. (1.5L)
4-Speed (76 MM)	2.5 pts. (1.2L)
4-Speed (77.5 MM)	4.9 pts. (2.3L)
4-Speed (89 MM)	8.5 pts. (4.0L)
4-Speed (117 MM)	8.5 pts. (4.0L)
5-Speed (77 MM)	4.2 pts. (2.0L)

ADJUSTMENTS

NOTE: **The 4-speed 117 MM transmission has no shift rods, the shift lever mounts directly to the top of the transmission, and is therefore not adjustable.**

SHIFT LINKAGE

All With Column Shifter

1) Remove shift rods from transmission. Place First and Reverse gear selector lever on transmission in Reverse position. Move second and third transmission shift lever to forward detent, then back one.

2) Place column shifter in Reverse position. Turn ignition switch to "LOCK" position. Turn ignition switch to "LOCK" position. Move columm shifter to Neutral position and put a 1/4" gauge pin through holes in shift levers at base of steering column.

3) Loosen slide swivel on First and Reverse rod and place in First and Reverse transmission shift lever. Hold tightly in place and tighten swivel adjusting bolt. Install Second and Third shift rod.

4) Unlock steering wheel and remove gauge pin. Lubricate all rod and swivel connections.

All With Floor-Mounted Shifter (Except 4-Speed 89 MM)

1) Disconnect all shift rods from transmission shift levers. With shift control lever in Neutral position, insert a 1/4" diameter pin through alignment holes in shifter assembly.

2) Align both shift levers on the transmission in the forward detent, then back one detent. Loosen lock nuts on shift swivel ends and align rod ends with shift lever holes. Install shift rods in levers, tighten lock nuts and install lock pins.

3) Remove alignment pin and check for proper linkage operation.

Floor-Mounted Shifter (4-Speed 89 MM)

1) Loosen all shift rod adjustment nuts at transmission shift levers. Move shift control lever to Neutral position. Move all 3 transmission shift levers into Neutral.

2) Put a 1/4" gauge pin through control levers at base of shifter assembly. Hold shift rods forward tightly in their swivels and tighten adjustment nuts in that position.

3) Remove gauge pin. Lubricate all swivel joints and shift control.

JEEP

LUBRICATION

SERVICE INTERVALS

Under normal driving conditions, check fluid level every 5000 miles or when serviced. Under severe driving conditions, check fluid level every 3000 miles. Transmission lubricant should be changed at 27,500 mile intervals.

CHECKING FLUID LEVEL

Check lubricant level at transmission filler plug hole. Lubricant should be level with bottom of hole. Add lubricant as needed.

RECOMENDED FLUID

Recommended lubricant for Jeep with manual transmission is AMC/Jeep Manual Transmission Fluid (Part No. 89 83 000 000) or 75W-90 GL-5 gear lubricant.

JEEP (Cont.)

FLUID CAPACITY

TRANSMISSION REFILL CAPACITIES

Application	Quanity
4-Speed	
AX4	7.4 pts. (3.5L)
T4	3.9 pts. (1.8L)
T-176	3.5 pts. (1.7L)
5-Speed	
AX5	7.0 pts. (3.3L)
T5	4.5 pts. (2.1L)

NOTE: Capacities given are approximate. Correct fluid level should be determined by level at filler plug hole.

ADJUSTMENTS

SHIFT LINKAGE

NOTE: All Jeep models use transmission shift linkage which does not require an external adjustment.

AMERICAN MOTORS

REMOVAL & INSTALLATION

EAGLE

Removal

1) Shift transmission into neutral. Remove console (if equipped). Remove gearshift lever, bezel and boot from floor pan. Slide boot upward on lever. Remove bolts attaching gearshift lever to lever mounting cover.

2) Remove gearshift lever. Raise vehicle and support on jack stands. Remove skid pan and mark position of speedometer adapter for installation reference. Remove speedometer retainer, adapter and cable. Plug adapter hole to prevent oil spillage.

3) Disconnect drive shafts and mark for installation reference. Disconnect exhaust (if necessary). Disconnect back-up light switch wire. Place a jack stand under engine. Support transmission and transfer case with a transmission jack.

4) Remove rear crossmember. Remove catalytic converter bracket from transfer case. Remove bolts attaching transmission to clutch housing. Remove transmission and transfer case as an assembly.

ALLIANCE & ENCORE

Removal

1) Raise vehicle and support on jack stands. Remove wheel assemblies and disconnect axle shafts. Disconnect gearshift lever linkage and engine-to-transaxle rod. Remove clutch shield and all mounting pad nuts.

2) Remove air filter. Disconnect back-up light switch wire connector and remove sensor. Disconnect clutch cable, speedometer cable and ground wire. Remove radiator and lay it on engine without disconnecting hoses.

3) Raise engine enough to free rear mounts. Remove starter motor. Remove transaxle retaining bolts, separate transaxle from engine and lift it free of chassis. On models with JB 1 transaxle, slide 5th gear casing between side members.

Installation

To install, reverse removal procedure and note the following: Fill transmission/transaxle with fluid to proper level. See MANUAL TRANSMISSION SERVICING in this section.

Raise vehicle and support on jack stands. Remove wheel assemblies and disconnect axle shafts. Disconnect gearshift lever linkage and engine-to-transaxle rod. Remove clutch shield and all mounting pad nuts.

TIGHTENING SPECIFICATIONS

Application	Ft. Lbs. (N.m)
Alliance & Encore	
Transaxle-to-Engine Bolts	32 (42)
Starter Motor Bolts	32 (42)
Eagle	
Bell Housing-to-Engine	
6-Cylinder	
Top Bolts	27 (37)
Bottom Bolts	43 (58)
Transmission-to-Bell Housing	55 (75)
Rear Crossmember Studs	30 (41)
Support-to-Crossmember	18 (24)

CHRYSLER CORP.

REMOVAL & INSTALLATION

FWD MODELS

Removal

1) Disconnect negative battery cable. Support engine with engine support fixture. Disconnect shift linkage from transaxle selector shaft. Disconnect back-up light switch wire. Remove starter.

2) Disconnect clutch cable. Remove bolt securing speedometer adapter to transaxle. Carefully work adapter and pinion out of transaxle.

3) Loosen wheel hub nuts with vehicle on floor. Raise and support vehicle. Remove wheel assemblies. Disconnect right drive axle shaft and tie out of the way. Remove left drive axle shaft and set aside.

4) Remove left splash shield. Remove small dust cover at bell housing. Remove large dust cover bolts at bell housing.

5) Drain fluid from transaxle. Place jack under transaxle and chain in place. Remove bolts from left engine mount. Remove bolt attaching transaxle-to-engine. Slide transaxle assembly to the left and rear of vehicle.

Installation

To install, reverse removal procedure and note the following: Adjust clutch cable and fill transaxle with fluid to proper level. See MANUAL TRANSMISSION SERVICING in this section.

TIGHTENING SPECIFICATIONS

Application	Ft. Lbs. (N.m)
Ball Joint Clamp Bolt	50 (68)
Strut-to-Block & Case	70 (95)
Transaxle Case-to-Engine Block	70 (95)

Manual Transmission Removal

FORD MOTOR CO.

REMOVAL & INSTALLATION

EXC. ESCORT, EXP, LYNX TEMPO & TOPAZ

Removal (85 ET 4-Speed)

1) Remove shift lever. From under vehicle, remove upper bolts from clutch housing. Raise vehicle on a hoist. Mark position of and remove drive shaft. Remove clutch release cover and cable.

2) Remove starter motor and speedometer cable. Support rear of engine and remove crossmember bolts. Remove bolts that attach crossmember to extension housing of transmission. Lower engine to permit removal of clutch housing bolts. Slide transmission from engine and lower from vehicle.

Removal (T50D)

1) Raise vehicle on hoist. Mark position of and remove drive shaft. Remove 4 bolts and catalytic converter. Remove 2 nuts attaching rear transmission support-to-crossmember. On 2.3L Turbo models, remove header pipe from exhaust manifold.

2) Support engine and transmission with a jack. Remove 2 nuts from crossmember bolts. Remove bolts and crossmember. Lower transmission to expose 2 bolts securing shift handle to shift tower. Remove 2 nuts and bolts and shift handle.

3) Disconnect wiring harness from back-up light switch. On 5.0L engine, disconnect top gear sensing switch. Remove speedometer cable from housing. Remove 4 bolts securing transmission to clutch housing. Slide transmission from engine and lower from vehicle.

Installation

Reverse removal procedure and note the following: Fill transmission with fluid to proper level. See MANUAL TRANSMISSION SERVICING in this section.

TEMPO & TOPAZ

Removal (MTX 5-speed)

1) Wedge a wood block (7" long) under clutch pedal. Disconnect clutch cable clutch release lever. Remove 2 top transaxle-to-engine bolts. Remove air cleaner. Raise vehicle on a hoist.

2) Remove front stabilizer bar. Remove pinch bolts and nuts from lower control arm ball joints. Pry control arms away from knuckle. Using Joint Fork (D83P-4026-A), pry inboard CV joint from transaxle. Install Shipping Plugs (T81P-1177-B).

3) Remove inboard CV joint from transaxle by grasping left hand steering knuckle and swinging knuckle and halfshaft outward from transaxle. Tie halfshaft in a near level position. Remove back-up light switch connector.

4) Remove engine roll restrictor and starter motor. Remove shift mechanism stabilizer bar-to-transaxle attaching bolt. Remove sheet metal screw and control select indicator switch and bracket. Remove speedometer cable.

5) Remove 2 bolts from oil pan to clutch housing. Position jack under transaxle. Remove 2 nuts securing left hand front insulator to body bracket. Lower jack until transaxle clears rear insulator.

6) Support engine with a screw jack stand under oil pan. Use a 2x4 block on top of jack stand. Remove 4 engine-to-transaxle attaching bolts. Remove ground strap and wiring harness bracket.

Installation

Reverse removal procedure and note the following: Do not start engine until inner CV joints are installed. Fill transaxle with fluid to proper level. See MANUAL TRANSMISSION SERVICING in this section.

ESCORT, EXP & LNYX

Removal (MTX 5-Speed)

1) Wedge a block of wood (7" long) under clutch pedal. Remove clutch cable from clutch release lever and from rib on top surface of transaxle case. Remove 2 top transaxle-to-engine mounting bolts.

2) On 1.6L engines, remove top bolt that secures air management valve bracket. Raise vehicle on a hoist. Remove pinch bolt and nut from left lower control arm ball joint. Pry lower control from steering knuckle.

3) Pry left inboard CV joint from transaxle. Install Shipping Plug (T81P-1177-B) to prevent fluid loss. Tie halfshaft up, in a near level position. Remove pinch bolt and nut from right lower control arm ball joint. Pry lower control arm from steering knuckle. Pry right CV joint from transaxle and install Shipping Plug (T81P-1177-B).

4) Remove back-up light switch connector. On EFI vehicles, remove neutral sensing switch. Remove starter motor. Remove shift mechanism-to-shift shaft attaching bolt and nut and selector indicator switch arm.

5) Remove shift shaft. Remove shift mechanism stabilizer bar-to-transaxle attaching bolt, switch and bracket. Remove speedometer cable from housing. Remove stiffener brace bolts. Remove 2 bolts securing rear mount to floor pan brace.

6) Loosen nut in bottom of front mount. Remove 3 bolts securing front mount. Lower transaxle jack until transaxle clears rear mount. Support engine with screw jack (use a 2x4 piece of wood) under oil pan. Remove 4 engine to transaxle attaching bolts. Slide transaxle from engine and lower from vehicle.

Installation

Reverse removal procedure and note the following: Do not start engine until inner CV joints are installed. Fill transaxle with fluid to proper level. See MANUAL TRANSMISSION SERVICING in this section.

SABLE & TAURUS

NOTE: **Removal and Installation procedures were not available from the manufacturer.**

TIGHTENING SPECIFICATIONS

Application	Ft. Lbs. (N.m)
Escort, EXP, Lynx, Tempo & Topaz	
Front Mounting Bolts	25-35 (34-47)
Lower Ball Joint	37-44 (50-60)
Rear Mounting Bolts	35-50 (47-68)
Transaxle-to-Engine	25-35 (34-47)
All Others	
Bell Housing-to-Engine	38-55 (52-75)
Transmission-to-Support	36-50 (48-68)

Manual Transmission Removal

GENERAL MOTORS CORP.

REMOVAL & INSTALLATION

CHEVETTE, 1000, CAMARO & FIREBIRD (70 MM 4-SPEED & 77 MM 5-SPEED)

Removal

1) Disconnect negative battery cable. Remove screws from transmission shaft lever boot retainer and slide boot up lever. Remove shift lever attaching bolts at transmission and remove lever. Raise vehicle on a hoist. On Camaro and Firebird models, remove torque arm on rear suspension.

2) Mark position and remove drive shaft. Disconnect speedometer cable. Remove back-up light switch connector and clutch cable from clutch release lever. Remove crossmember-to-transmission mount bolts.

3) Remove header pipe and catalytic converter. Remove crossmember-to-frame bolts. Remove dust cover and clutch housing retaining bolts. Slide transmission back and lower from vehicle.

CORVETTE (83 MM 4-SPEED W/OVERDRIVE)

Removal

1) Disconnect negative battery cable. Remove air cleaner and disconnect T.V. cable at throttle lever. Remove distributor cap. Raise vehicle on a hoist. Disconnect O_2 sensor lead. Remove entire exhaust system.

2) Support transmission with a jack. Remove bolts attaching drive line beam at axle and transmission. Remove drive line beam from vehicle. Mark position of and remove drive shaft. Disconnect overdrive cooling lines. Disconnect T.V. cable at overdrive lever.

3) Disconnect shift linkage and electrical connectors from transmission switches. Lower transmission and support engine. Remove bolts from transmission-to-clutch housing. Slide transmission from engine and lower from vehicle.

FIERO

Removal

1) Remove air cleaner and negative battery cable. Remove ground strap and shifter cables. Install engine Support Fixture (J-28467).

2) Raise vehicle on a hoist. Remove both rear wheels and drive axles. Remove the catalytic converter heat shield. Remove the header pipe from the exhaust manifold.

3) Remove cradle-to-engine nuts. Support cradle with a screw jack and remove remaining cradle nuts. Lower cradle from vehicle. Remove starter shield and starter. Support transaxle with a jack and remove lower transaxle-to-engine bolts. Slide transaxle from engine and lower from vehicle.

ALL MODELS

Installation

To install, reverse removal procedures. Adjust T.V. cable and clutch cable. Fill transmission (transaxle) with lubricant to proper level. See MANUAL TRANSMISSION SERVICING in this section.

FRONT WHEEL DRIVE MODELS

Removal

1) Disconnect negative battery cable. On all models (except Nova), install engine holding fixture (J-28467) and raise engine to take pressure off engine mounts. On models with hydraulic clutch, remove lower bezel under steering column. Remove clutch pedal actuating rod and remove slave cylinder from transaxle.

2) On all other models, remove heater hose clamp from mount bracket. Disconnect and remove horns and air cleaner. Disconnect clutch cable from clutch shift lever. If V6 equipped, remove fuel lines and clamps at clutch cable bracket and remove crossover pipe.

3) On all models, remove transaxle mount(s) and bracket or center support. Disconnect shift cables, retaining clamps and ground strap. Remove upper transaxle-to-engine bolts.

4) Raise vehicle on a hoist, and drain the fluid. Remove the air management valve attaching bolts, if equipped. On Nova models, remove the starter and the splash shields. On all models, remove the front wheels and remove the drive axles. Disconnect the speedometer cable from the drive axle housing.

5) On Nova models, support engine with a jack. Remove left engine mount and lower assembly slightly. Support transaxle. Remove remaining bolts. Slide transaxle back and lower from vehicle.

6) On all other models, support transaxle with a jack and remove lower transaxle-to-engine bolts. Slide transaxle back and lower from vehicle.

Installation

To install, reverse removal procedure and note the following: When installing transaxle, guide right axle shaft (if necessary) into bore as transaxle is being raised. Fill transaxle with fluid to proper level. See MANUAL TRANSMISSION SERVICING in this section.

TIGHTENING SPECIFICATIONS

Application	Ft. Lbs. (N.m)
Front Wheel Drive Models	
Nova	
Bell Housing-to-Engine (10 mm Bolts)	34 (46)
Bell Housing-to-Engine (12 mm Bolts)	50 (64)
Center Support-to-Frame	30 (40)
Center Support-to-Mounts	30 (40)
Left Engine Mount	40 (52)
All Other Front Wheel Drive Models	
Bell Housing-to-Engine	55 (75)
Support-to-Body	75 (100)
Transaxle-to-Support	40 (50)
Fiero	
Engine Mount-to-Cradle	40 (55)
Cradle-to-Body	70 (95)
Transaxle-to-Engine	55 (75)
Transaxle Mount-to-Cradle	
Front	36 (48)
Rear	18 (24)
All Other Models	
Bell Housing-to-Engine	30 (40)
Drive Line Beam-to-Transmission	50 (60)
Support-to-Transmisison	30 (40)
Transmission Filler Plug	30 (40)
Transmission-to-Bell Housing	
83 mm 4-Speed Overdrive	52 (70)

Manual Transmission Removal

CHRYSLER CORP. FWD LIGHT TRUCKS

TRANSAXLE

NOTE: **Transaxle removal does not require engine removal.**

REMOVAL

1) Disconnect battery negative cable. Install a "lifting eye" on No. 4 cylinder exhaust manifold bolt and install engine support fixture. Disconnect gearshift operating lever from selector shaft. Remove clutch housing upper bolts. Remove both front wheel and tire assemblies.

2) Remove left front splash shield. Remove engine left mount from transaxle. Remove both drive axles. Remove speedometer adapter, cable and pinion as an assembly. Disconnect sway bar. Remove both lower ball joint-to-steering knuckle bolts.

3) Pry lower ball joint from steering knuckle. Remove both driveshafts. Remove dust cover, mark torque converter and drive plate, and remove torque converter mounting bolts. Remove access plug in right splash shield to rotate engine crankshaft.

4) Remove neutral safety switch connector. Remove engine mount bracket from front crossmember. Remove front mount insulator through-bolt and bell housing bolts. Position transmission jack under transaxle. Remove left engine mount. Remove starter and lower bell housing bolts.

5) Slowly lower transaxle. It may be necessary to pry at engine to provide for clearance.

INSTALLATION

NOTE: **When installing transaxle, it may be helpful to use 2 locating pins in place of top 2 transaxle-to-engine block bolts.**

1) Make locating pins from 2 stock (transaxle case-to-block) bolts. Using a hacksaw, remove bolt heads, and cut slot in end of bolts for a screwdriver. Remove burrs with a grinding wheel. Install locating pins into engine block and proceed with transaxle installation

2) After transaxle is in place, remove locating pins and install mounting bolts before removing transmission jack. To complete installation, reverse removal procedure. Be sure to adjust gearshift and throttle cables. Refill transaxle with Dexron II type automatic transmission fluid.

TIGHTENING SPECIFICATIONS

Application	Ft. Lbs. (N.m)
Bell Flex Plate-to-Crank	
A-413	65 (88)
A-470	100 (136)
Flex Plate-to-Torque Converter	40 (54)
Transaxle-to-Cylinder Block	70 (95)
Starter-to-Transaxle Bell Housing	40 (54)
Manual Cable-to-Transaxle Case	21 (28)
Front Motor Mount	40 (54)
Left Motor Mount	40 (54)
	INCH lbs.
Housing Cover	108 (12)
Lower Bell Housing Cover	108 (12)
Manual Control Lever	108 (12)
Speedometer-to-Extension	60 (7)
Throttle Cable-to-Transaxle Case	108 (12)
Throttle Lever-to Transaxle Shaft	108 (12)

CHRYSLER CORP. RWD LIGHT TRUCKS

TRANSFER CASE

MODEL NP-205

Removal

1) Raise and support vehicle. Remove drain plug and drain transfer case. Replace plug. Disconnect speedometer cable. Remove skid plate, crossmember and strut rods as needed. Disconnect propeller shafts and wire out of way. DO NOT allow propeller shafts to hang free, as damage to universal joints may result.

2) Disconnect shift lever rod from shift rail link. Support transfer case and remove transfer case-to-transmission adapter bolts. Move transfer case to rear until input shaft clears adapter. Lower transfer case from vehicle.

Installation

To install transfer case, reverse removal procedure. Ensure that all attaching bolts are tight. Fill transfer case with lubricant.

MODEL NP-208

Removal

1) Raise vehicle, remove drain plug and drain transfer case. Mark front and rear output shaft yokes and propeller shafts for reassembly reference. Disconnect speedometer cable and indicator switch wires. Disconnect shift lever link from operating lever.

2) Support transfer case with transmission jack and remove crossmember. Disconnect front and rear propeller shafts at yokes and wire to frame.

3) If necessary, disconnect parking brake cable guide from pivot on right frame rail. Remove bolts attaching exhaust pipe support bracket to transfer case. Remove transfer case-to-transmission bolts. Move assembly to the rear until clear of output shaft. Lower transfer case from vehicle.

4) Remove all gasket material from rear of transmission adapter housing.

Installation

1) Install new transmission-to-transfer case gasket with sealer on both sides. Align transfer case with transmission. Rotate transfer case output shaft until transmission output shaft engages transfer case input shaft.

2) Move transfer case until case seats flush against transmission. Install transfer case attaching bolts. To complete installation, reverse removal procedures.

Manual Transmission Removal

CHRYSLER CORP. RWD LIGHT TRUCKS (Cont.)

TRANSMISSION

REMOVAL

1) Disconnect negative battery cable. Remove retaining screws from floor pan and slide boot up and off shift lever.

2) On models equipped with New Process 435 transmission, remove shift lever retainer by pressing down, rotating retainer clockwise and releasing.

3) On models equipped with Overdrive 4-Speed transmission, remove shift lever by inserting a .010" (.25 mm) feeler gauge between floor shift assembly and shift lever, and disengaging internal spring clip. *See Fig. 1.*

Fig. 1: Removing Overdrive 4-Speed Shift Lever

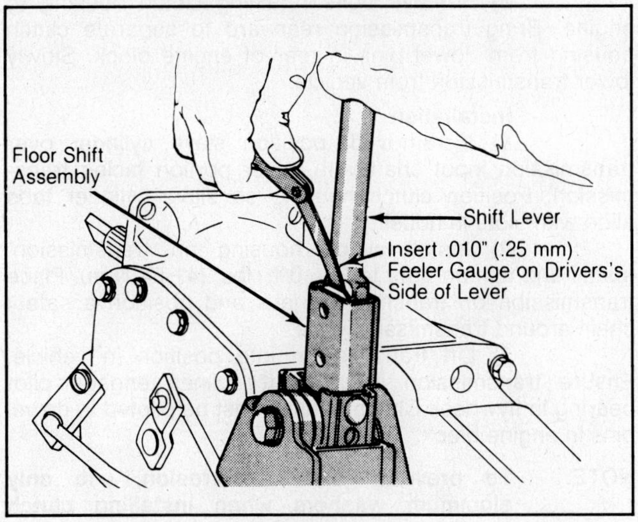

Insert feeler gauge to remove spring clip.

4) Remove bolts and washers securing shift lever to mounting plate on extension housing and remove.

5) On all models, drain fluid from transmission. On 4WD models, remove transfer case. On all vehicles, remove propeller shaft from transmission at rear universal joint. Disconnect speedometer cable and back-up light switch. Install Engine Support Fixture (C-3487-A).

6) On models equipped with New Process 435 transmission, place Adapters (DD-1279) firmly over frame rails. On all models, make sure support ends of engine fixture tool are up against underside of oil pan flange.

7) Raise engine slightly with support fixture. On models with Overdrive 4-Speed transmission, disconnect extension housing from removable center crossmember.

8) On all models, support transmission with a jack and remove crossmember. Remove transmission-to-clutch housing bolts. Slide transmission rearward until drive pinion shaft clears clutch disc, then lower and remove transmission.

INSTALLATION

1) To install transmission, reverse removal procedure. Apply a small amount of high-temperature grease to the pilot shaft bushing in the flywheel and on pinion bearing release sleeve area before installing transmission.

2) As transmission is installed, engage pinion shaft with clutch disc by slowly turning shaft to engage teeth. DO NOT allow transmission to hang free once clutch disc has been engaged.

TIGHTENING SPECIFICATIONS

Application	Ft. Lbs. (N.m)
Transfer Case-to-Transmission	40 (54)
Crossmember-to-Frame	30 (41)
Ext. Housing-to-Rear Mount Bolt	50 (68)
Transmission Case-to-Clutch Housing	
Overdrive 4-Speed	50 (68)
NP-435	105 (142)

FORD LIGHT TRUCKS

TRANSFER CASE

NP-208 (BRONCO, F-150 & F-250)

Removal

1) Raise and support vehicle. Remove drain plug and drain fluid from transfer case. Replace plug. Disconnect 4WD indicator switch connector at transfer case. Disconnect speedometer driven gear from transfer case rear bearing retainer.

2) Remove transmission shift lever-to-transfer case retaining nut. Remove skid plate from frame. Support transfer case with transmission jack. Disconnect front and rear propeller shafts from transfer case output shaft yokes and wire out of way. DO NOT allow shafts to hang free as damage to universal joints may result.

3) Remove transfer case-to-transmission adapter bolts. Remove gasket between transfer case and adapter and lower transfer case out of vehicle.

Installation

To install transfer case, reverse removal procedures. Fill case with 7 pints (3.3 liters) of Dexron II type automatic transmission fluid.

BORG-WARNER 1345 (F-150 & F-350)

Removal

1) Raise vehicle. Remove drain plug and drain fluid from transfer case. Replace plug. Disconnect 4WD indicator switch connector at transfer case. If equipped, remove skid plate.

2) Disconnect front and rear propeller shafts from transfer case output shaft yokes, and wire out of way. DO NOT allow shafts to hang free as damage to universal joints may result.

3) Disconnect speedometer driven gear from rear bearing retainer. Remove retaining clips and shift rod from transfer case control and transfer case shift levers. Disconnect vent hose from case.

4) Remove heat shield. Support transfer case with transmission jack, remove transfer case-to-transmission adapter bolts and slide transfer case off of transmission output shaft (towards rear). Lower transfer case out of vehicle and remove gasket from between transfer case and adapter.

Installation

Reverse removal procedures to install transfer case. Fill case with 6.5 pints (3.1 liters) of Dexron II type automatic transmission fluid.

BORG-WARNER 1350 (BRONCO II & RANGER)

Removal

1) Raise vehicle. Remove skid plate (if equipped). Remove drain plug and drain fluid from case. Replace plug. Disconnect 4WD indicator switch connector at transfer case. Disconnect front propeller shaft from front axle. Loosen front shaft boot clamp and slide out propeller shaft and boot as an assembly.

2) Disconnect rear propeller shaft from transfer case. Disconnect speedometer driven gear from transfer case rear cover. Disconnect vent hose from control lever.

3) Loosen bolts retaining shifter to extension housing. Pull on control lever until bushing slides off transfer case shift lever pin. Unscrew shift lever from control lever, as needed.

4) Remove heat shield from transfer case. Support transfer case with jack and remove transfer case-to-transmission extension housing bolts (5). Slide transfer case to the rear and off of transmission output shaft. Lower case from vehicle. Remove gasket from between transfer case and extension housing.

Installation

1) To install transfer case, reverse removal procedures. When installing shift lever assembly, tighten large bolt first, then small bolt.

2) When installing vent assembly, White marking on hose should be positioned in notch in shifter with upper end of hose 2 inches above top of shifter, inside of shift lever boot.

3) Before installing front propeller shaft into transfer case, lubricate female splines of transfer case input shaft with multipurpose grease.

4) Fill transfer case to bottom of fill plug hole with Dexron-II automatic transmission fluid.

TRANSMISSION

5-SPEED MAZDA (AEROSTAR)

Removal

1) Disconnect negative battery cable from battery. Shift transmission into Neutral. Remove 4 bolts retaining boot assembly to floor. Lift boot up shift lever assembly.

2) Remove 4 bolts retaining shift lever assembly to transmission remote shift rail adaptor. Remove lever, knob and boot assembly. Raise vehicle on a hoist. Disconnect starter cable and wires. Remove starter retaining bolts and remove starter.

3) Remove clip retaining tube to hydraulic clutch slave cylinder. Remove tube and fitting from slave cylinder. Cap end of tube and slave cylinder to prevent foreign object damage.

4) Disconnect back-up lamp switch, shift indicator and neutral position wires from senders on transmission. Remove cable (conventional speedometer) or disconnect wire (electronic speedometer) from fitting.

5) Scribe a mark on driveshaft and rear axle flange, marking propeller shaft position for installation. Remove "U" bolts and nuts from rear axle flange. Remove propeller shaft.

6) Cap transmission extension housing to prevent lubricant spillage. Remove nuts retaining insulator to crossmember. Loosen nut and washer assemblies attaching front insulators to crossmember brackets.

7) Position transmission jack under transmission. Place jack safety chain around transmission. Slightly raise transmission. Remove nuts and bolts retaining crossmember to frame and remove crossmember.

8) Remove bolts retaining clutch housing to engine. Bring transmission rearward to separate clutch housing from dowel pins in rear of engine block. Slowly lower transmission from vehicle.

Installation

1) If removed, position slave cylinder over transmission input shaft with tower portion facing transmission. Position clutch housing so slave cylinder tabs align with slots in housing.

2) Install clutch housing on transmission. Install and tighten nuts to 30-40 ft. lbs. (41-54 N.m). Place transmission on transmission jack and position a safety chain around transmission case.

3) Lift transmission into position in vehicle. Ensure transmission input shaft splines engage pilot bearing in flywheel. Clutch housing mst be piloted in dowel pins in engine block.

NOTE: **To prevent galvanic corrosion, use only aluminum washers when installing clutch housing to engine.**

4) Install bolts retaining clutch housing to engine block. Tighten bolts to 28-33 ft. lbs. (38-51 N.m). If removed, position insulator on transmission. Install and tighten bolts to 60-80 ft. lbs. (82-108 N.m).

5) Position crossmember in frame brackets. Install nuts and bolts and finger tighten. Lower transmission so insulator studs are piloted in proper holes in crossmember. Tighten nuts to 71-94 ft. lbs. (97-127 N.m).

6) Remove cap from extension housing. Install propeller shaft, ensuring that marks scribed on propeller shaft and rear axle flange are in alignment. Install "U" bolts and nuts and tighten 96-180 INCH lbs. (11-20 N.m).

7) Install speedometer cable (conventional speedometer) or connect wire (electronic speedometer). Connect back-up lamp switch and shift indicator wire to senders on transmission. Remove cap from hydraulic clutch tube.

8) Install clip retaining tube and fitting to slave cylinder. To complete installation, reverse removal procedure.

5-SPEED MAZDA (BRONCO II & RANGER)

Removal

1) Place shift lever in neutral position. Remove boot retainer screws and bolts attaching retainer cover to gearshift lever retainer. Disconnect clutch master cylinder push rod from clutch pedal.

2) Pull gearshift lever assembly, shim and bushing straight up and away from lever retainer. Cover shift tower in extension housing with a cloth to avoid dropping foreign material into transmission.

3) Disconnect clutch hydraulic system master cylinder push rod from clutch pedal. Open hood and disconnect battery negative cable from battery terminal. Raise vehicle. Disconnect drive shaft at rear axle drive flange.

4) Pull drive shaft rearward and disconnect from transmission. Install a suitable plug in extension housing to prevent lubricant leakage. Remove clutch housing dust shield and slave cylinder and secure it at one side.

5) Remove speedometer cable from extension housing. Disconnect starter motor and back-up lamp switch wires. Place jack under engine, protecting oil pan with a wood block.

6) On 4WD vehicles, remove transfer case. Remove starter motor. Position a transmission jack under transmission. Remove bolts, lock washers and flat washers attaching transmission to engine rear plate.

7) Remove nuts and bolts attaching transmission mount and damper to crossmember. Remove nuts attaching crossmember to frame side rails and remove crossmember.

8) Lower engine jack. Work clutch housing off locating dowels and slide transmission rearward until input shaft spline clears clutch disc. Remove transmission from vehicle.

Installation

To install, reverse removal procedure.

5-SPEED MITSUBISHI (BRONCO II & RANGER)

Removal

1) Place gearshift selector in neutral. Remove boot retainer bolts. Remove bolts attaching retainer cover to gearshift lever retainer. Pull gearshift lever assembly out of transfer case adapter. Cover opening in transfer case adapter with a cloth to prevent dirt from falling into adapter.

2) Open hood and disconnect battery negative cable from battery terminal. Raise vehicle. Index rear drive shaft to front axle flange and transfer case. Disconnect drive shaft at rear axle flange. Pull rear drive shaft rearward and disconnect drive shaft from transmission.

3) Install a suitable plug in transfer case adapter to prevent lubricant leakage. Remove clutch housing dust shield. Disconnect hydraulic fluid line from clutch slave cylinder. Plug line to prevent fluid leakage. Disconnect speedometer from transfer case adapter.

4) Disconnect starter motor cable, back-up lamp switch wire and shift indicator switch wire. Disconnect neutral position switch (2.3L EFI engine). Place jack under engine block, protecting oil pan with wood block. Remove transfer case from vehicle.

5) Remove starter. Place a transmission jack under transmission. Remove bolts, lock washers and flat washers attaching transmission to engine and plate. Remove nuts and bolts attaching transmission mount and damper to crossmember.

6) Remove nuts attaching crossmember to frame side rails and remove crossmember. Lower engine jack. Work clutch housing off locating dowels and slide transmission rearward until input shaft clears clutch disc. Remove transmission from vehicle.

Installation

To install, reverse removal procedure.

3.03 3-SPEED ("E" SERIES)

Removal

1) Raise and support vehicle. Remove lower extension housing-to-transmission bolt to drain lubricant. Disconnect propeller shaft from flange at transmission and wire out of way. Do not allow shaft to hang free as damage to universal joint may result.

2) Disconnect speedometer cable and shift control rods from transmission shift levers. Place jack under transmission and secure transmission to jack with safety chain.

3) Raise transmission slightly and remove 4 bolts retaining transmission extension housing to insulator and retainer assembly. Remove transmission-to-clutch housing bolts. Install engine support bar on frame, under engine, and lower transmission out of vehicle.

Installation

Reverse removal procedures to install. Fill transmission with lubricant. Adjust clutch and shift linkages.

3.03 3-SPEED ("F" SERIES)

Removal

1) Raise vehicle and support on safety stands. Support engine with jack and wood block under oil pan. To drain fluid from transmission, remove lower extension housing-to-transmission bolt.

2) Place jack under transmission and secure transmission to jack with safety chain. Disconnect shift linkage at transmission. Disconnect speedometer cable and back-up switch wires.

3) Disconnect propeller shaft and wire out of way. Do not allow shaft to hang free as damage to universal joint may result. Raise transmission and remove rear support, insulator and retainer.

4) Remove transmission-to-clutch housing attaching bolts. Move transmission rearward until input shaft clears clutch housing. Lower transmission out of vehicle. DO NOT depress clutch pedal at any time while transmission is out of vehicle.

Installation

To install, reverse removal procedures. Apply a thin film of multipurpose grease to the release bearing inner hub surfaces, release lever fulcrum and fork, and transmission front bearing retainer. With installation complete, fill transmission with lubricant. Adjust clutch and shift linkage.

4-SPEED OVERDRIVE ("E" SERIES)

Removal

1) Raise and support vehicle. Mark propeller shaft position for reassembly reference. Disconnect propeller shaft from rear axle and slide shaft out of transmission. Disconnect speedometer cable and shift rods. Remove bolts connecting shift control to transmission case.

2) Remove rear transmission support-to-crossmember bolts. Support engine with transmission jack and raise transmission enough to take weight off number 3 crossmember. Remove bolts holding crossmember to frame side supports. Remove crossmember.

3) Place jack under rear of engine and raise high enough to remove weight from forward crossmember. Remove crossmember. With transmission supported by and secured to transmission jack, remove clutch housing-to-transmission bolts.

FORD LIGHT TRUCKS (Cont.)

4) Move transmission to the rear until input shaft clears clutch housing and remove transmission. DO NOT depress clutch pedal while transmission is out of vehicle.

Installation

To install, reverse removal procedures.

(T.O.D.) 4-SPEED OVERDRIVE ("F" SERIES 2WD)

Removal

1) Raise vehicle on hoist. Mark drive shaft to aid as reference at reassembly. Disconnect drive shaft from rear flange. Slide drive shaft off transmission output shaft and install extension housing seal installer into extension housing to prevent lubrication leakage.

2) Disconnect speedometer cable from extension housing. Disconnect back-up lamp switch and high gear switch wires. Remove shift lever from transmission. Support engine with a transmission jack and remove extension housing-to-engine rear support attaching bolts.

3) Raise rear of engine high enough to remove weight from crossmember. Remove bolts retaining crossmember to frame side supports and remove crossmember. Support transmission on a jack and remove bolts attaching transmission to flywheel housing.

4) Move transmission and jack rearward until transmission input shaft clears flywheel housing. If necessary, lower engine enough to obtain clearance for transmission removal. DO NOT depress clutch pedal while transmission is removed.

Installation

To install, reverse removal procedure.

(T.O.D.) 4-SPEED OVERDRIVE (BRONCO & F-150 4WD)

Removal

1) Raise vehicle on a hoist. Drain transmission and transfer case. Disconnect 4WD indicator switch wire connector at transfer case. Disconnect back-up lamp switch wire connector at transmission. If equipped, remove skid plate. Mark front and rear drive shafts for reference at reassembly.

2) Disconnect rear drive shaft from transfer case and wire it out of way. Disconnect front drive shaft from transfer case and wire out of way. Remove speedometer cable from transfer case. Remove retaining clips and shift rod from transfer case control lever and transfer case shift lever.

3) Disconnect vent hose from transfer case. Remove shift lever from transmission. Support transmission with a transmission jack and remove transmission housing-to-engine rear support bracket. Raise rear of transmission high enough to remove weight from crossmember.

4) Remove 2 nuts connecting upper gusset to frame on both sides of frame. Remove nut and bolt assembly connecting gusset to support. Remove gusset on left side. Remove bolts holding transmission to transmission support plate on crossmember. Raise transmission with a transmission jack.

5) Remove nut and bolt assemblies connecting support plate to crossmember. Remove support plate and right gusset. Remove nut and bolt assemblies connecting crossmember to frame. Remove crossmember. Remove heat shield from transfer case. Support transfer case with a transmission jack.

6) Remove 6 bolts retaining transfer case to transmission adapter. Slide transfer case rearward off of transmission output shaft and lower transfer case from vehicle. Remove gasket between transfer case and adapter. Support transmission on a jack and remove bolts attaching transmission to flywheel housing.

7) Move transmission and jack rearward until transmission input shaft clears flywheel housing. If necessary, lower engine enough to obtain clearance for transmission removal. DO NOT depress clutch pedal while transmission is removed.

Installation

To install, reverse removal procedure.

NP 435 4-SPEED (BRONCO & "F" SERIES)

Removal

1) Remove floor mat. Remove shift lever, shift ball and boot as an assembly. On 4WD models, remove transfer case shift lever, shift ball and boot as an assembly. On F150-350 models, remove floor pan transmission cover or weather pad. Remove seat if necessary.

2) To remove gearshift lever and knob, first remove inner cap with Puller (T73T 7220 A). Remove seat and spring. Remove gearshift lever. Disconnect back-up light.

3) Raise vehicle. Disconnect speedometer cable and rear propeller shaft. Wire shaft out of way. On 4WD models, drain transfer case, remove front propeller shaft from case and wire out of way.

4) Remove cotter pin holding shift link and remove link. Remove bolts holding bracket to transfer case. Position transmission jack under transfer case.

5) Remove transfer case-to-transmission bolts and remove transfer case. On all models, place transmission jack under transmission and lift slightly. Remove transmission-to-insulator, insulator-to-crossmember and crossmember-to-frame bolts. Remove insulator and crossmember.

6) Remove transmission-to-clutch housing bolts and lower transmission out of vehicle.

Installation

To install transmission, reverse removal procedures.

WARNER T-18 ("F" SERIES 2WD)

Removal

1) Working from inside vehicle, remove floor mat and body floor pan cover. Remove gearshift lever, shift ball and boot as an assembly. Remove weather pad. Raise and support vehicle. Disconnect speedometer cable.

2) Disconnect back-up light switch from rear of gear shift housing cover. Disconnect propeller shaft from transmission and wire out of way. DO NOT allow shaft to hang free as damage to universal joint may result. Disconnect clutch linkage.

3) Remove skid plate (if equipped) and heat shield. Support transmission with jack. Remove crossmember gusset-to-frame bolts and gusset-to-crossmember bolts. Remove transmission-to-insulator bolts. Raise transmission and remove insulator-to-crossmember bolts. Remove insulator.

4) Remove right gusset, crossmember-to-frame bolts and crossmember. Remove transmission-to-clutch housing bolts. Move transmission away from clutch

FORD LIGHT TRUCKS (Cont.)

housing until input shaft clears housing. Lower transmission out of vehicle.

Installation

To install, reverse removal procedures. When installing shift lever, shift ball and boot assembly, lubricate the spherical ball seat with multipurpose grease.

WARNER T-18 (BRONCO & "F" SERIES 4WD)

Removal

1) Working from inside vehicle, remove floor mat and access cover to floor pan. Place shift lever in reverse position and remove cover, insulator and dust cover. Remove transfer case shift lever, shift ball and boot as an assembly.

2) Remove transmission shift lever, shift ball and boot as an assembly. Raise vehicle. Remove drain plug and allow transmission to drain. Replace plug. Disconnect front and rear propeller shafts from transfer case and wire out of way. DO NOT allow shafts to hang free as damage to universal joint may result.

3) Remove shift link retainer ring and remove shift link from transfer case. Disconnect speedometer cable. Place transmission jack under transfer case. Remove transfer case-to-transmission bolts and lower transfer case out of vehicle.

4) Remove rear support bracket-to-transmission bolts (8), position transmission jack under transmission and remove rear support bracket and brace. Remove transmission-to-clutch housing bolts (4), and remove transmission.

Installation

To install the transmission, reverse removal procedures.

WARNER T19B ("F" SERIES 2WD)

Removal

1) Working from inside vehicle, remove floor mat and body floor pan cover. Remove gearshift lever, shift ball and boot as an assembly. Remove weather pad.

2) Raise vehicle. Place transmission jack under transmission and disconnect speedometer cable. Disconnect back-up light switch from rear of gear shift housing cover. Disconnect propeller shaft and clutch linkage. Wire out of way.

3) Remove transmission rear insulator and lower retainer. Remove skid plate (if equipped) and heat shield. Remove upper gusset bolts and gusset-to-crossmember bolts. Remove left side gusset.

4) Remove transmission-to-support plate bolts, raise transmission slightly and remove support plate-to-crossmember bolts. Remove support plate and right gusset. Remove crossmember-to-frame bolts and remove crossmember.

5) Remove transmission-to-clutch housing bolts. Move transmission to the rear until input shaft clears housing and remove transmission.

Installation

To install transmission, reverse removal procedures. When installing shift lever, shift ball and boot assembly, lubricate spherical ball seat with multipurpose grease.

WARNER T19B & T19D ("F" SERIES 4WD)

Removal

1) Working from inside vehicle, remove floor mat and access cover to floor pan (shift lever in reverse when removing cover). Remove insulator and dust cover. Remove transfer case shift lever, shift ball and boot as an assembly.

2) Remove transmission shift lever, shift ball and boot as an assembly. Raise vehicle. Drain transmission and replace drain plug. Disconnect front and rear drive shafts from transfer case and wire out of way.

3) Remove shift link retainer ring and remove link from transfer case. Disconnect speedometer cable. Place transmission jack under transfer case and remove transfer case-to-transmission bolts (6). Lower transfer case out of vehicle.

4) Remove rear support bracket-to-transmission bolts (8). Place transmission jack under transmission and remove rear support bracket and brace. Remove transmission-to-clutch housing bolts (4) and remove transmission.

Installation

To install the transmission, reverse removal procedures.

TIGHTENING SPECIFICATIONS

Application	Ft. Lbs. (N.m)
Transmission-to-Clutch Housing	
Bronco II & Ranger	30-40 (42-56)
All Others	
3-Speed	42-50 (59-70)
4-Speed	35-50 (49-70)
Transfer Case-to-Transmission	
NP-208	20-25 (28-35)
Borg-Warner 1345	25-43 (35-60)
Borg-Warner 1350	25-35 (35-49)
Insulator-to-Crossmember	
3-Speed	50-70 (70-98)
4-Speed Overdrive	50-70 (70-98)
Bronco II & Ranger	71-94 (98-132)
Insulator-to-Transmission	
3-Speed ("E" Models)	50-70 (70-98)
4-Speed Overdrive	50-70 (70-98)
T19B 4-Speed	45-60 (63-84)
All Others	60-80 (84-112)

Manual Transmission Removal

GENERAL MOTORS LIGHT TRUCKS

TRANSFER CASE

NP-205 (30 SERIES)

Removal

1) Raise and support vehicle on hoist. Drain transfer case. Disconnect speedometer cable. Remove skid plate and crossmember supports as necessary. Disconnect rear drive shaft from transfer case and tie up away from work area.

2) Disconnect front drive shaft from transfer case and tie up shaft away from work area. Disconnect shift lever rod from shift rail link. Support transfer case and remove bolts attaching transfer case to transmission adapter.

3) Move transfer case to rear until input shaft clears adapter and lower assembly from vehicle.

Installation

To install, reverse removal procedure.

NP-207 ("S" SERIES)

Removal

1) With transfer case shift lever in "4H" position, disconnect negative battery cable. Raise vehicle and remove skid plate. Drain transfer case. Mark front and rear output shaft yokes and propeller shafts for reassembly reference and remove shafts.

2) Disconnect speedometer cable and vacuum harness from transfer case. Remove shift lever from case. Remove catalytic converter hanger bolts at converter. Raise transmission and transfer case assembly with jack and remove transmission mount bolts. Remove mount.

3) Lower complete assembly. Support transfer case alone and remove transmission-to-transfer case bolts. Remove shift lever bracket from transfer case adapter in order to reach upper left attaching bolt.

4) Separate transfer case from transmission adapter and remove from vehicle.

Installation

To install, reverse removal procedure. Always use a new gasket between the transfer case and adapter.

NP-208 (10 & 20 SERIES)

Removal

1) Place transfer case in "4H". Raise vehicle. Drain lubricant from transfer case. Remove cotter pin from shift lever swivel. Mark transfer case front and rear output shaft yokes and propeller shafts for assembly alignment reference.

2) Disconnect speedometer cable and indicator switch wires. Disconnect front drive shaft at transfer case yoke. Disconnect parking brake cable guide from pivot located on right frame rail, if necessary. Remove engine strut rod from transfer case.

3) Place support under transfer case and remove transfer case-to-transmission adapter bolts. Move transfer case assembly rearward until free of transmission output shaft and remove assembly. Remove all gasket material from rear of transmission adapter housing.

Installation

To install, reverse removal procedure.

TRANSMISSION

ALL EXCEPT "K" & "S" SERIES

Removal

1) On models with 117 MM 4-speed transmission, remove attaching screws from shift lever boot retainer. Slide boot assembly upshift lever and remove lever. To remove shift lever, push down on collar and turn counterclockwise.

2) On all models, raise and support vehicle under frame. Drain fluid from transmission. Disconnect speedometer cable at transmission. Remove shift controls from transmission (if not already removed). Remove parking brake lever, controls, and back-up switch wire as needed.

3) Disconnect propeller shaft at transmission and position support under transmission assembly. Disconnect exhaust pipes from exhaust manifolds as needed. Remove frame crossmember and flywheel inspection plate.

4) On 117 MM 4-speed, remove top 2 transmission-to-clutch housing bolts and install guide pins. On all models, remove all transmission-to-clutch housing attaching bolts, slide transmission rearward until input shaft is clear of clutch hub and remove assembly from vehicle. Remove guide pins if used.

NOTE: **Support clutch release bearing and support assembly when removing transmission main drive gear from flywheel housing. This will prevent release bearing from falling out of flywheel housing.**

Installation

Apply a light coating of high temperature grease to main drive gear bearing retainer and splined portion of transmission main drive gear shaft. Reverse removal procedures to complete installation.

ALL "K" SERIES

Removal

1) On models with 117 MM 4-speed, remove attaching screws from shift lever boot retainer. Slide boot assembly up shift lever and remove lever. To remove shift lever, push down on collar and turn counterclockwise.

2) On all models, raise and support vehicle under frame. Drain fluid from transmission and transfer case. Disconnect speedometer cable. Disconnect front and rear propeller shafts at transfer case and wire out of way. Disconnect transfer case shift lever.

3) Position support under transfer case. Remove transfer case-to-adapter bolts and remove transfer case. Disconnect shift control rods from shifter levers if not already removed. Separate exhaust pipes from exhaust manifolds as needed.

4) Support rear part of engine and remove 2 adapter bolts. Remove crossmember. Remove 2 top transmission-to-clutch housing cap screws. Insert 2 Guide Pins (J-1126 on 117 MM, J-2216 all others) in holes. Remove 2 lower transmission-to-clutch housing cap screws.

5) Slide transmission and adapter assembly rearward until clutch gear is free of splines in clutch disc. Guide pins will support transmission and prevent damage to clutch disc. Remove transmission and adapter as an assembly. Remove adapter from transmission.

GENERAL MOTORS LIGHT TRUCKS (Cont.)

Installation

Apply a light coating of high temperature grease to main drive gear bearing retainer and splined portion of transmission main drive gear shaft. Reverse removal procedures to complete installation.

ALL "S" SERIES

NOTE: **If vehicle is a 4WD model, refer to TRANSFER CASE removal procedures and remove case.**

Removal

1) Disconnect negative battery cable. On 77.5 MM 4-speed, remove upper starter motor nut. On all models, remove shift lever boot screws and slide boot up shift lever. Shift transmission into neutral and remove shift lever bolts at transmission. Remove shift lever.

2) Disconnect electrical connector and clip at transmission, if present. Raise vehicle and remove propeller shaft. Disconnect exhaust pipe at manifold, (if needed).

3) Disconnect speedometer cable, electrical connector and clutch cable at transmission. Support transmission on jack and remove mount attaching bolts. Remove catalytic converter hanger. Remove crossmember attaching bolts and crossmember. Remove flywheel inspection cover.

4) On 77.5 MM 4-speed, remove lower starter motor attaching bolt. Remove body mounting bolts on left side of body and loosen radiator support bolt. Raise cab on left side as needed to remove upper bell housing attaching bolts. Support cab with wood block between frame and cab.

5) Remove transmission-to-engine bolts on all models. Remove transmission.

Installation

To install transmission, reverse removal procedures. On 77 MM 4-speed, coat main drive gear bearing retainer and splined portion of transmission main drive gear with high temperature grease before installation.

TIGHTENING SPECIFICATIONS

Application	Ft. Lbs. (N.m)
Transmission-to-Clutch Housing	
All Except "S" Series	75 (102)
"S" Series	
1.9L 4-Cylinder	25 (35)
2.8L V6	55 (75)
Crossmember-to-Frame	
"S" Series	25 (30)
All Others	55-65 (75-88)
Crossmember-to-Mount	
"S" Series	25 (30)
All Others	40-45 (54-61)
Mount-to-Transmission Bolt	35 (50)
Radiator Support Mounting Bolt	45-60 (60-80)
Cab Mounting Bolts	45-60 (60-80)
Transfer Case-to-Extension Housing	
"S" Series	19-29 (26-40)
All Others	26-40 (36-56)
Adapter-to-Transmission	
All Others	26-40 (36-56)

JEEP

TRANSFER CASE

MODEL NP-207

Removal

1) Shift transfer case into "4H" position. Raise and support vehicle. Drain lubricant from transfer case. Mark rear axle yoke and drive shaft for installation reference. Remove rear drive shaft. Disconnect the speedometer cable, vacuum hoses and vent hose from transfer case.

2) Raise transmission and transfer case and remove transmission crossmember attaching bolts. Remove crossmember and lower transmission and transfer case. Mark transfer case front output shaft flange and drive shaft for installation reference.

3) Disconnect front drive shaft from transfer case. Disconnect shift lever linkage rod at transfer case. Remove shift lever bracket bolts. Support transfer case and remove transfer case attaching bolts. Remove transfer case assembly.

Installation

1) To install, reverse removal procedure. Align splines of input shaft with transmission and slide transfer case forward until mated with transmission. Install transfer case attaching bolts and tighten.

2) Install shift lever bracket bolts. Attach shift lever linkage rod at transfer case. Connect speedometer cable and vacuum hoses to transfer case.

3) Connect front and install rear propeller shaft. Ensure reference marks made during removal are aligned. Raise transmission and transfer case and install crossmember.

4) Install attaching bolts and tighten. Fill transfer case. Lower vehicle. Road test vehicle. Check to ensure that transfer case shifts and operates in all ranges.

MODEL NP-208

Removal

1) Raise vehicle. Drain lubricant from transfer case. Disconnect speedometer cable and indicator switch wires and disconnect transfer case shift lever link at operating lever. Place a safety stand under transmission and remove the rear crossmember.

2) Mark transfer case front and rear output shaft yokes and drive shafts for assembly alignment reference. Disconnect front and rear drive shafts at transfer case yokes. Secure shafts to frame rails with wire. Disconnect parking brake cable guide from pivot located on right frame rail, if necessary.

3) Remove bolts attaching exhaust pipe support bracket-to-transfer case, if necessary. Remove transfer case-to-transmission bolts. Move transfer case assembly rearward until free of transmission output shaft and remove assembly. Remove all gasket material from rear of transmission adapter housing.

Installation

To install, reverse removal procedure.

JEEP (Cont.)

MODEL NP-229

Removal

1) Raise and support vehicle. Drain lubricant from transfer case. Disconnect speedometer cable and vent hose. Disconnect transfer case shift lever link at operating lever. Place a safety stand under transmission and remove rear crossmember.

2) Mark transfer case front and rear output shafts at transfer case yokes and drive shafts for installation alignment reference. Disconnect front and rear drive shafts at transfer case yokes. Secure shafts. Disconnect shift motor vacuum hoses.

3) Disconnect transfer case shift linkage. Remove transfer case-to-transmission bolts. Move transfer case assembly rearward until clear of transmission output shaft and remove assembly. Remove all gasket material from rear of transmission adapter housing.

Installation

To install, reverse removal procedure.

MODEL NP-300

Removal

1) Remove floor covering (if equipped) and remove transmission access cover from floorpan. Raise vehicle and drain lubricant from transfer case. Position support stand under clutch housing to support engine and transmission and remove rear crossmember.

2) Disconnect front and rear drive shafts at transfer case. Mark drive shaft yokes for assembly reference. Disconnect speedometer cable at transfer case. If necessary, disconnect parking brake cable at equalizer. Disconnect exhaust pipe support bracket at transfer case, if equipped. Remove bolts attaching transfer case to transmission and remove transfer case.

Installation

1) To install, reverse removal procedure. Shift transfer case to "4L" position. Rotate transfer case output shaft by turning yoke until transmission output shaft gear engages transfer case input shaft.

2) Move transfer case forward until case seats against transmission. Ensure transfer case is flush against transmission.

NOTE: **Severe damage to transfer case will result if attaching bolts are tightened while transfer case is cocked or in a bind.**

3) Install transfer case attaching bolts. Tighten bolts to 30 ft. lbs. (41 N.m). Fill transfer with fluid. Connect speedometer drive gear. Connect transfer case shift lever and control links to transfer case shift rods.

4) Connect front and rear propeller shafts to transfer case. Make sure to align shafts to yokes using reference marks made during removal. Tighten shaft-to-yoke clamp strap nuts.

5) Install rear crossmember and remove support stand from under clutch housing. Connect parking brake cable to equalizer and connect exhaust pipe support bracket to transfer case if disconnected.

6) Lower vehicle. Install transmission access cover plate on floorpan. Install floor covering. Install boots, trim rings and shift knobs.

TRANSMISSION

ALL MODELS

Removal

1) Remove screws attaching shift lever boot to floorpan. Slide boot over lever. On models with T4 or T5 transmission, remove shift lever and lever housing from transmission.

2) On models with T-176 transmission, press and turn shift lever retainer counterclockwise to release lever. Remove lever, boot, spring and seat as an assembly.

3) On all models, raise vehicle and support with safety stands. Disconnect rear drive shaft from transfer case and wire out of way. DO NOT allow shaft to hang free, as damage to universal joint may result.

4) Disconnect front parking brake cable at equalizer. Remove rear cable clip from crossmember. Place a jack under clutch housing to support engine. Remove rear crossmember from frame.

5) Disconnect speedometer cable, back-up light switch wire and 4WD indicator switch wire. Disconnect transfer case vent hose. Disconnect front drive shaft and wire out of way.

6) On CJ model, remove transfer case shift lever by removing shifter shaft retaining nut. Remove cotter pins retaining shift control link pins in shift rods and remove pins. Remove shifter shaft and disengage shift lever from shift control links. Move lever out of the way.

NOTE: **On some models, shifter shaft must be unthreaded from shift lever in order to be removed. On other models, shaft can be removed by sliding it out of lever.**

7) Remove cotter pin and washers connecting link to shift lever. Separate link from lever. Support transmission and transfer case with jack.

8) Remove bolts securing transmission to clutch housing and remove transmission and transfer case. Separate transfer case and transmission.

Installation

1) Install pilot bushing lubricating wick and align throwout bearing with splines in driven plate hub. Shift transmission into gear using shift lever or a long screwdriver. This prevents clutch shaft from rotating during installation and makes clutch shaft-to-driven plate spline alignment easier.

2) Mount transmission on transmission jack. Raise transmission and align transmission clutch shaft with splines in driven plate hub.

3) When transmission is seated on clutch housing, install and tighten transmission-to-clutch housing bolts. Apply Permatex No. 3 sealer to both sides of replacement transmission output shaft and transfer case input shaft splines.

4) To install transmission, reverse removal procedure. Adjust clutch and shift linkage.

TIGHTENING SPECIFICATIONS

Application	Ft. Lbs. (N.m)
Transmission-to-Clutch Housing	55 (75)
Transmission Cover Bolts	55-65 (75-88)
Housing-to-Transmission Case	40-45 (54-61)
Crossmember Attaching Bolts	34-40 (47-54)
Filler Plug	13-15 (18-20)

GENERAL MANUAL TRANSMISSION/TRANSAXLE TROUBLE SHOOTING

It is essential that thorough trouble shooting and diagnostic procedures be followed prior to disassembly of any transmission/transaxle components for repair. Shift difficulties are frequently caused by conditions outside the transmission-/transaxle; such as linkage, cable, alignment of assemblies, or clutch problems.

Drive train noises may come from many sources; such as tires, road surfaces, wheel bearings, drive axles, engine, or exhaust system, etc. Adjustment or replacement of transmission/transaxle parts will not correct these problems. Gear "roll-over" noise is inherent in most constant-mest transmissions and will disappear when clutch is disengaged or transmission is in gear. Clutch release bearing noise will disappear when clutch release mechanism is moved enough to slide release bearing away from contact with pressure plate. DO NOT attempt transmission/transaxle repairs to correct gear "roll-over" or clutch release bearing noise.

If noise persists, drive vehicle on a smooth asphalt road to reduce tire and body noises. With vehicle fully warmed up, note speed and in which gear noise appears, whether noise occurs on pull, coast, or steady drive conditions. Refer to following conditions, possible cause, and correction for appropriate action.

CONDITION	POSSIBLE CAUSE	CORRECTION
Noisy in Forward Gears	Improper fluid level or type	Check fluid level and type; See GENERAL SERVICING
	Contaminated fluid	Check fluid condition; See GENERAL SERVICING
	Road or tire noise	Determine cause and service as required
	Drive axle/shaft noise telescoped to transmission	Determine cause and service as required
	Vehicle body components or exhaust system grounding on chassis	Determine cause and service as required
	Transmission or clutch housing bolts loose	Tighten bolts to specification
	Clutch housing misaligned with crankshaft	Check and align clutch housing
	Worn bearings or gears	Replace bearings or gears
	Brake noise telescoped through drive train	Determine cause and service as required
	Loose or worn engine mounts	Tighten or replace engine mounts
	Speedometer gear or teeth worn	Replace speedometer gear
Gear Clash When Shifting Forward Gears	Engine idle speed too high	Adjust engine idle speed
	Clutch out of adjustment	Adjust clutch
	Shift linkage damaged or out of adjustment	Adjust or replace linkage; See GENERAL SERVICING
	Pilot bushing or bearing damaged	Replace bushing or bearing
	Gears or synchronizers damaged	Service as required
	Insufficient or improper fluid	Check fluid level and type; See GENERAL SERVICING
Transmission Shifts Hard	Clutch out of adjustment	Adjust clutch
	Insufficient or improper fluid	Check fluid level and type; See GENERAL SERVICING
	Clutch disc warped or deformed	Replace clutch disc
	Shift lever or rail binding or deformed	Determine cause of condition and service as required
	Sliding gears or synchronizers binding	Determine cause of condition and service as required
	Pilot bushing or bearing binding	Determine cause of condition and service as required
	Housing and/or shafts out of alignment	Check and adjustment alignment
	Shift linkage binding or requires lubricant	Service or lubricate linkage

GENERAL MANUAL TRANSMISSION/TRANSAXLE TROUBLE SHOOTING (Cont.)

CONDITION	POSSIBLE CAUSE	CORRECTION
Will Not Shift into One Gear - Shifts into All Others	Shift linkage out of adjustment or damaged or worn	Adjust or replace linkage; See GENERAL SERVICING
	Back-up switch ball frozen or damaged	Replace switch ball
	Damaged or worn synchronizer sleeves or hubs	Replace sleeves or hubs
	Internal gearshift mechanism worn, damaged or improperly adjusted	Adjust or replace internal gearshift mechanism
Locked in One Gear - Cannot be Shifted Out	Shift linkage out of adjustment or damaged or worn	Adjust or replace linkage; See GENERAL SERVICING
	Internal gearshift mechanism worn, damaged or improperly adjusted	Adjust or replace internal gearshift mechanism
	Broken gear teeth on clutch shaft, countershaft gear or reverse idler gear	Replace clutch shaft, countershaft gear or reverse idler gear
	Shift fork loose on shift rail	Tighten or replace shift fork or rail
Transmission Jumps Out of Gear	Shift linkage damaged or out of adjustment	Adjust or service linkage; See GENERAL SERVICING
	Engine mounts loose or broken	Tighten or replace mounts
	Engine, transmission, or shift lever bolts loose	Tighten bolts to specification
	Clutch shaft or roller bearings worn	Replace shaft or bearings
	Pilot bushing or bearing worn	Replace bushing or bearing
	Gear teeth worn or tapered	Replace gear
	Internal shift mechanism worn, damaged or misadjusted	Adjust or service interal shift mechanism
	Shift lever seal binding	Determine cause and service as required
Shift Linkage Binds, Sticks or Rattles	Shift rods or cables out of adjustment	Adjust shift rods or cables; See GENERAL SERVICING
	Steering column shift tube out of alignment	Align shift tube
	Console shift assembly damaged or worn	Service as required
	Engine and/or transmission/transaxle mounts worn or broken	Replace mounts
	Shift lever pivot balls worn or loose	Replace shift lever pivot assembly
	Control assembly body weld bolts missing or loose	Tighten or replace bolts
	Shift linkage bushings worn, broken or missing	Replace bushings
Transmission Leaks	Improper fluid level or type	Check fluid; See GENERAL SERVICING
	Worn or damaged shift lever seal	Replace seal
	Propeller shaft yoke worn	Replace yoke
	Extension housing oil seal worn or damaged	Replace housing oil seal
	Components other than tranmission/transaxle leaking	Check and service other components

General Servicing

DRIVE AXLE GEAR TOOTH PATTERNS

INSPECTION

Wipe lubricant from internal parts. Rotate gears and inspect for wear or damage. Mount a dial indicator to housing and check backlash at several points around ring gear. Backlash must be within specifications at all points. If no defects are found, check gear tooth contact patterns.

GEAR TOOTH CONTACT PATTERN

NOTE: **Drive pattern should be well centered on ring gear teeth. Coast pattern should be centered but may be slightly toward toe of ring gear teeth.**

1) Paint ring gear teeth with gear marking compound. Apply some form of load to differential case to resist rotation. Rotate pinion gear until ring gear has made 1 full revolution.

2) Turn pinion gear in opposite direction to complete 1 full revolution of ring gear. Examine ring gear teeth for contact pattern. Correct as necessary by moving appropriate shims.

ADJUSTMENTS

GEAR BACKLASH & PINION SHIM CHANGES

NOTE: **Change in tooth pattern is directly related to change in shim and/or backlash adjustment.**

1) With no change in backlash, moving pinion further from ring gear moves drive pattern toward heel and top of tooth, and moves coast pattern toward toe and top of tooth.

2) With no change in backlash, moving pinion closer to ring gear moves drive pattern toward toe and bottom of tooth, and moves coast pattern toward heel and bottom of tooth.

3) With no change in pinion shim thickness, an increase in backlash moves ring gear further from pinion. Drive pattern moves toward heel and top of tooth, and coast pattern moves toward heel and top of tooth.

4) With no change in pinion shim thickness, a decrease in backlash moves ring gear closer to pinion gear. Drive pattern moves toward toe and bottom of tooth, and coast pattern moves toward toe and bottom of tooth.

Fig. 1: Drive Axle Gear Tooth Patterns Showing Necessary Corrections

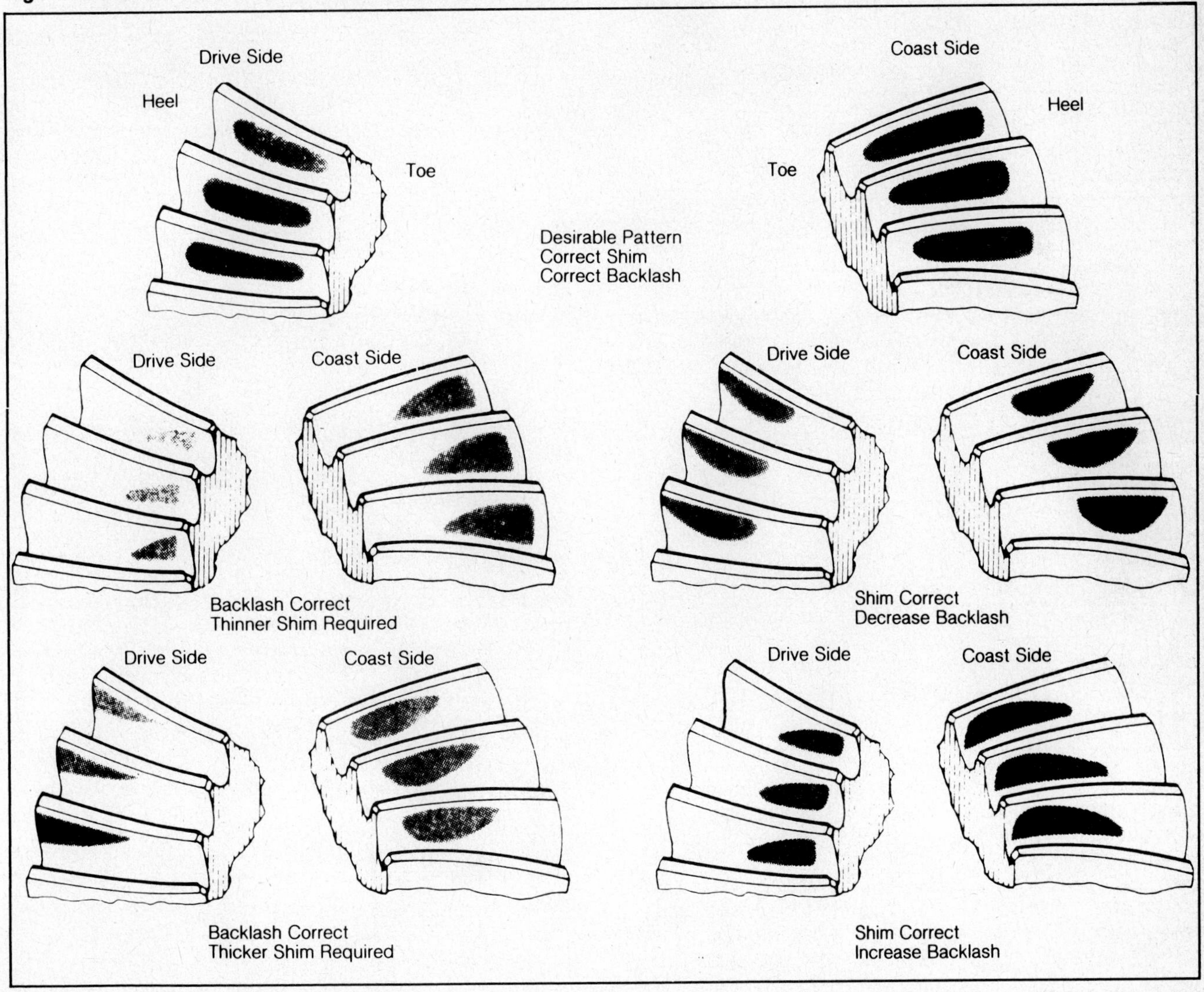

SECTION 2

DOMESTIC AUTOMATIC TRANSMISSIONS

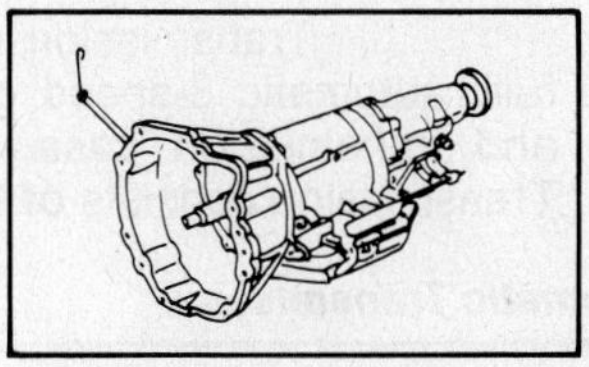

NOTE: ALSO SEE GENERAL INDEX.

Automatic Transmissions

AMERICAN MOTORS, CHRYSLER CORP. & JEEP
727, 904, 998 & 999

APPLICATIONS

CHRYSLER CORP.

Chrysler Corp. passenger cars use A-904LA Torqueflite transmissions. All models (except some fleet engines) use lock-up type torque converter. Dodge and Plymouth trucks and vans use Loadflite A-727, A-904T or A-999 transmissions. Those with A-904T and A-999 transmissions use lock-up converter, while A-727 equipped models may use either lock-up or conventional type torque converter, depending on GVWR and application.

AMC/JEEP

AMC Eagle uses 998 model. Jeep CJ7 and Scrambler use 999 model. Cherokee and Wagoneer use 904 model. Grand Wagoneer and J-10/20 trucks use 999 model in 6-cylinder models and 727 model in 8-cylinder models. The 727 is also used in 6-cylinder models with 3.31 axle ratio. Lock-up torque converter may be used with any of these applications.

NOTE: **All future references to transmission will be by number only (i.e. 727, 904, 999). Unless otherwise specified, model reference will include all models of that series. For example, reference to 904 will include 904, A-904, A-904LA and A-904T models.**

IDENTIFICATION

Transmission identification number is stamped on pad on left side of transmission case oil pan flange. Identification number is decoded as shown in *Fig. 1*.

Fig. 2: Transmission Identification Number

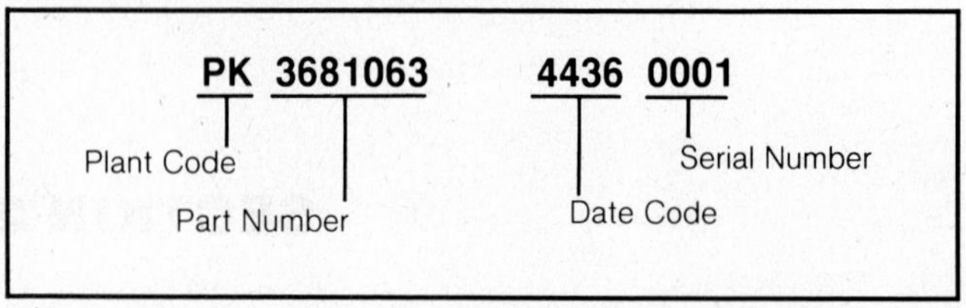

CAUTION: **Transmission operation requirements are different for each vehicle and engine combination, and some internal parts will differ between models. Always refer to 7-digit part number for positive transmission identification when replacing parts.**

DESCRIPTION

Transmission combines torque converter and fully automatic 3-speed gear system. Converter housing and transmission case are integral aluminum casting. Transmission consists of 2 multiple disc clutches, overrun-

Fig. 1: Cross-Sectional View Of Chrysler Corp. Model 727 Automatic Transmission

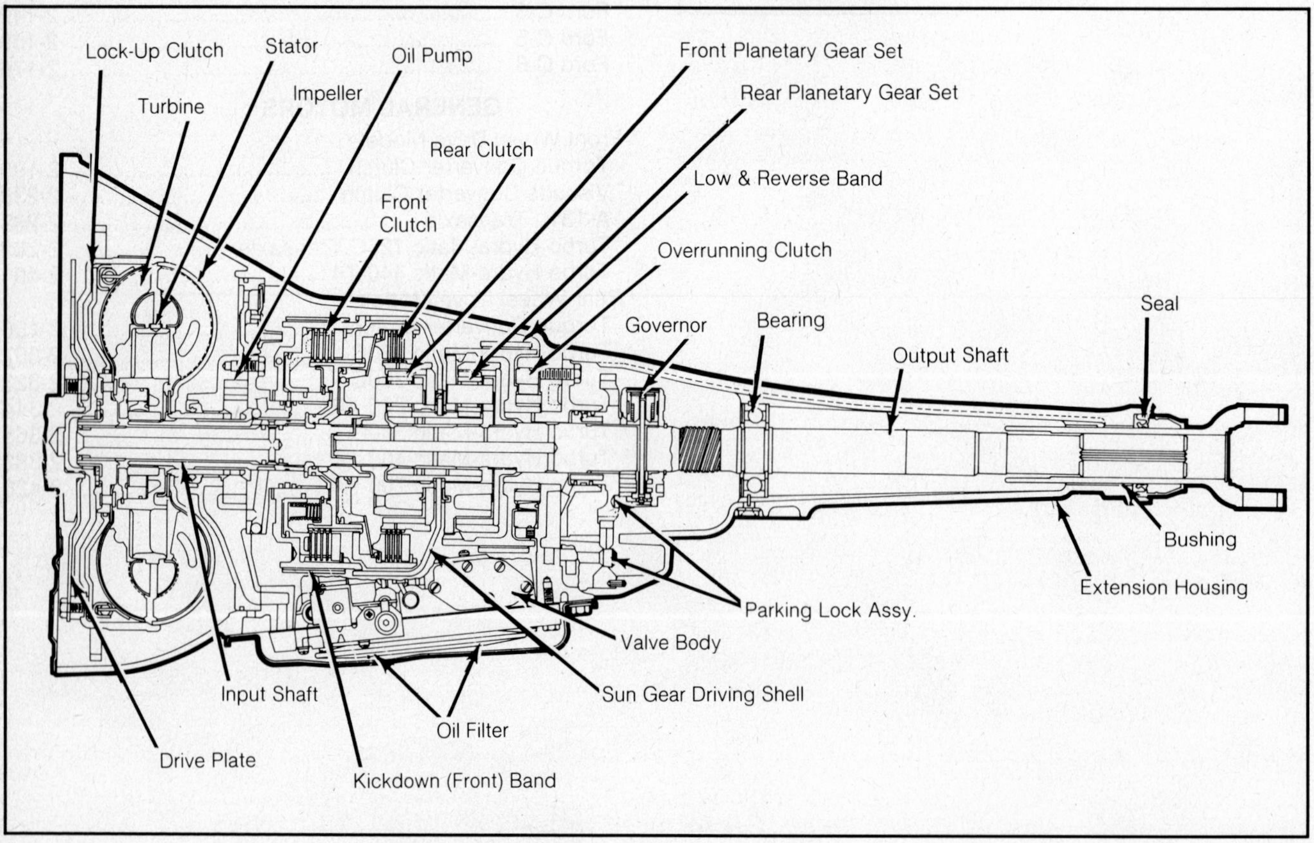

AMERICAN MOTORS, CHRYSLER CORP. & JEEP 727, 904, 998 & 999 (Cont.)

ning clutch, 2 servos and bands, and 2 planetary gear sets to provide 3 forward ratios and reverse ratio. Common sun gear of planetary gear sets is connected to front clutch by driving shell which is splined to sun gear and to front clutch retainer. Hydraulic system consists of oil pump and control valve body in which all valves except governor valve are found.

Torque converter is attached to crankshaft through flexible driving plate. Cooling of converter is accomplished by circulating transmission fluid through fluid-to-fluid type cooler, which is located in radiator lower tank. Torque converter assembly is sealed unit which cannot be disassembled.

Lock-up clutch is located inside most torque converters. Lock-up mode is activated only in direct drive and above minimum preset vehicle speed. At wider throttle openings, where 2-3 upshift occurs above minimum lock-up speed, lock-up shift will occur immediately after 2-3 upshift. Lock-up and conventional converters and transmissions are NOT interchangeable.

LUBRICATION & ADJUSTMENTS

See appropriate AUTOMATIC TRANSMISSION SERVICING article in DOMESTIC GENERAL SERVICING section.

TROUBLE SHOOTING

See appropriate AUTOMATIC TRANSMISSION TROUBLE SHOOTING article in DOMESTIC GENERAL SERVICING section.

TESTING

ROAD TEST

1) Before road testing, be certain that fluid level and control linkage adjustments have been checked

AUTOMATIC SHIFT SPEEDS & GOVERNOR PRESSURES – CHRYSLER CORP. TRUCKS & VANS

Engine	3.7L		5.2L & 5.9L			
Model Axle Ratio Tire Size	150 3.21 P195/75R15	250 3.54 P235/75R15XL	150 2.71 P195/75R15	150 2.94 P195/75R15	250 3.21 P235/75R15XL	350 3.54 8.75 X 16.5-E
Throttle Closed						
1-2 Upshift	8-11	8-11	9-12	9-11	9-11	8-11
2-3 Upshift	11-14	11-14	13-17	12-15	12-16	12-16
3-1 Downshift	8-11	8-11	9-12	9-11	9-11	8-11
Throttle Wide Open						
1-2 Upshift	29-36	29-36	34-42	31-39	36-43	34-41
2-3 Upshift	55-60	55-60	65-73	60-69	63-70	60-67
Kickdown Range						
3-2 Downshift	50-57	50-57	60-68	55-63	58-65	55-62
3-1 Downshift	24-30	24-30	30-32	28-30	27-35	26-33
Governor Pressure [1]						
15 psi	16-18	16-18	19-21	17-19	17-20	16-19
50 psi	36-41	36-41	43-49	40-45	43-49	41-47
75 psi	54-59	54-59	64-70	59-65	62-68	59-65

[1] – Governor pressure should be from zero to 1.5 psi at stand-still or downshift may not occur.

CLUTCH & BAND APPLICATION CHART (ELEMENTS IN USE)

Selector Lever Position	Front Clutch	Rear Clutch	Over-running Clutch	Converter Lock-up Clutch	Front (Kickdown) Band	Rear (Low-reverse) Band
D - DRIVE						
First		X	X			
Second		X			X	
Third	X	X		X		
2 - SECOND						
First		X	X			
Second		X			X	
1 - LOW (First)		X				X
R - REVERSE	X					X
NEUTRAL or PARK – All clutches and bands released and/or ineffective.						

Automatic Transmissions

AMERICAN MOTORS, CHRYSLER CORP. & JEEP 727, 904, 998 & 999 (Cont.)

Fig. 3: Cross-Sectional View Of Chrysler Corp. Model 904/999 & AMC/Jeep Model 904 Automatic Transmission

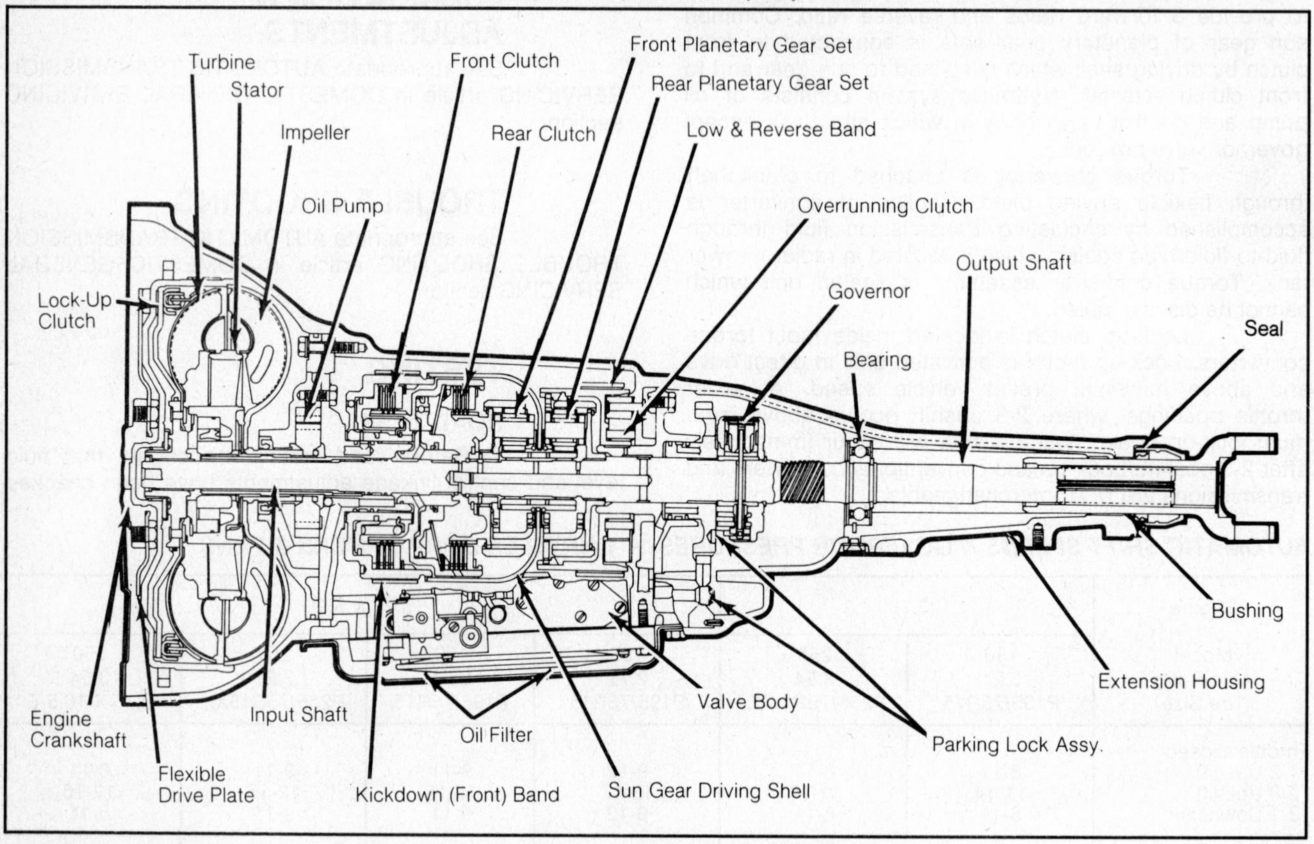

Fig. 4: Cross-Sectional View Of AMC/Jeep Model 727 Automatic Transmission

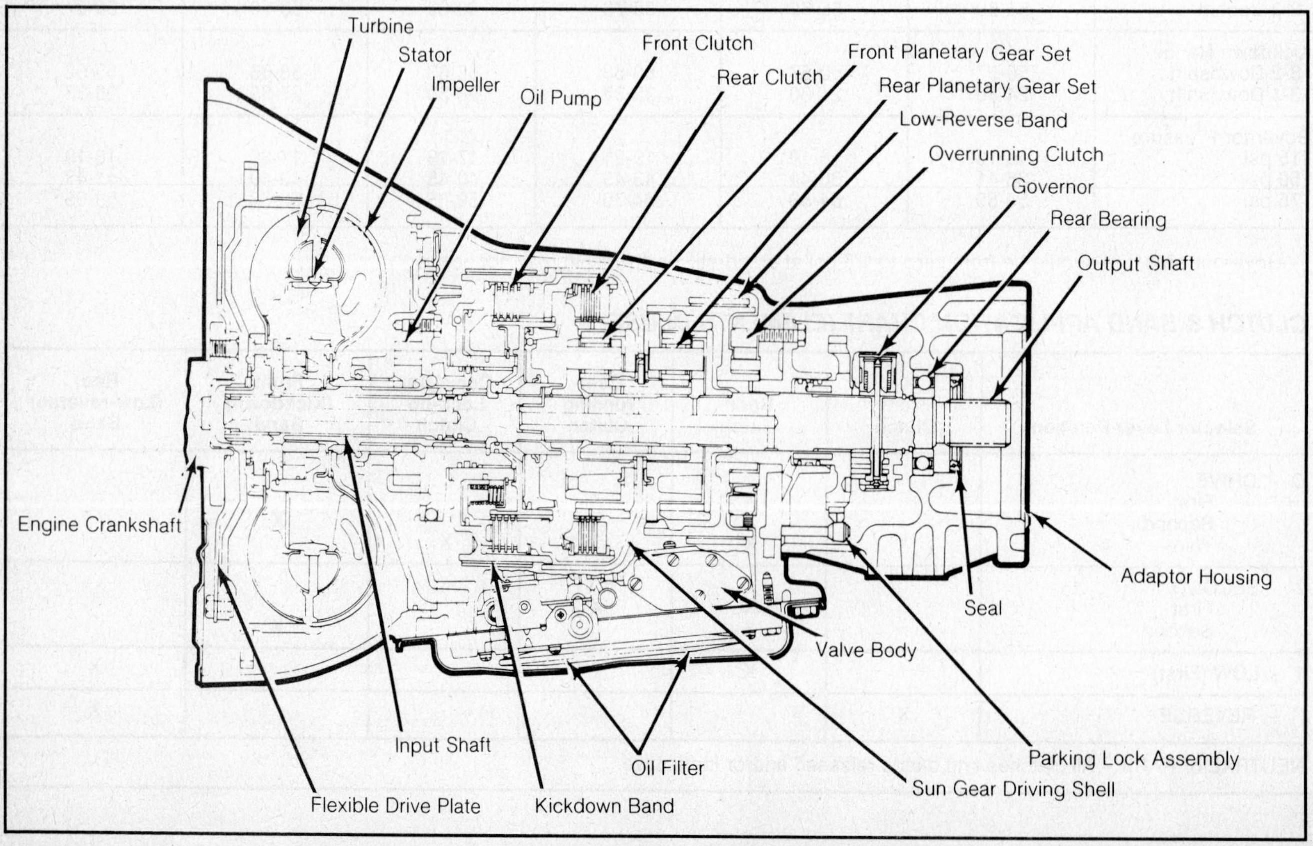

AMERICAN MOTORS, CHRYSLER CORP. & JEEP 727, 904, 998 & 999 (Cont.)

Fig. 5: Cross-Sectional View Of AMC/Jeep Model 998/999 Automatic Transmission

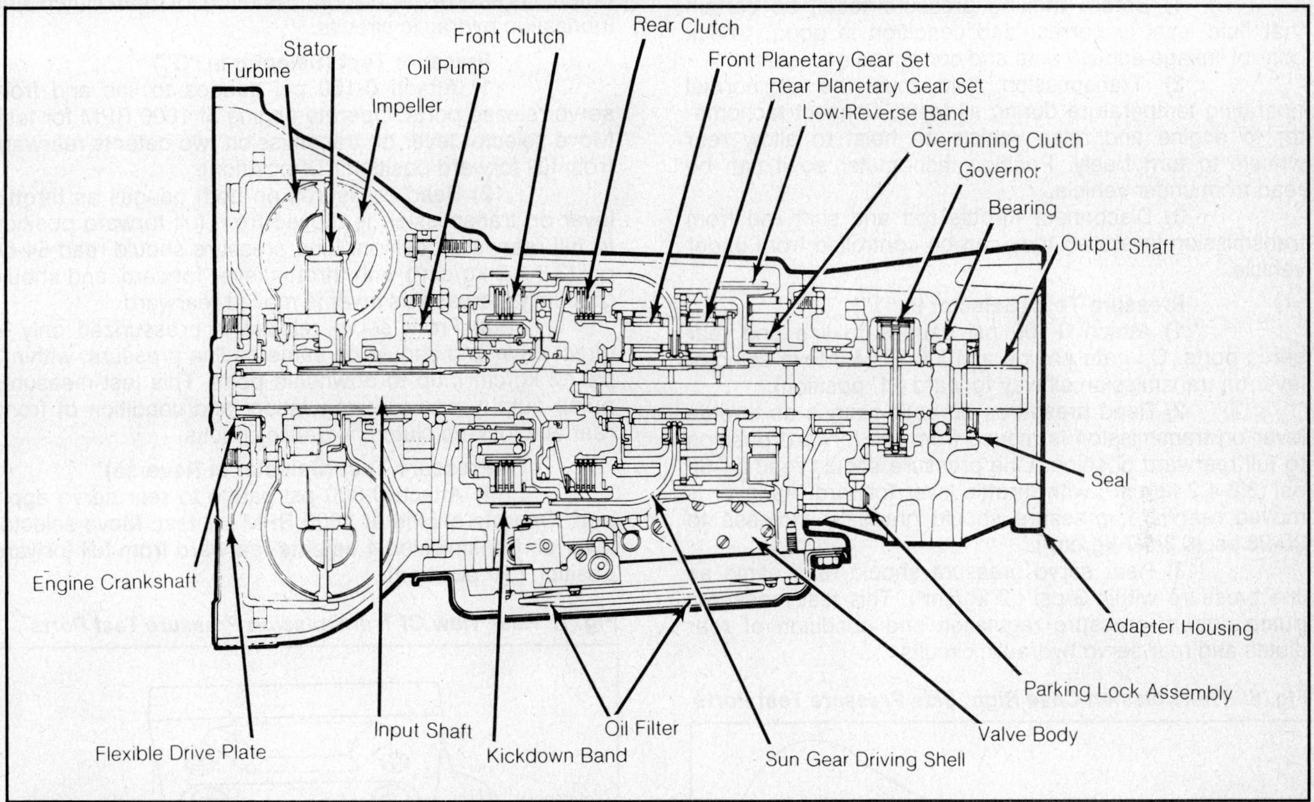

AUTOMATIC SHIFT SPEEDS & GOVERNOR PRESSURES CHRYSLER CORP. PASSENGER CARS

Application	2.26 Axle Ratio [1] (MPH)	2.94 Axle Ratio [1] (MPH)
Throttle Closed		
1-2 Upshift	12-15	9-11
2-3 Upshift	16-20	13-16
Lock-Up	38-53	30-41
Throttle Wide Open		
1-2 Upshift	37-56	31-43
2-3 Upshift	75-93	58-72
Kickdown Range		
3-2 Downshift	69-87	54-67
3-1 Downshift	35-40	27-31
Governor Pressure [2]		
15 psi	23-25	17-20
50 psi	51-59	39-45
75 psi	78-85	60-66

[1] – With standard tire size P205/75R15.
[2] – Governor pressure should be from zero to 1.5 psi at stand-still or downshift may not occur.

and corrected as needed. During testing, transmission should upshift and downshift automatically at approximate speeds shown in AUTOMATIC SHIFT SPEEDS & GOVERNOR PRESSURES chart.

2) Exact speeds will vary somewhat from 1 vehicle to another. This is due to differences in production tolerances, rear axle ratio and tire size. Of greater importance than shift speed is quality of shifts. All shifts should be smooth and responsive with no slipping or engine speed flare-up.

3) Slipping or flare-up in any gear usually indicates clutch, band or overrunning clutch problems. Clutch or band which is slipping can be determined by noting transmission operation in all selector positions and by comparing which internal units are applied in those positions.

4) For example, if transmission slips in high gear with selector lever in "D", either front or rear clutch is slipping. By selecting another gear which uses 1 but not both of these assemblies, unit which is slipping can be identified. If transmission also slips in Reverse, front clutch is slipping. If transmission does not also slip in Reverse, rear clutch is slipping.

5) Although this process of elimination can be used to detect any unit which slips and to confirm proper operation of good units, actual cause of malfunction usually cannot be determined. Practically any condition can be caused by leaking hydraulic circuits or sticking valves.

6) Unless obvious condition exists, transmission should never be disassembled until hydraulic and air pressure tests have been performed. Engine tachometer can be used to determine if lock-up clutch in converter is functioning.

7) Instantaneous rise in engine speed of more than 150 RPM at 45 MPH when throttle is opened just short of kickdown, indicates lock-up clutch is slipping more than normal. Slippage less than 150 RPM is normal.

AMERICAN MOTORS, CHRYSLER CORP. & JEEP 727, 904, 998 & 999 (Cont.)

HYDRAULIC PRESSURE TESTS

1) Before making pressure tests, be certain that fluid level is correct and condition is good. Check control linkage adjustments and correct as necessary.

2) Transmission fluid must be at normal operating temperature during all tests. Connect tachometer to engine and raise vehicle on hoist to allow rear wheels to turn freely. Position tachometer so it can be read from under vehicle.

3) Disconnect throttle rod and shift rod from transmission levers so they can be controlled from under vehicle.

Pressure Test (Selector in "1")

1) Attach 0-100 psi gauges to line and rear servo ports. Operate engine at 1000 RPM. Move selector lever on transmission all way forward ("1" position).

2) Read pressures on both gauges as throttle lever on transmission is moved from full forward position to full rearward position. Line pressure should read 54-60 psi (3.8-4.2 kg/cm²) with throttle lever forward. As lever is moved rearward, pressure should gradually increase to 90-96 psi (6.3-6.7 kg/cm²).

3) Rear servo pressure should read same as line pressure within 3 psi (.2 kg/cm²). This test measures pump output, pressure regulation and condition of rear clutch and rear servo hydraulic circuits.

Fig. 6: Transmission Case Right Side Pressure Test Ports

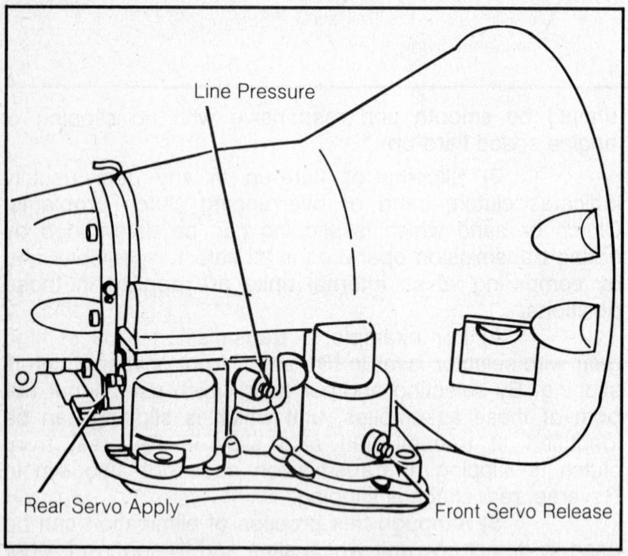

Fluid level, condition and control linkage adjustments must be correct before performing hydraulic tests.

Pressure Test (Selector in "2")

1) Install "T" fitting at rear cooler line fitting. Attach 0-100 psi gauges to "T" connection and line pressure port. Operate engine at 1000 RPM for test. Move selector lever on transmission 1 detent rearward from full forward position ("2" position).

2) Read pressures on both gauges as throttle lever on transmission is moved from full forward position to full rearward position. Line pressure should read 54-60 psi (3.8-4.2 kg/cm²) with throttle lever forward. As lever is moved rearward, pressure should gradually increase to 90-96 psi (6.3-6.7 kg/cm²).

3) Lubrication pressure should be 5-15 psi (.35-1.05 kg/cm²) with lever forward, and 10-30 psi (.7-2.1 kg/cm²) with lever rearward. This test measures pump output, pressure regulation, conditon of rear clutch and lubrication hydraulic circuits.

Pressure Test (Selector in "D")

1) Attach 0-100 psi gauges to line and front servo release ports. Operate engine at 1600 RPM for test. Move selector lever on transmission two detents rearward from full forward position ("D" position).

2) Read pressures on both gauges as throttle lever on transmission is moved from full forward position to full rearward position. Line pressure should read 54-60 psi (3.8-4.2 kg/cm²) with throttle lever forward, and should gradually increase as lever is moved rearward.

3) Front servo release is pressurized only in direct drive and should be same as line pressure, within 3 psi (.2 kg/cm²), up to downshift point. This test measures pump output, pressure regulation, and condition of front, rear and lock-up clutch hydraulic circuits.

Pressure Test (Selector in Reverse)

1) Attach 0-300 psi gauge to rear servo apply port. Operate engine at 1600 RPM for test. Move selector lever on transmission 4 detents rearward from full forward position ("R" position).

Fig. 7: Rear View Of Transmission Pressure Test Ports

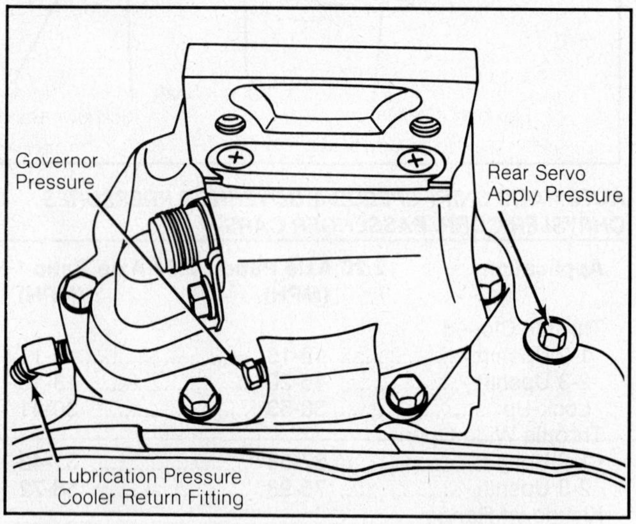

Gauge used to check pressure at rear servo apply port (shift lever in "R") MUST read to 300 psi (21 kg/cm²).

2) Rear servo pressure should read 145-175 psi (10.2-12.3 kg/cm²) with throttle lever forward and should gradually increase, as lever is moved rearward, to 230-280 psi (16.2-19.7 kg/cm²). This tests pump output, pressure regulation, condition of front clutch and rear servo hydraulic circuits.

3) Move selector lever on transmission to "D" position and check that rear servo pressure drops to zero. This test checks for leakage into rear servo due to case porosity, which can cause reverse band to burn out.

Governor Pressure

1) Connect 0-100 psi gauge to governor pressure port. Operate transmission in 3rd gear and read pressures. Compare readings with those shown in AUTOMATIC SHIFT SPEEDS & GOVERNOR PRESSURES chart.

AMERICAN MOTORS, CHRYSLER CORP. & JEEP 727, 904, 998 & 999 (Cont.)

NOTE: This test should only be performed if transmission shifts at wrong vehicle speeds when throttle rod is correctly adjusted.

2) If governor pressures are incorrect at given speeds, governor valve and/or weights are sticking. Governor pressure should return to 0-1.5 psi (0-.11 kg/cm²) when vehicle is stopped.

NOTE: High governor pressure (above 2 psi) at stand-still will prevent transmission from downshifting.

Throttle Pressure

No gauge port is provided for testing throttle pressure. Incorrect throttle pressure should only be suspected if part throttle upshift speeds are either delayed or occur too soon in relation to vehicle speeds. Engine runaway on either upshifts or downshifts can also be indicator of incorrect (low) throttle pressure.

Pressure Test Diagnosis

1) If line pressure is normal (minimum to maximum) in any one test, pump and pressure regulator are working properly.

2) If line pressure is normal in "R" but low in all forward gears ("D", "2" and "1"), rear clutch circuit leakage is indicated (servo, clutch seals or governor support seal rings).

3) Normal line pressure in "1" with low pressure in "D" and "R" indicates leakage in front clutch area (servo, clutch seals, retainer bore or pump seal rings).

4) Normal line pressure in "2" with low pressure in "R" and "1" indicates leakage in rear servo circuit.

5) Low line pressure in all positions indicates defective pump, clogged filter or stuck pressure regulator valve.

HYDRAULIC PRESSURE ADJUSTMENTS

NOTE: Throttle rod should always be checked and adjusted before checking or adjusting throttle pressure.

Throttle Pressure

1) Throttle pressures cannot be tested accurately. Adjustment should be measured if malfunction is evident.

2) Remove valve body assembly from transmission. Loosen throttle lever stop screw lock nut and back off screw approximately 5 turns.

3) Insert gauge pin of Gauge (C-3763 on Chrysler Corp. models; J-24031 on AMC/Jeep models) between throttle lever cam and kickdown valve. Push in on gauge and compress kickdown valve against spring so valve is completely bottomed inside valve body.

4) As force is being exerted to compress spring, turn throttle lever stop screw with Allen wrench. Adjustment is correct when head of screw touches throttle lever tang, with throttle lever cam touching gauge and throttle valve bottomed.

CAUTION: Be sure adjustment is made with spring fully compressed and valve bottomed in valve body.

Fig. 8: Adjusting Throttle Pressure

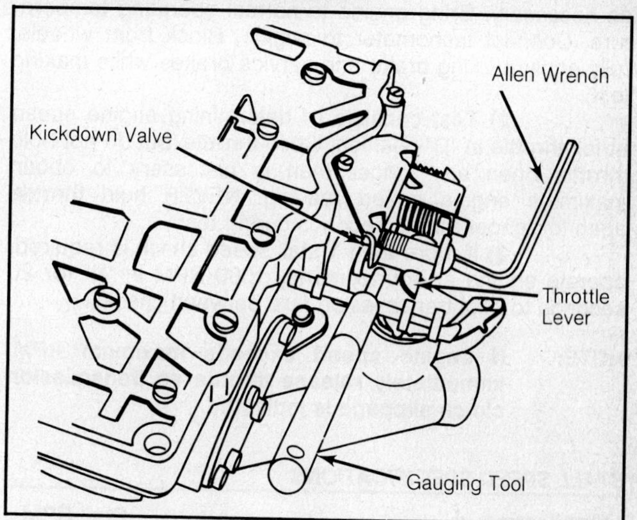

Gauge must be used to obtain proper adjustment.

Line Pressure

1) Incorrect throttle pressure setting will cause incorrect line pressure readings even though line pressure adjustment is correct. Always inspect and correct throttle pressure adjustment before adjusting line pressure.

2) Turn Allen screw in end of pressure regulator spring bracket so measurement between valve body and inner edge of adjusting nut is 1 5/16" (33.34 mm). Due to manufacturing tolerances, adjustment can be varied to obtain specified line pressure.

Fig. 9: Measuring Line Pressure Adjustment

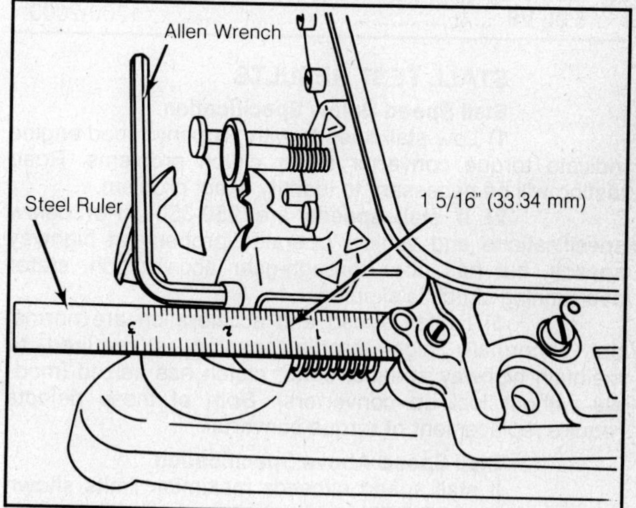

Exact adjustment may be varied slightly to obtain correct pressure reading.

3) One complete turn of adjusting screw changes closed throttle line pressure approximately 1.7 psi (.12 kg/cm²). Turning adjusting screw counterclockwise increases pressure; clockwise decreases pressure.

STALL TEST

CAUTION: Do NOT allow anyone to stand in front of vehicle during this test.

AMERICAN MOTORS, CHRYSLER CORP. & JEEP 727, 904, 998 & 999 (Cont.)

1) Check transmission fluid level and correct as necessary. Bring engine to normal operating temperature. Connect tachometer to engine. Block front wheels, fully apply parking brake and service brakes while making test.

2) Test consists of determining engine speed at full throttle in "D" position. Open throttle, but do not hold throttle open any longer than is necessary to obtain maximum engine speed reading. NEVER hold throttle open for longer than 5 seconds during test.

3) If more than 1 stall speed check is required, operate engine at approximately 1000 RPM in "N" for 20 seconds to cool transmission fluid between checks.

NOTE: **If engine speed exceeds maximum RPM, immediately release throttle as transmission clutch slippage is indicated.**

STALL SPEED SPECIFICATIONS

Application	Stall RPM
AMC	
4.2L 6-Cylinder	1850-2150
Chrysler Corp.	
3.7L 6-Cylinder	1800-2100
5.2L V8	1700-2000
5.9L V8 2-Bbl	1775-2075
5.9L V8 4-Bbl	1700-2000
Jeep	
Model 904	
2.5L 4-Cylinder	2350-2550
2.8L V6	2100-2300
All Other Models	
4.2L 6-Cylinder	1850-2150
5.9L V8	1700-2000

STALL TEST RESULTS

Stall Speed Below Specification

1) Low stall speeds with properly tuned engine indicate torque converter stator clutch problems. Road testing will be necessary to identify exact problem.

2) If stall speeds are 250-350 RPM below specifications and vehicle operates properly at highway speeds, but has poor through-gear acceleration, stator overrunning clutch is slipping.

3) If stall speed and acceleration are normal but abnormally high throttle opening is required to maintain highway speeds, stator clutch has seized (models without lock-up converters). Both of these defects require replacement of torque converter.

Stall Speed Above Specification

If stall speed exceeds maximum limits shown by more than 200 RPM, transmission clutch slippage is indicated. Make hydraulic pressure and air pressure checks to determine cause of slippage.

Noise During Stall Test

1) Whining or siren-like noise due to fluid flow is normal during stall test with some converters. However, loud metallic noises from loose parts or interference within assembly indicates defective converter.

2) To be sure noise originates in converter, raise vehicle on hoist and operate at light throttle in "D" and "N" while listening under transmission bellhousing.

AIR PRESSURE TESTS

"No Drive" condition can exist even with correct fluid pressure because of inoperative clutches and/or bands. Cause can be located by applying compressed air to appropriate case passages after valve body has been removed. If clutches and servos operate correctly, no upshift and/or erratic shift condition indicates malfunction in valve body.

NOTE: **Compressed air must be free of any dirt or moisture. Use air pressure of 30 psi (2.1 kg/cm²) for tests.**

Front Clutch

Direct air pressure into front clutch apply passage. Operation of clutch is indicated by dull thud which may be heard or felt. Hold air pressure for few seconds to check system for excessive air leaks.

Fig. 10: Air Pressure Test Points In Bottom Of Transmission Case

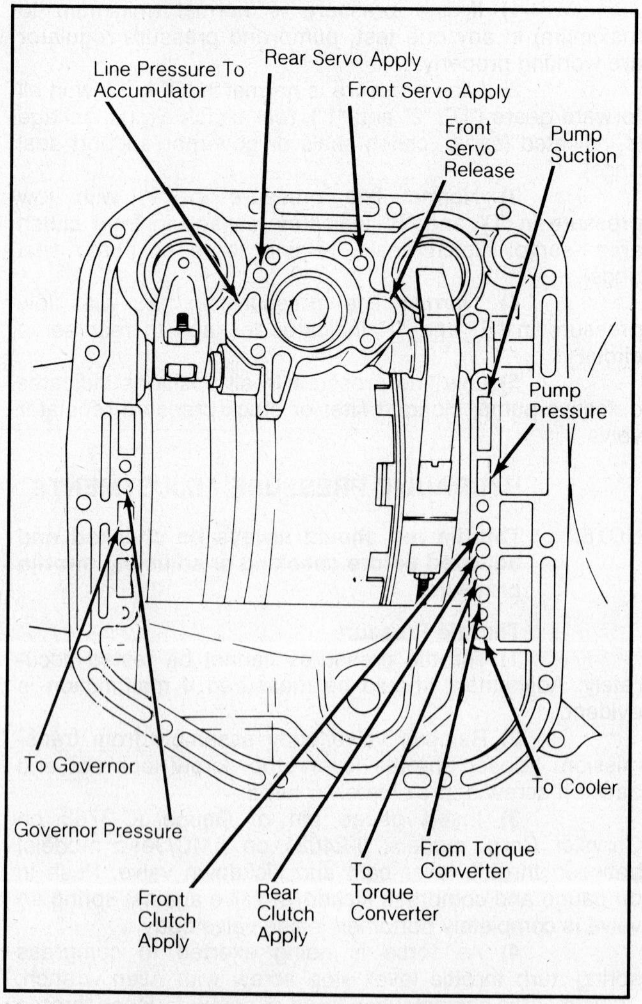

Use only filtered, compressed air to check system.

Rear Clutch

1) Direct air pressure into rear clutch apply passage. Operation of clutch is indicated by dull thud which may be heard or felt.

AMERICAN MOTORS, CHRYSLER CORP. & JEEP 727, 904, 998 & 999 (Cont.)

2) If clutch operation is not detected, place finger tips on clutch housing and again apply air pressure. Movement of piston can be felt as air is applied. Also check for excessive air leaks.

Front (Kickdown) Servo

Direct air pressure into front servo apply passage. Operation of servo is indicated by tightening of front band. Spring tension on servo piston should release band.

Rear (Low-Reverse) Servo

Direct air pressure into rear servo apply passage. Operation of servo is indicated by tightening of rear band. Spring tension of servo piston should release band.

SERVICE (IN VEHICLE)

SPEEDOMETER PINION

Removal

Remove bolt and clamp securing speedometer pinion adapter in extension housing. With cable housing connected, carefully work adapter and pinion out of extension housing.

Fig. 11: Exploded View Of Speedometer Drive Assembly

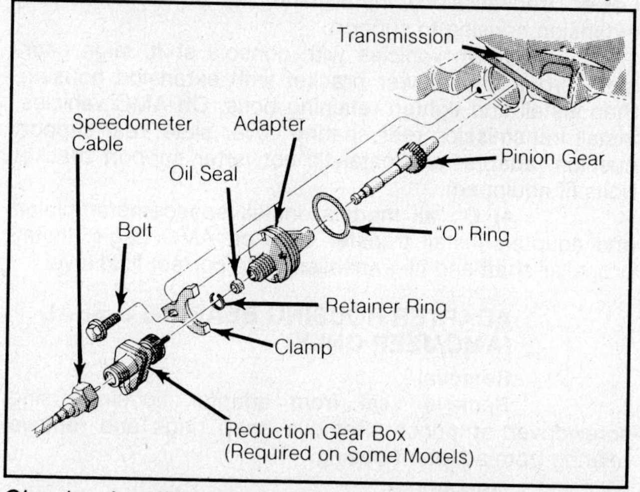

Chrysler Loadflite model is shown; other models are similar.

Seal Replacement

If transmission fluid is found inside cable housing, replace seal in adapter (if used) or speedometer pinion and seal assembly (Torqueflite models). Start seal and retainer ring in adapter. Push into adapter using Seal Installer (C-4004) until tool bottoms.

Fig. 12: Installing Speedometer Cable Adapter Oil Seal

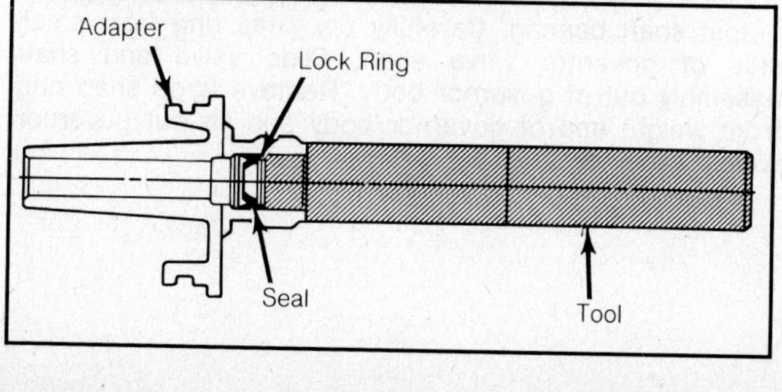

Installation

1) Note number on adapter, which corresponds to number of teeth on gear. Install correct speedometer pinion gear into adapter. Rotate pinion gear and adapter assembly so number on adapter is in 6 o'clock position.

NOTE: **To avoid misalignment and possible damage to speedometer pinion gear, make sure adapter flange and mating surfaces are clean before installation.**

2) Install pinion gear and adapter assembly. Install clamp and bolt with clamp tangs in adapter positioning slots. Tap adapter firmly into extension housing and tighten bolt.

Fig. 13: Speedometer Pinion & Adapter Installation

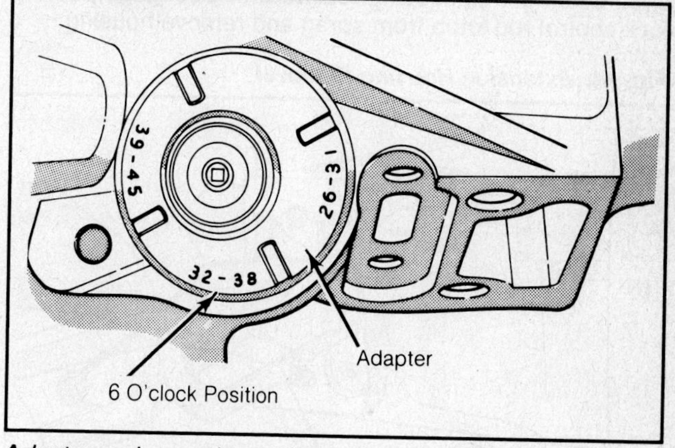

Adapter and mounting surface must be clean.

NEUTRAL SAFETY SWITCH

Refer to appropriate AUTOMATIC TRANSMISSION SERVICING article in DOMESTIC GENERAL SERVICING section.

OUTPUT SHAFT OIL SEAL

Removal

Mark propeller shaft and rear axle flange for reassembly and remove propeller shaft, being careful not to nick or scratch splined yoke. Using removal tool or large screwdriver, remove seal from extension housing.

Installation

Position new seal in opening of extension housing and drive seal into housing. Install propeller shaft, aligning marks made during disassembly.

EXTENSION HOUSING, BEARING & BUSHING

Removal

1) On 4WD models, remove transfer case. On all models, disconnect propeller shaft at rear axle and slide shaft assembly out of extension housing. Remove extension housing oil seal, speedometer pinion and adapter assembly. Drain about 2 quarts of transmission fluid.

2) Remove bolts holding extension housing to crossmember and support. Raise transmission slightly with jack and remove crossmember and support. On AMC passenger cars, remove catalytic converter support bracket bolts, rear support cushion with adapter and

AMERICAN MOTORS, CHRYSLER CORP. & JEEP 727, 904, 998 & 999 (Cont.)

transmission rear bearing cover plate from extension housing.

3) On models equipped with console shift mechanism, remove 2 bolts securing gearshift torque shaft lower bracket to housing, then swing bracket out of way for extension housing removal.

NOTE: **When removing or installing extension housing, gearshift lever must be in "1" (Low) position. This positions parking lock control rod rearward so it can be disengaged or engaged with parking lock sprag.**

4) Remove bolts holding extension housing to transmission. Remove 2 retaining screws, plate and gasket from bottom of housing mounting pad. With large snap ring pliers, spread snap ring on output shaft bearing as far as possible and tap extension housing off output shaft bearing. Pull housing rearward to disengage parking lock control rod knob from sprag and remove housing.

Fig. 14: Extension Housing Removal

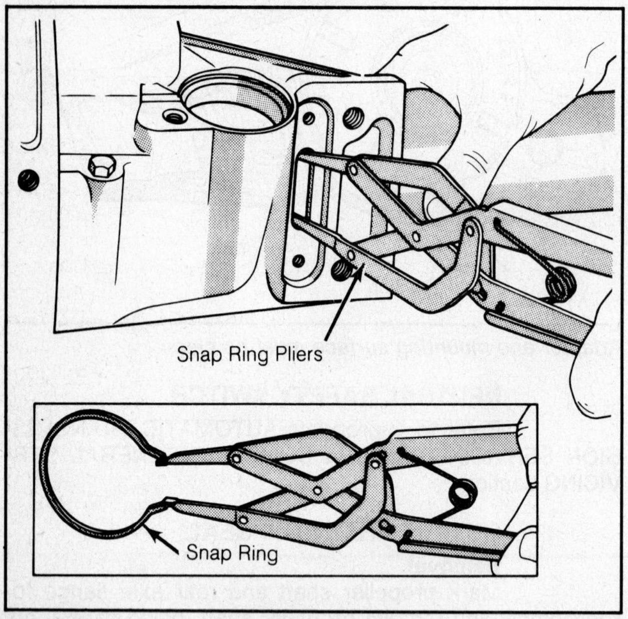

Spread snap ring as far as possible and remove extension housing.

Fig. 15: Output Shaft Rear Bearing Installation

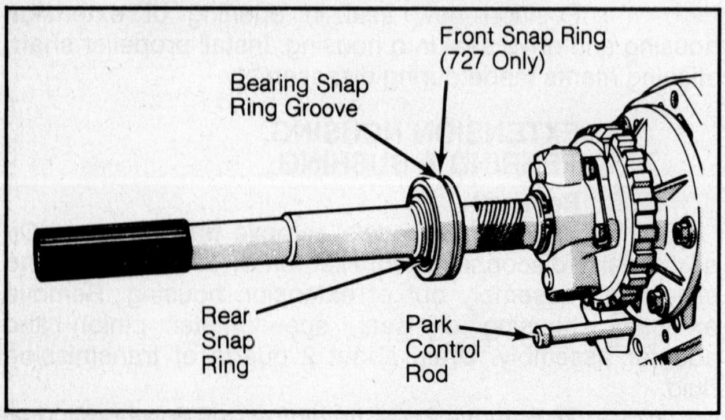

Snap ring groove on outer race must face toward front.

Bushing Replacement

Remove bushing from extension housing with bushing driver. Align hole in new bushing with oil slot in extension housing. Drive or press bushing into housing and install new oil seal.

Bearing Replacement

Remove output shaft bearing rear snap ring and bearing from output shaft. Replace snap ring in front groove on output shaft (if removed). Install new bearing on output shaft with ring groove on outer race toward front. Install rear snap ring.

Installation

1) Install new gasket on transmission case. Position output shaft bearing retaining snap ring in extension housing. Slide extension housing on output shaft, guiding parking lock control rod knob past parking sprag. While spreading large snap ring in housing, carefully tap housing into place and release snap ring.

NOTE: **Ensure snap ring is fully seated in bearing outer race ring groove.**

2) Install and tighten bolts holding extension housing to transmission case. Install gasket, plate and screws on bottom of extension housing mounting pad. Install center crossmember and rear mount assembly. Lower transmission. Install and tighten bolts holding extension housing to support.

3) On vehicles with console shift, align gearshift torque shaft lower bracket with extension housing, then install and tighten retaining bolts. On AMC vehicles, install transmission rear bearing cover plate, rear support cushion, adapter and catalytic converter support bracket bolts (if equipped).

4) On all models, install speedometer pinion and adapter. Install transfer case on AMC Eagle. Install propeller shaft and fill transmission to correct fluid level.

ADAPTER HOUSING BEARING & SEAL (AMC/JEEP ONLY)

Removal

Remove seal from adapter housing using screwdriver or punch. Remove snap rings and remove bearing from adapter housing.

Installation

Install new bearing in housing and install snap rings. Install new seal in housing. Seal should be seated flush with edge of seal bore.

GOVERNOR & PARKING GEAR

Removal

NOTE: **To remove governor and parking gear from 4WD models, transfer case must be removed.**

1) Remove adapter or extension housing and output shaft bearing. Carefully pry snap ring from small side of governor valve shaft. Slide valve and shaft assembly out of governor body. Remove large snap ring from weight end of governor body and lift out governor weight assembly.

AMERICAN MOTORS, CHRYSLER CORP. & JEEP 727, 904, 998 & 999 (Cont.)

Fig. 16: Governor, Support & Parking Gear Assembly

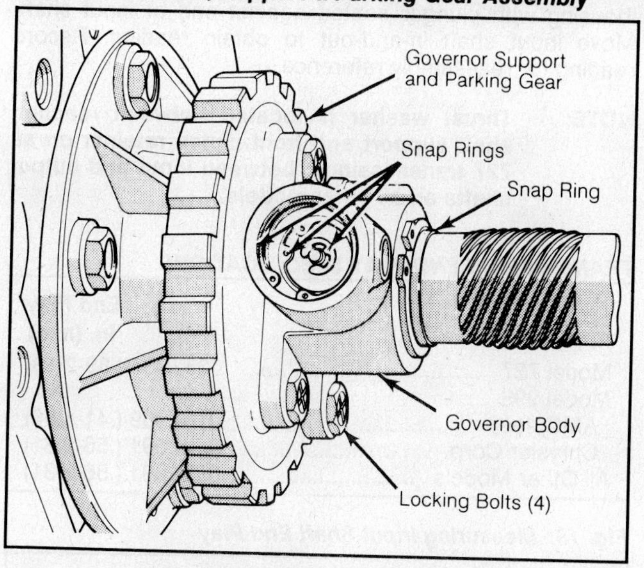

2) Remove snap ring from inside governor weight. Remove inner weight and spring from outer weight. Remove snap ring from behind governor body. Slide body and support assembly off output shaft. Remove bolts and separate governor body from support and parking gear.

Inspection

Inspect all parts for wear or damage. Check spring for distortion. Weights and valves should fall freely in bores when clean and dry. Remove any roughness with crocus cloth.

Installation

1) Assemble governor body to suppport and tighten bolts finger tight, making sure oil passage in governor body aligns with passage in support. Position support and governor assembly on output shaft. Align assembly so valve shaft hole in body mates with hole in output shaft.

2) Slide assembly into place, install snap ring behind governor body and tighten bolts holding body to support. Assemble governor weights and spring. Secure with snap ring inside large governor weight.

3) Place assembly in governor body and install snap ring. Place governor valve on valve shaft. Insert assembly into body and through governor weights. Install valve shaft retaining snap ring.

Fig. 17: Exploded View Of Governor Assembly

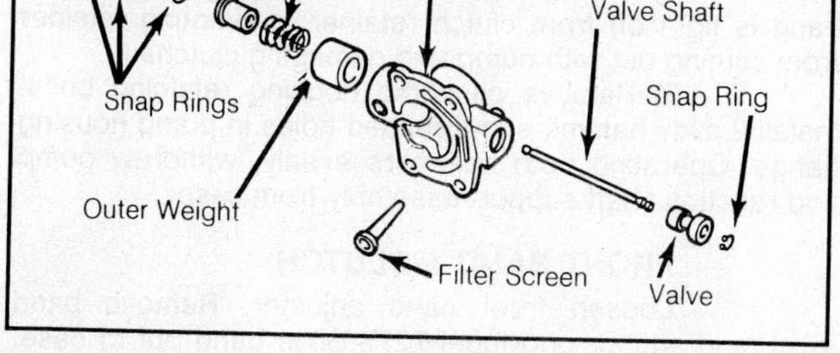

4) Inspect valve and weight assembly for free movement. Install output shaft bearing and extension housing or adapter housing.

PARKING LOCK

Removal

With extension or adapter housing removed, slide shaft out of housing to remove parking sprag and spring. Remove snap ring and slide reaction plug and pin assembly out of housing.

Inspection

Check sprag shaft for scores and free movement in housing and sprag. Check springs for loss of tension or distortion. Check square lug on sprag and lugs on governor support (park gear) for broken edges. Check knob on end of control rod for nicks, burrs and free movement.

Fig. 18: Parking Lock Component Installation

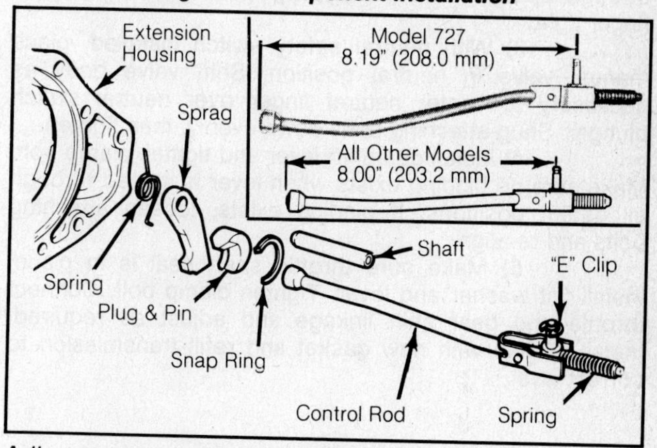

Adjust control rod to length as shown.

Installation

Install reaction plug and pin assembly in housing and secure with snap ring. Position sprag and spring in housing and insert shaft, making sure square lug on sprag is toward parking gear and spring is positioned so it moves sprag away from gear. Control rod length should be adjusted to 8.19" (208.0 mm) on 727 transmissions and 8.00" (203.2 mm) on all others. Install extension or adapter housing.

VALVE BODY ASSEMBLY & ACCUMULATOR PISTON

Removal

1) Loosen oil pan bolts, tap on pan to break it loose and allow fluid to drain. Remove oil pan. Loosen clamp bolts and remove transmission levers. Remove neutral safety switch.

2) While holding valve body in position, remove bolts holding valve body to transmission case. Move valve body down and forward to remove. Rotate propeller shaft as needed to align parking gear and sprag to allow knob on end of control rod to pass sprag.

3) Remove accumulator piston and spring from case. Inspect all parts for wear or damage and replace as needed.

AMERICAN MOTORS, CHRYSLER CORP. & JEEP 727, 904, 998 & 999 (Cont.)

Manual Lever Shaft Seal Replacement

If shaft seal requires replacement, drive seal from case with punch. Drive new seal into case using 15/16" socket and hammer.

NOTE: **Seal may be replaced without removing valve body from case by using small screwdriver to pry seal out of case. Take care not to damage shaft or seal bore in case.**

Installation

1) Place valve body manual lever in "1" position. Using screwdriver, push park sprag into engagement with parking gear, turning output shaft to verify engagement. This allows knob on end of control rod to move past sprag as valve body is installed.

2) Install accumulator piston in transmission case and accumulator spring between piston and valve body. Lift valve body into position, working park rod through opening and past sprag. Install retaining bolts finger tight.

3) With neutral safety switch installed, place manual valve in neutral position. Shift valve body as necessary to center neutral finger over neutral switch plunger. Snug attaching bolts down evenly, then tighten.

4) Install gearshift lever and tighten clamp bolt. Make sure no binding exists when lever is moved through all detent positions. If binding exists, loosen attaching bolts and re-align.

5) Make sure throttle shaft seal is in place. Install flat washer and lever. Tighten clamp bolt. Connect throttle and gear shift linkage and adjust as required. Install oil pan with new gasket and refill transmission to correct level.

REMOVAL & INSTALLATION

See appropriate AUTOMATIC TRANSMISSION REMOVAL article in DOMESTIC GENERAL SERVICING section.

TORQUE CONVERTER

1) Torque converter is welded assembly and is not serviceable. If malfunction occurs or if converter becomes contaminated with foreign material, it must be replaced. It cannot be flushed or repaired.

2) Input shaft and valve body used with lock-up converter are significantly different from those used in transmissions utilizing conventional converter. Two different types of converters are NOT INTERCHANGEABLE.

3) If starter ring gear on lock-up type torque converter requires replacement, complete converter must be replaced. Welding new ring gear onto lock-up converter will damage friction material used in converter.

TRANSMISSION DISASSEMBLY

INPUT SHAFT END PLAY

1) Measuring end play before disassembly will usually indicate whether change in thrust washer is required to properly adjust end play during reassembly (except when major parts are replaced).

2) Attach dial indicator to transmission bellhousing with plunger seated against end of input shaft. Move input shaft in-and-out to obtain reading. Record reading for reassembly reference.

NOTE: **Thrust washer is located between reaction shaft support and front clutch retainer on all 727 transmissions; between input and output shafts on all other models.**

TRANSMISSION END PLAY SPECIFICATIONS

Application	End Play In. (mm)
Model 727	.035-.084 (.89-2.13)
Model 999	
AMC/Jeep	.016-.059 (.41-1.50)
Chrysler Corp.	.022-.091 (.56-2.31)
All Other Models	.022-.091 (.56-2.31)

Fig. 19: Measuring Input Shaft End Play

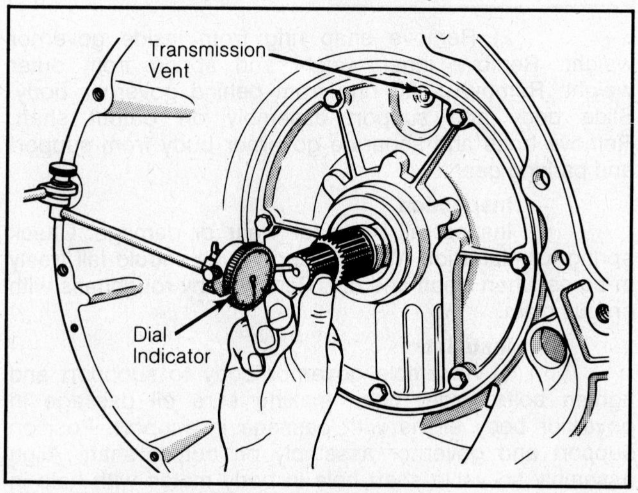

Measure end play before disassembly.

VALVE BODY & ACCUMULATOR PISTON

See SERVICE (IN VEHICLE).

EXTENSION/ADAPTER HOUSING

See SERVICE (IN VEHICLE).

GOVERNOR

See SERVICE (IN VEHICLE).

OIL PUMP & REACTION SHAFT SUPPORT

1) Tighten front band adjusting screw until band is tight on front clutch retainer, preventing retainer from coming out with pump and damaging clutches.

2) Remove oil pump housing retaining bolts. Install 2 slide hammers in threaded holes in pump housing flange. Operating both hammers evenly, withdraw pump and reaction shaft support assembly from case.

FRONT BAND & CLUTCH

Loosen front band adjuster. Remove band strut (and anchor on Model 727). Slide band out of case. Slide front clutch out of case.

AMERICAN MOTORS, CHRYSLER CORP. & JEEP 727, 904, 998 & 999 (Cont.)

INPUT SHAFT & REAR CLUTCH

Grasp input shaft by hand. Slide input shaft and rear clutch assembly out of case.

CAUTION: Do not lose thrust washer located between rear end of input shaft and forward end of output shaft.

PLANETARY GEAR ASSEMBLIES, SUN GEAR & DRIVING SHELL

While supporting output shaft and driving shell, carefully slide assembly forward and out through case.

CAUTION: Do not damage machined surfaces on output shaft during removal.

REAR BAND & LOW-REVERSE DRUM

AMC/Jeep

Remove low-reverse drum. Loosen rear band adjusting screw and thread 1/4" bolt into actuating lever pivot pin. Remove pin from case. Remove lever, linkage and rear band from case.

Chrysler Corp.

Remove drum, loosen rear band adjuster and remove band strut and link. Remove band from case. On models with double-wrap band, loosen band adjusting screw. Remove band and low-reverse drum.

OVERRUNNING CLUTCH

Note relative positions of overrunning clutch rollers and springs for reassembly reference.Carefully slide out clutch hub, then remove rollers and springs.

FRONT (KICKDOWN) SERVO

Compress kickdown servo and remove snap ring. Remove rod guide, springs and piston rod from case. Take care not to damage piston rod or guide. Remove piston from transmission case.

REAR (LOW-REVERSE) SERVO

Compress low-reverse servo piston spring and remove snap ring. Remove spring retainer, spring, servo piston and plug assembly from case. Tag spring for reassembly reference.

COMPONENT DISASSEMBLY & REASSEMBLY

VALVE BODY DISASSEMBLY

NOTE: Tag all valves and springs for reassembly reference as they are removed.

Filter, Transfer Plate & Pressure Regulators

1) Place valve body assembly on stand, remove filter retaining screws and filter. Remove top and bottom screws from spring retainer/adjustment screw bracket. Holding spring retainer firmly against spring pressure, remove last screw from side of valve body.

2) Remove spring retainer with line and throttle pressure adjusting screws (do not disturb settings). Remove line pressure and switch valve regulator springs.

3) Slide switch valve and line pressure valve from bores. Remove screws from lock-up module (stiffener plate on models with conventional converter) and carefully remove tube and lock-up module (or stiffener plate). Disassemble lock-up module, tagging springs for reassembly reference.

4) Remove transfer plate retaining screws and lift off transfer plate and separator plate assembly. Remove screws from stiffener and separator plate and

Fig. 20: Valve Body Assembly Prepared For Disassembly

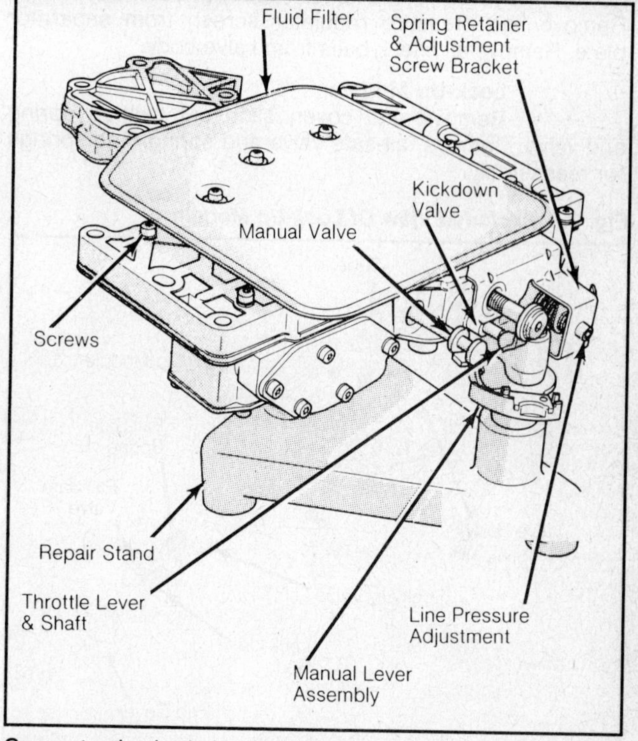

Support valve body in stand during disassembly procedure.

Fig. 21: Transfer & Separator Plate

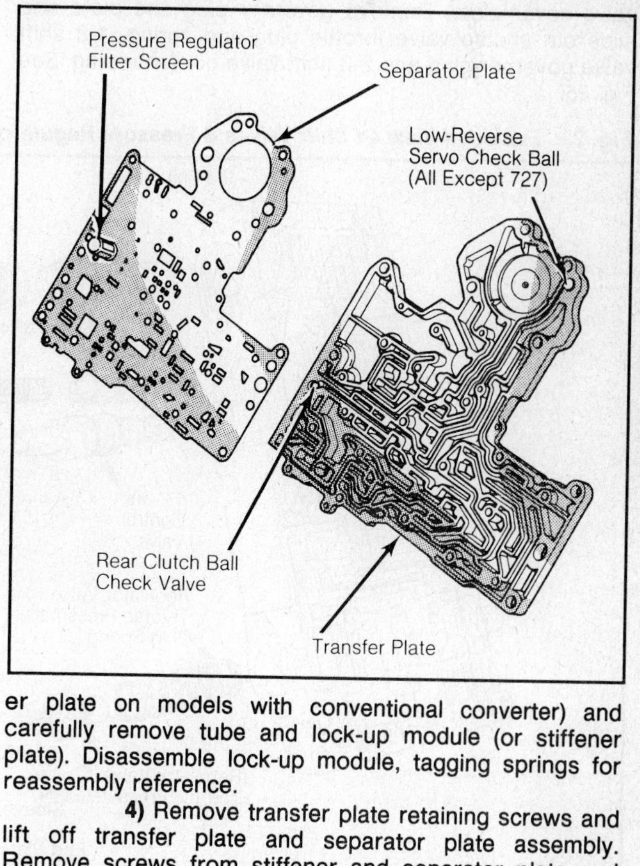

AMERICAN MOTORS, CHRYSLER CORP. & JEEP 727, 904, 998 & 999 (Cont.)

separate parts for cleaning. Remove rear clutch check ball and low-reverse servo check ball (Model 904 only). Remove line pressure regulator screen from separator plate. Remove all check balls from valve body.

Lock-Up Module

Remove end cover, slide out lock-up spring and valve. Remove fail-safe valve and spring. Tag springs for reassembly.

Fig. 22: Exploded View Of Lock-Up Module

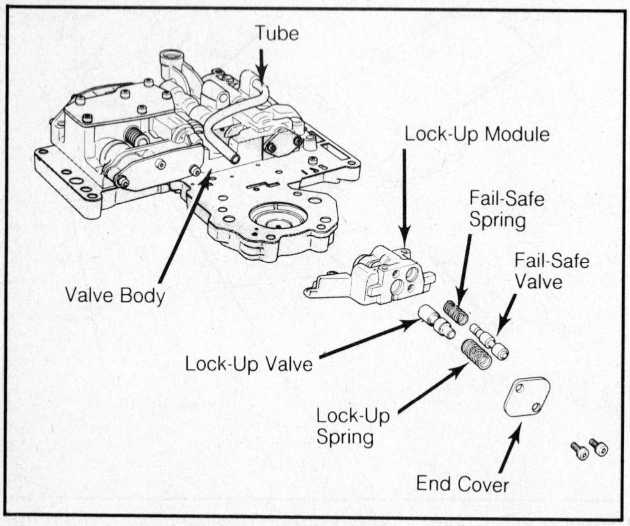

Shuttle Valve & Governor Plugs

1) Turn valve body over and remove shuttle valve cover plate. Remove governor plug end plate and slide out shuttle valve throttle plug and spring, 1-2 shift valve governor plug and 2-3 shift valve governor plug. *See Fig. 25.*

2) Remove shuttle valve "E" clip and slide shuttle valve from bore. Also remove secondary spring and guides retained by "E" clip. Remove "E" clip and park control rod from manual lever.

Pressure Regulators & Manual Control

1) Remove "E" clip and washer from throttle lever shaft. Remove any burrs from shaft. While holding manual lever detent ball and spring in bore, slide manual lever off throttle shaft. *See Fig. 24.*

2) Remove detent ball and spring. Slide manual valve from bore and remove kickdown detent, kickdown valve, throttle valve spring and throttle valve.

Shift Valves & Regulator Valve Pressure Sensing Plugs

1) Remove line pressure regulator valve end plate. *See Fig. 23.* Slide out regulator valve sleeve, line pressure plug, throttle pressure plug and spring.

2) Remove end plate. On models with downshift valve housing, remove housing assembly. Remove throttle plug, slide out retainer and remove spring and limit valve from housing. On all models, remove shift valves and springs (3) from valve body.

VALVE BODY INSPECTION

1) Wash all parts in solvent and dry with compressed air. Inspect all parts for nicks, burrs, scratches or distortion. Small nicks and burrs can be removed with crocus cloth. Use extreme care not to round off any machined sharp edges. These edges are necessary to prevent foreign matter from lodging between valve and bore, which could cause valve to stick or drag.

2) Make sure all passages are clean and free of obstructions. All metering holes in steel plate and valve body must be open. Insert 1/32" drill through orifice into 1-

Fig. 23: Exploded View Of Shift Valves & Pressure Regulator Valve Plugs

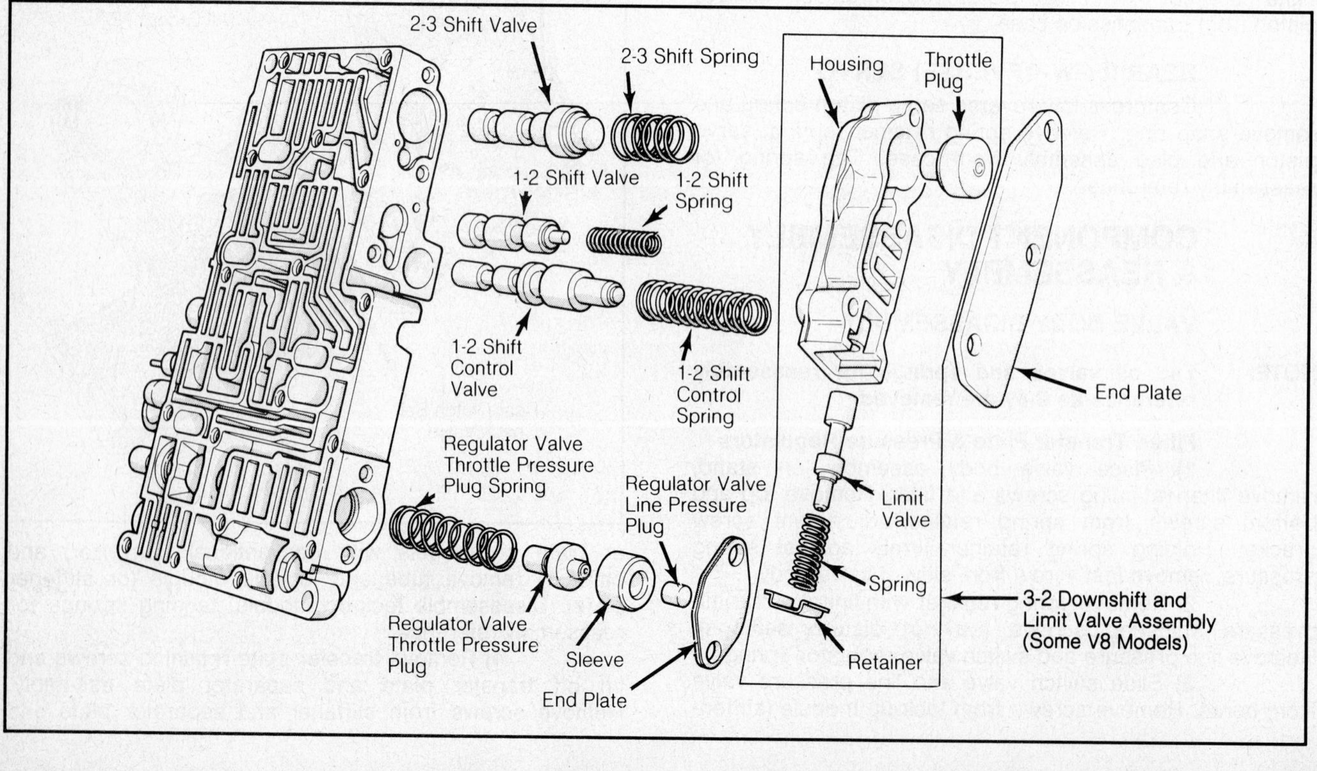

AMERICAN MOTORS, CHRYSLER CORP. & JEEP 727, 904, 998 & 999 (Cont.)

2 shift control bore to make sure it is open. Inspect all springs for distortion and/or collapsed coils.

3) Inspect manual and throttle valve operating levers and shafts. If bent, worn or loose on shaft, assembly should be replaced. DO NOT attempt to straighten bent levers.

4) When bores, valves and plugs are clean and dry, valves and plugs should fall freely into bores.

VALVE BODY REASSEMBLY

Shift Valves & Regulator Valve Pressure Sensing Plugs

1) Slide shift valves and springs into proper valve body bores. On models with downshift housing assembly, insert limit valve and spring into housing and slide spring retainer into groove. Install throttle plug in housing bore. Position assembly against shift valve springs.

2) On all models, install end plate and tighten retaining screws. Install throttle pressure spring, plug, sleeve and regulator valve plug. Install end plate and tighten retaining screws.

Shuttle Valve & Governor Plugs

1) Place 1-2 and 2-3 shift valve governor plugs in bores. Install shuttle valve into bore. Install spring guides, secondary spring and "E" clip on opposite end of valve.

2) Install primary shuttle valve spring and throttle plug into bore. Install governor plug end plate. Install and tighten retaining screws. Install shuttle valve cover plate and tighten retaining screws.

Fig. 24: Exploded View Of Pressure Regulators & Manual Controls

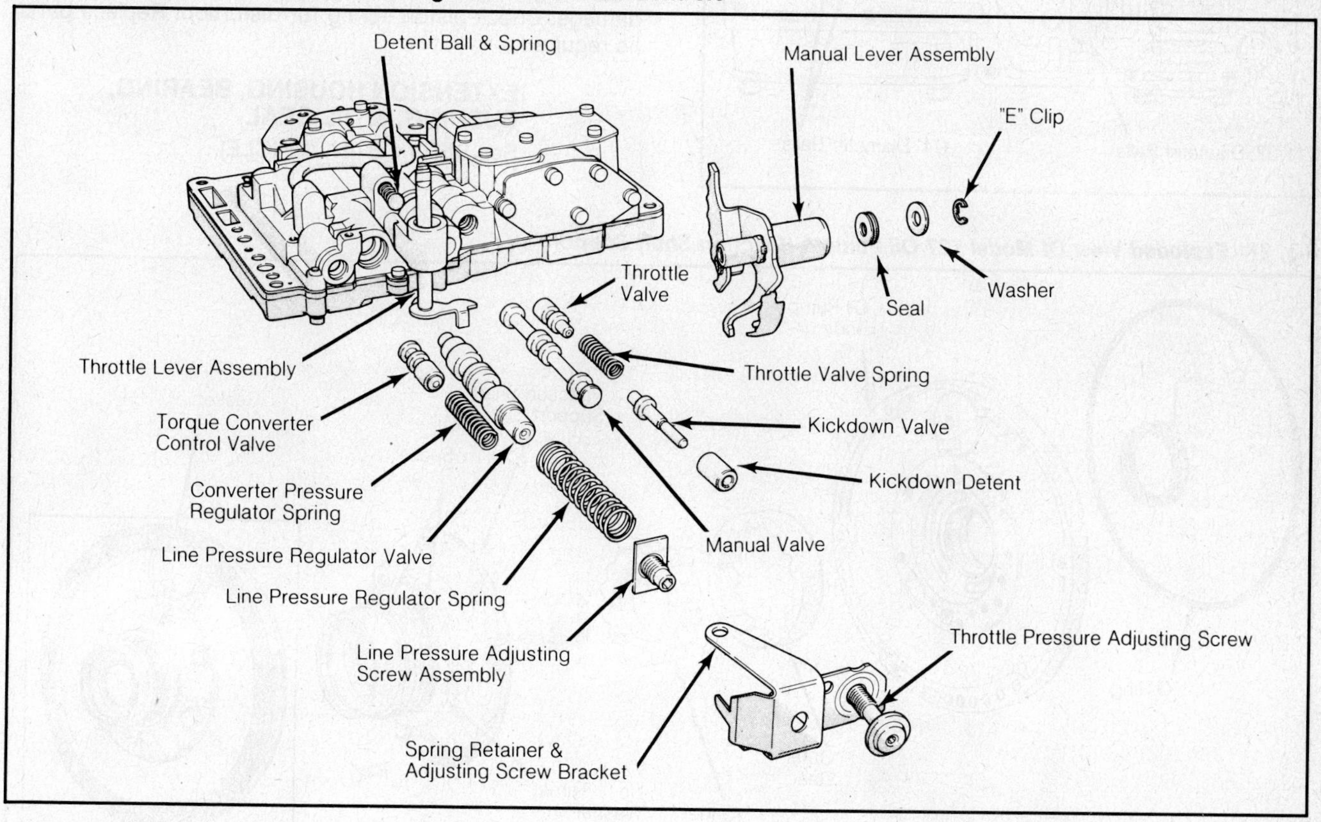

Pressure Regulators & Manual Control

1) Install throttle valve, valve spring, kickdown valve and detent into bore. Slide manual valve into its bore. Install throttle lever and shaft on valve body. Insert detent ball and spring into bore.

Fig. 25: Exploded View Of Shuttle Valve & Governor Plugs

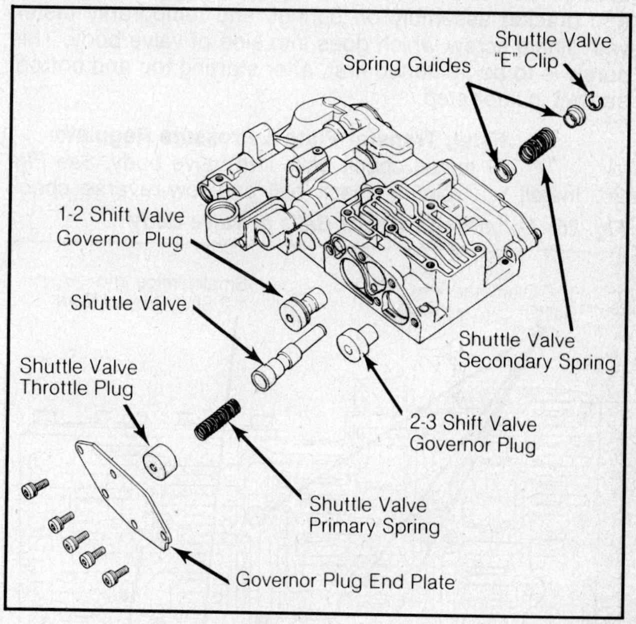

AMERICAN MOTORS, CHRYSLER CORP. & JEEP 727, 904, 998 & 999 (Cont.)

2) Depress ball and spring in bore. Slide manual lever over throttle shaft so it engages manual valve and detent ball. Install seal, retaining washer and "E" clip on throttle shaft. Insert switch valve and spring into valve body.

3) Insert line pressure regulator valve and spring into valve body. Install pressure adjusting screw and bracket assembly on springs and temporarily fasten with single screw which goes into side of valve body. This screw is to be tightened first, after starting top and bottom screws in later step.

Filter, Transfer Plate & Pressure Regulator

1) Install check balls into valve body. *See Fig. 26.* Install rear clutch check ball and low-reverse check

Fig. 26: Location Of Check Balls In Valve Body

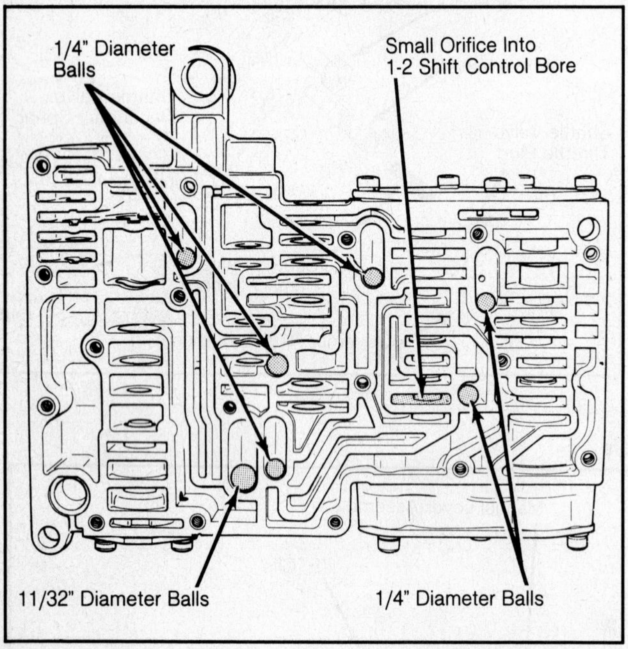

ball (Model 904 only) in transfer plate. Install regulator valve screen in separator plate. Install 3 screws in separator plate.

2) Place transfer plate assembly on valve body. Install 17 short screws into assembly finger tight (3 long screws are for oil filter), aligning holes for filter screen at same time. Tighten screws starting from center and working outward.

3) Slide switch valve, line pressure valves and springs into respective bores. Install pressure adjusting screw and bracket assembly on springs and temporarily fasten single screw which goes into side of valve body. This screw will be tightened first, after starting top and bottom screws in later step.

4) Install oil filter and tighten screws. Install lock-up valve and spring. Install fail-safe spring and valve into lock-up module. Install lock-up module to transfer and separator plate assembly with 3 screws (install stiffener plate on models with conventional converter).

5) After valve body has been reassembled, check throttle and line pressure adjustments. Make adjustments as required. Do not disturb settings if adjustments were correct prior to valve body disassembly. Install parking lock rod and "E" clip retainer to manual lever.

ACCUMULATOR PISTON & SPRING

Inspection

1) Inspect seal rings for wear or damage and ensure they turn freely in grooves. Do not remove seal rings unless replacement is required.

2) Inspect piston for nicks, burrs, scores or wear. Check piston bore in case for scores or other damage. Check piston spring for distortion. Replace parts as required.

EXTENSION HOUSING, BEARING, BUSHING, & OIL SEAL

See SERVICE (IN VEHICLE).

Fig. 27: Exploded View Of Model 727 Oil Pump & Reaction Shaft Support

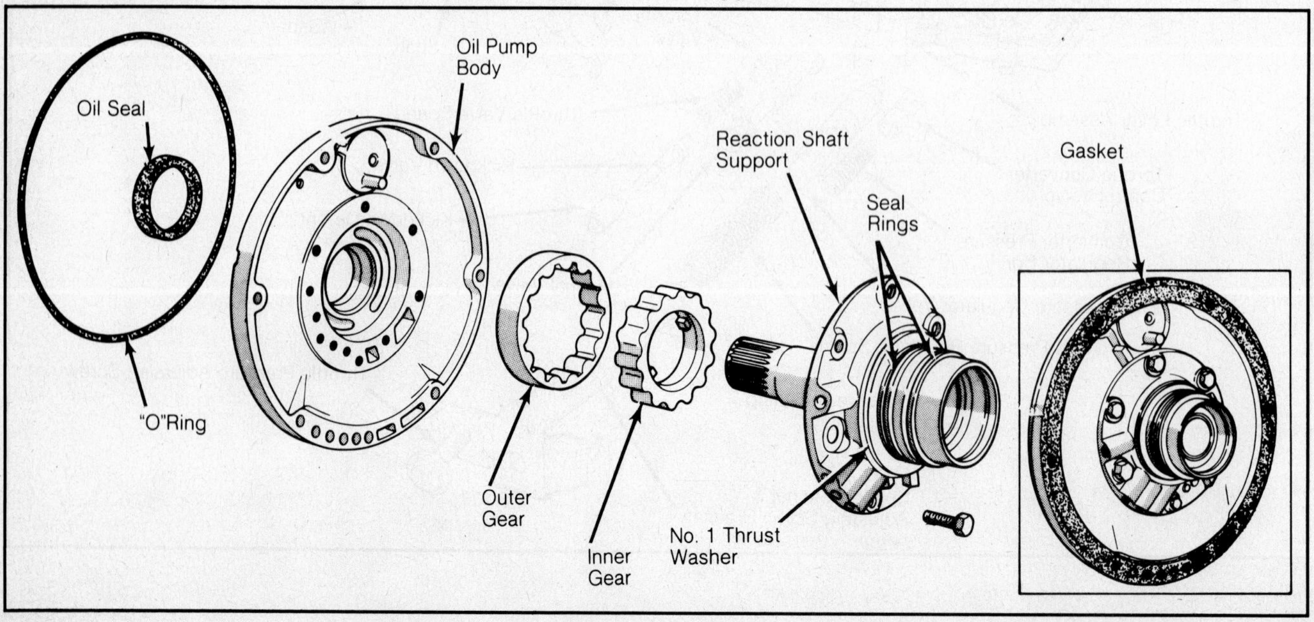

AMERICAN MOTORS, CHRYSLER CORP. & JEEP 727, 904, 998 & 999 (Cont.)

PARKING SPRAG & LEVER

See SERVICE (IN VEHICLE).

GOVERNOR

See SERVICE (IN VEHICLE).

OIL PUMP/REACTION SHAFT SUPPORT

Disassembly

Remove bolts from rear side of reaction shaft support and lift support off pump. Remove rubber seal ring from pump body flange. Drive out oil seal with blunt punch. Mark top of pump rotors with chalk to ensure proper installation during reassembly.

Fig. 28: Exploded View Of Oil Pump & Reaction Shaft Support

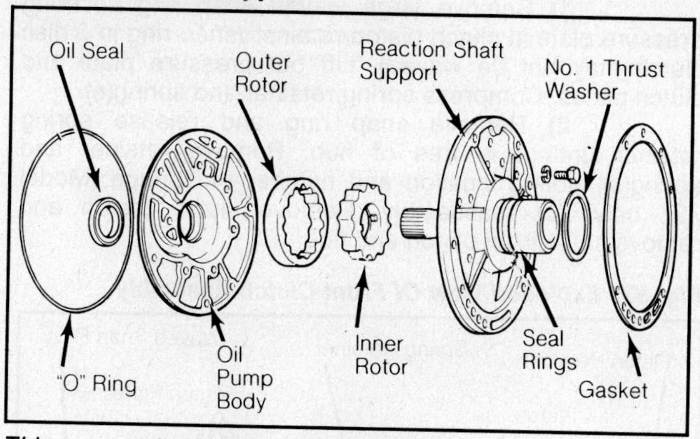

This covers all versions except Model 727.

Inspection

1) Inspect interlocking seal rings on support for wear or damage. Make sure rings turn freely in grooves. Do not remove rings unless replacement is required. Inspect pump body and support bushings for wear or scores.

2) Check machined surfaces of pump body and support for nicks or burrs. Check pump rotors for scoring or pitting. With rotors cleaned and installed in pump body, place straightedge across face of rotors and pump body. Using feeler gauge, measure clearance between straightedge and rotor faces. Clearance should be .001-.0025" (.03-.06 mm).

3) Measure rotor tip clearance between inner and outer rotor teeth. Clearance should be .005-.010" (.13-.25 mm). Clearance between outer rotor and oil pump body bore should be .004-.008" (.10-.20 mm).

NOTE: **On all models except 727, remove seal rings so that thrust washer between front clutch retainer and reaction shaft can be removed. If washer thickness is not .061-.063" (1.55-1.60 mm), it should be replaced.**

Pump Bushing Replacement

1) Place pump housing (rotor cavity down) on clean smooth surface. Drive bushing straight down and out of bore, being careful not to cock tool in bore.

2) With hub end of pump housing down, drive new bushing into place in pump cavity. Stake bushing in place using blunt punch.

3) Using narrow blade knife, remove high points or burrs around staked area. Do not use file or any tool that would remove more metal than necessary.

Fig. 29: Installing New Oil Pump Bushing

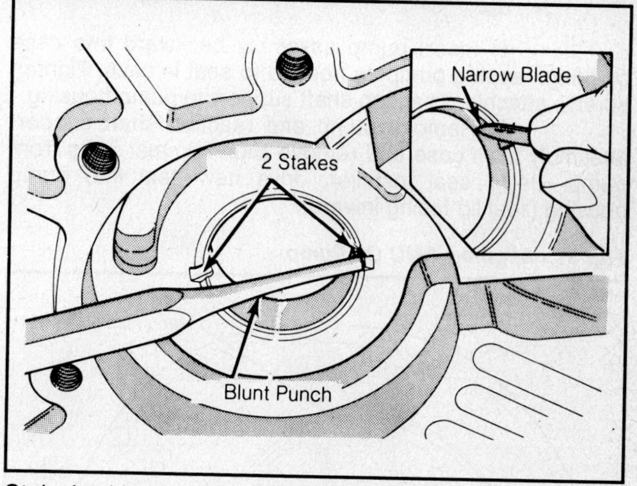

Stake bushing in place with blunt punch.

Reaction Shaft Bushing Replacement

1) Thread bushing remover into bushing. Remove bushing from reaction shaft. Support reaction shaft upright on clean smooth surface.

2) Using bushing installer, drive new bushing (chamfered end up) into place in reaction shaft.

NOTE: **Do not clamp any part of reaction shaft or support in vise.**

Fig. 30: Replacing Reaction Shaft Bushing

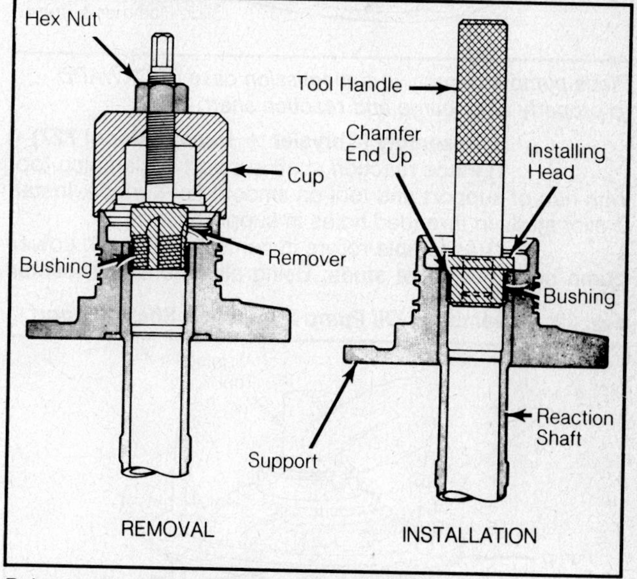

Drive in new bushing with chamfered end up.

Reassembly (AMC/Jeep)

1) Install rotors in pump housing (marks made at disassembly facing up). Align and loosely assemble reaction shaft support to pump housing. Do not tighten bolts at this time.

2) Thread 2 slide hammer bolts (from back-to-front) into threaded reaction shaft support holes, until bolt ends are recessed 1/16" below front machined surface of pump housing. Install 1 pilot stud into case pump opening.

AMERICAN MOTORS, CHRYSLER CORP. & JEEP 727, 904, 998 & 999 (Cont.)

NOTE: New rotors may be installed with either face up.

3) Insert pump assembly backward into case opening, tapping pump as needed to seat in case. Tighten screws attaching reaction shaft support to pump housing.

4) Remove pump and reaction shaft support assembly from case and remove slide hammer bolts from pump. Using seal installer, drive new seal into pump housing (seal lip facing inward).

Fig. 31: Aligning AMC Oil Pump

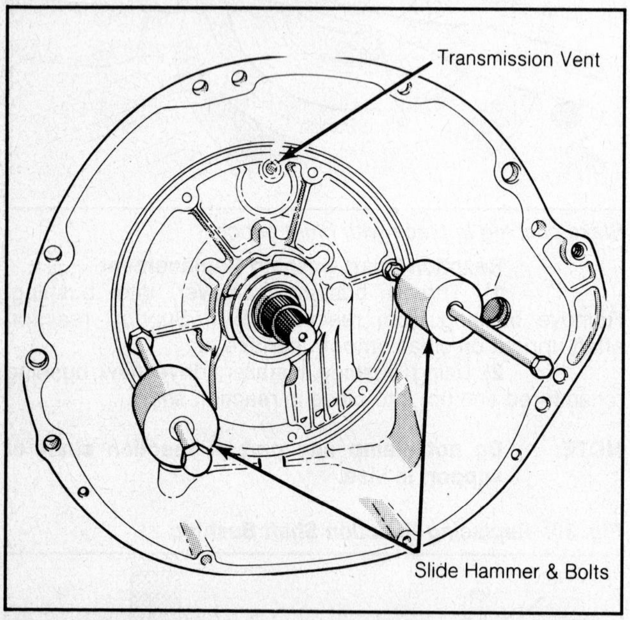

Place pump assembly in transmission case BACKWARD to properly align pump and reaction shaft.

Reassembly (Chrysler – Except Model 727)

1) Place reaction shaft support in clamping tool with hub of support and tool on smooth flat surface. Install 2 pilot studs in threaded holes in support flange.

2) Assemble rotors in center of support. Lower pump body over pilot studs. Using alignment tool, center rotors in pump body. With pump body firmly against reaction shaft support, tighten clamping tool securely. *See Fig. 32.*

Fig. 32: Assembling Oil Pump & Reaction Shaft Support

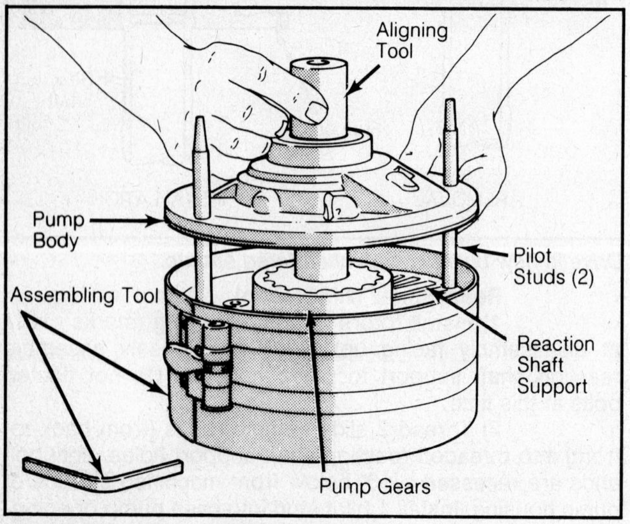

All Chrysler Corp. models except 727.

3) Invert pump and tool assembly. Install and evenly tighten bolts holding support to pump bolts. Remove clamping tool, pilot studs and aligning tool. Drive new pump oil seal into housing with lip of seal facing in.

Reassembly (Chrysler – 727)

Install pump rotors and "O" ring in pump housing. Install reaction shaft support and retaining bolts. Place new seal in opening of pump housing with lip of seal facing inward and press into place with driver.

FRONT CLUTCH

Disassembly

1) Remove large waved snap ring securing pressure plate in clutch piston retainer (snap ring in 5 disc clutch may not be waved). Lift out pressure plate and clutch plates. Compress spring retainer and spring(s).

2) Remove snap ring and release spring retainer until it is free of hub. Remove retainer and spring(s), noting location and number of springs (Model 727 only) for reassembly. Remove clutch piston and remove seals from piston and hub.

Fig. 33: Exploded View Of Front Clutch Assembly

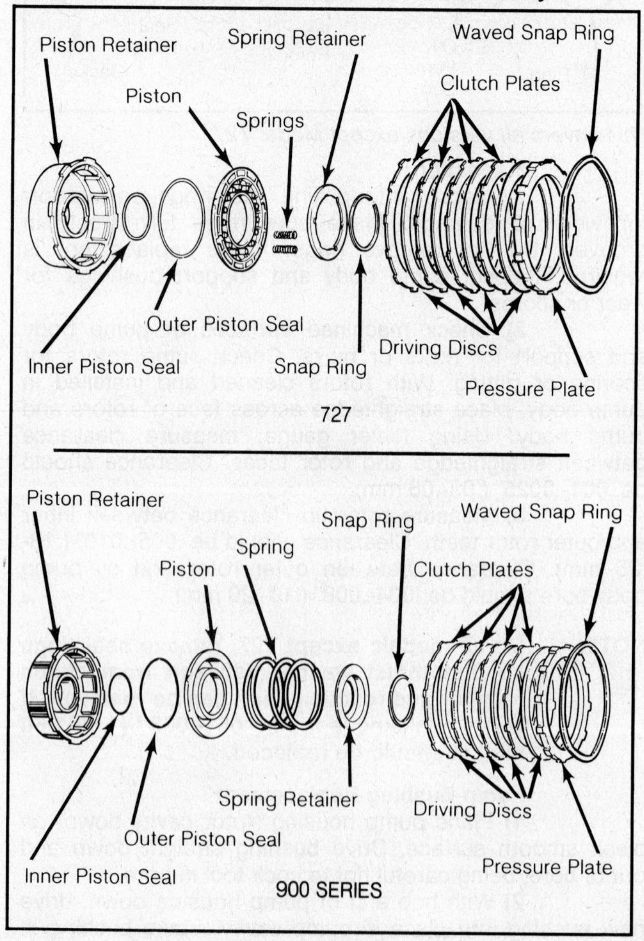

AMERICAN MOTORS, CHRYSLER CORP. & JEEP 727, 904, 998 & 999 (Cont.)

Inspection

1) Inspect plates and discs for flatness. They must not be warped or cone-shaped. Inspect facing material on all driving discs. Replace discs as needed.

2) Inspect discs and plates for wear on splines or lugs. Check clutch retainer for damaged lug grooves or band contacting surface. Make sure check ball in clutch retainer moves freely.

3) Check neoprene seals for wear, hardness or deterioration. Inspect piston spring(s), retainer and snap ring for distortion.

Front Clutch Retainer Bushing Replacement

1) Lay clutch retainer (open end down) on clean smooth surface. Drive bushing straight down and out of bore, taking care not to cock tool in bore.

2) To install, lay clutch retainer (open end up) on clean smooth surface. Drive bushing into place in clutch retainer bore with bushing installer.

Reassembly

1) Lubricate and install inner seal on hub of clutch retainer. Make sure lip of seal faces down and is properly seated in groove. Install outer seal on clutch piston with lip of seal toward bottom of clutch retainer.

2) Lubricate seals to ease installation. Install and carefully seat piston in bottom of retainer. Install return spring on piston hub. On Model 727, install same number of springs as were removed. See *Fig. 34* for spring location.

3) Position spring retainer and snap ring over hub. Compress and install snap ring in hub groove. Remove compressor tool. Lubricate all clutch plates. Install 1 steel plate followed by 1 faced disc until all clutch plates are installed. See FRONT CLUTCH PLATE USAGE chart.

4) Install pressure plate and snap ring. Make sure snap ring is properly seated. With front clutch completely assembled, measure maximum clearance where snap ring is waved away from pressure plate. Refer to FRONT CLUTCH PLATE CLEARANCES chart for specified clearance.

Fig. 35: Measuring Front Clutch Plate Clearance

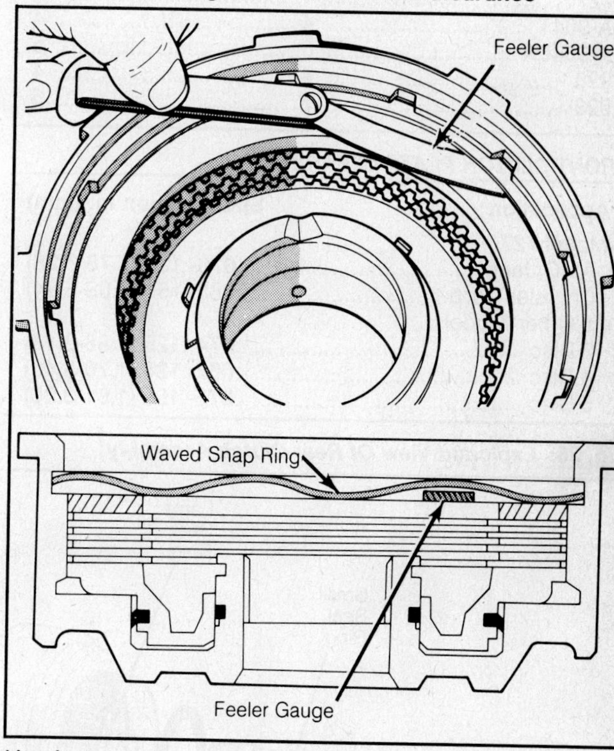

Use feeler gauge to measure gap.

Fig. 34: Model 727 Front Clutch Spring Installation

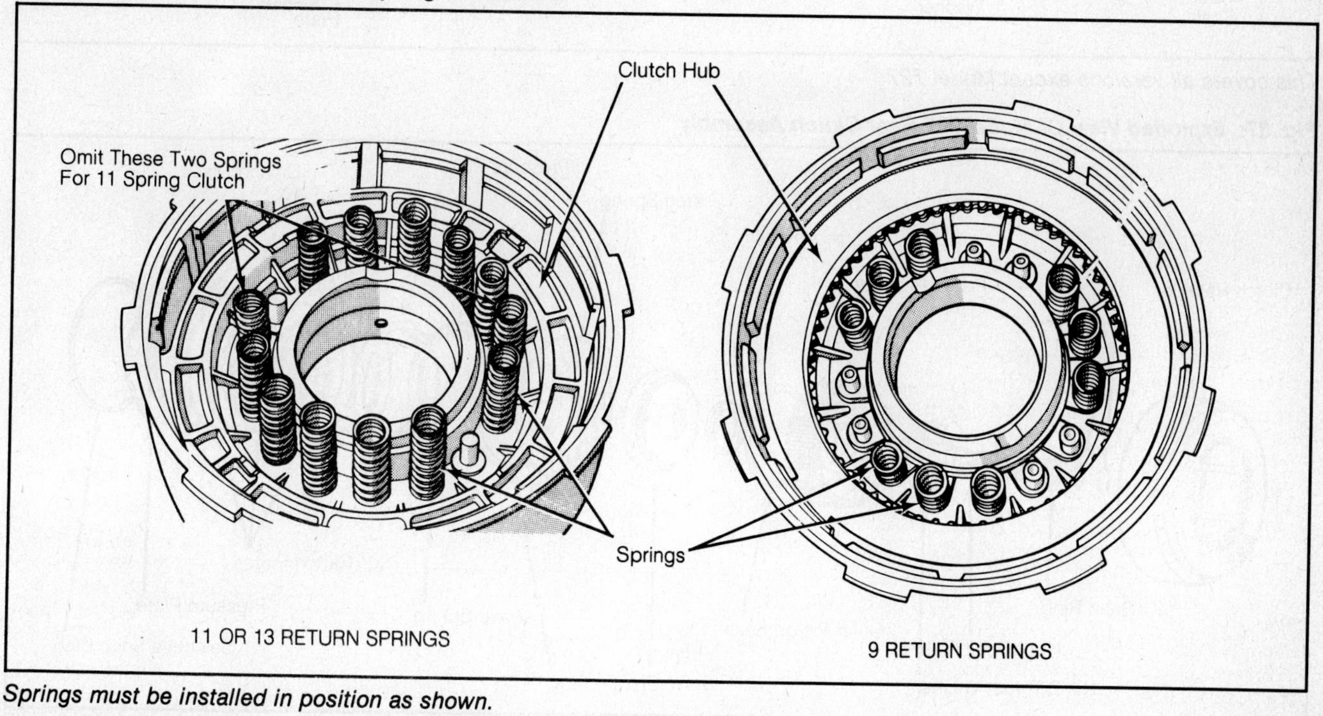

Springs must be installed in position as shown.

AMERICAN MOTORS, CHRYSLER CORP. & JEEP 727, 904, 998 & 999 (Cont.)

FRONT CLUTCH PLATE USAGE

Application	Steel Plates	Composition Plates
727	4	4
A-904T	4	4
A-904LA	5	5
998	4	4
999	5	5

FRONT CLUTCH PLATE CLEARANCES

Application	Specification In. (mm)
Model 727	
AMC/Jeep	.070-.129 (1.78-3.28)
Chrysler Corp.	.082-.151 (2.08-3.84)
All Other Models	
3 Disc	.074-.125 (1.88-3.18)
4 Disc	.067-.134 (1.70-3.40)
5 Disc	.075-.152 (1.91-3.86)

REAR CLUTCH

Disassembly

1) Remove large selective snap ring securing pressure plate in clutch retainer. Lift pressure plate, clutch plates and inner pressure plate out of retainer. Pry one end of wave spring out of groove in clutch retainer. Remove wave spring, spacer ring (Model 727) and clutch piston spring.

2) Invert clutch piston retainer assembly and bump on wood block to remove piston. Remove seals from piston. If necessary, remove snap ring and press input shaft from clutch piston retainer.

Inspection

1) Inspect plates and discs for flatness. Replace any that are warped or cone-shaped. Inspect facing material on all drive discs; replace if damaged. Inspect disc and plates for wear on splines or lugs and check lug grooves in clutch retainer for damage.

Fig. 36: Exploded View Of Rear Clutch Assembly

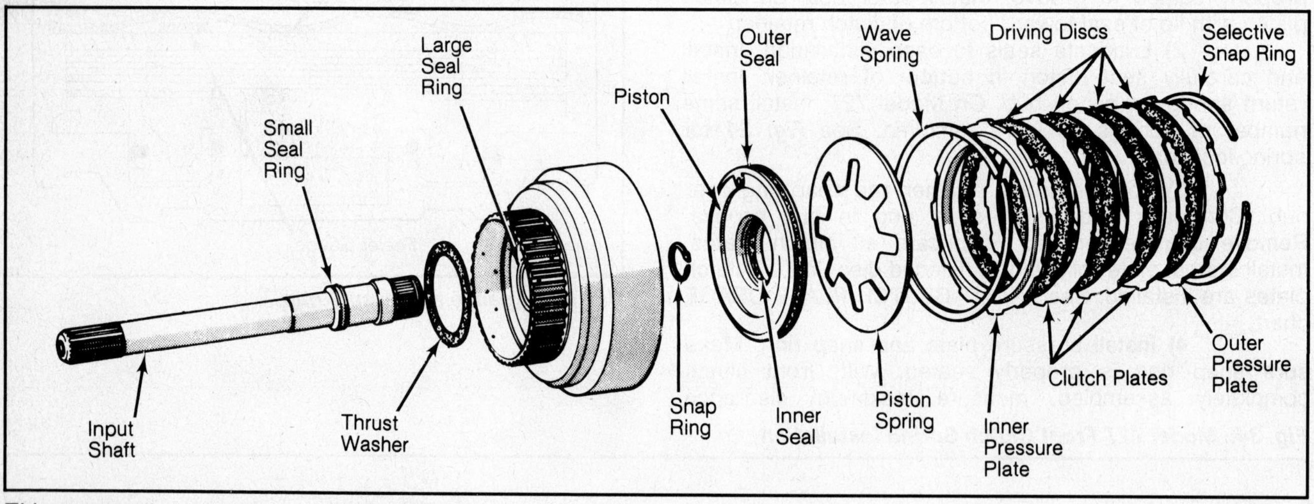

This covers all versions except Model 727

Fig. 37: Exploded View Of Model 727 Rear Clutch Assembly

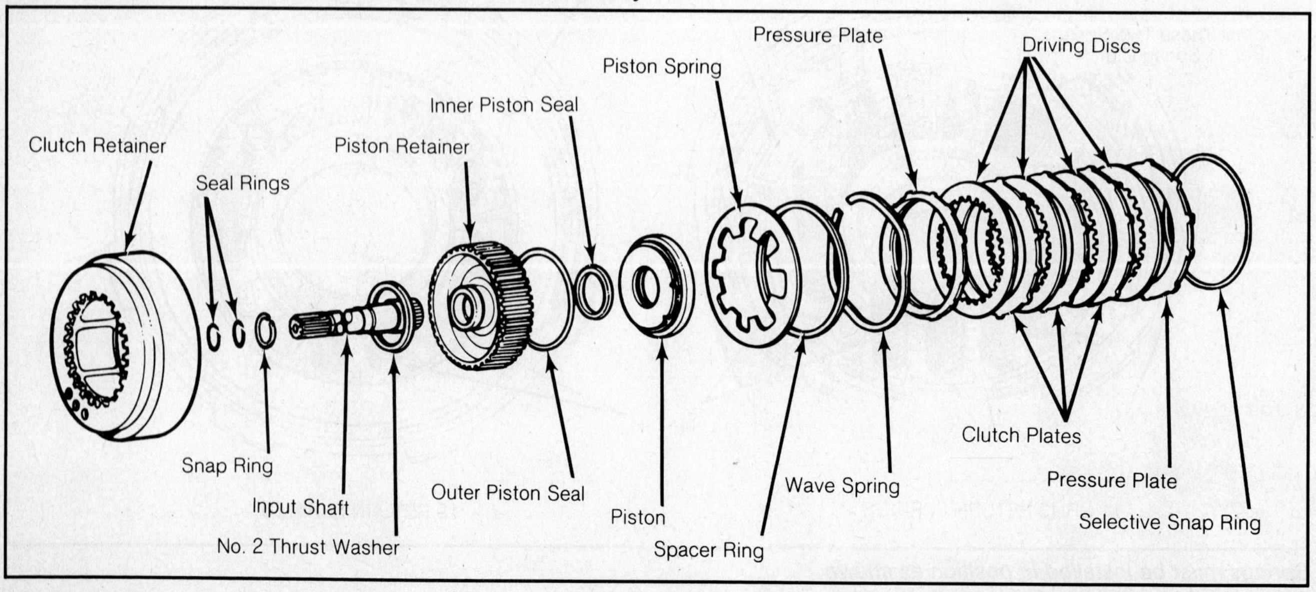

AMERICAN MOTORS, CHRYSLER CORP. & JEEP 727, 904, 998 & 999 (Cont.)

2) Make sure check ball in piston moves freely. Check seal ring surfaces in clutch retainer for nicks and scratches. Check neoprene seals for wear, hardness or deterioration.

3) Inspect interlocking seal rings on input shaft for wear or broken locks. Make sure rings turn freely in grooves. Do not remove rings unless replacement is required.

4) Check bushing in input shaft for wear or scores. Measure thrust washer between rear clutch and front clutch for wear. If washer is not .061-.063" (1.55-1.60 mm) thick, it should be replaced.

Input Shaft Bushing Replacement (727)

1) Clamp input shaft in soft-jawed vise, taking care not to clamp seal ring lands or journals. Thread bushing remover into bushing and withdraw bushing from shaft.

2) Thoroughly clean input shaft to remove any metal chips made by tool. Drive new bushing into place.

Fig. 38: Replacing Input Shaft Bushing

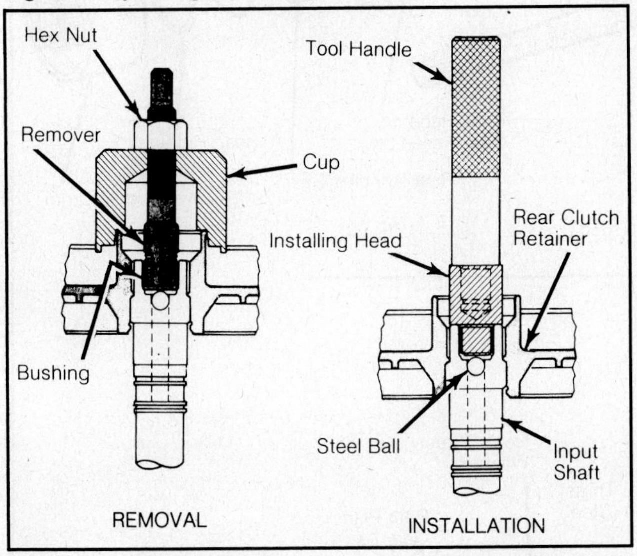

Clean input shaft to remove any metal chips made by tool.

Reassembly

1) If removed, press input shaft into clutch piston retainer and install snap ring. Lubricate and install inner and outer seal rings on clutch piston. Make sure lips of seals face toward head of clutch retainer and are properly seated in grooves.

2) Place piston assembly in retainer. Seat piston in bottom of retainer with twisting motion. On Model 727, position clutch retainer over piston retainer splines and support assembly so clutch retainer remains in place.

3) On all models, place piston spring and spacer ring (Model 727) on top of piston. Make sure they are positioned in retainer recess. Start one end of wave spring in retainer groove. Progressively push or tap spring into place. Make sure spring is fully seated in groove.

4) Install inner pressure plate in retainer with raised portion of plate against spring. Lubricate all clutch plates with ATF. Install 1 faced disc followed by 1 steel plate until all clutch plates are installed. See REAR CLUTCH PLATE USAGE chart. Install outer pressure plate and selective snap ring.

REAR CLUTCH PLATE USAGE

Application	Steel Plates	Composition Plates
All Models	3	4

5) Compress clutch pack by pressing down firmly on outer pressure plate. Maintain steady pressure with "C" clamp or press. Measure rear clutch plate clearance by inserting feeler gauge between plate and snap ring. See REAR CLUTCH PLATE CLEARANCES table for correct clearance range. If possible, lower limit is preferred setting.

REAR CLUTCH PLATE CLEARANCES

Application	[1] Clearance In. (mm)
727	.025-.045 (.64-1.14)
All Others	.032-.055 (.81-1.40)

[1] - Lower limit of range is preferred.

6) If clearance is incorrect, adjust it by installing different size snap ring. Selective snap rings are available in thicknesses of .060", .074", .088" and .106" (1.52, 1.88, 2.24, 2.69 mm) for Model 727, .060", .068" and .076" (1.52, 1.73, 1.93 mm) for all other Chrysler models and .060", .074 and .098" (1.52, 1.88, 2.49 mm) for all other AMC/Jeep models.

PLANETARY GEAR TRAIN

End Play Check

1) Measure end play of planetary gear assemblies, sun gear and driving shell before removing from output shaft. Stand assembly upright with forward end of output shaft supported on wood block so all parts will move forward against snap ring at front of shaft.

2) Insert feeler gauge between rear annulus gear support hub and shoulder on output shaft. Clearance should be .009-.044" (.23-1.12 mm) for Model 727, and .001-.047" (.025-1.20 mm) for all other models. If not, replace thrust washer and/or necessary parts.

Fig. 39: Checking Planetary Gear Train End Play

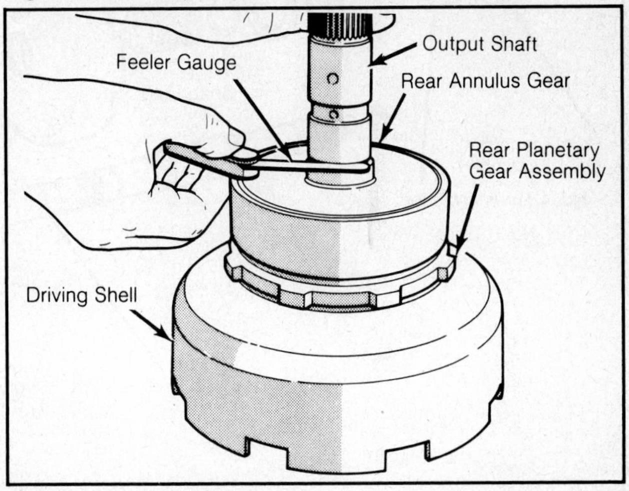

Measure end play of planetary gear before disassembly.

AMERICAN MOTORS, CHRYSLER CORP. & JEEP
727, 904, 998 & 999 (Cont.)

Fig. 40: Exploded View Of Planetary Gear Train & Output Shaft

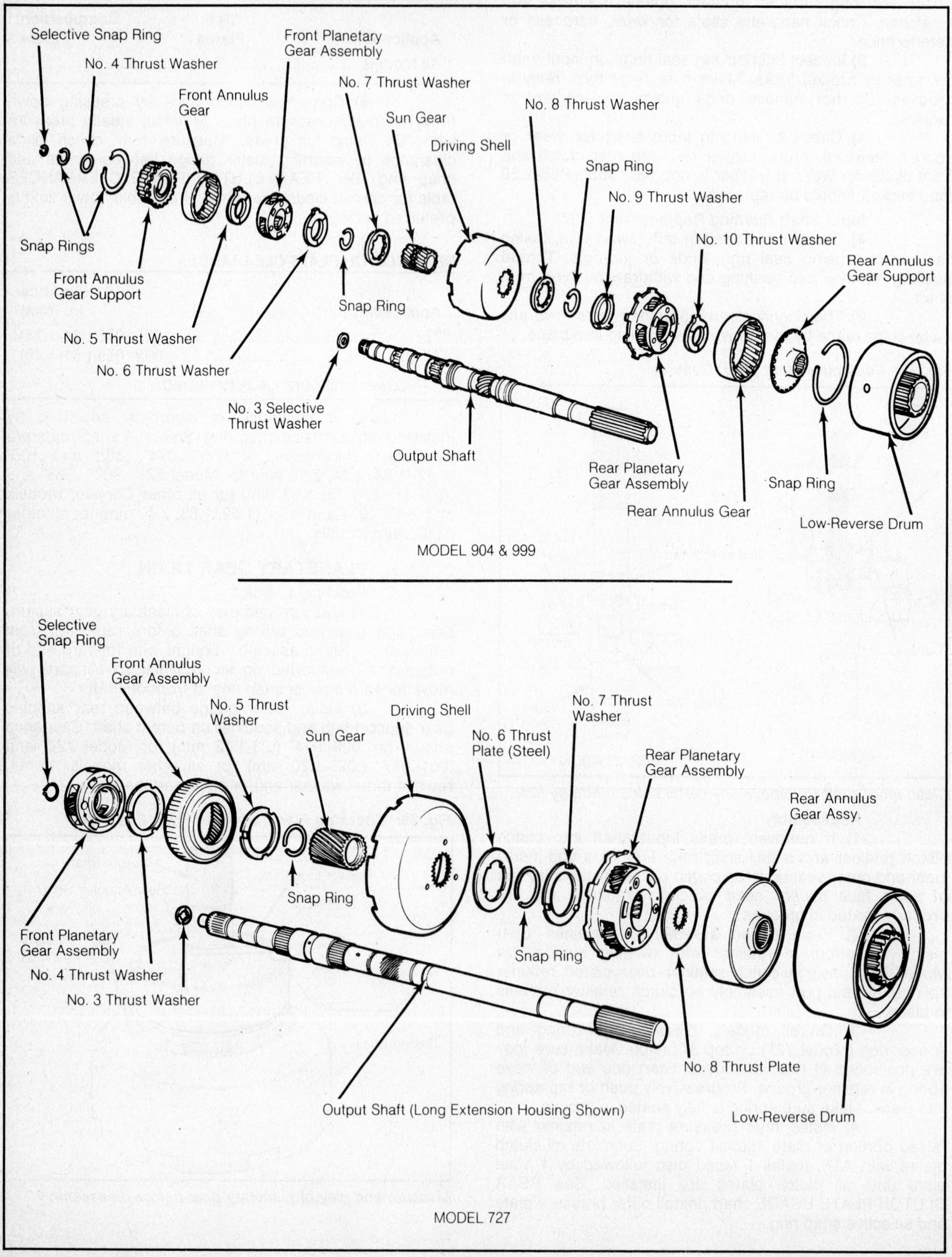

AMERICAN MOTORS, CHRYSLER CORP. & JEEP 727, 904, 998 & 999 (Cont.)

Disassembly (Model 727)

1) Remove thrust washer and selective snap ring from forward end of output shaft. Slide front planetary assembly off shaft. Slide front annulus gear off planetary gear set. Remove thrust washer from rear side of gear set.

2) Slide sun gear, driving shell and rear planetary assembly off output shaft. Lift sun gear and driving shell off rear planetary assembly. Remove thrust washer from inside driving shell.

3) Remove snap ring and steel washer from sun gear (rear side of driving shell) and slide gear out of shell, removing front snap ring from sun gear if necessary. Note that front end of sun gear is longer than rear.

4) Remove thrust washer from forward side of rear planetary assembly. Remove planetary gear set and thrust plate from annulus gear.

Disassembly (All Other Models)

1) Remove thrust washer and selective snap ring from forward end of output shaft. Slide front planetary assembly off of shaft. Remove snap ring and thrust washer from forward hub of front planetary gear assembly. Slide front annulus gear and support off planetary gear set.

2) Remove thrust washer from front side of planetary gear set, then remove thrust washer from rear side of planetary gear assembly. Separate support from annulus gear, removing snap ring from front of annulus gear if necessary. Slide sun gear, driving shell and rear planetary assembly off output shaft.

3) Lift sun gear and driving shell off rear planetary assembly. Remove snap ring and thrust plate from sun gear at rear side of driving shell. Slide sun gear out of shell.

4) Remove snap ring (or spacer on wide ratio model) and thrust plate from opposite end of sun gear. Remove thrust washer from forward side of rear planetary assembly and remove planetary gear set from assembly. Remove thrust washer from rear of gear set. If necessary, remove snap ring from rear of annulus gear to separate support from gear.

Inspection

1) Inspect all parts for nicks, burrs, scores or other damage. Light scratches, small nicks or burrs may be removed with crocus cloth or fine stone. Inspect bushings in sun gear for wear or scores. Replace assembly if bushings are damaged.

2) Inspect all thrust washers for wear and scores. Replace if damaged or worn below specifications. Make sure oil passages in shaft are open and clean. Replace distorted lock rings.

Reassembly (Model 727)

1) Install rear annulus gear on output shaft. Lightly grease thrust plate and place it on shaft, in annulus gear. Make sure teeth are over shaft splines. Position rear planetary gear assembly in rear annulus gear and install thrust washer on front side of gear assembly.

2) Install snap ring in front groove of sun gear (long end of gear). Insert sun gear through front side of driving shell. Install rear steel washer and snap ring. Slide driving shell and sun gear assembly on output shaft. Engage sun gear teeth with rear planetary pinion teeth.

3) Place thrust washer inside front of driving shell. Place thrust washer on rear hub of planetary gear set. Slide assembly into front annulus gear. Work front planetary and annulus gear assembly onto output shaft. Mesh planetary pinions with sun gear teeth.

4) With all components installed, place selective snap ring on front end of output shaft. Measure end play of assembly. Replace snap ring to obtain correct end play as needed. Snap rings are available in thicknesses of .048", .055" and .062" (1.22, 1.40, 1.57 mm).

Reassembly (All Other Models)

1) Install rear annulus gear support in annulus gear and install snap ring. Install thrust washer on rear side of rear planetary gear assembly and install in annulus gear. Install thrust washer on front of rear planetary gear assembly.

2) Insert output shaft in rear opening of rear annulus gear. Carefully work shaft through annulus gear support and planetary gear assembly, making sure shaft splines are fully engaged in splines of annulus gear support.

3) Install thrust plate and snap ring (or spacer on wide-ratio models) on end of sun gear. Insert sun gear through front side of driving shell. Install thrust plate and snap ring on opposite end.

4) Carefully slide driving shell and sun gear assembly onto output shaft, engaging sun gear teeth with rear planetary pinion teeth. Place front annulus gear support in annulus gear and install snap ring.

5) Place thrust washer on front of front planetary gear assembly and position assembly in front annulus gear. Place thrust washer over planetary gear assembly hub and install snap ring.

6) Position thrust washer on rear of planetary gear assembly. Carefully work front planetary and annulus gear assembly onto output shaft, meshing planetary pinions with sun gear teeth.

7) With all components properly positioned, install selective snap ring on front end of output shaft. Remeasure end play of assembly. Clearance may be adjusted with various thicknesses of selective snap rings. Snap rings are available in thicknesses of .042, .064 and .084" (1.02, 1.63, 2.13 mm).

OVERRUNNING CLUTCH

Inspection

Check clutch rollers for smooth round edges. Inspect roller contacting surfaces in cam and race for wear. Check roller springs for distortion, wear or other damage. Inspect cam set screw for tightness (Model 727). Tighten and restake case around screw if loose.

Overrunning Clutch Cam Replacement (Model 727)

1) Remove set screw from case (below clutch cam) and remove bolts securing output shaft support to rear of case. Insert punch through bolt holes and drive cam from case. Alternate punch from one hole to another so cam will be driven evenly from case.

2) If support requires replacement, tap support rearward with soft-faced hammer. To install, screw 2 pilot studs into case and position support over studs. Tap firmly into place using soft-faced hammer.

CAUTION: **Output shaft support must be in case to install overrunning clutch cam.**

AMERICAN MOTORS, CHRYSLER CORP. & JEEP 727, 904, 998 & 999 (Cont.)

3) Clean all burrs and chips from case. Place spring retainer on cam and make sure retainer lugs snap firmly into notches on cam. Position cam in case, aligning cam serrations with case grooves.

4) Tap cam evenly into case as far as possible with soft mallet. Using Cam Aligner and Adapter (C-3863-A and SP-5124) tighten nut on aligner to seat cam in case.

5) Make sure cam is firmly bottomed in case. Install cam retaining set screw. Stake case around set screw to prevent it from coming loose. Remove aligner and pilot studs. Install and tighten support retaining bolts. Stake case around cam in 12 places with blunt chisel.

Fig. 41: Installing Model 727 Overrunning Clutch Cam

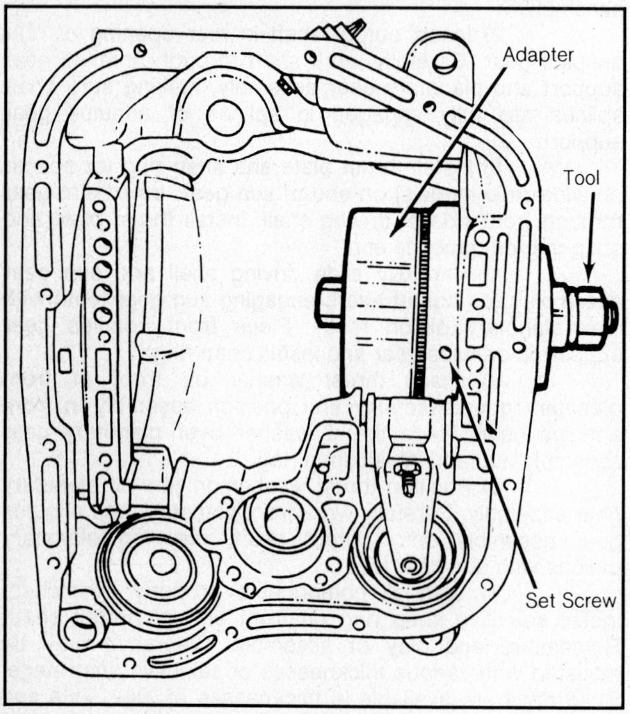

Tighten nut on tool to seat cam in case.

Overrunning Clutch Cam Replacement (All Except Model 727)

1) Replacement parts are retained in case with bolts instead of rivets. To install, remove 4 bolts securing output shaft support to rear of transmission case. Tap support rearward out of case with soft-faced hammer.

2) Center punch rivets in center of each rivet head. Drill out rivet with 3/8" drill, being careful not to drill into transmission case. Remove rivet heads with small chisel.

3) Drive rivets and cam from case with blunt punch. Carefully enlarge rivet holes in case with 17/64" drill. Remove any metal chips, burrs and/or foreign material from case.

NOTE: Alternate punch from one hole to another so cam will be driven evenly from case.

4) Install replacement cam and spring retainer into case with bolt holes in cam and retainer aligned with holes in case. Thread retaining screws and washers into cam and install cam in case using soft-faced hammer.

5) Alternately and evenly tighten retaining screws to 100 INCH lbs. (11 N.m). Thread 2 pilot studs into case. Position support over studs. Tap support firmly into place using soft-faced hammer. Remove pilot studs and install and tighten retaining bolts.

KICKDOWN SERVO & BAND (FRONT)

Disassembly

Disassemble controlled load servo piston by removing small snap ring from servo piston. Remove washer, spring and piston rod from servo piston.

Fig. 42: Exploded View Of Kickdown Servo

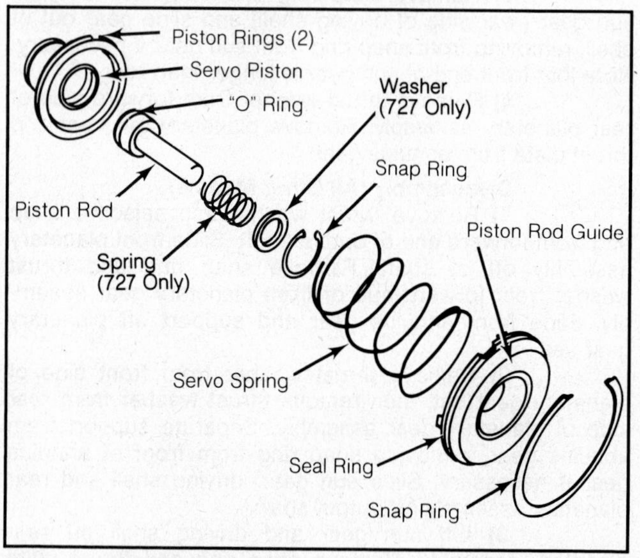

This is controlled load type.

Inspection

1) Inspect all parts for wear or damage. Be sure piston and guide seal rings turn freely in grooves. Do not remove seal rings unless replacement is required. Inspect piston bore in case for scoring or other damage. Inspect fit of guide on piston rod. Check position spring for distortion.

Fig. 43: Exploded View Of Kickdown Servo

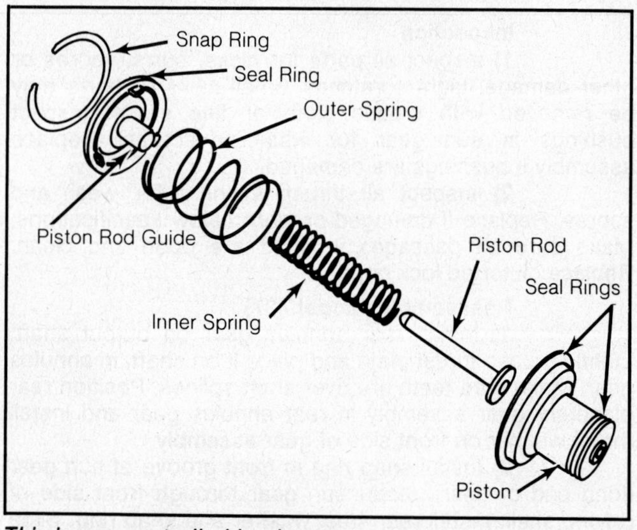

This is non-controlled load type.

2) If equipped with controlled load servo piston, inspect bore in piston and "O" ring on piston rod. Inspect band lining for wear or damage; if lining is worn so

AMERICAN MOTORS, CHRYSLER CORP. & JEEP 727, 904, 998 & 999 (Cont.)

grooves are not visible at ends, or at any portion of band, replace band.

Reassembly

Assemble controlled load servo piston as follows: Grease "O" ring and install on piston rod. Install piston rod into servo piston. Install spring, flat washer and snap ring.

LOW-REVERSE SERVO & BAND (REAR)

Disassembly

Remove snap ring from piston and remove piston plug and spring.

Fig. 44: Exploded View Of Low-Reverse Servo

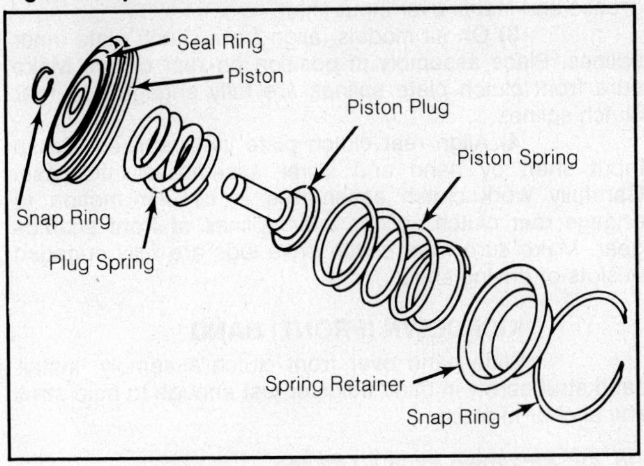

Inspection

1) Inspect seal for wear, deterioration and hardness. Inspect piston and plug for cracks, burrs, scores and wear. Piston plug must operate freely in piston. Inspect piston bore for scores or damage.

2) Check springs for distortion. Inspect band lining for wear and bond of lining to band. If lining is worn so grooves are not visible at end or any portion of band, replace band.

Reassembly

Lubricate and insert piston plug and spring in piston. Secure with snap ring.

TRANSMISSION REASSEMBLY

NOTE: Use only Dexron ATF to lubricate transmission parts during reassembly.

OVERRUNNING CLUTCH

With transmission case in upright position, insert clutch hub inside cam. Install overrunning clutch rollers and springs. *See Fig. 45.*

LOW-REVERSE SERVO & BAND (REAR)

1) Carefully work servo piston into case with twisting motion. Place spring, retainer and snap ring over piston. Compress low-reverse servo piston and install snap ring.

2) On models with double-wrap band, install replacement "O" ring on reaction pin. Insert pin into case until flush with gasket surface. Position band in case so both lugs rest against reaction pin. Install low-reverse drum into rear band. Install operating lever and pivot pin.

3) On all other models, position rear band in case and install short strut. Connect long link and anchor to band. Screw in band adjuster enough to hold strut in place. Install low-reverse drum.

Fig. 45: Installed View Of Overrunning Clutch

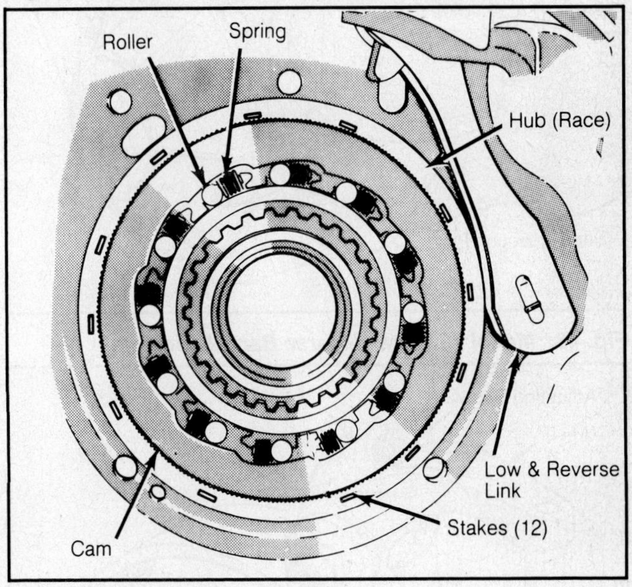

Install parts as shown.

Fig. 46: Double-Wrap Low-Reverse Band & Linkage

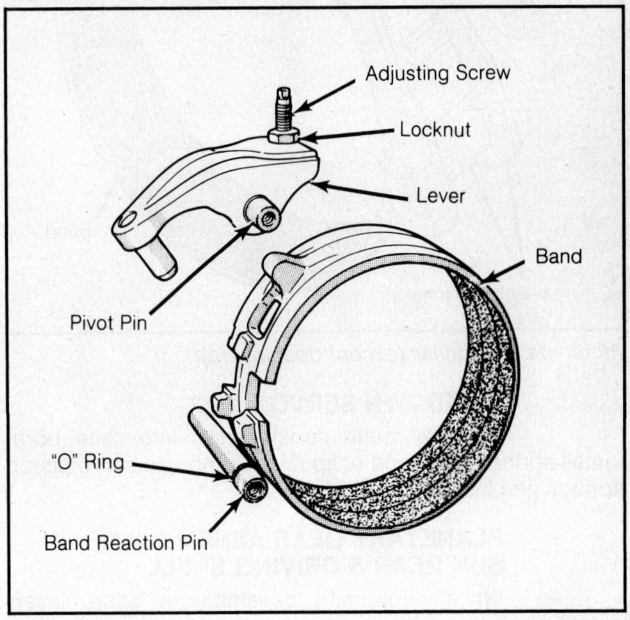

AMERICAN MOTORS, CHRYSLER CORP. & JEEP 727, 904, 998 & 999 (Cont.)

Fig. 47: Double-Wrap Band Linkage Installation

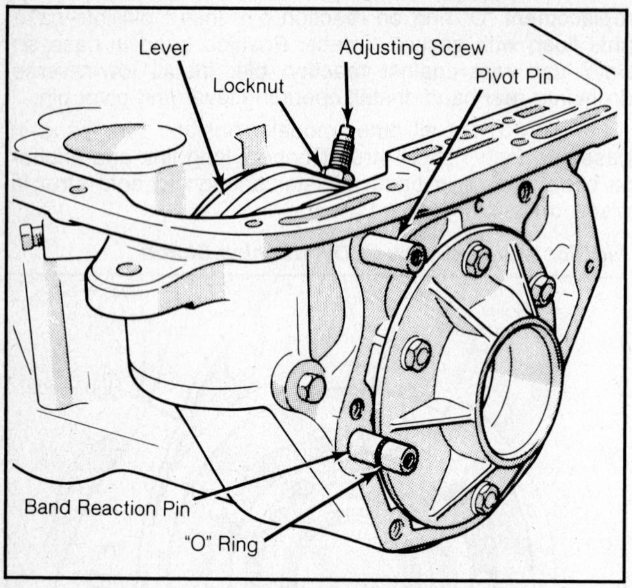

Fig. 48: Model 727 Low-Reverse Band & Linkage

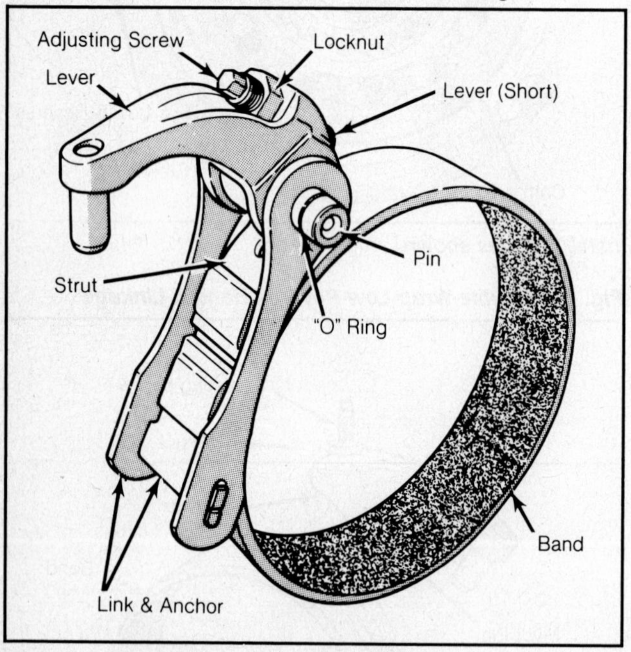

All others are similar (except double-wrap).

KICKDOWN SERVO

Carefully push servo piston into case bore. Install spring, guide and snap ring. Compress servo piston springs and install snap ring.

PLANETARY GEAR ASSEMBLIES, SUN GEAR & DRIVING SHELL

While supporting assembly in case, insert output shaft through rear support. Carefully work assembly rearward, engaging rear planetary carrier lugs into low-reverse drum slots.

CAUTION: Do not damage machined surfaces on output shaft during installation.

FRONT & REAR CLUTCH ASSEMBLIES

NOTE: Front and rear clutches, front band, oil pump and reaction shaft support are easier to install with transmission in upright position.

1) Apply thin coat of grease on thrust washer that goes between input shaft and output shaft. Install washer on front end of output shaft. If end play was incorrect when checked during disassembly (all except Model 727), replace washer with one of correct thickness. See THRUST WASHER chart.

2) On Model 727, apply thin coating of grease to thrust washer and install in rear clutch piston retainer. On all other models, coat input shaft thrust washer with grease and install over input shaft.

3) On all models, align front clutch plate inner splines. Place assembly in position on rear clutch. Make sure front clutch plate splines are fully engaged on rear clutch splines.

4) Align rear clutch plate inner splines. Grasp input shaft by hand and lower assemblies into case. Carefully work clutch assemblies in circular motion to engage rear clutch splines over splines of front annulus gear. Make sure front clutch drive lugs are fully engaged in slots of driving shell.

KICKDOWN (FRONT) BAND

Slide band over front clutch assembly. Install band strut screw in band adjuster just enough to hold strut and anchor in place.

Fig. 49: Kickdown Band & Linkage

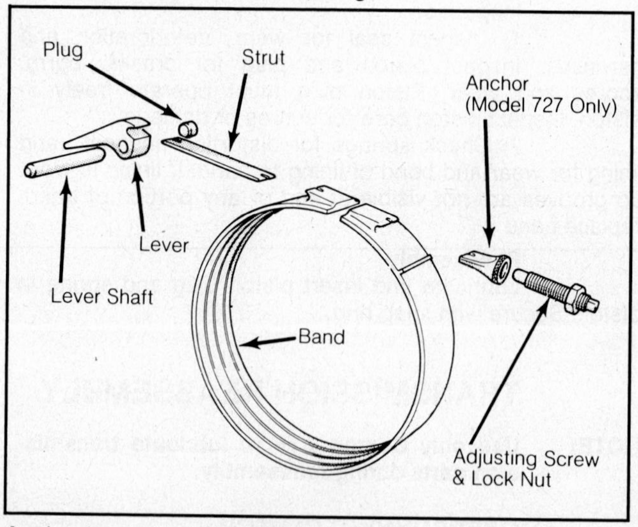

Anchor is used on Model 727 only.

OIL PUMP & REACTION SHAFT SUPPORT

NOTE: If difficulty was encounterd in removing pump assembly due to an exceptionally tight fit, it may be necessary to expand case in pump area with heat lamp prior to installation.

1) Install thrust washer on reaction shaft support hub. If input shaft end play was incorrect when checked during disassembly (Model 727), replace thrust

AMERICAN MOTORS, CHRYSLER CORP. & JEEP 727, 904, 998 & 999 (Cont.)

THRUST WASHER CHART

Thrust Washer	A-727 Washer No.	A-727 Thickness Inches (mm)	ALL OTHERS Washer No.	ALL OTHERS Thickness Inches (mm)
Reaction Shaft Support Thrust Washer	1	Selective Natural: .061-.063 (1.55-1.60) Red: .084-.086 (2.13-2.18) Yellow: .102-.104 (2.59-2.64)	1	.061-.063 (1.55-1.60)
Rear Clutch Retainer	2	Natural: .061-.063 (1.55-1.60)	2	.061-.063 (1.55-1.60)
Input Shaft Thrust Plate		....		.024-.026 (.61-.66)
Output Shaft Thrust Washer	3	.062-.064 (1.57-1.63)	3	Selective Tin: .052-.054 (1.32-1.37) Red: .068-.070 (1.73-1.78) Green: .083-.086 (2.11-2.18)
Output Shaft Thrust Plate		.030-.032 (.76-.81)		....
Front Annulus Thrust Washer		....	4	.121-.125 (3.07-3.18)
Front Carrier (To Annulus) Thrust Washer	4	.059-.062 (1.50-1.57)	5	.048-.050 (1.22-1.27)
Drive Shell (To Front Annulus) Thrust Washer	5	.059-.062 (1.50-1.57)		....
Front Carrier (To Drive Shell) Thrust Washer		....	6	.048-.050 (1.22-1.27)
Sun Gear Drive Shell Thrust Plate	6	.034-.036 (.86-.91)	7 8	.050-.052 (1.27-1.32) .050-.052 (1.27-1.32)
Rear Carrier (To Drive Shell) Thrust Washer	7	.059-.062 (1.50-1.57)	9	.048-.050 (1.22-1.27)
Rear Carrier (To Annulus) Thrust Plate	8	.034-.036 (.86-.91)		....
Rear Carrier (To Annulus) Thrust Washer		....	10	.048-.050 (1.22-1.27)

washer with one of proper thickness. Refer to THRUST WASHER chart.

2) Screw 2 pilot studs into pump opening in case. Install new gasket over studs. Place new rubber seal ring in groove on outer flange of pump housing, make sure seal is not twisted.

3) Coat seal ring with grease. Install pump assembly into case, tapping lightly with soft mallet if necessary. Remove pilot studs. Install bolts and snug down evenly.

4) Rotate input and output shafts to see that no binding exists. Tighten pump attaching bolts. Check shafts again for free rotation. Adjust both bands.

GOVERNOR

See SERVICE (IN VEHICLE).

EXTENSION/ADAPTER HOUSING

See SERVICE (IN VEHICLE).

VALVE BODY ASSEMBLY & ACCUMULATOR PISTON

See SERVICE (IN VEHICLE).

AMERICAN MOTORS, CHRYSLER CORP. & JEEP
727, 904, 998 & 999 (Cont.)

TIGHTENING SPECIFICATIONS

Application	Ft. Lbs. (N.m)
Band Adjusting Screw Lock Nut	30 (41)
Flex Plate-to-Crankshaft Bolt	55 (75)
Flex Plate-to-Torque Converter Bolt	
AMC/Jeep	40 (54)
Chrysler Corp.	23 (31)
Neutral Safety Switch	25 (34)
Output Shaft Housing-to-Insulator Bolt	50 (68)
Output Shaft Housing-to-Transmission Bolt	
Chrysler Corp	32 (43)
AMC/Jeep	24 (33)
Transmission-to-Engine Bolts	
Jeep Turbo Diesel	55 (75)
All Other Models	30 (41)
	INCH Lbs. (N.m)
Cooler Line Fitting	110 (12)
Cooler Line Nut	
AMC/Jeep	175 (20)
Chrysler Corp.	85 (10)
Governor Body-to-Support Bolts	100 (11)
Kickdown Lever Shaft Plug	150 (17)
Oil Pan Bolts	130 (15)
Output Shaft Support Bolt	150 (17)
Overrunning Clutch Cam Set Screw	40 (5)
Pressure Test Port Plug	110 (12)
Pump Hsg.-to-Transmission Case	175 (20)
Reaction Shaft Support-to-Oil Pump Bolt	148 (17)
Valve Body Screws	35 (4)
Valve Body-to-Transmission Case Bolt	100 (11)

AMC/RENAULT MB1

APPLICATION

All Alliance/Encore 1.4L and 1.7L models with automatic transaxle use the Renault model MB1.

IDENTIFICATION

Transmission identification number is stamped on metal tag attached to transaxle case under a rear case-to-intermediate case attaching bolt. Models are identified by tag on front upper side of transaxle.

Fig. 1: Transaxle Identification Tag

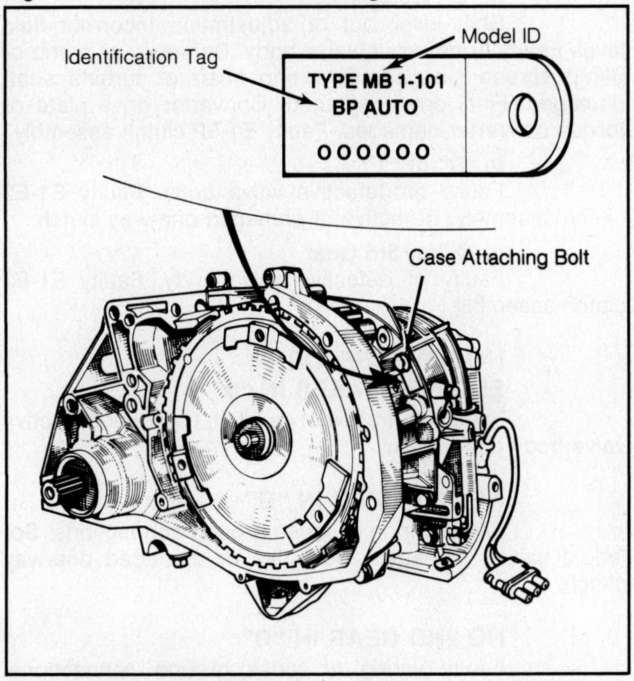

Always replace tag when reassembling transaxle case.

DESCRIPTION

The Renault MB1 automatic transaxles are computer controlled, 3-speed unit consisting of the torque converter, differential assembly and transmissions. The differential assembly consists primarily of the differential case and 2 planetary gears. Step down gears are used to change direction of the drive centerline.

The transmission assembly consists of 2 planetary gear sets, a clutch assembly (containing 2 clutches), 2 brakes, a one-way clutch and the transmission control systems. Control systems are of 3 types: mechanical, hydraulic and electrical.

ELECTRICAL COMPONENTS

Control Module

The control module is a microprocessor which recieves information from the vehicle speed sensor, throttle position sensor, neutral/safety switch, and kickdown switch. It converts this information into electrical signals which are sent to the solenoid valves to control gear shifts.

Solenoid Valves

Located on the valve body, the solenoid valves directly control pilot valve position in the valve body.

Neutral/Safety Switch

Switch is mounted on the rear of the transaxle and actuated by selector lever position. Depending on lever position, switch controls starting circuit, back-up lights and shift solenoid valves.

Throttle Position & Vehicle Speed Sensors

The throttle position sensor is a potentiometer which provides variable voltage to the control module depending on throttle position. The vehicle speed sensor is fitted opposite the park ring which senses vehicle speed.

LUBRICATION & ADJUSTMENTS

See appropriate AUTOMATIC TRANSMISSION SERVICING article in DOMESTIC GENERAL SERVICING section.

VACUUM MODULATOR VALVE

Adjustment

1) Remove lower plug on side of transaxle case. *See Fig. 3.* Install Pressure Gauge (B.Vi 466-04) at port and position gauge so that it may be seen from inside vehicle.

2) Test drive vehicle at full throttle and note pressure on gauge just before full-throttle 2-3 upshift. Pressure reading should be 75 psi (5.3 kg/cm^2). If fluid pressure is incorrect it may be adjusted by turning the vacuum capsule.

3) To increase fluid pressure, turn capsule clockwise. Counterclockwise rotation of capsule will reduce pressure. Turning capsule 2 notches changes pressure by about 1.5 psi (.11 kg/cm^2).

THROTTLE POSITION SENSOR

Adjustment

1) With engine off, turn ignition switch to "ON" position. With electrical connector attached, insert negative probe of digital volt-ohmmeter through back of connector at terminal "C", until probe contacts terminal. Insert positive lead of meter into terminal "B".

2) Hold throttle at wide open position, ensuring that throttle contacts stop. Note exact voltage reading on meter. Reading should be about 4.3 volts. This is input voltage.

3) Remove positive probe from terminal "B" and insert in terminal "A" of connector. With throttle still held in wide open position, check voltage reading. This is output voltage.

4) Output voltage should be within 3.5-4.5% of input voltage. For example, if input voltage is 5.0 volts, output voltage should be within .03 (.5% of 5) of .20 volts (4% of 5), or .17-.23 volts.

5) If voltage relationship is incorrect, loosen bottom mounting screw and pivot sensor to make coarse adjustment. Tighten screw. Loosen upper mounting screw and pivot sensor to make fine adjustment.

AMC/RENAULT MB1 (Cont.)

Fig. 2: Throttle Position Sensor Location and Adjustment

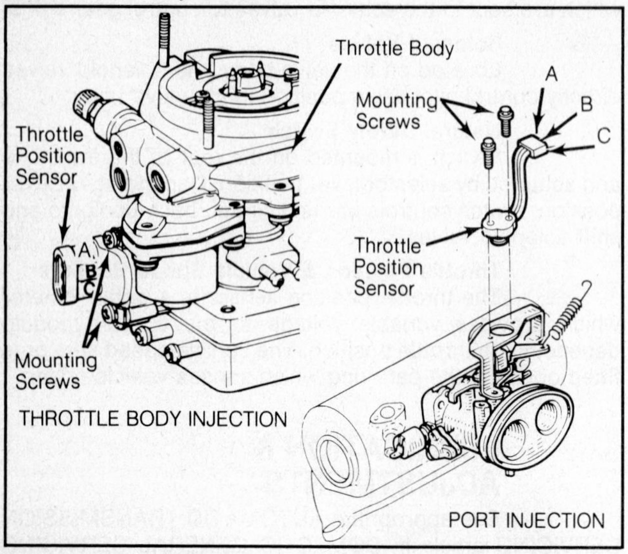

Loosen lower mounting screw to make coarse sensor adjustment, upper screw for fine adjustment.

TROUBLE SHOOTING

After each vehicle condition, several possible causes of that condition are listed. See COMPONENT TESTING when specific components are called out.

ENGINE IDLES ROUGH OR STALLS

Idle speed incorrect. Check ignition timing and spark plug condition. Check throttle cable adjustment. Check vacuum modulator valve and line for leak in vacuum circuit.

VEHICLE CREEPS IN "N"

Shift lever out of adjustment. E1-E2 clutch defective or damaged.

EXCESSIVE CREEPING IN "D"

Idle speed incorrect. Check throttle cable adjustment. Torque converter damaged.

SLIPS WHEN STARTING IN "D" OR "R"

Incorrect fluid level. Vacuum modulator valve adjustment (oil pressure) incorrect. Faulty or defective valve body. Torque converter damaged.

SLIPS WHEN STARTING IN "D", ONLY

Defective E1-E2 clutch. Defective or damaged one-way clutch.

SLIPS DURING SHIFTS

Vacuum modulator valve adjustment (oil pressure) incorrect. Faulty or defective valve body. Oil pump screen clogged. Faulty E1-E2 clutch assembly or F2 brake.

SURGES WHEN MOVING OFF

Idle speed incorrect. Check throttle cable adjustment and fluid level.

SURGES DURING SHIFTS

Vacuum modulator valve adjustment (oil pressure) incorrect. Leak in vacuum circuit. Faulty or defective valve body.

SHIFT SPEEDS INCORRECT

Check throttle cable and throttle position sensor adjustment. Faulty wiring or loose ground connections. Kickdown switch or control computer faulty. Defective vehicle speed sensor.

NO MOVEMENT

In "D" Only

Shift lever out of adjustment. Incorrect fluid level. Faulty or defective valve body. Defective oil pump or pump screen clogged. Oil pump shaft or turbine shaft damaged. Final drive damaged. Converter drive plate or torque converter damaged. Faulty E1-E2 clutch assembly.

In "D" or "1"

Faulty or defective valve body. Faulty E1-E2 clutch assembly. Defective or damaged one-way clutch.

In "R" or 3rd Gear

Faulty or defective valve body. Faulty E1-E2 clutch assembly.

NO REVERSE, OR, ENGINE BRAKES IN "1"

Faulty neutral/safety switch. Faulty or defective valve body or F1 brake.

NO 1ST GEAR IN "D"

Faulty wiring or loose ground connections. Solenoid valves damaged. Defective or damaged one-way clutch.

NO 2ND GEAR IN "D"

Faulty wiring or loose ground connections. Faulty or defective valve body or F2 brake.

NO 3RD GEAR IN "D"

Faulty wiring or loose ground connections. Control computer faulty. Solenoid valves damaged. Faulty neutral/safety switch. Faulty or defective valve body.

NO 1ST GEAR HOLD

Shift lever out of adjustment. Faulty wiring or loose ground connections. Control computer faulty. Faulty neutral/safety switch or valve body.

NO 2ND GEAR HOLD

Shift lever out of adjustment. Faulty wiring or loose ground connections. Control computer faulty. Faulty neutral/safety switch.

REMAINS IN 1ST IN "D"

Faulty wiring or loose ground connections. Control computer faulty. Solenoid valves damaged. Vehicle speed sensor defective. Faulty or defective valve body.

REMAINS IN 3RD GEAR

Check fuses. Check for damaged wiring or loose ground connections. Control computer faulty. Defective oil pump. Faulty or defective valve body.

AMC/RENAULT MB1 (Cont.)

SKIPS SOME GEARS, SHIFT LEVER ABNORMAL

Shift lever or selector control out of adjustment. Faulty manual valve control.

IMPROPER OPERATION IN "P"

Shift lever out of adjustment. Faulty manual valve control.

STARTER NOT WORKING

Shift lever or selector control incorrectly adjusted. Faulty wiring or loose ground connections. Control computer faulty. Faulty neutral/safety switch.

NO BACK-UP LIGHTS

Shift lever or selector control incorrectly adjusted. Faulty wiring or loose ground connections. Control computer faulty. Faulty neutral/safety switch.

TESTING

TESTING EQUIPMENT

Diagnosis of the electrical control system of the MB1 transaxle is possible with a volt-ohmmeter. However, use of Renault test box B. Vi. 958 will both reduce diagnosis time and give more accurate test results. Instructions for use are included with the test box. Procedures given here are for testing with volt-ohmmeter.

CONTROL PRESSURE TEST

1) Bring engine to normal operating temperature. Check fluid level and control linkage (cable) adjustment. Connect a pressure gauge to plug orifice on side of transaxle. There should be enough connecting hose so that gauge may held inside of vehicle. *See Fig. 3*.

2) Drive a few miles to ensure fluid is at operating temperature. Place selector lever in 2nd gear. Press accelerator pedal to floor. Apply brakes and stabilize speed to 50 MPH (80 km/h). Pressure should be 64 psi (4.5 kg/cm^2).

ROAD TEST

1) Before road testing, check fluid level and control linkage (cable) adjustments have been checked and corrected as needed. Also check fluid condition. During test, transaxle should upshift and downshift at approximately the specified speeds. See SHIFT SPEED SPECIFICATIONS chart.

Fig. 3: Testing Control Pressure

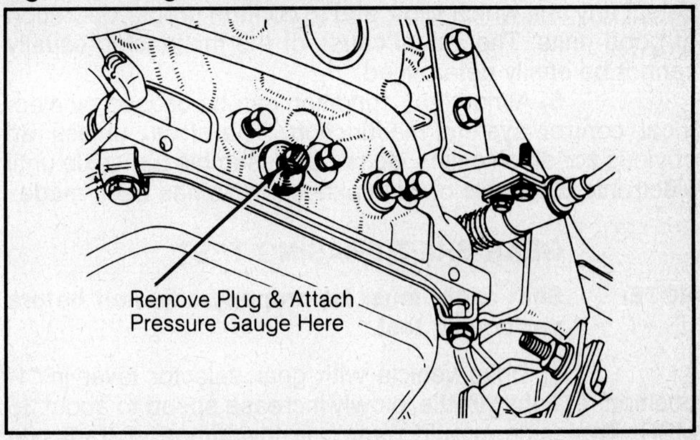

2) All shifts may vary somewhat due to production tolerances or tire size. What is important is the quality of the shifts. All shifts should be smooth, responsive, and with no slippage or engine speed runaway.

SHIFT SPEED SPECIFICATIONS

Application	Shift Speed (MPH)
Closed Throttle	
1-2 Upshift	16
2-3 Upshift	28
3-2 Downshift	16
2-1 Downshift	9
Full Throttle [1]	
1-2 Upshift	37
2-3 Upshift	62
3-2 Downshift	40
2-1 Downshift	25
Kickdown [1]	
1-2 Upshift	43
2-3 Upshift	68
3-2 Downshift	59
2-1 Downshift	34

[1] – Full throttle test is with kickdown switch disconnected. Connect switch for kickdown test.

3) Slippage or engine speed runaway in any gear usually indicates clutch or brake problems. The slipping unit in a particular gear can usually be identified by noting transaxle operation in other selector positions and comparing which internal units are applied in those positions. See TRANSAXLE COMPONENT APPLICATION Chart.

TRANSAXLE COMPONENT APPLICATION CHART (ELEMENTS IN USE)

Selector Lever Position	E1 Clutch	E2 Clutch	F1 Brake	F2 Brake	One-Way Clutch	Solenoid Valve 1	Solenoid Valve 2
D — DRIVE							
First	X				X		X
Second	X			X		X	X
Third	X	X					
2 — SECOND HOLD	X			X		X	X
1 — FIRST HOLD	X		X				X
R — REVERSE		X	X				X
NEUTRAL OR PARK							X

AMC/RENAULT MB1 (Cont.)

4) This process of elimination can be used to detect any unit which slips, and to confirm proper operation of good units. The actual cause of the malfuncion usually cannot be easily determined.

5) Almost any condition can be caused by electrical control system malfunction. Therefore, unless an obvious condition exists, do not disassemble transaxle until electronic diagnosis of transaxle controls has been made.

GEAR SHIFT PHASING TEST

NOTE: Shift cable must be properly adjusted before performing test.

1) Drive vehicle with gear selector lever in "1" position. At light throttle, slowly increase speed to about 35 MPH. Transaxle should remain in low range. If transaxle shifts to 2nd gear, replace neutral/safety switch.

2) Move selector lever to "2" position and maintain sustained speed of 35 MPH. Transaxle should shift automatically from low range to 2nd gear. If not, neutral/safety switch should be replaced.

3) With gear selector lever still in "2" position, increase vehicle speed to 50 MPH. Transaxle should remain in 2nd gear. If shift to 3rd occurs, replace neutral/safety switch. If all tests are satisfactory, shift operation is correct.

4) In any test, if neutral/safety switch is replaced and problem remains, check control module electrical connections. If connections are good, replace control module.

Fig. 4: 6-Way Connector Terminal Identification

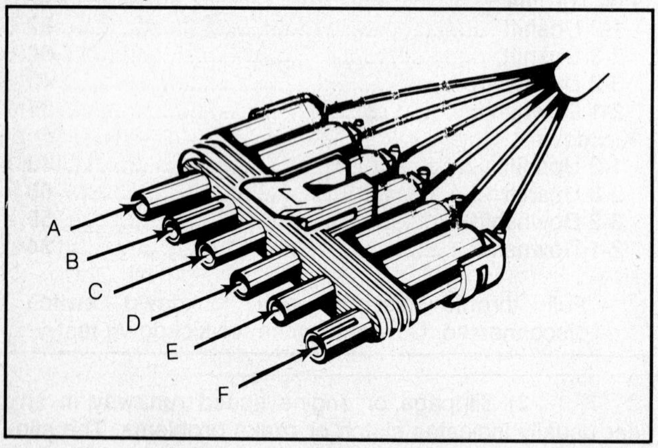

ELECTRONIC CONTROL COMPONENT TESTING

6-Way Connector

1) Turn ignition off. Unplug connector from control module. Using an ohmmeter, check resistance between pin "B" and ground. If resistance is not 1-7 ohms, check back-up light bulbs and wiring circuit. Repair as needed.

2) Connect voltmeter between terminal "A" and ground. With ignition off, voltage should be 10-14 volts. If not, check back-up light fuse and accessory plate wiring. Repair as needed.

3) Turn ignition switch on. Using an ohmmeter, check resistance from terminal "E" to ground. If resistance is not zero, check chassis ground circuit and repair as needed.

4) Connect voltmeter between terminal "F" and ground with ignition switch on. Voltage reading should be 10-14 volts. If not, check power supply circuit to control module. Repair wiring as needed.

5) Connect voltmeter between terminal "C" and ground. Check voltage reading while operating starter. If reading is not 10-14 volts, check starter, starter relay and wiring circuit. Repair or replace as needed.

3-Way Connector

Turn ignition off. Unplug 3-way connector. Turn ignition on and connect voltmeter between terminal "B" (center terminal) and ground. Reading should be 3.8-4.8 volts. If not, perform 6-way connector test. If 6-way connector check reveals no problems, control module is defective and should be replaced.

Solenoid Valves & Harness

1) Turn ignition off. Unplug solenoid valve connector at control module. Using an ohmmeter, check resistance between terminals "A" and "C" of connector. *See Fig. 5.* Reading on ohmmeter should be 20-40 ohms. If resistance is zero, closely inspect wiring harness from connector to solenoid valves and repair or replace as needed. If harness is okay, replace solenoid valves.

Fig. 5: 3-Way Connector Terminal Identification

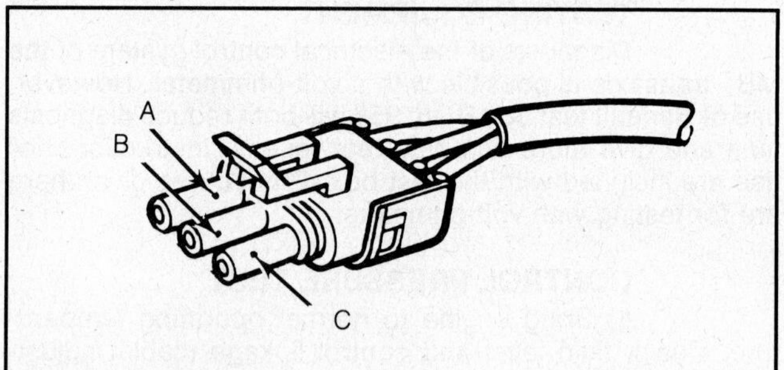

Terminal identification is the same for both 3-way connectors.

2) If resistance value in step **1)** is between 40 and 80 ohms, connection is loose or dirty. Inspect and repair.

3) Check resistance between terminals "B" and "C". If resistance value is not 20-40 ohms, inspect wiring and replace if damaged. If wiring harness is OK, replace solenoid valves.

4) Connect ohmmeter between terminal "C" and ground. Resistance value should be infinite. If not, solenoid valves are shorted to ground. Check wiring harness for short and repair or replace as needed. If harness is OK, replace solenoid valves.

Solenoid Valves

1) Disconnect wiring harness connector at solenoid valves. Check resistance value between terminals "A" and "C" of solenoid connector. *See Fig. 6.* Check value between terminals "B" and "C". Resistance value should be 20-40 ohms in both cases.

2) If either reading is zero, replace the solenoid valves. If resistance value obtained is greater than 40 ohms, but less than 80 ohms, check wiring and connections to solenoid valves. Clean or repair as needed.

3) If resistance between either set of terminals is infinite, replace solenoid valves. Finally, check resistance from terminal "C" to ground. Reading should be infinite. If it is not, there is a short between solenoid valve windings and ground. Replace valves.

Fig. 6: Solenoid Valve Connector Terminal Identification

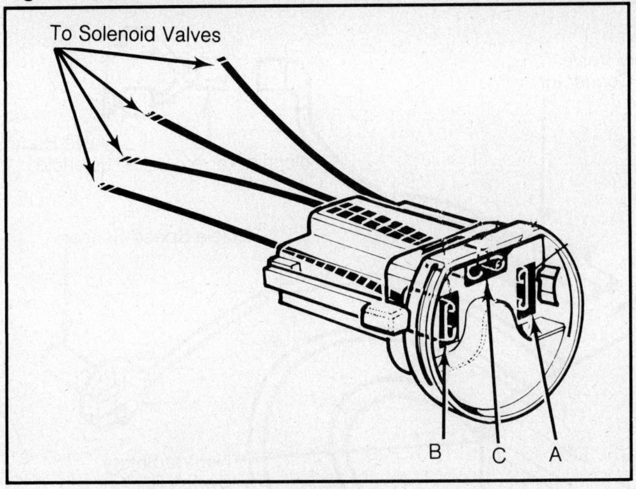

Throttle Position Sensor

1) Unplug throttle position sensor connector. With throttle closed, check resistance between connector sockets "C" and "B". *See Fig. 7*. Value should be 3000-5000 ohms. Check resistance between sockets "A" and "B". Value should be 1500-3500 ohms.

Fig. 7: Throttle Position Sensor Socket Identification

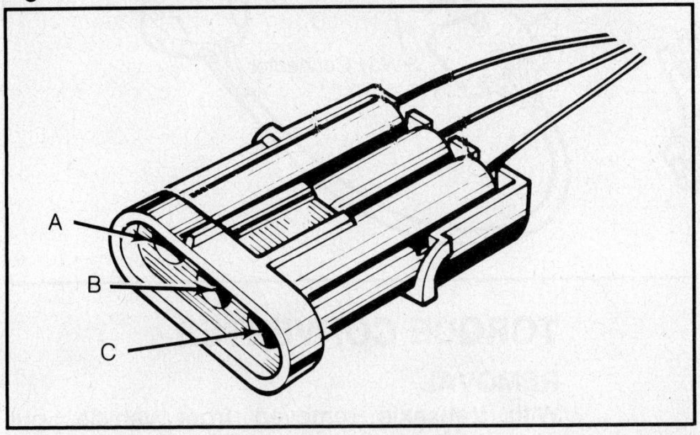

2) If either reading in step **1)** is incorrect, sensor is either faulty or incorrectly adjusted.

3) With ohmmeter connected between terminals "A" and "B", slowly open throttle from closed to full open position. Resistance should change with respect to throttle valve position, but never go to infinity. If so, TPS is faulty or out of adjustment.

Fig. 8: Neutral/Safety Switch Socket Identification

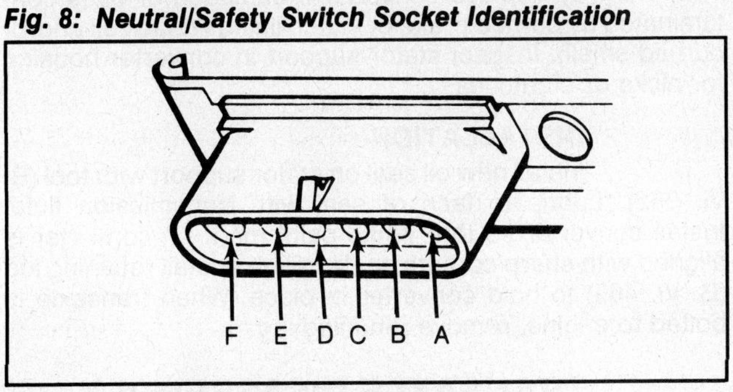

Neutral/Safety Switch

1) Turn ignition off. Unplug 6-way connector from control module. With gear selector lever in "R", check resistance value between sockets "A" and "B" in control module connection. Value should be zero.

2) With gear selector lever in "P" or "N", check resistance between sockets "E" and "C". As in step **1)**, value should be zero. If either resistance is incorrect (not zero), ensure proper electrical connections. If connections are good, replace neutral/safety switch.

NOTE: **Renault tester (B. Vi. 958) is required for complete testing of switch.**

SERVICE (IN VEHICLE)

DRIVE AXLE SHAFTS

See appropriate DRIVE AXLE SHAFT article in DOMESTIC FWD AXLE SHAFTS & TRANSFER CASES section.

VACUUM MODULATOR VALVE

Removal & Installation

Drain about 2 qts. (1.9L) of fluid from transaxle. Remove vacuum hose from modulator valve. Remove retaining bolt and retainer. Remove valve. Reverse removal procedure to install valve. Add fluid to proper level. Adjust vacuum modulator valve. See LUBRICATION and ADJUSTMENTS in this article.

VALVE BODY

Removal

1) Raise and support vehicle. Drain transaxle fluid. Remove front transaxle mount bolt and raise transaxle enough to gain clearance for oil pan removal. Remove pan, filter and "O" ring.

2) Remove valve body retaining bolts (8) and carefully remove valve body and seals (2). Remove regulator valve. Remove vacuum modulator valve from pressure regulator valve, then remove manual valve from manual lever assembly. *See Fig. 10*.

3) Locate electrical connector in corner of case, remove retaining clip and disconnect connector.

Installation

1) Assemble electrical connector and install in case. Retain with clip. Place valve body and seals in position and install center valve body bolt finger tight.

2) Install manual valve and connect to manual lever. Install vacuum modulator valve and position it against regulator valve. Install remaining valve body bolts finger tight.

3) Tighten 2 locating bolts. *See Fig. 10*. Tighten remaining bolts, center bolt first. Install oil filter and seal. Install oil pan. Lower transaxle and install transaxle mount bolt. Lower vehicle and fill transaxle with fluid.

THROTTLE POSITION SWITCH

Throttle position information is supplied to the computer by the throttle position sensor. This information is used, in part, to determine optimum gear selection under any given set of operating conditions. Proper sensor adjustment is essential to smooth transaxle operation.

Removal & Installation

Remove air cleaner assembly. Disconnect electrical connector from throttle position sensor. Remove attaching screws (2) and remove sensor. Reverse removal procedure to install sensor. Whenever sensor is removed,

AMC/RENAULT MB1 (Cont.)

Fig. 9: Electronic Control Module With Electrical Components & Connectors

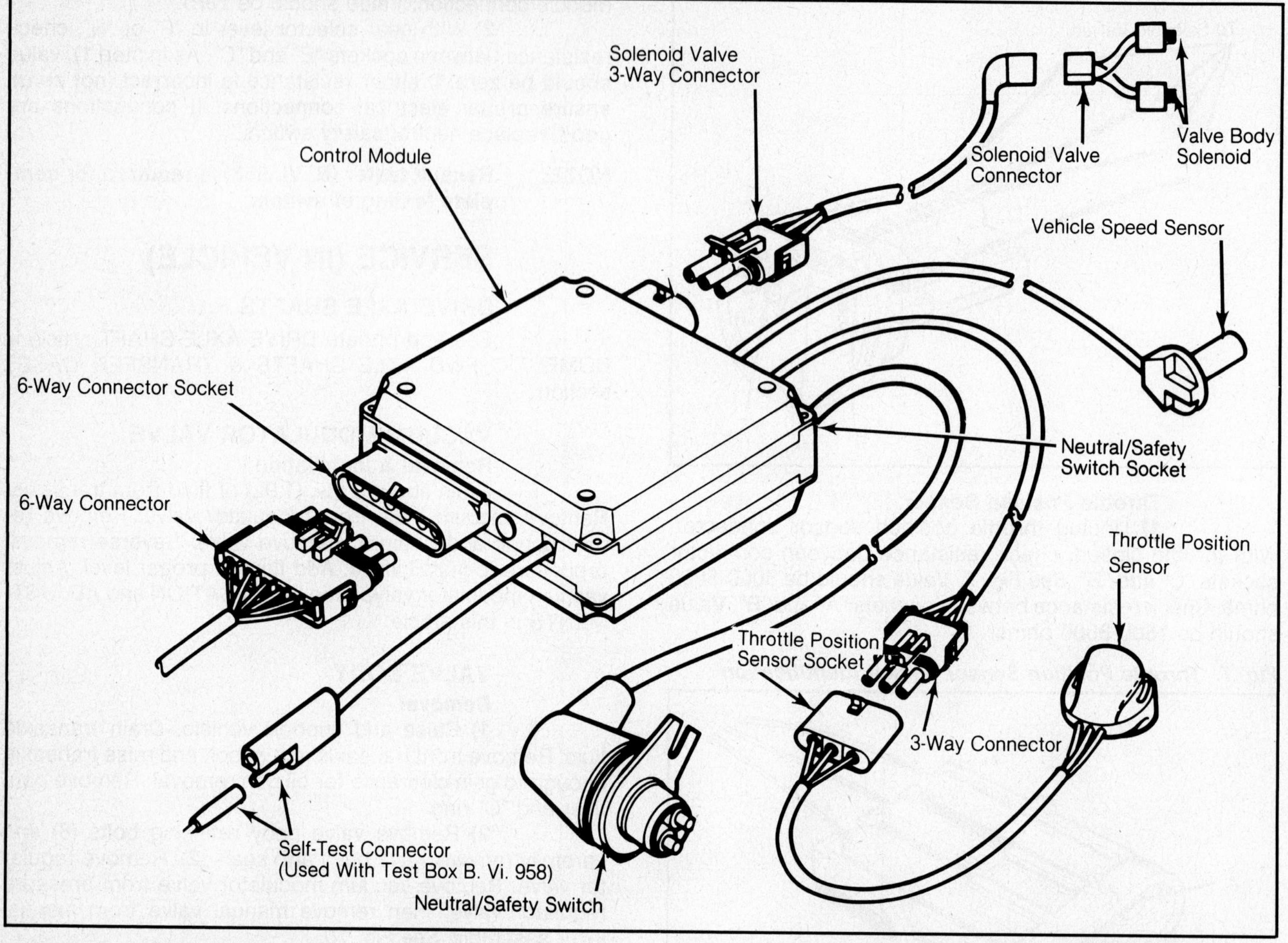

or if a new sensor is installed, it must be adjusted. See THROTTLE POSITION SENSOR in LUBRICATION & ADJUSTMENTS in this article.

SPEEDOMETER PINION OIL SEAL

Removal

NOTE: Special Puller (B. Vi. 905) should be used to remove seal. It includes an extractor, nut, 2 spacers and an inserting tool.

1) Disconnect speedometer cable at transaxle. With nut and thin spacer installed on extractor, screw extractor into case until it contacts seal.

2) Turn extractor in an additional 3 turns to engage seal. Tighten nut while holding extractor in position. As nut is tightened, seal will be pulled from case.

Installation

To install new seal, install seal on inserting tool, lip first. Lubricate seal with transmission fluid and push into case.

REMOVAL & INSTALLATION

TRANSAXLE

See appropriate AUTOMATIC TRANSMISSION REMOVAL article in DOMESTIC GENERAL SERVICING section.

TORQUE CONVERTER

REMOVAL

With transaxle removed from vehicle, pull torque converter straight out of converter housing. Pry oil seal off of stator support.

INSPECTION

1) Check general condition of the following converter components: Center boss on flywheel side, seal bearing surface, bushings on 3 mounting points, and timing target.

2) Replace converter if damaged or oil is contaminated by burned brake or clutch linings (black oil and/or burned smell). Inspect stator support in converter housing for nicks or scratches.

INSTALLATION

Install new oil seal on stator support with tool (B. Vi. 962). Lubricate face of seal with transmission fluid. Install converter so that White paint mark on converter is aligned with sharp corners on flex plate. Install retaining lug (B. Vi. 465) to hold converter in place. When transaxle is bolted to engine, remove retaining lug.

TRANSAXLE DISASSEMBLY

NOTE: All components must be kept clean and free of dust, dirt, or lint during the following proce-

AMC/RENAULT MB1 (Cont.)

dures. Disassembly and assembly procedures should be carried out on a shock resistant bench (rubber or thick plastic).

Fig. 10: Removing Valve Body From Transaxle Case

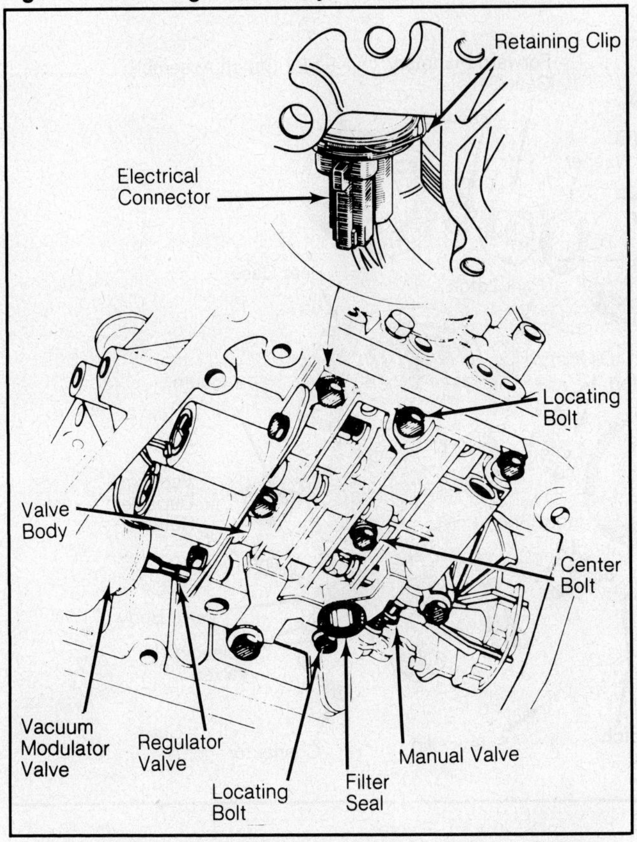

Use center bolt to support valve body during installation. Tighten locating bolts first. Then tighten remaining bolts.

Fig. 11: Replacing Speedometer Pinion Oil Seal

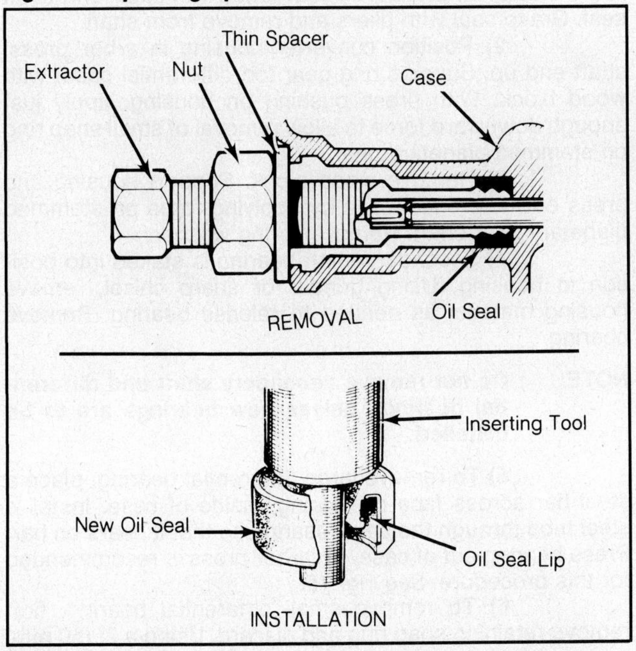

Place seal on inserting tool as shown and push into case.

VACUUM MODULATOR VALVE

See SERVICE (IN VEHICLE).

VALVE BODY

See SERVICE (IN VEHICLE)

Fig. 12: Removing F1 Piston

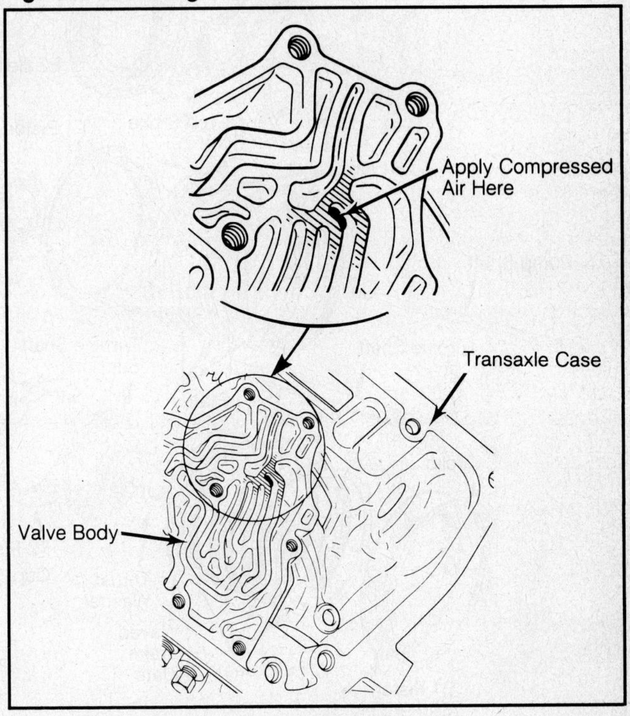

To remove piston, apply compressed air at valve body passage indicated.

REAR CASE

1) Remove torque converter from transaxle assembly. With transaxle on work bench, remove case attaching bolts indicated in *Fig. 23*. Remove "O" ring from locator bolt.

2) When separating cases, leave end play adjusting shim and spacer in position on output shaft. *See Fig. 17.* Lift park wheel and nylon washer from rear case. Remove park latch linkage and safety clip.

3) Remove large circlip. Lift out one-way clutch and reverse planetary gear set. Remove F1 plates and discs. To remove F1 piston, apply compressed air to valve body passage indicated in *Fig. 12.* Note position of springs on piston for reassembly reference and remove springs.

4) Lift out washer, E2 bellhousing, washer, forward planetery gear set, bearing, and E1-E2 clutch assembly.

5) Remove circlip and lift out F1 piston carrier, F2 plates and discs, thrust bearing, and turbine shaft support. Remove F2 piston cup and springs. Lift out F2 piston with Remover (B.Vi. 952). *See Fig. 14.*

INTERMEDIATE CASE

1) Remove remaining attaching bolts and separate intermediate case from differential and converter housing. Remove secondary shaft and output shaft snap rings. Remove output shaft assembly, secondary shaft, and step down driven gear.

AMC/RENAULT MB1 (Cont.)

Fig. 13: Exploded View of MB1 Automatic Transaxle Rear Case Assembly

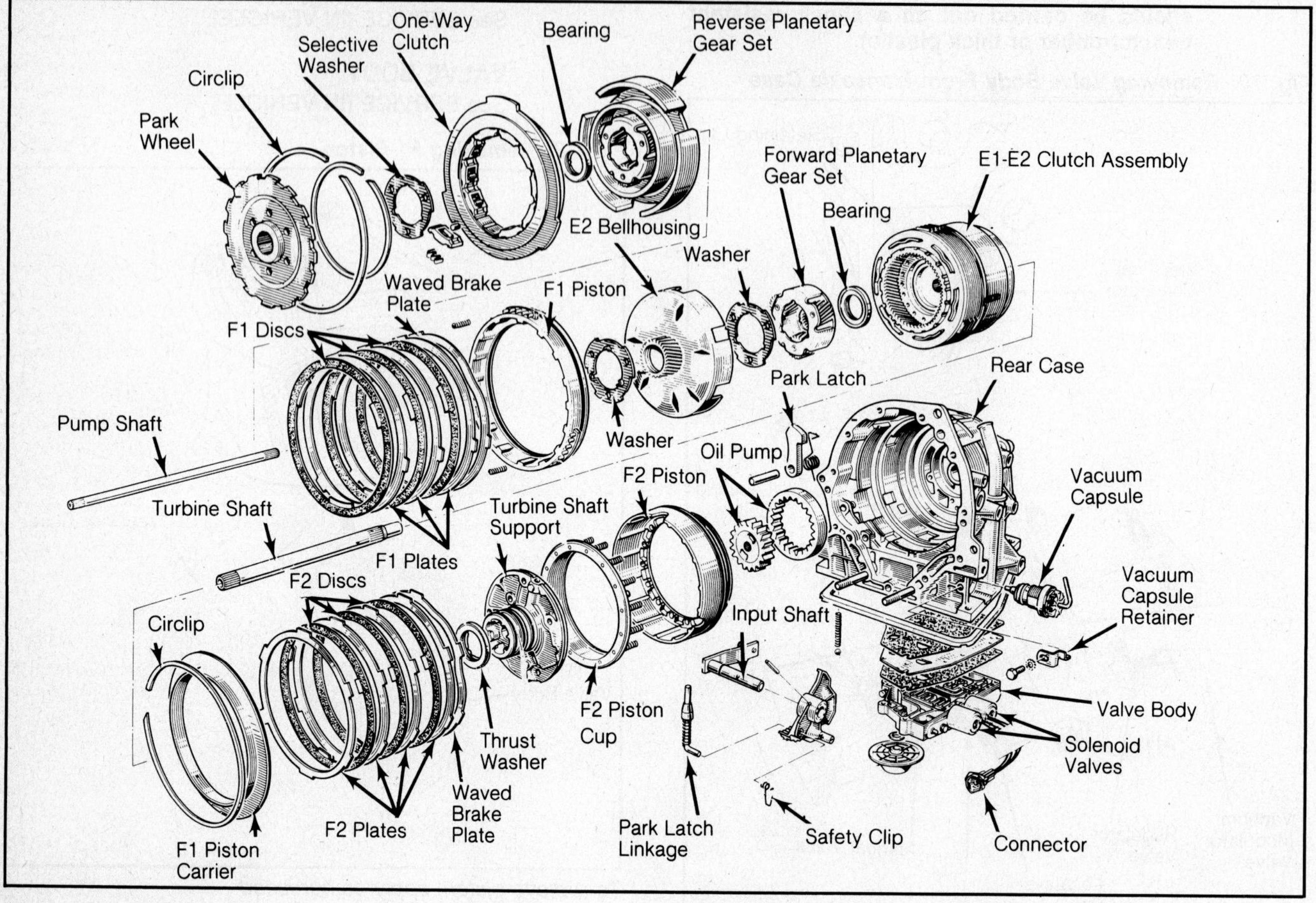

Fig. 14: Removing F2 Piston

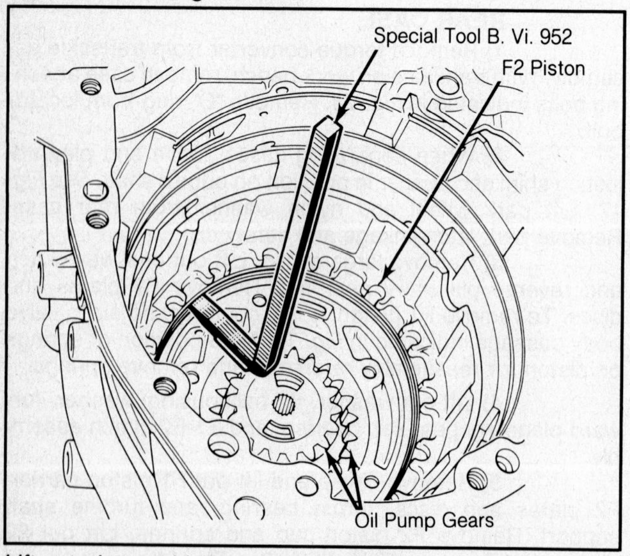

Lift out piston with Remover (B.Vi. 952).

2) If bearings are to be replaced, remove bearing retaining snap rings and, using a bearing puller, remove bearings from case. It is not necessary to remove bearings unless new bearings are to be installed.

DIFFERENTIAL & CONVERTER HOUSING

1) Remove "O" ring from planetary gear shaft. Tap 1 side of differential oil seal lightly with small drift to tilt seal. Grasp seal with pliers and remove from shaft.

2) Position converter housing in arbor press, shaft end up. Support ring gear (on differential case) with wood block. With press pushing on housing, apply just enough downward force to allow removal of small snap ring on stemmed planetary gear.

3) Remove wood block. Support housing and press out differential case by applying force on stemmed planetary gear shaft. Remove spring washer.

4) Secondary shaft bearing is staked into position in housing. Using grinder or sharp chisel, remove housing material as needed to release bearing. Remove bearing.

NOTE: **Do not remove secondary shaft and differential bearings unless new bearings are to be installed.**

5) To remove large differential bearing, place a steel bar across face of bearing, inside of case. Install a steel tube through the small bearing so that it bears on bar. Press bearing out of case. An arbor press is recommended for this procedure. *See Fig. 15.*

6) To remove small differential bearing, first remove retaining snap ring and discard. Using a 2" (50 mm) tube and arbor press, remove bearing by pressing it INTO

AMC/RENAULT MB1 (Cont.)

Fig. 15: Removing Large Differential Bearing

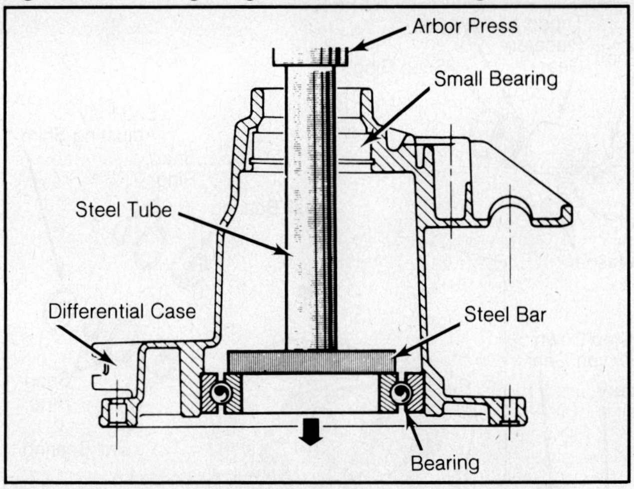

Pass steel tube through small bearing to bear against bar on large bearing.

tube and arbor press, remove bearing by pressing it INTO the case. Remove bearing through large bearing opening. *See Fig. 16.*

Fig. 16: Removing Small Differential Bearing

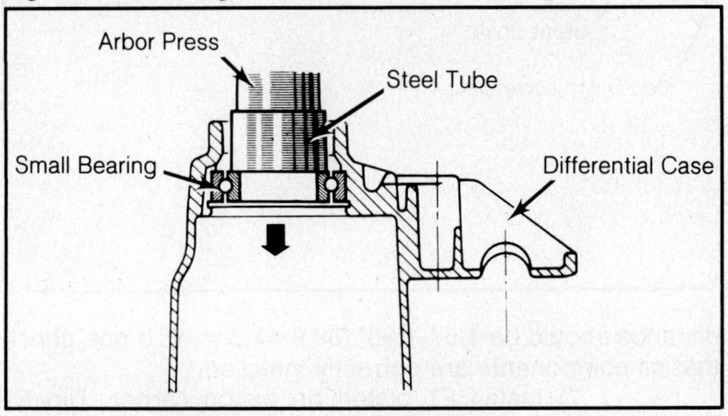

COMPONENT DISASSEMBLY & REASSEMBLY

VALVE BODY

Disassembly

1) Remove manual valve. Carefully remove cover plate retaining bolts (2) while holding plate in position. Slowly release plate to ensure that springs and valves remain in position.

2) While removing components, be sure to note position in valve body for reassembly reference. Withdraw pressure regulating valve, spring and plunger. Remove pilot valves and plungers.

3) Remove sequence valves and spring. Remove pressure limiting valve seal. Remove pressure limiting valve, spring and check ball.

Cleaning & Inspection

1) Check all valves for scratches or excessive wear. If any valve or valves is damaged, entire valve body must be replaced. All valves should slide freely in their bores without sticking or binding.

2) Check springs for damage or collapsed coils. Inspect check ball closely for scratches or other signs of unusual wear. Clean valve body with mineral spirits and lint free rags. Blow out passages and dry valve body with compressed air.

Reassembly

Reverse disassembly procedure to assemble valve body, noting the following: Install sequence valve with larger head towards spring. Solenoid valve marked with arrow must be installed on pressure regulating valve side. *See Fig. 18.*

DIFFERENTIAL

Disassembly

Remove speedometer drive gear from stemmed planetary gear shaft. With case held in soft-jawed vise, remove snap ring and washer. Lift out planetary gears, shaft, and side gears (with washers). Tie side gear washers to their respective side gears to ensure that washers are installed with correct gears during transaxle reassembly.

Inspection

Check all components for signs of scoring or excessive wear. Differential case components are designed as matched sets. If any differential component is damaged (planetary gear, differential case, side gears, washers or shaft), entire assembly must be replaced.

Reassembly

To assemble differential, reverse disassembly procedures. Dip all components in automatic transmission fluid before assembly. Ensure tab on speedometer drive gear is aligned with notch in differential case when parts are assembled.

TRANSAXLE INSPECTION, REASSEMBLY & ADJUSTMENT

INSPECTION

1) Clean case and housings thoroughly with solvent and lint free rags. DO NOT use solvents containing trichloroethylene as it may damage seals. Dry components with compressed air. Direct air stream into all holes, oil feed passages and lubrication channels.

2) Check condition of F1 and F2 brake plates and discs. Any plates which show signs of overheating (discoloration) should be replaced. Check for damage to plate surfaces, excessive runout or taper. Replace as needed.

3) Inspect discs for excessive wear and burned or torn linings. In most cases, if either or both brakes show signs of having been severely overheated, E1-E2 clutch assembly as well as all F1 and F2 plates and discs should be replaced.

4) Check sealing ring lands on turbine shaft support. If excessively worn, or if bottom of lands is not square, support should be replaced. Ensure that seal ring ends are square and hooked together properly.

5) Inspect all snap ring and circlip grooves. Worn or damaged grooves will prevent proper seating of retainers. Therefore, any component with worn grooves should be replaced. Check condition of machined surfaces and sleeves on all components. Replace as needed.

6) Check condition of teeth on all geared components. Ensure that forward and reverse planetary gear sets rotate freely on shafts.

7) Inspect secondary shaft bearing seat area in converter housing. Remove any burrs or scratches with emery cloth. Wipe bore clean with dry cloth and blow out with compressed air.

AMC/RENAULT MB1 (Cont.)

Fig. 17: Exploded View of Intermediate Case, Differential & Converter Housing Assemblies

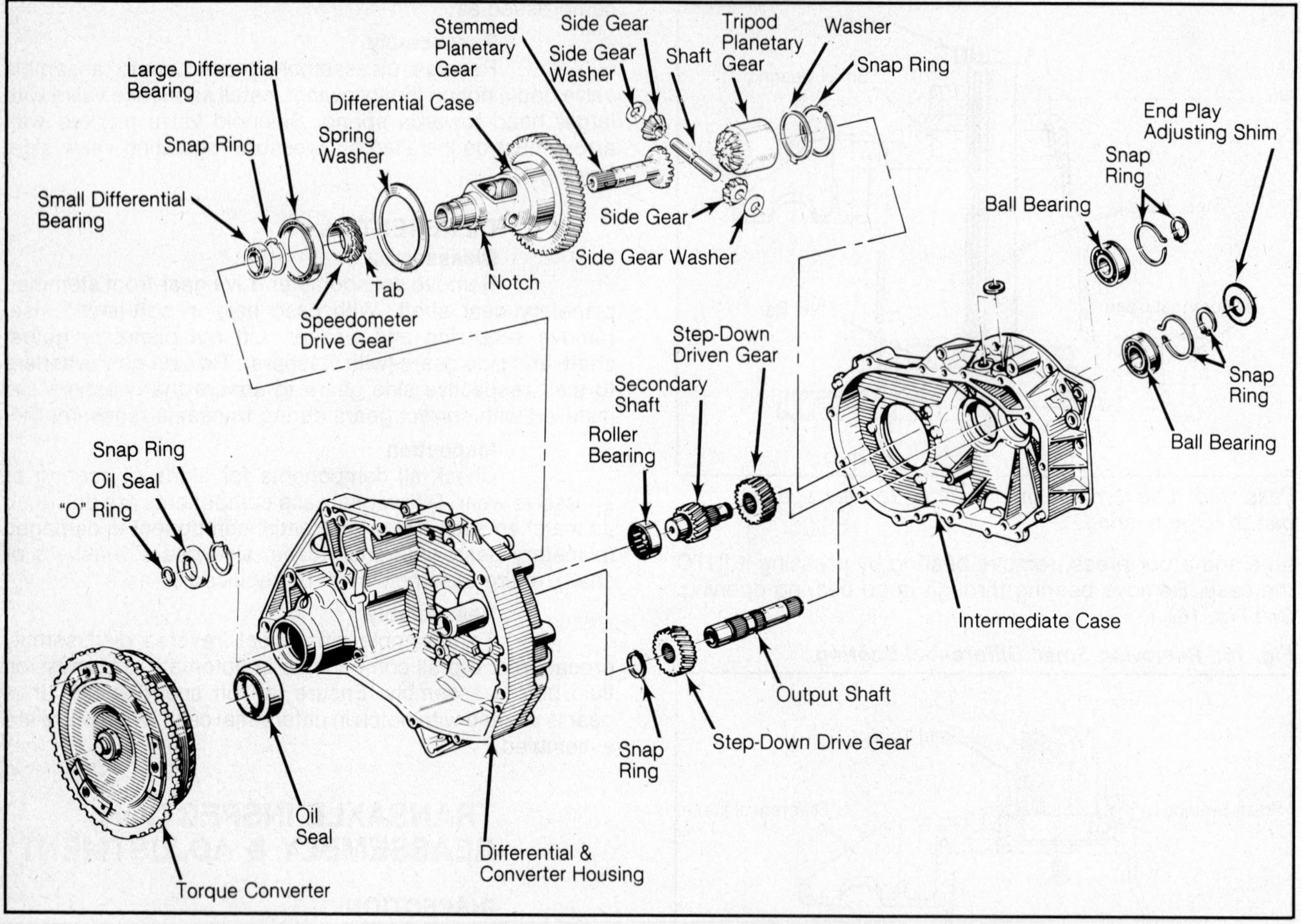

REASSEMBLY

Rear Case

1) Install oil pump gears in case. Ensure that gears rotate freely. Replace seals on F2 piston and install piston and piston cup in case. Make sure that piston springs are seated correctly in piston.

2) Install Guide Pins (B. Vi. 952) in case and install turbine shaft support, using pins to guide support into position. *See Fig. 19.* Remove pins, install retaining bolts and tighten alternately and evenly. Install thrust bearing. Install F2 brake steel clips.

3) Install waved brake plate. Dip F2 plates and discs in transmission fluid. Install 1 disc, then 1 plate in case. Continue alternating discs and plates until all have been installed. Install F1 piston carrier and large circlip.

4) Check clearance between discs and plates. Clearance should be .05-.13" (1.3-3.2 mm). If clearance is incorrect, check that all plates and discs are in correct position and re-check plate and disc condition. Ensure that circlip is fully seated in its groove.

5) Assemble E1-E2 clutch, roller bearing, forward planetary gear set, .06" (1.5 mm) washer, E2 bellhousing and turbine shaft. Ensure that tabs of clutch assembly fit into notches of E2 bellhousing. Install complete assembly in case so that tabs of F2 plates and discs are located in notches of E2 bellhousing.

6) Measure distance from face of F1 piston carrier to outside face of E1-E2 clutch assembly. Total distance should be 1.57-1.63" (39.9-41.3 mm). If not, check that all components are correctly installed.

7) Install F1 piston on piston carrier. Dip F1 plates and discs in transmission fluid. Install 1 plate, then 1 disc in case. Continue alternating plates and discs until all have been installed.

8) Check clearance between plates and discs. Operating clearance should be .03-.10" (.8-2.7 mm). If clearance is incorrect, check that all plates and discs are in correct position and re-check plate and disc condition.

9) Install one-way clutch in reverse planetary gear set. Install .06" (1.5 mm) washer on E2 bellhousing. Install reverse planetary gear set/one-way clutch assembly in case. Make sure that tabs on washer engage slots in planetary gear set. Install large circlip.

10) If any component in rear case was removed or replaced during transaxle overhaul, reverse planetary gear set adjustment and total end play adjustment must be checked. These adjustments must be made before final assembly of transaxle cases. See Reverse Planetary Gear Set Adjustment in ADJUSTMENT section in this article. Install valve body, filter and pan.

Differential/Converter Housing & Intermediate Case

1) Install large bearing retaining snap rings in intermediate case. Install bearings with Driver (B. Vi. 947). Assemble step down drive gear on output shaft and retain with snap ring. Install assembly in intermediate case and install snap ring.

AMC/RENAULT MB1 (Cont.)

Fig. 18: Exploded View of Renault Models MB1/3 Valve Body Assembly

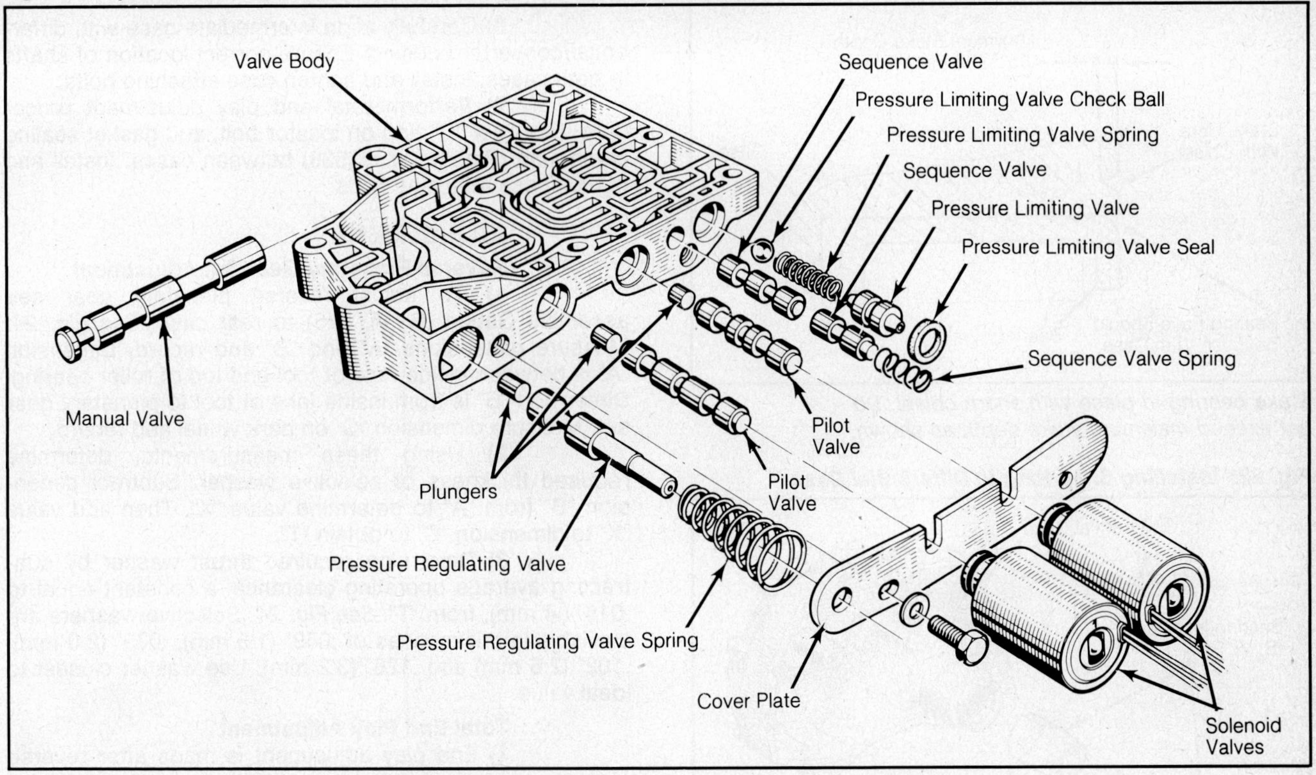

Fig. 19: Installing Turbine Shaft Support in Rear Case

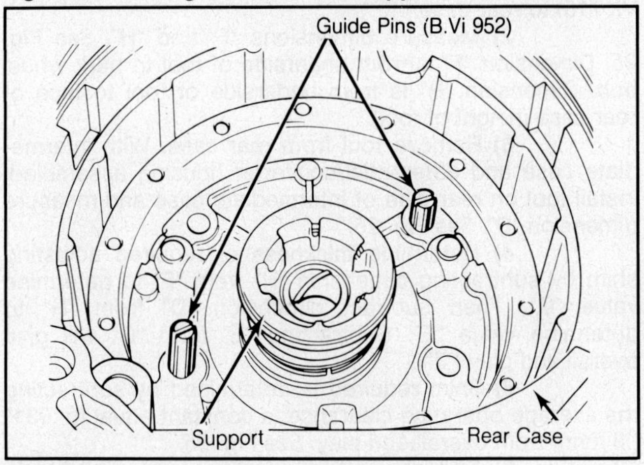

Install guide pins in case to align support.

Fig. 20: E1-E2 Clutch Assembly

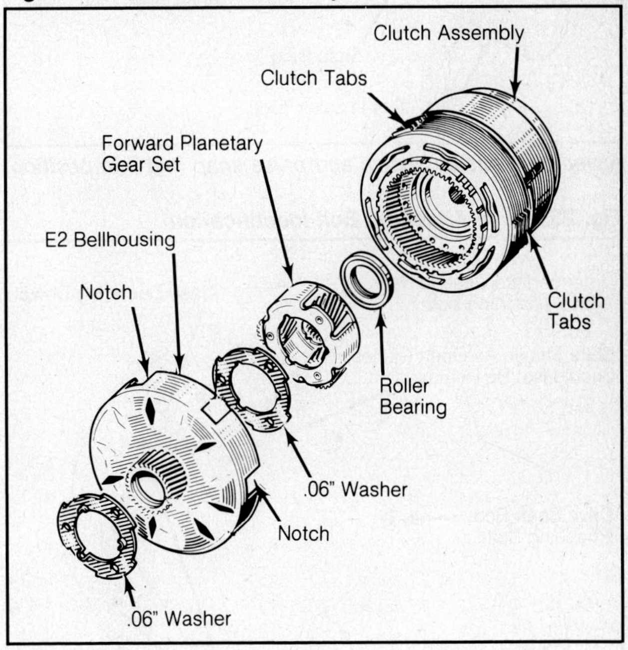

Tabs of clutch must align with slots in bellhousing.

2) Install step down driven gear and secondary shaft in intermediate case and retain with snap ring.

3) Position small differential bearing in housing and press into place with arbor press and 2.5" (65 mm) pipe. Install new snap ring. Place large differential bearing in position. Place a slightly shouldered bar or 5.0" (127 mm) steel pipe on bearing and press bearing into case.

4) Install secondary shaft bearing in converter housing. Press bearing in until it is flush with face of case. Stake in place with chisel. *See Fig. 21.*

5) Using Seal Installer (B. Vi. 962), install new converter oil seal over stator shaft support. Tap new seal onto shaft until outer face of tool is flush with end of support.

6) Install spring washer on base of differential case with outside edge of washer against gear. Install differential in housing.

7) Support differential case with wood block. Install part C of Tool Set (B. Vi. 946) on planetary gear stem and install snap ring on part C. *See Fig. 22.* Position part D of Tool Set (B. Vi. 946) on part C and press snap ring into groove. Install oil seal on planetary gear shaft.

AMC/RENAULT MB1 (Cont.)

Fig. 21: Secondary Shaft Bearing Installation

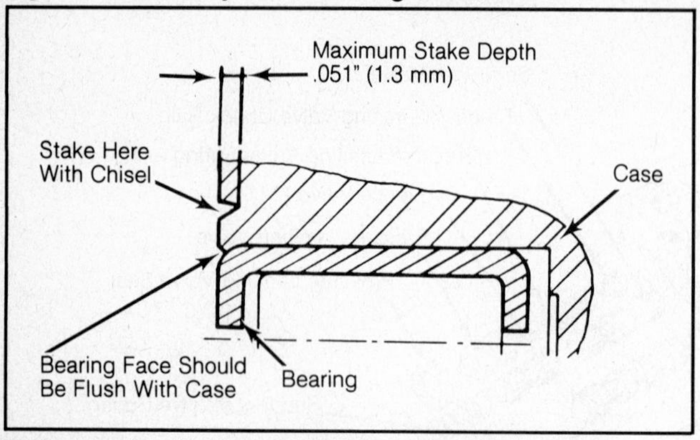

Stake bearing in place with sharp chisel. Do not exceed maximum stake depth as shown.

Fig. 22: Installing Snap Ring in Differential Case

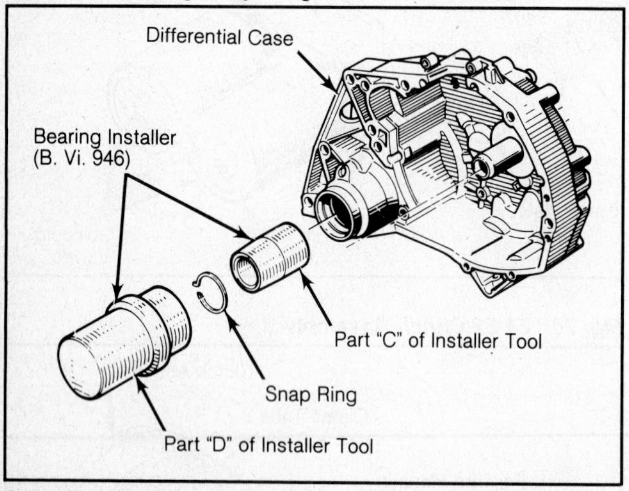

Assemble tools as shown and press snap ring into position.

Fig. 23: Case Attaching Bolt Identification

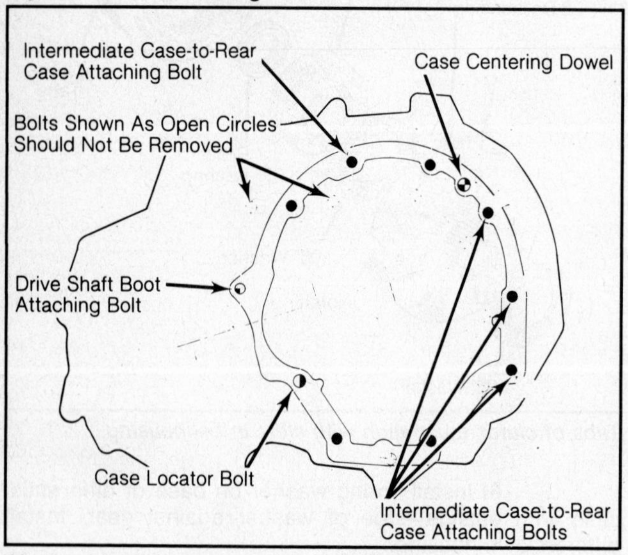

Always install new "O" ring on locator bolt.

NOTE: Use arbor press when installing snap ring.

8) Carefully align intermediate case with differential/converter housing. Ensure correct location of shafts in both cases. Install and tighten case attaching bolts.

9) Perform total end play adjustment procedure. Use new "O" ring on locator bolt, and gasket sealing compound (Part No. 8993539) between cases. Install and tighten case attaching bolts.

ADJUSTMENT

Reverse Planetary Gear Set Adjustment

1) To adjust reverse planetary gear set, assemble Gauge (B. Vi. 715) to rear case. *See Fig. 24.* Measure dimensions "A" and "B" and record. Dimension "A" is between inside face of tool and top of roller bearing. Dimension "B" is from inside face of tool to planetary gear set. Measure dimension "C" on park wheel and record.

2) Using these measurements, determine required thickness of selective washer. Subtract dimension "B" from "A" to determine value "X". Then add value "X" to dimension "C" to obtain "T".

3) Determine required thrust washer by subtracting average operating clearance, a constant equal to .016" (.4 mm), from "T". *See Fig. 24*. Selective washers are available in thicknesses of .059" (1.5 mm), .079" (2.0 mm), .102" (2.6 mm) and .126" (3.2 mm). Use washer closest to ideal value.

Total End Play Adjustment

1) End play adjustment is made after reverse planetary gear set adjustment. With gear set selective washer in place, install park gear and assemble Gauge (B. Vi. 715) to rear case.

2) Measure dimensions "F" and "H". *See Fig. 25.* Dimension "F" is from underside of tool to park wheel hub. Dimension "H" is from underside of tool to face of rear case (height of tool).

3) Remove tool from rear case. With intermediate case and differential/converter housing assembled, install tool on rear side of intermediate case and measure dimension "D". *See Fig. 25.*

4) Determine thickness of required adjusting shim by subtracting dimension "H" from "F" to determine value "G". Then subtract dimension "D" from "H" to determine value "E". Subtracting "E" from "G" will give overall end play ("T").

5) Shim required is determined by subtracting the average operating clearance, a constant equal to .031" (.8 mm), from overall end play. *See Fig. 25.*

6) End play adjusting shims are available in thicknesses of .010" (.25 mm), .028" (.70 mm), .043" (1.1 mm), .067" (1.7 mm) and .090" (2.3 mm). Use washer which is closest to ideal value.

TIGHTENING SPECIFICATIONS

Application	Ft. Lbs. (N.m)
Differential & Converter Housing-to-Intermediate Case	18 (25)
Rear Case-to-Intermediate Case	18 (25)
Transaxle-to-Engine Block	31 (42)
Turbine Shaft Retaining Bolts	11 (15)
	INCH Lbs. (N.m)
Transaxle Oil Pan Bolts	54 (6)
Valve Body Attaching Bolts	90 (10)

AMC/RENAULT MB1 (Cont.)

Fig. 24: Measuring Reverse Planetary Gear Set Adjustment

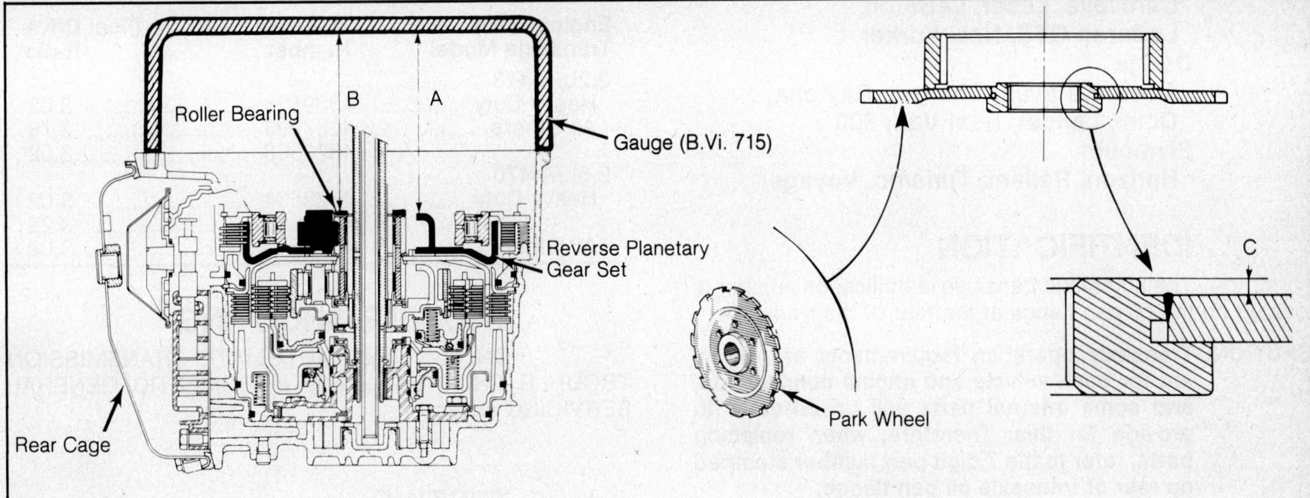

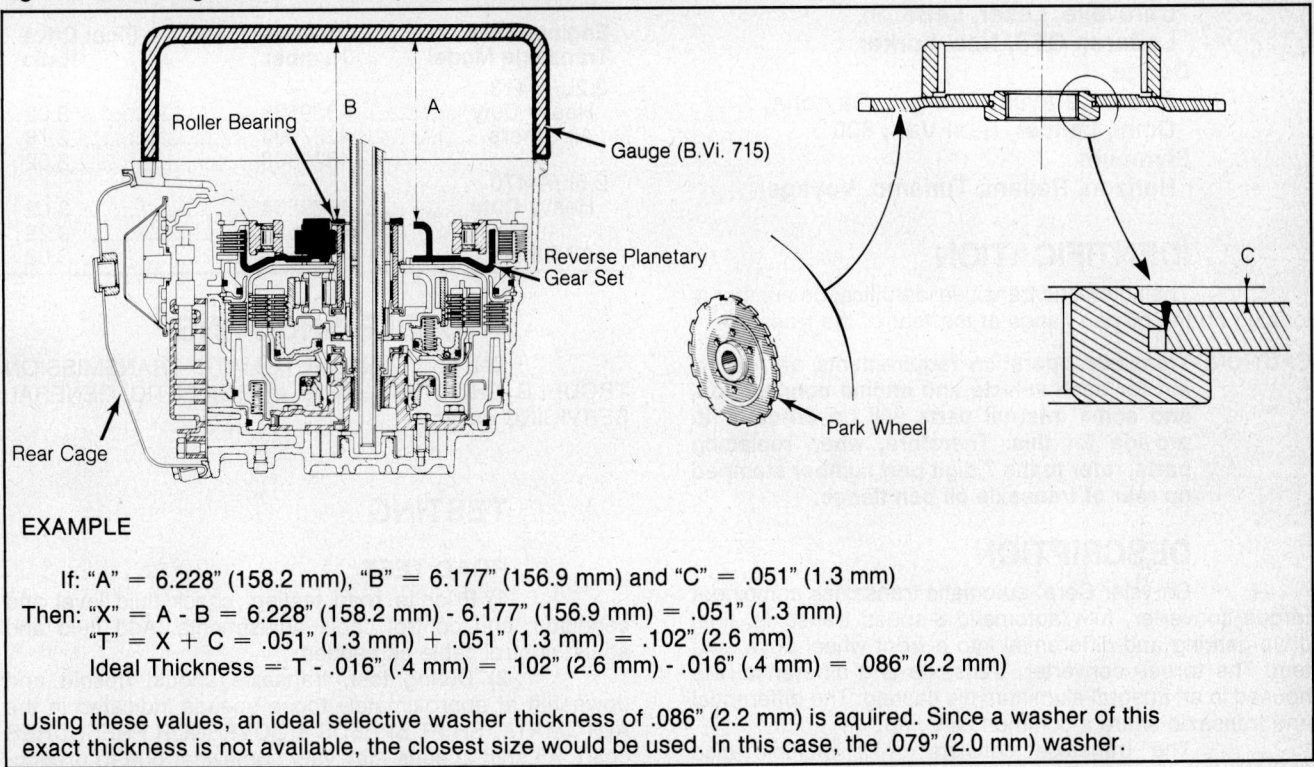

EXAMPLE

If: "A" = 6.228" (158.2 mm), "B" = 6.177" (156.9 mm) and "C" = .051" (1.3 mm)
Then: "X" = A - B = 6.228" (158.2 mm) - 6.177" (156.9 mm) = .051" (1.3 mm)
"T" = X + C = .051" (1.3 mm) + .051" (1.3 mm) = .102" (2.6 mm)
Ideal Thickness = T - .016" (.4 mm) = .102" (2.6 mm) - .016" (.4 mm) = .086" (2.2 mm)

Using these values, an ideal selective washer thickness of .086" (2.2 mm) is aquired. Since a washer of this exact thickness is not available, the closest size would be used. In this case, the .079" (2.0 mm) washer.

Measure dimensions shown and use values to determine required selective washer thickness.

Fig. 25: Measurements Required for Total End Play Adjustment

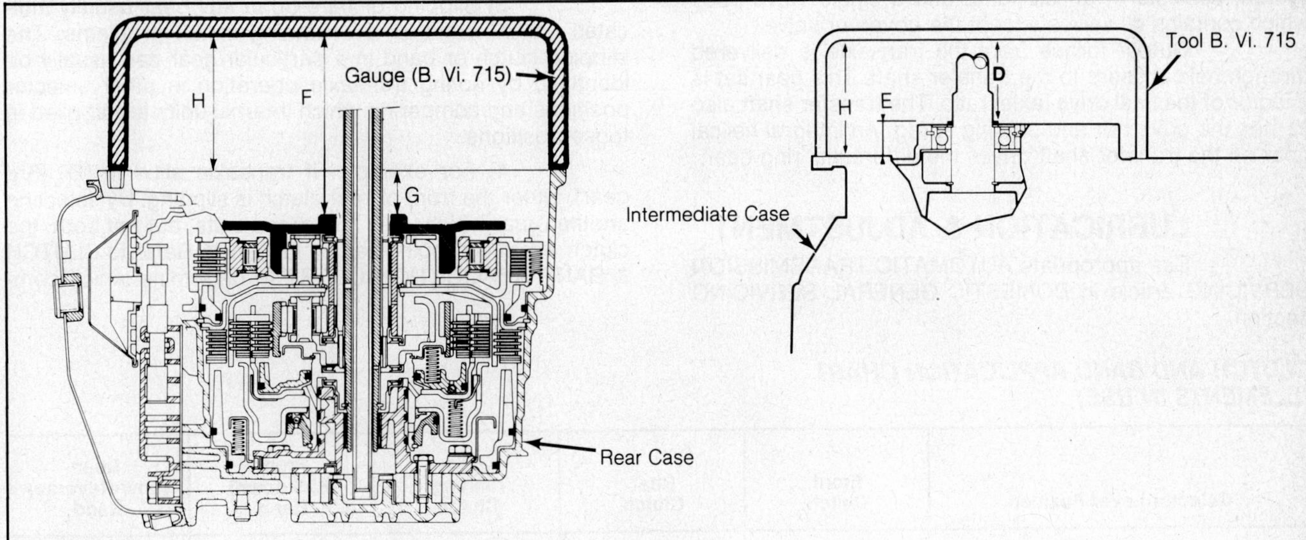

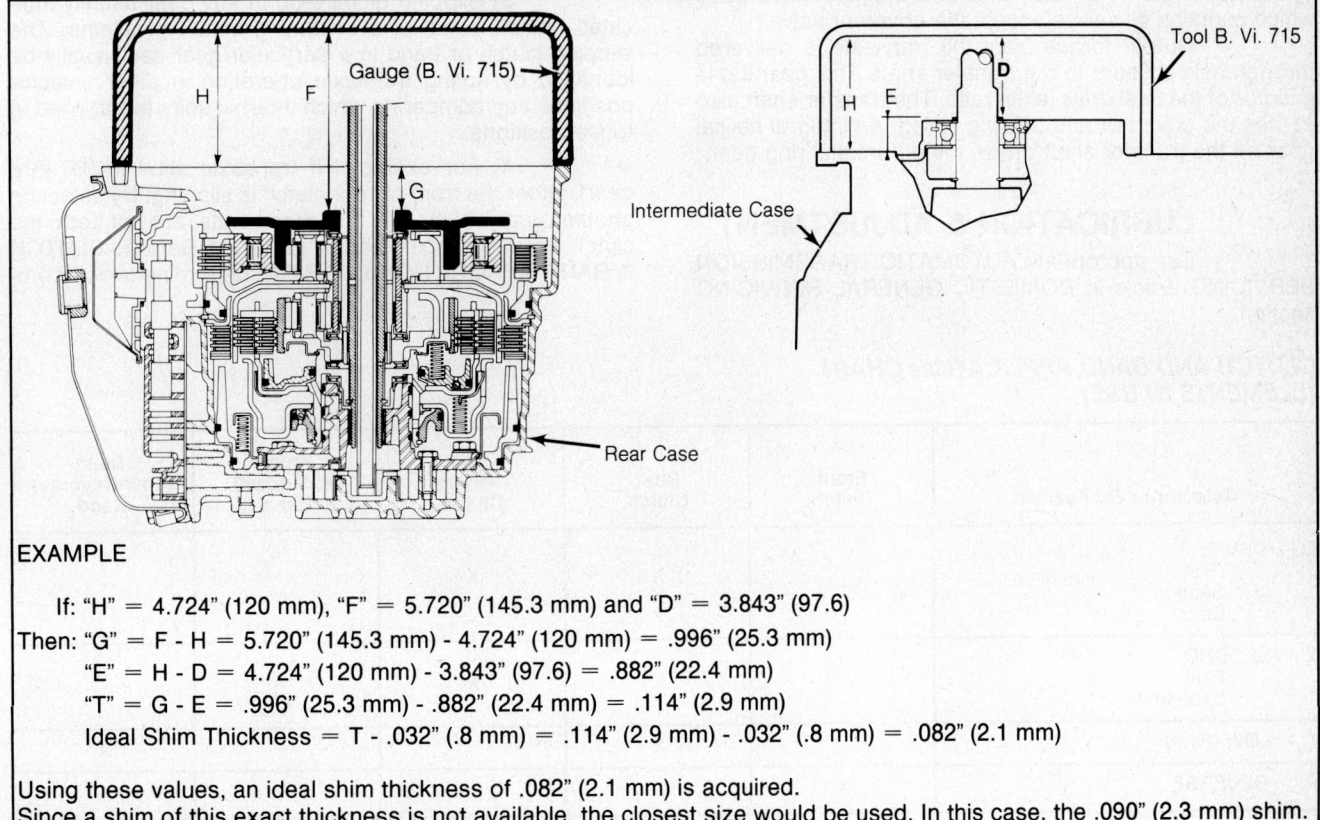

EXAMPLE

If: "H" = 4.724" (120 mm), "F" = 5.720" (145.3 mm) and "D" = 3.843" (97.6)
Then: "G" = F - H = 5.720" (145.3 mm) - 4.724" (120 mm) = .996" (25.3 mm)
"E" = H - D = 4.724" (120 mm) - 3.843" (97.6) = .882" (22.4 mm)
"T" = G - E = .996" (25.3 mm) - .882" (22.4 mm) = .114" (2.9 mm)
Ideal Shim Thickness = T - .032" (.8 mm) = .114" (2.9 mm) - .032" (.8 mm) = .082" (2.1 mm)

Using these values, an ideal shim thickness of .082" (2.1 mm) is acquired.
Since a shim of this exact thickness is not available, the closest size would be used. In this case, the .090" (2.3 mm) shim.

Measure dimensions shown and use values to determine required shim thickness.

Automatic Transmissions

CHRYSLER CORP. A-413 & A-470

Chrysler
Caravelle, Laser, LeBaron, LeBaron GTS, New Yorker
Dodge
Aries, Caravan, Charger, Daytona, Omni, Lancer, Ram Van, 600
Plymouth
Horizon, Reliant, Turismo, Voyager

IDENTIFICATION

The automatic transaxle identification number is located on the oil pan flange at the rear of the transaxle.

CAUTION: Transaxle operation requirements are different for each vehicle and engine combination, and some internal parts will be different to provide for this. Therefore, when replacing parts, refer to the 7 digit part number stamped on rear of transaxle oil pan flange.

DESCRIPTION

Chrysler Corp. automatic transaxles combine a torque converter, fully automatic 3-speed transaxle, final drive gearing and differential into a front wheel drive system. The torque converter, transaxle and differential are housed in an integral aluminum die casting. The differential and transaxle share a common oil sump.

The transaxle consists of 2 multiple disc clutches, an overrunning clutch, 2 servos, a hydraulic accumulator, 2 bands and 2 planetary gear sets to provide 3 forward gear ratios and a reverse ratio. The hydraulic system consists of an oil pump and a single valve body which contains all valves except the governor valve.

Output torque from the transaxle is delivered through helical gears to the transfer shaft. This gear set is a factor of the final drive (axle) ratio. The transfer shaft also carries the governor and parking sprag. An integral helical gear on the transfer shaft drives the differential ring gear.

LUBRICATION & ADJUSTMENT

See appropriate AUTOMATIC TRANSMISSION SERVICING article in DOMESTIC GENERAL SERVICING section.

TRANSAXLE APPLICATION

Engine Size/ Transaxle Model	Transaxle Number	Final Drive Ratio
2.2L/A-413		
Heavy Duty	4329538	3.02
All Others	4207905	2.78
	4329506	3.02
2.6L/A-470		
Heavy Duty	4329564	3.02
	4329565	3.22
All Others	4329547	3.02

TROUBLE SHOOTING

See appropriate AUTOMATIC TRANSMISSION TROUBLE SHOOTING article in DOMESTIC GENERAL SERVICING section.

TESTING

ROAD TEST

1) Prior to road testing, check fluid level and condition, and control cable adjustments. Add fluid and adjust control cable as needed.

2) During test, transaxle should upshift and downshift at approximately those speeds indicated in the AUTOMATIC SHIFT SPEEDS & GOVERNOR PRESSURES chart. All shift speeds may vary somewhat due to production tolerances, rear axle ratio, or tire size. The important factor is the quality of the shifts. All shifts should be smooth, responsive, and with no slipping or engine speed flare-up.

3) Slipping or flare-up in any gear usually indicates clutch, band or overrunning clutch problems. The slipping clutch or band in a particular gear can usually be identified by noting transaxle operation in other selector positions and comparing which internal units are applied in those positions.

4) For example, if transaxle slips in "D" (3rd gear), either the front or rear clutch is slipping. By selecting another gear which uses 1 of those units, but not both, the clutch which is slipping can be identified. Refer to CLUTCH & BAND APPLICATION CHART to determine which com-

CLUTCH AND BAND APPLICATION CHART (ELEMENTS IN USE)

Selector Lever Position	Front Clutch	Rear Clutch	Over-running Clutch	Front (Kickdown) Band	Rear (Low-Reverse) Band
D - DRIVE					
First		X	X		
Second		X		X	
Direct	X	X			
2 - SECOND					
First		X	X		
Second		X		X	
1 - LOW (First)		X			X
R - REVERSE	X				X
NEUTRAL OR PARK - All clutches and bands released and/or ineffective.					

CHRYSLER CORP. A-413 & A-470 (Cont.)

Fig. 1: Cutaway View of Chrysler Corp. Automatic Transaxle

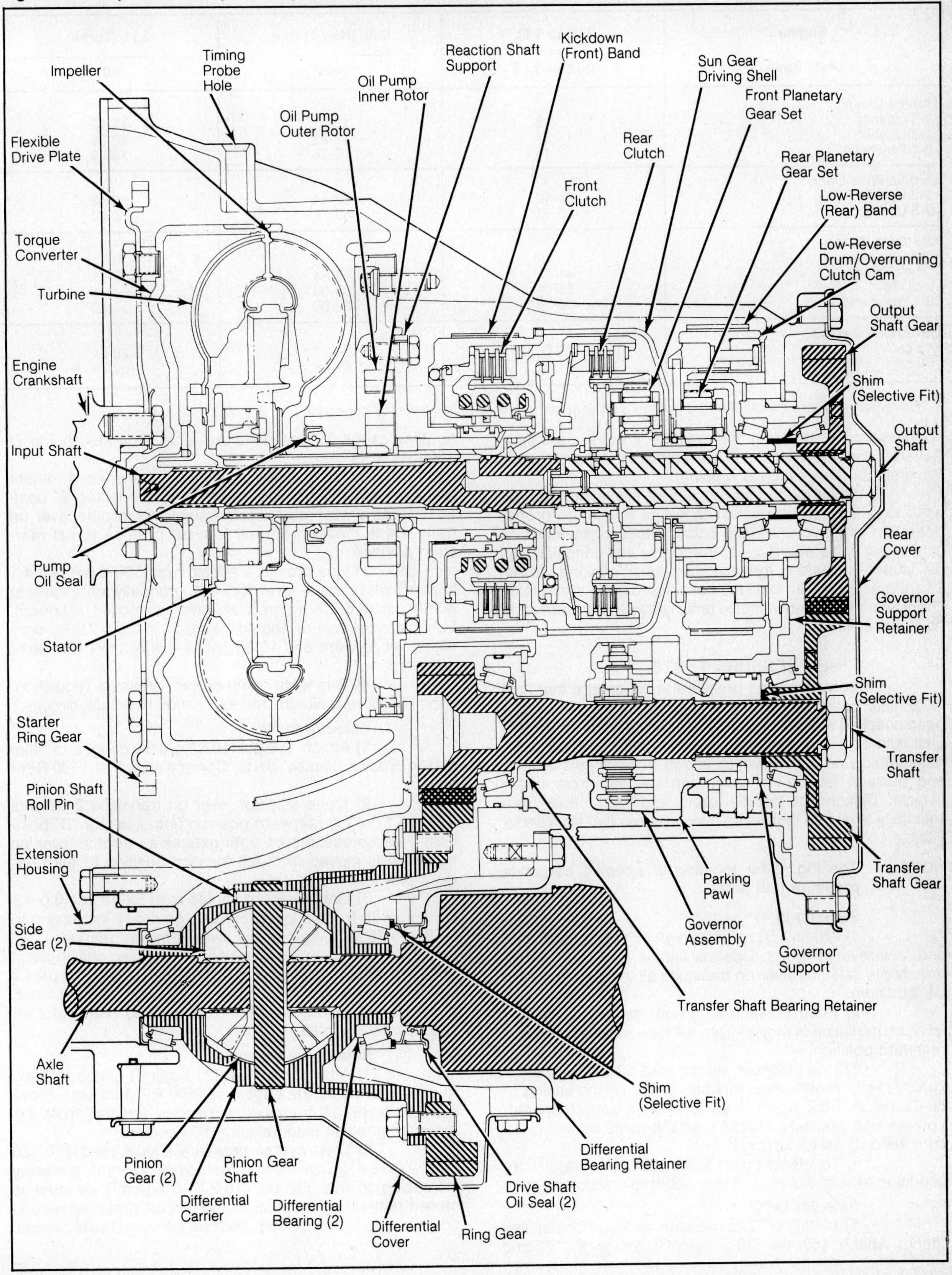

CHRYSLER CORP. A-413 & A-470 (Cont.)

AUTOMATIC SHIFT SPEEDS & GOVERNOR PRESSURES

Engine	2.2L or 2.6L	2.2L (Non-Turbo)	2.2L (Turbo)
Axle Ratio	2.78 or 3.22	3.02	3.02
Throttle Closed			
1-2 Upshift	13-16	13-17	15-19
2-3 Upshift	17-21	18-22	20-25
3-1 Downshift	12-15	13-16	15-19
Throttle Wide Open			
1-2 Upshift	34-42	36-44	38-42
2-3 Upshift	60-67	63-71	70-80
Kickdown Range			
3-2 Downshift			
Part Throttle	44-52	46-54	48-59
WOT	55-64	58-66	64-74
3-1 Downshift	30-38	32-39	37-40
Governor Pressure [1]			
15 psi	23-26	24-27	28-31
50 psi	57-65	61-68	69-76

[1] – Governor pressure should be from zero to 3.0 psi at stand-still or downshift may not occur.

ponents are in use. Using this example, if transaxle slips in Reverse also, the front clutch is slipping. If it does not slip in Reverse, the rear clutch is slipping.

5) Although this process of elimination can be used to detect any unit which slips and to confirm proper operation of good units, the actual cause of malfunction cannot easily be determined. Practically any condition can be caused by leaking hydraulic circuits or sticking valves. Therefore, unless an obvious condition exists, a transaxle should never be disassembled until hydraulic pressure tests have been made.

LINE PRESSURE TESTS

Before making pressure tests, ensure that fluid level, fluid condition, and control cable adjustments have been checked and corrected as needed. Operate transaxle until fluid is at operating temperature. Install a tachometer, raise vehicle on a hoist which allows front wheels to turn, and position tachometer so it can be read from under vehicle. Disconnect throttle cable and shift cable from transaxle levers so that levers may be controlled from under vehicle.

NOTE: See Fig. 2 for location of specific transaxle pressure test ports.

Selector in "1"

1) Attach 150 psi (10.5 kg/cm²) gauges to "line" and "low-reverse" ports. Operate engine at 1000 RPM for test. Move selector lever on transaxle all the way rearward ("1" position).

2) Read pressures on both gauges as throttle lever on transaxle is moved from full forward position to full rearward position.

3) Line pressure should read 52-58 psi (3.6-4.1 kg/cm²) with throttle lever forward, gradually increasing to 80-88 psi (5.6-6.2 kg/cm²) as lever is moved rearward. Low-reverse pressure should read the same as line pressure within 3 psi (.2 kg/cm²).

4) This tests pump output, pressure regulation, condition of rear clutch, and rear servo hydraulic circuits.

Selector in "2"

1) Install a "T" connection at lower cooler line fitting. Attach 150 psi (10.5 kg/cm²) gauge to "T" and another gauge to "line pressure" port. Operate engine at 1000 RPM for test.

2) Move selector lever on transaxle 1 detent forward from full rearward position (into selector "2" position). Read pressures on both gauges as throttle lever on transaxle is moved from full forward position to full rearward position.

3) Line pressure should read 52-58 psi (3.6-4.1 kg/cm²) with throttle lever forward, gradually increasing to 80-88 psi (5.6-6.2 kg/cm²) as lever is moved rearward. Lubrication pressure should be 10-25 psi (.7-1.8 kg/cm²) with lever forward and 10-35 psi (.7-2.5 kg/cm²) with lever rearward.

4) This tests pump output, pressure regulation, condition of rear clutch, and lubrication hydraulic circuits.

Selector in "D"

1) Attach 150 psi (10.5 kg/cm²) gauges to "line" and "kickdown release" ports. Operate engine at 1600 RPM for test.

2) Move selector lever on transaxle 2 detents forward from full rearward position (into selector "D" position). Read pressures on both gauges as throttle lever on transaxle is moved from full forward position to full rearward position.

3) Line pressure should read 52-58 psi (3.6-4.1 kg/cm²) with throttle lever forward, gradually increasing to 80-88 psi (5.6-6.2 kg/cm²) as lever is moved rearward.

4) Kickdown release is pressurized only in direct drive and should be same as line pressure within 3 psi (.2 kg/cm²), up to kickdown point. This tests pump output, pressure regulation, condition of front and rear clutches, and hydraulic circuits.

Selector in Reverse

1) Attach a 300 psi (21 kg/cm²) gauge to "low-reverse" port. Operate engine at 1600 RPM for test. Move selector lever on transaxle 4 detents forward from full rearward position (into selector "R" position).

2) Low-reverse pressure should read 180-220 psi (12.6-15.4 kg/cm²) with throttle lever forward, gradually increasing to 260-300 psi (18.2-21.0 kg/cm²) as lever is moved rearward. This tests pump output, pressure regulation, condition of front clutch, and rear servo hydraulic circuits.

CHRYSLER CORP. A-413 & A-470 (Cont.)

Fig. 2: View of Left Side of Transaxle Case Showing Pressure Test Port Locations

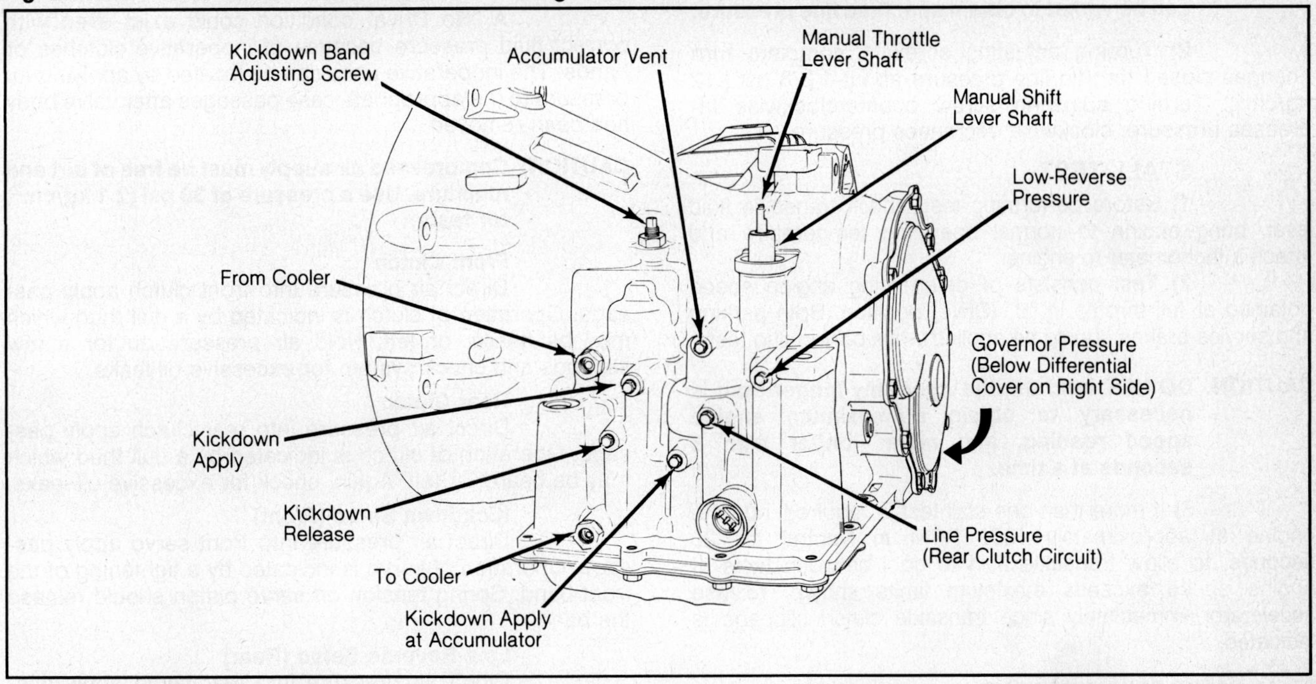

3) Move selector lever on transaxle to "D" position to check that rear servo pressure drops to zero. This tests for leakage into rear servo, due to case porosity, which can cause reverse band burn out.

PRESSURE TEST INDICATIONS

1) If proper minimum-to-maximum line pressure is found in any test, pump and pressure regulator are working properly.

2) Low pressure in "D", "1", and "2", but correct pressure in "R", indicates rear clutch circuit leakage.

3) Low pressure in "D" and "R", but correct pressure in "1", indicates front clutch circuit leakage.

4) Low pressure in "R" and "1", but correct pressure in "2", indicates rear servo circuit leakage.

5) Low line pressure in all positions indicates a defective pump, clogged filter, or stuck pressure regulator valve.

NOTE: The following GOVERNOR PRESSURE TEST need only be performed if transaxle shifts at wrong vehicle speed with throttle cable correctly adjusted.

GOVERNOR PRESSURE TEST

1) Connect a 150 psi (10.5 kg/cm^2) pressure gauge to governor pressure take-off point, located below differential cover at lower right side of case.

2) Operate transaxle in 3rd gear to read pressures. Compare pressure readings obtained with governor pressure specifications given in AUTOMATIC SHIFT SPEEDS & GOVERNOR PRESSURES chart.

3) If governor pressures are incorrect at given vehicle speed, governor valves are probably sticking.

4) Governor pressure should respond smoothly to changes in MPH and should return to 0-3 psi (0-.2 kg/cm^2) when vehicle is stopped. Pressure above 3 psi (.2 kg/cm^2) at standstill will prevent the transaxle from downshifting.

THROTTLE PRESSURES

No gauge port is provided for testing throttle pressure. Incorrect throttle pressure should only be suspected if part throttle upshift speeds are either delayed or occur too early in relation to vehicle speeds. Engine runaway on either upshifts or downshifts can also be an indication of incorrect (low) throttle pressure setting.

CAUTION: In no case should throttle pressure be adjusted until transaxle throttle cable adjustment has been checked and corrected as needed.

HYDRAULIC PRESSURE ADJUSTMENTS

NOTE: An incorrect throttle pressure setting will cause incorrect line pressure readings even though line pressure adjustment is correct. Therefore, always inspect and correct throttle pressure adjustment before adjusting line pressure.

Throttle Pressure

1) Remove valve body from transaxle. Back off throttle lever stop screw approximately 5 turns. Insert gauge pin of Gauge (C-3763) between throttle lever cam and kickdown valve.

2) By pushing in on tool, compress kickdown valve against spring so that valve is completely bottomed.

3) Turn throttle lever stop screw until head of screw touches throttle lever tang with throttle lever cam touching tool and throttle valve bottomed.

CAUTION: Ensure adjustment is made with spring fully compressed and valve bottomed in valve body bore.

Line Pressure

1) Turn Allen screw in end of pressure regulator spring bracket so measurement between valve body and inner edge of adjusting nut is 1 5/16".

CHRYSLER CORP. A-413 & A-470 (Cont.)

NOTE: Due to manufacturing tolerances, adjustment can be varied to obtain specified line pressure.

2) Turning adjusting screw 1 complete turn changes closed throttle line pressure about 1 2/3 psi (.12 kg/cm^2). Turning adjusting screw counterclockwise increases pressure; clockwise decreases pressure.

STALL TEST

1) Before performing test, check transaxle fluid level, bring engine to normal operating temperature and attach a tachometer to engine.

2) Test consists of determining engine speed obtained at full throttle in "D" (Drive) position. Both parking and service brakes should be applied while performing test.

CAUTION: DO NOT hold throttle open any longer than is necessary to obtain a maximum engine speed reading, and never longer than 5 seconds at a time.

3) If more than one stall test is required, operate engine at approximately 1000 RPM in Neutral for 20 seconds, to allow transaxle fluid to cool between tests. If engine speed exceeds maximum limits shown, release accelerator immediately since transaxle clutch slippage is indicated.

STALL SPEED SPECIFICATIONS

Engine	Transaxle Models	Stall Speed RPM
2.2L		
Carbureted	A-413	2620-2820
EFI	A-413	[1] 2210-2410
Turbo	A-413	3150-3350
2.6L	A-470	2400-2600

[1] - 2620-2820 on Daytona and Lazer models.

STALL TEST RESULTS

Stall Speed Above Specification

If stall speed exceeds maximum limits shown by more than 200 RPM, transaxle clutch slippage is indicated. Make hydraulic pressure and air pressure checks to determine cause of slippage.

Stall Speed Below Specification

1) Low stall speeds (with a properly tuned engine) indicate torque converter stator clutch problems. A road test will be necessary to identify exact problem.

2) If stall speeds are 250-350 RPM below specifications, and vehicle operates properly at highway speeds, but has poor through-gear acceleration, stator overrunning clutch is slipping.

3) If stall speed and acceleration are normal, but abnormally high throttle opening is required to maintain highway speeds, stator clutch has seized.

4) Both of the preceding stator defects require replacement of the torque converter.

Noise During Stall Test

1) A whining or siren-like noise due to fluid flow is normal during stall operation with some converters; however, loud metallic noises from loose parts or interference within the assembly indicate a defective torque converter.

2) To be sure that noise originates within the converter, raise vehicle on hoist and operate at light throttle in "D" and "N" while listening under transaxle bellhousing.

AIR PRESSURE TESTS

A "No Drive" condition could exist even with correct fluid pressure because of inoperative clutches or bands. The inoperative units can be located by applying air pressure to the appropriate case passages after valve body has been removed.

CAUTION: Compressed air supply must be free of dirt and moisture. Use a pressure of 30 psi (2.1 kg/cm^2) for tests.

Front Clutch

Direct air pressure into front clutch apply passage. Operation of clutch is indicated by a dull thud which may be heard, or felt. Hold air pressure on for a few seconds and check system for excessive oil leaks.

Rear Clutch

Direct air pressure into rear clutch apply passage. Operation of clutch is indicated by a dull thud which may be heard, or felt. Again, check for excessive oil leaks.

Kickdown Servo (Front)

Direct air pressure into front servo apply passage. Operation of servo is indicated by a tightening of the front band. Spring tension on servo piston should release the band.

Low-Reverse Servo (Rear)

Direct air pressure into rear servo apply passage. Operation of servo is indicated by a tightening of the rear band. Spring tension of servo piston should release the band.

NOTE: If clutches and servos operate properly, no upshift or erratic shift conditions indicate malfunctions in valve body assembly

SERVICE (IN VEHICLE)

NOTE: The valve body, extension housing oil seal, parking sprag, and governor assembly may be removed with transaxle still installed in vehicle. See procedures given in TRANSAXLE DISASSEMBLY and TRANSAXLE REASSEMBLY & ADJUSTMENT.

SPEEDOMETER PINION GEAR

NOTE: Any time that speedometer pinion adapter is removed, a new "O" ring must be installed on outside diameter of adapter. Speedometer pinion must be removed before removing right drive axle shaft.

Removal

Remove bolt and washer securing speedometer pinion adapter in extension housing. With cable housing connected, carefully work adapter and pinion out of extension housing. Remove retainer and remove pinion from adapter.

Seal Replacement

If transaxle fluid is found in cable housing, install a new speedometer pinion and seal assembly. If fluid is found between cable and adapter, replace small "O" ring on cable.

CHRYSLER CORP. A-413 & A-470 (Cont.)

Fig. 3: Bottom View of Transmission Case (With Valve Body Removed) Showing Air Pressure Test Points

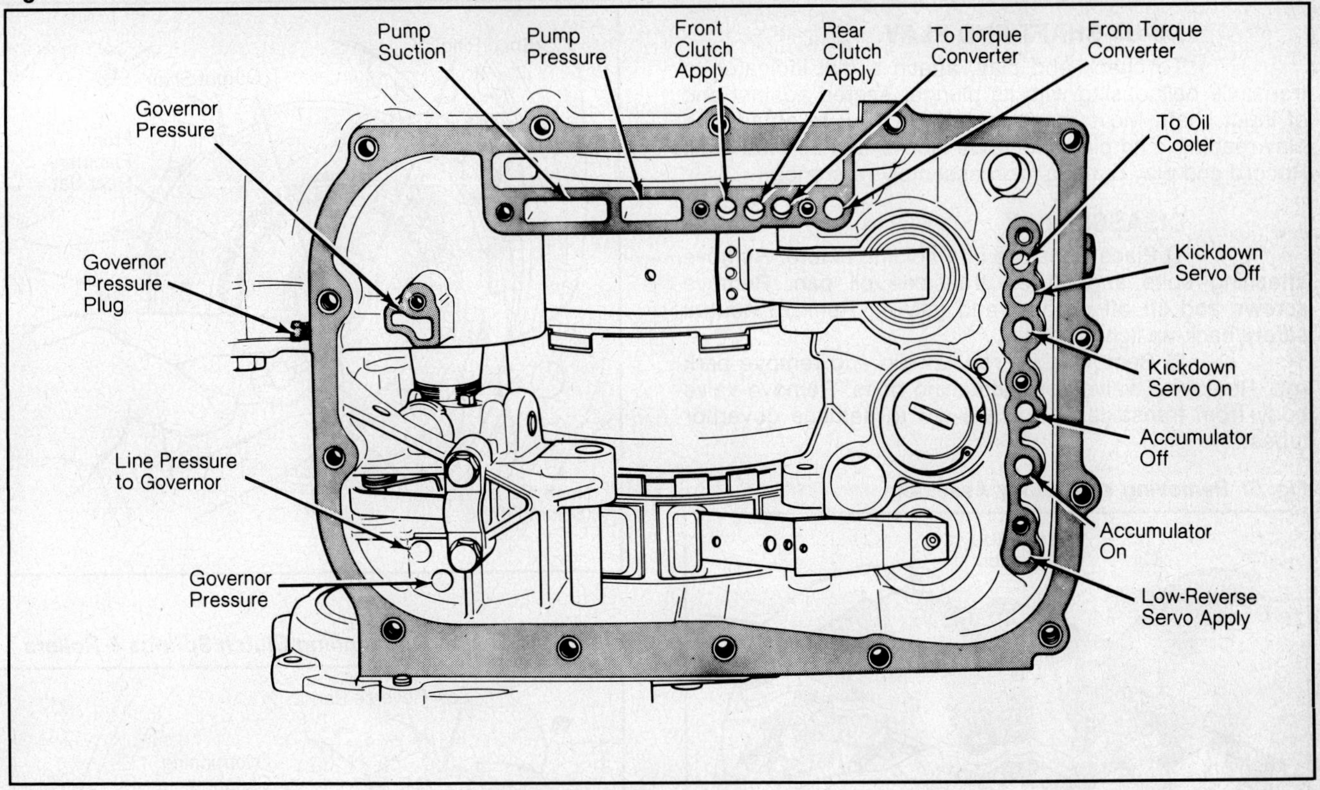

Installation

Before installing pinion, adapter and cable assembly ensure adapter flange and its mating areas on
xtension housing are clean. Dirt or sand will cause mis-
nment resulting in speedometer pinion gear damage.
ll and tighten bolt.

Exploded View of Speedometer Assembly

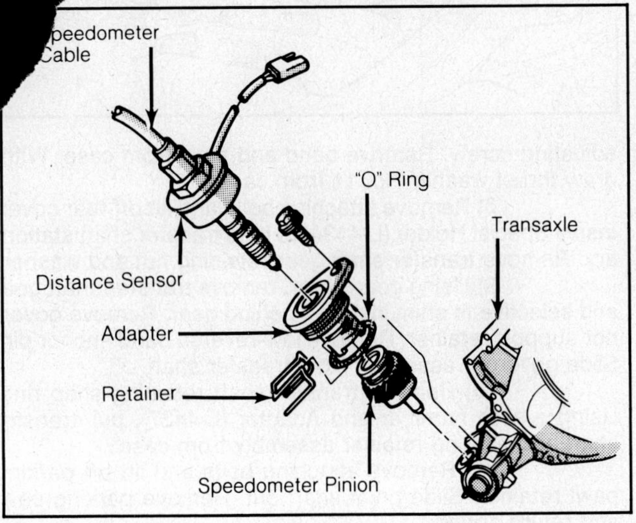

NEUTRAL SAFETY SWITCH

See appropriate AUTOMATIC TRANSMISSION SERVICING article in DOMESTIC GENERAL SERVICING section.

DRIVE AXLE SHAFTS

See appropriate DRIVE AXLE SHAFT article in DOMESTIC AXLE SHAFTS & TRANSFER CASES section.

REMOVAL & INSTALLATION

See appropriate AUTOMATIC TRANSMISSION REMOVAL article in DOMESTIC GENERAL SERVICING section.

TORQUE CONVERTER

The torque converter is a welded assembly and is not serviceable. Therefore, if a malfunction occurs or if the converter becomes contaminated with foreign material, it must be replaced. It cannot be flushed or repaired.

CHRYSLER CORP. A-413 & A-470 (Cont.)

TRANSAXLE DISASSEMBLY

INPUT SHAFT END PLAY

To check end play, attach a dial indicator to transaxle bellhousing with its plunger seated against end of input shaft. Move input shaft in and out to obtain end play reading. End play should be .008-.060" (.20-1.52 mm). Record end play reading for reassembly reference.

DISASSEMBLY

1) Place transaxle in a holding fixture. Remove attaching bolts and lift off transaxle oil pan. Remove screws and lift off oil filter and gasket. Remove neutral safety/back-up light switch.

2) Remove park rod "E" clip and remove park rod. Remove 7 valve body attaching bolts. Remove valve body from transaxle using care not to damage governor tubes.

Fig. 5: Removing Valve Body Assembly

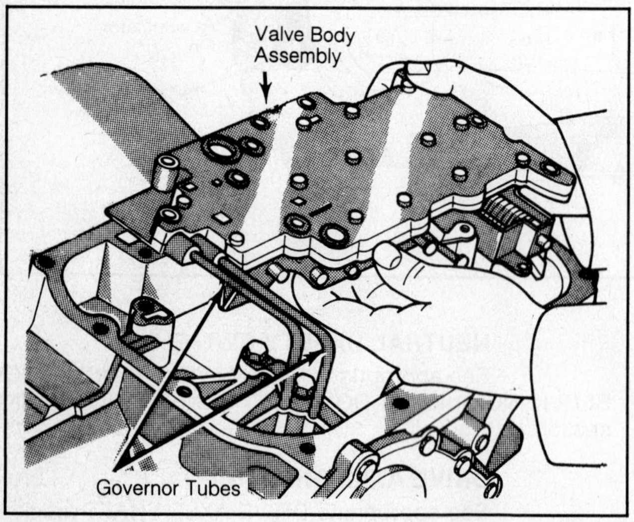

Use care when removing valve body to avoid damaging governor tubes.

3) Tighten kickdown band adjusting screw to retain parts when oil pump is removed. Remove oil pump attaching bolts. Using 2 slide hammer pullers, installed on opposite sides of pump, pull oil pump and No. 1 thrust washer from case. Loosen kickdown band adjusting screw.

4) Slide kickdown band and strut from case. Remove front clutch assembly. Slide rear clutch assembly out of case by pulling input shaft. Remove No. 2 thrust washer from input shaft and clutch drum.

5) Remove No. 3 thrust washer from end of output shaft. *See Fig. 6*. Remove snap ring retaining front planetary gear assembly in case. Slide out gear assembly.

6) Remove No. 6 thrust washer from sun gear driving shell, then slide out driving shell. Remove No. 9 thrust washer from rear planetary gear set. Remove gear set from case.

NOTE: No. 7 and No. 8 thrust washers are assembled with sun gear driving shell assembly.

7) Remove No. 10 thrust washer. Withdraw overrunning clutch cam assembly. Remove 8 overrunning clutch rollers and springs. Loosen low-reverse band adjusting screw. Remove band and strut from case. Withdraw thrust washer No. 11 from case.

Fig. 6: Removing No. 3 Thrust Washer

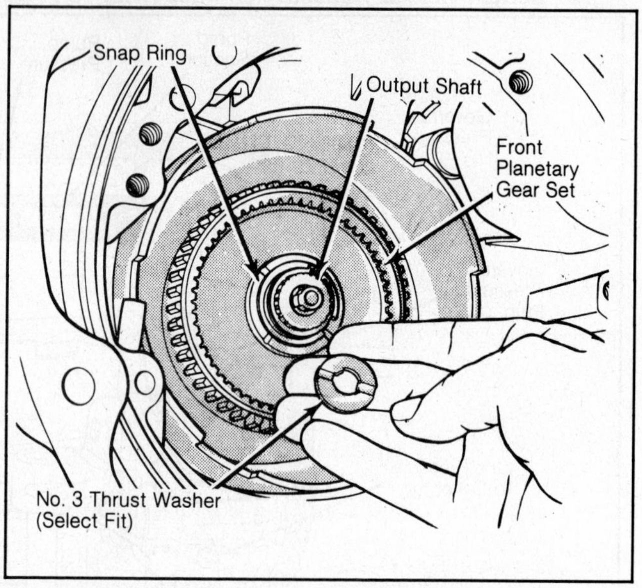

Fig. 7: Removing Overrunning Clutch Springs & Rollers

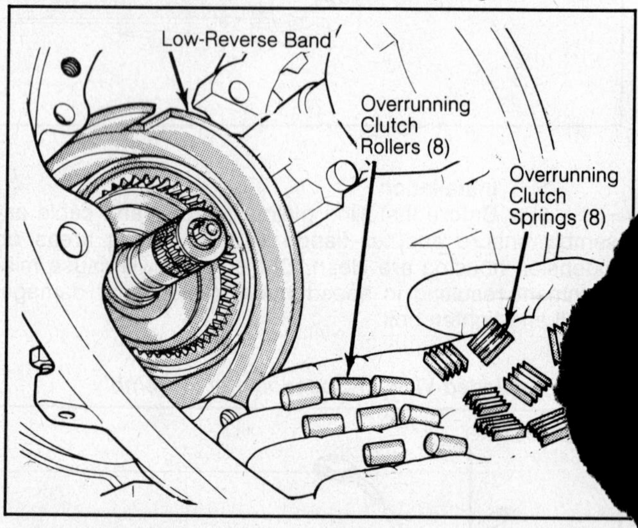

8) Remove attaching bolts and lift off rear cover. Install Special Holder (L-4434) to hold transfer shaft stationary. Remove transfer shaft gear retaining nut and washer.

9) Using gear puller, remove transfer shaft gear and selective fit shim installed behind gear. Remove governor support retainer. Remove low-reverse band anchor pin. Slide governor assembly from transfer shaft.

10) Remove transfer shaft retaining snap ring. Using a slide hammer and Adapter (L-4437), pull transfer shaft and bearing retainer assembly from case.

11) Remove attaching bolts and lift off parking pawl retainer. Slide pivot shaft out. Remove parking pawl and return spring.

12) Hold output shaft stationary with Holder (L-4434). Remove output shaft retaining nut and washer. Remove output shaft gear with puller. Slide out selective fit shim installed behind gear. From front of case slide out output shaft and annulus gear.

Fig. 8: Removing Parking Pawl & Pivot Shaft

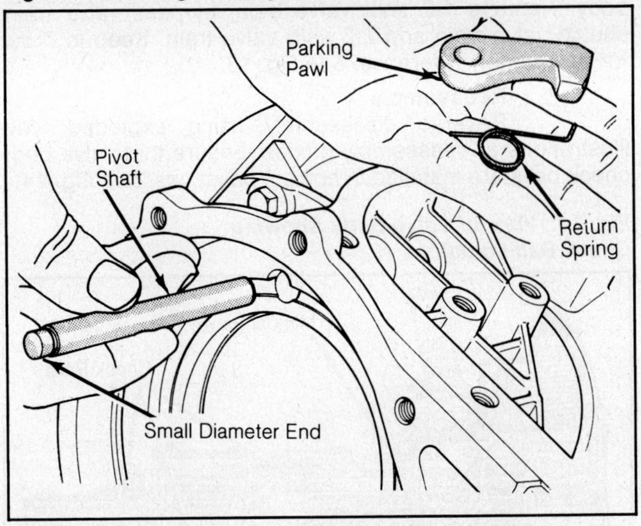

Pivot shaft is installed with small diameter to rear.

Fig. 9: Removing Differential Bearing Retainer

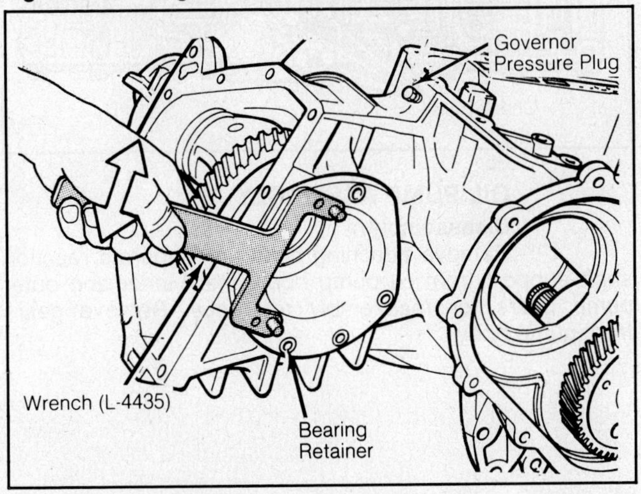

Rock wrench back and forth to remove retainer.

13) Using a screwdriver, pry oil seal out of extension housing. Remove attaching bolts and lift off differential cover.

14) Remove differential bearing retainer bolts. Rotate retainer back and forth with Wrench (L-4435) to remove.

15) Remove extension housing attaching bolts. Rotate housing back and forth to remove. Lift differential assembly out of transaxle case.

CAUTION: Hold on to differential assembly to prevent it from falling out of case when removing extension housing.

COMPONENT DISASSEMBLY & REASSEMBLY

VALVE BODY ASSEMBLY

NOTE: To simplify reassembly, place individual parts in correct order in relative position to valve body, as valve trains are removed from valve body bores.

1) Remove attaching screw and lift detent spring assembly from valve body. Remove 16 valve body screws, using Socket (L-4553). Lift separator plate and transfer plate from valve body, noting position of oil screen.

2) Note position of 8 valve body check balls for reassembly reference. Remove check balls from valve body.

3) Remove "E" clip and washer from end of throttle valve lever assembly. Slide manual valve lever assembly off throttle valve lever. Slide throttle valve lever assembly from valve body.

4) Remove manual valve from valve body. Remove pressure regulator and adjusting screw bracket attaching screws. Lift off bracket and adjusting screws. Slide out pressure regulator and manual control valve trains. *See Fig. 10.*

Fig. 10: Exploded View of Pressure Regulator & Manual Control Valves

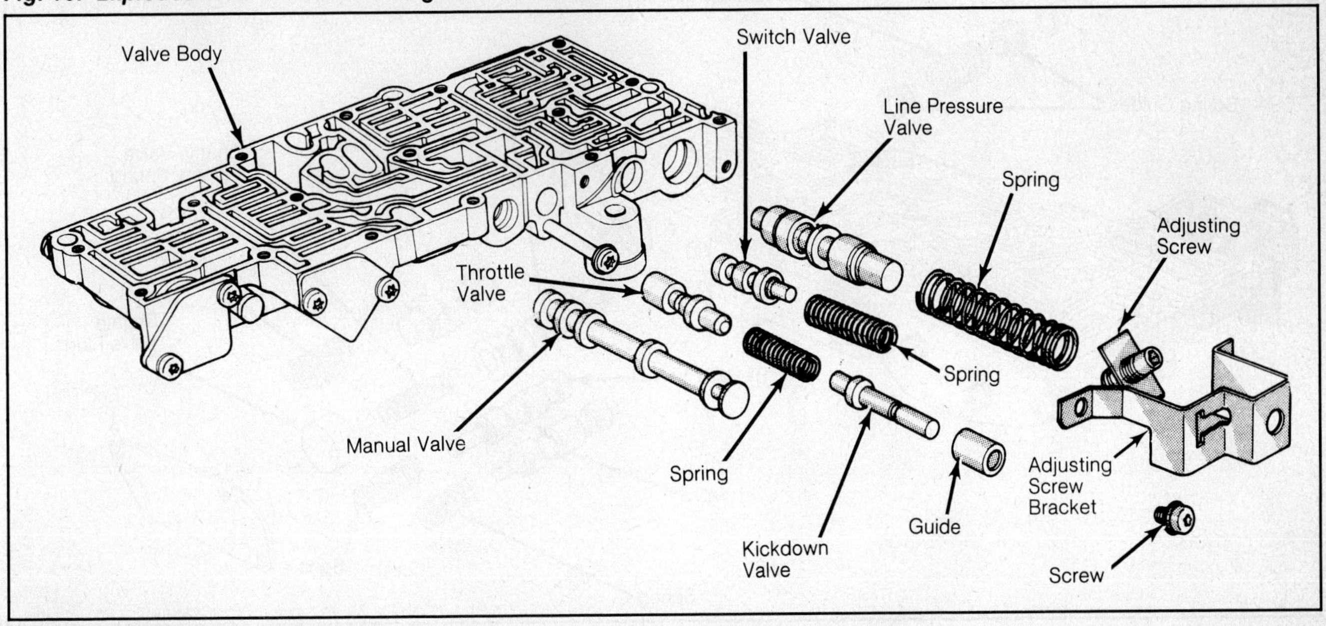

CHRYSLER CORP. A-413 & A-470 (Cont.)

5) Remove end plate and slide out 2-3 shift valve governor plug. Remove next end plate and slide out 1-2 shift valve governor plug. *See Fig. 11.*

Fig. 11: Exploded View of Governor Plugs

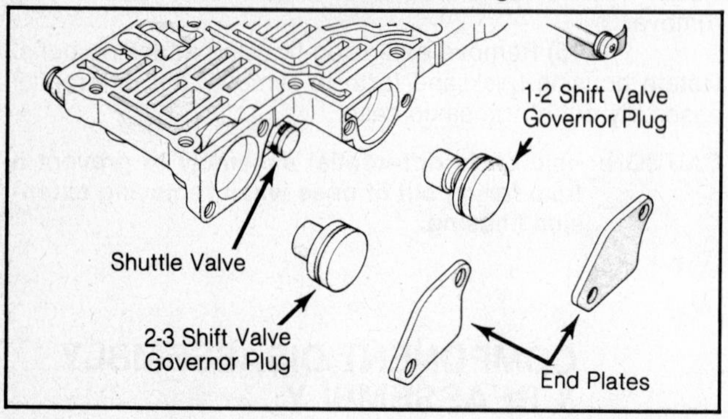

6) Remove end plate screws and carefully remove end plate. Remove regulator valve throttle pressure plug spring and regulator valve throttle pressure plug. *See Fig. 12.*

Fig. 12: Exploded View of Regulator Valve Throttle Pressure Plug Assembly

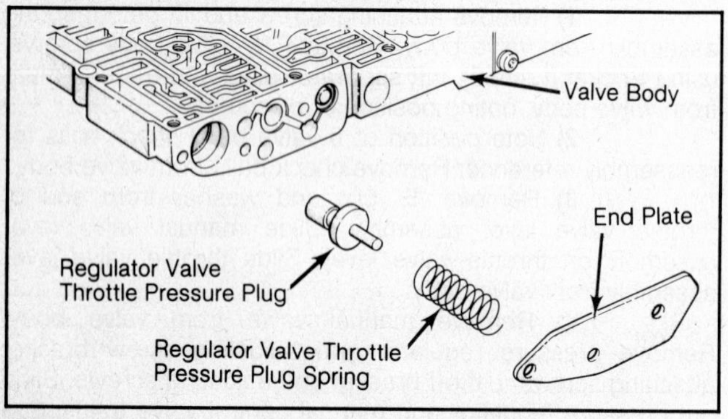

Remove end plate carefully to avoid losing spring.

Fig. 13: Exploded View of Shuttle Valve & Shift Valve Trains

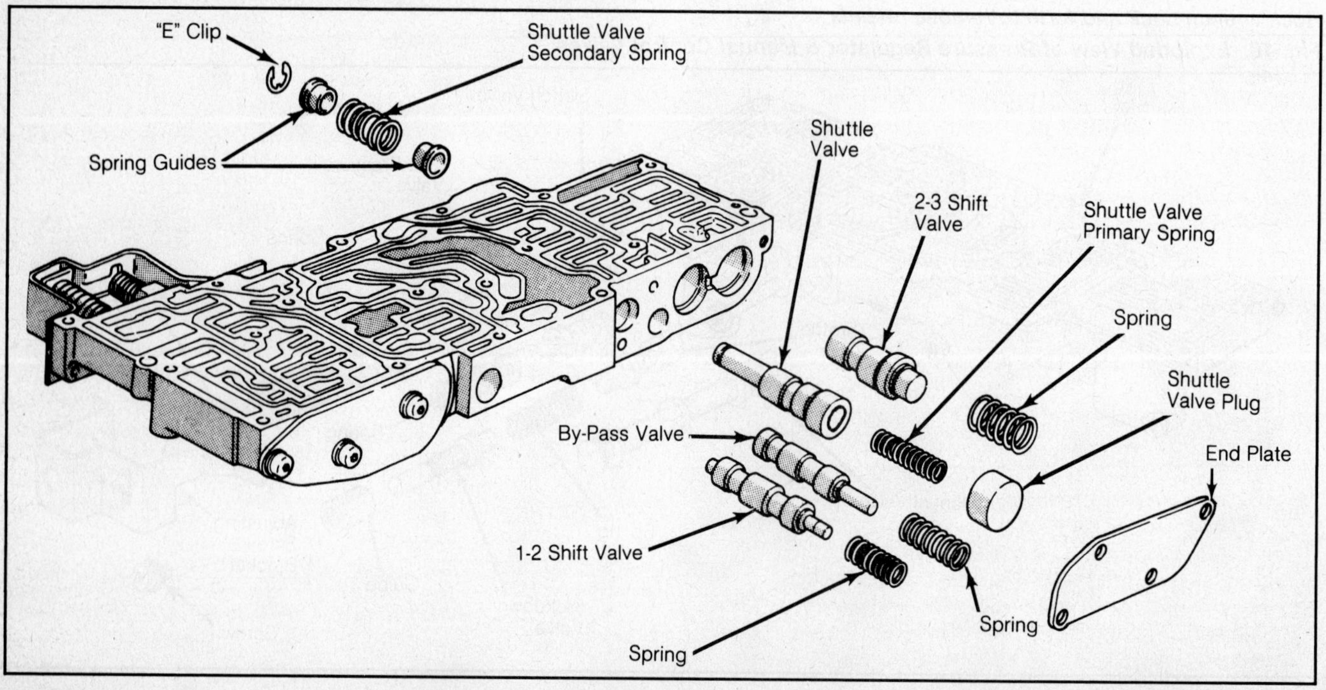

7) Remove remaining end plate from valve body. Remove 1-2 shift valve train, by-pass valve train, shuttle valve train and 2-3 shift valve train. Keep in order for reassembly reference. *See Fig. 13.*

Reassembly

Reverse disassembly using exploded view illustrations as reassembly guides. Ensure that valve body check balls are installed in correct passages. *See Fig. 14.*

Fig. 14: View of Valve Body Showing Check Ball Locations

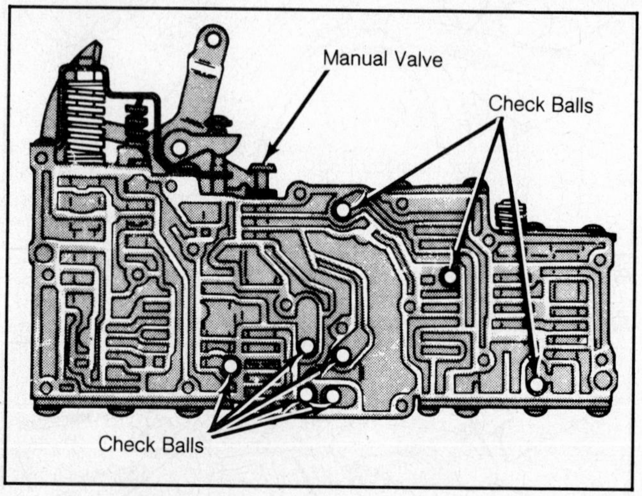

OIL PUMP ASSEMBLY

Disassembly

Remove attaching bolts and separate reaction shaft support from oil pump body. Mark inner and outer pump gears for reassembly reference. Remove gears from pump body.

OIL PUMP SPECIFICATIONS

Measurement	Clearance In. (mm)
Outer Gear-to-Pocket	.002-.006 (.045-.141)
Outer Gear I.D.-to-Crescent	.006-.012 (.150-.306)
Outer Gear Side Clearance	.001-.002 (.025-.050)
Inner Gear O.D.-to-Crescent	.006-.012 (.160-.316)
Inner Gear Side Clearance	.001-.002 (.025-.050)

Reassembly

1) Install inner and outer gears into pump body. Using feeler gauge, measure oil pump clearances indicated in OIL PUMP SPECIFICATIONS table.

2) If oil pump clearances are not within specifications, oil pump assembly should be replaced. After clearances have been measured, install reaction shaft support-to-pump body and install attaching bolts.

FRONT CLUTCH ASSEMBLY

Disassembly

1) Using a screwdriver, pry waved snap ring from clutch drum. Lift out reaction plate along with clutch plates and driving discs.

Fig. 15: Removing Front Clutch Return Spring Snap Ring

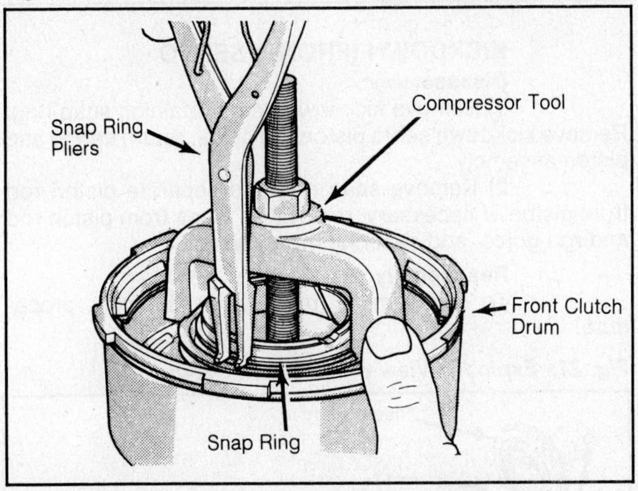

Fig. 16: Installing Front Clutch Plates & Driving Discs Into Clutch Drum

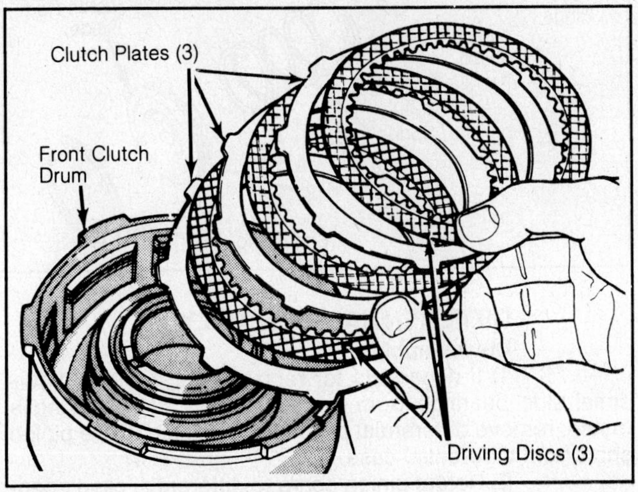

2) Compress clutch return spring and remove retaining snap ring. Remove compressor and lift out return spring retainer, return spring and clutch piston.

3) If necessary for replacement, remove lip seals from clutch piston and from inside of clutch drum.

Reassembly

1) Reverse disassembly procedure to assemble clutch, noting the following:

2) Install clutch plates (3) and driving discs (3) into clutch drum. With clutch plates and discs correctly installed, install reaction plate and retaining snap ring.

3) With front clutch assembly reassembled, use a feeler gauge to measure clearance from reaction plate to farthest wave on waved snap ring. Clearance should be .087-.133" (2.2-3.4 mm) on all models.

REAR CLUTCH ASSEMBLY

Disassembly

1) Pry selective snap ring from rear clutch drum. Lift out reaction plate, clutch plates, driving discs and pressure plate. Record number of clutch plates and driving discs for reassembly reference.

2) Pry piston spring waved snap ring from clutch drum. Remove piston spring and piston. If necessary, remove seals from piston. If necessary, remove input shaft snap ring from inside clutch drum. Press input shaft out of drum.

Fig. 17: Removing Rear Clutch Piston & Spring

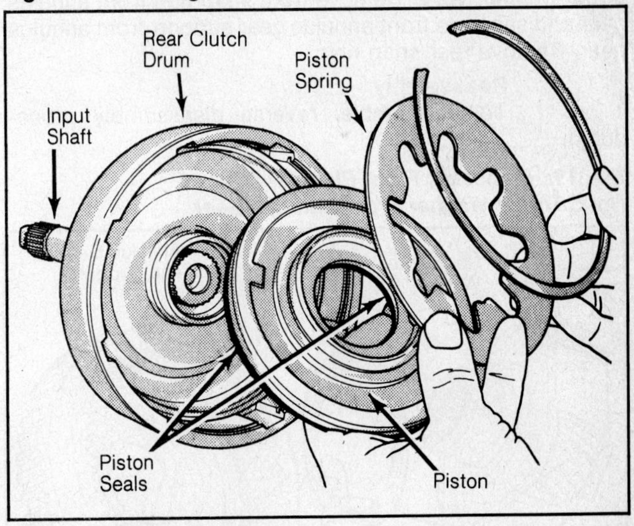

Reassembly

1) To reassemble, reverse disassembly procedure. Install clutch plates and driving discs into rear clutch drum. *See Fig. 18*.

2) With rear clutch reassembled, measure clearance between waved snap ring and reaction plate using a feeler gauge. Clearance should be .026-.043" (.67-1.10 mm), regardless of number of discs used.

3) If clearance is not to specification, install selective snap ring as required to obtain correct clearance. Snap rings are available in thicknesses of .048-.050" (1.22-1.27 mm), .060-.062" (1.52-1.57 mm), .068-.070" (1.73-1.78 mm), .074-.076" (1.88-1.93 mm) and .087-.089" (2.21-2.26 mm).

Fig. 18: Installing Clutch Plates & Driving Discs

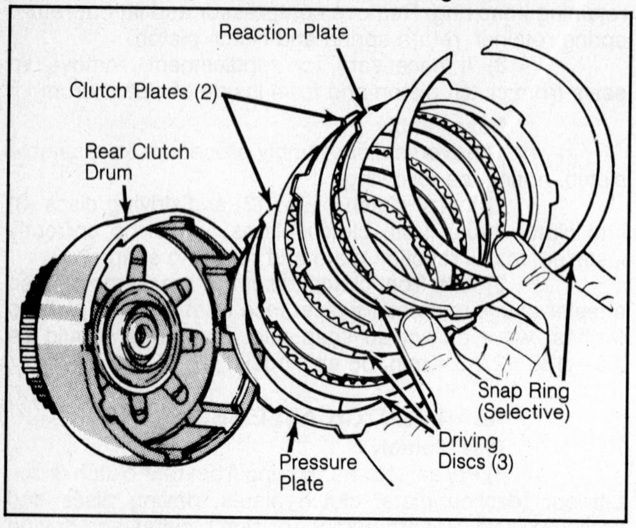

FRONT PLANETARY & ANNULUS GEAR

Disassembly

1) Remove snap ring retaining front planetary gear set in annulus gear. Remove thrust washer No. 4 which is located under snap ring.

2) Lift planetary gear from annulus gear. Lift out thrust washer No. 5. Remove front snap ring from annulus gear and separate front annulus gear support from annulus gear. Remove rear snap ring.

Reassembly

To reassemble, reverse disassembly procedure.

Fig. 19: Removing Front Planetary Gear & No. 5 Thrust Washer From Annulus Gear

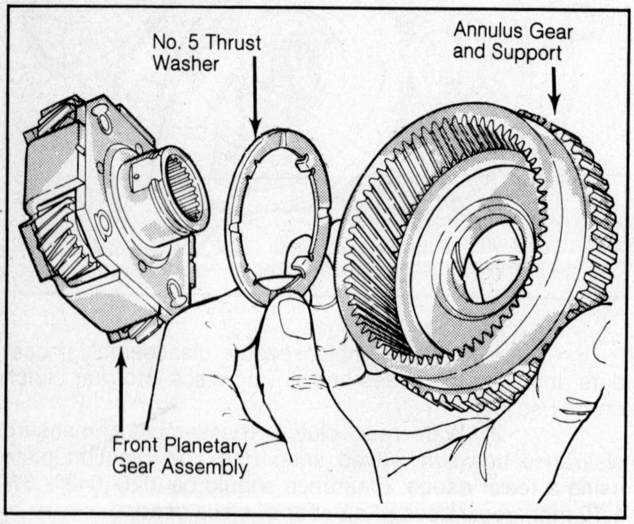

LOW-REVERSE SERVO

Disassembly & Reassembly

Remove servo retainer snap ring from servo bore in case. Lift out servo retainer, return spring and low-reverse servo assembly. Reverse disassembly procedure. Replace servo assembly lip seal if necessary.

ACCUMULATOR ASSEMBLY

Disassembly & Reassembly

Remove accumulator retaining snap ring. Lift accumulator plate from case bore. Withdraw accumulator spring and piston. If necessary, remove seal rings from piston. To reassemble, reverse disassembly procedure.

Fig. 20: Removing Accumulator Piston & Spring

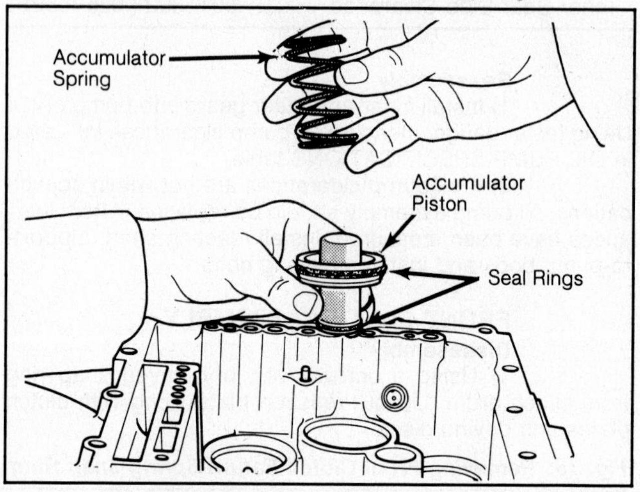

KICKDOWN (FRONT) SERVO

Disassembly

1) Remove kickdown servo retaining snap ring. Remove kickdown servo piston rod guide, return spring and piston assembly.

2) Remove snap ring and separate piston rod from piston. If necessary, remove "O" rings from piston rod and rod guide, and seal rings from piston.

Reassembly

To reassemble, reverse disassembly procedure.

Fig. 21: Exploded View of Kickdown Servo

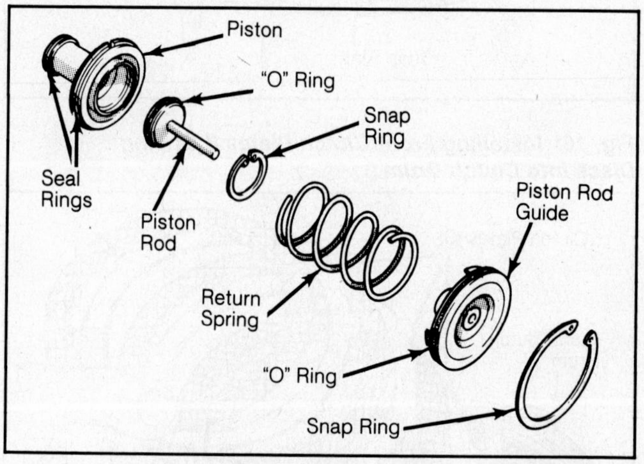

DIFFERENTIAL ASSEMBLY

Disassembly

1) If necessary for replacement, remove differential side bearings from carrier using a puller. Using a punch, remove differential pinion shaft roll pin. Drive pinion shaft from differential case.

2) Rotate pinion gears to differential case opening, then remove pinion gears, side gears and the 4 thrust washers. If necessary for replacement, remove ring gear attaching bolts. Press ring gear off differential case.

Reassembly

To reassemble, reverse disassembly procedure. Immerse ring gear in boiling water for 15 minutes before installing on differential case.

Fig. 22: Exploded View of Differential Gears, Thrust Washers & Pinion Shaft

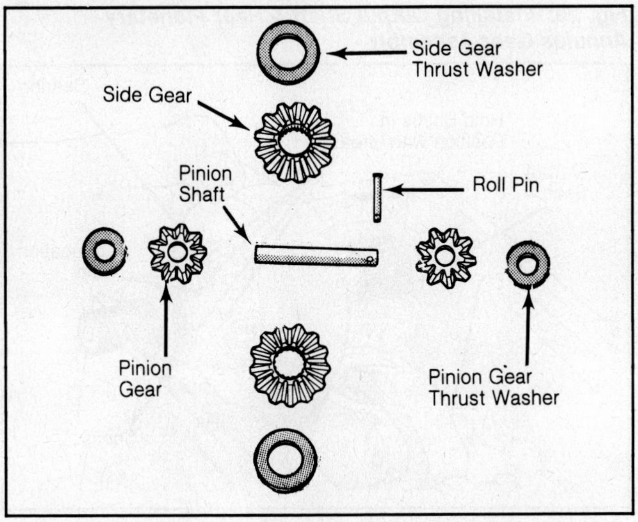

TRANSAXLE REASSEMBLY & ADJUSTMENT

DIFFERENTIAL ASSEMBLY

Differential bearing preload must be adjusted if any of the following components have been replaced:

- Transaxle Case
- Differential Carrier
- Differential Bearing Retainer
- Extension Housing
- Differential Bearings

If none of these parts are replaced, differential may be reassembled using the original adjusting shims.

1) Remove differential bearing outer race and preload adjusting shim from differential bearing retainer. If differential bearings have been replaced, also replace outer race in extension housing.

2) Install .020 (.50 mm) gauging shim in differential bearing retainer and reinstall bearing outer race. Install a new outer race in extension housing (if removed).

3) Position differential assembly in transaxle case. Install extension housing on case and tighten attaching bolts. Install differential bearing retainer and tighten attaching bolts.

4) Position transaxle assembly vertically in support stand and install Adapter (L-4436) into extension housing. Rotate differential at least one full turn to ensure tapered roller bearings are fully seated.

NOTE: **Adapter (L-4436) fits through extension housing and rests on pinion shaft.**

5) Attach dial indicator to case. *See Fig. 23.* Position indicator tip on end of adapter and zero dial indicator.

Fig. 23: Measuring Differential End Play

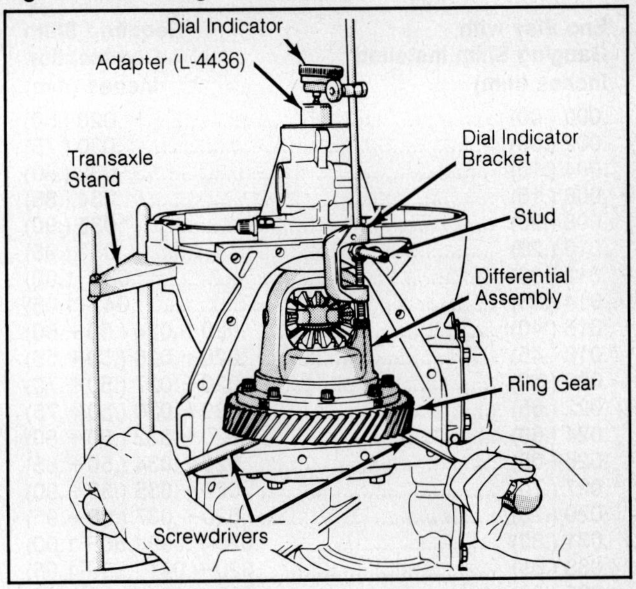

Lift ring gear with 2 large screwdrivers.

6) Place a large screwdriver under each side of ring gear and lift. Check dial indicator for amount of end play.

CAUTION: **Do not damage transaxle case or differential cover sealing surface when lifting ring gear.**

7) To determine shim combination required to obtain correct differential bearing preload, refer to DIFFERENTIAL BEARING SHIM CHART.

8) Remove differential bearing retainer. Remove differential bearing outer race and gauging shim from retainer. Install proper shim combination, as determined in step 7), under bearing race. Ensure oil baffle is installed properly in retainer, below bearing shims and race. Reinstall bearing retainer in case. Use RTV sealant between retainer and case.

9) To check adjustment, oil differential bearings. Insert Adapter (L-4436) through extension housing to engage differential assembly.

Fig. 24: Measuring Differential Turning Torque Usng Adapter (L-4436)

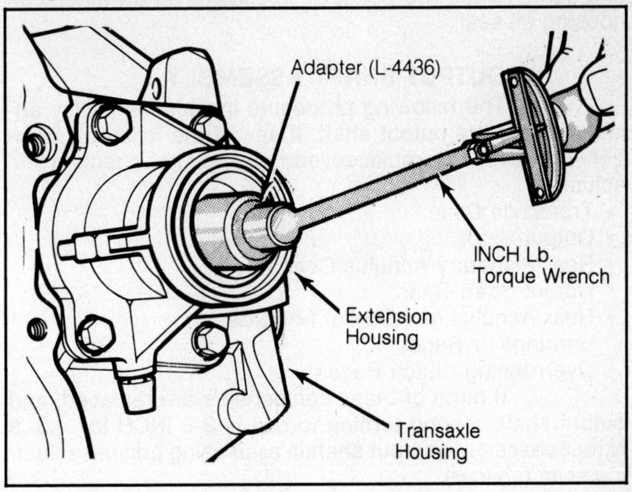

CHRYSLER CORP. A-413 & A-470 (Cont.)

DIFFERENTIAL BEARING SHIM CHART

End Play with Gauging Shim Installed Inches (mm)	Required Shim Combination Inches (mm)
.000 (.00)	[1] .020 (.50)
.002 (.05)	.030 (.75)
.004 (.10)	.032 (.80)
.006 (.15)	.034 (.85)
.008 (.20)	.035 (.90)
.010 (.25)	.037 (.95)
.012 (.30)	.039 (1.00)
.014 (.35)	.041 (1.05)
.016 (.40)	.020+.024 (.50+.60)
.018 (.45)	.020+.026 (.50+.65)
.020 (.50)	.020+.027 (.50+.70)
.022 (.55)	.020+.030 (.50+.75)
.024 (.60)	.020+.032 (.50+.80)
.026 (.65)	.020+.034 (.50+.85)
.027 (.70)	.020+.035 (.50+.90)
.029 (.75)	.020+.037 (.50+.95)
.031 (.80)	.020+.039 (.50+1.00)
.033 (.85)	.020+.041 (.50+1.05)
.035 (.90)	.039+.024 (1.00+.60)
.037 (.95)	.039+.026 (1.00+.65)
.039 (1.00)	.039+.027 (1.00+.70)
.041 (1.05)	.039+.030 (1.00+.75)
.043 (1.10)	.039+.032 (1.00+.80)
.045 (1.15)	.039+.034 (1.00+.85)
.047 (1.20)	.039+.035 (1.00+.90)
.049 (1.25)	.039+.037 (1.00+.95)
.051 (1.30)	.039+.039 (1.00+1.00)
.053 (1.35)	.039+.041 (1.00+1.05)
.055 (1.40)	.041+.041 (1.05+1.05)

[1] – Gauging shim.

10) Using an INCH lbs. torque wrench, check differential turning torque. Turning torque with differential bearing preload correctly adjusted should be 5-18 INCH lbs. (.55-2.0 N.m). If not, install a .002" (.05 mm) thinner shim to decrease torque or a .002" (.05 mm) thicker shim to increase torque.

11) When correct torque has been obtained, remove torque wrench, apply 1/8" bead of RTV sealant around differential cover and install cover on case. Install and tighten attaching bolts. Oil and install a new extension housing oil seal.

OUTPUT SHAFT ASSEMBLY

The following procedure includes end play adjustment for the output shaft. If any of the following components have been replaced, end play must be checked and adjusted.

- Transaxle Case
- Output Shaft
- Rear Planetary Annulus Gear
- Output Shaft Gear
- Rear Annulus and Output Shaft Gear Bearings or Races
- Overrunning Clutch Races

If none of these components are replaced, and output shaft bearing turning torque is 3-8 INCH lbs. (.3-.9 N.m), reassemble output shaft in case using original adjusting shim (spacer).

1) Install output shaft into transaxle case. Install .537" (13.65 mm) and .053" (1.34 mm) gauging shims on planetary rear annulus gear hub using grease to hold shims in place.

NOTE: The .537" (13.65 mm) gauging shim has a larger inside diameter and must be installed over output shaft first. The .053" (1.34 mm) shim pilots on the output shaft.

Fig. 25: Installing Output Shaft & Rear Planetary Annulus Gear Assembly

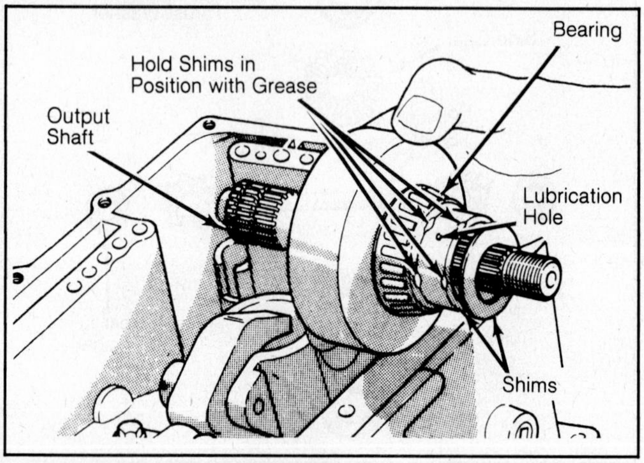

OUTPUT SHAFT BEARING SHIM CHART

End Play with Gauging Shims Installed Inches (mm)	Required Shim Combination Inches (mm)
.000 (.00)	[1] .537+.053 (13.65+1.34)
.002 (.05)	.537+.049 (13.65+1.24)
.004 (.10)	.537+.047 (13.65+1.19)
.006 (.15)	.537+.045 (13.65+1.14)
.008 (.20)	.537+.043 (13.65+1.09)
.010 (.25)	.537+.041 (13.65+1.04)
.012 (.30)	.537+.039 (13.65+.99)
.014 (.35)	.537+.037 (13.65+.94)
.016 (.40)	.518+.055 (13.15+1.39)
.018 (.45)	.518+.053 (13.15+1.34)
.020 (.50)	.518+.051 (13.15+1.29)
.022 (.55)	.518+.049 (13.15+1.24)
.024 (.60)	.518+.047 (13.15+1.19)
.026 (.65)	.518+.045 (13.15+1.14)
.028 (.70)	.518+.043 (13.15+1.09)
.030 (.75)	.518+.041 (13.15+1.04)
.032 (.80)	.518+.039 (13.15+.99)
.034 (.85)	.518+.037 (13.15+.94)
.036 (.90)	.498+.055 (12.65+1.39)
.038 (.95)	.498+.053 (12.65+1.34)
.040 (1.00)	.498+.051 (12.65+1.29)
.042 (1.05)	.498+.049 (12.65+1.24)
.044 (1.10)	.498+.047 (12.65+1.19)
.046 (1.15)	.498+.045 (12.65+1.14)
.048 (1.20)	.498+.043 (12.65+1.09)
.049 (1.25)	.498+.041 (12.65+1.04)
.051 (1.30)	.498+.039 (12.65+.99)
.053 (1.35)	.498+.037 (12.65+.94)

[1] – Gauging shims.

2) Place output shaft gear in position on output shaft. Install washer and retaining nut. Hold output shaft stationary and tighten retaining nut to 200 ft. lbs. (271 N.m).

3) Attach Holder (L-4432) to output shaft gear. Mount a steel ball into end of output shaft and retain in place with grease. Push and pull gear while rotating back and forth to ensure seating of roller bearings. Attach a dial indicator to case and position plunger against steel ball.

4) Move output shaft in and out and measure end play. Refer to OUTPUT SHAFT BEARING SHIM CHART to determine required shim combination.

NOTE: **The .537" (13.65 mm), .518" (13.15 mm) and .498" (12.65 mm) shims are always installed first. These shims have lubrication slots which are necessary for proper bearing lubrication.**

5) With proper shim combination determined, remove output shaft gear from case. Remove gauging shims from annulus gear hub and install correct shims. Hold shims in place with grease. Reinstall output shaft gear and tighten retaining nut.

6) Using an INCH lb. torque wrench, check output shaft bearing turning torque. Turning torque should be 3-8 INCH lbs. (.3-.9 N.m). If torque is not within limits, correct by changing shim thickness in increments of .002" (.05 mm). To reduce torque, increase total shim thickness. To increase torque, decrease shim thickness.

TRANSFER SHAFT, GOVERNOR & PARKING PAWL ASSEMBLIES

1) Position parking pawl and return spring in place in transaxle case. Slide parking pawl pivot shaft (small diameter to rear) through case bore and into parking pawl and spring. Install parking pawl retainer and tighten attaching bolts.

2) If necessary for replacement, install new oil seal and "O" rings on transfer shaft bearing retainer. Slide retainer onto transfer shaft.

3) Using Installer (L-4512), install transfer shaft into transaxle case. Install transfer shaft bearing retainer snap ring. Snap ring must be fully seated in groove in case.

Fig. 26: Installing Transfer Shaft Into Case Using Installer (L-4512)

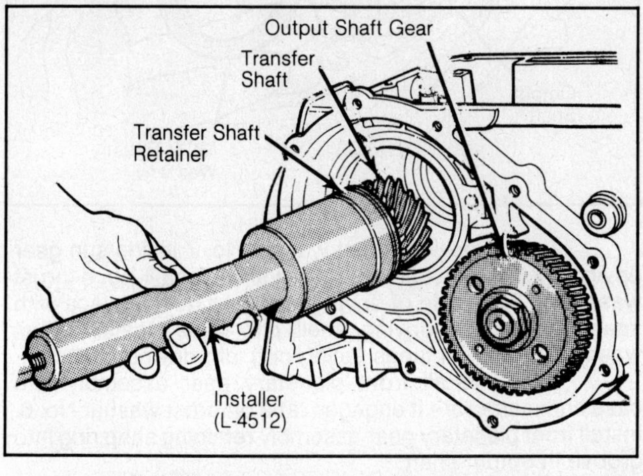

4) Slide governor assembly onto transfer shaft. Install low-reverse band anchor pin into bore in transaxle case. Install governor support retainer.

Fig. 27: Installing Governor Support Retainer

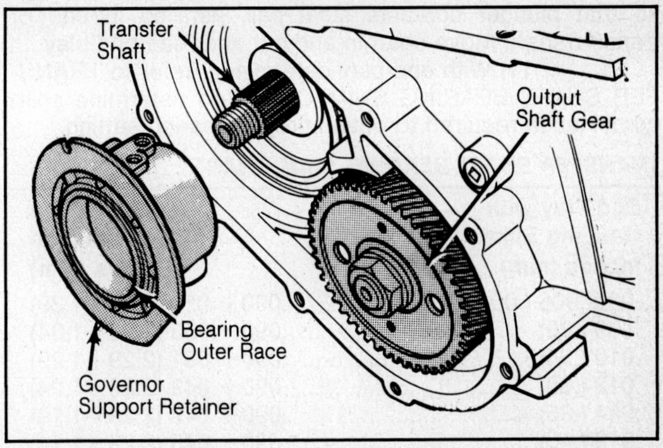

5) If one or more of the following components have been replaced, transfer shaft end play must be measured and adjusted:

- Transaxle Case
- Transfer Shaft
- Transfer Shaft Gear
- Transfer Shaft Bearings
- Governor Support Retainer
- Transfer Shaft Bearing Retainer
- Retainer Snap Ring
- Governor Support

6) If none of these components are replaced, skip steps **7)** through **12)** and reassemble transfer shaft assembly using original adjusting shims. *See Fig. 28* for location of shim.

7) Install .090" (229 mm) and .055" (1.39 mm) gauging shims on transfer shaft, behind governor support. Install transfer shaft gear and bearing assembly.

8) Hold transfer shaft stationary with holder. Install gear retaining nut and washer. Tighten nut to 200 ft. lbs. (271 N.m).

9) With holder installed, mount a steel ball into end of transfer shaft and hold in place with grease. Push and pull transfer shaft gear while rotating back and forth to ensure seating of bearings.

Fig. 28: View of Transfer Shaft With Gear Removed Showing Location of Adjusting Shim

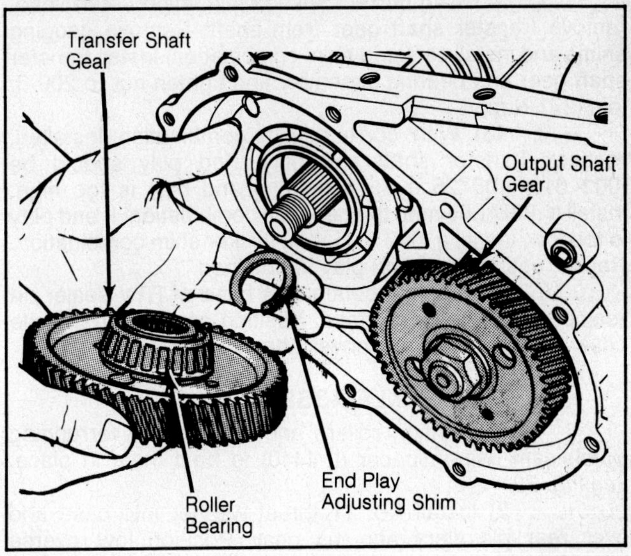

CHRYSLER CORP. A-413 & A-470 (Cont.)

10) Attach a dial indicator to case and position so that plunger contacts steel ball installed in end of transfer shaft. Move shaft in and out and read end play.

11) With end play determined, refer to TRANSFER SHAFT BEARING SHIM CHART to determine shim combination required to obtain proper bearing setting.

TRANSFER SHAFT BEARING SHIM CHART

End Play with Gauging Shims Installed Inches (mm)	Required Shim Combination Inches (mm)
.000-.006 (.00-.15)	[1] .090+.055 (2.29+1.39)
.008 (.20)	.090+.053 (2.29+1.34)
.010 (.25)	.090+.051 (2.29+1.29)
.012 (.30)	.090+.049 (2.29+1.24)
.014 (.35)	.090+.047 (2.29+1.19)
.016 (.40)	.090+.045 (2.29+1.14)
.018 (.45)	.090+.043 (2.29+1.09)
.020 (.50)	.090+.041 (2.29+1.04)
.022 (.55)	.090+.039 (2.29+.99)
.024 (.60)	.072+.055 (1.84+1.39)
.026 (.65)	.072+.053 (1.84+1.34)
.028 (.70)	.072+.051 (1.84+1.29)
.030 (.75)	.072+.049 (1.84+1.24)
.032 (.80)	.072+.047 (1.84+1.19)
.034 (.85)	.072+.045 (1.84+1.14)
.036 (.90)	.072+.043 (1.84+1.09)
.038 (.95)	.072+.041 (1.84+1.04)
.040 (1.00)	.072+.039 (1.84+.99)
.042 (1.05)	.055+.055 (1.39+1.39)
.044 (1.10)	.055+.053 (1.39+1.34)
.046 (1.15)	.055+.051 (1.39+1.29)
.048 (1.20)	.055+.049 (1.39+1.24)
.049 (1.25)	.055+.047 (1.39+1.19)
.050 (1.30)	.055+.045 (1.39+1.14)
.052 (1.35)	.055+.043 (1.39+1.09)
.055 (1.40)	.055+.041 (1.39+1.04)
.057 (1.45)	.055+.039 (1.39+.99)
.059 (1.50)	.037+.055 (.94+1.39)
.061 (1.55)	.037+.053 (.94+1.34)
.063 (1.60)	.037+.051 (.94+1.29)

[1] – Gauging shims.

12) With correct shim combination determined, remove transfer shaft gear from shaft. Remove gauging shims and install selected shim combination. Install transfer shaft gear and bearing assembly and tighten nut to 200 ft. lbs. (271 N.m).

13) With correct shim combination installed, recheck transfer shaft end play. End play should be .002-.010" (.05-.25 mm). If bearing end play is too high, install a .002" (.05 mm) thinner shim combination. If end play is too low, install a .002" (.05 mm) thicker shim combination. Repeat until correct end play is obtained.

14) Apply a continuous bead of RTV sealer on rear cover mounting surface. Position cover on transaxle case. Install and tighten cover attaching bolts.

TRANSAXLE ASSEMBLY

1) Position rollers and springs in overrunning clutch cam using Spacer (L-4440) to hold them in place. *See Fig. 29.*

2) Install No. 11 thrust washer into case and over rear planetary annulus gear. Position low-reverse band around annulus gear in case. Install band strut.

Fig. 29: Installing Rollers & Springs in Overrunning Clutch Cam Assembly

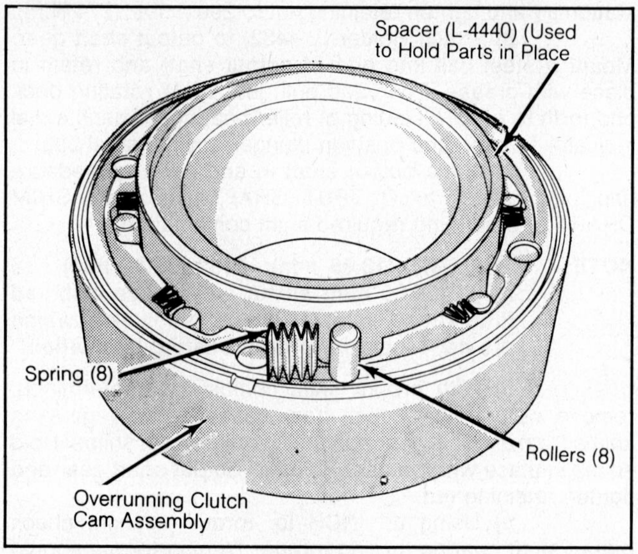

3) Install overrunning clutch cam assembly (Spacer L-4440 installed) into case and remove spacer. Install thrust washer No. 10 (with tangs facing out) into position in rear planetary annulus gear.

4) Install rear planetary gear assembly into rear annulus gear. Install thrust washer No. 9 into case and ensure tabs on washer engage slots in planetary assembly.

Fig. 30: Installed View of Rear Planetary Assembly

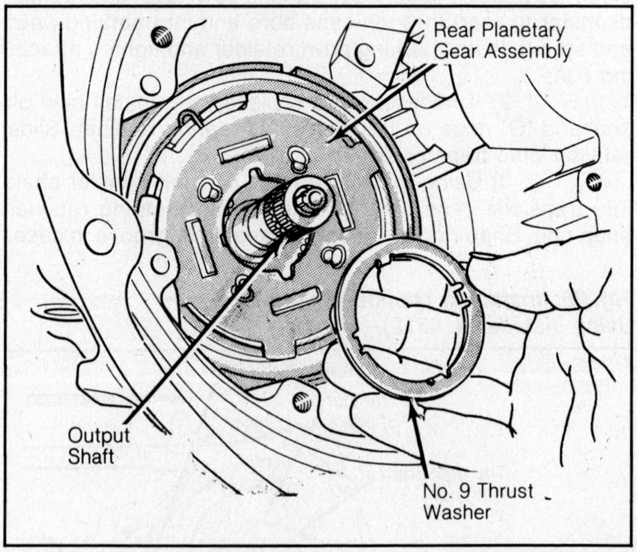

5) Position thrust washer No. 7 inside sun gear driving shell and install sun gear in shell. Install No. 8 thrust washer on back side of driving shell and hold in place with snap ring. Install driving shell into case. Install thrust washer No. 6 (with tangs facing out) into driving shell.

6) Install front planetary gear assembly into case and make sure it engages tabs of thrust washer No. 6. Install front planetary gear assembly retaining snap ring into groove in output shaft.

7) Slide thrust washer No. 3 onto end of output shaft. Position thrust washer No. 2 in rear clutch drum. Install rear clutch/input shaft assembly in case.

CHRYSLER CORP. A-413 & A-470 (Cont.)

Fig. 31: Installing Front Planetary Gear Assembly Retaining Snap Ring

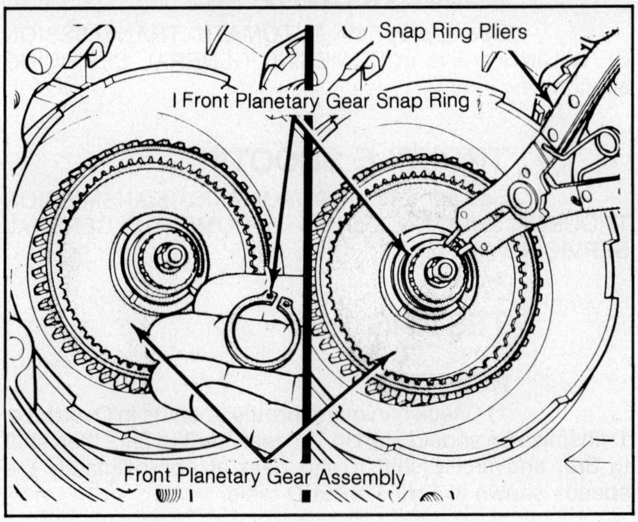

CAUTION: No. 3 thrust washer controls input shaft end play. Refer to INPUT SHAFT END PLAY in this article. If necessary, install a new thrust washer of correct thickness.

8) Install front clutch assembly in case. Ensure tabs on front clutch drum engage slots in rear clutch drum.

9) Position kickdown (front) band in place on front clutch drum. Install band strut. Tighten kickdown band adjusting screw just enough to hold parts in place.

10) Install oil pump gasket in case. Ensure oil holes in gasket align with holes in case. Install oil pump assembly and No. 1 thrust washer in case. Use NEW bolts when installing pump.

NOTE: Input shaft end play should be rechecked to ensure correct No. 3 thrust washer has been installed.

11) If necessary, remove oil pump seal using Seal Remover (C-3981). *See Fig. 32*. Drive new seal (seal lip facing inward) into oil pump until it is fully seated.

Fig. 32: Removing Oil Pump Seal

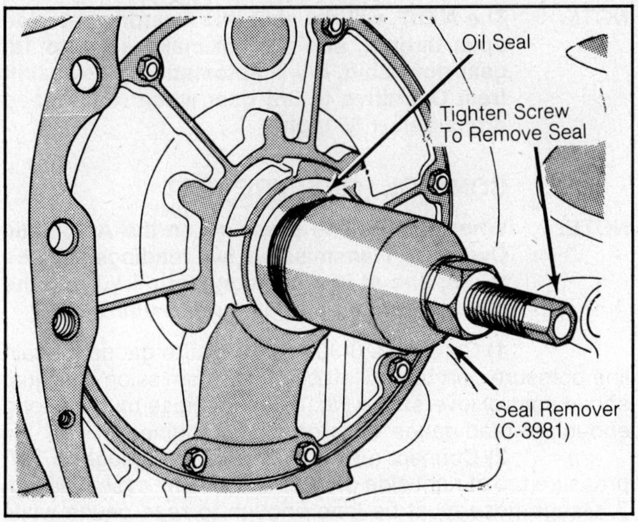

12) Carefully install valve body in case while guiding governor tubes into position. Install valve body attaching bolts. Tighten bolts alternately and evenly.

13) Install park rod into case and secure to throttle valve lever with "E" clip. Install neutral safety/back-up light switch. Install oil filter on valve body and tighten attaching screws. Install oil pan on case using only RTV sealer.

THRUST WASHER CHART

Thrust Washer (No.)	Thickness In. (mm)
Reaction Shaft Support (1)	.061-.063 (1.55-1.60)
Rear Clutch Retainer (2)	.061-.063 (1.55-1.60)
Output Shaft - Selective (3)	.077-.080 (1.98-2.03)
	.085-.087 (2.15-2.22)
	.092-.095 (2.34-2.41)
Front Annulus (4)	.116-.120 (2.95-3.05)
Front Carrier (5 & 6)	.048-.050 (1.22-1.28)
Sun Gear (7 & 8)	.033-.036 (.85-.91)
Rear Carrier (9 & 10)	.048-.050 (1.22-1.28)
Reverse Drum (11)	.061-.063 (1.55-1.60)

TIGHTENING SPECIFICATIONS

Application	Ft. Lbs. (N.m)
Converter-to-Drive Plate Bolt	55 (75)
Differential Bearing Retainer-to-Case Bolt	21 (28)
Drive Plate-to-Crankshaft Bolt	70 (95)
Extension Housing-to-Case Bolt	21 (28)
Front Mount-to-Engine Bolt	21 (28)
Governor Counterweight Screw	21 (28)
Kickdown (Front) Band Adjusting Screw Lock Nut	35 (47)
Neutral Safety Switch	25 (34)
Oil Pump-to-Case Bolts	23 (31)
Output Shaft Gear Nut	200 (271)
Reaction Shaft Bolt	21 (28)
Ring Gear-to-Carrier Bolt	70 (95)
Side Mount-to-Engine Bolt	40 (54)
Starter-to-Bellhousing Bolt	40 (54)
Transaxle-to-Engine Bolt	70 (95)
Transfer Shaft Gear Nut	200 (271)
Valve Body Sprag Retainer-to-Case Bolt	21 (28)
	INCH Lbs. (N.m)
Bellhousing Cover Bolts	105 (12)
Differential Cover-to-Case Bolt	165 (19)
Governor-to-Support Bolt	60 (7)
Oil Pan-to-Case Bolt	165 (19)
Rear Cover-to-Case Bolt	165 (19)
Reverse Band Shaft Plug	60 (70
Speedometer Pinion Retaining Bolt	60 (7)
Valve Body	
Attaching Bolts	40 (5)
Oil Filter Screws	40 (5)
Transfer Plate Screws	40 (5)
Transfer Plate to-Case Bolt	105 (12)

Automatic Transmissions
FORD MOTOR CO. AOT

Capri, Continental, Cougar, Crown Victoria, Grand Marquis, LTD, Mark VII, Marquis, Mustang, Thunderbird, Town Car, E150/250, F150/250, Bronco

IDENTIFICATION

The Automatic Overdrive Transmission (A.O.T.) is identified by the code letter "T". The identification code letter is found on the lower line of Vehicle Certification Label under "TR". This label is attached to the left (driver's) side door lock post.

The transmission model may be identified by a metal tag attached to transmission by the lower extension housing retaining bolt. Top line of tag shows transmission Model Number and Line Shift Code. Bottom line on tag shows the Build Date Code. *See Fig. 1.*

Fig. 1: Service Identification Tag

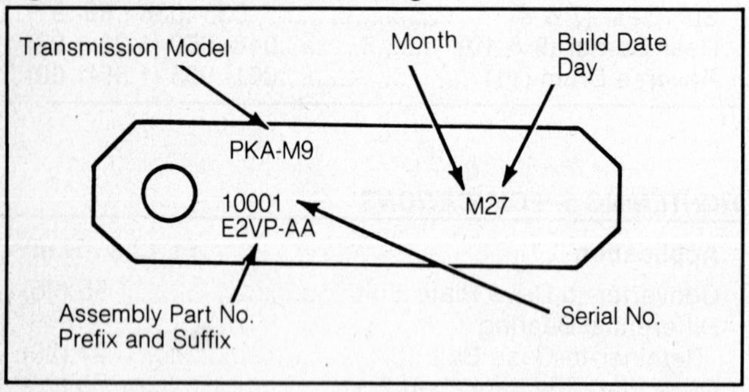

DESCRIPTION

The Automatic Overdrive Transmission (A.O.T.) is a 4-speed, fully automatic transmission which combines automatic shifting with two fuel saving features: An overdrive gear ratio and mechanical lock-out split torque path in 3rd gear. In this range, 40% of the torque is transmitted hydraulically through the torque converter as in conventional automatic transmissions while the remaining 60% of engine torque is transmitted mechanically.

The torque converter operation is similar to other automatics, but has an added damper assembly and an input shaft which is used in 3rd (direct drive) and overdrive gears.

Overdrive is accomplished by band application which locks the reverse sun gear while driving the planet carrier. In this ratio, engine torque flows through the damper assembly and in doing so, by-passes the torque converter. Power flow from the engine into the transmission is then direct.

Transmission consists basically of the torque converter assembly, 4 multi-disc clutches, 2 bands, 2 one-way roller clutches, and a hydraulic control system. The hydraulic system differs from that on other Ford automatic transmissions in that the vacuum diaphragm that is normally used for the "engine load" input has been eliminated. In place of this vacuum device, mechanical linkage is employed from the carburetor to the transmission. As a result, throttle (T.V.) fluid pressure is controlled mechanically rather than by vacuum.

LUBRICATION & ADJUSTMENTS

See appropriate AUTOMATIC TRANSMISSION SERVICING article in DOMESTIC GENERAL SERVICING section.

TROUBLE SHOOTING

See appropriate AUTOMATIC TRANSMISSION TROUBLE SHOOTING article in DOMESTIC GENERAL SERVICING section.

TESTING

ROAD TEST

1) Check minimum throttle upshifts in Overdrive. Transmission should start in 1st gear, shift to 2nd, then shift to 3rd, and finally shift to 4th gear at approximately the speeds shown in SHIFT SPEED table.

NOTE: Choke must be "OFF" when checking minimum throttle upshifts. If not, shift points will be affected.

2) With transmission in 4th gear (overdrive), depress accelerator pedal to the floor. Transmission should downshift to 3rd or to 2nd gear, depending on vehicle speed. See SHIFT SPEED table.

3) Since closed throttle downshifts are extremely difficult to detect, it may be necessary to attach 0-100 psi pressure gauges to forward and direct clutch pressure taps in order to detect O/D to 3rd gear and 3rd to 2nd gear coast downshifts. *See Fig. 3.*

4) With gauges attached, a 4th to 3rd gear coast (closed throttle) downshift is signified by the application of the forward clutch (pressure reading will increase from 0 to 60 psi), and 3rd to 2nd gear coast downshift is signified by the release of the direct clutch (pressure reading will decrease from 60 to 0 psi). See SHIFT SPEED table. A 2nd to 1st gear downshift should not be felt.

5) When selector lever is moved from either Overdrive or Drive ranges to "1" position, transmission should downshift into 2nd gear if vehicle speed is above 25 MPH, and into 1st gear if speed is less than 25 MPH.

NOTE: The A.O.T. will not shift into Overdrive at wide open throttle, and will not make a 4th to 1st gear downshift. It will automatically downshift from Overdrive to 3rd gear when road speed drops below 35 mph.

CONTROL PRESSURE TEST

NOTE: When testing line pressure on the Automatic Overdrive Transmission, two readings must be taken; one at idle position (zero T.V.) and the other at wide open, full throttle (full T.V.).

1) Connect a 0-300 psi pressure gauge to main line pressure port tap on left side of transmission case just above control levers. *See Fig. 3*. Gauge hose must be long enough to read gauge while operating engine.

2) Connect a 0-100 psi pressure gauge to T.V. pressure tap at right side of the transmission case. *See Fig. 3*. Gauge hose must be long enough to read gauge while operating engine.

Fig. 2: Cross-Sectional View of Automatic Overdrive Transmission

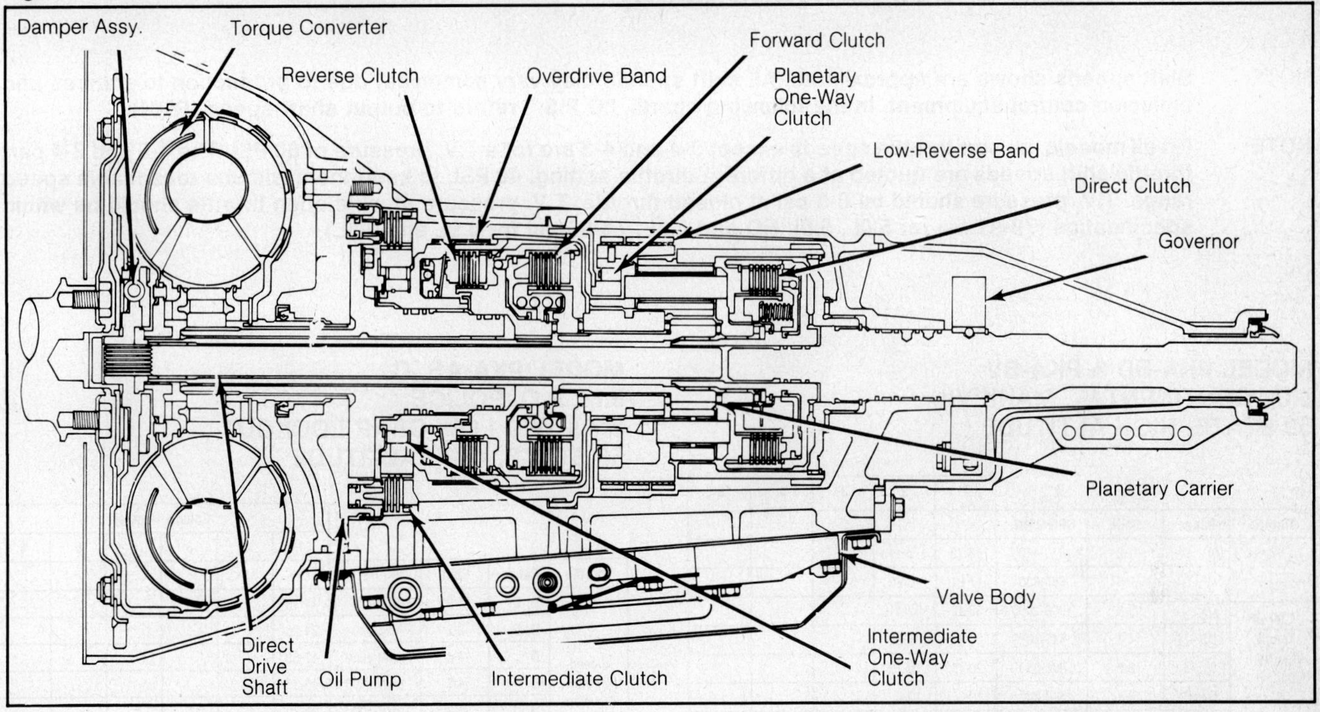

3) Ensure T.V. linkage is properly adjusted.

CAUTION: Pressure gauges affect the shift quality of the transmission. Do not accelerate or decelerate rapidly. Possible transmission failure could result.

4) With engine at normal operating temperature, apply parking and service brakes. Check line pressure and throttle pressure in all ranges. Pressures should be approximately as specified. See CONTROL PRESSURE SPECIFICATIONS table.

NOTE: Pressure test at idle position must be taken with throttle off fast idle cam. Pressure test at wide open throttle position should be taken at full stall conditions. Run engine at a fast idle in Neutral for cooling between tests.

CONTROL PRESSURE TEST RESULTS

Low in "P"
Faulty valve body or low-reverse servo.

Low in "R"
Faulty reverse clutch or low-reverse servo.

CLUTCH AND BAND APPLICATION CHART (ELEMENTS IN USE)

Selector Lever Position	Intermed. Clutch	Intermed. One-Way Clutch	Overdrive Band	Reverse Clutch	Forward Clutch	Planetary One-Way Clutch	Low-Reverse Band	Direct Clutch
O/D — OVERDRIVE								
First Gear					X	X		
Second Gear	X	X			X			
Third Gear	X				X			X
Fourth Gear	X		X					X
3 — OVERDRIVE LOCKOUT								
First Gear					X	X		
Second Gear	X	X			X			
Third Gear	X				X			X
1 — LOW								
First Gear					X	X	X	
Second Gear	X	X	X		X			
R — REVERSE				X			X	

NEUTRAL — All clutches and bands released and/or ineffective.

Automatic Transmissions
FORD MOTOR CO. AOT (Cont.)

SHIFT SPEED SPECIFICATIONS (MPH)

NOTE: Shift speeds shown are approximate. All shift speeds may vary somewhat due to production tolerances and emission control equipment. In the following charts, "O.P.S." refers to output shaft speed (RPM).

NOTE: On all models, all part throttle speeds except 3-4 and 4-3 are for a T.V. pressure of 60 PSI. The 4-3 and 3-4 part throttle shift speeds are quoted at a different throttle setting, 40 PSI, to keep them within a reasonable speed range. T.V. pressure should be 0-5 psi at closed throttle. T.V. pressure at wide open throttle should be within specification (79-91 psi for 5.0L, 5.0L HO and 5.8L, 74-86 psi for 4.9L and 3.8L).

MODEL PKA-BD & PKA-BV
5.0L CONTINENTAL, MARK VII
50 STATE, HIGH ALTITUDE

Throttle	Range	Shift	OPS-R.P.M.	1	2	3	4	5
Closed Throttle See Note	Ⓓ, D	1-2	310-460	8-12	7-11			
	Ⓓ, D	2-3	680-830	17-21	16-20			
	Ⓓ	3-4	1300-1680	32-42	32-41			
	Ⓓ	4-3	1440-1060	36-27	35-26			
	Ⓓ, D	3-2	800-600	20-15	19-15			
	Ⓓ, D	2-1	410-240	10-6	10-6			
	1	3-1, 2-1	1110-730	28-18	27-18			
Part Throttle See Note	Ⓓ, D	1-2	670-1020	17-26	16-25			
	Ⓓ, D	2-3	1330-1710	33-43	32-42			
	Ⓓ	3-4	1600-2210	40-56	39-54			
	Ⓓ	4-3	1600-1200	40-30	39-29			
	Ⓓ, D	3-2	1440-1020	36-26	35-25			
	Ⓓ, D	2-1	690-480	17-12	17-12			
Wide Open See Note	Ⓓ, D	1-2	1370-1800	34-45	33-44			
	Ⓓ, D	2-3	2470-2810	62-71	60-68			
	Ⓓ, D	3-2	2420-2080	61-52	59-51			
	Ⓓ, D	2-1	1450-1020	36-26	35-25			

NOTE: Part throttle shift speeds can not be checked unless a TV pressure gauge is installed.

Tire Size	Axle Ratio
	3.08
P215/70R15	1
P215/65R15	2

MODEL PKA-AS, C
5.8L H.O. POLICE,
W/ & W/O LOW GEAR LOCKOUT
50 STATE, HIGH ALTITUDE

Throttle	Range	Shift	OPS-R.P.M.	Column Number 1	2	3	4	5	6
Closed Throttle See Note	D, D	1-2	370-530	11-15					
	D, D	2-3	720-890	21-26					
	D	3-4	1460-1850	42-53					
	D	4-3	1580-1200	46-35					
	D, D	3-2	870-700	25-20					
	D, D	2-1	470-320	14-9					
	1	3-1, 2-1	730-810	21-23					
Part Throttle See Note	D, D	1-2	670-1050	19-30					
	D, D	2-3	1350-1780	39-51					
	D	3-4	1790-2420	52-70					
	D	4-3	1760-1340	51-39					
	D, D	3-2	1390-830	40-24					
	D, D	2-1	750-500	22-14					
Wide Open See Note	D, D	1-2	1400-1940	40-56					
	D, D	2-3	2650-3020	77-87					
	D, D	3-2	2530-2170	73-63					
	D, D	2-1	1560-1060	45-31					

Tire Size	Use Column Number					
Axle Ratio	2.73					
P225/70R15	1					

Automatic Transmissions

FORD MOTOR CO. AOT (Cont.)

SHIFT SPEED SPECIFICATIONS (Cont.)

MODEL PKA-CZ
5.0L COUGAR, THUNDERBIRD
50 STATE, HIGH ALTITUDE

				COLUMN NUMBER					
				1	2	3	4	5	6
Throttle	Range	Shift	OPS-R.P.M.						
Closed Throttle See Note	D . D	1-2	310-460	8-13	8-12				
	D . D	2-3	680-830	19-23	18-22				
	D	3-4	1300-1680	35-46	34-44				
	D	4-3	1440-1060	39-29	38-28				
	D . D	3-2	800-660	22-18	21-17				
	D . D	2-1	410-240	11-7	11-6				
	1	3-1, 2-1	1100-730	30-20	29-19				
Part Throttle See Note	D . D	1-2	670-1020	18-28	18-27				
	D . D	2-3	1330-1710	36-47	35-45				
	D	3-4	1600-2210	44-60	42-58				
	D	4-3	1600-1200	44-33	42-32				
	D . D	3-2	1440-1020	39-28	38-27				
	D . D	2-1	690-480	19-13	18-13				
Wide Open See Note	D . D	1-2	1370-1800	37-49	36-48				
	D . D	2-3	2470-2810	67-77	65-74				
	D . D	3-2	2420-2080	66-57	64-55				
	D . D	2-1	1450-1020	39-28	38-27				

	TIRE SIZE	USE COLUMN NUMBER						
Axle Ratio		2.73	2.73					
	P215/70R14	1						
	215/70HR14	1						
	220/55R390		2					

MODEL PKA-CL, CR
5.0L CROWN VICTORIA, GRAND MARQUIS, TOWN CAR, 50 STATE

				COLUMN NUMBER					
				1	2	3	4	5	6
Throttle	Range	Shift	OPS-R.P.M.						
Closed Throttle See Note	Ⓓ. D	1-2	310-460	9-13					
	Ⓓ. D	2-3	640-800	18-23					
	Ⓓ	3-4	1180-1580	34-45					
	Ⓓ	4-3	1330-900	38-26					
	Ⓓ. D	3-2	770-620	22-18					
	Ⓓ. D	2-1	410-240	12-7					
	1	3-1, 2-1	1100-730	31-21					
Part Throttle See Note	Ⓓ. D	1-2	640-1000	18-29					
	Ⓓ. D	2-3	1250-1640	36-47					
	Ⓓ	3-4	1500-2140	43-61					
	Ⓓ	4-3	1500-1060	43-30					
	Ⓓ. D	3-2	1310-800	37-23					
	Ⓓ. D	2-1	680-460	19-13					
Wide Open See Note	Ⓓ. D	1-2	1340-1800	38-51					
	Ⓓ. D	2-3	2430-2770	69-79					
	Ⓓ. D	3-2	2350-1990	67-57					
	Ⓓ. D	2-1	1440-980	41-28					

	TIRE SIZE	USE COLUMN NUMBER					
Axle Ratio		2.73					
	P215/70R15	1					
	P205/75R15	1					

MODEL PKA-CT, CW
5.0L CONTINENTAL, MARK VII
50 STATE

				COLUMN NUMBER					
				1	2	3	4	5	6
Throttle	Range	Shift	OPS-R.P.M.						
Closed Throttle See Note	Ⓓ. D	1-2	310-460	9-13	8-13				
	Ⓓ. D	2-3	680-830	19-23	19-23				
	Ⓓ	3-4	1180-1580	33-45	32-43				
	Ⓓ	4-3	1330-900	38-25	36-25				
	Ⓓ. D	3-2	800-660	23-19	22-18				
	Ⓓ. D	2-1	410-240	12-7	11-7				
	1	3-1, 2-1	1100-730	31-21	30-20				
Part Throttle See Note	Ⓓ. D	1-2	670-1020	19-29	18-28				
	Ⓓ. D	2-3	1330-1710	38-48	36-47				
	Ⓓ	3-4	1500-2140	42-60	41-59				
	Ⓓ	4-3	1500-1060	42-30	41-29				
	Ⓓ. D	3-2	1440-1020	41-29	39-28				
	Ⓓ. D	2-1	690-480	19-14	19-13				
Wide Open See Note	Ⓓ. D	1-2	1370-1800	39-51	37-49				
	Ⓓ. D	2-3	2470-2810	70-79	68-77				
	Ⓓ. D	3-2	2420-2080	68-59	66-57				
	Ⓓ. D	2-1	1450-1020	41-29	40-28				

	TIRE SIZE	USE COLUMN NUMBER					
Axle Ratio		2.73					
	P215/70R15	1					
	P215/65R15	2					

MODEL PKA-CB, CD
3.8L CAPRI, COUGAR, LTD, MARQUIS, MUSTANG, THUNDERBIRD
49 STATE, HIGH ALTITUDE

				COLUMN NUMBER					
				1	2	3	4	5	6
Throttle	Range	Shift	OPS-R.P.M.						
Closed Throttle See Note	Ⓓ. D	1-2	370-530	8-12	8-11				
	Ⓓ. D	2-3	740-910	17-20	16-19				
	Ⓓ	3-4	1680-2060	38-46	36-44				
	Ⓓ	4-3	1840-1460	41-33	39-31				
	Ⓓ. D	3-2	870-720	20-16	19-15				
	Ⓓ. D	2-1	470-320	11-7	10-7				
	1	3-1, 2-1	1230-810	28-18	26-17				
Part Throttle See Note	Ⓓ. D	1-2	730-1140	16-26	16-24				
	Ⓓ. D	2-3	1500-1890	34-43	32-40				
	Ⓓ	3-4	1970-2590	44-58	42-55				
	Ⓓ	4-3	1990-1780	45-40	43-38				
	Ⓓ. D	3-2	1580-1170	36-26	34-25				
	Ⓓ. D	2-1	770-540	17-12	16-12				
Wide Open See Note	Ⓓ. D	1-2	1430-1900	32-43	31-41				
	Ⓓ. D	2-3	2630-3000	59-68	56-64				
	Ⓓ. D	3-2	2570-2220	58-50	55-47				
	Ⓓ. D	2-1	1520-1060	34-24	32-23				

	TIRE SIZE	USE COLUMN NUMBER					
Axle Ratio		3.27	3.45				
	P195/75R14	1	2				
	P205/70R14	1	2				

Automatic Transmissions

FORD MOTOR CO. AOT (Cont.)

SHIFT SPEED SPECIFICATIONS (Cont.)

MODELS PKA-DB
5.0L CROWN VICTORIA, GRAND MARQUIS, TOWN CAR, 50 STATE, HIGH ALTITUDE

				COLUMN NUMBER					
Throttle	Range	Shift	OPS-R.P.M.	1	2	3	4	5	6
Closed Throttle See Note	(D), D	1-2	310-460	7-11					
	(D), D	2-3	680-830	16-20					
	(D)	3-4	1420-1780	34-42					
	(D)	4-3	1560-1200	37-29					
	(D), D	3-2	800-650	19-15					
	(D), D	2-1	410-240	10-6					
	1	3-1, 2-1	1100-730	26-17					
Part Throttle See Note	(D), D	1-2	700-1100	17-26					
	(D), D	2-3	1400-1770	33-42					
	(D)	3-4	1700-2290	40-55					
	(D)	4-3	1720-1320	41-31					
	(D), D	3-2	1500-1120	36-27					
	(D), D	2-1	710-510	17-12					
Wide Open See Note	(D), D	1-2	1440-1850	34-44					
	(D), D	2-3	2510-2850	60-68					
	(D), D	3-2	2460-2130	59-51					
	(D), D	2-1	1480-1080	35-26					

	TIRE SIZE	USE COLUMN NUMBER				
Axle Ratio		3.27				
	P215/70R15	1				
	P205/75R15	1				

MODEL PKA-CY, CV
5.0L CAPRI, MUSTANG, MARK VII LSC 50 STATE, HIGH ALTITUDE

				Column Number					
Throttle	Range	Shift	OPS-R.P.M.	1	2	3	4	5	6
Closed Throttle See Note	(D), D	1-2	370-530	8-12	8-12	9-12			
	(D), D	2-3	740-1100	17-25	16-24	17-26			
	(D)	3-4	1560-1940	35-44	35-43	36-45			
	(D)	4-3	1700-1320	38-30	38-29	39-31			
	(D), D	3-2	1000-720	22-16	22-16	23-17			
	(D), D	2-1	470-320	11-7	10-7	11-7			
	1	3-1, 2-1	1360-920	31-21	30-20	32-21			
Part Throttle See Note	(D), D	1-2	720-1300	16-29	16-29	17-30			
	(D), D	2-3	1590-1970	36-44	35-44	37-46			
	(D)	3-4	1870-2490	42-56	42-55	43-58			
	(D)	4-3	1860-1450	42-33	41-32	43-34			
	(D), D	3-2	1700-1290	38-29	38-29	39-30			
	(D), D	2-1	770-540	17-12	17-12	39-13			
Wide Open See Note	(D), D	1-2	1630-2070	37-47	36-46	38-48			
	(D), D	2-3	2790-3130	63-70	62-70	65-73			
	(D), D	3-2	2710-2370	61-53	60-53	63-55			
	(D), D	2-1	1710-1280	38-29	38-28	40-30			

	Tire Size	Use Column Number					
Axle Ratio		3.27					
	P195/75R14	1					
	P205/70R14	2					
	205/70VR14	2					
	225/60VR15	1					
	P215/70R15	3					
	P215/65R15	3					

Automatic Transmissions

FORD MOTOR CO. AOT (Cont.)

SHIFT SPEED SPECIFICATIONS (Cont.)

MODEL PKB-J
5.0L F-150/250, E-150/250
50 STATE, HIGH ALTITUDE

Throttle	Range	Shift	OPS — R.P.M.	COLUMN NUMBER 1	2	3	4	5	6
Closed Throttle See Note	Ⓓ, D	1-2	370-530	8-12	8-11	9-12	9-13		
	Ⓓ, D	2-3	720-890	16-20	15-19	17-21	18-22		
	Ⓓ	3-4	1460-1850	33-41	31-40	34-44	36-46		
	Ⓓ	4-3	1580-1200	35-27	34-26	37-28	39-30		
	Ⓓ, D	3-2	870-700	19-16	19-15	20-16	21-17		
	Ⓓ, D	2-1	470-320	11-7	10-7	11-8	12-8		
	1	3-1, 2-1	1230-810	28-18	26-17	29-19	30-20		
Part Throttle See Note	Ⓓ, D	1-2	670-1050	15-24	14-22	16-25	17-26		
	Ⓓ, D	2-3	1350-1780	30-40	29-38	32-42	33-44		
	Ⓓ	3-4	1790-2420	40-54	38-52	42-57	44-60		
	Ⓓ	4-3	1760-1340	39-30	38-29	41-32	44-33		
	Ⓓ, D	3-2	1390-830	31-19	30-18	33-20	34-21		
	Ⓓ, D	2-1	750-500	17-11	16-11	18-12	19-12		
Wide Open See Note	Ⓓ, D	1-2	1400-1940	31-43	30-42	33-46	35-48		
	Ⓓ, D	2-3	2650-3020	59-68	57-65	62-71	66-75		
	Ⓓ, D	3-2	2530-2170	57-49	54-47	60-51	63-54		
	Ⓓ, D	2-1	1560-1060	35-24	33-23	37-25	39-26		

Axle Ratio	TIRE SIZE	USE COLUMN NUMBER 3.55	3.73	3.50				
	P215/75R 15SL	1						
	P195/75R 15SL	2						
	P235/75R 15XL	3						
	7.50 x 16D		4					
	LT235/85R 16D		4					
	LT235/85R 16E		4					
	LT235/85R 16D		3					
	LT215/85R 16C		3					
	LT215/85R 16D		1					
	LT215/85R 16E		1					
	31-10.5R x 15C	4						
	P235/75R 15XL			3				
	P205/75R 15SL			1				
	P235/75R 15SL			3				

MODEL PKB-L
5.0L EFI F-250, 50 STATE,
HIGH ALTITUDE

Throttle	Range	Shift	OPS — R.P.M.	COLUMN NUMBER 1	2	3	4	5	6
Closed Throttle See Note	Ⓓ, D	1-2	370-530	8-12	8-11				
	Ⓓ, D	2-3	740-900	17-20	16-19				
	Ⓓ	3-4	1600-1960	36-44	34-42				
	Ⓓ	4-3	1720-1350	39-30	37-29				
	Ⓓ, D	3-2	870-720	20-16	19-15				
	Ⓓ, D	2-1	470-320	11-7	10-7				
	1	3-1, 2-1	1320-810	28-18	26-17				
Part Throttle See Note	Ⓓ, D	1-2	770-1220	17-27	16-26				
	Ⓓ, D	2-3	1570-1940	35-44	34-42				
	Ⓓ	3-4	1890-2510	42-56	40-54				
	Ⓓ	4-3	1890-1480	41-33	39-32				
	Ⓓ, D	3-2	1670-1270	38-29	36-27				
	Ⓓ, D	2-1	790-580	18-13	17-12				
Wide Open See Note	Ⓓ, D	1-2	1610-2030	36-46	34-43				
	Ⓓ, D	2-3	2760-3110	62-70	59-67				
	Ⓓ, D	3-2	2690-2360	60-53	58-50				
	Ⓓ, D	2-1	1630-1220	37-27	35-26				

Axle Ratio	TIRE SIZE	USE COLUMN NUMBER 4.10						
	7.50R x 16D	1						
	LT215/85R 16C	2						
	LT215/85R 16D	2						
	LT235/85R 16D	1						
	LT235/85R 16E	1						

MODEL PKA-CM, CP, CN, CS, CU
5.0L CROWN VICTORIA, GRAND MARQUIS,
POLICE (W/ & W/O LOW GEAR LOCKOUT)
50 STATE, HIGH ALTITUDE

Throttle	Range	Shift	OPS-R.P.M.	COLUMN NUMBER 1	2	3	4	5	6
Closed Throttle See Note	Ⓓ, D	1-2	310-460	8-12					
	Ⓓ, D	2-3	680-830	17-21					
	Ⓓ	3-4	1300-1680	33-43					
	Ⓓ	4-3	1440-1060	36-27					
	Ⓓ, D	3-2	800-660	20-17					
	Ⓓ, D	2-1	410-240	10-6					
	1	3-1, 2-1	1100-730	28-18					
Part Throttle See Note	Ⓓ, D	1-2	670-1020	17-26					
	Ⓓ, D	2-3	1330-1710	34-43					
	Ⓓ	3-4	1600-2210	41-56					
	Ⓓ	4-3	1600-1200	41-30					
	Ⓓ, D	3-2	1440-1020	36-26					
	Ⓓ, D	2-1	690-480	17-12					
Wide Open See Note	Ⓓ, D	1-2	1370-1800	35-46					
	Ⓓ, D	2-3	2470-2810	63-71					
	Ⓓ, D	3-2	2420-2080	61-53					
	Ⓓ, D	2-1	1450-1020	37-26					

Axle Ratio	TIRE SIZE	USE COLUMN NUMBER 3.08					
	P215/70R15	1					
	P205/75R15	1					
	P225/70R15						
	P215/65R15						

MODEL PKB-E
4.9L F-150, 49 STATE

Throttle	Range	Shift	OPS — R.P.M.	COLUMN NUMBER 1	2	3	4	5	6
Closed Throttle See Note	Ⓓ, D	1-2	290-420	7-10	7-11	8-11			
	Ⓓ, D	2-3	650-810	16-20	17-21	18-22			
	Ⓓ	3-4	1470-1820	36-45	38-47	40-49			
	Ⓓ	4-3	1620-1270	40-31	42-33	44-35			
	Ⓓ, D	3-2	780-630	19-16	20-16	21-17			
	Ⓓ, D	2-1	370-230	9-6	10-6	10-6			
	1	3-1, 2-1	1100-730	27-18	28-19	30-20			
Part Throttle See Note	Ⓓ, D	1-2	590-860	15-21	15-22	16-23			
	Ⓓ, D	2-3	1180-1570	29-39	30-41	32-43			
	Ⓓ	3-4	1730-2300	43-57	45-59	47-62			
	Ⓓ	4-3	1750-1380	43-34	45-36	47-37			
	Ⓓ, D	3-2	1210-760	30-19	31-20	33-21			
	Ⓓ, D	2-1	640-420	16-10	17-11	17-11			
Wide Open See Note	Ⓓ, D	1-2	1130-1640	28-41	30-42	31-44			
	Ⓓ, D	2-3	2260-2620	56-65	58-68	61-71			
	Ⓓ, D	3-2	2180-1820	54-45	56-47	59-49			
	Ⓓ, D	2-1	1300-770	32-19	34-20	35-21			

Axle Ratio	TIRE SIZE	USE COLUMN NUMBER 3.08						
	P195/75R15SL	1						
	P215/75R15SL	2						
	P235/75R15XL	3						

Automatic Transmissions

FORD MOTOR CO. AOT (Cont.)

SHIFT SPEED SPECIFICATIONS (Cont.)

MODEL PKB-F
4.9L E-150, F-150
50 STATE, HIGH ALTITUDE

				COLUMN NUMBER					
Throttle	Range	Shift	OPS — R.P.M.	1	2	3	4	5	6
Closed Throttle See Note	Ⓓ, D	1-2	290-420	6-9	7-10	6-9			
	Ⓓ, D	2-3	650-810	15-18	15-19	14-17			
	Ⓓ	3-4	1590-1890	36-42	38-45	34-41			
	Ⓓ	4-3	1700-1410	38-32	40-34	36-30			
	Ⓓ, D	3-2	780-630	17-14	19-15	17-14			
	Ⓓ, D	2-1	370-230	8-5	9-5	8-5			
	1	3-1, 2-1	1100-730	24-16	26-17	24-16			
Part Throttle See Note	Ⓓ, D	1-2	590-860	13-19	14-20	13-18			
	Ⓓ, D	2-3	1180-1570	26-35	28-37	25-34			
	Ⓓ	3-4	1830-2360	41-53	44-56	39-51			
	Ⓓ	4-3	1830-1500	41-34	44-36	39-32			
	Ⓓ, D	3-2	1210-760	27-17	29-18	26-16			
	Ⓓ, D	2-1	640-420	14-9	15-10	14-9			
Wide Open See Note	Ⓓ, D	1-2	1130-1640	25-37	27-39	24-35			
	Ⓓ, D	2-3	2260-2620	51-59	54-62	49-56			
	Ⓓ, D	3-2	2180-1820	49-41	52-43	47-39			
	Ⓓ, D	2-1	1300-770	29-17	31-18	28-17			

	TIRE SIZE	USE COLUMN NUMBER						
Axle Ratio		3.50	3.55					
	P205/75R 15SL	1						
	P235/75R 15SL	2						
	P235/75R 15XL	2						
	P215/75R 15SL		1					
	P235/75R 15XL		2					
	P195/75R 15SL		3					

MODEL PKB-K
5.0L BRONCO/F-150,(4x4)
50 STATE, HIGH ALTITUDE

				COLUMN NUMBER					
Throttle	Range	Shift	OPS — R.P.M.	1	2	3	4	5	6
Closed Throttle See Note	Ⓓ, D	1-2	370-530	9-13	9-12				
	Ⓓ, D	2-3	720-890	18-22	17-21				
	Ⓓ	3-4	1460-1850	36-46	34-44				
	Ⓓ	4-3	1580-1200	39-30	37-28				
	Ⓓ, D	3-2	870-700	21-17	20-16				
	Ⓓ, D	2-1	470-320	12-8	11-8				
	1	3-1, 2-1	1230-810	30-20	29-19				
Part Throttle See Note	Ⓓ, D	1-2	670-1050	16-26	16-25				
	Ⓓ, D	2-3	1350-1780	33-44	32-42				
	Ⓓ	3-4	1790-2420	44-60	42-57				
	Ⓓ	4-3	1760-1340	44-33	41-32				
	Ⓓ, D	3-2	1390-830	34-20	33-20				
	Ⓓ, D	2-1	750-500	18-12	18-12				
Wide Open See Note	Ⓓ, D	1-2	1400-1940	34-48	33-46				
	Ⓓ, D	2-3	2650-3020	65-74	62-71				
	Ⓓ, D	3-2	2530-2170	62-53	60-51				
	Ⓓ, D	2-1	1560-1060	38-26	27-25				

	TIRE SIZE	USE COLUMN NUMBER						
Axle Ratio		3.55						
	31-10.5R x 15C	1						
	P235/75R 15XL	2						

MODEL PKB-M
5.0L EFI BRONCO/F-150/250 (4x4),
F-250 (4x2), 50 STATE, HIGH ALTITUDE

				COLUMN NUMBER					
Throttle	Range	Shift	OPS — R.P.M.	1	2	3	4	5	6
Closed Throttle See Note	Ⓓ, D	1-2	370-530	8-11	7-11	8-12	8-12		
	Ⓓ, D	2-3	740-900	16-19	15-18	17-20	16-20		
	Ⓓ	3-4	1600-1960	34-42	32-40	36-44	35-43		
	Ⓓ	4-3	1720-1350	37-29	35-27	39-30	38-30		
	Ⓓ, D	3-2	870-720	18-15	18-15	20-16	19-16		
	Ⓓ, D	2-1	470-320	10-7	10-6	11-7	10-7		
	1	3-1, 2-1	1230-810	26-17	25-16	28-18	27-18		
Part Throttle See Note	Ⓓ, D	1-2	770-1220	16-26	16-25	17-27	17-27		
	Ⓓ, D	2-3	1570-1940	33-41	32-39	35-44	34-42		
	Ⓓ	3-4	1890-2510	40-53	38-51	42-56	41-55		
	Ⓓ	4-3	1890-1480	40-31	38-30	42-33	41-32		
	Ⓓ, D	3-2	1670-1270	35-27	34-26	37-29	37-28		
	Ⓓ, D	2-1	790-580	17-12	16-12	18-13	17-13		
Wide Open See Note	Ⓓ, D	1-2	1610-2030	34-43	33-41	36-46	35-44		
	Ⓓ, D	2-3	2760-3110	59-66	56-63	62-70	60-68		
	Ⓓ, D	3-2	2690-2360	57-50	55-48	60-53	59-52		
	Ⓓ, D	2-1	1630-1220	35-26	33-25	37-27	36-27		

	TIRE SIZE	USE COLUMN NUMBER					
Axle Ratio		4.10	4.11				
	31-10.5R x 15C		1				
	P235/75R15XL		2				
	LT235/85R16D	3					
	LT235/85R16E	4					
	LT215/85R16C	1					
	LT215/85R16D	1					
	7.50 x 16D	3					

CONTROL PRESSURE SPECIFICATIONS [1]

Throttle Position	Line Pressure psi (kg/cm²)	T.V. Limit Pressure psi (kg/cm²)
At Idle		
In "R"	75-90 (5.3-6.3)	0
All Other Ranges	55-65 (3.9-4.6)	0
At W.O.T. Stall		
In "R"		
3.8L & 4.9L	241-279 (16.9-19.6)	74-86 (5.2-6.0)
All Others	250-290 (17.5-20.3)	79-91 (5.5-6.4)
All Other Ranges		
3.8L & 4.9L	176-204 (12.4-14.3)	74-86 (5.2-6.0)
All Others	180-215 (12.6-15.1)	79-91 (5.5-6.4)

1 – With governor pressure at zero.

Fig. 3: Transmission Case showing Control Pressure Connecting Points

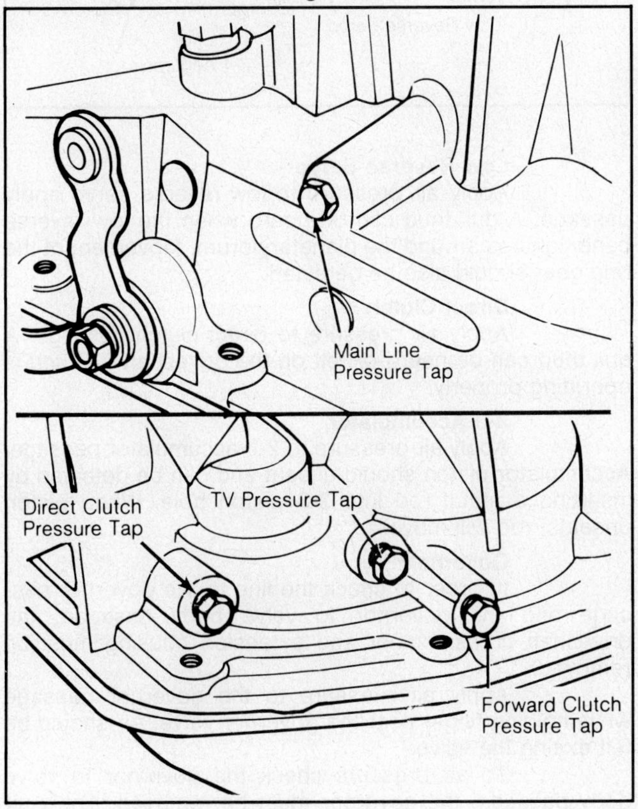

Low in "N"
Faulty valve body.

Low in "O/D"
Check for faulty forward clutch, overdrive servo, or for faulty valve body.

Low in Drive
Faulty forward clutch or intermediate servo.

Low in "1"
Faulty forward clutch or low-reverse servo.

Low at Idle in All Ranges
Check for low fluid level, restricted intake screen or filter, loose valve body bolts, pump leakage, case leakage, faulty valve body, excessively low engine idle, fluid too hot.

High at Idle in All Ranges
Check throttle valve linkage adjustment and condition and for faulty valve body.

Pressure Okay at Idle but Low at W.O.T.
Check for internal leakage, pump leakage, restricted intake screen of filter, damaged or out of adjustment T.V. valve linkage. Also check for sticking T.V. or T.V. limit valve in valve body.

DIRECT CLUTCH PRESSURE TEST

1) Attach accurate 0-300 psi pressure gauges to the forward and direct clutch pressure taps on right side of transmission. *See Fig. 3.* Have sufficient hose so gauges may be read in vehicle.

2) Drive the vehicle. When pressure is applied to direct clutch, note the difference between the line pressure on forward clutch gauge and direct clutch gauge. If difference is less than 15 psi (1.1 kg/cm²), direct clutch circuit is good.

3) If difference is greater than 15 psi (1.1 kg/cm²), there could be a leak in the direct clutch pressure circuit.

GOVERNOR CHECK

Accelerate vehicle to 25 MPH and back off throttle completely. If governor is operating properly, transmission will shift to 3rd gear.

STALL TEST

Testing Precautions

When performing stall test, do not hold throttle open longer than 5 seconds. Allow a cooling period of 15 seconds with transmission in Neutral and engine speed at 1000 RPM between each test. If engine speed exceeds maximum limits shown, release accelerator immediately as this is an indication of clutch or band slippage.

Testing Procedure

Bring engine to normal operating temperature. Apply parking and service brakes. Stall test transmission in each driving range at full throttle. Note maximum RPM obtained. Engine speed should be within limits. See STALL SPEED SPECIFICATIONS table.

STALL TEST RESULTS

Stall Speed Too High

In "O/D", Drive, "1" and "R"; general transmission problems are indicated and a control pressure test should be made to locate faulty unit(s). In "O/D" and Drive only; planetary one-way clutch slippage is indicated. In "O/D", Drive and "1"; forward clutch slippage is indicated. In "R" only; reverse clutch and/or low-reverse band slippage is indicated.

Stall Speed Too Low

Converter stator one-way clutch or engine performance is faulty.

AIR PRESSURE TESTS

A "No Drive" condition can exist even with correct transmission fluid pressure, because of inoperative

Automatic Transmissions
FORD MOTOR CO. AOT (Cont.)

STALL SPEED SPECIFICATIONS

Application	Stall RPM
Capri, Cougar, Mustang, Thunderbird	
3.8L	2067-2391
Capri & Mustang	
5.0L (HO) SEFI	2003-2390
Continental & Mark VII	
5.0L SEFI	2038-2357
Lincoln Town Car	
5.0L SEFI	2072-2421
Cougar & Thunderbird	
5.0L SEFI	2032-2350
Ford & Mercury	
5.0L SEFI	2038-2357
5.8L (HO)	1523-1838
Mark VII LSC	
5.0L (HO) SEFI	1992-2382
E150/250	
4.9L	1950-2232
5.0L EFI	2091-2434
F150/250	
4.9L	1965-2245
F150/250 & Bronco	
5.0L EFI	2075-2421

clutches or bands. The inoperative units can be located by substituting air pressure for fluid pressure to determine location of malfunction.

To make air pressure checks, drain transmission fluid. Remove oil pan and control valve body assembly. Install adapter plate (T82L-7006-A), with adapter plate attaching screws (T82P-7006-C), and control valve body gasket, in place of control valve body. With a rubber tipped air nozzle, apply air pressure in the following order at points noted in *Fig. 4*.

NOTE: **Air pressure should be regulated between 40 psi (2.8 kg/cm^2) and 90 psi (6.3 kg/cm^2). Compressed air used for test should be filtered and dry to avoid contaminating transmission fluid.**

3-4 Accumulator

Apply air pressure to 3-4 accumulator passage. The accumulator piston should unseat.

Reverse Clutch

Apply air pressure to reverse clutch passage. A dull thud can be heard when clutch piston is applied, or movement can be felt by placing fingertips on clutch drum.

Forward Clutch

Apply air pressure to the forward clutch apply passage in the adapter plate. A dull thud can be heard when clutch piston is applied, or movement can be felt by placing fingertips on input shell.

Intermediate Clutch

Apply air pressure to intermediate clutch apply passage. A dull thud can be heard or felt if clutch is operating properly.

Overdrive Servo

Pressurize overdrive servo apply passage. Operation of the band is indicated by tightening of the band around reverse clutch drum. A thud can be felt on the servo cover when the servo returns to the release position as a result of spring force from the release spring. The band will then relax.

Fig. 4: Air Pressure Test Apply Ports on Adapter Plate

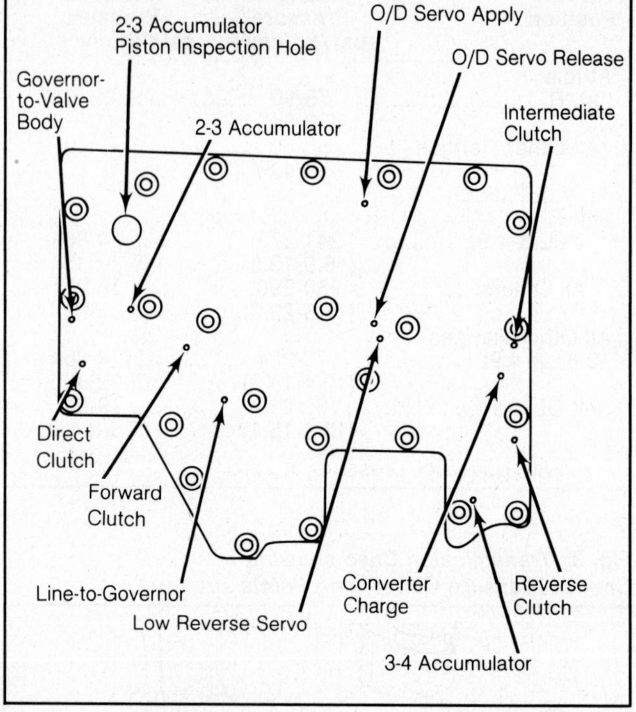

Low-Reverse Servo

Apply air pressure to low-reverse servo apply passage. A dull thud can be heard when the low-reverse band tightens around the planetary drum. Movement of the ring gear should also be detected.

Direct Clutch

Apply air pressure to direct clutch passage. A dull thud can be heard or felt on the driveshaft if clutch is operating properly.

2-3 Accumulator

Apply air pressure to 2-3 accumulator passage. Accumulator piston should unseat and can be detected by inserting a metal rod into 2-3 piston hole. When piston unseats, rod will move.

Governor

In order to check the line to the governor passage and the governor to valve body passage, the driveshaft crossmember and extension housing must be removed.

Apply air pressure to the governor passage while holding finger near the governor valve. Air should be felt exiting the valve.

To air pressure check the governor to valve body passage, the governor must be removed. Apply air pressure to the passage while holding finger over holes in the output shaft. Air should be felt exiting one of the holes.

SERVICE (IN VEHICLE)

VALVE BODY ASSEMBLY

Removal

1) Raise vehicle on a hoist. Loosen oil pan retaining bolts and allow transmission fluid to drain. Remove oil pan and gasket. Discard gasket.

Fig. 5: Automatic Overdrive Transmission Hydraulic Circuits Diagram

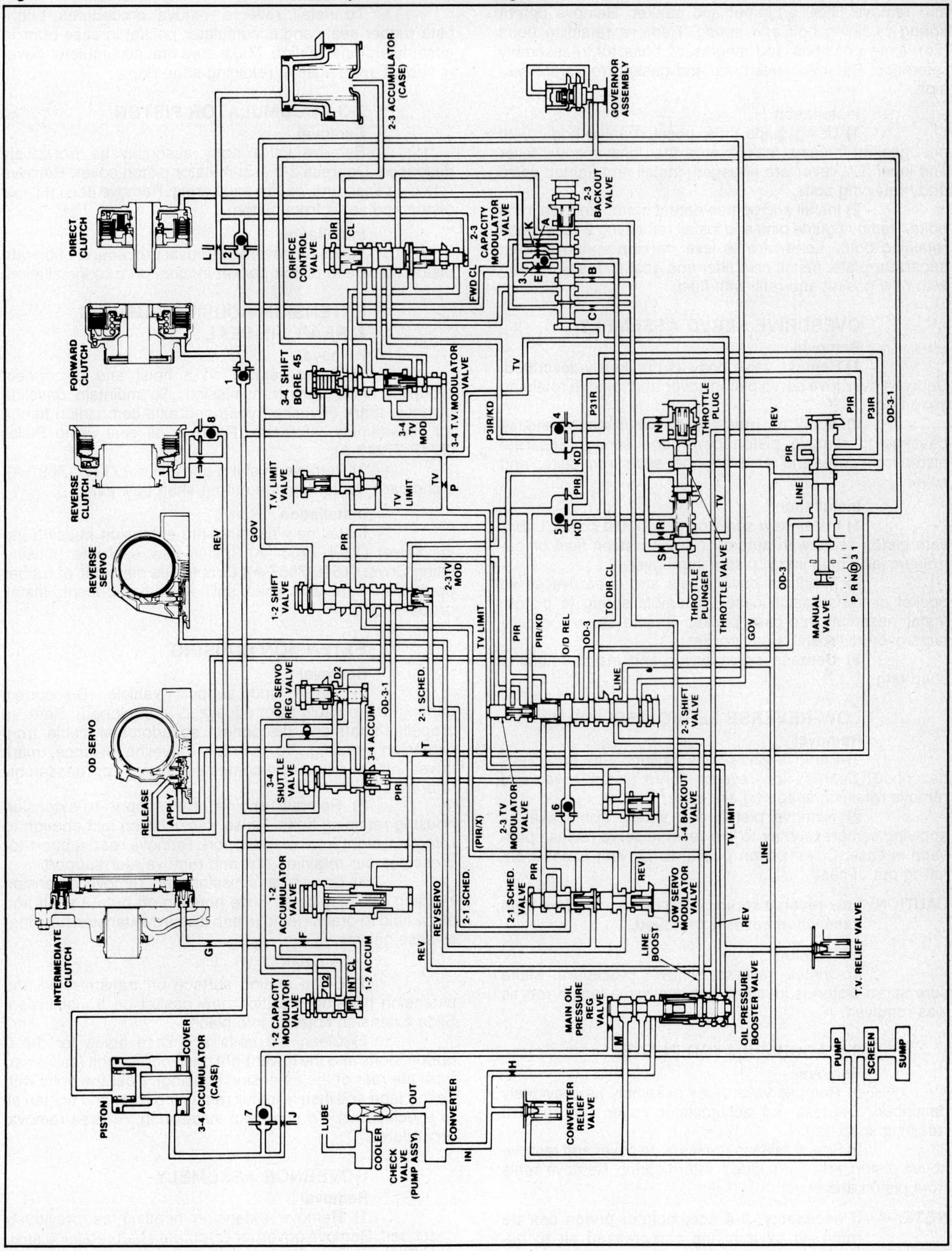

2) Remove 3 filter-to-valve body retaining bolts and remove filter, grommet and gasket. Remove detent spring retaining bolt and spring. Remove retaining bolts (24). Note positions and lengths of bolts for reassembly reference. Remove valve body and gasket from transmission.

Installation

1) Using guide pins, position valve body (with new gasket) in case, making sure that inner manual lever and inner T.V. lever are engaged. Install and tighten valve body retaining bolts.

2) Install and tighten detent spring and retaining bolts. Remove guide pins and install remaining 2 valve body retaining bolts. Load throttle lever torsion spring against separator plate. Install new filter and gasket. Install oil pan with new gasket and refill with fluid.

OVERDRIVE SERVO ASSEMBLY

Removal

1) Remove valve body as previously described. Depress overdrive servo piston cover and remove retaining snap ring.

2) Apply air pressure to servo piston release passage to remove piston cover and spring. Separate piston from cover and remove rubber seals from piston and cover.

Installation

1) Install new seals on piston and cover. Lubricate piston seals with automatic transmission fluid or petroleum jelly, then install piston into cover.

2) Lubricate cover seals and overdrive servo pocket in transmission case. Assemble spring to piston. Install assembly into case pocket. Ensure servo rod contacts overdrive band apply pocket.

3) Depress servo cover and install retaining snap ring.

LOW-REVERSE SERVO ASSEMBLY

Removal

1) Remove valve body assembly as previously described. Depress low-reverse servo piston cover and remove retaining snap ring and cover.

2) Remove piston and spring from case by applying compressed air to low-reverse servo release passage in case. Cover piston pocket to prevent piston from falling out of case.

CAUTION: Low-reverse servo piston may spring free from case when cover is removed.

Installation

To install, reverse removal procedure. Make sure servo piston is installed with the same length rod as was removed.

3-4 ACCUMULATOR PISTON

Removal

1) Remove valve body assembly as previously described. Depress 3-4 accumulator cover and remove retaining snap ring.

2) Slowly release pressure on cover and remove cover, piston, and (if equipped) return spring. Remove seals from piston and cover.

NOTE: If necessary, 3-4 accumulator piston can be removed by applying compressed air to hydraulic apply passage.

Installation

To install, reverse removal procedures. Lubricate rubber seals and accumulator pocket in case prior to accumulator installation. Make sure that accumulator cover is seated snug against retaining snap ring.

2-3 ACCUMULATOR PISTON

Removal

Remove valve body assembly as previously described. Depress 2-3 accumulator piston cover. Remove retaining snap ring, cover, and spring. Remove accumulator piston and seals from piston.

Installation

To install, reverse removal procedure. Lubricate piston seals and piston pocket in case prior to installation.

EXTENSION HOUSING BUSHING & REAR OIL SEAL

Removal

1) Raise vehicle on a hoist and disconnect propeller shaft from transmission. To maintain driveline balance, mark driveshaft yoke and axle companion flange for reassembly reference. Remove oil seal using Puller (T74P-77248-A).

2) Remove bushing using Puller (T77L-7697-A), using care not to damage output shaft splines.

Installation

Install new bushing into extension housing using Driver (T80L-77034-A). Install new seal into housing using Driver (T61L-7657-A). Coat inside diameter of rubber portion of seal and yoke splines with lubricant. Install propeller shaft.

EXTENSION HOUSING

Removal

1) Raise and support vehicle. Disconnect parking brake cable from equalizer, (if equipped). Remove propeller shaft and disconnect speedometer cable from extension housing. To maintain driveline balance, mark driveshaft yoke and axle companion flange for reassembly reference.

2) Remove engine rear support-to-extension housing retaining bolts. Raise transmission just enough to remove weight from rear support. Remove rear support-to-crossmember retaining bolt and remove rear support.

3) Lower transmission and remove extension housing retaining bolts. Slide housing off output shaft and allow fluid to drain. Remove and discard extension housing-to-case gasket.

Installation

1) Clean mating surface on transmission and extension housing. Position new gasket on transmission. Slide extension housing into place.

2) Clean the bolts and case holes for the 2 bottom bolts and the lower right hand corner bolt (as viewed from the rear of the extension housing). Coat the bolts with Teflon tape and install. Install remaining bolts and tighten all to specification. To complete installation, reverse removal procedures.

GOVERNOR ASSEMBLY

Removal

1) Remove extension housing as previously described. Remove governor-to-output shaft retaining snap ring. Using a mallet, tap governor assembly off output shaft.

2) Remove governor drive ball. Remove governor-to-counterweight retaining screws and lift governor from counterweight.

Installation

1) Lubricate governor parts with clean transmission fluid and make sure valve moves freely in bore. Position governor body on counterweight with cover facing toward front of vehicle. Install and tighten 2 retaining screws.

2) Position governor drive ball into pocket on output shaft. Align keyway in counterweight with drive ball and drive assembly onto output shaft with mallet. Install governor-to-output shaft retaining snap ring. To complete installation, reverse removal procedures.

INTERNAL & EXTERNAL SHIFT LINKAGE

NOTE: **On some vehicles it may be necessary to loosen the fan shroud and lower the transmission to remove linkage.**

Removal

1) Raise vehicle on a hoist. Disconnect any interfering exhaust system components. Apply penetrating oil to outer throttle lever retaining nut to prevent breaking inner throttle lever.

2) Hold the outer throttle lever stationary and remove the retaining nut and lockwasher. Swing lever and T.V. rod or cable out of the way for clearance. Disconnect manual rod from manual lever at transmission.

3) Loosen oil pan retaining bolts and allow fluid to drain. Remove oil pan. Remove manual lever detent spring and roller assembly.

4) Remove manual lever retaining pin carefully using a narrow sharp screwdriver. Note assembled position of T.V. lever torsion spring. Remove torsion spring.

5) Securely hold the inner manual lever with a suitable tool while using a 21 mm wrench to break free the manual lever attaching nut. DO NOT allow the tool to contact the "rooster comb" area. Remove outer manual lever from case.

6) Remove inner throttle lever and shaft assembly. Remove inner manual lever and park pawl rod assembly. Disconnect park pawl rod from inner manual lever. Remove manual lever oil seal using a screwdriver.

Installation

1) Install new manual lever oil seal into case using a driver. With manual lever nut on inner throttle lever, slide inner throttle lever through inner manual lever. *See Fig. 12.*

2) Install outer manual lever in case ensuring lever is in proper position (either up or down). Install inner throttle lever and shaft into outer manual lever.

3) Tighten manual lever attaching nut to specifications making sure the flats are aligned. Install T.V. lever torsion spring. Push manual lever into case. Ensure inner manual lever pin is engaged on manual valve detent slot and inner throttle lever is acting on T.V. valve. Neutral start switch plunger must also contact cam surface of inner manual lever.

4) Install new manual lever retaining pin in case. Pin must be flush or below pan gasket surface. Install new throttle lever seal.

5) Install detent spring. Install throttle valve outer lever (do not push inner lever past throttle valve), lockwasher, and nut. Tighten retaining nut to specification. Check Park function and operation of T.V. and manual levers. Connect shift linkage. Adjust linkage as necessary.

See appropriate AUTOMATIC TRANSMISSION SERVICING article in DOMESTIC GENERAL SERVICING section.

REMOVAL & INSTALLATION

TRANSMISSION

See appropriate AUTOMATIC TRANSMISSION REMOVAL article in DOMESTIC GENERAL SERVICING section.

TORQUE CONVERTER

LEAKAGE CHECK

See procedures given in FORD MOTOR CO. C-6 article.

FLUSHING CONVERTER

See procedures given in FORD MOTOR CO. C-6 article.

TURBINE & STATOR END PLAY CHECK

See procedures given in FORD MOTOR CO. C-6 article.

TRANSMISSION DISASSEMBLY

1) Mount transmission in a holding fixture. Remove torque converter. Remove retaining bolts and lift off oil pan and gasket. Remove oil filter, grommet, and gasket.

2) Remove detent spring and roller assembly. Remove valve body retaining bolts and lift off valve body and gasket. Note length of bolts for reassembly. Push down on 3-4 accumulator cover and remove retaining snap ring. Remove cover, piston, and spring.

NOTE: **If necessary, accumulator cover and piston can also be removed by applying compressed air to accumulator hydraulic apply passage. Also, some models do not use a spring on the 3-4 accumulator piston.**

Fig. 6: Bottom View of Transmission Case

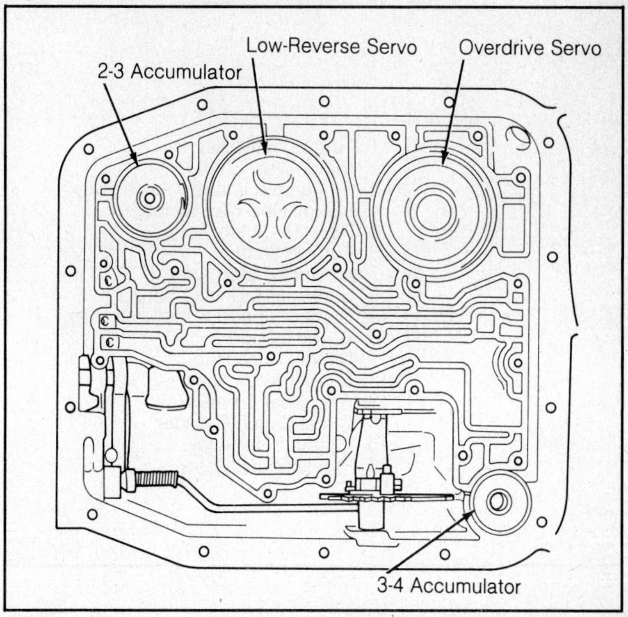

Automatic Transmissions

FORD MOTOR CO. AOT (Cont.)

Fig. 7: Exploded View of Automatic Overdrive Transmission

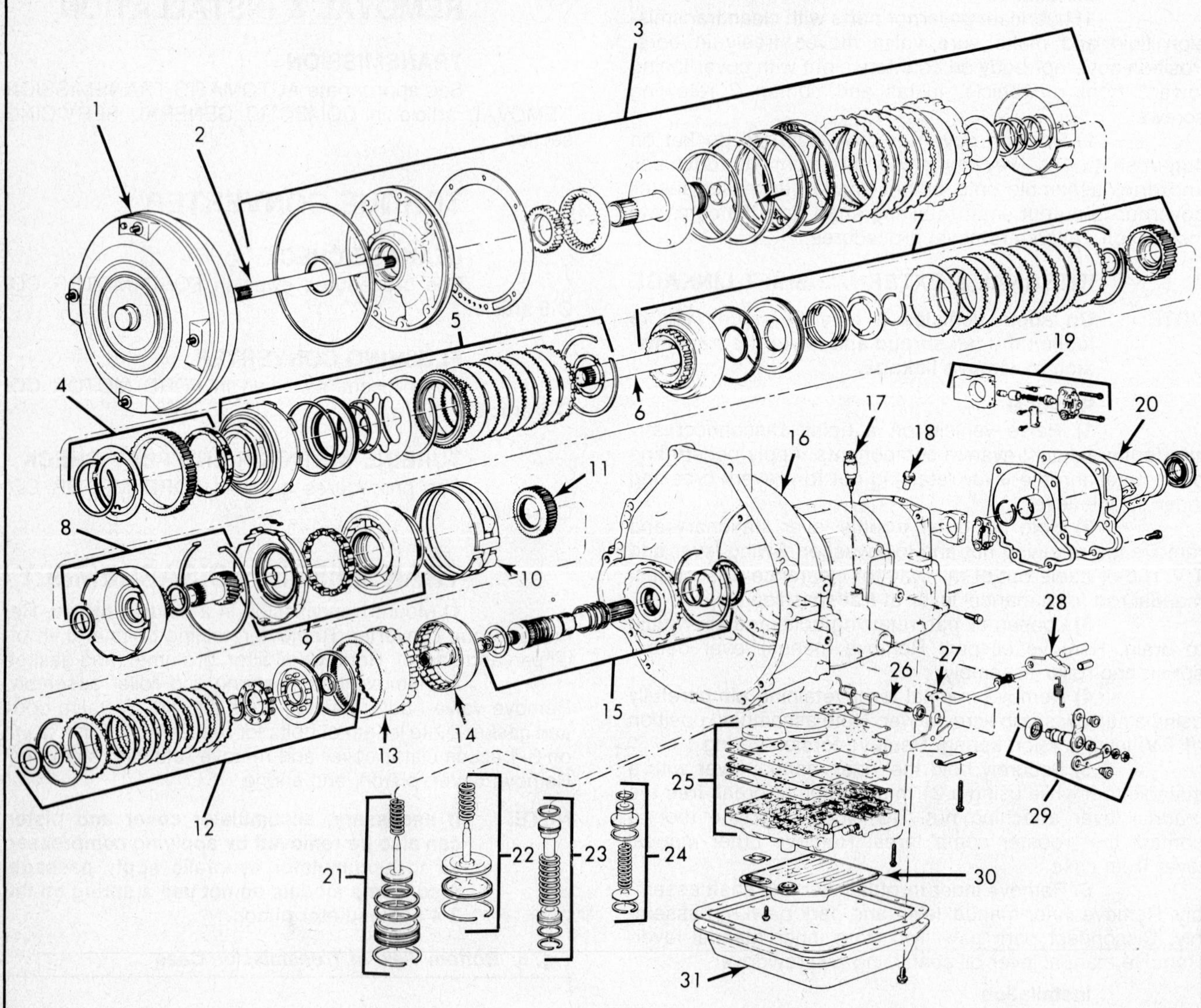

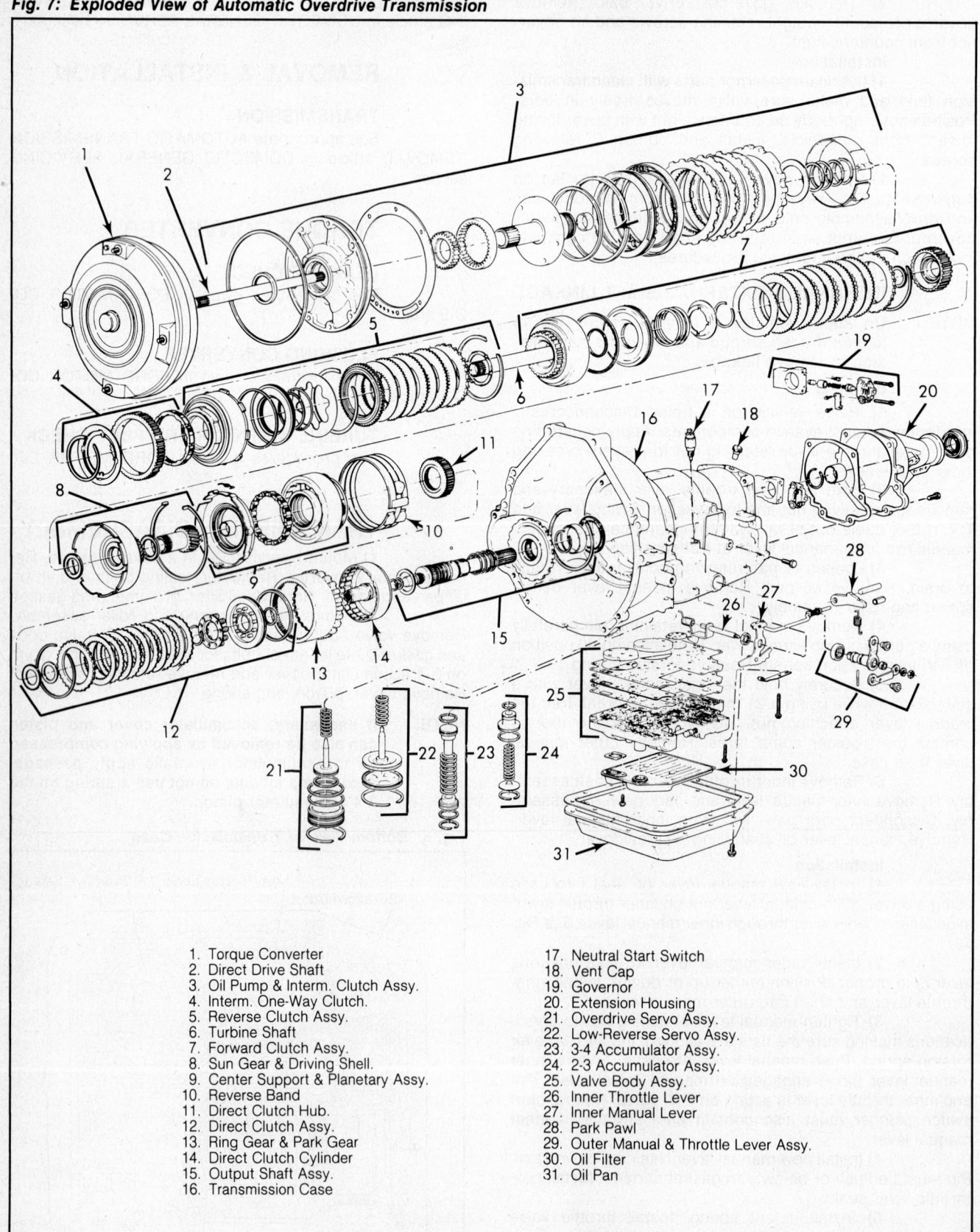

1. Torque Converter
2. Direct Drive Shaft
3. Oil Pump & Interm. Clutch Assy.
4. Interm. One-Way Clutch.
5. Reverse Clutch Assy.
6. Turbine Shaft
7. Forward Clutch Assy.
8. Sun Gear & Driving Shell.
9. Center Support & Planetary Assy.
10. Reverse Band
11. Direct Clutch Hub.
12. Direct Clutch Assy.
13. Ring Gear & Park Gear
14. Direct Clutch Cylinder
15. Output Shaft Assy.
16. Transmission Case
17. Neutral Start Switch
18. Vent Cap
19. Governor
20. Extension Housing
21. Overdrive Servo Assy.
22. Low-Reverse Servo Assy.
23. 3-4 Accumulator Assy.
24. 2-3 Accumulator Assy.
25. Valve Body Assy.
26. Inner Throttle Lever
27. Inner Manual Lever
28. Park Pawl
29. Outer Manual & Throttle Lever Assy.
30. Oil Filter
31. Oil Pan

NOTE: Length of low-reverse piston rod may vary. Three possible rod lengths are available.

3) Remove 2-3 accumulator assembly, low-reverse servo assembly, and overdrive servo assembly by pushing down on the servo covers and removing the retaining snap rings. Note length of low-reverse servo piston rod for reassembly purposes.

4) Remove direct drive shaft by pulling it straight out from case. Remove pump body retaining bolts. Remove pump from case using 2 slide hammers installed in opposite pump retaining bolt holes. Remove pump-to-case gasket.

5) Grasp turbine shaft and pull intermediate clutch pack, intermediate one-way clutch, reverse clutch, and forward clutch from transmission case as an assembly. Disconnect overdrive band from anchor pins and remove band from case.

6) Remove forward clutch hub and No. 3 needle bearing as an assembly. Remove forward sun gear, No. 5 needle bearing, reverse sun gear and drive shell, and No. 4 needle bearing from case as an assembly.

7) Note position of center support snap ring tangs for installation reference. Remove snap ring. Using a screwdriver, pry anti-clunk spring from between center support and case. Prior to removal, note installation position of anti-clunk spring to ensure it is reinstalled in the same position.

8) Remove center support and planetary carrier from case as an assembly. Remove reverse band from case. If direct clutch hub did not come out with planetary carrier, remove it from direct clutch.

9) Remove retaining bolts and slide extension housing from transmission. Remove and discard housing-to-case gasket. Remove retaining snap ring and slide governor assembly off output shaft. Remove governor drive ball from output shaft.

CAUTION: If transmission is positioned with output shaft pointing up, do not allow shaft assembly to fall through case when governor is removed.

10) Remove output shaft, ring gear, and direct clutch as an assembly, through front of case. Remove output shaft No. 9 needle bearing from rear of case.

COMPONENT DISASSEMBLY & REASSEMBLY

NOTE: Handle all parts carefully to avoid damage. Lubricate parts with clean transmission fluid before reassembly (petroleum jelly may be used on gaskets and thrust washers). Use all new gaskets and seals.

GOVERNOR ASSEMBLY

Disassembly

Remove retaining screws and separate counterweight from governor body. Remove cover screws and cover. Remove plug, sleeve, and valve from governor body. *See Fig. 8*.

Reassembly

1) If removed, install clip and spring on valve. Install valve into governor body. Install sleeve in body with points outward.

Fig. 8: Exploded View of Governor Assembly

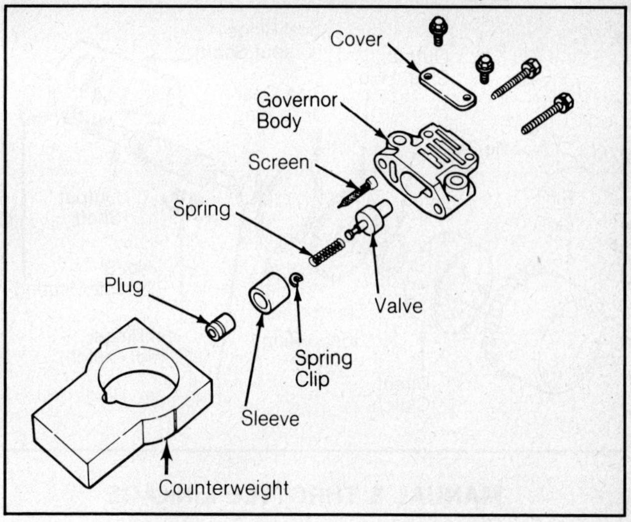

2) Install plug in sleeve with knurled face inward. Install cover. Install screen in body with steel band (brass colored) forward and tip of screen facing outward.

3) Position governor body on counterweight and install retaining screws. When correctly assembled, the finished face of governor body should be flush with face of counterweight.

INTERMEDIATE ONE-WAY CLUTCH

Disassembly & Reassembly

Remove clutch retaining ring and lift off clutch retaining plate. Remove clutch outer race by lifting on race while turning counterclockwise. Carefully lift one-way clutch from inner race. *See Fig. 9*. To assemble, reverse disassembly procedures.

Fig. 9: Intermediate One-Way Clutch Assembly

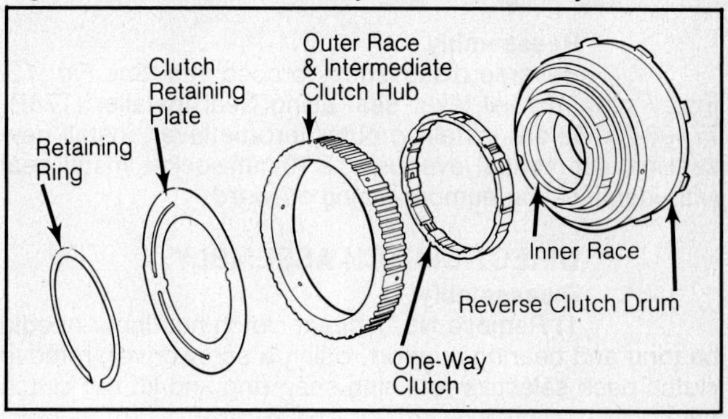

NOTE: If a roller is damaged or lost, entire one-way clutch assembly must be replaced.

OUTPUT SHAFT ASSEMBLY

Disassembly & Reassembly

1) Remove retaining ring and separate output shaft and hub assembly from ring gear. Remove direct clutch from ring gear and No. 8 needle bearing from rear of direct clutch.

2) Remove 4 output shaft seal rings and hub-to-shaft retaining ring. Separate hub from output shaft. Remove the 2 direct clutch seal rings from end of output shaft. *See Fig. 10*. To assemble, reverse disassembly procedures.

Fig. 10: Exploded View of Output Shaft Assembly

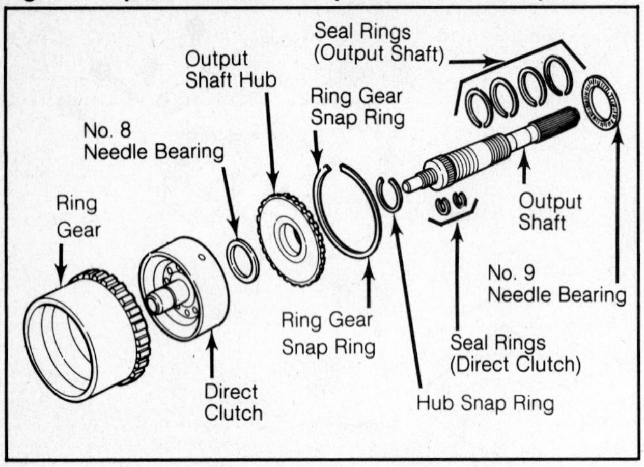

MANUAL & THROTTLE LINKAGE

Disassembly

1) Hold outer throttle lever stationary and remove retaining nut, lock washer, and throttle lever. Using a small screwdriver, remove oil seal from outer manual lever counterbore.

CAUTION: Failure to hold outer throttle lever stationary when removing retaining nut will allow inner throttle lever to rotate against valve body surface, which could result in damage to surface.

2) Using a narrow sharp screwdriver, remove manual shaft retaining pin from case. Hold inner manual lever stationary and remove manual lever retaining nut with a 21 mm wrench. Remove throttle lever. Remove inner throttle lever and torsion spring. *See Fig. 11.*

3) Remove inner manual lever and parking pawl actuating rod as an assembly. Separate rod from lever if necessary. Remove manual lever shaft seal from case using a seal puller.

Reassembly

Reverse disassembly procedures. *See Fig. 12.* Install new manual lever seal using Seal Installer (T74P-77498-A). Before installing outer throttle lever, install new seal in outer manual lever using a 13 mm socket. Install seal with identification number facing outward.

DIRECT CLUTCH ASSEMBLY

Disassembly

1) Remove No. 7 direct clutch hub inner needle bearing and bearing support. Using a screwdriver, remove clutch pack selective retaining snap ring and lift out clutch pack.

2) Using a compressor tool, compress piston return springs and remove retaining snap ring. Remove tool and lift spring retainer assembly and piston from clutch drum. If necessary, piston can be removed by applying compressed air to lubrication hole in clutch drum.

3) Noting position and direction of lip seals, remove seals from drum and piston.

Inspection

1) Check piston check ball for freedom of movement. Check for leakage by turning piston upside down (flat side up), allowing check ball to seat in piston.

2) Pour small quantity of solvent over check ball. If solvent drips past check ball, replace piston.

Fig. 11: Bottom View of Transmission Case

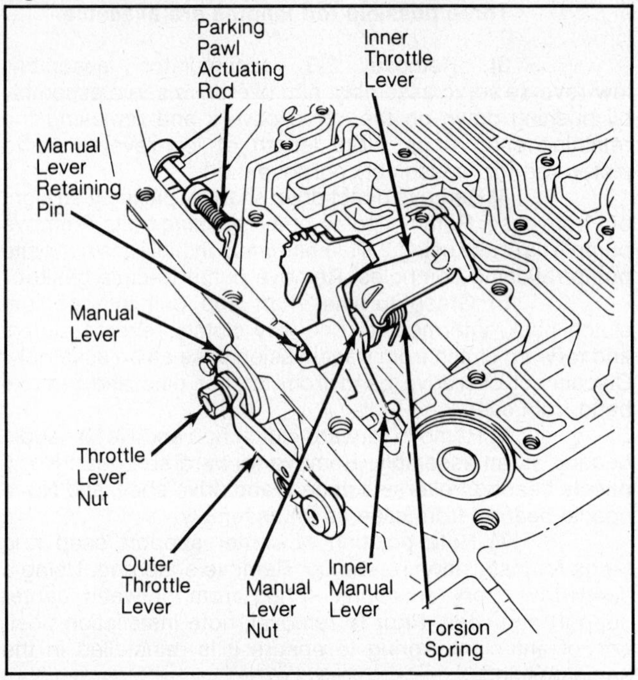

Illustration shows manual and throttle linkage locations.

Fig. 12: Exploded View of Manual and Throttle Linkage

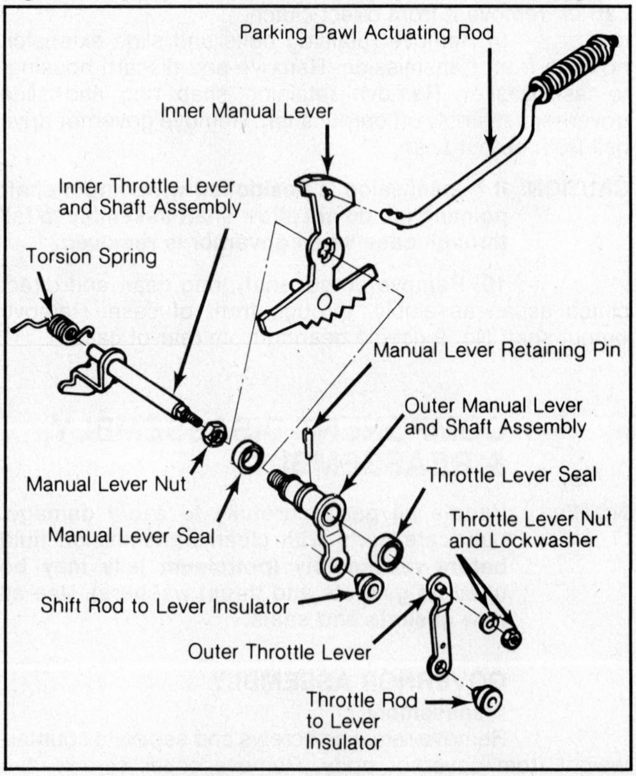

Reassembly

1) Using a Seal Protector (T80L-77234-A), install inner seal on clutch drum hub with sealing lip facing down into drum. Lubricate seals and seal protector with petroleum jelly prior to installation. Install outer seal on piston with lip pointing away from spring posts.

2) Coat piston seals, clutch drum sealing area, and piston inner seal area with petroleum jelly. Install piston into clutch drum using Seal Protector (T80L-77254-A) to prevent damaging seals.

3) Position piston spring and retainer assembly in clutch drum. Compress assembly and install retaining snap ring. Install clutch pack into drum. Install pressure plate on top of clutch pack. Install clutch pack selective retaining ring.

DIRECT CLUTCH PLATE USAGE CHART

Application	Steel Plates	Friction Plates
3.8L	4	4
All Others	5	5

Fig. 13: Checking Direct Clutch Operation

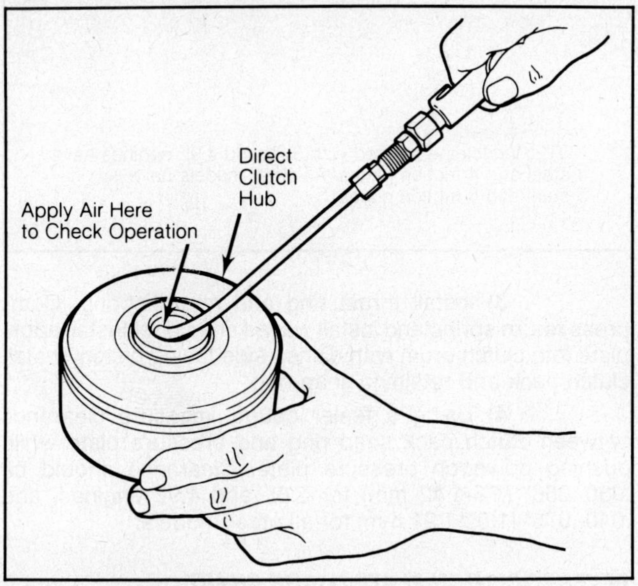

Apply no more than 30 psi (2.1 kg/cm²) to check operation.

4) Using a feeler gauge, measure clearance between clutch pack retaining ring and pressure plate with pressure plate held down. Clearance should be .040-.057" (1.02-1.45 mm) if equipped with 3.8L engine and .050-.067" (1.27-1.70 mm) for all others.

5) If clearance is not within limits, selective snap rings are available in the following thicknesses: .050-.054", .064-.068", .078-.082" and .092-.096". Install correct size snap ring and recheck clearance.

6) To check clutch for proper operation use compressed air at 30 psi (2.1 kg/cm^2). *See Fig. 13.* Clutch should be heard and felt to apply smoothly and without leakage.

FORWARD CLUTCH

Disassembly

1) Lift clutch hub and No. 3 needle bearing from forward clutch assembly. Using a screwdriver, pry clutch pack retaining snap ring from drum. Remove clutch pack.

2) Using a compressor tool, compress piston return spring and remove retaining snap ring. Lift out retainer and return spring.

3) Remove clutch piston from drum. Note position of inner and outer piston seals, then remove seals. Ensure check balls in piston are free.

Reassembly

1) Lubricate and install inner and outer seals on piston with seal lips facing into clutch drum. Lubricate piston seals and drum sealing area with petroleum jelly. Install piston into drum using a Seal Protector (T80L-77140-A) to prevent damaging seals.

2) Position return spring and retainer on piston. Compress return spring and install retaining snap ring. Install clutch pack into clutch drum starting with waved plate. Install clutch pack retaining snap ring.

3) Using a feeler gauge, measure clearance between retaining snap ring and pressure plate with pressure plate held downward. Clearance should be .040-.071" (1.02-1.80 mm) for 3.8L and 4.9L engines, and .050-.089" (1.27-2.26 mm) for all others.

Fig. 14: Exploded View of Direct Clutch Assembly

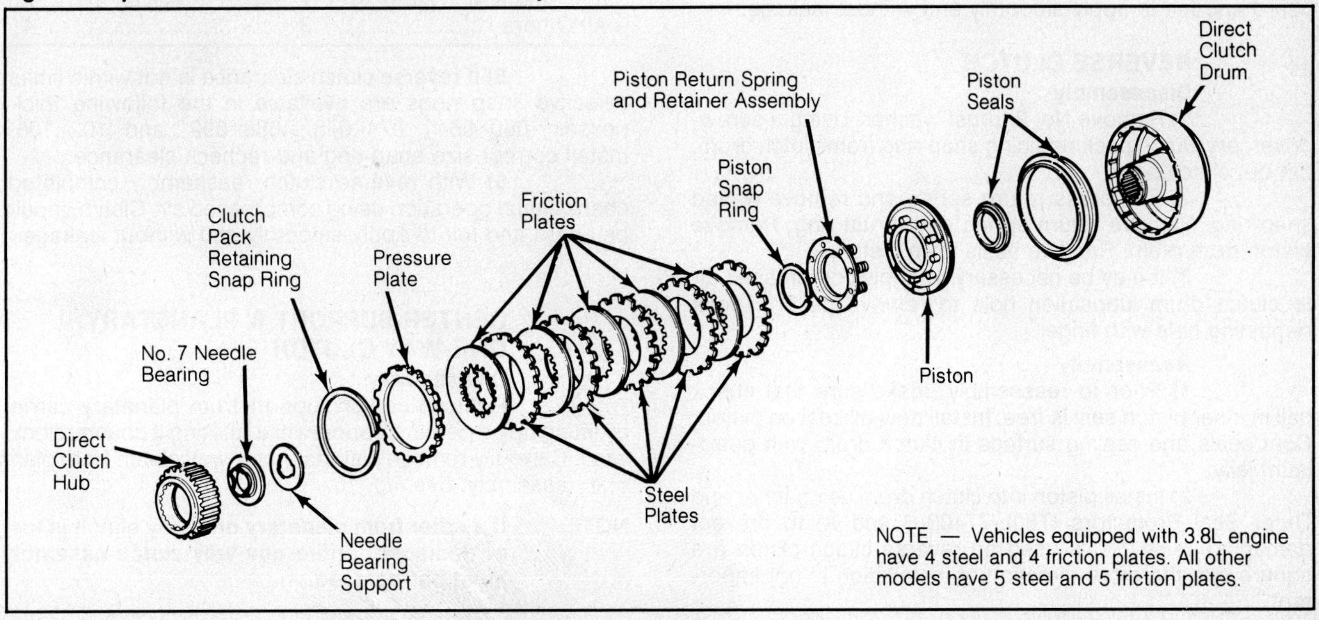

Fig. 15: Exploded View of Forward Clutch Assembly

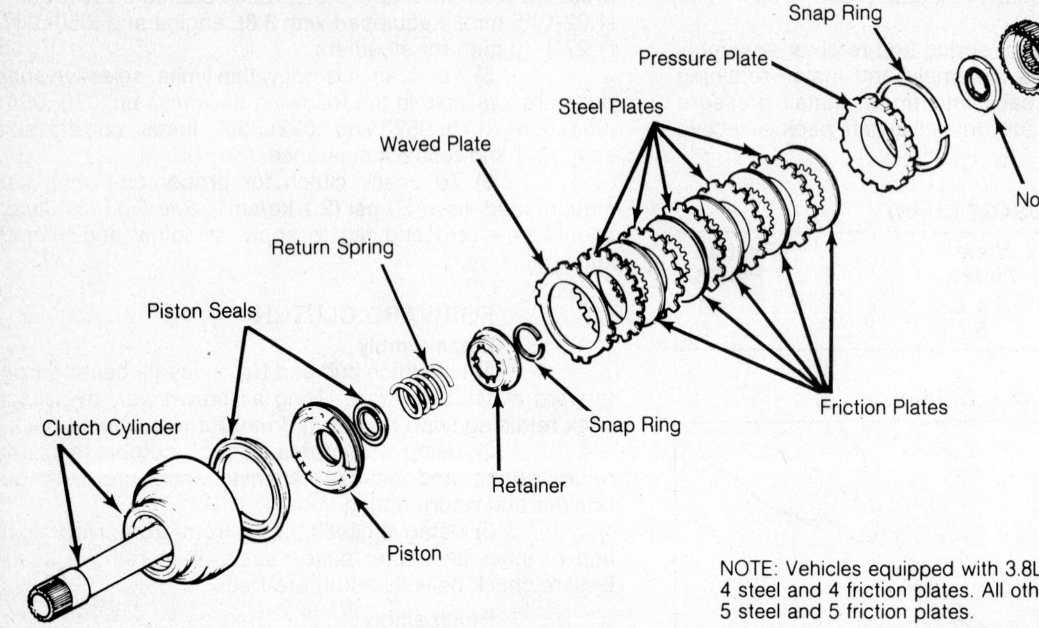

NOTE: Vehicles equipped with 3.8L and 4.9L engines have 4 steel and 4 friction plates. All other models have 5 steel and 5 friction plates.

FORWARD CLUTCH PLATE USAGE CHART

Application	Steel Plates	Friction Plates
3.8L & 4.9L	4 [1]	4
All Others	5 [1]	5

1 – Plus 1 waved plate installed next to piston.

4) If forward clutch clearance is not within limits, selective snap rings are available in the following thicknesses: .060-.064", .074-.078", .088-.092" and .102-.106". Install correct size snap ring and recheck clearance.

5) With reassembly completed, use compressed air and check forward clutch operation. Clutch should be heard and felt to apply smoothly and without leakage.

REVERSE CLUTCH

Disassembly

1) Remove No. 2 thrust washer. Using a screwdriver, pry clutch pack retaining snap ring from clutch drum. Lift out clutch pack.

2) Compress return spring and remove waved snap ring. Remove return spring and thrust ring. Remove piston from drum. Remove seals from piston.

3) It may be necessary to apply compressed air to clutch drum lubrication hole to remove piston. Block remaining hole with finger.

Reassembly

1) Prior to reassembly, make sure that check ball in inner piston seal is free. Install new oil seal on piston. Coat seals and sealing surface in clutch drum with petroleum jelly.

2) Install piston into clutch drum using Inner and Outer Seal Protectors (T80L-77403-B and A) to prevent damaging seals. Seals used on reverse clutch piston are square cut, therefore direction of installation is not important.

3) Install thrust ring and return spring. Compress return spring and install waved snap ring. Install apply plate into clutch drum with dished side facing piston. Install clutch pack and retaining snap ring.

4) Using a feeler gauge, measure clearance between clutch pack snap ring and pressure plate while pushing down on pressure plate. Clearance should be .030-.056" (.76-1.42 mm) for 3.8L and 4.9L engines, and .040-.075" (1.02-1.91 mm) for all other models.

REVERSE CLUTCH PLATE USAGE CHART

Engine Application	Steel Plates	Friction Plates
3.8L and 4.9L	2	3
All Others	3	4

5) If reverse clutch clearance is not within limits, selective snap rings are available in the following thicknesses: .060-.064", .074-.078", .088-.092", and .102-.106". Install correct size snap ring and recheck clearance.

6) With reverse clutch reassembly completed, check clutch operation using compressed air. Clutch should be heard and felt to apply smoothly and without leakage.

CENTER SUPPORT & PLANETARY ONE-WAY CLUTCH

Disassembly

Remove center support from planetary carrier by lifting up on center support while rotating it counterclockwise. Carefully remove planetary one-way clutch from planetary assembly. *See Fig. 16.*

NOTE: If a roller from planetary one-way clutch is lost or damaged, entire one-way clutch assembly must be replaced.

Fig. 16: Center Support and Planetary Assembly

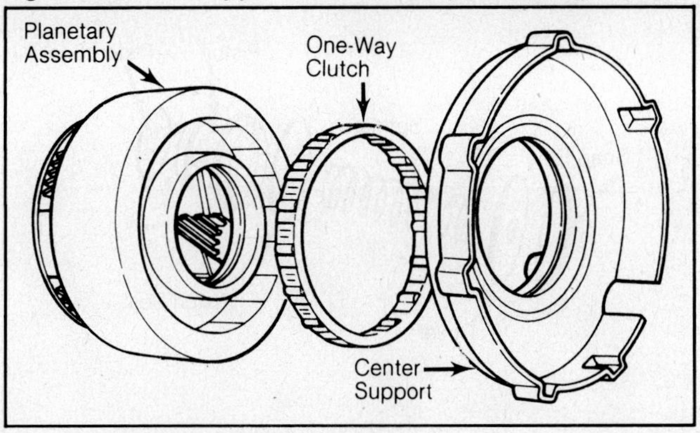

Reassembly

If necessary, assemble one-way clutch. *See Fig. 17.* Lubricate clutch races and clutch assembly with petroleum jelly to aid in assembly. Install one-way clutch in planetary carrier. Install center support into one-way clutch by rotating center support counterclockwise.

SUN GEAR & DRIVING SHELL

Disassembly

Remove No. 4 needle bearing from driving shell. Remove forward sun gear and No. 5 needle bearing from shell. Remove needle bearing from forward sun gear. *See Fig. 19.*

Fig. 17: Assembling Planetary One-Way Clutch

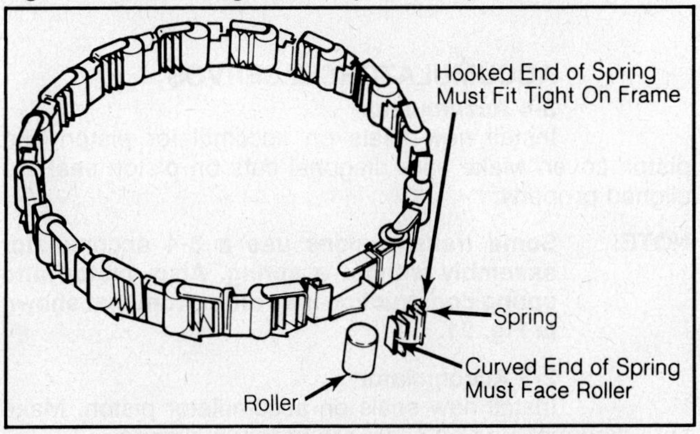

Reassembly

Sun gear and driving shell will be reassembled as part of TRANSMISSION REASSEMBLY.

Fig. 19: Exploded View of Sun Gear and Driving Shell

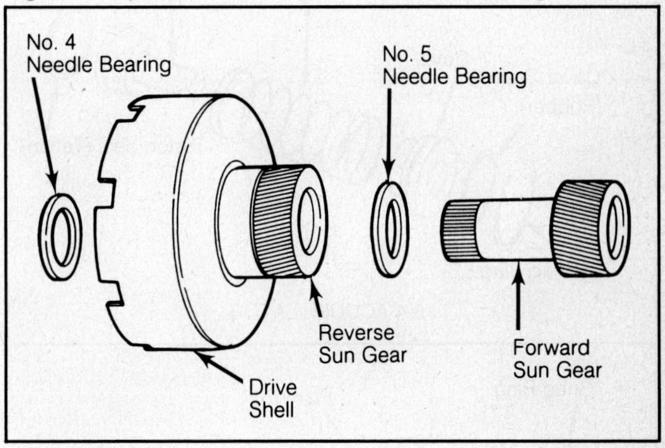

Fig. 20: Exploded View of Oil Pump and Intermediate Clutch Piston

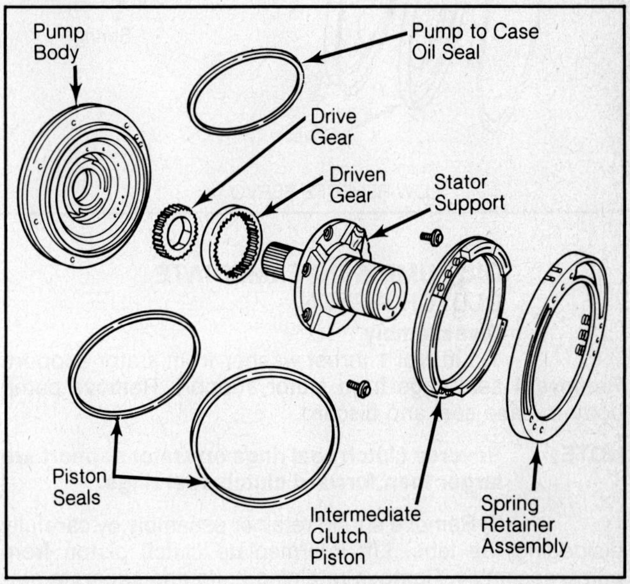

Fig. 18: Exploded View of Reverse Clutch Assembly

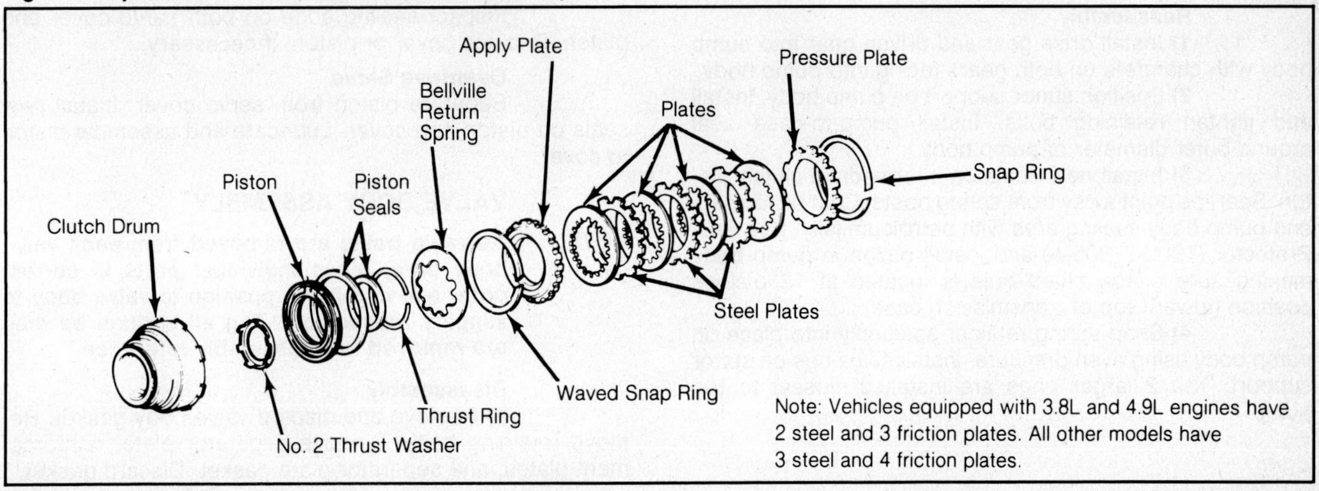

Fig. 21: Exploded View of Accumulator and Servo Assemblies

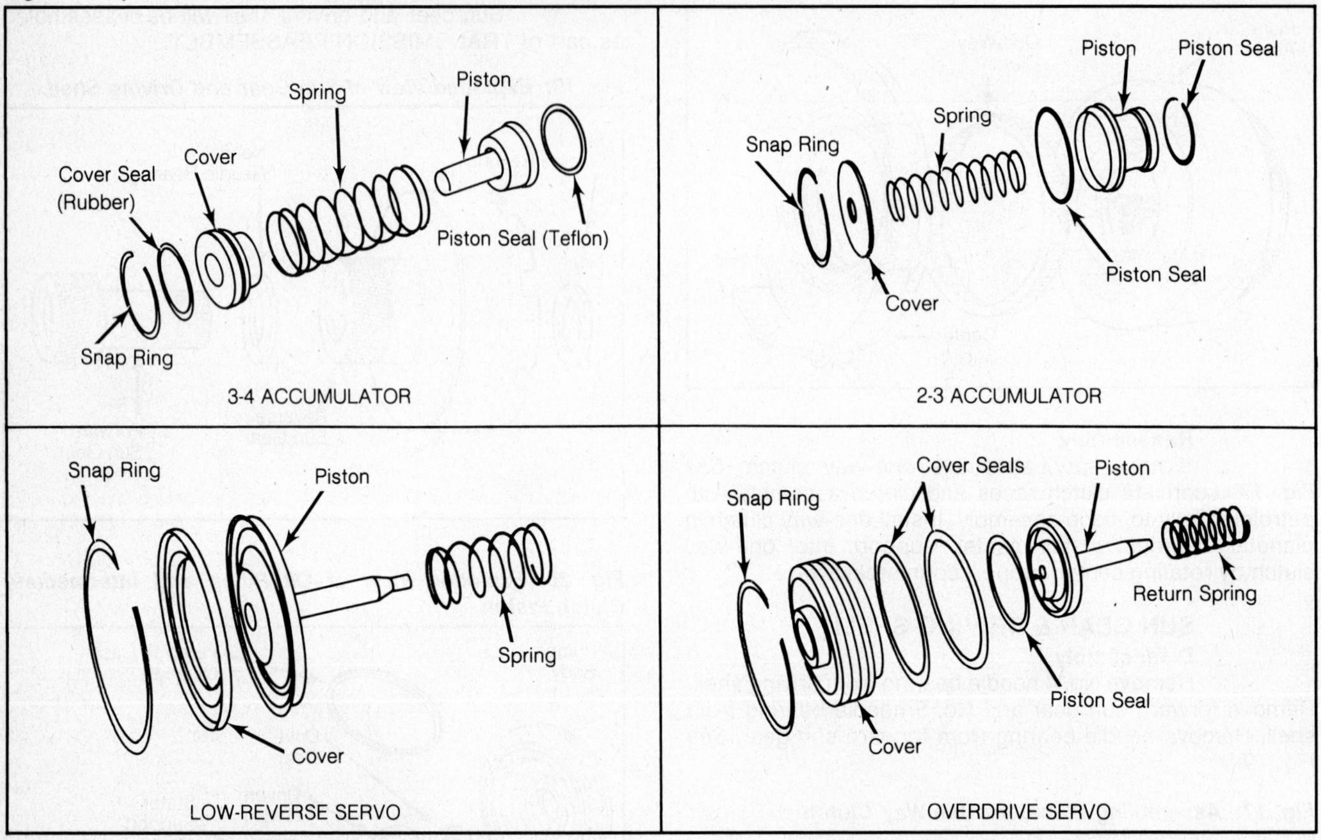

OIL PUMP & INTERMEDIATE CLUTCH PISTON

Disassembly

1) Lift No. 1 thrust washer from stator support. Remove 4 seal rings from stator support. Remove pump body-to-case seal and discard.

NOTE: **Reverse clutch seal rings on stator support are larger than forward clutch seal rings.**

2) Remove spring retainer assembly by carefully dislodging the tabs. Lift intermediate clutch piston from pump assembly. Remove retaining bolts and separate stator support from pump body. Remove drive and driven gears from pump body.

Reassembly

1) Install drive gear and driven gear into pump body with chamfers on both gears facing into pump body.

2) Position stator support on pump body. Install and tighten retaining bolts. Install pump-to-case seal around outer diameter of pump body.

3) Install new seals on intermediate clutch piston. Seal lips point away from spring posts. Coat piston seal and pump body sealing area with petroleum jelly. Use Seal Protector (T80L-77005-A) and install piston in pump body making sure piston bleed hole is located at 12 o'clock position (toward top of transmission case).

4) Snap spring retainer assembly into place on pump body using even pressure. Install seal rings on stator support. The 2 larger rings are installed closest to the pump.

ACCUMULATORS & SERVOS

3-4 Accumulator

Install new seals on accumulator piston and piston cover. Make sure diagonal cuts on piston seal are aligned properly.

NOTE: **Some transmissions use a 3-4 accumulator assembly without a spring. Also, piston and spring construction may differ from that shown in Fig. 21.**

2-3 Accumulator

Install new seals on accumulator piston. Make sure diagonal cuts on seals are properly aligned.

Low-Reverse Servo

Inspect sealing edge on both servo cover and piston. Replace cover or piston, if necessary.

Overdrive Servo

Separate piston from servo cover. Install new seals on piston and cover. Lubricate and assemble piston to cover.

VALVE BODY ASSEMBLY

NOTE: **As valve trains are removed from each valve body bore, place individual parts in correct order and in relative position to valve body to simplify reassembly. Tag all springs as they are removed for reassembly reference.**

Disassembly

1) Remove and discard valve body gasket. Remove retaining bolts. Remove separator plate, reinforcement plates, and separator plate gasket. Discard gasket.

2) Remove 2 relief valves and 7 check balls from valve body. Note location of Orange check ball, it is not interchangeable with 6 Black check balls. *See Fig. 24.*

3) Remove retaining clip and manual valve. Remove retaining clip and slide throttle control valve train from valve body. Remove retaining clip and 2-3 backout valve train. *See Fig. 25.*

4) Remove 2 retaining plates, 2-3 capacity modulator valve, and orifice control valve trains. Remove retaining clip, 3-4 throttle valve modulator valve, and 3-4 shift valve train. Remove retaining plate and throttle valve limit valve train. Remove retaining clip and 1-2 shift valve train. *See Fig. 22.*

5) Remove retaining plate and overdrive servo regulator valve train. Remove retaining plate and 3-4 shuttle valve train. Remove retaining clip and 1-2 accumulator valve train. Remove retaining clip and 1-2 capacity modulator valve train. *See Fig. 23.*

6) Remove retaining clip and boost valve and main pressure regulator valve trains. Remove 2 retaining plates, 2-1 scheduling valve, and low servo modulator valve trains. Remove retaining plate and 3-4 backout valve train. *See Fig. 26.*

7) Remove the retaining clip, 2-3 shift valve, 3-2 control valve, and 2-3 throttle valve modulator valve trains. *See Fig. 26.*

Fig. 22: Exploded View of 2-3 Modulator Valve, 3-4 T.V. Modulator Valve, 3-4 Shift Valve, T.V. Limit Valve and 1-2 Shift Valve

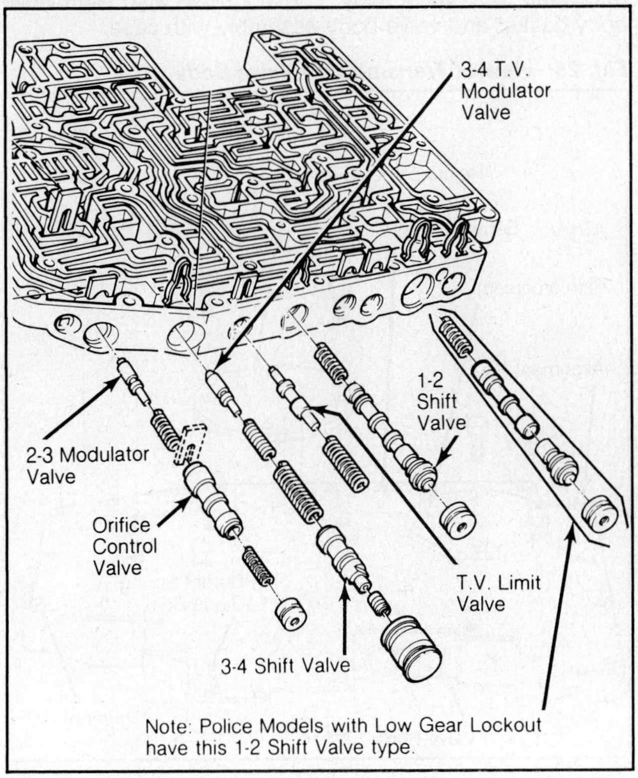

Cleaning & Inspection

1) Clean all parts thoroughly in clean solvent, and blow dry with moisture-free compressed air. Inspect all valves and plug bores for scores. Check all fluid passages for obstructions.

Fig. 23: Exploded View of O/D Servo Valve, 3-4 Shuttle Valve, 1-2 Accumulator Valve and 1-2 Modulator Valve

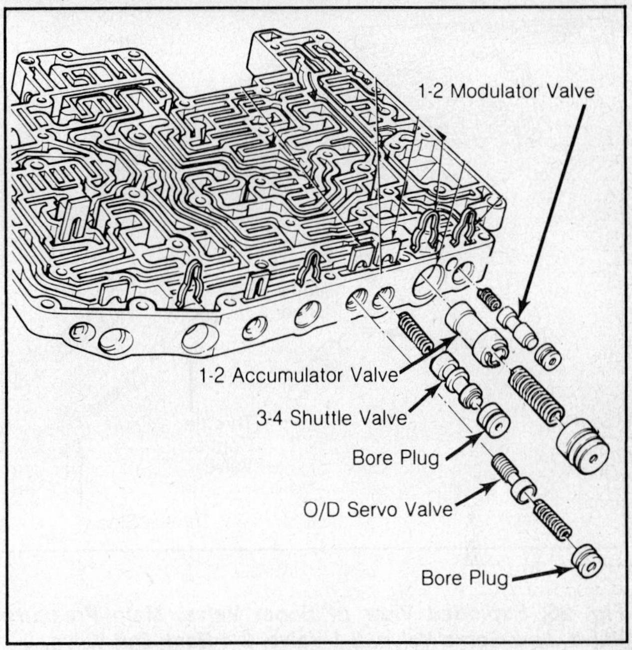

2) Inspect all mating surfaces, plugs, and valves for burrs and scores. If necessary, use crocus cloth to polish valves and plugs.

3) Inspect all springs for distortion. Check all valves and plugs for free movement in their respective bores. Valves and plugs, when dry, must fall free from their own weight in their respective bores.

CAUTION: Avoid rounding off the sharp edges of valves and plugs with the crocus cloth. These edges perform a cleaning action.

Fig. 24: Check Ball Locations in Valve Body

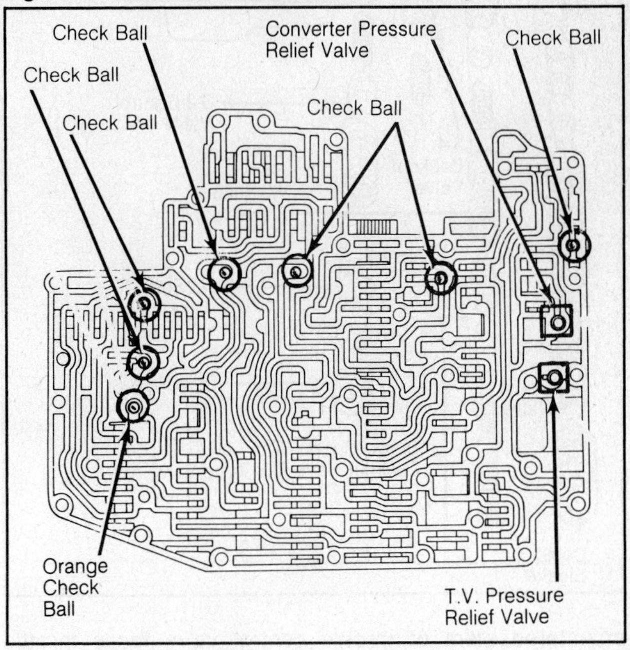

Reassembly

1) Install all valve trains into their respective bores using illustrations as assembly guides. Note

Automatic Transmissions

FORD MOTOR CO. AOT (Cont.)

Fig. 25: Exploded View of Manual Valve, Throttle Control Valve Train and 2-3 Backout Valve Train

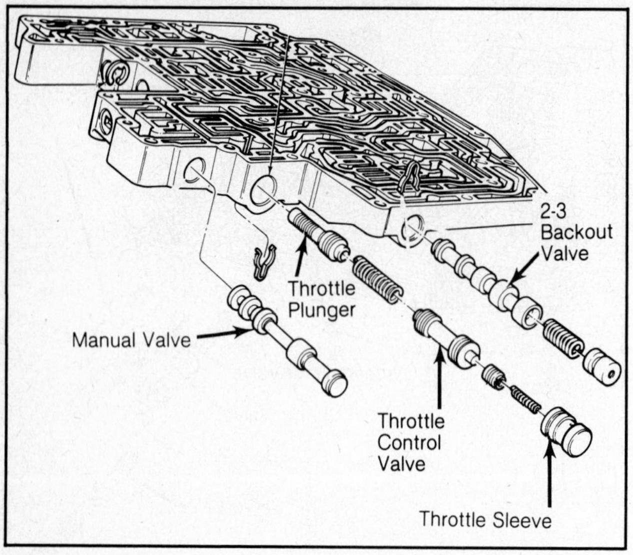

Fig. 26: Exploded View of Boost Valve, Main Pressure Valve, Low Servo Valve, 2-1 Valve, 3-4 Back Out Valve, 2-3 Shift Valve, 3-2 Valve and 2-3 Modulator Valve

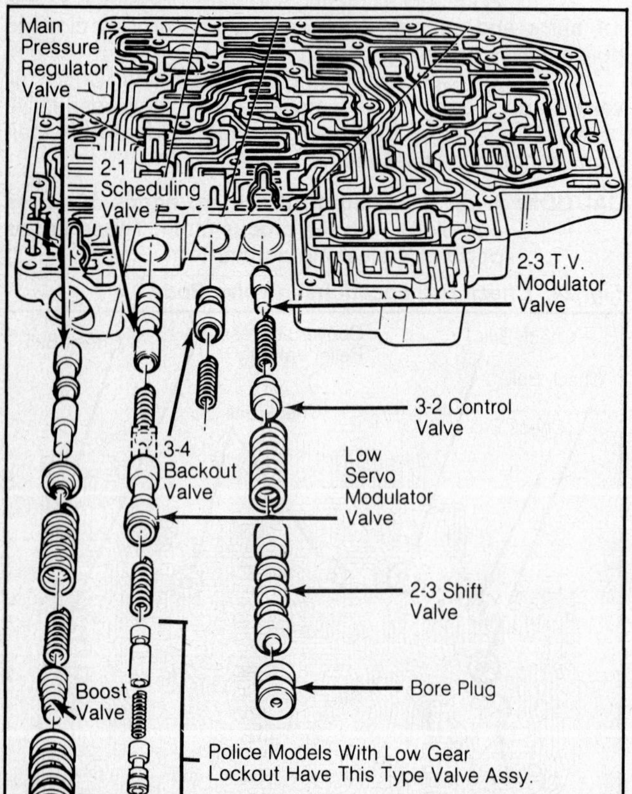

chamfered stem of throttle control valve faces throttle plunger. Retainer plate used for 2-3 capacity modulator valve is thicker and longer than other retainer plates. Note notch in plugs face bottom of bore.

2) The 1-2 accumulator valve and valve body diameters are not the same for all models. The 1-2 accumulator valve bore plug "O" ring must face outside of valve body. To install the O/D servo valve bore plug turn the retaining plate into the plug slot.

3) Install valve body check balls. *See Fig. 24.* Make sure that Orange check ball is correctly installed. This check ball is larger than the others and is not interchangeable. Install pressure relief valves and springs. *See Fig. 27.*

Fig. 27: Installing Pressure Relief Valves

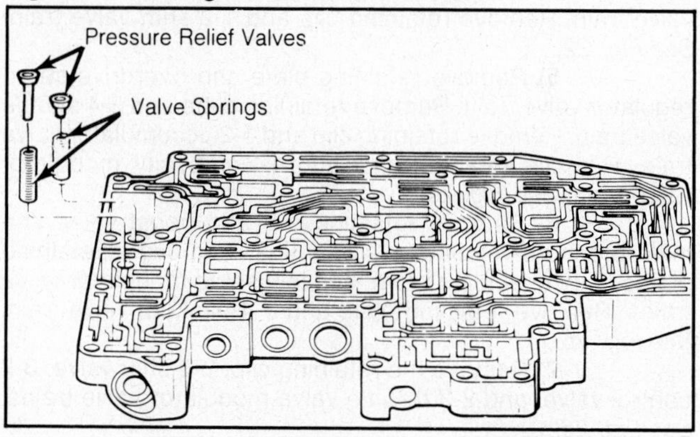

4) Install Alignment Pins (T80L-77100-A) into holes. *See Fig. 28.* These 2 holes are smaller than the other bolt holes to assure proper alignment of gasket and separator plate with valve body. These 2 holes also align valve body gasket and valve body assembly with case.

Fig. 28: View of Transmission Valve Body

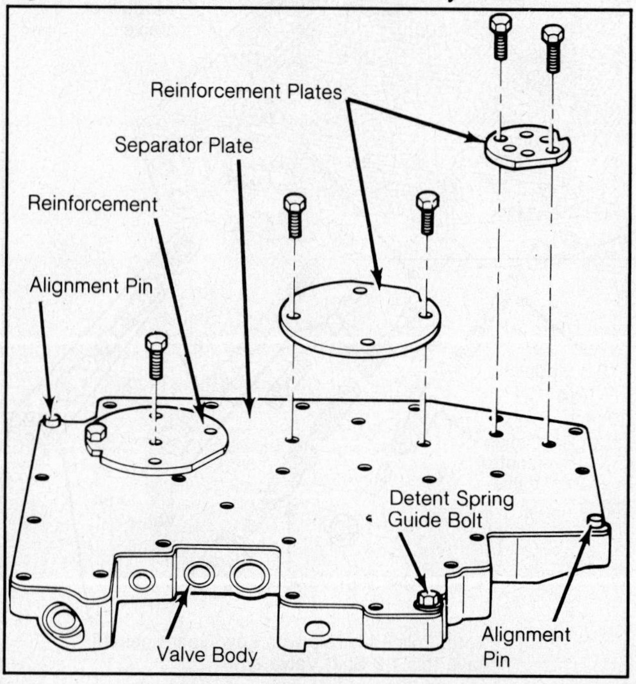

5) Using a new separator plate gasket, slide plate, and gasket over alignment pins. Position the 3 reinforcement plates and loosely install retaining bolts.

6) Loosely install detent spring guide bolt. Detent spring guide bolt is the same length as short valve body-to-case retaining bolts. Starting at center (large) reinforcement plate and working outward, tighten retaining bolts. Remove alignment pins.

TRANSMISSION REASSEMBLY

NOTE: Handle all parts carefully to avoid damaging bearings and mating surfaces. Lubricate all parts with clean transmission fluid. Use petroleum jelly on gaskets, thrust washers, and needle bearings to retain in place. Use new gaskets and seals.

1) Install No. 9 output shaft needle bearing in transmission case. Install bearing support, No. 7 needle bearing and direct clutch hub in direct clutch assembly. Assemble output shaft hub to output shaft and install retaining snap ring.

2) Place No. 8 needle bearing on rear of direct clutch drum. Slide output shaft into direct clutch drum. Attach output shaft hub to ring gear with retaining ring. Install output shaft, ring gear, and direct clutch assembly into transmission case. *See Fig. 29.*

Fig. 29: Installing Direct Clutch Assembly

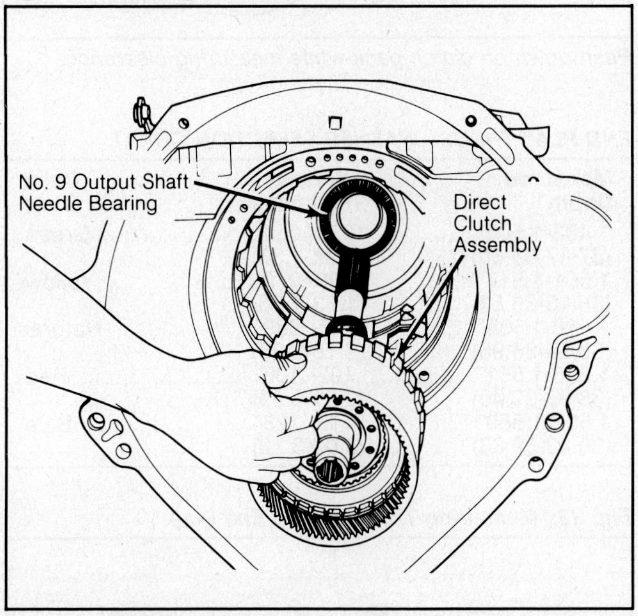

Fig. 30: Aligning Center Support Notch with Overdrive Band Anchor Pin.

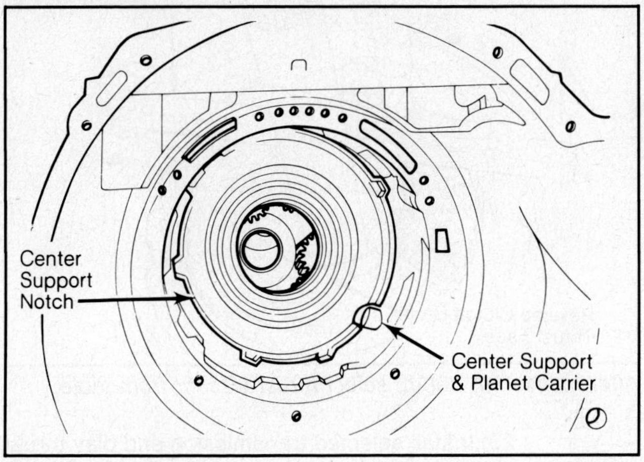

3) Position governor drive ball in pocket on output shaft. Slide governor assembly onto output shaft with cover and attaching screws facing toward front of case. Install governor retaining snap ring.

4) Clean mating surface on transmission and extension housing. Position new gasket on transmission. Slide extension housing into place.

5) Clean the bolts and case holes for the 2 bottom bolts and the lower right hand corner bolt (as viewed from the rear of the extension housing). Coat the bolts with Teflon tape and install. Install remaining bolts and tighten all to specification.

6) Install low-reverse band into transmission case and make sure band is seated on anchor pins. When properly installed, center of band actuating rod seat can be seen through servo piston bore.

7) Install center support and planetary assembly into case. If necessary, rotate output shaft to align planet carrier splines with direct clutch hub splines. Install center support anti-clunk spring using a hammer handle or wooden dowel. Spring tabs must face out.

NOTE: Center support and planet carrier cannot be installed unless notch cut in center support is aligned with overdrive band anchor pin. *See Fig. 30.*

8) Install center support retaining ring.

9) Determine correct length of low-reverse servo pin to use. Lubricate and install servo piston and return spring. Do not install cover or retaining ring. Install Servo Selector Gauge (T80L-77030-A) into servo bore.

10) Tighten band apply bolt on tool to 50 INCH lbs. (5.6 N.m). Attach dial indicator. *See Fig. 31.* Position indicator stem on flat portion of servo piston. Zero dial indicator.

11) Thread bolt out of selector tool until piston stops against bottom of tool. Read amount of piston travel on dial indicator. If travel is 0.112"-.237" (2.845-6.020 mm), correct servo pin is installed. If travel is not within specifications, selective pistons are available in lengths of: 2.936" identified by 1 groove, 2.989" (2 grooves), and 3.043" (3 grooves).

12) Length is measured from base of piston to end of rod. Select proper servo rod to bring servo travel within specifications. Remove selector tool and dial indicator.

Fig. 31: Low-Reverse Servo Pin Selection

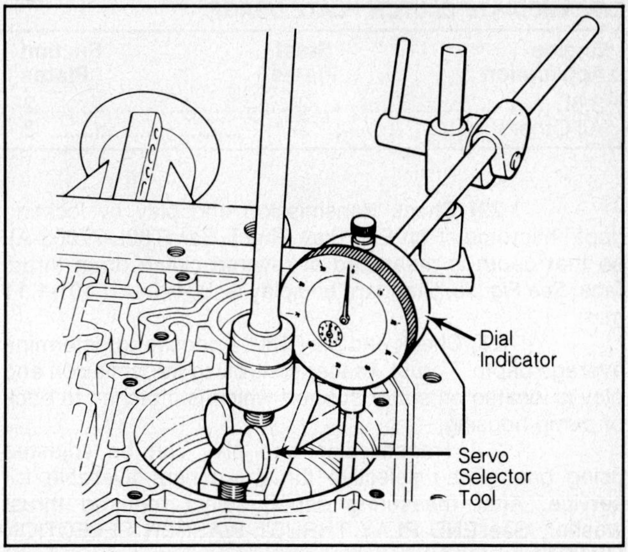

Position indicator stem on flat portion of servo piston.

Automatic Transmissions
FORD MOTOR CO. AOT (Cont.)

13) Install selected low-reverse servo piston. Install servo cover and cover retaining snap ring.

14) Make sure No. 2 thrust washer is in position in reverse clutch. Assemble reverse clutch on forward clutch. Install No. 3 needle bearing and forward clutch hub in forward clutch. Position No. 4 needle bearing on forward clutch hub.

15) Install drive shell over clutch assemblies. Install No. 5 needle bearing and forward sun gear on drive shell. Install complete assembly into case, rotating output to aid in engaging sun gear with planetary gears.

16) Install overdrive band into case and around drive shell assembly. Ensure band anchor is properly positioned on anchor pin. Using a screwdriver to hold overdrive band in position, lubricate and install overdrive servo.

17) With overdrive servo installed, inspect band and apply pin for proper position and engagement. If band anchor and apply pin are not properly engaged, remove servo and reposition band as necessary.

18) Install intermediate clutch pack components into case in the following order: Pressure plate, clutch pack (starting with a friction plate and alternating steel and friction plates) and selective steel plate. Measure intermediate clutch clearance as follows.

19) Intermediate clutch clearance is measured using a depth micrometer and End Play Checking Tool (T80L-77003-A). *See Fig. 32.* Set end play tool across pump case mounting surface. Locate micrometer end play bar and read depth.

20) Check depth again with micrometer at 180° opposite from previous measurement. Depth at intermediate clutch selective steel plate should be 1.629-1.640" (41.38-41.66 mm) if vehicle is equipped with 3.8L engine, and 1.634-1.646" (41.50-41.81 mm) for all other models. Average of the 2 measurements should be within this range.

NOTE: A downward pressure must be applied to clutch pack while measuring intermediate clutch clearance.

21) If intermediate clutch clearance is not within tolerance, the following size selective steel plates are available: .067-.071", .077-.081", .087-.091", and .097-.101". Install correct size plate and recheck clearance.

INTERMEDIATE CLUTCH PLATE USAGE

Engine Application	Steel Plates	Friction Plates
3.8L	2	2
All Others	3	3

22) Check transmission end play by locating depth micrometer on End Play Check Bar (T80L-77003-A), so that depth is measured at reverse clutch drum thrust face. *See Fig. 33.* Standard end play is .004-.044" (.101-1.11 mm).

23) Check end play 180° opposite to determine average depth. Thrust washer controlling transmission end play is located on stator support which is attached to back of pump housing.

24) Transmission end play can be adjusted using one of the selective thrust washers available for service. After measuring depth, select required thrust washer. See END PLAY THRUST WASHER SELECTION CHART.

Fig. 32: Measuring Intermediate Clutch Clearance

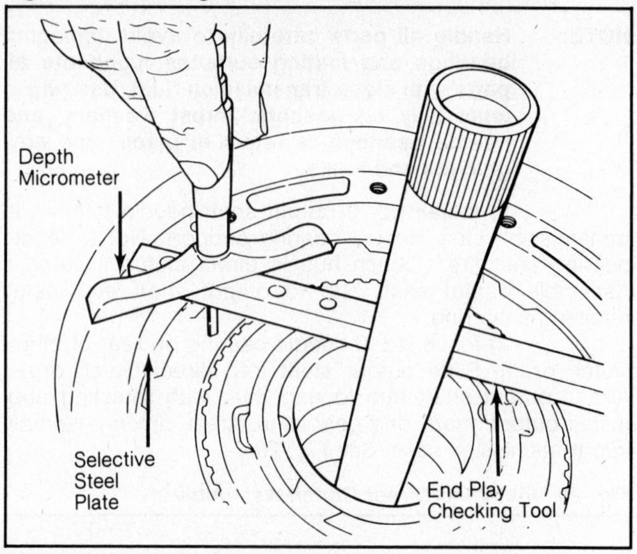

Push down on clutch pack while measuring clearance.

END PLAY THRUST WASHER SELECTION CHART

Measured Depth	Washer Thickness	Color Code
1.483-1.500" (37.67-38.10)	.050-.054" (1.27-1.37)	Green
1.501-1.517" (38.13-38.53)	.068-.072" (1.73-1.83)	Yellow
1.518-1.534" (38.56-38.96)	.085-.089" (2.16-2.26)	Natural
1.535-1.551" (38.99-39.40)	.102-.106" (2.59-2.69)	Red
1.552-1.568" (39.42-39.83)	.119-.123" (3.02-3.12)	Blue

Fig. 33: Measuring Transmission End Play

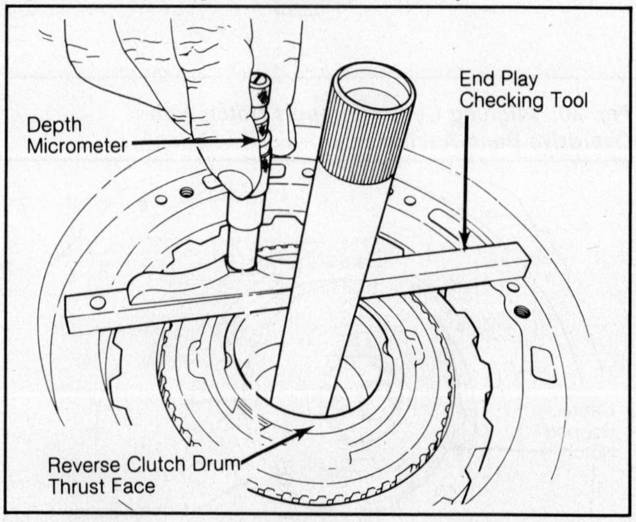

After measuring depth, select thrust washer from table.

25) Install selected transmission end play thrust washer on stator support. Use petroleum jelly to hold it in place. Install pump alignment dowel, made by cutting the head from a M8-1.25 bolt, into pump mounting bolt hole at 6 o'clock position.

place. Install pump alignment dowel, made by cutting the head from a M8-1.25 bolt, into pump mounting bolt hole at 6 o'clock position.

26) Install new pump gasket into case. Install pump assembly into case using 2 slide hammers to lower pump into position. Remove alignment dowel.

27) Coat all pump-to-case bolts with threadlock or sealant and install. Alternately tighten bolts a few turns at a time to draw pump into case.

28) Assemble 3-4 accumulator. Install piston (and spring, if so equipped) into case. Lubricate rubber seal on accumulator cover and top of bore to help cover installation. Install cover and retaining ring. Install 2-3 accumulator assembly.

CAUTION: After installation, 3-4 accumulator cover must be seated firmly against retaining ring. Use air pressure if necessary to seat cover against ring.

29) Install 2 valve body Alignment Pins (T80L-77100-A) into valve body. Install valve body gasket and valve body assembly over pins, making sure manual and throttle levers are properly positioned before installing valve body retaining bolts.

30) Loosely install valve body retaining bolts. Starting at center and working outward, tighten bolts. Remove alignment pins and install bolts. Install detent spring and roller assembly and tighten bolts.

NOTE: Two different length valve body retaining bolts are used. Shorter bolts are used at the 4 front, 1 center and 3 rear locations.

31) Position torsion spring against separator plate "V" notch. This spring pushes the throttle lever in direction of wide open throttle.

32) Install filter grommet, new filter gasket, and filter on valve body. Install filter attaching bolts and tighten. Position new pan gasket on case and install oil pan.

33) Slide direct drive shaft into turbine input shaft. Install torque converter, making sure it is fully seated in pump.

TIGHTENING SPECIFICATIONS

Application	Ft. Lbs. (N.m)
Converter-to-Flywheel	20-34 (27-46)
Converter Plug-to-Converter	8-28 (11-38)
Cooler Line-to-Case	18-23 (24-31)
Extension-to-Case	16-20 (22-27)
Inner Manual Lever-to-Shaft	19-27 (26-37)
Oil Pan-to-Case	6-10 (8-13)
Outer Throttle Lever-to-Shaft	12-16 (16-22)
Pressure Plug-to-Case	6-12 (8-16)
Pump-to-Case	16-20 (22-27)
Stator Support-to-Pump	12-16 (16-22)
Transmission-to-Engine	40-50 (54-68)
	INCH Lbs (N.m)
Cover-to-Governor Body	20-30 (2.3-3.4)
Filter-to-Valve Body	80-120 (9-14)
Governor Body-to-Counterweight	50-60 (6-7)
Reinforcing Plate-to-Valve Body	80-120 (9-14)
Separator Plate-to-Valve Body	80-100 (9-11)
Valve Body-to-Case	80-100 (9-11)

FORD MOTOR CO. ATX – AUTOMATIC TRANSAXLE

Escort, EXP, Lynx, Sable, Taurus, Tempo, Topaz

IDENTIFICATION

Transaxle can be identified by the letter "B" or "O" on lower line of Vehicle Certification Label under "TR". Gear ratio is determined by the letter code under "AX" of Vehicle Certification Label. The label is attached to left side door lock panel.

Transaxle can be identified by a metal tag attached to valve body cover. First line on tag shows build date code and model number. Bottom line on tag shows serial and assembly part number prefix and suffix.

TRANSAXLE IDENTIFICATION CODES

Application	Axle Ratio	Code
All Models		
Auto. Trans.	3.23:1	2

DESCRIPTION

The ATX combines an automatic transmission and differential into a single unit designed for front wheel drive vehicles. Transmission and differential are housed in a light-alloy housing. The transmission uses 3 friction clutches, 1 band, and a single one-way clutch. These components are applied as necessary to transmit engine torque through a compound planetary gear set.

The planetary provides 3 forward gear ratios and 1 reverse. The planetary transmits engine torque to the input gear, which meshes with the differential idler gear. The idler gear meshes with the differential ring gear, which is riveted to differential case. Engine torque flows outward to the wheels through differential gears.

To minimize torque converter inefficiency, the ATX contains a splitter gear to provide a mechanical connection between the engine and transaxle. Splitter gear is similiar to a planetary gear set. In 1st and reverse, engine torque is hydraulically transmitted. In 2nd gear, 62% of engine torque is transmitted mechanically through the splitter gear. Converter slip is less than 7% when ATX is in 3rd gear.

Taurus and Sable models use a new CLC (Centifugal Locking Converter), which resembles other ATX converters, but has a centrifugal clutch added. This converter is similar to one used in C-5 transmission. The converter changes the hydraulic coupling to a 100% mechanical coupling after input shaft speed reaches 900 RPM. The overall effect of the CLC converter is to provide an improved shift feel and to reduce tip-in back-out clunk.

LUBRICATION & ADJUSTMENTS

See appropriate AUTOMATIC TRANSMISSION SERVICING article in DOMESTIC GENERAL SERVICING section.

TROUBLE SHOOTING

See appropriate AUTOMATIC TRANSMISSION TROUBLE SHOOTING article in DOMESTIC GENERAL SERVICING section.

TESTING

ROAD TEST

This check will determine if governor pressure and shift control valves are functioning properly.

1) Check minimum throttle upshifts in Drive. Transaxle should start in 1st gear, shift to 2nd, and then shift to 3rd at approximately the speeds shown in ATX SHIFT SPEEDS tables.

2) With transaxle in 3rd, depress accelerator pedal to floor. Transaxle should shift from 3rd to 2nd or 1st, depending on vehicle speed. See ATX SHIFT SPEEDS tables.

3) Check closed throttle downshifts from 3rd to 1st by coasting down from approximately 30 MPH in 3rd gear. Shift should occur at approximate speed shown in ATX SHIFT SPEEDS tables.

NOTE: When selector lever is at "2", transaxle will operate in 1st and 2nd gears.

4) With transaxle in 3rd and road speed above 30 MPH, transaxle should shift to 2nd gear when selector lever is moved from to 3rd to 1st. Transaxle will shift into 1st when road speed is less than 30 MPH. When transaxle is shifted from Drive to 2nd, it should always, regardless of vehicle speed, shift into 2nd gear.

GOVERNOR CHECK

Accelerate vehicle to 30-40 MPH, then back off throttle completely. If governor is functioning properly, transaxle will shift to 3rd gear.

LINE PRESSURE TEST

1) Connect a 0-300 psi pressure gauge to line pressure test port on transaxle case. *See Fig. 1.* Run engine until normal operating temperature is reached.

2) Apply service and parking brakes. Check line pressure in all selector lever positions with engine at idle and then with engine at wide open throttle. Pressures should be as specified. See LINE PRESSURE SPECIFICATIONS table.

LINE PRESSURE TEST RESULTS

Low at Idle in All Ranges

Check engine EGR system. Check for low fluid level, restricted intake screen or filter, loose valve body or regulator-to-case bolts, loose oil tubes, excessive leakage in oil pump, case, valve body or sticking control pressure regulator valve.

High at Idle in All Ranges

Check throttle valve or control rod adjustment, and T.V. linkage return spring, or sticking regulator boost valve(s).

Low in "P" or "N"

Faulty valve body.

Low in "D"

Faulty servo or valve body.

Low in "2"

Faulty valve body and/or intermediate servo.

Low in "1"

Faulty direct clutch and/or valve body.

Low in "R"

Faulty direct clutch and/or reverse clutch. Faulty valve body.

Automatic Transmissions

FORD MOTOR CO. ATX – AUTOMATIC TRANSAXLE (Cont.)

STALL TEST

1) Start engine and allow it to reach normal operating temperature. Apply both parking and service brakes. Stall test is made in all Drive ranges and Reverse at full throttle.

2) Stall testing is to check engine performance, converter operation or installation and holding ability of the direct clutch, reverse clutch and low-intermediate band brake and gear train one-way clutch.

NOTE: **While performing this test, DO NOT hold throttle open for more than 5 seconds at a time.**

3) After test, move gear selector lever to "N" and run engine at 1000 RPM for about 15 seconds to cool converter before making next test. If engine speed recorded by tachometer exceeds maximum limits given in specifications, RELEASE ACCELERATOR IMMEDIATELY because clutch or band brake slippage is indicated.

STALL SPEED SPECIFICATIONS

Application	Stall RPM
1.9L (EFI)	2959-3475
1.9L (2 Barrel)	2951-3431
2.3L (HSC CFI)	2422-2808
2.3L (HSC IV)	2214-2607
2.5L (HSC CFI)	2422-2808

STALL TEST RESULTS

1) If stall speed(s) are high (slip) in "D" or "2", check turbine shaft one-way clutch. If condition exists in "D", "2" and "1", check low-intermediate band or servo. If

CLUTCH AND BAND APPLICATION CHART (ELEMENTS IN USE)

Selector Lever Position	Band	Direct Clutch	Intermed. Clutch	Reverse Clutch	Intermed. One-Way Clutch
D — DRIVE					
First Gear	X				X
Second Gear	X		X		
Third Gear		X	X		
2 — INTERMEDIATE					
Second Gear	X		X		
1 — LOW					
First Gear	X	X			X
R — REVERSE		X		X	X
P — Park					X
N — Neutral					X

ATX SHIFT SPEEDS – ACTUAL M.P.H.

MODEL PMA-AD, AM
1.9L 2V ESCORT/LYNX

Throttle Opening	Drive Range	Shift	Km/Hr (MPH)
Idle (Closed Throttle)	*D	1-2	18-30 (11-18)
	*D	2-3	25-50 (16-31)
	D	3-2	27-39 (17-24)
	D	2-1	15-23 (9-15)
	1	2-1	40-69 (25-43)
Part Throttle @	D	1-2	23-48 (14-30)
	D	2-3	53-80 (30-50)
	D	3-2	42-71 (26-44)
	D	2-1	23-35 (14-22)
Wide Open Throttle (WOT)	D	1-2	45-74 (28-46)
	D	2-3	95-124 (59-77)
	D	3-2	87-113 (54-70)
	D	2-1	28-55 (18-34)

* Upshifts are taken at minimum throttle (10′ throttle rotation from idle step).

@ Partial throttle shift speeds were made with line pressure at 648-772 kPa (94-112 psi)

Tire Size	Axle Ratio
P165/80R13	3.23:1
P175/80R13	
P185/70R14 (29/25 EXP)	

MODEL PMA-AP
1.9L 2V ESCORT/LYNX

Throttle Opening	Drive Range	Shift	Km/Hr (MPH)
Idle (Closed Throttle)	*D	1-2	24-35 (15-22)
	*D	2-3	34-58 (21-36)
	D	3-2	29-41 (18-25)
	D	2-1	15-23 (9-15)
	1	2-1	42-71 (26-44)
Part Throttle @	D	1-2	24-50 (15-31)
	D	2-3	55-82 (34-51)
	D	3-2	39-68 (24-42)
	D	2-1	24-36 (15-23)
Wide Open Throttle (WOT)	D	1-2	53-82 (33-51)
	D	2-3	100-129 (62-80)
	D	3-2	92-117 (57-73)
	D	2-1	34-60 (21-37)

* Upshifts are taken at minimum throttle (10′ throttle rotation from idle step).

@ Partial throttle shift speeds were made with line pressure at 600-724 kPa (87-105 psi)

Tire Size	Axle Ratio
P185/70R14 Handling EXP	3.23:1
P195/60HR15	

FORD MOTOR CO. ATX – AUTOMATIC TRANSAXLE (Cont.)

ATX SHIFT SPEEDS – ACTUAL M.P.H. (Cont.)

MODEL PMA-N
2.3L HSC-CFI TEMPO/TOPAZ

Throttle Opening	Drive Range	Shift	Km/Hr (MPH)
Idle (Closed Throttle)	*D	1-2	16-28 (10-17)
	*D	2-3	24-48 (15-30)
	D	3-2	27-42 (17-26)
	D	2-1	14-24 (9-15)
	1	2-1	35-64 (22-40)
Part Throttle @	D	1-2	19-45 (12-28)
	D	2-3	43-71 (27-44)
	D	3-2	34-64 (21-40)
	D	2-1	19-31 (12-19)
Wide Open Throttle (WOT)	D	1-2	38-67 (24-42)
	D	2-3	85-113 (53-70)
	D	3-2	77-104 (48-65)
	D	2-1	24-50 (15-31)

* Upshifts are taken at minimum throttle (10′ throttle rotation from idle step).

@ Partial throttle shift speeds were made with line pressure at 586-710 kPa (85-103 psi)

Tire Size	Axle Ratio
P185/70R14	3.23:1
P185/70R14 Handling	
P195/60HR15	

MODEL PMB-S, T
1.9L 2V ESCORT/LYNX

Throttle Opening	Drive Range	Shift	Km/Hr (MPH)
Idle (Closed Throttle)	*D	1-2	18-30 (12-19)
	*D	2-3	25-50 (16-31)
	D	3-2	27-39 (17-24)
	D	2-1	15-23 (9-15)
	1	2-1	40-69 (25-43)
Part Throttle @	D	1-2	20-45 (12-28)
	D	2-3	48-76 (30-47)
	D	3-2	37-66 (23-41)
	D	2-1	23-35 (14-22)
Wide Open Throttle (WOT)	D	1-2	50-79 (31-49)
	D	2-3	95-124 (59-77)
	D	3-2	85-113 (54-70)
	D	2-1	28-55 (18-34)

* Upshifts are taken at minimum throttle (10′ throttle rotation from idle step).

@ Partial throttle shift speeds were made with line pressure at 648-772 kPa (94-112 psi)

Tire Size	Axle Ratio
P165/80R13	3.23:1
P175/80R13	
P185/70R14 (29/25 EXP)	

MODEL PMA-AK
2.5L CLC TAURUS/SABLE

Throttle Opening	Drive Range	Shift	Km/Hr (MPH)
Idle (Closed Throttle)	*D	1-2	16-28 (10-17)
	*D	2-3	24-48 (15-30)
	D	3-2	23-37 (14-23)
	D	2-1	10-20 (6-12)
	1	2-1	29-58 (18-36)
Part Throttle @	D	1-2	19-45 (12-28)
	D	2-3	42-70 (26-43)
	D	3-2	24-54 (15-34)
	D	2-1	13-24 (8-15)
Wide Open Throttle (WOT)	D	1-2	45-74 (28-46)
	D	2-3	89-116 (55-72)
	D	3-2	80-108 (50-67)
	D	2-1	20-45 (12-28)

* Upshifts are taken at minimum throttle (10′ throttle rotation from idle step).

@ Partial throttle shift speeds were made with line pressure at 414-538 kPa (60-78 psi)

Tire Size	Axle Ratio
P195/70R14	3.23:1
P205/70R14	
P205/65R15	

MODEL PMA-P
1.9L EFI ENGINE
MODEL PMA-N
2.3L HSC ENGINE

		PMA-P		PMA-N	
		1.9 EFI Engine		2.3L HSC Engine	
Drive Range		km/h	mph	km/h	mph
Idle:	1-2	16-30	10-19	17-29	11-18
	2-3	24-50	15-31	25-50	16-31
	3-2	22-40	14-25	26-40	16-25
	2-1	16-24	10-15	15-23	9-14
Part Throttle:	1-2	18-27	11-17	19-44	12-27
	2-3	38-67	24-42	42-70	26-43
	3-2	32-61	20-38	36-45	22-41
WOT:	1-2	54-82	34-51	38-66	23-41
	2-3	98-125	61-78	84-112	52-69
	3-2	88-117	55-73	76-102	49-64
	2-1	45-70	28-44	24-51	15-32
Manual Low:	2-1	32-61	20-38	32-61	20-38

FORD MOTOR CO. ATX – AUTOMATIC TRANSAXLE (Cont.)

Fig. 1: Line Pressure Test Port

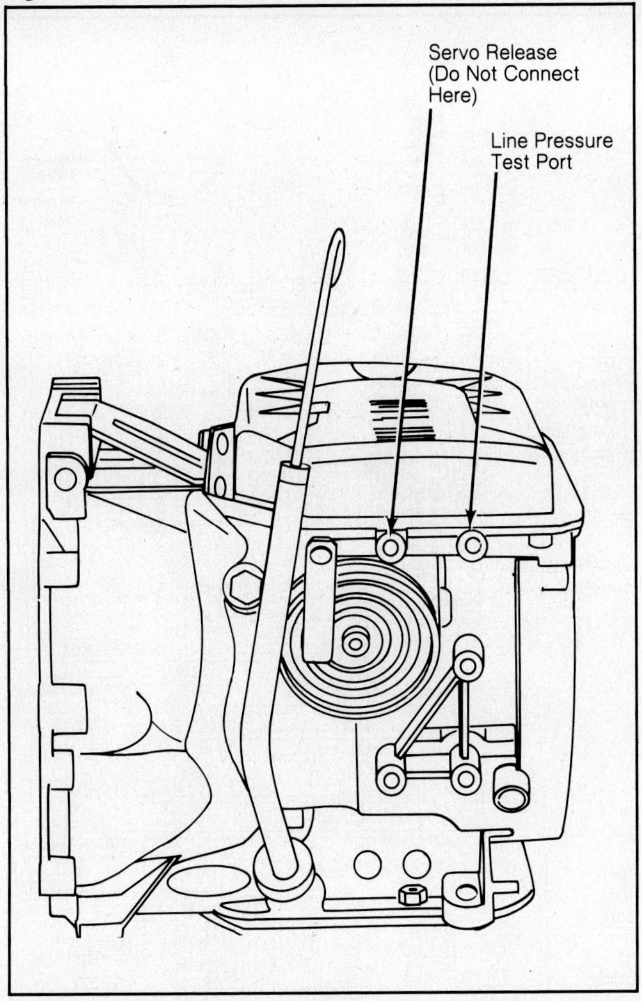

condition exists in "R", check reverse clutch. If condition exists in all driving ranges, check T.V. control adjustment and perform line pressure test.

2) If stall speeds are low, check engine for tune-up. If tune is okay, remove torque converter and bench test for reactor one-way clutch slippage.

AIR PRESSURE TESTS

"No Drive" condition can exist even with correct transaxle fluid pressure, because of inoperative clutches or band. Erratic shifts could be caused by a stuck governor valve. Inoperative units can be located through a series of checks by substituting air pressure for fluid pressure to determine location of malfunction.

To make air pressure checks, loosen valve body cover bolts, then remove cover and valve body assembly. Install Special Adapter Plate (T82P-7006-B) in place of valve body. *See Fig. 2.* Inoperative units can be located by applying air pressure in transaxle case passages, through adapter plate, leading to clutches, servo, and governor. *See Fig. 2.*

NOTE: **Air pressure test adapter plate should be installed with a new valve body gasket. Tighten attaching bolts to 80-100 INCH lbs. (9-11 N.m).**

LINE PRESSURE SPECIFICATIONS

Selector Position	Pressure Psi (kg/cm²)
PMA, AD2, AM, PMB-S2, T Models	
At Idle	
"D", "1", "2", "P", "N"	57-70 (4.0-4.9)
"R"	79-115 (5.5-8.0)
At WOT Stall	
"D", "1", "2", "P", "N"	101-119 (7.1-8.3)
"R"	206-258 (14.4-18.1)
PMA-U & PMA-AP	
At Idle	
"D", "1", "2", "P", "N"	56-69 (3.9-4.8)
"R"	84-120 (5.9-8.4)
At WOT Stall	
"D", "1", "2", "P", "N"	105-123 (7.3-8.6)
"R"	215-267 (15.1-18.7)
PMA-N9	
At Idle	
"D", "1", "2", "P", "N"	48-60 (3.3-4.2)
"R"	65-99 (4.5-6.9)
At WOT Stall	
"D", "1", "2", "P", "N"	99-115 (6.9-8.0)
"R"	195-247 (13.7-17.4)
PMA-AK	
At Idle	
"D", "1", "2", "P", "N"	45-57 (3.1-4.0)
"R"	56-92 (3.9-6.4)
At WOT Stall	
"D", "1", "2", "P", "N"	98-114 (6.8-8.0)
"R"	196-246 (13.7-17.2)

Fig. 2: Air Pressure Test Apply Ports on Adapter Plate

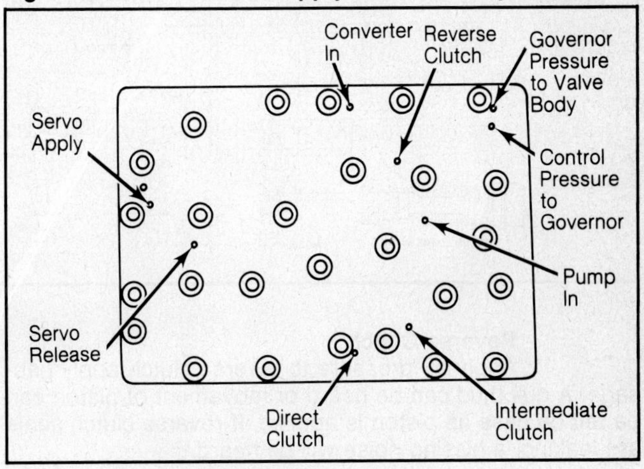

Band Apply Servo

Apply air pressure to servo apply passage. Band should apply. A dull thud should be heard when air pressure is removed, allowing servo piston to return to release position.

Direct Clutch

Apply air pressure to direct clutch apply passage. A dull thud can be heard or movement of piston can be felt as piston is applied. If direct clutch seals are leaking, a hissing noise will be heard.

Intermediate Clutch

Apply air pressure to intermediate clutch apply passage. A dull thud can be heard or movement of piston can be felt on case as piston is applied. If intermediate clutch seals are leaking, a hissing noise will be heard.

FORD MOTOR CO. ATX – AUTOMATIC TRANSAXLE (Cont.)

Fig. 3: ATX Automatic Transaxle Hydraulic Circuits Diagram

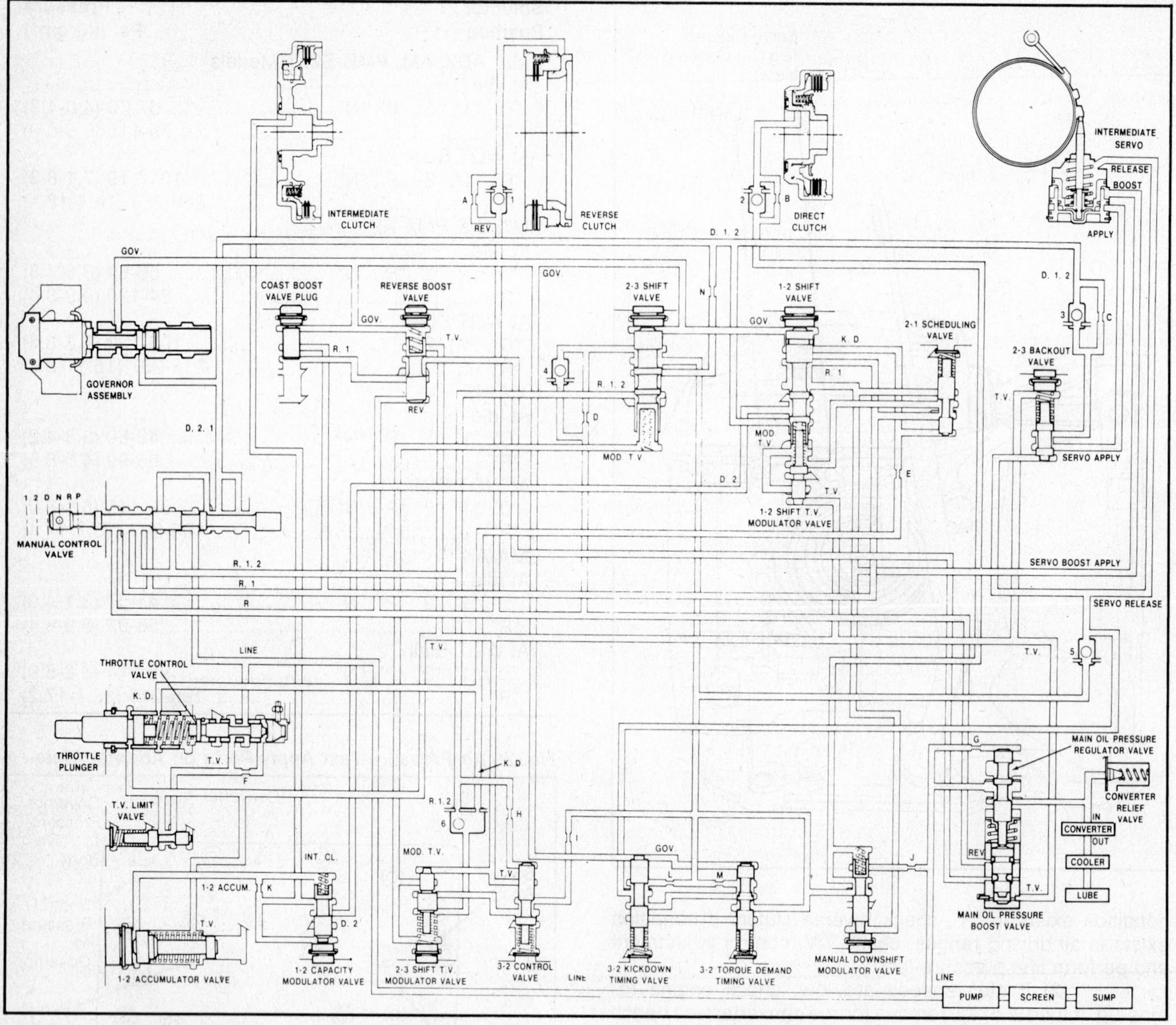

Reverse Clutch

Apply air pressure to reverse clutch apply passage. A dull thud can be heard or movement of piston can be felt on case as piston is applied. If reverse clutch seals are leaking, a hissing noise will be heard.

Converter In

This passage can only be checked for blockage. If passage holds air pressure, remove adapter plate and check for an obstruction or damage.

Control Pressure-to-Governor

Remove governor cover. Apply air pressure to control pressure-to-governor apply passage. Watch for movement of governor valve.

Governor Pressure-to-Valve Body

This passage can only be checked for blockage. If passage holds air pressure, remove adapter plate and check for an obstruction or damage.

Pump In (Bench Test)

With transaxle removed from vehicle and converter removed, apply air pressure to pump in apply passage. Rotation of pump gears should be heard when air pressure is applied.

NOTE: "Pump In" check is normally performed during assembly of an overhauled transaxle.

SERVICE (IN VEHICLE)

DRIVE AXLE SHAFTS

See appropriate DRIVE AXLE SHAFT article in DOMESTIC FWD AXLE SHAFTS, OVERDRIVES & TRANSFER CASES section.

VALVE BODY

Removal

1) Apply parking brake. Open hood and remove battery and battery tray. Remove ignition coil and transaxle dipstick. Remove air cleaner assembly.

2) Disconnect supply hoses and vacuum lines from managed air valve (if equipped), then remove valve from valve body cover.

FORD MOTOR CO. ATX – AUTOMATIC TRANSAXLE (Cont.)

3) Remove attaching bolts, then lift off valve body cover and gasket. Remove valve body-to-case attaching bolts, then remove valve body and gasket from transaxle case.

Installation

1) Install 2 Alignment Pins (T80L-77100-A) into opposing valve body attaching bolt holes, then install valve body-to-case gasket. Install valve body assembly into case, removing 1 alignment pin to allow attachment of manual valve to "Z" link. Reinstall alignment pin.

NOTE: Ensure roller on end of throttle valve plunger has engaged cam on end of throttle lever shaft.

2) Connect throttle valve control spring. Remove alignment pins. Install 27 valve body attaching bolts, detent spring, main oil pressure regulator baffle plate and transaxle control baffle plate. Tighten valve body attaching bolts.

3) Install new valve body cover gasket on case, then install and tighten cover attaching bolts, making sure transaxle I.D. tag is installed in its original position.

4) To complete installation, reverse removal procedure. Check and adjust transaxle fluid level.

GOVERNOR

Removal

Apply parking brake and disconnect battery. Remove air cleaner. Using a long screwdriver, remove governor retaining clip. Remove governor cover and pull out governor.

Installation

To install governor, reverse removal procedure. Slide governor in carefully, allowing gear teeth to mesh. DO NOT force in. Install a new "O" ring seal on governor cover. Check transaxle fluid level and add fluid if necessary.

LOW-INTERMEDIATE SERVO

Removal

1) Apply parking brake and disconnect battery. Disconnect fan motor and water temperature sending unit wiring. If equipped, disconnect FM capacitor wiring.

2) Remove fan and shroud assembly. Place drain pan under transaxle. Remove filler tube-to-case attaching bolt using care not to lose service I.D. tag which is attached with bolt. Remove filler tube.

3) From left front mount remove lower left mount-to-case attaching bolt. Using a Servo Compressor (T81P-70027-A), compress servo cover and remove retaining snap ring, then remove cover and servo assembly.

Installation

To install servo, reverse removal procedure. Refill transaxle with fluid.

REMOVAL & INSTALLATION

TRANSAXLE

See appropriate AUTOMATIC TRANSMISSION REMOVAL article in DOMESTIC GENERAL SERVICING section.

TORQUE CONVERTER

LEAKAGE CHECK

See procedures given in FORD MOTOR CO. C-6 article.

FLUSHING CONVERTER

See procedures given in FORD MOTOR CO. C-6 article.

STATOR TO IMPELLER INTERFERENCE CHECK

See procedures given in FORD MOTOR CO. C-6 article.

STATOR TO TURBINE INTERFERENCE CHECK

See procedures given in FORD MOTOR CO. C-6 article.

REACTOR ONE-WAY CLUTCH CHECK

See procedures given in FORD MOTOR CO. C-6 article.

CONVERTER END PLAY CHECK

See procedures given in FORD MOTOR CO. C-6 article.

TRANSAXLE DISASSEMBLY

1) Mount transaxle in a holding stand. Pull torque converter from case, then remove oil pump drive shaft. Remove filler tube from case. Remove governor cover retainer from case. Pry off cover and pull governor from case. Remove 13 oil pan attaching bolts, then remove oil pan. Remove 3 attaching bolts and lift out oil filter and seal.

2) Remove 6 differential bearing retainer-to-case attaching bolts, then pry retainer from case. Remove differential bearing preload and tapered shims located under bearing retainer. Remove differential assembly from transaxle case.

3) Remove 10 valve body cover bolts and remove cover. Disconnect and remove throttle lever return spring. Remove 27 valve body attaching bolts. Remove main oil pressure regulator baffle plate. Remove transaxle control baffle plate. Remove detent spring and roller assembly. Disengage "Z" link from manual valve and remove valve body assembly.

NOTE: The 7 main oil pressure regulator baffle plate attaching bolts are longer than the other valve body attaching bolts.

4) Lift governor screen from bore in case (located under valve body). Pry speedometer driven gear retaining pin partially out of case, then remove pin using side cutters. Tap driven gear from case using a hammer handle.

5) Remove 7 oil pump attaching bolts and washers. Remove pump from case using a slide hammer puller. Remove selective thrust washer from under pump body. Remove and discard pump gasket. Remove No. 11 thrust bearing (needle) from top of intermediate clutch, then remove clutch assembly from case.

FORD MOTOR CO. ATX – AUTOMATIC TRANSAXLE (Cont.)

6) Remove No. 10 thrust bearing (needle) from direct clutch, then remove direct clutch from case. Remove intermediate clutch hub and ring gear assembly. Remove No. 7 thrust washer from planetary assembly.

7) Remove large snap ring securing reverse clutch in case, then pull reverse clutch pack from case. Remove planetary assembly and No. 5 thrust washer from case. Remove reverse clutch return springs and holder assembly. Pull reverse clutch piston from case. Pry reverse clutch drum up to loosen and remove from case.

8) Using a compressor tool, compress servo and remove retaining snap ring. Slowly release spring pressure, then remove compressor tool and servo assembly. Remove low-intermediate band from inside case.

9) Remove sun gear and drum assembly from case, then remove thrust washer No. 4 from final drive housing at rear of case. Remove 5 final drive housing-to-case attaching bolts. Use a screwdriver and pry housing from idler gear shaft and remove from case. DO NOT pry downward against transfer gear teeth or damage will result.

NOTE: **Discard final drive gear housing bolts. Replace with new bolts and use high strength thread adhesive.**

10) Remove No. 3 thrust bearing (needle) from input gear and remove input gear from case. Remove input gear caged needle bearing No. 2, and No. 1 thrust bearing (needle) located under it, from case.

11) Position a 12 mm Allen wrench in idler gear shaft and allow wrench to catch on side of case. With wrench holding idler gear shaft, remove nut from rear of shaft using a 32 mm/12 point socket. Tap idler gear shaft with a hammer handle to loosen "O" ring, then remove shaft from case.

12) Remove reactor support from case if damaged or unservicable. Reactor support is pressed in case. Remove with Puller (T81P-70363-A).

COMPONENT DISASSEMBLY & REASSEMBLY

OIL PUMP

Disassembly

1) Remove No. 12 selective fit thrust washer and oil seal rings from clutch support. Remove pump-to-case oil seal ring from outside diameter of clutch support.

2) Remove 5 clutch support-to-pump body attaching bolts, then separate support from pump body. Remove insert from pump drive gear. Remove driven gear and drive gear from pump body.

Fig. 5: Exploded View of Oil Pump

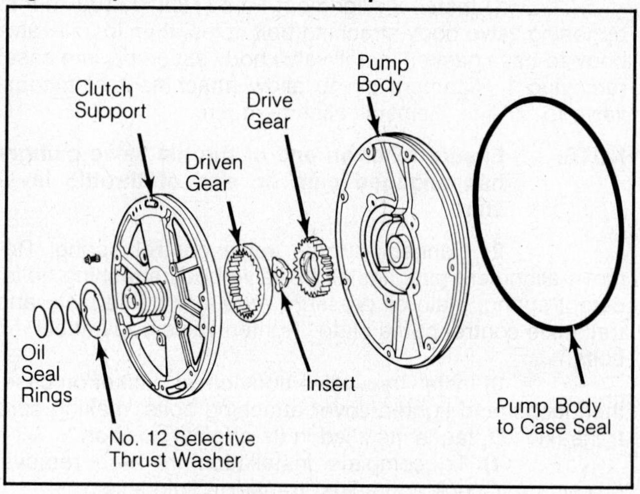

Reassembly

Reverse disassembly procedure making sure ends of scarf-cut oil seal rings are correctly positioned. Tighten support-to-pump bolts to specifications.

INTERMEDIATE CLUTCH

Disassembly

1) Remove intermediate shaft snap ring, then pull shaft from intermediate clutch drum. If damaged, remove stop ring from intermediate shaft.

2) Remove clutch pack retaining snap ring and withdraw pressure plate, wave spring, and clutch pack. Remove seal rings from clutch drum hub.

3) Using Clutch Spring Compressor (T81P-70222-A), compress clutch return springs and remove retaining snap ring. Remove tool and lift return spring retainer and spring assembly from clutch drum.

4) Using pliers, remove clutch piston from drum. Remove inner piston seal from clutch drum and outer piston seal from clutch piston.

Fig. 4: Exploded View of Intermediate Clutch Assembly

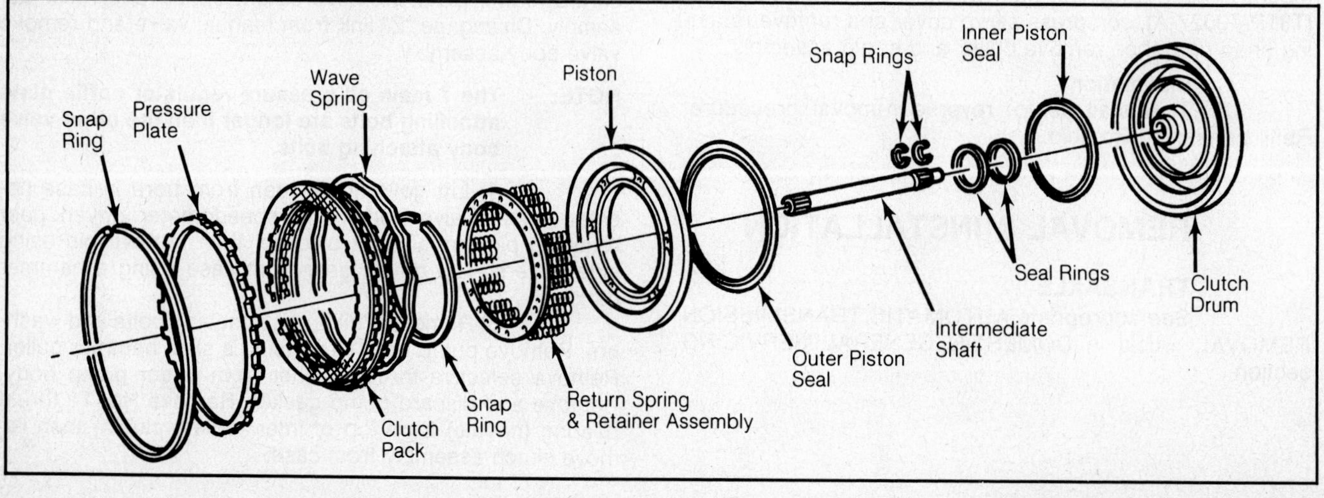

FORD MOTOR CO. ATX – AUTOMATIC TRANSAXLE (Cont.)

Fig. 6: Exploded View of Direct Clutch Assembly

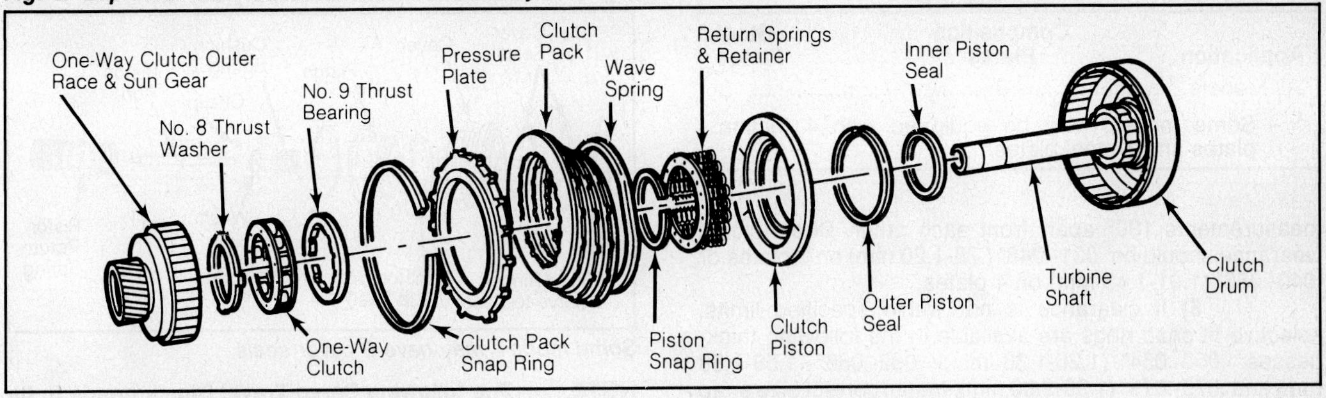

Cleaning & Inspection

1) Inspect clutch drum thrust surfaces, piston bore, and clutch plate serrations for scores or burrs. Minor scores or burrs may be removed with crocus cloth. Replace drum if it is badly scored or damaged.

2) Check fluid passage in clutch drum for obstructions. Clean out all passages. Inspect clutch piston for scores and replace if necessary. Inspect piston check ball for freedom of movement and proper seating.

3) Inspect clutch return springs for distortion and cracks. Inspect composition plates, steel plates and pressure plate for worn or scored bearing surfaces. Replace all parts that are deeply scored.

4) Check clutch plates for flatness and fit on clutch drum hub serrations. Replace any plate that does not slide freely on serrations or that is not flat.

5) Check clutch hub thrust surfaces for scores and clutch hub splines for wear. Inspect shaft bearing surfaces for scores. Check shaft splines for wear.

Reassembly

1) Inspect piston check ball and ensure ball is free in cage. Install outer piston seal on piston with lip facing up and inner piston seal in clutch drum with lip facing down. Apply a light film of petroleum jelly to piston seals, drum seal area and piston inner seal area.

2) Install clutch piston into drum by pushing down on piston while rotating. Position return spring and retainer assembly into drum, then compress return springs and install retaining snap ring.

3) Install scarf-cut seal rings on clutch drum hub. Ensure seals overlap at the bevel edge. Install wave spring into drum. Install clutch pack into drum starting with a steel plate. Alternate composition and steel plates until correct number of plates are installed. See INTERMEDIATE CLUTCH PLATE USAGE chart. Install pressure plate and clutch pack retaining snap ring.

INTERMEDIATE CLUTCH PLATE USAGE CHART

Application	Composition Plates	Steel Plates
All Models	3	3

4) Use dial indicator to measure clearance between clutch pack retaining snap ring and pressure plate with pressure plate held downward. Take 2 readings 180° apart and average readings. Clearance should be .030-.044" (.75-1.22 mm).

5) On all models, if clearance is not within specifications, selective snap rings are available in the following thicknesses: .049-.053" (1.245-1.346 mm), .059-.063" (1.499-1.600 mm), and .070-.074" (1.788-1.880 mm). Install correct size snap ring and recheck clearance.

6) If removed, install stop ring on intermediate shaft. Install shaft into clutch drum, then install intermediate shaft retaining snap ring.

DIRECT CLUTCH

Disassembly

1) Remove sun gear/one-way clutch race assembly. Remove No. 8 thrust washer, then withdraw one-way clutch.

2) Remove clutch pack retaining snap ring. Remove pressure plate, clutch pack, and wave spring from clutch drum. Remove No. 9 thrust bearing. Using Compressor (T81P-70235), compress piston return spring retainer and remove retaining snap ring. Remove tool and piston return spring retainer.

3) Remove piston from clutch drum using pliers. Remove piston seals from clutch drum and piston.

Inspection

See INTERMEDIATE CLUTCH inspection.

Reassembly

1) Inspect clutch drum check ball and ensure it is free in cage. Install seal on clutch drum with seal lip facing down. Install piston seal on piston with seal lip facing up. Apply a light film of petroleum jelly to piston seals, then install piston into drum using a rotating motion while applying downward pressure.

2) Position return springs, retainer and retaining snap ring in clutch drum, then compress retainer and install snap ring in groove. Install thrust bearing No. 9 on top of return spring retainer.

3) Install wave spring. Install clutch pack into drum starting with a steel clutch plate and alternating composition clutch plates and steel plates until correct number of clutch plates have been installed. See DIRECT CLUTCH PLATE USAGE chart. Install pressure plate and clutch pack snap ring.

4) Install one-way clutch over turbine shaft and into clutch drum. Install thrust washer into drum and ensure that tabs of washer are facing down against shoulder of one-way clutch inner race.

5) Using feeler gauge or dial indicator, measure clearance between clutch pack retaining snap ring and pressure plate with pressure plate held down. Take 2

FORD MOTOR CO. ATX – AUTOMATIC TRANSAXLE (Cont.)

DIRECT CLUTCH PLATE USAGE CHART

Application	Composition Plates	Steel Plates
All Models [1]	3	3

[1] – Some models may be equipped with 4 friction plates and 4 steel plates.

measurements 180° apart from each other. Direct clutch clearance should be .031-.048" (.78-1.20 mm) on 3 plates or .040-.056" (1.01-1.43 mm) on 4 plates.

6) If clearance is not within specified limits, selective fit snap rings are available in the following thicknesses: .050-.054" (1.26-1.36 mm), .062-.066" (1.58-1.68 mm) and .075-.079" (1.90-2.00 mm). Install correct size snap ring and recheck clearance.

7) Install sun gear/one-way clutch outer race assembly over turbine shaft and into clutch drum. Check operation of one-way clutch. When properly assembled the one-way clutch allows sun gear/outer race assembly to rotate in one direction only.

REVERSE CLUTCH

NOTE: **Reverse clutch was disassembled under Transaxle Disassembly and will be reassembled during Transaxle Reassembly. The following procedure is for replacing piston seals.**

Piston Seal Replacement

Remove seals from clutch cylinder and clutch piston. Install new seal (large) on clutch cylinder with seal lips facing up. Install new inner seal (small) on piston with seal lip facing down, then install new outer seal on piston.

NOTE: **Outer piston seal is square-cut, making direction of installation unimportant.**

Inspection

1) Inspect clutch piston bore and piston inner and outer bearing surfaces for scores. Check air bleed ball valve in piston for free movement. Check orifice for obstructions.

2) Check fluid passages for obstructions. All passages must be clean and free of obstructions. Inspect clutch plates for wear, scoring and fit on clutch hub serrations. Replace all plates that are badly scored, worn, or do not fit freely in hub serrations.

3) Inspect clutch pressure plate for scores on clutch plate bearing surface. Check clutch return springs for distortion or collapsed coils.

BAND APPLY SERVO

Disassembly

Remove piston return spring, then separate servo piston from cover. Remove piston rod circlip, then slide piston rod, cushion spring and spring retaining washer from piston. Remove seals from servo cover and piston.

Inspection

1) Inspect servo body for cracks and piston bore for scores. Check fluid passages for obstructions. Inspect band and struts for distortion. Inspect band ends for cracks.

2) Inspect servo spring for distortion. Inspect band lining for excessive wear and bonding to metal band. Replace damaged seals.

Fig. 7: Exploded View of Band Apply Servo

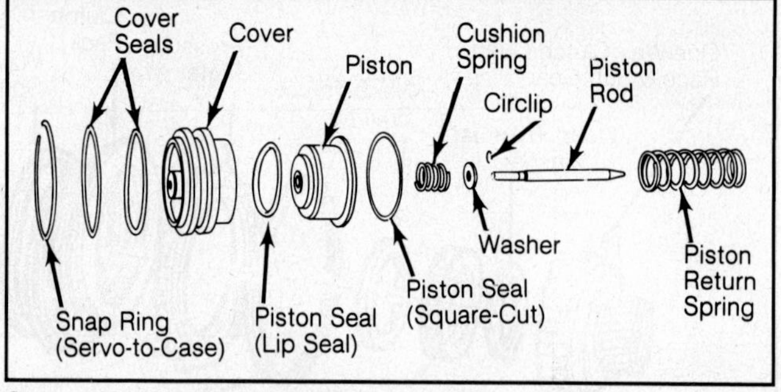

Some models may have 3 cover seals.

NOTE: **The following Servo Travel Check needs to be performed only if one of the following components has been replaced:**
- **Transaxle Case**
- **Band Assembly**
- **Drum and Sun Gear Assembly**
- **Servo Piston Rod**
- **Servo Piston**
- **Band Anchor Strut**

Servo Travel Check

1) Clean and assemble servo piston without piston seals. Install Return Spring (T81P-70027-A) on piston rod and position piston in case.

2) Install Servo Piston Selector (T81P-70023-A) and secure in case using servo cover retaining snap ring. Tighten gauge disc screw to 10 ft. lbs. (14 N.m). *See Fig. 8*.

3) Mount a dial indicator and position indicator stylus through hole in gauge disc, making sure stylus contacts servo piston. Zero dial indicator.

4) Back-off gauge disc screw until piston movement stops and read dial indicator. Amount of piston travel shown on indicator will determine piston rod length to install.

5) If piston travel is .203-.247" (5.15-6.27 mm), correct piston rod is installed and no change is required. If travel is less than specifications, piston rod is too long and a shorter rod (more grooves) will have to be installed. If travel is more than specified, rod is too short and a longer rod (less grooves) will have to be installed.

6) Select new piston rod if necessary. See SERVO PISTON ROD SELECTION table. Install selected rod and recheck servo travel.

SERVO PISTON ROD SELECTION

Rod Length [1] In. (mm)	Rod I.D.
6.313-6.324 (160.22-160.52)	No Grooves
6.289-6.300 (159.61-159.90)	1 Groove
6.265-6.276 (159.00-159.30)	2 Grooves
6.240-6.252 (158.39-158.69)	3 Grooves
6.216-6.189 (157.78-158.08)	4 Grooves
6.197-6.209 (157.17-157.47)	5 Grooves

[1] – From far end of snap ring groove to end of rod.

Reassembly

1) Position cushion spring retaining washer and cushion spring on piston rod, then install spring and rod assembly in servo piston. Compress cushion spring and install circlip on piston rod.

Fig. 8: Measuring Servo Piston Travel

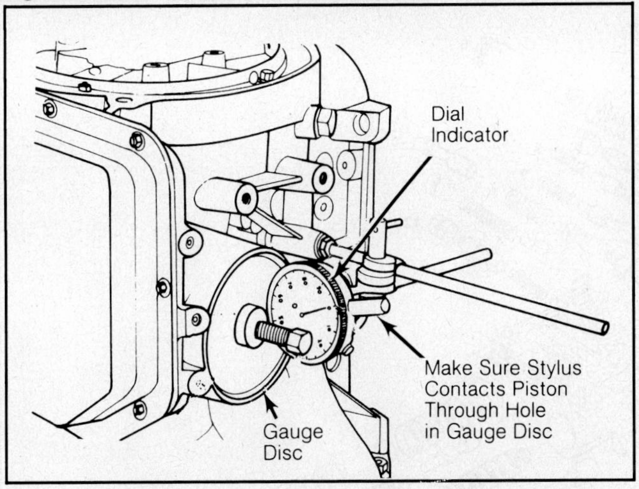

2) Install square-cut seal on piston. Install seals on servo cover. Lubricate piston seals with petroleum jelly, then install piston into cover. Install piston return spring on piston rod.

VALVE BODY ASSEMBLY

Disassembly

1) Remove 2 separator plate attaching screws and remove separator plate from valve body, then remove check balls and relief valve from valve body core passages. *See Fig. 9.*

2) Compress reverse boost valve plug. Using tweezers, remove retainer and slide out valve plug, spring and reverse boost valve.

3) Compress 2-3 shift valve plug, remove retainer and slide out valve plug, 2-3 shift valve and valve spring.

4) Compress 1-2 shift valve, remove retainer, then slide out valve plug, 1-2 shift valve, modulator valve spring and 1-2 T.V. modulator valve.

5) Compress 2-1 scheduling valve, remove retainer, then slide out valve spring and 2-1 scheduling valve.

6) Compress 2-3 backout valve, remove retainer, then slide out valve plug, valve spring and 2-3 backout valve.

7) Compress main oil pressure regulator and remove retainer. Slide out main oil pressure booster sleeve, main oil regulator boost valve, regulator valve spring, spring retainer and main oil regulator valve.

8) Compress manual low downshift modulating valve and remove retainer. Slide out valve plug, manual low downshift valve and valve spring.

9) Compress 3-2 torque demand timing valve, remove retainer, then slide out valve spring and 3-2 torque demand timing control valve.

10) Compress 3-2 kickdown timing valve, remove retainer, then slide out valve spring and 3-2 kickdown timing valve.

11) Compress 3-2 control valve and remove retainer. Slide out valve spring and 3-2 control valve.

12) Compress 2-3 shift T.V. modulator valve and remove retainer. Slide out valve plug, valve spring and 2-3 shift T.V. modulator valve.

13) Compress 1-2 capacity modulator valve and remove retainer. Slide out valve plug, 1-2 capacity modulator valve and valve spring.

14) Compress 1-2 accumulator valve and remove retainer. Slide out valve plug, 1-2 accumulator valve and valve spring.

15) Compress T.V. limit valve and remove retainer. Slide out valve spring and T.V. limit valve.

16) Compress throttle pressure valve and remove retainer. Slide out throttle valve plunger sleeve, throttle pressure valve, plunger return spring (large), throttle valve spring (small) and small throttle pressure valve and washer.

CAUTION: DO NOT turn throttle valve adjusting screw and lock nut. Adjustment screw is set during manufacture and must not be altered.

17) Using a drift, drive out retaining pin and remove throttle pressure adjusting sleeve. Slide manual control valve from valve body bore.

Cleaning & Inspection

1) Clean all parts thoroughly in clean solvent, and blow dry with moisture-free compressed air.

2) Inspect all valve and plug bores for scores. Check all fluid passages for obstructions. Inspect all mating surfaces for burrs or distortion. Inspect all plugs and valves for burrs and scores.

NOTE: If necessary, use crocus cloth to polish valve and plugs. Avoid rounding off sharp edges of valves and plugs with cloth.

3) Inspect all springs for distortion. Check all valves and plugs for free movement in their bores. Valves and plugs, when dry, must fall from their own weight in their respective bores. Roll manual control valve on a flat surface to check for bent condition.

Reassembly

1) Reverse disassembly procedure and note following: Install 5 check balls and relief valve into valve body passages. *See Fig. 10.*

2) Use Alignment Pins (T80L-77100-A) when installing separator plate and gasket to ensure that they are properly aligned with valve body. Tighten separator plate bolts to specification.

GOVERNOR

Disassembly

Support governor on a vise and remove 3/32" roll pin securing gear to shaft. DO NOT place governor assembly or governor shaft in vise jaws. DO NOT damage ring lands. Clamp plastic gear in vise. Grip shaft firmly and twist and pull to remove gear from shaft.

Inspection

1) Inspect governor valve and bore for scores. Minor scores may be removed from valve with crocus cloth. Replace governor if valves or body are deeply scored.

2) Inspect governor screen for obstructions. Screen must be free of foreign material. If contaminated, clean thoroughly in solvent and blow dry with compressed air.

3) Check for free movement of valves in bores. Valves should slide freely of their own weight in bores when dry. Inspect fluid passages in valve body and counterweight for obstructions. All fluid passages must be clean.

4) Inspect governor drive gear and replace it if teeth are broken, chipped or excessively worn.

Reassembly

1) Align driven gear to shaft gear bore. Ensure driven gear is properly aligned and tap gear into position

FORD MOTOR CO. ATX – AUTOMATIC TRANSAXLE (Cont.)

Fig. 9: Exploded View of Valve Body Valve Trains

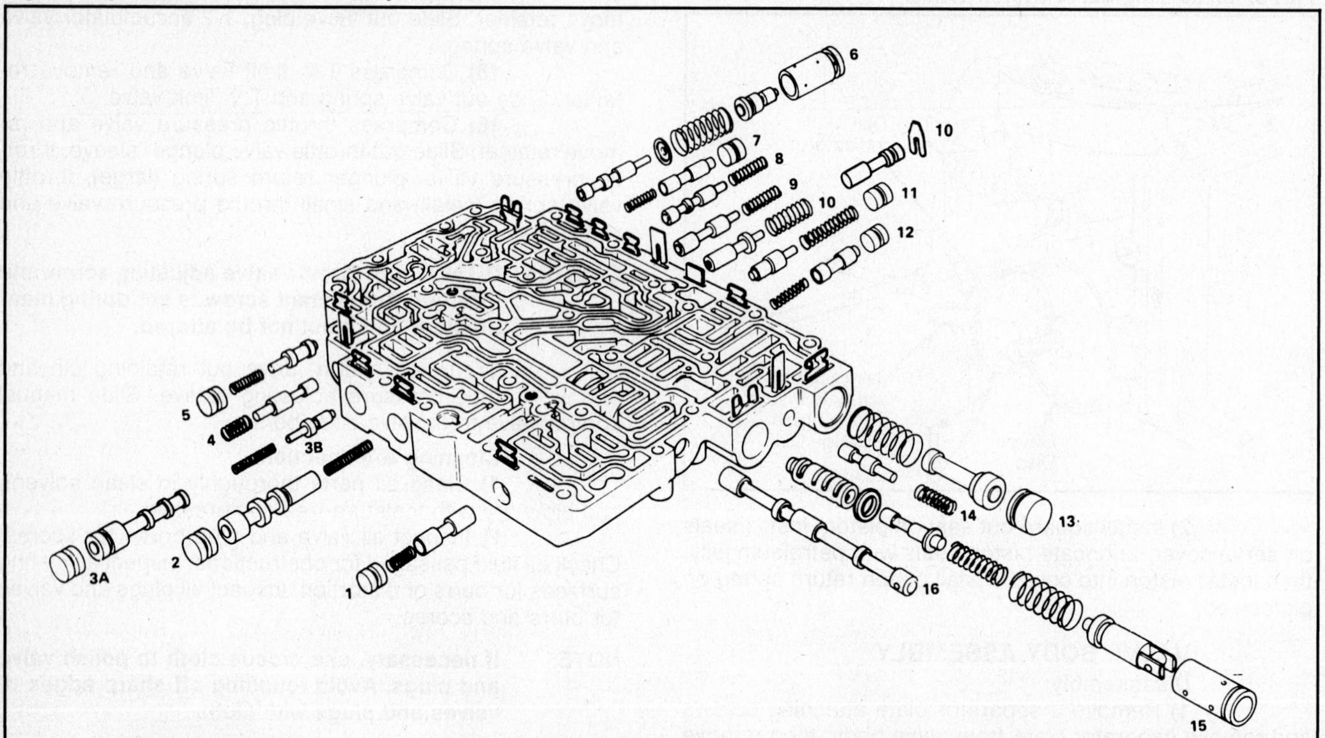

1. Reverse Boost Valve
2. 2-3 Shift Valve
3A. 1-2 Shift Valve
3B. 1-2 T.V. Modulator Valve
4. 2-1 Scheduling Valve
5. 2-3 Backout Valve
6. Main Oil Pressure Regulator
7. Manual Low Downshift Modulating Valve
8. 3-2 Torque Demand Timing Valve
9. 3-2 Kickdown Timing Valve
10A. 3-2 Control Valve (Taurus/Sable)
10B. Plug 3-2 Downshift Control
11. 2-3 Shift T.V. Modulator Valve
12. 1-2 Capacity Modulator Valve
13. 1-2 Accumulator Valve
14. T.V. Limit Valve
15. Throttle Pressure Control Valve
16. Manual Control Valve

Fig. 10: View of Valve Body Showing Location of Check Balls and Relief Valve

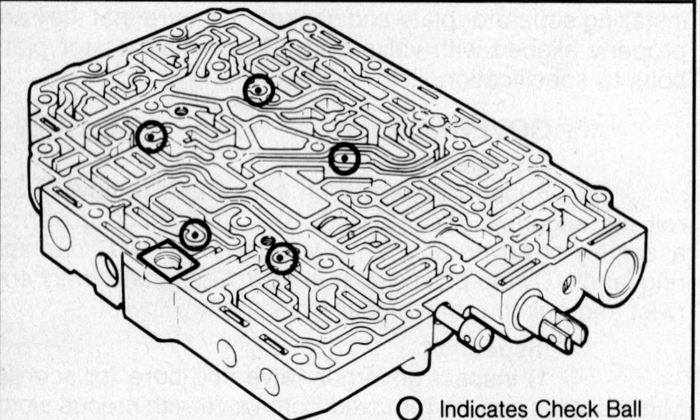

using a plastic mallet. Gear is in correct position when shoulder is seated against governor shaft.

2) Support governor on a non-machined surface. Using a drill press, align drill bit to prevent damaging governor shaft and drill a 1/8" hole through driven gear. Install NEW roll pin.

MANUAL AND THROTTLE LINKAGE

Disassembly

1) Hold outer throttle lever stationary to prevent damage to throttle shaft cam and remove throttle valve outer lever nut and washer. Remove attaching screws and washers, then slide neutral safety switch from shaft.

2) Using needle nose pliers, remove manual lever retaining pin and parking pawl ratcheting spring. Remove nut attaching inner manual lever (detent) and parking pawl actuating lever to manual lever shaft.

3) Remove manual lever and shaft assembly, then remove throttle valve lever and components on throttle valve lever shaft. Remove parking pawl return spring. Using a screwdriver, pry manual lever shaft oil seal from case and throttle valve lever shaft seal from manual lever. Remove insulator from manual lever.

Reassembly

1) Install new manual lever shaft seal in case. Install new seal on throttle lever shaft. Install new insulator on manual lever. Install parking pawl return spring.

2) Install the following on throttle shaft in this order: Parking pawl actuator, inner manual lever, inner manual lever/parking pawl actuator nut. Position throttle shaft in case and install manual lever and shaft assembly.

3) Position parking pawl actuator and inner manual lever on manual shaft, then install and tighten attaching nut. Install parking pawl ratcheting spring. Install manual lever retaining pin.

4) Install neutral safety switch in case. Install, but do not tighten, attaching screws and washers. Adjust neutral safety switch. See appropriate article in AUTOMATIC TRANSMISSION SERVICING in GENERAL TRANSMISSION SERVICING for switch adjustment.

FORD MOTOR CO. ATX – AUTOMATIC TRANSAXLE (Cont.)

Fig. 11: Exploded View of Manual and Throttle Linkage Components

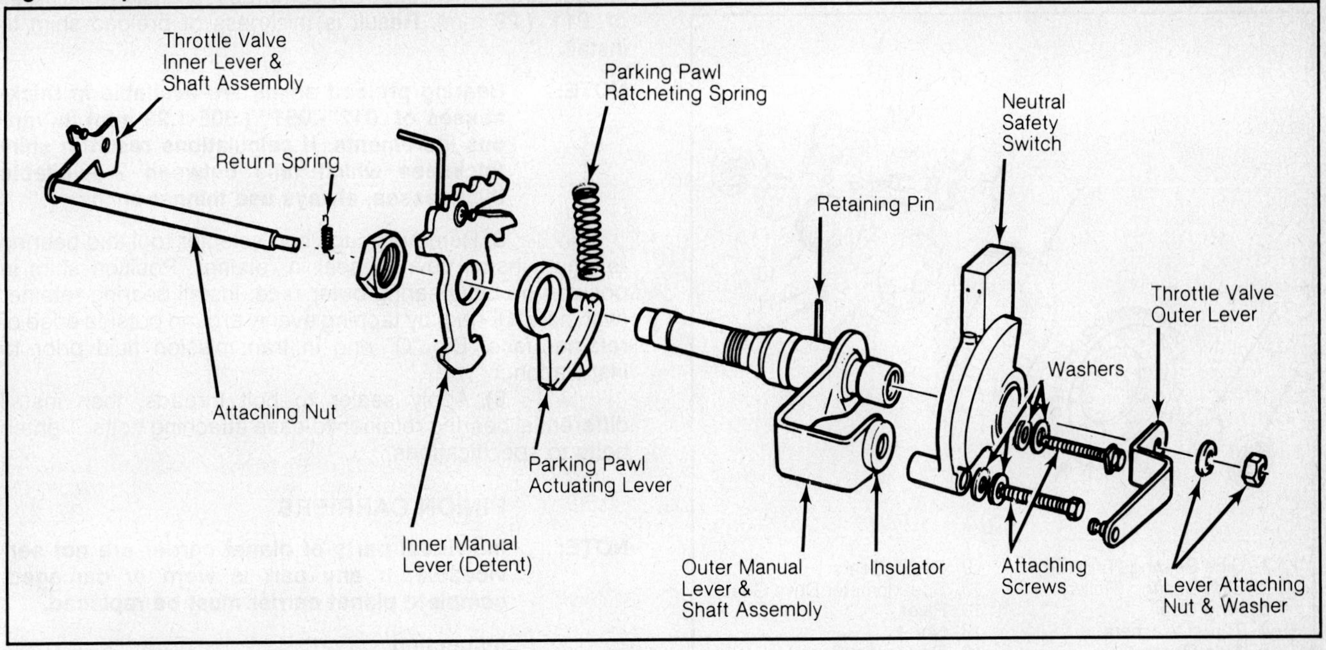

5) Tighten attaching screws. Install outer throttle lever. Tighten attaching nut while holding lever stationary to prevent damage to throttle shaft cam.

DIFFERENTIAL ASSEMBLY

Disassembly

1) Remove bolts attaching differential bearing retainer to case. Using 2 screwdrivers, remove retainer. Remove bearing spacer shims. Remove differential from case. Using Puller (T77F-4220-B1), remove differential carrier bearings. Pull speedometer drive gear from case.

2) Remove side gears and thrust washers from differential case by rotating gears toward case windows. Using a punch, drive out differential pinion gear shaft retaining pin, then remove gears and thrust washers from case.

3) If necessary, remove ring gear from differential case as follows: Using 5/16" drill, drill formed side of attaching rivets, then remove heads of rivets with a chisel. Using a punch, drive remaining rivet shank from case and remove ring gear.

Cleaning & Inspection

1) Thoroughly clean all parts in new solvent. Do not spin dry bearings using compressed air. Oil side bearings immediately after cleaning to prevent corrosion. Inspect parts for any major defect.

NOTE: **When a scored or chipped gear is replaced, transaxle case must be cleaned thoroughly to insure all chips are removed.**

2) Examine pinion and side gears for scoring, excessive wear, nicks and chips. Worn, scored and damaged gears must be replaced.

3) Make sure differential case bearing journals are smooth. Inspect case bearing shoulders for damage caused by bearing removal. Check fit (free rotation) of side gears in their cavities.

4) Check bearing races for deep scores, galling or chipping. If races are not damaged, do not remove from transaxle case or differential retainer. If races must be replaced, remove and install with appropriate tools.

5) Check side bearings for smooth rotation in races. Examine bearing roller ends for step wear. If inspection reveals either a damaged race or bearing, both parts must be replaced as they are a matched set.

Reassembly

1) To reassemble differential assembly, reverse disassembly procedure. Lubricate all thrust washers and thrust surfaces on gears and in case with automatic transmission fluid.

2) If removed, press ring gear onto differential case and attach to case with service replacement nuts and bolts. Install bolts with heads on parking pawl gear side of ring gear.

3) Install speedometer drive gear with bevel on inside diameter facing differential case.

NOTE: **Differential side gears must be aligned in case. This alignment must be held after installing differential assembly in case. Use Shipping Plugs (T81P-1177-B) to maintain alignment. Failure to maintain alignment will make it impossible to install axle drive shafts through side gears.**

Differential Bearing Preload Adjustment

1) Differential bearing preload is set at factory and need not be checked or adjusted unless one of the following parts is replaced:

- Transaxle Case
- Differential Case
- Differential Bearings
- Differential Bearing Retainer

2) To adjust preload, install differential assembly into transaxle case. Place Shim Spacer (T83P-4451-BH) on differential ball bearing outer race. Thickness of spacer tool should be .054-.055" (1.39-1.41 mm).

3) Remove bearing retainer oil seal and "O" ring. Install bearing retainer in case. Install Differential Bearing Preload Shim Selector (T81P-4451-A) in differential retainer.

FORD MOTOR CO. ATX – AUTOMATIC TRANSAXLE (Cont.)

Fig. 12: Exploded View of Differential Assembly

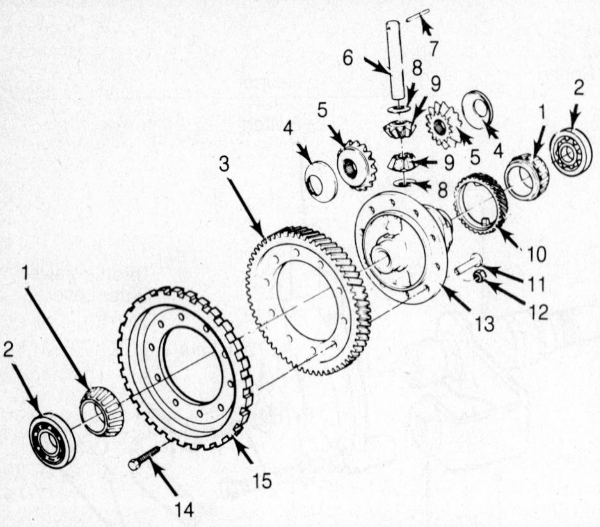

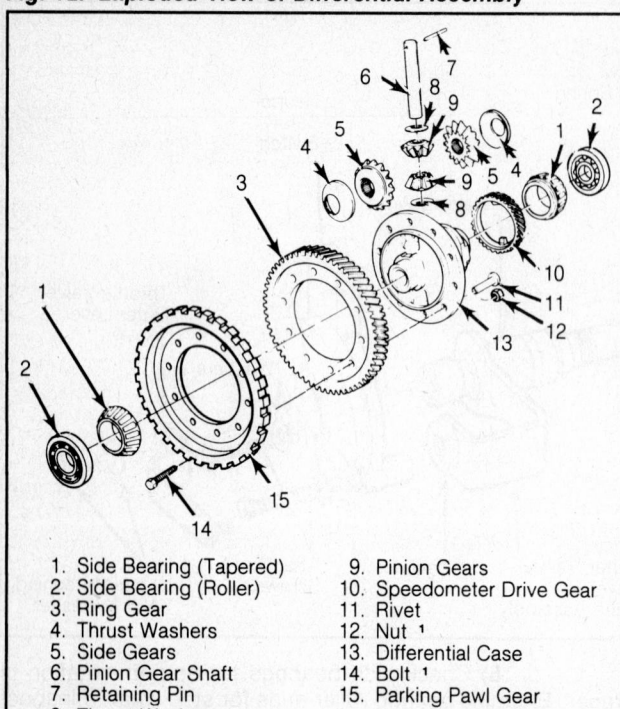

1. Side Bearing (Tapered)
2. Side Bearing (Roller)
3. Ring Gear
4. Thrust Washers
5. Side Gears
6. Pinion Gear Shaft
7. Retaining Pin
8. Thrust Washers
9. Pinion Gears
10. Speedometer Drive Gear
11. Rivet
12. Nut [1]
13. Differential Case
14. Bolt [1]
15. Parking Pawl Gear

[1] — Service replacement for attaching ring gear.

4) Ensure tool is centered in differential seal bore. Position gauge bar of selector tool across bearing retainer and install 2 attaching bolts fingertight. *See Fig. 13.*

5) Tighten center screw of gauge bar fingertight, then rotate differential assembly several times to seat bearings. Retighten screw fingertight.

Fig. 13: Differential Bearing Preload Tool Installation

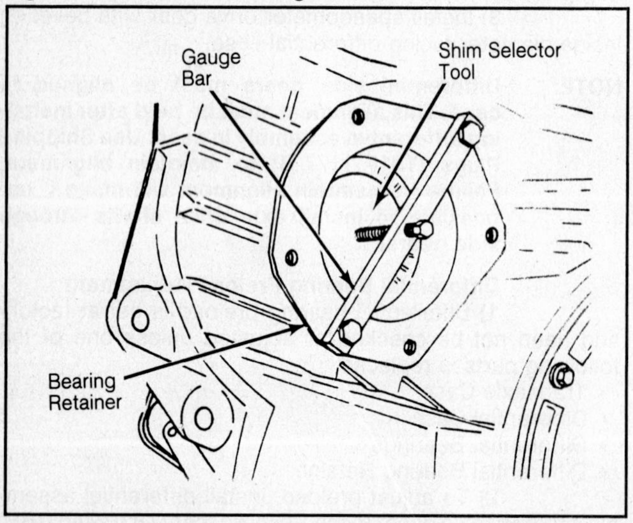

6) Using a feeler gauge, measure clearance between bearing retainer and transaxle case at 3 positions around retainer. Add the 3 measurements together and divide by 3 to obtain average of all measurements.

7) To determine shim needed for correct bearing preload, subtract average measurement obtained in step **6)** from 1.35 mm (1.35 mm or .053" is a constant based on spacer tool). Then subtract compressed gasket thickness of .011" (.29 mm). Result is thickness of preload shim to install.

NOTE: **Bearing preload shims are available in thicknesses of .012"-.051" (.305-1.29 mm) in various increments. If calculations result in shim thickness which falls between 2 available thicknesses, always use thinner shim.**

8) Remove gauge bar, selector tool and bearing retainer. Install new oil seal in retainer. Position shim in position on ball bearing outer race. Install bearing retainer (with new "O" ring) by tapping evenly around outside edge of retainer face. Dip "O" ring in transmission fluid prior to installation.

9) Apply sealer to bolt threads, then install differential bearing retainer-to-case attaching bolts. Tighten bolts to specifications.

PINION CARRIERS

NOTE: **Individual parts of planet carrier are not serviceable. If any part is worn or damaged, complete planet carrier must be replaced.**

Inspection

Inspect pins and shafts for loose fit and/or complete disengagement. Check shaft welds. Inspect pinion gears for damage or excessively worn teeth. Check for free rotation of pinion gears.

INPUT, IDLER & FINAL DRIVE GEARS

Inspection

Inspect gear teeth. They should be smooth with a uniform contact pattern without signs of excessive wear. Replace any gear which is cracked, chipped, broken or excessively worn.

TRANSAXLE CASE

Inspection

Inspect case for cracks and stripped threads. Inspect gasket surfaces and mating surfaces for burrs. Check vent for obstructions, and check all fluid passages for obstructions and leakage. Inspect case bushing for scores. Check all parking linkage parts for wear or damage.

NOTE: **Service kits are available for repairing damaged case threads.**

TRANSAXLE REASSEMBLY

NOTE: **Handle all parts carefully to avoid damaging bearings and mating surfaces. Lubricate all parts with clean automatic transmission fluid (use petroleum jelly on gaskets, thrust washers and needle bearings to retain them in place). Use all new gaskets and seals, and tighten bolts evenly.**

1) Clean up threads of idler gear shaft and install a new "O" ring. Place idler gear and shaft in case. Insert a 12 mm Allen wrench in idler gear shaft and position it to catch on band anchor strut.

2) Apply thread locking sealant (E0AZ-19554-A) to attaching nut. Install and tighten nut to specification using a 32 mm 12-point socket. Install No. 1 thrust bearing and input gear No. 2 caged needle bearing. *See Fig. 14.*

FORD MOTOR CO. ATX – AUTOMATIC TRANSAXLE (Cont.)

Fig. 14: Installing Thrust Bearing and Caged Needle Bearing

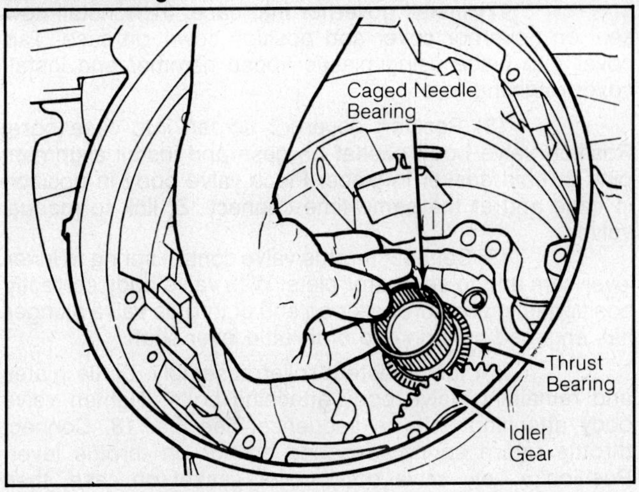

3) Install input gear over reactor support, then install No. 3 thrust bearing (needle) on input gear. Position transfer housing in case and ensure it is firmly seated on alignment dowels. Install NEW transfer housing attaching bolts and tighten to specifications.

NOTE: Before installing transfer housing, ensure that band strut is rotated into its operating position. Also, transmission case and housing are matched parts. If one is damaged, both must be replaced.

4) Install No. 4 thrust washer on transfer case. Install sun gear and drum. Install intermediate band. Ensure band lug engages stud. Place servo piston in case and install Remover/Installer (T81P-70027-A).

5) Compress piston spring far enough to allow installation of retaining ring. Install servo retaining ring and before removing tool, ensure piston rod has engaged band lug.

Fig. 15: Measuring Reverse Clutch Clearance

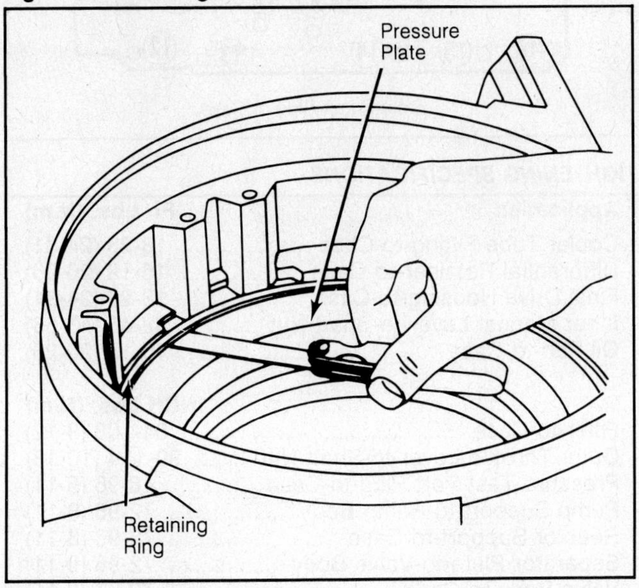

6) Place reverse clutch cylinder in case and tap cylinder in using a hammer handle. Using Seal Protector (T81P-70402-A), apply even pressure and install reverse clutch piston in clutch cylinder. Remove seal protector. Install No. 5 thrust washer on planetary gear set, then install assembly on sun gear.

NOTE: Before installing reverse clutch piston return spring and holder assembly, reverse clutch clearance must be checked as follows:

7) Install clutch pack wave spring, clutch pack and pressure plate, then install clutch pack retaining ring. Using a feeler gauge, measure clearance between retaining ring and pressure plate at 2 places 180 degrees apart.

8) If average clearance is .030-.055" (.76-1.40 mm), clutch clearance is correct. If clearance is less than .030" (.76 mm), install a thinner retaining ring. If clearance is greater than .055" (1.40 mm), install a thicker retaining ring.

NOTE: Whenever new retaining ring is installed, repeat clearance check. Reverse clutch retaining rings are available in the following thicknesses: .049-.053" (1.24-1.34 mm), .066-.070" (1.68-1.78 mm), .083-.087" (2.11-2.21 mm),and .099-.103" (2.53-2.63 mm).

REVERSE CLUTCH PLATE USAGE CHART

Application	Composition Plates	Steel Plates
All Models	3	3

9) Remove reverse clutch pack retaining ring, pressure plate, clutch pack and wave spring. Install reverse clutch return spring and holder assembly, then reinstall wave spring, clutch pack, pressure plate and retaining ring.

10) Install No. 7 thrust washer on planetary assembly. Install intermediate clutch hub and ring gear assembly into case. Install direct clutch assembly into case, then position No. 10 thrust bearing (needle) on direct clutch.

11) Install intermediate clutch assembly into case and check for proper clutch engagement as follows: Position No. 11 thrust bearing on one of the machined tabs and push it up against case. If bearing is flush with, or slightly below machined pump housing surface in case, clutch is fully engaged. *See Fig. 16*. Position No. 11 thrust bearing on clutch drum.

Fig. 16: Checking Intermediate Clutch for Proper Engagement

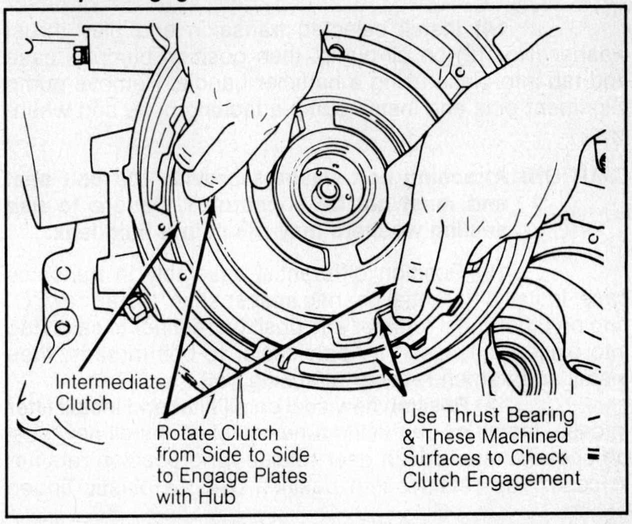

FORD MOTOR CO. ATX – AUTOMATIC TRANSAXLE (Cont.)

12) Install pump Alignment Pins (T81P-77100-A) and pump housing gasket. Position transaxle End Play Checking Tools (T81P-77389-A and T80L-77003-A) in intermediate clutch as shown in *Fig. 17*.

Fig. 17: Assembling Transaxle End Play Measuring Tools

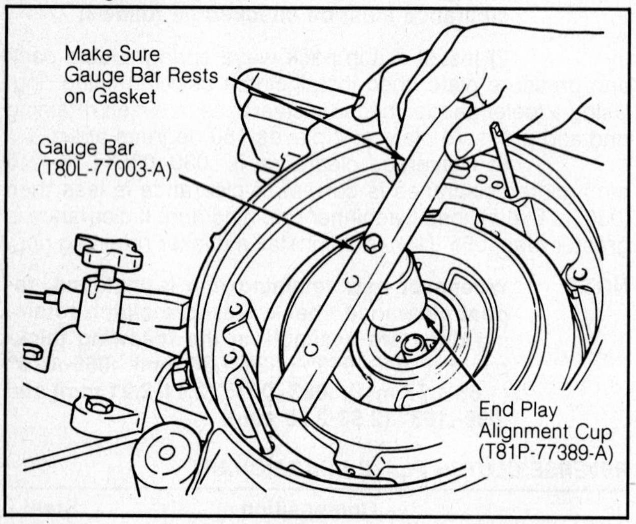

13) Using a micrometer, measure distance from top of gauge bar to top of No. 11 thrust bearing installed on intermediate clutch. Make measurement at 2 places 180 degrees apart and use average. From micrometer reading, choose correct end play thrust washer to install. See END PLAY THRUST WASHER SELECTION CHART.

END PLAY THRUST WASHER SELECTION CHART

End Play Measurement	[1] Thrust Washer Part I.D.
.070-.079" (1.77-2.00 mm)	AA
.079-.087" (2.00-2.20 mm)	BA
.087-.095" (2.20-2.41 mm)	CA
.057-.070" (1.46-1.77 mm)	EA

[1] – If washer thickness is not known, measure its thickness using a micrometer. Washer "AA" is .055-.057" (1.40-1.45 mm); washer "BA" is .063-.065" (1.60-1.65 mm); washer "CA" is .071-.073" (1.80-1.85 mm); washer "EA" is .045-.047" (1.15-1.20 mm).

14) Install selected transaxle end play thrust washer (No. 12) on oil pump, then position pump in case and tap into place using a hammer handle. Remove pump alignment pins and install pump attaching bolts and washers.

CAUTION: Attaching bolt washers provide the bolt seal and must not be substituted. Failure to use sealing washers may result in a fluid leak.

15) Position differential assembly in transaxle case. Install differential bearing spacer shim. Install new "O" ring on differential retainer and position retainer in case (tap into place if necessary). Apply sealer to bolt threads, then install and tighten retainer attaching bolt.

16) Position new seal on oil filter and install filter in case. Install oil pan using a new gasket. Install new seal on speedometer driven gear retainer and position retainer in case. Tap retainer into position using a plastic tipped hammer. With retainer properly positioned, tap retaining pin into case.

17) Install governor into case, then install new seal on governor cover and position cover on case. Tap cover into place using plastic tipped hammer and install cover retaining wire.

18) Position governor screen into case bore. Position valve body gasket on case and install alignment pins to hold gasket in place. Place valve body in position in case and at the same time connect "Z" link to manual valve.

19) Connect throttle valve control spring to inner lever cam and to separator plate. With valve body correctly positioned, make sure roller on end of throttle valve plunger has engaged cam on end of throttle lever shaft.

20) Install detent roller assembly, baffle plates and remaining valve body attaching bolts. Tighten valve body attaching bolts in sequence. *See Fig. 18*. Connect throttle return spring to spring anchor on throttle lever. Position a new valve body cover gasket on case, then install cover and tighten attaching bolts.

21) Install oil pump shaft. Install new seal on dipstick tube and install tube in case. Install torque converter into transaxle case.

Fig. 18: Tightening Sequence for Valve Body Attaching Bolts

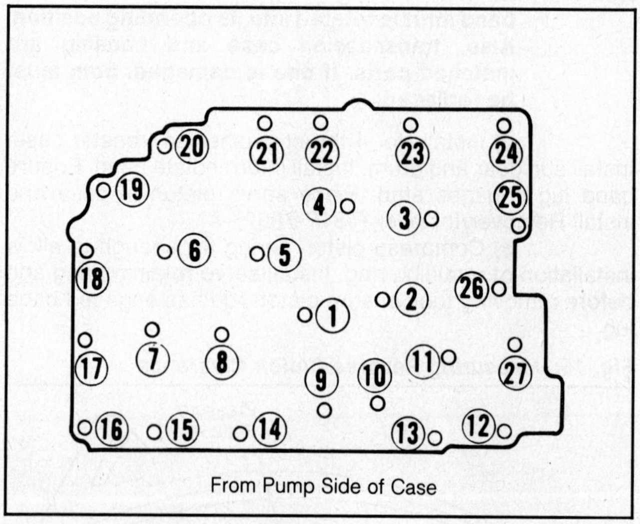

TIGHTENING SPECIFICATIONS

Application	Ft. Lbs. (N.m)
Cooler Tube Fitting-to-Case	18-23 (24-31)
Differential Retainer-to-Case	15-19 (20-26)
Final Drive Housing-to-Case	18-23 (24-31)
Inner Manual Lever-to-Shaft Nut	32-48 (43-65)
Oil Pan-to-Case	15-19 (20-26)
	INCH Lbs. (N.m)
Filter-to-Case	84-108 (9-12)
Outer Throttle Lever-to-Shaft Nut	90-114 (10-13)
Pressure Test Port Plug-to-Case	48-96 (5-11)
Pump Support-to-Pump Body	72-96 (8-11)
Reactor Support-to-Case	72-96 (8-11)
Separator Plate-to-Valve Body	72-96 (8-11)
Valve Body-to-Case	72-96 (8-11)
Valve Body Cover-to-Case	84-108 (9-12)

Automatic Transmissions

FORD MOTOR CO. ATX – AUTOMATIC TRANSAXLE (Cont.)

Fig. 19: Exploded View of ATX Automatic Transaxle Assembly

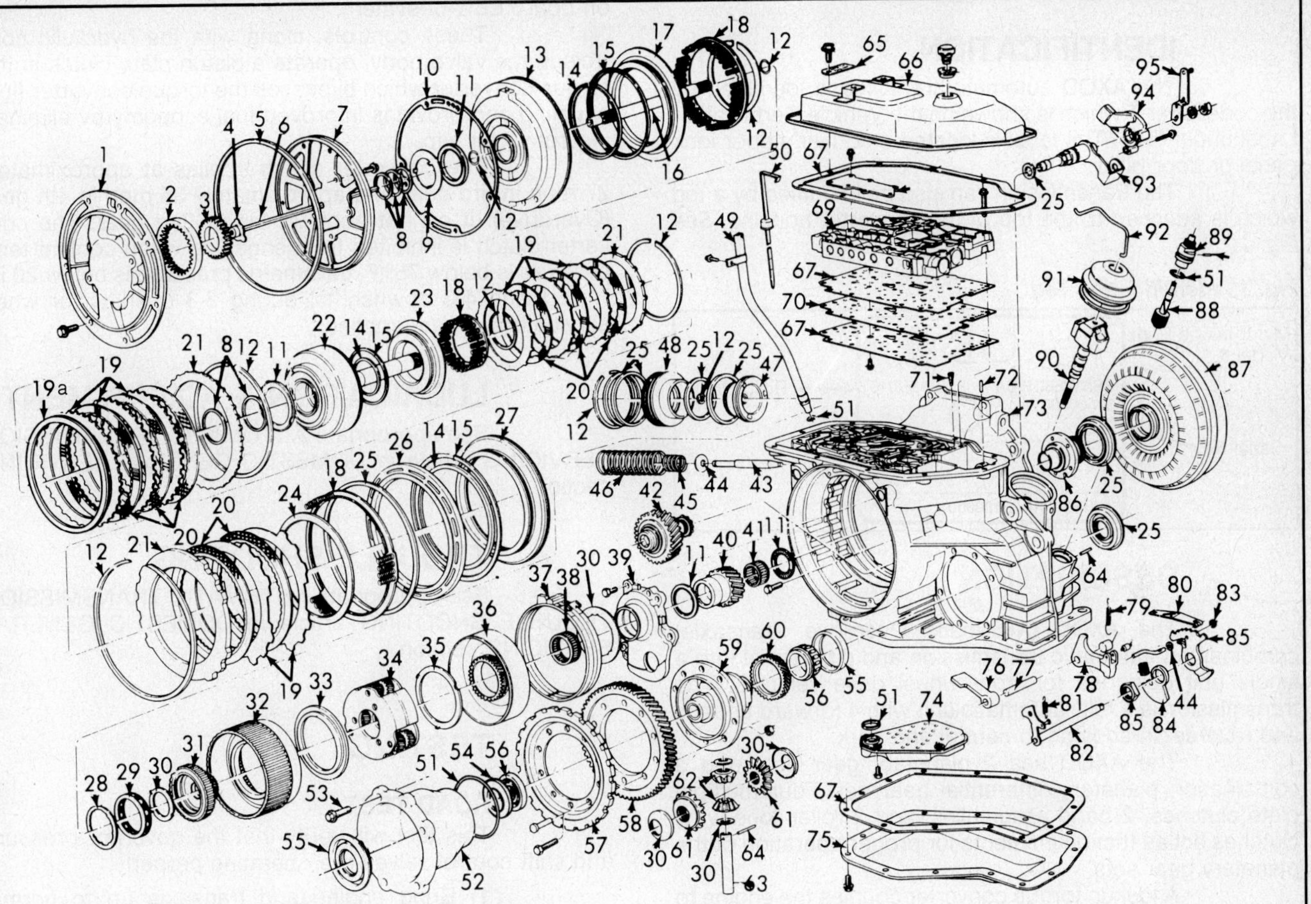

1. Oil Pump Body
2. Pump Driven Gear
3. Pump Drive Gear
4. Pump Gear Insert
5. Oil Pump Seal
6. Oil Pump Shaft
7. Clutch Support
8. Teflon Oil Seals
9. End Play Thrust Washer
10. Pump Gasket
11. Thrust Bearing
12. Snap Ring
13. Interm. Clutch Drum
14. Inner Piston Seal
15. Outer Piston Seal
16. Interm. Clutch Shaft
17. Interm. Clutch Piston
18. Return Spring Assy.
19. Steel Clutch Plates
19a. Wave Spring
20. Composition Clutch Plates
21. Pressure Plate
22. Direct Clutch Drum
23. Direct Clutch Piston
24. Wave Spring
25. Seal
26. Reverse Clutch Piston
27. Reverse Clutch Drum
28. One-Way Clutch Bearing
29. Spring & Roller Assy.
30. Thrust Washer
31. 1st/3rd, Reverse Gear
32. Interm. Clutch Hub & Ring Gear
33. Planet Rear Thrust Bearing
34. Planetary Assy.
35. Planet Front Thrust Washer
36. Sun Gear & Drum Assy.
37. Band
38. Transfer Hsg. Bearing
39. Final Drive Gear Housing
40. Input Gear, Final Drive
41. Input Gear Bearing
42. Idler Gear
43. Servo Rod
44. Washer
45. Cushion Spring
46. Piston Spring
47. Servo Piston
48. Servo Cover
49. Oil Filler Tube
50. Dipstick
51. "O" Ring
52. Differential Retainer
53. Retainer Bolt
54. Side Bearing Preload Shim
55. Oil Seal
56. Differential Side Bearing
57. Parking Pawl Gear
58. Ring Gear
59. Differential Case
60. Speedometer Drive Gear
61. Side Gears
62. Pinion Gears
63. Pinion Gear Shaft
64. Retaining Pin
65. Transaxle I.D. Tag
66. Valve Body Cover
67. Gasket
68. Baffle Plate
69. Valve Body Assy.
70. Separator Plate
71. Governor Screen
72. Dowel Pin
73. Transaxle Case
74. Oil Filter
75. Oil Pan
76. Band Anchor Strut
77. Park Pawl Shaft
78. Park Pawl Assembly
79. Park Pawl Return Spring
80. Manual Valve Detent Spring
81. TV Lever Control Spring
82. TV Lever Actuating Shaft
83. Nut
84. Park Pawl Actuating Lever
85. Manual Valve Inner Lever
86. Reactor Support
87. Torque Converter
88. Speedometer Driven Gear
89. Speedometer Gear Retainer
90. Governor
91. Governor Cover
92. Retainer Wire
93. Manual Lever
94. Neutral Safety Switch
95. TV Outer Lever

Automatic Transmissions

FORD MOTOR CO. AXOD

Sable, Taurus

IDENTIFICATION

The AXOD automatic transaxle is identified by the code letter T which is shown on the Vehicle Certification Label under "TR". The label is located on driver's door lock panel or door pillar.

The transmission can also be identified by a tag which is attached to the top of the converter housing. *See Fig. 1.*

Fig. 1: Identification Tag

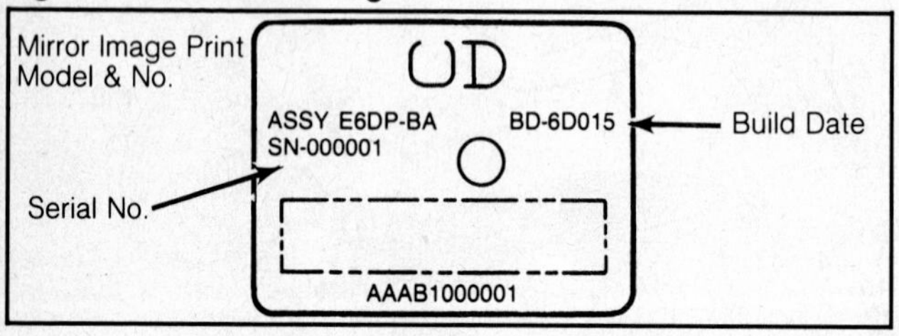

DESCRIPTION

The AXOD (Automatic Overdrive Transaxle) combines an automatic transmission and differential into a single unit designed for front wheel drive vehicles. The transmission is a fully automatic unit with 4 forward speeds and reverse, in addition to neutral and park.

The AXOD has 2 planetary gear sets and a combination planetary/differential gear set. Four multiple plate clutches, 2 band assemblies, and 2 roller (one-way) clutches act as friction elements for proper operation of the planetary gear sets.

A lockup torque converter couples the engine to the planetary gears and overdrive unit by means of a drive link assembly (chain) that connects the drive and driven gears.

OPERATION

TORQUE CONVERTER CLUTCH

The application of the converter clutch is controlled by a bypass solenoid and 3 pressure switch sensors mounted on the valve body that are integrated into the on-board EEC-IV system.

These controls, along with the hydraulic controls in the valve body, operate a piston plate clutch in the torque converter which bypasses the torque converter fluid coupling and provides improved fuel economy by eliminating converter slip.

The converter clutch applies at approximately 27 mph in 3rd gear and approximately 35 mph in 4th gear (Overdrive). It cannot apply in 1st or 2nd gear. The converter clutch is inhibited from engaging when coolant temperature is below 75° F, barometric pressure is below 20 in. Hg., during 4-3 downshifts, during 2-3 upshifts, or when service brakes are applied.

LUBRICATION & ADJUSTMENT

See appropriate AUTOMATIC TRANSMISSION SERVICING article in DOMESTIC GENERAL SERVICING section.

TROUBLE SHOOTING

See appropriate AUTOMATIC TRANSMISSION TROUBLE SHOOTING article in DOMESTIC GENERAL SERVICING section.

TESTING

ROAD TEST

This test will verify that the governor pressure and shift control valves are operating properly.

1) Bring engine and transaxle up to normal operating temperature. Check minimum throttle upshifts with transaxle in Overdrive. Note upshift speeds and speed at which converter clutch applies. Refer to SHIFT SPEEDS table.

2) Shift transaxle to Drive and repeat Step **1)**. Transaxle should make all upshifts except 3-4 and converter clutch should apply above 27 mph.

3) With transaxle still in Drive, depress accelerator to floor (Wide Open Throttle). Transaxle should shift from 3rd to 2nd, or 3rd to 1st, depending on vehicle speed. Converter clutch should also release.

CLUTCH AND BAND APPLICATION CHART (ELEMENTS IN USE)

Selector Lever Position	Low-Intermed. Band	Overdrive Band	Forward Clutch	Intermed. Clutch	Direct Clutch	Reverse Clutch	Low One-Way Clutch	Direct One-Way Clutch
1st Manual Low	X		X		X		X	X
Drive - 1st Gear	X		X				X	
Drive - 2nd Gear	X		X	X			X	
Drive - 3rd Gear			X	X	X			
Overdrive - 4th Gear		X		X	X			X
Reverse			X			X	X	

PARK & NEUTRAL – All clutches and bands released and/or ineffective.

Automatic Transmissions

FORD MOTOR CO. AXOD (Cont.)

NOTE: With transaxle in Overdrive, a 4-3 WOT downshift can be obtained regardless of vehicle speed.

4) With vehicle speed above 30 mph, shift transaxle from Drive to "1" (Low) and remove foot from accelerator. Transaxle should immediately downshift to 2nd gear. When vehicle speed drops below 20 mph, transaxle should downshift into 1st gear.

IN-SHOP TEST

The governor circuit, shift delay pressures and throttle boost can be checked during this test.

CAUTION: Do not exceed 60 mph indicated speedometer speed.

1) Raise vehicle so front wheels are off floor. To check shift valves and governor circuit, place transaxle in Overdrive and apply minimum throttle, noting upshift speeds and speeds at which the converter clutch locks up.

2) The transaxle should shift in the following order: 1-2, 2-3, Converter Lockup, 3-4. Converter will remain locked up when in 4th (Overdrive).

3) To check downshift valve operation, disconnect throttle valve linkage from throttle lever and pull out to maximum travel. DO NOT crimp or kink cable.

4) Place transaxle in Drive and apply minimum throttle pressure. Observe speed at which 1-2 upshift occurs.

5) If shift speeds are not within specifications, perform GOVERNOR TEST. If shift speeds are too low, the shift modulator valves may be faulty.

SHIFT SPEEDS (MPH)

Throttle	Range	Shift	OPS—R.P.M.	Column Number		
				1	2	3
Closed Throttle	OD,D	1-2	570-724	12-15	12-15	12-15
	OD, D	2-3	777-1085	16-23	16-23	16-23
	OD	3-4	1434-1903	29-40	30-41	30-41
	OD	4-3	1144-1648	23-34	24-35	24-35
	OD, D	3-2	399-539	8-11	8-11	8-11
	OD, D	2-1	399-539	8-11	8-11	8-11
	1	2-1				
Part Throttle (See note below)	OD, D	1-2	915-1114	19-23	19-24	19-24
	OD, D	2-3	1648-1968	33-41	34-42	34-42
	*OD	3-4	1854-2179	38-45	38-46	38-47
	*OD	4-3	1359-1795	27-37	28-38	28-38
	OD, D	3-2	1175-1527	24-32	24-33	24-33
	OD, D	2-1	737-808	15-17	15-17	15-17
Wide Open Throttle	OD, D	1-2	1368-1757	28-37	28-37	28-38
	OD, D	2-3	2849-3302	58-69	59-70	59-70
	OD, D	3-2	2581-3026	52-62	53-64	54-65
	OD, D	2-1	987-1418	20-29	20-30	20-30

NOTE: All shifts at 60 psi T.V. pressure except * which are at 40 psi T.V. pressure.

Tire Size	Axle Ratio
	Use Column No.
P195/70R14	1
P205/70R14	2
P205/65R15	3

CONTROL PRESSURE TEST

1) Connect a pressure gauge to line pressure port. *See Fig. 2.*

2) Start engine, apply service and parking brakes, and check line pressure in all gears. Refer to LINE PRESSURE table.

3) If line pressure is not within specification, perform AIR PRESSURE TESTS.

CONTROL PRESSURE TEST RESULTS

High or Low Oil Pressure

Check for low oil level. TV cable or linkage could be stuck or damaged. Pressure regulator valve or spring could be damaged. Pressure relief valve could be damaged, missing spring, or missing check ball. Oil pump slide could be stuck, seals damaged, vanes broken or driveshaft damaged or broken.

Fig. 2: Control Pressure Port Location

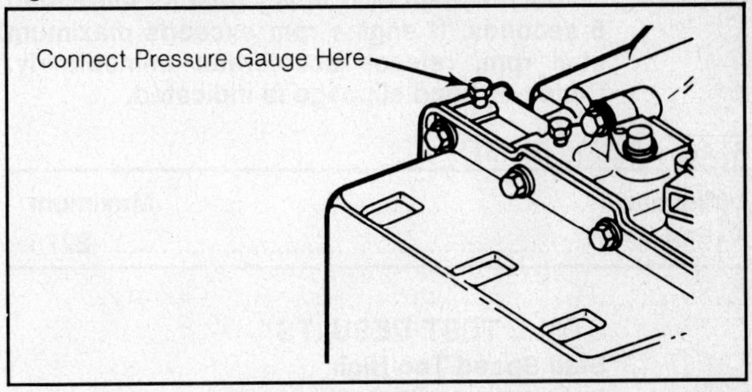

LINE PRESSURE SPECIFICATIONS (PSI)

Range	Idle	WOT Stall
"OD","D"	81-91	158-183
"1"	112-169	158-183
"R"	93-152	242-279
"P", "N"	81-95	158-183

CONVERTER CLUTCH TEST

1) Connect a tachometer to the vehicle (if not equipped). Bring engine and transaxle up to normal operating temperature by driving at highway speeds for about 15 minutes in Overdrive.

2) Maintaining a constant speed of 50 mph, tap the brake pedal. Engine rpm should increase. It should decrease about 5 seconds after the pedal is released. If this does not occur, refer to CONVERTER CLUTCH TEST RESULTS.

CONVERTER CLUTCH TEST RESULTS

Converter Clutch Does Not Apply

- Transaxle electrical system or EEC are malfunctioning: No lock-up signal, by-pass solenoid damaged or inoperative, bulkhead connector damaged, pinched wires, 4-3 pressure switch or 3-2 pressure switch inoperative.
- Converter clutch blowoff check ball in channel plate not seating or damaged.
- Turbine shaft has damaged seals.
- Bypass clutch control valve stuck or bypass plunger stuck.
- Pump shaft seals missing or damaged.
- Valve body pilot sleeve misaligned or damaged.

FORD MOTOR CO. AXOD (Cont.)

Converter Clutch Does Not Release

- EEC is malfunctioning: No unlock signal or bypass solenoid damaged or inoperative.
- Bypass clutch control valve or plunger valve stuck, nicked or damaged.

STALL TEST

The stall test checks the operation of the following items: converter one-way clutch, forward clutch, low one-way clutch, reverse clutch, low-intermediate band and engine performance.

NOTE: **After each test, shift transaxle into Neutral and run engine for at least 15 seconds to cool converter.**

Apply service and parking brakes. Connect tachometer to engine, and record rpm reached in each range at WOT (Wide Open Throttle).

CAUTION: **Do not maintain WOT in any gear for more than 5 seconds. If engine rpm exceeds maximum stall rpm, release accelerator immediately. Clutch or band slippage is indicated.**

STALL SPEEDS (RPM)

Minimum	Maximum
1950	2275

STALL TEST RESULTS

Stall Speed Too High

In Overdrive, Drive, "1" and "R"; general transmission problems are indicated and a control pressure test should be made to locate faulty unit(s).

In Overdrive, Drive or "1"; forward clutch, low-intermediate clutch, or low-intermediate band slippage is indicated. The low-intermediate servo may also be malfunctioning.

In "R", the forward clutch, low-intermediate clutch or reverse clutch may be slipping.

Stall Speed Too Low

Converter reactor one-way clutch is slipping or engine performance is faulty.

AIR PRESSURE TESTS

A "No Drive" condition can exist even with correct transaxle fluid pressure because of inoperative clutches or bands. A "No Drive" condition in a forward gear range may be caused by an inoperative forward clutch, low-intermediate one-way clutch or low-intermediate band.

No manual low ("1") coast could be caused by a faulty direct clutch or direct one-way clutch.

Failure to drive in Reverse may be caused by a malfunctioning reverse clutch, forward clutch or low-intermediate one-way clutch.

To perform air pressure tests, drain transaxle fluid and remove oil pan. Remove valve body cover, and oil pump and valve body assembly. Install Air Pressure Test Plate (T86P-7006-B) with valve body assembly-to-chain cover gasket.

Forward Clutch

Apply air pressure to forward clutch test port. A dull thud can be heard, or movement of piston felt when clutch piston is applied. If clutch seal(s) are leaking, a hissing sound will be heard.

Fig. 3: Air Pressure Test Plate Locations

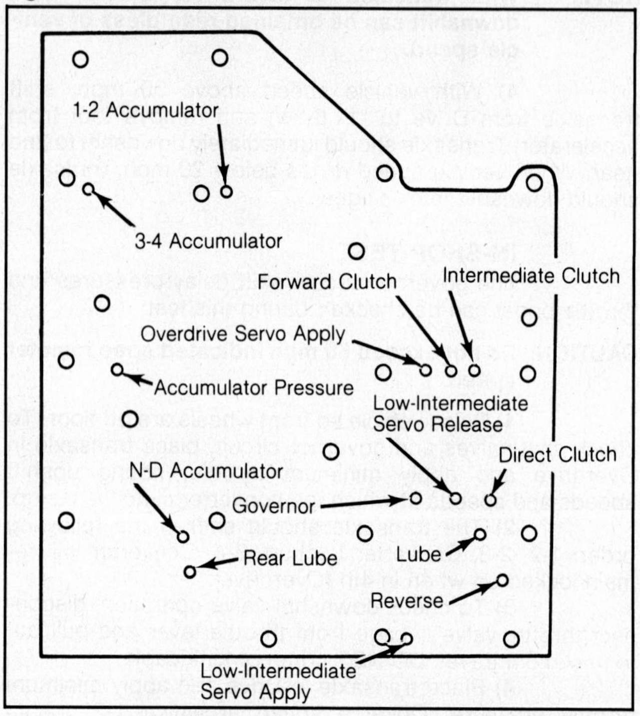

Governor

Apply air pressure to governor test port and listen for a sharp clicking or whistling noise. The noise indicates proper governor movement.

Overdrive Servo

Apply air pressure to overdrive servo test port. Operation of servo is indicated by the tightening of overdrive band around overdrive drum. Because of the cushioning effect of the servo release spring, this may not be heard or felt. The servo should hold air pressure and a dull thud should be heard when air pressure is released.

Direct Clutch

Apply air pressure to direct clutch test port. A dull thud can be heard, or movement of piston felt on case as piston is applied. If clutch seal(s) are leaking, a hissing sound will be heard.

Intermediate Clutch

Apply air pressure to intermediate clutch test port. A dull thud can be heard, or movement of piston felt on case as piston is applied. If clutch seal(s) are leaking, a hissing sound will be heard.

NOTE: **If air pressure fails to operate a clutch, or operates clutches simultaneously, remove and check fluid passages in the clutches, chain cover and driven sprocket support.**

Low-Intermediate Servo

Apply air pressure at low-intermediate servo apply test port. The low-intermediate band should tighten around sun gear of rear planetary gear set. Because of the cushioning effect of the servo release spring, this may not be heard or felt. The servo should hold air pressure and a dull thud should be heard when air pressure is removed.

Apply air pressure to low-intermediate servo release test port while continuing to pressurize the apply port. Servo piston should return to the release position. The band should loosen and a dull thud should be heard.

Automatic Transmissions

FORD MOTOR CO. AXOD (Cont.)

Release the apply test port. The release test port should hold air pressure. Any leakage or failure of piston movement requires servo service.

Lube and Rear Lube

Apply air pressure to lube and rear lube test ports. These passages can only be checked for blockage. If either passage holds air pressure, remove test plate and check for damage or an obstruction.

1-2, 3-4 and N-D Accumulators

Apply air pressure to each accumulator test port. Accumulator should apply. Because of the cushioning effect of the release spring, this may not be heard or felt.

The accumulator should hold air pressure without leaking and a dull thud should be heard when air pressure is removed.

NOTE: **If air pressure applied to the accumulator passages fails to operate an accumulator, remove and check fluid passages in the accumulator and chain cover.**

ELECTRICAL SYSTEM TEST

Circuit Test

NOTE: Perform this test only when KEY ON/ENGINE OFF SELF-TEST service codes 62, 67, and 89 are present; when ENGINE RUNNING SELF-TEST service code 62 is displayed; or when CONTINUOUS SELF-TEST service codes 29, 39, 57, 59, and 69 are displayed. Ensure that all components are connected before performing test. Perform AXOD DRIVE CYCLE TEST on a slight upgrade or flat terrain.

AXOD Drive Cycle Test. Record and zero service codes. Warm engine to operating temperature. With transaxle in "D" range, lightly accelerate from a stop to 40 MPH to allow transaxle to shift into 3rd gear. Hold speed and throttle opening steady for a minimum of 15 seconds (30 seconds above 4000 feet altitude).

Shift transaxle into overdrive and accelerate lightly from 40 to 50 MPH to allow transaxle to shift into 4th gear. Hold speed and throttle opening steady for a minimum of 15 seconds.

With transaxle in 4th gear, throttle open and speed steady, lightly apply and release brakes (enough to light brake lamps). Hold speed and throttle opening steady for an additional 15 seconds minimum.

Brake to a stop and remain stopped for a minimum of 20 seconds with transaxle in overdrive. Perform QUICK TEST and record service codes.

1) Continuous Code 29 Displayed. Perform AXOD DRIVE CYCLE TEST and return to this step. If continuous code 29 is not displayed, fault cannot be duplicated at this time. If any other codes are present, return to QUICK TEST for instructions. If none, test is complete. If continuous code 29 is displayed, go to next step.

2) Turn key off and wait 10 seconds. Disconnect ECA 60-pin connector. Inspect for and repair any damaged wiring. Install breakout box, leaving ECA and Vehicle Speed Sensor (VSS) disconnected. Set DVOM on 200-ohm scale. Measure resistance between test pin 3 and VSS + circuit at harness connector. Measure resistance between test pin 6 and VSS - circuit at harness connector. If both readings are 5 ohms or more, repair open(s) in VSS harness, then repeat step **1)**. If both readings are 5 ohms or less, go to next step.

3) With key off, ECA and VSS disconnected, set DVOM on 200,000-ohm sacle. Measure resistance between test pin 3 and test pins 37, 40, and 6. Then measure resistance between test pin 6 and test pins 37 and 40. If all readings are less than 1000 ohms, repair short(s) in VSS harness, then repeat step **1)**. If all readings are more than 1000 ohms, go to next step.

4) Substitute original VSS with a good known VSS. With ECA and VSS connected, perform AXOD DRIVE CYCLE TEST and return to this step. If continuous code 29 is displayed, replace ECA then repeat step **1)**. If continuous code 29 is not displayed, replace original VSS then repeat QUICK TEST.

Circuit Test (Cont.)

5) Continuous Code 69 Displayed. Perform AXOD DRIVE CYCLE TEST and return to this step. If continuous code 69 is not displayed, fault cannot be duplicated at this time. If any other codes are present, return to QUICK TEST for instructions. If none, test is complete. If continuous code 69 is displayed, go to next step.

6) Turn key off and wait 10 seconds. Disconnect ECA 60-pin connector. Inspect for and repair any damaged wiring. Install breakout box, leaving ECA and AXOD harness disconnected. Set DVOM on 200-ohm scale. Measure resistance between test pin 19 and THS 3/2 circuit at AXOD harness connector. If reading is more than 5 ohms, repair open in THS 3/2 circuit then repeat step **5)**. If reading is 5 ohms or less, go to next step.

7) With key off, breakout box installed, and ECA and AXOD harness disconnected, set DVOM on 200,000-ohm scale. Measure resistance between test pin 19 and test pin 37. If reading is less than 10,000 ohms, repair short to power in THS 3/2 circuit, then repeat step **5)**. If reading is more than 10,000 ohms, go to next step.

8) With key off and breakout box installed, connect ECA and AXOD harness. Install a jumper wire between test pin 19 and 40. Perform KEY ON/ENGINE OFF SELF-TEST. If code 62 is displayed, remove jumper wire and go to AXOD TRANSAXLE ELECTRICAL SYSTEM DIAGNOSIS. If code 62 is not displayed, remove jumper wire, replace ECA, and then repeat step **5)**.

9) Continuous Code 59 Displayed. Perform AXOD DRIVE CYCLE TEST and return to this step. If continuous code 59 is not displayed, fault cannot be duplicated at this time. If any other codes are present, return to QUICK TEST for instructions. If none, test is complete. If continuous code 59 is displayed, go to next step.

10) Turn key off and wait 10 seconds. Disconnect ECA 60-pin connector. Inspect for and repair any damaged wiring. Install breakout box, leaving ECA and AXOD harness disconnected. Set DVOM on 200-ohm scale. Measure resistance between test pin 18 and THS 4/3 circuit at AXOD harness connector. If reading is more than 5 ohms, repair open in THS 4/3 harness, then repeat step **9)**. If reading is 5 ohms or less, go to next step.

11) With key off, breakout box installed, and ECA and AXOD harness disconnected, set DVOM on 200,000-ohm scale. Measure resistance between pin 18 and test pin 37. If reading is less than 10,000 ohms, repair short to power in THS 4/3 circuit, then repeat step **9)**. If reading is higher than 10,000 ohms, go to next step.

12) With key off and breakout box installed, connect ECA and AXOD harness. Install a jumper wire between test pin 18 and 40. Perform KEY ON/ENGINE OFF SELF-TEST. If code 62 is displayed, remove jumper wire and go to AXOD TRANSAXLE ELECTRICAL SYSTEM DIAGNOSIS. If code 62 is not displayed, remove jumper wire, replace ECA, and then repeat step **9)**.

13) Continuous Code 39 Displayed. Perform AXOD DRIVE CYCLE TEST then return to this step. If continuous code 59 is also present, go directly to step **9)**. If continuous code 39 is displayed, go to AXOD TRANSAXLE ELECTRICAL SYSTEM DIAGNOSIS. If continuous code 39 is not displayed, fault cannot be duplicated at this time. If any other codes are present, return to QUICK TEST for instructions. If none, test is completed.

14) Continous Code 57 Displayed. Perform AXOD DRIVE CYCLE TEST and then return to this step. If continuous code 57 is not displayed, fault cannot be duplicated at this time. If any other codes are present, return to QUICK TEST for instructions. If none, test is completed. If continuous code 57 is displayed, go to next step.

15) Turn key off and wait 10 seconds. Disconnect ECA 60-pin connector. Inspect for and repair any damaged wiring. Install breakout box, leaving ECA and AXOD harness disconnected. Set DVOM on 200-ohm scale. Measure resistance between test pin 30 and NPS circuit at AXOD harness connector. If reading is more than 5 ohms, repair open in NPS circuit, then repeat step **14)**. If reading is 5 ohms or less, go to AXOD TRANSAXLE ELECTRICAL SYSTEM DIAGNOSIS.

16) Code 89 Displayed. Turn key off and wait 10 seconds. Disconnect ECA 60-pin connector. Inspect for and repair any damaged wiring. Install breakout box, leaving ECA and AXOD harness disconnected. Set DVOM on 200-ohm scale. Measure resistance between test pin 37 and VPWR circuit at AXOD harness connector. If reading is more than 5 ohms, repair open in VPWR circuit then repeat QUICK TEST. If reading is 5 ohms or less, go to next step.

FORD MOTOR CO. AXOD (Cont.)

Circuit Test (Cont.)

17) With key off, breakout box installed, and ECA and AXOD harness disconnected, set DVOM on 200-ohm scale. Measure resistance between test pin 53 and LUS circuit at AXOD harness connector. If reading is more than 5 ohms, repair open in LUS circuit then repeat QUICK TEST. If reading is 5 ohms or less, go to next step.

18) With key off, breakout box installed, and ECA and AXOD harness disconnected, set DVOM on 200,000-ohm scale. Measure resistance between test pin 53 and test pins 37 and 40. If both readings are less than 10,000 ohms, repair shorts in LUS harness. Repeat QUICK TEST. If code 89 is still displayed, replace ECA and repeat QUICK TEST. If both readings are higher than 10,000 ohms, go to next step.

19) With key off, breakout box installed, and ECA disconnected, connect AXOD harness. Set DVOM on 200,000-ohm scale. Measure resistance between test pin 53 and test pin 57. If resistance is between 20 and 40 ohms, replace ECA and repeat QUICK TEST. If resistance is not between 20 and 40 ohms, go to AXOD TRANSAXLE ELECTRICAL SYSTEM DIAGNOSIS.

20) Code 62 Displayed. Perform ENGINE RUNNING SELF-TEST and record codes. If code 62 is displayed, fault is in THS 4/3 circuit. Go to next step. If code 62 is not displayed, fault is in THS 3/2 circuit. Go to next step.

21) Turn key off and disconnect AXOD harness. Perform KEY ON/ENGINE OFF SELF-TEST. If code 62 is not displayed, go to AXOD TRANSAXLE ELECTRICAL SYSTEM DIAGNOSIS. If code 62 is displayed, go to next step.

22) Turn key off, install breakout box, leaving ECA and AXOD harness disconnected. Set DVOM on 200,000-ohm scale. Measure resistance between test pin 18 and test pins 40 and 60. Also measure resistance between test pin 19 and test pins 40 and 60. If all readings are less than 10,000 ohms, repair short(s) to ground. Repeat QUICK TEST. If all readings are higher than 10,000 ohms, replace ECA and repeat QUICK TEST.

23) Verify that code 62 is present in ENGINE RUNNING SELF-TEST. If code 62 is displayed, go to AXOD TRANSAXLE ELECTRICAL SYSTEM DIAGNOSIS. If code is not displayed, fault cannot be duplicated at this time. If any other codes are present, return to QUICK TEST for instructions. If none, test is completed.

24) Code 67 Displayed. Turn key on, leaving engine off. Disconnect ECA 60-pin connector. Inspect for and repair any damaged wiring. Install breakout box and connect ECA to box. Set DVOM on 20-volt scale. Measure voltage between test pin 30 and 46. If reading is more than 4.0 volts, go to CIRCUIT TEST M, step **4**). If reading is less than 4.0 volts, go to next step.

25) With key off, breakout box installed, and ECA and AXOD harness disconnected, set DVOM on 200,000-ohm scale. Measure resistance between test pin 30 and test pins 40 and 60. If all readings are less than 10,000 ohms, repair short to ground in NPS circuit. Repeat QUICK TEST. If all readings are higher than 10,000 ohms, go to next step.

26) With key off and breakout box installed, connect ECA. Leave AXOD harness disconnected. Perform KEY ON/ENGINE OFF SELF-TEST. If code 67 is displayed, replace ECA and repeat QUICK TEST. If code 67 is not displayed, go to AXOD TRANSAXLE ELECTRICAL SYSTEM DIAGNOSIS.

AXOD Transaxle Circuits

Breakout Box
Test Pins

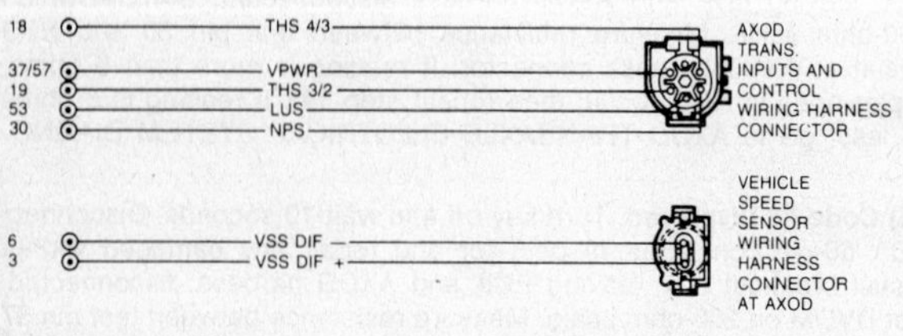

Circuit Test (Cont.)

Breakout Box
Test Pins

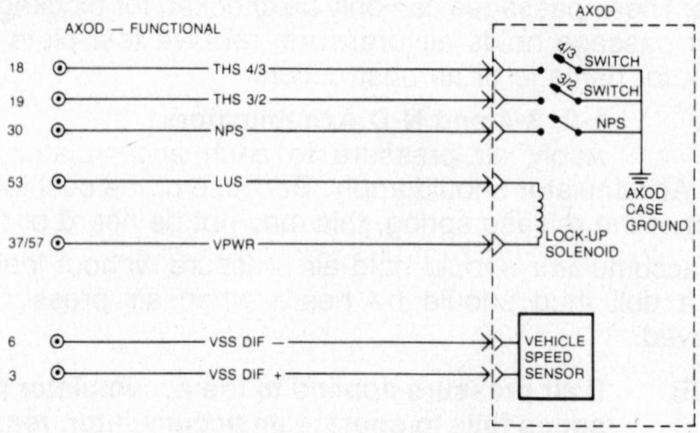

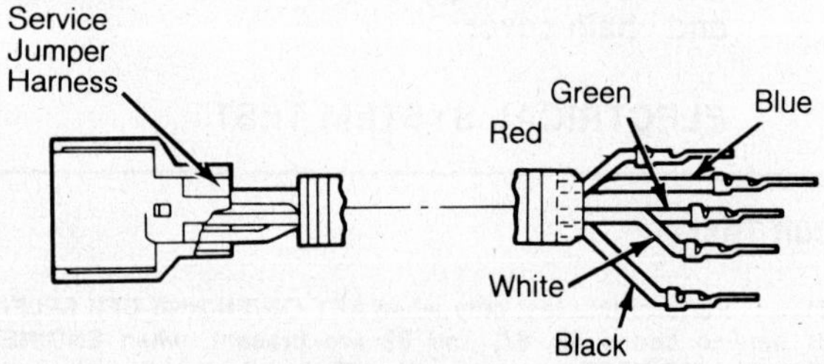

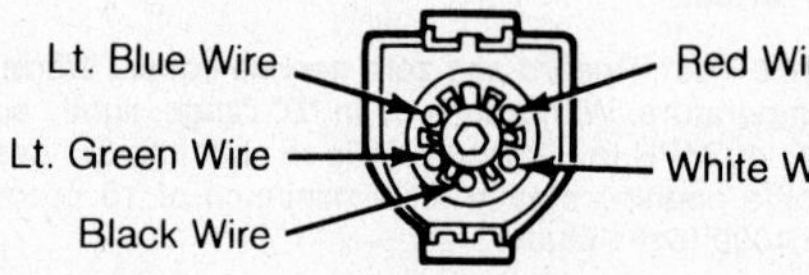

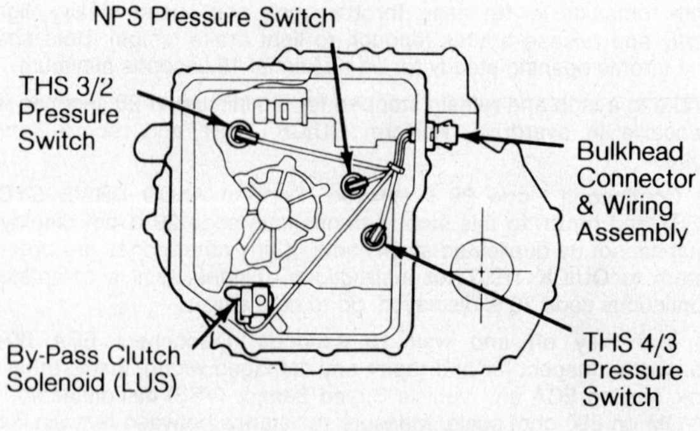

FORD MOTOR CO. AXOD (Cont.)

Diagnosis

This test should be performed only if a problem has been detected in transaxle. If any of these service codes appeared during SELF-TESTS, the AXOD DRIVE CYCLE TEST should be performed. The following AXOD transaxle related items have malfunctioned or failed as indicated:

- **Code 39 Displayed.** Transaxle converter by-pass clutch is not operating properly.
- **Code 59 Displayed.** THS 4/3 pressure switch circuit has failed open.
- **Code 62 Displayed.** THS 4/3 pressure switch circuit failed closed. If code appears in KEY ON/ENGINE OFF SELF-TEST, THS 3/2 circuit has failed. If code appears in ENGINE RUNNING SELF-TEST, THS 4/3 circuit has failed. If code appears in both SELF-TESTS, both circuits have failed and must be checked.
- **Code 69 Displayed.** THS 3/2 circuit has failed open.
- **Code 89 Displayed.** Transaxle converter by-pass clutch solenoid has stayed always open or always closed.

The following service codes are not AXOD transaxle related, but can affect converter clutch by-pass operation. Service these components before servicing AXOD transaxle codes:

- **Code 21 Displayed.** Engine Coolant Temperature (ECT) sensor out of range.
- **Code 22 Displayed.** Manifold Absolute Pressure (MAP) sensor out of range.
- **Code 23 Displayed.** Throttle Position Sensor (TPS) out of range.
- **Code 24 Displayed.** Air Charge Temperature (ACT) sensor out of range.
- **Code 23 Displayed.** Vehicle Speed Sensor (VSS) not functioning.
- **Code 74 Displayed.** Brake ON/OFF (BOO) switch always open or brake not applied during ENGINE RUNNING SELF-TEST.
- **Code 75 Displayed.** Brake ON/OFF (BOO) switch always closed.

The following service code indicates that a transaxle component may have caused faulty engine idle speed control:

- **Code 57 Displayed.** Neutral Pressure Switch (NPS) failed in Neutral (open). The NPS is normally open and closes with hydraulic pressure. Failure of transaxle to engage in "D" or "R" will cause service code 57 to be displayed. Check for proper hydraulic pressure before testing AXOD transaxle electrical components.

NOTE: Ensure that all components are connected before performing test. Perform AXOD DRIVE CYCLE TEST on a slight upgrade or flat terrain. If any other non-AXOD related codes appear, service those codes first as they could affect the electrical operation of transaxle.

AXOD Drive Cycle Test. Record and zero service codes. Warm engine to operating temperature. With transaxle in "D" range, lightly accelerate from a stop to 40 MPH to allow transaxle to shift into 3rd gear. Hold speed and throttle opening steady for a minimum of 15 seconds (30 seconds above 4000 feet altitude).

Shift transaxle into overdrive and accelerate lightly from 40 to 50 MPH to allow transaxle to shift into 4th gear. Hold speed and throttle opening steady for a minimum of 15 seconds.

With transaxle in 4th gear, throttle open and speed steady, lightly apply and release brakes (enough to light brake lamps). Hold speed and throttle opening steady for an additional 15 seconds minimum.

Brake to a stop and remain stopped for a minimum of 20 seconds with transaxle in overdrive. Perform QUICK TEST and record service codes.

1) Code 39 Displayed. Check that vehicle harness connector is fully attached to transaxle bulkhead connector and that vehicle harness connector terminals are fully engaged in connector. If connector or terminals are not okay, repair as required. Repeat QUICK TEST. If connector and terminals are okay, go to next step.

2) Install service jumper harness to transaxle bulkhead connector. Connect VOM positive test lead to Red wire and negative test lead to Black wire. Check resistance. If reading is between 20 and 40 ohms, go to QUICK TEST and service codes as required. If reading is not between 20 and 40 ohms, go to next step.

3) Connect service jumper harness Red wire to battery positive post. With engine running and transaxle in 3rd gear, connect service jumper harness Black wire to ground (to energize by-pass clutch solenoid). DO NOT connect with polarity reversed, otherwise solenoid diode will be damaged.

Diagnosis (Cont.)

4) If by-pass clutch is applied (engine RPM drops), there is no electrical component failure. By-pass clutch solenoid is operating properly. Error code may be indicating a slipping by-pass clutch. Service transaxle for a no converter clutch apply condition and repeat QUICK TEST.

5) If by-pass clutch is not applied (engine RPM does not drop), check main control by-pass clutch control valve (in valve body) for sticking. If valve is sticking, service spool valve as required. If okay, go to next step.

6) Remove by-pass solenoid. Check condition of "O" ring. Shake solenoid vigorously to check for free armature. If not okay, replace by-pass solenoid and repeat QUICK TEST. If okay, service transaxle for a no converter clutch apply condition and repeat QUICK TEST.

NOTE: The THS 4/3 and 3/2 pressure switches are normally open and close with hydraulic pressure. Failure of transaxle to engage in "D" will cause code 59 to be displayed. Failure of transaxle to shift into 3rd gear will cause code 69 to be displayed. Check for proper hydraulic operation before testing electrical components.

7) Code 59 Displayed. Check that vehicle harness connector is fully attached to transaxle bulkhead connector and that vehicle harness connector terminals are fully engaged in connector. If connector or terminals are not okay, repair as required. Repeat QUICK TEST. If connector and terminals are okay, go to next step.

8) Install service jumper harness to transaxle bulkhead connector. Using VOM, check for continuity between engine ground and Blue wire. With engine running and transaxle in Neutral, VOM should indicate no continuity (infinite resistance).

9) Shift transaxle into "D". Switch should close and resistance should be less than 10 ohms. Switch should stay closed in 1st, 2nd and 3rd gear, then open in 4th gear. If circuit is okay, go to QUICK TEST and service codes as required. If circuit is not okay, go to next step.

10) Remove transaxle side oil pan and check that internal connector with Blue wire is firmly attached to THS 4/3 pressure switch. Connector should not pull off easily or fit loosely. If connector is not okay, replace bulkhead connector and wiring assembly. Repeat QUICK TEST. If connector is okay, go to next step.

11) Remove connector from pressure switch by pushing on end of connector, while pulling on connector wire. Check for continuity in bulkhead connector by measuring resistance between Blue wire and terminal inside connector just removed. If reading is more than 2 ohms, replace bulkhead connector and wiring assembly. Repeat QUICK TEST. If reading is less than 2 ohms, go to next step.

12) Remove THS 4/3 pressure switch. Install a 1/8-27 pipe fitting that can be connected to LOW pressure air supply in order to pressure leak and test switch closure. With 50 psi (3.5 kg/cm²) applied, check for ruptured diaphragm by submerging switch in clean transmission fluid. Check for bubbles coming out of small vent hole near switch terminal. If bubbles show, diaphragm has failed. Replace THS 4/3 pressure switch and repeat QUICK TEST. If no bubbles show, go to next step.

13) With 50 psi (3.5 kg/cm²) applied to switch, check resistance between switch terminal and switch case. If reading is 8 ohms or less, hydraulic pressure circuit to switch may have excessive leaks. Service transaxle as required. If reading is more than 8 ohms, replace switch. Repeat step **8)**, then QUICK TEST. Codes 39, 59, 62, 69 and 89 should no longer be displayed.

NOTE: If code 62 appears in KEY ON/ENGINE OFF SELF-TEST, THS 3/2 circuit has failed. If code appears in ENGINE RUNNING SELF-TEST, THS 4/3 circuit has failed. If code appears in both SELF-TESTS, follow entire test procedure to determine which circuit has failed.

14) Code 62 Displayed. Remove vehicle harness connector from transaxle bulkhead connector and install service jumper harness. Using VOM, measure continuity between engine ground and White wire (THS 3/2 circuit). With engine off, VOM should indicate no continuity (infinite resistance).

Automatic Transmissions

FORD MOTOR CO. AXOD (Cont.)

Diagnosis (Cont.)

15) Measure continuity between engine ground and Blue wire (THS 4/3 circuit). With engine off, VOM should indicate no continuity (infinite resistance). With engine running and transaxle in Neutral, VOM should also indicate no continuity (infinite resistance). If all readings show no continuity, go to QUICK TEST and service codes as required. If any reading indicates continuity, go to next step.

16) Remove transaxle side oil pan and check for pinched, cut or otherwise grounded wiring. If wiring is pinched, cut or grounded, replace bulkhead connector and wiring assembly. Repeat QUICK TEST. If THS 4/3 switch wiring is okay, go to step **18)**. If THS 3/2 switch wiring is okay, go to next step.

17) Remove wiring from THS 3/2 pressure switch. Using VOM, check pressure switch for continuity to engine ground by connecting one lead to switch terminal and other lead to valve body. If there is no continuity (infinite resistance), go to step **19)**. If there is continuity to ground, replace THS 3/2 pressure switch and repeat QUICK TEST.

18) Remove wiring from THS 4/3 pressure switch. Using VOM, check pressure switch for continuity to engine ground by connecting one lead to switch terminal and other lead to valve body. If there is continuity to ground, replace 4/3 pressure switch and repeat QUICK TEST. If there is no continuity (infinite resistance), go to next step.

19) Using VOM and with wiring removed from both pressure switches, check for continuity to ground. Connect one test lead to White wire and other test lead to ground. Then connect one test lead to Blue wire and other test lead to ground. Make sure that internal terminals are not touching any metallic parts. If there is continuity to ground, replace bulkhead connector and wiring assembly. Repeat QUICK TEST. If there is no continuity (infinite resistance), go to QUICK TEST and service codes as required.

NOTE: The THS 4/3 and 3/2 pressure switches are normally open, and close with hydraulic pressure. Failure of transaxle to engage in "D" will cause service code 59 to be displayed. Failure of transaxle to shift into 3rd gear will cause service code 69 to be displayed. Check for proper hydraulic operation before testing electrical components.

20) Code 69 Displayed. Check that vehicle harness connector is fully attached to transaxle bulkhead connector and that vehicle harness terminals are fully engaged in connector. If connector or terminals are not okay, repair as required. Repeat QUICK TEST. If connector and terminals are okay, go to next step.

21) Install service jumper harness to transaxle bulkhead connector. Using VOM, check for continuity between engine ground and White wire. With engine running and transaxle in Drive, 1st or 2nd gear, VOM should indicate no continuity (infinite resistance).

22) When transaxle shifts into 3rd or 4th gear, the switch should close, resistance should be less than 10 ohms between White wire and engine ground. If circuit is okay, go to QUICK TEST and service codes as required. If circuit is not okay, go to next step.

23) Remove transaxle side oil pan and check that internal connector with White wire is firmly attached to THS 3/2 pressure switch. Connector should not pull off easily or fit loosely. If connector is not okay, replace bulkhead connector and wiring assembly. Repeat QUICK TEST. If connector is okay, go to next step.

24) Check for continuity in bulkhead connector by measuring resistance between White wire and terminal inside connector just removed. If reading is more than 2 ohms, replace bulkhead connector and wiring assembly. Repeat QUICK TEST. If reading is less than 2 ohms, go to next step.

25) Remove THS 3/2 pressure switch. Install a 1/8-27 pipe fitting that can be connected to LOW pressure air supply in order to pressure leak and test switch closure. With 50 psi (3.5 kg/cm²) applied, check for ruptured diaphragm by submerging switch in clean transmission fluid. Check for bubbles coming out of small vent hole near switch terminal. If bubbles show, diaphragm has failed. Replace THS 3/2 pressure switch and repeat QUICK TEST. If no bubbles show, go to next step.

26) With 50 psi (3.5 kg/cm²) applied to switch, check resistance between switch terminal and switch case. If reading is 8 ohms or less, hydraulic pressure circuit to switch may have excessive leaks, service transaxle as required. If reading is more than 8 ohms, replace switch. Repeat steps **21)** and **22)**, then repeat QUICK TEST. Codes 39, 59, 62, 69 and 89 should no longer be displayed.

Diagnosis (Cont.)

27) Code 89 Displayed. If code 39 is also displayed, go to step **1)**. Check that vehicle harness connector is fully attached to transaxle bulkhead connector and that vehicle harness terminals are fully engaged in connector. If connector or terminals are not okay, repair or replace as required. Repeat QUICK TEST. If connector and terminals are okay, go to next step.

28) Install service jumper harness to transaxle bulkhead connector. Connect VOM positive test lead to Red wire and negative test lead to Black wire. Check resistance. If reading is between 20 and 40 ohms, go to QUICK TEST and service codes as required. If reading is not between 20 and 40 ohms, go to next step.

29) Remove transaxle side oil pan and check that internal connector is fully attached to solenoid. If connector is okay, go to next step. If connector is not okay, fully engage connector and check continuity once more. If resistance is still not between 20 and 40 ohms, go to next step. If resistance is now okay, repeat QUICK TEST.

30) Remove connector from solenoid by pulling on wires at 2-way connector. Check solenoid continuity by connecting VOM positive test lead to positive terminal and negative test lead to negative terminal (polarity symbols are stamped on solenoid frame).

31) If circuit is open (infinite resistance), replace solenoid and then repeat QUICK TEST. If solenoid is okay (20 to 40 ohms resistance), replace bulkhead connector and wiring assembly. Connect all internal connectors and repeat step **28)**. If circuits test okay, install oil pan. Repeat KEY ON/ENGINE OFF SELF-TEST. Code 89 should no longer be displayed.

NOTE: The NPS is normally open and closes with hydraulic pressure. Failure of transaxle to engage in "D" or "R" will cause service code 57 to be displayed. Check for proper hydraulic pressure before testing transaxle electrical components.

32) Code 57 Displayed. Check that vehicle harness connector is fully attached to transaxle bulkhead connector and that vehicle harness terminals are fully engaged in connector. If connector or terminals are not okay, repair as required. Repeat QUICK TEST. If connector and terminals are okay, go to next step.

33) Install service jumper harness to transaxle bulkhead connector. Using VOM, check continuity between Green wire and engine ground. With engine running and transaxle in "P" or "N", VOM should indicate no continuity (infinite resistance). Shift transaxle into "R" and "D", switch should close, resistance should be less than 10 ohms in both ranges. If circuit is okay, go to QUICK TEST and service codes as required. If circuit is not okay, go to next step.

34) Remove transaxle side oil pan and check that internal connector with Green wire is firmly attached to NPS. Connector should not pull off easily or fit loosely. If connector is not okay, replace bulkhead connector and wiring assembly. Repeat QUICK TEST. If connector is okay, go to next step.

35) Remove connector from NPS by pushing on end of connector, while pulling on connector wire. Check for continuity in bulkhead connector by measuring resistance between Green wire and terminal inside connector just removed. If reading is more than 2 ohms, replace bulkhead connector and wiring assembly. Repeat QUICK TEST. If reading is less than 2 ohms, go to next step.

36) Remove NPS. Install a 1/8-27 pipe fitting that can be connected to LOW pressure air supply in order to pressure leak and test switch closure. With 50 psi (3.5 kg/cm²) applied, check for ruptured diaphragm by submerging switch in clean transmission fluid. Check for bubbles coming out of small vent hole near switch terminal. If bubbles show, diaphragm has failed. Replace NPS and repeat QUICK TEST. If no bubbles show, go to next step.

37) With 50 psi (3.5 kg/cm²) applied to switch, check resistance between switch terminal and switch case. If reading is 8 ohms or less, hydraulic pressure circuit to switch may have excessive leaks. Service transaxle as required. If reading is more than 8 ohms, replace switch. Repeat step **33)**, then repeat QUICK TEST. Codes 39, 59, 62, 69 and 89 should no longer be displayed.

Automatic Transmissions

FORD MOTOR CO. AXOD (Cont.)

Fig. 4: Cutaway View of Ford Motor Co. AXOD Transaxle

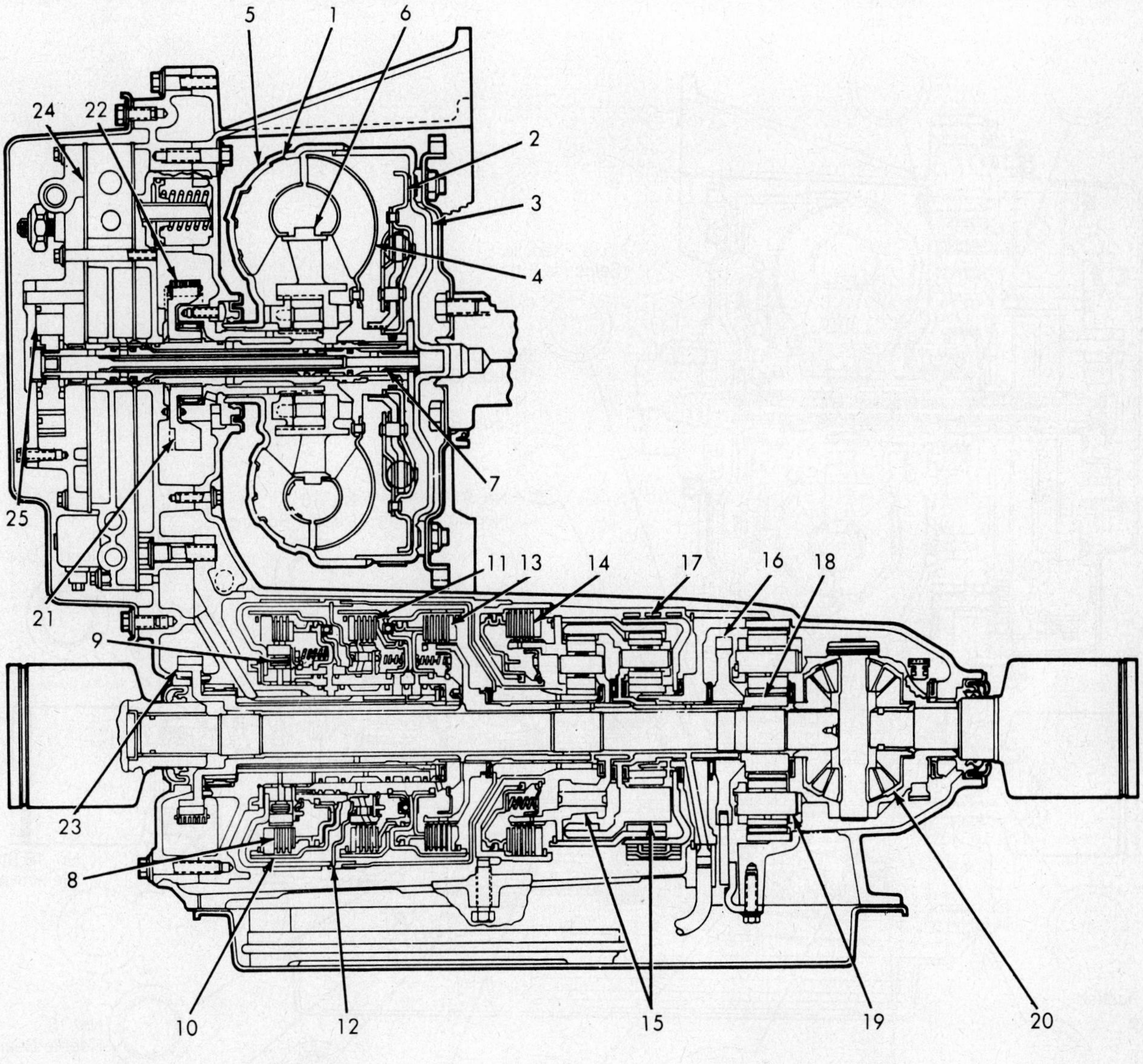

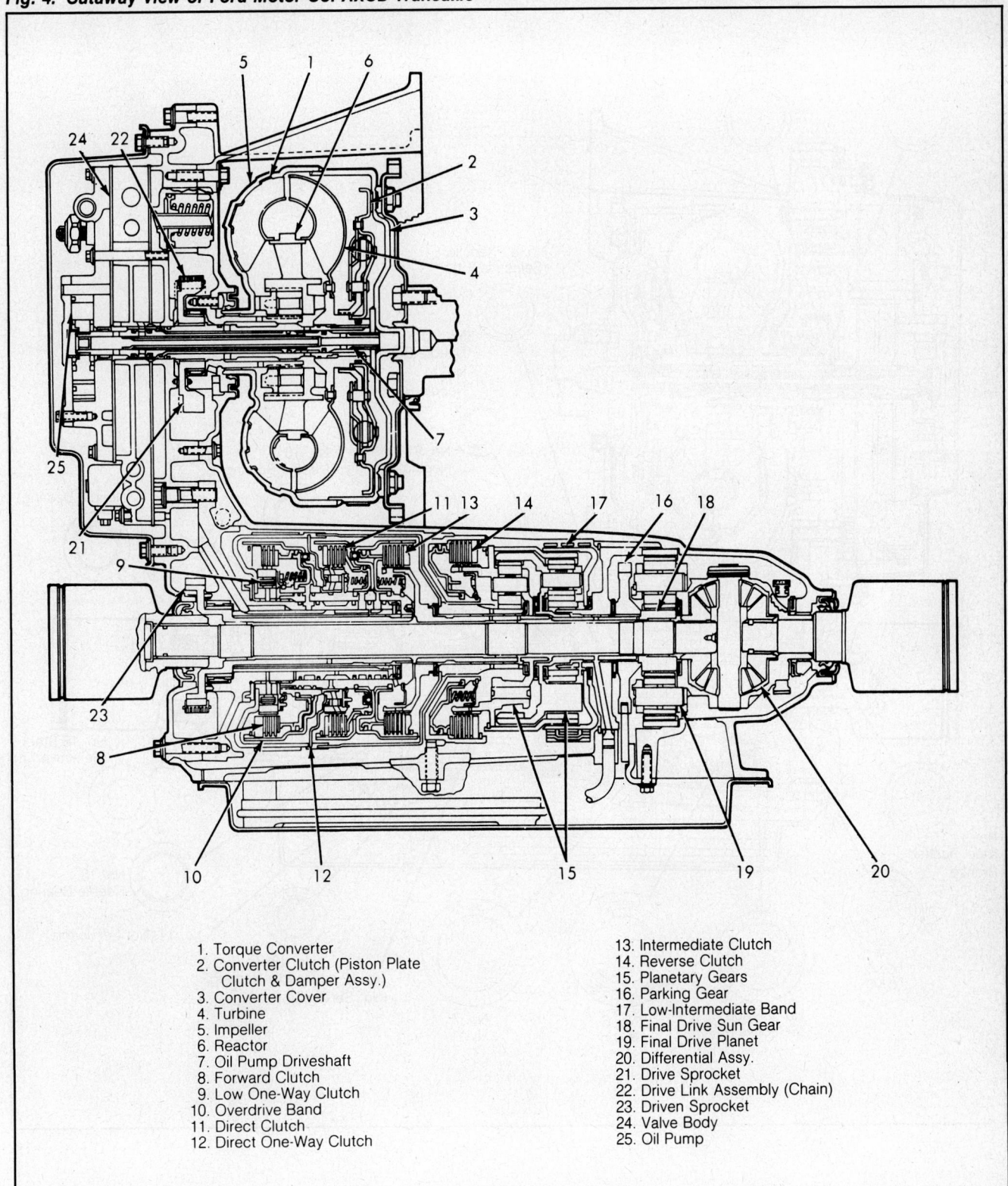

1. Torque Converter
2. Converter Clutch (Piston Plate Clutch & Damper Assy.)
3. Converter Cover
4. Turbine
5. Impeller
6. Reactor
7. Oil Pump Driveshaft
8. Forward Clutch
9. Low One-Way Clutch
10. Overdrive Band
11. Direct Clutch
12. Direct One-Way Clutch
13. Intermediate Clutch
14. Reverse Clutch
15. Planetary Gears
16. Parking Gear
17. Low-Intermediate Band
18. Final Drive Sun Gear
19. Final Drive Planet
20. Differential Assy.
21. Drive Sprocket
22. Drive Link Assembly (Chain)
23. Driven Sprocket
24. Valve Body
25. Oil Pump

Automatic Transmissions

FORD MOTOR CO. AXOD (Cont.)

Fig. 5: Thrust Washer and Needle Bearing Location

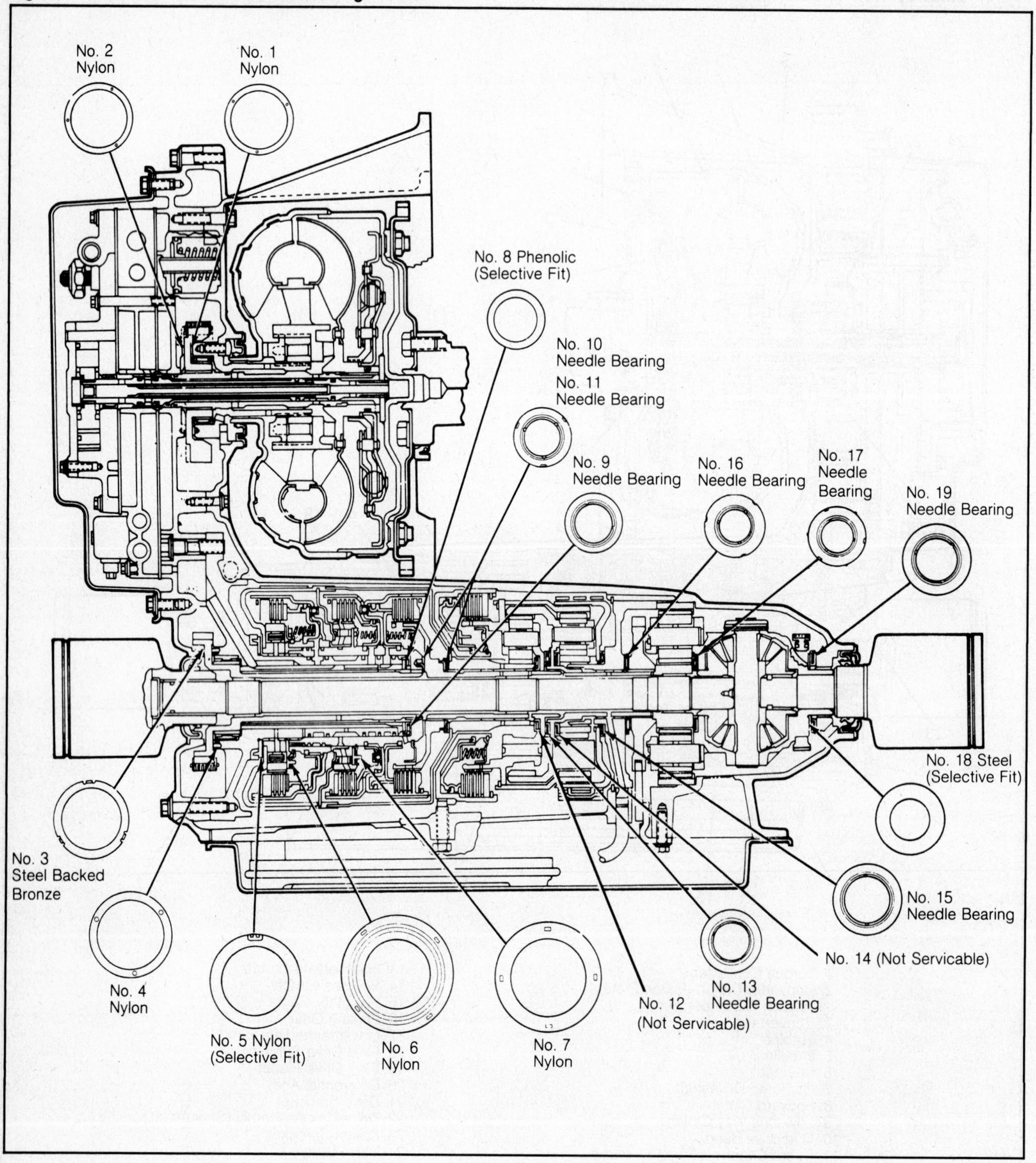

Automatic Transmissions

FORD MOTOR CO. AXOD (Cont.)

Fig. 6: Oil Pump and Valve Body Bolt Removal and Tightening Sequence

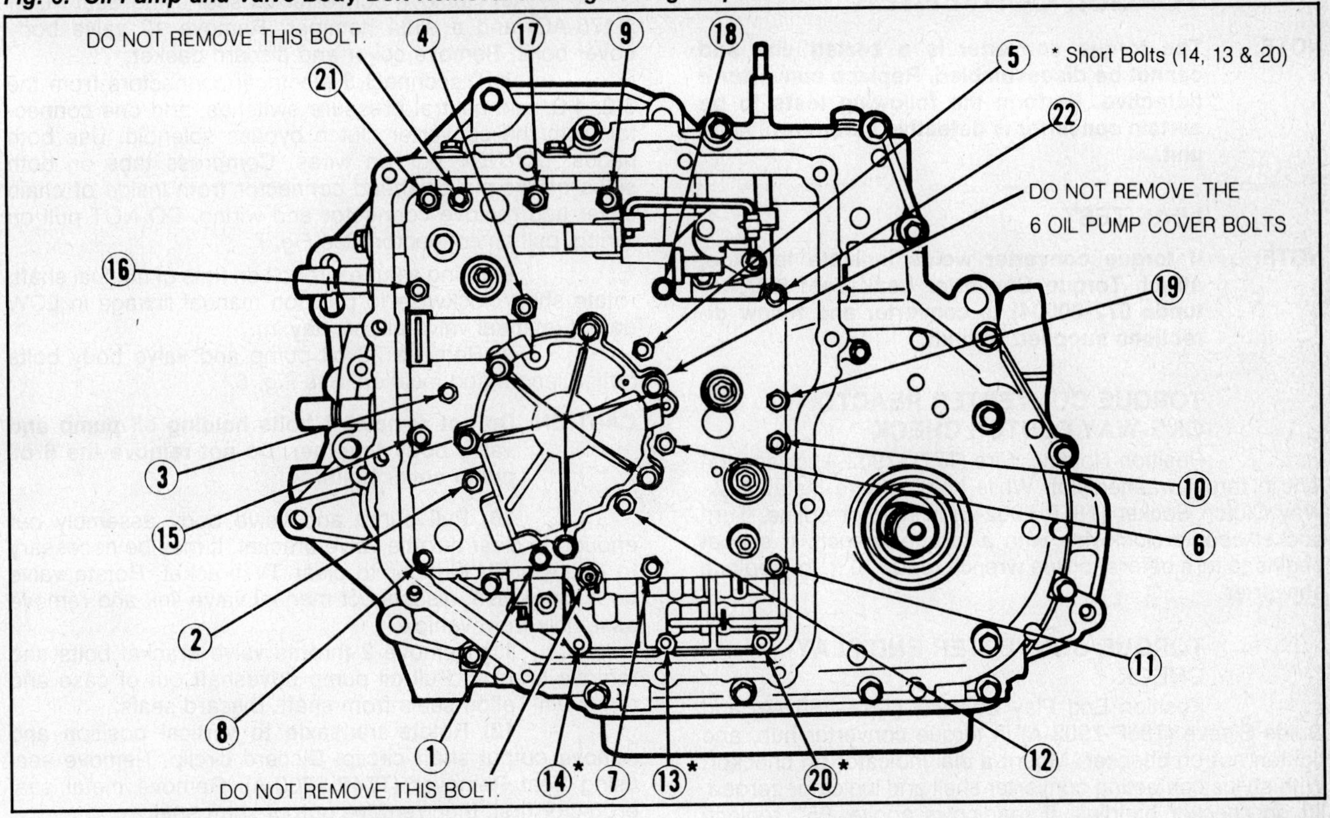

SERVICE (IN VEHICLE)

OIL PUMP & VALVE BODY ASSEMBLY

Removal

1) Disconnect battery ground cable. Remove battery and battery tray. Remove remote air cleaner. Secure supply hoses, vacuum lines and wiring away from valve body cover.

2) Raise vehicle on hoist. Support engine and transaxle and remove left side engine mounts and supports. See appropriate AUTOMATIC TRANSMISSION REMOVAL article in DOMESTIC GENERAL SERVICING section.

3) Loosen valve body cover bolts and drain fluid. Remove cover and gasket. Remove 22 pump and valve body assembly-to-chain cover bolts. *See Fig. 6.*

4) Pull pump and valve body assembly out enough to clear throttle valve bracket. It may be necessary to depress TV plunger to clear TV bracket. Rotate valve body clockwise, disconnect manual valve link and remove assembly from vehicle.

Installation (Method No. 1)

1) Install new cover gasket. Slide pump and valve body assembly onto oil pump shaft. Rotate assembly clockwise and connect manual valve link.

2) Slightly rotate or jiggle assembly to engage splines on oil pump shaft with splines in oil pump rotor. Valve body should slide flush onto chain cover without force. It may be necessary to rotate engine using a 7/8" socket on crankshaft to complete engagement of pump shaft to pump.

3) Use Valve Body Alignment Pin (T86P-70100-C) to position valve body. Install bolts and tighten in sequence shown. *See Fig. 6.*

CAUTION: Do not use bolts to draw pump and valve body into position.

4) Install cover using a new gasket. To complete installation, reverse removal procedures.

NOTE: If full engagement of the pump and valve body assembly is not obtained using Method No. 1, the following alternate method may be used.

Installation (Method No. 2)

1) Install new cover gasket. Remove manual valve from valve body. Slide pump and valve body assembly onto oil pump shaft. Rotate assembly as necessary to allow full engagement (360° rotation possible). After full engagement, return assembly to installed position and install manual valve.

2) Use Valve Body Alignment Pin (T86P-70100-C) to position valve body. Install bolts and tighten in sequence shown. *See Fig. 6.*

CAUTION: Do not use bolts to draw pump and valve body into position.

3) Install cover using a new gasket. To complete installation, reverse removal procedures.

REMOVAL & INSTALLATION

TRANSMISSION

See appropriate AUTOMATIC TRANSMISSION REMOVAL article in DOMESTIC GENERAL SERVICING section.

TORQUE CONVERTER

NOTE: The torque converter is a sealed unit and cannot be disassembled. Replace converter if defective. Perform the following tests to be certain converter is defective before replacing unit.

LEAK TEST

NOTE: If torque converter welds indicate leakage, attach Torque Converter Leak Test Kit (Rotunda 072-00004) to converter and follow directions supplied with kit.

TORQUE CONVERTER REACTOR ONE-WAY CLUTCH CHECK

Position Holding Wire (T77L-7902-A) or equivalent in thrust washer slot. While holding wire install One-Way Clutch Socket (T81P-7902-B) in reactor spline. Turn socket counterclockwise with a torque wrench. If socket begins to turn before torque wrench reads 10 ft. lb., replace converter.

TORQUE CONVERTER END PLAY CHECK

Position End Play Checker (T80L-7902-A) and Guide Sleeve (T86P-7902-A) in torque converter hub, and tighten nut on checker. Mount a dial indicator on checker. With stylus contacting converter shell and indicator zeroed, lift on checker handles. If reading is above .05", replace converter.

STATOR TO IMPELLER INTERFERENCE CHECK

Position stator support assembly on a bench with spline end pointing up. Mount a converter on the stator support with the splines on the one-way clutch engaging the splines on the stator support. Hold support stationary, and try to rotate the converter both clockwise and counterclockwise. It should rotate freely without interference or scraping. If there is any indication of interference or scraping, replace the converter.

TRANSAXLE DISASSEMBLY

1) Remove torque converter. Mount transaxle in a holding fixture. Turn to a vertical position, remove shipping plug and drain fluid.

2) Return transaxle to horizontal position and remove 2 governor cover bolts, cover and seal. Discard seal. Lift governor and speedometer drive gear assembly, and bearing (on top of speedometer drive gear) from case.

3) Remove 3 bolts on both the overdrive servo cover and the low-intermediate servo cover. Remove both servo assemblies and discard gaskets or seals.

4) Remove right side 2 piece output shaft seal using Shaft Protector (D80L-625-A) and Seal Remover (T74P-6700-A). Remove metal seal protector first, then remove output shaft seal.

5) Remove 2 neutral safety switch bolts and remove switch. Remove dipstick tube attaching bolt and pull tube from case. Remove 9 chain cover bolts from inside torque converter housing.

6) Remove converter oil seal using Seal Puller (1175-AC) and a slide hammer. Remove 12 valve body cover bolts. Remove cover and discard gasket.

7) Disconnect 3 electrical connectors from the 3-2, 4-3, and neutral pressure switches, and one connector from the converter clutch bypass solenoid. Use both hands. DO NOT pull on wires. Compress tabs on both sides of five-pin bulkhead connector from inside of chain cover and remove connector and wiring. DO NOT pull on wiring, pull on connector. *See Fig. 7*.

8) Using a 9mm wrench on flats of manual shaft, rotate shaft clockwise to position manual linkage in LOW detent (manual valve all the way in).

9) Remove 22 oil pump and valve body bolts noting length and location. *See Fig. 6*.

CAUTION: Do not remove 2 bolts holding oil pump and valve body together. Do not remove the 6 oil pump cover bolts.

10) Pull pump and valve body assembly out enough to clear throttle valve bracket. It may be necessary to depress TV plunger to clear TV bracket. Rotate valve body clockwise, disconnect manual valve link and remove assembly from vehicle.

11) Remove 2 throttle valve bracket bolts and remove bracket. Pull oil pump driveshaft out of case and remove 4 Teflon seals from shaft. Discard seals.

12) Rotate transaxle to vertical position and remove output shaft circlip. Discard circlip. Remove seal using Seal Remover (T74P-6700-A). Remove metal seal protector first, then remove output shaft seal.

13) Remove fourteen 10mm, one 13mm, and one 8mm chain cover bolts. Note length and location of bolts. *See Fig. 8*. Remove chain cover, discard gasket and tag accumulator springs for reassembly reference. Remove No. 1 (plastic) and No. 3 (metal) thrust washers from chain cover.

14) Simultaneously lift out both sprockets with chain assembly. Remove No. 2 and No. 4 thrust washers from drive and driven sprocket supports. Inspect drive sprocket support bearing to determine if it needs replacing. If bearing is okay, remove 6 Torx bolts attaching support to case.

15) Remove lockpin and 2 roll pins from manual shaft using Remover (D81P-3504-N) or equivalent. Be careful not to damage any machined surfaces. Slide shaft out of case, then pry seal from case. *See Fig. 9*.

16) Remove driven sprocket support assembly. If support binds it may be necessary to back out reverse clutch anchor bolt. Remove 5 Teflon seals from support and the No. 5 selective thrust washer.

17) Using a wire hook remove No. 8 selective thrust washer and No. 9 needle bearing from bottom of cylinder. Remove plastic overdrive band retainer and overdrive band.

18) Using Clutch Pack Holder (T86P-70389-A) or equivalent, lift front sun gear and shell assembly out of case. Remove 17 oil pan cover bolts, remove cover and discard gasket. Remove reverse apply tube/oil filter bolt and bracket. Remove oil filter screen and discard 2 "O" rings.

19) Remove tube bracket bolts and brackets. If necessary, use Tube Remover (T86P-70001-A) and a slide hammer to remove lube tubes. Tubes are held in with Loctite.

FORD MOTOR CO. AXOD (Cont.)

Fig. 7: Disconnecting Electrical Connectors from Pressure Switches and Solenoid

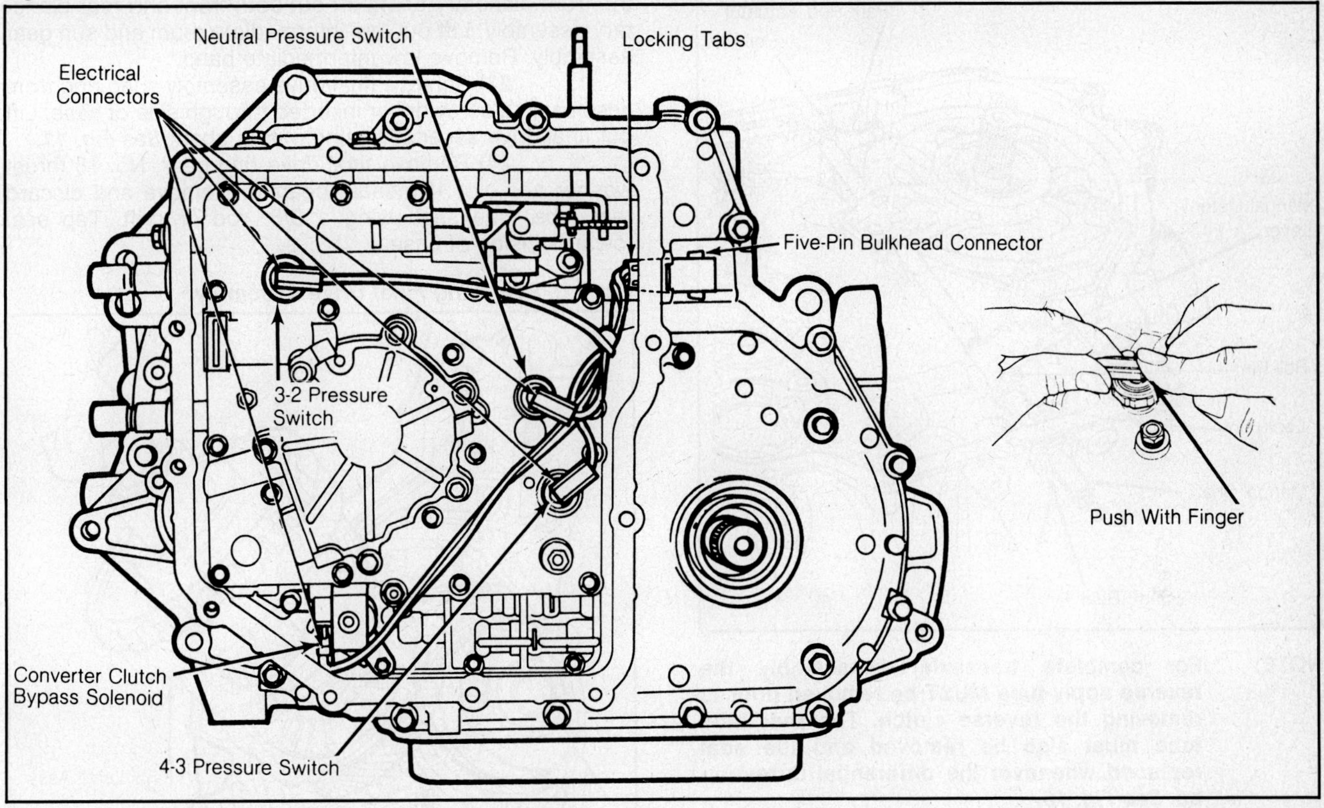

Fig. 8: Chain Cover Bolt Locations

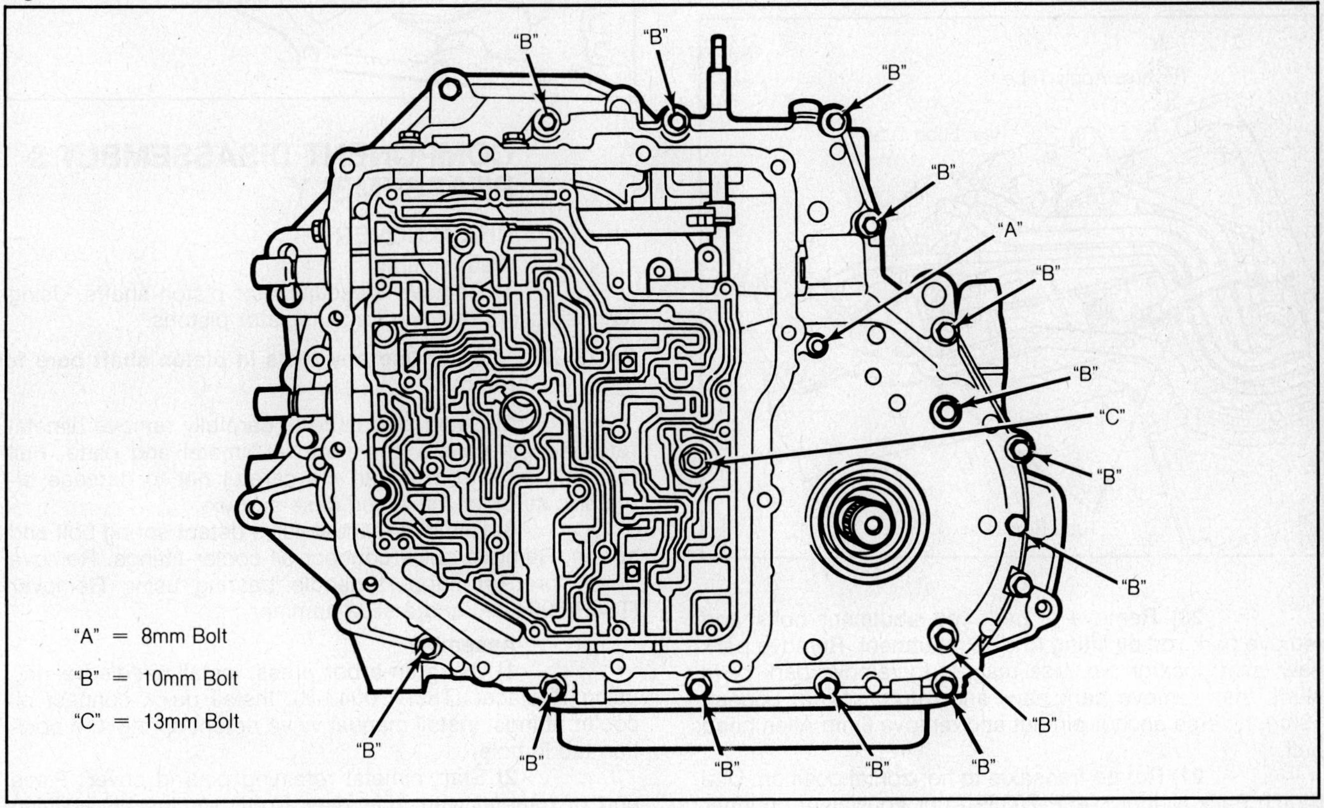

Automatic Transmissions

FORD MOTOR CO. AXOD (Cont.)

Fig. 9: Manual Shaft Lock Pin, Roll Pins and Seal Removal

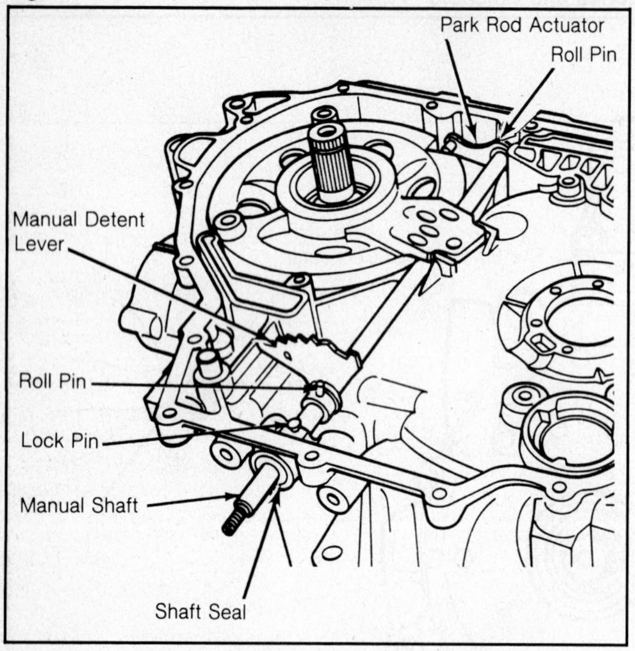

NOTE: **For complete transaxle disassembly the reverse apply tube MUST be removed prior to removing the reverse clutch. The rear lube tube must also be removed and the seal replaced whenever the differential is removed. *See Fig. 10*.**

Fig. 10: Oil Tube Locations

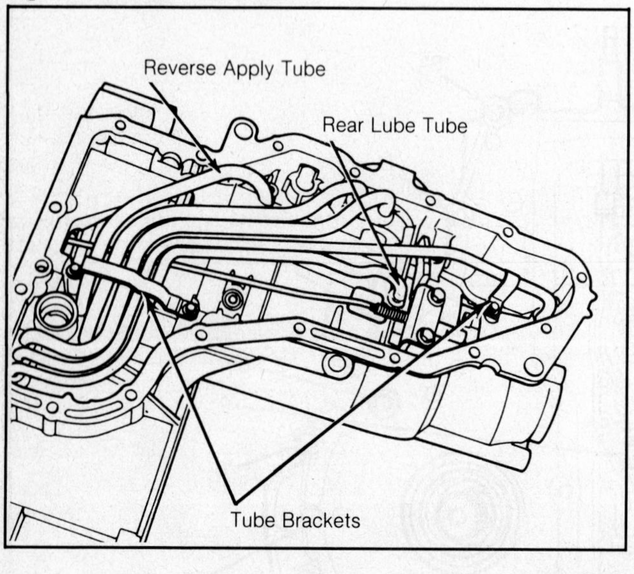

20) Remove 2 park rod abutment bolts and remove park rod by lifting to clear abutment. Remove park pawl shaft locator pin. Use magnet to remove park pawl shaft, then remove park pawl and return spring. Loosen 19mm reverse anchor pin nut and remove 6mm Allen head bolt.

21) Rotate transaxle to horizontal position. Use Clutch Pack Holder (T86P-70389-A) or equivalent on inner diameter of reverse clutch cylinder and slide clutch assembly out of case.

22) Rotate transaxle to vertical position. Holding the front planetary shaft, lift out both front and rear planetary assembly. Lift out low-intermediate drum and sun gear assembly. Remove low-intermediate band.

23) Remove final drive assembly snap ring from case using a screwdriver inserted through side of case. Lift out final drive assembly using output shaft. *See Fig. 11*.

24) Remove final drive ring gear, No. 18 thrust washer and No. 19 needle bearing. Remove and discard rear lube tube seal using a 3/8" rod or drift. Tap seal towards inside of case.

Fig. 11: Removing Final Drive Assembly

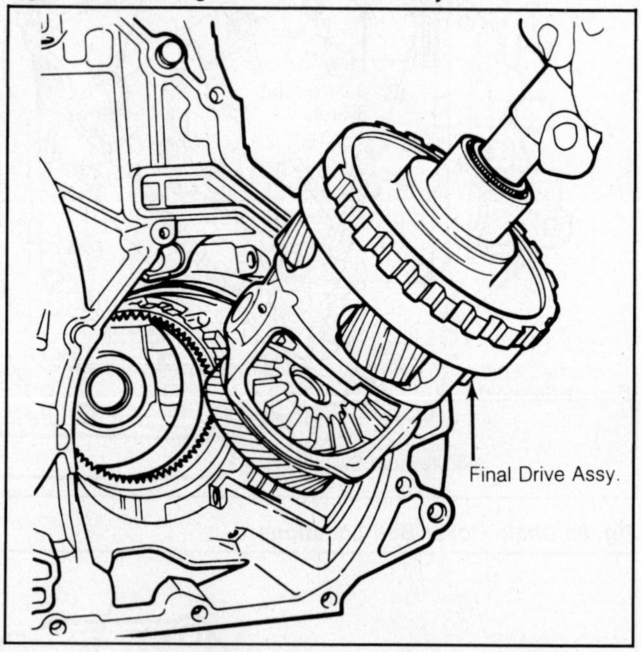

COMPONENT DISASSEMBLY & REASSEMBLY

CHAIN COVER

Disassembly

1) Remove 3 accumulator piston shafts. Using flatnose pliers remove 3 accumulator pistons.

CAUTION: **Do not use any tools in piston shaft bore for removal.**

2) Using side cutters, carefully remove bimetal retaining pin collars and remove bimetal and plate. Pull retaining pins from cover. Be careful not to damage bimetallic strips or machined case surface.

3) Remove manual valve detent spring bolt and spring. Remove quick connect oil cooler fittings. Remove drive sprocket support needle bearing using Remover (T86P-70043-A) and a slide hammer.

Assembly

1) Using an arbor press, install needle bearing using Replacer (T86P-70043-B). Install quick connect oil cooler fittings. Install manual valve detent spring and position tab in hole.

2) Start bimetal retaining pins in cover. Place end of bimetal with hole over front pin. Install retaining collars. Place Height Gauge (T86P-70422-A) or equivalent against pin and under bimetal. Gently tap collar onto pin until it seats against tool. *See Fig. 12*.

FORD MOTOR CO. AXOD (Cont.)

3) Engage slotted end of bimetal under rear retaining pin and repeat above step to set proper height. Remove slotted end of bimetal and set center retaining pin height using same gauge. Position slotted ends of plate onto rear and middle pins. Install slotted end of bimetal under rear pin.

Fig. 12: Setting Bimetal Height

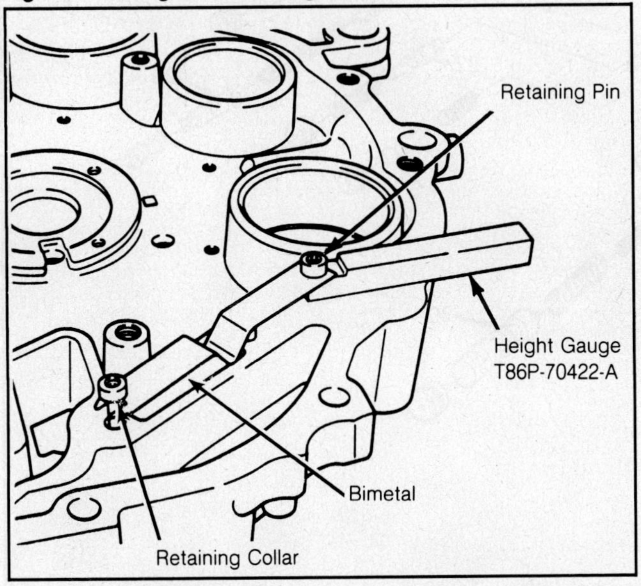

4) Install new seals and "O" rings on accumulator pistons, and install into their respective cylinder. Install 3 accumulator piston shafts.

OIL PUMP & VALVE BODY

Disassembly & Reassembly

Remove 2 bolts holding oil pump to valve body and separate. Remove gasket.

Using a new gasket, position valve body on oil pump. Insert Guide Pins (T86P-70370-A) and (T86P-70100-C), the 2 bolts and tighten to specification. *See Fig. 13.*

Fig. 13: Valve Body and Oil Pump Guide Pin Location

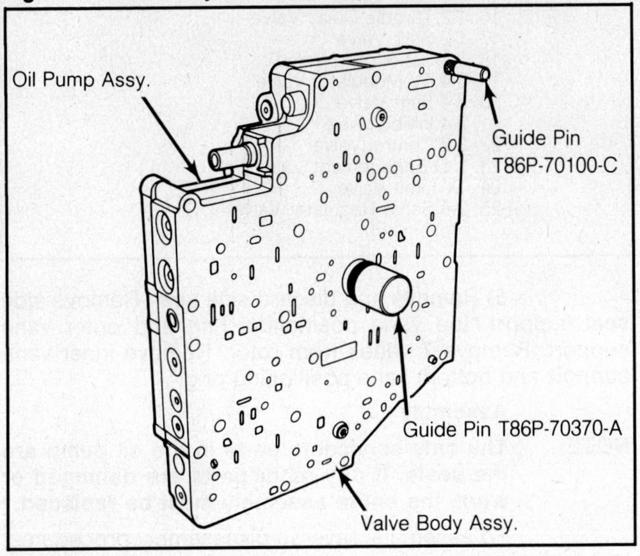

VALVE BODY

Disassembly

1) Place valve body on bench with separator plate up and remove 2 Torx bolts holding plate to valve body. Remove plate and gasket.

2) Remove 7 check balls, 2 relief valves and by-pass solenoid filter. *See Fig. 14.*

Fig. 14: Valve Body Check Balls, Relief Valves and By-Pass Solenoid Filter Locations

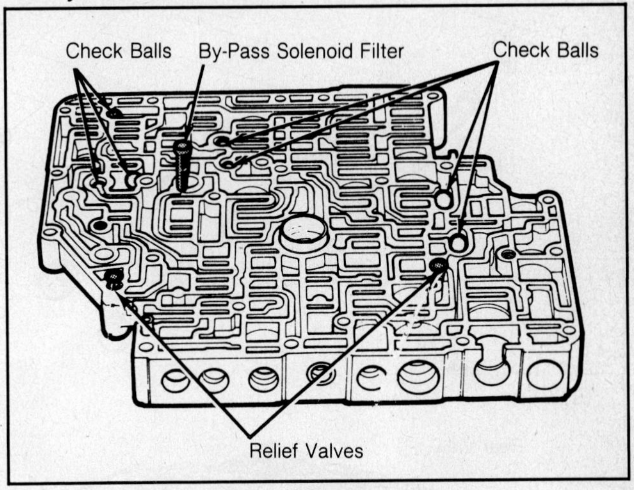

3) Remove retaining clips and bore plugs to remove individual valves and springs from valve body. *See Fig. 15.* DO NOT turn the throttle valve adjusting screw.

CAUTION: **Most valves are aluminum and cannot be removed using a magnet. Remove valves by tapping valve body on palm of hand. It may be necessary to use a pick to remove valves. Be extremely careful not to damage valve or bore.**

Inspection

Roll manual valve on a flat surface to check if it is bent. Inspect all valves, plugs and bores for scores or burrs. Valves and plugs, when dry, must fall from their own weight in their respective bores. Inspect all springs for distortion.

Assembly

NOTE: **If needed, use crocus cloth to polish valves and plugs. Avoid rounding sharp edges of the valves and plugs with the crocus cloth.**
Use NEW retaining clips on the 2-3 shift, 1-2 shift, 3-4 shift, 2-4 inhibit, 3-2 control, 2-3 servo regulator, TV/line modulator, backout and accumulator valves.

Reverse disassembly procedures. Use a new valve body gasket. Use Guide Pins (T86P-70100-A) to align separator plate with valve body. *See Fig. 16.*

OIL PUMP

Disassembly

1) Remove 2 Torx bolts holding separator plate to oil pump housing. Remove 9 check balls and a relief valve. *See Fig. 17.*

2) Remove 2 retaining clips and remove line pressure blowoff spring and ball, bore plug, 1-2 capacity modulator valve and spring. *See Fig. 19.*

FORD MOTOR CO. AXOD (Cont.)

Fig. 15: Exploded View of Valve Body Components

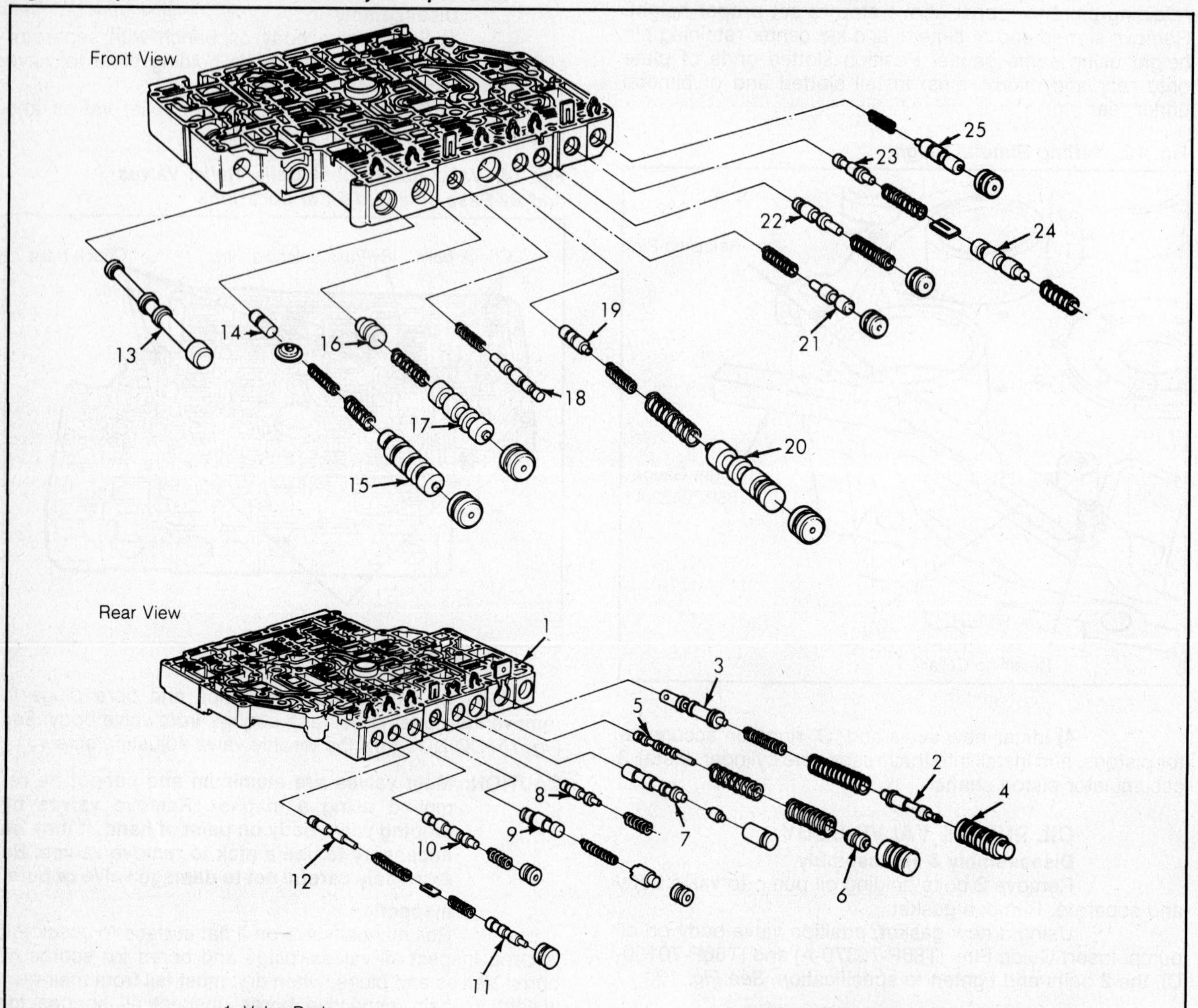

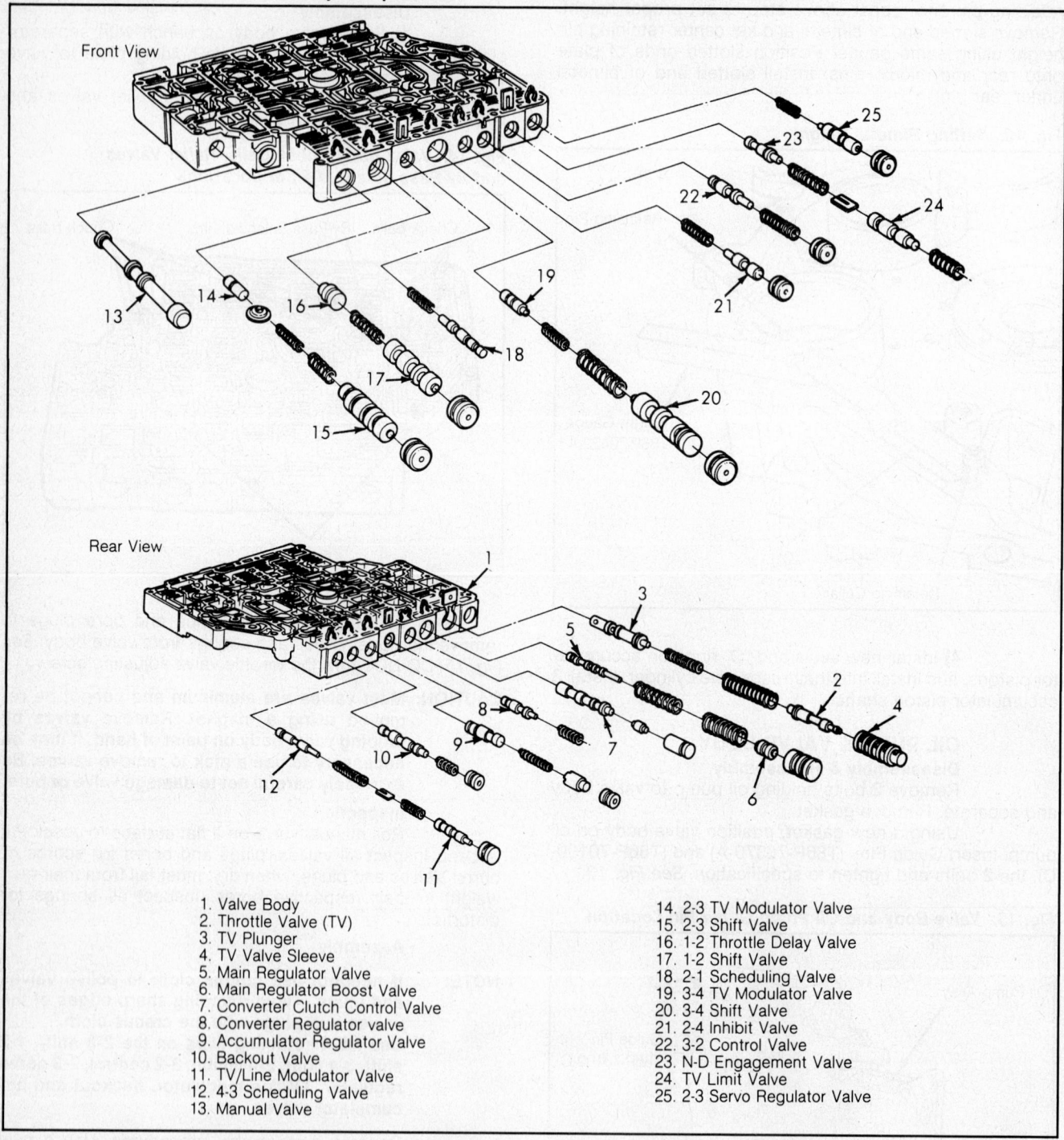

1. Valve Body
2. Throttle Valve (TV)
3. TV Plunger
4. TV Valve Sleeve
5. Main Regulator Valve
6. Main Regulator Boost Valve
7. Converter Clutch Control Valve
8. Converter Regulator valve
9. Accumulator Regulator Valve
10. Backout Valve
11. TV/Line Modulator Valve
12. 4-3 Scheduling Valve
13. Manual Valve
14. 2-3 TV Modulator Valve
15. 2-3 Shift Valve
16. 1-2 Throttle Delay Valve
17. 1-2 Shift Valve
18. 2-1 Scheduling Valve
19. 3-4 TV Modulator Valve
20. 3-4 Shift Valve
21. 2-4 Inhibit Valve
22. 3-2 Control Valve
23. N-D Engagement Valve
24. TV Limit Valve
25. 2-3 Servo Regulator Valve

3) Remove 6 bolts retaining cover to housing and remove. Remove bore spring by prying out of housing using a screwdriver.

CAUTION: Use extreme caution when removing bore spring to prevent personal injury. Place a piece of suitable material under screwdriver to prevent damage to housing surface.

4) Remove outside vane support retaining pin. Remove metal "O" ring retainer and "O" ring from outer vane support. Discard "O" ring.

5) Remove and discard side seal. Remove side seal support, top vane positioning ring and outer vane support. Remove 7 vanes from rotor. Remove inner vane support and bottom vane positioning ring.

Assembly

NOTE: The only servicable parts in the oil pump are the seals. If any other parts are damaged or worn, the entire assembly must be replaced.

To assemble, reverse disassembly procedures. Install inner vane support with small inside diameter counter bore facing up. Shiny portion of the 7 vane blades is

Automatic Transmissions

FORD MOTOR CO. AXOD (Cont.)

Fig. 16: ***Valve Body to Separator Plate Guide Pin Locations***

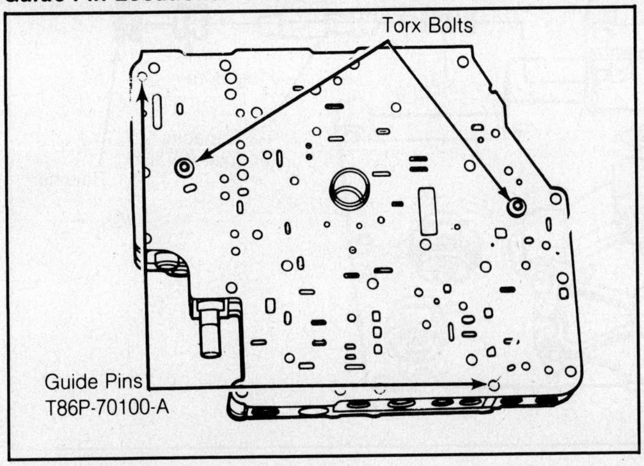

Fig. 17: ***Oil Pump Check Balls and Relief Valve Locations***

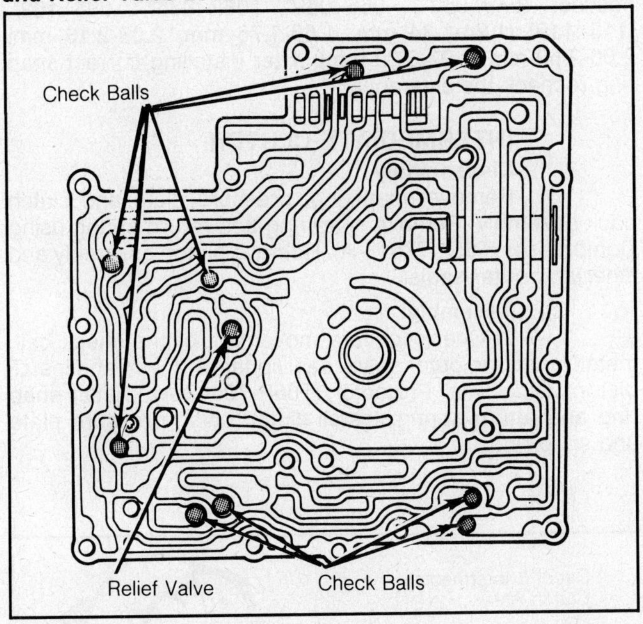

installed toward outer vane support. Use Guide Pins (T86P-70100-A and B) to align separator plate and pump housing. *See Fig. 18*. Use a new gasket.

SHELL ASSEMBLY

Disassembly

1) Set assembly on overdrive drum and remove sun gear and shell assembly. Remove No. 11 needle bearing, intermediate clutch hub and No. 10 needle bearing.

2) Turn assembly onto intermediate cylinder hub and remove overdrive drum and one-way clutch assembly. Remove No. 6 thrust washer. Remove forward clutch assembly by prying up on each side with 2 screwdrivers.

NOTE: **Direct clutch hub "O" ring seals retain forward clutch on hub. Pry evenly and do not locate screwdriver ends on or near forward clutch check ball.**

3) Remove direct one-way clutch and No. 7 thrust washer.

Fig. 18: ***Oil Pump and Separator Plate Guide Pin Locations***

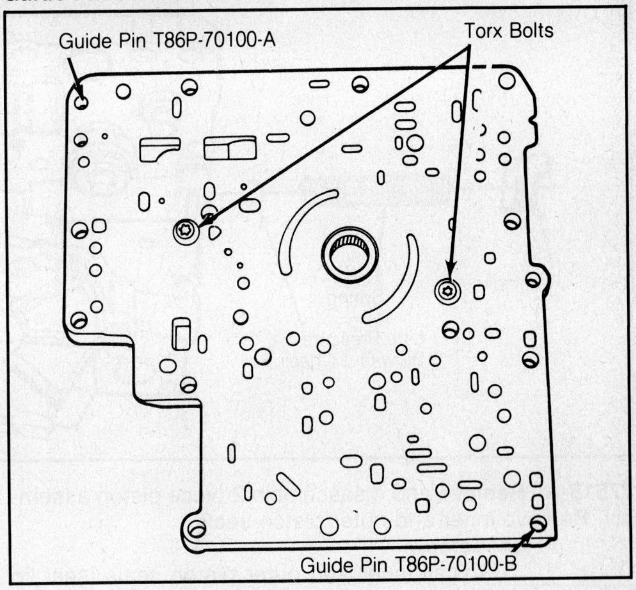

Assembly

To assemble, reverse disassembly procedures. Ensure No. 7 thrust washer tabs are aligned with slots in direct clutch. One-way clutch must turn clockwise when installed. Install No. 11 needle bearing with outer lip facing down.

FORWARD CLUTCH

Disassembly

Remove snap ring, pressure plate, clutch pack and wave spring. Remove snap ring and return spring using Compressor (T65L-77515-A). Remove piston assembly from hub. Remove piston inner and outer seals.

Assembly

1) Install inner and outer seals (seal lip faces down), and install piston assembly using Seal Protector (T86P-70548-A). Install return spring and snap ring. Install wave spring, clutch pack (4 friction and 4 steel), pressure plate and snap ring.

NOTE: **Soak new clutch plates in transmission fluid for 15 minutes before assembling.**

2) Check clutch pack clearance using dial indicator. Push down on clutch pack with a minimum of 10 lbs. force. Release pressure and zero indicator. Lift pressure plate to bottom of snap ring and note reading. Take 2 readings 180° apart and determine the average. Clearance should be .055-.075" (1.40-1.89 mm).

3) If clearance is not within specifications, selective snap rings are available in the following thicknesses: .049-.053", .063-.067", .077-.081", .091-.094", .104-.108" (1.24-1.54 mm, 1.60-1.70 mm, 1.95-2.05 mm, 2.30-2.40 mm, 2.64-2.75 mm). After installing correct snap ring recheck the clearance.

DIRECT CLUTCH

Disassembly

Remove direct clutch bushing (if necessary) using Remover (T86P-70043-A) and a slide hammer. Remove snap ring, pressure plate and clutch pack. Remove snap ring and return spring using Compressor (T65L-

Automatic Transmissions

FORD MOTOR CO. AXOD (Cont.)

Fig. 19: Exploded View of Oil Pump

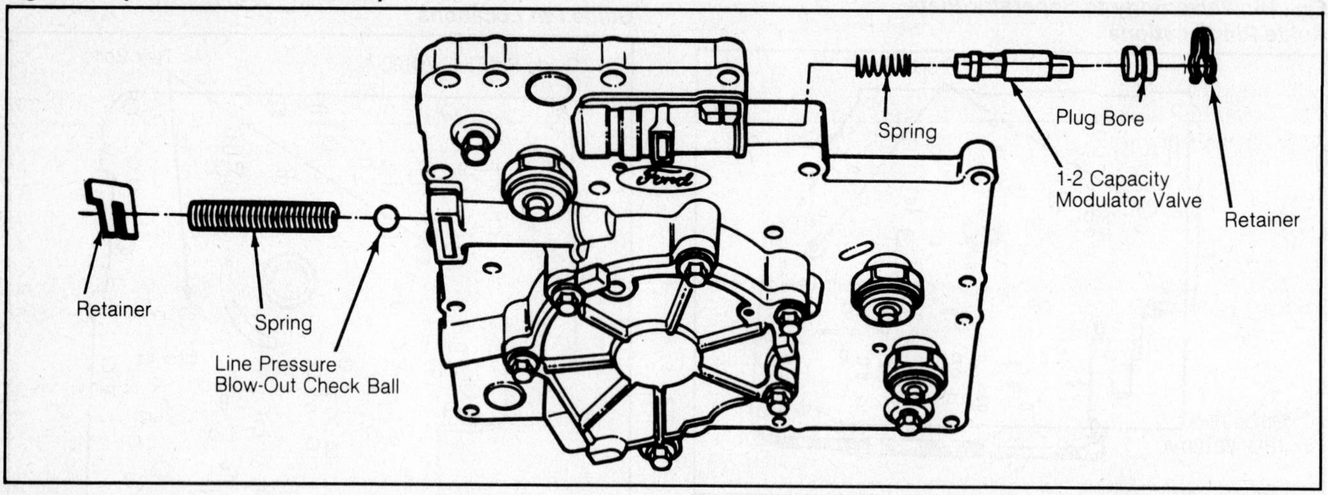

77515-A). Remove and disassemble 2 piece piston assembly. Remove inner and outer piston seals.

Assembly

1) Install inner and outer piston seals (seal lip faces down), and install piston into hub using Seal Protector (T86P-70234-A). Verify free movement of the check ball. Install piston outer ring and return spring in cylinder. Align notch in return spring with check ball. Install snap ring, clutch pack, pressure plate and snap ring. If removed, install direct clutch bushing.

NOTE: Soak new clutch plates in transmission fluid for 15 minutes before assembling.

2) Check clutch pack clearance using dial indicator. Push down on clutch pack with a minimum of 10 lbs. force. Release pressure and zero indicator. Lift pressure plate to bottom of snap ring and note indicator reading. Take 2 readings 180° apart and take average. Clearance should be: (3-plate) .027-.044" (.69-1.12mm), (4-plate) .038-.060" (.97-1.53 mm).

3) If clearance is not to within specification, selective snap rings are available in the following thicknesses: .049-.053", .065-.069", .082-.086", .098-.102", .115-.119" (1.24-1.34 mm, 1.66-1.76 mm, 2.08-2.18 mm, 2.50-2.60 mm, 2.92-3.02 mm). After installing correct snap ring recheck the clearance.

INTERMEDIATE CLUTCH

Disassembly

Remove snap ring, pressure plate and clutch pack assembly. Remove snap ring and return spring using Compressor (T65L-77515-A). Remove piston assembly and inner and outer seals.

Assembly

1) Check for free movement of the check ball. Install inner and outer seals (seal lip faces down) and install piston using Seal Protector (T86P-70548-A). Install snap ring and return spring. Install clutch pack, pressure plate and snap ring.

Fig. 20: Exploded View of Shell Assembly

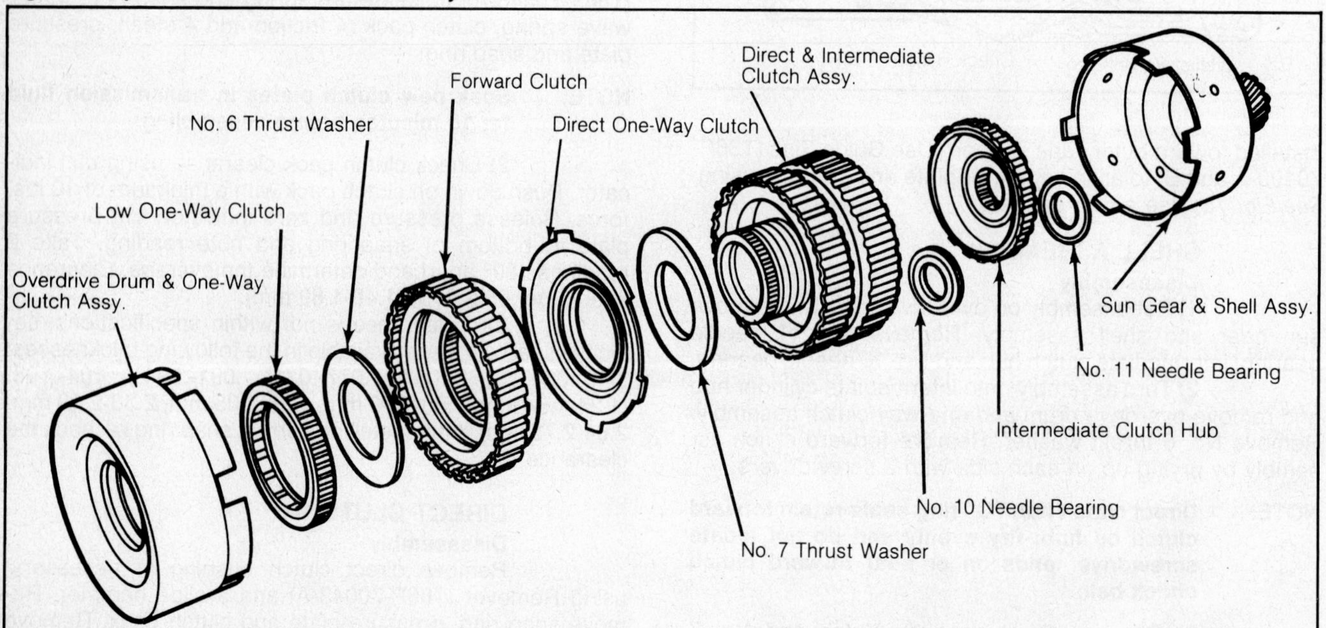

FORD MOTOR CO. AXOD (Cont.)

Fig. 21: Exploded View of Forward Clutch Assembly

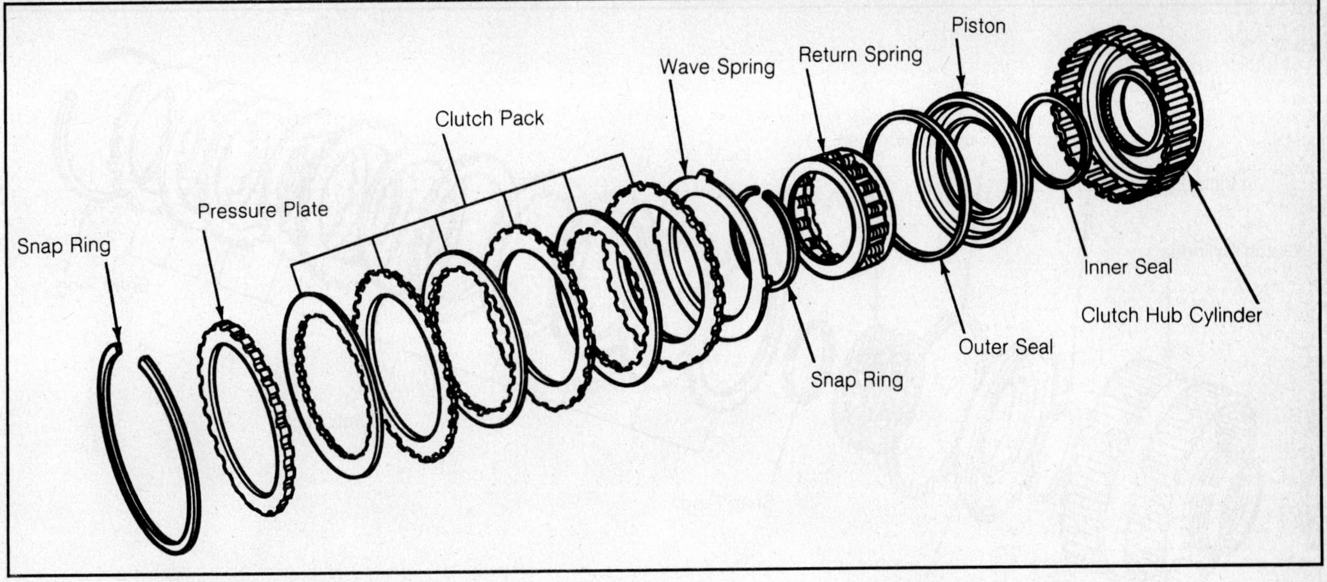

NOTE: **Soak new clutch plates in transmission fluid for 15 minutes before assembling.**

2) Check clutch pack clearance using dial indicator. Push down on clutch pack with a minimum of 10 lbs. force. Release pressure and zero the indicator. Lift pressure plate to bottom of snap ring and note reading. Take 2 readings 180° apart and average. The clearance should be: (4-plate) .035-.052" (.89-1.31 mm), (5-plate) .063-.067" (1.61-1.69 mm).

3) If clearance is not to within specification, selective snap rings are available in the following thicknesses: .044-.048", .059-.063", .075-.079", .091-.095", .107-.111" (1.11-1.21 mm, 1.51-1.61 mm, 1.91-2.01 mm, 2.31-2.41 mm, 2.71-2.81 mm). After installing the correct snap ring recheck clearance.

REVERSE CLUTCH

Disassembly

Remove snap ring, pressure plate, clutch pack and wave spring. Remove snap ring and return spring using Compressor (T65L-77515-A). Lift out piston and remove inner and outer seals.

Assembly

1) Install inner and outer seals (seal lip faces down) and install piston using Seal Protector (T86P-70403-A). Install snap ring and return spring. Install wave spring, clutch pack (3 friction and 3 steel), pressure plate and snap ring.

NOTE: **Soak new clutch plates in transmission fluid for 15 minutes before assembling.**

2) Check clutch pack clearance using dial indicator. Push down on clutch pack with a minimum of 10 lbs. force. Release pressure and zero indicator. Lift pressure

Fig. 22: Exploded View of Direct Clutch Assembly

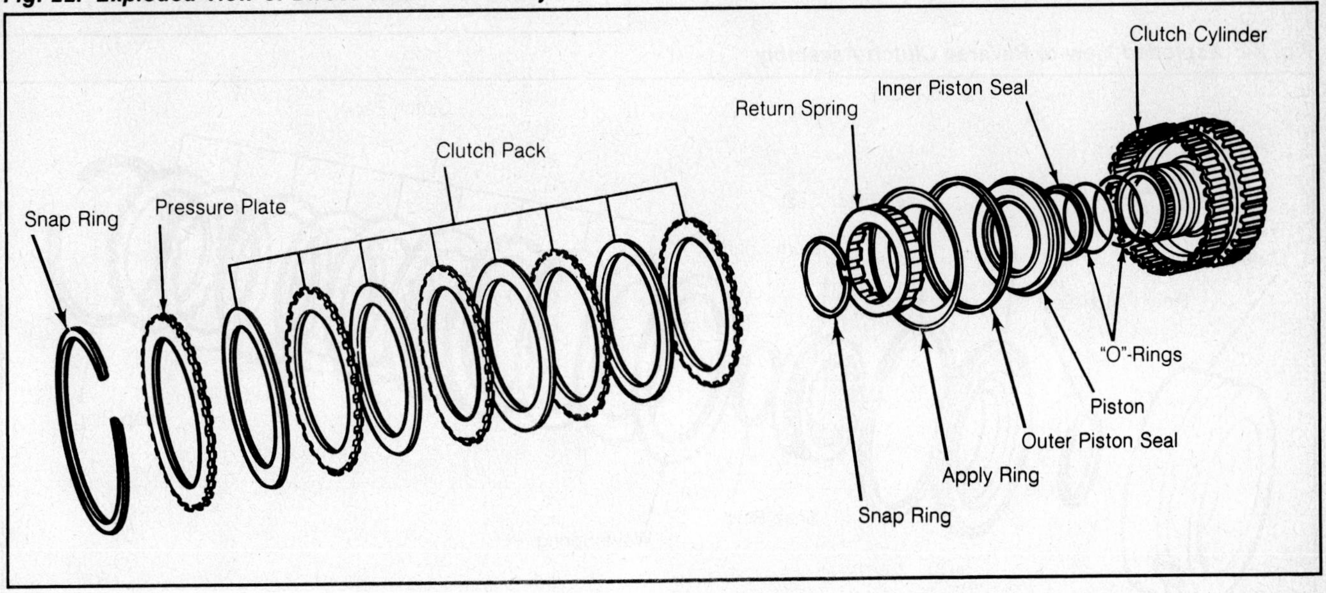

Automatic Transmissions

FORD MOTOR CO. AXOD (Cont.)

Fig. 23: Exploded View of Intermediate Clutch Assembly

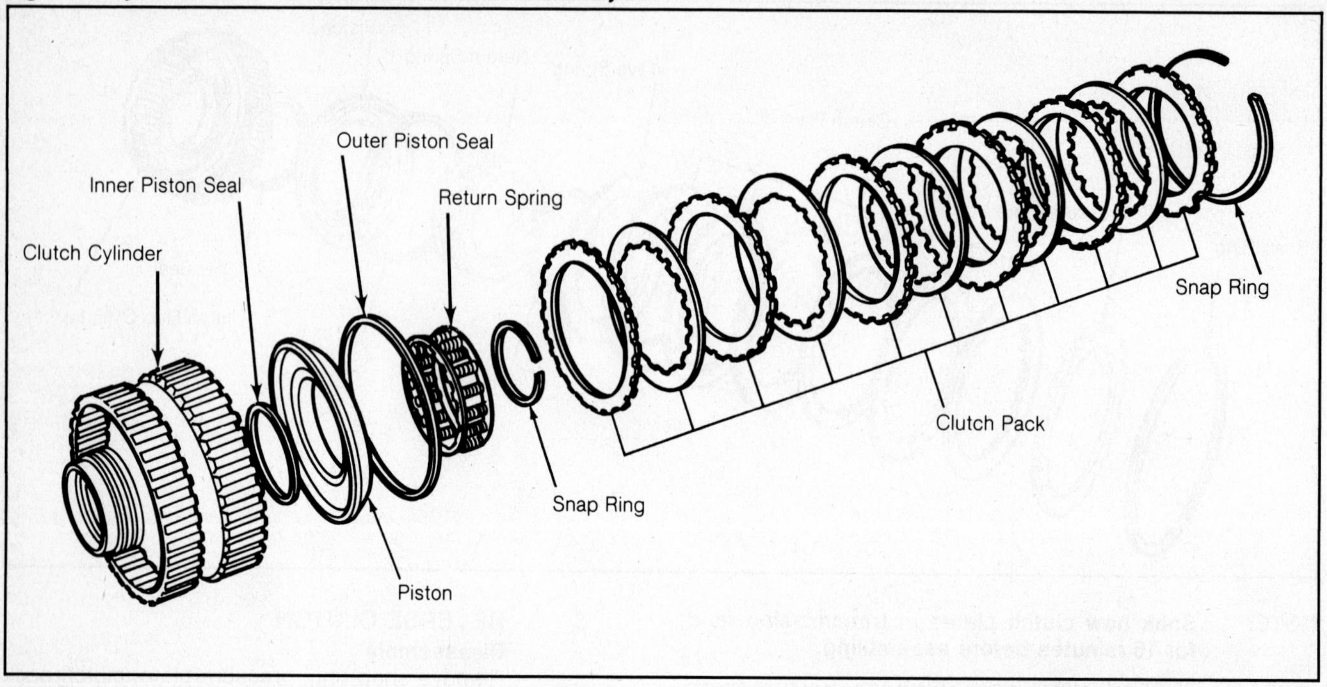

plate to bottom of snap ring and note reading. Take 2 readings 180° apart and average. The clearance should be .038-.064" (.97-1.63 mm).

3) If clearance is not within specification, selective snap rings are available in the following thicknesses: .059-.064", .078-.081", .096-.100", .115-.118" (1.52-1.62 mm, 1.98-2.08 mm, 2.45-2.55 mm, 2.92-3.02 mm).

PLANETARY ASSEMBLY

NOTE: Individual components of the planet carrier are not serviceable except for the differential components.

Disassembly & Assembly

Remove snap ring, front planetary and No. 13 needle bearing. Remove rear planetary from shell and ring gear assembly.

To assemble, reverse disassembly procedures. *See Fig. 25.*

Fig. 25: Planetary Assembly

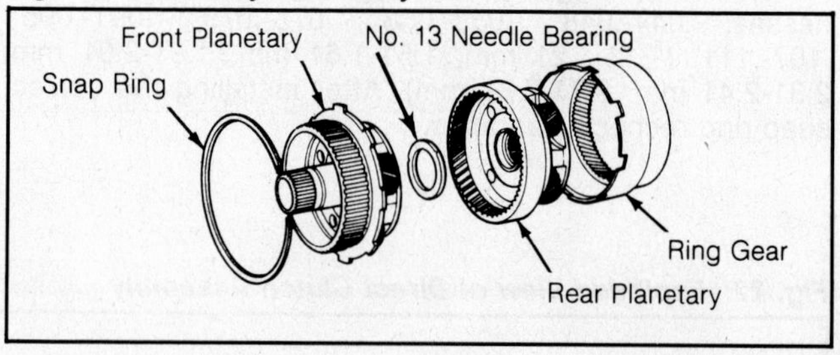

Fig. 24: Exploded View of Reverse Clutch Assembly

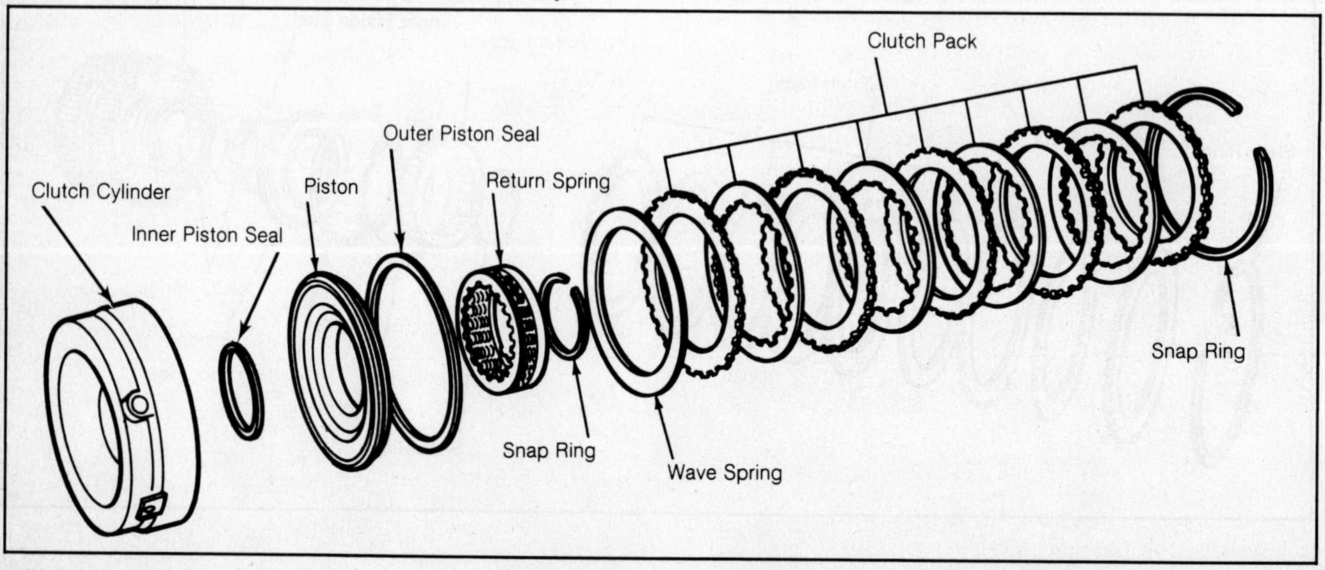

DIFFERENTIAL & GEAR SET

Disassembly

1) Remove planetary pinion shaft retaining snap ring. Using a magnet, work pinion shafts out of differential case housing. Slide out pinion gears and thrust washers. Inspect needle bearings and pinion shafts and replace if necessary.

2) Remove No. 17 needle bearing from top of planetary assembly. Drive out pinion shaft roll pin. Tap out pinion shaft. Remove pinion gears and thrust washers by rotating output shaft. Remove right side gear and thrust washer.

3) Push output shaft toward center of housing and remove left side gear to gain access to retaining ring. Remove retaining ring and slide shaft out. Remove pinion gear and thrust washer.

Assembly

1) With output shaft inside of case, slide thrust washer and left side gear onto output shaft. Install retaining ring and slide gear down over ring. *See Fig. 26*. Install thrust washer and right side gear into case. Install thrust washers on pinion gears ensuring inner lips on washers are seated into recess of pinion gears.

Fig. 26: Differential Left Side Gear Installation

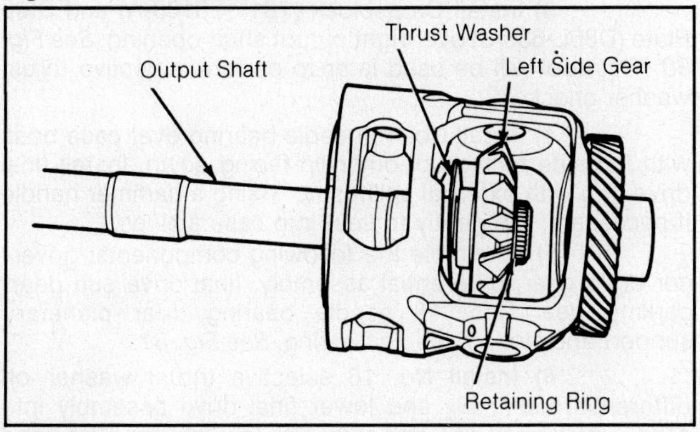

2) Position pinion gears on side gears and turn output shaft to walk gears into position. Tap pinion shaft through case making sure to align roll pin hole in shaft with hole in case. Install roll pin.

3) Install No. 17 needle bearing with tabs facing up. Install upper and lower pinion gear thrust washers onto pinion gears, and install in case. Push pinion shafts through case and gears until lower step on shaft is level with case. Lower step should also face inward. Be careful not to disturb needle bearings. Install retaining ring.

LOW-INTERMEDIATE SERVO

Disassembly

Remove 3 cover bolts and piston return spring. Remove piston and rod from cover. Remove rod retaining clips and remove rod and cushion spring. Remove piston seal and seal and gasket from cover. *See Fig. 27*.

Assembly

To assemble, reverse disassembly procedures. Lubricate seals with petroleum jelly. Ensure spring is correctly positioned in case.

OVERDRIVE SERVO

Disassembly

Remove 3 cover bolts and return spring and rod. Remove piston from cover. Remove rear rod clip, washer, piston, seal, cushion spring and front rod clip. Remove cover seal. *See Fig. 28*.

Fig. 27: Exploded View of Low-Intermediate Servo

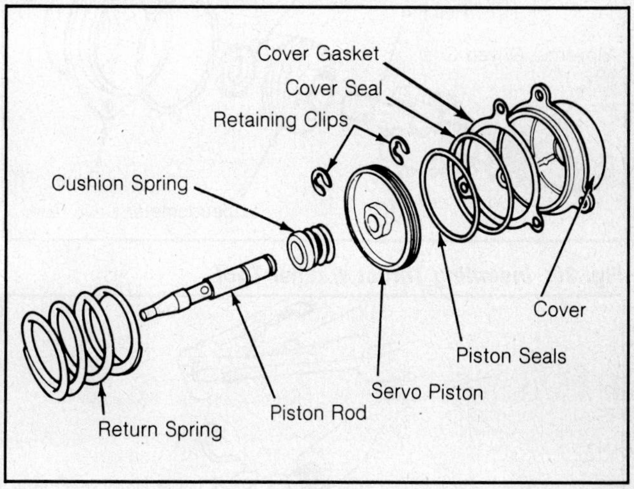

Fig. 28: Exploded View of Overdrive Servo

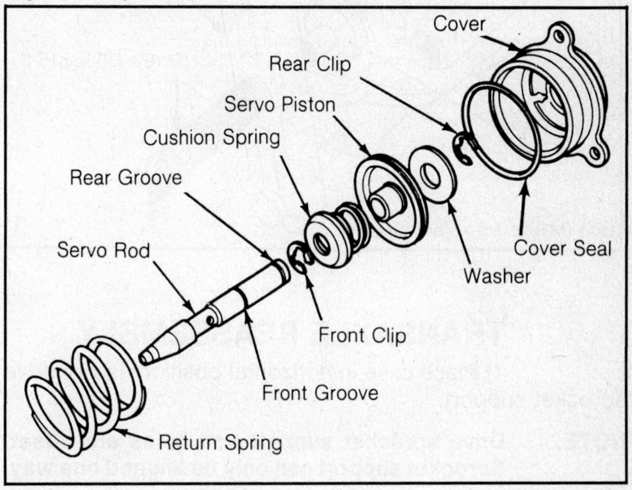

Assembly

To assemble, reverse disassembly procedures. Lubricate seals with petroleum jelly. Ensure spring is correctly positioned in case.

GOVERNOR

Disassembly

Remove 2 cover bolts, remove cover and discard seal. Remove governor assembly. Remove speedometer drive gear and drive gear bearing from shaft.

Assembly

Push speedometer drive gear onto shaft aligning slots in gear with shaft roll pin. Install bearing on speedometer gear with outer race facing up. Install new seal and cover. *See Fig. 29*.

DRIVEN SPROCKET SUPPORT

Disassembly & Assembly

Remove needle bearing using Remover (T58L-101-A) and a slide hammer.

Install needle bearing using Replacer (T86P-70043-B).

FORD MOTOR CO. AXOD (Cont.)

Fig. 29: Governor Assembly

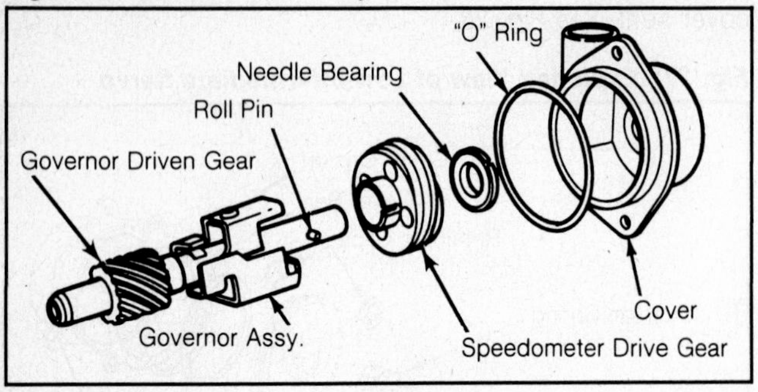

Fig. 30: Installing Thrust Washer Tool

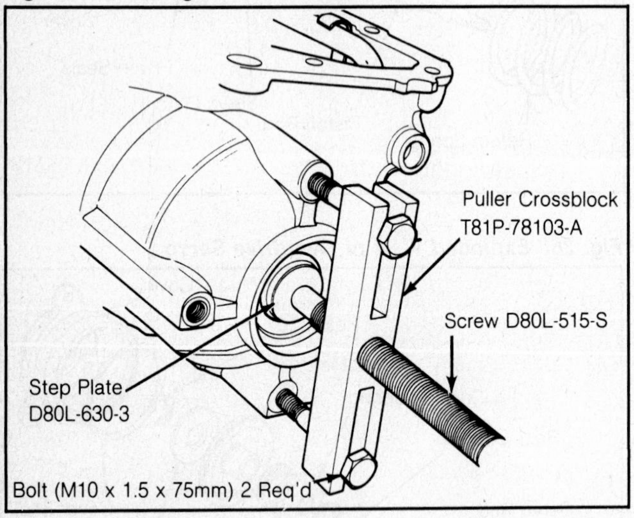

TRANSAXLE REASSEMBLY

1) Place case in horizontal position. Install drive sprocket support.

NOTE: Drive sprocket support bolt holes are offset. Sprocket support can only be aligned one way.

2) Install converter oil seal using Replacer (T86P-70401-A). Install right output shaft seal using Replacer (T86P-1177-B). After installation, make sure garter springs are present.

Fig. 32: Output Shaft End Play Check

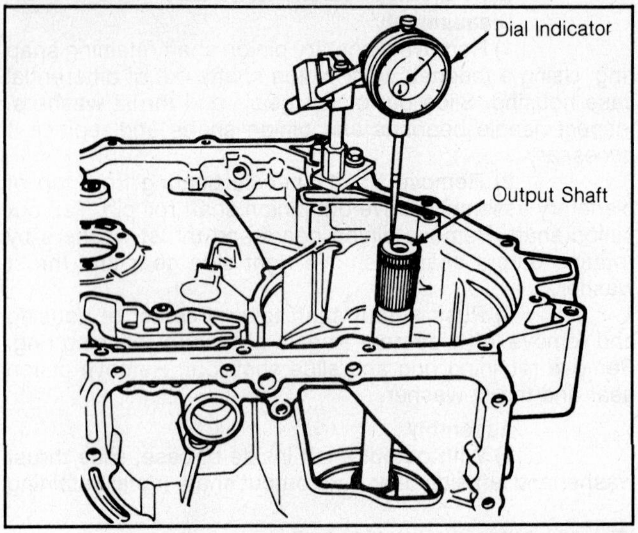

3) Install Crossblock (T81P-78103-A) and Step Plate (D80L-630-3) over right output shaft opening. *See Fig. 30*. This tool will be used later to perform selective thrust washer checks.

4) Install No. 19 needle bearing over case boss with flat side facing up, outer lip facing down. Install final drive ring with external splines up. Using a hammer handle if necessary, tap gently to seat into case splines.

5) Assemble the following components: governor drive gear, differential assembly, final drive sun gear, parking gear, No. 16 needle bearing, rear planetary support and No. 15 needle bearing. *See Fig. 31.*

6) Install No. 18 selective thrust washer on differential assembly and lower final drive assembly into case. Install snap ring and align with low-intermediate band anchor pin.

7) Mount a dial indicator with stylus on end of output shaft. *See Fig. 32*. Back out screw on tool installed in step **3)** until it no longer touches shaft. Zero dial indicator. Tighten screw to 35-44 lbs. in. (4-5 N.m). Observe reading. Clearance should be .004-.025" (.1-.65 mm).

8) If clearance is not within specification, selective thrust washers are avsilable in the following thicknesses: .045-.049" (1.15-1.25 mm) Orange, .055-.059" (1.40-1.50 mm) Purple, .064-.069" (1.65-1.75 mm) Yellow. After installing correct thrust washer, recheck clearance.

Fig. 31: Assembling Final Drive Components

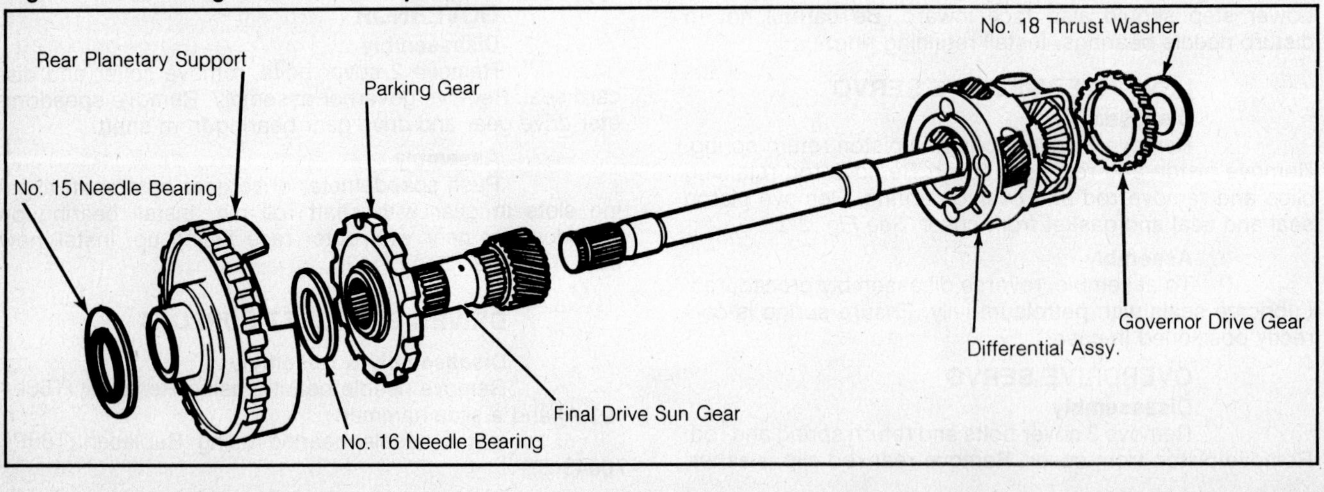

Automatic Transmissions

FORD MOTOR CO. AXOD (Cont.)

After completing end clearance check, back off screw on tool and leave in position for No. 5 and No. 8 selective thrust washer clearance check.

9) Place transaxle in vertical position. Install park pawl, return spring, park pawl shaft and locator pin. Install park rod actuating lever and park rod. Install park rod abutment and start abutment bolts. Push in park pawl and locate rod between pawl and abutment.

10) Using a 3/8 drift, gently install lube tube seal flush against rear case support. Install No. 15 needle bearing on rear planetary support. Install low-intermediate band and position against anchor pin. Install low-intermediate drum and sun gear.

11) Assemble the following components: ring gear and shell assembly, rear planetary, No. 13 needle bearing, front planetary and snap ring. *See Fig. 25*. Carefully slide planetary assembly over output shaft.

12) Lower reverse clutch into case and start clutch plate engagement to seat clutch. The intermediate clutch hub can be used as a tool to complete clutch plate engagement and fully seat reverse clutch. Rotate planet with hub to engage splines.

13) Start reverse anchor pin bolt but do not tighten. Assemble forward, direct and intermediate clutch assembly. Using Clutch Pack Holder (T86P-70389-A), lower assembly into case, aligning shell and sun gear splines into forward planetary. Ensure assembly is fully seated before removing tool.

14) Install overdrive band into case. Install plastic retainer with crosshairs facing up.

15) Tighten screw on tool used in step **7)** to 10 ft. lbs. (13.5 N.m). Remove all 5 Teflon seals from driven sprocket support. Install No. 9 needle bearing over output shaft with outer lip facing up. Install No. 8 selective thrust washer. Install driven sprocket support and driven sprocket.

16) To measure No. 8 thrust washer clearance, it must first be determined if machined bolt hole surfaces on driven sprocket support are ABOVE or BELOW case machined surface. *See Fig. 33*.

17) ("A") Above case machined surface: Place depth micrometer on machined bolt hole surface and measure distance to case machined surface.

("B") Below case machined surface: Place depth micrometer on case machined surface and measure distance to machined bolt hole surface.

18) Measure at both bolt hole surfaces and take an average of both readings. If average reading exceeds .008" (.21 mm) ("A"), or .018" (.46 mm) ("B") refer to NO. 8 THRUST WASHER SELECTION table to determine correct size thrust washer to install. Install correct thrust washer, check measurement and record reading.

NO. 8 THRUST WASHER SELECTION TABLE

Thickness	Color
.056-.060" (1.43-1.53 mm)	Natural
.066-.070" (1.68-1.78 mm)	Dark Green
.075-.079" (1.92-2.02 mm)	Light Blue
.085-.089" (2.17-2.27 mm)	Red

19) Remove driven sprocket support, No. 8 thrust washer and No. 9 needle bearing. Install No. 5 thrust washer on driven sprocket support, aligning tab with slot. Install driven sprocket support without No. 8 thrust washer and No. 9 needle bearing.

20) Position depth micrometer on machined case surface and measure distance betwween machined bolt hole surface and case surface. Measure at both bolt hole surfaces and take an average of both readings.

21) The difference between this reading and the reading for the No. 8 thrust washer recorded in step **18)**

Fig. 33: Measuring For No. 8 Thrust Washer

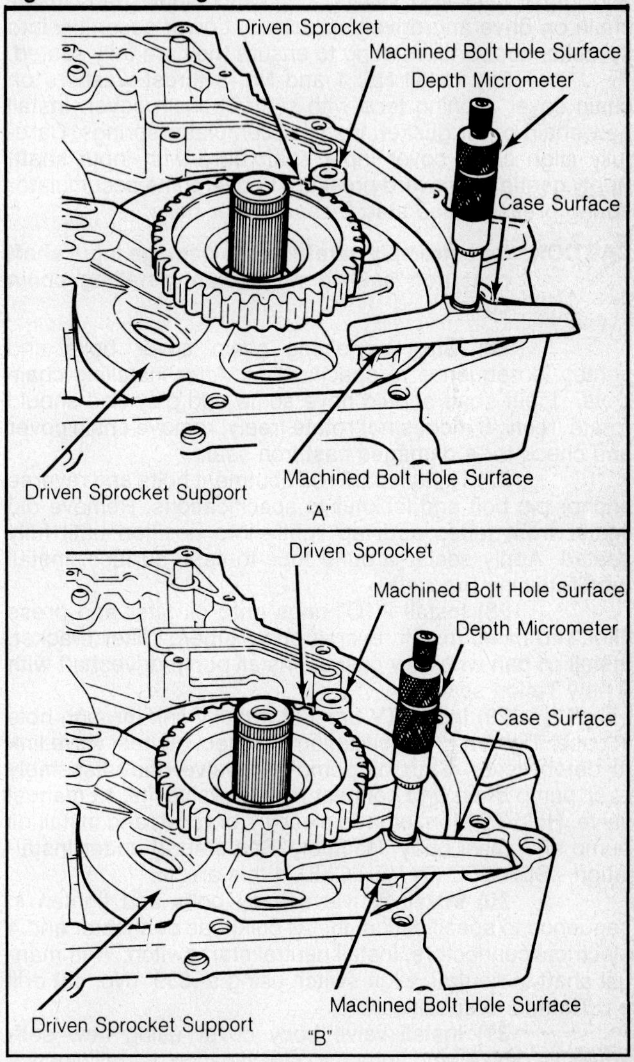

must be greater than zero but less than .033" (.85 mm). If measurement exceeds specification, refer to NO. 5 THRUST WASHER SELECTION table to determine correct size thrust washer to install.

NO. 5 THRUST WASHER SELECTION TABLE

Thickness	Color
.086-.090" (2.18-2.28 mm)	Green
.095-.099" (2.43-2.53 mm)	Black
.105-.109" (2.67-2.77 mm)	Natural
.115-.118" (2.92-3.02 mm)	Red

22) Remove driven sprocket support and install No. 9 needle bearing and correct No. 8 thrust washer. Install Teflon seals and correct No. 5 thrust washer. Install driven sprocket support.

FORD MOTOR CO. AXOD (Cont.)

23) Install manual shaft seal, slide manual shaft through seal, and slide manual detent lever onto shaft. Slide shaft through park rod actuating lever and tap shaft into case hole. Install new lock pin through case hole, aligning with groove in shaft. Install new roll pins.

24) Align tabs on No. 2 and No. 4 thrust washers with holes in drive and driven sprocket supports. Lubricate and install cast iron sealing ring onto input shaft. Install chain on drive and driven sprockets. Lower assembly into sprocket supports, rotating to ensure they are fully seated.

25) Install No. 1 and No. 3 thrust washers on chain cover aligning tabs with slots in chain cover. Install new chain cover gasket. Install accumulator springs. Carefully align chain cover input shaft bore with input shaft. Apply gentle downward pressure to overcome accumulator spring pressure and start 2 chain cover bolts.

CAUTION: Be extremely careful not to damage input shaft cast iron sealing ring when installing chain cover.

26) Start remaining chain cover bolts and tighten in sequence to specification. After installing chain cover, input shaft should have some end play and should rotate freely. If it does not rotate freely, remove chain cover and check for a damaged cast iron seal.

27) Tighten park rod abutment bolts and reverse anchor pin bolt and locknut to specifications. Remove old sealer from tubes and tap lightly into position until fully seated. Apply sealer around tube-to-case surface. Install tube retaining brackets.

28) Install 2 "O" rings onto oil filter and press filter into case. Install reverse apply tube/oil filter bracket. Install oil pan with new gasket. Install pump driveshaft with 4 new Teflon seals.

29) Install TV bracket with TV link through hole in case. Tighten to specification. Connect manual valve link to detent lever. Start oil pump and valve body assembly over pump shaft and connect manual valve link to manual valve. Hold TV plunger in to clear TV bracket, and install oil pump and valve body assembly. See step **2)** under Installation - SERVICE (IN VEHICLE) in this article.

30) Install 22 valve body bolts and tighten in sequence to specification. Install bulkhead connector and 4 electrical connectors. Install neutral start switch. With manual shaft in neutral, align switch using a .089" (No. 43) drill bit. Tighten to specification.

31) Install valve body cover using new self-adhesive gasket and tighten to specification. Install dipstick tube grommet and dipstick tube in case.

SERVO TRAVEL CHECK

NOTE: The following servo travel check of both the overdrive and low-intermediate servos should only be performed if the transaxle case, band assembly, drum and sun gear assembly, servo piston rod or servo piston were replaced during assembly of the transaxle.

Overdrive Servo

1) Place transaxle in horizontal position. Install Test Spring (T86P-70023-B), servo piston and rod in case. Install Servo Piston Gauge (T86P-70023-B) and secure in case using servo cover bolts. Tighten gauge screw to 10 INCH lbs. *See Fig. 34*.

2) Mount a dial indicator and position stylus through hole in gauge. Be sure stylus has contacted piston on a flat surface. DO NOT contact step on piston. Zero dial indicator.

3) Back off gauge screw until piston movement stops and read indicator. The amount of piston travel as indicated determines the rod length to be installed. Reading should be .070-.149" (1.8-3.8 mm).

4) Select new piston rod using measurement obtained in step **3)**. Repeat steps **1)** through **3)** to verify piston travel. Install servo piston and spring being sure they are fully seated. Install new seals on cover and tighten cover bolts to specification.

Low-Intermediate Servo

1) Place transaxle in horizontal position. Install Test Spring (T86P-70023-A), servo piston (without seal) and rod in case. Install Servo Piston Gauge (T86P-70023-A) and secure in case using servo cover bolts. Tighten gauge screw to 30 INCH lbs. *See Fig. 35*.

2) Mount a dial indicator and position stylus through hole in gauge. Be sure stylus has contacted piston on a flat surface. DO NOT contact step on piston. Zero dial indicator.

3) Back off gauge screw until piston movement stops and read indicator. The amount of piston travel as indicated determines the rod length to be installed. Reading should be .216-.255" (5.5-6.5 mm). If a new low-intermediate band was installed, reading should be .196-.236" (5.0-6.0 mm).

4) Select new piston rod using measurement obtained in step **3)**. Repeat steps **1)** through **3)** to verify piston travel. Install seals on piston. Install servo piston and spring being sure they are fully seated. Install new gasket on cover and tighten cover bolts to specification.

NOTE: Be sure and align low-intermediate servo cover tab with port on case.

Fig. 34: Overdrive Servo Check

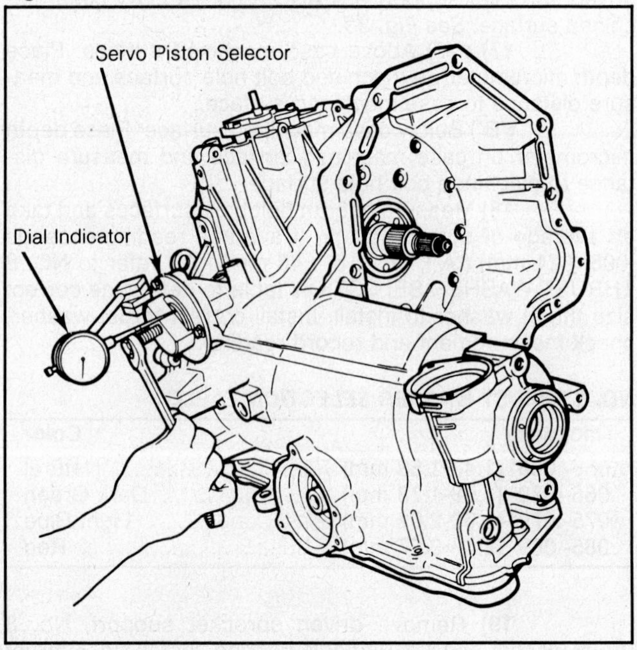

Automatic Transmissions

FORD MOTOR CO. AXOD (Cont.)

Fig. 35: Low-Intermediate Servo Check

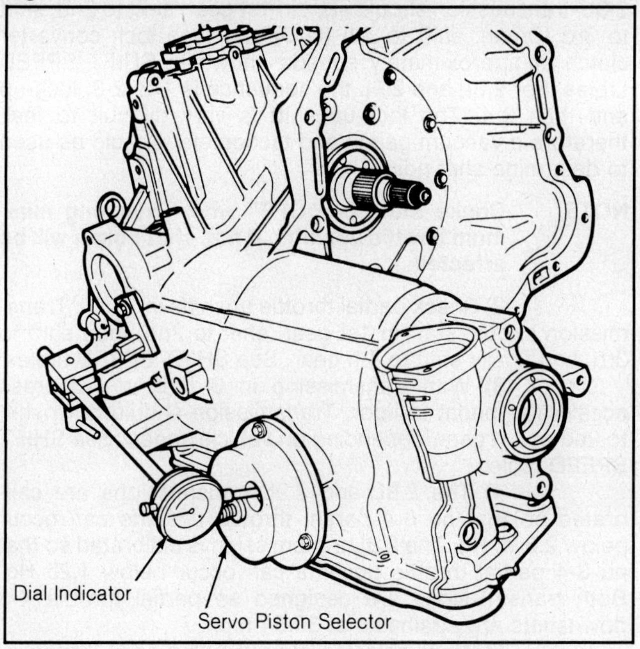

TIGHTENING SPECIFICATIONS

Application	Ft. Lbs. (N.m)
Anchor Bolt Locknut	25-35 (33-48)
Anchor Bolt (6 mm Allen)	7-9 (9-12)
Chain Cover Bolt to Case (13 mm)	25-35 (33-48)
Chain Cover Bolts to Case (10 mm)	20-26 (27-34)
Chain Cover Bolt to Case (8 mm)	7-9 (9-12)
Drive Sprocket Support to Case (Torx)	7-9 (9-12)
Governor and Servo Covers to Case	7-9 (9-12)
Manual Valve Detent Spring Bolt	7-9 (9-12)
Neutral Start Switch to Case	7-9 (9-12)
Oil Pan to Case	10-12 (14-16)
Oil Pump to Valve Body	7-9 (9-12)
Oil Pump Cover to Oil Pump	7-9 (9-12)
Park Rod Abutment Bolts to Case	20-22 (27-30)
Separator Plate to Valve Body	7-9 (9-12)
Separator Plate to Oil Pump	7-9 (9-12)
TV Bracket to Case	7-9 (9-12)
Valve Body to Case	7-9 (9-12)
Valve Body Cover to Case	7-9 (9-12)

Automatic Transmissions

FORD MOTOR CO. A4LD

Aerostar, 2WD/4WD Bronco II, Ranger

IDENTIFICATION

The A4LD automatic transmission is identified by code letter "T", which is shown on lower line of Vehicle Certification Label under "TRANS". Label is attached to driver's front door lock panel or pillar.

Transmission model may be identified by metal tag attached to transmission at lower extension housing retaining bolt. Top line of tag shows transmission model number and line shift code. Bottom line on tag shows build date code. *See Fig. 1.*

Fig. 1: Service Identification Tag

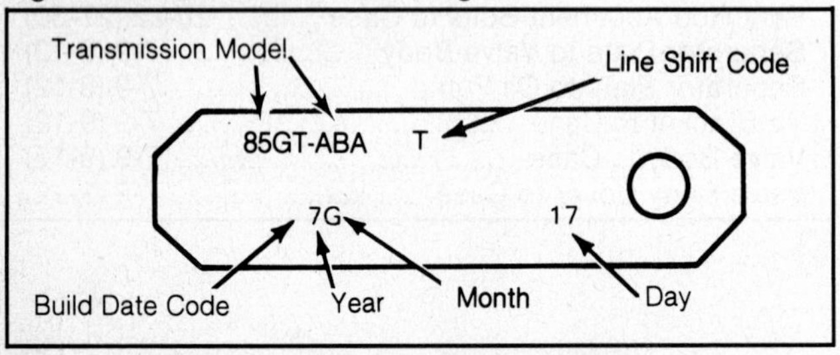

Tag is on lower left extension housing bolt.

DESCRIPTION

The A4LD is a 4-speed automatic overdrive derivative of the C3 3-speed automatic transmission. Manual selection of all gears is provided.

It is the first Ford Motor Company production automatic transmission to use electronic controls integrated in the on-board EEC-VI system. These controls operate a piston/plate clutch in the torque converter that eliminates torque converter slip when applied.

Transmission consists of torque converter, planetary gear train, 3 multiple disc clutch packs, one-way clutch and hydraulic control system.

LUBRICATION & ADJUSTMENT

See appropriate AUTOMATIC TRANSMISSION SERVICING article in DOMESTIC GENERAL SERVICING section.

TROUBLE SHOOTING

See appropriate AUTOMATIC TRANSMISSION TROUBLE SHOOTING article in DOMESTIC GENERAL SERVICING section.

TESTING

Check fluid level and correct if necessary. Use initial road test to verify malfunction of transmission. Make sure that engine appears to be running properly. If transmission problems occur on initial road test, check adjustments and fluid levels.

ROAD TEST

This test will determine if governor pressure and shift control valves are functioning properly.

1) Check minimum throttle upshifts in "O/D". For 2.3L, transmission should start in 1st gear, shift to 2nd, shift to 3rd (Drive), shift to 4th (O/D) and then lock converter clutch at approximately speeds shown in SHIFT SPEED tables. For 2.8L and 2.9L the sequence is 1-2, 2-3, lock-up and then 3-4. The lock-up shift is very difficult to feel, therefore a vacuum gauge and tachometer should be used to determine shift points.

NOTE: Choke must be "OFF" when checking minimum throttle upshifts. If not, shift points will be affected.

2) Check partial throttle upshifts in "O/D". Transmission should start in 1st gear, shift to 2nd, then shift to 3rd, and finally shift to 4th gear. See SHIFT SPEED tables.

3) With transmission in 3rd (Drive), depress accelerator pedal to floor. Transmission should downshift to 2nd or 1st gear, depending on vehicle speed. See SHIFT SPEED tables.

4) The 2.8L and 2.9L transmissions are calibrated so that no 3-4 partial throttle upshifts can occur below 2.8 in. Hg. The 2.3L transmission is calibrated so that no 3-4 partial throttle upshifts can occur below 1.25 Hg. Both transmissions are designed so partial throttle 4-3 downshifts are attainable at 50-54 mph.

5) When selector lever is in 2nd gear, transmission can operate only in 2nd gear.

6) With vehicle speed over 45 mph and transmission in O/D or Drive (3rd), move selector to 1st gear (closed throttle). The transmission will immediately shift to 2nd gear. As vehicle speed drops below 30 mph, the transmission will downshift to 1st gear.

VACUUM MODULATOR

1) Remove hose from vacuum modulator unit. If transmission fluid is evident on vacuum side of diaphragm or in vacuum hose, replace modulator unit. Fluid indicates that diaphragm is broken.

2) Hook up vacuum pump to fitting on modulator. Operate pump until gauge shows 18 in. Hg. If gauge reading holds steady, modulator unit is good. If gauge reading drops, modulator unit is bad and must be replaced.

3) With modulator removed from transmission, draw 18 in. Hg. on vacuum pump attached to vacuum port of unit. Hold finger over end of control rod of modulator unit. When hose is removed, good modulator unit will push out on control rod due to internal spring pressure.

ENGINE VACUUM PRESSURE

1) If vacuum modulator is working properly and downshift linkage is adjusted correctly, all shifts should occur within certain road speed limits. See SHIFT SPEEDS tables. If shifts do not occur at proper points or slipping occurs during shifts, check engine vacuum, vacuum supply, and vacuum units for possible cause of problem.

2) Connect tachometer to engine. Connect vacuum gauge to manifold vacuum line, using "T" fitting at modulator hookup. Attach pressure gauge to control pressure outlet on transmission case. *See Fig. 2.* Plug for pressure take-off is located on left side of case just behind manual shift linkage.

CAUTION: Pressure gauge affects quality of transmission shifting. When gauge is installed in transmission port, DO NOT accelerate or decelerate rapidly as transmission failure could occur.

FORD MOTOR CO. A4LD (Cont.)

SHIFT SPEEDS (MPH)

NOTE: **Figures given below are approximate. All shift speeds may vary somewhat due to production tolerances, rear axle ratio, or emission control equipment.**

2.9L V6-EFI
RANGER/BRONCO II 4x2/4x4
MODEL 86GT-ABA, ACA, BAA, CAA, DAA, EAA

Throttle	Range	Shift	OPS—R.P.M.	Column Number 1	2	3	4	5
Closed Throttle 10-15 in Hg Vacuum	(D),D	1-2	560-865	11-18	12-19	11-17	11-18	10-16
	(D),D	2-3	865-1275	18-27	19-28	16-25	17-27	15-23
	(D)	3-4	1780-2290	37-49	39-51	34-46	36-49	31-42
	(D),D	CL	1730-2140	36-45	38-47	33-43	35-46	30-39
	(D),D	CU	See Note 1					
	(D)	4-3	865-1170	18-25	18-26	16-23	17-25	15-21
	(D),D	3-2	458-763	9-16	10-17	9-15	9-16	8-14
	(D),D	2-1	407-610	8-13	9-14	8-12	8-13	7-11
	1	2-1	1475-1985	30-42	32-45	28-40	30-43	26-36
To Detent 2.0 in Hg Vacuum	(D),D	1-2	1476-1781	30-37	32-40	28-36	30-38	26-32
	(D),D	2-3	2240-2545	46-54	49-57	43-51	46-55	39-46
	(D)	3-4	2950-3610	61-77	64-82	57-73	60-78	51-66
	(D),D	CL	See Note 1					
	(D),D	CU	See Note 1					
	(D)	4-3	1880-2190	39-46	41-49	36-44	38-47	33-40
	(D),D	3-2	1630-1935	34-41	35-44	31-39	33-41	28-35
Through Detent WOT 1.0 in Hg Vacuum	(D),D	1-2	1880-2190	39-46	41-49	36-44	38-47	33-40
	(D),D	2-3	3100-3410	64-72	68-77	60-69	63-73	54-62
	(D),D	CL	See Note 1					
	(D),D	CU	See Note 1					
	(D),D	3-2	2850-3156	59-66	62-71	55-63	58-68	50-58
	(D),D	3-1	1630-1935	34-41	35-44	31-39	33-41	28-35

CL—Converter Clutch Lockup
CU—Converter Clutch Unlock

Tire Size	Axle Ratio 3.45	3.73	4.10
	Use Column No.		
P185/75R14SL	1	3	5
P195/75R14SL	1	3	5
P205/70R14SL	1	3	5
P205/75R14SL	2	3	5
P215/75R14SL	2	4	—
P195/75R15SL	2	4	—
P205/75R15SL	2	4	—
P215/75R15SL	—	4	—

NOTE:

1 The converter clutch upshift/downshift is scheduled hydraulically but can be overridden electronically. The converter clutch is prevented from engaging or is disengaged during the following driving modes:

- engine coolant below 128°F or above 240°F
- application of brakes
- closed throttle
- heavy or W.O.T. throttle accelerations
- quick tip-ins
- quick tip-outs
- when the actual engine speed is below a certain value at lower vacuums (this ensures all 4-3 torque demands will be made on an unlocked converter).

2.9L V6-EFI
RANGER/BRONCO II 4x2/4x4
MODEL 86GT-ABA, ACA, BAA, CAA, DAA, EAA

Throttle	Range	Shift	OPS—R.P.M.	Column Number 1
Closed Throttle 10-15 in Hg Vacuum	(D),D	1-2	560-865	10-17
	(D),D	2-3	865-1275	16-25
	(D)	3-4	1780-2290	33-45
	(D),D	CL	1730-2140	32-42
	(D),D	CU	See Note 1	
	(D)	4-3	865-1170	16-23
	(D),D	3-2	458-763	8-15
	(D),D	2-1	407-610	7-12
	1	2-1	1475-1985	27-39
To Detent 2.0 in Hg Vacuum	(D),D	1-2	1476-1781	27-35
	(D),D	2-3	2240-2545	41-50
	(D)	3-4	2950-3610	55-71
	(D),D	CL	See Note 1	
	(D),D	CU	See Note 1	
	(D)	4-3	1880-2190	35-43
	(D),D	3-2	1630-1935	30-38
Through Detent WOT 1.0 in Hg Vacuum	(D),D	1-2	1880-2190	35-43
	(D),D	2-3	3100-3410	57-67
	(D),D	CL	See Note 1	
	(D),D	CU	See Note 1	
	(D),D	3-2	2850-3156	53-62
	(D),D	3-1	1630-1935	30-38

CL—Converter Clutch Lockup

CU—Converter Clutch Unlock

Tire Size	Axle Ratio 3.45	3.73	4.10
	Use Column No.		
P185/75R14SL			—
P195/75R14SL			—
P205/70R14SL			—
P205/75R14SL			—
P215/75R14SL			1
P195/75R15SL			1
P205/75R15SL			1
P215/75R15SL			1

Automatic Transmissions

FORD MOTOR CO. A4LD (Cont.)

SHIFT SPEEDS (MPH) (Cont.)

2.3L EFI
RANGER 4x2, AEROSTAR
MODEL 85GT-ACA & MODEL 86GT-AAA

Throttle	Range	Shift	OPS—R.P.M.	Column Number 1	2	3	4
Closed Throttle 10-15 in Hg Vacuum	(D),D	1-2	509-764	10-16	11-17	10-15	10-15
	(D),D	2-3	713-1069	15-23	15-24	13-21	14-22
	(D)	3-4	1832-2240	38-48	40-50	35-44	37-46
	(D),D	CL	2036-2494	42-53	44-55	39-49	41-51
	(D),D	CU	See Note 1				
	(D)	4-3	814-1120	17-24	18-25	15-22	16-23
	(D),D	3-2	509-814	10-17	11-18	10-16	10-16
	(D),D	2-1	356-560	7-12	7-12	7-11	7-11
	1	2-1	1476-1781	31-38	32-39	28-35	30-36
To Detent 2.0 in Hg Vacuum	(D),D	1-2	1425-1731	29-37	31-38	27-34	28-35
	(D),D	2-3	2036-2341	42-50	44-52	39-46	41-48
	(D)	3-4*	2499-2804	52-60	54-62	48-55	50-58
	(D),D	CL*	2433-2738	50-58	53-61	47-54	49-56
	(D),D	CU	See Note 1				
	(D)	4-3	2647-2952	55-63	58-65	51-58	53-61
	(D),D	3-2	1629-1934	34-41	35-43	31-38	33-40
Through Detent WOT 1.0 in Hg Vacuum	(D),D	1-2	1832-2138	38-45	40-47	35-42	37-44
	(D),D	2-3	3156-3461	66-74	69-77	61-68	63-71
	(D),D	CL	See Note 1				
	(D),D	CU	See Note 1				
	(D),D	3-2	2952-3258	61-69	64-72	58-64	59-67
	(D),D	3-1	1527-1832	32-39	33-41	30-36	31-37

*Check 3-4 upshift and converter clutch lockup at 5.0 in Hg vacuum.
CL—Converter Clutch Lockup
CU—Converter Clutch Unlock

Tire Size	Axle Ratio 3.45	3.73
	Use Column No.	
P185/75R14SL	1	3
P195/75R14SL	1	3
P205/70R14SL	1	3
P205/75R14SL	2	4
P215/75R14SL	2	4

2.8L 2-Barrel V6
AEROSTAR
MODEL 85GT-AMA/BCA

Throttle	Range	Shift	OPS—R.P.M.	Column Number 1	2	3	4
Closed Throttle 10-15 in Hg Vacuum	(D),D	1-2	458-712	9-15	10-15	9-14	8-13
	(D),D	2-3	814-1221	17-26	17-26	15-24	15-22
	(D)	3-4	1781-2290	37-48	39-50	34-46	32-42
	(D),D	CL	1578-1985	33-42	34-43	30-40	29-36
	(D),D	CU	See Note 1				
	(D)	4-3	865-1170	18-25	19-25	16-23	16-21
	(D),D	3-2	458-763	9-16	10-16	9-15	8-14
	(D),D	2-1	356-560	7-12	7-12	7-11	6-10
	1	2-1	1425-1935	29-41	31-42	27-39	26-35
To Detent 2.0 in Hg Vacuum	(D),D	1-2	1325-1625	27-34	29-35	25-33	24-30
	(D),D	2-3	1880-2180	39-46	41-47	36-44	34-40
	(D)	3-4*	2372-2677	49-57	51-58	45-54	43-49
	(D),D	CL*	1990-2296	41-48	43-50	38-46	36-42
	(D),D	CU	See Note 1				
	(D)	4-3	2035-2550	42-54	44-55	39-51	37-47
	(D),D	3-2	1680-1985	35-42	36-43	32-40	31-36
Through Detent WOT 2.0 in Hg Vacuum	(D),D	1-2	1781-2087	37-44	39-45	34-42	32-38
	(D),D	2-3	3003-3308	63-70	65-72	58-67	55-61
	(D),D	CL	See Note 1				
	(D),D	CU	See Note 1				
	(D),D	3-2	2850-3156	59-67	62-69	55-63	52-58
	(D),D	3-1	1578-1883	33-40	34-41	30-38	29-34

*Check 3-4 upshift and converter clutch lockup at 7.0 in Hg vacuum.
CL—Converter Clutch Lockup
CU—Converter Clutch Unlock

2.3L EFI
RANGER 4x2, AEROSTAR
MODEL 85GT-ACA & MODEL 86GT-AAA

Throttle	Range	Shift	OPS—R.P.M.	Column Number 1	2
Closed Throttle 10-15 in Hg Vacuum	(D),D	1-2	509-764	9-13	9-14
	(D),D	2-3	713-1069	12-19	13-20
	(D)	3-4	1832-2240	32-40	33-42
	(D),D	CL	2036-2494	35-44	37-46
	(D),D	CU	See Note 1		
	(D)	4-3	814-1120	14-20	15-21
	(D),D	3-2	509-814	9-14	9-15
	(D),D	2-1	356-560	6-10	6-10
	1	2-1	1476-1781	26-32	27-33
To Detent 2.0 in Hg Vacuum	(D),D	1-2	1425-1731	25-31	26-32
	(D),D	2-3	2036-2341	35-42	37-44
	(D)	3-4*	2499-2804	44-50	46-52
	(D),D	CL*	2433-2738	42-49	44-51
	(D),D	CU	See Note 1		
	(D)	4-3	2647-2952	46-53	48-55
	(D),D	3-2	1629-1934	28-34	30-36
Through Detent WOT 1.0 in Hg Vacuum	(D),D	1-2	1832-2138	32-38	33-40
	(D),D	2-3	3156-3461	55-62	58-65
	(D),D	CL	See Note 1		
	(D),D	CU	See Note 1		
	(D),D	3-2	2952-3258	51-58	54-61
	(D),D	3-1	1527-1832	26-33	28-34

*Check 3-4 upshift and converter clutch lockup at 5.0 in Hg vacuum.
CL—Converter Clutch Lockup
CU—Converter Clutch Unlock

Tire Size	Axle Ratio 4.10
	Use Column No.
P185/75R14SL	1
P195/75R14SL	1
P205/70R14SL	1
P205/75R14SL	2
P215/75R14SL	2

Tire Size	Axle Ratio 3.45	3.73	4.10
	Use Column No.		
P185/75R14SL	1	3	—
P195/75R14SL	1	3	—
P205/75R14SL	2	3	4

FORD MOTOR CO. A4LD (Cont.)

Fig. 2: Gauge Hookup for Pressure Testing

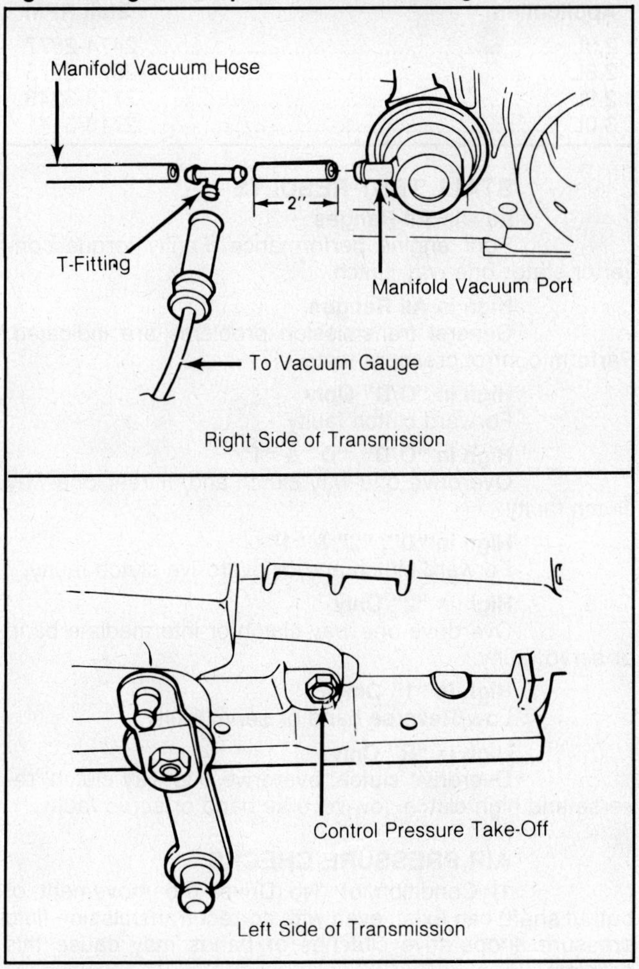

3) Apply parking brake firmly. Start engine. Adjust engine idle speed to correct RPM. If engine idle cannot be brought within limits, check throttle and downshift linkages for binding. Check for vacuum leaks in hoses and tubes if linkage is correctly in place. Check vacuum units such as power brake booster for leaks.

4) Vacuum reading at gauge should be steady with engine idling. Reading must be acceptable for altitude where test is being done. If vacuum reading is correct at idle, accelerate engine rapidly and release throttle immediately. Vacuum reading must drop rapidly during acceleration.

5) Vacuum should return as soon as throttle is released. If vacuum reading does not respond correctly, check lines for restriction or plugging. Also make sure that vacuum line is not hooked up to reservoir.

CONTROL PRESSURE TEST

NOTE: **Governor can be checked at same time control pressure test is performed and in same manner.**

1) Disconnect engine vacuum line from modulator unit. Hookup vacuum pump to unit. Apply parking and service brakes. Start engine and apply 15 in. Hg. vacuum to modulator. Select all ranges of transmission. Read and record control pressures.

2) Run engine up to 1000 RPM and set vacumm pump at 10 in. Hg. Read and record control pressures in 4 forward ranges. Keeping engine speed at 1000 RPM, reduce vacuum to 1 in. Hg. Read and record control pressures in 4 forward ranges and in Reverse range.

CONTROL PRESSURE SPECIFICATIONS (PSI)

Transmission Type	Transmission Model	Range	Idle 15" & Above	10"	WOT Stall Thru Detent
A4LD	85GT-ACA/AMA/ BCA 86GT-AAA	*OD,D,2,1	50-70	92-113	167-195
		R	75-109	158-178	282-316
		P,N	50-70		
A4LD	85GT-AMA	%OD,D,2,1	50-60	70-93	144-177
		R	66-78	122-145	247-282
		P,N	50-60		
A4LD	86GT-ABA/ACA/ BAA/CAA/DAA/ EAA	*OD,D,2,1	57-78	114-134	205-235
		R	67-105	157-177	282-316
		P,N	57-78		
A4LD	86GT-ACA/CAA/ EAA	%OD,D,D,2,1	57-67	90-110	180-210
		R	67-77	124-144	247-280
		P,N	57-67		

*Barometric pressure 29.0-30.0 in. hg.
%Barometric pressure 24.0-25.0 in. hg.

CONTROL PRESSURE RESULTS

Compare recorded control pressures to control pressures listed in table. See CONTROL PRESSURE SPECIFICATIONS (PSI) table. If control pressures are outside of specified ranges, use following list to determine cause of trouble:

High at Idle in All Ranges

Check engine EGR system, vacuum diaphragm unit and manifold vacuum line. Check throttle valve, control rod and regulator boost valves for sticking.

Low at Idle in All Ranges

Check engine EGR system. Check fluid level. Check for restricted intake screen or filter. Check for loose oil tubes. Check if valve body-to-case or regulator-to-case bolts are loose. Check for excessive leakage in oil pump, control valve body and case. Check control pressure regulator valve for sticking.

Normal at Idle; Low at 10 in. Hg

Check vacuum diaphragm unit. Control rod or throttle valve stuck.

Normal at Idle and 10 in. Hg.; Low at 1 in. Hg

Check for excessive leakage, low pump capacity or restricted oil pan screen.

Low in "P" or "N"

Check valve body.

Low in "O/D"

Check forward clutch and/or overdrive servo.

Low in "D"

Check forward clutch and/or overdrive clutch.

Low in "2"

Check forward clutch or overdrive clutch and/or intermediate servo.

Low in "1"

Check forward clutch or overdeive clutch and/or reverse clutch and servo.

Low in "R"

Check reverse-high clutch or overdrive clutch and/or low and reverse servo.

Automatic Transmissions

FORD MOTOR CO. A4LD (Cont.)

CONVERTER CLUTCH TEST

NOTE: Engine coolant temperature must be above 128°F (53°C) and below 240°F (116°C). This temperature can be obtained after approximately 15 minutes of highway driving. Since most converter clutch shifts are difficult to feel a tachometer and/or vacuum gauge must be connected to engine.

1) To check converter for engagement to disengagement, drive vehicle at approximately 50 MPH. While maintaining this speed tap brake pedal with left foot.

2) Engine RPM and vacuum should increase when clutch disengages, with light brake pedal application. RPM will decrease when pedal is released and clutch engages.

3) If converter clutch does not engage, see appropriate AUTOMATIC TRANSMISSION TROUBLE SHOOTING article in DOMESTIC GENERAL SERVICING section.

GOVERNOR PRESSURE TEST

CAUTION: Never exceed 60 MPH speedometer reading during governor pressure test. After each test, move selector lever to Neutral and run engine at 1000 RPM to cool transmission.

1) Raise vehicle until rear wheels are clear of ground. Disconnect and plug vacuum line to vacuum diaphragm unit. Connect hand-held vacuum pump to diaphragm unit.

2) Place transmission in "D2". Apply 10 in. Hg to diaphragm unit with no load on engine. Increase speed slowly and watch speedometer. Note speed at which control pressure cut-back occurs. It should occur between 8-12 MPH.

3) Decrease vacuum to 0-2 in. Hg and repeat test. Control pressure cut-back should occur at 10-14 MPH. Governor is okay if cut-back occurs as specified. If not, check shift speeds to verify that problem is in governor and not due to stuck cut-back valve. Repair or replace governor.

STALL TEST

Testing Precautions

1) Engine coolant and transmission fluid must be at proper levels and operating temperatures. T.V. linkage must be set properly. Hold accelerator down just long enough to get stable tachometer reading. Do not floor accelerator for more than 5 seconds.

2) Do not exceed maximum specified RPM for vehicle. Before shifting into each selector position, run engine in "N" at 1000 RPM for 15 to 20 seconds to cool transmission. If engine speed exceeds upper specification, release accelerator immediately as this is an indication of clutch or band slippage.

Testing Procedure

1) Connect tachometer to engine. Apply parking and service brakes firmly. Place selector lever in "O/D" position, and push accelerator completely to floor. Record tachometer reading.

2) Engine speed should be within specifications given in STALL SPEEDS table. Repeat procedure in "D", "2", "1", and "R" positions.

STALL SPEEDS

Application	Stall RPM
2.3L	2474-2877
2.8L	2576-2975
2.9L	2758-3248
3.0L	2718-3141

STALL TEST RESULTS

Low in All Ranges

Poor engine performance. Faulty torque converter stator one-way clutch.

High in All Ranges

General transmission problems are indicated. Perform control pressure tests.

High in "O/D" Only

Forward clutch faulty.

High in "O/D", "D" & "1"

Overdrive one-way clutch and/or rear one-way clutch faulty.

High in "D", "2" & "1"

Forward clutch and/or overdrive clutch faulty.

High in "2" Only

Overdrive one-way clutch or intermediate band or servo faulty.

High in "1" Only

Low/Reverse band or servo faulty.

High in "R" Only

Overdrive clutch, overdrive one-way clutch, reverse and high clutch, low/reverse band or servo faulty.

AIR PRESSURE CHECKS

1) Condition of "No Drive" (no movement of output shaft) can exist, even with correct transmission fluid pressure. Inoperative clutches or bands may cause this problem.

2) Inoperative units can be located through series of checks by substituting air pressure for fluid pressure to determine location of malfunction.

3) Loosen oil pan bolts and allow transmission fluid to drain. Remove oil pan and control valve body. Apply air at points noted in *Fig. 3.* Check unit operation as follows:

Forward Clutch

Apply air pressure into forward clutch passage. Dull thud can be heard when clutch piston is applied. Movement of piston can be felt by placing finger tips on input shell if no thud is heard.

Governor

Apply air pressure into the control pressure-to-governor passage. Listen for sharp clicking or whistling noise indicating governor valve movement.

Overdrive Servo

1) Hold air nozzle in overdrive servo apply passage. Operation of servo is indicated by a tightening of overdrive band around overdrive drum.

2) While continuing to apply air pressure to servo apply passage, introduce air pressure into overdrive servo release passage. The overdrive servo should release overdrive band.

Overdrive Clutch

Apply air pressure to overdrive clutch feed passage. A dull thud indicates that the overdrive clutch piston has moved to the applied position.

Fig. 3: Bottom View of Transmission Case

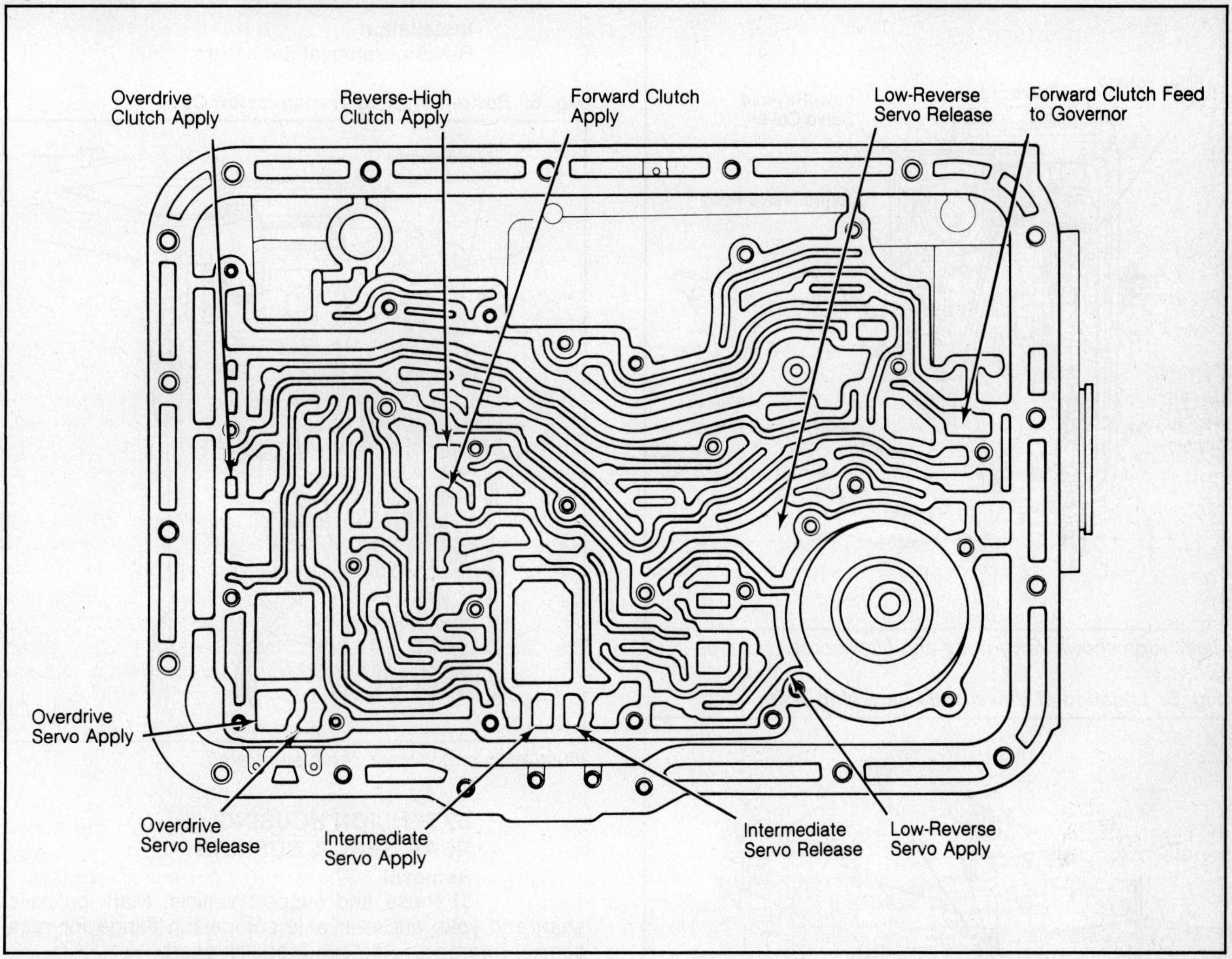

Note points for air testing of clutches and bands.

Reverse-High Clutch

Apply air pressure into reverse-high clutch passage. Dull thud can be heard when clutch piston is applied. Movement of piston can be felt by placing finger tips on clutch drum.

Intermediate Servo

1) Hold air nozzle in intermediate servo apply passage. Operation of servo is indicated by tightening of intermediate band around drum.

2) While continuing to apply air pressure at servo apply passage, apply air pressure to intermediate servo release passage. Intermediate servo should then release band against pressure in apply passage.

Low-Reverse Servo

Apply air pressure to low-reverse servo apply passage. Low-reverse band should tighten around drum if servo is operating properly.

NOTE: **If air pressure applied to either clutch passages fails to operate clutch, or operates both clutches at once, remove and check fluid passages in case and oil pump. Use air pressure to detect obstructions.**

SERVICE (IN VEHICLE)

CONTROL VALVE BODY

Removal

Remove oil pan, filter screen and "O" ring. Remove rear servo cover and gasket. Disconnect 2 wires at converter clutch solenoid. Remove valve body retaining bolts. Carefully ease valve body from case while unlocking and detaching selector lever connecting rod ("Z" link).

NOTE: **Note size and location of valve body retaining bolts. Bolts are of different sizes and must be replaced in proper position at reassembly.**

Installation

1) Attach and lock selector lever connecting rod ("Z" link) to manual valve. Ease control valve body to case. Install bolts "A" and "B" fingertight to align body to case. *See Fig. 5.* Install and tighten remaining valve body bolts. Install detent spring, hooking it to bolt "A". Tighten bolts "A" and "B" to specification.

2) Install rear servo cover with new gasket. Connect wires to converter clutch solenoid. Clean filter screen. Install filter screen and "O" ring. Install oil pan using new gasket. Tighten pan bolts evenly. Lower vehicle and fill

FORD MOTOR CO. A4LD (Cont.)

Fig. 4: Bottom View of Transmission Case

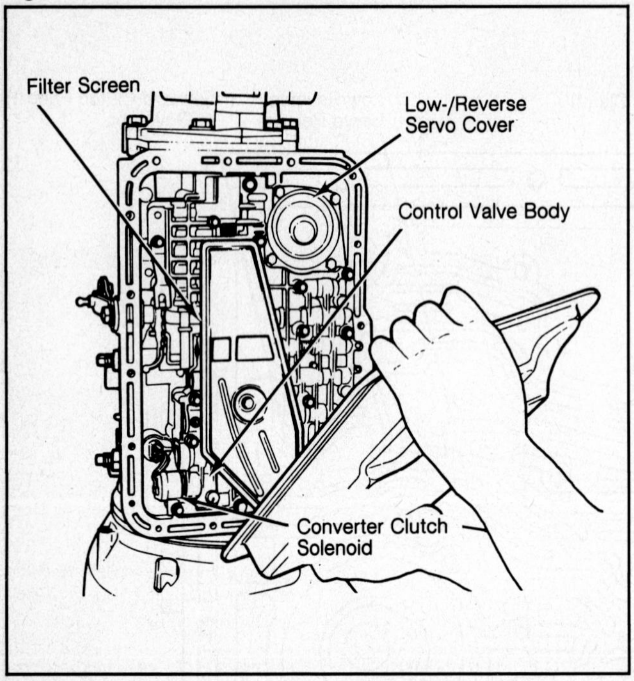

Illustration shows valve body and filter screen position

Fig. 5: Location of Valve Body Retaining Bolts

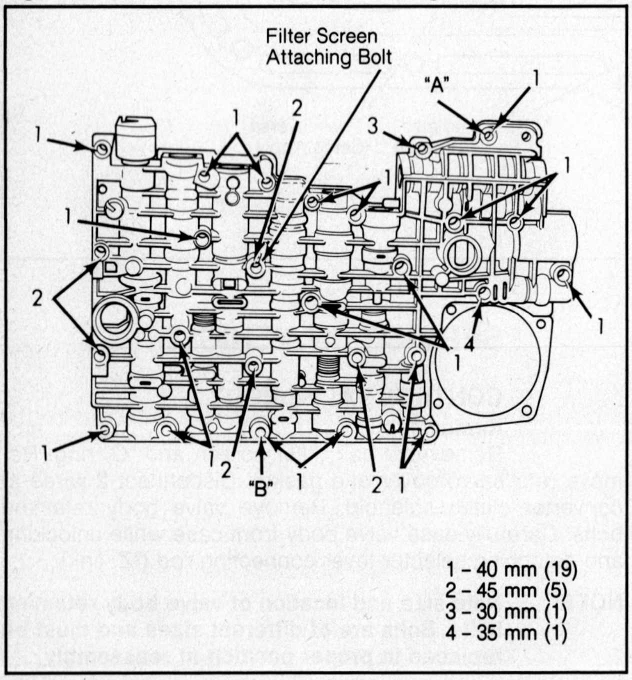

Use "A" and "B" bolts for locating valve body. Bolts must go into original locations.

transmission with 3 quarts of fluid. Start engine and add fluid as necessary. Check for leaks.

REAR SERVO

Removal

With oil pan and filter screen removed, remove rear servo cover retaining bolts, cover, gasket, servo piston, and spring.

NOTE: Force of servo spring will push cover off.

Installation

Reverse removal procedure.

Fig. 6: Bottom View of Transmission Case

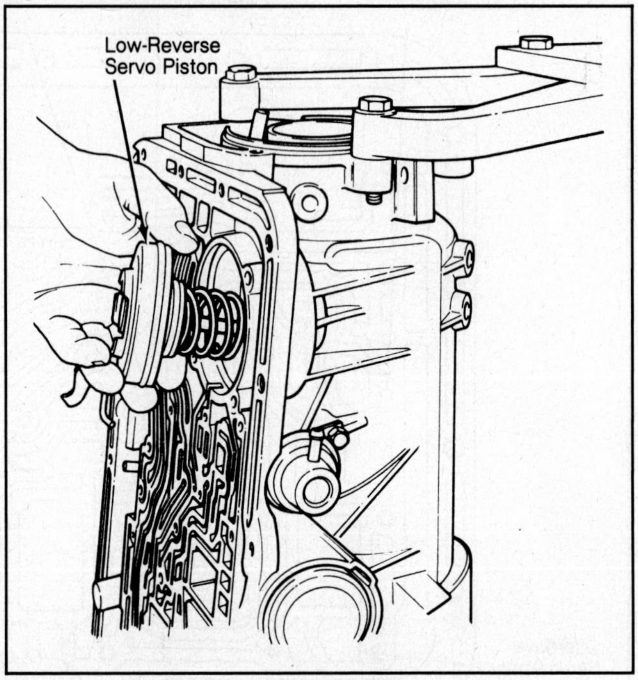

Illustration shows rear servo separated.

EXTENSION HOUSING REAR SEAL & BUSHING

Removal

1) Raise and support vehicle. Mark propeller shaft end yoke and rear axle companion flange for reassembly reference. Remove propeller shaft.

2) Remove extension housing rear oil seal and bushing using Pullers (T71P-7657-A for seal and T77L-7697-E for bushing). *See Fig. 7.*

Fig. 7: Removing Extension Housing Oil Seal & Bushing

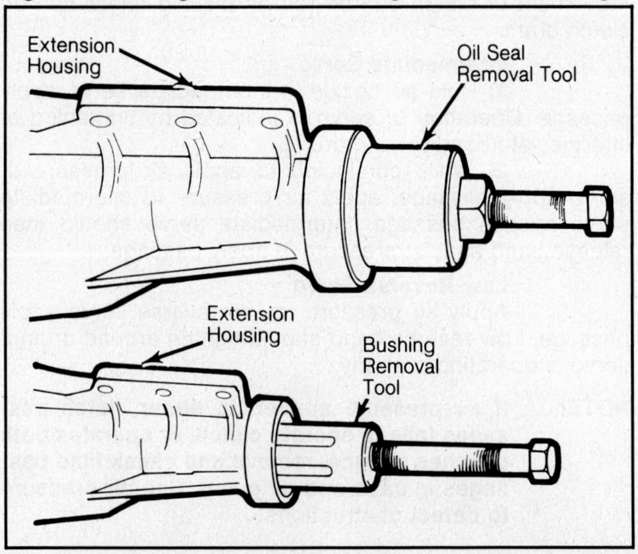

Installation

Check sealing surface of yoke for scoring. Replace if scoring found. Check housing counterbore for burrs and remove with crocus cloth if necessary. Drive new bushing and oil seal into extension housing using Drivers (T77L-7697-F for bushing and T74P-77052-A for oil seal). Install propeller shaft, aligning reference marks made at removal.

EXTENSION HOUSING

Removal

1) Raise and support vehicle. Mark propeller shaft for installation reference. Remove shaft. Disconnect speedometer cable from extension housing. Support transmission with jack.

2) Remove rear support-to-crossmember bolts. Raise transmission slightly and remove rear support from extension housing.

3) Loosen extension housing retaining bolts and allow transmission fluid to drain. Remove bolts and slide extension housing off output shaft.

Installation

Use new gasket. Position extension housing on case. Pay special attention to correctly seating park pawl operating rod in guide cup. Install and tighten bolts. To complete installation, reverse removal procedure.

GOVERNOR

Removal

Remove extension housing as previously described. Remove 2 governor body-to-oil collector body retaining bolts. Remove governor body from collector body. *See Fig. 8*.

NOTE: Components are not retained once governor body bolts have been removed. It is necessary to hold body and components while removing and installing governor.

Fig. 8: Removing Governor Assembly

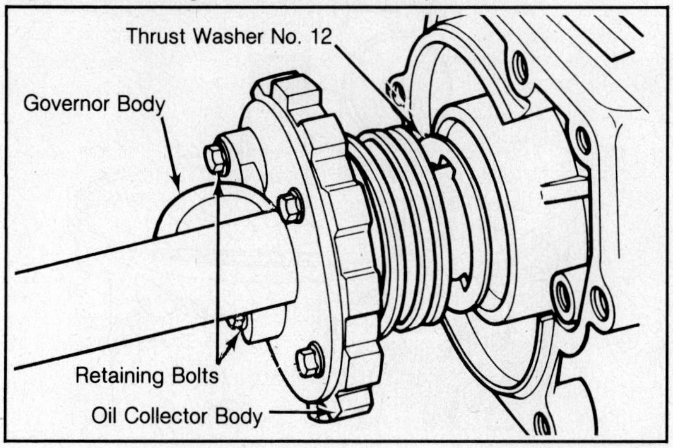

Installation

Assemble governor body and components. Position body over oil feed holes of oil collector body. Install retaining bolts. Install extension housing.

VACUUM DIAPHRAGM ASSEMBLY

Removal

Disconnect hoses from unit. Remove retaining bracket (do not pry or bend bracket). Remove vacuum diaphragm, actuating pin and throttle valve from case. Remove "O" ring from assembly. *See Fig. 9*.

Fig. 9: Side View of Transmission Case

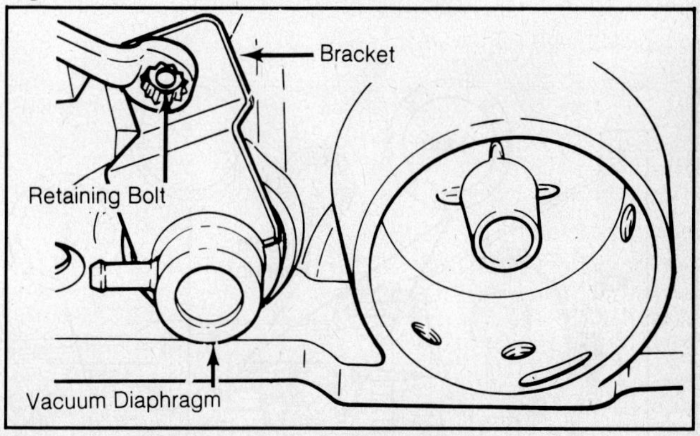

Illustration shows vacuum diaphragm installed.

Installation

Install new "O" ring. Install throttle valve, actuating pin and vacuum diaphragm (with tube pointing rearward). Install retaining bracket and tighten bolt.

REMOVAL & INSTALLATION

TRANSMISSION

See appropriate AUTOMATIC TRANSMISSION REMOVAL article in DOMESTIC GENERAL SERVICING section.

TORQUE CONVERTER

LEAKAGE CHECK

See procedure given in FORD C-6 article.

FLUSHING CONVERTER

See procedure given in FORD C-6 article.

TURBINE & STATOR END PLAY CHECK

See procedure given in FORD C-6 article. Only difference is end play specifications. Replace a new or rebuilt converter if end play exceeds .023" (.58 mm). Replace a used converter if end play exceeds .050" (1.27 mm).

STATOR ONE-WAY CLUTCH CHECK

See procedure given in FORD C-6 article.

STATOR INTERFERENCE CHECKS

See procedure given in FORD C-6 article.

TRANSMISSION DISASSEMBLY

NOTE: There are 10 thrust washers and 2 thrust bearing being used in this transmission, with No. 1 at front pump and No. 12 at governor. Note that No. 2 and No. 8 are needle roller bearings performing thrust function. Refer to Fig. 10 for identification and location of thrust washers.

REAR SERVO, VALVE BODY & OIL PUMP

1) Remove torque converter, input shaft, and oil pan. Remove oil filter screen, gasket. Remove detent spring.

Automatic Transmissions

FORD MOTOR CO. A4LD (Cont.)

Fig. 10: Cutaway View of Transmission Showing Thrust Washer Identification and Location

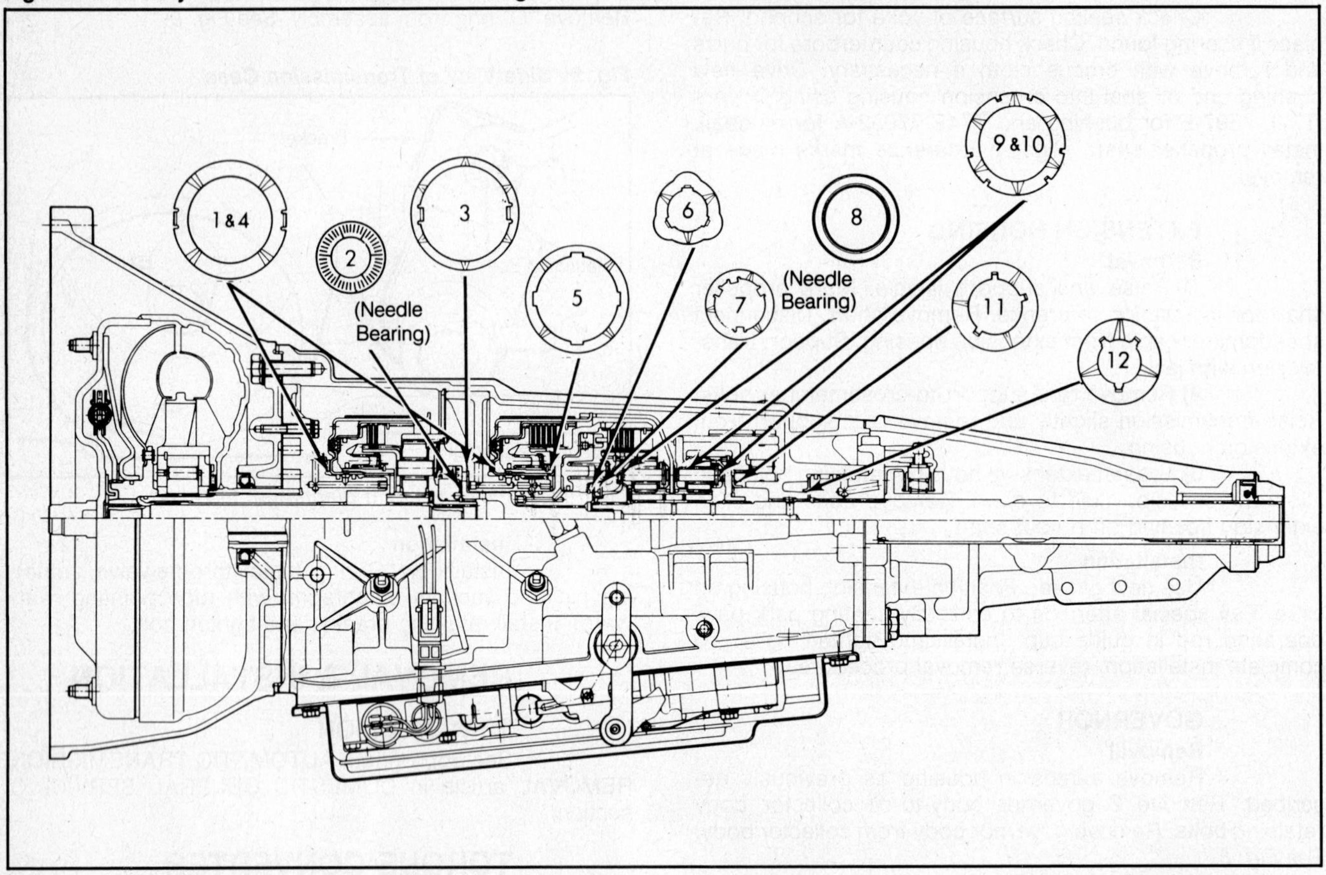

2) Remove rear servo cover and gasket (spring force will raise cover). Disconnect 2 wires at converter clutch solenoid. Remove bolts from valve body. Note size, length, and location of bolts for reassembly reference.

3) Slowly remove valve body from transmission, unlocking and detaching selector lever connecting link. Remove valve body and gasket. Remove 5 mm Allen head retaining bolt that holds center support.

4) Remove converter housing bolts. Remove housing and oil pump as an assembly. Remove No. 1 thrust washer and gasket. Remove oil pump seal with Puller (T74P-77248-A). Remove oil pump from converter housing. Remove steel plate (behind oil seal) with "O" ring.

NOTE: Before continuing with disassembly, transmission end play should be measured.

TRANSMISSION END PLAY CHECK

1) Install oil pump (without gasket) and existing No. 1 thrust washer into transmission case. Make sure pump body is below case gasket surface.

2) Mount dial indicator on oil pump with plunger resting on transmission housing. *See Fig. 11.* Zero dial indicator, then swing indicator around so plunger contacts oil pump.

3) Check reading on dial and record for future reference. Move dial indicator assembly to opposite side of pump. Make another end play check. Take average of 2 readings.

4) End play range is .001-.025" (.03-.64 mm). If end play exceeds limits, replace thrust washer No. 1 with one that will bring end play within specifications.

Fig. 11: Tool Set-Up for Transmission End Play Check

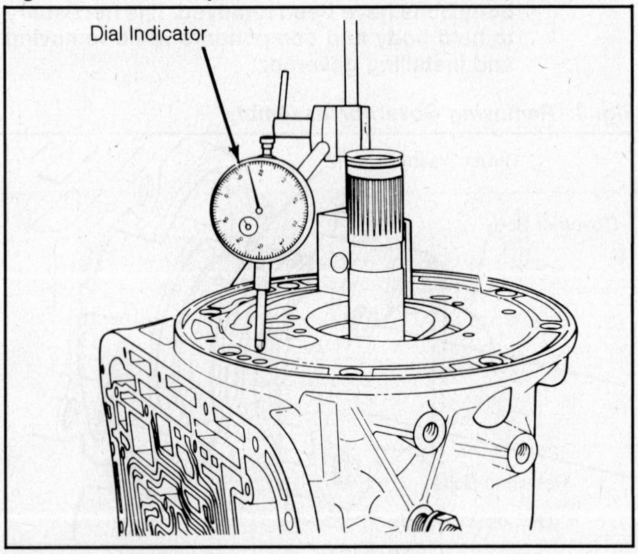

Take average of 2 readings 180° apart.

5) After end play check has been completed, remove oil pump and No. 1 selective thrust washer. Mark installed position of oil pump gears in relation to one another and remove.

OVERDRIVE CLUTCH ASSEMBLY

1) Loosen overdrive band lock nut and back off adjusting screw. Replace lock nut with new one during reassembly.

SELECTIVE THRUST WASHER NO. 1

Identification Number	Thickness Inch (mm)
"1"	.053-.055 (1.35-1.40)
"2"	.060-.062 (1.52-1.57)
"3"	.068-.070 (1.73-1.78)
"4"	.076-.078 (1.93-1.98)
"5"	.084-.086 (2.13-2.18)
"6"	.092-.094 (2.34-2.39)

2) Remove anchor and apply struts. Lift out overdrive clutch assembly and band. Lift out overdrive one way clutch and planetary assembly. Remove center support retaining snap ring.

3) Remove overdrive apply lever and shaft. Remove overdrive control bracket from valve body side of case.

NOTE: **Overdrive apply lever does not have a boss on shaft hole as compared to intermediate apply lever. Overdrive apply lever shaft is longer as compared to the intermediate apply lever shaft.**

4) Remove thrust washer on top of center support. Identify thrust washer for reassembly.

5) Remove center support being careful to pry upward evenly. Remove thrust washer below center support. Identify thrust washer for reassembly.

REVERSE-HIGH & FORWARD CLUTCH ASSEMBLY

1) Loosen intermediate band lock nut and back off adjusting screw. Replace lock nut with new one during reassembly. Remove anchor and apply struts.

2) Remove reverse-high and forward clutch assembly. Remove intermediate band. Remove forward planet gear assembly. Identify thrust washer for reassembly.

CASE & EXTENSION HOUSING PARTS

1) Remove extension housing bolts. Remove housing and gasket. Remove return spring and parking pawl. Remove large snap ring from rear planet gear carrier.

2) Remove reverse planet gear carrier with thrust washer. Identify thrust washer for reassembly. Remove small snap ring from output shaft.

3) Remove output shaft ring gear and thrust washer. Remove reverse brake drum. Remove low-reverse servo from valve body side of case. Remove rear band assembly and thrust washer.

NOTE: **Inner race of rear one-way clutch is not removable from case.**

4) Remove intermediate apply lever and shaft. This apply lever has a boss on the shaft hole and shaft is shorter than overdrive shaft. Remove output shaft.

5) Remove park gear/collector body assembly from rear of case. Remove thrust washer. Remove vacuum diaphragm unit and throttle valve actuator rod. Use magnet to verify that throttle valve moves freely in bore, then remove throttle valve.

6) Remove intermediate servo cover snap ring. Remove intermediate servo cover, piston and spring. Remove overdrive servo cover snap ring. Remove overdrive cover, piston and spring. Air pressure may be used on release side of pistons. Do not exceed 20 psi (1.4 kg/cm^2) air pressure.

7) Remove neutral safety switch. Use thin-walled socket to remove neutral safety switch. Open-end wrench will crush switch. Remove kickdown lever nut, lever and "O" ring seal.

8) Remove linkage centering pin. Remove manual lever, internal kickdown lever and park pawl rod and detent plate assembly. Remove lever shaft oil seal.

9) Remove torque converter clutch solenoid connector. Tab on outside of case on backside of connector must be depressed while pulling with pliers. The tab is depressed with a small pair of locking pliers.

NOTE: **Clutch solenoid connector does not need to be removed unless it is to be replaced and/or if case is immersed in degreaser.**

COMPONENT DISASSEMBLY & REASSEMBLY

OVERDRIVE CLUTCH

Disassembly

Disassembly of overdrive clutch is the same as reverse-high clutch except for removing clutch piston. Piston is removed by air pressure. Use finger to close off air leak.

Reassembly

Reassembly of overdrive clutch is the same as reverse-high clutch with the exception of the following.

1) Install clutch plates beginning with a steel plate, then alternate friction, steel, friction. Install pressure plate and retaining clip. Use feeler gauge to check clearance between retaining ring and pressure plate. Push down on plates while making this check.

2) Clearance should be between .026"-.053" (.65-1.35 mm). Selective snap rings are available in following thicknesses: .054", .068", .082", and .096" (1.37, 1.73, 2.08, and 2.44 mm).

FORWARD GEAR TRAIN ASSEMBLY

Disassembly

Remove clutch hub and sun gear. Remove front planet gear carrier with internal gear and needle bearing No. 8. If necessary, remove sun gear from input shell after removing retainer. Replace thrust washer No. 9 if damaged. Remove forward drive clutch and thrust washer No. 5.

NOTE: **Reassembly of forward gear train assembly is covered at end of COMPONENT DISASSEMBLY and REASSEMBLY.**

REVERSE-HIGH CLUTCH

Disassembly

1) Remove large pressure plate retaining ring. Remove pressure plate and clutch pack. Using Spring Compressor (T65L-77515-A), compress piston return springs and remove small retaining ring. *See Fig. 14.* Carefully release pressure on springs.

Automatic Transmissions

FORD MOTOR CO. A4LD (Cont.)

Fig. 12: Exploded View of Forward Gear Train

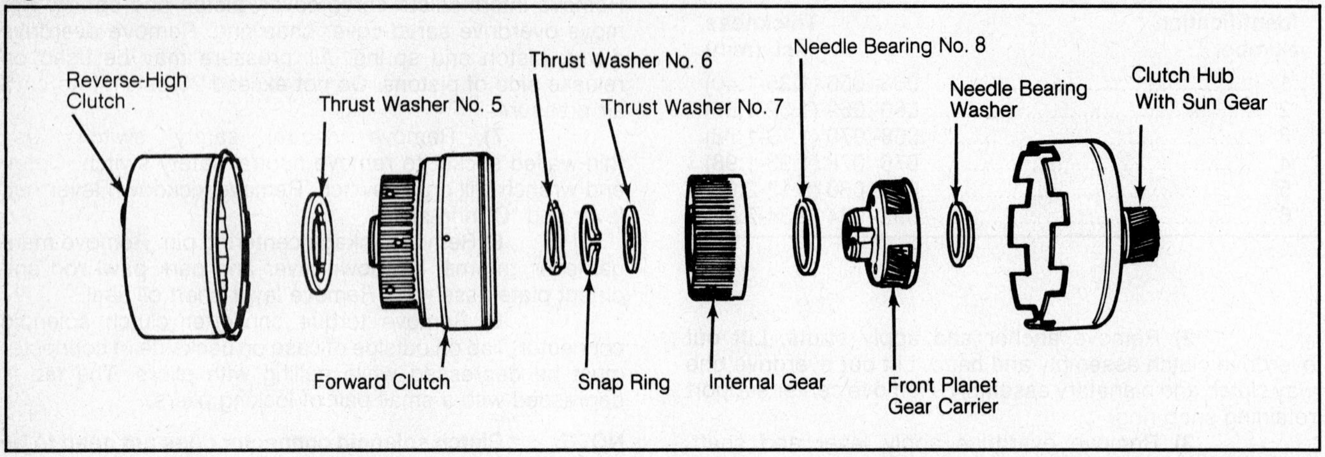

2) Remove spring retainer and return springs. Turn clutch body over and carefully force out piston with compressed air. *See Fig. 15.* Remove "O" rings from piston and clutch body.

Reassembly

1) Inspect all parts for wear, damage, or effects of overheating. If new composition clutch plates are to be used, soak in transmission fluid for 30 minutes before installing.

2) Install new "O" rings on piston and clutch body. Carefully install clutch piston, using Seal Protector (T74P-77404-A) to protect inner and outer seals. *See Fig. 17.*

3) Install 20 piston return springs and spring retainer. Compress springs with tool used at disassembly. Install snap ring and remove compressing tool. Install clutch plates, starting with steel plate.

4) Alternate composition and steel plates until all clutch plates are installed. See CLUTCH PLATE USAGE chart. Install pressure plate and secure with snap ring. Push down on pressure plate. Measure clearance between pressure plate and snap ring with feeler gauge. Clearance should be .051-.079" (1.29-2.01 mm).

5) If clearance is not within specifications, install correct thickness selective snap ring. Reverse-High clutch selective snap rings are available in following thicknesses: .054", .068", .082" and .096" (1.37, 1.73, 2.08 and 2.44 mm).

Fig. 14: Compressing Piston Return Springs and Retainer

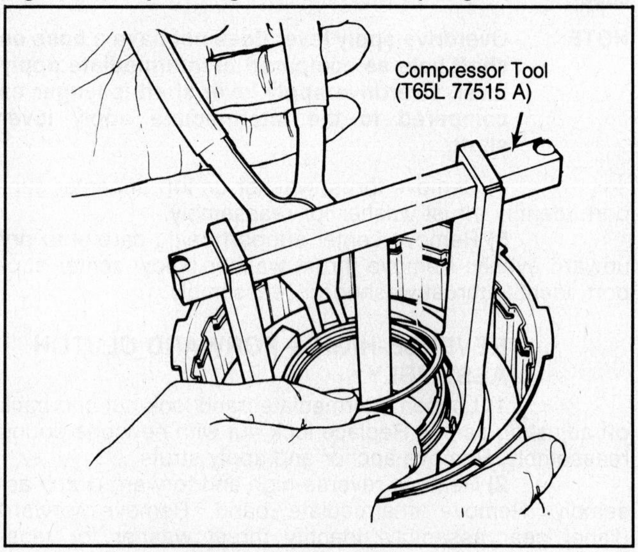

FORWARD CLUTCH

Disassembly

1) Remove large retaining ring. Lift out pressure plate, clutch pack, and rubber cushion spring. Using Spring

Fig. 13: Exploded View of Reverse-High Clutch Assembly

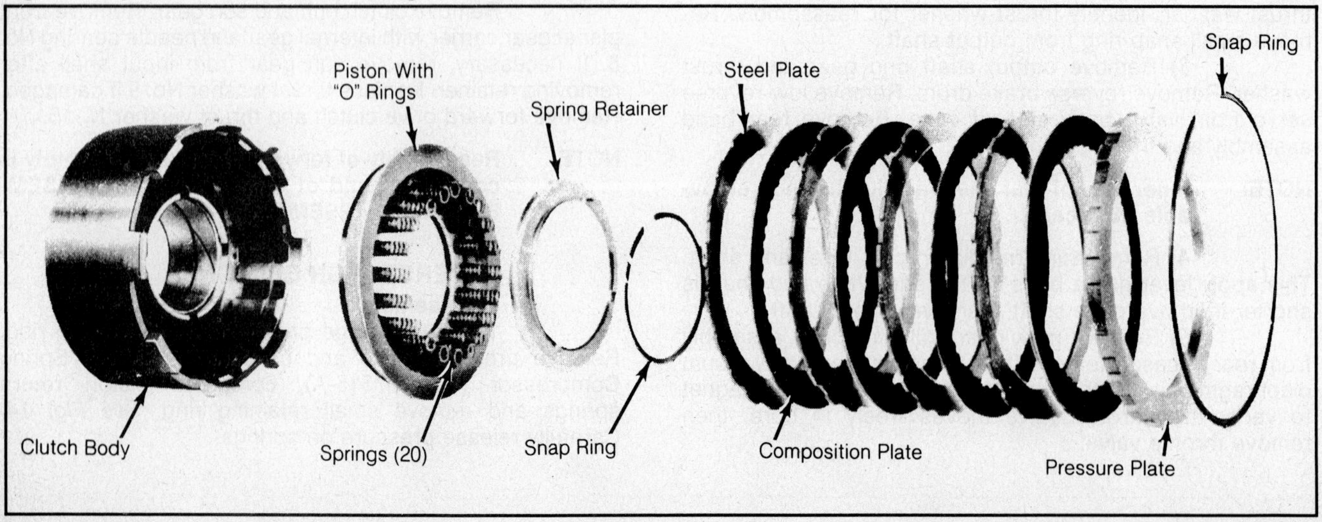

Automatic Transmissions

FORD MOTOR CO. A4LD (Cont.)

Fig. 15: Using Compressed Air to Remove Reverse-High Clutch Piston

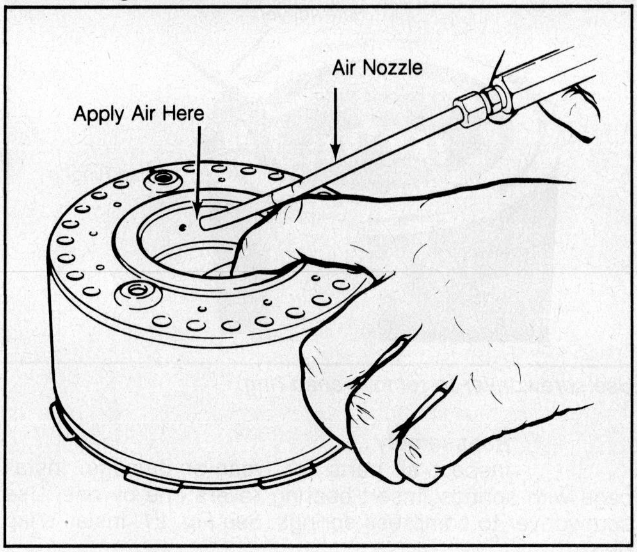

CLUTCH PLATE USAGE

Application	Composition Plates	Steel Plates
All Models		
Forward Clutch	5	5
2.3L		
Reverse-High Clutch	4	4
2.8L, 2.9L & 3.0L		
Reverse-High Clutch	5	5
All Models		
Overdrive Clutch	2	2

Compressor (T65L-77515-A), compress piston return springs. Remove small retaining ring. *See Fig. 16.*

2) Carefully release pressure on springs. Remove spring retainer and springs. Install center support on forward clutch cylinder. Apply air pressure to left (middle sized) port in center support to force clutch piston from

Fig. 17: Reverse-High Clutch Piston Installation

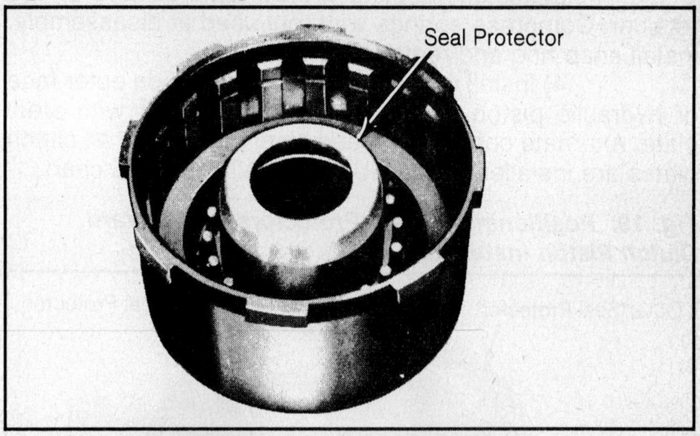

Note installed position of seal protector.

Fig. 18: Clutch Pressure Plate Clearance

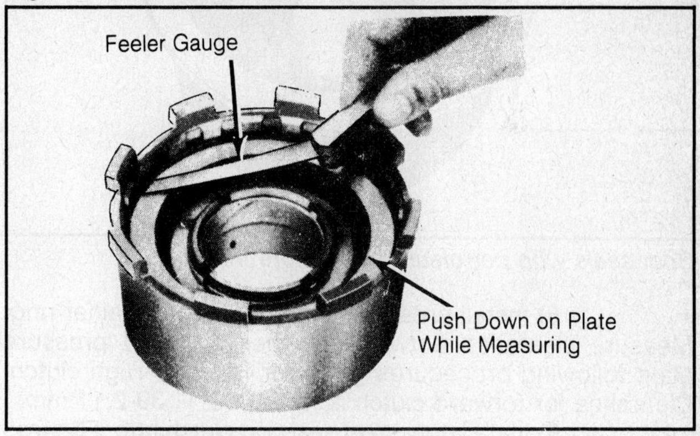

Use feeler gauge to measure clearance.

clutch cylinder. Remove "O" rings from piston and clutch body.

Reassembly

1) Inspect all parts for wear, damage, or effects of overheating. If new composition clutch plates are to be used, soak in transmission fluid for 30 minutes before installing.

2) Use Protective Tool (T74P-77548-A and B) to prevent damage to inner and outer seals. *See Fig. 19*. Install new "O" rings. Apply petroleum jelly to rings and to shoulder at clutch stub. Carefully install piston.

Fig. 16: Exploded View of Forward Clutch Assembly

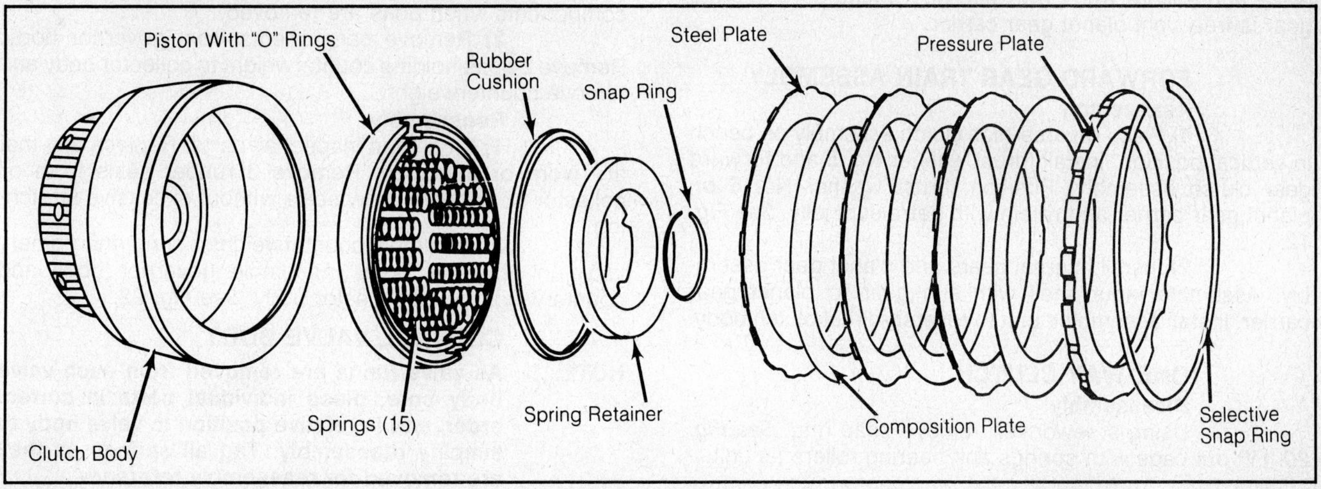

FORD MOTOR CO. A4LD (Cont.)

3) Install 15 piston return springs and spring retainer. Compress springs with tool used at disassembly. Install snap ring and remove tool.

4) Install rubber cushion in groove on outer face of hydraulic piston. Install clutch plates. Start with steel plate. Alternate composition and steel plates until all clutch plates are installed. See CLUTCH PLATE USAGE chart.

Fig. 19: Positioning of Seal Protectors for Forward Clutch Piston Installation

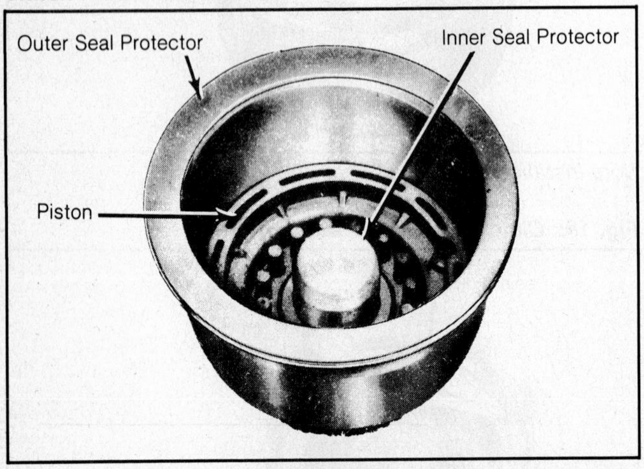

Coat seals with petroleum jelly before installing.

5) Install pressure plate and large retainer ring. Measure clearance between retainer ring and pressure plate following procedures given for Reverse-High clutch. Clearance for forward clutch is .055-.083" (1.39-2.11 mm).

6) Install new steel seals on clutch hub. Forward clutch selective snap rings are available in following thicknesses: .054", .068", .082" and .096" (1.37, 1.73, 2.08 and 2.44 mm).

INTERNAL GEAR & PLANET GEAR ASSEMBLY

Disassembly

Remove snap ring, planet gear carrier internal gear, and thrust washer No. 7. Separate planet gear carrier from internal gear. Remove needle bearing No. 8. *See Fig. 12.*

Reassembly

Insert planet gear carrier with needle bearing No. 8 into internal gear. Position thrust washer No. 7 in place and secure with new snap ring. Make sure internal gear is free from planet gear carrier.

FORWARD GEAR TRAIN ASSEMBLY

Reassembly

1) Place reverse-high clutch assembly on bench in vertical position. Install thrust washer No. 5 and forward gear clutch assembly. Position thrust washer No. 6 on planet gear carrier and retain with petroleum jelly. *See Fig. 12.*

2) Install internal gears and planet gear assembly. Assemble input shell with sun gear to planet gear carrier. Install assembled unit to reverse-direct clutch body.

ONE-WAY CLUTCH

Disassembly

Using screwdriver, remove snap ring. *See Fig. 20.* Lift out cage with springs and bearing rollers as unit.

Fig. 20: Removing Snap Ring from One-Way Clutch Cage

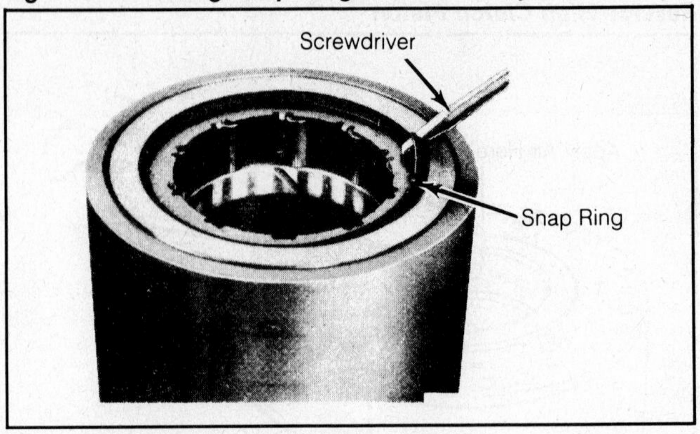

Use screwdriver to remove snap ring.

Reassembly

Inspect all parts for wear or damage. Install cage with springs. Insert bearing rollers one by one. Use screwdriver to compress springs. *See Fig. 21.* Install snap ring.

Fig. 21: Installing One-Way Clutch Bearing Rollers

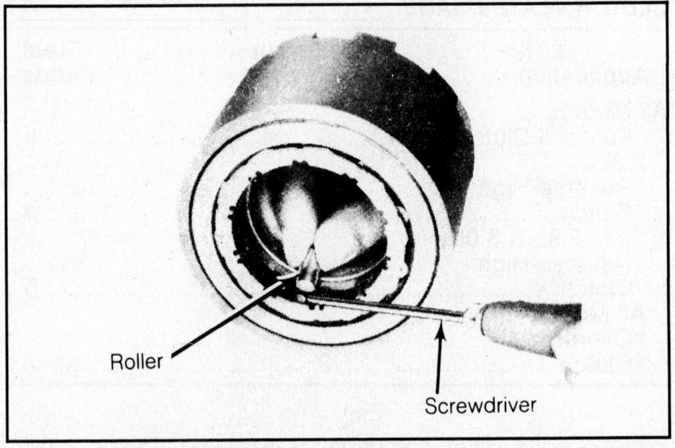

Use screwdriver to install rollers.

GOVERNOR

Disassembly

1) Remove 2 governor body-to-oil collector body retaining bolts. When these bolts are removed, governor components are no longer retained in position in body. Care must be taken not to drop governor body and components when bolts are removed.

2) Remove components from governor body. Remove 2 bolts holding counterweight to collector body and remove counterweight.

Reassembly

1) Clean and inspect all parts. Replace any that are worn or damaged. Remove 3 rubber seals from oil collector body. Install new seals without excessive stretching.

2) Assemble counterweight, spring and primary valve in governor body. Assemble governor body and counterweight to oil collector body. *See Fig. 22.*

CONTROL VALVE BODY

NOTE: **As valve trains are removed from each valve body bore, place individual parts in correct order, and in relative position to valve body to simplify reassembly. Tag all springs as they are removed for reassembly reference.**

FORD MOTOR CO. A4LD (Cont.)

Fig. 22: Exploded View of Governor Assembly

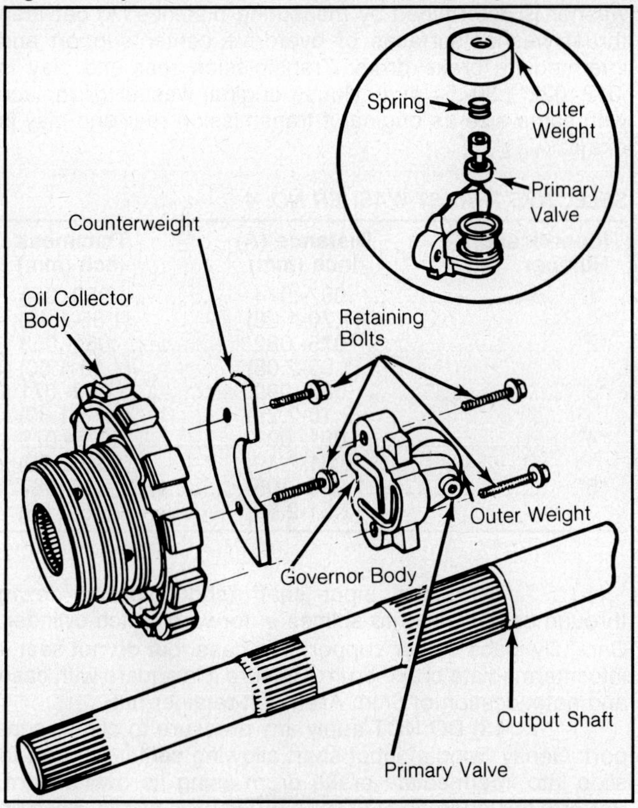

Attaching bolts also hold governor components together.

Fig. 23: Valve Body Separator Plate and Bolt Locations

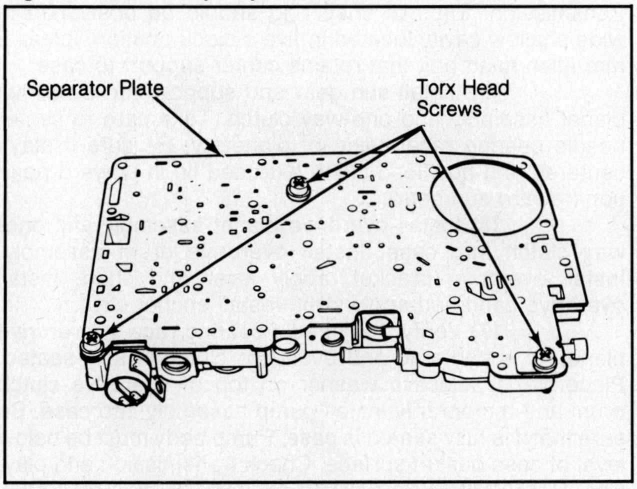

Disassembly

Remove separator plate bolts. Lift off separator plate and gasket. Remove 6 check balls, 2 check valves and both relief valves with springs. Refer to *Fig. 24* for correct placement. Remove retaining plates, dowels, plugs, and valves with springs from valve body.

Reassembly

Clean all parts and make sure passages are open. Inspect all parts for burring, unevenness, and gum deposits. Lubricate all parts with transmission fluid. Install valves, springs, plugs, and pins. *See Fig. 28.* Using new gasket, install separator plate.

Fig. 24: Locations of Check Balls, Check Valves and Pressure Relief Valves in Valve Body

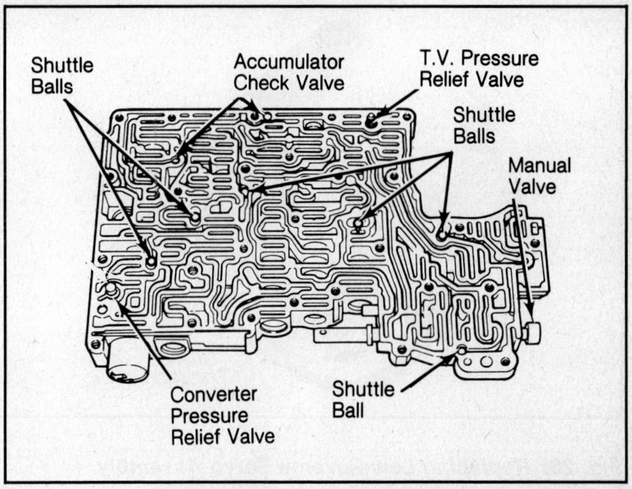

TRANSMISSION REASSEMBLY

NOTE: **Lubricate all parts with transmission fluid before reassembly. Thrust washers and gaskets should be held in place with petroleum jelly. See Fig. 10 for identification and location of thrust washers.**

1) Before installing center support into case, install new high clutch seals on support hub. It is also necessary to size these seals. Apply liberal amount of petroleum jelly to center support hub and seals.

NOTE: **If sizing is not done, the seals will be cut or rolled over when entering intermediate brake drum cavity.**

2) Use overdrive brake drum as a sizing tool. Carefully rotate center support while inserting it into drum housing. Observe seals as they enter cavity to see that they do not roll over or get cut.

3) Be sure center support is seated fully into overdrive drum. Allow to stand for several minutes so that seals seat in grooves. Set aside until required for reassembly.

4) Position thrust washer No. 12 in case. Install collector body in rear of case. Install output shaft and governor assembly, taking care to avoid damaging rubber oil seal rings.

5) Position thrust washer No. 11 in case. Install low-reverse brake drum. Install internal gear and attach with snap ring. Position thrust washer No. 10 to back of planet carrier. Install thrust washer No. 9. Install carrier and attach to rear brake drum with snap ring.

6) Install low-reverse band. Install low-reverse servo piston to hold band in position. *See Fig. 26.*

7) Install spiral spring on intermediate servo piston assembly. Install piston and cover. Press down on cover with Compressor (T74P-77028-A). Install snap ring. *See Fig. 27.*

8) Install spiral spring on overdrive servo piston assembly. Install piston and cover. Press down on cover with Compressor (T74P-77028-A). Install snap ring. *See Fig. 27.*

9) Install intermediate servo apply lever and shaft into case. Install complete forward clutch and high clutch assemblies.

FORD MOTOR CO. A4LD (Cont.)

Fig. 25: Clutch Replacing Guide Used to Install One-Way Clutch Inner Race

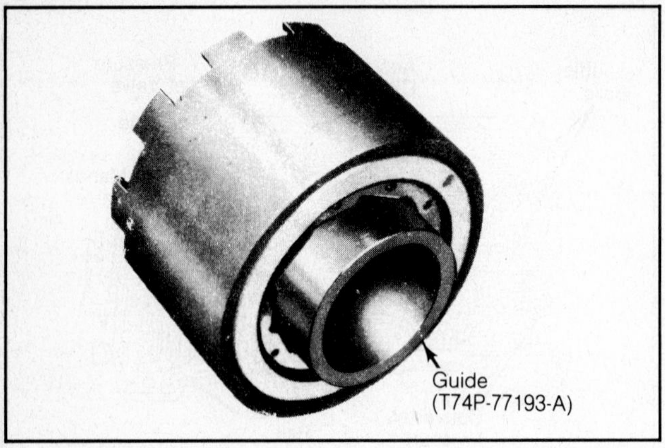

Fig. 26: Replacing Low-Reverse Servo Assembly

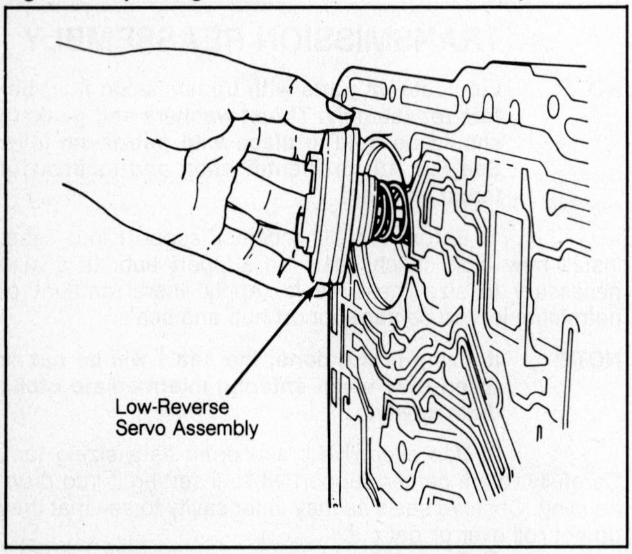

Fig. 27: Tool Set-Up for Servo Snap Ring Installation

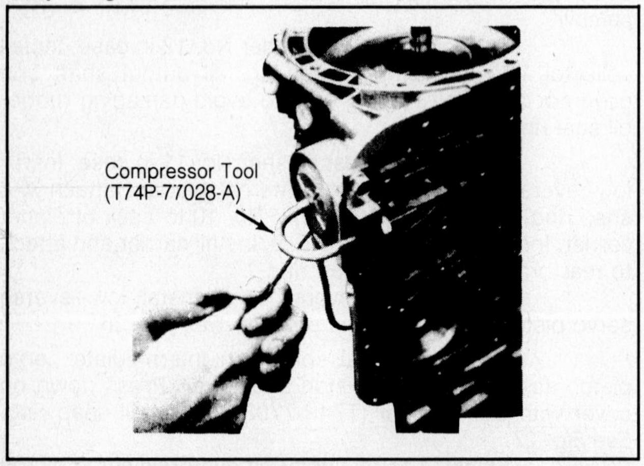

10) Turn transmission so output shaft points downward. Install intermediate band and apply strut. Install intermediate band anchor strut.

11) Remove center support from overdrive drum and position correct No. 4 selective washer on rear of center support using petroleum jelly. Correct No. 4 thrust washer is determined by measuring distance (A) between thrust washer surfaces of overdrive center support and intermediate brake drum. Transmission rear end play is .012-.022" (.30-.54 mm). Reuse original washer or replace with same size as original if transmission rear end play is okay.

SELECTIVE THRUST WASHER NO. 4

Identification Number	Distance (A) Inch (mm)	Thickness Inch (mm)
"1"	.067-.074 (1.70-1.88)	.053-.055 (1.35-1.40)
"2"	.075-.082 (1.90-2.08)	.061-.063 (1.55-1.60)
"3"	.083-.090 (2.10-2.29)	.069-.071 (1.75-1.80)
"4"	.091-.098 (2.31-2.49)	.077-.079 (1.95-2.00)
"5"	.099-.106 (2.51-2.69)	.085-.087 (2.15-2.20)

12) Insert input shaft (short splines down) through center and into splines in forward clutch cylinder. Carefully place center support into case, but do not seat it into intermediate brake drum. Be sure it is square with case and note location of 5mm Allen bolt retainer nut.

13) DO NOT apply any pressure to center support. Gently "wiggle" input shaft allowing center support to slide into intermediate brake drum using its own weight. Perform this operation until support is fully seated. Position No. 3 thrust washer on top of center support.

14) Install large snap ring to retain center support in position with taper of snap ring towards front of transmission. Ends of snap ring should be positioned in wide shallow cavity located in five o'clock postion. Install 5 mm Allen head bolt that retains center support to case.

15) Install sun gear and support into overdrive planet assembly and one-way clutch. Take care to center needle bearing race inside of planetary. Be sure it stays centered and positioned with extruded lip in upward position (toward sun gear).

16) Install overdrive planet assembly and one-way clutch into case. Install overdrive drum assembly. Install overdrive bracket, apply lever and shaft. Install overdrive band and apply strut. Install anchor strut.

17) Verify that needle bearing race in overdrive planetary is centered and overdrive clutch is fully seated. Place No. 1 selective washer on top of overdrive clutch drum and temporarily install pump assembly into case. Be sure that it is fully seated in case. Pump body must be below level of case gasket surface. Check transmission end play. See TRANSMISSION END PLAY CHECK in TRANSMISSION DISASSEMBLY section.

NOTE: Check for damaged or missing front pump support seal. Replace if necessary.

18) Position separator plate on converter housing. *See Fig. 30*. Place 2 pump gears into pump housing. The inside edge of small gear has a chamfer on one side. This chamfer must be positioned toward front of transmission. The larger gear has a dimple on one side which must be positioned towards rear of transmission. Position pump assembly onto separator plate and converter housing. Install bolts finger tight.

FORD MOTOR CO. A4LD (Cont.)

Fig. 28: Valve Body Assembly

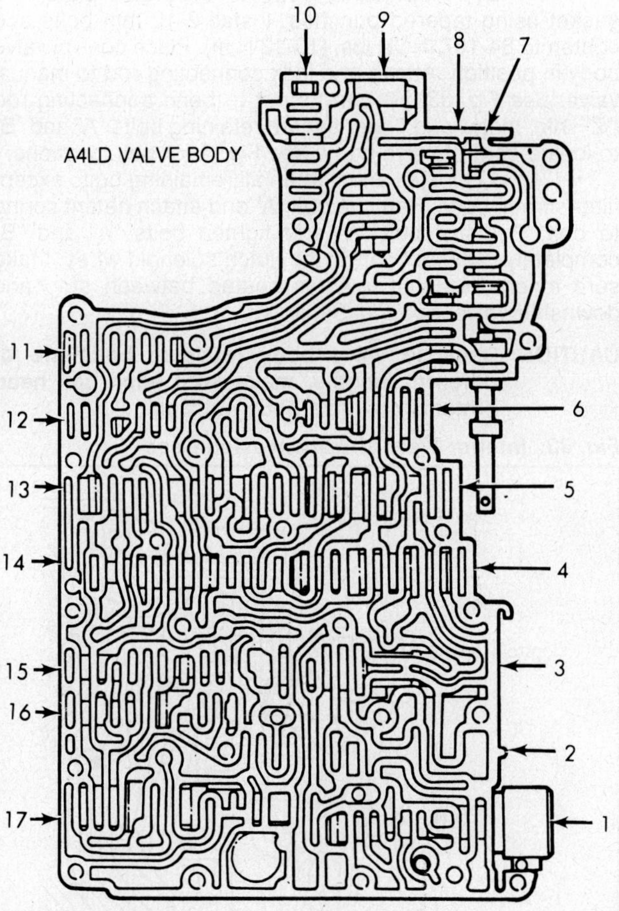

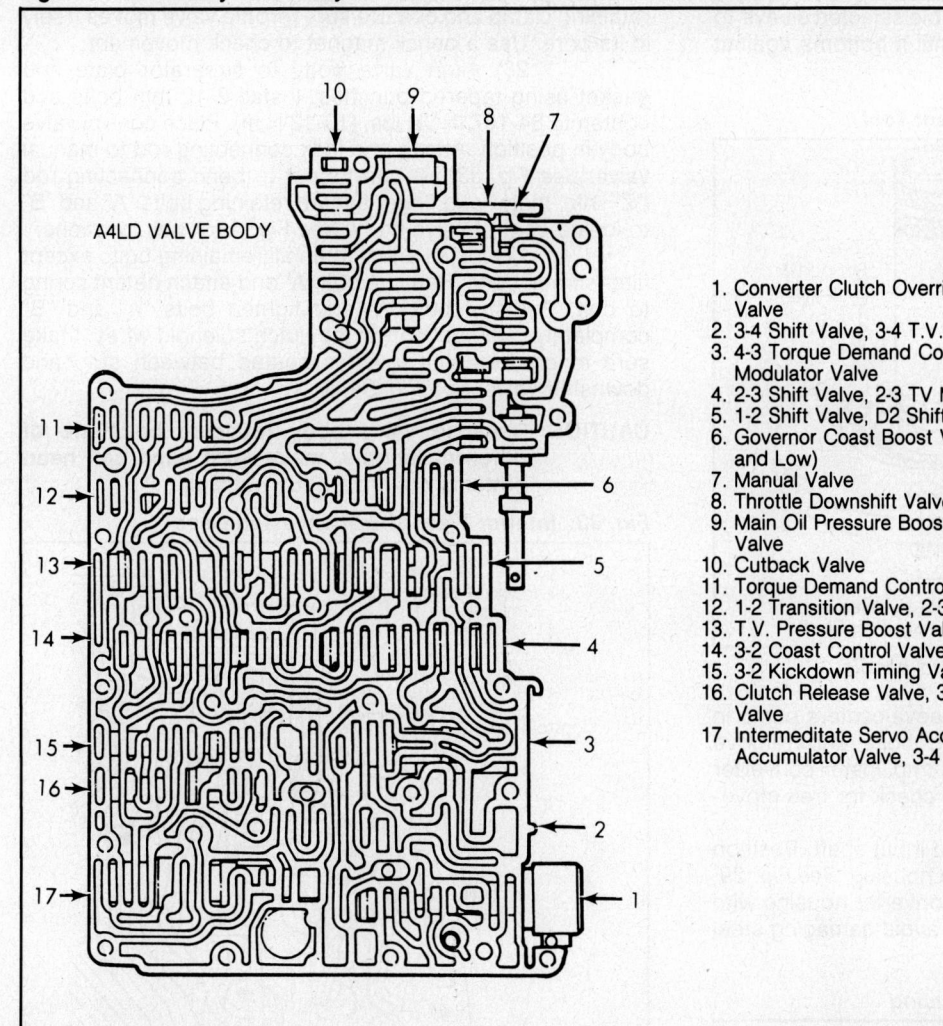

1. Converter Clutch Override Solenoid, Converter Clutch Control Valve
2. 3-4 Shift Valve, 3-4 T.V. Modulator Valve
3. 4-3 Torque Demand Control Valve, Converter Clutch T.V. Modulator Valve
4. 2-3 Shift Valve, 2-3 TV Modulator Valve
5. 1-2 Shift Valve, D2 Shift Valve
6. Governor Coast Boost Valve, Line Pressure Coast Boost Valve (2 and Low)
7. Manual Valve
8. Throttle Downshift Valve (Kickdown)
9. Main Oil Pressure Booster Valve, Main Oil Pressure Regulator Valve
10. Cutback Valve
11. Torque Demand Control Valve
12. 1-2 Transition Valve, 2-3 Backout Valve, Orifice Control Valve
13. T.V. Pressure Boost Valve
14. 3-2 Coast Control Valve
15. 3-2 Kickdown Timing Valve
16. Clutch Release Valve, 3-2 Intermediate Servo Release Control Valve
17. Intermeditate Servo Accumulator Valve, Overdrive Servo Accumulator Valve, 3-4 Backout Valve

Fig. 29: Installing Pump Into Case

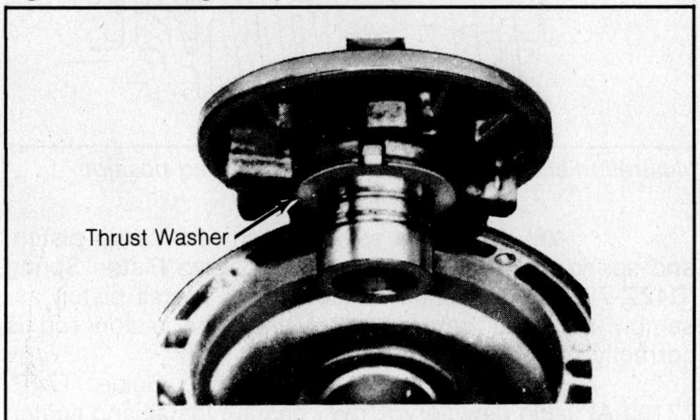

NOTE: The rough appearance of pump stator casting is intentional and is not a flaw. Function of pump is not affected, and it should not be replaced due to this appearance.

19) Front pump alignment requires special Pump Aligner (T74P-77103-X). Aligner consists of 4 special sleeves and handle. Each sleeve has same O.D. but different I.D. *See Fig. 31*.

Fig. 30: Correct Positioning of Adapter Plate on Housing

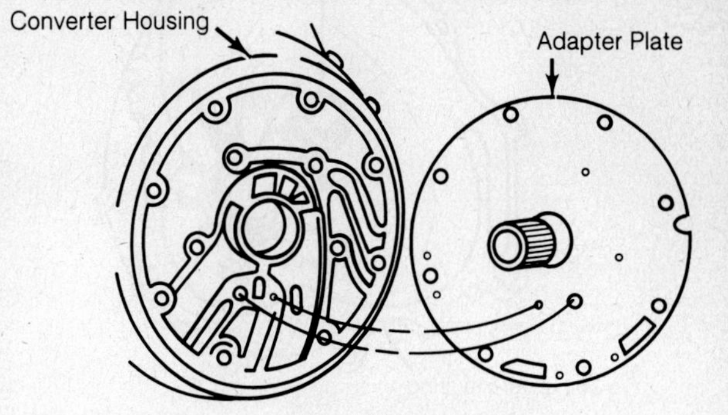

CAUTION: As this measurement is critical, make sure that sleeve gauging surfaces are in good condition. Damage to sleeve gauging surfaces may result in incorrect pump-to-converter housing alignment. Pump seal leakage, pump gear breakage, or bushing failure will occur.

FORD MOTOR CO. A4LD (Cont.)

20) Select smallest I.D. sleeve which will fit completely over support shaft. Assemble selected sleeve to handle. Slide tool down over shaft until it bottoms against pump.

Fig. 31: Special Front Pump Alignment Tool

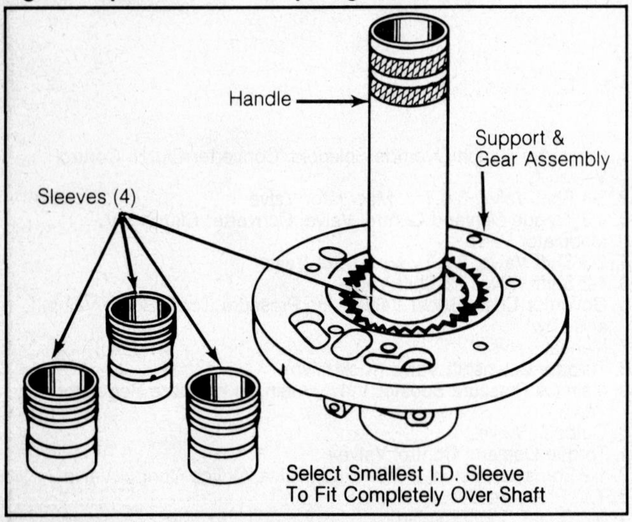

T74P-77103-X consists of 4 sleeves and handle.

21) Outside diameter of sleeve centers pump in converter housing. Tighten retaining bolts and remove centering tool. Install input shaft into pump. Install converter into pump gears. Rotate converter to check for free movement.

22) Remove converter and input shaft. Position selected No. 1 thrust washer to pump housing. *See Fig. 29.* Install new "O" ring. Carefully install converter housing with pump using new gasket. Use care to avoid damaging steel oil seals.

Fig. 32: Front View of Converter Housing

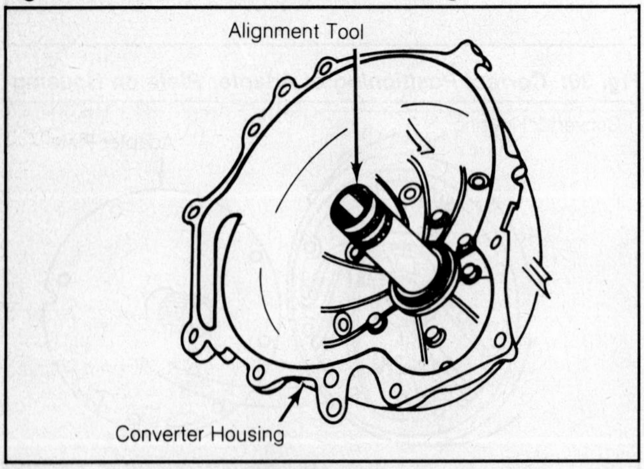

Illustration shows position of pump alignment tools.

23) Install bolts and tighten. Be sure to use new aluminum washers. Adjust overdrive and intermediate bands. Perform air pressure tests to ensure proper transmission operation as described under AIR PRESSURE CHECKS in this article.

24) Install shift lever oil seal using Shift Lever Seal Replacer (74P-77498-A). Install internal shift linkage and centering pin. Install "O" ring, kickdown lever and 13 mm nut. Install converter clutch solenoid connector.

25) Install throttle valve, vacuum diaphragm, retaining clamp and bolt. Be sure throttle valve moves freely in its bore. Use a pencil magnet to check movement.

26) Align valve body to separator plate and gasket using tapered punches. Install 2 10 mm bolts and tighten to 84-107 INCH lbs. (10-12 N.m). Place control valve body in position. Attach and lock connecting rod to manual valve. *See Fig. 33.* Be careful not to bend connecting rod ("Z" link). Install and finger tighten retaining bolts "A" and "B" to locate control valve body. *See Fig. 5* for bolt locations.

27) Install and tighten all remaining bolts except filter screen bolts. Remove bolt "A" and attach detent spring to bolt. Reinstall bolt "A" and tighten bolts "A" and "B" completely. Connect converter clutch solenoid wires. Make sure inner downshift lever is seated between stop and downshift valve. *See Fig. 34.*

CAUTION: Because valve body retaining bolts are of different lengths, make sure each bolt head bottoms on valve body housing.

Fig. 33: Interior View of Transmission Case

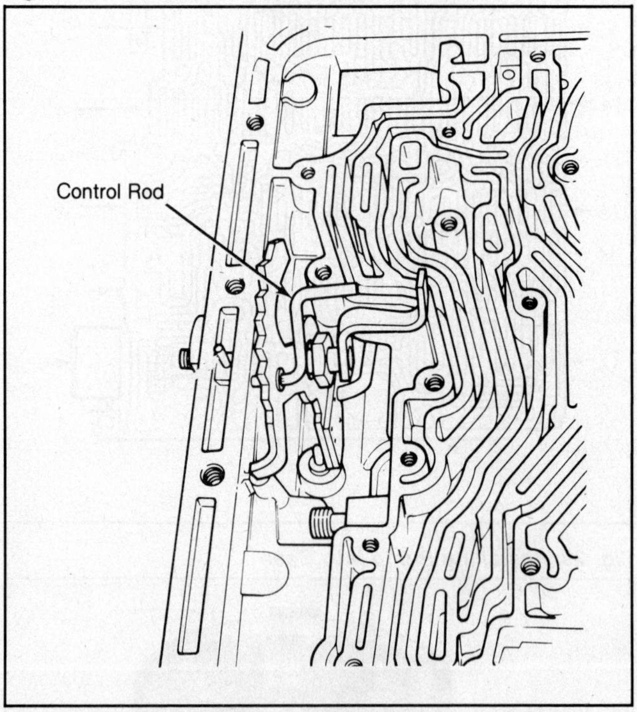

Illustration shows valve body installation and position.

28) Assemble servo piston rod, servo piston, and spring. Install additional reverse servo Piston Spring (D4ZZ-7D031-A) to check piston travel. Install piston assembly into rear servo bore. Make sure piston rod is correctly seated in reverse band apply end.

29) Install servo rod Selecting Guide (T74P-77190-A) using new servo cover gasket. Install and tighten 3 retaining bolts (servo cover bolts are not long enough to attach tool to case; use three valve body retaining bolts).

30) Tighten servo tool adjusting screw to 36 INCH lbs. (4 N.m). Install dial indicator on case. Position indicator tip on one of 3 servo piston pads accessible through cut-out of tool. Zero dial indicator. *See Fig. 35.*

31) Back out tool adjusting screw until servo piston bottoms out on tool. Record distance servo piston moved. If servo piston travel is .120-.220" (3.05-5.59 mm),

FORD MOTOR CO. A4LD (Cont.)

Fig. 34: Bottom of Transmission Case

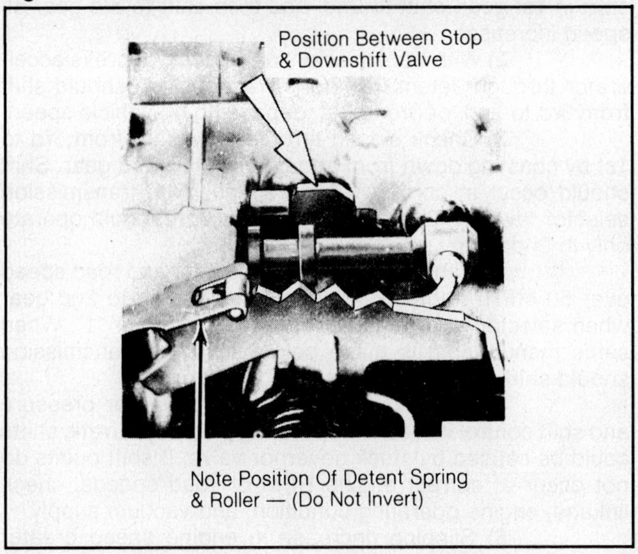

Illustration shows inner downshift lever position.

Fig. 35: Tool Set-Up for Rear Servo Pin Selection

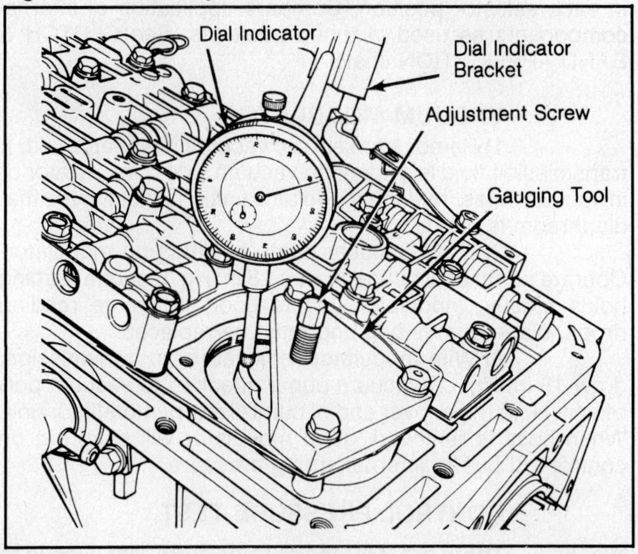

servo piston rod is acceptable. If piston travel is greater than .220" (5.59 mm), use next longer servo piston and rod.

NOTE: **Servo piston rods are available in 3 sizes and identified by grooves on rod. Rod sizes and I.D. are as follows: 2.085-2.112" (1 groove), 1.986-2.014" (no groove), and 1.888-1.915" (2 grooves).**

32) If travel is less than .120" (3.05 mm), use next shorter piston and rod. Install correct servo piston and rod. Recheck piston travel. Remove servo adjusting tool and additional reverse servo spring (only used for checking piston travel).

33) Reinstall servo assembly. Install servo cover and bolts. Install oil pan, using new gasket. Tighten pan bolts to specifications in 2 steps. Install neutral start switch. Install input shaft and torque converter.

34) Install parking pawl and its return spring in extension housing and preload. Using new gasket, install extension housing. Make sure to correctly seat operating parking rod in extension guide cup. Install and tighten bolts. Replace extension housing oil seal and bushing.

Fig. 36: Rear Servo Piston Travel Measurement

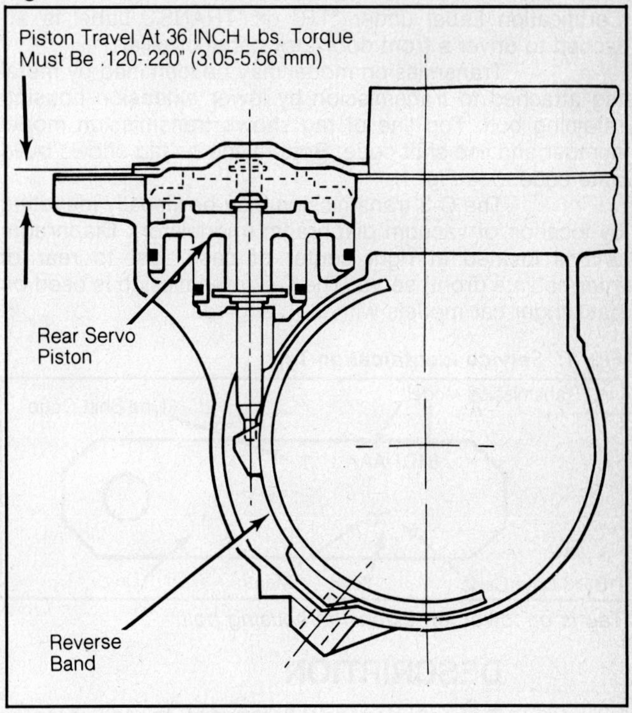

TIGHTENING SPECIFICATIONS

Application	Ft. Lbs. (N.m)
Converter Housing-to-Case	27-39 (37-53)
Converter Housing-to-Engine	28-38 (38-52)
Converter-to-Flywheel	20-34 (27-46)
Extension Housing-to-Case	27-39 (37-53)
Intermediate Band Adjusting Screw Lock Nut	35-45 (47-61)
Overdrive Band Adjusting Screw Lock Nut	35-45 (47-61)
Manual Lever Inner Nut	30-40 (41-54)
	INCH lbs.
Center Support-to-Case	71-97 (8-11)
Downshift Lever Outer Nut	84-132 (10-15)
Separator Plate-to-Valve Body	84-107 (10-12)
Governor-to-Collector Body	84-120 (10-14)
Oil Pan-to-Case	60-120 (7-14)
Oil Cooler Line or By-Pass Tube-to Connector	84-120 (10-14)
Neutral Switch-to-Case	84-120 (10-14)
Pump-to-Converter Housing	84-120 (10-14)
Rear Servo Cover-to-Case	80-115 (9-13)
Valve Body-to-Case	71-97 (8-11)
Vaccum Diaphragm Retaining Clip to Case	80-106 (9-12)

FORD MOTOR CO. C-3

Capri, Cougar, LTD, Marquis, Merkur, Mustang, Thunderbird

IDENTIFICATION

The C-3 automatic transmission is identified by code letter "V", which is shown on lower line of Vehicle Certification Label under "TR" or "TRANS". Label is attached to driver's front door lock panel or pillar.

Transmission model may be identified by metal tag attached to transmission by lower extension housing retaining bolt. Top line of tag shows transmission model number and line shift code. Bottom line on tag shows build date code. *See Fig. 1.*

The C-3 transmission may be visually identified by location of vacuum diaphragm (modulator). Diaphragm unit is located at right center of case, just to rear of intermediate (front) servo. The C-3 transmission is used on passenger car models with 2.3L engines.

Fig. 1: Service Identification Tag

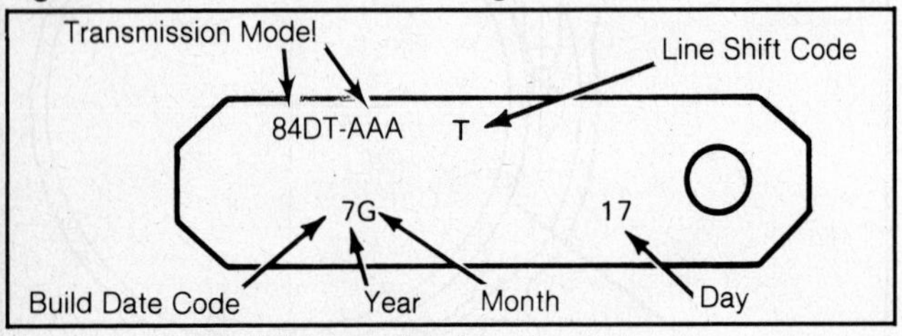

Tag is on lower left extension housing bolt.

DESCRIPTION

Transmission has 3 forward speeds. Manual selection of 1st and 2nd gears is provided. Transmission consists of torque converter, planetary gear train, 2 multiple disc clutches, one-way clutch, and hydraulic control system. Only front band adjustment is required.

LUBRICATION & ADJUSTMENT

See appropriate AUTOMATIC TRANSMISSION SERVICING article in DOMESTIC GENERAL SERVICING Section.

TROUBLE SHOOTING

See appropriate AUTOMATIC TRANSMISSION TROUBLE SHOOTING article in DOMESTIC GENERAL SERVICING section.

TESTING

Check fluid level and correct if necessary. Use initial road test to verify malfunction of transmission. Make sure that engine appears to be running properly. If transmission problems occur on initial road test, check adjustments and fluid levels.

ROAD TEST

1) If vehicle is not so equipped, attach tachometer to engine. Check minimum throttle upshifts in "D" position. See SHIFT SPEEDS tables. Transmission should start in 1st gear, shift to 2nd, and then shift to 3rd gear as speed increases.

2) With transmission in 3rd gear, depress accelerator through detent (to floor). Transmission should shift from 3rd to 2nd, or 3rd to 1st, depending on vehicle speed.

3) Check closed throttle downshift from 3rd to 1st by coasting down from about 30 MPH in 3rd gear. Shift should occur at correct vehicle speed. With transmission selector lever in "2" position, transmission should operate only in 2nd gear.

4) With transmission in 3rd gear and road speed over 50 MPH, transmission should downshift to 2nd gear when selector lever is moved from "D" to "2" or "1". When same manual shift is made below 25 MPH, transmission should shift from 2nd or 3rd to 1st.

5) Step **1)** will determine if governor pressure and shift control valves are operating properly. Erratic shifts could be caused by stuck governor valve. If shift points do not occur at correct engine RPM or road speeds, check linkage, engine operating condition, and vacuum supply.

6) Slipping (increase in engine speed greater than increase in road speed) in gear usually indicates clutch or band problems. Specific clutch or band that is slipping can usually be determined by noting transmission operation in each selector position. Compare application of internal components as used in those positions. See CLUTCH & BAND APPLICATION chart.

VACUUM MODULATOR

1) Remove hose from vacuum modulator unit. If transmission fluid is evident on vacuum side of modulator or in vacuum hose, replace modulator unit. Fluid indicates that diaphragm is broken.

2) Hook vacuum pump to fitting on modulator. Operate pump until gauge shows 18 in. Hg. If gauge reading holds steady, modulator unit is good. If gauge reading drops, diaphragm is bad and must be replaced.

3) With modulator removed from transmission, draw 18 in. Hg. on vacuum pump attached to vacuum port of unit. Hold finger over end of control rod of modulator unit. When hose is removed, good modulator will push out on control rod due to internal spring pressure.

CONTROL PRESSURE TEST

NOTE: There are 2 methods to perform test. One is to use engine vacuum, the other is using a hand operated vacuum pump. Governor can be checked at same time control pressure test is performed and in same manner.

ENGINE VACUUM PRESSURE

1) If vacuum modulator is working properly and downshift linkage is adjusted correctly, all shifts should occur within certain road speed limits. See SHIFT SPEEDS tables. If shifts do not occur at proper points or slipping occurs during shifts, check engine vacuum, vacuum supply, and vacuum unit for possible cause of problem.

2) Connect tachometer to engine. Connect vacuum gauge to manifold vacuum line, using "T" fitting at modulator hookup. Attach pressure gauge to control pressure outlet on transmission case. *See Fig. 3.*

CAUTION: Pressure gauge affects quality of transmission shifting. When gauge is installed in transmission port, DO NOT accelerate or decelerate rapidly as transmission failure could occur.

FORD MOTOR CO. C-3 (Cont.)

Fig. 2: Cutaway View of C-3 Automatic Transmission Assembly

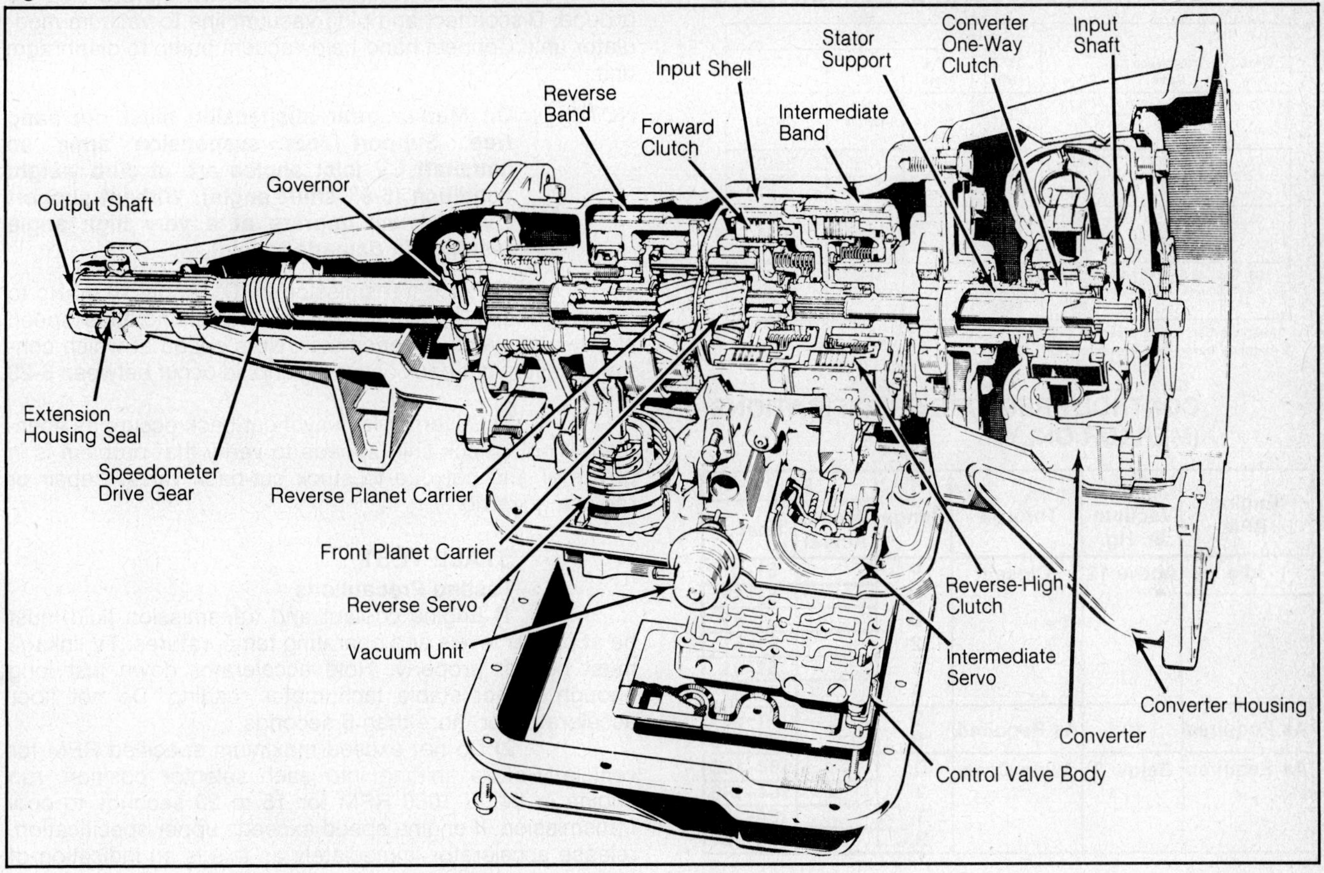

Fig. 3: Control Pressure Outlet Location

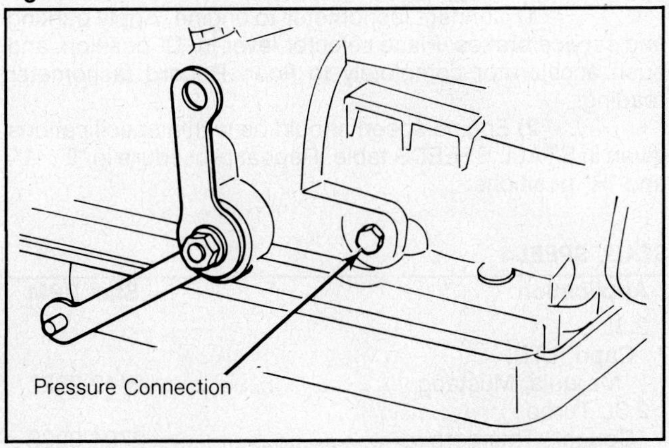

3) Apply parking brake. Start engine. On vehicle equipped with vacuum brake release, apply service brakes. Parking brake automatically releases when transmission is moved to "D".

4) Adjust engine idle speed to correct RPM. If engine idle cannot be brought within limits, check throttle and downshift linkages for binding. Check for vacuum leaks in hoses and tubes if linkage is correctly in place. Check vacuum units such as power brake booster for leaks.

VACUUM PUMP PROCEDURE

Disconnect and plug engine vacuum line from modulator. Hook up vacuum pump to unit. Apply parking and service brakes. Start engine and apply 15 in. Hg. vacuum to diaphragm. Select all ranges of transmission. Read and record control pressures.

VACUUM SUPPLY TEST

1) To check supply to vacuum modulator, disconnect vacuum line at modulator and connect to a vacuum gauge. Vacuum reading at gauge should be steady with engine idling. Reading must be acceptable for altitude where test is being done. If vacuum reading is correct at idle, accelerate engine rapidly and release throttle immediately. Vacuum reading must drop rapidly during acceleration.

2) Vacuum should return as soon as throttle is released. If vacuum reading does not respond correctly, check lines for restriction or plugging. Also make sure that vacuum line is not hooked up to reservoir.

CONTROL PRESSURE RESULTS

Compare recorded control pressures to control pressures listed in table. See CONTROL PRESSURE SPECIFICATIONS table. If control pressures are outside of specified ranges, use following list to determine cause of trouble:

High at Idle in All Ranges

Check engine EGR system, vacuum modulator unit, and manifold vacuum line. Check throttle valve, control rod, and regulator boost valves for sticking.

Low at Idle in All Ranges

Check engine EGR system. Check fluid level. Check for restricted intake screen or filter. Check for loose

Automatic Transmissions

FORD MOTOR CO. C-3 (Cont.)

CONTROL PRESSURE SPECIFICATIONS

				IDLE		
Trans. Type	Transmission Model	Range	16" & Above	15" & Above	10"	W.O.T. Stall Thru Detent
C3	86 DT-AAA/ ABA/ACA/ ADA	*D,2,1 R P,N		50-60 66-78 50-60	74-94 129-148	165-195 278-316
C3	86 DT-ACA/ ADA	@D,2,1 R P,N		50-60 66-78 50-60	53-75 94-116	144-177 244-282
C3	86 DT-AEA/ AFA/AGA AHA	*D,2,1 R P,N	51-61 67-82 51-61		70-90 123-143	180-222 302-330
C3	86 DT-AFA/ AHA	@D,2,1 R P,N	51-61 67-82 51-61		62-82 109-129	171-195 292-311

*Absolute barometric pressure (ABP) 29.0-30.0.
@Absolute barometric pressure (ABP) 24.0-25.0.

CONTROL PRESSURE SPECIFICATIONS (MERKUR ONLY)

Engine RPM	Manifold Vacuum In. Hg.	Throttle	Range	PSI Record Actual	PSI Spec.
Idle	Above 12	Closed	P		51-61
			N		51-61
			D		51-61
			2		51-61
			1		51-61
			R		67-82
As Required	10	As Required	D		51-90
			R		83-143
As Required	Below 3	Wide Open	D		164-188
			2		164-188
			1		164-188
			R		276-304

oil tubes. Check if valve body-to-case or regulator-to-case bolts are loose. Check for excessive leakage in oil pump, control valve body, and case. Check control pressure regulator valve for sticking.

Normal at Idle; Low at 10 in. Hg

Check vacuum modulator unit. Control rod or throttle valve stuck.

Normal at Idle and 10 in. Hg.; Low at 1 in. Hg

Check for excessive leakage, low pump capacity, or restricted oil pan screen.

Low in "P" or "N"

Check valve body.

Low in "D"

Check forward clutch.

Low in "2"

Check forward clutch and/or intermediate servo or clutch.

Low in "1"

Check forward clutch and/or reverse clutch and servo.

Low in "R"

Check reverse-direct clutch and/or reverse servo.

GOVERNOR PRESSURE TEST

CAUTION: Never exceed 60 MPH speedometer reading during governor pressure test. After each test, move selector lever to Neutral and run engine at 1000 RPM to cool transmission.

1) Raise vehicle until rear wheels are clear of ground. Disconnect and plug vacuum line to vacuum modulator unit. Connect hand-held vacuum pump to diaphragm unit.

NOTE: On Merkur, rear suspension must not hang free. Support rear suspension arms so halfshaft CV joint angles are at curb weight condition (5-9° shaft angle). Without support CV joint will operate at a very high angle resulting in damage to joint.

2) Place transmission in "D". Apply 10 in. Hg to diaphragm unit with no load on engine. Increase speed slowly and watch speedometer. Note speed at which control pressure cut-back occurs. It should occur between 6-20 MPH.

3) Governor is okay if cut-back occurs as specified. If not, check shift speeds to verify that problem is in governor and not due to stuck cut-back valve. Repair or replace governor.

STALL TEST

Testing Precautions

1) Engine coolant and transmission fluid must be at proper levels and operating temperatures. TV linkage must be set properly. Hold accelerator down just long enough to get stable tachometer reading. Do not floor accelerator for more than 5 seconds.

2) Do not exceed maximum specified RPM for vehicle. Before shifting into each selector position, run engine in "N" at 1000 RPM for 15 to 20 seconds to cool transmission. If engine speed exceeds upper specification, release accelerator immediately as this is an indication of clutch or band slippage.

Testing Procedure

1) Connect tachometer to engine. Apply parking and service brakes. Place selector lever in "D" position, and push accelerator completely to floor. Record tachometer reading.

2) Engine speed should be within specifications given in STALL SPEEDS table. Repeat procedure in "2", "1", and "R" positions.

STALL SPEEDS

Application	Stall RPM
2.3L	
Capri, LTD,	
Marquis, Mustang	2442-2827
2.3L Turbo	
Cougar, Thunderbird	2701-3222
Merkur	3000-3300

STALL TEST RESULTS

Low in All Ranges

Poor engine performance. Faulty torque converter stator one-way clutch.

High in All Ranges

General transmission problems are indicated. Perform control pressure tests.

High in "D" Only

Planetary one-way clutch faulty.

High in "D", "2" & "1"

Forward clutch faulty.

Automatic Transmissions

FORD MOTOR CO. C-3 (Cont.)

SHIFT SPEEDS (MPH)

NOTE: Figures given below are approximate. All shift speeds may vary somewhat due to production tolerances, rear axle ratio, or emission control equipment.

MODEL 86-DT-7000-AEA & AFA

Throttle	Range	Shift	OPS-RPM	COLUMN NUMBER 1	COLUMN NUMBER 2
Closed (Above 17″ Vacuum)	D	1-2	560-800	12-17	
	D	2-3	750-1180	16-25	
	D	3-2	470-800	10-17	
	D	2-1	235-560	5-12	
	1	2-1	1360-1830	29-39	
To Detent (Torque Demand)	D	1-2	1640-1930	35-41	
	D	2-3	2350-2630	50-56	
	D	3-2	1450-1740	31-37	
Through Detent (W.O.T.)	D	1-2	1880-2160	40-46	
	D	2-3	3100-3380	66-72	
	D	3-2	2730-3000	58-64	
	D	3-1, 2-1	1315-1690	28-36	

Axle Ratio	TIRE SIZE	USE COLUMN NUMBER		
		3.45		
	225/60VR15	1		
	220/55R390	1		

MODEL 86 DT-7000-AAA, ABA, ACA, ADA

Throttle	Range	Shift	OPS — R.P.M.	Column Number 1	Column Number 2
Closed (Above 17″ Vacuum)	D	1-2	445-670	10-15	9-14
	D	2-3	750-1070	17-24	16-23
	D	3-2	490-760	11-17	10-16
	D	2-1	220-490	5-11	4-10
	1	2-1	1425-1870	32-42	30-40
To Detent (Torque Demand)	D	1-2	1460-1735	33-39	31-37
	D	2-3	1960-2225	44-50	42-47
	D	3-2	1600-1870	36-42	34-40
Through Detent (W.O.T.)	D	1-2	1915-2180	43-49	41-46
	D	2-3	2980-3250	67-73	63-69
	D	3-2	2800-3070	63-69	60-65
	D	3-1 2-1	1600-1870	36-42	34-40

Axle Ratio	Tire Size	Use Column Number		
		3.27	3.45	
	P195/75R14	1	2	
	P205/70R14	1	2	
	P205/70VR14	1	2	
	225/60VR15	1	2	

MERKUR

SHIFT	MPH	OUTPUT SHAFT RPM
1-2 minimum 10-15 in. Hg.	12-16	580-790
2-3 minimum 10-15 in. Hg.	17-24	845-1215
1-2 to detent 6 psi boost pressure	35-41	1740-2060
2-3 to detent 6 psi boost pressure	50-56	2480-2800
1-2 thru detent (WOT) 10 psi boost pressure	41-47	2038-2325
2-3 thru detent (WOT) 10 psi boost pressure	65-71	3275-3560
3-2 torque demand lockout 1 psi boost pressure	33-39	1640-1955
3-2 thru detent (kickdown) max. lockout 5 psi boost pressure	57-63	2850-3170
3-1 or 2-1 thru detent (kickdown) max. lockout 3 psi boost pressure	28-36	1425-1795
3-2 closed throttle coast out	11-17	530-845
2-1 closed throttle coast out	8-15	425-740
2-1 manual low closed throttle coast out	30-41	1530-2060

Automatic Transmissions

FORD MOTOR CO. C-3 (Cont.)

Fig. 4: C-3 Automatic Transmission Hydraulic Circuits Diagram

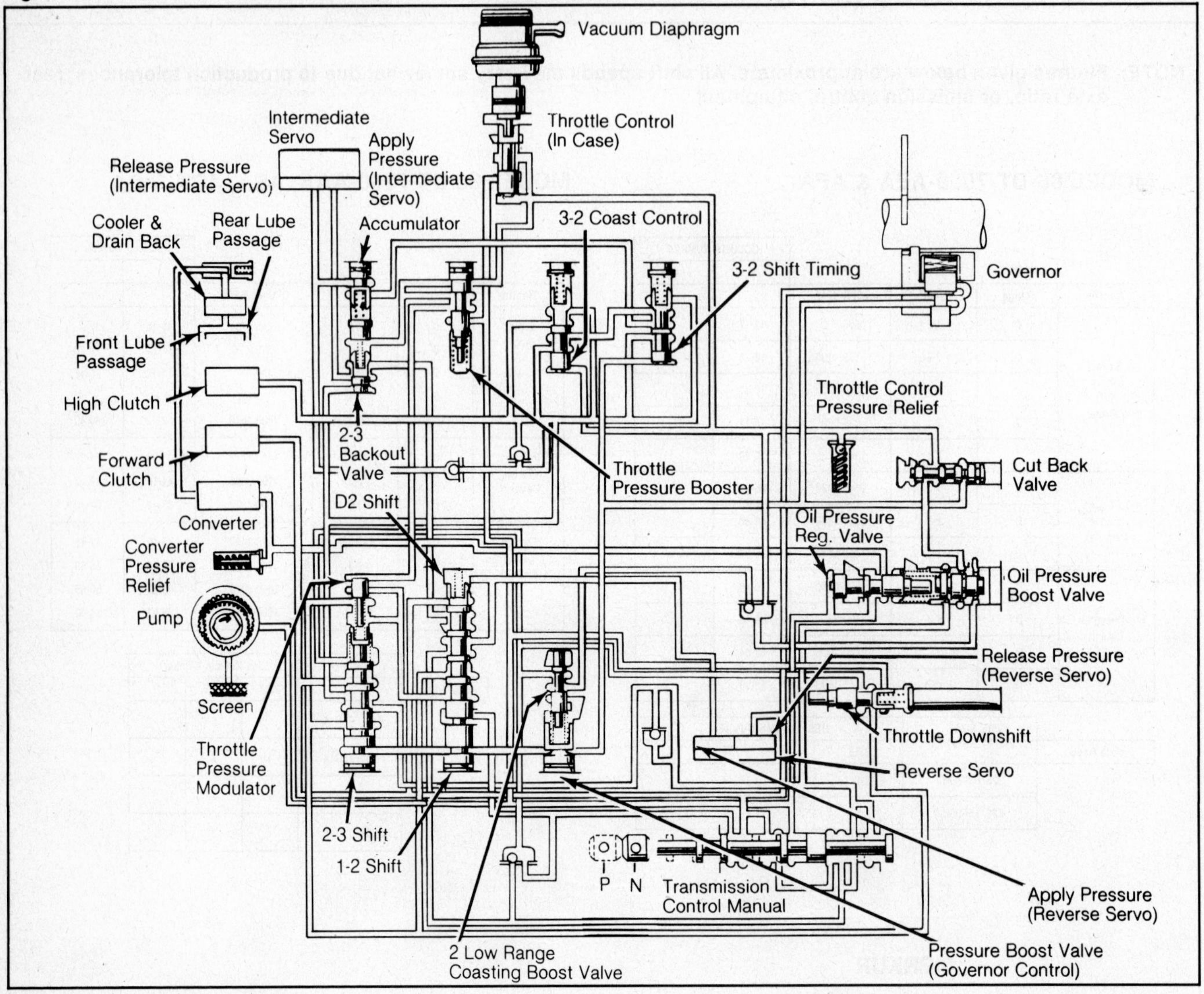

CLUTCH AND BAND APPLICATION (ELEMENTS IN USE)

Selector Lever Position	Intermediate Band	Low-Reverse Band	Forward Clutch	Reverse-Direct Clutch	One-Way Clutch
D - DRIVE					
First			Applied		Applied
Second	Applied		Applied		
Third			Applied	Applied	
2 - INTERMEDIATE					
Second	Applied		Applied		
1 - LOW					
First		Applied	Applied		
R - REVERSE		Applied		Applied	

NEUTRAL OR PARK – All clutches, brakes, and bands released and/or ineffective.

Fig. 5: Bottom View of Transmission Case

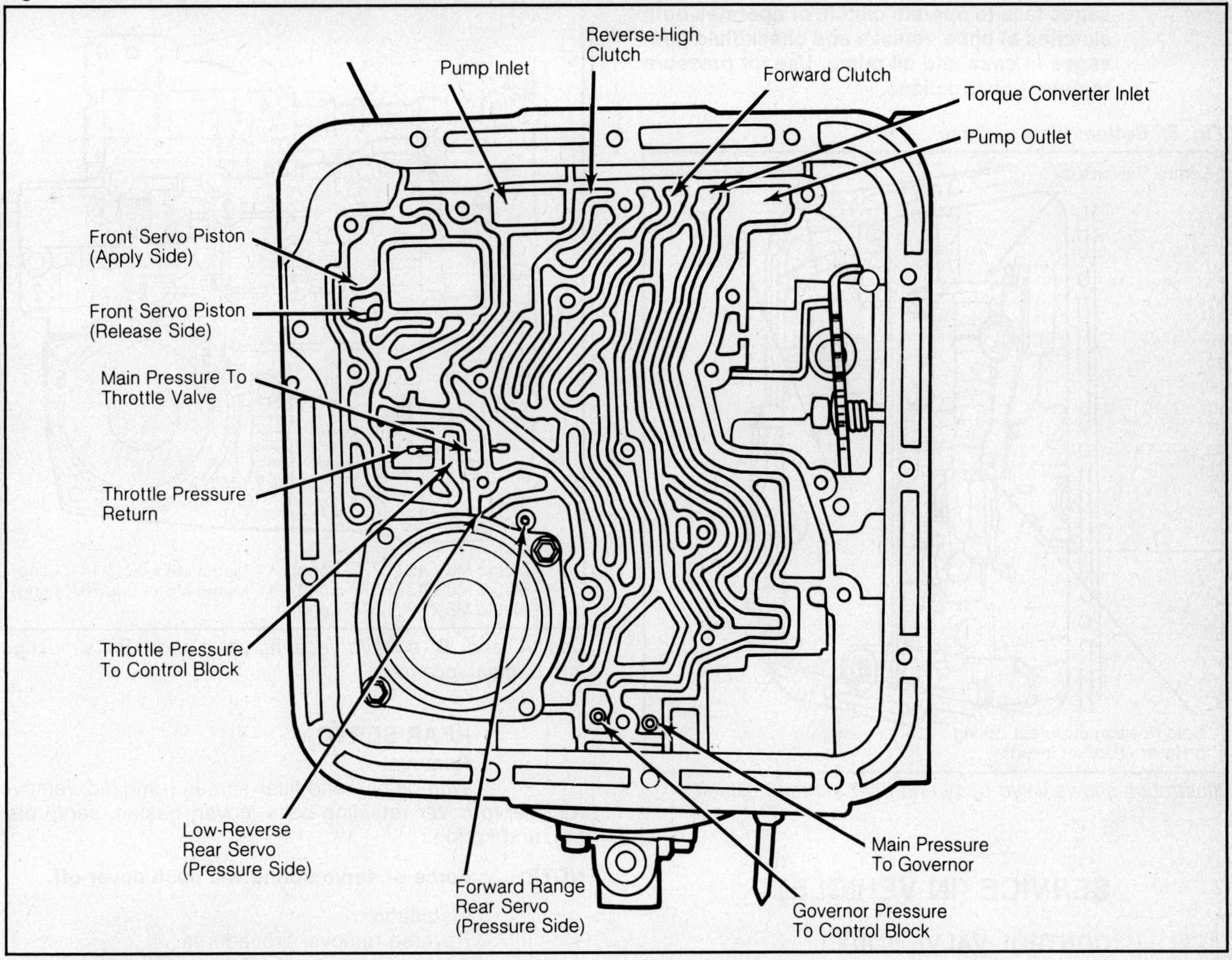

Note points for air testing of clutches and bands.

High in "2" Only
Intermediate band or servo faulty.

High in "1" Only
Low/Reverse band or servo faulty.

High in "R" Only
Reverse-Direct clutch faulty. Low/Reverse band faulty.

AIR PRESSURE CHECKS

1) Condition of "No Drive" (no movement of output shaft) can exist, even with correct transmission fluid pressure. Inoperative clutches or bands may cause this problem.

2) Inoperative units can be located through series of checks by substituting air pressure for fluid pressure to determine location of malfunction.

3) Loosen oil pan bolts and allow transmission fluid to drain. Remove oil pan and control valve body. Apply air at points noted in *Fig. 5.* Minimum of 40 psi or maximum of 90 psi is needed to pressure check transmission. Check unit operation as follows:

Forward Clutch
Apply air pressure into forward clutch passage. Dull thud can be heard when clutch piston is applied. Movement of piston can be felt by placing finger tips on input shell if no thud heard.

Governor
Apply some air pressure into the control pressure-to-governor passage. Listen for sharp clicking or whistling noise indicating governor valve movement.

Reverse-Direct Clutch
Apply air pressure into reverse-direct clutch passage. Dull thud can be heard when clutch piston is applied. Movement of piston can be felt by placing finger tips on clutch drum.

Intermediate Servo
1) Hold air nozzle in intermediate servo apply passage. Operation of servo is indicated by tightening of intermediate band around drum.

2) While continuing to apply air pressure at servo apply passage, apply air pressure to intermediate servo release passage. Intermediate servo should then release band against pressure in apply passage.

Low-Reverse Servo
Apply air pressure to low-reverse servo apply passage. Low-reverse band should tighten around drum if servo is operating properly.

NOTE: **If air pressure applied to either clutch passages fails to operate clutch, or operates both clutches at once, remove and check fluid passages in case and oil pump. Use air pressure to detect obstructions.**

Fig. 6: Bottom View of Case

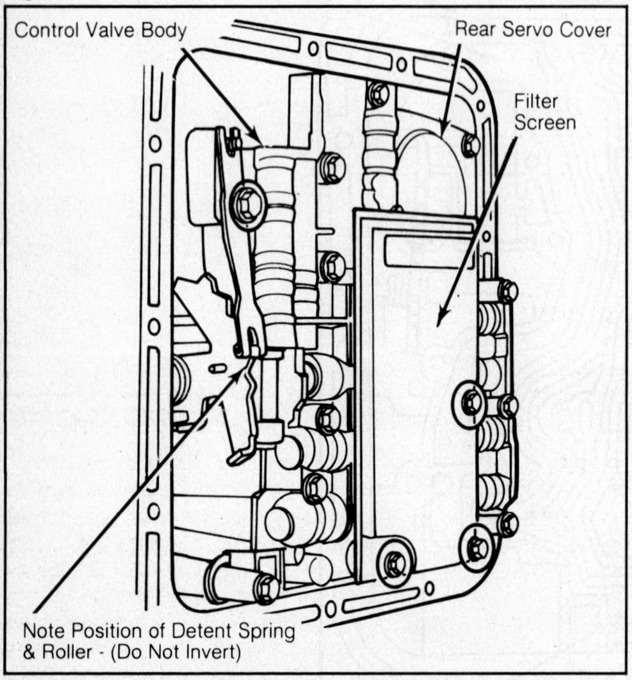

Illustration shows valve body and filter screen position

SERVICE (IN VEHICLE)

CONTROL VALVE BODY

Removal

Remove oil pan, filter screen, and gasket. Remove rear servo cover and gasket. Remove valve body retaining bolts. Carefully ease valve body from case while unlocking and detaching selector lever connecting rod.

NOTE: **Note size and location of valve body retaining bolts. Bolts are of different sizes and must be replaced in proper position at reassembly.**

Installation

1) Attach and lock selector lever connecting rod ("Z" link) to manual valve. Ease control valve body to case. Install and finger tighten valve body locating bolts "A" and "B". *See Fig. 7.* Install and tighten remaining valve body retaining bolts (except for filter screen). Remove bolt "A" and install detent spring, then reassemble and tighten bolts "A" and "B".

2) Install rear servo cover with new gasket. Clean filter screen. Install filter screen and gasket. DO NOT use spacers when installing screen and gasket, as was done on former models. To do this would reduce control pressure and malfunction or failure will result.

3) Install oil pan using new gasket. Tighten pan bolts evenly. Lower vehicle and fill transmission with 3 quarts of fluid. Start engine and add fluid as necessary. Check for leaks.

Fig. 7: Location of Valve Body Retaining Bolts

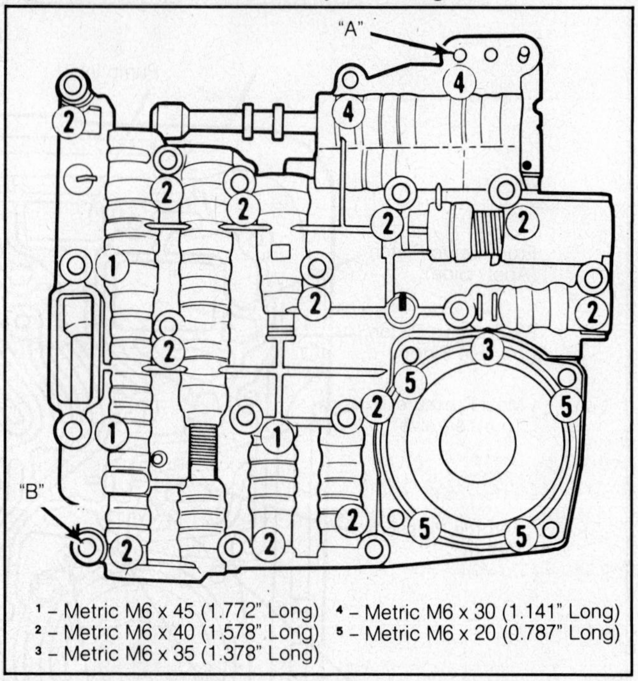

Use "A" and "B" bolts for locating valve body. Bolts must go into original locations.

REAR SERVO

Removal

With oil pan and filter screen removed, remove rear servo cover retaining bolts, cover, gasket, servo piston, and spring.

NOTE: **Force of servo spring will push cover off.**

Installation

Reverse removal procedures.

Fig. 8: Bottom View of Transmission Case

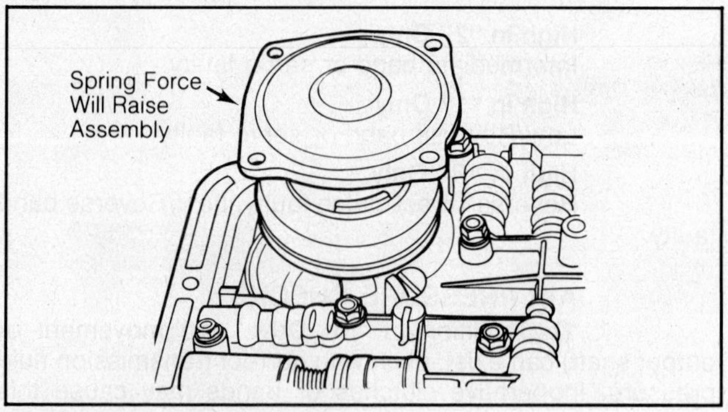

Illustration shows rear servo separated.

EXTENSION HOUSING REAR SEAL & BUSHING

Removal

1) Raise and support vehicle. Mark propeller shaft end yoke and rear axle companion flange for reassembly reference. Remove propeller shaft.

2) Remove extension housing rear oil seal and bushing using Pullers (T71P-7657-A for seal and T77L-7697-E for bushing). *See Fig. 9.*

Fig. 9: Removing Extension Housing Oil Seal & Bushing

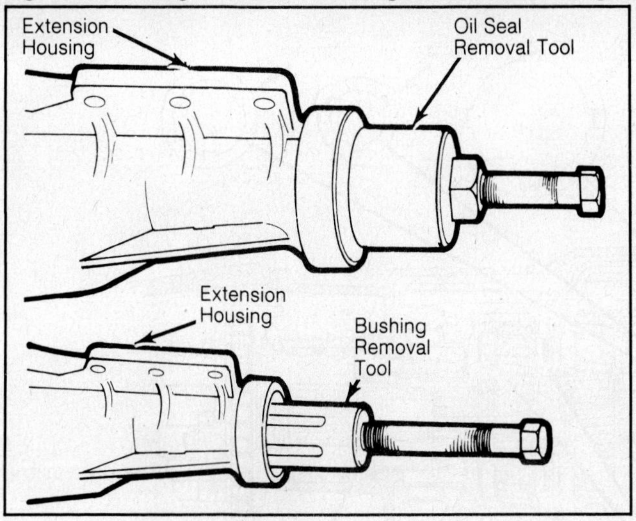

Installation

Check sealing surface of yoke for scoring. Replace if scoring found. Check housing counterbore for burrs and remove with crocus cloth (if necessary). Drive new bushing and oil seal into extension housing using Drivers (T77L-7697-F for bushing and T74P-77052-A for oil seal). Install propeller shaft, aligning reference marks made at removal.

EXTENSION HOUSING

Removal

1) Raise and support vehicle. Mark propeller shaft for installation reference. Remove shaft. Disconnect speedometer cable from extension housing. Support transmission with jack.

2) Remove rear support-to-crossmember bolts. Raise transmission slightly and remove rear support from extension housing.

3) Loosen extension housing retaining bolts and allow transmission fluid to drain. Remove bolts and slide extension housing off output shaft.

Installation

Soak new gasket in clean transmission fluid for 5 minutes. Position extension housing on case. Pay special attention to correctly aligning parking pawl actuating rod. Install and tighten bolts. To complete installation, reverse removal procedures.

GOVERNOR

Removal

Remove extension housing as previously described. Remove governor body-to-oil collector body retaining bolts. Remove governor body, valve, spring, and weight from collector body. *See Fig. 10.*

NOTE: Components are not retained once governor body bolts have been removed. It is necessary to hold body and components while removing and installing governor.

Installation

Assemble governor body and components. Position body over oil feed holes of oil collector body. Install retaining bolts. Install extension housing.

Fig. 10: Removing Governor Assembly

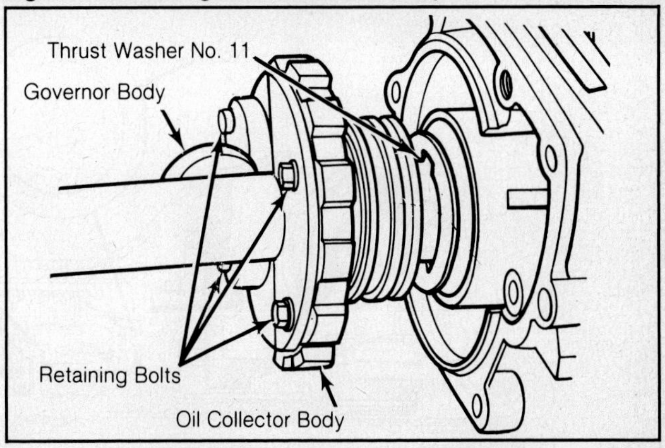

VACUUM DIAPHRAGM ASSEMBLY

Removal

Disconnect hose from unit. On Merkur, remove heat shield. Remove retaining bracket (do not pry or bend bracket). *See Fig. 11.* Remove vacuum diaphragm, actuating pin and throttle valve from case. Remove "O" ring from assembly.

Fig. 11: Side View of Transmission Case

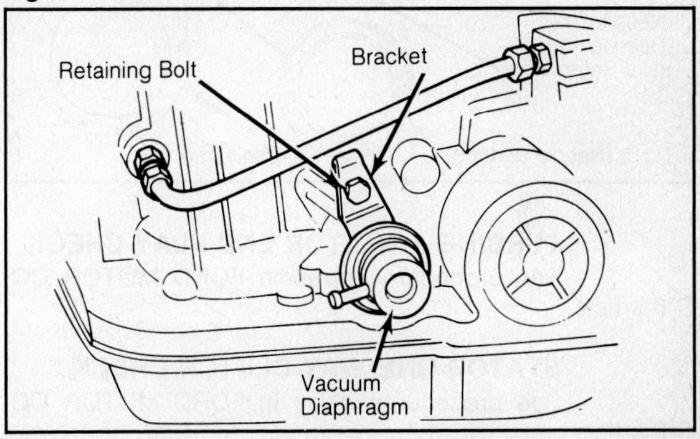

Illustration shows vacuum diaphragm installed.

Installation

Install new "O" ring. Install throttle valve, actuating pin and vacuum diaphragm (with tube pointing rearward). Install retaining bracket and tighten bolt. Install heat shield ensuring it does not touch diaphragm.

REMOVAL & INSTALLATION

See FORD MOTOR CO. articles in AUTOMATIC TRANSMISSION REMOVAL section.

TORQUE CONVERTER

LEAKAGE CHECK

See procedures given in FORD MOTOR CO. C-6 article.

FLUSHING CONVERTER

See procedures given in FORD MOTOR CO. C-6 article.

FORD MOTOR CO. C-3 (Cont.)

Fig. 12: Cutaway View of Transmission Showing Thrust Washer Identification and Location

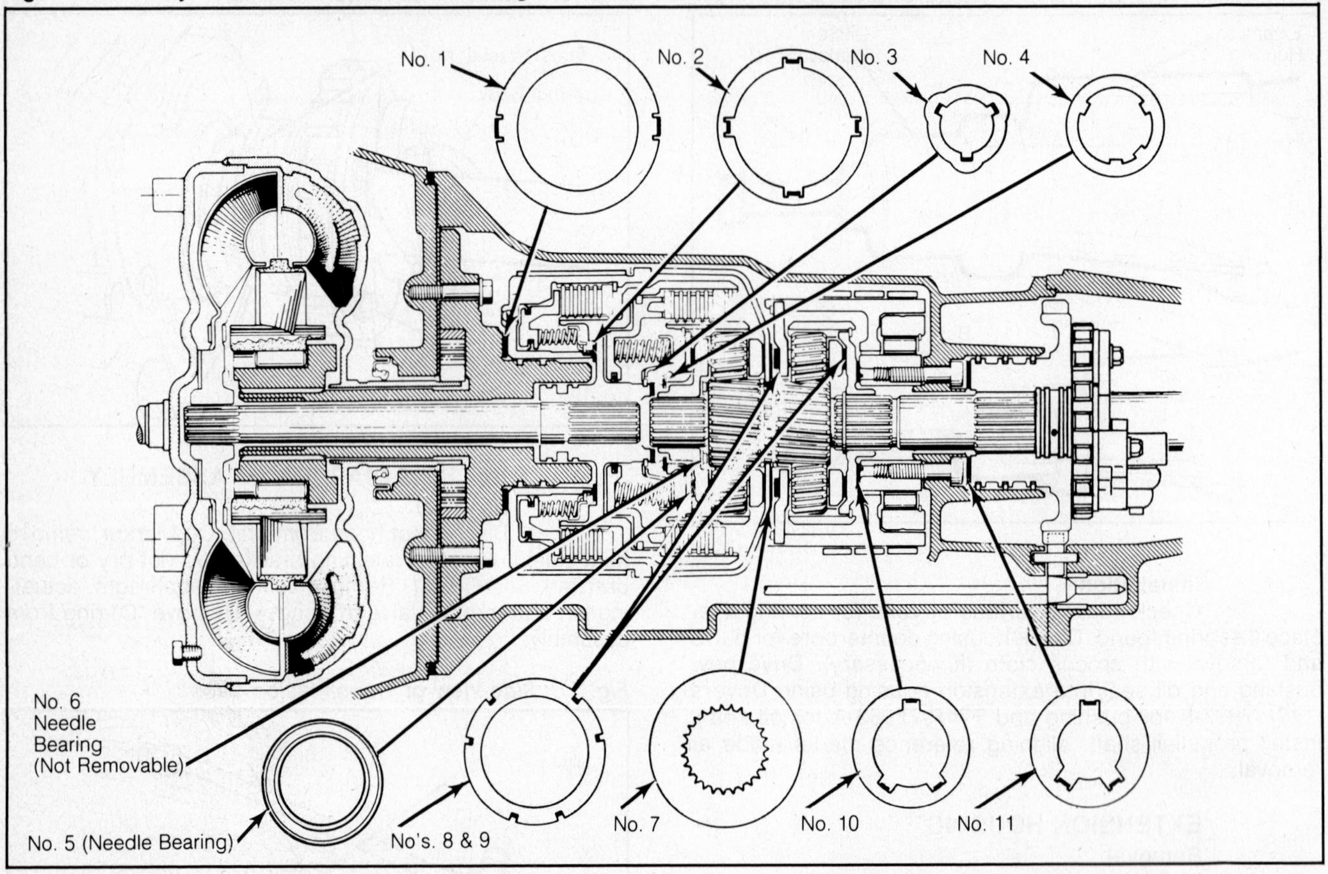

TURBINE & STATOR END PLAY CHECK

See procedures given in FORD MOTOR CO. C-6 article.

STATOR ONE-WAY CLUTCH CHECK

See procedures given in FORD MOTOR CO. C-6 article.

STATOR INTERFERENCE CHECKS

See procedures given in FORD MOTOR CO. C-6 article.

TRANSMISSION DISASSEMBLY

NOTE: **Ten thrust washers and one thrust bearing are used in this transmission, with No. 1 at front pump and No. 11 at governor. Note that No. 5 and No. 6, while performing thrust functions, are actually bearings. Because No. 6 bearing is part of staked portion of planet assembly, it is NOT removable. Refer to Fig. 12 for identification and location of thrust washers.**

REAR SERVO, VALVE BODY & OIL PUMP

1) Remove torque converter, input shaft, and oil pan. Remove oil filter screen and gasket. Remove detent spring.

2) Remove rear servo cover and gasket (spring force will raise cover). Remove bolts from valve body. Note size, length, and location of bolts for reassembly reference.

3) Slowly remove valve body from transmission, unlocking and detaching selector lever connecting link. Remove valve body and gasket. Remove converter housing bolts. Remove housing and oil pump as an assembly.

4) Remove No. 1 thrust washer and gasket. Remove oil pump seal with Puller (T74P-77248-A). Remove oil pump from converter housing. Remove steel plate (behind oil seal) with "O" ring.

NOTE: **Before continuing with disassembly, transmission end play should be measured.**

TRANSMISSION END PLAY CHECK

1) Install oil pump (without gasket) and existing No. 1 thrust washer into transmission case. Make sure pump body is below case gasket surface.

2) Mount dial indicator on oil pump with plunger resting on transmission housing. *See Fig. 13.* Zero dial indicator, then swing indicator around so plunger contacts oil pump.

3) Check reading on dial and record for future reference. Move dial indicator assembly to opposite side of pump. Make another end play check. Take average of 2 readings.

4) End play range is .001-.025" (.03-.64 mm). If end play exceeds limits, replace thrust washer No. 1 with one that will bring end play within specifications.

5) After end play check has been completed, remove oil pump and No. 1 selective thrust washer. Mark installed position of oil pump gears in relation to one another and remove.

Fig. 13: Tool Set-Up for Transmission End Play Check

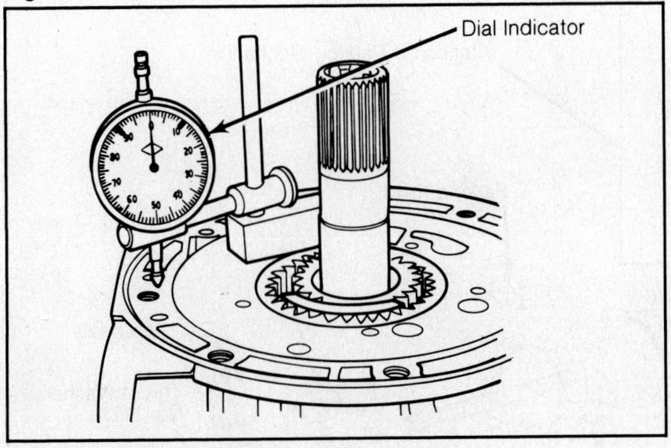

Take average of 2 readings 180° apart.

SELECTIVE THRUST WASHER NO. 1

ID Number	Thickness In (mm)
"1"	.053-.055 (1.35-1.40)
"2"	.060-.062 (1.55-1.60)
"3"	.068-.070 (1.75-1.80)
"4"	.076-.078 (1.95-2.00)
"5"	.084-.086 (2.15-2.20)
"6"	.092-.094 (2.35-2.40)

FRONT BAND & FRONT SERVO

1) Loosen lock nut, back out adjustment screw, and remove struts. Remove front band and front planet assembly, including thrust washer No. 8. *See Fig. 14.*

NOTE: Thrust washers No. 8 and No. 9 are identical.

Fig. 14: Front Band Removal

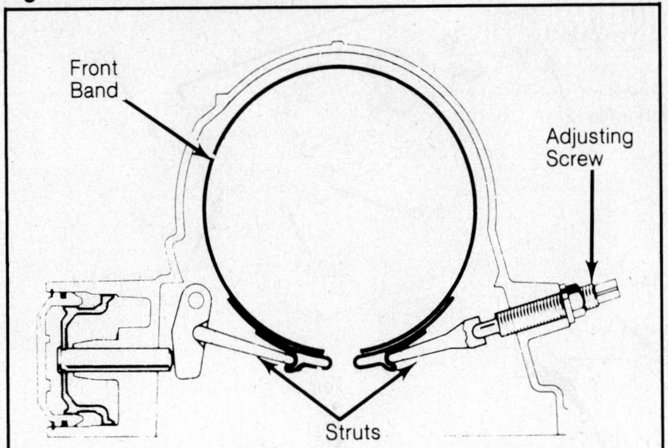

2) Press inward slightly on front servo cover and remove snap ring. Carefully force out servo piston assembly using compressed air through bottom of transmission case. *See Fig. 15.*

Fig. 15: Bottom View of Transmission Case

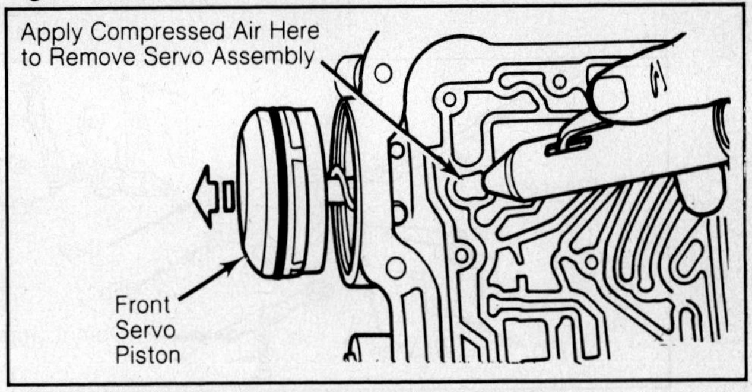

Illustration shows front servo piston removal.

CASE & EXTENSION HOUSING PARTS

1) Remove extension housing bolts. Remove housing and gasket. Remove return spring and parking pawl.

2) Remove large snap ring from rear planet gear carrier. Remove planet gear carrier with thrust needle bearing No. 5 from case. Remove small snap ring from output shaft. *See Fig. 16.*

3) Remove output shaft and governor with thrust washer No. 11. *See Fig. 10.*

Fig. 16: Locations of Planet Gear Carrier Snap Rings

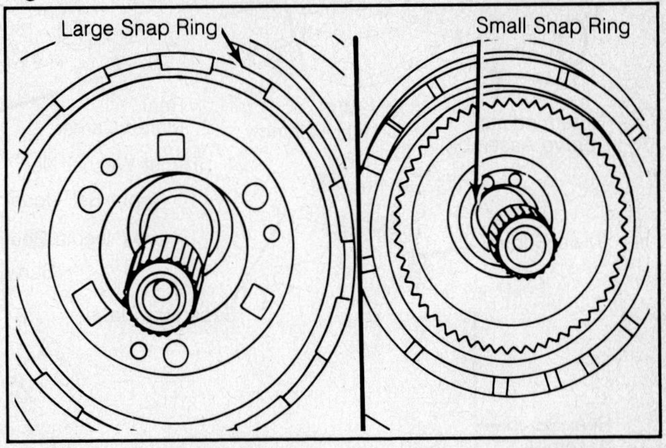

4) Remove internal gear, No. 10 thrust washer, and reverse brake drum. Remove reverse band assembly. Remove vacuum diaphragm unit. Remove neutral safety switch.

CAUTION: Use thin-walled socket to remove neutral safety switch. Open-end wrench will crush switch.

5) If replacing shift lever oil seal, press inward on downshift lever and remove "O" ring. Remove shift lever roll pin from case. Remove shift lever nut (outside). Remove parking pawl actuating rod.

6) Remove selector lever from outside case. Remove downshift lever shaft from inside case. Pry out shift lever oil seal with screwdriver. Install new oil seal using Seal Driver (T74P-77498-A).

7) Install downshift lever inside case and shift lever outside. Install nuts and parking pawl actuating rod. Install roll pin, new "O" ring, and downshift lever.

Fig. 17: Exploded View of C-3 Automatic Transmission Assembly

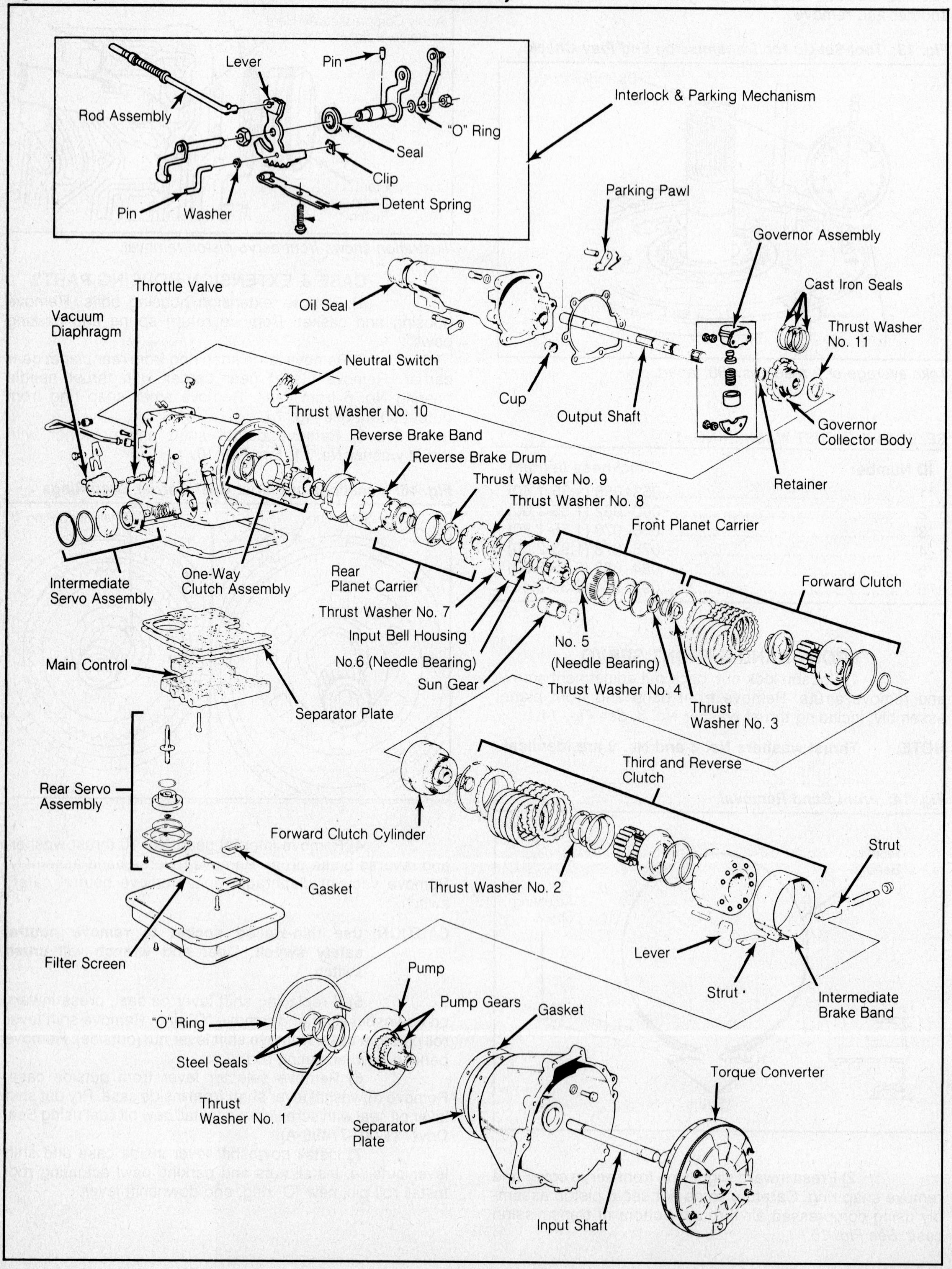

FORD MOTOR CO. C-3 (Cont.)

Fig. 18: Exploded View of Forward Part of Transmission Gear Train

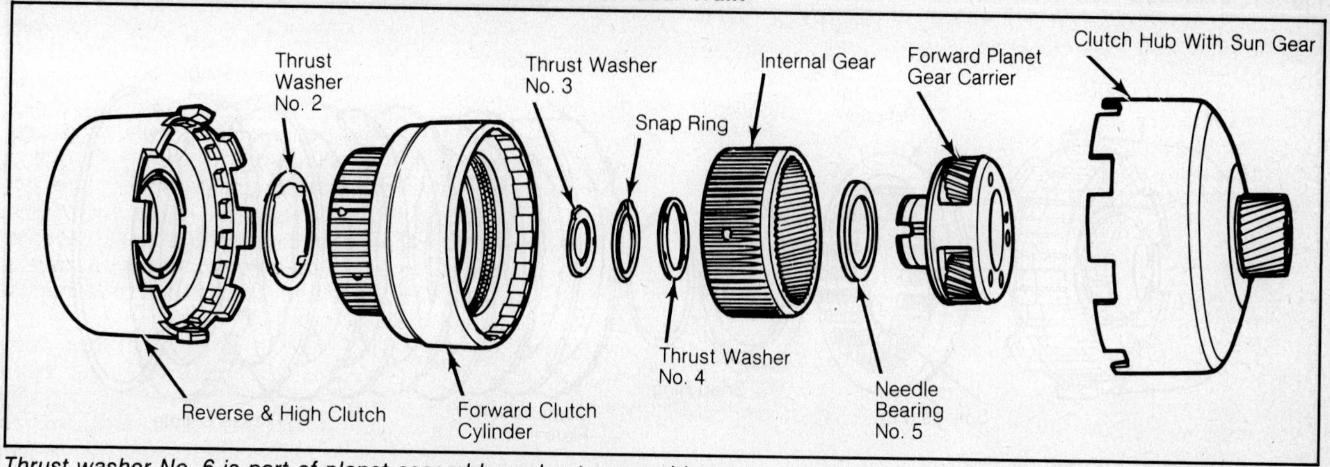

Thrust washer No. 6 is part of planet assembly and not removable.

Fig. 19: Compressing Piston Return Springs and Retainer

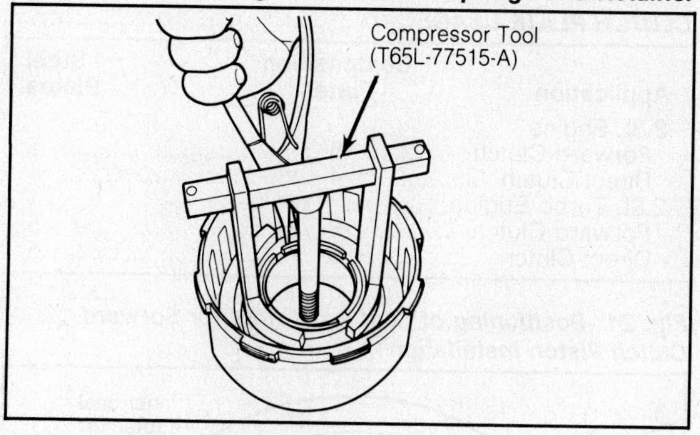

Fig. 20: Using Compressed Air to Remove Reverse-Direct Clutch Piston

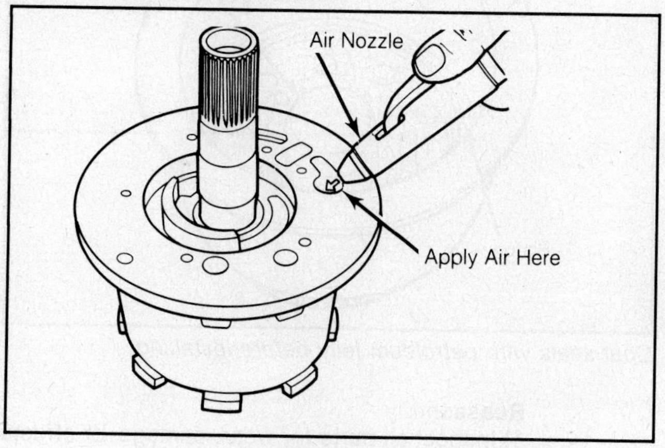

COMPONENT DISASSEMBLY & REASSEMBLY

FRONT ASSEMBLY

Disassembly

Remove clutch hub and sun gear. Remove front planet gear carrier with internal gear and needle bearing No. 5. If necessary, remove sun gear from input shell after removing retainer. Replace thrust washer No. 7, if damaged. Remove forward drive clutch and thrust washer No. 2.

NOTE: **Reassembly of front assembly is covered at end of COMPONENT DISASSEMBLY and REASSEMBLY.**

REVERSE-DIRECT CLUTCH

Disassembly

1) Remove large pressure plate retaining ring. Remove pressure plate and clutch pack. Using Spring Compressor (T65L-77515-A), compress piston return springs and remove small retaining ring. *See Fig. 19.* Carefully release pressure on springs.

2) Remove spring retainer and return springs. Turn clutch body over and carefully force out piston with compressed air. *See Fig. 20.* Remove hydraulic pump and "O" rings from piston and clutch body.

Reassembly

1) Inspect all parts for wear, damage, or effects of overheating. If new composition clutch plates are to be used, soak in transmission fluid for 30 minutes before installing.

2) Install new "O" rings on piston and clutch body. Carefully install clutch piston, using Seal Protectors (T74P-77404-A) to protect inner and outer seals. *See Fig. 22.*

3) Install 20 piston return springs and spring retainer. Compress springs with tool used at disassembly. Install snap ring and remove compressing tool. Install clutch plates, starting with steel plate.

4) Alternate composition and steel plates until all clutch plates are installed. See CLUTCH PLATE USAGE chart. Install pressure plate and secure with snap ring. Push down on pressure plate. Measure clearance between pressure plate and snap ring with feeler gauge. *See Fig. 23.* Clearance should be .054-.082" (1.39-2.11 mm).

5) If clearance is not within specifications, install correct thickness selective snap ring. Reverse-Direct clutch selective snap rings are available in following thicknesses: .054", .068", .082", and .096" (1.37, 1.73, 2.08, and 2.44 mm).

FORWARD CLUTCH

Disassembly

1) Remove large retaining ring. Lift out pressure plate, clutch pack, and rubber cushion spring. Using Spring Compressor (T65L-77515-A), compress piston return springs. Remove small retaining ring. *See Fig. 25.*

FORD MOTOR CO. C-3 (Cont.)

Fig. 21: Exploded View of Reverse-Direct Clutch Assembly

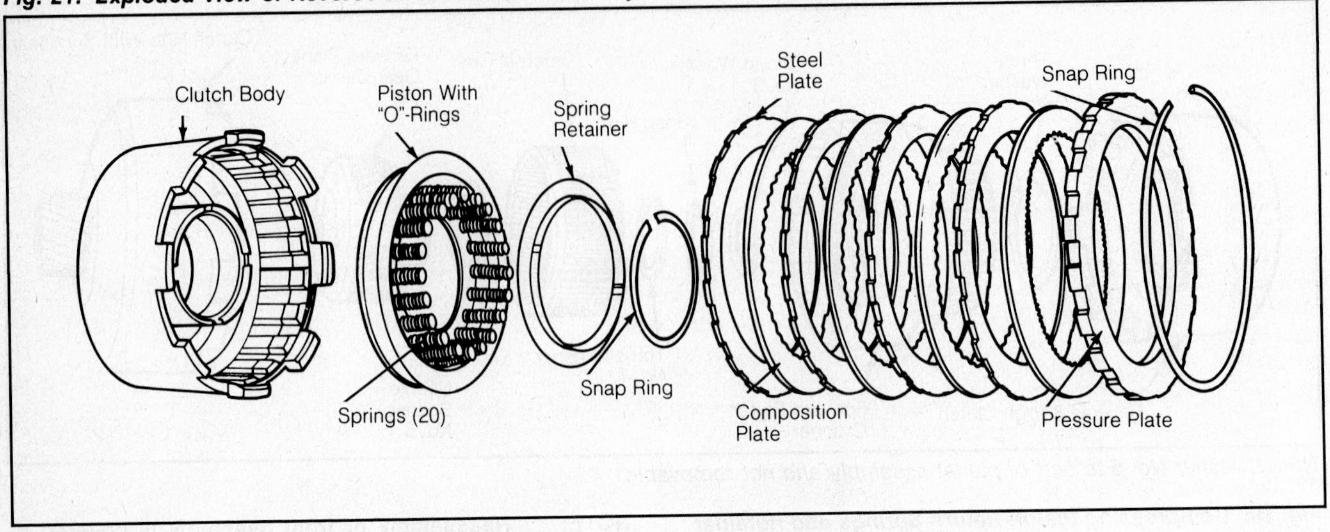

Fig. 22: Reverse-Direct Clutch Piston Installation

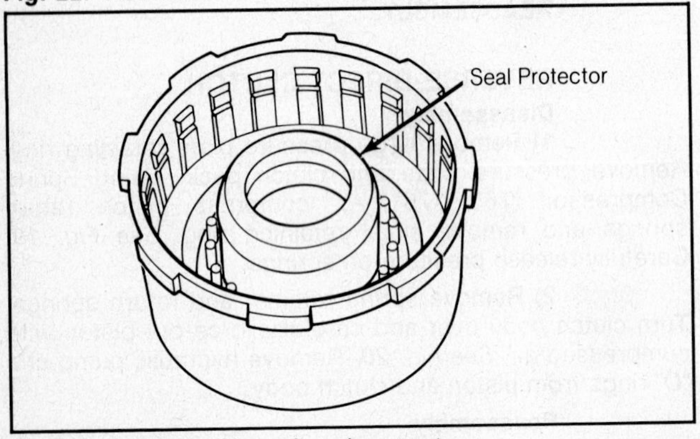

Note installed position of seal protector.

Fig. 23: Clutch Pressure Plate Clearance

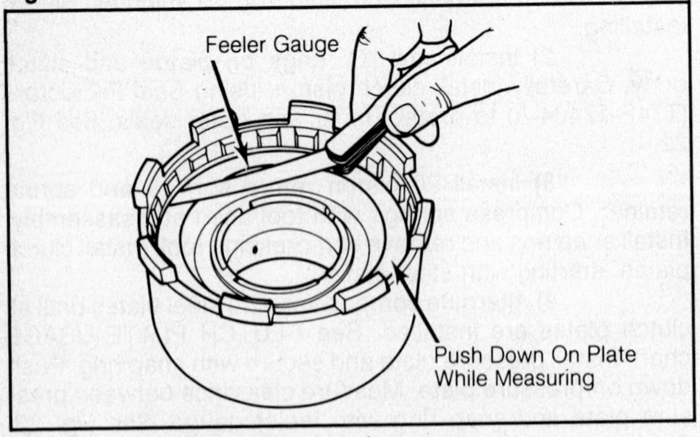

Use feeler gauge to measure clearance.

FORWARD CLUTCH

Disassembly

1) Remove large retaining ring. Lift out pressure plate, clutch pack, and rubber cushion spring. Using Spring Compressor (T65L-77515-A), compress piston return springs. Remove small retaining ring. *See Fig. 25.*

2) Carefully release pressure on springs. Remove spring retainer and springs. Using compressed air, carefully force clutch piston from clutch body. Remove "O" rings from piston and clutch body.

CLUTCH PLATE USAGE

Application	Composition Plates	Steel Plates
2.3L Engine		
Forward Clutch	5	5
Direct Clutch	4	4
2.3L Turbo Engine		
Forward Clutch	5	5
Direct Clutch	5	5

Fig. 24: Positioning of Seal Protectors for Forward Clutch Piston Installation

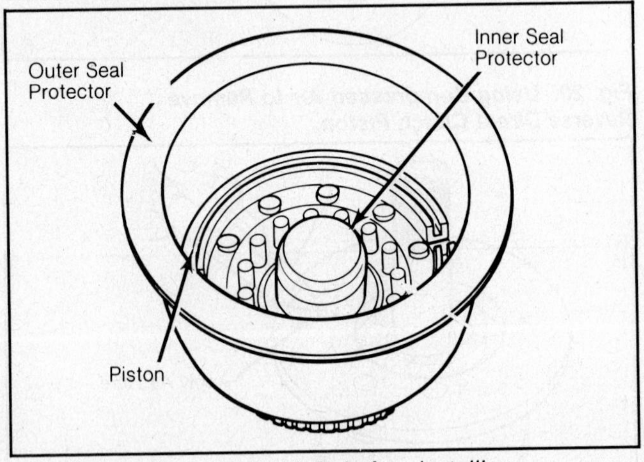

Coat seals with petroleum jelly before installing.

Reassembly

1) Inspect all parts for wear, damage, or effects of overheating. If new composition clutch plates are to be used, soak in transmission fluid for 30 minutes before installing.

2) Use Protector (T74P-77548-A & B) to prevent damage to inner and outer seals. Install new "O" rings. Apply petroleum jelly to rings and to shoulder at clutch stub. Carefully install piston.

3) Install piston return springs and spring retainer. Compress springs with tool used at disassembly. Install snap ring and remove tool.

4) Install rubber cushion in groove on outer face of hydraulic piston. Install clutch plates. Start with steel

Fig. 25: Exploded View of Forward Clutch Assembly

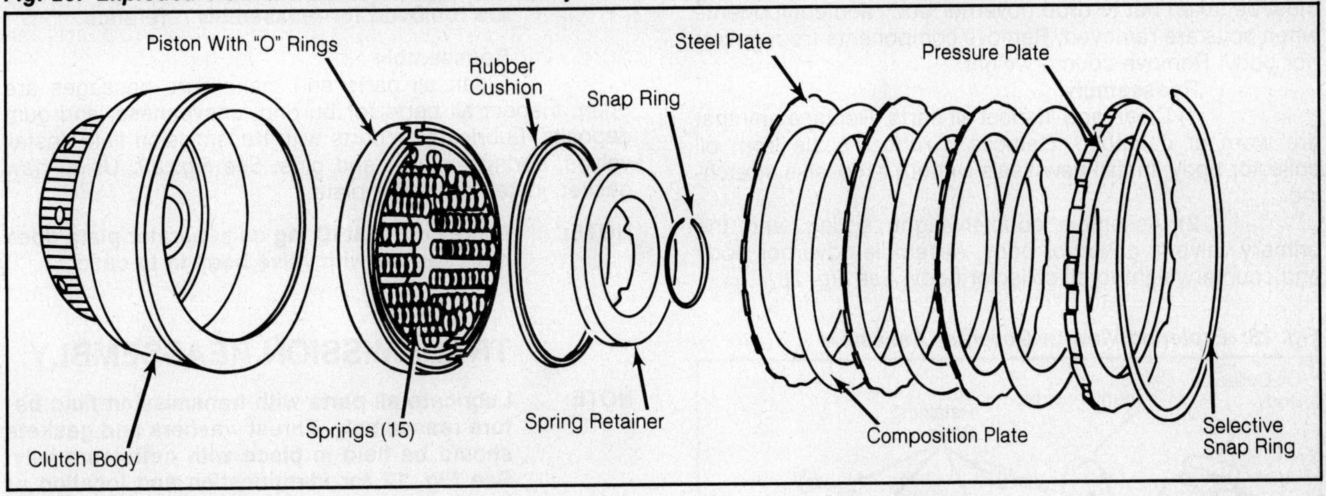

plate. Alternate composition and steel plates until all clutch plates are installed. See CLUTCH PLATE USAGE chart.

5) Install pressure plate and large retainer ring. Measure clearance between retainer ring and pressure plate following procedures given for Reverse-Direct clutch. Clearance for forward clutch is .051-.079" (1.3-2.0 mm).

6) Install new steel seals on clutch hub. *See Fig. 24.* Forward clutch selective snap rings are available in following thicknesses: .054", .068", .082", and .096" (1.37, 1.73, 2.08, and 2.44 mm).

INTERNAL GEAR & PLANET GEAR ASSEMBLY

Disassembly

Remove snap ring, planet gear carrier internal gear, and thrust washer No. 4. Separate planet gear carrier from internal gear. Remove needle bearing No. 5.

Reassembly

Insert planet gear carrier with needle bearing No. 5 into internal gear. Position thrust washer No. 4 in place and secure with new snap ring. Make sure internal gear is free from planet gear carrier.

NOTE: Needle roller bearing (No. 6 washer) can only be replaced complete, with planet gear carrier. If needle bearing thrust washer is removed, washer must be positioned with collar pointing toward rear.

FRONT ASSEMBLY

Reassembly

1) Place reverse-direct clutch assembly on bench in vertical position. Install thrust washer No. 2 and forward gear clutch assembly. Position thrust washer No. 3 on planet gear carrier and retain with petroleum jelly. *See Fig. 18.*

2) Install internal gears and planet gear assembly. Assemble input shell with sun gear to planet gear carrier. Install assembled unit to reverse-direct clutch body.

ONE-WAY CLUTCH

Disassembly

Using screwdriver, remove snap ring. *See Fig. 26.* Lift out cage with springs and bearing rollers as unit.

Fig. 26: Removing Snap Ring from One-Way Clutch Cage

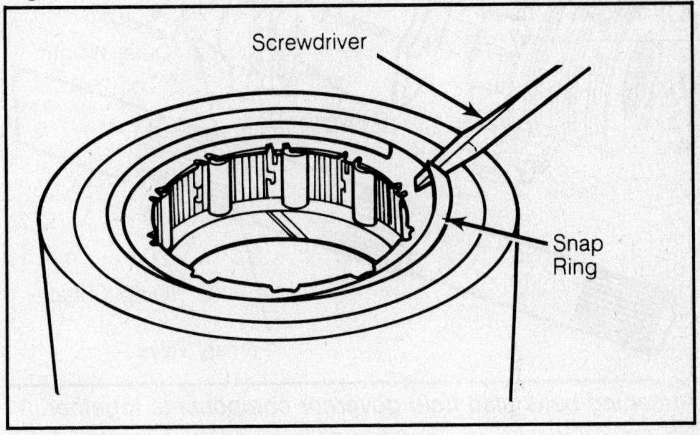

Use screwdriver to remove snap ring.

Reassembly

Inspect all parts for wear or damage. Install cage with springs. Insert bearing rollers one by one. Use screwdriver to compress springs. Install snap ring. *See Fig. 27.*

Fig. 27: Installing One-Way Clutch Bearing Rollers

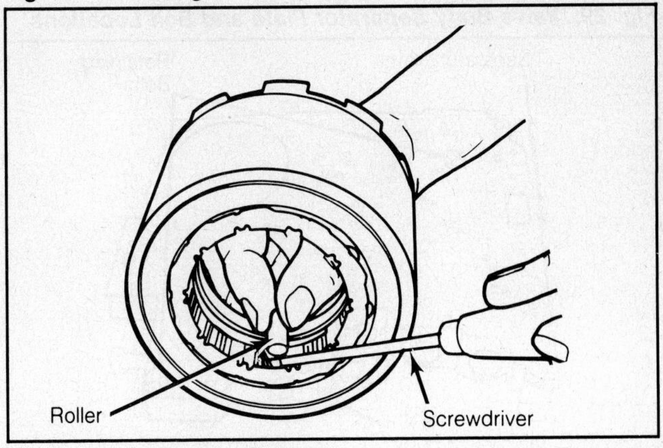

Use screwdriver to install rollers.

GOVERNOR

Disassembly

Remove governor body-to-oil collector body retaining bolts. When these bolts are removed, governor

Automatic Transmissions

FORD MOTOR CO. C-3 (Cont.)

components are no longer retained in position in body. Care must be taken not to drop governor body and components when bolts are removed. Remove components from governor body. Remove counterweight.

Reassembly

1) Clean and inspect all parts. Replace any that are worn or damaged. Remove 3 rubber seals from oil collector body. Install new seals without excessive stretching.

2) Assemble counterweight, spring, and the primary valve in governor body. Assemble governor body and counterweight to oil collector body. *See Fig. 28.*

Fig. 28: Exploded View of Governor Assembly

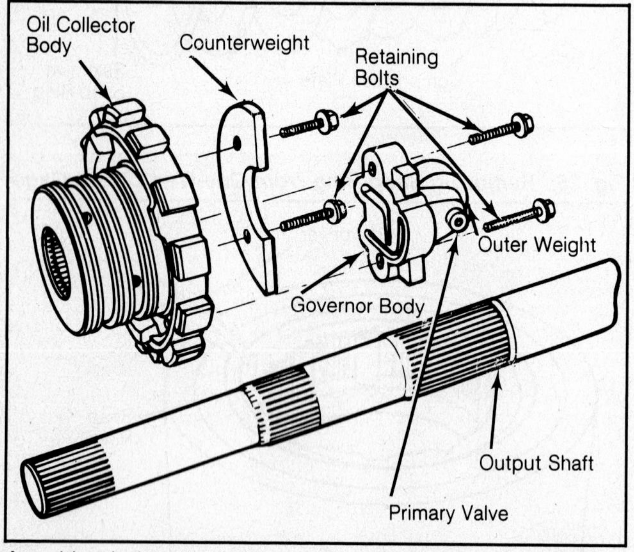

Attaching bolts also hold governor components together.

CONTROL VALVE BODY

Disassembly

Remove separator plate bolts. *See Fig. 29.* Lift off separator plate and gasket. Remove 4 check balls, 1 check puck and both relief valves with springs. Refer to *Fig. 30* for correct placement. Remove retaining plates, dowels, plugs, and valves with springs from valve body.

Fig. 29: Valve Body Separator Plate and Bolt Locations

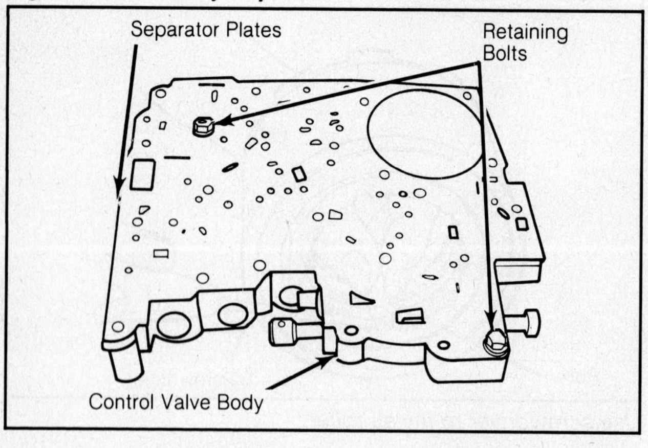

NOTE: **As valve trains are removed from each valve body bore, place individual parts in correct order, and in relative position to valve body to simplify reassembly. Tag all springs as they are removed for reassembly reference.**

Reassembly

Clean all parts and make sure passages are open. Inspect all parts for burring, unevenness, and gum deposits. Lubricate all parts with transmission fluid. Install valves, springs, plugs, and pins. *See Fig. 33.* Using new gasket, install separator plate.

NOTE: **Make sure that ID tag on separator plate does not interfere with valve body fit to case.**

TRANSMISSION REASSEMBLY

NOTE: **Lubricate all parts with transmission fluid before reassembly. Thrust washers and gaskets should be held in place with petroleum jelly. See Fig. 12 for identification and location of thrust washers.**

1) Install new pump oil seal, using Front Pump Alignment Set (T74P-77103-A) and Front Pump Seal Replacer (T74P-77248-B). Install vacuum diaphragm unit.

2) Position thrust washer No. 11 in case. Install output shaft and governor assembly, taking care to avoid damaging rubber oil seal rings.

3) Position rear band in housing. Make sure it is aligned with guide pilots. Position thrust washer No. 10 in case. Install reverse brake drum using Clutch Replacing Guide (T74P-77193-A).

4) Remove guide. Install internal gear and attach with snap ring. Position thrust washer No. 9 to back of planet carrier. Install carrier and attach to reverse brake drum with snap ring.

5) Position thrust washer No. 8 on planet gear carrier and install front assembly.

6) Replace front servo piston or "O" rings at this time, if necessary. Install spiral spring on front servo piston assembly. Install piston and cover. Press down on cover with Compressor (T74P-77028-A). Install snap ring. *See Fig. 32 and Fig. 34.*

7) Install brake band and struts, starting with strut at servo piston lever. Being careful not to damage oil seals, turn transmission so output shaft points downward.

8) Install oil pump and thrust washer No. 1. *See Fig. 35.* Recheck transmission end play as described this article under TRANSMISSION DISASSEMBLY. Replace thrust washer if end play is not within range.

CAUTION: **End play setting is critical. Be sure to check end play during reassembly procedure.**

9) Remove oil pump and thrust washer again. Install inside and outside pump gears. Make sure small gear has I.D. pump drive flat recess facing upward, and large gear has chamfer facing downward.

10) Position steel adapter plate on oil pump in exact position required. *See Fig. 36.* Install complete assembly to converter housing and tighten retaining bolts finger tight.

11) Front pump alignment requires special Pump Alignment Set (T74P-77103-X). Tool consists of 4 special sleeves and handle. Each sleeve has same O.D. but different I.D. *See Fig. 37*

Fig. 30: Locations of Check Balls and Pressure Relief Valve in Valve Body

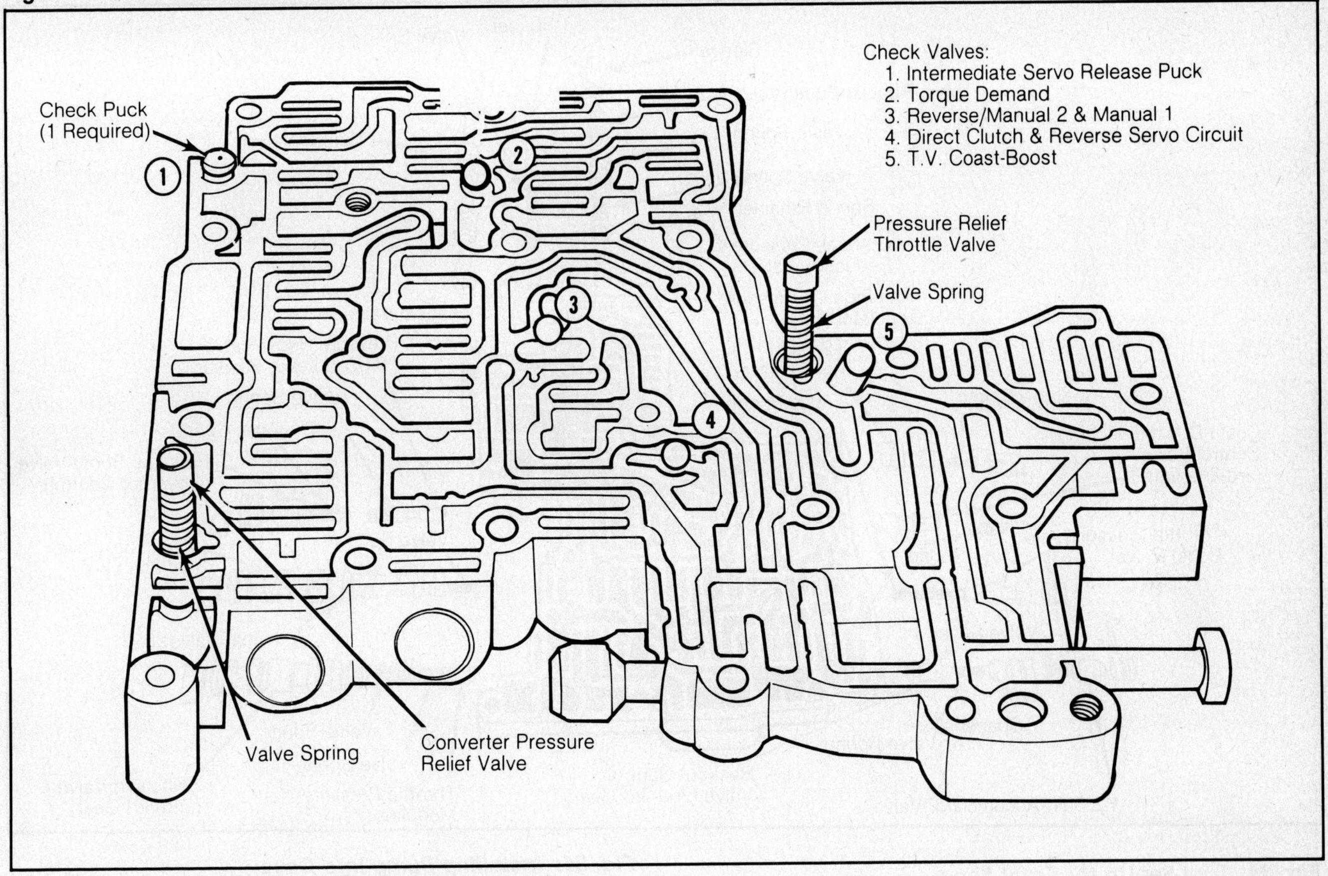

Note that 4 check balls and 1 check puck are used.

Fig. 31: Clutch Replacing Guide Used to Install One-Way Clutch Inner Race

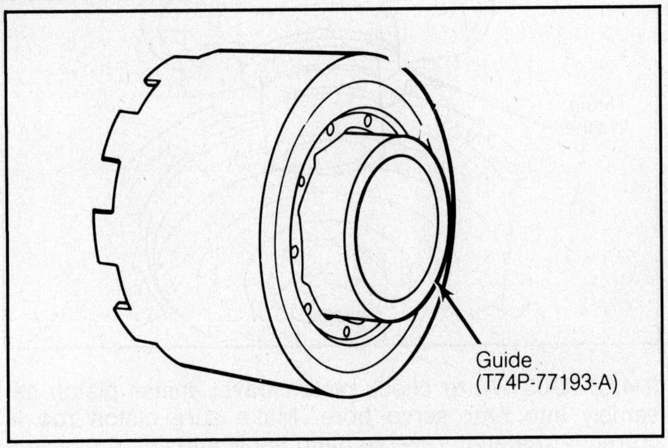

Fig. 32: Exploded View of Front Servo Assembly

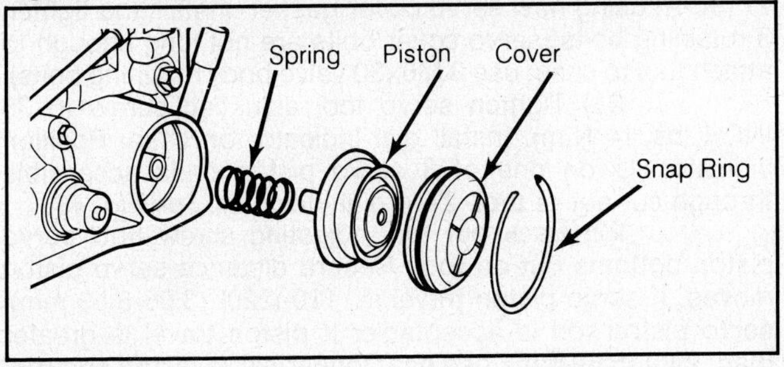

CAUTION: As this measurement is critical, make sure that sleeve gauging surfaces are in good condition. Damage to sleeve gauging surfaces may result in incorrect pump-to-converter housing alignment. Pump seal leakage, pump gear breakage, or bushing failure will occur.

12) Select smallest I.D. sleeve which will fit completely over support shaft. Assemble selected sleeve to handle. Slide tool down over shaft until it bottoms against pump. *See Fig. 38*.

13) Outside diameter of sleeve centers pump in converter housing. Tighten retaining bolts and remove centering tool. Install input shaft into pump. Install converter into pump gears. Rotate converter to check for free movement.

14) Remove converter and input shaft. Position selected No. 1 thrust washer to pump housing. Install new "O" ring. Carefully install converter housing with pump using new gasket. Use care to avoid damaging steel oil seals.

15) Install bolts and tighten. Be sure to use new aluminum washers. Adjust front band. Perform air pressure tests to ensure proper transmission operation as described under AIR PRESSURE CHECKS in this article.

16) Install parking pawl and its return spring in extension housing and preload. *See Fig. 39*. Using new gasket, install extension housing. Make sure to correctly seat operating parking rod in extension guide cup. *See Fig. 40*. Install and tighten bolts. Replace extension housing oil seal and bushing.

Automatic Transmissions

FORD MOTOR CO. C-3 (Cont.)

Fig. 33: Exploded View of Valve Body Assembly

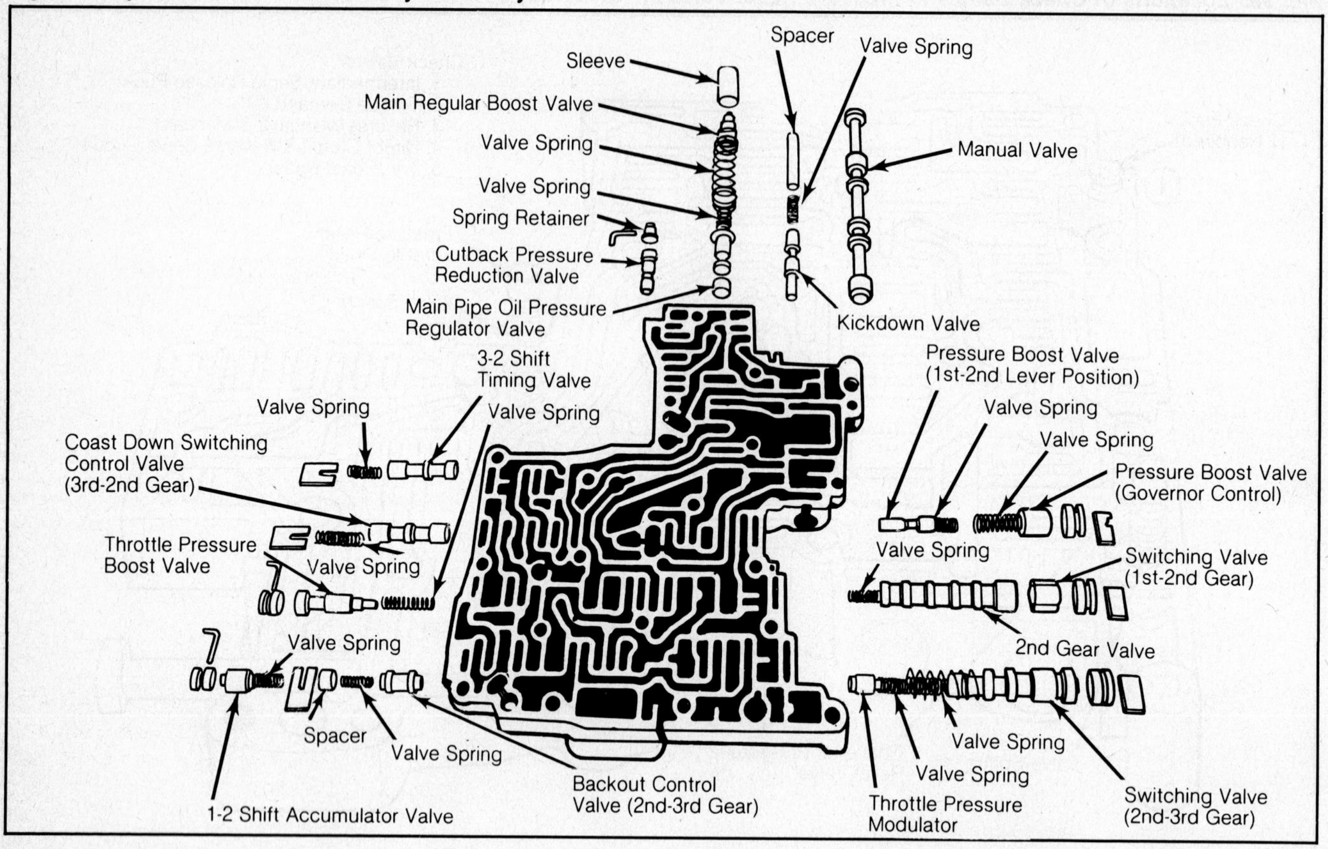

Fig. 34: Tool Set-Up for Front Servo Snap Ring Installation

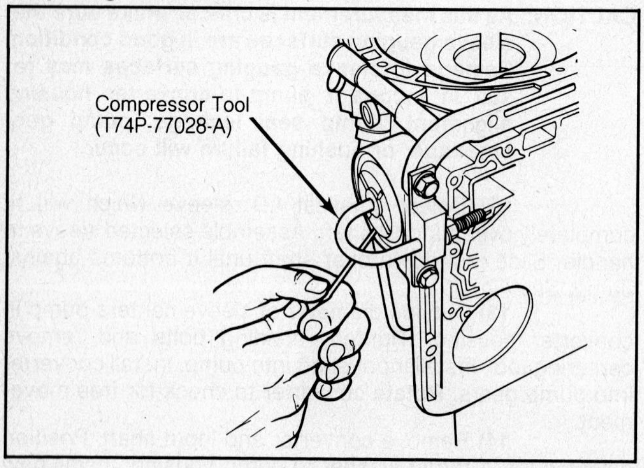

Fig. 35: Installing Pump Into Case

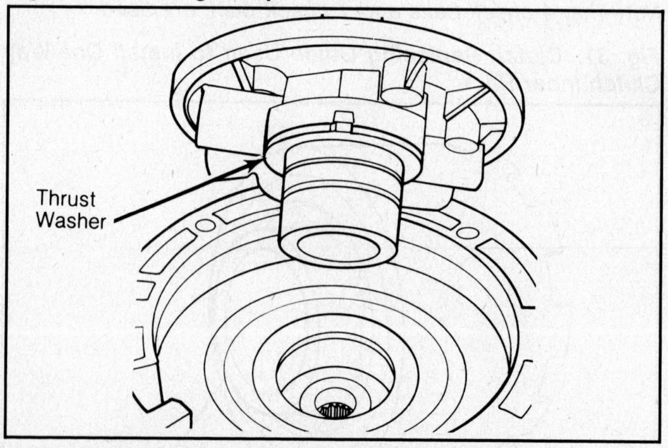

17) Using new gasket, place control valve body in position. Attach and lock connecting rod to manual valve. *See Fig. 41*. Be careful not to bend connecting rod ("Z" link). Install and finger tighten retaining bolts "A" and "B" to locate control valve body. *See Fig. 7* for bolt locations.

18) Install and tighten all remaining bolts except filter screen bolts. Remove bolt "A" and attach detent spring to bolt. Reinstall bolt "A" and tighten bolts "A" and "B" completely. Make sure inner downshift lever is seated between stop and downshift valve as shown in *Fig. 42*.

19) Assemble servo piston rod, servo piston, and spring. Install additional reverse servo Piston Spring (D4ZZ-7D031-A) to check piston travel. Install piston assembly into rear servo bore. Make sure piston rod is correctly seated in reverse band apply end.

20) Install servo rod Selecting Guide (T74P-77190-A) using new servo cover gasket. Install and tighten 3 retaining bolts (servo cover bolts are not long enough to attach tool to case; use 3 M6x30 valve body retaining bolts).

21) Tighten servo tool adjusting screw to 36 INCH lbs. (4 N.m). Install dial indicator on case. Position indicator tip on one of 3 servo piston pads accessible through cut-out of tool. Zero dial indicator. *See Fig. 43*.

22) Back out tool adjusting screw until servo piston bottoms out on tool. Record distance servo piston moved. If servo piston travel is .120-.220" (3.05-5.59 mm), servo piston rod is acceptable. If piston travel is greater than .220" (5.59 mm), use next longer servo piston and rod.

Fig. 36: *Correct Positioning of Adapter Plate on Housing*

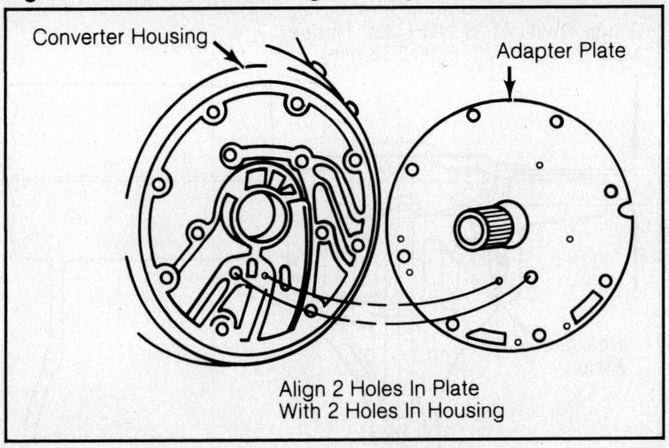

Fig. 37: *Special Front Pump Alignment Tool*

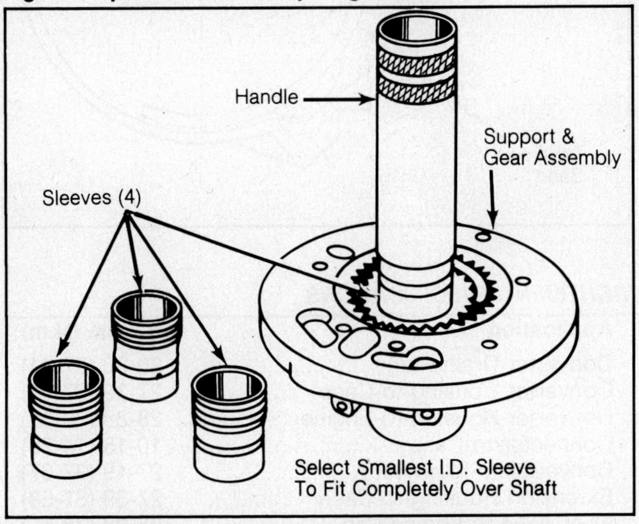

Tool T74P 77103 X consists of 4 sleeves and handle.

Fig. 38: *Front View of Converter Housing.*

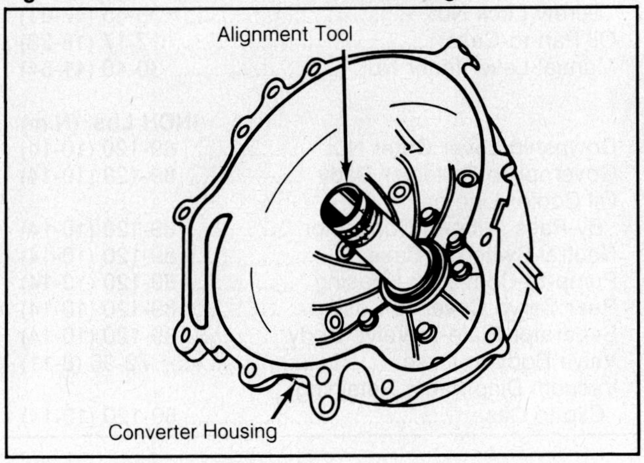

Illustration shows position of pump alignment tools.

22) Back out tool adjusting screw until servo piston bottoms out on tool. Record distance servo piston moved. If servo piston travel is .120-.220" (3.05-5.59 mm), servo piston rod is acceptable. If piston travel is greater than .220" (5.59 mm), use next longer servo piston and rod.

Fig. 39: *Interior View of Extension Housing*

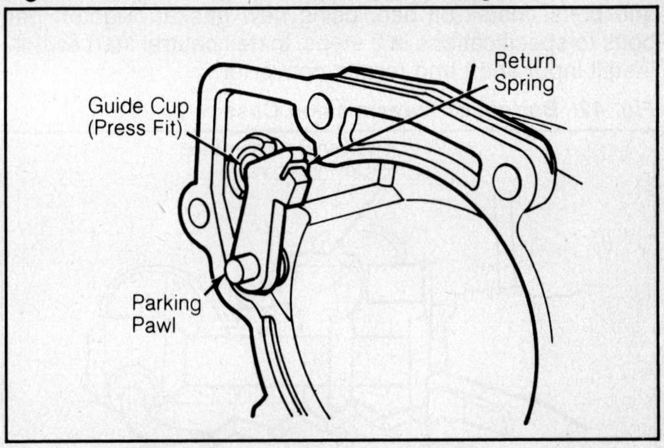

Note correct installation of parking pawl.

Fig. 40: *Rear of Transmission Housing*

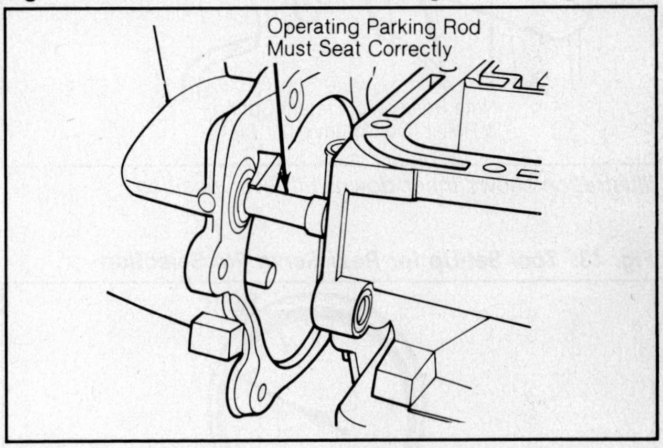

Note proper installation of extension housing.

Fig. 41: *Interior View of Transmission Case*

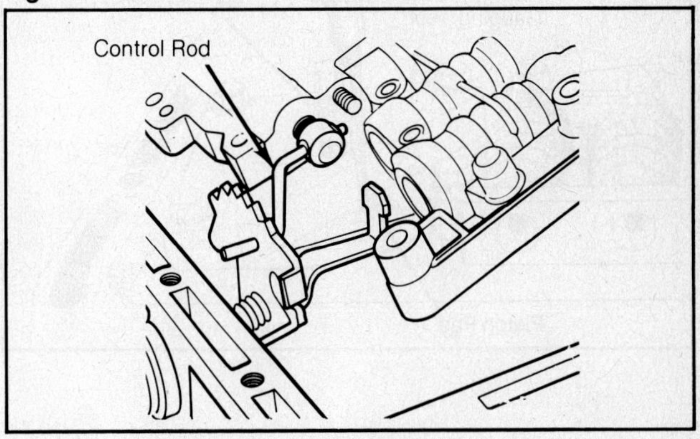

Illustration shows valve body installation and position.

NOTE: Servo piston rods are available in 3 sizes and identified by grooves on rod. Rod sizes and I.D. are as follows: 2.085-2.112" (1 groove), 1.986-2.014" (no groove), and 1.888-1.915" (2 grooves).

23) If travel is less than .120" (3.05 mm), use next shorter piston and rod. Install correct servo piston and rod. Recheck piston travel. *See Fig. 44.* Remove servo adjusting tool and additional reverse servo spring (only used for checking piston travel).

Automatic Transmissions

FORD MOTOR CO. C-3 (Cont.)

24) Reinstall servo assembly. Install servo cover and bolts. Install oil pan, using new gasket. Tighten pan bolts to specifications in 2 steps. Install neutral start switch. Install input shaft and torque converter.

Fig. 42: Bottom of Transmission Case

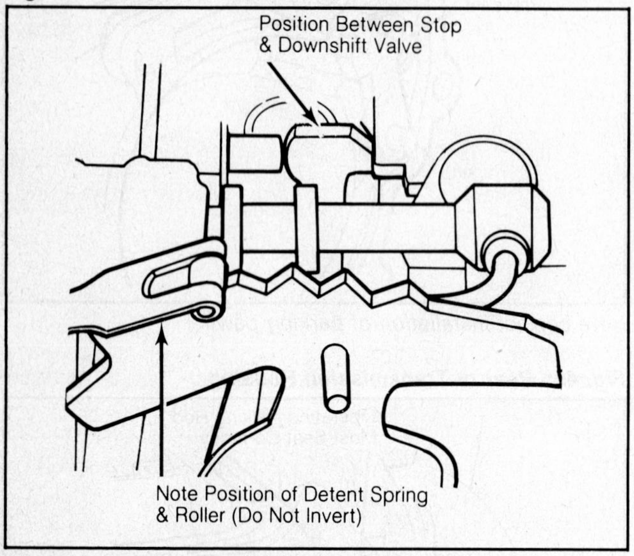

Illustration shows inner downshift lever position.

Fig. 43: Tool Set-Up for Rear Servo Pin Selection

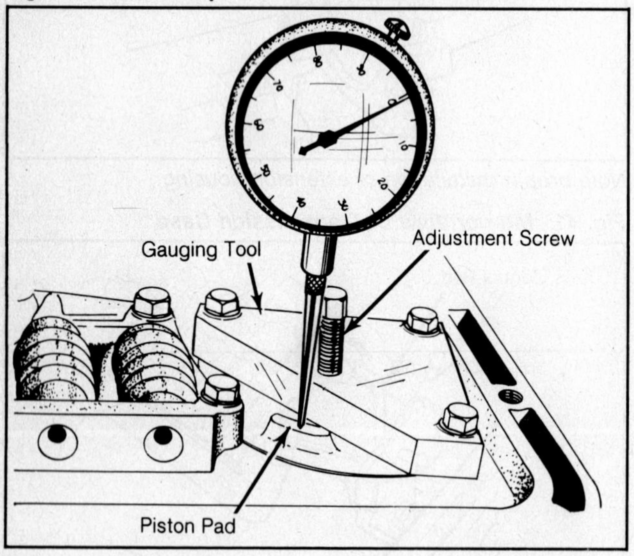

Fig. 44: Rear Servo Piston Travel Measurement

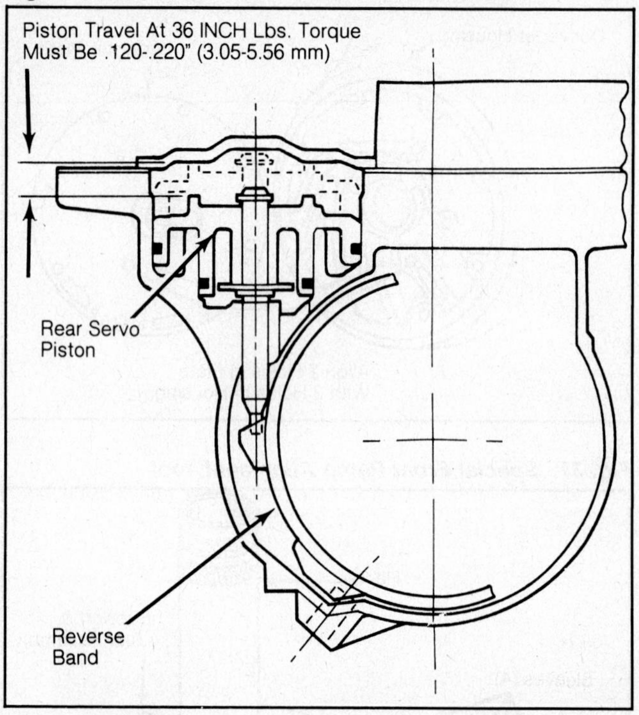

TIGHTENING SPECIFICATIONS

Application	Ft. Lbs. (N.m)
Converter Drain Plug	20-30 (27-41)
Converter Housing-to-Case	27-39 (37-53)
Converter Housing-to-Engine	28-38 (38-52)
Connector-to-Case	10-15 (14-20)
Converter-to-Flywheel	27-49 (37-67)
Extension Housing-to-Case	27-39 (37-53)
Filler Tube to Engine Clip	28-38 (38-52)
Flywheel-to-Crankshaft	48-53 (65-72)
Front Band Adjusting Screw Lock Nut	35-45 (47-61)
Oil Pan-to-Case	12-17 (16-23)
Manual Lever Inner Nut	30-40 (41-54)
	INCH Lbs. (N.m)
Downshift Lever Outer Nut	89-120 (10-14)
Governor-to-Collector Body	89-120 (10-14)
Oil Cooler Line or By-Pass Tube-to Connector	89-120 (10-14)
Neutral Switch to Case	89-120 (10-14)
Pump-to-Converter Housing	89-120 (10-14)
Rear Servo Cover-to-Case	89-120 (10-14)
Separator Plate-to-Valve Body	89-120 (10-14)
Valve Body-to-Case	72-96 (8-11)
Vacuum Diaphragm Retaining Clip to Case	89-120 (10-14)

Automatic Transmissions

FORD MOTOR CO. C-5

Capri, Cougar, LTD, Marquis,
Mustang, Thunderbird, F150 Pickups

IDENTIFICATION

The C-5 automatic transmission is identified by code letter C (passenger cars) or W (truck models), which is shown on lower line of Vehicle Certification Label under "TR" or "TRANS". Label is located on driver's door lock panel of pillar.

Transmission may also be identified by a metal tag which is attached under lower front intermediate servo cover bolt. The first line on tag shows transmission model prefix and suffix. A number appearing after the suffix indicates that internal parts have been changed after initial production start up.

TRANSMISSION IDENTIFICATION CODES

Application	Code
F150 Pickups	"W"
Passenger Cars	"C"

Fig. 1: Service Identification Tag

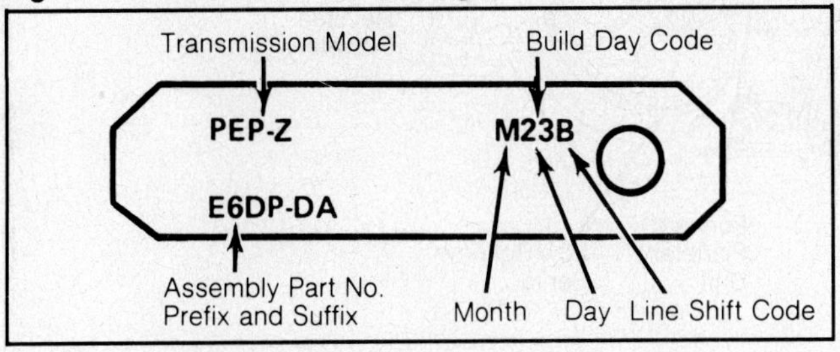

DESCRIPTION

The C-5 transmission is a fully automatic 3-speed unit capable of providing automatic upshifts and downshifts through 3 forward gear ratios and also capable of providing manual selection of 1st and 2nd gears.

The unit consists essentially of a converter clutch torque converter, a compound planetary gear train controlled by 2 bands, 2 disc clutches, a one-way clutch and a hydraulic control system.

LUBRICATION & ADJUSTMENTS

See appropriate AUTOMATIC TRANSMISSION SERVICING article in DOMESTIC GENERAL SERVICING section.

TROUBLE SHOOTING

See appropriate AUTOMATIC TRANSMISSION TROUBLE SHOOTING article in DOMESTIC GENERAL SERVICING section.

TESTING

STALL TEST

Testing Precautions

1) When making test, DO NOT hold throttle open longer than 5 seconds. Allow a cooling period of 15 seconds with transmission in Neutral and engine speed at 1000 RPM between each test.

2) If engine speed exceeds maximum limits shown, release accelerator immediately as this is an indication of clutch or band slippage.

Testing Procedure

1) Install tachometer and fully apply parking and service brakes. Start engine and run at curb idle and at normal operating temperature.

2) Stall test transmission in each driving range at full throttle. Note maximum RPM obtained. Engine speed should be within limits shown in STALL SPEED SPECIFICATIONS table.

STALL SPEED SPECIFICATIONS

Engine Size	Converter Size	Stall Speed RPM
3.8L C.F.I.	12"	1760-2050
4.9L [1]	12"	1549-1788

[1] – F150 pickup only.

STALL TEST RESULTS

Stall Speed Too High

In "D", "2", "1" and "R"; general transmission problems are indicated and control pressure test should be made to locate faulty unit(s). In "D" only; planetary one-way clutch slippage is indicated. In "D", "2" and "1"; forward clutch slippage is indicated. In "R" only; high clutch or reverse band slippage is indicated.

Stall Speed Too Low

Converter stator one-way clutch or engine performance is faulty.

ROAD TEST

1) Check minimum throttle upshifts in "D". Transmission should start off in 1st gear, shift to 2nd, and then shift to 3rd as speed increases.

2) With transmission in 3rd gear, depress accelerator pedal through detent (to floor). Transmission should shift from 3rd to 2nd, or 3rd to 1st, depending on vehicle speed. See SHIFT SPEEDS chart.

3) Check closed throttle downshift from 3rd to 1st by coasting down from about 30 MPH in 3rd gear. Shift should occur as shown in table.

4) With transmission in "2" position, transmission should operate only in 2nd gear.

5) With transmission in 3rd gear and road speed above 30 MPH, transmission should shift to 2nd gear when selector lever is moved from "D", to "2" or "1". When same manual shift is made below 25 MPH, transmission will shift from 2nd or 3rd to 1st.

NOTE: Preceding check will determine if governor pressure and shift control valves are operating properly.

6) Slipping or engine speed flare-up in any gear usually indicates clutch or band problems. In most cases, clutch or band that is slipping can be determined by noting transmission operation in all selector lever positions, and comparing which internal units are applied in those positions. See CLUTCH and BAND APPLICATION chart.

Automatic Transmissions

FORD MOTOR CO. C-5 (Cont.)

Fig. 2: Cutaway View of Ford Motor Co. C-5 Automatic Transmission Assembly

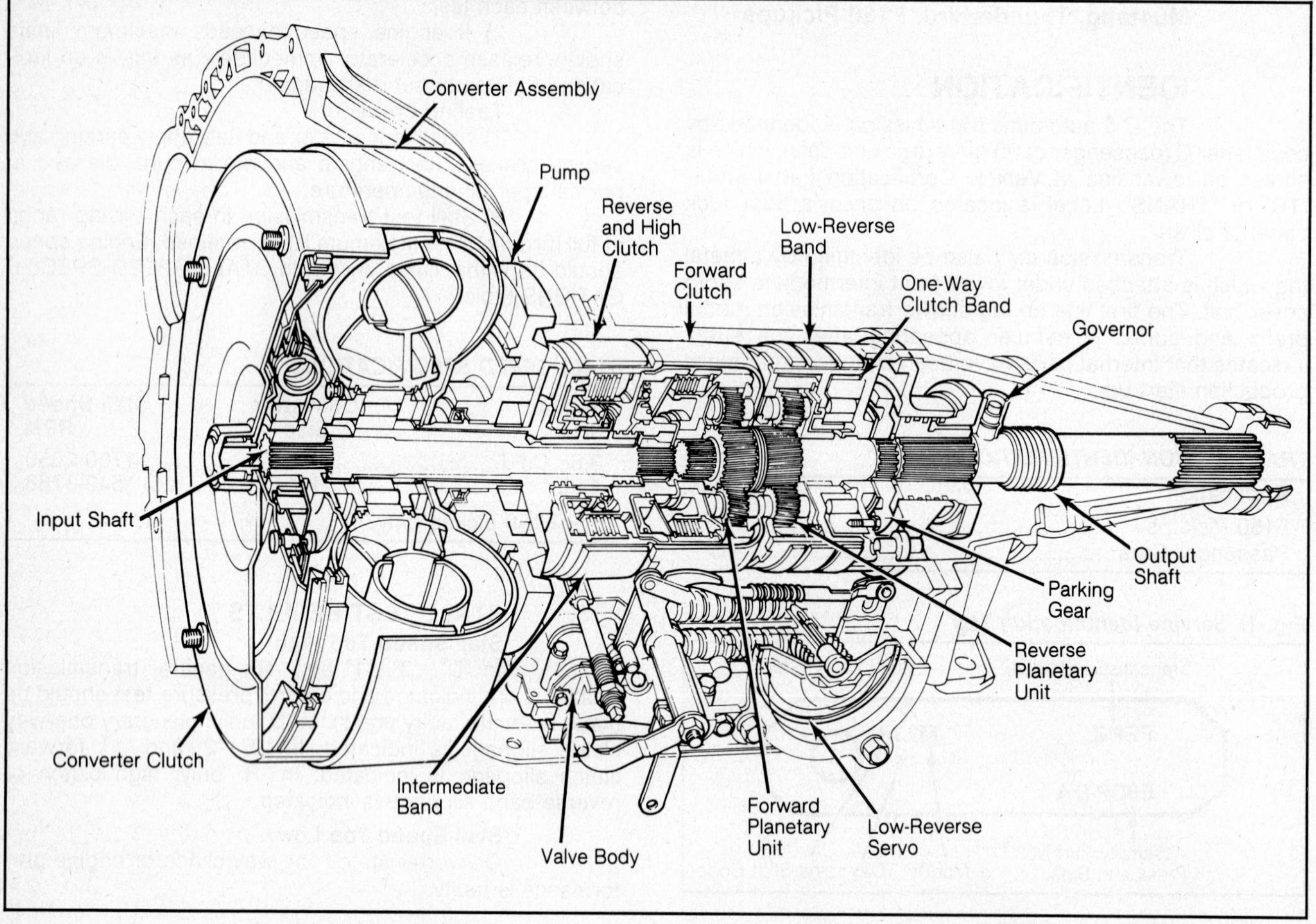

CONTROL PRESSURE TEST

NOTE: There are 2 methods to perform test. One is to use engine vacuum. The other is to use a hand operated vacuum pump. Governor can be checked at the same time and in the same manner.

ENGINE VACUUM PRESSURE

1) If vacuum diaphragm is working properly and manual and downshift linkages are adjusted correctly, all shifts should occur within certain road speed limits. See SHIFT SPEEDS tables. If shifts do not occur at proper points or slipping occurs during shifts, check engine vacuum, vacuum supply, vacuum units, and valve body for possible cause of problem.

2) Attach tachometer to engine and vacuum gauge to transmission vacuum line. Attach pressure gauge to control pressure outlet on transmission. *See Figs. 3 and 4.*

Fig. 3: Vacuum Gauge Installation

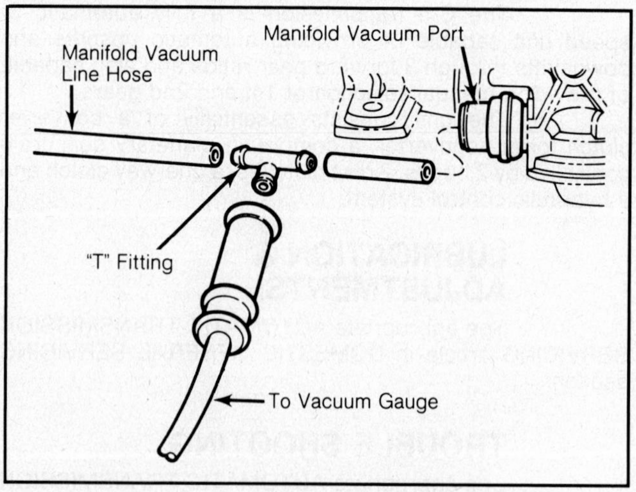

CLUTCH & BAND APPLICATION (ELEMENTS IN USE)

Gear	Rev. & High Clutch	Forward Clutch	One-Way Clutch	Intermediate Band	Low-Reverse Band
1st (D Range)		Applied	Applied		
1st (1 Range)		Applied			Applied
2nd		Applied		Applied	
3rd	Applied	Applied			
Reverse	Applied				Applied

CAUTION: Pressure gauge affects quality of transmission shifting. When gauge is installed in transmission outlet, DO NOT accelerate or decelerate rapidly as transmission failure could result.

3) Apply parking brake. If equipped with vacuum brake release, apply service brake. Parking brake will automatically release when transmission is shifted into DRIVE. Start engine and allow it to reach normal operating temperature. Set idle speed to specifications.

4) If idle speed cannot be brought within limits, check linkage for binding. If linkage is okay, check for vacuum leaks in modulator and its hoses and tubes. Check all other vacuum operated units such as power brake for leaks.

VACUUM PUMP METHOD

1) Disconnect and plug vacuum line at vacuum modulator. Attach vacuum pump to modulator. Apply both parking and service brakes. Start engine and set vacuum at 15 Hg. Read and record control pressure at all selector positions.

2) Adjust engine speed to 1000 RPM and reduce vacuum to 10 in. Hg. Read and record control pressure in DRIVE, 2 and 1. Keep engine rpm at 1000 and reduce vacuum to 1 Hg. Read and record pressure in DRIVE, 1, 2, and REVERSE. Compare obtained pressure readings with readings in CONTROL PRESSURE table.

THROTTLE VALVE ROD CODES

Color Code	Rod Length Inches (mm)
Green	1.5875-1.5925 (40.3-40.4)
Blue	1.6025-1.6075 (40.7-40.8)
Orange	1.6175-1.6225 (41.1-41.2)
Black	1.6325-1.6375 (41.5-41.6)
Pink & White	1.6535-1.6585 (42.0-42.1)

Fig. 4: View of Left Side of Transmission Case

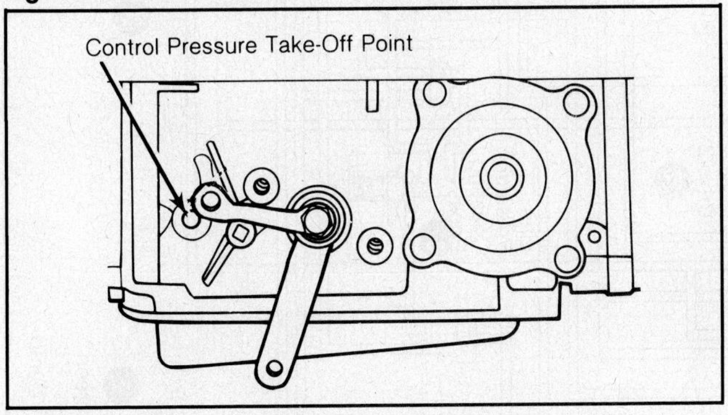

Illustration shows location of control pressure outlet.

CONTROL PRESSURE RESULTS

If control pressures are not within specification, use the following to determine cause of trouble:

Control Pressure Low at Idle in All Ranges

Check for low fluid level, restricted oil filter, loose valve body to case bolts, low engine idle, pump leakage, case leakage, valve body leakage, fluid is too hot, or main oil regulator valve sticking.

Control Pressure High at Idle in All Ranges

Check engine EGR system. Check vacuum diaphragm unit, manifold vacuum line, throttle valve linkage, and control rod. Check for sticking regulator boost valve(s).

Control Pressure OK at Idle in All Ranges, But Low at 10 in. Hg

Check vacuum diaphragm unit. Control rod or throttle valve are stuck.

Control Pressure OK at Idle in All Ranges, OK at 10 in. Hg, But Low at 1 in. Hg

Check for excessive leakage, low pump capacity, or restricted oil pan screen.

Control Pressure Low In "2"

Check forward clutch and/or intermediate servo.

Control Pressure Low In "D"

Check for faulty forward clutch.

Control Pressure Low In "1"

Check forward clutch and/or reverse/high servo.

Control Pressure Low In "R"

Check reverse-high clutch and/or rear servo.

CONTROL PRESSURES

Transmission Model	Range	Idle		
		15″ & Above	10″	WOT Stall Thru Detent
PEA-CU	D	57-73	93-103	150-164
	2,1	95-108	93-103	150-164
	R	61-121	155-172	250-274
	P,N	57-73	93-103	150-164

Trans. Type	Transmission Model	Range	IDLE		
			15″ & Above	10″	W.O.T. Stall Thru Detent
C5	PEP-Z,AC AD,AE,AP,AF2	@D	53-70	93-107	162-182
		@2,1	107-121	100-112	162-182
		@R	88-116	156-178	271-303
		@P,N	53-70	93-107	162-182
C5	PEP-AF1	@D	64-68	86-97	160-176
		@2,1	105-115	100-110	160-176
		@R	73-95	144-162	267-294
		@P,N	64-68	67-85	160-176

@ At sea level barometric pressure 29.5

GOVERNOR CHECK

1) Raise and support vehicle so that rear wheels are clear of floor. Disconnect and plug vacuum line to vacuum modulator. Connect hose from remote vacuum pump to vacuum modulator.

2) Attach tachometer to engine. Attach 0-400 psi pressure gauge to control pressure take-off point at transmission.

CAUTION: Do not exceed 60 MPH speedometer speed during governor pressure test.

3) Place transmission in DRIVE, no load on engine, and apply 10 in. Hg to modulator. Increase speed slowly and watch speedometer. Check MPH at which control pressure cutback occurs. It should occur between 10-20 MPH on F150, and 6-20 MPH on all other models.

NOTE: After each test, shift into Neutral and run engine at 1000 RPM to cool transmission.

Automatic Transmissions

FORD MOTOR CO. C-5 (Cont.)

Fig. 5: C-5 Automatic Transmission Hydraulic Circuits Diagram

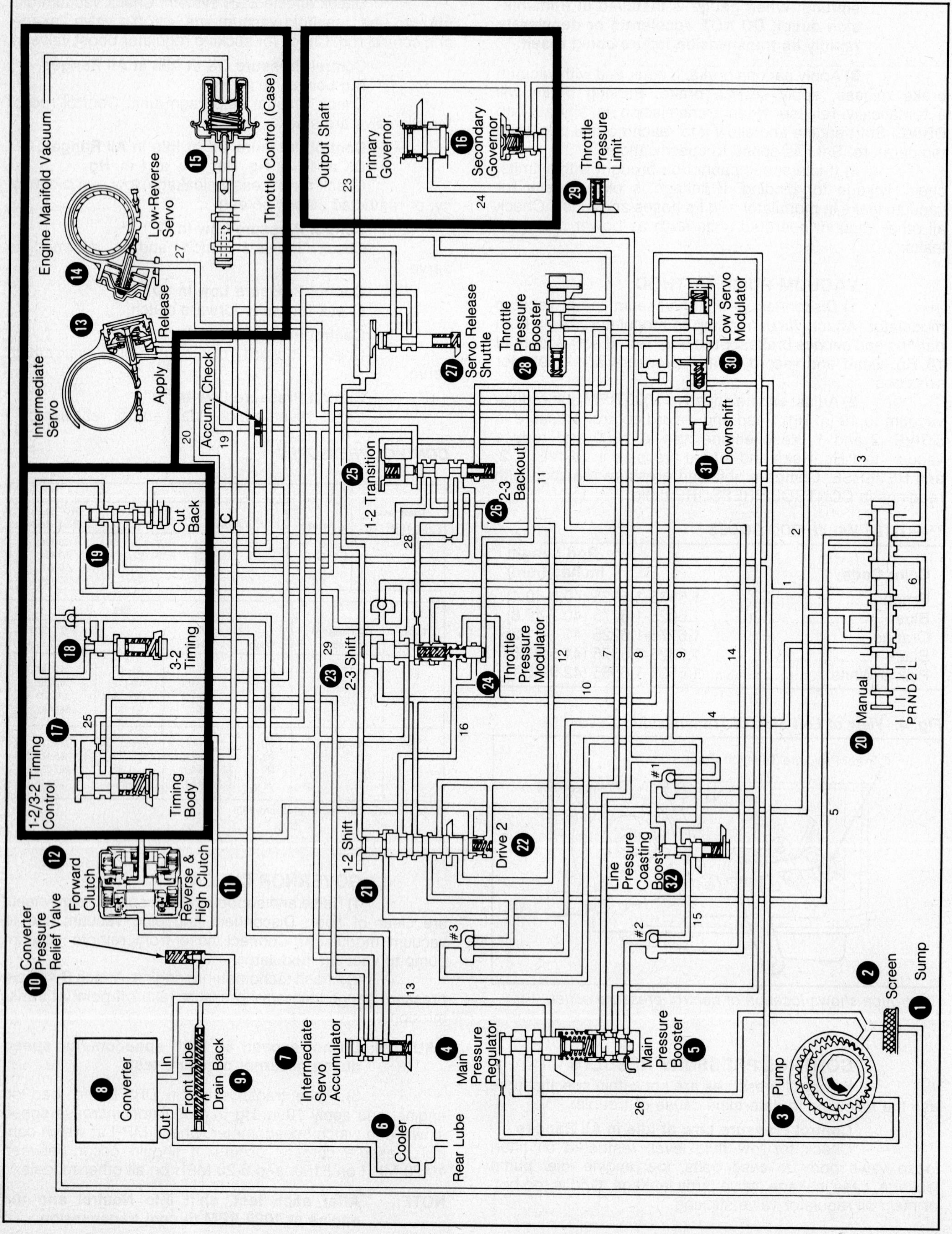

Automatic Transmissions

FORD MOTOR CO. C-5 (Cont.)

SHIFT SPEEDS (MPH)

NOTE: **Figures given are approximate. All shift speeds may vary somewhat due to production tolerances, rear axle ratio, or emission equipment.**

MODEL PEA-CU
4.9L F150, 49 STATE

Throttle	Range	Shift	OPS—R.P.M.	Column Number			
				1	2	3	4
Closed (Above 17" Vacuum)	D	1-2	405-449	10-11	10-12	10-12	
	D	2-3	574-776	14-19	15-21	14-20	
	D	3-1, 2-1	331-366	8-9	8-9	8-10	
	1	2-1	1004-1192	25-30	27-32	25-31	
To Detent (Torque Demand)	D	1-2	724-995	18-25	19-27	18-26	
	D	2-3	1341-1536	36-38	36-41	34-40	
	D	3-2	1070-1259	26-31	29-34	27-33	
Through Detent (WOT)	D	1-2	1373-1598	34-40	37-43	35-41	
	D	2-3	2413-2681	60-67	65-73	62-69	
	D	3-2	2170-2324	54-58	58-63	56-60	
	D	3-1, 2-1	998-1218	24-30	27-33	25-32	

Tire Size	Axle Ratio
	3.08
	Use Column No.
P195/75R15SL	1
P215/75R15SL	2
P235/75R15XL	3

MODELS PEP-AC, AD, AE, AP, Z, AF2
3.8L CAPRI, COUGAR, LTD, MUSTANG, MARQUIS, THUNDERBIRD
50 STATE

Throttle	Range	Shift	OPS—R.P.M.	Column Number			
				1	2	3	4
Closed (Above 17" Vacuum)	D	1-2	399-446	10-12	10-12	9-11	9-11
	D	2-3	500-744	13-20	13-20	11-18	12-18
	D	3-1, 2-1	331-366	9-10	9-10	7-9	8-9
	1	2-1	1091-1317	29-35	29-36	25-31	26-32
To Detent (Torque Demand)	D	1-2	609-1061	16-28	16-29	14-25	15-26
	D	2-3	1237-1656	33-44	33-45	29-39	30-40
	D	3-2	1242-1564	32-42	32-43	29-37	30-38
Through Detent (WOT)	D	1-2	1514-1775	40-48	41-49	35-42	36-43
	D	2-3	2666-2981	70-80	72-82	62-71	64-72
	D	3-2	2407-2602	63-70	65-71	56-62	58-63
	D	3-1, 2-1	1094-1344	28-36	29-37	25-32	26-33

Tire Size	Axle Ratio	
	2.73	3.08
	Use Column No.	
P195/75R14	1	3
P205/70R14	1	3
P215/70R14	2	4
215/70HR14	2	4
220/55R390	1	3

MODEL PEP-AF1
3.8L CAPRI, MUSTANG
HIGH ALTITUDE

Throttle	Range	Shift	OPS—R.P.M.	Column Number
				1
Closed (Above 17" Vacuum)	D	1-2	409-444	10-12
	D	2-3	580-761	15-21
	D	3-1, 2-1	331-366	8-10
	1	2-1	1074-1273	28-34
To Detent (Torque Demand)	D	1-2	588-1035	15-28
	D	2-3	1226-1638	32-44
	D	3-2	1242-1491	33-40
Through Detent (WOT)	D	1-2	1489-1726	39-46
	D	2-3	2633-2912	69-78
	D	3-2	2381-2539	63-68
	D	3-1, 2-1	1076-1306	28-35

Tire Size	Axle Ratio
	2.73
	Use Column No.
P195/75R14	1
P205/70R14	1
205/70VR14	1

MODEL PEP-AF1
3.8L CAPRI, MUSTANG
50 STATE

Throttle	Range	Shift	OPS—R.P.M.	Column Number
				1
Closed (Above 17" Vacuum)	D	1-2	409-444	10-12
	D	2-3	580-761	15-21
	D	3-1 2-1	331-366	8-10
	1	2-1	1074-1273	28-34
To Detent (Torque Demand)	D	1-2	536-1063	14-29
	D	2-3	1175-1675	31-45
	D	3-2	1191-1502	31-40
Through Detent (WOT)	D	1-2	1480-1733	39-47
	D	2-3	2621-2921	69-79
	D	3-2	2370-2547	62-68
	D	3-1 2-1	1068-1311	28-35

Tire Size	Axle Ratio
	2.73
	Use Column No.
P195/75R14	1
P205/70R14	1
205/70VR14	1

4) On all models, if cutback does not occur within specifications, check shift speeds to verify that it is the governor and not a stuck cutback valve, then repair or replace governor.

VACUUM MODULATOR CHECK

Vacuum Supply to Modulator

1) Check supply by disconnecting vacuum line at vacuum unit and connect it to vacuum gauge. With engine idling, gauge must show steady acceptable vacuum.

2) If reading is low, check for vacuum leak or poor engine vacuum. If reading is OK, rapidly accelerate engine momentarily. Reading must drop rapidly at acceleration and return immediately upon release of accelerator.

3) If reading does not change or changes slowly, transmission vacuum line is plugged, restricted, or connected to reservoir supply. Correct as necessary.

Vacuum Modulator

1) Remove unit from transmission. Use a distributor tester equipped with vacuum pump. Start pump and set regulator knob so that vacuum gauge reads 18 in. Hg, with end of hose blocked off.

2) Connect vacuum hose to manifold vacuum port. If gauge still reads 18 in. Hg, vacuum modulator is not leaking. If reading does not hold at 18 in. Hg, but drops, diaphragm is leaking and unit must be replaced.

3) As hose is removed from modulator, hold a finger over end of control rod. When hose is removed, internal spring of modulator should push control rod outward.

4) Check also for presence of transmission fluid in vacuum side of modulator or in vacuum hose. If fluid is present, diaphragm is leaking and must be replaced.

Vacuum Modulator Replacement

When replacement vacuum modulator is installed, line pressure must be checked. If not within specification, a longer or shorter throttle valve rod must be installed. The following procedure will determine if a change in rod length is necessary.

1) Attach tachometer to engine and hand vacuum pump to vacuum diaphragm. Attach pressure gauge to control pressure outlet on transmission.

2) Apply parking and service brakes. Start engine and set normal idle speed. Raise engine speed to 1000 rpm and apply 10 Hg. of vacuum to modulator. If not to specification, rod must be replaced. Low pressure reading means to use next longest rod, high reading means to use next shortest rod.

AIR PRESSURE CHECKS

1) "No Drive" condition can exist, even with correct transmission fluid pressure, because of inoperative clutches or bands. Erratic shifts could be caused by stuck governor valve.

2) Inoperative units can be located through a series of checks by substituting air pressure for fluid pressure to determine location of malfunction.

3) To make air pressure checks, loosen oil pan bolts and allow transmission to drain. Remove oil pan and control valve body. Apply air to fluid passages to ensure that unit operation is as follows:

Forward Clutch

Apply air pressure to forward clutch passage. A dull thud can be heard when clutch piston is applied, or movement of piston can be felt by placing finger tips on input shell.

Governor

Apply air pressure to the control pressure-to-governor passage and listen for sharp clicking or whistling noise indicating governor valve movement.

Reverse-High Clutch

Apply air pressure to reverse-high clutch passage. A dull thud can be heard when clutch piston is applied, or movement of piston can be felt by placing finger tips on clutch drum.

Intermediate Servo

1) Hold air nozzle in intermediate servo apply passage. Operation of servo is indicated by tightening of intermediate band around drum.

2) While continuing to apply air pressure at servo apply passage, apply air pressure to intermediate servo release passage or front release tube. Front or intermediate servo should release band against applied pressure.

Low-Reverse Servo

Apply air pressure to low-reverse servo apply passage. Low-Reverse band should tighten around drum if servo is operating properly.

NOTE: **If the air pressure applied to either clutch passage fails to operate clutch or operates both clutches at once, remove clutch and check fluid passages in case and oil pump with air pressure to detect obstructions.**

SERVICE (IN VEHICLE)

CONTROL VALVE BODY

Removal

1) Raise and support vehicle. Drain transmission fluid. Remove oil pan retaining bolts, pan and gasket. Shift transmission manual lever to "P".

2) Remove filter retaining bolt and remove filter. Remove valve body-to-case retaining bolts. Hold manual valve in valve body to prevent damaging valve. Remove valve body from case.

NOTE: **Nylon plug will be found in transmission pan. It is used to retain transmission fluid within transmission during shipment and should be discarded when oil pan is removed.**

Installation

1) Place manual lever in "P" position. Position valve body in case. Place inner downshift lever between downshift lever stop and downshift valve.

2) Make sure that 2 lands on end of manual valve engage actuating pin on manual detent lever. Install 7 body-to-case bolts, but do not tighten at this time.

3) Position detent spring on lower valve body. Install spring-to-case bolt finger tight. Hold detent spring roller in center of manual lever and install detent spring-to-lower valve body bolt. Tighten retaining bolt.

4) Tighten all control body-to-case retaining bolts. Position filter and install retaining bolt and tighten. Position gasket on pan and install pan and retaining bolts and tighten.

INTERMEDIATE SERVO

Removal

1) Raise and support vehicle. Remove servo cover retaining bolts. Remove identification tag. Remove servo cover, gasket, piston and piston return spring. Remove piston from cover and seals from piston and cover. *See Fig. 8*.

NOTE: On models equipped with 3.8L engine it may be necessary to loosen fan shroud, remove crossmember and/or oil cooler lines, and lower transmission to gain access to servo cover bolts.

Installation

1) Install new seals on piston, lubricate seals with transmission fluid. Install piston into cover. Install return spring into case. Install new gasket to cover so that notch in gasket aligns with fluid passage in case.

2) Install piston and cover into transmission case. Use two 5/16-18 x 1 1/4 bolts, 180° apart to position cover against case. Install identification tag and 2 retaining bolts. Remove aligning bolts.

3) Install remaining retaining bolts and tighten. Install crossmember and adjust intermediate band. Check fluid level.

NOTE: If band cannot be adjusted properly, band struts are not in position. Remove oil pan and valve body, install struts. Reinstall valve body and pan. Adjust band and check fluid level.

LOW-REVERSE SERVO

Removal

1) Raise vehicle on hoist, loosen reverse band adjusting screw lock nut. Tighten band adjusting screw to 10 ft. lbs. (14 N.m) to prevent band strut from falling down when servo is removed.

2) Disengage neutral start switch wiring harness. Remove servo cover-to-case retaining bolts, servo cover and seal. Remove servo piston from case. *See Fig. 9*.

NOTE: On 3.8L Capri and Mustang models, it is necessary to loosen fan shroud, remove crossmember, and lower transmission to gain access to Low Reverse Servo. Piston seal cannot be replaced without replacing piston. Seal is bonded to piston.

Installation

1) Install piston into case. Install a new seal on cover. Install cover by using two 5/16-18 x 1 1/4" bolts, 180° apart to position servo cover on case. Install 2 cover retaining bolts.

2) Remove aligning bolts and install remaining 2 retaining bolts. Tighten all retaining bolts. Position neutral start switch wiring harness. Adjust low-reverse band. Lower vehicle and check transmission fluid level.

NOTE: If band cannot be adjusted properly, low-reverse band struts are not in position. Remove oil pan and valve body. Install struts, valve body and oil pan. Adjust band. Refill transmission with fluid.

EXTENSION HOUSING BUSHING & SEAL

Removal

Raise vehicle and support. Disconnect propeller shaft from transmission. To maintain driveshaft balance, mark yoke and axle companion flange for reassembly reference. Remove seal using tapered chisel or seal remover tool. Remove bushing using puller.

CAUTION: When bushing is installed, fluid return drain hole must face downward in alignment with extension housing fluid return groove.

Installation

1) Install new bushing using driver. Inspect sealing surface of universal joint yoke. If damaged, replace yoke. Remove any scores in counter bore of housing with crocus cloth.

2) Using driver, install new seal into extension housing. Lubricate seal, yoke and splines. Install propeller shaft.

EXTENSION HOUSING

Removal

1) Raise and support vehicle. Disconnect propeller shaft and speedometer cable from transmission. To maintain driveshaft balance, mark yoke and companion flange for reassembly reference. Support transmission with jack.

2) Remove the engine rear support-to-crossmember nuts. Raise transmission and remove rear support-to-body bolts. Remove crossmember. Loosen extension housing bolts and allow transmission to drain.

3) Remove extension housing-to-case retaining bolts and vacuum tube clip. Remove extension housing.

Installation

To install, reverse removal procedures. Lubricate slip yoke splines. Tighten all bolts and adjust fluid level.

GOVERNOR

Removal

With extension housing removed, remove governor housing-to-governor distributor retaining bolts. Slide governor away from distributor body and off output shaft.

Installation

To install, reverse removal procedures. Tighten all bolts, and adjust fluid level.

REMOVAL & INSTALLATION

TRANSMISSION

See FORD MOTOR CO. articles in AUTOMATIC TRANSMISSION REMOVAL section.

TORQUE CONVERTER

LEAKAGE CHECK

See procedures given in FORD MOTOR CO. C-6 article.

FLUSHING CONVERTER

See procedures given in FORD MOTOR CO. C-6 article.

TURBINE & STATOR END PLAY CHECK

See procedures given in FORD MOTOR CO. C-6 article.

STATOR ONE-WAY CHECK

See procedures given in FORD MOTOR CO. C-6 article.

FORD MOTOR CO. C-5 (Cont.)

Fig. 6: Exploded View of C-5 Valve Body Assembly

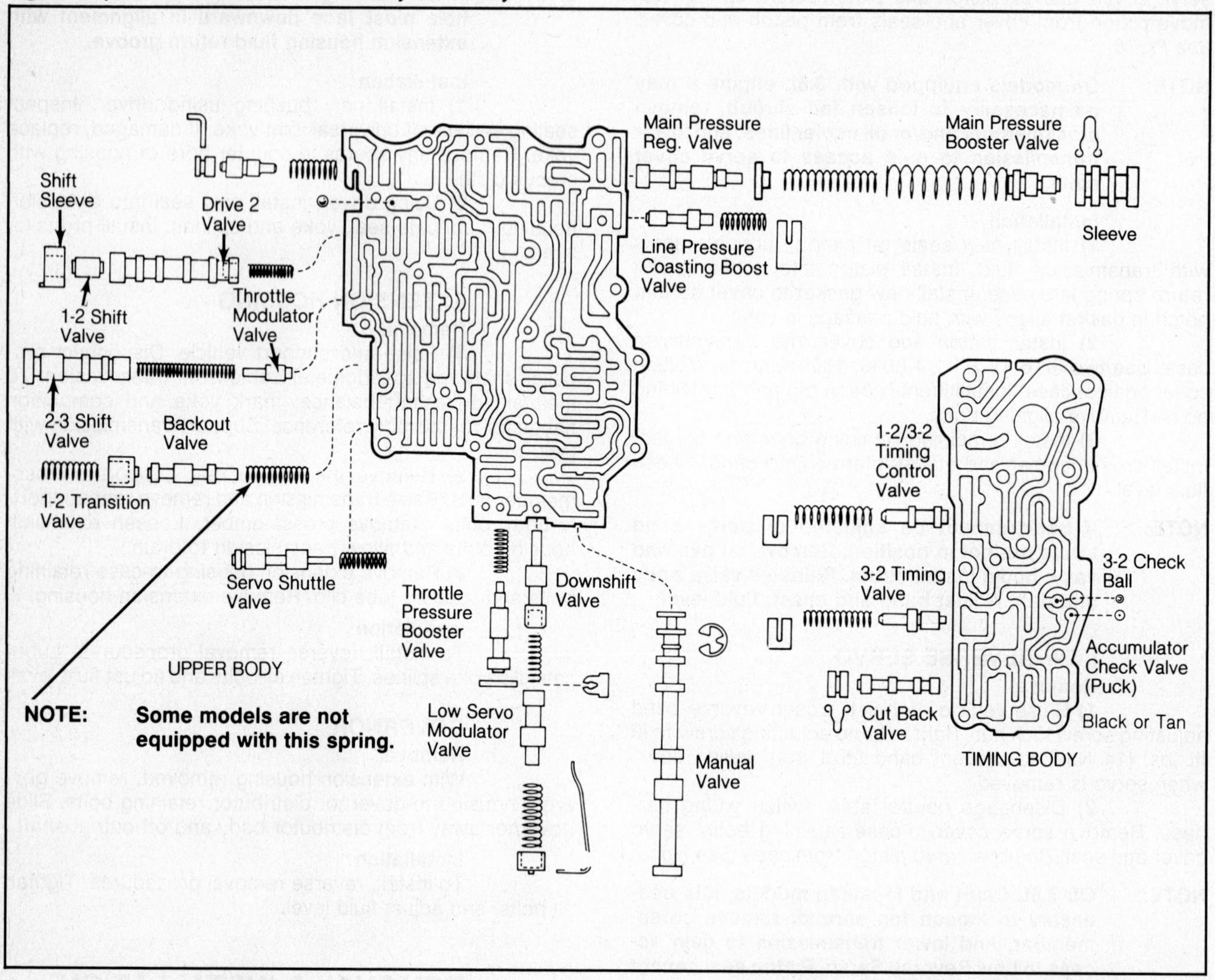

STATOR INTERFERENCE CHECKS

See procedures given in FORD MOTOR CO.C-6 article.

TRANSMISSION DISASSEMBLY

1) Remove converter assembly. Remove input shaft. Mount transmission to holding fixture. Loosen transmission oil pan retaining bolts and allow fluid to drain. Remove oil pan bolts, pan and gasket.

2) Locate oil filler tube shipping plug in case. Remove and discard plug. Remove filter screen retaining bolt and filter screen. Remove 9 valve body retaining bolts and lift valve body out of transmission case. Remove pump inlet screen from pick-up passage.

3) Remove converter housing retaining bolts and detach housing from case. Insert large screwdriver between input shell and reverse planet carrier, and pry input shell forward until pump can be removed from case. Remove and discard pump gasket.

NOTE: **Check stator support for No. 1 and No. 2 thrust washers. If washers are not present, remove them from top of reverse-high clutch.**

4) Loosen intermediate band adjusting screw lock nut, thread adjusting screw out of case, and remove band struts. Turn intermediate band counterclockwise until band lugs are aligned with clearance relief provided in case and remove band.

5) Remove clutch packs, front planetary, and input shell as an assembly. Position assembly with sun gear facing up. Remove reverse planetary assembly. Remove No. 6 and No. 7 thrust washers from carrier thrust faces. Loosen low-reverse band adjusting screw lock nut, thread adjusting screw out of case, and remove band struts.

6) Rotate low-reverse band until lugs are aligned with clearance relief provided in case. Remove band. Remove extension housing retaining bolts and vacuum diaphragm. Using magnet, remove throttle valve rod and throttle valve. Remove vacuum and vent hose clips. Note position of throttle rod in bore and location of clips.

7) Remove extension housing and discard gasket. Remove and discard rubber shipping plug from output shaft. Remove governor retaining bolts and slide governor off output shaft.

8) Using magnet, lift governor filter out of governor distributor body. Using snap ring pliers, remove snap ring retaining reverse ring gear and hub assembly to output shaft. To gain access to snap ring, it may be necessary to push output shaft forward.

9) Remove reverse ring gear hub and assembly. Remove low-reverse drum and detach No. 8 thrust washer from drum. Lift output shaft out of case. Lift governor oil collector body out of case.

10) Remove distributor sleeve retaining bolts and lift sleeve from case taking care not to bend oil tubes. Remove parking gear and No. 10 thrust washer.

11) Remove parking pawl, pivot pin, and return spring from case as an assembly. Using Socket (T65P-7B456-B) remove one-way clutch outer race retaining bolts, positioning one hand in case to catch clutch assembly before last bolt is removed. Remove No. 9 thrust washer from back of case or from one way clutch.

COMPONENT DISASSEMBLY & REASSEMBLY

NOTE: **Handle all parts carefully to avoid damaging bearing or mating surfaces. Lubricate all internal parts with clean automatic transmission fluid only (gaskets and thrust washers may be held in place with petroleum jelly). Use all new gaskets, and tighten all bolts evenly.**

CONTROL VALVE BODY

Disassembly

1) Remove timing body retaining bolts. Remove timing body and relief valve from lower body. Remove timing body separator plate retaining screw, separator plate, check valve, and check ball from timing body.

2) Remove upper body to lower body retaining bolts, turn valve body over and remove lower body to upper body retaining bolts. Remove detent spring. Hold separator plate against lower body and lift lower body half away from upper body half.

3) Turn lower body over and place it on bench with separator plate facing up. Remove separator plate and gasket from body and discard gasket.

4) Remove check balls and pressure limit valve from lower body half. Remove check ball from upper body half.

Reassembly

NOTE: **Depending upon vehicle application, there may be either a black or tan check valve (puck) in timing body. Be sure correct valve is used when replacing or reassembling.**

1) Install check valve and check ball in timing body. Position separator and gasket with plate on timing body. Install retaining bolts and tighten using alignment pins to prevent plate from turning.

2) Install check balls and pressure limit valve in lower half of valve body. Steel ball is larger than other check balls and must be positioned as shown in *Fig. 7.*

3) Install gasket and separator plate on lower body half. Install check ball in upper body half. Hold separator plate firmly against lower body half while turning it over.

4) Position lower body half on upper body half. Align the bodies using 2 1/4-20 x 1.5" bolts. Install the one 10-24 x .875" bolt, and tighten. Remove alignment bolts.

5) Install detent spring and roller assembly on lower body half. Position a drift punch in valve body to hold assembly in alignment. Install retaining bolt and tighten. Install 9 additional bolts and tighten. Remember to tighten screw in suction passage under center screw.

6) Install gasket on lower valve body. Install check valve and spring in lower body half and position timing body on lower body half. Install timing body retaining bolts and tighten.

GOVERNOR

Disassembly

Remove snap ring from governor bore. Remove primary valve spring, spring seat washer, and primary

Fig. 7: Check Ball Location in Valve Body Components

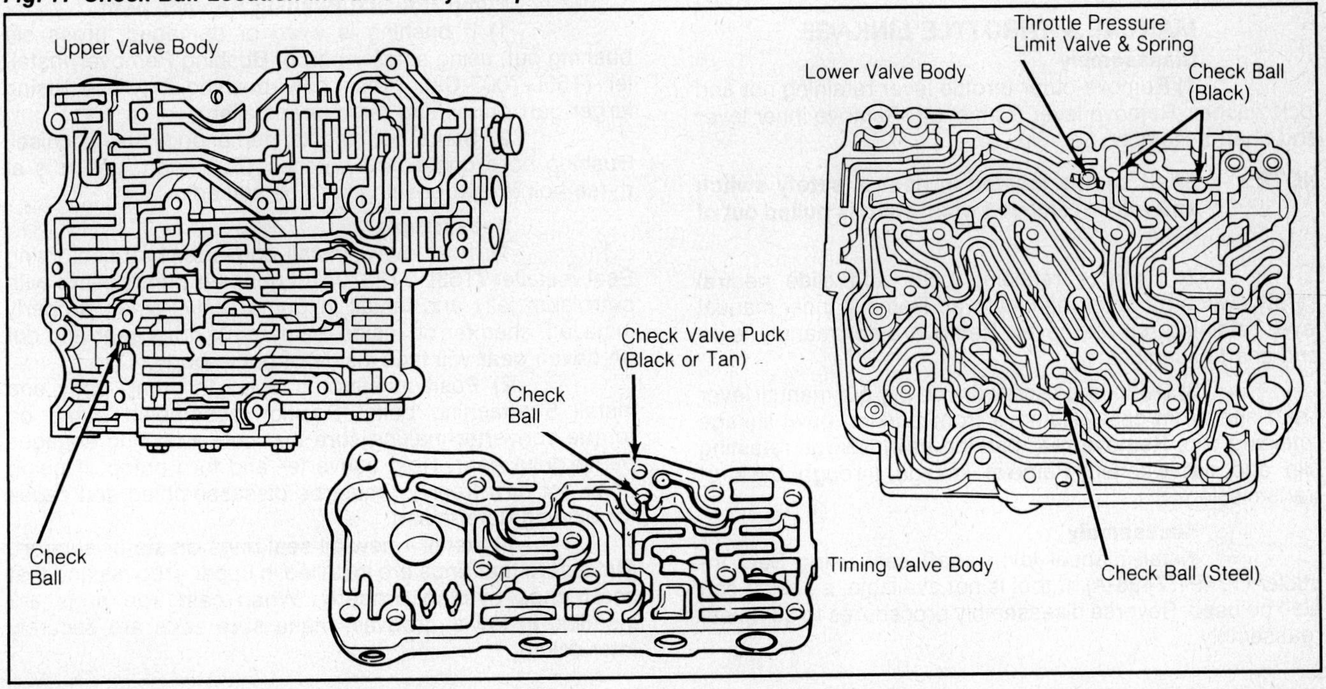

Automatic Transmissions

FORD MOTOR CO. C-5 (Cont.)

Fig. 8: Exploded View of Intermediate Servo

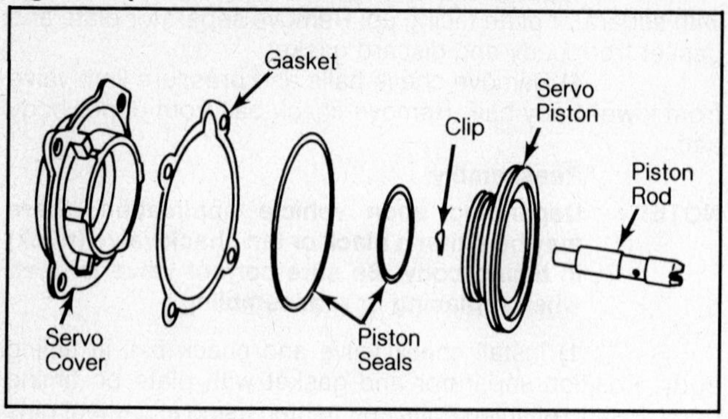

Fig. 9: Exploded View of Low-Reverse Servo

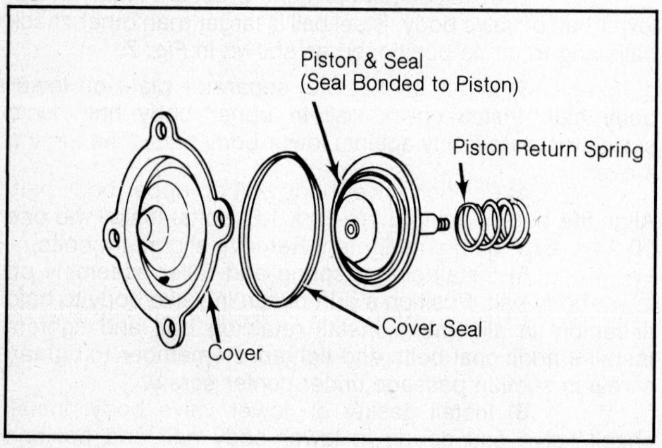

valve. Remove secondary valve spring retaining plate. Remove secondary valve and spring from governor bore. *See Fig. 11.*

Reassembly

Reverse disassembly procedures. Ensure concave area on retaining plate faces spring.

MANUAL & THROTTLE LINKAGE

Disassembly

1) Remove outer throttle lever retaining nut and lock washer. Remove lever from shaft. Remove inner lever and shaft assembly. *See Fig. 10.*

NOTE: **Shaft seal is located in neutral safety switch and will be removed when shaft is pulled out of case.**

2) Remove retaining bolts and slide neutral safety switch off outer manual lever. Remove inner manual lever retaining nut and lever. Remove outer manual lever and shaft assembly.

3) Using large screwdriver, pry out manual lever shaft seal from case. Remove front parking pawl linkage retaining clip. Remove rear parking pawl linkage retaining clip and flat washer. Remove linkage through back of transmission.

Reassembly

Install manual lever shaft seal using Seal Installer (T74P-77498-A). If tool is not available, a socket can also be used. Reverse disassembly procedures to complete reassembly.

Fig. 10: Exploded View of Manual and Throttle Linkage

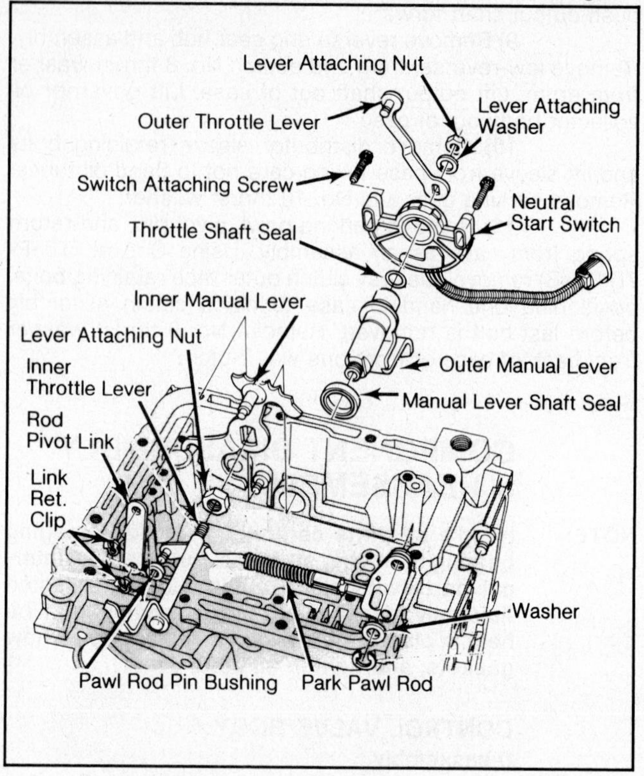

FRONT PUMP

Disassembly

1) Remove No. 1 and No. 2 thrust washers from stator support. Remove teflon and cast iron seal rings from stator support.

2) Remove retaining bolts and lift stator support out of pump body. Remove gears from pump body. Using hammer and punch, drive out converter hub seal from pump body. *See Fig. 12.*

Pump Housing Bushing Replacement

1) If bushing is worn or damaged, press old bushing out, using smaller part of Bushing Remover/Installer (T66L-7003-C2). Press new bushing in place, using larger part of bushing remover/installer.

2) Stake bushing to pump body using chisel. Bushing bore contains 2 notches 180° apart, and it is at these points that bushing is to be staked.

Reassembly

1) If removed, install converter hub seal using Seal Installer (T63L-778370A). Lubricate pump gears with petroleum jelly and install in pump body. When properly installed, chamfer on inside diameter of drive gear and dot on driven gear will face inside of pump body.

2) Position stator support in pump body and install 5 attaching bolts. Position assembled pump on torque converter making sure that converter hub engages pump drive gear. Hold converter and turn pump. If pump does not turn freely, it must be dissassembled and cause for binding determined.

3) Install 4 new oil seal rings on stator support. Make sure that rings are installed in upper grooves and that scarf ends overlap properly. When cast iron rings are installed in lower grooves, make sure ends are securely interlocked.

Fig. 11: Exploded View of Governor Assembly

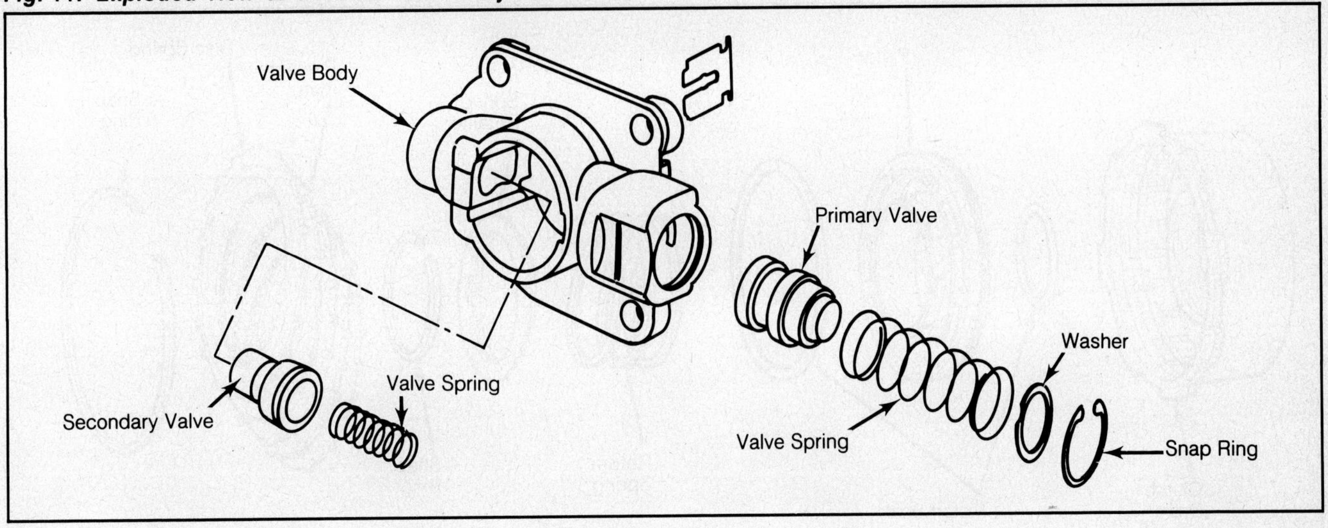

NOTE: Number 1 and Number 2 thrust washers are selective fit washers used to determine transmission end play. These washers should be replaced in pairs to obtain an end play of .008-.042" (.20-1.07 mm).

4) If end play is known, select proper washers to obtain desired end play. If end play is not known, use original thrust washers. End play will be checked and corrected during transmission assembly. Lubricate No. 1 and No. 2 thrust washers with petroleum jelly and install to stator support.

REVERSE-HIGH CLUTCH

Disassembly

1) Remove clutch pack retaining ring and clutch pack from drum. Using clutch spring Compressor (T65L-77515-A) , compress piston return spring. Remove spring retaining ring using external snap ring pliers.

2) Remove clutch piston. If piston is difficult to remove, air pressure can be used to help remove piston. Remove clutch piston seal and inner seal from clutch drum hub.

Reassembly

1) Install new seal on clutch drum hub and clutch piston. Lubricate seals with petroleum jelly. Lubricate inside of Seal Protector (T82L-77404-A) with petroleum jelly and place piston in tool. Position tool in hub and push piston to bottom of hub using even thumb pressure.

2) To complete reassembly, reverse disassembly procedure. If new composition plates are to be installed, soak in transmission fluid for 15 minutes before installing.

3) To check clutch pack clearance, install steel plate in clutch drum. Install composition and steel plates alternately until 2 composition plates remain.

4) Install remaining 2 composition plates, disc spring and pressure plate (thicker steel plate). Install retaining ring.

Fig. 12: Exploded View of Oil Pump Assembly

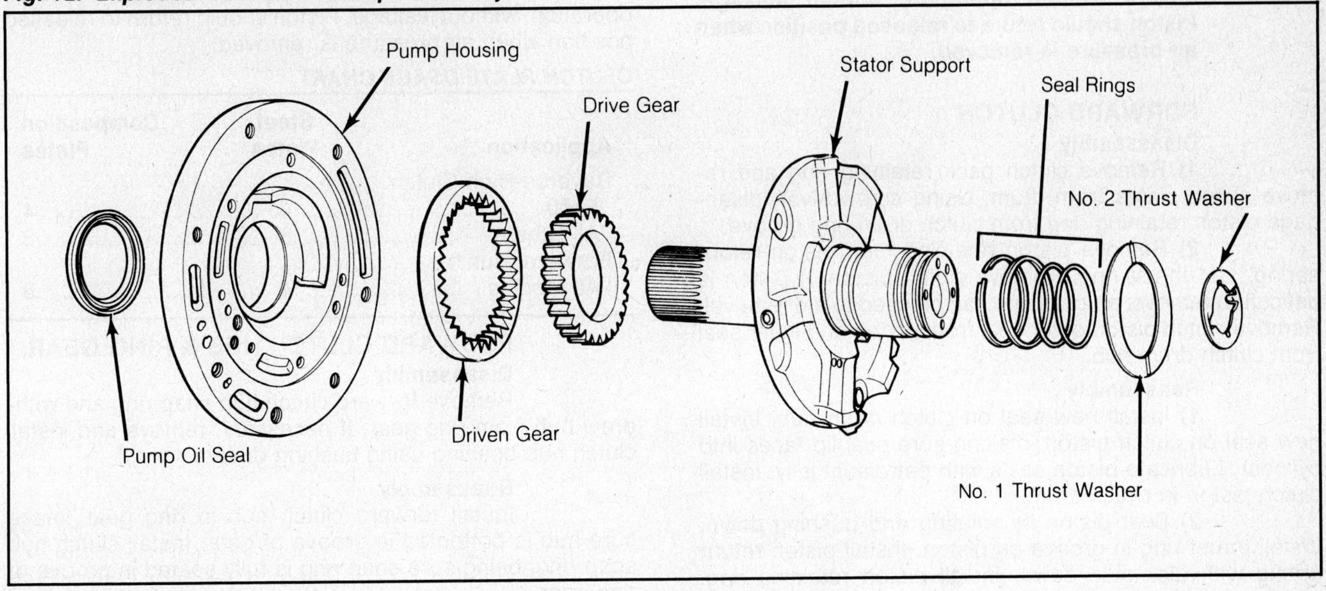

Fig. 13: Exploded View of Reverse-High Clutch Assembly

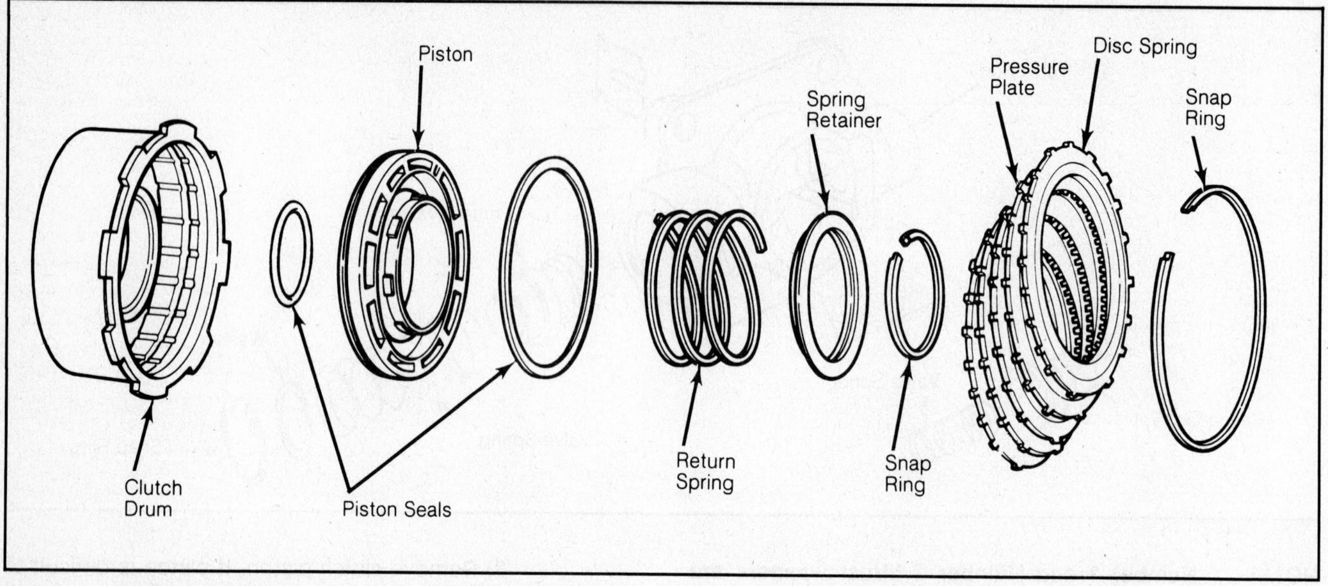

NOTE: **This is not correct plate installation sequence. This sequence is only used to check clutch pack clearance.**

5) Using a feeler gauge, check clearance between pressure plate and retaining ring. Pressure plate should be held down when checking clearance. If clearance exceeds .025-.050" (.64-1.35 mm), install snap ring of required thickness. Snap rings are available in .050-.054" (1.27-1.37 mm), .064-.068" (1.62-1.72 mm), .078-.082" (1.98-2.08 mm) and .092-.096" (2.34-2.44 mm) thicknesses.

6) After clearance has been checked and proper snap ring selected, remove clutch plates from clutch drum and reinstall as follows: install a steel plate, then alternately install composition and steel plates. Install pressure plate and disc spring with splines facing snap ring. Install retaining ring.

NOTE: **Using air pressure, check clutch for proper operation. Clutch should be heard and felt to assure smooth operation, without leakage. Piston should return to released position when air pressure is removed.**

FORWARD CLUTCH

Disassembly

1) Remove clutch pack retaining ring and remove clutch plates from drum. Using screwdriver, disengage piston retaining ring from clutch drum ring groove.

2) Remove piston retaining ring, piston return spring, and thrust ring. Remove clutch piston. If piston is difficult to remove, air pressure can be used to aid removal. Remove clutch piston outer seal from piston and inner seal from clutch drum hub.

Reassembly

1) Install new seal on clutch drum hub. Install new seal on clutch piston, making sure seal lip faces into cylinder. Lubricate piston seals with petroleum jelly. Install clutch piston in clutch drum.

2) Seat piston by rotating and pushing down. Install thrust ring in groove on piston. Install piston return spring with disk side down. Install piston retaining ring. Make sure ring is fully seated in clutch drum groove. Install forward pressure plate.

3) Dished side of plate should face piston. Install clutch pack. If new clutch plates are installed, they must be soaked in transmission fluid for 15 minutes before clutch pack is assembled. Starting with composition plate, alternately install composition and steel plates. Last plate to be installed is rear pressure plate.

4) Install clutch pack retaining ring. Using feeler gauge, check clearance between pressure plate and retaining ring. Hold pressure plate down when making measurement.

5) Clearance should be .025-.050" (.64-1.35 mm). If clearance is not within limits, install snap ring of required thickness. Snap rings are available in .050-.054" (1.27-1.37 mm), .064-.068" (1.62-1.72 mm), .078-.082" (1.98-2.08 mm), .092-.096" (2.34-2.44 mm), and .104-.108" (2.64-2.74 mm) thicknesses.

6) Apply air pressure to clutch and check operation. Clutch should be heard and felt to assure smooth operation, without leakage. Piston should return to released position when air pressure is removed.

CLUTCH PLATE USAGE CHART

Application	Steel Plates	Composition Plates
Reverse-High Clutch		
F150	4	4
All Others	3	3
Forward Clutch		
All Models	4	5

FORWARD CLUTCH HUB & RING GEAR

Disassembly

Remove forward clutch hub snap ring and withdraw hub from ring gear. If necessary, remove and install clutch hub bushing using bushing drivers.

Reassembly

Install forward clutch hub in ring gear, make sure hub is bottomed in groove of gear. Install clutch hub snap ring, being sure snap ring is fully seated in groove of ring gear.

FORD MOTOR CO. C-5 (Cont.)

Fig. 14: View of Forward Clutch Hub and Ring Gear

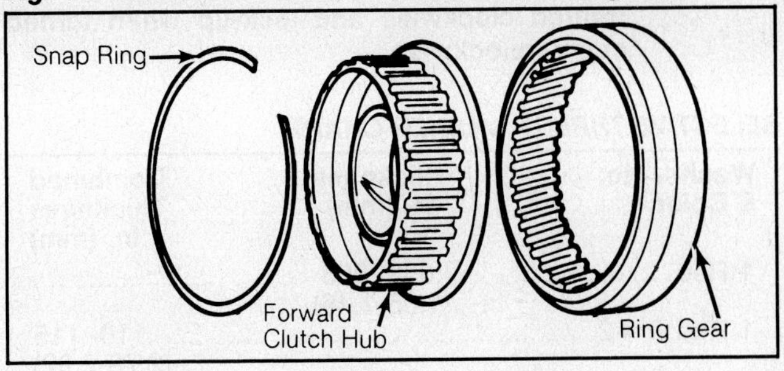

Fig. 15: Input Shell and Sun Gear Assembly

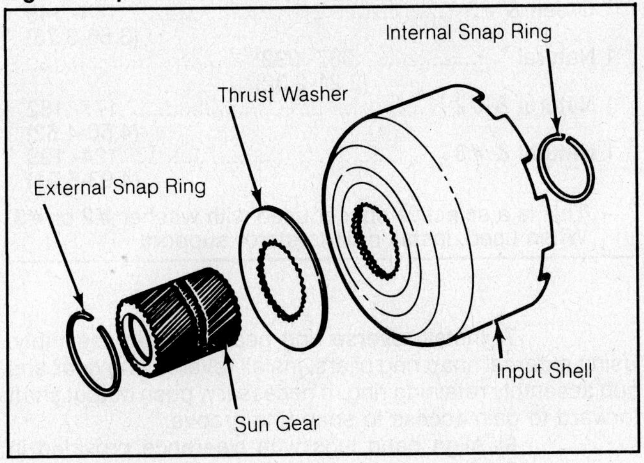

INPUT SHELL & SUN GEAR

Disassembly

Using snap ring pliers remove rear snap ring from sun gear. Remove thrust washer No. 5. Remove sun gear from input shell. Remove internal snap ring from sun gear.

Sun Gear Bushing Replacement

Remove old bushings by using bushing remover to press both bushings through and out of gear. Install new bushings separately using bushing installer to press new bushing in each end of gear.

Reassembly

Reverse disassembly procedures.

SUN GEAR BUSHING TOOLS

Application	Tool Number
Bushing Remover	
F150	T66L-7003-B6
All Others	T66L-7003-C5
Bushing Installer (All Models)	T66L-7003-C3

OUTPUT SHAFT & GOVERNOR DISTRIBUTOR

Disassembly

Using expanding type snap ring pliers, remove distributor to output shaft snap ring. Slide governor distributor off output shaft. Using snap ring pliers, remove seal rings on distributor body.

Reassembly

Install seal rings on distributor body, and reverse disassembly procedures.

REVERSE RING GEAR & HUB

Disassembly

Remove hub snap ring from reverse ring gear and withdraw hub from ring gear. *See Fig. 17.*

Reassembly

Install hub in reverse ring gear, make sure hub is fully seated in groove. Install snap ring in reverse ring gear, making sure snap ring is fully seated in snap ring groove of ring gear.

Fig. 16: Exploded View of Forward Clutch Assembly

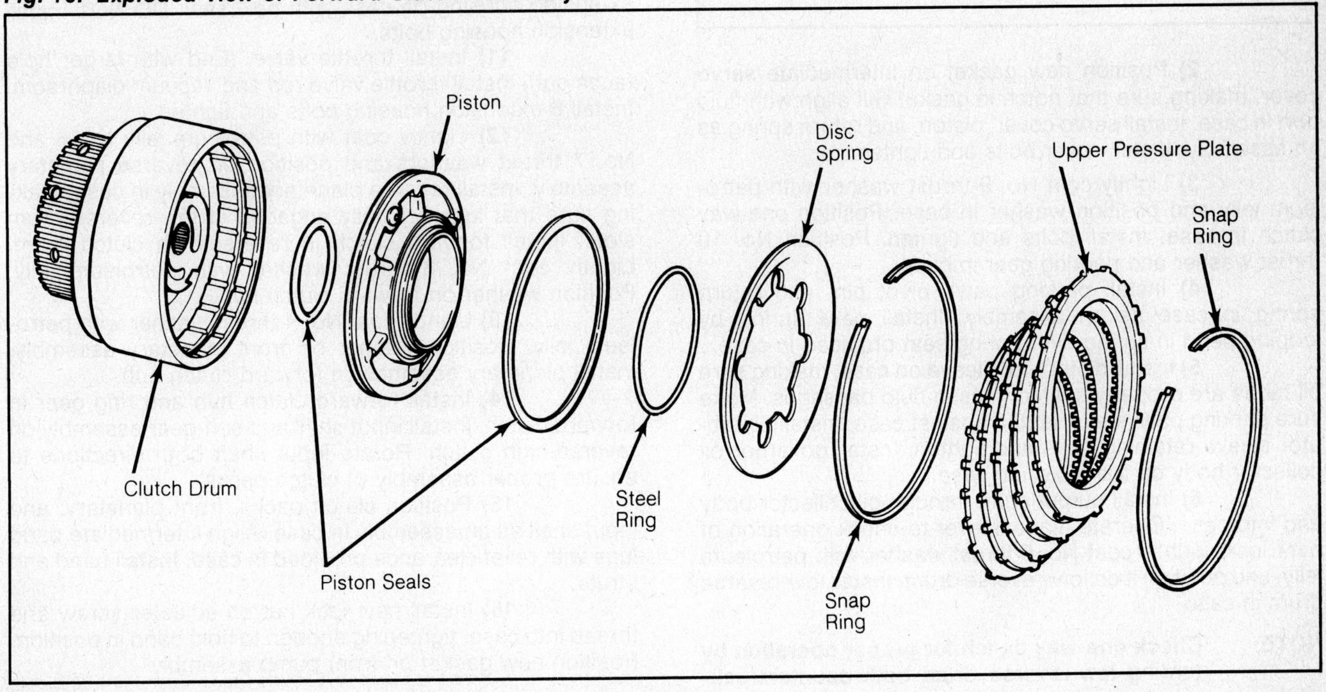

LOW-REVERSE BRAKE DRUM BUSHING REPLACEMENT

To remove bushing, use cape chisel and cut along bushing seam until chisel breaks through bushing wall. Pry loose ends of bushing up with an awl and remove bushing. Use bushing Driver (T66L-7003-C7) to install new bushing.

TRANSMISSION REASSEMBLY

NOTE: **Handle all parts carefully to avoid damaging bearing and mating surfaces. Lubricate all parts with clean automatic transmission fluid only (gaskets and thrust washers may be held in place with petroleum jelly). Use all new gaskets and seals. Tighten all bolts evenly.**

1) Install low-reverse servo piston and return spring in transmission case. Place new seal on servo cover and position cover on case, install bolts and tighten. Route neutral start switch through clip. Bend clip over slightly to hold harness in position.

Fig. 17: Reverse Ring Gear and Hub

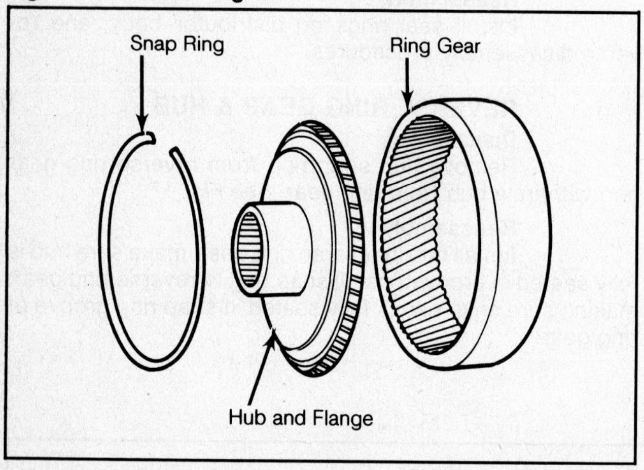

2) Position new gasket on intermediate servo cover, making sure that notch in gasket will align with fluid port in case. Install servo cover, piston, and return spring as an assembly. Install cover bolts and tighten.

3) Lightly coat No. 9 thrust washer with petroleum jelly and position washer in case. Position one-way clutch in case. Install bolts and tighten. Position No. 10 thrust washer and parking gear in case.

4) Install parking pawl, pivot pin, and return spring in case as an assembly. Install pawl spring by looping bend in spring over spring seat provided in case.

5) Install distributor sleeve on case, making sure oil tubes are properly seated in case fluid passages. Make sure parking pawl stays seated against case. Install distributor sleeve retaining bolts and tighten. Install governor oil collector body on transmission case.

6) Install output shaft through oil collector body and into case. Operate manual lever to check operation of park lock. Lightly coat No. 8 thrust washer with petroleum jelly, and position it on low-reverse drum. Install low-reverse drum in case.

NOTE: **Check one-way clutch for proper operation by turning low-reverse drum both counterclockwise and clockwise. Drum should turn when rotated clockwise and lock-up when turned counterclockwise.**

SELECTIVE THRUST WASHER CHART

Washer No. & Color	Thickness In. (mm)	Combined Thickness In. (mm)
1 Red	.053-.058 (1.35-1.46)	....
1 Red & #2	....	.110-.115 (2.79-2.92)
1 Green	.070-.075 (1.78-1.90)	....
1 Green & #3	....	.144-.149 (3.66-3.78)
1 Natural [1]	.087-.092 (2.21-2.32)	....
1 Natural & #2 [1]	....	.177-.182 (4.50-4.62)
1 Natural & #3 [1]	....	.194-.199 (4.93-5.01)

[1] – This is a selective spacer used with washer #2 or #3. When used, install next to stator support.

7) Install reverse ring gear and hub assembly. Using external snap ring pliers, install reverse ring gear and hub assembly retaining ring. If necessary, push output shaft forward to gain access to snap ring groove.

8) Align band lugs with clearance provided in case. Install low-reverse band, making sure double lug faces adjuster screw.

9) Install band struts, using a new lock nut on adjuster screw, and thread screw into case tightening it enough to hold band in place. Install governor screen in governor distributor body.

10) Position governor on governor collector body and install and tighten retaining bolts in a cross pattern. Install new gasket to extension housing. Position extension housing on case with new seal. DO NOT install extension housing bolts.

11) Install throttle valve. (End with larger hole faces out.) Install throttle valve rod and vacuum diaphragm. Install 6 extension housing bolts and tighten.

12) Lightly coat with petroleum jelly No. 6 and No. 7 thrust washers and position on reverse planetary assembly. Install reverse planetary assembly in case, making sure that lugs are fully engaged in low-reverse drum slots. Install forward clutch in reverse-high clutch drum. Lightly coat No. 3 thrust washer with petroleum jelly. Position washer on forward clutch hub.

13) Lightly coat No. 4 thrust washer with petroleum jelly. Position washer on front planetary assembly. Install planetary assembly in forward clutch hub.

14) Install forward clutch hub and ring gear in forward clutch. Install input shell and sun-gear assembly on reverse-high clutch. Rotate input shaft both directions to ensure proper assembly of clutch packs.

15) Position clutch packs, front planetary, and input shell as an assembly in case. Align intermediate band lugs with relief clearance provided in case. Install band and struts.

16) Install new lock nut on adjuster screw and thread into case, tightening enough to hold band in position. Position new gasket on front pump assembly.

Automatic Transmissions

FORD MOTOR CO. C-5 (Cont.)

Fig. 18: Exploded View of Transmission Showing Main Components

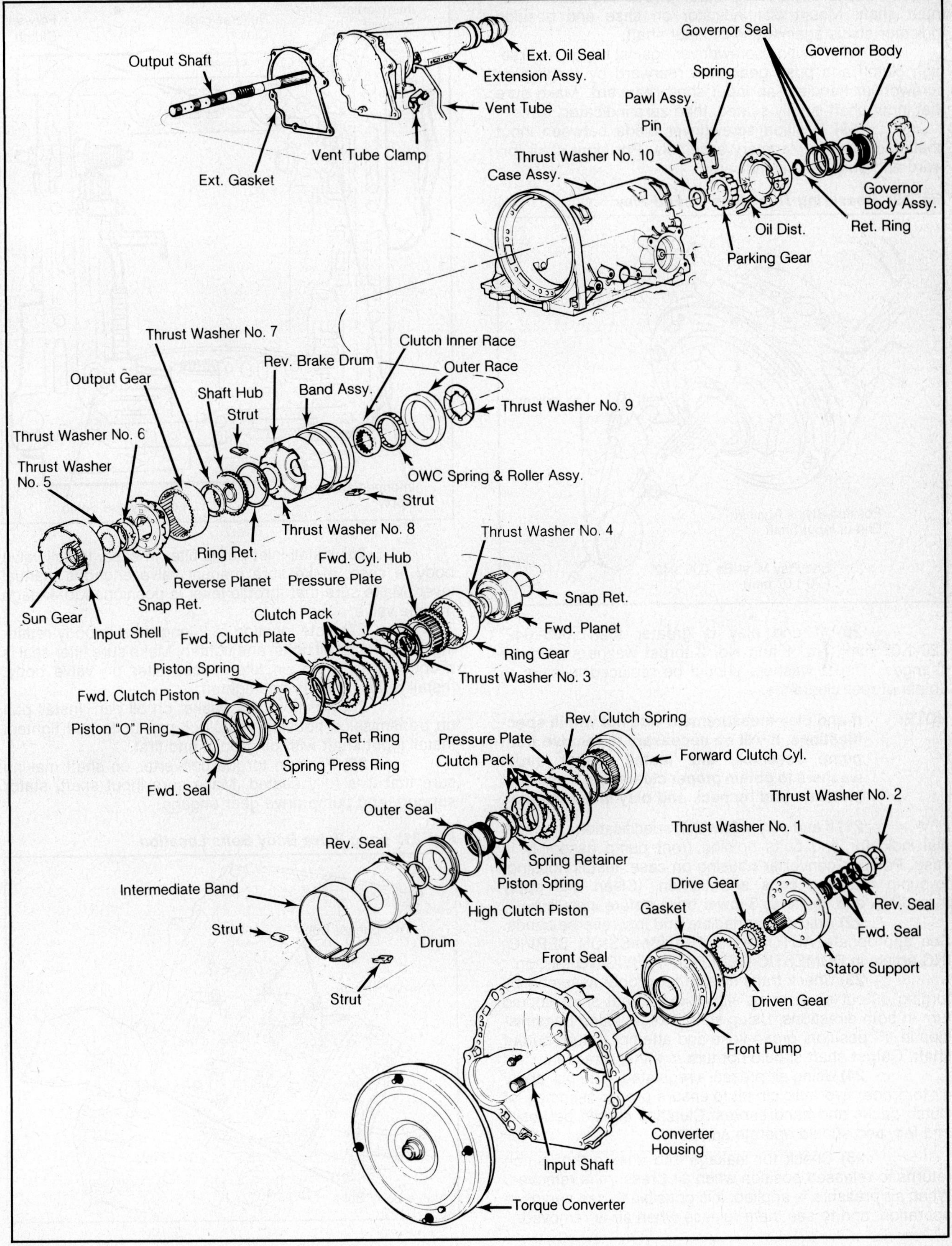

FORD MOTOR CO. C-5 (Cont.)

17) Place pump assembly in case. Install and tighten 2 converter housing-to-pump retaining bolts. Install input shaft. Mount dial indicator on case and position indicator stylus against end of input shaft.

18) Position screwdriver against lug on reverse-high clutch and push gear train rearward by tapping on screwdriver handle. Tap input shaft rearward. Make sure that input shaft is fully seated, then zero indicator.

19) Position screwdriver blade between input shell and reverse planetary assembly. Pry input shell forward and observe dial indicator.

Fig. 19: Measuring Transmission End Play

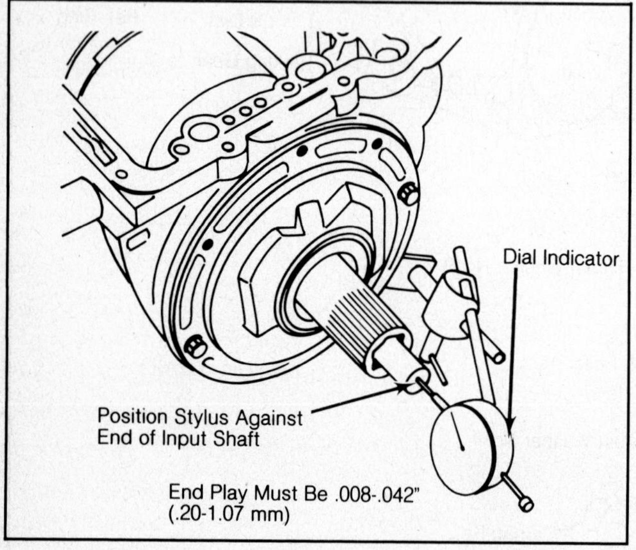

20) If end play is greater than .008-.042" (.20-1.07 mm), No. 1 and No. 2 thrust washers must be changed. Thrust washers should be replaced in pairs to obtain proper clearance.

NOTE: **If end play measurement was not within specifications, it will be necessary to remove front pump assembly and install proper thrust washers to obtain proper clearance. Install dial indicator and recheck end play measurement.**

21) If end play was within specifications, remove dial indicator and bolts holding front pump assembly in case. Position converter housing on case. Install housing-to-pump retaining bolts and tighten. (Clean and apply threadlock and sealer to 3 lower bolts before installing.)

22) Adjust intermediate and low-reverse bands. See appropriate AUTOMATIC TRANSMISSION SERVICING article in DOMESTIC GENERAL SERVICING section.

23) Check transmission for proper assembly by turning output shaft using slip yoke. Output shaft should turn in both directions. Using shift linkage, place transmission in "P" position, grasp yoke and attempt to turn output shaft. Output shaft should not turn in either direction.

24) Using air pressure regulated at 25 psi, apply air to proper hydraulic circuit to ensure proper assembly of clutch packs and band servos. Clutches should be heard and felt, and should operate smoothly.

25) Check for leakage and ensure that clutch returns to released position when air pressure is removed. When air pressure is applied, it is possible to see servos in operation, and to see them release when air is removed.

Fig. 20: Air Pressure Test Locations on Case

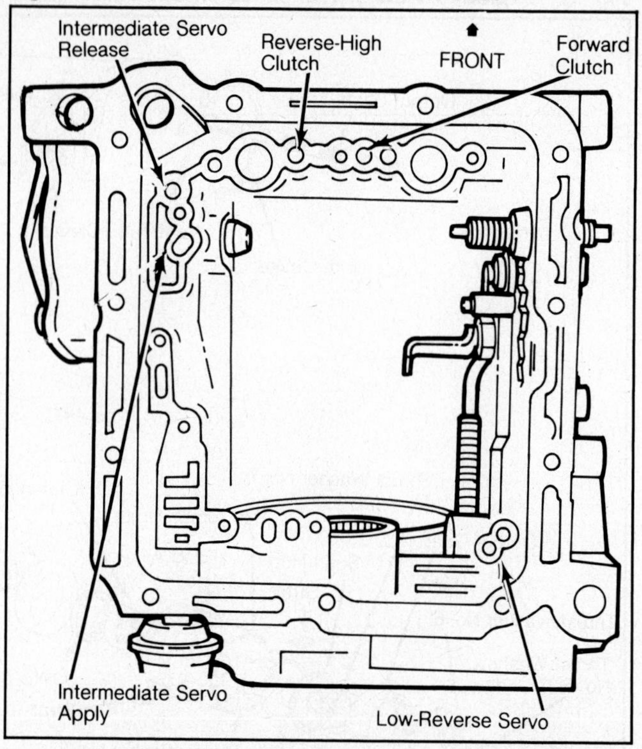

26) Install inlet pump filter in case. Install valve body in case, make sure manual valve engages manual lever. Make sure that throttle lever is positioned to engage throttle valve.

27) Note location of 2 longer valve body retaining bolts, install all bolts, and tighten. Make sure filter seal is properly positioned on filter. Place filter on valve body. Install retaining bolts and tighten.

28) Position new gasket on oil pan. Install pan on transmission housing. Install oil pan bolts and tighten. Install input shaft with oil groove end first.

29) Position torque converter on shaft making sure that it is fully seated. Make sure input shaft, stator support, and pump drive gear engage.

Fig. 21: Long Valve Body Bolts Location

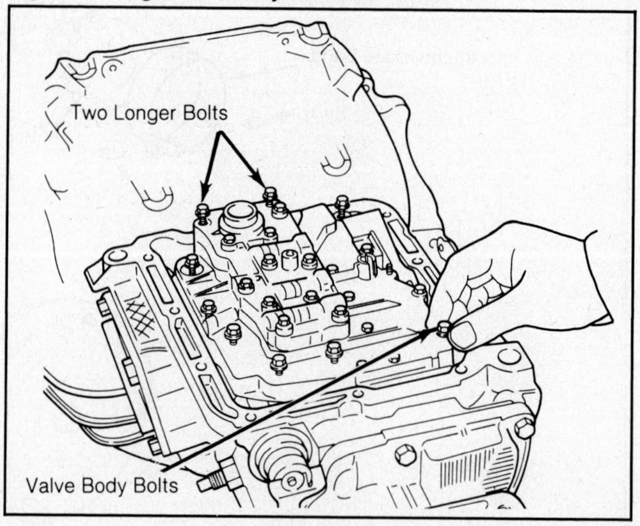

FORD MOTOR CO. C-5 (Cont.)

TIGHTENING SPECIFICATIONS

Application	Ft. Lbs. (N.m)
Oil Line-to-Transmission	18-23 (24-31)
Overrunning Clutch Race-to-Case	13-20 (18-27)
Oil Pan-to-Case	12-16 (17-21)
Reactor Support-to-Pump	12-20 (17-27)
Converter Hsg.	
Cover-to-Converter Hsg.	12-16 (17-21)
Converter Hsg.-to-Case	28-40 (38-55)
Pump-to-Case	28-40 (38-55)
Engine Rear Cover Plate-to-Trans.	12-16 (17-21)
Rear Servo Cover-to-Case	12-20 (17-27)
Oil Distributor Sleeve-to-Case	12-20 (17-27)
Extension Housing-to-Case	28-40 (38-55)
Engine-to-Trans. (3.8L)	28-38 (38-51)
Engine-to-Trans. (3.3L)	40-50 (55-67)
Outer Throttle Lever-to-Shaft	12-16 (17-21)
Inner Manual Lever-to-Shaft	30-40 (41-55)
Inter. & Reverse Lock Nut	35-45 (47-61)
Drain Plug-to-Converter Cover	12-17 (16-23)
	INCH Lbs. (N.m)
End Plates-to-Body	25-40 (2.8-4.5)
Separator Plate-to-Timing Body	25-40 (2.8-4.5)
Lower Body & Detent-to-Upper Body	40-60 (4.5-6.7)
Pan Screen-to-Timing Valve Body	25-40 (2.8-4.5)
Governor-to-Oil Collector	80-120 (9.0-12.5)
Pump Assembly-to-Case	20-38 (2.2-4.0)
Main Control-to-Case	80-120 (9.0-13.5)
Neutral Switch-to-Case	55-75 (6.2-8.5)
Upper Body-to-Lower Body (Long)	80-120 (9.0-12.5)
Upper Body-to-Lower Body (Short)	40-60 (4.5-6.7)
3-2 Timing Valve	
Body-to-Upper Body	40-60 (4.5-6.7)
Detent Spring & Lower	
Body-to-Upper Body	40-60 (4.5 6.7)
3-2 Timing Valve	
Body-to-Lower Body	
5/16" Bolts	40-60 (4.5-6.7)
3/8" Bolts	52-72 (6-8)
1/4-20 Bolts	52-72 (5.9-8.1)
10-24 Screws	40-60 (4.5-6.7)

FORD MOTOR CO. C-6

E150, 250 & 350,
F150, 250 & 350,
Bronco, F350 4WD

IDENTIFICATION

An identification tag is located under lower front intermediate servo cover bolt. A number appearing after the suffix indicates internal parts in transmission have been changed after initial production start-up.

For example, a PJA-AL 15 model transmission that has been changed internally would read PJA-AL 16. *See Fig. 1.*

Fig. 1: C-6 Transmission Identification Tag

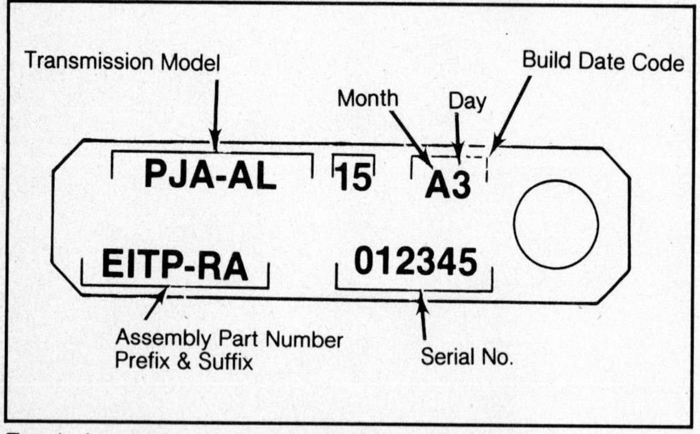

Tag is located under lower front intermediate servo cover bolt.

TRANSMISSION IDENTIFICATION CODES

Application	Models
Bronco, F150-250-350	K
E150-250-350	G

DESCRIPTION

Transmission is a 3-speed unit capable of providing automatic upshifts and downshifts through 3 forward gear ratios and also providing manual selection of 1st and 2nd gears.

Transmission consists basically of a torque converter, compound planetary gear train controlled by a single band, 3 multiple disc clutches, a one-way clutch and hydraulic control system.

LUBRICATION & ADJUSTMENTS

See appropriate AUTOMATIC TRANSMISSION SERVICING article in DOMESTIC GENERAL SERVICING section.

TROUBLE SHOOTING

See appropriate AUTOMATIC TRANSMISSION TROUBLE SHOOTING article in DOMESTIC GENERAL SERVICING section.

TESTING

ROAD TEST

1) Check minimum throttle upshift in "D". Transmission should start in 1st gear, shift to 2nd, and then shift to 3rd as speed increases. See SHIFT SPEEDS table.

2) With transmission in 3rd gear depress accelerator through detent (to floor). Transmission should shift from 3rd to 2nd or 3rd to 1st, depending on vehicle speed. See SHIFT SPEEDS table.

3) Check closed throttle downshift from 3rd to 1st by coasting down from about 30 MPH in 3rd gear. Shift should occur as shown in table.

4) With transmission selector lever in "2" position, transmission should operate only in 2nd gear.

5) With transmission in 3rd gear and road speed above 30 MPH, transmission should shift to 2nd gear when selector lever is moved from "D" into "2" or "1". When manual shift is made below 30 MPH, transmission should shift from 2nd or 3rd to 1st.

NOTE: **This check will determine if governor pressure and shift control valve are operating properly.**

6) Slipping or engine speed flare-up in any gear usually indicates clutch or band problems. In most cases, the clutch or band that is slipping can be determined by noting transmission operation in all selector positions and comparing which internal units are applied in those positions. See CLUTCH and BAND APPLICATION CHART.

CLUTCH AND BAND APPLICATION CHART (ELEMENTS IN USE)

Selector Lever Position	Intermediate Band	Reverse Clutch	Forward Clutch	High Clutch	One-Way Clutch
D - DRIVE					
First Gear			X		X
Second Gear	X		X		
Third Gear			X	X	
L2 - INTERMEDIATE					
Second Gear	X		X		
L1 - LOW		X	X		
R - REVERSE		X		X	

NEUTRAL OR PARK – All clutches, brakes, and bands released and/or ineffective.

Fig. 2: Side View of Transmission Case

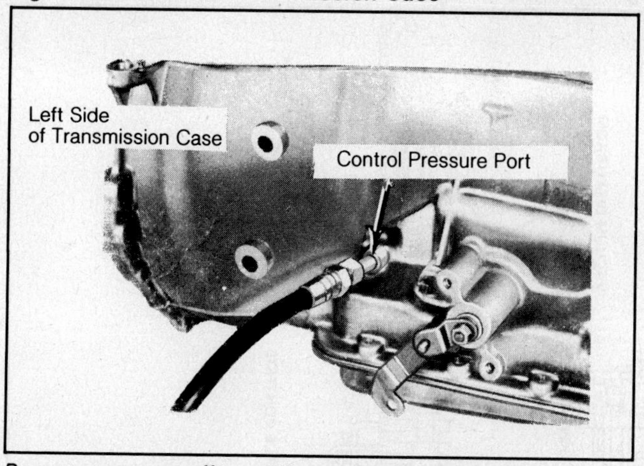

Pressure gauges affect shift quality of transmission.

CONTROL PRESSURE TEST

Engine Vacuum Method

1) Attach tachometer to engine. Install vacuum gauge (using "T") into manifold vacuum line at vacuum diaphragm unit. Attach a 0-400 psi gauge to control pressure take-off point at transmission. *See Figs. 2 and 4.*

2) Apply both parking and service brakes. Adjust the idle speed to the specified RPM. If engine idle speed cannot be brought within limits, check for a binding throttle and downshift linkage, vacuum leaks in the vacuum diaphragm, or vacuum leaks in all other vacuum operated units (such as the power brake).

3) With engine at curb idle speed and normal operating temperature, read and record control pressure in all selector positions at specified manifold vacuum. Com pare control pressures obtained in tests with pressures given in CONTROL PRESSURE table.

Fig. 4: Connecting Vacuum Gauge for Pressure Test

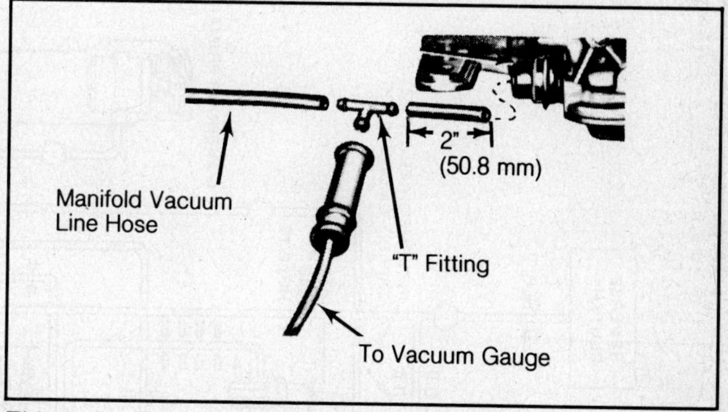

This is for the engine vacuum test method

Fig. 3: Sectional View of Ford C-6 Automatic Transmission Assembly

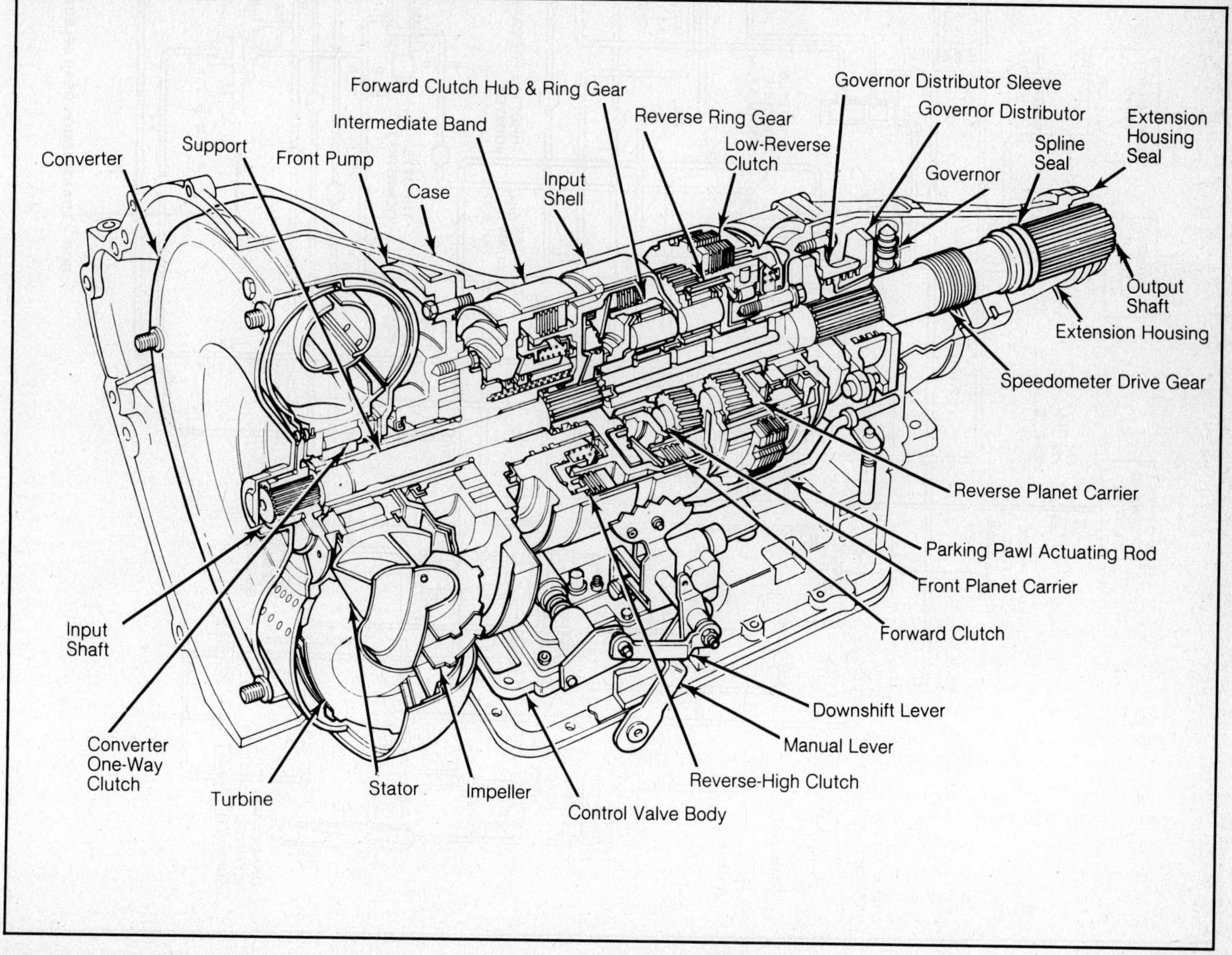

Automatic Transmissions

FORD MOTOR CO. C-6 (Cont.)

Fig. 5: Ford C-6 Automatic Transmission Hydraulic Circuits Diagram

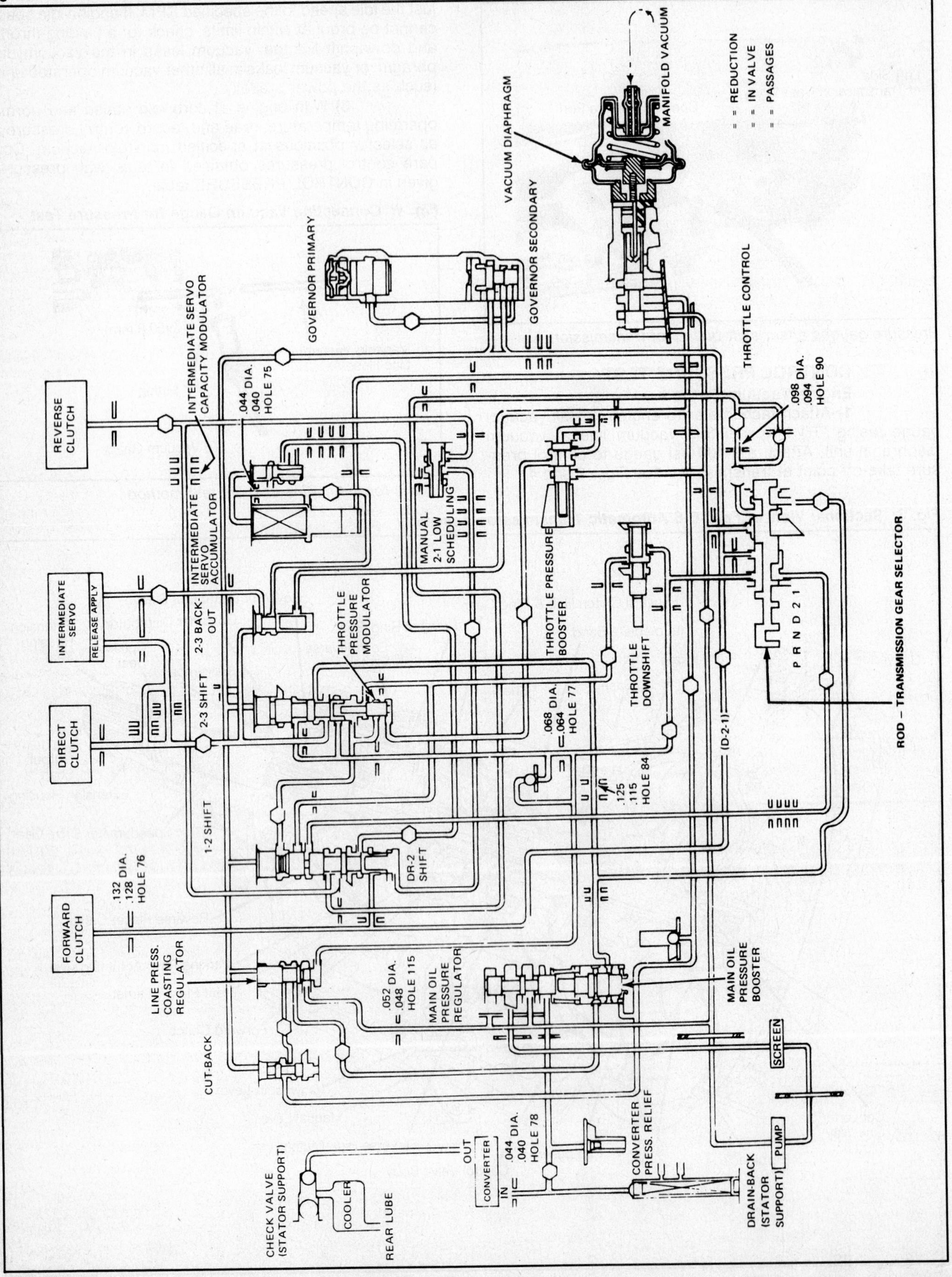

FORD MOTOR CO. C-6 (Cont.)

SHIFT SPEEDS (MPH)

NOTE: **Figures given below are approximate. All shift speeds may vary somewhat due to production tolerances, rear axle ratios, or emission control equipment.**

MODELS PJE-B, C HIGH ALTITUDE

Throttle	Range	Shift	OPS—R.P.M.	Column Number 1	2	3	4
Closed (Above 17″ Vacuum)	D	1-2	270 Min	8 Min	7 Min	6 Min	6 Min
	D	2-3	500 Min	13 Min	11 Min	10 Min	9 Min
	D	3-1	270-330	8-10	7-8	6-8	6-7
	1	2-1	600-870	19-27	16-23	14-21	13-19
To Detent (Torque Demand)	D	1-2	880-1290	26-38	26-33	21-79	19-27
	D	2-3	1530-2000	44-56	37-48	34-44	31-40
	D	3-2	1270-1780	36-50	31-42	28-39	26-35
Through Detent (WOT)	D	1-2	1120-1360	32-39	28-34	25-31	26-29
	D	2-3	1940-2180	53-62	45-52	42-49	38-45
	D	3-2	1810-2050	51-54	44-50	40-44	37-42
	D	3-1 2-1	750-1010	24-32	21-27	19-25	18-24

Tire Size	Axle Ratio 3.07	3.54	3.73	4.10
	Use Column No.			
LT215/85R16C		2	3	4
LT215/85R16D		2	3	4
LT235/85R16E		2	2	3
7.50D × 16D	1	2	2	3
7.50R × 16D		2		3
8.00 × 16.5D			2	3
8.75 × 16.5D		3	3	4
8.75 × 16.5E		2	3	4
8.75 × 16.5E	1	2	3	4
9.50 × 16.5E	1	2	3	4
9.50R × 16.5E		2	2	3

MODELS PJE-A

Throttle	Range	Shift	OPS—R.P.M.	Column Number 1	2	3	4
Closed (Above 17″ Vacuum)	D	1-2	270 Min	8 Min	7 Min	6 Min	6 Min
	D	2-3	450 Min	13 Min	11 Min	10 Min	9 Min
	D	3-1	270-330	8-10	7-8	6-8	6-7
	1	2-1	670-960	20-28	17-24	15-22	14-20
To Detent (Torque Demand)	D	1-2	940-1240	28-33	23-32	21-29	20-27
	D	2-3	1540-1840	45-54	39-46	35-42	32-40
	D	3-2	1050-1280	31-38	26-32	24-29	22-27
Through Detent (WOT)	D	1-2	1080-1310	32-39	27-33	25-30	23-27
	D	2-3	1800-2030	53-60	45-51	41-46	38-42
	D	3-2	1680-1900	49-56	42-48	38-43	35-40
	D	3-1 2-1	750-1010	22-30	19-25	17-23	16-21

Tire Size	Axle Ratio 3.07	3.54	3.73	4.10
	Use Column No.			
P195/75R15SL				
P205/75R15SL				
P215/75R15SL				
P225/75R15SL				
P235/75R15XL				
LT215/85R16C		2	3	4
LT215/85R16D		2	3	4
LT235/85R16D		2	2	3
LT235/85R16E	1	2	2	3
7.50D × 16D		2		3
7.50R × 16D			2	3
8.00 × 16.5D		3	3	4
8.75 × 16.5D		2	3	4
8.75 × 16.5E	1	2	3	4
8.75R × 16.5E	1	2	3	4
9.50 × 16.5E		2	2	3
9.50R × 16.5E	1	2	2	3

MODELS PJD-BA, BB, BC

Throttle	Range	Shift	OPS—R.P.M.	Column Number 1	2	3	4	5
Closed (Above 17″ Vacuum)	D	1-2	270-680	8-19	8-18	7-16	6-15	6-14
	D	2-3	390-1010	11-26	10-25	10-23	9-20	8-18
	D	3-1	270-330	8-10	8-9	7-8	6-8	6-7
	1	2-1	960-1340	26-36	25-34	23-31	20-28	18-25
To Detent (Torque Demand)	D	1-2	1140-1750	31-46	29-43	26-40	23-35	21-32
	D	2-3	1940-2750	51-22	47-67	44-62	39-55	35-50
	D	3-2	1100-1860	29-48	27-45	25-42	22-37	20-34
Through Detent (WOT)	D	1-2	1470-1810	39-48	37-45	34-41	30-36	28-33
	D	2-3	2540-2940	65-76	61-71	56-66	50-58	46-53
	D	3-2	2210-2590	58-67	54-63	50-58	44-51	40-47
	D	3-1 2-1	950-1300	26-35	24-33	22-30	20-27	18-24

Tire Size	Axle Ratio 3.07	3.54	3.73	4.10
	Use Column No.			
LT215/85R16C		3	4	5
LT215/85R16D		3	4	5
LT235/85R16D			3	4
LT235/85R16E	1	3	3	4
7.50 × 16D		3		4
7.50R × 16D			3	4
8.00 × 16.5D		4		5
8.75 × 16.5D		3		5
8.75 × 16.5E	2	3		5
8.75R × 16.5E	2	3		5
9.50 × 16.5E		3	3	4
9.50 × 16.5E	2	3	3	5

MODELS PGD-FB, FC

Throttle	Range	Shift	OPS—R.P.M.	Column Number 1	2	3	4
Closed (Above 17″ Vacuum)	D	1-2	270-420	7-11	7-11	6-9	6-10
	D	2-3	375-830	10-22	10-22	8-18	9-20
	D	3-1	270-330	7-9	7-9	6-7	6-8
	1	2-1	860-1200	22-31	23-33	19-27	21-29
To Detent (Torque Demand)	D	1-2	620-1310	16-34	17-36	14-29	15-31
	D	2-3	890-1780	23-46	24-48	20-40	21-42
	D	3-2	770-1380	20-36	21-37	17-31	18-33
Through Detent (WOT)	D	1-2	1270-1590	33-41	34-43	28-35	30-38
	D	2-3	2190-2560	57-66	59-69	49-57	52-61
	D	3-2	2120-2470	55-64	57-67	47-55	51-59
	D	3-1, 2-1	900-1220	23-31	24-33	20-27	21-29

Tire Size	Axle Ratio 3.00	3.50
	Use Column No.	
P205/75R15SL	1	3
P225/75R15SL	2	4
P235/75R15XL	2	4

Automatic Transmissions

FORD MOTOR CO. C-6 (Cont.)

SHIFT SPEEDS (MPH) (Cont.)

MODELS PGD-EV, EY HIGH ALTITUDE

Throttle	Range	Shift	OPS—R.P.M.	Column Number 1	2	3	4
Closed (Above 17″ Vacuum)	D	1-2	270-610	7-16	6-15	6-13	6-13
	D	2-3	400-980	11-26	10-24	9-21	8-21
	D	3-1	270-330	7-9	6-8	6-7	6-7
	1	2-1	990-1380	26-36	24-33	21-30	21-29
To Detent (Torque Demand)	D	1-2	1040-1820	27-48	25-43	22-39	22-38
	D	2-3	1780-2870	47-76	42-68	38-62	37-60
	D	3-2	1200-2450	32-64	29-58	26-53	25-51
Through Detent (WOT)	D	1-2	1480-1890	39-50	35-45	32-41	31-39
	D	2-3	2560-3060	67-81	61-73	56-67	53-63
	D	3-2	2240-2700	59-71	53-64	49-59	47-56
	D	3-1, 2-1	940-1360	25-36	22-32	20-30	20-28

Tire Size	Axle Ratio 3.50	3.54	3.55	3.73	4.10
	Use Column No.				
P195/75R15SL			3		
P205/75R15SL	3				
P215/75R15SL			3		
P225/75R15SL	2				
P235/75R15XL	2		2		
LT215/85R16C		1	1	2	3
LT215/85R16D		1	1	2	3
LT235/85R16D			1	1	3
LT235/85R16E		1	1	1	3
7.50D × 16D		1			3
7.50R × 16D			1	1	3
8.00 × 16.5D		2	3	3	4
8.75 × 16.5D		2	2	3	4
8.75 × 16.5E		2	2	3	4
8.75R × 16.5E		2	2	3	4
9.50 × 16.5E		1		2	3
9.50R × 16.5E		1		2	3

MODELS PGD-EV, EY, FD

Throttle	Range	Shift	OPS—R.P.M.	Column Number 1	2	3	4
Closed (Above 17″ Vacuum)	D	1-2	270-620	7-16	6-15	6-13	6-13
	D	2-3	400-990	11-26	10-24	9-21	8-21
	D	3-1	270-330	7-9	6-8	6-7	6-7
	1	2-1	990-1380	26-36	24-33	21-30	21-29
To Detent (Torque Demand)	D	1-2	1130-1790	30-47	27-43	25-39	24-37
	D	2-3	1920-2820	51-74	46-67	42-63	40-59
	D	3-2	1380-2390	36-63	33-57	30-52	29-50
Through Detent (WOT)	D	1-2	1510-1860	40-49	36-44	33-40	31-39
	D	2-3	2600-3020	68-79	62-72	57-66	54-63
	D	3-2	2270-2660	60-70	54-63	49-58	47-55
	D	3-1, 2-1	970-1340	26-35	23-32	21-29	20-28

Tire Size	Axle Ratio 3.50	3.54	3.55	3.73	4.10
	Use Column No.				
P195/75R15SL			3		
P205/75R15SL	3				
P215/75R15SL			3		
P225/75R15SL	2				
P235/75R15XL	2		2		
LT215/85R16C		1	1	2	3
LT215/85R16D		1	1	2	3
LT235/85R16D			1	1	3
LT235/85R16E		1	1	1	3
7.50D × 16D		1			3
7.50R × 16D			1	1	3
8.00 × 16.5D		2	3	3	4
8.75 × 16.5D		2	2	3	4
8.75 × 16.5E		2	2	3	4
8.75R × 16.5E		2	2	3	4
9.50 × 16.5E		1		2	3
9.50R × 16.5E		1		2	3

MODELS PGD-AW, EG HIGH ALTITUDE

Throttle	Range	Shift	OPS—R.P.M.	Column Number 1	2	3	4
Closed (Above 17″ Vacuum)	D	1-2	270-640	7-17	7-16	6-15	6-14
	D	2-3	375-930	10-25	9-3	9-21	8-19
	D	3-1	270-330	7-9	7-8	6-8	6-8
	1	2-1	890-1260	24-34	22-32	20-29	19-26
To Detent (Torque Demand)	D	1-2	770-1520	22-40	21-37	19-35	18-32
	D	2-3	1330-2330	35-63	33-59	30-53	27-50
	D	3-2	730-1640	21-45	20-42	18-38	18-35
Through Detent (WOT)	D	1-2	1250-1630	34-45	31-42	28-38	26-35
	D	2-3	2200-2630	59-70	55-65	50-59	46-55
	D	3-2	1980-2380	54-64	50-60	45-54	41-50
	D	3-1, 2-1	830-1230	23-32	21-30	19-27	18-25

Tire Size	Axle Ratio 3.50	3.54	3.55	3.73	4.10
	Use Column No.				
P195/75R15SL			3		
P205/75R15SL	3				
P215/75R15SL			3		
P225/75R15SL	3				
P235/75R15XL	2		2	2	4
LT215/85R16C		2	2	2	4
LT215/85R16D		2	2	2	3
LT235/85R16D			2	2	3
LT235/85R16E		1	2		
7.50D × 16D		2			3
7.50R × 16D			2	2	3
8.00 × 16.5D		3	3	3	4
8.75 × 16.5D		2	2	3	4
8.75 × 16.5E		2	2	3	4
8.75R × 16.5E		2	2	3	4
9.50 × 16.5E		2		2	3
9.50R × 16.5E		2		2	4

Automatic Transmissions

FORD MOTOR CO. C-6 (Cont.)

SHIFT SPEEDS (MPH) (Cont.)

MODELS PGD-AW, EG, EK

Throttle	Range	Shift	OPS—R.P.M.	Column Number 1	2	3	4
Closed (Above 17″ Vacuum)	D	1-2	270-560	7-15	7-14	6-13	6-12
	D	2-3	375-870	10-24	9-22	9-20	8-18
	D	3-1	270-330	7-9	7-8	6-8	6-8
	1	2-1	890-1260	24-34	22-32	20-29	19-26
To Detent (Torque Demand)	D	1-2	710-1310	19-35	18-33	16-30	15-27
	D	2-3	1260-1940	34-52	32-49	29-44	26-40
	D	3-2	600-1510	16-41	15-38	14-34	13-31
Through Detent (WOT)	D	1-2	1250-1590	34-43	31-40	28-36	26-33
	D	2-3	2190-2570	59-69	55-64	50-58	46-54
	D	3-2	1990-2340	54-63	50-59	45-53	41-49
	D	3-1, 2-1	840-1200	23-32	21-30	19-27	18-25

Tire Size	Axle Ratio 3.50	3.54	3.55	3.73	4.10
	Use Column No.				
P195/75R15SL			3		
P205/75R15SL	3				
P215/75R15SL			3		
P225/75R15SL	3				
P235/75R15XL	2		2	2	4
LT215/85R16C		2	2	2	4
LT215/85R16D		2	2	2	3
LT235/85R16D			2	2	3
LT235/85R16E		1	2		
7.50D × 16D		2			3
7.50R × 16D			2	2	3
8.00 × 16.5D		3	3	3	4
8.75 × 16.5D		2	2	3	4
8.75 × 16.5E		2	2	3	4
8.75R × 16.5E		2	2	3	4
9.50 × 16.5E		2		2	3
9.50R × 16.5E		2		2	4

MODELS PGD-FG

Throttle	Range	Shift	OPS—R.P.M.	Column Number 1	2
Closed (Above 17″ Vacuum)	D	1-2	270-740	7-16	6-15
	D	2-3	400-1010	11-26	10-24
	D	3-1	270-330	7-9	6-8
	1	2-1	1030-1430	26-36	24-33
To Detent (Torque Demand)	D	1-2	1220-1860	31-47	28-44
	D	2-3	1950-2830	51-74	46-67
	D	3-2	1370-2380	36-63	33-57
Through Detent (WOT)	D	1-2	1630-1980	41-50	37-44
	D	2-3	2710-3130	69-80	63-73
	D	3-2	2360-2760	59-69	53-62
	D	3-1 2-1	1090-1450	27-36	24-33

Tire Size	Axle Ratio 3.08
	Use Column No.
P195/75R15SL	
P205/75R15SL	2
P215/75R15SL	
P225/75R15SL	2
P235/75R15XL	1

MODELS PGD-FE, FF

Throttle	Range	Shift	OPS—R.P.M.	Column Number 1	2	3	4
Closed (Above 17″ Vacuum)	D	1-2	270-540	7-15	7-14	6-13	6-12
	D	2-3	375-780	10-23	9-21	9-19	8-17
	D	3-1	270-330	7-9	7-8	6-8	6-8
	1	2-1	880-1210	24-34	22-32	20-29	19-26
To Detent (Torque Demand)	D	1-2	840-1330	20-35	19-33	17-30	15-27
	D	2-3	1380-1980	35-52	33-49	30-44	27-40
	D	3-2	780-1540	17-41	16-38	15-34	14-31
Through Detent (WOT)	D	1-2	1220-1530	34-42	31-39	28-35	26-32
	D	2-3	2100-2450	60-70	56-65	51-59	47-55
	D	3-2	1910-2230	53-63	49-59	44-53	40-48
	D	3-1 2-1	850-1160	23-32	21-30	19-27	18-25

Tire Size	Axle Ratio 3.08	3.55	4.10
	Use Column No.		
P195/75R15SL		3	
P205/75R15SL	3		
P215/75R15SL		3	
P225/75R15SL	3		
P235/75R15XL	2		4
LT215/85R16C		2	4
LT215/85R16D		2	3
LT235/85R16D		2	3
LT235/85R16E		2	
7.50D × 16D			3
7.50R × 16D		2	3
8.00 × 16.5D		3	4
8.75 × 16.5D		2	4
8.75 × 16.5E		2	4
8.75 × 16.5E		2	4
9.50 × 16.5E		2	3
9.50 × 16.5E		2	4

CAUTION: Release throttle immediately if slippage is indicated. Also shift transmission to Neutral and run engine at 1000 RPM to cool transmission fluid between tests.

Vacuum Pump Method

1) Attach tachometer to engine and a 0-400 psi gauge to pressure take-off point at transmission. Disconnect and plug manifold vacuum line at diaphragm unit.

2) Connect vacuum source (vacuum pump in distributor tester) to vacuum diaphragm. Apply both parking and service brakes. Start engine and vacuum pump, setting vacuum to 15 in. Hg. Read and record control pressure in all shift selector positions.

3) Increase engine to 1000 RPM, and reduce vacuum to 10 in. Hg. Read and record control pressure in "D", "2" and "1" shift selector positions.

4) With engine still at 1000 RPM, reduce vacuum to 1 in. Hg. Read and record control pressure in "D", "2", "1" and "R". Compare control pressures obtained in tests with pressures given in CONTROL PRESSURE table.

NOTE: Governor can be checked at same time Control Pressure Test is performed.

5) With vehicle raised, place selector lever in DRIVE, no load on engine and apply 10 in. Hg. Increase speed slowly while watching speedometer, check speed at which control pressure cutback occurs. It should occur between 10-20 MPH.

6) If cutback does not occur within specifications, check shift speeds to make sure that it is the governor and not a stuck cutback valve.

CAUTION: Do not exceed 60 MPH speedometer speed during test. If control pressures are not within specifications, proceed to Control Pressure Test Results to determine problems.

CONTROL PRESSURE TEST RESULTS

Low at Idle in All Ranges

Check for low fluid level, restricted intake screen or filter, and loose oil tubes. Check for loose valve body or regulator-to-case bolts. Check for excessive leakage in front pump, case or control valve body. Check for sticking control pressure regulator valve.

OK at Idle in All Ranges, But Low at 10 in. Hg

Check vacuum diaphragm unit. Check if control rod or throttle valve is stuck.

High at Idle in All Ranges

Check vacuum diaphragm unit, manifold vacuum line, throttle rod, and control rod. Check for sticking regulator boost valve(s).

OK at Idle in All Ranges, OK at 10 in. Hg, But Low at 1 in. Hg

Check for excessive leakage, low pump capacity or restricted oil pan screen.

Low In "P"

Check valve body pressure regulator.

Low in "R"

Check high clutch and/or reverse clutch.

Low in "N"

Check valve body for correct operation.

Low in "D"

Check for faulty forward clutch operation.

Low in "2"

Check forward clutch and servo.

Low in "1"

Check forward clutch and/or reverse clutch.

CONTROL PRESSURE SPECIFICATIONS

Trans. Type	Transmission Model	Range	Idle 15" & Above Altitude	Idle 15" & Above Non Altitude	10" Vacuum Altitude	10" Vacuum Non Altitude	WOT Stall Altitude	WOT Stall Non Altitude
C6	PGD-EV-EY-FD FG	D,2,1	42-61# 53-81@	52-76	68-95# 86-113@	88-111	134-159# 150-185@	150-185
		R	66-95# 81-126@	81-119	106-148# 135-177@	137-173	209-249# 235-285@	245-275
		P,N	42-61# 53-81@	52-76				
C6	PGD-AW-EG-FE-FF PJE-B-C	D,2,1	42-61# 53-81@	42-63	68-95# 86-113@	75-110	134-159# 150-185@	155-180
		R	66-95# 81-126@	66-99	106-148# 135-177@	117-157	209-249# 235-285@	245-275
		P,N	42-61# 53-81@	42-63				
C6	PGD-EK-FB-FC PJE-A	D,2,1	42-63		75-110		155-180	
		R	66-99		117-157		245-275	
		P,N	42-63					
C6	PJD-BA-BB-BC	D,2,1	67-91		99-119		155-180	
		R	94-142		155-186		245-275	
		P,N	67-91					

\# At 500 ft Bar—24.5 @ At sea level Bar—29.5

VACUUM DIAPHRAGM UNIT

Vacuum Supply Check

1) Disconnect vacuum line at vacuum unit and connect vacuum gauge. With engine idling, gauge must show a steady acceptable vacuum. If reading is low, check for vacuum leak or poor engine vacuum.

2) If reading is acceptable, rapidly accelerate engine momentarily. Vacuum must drop rapidly at acceleration and return immediately upon deceleration. If vacuum reading does not change or changes slowly, vacuum line is plugged, restricted or connected to reservoir supply. Repair as required.

Vacuum Diaphragm Unit Check

1) Remove unit from transmission. Use tester equipped with vacuum pump. Start pump and set regulator knob so vacuum gauge reads 18 in. Hg with end of hose blocked off.

2) Connect vacuum hose to port on unit. If gauge still reads 18 in. Hg, unit is not leaking. If vacuum does not hold at 18 in. Hg, unit is leaking and must be replaced.

3) When hose is removed from unit, hold finger over end of control rod. Internal spring in unit should push control rod outward. Also, check for presence of transmission fluid in vacuum side of diaphragm or in vacuum hose. If fluid is present, unit is leaking and must be replaced.

VACUUM REGULATOR VALVE (VRV)

Operational Check & Adjustment

6.9L Diesel Only

1) Shut engine off. Disconnect 2 port vacuum connector from VRV which is located on left side of fuel injection pump. Remove throttle cable from lever on right side of pump.

2) Remove throttle return spring. Install 1 end of spring over throttle lever ball stud and other end over throttle cable support bracket.

3) Attach a vacuum pump to upper port of VRV (vacuum supply side). Attach a vacuum gauge to lower port of VRV, (labeled TRANS on VRV). Apply and maintain 20 in. Hg to VRV.

4) It will be necessary to pump vacuum up as it bleeds off. Cycle the throttle lever 5 times from idle to wide open throttle with vacuum applied. Insert Gauge Block

(T83T-7B200-AH), or 0.515" gauge block, between pump boss and throttle wide open stop. Ensure lever stop is against block. Gauge attached to lower port should indicate 6-8 in. Hg. If reading is incorrect, adjust VRV to 7 in. Hg.

5) To adjust, loosen 2 adjustment screws that attach VRV to fuel injection pump. Rotate VRV until proper vacuum is obtained. Tighten adjusting screws after correct vacuum is obtained. If VRV cannot be adjusted to proper specifications, replace VRV and repeat procedure in step **2)**.

6) Remove gauge block. Reattach throttle return spring and throttle cable. Again, apply and maintain 20 in. Hg to VRV. While maintaining vacuum, cycle the throttle lever from idle to wide open throttle 5 times. Vacuum gauge MUST indicate at least 13 in. Hg with throttle at idle position.

7) If vacuum gauge indicates less than 13 in. Hg, VRV must be replaced and procedure for adjustment must be repeated. After final adjustment, remove vacuum pump and gauge from VRV and reattach vacuum connector.

8) Start engine and check throttle operation and check transmission shifts.

STALL SPEED TEST

CAUTION: Do not hold throttle open longer than 5 seconds at a time during testing. If engine speed exceeds maximum limit of stall speed, release throttle immediately as clutches or bands are slipping.

Testing Procedure

Install tachometer and fully apply parking and service brakes. Start engine and run at curb idle and at normal operating temperature. Stall test transmission in each driving range at full throttle. Note maximum RPM obtained. Engine speed should be within limits shown in STALL SPEEDS table.

NOTE: Allow a cooling period of 15 seconds with transmission in Neutral and engine speed at 1000 RPM between each test.

STALL TEST RESULTS

Stall Speed Too High

In "D", "2", "1", and "R"; general transmission problems are indicated and a control pressure test should be made to locate faulty unit(s). In "D" only; planetary one-way clutch slippage is indicated. In "D", "2", and "1"; forward clutch slippage is indicated. In "R" only; high and/or reverse clutch slippage indicated.

STALL SPEEDS

Application	Stall RPM
F-Series (4x2/4x4)	
4.9L	1566-1808
E-Series	
4.9L	1537-1792
E/F Series & Bronco	
5.8L 2-Barrel	2091-2413
E/F Series & Bronco (under 8500 GVW)	
5.8L 4-Barrel	2162-2533
E/F Series & Bronco (over 8500 GVW)	
5.8L 4-Barrel	2090-2459
E/F Series (over 8500 GVW)	
6.9L Diesel	1758-2025
E/F Series (over 8500 GVW)	
7.5L	1831-2143

Stall Speed Too Low

Converter stator one-way clutch faulty.

CAUTION: Make sure engine performance is satisfactory before condemning converter assembly. Converter cannot be overhauled and must be replaced if defective.

AIR PRESSURE CHECKS

1) A "No Drive" condition can exist, even with correct transmission fluid pressure, because of inoperative clutches or bands. Erratic shifts could be caused by stuck governor valve.

2) The inoperative units can be located through a series of checks by substituting air pressure for the fluid pressure to determine location of malfunction.

3) To make air pressure checks, loosen oil pan bolts and allow transmission to drain. Remove oil pan and control valve body. Apply air at points noted. *See Fig. 6.* Check unit operations as follows:

Forward Clutch

Apply air pressure to transmission case forward clutch passage. A dull thud can be heard when clutch piston is applied, or movement of piston can be felt by placing a finger on input shell.

Governor

Apply air pressure to governor control pressure passage and listen for sharp clicking or whistling noise, indicating governor valve movement.

Fig. 6: Bottom View of Transmission Case

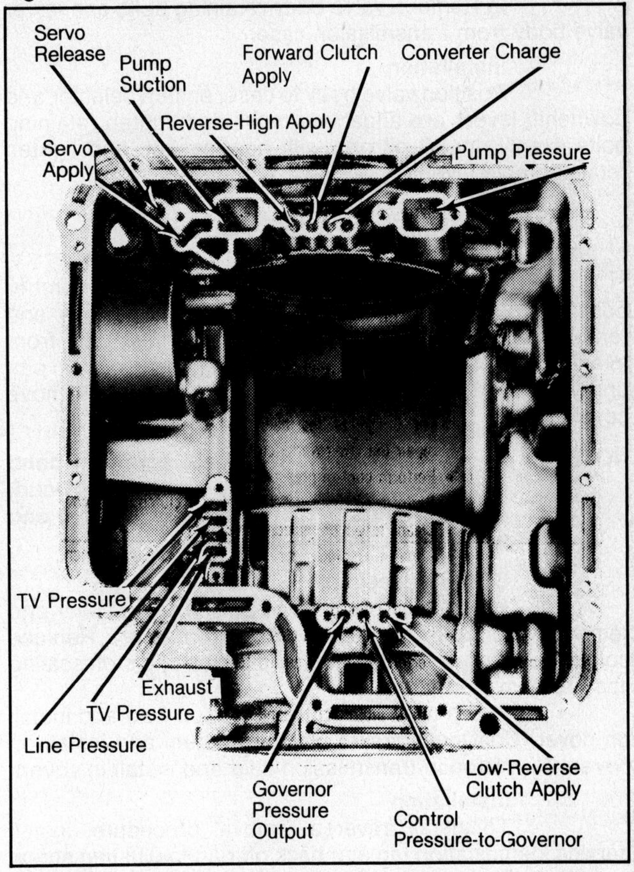

Illustration shows fluid passages for air pressure checks

FORD MOTOR CO. C-6 (Cont.)

Reverse-High Clutch

Apply air pressure to reverse-high clutch passage, dull thud should be heard when clutch piston is applied. If not, place finger tips on clutch drum, movement should be felt.

Intermediate Servo

Hold air nozzle in intermediate servo apply passages. Operation of servo will be indicated by tightening of intermediate band around drum. With air still applied at apply passage, use 2nd air nozzle to apply air at the servo release passage. Band should now release (combination of air pressure and spring on release side of piston should overcome apply pressure).

Low-Reverse Clutch

Apply air pressure to reverse clutch apply passage. A dull thud should be heard if clutch is operating properly.

SERVICE (IN VEHICLE)

VALVE BODY

Removal

1) Loosen oil pan retaining bolts, tap pan to break it loose allowing fluid to drain. Remove oil pan and gasket. Remove and discard nylon shipping plug from filler tube hole.

NOTE: **This plug is used to retain fluid in transmission during shipment and should be discarded when oil pan is removed.**

2) Remove valve body retaining bolts and lower valve body from transmission case.

Installation

Position valve body to case, ensure selector and downshift levers are engaged. Install and tighten retaining bolts evenly. Install oil pan with new gasket, and tighten retaining bolts evenly.

INTERMEDIATE SERVO

Removal

Remove engine rear support-to-crossmember bolt. Remove crossmember-to-frame retaining bolts and remove crossmember. Disconnect muffler inlet pipe from exhaust manifolds and allow pipe to hang. Place a drain pan under servo and remove cover retaining bolts. Remove cover, piston, spring and gasket.

NOTE: **As piston is being removed, screw in band adjusting screw. This keeps tension on band, keeping struts properly engaged in band end notches as piston is removed.**

Seal Replacement

1) Apply air pressure to port in servo cover and remove piston and rod. Remove seal from cover. Replace complete piston and rod assembly if piston or piston sealing lips are damaged.

2) Dip new seal in transmission fluid and install on cover. Coat new gasket with petrolatum and install on cover. Dip piston in transmission fluid and install in cover.

Installation

To install, reverse removal procedure. Install service identification tag and back off band adjusting screw as servo cover bolts are being tightened. Adjust intermediate band and refill transmission to correct fluid level.

Fig. 7: Disassembled View of Intermediate Servo

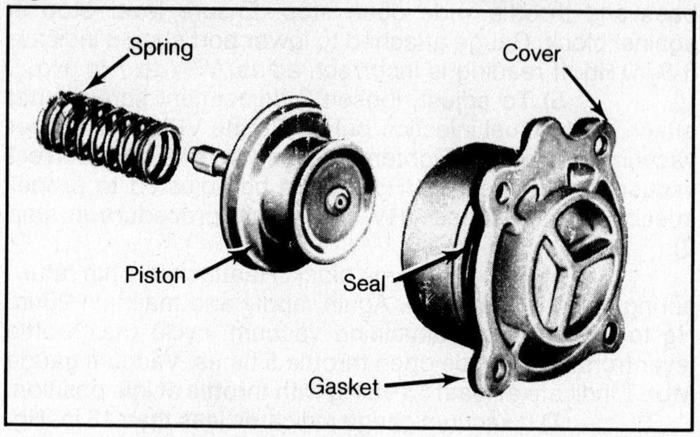

EXTENSION HOUSING SEAL & BUSHING

Removal

Disconnect propeller shaft at transmission. Using a tapered chisel, carefully remove rear seal. Using a bushing remover tool, remove bushing from extension housing.

NOTE: **Use tool carefully so that spline seal is not damaged.**

Installation

1) Install bushing into extension housing using a bushing driver. Before installing a new seal, inspect sealing surface of propeller shaft yoke for wear or damage. If scores are found, replace yoke.

2) Using a seal driver, install seal in extension housing, ensure that it is fully seated in bore. Coat inside of seal and yoke spline with wheel bearing grease and install propeller shaft.

EXTENSION HOUSING & GOVERNOR

Removal

1) Remove propeller shaft. Remove transfer case (if equipped) and speedometer cable. Remove engine rear support-to-extension housing bolts. Raise transmission with jack to take weight off support and remove support from crossmember.

2) Place drain pan under rear of transmission and remove extension housing-to-case bolts. Slide housing off output shaft. Remove governor housing-to-flange bolts and separate governor from flange.

Installation

To install, reverse removal procedure. Tighten all nuts and bolts. Make sure all mating surfaces are kept clean and refill transmission to correct fluid level.

REMOVAL & INSTALLATION

TRANSMISSION

See appropriate AUTOMATIC TRANSMISSION REMOVAL article in DOMESTIC GENERAL SERVICING section.

TORQUE CONVERTER

NOTE: **Converter is a sealed unit and cannot be disassembled for service. Replace if found to be defective. Make the following tests to be certain converter is defective before replacing unit.**

FORD MOTOR CO. C-6 (Cont.)

FLUSHING CONVERTER

Whenever transmission has been disassembled to replace worn or damaged parts or because valve body sticks due to foreign material, converter and oil cooler must be cleaned using a mechanically agitated cleaner (Rotunda 1400028). Under no conditions should converter or oil cooler be cleaned by hand agitation using solvent.

LEAK TEST

NOTE: **If torque converter welds indicate leakage, attach Torque Converter Leak Detector (Rotunda 7200004) to converter and follow detector kit instructions.**

TURBINE & STATOR END PLAY CHECK

1) Insert Tester (T80L-7902-D) into converter pump drive hub until it bottoms. Expand sleeve in turbine spline by tightening threaded inner post of tester until it is securely locked into spine.

Fig. 8: Checking Torque Converter Turbine and Stator End Play

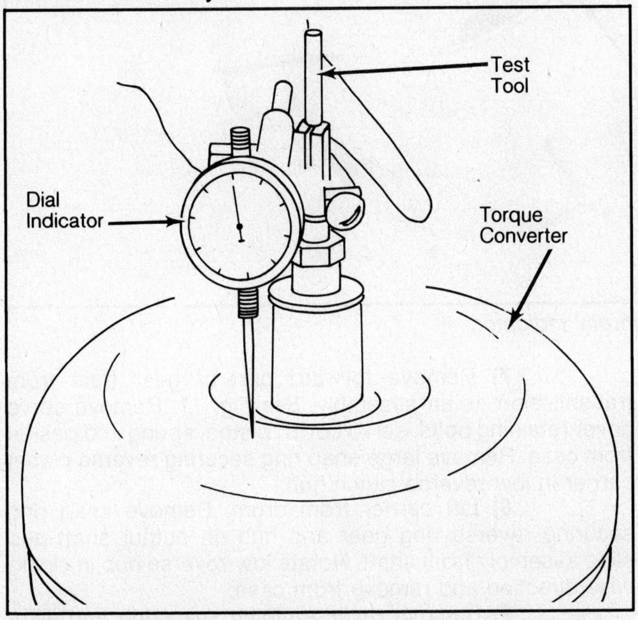

With test tool (T80L-7902-D) inserted and secured in hub, check end play.

2) Attach a dial indicator to tool with button on indicator on converter pump drive hub. Zero dial face. Lift tool upward as far as it will go and note indicator reading.

3) Reading is total end play of turbine and stator. If end play exceeds .021" (.53 mm) new or rebuilt converter, or .040" (1.02 mm) used converter, replace torque converter assembly.

STATOR ONE-WAY CLUTCH CHECK

1) Insert one-way clutch holding tool into one of the grooves in the stator thrust washer. Insert Torque Adapter (T83L-7902-A1) into converter pump drive hub so as to engage one-way clutch inner race.

2) Attach a torque wrench to torque adapter. With clutch holding wire held stationary, turn torque wrench counterclockwise. *See Fig. 9.* The converter one-way clutch should lock-up and hold a 10 ft. lb. (14 N.m) force. One-way clutch should rotate freely in a clockwise direction.

Fig. 9: Stator One-Way Clutch Check

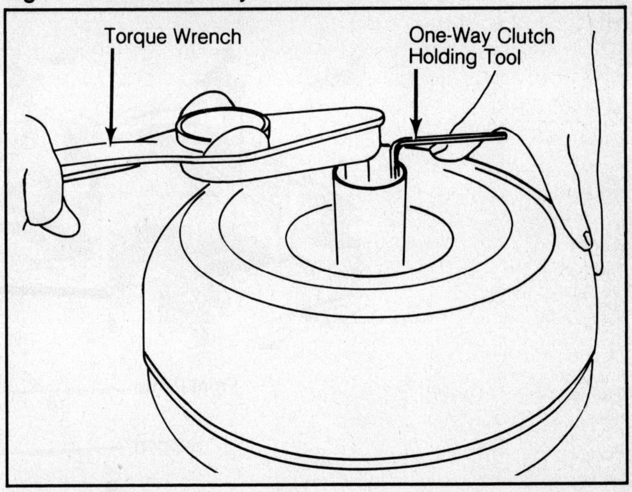

Use holding wire (T77L-7902-A) to check stator one-way clutch.

3) Repeat lock-up test in at least 5 different locations around torque converter. If clutch fails to lock-up and hold, replace torque converter.

STATOR INTERFERENCE CHECK

Stator-to-Impeller Interference Check

1) Position front pump assembly on bench with spline end of stator shaft pointing up. Mount converter on pump so splines of one-way clutch inner race engage splines of stator support and converter hub engages pump drive gear.

2) While holding pump stationary, rotate converter counterclockwise. Converter should rotate freely without interference or scraping within assembly. Should this condition exist, replace converter unit.

Stator-To-Turbine Interference Check

1) Place converter on bench, front side down. Install front pump assembly to engage mating splines of stator support, stator and pump drive gear lugs.

2) Install input shaft, engaging the splines with turbine hub. While holding pump stationary, rotate turbine with input shaft.

3) Turbine should rotate freely in both directions without interference or noise. If interference or noise exists, stator front thrust washer may be worn; the converter should be replaced.

TRANSMISSION DISASSEMBLY

1) With transmission in a holding fixture, remove oil pan and gasket. Remove retaining bolts and lift valve body assembly from transmission case.

2) Attach a dial indicator to front pump with indicator contact against input shaft. Install Oil Seal Replacer (T61L-7657-B) in extension housing to center output shaft.

3) Check transmission end play as follows: Push gear train to rear of case. Press input shaft inward until bottomed. Zero dial indicator.

4) Push gear train forward. Read and record end play for reference at reassembly. Remove checking tools from transmission. *See Fig. 10.*

Fig. 10: Checking Transmission End Play

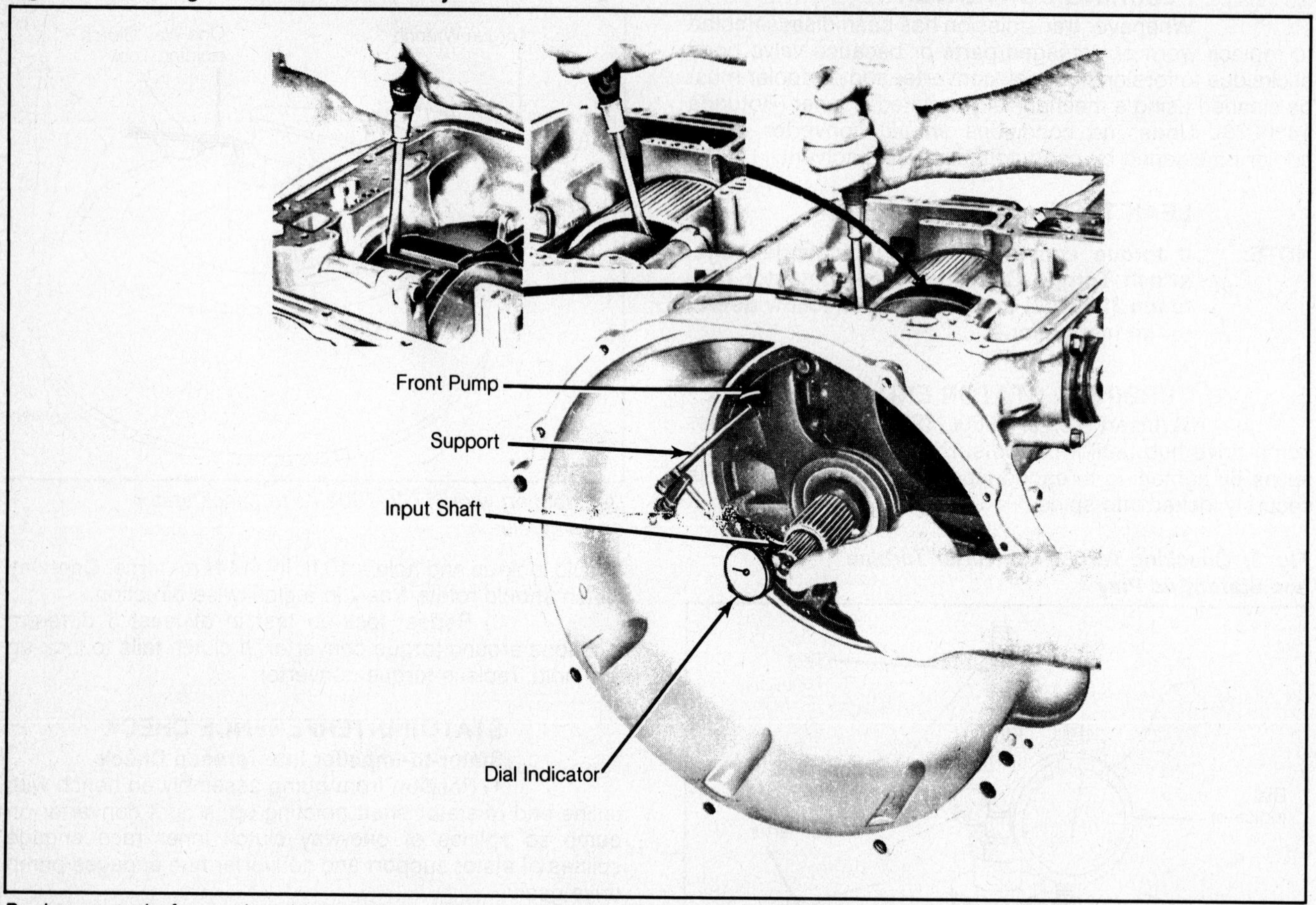

Push gear train forward and backward, and measure end play with dial indicator.

TRANSMISSION END PLAY

Application	In. (mm)
C-6	.008-.044 (.21-1.12)

5) Remove vacuum diaphragm, rod and primary throttle valve from case. Slide input shaft from front pump. Remove front pump retaining bolts, pry gear train forward and remove pump.

6) Loosen band adjusting screw and remove 2 band struts. Rotate band 90° counterclockwise to align band ends with slot in case. Remove band from reverse-high clutch drum.

Fig. 11: Removing Reverse-High Clutch Drum

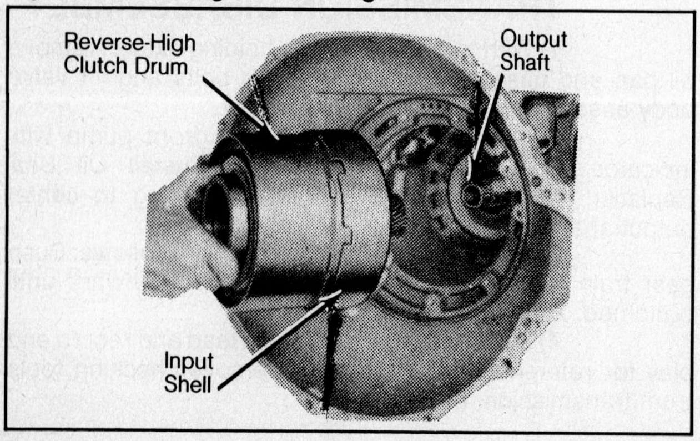

7) Remove forward part of gear train from transmission as an assembly. *See Fig. 11.* Remove servo cover retaining bolts, servo cover, piston, spring and gasket from case. Remove large snap ring securing reverse planet carrier in low-reverse clutch hub.

8) Lift carrier from drum. Remove snap ring securing reverse ring gear and hub on output shaft and slide assembly from shaft. Rotate low-reverse hub in clockwise direction and remove from case.

9) Remove reverse clutch snap ring and withdraw clutch discs, plates and pressure plate from case. Remove extension housing retaining bolts and vent tube from case.

10) Remove extension housing and gasket. Slide output shaft asssembly from case. Remove distributor sleeve retaining bolts. Remove sleeve, parking pawl gear and thrust washer.

NOTE: **If thrust washer is staked in place, use a sharp chisel and cut off metal from behind thrust washer. Remove any metal particles from case.**

11) Compress reverse clutch piston release spring. Remove snap ring and lift out springs and retainer assembly.

12) Remove one-way clutch inner race retaining bolts from rear of case and remove inner race. Remove reverse clutch piston by applying air pressure to low-reverse apply passage in case.

NOTE: See Fig. 6 for location of low-reverse apply passage.

COMPONENT DISASSEMBLY & REASSEMBLY

DOWNSHIFT & MANUAL LINKAGE

Disassembly

1) Remove nut and lock washer securing outer downshift lever to transmission and remove lever. Slide downshift lever out from inside case and remove seal from recess in manual lever shaft.

2) Remove neutral safety switch bolts and remove switch. Remove "C" clip securing parking pawl actuating rod to manual lever. Remove rod from case.

3) Remove nut retaining inner manual lever to shaft. Remove inner lever from shaft. Slide outer lever and shaft from case. Remove seal from case using a puller and slide hammer.

Fig. 12: Installed View of Downshift and Manual Linkage Components

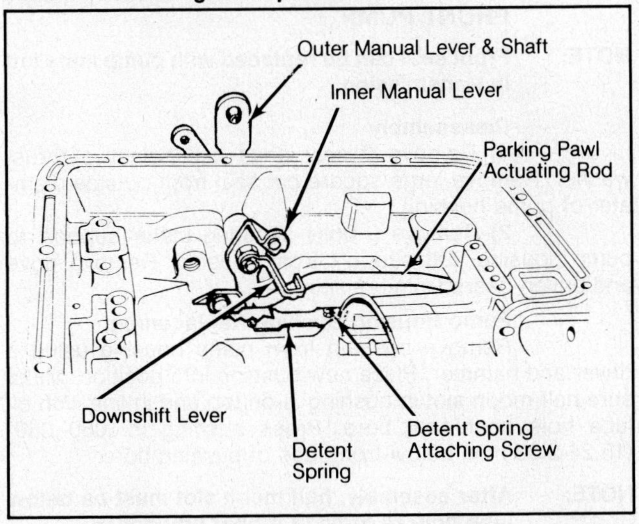

Reassembly

1) Dip new seal in transmission fluid and install into case using installing tools. Slide outer manual lever and shaft into case. Position inner lever on shaft, making sure leaf spring roller is positioned in inner manual lever detent.

2) Install retaining nut and tighten. Install parking pawl actuating rod and secure to inner manual lever with "C" clip. Slide neutral safety switch onto outer shaft lever.

3) Install retaining bolt. With manual lever in neutral, rotate switch and install gauge pin (No. 43 drill) into gauge pin hole. Tighten switch retaining bolt.

4) Install a new downshift lever seal in outer lever shaft recess. Slide downshift lever and shaft into position. Place outer downshift lever on shaft. Install and tighten lock washer and nut.

PARKING PAWL LINKAGE

Disassembly

1) Remove bolts retaining parking pawl guide plate to case. Remove plate. Remove spring, parking pawl and shaft from case.

2) Working from pan mounting surface, drill a 1/8" hole through center of cupped plug. Pull plug from case with a wire hook. *See Fig. 13.*

3) Unhook end of spring from park plate slot. Thread a 1/4-20 x 1 1/4" screw into park plate shaft. Pull shaft from case with screw. Remove spring and park plate.

Reassembly

1) Position spring and park plate in case and install shaft. Place end of spring into slot of park plate. Install a new cupped plug to retain shaft. Install parking pawl shaft in case.

2) Slip parking pawl and spring into place on shaft. Position guide plate on case, making sure actuating rod is seated in slot of plate. Secure plate with 2 bolts and lock washers.

Fig. 13: Installed View of Parking Pawl Linkage Assembly

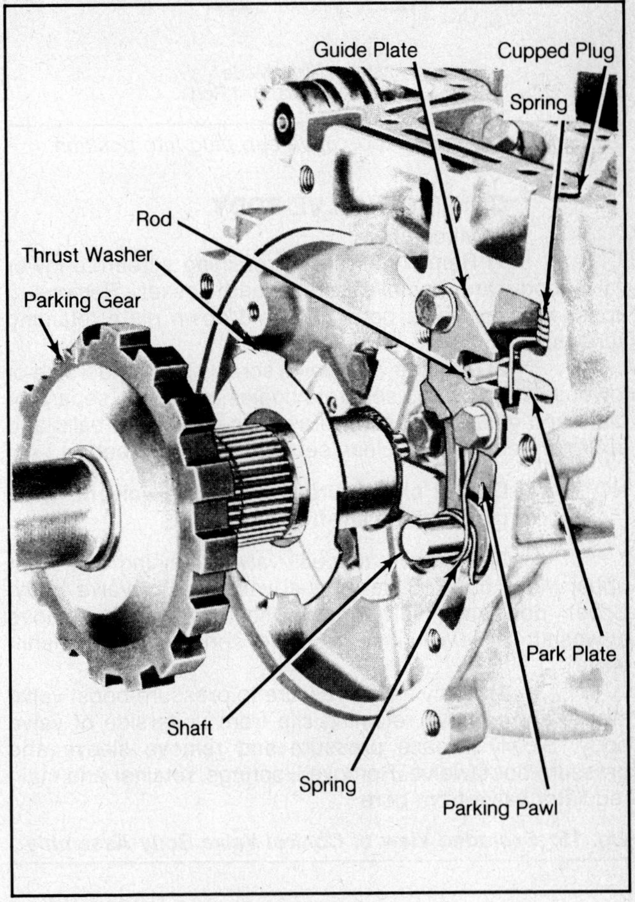

Note location of springs and guide pins.

SERVO APPLY LEVER

Disassembly

Working from inside case, carefully tap on servo apply lever shaft to remove the cup plug; shaft can be withdrawn by hand.

Reassembly

Hold servo apply lever in position and install shaft. Using fabricated shop tool shown in *Fig. 14*, drive cup plug into positon in case. Make sure plug is flush with shoulder of counterbore.

NOTE: Cup plug should be coated with Loctite to prevent leakage.

Fig. 14: Installing Servo Apply Lever Cup Plug

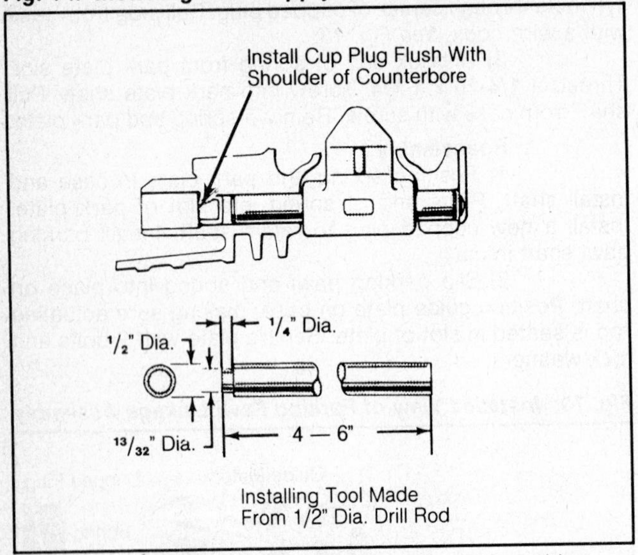

Using shop fabricated tool, drive cup plug into position.

CONTROL VALVE BODY

Disassembly

1) Remove 9 screws retaining screen-to-lower valve body and remove screen and gasket. Remove 5 upper-to-lower valve body and hold down plate retaining screws.

2) Remove 7 retaining screws from underside of lower valve body and separate bodies, removing separator plate and gasket. Be sure to avoid losing check balls and springs. Remove and clean separator plate screen.

NOTE: **Do not clean screen gasket in solvent; wipe clean with a lint-free cloth.**

3) Remove manual valve retaining pin from upper valve body. Slide manual valve out of valve body. Cover downshift valve port with finger and remove downshift valve retainer. Remove spring and downshift valve.

4) Apply hand pressure to pressure boost valve sleeve and remove retaining clip from underside of valve body. Slowly release pressure and remove sleeve and pressure boost valve. Remove 2 springs, retainer and main regulator valve from bore.

5) Apply hand pressure to throttle boost valve plate and remove 2 retaining screws. Release pressure and remove plate, throttle boost valve, spring and manual low 2-1 scheduling valve and spring from bore.

6) Apply hand pressure on remaining valve body plate and remove 8 retaining screws. Hold valve body so plate faces upward.

7) Release hand pressure on plate and remove. Remove spring and intermediate servo modulator valve from body. Remove intermediate servo accumulator valve and springs.

8) Remove 2-3 back-out valve and spring. Remove 2-3 shift valve, spring and throttle modulator valve.

9) Remove 1-2 shift valve, DR-2 shift valve and spring. Remove coasting regulator valve and cutback valve from body.

Reassembly

To reassemble, reverse disassembly procedure. Coat check balls with petrolatum to hold in place during reassembly. When installing screen in separator plate, make sure tabs are flush with separator plate surface. Tighten all bolts and screws evenly.

FRONT PUMP

NOTE: **Front seal can be replaced with pump installed in transmission.**

Disassembly

1) Remove 2 seal rings and selective thrust washer. Remove large square cut seal from outside diameter of pump housing.

2) Remove 5 bolts securing stator support to pump housing. Lift support from housing. Remove drive and driven gears from housing.

Pump Housing Bushing Replacement

Remove bushing from pump housing using a driver and hammer. Place new bushing into position. Make sure half moon slot in bushing is on top and in line with oil lube hole near seal bore. Press bushing in .060-.080" (15.24-2.03 mm) below front face of bushing bore.

NOTE: **After assembly, half moon slot must be below lube hole to provide proper lubrication.**

Reassembly

1) Install drive and driven gear into pump housing with identification mark or chamfered surface of each

Fig. 15: Exploded View of Control Valve Body Assembly

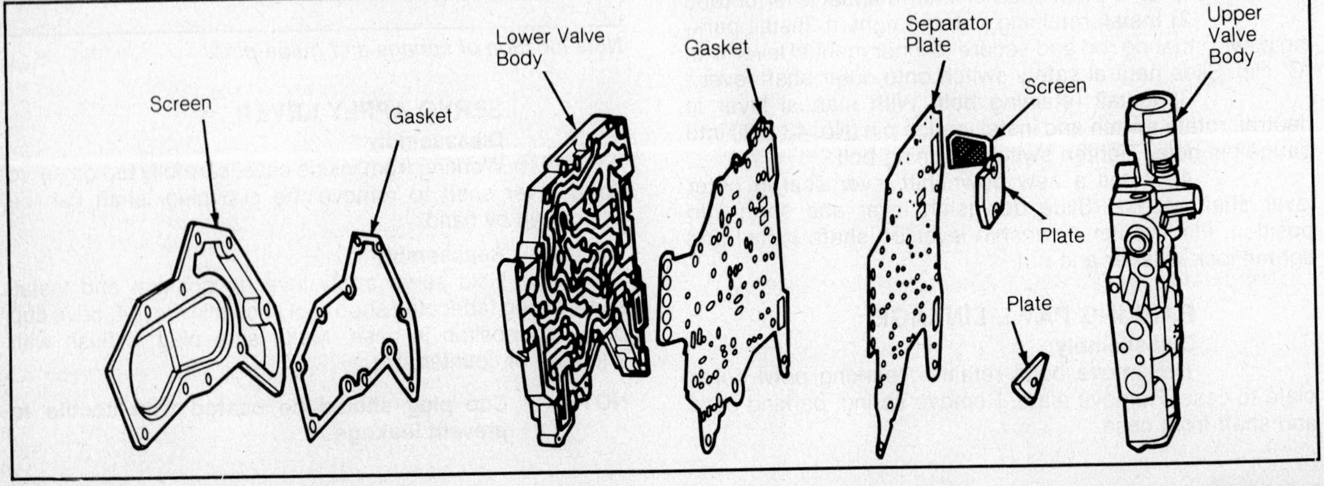

Fig. 16: View of Valve Body Showing Location of Check Valves and Balls

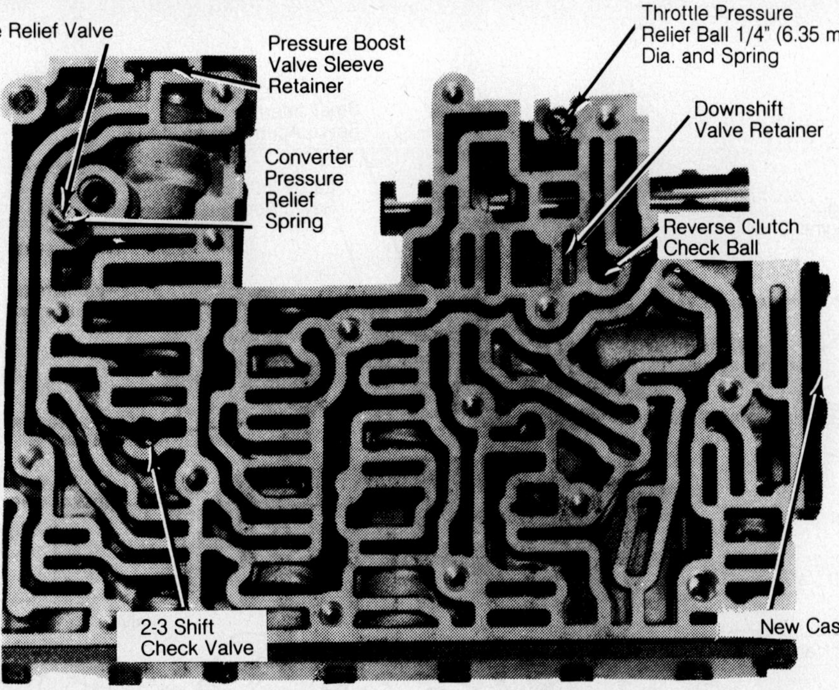

gear installed toward front of pump housing. Position stator support in pump housing. Install and tighten retaining bolts.

2) Carefully install 2 new seal rings on stator support. Make sure ends of rings are engaged to lock them in place. Install a new square cut seal on outside diameter of pump housing.

3) Install selective thrust washer. Place pump on torque converter. Make sure drive gear engages converter hub. Rotate pump to ensure that gears rotate freely.

FRONT PUMP SELECTIVE THRUST WASHERS

Color Code	Thickness In. (mm)
Blue	.056-.060 (1.42-1.52)
Natural (White)	.073-.077 (1.85-1.96)
Red	.088-.092 (2.24-2.34)

NOTE: **Different clutch assemblies are used in various models. When disassembling clutches, note number and location of plates used for reassembly reference.**

REVERSE-HIGH CLUTCH

Disassembly

1) Remove pressure plate snap ring by prying up with screwdriver. Remove pressure plate, drive and driven plates. Using Clutch Spring Compressor (T65L-77515-A) compress piston return springs.

2) Remove snap ring, spring retainer and springs. Apply air pressure to piston apply hole in drum and remove piston. Remove piston outer seal from piston and inner seal from clutch drum.

Bushing Replacement

To remove front bushing, use a cape chisel and cut along bushing seam until chisel breaks through bushing wall. Pry loose ends of bushing up to remove. Remove rear bushing using a press ram and bushing adapter. Install bushings using bushing drivers.

Reassembly

1) Dip new seals in transmission fluid and install one seal on piston and one in drum. Install piston into clutch drum. Position return springs in pockets as shown. Place spring retainer over springs. Using compressor tool, compress springs and install snap ring. Be sure snap ring is seated inside 4 guides on spring retainer. *See Fig. 21.*

NOTE: **Before releasing tool, make sure snap ring is seated inside 4 snap ring guides on spring retainer.**

2) Install clutch plates alternately starting with a steel drive plate. If new clutch plates are being installed, composition plates must be soaked in transmission fluid for 15 minutes before installation.

3) Install pressure plate and retaining snap ring. See CLUTCH PLATE CHART for the number of clutch plates required.

4) Using a feeler gauge, check clearance between pressure plate and snap ring. Hold pressure plate downward while measuring. Clearance should be .022-.036" (.56-.91 mm).

5) If clearance is not within specifications, selective snap rings are available in the following thicknesses:

.056-.060" (1.42-1.52 mm)
.065-.069" (1.65-1.75 mm)
.074-.078" (1.88-1.98 mm)
.083-.087" (2.11-2.21 mm)
.092-.096" (2.34-2.44 mm)

FORD MOTOR CO. C-6 (Cont.)

Fig. 17: Exploded View of Upper Valve Body Assembly

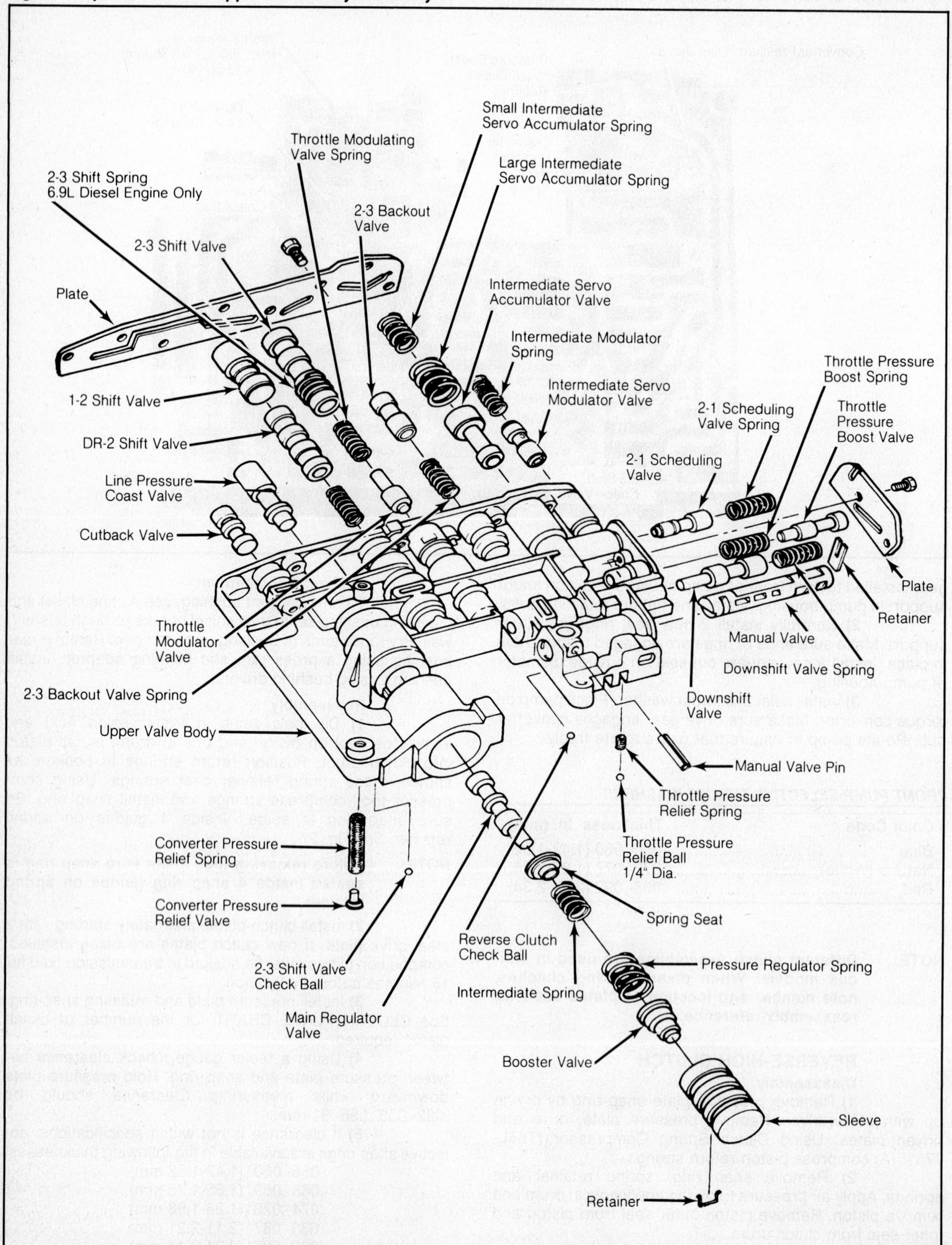

Small Intermediate Servo Accumulator Spring
Throttle Modulating Valve Spring
Large Intermediate Servo Accumulator Spring
2-3 Shift Spring 6.9L Diesel Engine Only
2-3 Backout Valve
2-3 Shift Valve
Plate
Intermediate Servo Accumulator Valve
Intermediate Modulator Spring
Throttle Pressure Boost Spring
Intermediate Servo Modulator Valve
1-2 Shift Valve
2-1 Scheduling Valve Spring
Throttle Pressure Boost Valve
DR-2 Shift Valve
2-1 Scheduling Valve
Line Pressure Coast Valve
Cutback Valve
Plate
Retainer
Throttle Modulator Valve
Manual Valve
Downshift Valve Spring
2-3 Backout Valve Spring
Downshift Valve
Upper Valve Body
Manual Valve Pin
Throttle Pressure Relief Spring
Converter Pressure Relief Spring
Throttle Pressure Relief Ball 1/4" Dia.
Converter Pressure Relief Valve
Spring Seat
Reverse Clutch Check Ball
2-3 Shift Valve Check Ball
Pressure Regulator Spring
Intermediate Spring
Main Regulator Valve
Booster Valve
Sleeve
Retainer

Automatic Transmissions

FORD MOTOR CO. C-6 (Cont.)

Fig. 18: Exploded View of Front Pump Assembly

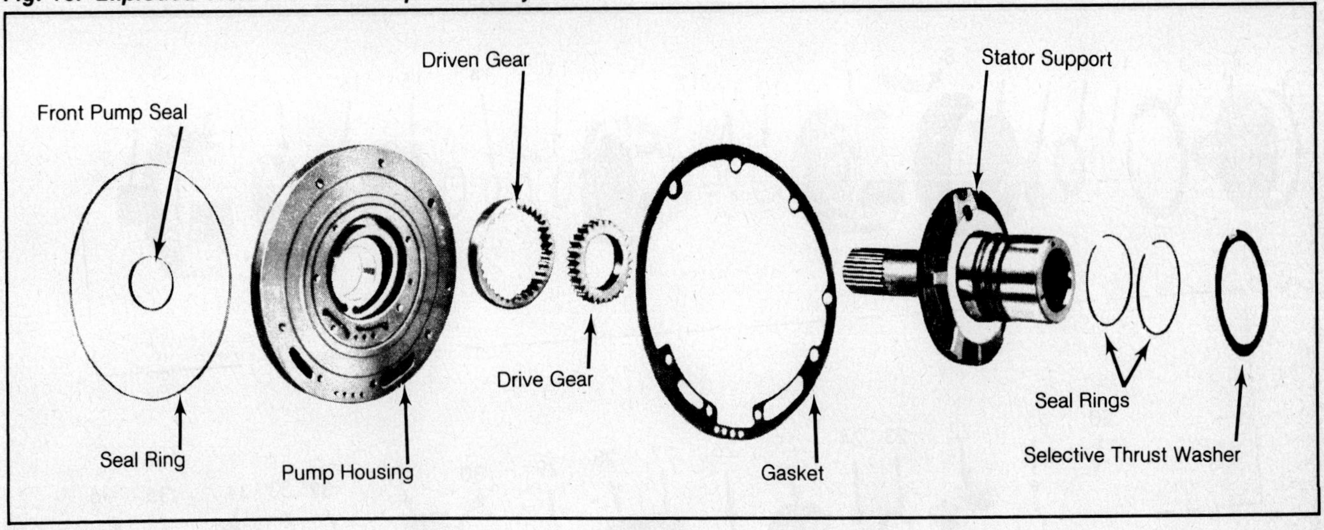

.110-.114" (2.79-2.90 mm)
.128-.132" (3.25-3.35 mm)

Install correct thickness snap ring and recheck clearance.

FORWARD CLUTCH

Disassembly

1) Remove clutch pressure plate retaining snap ring. Remove rear pressure plate, drive and driven plates and forward pressure plate from clutch drum.

2) Remove snap ring securing disc spring in drum and remove disc spring. Apply air pressure to clutch apply passage in drum and remove piston. Remove seals from piston and drum.

Reassembly

1) Dip 2 new seals in transmission fluid. Install smaller seal on clutch hub and other seal on piston. Install clutch piston in cylinder.

2) Make sure steel pressure ring is in groove on piston. Place disc spring in clutch drum with dished face downward. Secure in place with retaining snap ring.

NOTE: If new composition plates are being installed, soak them in transmission fluid for 15 minutes prior to installation.

3) Install forward pressure plate with flat side up and beveled side downward. Dip clutch plates in transmission fluid.

4) Install clutch plates starting with the waved plate, then a steel plate and a composition plate. Install remaining plates in this sequence.

NOTE: See CLUTCH PLATE CHART for the number of clutch plates required.

5) Using a feeler gauge, check clearance between snap ring and pressure plate. Hold pressure plate down while measuring.

6) Clearance should be .021-.046" (.53-1.17 mm). If clearance is not within specifications, selective snap rings are available in following thicknesses:

Fig. 19: Exploded View of Reverse-High Clutch Assembly

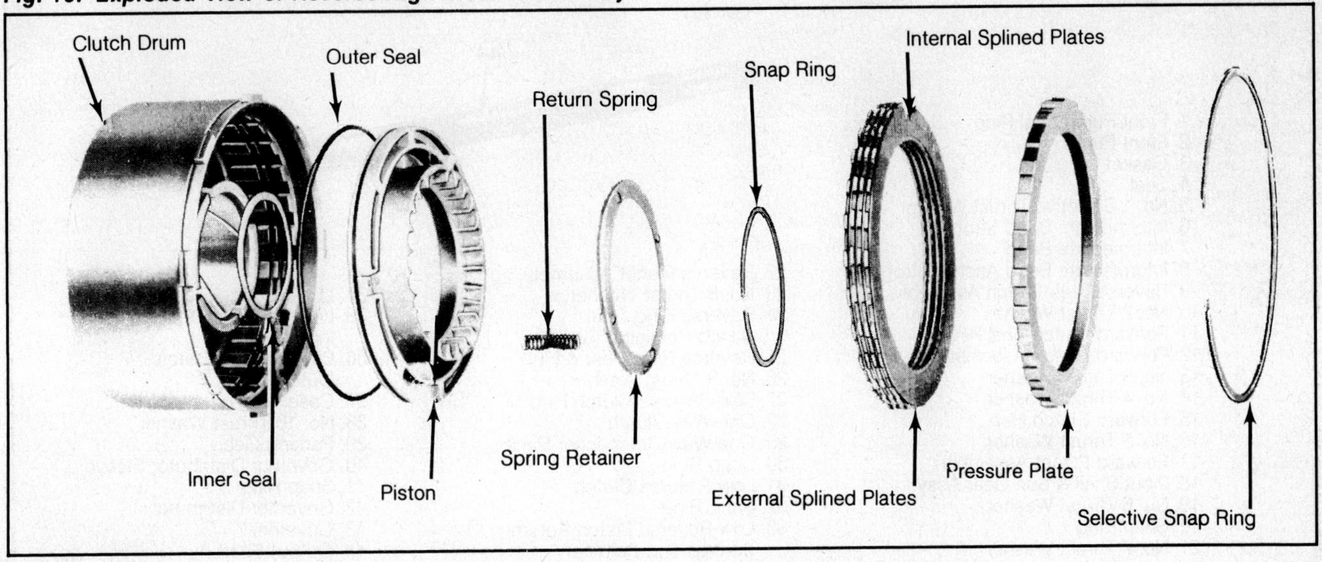

FORD MOTOR CO. C-6 (Cont.)

Fig. 20: Exploded View of Transmission Case and Drive Train Assembly

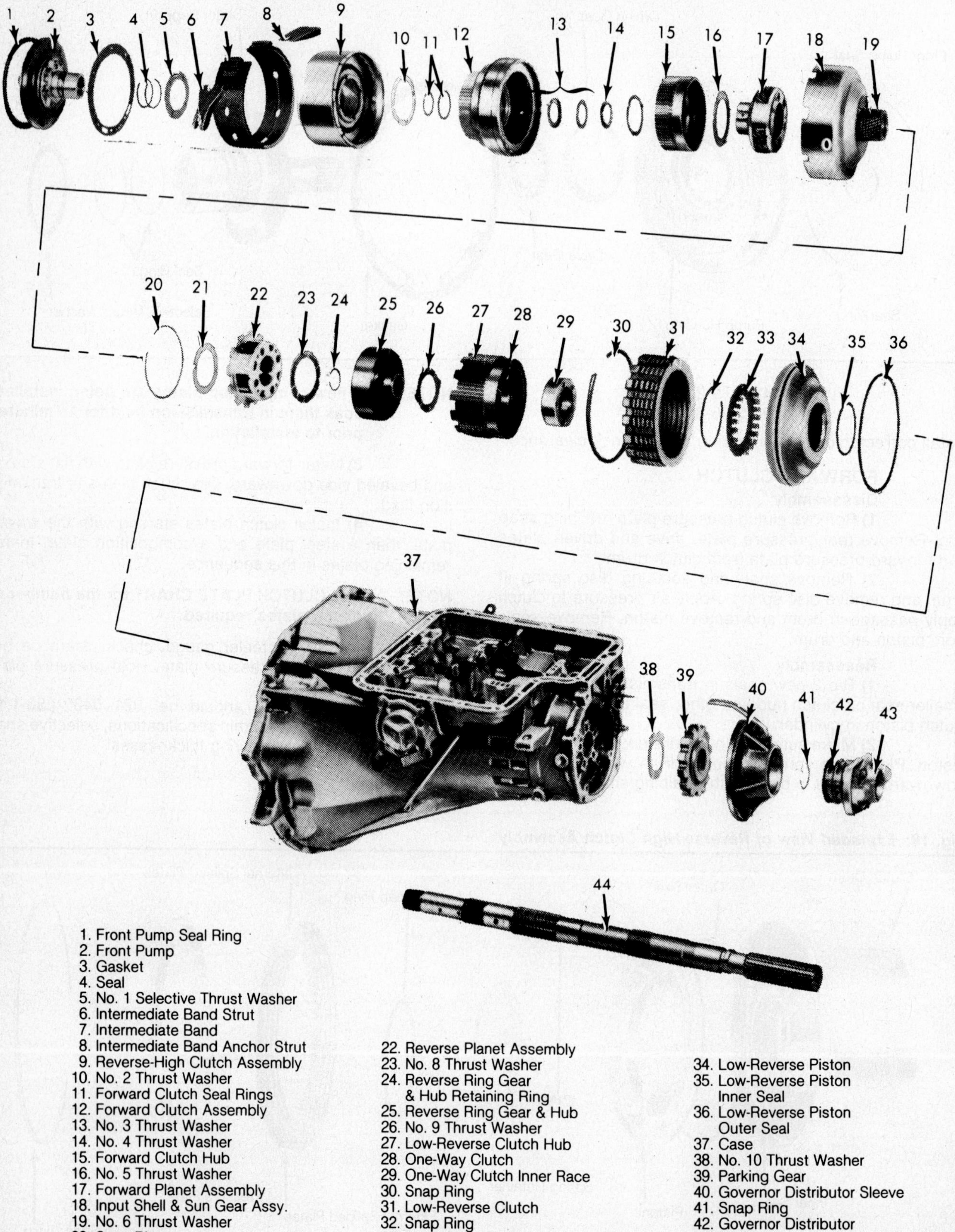

1. Front Pump Seal Ring
2. Front Pump
3. Gasket
4. Seal
5. No. 1 Selective Thrust Washer
6. Intermediate Band Strut
7. Intermediate Band
8. Intermediate Band Anchor Strut
9. Reverse-High Clutch Assembly
10. No. 2 Thrust Washer
11. Forward Clutch Seal Rings
12. Forward Clutch Assembly
13. No. 3 Thrust Washer
14. No. 4 Thrust Washer
15. Forward Clutch Hub
16. No. 5 Thrust Washer
17. Forward Planet Assembly
18. Input Shell & Sun Gear Assy.
19. No. 6 Thrust Washer
20. Snap Ring
21. No. 7 Thrust Washer
22. Reverse Planet Assembly
23. No. 8 Thrust Washer
24. Reverse Ring Gear & Hub Retaining Ring
25. Reverse Ring Gear & Hub
26. No. 9 Thrust Washer
27. Low-Reverse Clutch Hub
28. One-Way Clutch
29. One-Way Clutch Inner Race
30. Snap Ring
31. Low-Reverse Clutch
32. Snap Ring
33. Low-Reverse Piston Return Springs and Retainer
34. Low-Reverse Piston
35. Low-Reverse Piston Inner Seal
36. Low-Reverse Piston Outer Seal
37. Case
38. No. 10 Thrust Washer
39. Parking Gear
40. Governor Distributor Sleeve
41. Snap Ring
42. Governor Distributor
43. Governor
44. Output Shaft

.056-.060" (1.42-1.52 mm)
.065-.069" (1.65-1.75 mm)
.074-.078" (1.88-1.98 mm)
.083-.087" (2.11-2.21 mm)
.092-.096" (2.34-2.44 mm)
.110-.114" (2.79-2.90 mm)
.128-.132" (3.25-3.35 mm).

Install correct thickness snap ring and recheck clearance.

Fig. 21: View of Reverse-High Clutch Piston Return Springs

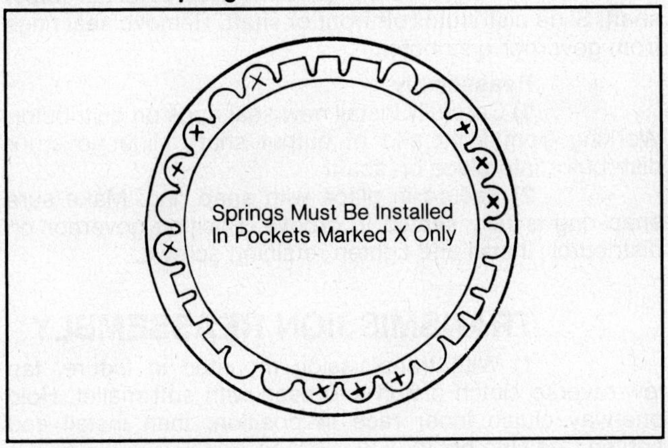

CLUTCH PLATE CHART

Application	Flat Steel Plates	Composition Plates
Forward Clutch		
PGD, PJD	[1] 4	4
High Clutch		
PGD, PJD	3	3
Reverse Clutch		
PJD	[2] 5	5
PGD	[2] 4	4

[1] - Plus one WAVED plate installed next to inner pressure plate.
[2] - Plus one WAVED plate installed next to piston.

Fig. 22: Exploded View of Forward Clutch Assembly

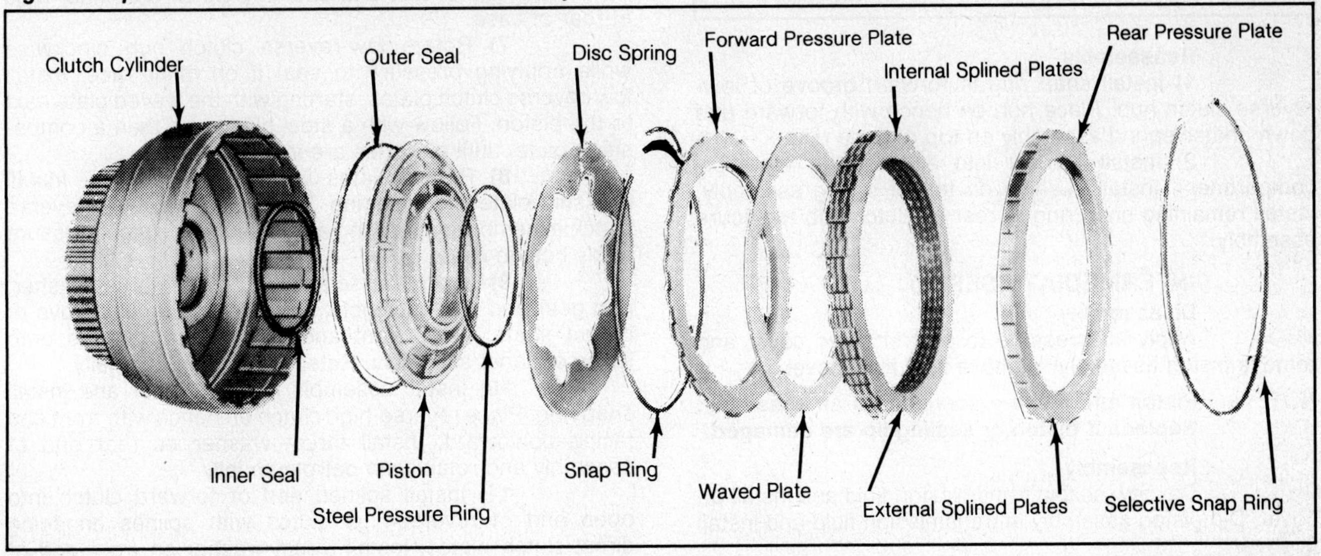

INPUT SHELL & SUN GEAR

Disassembly

Remove rear (external) snap ring from sun gear and remove thrust washer from sun gear and input shell. Working inside input shell, remove sun gear. Remove forward (internal) snap ring from gear.

Reassembly

Install forward snap ring on short end of sun gear. Working inside input shell, slide sun gear and snap ring into place. Making sure longer end of gear is at rear. Place thrust washer on rear side of input shell. Install rear snap ring. *See Fig. 23.*

Fig. 23: Exploded View of Input Shell & Sun Gear

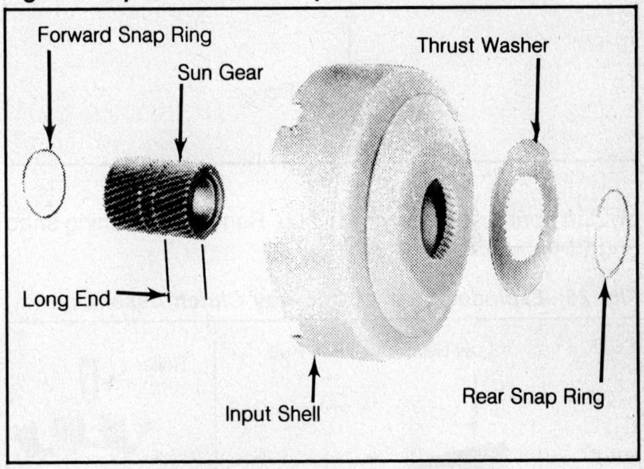

OUTPUT SHAFT HUB & RING GEAR

Disassembly & Reassembly

If it is necessary to remove these parts, remove hub retaining snap ring and lift hub from ring gear. When installing, secure hub with retaining snap ring. Make sure snap ring is fully engaged in groove.

ONE-WAY CLUTCH

Disassembly

Remove snap ring and bushing from rear of low-reverse clutch hub. Remove rollers from spring assem-

Fig. 24: Output Shaft Hub and Ring Gear Assembly

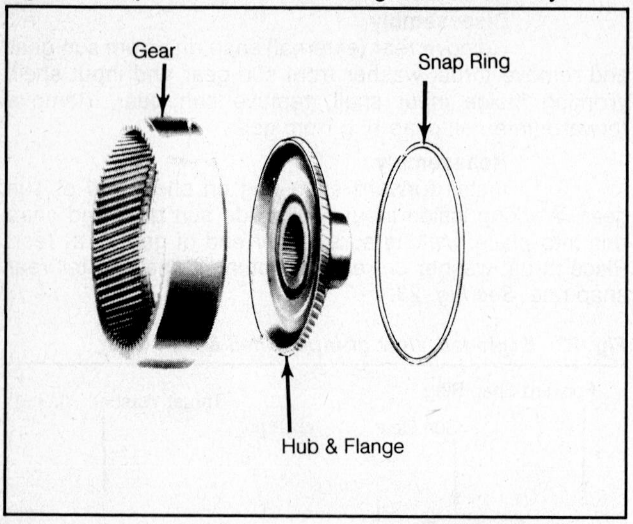

bly. Lift spring assembly from hub. Remove remaining snap ring from hub. *See Fig. 25.*

Fig. 25: Exploded View of One-Way Clutch Assembly

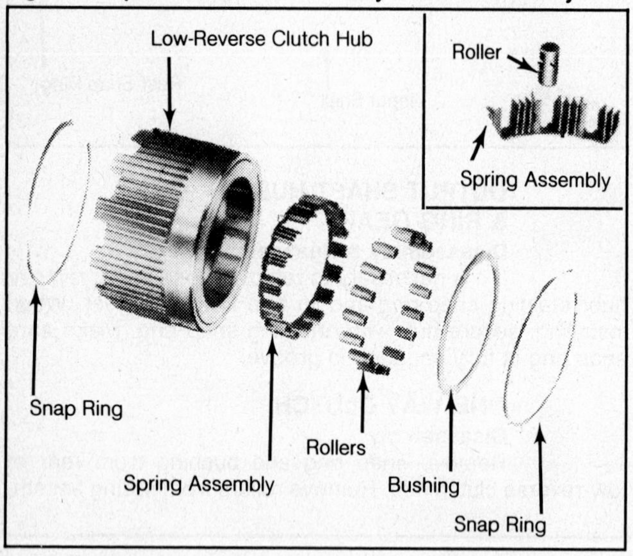

Reassembly

1) Install snap ring in forward groove of low-reverse clutch hub. Place hub on bench with forward end down. Install spring assembly on top of snap ring.

2) Install a roller into each spring assembly compartment. Install bushing on top of spring assembly. Install remaining snap ring at rear of clutch hub to secure assembly.

INTERMEDIATE SERVO

Disassembly

Apply air pressure to port in servo cover and remove piston assembly. Remove seal from cover.

NOTE: Piston and rod are serviced as an assembly. Replace if piston or sealing lip are damaged.

Reassembly

Dip new seal in transmission fluid and install on cover. Dip piston assembly in transmission fluid and install in cover.

LOW-REVERSE CLUTCH PISTON

NOTE: Clutch is assembled as part of transmission reassembly; replace seals as follows:

Remove inner and outer seals from clutch piston. Dip new seals in transmission fluid and install on piston.

GOVERNOR

Disassembly

Remove governor retaining bolts and governor. Remove snap ring securing governor distributor to output shaft. Slide distributor off front of shaft. Remove seal rings from governor distributor.

Reassembly

1) Carefully install new seal rings on distributor. Working from front end of output shaft, slide governor distributor into place on shaft.

2) Secure in place with snap ring. Make sure snap ring is fully seated in groove. Position governor on distributor. Install and tighten retaining screws.

TRANSMISSION REASSEMBLY

1) With transmission mounted in fixture, tap low-reverse clutch piston into case with soft mallet. Hold one-way clutch inner race in position, then install and tighten retaining bolts.

2) Install low-reverse clutch return spring and retainer assembly in clutch piston. Position snap ring on one-way clutch inner race. Compress return spring and retainer and seat snap ring in groove.

3) Place transmission case on bench with front end facing downward. Position parking gear thrust washer and gear on case. It is not necessary to restake thrust washer. Position oil distributor and tubes on rear of case.

4) Install and tighten retaining bolts. Install output shaft and governor as an assembly. Place a new gasket on rear of case. Install extension housing and retaining bolts. Tighten bolts to specifications.

5) Coat new servo cover gasket with petroleum jelly and position it on servo cover. Place servo spring on piston rod and install in case.

6) Install retaining bolts. Make sure identification tag is under one of the cover bolts and tighten. Align low-reverse clutch hub and one-way clutch with inner race at rear of case.

7) Rotate low-reverse clutch hub clockwise while applying pressure to seat it on inner race. Install low-reverse clutch plates, starting with the waved plate next to the piston. Follow with a steel plate, and then a composition plate, until all plates are installed.

8) Retain plates with petroleum jelly. Install pressure plate and snap ring. Test operation of low-reverse clutch assembly by applying air pressure to clutch pressure apply hole in case.

9) Install reverse planet ring gear thrust washer, ring gear and hub assembly. Install snap ring in groove of output shaft. Install front and rear thrust washers onto reverse planet assembly. Retain with petroleum jelly.

10) Install assembly into ring gear and install snap ring. Place reverse-high clutch on bench with front end facing downward. Install thrust washer on rear end of assembly and retain with petroleum jelly.

11) Install splined end of forward clutch into open end of reverse-high clutch with splines engaging direct clutch plates. Install thrust washer on front end of

FORD MOTOR CO. C-6 (Cont.)

Fig. 26: Exploded View of Output Shaft and Governor Assembly

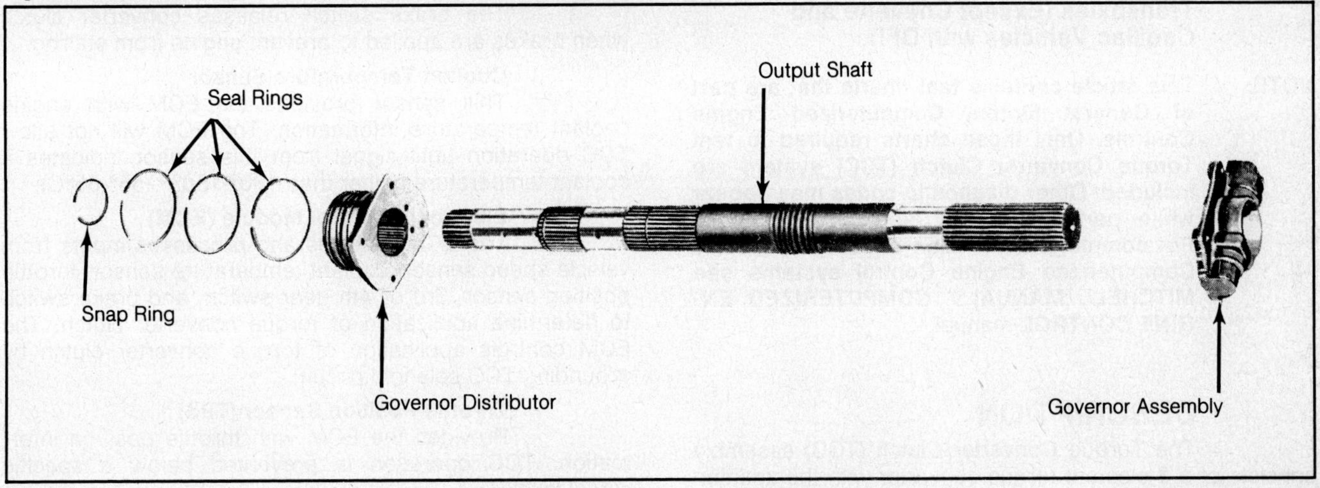

forward planet ring gear and hub. Retain with petroleum jelly.

12) Install ring gear into forward clutch and install thrust washer on front end of forward planet assembly and retain with petroleum jelly.

13) Install assembly into ring gear. Install input shell and sun assembly. Install reverse-high clutch, forward clutch, forward planet assembly, input shell and sun gear as an assembly into case.

14) Install intermediate band around direct clutch drum. Install band struts and tighten band adjusting screw enough to retain band.

15) Place selective bronze thrust washer on rear shoulder of stator support and retain with petroleum jelly.

16) If end play was not within specifications when disassembled, replace washer at this time with one of proper thickness. See TRANSMISSION END PLAY table in TRANSMISSION DISASSEMBLY.

17) Using 5/16 x 3" bolts, make 2 alignment studs by cutting the heads off and grinding a taper on the cut end. Install the studs opposite each other in case mounting holes.

18) Slide a new gasket onto studs. Position pump on case, being careful not to damage seal on pump housing, and remove studs. Install 6 of the mounting bolts and tighten.

19) Tighten intermediate band adjusting screw to 10 ft. lbs. (14 N.m). Back off screw exactly 1 1/2 turns. Hold adjusting screw in this position and tighten lock nut to specifications.

20) Install input shaft with long splined end inserted into forward clutch assembly. Check end play again to ensure correct assembly. Install control valve body into case, making sure levers engage valves properly.

21) Install primary throttle valve, rod and vacuum diaphragm in case. Install oil pan with new gasket. Install retaining bolts and tighten. Install torque converter.

TIGHTENING SPECIFICATIONS

Application	Ft. Lbs. (N.m)
Converter-to-Flywheel	20-34 (27-46)
Front Pump-to-Case	16-30 (22-41)
Overrunning Clutch Race-to-Case	18-25 (24-34)
Stator Support-to-Pump	12-16 (16-22)
Converter Cover-to-Housing	12-16 (16-22)
Guide Plate-to-Case	12-16 (16-22)
Intermediate Servo Cover-to-Case	14-20 (19-27)
Diaphragm Assembly-to-Case	12-16 (16-22)
Distributor Sleeve-to-Case	12-16 (16-22)
Extension Housing-to-Case	25-35 (34-48)
Band Adjusting Screw Lock Nut	35-45 (48-61)
Cooler Tube Connector Lock	20-35 (27-48)
Converter Drain Plug	8-28 (11-38)
Manual Valve Inner Lever-to-Shaft	30-40 (41-54)
Downshift Lever-to-Shaft	12-16 (16-22)
Filler Tube-to-Engine	
Econoline - 5.0L, 5.8L, 7.5L	40-50 (54-68)
Econoline - 4.9L	33-42 (45-57)
Econoline - 6.9L	24-35 (33-48)
Transmission-to-Engine (Diesel)	50-65 (68-88)
Transmission-to-Engine (Gasoline)	40-50 (54-68)
Rear Engine Support-to-Trans.	60-80 (82-109)
Yoke-to-Output Shaft	130 (15.0)
	INCH Lbs. (N.m)
End Plates-to-Valve Body	20-40 (2.5-4.5)
Inner Downshift Lever Stop	20-45 (2.5-5.0)
Reinforcement Plate-to-Valve Body	20-45 (2.5-5.0)
Screen & Lower-to-Upper Valve Body	40-55 (4.5-6.2)
Shift Valve Plate-to-Upper Body	20-45 (2.5-5.0)
Upper-to-Lower Body	40-55 (4.5-6.2)
Converter Housing-to-Converter Cover	
7.5L Engine Only	30-60 (3.5-6.5)
Control Assy.-to-Case	95-125 (11.0-14.0)
Governor Body-to-Collector Body	90-120 (10.5-13.5)
Detent Spring-to-Case	80-120 (9.5-13.5)
Neutral Switch-to-Case	55-75 (6.2-8.0)

GENERAL MOTORS TORQUE CONVERTER CLUTCH

All GM Automatic Transmissions and Transaxles (Except Chevette and Cadillac Vehicles with DFI)

NOTE: **This article contains test charts that are part of General Motors Computerized Engine Controls. Only those charts required to test Torque Converter Clutch (TCC) system are included. Other diagnostic codes may appear while performing TCC electrical diagnosis. For complete information on General Motors Computerized Engine Control systems see MITCHELL MANUALS' COMPUTERIZED ENGINE CONTROL manual.**

DESCRIPTION

The Torque Converter Clutch (TCC) assembly consists of a 3-element torque converter with the addition of a converter clutch. The converter clutch is an internal mechanism with friction material attached to front face. It is splined to the turbine assembly in converter.

The purpose of the automatic transaxle torque converter clutch feature is to eliminate power loss of torque converter stage when vehicle is in a cruise condition. This allows the convenience of an automatic transmission and the fuel economy of a manual transmission.

When the TCC solenoid is activated, the torque converter clutch is applied which results in a straight through mechanical coupling from engine to transmission. When TCC solenoid is deactivated, the torque converter clutch is released which allows the torque converter clutch to operate in a conventional manner.

Fig. 1: Torque Converter Assembly With TCC

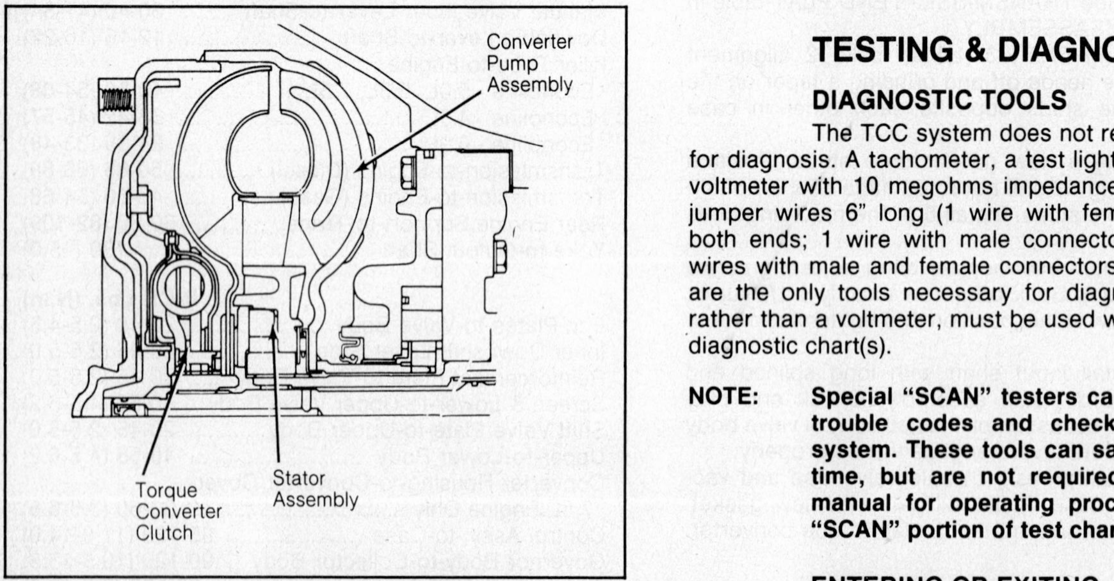

THM 700-R4 shown; other models are similar.

TCC CONTROL COMPONENTS

The following components are used to engage/disengage torque converter control clutch. Not all components will be present on all vehicles.

Brake Switch

The brake switch releases converter clutch when brakes are applied to prevent engine from stalling.

Coolant Temperature Sensor

This sensor provides the ECM with engine coolant temperature information. The ECM will not allow TCC operation until signal from this sensor indicates a coolant temperature higher than 130°-150°F (55°-65°C).

Electronic Control Module (ECM)

The ECM receives and processes inputs from vehicle speed sensor, coolant temperature sensor, throttle position sensor, 3rd or 4th gear switch, and brake switch to determine application of torque converter clutch. The ECM controls application of torque converter clutch by grounding TCC solenoid circuit.

Throttle Position Sensor (TPS)

Provides the ECM with throttle position information. TCC operation is prevented below a specific signal level.

3rd & 4th Gear Switch

The 3rd and 4th gear switches prevent TCC operation until direct drive (3rd and/or 4th gear) is obtained.

Vehicle Speed Sensor (VSS)

This sensor sends vehicle speed information to ECM. Vehicle speed must be above a certain value before TCC can be applied. This sensor is located in instrument cluster, behind speedometer.

TROUBLE SHOOTING

See GENERAL MOTORS TORQUE CONVERTER CLUTCH TROUBLE SHOOTING in DOMESTIC GENERAL SERVICING section.

TESTING & DIAGNOSIS

DIAGNOSTIC TOOLS

The TCC system does not require special tools for diagnosis. A tachometer, a test light, ohmmeter, digital voltmeter with 10 megohms impedance (minimum), and 6 jumper wires 6" long (1 wire with female connectors at both ends; 1 wire with male connector at both ends; 4 wires with male and female connectors at opposite ends) are the only tools necessary for diagnosis. A test light, rather than a voltmeter, must be used when indicated by a diagnostic chart(s).

NOTE: **Special "SCAN" testers can be used to read trouble codes and check voltages in the system. These tools can save a great deal of time, but are not required. Refer to tester manual for operating procedures. Also see "SCAN" portion of test chart(s).**

ENTERING OR EXITING DIAGNOSTIC MODE

All Passenger Cars & Trucks (Except Buick Riviera & Oldsmobile Toronado)

The ECM stores component failure information under a related trouble code which can be recalled for diagnosis and repair. When recalled, these codes will be displayed by flashes of the "CHECK ENGINE"/"SERVICE ENGINE SOON" light.

It is NOT necessary to enter diagnostic mode to use TCC test chart(s). It will be necessary to enter ECM diagnostic mode to verify the presence of Code 24, Codes 33 and 34 (4.3L TBI passenger car engine).

1) To enter diagnostic mode, turn ignition on but do not start engine. "CHECK ENGINE"/"SERVICE ENGINE SOON" light should glow. Locate Assembly Line Communication Link (ALCL) connector attached to ECM wiring harness under instrument panel. Insert jumper wire across diagnostic mode test terminal "B" and ground terminal "A". *See Fig. 2.*

CAUTION: Inserting spade lug in terminals of ALCL connector grounds "TEST" terminal lead. Do not ground ALCL connector until after ignition is on.

Fig. 2: ALCL Connector Terminal Locations

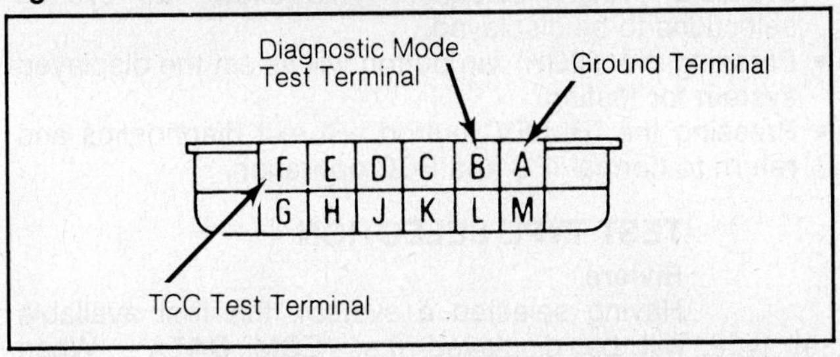

2) "CHECK ENGINE"/"SERVICE ENGINE SOON" light should flash Code 12 ("FLASH", pause, "FLASH", "FLASH") followed by a longer pause. Trouble Code 12 will be repeated 3 more times, then if any trouble codes are stored in the ECM memory, they will be displayed in the same manner.

3) Trouble codes will be displayed from lowest to highest numbered codes (3 times each) and be repeated as long as the "TEST" terminal of the ALCL connector is grounded.

4) To exit diagnostic mode, turn ignition off and remove jumper wire from ALCL connector.

CLEARING TROUBLE CODES

All Passenger Cars & Trucks (Except Buick Riviera & Oldsmobile Toronado)

Trouble codes are cleared by removing battery voltage from ECM for at least 10 seconds. Turn ignition off and remove ECM fuse from fuse block for 10 seconds. Remove "TEST" lead ground.

ENTERING SERVICE (DIAGNOSTIC) MODE

Buick Riviera & Oldsmobile Toronado

It will be necessary to enter service mode to use Riviera and Toronade TCC test chart(s). Enter appropriate test condition (i.e. ECM INPUTS, BCM CODE, etc.) as indicated in chart(s).

1) On Riviera, turn ignition on. Touch the "OFF" and "WARM" key pads on the Cathode Ray Tube (CRT) climate control page simultaneously and hold until a double "beep" is heard or a page entitled "SERVICE MODE" appears on the screen. *See Fig. 3.*

NOTE: Operating vehicle in service mode for extended periods of time will cause the battery to run down and possibly relate false diagnostic information. Connect battery charger on "trickle" charge if vehicle is to be in service mode for periods longer than 1/2 hour.

Fig. 3: Entering Riviera Service Mode

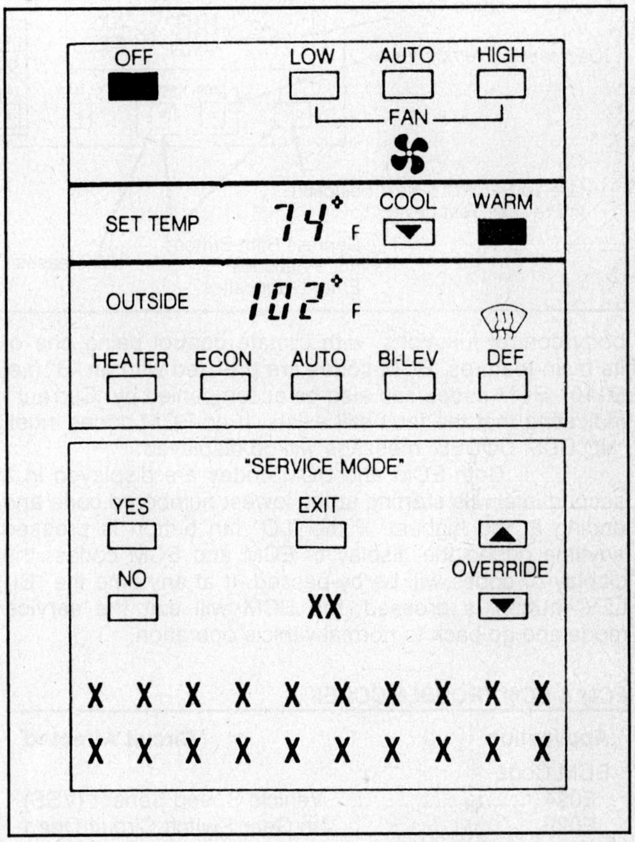

2) On Toronado, turn ignition on. Touch the "OFF" and "WARM" buttons on the ECC control panel simultaneously, and hold until a segment check is displayed on the Instrument Panel Cluster (IPC) and Electronic Climate Control (ECC) panel. *See Fig. 4.*

TROUBLE CODE DISPLAY

Riviera

After service mode is entered any trouble codes stored in the computer memory will be displayed. ECM codes will be displayed first. If no ECM codes are stored, the CRT will display "NO ECM CODES" for approximately 2 seconds.

After ECM codes have been displayed, the BCM codes will be displayed. BCM codes will also be accompanied by "Current" or "History". "History" indicates that the failure was not present when last tested. "Current" indicates the fault still exists.

If no BCM codes are present, the BCM will display "NO BCM CODES" message. Trouble codes for both the ECM and BCM will be displayed in numerical succession of lowest too highest numbered code.

Toronado

After service mode is entered, any trouble codes stored in the computer will be displayed. ECM codes will be displayed first. If no ECM codes are stored, the IPC will display "NO ECM CODES". All ECM codes will be prefixed by an "E" (i.e. E013).

When all ECM codes have been displayed, the BCM codes will be displayed. BCM codes mainly deal with

GENERAL MOTORS TORQUE CONVERTER CLUTCH (Cont.)

Fig. 4: Oldsmobile Toronado Electronic Climate Control (ECC) Panel

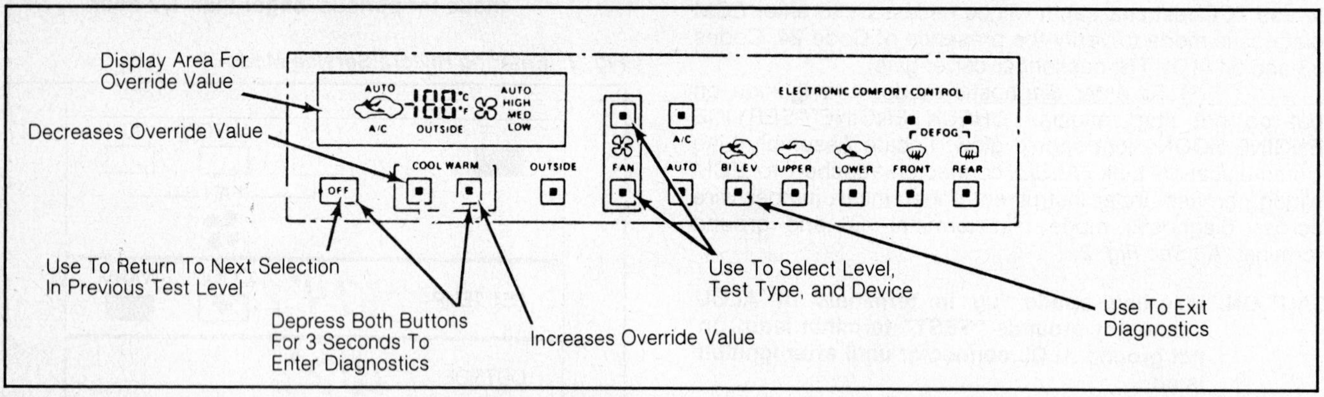

body control functions, with climate control being one of its main features. BCM codes are prefixed with an "B" (i.e. B110). BCM codes can also be accompanied by "Current", indicating that the fault still exists. If no BCM codes exist, "NO BCM CODES" message will be displayed.

Both ECM and BCM codes are displayed in 2 second intervals starting at the lowest numbered code and ending at the highest. If the "LO" fan button is pressed anytime during the display of ECM and BCM codes, the display of codes will be by-passed. If at any time the "BI-LEV" button is pressed, the BCM will exit the service mode and go back to normal vehicle operation.

ECM & BCM TROUBLE CODES

Application	Circuit Affected
ECM Code	
E024	Vehicle Speed Sensor (VSS)
E029	4th Gear Switch Circuit Open
BCM Code	
B124	Vehicle Speed Sensor (VSS) Circuit

SYSTEM SELECTION

Riviera

After trouble codes have been displayed, the service mode can be used to perform several tests on different systems one at a time. Upon completion of the trouble code display, a specific system may be selected for testing. Following the trouble code display, the first available system will be displayed (i.e. ECM). When making system selections there are 3 available alternatives:

- Pressing the "EXIT" key pad will stop the system selection process and return to the beginning of the trouble code sequence.
- Pressing the "NO" key pad will display the next available system selection.
- Pressing the "YES" key pad will select the displayed system for testing.

Toronado

After trouble codes have been displayed, the service mode can be used to perform several tests on different systems one at a time. Upon completion of trouble code display, a specific system may be selected for testing. Following trouble code display, the first available system will be displayed (i.e. ECM). When selecting a test, there are 4 available actions to be taken:

- Pressing the "OFF" button will stop the system selection process and return the display to the beginning of the trouble code sequence.
- Pressing the "LOW" fan button will display the next available system selection. This allows all system selections to be displayed.
- Pressing the "HIGH" fan button will select the displayed system for testing.
- Pressing the "BI-LEV" button will exit diagnostics and return to normal IPC and ECC operation.

TEST TYPE SELECTION

Riviera

Having selected a system, the first available test type will be displayed (i.e. "ECM DATA"). When making selection of test type there are 3 available alternatives:

- Pressing the "EXIT" key pad will stop the test type selection and return the display to the next available system selection.
- Pressing the "NO" key pad will display the next available test type for the selected system. This allows the display to be stepped through all available test type choices.
- Pressing the "YES" key pad will select the displayed test type. Here, the display will either indicate that the selected test type is in progress or the first of several specific tests will appear. If "NO DEVICES" appears, no test is available.

Toronado

Having selected a system, the first available test type will be displayed (i.e. "ECM DATA"). When selecting a specific test type there are 4 available actions to be taken:

- Pressing the "OFF" button will stop the test type selection process and return to the next available selection.
- Pressing the "LOW" fan button will display the next available test type for the selected system. This allows all available test types to be displayed for selection.
- Pressing the "HIGH" fan button will select the displayed test type. Here the display will either indicate whether the selected test type is in progress or the first of several tests will appear.
- Pressing the "BI-LEV" button will exit diagnostics.

TEST SELECTION

Riviera

Selection of "DATA", "INPUTS", "OUTPUTS", or "OVERRIDE" test types will result in the first available test being displayed. If a "Select ERR" message appears, this test is not allowed with the engine running. Turn engine off and try again.

GENERAL MOTORS TORQUE CONVERTER CLUTCH (Cont.)

Four characters of the display will contain a test code to identify the selection. The first 2 characters are letters which identify the system and test type (i.e. "ED" for "ECM DATA"), while the last 2 characters numerically identify the test. When selecting these tests, 3 alternatives are available:

- Pressing the "EXIT" key pad will stop the test selection process and return the display to the next test type for the selected system.
- Pressing the "NO" key pad will display the next smaller test number. If the lowest number is already displayed, the highest number will then be displayed.
- Pressing the "YES" key pad will display the next larger test number for the selected test type. If the highest number is already displayed, the lowest number will appear.

Fig. 5: Riviera Service Mode Operation Sequence

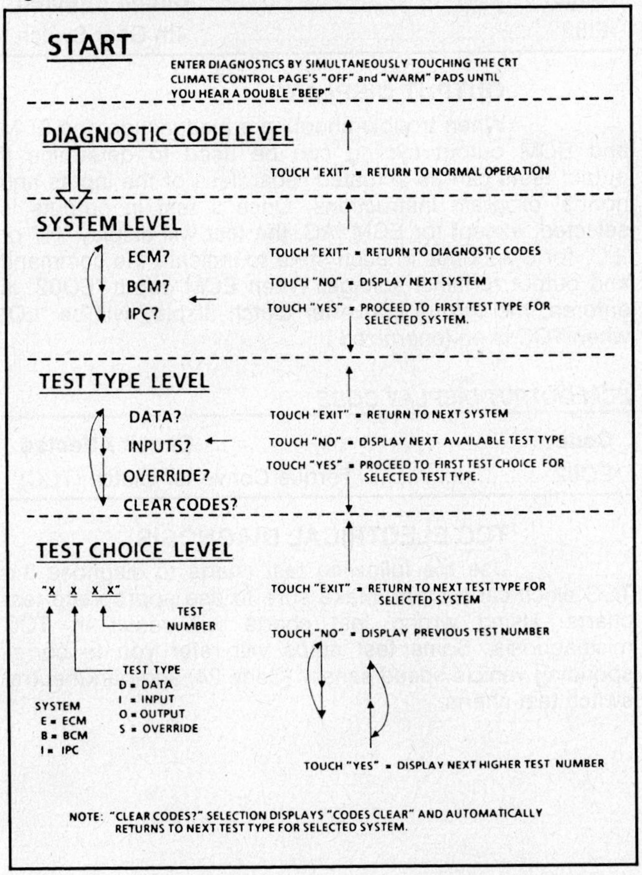

Toronado

Selection of "DATA", "INPUTS", or "OUTPUTS" test types will result in the first available test being displayed. If the message, "EEEE" appears it means that test is not allowed with the engine running. Turn engine off and repeat sequence.

The last 4 characters of the display will contain a test code to identify the selection. The first 2 of these characters are letters which identify the system and the test type (i.e. "ED" for "ECM DATA"), while the last 2 characters numerically identify the test. When selecting a specific test there are 3 available actions to be taken:

- Pressing the "OFF" button will stop the test selection process and return the display to the next available test type for the selected system.
- Pressing the "LOW" fan button will display the next smaller test number for the selected test type.
- Pressing the "HI" fan button will display the next larger test number for the selected test type.

Fig. 6: Toronado Service Mode Operation Sequence

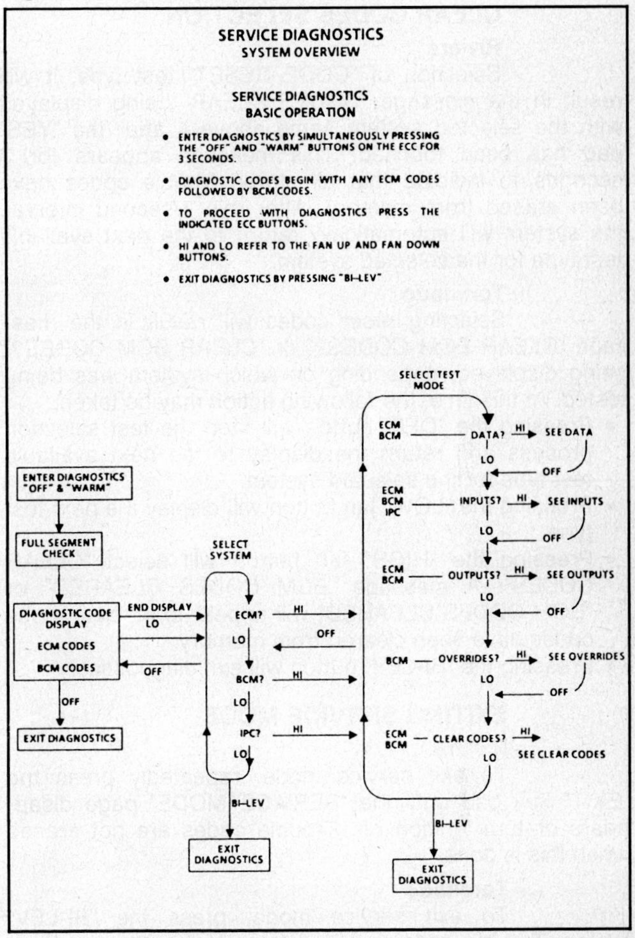

Upon selection of an "OVERRIDE" test function, current operation will be represented as a percentage of its full range. This value will be displayed on the ECC panel. The display will alternate between "--" and the normal program value. This alternating display is a reminder that the function is not currently being overridden.

Pressing the "WARM" or "COOL" buttons on the ECC panel begins the override, at which time the display will no longer alternate. Pressing the "WARM" button increases the value while pressing the "COOL" button decreases the value. Normal program control can be resumed in 1 of 3 ways.

- Selection of another override test will cancel the current override.
- Selection of another system (i.e. ECM, BCM) will cancel the current override.
- Overriding the value beyond either extreme (0 or 99) will display "--" momentarily and then jump to the opposite extreme. If the button is released while "--" is being displayed, normal program control will resume and the display will again alternate.

The override test type is unique in that any other test type within the selected system may be active at the same time. After selecting an override test, pressing the "OFF" button will allow selection of another test type, "DATA", "INPUTS" or "OUTPUTS". The ECC panel will

GENERAL MOTORS TORQUE CONVERTER CLUTCH (Cont.)

continue to display the selected override. By selecting another test type and test, while at the same time pressing the "WARM" or "COOL" button, it is possible to monitor the effect of the override on different vehicle parameters.

CLEAR CODES SELECTION

Riviera

Selection of "CODE RESET" test type, it will result in the message "CODES CLEAR" being displayed with the selected system name above it after the "YES" pad has been touched. This message appears for 3 seconds to indicate that all stored trouble codes have been erased from memory. After this 3-second interval, the system will automatically return to the next available test type for the selected system.

Toronado

Selecting reset codes will result in the message "CLEAR ECM CODES?" or "CLEAR BCM CODES?" being displayed, depending on which system was being tested. At this time, the following action may be taken:

- Pressing the "OFF" button will stop the test selection process and return the display to the next available test type for the selected system.
- Pressing the "LOW" fan button will display the next test type.
- Pressing the "HIGH" fan button will select "CLEAR CODES". A message "ECM CODES CLEARED" or "BCM CODES CLEARED" will appear to indicate those codes have been cleared from memory.
- Pressing the "BI-LEV" button will exit diagnostics.

EXITING SERVICE MODE

Riviera

To exit service mode, repeatedly press the "EXIT" key pad until the "SERVICE MODE" page disappears or turn ignition off. Trouble codes are not erased when this is done.

Toronado

To exit service mode, press the "BI-LEV" button. Trouble codes are not erased when this is done. Any mode button will exit diagnostics, however, the "BI-LEV" button was chosen for consistency.

DATA DISPLAYS

When trouble shooting a malfunction, the ECM and BCM data display can be used to compare the vehicle with problems, with a vehicle that is functioning properly. When ECM data "ED12" or BCM data "BD60" is entered, vehicle speed is displayed from "0" (zero) to "159" MPH.

ECM DATA & BCM DATA DISPLAY CODES

Application	Circuit Affected
ECM Code	
ED12	Vehicle Speed
BCM Code	
BD60	Vehicle Speed

INPUT DISPLAYS

When trouble shooting a malfunction, the ECM, BCM, or IPC input display can be used to determine if the switched inputs are properly interpreted. When one of the input tests is selected, the state of that device is displayed as "HI" or "LO". Basically, "HI" or "LO" represent the input terminal voltage for that circuit.

The display also indicates if the input changed state since it was last tested. If a change occurred, an "X" will appear next to the "HI"/"LO" indicator. On Riviera, if a change did not occur, a "O" will remain displayed. The "X" will only appear once per selected input. When input display "E182" is entered, the 4th gear switch is "HI" when vehicle is in 4th gear.

ECM INPUT DISPLAY CODE

Code	Circuit Affected
E182	4th Gear Switch

OUTPUT DISPLAYS

When trouble shooting a malfunction, the ECM and BCM output cycling can be used to determine if output tests can be actuated regardless of the inputs and normal program instructions. Once a test in outputs is selected, except for ECM IAC, the test will display "HI" or "LO" for 3 seconds in each state to indicate the command and output terminal voltage. When ECM ouput "EO02" is entered, the torque converter clutch display will be "LO" when TCC is on (energized.)

ECM OUTPUT DISPLAY CODE

Code	Circuit Affected
EO02	Torque Converter Clutch (TCC)

TCC ELECTRICAL DIAGNOSIS

Use the following test charts to diagnose the TCC electrical system. Make sure to use appropriate test charts. Using wrong test charts will result in TCC misdiagnosis. Some test steps will refer you to corresponding vehicle speed sensor (Code 24) and park/neutral switch test charts.

GENERAL MOTORS TORQUE CONVERTER CLUTCH (Cont.)

Fig. 7: TCC Test Charts For Passenger Cars With 2.8L, 3.8L, 5.0L & 5.7L Carbureted Engines

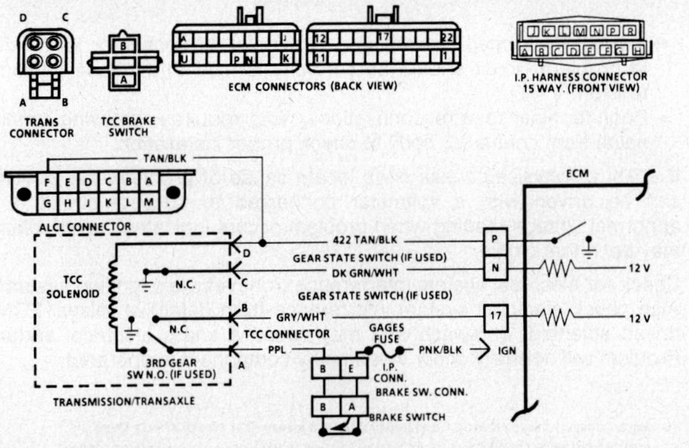

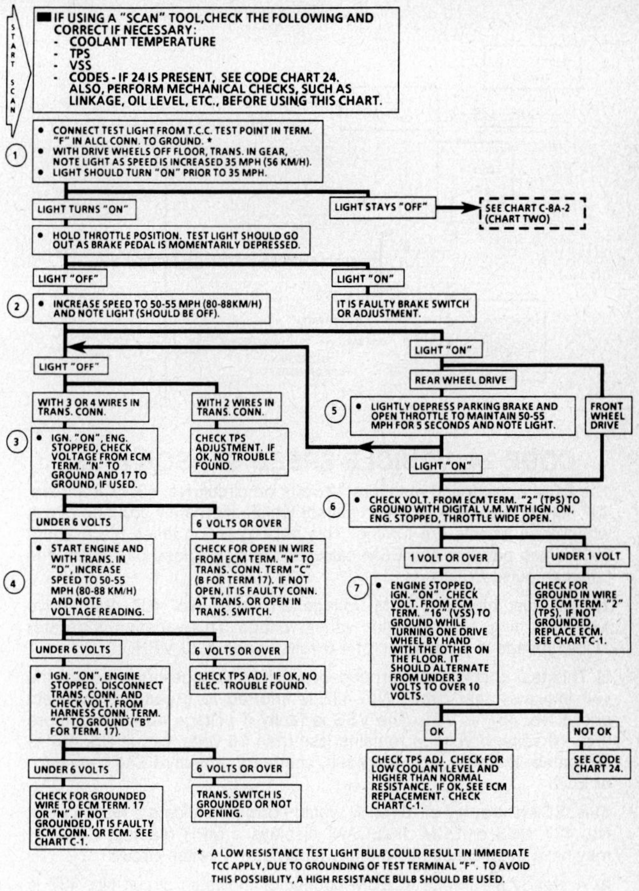

CHART C-8A-1
TCC ELECTRICAL DIAGNOSIS

1) This test checks voltage from ignition switch through brake switch, 3rd gear apply switch (if equipped) and TCC solenoid. Test light should light by 35 MPH. Test light may light momentarily between 3rd gear apply switch closing and ECM grounding TCC cirçuit from ECM terminal "P".

2) This test checks if ECM completes ground to energize TCC solenoid. Light should go off.

3) This test checks for open in circuits to terminals "N" and "17". The ECM supplies 12 volts to these terminals through a resistor. Normally both circuits have low voltage readings, since they involve normally closed circuits with vehicle stoppped. An open circuit would give a reading of about 12 volts.

4) Switch(es) open when transmission/transaxle upshifts. This checks that transmission circuit functions normally by voltage going high (about battery voltage) as switch opens.

5) This increases throttle opening to increase TPS output. If TPS output is too low, the clutch won't apply. On some applications, coasting doesn't require enough throttle opening to allow transmission to shift.

6) This tests for low TPS input voltage at ECM. At wide open throttle, voltage should be about 5 volts. Too low a TPS voltage output could prevent transmission from shifting.

7) This tests for VSS signal at ECM. VSS signal is necessary to engage TCC.

CHART C-8A-2
TCC ELECTRICAL DIAGNOSIS (Cont.)

1) This test checks for ground in circuit to ECM terminal "P". Normally light should be off.

2) This test checks for ignition voltage to terminal "A" of the transmission connector. Light should normally be on.

3) This test checks for complete circuit from transaxle to TCC test terminal. Normally light should go on if harness is good.

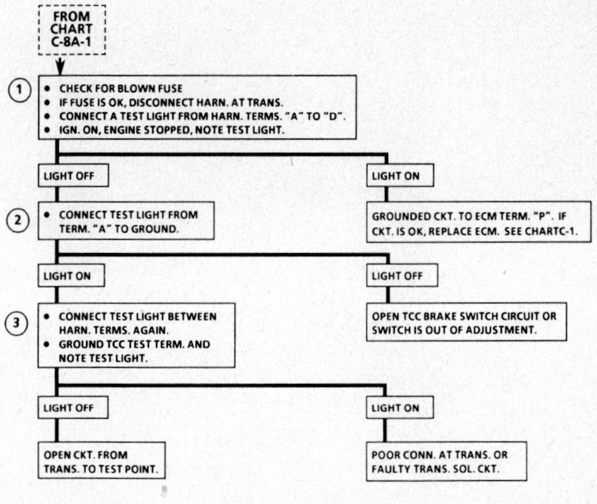

GENERAL MOTORS TORQUE CONVERTER CLUTCH (Cont.)

Fig. 8: Vehicle Speed Sensor (VSS) Test Chart For Passenger Cars With 2.8L, 3.8L, 5.0L & 5.7L Carbureted Engines

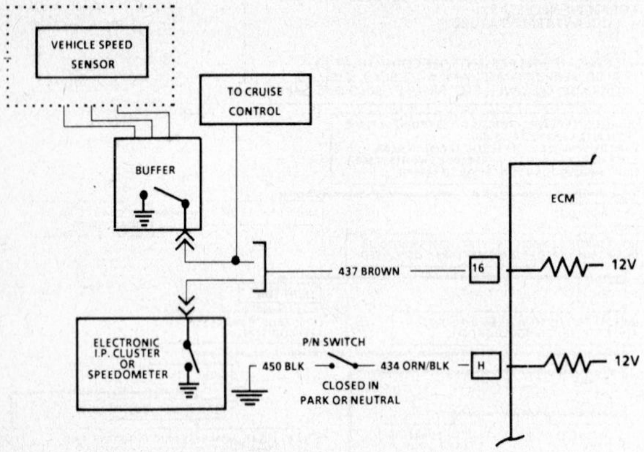

CODE 24, VEHICLE SPEED SENSOR (VSS)

The ECM applies and monitors 12 volts on circuit No. 437. Circuit No. 437 connects to vehicle speed sensor which alternately grounds circuit when drive wheels are turning. This pulsing action takes place about 2000 times per mile and ECM calculates vehicle speed based on time between pulses.

1) This test monitors ECM voltage on circuit No. 437. With drive wheels turning, pulsing action varies voltage. This variation is greater at low speeds to an average of 4-6 volts at about 20 MPH.

2) This test checks for a grounded circuit. A voltage of less than one volt indicates that circuit No. 437 is shorted to ground. Disconnect circuit No. 437 at VSS. The VSS is faulty if voltage now reads more than 10 volts. If voltage remains less than 10 volts, circuit No. 437 is grounded. If wire is not grounded, check for a faulty ECM connector or ECM.

3) A "SCAN" display of "0" MPH would normally indicate a faulty circuit No. 437, VSS or ECM. If "SCAN" displays a MPH reading, Code 24 may have been caused by a faulty park/neutral switch circuit.

4) A steady 8-12 volts at ECM connector indicates circuit No. 437 is open or a faulty VSS.

5) Normal voltage is 1-6 volts and varying. This may indicate an intermittent problem if Code 24 is shown.

Note on Intermittents: Most intermittent problems are caused by faulty electrical connections or wiring. Carefully check suspect circuit for:

- Poor mating of connector halves. Terminals not fully seated in connector body.
- Improperly formed or damaged terminals. All connector terminals in problem circuit should be carefully formed to increase contact tension.
- Poor terminal to wire connections. This requires removing terminal(s) from connector body to check proper installation.

If a visual (physical) check does locate cause of problem, the vehicle can be driven with a voltmeter connected to suspect circuit. An abnormal voltage reading when problem occurs indicates that problem may be in that circuit.

Check for electrical system interference from vehicle's ignition system. Also check electrical system interference from defective relays, ECM driven solenoid, or switch that may cause a sharp electrical surge. Problem will normally occur when faulty component is operated.

NOTE: TO PREVENT MISDIAGNOSIS, THE TECHNICIAN SHOULD IDENTIFY THE TYPE OF VEHICLE SPEED SENSOR USED PRIOR TO USING THIS CHART. DISREGARD CODE 24 WHEN DRIVE WHEELS ARE NOT TURNING.

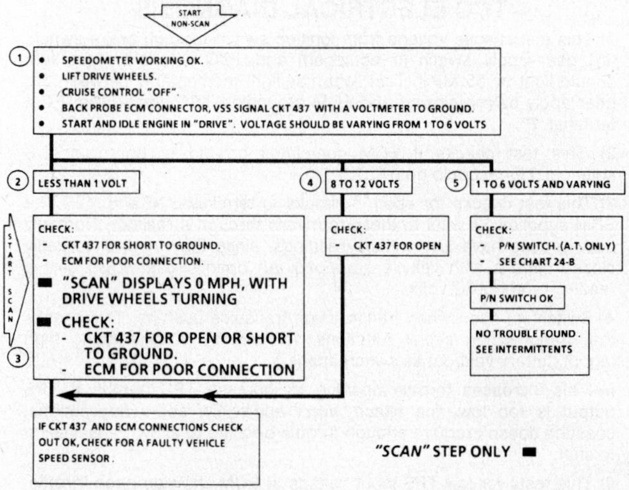

CLEAR CODES AND CONFIRM "CLOSED LOOP" OPERATION AND NO "SERVICE ENGINE SOON" LIGHT.

GENERAL MOTORS TORQUE CONVERTER CLUTCH (Cont.)

Fig. 9: Park/Neutral Switch Test Chart For Passenger Cars With 2.8L, 3.8L, 5.0L & 5.7L Carbureted Engines

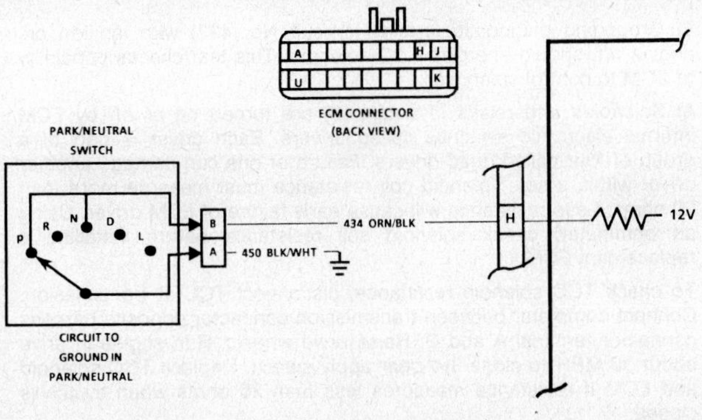

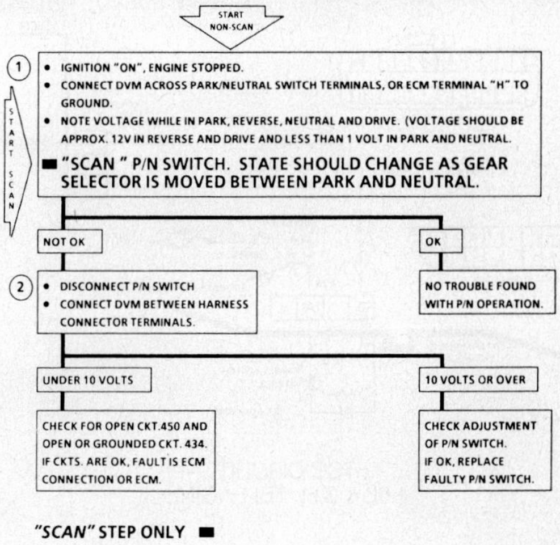

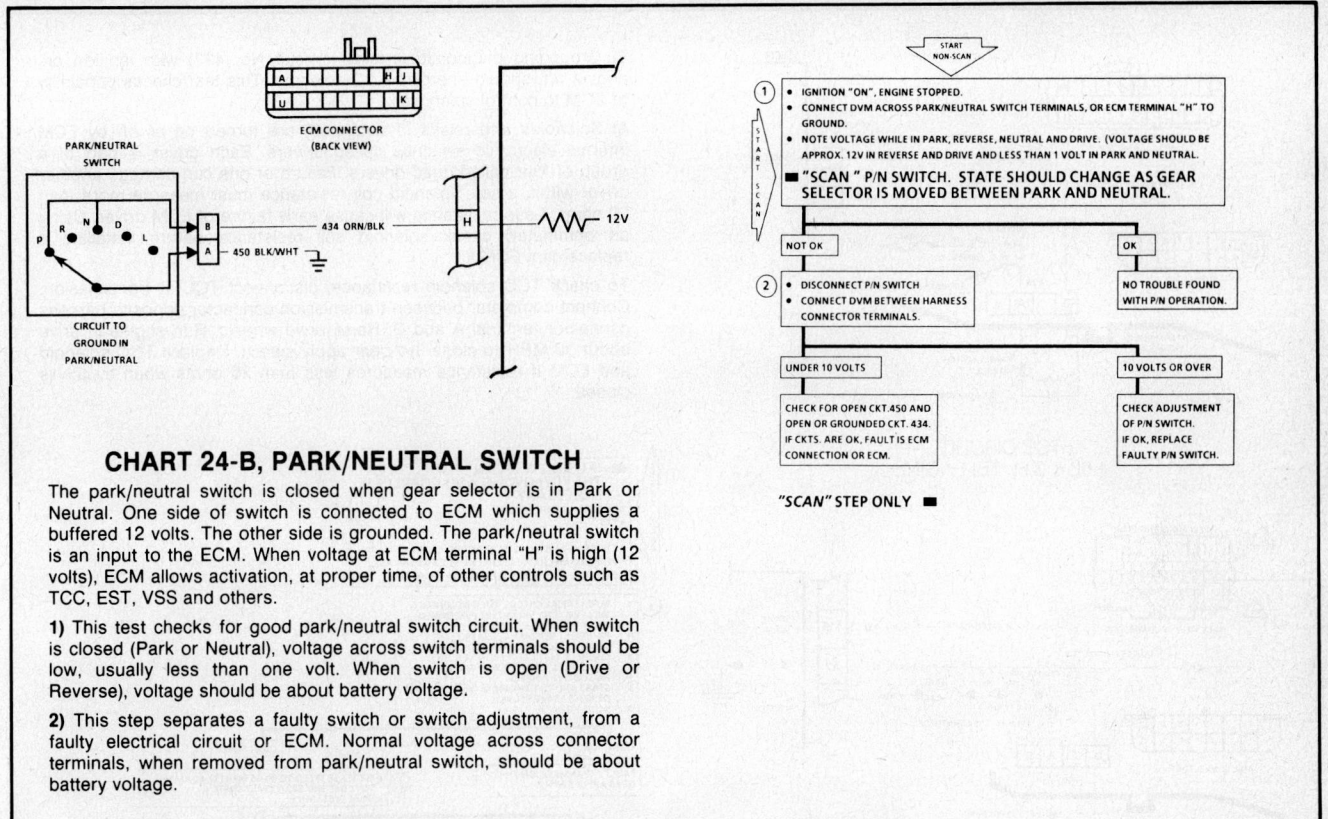

CHART 24-B, PARK/NEUTRAL SWITCH

The park/neutral switch is closed when gear selector is in Park or Neutral. One side of switch is connected to ECM which supplies a buffered 12 volts. The other side is grounded. The park/neutral switch is an input to the ECM. When voltage at ECM terminal "H" is high (12 volts), ECM allows activation, at proper time, of other controls such as TCC, EST, VSS and others.

1) This test checks for good park/neutral switch circuit. When switch is closed (Park or Neutral), voltage across switch terminals should be low, usually less than one volt. When switch is open (Drive or Reverse), voltage should be about battery voltage.

2) This step separates a faulty switch or switch adjustment, from a faulty electrical circuit or ECM. Normal voltage across connector terminals, when removed from park/neutral switch, should be about battery voltage.

Fig. 10: ECM Replacement Test Chart For Passenger Cars With 2.8L, 3.8L, 5.0L & 5.7L Carbureted Engines

CHART C-1, ECM REPLACEMENT CHECK

Before replacing ECM, test ECM circuit involved for poor ECM connector terminal contact, direct battery voltage short on ECM ground circuit, or shorted solenoid or relay. If a short is found, circuit must be repaired prior to replacing ECM to prevent further ECM failures.

1) This test checks for good terminal contact at ECM connector. Remove terminals to inspect. Replace if broken or dirty. If coolant is present, clean connector with alcohol or contact spray cleaner and replace ECM.

2) This test checks for a short to ignition or shorted solenoid or relay. All terminals must be tested because several are connected internally in the ECM. Any circuit testing below 20 ohms is shorted to ignition or shorted across relay or solenoid.

3) This test checks for shorted TCC solenoid. Some transmissions have a normally open 3rd gear switch in series with the solenoid. Ohmmeter will read infinity (open circuit) in these cases. If reading is less than 20 ohms, a short to ignition or shorted solenoid exists. A normal solenoid will read 20-50 ohms.

4) This test checks for shorted TCC circuit in units with a 3rd gear switch. Vehicle must be in 3rd gear to close switch to obtain a resistance reading. A normal solenoid will read 20-50 ohms.

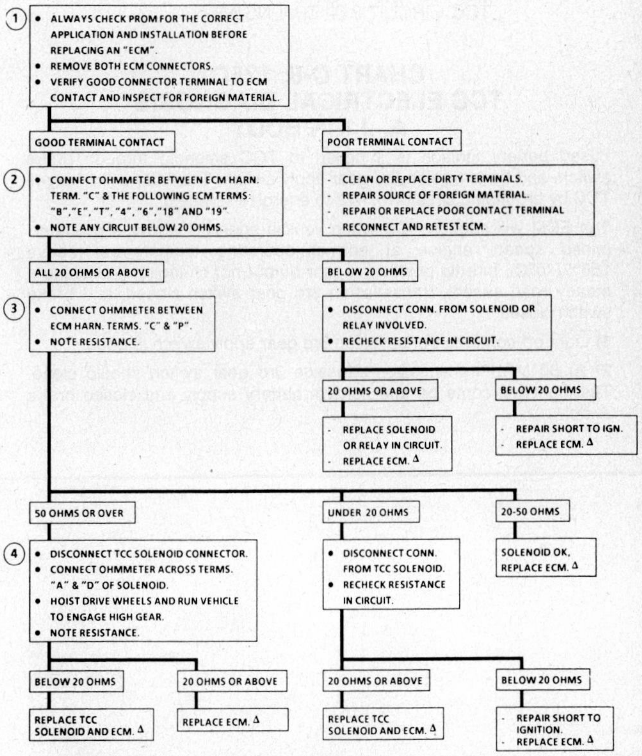

Δ 1. IF REPLACING AN ORIGINAL EQUIPMENT ECM, TRANSFER THE ORIGINAL BROADCAST CODE TO THE LABEL ON THE REPLACEMENT ECM.
2. IF, AFTER REPLACING THE "ECM', THE PROBLEM STILL EXISTS, THE "PROM" MAY BE FAULTY.

GENERAL MOTORS TORQUE CONVERTER CLUTCH (Cont.)

Fig. 11: TCC Test Chart For A, J & N Body Passenger Cars With 1.8L, 2.0L & 2.5L Throttle Body Injection (TBI) Engines

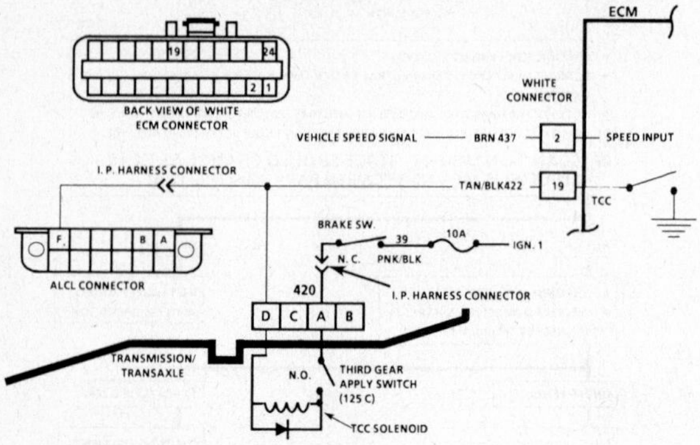

TCC CIRCUIT
1.8L & 2.5L TBI ENGINE

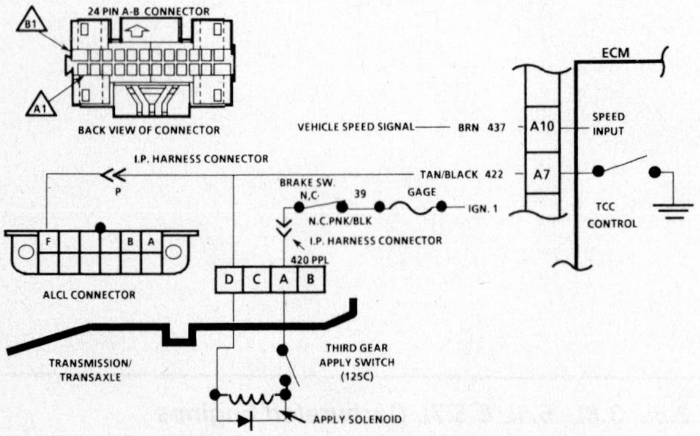

TCC CIRCUIT 2.0L TBI ENGINE

CHART C-8, 125C
TCC ELECTRICAL DIAGNOSIS
A, J & N BODY

Fused battery ignition is supplied to TCC solenoid through brake switch, and transmission 3rd gear apply switch. The ECM will engages TCC by grounding circuit No. 422 to energize solenoid.

The ECM will engage TCC when vehicle speed is above a predetermined speed, engine at normal operating temperature (above 158°F/70°C), throttle position sensor output not changing (indicating a steady road speed), transmission 3rd gear switch closed, and brake switch closed.

1) Light off confirms transmission 3rd gear apply switch is open.

2) At 30 MPH transmission/transaxle 3rd gear switch should close. Test light will come on and confirm battery supply and closed brake switch.

3) Grounding diagnostic terminal (circuit No. 422) with ignition on, engine off, should energize TCC solenoid. This test checks capability of ECM to control solenoid.

4) Solenoids and relays (if equipped) are turned on or off by ECM internal electronic switches called drivers. Each driver is part of a group of four called quad-drivers. Failure of one can damage another driver within a set. Solenoid coil resistance must measure more than 20 ohms. Less resistance will cause early failure of ECM driver. Using an ohmmeter, check solenoid coil resistance before installing a replacement ECM.

To check TCC solenoid resistance, disconnect TCC at transmission. Connect ohmmeter between transmission connector opposite harness connector terminal A and D. Raise drive wheels. Run engine in drive about 30 MPH to close 3rd gear apply switch. Replace TCC solenoid and ECM if resistance measures less than 20 ohms when switch is closed.

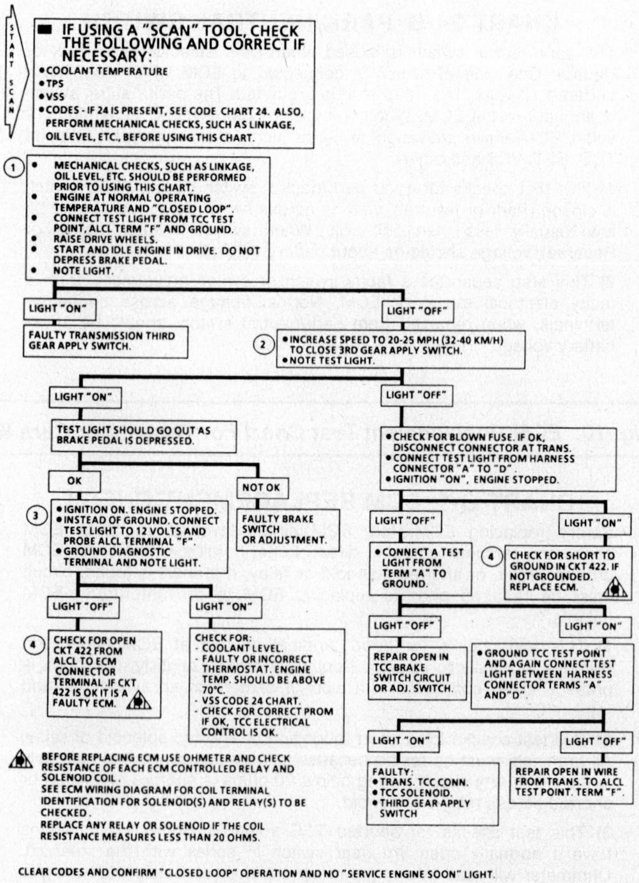

GENERAL MOTORS TORQUE CONVERTER CLUTCH (Cont.)

Fig. 12: TCC Test Chart For F Body Passenger Cars With 2.5L Throttle Body Injection (TBI) Engine

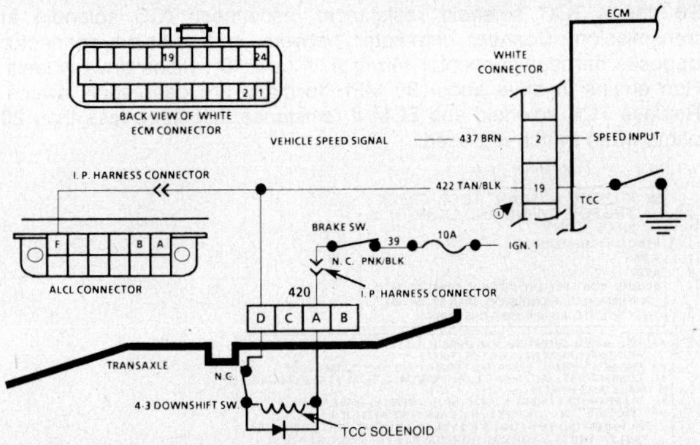

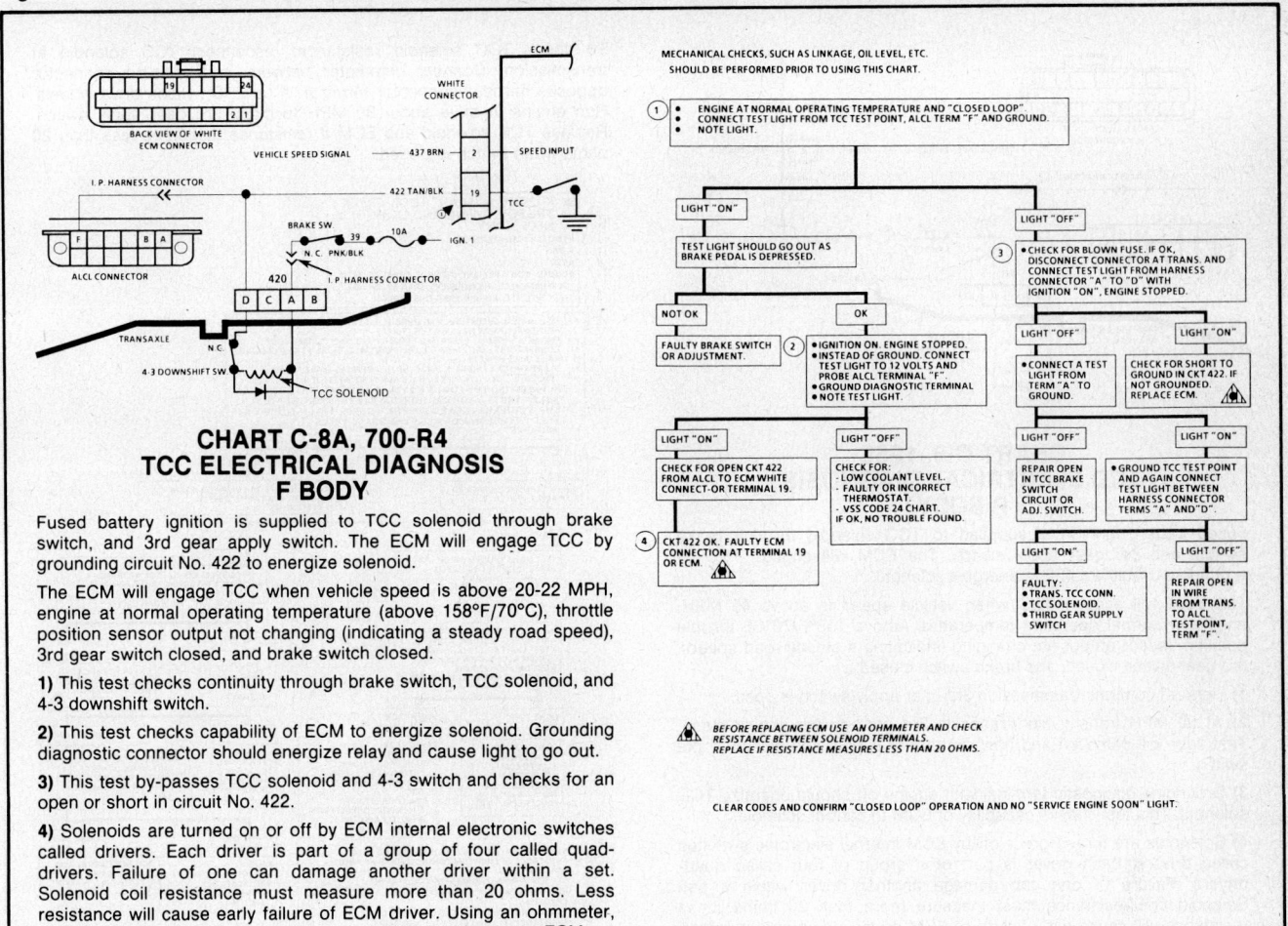

CHART C-8A, 700-R4
TCC ELECTRICAL DIAGNOSIS
F BODY

Fused battery ignition is supplied to TCC solenoid through brake switch, and 3rd gear apply switch. The ECM will engage TCC by grounding circuit No. 422 to energize solenoid.

The ECM will engage TCC when vehicle speed is above 20-22 MPH, engine at normal operating temperature (above 158°F/70°C), throttle position sensor output not changing (indicating a steady road speed), 3rd gear switch closed, and brake switch closed.

1) This test checks continuity through brake switch, TCC solenoid, and 4-3 downshift switch.

2) This test checks capability of ECM to energize solenoid. Grounding diagnostic connector should energize relay and cause light to go out.

3) This test by-passes TCC solenoid and 4-3 switch and checks for an open or short in circuit No. 422.

4) Solenoids are turned on or off by ECM internal electronic switches called drivers. Each driver is part of a group of four called quad-drivers. Failure of one can damage another driver within a set. Solenoid coil resistance must measure more than 20 ohms. Less resistance will cause early failure of ECM driver. Using an ohmmeter, check solenoid coil resistance before installing a replacement ECM.

MECHANICAL CHECKS, SUCH AS LINKAGE, OIL LEVEL, ETC. SHOULD BE PERFORMED PRIOR TO USING THIS CHART.

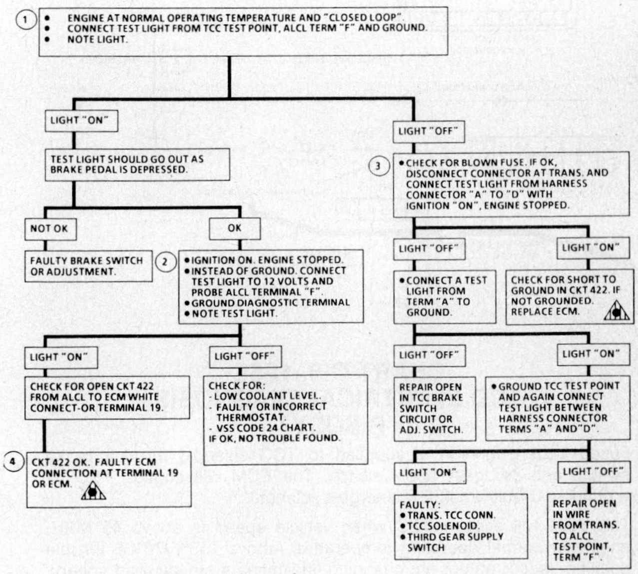

BEFORE REPLACING ECM USE AN OHMMETER AND CHECK RESISTANCE BETWEEN SOLENOID TERMINALS. REPLACE IF RESISTANCE MEASURES LESS THAN 20 OHMS.

CLEAR CODES AND CONFIRM "CLOSED LOOP" OPERATION AND NO "SERVICE ENGINE SOON" LIGHT.

GENERAL MOTORS TORQUE CONVERTER CLUTCH (Cont.)

Fig. 13: TCC Test Chart For P Body Passenger Cars With 2.5L Throttle Body Injection (TBI) Engine

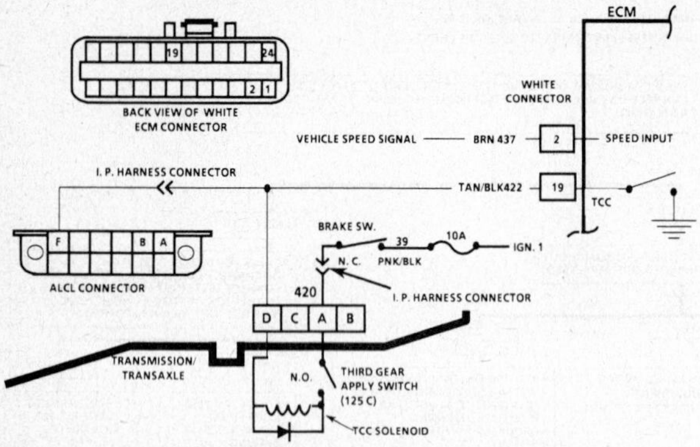

CHART C-8, 125C
TCC ELECTRICAL DIAGNOSIS
P BODY

Fused battery ignition is supplied to TCC solenoid through brake switch, and 3rd gear apply switch. The ECM will engage TCC by grounding circuit No. 422 to energize solenoid.

The ECM will engage TCC when vehicle speed is above 45 MPH, engine at normal operating temperature (above 158°F/70°C), throttle position sensor output not changing (indicating a steady road speed), 3rd gear switch closed, and brake switch closed.

1) Light off confirms transmission 3rd gear apply switch is open.

2) At 30 MPH transmission/transaxle 3rd gear switch should close. Test light will come on and confirm battery supply and closed brake switch.

3) Grounding diagnostic terminal with engine off should energize TCC solenoid. This test checks capability of ECM to control solenoid.

4) Solenoids are turned on or off by ECM internal electronic switches called drivers. Each driver is part of a group of four called quad-drivers. Failure of one can damage another driver within a set. Solenoid coil resistance must measure more than 20 ohms. Less resistance will cause early failure of ECM driver. Using an ohmmeter, check solenoid coil resistance before installing a replacement ECM.

To check TCC solenoid resistance, disconnect TCC solenoid at transmission. Connect ohmmeter between transmission connector opposite harness connector terminal "A" and "D". Raise drive wheels. Run engine in drive about 30 MPH to close 3rd gear apply switch. Replace TCC solenoid and ECM if resistance measures less than 20 ohms when switch is closed.

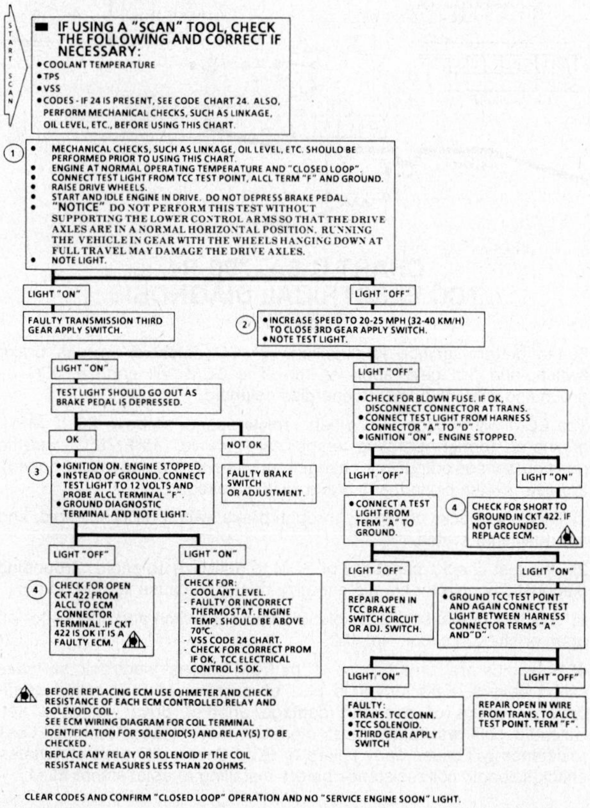

GENERAL MOTORS TORQUE CONVERTER CLUTCH (Cont.)

Fig. 14: Vehicle Speed Sensor (VSS) Test Chart For A, F, J, N & P Body Passenger Cars With 1.8L, 2.0L & 2.5L Throttle Body Injection (TBI) Engines

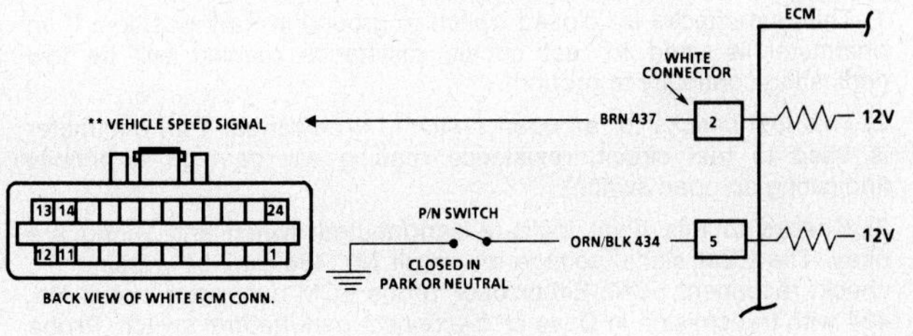

VSS CIRCUIT
1.8L & 2.5L TBI ENGINE

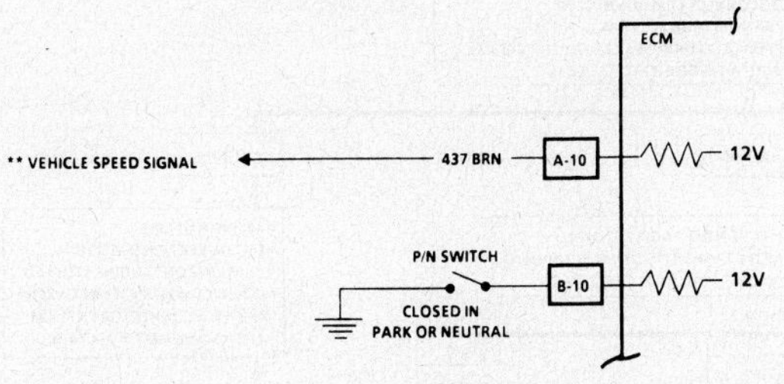

VSS CIRCUIT 2.0L TBI ENGINE

CODE 24, VEHICLE SPEED SENSOR (VSS) A, F, J, N & P BODY

The ECM applies and monitors 12 volts on circuit No. 437. Circuit No. 437 connects to vehicle speed sensor which alternately grounds circuit when drive wheels are turning. This pulsing action takes place 2000 times per mile. The ECM calculates vehicle speed based on the time between pulses.

1) This test monitors ECM voltage on circuit No. 437. With wheels turning, the pulsating action will result in a varying voltage. Variation will be greater at low speeds to an average of 4-6 volts at about 20 MPH.

2) A voltage of less than one volt at ECM connector indicates that wire in circuit No. 437 is shorted to ground. Disconnect circuit No. 437 at vehicle speed sensor. If voltage now reads above 10 volts, vehicle speed sensor is faulty. If voltage remains less than 10 volts, wire in circuit No. 437 is grounded. If circuit No. 437 is not grounded, check for faulty ECM connector or ECM.

NOTE: Some vehicles have a splice for cruise control (if equipped), which may supply voltage to circuit No. 437. Ensure that cruise control is off or disconnected.

3) A steady 8-12 volts at ECM connector indicates circuit No. 437 is open or a faulty vehicle speed sensor.

4) This normal voltage condition indicates a possible intermittent problem. See NOTE ON INTERMITTENTS.

5) If "SCAN" displays vehicle speed, check park/neutral switch using CHART C-1A. If switch is okay, check for intermittents.

Note on Intermittents: Most intermittent problems are caused by faulty electrical connections or wiring. Carefully check suspect circuit for:

- Poor mating of connector halves. Terminals not fully seated in connector body.
- Improperly formed or damaged terminals. All connector terminals in problem circuit should be carefully formed to increase contact tension.
- Poor terminal to wire connections. This requires removing terminal(s) from connector body to check proper installation.

If a visual (physical) check does locate cause of problem, the vehicle can be driven with a voltmeter connected to suspect circuit. An abnormal voltage reading when problem occurs indicates that problem may be in that circuit.

Check for electrical system interference from vehicle's ignition system. Also check electrical system interference from defective relays, ECM driven solenoid, or switch that may cause a sharp electrical surge. Problem will normally occur when faulty component is operated.

NOTE: TO PREVENT MISDIAGNOSIS, THE TECHNICIAN SHOULD IDENTIFY THE TYPE OF VEHICLE SPEED SENSOR USED PRIOR TO USING THIS CHART. DISREGARD CODE 24 WHEN DRIVE WHEELS ARE NOT TURNING.

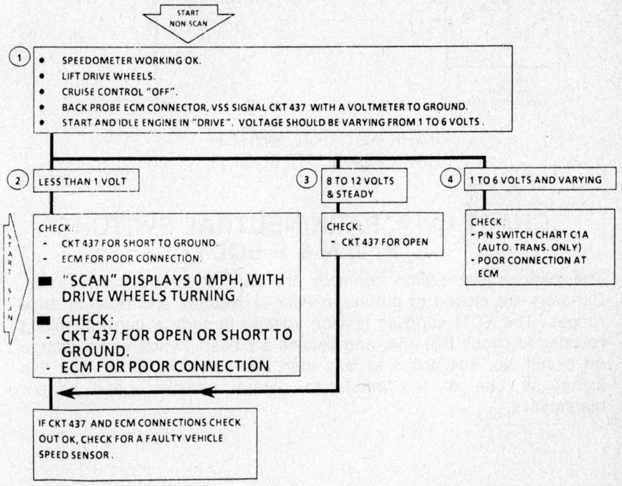

CLEAR CODES AND CONFIRM "CLOSED LOOP" OPERATION AND NO "SERVICE ENGINE SOON" LIGHT.

GENERAL MOTORS TORQUE CONVERTER CLUTCH (Cont.)

Fig. 15: Park/Neutral Switch Test Chart For A, F, J, N & P Body Passenger Cars With 1.8L, 2.0L & 2.5L Throttle Body Injection (TBI) Engines

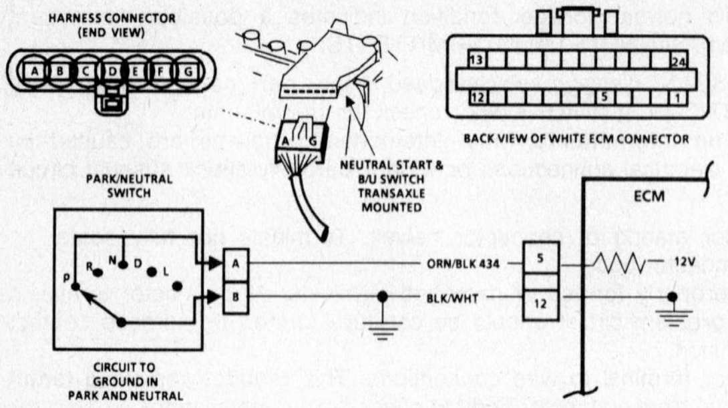

PARK/NEUTRAL SWITCH
CIRCUIT 1.8L & 2.5L TBI ENGINE

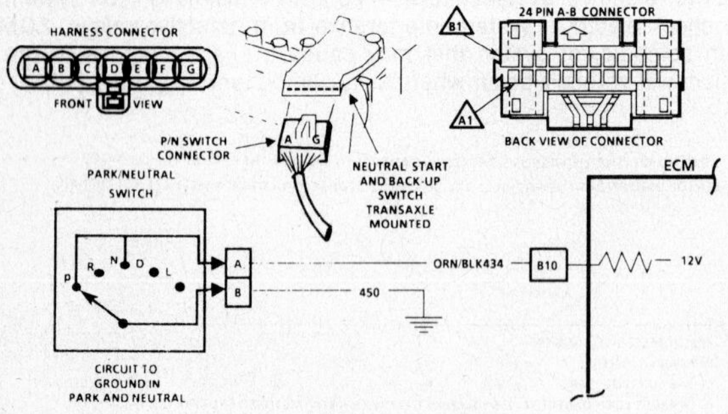

PARK/NEUTRAL SWITCH
CIRCUIT 2.0L TBI ENGINE

CHART C-1A, PARK/NEUTRAL SWITCH A, F, J, N & P BODY

The park/neutral switch contacts are part of neutral/start switch. Contacts are closed to ground in Park or Neutral, and open in drive ranges. The ECM supplies ignition voltage through a current limiting resistor to circuit No. 434, and senses a closed switch when voltage on circuit No. 434 drops to less than one volt. The ECM uses this signal as one of the inputs to control vehicle speed sensor diagnostics.

1) This test checks for closed switch to ground in Park position. If an ohmmeter is used to test circuit, resistance reading will be low (indicating continuity to ground).

2) This test checks for an open switch in drive range. If an ohmmeter is used to test circuit, resistance reading will be high or infinity (indicating an open switch).

3) Checks to this point indicate park/neutral switch and wiring are okay. The ECM signal voltage on circuit No. 434 may be missing. To check, reconnect ECM. Either back probe ECM connector circuit No. 434 with transmision in Drive or disconnect park/neutral switch. Probe harness connector circuit No. 434 with a voltmeter to ground.

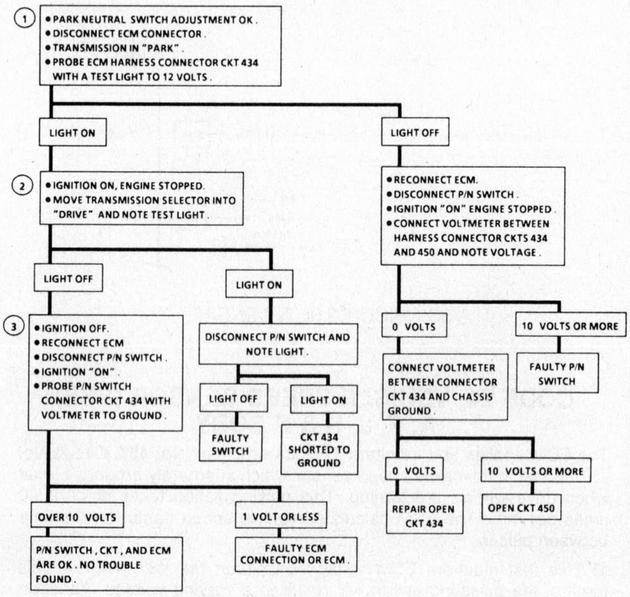

CLEAR CODES AND CONFIRM "CLOSED LOOP" OPERATION AND NO "SERVICE ENGINE SOON" LIGHT.

GENERAL MOTORS TORQUE CONVERTER CLUTCH (Cont.)

Fig. 16: TCC Test Chart For B & G Body Passenger Cars With 4.3L Throttle Body Injection (TBI) Engine

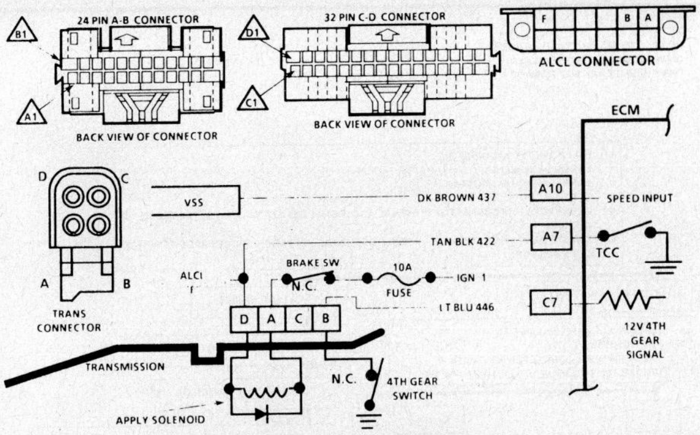

CHART C-8, 200-4R
TCC ELECTRICAL DIAGNOSIS
B & G BODY

Fused battery ignition is supplied to TCC solenoid through brake switch. The ECM will engage TCC by grounding circuit No. 422 to energize solenoid. The ECM will engage TCC when vehicle speed is above 24 MPH, engine is at normal operating temperature, throttle position sensor output not changing (indicating a steady road speed), and brake switch closed.

1) Test light on indicates battery voltage and continuity through TCC solenoid is okay.

2) This test checks for vehicle speed sensor signal to ECM. Voltage should vary from under 2 volts to over 8 volts.

3) This test checks for 4th gear switch signal to ECM. This signal will not prevent TCC engagement, but could cause a change in engage and disengage speed points.

4) Solenoids are turned on or off by ECM internal electronic switches called drivers. Each driver is part of a group of four called quad-drivers. Failure of one can damage any other driver within set.

Solenoid coil resistance must measure more than 20 ohms. Less resistance will cause early failure of ECM driver. Using an ohmmeter, check solenoid coil resistance of all ECM controlled solenoids and relays before installing a replacement ECM. Replace any solenoid or relay that measures less than 20 ohms resistance.

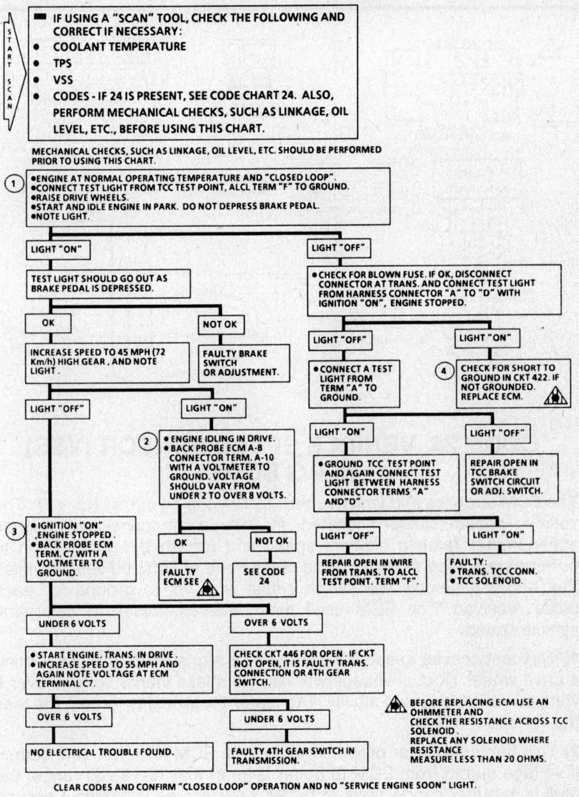

GENERAL MOTORS TORQUE CONVERTER CLUTCH (Cont.)

Fig. 17: Vehicle Speed Sensor (VSS) Test Chart For B & G Body Passenger Cars With 4.3L Throttle Body Injection (TBI) Engine

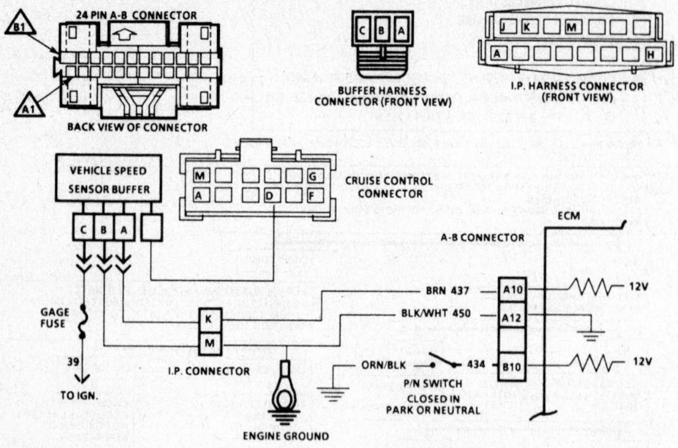

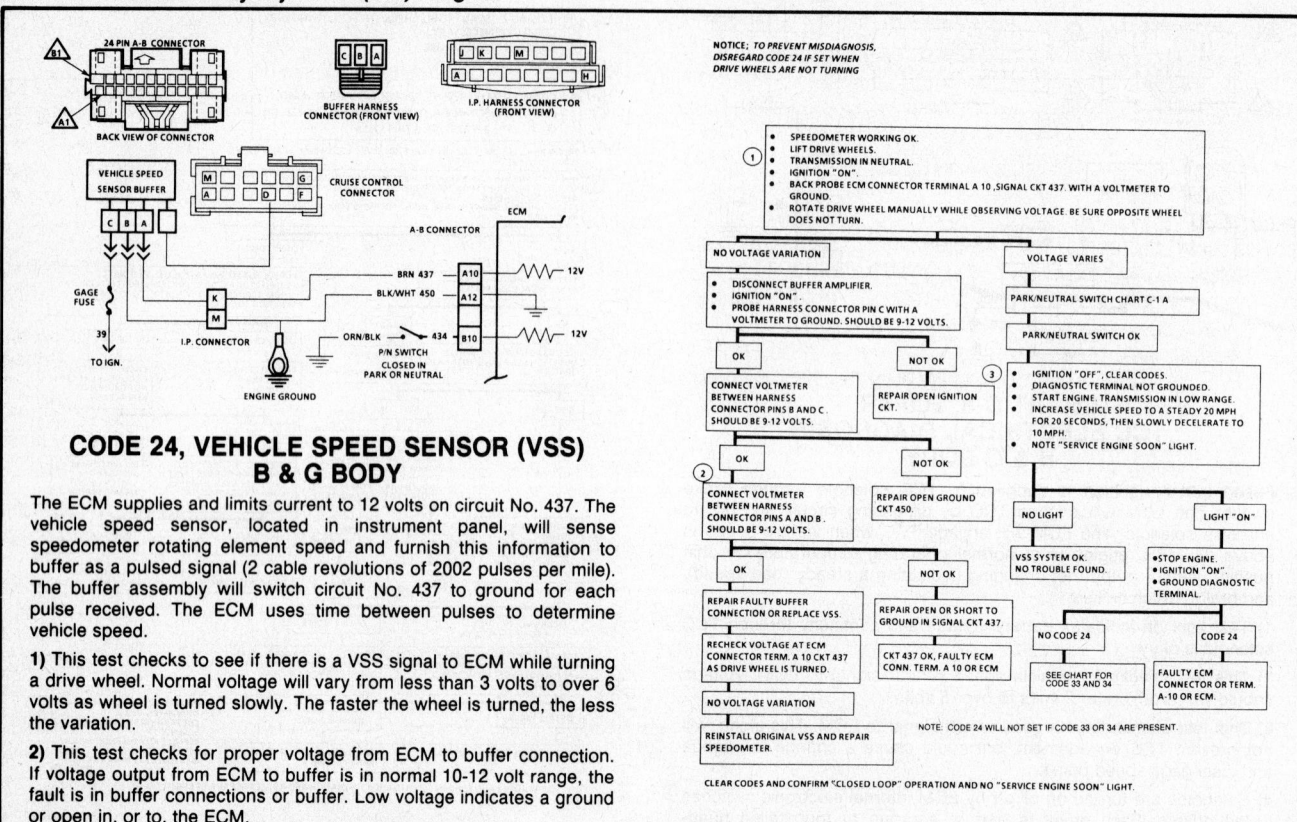

CODE 24, VEHICLE SPEED SENSOR (VSS) B & G BODY

The ECM supplies and limits current to 12 volts on circuit No. 437. The vehicle speed sensor, located in instrument panel, will sense speedometer rotating element speed and furnish this information to buffer as a pulsed signal (2 cable revolutions of 2002 pulses per mile). The buffer assembly will switch circuit No. 437 to ground for each pulse received. The ECM uses time between pulses to determine vehicle speed.

1) This test checks to see if there is a VSS signal to ECM while turning a drive wheel. Normal voltage will vary from less than 3 volts to over 6 volts as wheel is turned slowly. The faster the wheel is turned, the less the variation.

2) This test checks for proper voltage from ECM to buffer connection. If voltage output from ECM to buffer is in normal 10-12 volt range, the fault is in buffer connections or buffer. Low voltage indicates a ground or open in, or to, the ECM.

3) This step checks to see if ECM recognizes VSS signal.

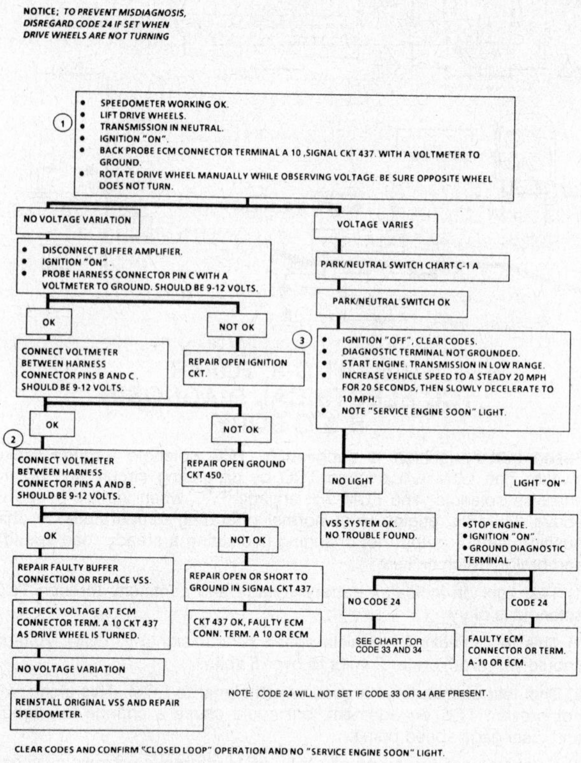

Fig. 18: Park/Neutral Switch Test Chart For B & G Body Passenger Cars With 4.3L Throttle Body Injection (TBI) Engine

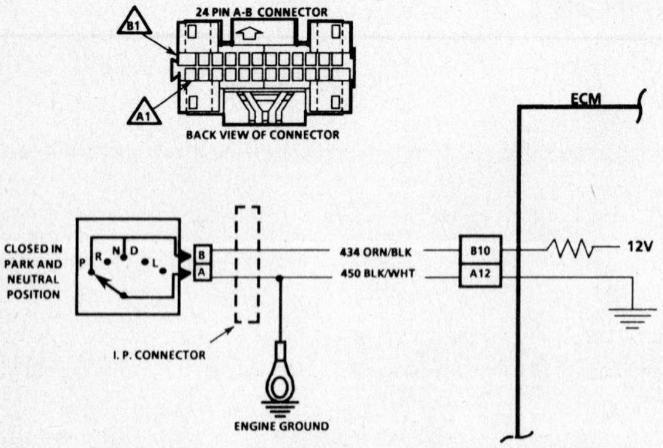

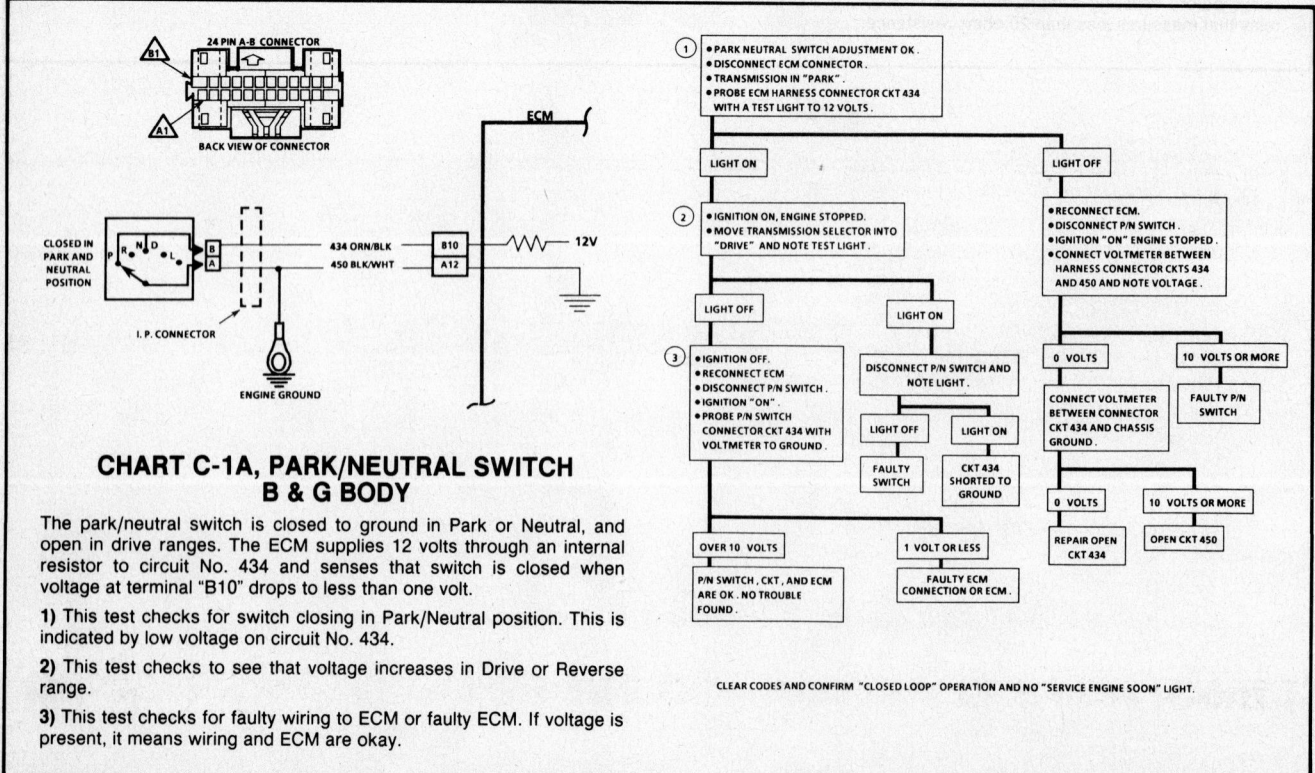

CHART C-1A, PARK/NEUTRAL SWITCH B & G BODY

The park/neutral switch is closed to ground in Park or Neutral, and open in drive ranges. The ECM supplies 12 volts through an internal resistor to circuit No. 434 and senses that switch is closed when voltage at terminal "B10" drops to less than one volt.

1) This test checks for switch closing in Park/Neutral position. This is indicated by low voltage on circuit No. 434.

2) This test checks to see that voltage increases in Drive or Reverse range.

3) This test checks for faulty wiring to ECM or faulty ECM. If voltage is present, it means wiring and ECM are okay.

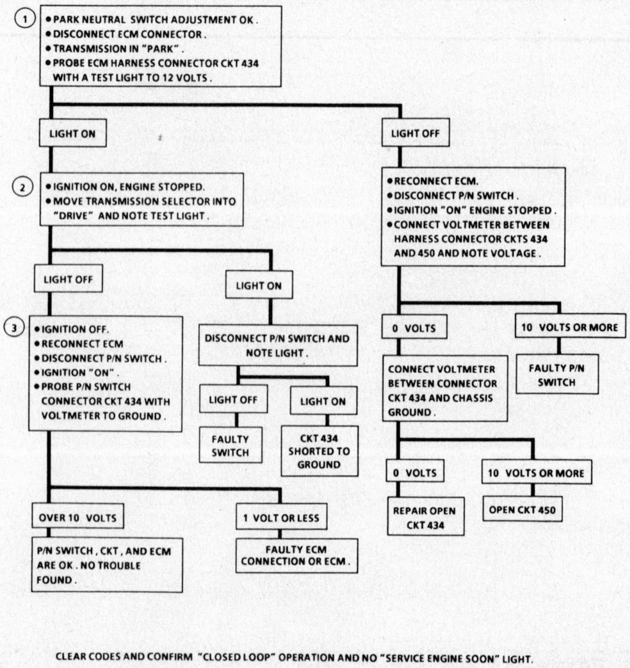

GENERAL MOTORS TORQUE CONVERTER CLUTCH (Cont.)

Fig. 19: Manifold Absolute Pressure (MAP) Sensor Test Charts For B & G Body Passenger Cars With 4.3L Throttle Body Injection (TBI) Engine

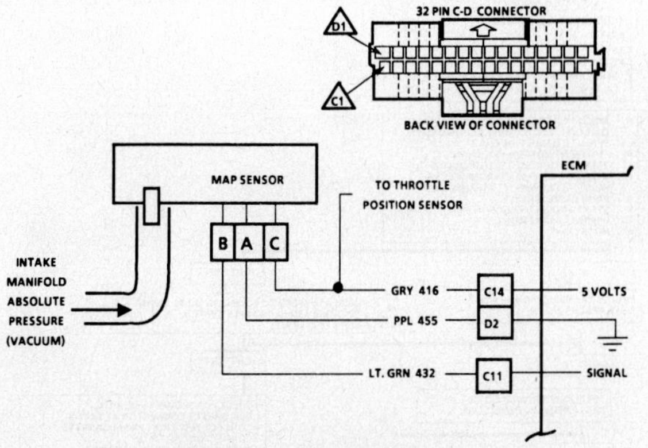

CODE 33, MAP SENSOR SIGNAL VOLTAGE HIGH B & G BODY

The Manifold Absolute Pressure (MAP) sensor responds to changes in manifold pressure (vacuum). The ECM receives this information as a signal voltage that will vary from about 1-1.5 volts at idle to 4-4.5 volts at wide open throttle. If MAP sensor fails, the ECM will substitute a fixed MAP value and use Throttle Position Sensor (TPS) to control fuel delivery.

Code 33 will set when signal reading is too high for a time greater than 5 seconds, when TPS voltage indicates throttle is closed and vehicle speed is zero MPH. Engine misfire or a low and unstable idle may set Code 33. Disconnect MAP sensor and system will go into back-up mode. If misfire or poor idle condition remains, have vehicle repaired.

1) This test confirms Code 33, and that fault is present.

2) If ECM recognizes and sets Code 34, low MAP signal, the ECM and wiring are okay.

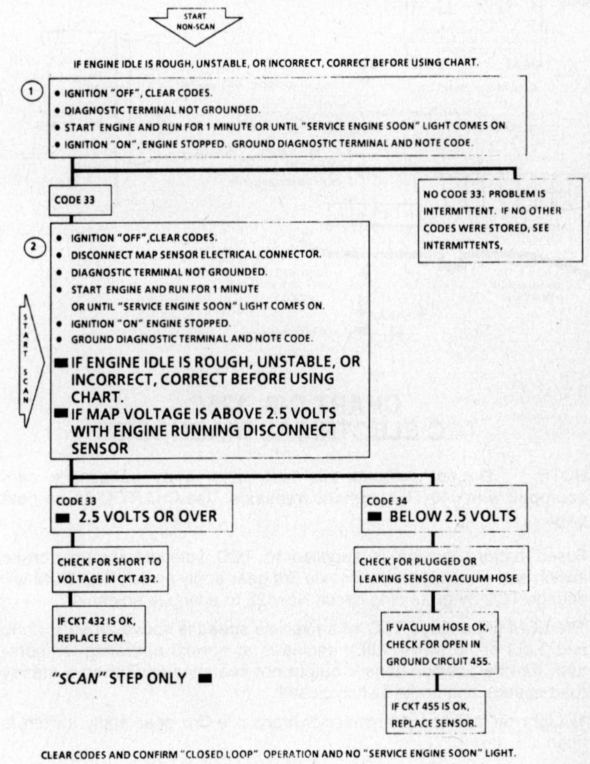

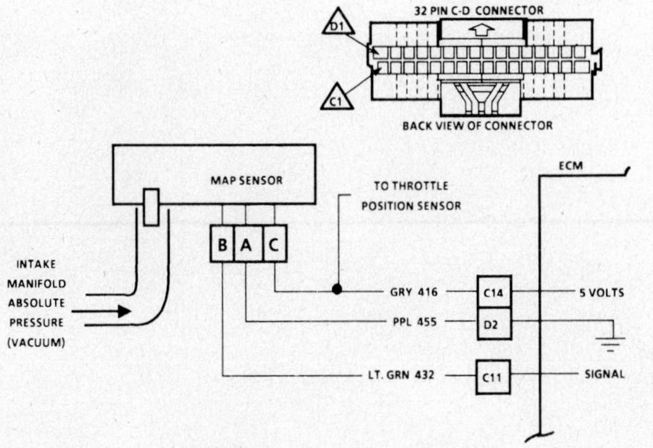

CODE 34, MAP SENSOR SIGNAL VOLTAGE LOW B & G BODY

The Manifold Absolute Pressure (MAP) sensor responds to changes in manifold pressure (vacuum). The ECM receives this information as a signal voltage that will vary from about 1-1.5 volts at idle to 4-4.5 volts at wide open throttle. If MAP sensor fails, the ECM will substitute a fixed MAP value and use Throttle Position Sensor (TPS) to control fuel delivery. Code 34 will set when signal is low and ignition is on.

1) This test confirms Code 34, and that fault is present.

2) If ECM recognizes and sets Code 33, high MAP signal, the ECM and wiring are okay.

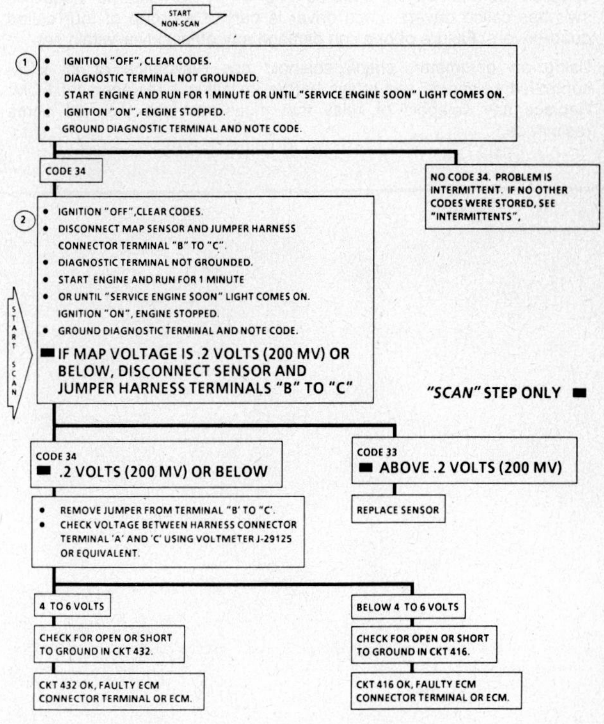

GENERAL MOTORS TORQUE CONVERTER CLUTCH (Cont.)

Fig. 20: TCC Test Chart For For A & J Body Passenger Cars With 1.8L & 2.8L Port Fuel Injected Engines

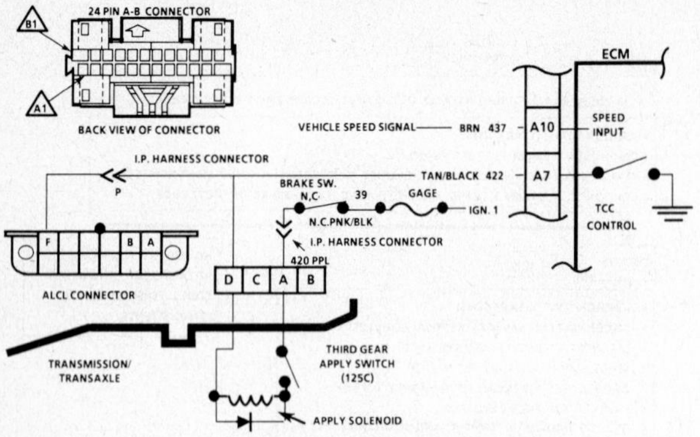

CHART C-8, 125C
TCC ELECTRICAL DIAGNOSIS

NOTE: Do not perform this test on A body passenger cars equipped with 440-T4 automatic transaxle. Use CHART C-8A on next page.

Fused battery ignition is supplied to TCC solenoid through brake switch and transmission/transaxle 3rd gear apply switch. The ECM will engage TCC by grounding circuit No. 422 to energize solenoid.

The ECM will engage TCC when vehicle speed is above 28 MPH (2.8L and 3.0L) or 40 MPH (1.8L), engine is at normal operating temperature, throttle position sensor output not changing (indicating a steady road speed), and brake switch closed.

1) Light off confirms transmission/transaxle 3rd gear apply switch is open.

2) At 20-25 MPH the transmission/transaxle 3rd gear switch should close. Test light will come on and confirm battery supply and closed brake switch.

3) Grounding diagnostic terminal with engine off should energize TCC solenoid. This test checks capability of ECM to control solenoid.

4) Solenoids and relays are turned on or off by ECM internal electronic switches called drivers. Each driver is part of a group of four called quad-drivers. Failure of one can damage any other driver within set.

Using an ohmmeter, check solenoid coil resistance of all ECM controlled solenoids and relays before installing a replacement ECM. Replace any solenoid or relay that measures less than 20 ohms resistance.

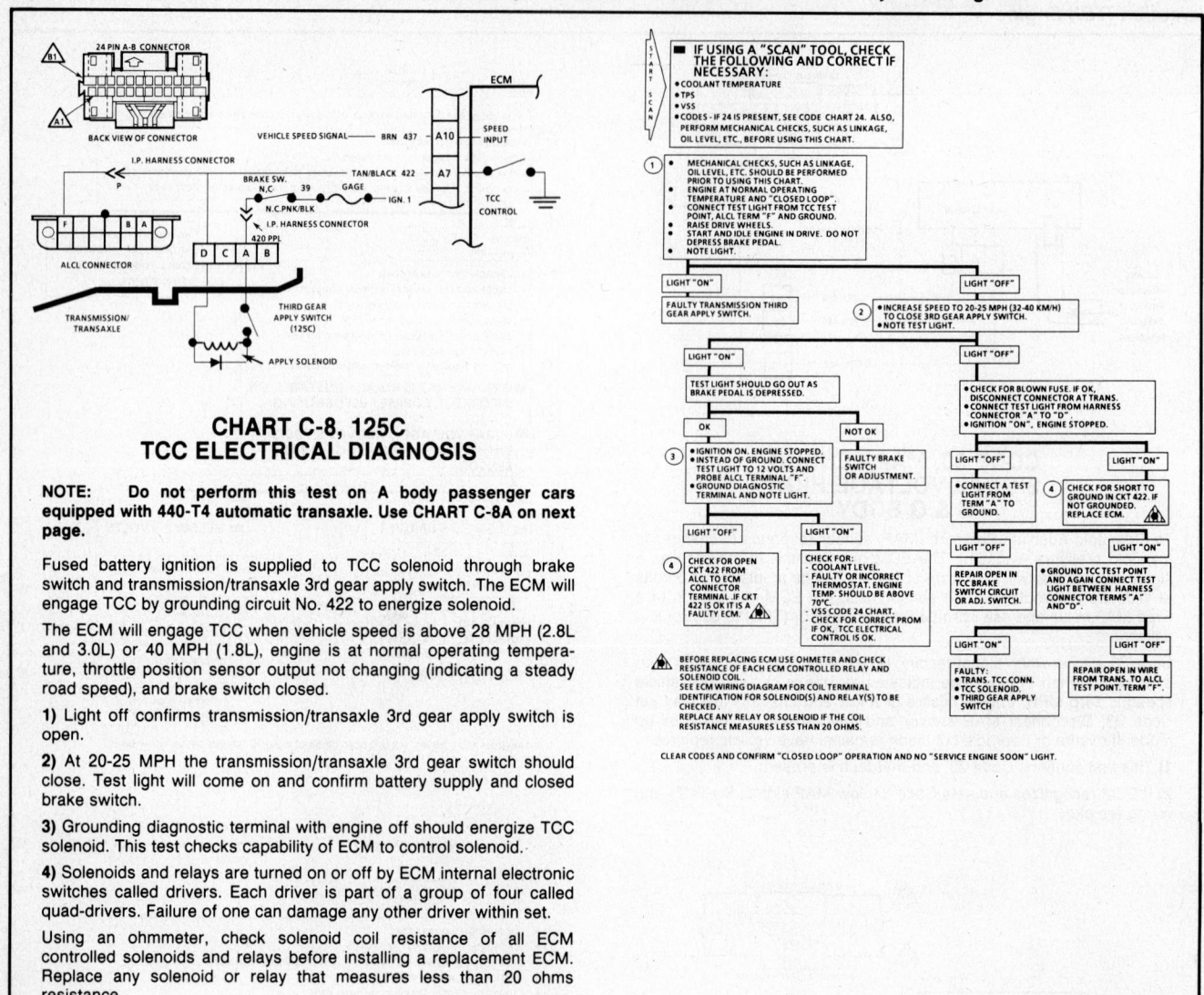

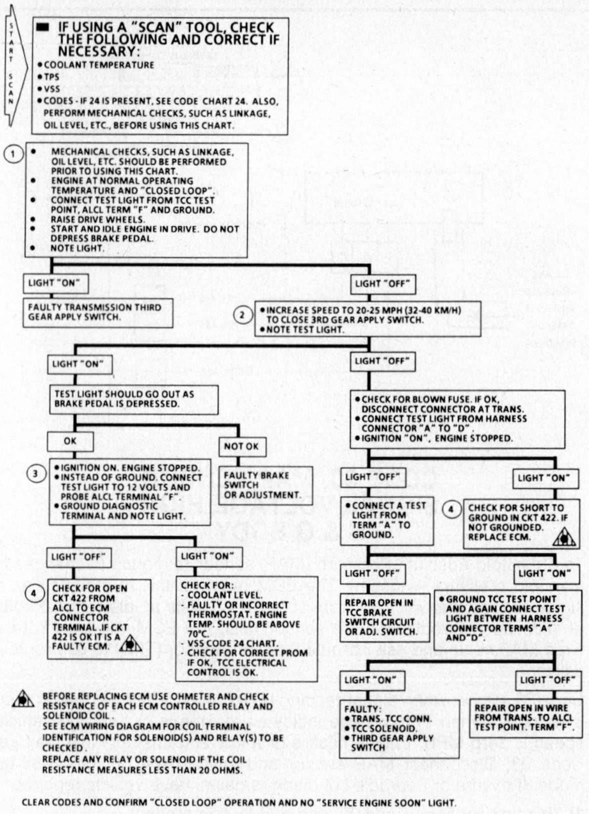

GENERAL MOTORS TORQUE CONVERTER CLUTCH (Cont.)

Fig. 21: TCC Test Charts For For A Body Passenger Cars With 2.8L Port Fuel Injected Engine

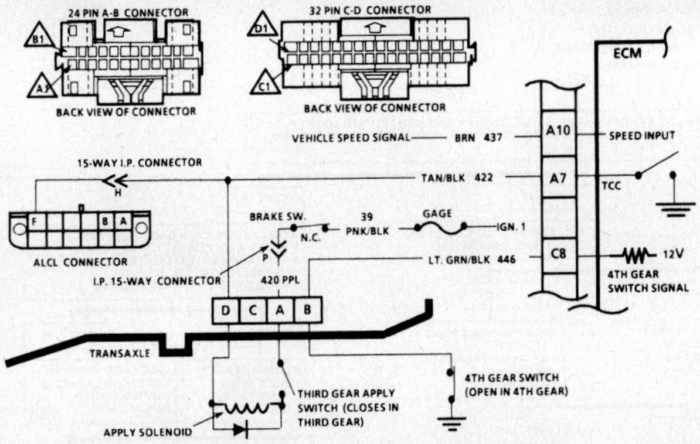

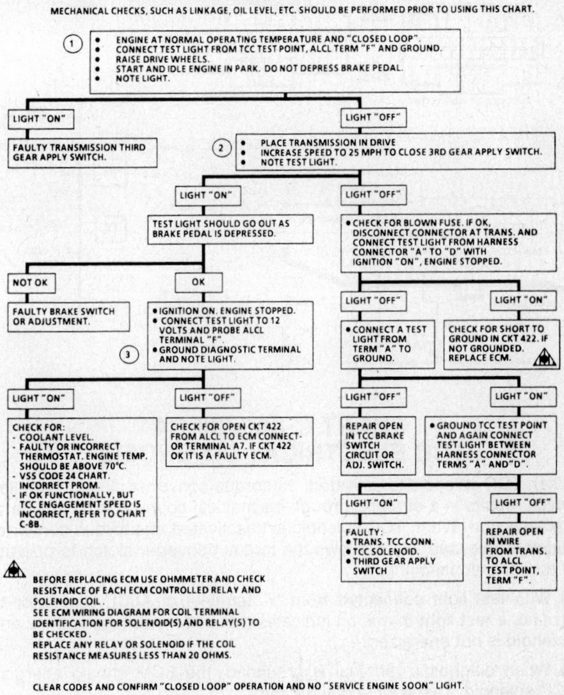

CHART C-8A, 440-T4
TCC ELECTRICAL DIAGNOSIS

When TCC solenoid is activated, the torque converter clutch is applied which results in a straight through mechanical coupling from engine to transmission. When TCC solenoid is deactivated, the torque converter clutch is released which allows the torque converter to operate in a conventional manner.

The ECM will engage TCC when vehicle speed is above 28 MPH, engine is at normal operating temperature, throttle position sensor output not changing (indicating a steady road speed), 4th gear switch open, and brake switch closed.

1) Light off confirms transaxle 3rd gear apply switch is open.

2) At 20-25 MPH the transaxle 3rd gear switch should close. Test light will come on and confirm battery supply and closed brake switch.

3) Grounding diagnostic terminal with engine off should energize TCC solenoid. This test checks capability of ECM to control solenoid. Solenoids and relays are turned on or off by ECM internal electronic switches called drivers.

Each driver is part of a group of four called quad-drivers. Failure of one can damage any other driver within set. Using an ohmmeter, check solenoid coil resistance of all ECM controlled solenoids and relays before installing a replacement ECM. Replace any solenoid or relay that measures less than 20 ohms resistance.

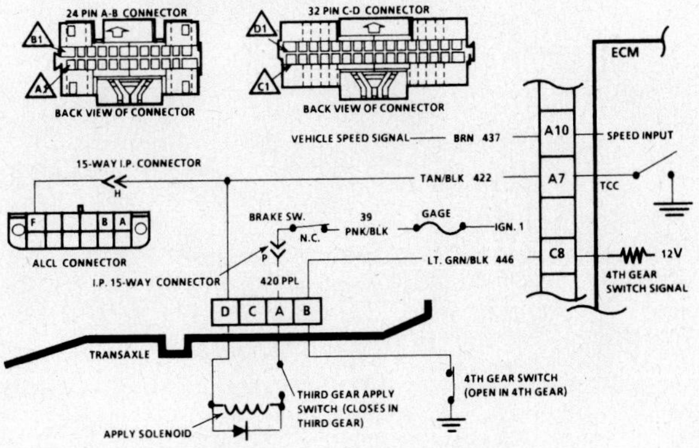

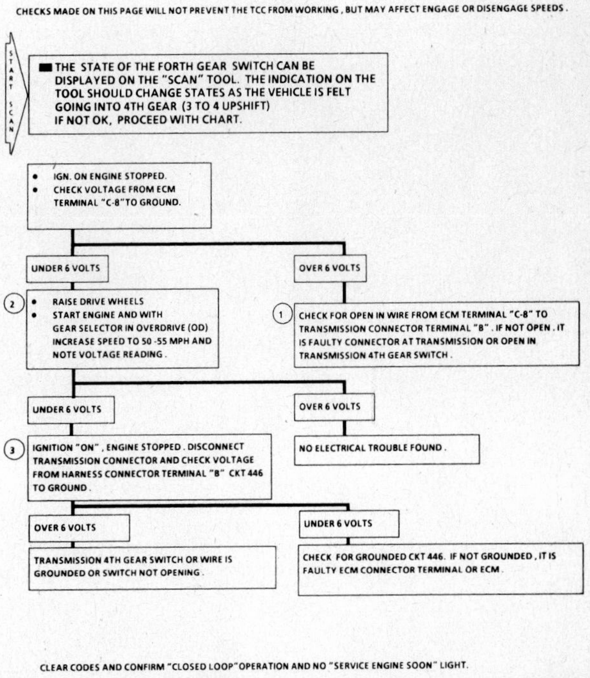

CHART C-8B, 440-T4
TCC ELECTRICAL DIAGNOSIS (Cont.)

1) If reading is over 6 volts, it indicates that circuit No. 446 is open. Transaxle connector is bad or 4th gear switch is stuck open.

2) With drive wheels turning, a voltage reading under 6 volts indicates that circuit No. 446 is shorted to ground. Also check for a faulty 4th gear switch, if transaxle is actually in 4th gear.

3) This test determines if problem with circuit No. 446 is an internal transaxle problem.

GENERAL MOTORS TORQUE CONVERTER CLUTCH (Cont.)

Fig. 22: TCC Test Chart For For F Body Passenger Cars With 2.8L Port Fuel Injected Engine

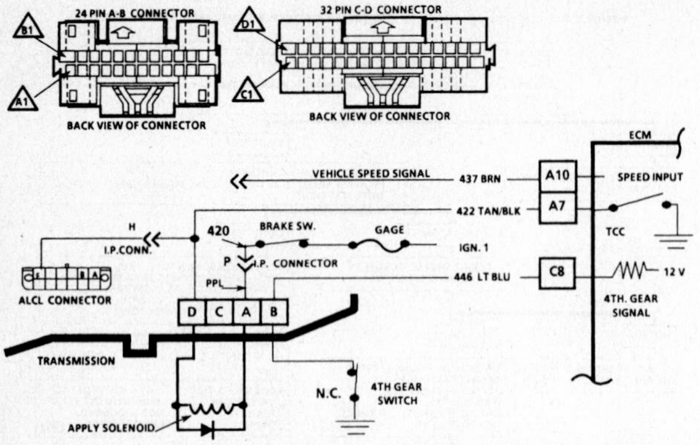

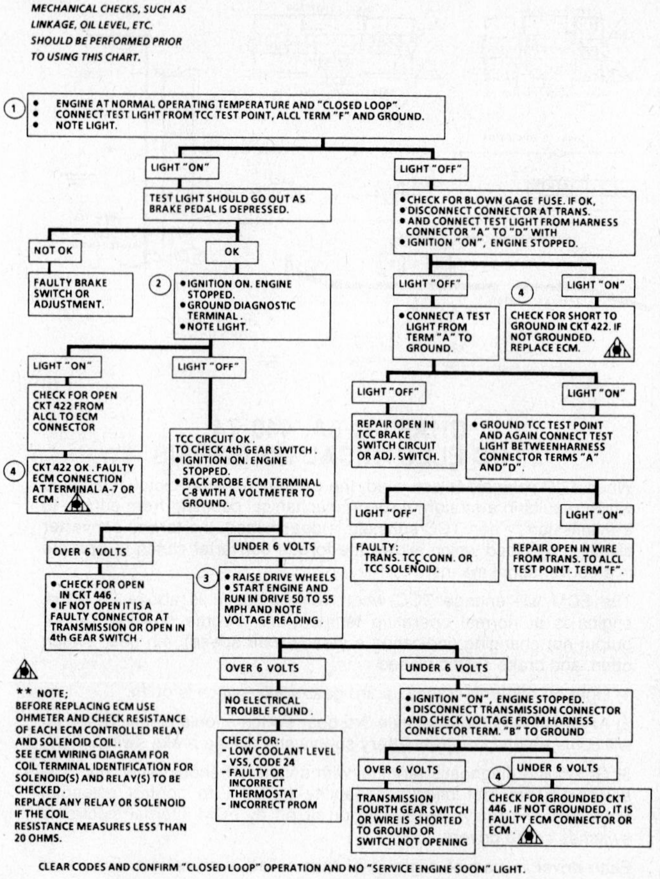

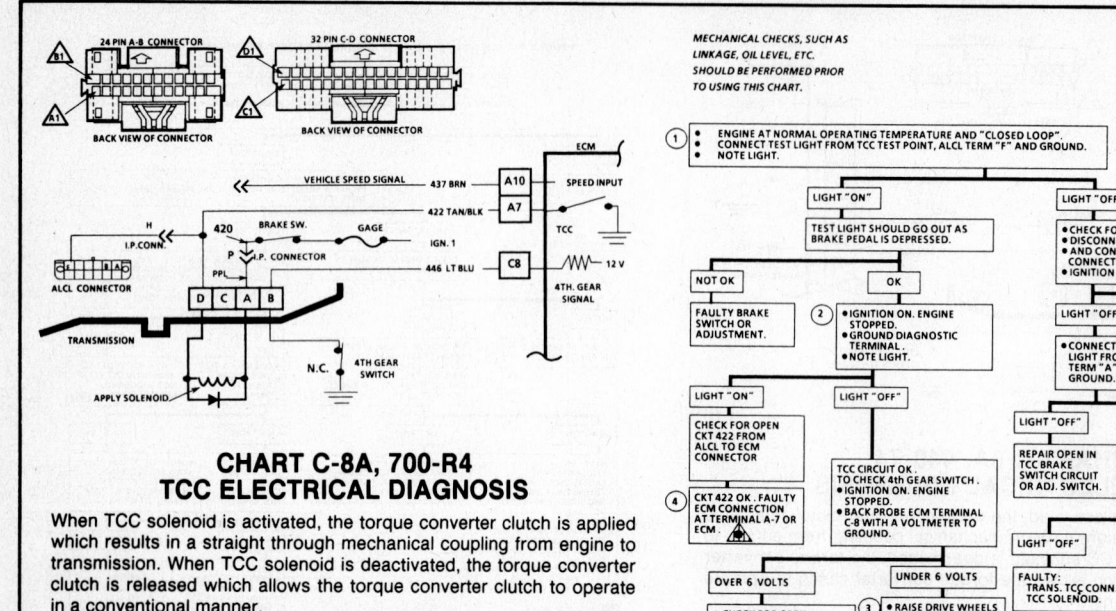

CHART C-8A, 700-R4
TCC ELECTRICAL DIAGNOSIS

When TCC solenoid is activated, the torque converter clutch is applied which results in a straight through mechanical coupling from engine to transmission. When TCC solenoid is deactivated, the torque converter clutch is released which allows the torque converter clutch to operate in a conventional manner.

1) With test light connected from "F" terminal of ALCL connector to ground, a test light that is on indicates that battery voltage is okay and solenoid is not energized.

2) When diagnostic terminal is grounded, the ECM should energize TCC solenoid. Test light should go out.

3) The 4th gear switch is normally closed. Switch should open around 50 MPH and cause voltage at ECM terminal "C8" to go over 6 volts.

4) Solenoids and relays are turned on or off by ECM internal electronic switches called drivers. Each driver is part of a group of four called quad-drivers. Failure of one can damage any other driver within set.

Using an ohmmeter, check solenoid coil resistance of all ECM controlled solenoids and relays before installing a replacement ECM. Replace any solenoid or relay that measures less than 20 ohms resistance.

GENERAL MOTORS TORQUE CONVERTER CLUTCH (Cont.)

Fig. 23: TCC Test Charts For For H & N Body Passenger Cars With 3.0L Port Fuel Injected Engine

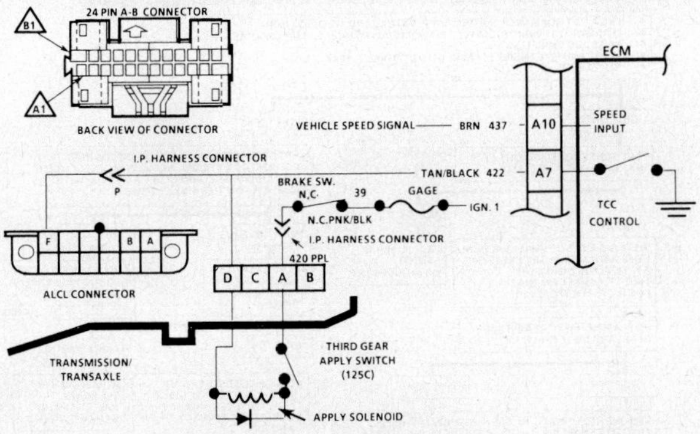

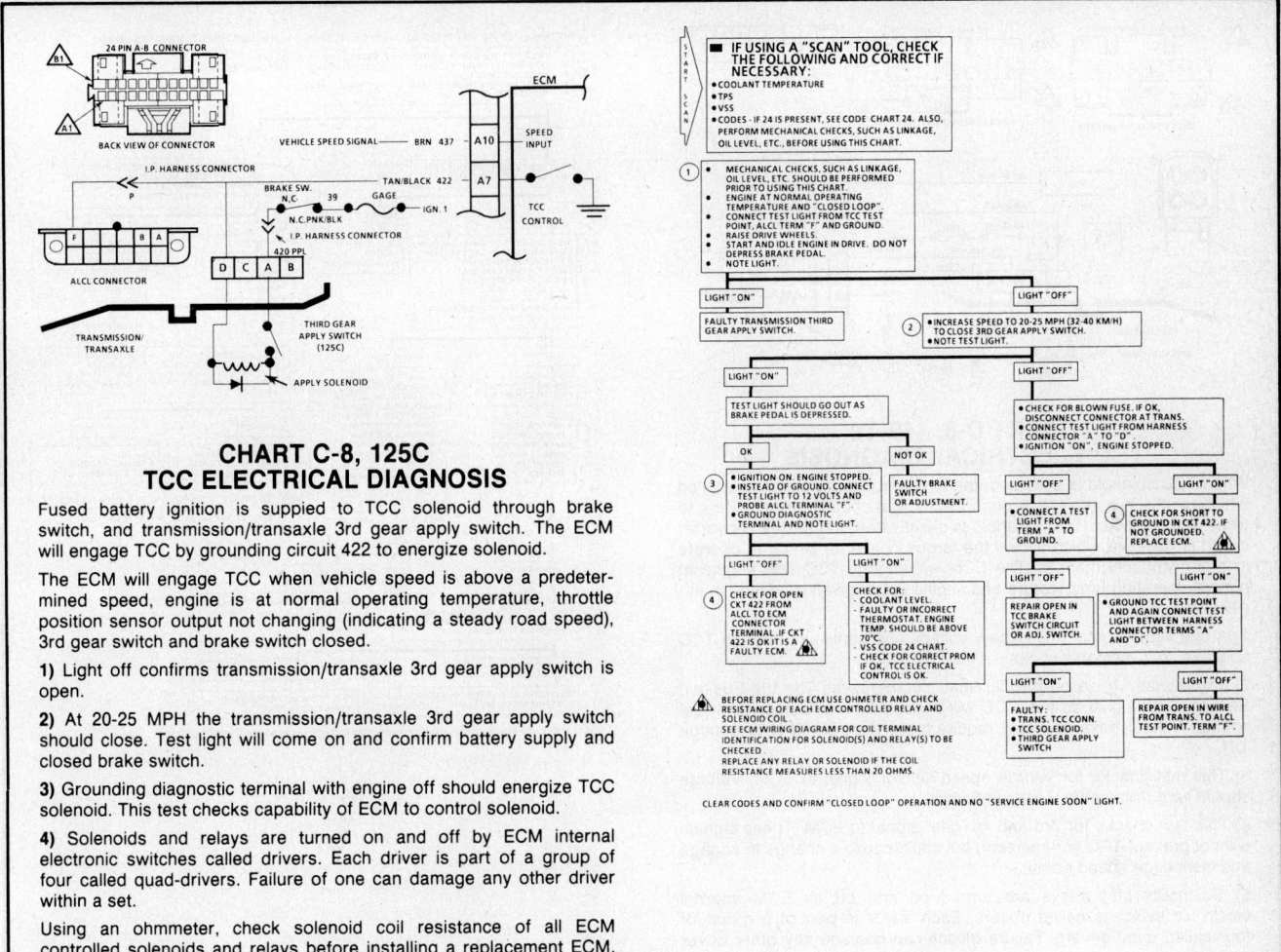

CHART C-8, 125C
TCC ELECTRICAL DIAGNOSIS

Fused battery ignition is suppied to TCC solenoid through brake switch, and transmission/transaxle 3rd gear apply switch. The ECM will engage TCC by grounding circuit 422 to energize solenoid.

The ECM will engage TCC when vehicle speed is above a predetermined speed, engine is at normal operating temperature, throttle position sensor output not changing (indicating a steady road speed), 3rd gear switch and brake switch closed.

1) Light off confirms transmission/transaxle 3rd gear apply switch is open.

2) At 20-25 MPH the transmission/transaxle 3rd gear apply switch should close. Test light will come on and confirm battery supply and closed brake switch.

3) Grounding diagnostic terminal with engine off should energize TCC solenoid. This test checks capability of ECM to control solenoid.

4) Solenoids and relays are turned on and off by ECM internal electronic switches called drivers. Each driver is part of a group of four called quad-drivers. Failure of one can damage any other driver within a set.

Using an ohmmeter, check solenoid coil resistance of all ECM controlled solenoids and relays before installing a replacement ECM. Replace any solenoid or relay that measures less than 20 ohms resistance.

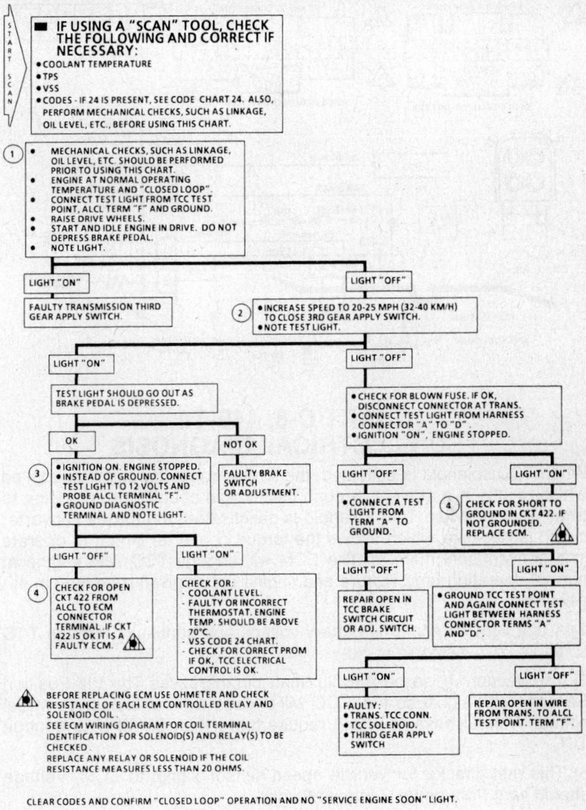

GENERAL MOTORS TORQUE CONVERTER CLUTCH (Cont.)

Fig. 24: TCC Test Charts For For Buick Regal With 3.8L (Turbo) Port Fuel Injected Engine

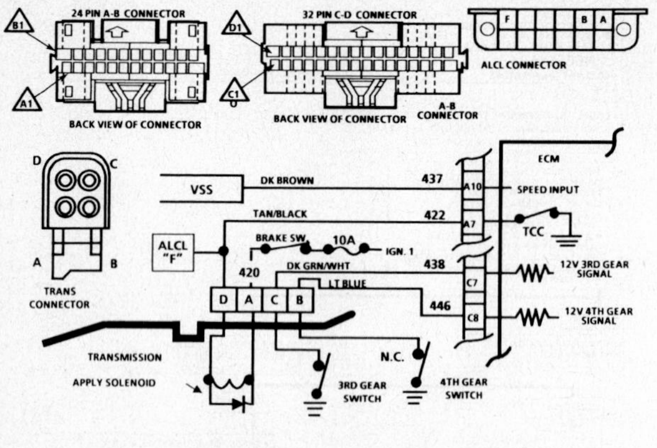

CHART C-8, 440-T4
TCC ELECTRICAL DIAGNOSIS

When TCC solenoid is activated, the torque converter clutch is applied which results in a straight through mechanical coupling from engine to transmission. When TCC solenoid is deactivated, the torque converter clutch is released which allows the torque converter clutch to operate in a conventional manner. The ECM will engage TCC with engine at normal operating temperature and engine under given road load in 4th gear only.

1) A test light on confirms battery voltage and continuity through TCC solenoid. TCC solenoid is okay.

2) The vacuum hose on throttle shaft pin increases Throttle Position Sensor (TPS) signal so that TCC will engage without excessive wheel speed. Without hose, it would require more than 65 MPH to engage TCC.

3) This test checks for vehicle speed sensor signal to ECM. Voltage should vary from under 2 to over 9 volts.

4) This test checks for 3rd and 4th gear signal to ECM. These signals will not prevent TCC engagement, but could cause a change in engage and disengage speed points.

5) Solenoids and relays are turned on and off by ECM internal electronic switches called drivers. Each driver is part of a group of four called quad-drivers. Failure of one can damage any other driver with in a set.

Using an ohmmeter, check solenoid coil resistance of all ECM controlled solenoids and relays before installing a replacement ECM. Replace any solenoid or relay that measures less than 20 ohms resistance.

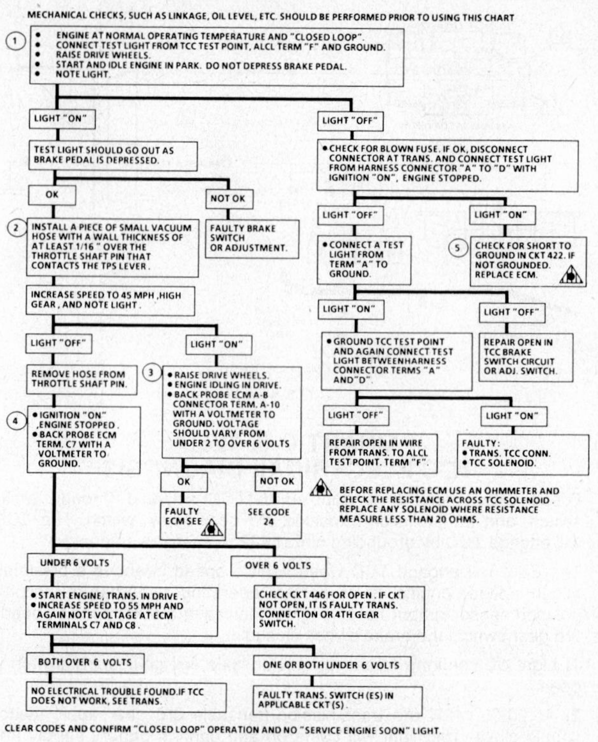

GENERAL MOTORS TORQUE CONVERTER CLUTCH (Cont.)

Fig. 25: TCC Test Charts For For A, C & H Body Passenger Cars With 3.8L Port Fuel Injected Engine

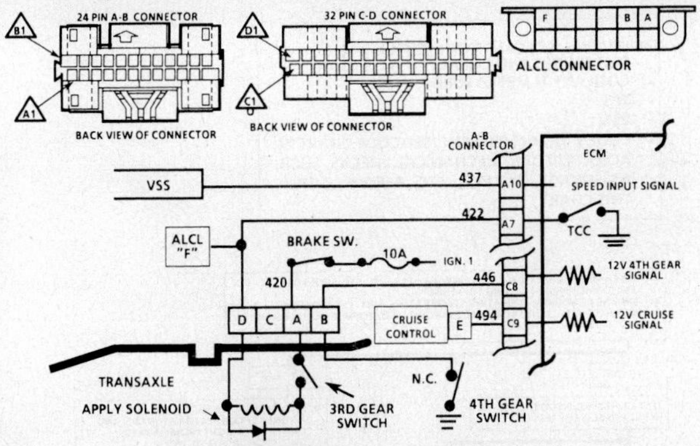

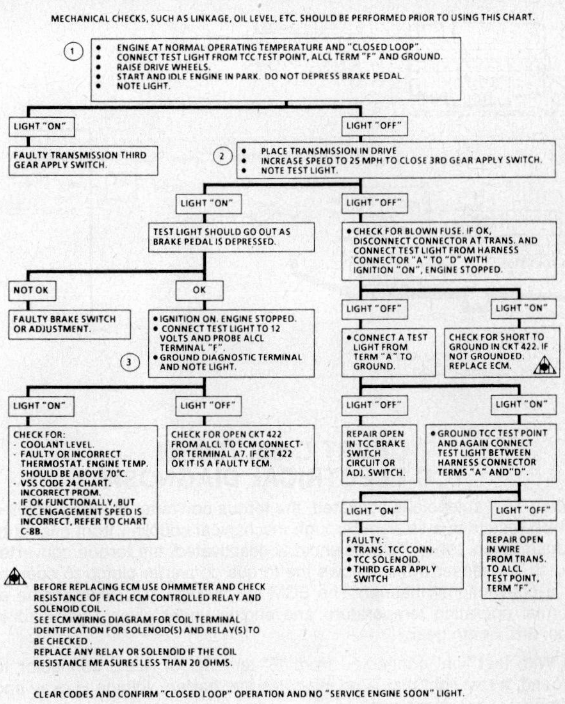

CHART C-8B, 440-T4
TCC ELECTRICAL DIAGNOSIS (Cont.)

When TCC solenoid is activated, the torque converter clutch is applied which results in a straight through mechanical coupling from engine to transmission. When TCC solenoid is deactivated, the torque converter clutch is released which allows the torque converter clutch to operate in a conventional manner.

The ECM will engage TCC when vehicle speed is above 28 MPH, engine is at normal operating temperature, throttle position sensor output not changing (indicating a steady road speed), 4th gear switch open, and brake switch closed.

1) Light off confirms transmission/transaxle 3rd gear apply switch is open.

2) At 25 MPH the transmission/transaxle 3rd gear switch should close. Test light will come on and confirm battery supply and closed brake switch.

3) Grounding diagnostic terminal with engine off should energize TCC solenoid. This test checks capability of ECM to control solenoid.

4) Solenoids and relays are turned on and off by ECM internal electronic switches called drivers. Each driver is part of a group of four called quad-drivers. Failure of one can damage any other driver within a set.

Using an ohmmeter, check solenoid coil resistance of all ECM controlled solenoids and relays before installing a replacement ECM. Replace any solenoid or relay that measures less than 20 ohms resistance.

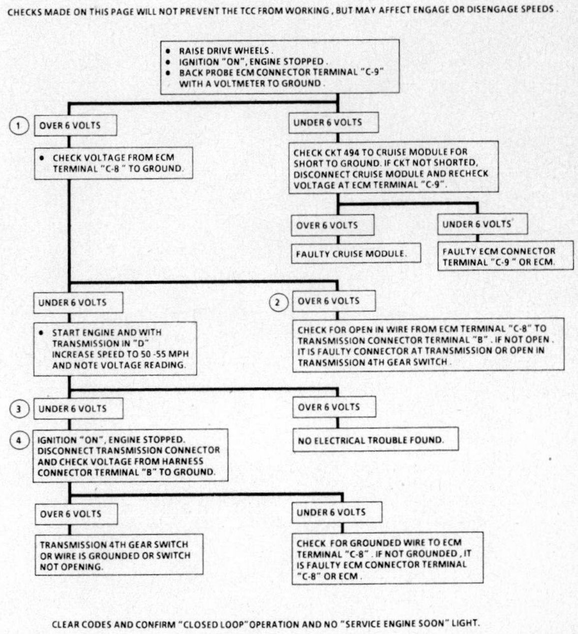

CHART C-8B, 440-T4
TCC ELECTRICAL DIAGNOSIS (CONT.)

1) Over 6 volts confirms ECM cruise signal voltage is okay and circuit No. 494 is not shorted to ground.

2) Over 6 volts indicates an open in circuit No. 446. Transmission/transaxle connector is bad, or 4th gear switch stuck open.

3) Over 6 volts confirms ECM cruise signal voltage is okay and circuit No. 494 is not shorted to ground.

2) Over 6 volts indicates an open in circuit No. 446. Transmission/transaxle connector is bad, or 4th gear switch stuck open.

3) With drive wheels turning (50-55 MPH), a reading under 6 volts indicates that circuit No. 446 is shorted to ground. Also check for a faulty 4th gear switch, if transaxle is actually in 4th gear.

4) This test determines if problem with circuit No. 446 is an internal transmission/transaxle problem.

Automatic Transmissions

GENERAL MOTORS TORQUE CONVERTER CLUTCH (Cont.)

Fig. 26: TCC Test Chart For F Body Passenger Cars With 5.0L Port Fuel Injected Engines

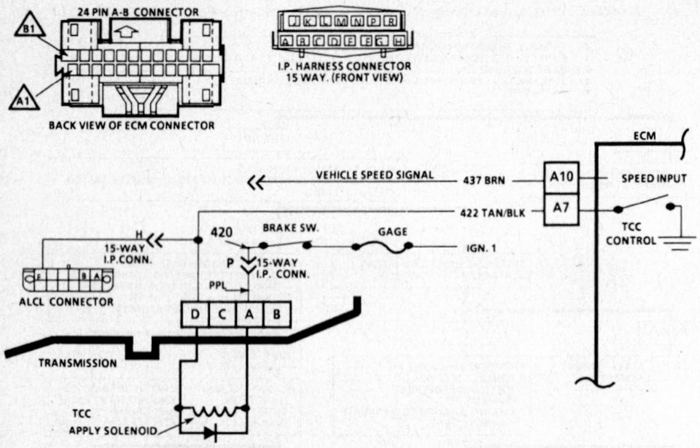

CHART C-8B, 700-R4
TCC ELECTRICAL DIAGNOSIS

When TCC solenoid is activated, the torque converter clutch is applied which results in a straight through mechanical coupling from engine to transmission. When TCC solenoid is deactivated, the torque converter clutch is released which allows the torque converter clutch to operate in a conventional manner. The ECM will engage TCC with engine at normal operating temperature and engine under given road load in 2nd, 3rd, or 4th gear.

1) With test light connected from "F" terminal of ALCL connector to ground, a test light that is on indicates that battery voltage is okay and solenoid is not energized.

2) When diagnostic terminal is grounded, the ECM should energize TCC solenoid. Test light should go out.

3) Solenoids and relays are turned on and off by ECM internal electronic switches called drivers. Each driver is part of a group of four called quad-drivers. Failure of one can damage any other driver within a set.

Using an ohmmeter, check solenoid coil resistance of all ECM controlled solenoids and relays before installing a replacement ECM. Replace any solenoid or relay that measures less than 20 ohms resistance.

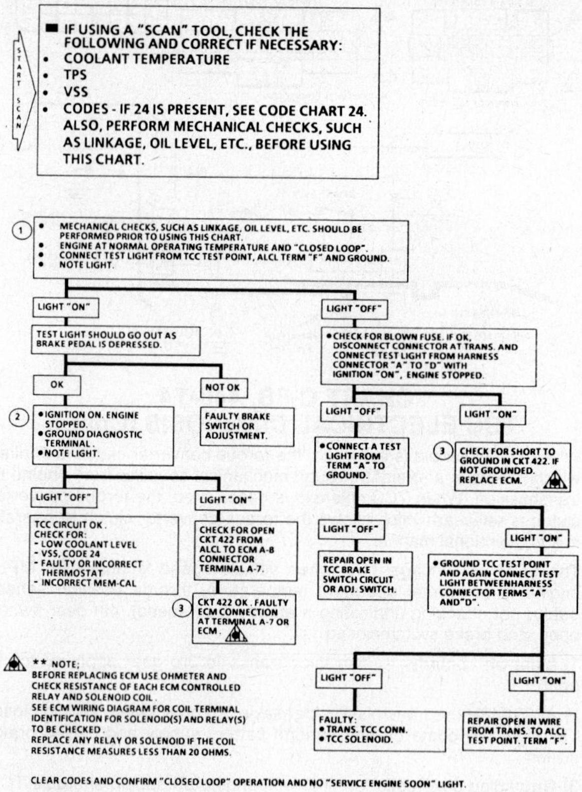

GENERAL MOTORS TORQUE CONVERTER CLUTCH (Cont.)

Fig. 27: TCC Test Chart For Y Body Passenger Cars With 5.7L Port Fuel Injected Engines

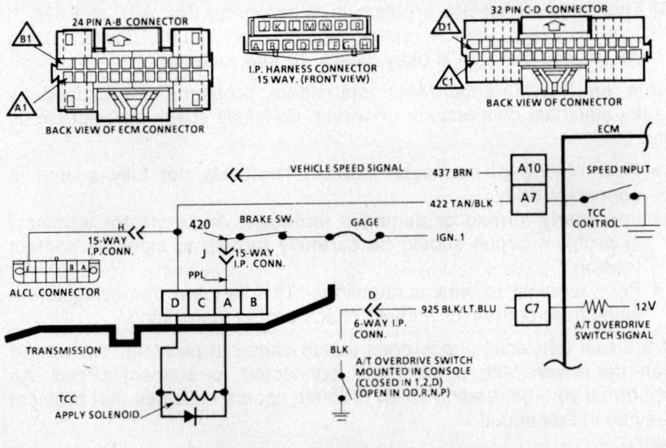

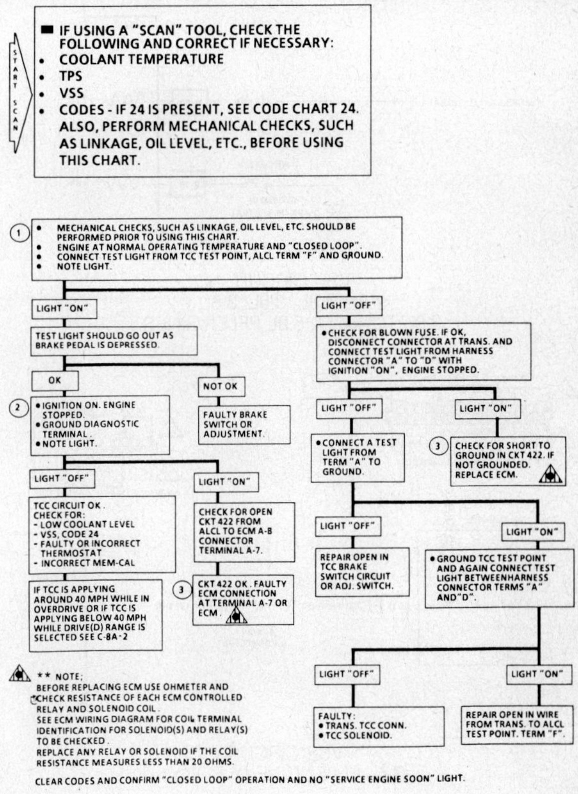

CHART C-8A-1, 700-R4
TCC ELECTRICAL DIAGNOSIS

When TCC solenoid is activated, the torque converter clutch is applied which results in a straight through mechanical coupling from engine to transmission. When TCC solenoid is deactivated, the torque converter clutch is released which allows the torque converter clutch to operate in a conventional manner. The ECM will engage TCC with engine at normal operating temperature and engine under given road load in 2nd, 3rd, or 4th gear. If "1", "2" or "D" range is selected, the overdrive switch should be closed and the ECM will not engage TCC until vehicle reaches 40 MPH. This will keep TCC from engaging and disengaging while in city traffic.

1) With test light connected from "F" terminal of ALCL connector to ground, a test light that is on indicates that battery voltage is okay and solenoid is not energized.

2) When diagnostic terminal is grounded, the ECM should energize TCC solenoid. Test light should go out.

3) Solenoids are turned on and off by ECM internal electronic switches called drivers. Each driver is part of a group of four called quad-drivers. Failure of one can damage any other driver within a set.

Using an ohmmeter, check solenoid coil resistance of all ECM controlled solenoids and relays before installing a replacement ECM. Replace any solenoid or relay that measures less than 20 ohms resistance.

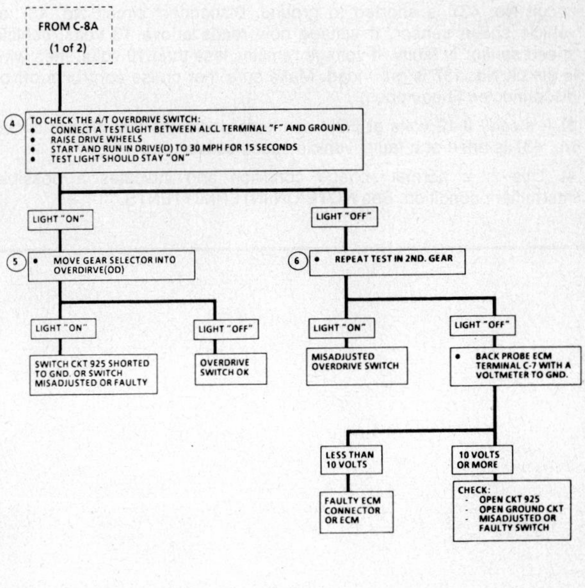

CHART C-8A-2, 700-R4
TCC ELECTRICAL DIAGNOSIS

4) The overdrive switch should be closed while in "D". This should keep the TCC disengaged until about 40 MPH. Test light should remain on at 30 MPH.

5) When the gear selector is moved into "OD" (overdrive), the overdrive switch should open, which will cause signal at ECM terminal "C7" to go high. The ECM will then engage TCC solenoid and test light should go out.

6) If test light remains on while in 2nd gear, the overdrive witch is staying open in "D" (drive) range. If test light remains off, the ECM is still turning engaging TCC. This condition is caused by a faulty signal at ECM terminal "C7", or because the ECM is not processing information correctly.

GENERAL MOTORS TORQUE CONVERTER CLUTCH (Cont.)

Fig. 28: Vehicle Speed Sensor (VSS) Test Chart For All Passenger Cars With Port Fuel Injected Engines

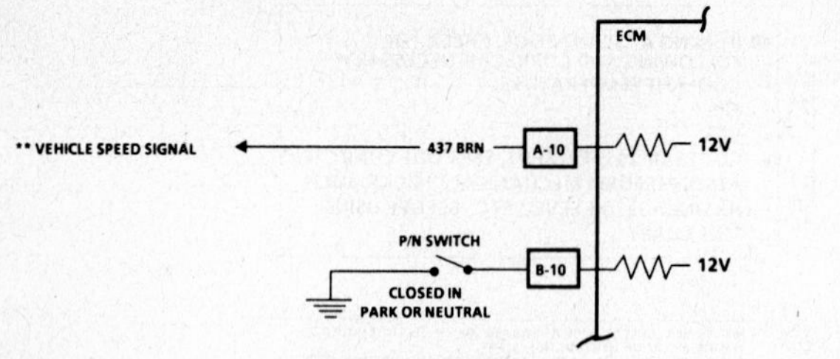

VSS CIRCUIT
1.8L, 2.8L, 3.0L, 3.8L
3.8L TURBO & 5.0L PFI ENGINES

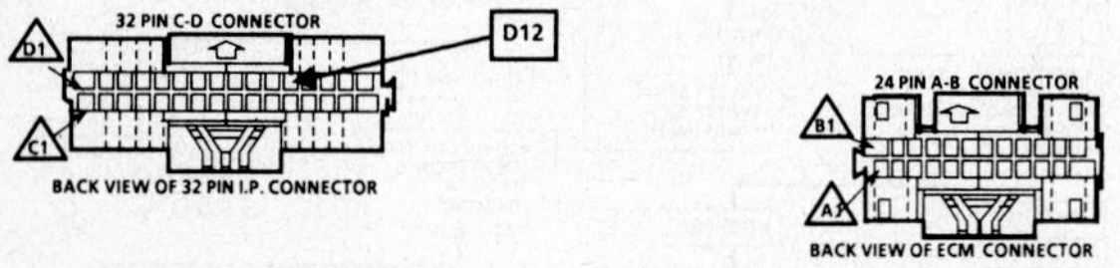

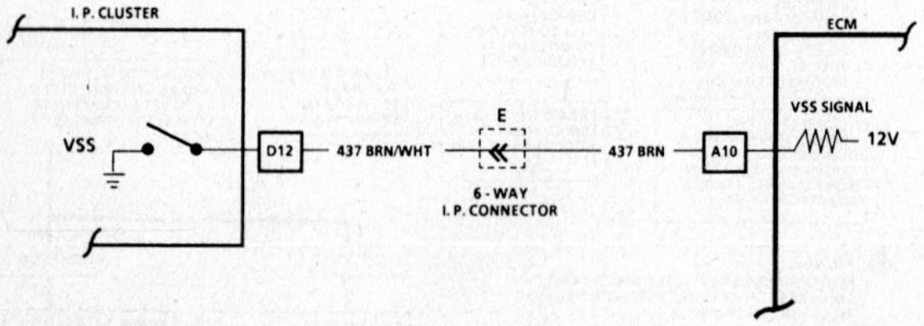

VSS CIRCUIT
5.7L PFI ENGINE (Y BODY)

CODE 24, VEHICLE SPEED SENSOR (VSS)

The ECM applies and monitors 12 volts on circuit 437. Circuit 437 connects to vehicel speed sensor which alternately grounds circuit when drive wheels are turning. This pulsating action takes place about 2000 times per mile. The ECM uses time between pulses to determine vehicle speed. Disregard Code 24 when drive wheels are not turning.

1) This test monitors ECM voltage on circuit No. 437. With wheels turning, the pulsating action will result in a varying voltage. The variation will be greater at low speeds and increase to an average of 4-6 volts at about 20 MPH.

2) A voltage less than one volt at ECM connector indicates that wire in circuit No. 437 is shorted to ground. Disconnect circuit No. 437 at vehicle speed sensor. If voltage now reads above 10 volts, vehicle speed sensor is faulty. If voltage remains less than 10 volts, then wire in circuit No. 437 is grounded. Make sure that cruise control is off or disconnected (if equipped).

3) A steady 8-12 volts at ECM connector indicates that wire in circuit No. 437 is open or a faulty vehicle speed sensor.

4) This is a normal voltage condition and indicates a possible intermittent condition. See NOTE ON INTERMITTENTS.

5) This step will isolate problem in either circuit No. 437 or ECM. If "SCAN" displays vehicle speed, check park/neutral switch using CHART C-1A. If switch is okay, check for intermittents.

Note on Intermittents: Most intermittent problems are caused by faulty electrical connections or wiring. Carefully check suspect circuit for:

- Poor mating of connector halves. Terminals not fully seated in connector body.
- Improperly formed or damaged terminals. All connector terminals in problem circuit should be carefully formed to increase contact tension.
- Poor terminal to wire connections. This requires removing terminal(s) from connector body to check proper installation.

If a visual (physical) check does locate cause of problem, the vehicle can be driven with a voltmeter connected to suspect circuit. An abnormal voltage reading when problem occurs indicates that problem may be in that circuit.

Check for electrical system interference from vehicle's ignition system. Also check electrical system interference from defective relays, ECM driven solenoid, or switch that may cause a sharp electrical surge. Problem will normally occur when faulty component is operated.

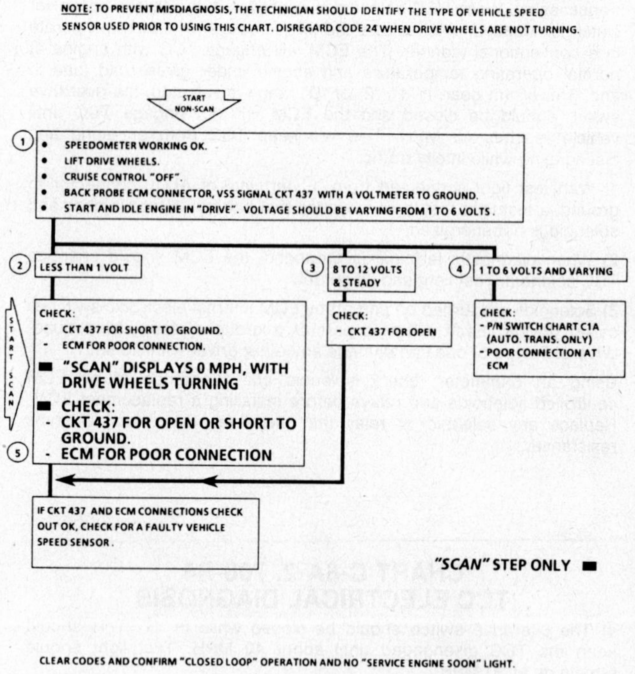

GENERAL MOTORS TORQUE CONVERTER CLUTCH (Cont.)

Fig. 29: ***Park/Neutral Switch Test Chart For All Passenger Cars With Port Fuel Injected Engines***

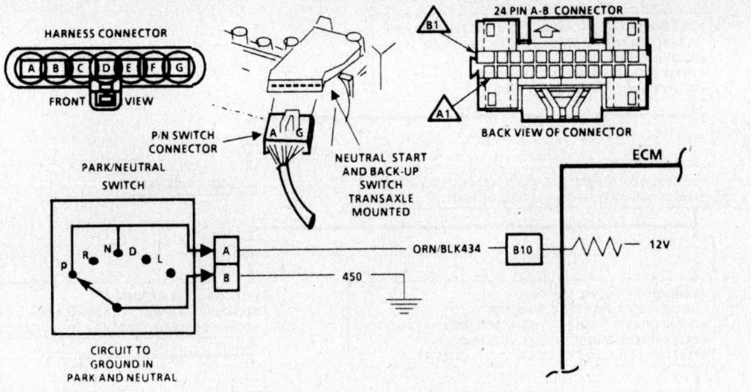

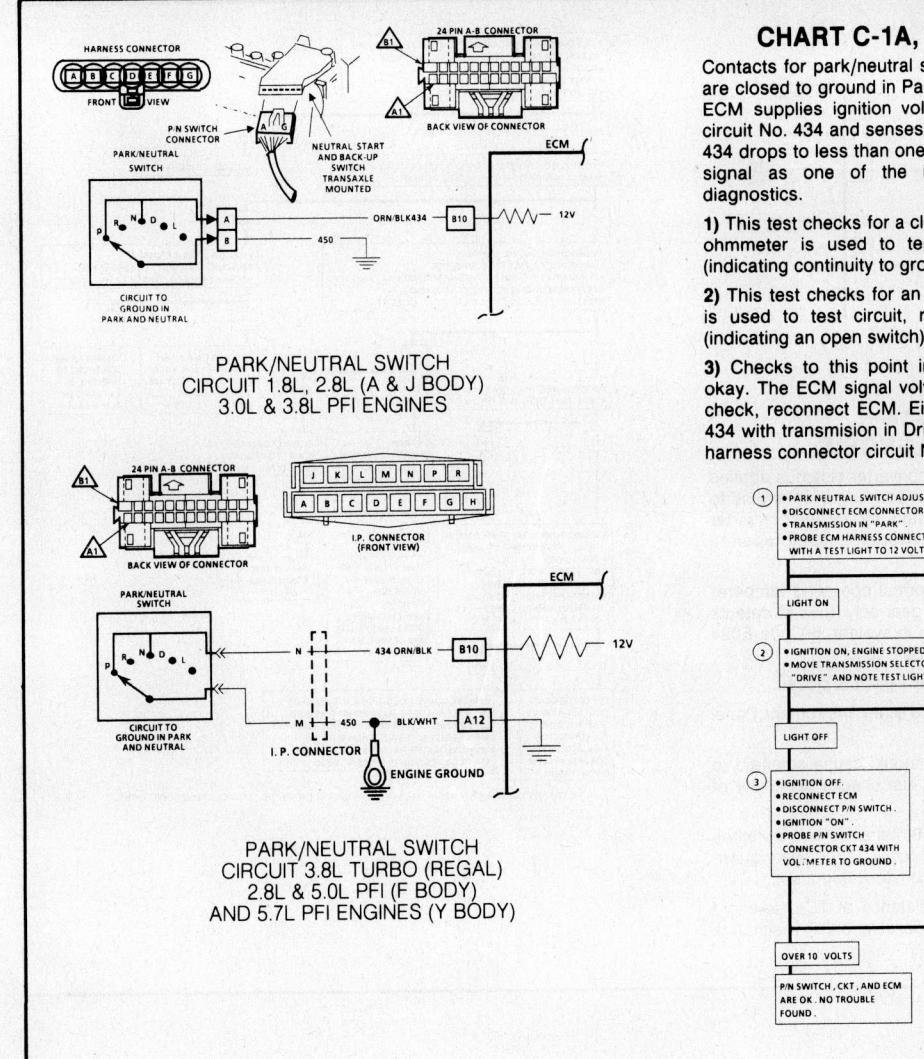

PARK/NEUTRAL SWITCH
CIRCUIT 1.8L, 2.8L (A & J BODY)
3.0L & 3.8L PFI ENGINES

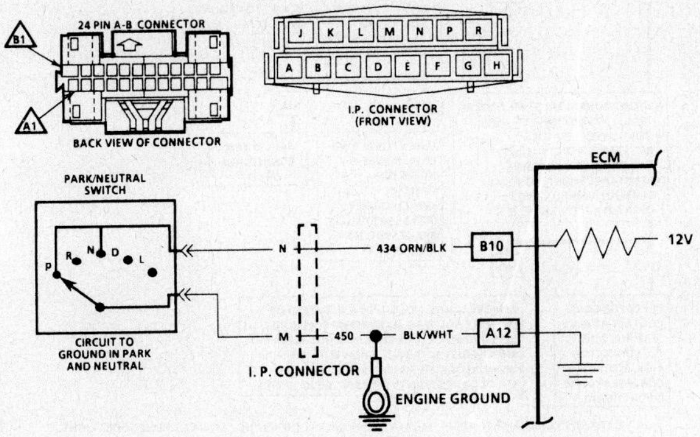

PARK/NEUTRAL SWITCH
CIRCUIT 3.8L TURBO (REGAL)
2.8L & 5.0L PFI (F BODY)
AND 5.7L PFI ENGINES (Y BODY)

CHART C-1A, PARK/NEUTRAL SWITCH

Contacts for park/neutral switch are a part of neutral/start switch and are closed to ground in Park or Neutral, and open in drive ranges. The ECM supplies ignition voltage through a current limiting resistor to circuit No. 434 and senses a closed switch when voltage on circuit No. 434 drops to less than one volt. The ECM uses the park/neutral switch signal as one of the inputs to control vehicle speed sensor diagnostics.

1) This test checks for a closed switch to ground in Park position. If an ohmmeter is used to test circuit, resistance reading will be low (indicating continuity to ground).

2) This test checks for an open switch in drive range. If an ohmmeter is used to test circuit, resistance reading will be high or infinity (indicating an open switch).

3) Checks to this point indicate park/neutral switch and wiring are okay. The ECM signal voltage on circuit No. 434 may be missing. To check, reconnect ECM. Either back probe ECM connector circuit No. 434 with transmision in Drive or disconnect park/neutral switch. Probe harness connector circuit No. 434 with a voltmeter to ground.

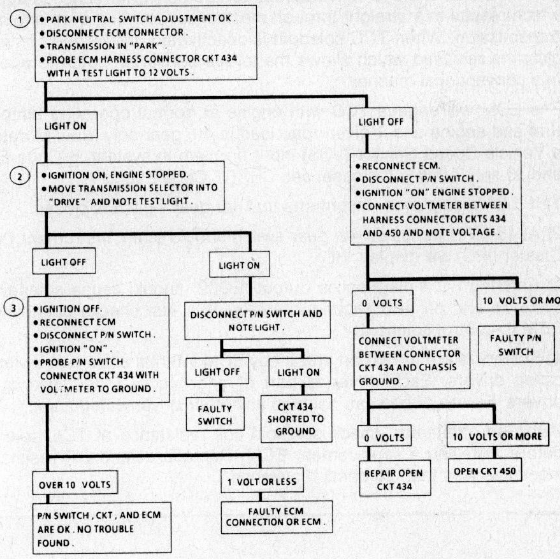

CLEAR CODES AND CONFIRM "CLOSED LOOP" OPERATION AND NO "SERVICE ENGINE SOON" LIGHT.

GENERAL MOTORS TORQUE CONVERTER CLUTCH (Cont.)

Fig. 30: TCC Test Chart For Buick Riviera & Oldsmobile Toronado

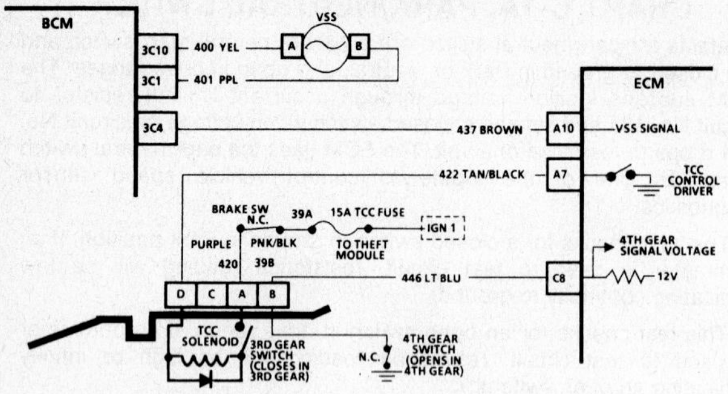

CHART C-8, 440-T4
TCC ELECTRICAL DIAGNOSIS

When TCC solenoid is activated, the torque converter clutch is applied which results in a straight through mechanical coupling from engine to transmission. When TCC solenoid is deactivated, the torque converter clutch is released which allows the torque converter clutch to operate in a conventional manner.

The ECM will engage TCC with engine at normal operating temperature and engine under given road load in 4th gear only. If ECM detects a Vehicle Speed Sensor (VSS) input problem in system, a Code E024 should set. If this is the case, see CHART Code E024.

1) If "LO" is displayed, it confirms that 4th gear switch is closed.

2) At 45 MPH transaxle 4th gear switch should open. Instrument Panel Cluster (IPC) will display "HI".

3) Entering ECM diagnostics output "EO02" should cause solenoid to cycle on and off at 3 second intervals. This test checks capability of ECM to control solenoid.

4) Solenoids are turned on and off by ECM internal electronic switches called drivers. Each driver is part of a group of four called quad-drivers. Failure of one can damage any other driver within a set.

Using an ohmmeter, check solenoid coil resistance of TCC solenoid before installing a replacement ECM. Replace solenoid if resistance measures less than 20 ohms resistance.

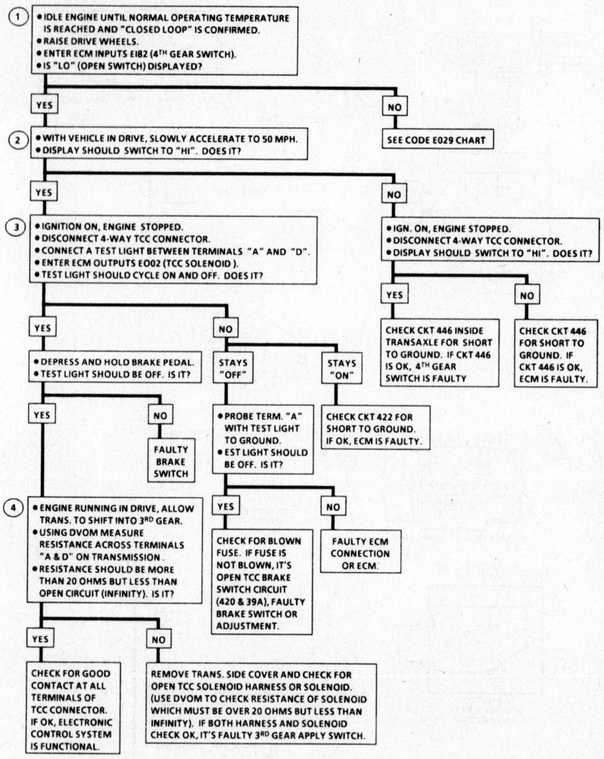

CLEAR ALL CODES AND CONFIRM "CLOSED LOOP" OPERATION AND NO "SERVICE ENGINE SOON" LIGHT.

GENERAL MOTORS TORQUE CONVERTER CLUTCH (Cont.)

Fig. 31: Vehicle Speed Sensor (VSS) Test Chart For Buick Riviera & Oldsmobile Toronado

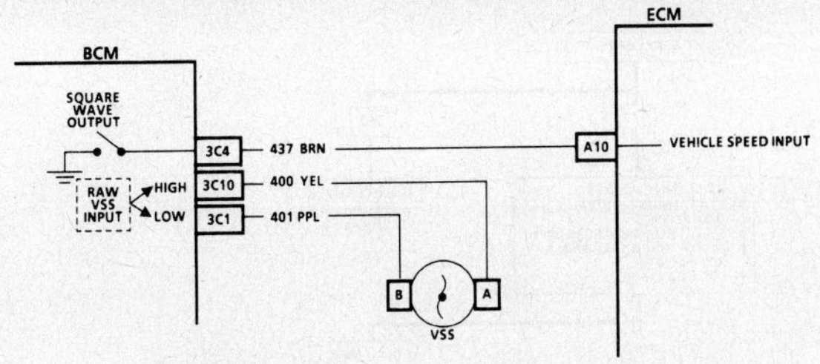

CODE E024, VEHICLE SPEED SENSOR

The VSS system incorporates 3 major components: The vehicle speed generator, the BCM, and the ECM. The vehicle speed generator is a permanent magnet assembly attached to transaxle. As the vehicle moves, the generator creates a "sine wave" electrical pulse which is monitored by the BCM. In the BCM, this signal is amplified and "cleaned up" via the same process as used in a buffer. Part of this "cleaning up" involves changing the "sine wave" signal into a "square wave" signal or on/off type of signal. By determining time between on and off portions of signal, the BCM can interpret vehicle speed. It then transmits this data to the ECM via circuit No. 437.

Because of the circuitry involved, it is highly unlikely that a Code E024 alone will caused by a faulty VSS. However, a combination of Codes E024 and B124 could represent this.

To set a Code E024, the following conditions must exist: Engine speed between 1500-4000 RPM, LV8 reading (Diagnostic Data ED23) between 40-150 counts, Codes E033 or E034 not present, vehicle speed less than 3 MPH, gear selector not in Park or Neutral, and the above conditions exist for 40 seconds or longer.

1) If code B124 is present, see CHART B124 before attempting to diagnose Code E024.

2) If ECM Data ED12 (vehicle speed) displays "0" MPH, the ECM is not receiving a vehicle speed sensor input from BCM.

3) A "0" MPH display at this point, indicates a fault which should have set Code B124. See CHART B124 for remainder of diagnosis. A display greater than zero indicates a fault in circuit No. 437, the connections at ECM or BCM, or a faulty ECM.

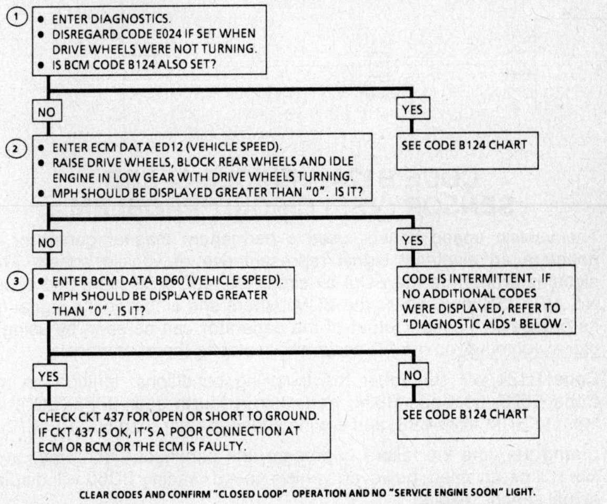

Fig. 32: Fourth Gear Switch Test Chart For Buick Riviera & Oldsmobile Toronado

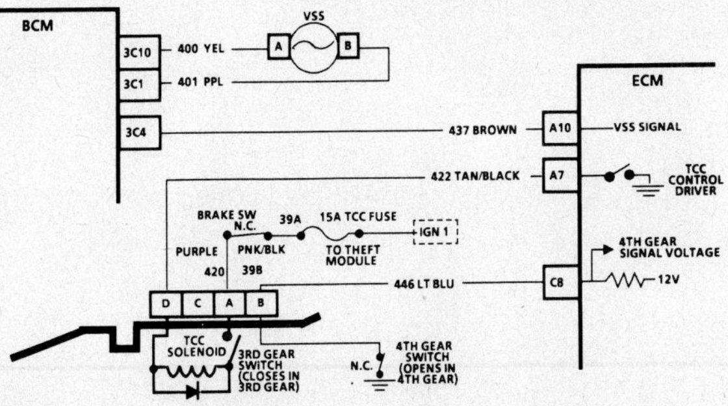

CODE E029, 4TH GEAR SWITCH CIRCUIT INOPERATIVE (OPEN)

The ECM applies 12 volts to circuit No. 446 through terminal "C8". When the normally closed 4th gear switch opens, the voltage on circuit No. 446 is allowed to increase and monitored inside the ECM. The 4th gear switch (located inside transaxle) allows the ECM to determine if transaxle has hydraulically applied 4th gear. This information is used by ECM to calculate TCC application.

1) Under normal conditions, display at this point should be "LO". This indicates that 4th gear switch is closed (4th gear disengaged).

2) This test verifies that circuit No. 446 from ECM terminal "C8" is complete and that ECM is supplying batery voltage. If battery voltage is available at transaxle connector terminal "B", fault is an open switch harness inside transaxle or a faulty 4th gear switch.

Diagnostic Aids An intermittent may be caused by a poor connection, rubbed through wire insulation or a wire broken inside the insulation. Check for:

- Inspect ECM harness connectors for backed out terminal "C8", improper mating, broken locks, improperly formed or damaged terminals, poor terminals wire connection or damaged harness.
- If connections and harness checks out okay, monitor "E128" 4th gear switch display while moving related connectors and wiring harness. If failure is induced, the 4th gear switch display will abruptly change. This will help isolate location of malfunction.

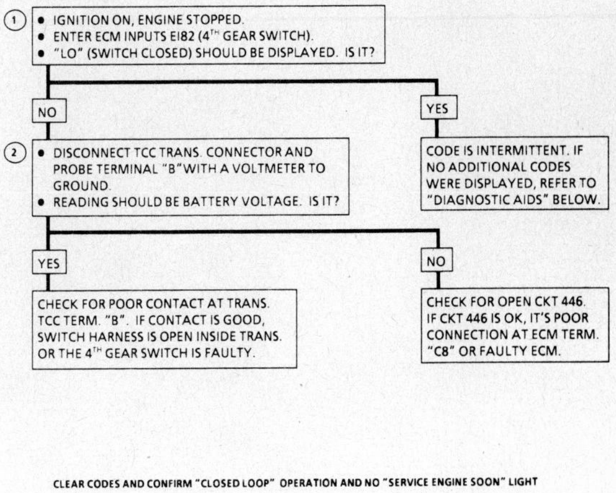

GENERAL MOTORS TORQUE CONVERTER CLUTCH (Cont.)

Fig. 33: Vehicle Speed Sensor (VSS) Circuit Test Chart For Buick Riviera & Oldsmobile Toronado

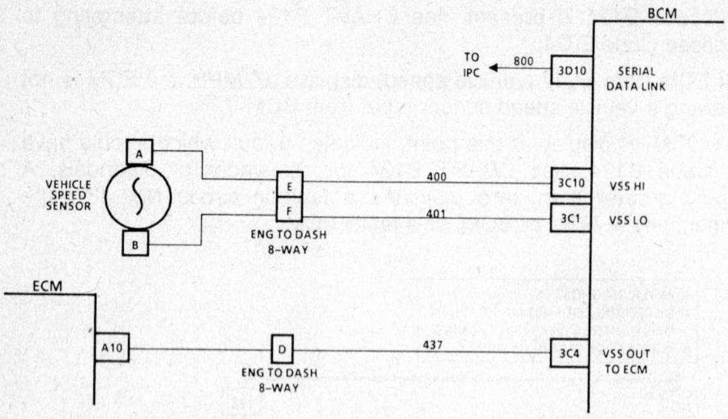

CODE B124, VEHICLE SPEED SENSOR (VSS) CIRCUIT PROBLEM

The vehicle speed sensor uses a permanent magnet generator to generate an electrical signal representative of vehicle speed. This signal is brought to the BCM by circuit No. 400 (VSS high) and circuit No. 401 (VSS low), where the BCM buffers and amplifies the signal for its prospective uses. Output of the generator can be seen by using a digital voltmeter on the AC scale while rotating the front wheels.

Code B124 will set under the following conditions: Ignition on, no Code E029, no Code B334, transaxle in fourth gear (EI82 "LO"), no input to BCM from VSS, and engine speed greater than 500 RPM.

During the time the failure is present, the continuous compressor at idle will be disabled, however, vehicle speed reading BD60 will display actual sensor reading.

1) Since the BCM amplifies and buffers the speed signal before it is sent to the ECM, Code E024 in the ECM will set along with Code B124 in the BCM if the permanent magnet generator, or circuits No. 400 and No. 401 have a problem. If Code B124 ever sets without setting a Code E024, there is an internal problem in the BCM.

2) BCM data value BD60 displays MPH.

3) With wheels turning, a voltage reading indicates that permanent magnet generator and wiring are okay.

4) This test checks for open in VSS circuit wiring.

5) This test checks for ground in VSS circuit wiring prior to replacing sensor.

Note On Intermittents: If an intermittent Code B124 is being set, move related wiring while observing BCM data parameter BD60. If failure is induced, the reading will jump from a normal value to zero MPH.

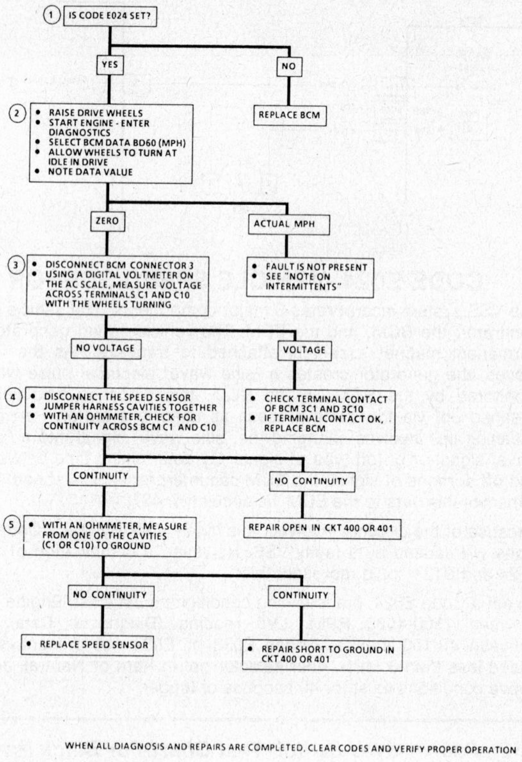

GENERAL MOTORS TORQUE CONVERTER CLUTCH (Cont.)

Fig. 34: TCC Test Chart For California Light Duty Trucks With 4.3L, 5.0L & 5.7L Carbureted Engines

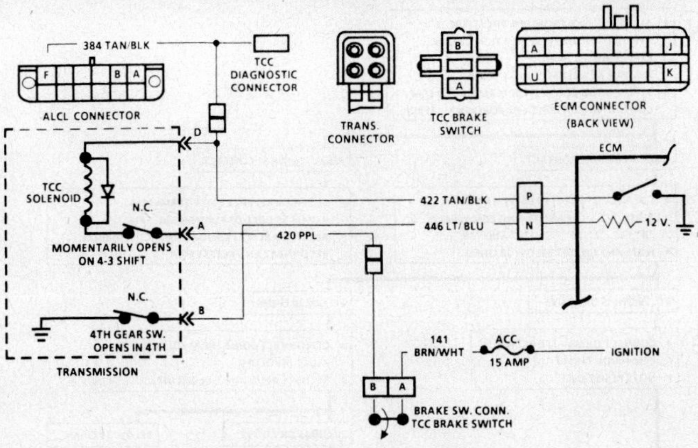

TCC CIRCUIT FOR 2WD
C SERIES WITH V8 ENGINE

CHART C-8B
TCC ELECTRICAL DIAGNOSIS

The transmission torque converter clutch is activated by a TCC solenoid located inside transmission. Ignition voltage is supplied to TCC solenoid and the ECM completes ground circuit to energize solenoid.

1) Ths test checks for complete circuit from ignition through TCC solenoid to ALCL TCC test terminal. Light should normally be on if circuit is not open or grounded.

2) This test checks to see if ECM completes ground circuit to energize TCC solenoid. Light should go out.

3) This procedure increases throttle opening to increase Throttle Position Sensor (TPS) output. If TPS output is too low, TCC clutch will not apply. Some applications do not require full throttle opening to allow transmission to shift.

4) This test checks for ground in circuit to P terminal at ECM. Light should normally be off.

5) This test checks for open in wire from TCC test point to transmission. It also checks for opens in TCC solenoid connections or TCC solenoid. If wiring is complete, test light should be on.

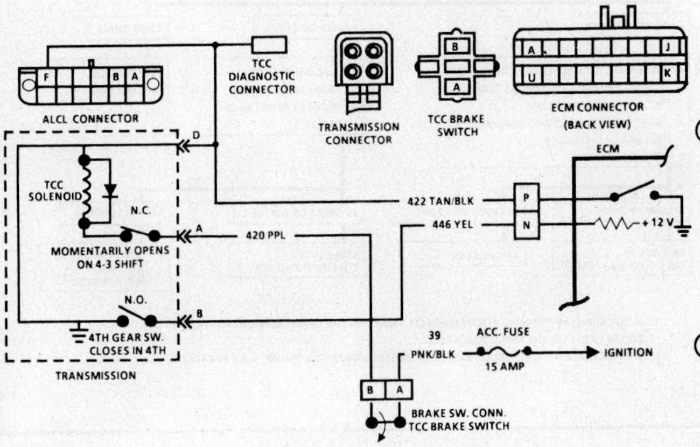

TCC CIRCUIT FOR G SERIES
WITH V6 OR V8 ENGINE

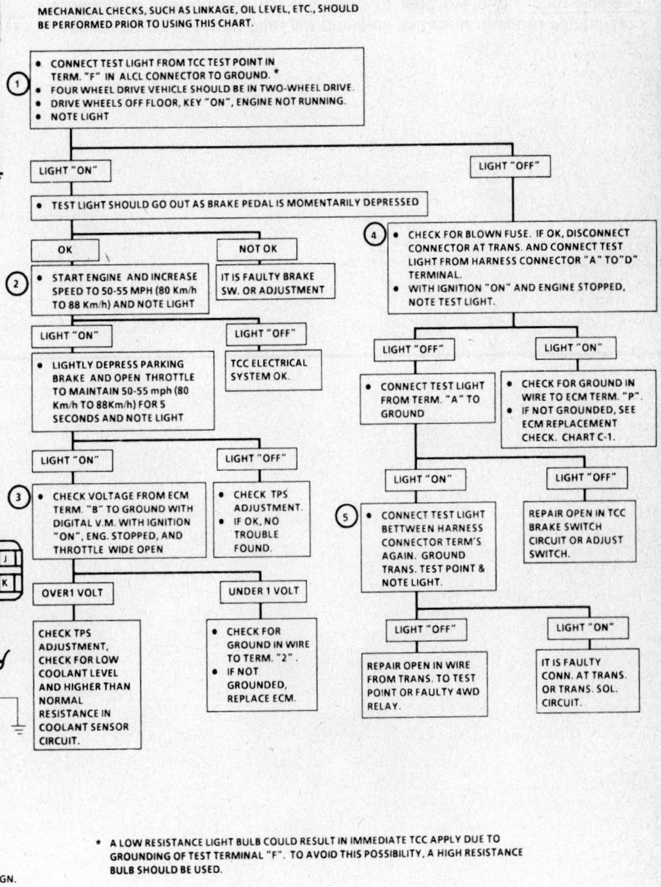

* A LOW RESISTANCE LIGHT BULB COULD RESULT IN IMMEDIATE TCC APPLY DUE TO GROUNDING OF TEST TERMINAL "F". TO AVOID THIS POSSIBILITY, A HIGH RESISTANCE BULB SHOULD BE USED.

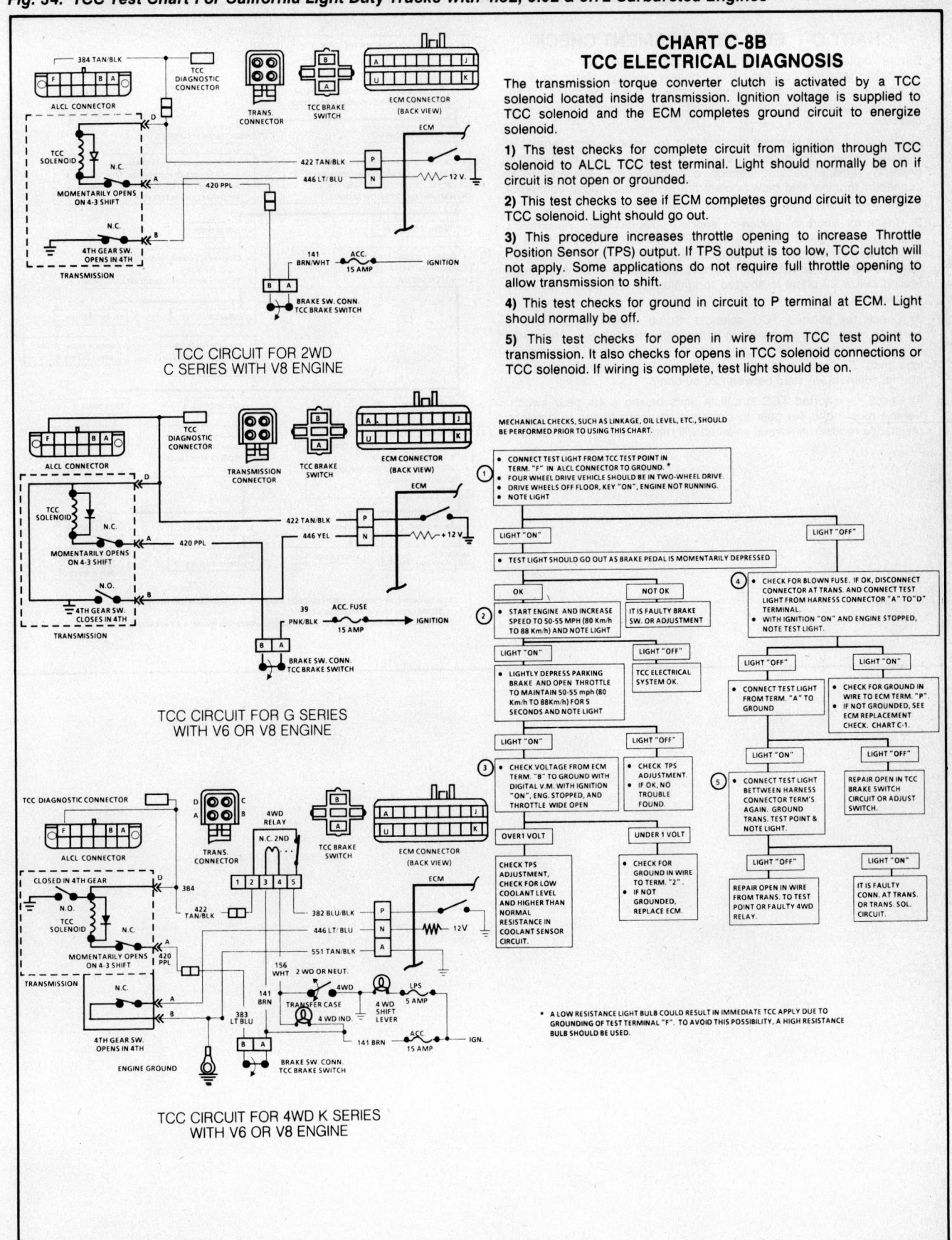

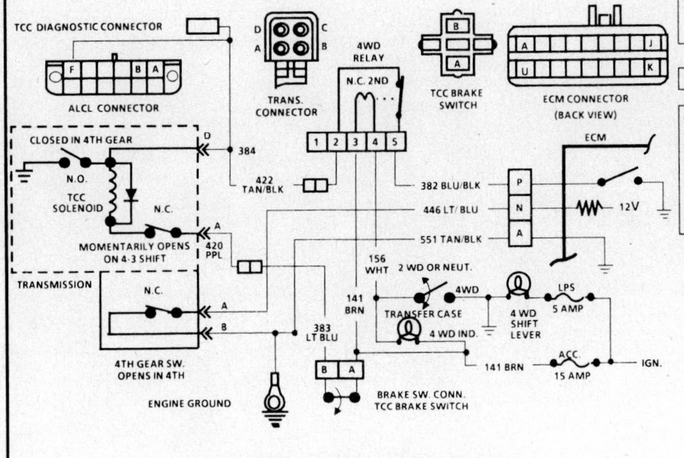

TCC CIRCUIT FOR 4WD K SERIES
WITH V6 OR V8 ENGINE

GENERAL MOTORS TORQUE CONVERTER CLUTCH (Cont.)

Fig. 35: ECM Replacement Test Chart For California Light Duty Trucks With 4.3L, 5.0L & 5.7L Carbureted Engines

CHART C-1, ECM REPLACEMENT CHECK

Before replacing ECM, test ECM circuit involved for poor ECM connector terminal contact, direct battery voltage short on ECM ground circuit, or shorted solenoid or relay. If a short is found, circuit must be repaired prior to replacing ECM to prevent further ECM failures.

1) Check for good terminal contact due to weak or dirty terminals. Remove terminal to inspect. Replace if broke or dirty. If coolant is present, replace coolant sensor and connector. Replace ECM connector terminal and blow coolant out of harness. Clean connector with alcohol or spray contact cleaner and replace ECM.

2) Check for short to ignition or shorted solenoid relay. All termials must be tested since several are connected internally in the ECM. A short in one circuit may cause another circuit in ECM to be inoperative even though that circuit does not have an external fault. Any circuit testing below 20 ohms is shorted to ignition, or shorted across relay or solenoid.

3) Check for shorted TCC solenoid. Some transmissions have a normally open 4th gear switch in series with the solenoid. Ohmmeter will read infinite resistance (open circuit) in these cases. If reading is less than 20 ohms, a short to ignition or faulty solenoid exists. A normal solenoid will read between 20-50 ohms.

4) Check for shorted TCC circuit in units having a 4th gear switch. Vehicle must be in 4th gear to close switch contacts and to obtain a resistance reading. A normal solenoid will read between 20-50 ohms.

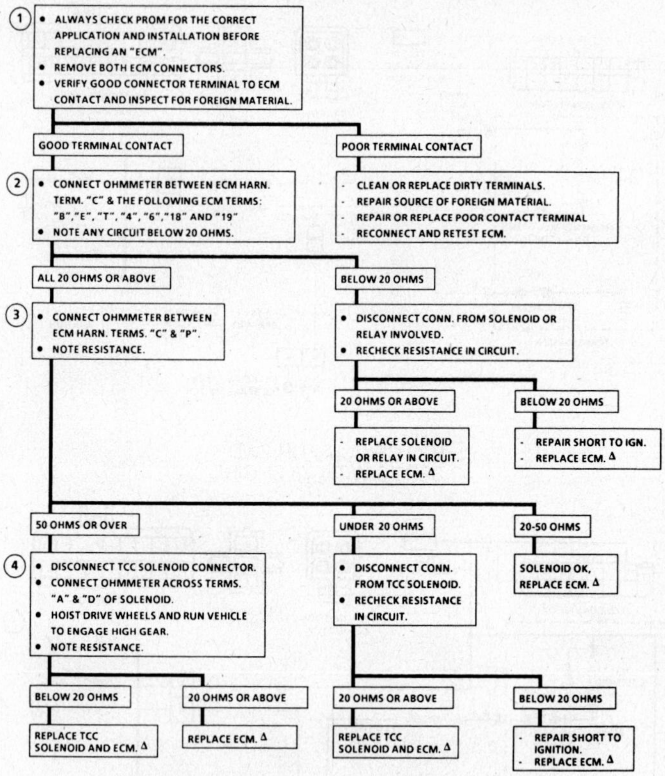

1. IF REPLACING AN ORIGINAL EQUIPMENT ECM, TRANSFER THE ORIGINAL BROADCAST CODE TO THE LABEL ON THE REPLACEMENT ECM.
2. IF AFTER REPLACING THE "ECM', THE PROBLEM STILL EXISTS, THE "PROM" MAY BE FAULTY.

GENERAL MOTORS TORQUE CONVERTER CLUTCH (Cont.)

***Fig. 36:** TCC Test Chart For Light Duty Trucks With 2.5L & 2.8L Throttle Body Injection (TBI) Engines*

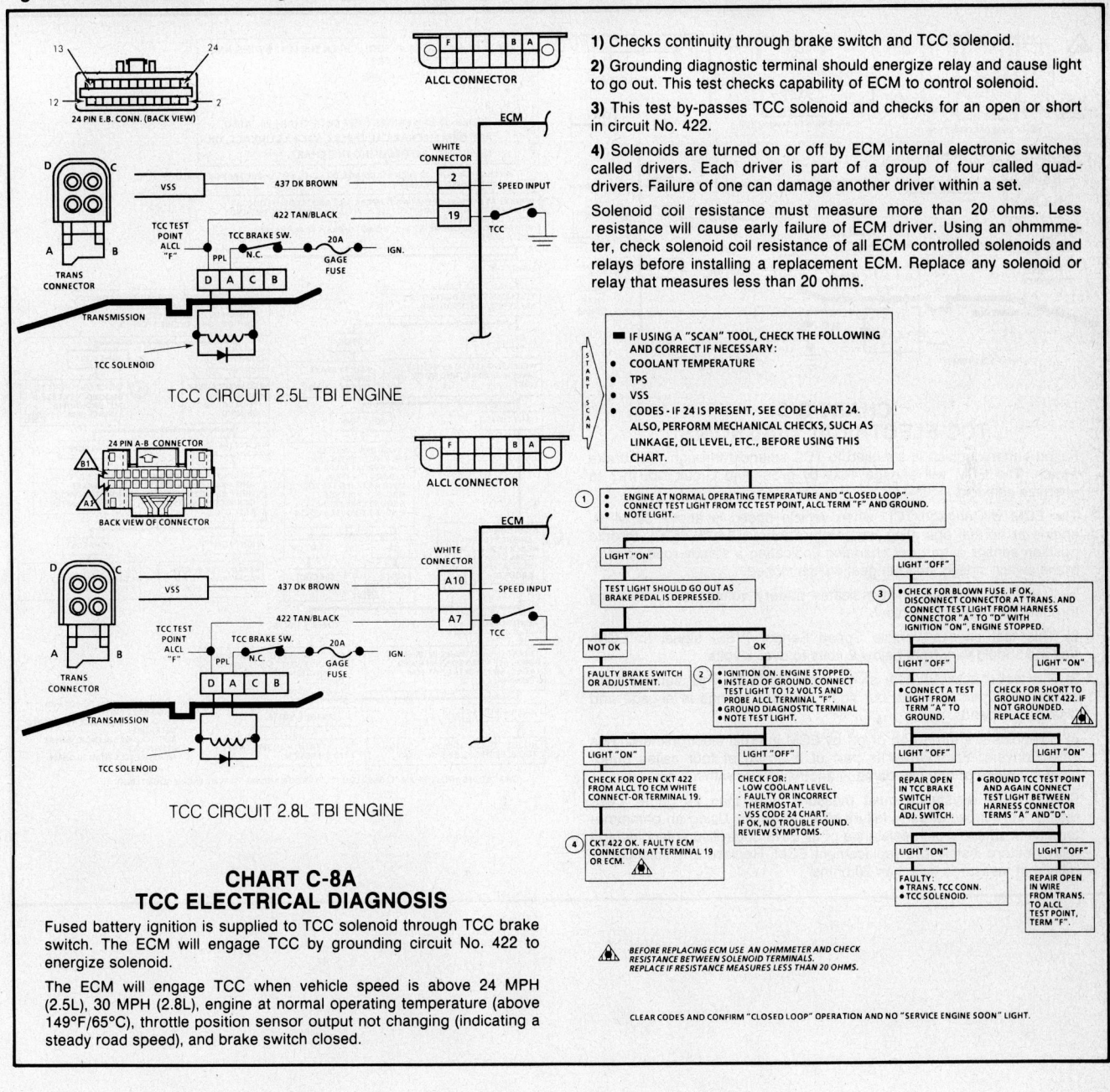

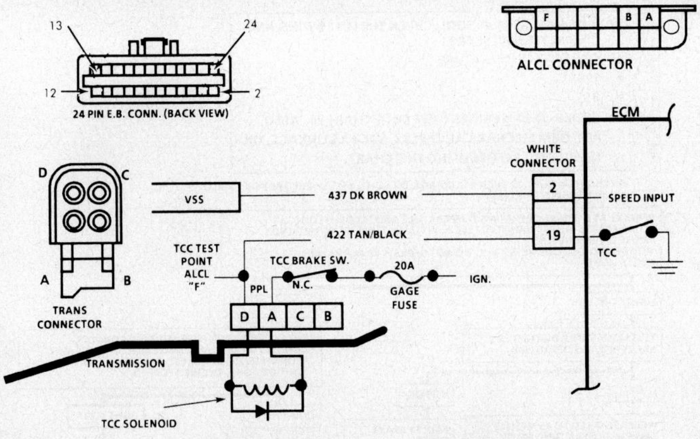

TCC CIRCUIT 2.5L TBI ENGINE

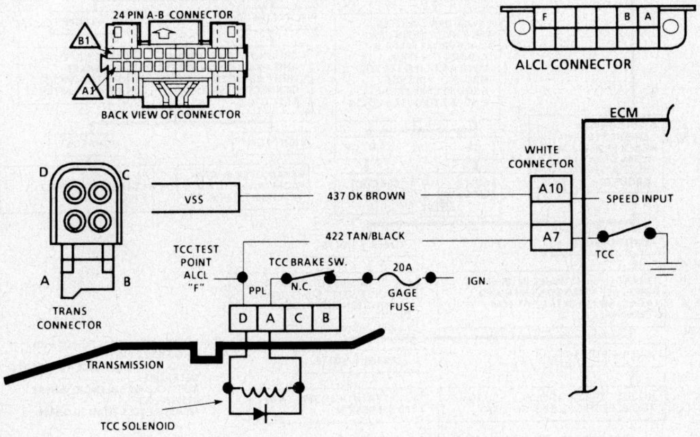

TCC CIRCUIT 2.8L TBI ENGINE

CHART C-8A
TCC ELECTRICAL DIAGNOSIS

Fused battery ignition is supplied to TCC solenoid through TCC brake switch. The ECM will engage TCC by grounding circuit No. 422 to energize solenoid.

The ECM will engage TCC when vehicle speed is above 24 MPH (2.5L), 30 MPH (2.8L), engine at normal operating temperature (above 149°F/65°C), throttle position sensor output not changing (indicating a steady road speed), and brake switch closed.

1) Checks continuity through brake switch and TCC solenoid.

2) Grounding diagnostic terminal should energize relay and cause light to go out. This test checks capability of ECM to control solenoid.

3) This test by-passes TCC solenoid and checks for an open or short in circuit No. 422.

4) Solenoids are turned on or off by ECM internal electronic switches called drivers. Each driver is part of a group of four called quad-drivers. Failure of one can damage another driver within a set.

Solenoid coil resistance must measure more than 20 ohms. Less resistance will cause early failure of ECM driver. Using an ohmmmeter, check solenoid coil resistance of all ECM controlled solenoids and relays before installing a replacement ECM. Replace any solenoid or relay that measures less than 20 ohms.

START SCAN

- IF USING A "SCAN" TOOL, CHECK THE FOLLOWING AND CORRECT IF NECESSARY:
  - COOLANT TEMPERATURE
  - TPS
  - VSS
  - CODES - IF 24 IS PRESENT, SEE CODE CHART 24. ALSO, PERFORM MECHANICAL CHECKS, SUCH AS LINKAGE, OIL LEVEL, ETC., BEFORE USING THIS CHART.

(1)
- ENGINE AT NORMAL OPERATING TEMPERATURE AND "CLOSED LOOP".
- CONNECT TEST LIGHT FROM TCC TEST POINT, ALCL TERM "F" AND GROUND.
- NOTE LIGHT.

LIGHT "ON"

TEST LIGHT SHOULD GO OUT AS BRAKE PEDAL IS DEPRESSED.

NOT OK — FAULTY BRAKE SWITCH OR ADJUSTMENT.

OK — (2)
- IGNITION ON, ENGINE STOPPED.
- INSTEAD OF GROUND, CONNECT TEST LIGHT TO 12 VOLTS AND PROBE ALCL TERMINAL "F".
- GROUND DIAGNOSTIC TERMINAL
- NOTE TEST LIGHT.

LIGHT "ON" — CHECK FOR OPEN CKT 422 FROM ALCL TO ECM WHITE CONNECT-OR TERMINAL 19.

(4) CKT 422 OK. FAULTY ECM CONNECTION AT TERMINAL 19 OR ECM. ⚠

LIGHT "OFF" — CHECK FOR:
- LOW COOLANT LEVEL.
- FAULTY OR INCORRECT THERMOSTAT.
- VSS CODE 24 CHART.

IF OK, NO TROUBLE FOUND. REVIEW SYMPTOMS.

LIGHT "OFF"

(3)
- CHECK FOR BLOWN FUSE. IF OK, DISCONNECT CONNECTOR AT TRANS. AND CONNECT TEST LIGHT FROM HARNESS CONNECTOR "A" TO "D" WITH IGNITION "ON", ENGINE STOPPED.

LIGHT "OFF"
- CONNECT A TEST LIGHT FROM TERM "A" TO GROUND.

LIGHT "OFF" — REPAIR OPEN IN TCC BRAKE SWITCH CIRCUIT OR ADJ. SWITCH.

LIGHT "ON"
- GROUND TCC TEST POINT AND AGAIN CONNECT TEST LIGHT BETWEEN HARNESS CONNECTOR TERMS "A" AND "D".

LIGHT "ON" — FAULTY:
- TRANS. TCC CONN.
- TCC SOLENOID.

LIGHT "OFF" — REPAIR OPEN IN WIRE FROM TRANS. TO ALCL TEST POINT, TERM "F".

LIGHT "ON" — CHECK FOR SHORT TO GROUND IN CKT 422. IF NOT GROUNDED, REPLACE ECM. ⚠

⚠ *BEFORE REPLACING ECM USE AN OHMMETER AND CHECK RESISTANCE BETWEEN SOLENOID TERMINALS. REPLACE IF RESISTANCE MEASURES LESS THAN 20 OHMS.*

CLEAR CODES AND CONFIRM "CLOSED LOOP" OPERATION AND NO "SERVICE ENGINE SOON" LIGHT.

GENERAL MOTORS TORQUE CONVERTER CLUTCH (Cont.)

Fig. 37: TCC Test Chart For Light Duty Trucks With 4.3L Throttle Body Injection (TBI) Engine

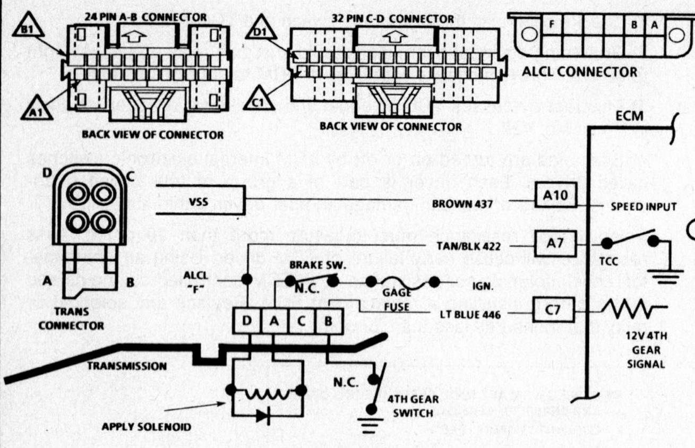

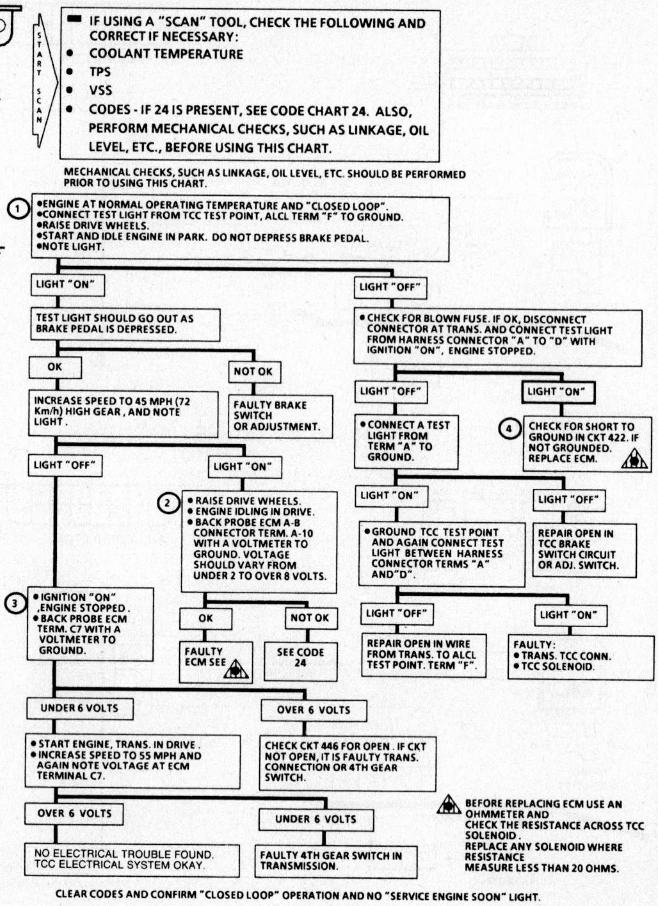

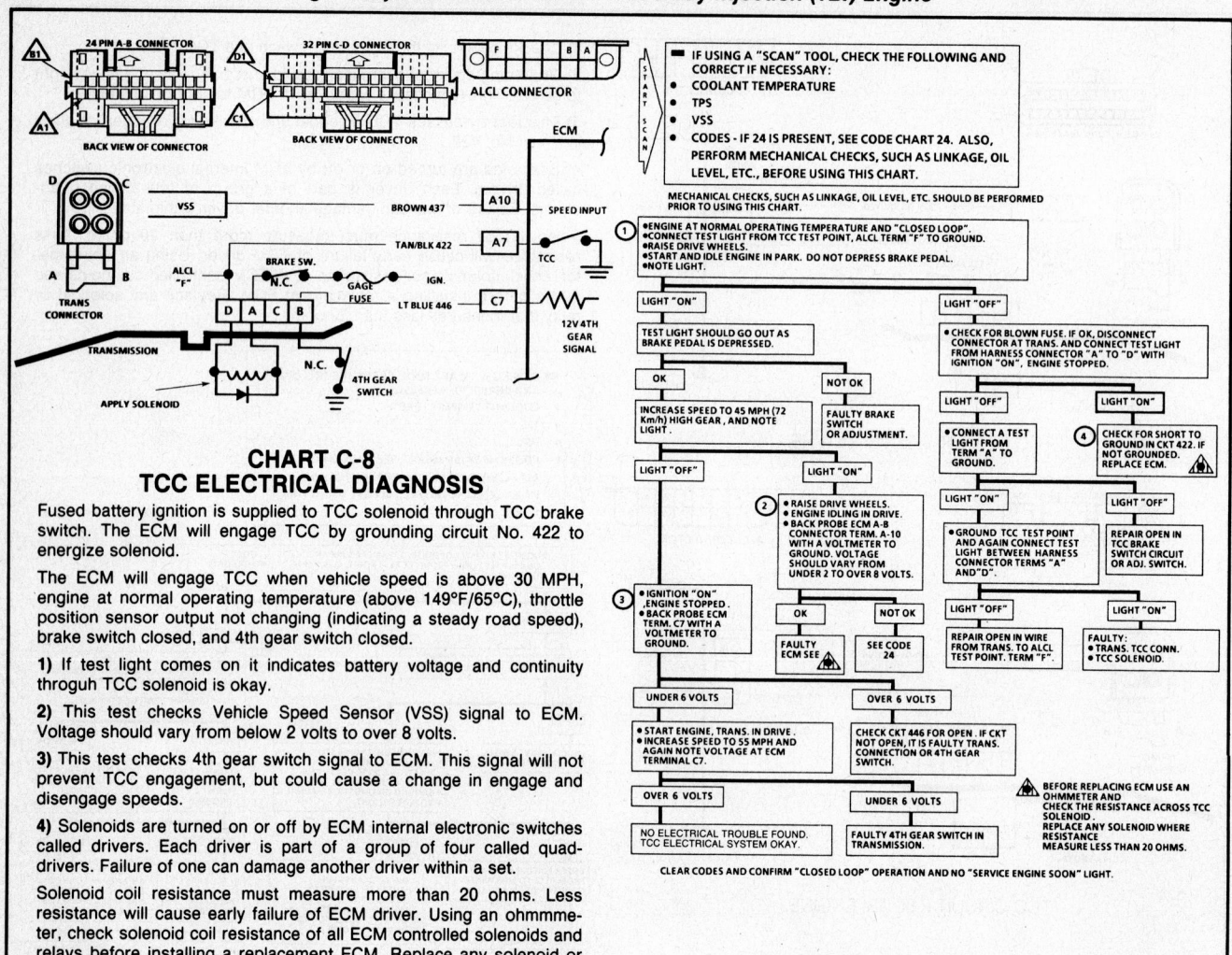

CHART C-8
TCC ELECTRICAL DIAGNOSIS

Fused battery ignition is supplied to TCC solenoid through TCC brake switch. The ECM will engage TCC by grounding circuit No. 422 to energize solenoid.

The ECM will engage TCC when vehicle speed is above 30 MPH, engine at normal operating temperature (above 149°F/65°C), throttle position sensor output not changing (indicating a steady road speed), brake switch closed, and 4th gear switch closed.

1) If test light comes on it indicates battery voltage and continuity throguh TCC solenoid is okay.

2) This test checks Vehicle Speed Sensor (VSS) signal to ECM. Voltage should vary from below 2 volts to over 8 volts.

3) This test checks 4th gear switch signal to ECM. This signal will not prevent TCC engagement, but could cause a change in engage and disengage speeds.

4) Solenoids are turned on or off by ECM internal electronic switches called drivers. Each driver is part of a group of four called quad-drivers. Failure of one can damage another driver within a set.

Solenoid coil resistance must measure more than 20 ohms. Less resistance will cause early failure of ECM driver. Using an ohmmmeter, check solenoid coil resistance of all ECM controlled solenoids and relays before installing a replacement ECM. Replace any solenoid or relay that measures less than 20 ohms.

GENERAL MOTORS TORQUE CONVERTER CLUTCH (Cont.)

Fig. 38: Vehicle Speed Sensor (VSS) Test Chart For Light Duty Trucks With Throttle Body Injection (TBI) Engines

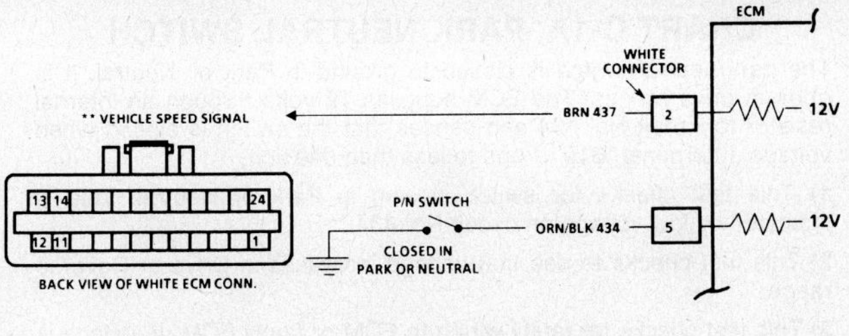

VSS CIRCUIT 2.5L TBI ENGINE

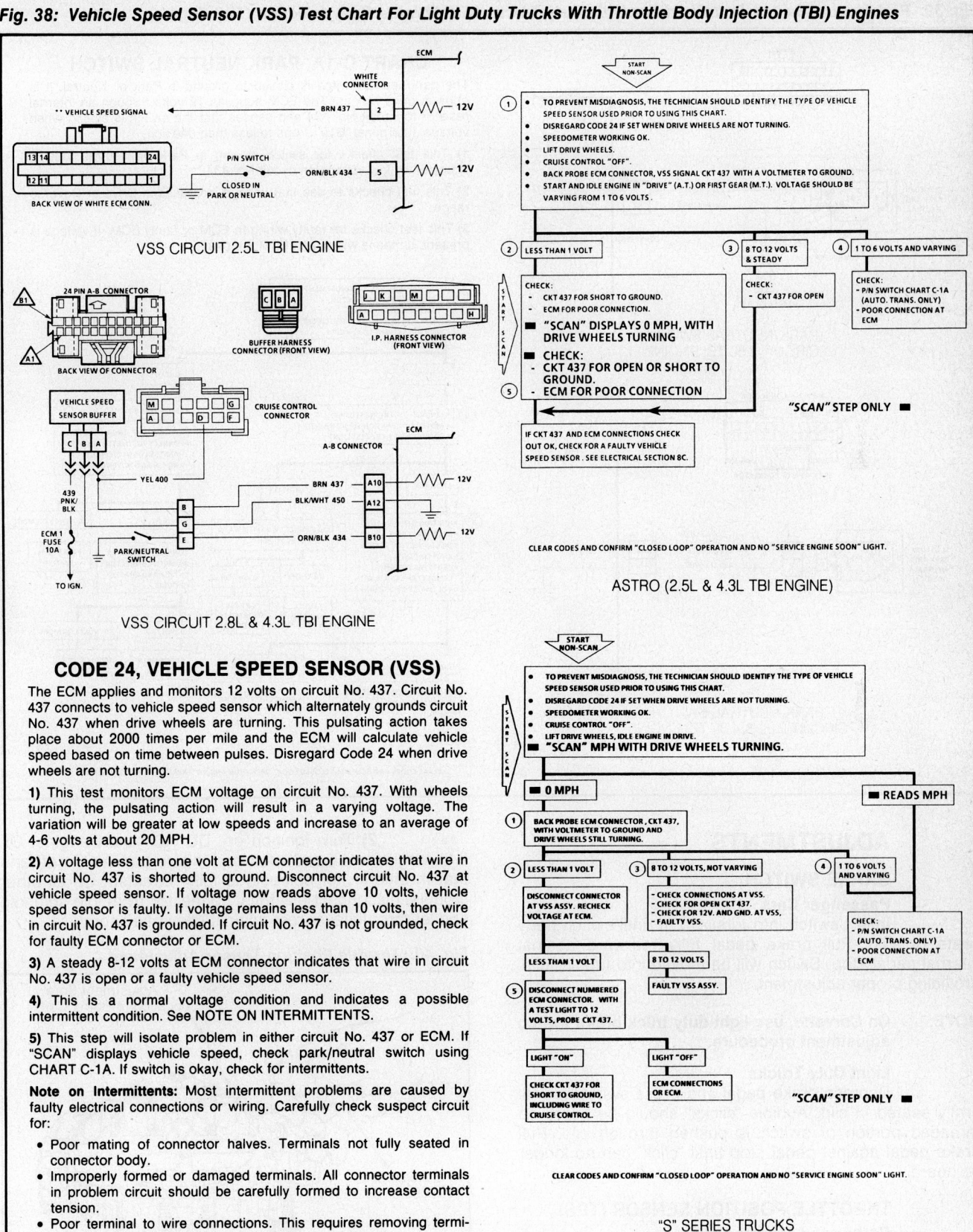

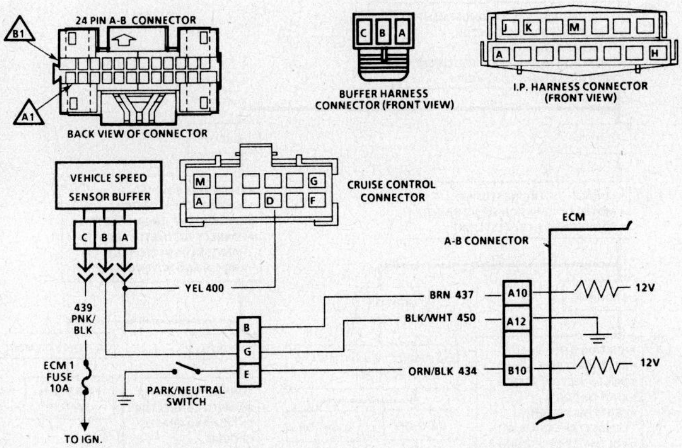

VSS CIRCUIT 2.8L & 4.3L TBI ENGINE

CODE 24, VEHICLE SPEED SENSOR (VSS)

The ECM applies and monitors 12 volts on circuit No. 437. Circuit No. 437 connects to vehicle speed sensor which alternately grounds circuit No. 437 when drive wheels are turning. This pulsating action takes place about 2000 times per mile and the ECM will calculate vehicle speed based on time between pulses. Disregard Code 24 when drive wheels are not turning.

1) This test monitors ECM voltage on circuit No. 437. With wheels turning, the pulsating action will result in a varying voltage. The variation will be greater at low speeds and increase to an average of 4-6 volts at about 20 MPH.

2) A voltage less than one volt at ECM connector indicates that wire in circuit No. 437 is shorted to ground. Disconnect circuit No. 437 at vehicle speed sensor. If voltage now reads above 10 volts, vehicle speed sensor is faulty. If voltage remains less than 10 volts, then wire in circuit No. 437 is grounded. If circuit No. 437 is not grounded, check for faulty ECM connector or ECM.

3) A steady 8-12 volts at ECM connector indicates that wire in circuit No. 437 is open or a faulty vehicle speed sensor.

4) This is a normal voltage condition and indicates a possible intermittent condition. See NOTE ON INTERMITTENTS.

5) This step will isolate problem in either circuit No. 437 or ECM. If "SCAN" displays vehicle speed, check park/neutral switch using CHART C-1A. If switch is okay, check for intermittents.

Note on Intermittents: Most intermittent problems are caused by faulty electrical connections or wiring. Carefully check suspect circuit for:

- Poor mating of connector halves. Terminals not fully seated in connector body.
- Improperly formed or damaged terminals. All connector terminals in problem circuit should be carefully formed to increase contact tension.
- Poor terminal to wire connections. This requires removing terminal(s) from connector body to check proper installation.

If a visual (physical) check does locate cause of problem, the vehicle can be driven with a voltmeter connected to suspect circuit. An abnormal voltage reading when problem occurs indicates that problem may be in that circuit.

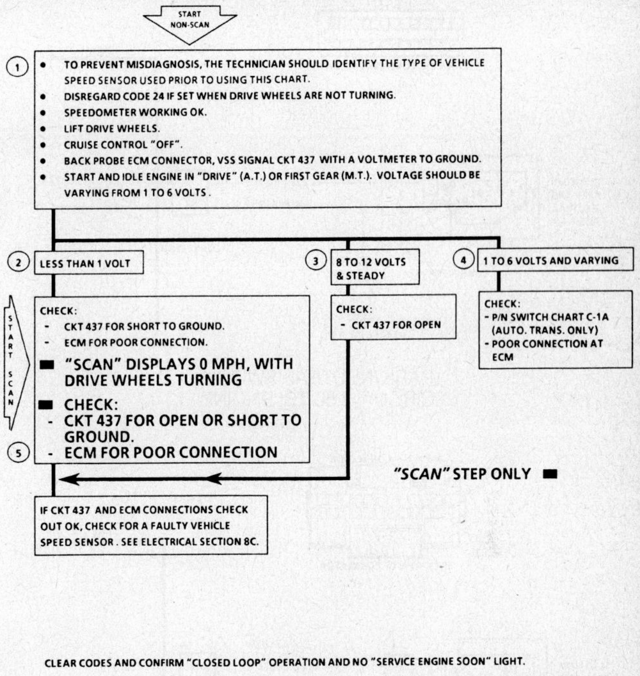

ASTRO (2.5L & 4.3L TBI ENGINE)

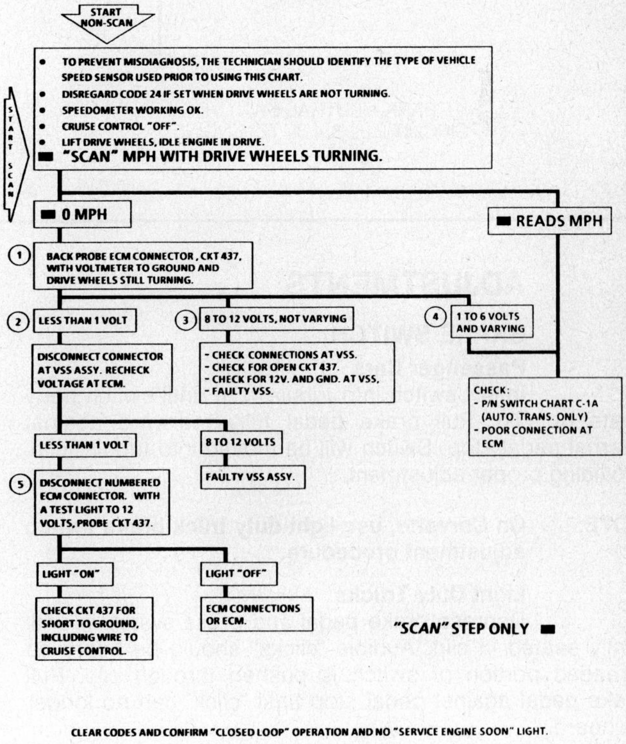

"S" SERIES TRUCKS
(2.5L & 2.8L TBI ENGINE)

GENERAL MOTORS TORQUE CONVERTER CLUTCH (Cont.)

Fig. 39: Park/Neutral Switch Test Chart For Light Duty Trucks With Throttle Body Injection (TBI) Engines

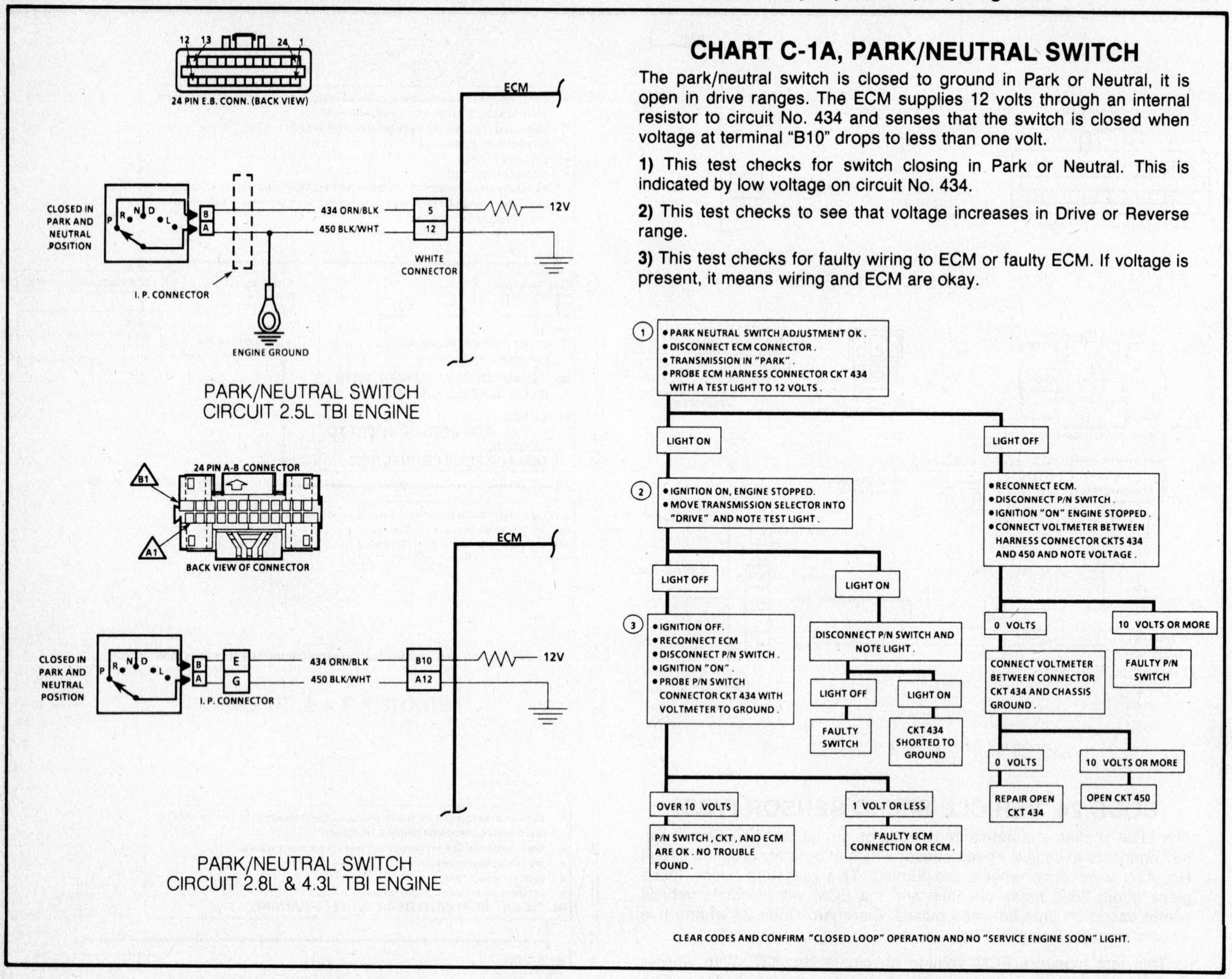

12 13 24 1
24 PIN E.B. CONN. (BACK VIEW)
ECM
CLOSED IN PARK AND NEUTRAL POSITION
P R N D L
B A
434 ORN/BLK
450 BLK/WHT
5
12
12V
WHITE CONNECTOR
I. P. CONNECTOR
ENGINE GROUND
PARK/NEUTRAL SWITCH CIRCUIT 2.5L TBI ENGINE
24 PIN A-B CONNECTOR
B1
A1
BACK VIEW OF CONNECTOR
ECM
CLOSED IN PARK AND NEUTRAL POSITION
E
G
I. P. CONNECTOR
434 ORN/BLK
450 BLK/WHT
B10
A12
12V
PARK/NEUTRAL SWITCH CIRCUIT 2.8L & 4.3L TBI ENGINE
CHART C-1A, PARK/NEUTRAL SWITCH
The park/neutral switch is closed to ground in Park or Neutral, it is open in drive ranges. The ECM supplies 12 volts through an internal resistor to circuit No. 434 and senses that the switch is closed when voltage at terminal "B10" drops to less than one volt.
1) This test checks for switch closing in Park or Neutral. This is indicated by low voltage on circuit No. 434.
2) This test checks to see that voltage increases in Drive or Reverse range.
3) This test checks for faulty wiring to ECM or faulty ECM. If voltage is present, it means wiring and ECM are okay.
1
• PARK NEUTRAL SWITCH ADJUSTMENT OK. • DISCONNECT ECM CONNECTOR. • TRANSMISSION IN "PARK". • PROBE ECM HARNESS CONNECTOR CKT 434 WITH A TEST LIGHT TO 12 VOLTS.
LIGHT ON
LIGHT OFF
2
• IGNITION ON, ENGINE STOPPED. • MOVE TRANSMISSION SELECTOR INTO "DRIVE" AND NOTE TEST LIGHT.
• RECONNECT ECM. • DISCONNECT P/N SWITCH. • IGNITION "ON" ENGINE STOPPED. • CONNECT VOLTMETER BETWEEN HARNESS CONNECTOR CKTS 434 AND 450 AND NOTE VOLTAGE.
LIGHT OFF
LIGHT ON
0 VOLTS
10 VOLTS OR MORE
3
• IGNITION OFF. • RECONNECT ECM • DISCONNECT P/N SWITCH. • IGNITION "ON". • PROBE P/N SWITCH CONNECTOR CKT 434 WITH VOLTMETER TO GROUND.
DISCONNECT P/N SWITCH AND NOTE LIGHT.
CONNECT VOLTMETER BETWEEN CONNECTOR CKT 434 AND CHASSIS GROUND.
FAULTY P/N SWITCH
LIGHT OFF
LIGHT ON
FAULTY SWITCH
CKT 434 SHORTED TO GROUND
0 VOLTS
10 VOLTS OR MORE
OVER 10 VOLTS
1 VOLT OR LESS
REPAIR OPEN CKT 434
OPEN CKT 450
P/N SWITCH, CKT, AND ECM ARE OK. NO TROUBLE FOUND.
FAULTY ECM CONNECTION OR ECM.
CLEAR CODES AND CONFIRM "CLOSED LOOP" OPERATION AND NO "SERVICE ENGINE SOON" LIGHT.

ADJUSTMENTS

BRAKE SWITCH

Passenger Cars

Insert switch into tubular clip until switch body seats on clip. Pull brake pedal fully rearward against internal pedal stop. Switch will be moved into tubular clip, providing proper adjustment.

NOTE: **On Corvette, use light duty truck brake switch adjustment procedure.**

Light Duty Trucks

Depress brake pedal and press switch in until firmly seated in clip. Audible "clicks" should be heard as threaded portion of switch is pushed through clip. Pull brake pedal against pedal stop until "click" can no longer be heard.

THROTTLE POSITION SENSOR (TPS)

Carbureted Models Only

1) Ensure that engine idle speed is correct. On 2.8L engine equipped vehicles, disconnect TPS connector and jumper all 3 terminals. On all models, connect digital voltmeter from TPS connector center terminal to bottom terminal.

2) Turn ignition on, DO NOT start engine. On 2.8L engine equipped vehicles, ensure that A/C is off and that throttle kicker solenoid is fully retracted. On all other models, disconnect electrical connector from idle solenoid and let throttle lever rest against idle speed screw.

Fig. 40: Throttle Position Sensor Adjustment

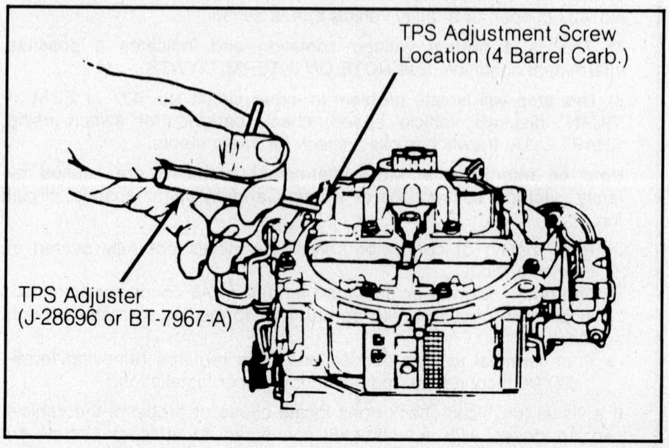

TPS Adjustment Screw Location (4 Barrel Carb.)
TPS Adjuster (J-28696 or BT-7967-A)

GENERAL MOTORS TORQUE CONVERTER CLUTCH (Cont.)

3) On all models, read TPS voltage. If reading is incorrect, use a 5/64" drill bit and carefully drill a hole in plug covering TPS adjustment screw. Plug is located next to TPS plunger bore. Start a No. 8, 1/2" long self-tapping screw in drilled hole turning screw in only enough to ensure good thread engagement.

4) Place a screwdriver between screw head and carburetor air horn casting, pry against screw head to remove plug. With ignition on, engine stopped, turn TPS adjustment screw to obtain specified voltage. After adjustment, a new plug or RTV sealant must be inserted in TPS adjustment screw hole.

THROTTLE POSITION SENSOR SPECIFICATIONS

Application	Voltage
Passenger Cars	
2.8L V6	.30
3.8L V6 (VIN A)	.30
5.0L V8 (VIN G & H)	.50-.58
5.0L V8 (VIN Y & 9)	.45-.47
5.7L (VIN 6)	.45-.47
Light Duty Trucks	
Calif. 4.3L, 5.0L & 5.7L V8	.30-.32

Fig. 41: THM 125C & 350-C Torque Converter Clutch Solenoid & Wiring

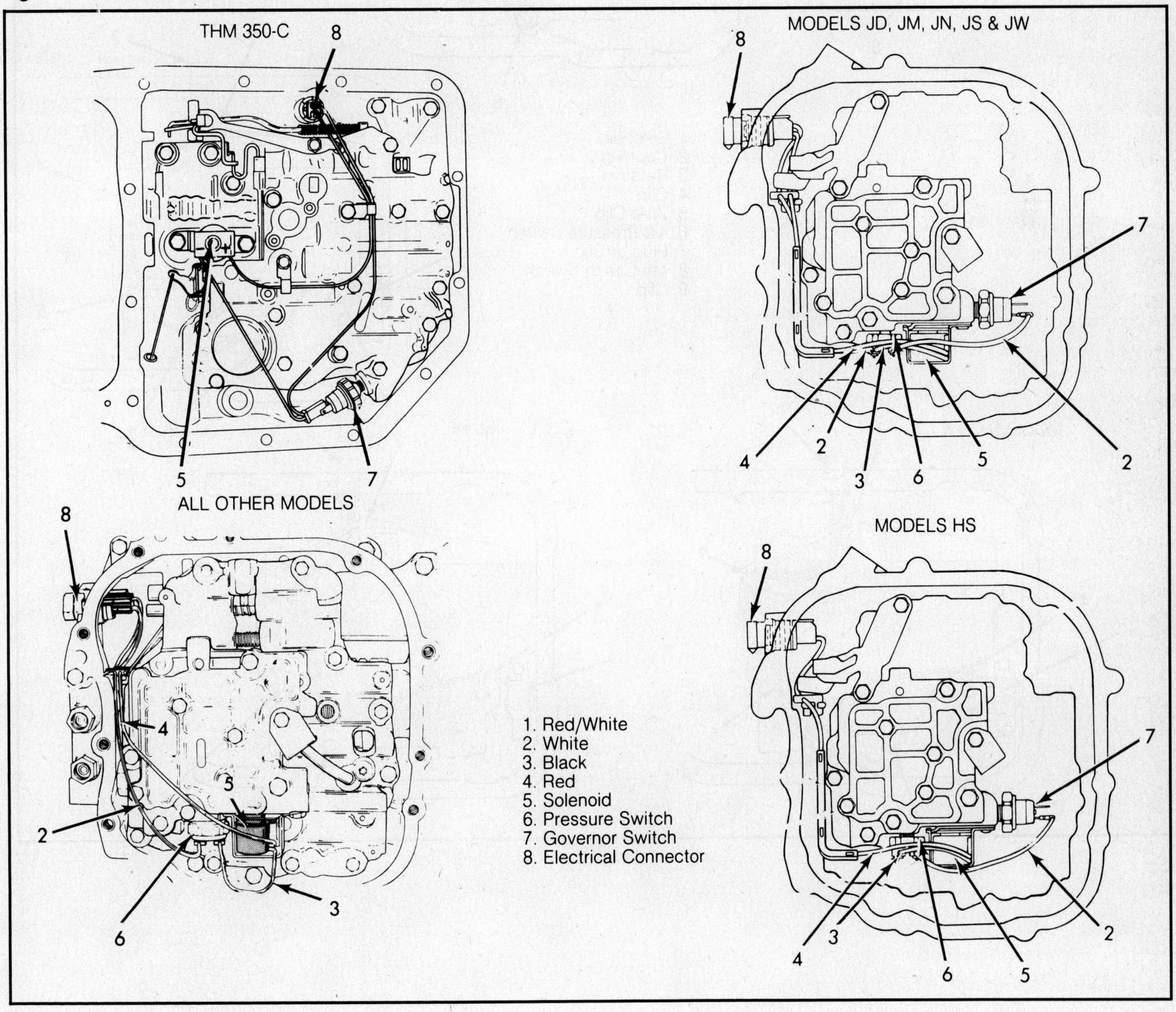

GENERAL MOTORS TORQUE CONVERTER CLUTCH (Cont.)

Fig. 42: THM 200-4R Torque Converter Clutch Solenoid & Wiring

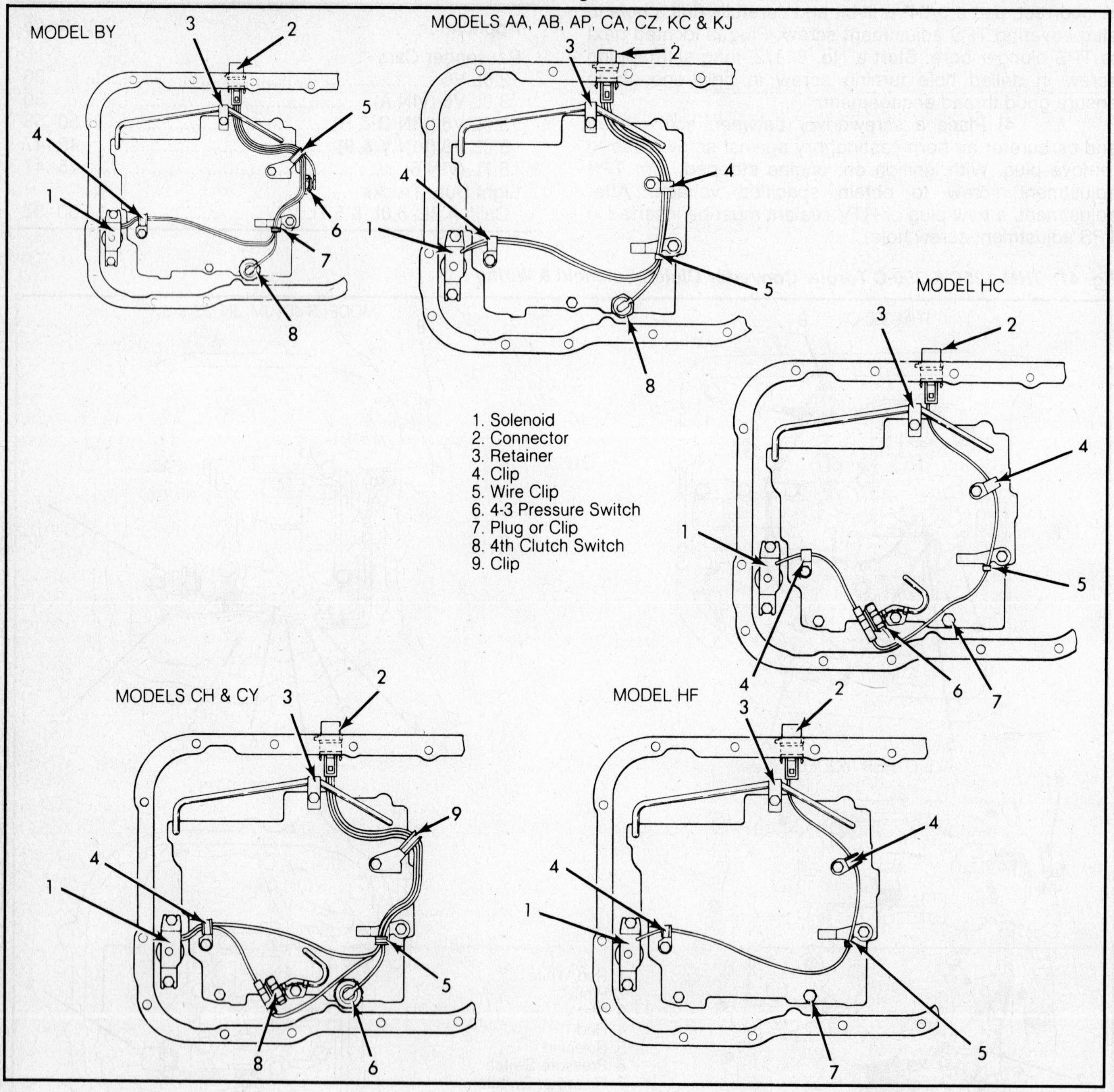

GENERAL MOTORS TORQUE CONVERTER CLUTCH (Cont.)

Fig. 43: THM 440-T4 Torque Converter Clutch Solenoid & Wiring

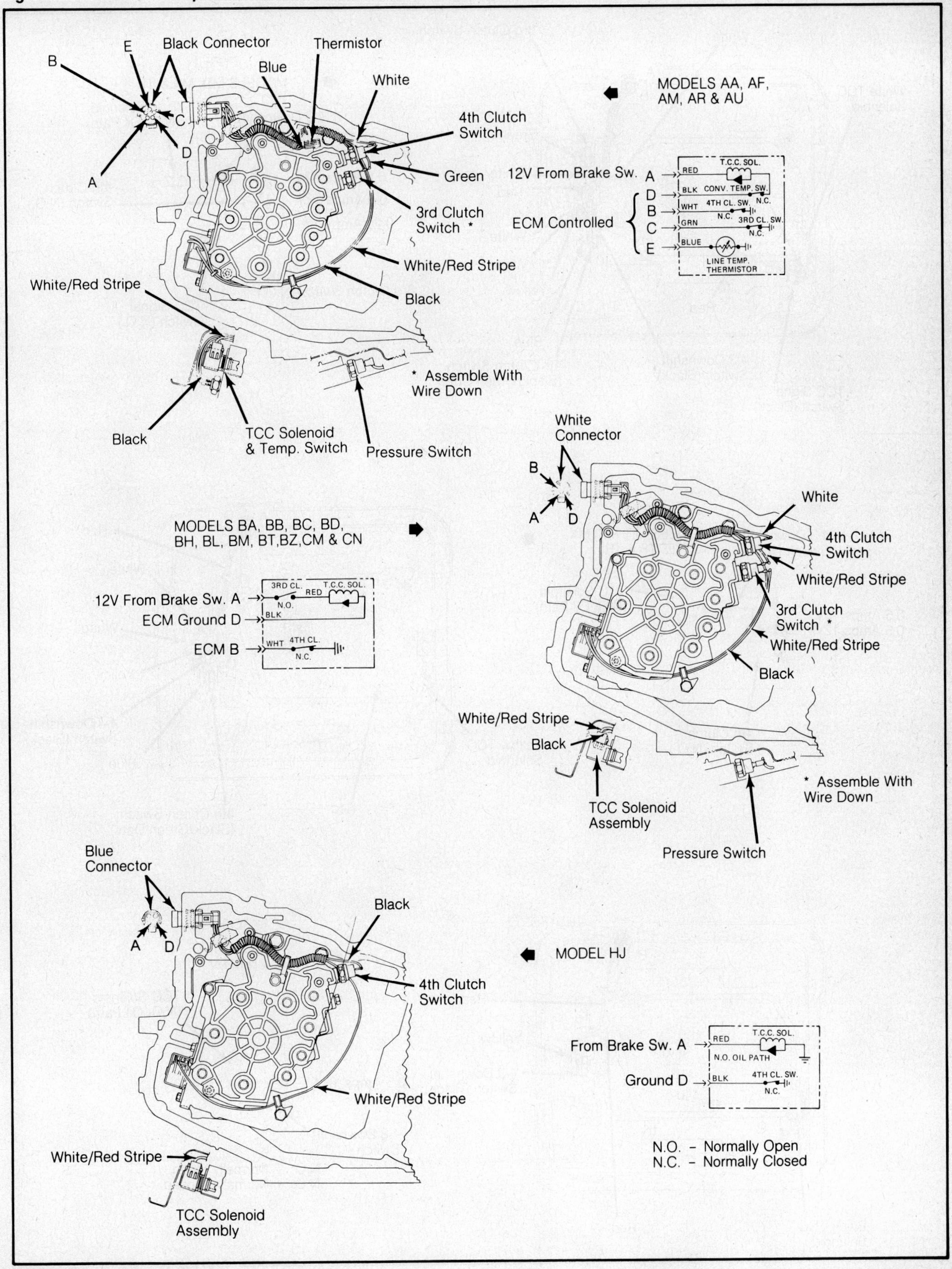

GENERAL MOTORS TORQUE CONVERTER CLUTCH (Cont.)

Fig. 44: THM 700-R4 Torque Converter Clutch Solenoid & Wiring

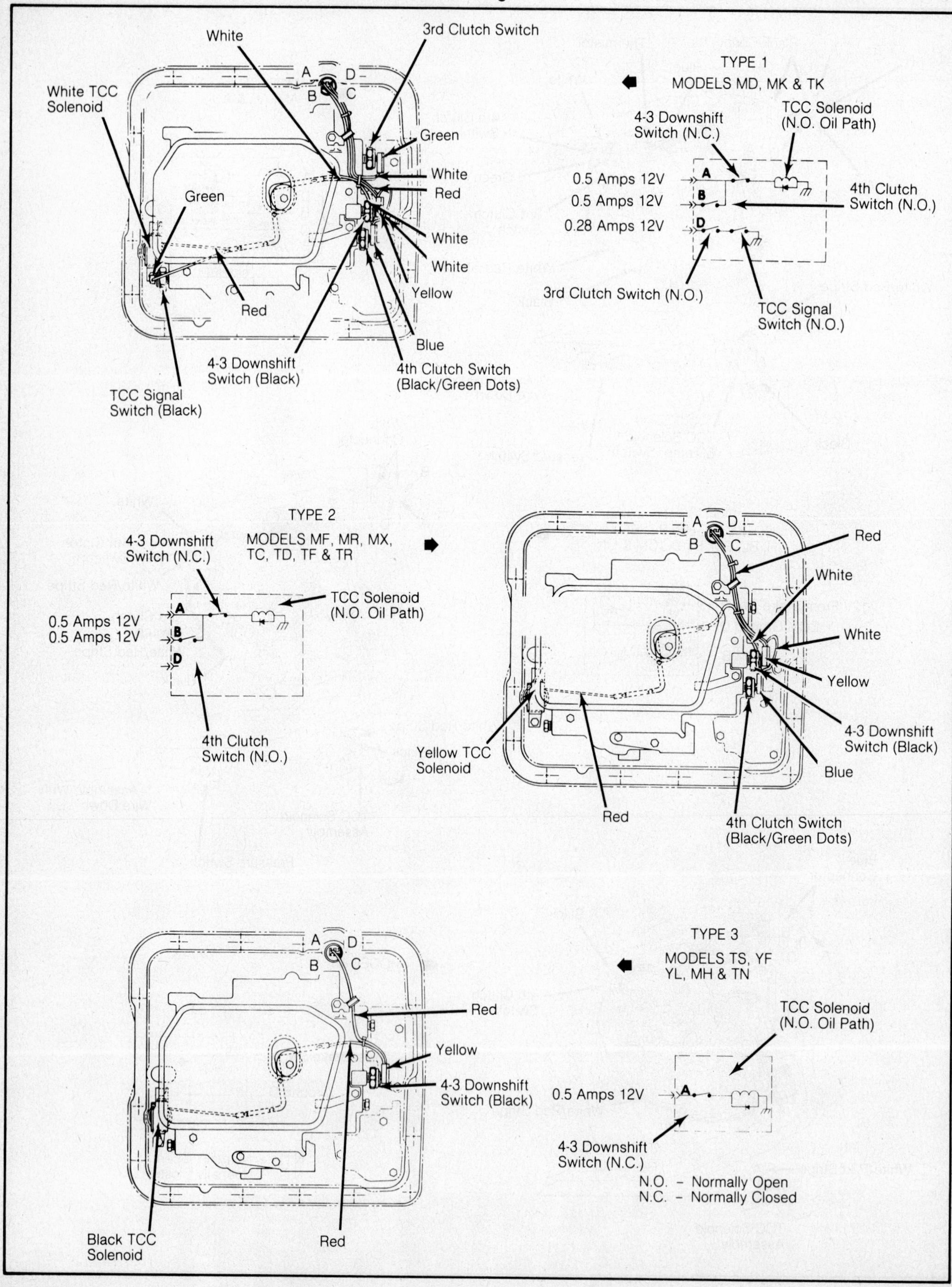

GENERAL MOTORS TORQUE CONVERTER CLUTCH (Cont.)

Fig. 45: THM 700-R4 Torque Converter Clutch Solenoid & Wiring (Cont.)

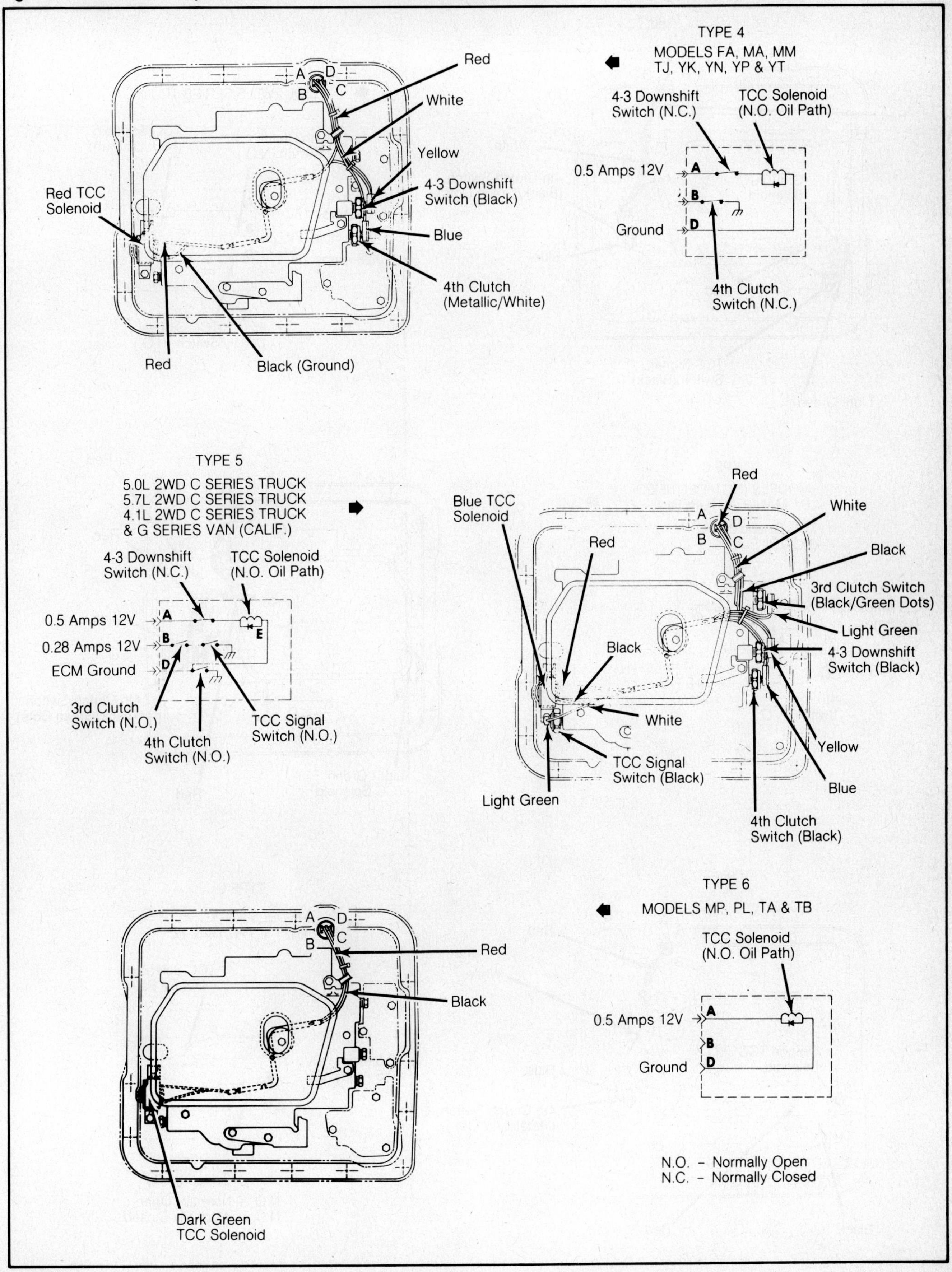

GENERAL MOTORS TORQUE CONVERTER CLUTCH (Cont.)

Fig. 46: THM 700-R4 Torque Converter Clutch Solenoid & Wiring (Cont.)

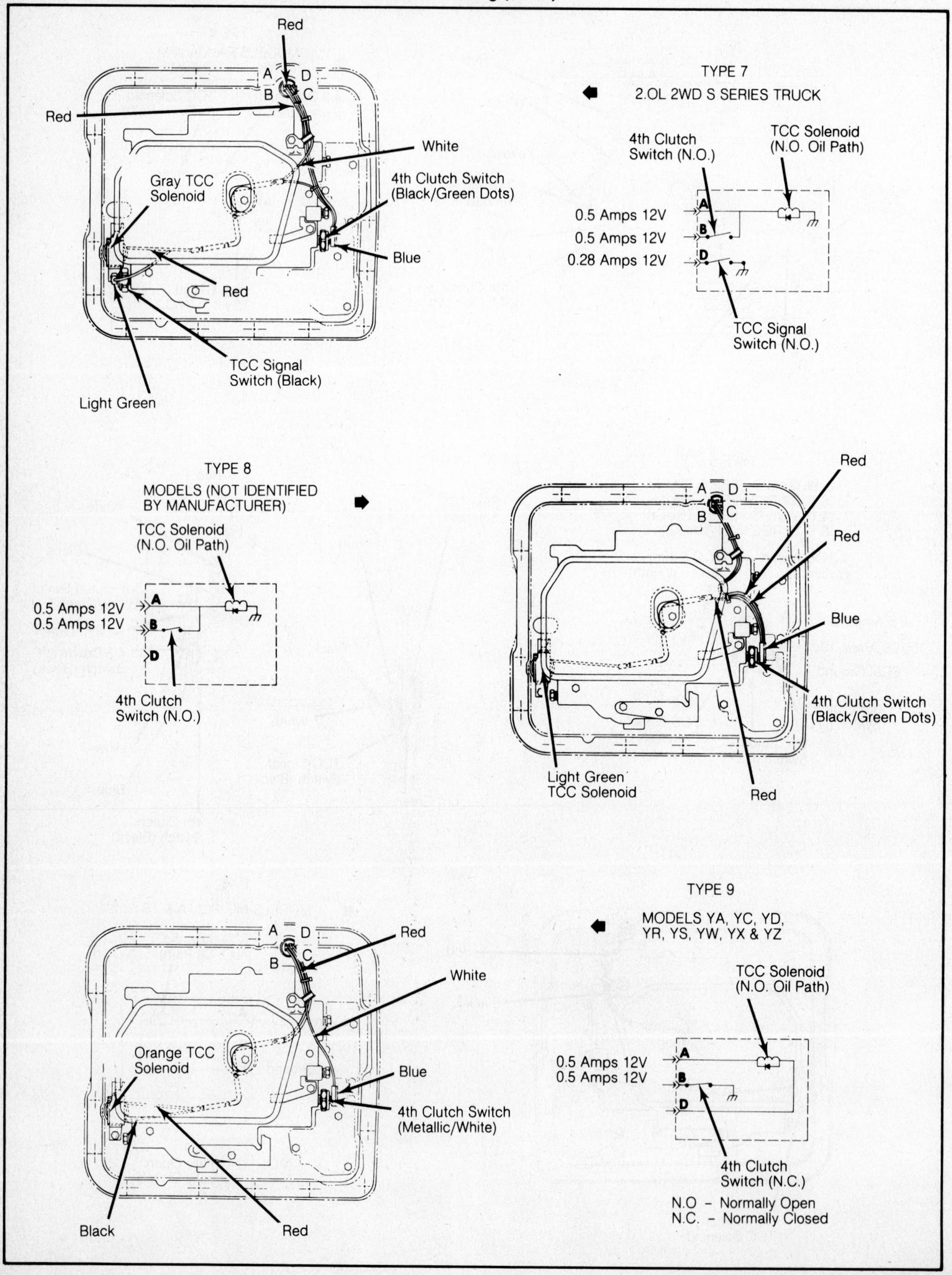

GENERAL MOTORS TORQUE CONVERTER CLUTCH (Cont.)

Fig. 47: THM 700-R4 Torque Converter Clutch Solenoid & Wiring (Cont.)

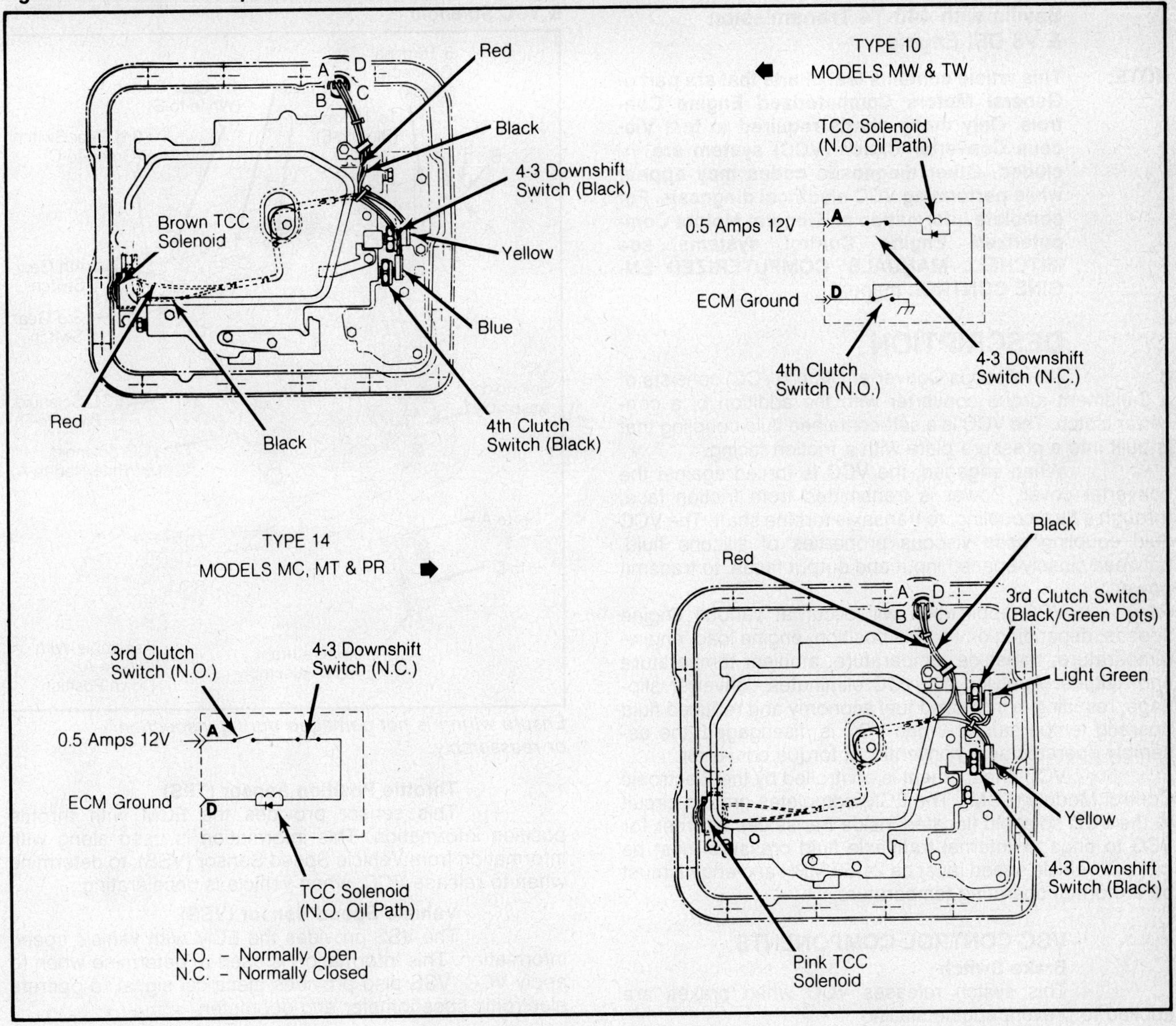

GENERAL MOTORS VISCOUS CONVERTER CLUTCH

Cadillac DeVille, Eldorado, Fleetwood Seville with 440-T4 Transmission & V8 DFI Engine

NOTE: **This article contains test charts that are part of General Motors Computerized Engine Controls. Only those charts required to test Viscous Converter Clutch (VCC) system are included. Other diagnostic codes may appear while performing VCC electrical diagnosis. For complete information on General Motors Computerized Engine Control systems see MITCHELL MANUALS' COMPUTERIZED ENGINE CONTROL manual.**

DESCRIPTION

The Viscous Converter Clutch (VCC) consists of a 3-element torque converter with the addition of a converter clutch. The VCC is a self-contained fluid coupling that is built into a pressure plate with a friction facing.

When engaged, the VCC is forced against the converter cover. Power is transmitted from friction face, through a fluid coupling, to transaxle turbine shaft. The VCC fluid coupling uses viscous properties of silicone fluid, between closely spaced input and output faces, to transmit power.

VCC application will occur at various engine speeds, depending on throttle position, engine load, engine temperature, transaxle temperature, ambient temperature and altitude. Applying the VCC eliminates converter slippage, resulting in improved fuel economy and reduced fluid operatig temperatures. When VCC is disengaged, the assembly operates as a conventional torque converter.

VCC engagement is controlled by the Electronic Control Module (ECM). The ECM completes ground circuit to the VCC solenoid (located inside transaxle). In order for VCC to engage, internal transaxle fluid pressure must be correct, vehicle speed must be 24-50 MPH and engine must be at normal operating temperature.

VCC CONTROL COMPONENTS

Brake Switch

This switch releases VCC when brakes are applied to prevent engine stalling.

Coolant Temperature Sensor

This sensor provides ECM with engine coolant temperature information. The ECM will not allow VCC operation until the signal from this sensor indicates a coolant temperature more than 140°F (60°C).

Manifold Absolute Pressure (MAP) Sensor

The MAP sensor provides the ECM with information on atmospheric pressure. If the MAP sensor detects low pressure, VCC engagement is delayed until vehicle speed is more than 50 MPH.

Thermistor Switch

The thermistor switch senses transaxle fluid temperature. If fluid temperature is more than 200°F (93°C), VCC engagement will be delayed until vehicle speed reaches 36 MPH.

Gear Switches

A 3rd and a 4th gear switch are used to tell the ECM that transaxle is in 3rd or 4th gear. The ECM uses this information to vary conditions under which VCC is applied or released. Transaxle does not have to be in 3rd or 4th gear to apply VCC.

Fig. 1: View of 440-T4 Valve Body, Sensors & VCC Solenoid

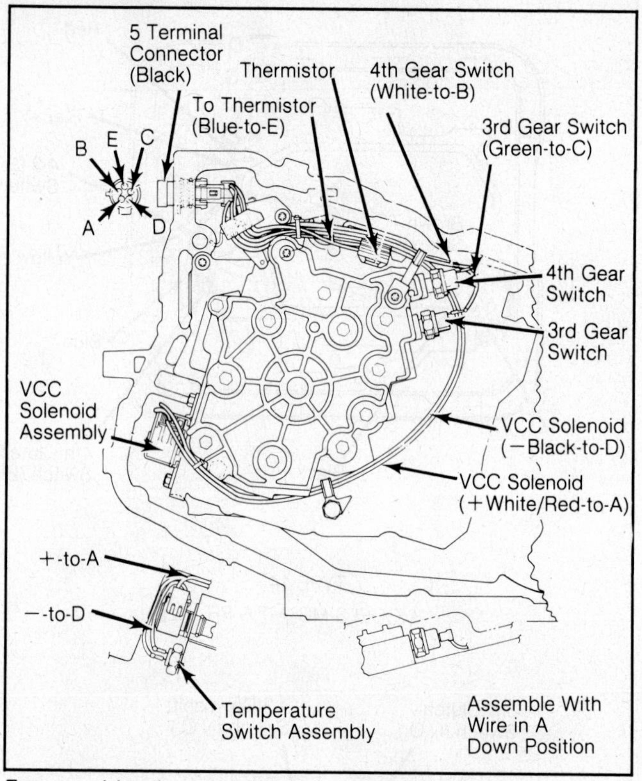

Ensure wiring is not damaged during inspection or reassembly.

Throttle Position Sensor (TPS)

This sensor provides the ECM with throttle position information. This information is used along with information from Vehicle Speed Sensor (VSS), to determine when to release VCC, when vehicle is decelerating.

Vehicle Speed Sensor (VSS)

The VSS provides the ECM with vehicle speed information. This information is used to determine when to apply VCC. VSS also provides electrical signal to operate electronic speedometer and odometer.

TROUBLE SHOOTING

CONDITION & CAUSE

No VCC Application

- Verify proper ECM operation. Check thermistor and coolant temperature circuits for damage.
- Verify control valve operation. Check for stuck clutch apply valve. Check for missing No. 10 check ball.
- Check converter clutch blow-off check ball in channel plate not seating or damaged.
- Check turbine shaft seals for damage.
- Check oil pump drive shaft seals for damage.

VCC Does Not Release

- Check VCC brake release switch operation.
- Check for converter clutch apply valve stuck in apply position.

TESTING

RETRIEVING STORED TROUBLE CODES

NOTE: **The terms "enter diagnostics" and "exit diagnostics" will be used periodically throughout this section. Follow step 1) of ENTERING DIAGNOSTIC MODE procedure when instructed to "enter diagnostics". Use EXITING DIAGNOSTIC MODE procedure when instructed to "exit diagnostics".**

Entering Diagnostic Mode (DeVille & Fleetwood)

1) Turn ignition on. Depress "OFF" and "WARMER" buttons on CCP panel simultaneously. Hold buttons until code "-1.8.8" appears on CCP panel and code "8.8.8" appears on Fuel Data Control (FDC) panel. This is a check of all display segments and indicates the beginning of diagnostic readout. *See Fig. 2.*

Fig. 2: Deville & Fleetwood Display Of "-1.8.8" On CCP Panel and "8.8.8" On FDC Panel

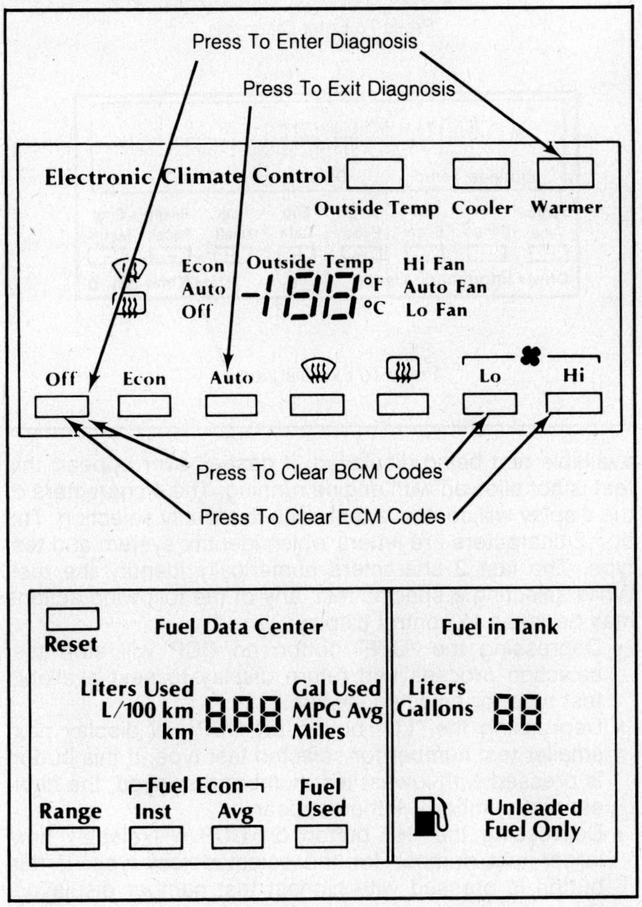

NOTE: **If all segments of read-out "-1.8.8" or "8.8.8" do not appear, diagnosis should not be attempted. This could lead to mis-diagnosis of the system (Code "34" appears as "31", etc.). If any of the segments (except periods) are inoperative, the affected display panel must be replaced.**

2) After the display segments check, any trouble codes stored in computer memory will be displayed in ascending order (from lowest to highest) on the FDC panel (except code "E51"). Trouble codes prefixed with an "E" indicate that the malfunction was recorded by the ECM. Trouble codes prefixed with an "F" indicate that the malfunction was recorded by the BCM.

NOTE: **If code "E51" is currently being detected, it will be continuously displayed until diagnostic mode is exited. During display of code "E51", no other diagnostic function is possible. PROM error must be corrected.**

3) An "..E" will appear before the first pass through the ECM-detected trouble codes. The first pass through ECM-detected troubled codes includes all detected malfunctions, even though they may not be currently present. If no trouble codes are stored, the "..E" will be by-passed.

4) Each trouble code will appear for 2 seconds until the highest stored code has been displayed. Record all codes. After display of highest stored code, ".E.E" will be displayed to indicate the second pass through ECM-stored codes. This second pass displays ONLY hard codes which indicate a present malfunction and are keeping the "SERVICE NOW/SOON" light on.

5) Therefore, any code which was displayed during the first cycle, but is not displayed during the second cycle is an intermittent failure. If all stored codes are intermittent, the ".E.E" display will be by-passed.

NOTE: **Trouble code "E30" will cause "SERVICE SOON" light to stay on throughout the ignition cycle, even though it may be an intermittent trouble code. This condition will exist until the ISC circuit is tested again during the next ignition cycle.**

6) After display of all ECM-stored trouble codes, all BCM-stored trouble codes will be displayed in same manner. The first pass of BCM codes will be preceded by an "..F" and second pass will be preceded by ".F.F".

7) After display of all ECM and BCM trouble codes, or if no codes are stored, code ".7.0" will be displayed on the FDC, indicating system is ready for next diagnostic feature. See INTERMITTENT FAILURE TEST PROCEDURES.

NOTE: **If code "F51" is currently being detected, it will be continuously displayed until diagnostic mode is exited. During display of code "F51", no other diagnostic function is possible. PROM error must be corrected.**

Entering Diagnostic (Service) Mode (Eldorado & Seville)

After diagnostic service mode is entered, any trouble codes stored in computer memory will be displayed. ECM codes will be displayed first. If no ECM trouble codes are stored, a "NO ECM CODES" message will be displayed. All ECM codes will be prefixed with a "E". The lowest numbered ECM code will be displayed first followed by progressively higher numbered codes present.

Following highest ECM code present or "NO ECM CODES" message, BCM codes will be displayed. All BCM codes will be prefixed with a "B". If no BCM trouble codes are stored, "NO BCM CODES" message will be displayed.

Any BCM and ECM codes displayed will also be accompanied by "Current" or "History". "History" indicates

GENERAL MOTORS VISCOUS CONVERTER CLUTCH (Cont.)

failure was not present last time code was tested, and "Current" indicates fault still exists. At any time during display of ECM or BCM codes, if "LO" button on CCP is depressed, the display of codes will be by-passed. At any time during display of trouble codes, if "RESET/RECALL" button on DIC is depressed, the system will exit service mode and go back to normal vehicle operation.

Upon entering service mode, the climate control will operate in whatever mode was being commanded just prior to depressing the "OFF" and "WARM" buttons. Even though display may change just as buttons are touched, the prior operating mode is remembered and will resume after service mode is entered. The Extended Compressor at Idle (ECI) is not allowed while in diagnostic service mode. This allows observation of system parameters during normal compressor cycles.

1) To operate diagnostic service modes, turn ignition on. Depress "OFF" and "WARM" buttons on Climate Control Panel (CCP) simultaneously. Hold buttons until segment check appears on Instrument Panel Cluster (IPC) and Climate Control Driver Information Center (CCDIC). *See Fig. 3.*

NOTE: The purpose of illuminating the IPC and CCDIC is to check that all segments of vacuum flourescent displays are working. On IPC however, the turn signal indicators do not light during this check. Diagnosis should not be attempted unless all CCDIC segments appear, as this could lead to misdiagnosis. If any portions or segments of CCDIC display are inoperative, it must be replaced.

2) After trouble codes have been displayed, the "SERVICE MODE" can be used to perform several test on different systems one at a time. Upon completion of code display, a specific system may be selected for testing.

3) Following the display of trouble codes, the first available system will be displayed. ECM will be the first available system, followed by BCM system and IPC system. While selecting a system to test, any of the following actions may be taken to control display:

- Depressing the "OFF" button, CCP will stop system selection process and return display to beginning of trouble code sequence.
- Depressing the "LO" button on CCP, will display next available system selection. This allows display to be stepped through all system choices. This list of systems can be repeated following end of system list.
- Depressing "HI" button on CCP will select displayed system for testing.

4) Having selected a system, the first available test type will be displayed. While slecting a specific test type any of the following actions may be taken to control display:

- Depressing the "OFF" button on CCP will stop test type selection process and return display to next available system selection.
- Depressing the "LO" button on CCP will display next available test type for selected system. This allows display to be stepped through all available test type choices. This list of test types can be repeated following display of last test type.
- Depress the "HI" button on CCP will select the displayed test type. At this point the first of several specific tests will appear.

5) Selection of "DATA?", "INPUTS?", "OUTPUTS?", or "OVERRIDE?" test types will result in first

Fig. 3: Eldorado & Seville Operation of "DIAGNOSTIC SERVICE MODE"

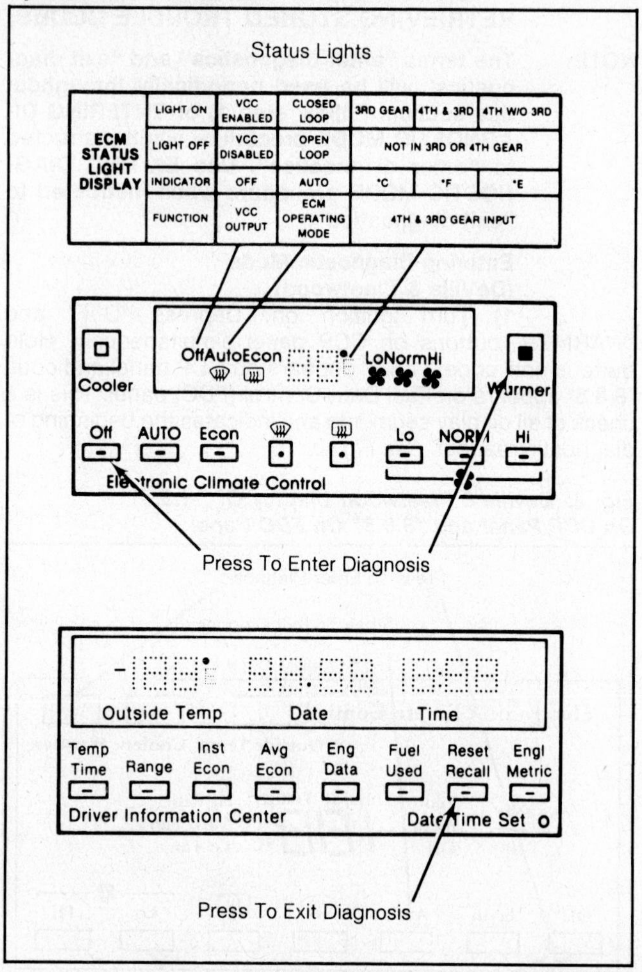

available test being displayed. If dashes ever appear, this test is not allowed with engine running. The 4 characters of the display will contain a test code to identify selection. The first 2 characters are letters which identify system and test type. The last 2 characters numerically identify the test. While selecting a specific test, any of the following actions may be taken to control display:

- Depressing the "OFF" button on CCP will stop test selection process and return display to next available test type for selected system.
- Depressing the "LO" button on CCP will display next smaller test number for selected test type. If this button is pressed with lowest test number displayed, the highest test number will then appear.
- Depressing the "HI" button on CCP will display next larger test number for the selected test type. If this button is pressed with highest test number displayed, the lowest test number will then appear.

6) Selection of "CLEAR CODES?" test type will result in message "CODES CLEAR" being displayed along with selected system name. This message will appear for 3 seconds to indicate that all stored trouble codes have been erased from that system's memory. After 3 seconds the display will automatically return to next available test type for selected system.

7) Selection of "SNAPSHOT?" test type will result in meassage "SNAPSHOT TAKEN" being displayed with selected system name preceeding it. This message will appear for 3 seconds to indicate that all system data and inputs have been stored in memory. After 3 seconds the display will automatically proceed to the first available snapshot test type. While selecting a snapshot test type, any of the following actions may be taken to control display:

- Depressing the "OFF" button on CCP will stop test type selection process and return display to next available system selection.
- Depressing the "LO" button will display the next available snapshot test type. This allows the display to be stepped through all available choices. This list of snapshot test types can be repeated following display of last choice.
- Depressing the "HI" button with "SNAP DATA?" or "SNAP INPUTS?" displayed will select that test type. At this point the display is controlled as it would be for non-snapshot data and inputs displays. However, all values and status information represents memorized vehicle conditions.
- Depressing the "HI" button with "SNAPSHOT?" displayed will again display "SNAPSHOT TAKEN" message to indicate that new information has been stored in memory. Access to this information is obtained the same as previously described.

NOTE: **Operating vehicle in "DIAGNOSTIC (SERVICE) MODE" for extended time periods without engine running or without a battery charger will cause battery to run down and possibly related false diagnostic information, or cause a no start condition. To ensure proper operation, attach a battery charger if vehicle is to be operated in "DIAGNOSTIC (SERVICE) MODE" without engine running for periods longer than 1/2 hour.**

Status Light Display (DeVille & Fleetwood)

While in diagnostic mode, the lights on the CCP control head function buttons indicate status of various operating modes. The different modes of operation are indicated by the light being either on or off. Lights and the mode they represent are as follows:

"AUTO" BUTTON – This light is illuminated when ECM is operating in "closed loop" fuel control mode. This light should come on when the coolant temperature and oxygen sensors reach operating temperature.

"ECON" BUTTON – This light is illuminated when oxygen sensor indicates a rich exhaust mixture (not enough oxygen). The light will be off when the signal indicates a lean mixture (too much oxygen). It should flicker on and off during warm steady throttle operation to verify that the oxygen sensor is providing signals to the ECM and that the ECM is in closed loop operation.

"OFF" BUTTON – This light will be on when ECM senses that throttle switch (part of TPS) is closed. This light should be off whenever throttle is applied.

"FRONT DEFOG" – This light is illuminated whenever ECM is commanding VCC to engage. This indicator only signals that VCC is enabled or disabled by ECM. Actual operation depends on integrity of VCC system.

"REAR DEFOG" – This light indicates when ECM senses that 4th gear pressure switch is open. Light should only be on during actual 4th gear operation.

"OUTSIDE TEMP" – This light is illuminated whenever the BCM is commanding the A/C compressor clutch to engage. This light only indicates whether clutch is enabled or disabled by BCM. Actual operation depends on integrity of compressor clutch system.

"AUTO FAN" – This light is turned on whenever feedback signal from cooling fans control module to BCM indicates that fans are running. Light should be off when fans are off.

"HI FAN" – This light is illuminated whenever BCM is commanding "UP-DOWN" mode door to divert airflow up away from the heater outlet. This light will be off whenever climate control system is in "heater" or "normal purge" modes.

"LO FAN" – This light is illuminated whenever BCM is commanding "A/C-DEF" mode door to divert airflow to A/C outlets as in "A/C" or "normal purge" modes. This light will be off whenever climate control system is in "heater", "intermediate", "defrost", and "cold purge" modes.

"°F" – This light is illuminated whenever BCM senses that A/C refrigerant low pressure switch is open. This light is illuminated when ambient temperature falls below about -5°F (-21°C) due to pressure-temperature relationship of R-12 refrigerant. This light should remain off under all conditions if refrigerant system is fully charged and being controlled properly.

"°C" – This light is illuminated whenever BCM is commanding heater water valve to block coolant flow through heater core. This light should remain off except when air mix door is being commanded to the "Max A/C" position (0%).

Status Light Display (Eldorado & Seville)

While in diagnostic service mode, the mode indicators on CCP of CCDIC are used to indicate status of certain operating modes. The differenct modes of operation are indicated by status light being turned on or turned off. Lights and the mode they represent are as follows:

"OFF" BUTTON – This status indicator is turned on whenever the ECM is commanding the VCC to engage. The light only indicates whether the VCC is enabled or disabled by ECM. Actual operation depends on integrity of VCC system.

"AUTO" BUTTON – This status indicator is turned on whenever ECM is operating in "closed loop" fuel control. This light should come on after coolant and oxygen sensors have reached normal operating temperatures.

"ECON" BUTTON – This status indicator is turned on whenever oxygen sensor signal to ECM indicates a "rich" exhaust condition. This light should switch between "rich" and "lean" (flashing on and off) during warm steady throttle operation.

"°C" – This status indicator is turned on whenever ECM senses that 3rd gear pressure switch is open. The light should be on while in 3rd gear operation.

"°F" – This status indicator is turned on whenever ECM senses that 3rd and 4th gear pressure switches are open. The light should be on while in 4th gear operation and ECM had received a 3rd gear input signal.

"°E" – This status indicator is turned on whenever ECM senses that 4th gear pressure switch is open, but not 3rd gear switch. This light should be on while in 4th gear operation and ECM had not received a 3rd gear input signal.

"FRONT DEFOG" – The status indicator is turned on whenever BCM is commanding ECC compressor clutch to engage. The light indicates whether clutch is enabled or disabled by BCM. Actual operation depends on integrity of compressor clutch system.

GENERAL MOTORS VISCOUS CONVERTER CLUTCH (Cont.)

"REAR DEFOG" - The status indicator is turned on whenever BCM senses that low refrigerant pressure switch is open. The light should remain off if refrigerant system is fully charged and being properly controlled. However, when ambient temperature drops below approximately -5°F (-21°C), the light will come on due to pressure/temperature relationship of refrigerant.

"LO FAN" - This status indicator is turned on whenever BCM is commanding A/C-DEF mode door to divert air-flow to A/C outlets (as in A/C or normal purge modes). This light will be off whenever ECC system is in "heater", "intermediate", "defrost" and "cold purge" modes.

"NORM FAN" - This status indicator is turned on whenever BCM is commanding heater water valve to block coolant flow through heater core. The light should remain off except when air-mixture door is being commanded to "Max A/C" position (0%).

"HI FAN" - This status indicator is turned on whenever BCM is commanding the "UP-DOWN" mode door to divert air-flow up and away from heater outlet. This light will be off whenever ECC system is in "heater" or "normal purge" mode.

Exiting Diagnostic Mode (DeVille & Fleetwood)

The cycle of trouble code displays may be exited at any time. To do so, simply press the "AUTO" CCP function key. Diagnostics may also be exited by turning ignition switch to "OFF" position for 10 seconds. Either method will take CCP panel out of diagnostic mode, but will not clear any trouble codes. Original temperature setting should appear on CCP panel.

Exiting Diagnostic Mode (Eldorado & Seville)

To exit diagnostic service mode, depress "Reset/Recall" button on DIC or turn ignition off. However, trouble codes are not erased when this is done. The temperature setting will reappear in display panel.

Clearing Trouble Codes (DeVille & Fleetwood)

After system is diagnosed and repaired, all stored trouble codes may be cleared from ECM/BCM memory. To clear ECM codes, enter diagnostic mode and depress "OFF" and "HI" buttons on CCP panel at the same time. Hold buttons until "E.0.0" appears. To clear BCM codes, enter diagnostic mode and depress "OFF" and "LO" buttons on CCP panel at the same time. Hold buttons until "F.0.0" appears. After "E.0.0" or "F.0.0" is displayed, code ".7.0" should appear. With code ".7.0" displayed, turn ignition off for at least 10 seconds before re-entering the diagnostic mode.

Clearing Trouble Codes (Eldorado & Seville)

Selection of "CLEAR CODES?" test type will result in the message "CODES CLEAR" being displayed along with selected system name. This message will appear for 3 seconds to indicate that all stored trouble codes have been erased from that system's memory. After 3 seconds the display will automatically return to next available test type for selected system.

INTERMITTENT FAILURE TEST PROCEDURES

Procedures (DeVille & Fleetwood)

When diagnosis of all hard codes is completed, or if no hard codes were stored, the following test procedres should be used to diagnose intermittent failures. At the end of the dagnostic cycle, code ".7.0" will appear on the ECC/FDC display panel. With this code displayed, the test procedure needed to isolate a specific intermittent failure can be chosen.

Procedures (Eldorado & Seville)

Selection of "DATA?", "INPUTS?", "OUTPUTS?", or "OVERRIDE?" test types will result in first available test being displayed. If dashes ever appear, this test is not allowed with engine running. The 4 characters of the display will contain a test code to identify selection. The first 2 characters are letters which identify system and test type. The last 2 characters numerically identify the test. While selecting a specific test, any of the following actions may be taken to control display.

Switch Test Procedure (DeVille & Fleetwood)

1) With engine running, enter diagnostics. With code ".7.0" displayed on FDC, depress and release brake pedal. This will start switch test procedure and code "E.7.1" will be displayed. If code "E.7.1" is NOT displayed, refer to "Trouble Code E.7.1" diagnostic chart.

NOTE: **Each test action must be performed within 10 seconds after codes appear on display panel or ECM will store code as failure and proceed to next code.**

2) With code "E.7.1" displayed, depress and release brake pedal again. Code "E.7.2" should appear. With code "E.7.2" displayed, depress throttle to wide open position and slowly release. This checks throttle switch for proper operation. Code "E.7.4" should appear.

3) With code "E.7.4" displayed, shift transmission to "R" and back to "N". This checks operation of the Park/Neutral switch. Code "E.7.5" should appear. With code "E.7.5" displayed, switch cruise control instrument panel switch on then off. This checks operation of the cruise control switch. Code "E.7.6" should appear.

4) With code "E.7.6" displayed, switch cruise control instrument panel switch on, then depress and release "Set/Coast" button. This checks operation of the "Set/Coast" switch. Code "E.7.7" should appear. With code "E.7.7" displayed, switch cruise control instrument panel switch on, then depress and release "Resume/Acceleration" switch. This checks operation of the "Resume/Acceleration" switch. Code "E.7.8" should appear.

NOTE: **To pass codes "E.7.5", "E.7.6" and "E.7.7" on vehicles without cruise control, allow codes to appear for 10 seconds each, then proceed with step 5). Codes will cycle through ECM and be processed as failures.**

5) With code "E.7.8" displayed, turn wheels from straight ahead to either full right or full left and then return to straight ahead position. This checks the power steering pressure switch for proper operation.

6) When switch tests are completed, FDC will display codes which did not pass test. Each code will appear beginning with lowest code. Codes will not disappear until affected switch circuit is repaired and retested.

NOTE: **Refer to appropriate diagnostic chart for affected system**

7) After switch tests are completed and all circuits passed, FDC will display code "E.0.0" and returns to code ".7.0". Code "E.0.0" indicates all switch circuits are operating properly. Remember that "E.0.0" will never be obtained on vehicles without cruise control.

Engine Data Display Procedure (DeVille & Fleetwood)

1) Enter diagnostics and with code ".7.0" displayed on FDC, depress and release "LO" button on CCP. Code "E.9.0" should appear. It is possible to leave data series at any time and return to code ".7.0" by clearing ECM/BCM codes.

2) To advance display, depress "HI" button on CCP. To return to a lower numbered parameter or jump directly from "E.9.0" to end of parameter list ("P.1.3"), depress "LO" button on CCP.

3) Parameter numbers "P.0.1-P.1.3" will be displayed for 1 second on FDC, followed by numerical value. The parameter value will be displayed for 9 seconds. Each parameter and value will be repeated until manually advanced to next parameter.

4) When trouble shooting a malfunction, ECM data display can be used to compare vehicle with a vehicle that is functioning properly. A summary of parameters with ranges and display units is contained in the ENGINE DATA PARAMETERS table.

ENGINE DATA PARAMETERS (DEVILLE & FLEETWOOD)

Display	Parameter	Range
P.0.1	TPS	-10-90°
P.0.2	MAP	14-109 kPa
P.0.3	BARO	61-103 kPa
P.0.4	Coolant Temp.	-40-151°C
P.0.5	MAT	-40-151°C
P.0.6	Injector Pulse	0-99.9 ms
P.0.7	Oxygen Sensor	0-1.14 volts
P.0.8	Spark Advance	0-52°
P.0.9	Ignition Cycles	0-50
P.1.0	Battery Volts	0-25.5 volts
P.1.1	Engine RPM	[1] 0-6370
P.1.2	Vehicle Speed	0-25 MPH
P.1.3	Cross Counts	0-255
P.1.4	Fuel Integrator	0-255
P.1.5	VCC Volts	0-5.1 volts
P.1.6	ECM PROM I.D.	[2]

[1] – RPM reading on FDC is 10 of actual RPM.
[2] – Displayed as a number up to three digits long.

Engine Data Display Procedure (Eldorado & Seville)

1) Depressing the "OFF" button on CCP will stop test selection process and return display to next available test type for selected system.

2) Depressing the "LO" button on CCP will display next smaller test number for selected test type. If this button is pressed with lowest test number displayed, the highest test number will then appear.

3) Depressing the "HI" button on CCP will display next larger test number for the selected test type. If this button is pressed with highest test number displayed, the lowest test number will then appear.

ENGINE DATA PARAMETERS (ELDORADO & SEVILLE)

Display	Parameter	Range
ED01	TPS	-10-90°
ED02	MAP	14-109 kPa
ED03	BARO	61-103 kPa
ED04	Coolant Temp.	-40-151°C
ED05	MAT	-40-151°C
ED06	Injector Pulse	0-99.9 ms
ED07	Oxygen Sensor	0-1.14 volts
ED08	Spark Advance	-30-60°
ED10	Battery Volts	0-25.5 volts
ED11	Engine RPM	[1] 0-6370
ED12	Vehicle Speed	0-25 MPH
ED18	0_2 Cross Counts	0-255
ED19	Fuel Integrator	0-255
ED26	VCC Volts	0-5.1 volts
ED98	Ignition Cycles	0-50
ED99	ECM PROM I.D.	[2] 0-999

[1] – RPM reading on FDC is 10 of actual RPM.
[2] – Displayed as a number up to three digits long.

ADJUSTMENTS

BRAKE SWITCH

1) Remove wiring connector from switch. Depress brake pedal. Push brake switch into retainer until body seats on retainer.

2) Pull brake switch rearward until audible clicking of switch can no longer be heard.

3) Release brake pedal and repeat step **2)** to ensure proper adjustment. Reconnect wiring connector.

TPS POSITION

1) Open throttle valve and close it against throttle stop screw. Turn ignition on. Back probe TPS connector terminals "B" and "C" using a voltmeter. This is the reference voltage. Record reference voltage.

2) Connect digital voltmeter, set on 2-volt scale, to TPS connector. Back probe positive test lead to TPS connector terminal "A". Connect negative test lead to TPS connector terminal "B". *See Fig. 8*.

3) Ensure throttle is against throttle stop screw. Check TPS voltage. If voltage is .45-.55 volts, TPS position is okay. If voltage is not within specification, loosen TPS mounting screws just enough to permit sensor adjustment.

4) Open and close throttle. Allow throttle to snap close against against minimum air screw. Adjust TPS so that voltage reading is .5 volts. Tighten TPS mounting screws. Recheck voltage reading to ensure TPS voltage did not change. Readjust TPS as necessary.

GENERAL MOTORS VISCOUS CONVERTER CLUTCH (Cont.)

Fig. 4: DeVille & Fleetwood ECM/BCM Diagnostic Chart

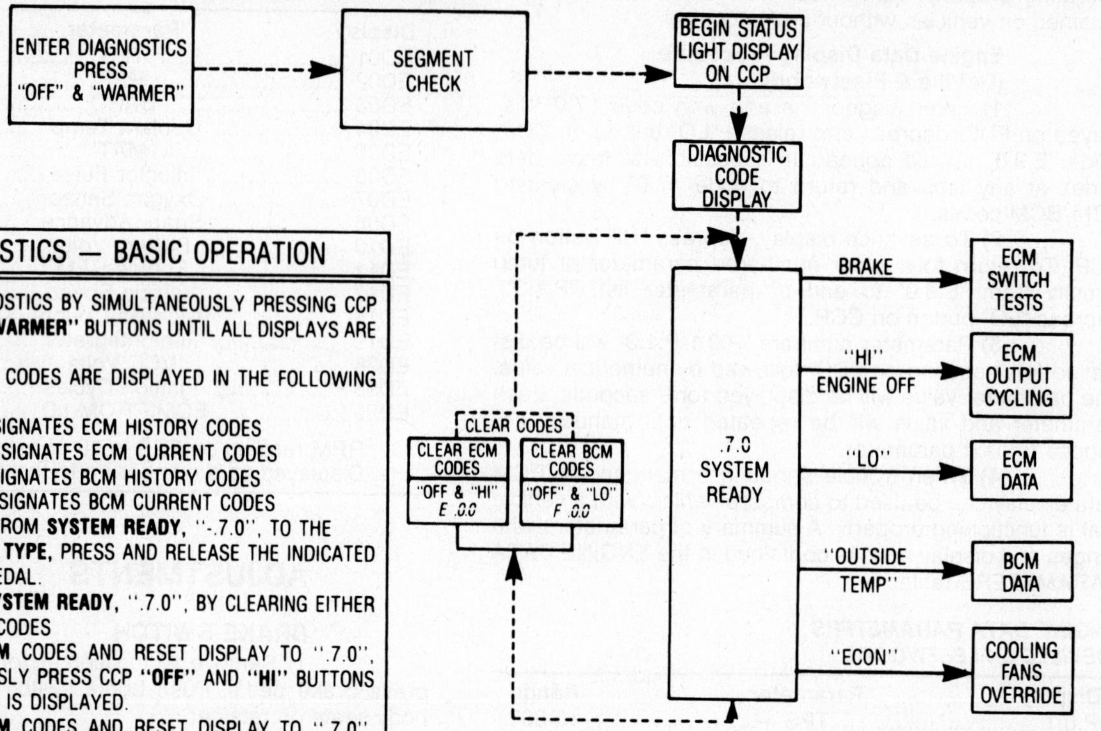

DIAGNOSTICS — BASIC OPERATION

- ENTER DIAGNOSTICS BY SIMULTANEOUSLY PRESSING CCP **"OFF"** AND **"WARMER"** BUTTONS UNTIL ALL DISPLAYS ARE LIT.
- MALFUNCTION CODES ARE DISPLAYED IN THE FOLLOWING SEQUENCE:
  - ..E—DESIGNATES ECM HISTORY CODES
  - .E.E—DESIGNATES ECM CURRENT CODES
  - ..F—DESIGNATES BCM HISTORY CODES
  - .F.F—DESIGNATES BCM CURRENT CODES
- TO PROCEED FROM **SYSTEM READY**, "-.7.0", TO THE DESIRED **TEST TYPE**, PRESS AND RELEASE THE INDICATED BUTTON OR PEDAL.
- RETURN TO **SYSTEM READY**, ".7.0", BY CLEARING EITHER ECM OR BCM CODES
- TO CLEAR **ECM** CODES AND RESET DISPLAY TO ".7.0", SIMULTANEOUSLY PRESS CCP **"OFF"** AND **"HI"** BUTTONS UNTIL "E.0.0" IS DISPLAYED.
- TO CLEAR **BCM** CODES AND RESET DISPLAY TO ".7.0", SIMULTANEOUSLY PRESS CCP **"OFF"** AND **"LO"** BUTTONS UNTIL "F.0.0" IS DISPLAYED.
- EXIT DIAGNOSTICS BY PRESSING **"AUTO"** BUTTON.

STATUS LIGHTS

ECM STATUS LIGHT DISPLAY						
LIGHT ON	IN 4TH GEAR	VCC ENABLED	CLOSED THROTTLE	RICH	CLOSED LOOP
LIGHT OFF	NOT IN 4TH GEAR	VCC DISABLED	OPEN THROTTLE	LEAN	OPEN LOOP
INDICATOR	(defrost symbol)	(defrost symbol)	OFF	ECON	AUTO
FUNCTION	4TH GEAR INPUT	VCC OUTPUT	THROTTLE SWITCH INPUT	OXYGEN SENSOR INPUT	ECM OPERATING MODE

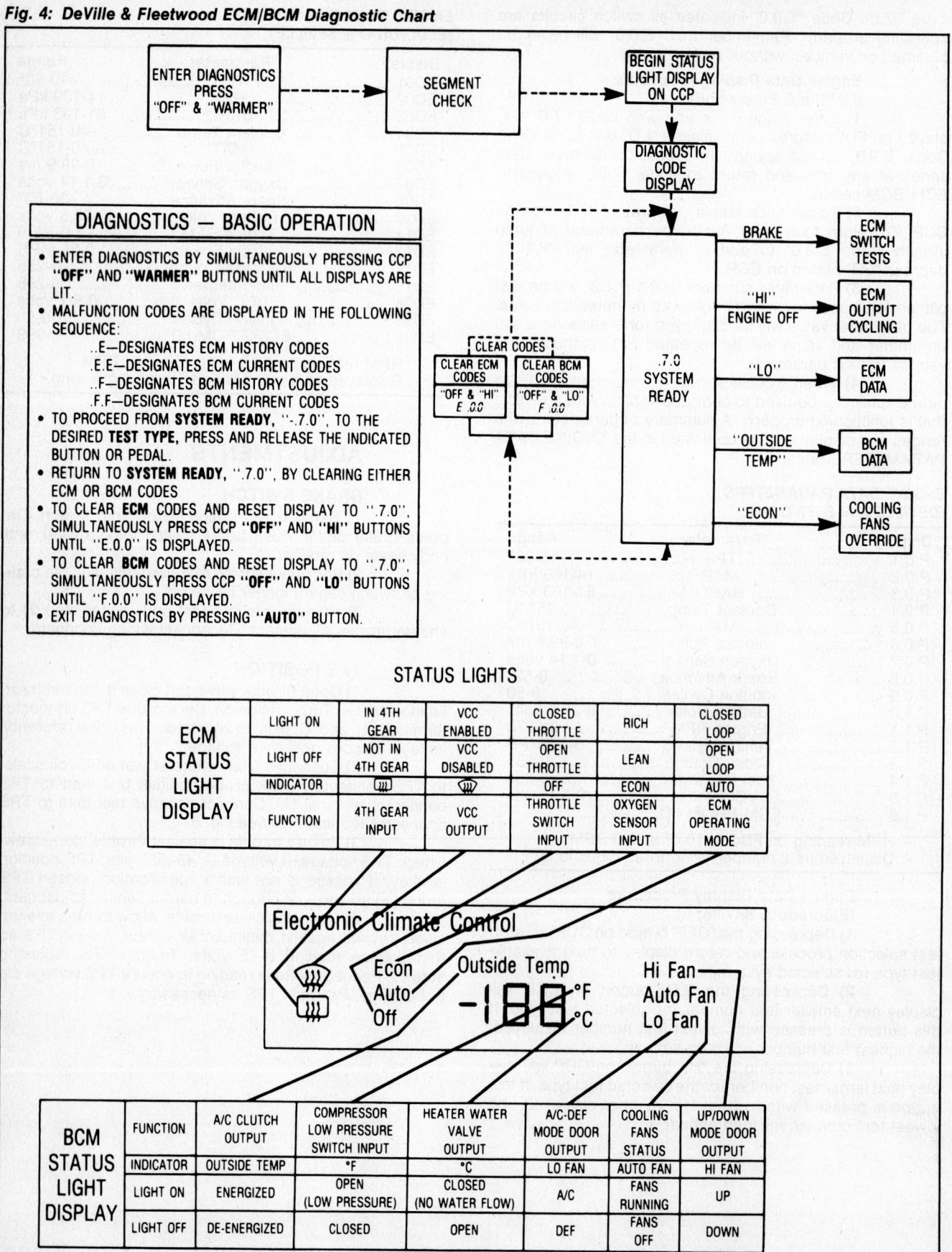

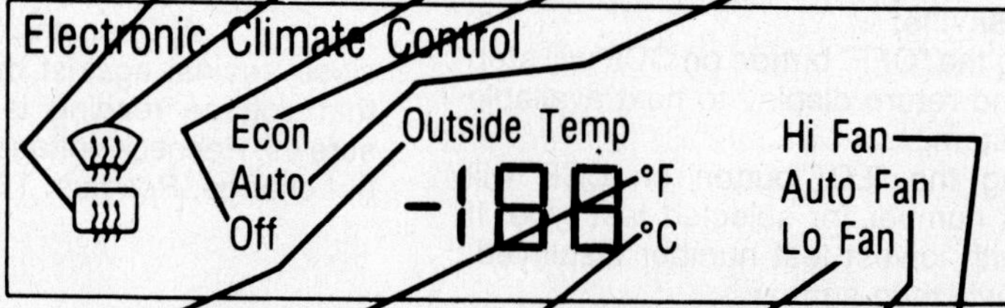

BCM STATUS LIGHT DISPLAY							
FUNCTION	A/C CLUTCH OUTPUT	COMPRESSOR LOW PRESSURE SWITCH INPUT	HEATER WATER VALVE OUTPUT	A/C-DEF MODE DOOR OUTPUT	COOLING FANS STATUS	UP/DOWN MODE DOOR OUTPUT
INDICATOR	OUTSIDE TEMP	°F	°C	LO FAN	AUTO FAN	HI FAN
LIGHT ON	ENERGIZED	OPEN (LOW PRESSURE)	CLOSED (NO WATER FLOW)	A/C	FANS RUNNING	UP
LIGHT OFF	DE-ENERGIZED	CLOSED	OPEN	DEF	FANS OFF	DOWN

GENERAL MOTORS VISCOUS CONVERTER CLUTCH (Cont.)

Fig. 5: DeVille & Fleetwood ECM Diagnostic Chart

ECM SWITCH TESTS	
DIAGNOSTIC DISPLAY	CIRCUIT TEST
E.7.1	Brake Switch
E.7.2	Throttle Switch
E.7.4	Park/Neutral Switch
E.7.5	Cruise "ON-OFF"
E.7.6	Cruise "SET/COAST" †
E.7.7	Cruise "RESUME/ACCEL." †
E.7.8	Power Steering Pressure Switch (Engine Running)

† Switch Cruise "ON" Before Testing

ECM OUTPUT CYCLING
"COOLANT TEMP FAN" Light
"SERVICE ELECTRICAL SYSTEM" Light
Air Switch Solenoid
Air Divert Solenoid
ISC Motor
Cruise Vacuum Solenoid & Engage Light*
Cruise Power Solenoid*
Canister Purge Solenoid
EGR Solenoid
VCC Solenoid
EFE Relay

**To Activate These Outputs, The Following Must Occur:*

A) Engine Running
B) Cruise Switch "ON"
C) Key OFF And ON Within 2 Seconds Prior To Entering Diagnostics.

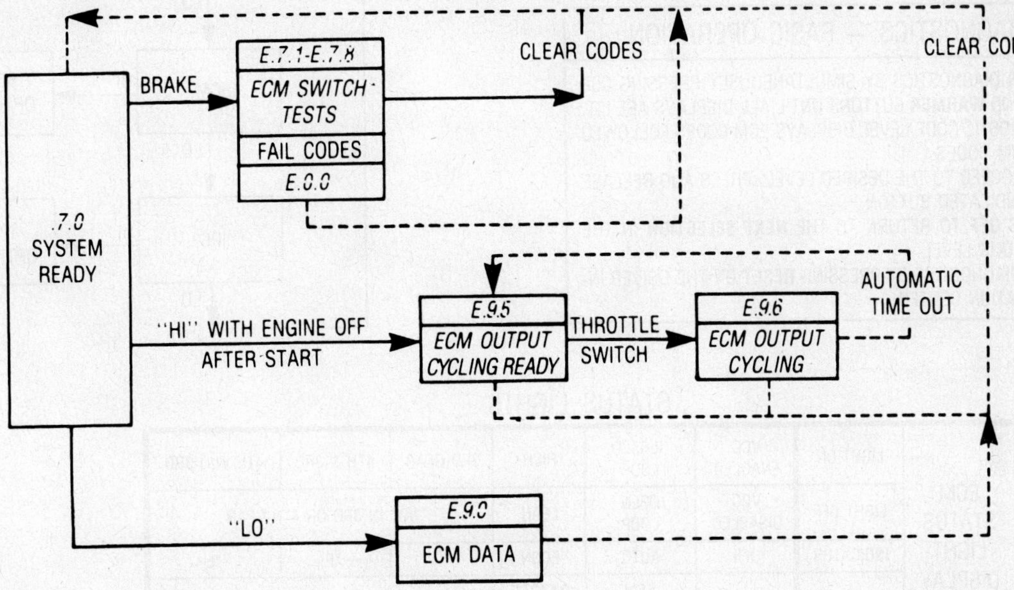

KEY
To Select Another Test Press: "HI" — To Increment "LO" — To Decrement
ECM DATA P.1.6 "LO" ↓ ↑ "HI" P.0.1

ECM DATA			
PARAMETER NUMBER	PARAMETER	DISPLAY RANGE	DISPLAY UNITS
P.0.1	Throttle Position	– 10.0 - 90.0	Degrees
P.0.2	MAP	14 - 109	kPa
P.0.3	Computed BARO	61 - 103	kPa
P.0.4	Coolant Temperature	– 40 - 151	°C
P.0.5	MAT	– 40 - 151	°C
P.0.6	Injector Pulse Width	0 - 99.9	ms
P.0.7	Oxygen Sensor Voltage	0 - 1.14	Volts
P.0.8	Spark Advance	– 30 - 60	Degrees
P.0.9	Ignition Cycle Counter	0 - 50	Key Cycles
P.1.0	Battery Voltage	0 - 25.5	Volts
P.1.1	Engine RPM	0 - 6370	RPM ÷ 10
P.1.2	Car Speed	0 - 255	MPH
P.1.3	Oxygen Sensor Cross Cts.	0 - 255	Number
P.1.4	Fuel Integrator	0 - 255	Counts
P.1.5	VCC Volts	0 - 5.12	Volts
P.1.6	ECM PROM ID	0 - 999	Code •

FIXED SPARK
Exit Diagnostics And Connect Pins A&B Of ALDL Test Connector. Vehicle Will Be In Fixed Spark Mode If At Curb Idle With Transmission In Park.

• PROM ID
PROM ID Code Number Identifies An Individual Calibration And Is Periodically Updated; Refer To Latest Service Publication For Correct ID Number.

GENERAL MOTORS VISCOUS CONVERTER CLUTCH (Cont.)

Fig. 6: Eldorado & Seville ECM/BCM Diagnostic Chart

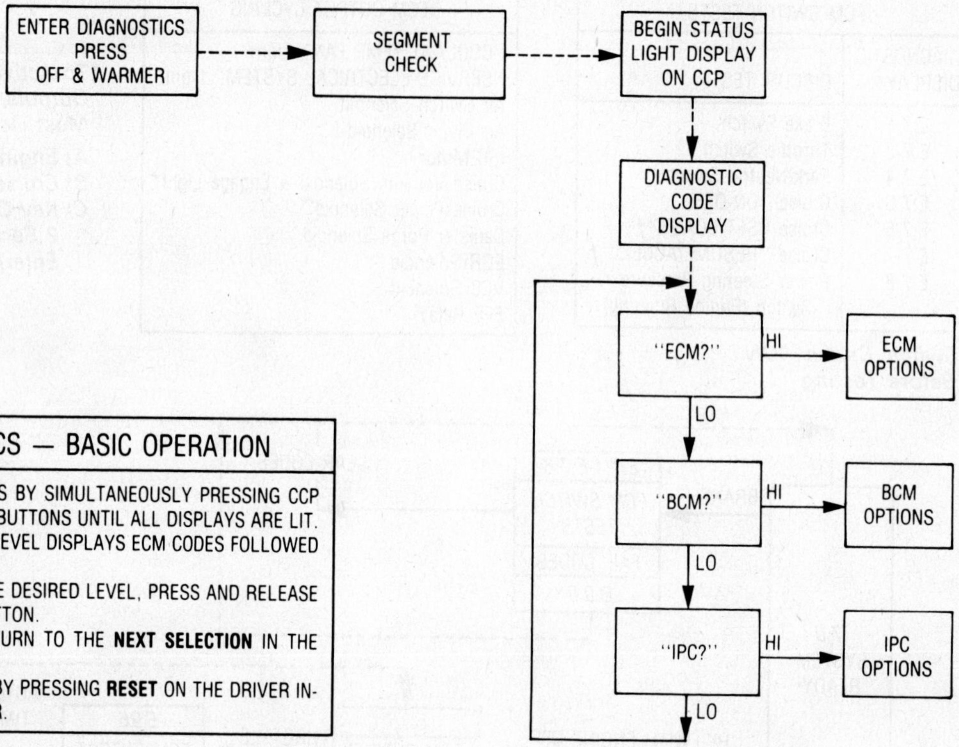

DIAGNOSTICS — BASIC OPERATION

- ENTER DIAGNOSTICS BY SIMULTANEOUSLY PRESSING CCP **OFF** AND **WARMER** BUTTONS UNTIL ALL DISPLAYS ARE LIT.
- DIAGNOSTIC CODE LEVEL DISPLAYS ECM CODES FOLLOWED BY BCM CODES.
- TO PROCEED TO THE DESIRED LEVEL, PRESS AND RELEASE THE INDICATED BUTTON.
- PRESS **OFF** TO RETURN TO THE **NEXT SELECTION** IN THE **PREVIOUS** LEVEL.
- EXIT DIAGNOSTICS BY PRESSING **RESET** ON THE DRIVER INFORMATION CENTER.

STATUS LIGHTS

ECM STATUS LIGHT DISPLAY							
LIGHT ON	VCC ENABLED	CLOSED LOOP	RICH	3RD GEAR	4TH & 3RD	4TH W/O 3RD
LIGHT OFF	VCC DISABLED	OPEN LOOP	LEAN	NOT IN 3RD OR 4TH GEAR		
INDICATOR	OFF	AUTO	ECON	°C	°F	°E
FUNCTION	**VCC OUTPUT**	**ECM OPERATING MODE**	**OXYGEN SENSOR INPUT**	**4TH & 3RD GEAR INPUT**		

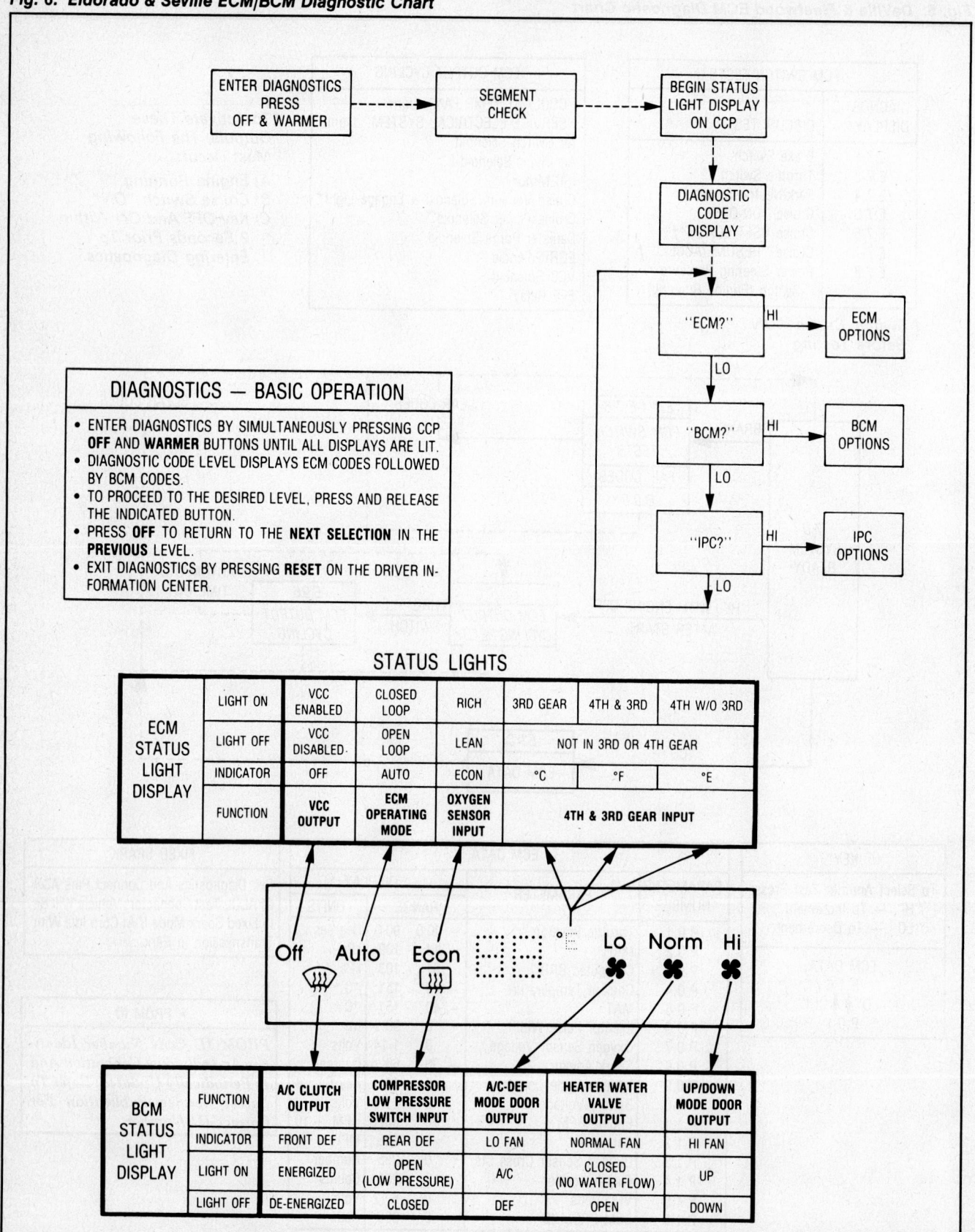

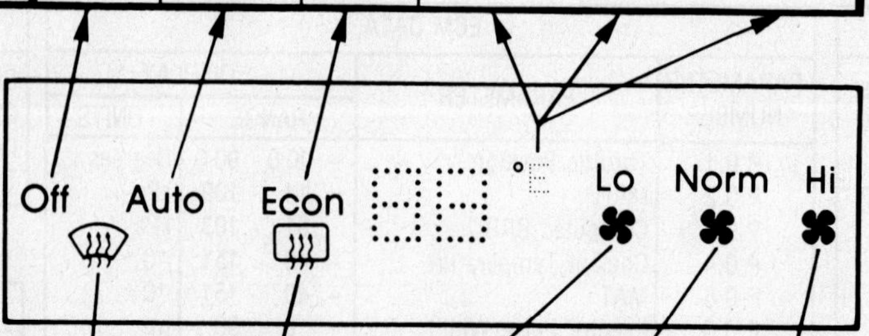

BCM STATUS LIGHT DISPLAY					
FUNCTION	**A/C CLUTCH OUTPUT**	**COMPRESSOR LOW PRESSURE SWITCH INPUT**	**A/C-DEF MODE DOOR OUTPUT**	**HEATER WATER VALVE OUTPUT**	**UP/DOWN MODE DOOR OUTPUT**
INDICATOR	FRONT DEF	REAR DEF	LO FAN	NORMAL FAN	HI FAN
LIGHT ON	ENERGIZED	OPEN (LOW PRESSURE)	A/C	CLOSED (NO WATER FLOW)	UP
LIGHT OFF	DE-ENERGIZED	CLOSED	DEF	OPEN	DOWN

GENERAL MOTORS VISCOUS CONVERTER CLUTCH (Cont.)

Fig. 7: Eldorado & Seville ECM Diagnostic Chart

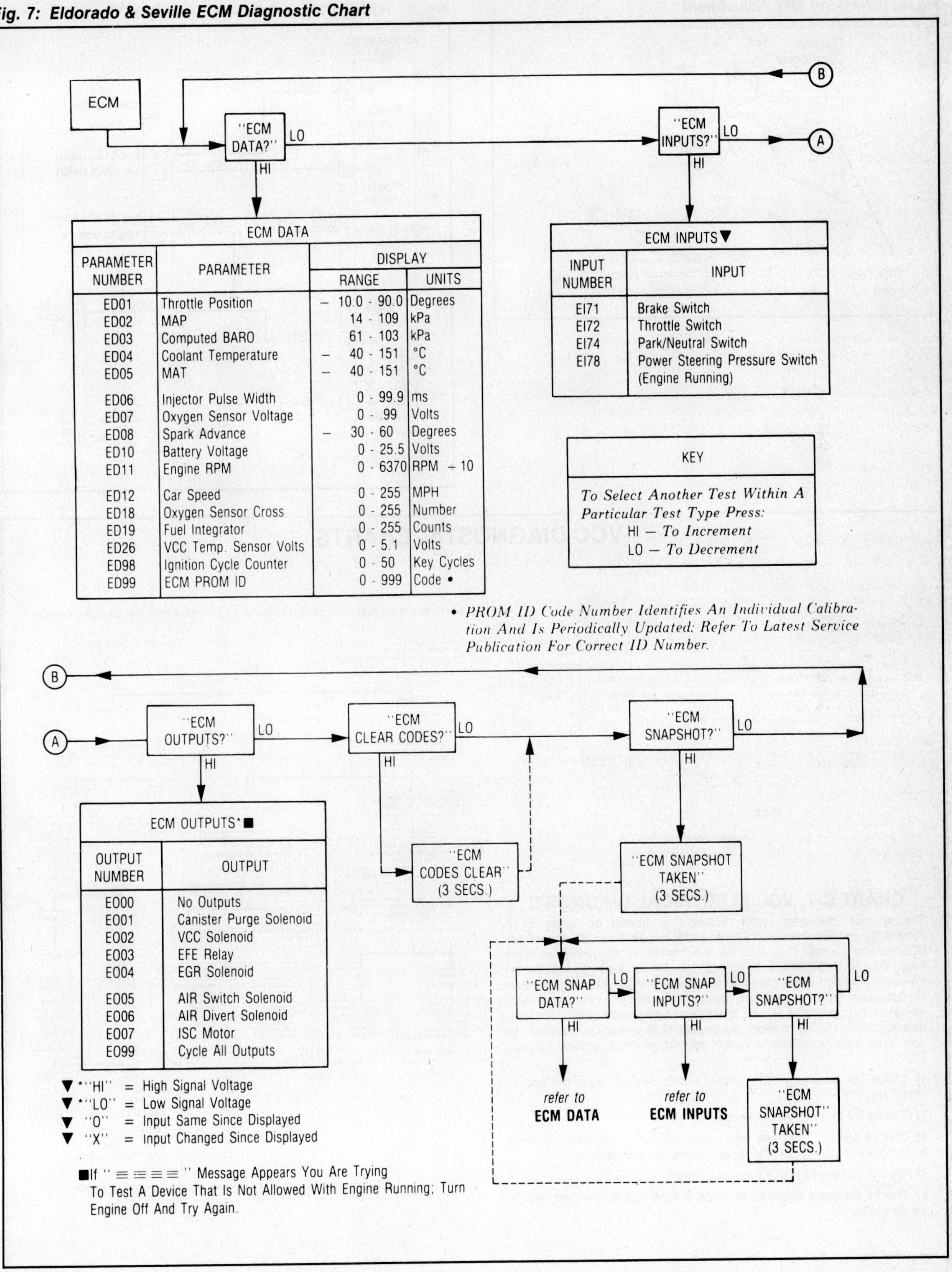

ECM DATA

PARAMETER NUMBER	PARAMETER	DISPLAY RANGE	DISPLAY UNITS
ED01	Throttle Position	– 10.0 - 90.0	Degrees
ED02	MAP	14 - 109	kPa
ED03	Computed BARO	61 - 103	kPa
ED04	Coolant Temperature	– 40 - 151	°C
ED05	MAT	– 40 - 151	°C
ED06	Injector Pulse Width	0 - 99.9	ms
ED07	Oxygen Sensor Voltage	0 - .99	Volts
ED08	Spark Advance	– 30 - 60	Degrees
ED10	Battery Voltage	0 - 25.5	Volts
ED11	Engine RPM	0 - 6370	RPM ÷ 10
ED12	Car Speed	0 - 255	MPH
ED18	Oxygen Sensor Cross	0 - 255	Number
ED19	Fuel Integrator	0 - 255	Counts
ED26	VCC Temp. Sensor Volts	0 - 5.1	Volts
ED98	Ignition Cycle Counter	0 - 50	Key Cycles
ED99	ECM PROM ID	0 - 999	Code •

ECM INPUTS▼

INPUT NUMBER	INPUT
EI71	Brake Switch
EI72	Throttle Switch
EI74	Park/Neutral Switch
EI78	Power Steering Pressure Switch (Engine Running)

KEY

To Select Another Test Within A Particular Test Type Press:
HI — *To Increment*
LO — *To Decrement*

• *PROM ID Code Number Identifies An Individual Calibration And Is Periodically Updated; Refer To Latest Service Publication For Correct ID Number.*

ECM OUTPUTS*■

OUTPUT NUMBER	OUTPUT
E000	No Outputs
E001	Canister Purge Solenoid
E002	VCC Solenoid
E003	EFE Relay
E004	EGR Solenoid
E005	AIR Switch Solenoid
E006	AIR Divert Solenoid
E007	ISC Motor
E099	Cycle All Outputs

▼ *"HI" = High Signal Voltage
▼ *"LO" = Low Signal Voltage
▼ "O" = Input Same Since Displayed
▼ "X" = Input Changed Since Displayed

■If " ≡≡≡≡ " Message Appears You Are Trying To Test A Device That Is Not Allowed With Engine Running; Turn Engine Off And Try Again.

GENERAL MOTORS VISCOUS CONVERTER CLUTCH (Cont.)

Fig. 8: Checking TPS Adjustment

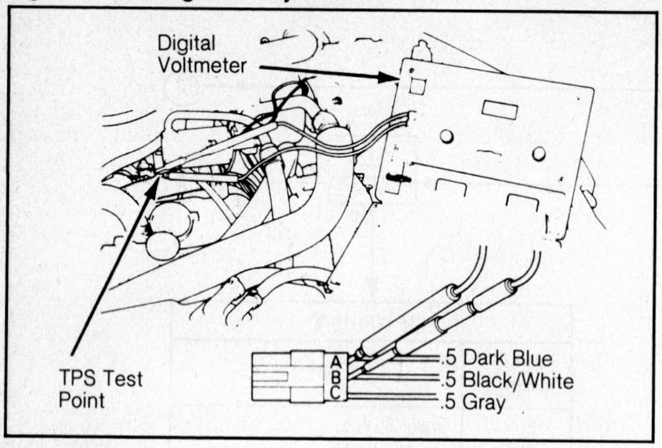

Fig. 9: Wiring Diagram for 440-T4 With VCC

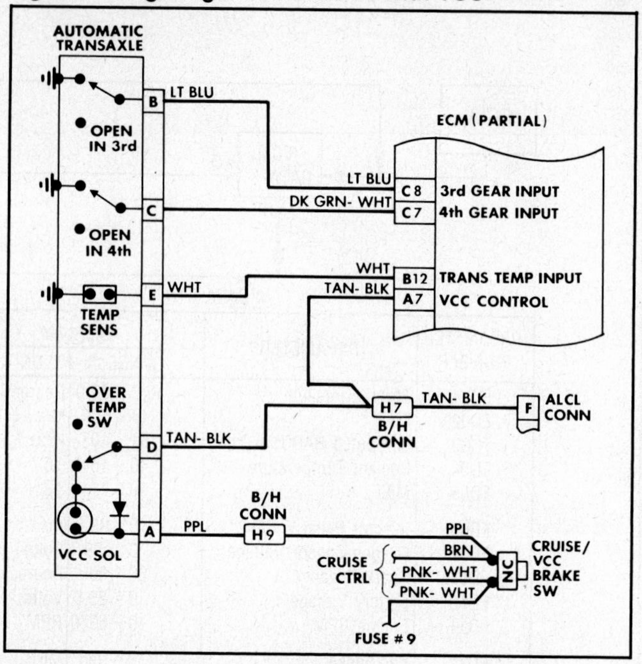

VCC DIAGNOSTIC CHARTS

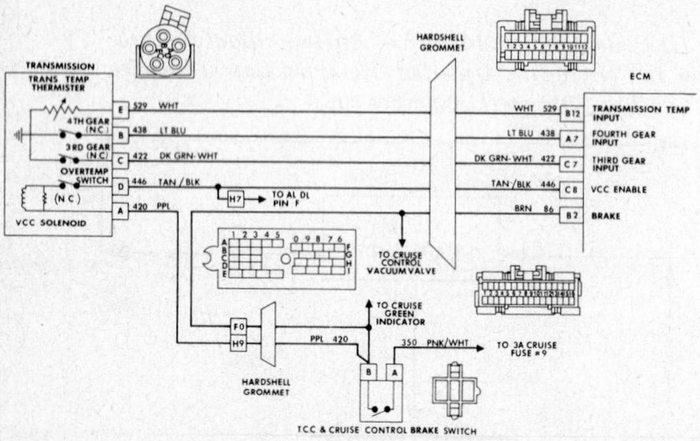

NOTE: THIS PROCEDURE MUST NOT BE FOLLOWED IF A CODE E016, E024, E051 OR E059 IS CURRENT

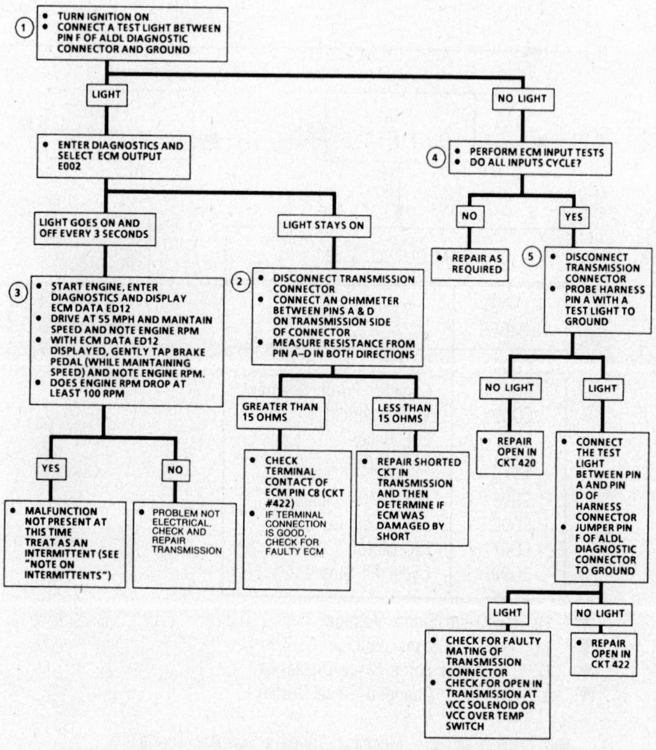

WHEN ALL DIAGNOSIS AND REPAIRS ARE COMPLETED, CLEAR CODES AND VERIFYOPERATION

CHART C-7, VCC ELECTRICAL DIAGNOSIS

The viscous converter clutch solenoid is turned on when ECM completes ground through VCC solenoid circuit No. 422. Power for VCC solenoid comes from fuse No. 9 in fuse block. Current flows from fuse, through VCC brake switch, to pin "A" of 5-pin connector on transaxle. Current then flows into transaxle to VCC solenoid and then to transaxle over-temperature switch. Transaxle over-temperature switch is normally closed and opens when transaxle sump temperature is 315°F (157°C) or more, to disable VCC and allow transaxle to cool. From over-temperature switch, current returns to ground through ECM.

1) Check for continuity from brake switch through solenoid coil to circuit No. 422.

2) Checks for shorted VCC solenoid.

3) Checks for VCC release when solenoid is de-energized. If RPM does not increase, check and repair transaxle as necessary.

4) Checks for proper brake switch operation.

5) Checks for open in circuit No. 422. If light comes on, then fault is inside transaxle.

GENERAL MOTORS VISCOUS CONVERTER CLUTCH (Cont.)

VCC DIAGNOSTIC CHARTS (Cont.)

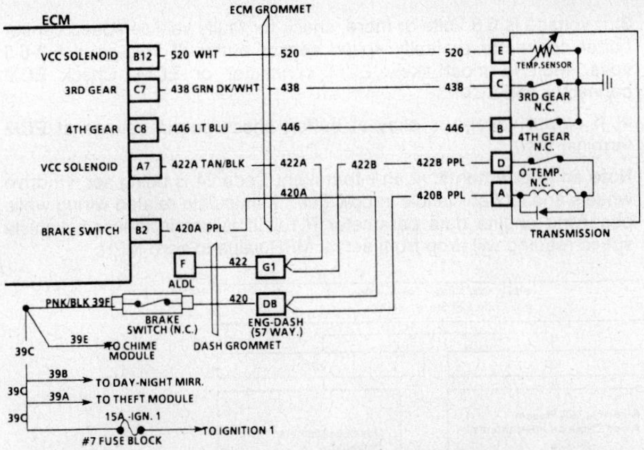

NOTE: THIS PROCEDURE MUST NOT BE FOLLOWED IF A CODE E21, E22 OR E24 IS STORED HARD

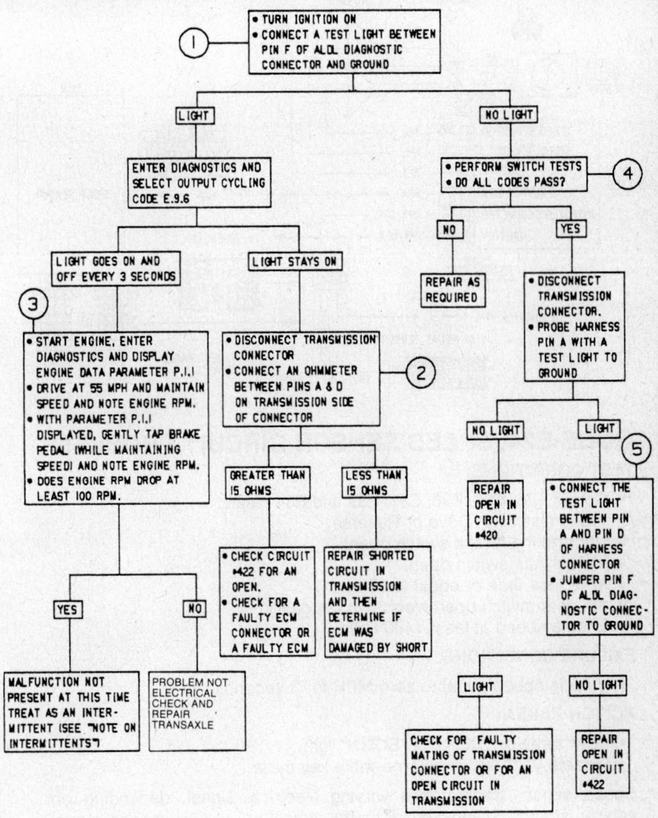

CHART C-8, VCC ELECTRICAL DIAGNOSIS

The viscous converter clutch solenoid is turned on when ECM completes ground through VCC solenoid circuit No. 422. Power for VCC solenoid comes from "IGN. 1" fuse in fuse block. Current flows from fuse, through VCC brake switch, to pin "A" of 5-pin connector on transaxle. Current then flows into transaxle to VCC solenoid and then to transaxle over-temperature switch. Transaxle over-temperature switch is normally closed and opens when transaxle sump temperature is 315°F (157°C) or more, to disable VCC and allow transaxle to cool. From over-temperature switch, current returns to ground through ECM.

1) Check for continuity from brake switch through solenoid coil to circuit No. 422.

2) Checks for shorted VCC solenoid.

3) Checks for VCC release when solenoid is de-energized. If RPM does not increase, check and repair transaxle as necessary.

4) Checks for proper brake switch operation.

5) Checks for open in circuit No. 422. If light comes on, then fault is inside transaxle.

GENERAL MOTORS VISCOUS CONVERTER CLUTCH (Cont.)

VCC DIAGNOSTIC CHARTS (Cont.)

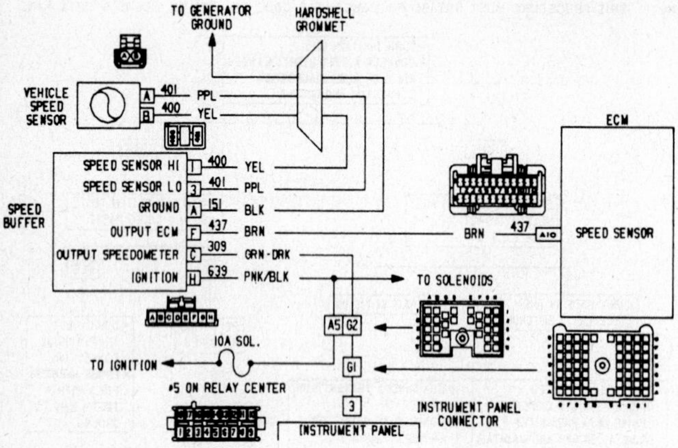

CODE E24, SPEED SENSOR CIRCUIT PROBLEM

TEST CONDITIONS:

- Codes E26, E27, E28, E31, E32 and E34 clear.
- Transmission in Drive or Reverse.
- Not braking (brake switch open).
- ISC throttle switch open.
- MAP less than or equal to 85 kpa.
- 4th gear switch open (vehicle in 4th gear).
- Engine speed at least 1400 RPM.

FAILURE CONDITIONS:

- Vehicle speed equal to zero MPH for 3 seconds.

ACTION TAKEN:

- ECM turns on "SERVICE SOON" light.
- Disable VCC and cruise for entire key cycle.

Speed sensor generates a varying electrical signal, depending on vehicle speed. Speed sensor buffer amplifies and conditions signal from speed sensor to ECM. Code E24 indicates speed sensor signal is not being received by ECM when transaxle is in 4th gear. This can be observed in engine data display as a vehicle speed reading (parameter P.1.2) of zero MPH while driving.

1) Determine if speedometer is operating properly. Repair as necessary.

2) If speedometer is operating properly, determine if speed signal is being received by ECM. This can be observed by noting vehicle speed sensor reading (parameter P.1.2) with drive wheels turning.

3) If voltage is 6.5 volts or more, check for faulty vehicle speed sensor buffer connector or faulty speed sensor buffer. If voltage is 5.0-6.5 volts, fault is most likely ECM connector or ECM. Check ECM connector and ECM.

4) If output voltage is okay at buffer, check output voltage at ECM terminal "A10".

Note on Intermittents: If an intermittent Code 24 is being set, lift drive wheels and let vehicle idle in Low gear. Manipulate related wiring while observing engine data parameter P.1.2. If failure is induced, vehicle speed reading will drop from actual MPH value to zero MPH.

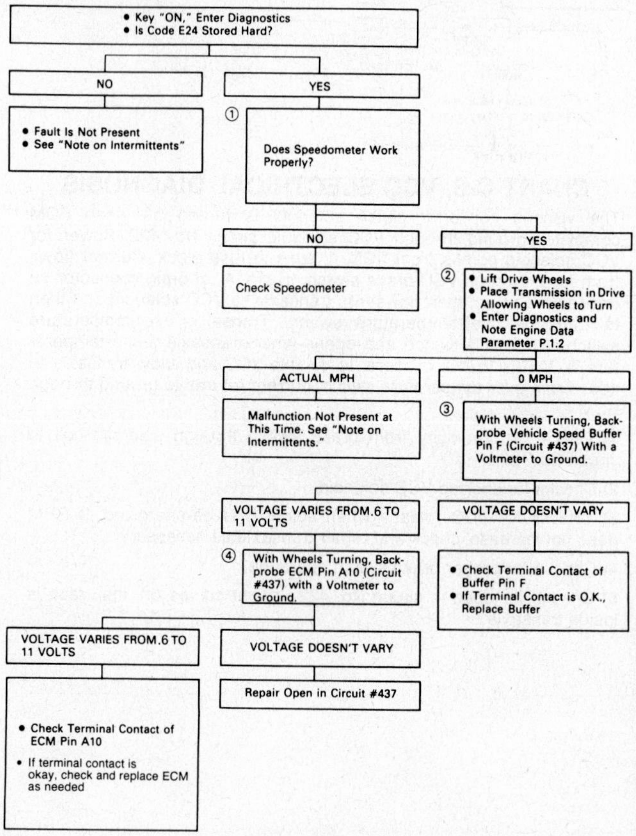

GENERAL MOTORS VISCOUS CONVERTER CLUTCH (Cont.)

VCC DIAGNOSTIC CHARTS (Cont.)

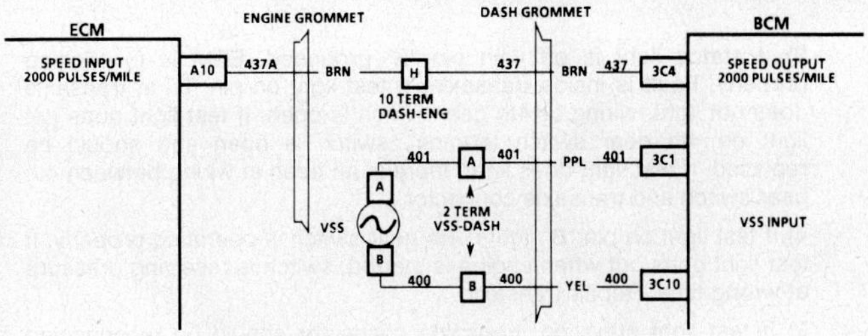

CODE EO24, SPEED SENSOR CIRCUIT PROBLEM

TEST CONDITIONS:

- Codes EO26, EO27, EO28, EO31, EO32 and EO34 clear.
- Transmission in Drive or Reverse.
- Not braking (brake switch open).
- ISC throttle switch open.
- MAP less than or equal to 85 kpa.
- 4th gear switch open (vehicle in 4th gear).
- Engine speed at least 1400 RPM.

FAILURE CONDITIONS:

- Vehicle speed equal to zero MPH for 3 seconds.

ACTION TAKEN:

- ECM turns on "ENGINE CONTROL SYSTEM" light.
- ECM commands BCM to turn on "SERVICE SOON" message.
- Disable VCC and cruise for entire key cycle.
- Use vehicle speed information from BCM on UART as VSS input.

Speed sensor generates an electrical signal of 4000 pulses per mile. BCM receives the signal from vehicle speed sensor, and changes signal to 2000 pulses per mile. BCM sends this modified signal to ECM on circuit No. 437. ECM uses speed sensor input for VCC apply and release determinations, to select between RPM and throttle angle control of ISC. ECM also uses this information as a test condition for many fault codes.

1) Checking for proper voltage from BCM at ECM connector.

2) Checking for voltage sent from BCM.

3) Before replacing ECM or BCM, remove and replace BCM connectors "J1" and "J3". Ensure connectors are latched properly.

Note on Intermittents: Backprobe ECM pin "A10" with a voltmeter. Connect other voltmeter lead to ground. Lift drive wheels and let vehicle idle in Drive. Manipulate related wiring and watch for sudden loss of voltage at ECM terminal "A10".

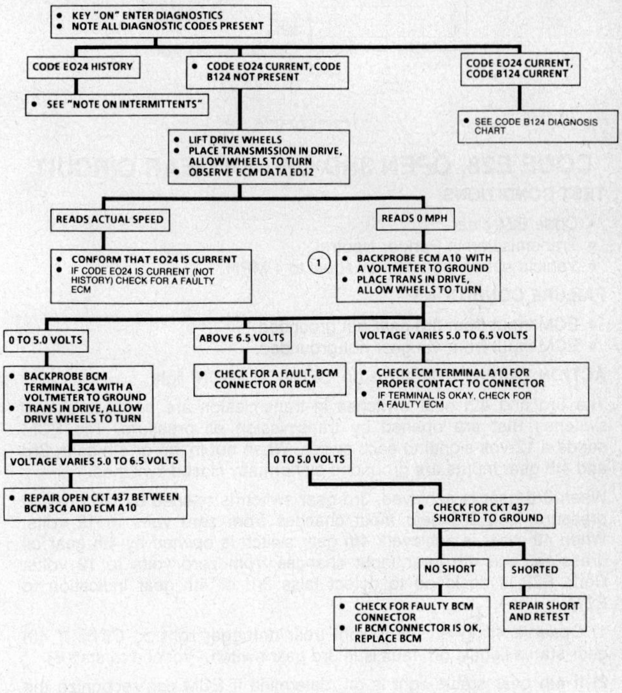

WHEN ALL DIAGNOSIS AND REPAIRS ARE COMPLETED, CLEAR CODES AND VERIFY OPERATION

GENERAL MOTORS VISCOUS CONVERTER CLUTCH (Cont.)

VCC DIAGNOSTIC CHARTS (Cont.)

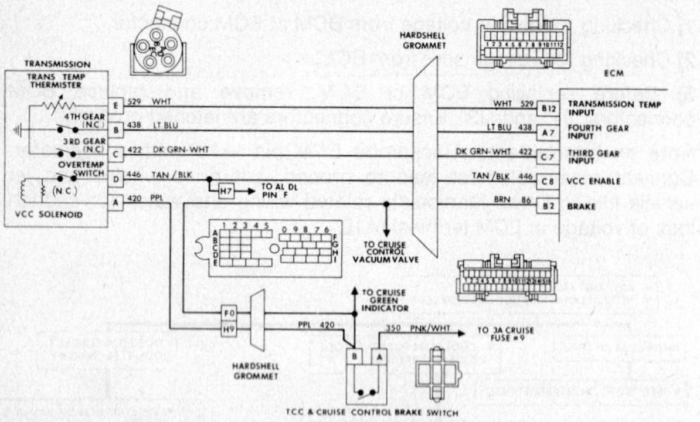

CODE E28, OPEN 3RD OR 4TH GEAR CIRCUIT

TEST CONDITIONS:

- Code E24 clear.
- Transmission in Park or Neutral.
- Vehicle speed less than or equal to 4 MPH.

FAILURE CONDITIONS:

- ECM input from 3rd gear not grounded.
- ECM input from 4th gear not grounded.

ACTION TAKEN: ECM turns on "SERVICE SOON" light.

The 3rd and 4th gear switches in transmission are normally closed switches that are opened by transmission oil pressure. The ECM sends a 12-volt signal to each switch. When not in 3rd or 4th gear, 3rd and 4th gear inputs are grounded by normally closed switches.

When 3rd gear is achieved, 3rd gear switch is opened by 3rd gear oil pressure, and 3rd gear input changes from zero volts to 12 volts. When 4th gear is achieved, 4th gear switch is opened by 4th gear oil pressure, and 4th gear input changes from zero volts to 12 volts. Code E28 is designed to detect false 3rd or 4th gear indication to ECM.

1) Observe 4th gear status light (rear defogger light on CCP). If 4th gear status light is off, fault is in 3rd gear switch. Proceed to step **6)**.

2) If 4th gear status light is on, determine if ECM can recognize the grounding of circuit No. 438 at transmission connector. If 4th gear status light remains on, there is an open in circuit No. 438 or ECM. If light remains on when circuit No. 438 is grounded at ECM, ECM or connector is defective. If light goes off, circuit No. 438 is open.

3) If status light is off with pin "B" grounded, ECM is functioning properly. Fault is inside transaxle. If test light on pin "B" at transaxle does not light, wiring or 4th gear switch is open. If test light does not light on 4th gear switch terminal, switch is open and should be replaced. If test light does light, there is an open in wiring between 4th gear switch and transaxle connector.

4) If test light on pin "B" lights, 4th gear switch is operating properly. If test light goes out when engine is started, switch is receiving pressure at wrong time. Repair transaxle.

5) If test light stays on, transaxle connector should be reconnected and 4th gear status light should be checked for proper operation. If light is on, fault is improper mating of circuit No. 446 terminals at pin "B" of transaxle connector. If light is off, malfunction is not present at this time.

6) If 4th gear status light was off without pin "B" grounded, determine if ECM can recognize grounding of circuit No. 422 at transaxle connector. If "SERVICE SOON" light is on when out of diagnostic mode, there is an open in circuit No. 422 or ECM. If light remains on with circuit No. 422 grounded at ECM, connector or ECM is faulty. If light goes off, circuit No. 422 is open.

7) If "SERVICE SOON" light is off with pins "B" and "C" grounded, ECM is functioning properly. Fault is inside transaxle. If test light on pin "C" at transaxle connector does not light, there is an open in wiring or 3rd gear switch. If test light fails to light on 3rd gear switch terminal, switch is open and should be replaced. If test light does light, there is an open in wiring between transaxle connector and 3rd gear switch.

8) If test light on pin "C" lights, 3rd gear switch is operating properly. If test light goes out when engine is started, switch is receiving oil pressure at wrong time. Repair transaxle.

9) If test light stays on, transaxle connector should be reconnected and "SERVICE SOON" light checked for proper operation. If light is on, fault must be improper mating of circuit No. 422 terminals at pin "C" of transaxle connector. If light is off, malfunction is not present at this time.

Notes on Intermittents – With ignition on, engine off and transmission in Park, manipulate affected wiring and connectors while observing "SERVICE SOON" light. If "SERVICE SOON" light flashes on, repair intermittent open in circuit No. 422 (3rd gear) or circuit No. 438 (4th gear).

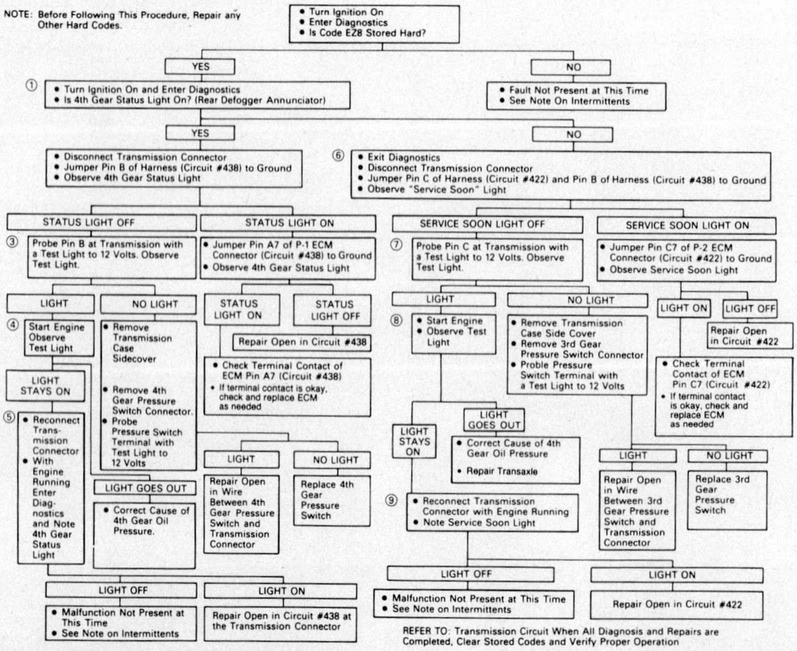

GENERAL MOTORS VISCOUS CONVERTER CLUTCH (Cont.)

VCC DIAGNOSTIC CHARTS (Cont.)

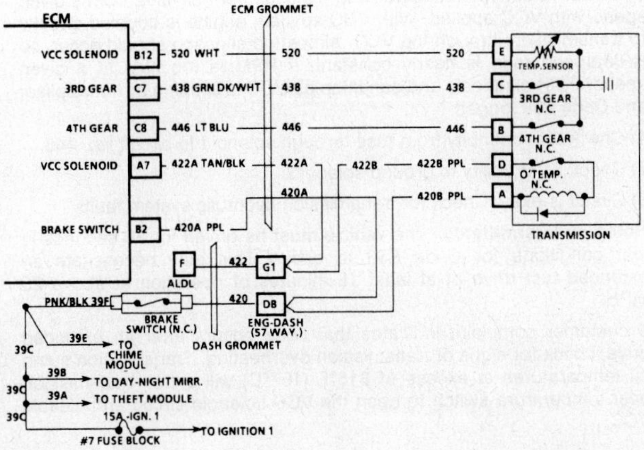

CODE EO28, OPEN 3RD OR 4TH GEAR CIRCUIT

TEST CONDITIONS:

- Code EO24 clear.
- Transmission in Park or Neutral.
- Vehicle speed less than or equal to 4 MPH.

FAILURE CONDITIONS:

- ECM input from 3rd gear not grounded.
- ECM input from 4th gear not grounded.

ACTION TAKEN:

- ECM turns on "ENGINE CONTROL SYSTEM" light.
- ECM commands BCM to turn on "SERVICE SOON" meaasge.

The 3rd and 4th gear switches in transmission are normally closed switches that are opened by transmission oil pressure. The ECM sends a 12-volt signal to each switch. When not in 3rd or 4th gear, 3rd and 4th gear inputs are grounded by normally closed switches.

When 3rd gear is achieved, 3rd gear switch is opened by 3rd gear oil pressure, and 3rd gear input changes from zero volts to 12 volts. When 4th gear is achieved, 4th gear switch is opened by 4th gear oil pressure, and 4th gear input changes from zero volts to 12 volts. Code EO28 is designed to detect false 3rd or 4th gear indication to ECM.

Notes on Intermittents – With ignition on and engine off, manipulate affected wiring and connectors while observing 3rd/4th gear status light. If 3rd/4th gear status light flashes on, repair intermittent open in circuit No. 438 (3rd gear) or circuit No. 446 (4th gear).

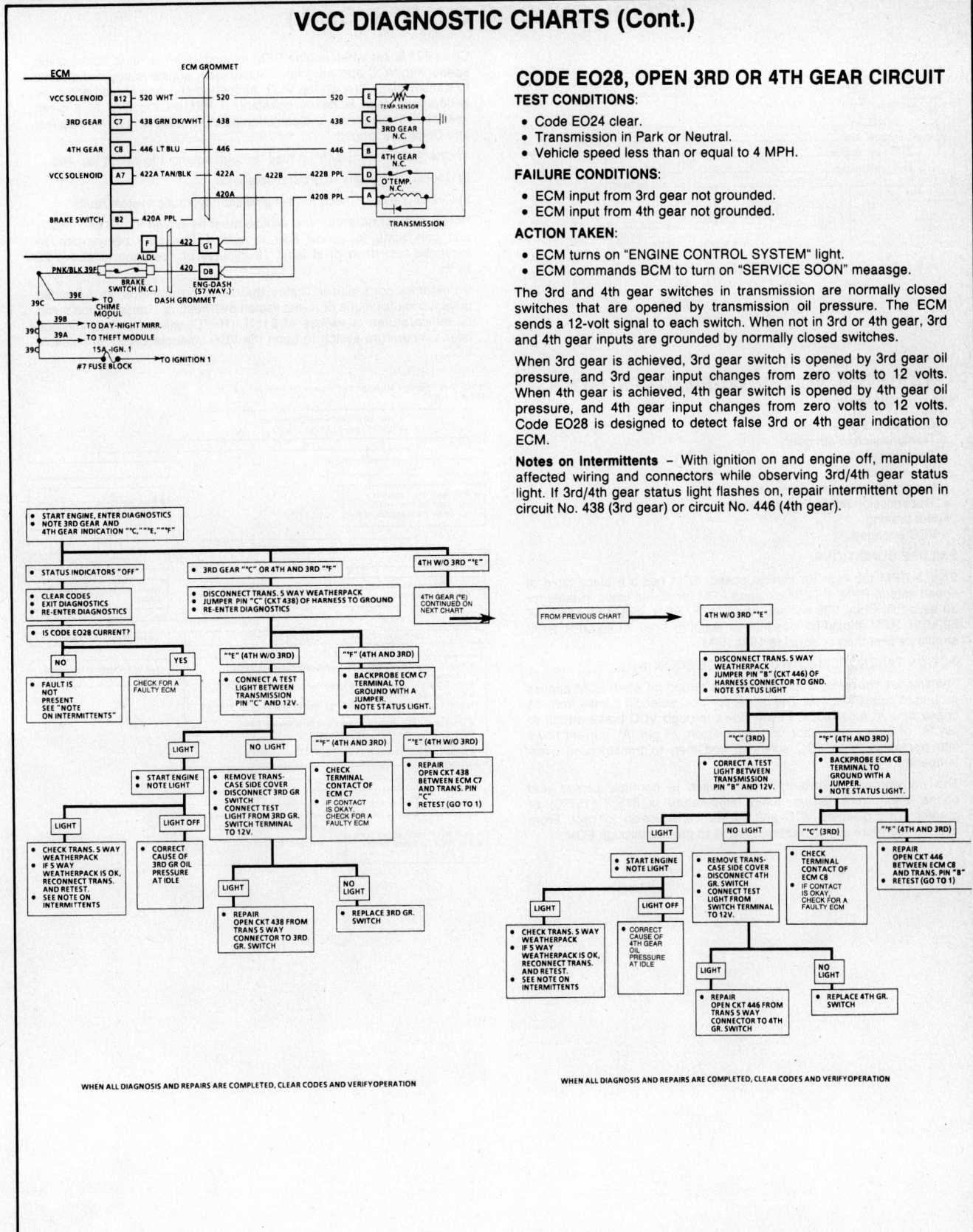

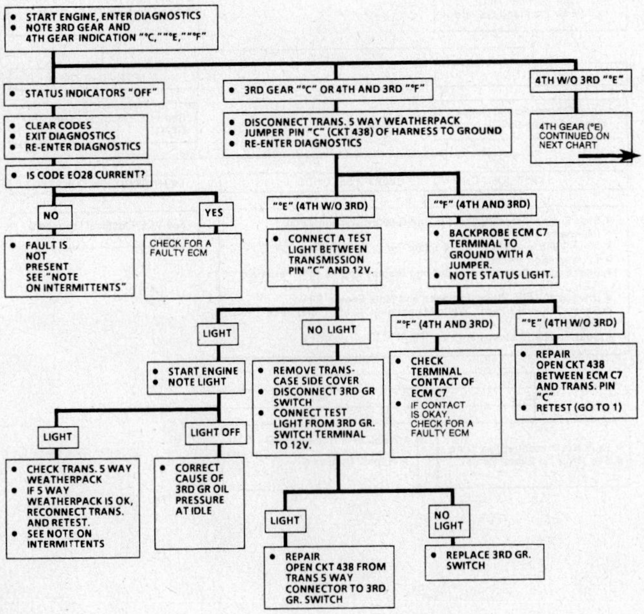

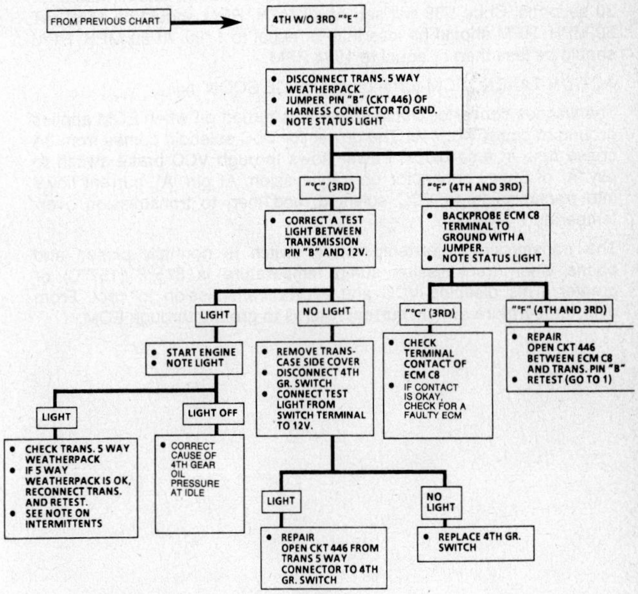

WHEN ALL DIAGNOSIS AND REPAIRS ARE COMPLETED, CLEAR CODES AND VERIFYOPERATION

WHEN ALL DIAGNOSIS AND REPAIRS ARE COMPLETED, CLEAR CODES AND VERIFYOPERATION

GENERAL MOTORS VISCOUS CONVERTER CLUTCH (Cont.)

VCC DIAGNOSTIC CHARTS (Cont.)

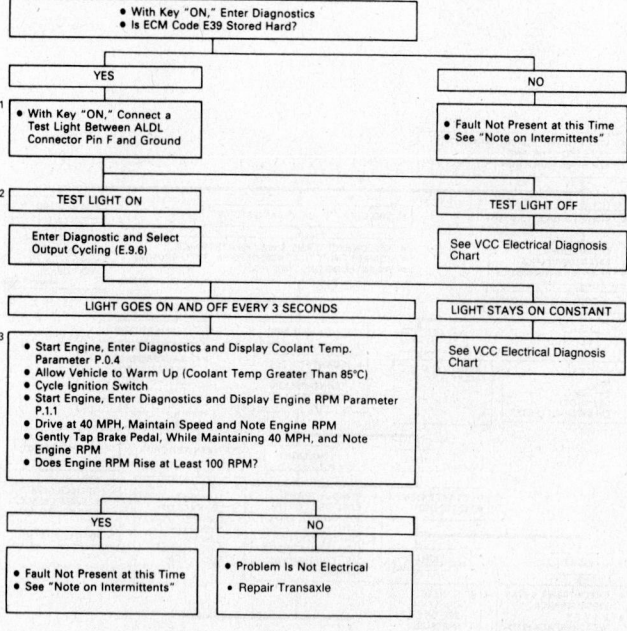

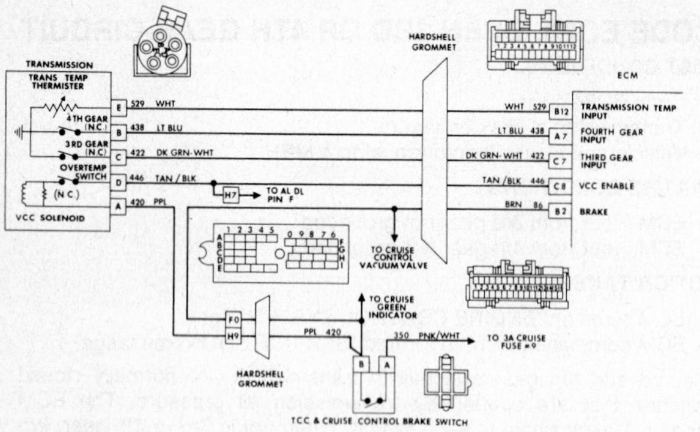

Code E39 is set when engine RPM exceeds normal value from a given speed with VCC applied. With VCC applied, engine is coupled directly to transmission through the VCC. Almost no slippage should occur, so RPM/speed ratio is nearly constant. If RPM is too high at a given speed, ECM diagnosis and condition as VCC is slipping or not applied, and Code E39 logged.

1) Check for continuity from fuse through solenoid to circuit No. 446.

2) Check ECM ability to ground solenoid.

3) Circuit is okay. Check for transmission hydraulic system faults.

Notes on Intermittents: The vehicle must be driven for 30 seconds in test conditions for Code E39 to occur. This may necessitate an extended test drive of at least 15 minutes of operation at above 25 MPH.

If customer complaint indicates that code occurs after an extended drive, check for signs of transmission overheating. Transmission sump oil temperatures in excess of 315°F (157°C) will cause transmission over-temperature switch to open the VCC solenoid circuit and disable VCC.

CODE E39, VCC ENGAGEMENT PROBLEM

TEST CONDITIONS:

- Code E28 is clear.
- Transmission in 4th gear.
- Throttle switch open.
- In closed loop.
- Not accelerating or decelerating.
- Transmission not in Park or Neutral.
- Not braking.
- VCC engaged.

FAILURE CONDITIONS:

Engine RPM too high for vehicle speed. ECM has a 9 place table of speed versus RPM. If RPM exceeds RPM for speed listed in table for 30 seconds, Code E39 will set. At 40 MPH, RPM should be 1650. AT 50 MPH, RPM should be less than or equal to 1790. At 60 MPH, RPM should be less than or equal to 1994 RPM.

ACTION TAKEN: ECM turns on "SERVICE SOON" light.

The viscous convertor clutch solenoid is turned on when ECM applies ground to circuit No. 446. The power for VCC solenoid comes from 3A cruise fuse in fuse block. Power flows through VCC brake switch to pin "A" of 5-way connector on transmission. At pin "A", current flows into transmission to VCC solenoid, and then to transmission over-temperature switch.

The transmission over-temperature switch is normally closed and opens when transmission sump temperature is 315°F (157°C) or greater. This disables VCC and allows transmission to cool. From over-temperature switch, current returns to ground through ECM.

NOTE: This Procedure Must Not Be Followed if a Code E21, E22, or E24 Is Current.

- With Key "ON," Enter Diagnostics
- Is ECM Code E39 Stored Hard?

YES

1
- With Key "ON," Connect a Test Light Between ALDL Connector Pin F and Ground

2 **TEST LIGHT ON**

Enter Diagnostic and Select Output Cycling (E.9.6)

LIGHT GOES ON AND OFF EVERY 3 SECONDS

3
- Start Engine, Enter Diagnostics and Display Coolant Temp. Parameter P.0.4
- Allow Vehicle to Warm Up (Coolant Temp Greater Than 85°C)
- Cycle Ignition Switch
- Start Engine, Enter Diagnostics and Display Engine RPM Parameter P.1.1
- Drive at 40 MPH, Maintain Speed and Note Engine RPM
- Gently Tap Brake Pedal, While Maintaining 40 MPH, and Note Engine RPM
- Does Engine RPM Rise at Least 100 RPM?

YES
- Fault Not Present at this Time
- See "Note on Intermittents"

NO
- Problem Is Not Electrical
- Repair Transaxle

LIGHT STAYS ON CONSTANT

See VCC Electrical Diagnosis Chart

TEST LIGHT OFF

See VCC Electrical Diagnosis Chart

NO
- Fault Not Present at this Time
- See "Note on Intermittents"

GENERAL MOTORS VISCOUS CONVERTER CLUTCH (Cont.)

VCC DIAGNOSTIC CHARTS (Cont.)

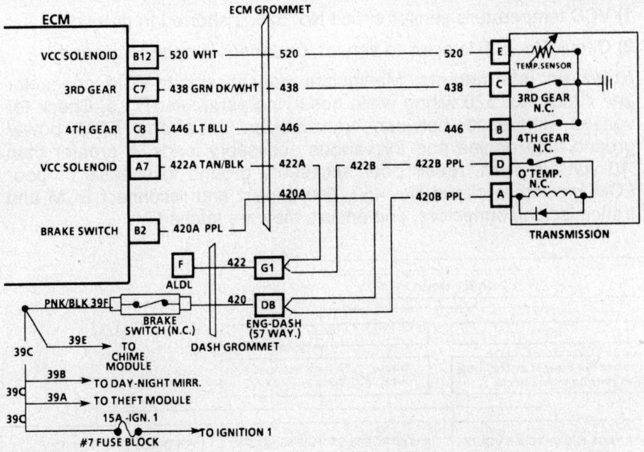

1) Check for continuity from fuse through solenoid to circuit No. 422.

2) Check ECM ability to ground solenoid.

3) Circuit is okay. Check for transmission hydraulic system faults.

Notes on Intermittents: The vehicle must be driven for 30 seconds in test conditions for Code EO39 to occur. This may necessitate an extended test drive of at least 15 minutes of operation at above 25 MPH.

If customer complaint indicates that code occurs after an extended drive, check for signs of transmission overheating. Transmission sump oil temperatures in excess of 315°F (157°C) will cause transmission over-temperature switch to open the VCC solenoid circuit and disable VCC.

CODE EO39, VCC ENGAGEMENT PROBLEM

TEST CONDITIONS:

- Code EO28 is clear.
- Transmission in 4th gear.
- Throttle switch open.
- In closed loop.
- Not accelerating or decelerating.
- Transmission not in Park or Neutral.
- Not braking.
- VCC engaged.

FAILURE CONDITIONS:

Engine RPM too high for vehicle speed. ECM has a 9 place table of speed versus RPM. If RPM exceeds RPM for speed listed in table for 30 seconds, Code EO39 will set. At 40 MPH, RPM should be 1650. AT 50 MPH, RPM should be less than or equal to 1790. At 60 MPH, RPM should be less than or equal to 1994 RPM.

ACTION TAKEN:

- ECM turns on "ENGINE CONTROL SYSTEM" light.
- ECM commands BCM to turn on "SERVICE SOON" message.

The viscous convertor clutch solenoid is turned on when ECM applies ground to circuit No. 422. The power for VCC solenoid comes from "IGN 1" fuse in fuse block. Power flows through VCC brake switch to pin "A" of 5-way connector on transmission. At pin "A", current flows into transmission to VCC solenoid, and then to transmission over-temperature switch.

The transmission over-temperature switch is normally closed and opens when transmission sump temperature is 315°F (157°C) or greater. This disables VCC and allows transmission to cool. From over-temperature switch, current returns to ground through ECM.

Code EO39 is set when engine RPM exceeds normal value from a given speed with VCC applied. With VCC applied, engine is coupled directly to transmission through the VCC. Almost no slippage should occur, so RPM/speed ratio is nearly constant. If RPM is too high at a given speed, ECM diagnosis and condition as VCC is slipping or not applied, and Code EO39 logged.

NOTE: THIS PROCEDURE MUST NOT BE FOLLOWED IF A CODE EO16, EO24, EO51 OR EO59 IS CURRENT

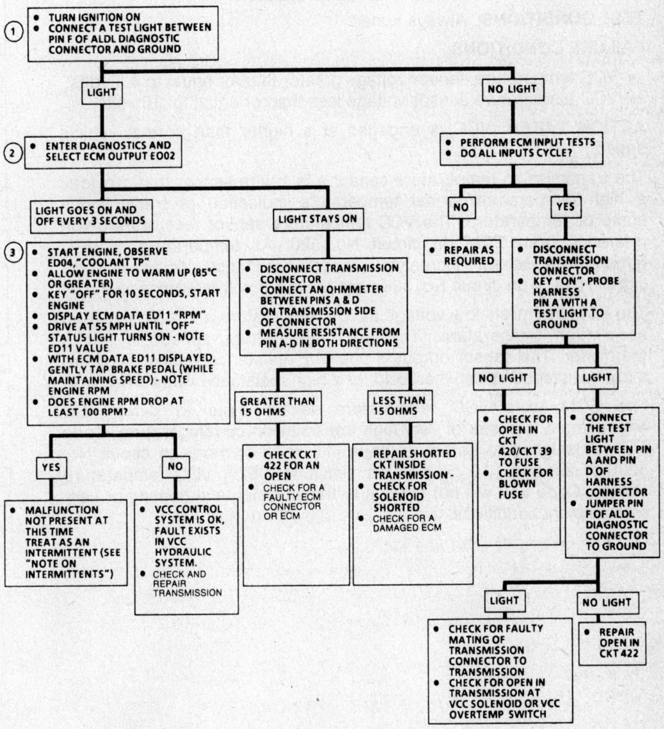

WHEN ALL DIAGNOSIS AND REPAIRS ARE COMPLETED, CLEAR CODES AND VERIFY OPERATION

GENERAL MOTORS VISCOUS CONVERTER CLUTCH (Cont.)

VCC DIAGNOSTIC CHARTS (Cont.)

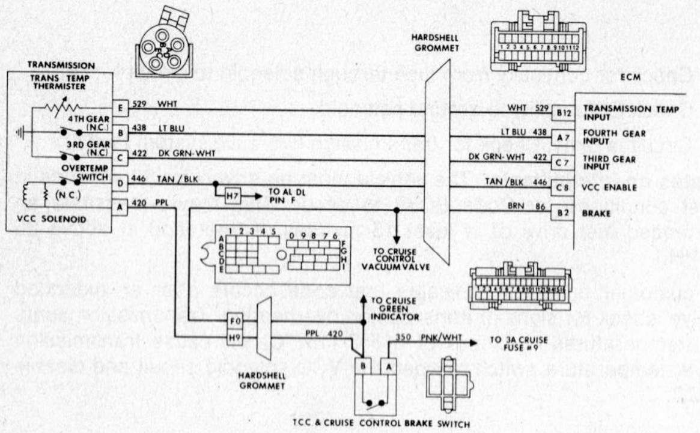

CODE E59, VCC TEMPERATURE SENSOR CIRCUIT PROBLEM

TEST CONDITIONS: Always tested.

FAILURE CONDITIONS:

- VCC temperature sensor voltage greater than or equal to 4.5 volts.
- VCC temperature sensor voltage less than or equal to .10 volts.

ACTION TAKEN: VCC is engaged at a higher than normal vehicle speed.

The transmission temperature sensor a is 1-wire sensor that provides a high temperature/normal temperature indication of transmission sump oil temperature. The VCC temperature sensor receives a 5-volt reference from ECM on circuit No. 520. As temperature of VCC temperature sensor increases, sensor resistance increases, and signal voltage on circuit No. 520 rises toward 5-volt reference value.

The ECM interprets low voltage as low temperature and a high voltage as a high temperature. The VCC temperature sensor is not a thermistor. The sensor output is one of 2 resistance values. They are a low resistance value when cold, or a high resistance value when hot.

The ECM uses VCC temperature sensor input to delay VCC engagement in cases of very high transmission oil temperature. Code E59 is designed to detect an open (4.5 volts or more on circuit No. 520) or shorted (.10 or less on circuit No. 520) VCC temperature sensor. Code E59 will not set due to transmission overheating or very cold ambient conditions.

1) VCC temperature sensor circuit No. 520 is shorted to ground.

2) Circuit No. 520 is open to sensor, or sensor is open to ground.

Notes on Intermittents: Manipulate transmission-to-ECM connector and circuit No. 520 wiring while observing parameter P.1.5. Check for voltage difference between transmission case and ECM power ground. Idle engine and try various accessory loads. If greater than .10 volts is seen, repair poor accessory ground to chassis or poor ECM ground to circuit No. 450. Disconnect and reconnect ECM and transmission connectors, and ensure they are latched.

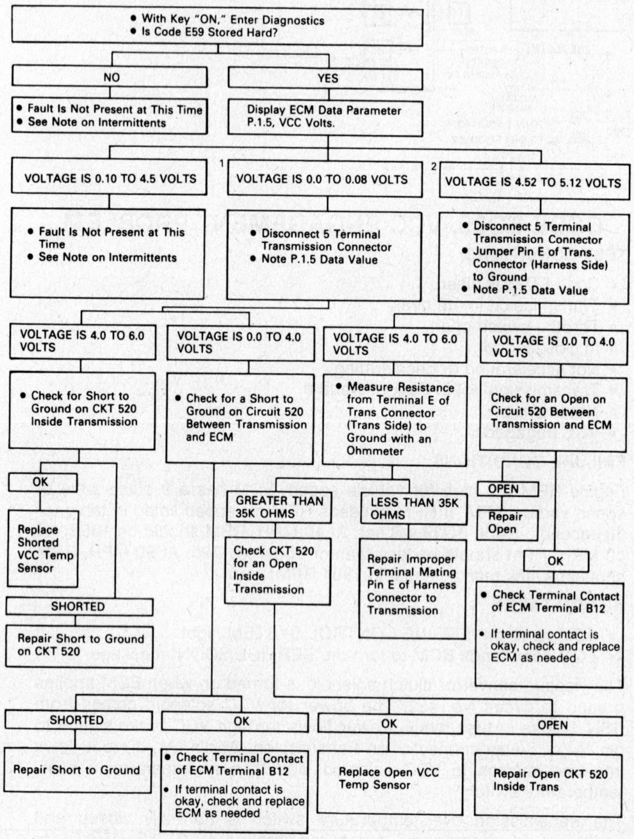

GENERAL MOTORS VISCOUS CONVERTER CLUTCH (Cont.)

VCC DIAGNOSTIC CHARTS (Cont.)

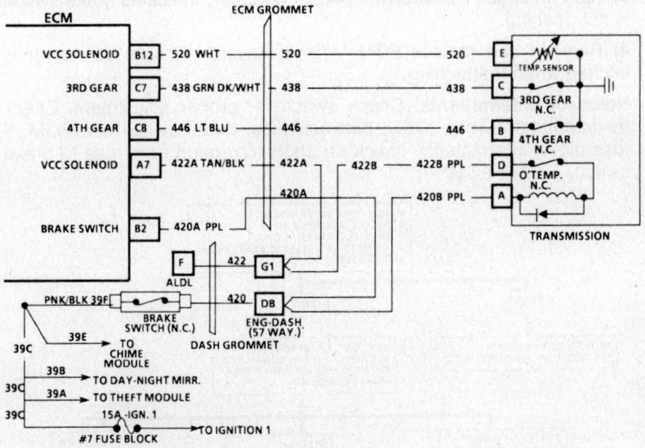

CODE E059, VCC TEMPERATURE SENSOR CIRCUIT PROBLEM

TEST CONDITIONS: Always tested.

FAILURE CONDITIONS:

- VCC temperature sensor voltage greater than or equal to 4.5 volts.
- VCC temperature sensor voltage less than or equal to .10 volts.

ACTION TAKEN:

- VCC is engaged at a higher than normal vehicle speed.
- Code E059 is logged as history code.

The transmission temperature sensor a is 1-wire sensor that provides a high temperature/normal temperature indication of transmission sump oil temperature. The VCC temperature sensor receives a 5-volt reference from ECM on circuit No. 520. As temperature of VCC temperature sensor increases, sensor resistance increases, and signal voltage on circuit No. 520 rises toward 5-volt reference value.

The ECM interprets low voltage as low temperature and a high voltage as a high temperature. The VCC temperature sensor is not a thermistor. The sensor output is one of 2 resistance values. They are a low resistance value when cold, or a high resistance value when hot.

The ECM uses VCC temperature sensor input to delay VCC engagement in cases of very high transmission oil temperature. Code E059 is designed to detect an open (4.5 volts or more on circuit No. 520) or shorted (.10 or less on circuit No. 520) VCC temperature sensor. Code E59 will not set due to transmission overheating or very cold ambient conditions.

1) VCC temperature sensor circuit No. 520 is shorted to ground.

2) Circuit No. 520 is open to sensor, or sensor is open to ground.

Notes on Intermittents: Manipulate transmission-to-ECM connector and circuit No. 520 wiring while observing parameter ED26. Check for voltage difference between transmission case and ECM power ground. Idle engine and try various accessory loads. If greater than .10 volts is seen, repair poor accessory ground to chassis or poor ECM ground to circuit No. 450. Disconnect and reconnect ECM and transmission connectors, and ensure they are latched.

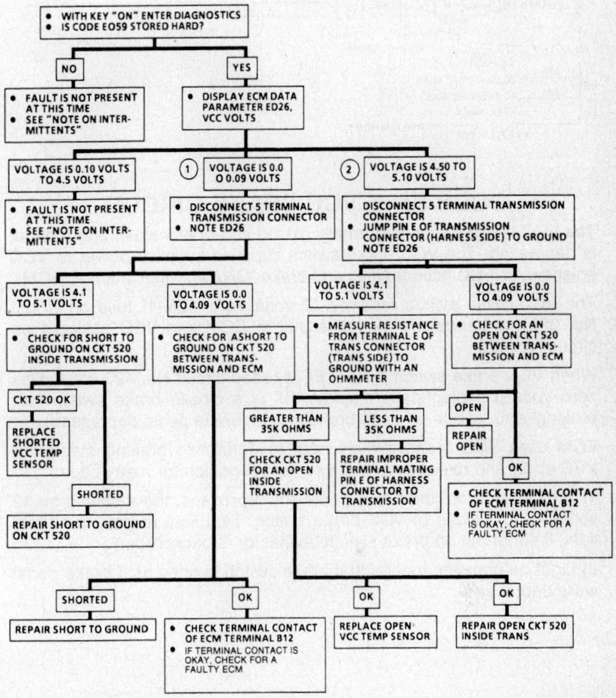

WHEN ALL DIAGNOSIS AND REPAIRS ARE COMPLETED, CLEAR CODES AND VERIFY OPERATION

GENERAL MOTORS VISCOUS CONVERTER CLUTCH (Cont.)

VCC DIAGNOSTIC CHARTS (Cont.)

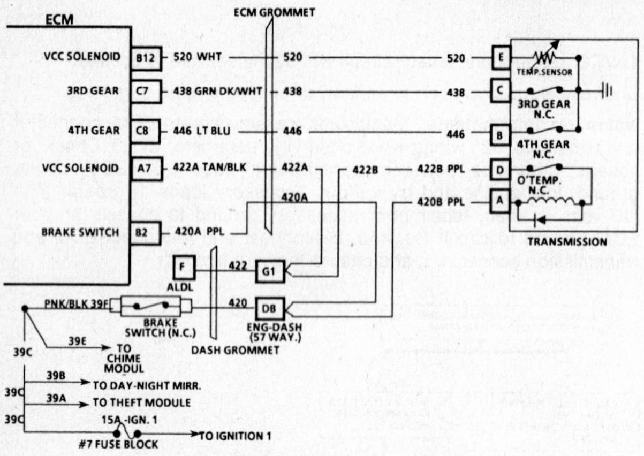

CODE E171, VCC BRAKE CIRCUIT

The VCC brake switch is normally closed and opens when brake pedal is depressed. The VCC brake switch supplies supplies power to VCC solenoid, cruise vacuum valve and brake "ON/OFF" indication to ECM.

The VCC brake switch receives 12 volts from "IGN 1" fuse on circuit No. 39, and sends the 12-volt signal to ECM and VCC solenoid on circuit No. 420.

When VCC brake switch opens, ECM reads circuit No. 420 voltage as zero volts. On diagnostic display, "HI" is a closed brake switch (not braking) and "LO" is an open brake switch (brake pedal depressed).

ECM uses VCC brake switch input to determine braking status for VCC apply and release, as well as a test condition for many codes.

1) With ignition on and brake pedal not depressed, there should be 12 volts on both sides of VCC brake switch. Test light to ground should light, if either pin on brake switch connector is backprobed.

2) Light on one side means that brake switch is open as if brake pedal were depressed.

3) Light on circuit No. 420 with pedal depressed indicates brake switch is not opening.

4) Remove and replace ECM "A/B" connector. Ensure connector is latched when reattaching.

Notes on Intermittents: Check switch for proper adjustment. Check for intermittent open circuit between fuse, brake switch and ECM. If fuse blows intermittenly, check for short to ground from fuse to brake switch, VCC or ECM.

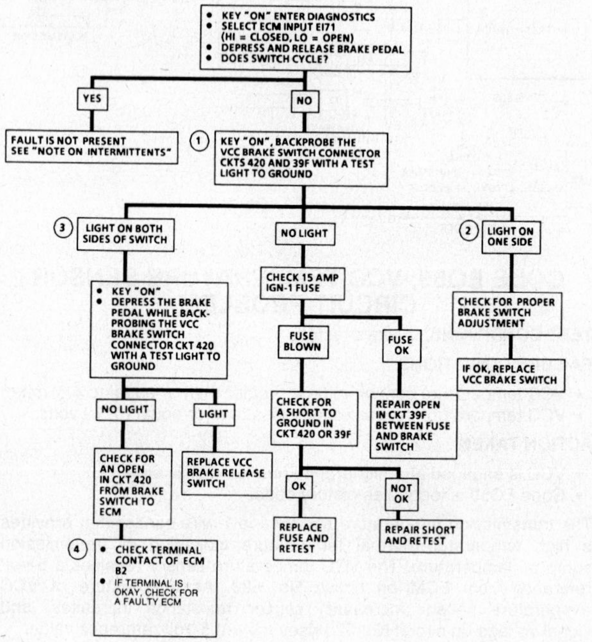

WHEN ALL DIAGNOSIS AND REPAIRS ARE COMPLETED, CLEAR CODES AND VERIFY OPERATION

GENERAL MOTORS VISCOUS CONVERTER CLUTCH (Cont.)

VCC DIAGNOSTIC CHARTS (Cont.)

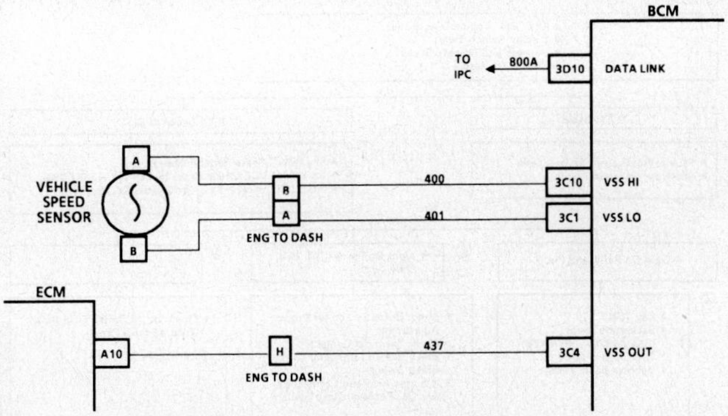

CODE B124, VEHICLE SPEED SENSOR CIRCUIT PROBLEM

Vehicle speed sensor uses a permanent magnet (P.M.) generator to produce an electrical signal representative of vehicle speed. This signal is sent to BCM on circuit No. 400 (VSS High) and circuit No. 401 (VSS Low). BCM buffers and amplifies signal for its prospective uses. Output of the generator can be seen using a digital voltmeter on AC scale while rotating generator drive (rotate front wheels).

Code B124 will set if ignition is on, no code EO28 or B334 set, transaxle in 4th gear (EI82 Low), no input to BCM from VSS and engine RPM greater than 1300 RPM. During the time the failure is present, continuous compressor at idle will be disabled. Vehicle speed reading BD60 will display actual sensor reading.

1) Since BCM amplifies and buffers speed signal before it is sent to ECM, code EO24 in ECM will set with code B124 in BCM, if P.M. generator or circuits No. 400 or No. 401 have a problem. If code B124 sets without setting code EO24, there is an internal problem in BCM.

2) BCM data value BD60 displays MPH.

3) With front wheels turning, a voltage reading indicates P.M. generator and wiring are okay.

4) Checks for open in VSS circuit wiring.

5) Checks for ground in VSS circuit wiring, prior to replacing sensor.

Notes on Intermittents: If an intermittent code B124 bas been set, manipulate related wiring while observing BCM data parameter BD60. If failure is induced, reading will jump from a normal reading value to zero MPH.

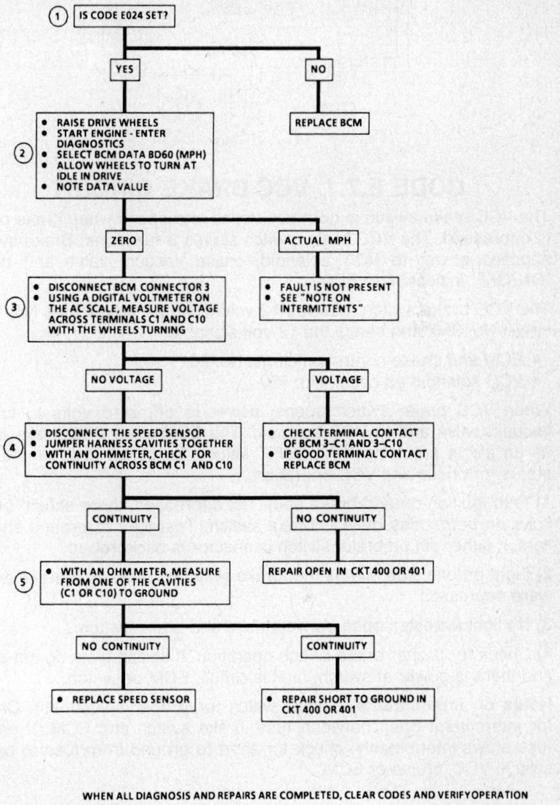

GENERAL MOTORS VISCOUS CONVERTER CLUTCH (Cont.)

VCC DIAGNOSTIC CHARTS (Cont.)

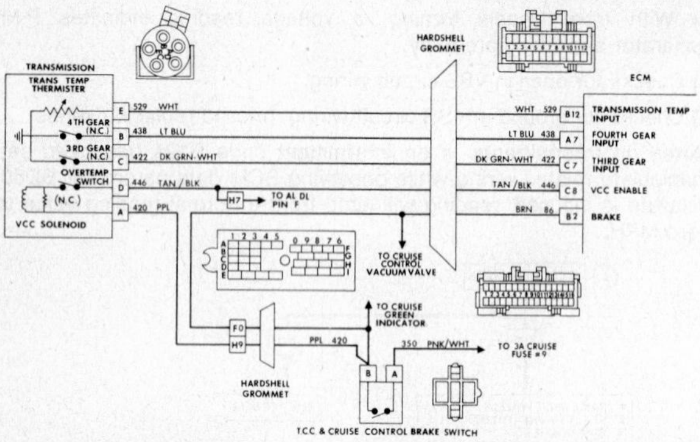

CODE E.7.1, VCC BRAKE CIRCUIT

The VCC brake switch is normally closed and opens when brake pedal is depressed. The VCC brake switch serves 3 functions: Brake switch supplies power to VCC solenoid, cruise vacuum valve and brake "ON/OFF" indication to ECM.

The VCC brake switch receives 12 volts from 3A cruise fuse No. 9 on circuit No. 350, and sends the 12-volt signal to:

- ECM and cruise control on circuit No. 86.
- VCC solenoid on circuit No. 420.

When VCC brake switch opens, power is off, zero volts to cruise vacuum valve and to VCC solenoid. The ECM uses VCC brake input as an aid in providing "FAILSOFT" values for codes and for braking status for cruise and VCC operation.

1) With ignition on and brake pedal not depressed, there should be 12 volts on both sides of VCC brake switch. Test light to ground should light, if either pin on brake switch connector is backprobed.

2) Light on one side means that brake switch is open as if brake pedal were depressed.

3) No light indicates open between fuse and brake switch.

4) Check for proper brake switch operation. If switch tests do not pass and there is power at switch, fault is circuit, ECM or switch.

Notes on Intermittents: Check switch for proper adjustment. Check for intermittent open between fuse, brake switch and ECM. If cruise fuse blows intermittenly, check for short to ground from fuse to brake switch, VCC, cruise or ECM.

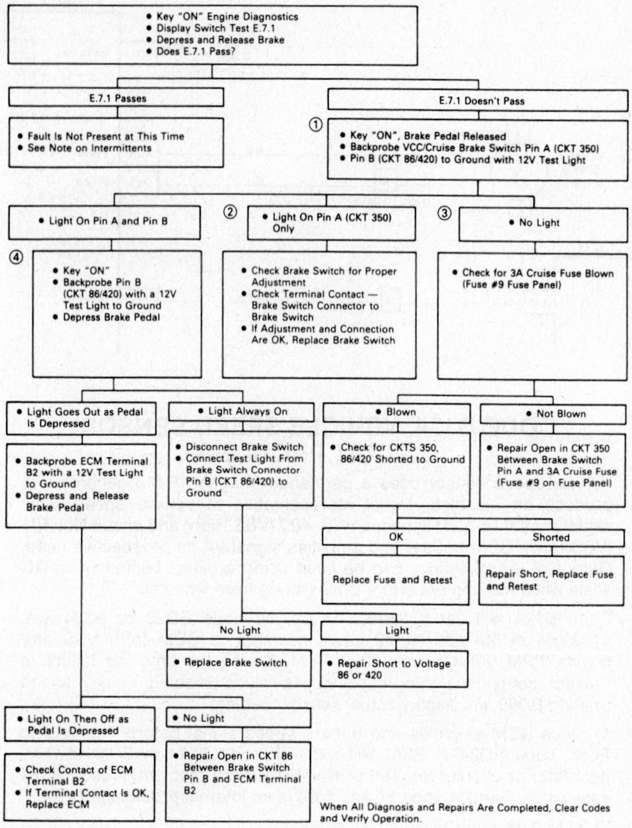

GENERAL MOTORS VISCOUS CONVERTER CLUTCH (Cont.)

VCC DIAGNOSTIC CHARTS (Cont.)

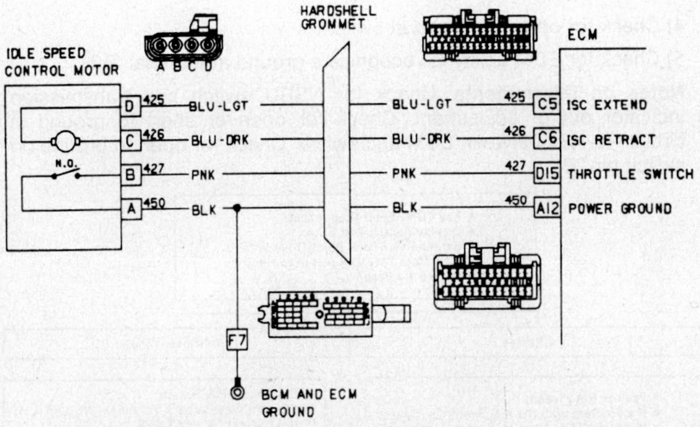

CODE E.7.2, THROTTLE SWITCH CIRCUIT

The throttle switch is part of ISC motor. Pin "B" of 4-wire weatherpack connector on ISC is throttle switch or closed throttle input to ECM. The ISC throttle switch contacts are normally open and closed when throttle linkage contacts ISC plunger (closed throttle, ISC in control of idle speed).

The ECM sends a 5-volt signal to pin "B" of ISC motor on circuit No. 427. When throttle linkage resets on ISC plunger, throttle switch contacts close, shorting ISC pin "B" to pin "A" on circuit No. 450 ground. The 5-volt signal from ECM is grounded at closed throttle, resulting in zero volts at ECM pin "D15". When throttle is opened, the throttle switch opens pin "B" on circuit No. 427, resulting in 5 volts at ECM pin "D15".

1) ISC plunger depressed and released should allow switch test to pass. If "E.7.2" does not pass, check for ISC circuit problems.

2) When ISC motor is completely retracted, throttle switch will open due to ISC internal design. Ensure ISC is extended partially before continuing diagnosis.

3) Check for ISC or circuit problem. If "E.7.2" passes, problem is at ISC motor or connector.

4) Check for continuity on circuit No. 427 between ECM and ISC motor.

Notes on Intermittents: Check for binding throttle linkage due to TV, cruise, throttle cables, TPS installed improperly, or throttle shaft binding. Check for proper throttle return spring and throttle return spring installation.

Probe ECM "D15" to ground with a voltmeter. Manipulate wiring and connnectors at closed throttle and watch for 5.0 volts, indicating an open from "D15" to ground. Manipulate wiring and connectors at open throttle and watch for zero volts, indicating short to ground on circuit No. 427.

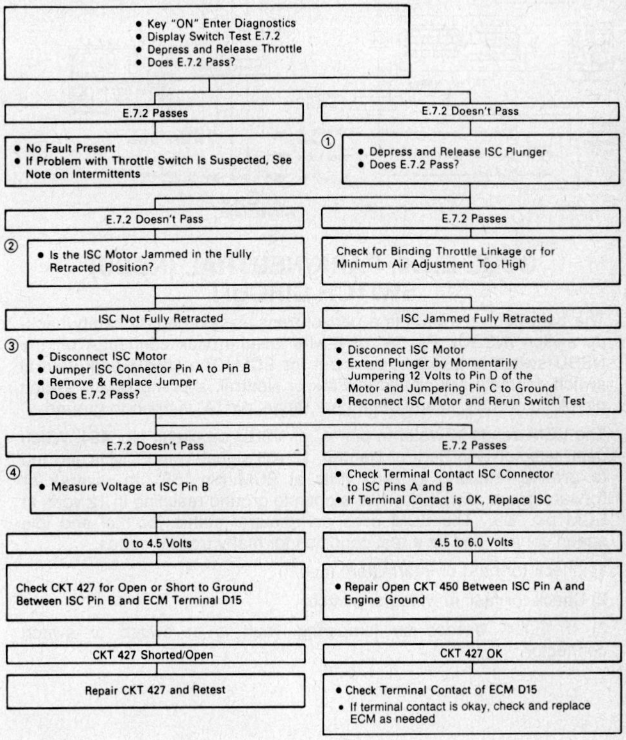

When All Diagnosis and Repairs Are Completed, Clear Codes and Verify Operation.

GENERAL MOTORS VISCOUS CONVERTER CLUTCH (Cont.)

VCC DIAGNOSTIC CHARTS (Cont.)

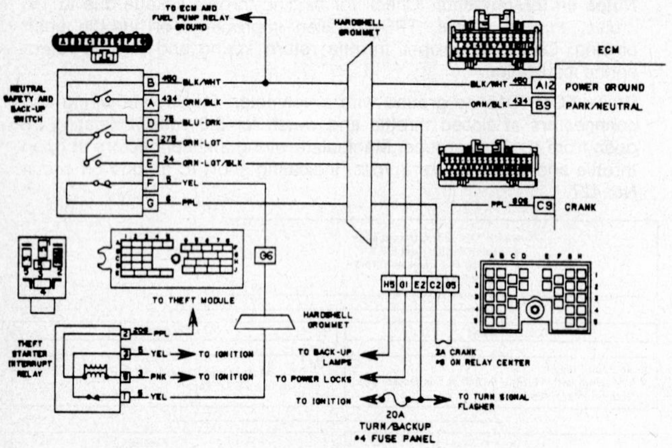

CODE E.7.4, PARK/NEUTRAL (NSBU) SWITCH CIRCUIT

The park neutral switch is a part of transmission neutral safety/back-up switch (NSBU). Pin "A" of 6-wire weatherpack connector on the NSBU switch is park/neutral input for ECM. The NSBU park/neutral switch contacts are closed in Park or Neutral, shorting NSBU switch pin "A" to ground. In any other gear range, pin "A" is open to ground.

The ECM sends 12 volts to pin "A" of NSBU on circuit No. 434. When gear selector is in Park or Neutral, 12-volt signal from ECM is shorted to ground resulting in zero volts at ECM pin "B9". In reverse or forward gears, circuit No. 434 is open to ground resulting in 12 volts at ECM pin "B9". The ECM uses park/neutral status for fuel and idle speed control, and as a test condition for many trouble codes.

1) Check for hard or intermittent fault.

2) Check for fault in wiring or switch.

3) If "E.7.4" passes by jumpering, fault is at switch or switch connector.

4) Check for open to ground at switch.

5) Check for ECM ability to recognize a ground at terminal "B9".

Notes on Intermittents: Check for NSBU switch and transmission indicator out of adjustment. Check for open or short to ground in circuit No. 434 between ECM and switch. Check for open to ground on switch pin "B".

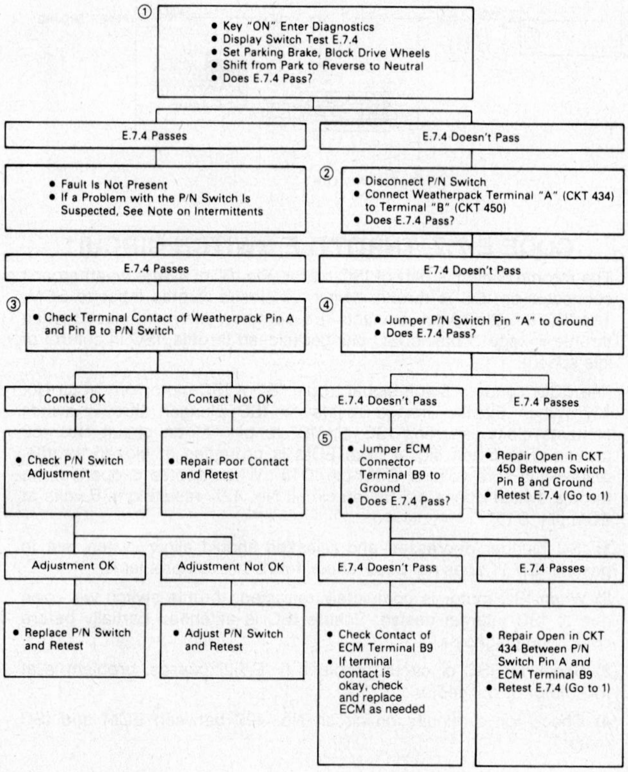

When All Diagnosis and Repairs Are Complete, Clear Codes and Verify Operation.

GENERAL MOTORS A-131L TRANSAXLE

Chevrolet Nova

DESCRIPTION

Model A-131L transaxles have 3 forward speeds and reverse. Transaxle assembly consists of a 3-element torque converter, a gear driven oil pump, a valve body, a differential, and 2 planetary gear sets actuated by 3 multi-disc brakes and 2 clutches. Engine load and speed determine gear changes by use of throttle valve position and output shaft speed. Torque convertor is equipped with a built-in lock-up clutch.

LUBRICATION & ADJUSTMENT

See appropriate AUTOMATIC TRANSMISSION SERVICNG article in DOMESTIC GENERAL SERVICING section.

TROUBLE SHOOTING

PRELIMINARY CHECKS

Trouble occuring with the automatic transaxle can be caused by either the engine or the transaxle. Isolate trouble to engine or transaxle before proceeding with trouble shooting. Trouble shooting should begin with simplest test procedure, working up in order of difficulty, and in the following sequence:

- Check oil level.
- Check throttle cable.
- Check shift linkage.
- Check neutral safety switch.
- Check idle speed (cooling fan and A/C unit off).
- Check tire pressure.

CHECK ENGINE & TORQUE CONVERTER

Perform stall test and repair as necessary.

CHECK TRANSAXLE

Check each clutch, brake and gear for wear by performing time lag test. Confirm test results with road test. Repair as necessary.

CHECK LINE PRESSURE

Perform hydraulic test. Confirm shift point and extent of shock with road test. Repair as necessary.

ROAD TEST VEHICLE

Road test vehicle and confirm that trouble lies within transaxle. Perform in vehicle service or overhaul transaxle.

TESTING

ROAD TEST

"D" Range Test

1) Allow ATF to reach a normal operating temperature of 122-176°F (50-80°C). Shift into "D" range, and while driving, hold throttle half open and then wide open.

2) Check that 1st to 2nd upshift takes place, then check that 2nd to 3rd upshift take place, and that upshift points conform to those indicated in diagram. *See Fig. 1*.

3) If there is no 1st to 2nd upshift, governor valve is defective or 1-2 shift valve is stuck. If there is no 2nd to 3rd upshift, 2-3 shift valve is stuck. If shift points are incorrect, throttle valve, 1-2 or 2-3 shift valves are stuck or defective.

4) Repeat procedure and check shock and slip from 1st to 2nd and from 2nd to 3rd. If shock is severe, line pressure is too high, accumulator is defective or check ball is defective.

5) While driving in "D" range, check for unusual noise and vibration. Abnormal noise and vibration may be due to an unbalanced propeller shaft, differential, tires, torque converter, or other drive train components.

6) With vehicle in "D" range, and while driving, hold throttle half open and then wide open. Check to see that 2nd to 1st, 3rd to 1st, and 3rd to 2nd kickdown speeds conform to those indicated in diagram. *See Fig. 1*. Also check for abnormal shock and slip at kickdown.

7) While driving in "D" range, shift to "2" and "L" range and check engine braking power. If there is no engine braking at "2" range, 2nd coast brake is defective. If there is no engine braking at "L" range, 1st and reverse is defective.

8) While driving in "D" range, remove foot from accelerator pedal and shift into "L" range. Check to see that 3rd to 2nd, and 2nd to 1st downshift points conform to those indicated indicated in diagram. *See Fig. 1*.

Lock-Up Mechanism

Connect a tachometer to engine and drive vehicle at around 40 MPH. Depress accelelator pedal and read tachometer. If there is a large jump in engine RPM, lock-up mechanism is not working.

"2" Range Test

1) Shift into "2" range and drive with throttle half open and then wide open. Check 1st to 2nd upshift points at each of the throttle valve openings to see that they conform with those indicated in diagram. *See Fig. 1*.

2) While driving in "2" range, release accelerator pedal and check for engine braking. Perform a kickdown in "2" range and check 2nd to 1st kickdown speed. Kickdown speed must conform with that indicated in diagram. Check for abnormal noise at acceleration and deceleration, and for shock at upshift and downshift.

"L" Range Test

While driving in "L" range, check to see that ther is no upshift to 2nd gear. Release accelerator pedal and check for engine braking. Also check for abnormal noise at acceleration and deceleration

"R" Range Test

Shift into "R" range and, while starting at full throttle, check for slipping.

"P" Range Test

Stop vehicle on a hill with more than a 9% grade and, after shifting into "P" range, release the parking brake. Check to see that parking lock pawl prevents the vehicle from moving.

HYDRAULIC PRESSURE TESTS

Governor Pressure Test

1) Allow ATF to reach a normal operating temperature of 122-176°F (50-80°C). Block rear wheels and apply parking brake. Raise and support front of vehicle with safety stands.

2) Remove transmission test plugs and connect pressure gauges. Measurements can be made at 800 RPM.

Automatic Transmissions

GENERAL MOTORS A-131L TRANSAXLE (Cont.)

Fig. 1: A-131L TRANSAXLE DOWNSHIFT & UPSHIFT POINTS

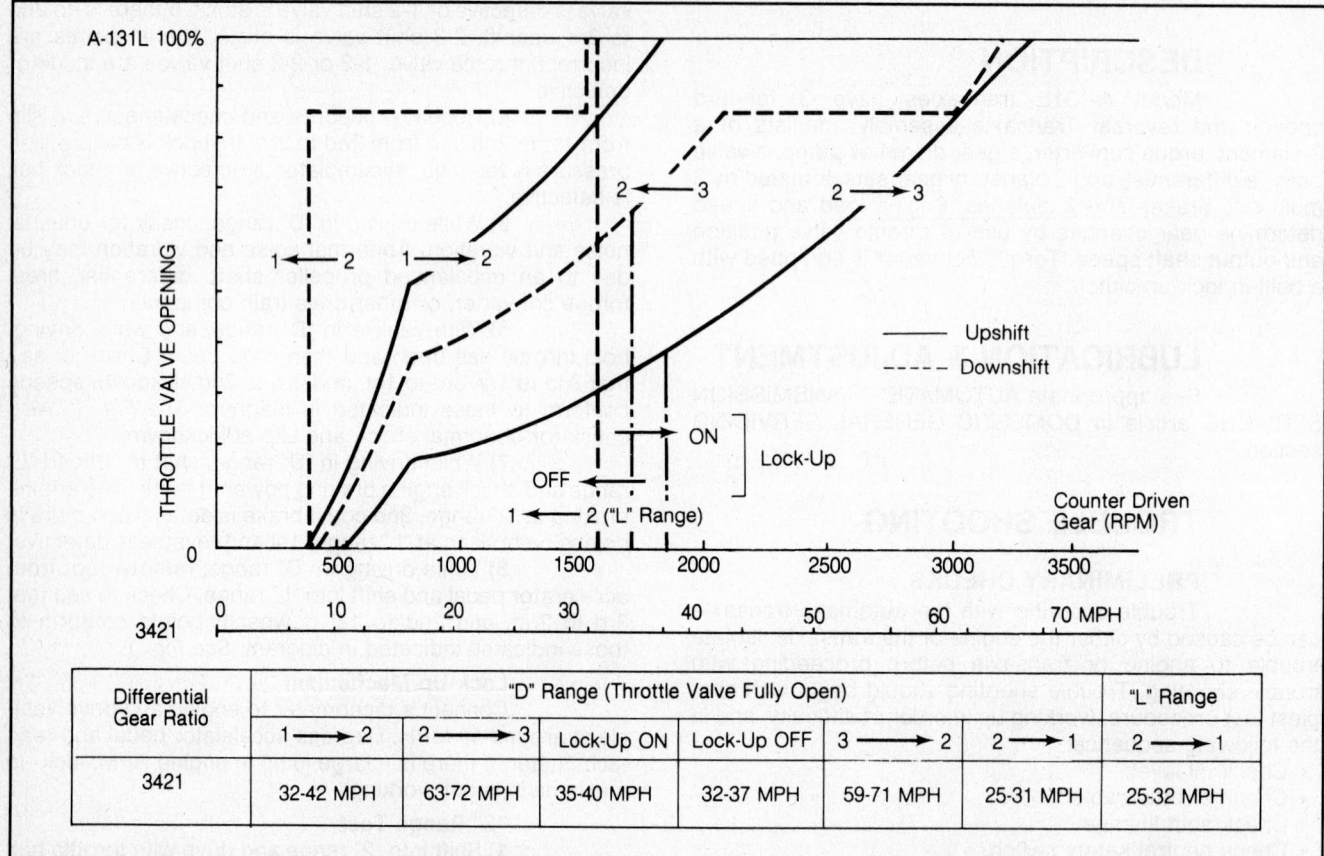

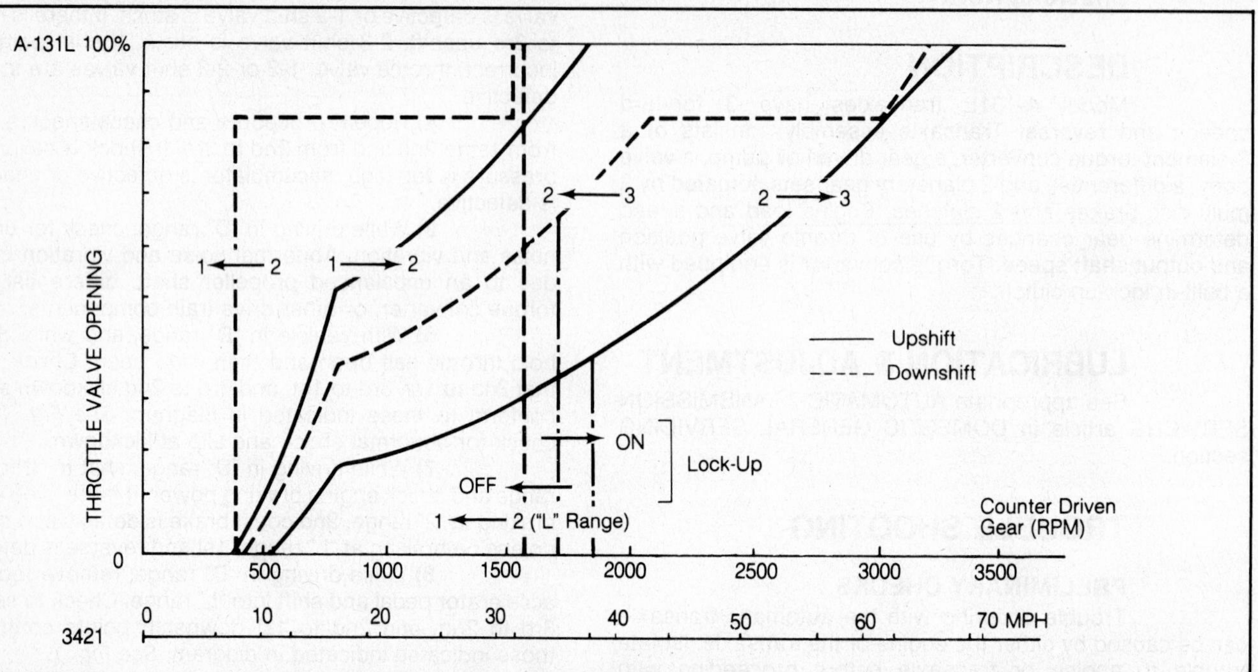

Differential Gear Ratio	"D" Range (Throttle Valve Fully Open)						"L" Range
	1 → 2	2 → 3	Lock-Up ON	Lock-Up OFF	3 → 2	2 → 1	2 → 1
3421	32-42 MPH	63-72 MPH	35-40 MPH	32-37 MPH	59-71 MPH	25-31 MPH	25-32 MPH

If tests are to be made at 1600 RPM or at 3500 RPM, perform these test on a road or a chassis dynamometer.

3) Ensure that parking brake is applied and start the engine. Shift into "D" range and measure governor pressure at specified speeds. If governor pressure is incorrect, line pressure may be incorrect, governor pressure circuit may be leaking or governor valve may be defective.

GOVERNOR PRESSURE SPECIFICATIONS

Application	psi (kg/cm²)
At 800 RPM [1]	13-24 (.91-1.69)
At 1600 RPM [2]	24-36 (1.69-2.53)
At 3500 RPM [3]	44-55 (3.09-3.87)

[1] – Approximate vehicle speed is 19 MPH.
[2] – Approximate vehicle speed is 38 MPH.
[3] – Approximate vehicle speed is 57 MPH.

Line Pressure Test

1) Block all wheels and apply parking brake. Start engine and shift into "D" range. Step on brake pedal with left foot and with right foot control accelerator pedal. Measure line pressure at idle and stall speeds. Repeat test in "R" range.

2) If pressure is lower than specified, check throttle cable adjustment and retest. If pressure in both ranges is higher than specified, throttle cable may be out of adjustment, throttle valve or regulator valve may be defective.

3) If pressure in both ranges is lower than specified, throttle cable may be out of adjustment, oil pump may be defective, throttle valve or regulator valve may be defective.

4) If pressure is low in "D" range only, "D" range circuit may be leaking or forward clutch may be defective. If pressure is low in "R" range only, "R" range circuit may be leaking, direct clutch may be defective, or 1st and reverse may be defective.

LINE PRESSURE SPECIFICATIONS IN "D" RANGE

Application	psi (kg/cm²)
At Idle Speed	53-61 (3.73-4.29)
At Stall Speed	131-152 (9.21-10.69)

LINE PRESSURE SPECIFICATIONS IN "R" RANGE

Application	psi (kg/cm²)
At Idle Speed	77-102 (5.41-7.17)
At Stall Speed	205-239 (14.41-16.80)

STALL TEST

NOTE: **The object of this test is to check the overall performance of the transaxle and engine by measuring maximum engine speeds in the "D" and "R" ranges. Perform this test with ATF at a normal operating temperature of 122-176°F (50-80°C). DO NOT continously run this test longer than 5 seconds.**

GENERAL MOTORS A-131L TRANSAXLE (Cont.)

CLUTCH & BAND APPLICATION – A-131L (ELEMENTS IN USE)

Selector Lever Position	Direct (Front) Clutch	Forward (Rear) Clutch	2nd Coast Brake Band	2nd Gear Brake Drum	1st & Reverse Gear Brake (Piston)	No. 1 One-Way Clutch	No. 2 One-Way Clutch
P – PARK							
R – REVERSE		X			X		
N – NEUTRAL							
D – DRIVE							
First	X						X
Second	X			X		X	
Third	X	X		X			
2 – SECOND							
First	X						X
Second	X		X	X		X	
1 – LOW							
First	X				X		X
Second [1]	X		X	X		X	

[1] – Downshift in "L" range, 2nd gear only; no upshift.

1) Block front and rear wheels and fully apply parking brake. Install tachometer. Depress brake pedal and start the engine. Shift into "D" range and fully depress accelerator pedal. Immediately read highest engine RPM.

2) Stall speed should be 1950-2250 RPM. Repeat test in "R" range. If stall speed is the same for both ranges but lower than specified, then engine output may be insufficient or stator one-way clutch is not operating properly. If stall speed is more than 600 RPM below the specified value, the torque converter could be at fault.

3) If stall speed in "D" range is higher than specified, line pressure may be too low, forward clutch may be slipping or No. 2 one-way clutch may not be operating properly.

4) If stall speed in "R" range is higher than specified, line pressure may be too low, direct clutch may be slipping or 1st and reverse brake may be slipping. If stall speed in "D" and "R" range is higher than specified, fluid level may be low or line pressure may be too low.

TIME LAG TEST

NOTE: **If the shift lever is moved while the engine is idling, there will be a certain time lapse or lag before shock can be felt. This time lapse is used to check the condition of the forward clutch, direct clutch, and 1st and reverse brake. Allow a 1 minute interval between tests. Make 3 tests and take average value.**

1) With ATF at a normal operating temperature of 122-176°F (50-80°C), apply parking and check idle speed. Using a stop watch, measure the time that it takes for shock to be felt when moving shift lever from "N" to "D" range. Time lag must be less than 1.2 seconds.

2) Repeat procedure from "N" to "R" range, time lag must be less than 1.5 seconds. If "N" to "D" time lag is longer than specified, line pressure may be too low or forward clutch may be worn. If "N" to "R" time lag is longer than specified, line pressure may be too low, direct clutch may be worn, or 1st and reverse brake may be worn.

ENGINE IDLE SPEED

Application	Range	RPM
With P/S	"N"	800
Without P/S	"N"	900

SERVICE (IN VEHICLE)

GOVERNOR ASSEMBLY

Removal & Installation

Remove left drive shaft. Remove transaxle dust cover. Remove bracket bolts, governor cover and "O" ring. Remove governor body and thrust washer. Remove washer and governor body adapter. To install, reverse removal procedure.

THROTTLE CABLE

Removal

Disconnect throttle cable from throttle linkage. Disconnect transaxle control cable from manual shift lever and remove manual shift lever. Remove neutral safety switch. Remove valve body. Remove throttle cable bolt and retaining plate. Pull throttle cable out of transaxle.

Installation

1) Install throttle cable in transaxle case. Install retaining plate and bolt. If throttle cable is new, bend cable in about a 7.87" (200 mm) radius.

2) Pull inner cable lightly, until a slight resistance is felt. Hold cable in place. Stake stopper on inner cable, leaving a 0.031-0.059" (0.8-1.5 mm) gap between cable housing and stopper. *See Fig. 2.*

3) Connect throttle cable to throttle linkage. Adjust throttle cable. See appropriate AUTOMATIC TRANSMISSION SERVICNG article in DOMESTIC GENERAL SERVICING section.

4) Install neutral safety switch and manual shift lever. Adjust neutral safety switch. See appropriate AUTOMATIC TRANSMISSION SERVICNG article in DOMESTIC GENERAL SERVICING section. Connect transaxle control cable. Test drive vehicle.

Fig. 2: Throttle Cable Stopper Installation

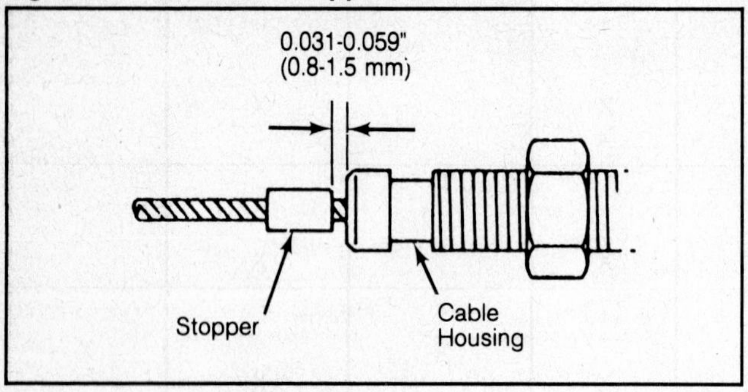

VALVE BODY

Removal

1) Clean exterior of transaxle to prevent contamination of valve body. Remove drain plug and drain ATF. Remove oil pan and gasket. Remove bolts and apply tube bracket. Remove 3 bolts and carefully remove oil strainer. Note position of oil tubes and, using a large screwdriver, remove oil tubes.

2) Remove manual detent spring. Remove manual valve. Remove 6 manual valve body bolts and note their length. Remove valve body. Remove 14 valve body bolts and note their length. Remove valve body. Remove governor pressure line strainer. Remove governor apply gasket.

Installation

1) Install governor apply gasket. Install governor pressure line strainer. Hold valve body cam down, and slip cable into slot. Install valve body in transaxle.

2) Install 14 valve body bolts finger tight, then tighten to specification. Align manual valve with pin on manual shift lever. Lower valve body into place. Install 6 manual valve body bolts finger tight, then tighten to specification.

3) Install detent spring and tighten bolts. Check that manual valve lever is in contact with center of roller at tip of detent spring. Using a plastic hammer, tap oil tubes into place.

4) Install apply tube bracket. Install oil strainer. Install magnet in oil pan. Ensure that magnet does not interfere with oil tubes. Install oil pan and drain plug. Fill transaxle with Dexron II ATF and check fluid level. Do not overfill.

REMOVAL & INSTALLATION

TRANSAXLE

See appropriate AUTOMATIC TRANSMISSION REMOVAL article in DOMESTIC GENERAL SERVICING section.

TORQUE CONVERTER

NOTE: The torque converter is a sealed unit and cannot be disassembled for service. Make the following tests to be certain that converter is defective. If transaxle is contaminated, the torque converter and transaxle cooler must be thoroughly cleaned and flushed.

ONE-WAY CLUTCH TEST

1) Insert rotator in inner race of one-way clutch. Insert One-Way Clutch Tester (J-35467) so that it fits into notch of converter hub and into one-way clutch.

2) With converter positioned upright, one-way clutch should lock when turned counterclockwise. Clutch should rotate freely and smoothly when turned clockwise.

3) Less than 22 INCH lbs. (2.5 N.m) should be required to rotate clutch. If necessary, clean converter and retest. If clutch still fails test, replace torque converter.

RUNOUT TEST

1) Mount dial indicator on engine and measure flex plate runout. If flex plate exceeds .0079" (.20 mm) or if ring gear is damaged, replace flex plate. If installing a new flex plate, note orientation of spacers and tighten bolts.

2) Temporarily mount torque converter to engine flex plate. Place dial indicator tip on torque converter hub. Rotate converter and check runout. If runout exceeds .0118" (.30 mm), try to correct runout by changing position of converter on flex plate.

3) If excessive runout cannot be corrected, replace torque converter. If runout is okay, mark converter position to ensure correct installation. Remove converter from flex plate.

TRANSAXLE DISASSEMBLY

1) Remove oil cooler pipes, manual shift lever, and neutral safety switch. Remove filler tube and dipstick. Remove throttle cable retaining plate. Remove governor cover bracket.

2) Remove governor cover and "O" ring. Remove thrust washer and remove governor body. Remove plate washer and governor body adapter. Remove oil pan bolts. Remove oil pan and gasket. Remove magnet from oil pan.

3) Turn transaxle over and remove tube bracket and oil strainer. Using a large screwdriver, pry and remove oil tubes. Remove detent spring. Remove manual valve and its valve body.

4) Remove 14 bolts from valve body. Disconnect throttle cable from cam and remove valve body. Remove throttle cable from case. Remove governor apply gasket and line strainer.

5) Loosen 5 bolts from accumulator piston cover 1 turn at a time until spring tension is released. Remove cover and gasket. Remove piston and spring. Apply 14 psi (1 kg/cm²) to hole below center piston to force piston and spring out of bore.

6) Install 2nd Coast Brake Piston Compressor (J-35549). Remove snap ring, cover and 2nd coast brake piston assembly. Remove 7 bolts holding oil pump to transaxle case. Firmly push brake band into case, being careful not to catch it on direct clutch drum.

7) Using Pullers (J-6125-B) and Adapters (J-35496), pull oil pump out of case. Remove direct clutch and

GENERAL MOTORS A-131L TRANSAXLE (Cont.)

Fig. 3: Exploded View of A-131L Automatic Transaxle

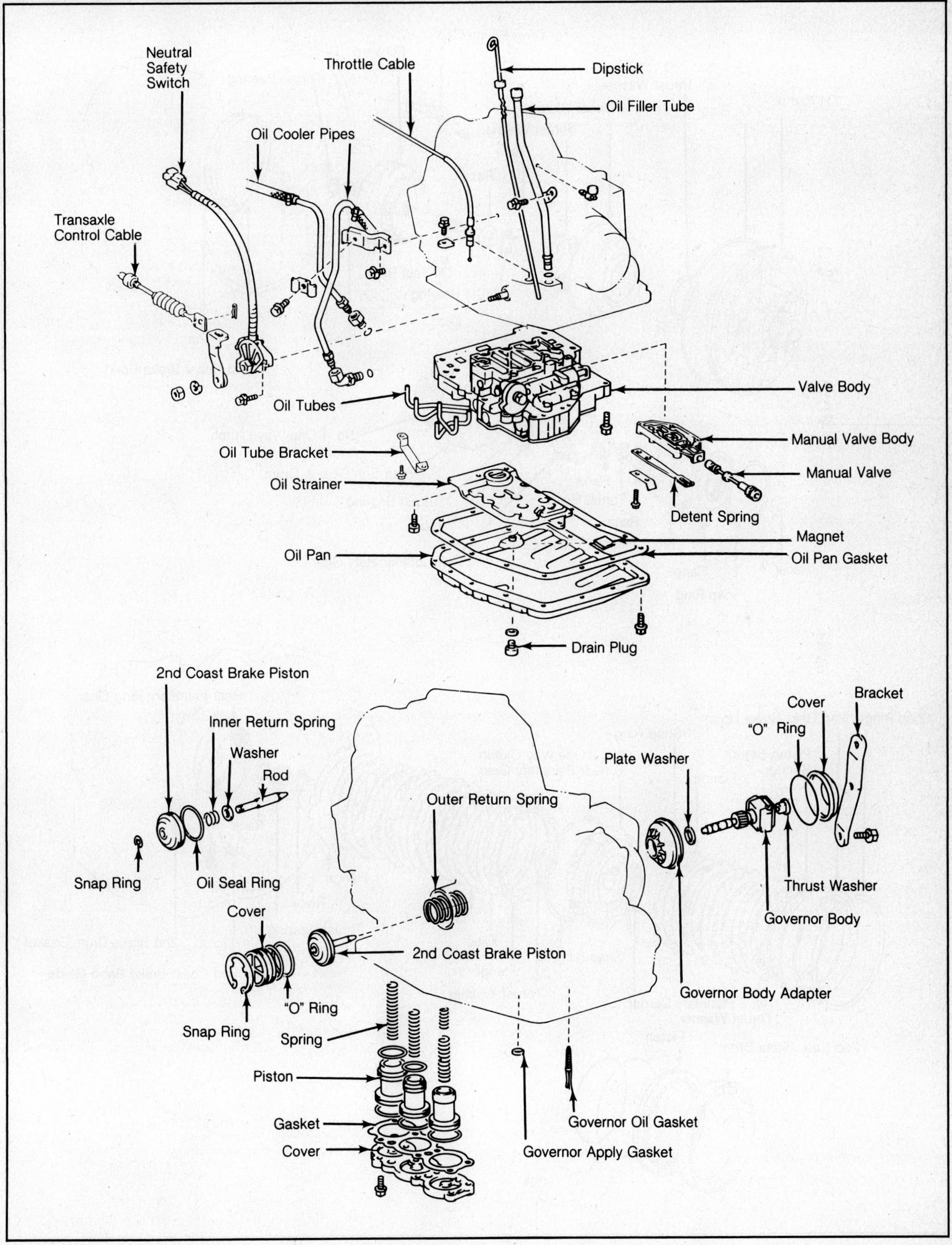

Automatic Transmissions

GENERAL MOTORS A-131L TRANSAXLE (Cont.)

Fig. 4: Exploded View of A-131L Automatic Transaxle

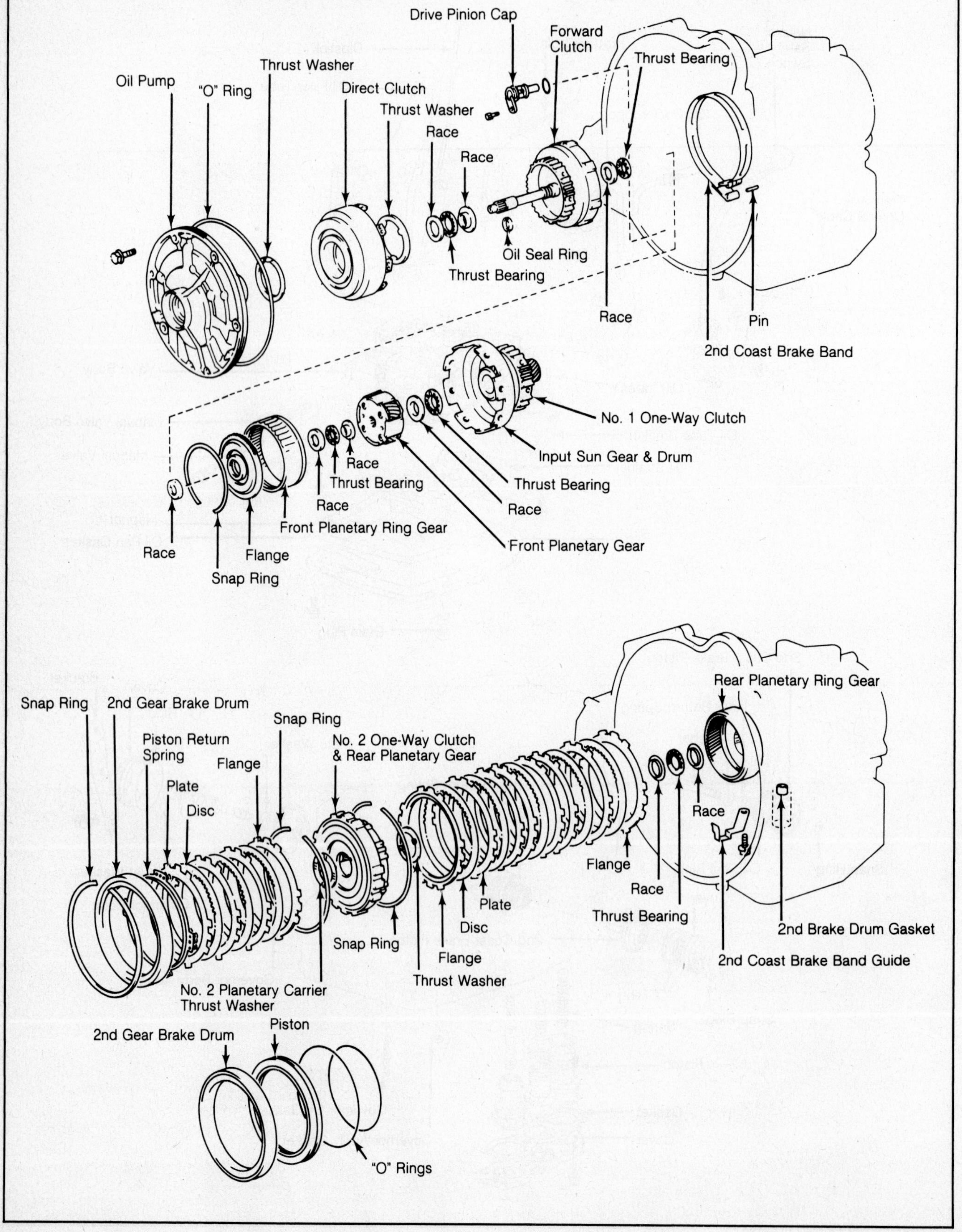

GENERAL MOTORS A-131L TRANSAXLE (Cont.)

Fig. 5: Exploded View of A-131L Automatic Transaxle

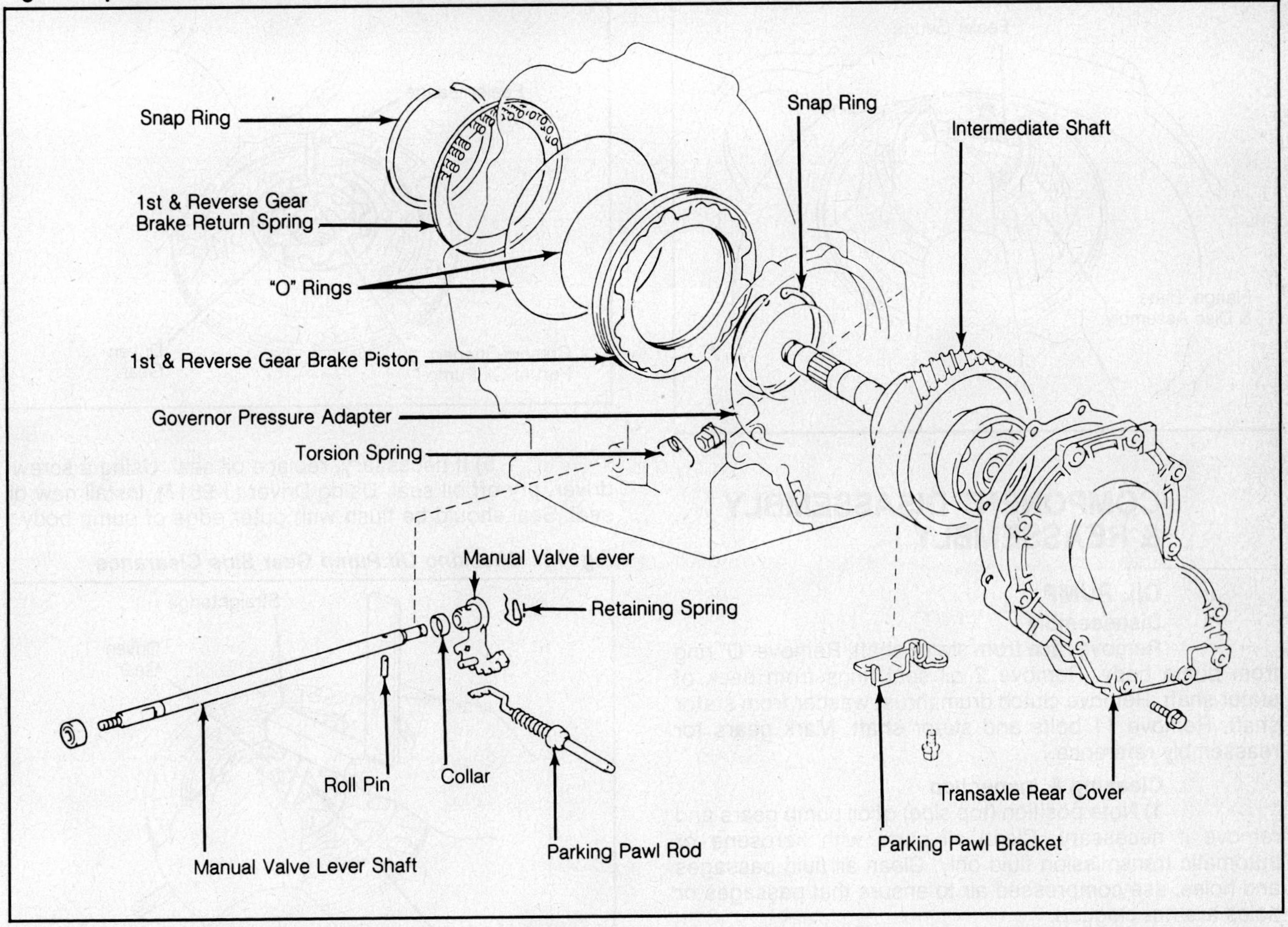

thrust washer from rear of oil pump. Remove thrust washer, bearings and races from forward (rear) clutch. Remove forward clutch. Remove bearing and race from rear of forward clutch.

8) Push 2nd coast brake band pin with a small screwdriver and remove it from oil pump mounting bolt hole. Remove 2nd coast brake band. Remove front planetary ring gear. Remove race and bearing from ring gear. Remove planetary gear. Remove bearing and race from planetary gear.

9) Remove sun gear, sun gear input drum, 2nd brake hub and No. 1 one-way clutch. Remove 2nd coast brake band guide. Using a feeler gauge, measure the clearance between 2nd brake piston return spring assembly seat and top of plate. *See Fig. 6.* Clearance should be 0.0193-0.0626" (0.49-1.59 mm). If clearance exceeds specification, replace discs.

10) Remove snap ring holding 2nd brake drum to case. Remove 2nd brake drum, if piston is difficult to remove, lightly tap drum with a wooden block. Remove 2nd brake drum gasket. Using a pin punch and hammer, tap out 2nd brake drum seal.

11) Remove plate, disc and flange. Using compressed air, blow piston and oil seal out of 2nd brake drum. Remove snap ring holding No. 2 one-way clutch outer race to case.

12) Remove No. 2 one-way clutch and rear planetary gear. Remove thrust washers from both sides of planetary carrier. Remove rear planetary ring gear and bearing. Remove bearing and race from ring gear.

Fig. 6: Measuring 2nd Brake Piston Clearance

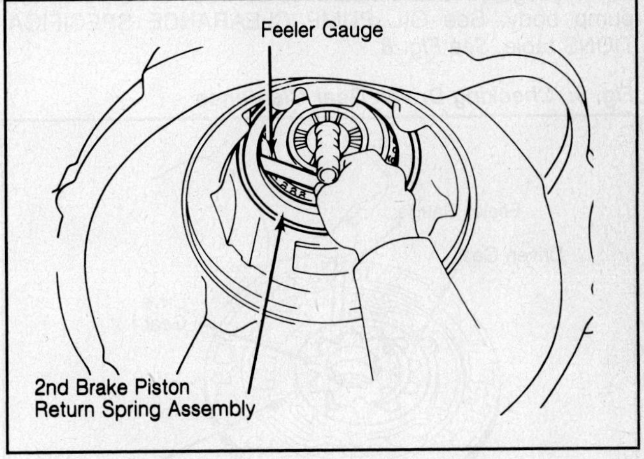

13) Using a feeler gauge, measure clearance between 1st and reverse brake piston and flange. *See Fig. 7.* Clearance should be 0.0465-0.0953" (1.18-2.42 mm).

14) Remove snap ring holding flange to case. Remove flange, plate, and disc assembly. Remove 11 bolts holding rear cover to transaxle case. Remove rear cover and intermediate shaft from case. Remove parking pawl bracket and parking pawl rod. Remove parking pawl shaft, spring and parking pawl.

GENERAL MOTORS A-131L TRANSAXLE (Cont.)

Fig. 7: Measuring 1st & Reverse Brake Clearance

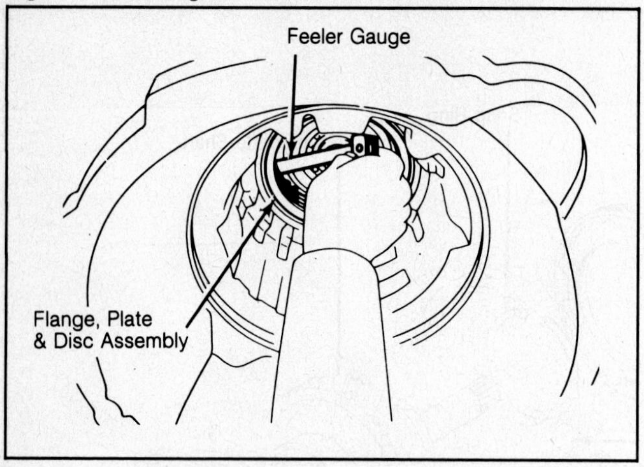

Fig. 9: Checking Driven Gear Tip Clearance

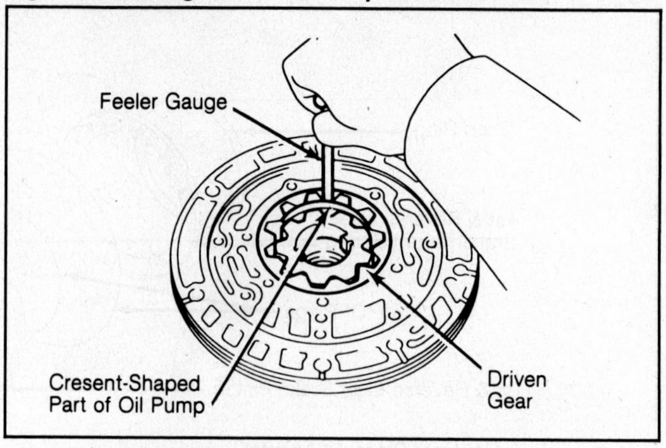

COMPONENT DISASSEMBLY & REASSEMBLY

OIL PUMP

Disassembly

Remove race from stator shaft. Remove "O" ring from pump body. Remove 2 oil seal rings from back of stator shaft. Remove clutch drum thrust washer from stator shaft. Remove 11 bolts and stator shaft. Mark gears for reassembly reference.

Cleaning & Inspection

1) Note position (top side) of oil pump gears and remove if necessary. Clean all parts with kerosene or automatic transmission fluid only. Clean all fluid passages and holes, use compressed air to ensure that passages or holes are not clogged.

2) Push driven gear to one side of body. Using a feeler gauge, measure clearance between driven gear and pump body. See OIL PUMP CLEARANCE SPECIFICATIONS table. *See Fig. 8.*

Fig. 8: Checking Driven Gear Clearance

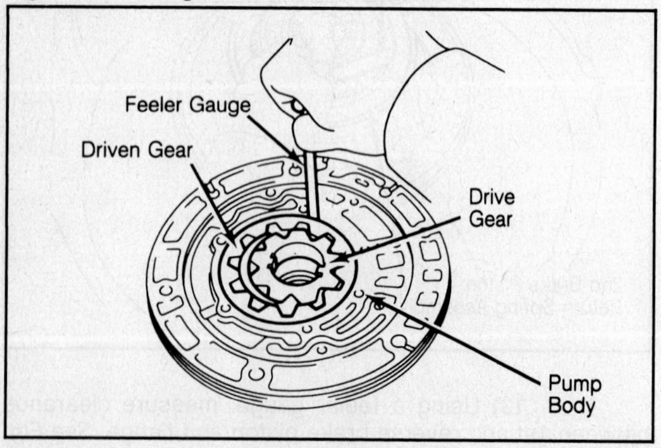

3) Using a feeler gauge, measure clearance between driven gear and crescent-shaped part of pump body. *See Fig. 9.* See OIL PUMP CLEARANCE SPECIFICATIONS table.

4) Using a feeler gauge and straightedge, measure oil pump gear side clearance. *See Fig. 10.* See OIL PUMP CLEARANCE SPECIFICATIONS table. Inspect front oil seal for wear, damage, or cracks.

5) If necessary, replace oil seal. Using a screwdriver, pry off oil seal. Using Driver (J-9617), install new oil seal. Seal should be flush with outer edge of pump body.

Fig. 10: Checking Oil Pump Gear Side Clearance

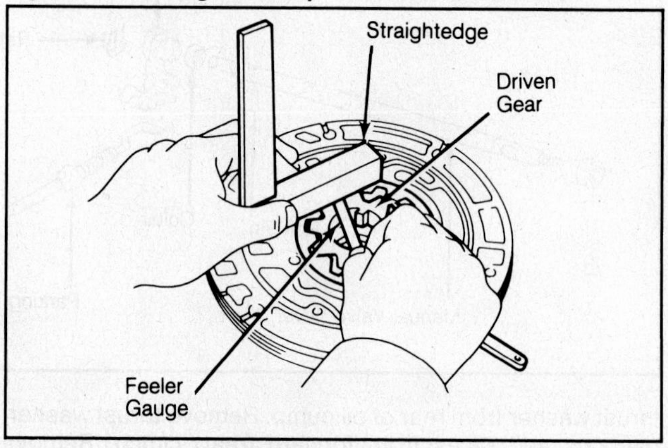

Reassembly

1) Coat parts with ATF. Install oil pump gears with top side facing up. Align stator shaft with pump body, install bolts and tighten to specification. Coat thrust washer with petroleum jelly and align tab of washer with pump body.

2) Being careful not to spread seal rings too much, install rings on pump. Turn drive gear with 2 screwdrivers, ensure that drive gear rotates smoothly. Install "O" ring. Install race on stator shaft.

OIL PUMP CLEARANCE SPECIFICATIONS

Application	Specification Inches (mm)
Driven Gear-to-Pump Body	
Standard	.0028-.0059 (.07-.15)
Maximum	.012 (.30)
Driven Gear-to-Cresent	
Standard	.0043-.0055 (.110-.140)
Maximum	.012 (.30)
Gear Side Clearance	
Standard	.0008-.0020 (.020-.050)
Maximum	.004 (.10)

GENERAL MOTORS A-131L TRANSAXLE (Cont.)

Fig. 11: Exploded View of Oil Pump Assembly

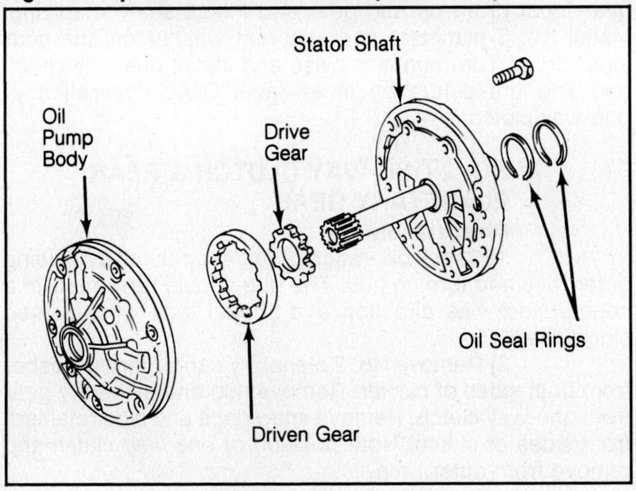

Fig. 12: Direct Clutch Assembly

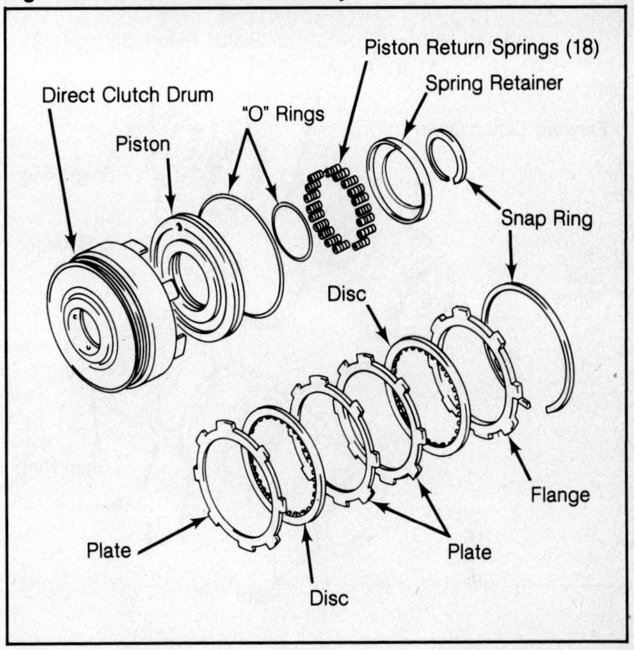

DIRECT CLUTCH

Disassembly

1) Using a feeler gauge, measure clearance between snap ring and flange. Clearance should be 0.0350-0.0575" (0.89-1.46 mm). Remove snap ring from clutch drum. Remove flange, discs and plates. Compress spring retainer and springs. Using a screwdriver, remove snap ring, spring retainer and 18 springs.

2) Install direct clutch on oil pump and apply compressed air to oil pump oval shaped passage to remove piston. If piston did not come out, use needle-nose pliers to remove it. Remove clutch piston "O" ring.

Cleaning & Inspection

Clean all parts with kerosene or automatic transmission fluid only. Use compressed air to dry all parts. Shake piston to ensure that check ball in piston is free. Check that valve does not leak by applying low pressure compressed air.

Reassembly

NOTE: New discs or plates that are to be used for replacement must be soaked in transmission fluid for at least 2 hours before assembly.

1) Coat new "O" rings with ATF and install on piston. Press piston into drum with cupped side up. Do not damage "O" rings. Install 18 piston return springs, retainer and snap ring. Ensure that snap ring gap is not aligned with spring retainer claw.

2) Install 1 plate, 1 disc, 2 plates and 1 disc. *See Fig. 12*. Install flange with flat side facing downward. Install outer snap ring and check that snap ring gap is not aligned with a cut-out.

3) Using a feeler gauge, measure clearance between snap ring and flange. Clearance should be 0.0350-0.0575" (0.89-1.46 mm). Install direct clutch on oil pump and apply compressed air to oil pump oval shaped passage. Check to see that piston moves, if not, disassemble piston and inspect.

FORWARD (REAR) CLUTCH

Disassembly

1) Remove thrust washer. Remove thrust bearings and races from both sides of clutch. Using a feeler gauge, measure clearance between snap ring and flange. Clearance should be .0161-.0425" (.410-1.080 mm).

2) Remove snap ring from clutch drum. Remove flange, discs and plates. Compress spring retainer and return springs. Remove snap ring with snap ring pliers. Remove spring retainer and 18 springs.

3) Apply compressed air to oil passage hole (nearest piston) on rear of forward clutch shaft. If piston does not come out, use needle-nose pliers to remove it. Remove oil seal rings.

Cleaning & Inspection

Clean all parts with kerosene or automatic transmission fluid only. Use compressed air to dry all parts. Shake piston to ensure that check ball in piston is free. Check that valve does not leak by applying low pressure compressed air.

Reassembly

NOTE: New discs or plates that are to be used for replacement must be soaked in transmission fluid for at least 2 hours before assembly.

1) Being careful not to spread oil seal rings too much, install rings on shaft. Coat new "O" rings with ATF and install on piston. Press piston into drum with cupped side up. Do not damage "O" rings. Install 18 piston return springs, retainer and snap ring.

2) Ensure that snap ring gap is not aligned with spring retainer claw. Install 1 plate, 1 disc, 1 plate, 1 disc, 1 plate and 1 disc. *See Fig. 13*. Install flange with flat side facing downward. Install outer snap ring and check that snap ring gap is not aligned with a cut-out.

3) Using a feeler gauge, measure clearance between snap ring and flange. Clearance should be 0.0161-0.0425" (0.410-1.080 mm). Apply compressed air to oil passage hole (nearest piston) on rear of forward clutch shaft. Check to see that piston moves, if not, disassemble piston and inspect.

NO. 1 ONE-WAY CLUTCH & SUN GEAR

Disassembly

1) Check operation of one-way clutch by holding sun gear and turning hub. The hub should turn freely in a

GENERAL MOTORS A-131L TRANSAXLE (Cont.)

Fig. 13: Forward (Rear) Clutch Assembly

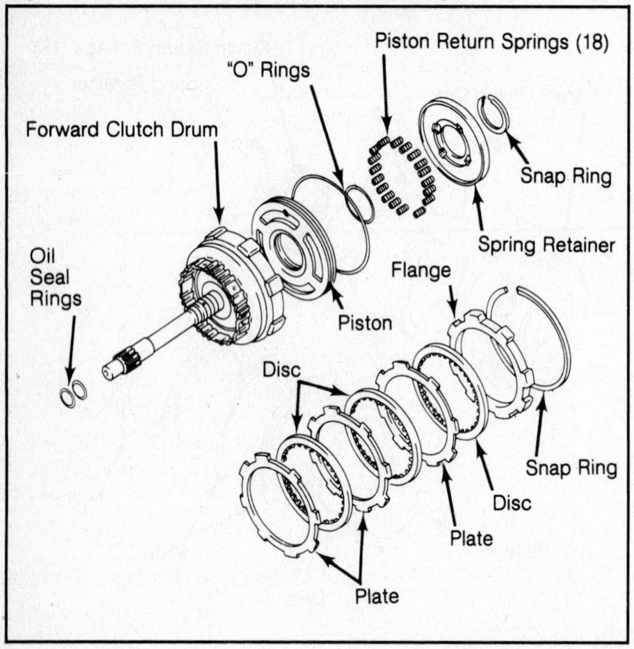

clockwise direction and should lock when turned counterclockwise.

2) Remove No. 2 brake hub and one-way clutch from inner race. Remove No. 3 planetary carrier thrust washer from sun gear input drum. Remove shaft snap ring and remove sun gear input drum. Remove shaft snap ring. If necessary, pry off one-way clutch retainer and remove one-way clutch from hub.

Cleaning & Inspection

Clean all parts with kerosene or automatic transmission fluid only. Use compressed air to dry all parts. Check thrust bearings, races, and one-way clutch for wear or damage. Replace if necessary.

Reassembly

1) Coat parts with ATF. If one-way clutch was removed, install clutch on hub with spring cage toward rear cover. Hold brake hub in soft-jawed vise and flatten retainer ears with a chisel. Ensure that retainer is centered. Check operation of one-way clutch.

Fig. 14: No. 1 One-Way Clutch & Sun Gear Assembly

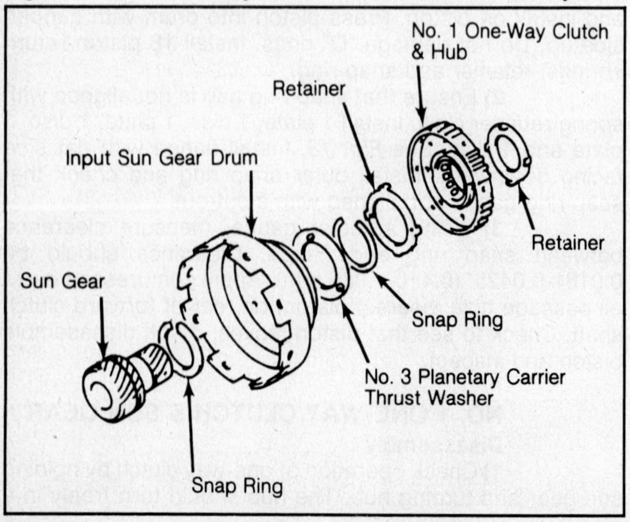

2) Install shaft snap ring on sun gear. Install sun gear input drum on sun gear and install shaft snap ring. Install No. 3 planetary carrier thrust washer on sun gear input drum. Turn hub clockwise and install one-way clutch and 2nd brake hub on inner race. Check operation of one-way clutch.

NO. 2 ONE-WAY CLUTCH & REAR PLANETARY GEAR

Disassembly

1) Check operation of one-way clutch by holding outer race and turning hub. The hub should turn freely in a counterclockwise direction and should lock when turned clockwise.

2) Remove No. 2 planetary carrier thrust washer from both sides of carrier. Remove hub and planetary gear from one-way clutch. Remove snap rings and side retainers from sides of clutch. Note position of one-way clutch and remove from outer race.

Cleaning & Inspection

Clean all parts with kerosene or automatic transmission fluid only. Use compressed air to dry all parts. Check one-way clutch for wear or damage.

Reassembly

1) Coat all parts with ATF. Install one-way clutch into outer race. Flanged side of one-way clutch should face inward from shiny side of outer race. Install both retainers and snap rings. Install planetary gear into one-way clutch.

2) Inner race of planetary gear should face inward from Black side of outer race. Check operation of one-way clutch. Install No. 2 planetary carrier thrust washers on both sides of carrier. Coat thrust washers with petroleum jelly and align thrust washer tab with hollow in carrier.

Fig. 15: No. 2 One-Way Clutch & Rear Planetary Gear Assembly

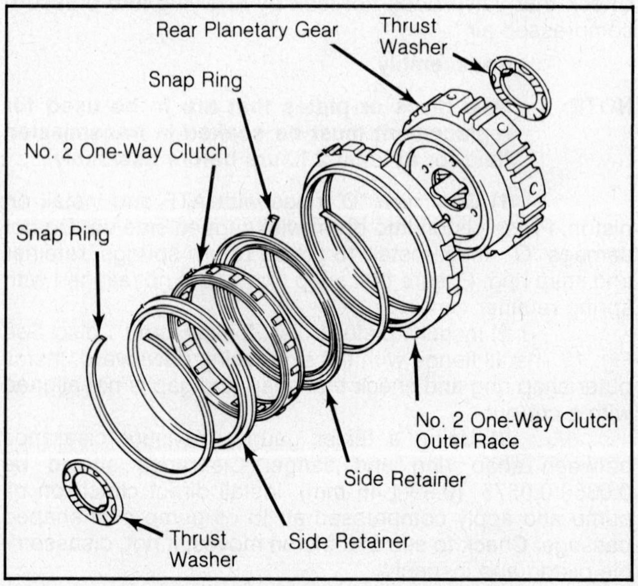

1ST & REVERSE BRAKE PISTON

Disassembly

1) Using Clutch Spring Compressor (J-23327) and Adapter (J-35683), compress springs by tightening bolt gradually. Remove spring retainer snap ring. Remove compressor.

2) Remove snap ring and return spring assembly. Apply compressed air to oil passage in transaxle case to remove piston. *See Fig. 16*. If piston does not pop out, remove piston with needle-nose pliers. Remove "O" rings from piston.

Fig. 16: 1st & Reverse Brake Piston Removal

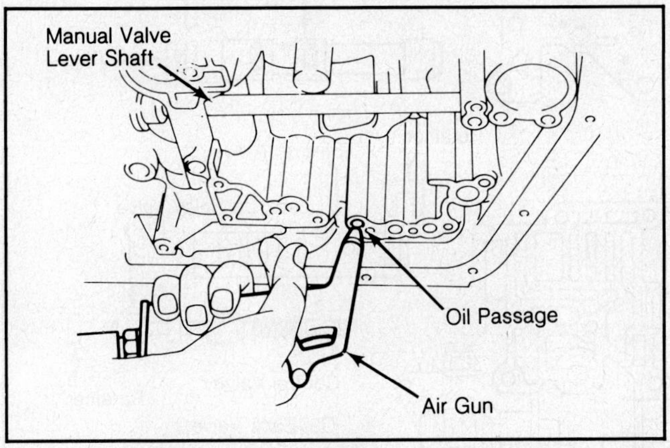

Cleaning & Inspection

Clean all parts with kerosene or automatic transmission fluid only. Use compressed air to dry all parts.

Reassembly

1) Coat new "O" rings with ATF and install on piston. Push piston into transaxle case with spring seats facing (up) forward. Install piston return spring assembly and snap ring in place.

2) Compress piston return springs to allow installation of snap ring. Avoid bending spring retainer or damaging case by overtightening compressor. Push snap ring into place with fingers.

3) Visually check snap ring to ensure that it is fully seated and centered by 3 lugs on spring retainer. Ensure that snap ring gap is not aligned with spring retainer claw. Remove compressor.

INTERMEDIATE SHAFT

Disassembly

Press intermediate shaft front bearing from shaft using Bearing Plate (J-22912-01). Press rear bearing from shaft using bearing plate and Pilot (J-35378).

Reassembly

Press new front bearing on shaft using Bearing Installer (J-35565). Press new rear beaing on shaft using Bearing Installer (J-35565). Ensure that distance from gear flange end to intermediate shaft end should be about .197" (5 mm).

VALVE BODY

Disassembly

1) Remove 14 bolts. Remove lower valve body cover and gasket. Turn assembly over and remove 12 bolts from upper valve body and upper valve body cover. Remove upper valve body cover, strainer and gasket.

2) Turn assembly over and remove 3 bolts from lower valve body. Hold valve body plate against lower valve body and carefully remove lower valve body. DO NOT allow check valve and ball to fall out. Note location of steel ball, retainers, and pins in valve body.

3) From upper valve body, remove throttle valve retainer and check ball. Remove plug retainer with a magnet and remove plug. Remove lock-up relay valve, control valve, and spring. Remove sleeve retainer with a magnet, then remove sleeve. *See Fig. 17*.

4) Remove retainer with a magnet and remove cut-back valve. Remove retainer with a magnet and remove plug, throttle modulator valve, and spring. Remove retainer with a magnet and remove plug, spring, and accumulator control valve.

5) Remove pin with a magnet and remove plug, spring, and low coast modulator valve. Remove retainer with a magnet and remove spring and 2nd coast modulator valve. Loosen throttle cam bolt. Remove bolt, throttle cam, spring, and collar.

6) Remove pin with a magnet and remove downshift plug, sleeve, and spring. Remove throttle valve. Remove springs and adjustment rings from upper valve body. Note and record number of adjustment rings.

7) From lower valve body, remove lower valve body plate and gaskets. Remove cooler by-pass valve and spring. *See Fig. 18*. Remove damping check valve and spring. Note position of 3 lower valve body check balls. Remove check balls.

8) Remove retainer with a magnet and remove plug, sleeve, and plunger. Remove spring and primary regulator valve. Note and record number of adjustment rings. Remove retainer with a magnet and remove plug, secondary regulator valve, and spring.

9) Remove retainer with a magnet and remove plug, 1-2 shift valve, and spring. Remove retainer with a magnet and remove plug and low coast shift valve. Remove retainer with a magnet and remove plug and lock-up control valve.

10) Remove retainer with a magnet and remove plug, detent regulator valve, and spring. Remove retainer with a magnet and remove plug, 2-3 shift valve, and spring. Remove retainer with a magnet and remove plug and intermediate shift valve.

11) Remove retainer with a magnet and remove plug, lock-up signal valve, and spring. Remove retainer with a magnet and remove plug and 3-4 coast shift plug. Remove retainer with a magnet and remove plug and 3-4 shift plug.

Cleaning & Inspection

1) Clean all parts with kerosene or automatic transmission fluid only. Clean all fluid passages and holes, use compressed air to ensure that passages or holes are not clogged. After cleaning, arrange parts in proper order for inspection.

2) Inspect valve springs for damage, squareness, rust and collapsed coils. Measure spring free length and replace any spring whose length is less than specified. Keep valve body springs together with corresponding valve.

Reassembly

1) Reassemble upper valve body coating parts with ATF. With valve body in a horizontal position install sleeve into bore. Coat retainer with petroleum jelly and install it on end of sleeve.

2) Install control valve, spring and lock-up relay valve. Push in on lock-up relay valve until control valve touches end of sleeve. Install plug and retainer. Install cut-back valve (small end first) into bore. Install plug and retainer. Install throttle modulator valve into bore. Install plug and retainer.

3) Install accumulator control valve and spring into bore. Install plug and retainer. Install low coast modu-

GENERAL MOTORS A-131L TRANSAXLE (Cont.)

Fig. 17: Upper Valve Body Assembly

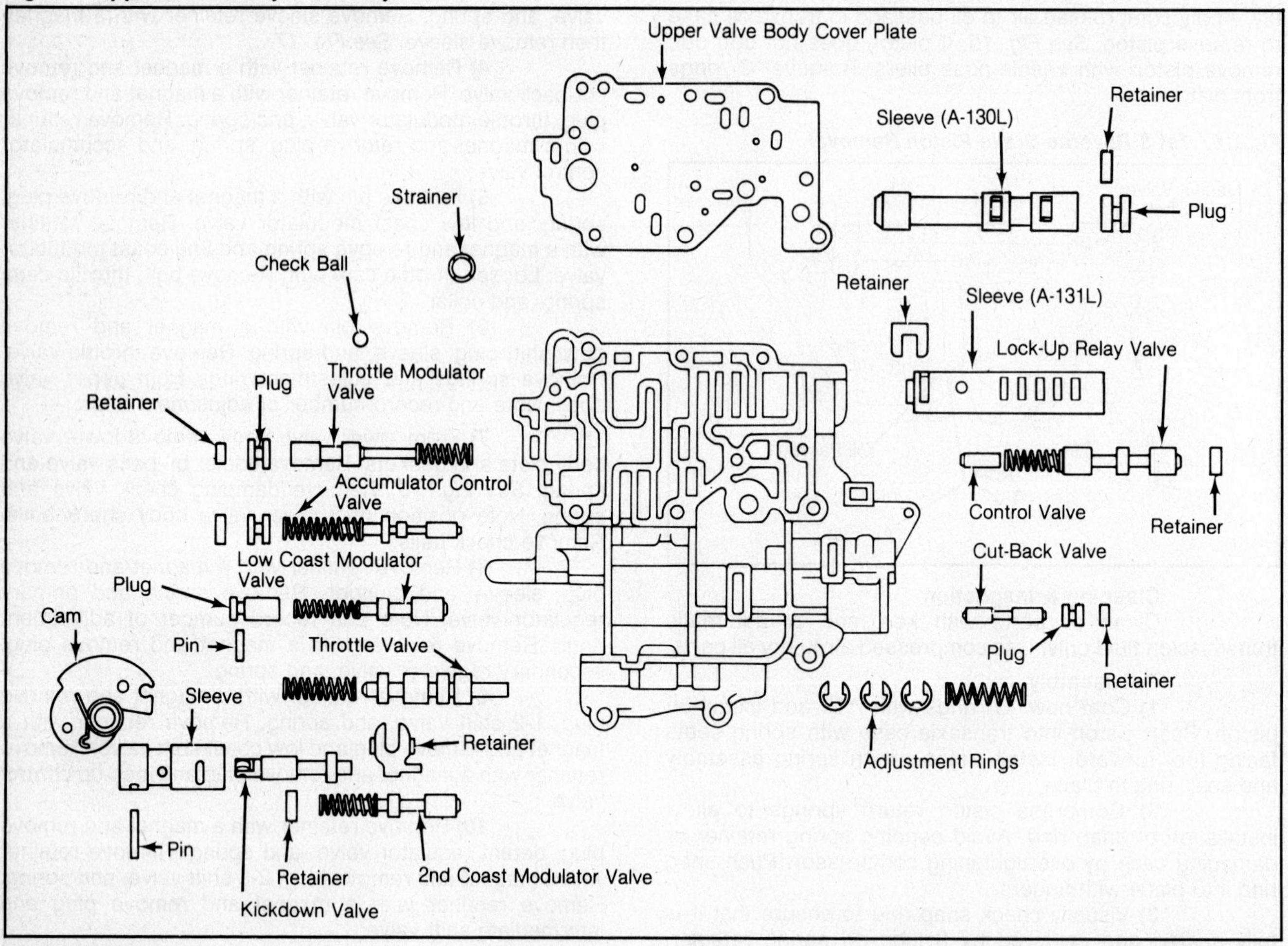

UPPER VALVE BODY SPRING FREE LENGTHS

Application	In. (mm)
Accumulator Control Valve Spring	1.3071 (33.20)
Downshift Plug Spring	1.1717 (29.76)
Lock-Up Relay Valve Spring	1.0457 (26.56)
Low Coast Modulator Valve Spring	.9213 (23.40)
Throttle Modulator Valve Spring	.8543 (21.70)
Throttle Valve Spring	1.2087 (30.70)
2nd Coast Modulator Valve Spring	.8240 (20.93)

LOWER VALVE BODY SPRING FREE LENGTHS

Application	In. (mm)
Detent Regulator Valve Spring	1.2063 (30.64)
Cooler By-Pass Valve Spring	.7335 (19.90)
Damping Check Valve Spring	.4409 (11.20)
Lock-Up Signal Valve Spring	1.6476 (41.85)
Primary Regulator Valve Spring	2.6240 (66.65)
Secondary Regulator Valve Spring	1.7165 (43.60)
1-2 Shift Valve Spring	1.0697 (27.17)
2-3 Shift Valve Spring	1.0921 (27.74)

lator valve and spring into bore. Install plug (thick end first) and retainer. Install throttle valve into bore. Coat retainer with petroluem jelly and install it in valve body.

4) Install adjustment rings (number removed) on throttle valve shaft. Slip spring over end of valve shaft. Compress spring and slide it into place. Install spring on throttle valve. Install downshift plug and sleeve. Coat pin with petroluem jelly and install to hold sleeve in place.

5) Install 2nd coast modulator valve and spring into bore. Compress spring and allow retainer to fall into place. Ensure that retainer fully covers end of spring. Install hook of spring through hole in cam and install sleeve on side of cam.

6) Install cam assembly on upper valve body. Check position of spring ends. Tighten cam bolt. Ensure that cam moves on roller of downshift plug. Install check ball. Ensure that pins and retainers are correctly installed and in place. *See Fig. 19.*

7) Reassemble lower valve body coating parts with ATF. Place valve body in a horizontal position. Install adjustment rings (number removed) and spring seat on primary regulator valve. Place valve in bore. Stand valve body up and push valve in until it bottoms in bore. Install spring.

8) Insert plunger (short end first) into sleeve. Ensure that plunger is fully inserted in sleeve. Install sleeve and plunger in primary regulator valve bore. Install retainer.

9) Install spring and secondary regulator valve in bore. Install plug and retainer. Install spring and 1-2 shift valve in bore. Install plug and retainer. Install lock-up control valve in bore. Coat retainer with petroluem jelly and install plug and retainer.

Automatic Transmissions

GENERAL MOTORS A-131L TRANSAXLE (Cont.)

Fig. 18: Lower Valve Body Assembly

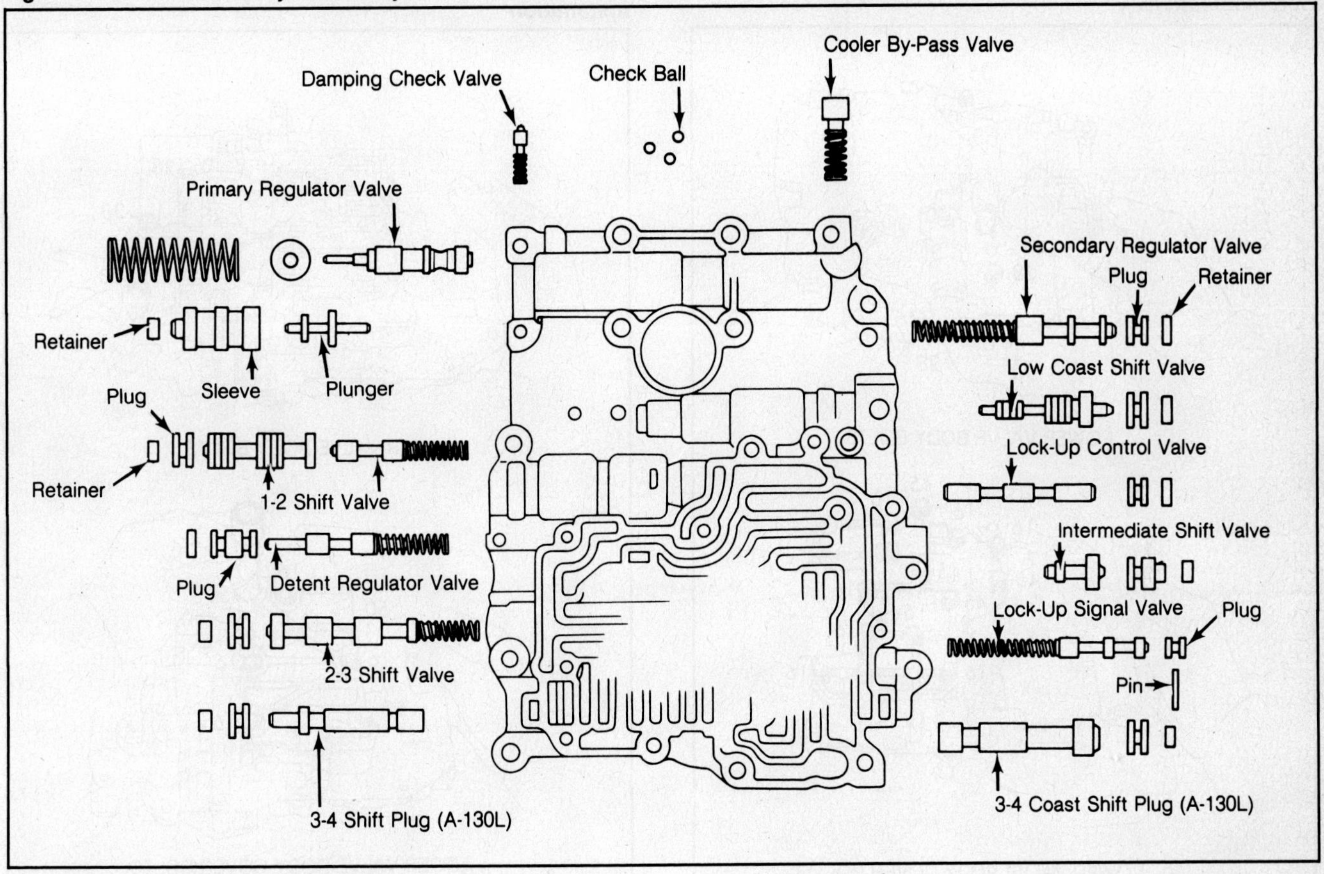

Fig. 19: Upper Valve Body Check Ball, Pin & Retainer Locations

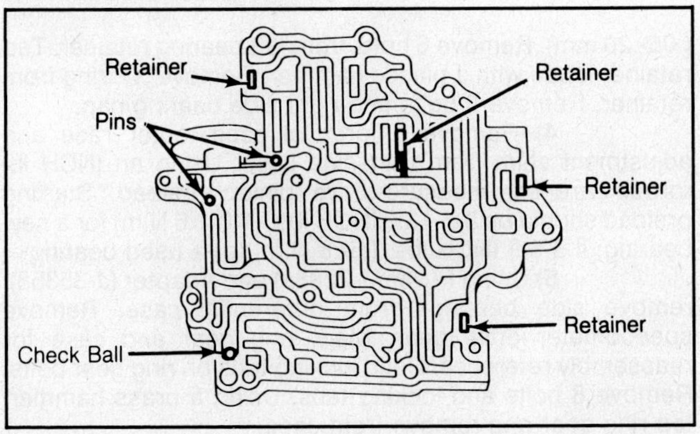

10) Install spring and detent regulator valve (thin end first) into bore. Install plug and retainer. Install intermediate shift valve (small end first) into bore. Install plug and retainer. Install spring and 2-3 shift valve into bore. Install plug and retainer.

11) Install spring and lock-up signal valve in bore. Install plug and pin. Install 3-4 coast shift plug. Install plug and retainer. Install spring and cooler by-pass valve. Install spring and damping valve. Ensure that pin and retainers are correctly installed and in place. Install 3 check balls. *See Fig. 20.*

12) Place gasket having larger cooler by-pass valve hole against lower valve body. Place plate and second gasket on top of first gasket. Align bolt holes in valve body with gaskets and plate.

13) Tightly hold lower valve body, gaskets and plate. Place lower valve body, gaskets and plate on top of upper valve body. Align bolt holes in valve bodies, gaskets and plate. Install and finger tighten 3 bolts in lower valve body. *See Fig. 21.*

Fig. 20: Lower Valve Body Check Ball, Pin & Retainer Locations

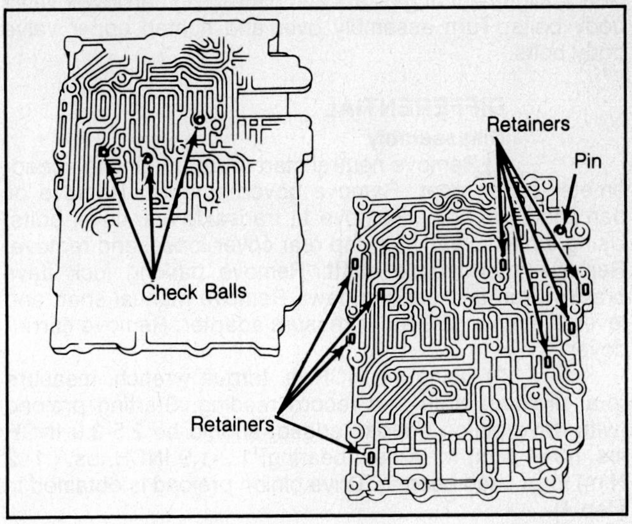

GENERAL MOTORS A-131L TRANSAXLE (Cont.)

Fig. 21: Lower Valve Body & Valve Body Cover Bolt Installation

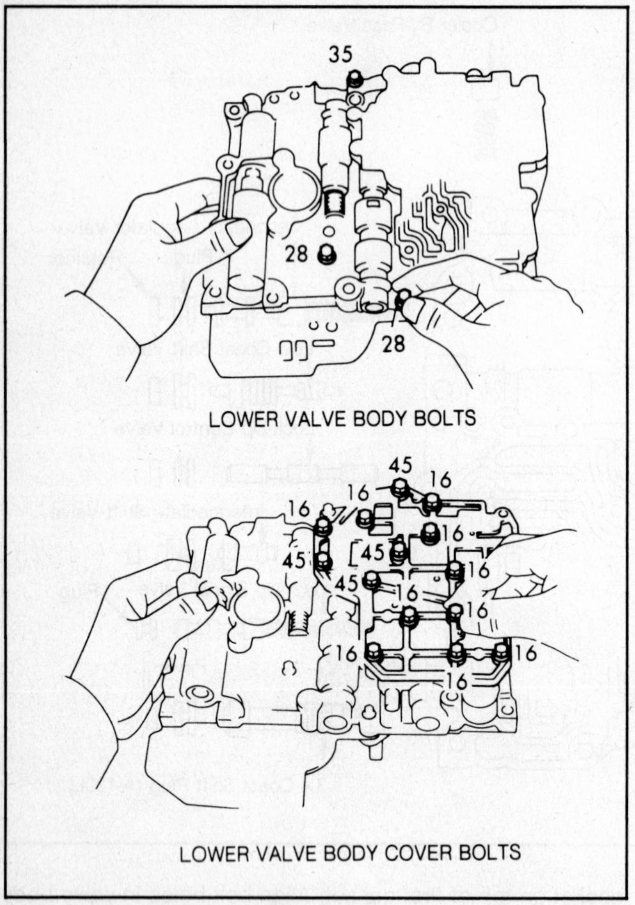

Bolt length (mm) is shown in figure.

Fig. 22: Upper Valve Body & Valve Body Cover Bolt Installation

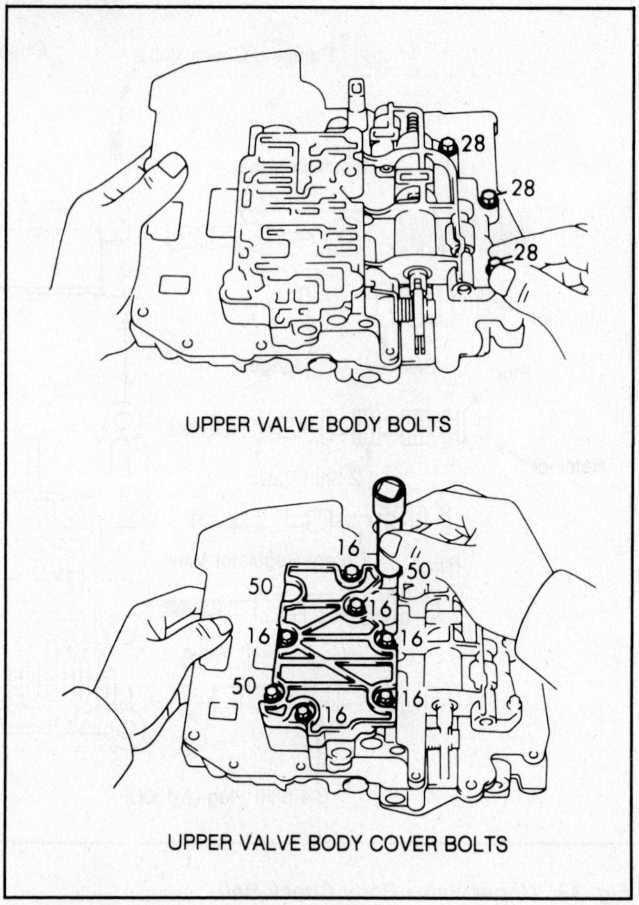

Bolt length (mm) is shown in figure.

14) Turn assembly over. Install and finger tighten 3 bolts in upper valve body. *See Fig. 22*. Install gasket, plate, and gasket on upper valve body. Install strainer on plate. Install upper valve body cover and finger tighten 9 bolts. *See Fig. 22*.

15) Turn assembly over. Install lower valve body gasket, cover, and finger tighten 14 bolts. *See Fig. 21*. Check alignment of gaskets and plates. Tighten lower valve body bolts. Turn assembly over and tighten upper valve body bolts.

DIFFERENTIAL

Disassembly

1) Remove neutral start switch. Remove speedometer driven gear. Remove governor body. Remove oil pan and valve body. Remove 11 transaxle rear cover bolts. Using a plastic hammer, tap rear cover loose, and remove. Remove intermediate shaft. Remove parking lock pawl bracket, rod and parking pawl. Remove manual shaft and lever. Remove governor pressure adapter. Remove carrier cover.

2) Using an INCH lb. torque wrench, measure total preload. Note and record reading. Starting preload (with drive pinion preload added) should be 2.5-3.9 INCH lbs. (.3-.4 N.m) for a new bearing; 1.2-1.9 INCH lbs. (.1-.2 N.m) for a used bearing. Drive pinion preload is obtained in step **4)**.

3) Measure side gear backlash while holding 1 pinion toward case. Backlash should be .0020-.0079" (.05-.20 mm). Remove 6 bolts from left bearing retainer. Tap retainer loose with a plastic hammer. Remove "O" ring from retainer. Remove 2 bolts and right side bearing cap.

4) Remove differential case, outer race and adjustment shim from transaxle case. Using an INCH lb. torque wrench, measure drive pinion preload. Starting preload should be 8.7-13.9 INCH lbs. (1.0-1.6 N.m) for a new bearing; 4.3-6.9 INCH lbs. (.5-.8 N.m) for a used bearing.

5) Using Puller (J-22888) and Adapter (J-35358), remove side bearings from differential case. Remove speedometer drive gear. Mark ring gear and case for reassembly reference. Bend locking tabs on ring gear bolts. Remove 8 bolts and locking tabs. Using a brass hammer, tap ring gear and remove from case.

6) While holding 1 pinion against case, measure side gear backlash. If backlash is incorrect, disassemble case and change thrust washer on side gears. Drive out pinion shaft lock pin and remove pinion shaft. Remove pinions, side gears and 4 thrust washers from each gear.

7) Remove oil seal from left bearing retainer. Press out left bearing outer race and shim. Using a long screwdriver, remove right bearing oil seal from transfer case.

Cleaning & Inspection

Clean all parts with kerosene or automatic transmission fluid only. Use compressed air to dry all parts. Check bearings and gears for wear or damage. Replace if necessary.

Reassembly

1) Coat lip of oil seals with multipurpose grease. Install oil seals. Install shim in left bearing retainer. Using Driver (J-35552), install bearing outer race.

2) Select thrust washers that will ensure correct backlash. Install thrust washers and side gears in case. If possible, install same size washers on both sides of gears. Install pinions and pinion shaft.

3) While holding 1 pinion against case, check side gear backlash. Backlash should be .0020-.0079" (.05-.20 mm). If backlash is incorrect, disassemble case and change thrust washer on side gears.

NOTE: **Side gear thrust washers are available in the following thickness variations: .0374" (.95 mm), .0394" (1.00 mm), .0413" (1.05 mm), .0433" (1.10 mm), .0453" (1.15 mm) and .0472" (1.20 mm).**

4) Using a hammer and punch, drive lock pin through case and into pinion shaft. Stake differential case to hold pin in place. Clean ring gear contact surface of case. Heat ring gear to 212°F (100°C) in an oil bath.

5) Clean contact surface of ring gear with cleaning solvent. Align ring gear with differential case, and quickly install ring gear on case. Install locking tabs and bolts. Tighten bolts evenly and a little at a time.

6) Using a hammer and punch, bend locking tabs. Stake 1st tab flush with flat surface of nut. Stake 2nd tab against corner of nut. Install speedometer drive gear. Using Bearing Installer (J-35409), press bearings onto differential case.

7) Install outer race and adjustment shim on right bearing. Install differential in transaxle case. Install left bearing retainer without "O" ring. Snug bolts evenly and gradually while turning ring gear, then tighten bolts.

8) Install right bearing cap. Snug bolts evenly and gradually while turning ring gear, then tighten bolts. Using Differential Preload Adapter (J-35405) and an INCH lb. torque wrench, measure differential bearing preload.

9) Starting preload should be 6.9-13.9 INCH lbs. (.8-1.6 N.m) for a new bearing; 4.3-8.7 INCH lbs. (.5-1.0 N.m) for a used bearing. If preload is incorrect, remove differential from case and change adjustment shim.

NOTE: **Preload will change about 2.6-3.5 INCH lbs. (.3-.4 N.m) with each shim thickness.**

Fig. 23: Measuring Differential Bearing Preload

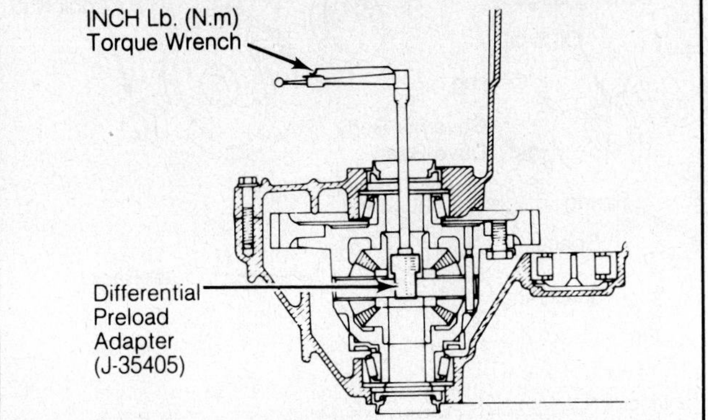

10) If preload is within specification, remove left bearing retainer, differential and shim. Do not lose selected adjustment shim. Reinstall outer race and adjustment shim on right bearing. Install "O" ring on left bearing retainer.

DIFFERENTIAL BEARING PRELOAD SHIM SELECTION

I.D. Mark	Thickness In. (mm)
A-131L	
None	.0630 (1.60)
None	.0650 (1.65)
None	.0669 (1.70)
None	.0689 (1.75)
None	.0709 (1.80)
None	.0728 (1.85)
None	.0748 (1.90)
None	.0768 (1.95)
None	.0787 (2.00)
None	.0807 (2.05)
None	.0827 (2.10)
None	.0846 (2.15)
None	.0866 (2.20)
None	.0886 (2.25)
None	.0906 (2.30)
None	.0925 (2.35)
None	.0945 (2.40)
None	.0965 (2.45)
None	.0984 (2.50)
None	.1004 (2.55)
None	.1024 (2.60)
None	.1043 (2.65)

11) Install differential and retainer on case. Clean threads of bolts and case with White gasoline. Coat bolt threads with sealer. Snug bolts evenly and gradually while turning ring gear. Install right bearing cap. Snug bolts evenly and gradually while turning ring gear. Tighten cap and left bearing retainer bolts.

12) With drive pinion installed in case, measure total preload. Starting preload (with drive pinion preload added) should be 2.5-3.9 INCH lbs. (.3-.4 N.m) for a new bearing; 1.2-1.9 INCH lbs. (.1-.2 N.m) for a used bearing.

NOTE: **If drive pinion was diassembled, use bearing preload obtained during reassembly.**

13) If total preload is not within specification, disassemble differential and readjust. If total preload is correct, stake counter driven gear lock nut. Install drive pinion cap.

14) Clean threads of bolts and case with White gasoline. Coat bolt threads with sealer. Install carrier cover over gasket. Install cover and tighten bolts.

15) Install intermediate shaft while turning counter driven gear. Do not damage bushing and oil seal. Install transaxle rear cover and tighten bolts. Install speedometer driven gear.

DIFFERENTIAL DRIVE PINION

Disassembly

1) Using an INCH lb. torque wrench, measure drive pinion preload. Starting preload should be 8.7-13.9 INCH lbs. (1.0-1.6 N.m) for a new bearing; 4.3-6.9 INCH lbs. (.5-.8 N.m) for a used bearing.

2) Remove drive pinion cap. Using a chisel, loosen staked part of counter driven gear lock nut. Install Holder (J-8614-01) on gear. Using socket, remove counter driven gear lock nut. Using Puller (J-1859-03), remove gear and bearing.

Automatic Transmissions

GENERAL MOTORS A-131L TRANSAXLE (Cont.)

Fig. 24: Exploded View of A-131L Transaxle Differential & Drive Pinion Assemblies

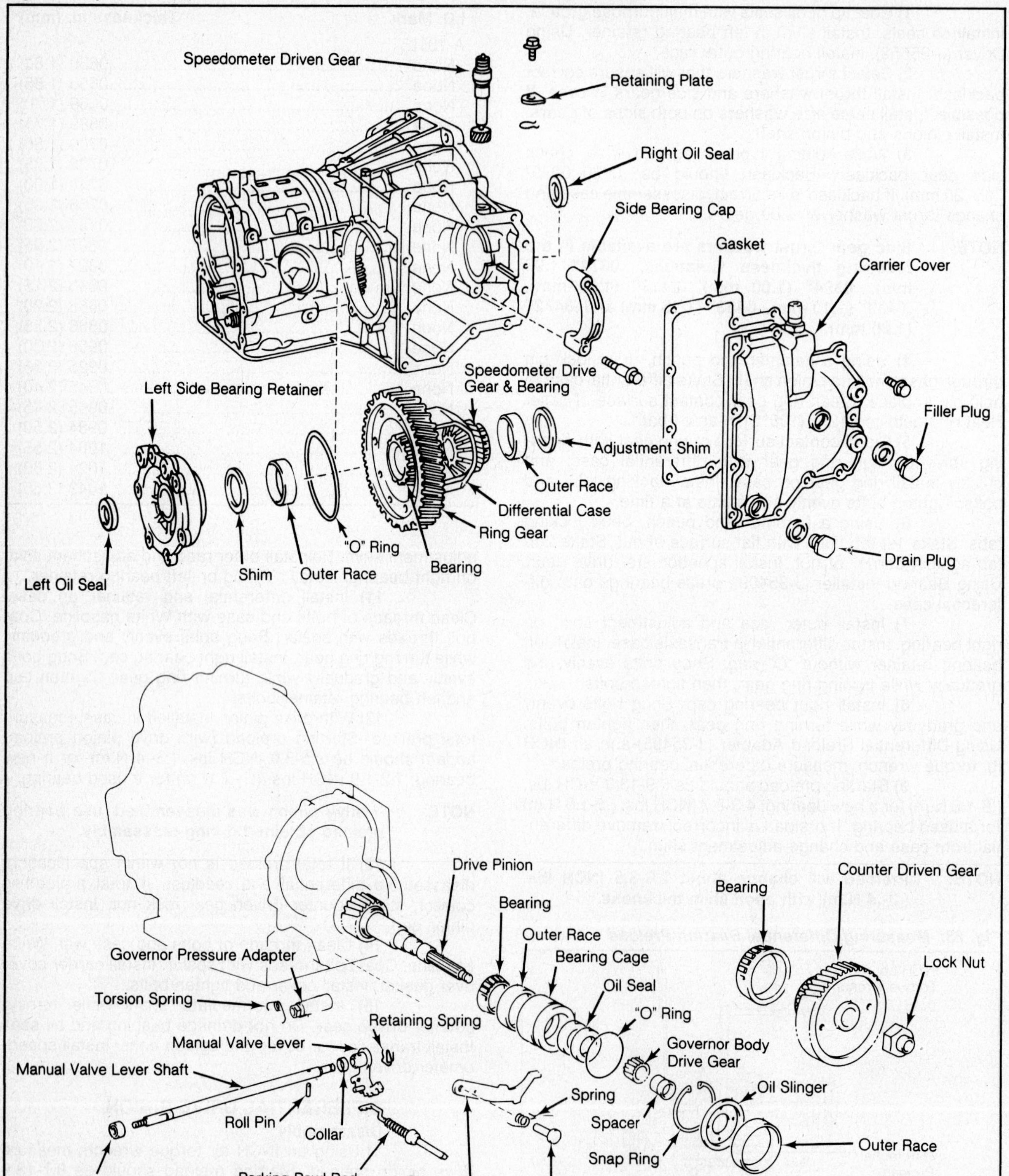

3) Using Puller (J-26941) and slide hammer, remove bearing outer race. Remove oil slinger, bearing spacer and governor body drive gear. If gear is too tight, remove it later. Remove snap ring using snap ring pliers.

4) Insert brass bar into hole and drive out drive pinion and bearing cage from bore. Press governor drive gear out of drive pinion shaft. Remove bearing cage from drive pinion. Remove "O" ring from bearing cage.

5) Using Bearing Remover (J-22912-01) and Adapter (J-23454), press bearing out of counter driven gear. Using bearing remover, press bearing out of pinion shaft. Using Puller (J-26941) without bolt, drive bearing outer race from cage. Note position of lip on oil seals, and press seals out of cage.

Cleaning & Inspection

Clean all parts with kerosene or automatic transmission fluid only. Use compressed air to dry all parts. Check bearings and gears for wear or damage. Replace if necessary.

Reassembly

1) Coat lip of cage oil seals with multipurpose grease. With lip of inner seal facing downward, press in oil seal until top of seal is at a depth of .43" (10 mm). With lip of outer seal facing upward, press in oil seal until it is flush with cage surface. Press outer bearing race into bearing cage.

2) Using Bearing Installer (J-35664), press bearing onto pinion shaft. Using bearing installer, press bearing onto counter driven gear. Install "O" ring on bearing cage. Install cage on drive pinion shaft. Do not damage oil seals with splines.

3) Press governor drive gear onto drive pinion shaft. Install shaft assembly into case. Tap bearing cage into case. Ensure that cage is past snap ring groove in bore, and that groove can be seen.

4) Install snap ring using snap ring pliers. Insert brass bar into hole and tap drive pinion shaft against snap ring. Ensure that snap ring is properly installed. Install oil slinger with lip facing outward. Drive outer race into case.

5) Install new bearing spacer, small end first. Insert a bar into hole and position against drive pinion shaft. Position other end of bar against a solid object. Drive counter driven gear onto shaft until lock nut can be installed. Do not tap on transaxle case.

6) Coat threads and lock nut with multipurpose grease. Install nut on shaft. Install Holder (J-8614-01) on gear. Using socket, tighten counter driven gear lock nut. Turn gear counterclockwise and then clockwise several times.

7) Using an INCH lb. torque wrench, measure drive pinion preload. Starting preload should be 8.7-13.9 INCH lbs. (1.0-1.6 N.m) for a new bearing; 4.3-6.9 INCH lbs. (.5-.8 N.m) for a used bearing. If preload is greater than specified, replace bearing spacer and repeat preload procedure.

8) If preload is less than specified, retighten lock nut 9 ft. lbs. (13 N.m) at a time until specified preload is obtained. If maximum torque of 213 ft. lbs. (289 N.m) is exceeded while retightening nut, replace bearing spacer and repeat procedure. DO NOT back off nut to reduce preload.

TRANSAXLE REASSEMBLY

1) Place parking pawl and manual valve lever shaft in transaxle case. Hook spring end on pawl and case. Install pin in case, through spring and pawl. Install parking lock rod.

2) Install parking pawl bracket and tighten bolt. Check operation of pawl to ensure that counter driven gear is locked when manual valve lever is in the "P" range.

3) Install intermediate shaft. Install transaxle rear cover over gasket. Install cover and tighten bolts. Ensure that intermediate shaft turns smoothly. Check intermediate shaft end play. End play should be .0193-.0594" (.049-1.51 mm).

4) Install 1st and reverse inner flange with flat side facing (oil pump) forward. Install 1 disc, 1 plate, 1 disc, 2 plates, 1 disc, 1 plate, 2 plates, 1 disc, 1 plate and 1 disc. Install outer flange with flat side toward piston. Install snap ring.

5) Using a feeler gauge, measure clearance between 1st and reverse brake piston and flange. *See Fig. 7*. Clearance should be .0465-.0953" (1.18-2.42 mm).

6) Apply compressed air to oil passage and check that piston moves. *See Fig. 16*. Coat No. 2 planetary carrier thrust washer with petroleum jelly and install on carrier. Ensure thrust washer lugs match openings in carrier.

7) Coat rear ring gear races and bearing with petroleum jelly and install them onto ring gear. Install planetary gear onto ring gear. Ensure that thrust bearing is installed in center of ring gear flange.

8) Align tabs of discs with 1st and reverse brake. Align splines of planetary carrier with tabs of discs and install rear planetary gear into 1st and reverse brake discs.

9) Place No. 2 one-way clutch in case. Install one-way clutch onto inner race while turning the planetary pinion counterclockwise with a screwdriver. Check operation on clutch by turning planetary carrier. The carrier should turn freely clockwise and should lock when turned counterclockwise. Install snap ring.

10) Install 2nd coast brake band guide and 2nd brake drum guide. Install band guide so that its tip touches case. Install 2nd brake flange with flat side toward 2nd brake piston. Install 1 disc, 1 plate, 1 disc, 1 plate, 1 disc and 1 plate.

11) Install piston return spring assembly. Install each spring over protrusions in case. Align groove of 2nd brake drum with guide and install drum in case. Install snap ring so that end gap is installed in groove. Using 2 hammers, compress piston return springs with handles. Install snap ring into groove.

12) Using a feeler gauge, measure the clearance between 2nd brake piston return spring assembly seat and top of plate. *See Fig. 6*. Clearance should be .0193-.0626" (.49-1.59 mm). Apply compressed air to center oil passage (next to manual valve lever shaft) and ensure that piston moves.

13) Install 2nd brake drum seal in center oil passage until the distance between surface of case (passage) and top of seal is 1.138-1.142" (28.95-29.05 mm).

14) Align tabs of discs in 2nd brake. Align splines of 2nd brake hub and No. 1 one-way clutch with tabs of discs and install hub on 2nd brake discs. Install sun gear and sun gear input drum onto one-way clutch while turning sun gear clockwise.

NOTE: **Place sun gear in center of intermediate shaft to protect bushings from damage.**

15) Coat front ring gear races and bearing with petroleum jelly and install them onto ring gear. Coat race

GENERAL MOTORS A-131L TRANSAXLE (Cont.)

and bearing with petroluem jelly and install them onto carrier. Install front planetary gear onto ring gear. Install front planetary gear assembly onto sun gear.

16) If planetary gear and other parts are installed correctly in case, the bushing on the ring gear flange will be flush with shoulder of intermediate shaft. Coat race with petroluem jelly and install it onto tip of ring gear flange.

17) Install 2nd coast brake band in case. Install pin through oil pump mounting bolt hole. Coat forward (rear) clutch races and bearing with petroleum jelly and install them onto both sides of clutch drum. Align tabs of discs in forward clutch.

18) Install clutch on sun gear. Hold sun gear input drum and rotate input shaft to mesh hub with clutch discs of forward clutch. Align center of input shaft and intermediate shaft, and while pushing on input shaft, rotate it to mesh hub and disc.

19) If tabs of discs are correctly meshed with hub, the protrusion around clutch drum will be flush with tip of input sun gear drum. Coat direct clutch drum thrust washer with petroleum jelly and install it with oil groove facing upward onto drum.

20) Align tabs of discs in direct clutch. Hold input shaft, and install clutch drum through and into 2nd coast brake band. Mesh hub with tabs of direct clutch while turning clutch drum. If tabs of discs are correctly meshed with hub, the end of bushing on direct clutch drum will be flush with thrust bearing on forward clutch.

21) Coat oil pump race with petroleum jelly and install it onto stator shaft. Insert oil pump (without "O" ring) through input shaft, and aling bolt holes with case. Hold input shaft and lightly press oil pump body to slide oil seal rings on stator shaft through direct clutch drum. Install and tighten bolts.

NOTE: **Do not push strongly on oil pump or the seal rings will stick to direct clutch drum.**

22) Ensure that input shaft rotates smoothly. Using a dial indicator, measure input shaft end play. End play should be .012-.035" (.30-.90 mm). If end play is incorrect, remove oil pump and install a new oil pump race. Oil pump races are available in thicknesses of .031" (.80 mm) and .055" (1.40 mm).

23) If input shaft end play is correct, remove oil pump. Install "O" ring around pump body. Insert oil pump through input shaft, and align bolt holes with case. Hold input shaft and lightly press oil pump body to slide oil seal rings on stator shaft through direct clutch drum. Install and tighten bolts.

24) Ensure that input shaft rotates smoothly and recheck input shaft end play. Install 2nd coast brake piston (without outer spring) and install snap ring. Firmly push brake apply rod into case.

25) Measure distance between outer side of snap ring and tip of piston rod. Piston travel must be within .059-.118" (1.5-3.0 mm). If travel is not within specifications, select a longer brake apply rod. Brake apply rods are available in lenghts of 2.870" (72.9 mm) and 2.811" (71.4 mm).

26) Re-measure piston travel. If travel is still more than specified, replace 2nd coast brake band with a new one. If travel is correct, remove installed parts from bore. Install outer spring, piston, and cover. Compress spring and install snap ring.

27) Apply compressed air to hole and check that piston rod moves. *See Fig. 25.* Install accumulator springs and pistons. Install cover, gasket, and bolts. Tighten bolts a little at a time.

Fig. 25: Cheking 2nd Coast Brake Band.

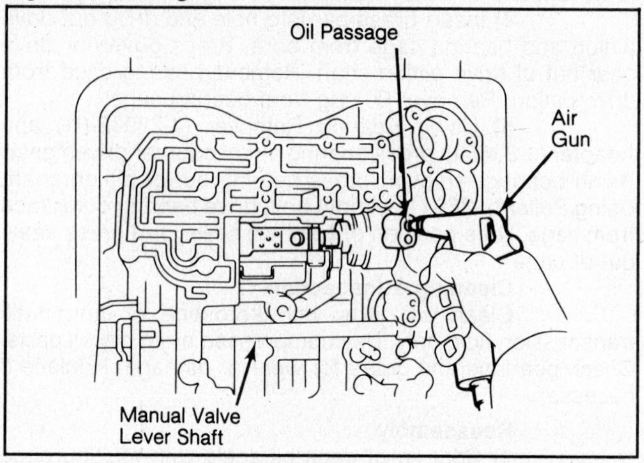

28) Install governor apply gasket and governor line strainer. Push throttle cable through case, being careful not to damage "O" ring. Ensure that cable is fully seated in case.

29) Place valve body in transaxle, and while holding cam down with your hand, slip cable end into slot in cam. Lower valve body into place. Install valve body bolts finger tight, and then tighten to specification. *See Fig. 26.*

Fig. 26: Valve Body Bolt Installation

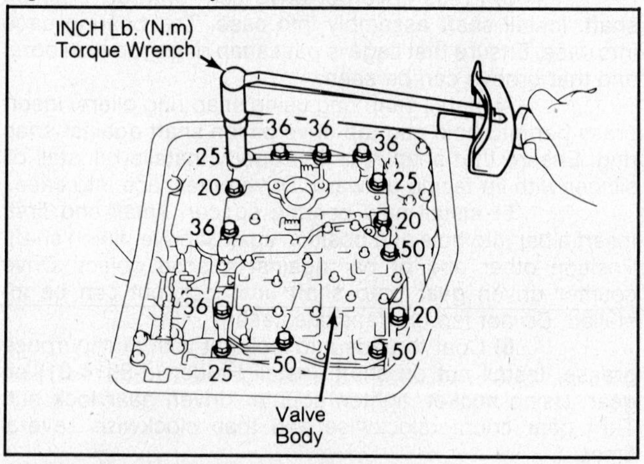

Bolt length (mm) is shown in figure.

30) Align manual valve with pin on manual shaft lever. Lower valve body into place. Install detent spring. Check that manual valve lever is touching center of detent spring roller. Install valve body bolts finger tight, and then tighten to specification. *See Fig. 27.*

31) Using a plastic hammer, install oil tubes. Be careful not to bend or damage tubes. Install tube bracket. Install oil strainer. Tighten mounting bolts to specification.

32) Install magnet in oil pan. Ensure that magnet does not interfere with oil tubes. Install oil pan and gasket. Tighten bolts. Install governor body adapter. Install governor body with plate washer.

33) Install thrust washer onto governor body. Install cover over "O" ring. Install cover bracket with 2 bolts. Install throttle cable retaining plate. Install filler tube and

GENERAL MOTORS A-131L TRANSAXLE (Cont.)

Fig. 27: Manual Valve Body Bolt Installation

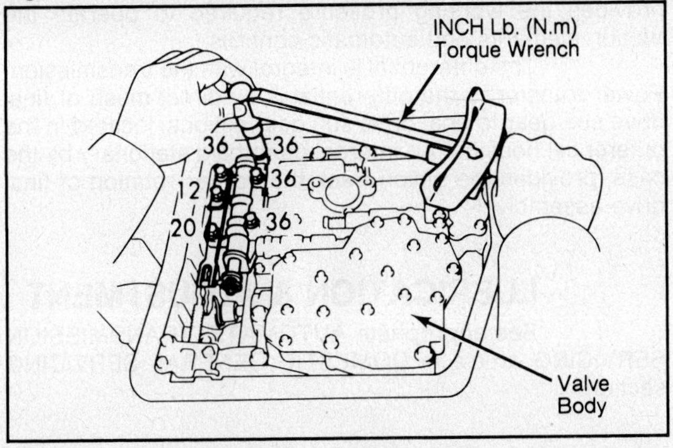

Bolt length (mm) is shown in figure.

dipstick. Install seal (lip facing inward) and neutral safety switch. Tighten nut and secure with lock washer. Install shift handle.

34) Connect an ohmmeter between neutral switch terminals. Shift lever into "N" position. Adjust switch so that there is continuity between terminals. Tighten neutral switch bolts. Install oil pipe bracket onto case. Connect pipes to union. Clamp pipes onto braket. Tighten union nuts.

TIGHTENING SPECIFICATIONS

Application	Ft. Lbs (N.m)
Carrier Cover Bolts	18 (25)
Counter Driven Gear Lock Nut	127 (172)
Flex Plate Bolts	61 (83)
Left Bearing Retainer Bolts	14 (19)
Oil Cooler Pipes	25 (34)
Oil Pump Bolts	16 (22)
Right Bearing Cap Bolts	36 (49)
Ring Gear Bolts	71 (96)
Torque Converter Bolts	13 (18)
Transaxle Mounting Bolts	
10 mm	34 (46)
12 mm	47 (64)
Transaxle Rear Cover Bolts	18 (25)
	INCH Lbs. (N.m)
Governor Bracket Bolts	108 (12)
Manual Valve Body-to-Transaxle	84 (10)
Neutral Start Switch	48 (5.4)
Oil Pan Bolts	43 (5)
Oil Pump Stator Shaft Bolts	84 (10)
Oil Strainer Bolts-to-Valve Body	84 (10)
Oil Tube Bracket Bolts	84 (10)
Parking Pawl Bracket Bolt	65 (7)
Upper Valve Body Cam Bolt	65 (7)
Valve Body Bolts	48 (5.4)
Valve Body-to-Transaxle Case Bolts	84 (10)

GENERAL MOTORS TURBO HYDRA-MATIC 125C TRANSAXLE

Buick
Century, Skyhawk, Skylark
Somerset Regal
Cadillac
Cimmaron
Chevrolet
Cavalier, Celebrity,
Oldsmobile
Calais, Cutlass Ciera, Firenza
Pontiac
Fiero, Grand Am, Sunbird, 6000

IDENTIFICATION

MODEL IDENTIFICATION

Models	Body Code
Celebrity, Century Cutlass Ciera, 6000	A
Cavalier, Cimarron Firenza, Skyhawk, Sunbird	J
Calais, Grand Am, Somerset Regal	N
Skylark	X
Fiero	P

The transaxle Vehicle Identification Number (VIN) code is stamped on a machined pad located to the rear of the valve body cover and to the right of the dipstick tube. The transaxle model code is stamped on a machined pad located on the top center of the transaxle case.

TRANSAXLE CODES

Application	Code Letters
Buick	BA, BP, CA, CB, CC CJ, CL, PD, PN, PW
Cadillac	CA, CB, CC, CJ, CM
Chevrolet	CA, CB, CC, CJ, CL CM, CT, CX, PD, PW
Oldsmobile	BA, BC, BD, BP, CA, CB, CC CL, CT, CX, PD, PM, PR, PW
Pontiac	BA, BP, CA, CB, CC, CD CK, CL, CM, CT, CU, CX PA, PD, PF, PN, PR, PW

DESCRIPTION

The THM-125C transaxle combines a torque converter, fully automatic 3-speed transmission, final drive gearing and differential into a front wheel drive system (except RWD Fiero). The 4-element torque converter couples the engine crankshaft to the planetary gear set through a dual sprocket and drive link assembly.

The 4-element torque converter consists of a pump, a turbine, a pressure plate splined to the turbine and a stator assembly. The pressure plate, when applied, provides a mechanical direct drive coupling between the engine and the planetary gear set.

Three multi-disc clutches, a roller clutch and a single band provide the friction elements required to obtain the desired function of the planetary gear sets. The hydraulic system is pressurized by a vane-type pump which provides the working pressure required to operate the friction elements and automatic controls.

The differential is integral with the transmission. Power transfer to the differential is by direct mesh of final drive sun gear to final drive sun gear pinions, located in the differential housing. An internal gear, held stationary by the case, provides the pinion track that forces rotation of final drive assembly.

LUBRICATION & ADJUSTMENT

See appropriate AUTOMATIC TRANSMISSION SERVICING article in DOMESTIC GENERAL SERVICING section.

TROUBLE SHOOTING

See appropriate AUTOMATIC TRANSMISSION TROUBLE SHOOTING article in DOMESTIC GENERAL SERVICING section.

TESTING

ROAD TEST

"D" Range

1) With selector lever in "D" range, accelerate from a standstill. A 1-2 and 2-3 shift should occur at all throttle openings (shift points will vary depending upon throttle opening).

2) Check part throttle 3-2 downshift at 30 MPH by quickly opening throttle approximately 3/4. At 50 MPH, transmission should downshift 3-2 by depressing accelerator fully.

"2" Range

1) With selector lever in "2", accelerate vehicle from a standstill. A 1-2 shift should occur at all throttle openings (no 2-3 shift can be obtained in this range). The 1-2 shift point will vary with throttle opening.

2) At approximately 20 MPH move selector from "2" to "1", a 2-1 downshift should occur. The 1-2 shift in "2" range is normally somewhat firmer than in "D" range.

3) With selector lever in "D" range and vehicle speed at approximately 50 MPH, release accelerator and move selector lever to "2" range. A 3-2 downshift should occur accompanied by an increase in engine speed and an engine braking effect.

"1" Range

1) With selector lever in "1" range, accelerate vehicle from a standstill. No upshift should occur in this range. At 40 MPH in "2" range, with throttle closed, move selector lever to "1".

2) A 2-1 downshift should occur between approximately 25 to 45 MPH, depending on valve body calibration. A 2-1 downshift at closed throttle should be accompanied by increased engine speed and an engine braking effect.

Converter Clutch

Install a tachometer and bring engine to normal operating temperature. With vehicle speed between 40-45 MPH, in 3rd gear, converter clutch should apply. Observing tachometer, a drop of 200 RPM's will occur when clutch is applied.

Automatic Transmissions

GENERAL MOTORS TURBO HYDRA-MATIC 125C TRANSAXLE (Cont.)

Fig. 1: Exploded View of Transaxle Case and Related Components

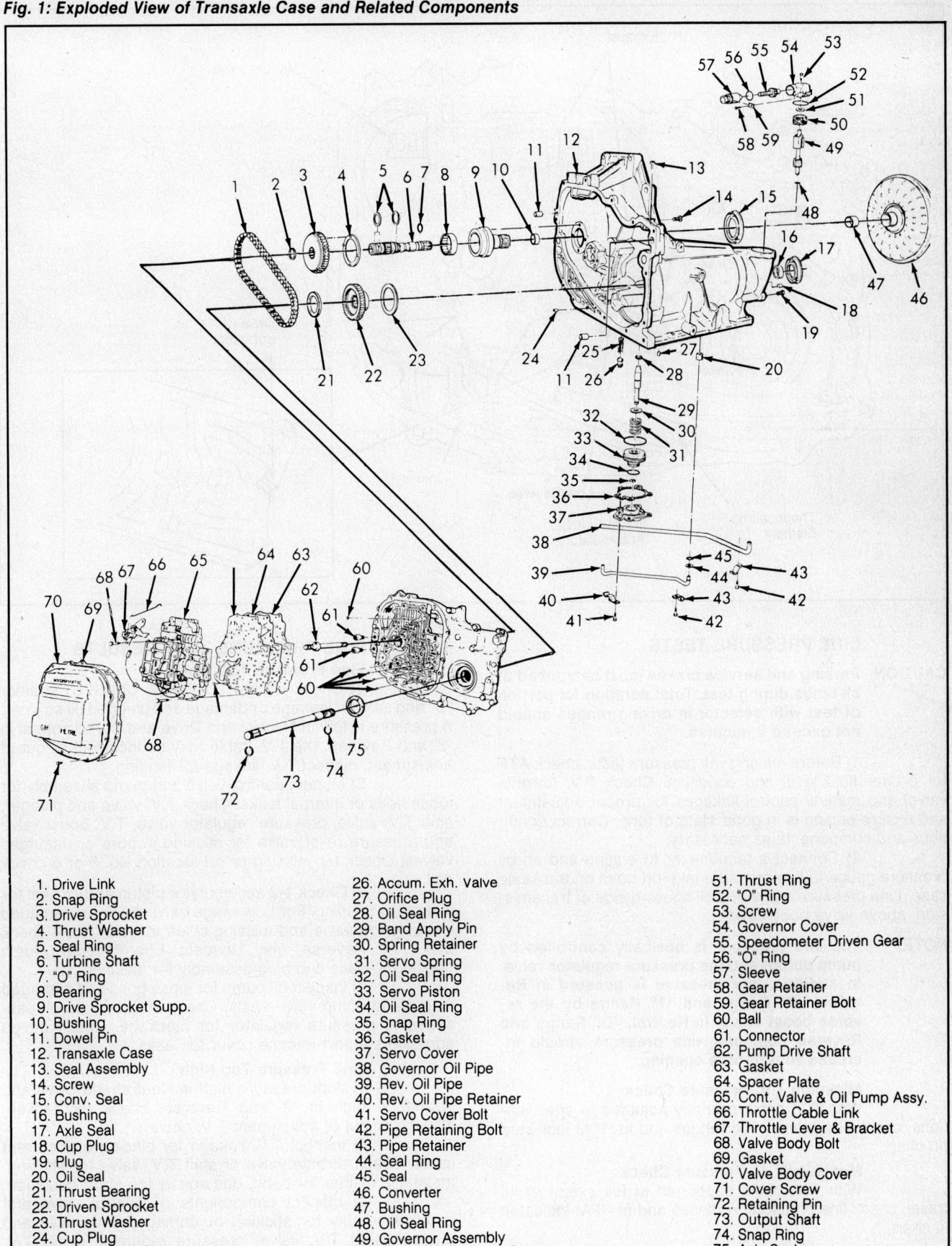

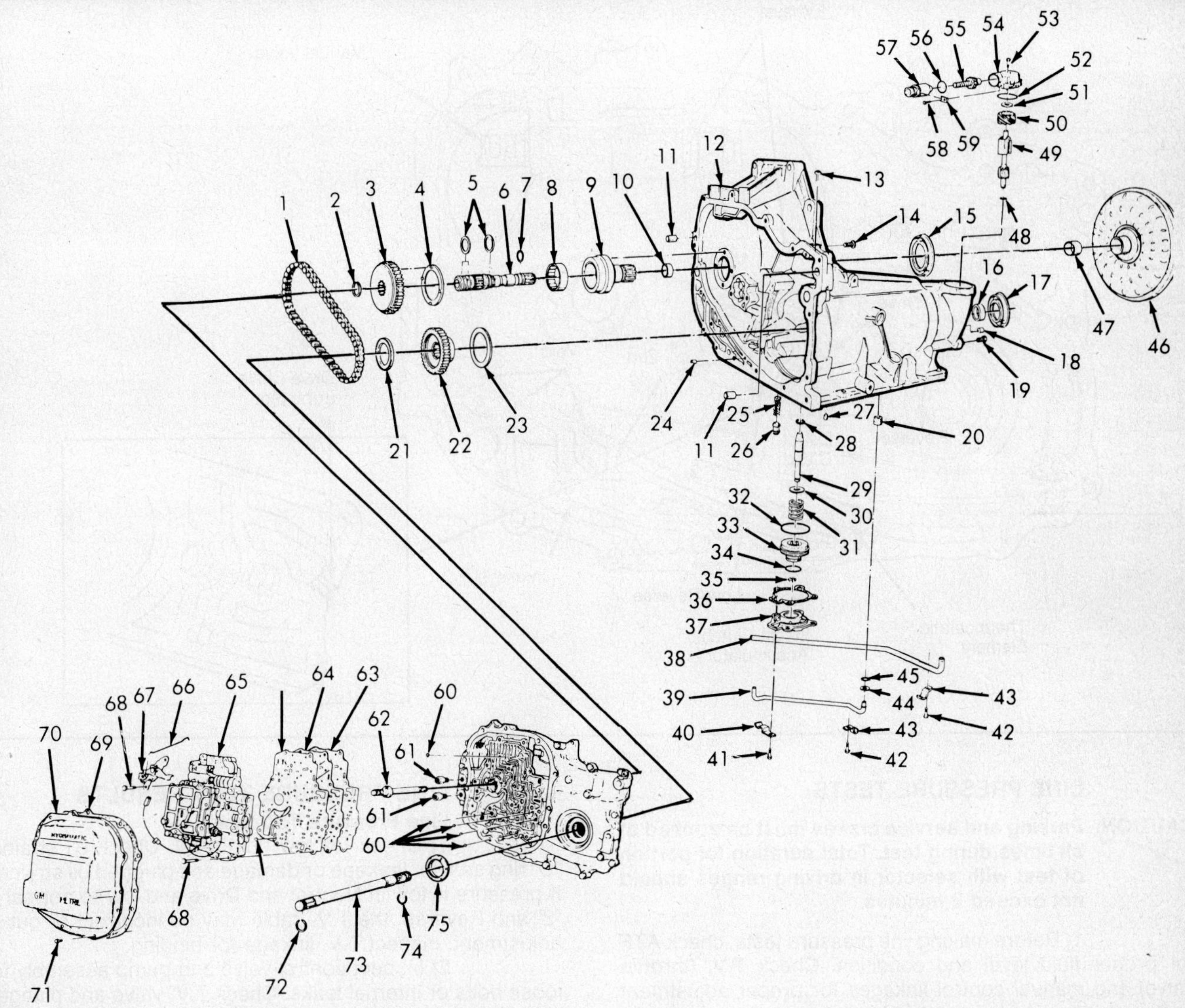

1. Drive Link
2. Snap Ring
3. Drive Sprocket
4. Thrust Washer
5. Seal Ring
6. Turbine Shaft
7. "O" Ring
8. Bearing
9. Drive Sprocket Supp.
10. Bushing
11. Dowel Pin
12. Transaxle Case
13. Seal Assembly
14. Screw
15. Conv. Seal
16. Bushing
17. Axle Seal
18. Cup Plug
19. Plug
20. Oil Seal
21. Thrust Bearing
22. Driven Sprocket
23. Thrust Washer
24. Cup Plug
25. Accum. Exh. Spring
26. Accum. Exh. Valve
27. Orifice Plug
28. Oil Seal Ring
29. Band Apply Pin
30. Spring Retainer
31. Servo Spring
32. Oil Seal Ring
33. Servo Piston
34. Oil Seal Ring
35. Snap Ring
36. Gasket
37. Servo Cover
38. Governor Oil Pipe
39. Rev. Oil Pipe
40. Rev. Oil Pipe Retainer
41. Servo Cover Bolt
42. Pipe Retaining Bolt
43. Pipe Retainer
44. Seal Ring
45. Seal
46. Converter
47. Bushing
48. Oil Seal Ring
49. Governor Assembly
50. Speedometer Drive Gear
51. Thrust Ring
52. "O" Ring
53. Screw
54. Governor Cover
55. Speedometer Driven Gear
56. "O" Ring
57. Sleeve
58. Gear Retainer
59. Gear Retainer Bolt
60. Ball
61. Connector
62. Pump Drive Shaft
63. Gasket
64. Spacer Plate
65. Cont. Valve & Oil Pump Assy.
66. Throttle Cable Link
67. Throttle Lever & Bracket
68. Valve Body Bolt
69. Gasket
70. Valve Body Cover
71. Cover Screw
72. Retaining Pin
73. Output Shaft
74. Snap Ring
75. Axle Seal

Automatic Transmissions
GENERAL MOTORS TURBO HYDRA-MATIC 125C TRANSAXLE (Cont.)

Fig. 2: Inside View of Case Cover Showing Oil Passages

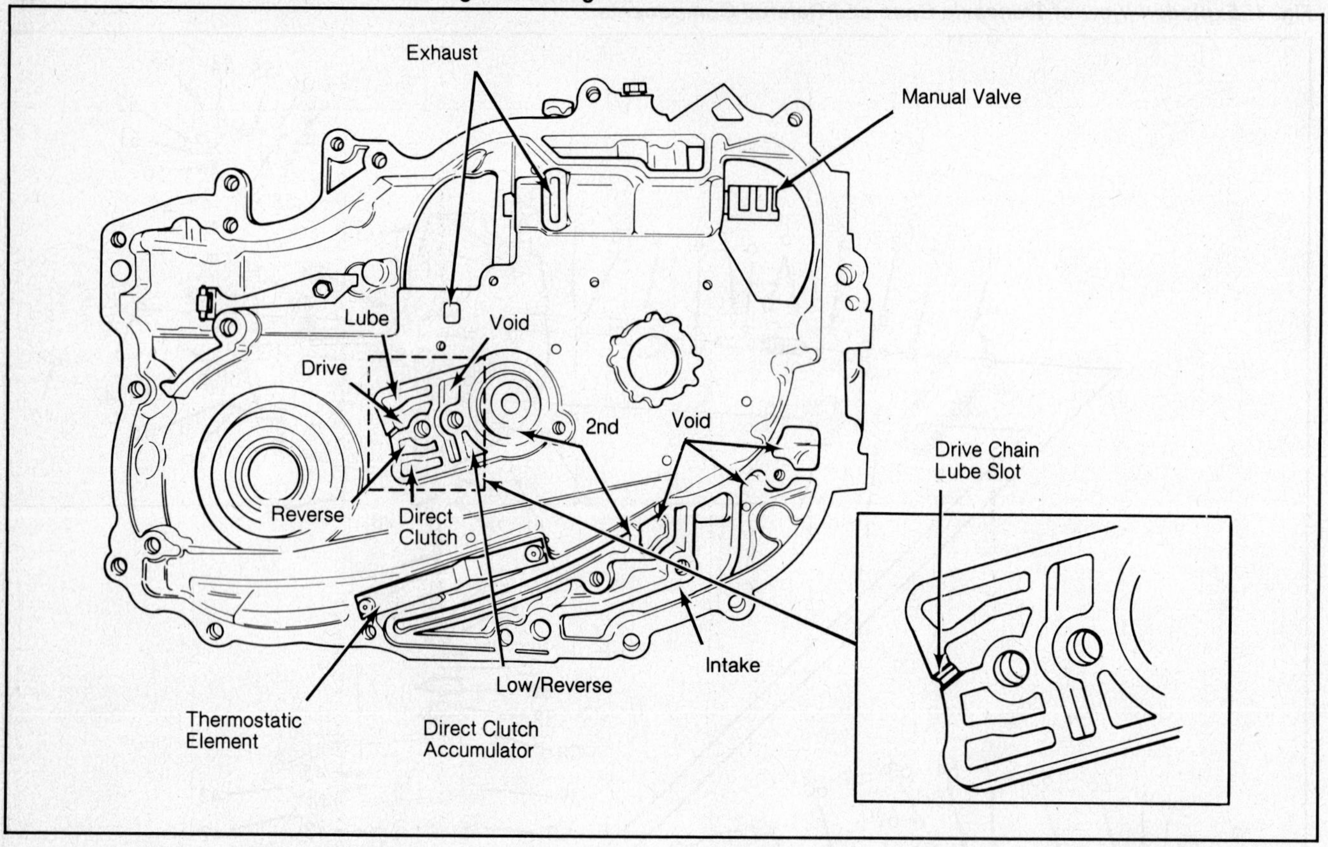

LINE PRESSURE TESTS

CAUTION: Parking and service brakes must be applied at all times during test. Total duration for portion of test with selector in driving ranges should not exceed 2 minutes.

1) Before making line pressure tests, check ATF for proper fluid level and condition. Check T.V. (throttle valve) and manual control linkages for proper adjustment and ensure engine is in good state of tune. Correct conditions and components as necessary.

2) Connect a tachometer to engine and an oil pressure gauge to line pressure take-off point on transaxle case. Line pressure tap is on bell housing side of transmission, above valve body cover.

NOTE: The line pressure is basically controlled by pump output and the pressure regulator valve. In addition, line pressure is boosted in Reverse, "2" Range and "1" Range by the reverse boost valve. In Neutral, "D" Range and Reverse positions, line pressure should increase with throttle opening.

Minimum T.V. Pressure Check

With T.V. cable properly adjusted to specifications, check line pressure in ranges and at RPM indicated on chart.

Maximum T.V. Pressure Check

With T.V. cable supported at full extent of its travel, check line pressure in ranges and at RPM indicated in chart.

LINE PRESSURE TEST RESULTS

Line Pressure Too Low

1) Check for low fluid level. Check oil strainer "O" ring seal for leakage or damage and plugged oil strainer. If pressure is low in Neutral and Drive and low to normal in "2" and Reverse, the T.V. cable may be incorrect or out of adjustment. Inspect T.V. linkage for binding.

2) Inspect control valve and pump assembly for loose bolts or internal leaks. Check T.V. valve and plunger, shift T.V. valve, pressure regulator valve, T.V. boost valve and pressure relief valve for sticking in bore or damaged valves. Check for missing or off location No. 5 or 6 check ball.

3) Check 1-2 accumulator piston and/or seal for leaking or missing. For Low range only, check for damaged low blow-off valve and missing or off location No. 4 check ball. For Reverse only, inspect Low-Reverse clutch housing-to-case cup plug assembly for leaking.

4) Inspect oil pump for loose bolts and damaged or missing pump valve seals. Check intermediate oil passages to pressure regulator for blockage. Check driven sprocket support-to-case cover for leaks.

Line Pressure Too High

1) With pressure high in Neutral and Drive and normal to high in "2" and Reverse, check for broken, sticking or out of adjustment T.V. cable.

2) Inspect T.V. linkage for binding or incorrect cable. Check throttle valve or shift T.V. valve for sticking. Inspect T.V. lifter for bend, damage or too short condition.

3) Inspect components of control valve and pump assembly for sticking or damaged T.V. valve and plunger, shift T.V. valve, pressure regulator valve, T.V. boost valve and/or pump slide.

Automatic Transmissions
GENERAL MOTORS TURBO HYDRA-MATIC 125C TRANSAXLE (Cont.)

Fig. 3: Outside View of Case Cover Showing Oil Passages

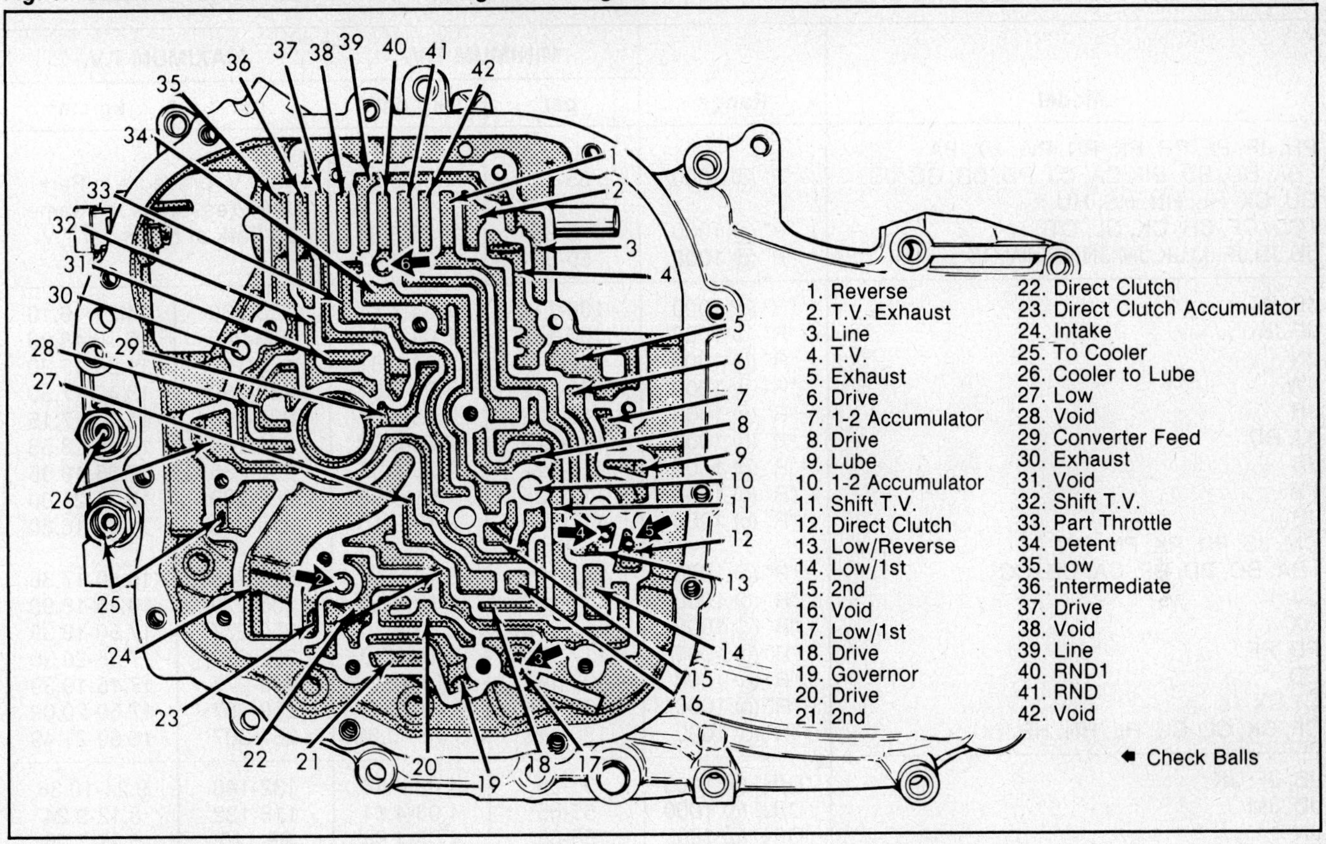

4) Check for worn or missing pressure regulator valve retaining pin. For Low only, check Low blow-off valve for sticking closed. Inspect internal pump or case cover for leaks.

SERVICE (IN VEHICLE)

DRIVE AXLE SHAFTS

See appropriate DRIVE AXLE SHAFT article in DOMESTIC FWD AXLE SHAFTS & TRANSFER CASES section.

CLUTCH AND BAND APPLICATION CHART (ELEMENTS IN USE)

Selector Lever Position	Direct Clutch	Forward Clutch	Low & Reverse Clutch	Intermediate Band	Low Roller Clutch
D – Drive					
First Gear		X			X
Second Gear		X		X	
Third Gear	X	X			
2 – Intermediate					
First Gear		X			X
Second Gear		X		X	
1 – Low					
First Gear		X	X		X
R – Reverse	X		X		
NEUTRAL OR PARK – All clutches and bands released and/or ineffective.					

REMOVAL & INSTALLATION

TRANSAXLE

See appropriate AUTOMATIC TRANSMISSION REMOVAL article in DOMESTIC GENERAL SERVICING section.

TORQUE CONVERTER

NOTE: **Torque converter is a sealed unit and cannot be disassembled for service or repair.**

Automatic Transmissions

GENERAL MOTORS TURBO HYDRA-MATIC 125C TRANSAXLE (Cont.)

THROTTLE VALVE LINE PRESSURE CHECK

Model	Range	MINIMUM T.V.		MAXIMUM T.V.	
		psi	kg/cm²	psi	kg/cm²
PH, JP, PF, PR, PK, PN, PW, HX, PA BA, BC, BD, BP, CA, CJ, PD, CB, CC, JS,	"P" @ 1000	65-75	4.64-5.20	No T.V. pressure in Park. Line Pressure is the same as Park at Minimum T.V.	
CU, CX, HL, HN, HS, HU CD, CF, CH, CK, CL, CT	"P" @ 1000	75-85	5.25-5.98		
JB,JD,JF,JJ,JK,JM,JN,JR,JW,RD	"P" @ 1000	55-65	4.03-4.64		
JD,JM	"R" @ 1000	100-112	7.04-7.81	203-230	14.21-16.10
JF,JK	"R" @ 1000	100-112	7.04-7.81	230-260	16.10-18.20
JN	"R" @ 1000	100-112	7.04-7.81	170-190	11.90-13.30
JW	"R" @ 1000	100-112	7.04-7.81	220-250	15.40-17.50
JR	"R" @ 1000	110-122	7.75-8.57	220-245	15.40-17.15
JJ, RD	"R" @ 1000	110-122	7.75-8.57	235-265	16.45-18.55
JB	"R" @ 1000	110-122	7.75-8.57	255-285	17.85-19.95
PA	"R" @ 1000	113-125	7.91-8.75	262-300	18.34-21.00
JP	"R" @ 1000	117-130	8.19-9.10	215-240	15.05-16.80
CM, JS, PH, PK, PN, PW BA, BC, BD, BP, CA, CB, CC	"R" @ 1000	117-130	8.19-9.10	220-248	15.40-17.36
CJ	"R" @ 1000	117-130	8.19-9.10	235-270	16.45-18.90
HX	"R" @ 1000	117-130	8.19-9.10	250-277	17.50-19.39
PD, PF	"R" @ 1000	117-130	8.19-9.10	255-290	17.85-20.30
CD	"R" @ 1000	130-148	9.10-10.36	245-277	17.15-19.39
CT,CX	"R" @ 1000	130-148	9,10-10.36	250-287	17.50-20.09
CF, CK, CL, CU, HL, HN, HS, HU	"R" @ 1000	130-148	9.10-10.36	267-307	18.69-21.49
JB, JF, JK	"D/N" @ 1000	55-65	4.03-4.46	132-148	9.24-10.36
JD, JM	"D/N" @ 1000	55-65	4.03-4.64	116-132	8.12-9.24
JN	"D/N" @ 1000	55-65	4.03-4.64	98-110	6.86-7.75
JR	"D/N" @ 1000	55-65	4.03-4.64	114-127	7.98-8.89
JJ, RD	"D/N" @ 1000	55-65	4.03-4.64	125-138	8.75-9.66
JW	"D/N" @ 1000	55-65	4.03-4.64	125-143	8.75-10.01
JP	"D/N" @ 1000	67-74	4.69-5.18	123-137	7.82-9.59
CM, JS, PH, PR, PK, PN, PW BA, BC, BD, BP, CA, CC, CB	"D/N" @ 1000	67-74	4.69-5.18	125-142	8.75-9.94
CJ	"D/N" @ 1000	67-76	4.69-5.32	135-153	9.45-10.71
HX	"D/N" @ 1000	67-74	4.69-5.18	142-158	9.94-11.06
PD, PF	"D/N" @ 1000	67-74	4.69-5.18	145-165	10.15-11.55
PA	"D/N" @ 1000	67-74	4.69-5.18	155-176	10.85-12.32
CD	"D/N" @ 1000	74-85	5.18-5.95	140-158	9.80-11.06
CX, CT	"D/N" @ 1000	74-85	5.18-5.95	142-164	9.94-11.48
CF, CK, CL, CU, HL, HN, HS, HU	"D/N" @ 1000	74-85	5.18-5.95	152-175	10.64-12.25
JD, JF, JK, JM, JN, JW	2/Low @ 1000	99-109	6.93-7.63	No T.V. in intermediate or low. Line Pressure same as intermediate or low at minimum.	
JP, JS, PD, PF, PH, PR, PK, PN, PW BA, BC, BD, BP, CA, CB, CC, CM, CJ, HX	2/Low @ 1000	114126	7.98-8.82		
JB, JR, JJ, RD	2/Low @ 1000	120-132	8.40-9.24		
CX, HL, HN, NS, HU CD, CF, CK, CL, CT, CU	2/Low @ 1000	127-145	8.89-10.15		
PA	2/Low @ 1000	139-154	9.73-10.78		

LEAKAGE CHECK

1) Install Pressure Tester (J-21369-B) into converter hub. Tighten hex nut on tool to expand it. Ensure safety strap is installed to prevent tool from blowing out when air pressure is applied. *See Fig. 4*. Apply 80 psi (5.6 kg/cm²) air pressure to air valve in tool. Submerge converter in water and check for air bubbles in water indicating leaks.

CAUTION: After leak checking converter, bleed air pressure from test tool before removing tool from converter hub.

Automatic Transmissions
GENERAL MOTORS TURBO HYDRA-MATIC 125C TRANSAXLE (Cont.)

Fig. 4: Installing Torque Converter Leakage Tester

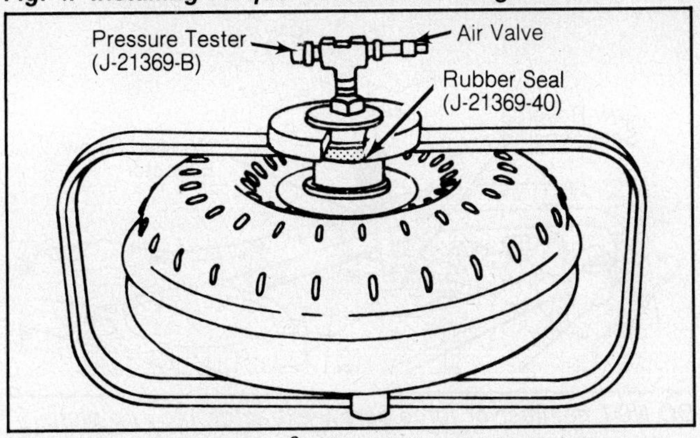

Apply 80 psi (5.6 kg/cm^2) air pressure to air valve.

2) With leakage tester removed, inspect converter hub surfaces for signs of scoring or wear. Check converter bushing for damage, cracks or scoring. If any components are excessively worn or damaged, replace torque converter assembly.

END CLEARANCE CHECK

1) Install collet end of End Clearance Checker (J-28538) into converter hub and hand tighten counterclockwise. Mount dial indicator onto hub of tool collet so dial indicator plunger rests on converter.

2) Zero dial indicator. Lift up on tool and read clearance at dial indicator. Converter end clearance should be 0-.050" (0-1.27 mm). If clearance is greater than .050" (1.27 mm), replace torque converter assembly.

Fig. 5: Measuring Torque Converter End Play

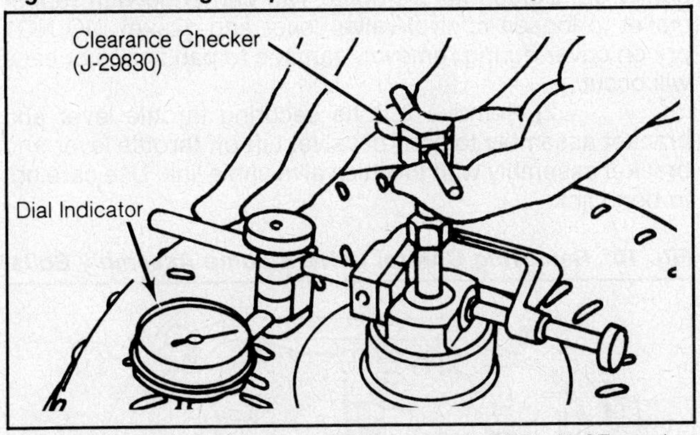

The converter end play must not exceed .050" (1.27 mm).

3) When replacing torque converter, ensure converter is installed fully toward rear of transaxle. Ensure converter is installed so that there is at least .50" (13 mm) between engine mounting face of case and front face of converter cover lugs.

NOTE: **After end play and leakage tests, check torque converter stator assembly for freewheeling in both directions or assembly remains locked up at all times. Replace converter assembly if either condition exists.**

TRANSAXLE DISASSEMBLY

Before disassembling unit, throughly clean exterior of transaxle case to prevent dirt from entering transaxle internal mechanism. During inspection and reassembly, all parts should be washed with cleaning solvent and air dried. DO NOT use rags to dry components. Remove torque converter by pulling it straight out. Place transaxle in Holding Fixtures (J-28664 and J-3289-20). Position so right side axle end is down to drain fluid.

SPEEDOMETER DRIVE GEAR & GOVERNOR ASSEMBLY

Reposition transaxle to normal position. Remove speedometer driven gear mount bolt with retainer. Withdraw driven gear assembly from governor cover. Remove governor cover bolts and lift off cover with "O" ring. Lift out governor and speedometer drive gear as an assembly.

INTERMEDIATE SERVO ASSEMBLY

1) Position transaxle so oil pan is up. Remove oil pan, gasket and oil strainer assembly from lower case assembly. Remove and discard oil strainer "O" ring.

2) Remove bolt holding reverse oil pipe retaining bracket to servo cover. Remove remaining servo cover bolts. Lift off servo cover and gasket. Withdraw intermediate servo assembly. *See Fig. 7.*

3) If necessary, detach "E" clip and remove intermediate band apply pin from intermediate servo piston. Discard "O" ring seals. Remove 3rd accumulator check valve and spring. *See Fig. 6.*

NOTE: **Make intermediate band apply pin selection check at this time to determine correct pin to use during reassembly.**

Fig. 6: Removing 3rd Accumulator Check Valve & Spring

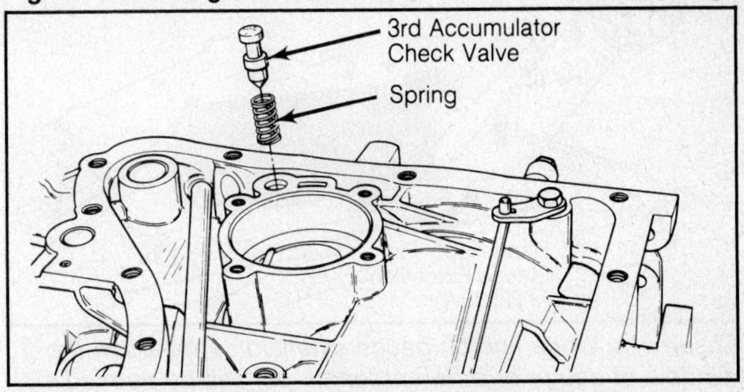

Inspect spring and check valve for wear or damage.

Band Apply Pin Selection Check

1) Install Intermediate Band Apply Pin Gauge (J-28535) over intermediate servo bore. Retain with 2 servo cover bolts. Remove band apply pin from intermediate servo assembly.

2) Install Band Apply Ain Gauge Extension (J-28535-4) onto servo piston end of band apply pin. Install band apply pin and gauge extension into gauge on servo bore. *See Fig. 8.*

3) Apply 100 INCH lbs. (11.2 N.m) of torque to hex nut on selection gauge to compress band. White line, on gauge extension, should appear in window on selection gauge to indicate proper pin installed.

4) If White line cannot be seen, change band apply pin (longer or shorter as necessary) and recheck. See INTERMEDIATE BAND APPLY PIN table. With proper apply pin selected, remove gauge. Install new seals, assemble and install components in reverse of removal procedure.

Fig. 7: Removing Intermediate Servo Assembly

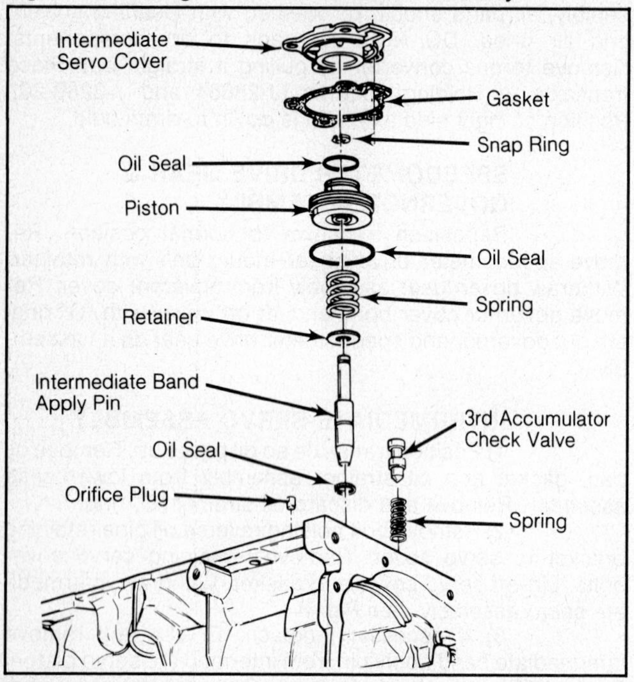

Do not remove the servo piston "O" ring seals unless replacement is necessary.

Fig. 8: Checking for Proper Band Apply Pin

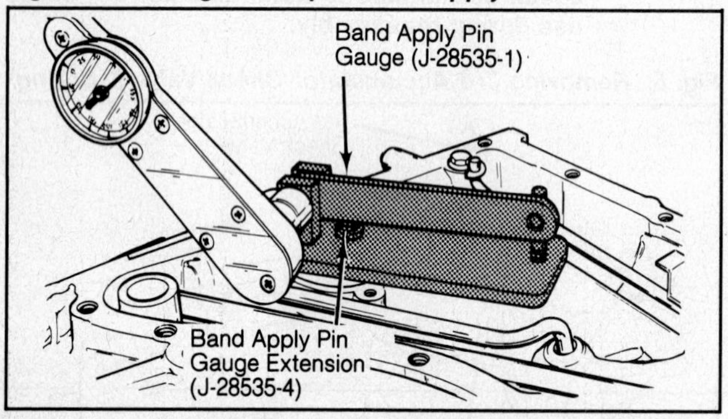

Ensure the White line on gauge extension appears in the window of gauge or different length pin will be needed.

INTERMEDIATE BAND APPLY PIN

Length	Identification
Short	2 Grooves
Medium	1 Groove
Long	No Grooves

OUTPUT SHAFT & LOW-REVERSE SEAL

1) With oil pan, gasket, strainer assembly, reverse oil pipe bracket, intermediate servo assembly and 3rd accumulator check valve (with spring) removed, detach Low-Reverse oil pipe, oil pipe seal back-up washer and "O" ring seal.

2) Grind approximately .75" (20 mm) from end of a No. 4 screw extractor. Insert ground end into Low-Reverse cup plug. DO NOT hammer or force screw extractor into cup plug. Carefully twist screw extractor to remove cup plug. *See Fig. 9.*

Fig. 9: Removing Low-Reverse Cup Plug Assembly

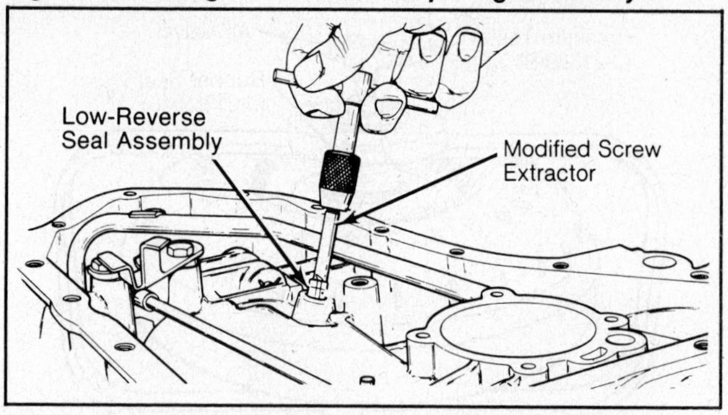

DO NOT hammer or force screw extractor into cup plug.

3) Remove dipstick stop and parking lock bracket from above parking pawl and parking pawl actuator rod. Rotate final drive unit until open ends of output shaft retaining "C" ring are visible through access window of differential carrier.

4) Using output shaft "C" Ring Remover (J-28583), push both ends of retaining "C" ring down to partially dislodge from output shaft. Rotate output shaft/final drive until retaining "C" ring is visible through access window.

5) Carefully remove retaining "C" ring by pulling it up and out using needle nose pliers, then discard retaining ring. Remove output shaft.

CONTROL VALVE BODY & OIL PUMP ASSEMBLY

1) Rotate transaxle so that control valve body oil pan is up. Detach mount bolts. Tap pan edge with rubber mallet to loosen control valve cover and gasket. DO NOT pry on cover during removal, damage to pan flange or case will occur.

2) Remove 2 bolts securing throttle lever and bracket assembly to control valve. Lift off throttle lever and bracket assembly with throttle valve cable link. Use care not to bend link.

Fig. 10: Removing Control Valve & Pump Assembly Bolts

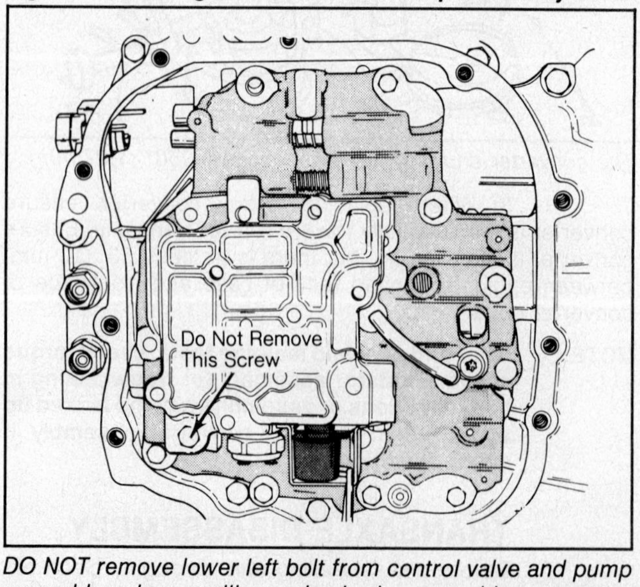

DO NOT remove lower left bolt from control valve and pump assembly unless auxiliary valve body removal is necessary.

GENERAL MOTORS TURBO HYDRA-MATIC 125C TRANSAXLE (Cont.)

3) Remove the auxiliary valve body screws EXCEPT for the lower left screw. *See Fig. 10*. Remove remaining control valve assembly bolts. Carefully lift off control valve and pump assembly. Place on bench with machined surface up.

4) Remove No. 1 check ball from direct clutch passage on spacer plate. Lift out oil pump drive shaft. Carefully remove spacer plate and spacer plate gaskets. Remove the 5 check balls from case cover. *See Fig. 11*.

Fig. 11: Check Ball Locations in Case Cover

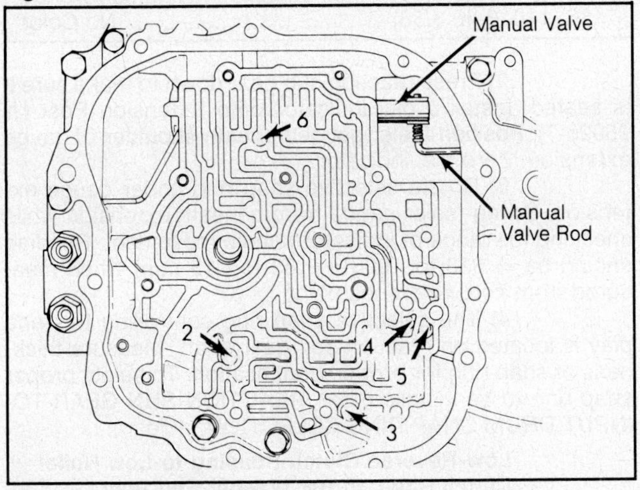

The No. 1 check ball is located in the direct clutch passage on the spacer plate.

NOTE: Before proceeding with transaxle disassembly, input shaft-to-case cover end play must be checked to determine proper selective snap ring to install during reassembly.

Input Shaft-to-Case Cover End Play

1) Rotate transaxle assembly until right axle end is up. Install Output Shaft Loader Adapter Plug (J-26958-10) into right side axle end. Mount Output Shaft Aligner/Loader (J-26958) and Bracket (J-26958-11) to right side axle end of case as shown in *Fig. 12*.

2) Install Input Shaft Lifter (J-28544) into input shaft bore and tighten by turning handle clockwise. Install dial indicator with Extension Post (J-25025-7), placing indicator plunger on end of lifter.

3) Press down on lifter and zero dial indicator. Lift up tool and record indicator end play reading. End play should be .004-.033" (.10-.84 mm).

4) Selective snap ring controlling end play is located on input shaft beneath driven sprocket. If end play is not within specifications, select proper snap ring. See INPUT SHAFT END PLAY SELECTIVE SNAP RINGS table.

INPUT SHAFT END PLAY SELECTIVE SNAP RINGS

Thickness In. (mm)	Color Code
.071-.076 (1.83-1.93)	White
.078-.084 (2.03-2.13)	Blue
.088-.092 (2.23-2.33)	Brown
.095-.099 (2.43-2.53)	Yellow
.103-.107 (2.63-2.73)	Green

Fig. 12: Positioning Output Shaft Aligner and Loader on Transaxle

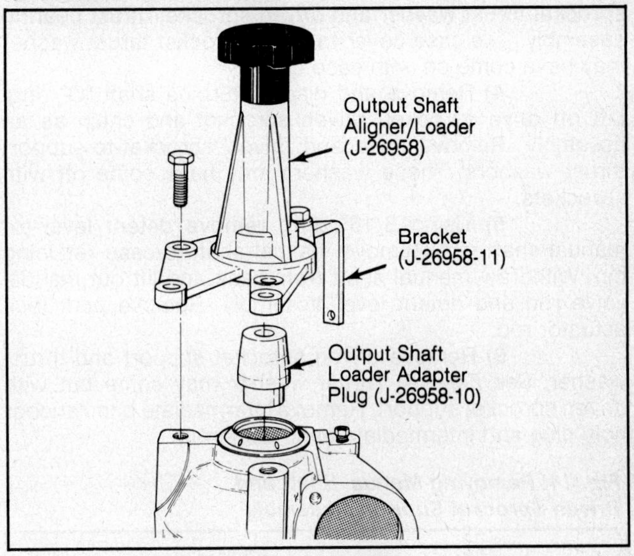

Adjust the loader to the correct load by turning the handle until the knob bottoms.

CAUTION: Oil soaked snap rings may tend to discolor. Measure snap ring for its actual thickness and replace as necessary.

TRANSMISSION CASE COVER & INPUT UNIT ASSEMBLY

1) Disconnect manual valve rod from manual valve. *See Fig. 11*. Remove remaining transmission case cover mount bolts. Install two M12 X 1.75 X 50 bolts into case cover dowel pin holes. *See Fig. 13*.

Fig. 13: Removing Transmission Case Cover from Case

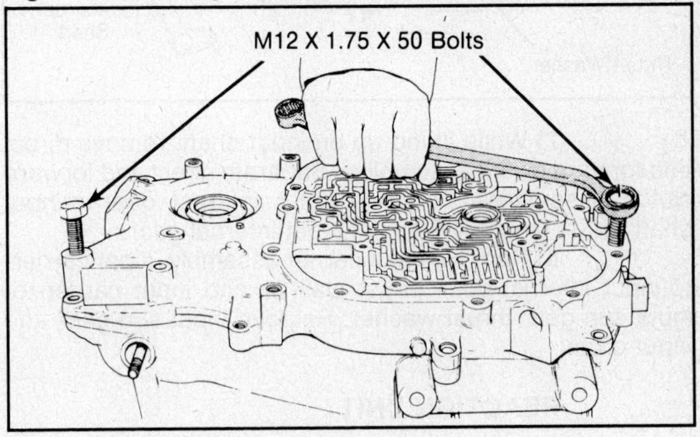

Bolts installed in cover dowel pin holes will self tap, bottom out on dowel pins and separate cover from case.

2) The bolts will self-tap, bottom out on dowel pins and separate case cover from case. DO NOT pry cover from case or damage to machined surfaces will result. Remove case cover.

NOTE: When removed, lay case cover with 1-2 accumulator side up or 1-2 accumulator pin may drop out of cover.

GENERAL MOTORS TURBO HYDRA-MATIC 125C TRANSAXLE (Cont.)

3) Remove 1-2 accumulator spring and center case-to-cover gasket. Remove case cover-to-drive sprocket thrust washer and driven sprocket thrust bearing assembly. The case cover-to-drive sprocket thrust washer may have come off with case cover.

4) Remove and discard turbine shaft "O" ring. Lift off drive sprocket, driven sprocket and chain as an assembly. Remove drive and driven sprocket-to-support thrust washers. These washers may have come off with sprockets.

5) Using 3/16" drift, remove detent lever-to-manual shaft pin. Remove manual shaft-to-case retaining pin. Withdraw manual shaft from case and lift out manual valve rod and detent lever assembly. Remove park lock actuator rod.

6) Remove driven sprocket support and thrust washer. *See Fig. 14*. Thrust washer may come out with driven sprocket support. Remove intermediate band anchor hole plug and intermediate band assembly.

Fig. 14: Removing Manual Shaft and Driven Sprocket Support Assembly

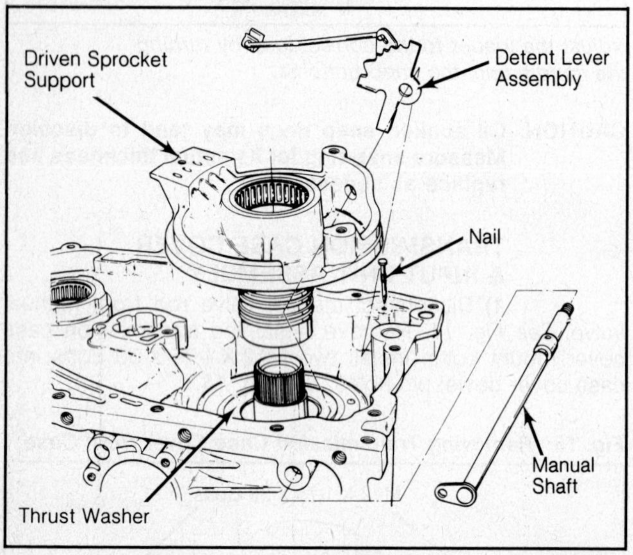

7) While lifting up on input shaft, remove direct and forward clutch assemblies. Separate direct and forward clutch assemblies. Remove input internal gear-to-input shaft thrust washer. Remove input internal gear.

8) Remove input carrier assembly, input carrier-to-input internal gear thrust washer and input carrier-to-input sun gear thrust washer. Remove input sun gear and input drum.

REACTION UNIT

NOTE: **Before proceeding with disassembly of reaction unit parts, reaction sun gear-to-input drum selective snap ring and Reverse clutch housing-to-Low race selective thrust washer end play measurements should be taken to determine correct snap ring and thrust washer to install during reassembly.**

Reaction Sun Gear-to-Input Drum End Play

1) Install Output Shaft Aligner/Loader (J-26958) in fully loaded position. Install Reaction Sun Gear Snap Ring Gauge (J-28588) to case using 2 case cover bolts. Position gauge extension between open ends of selective snap ring.

REACTION SUN GEAR-TO-INPUT DRUM SNAP RING SELECTION

Thickness In. (mm)	Color Code
.089-.093 (2.27-2.36)	Pink
.096-.100 (2.44-2.54)	Brown
.103-.107 (2.61-2.71)	Lt. Blue
.109-.113 (2.78-2.88)	White
.116-.120 (2.95-3.05)	Yellow
.123-.127 (3.12-3.22)	Lt. Green
.129-.133 (3.29-3.39)	Orange
.136-.140 (3.46-3.56)	No Color

2) Press reaction sun gear down to make sure it is seated. Install a dial indicator onto Extension Post (J-25025-7). Position feeler gauge beneath shoulder of gauge extension. Zero dial indicator.

3) Rotate selective snap ring under gauge extension. Swing feeler gauge from beneath extension while checking full range of indicator needle movement. Reading should be +.013 to -.005" (+.33 to -.13 mm) when measured from zero reference point.

4) The selective snap ring controlling this end play is located on reaction sun gear shaft. Measure thickness of snap ring for proper identification. To select proper snap ring to be installed, see REACTION SUN GEAR-TO-INPUT DRUM SNAP RING SELECTION table.

Low-Reverse Clutch Housing-to-Low Roller Clutch Race Thrust Washer End Play

1) With dial indicator and output shaft aligner/loader installed as it was for measurement of reaction sun gear-to-input drum snap ring, press down reaction sun gear to ensure it is seated. Zero dial indicator.

Fig. 15: Checking Low-Reverse Clutch Housing-to Low Roller Clutch Race Thrust Washer End Play

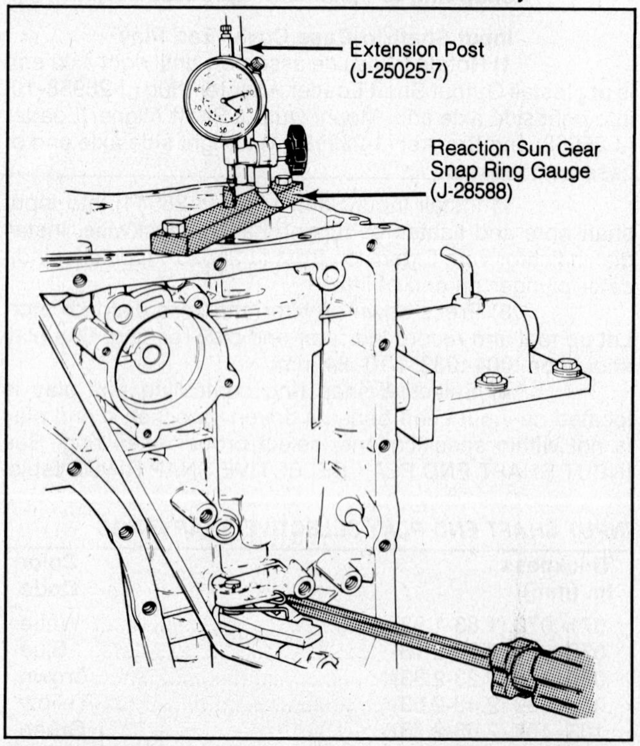

DO NOT rest screwdriver on spacer in parking pawl case opening when prying reaction internal gear.

GENERAL MOTORS TURBO HYDRA-MATIC 125C TRANSAXLE (Cont.)

2) Insert screwdriver through parking pawl case opening next to parking pawl. Lift reaction internal gear to check Low-Reverse clutch selective end play. Read resulting end play. DO NOT rest screwdriver on spacer in parking pawl case opening when prying reaction internal gear. Spacer damage will result. *See Fig. 15.*

3) End play should be .003-.046" (.08-1.17 mm). The selective washer controlling this end play is located between Low-Reverse clutch housing and low roller clutch assembly. Select proper thrust washer. See REVERSE CLUTCH HOUSING-TO-LOW RACE WASHER table.

REVERSE CLUTCH HOUSING-TO-LOW RACE WASHER

Thickness In. (mm)	Identification Code
.039-.043 (1.00-2.20)	1
.056-.060 (1.42-1.52)	2
.072-.076 (1.84-1.94)	3
.089-.093 (2.26-2.36)	4
.105-.109 (2.68-2.78)	5
.122-.126 (3.10-3.20)	6

4) Remove dial indicator, gauge and output shaft loading/aligning tool. Leave output shaft loader adapter in place for use when final drive-to-case end play is measured.

5) Remove reaction sun gear. Sun gear will lift straight out. Remove Low-Reverse clutch housing-to-case snap ring. Snap ring is .092" (2.36 mm) thick. Using Low-Reverse Clutch Housing Remover/Installer (J-28542), lift out Low-Reverse Clutch housing. *See Fig. 16.*

Fig. 16: Removing Low-Reverse Clutch Housing

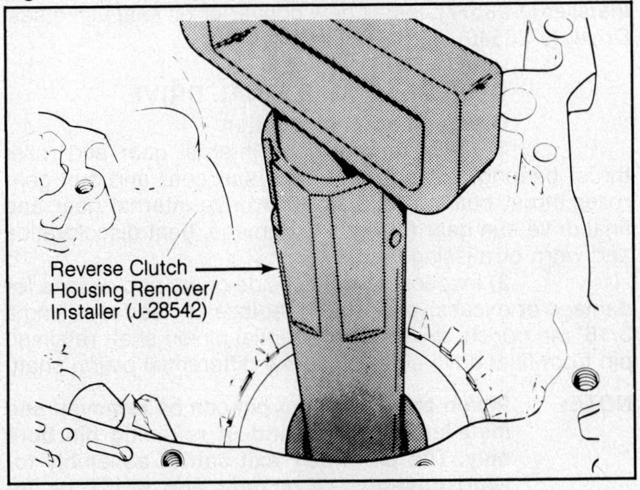

Use lifter to lift out Low-Reverse Clutch housing.

6) Remove the Low-Reverse clutch housing-to-case spacer ring from groove in case. Spacer ring is .042" (1.07 mm) thick. Lift out final drive sun gear shaft and reaction gear set as an assembly.

7) Remove roller clutch and reaction carrier assembly off final drive sun gear shaft. Remove 4 tanged reaction carrier-to-reaction internal gear thrust washers off end of reaction carrier (or inside reaction internal gear).

8) Remove Low-Reverse clutch plates off final drive sun gear shaft. Remove reaction internal gear-to-reaction sun gear thrust bearing assembly off reaction gear. Remove reaction internal gear off final drive sun gear shaft.

FINAL DRIVE UNIT

NOTE: **Before proceeding with transaxle disassembly, final drive-to-case end play should be checked to determine proper final drive differential-to-case selective thrust washer for install during reassembly. Also, case bushing should be inspected for wear and replaced if necessary.**

Final Drive-to-Case End Play

1) Rotate transaxle so right hand axle end is up. With Output Shaft Aligner/Loader Adapter Plug (J-26958-10) in place, press down on adapter to fully seat final drive onto final drive internal gear-to-case snap ring.

2) Install dial indicator onto post and install post into one of the motor mount bolt holes. Ensure indicator plunger rests on top of adapter. Zero dial indicator while pressing down on adapter.

3) Insert large screwdriver into transaxle governor bore. Lift final drive by prying up on governor drive gear. Read end play at dial indicator. End play should be .005-.032" (.12-.82 mm).

4) Selective washer controlling end play is located between differential carrier and differential carrier case thrust bearing assembly. Select correct thrust washer. See FINAL DRIVE-TO-CASE END PLAY table.

FINAL DRIVE-TO-CASE END PLAY

Thickness In. (mm)	Identification Code
.055-.059 (1.40-1.50)	0
.059-.062 (1.50-1.60)	1
.062-.066 (1.60-1.70)	2
.066-.070 (1.70-1.80)	3
.070-.074 (1.80-1.90)	4
.074-.078 (1.90-2.00)	5
.078-.082 (2.00-2.10)	6
.082-.086 (2.10-2.20)	7
.086-.091 (2.20-2.30)	8
.091-.095 (2.30-2.40)	9

5) Remove dial indicator, indicator post and loader/aligner adapter. Remove final drive internal gear spacer-to-case snap ring. The snap ring is .092" (2.36 mm) thick. Remove final drive internal gear spacer. DO NOT deform or bend spacer when removing.

6) Using Final Drive Unit Remover/Installer (J-28545), lift final drive unit from case. Remove final drive differential-to-case selective thrust washer. Remove differential carrier-to-case thrust roller bearing assembly from final drive assembly. The thrust washer and thrust bearing may be located in case.

COMPONENT DISASSEMBLY & REASSEMBLY

NOTE: **During disassembly, note component locations for reassembly reference. When reassembling transaxle unit, lubricate all bushings, seals, thrust bearings and internal mating surfaces with transmission fluid. Use petroleum jelly to lubricate and retain all thrust washers.**

GENERAL MOTORS TURBO HYDRA-MATIC 125C TRANSAXLE (Cont.)

TRANSAXLE CASE

NOTE: Disassembly procedures include drive sprocket support, drive sprocket roller bearing, third oil cup plug, parking pawl and governor oil pipe removal. It is not necessary to remove and service these components unless they are damaged or worn.

Disassembly

1) Rotate transaxle case until case cover side is up. Using slide hammer and Adapter (J-26941), remove drive sprocket support roller bearing assembly. Inspect bearing bore and roller bearing race on drive sprocket for wear or damage. Replace components as needed.

2) Inspect drive sprocket support for damaged journals or splines. If removal is needed, turn transaxle case so right axle side is up. Remove converter oil seal. From inside torque converter housing, unbolt and remove drive sprocket support.

3) Inspect parking pawl shaft cup plug for damage. If replacement is needed, turn transaxle case so oil pan side is up. Using a 3/8" drift, remove parking pawl shaft cup plug from oil pan side of case. Inspect parking pawl for damage.

4) If replacement is needed, remove parking pawl shaft retainer, parking pawl shaft, parking pawl and return spring from case. Check governor pipe for damage, cracks or possible leak points. If replacement is necessary, remove governor oil pipe clamp screw and clamp.

CAUTION: If governor pipe needs replacement, remove right hand axle end first. The pipe is sealed strongly in place and may require a high effort to break loose. DO NOT damage machined case surface if pipe must be pryed out.

5) Pry right side end up first, then pry left side end of pipe from case. Remove pipe. Inspect third oil cup plug for wear or damage. If removal is needed, grind .50" (13 mm) from end of No. 3 easy out and install into third oil cup plug. Twist screw extractor out counterclockwise and remove cup plug.

6) Check manual shaft oil seal for damage. If removal is needed, rotate transaxle case so oil pan side is down. Remove manual shaft seal. Inspect axle oil seal and guard for damage. If seal guard is damaged, seal will need replacement also. Pry axle seal from case.

NOTE: If final drive case bushing is worn or scored, bushing must be replaced to prevent damage to right axle shaft or seal.

7) With final drive assembly and right axle shaft removed from case, inspect final drive case bushing for wear or scoring. If bushing removal is needed, remove right axle seal assembly from case. Using Bushing Remover (J-28537-6) with Driver (J-8092), remove bushing.

Inspection

1) Inspect case assembly for damage, cracks, porosity or interconnected oil passages. Inspect exhaust vent holes and ensure they are open. Inspect for damaged or stripped bolt holes.

2) Check case lugs, intermediate servo bore and snap ring grooves for damage. Inspect case bushings for wear or scoring. Inspect drive sprocket support bearing assembly for pitting and scoring to carrier and rollers. Check rollers for excessive clearance.

3) Inspect drive sprocket support for damage to journal splines. Check for heat discoloration and cracks on support assembly. Inspect governor pipe for damage, cracks and possible point of leakage. Check parking pawl shaft cup plug, parking pawl shaft and parking pawl for damage and excessive wear.

4) Inspect third oil cup plug for tightness in bore or damage. Use a straightedge to check all sealing and mating surfaces for straightness. If final drive case bushing was removed, inspect case and new bushing for loose aluminum or burrs. remove all loose material.

Reassembly

1) If final drive case bushing was removed, install new bushing using Bushing Installer (J-28537-2) with Driver Handle (J-8092). Press or drive bushing into position until tool bottoms.

2) Using Seal Driver (J-26938 or J-29130) and Handle (J-8092), install new right hand axle seal assembly. DO NOT damage seal guard during installation. If manual shaft oil seal needs replacement, install seal with lip up, using a 9/16" socket.

3) Install new third cup plug using a 1/4" drift. Cup plug should seat fully in bore when installed. Before installing, coat ends of governor oil pipe with sealing compound (Loctite), to seal against leakage. Install governor pipe and retaining clamp. Lightly tap pipe into place to secure against leakage.

4) Install parking pawl and spring, parking pawl shaft and retainer. Ensure large loop of pawl spring is positioned on right side of pawl. Coat parking pawl shaft cup plug with sealant and install plug using a 3/8" drift.

5) Install drive sprocket support roller bearing assembly with bearing identification facing up. Lightly tap drive sprocket support bearing in place using Bearing Installer (J-28677). Install new converter oil seal using seal Driver (J-28540).

DIFFERENTIAL & FINAL DRIVE

Disassembly & Inspection

1) Remove final drive internal gear and roller thrust bearing. Lift out final drive sun gear and sun gear roller thrust bearing. Inspect final drive internal gear and final drive sun gear for cracks, damage, heat discoloration and worn or missing teeth.

2) Inspect differential side gears and pinions for damage or excessive wear and replace as needed. Using a 3/16" pin punch, drive out differential pinion shaft retaining pin from final drive side. Withdraw differential pinion shaft.

NOTE: Pinion shaft retaining pin can be removed and installed from one end of retaining pin bore only. The pin MUST exit carrier assembly toward governor drive gear and MUST be installed from governor drive gear end toward final drive end of carrier.

3) Remove differential pinion gears and thrust washers by rotating 1 differential side gear (until gear is in differential carrier window) while holding the other in place. Push pinion gears from differential. Ensure dished pinion thrust washers are removed with pinion gears.

4) Slide 1 differential side gear toward center of carrier and remove, then remove other gear in same manner. Remove side gear thrust washers, making sure they are kept with gear from which they were removed.

5) Inspect side gear and pinion thrust washers for scoring, elongated inside diameter, heat discoloration

GENERAL MOTORS TURBO HYDRA-MATIC 125C TRANSAXLE (Cont.)

Fig. 17: Exploded View of Differential and Final Drive Unit

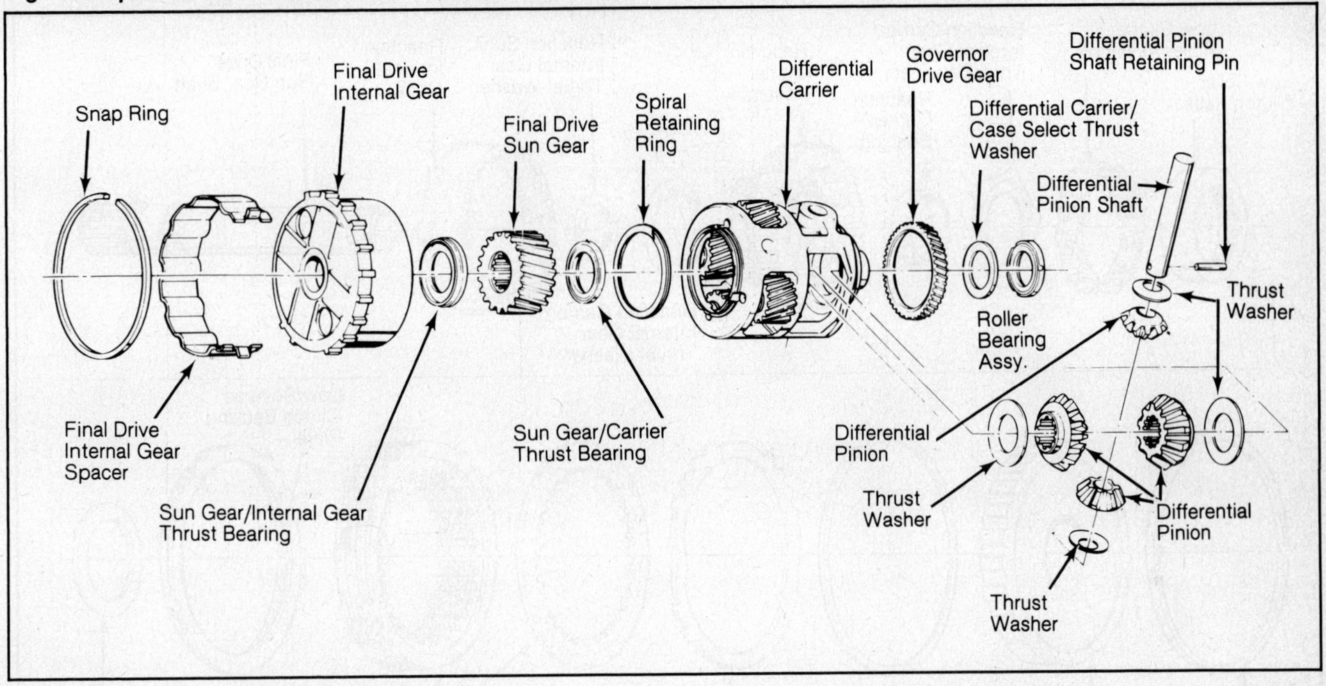

and flattened outer edges. Check final drive pinion end play by inserting feeler gauge between carrier and final drive pinion.

6) End play is .009-.025" (.24-.63 mm). Inspect final drive pinions for excessive wear or damage. If pinions must be removed, detach spiral pinion pin snap ring. Withdraw pinion pins.

7) Carefully remove pinion gears and thrust washers together to prevent dropping needle roller bearings. Remove 36 upper and lower needle bearings from each pinion gear. Inspect all parts for damage.

NOTE: **It is not necessary to remove governor drive gear for inspection or repair of differential and final drive unit. Remove gear only if replacement is necessary.**

8) Using Puller (J-8433) and a heavy flat washer positioned on end of carrier assembly (to protect carrier when puller ram is tightened), pull governor drive gear from differential.

Reassembly

1) If removed, lightly tap governor drive gear into place with a plastic mallet. Lube pinion pin with petroleum jelly and slide 1 steel thrust washer onto end of pin. Install 18 needle bearings around diameter of pin, against steel thrust washer.

2) Install needle bearing spacer onto pin and install remaining 18 needle bearings to pin on opposite side of spacer. Push needle bearing and pinion pin assembly into pinion gear.

3) Install steel pinion thrust washer onto end of pin (side opposite first thrust washer). Install 1 bronze pinion thrust washer to each end of pin. Slide pinion pin from assembly (keeping bearings intact in gear).

4) Install pinion gear assembly into final drive carrier. Install pinion pin (stepped end last) into carrier through pinion gear assembly. Repeat this procedure for remaining final drive pinion gears. Install spiral pinion pin snap ring.

NOTE: **Install pinion pin so step is outside. Ensure that there is a bronze thrust washer between carrier and steel thrust washer on each end of final drive pinion.**

5) Install differential side gear thrust washers and side gears. Retain in place with petroleum jelly. Coat side gear pinion dished thrust washers with petroleum jelly and install onto side gear pinions. Install pinion gears in differential carrier windows.

NOTE: **The side gear clearance on left side of differential is greater than on right side. Do not replace carrier due to looseness on left side. Left side gear-to-carrier clearance is .023-.032" (.58-.81 mm). Right side gear-to-carrier clearance is .0020-.0050" (.051-.127 mm).**

6) Slide differential pinion shaft through both pinion gears to align. Remove shaft, without disturbing pinion location. Rotate pinions into place. Install pinion shaft into carrier through both pinion gears. Install pinion shaft retaining pin.

7) Install final drive sun gear-to-differential carrier thrust bearing outer race against carrier. Install sun gear with step side up. Install sun gear-to-final drive internal gear thrust bearing with cupped race side onto final drive internal gear. Retain with petroleum jelly.

8) Install internal gear on final drive carrier. Install differential selective thrust washer onto differential carrier. Install case-to-differential roller bearing thrust washer with inner race against differential selective thrust washer.

REACTION INTERNAL GEAR

Inspection

Check final drive sun gear shaft, splines and journals for damage or excessive wear. Inspect reaction

GENERAL MOTORS TURBO HYDRA-MATIC 125C TRANSAXLE (Cont.)

Fig. 18: Exploded View of Reaction Carrier and Low-Reverse Clutch Assembly

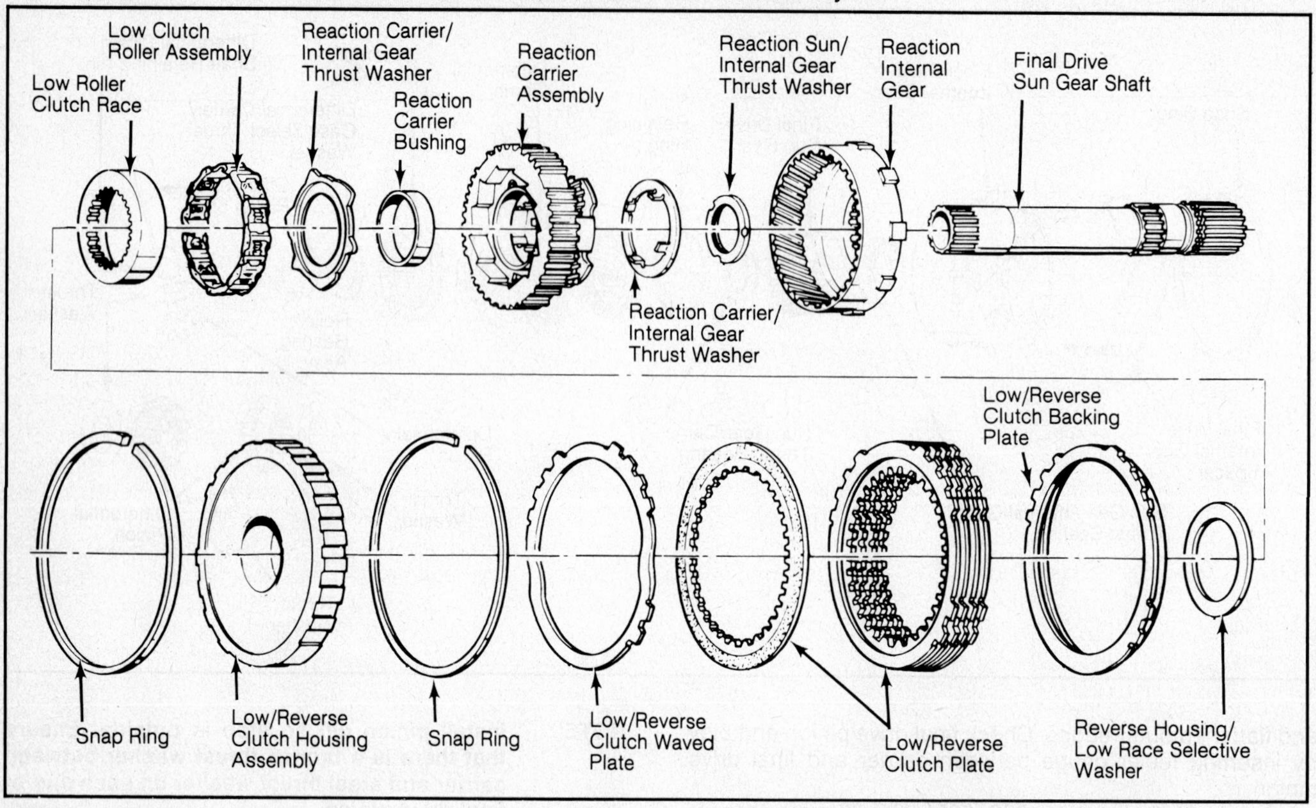

When low-reverse clutch assembly uses an apply ring, the adjoining steel clutch plate will be flat.

internal gear splines, teeth and bearing surface for wear, cracks and damage. Inspect reaction internal gear-to-reaction sun gear roller thrust bearing for damage. Inspect reverse clutch housing-to-low race selective washer for wear. Inspect parking pawl lugs for cracks or damage. Replace components as necessary.

LOW ROLLER CLUTCH & REACTION CARRIER ASSEMBLY

Disassembly

With transaxle rotated so case cover side is up, remove spacer and low roller clutch race. Pull low roller clutch from reaction carrier assembly. Lift reaction carrier-to-low roller clutch thrust washer from carrier. Pull final drive sun gear shaft from reaction internal gear.

Inspection

1) Inspect low roller clutch race and splines for scoring or wear. With low roller clutch assembly removed, inspect roller clutch bearings, cage and springs for wear, heat discoloration and damage.

2) Inspect the 4 tanged thrust washers for scoring, excessive wear and distorted tangs. Inspect reaction carrier, roller clutch cam ramps and bushing for damage or scoring.

3) Inspect reaction pinions for damage, rough bearings or tilt. Check pinion pins for tightness. Ensure pinion pins do not rotate. Using a feeler gauge, check pinion end play. Pinion end play should be .009-.027" (.24-.69 mm).

Reassembly

1) Install thrust washer into reaction carrier. Install all rollers that may have come out of roller clutch cage by compressing energizing spring with finger and inserting roller from outer edge.

2) Install roller clutch into carrier, then install clutch race, (splined side out) and rotate race clockwise until it drops into position. Install 4 tanged thrust washers onto reaction carrier assembly.

3) Align washer tangs into slot on pinion side of carrier and retain with petroleum jelly. Install reaction internal gear onto final drive sun gear shaft. Install reaction internal gear-to-reaction sun gear roller thrust bearing onto shaft.

4) Install reaction carrier and roller clutch assembly into reaction internal gear. Install Low-Reverse clutch housing-to-Low roller clutch race selective washer. Install reaction gear set into transaxle.

LOW-REVERSE CLUTCH HOUSING

Disassembly

Compress Low-Reverse clutch spring retainer, remove snap ring, then lift out retainer. Remove waved release spring and clutch piston from housing. Remove inner and outer piston seals and clutch apply ring (if equipped).

Inspection

1) Inspect clutch housing for damage or plugged feel hole. Check backing plate for cracks, damage or warpage. Inspect clutch splines and snap ring groove for damage or burrs. Remove any burrs on splines or snap ring groove.

2) Inspect clutch piston for distortion, cracks or damage. Inspect piston seals for nicks, cuts or hardening. Check apply ring for distortion, cracks or damage.

3) Inspect composite and steel clutch plates for signs of wear or burning. Inspect all other parts for damage or wear and replace components as necessary.

GENERAL MOTORS TURBO HYDRA-MATIC 125C TRANSAXLE (Cont.)

Fig. 19: Piston Seal Installer

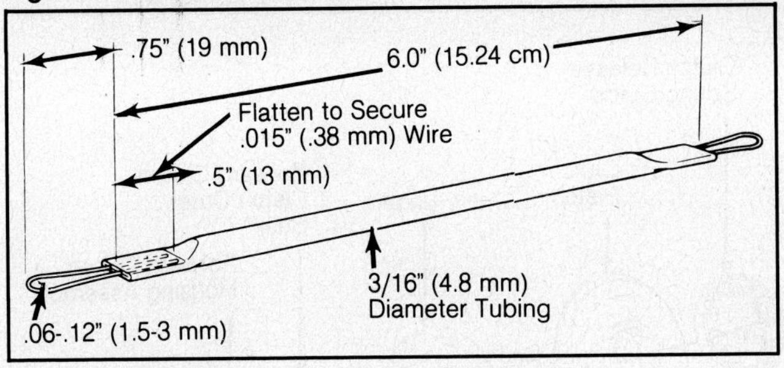

Use fabricated tool to install Low-Reverse and Forward Clutch pistons.

NOTE: **When using old design Low-Reverse clutch assembly, the clutch housing oil feed orifice will be .157" (4 mm) in diameter. New design housing feed hole is .079" (2 mm) in diameter. Use only new design components together and vice versa.**

Reassembly

1) Install Low-Reverse backing plate with stepped side down. When installing composite clutch plates, lubricate with ATF and install plates alternately, starting with one composite plate. Install waved steel plate last.

2) Install Low-Reverse clutch housing-to-case spacer ring. Spacer ring is .0042" (1.07 mm) thick. Install new inner and outer seals onto piston with lips facing Low-Reverse housing. Lubricate seal lips with transmission fluid.

NOTE: **It will be necessary to fabricate a piston installing tool to aid in proper installation and positioning of clutch seals. Using a 6" length of 3/16" diameter tubing and two 2 3/4" sec tions of .015" diameter wire, fabricate tool to dimensions in Fig. 19.**

3) Using fabricated tool, install clutch piston into housing and work inner seal down partially, then work outer seal down. Alternate from inner seal to outer seal until piston is fully seated.

4) Install waved spring and spring retainer (cupped side down). Compress retainer and install snap ring. Using Handle (J-28542), install Low-Reverse clutch housing. Ensure oil feed hole in housing lines up with feed hole in case. Check for piston movement by applying air to feed hole. Piston must apply and release when pressure is removed.

REACTION SUN GEAR & INPUT DRUM

Inspection

Check reaction sun gear (shaft) for cracks, splits, spline damage, gear-to-journal wear and for plugged lubrication passages. Inspect input drum for distortion, damaged splines and pins. Angle of roll pins is normal. DO NOT attempt to straighten pins.

INPUT CARRIER, INPUT SUN GEAR & INTERNAL GEAR

Inspection

1) Check all parts for pitting, scoring, damaged gear teeth and cracks. Ensure all lubrication holes are open.

Fig. 20: Exploded View of Input Unit

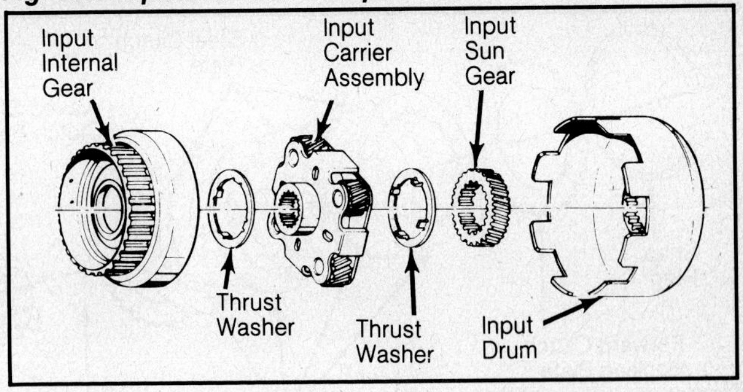

Check input carrier thrust washers for wear and distortion of tangs.

2) Check carrier pinion pins for tightness. Pin should not rotate. Using a feeler gauge, check input carrier pinion end play. End play should be .009-.027" (.24-.69 mm).

FORWARD CLUTCH ASSEMBLY

NOTE: **Some models may not be equipped with an apply ring.**

Disassembly

1) Place forward clutch housing in a holding fixture, clutch pack facing up. Remove clutch pack retaining snap ring. Remove backing plate, composite and steel clutch plates from housing.

2) Using an arbor press and/or Clutch Pack Compressor (J-23456) and Adapter (J-23327-1), compress retainer and spring assembly. Remove snap ring. Remove tool. Lift retainer and spring assembly from clutch housing. Remove piston from housing and seals from piston.

NOTE: **Do not remove clutch apply ring from piston unless piston or apply ring requires replacement.**

Inspection

1) Inspect input shaft teflon oil seal rings for missing, free fit in grooves and damage. Do not remove seals unless replacement is necessary. If new seal rings are installed, ensure cut ends are installed the same way they are cut.

2) Inspect composite and steel clutch plates for signs of wear or burning. Inspect backing plate for scratches and damage. Check forward clutch housing for broken welds. Check housing for cracks by applying compressed air, at 30 psi (2.11 kg/cm^2), to hole in input shaft (next to sealing rings).

3) With check ball removed, air pressure will exhaust when air nozzle is removed. With check ball installed, apply pressure to hole in clutch housing (input shaft side) and block input shaft hole with finger. Replace forward clutch housing if leak is found.

4) Check forward housing check ball for damage or improper sealing. Inspect release spring retainer for distortion and release springs for collapsed coils. Inspect piston and clutch apply ring assembly for cracks and damage. Apply ring width should be .47" (11.9 mm).

5) Check snap ring groove in clutch housing for damage or burrs. Inspect input shaft splines and journals for distortion or damage. Input shaft sleeve must not turn. The slot in sleeve must align with hole in input shaft. Replace components as necessary.

GENERAL MOTORS TURBO HYDRA-MATIC 125C TRANSAXLE

Fig. 21: Exploded View of Forward Clutch Assembly

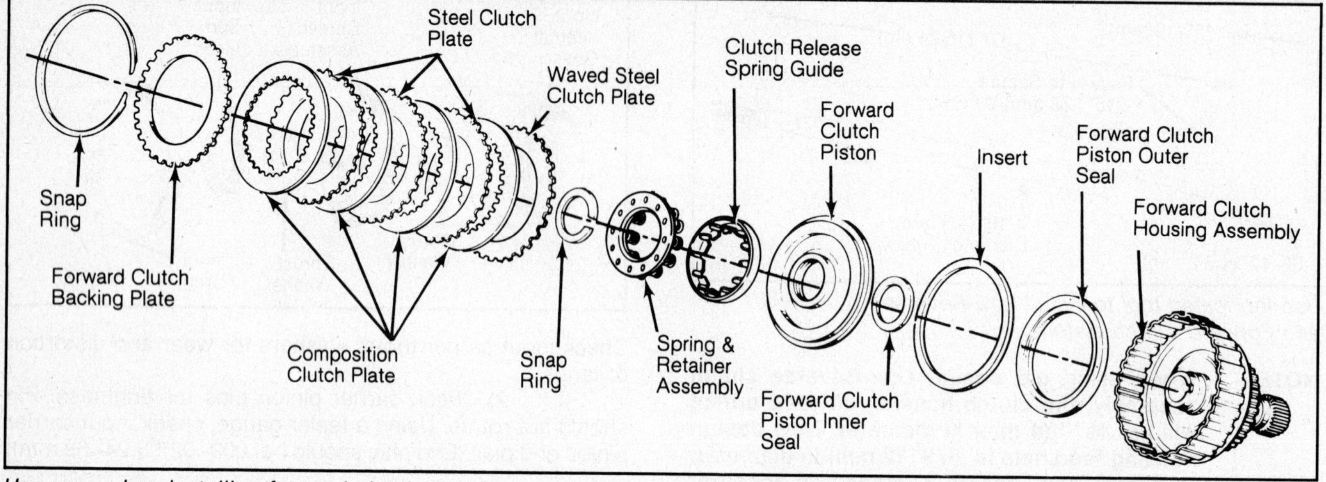

Use care when installing forward clutch piston past large forward clutch snap ring groove or seal could be cut.

Reassembly

1) If removed, install apply ring on piston. Install new inner and outer seals on piston with lips facing away from apply ring side. Lubricate seals and install piston into clutch housing using tool fabricated for Low-Reverse clutch piston installation.

2) Position spring guide, retainer and spring assembly into clutch housing. Compress retainer and spring assembly past snap ring groove and install snap ring. Remove compressor.

3) Lubricate and install forward clutch plates into housing. Start with waved steel plate then install a composition plate. Waved steel plate should be .06" (1.6 mm) thick. Alternate until 4 composition and 3 flat steel plates are installed. See FORWARD CLUTCH PLATE USAGE table.

FORWARD CLUTCH PLATE USAGE

Application	Flat Steel	Composition
All Models	[1] 3	4

[1] – Plate thickness is .08" (1.9 mm)

Fig. 22: Installing Input Shaft Seal Ring

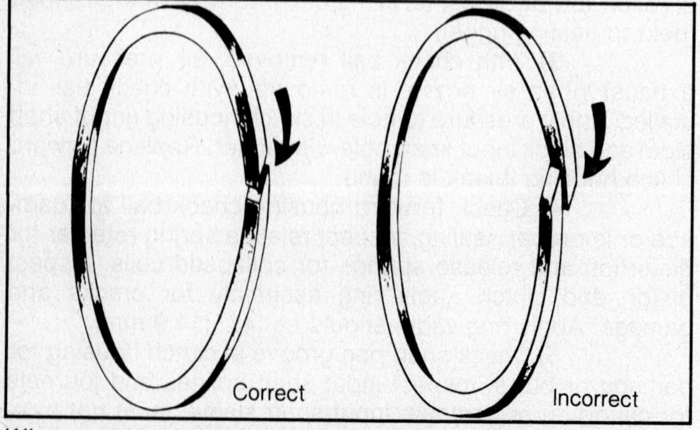

When new seal rings are installed, ensure the cut ends are installed the same way that they are cut.

4) Install clutch backing plate into housing with identification side up. Install snap ring. Ensure composition clutch plates turn freely. Measure clearance between backing plate and snap ring with a feeler gauge. DO NOT compress waved clutch plate.

5) If clearance is not within .04-.07" (1.0-1.5 mm), choose a selective thickness backing plate to correct clearance. Backing plates are available in the following sizes: .18-.19" (4.6-4.8 mm), .20-.2l" (5.1-5.3 mm) and .23-.24" (5.8-6.1 mm).

6) If removed, install new input shaft seal rings, making sure cut ends are assembled in same relationship as cut. Rings must be seated in groove. Retain with petroleum jelly. *See Fig. 22.*

DIRECT CLUTCH ASSEMBLY

NOTE: All THM 125C transmissions being serviced for a burnt band and direct clutch condition must have a new dual land third accumulator check valve and conical spring installed.

Disassembly

1) Remove clutch pack snap ring. Withdraw backing plate, composite and steel clutch plates from clutch housing. Ensure direct clutch plates are kept separated from forward clutch plates (if forward clutch is disassembled).

2) Remove snap ring holding apply ring and release spring assembly. Withdraw ring and spring assembly from housing. Remove direct clutch piston from clutch housing. Remove inner and outer seals from piston. Remove center seal from clutch housing.

Inspection

1) Inspect direct clutch housing bushings for damage, cracks or scoring. Inspect composition plates, steel plates and backing plate for wear, burning or scoring. Inspect apply ring, retainer and release spring assembly for damage, collapsed springs and proper apply ring width.

2) The apply ring width should be .750" (19.05 mm). Inspect direct clutch piston for distortion, cracks or damage. Inspect clutch housing for excessive wear, distortion and damaged check ball capsule.

3) If removal is necessary, drive check ball capsule (toward direct clutch side of housing) from housing, using a 3/8" drift. Install new capsule, from direct clutch side of housing, and seat with a 3/8" drift.

GENERAL MOTORS TURBO HYDRA-MATIC 125C TRANSAXLE (Cont.)

Fig. 23: Exploded View of Direct Clutch Assembly

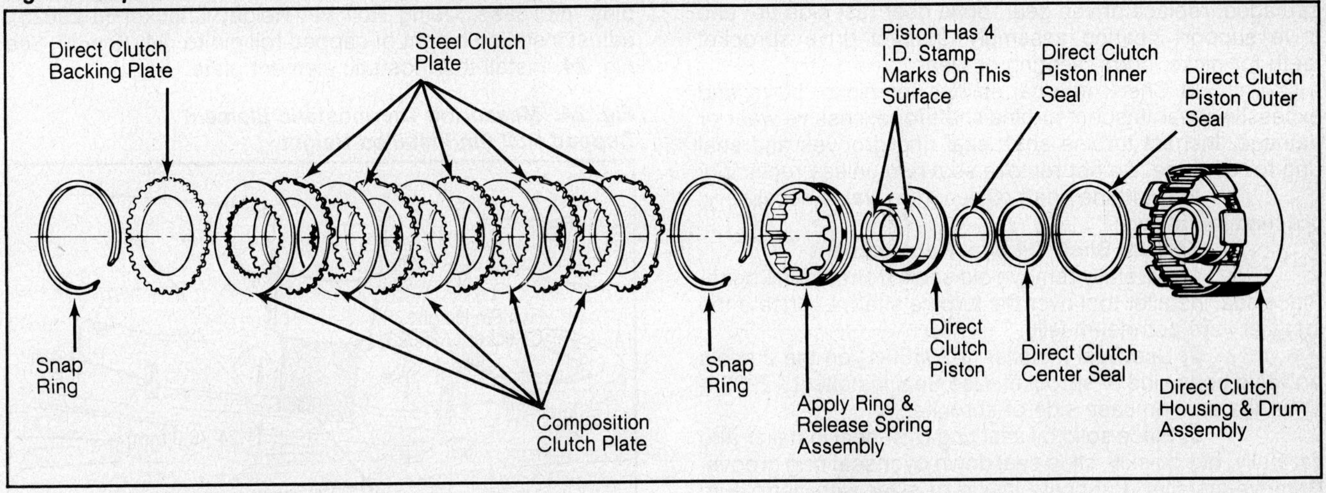

4) If burned band/direct clutch condition exists, remove intermediate servo cover and gasket. Remove third accumulator check valve and spring. Inspect third accumulator valve bore for presents of valve seat and excessive seat wear or damage.

5) Plug feed and release holes in bore with petroleum jelly. Install a dual land check valve. Ensure valve is centered in seat. Pour solvent into valve bore and check for leakage on inside of case. Small amount of seepage is acceptable.

6) If valve leaks, replace transmission case. If valve does not leak, remove check valve and install new conical spring onto the valve (small end first). Install valve with spring into bore. Replace servo gasket and cover.

Reassembly

1) Install inner and outer seals onto pistons with lips facing away from apply ring side. Install center seal on housing wih lip facing up. Lubricate all seals, then install piston into clutch housing.

CAUTION: **Use care when installing piston seals past snap ring grooves. Grooves could cut outer seal on piston.**

2) Install apply ring, retainer and release spring assembly and snap ring. Oil and install direct clutch plates into housing, starting with a flat steel plate and alternating 4 composition and 4 flat steel plates. See DIRECT CLUTCH PLATE USAGE table.

DIRECT CLUTCH PLATE USAGE

Application	Flat Steel	Composition
All Models	[1] 4	4

[1] - Plate thickness is .09" (2.3 mm).

3) Install backing plate into housing with flat side up. Backing plate thickness should be .190" (4.92 mm). Install snap ring. Ensure composition plates turn freely.

NOTE: **When servicing direct clutch/intermediate band assembly, check direct clutch for proper width compaired to intermediate band. DO NOT use old design, narrow 1.490" (37.84 mm), direct clutch housing with new design, wider 1.74" (44.2 mm) intermediate band or interference will result.**

INTERMEDIATE BAND ASSEMBLY

Inspection & Installation

Inspect intermediate band for burns, flaking or damage and replace as necessary. Install intermediate band, locating eye end into case and aligning lugged end with apply pin bore. Install band anchor hole plug.

CAUTION: **When installing, ensure lugged end of intermediate band is properly located or band will be inoperative.**

DRIVEN SPROCKET SUPPORT

Inspection

1) Inspect driven sprocket support and sleeve for cracks, burrs or damage. Sleeve must be tight in its bore and align with holes in support. Inspect driven sprocket support bushing and bearing assembly for damage and wear.

2) If necessary to replace bearing assembly, pull out using slide hammer and Bearing Remover (J-26941). Using Bearing Installers (J-28677 and J-8092), install bearing with manufacturing identification facing up.

3) Check bearing race on driven sprocket. If race requires replacement, driven sprocket support must be replaced. Inspect seal rings for nicks or cuts. Replace worn or damaged components as needed.

MANUAL SHAFT

Inspection

1) Inspect manual valve rod, rod retainer and detent lever for damage. Check threads of manual shaft for damage and check flats for any raised edges. File down any raised edges.

2) Inspect parking lock actuator rod for damage or broken retainer lugs. If removed, install parking lock actuator rod into manual shaft lever. The manual shaft and detent lever assembly are made as a matched set. Replace as an assembly only.

DRIVE LINK ASSEMBLY (CHAIN, DRIVE & DRIVEN SPROCKETS)

Inspection

1) Inspect drive chain for damage, stretching or loose links. With drive link assembly installed, check chain slack at each extreme and mark case for reference. If chain slack is more than 1.063" (27 mm), replace drive chain.

GENERAL MOTORS TURBO HYDRA-MATIC 125C TRANSAXLE (Cont.)

2) Inspect driven gear thrust bearing race. If damaged, replace driven gear, drive gear (flat side up) and drive support bearing assembly. Inspect drive sprocket teeth for nicks, burrs, scoring or wear.

3) Check internal splines for nicks, burrs and excessive wear. Inspect turbine shaft for excessive wear or damage. Inspect turbine shaft seal ring grooves and seal ring for damage. Do not remove seal ring unless replacing.

4) If turbine shaft oil seal removal is necessary, proceed as follows:

Turbine Shaft Oil Seal Replacement

1) Carefully remove old seals from turbine shaft. Place seal installer tool over the turbine shaft. Lubricate the installer with petroleum jelly.

2) Use Seal Installer (J-29569-1) on the 2 seals on valve body side of sprocket. Use Seal Installer (J-29829-1) on the seal on case side of sprocket.

3) Place solid oil seal ring over seal installer and carefully, but quickly, slide seal down over seal ring groove. Remove installer. Lubricate inside of sizer with petroleum jelly.

4) Use Sizer (J-29569-2) on 2 seals on valve body side of sprocket and Sizer (J-29829-2) on the seal on case side of sprocket. Push sizer down over seal and turn. Remove tool and inspect seal to be sure it is properly seated in the groove. Repeat procedure as needed.

CASE COVER

Disassembly

1) Remove detent spring/roller assembly retaining screw and spring/roller assembly. Remove 2 thermostatic roll pin washers. Remove thermostatic element and plate. Remove axle oil seal and guard if necessary.

2) Using a drift, drive out manual valve cup plug. Carefully withdraw manual valve. DO NOT use manual valve to drive out cup plug.

Inspection

1) Inspect case cover for damage, cracks, porosity or interconnected oil passages. Check for damaged threads in any threaded hole and repair with Heli-coil kit. Inspect vent assembly for damage and clogging. Check manual valve for damage and freedom of movement.

2) Check manual valve electrical connector for damage and replace as needed. Inspect manual detent spring and roller assembly for damage. Check case cover sleeve. Ensure hole in sleeve aligns with case cover passages that intersect case cover (pump shaft) bore.

3) Inspect 1-2 accumulator piston seals for damage and for free fit in grooves. Inspect thermostatic element for damage or distortion. Inspect vent assembly and cooler line connectors for damage. Replace components as necessary.

NOTE: **Do not disassemble case cover unless repair or replacement of cover and/or components is necessary.**

Reassembly

1) Using Seal Installer (J-26938 or J-29130), install new axle oil seal. Install seal guard if removed. Install detent spring and roller assembly. If 1-2 accumulator piston seal was removed, install new seal ring as shown in *Fig. 28*. Install 1-2 accumulator piston (flat side down).

2) Install 1-2 accumulator piston pin. Install manual valve assembly with small diameter first. Using a 3/8" drift, replace manual valve cup plug. Coat cup plug with sealant before installing. With new "O" ring on electrical connector, install connector with tab located at case slot.

3) If removed, install thermostatic element roll pins into case. Using Roll Pin Height Checker (J-29023), adjust installed height of capped roll pin to .24" (6 mm). *See Fig. 24*. Install thermostatic element plate.

Fig. 24: Measuring Thermostatic Element Capped Roll Pin Installed Height

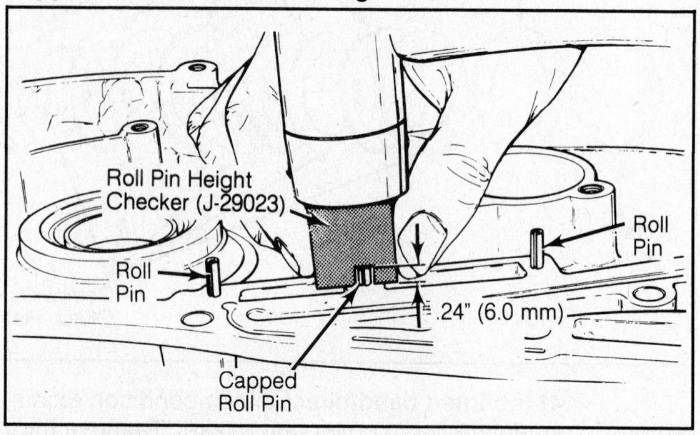

Always use measuring tool to check thermostatic element roll pin for proper installed height.

4) Install thermostatic element onto roll pins. Place Roll Pin Height Checker (J-29023) against roll pin, between case surface and thermostatic element. Install roll pin washers and tap them down onto roll pins until element contacts gauge. Set roller pin washer height to .21" (5.4 mm). *See Fig. 25*.

Fig. 25: Adjusting Thermostatic Element Roll Pin Washer Height

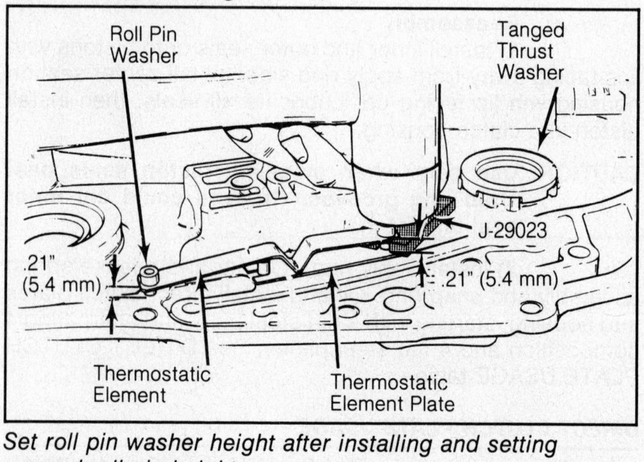

Set roll pin washer height after installing and setting capped roll pin height.

NOTE: **This adjustment is important for thermostatic element operation. Thermostatic element controls fluid level in control valve cover oil sump.**

CONTROL VALVE BODY & OIL PUMP ASSEMBLIES

NOTE: **As valve train assemblies are removed from their bore, place individual parts, in correct order, in relative position to valve body. Valves, bushings and springs are not interchangeable.**

GENERAL MOTORS TURBO HYDRA-MATIC 125C TRANSAXLE (Cont.)

Disassembly

1) Position control valve body with cored face up and line boost valve at top. Check operation of line boost valve. If replacement is needed, grind a taper on one end of a No. 49 (.073") drill.

NOTE: Remove roll pins by pushing through from case side of body, except for blind hole roll pins.

2) Use modified drill to remove all blind hole roll pins from valve body. Lightly tap drill into line boost valve roll pin. Pull out drill and roll pin. Remove line boost valve and plug by pushing valve out of valve body.

3) Check operation of Throttle Valve (T.V.) by moving valve against spring. If necessary to remove valve, remove roll pin holding T.V. plunger bushing. Withdraw throttle valve bushing, plunger and spring.

4) Tap drill into throttle valve roll pin and remove pin. Remove throttle valve. Remove pin from next bore down (same side). Withdraw T.V. boost valve assembly with bushing, reverse boost valve with bushing, pressure regulator valve and spring.

CAUTION: Remaining roll pins in valve body have pressure against them. Use caution when removing to prevent personal injury, loss or damage to parts.

5) Remove roll pin from next bore down, left side of valve body assembly. Slide out 3-2 shift T.V. valve and spring. Turn valve body over and remove roll pin, valve bore plug, shift T.V. valve and spring.

6) Remove spring retaining sleeve. Withdraw pressure relief spring and check ball. Remove roll pin from next bore down and withdraw 1-2 accumulator valve bore plug, valve, bushing and spring.

7) Remove roll pin from next bore down and remove 2-3 throttle valve bushing, spring, throttle valve and shift valve. Remove roll pin from next bore down and remove 1-2 throttle valve bushing, spring, valve and 1-2 shift valve.

8) Remove spring retaining sleeve from 3-2 control valve bore in the lower right hand corner. Remove 3-2 control valve and spring. Using a 1/4" punch, remove low-blowoff spring, plug assembly and ball.

NOTE: The low-blowoff assembly must be removed and replaced if valve body is washed in solvent.

9) Turn control valve body so oil pump side is facing up. If pump assembly must be serviced, remove roll pin from oil pump priming spring bore. Remove priming spring cup plug and priming spring.

10) Remove auxiliary valve body cover screw, auxiliary valve body, gasket and cover. Remove pump slide, rotor, 7 vanes and 2 vane rings.

CAUTION: DO NOT service oil pump rotor if pump pocket or auxiliary valve body/pump cover surfaces are scored. Service oil pump rotor and slide ONLY if selective pump rotor, pump drive shaft or pump slide is worn.

Inspection

1) Using solvent, wash control valve body, valves, springs, other valve train components, pump cover, pump slide, pump rotor, vanes and vane rings. DO NOT wash pump seals in solvent.

2) Inspect control valve body/oil pump body for cracks, damage or scoring of valve bores, pump pocket and pump cover. Inspect pump shaft seal and bearing for smooth operation and damage. If seal is damaged, pry out with screwdriver.

3) If necessary, replace bearing assembly using Bearing Remover/Installers (J-28698 and J-7092-2). Drive bearing out toward case cover side. Using bearing installers, install new bearing from pump pocket side. Install bearing until race is .040-.048" (1.00-1.20 mm) ABOVE pump pocket face.

4) After installation, check bearing installed height with feeler gauge. Using installer tools, install new oil seal (with steel side up) from case cover side. Ensure seal is .02" (.5 mm) to flush above case surface. DO NOT drive seal below case surface.

5) Recheck bearing race height once seal is installed. Inspect valve bushings for cracks and scored bores. Inspect bore plugs, pump slide, pump rotor, pump vanes and pump vane rings for damage, cracks or wear. Inspect springs for distortion or collapsed coils.

Oil Pump Rotor & Slide Replacement

1) If pump rotor and/or slides are defective, the replacement parts must provide the same end play originally built into the transaxle. Use the following procedure to obtain an end clearance of .0026-.0036" (.066-.092 mm).

2) Use a micrometer to measure the pump/rotor or slide thickness. Measure on flat, undamaged surface. Using the original measurement, order replacement part using SELECTIVE PUMP ROTOR and SELECTIVE PUMP SLIDE tables.

SELECTIVE PUMP SLIDE REPLACEMENT

Part No.	Thickness In. (mm)
8631800	.7070-.7074 (17.958-17.968)
8631801	.7075-.7079 (17.971-17.981)
8631802	.7080-.7084 (17.983-17.993)
8631803	.7085-.7089 (17.996-18.006)
8631804	.7090-.7094 (18.009-18.019)

SELECTIVE PUMP ROTOR REPLACEMENT

Part No.	Thickness In. (mm)
8637768	.7055-.7059 (17.920-17.930)
8637769	.7060-.7064 (17.932-17.943)
8637178	.7065-.7069 (17.945-17.955)
8637179	.7070-.7074 (17.958-17.968)
8637180	.7075-.7079 (17.971-17.981)

GENERAL MOTORS TURBO HYDRA-MATIC 125C TRANSAXLE (Cont.)

Fig. 26: Exploded view of Control Valve Body and Oil Pump Assembly

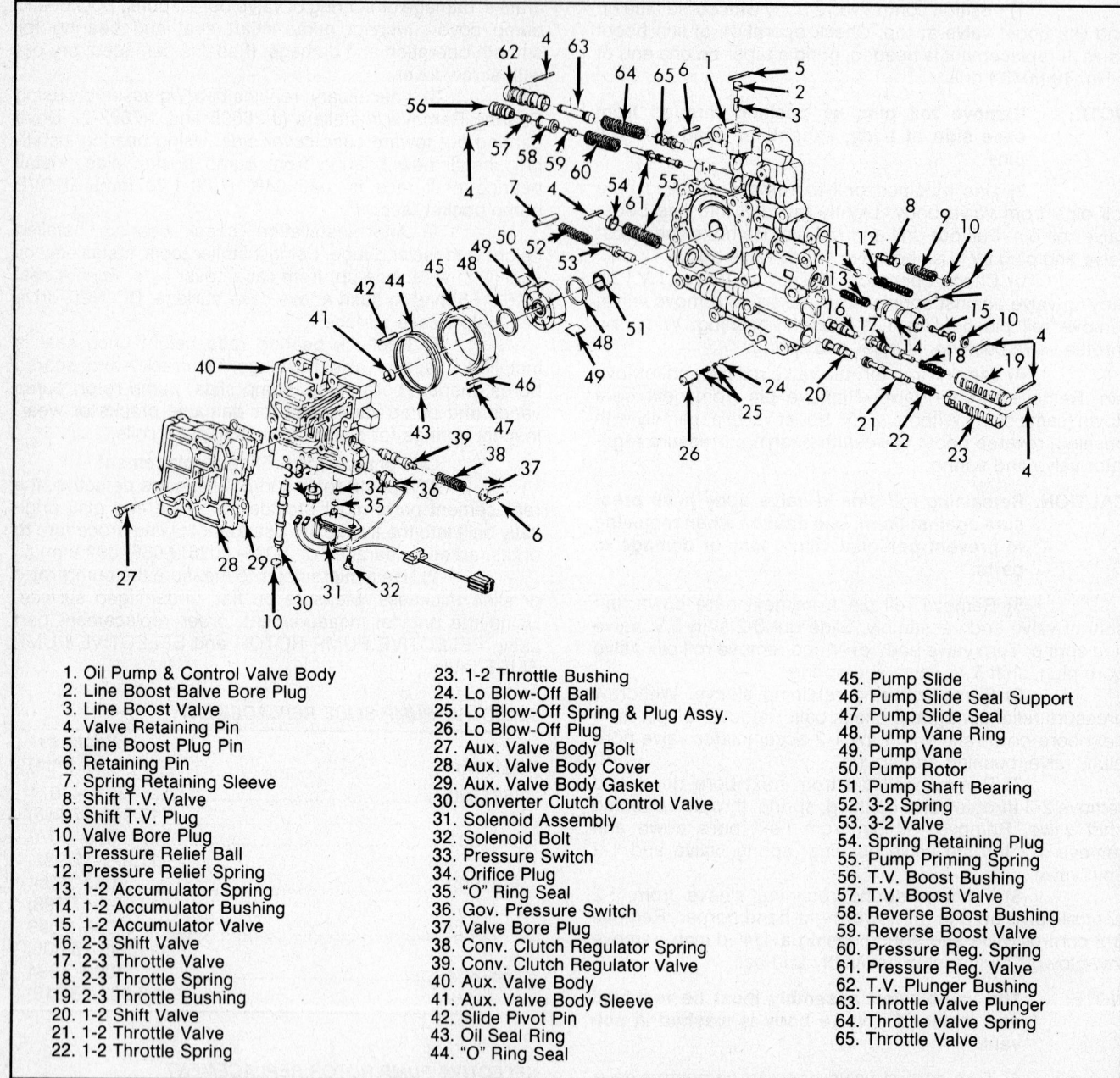

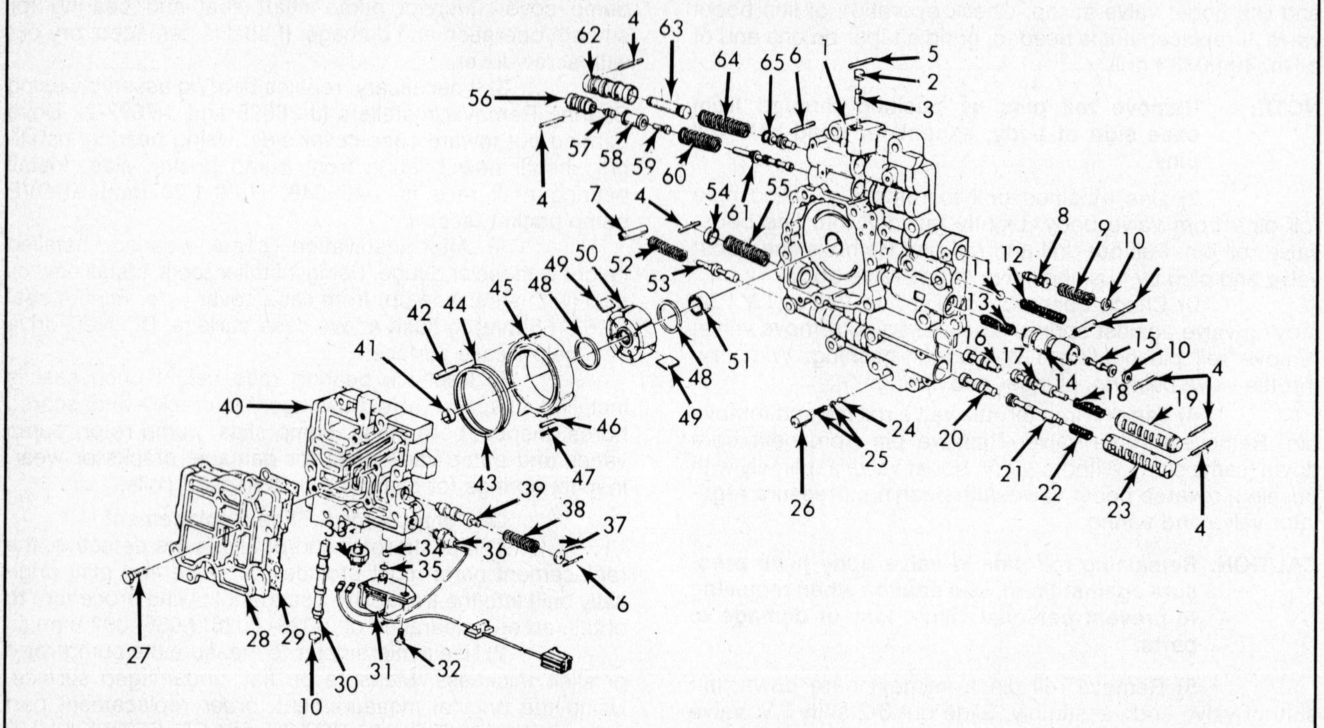

1. Oil Pump & Control Valve Body
2. Line Boost Balve Bore Plug
3. Line Boost Valve
4. Valve Retaining Pin
5. Line Boost Plug Pin
6. Retaining Pin
7. Spring Retaining Sleeve
8. Shift T.V. Valve
9. Shift T.V. Plug
10. Valve Bore Plug
11. Pressure Relief Ball
12. Pressure Relief Spring
13. 1-2 Accumulator Spring
14. 1-2 Accumulator Bushing
15. 1-2 Accumulator Valve
16. 2-3 Shift Valve
17. 2-3 Throttle Valve
18. 2-3 Throttle Spring
19. 2-3 Throttle Bushing
20. 1-2 Shift Valve
21. 1-2 Throttle Valve
22. 1-2 Throttle Spring
23. 1-2 Throttle Bushing
24. Lo Blow-Off Ball
25. Lo Blow-Off Spring & Plug Assy.
26. Lo Blow-Off Plug
27. Aux. Valve Body Bolt
28. Aux. Valve Body Cover
29. Aux. Valve Body Gasket
30. Converter Clutch Control Valve
31. Solenoid Assembly
32. Solenoid Bolt
33. Pressure Switch
34. Orifice Plug
35. "O" Ring Seal
36. Gov. Pressure Switch
37. Valve Bore Plug
38. Conv. Clutch Regulator Spring
39. Conv. Clutch Regulator Valve
40. Aux. Valve Body
41. Aux. Valve Body Sleeve
42. Slide Pivot Pin
43. Oil Seal Ring
44. "O" Ring Seal
45. Pump Slide
46. Pump Slide Seal Support
47. Pump Slide Seal
48. Pump Vane Ring
49. Pump Vane
50. Pump Rotor
51. Pump Shaft Bearing
52. 3-2 Spring
53. 3-2 Valve
54. Spring Retaining Plug
55. Pump Priming Spring
56. T.V. Boost Bushing
57. T.V. Boost Valve
58. Reverse Boost Bushing
59. Reverse Boost Valve
60. Pressure Reg. Spring
61. Pressure Reg. Valve
62. T.V. Plunger Bushing
63. Throttle Valve Plunger
64. Throttle Valve Spring
65. Throttle Valve

3) Hone both sides of the replacement rotor and/or slide to remove any burrs. After assembly, the pump drive shaft should turn freely. If not, recheck the pump rotor and slide.

Reassembly

1) Turn valve body so pump pocket side is up. Install pump slide into pump pocket. Ensure slide is in correct position. Install pump slide seal and seal support. Retain slide parts with petroleum jelly.

2) Position slide with the pump slide pivot hole and install pump slide pivot pin. Install vane ring and pump rotor into pump pocket. Install 7 vanes into pump.

3) Ensure vane wear pattern is against centering ring and each vane is seated flush with rotor. Install top vane ring. Install new slide "O" ring seal in the pump slide.

4) Install pump slide-to-auxiliary valve body oil seal ring. Check auxiliary valve body sleeve for damage. Install auxiliary valve body, gasket and cover. Align pump rotor step with auxiliary valve body sleeve.

NOTE: When pressure regulator valve is replaced, ensure new design steel retaining pin (part No. 112496) is inserted from and flush with machined face side of control valve and oil pump assembly.

5) To complete reassembly, reverse disassembly procedure, using *Fig. 26* as a guide. Care must be taken during reassembly of remaining components to avoid damage to valve bores and control valve body-to-case cover mating surfaces.

Fig. 27: Assembled View of Oil Pump

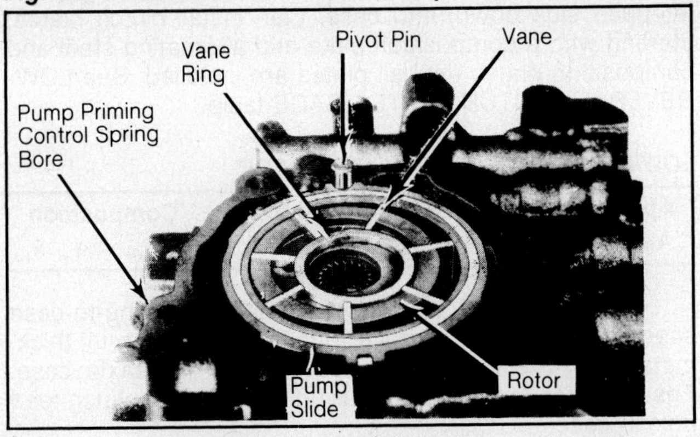

AUXILIARY VALVE BODY

Disassembly

1) Remove solenoid screw and solenoid. Using 24 mm socket, remove pressure switch and, if equipped, governor pressure switch. Remove auxiliary valve body cover, gasket and screw.

2) Remove converter clutch control valve and bore plug. With end of bore covered, remove roll pin (under pressure) from converter clutch control regulator valve. Remove bore plug, valve and spring. *See Fig. 28.*

Fig. 28: Exploded View of Auxiliary Valve Body

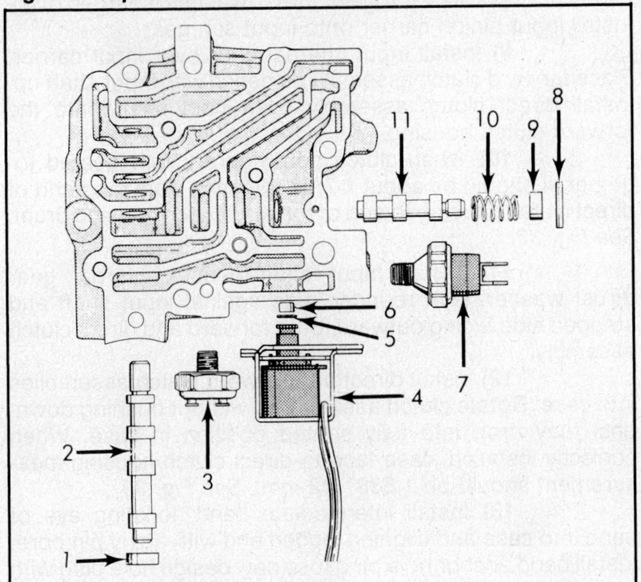

1. Valve Bore Plug
2. Converter Clutch Control Valve
3. Pressure Switch
4. Solenoid
5. "O" Ring Seal
6. Orifice Cup Plug
7. Governor Pressure Switch (Diesel)
8. Retaining Pin
9. Valve Bore Plug
10. Conv. Clutch Reg. Spring
11. Conv. Clutch Reg. Valve

Cover end of bore, during roll pin removal, to prevent loss of spring which is under pressure.

Inspection

1) Wash all auxiliary valve body parts, except solenoid, in solvent. Inspect valves and valve body for cracks, scoring valve bores or pump face and other damage. Inspect spring for distortion or collapsed coils.

2) Ensure orifice cup plugs are present in solenoid bore and pressure switch parts. Inspect solenoid "O" ring and bore plug for damage.

3) To prevent oil exhausting from vent after reassembly, check length of auxiliary valve body bolts. Bolts must be M6 X 1.0 X 20 mm. Tighten to 8 ft. lbs. (11 N.m).

Reassembly

1) Install converter clutch control regulator valve, spring and bore plug. Compress spring and install roll pin. Install converter clutch control valve and bore plug.

2) Install auxiliary valve body, gasket and screws. Ensure auxiliary valve body sleeve is aligned with step in pump rotor. Tighten mount screw to 8 ft. lbs. (11 N.m). Install pressure switches and tighten to 8 ft. lbs. (11 N.m).

3) Before installing solenoid, check for metal clip attached to valve body and discard if found. Install new design solenoid with new "O" ring and plastic wire routing clip. Install cover gasket and screw.

INTERMEDIATE SERVO

NOTE: **Ensure proper apply ring size is determined before final reassembly and installation.**

Disassembly & Inspection

1) Remove "E" clip from apply pin. Separate intermediate servo piston, cushion spring, spring retainer and apply pin. Remove and discard all "O" ring seals. *See Fig. 29.*

Fig. 29: Exploded View of Intermediate Servo Assembly

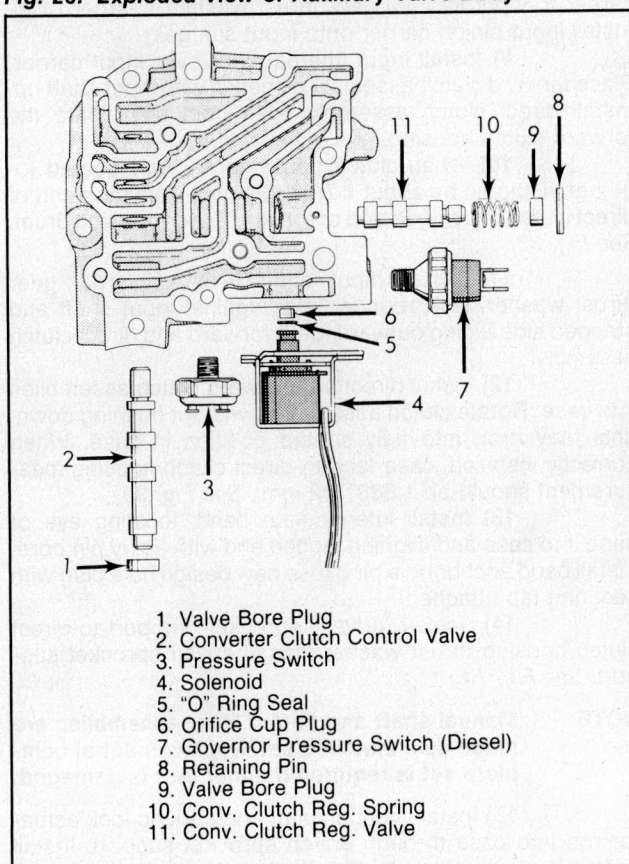

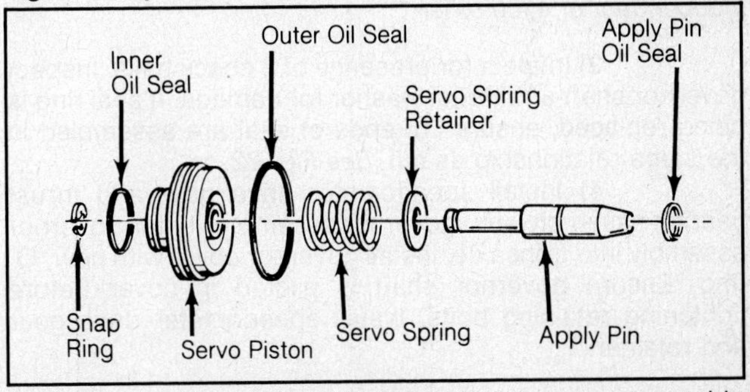

Remove and discard all of the intermediate servo assembly "O" ring seals whenever assembly is removed.

NOTE: **If THM 125C transaxle (code BL, CE, CT or OP) is being serviced for 3-2 coast-down clunk condition, check for broken, cracked or damaged intermediate servo spring. If spring (White) needes replacement, be sure to use spring (Violet) with part No. 8652057.**

2) Inspect all parts for damage, cracks, scoring and distortion. Check apply pin for free fit in bore. Check servo cover and piston assembly for porosity.

3) Reassemble servo using new inner and outer oil seals on piston and new seal on apply pin (proper apply pin size determined during disassembly).

GOVERNOR/SPEEDOMETER GEAR ASSEMBLY

Inspection

1) Check for plugged oil passage, wash in solvent and blow out oil passage. If necessary, remove

GENERAL MOTORS TURBO HYDRA-MATIC 125C TRANSAXLE (Cont.)

speedometer drive gear from governor shaft and inspect gear for nicks or damage. Check governor cover for damage or distortion of mating surface. Remove and discard cover "O" ring.

2) Inspect governor driven gear for nicks or damage. Check governor shaft seal rings for cuts, damage and free fit in groove. Check for free operation of governor weights. The weights must operate freely and independent of each other. Check for damaged, mispositioned or tilted springs. *See Fig. 30.*

Fig. 30: Sectional View of Governor Assembly

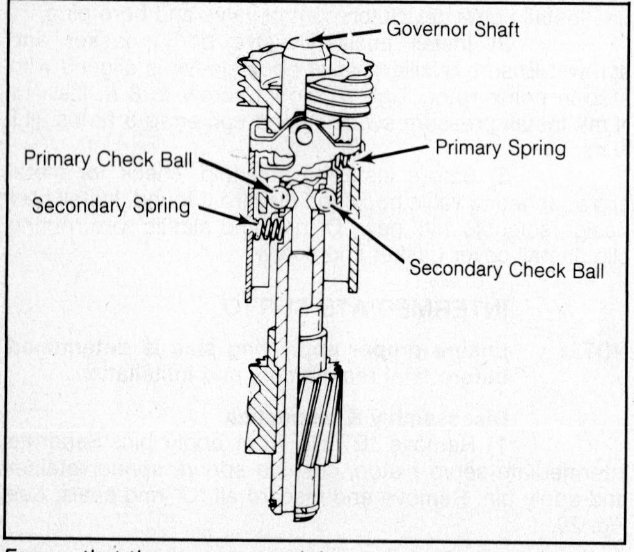

Ensure that the governor weights operate freely and are independent of each other.

3) Inspect for presence of 2 check balls. Inspect governor shaft and thrust washer for damage. If seal ring is being replaced, ensure cut ends of seal are assembled in the same relationship as cut. *See Fig. 22.*

4) Install speedometer drive gear and thrust bearing assembly onto governor assembly. Install governor assembly into transaxle. Install governor cover with new "O" ring. Ensure governor shaft is piloted in cover before tightening retaining bolts. Install speedometer drive gear and retainer.

TRANSAXLE REASSEMBLY

NOTE: All selective snap ring and thrust washer measurements taken during disassembly should be rechecked at appropriate stage of reassembly. Follow procedures given in TRANSAXLE DISASSEMBLY.

1) Turn transaxle so case cover end is up. Install proper final drive-to-case thrust washer and thrust bearing assembly to final drive unit (inner race of bearing against selective washer). Install differential and final drive assembly into case.

2) Install final drive internal gear spacer (cupped side against final drive internal gear). Ensure opening in spacer aligns with parking pawl opening in case. Check to see that parking pawl passes through spacer freely.

3) Install final drive spacer-to-case snap ring with ring gap away from parking pawl opening in case. Install reaction sun gear set into case.

4) Install Low-Reverse clutch backing plate (stepped side down) into case, then install clutch plates, starting with a composition plate and alternating steel and composition plates until all plates are installed. See LOW-REVERSE CLUTCH PLATE USAGE table.

LOW-REVERSE CLUTCH PLATE USAGE

Application	Flat Steel	Composition
All Models	4	5

5) Install Low-Reverse clutch housing-to-case spacer ring. This case spacer ring is .042" (1.07 mm) thick. Install Low-Reverse clutch housing into transaxle case. Ensure clutch feed hole in housing lines up with clutch feed hole in case.

6) Install proper selective snap ring onto reaction sun gear. Install reaction sun gear onto final drive sun gear shaft in transaxle. Rotate reaction sun gear while pushing down on the Low-Reverse clutch housing until clutch housing drops below snap ring groove in case.

7) Install Low-Reverse clutch housing-to-case snap ring. This snap ring is .092" (2.36 mm) thick. Install input drum onto reaction sun gear. Install input sun gear into input drum. Install input carrier-to-input sun gear tanged thrust washer to pinion side of carrier.

8) Install input carrier-to-input internal gear tanged thrust washer to internal gear side of carrier (input carrier-to-input internal gear thrust washer is larger of 2). Install input pinion carrier onto input sun gear.

9) Install input internal gear over input carrier. Place forward clutch assembly on bench with input shaft up. Install direct clutch assembly over input shaft onto the forward clutch housing.

10) When clutch housings are fully seated together, it should be about 1 7/32" (31 mm) from tang end of direct clutch housing to end of forward clutch housing drum. *See Fig. 32.*

11) Install input shaft-to-input internal gear thrust washer, with rounded side against input shaft and stepped side facing outward, onto forward and direct clutch assembly.

12) Install direct and forward clutch assemblies into case. Rotate clutch assemblies, without pushing down, until they drop into fully seated position in case. When correctly installed, case face-to-direct clutch housing measurement should be 1.688" (42 mm). *See Fig. 33.*

13) Install intermediate band, locating eye of band into case and aligning lugged end with apply pin bore. Install band anchor hole plug (use new design hole plug with securing tab attached).

14) Install driven sprocket support-to-direct clutch housing thrust washer. Install driven sprocket support. *See Fig. 14.*

NOTE: Manual shaft and detent lever assemblies are made as a matched set. Replacement of complete set is required if either part is damaged.

15) Install manual shaft and parking lock actuator rod into case through driven sprocket support. Install detent lever on manual shaft (hub side away from driven sprocket support) and push manual shaft in place.

16) Install detent lever-to-manual shaft retaining nail. Install manual shaft-to-case retaining pin. *See Fig. 14.*

17) Assemble drive and driven sprockets with link assembly and install drive and driven thrust washers to

GENERAL MOTORS TURBO HYDRA-MATIC 125C TRANSAXLE (Cont.)

Fig. 31: Thrust Bearing, Thrust Washer and Bushing Locations

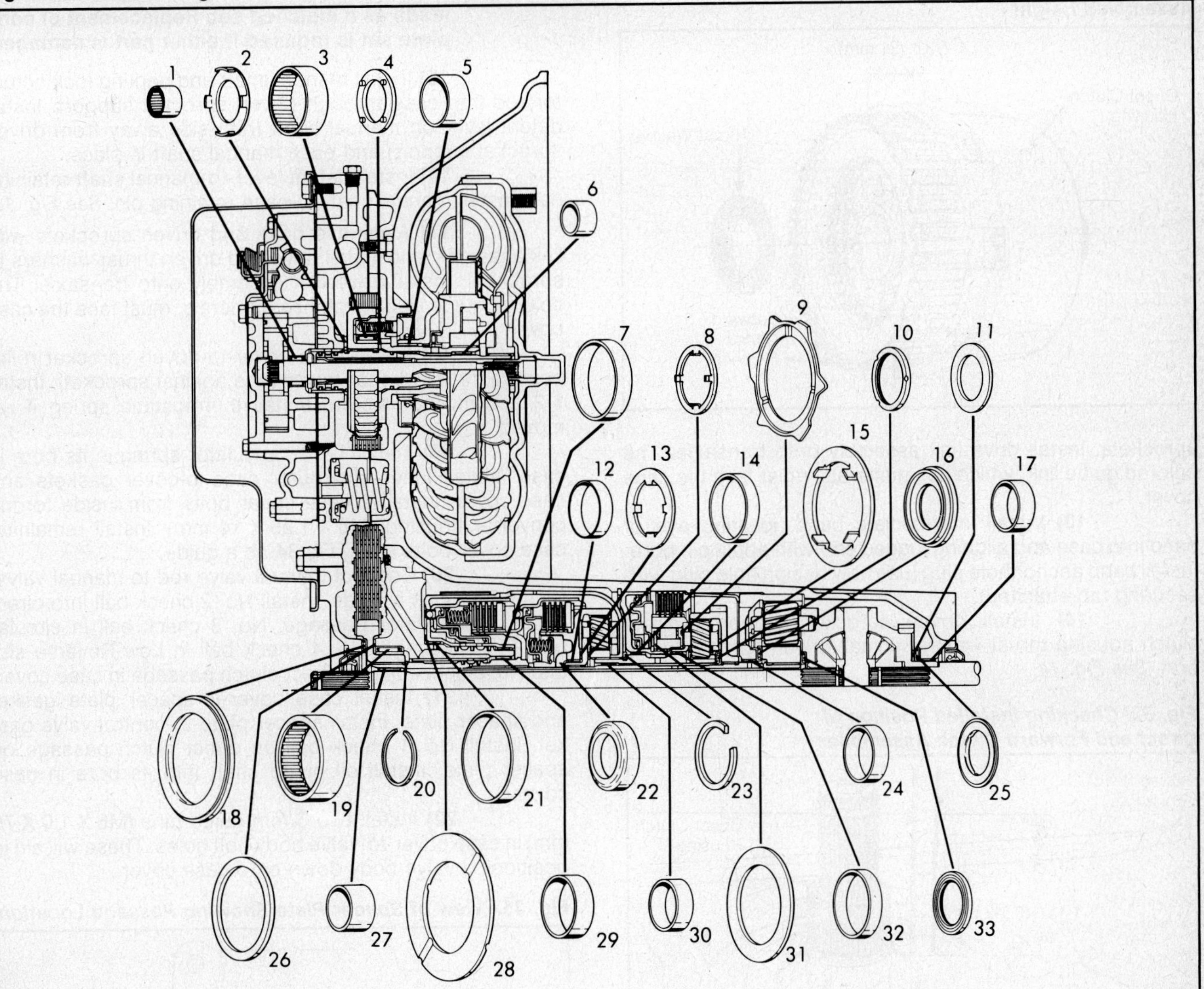

1. Pump Shaft Bearing Assembly
2. Case Cover-to-Driven Sprocket Thrust Washer
3. Bearing Assembly
4. Case Cover-to-Drive Sprocket Thrust Washer
5. Converter Bushing
6. Drive Sprocket Support Bushing
7. Direct Clutch Drum Bushing
8. Input Carrier-to-Input Sun Gear Thrust Washer
9. Reaction Carrier-to-Lo Race Thrust Washer
10. Reaction Sun Gear-to-Internal Gear Thrust Bearing
11. Differential Carrier-to-Case Selective Thrust Washer
12. Input Internal Gear Bushing
13. Input Carrier-to-Input Internal Gear Thrust Washer
14. Low & Reverse Clutch Housing Bushing
15. Reaction Carrier-to-Internal Gear Thrust Washer
16. Sun Gear-to-Internal Gear Thrust Bearing
17. Case Bushing
18. Driven Sprocket Thrust Bearing Assembly
19. Bearing Assembly
20. Selective Snap Ring
21. Direct Clutch Bushing
22. Input Shaft Thrust Washer
23. Selective Snap Ring
24. Final Drive Internal Gear Bushing
25. Differential Case Thrust Bearing Assembly
26. Driven Sprocket Support Thrust Washer
27. Input Shaft Bushing
28. Thrust Washer
29. Driven Sprocket Support Bushing
30. Reaction Sun Gear Bushing
31. Reverse Housing-to-Lo Race Selective Thrust Washer
32. Reaction Carrier Bushing
33. Sun Gear-to-Carrier Thrust Bearing

GENERAL MOTORS TURBO HYDRA-MATIC 125C TRANSAXLE (Cont.)

Fig. 32: Measuring Forward Clutch-to-Direct Clutch Assembled Height

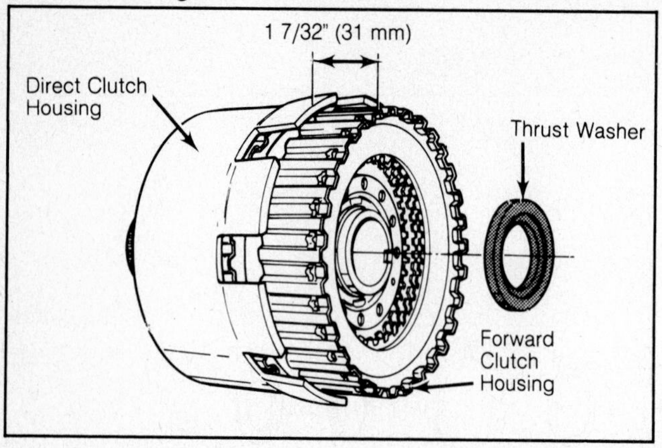

sprockets. Install drive link assembly onto transaxle. The colored guide link, which has numerals, must face the case cover.

13) Install intermediate band, locating eye of band into case and aligning lugged end with apply pin bore. Install band anchor hole plug (use new design hole plug with securing tab attached).

14) Install driven sprocket support-to-direct clutch housing thrust washer. Install driven sprocket support. *See Fig. 14.*

Fig. 33: Checking Installed Position of Direct and Forward Clutch Assemblies

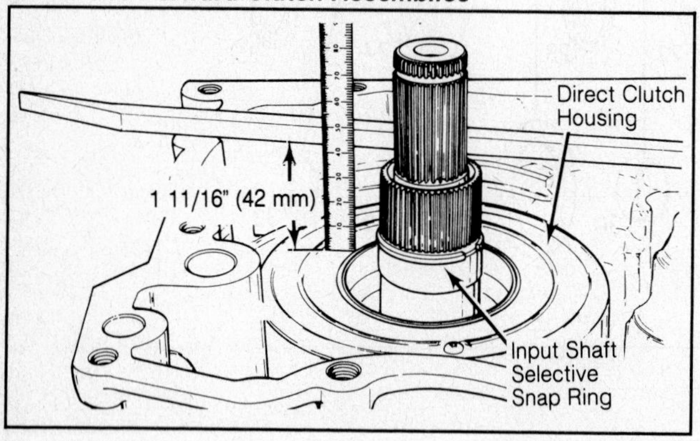

Fig. 34: Case Cover Bolt Locations

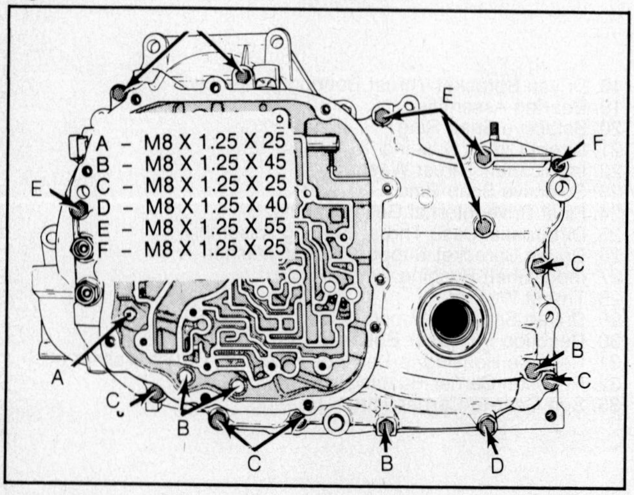

NOTE: **Manual shaft and detent lever assemblies are made as a matched set. Replacement of complete set is required if either part is damaged.**

15) Install manual shaft and parking lock actuator rod into case through driven sprocket support. Install detent lever on manual shaft (hub side away from driven sprocket support) and push manual shaft in place.

16) Install detent lever-to-manual shaft retaining nail. Install manual shaft-to-case retaining pin. *See Fig. 14.*

17) Assemble drive and driven sprockets with link assembly and install drive and driven thrust washers to sprockets. Install drive link assembly onto transaxle. The colored guide link, which has numerals, must face the case cover.

18) Install case cover-to-driven sprocket roller bearing thrust washer (outer race against sprocket). Install 1-2 accumulator piston. Install thermostatic spring if removed.

19) Install 1-2 accumulator spring in its bore in case. Install inner and outer case-to-cover gaskets and case cover. Install 2 case cover bolts from inside torque converter housing (M8 X 1.25 X 14 mm). Install remaining case cover bolts using *Fig.34* as a guide.

20) Connect manual valve rod to manual valve. Using *Fig 11* as a guide, install No. 2 check ball into direct clutch accumulator passage, No. 3 check ball in circular Low-First passage, No. 4 check ball in Low-Reverse slot and No. 5 check ball in direct clutch passage in case cover.

21) Install case cover-to-spacer plate gasket and spacer plate. Install spacer plate-to-control valve gasket. Install No. 1 check ball on direct clutch passage on spacer plate. Install oil pump shaft into its bore in case cover.

22) Install two 6 mm guide pins (M6 X 1.0 X 75 mm) in case cover-to-valve body bolt holes. These will aid in positioning valve body down onto case cover.

Fig. 35: View of Spacer Plate Showing Passage Location

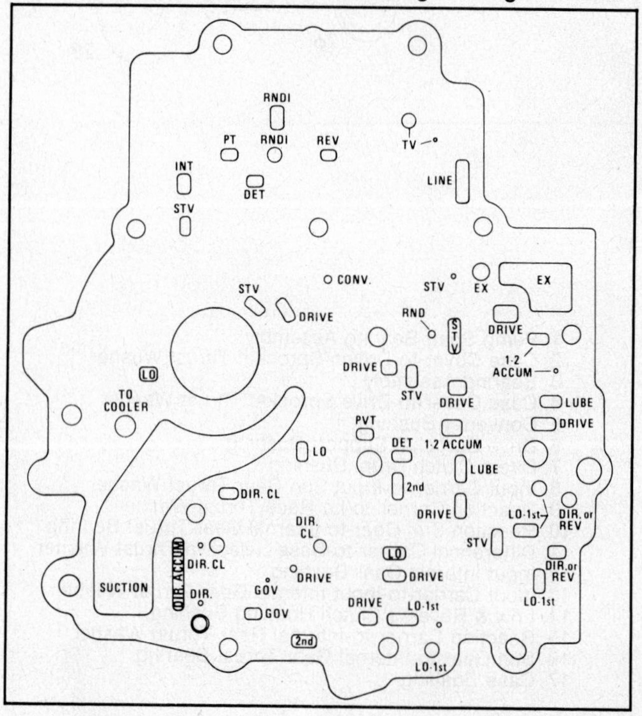

GENERAL MOTORS TURBO HYDRA-MATIC 125C TRANSAXLE (Cont.)

23) Install control valve body with bolts and tighten. Install valve body wiring harness as shown in *Figs. 37 and 38*. Connect lever link to T.V. bracket. Install T.V. bracket onto valve body.

Fig. 36: Control Valve Body Bolt Locations

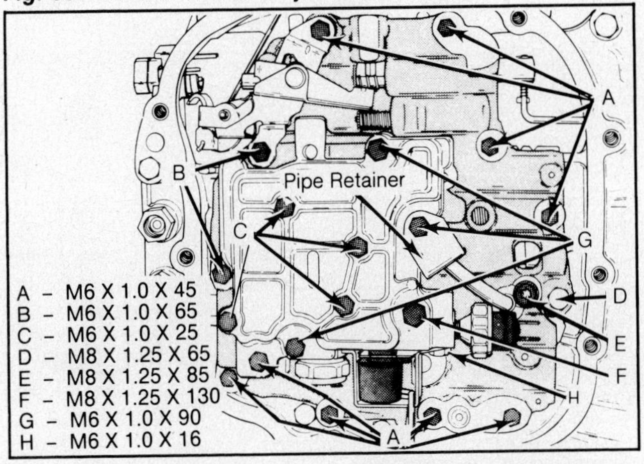

24) Remove guide bolts used to install valve body and install remaining 2 valve body bolts. Thoroughly clean valve body cover and install using new gasket.

25) Turn transaxle so oil pan side is up. Install output shaft into transaxle. Rotate final drive so retaining ring groove is visible through access window in case. Install new retaining ring onto shaft groove.

Fig. 37: Wiring Harness Connections For Vehicles Equipped With Gasoline Engine

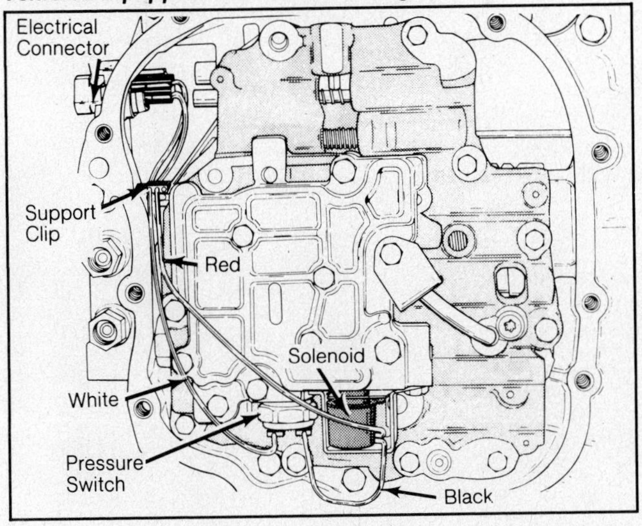

26) Install parking lock bracket and dipstick stop. Using a 3/8" drift, install new Low-Reverse oil pipe seal assembly. Install "O" ring back-up washer and "O" ring seal onto end of Low-Reverse pipe. Install pipe, plain end in first, then "O" ring end. Install retainer bracket.

27) Install intermediate servo piston assembly. Install third accumulator check valve and spring into check valve bore next to servo piston. Install intermediate servo cover and 3 bolts.

28) Install reverse oil pipe bracket to oil pipe and servo cover. Install remaining servo cover bolt through bracket and cover. Tighten servo cover bolts.

Fig. 38: Wiring Harness Connections For Vehicles Equipped With Diesel Engine

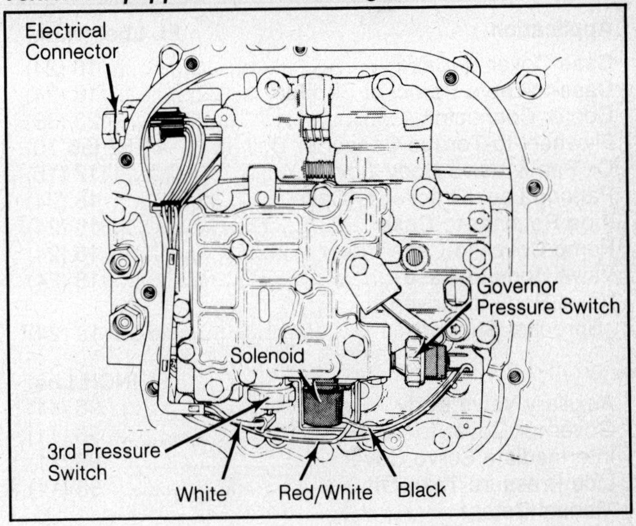

NOTE: **If transaxle was equipped with a third accumulator check valve cup plug, and plug was removed, DO NOT install a new plug or old servo cover. Replace servo cover and gasket with replacement version. Replacement version has cast lug to take place of cup plug.**

29) Install new oil strainer and "O" ring. Install oil pan gasket and oil pan. Rotate transaxle so oil pan side is down. Install governor assembly. Install new "O" ring to governor cover and install cover onto case. Install speedometer driven gear assembly into governor cover.

NOTE: **Ensure governor shaft is piloted in governor cover before tightening cover bolts.**

30) Install torque converter. Converter is properly installed if the distance is .50" (13 mm) minimum between engine mount face of case and front face of converter cover lugs.

GENERAL MOTORS TURBO HYDRA-MATIC 125C TRANSAXLE (Cont.)

TIGHTENING SPECIFICATIONS

Application	Ft. Lbs. (N.m.)
Case Cover-to-Case	18 (24)
Case-to-Drive Sprocket Support	18 (24)
Cooler Connector	23 (38)
Flywheel-to-Torque Converter Bolt	41-52 (55-70)
Oil Pan & Valve Body Cover	12 (16)
Parking Lock Bracket-to-Case	18 (24)
Pipe Retainer-to-Case	18 (24)
Pump Cover-to-Case Cover	18 (24)
Valve Body-to-Case	18 (24)
Valve Body-to-Driven Sprocket Support	18 (24)
	INCH Lbs.
Auxiliary Valve Body	96 (11)
Governor Cover-to-Case	96 (11)
Intermediate Servo Cover	96 (11)
Line Pressure Take-Off	96 (11)
Manual Detent Spring-to-Case	96 (11)
Oil Pan & Valve Body Cover	96 (11)
Pressure Switch	96 (11)
Pump Cover-to-Valve Body	96 (11)
Solenoid-to-Valve Body	96 (11)
T.V. Cable-to-Case	72 (9)
Valve Body-to-Case Cover	96 (11)

[1] – Discard hub nut whenever it is removed and use only a new hub nut during installation.

GENERAL MOTORS TURBO HYDRA-MATIC 180C

Chevrolet Chevette
Pontiac 1000

TRANSMISSION IDENTIFICATION

The transmission identification code is stamped on a tag located on left side of transmission case near rear edge of torque converter housing.

DESCRIPTION

The 180C transmission is a fully automatic unit consisting primarily of a 4-element hydraulic torque converter and a compound planetary gear set. Three multiple-disc clutches, a roller clutch and a band provide the friction elements required to obtain the desired function of the compound planetary gear set. A hydraulic system pressurized by a gear-type pump provides the working pressure required to operate the friction elements and automatic controls.

LUBRICATION & ADJUSTMENTS

See appropriate AUTOMATIC TRANSMISSION SERVICING article in DOMESTIC GENERAL SERVICING section.

TROUBLE SHOOTING

See appropriate AUTOMATIC TRANSMISSION TROUBLE SHOOTING article in DOMESTIC GENERAL SERVICING section.

CLUTCH AND BAND APPLICATION CHART (ELEMENTS IN USE)

Selector Lever Position	Reverse Clutch	2nd Clutch	3rd Clutch	Sprag Clutch	Low Band
D - Drive					
1st Gear				X	X
2nd Gear		X			X
3rd Gear		X	X	X	
L2 - Intermediate 2nd Gear		X			X
L1 - Low			X	X	X
R - Reverse	X		X	X	

NEUTRAL OR PARK - All clutches and bands released and/or ineffective.

TESTING

ROAD TEST

Drive Range ("D")

With selector lever in "D" range, accelerate vehicle from a standstill. A 1-2 and 2-3 shift should occur at all throttle openings (shift points will vary with throttle openings). As vehicle speed decreases to zero MPH, a 3-2 and 2-1 downshift should occur.

Intermediate Range ("L2")

Place selector lever in "L2" and accelerate vehicle from a standstill. A 1-2 shift should occur at all throttle openings. No 2-3 shift can be obtained in this range. The 1-2 shift point will vary with throttle opening. As vehicle speed decreases to zero MPH, a 2-1 downshift should occur.

Low Range ("L1")

Place selector lever in "L1" and accelerate vehicle from a standstill. No upshift should occur in this range.

2nd Gear ("L2") Overrun Braking

With selector lever in "D" range and vehicle moving in high gear, lift foot off accelerator and move selector lever to intermediate range ("L2"). An increase in engine RPM and an engine braking effect should be noted.

1st Gear ("L1") Overrun Braking

With selector lever in "L2" range, and vehicle speed approximately 30 MPH at constant throttle, move selector lever to "L1" range. An increase in engine RPM and an engine braking effect should be noted.

CONTROL PRESSURE TEST

Remove transmission crossmember side bolts and lower transmission slightly to gain access to line pressure take-off point. Connect a tachometer to engine and a pressure gauge to line pressure take-off point on left side of transmission case. With transmission fluid at correct level and operating temperature, pressure can be checked by road testing or by running engine with vehicle on a hoist as follows:

GENERAL MOTORS TURBO HYDRA-MATIC 180C (Cont.)

Stationary Test (Modulator Disconnected)

Make test with vehicle stationary, service brakes applied, engine speed set at 1500 RPM, vacuum modulator line disconnected, and pressure gauge installed. Transmission line pressure should be approximately as shown in CONTROL PRESSURES table.

CONTROL PRESSURES

Shift Lever Position	[1] psi (kg/cm²)
Drive ("D")	118 (8.3)
Intermediate ("L2")	118 (8.3)
Low ("L1")	160 (11.2)

[1] – Maximum pressure.

Coasting Check (Modulator Connected)

With vehicle coasting at 30 MPH (foot off throttle), pressure gauge installed and vacuum modulator line connected, transmission line pressure should be approximately as shown in CONTROL PRESSURES table.

CONTROL PRESSURES

Shifter Position	[1] psi (kg/cm²)
Drive ("D")	65 (4.6)
Intermediate ("L2")	65 (4.6)
Low ("L1")	95 (6.7)

[1] – Minimum pressure.

CONTROL PRESSURE TEST RESULTS

Control Pressure Too Low

- Low oil level.
- Clogged suction screen.
- Leak in oil pump suction circuit.
- Leak in oil pressure circuit.
- Pressure regulator valve mulfunction.
- Sealing ball in valve body dropped out.

Control Pressure Too High

- Modulator vacuum line leaking or interrupted.
- Failed vacuum modulator.
- Vacuum leak in engine or accessory vacuum system.
- Pressure regulator valve malfunction.

SERVICE (IN VEHICLE)

The following components may be removed from transmission for inspection or repair, without removing transmission from vehicle:

- Governor Cover, Seals & Assembly
- Governor Pressure Switch (Diesel Only)
- Intermediate Servo Cover, Seal & Assembly
- Oil Pan & Screen Assembly
- Control Valve Assembly
- Check Balls & Valve Body Space Plates & Gaskets
- Inside Detent Range Lever
- Manual Detent Roller & Spring Assembly
- Throttle Lever & Bracket Assembly
- TV Detent Cable & "O" Ring
- Parking Pawl Actuator Rod
- Parking Pawl & Bracket
- Manual Shift & Seal
- Manual Valve
- Manual Valve Link
- Extension Housing, Gasket & Rear Seal
- 1-2 Accumulator Assembly
- Vacuum Modulator
- Cooler Fittings
- Oil Filter Pipe & "O" Ring
- Speedometer Driven Gear & Assembly
- Converter Clutch Solenoid
- Solenoid Wire Clips
- Electrical Connectors
- Governor Feed Screen
- Modulator Valve
- Low Band Adjustment

NOTE: **For removal and installation procedures on these components, see TRANSMISSION DISASSEMBLY and TRANSMISSION REASSEMBLY in this article.**

REMOVAL & INSTALLATION

TRANSMISSION

REMOVAL See appropriate AUTOMATIC TRANSMISSION article in DOMESTIC GENERAL SERVICING section.

TORQUE CONVERTER

NOTE: **Torque converter is a sealed unit and cannot be disassembled for service.**

LEAKAGE CHECK

See procedure given in G.M. Turbo Hydra-Matic 400 article in this section.

NOTE: **For additional information on the Torque Converter Clutch (TCC) system used with this transmission see GENERAL MOTORS TORQUE CONVERTER CLUTCH (TCC) SYSTEM article in this section.**

TRANSMISSION DISASSEMBLY

TORQUE CONVERTER & CONVERTER HOUSING OIL SEAL

1) Remove oil filter tube. Remove converter by pulling straight out. Install transmission in a holding fixture with oil pan up.

2) If converter housing oil seal replacement is necessary, remove oil seal using puller and slide hammer.

INPUT SHAFT END PLAY

See SELECTING TRANSMISSION END PLAY SELECTIVE THRUST WASHER section in this article.

GENERAL MOTORS TURBO HYDRA-MATIC 180C (Cont.)

Fig. 1: Exploded View of 180C Automatic Transmission THM 180C

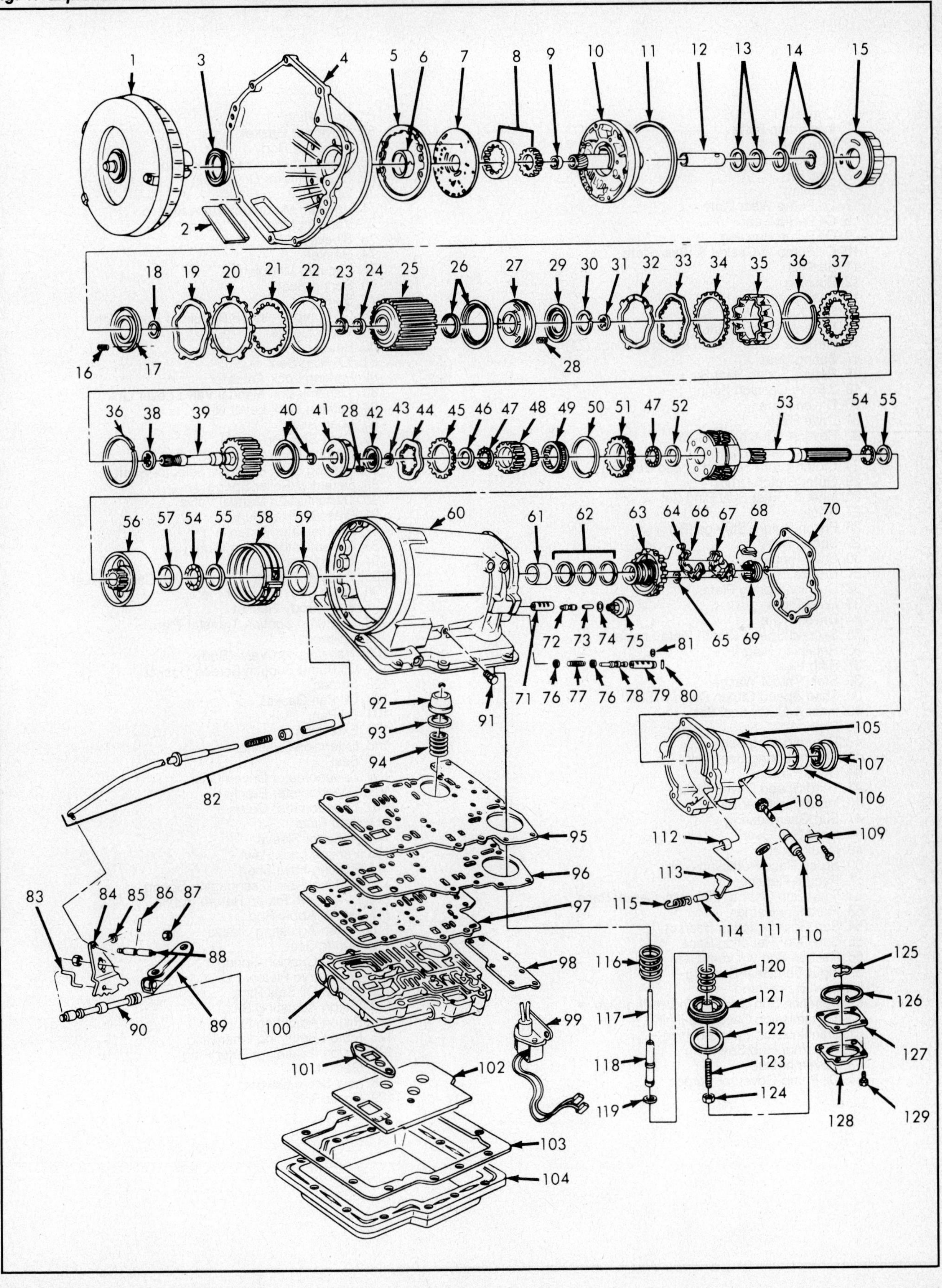

GENERAL MOTORS TURBO HYDRA-MATIC 180C (Cont.)

Automatic Transmission Components (Use With Fig. 1)

1. Converter
2. Inspection Plate
3. Hub Seal
4. Converter Housing
5. Seal Kit
6. Bushing
7. Oil Pump Wear Plate
8. Oil Pump Gear
9. Oil Pump Bushing
10. Oil Pump w/Gasket & Wear Plate
11. Seal Kit
12. Bushing
13. Seal
14. Seal Kit
15. Reverse Clutch Piston
16. Reverse Clutch Piston Return Springs (24)
17. Spring Seat
18. Return Spring Seat Ring
19. 3 Pong Cushion Spring
20. Driven Plate
21. Drive Plate
22. Reverse Clutch Pressure
23. Thrust Washer
24. Clutch Drum Second Speed Bushing
25. Outer Clutch Drum
26. Inner & Outer Seal Ring Set
27. Piston
28. Piston Return Springs (24)
29. Spring Seat
30. Snap Ring
31. Bronze Thrust Washer
32. Cushion Spring Plate
33. Drive Plate
34. Driven Plate
35. Second Speed Clutch Plate Spacer
36. Retaining Ring
37. Ring Gear
38. Steel Thrust Washer
39. Third Speed Clutch Drum w/Shaft
40. Inner & Outer Seal Set
41. Piston
42. Return Spring Seat
43. Return Spring Seat Ring
44. Drive Plate
45. Third Speed Driven Plate
46. Input Sun Gear Race
47. Sun Gear Bearing
48. Input Sun Gear
49. Input Sprag
50. Sprag Race Retaining Ring
51. Race & Retainer
52. Input Sun Gear to Planetary Carrier Race
53. Planetary Carrier
54. Sun Gear Reaction Bearing
55. Sun Gear Reaction Race
56. Rection Sun w/Drum Gear
57. Input Sun Gear Bushing
58. Low Brake Band
59. Reaction Sun Gear Drum Bearing Sleeve
60. Transmission Case w/Bushing
61. Transmission Case Bushing
62. Governor Hub Seal Ring
63. Governor Hub
64. Oil Pump Governor Screen
65. Snap Ring
66. Governor Gasket
67. Governor Body
68. Speedometer Drive Gear Clip
69. Speedometer Drive Gear
70. Gasket
71. Vacuum Modulator Valve Sleeve
72. Vacuum Modulator Valve
73. Sleeve
74. Gasket
75. Vacuum Modulator
76. Spring Seat
77. Spring
78. Oil Pump Pressure Regulator Boost Valve
79. Valve Sleeve
80. Retainer Pin
81. "O" Ring Seal
82. Parking Lock Actuator
83. Transmission Manual Valve Lever Link
84. Parking Lock Lever Nut
85. Snap Ring
86. Case Side Pin
87. Parking Lock Lever Nut
88. Parking Lock & Range Selector Shaft
89. Detent w/Roller Spring
90. Transmission Manual Valve
91. Pressure Tap Plug
92. Accumulator Piston
93. Accumulator Piston Ring
94. Thrust Ring
95. Transfer Plate to Transmission Case Gasket
96. Valve Body Transfer Plate
97. Valve Body Gasket
98. Oil Pump Suction Transfer Plate
99. Solenoid
100. Transmission Valve Body
101. Oil Pump Suction Screen Gasket
102. Screen
103. Oil Pan Gasket
104. Oil Pan
105. Extension
106. Extension Bushing
107. Seal
108. Speedometer Driven Gear
109. Speedometer Bracket
110. Speedometer Guide
111. Seal Ring
112. Actuator Sleeve
113. Parking Lock Pawl
114. Parking Pawl Shaft
115. Parking Pawl Disengaging Spring
116. Low Servo Piston Return Spring
117. Piston Apply Rod
118. Piston Adjusting Sleeve
119. Spring Seat
120. Piston Cushion Spring
121. Low Servo Piston
122. Piston Oil Seal Ring
123. Piston Adjusting Stud
124. Piston Adjusting Nut
125. Piston Retaining Inner Ring
126. Piston Retaining Outer Ring
127. Gasket
128. Low Servo Cover
129. Cover Bolt

GENERAL MOTORS TURBO HYDRA-MATIC 180C (Cont.)

OIL PAN, VALVE BODY & SERVO PISTON

1) Remove attaching bolts and lift off oil pan. Remove oil pan gasket. Remove manual detent roller and spring assembly. Remove oil strainer assembly and discard gasket.

2) Disconnect governor pressure switch electrical connector and solenoid wiring harness. Remove governor pressure switch, converter clutch solenoid and solenoid pipes. DO NOT bend solenoid pipes when removing.

3) Remove transfer plate reinforcement attaching bolts and remove reinforcement. Remove servo cover attaching bolts and remove cover and gasket. Remove remaining bolts attaching valve body to case. Carefully remove valve body with gasket and transfer plate. *See Fig. 2.*

Fig. 2: Removing Valve Body from Transmission

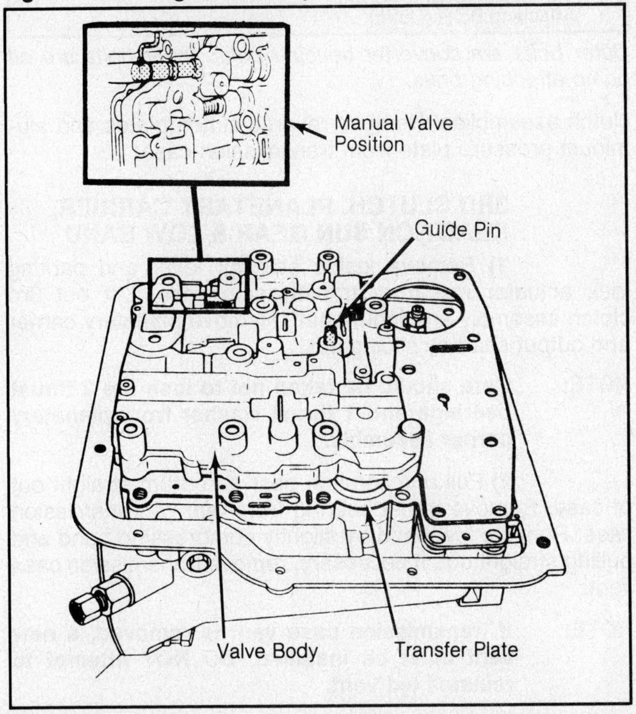

Care must be taken so that manual valve and link are not damaged or lost during valve body removal.

4) Remove 2 bolts holding transfer plate to valve body, then remove plate and gasket. Remove 2 check balls located in oil passages in transmission case.

NOTE: **Location of these 2 check balls must be noted to ensure that they are reinstalled correctly.**

5) Using Compressor (J-23075), compress servo piston and remove retaining snap ring. Remove compressor and servo piston assembly.

MODULATOR ASSEMBLY

Remove vacuum modulator from transmission case. Use care not to lose the modulator plunger. Remove modulator valve and sleeve from case. Remove "O" ring seal, by using internal snap ring pliers.

Fig. 3: Location of Check Balls in Case Oil Passages

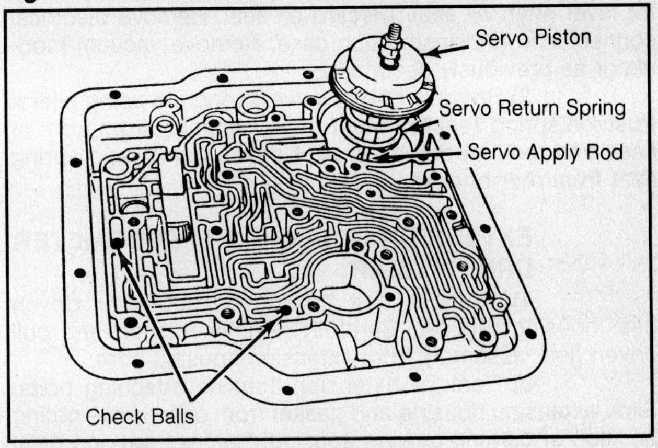

Arrows indicate check ball location.

Fig. 4: Compressing Servo Piston to Remove Snap Ring

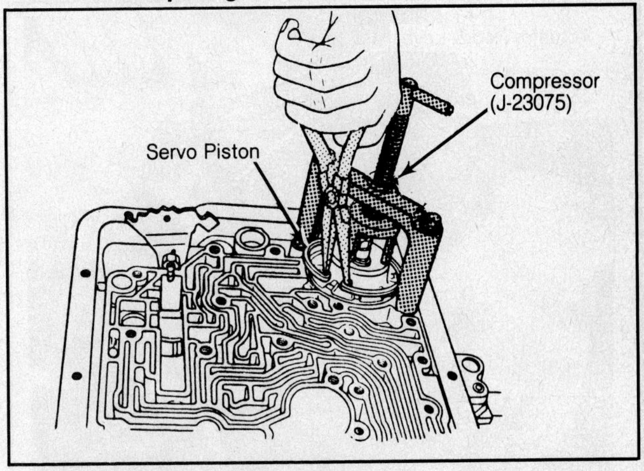

Servo is under high spring tension.

SELECTOR LEVER, SHAFT & DETENT VALVE ASSEMBLY

1) Remove lock nut securing inner lever to selector shaft, then remove inner lever. Remove selector lever shaft spring pin by pulling upwards with pliers. *See Fig. 5.*

Fig. 5: Removing Selector Lever Shaft Spring Pin

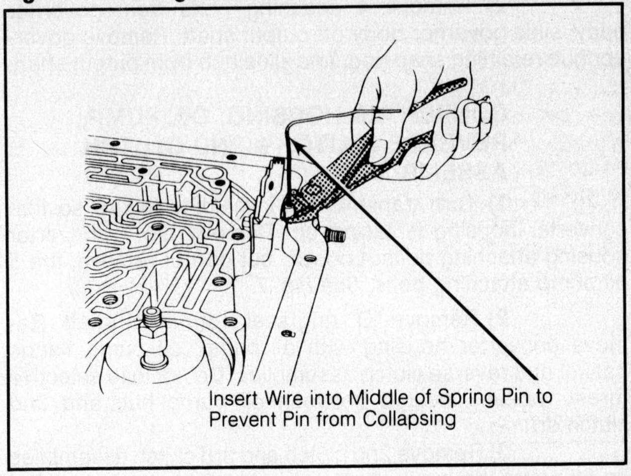

Insert Wire into Middle of Spring Pin to Prevent Pin from Collapsing

GENERAL MOTORS TURBO HYDRA-MATIC 180C (Cont.)

2) Remove selector lever shaft. Remove selector lever shaft oil seal. Discard oil seal. Remove electrical connector from transmission case. Remove vacuum modulator as previously described.

3) Remove detent valve spring pin using pliers. Push on spring seat of detent valve assembly from front of case and remove detent valve, sleeve, spring, and spring seat from rear of case.

EXTENSION HOUSING & SPEEDOMETER DRIVEN GEAR

1) Remove bolt holding speedometer driven gear housing retainer. Carefully remove retainer and pull driven gear assembly from extension housing bore.

2) Remove extension housing attaching bolts. Slide extension housing and gasket from case, while noting position of parking pawl in housing. Remove parking pawl actuator lever and actuator rod from transmission case. *See Fig. 6.*

Fig. 6: Removing Parking Pawl Actuator Rod

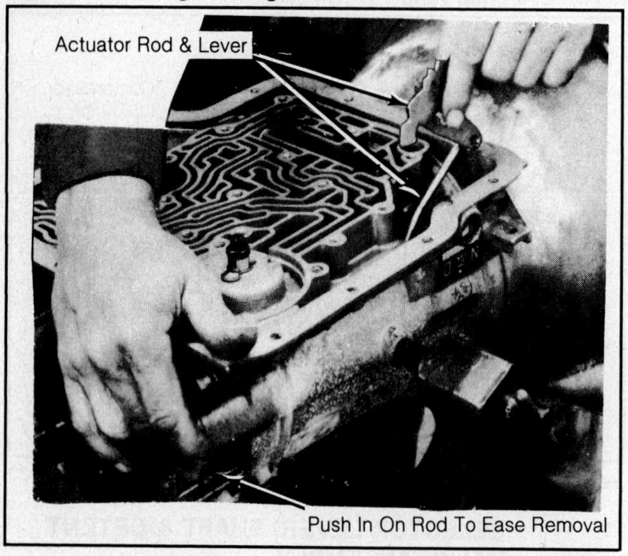

SPEEDOMETER DRIVE GEAR, GOVERNOR BODY & HUB

1) Depress speedometer drive gear retaining clip and slide gear off output shaft.

2) Remove 4 attaching bolts from governor body, slide governor body off output shaft. Remove governor hub retaining snap ring, and slide hub from output shaft.

CONVERTER HOUSING, OIL PUMP, REVERSE CLUTCH & 2ND CLUTCH ASSEMBLY

1) Turn transmission in holding fixture so that converter housing is facing up. Remove the 7 converter housing attaching bolts. Loosen, but do not remove, the 5 oil pump attaching bolts. *See Fig. 7.*

2) Remove "O" ring seal from input shaft. Remove converter housing with oil pump, oil pump flange gasket and reverse clutch assemblies. Do not lose selective thrust washer, located between oil pump hub and 2nd clutch drum.

3) Remove 2nd clutch and 3rd clutch assemblies by lifting up on input shaft. Separate 2nd clutch and 3rd clutch assemblies. Remove reverse clutch plates and aluminum pressure plate from transmission case.

Fig. 7: View of Converter Housing Showing Housing & Oil Pump Attaching Bolts

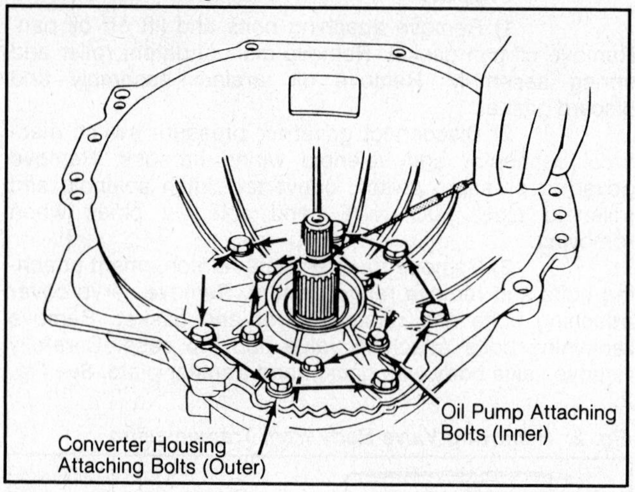

Outer bolts are converter housing bolts. Inner bolts are oil pump attaching bolts.

3RD CLUTCH, PLANETARY CARRIER, REACTION SUN GEAR & LOW BAND

1) Remove inside selector lever and parking lock actuator rod from transmission case. Lift out 3rd clutch assembly and input shaft. Remove planetary carrier and output shaft by sliding out.

NOTE: **Care should be taken not to lose the 2 thrust bearings and 1 thrust washer from planetary carrier assembly.**

2) Pull reaction sun gear and drum straight out of case. Remove thrust bearing from rear of transmission case. Remove low band by slightly compressing band and pulling straight out. If necessary, remove transmission case vent.

NOTE: **If transmission case vent is removed, a new vent must be installed. DO NOT attempt to reinstall old vent.**

COMPONENT DISASSEMBLY & REASSEMBLY

CONVERTER HOUSING, OIL PUMP & REVERSE CLUTCH

Disassembly

1) Remove 2nd clutch assembly from oil pump shaft. Remove selective washer from oil pump shaft.

2) Remove oil pump outer seal. Remove oil pump bolts from converter housing. Separate oil pump from housing. Remove oil pump wear plate. *See Fig. 8.*

3) Remove converter housing oil seal, and if necessary, remove housing bushing using a bushing driver. Mark relative location of oil pump gears and remove gears from oil pump body.

4) Using compressor, compress reverse clutch return springs and remove snap ring. Remove reverse

GENERAL MOTORS TURBO HYDRA-MATIC 180C (Cont.)

clutch retaining ring and 24 return springs. Remove reverse clutch piston.

Fig. 8: Removing Converter Housing & Oil Pump from Transmission

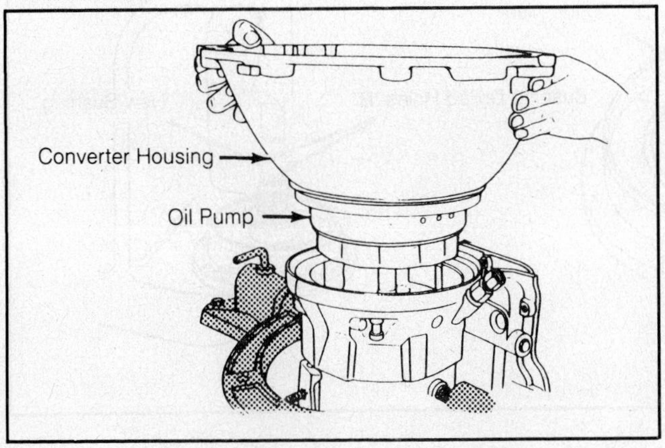

NOTE: **Pressure regulator valve and boost valve should not be removed unless it was determined by oil pressure checks to have been malfunctioning.**

Inspection

1) Clean converter housing thoroughly. Check converter pump hub for nicks, burrs or other damage. Remove nicks and burrs. Inspect the pressure regulator boost valve, the pressure regulator valve and the converter clutch actuator valve for nicks or damage.

2) Thoroughly clean the pressure regulator boost valve, pressure regulator valve and converter clutch actuator valve. Immerse valves in transmission fluid before installing in their bores. Inspect oil pump hub oil seal rings. Replace if damage or side wear is found.

3) Inspect reverse clutch piston for damage and replace if necessary. Inspect reverse clutch piston springs for wear or distortion and replace as necessary.

Fig. 9: Exploded View of Valves in Oil Pump

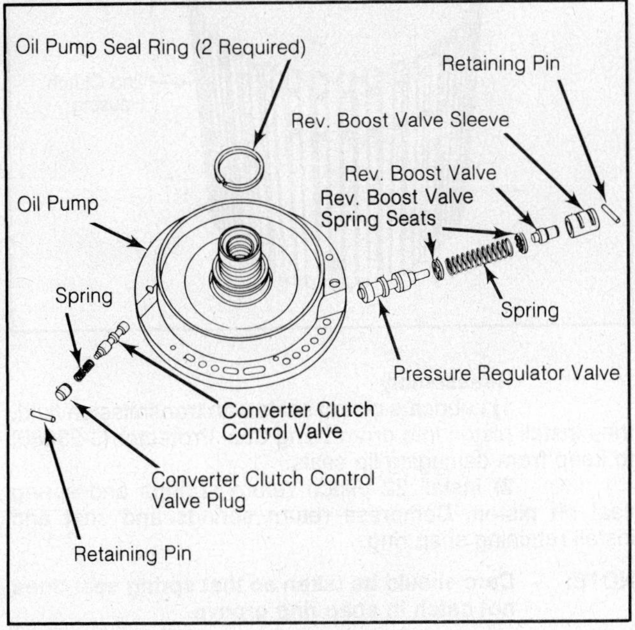

4) Inspect oil pump and gears for any signs of wear or damage, and replace as necessary. Install gears into oil pump and check end clearance of both gears.

5) Use a straightedge and feeler gauge and measure clearance between face of gears and pump face. Clearance should be .0005-.0035" (.013-.089 mm).

6) Next, measure clearance between drive gear and crescent while rotating gears one complete revolution. Clearance should be .005-.009" (.127-.229 mm).

7) Measure clearance between outside of driven gear and housing. Clearance here should be .003-.007" (.076-.178 mm). Finally, measure between inside of driven gear and crescent segment. Rotate gear one revolution. Clearance should be a minimum of .005" (.127 mm).

Oil Pump Hub Bushing Replacement

1) Inspect oil pump hub bushing for wear or damage and replace as necessary. If replacement is needed, thread a 3/4" standard pipe tap into bushing. Using a drift on tap, press oil pump bushing out with arbor press.

NOTE: **Use rag or cloth to protect oil pump face when pressing out bushing.**

2) Clean pump body, including all holes and pockets thoroughly. With oil pump shaft hole "A" facing downward, scribe an alignment mark on oil pump shaft inner diameter at the center of oil groove to right of hole "A". *See Fig. 10*.

3) Scribe mark on outer edge of bushing through centers of small and large drilled holes "B". Place bushing into oil pump shaft with small hole up, and align scribe marks on bushing with those made in oil pump shaft.

4) Use arbor press to drive bushing into oil pump shaft until seated in bore.

CAUTION: **Care must be taken so that bushing is pressed in straight, using scribe marks as a guide until firmly seated.**

Reassembly

1) If removed, install a new converter housing bushing using a driver. Install bushing flush with front face of housing. Install new converter housing oil seal.

2) Immerse pressure regulator valve in transmission fluid, install valve in oil pump body bore. Install pressure regulator spring, 2 spring seats, boost valve and sleeve into pump bore. Depress regulator boost valve sleeve until back end lines up with pin holes. Install retaining spring pin.

3) Install 2 new oil seals on reverse clutch piston. Install reverse clutch piston onto rear face of oil pump using a liberal amount of transmission fluid.

4) Install 24 reverse clutch piston return springs, then install retaining seat. Compress return springs and seat and install retaining snap ring.

CAUTION: **DO NOT air check reverse clutch as the clutch is not complete and damage to return spring retaining seat may occur.**

5) Turn oil pump and reverse clutch assembly so that oil pump face is up. Install oil pump gears using location marks made at disassembly. Install oil pump wear plate onto oil pump.

6) Insert guide pin into oil pump for alignment of converter housing and lower housing onto pump. Loosely install bolts into converter housing.

GENERAL MOTORS TURBO HYDRA-MATIC 180C (Cont.)

Fig. 10: Installing Oil Pump Hub Bushing

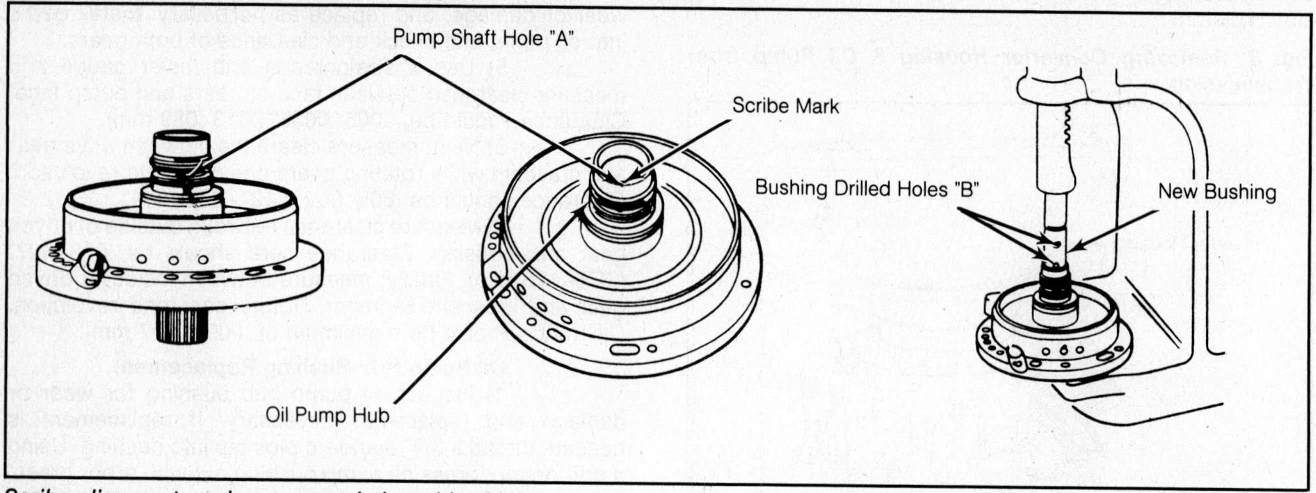

Scribe alignment marks on pump hub and bushing.

7) Use Aligner (J-23082-01) to align converter housing to pump. *See Fig. 11.* Aligner should bottom on oil pump gear.

Fig. 11: Using Aligner to Align Converter Housing to Oil Pump

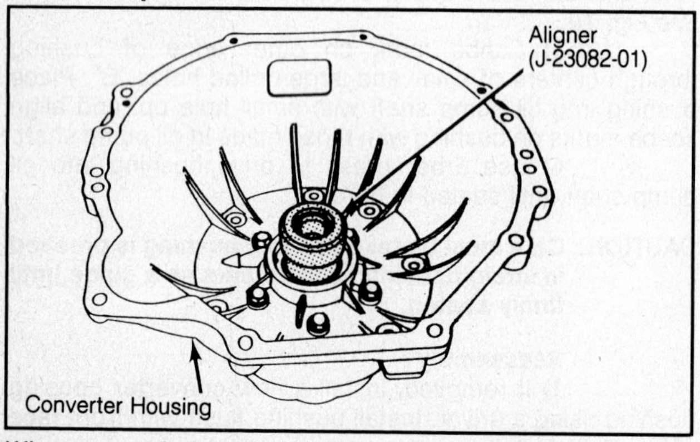

When correctly installed aligner should bottom on oil pump gear.

8) Tighten oil pump attaching bolts in two stages to specified torque. Remove aligner. Install new converter housing-to-case rubber oil seal.

2ND CLUTCH ASSEMBLY

Disassembly

1) Remove ring gear retaining ring from 2nd clutch drum, then pull ring gear from drum. Remove 2nd clutch spacer plate retaining ring, then remove spacer plate, steel and composition clutch plates from clutch drum.

NOTE: **Keep clutch plates in same sequence as they were installed in clutch drum.**

2) Remove 2nd clutch-to-3rd clutch thrust washer. Using compressor, compress 2nd clutch return springs and remove retaining snap ring. Remove compressor and withdraw spring retaining seat and return springs. Remove clutch piston from drum.

Inspection

1) Inspect clutch piston. If piston is damaged or if check ball falls out upon inspection, replace piston. Also, inspect piston lip seals and replace if worn or damaged.

2) Inspect piston return springs for wear and distortion and replace as necessary. Inspect clutch hub bushing, and if necessary use a driver to remove and install bushing.

3) Inspect clutch plates for wear, damage or signs of burning or glazing. Replace as necessary.

NOTE: **If the surface of steel clutch plate; is smooth and an even color smear is indicated, plate should be reused. If severe heat spot discoloration or surface scuffing is indicated, plate should be replaced.**

Fig. 12: Installing 2nd Clutch Piston

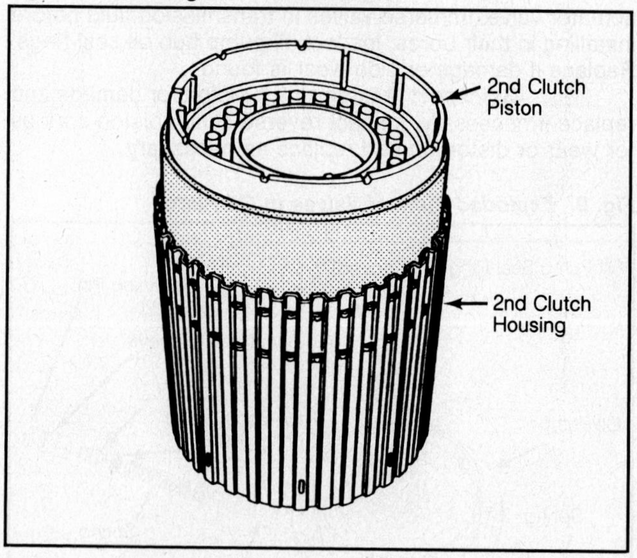

Reassembly

1) Lubricate piston seals with transmission fluid, then install piston into drum using Seal Protector (J-23080) to keep from damaging lip seals.

2) Install 22 piston return springs and spring seat on piston. Compress return springs and seat and install retaining snap ring.

NOTE: **Care should be taken so that spring seat does not catch in snap ring groove.**

GENERAL MOTORS TURBO HYDRA-MATIC 180C (Cont.)

Fig. 13: Exploded View of 2nd Clutch Assembly

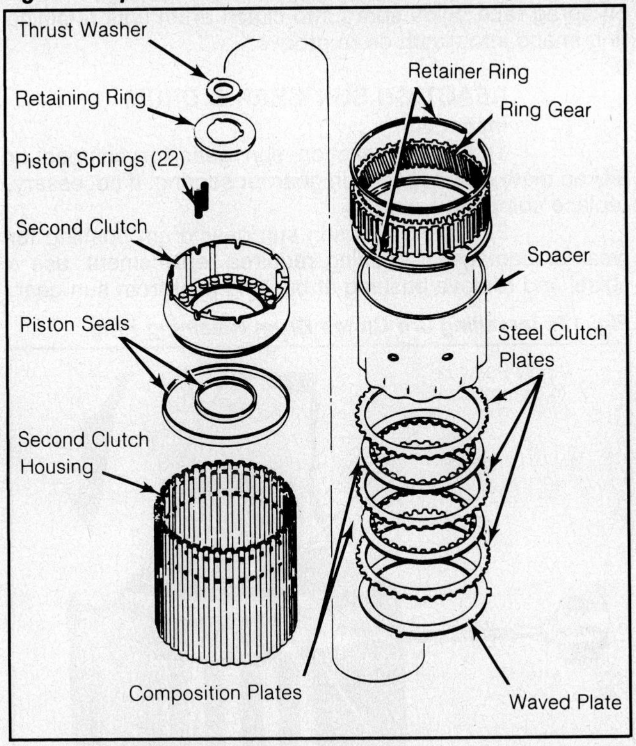

3) Install 2nd clutch-to-3rd clutch thrust washer so that tang seats in slot of 2nd clutch hub. Retain washer with petrolatum. *See Fig. 14.*

4) Lubricate clutch plates with transmission fluid. Install plates into drum starting with cushion plate (wave washer), alternating steel and composition plates until all clutch plates are installed.

Fig. 14: Installing 2nd Clutch-to-3rd Clutch Thrust Washer

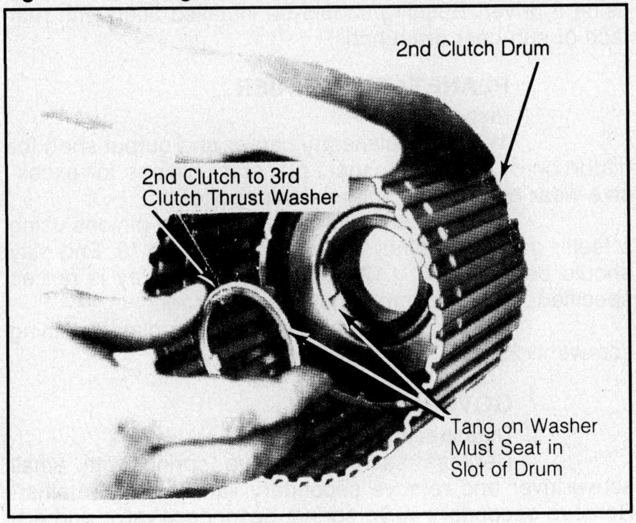

5) Install 2nd clutch spacer plate into drum. If necessary, expand spacer plate with screwdriver until ends are evenly butted together seating tightly into drum. Install spacer plate retaining snap ring. Install ring gear into drum with grooved edge facing up, then install retaining snap ring.

3RD CLUTCH ASSEMBLY, SPRAG & INPUT SUN GEAR

Disassembly

1) Mount 3rd clutch assembly in vise at a 90 degree angle. Position the 5 pins of Sprag Retaining Ring Remover (J-29351) into elongated slots of 3rd clutch drum. *See Fig. 15.*

NOTE: **Do not put a pin into slot if the internal retaining ring is not visible in that slot.**

2) Slide compressing ring of remover over pin cage to compress retaining ring. Pull up on remover to withdraw sprag assembly from clutch drum. Remove input shaft-to-input sun gear thrust washer and thrust bearing from clutch drum.

NOTE: **If sprag retaining ring hangs up on one side causing clutch hub to cock, insert a punch in slot to compress ring.**

3) Lift clutch plates from drum, noting the number and installation sequence for reassembly reference.

Fig. 15: Installing Retaining Ring Remover on 3rd Clutch Assembly

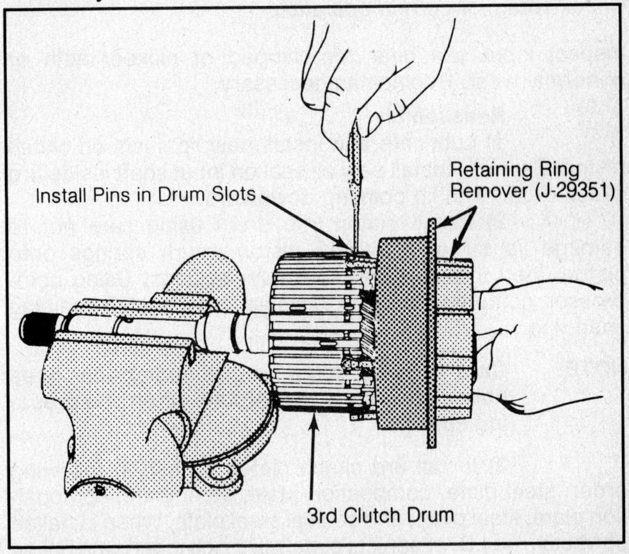

Insert punch in slot only if ring is visible.

4) Remove input sprag race and retainer assembly from clutch hub and input sun gear assembly. Push sprag assembly and retaining rings from sprag race and retainer.

5) Using compressor, compress 3rd clutch piston return springs and remove snap ring. Remove retaining seat and 12 piston return springs. Remove piston from drum.

Inspection

1) Inspect piston return springs for wear and distortion. Replace as necessary. Inspect clutch piston for wear, damage and condition of check ball. If check ball is missing or falls out upon inspection, replace piston.

2) Inspect steel thrust washer on front face of 3rd clutch drum. Replace if scored or damaged. Inspect all other thrust washers and thrust bearing for wear or damage and replace as necessary.

3) Inspect condition of composition and steel clutch plates. Replace as necessary. Inspect sprag assembly for wear, damage or sprags that fall freely out of cage.

GENERAL MOTORS TURBO HYDRA-MATIC 180C (Cont.)

Fig. 16: Sprag Assembly

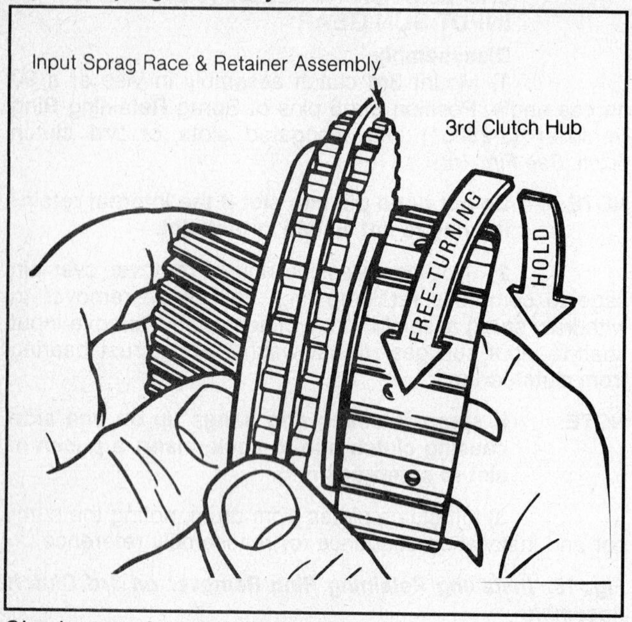

Check sprag for correct operation.

Inspect input sun gear for chipped or nicked teeth or abnormal wear. Replace as necessary.

Reassembly

1) Lubricate and install new lip seals on clutch piston. Carefully install new oil seal on input shaft inside 3rd clutch drum, with lip pointing downward.

2) Install piston into drum using care not to damage lip seals. Install 12 piston return springs onto piston, then install spring seat over springs. Using compressor, compress return springs and seat. Install retaining snap ring.

NOTE: **Care must be taken so that spring seat does not catch in snap ring groove when compressing springs.**

3) Install 3rd clutch plates on hub in following order: steel plate, compostion plate, steel plate, composition plate, steel plate, and conical steel plate. When installed correctly, the I.D. of conical plate will touch steel plate below it but, O.D. will not.

NOTE: **Install the same number of clutch plates as were removed. Also, lubricate plates with transmission fluid before installing.**

4) Install thrust washer and thrust bearing onto input shaft, with inner lips of bearing toward washer. Retain in place with petrolatum.

5) Install sprag onto clutch hub with flare shoulder on cage outer diameter toward input sun gear. Install sprag race and retainer assembly over sprag assembly.

NOTE: **When correctly assembled, sprag should rotate when turned counterclockwise and lock up when turned clockwise.**

6) Slightly turn clutch hub and sprag assembly to engage it to clutch plate splines until sprag race rests on clutch drum.

7) Align teeth of sprag race with splines of clutch drum. Using a small screwdriver, press retaining ring all around into ring groove, at the same time applying pressure on sprag race. Slide sprag into clutch drum until retaining ring snaps into clutch drum groove.

REACTION SUN GEAR & DRUM

Inspection

1) Inspect reaction sun gear for chipped or nicked teeth and inspect sun gear for scoring. If necessary, replace complete assembly.

2) Inspect reaction sun gear drum bushing for wear or damage. If bushing requires replacement, use a chisel and remove bushing at bushing joint from sun gear.

Fig. 17: Installing 3rd Clutch Drum Retaining Ring

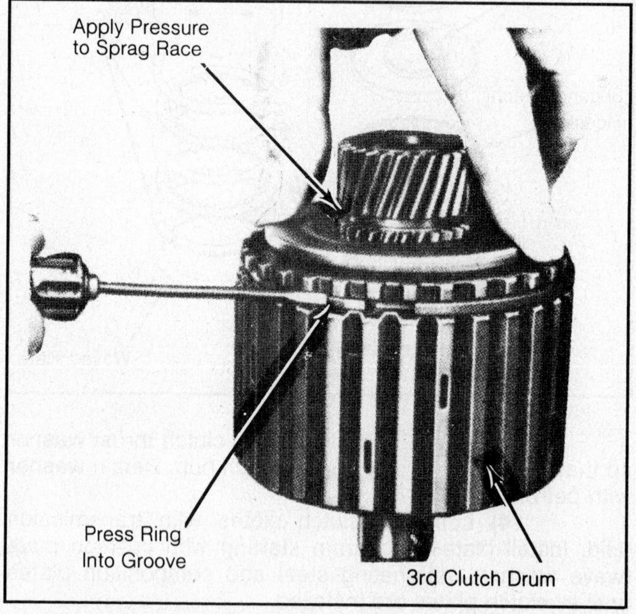

3) Thoroughly clean drum. Install new bushing using a driver. Bushing should be installed flush with rear face of sun gear drum hub.

PLANETARY CARRIER

Inspection

1) Inspect planetary carrier and output shaft for distortion or damage. Inspect planetary pinions for excessive wear or damage, such as chipped teeth.

2) Check end play of all planetary pinions using a feeler gauge at points "A" and "B". *See Fig. 19.* End play should be .005-.035" (.127-.89 mm). If end play is not as specified, replace complete planetary carrier.

3) Tighten planetary carrier lock plate retaining screws to 20-35 ft. lbs. (27-48 N.m.)

GOVERNOR BODY

Disassembly

Depress secondary valve spring with small screwdriver and remove secondary valve spring retainer. Remove secondary valve spring, secondary valve and primary valve from governor body.

Inspection

1) Inspect primary and secondary valves for nicks, burrs and other damage. If necessary, use crocus cloth to remove small burrs.

NOTE: **Do not remove the sharp edges of the valve since these edges perform a cleaning action within the valve bore.**

GENERAL MOTORS TURBO HYDRA-MATIC 180C (Cont.)

Fig. 18: Exploded View of 3rd Clutch Assembly, Sprag & Input Sun Gear Assembly

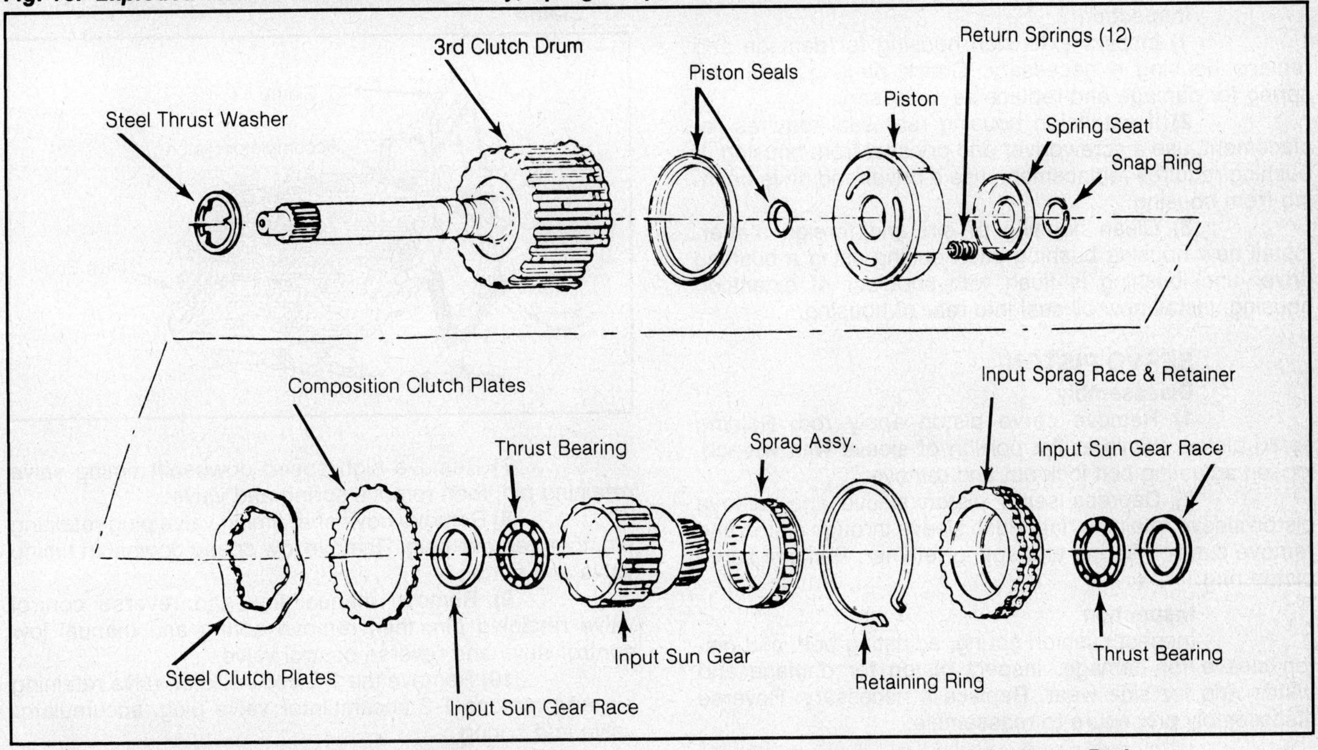

Fig. 19: Checking Planetary Carrier & Pinion End Play

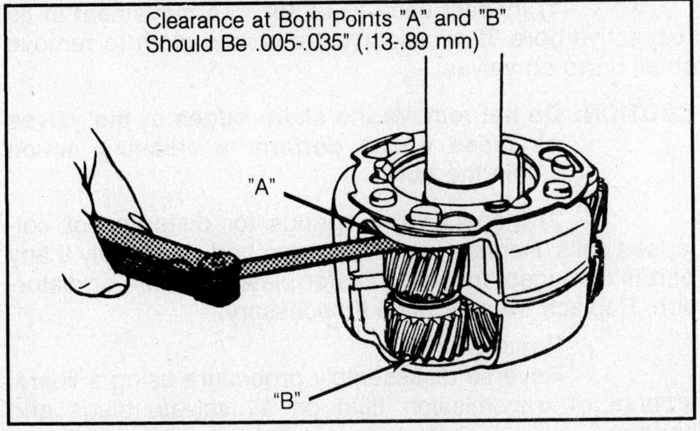

Fig. 20: Exploded View of Governor Body

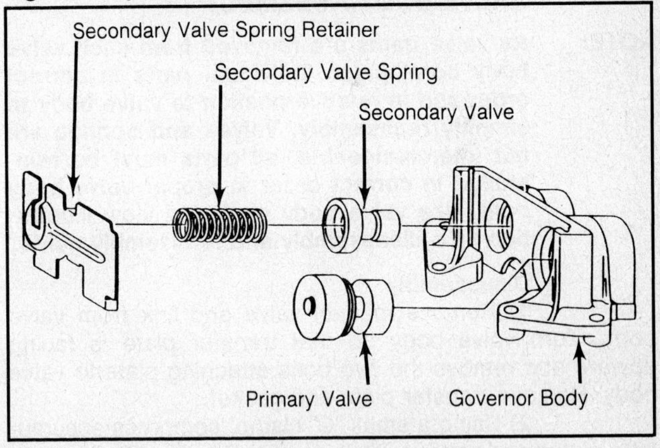

Fig. 21: Exploded View of Servo Piston Assembly

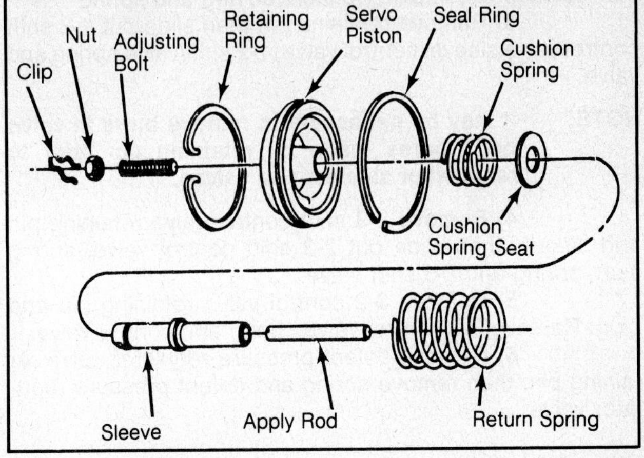

2) Inspect secondary valve spring for distortion or breakage. Clean governor body in solvent and below out all passages with compressed air. Replace governor body if damaged or worn.

NOTE: Lubricate governor valves with transmission fluid before installation.

Reassembly

Install primary valve in governor, small end first. Install secondary valve (small end first) into governor body. Install secondary valve spring, then depress spring and install retainer.

GOVERNOR HUB

Inspection

1) Inspect governor hub oil seal rings for wear or damage, and if necessary replace. Remove governor hub oil screen, using care not to lose or damage screen.

2) Inspect screen and clean with solvent and air dry. Install governor screen flush with hub. Inspect governor hub splines for cracks or chipped teeth in splines. Replace governor hub if required.

GENERAL MOTORS TURBO HYDRA-MATIC 180C (Cont.)

EXTENSION HOUSING

Inspection

1) Inspect extension housing for damage and replace housing if necessary. Check parking pawl and spring for damage and replace as necessary.

2) If extension housing rear seal requires replacement, use a screwdriver and pry seal from housing. If bushing requires replacement, use a driver and drive bushing from housing.

3) Clean housing of dirt and foreign matter. Install new housing bushing into housing using a bushing driver until bushing is flush with shoulder of extension housing. Install new oil seal into rear of housing.

SERVO PISTON

Disassembly

1) Remove servo piston apply rod. Holding servo piston sleeve at flat portion of sleeve with wrench, loosen adjusting bolt lock nut and remove.

2) Depress servo piston sleeve and remove piston sleeve retaining ring. Push sleeve through piston and remove cushion spring and spring retainer. Remove servo piston ring.

Inspection

Inspect cushion spring, adjusting bolt, and piston sleeve for damage. Inspect piston for damage and piston ring for side wear. Replace if necessary. Reverse disassembly procedure to reassemble.

VALVE BODY ASSEMBLY

NOTE: **As valve trains are removed from each valve body bore, place individual parts in correct order and in relative postion to valve body to simplify reassembly. Valves and springs are not interchangeable, all parts must be reinstalled in correct order in proper valve body bore. Use valve body exploded view illustration as a disassembly and reassembly guide.**

Disassembly

1) Remove manual valve and link from valve body. Turn valve body so that transfer plate is facing upward and remove the two bolts attaching plate to valve body. Remove transfer plate and gasket.

2) Using a small "C" clamp, compress accumulator piston and remove retaining ring. *See Fig. 22.* Carefully loosen "C" clamp as accumulator is under spring tension, then remove accumulator piston, oil ring and spring.

3) Remove retaining pin then slide out 1-2 shift control valve sleeve, control valve, 1-2 shift valve spring and valve.

NOTE: **It may be necessary to remove burrs in valve body bores made by retaining pin prior to removal of sleeves and valves.**

4) Remove 2-3 shift control valve retaining pin and sleeve, then slide out 2-3 shift control valve, spring seat, spring and 2-3 shift valve.

5) Remove 3-2 control valve retaining pin and plug. Remove 3-2 control valve spring and control valve.

6) Remove detent pressure regulator valve retaining pin, then remove spring and detent pressure regulator valve.

Fig. 22: Removing Accumulator Piston Retaining Ring with "C" Clamp

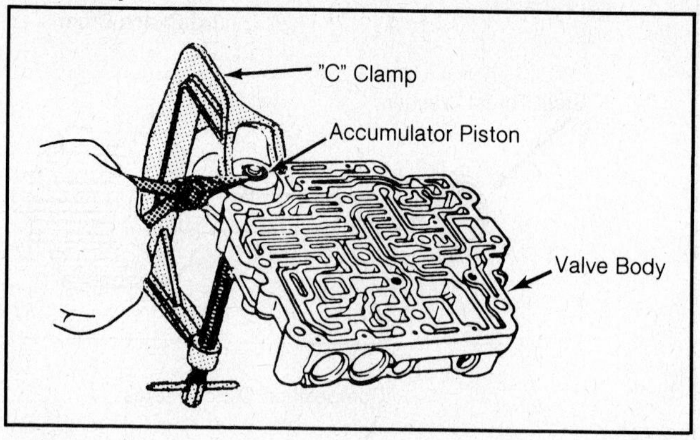

7) Remove high speed downshift timing valve retaining pin, then remove spring and valve.

8) Remove downshift timing valve plug retaining pin, then remove plug. Remove low speed downshift timing valve and spring.

9) Remove manual low and reverse control valve retaining pin, then remove spring and manual low control valve and reverse control valve.

10) Remove the 1-2 accumulator valve retaining pin and remove 1-2 accumulator valve plug, accumulator valve and spring.

Inspection

1) Inspect each valve for free movement in its respective bore. If necessary, use crocus cloth to remove small burrs on valves.

CAUTION: **Do not remove the sharp edges of the valves as these edges perform a cleaning action within the bore.**

2) Inspect valve springs for distortion or collapsed coils. Replace complete valve body assembly if any part is damaged. Inspect transfer plate for dents or distortion. Replace transfer plate if necessary.

Reassembly

Reverse disassembly procedure using a liberal amount of transmission fluid on all valves, plugs and springs.

TRANSMISSION CASE

Inspection

1) Inspect case for damage. Clean oil passages with cleaning solvent and air. Check for good retention of band anchor pins. Inspect all threaded holes for thread damage.

2) Inspect detent valve and modulator valve bores for scratches or scoring. Inspect case bushing inside case at rear. If damaged, remove and install bushing using a driver. Install bushing flush with rear of case.

3) Inspect reaction sun gear drum bushing sleeve inside case at rear for scoring. If necessary, replace sleeve before installing new case bushing.

CAUTION: **Care must be used when removing sleeve in order that aluminum case is not damaged.**

Fig. 23: Exploded View of Valve Body Assembly

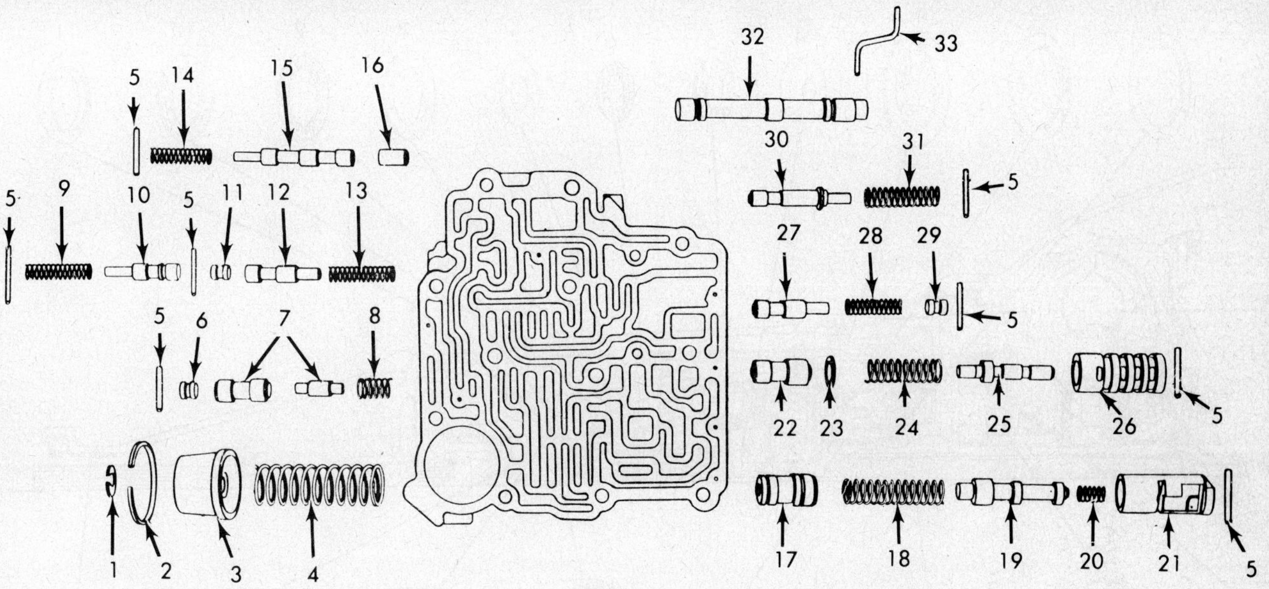

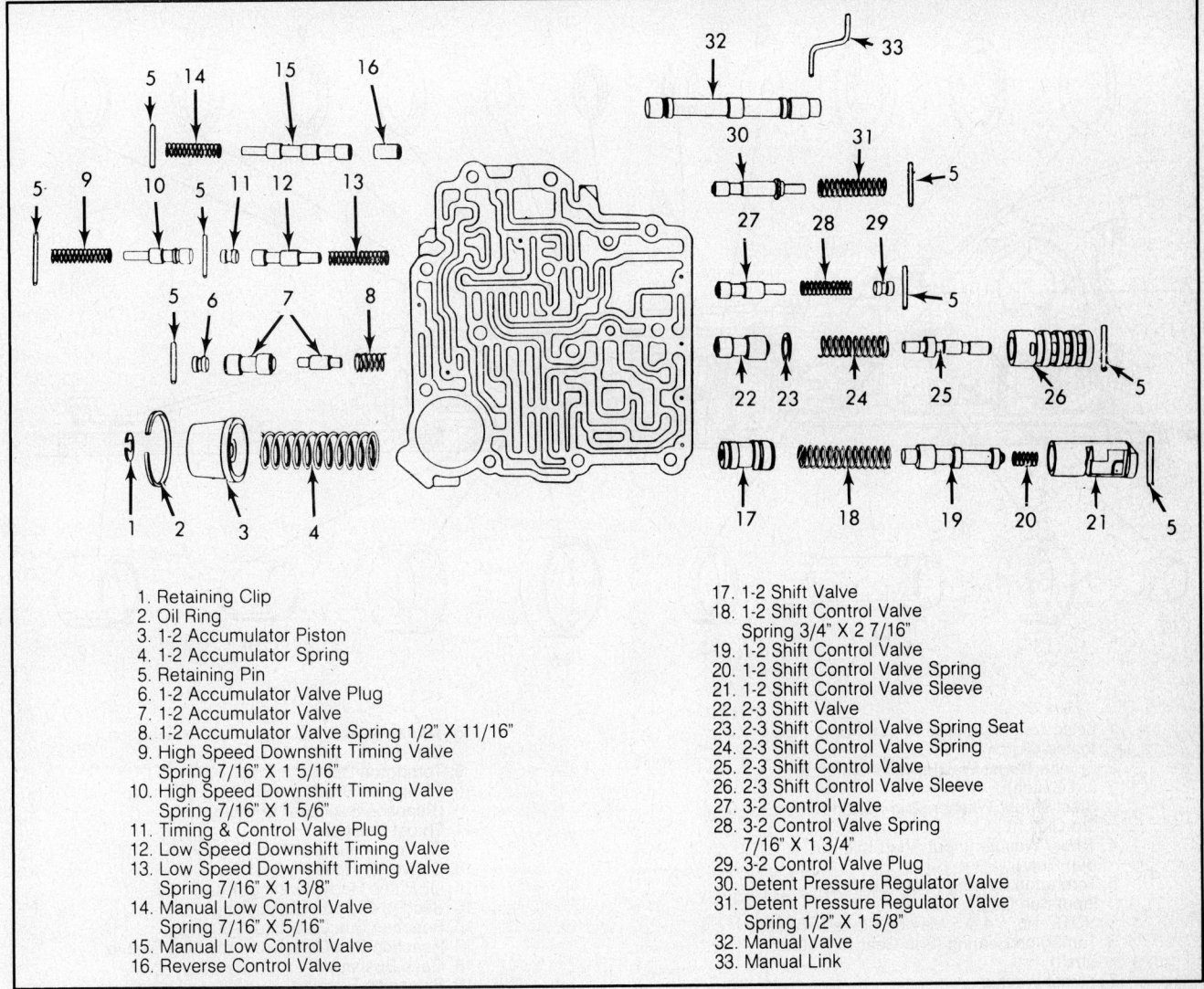

1. Retaining Clip
2. Oil Ring
3. 1-2 Accumulator Piston
4. 1-2 Accumulator Spring
5. Retaining Pin
6. 1-2 Accumulator Valve Plug
7. 1-2 Accumulator Valve
8. 1-2 Accumulator Valve Spring 1/2" X 11/16"
9. High Speed Downshift Timing Valve Spring 7/16" X 1 5/16"
10. High Speed Downshift Timing Valve Spring 7/16" X 1 5/6"
11. Timing & Control Valve Plug
12. Low Speed Downshift Timing Valve
13. Low Speed Downshift Timing Valve Spring 7/16" X 1 3/8"
14. Manual Low Control Valve Spring 7/16" X 5/16"
15. Manual Low Control Valve
16. Reverse Control Valve
17. 1-2 Shift Valve
18. 1-2 Shift Control Valve Spring 3/4" X 2 7/16"
19. 1-2 Shift Control Valve
20. 1-2 Shift Control Valve Spring
21. 1-2 Shift Control Valve Sleeve
22. 2-3 Shift Valve
23. 2-3 Shift Control Valve Spring Seat
24. 2-3 Shift Control Valve Spring
25. 2-3 Shift Control Valve
26. 2-3 Shift Control Valve Sleeve
27. 3-2 Control Valve
28. 3-2 Control Valve Spring 7/16" X 1 3/4"
29. 3-2 Control Valve Plug
30. Detent Pressure Regulator Valve
31. Detent Pressure Regulator Valve Spring 1/2" X 1 5/8"
32. Manual Valve
33. Manual Link

TRANSMISSION REASSEMBLY

SELECTOR LEVER & SHAFT

1) Install new selector lever shaft oil seal in case, with grooved end (with metric threads) outside of case. Insert selector shaft through case from outside.

NOTE: Use care not to damage oil seal when installing shaft.

2) Insert spring pin in case to secure selector lever shaft. Guide selector lever over shaft and secure with lock nut. Insert parking pawl actuator rod from front of case and through hole in rear of case, then install retaining ring.

LOW BAND & REACTION SUN GEAR & DRUM

1) Turn transmission case so that front of case is upward. Place band in case and locate onto anchor pins in case.

2) Place thrust bearing into case and retain with petrolatum. The case bushing acts as a guide to center bearing.

3) Insert reaction sun gear and drum into low band with reaction sun gear facing upward. Install thrust bearing onto sun gear and hold in place with petrolatum.

OUTPUT SHAFT & PLANETARY CARRIER

1) Install thrust washer and Torrington bearing into planetary carrier. Retain in place with petrolatum.

2) Insert output shaft and planetary carrier from front of case. Ensure that planetary carrier engages reaction sun gear.

2ND & 3RD CLUTCH ASSEMBLIES

1) With 2nd clutch assembly on bench, align drive plates in drum. Insert 3rd clutch drum and input shaft through top of 2nd clutch drum, seating 3rd clutch drum splines with 2nd clutch plate splines.

2) Holding clutch assemblies by input shaft, lower into transmission case, indexing 2nd clutch drum ring gear with long planetary pinion gear teeth.

GENERAL MOTORS TURBO HYDRA-MATIC 180C (Cont.)

Fig. 24: Cutaway View of Transmission Case Showing Location of Washers & Bushings

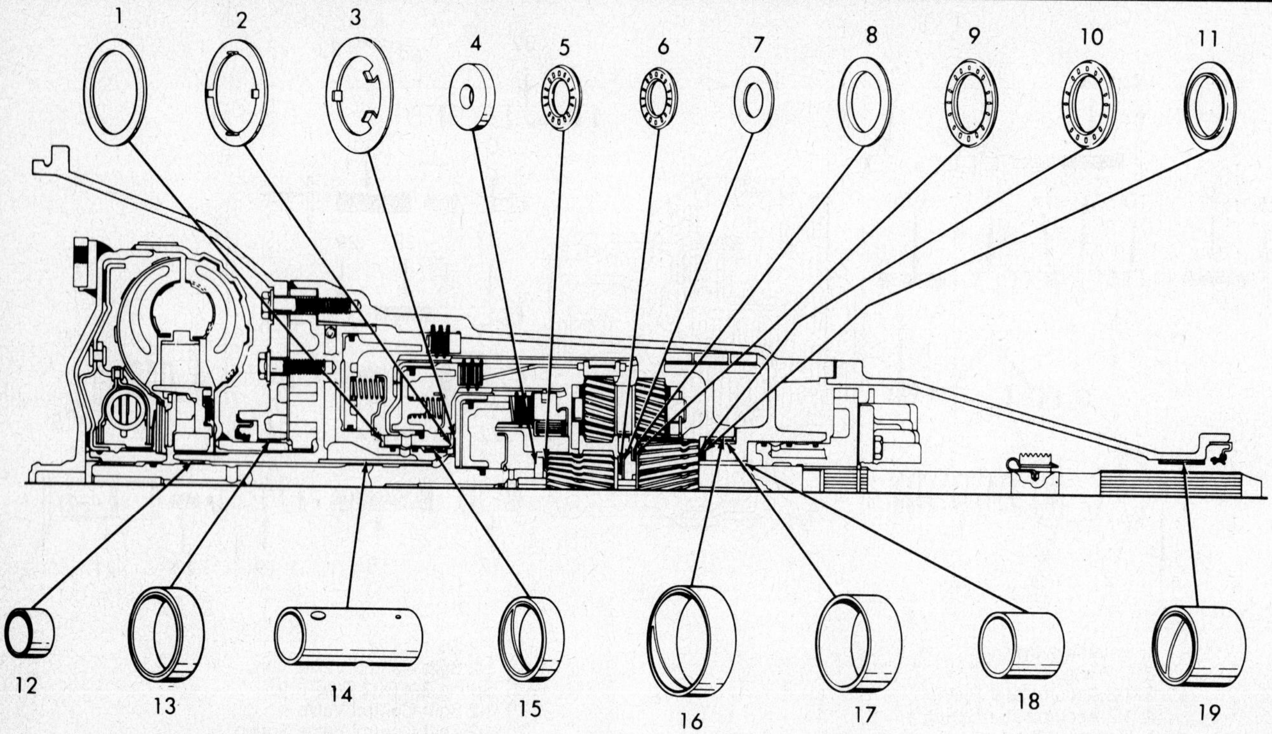

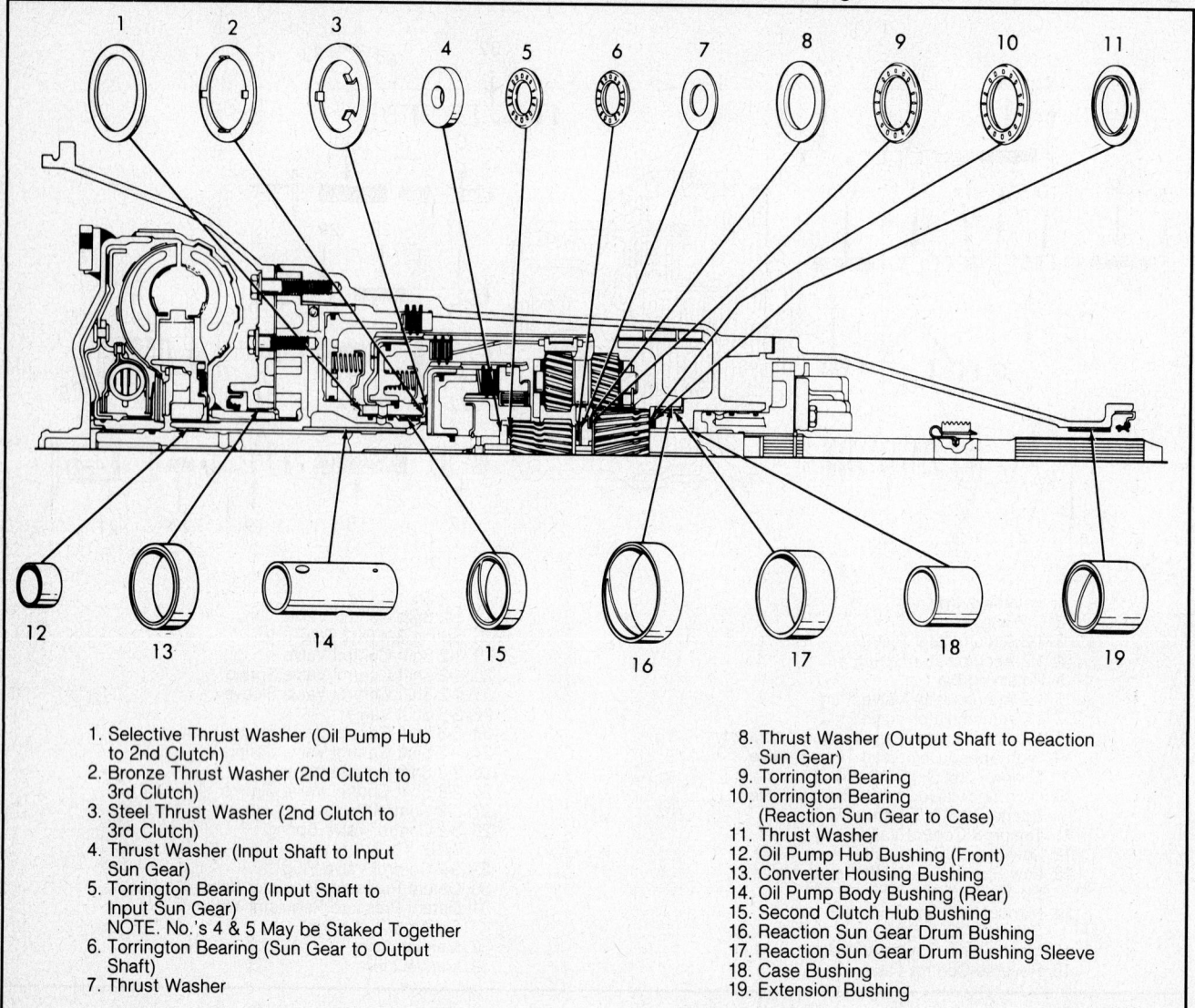

1. Selective Thrust Washer (Oil Pump Hub to 2nd Clutch)
2. Bronze Thrust Washer (2nd Clutch to 3rd Clutch)
3. Steel Thrust Washer (2nd Clutch to 3rd Clutch)
4. Thrust Washer (Input Shaft to Input Sun Gear)
5. Torrington Bearing (Input Shaft to Input Sun Gear)
   NOTE. No.'s 4 & 5 May be Staked Together
6. Torrington Bearing (Sun Gear to Output Shaft)
7. Thrust Washer
8. Thrust Washer (Output Shaft to Reaction Sun Gear)
9. Torrington Bearing
10. Torrington Bearing (Reaction Sun Gear to Case)
11. Thrust Washer
12. Oil Pump Hub Bushing (Front)
13. Converter Housing Bushing
14. Oil Pump Body Bushing (Rear)
15. Second Clutch Hub Bushing
16. Reaction Sun Gear Drum Bushing
17. Reaction Sun Gear Drum Bushing Sleeve
18. Case Bushing
19. Extension Bushing

REVERSE CLUTCH PLATES

1) Install aluminum pressure plate into transmission case with flat side up. Ensure lug on pressure plate engages with one of the narrow notches in case.

2) Lubricate steel and composition reverse clutch plates with transmission fluid. Install clutch plates into transmission case starting with a steel plate and alternating composition and steel clutch plates until all plates are installed.

3) Install reverse clutch cushion plate (wave washer) into case, so that all three of its lugs are engaged into narrow notches in case.

SELECTING TRANSMISSION END PLAY SELECTIVE THRUST WASHER

1) Place Gauge (J-23085) on case flange and against input shaft. *See Fig. 26.* Loosen thumb screw to allow inner shaft of gauge to drop onto 2nd clutch drum hub.

2) Tighten thumb screw and remove gauge. Compare thickness of selective thrust washer No. "1" removed during transmission disassembly with protruding portion of gauge inner shaft.

3) Selective thrust washer used in reassembly should be the thickest washer available without exceeding the dimension of shaft protruding from gauge.

NOTE: The dimension of thrust washer selected should be equal to or slightly less than inner shaft dimension for correct transmission end play. Selective thrust washers for end play are available in the following thicknesses: .069-.074", .075-.079", .080-.084", .085-.089", .090-.094", and .095-.100" (1.7-1.8 mm, 1.9-2.0 mm, 2.0-2.1 mm, 2.2-2.3 mm, 2.3-2.4 mm, and 2.4-2.5 mm).

4) If correct thickness thrust washer has been installed, transmission end play should be .014-.031" (.36-.79 mm).

Fig. 25: Converter Housing Oil Passages

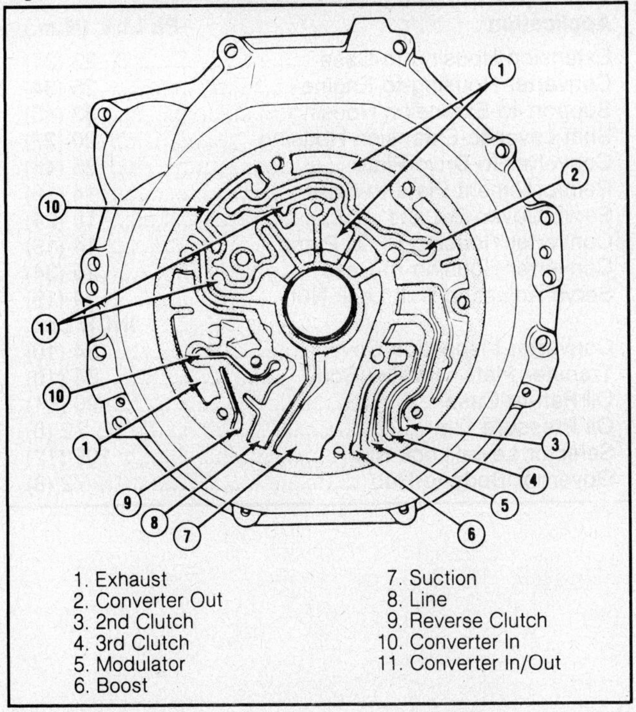

Fig. 26: Using Gauge to Select Transmission End Play Thrust Washer

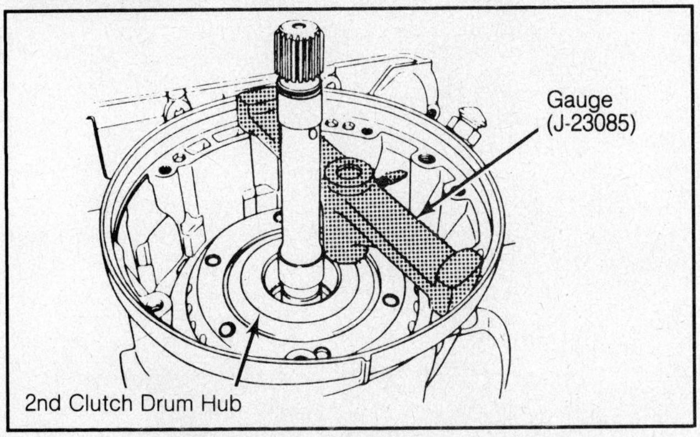

CONVERTER HOUSING, OIL PUMP & REVERSE CLUTCH ASSEMBLY

1) Install new oil pump flange gasket. Place transmission end play thrust washer, as previously determined, onto oil pump shaft and retain with petroleum jelly.

2) Install guide pin in case and lower converter housing and oil pump into case. Use Oil Pump Aligner (K-23082) to align converter housing with oil pump and case, then install and tighten converter housing attaching bolts.

3) Check for correct assembly by turning input shaft by hand. Shaft should rotate freely without binding.

GOVERNOR ASSEMBLY & SPEEDOMETER DRIVE GEAR

1) Turn transmission so that bottom face is upward. Lubricate governor hub seal rings with transmission fluid, then slide hub onto output shaft until it seats in case. Install snap ring into output shaft groove to lock hub in place.

2) Install new governor body gasket. Install governor body to governor hub, then install and tighten attaching bolts.

NOTE: **Ensure governor valves move freely after governor body is installed on hub.**

3) Install speedometer drive gear retaining clip into hole in output shaft. While depressing retaining clip, slide drive gear over output shaft and onto retaining clip.

Fig. 27: Installing Speedometer Drive Gear & Governor Body

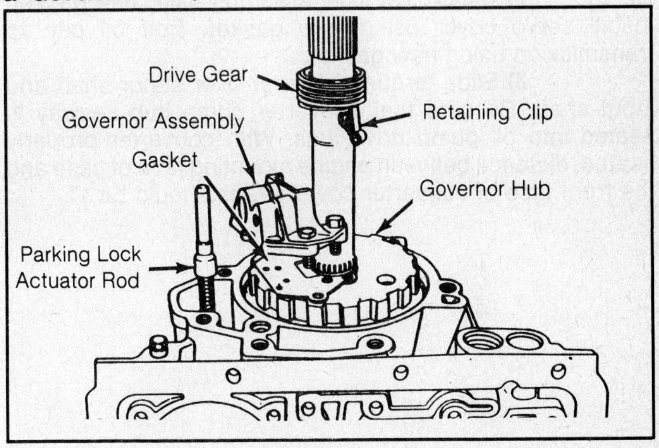

EXTENSION HOUSING & SPEEDOMETER DRIVEN GEAR

1) Install new extension housing lubricate with transmission fluid, then install detent valve, sleeve, spring and spring seat into case bore. Depress detent valve spring and insert spring pin to secure valve assembly.

NOTE: **Detent valve sleeve must be installed with slot facing oil pan. Also, care should be taken so that spring pin is inserted into groove provided in sleeve and not into oil passage slots in sleeve.**

2) Install modulator valve and sleeve into case with small end of valve installed first. Use a new "O" ring on modulator, then install plunger and thread modulator into case and tighten.

SERVO ASSEMBLY

1) Install servo apply rod, spring and piston into case using a liberal amount of transmission fluid. Compress servo piston spring and install retaining ring while lightly tapping piston until piston is seated.

2) To adjust servo, use a 3/16" hex head wrench on servo adjusting bolt and tighten bolt to 40 INCH lbs. Back off bolt EXACTLY 5 turns. Hold adjusting bolt stationary and tighten lock nut.

VALVE BODY ASSEMBLY

1) Position steel check balls into case oil passages. *See Fig. 3*. Locate guide pin in case. *See Fig. 2*. Install new transfer plate-to-case gasket. Install bolts holding transfer plate to valve body.

2) Install manual valve into valve body bore using liberal amount of transmission fluid. Install long side of manual valve link into valve, then install short end of link into selector lever as valve body and transfer plate are installed over guide pins.

GENERAL MOTORS TURBO HYDRA-MATIC 180C (Cont.)

3) Install selector lever roller spring and retainer. Tighten valve body attaching bolts by starting at the center and working outward. Install reinforcement plate bolts to case and tighten.

EXTERNAL PARTS

Installation

1) Install governor pressure switch. Install solenoid valve and piping. Connect electrical wires. Negative wire connects to governor pressure switch and positive wire connects to case electrical connector.

2) Install oil strainer assembly using new gasket. Install servo cover using new gasket. Bolt oil pan to transmission using new gasket.

3) Slide torque converter over stator shaft and input shaft. Be sure that converter pump hub keyway is seated into oil pump drive lugs. With converter properly seated, distance between engine mounting face of case and the front face of converter cover straps should be 1".

TIGHTENING SPECIFICATIONS

Application	Ft. Lbs. (N.m.)
Extension Housing-to-Case	23 (31)
Converter Housing-to-Engine	25 (34)
Support-to-Extension Housing	33 (45)
Shift Lever-to-Extension Housing	20 (27)
Converter-to-Drive Plate	35 (48)
Reinforcement Plate-to-Case	14 (19)
Servo Cover-to-Case	18 (24)
Converter Housing-to-Oil Pump	14 (19)
Converter Housing-to-Case	25 (34)
Servo Adjusting Bolt Lock Nut	14 (19)
	INCH Lbs.
Converter Inspection Cover	84 (10)
Transfer Plate-to-Valve Body	84 (10)
Oil Pan-to-Case	96 (11)
Oil Pressure Tap	72 (8)
Selector Lever Lock Nut	108 (12)
Governor Body-to-Hub	72 (8)

GENERAL MOTORS TURBO HYDRA-MATIC 200C

Buick
LeSabre, Regal
Chevrolet
Caprice, El Camino, Impala, Monte Carlo, S/T10
GMC
Caballero, S/T15
Oldsmobile
Cutlass Supreme, Delta 88
Pontiac
Bonneville, Grand Prix, Parisienne

TRANSMISSION IDENTIFICATION

Transmission model may be identified by the production code number, located on an identification plate attached to right side of transmission case, near modulator. Number consists of a year code, 2 letter model code, and a build date code. Transmission model codes are listed in the following table.

TRANSMISSION MODEL CODES

Application	Code
Buick	BH, HH, HL, KA
Chevrolet	CA, CU, HH, HL
GMC	CA, CU, HH, HL
Oldsmobile	BH, HH, HL, KA
Pontiac	BH, CA, CU, HH, HL, KA

DESCRIPTION

The Turbo Hydra-Matic 200C automatic transmission is a fully automatic unit consisting primarily of a 3-element hydraulic torque converter with the addition of a converter clutch and a compound planetary gear set. Three multiple-disc clutches, a roller clutch and a band provide friction elements required to obtain the desired function of the compound planetary gear set. A hydraulic system pressurized by a gear type pump provides the working pressure required to operate the friction elements and automatic controls.

The 3-element torque converter consists of a pump or driving member, a turbine or driven member, and a stator assembly. The stator assembly is mounted on a one-way roller clutch which will allow stator to turn clockwise but not counterclockwise. The converter clutch is splined to the turbine assembly, and when operated, applies against the converter cover, providing mechanical direct drive coupling of the engine to the transmission planetary gears. When converter clutch is released, the assembly operates as a normal torque converter.

NOTE: **See GENERAL MOTORS TORQUE CONVERTER CLUTCH article in this section for information on the Torque Converter Clutch (TCC) system used in the THM 200C.**

LUBRICATION & ADJUSTMENTS

See appropriate AUTOMATIC TRANSMISSION SERVICING article in DOMESTIC GENERAL SERVICING section.

TROUBLE SHOOTING

See appropriate AUTOMATIC TRANSMISSION TROUBLE SHOOTING article in DOMESTIC GENERAL SERVICING section.

TESTING

ROAD TEST

Drive Range

Position selector lever in Drive range and accelerate vehicle. A 1-2 and 2-3 shift should occur at all throttle openings (shift points will vary with throttle opening). Check part throttle 3-2 downshift at 30 MPH by quickly opening throttle approximately three-fourths, transmission should downshift 3-2. Check for 3-2 downshifts at 50 MPH, by depressing accelerator fully.

Intermediate Range

Position selector lever in Intermediate range and accelerate vehicle. A 1-2 shift should occur at all throttle openings (shift point will vary with throttle opening). No 2-3 shift can be obtained in this range. Check detent 2-1 downshift at 20 MPH. Transmission should downshift 2-1.

Low Range

Position selector lever in Low range and accelerate vehicle. No upshift should occur in this range.

Intermediate Range Overrun Braking

Position selector lever in Drive range and with vehicle speed at approximately 50 MPH, with closed throttle, move selector lever to Intermediate range. Transmission should downshift to 2nd. An increase in engine RPM and an engine braking effect should be noticed.

Low Range Overrun Braking

At 40 MPH, with throttle closed, move selector lever to Low. A 2-1 downshift should occur in speed range of approximately 40-25 MPH, depending on axle ratio and control valve assembly calibration. The 2-1 downshift at closed throttle will be accompanied by increasing engine RPM and an engine braking effect should be noticed.

Reverse Range

Position selector lever in Reverse range and check for reverse operation.

CONTROL PRESSURE TEST

Preliminary Checking Procedure

Perform the following prior to making control pressure test:

- Check transmission fluid level.
- Check and adjust T.V. cable.
- Check and adjust outside manual linkage.
- Check engine tune-up.
- Install oil pressure gauge. *See Fig. 2.*
- Connect tachometer to engine

Minimum T.V. Pressure Check

With T.V. cable adjusted to specifications and brake applied, check line pressure in ranges and at engine RPM indicated in CONTROL PRESSURE SPECIFICATIONS chart.

Full T.V. Pressure Check

With T.V. cable at full extent of its travel and brakes applied, check line pressure in ranges and at engine RPM indicated in CONTROL PRESSURE SPECIFICATIONS chart.

GENERAL MOTORS TURBO HYDRA-MATIC 200C (Cont.)

Fig. 1: Sectional View of Turbo Hydra-Matic 200C Automatic Transmission

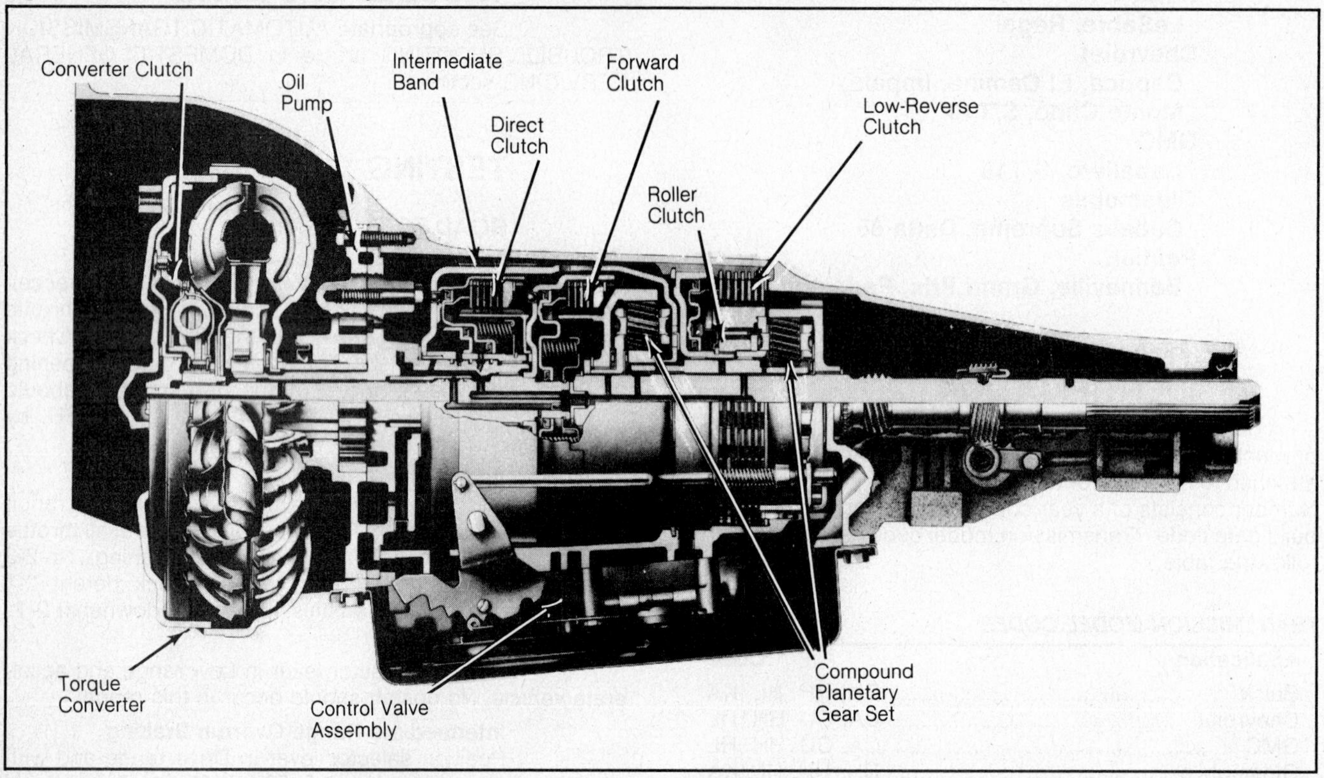

Fig. 2: View of Transmission Showing Location of Control Pressure Test Take-Off Point

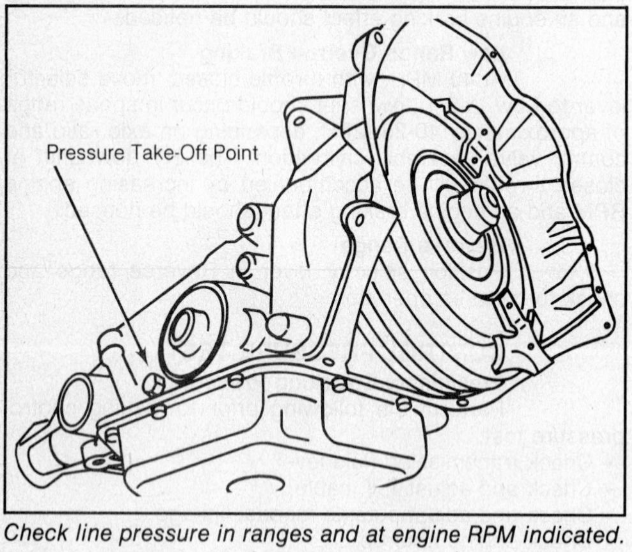

Check line pressure in ranges and at engine RPM indicated.

High Or Low Oil Pressures

- T.V. cable misadjusted, binding, unhooked or broken.
- Throttle lever and bracket assembly binding, unhooked or mispositioned.
- Throttle valve or plunger binding.
- Shift T.V. valve binding.
- No. 1 check ball missing or leaking.
- Pressure regulator valve binding.
- Wrong pressure regulator valve spring installed.
- Oil pressure control orifice in pump cover plugged (causes high oil pressure).
- Pressure regulator bore plug leaking.
- Manual valve not connected.
- Intermediate boost valve binding (pressure will be incorrect in intermediate and low ranges only).
- Orifice in spacer plate at end of intermediate boost valve plugged.
- Reverse boost valve binding (pressures will be incorrect in reverse only).
- Orifice in spacer plate at end of reverse boost valve plugged.

SERVICE (IN VEHICLE)

The following components may be removed from transmission without removing transmission from vehicle.

- Governor Assembly.
- Governor Pressure Switch (Diesel Only).
- Intermediate Servo Assembly.
- Oil Pan and Oil Screen (Intake Pipe) Assembly.
- 3rd Accumulator Check Valve Assembly.
- Control Valve Body Assembly.
- Check Balls and Valve Body Spacer Plate and Gaskets.
- Pressure Regulator Parts.
- Inside Detent/Range Lever.
- Manual Detent and Roller Assembly.
- Throttle Lever and Bracket Assembly.
- T.V. Cable and "O" Ring.
- Parking Pawl Actuator Rod, Bracket, and Parking Pawl.
- Manual Shaft and Seal.
- Manual Valve.
- Rear Seal.
- 1-2 Accumulator and Spring.
- Low-Reverse Clutch Cup Plug.
- Cooler Fittings.
- Oil Filter Pipe & "O" Ring.
- Speedometer Driven Gear Assembly.

GENERAL MOTORS TURBO HYDRA-MATIC 200C (Cont.)

CONTROL PRESSURE SPECIFICATIONS

Model	Range @ RPM [1]	MINIMUM T.V. psi	MINIMUM T.V. kg/cm[1]	MAXIMUM T.V. psi	MAXIMUM T.V. kg/cm[1]
BH, CA, CU, HH, HL, KA	Park @ 1000	66-74	4.64-5.20	66-74	4.64-5.20
	Reverse @ 1000 [2]	144-217	10.12-15.26	205-264	14.55-17.93
	Neutral @ 1000	66-79	4.64-5.55	127-143	8.93-10.05
	Drive @ 1000	66-79	4.64-5.55	127-143	8.93-10.05
	Intermediate @ 1000	130-155	9.14-10.90	130-155	9.14-10.90
	Low @ 1000	130-155	9.14-10.90	130-155	9.14-10.90

[1] – Total running time for this combination of tests is not to exceed 2 minutes. Brakes must be applied at all times.
[2] – Maximum T.V. reverse line pressure to be checked at 2000 RPM.

- Solenoid Wire Clips.
- Electrical Connector

For removal and installation of these components, see TRANSMISSION DISASSEMBLY and TRANSMISSION REASSEMBLY.

REMOVAL & INSTALLATION

TRANSMISSION

See appropriate AUTOMATIC TRANSMISSION REMOVAL article in DOMESTIC GENERAL SERVICING section.

TORQUE CONVERTER

NOTE: Torque converter is a sealed unit and cannot be disassembled for service.

LEAKAGE CHECK

See procedure given in GENERAL MOTORS TURBO HYDRA-MATIC 400 article in this section.

END CLEARANCE CHECK

See procedure given in GENERAL MOTORS TURBO HYDRA-MATIC 400 article in this section.

CONVERTER FLUSHING

See procedure given in GENERAL MOTORS TURBO HYDRA-MATIC 400 article in this section.

NOTE: For additional information on Torque Converter Clutch (TCC) system used on THM 200C transmission, see GENERAL MOTORS TORQUE CONVERTER CLUTCH article in this section.

TRANSMISSION DISASSEMBLY

EXTERNAL PARTS

1) Mount transmission in holding fixture and remove torque converter by pulling straight out. Remove oil pan and discard gasket. Remove oil screen and discard gasket.

NOTE: The two oil screen attaching bolts are about 3/8" (10 mm) longer than valve body attaching bolts, and they are not interchangeable.

CLUTCH AND BAND APPLICATION CHART (ELEMENTS IN USE)

Selector Lever Position	Direct Clutch	Forward Clutch	Low & Reverse Clutch	Intermediate Band	Low Roller Clutch
D – DRIVE					
First Gear		X			X
Second Gear		X		X	
Third Gear	X	X			
S or L2 – INTERMEDIATE					
First Gear		X			X
Second Gear		X		X	
L or L1 – LOW					
First Gear		X	X		
R – REVERSE	X		X		
NEUTRAL OR PARK – Band and clutches released and/or ineffective.					

GENERAL MOTORS TURBO HYDRA-MATIC 200C (Cont.)

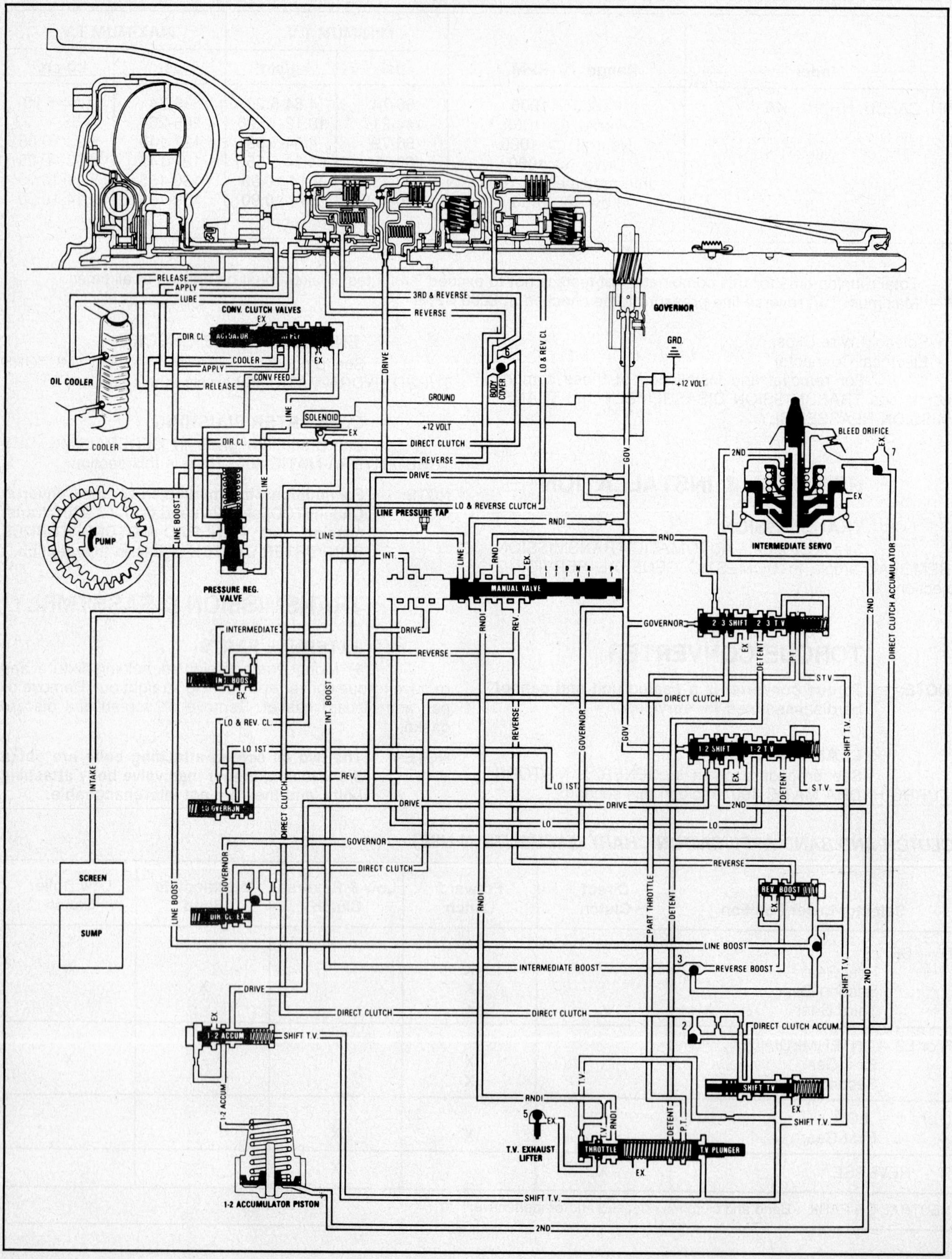

Fig. 3: Turbo Hydra-Matic 200C Hydraulic Circuits Diagram (All Except Diesel Models)

GENERAL MOTORS TURBO HYDRA-MATIC 200C (Cont.)

Fig. 4: Turbo Hydra-Matic 200C Hydraulic Circuits Diagram (Models With Diesel Engines)

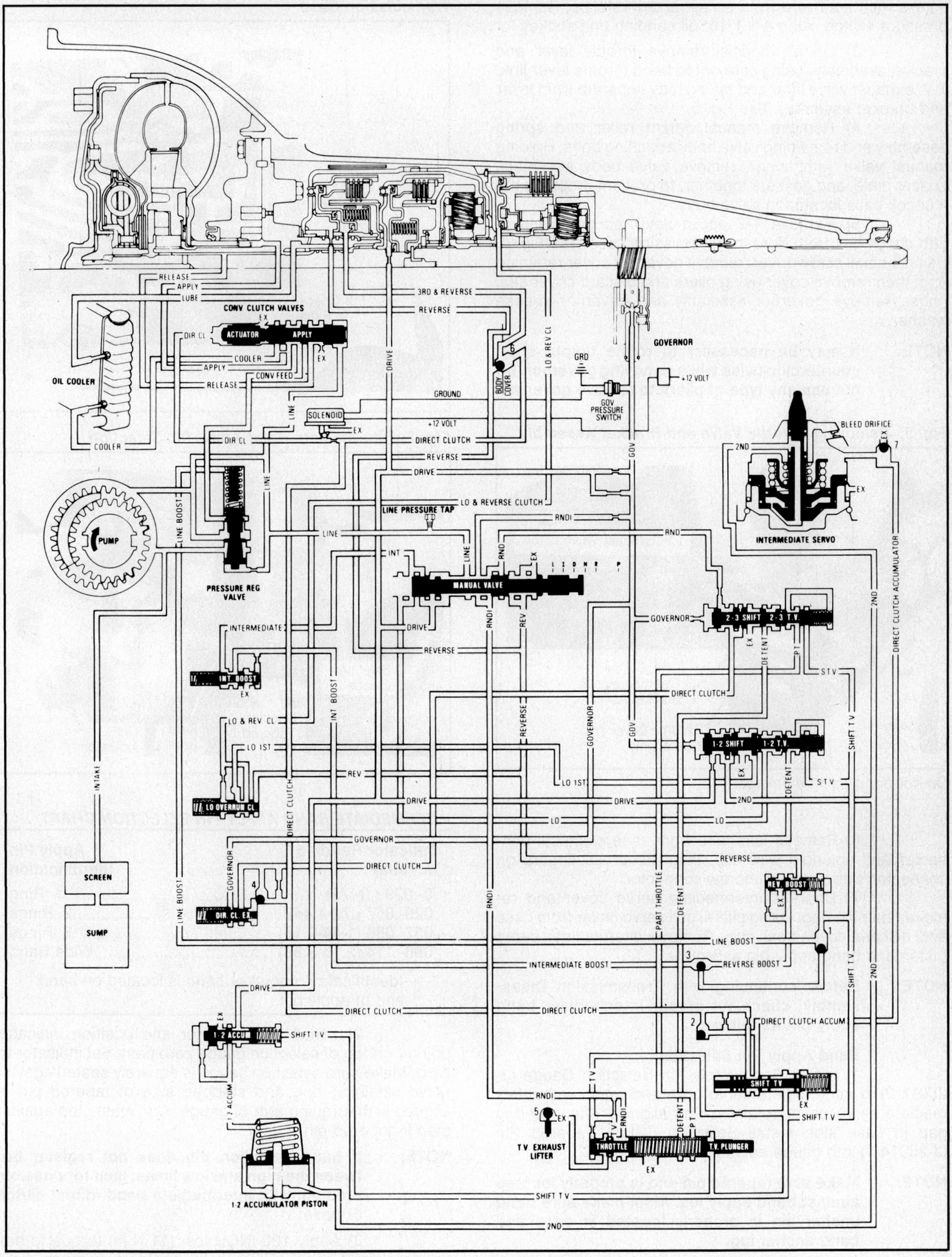

2) On diesel models, remove governor pressure switch lead wire from switch and wire clips. Remove pressure switch using a 1 1/16" oil sending unit socket.

3) On all models, remove throttle lever and bracket assembly, using care not to bend throttle lever link. T.V. exhaust valve lifter and spring may separate from lever and bracket assembly. *See Fig. 5.*

4) Remove manual detent roller and spring assembly and remaining valve body attaching bolts. Holding manual valve with finger, remove valve body assembly, spacer plate, and gaskets together, to prevent dropping the 4 check balls located in valve body.

5) Remove 1-2 accumulator spring. Remove fifth check ball from bore in transmission case. *See Fig. 6.* Using a small screwdriver, remove governor cover retaining ring, then remove cover using pliers and discard cover seal rings. Remove governor assembly and governor-to-case washer.

NOTE: **It may be necessary to rotate output shaft counterclockwise while removing governor. Do not use any type of pliers to remove governor.**

Fig. 5: Removing Throttle Valve and Bracket Assembly

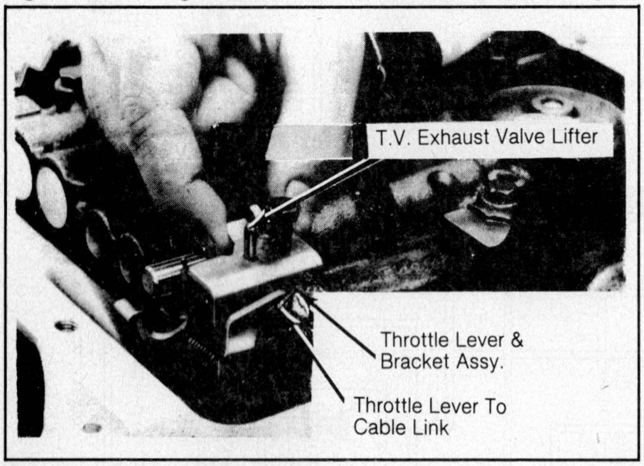

Do not bend throttle linkage.

6) Remove lead wire from case electrical connector and solenoid wire clip, then compress fingers on connector sleeve and withdraw connector.

7) Depress intermediate servo cover and remove retaining ring. Using pliers, pull servo cover from case and discard cover seal ring. Remove intermediate servo piston and band apply pin assembly.

NOTE: **Before continuing with Transmission Disassembly, check for proper intermediate band apply pin as follows:**

Band Apply Pin Selection

1) Install Band Apply Pin Selection Gauge (J-25014-2) in intermediate servo bore and retain with intermediate servo cover retaining ring aligning retaining ring gap in case slot. Install Selection Gauge Tapered Pin (J-25014-1) into gauge as shown in *Fig. 7.*

NOTE: **Make sure tapered pin end is properly located against band apply lug. Also, make sure band anchor pin is properly located in case and band anchor lug.**

Fig. 6: Removing Fifth Check Ball From Transmission Case

Fig. 7: Intermediate Band Apply Pin Selection

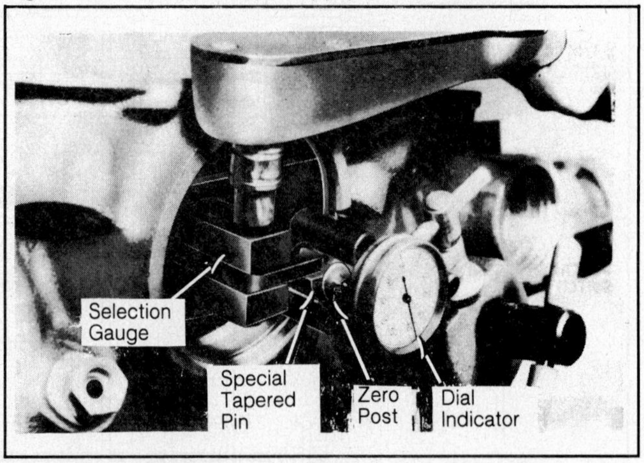

INTERMEDIATE BAND APPLY PIN SELECTION CHART

Indicator Reading In. (mm)	[1] Apply Pin Identification
.0-.029 (.0-.72)	1 Ring
.029-.057 (.72-1.44)	2 Rings
.057-.086 (1.44-2.16)	3 Rings
.086-.114 (2.16-2.88)	Wide Band

[1] – Identification ring(s) or band is located on band end of apply pin.

2) Install dial indicator and position indicator pointer on top of selection gauge zero post. Set indicator to zero. Make sure selection gauge is squarely seated against servo retaining ring and stepped side of tapered pin is aligned with torquing arm of gauge. Arm must stop against step in tapered pin.

NOTE: **If band selection pin does not register between the high and low limits, look for possible problem with intermediate band, direct clutch or case.**

3) Apply 100 INCH lbs. (11 N.m) torque to hex nut on side of gauge. Slide dial indicator over tapered pin and read dial indicator travel. Select correct band apply pin from the following chart:

NOTE: **Dial indicator travel is reversed, making the indicator readings backwards. On an indicator that ranges from 0-100, a .020" (.51 mm) travel will read .080" (2.03 mm), a .060" (1.52 mm) travel will read .040" (1.02 mm).**

4) Remove apply pin selection tools. Inspect third accumulator valve for the following: Missing check ball, check ball binding or stuck in tube, oil feed slot in tube missing or restricted, improperly assembled, loose fitting or not fully seated in case. *See Fig. 8.*

Fig. 8: Third Accumulator Check Valve Assembly

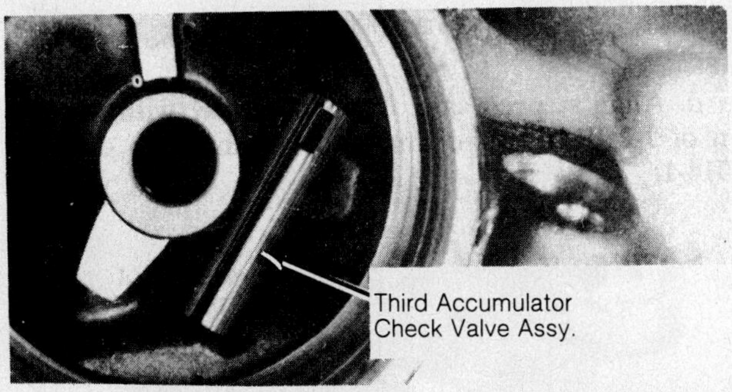

Third Accumulator Check Valve Replacement

1) Using a No. 4 screw extractor, remove check valve assembly from case by turning and pulling straight out. *See Fig. 9.*

2) Install new check valve assembly, small end first, into case. Position oil feed slot in tube so it faces servo cover. Using a 3/8" diameter metal rod and hammer, drive assembly in until it is flush or below surface of third accumulator case hole.

Fig. 9: Removing Third Accumulator Check Valve

Remove check valve assembly from case by turning and pulling.

OIL PUMP & FRONT UNIT COMPONENTS

NOTE: **Prior to removing oil pump and front unit components, check front unit end play to determine correct end play thrust washer for use at reassembly. See FRONT UNIT END PLAY CHECK under TRANSMISSION REASSEMBLY.**

1) Turn transmission so oil pump faces upward. If necessary, remove and discard pump oil seal. Remove oil pump-to-case attaching bolts and washers, then withdraw oil pump and gasket from case using a puller.

2) Grasp turbine shaft and pull direct and forward clutch assemblies from transmission case. Pull direct clutch assembly off forward clutch assembly.

NOTE: **Direct-to-forward clutch thrust washer may stick to end of direct clutch housing.**

3) Remove intermediate band assembly and anchor pin from case. Withdraw output shaft-to-turbine shaft front selective thrust washer.

NOTE: **Output shaft-to-turbine shaft selective thrust washer may be stuck to end of turbine shaft.**

FRONT INTERNAL GEAR

NOTE: **At this time, check rear unit end play to determine correct end play thrust washer for use at reassembly. See Rear Unit End Play Check under TRANSMISSION REASSEMBLY.**

Using snap ring pliers, remove output shaft-to-selective washer snap ring, then withdraw front internal gear, rear selective thrust washer, and thrust washer. Remove front carrier assembly and front internal gear-to-front carrier roller bearing assembly. Remove front sun gear, and front sun gear-to-front carrier thrust bearing assembly. *See Fig. 10.*

INPUT DRUM, REAR SUN GEAR & LOW-REVERSE CLUTCH HOUSING

1) Remove input drum and rear sun gear from case. Remove the 4-tanged input drum-to-reverse clutch housing thrust washer from rear of input drum or from reverse clutch housing.front carrier roller bearing assembly. Remove front sun gear, and front sun gear-to-front carrier thrust bearing assembly. *See Fig. 10.*

Fig. 10: Removing Front Internal Gear

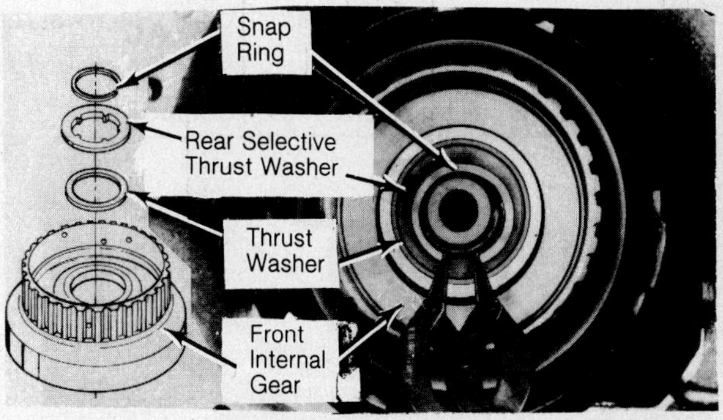

The front sun gear-to-front carrier thrust bearing may come out with front carrier.

INPUT DRUM, REAR SUN GEAR & LOW-REVERSE CLUTCH HOUSING

1) Remove input drum and rear sun gear from case. Remove the 4-tanged input drum-to-reverse clutch housing thrust washer from rear of input drum or from reverse clutch housing.

GENERAL MOTORS TURBO HYDRA-MATIC 200C (Cont.)

2) Grind approximately 3/4" from end of a No. 4 screw extractor to remove housing-to-case cup plug. Remove cup plug assembly by turning easy-out 2 or 3 turns and pulling straight out. *See Fig. 11.*

3) Remove low-reverse clutch housing-to-case beveled snap ring. Flat side of snap ring should have been against housing with beveled side up. Withdraw low-reverse clutch housing assembly from case. Remove clutch housing-to-case spacer ring.

Fig. 11: Removing Low-Reverse Clutch Housing To Case Cup Plug

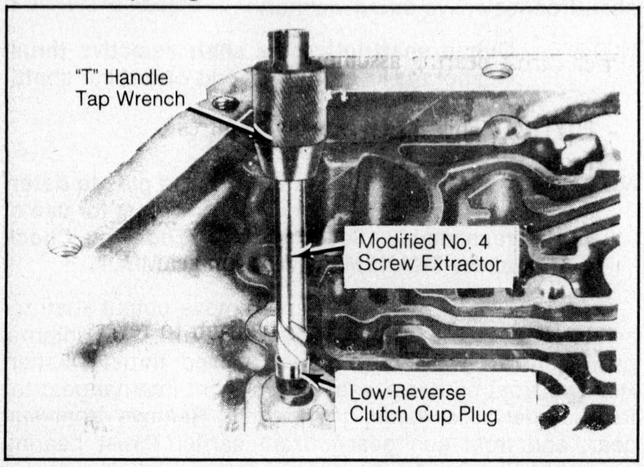

REAR GEAR COMPONENTS

NOTE: Make sure governor has been removed before removing rear gear components.

1) Grasp output shaft and lift out rear unit parts and lay them down in a horizontal position. *See Fig. 12.* Slide roller clutch and rear carrier assembly off output shaft. Remove 4-tanged rear carrier-to-rear internal gear thrust washer off end of rear carrier or inside rear internal gear.

2) Remove low-reverse clutch plates from output shaft. Remove rear internal gear-to-rear sun gear thrust bearing assembly from rear internal gear. Remove rear internal gear from output shaft.

Fig. 12: Removing Rear Internal Gear Components

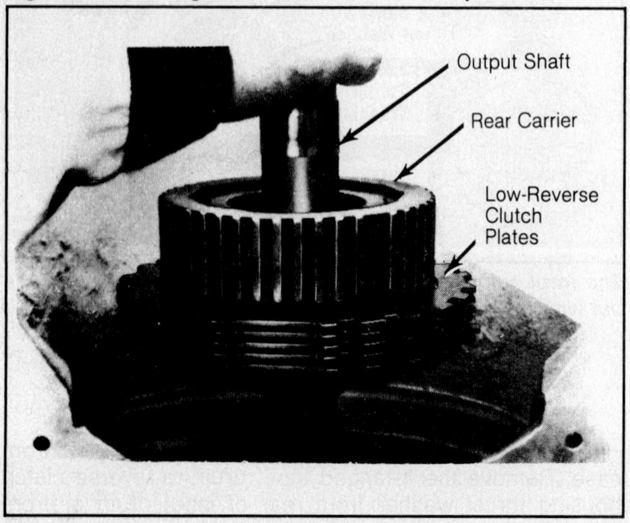

MANUAL SHAFT & PARKING LINKAGE

1) Remove hex nut holding inside detent lever to manual shaft, then remove parking actuator rod and detent lever. Remove manual shaft retaining pin from case and slide manual shaft out. If necessary, pry manual shaft seal from case.

2) Remove parking lock bracket. Remove parking pawl shaft retaining pin. Grind approximately 3/4" from end of a No. 4 screw extractor. Remove parking pawl cup plug and discard. *See Fig. 13.*

3) Using sheet metal screw or No. 3 screw extractor, remove parking pawl shaft. Remove parking pawl and return spring.

Fig. 13: Removing Parking Pawl Shaft Cup Plug

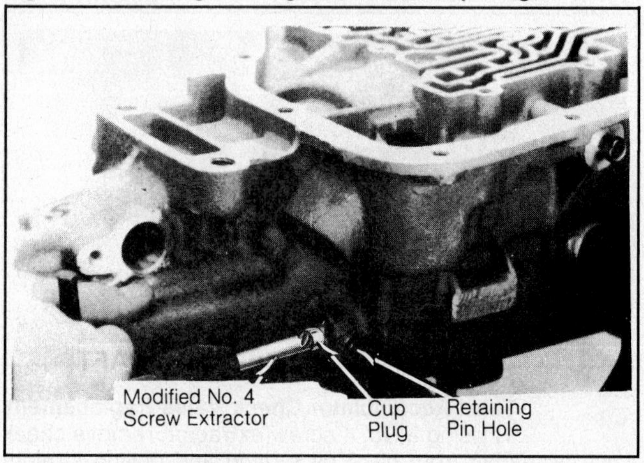

COMPONENT DISASSEMBLY & REASSEMBLY

VALVE BODY

As valve trains are removed from each valve body bore, place individual parts in correct order in relative position to valve body to simplify reassembly.

Valves and springs are not interchangeable, and all parts must be installed in correct order in proper valve body bore. *See Fig. 15.* Remove all coiled pins by pushing through from rough case surface of body, except the 2 pins which retain throttle valve and throttle valve plunger.

Disassembly

1) Position valve body with cored face upward and 1-2 accumulator pocket at lower left. *See Fig. 16.* Remove four check balls from cored passages of valve body (5th check ball is in case), then remove 1-2 accumulator piston. From upper bore, remove manual valve.

CAUTION: Some coiled pins in valve body assembly have pressure against them. Hold a shop towel over bore while removing pin to prevent losing bore plug or spring.

2) From upper right side bore, remove 2-3 valve train. From next bore down, remove the 1-2 valve train. From next bore down, remove reverse boost valve train.

NOTE: Some valves and springs may be inside valve bushings.

3) If necessary to remove shift T.V. valve train, remove coiled pin and place valve body with rough casting

GENERAL MOTORS TURBO HYDRA-MATIC 200C (Cont.)

Fig. 14: Exploded View of Turbo Hydra-Matic 200C Valve Body Assembly

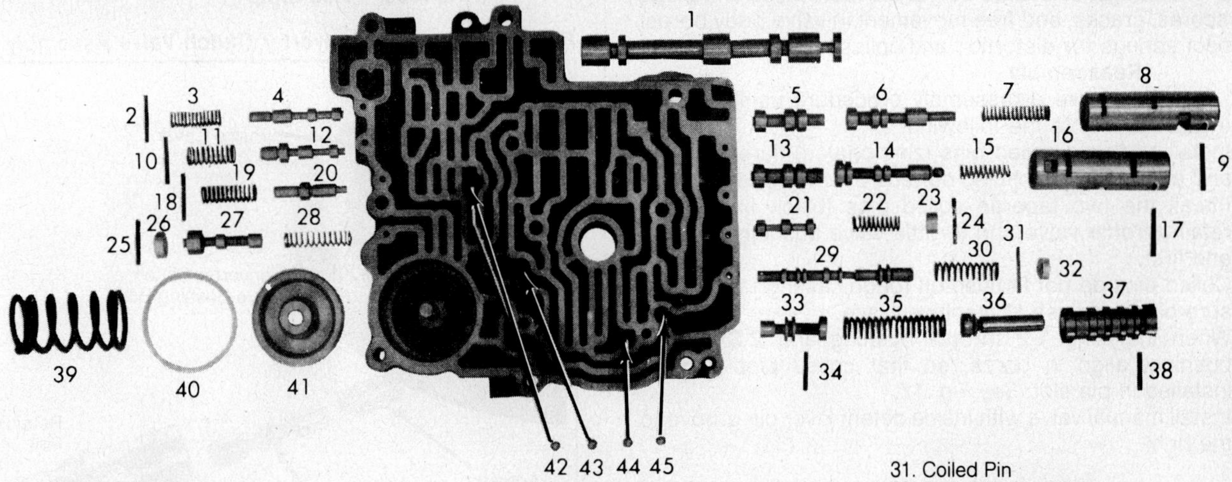

1. Manual Valve
2. Coiled Pin
3. Intermediate Boost Spring
4. Intermediate Boost Valve
5. 2-3 Shift Valve
6. 2-3 Throttle Valve
7. 2-3 Throttle Spring
8. 2-3 Throttle Bushing
9. Coiled Pin
10. Coiled Pin
11. Low Overrun Clutch Spring
12. Low Overrun Clutch Valve
13. 1-2 Shift Valve
14. 1-2 Throttle Valve
15. 1-2 Throttle Spring
16. 1-2 Throttle Bushing
17. Coiled Pin
18. Coiled Pin
19. Direct Clutch Exhaust Spring
20. Direct Clutch Exhaust Valve
21. Reverse Boost Valve
22. Reverse Boost Spring
23. Reverse Boost Bore Plug
24. Coiled Pin
25. Coiled Pin
26. 1-2 Accumulator Bore Plug
27. 1-2 Accumulator Valve
28. 1-2 Accumulator Spring
29. Shift T.V. Valve
30. Shift T.V. Spring
31. Coiled Pin
32. Shift T.V. Bore Plug
33. Throttle Valve
34. Coiled Pin
35. Throttle Valve Spring
36. Throttle Valve Plunger
37. Throttle Valve Plunger Bushing
38. Coiled Pin
39. 1-2 Accumulator Spring
40. 1-2 Accumulator Piston Seal
41. 1-2 Accumulator Piston
42. Check Ball No. 4
43. Check Ball No. 3
44. Check Ball No. 2
45. Check Ball No. 1

(NOTE: 5th Check Ball in Case)

Fig. 15: Removing Shift T.V. Valve Train

Valves and valve springs are not interchangeable.

Fig. 16: Removing Throttle Valve Inner Pin

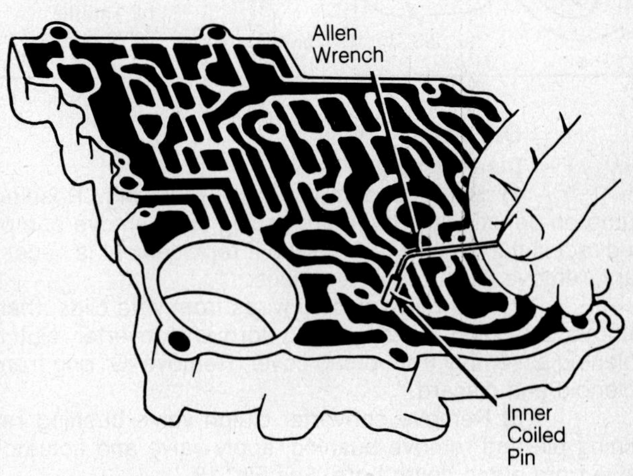

Use modified Allen Wrench.

surface up. Use needle nose pliers and push in on valve, then hold in place with a small screwdriver.

4) Position a 1/4" diameter rod, 3/8" long against end of valve, pry on rod with a screwdriver, remove small screwdriver, and remove plug, spring, and valve.

5) From lower right side bore, remove outer coiled pin and withdraw throttle valve bushing, plunger and spring. Remove throttle valve detent pin. Using 1/16" Allen wrench, with sides ground to fit inside pin, remove inner coiled pin, and then withdraw throttle valve. *See Fig. 15.*

6) From upper left side bore, remove intermediate boost valve train. From next bore down, remove low overrun clutch valve train. From next bore down, remove direct clutch exhaust valve train. From lower left side bore, remove 1-2 accumulator valve train.

Inspection

Wash all parts in solvent and air dry. Inspect 1-2 accumulator piston and seal for damage; do not remove

GENERAL MOTORS TURBO HYDRA-MATIC 200C (Cont.)

seal unless replacement is required. Check valve body for cracks, damage, or scored bores. Inspect valves and plugs for scores, cracks, and free movement in valve body bores. Inspect springs for distortion and collapsed coils.

Reassembly

Reverse disassembly procedure using *Fig. 16* as a guide and note the following:

- Install all flared coiled pins (zinc coated) flare end out, and away from machined surface of valve body.
- Install the two tapered coiled pins (black finish) that retain throttle valve and throttle valve bushing, tapered end first.
- Coiled pins do not fit flush on rough casting face. Make sure pins are flush at machined face.
- When installing 1-2 throttle bushing and 2-3 throttle bushing, align in bores, so that coiled pins can be installed in pin slot. *See Fig. 17.*
- Install manual valve with inside detent lever pin groove to the right.

Fig. 17: Installing Throttle Valve Bushings

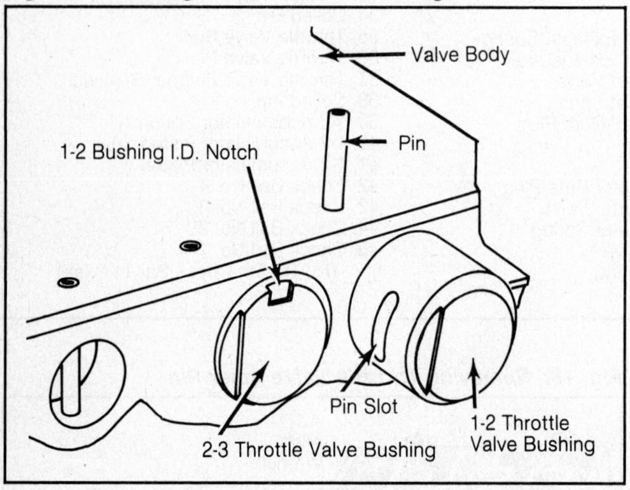

OIL PUMP

Disassembly

1) Remove pump-to-case seal ring. Position pump on bench with cover side facing up. Remove pump-to-direct clutch thrust washer, and if replacement is necessary, remove 3 Teflon oil seal rings.

2) Remove solenoid wires from wire clips, then remove attaching bolts and lift torque converter clutch solenoid assembly from pump cover. Remove "O" ring from solenoid and discard.

3) Remove converter clutch valve bushing retaining pin and remove bushing, apply valve and actuator valve from pump cover bore. *See Fig. 18.*

4) Using a small screwdriver, push in on pressure regulator bore plug and remove retaining ring. Release spring tension slowly and remove pressure regulator valve train.

5) Remove attaching bolts and separate pump cover from body using care not to drop check ball from body. Remove check ball. Remove pump gears, marking them for reassembly in same position.

NOTE: **Keep pump check ball separate from the 5 check balls used in case and valve body. Pump check ball diameter is .281" (7.14 mm), while case and valve body check ball diameter is .250" (6.35 mm).**

Fig. 18: Removing Converter Clutch Valve Assembly

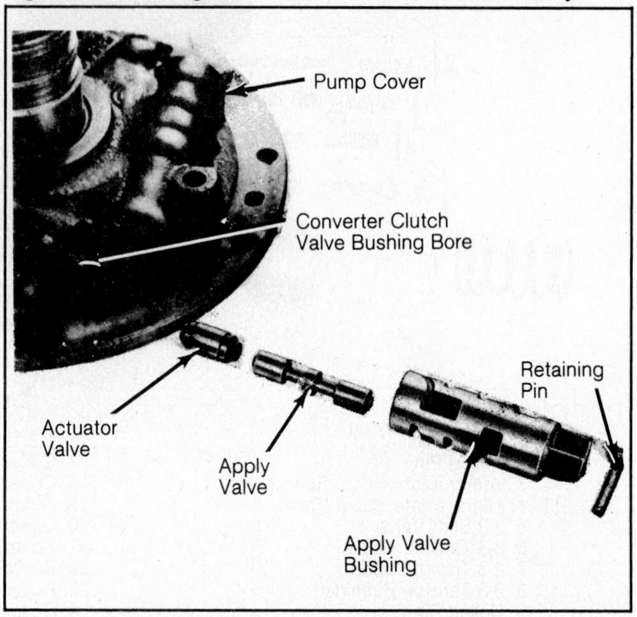

Inspection

1) Check drive and driven gears for scoring, galling, or other damage. Inspect gear pocket and crescent in body for scoring or damage.

2) Check pump cover and body for nicks, open oil passages, and overall flatness. Using a straightedge and feeler gauge, measure pump body face-to-gear face clearance; clearance should be .0007-.0021" (.020-.055 mm).

3) Inspect torque converter clutch solenoid wires for loose connections and damaged or cut insulation. Inspect solenoid assembly ball check valve for nicks or damage. Check for defective ball or ball seat as follows:

- Blow air into ball seat with solenoid de-energized; air should pass through ball seat.
- Noting polarity, energize solenoid with +12 volts D.C. and again blow air into ball seat; air should not pass through ball seat.

Fig. 19: Exploded View of Oil Pump Assembly

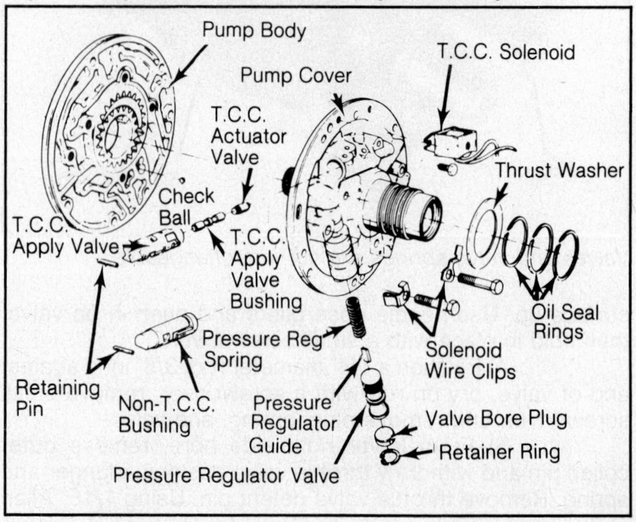

GENERAL MOTORS TURBO HYDRA-MATIC 200C (Cont.)

NOTE: **Do not use compressed air to check ball and ball seat. The use of compressed air may cause a false reading.**

4) Inspect converter clutch apply and actuator valves for nicks or damage. Check valves for free operation in bushing bore.

5) Grind approximately 1/2" from end of a No. 4 screw extractor. Using modified screw extractor, remove and discard cup plug from pump body. *See Fig. 20*. Discard cup plug. Withdraw screen from plug bore.

Fig. 20: Removing Cup Plug From Pump Body

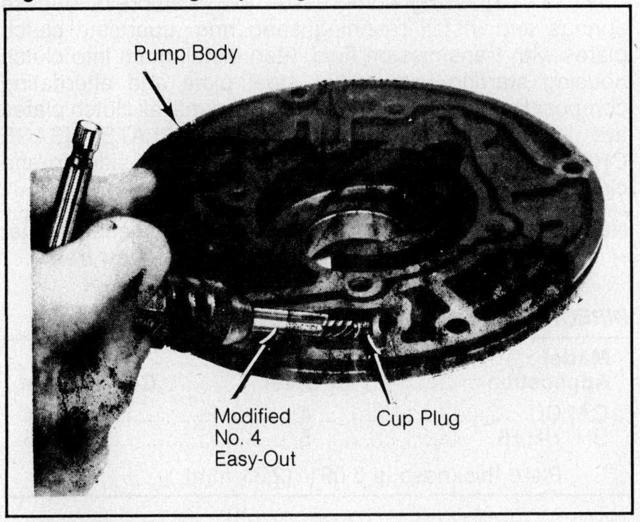

6) Clean screen in clean solvent and air dry, then reinstall screen in pump body bore. Install new cup plug, small diameter end first, into hole in pump body. Using a 5/16" diameter metal rod and hammer, drive cup plug until just below surface of hole.

7) Inspect pressure regulator valve bore in pump cover and pressure regulator valve assembly for wear or damage and make sure parts operate freely in bore. Inspect the 6 cup plugs in pump cover for damage or leaks. If necessary, replace cup plug.

Pump Cover Cup Plug Replacement

Remove old cup plugs using care not to damage pump cover. Drive new cup plugs to 1/32" below top of hole, using a 1/4" diameter rod on smaller plug and a 5/16" rod on the 5 larger plugs. Stake top of hole in 2 places, directly opposite each other, to retain plugs.

Reassembly

1) Install driven gear into pump body with identification mark down against gear pocket. *See Fig. 22*. Install drive gear into pump body with identification marks on tangs up. *See Fig. 23*. Place check ball into pocket in pump body as shown in *Fig. 21*. Retain with petroleum jelly.

2) Assemble pump cover and body using Alignment Strap (J-25015) and lace bolt or screwdriver through pump-to-case bolt hole. Install and tighten pump cover attaching bolts and remove strap.

3) Install pressure regulator spring, spring guide, valve (stem end out), and bore plug (hole end out) into pump cover bore. Compress pressure regulator valve assembly and install retaining ring.

4) Install actuator valve into bushing bore of pump cover. Install apply valve into bushing, then install

Fig. 21: Pump Body Oil Passages

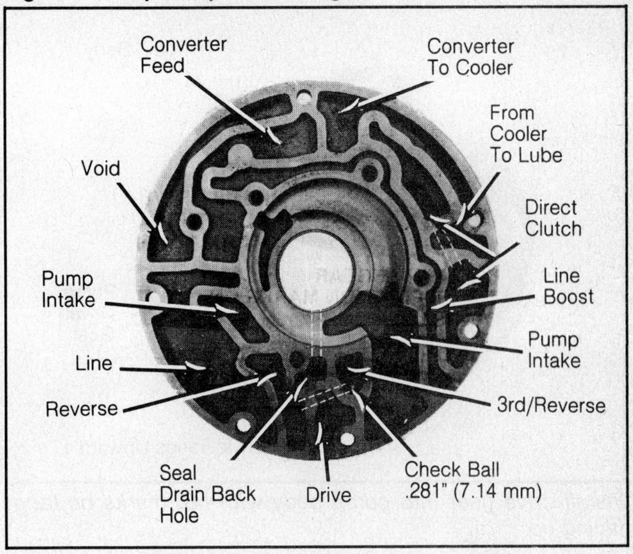

Make sure all castings are clean and true.

Fig. 22: Pump Driven Gear Identification Marks

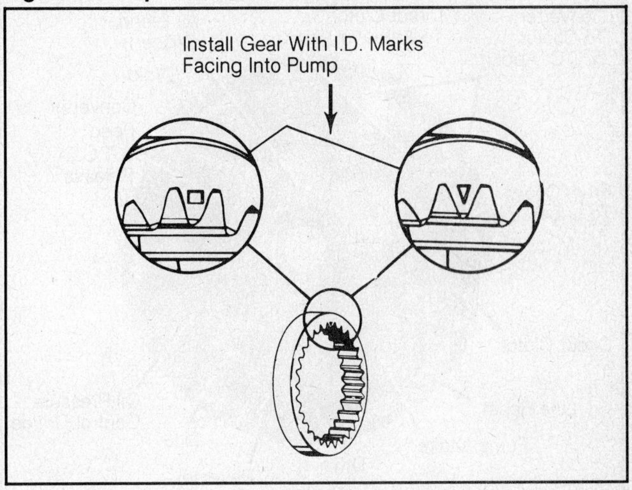

bushing into cover. Install apply valve bushing retaining pin and pin clip and bolt. *See Fig. 18*.

5) Install new pump-to-case gasket on pump and retain with petroleum jelly. Lubricate with petroleum jelly and install new "O" ring on solenoid assembly, then install solenoid on pump and tighten attaching bolts. Install solenoid wires into wire clip.

6) If removed, install 3 new oil seal rings on pump cover stator shaft, making sure cut ends are assembled in the same relationship as cut. Also, make sure rings are seated in grooves to prevent damage during transmission reassembly. Retain rings with petroleum jelly.

7) Install pump-to-case seal ring (chamfered side out), making sure ring is not twisted. Install pump-to-direct clutch thrust washer and retain with petroleum jelly.

DIRECT CLUTCH

Disassembly

1) Using *Fig. 25* as a guide, remove clutch pack snap ring. Remove backing plate from clutch housing. Remove clutch plates from housing and keep them separate from the forward clutch plates.

GENERAL MOTORS TURBO HYDRA-MATIC 200C (Cont.)

Fig. 23: Pump Drive Gear Identification Marks

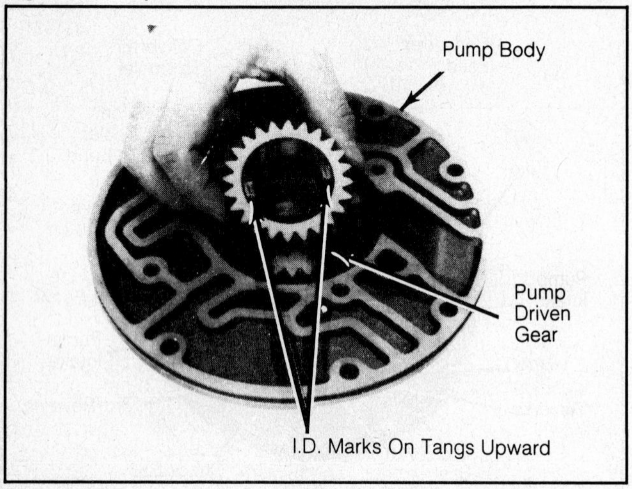

Install drive gear into pump body with I.D. marks on tangs facing up.

Fig. 24: Pump Cover Oil Passages

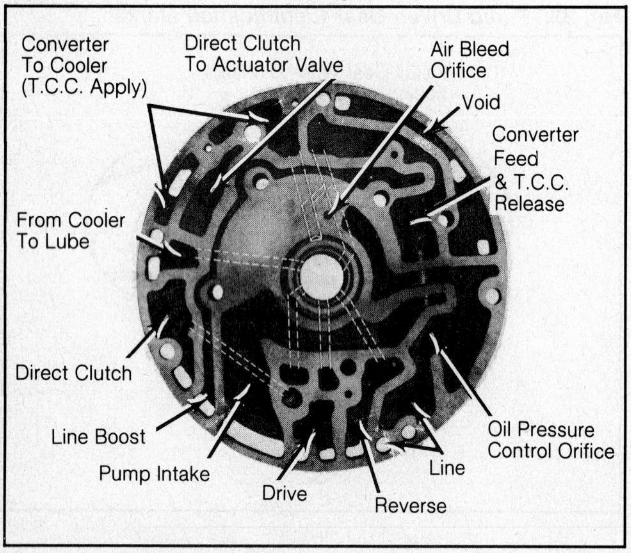

Make sure castings are clean.

2) Using a compressor tool, compress retainer and spring assembly and removed snap ring. Remove tool and lift retainer and spring assembly from clutch housing.

3) Remove release spring guide from clutch housing. Remove clutch piston from housing. Remove inner and outer seals from piston and center seal from housing.

NOTE: **Do not separate apply ring from clutch piston unless ring or piston requires replacement.**

Inspection

1) Inspect composition plates, steel plates, and backing plate for wear, burning, or scoring. Check release springs and retainer for damage or a collapsed condition. Inspect clutch piston for distortion, cracks and free operation of check ball.

2) Check clutch housing for cracks, wear, and open passages, and for free operation of check ball. Inspect snap ring grooves and bushing in housing for wear or damage.

Reassembly

1) Install apply ring on clutch piston, then install new inner and outer seals on piston, with seal lips facing away from clutch apply ring side. Install new center seal into direct clutch housing, with seal lip facing upward. Install Seal Protector (J-25010) over oil seals, lubricate seals with transmission fluid, and install clutch piston.

CAUTION: **Use care when installing piston past larger snap ring groove in clutch housing as groove could cut outer seal on piston.**

2) Install release spring guide with omitted rib over check ball in piston as shown in *Fig. 26*. Install retainer and spring assembly into housing, making sure all parts are positioned correctly.

3) Using compressor tool, compress release springs and install retaining snap ring. Lubricate clutch plates with transmission fluid, then install them into clutch housing starting with a flat steel plate and alternating composition plates and flat steel plates until all clutch plates are installed. See DIRECT CLUTCH PLATE USAGE CHART. Install backing plate with chamfered side up and clutch pack retaining snap ring.

NOTE: **After reassembly is completed, ensure that composition faced clutch plates turn freely.**

DIRECT CLUTCH PLATE USAGE CHART

Model Application	Flat Steel [1]	Composition
CA, CU	4	4
BH, HH,HL	5	5

[1] – Plate thickness is 0.091" (2.31 mm).

FORWARD CLUTCH

Disassembly

1) Remove forward clutch-to-direct clutch thrust washer. If replacement is required, remove teflon oil seal rings from turbine shaft. Remove clutch pack snap ring and lift out backing plate and clutch plates. *See Fig. 27.*

NOTE: **Keep forward clutch plates separate from direct clutch plates.**

2) Using an arbor press, compress retainer and spring assembly and remove retaining snap ring. Release arbor press slowly, then remove retainer and spring assembly. Remove piston from clutch housing, then remove inner and outer seals from piston.

NOTE: **Do not remove clutch apply ring from piston unless piston or apply ring requires replacement.**

Inspection

1) Inspect composition, steel and backing plates for wear, scores or other damage. Check spring retainer and release springs for distortion or collapse. Inspect piston and housing for cracks, distortion, open oil passages, or other damage. Inspect snap ring grooves for wear or damage, and make sure ball check in housing operates freely.

2) Check turbine shaft for open passages on both ends of shaft, and check journals for damage. Inspect clutch housing cup plug and if damaged, remove using No. 3 screw extractor (grind to fit). Install new cup plug to .039" (1.0 mm) below surface (grind to fit). Install new cup plug to .039" (1.0 mm) below surface.

Reassembly

1) Install clutch apply ring on piston, then install new inner and outer seals on piston, with seal lips facing

GENERAL MOTORS TURBO HYDRA-MATIC 200C (Cont.)

Fig. 25: Exploded View of Direct Clutch Assembly

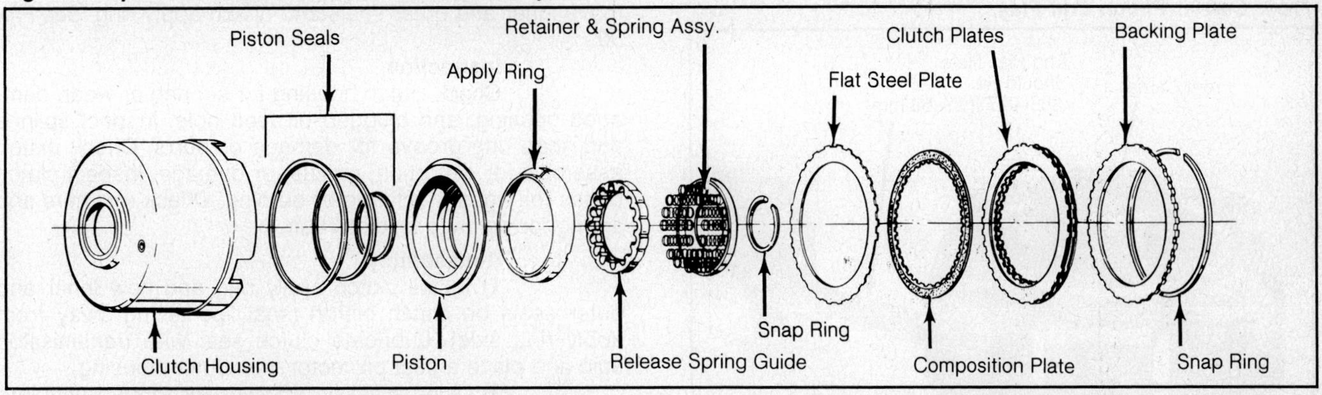

Fig. 26: Assembling Release Spring Guide to Piston

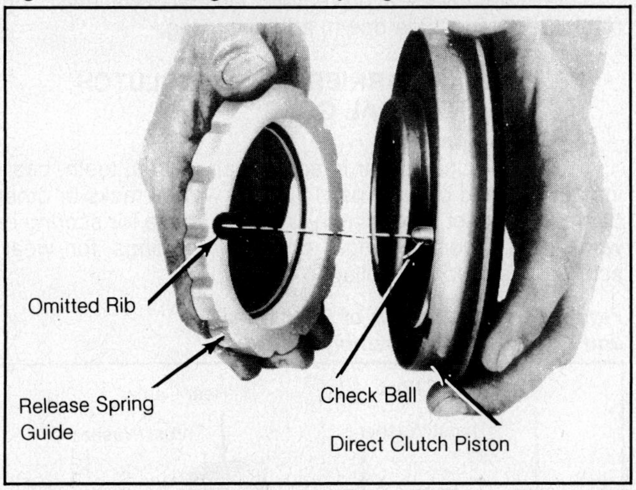

Install release spring guide with omitted rib over check ball in piston.

away from apply ring side. Lubricate seals with transmission fluid, then install piston into housing. Install retainer and spring assembly into housing, compress retainer and springs, and install retaining snap ring.

CAUTION: Use care when installing piston past large snap ring groove as groove could cut outer piston seal.

2) Lubricate with transmission fluid then install forward clutch plates into housing starting with waved steel plate then alternating composition plates and flat steel plates until all clutch plates are installed. See FORWARD CLUTCH PLATE USAGE CHART. Install backing plate (chamfered side up) and clutch pack snap ring. If removed, install new turbine shaft seal rings and forward clutch-to-direct clutch thrust washer.

FORWARD CLUTCH PLATE USAGE CHART

Model Application	Flat Steel [1]	Composition
CA, CU	2 [2]	3
BH, HH, HL	3 [2]	4

[1] – Plate thickness is 0.077" (1.96 mm).
[2] – Plus 1 WAVED steel plate 0.062" (1.57 mm) thick, installed first.

NOTE: After reassembly is completed, ensure that composition faced clutch plates turn freely.

FRONT CARRIER, SUN GEAR & INTERNAL GEAR

Inspection

Check all parts for pitting, scoring, damaged gear teeth and cracks. Make sure all lubrication holes are open. Check front internal gear thrust washers for wear or other damage and front carrier roller thrust bearing for roughness and pitting. Check pinion end play of front carrier. End play should be .009-.027" (.23-.69 mm). *See Fig. 28.*

Fig. 27: Exploded View of Forward Clutch Assembly

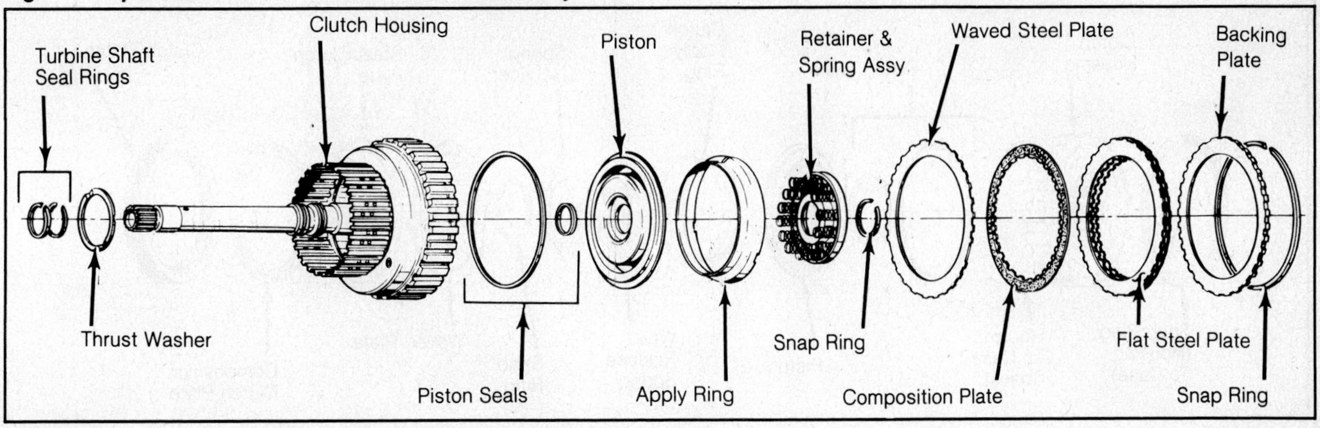

GENERAL MOTORS TURBO HYDRA-MATIC 200C (Cont.)

Fig. 28: Using Feeler Gauge to Measure Front Carrier Pinion End Play

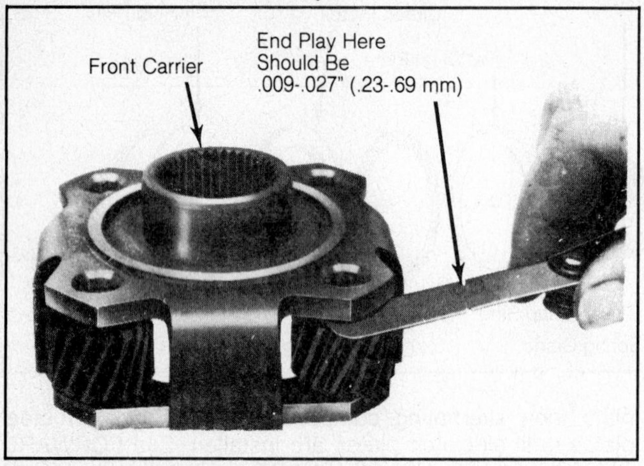

If not within specifications, replace.

Fig. 29: Exploded View of Rear Sun Gear and Input Drum Assembly

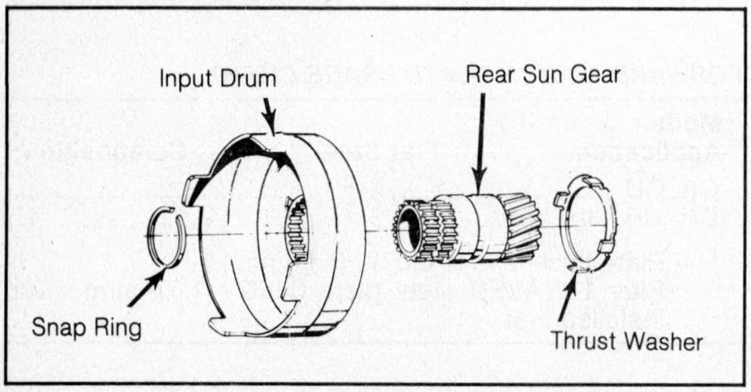

REAR SUN GEAR & INPUT DRUM

Inspection

Check rear sun gear for cracks, splits, spline damage, gear or journal wear, and for plugged lubrication holes. If necessary, remove snap ring and separate sun gear from input drum and inspect drum splines for damage. Check input drum-to-low-reverse clutch housing thrust washer for scoring or distorted tangs.

LOW-REVERSE CLUTCH

Disassembly

Compress low-reverse clutch spring retainer, remove snap ring and retainer. Check for damage and distortion. Withdraw waved spring and clutch piston. Remove inner and outer seals and clutch apply ring. *See Fig. 30.*

Inspection

Check clutch housing for scoring or wear, damaged bushing, and plugged oil feed hole. Inspect splines and snap ring groove for damage or burrs. Check piston assembly for distortion, cracks, or damage. Inspect clutch plates for signs of scoring or burning. Check retainers and spring for damage or distortion.

Reassembly

1) Install clutch apply ring and new inner and outer seals on clutch piston (seal lips facing away from apply ring side). Lubricate clutch seal with transmission fluid and place a seal protector into clutch housing.

2) Using a flat tip screwdriver to start seal into housing, install clutch piston, rotating while pushing down into bore. Remove seal protector, then install waved spring, retainer (cupped side down) and snap ring.

REAR CARRIER, ROLLER CLUTCH & INTERNAL GEAR

Inspection

1) Check rear internal gear splines, teeth, bearing surface and parking pawl lugs for wear, cracks or other damage. Inspect roller clutch race and spline for scoring or wear, and roller bearings, cage and springs for wear, scoring, distortion or collapse.

Fig. 31: Exploded View of Rear Carrier and Roller Clutch Assembly

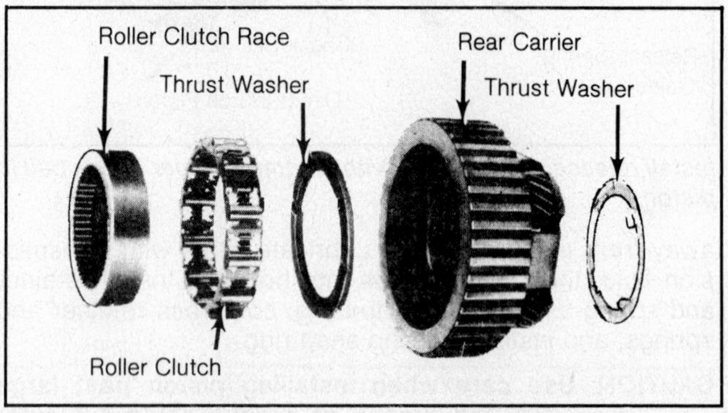

2) Inspect thrust washers for excessive wear or damaged tangs. Check rear carrier roller clutch cam ramps and bushing for scoring or other damage. Inspect planet

Fig. 30: Exploded View of Low-Reverse Clutch Assembly

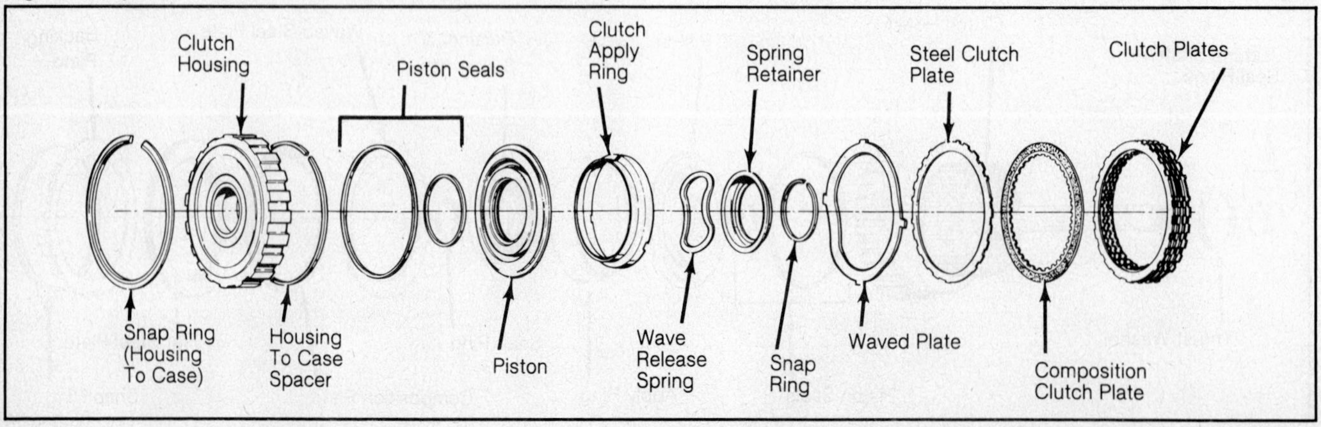

pinions for damage, rough bearings, tilt and correct end play. End play should be .009-.027" (.23-.69 mm).

OUTPUT SHAFT

Inspection

Inspect journals and snap ring grooves for wear or damage. Check for plugged or damaged lubrication holes. Inspect shaft splines and governor drive gear for holes. Inspect shaft splines and governor drive gear for rough or damaged surfaces. Check speedometer drive gear and retaining clip for wear or damage.

NOTE: Service replacement output shaft has one speedometer drive gear clip hole at the front speedometer gear location which is about 1/4" diameter and opposite this hole is another clip hole which is about 5/32". The shaft also has same size holes at rear speedometer gear location.

Speedometer Drive Gear Replacement

1) If equipped with a nylon gear, depress gear clip and slide drive gear and clip off output shaft. To install, place gear clip with tanged end in correct hole in shaft, then align slot of gear with slip and install gear. *See Fig. 32.*

2) If equipped with steel gear, remove gear using puller. To install, position front end of shaft on a block of wood to prevent damaging shaft during installation. Position gear (large chamfered inside diameter first) over rear end of output shaft. Using driver, drive gear onto shaft until distance from rear end of shaft to rear face of gear is 6 5/32" (156.37 mm).

Fig. 32: Output Shaft and Speedometer Drive Gear

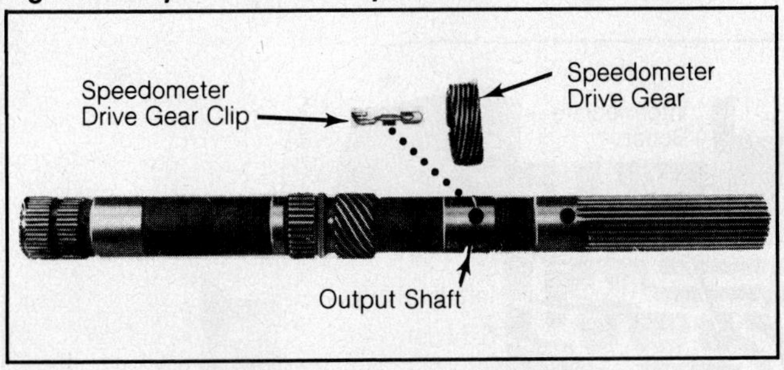

Align slot of gear with clip and install gear.

INTERMEDIATE SERVO

Disassembly

Compress intermediate servo piston spring. Using small flat blade screwdriver, remove servo pin-to-piston snap ring. Separate band apply pin, spring and washer from servo piston. *See Fig. 33.*

Inspection

1) Check intermediate servo pin for wear, damage and proper fit in case bore. Inspect inner and outer seal rings for damage and proper fit in seal ring grooves of piston.

CAUTION: Do not remove seal rings from piston unless replacement is required.

2) Check servo piston and cover for cracks or other damage. Inspect servo spring for collapsed coils or distortion. Check intermediate servo cover and piston assembly for proper combination and usage. See INTERMEDIATE SERVO COVER & PISTON USAGE chart.

INTERMEDIATE SERVO COVER & PISTON USAGE

Application Model	Cover I.D. No.	Piston Casting No.	Piston I.D.
BH, CA, CU, HH [1]	8635692	8633563	3 Steps
HL, KA	8635692	8633563	3 Steps

[1] – Use orificed cup plug with piston.

Reassembly

1) Install retainer on band apply pin and install snap ring. Install band apply pin (retainer end first) through servo pistons. If removed, install new inner and outer seal rings on piston, making sure seal ring ends are assembled in the same relationship as cut and seal rings are seated in grooves.

2) Lubricate with petroleum jelly and install new seal ring on intermediate servo cover. Install servo piston assembly into servo cover.

Fig. 33: Exploded View of Intermediate Servo Assembly

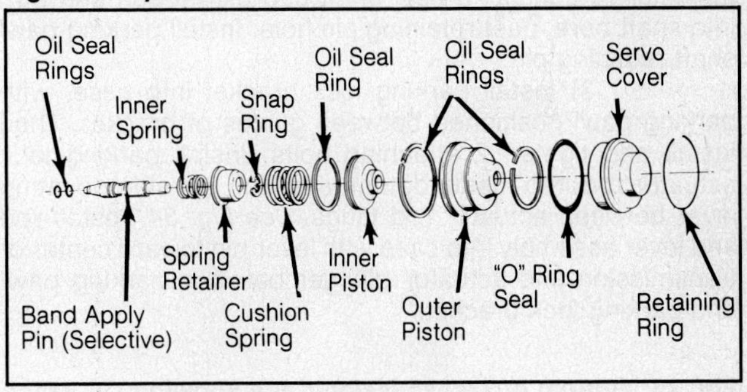

GOVERNOR ASSEMBLY

Inspection

1) Inspect governor cover for damage, scored or worn bore and plugged oil passage. Wash governor assembly in cleaning solvent and blow out oil passage. Inspect governor driven gear, weights, springs, shaft and washer for wear or damage.

2) Check governor shaft seal ring for cuts, damage and free fit in groove. If damaged, cut ring off shaft and install new seal ring. Lubricate seal with petroleum jelly. Inspect for presence of two check balls.

TRANSMISSION CASE

Inspection

1) Check case assembly for cracks, porosity and interconnected oil passages. Inspect reverse clutch lugs, governor bore, intermediate servo bore, speedometer bore and snap ring grooves for wear and other damage. Make sure all vents and passages are open and clear.

2) Inspect vent assembly in case for damage. DO NOT remove unless replacement is required. Check cooler line connectors for damage. DO NOT remove unless replacement is required.

TRANSMISSION REASSEMBLY

MANUAL SHAFT & PARKING LINKAGE

1) Place transmission in horizontal position, oil pan side up. Install new manual shaft seal into case with seal lip facing inward. Place parking pawl and return spring into case, making sure pawl tooth faces inside of case. Be sure spring is positioned under pawl tooth and spring ends locate against case pad.

GENERAL MOTORS TURBO HYDRA-MATIC 200C (Cont.)

Fig. 34: Installing Parking Actuator Rod

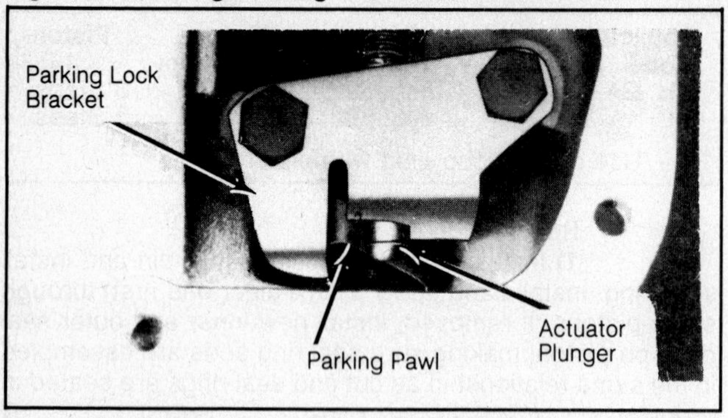

Be careful not to bend rod during installation.

2) Align pawl and spring with shaft bore in case and install pawl shaft (tapered end first). Using a 3/8" diameter rod, install a new shaft cup plug (open end out) into shaft bore, past retaining pin hole. Install parking pawl shaft retaining pin.

3) Install parking lock bracket into case, with parking pawl positioned between guides of bracket. Then install and tighten 2 attaching bolts. Install parking lock actuator rod into inside detent lever (on pin side) locating lever between actuator rod tangs. *See Fig. 34*. Install rod and lever assembly into case with lever pin toward center of transmission and actuator plunger between parking pawl and parking lock bracket.

NOTE: **File off any burrs or raised edges on manual shaft that could damage seal during installation of shaft.**

4) Install manual shaft (small I.D. ring groove first) through case. Install manual shaft-to-case retaining pin, indexing with larger groove on manual shaft. Align inside detent lever with flats on manual shaft, position lever on shaft, then install and tighten nut on manual shaft.

OUTPUT SHAFT & REAR INTERNAL GEAR

If removed, install new rear internal gear-to-output shaft snap ring into groove on output shaft, then install rear internal gear (hub end first) onto shaft. Position rear internal gear-to-rear sun gear roller thrust bearing assembly over shaft by placing small diameter race against rear internal gear.

ROLLER CLUTCH & REAR CARRIER

1) Install rear internal gear, hub end first, on output shaft. Install internal gear-to-rear sun gear roller thrust bearing assembly into internal gear by placing small diameter race over output shaft.

2) Install roller clutch-to-rear carrier thrust washer into rear carrier. Install rollers that may have come out of roller clutch cage, by compressing energizing spring with forefinger and inserting roller from outer edge. Install roller clutch assembly into roller clutch cam.

3) Install roller clutch race, spline side out and rotate clutch race counterclockwise into position. Install 4

Fig. 35: Bottom of Transmission Case Showing Oil Passages

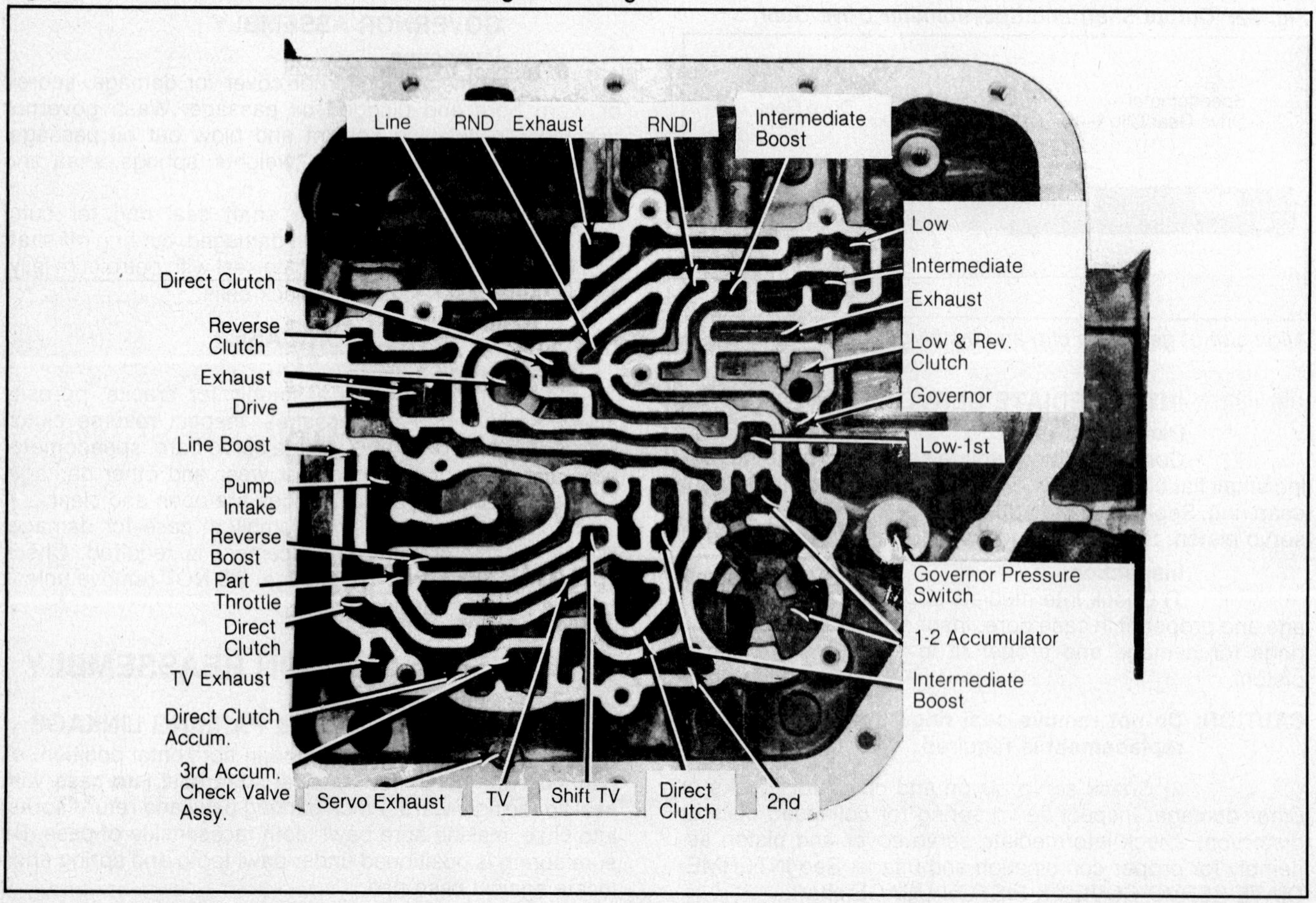

GENERAL MOTORS TURBO HYDRA-MATIC 200C (Cont.)

Fig. 36: Exploded View of Manual and Parking Linkage

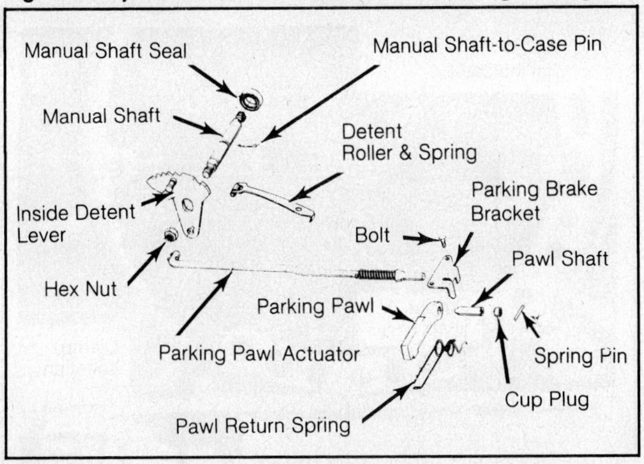

tanged rear carrier-to-rear internal gear thrust washer onto carrier and align tangs into slots of carrier. Retain washer with petroleum jelly. Install roller clutch and carrier assembly into rear internal gear on output shaft.

4) Install Output Shaft Support (J-25013) on rear of transmission as follows: Place Support Sleeve into rear of case, open end first. Then bolt Bracket (J-25013-5) into rear mount bolt holes on extension housing. *See Fig. 37*.

5) Turn case to vertical position, with pump end upward. Install rear unit parts (output shaft, rear internal gear, and rear carrier previously assembled) into transmission case and into support sleeve, indexing rear internal gear parking pawl lugs to pass by parking pawl tooth.

6) Using adjusting screw on bracket and looking through parking pawl case slot, adjust height of the rear internal gear parking pawl lugs to align flush with the parking pawl tooth.

CAUTION: With rear internal gear parking pawl lugs correctly aligned, make sure speedometer drive gear is visible through speedometer gear bore of case. If gear is not visible, it may be located on wrong journal of output shaft.

Fig. 37: Installing Output Shaft Support

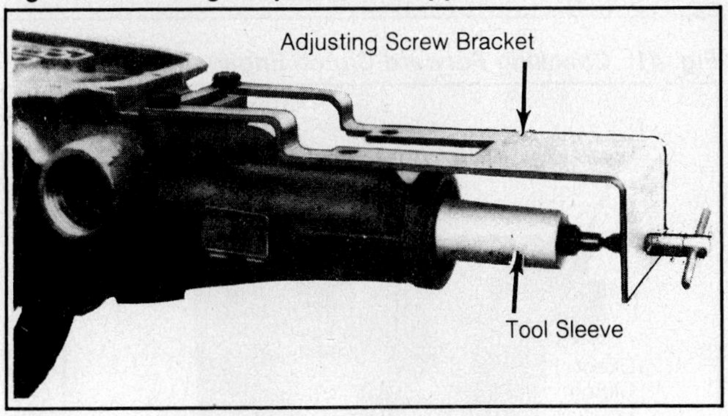

LOW-REVERSE CLUTCH

1) Lubricate with transmission fluid then install low-reverse clutch plates, starting with a flat steel plate, and alternating composition and flat steel plates until all clutch plates are installed. See LOW-REVERSE CLUTCH PLATE USAGE CHART. Install waved steel clutch plate on top of last flat steel plate.

2) Install low-reverse clutch housing-to-case spacer ring into case, then install low-reverse clutch housing assembly, aligning housing oil feed hole with case oil feed passage. *See Fig. 38*.

3) If housing does not seat past snap ring groove, proceed as follows: Install input drum and rear sun gear assembly into case and rotate back and forth to align roller clutch race and low-reverse clutch hub splines, then remove input drum and sun gear.

LOW-REVERSE CLUTCH PLATE USAGE CHART

Model Application	Flat Steel [1]	Composition
All Models	7 [2]	6

[1] – Plate thickness is 0.077" (1.96 mm).
[2] – Plus 1 WAVED steel plate 0.077" (1.96 mm) thick, installed last.

Fig. 38: Installing Low-Reverse Clutch Housing To Case Snap Ring

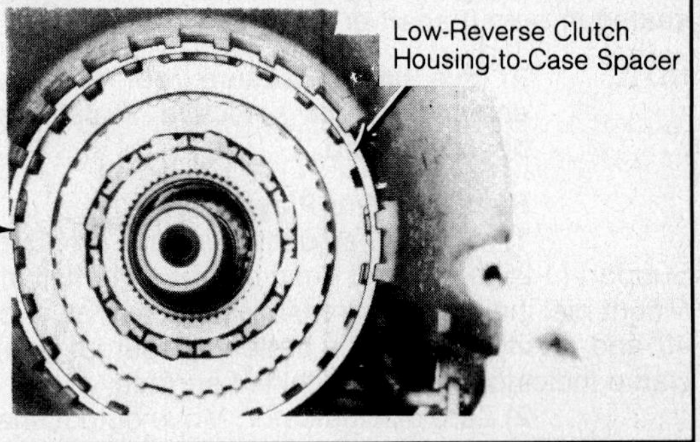

Align housing oil feed hole with case oil feed passage.

3) Repeat preceding step if low-reverse clutch housing still is not seated past case snap ring groove. With parts properly seated, install low-reverse clutch housing-to-case snap ring, with flat side of ring against housing (beveled side upward). Locate snap ring gap opposite parking pawl rod.

NOTE: It may be necessary to loosen adjusting screw on output shaft support tool to install low-reverse clutch housing-to-case snap ring.

REAR SUN GEAR, INPUT DRUM & FRONT SUN GEAR

Position thrust washer (four tangs) on input drum over sun gear end, align washer tangs with slots in drum, and retain with petroleum jelly. Install rear sun gear and input drum assembly into case. Install front sun gear, with drill spot or groove on face against input drum-to-rear sun gear snap ring. Install front sun gear-to-front carrier thrust bearing and race assembly with roller thrust bearing against front sun gear.

NOTE: The front sun gear-to-front carrier thrust bearing requires only one thrust race.

FRONT CARRIER

Position front carrier-to-front internal ring gear thrust bearing assembly on front carrier, with small diameter race against carrier and retain in place with petroleum jelly. Install front carrier and thrust bearing assembly into case, engaging front sun gear.

GENERAL MOTORS TURBO HYDRA-MATIC 200C (Cont.)

Fig. 39: Front Sun Gear Identification Marks

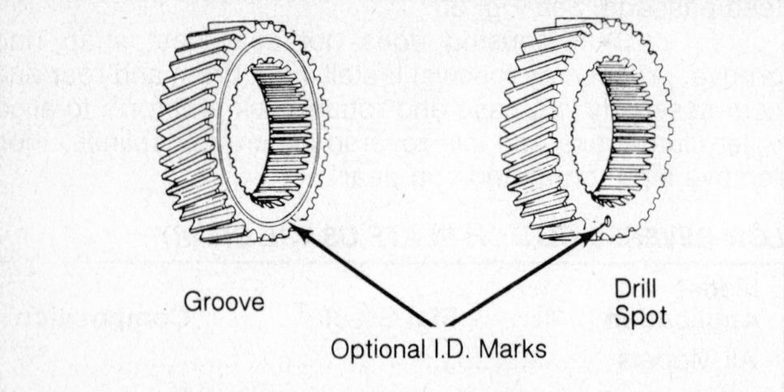

FRONT INTERNAL GEAR

Install thrust washer on front internal gear and retain with petroleum jelly, then install front internal gear into case. Install rear unit selective thrust washer on top of internal gear thrust washer, then install output shaft-to-thrust washer snap ring and make sure snap ring is fully seated in output shaft groove.

NOTE: At this time, measure rear unit end play to ensure correct selective thrust washer has been installed.

Rear Unit End Play Check

1) Loosen adjusting screw on Output Shaft Support (J-25013-5) and push output shaft fully downward. Mount dial indicator on transmission case as shown in *Fig. 40* and position indicator button on output shaft. Do not clamp indicator to any machined surface.

2) Zero dial indicator. Move output shaft upward by turning adjusting screw on output shaft support tool, until white or scribed line on tool sleeve begins to disappear. Read resulting end play on indicator.

3) Rear unit end play should be .004-.025" (.10-.64 mm). If not, selective thrust washer located between front internal gear thrust washer and output shaft snap ring must be changed. See REAR UNIT SELECTIVE THRUST WASHER CHART. Install correct thickness thrust washer (with I.D. number toward front of case), then reinstall output shaft snap ring making sure it is fully seated in groove.

4) Remove dial indicator assembly and loosen adjusting screw on output shaft support tool. Install output shaft-to-turbine shaft front selective thrust washer, locating it on output shaft and retain with petroleum jelly.

DIRECT CLUTCH, FORWARD CLUTCH & INTERMEDIATE BAND

NOTE: Align direct clutch composition clutch plate teeth one above the other to make forward clutch assembly easier to install.

1) Position direct clutch over hole in bench with clutch plate end upward. Make sure forward clutch-to-direct clutch thrust washer is still in place on forward clutch, then install forward clutch (turbine shaft first) into direct clutch. Hold direct clutch housing and rotate forward clutch back and forth until forward clutch is seated.

NOTE: When properly seated, end of forward clutch drum will be approximately 5/8" (15.88 mm) from tang end of direct clutch housing.

2) Position intermediate band into case, locating band apply lug and anchor pin lug in case slots. Install direct and forward clutch assemblies into case as a unit, rotating into position.

Fig. 40: Checking Rear Unit End Play

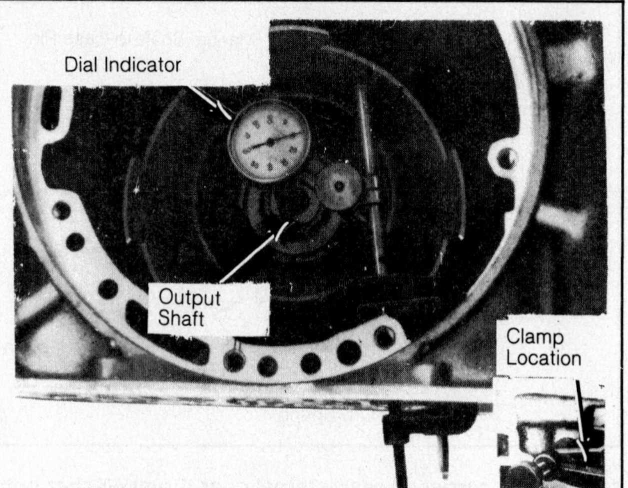

Dial indicator is located on output shaft.

REAR UNIT SELECTIVE THRUST WASHER CHART

Washer Thickness In. (mm)	I.D. Number	I.D. Color
.114-.119 (2.90-3.01)	1	Orange
.121-.126 (3.08-3.19)	2	White
.128-.133 (3.26-3.37)	3	Yellow
.135-.140 (3.44-3.55)	4	Blue
.143-.147 (3.62-3.73)	5	Red
.150-.154 (3.80-3.91)	6	Brown
.157-.161 (3.98-4.09)	7	Green
.164-.168 (4.16-4.27)	8	Black
1.71-.175 (4.34-4.45)	9	Purple

Fig. 41: Checking Forward Clutch Engagement

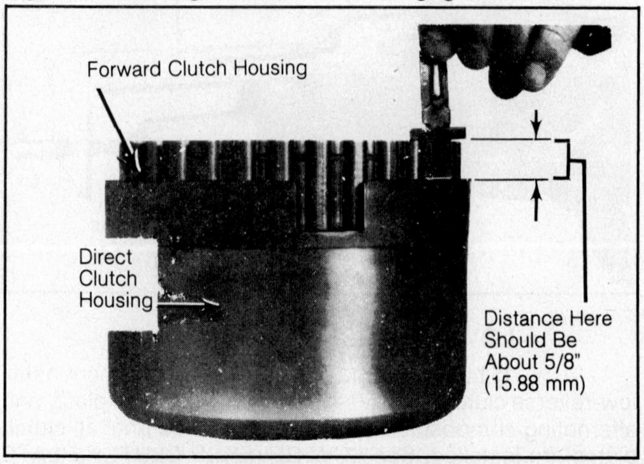

GENERAL MOTORS TURBO HYDRA-MATIC 200C (Cont.)

Fig. 42: Checking for Proper Installation of Direct and Forward Clutch Assemblies

Assembly must be completely seated before measuring.

NOTE: **When correctly seated, the direct clutch housing will be approximately 1 5/16" (33.34 mm) from pump face in case.**

OIL PUMP

1) Install new pump-to-case gasket on pump and retain with petroleum jelly. Install 2 pump-to-case alignment pins in case, opposite each other.

NOTE: **Before installing pump, ensure intermediate band anchor pin lug is aligned with band anchor pin hole in case.**

2) Install pump assembly and finger start pump-to-case bolts and new washers, except one bolt which will be used to make front unit end play check.

CAUTION: **If turbine shaft cannot be rotated as pump is pulled into place, forward or direct clutch housings are not properly indexed with all clutch plates. This condition must be corrected before pump is pulled fully into place.**

3) Remove alignment pins and install 2 pump attaching bolts and new washers. Tighten pump-to-case bolts evenly and make sure turbine shaft rotates freely.

Front Unit End Play Check

1) With transmission in vertical position (pump side up), install an 11" long bolt into pump attaching bolt hole. Push turbine shaft downward.

NOTE: **Output Shaft Support (J-25013-5 and J-25013-1) should still be attached to rear of transmission; if not, reinstall using procedure given in Roller Clutch and Rear Carrier section of TRANSMISSION REASSEMBLY.**

2) Install End Play Gauging Fixture and Adapter (J-24773 and J-25022) on end of turbine shaft. *See Fig. 43.* Mount dial indicator on bolt and position indicator button against cap nut of gauging fixture.

3) Move output shaft upward by turning adjusting screw on output shaft support tool until white or scribed line on sleeve begins to disappear, then zero dial indicator. Pull turbine shaft upward and read end play on indicator. Front unit end play should be .022-.051" (.56-1.30 mm).

Fig. 43: Checking Front Unit End Play

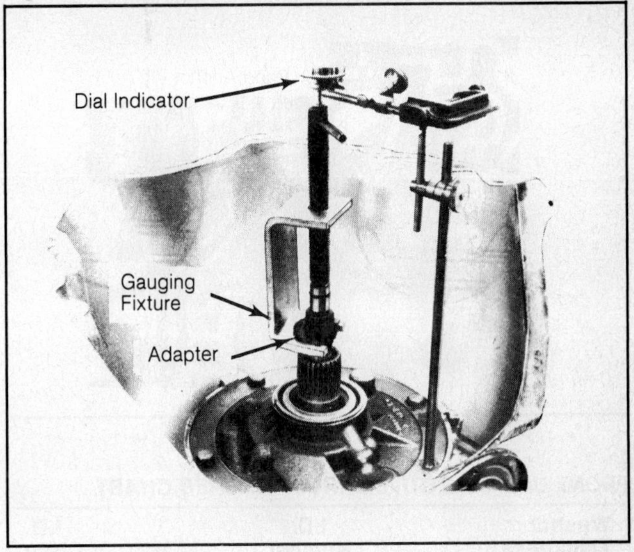

4) Selective thrust washer controlling front unit end play is located between output shaft and turbine shaft. If more or less washer thickness is required to bring end play within specifications, remove oil pump and forward and direct clutch assemblies, and install correct thickness washer on end of output shaft. See FRONT UNIT SELECTIVE THRUST WASHER CHART.

5) Remove front unit end play checking tools. Install remaining pump-to-case bolt and tighten. Remove output shaft support.

GOVERNOR

1) If removed, install new seal ring on governor shaft and place seal ring end into governor cover to size seal. Lubricate seal with petroleum jelly. Lubricate and install 2 new seal rings on governor cover.

NOTE: **Make sure 2 check balls are in governor before installation.**

2) Install governor assembly (seal end first) into cover. Install governor assembly and cover into case, aligning governor shaft with shaft hole in case. Rotate assembly and output shaft slightly to ease installation. Install governor retaining ring and align ring gap with an end showing in case slot.

NOTE: **If retaining ring cannot be installed, governor shaft is not aligned with case hole. Also, governor cover fits tight in case bore the last 1/16" (1.59 mm).**

BAND ANCHOR PIN & INTERMEDIATE SERVO

Install anchor pin (stem end first) into case, making sure stem locates in hole of intermediate band lug. Install servo assembly into case and make sure tapered end of band apply pin is properly located against band apply lug. Compress servo cover and install retaining ring. Align ring gap with an end showing in case slot.

GENERAL MOTORS TURBO HYDRA-MATIC 200C (Cont.)

Fig. 44: Installing Intermediate Band Anchor Pin

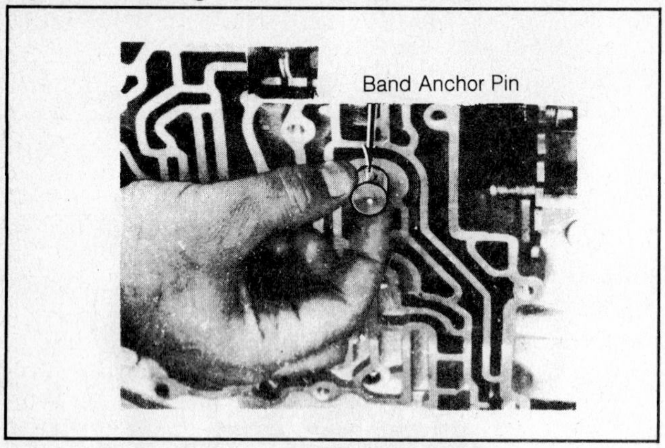

Fig. 45: Installing Low-Reverse Clutch Housing to Case Cup Plug and Seal Assembly

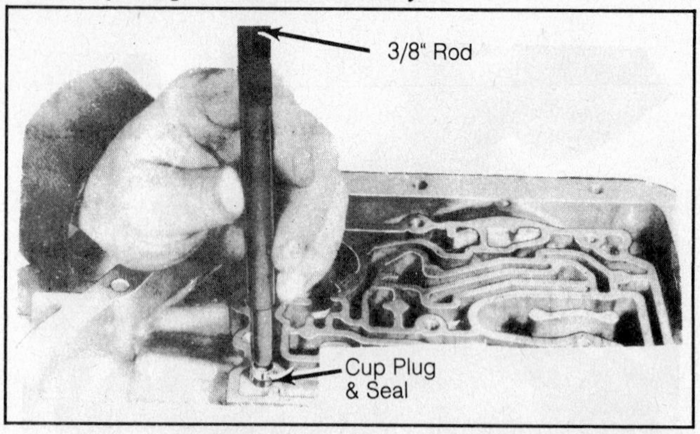

FRONT UNIT SELECTIVE THRUST WASHER CHART

Washer Thickness In. (mm)	I.D. Number	I.D. Color
.065-.070 (1.66-1.77)	1	
.070-.075 (1.79-1.90)	2	
.076-.080 (1.92-2.03)	3	Black
.081-.085 (2.05-2.16)	4	Light Green
.086-.090 (2.18-2.29)	5	Scarlet
.091-.095 (2.31-2.42)	6	Purple
.096-.100 (2.44-2.55)	7	Cocoa Brown
.101-.106 (2.57-2.68)	8	Orange
.106-.111 (2.72-2.81)	9	Yellow
.111-.116 (2.83-2.94)	10	Light Blue
.117-.121 (2.96-3.07)	11	Blue
.122-.126 (3.09-3.20)	12	
.127-.131 (3.22-3.33)	13	Pink
.132-.136 (3.35-3.46)	14	Green
.137-.141 (3.48-3.59)	15	Gray

VALVE BODY

1) Install new low-reverse clutch housing-to-case cup plug and seal assembly, with seal end first, into hole in case. *See Fig. 45*. Using a 3/8" diameter metal rod and hammer, drive plug and seal assembly into case until it seats against low-reverse clutch housing.

2) Lubricate with petroleum jelly and install new "O" ring seal on torque converter clutch electrical connector. Connect solenoid lead wire to electrical connector. Install connector into case with lock tabs facing into case and locator tab in notch on side of case.

3) Install 1-2 accumulator spring into case pocket. Install fifth check ball into case. *See Fig. 4*. Install two guide pins into case to align valve body parts. Install remaining four check balls into ball seat pockets in valve body and retain with petroleum jelly. *See Fig. 14*.

4) Position valve body-to-spacer plate gasket (marked "VB") on valve body, then place spacer plate on top of gasket. Place spacer plate-to-case gasket (marked "C") on top of spacer plate.

5) Insert 2 valve body attaching bolts through valve body, gaskets and spacer plate, then install valve body assembly, aligning manual valve with detent lever pin.

NOTE: **Make sure check balls, 1-2 accumulator piston and manual valve do not fall out during valve body installation.**

6) Start valve body attaching bolts, except throttle lever, bracket assembly and oil screen attaching bolts. Remove guide pins and replace with bolts and inside manual detent roller and spring assembly, locating tang in valve body and roller on inside detent lever.

7) If removed, install spring on top of throttle lever and bracket assembly lifter, then place lifter and spring into throttle bracket. Install link on throttle lever, making sure link is hooked. *See Fig. 46*.

Fig. 46: Throttle Lever and Bracket Assembly

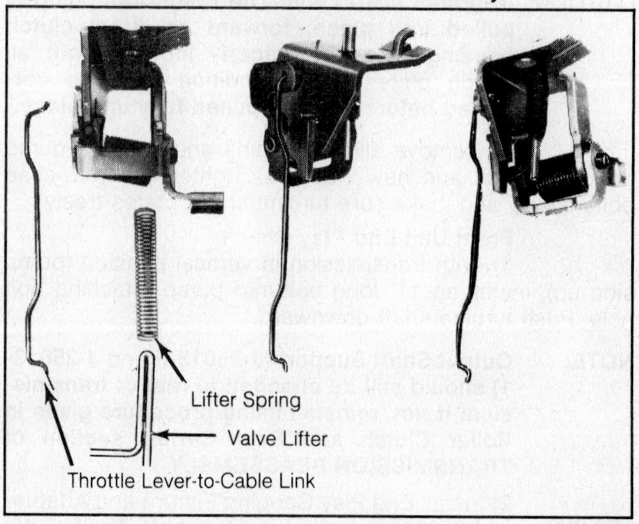

8) Install lever and bracket assembly, locating slot in bracket with coiled pin, aligning lifter through valve body hole and link through T.V. linkage case bore. Install

GENERAL MOTORS TURBO HYDRA-MATIC 200C (Cont.)

Fig. 47: Cutaway View of Transmission Showing Location of Thrust Washers, Thrust Bearings and Bushings

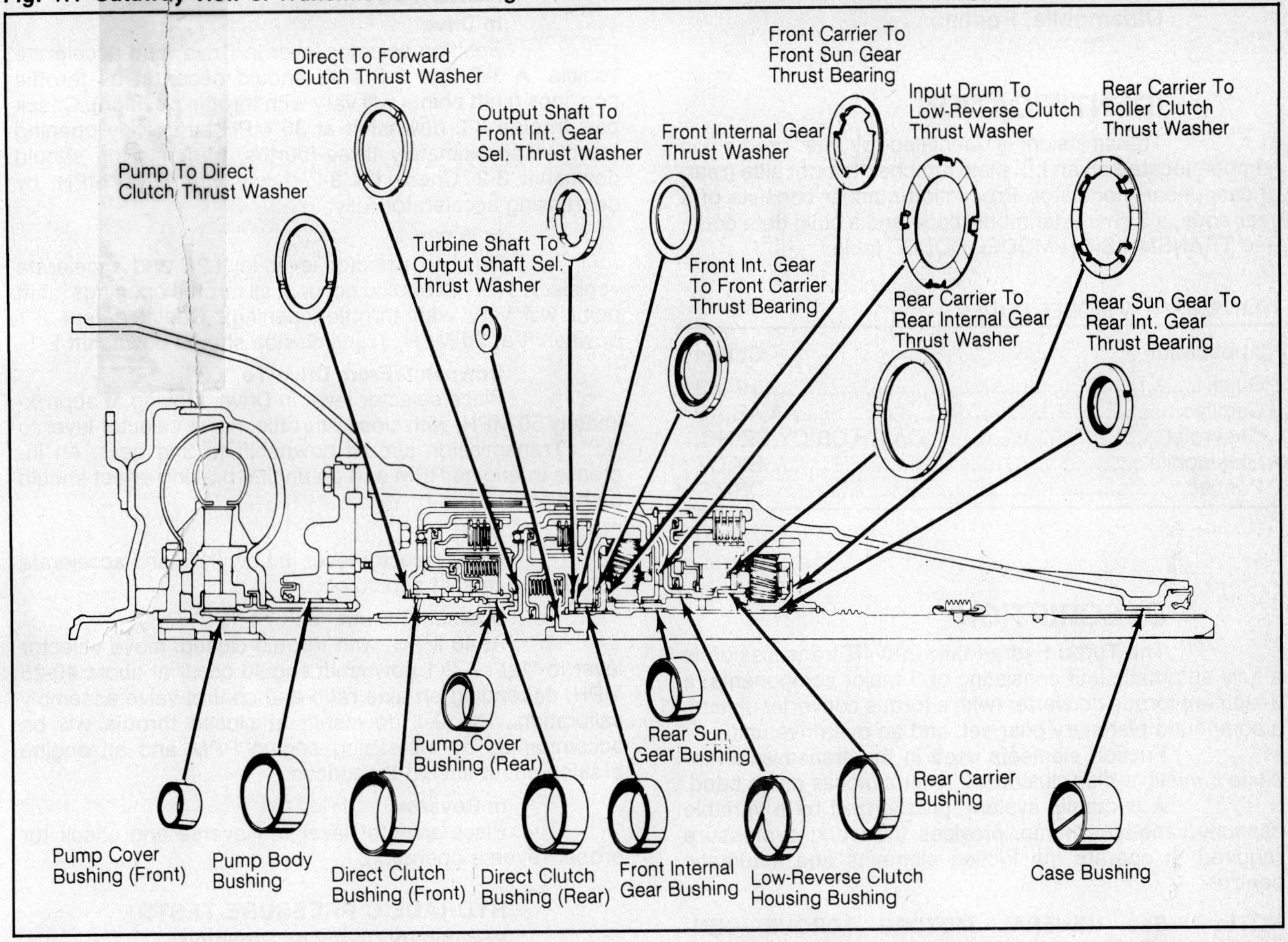

attaching bolts. Tighten all valve body attaching bolts evenly.

9) On diesel models, install governor pressure switch using a 1 1/16" oil pressure sending unit socket. Connect long solenoid lead wire to governor pressure switch terminal. Press solenoid lead wires into wire clip.

OIL SCREEN, OIL PAN & SPEEDOMETER DRIVEN GEAR

Install new screen gasket on oil screen, retain with petroleum jelly, then install screen on valve body and install and tighten attaching bolts. Position new pan gasket on case, install oil pan and attaching bolts and tighten. If necessary, install new "O" ring seal on speedometer driven gear housing, install housing into case, then install retainer and attaching bolt, aligning slot in housing with retainer.

TORQUE CONVERTER

Install torque converter into pump assembly. Ensure converter hub drive slots are fully engaged with pump drive gear tangs. Converter must be fully installed towards rear of transmission.

NOTE: **When properly installed, the distance between engine mounting face of transmission case and front face of converter cover drive lugs will be at least 1".**

TIGHTENING SPECIFICATIONS

Application	Ft. Lbs. (N.m)
Converter-to Flywheel	41-52 (55-70)
Manual Shaft-to-Detent Lever	20-25 (27-34)
Pump Body-to-Pump Cover	15-20 (20-27)
Pump-to-Case	15-20 (20-27)
Park Lock Bracket-to-Case	15-20 (20-27)
Transmission-to-Engine	
V6 (2.8L)	55 (75)
All Others	35 (47)
	INCH Lbs. (N.m)
Governor Pressure Switch (Diesel)	62-124 (7-14)
Line Pressure Take Off	62-124 (7-14)
Oil Pan-to-Case	124-160 (14-18)
Oil Screen-to-Case	115-151 (13-17)
Speedo Driven Gear Retainer-to-Case	71-124 (8-14)
Throttle Lever Bracket-to-Case	115-151 (13-17)
T.C.C. Solenoid-to-Pump	27-44 (3-5)
Valve Body-to-Case	115-151 (13-17)

GENERAL MOTORS TURBO HYDRA-MATIC 200-4R

Buick, Cadillac, Chevrolet, Oldsmobile, Pontiac

IDENTIFICATION

Transmission is identified by the production number, located on an I.D. plate attached to right side (rear) of case, near modulator. Production number consists of a year code, a 2 character model code and a build date code. See TRANSMISSION MODEL CODES table.

TRANSMISSION MODEL CODES

Application	Codes
Buick	HF,KJ
Cadillac	AA,AB,AP
Chevrolet	CA,CH,CR,CY,CZ,HC,
Oldsmobile	BY,CZ
Pontiac	CR,KC

DESCRIPTION

The Turbo Hydra-Matic 200-4R transmission is a fully automatic unit consisting of 3 major components; a 3-element torque converter (with a torque converter clutch), a compound planetary gear set, and an overdrive unit.

Friction elements used in this transmission include 5 multiple-disc clutches, 2 roller clutches and a band.

A hydraulic system, pressurized by a variable capacity vane-type pump, provides the working pressure required to operate the friction elements and automatic controls.

NOTE: **See GENERAL MOTORS TORQUE CONVERTER CLUTCH article in this section for information on the converter clutch system used in the THM 200-4R.**

LUBRICATION & ADJUSTMENTS

See appropriate AUTOMATIC TRANSMISSION SERVICING article in DOMESTIC GENERAL SERVICING section.

TROUBLE SHOOTING

See appropriate AUTOMATIC TRANSMISSION TROUBLE SHOOTING article in DOMESTIC GENERAL SERVICING section.

TESTING

LEAKAGE

See procedure FOR G.M. TURBO HYDRA-MATIC 400.

ROAD TEST

In Drive

Position selector lever in Drive, and accelerate vehicle. A 1-2 and 2-3 shift should occur at all throttle positions (shift points will vary with throttle position). Check part throttle 3-2 downshift at 30 MPH by quickly opening throttle approximately three-fourths, transmission should downshift 3-2. Check for 3-2 downshifts at 50 MPH, by depressing accelerator fully.

In "L2"

Position selector lever in "L2", and accelerate vehicle. A 1-2 shift should occur at all throttle openings (shift point will vary with throttle opening). Check detent 2-1 downshift at 20 MPH. Transmission should downshift 2-1.

Downshift From Drive To "L2"

Place selector lever in Drive. Moving at approximately 50 MPH, with closed throttle, move selector lever to "L2". Transmission should downshift to 2nd gear. An increase in engine RPM and an engine braking effect should be noticed.

In ("L1")

Place selector lever in Low ("1"), and accelerate vehicle. No upshift should occur.

Downshift From "L2" To "L1"

At 40 MPH, with throttle closed, move selector lever to "1st". A 2-1 downshift should occur at about 40-25 MPH, depending on axle ratio and control valve assembly calibration. The 2-1 downshift at closed throttle will be accompanied by increasing engine RPM and an engine braking effect should be noticed.

In Reverse

Place selector lever in Reverse and check for proper reverse operation.

HYDRAULIC PRESSURE TESTS

Preliminary Checking Procedure

Prior to making control pressure test: check transmission fluid level, check and adjust T.V. cable, check and adjust outside manual linkage, check engine tune, install oil pressure gauge to transmission and connect tachometer to engine.

CAUTION: **When performing T.V. pressure checks, DO NOT sustain engine test speed more than 2 minutes.**

Minimum T.V. Pressure Check

With T.V. cable adjusted to specifications and brakes applied, check line pressure in selector lever positions and at 1000 RPM. See CONTROL PRESSURE SPECIFICATIONS table.

Maximum T.V. Pressure Check

With T.V. cable held at in fully extended position, and brakes applied, check for correct line pressure in selector lever positions and at 1000 RPM. See CONTROL PRESSURE SPECIFICATIONS table.

PRESSURE TEST RESULTS

High or Low Pressures

- T.V. cable out of adjustment, binding, unhooked, broken or wrong link.
- Throttle lever and bracket assembly binding, unhooked or mispositioned.
- Throttle valve or plunger valve binding.

GENERAL MOTORS TURBO HYDRA-MATIC 200-4R (Cont.)

Fig. 1: Cutaway View of Turbo Hydra-Matic 200-4R Transmission

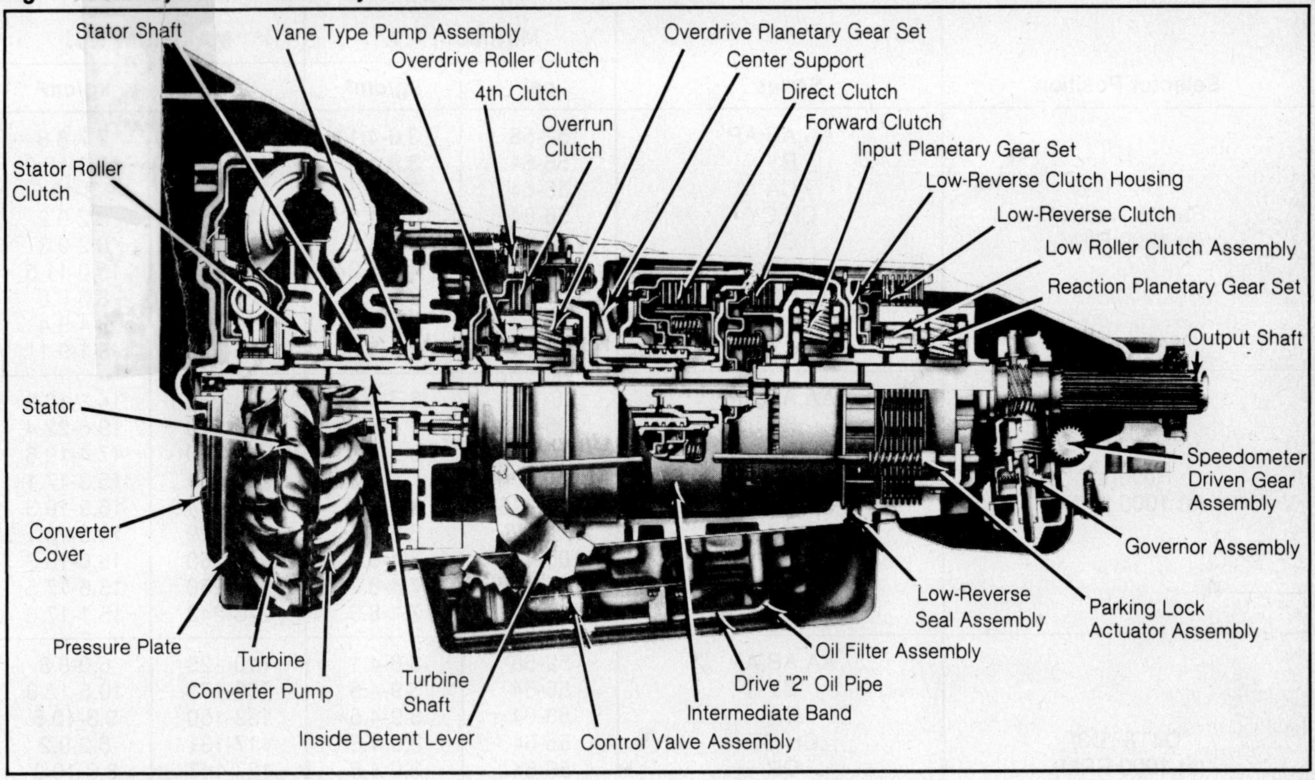

- Pressure regulator valve binding.
- T.V. Boost valve binding or wrong valve installed (causing low oil pressure only).
- Reverse Boost valve binding.
- Manual valve unhooked, or mispositioned.
- Pressure relief valve ball missing or spring damaged.
- Oil pump slide stuck, or slide seal missing or damaged.
- Pump decrease air bleed orifice missing or damaged (causing low oil pressure only).
- Pump decrease air bleed orifice plugged (causing low oil pressure only).
- T.V. Limit valve binding.
- Line Bias valve binding in open position (causing high oil pressure).
- Line Bias valve binding in closed position (causing low oil pressure).

NOTE: Control valve assembly spacer plate and case should be closely inspected for corroded orifices and passages.

CLUTCH AND BAND APPLICATION CHART (ELEMENTS IN USE)

Selector Lever Position	Overrun Clutch	Intermediate Band	Overdrive Roller Clutch	Direct Clutch	Low Roller Clutch	4th Clutch	Forward Clutch	Low-Reverse Clutch
D - DRIVE								
1st Gear			X		X		X	
2nd Gear		X	X				X	
3rd Gear			X	X			X	
Overdrive				X	X	X		
"3" - MANUAL 3rd	X			X			X	
"L2" - MANUAL 2nd	X	X					X	
"L1" - MANUAL LOW	X						X	X
"R" - REVERSE			X	X				X
NEUTRAL or PARK			X					

GENERAL MOTORS TURBO HYDRA-MATIC 200-4R (Cont.)

CONTROL PRESSURE SPECIFICATIONS

Selector Position	Series [1]	MINIMUM T.V.		MAXIMUM T.V.	
		psi	kg/cm²	psi	kg/cm²
Park & Neutral (at 1000 RPM)	AA,AB,AP	52-58	3.6-4.1	110-125	7.7-8.8
	BY	56-64	3.9-4.5	150-171	10.5-12.0
	CA	56-64	3.9-4.5	133-150	9.3-10.5
	CH,CY	56-64	3.9-4.5	117-131	8.2-9.2
	CR	56-64	3.9-4.5	117-132	8.2-9.3
	CZ	65-75	4.6-5.3	142-163	10.0-11.5
	HC	56-64	3.9-4.5	123-140	8.6-9.8
	HF	56-64	3.9-4.5	119-134	8.4-9.4
	KC,KJ	56-64	3.9-4.5	116-130	8.1-9.1
Reverse (at 1000 RPM)	AA,AB,AP	96-109	6.7-7.7	204-233	14.3-16.3
	BY	105-118	7.4-8.3	279-319	19.6-22.4
	CA	105-118	7.4-8.3	248-280	17.4-19.6
	CH,CY	105-118	7.4-8.3	218-244	15.3-17.1
	CR	105-118	7.4-8.3	240-274	16.9-19.3
	CZ	92-106	6.5-7.4	200-229	14.0-16.1
	HC	105-118	7.4-8.3	228-260	16.0-18.3
	HF	105-118	7.4-8.3	222-250	15.6-17.5
	KC,KJ	105-118	7.4-8.3	215-242	15.1-17.0
"D4" & "D3" (at 1000 RPM)	AA,AB,AP	52-58	3.6-4.1	110-125	6.0-8.8
	BY	56-64	3.9-4.5	150-171	10.5-12.0
	CA	56-64	3.9-4.5	133-150	9.3-10.5
	CH,CY	56-64	3.9-4.5	117-131	8.2-9.2
	CR	56-64	3.9-4.5	127-147	8.9-10.3
	CZ	65-75	4.6-5.3	142-163	10.0-11.5
	HC	56-64	3.9-4.5	123-140	8.6-9.8
	HF	56-64	3.9-4.5	119-134	8.4-9.4
	KC,KJ	56-64	3.9-4.5	116-130	8.1-9.1
"D2" & "D1" (at 1000 RPM)	AA,AB,AP,	112-127	7.9-8.9	112-127	7.9-8.9
	BY,CA,CH,CR,CY	123-138	8.6-9.7	123-138	8.6-9.7
	CZ	132-152	9.3-10.7	132-152	9.3-10.7
	HC,HF,KC,KJ	123-138	8.6-9.7	123-138	8.6-9.7

[1] – Information on 5CY series transaxle not available from manufacturer at time of publication.

SERVICE (IN VEHICLE)

The following components can be removed from transmission without removing transmission from vehicle. For removal and installation procedures for these components, see TRANSMISSION DISASSEMBLY in this article.

- Extention Housing Seal
- Governor Assembly
- Intermediate Servo Piston Assembly
- Oil Pan and Screen
- Control Valve Assembly
- Check Balls and Valve Body Spacer Plate and Gaskets
- Pressure Regulator Parts
- Inside Detent/Selector Lever
- Manual Detent Roller and Spring Assembly
- Throttle Lever and Bracket Assembly
- T.V. Cable and "O" Ring
- T.V. Boost Valve and Bushing
- Parking Pawl Actuator Rod, Bracket and Pawl
- Manual Shaft and Seal
- Manual Valve and Link
- Rear Seal
- 1-2 Accumulator Assembly
- 3-4 Accumulator Assembly
- Low/Reverse Cup Plug
- Reverse Boost Valve and Bushing
- Stop Valve
- Intermediate Band Anchor Pin
- 4-3 Pressure Switch
- 4th Clutch Pressure Switch
- Speedometer Driven Gear Assembly
- Converter Clutch Valve and Spring
- Converter Clutch Solenoid
- Solenoid Wire Clips
- Electrical Connectors
- Cooler Fittings
- Oil Filter Pipe and "O" Ring

REMOVAL & INSTALLATION

TRANSMISSION

See appropriate AUTOMATIC TRANSMISSION REMOVAL article in DOMESTIC GENERAL SERVICING section.

NOTE: **See GENERAL MOTORS TORQUE CONVERTER CLUTCH article in this section for information on the converter clutch system used in the THM 200-4R.**

GENERAL MOTORS TURBO HYDRA-MATIC 200-4R (Cont.)

TRANSMISSION DISASSEMBLY

INPUT SHAFT END PLAY

See procedure FOR G.M. TURBO HYDRA-MATIC 400.

EXTERNAL PARTS

1) Mount transmission in a holding fixture and remove torque converter. Rotate transmission so that oil pan is facing up. Remove oil pan and gasket. Remove oil filter intake pipe and "O" rings. "O" rings may be located in pump bore.

2) Disconnect wire leads at electrical connector and pressure switches. *See Fig. 2.* Using a 3/4" box wrench to compress connector tangs, withdraw electrical connector and "O" ring from case. Remove converter clutch solenoid assembly bolts, clips and solenoid.

Fig. 2: Bottom View of Transmission Case

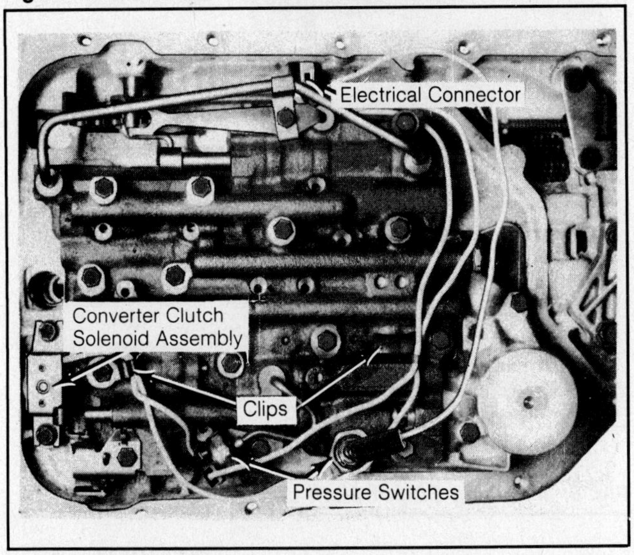

3) Using care not to bend throttle lever link, remove throttle lever and bracket assembly. T.V. exhaust valve lifter and spring may separate from lever and bracket assembly. Remove manual detent roller and spring assembly, signal (Drive "2") oil pipe retaining clip and oil pipe.

4) Remove 4-3 pressure switch and retaining bolt, then remove remaining valve body attaching bolts. Hold manual valve in bore and carefully lift control valve assembly from case. Care must be taken as 3 check balls are located on top of spacer plate-to-valve body gasket. Remove check balls.

5) Remove 1-2 accumulator housing, then withdraw spring, gasket, plate and piston from housing. It may be necessary to apply low air pressure (approximately 3 psi) to orifice in accumulator housing passage to remove piston.

6) Remove control valve assembly gaskets and spacer plate from transmission case. Withdraw 3-4 accumulator spring, piston and pin from bore in case. It may be necessary to apply low air pressure (approximately 3 psi) to orifice in case core passage to remove piston. *See Fig. 3.*

7) Remove 8 check balls from core passages in case. *See Fig. 4.* Remove governor cover and gasket from case, then remove governor assembly while rotating output shaft counterclockwise to ease removal.

Fig. 3: View of Case Core Passage

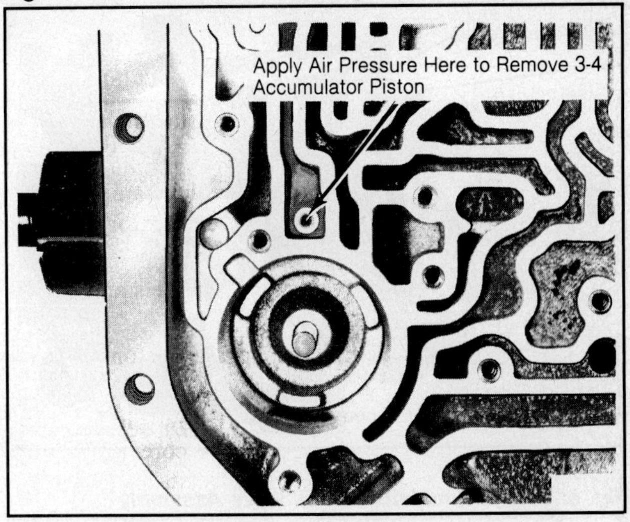

Use approximately 3 psi to remove piston.

Fig. 4: Removing Check Balls From Case

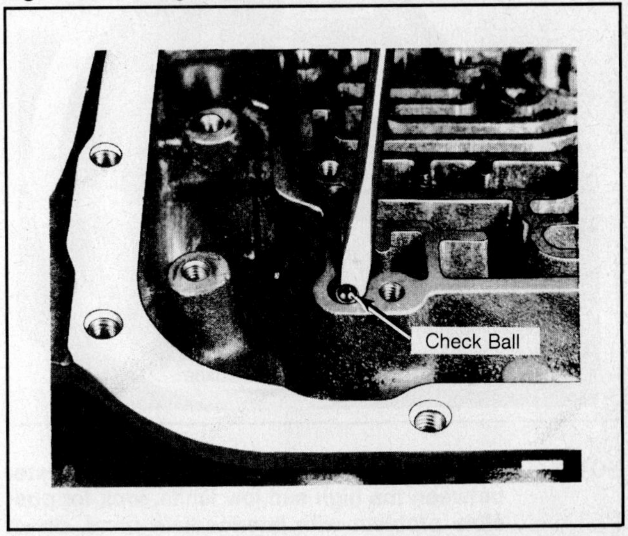

CAUTION: Do not use pliers to remove governor assembly.

8) Pry intermediate servo cover retaining ring from groove in case. Remove servo cover and discard seal ring. Remove servo piston and band apply pin from bore in case.

NOTE: Before continuing with Transmission Disassembly, check for proper intermediate band apply pin as follows.

Intermediate Band Apply Pin Selection

1) Install Band Apply Pin Selection Gauge (J-25014-2) in intermediate servo bore and retain with servo cover retaining ring, aligning ring with gap at case slot. Install Selection Gauge Tapered Pin (J-25014-1) into gauge. *See Fig. 5.*

NOTE: Ensure tapered pin end is properly located against band apply lug. Also, ensure band anchor pin is properly located in case and band anchor lug.

GENERAL MOTORS TURBO HYDRA-MATIC 200-4R (Cont.)

Fig. 5: Intermediate Band Apply Pin Selection

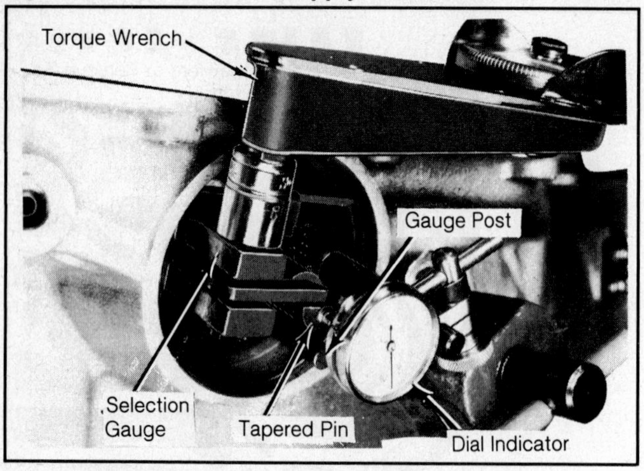

Fig. 6: 3rd Accumulator Check Valve Assembly

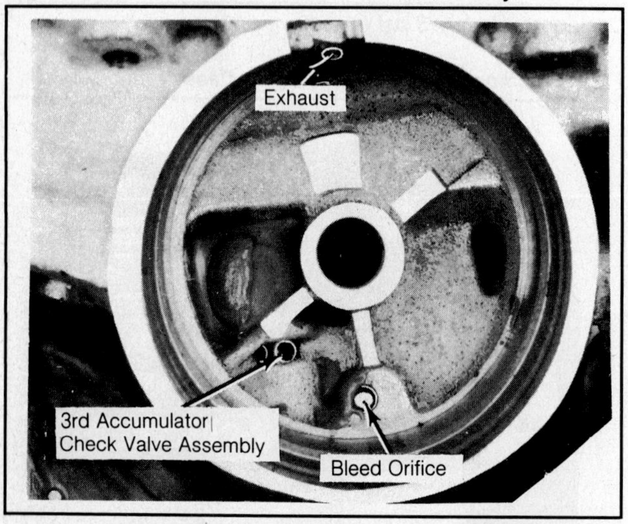

NOTE: If band selection tapered pin does not register between the high and low limits, look for possible problem with intermediate band, direct clutch housing or transmission case.

2) Install dial indicator and position indicator point on top of selection gauge post. Set indicator to zero. Ensure selection gauge is squarely seated against servo retaining ring and stepped side of tapered pin is aligned with torquing arm of gauge.

NOTE: Dial indicator travel is reversed, making the indicator readings backwards. On an indicator that ranges from 0-100, a .020" (.51 mm) travel will read .080" (2.03 mm), a .060" (1.52 mm) travel will read .040" (1.02 mm).

INTERMEDIATE BAND APPLY PIN SELECTION

Indicator Reading Inches (mm)	Apply Pin I.D.
0-.029 (0-.72)	1 Groove
.029-.057 (.72-1.44)	2 Grooves
.057-.086 (1.44-2.16)	3 Grooves
.086-.114 (2.16-2.88)	None

3rd Accumulator Check Valve Replacement

1) Inspect 3rd accumulator check valve for the following conditions: Missing check ball, check ball binding or stuck in tube, oil feed slot in tube missing or restricted, improperly assembled, loose fitting or not fully seated in case. If check valve requires replacement, go to step **2)**.

2) Using a No. 4 screw extractor, remove check valve assembly from case by turning and pulling straight out. *See Fig. 7.*

3) Install new check valve assembly, small end first, into case. Position oil feed slot in tube so it faces servo. Using a 3/8" diameter metal rod and hammer, drive assembly until it is seated in case hole.

Fig. 7: Removing 3rd Accumulator Check Valve Assembly

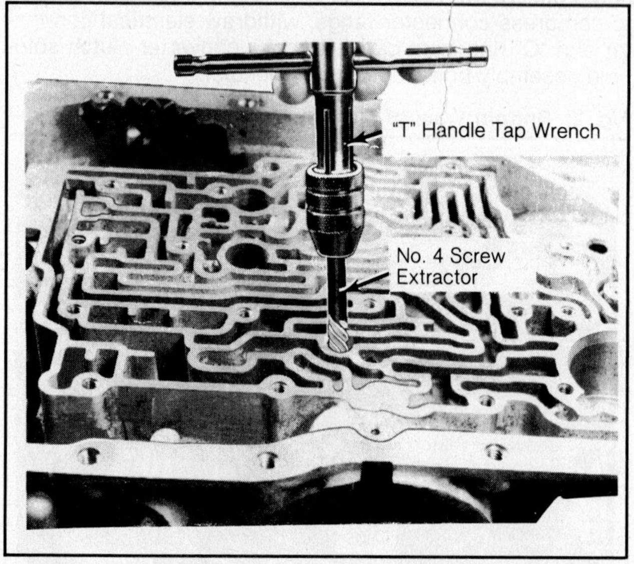

Fig. 8: Installing Output Shaft Loader

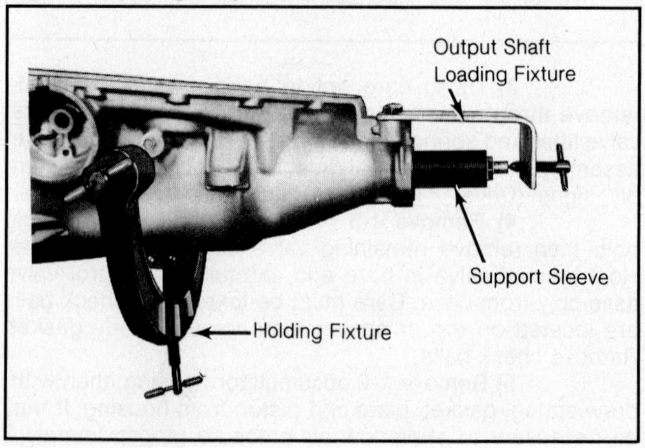

OVERDRIVE UNIT PARTS

NOTE: Prior to removing overdrive unit parts, check overdrive unit end play to determine correct end play thrust washer for use during reassembly.

Overdrive End Play

1) Install Output Shaft Loading Fixture (J-29332) and Support Sleeve (J-25013-1) on output shaft. *See Fig. 8.* Turn transmission to vertical position, pump side up.

GENERAL MOTORS TURBO HYDRA-MATIC 200-4R (Cont.)

2) Remove one pump-to-case bolt and washer and install an 11" long bolt into pump bolt hole. Attach Overdrive End Play Checker (J-25022) and Oil Pump Remover (J-24773-5) to turbine shaft. *See Fig. 9.*

Fig. 9: Checking Overdrive Unit End Play

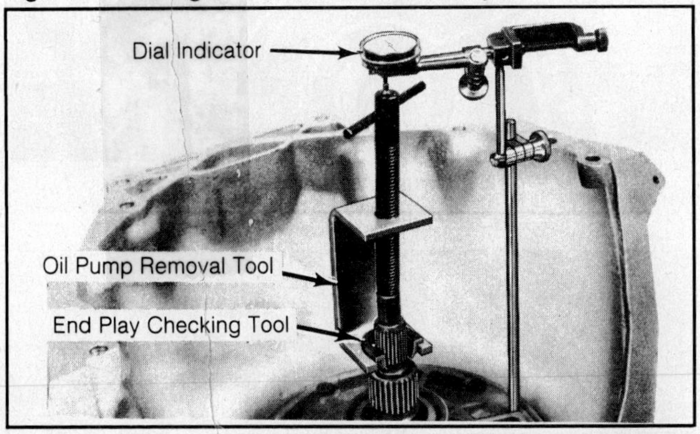

NOTE: **The following step must be performed to eliminate the tolerance difference between turbine shaft snap ring and overdrive carrier.**

3) Mount a dial indicator and clamp assembly on long bolt, positioning indicator point cap on top of pump remover. Lift upward on remover with approximately 3 lbs. force and zero indicator while maintaining the upward force.

4) With dial indicator zeroed, increase upward force to approximately 20 lbs. (9.1 kg) and read end play on indicator. Overdrive unit end play should be .004-.027" (.10-.69 mm). The selective thrust washer controlling this end play is located between pump cover and overdrive clutch housing. If more or less washer thickness is required to bring end play within specification, select correct washer. See OVERDRIVE UNIT END PLAY WASHER SELECTION chart.

OVERDRIVE UNIT END PLAY WASHER SELECTION

Washer Thickness	I.D. Number	I.D. Color
.167-.171"	0	Scarlet
.172-.176"	1	White
.177-.180"	2	Brown
.181-.185"	3	Grey
.186-.190"	4	Yellow
.191-.195"	5	Lt. Blue
.196-.200"	6	Purple
.201-.204"	7	Orange
.205-.209"	8	Green

Component Removal

1) If necessary, pry oil pump seal from pump. Remove pump-to-case bolts and washers. Install Oil Pump Remover (J-24773-A) on turbine shaft. *See Fig. 9.* Remove oil pump assembly from case. Remove pump-to-case gasket and tanged oil deflector plate located under pump.

2) Remove 4th clutch plate-to-case snap ring, then grasp turbine shaft and lift overdrive assembly and 4th clutch plates from case. Remove clutch plates from overdrive assembly and the remaining steel plate from case.

3) Remove overdrive internal gear-to-carrier thrust washer from inside internal gear. Remove internal gear and internal gear-to-support thrust washer from case.

4) Using a spring compressor, compress 4th clutch spring and retainer assembly. Remove support-to-clutch snap ring, spring and retainer. Remove compressor from retainer assembly. Lift 4th clutch piston from case.

FRONT UNIT PARTS

NOTE: **Prior to removing front unit parts, check front unit end play to determine correct thrust washer to install at reassembly.**

Front Unit End Play

1) Push forward clutch shaft downward, then install Forward And Direct Clutch Remover (J-29337) in end of shaft. Mount dial indicator and clamp assembly. *See Fig. 10.* Position indicator point on top of clutch remover.

NOTE: **Perform this check with output shaft loading fixture and support sleeve in place.**

Fig. 10: Checking Front Unit End Play

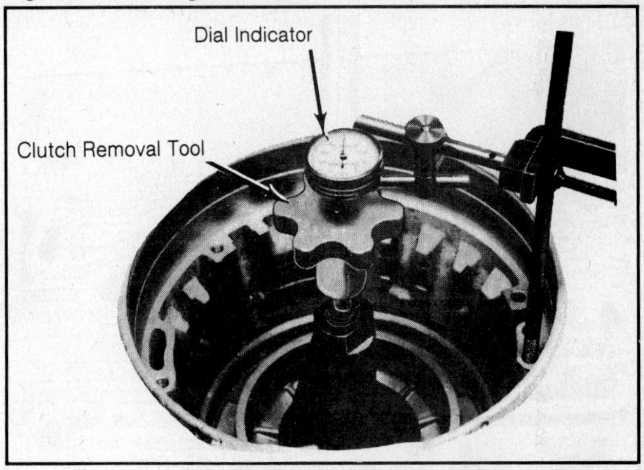

2) Move output shaft upward by turning adjusting screw on output shaft loading fixture. Move shaft upward until White or scribed line on support sleeve begins to disappear. Zero dial indicator.

3) Pull clutch remover upward and read resulting end play on dial indicator. Front unit end play should be .022-.051" (.56-1.30 mm). Selective thrust washer controlling this end play is located between output shaft and forward clutch shaft. If more or less washer thickness is required to bring end play within specification, select proper washer. See FRONT UNIT END PLAY WASHER SELECTION chart.

Component Removal

1) Remove 2 center support bolts. *See Fig. 11.* From inside case, remove center support beveled snap ring. Lift center support from case using Slide Hammer (J-7004) and Puller (J-29334-1). Remove center support/direct clutch thrust washer.

NOTE: **Center support/direct clutch thrust washer may be stuck to back of direct clutch.**

2) Install Direct And Forward Clutch Remover (J-29337) in end of forward clutch shaft. *See Fig. 10.* Pull direct and forward clutch assemblies from case. Separate direct clutch from forward clutch. Remove intermediate band assembly and band anchor pin from case. Remove output shaft/forward clutch shaft selective thrust washer.

GENERAL MOTORS TURBO HYDRA-MATIC 200-4R (Cont.)

FRONT UNIT END PLAY WASHER SELECTION

Washer Thickness	I.D. Number	I.D. Color
.065-.070"	1	.....
.070-.075"	2	.....
.076-.080"	3	Black
.081-.085"	4	Lt. Green
.086-.090"	5	Scarlet
.091-.095"	6	Purple
.096-.100"	7	Brown
.101-.106"	8	Orange
.106-.111"	9	Yellow
.111-.116"	10	Lt. Blue
.117-.121"	11	.....
.122-.126"	12	.....
.127-.131"	13	Pink
.132-.136"	14	Green
.137-.141"	15	Grey

Fig. 11: Removing Center Support Bolts

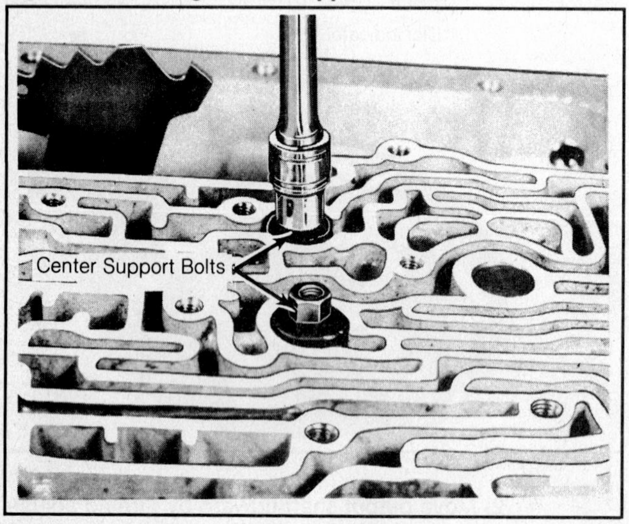

NOTE: The direct-to-forward clutch thrust washer may stick to end of direct clutch housing when separating clutch assemblies.

FRONT GEAR PARTS

NOTE: Prior to removing front gear parts, check rear unit end play to determine correct thrust washer to install at transmission reassembly.

Rear Unit End Play

1) Loosen adjusting screw on output shaft loading fixture (installed at overdrive end play check) and push output shaft downward. Install a "C" clamp on case. *See Fig. 12.* Mount a dial indicator and extension on "C" clamp.

2) Position dial indicator extension against end of output shaft and set indicator to zero. Move output shaft upward by turning screw on loading fixture until White or scribed line on support sleeve begins to disappear, then read indicator end play.

3) Rear unit end play should be .004-.025" (.10-.64 mm). Selective thrust washer controlling this end play is located between front internal gear thrust washer and output shaft snap ring. If more or less thrust washer thickness is required to bring end play within specification, select proper washer. REAR UNIT END PLAY WASHER SELECTION chart. Remove dial indicator and "C" clamp.

Fig. 12: Checking Rear Unit End Play

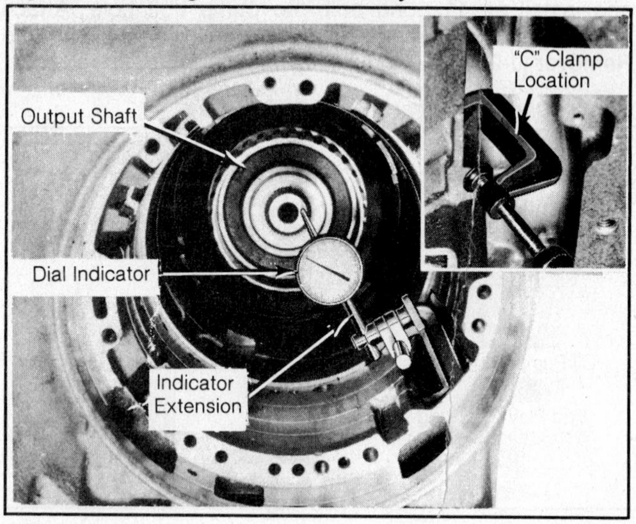

REAR UNIT END PLAY WASHER SELECTION

Washer Thickness	I.D. Number	I.D. Color
.097-.102"	0	.....
.114-.119"	1	Orange
.121-.126"	2	White
.128-.133"	3	Yellow
.135-.140"	4	Blue
.143-.147"	5	Red
.150-.154"	6	Brown
.157-.161"	7	Green
.164-.168"	8	Black
.171-.175"	9	Purple

Component Removal

1) Remove output shaft-to-selective washer snap ring, then lift front internal gear, rear selective washer and thrust washer from case and remove washers from front internal gear.

2) Remove front carrier assembly and front internal gear-to-front carrier thrust bearing assembly. If it did not come out with front carrier, remove front sun gear and sun gear-to-front carrier thrust bearing assembly.

Fig. 13: Removing Output Shaft Snap Ring

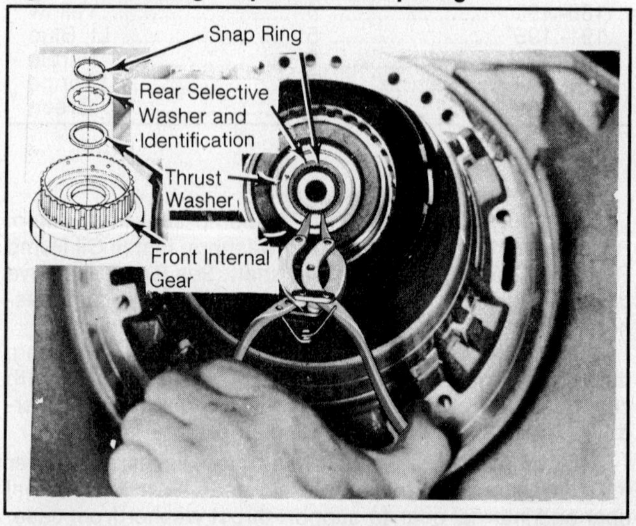

GENERAL MOTORS TURBO HYDRA-MATIC 200-4R (Cont.)

NOTE: **The front sun gear-to-front carrier thrust bearing requires only one race.**

3) Remove input drum and rear sun gear. Remove the 4-tanged input drum-to-reverse clutch housing thrust washer from rear of drum or front clutch housing.

4) Grind approximately 3/4" from end of a No. 4 screw extractor, then insert screw extractor into low/reverse clutch housing-to-case cup plug. Turn screw extractor 2 or 3 turns and pull out cup plug. Remove low/reverse clutch-to-case beveled snap ring. Lift clutch assembly from case. Remove low/reverse clutch housing-to-case spacer ring.

NOTE: **Do not reuse low/reverse clutch housing cup plug and seal assembly.**

Fig. 14: Removing Low/Reverse Clutch Housing Cup Plug

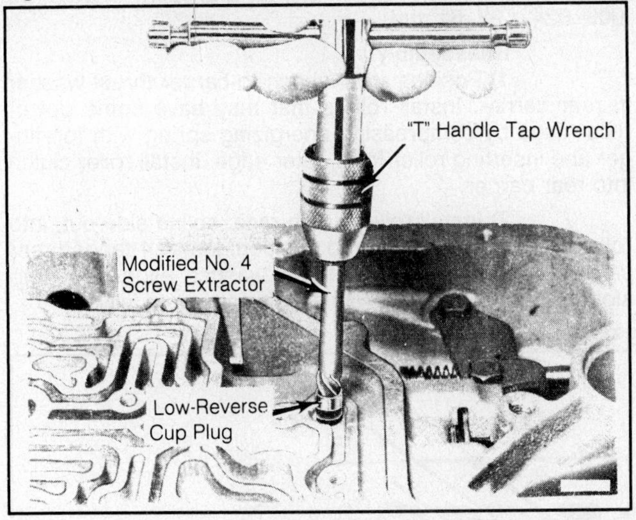

REAR GEAR PARTS

NOTE: **Governor assembly must be removed before removing rear gear parts.**

1) Grasp output shaft and lift out remaining rear unit parts and lay in a horizontal position. Remove roller clutch and rear carrier from output shaft. Remove the 4-tanged rear carrier-to-rear internal gear thrust washer from end of carrier or from inside rear internal gear.

2) Pull low/reverse clutch plates from output shaft. Remove rear internal gear-to-rear sun gear thrust bearing assembly from internal gear, then remove internal gear from output shaft. If necessary, remove rear oil seal from transmission case.

MANUAL SHAFT & PARKING PAWL PARTS

1) Turn transmission to a horizontal position, oil pan side up. If necessary, remove manual shaft and parking pawl linkage.

2) Remove hex nut securing inside detent lever to manual shaft. Remove parking lock actuator rod and inside detent lever. Remove manual shaft retaining pin from case and slide shaft out. If damaged, pry manual shaft oil seal from case.

3) Remove parking lock bracket. Remove parking pawl shaft retaining pin, then remove parking pawl cup plug using a No. 4 screw extractor with 3/4" ground from end. Using No. 4 screw extractor, remove parking pawl shaft from case. Remove parking pawl and spring.

Fig. 15: Removing Parking Pawl Cup Plug

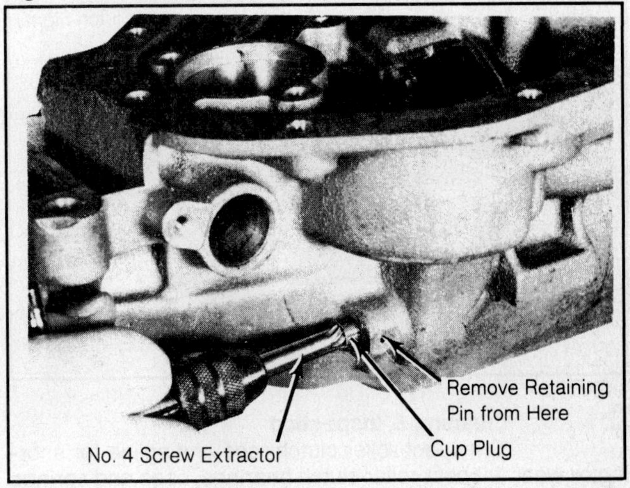

TORQUE CONVERTER

NOTE: **The torque converter is a sealed unit and cannot be disassembled for service.**

COMPONENT DISASSEMBLY & REASSEMBLY

TRANSMISSION CASE

Cleaning & Inspection

1) Inspect case assembly for damage, cracks, porosity or interconnected oil passages. Inspect orifice plug in intermediate servo bore. If plug requires replacement, install new plug, orifice end first, flush to slightly below top of plug hole.

2) Inspect case exhaust passages for restrictions. Inspect reverse clutch lugs, governor, intermediate servo bore, speedometer bore, and snap ring grooves for damage. Inspect all bolt holes for damage or stripped holes. Inspect case bushing for damage and scoring.

REAR GEAR PARTS

Cleaning & Inspection

1) Inspect output shaft journals, snap ring groove and splines for wear or damage. Check lubrication passages for damage or obstructions. Check governor drive gear for rough or damaged teeth.

2) Inspect rear internal gear splines, teeth and bearing surface for wear, cracks or damage. Inspect parking pawl lugs for cracks or damage. Thoroughly clean, air dry and inspect rear internal gear-to-rear sun gear thrust bearing assembly for pitted or rough conditions.

ROLLER CLUTCH & REAR CARRIER ASSEMBLY

Disassembly

Remove roller clutch inner race and lift roller clutch assembly from rear carrier. Remove rear carrier-to-clutch thrust washer (4 tangs) from rear of carrier and roller clutch-to-rear carrier thrust washer from inside carrier.

GENERAL MOTORS TURBO HYDRA-MATIC 200-4R (Cont.)

Fig. 16: Front View of Transmission Case Showing Oil Passages

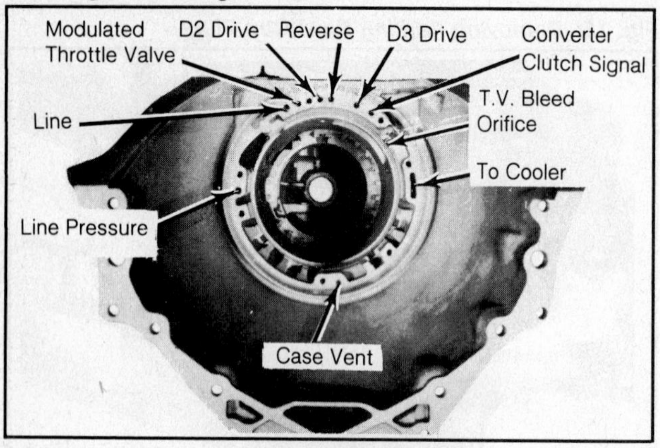

Cleaning & Inspection

1) Inspect roller clutch race and spline for scoring or wear. Inspect roller clutch bearings, cage and springs for damage or wear. Inspect thrust washers for signs of scoring or excessive wear and check tanged thrust washer for bent tangs.

2) Inspect rear carrier for damage to roller clutch cam ramps. Inspect bushing for damage and scoring. Inspect planet pinions for damage, rough bearings or tilt. Check pinion end play using a feeler gauge inserted between carrier and pinion gears. End play should be .009-.024" (.23-.61 mm).

Fig. 18: Exploded View of Roller Clutch and Rear Carrier Assembly

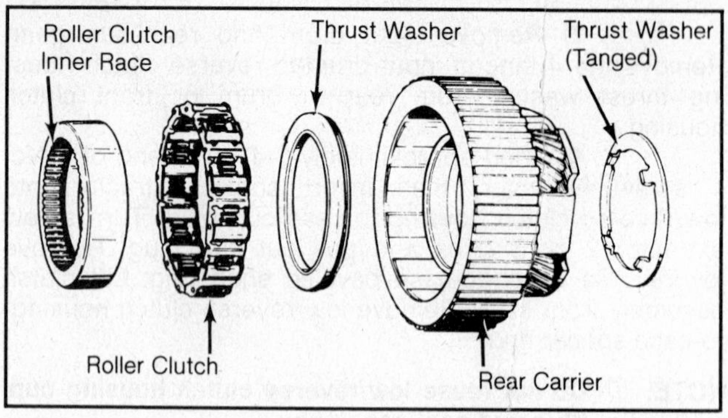

Reassembly

1) Position roller clutch-to-carrier thrust washer in rear carrier. Install rollers that may have come out of roller cage by compressing energizing spring with forefinger and inserting roller from outer edge. Install roller clutch into rear carrier.

2) Install roller clutch race, spline side out, into roller clutch and rotate it into position. Install 4-tanged rear carrier-to-rear internal gear thrust washer. Align tangs into slots of rear carrier and retain with petroleum jelly.

Fig. 17: Bottom View of Transmission Case Showing Oil Passages

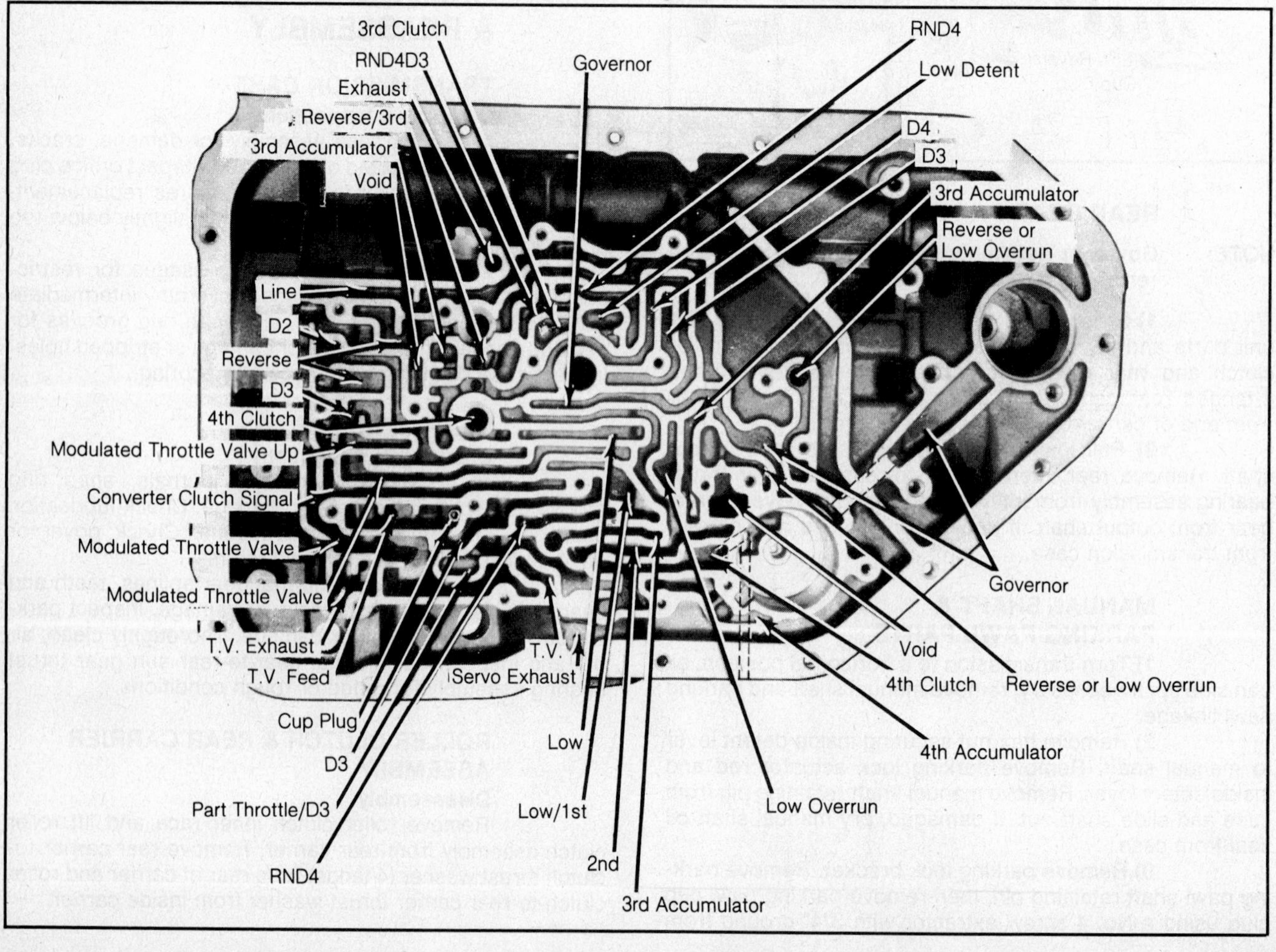

GENERAL MOTORS TURBO HYDRA-MATIC 200-4R (Cont.)

Fig. 19: Exploded View of Low/Reverse Clutch Assembly

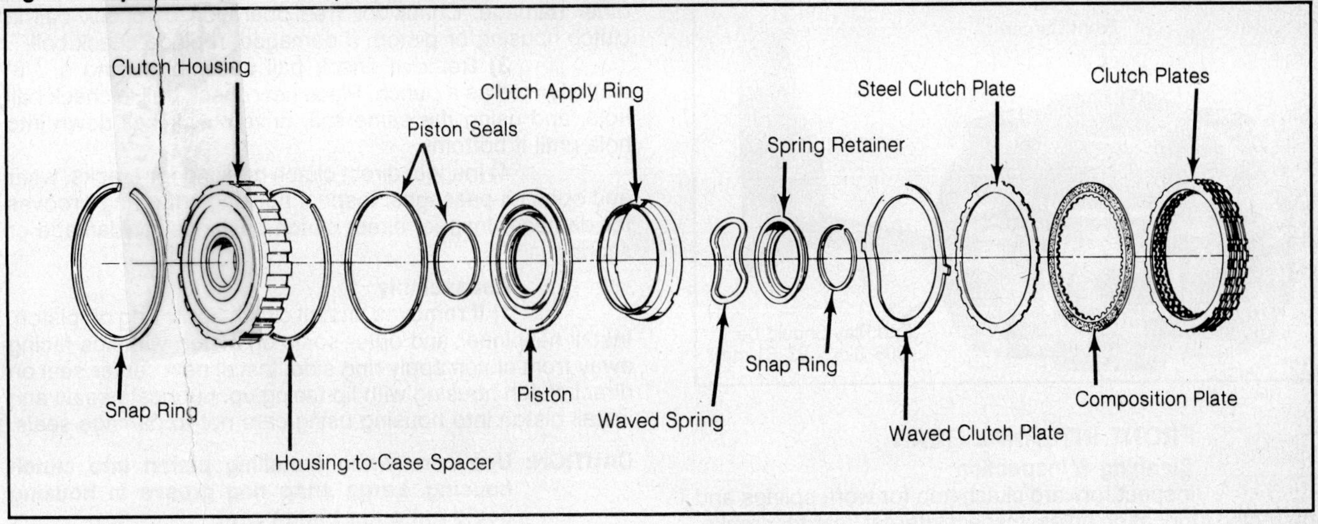

LOW/REVERSE CLUTCH

Disassembly

Compress low/reverse clutch spring retainer and remove snap ring. Remove waved spring from top of piston, then remove piston from housing. Remove inner and outer seals from piston. Remove clutch apply ring.

NOTE: **Low/reverse clutch assembly clutch plates and disc were removed during Transmission Disassembly.**

Cleaning & Inspection

1) Inspect composition, steel and waved clutch plates for signs of wear or burning. Check spring retainer and waved spring for damage or distortion. Inspect clutch housing for damage or plugged feed hole. Inspect clutch housing bushing for damage or scoring.

2) Inspect clutch housing splines and snap ring groove for damage or burrs. Remove burrs with crocus cloth. Inspect clutch piston and apply ring assembly for distortion, cracks or damage. Inspect clutch housing-to-case spacer ring for damage.

Reassembly

1) Position clutch apply ring on piston, then install new inner and outer seals on piston with seal lips facing away from apply ring side. Lubricate seals with automatic transmission fluid, then install piston into housing using care not to damage seals.

2) Install waved release spring on clutch piston. Install spring retainer, cupped face up, on top of piston, then compress retainer and install snap ring.

REAR SUN GEAR & INPUT DRUM

NOTE: **Rear sun gear and input drum need not be disassembled unless inspection shows it to be necessary.**

Disassembly

Remove input drum-to-rear sun gear snap ring. Separate sun gear from input drum. Remove tanged thrust washer from drum.

Cleaning & Inspection

Inspect rear sun gear for cracks, splits, damaged spline, worn gear or journals and plugged lubrication holes. Inspect sun gear bushing for damage or scoring. Inspect input drum for damage. Inspect 4-tanged input drum-to-low and reverse clutch housing thrust washer for scoring or distorted tangs. If damaged, replace sun gear-to-input drum snap ring.

Reassembly

Install sun gear into input drum, spline side first, and retain with snap ring. Install 4-tanged thrust washer on drum over sun gear end. Align tangs into drum and retain with petroleum jelly.

Fig. 20: Disassembled View of Rear Sun Gear and Input Drum Assembly

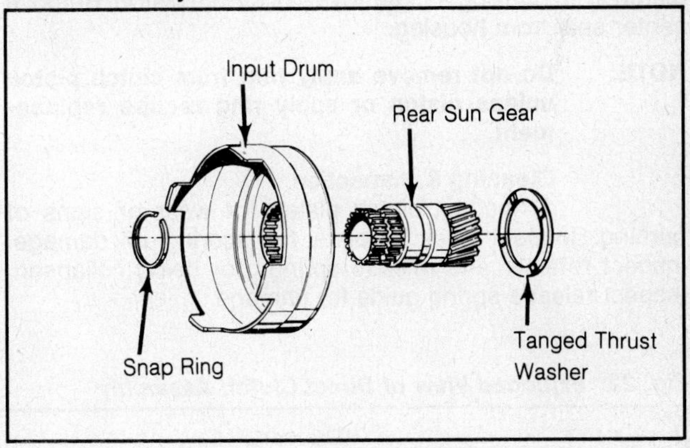

FRONT SUN GEAR

Cleaning & Inspection

Inspect front sun gear splines and teeth for damage or wear. Inspect machined face for pitting, scoring or damage.

FRONT CARRIER ASSEMBLY

Cleaning & Inspection

1) Inspect front carrier for damage. Check pinions for damage, rough bearings or tilt. Check pinion end play using a feeler gauge. *See Fig. 21.* End play should be .009-.024" (.23-.61 mm).

2) Inspect front carrier-to-front internal gear thrust bearing assembly for pitted or rough conditions.

Fig. 21: Checking Front Carrier Pinion End Play

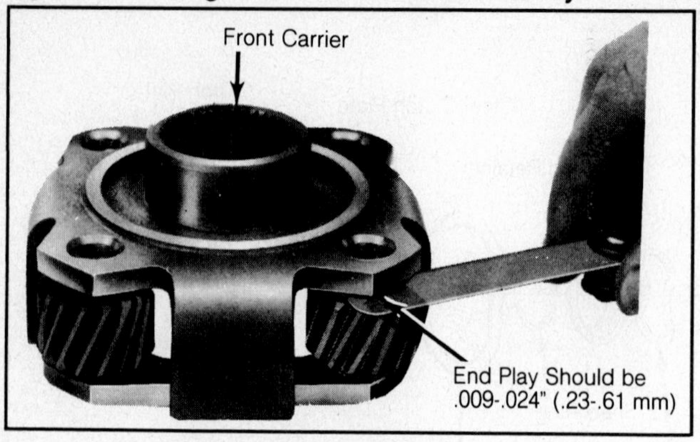

FRONT INTERNAL GEAR

Cleaning & Inspection

Inspect forward clutch hub for worn splines and restricted lubrication holes. Inspect internal gear for cracks, damage and worn gear teeth. Check bushing for damage or scoring. Inspect front internal gear-to-selective thrust washer for scoring or damage. *See Fig. 13.*

DIRECT CLUTCH ASSEMBLY

Disassembly

1) Remove snap ring and lift out clutch backing plate, composition clutch plates and steel clutch plates. Keep clutch plates separated from forward clutch plates.

2) Compress retainer and spring assembly and remove snap ring. Withdraw retainer and spring assembly from clutch housing. Remove release spring guide. Remove piston from housing and remove seals from piston. Remove center seal from housing.

NOTE: **Do not remove apply ring from clutch piston unless piston or apply ring require replacement.**

Cleaning & Inspection

1) Inspect clutch plates for wear or signs of burning. Inspect backing plate for scoring or damage. Inspect retainer and release springs for being collapsed. Inspect release spring guide for damage.

2) Inspect clutch piston for distortion, cracks or other damage. Check for free operation of check ball in clutch housing or piston. If damaged, replace check ball.

3) Remove check ball assembly using a 3/8" diameter rod as a punch. Place new check ball in check ball hole, and using the same rod, drive check ball down into hole until it bottoms.

4) Inspect direct clutch housing for cracks, wear and open oil passages. Inspect housing snap ring grooves for damage. Inspect direct clutch bushings for damage or scoring.

Reassembly

1) If removed, install clutch apply ring on piston. Install new inner and outer seals on piston with lips facing away from clutch apply ring side. Install new center seal on direct clutch housing with lip facing up. Lubricate seals and install piston into housing using care not to damage seals.

CAUTION: **Use care when installing piston into clutch housing. Large snap ring groove in housing could cut outer piston seal.**

2) Install release spring guide with the omitted rib over check ball in piston. *See Fig. 23.* Install retainer and spring assembly, compress springs and install snap ring.

Fig. 23: Installing Direct Clutch Release Spring Guide

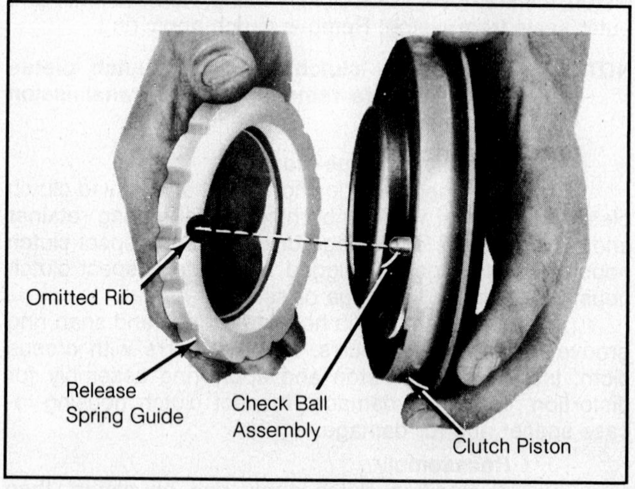

Fig. 22: Exploded View of Direct Clutch Assembly

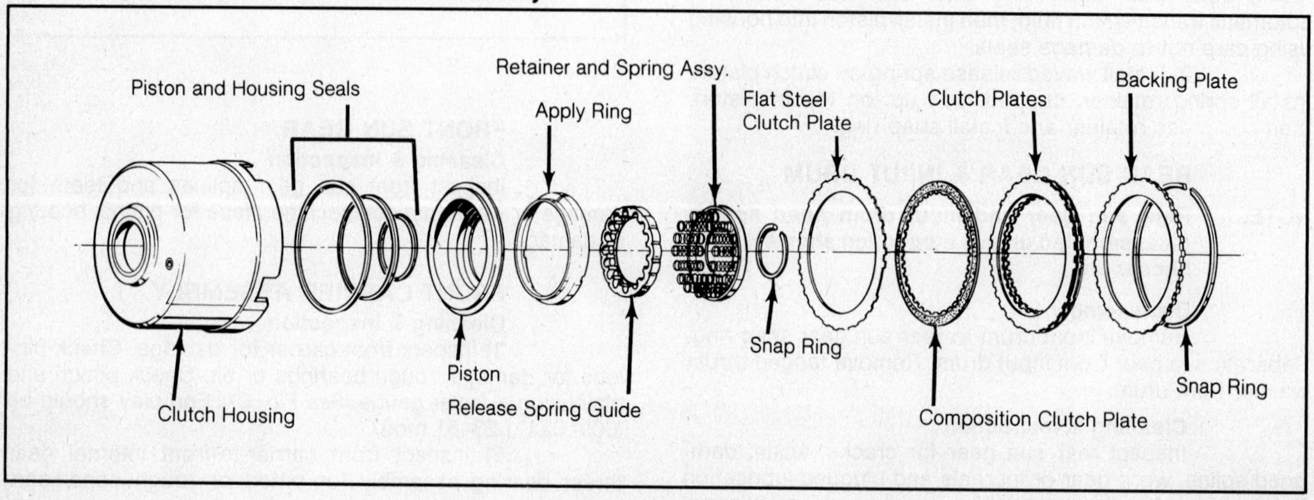

GENERAL MOTORS TURBO HYDRA-MATIC 200-4R (Cont.)

3) Oil and install clutch plates into clutch housing. Start with a flat steel and alternate composition and flat steel clutch plates. See DIRECT CLUTCH PLATE USAGE chart. Install backing plate, micro-finish down. Install clutch pack retaining snap ring. Ensure composition clutch plates turn freely.

DIRECT CLUTCH PLATE USAGE

Application	Steel	Composition
All Models	6	6

FORWARD CLUTCH ASSEMBLY

Disassembly

1) If damaged, remove Teflon oil seal rings from forward clutch shaft. Remove forward clutch-to-direct clutch thrust washer. Remove retaining snap ring and withdraw backing plate, composition plates and steel plates from clutch housing and keep them separated from direct clutch plates.

2) Compress retainer and release spring assembly and remove snap ring. Remove retainer and spring assembly from housing. Remove forward clutch piston from housing, then remove inner and outer oil seals from piston. If necessary, remove clutch apply ring from piston.

NOTE: **Clutch apply ring should not be removed from piston unless apply ring or piston requires replacement.**

Cleaning & Inspection

Forward clutch assembly inspection is identical to direct clutch assembly inspection except for the following differences; Replace forward clutch housing cup plug if damaged or missing. Remove plug using a No. 3 screw extractor (grind to fit). Install new cup plug .039" (1 mm) below surface.

Reassembly

1) If removed, install clutch apply ring on clutch piston. Install new inner and outer seals on clutch piston. Lubricate piston seals and install piston into clutch housing using care to prevent seals from being damaged when installing piston past large snap ring groove in housing.

Fig. 25: Forward Clutch Housing

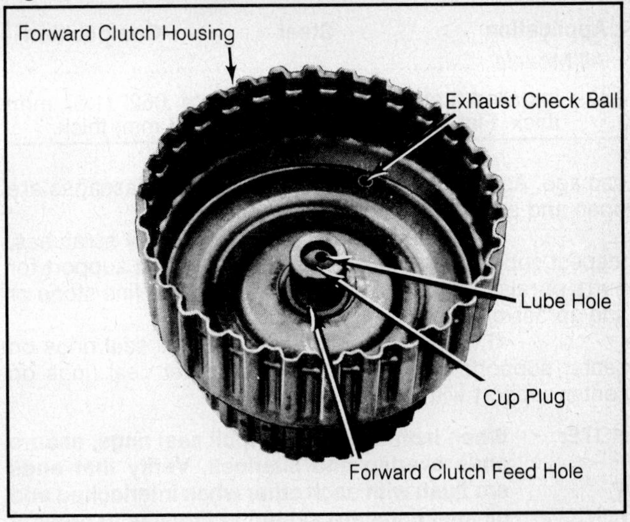

2) Install release springs and retainer assembly on piston. Compress retainer and install snap ring. Lubricate (ATF) and install clutch plates into housing, starting with the waved steel plate and alternating compostion plates and flat steel plates. See FORWARD CLUTCH PLATE USAGE chart.

3) Install backing plate into housing with micro-finish side down. Install clutch pack retaining snap ring and ensure composition clutch plates rotate freely in housing. Install forward-to-direct clutch thrust washer and retain with petrolatum.

4) If removed, install new forward clutch shaft oil seal rings, making sure cut ends are assembled in the same relationship as cut and that rings are seated in their groove. Retain with petrolatum.

CENTER SUPPORT

Cleaning & Inspection

1) Remove 4th clutch inner and outer seal rings from center support. Check condition of cast iron oil rings, and if necessary, remove from center support.

2) Inspect bushings for scoring, wear or galling. Check oil ring grooves and oil rings for nicks or other

Fig. 24: Exploded View of Forward Clutch Assembly

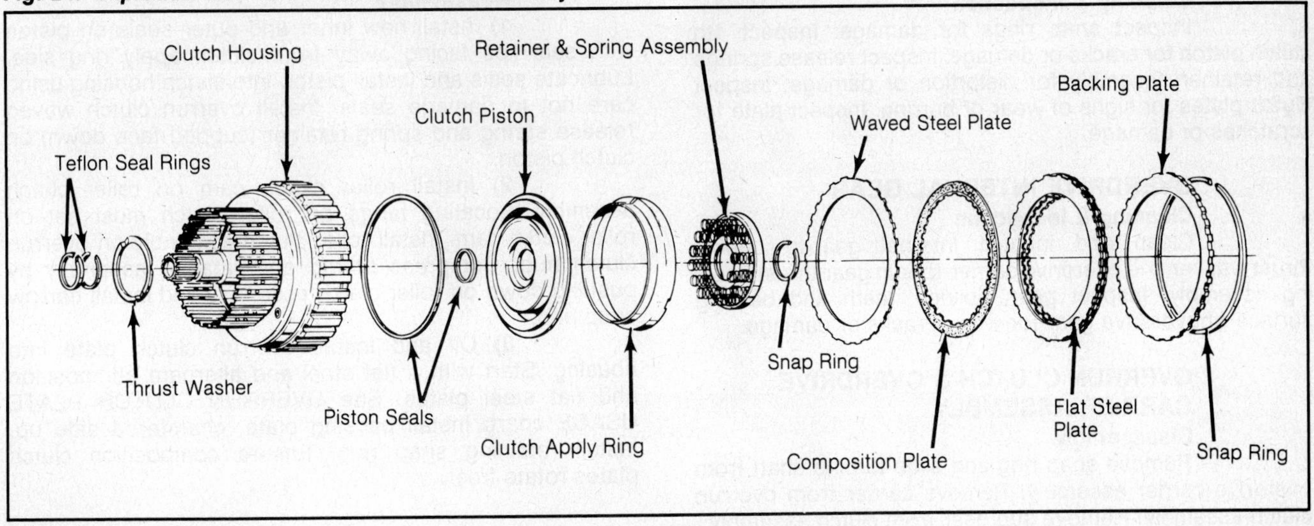

GENERAL MOTORS TURBO HYDRA-MATIC 200-4R (Cont.)

FORWARD CLUTCH PLATE USAGE

Application	Steel	Composition
All Models	4 [1]	4

[1] – Installed first is 1 waved steel plate .062" (1.57 mm) thick. Flat steel plates are .077" (1.96 mm) thick.

damage. Apply air to oil passages to ensure passages are open and are not interconnected.

3) Inspect piston sealing surfaces for scratches. Inspect support for cracks or porosity. Inspect support for burrs or raised edges. If present, remove with fine stone or fine abrasive paper.

4) If removed, install cast iron oil seal rings on center support. Install new inner and outer seal rings on center support with seal lips down.

NOTE: When installing cast iron oil seal rings, ensure ends overlap and interlock. Verify that ends are flush with each other when interlocked and oil seal rings are seated in grooves to prevent damage to ring during assembly of mating parts.

Fig. 26: Location of Cast Iron Seals on Center Support

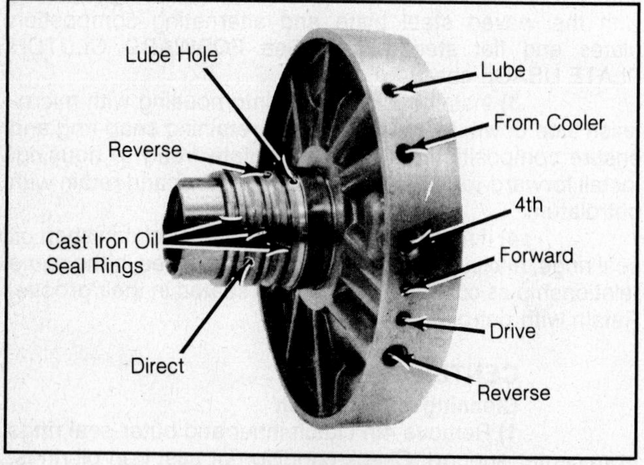

4TH CLUTCH ASSEMBLY

NOTE: The 4th clutch assembly was disassembled during Transmission Disassembly.

Cleaning & Inspection

Inspect snap rings for damage. Inspect 4th clutch piston for cracks or damage. Inspect release springs and retainer assembly for distortion or damage. Inspect clutch plates for signs of wear or burring. Inspect plate for scratches or damage.

OVERDRIVE INTERNAL GEAR

Cleaning & Inspection

Clean and inspect internal gear-to-support thrust washer and overdrive carrier-to-sun gear thrust bearing assembly. Inspect gear, splines, teeth and bearing surface of overdrive gear for wear, cracks or damage.

OVERRUN CLUTCH & OVERDRIVE CARRIER ASSEMBLY

Disassembly

Remove snap ring and slide turbine shaft from overdrive carrier assembly. Remove carrier from overrun clutch assembly. Remove sun gear from clutch assembly.

NOTE: Reassembly of this unit follows the disassembly and reassembly of the individual components.

OVERRUN CLUTCH ASSEMBLY

Disassembly

1) Remove retaining snap ring and lift backing plate, steel clutch plates and composition clutch plates from overrun clutch housing. Keep clutch plates separated from the other plate assemblies.

2) Using snap ring pliers, remove overrun clutch hub snap ring. Lift overdrive roller clutch cam assembly from housing, then separate roller clutch from cam assembly.

3) Remove retainer and wave spring assembly from clutch housing. Remove overrun clutch piston from housing, then remove inner and outer seals from piston.

Fig. 27: Removing Overdrive Roller Clutch Cam Assembly

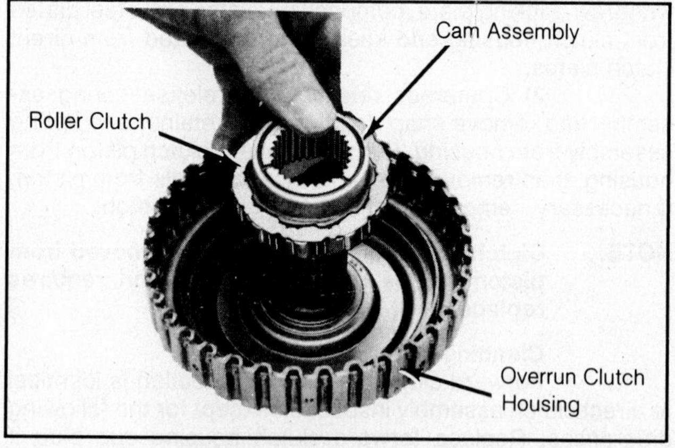

Cleaning & Inspection

1) Inspect clutch plates for signs of wear or burning. Inspect roller clutch cam ramps for damage. Check roller bearings, cage and springs of roller clutch for wear or damage.

2) Inspect retainer and wave spring for damage. Inspect clutch piston for distortion, cracks and damage. Inspect housing for cracks, wear and open oil passages. Check clutch housing snap ring groove and bushing for damage or scoring.

Reassembly

1) Install new inner and outer seals on piston with seal lips facing away from clutch apply ring side. Lubricate seals and install piston into clutch housing using care not to damage seals. Install overrun clutch waved release spring and spring retainer (cupped face down) on clutch piston.

2) Install roller clutch cam on roller clutch assembly. Locating tangs on roller clutch must set on roller clutch cam. Install roller clutch assembly on overrun clutch hub. Compress spring and retainer assembly by pushing down on roller clutch assembly and install narrow snap ring.

3) Oil and install overrun clutch plate into housing. Start with a flat steel and alternate composition and flat steel plates. See OVERRUN CLUTCH PLATE USAGE chart. Install backing plate, chamfered side up. Install retaining snap ring. Ensure composition clutch plates rotate freely.

OVERRUN CLUTCH PLATE USAGE

Application	Flat Steel	Composition
All Models	2 [1]	2

[1] - Plate thickness is .077" (1.96 mm).

OVERDRIVE CARRIER

Disassembly

1) Remove overdrive carrier snap ring. Using pliers, remove pinion pins. Remove pinions, thrust washers and roller bearings. Inspect pinion pocket thrust faces for burrs, and remove if present.

2) Remove overdrive sun gear-to-overdrive carrier thrust bearing assembly. Thoroughly clean, air dry and closely inspect thrust bearing assembly for pitting or rough condition.

Cleaning & Inspection

1) Inspect locating splines for damage and roller clutch race for scratches and wear. Inspect carrier housing for cracks and wear.

2) Inspect pinions for damage, rough bearings or tilt. Using a feeler gauge, measure pinion end play between pinion and carrier. End play should be .009-.024" (.23-.61 mm). If necessary to disassemble carrier, go to disassembly procedure.

Fig. 28: Assembling Overdrive Carrier Pinions

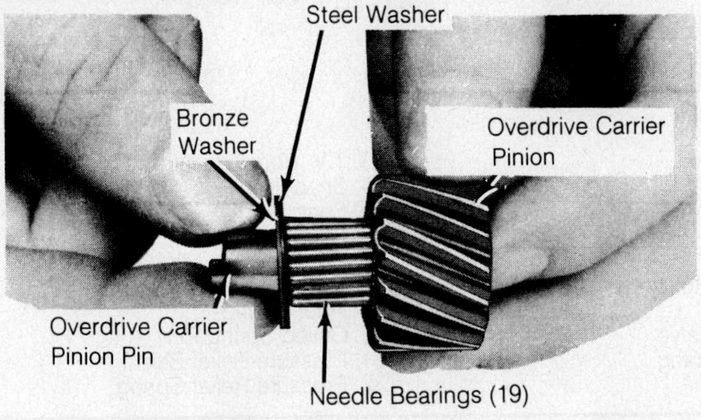

Reassembly

1) Install thrust bearing into carrier housing with small diameter race down. Retain bearing in place with petroleum jelly. Install 19 needle bearings into each pinion and hold them in place. Place a bronze and steel thrust washer on each side of pinion so that steel washer is against pinion. Hold washers in place with petroleum jelly.

2) Install a pinion assembly in place in housing and use a pilot shaft to align parts. Push pinion pin into place while rotating pinions from the side. Repeat procedure for remaining pinions. Install overdrive carrier snap ring to retain pinion pins.

TURBINE SHAFT

Cleaning & Inspection

1) Inspect Teflon oil seals on turbine shaft for damage and free fit in grooves. Do not remove seal unless replacement is necessary. Inspect snap ring for damage. Check journals and snap ring grooves for wear or damage.

2) Inspect both ends of turbine shaft for open oil passages. Inspect journals for damage. Check for free operation of check ball in end of shaft. If check ball is damaged, go to step **3)**.

3) Straighten tangs of retainer and check valve assembly capsule in end of shaft. Remove check ball. Using a No. 4 screw extractor, and remove check valve retainer from turbine shaft by turning and pulling straight out.

4) Install new check valve assembly, check valve seat first, into turbine shaft. Using a 3/8" diameter rod, drive retainer and check valve assembly until it is 1/8" below top surface of turbine shaft.

Fig. 29: Turbine Shaft Assembly

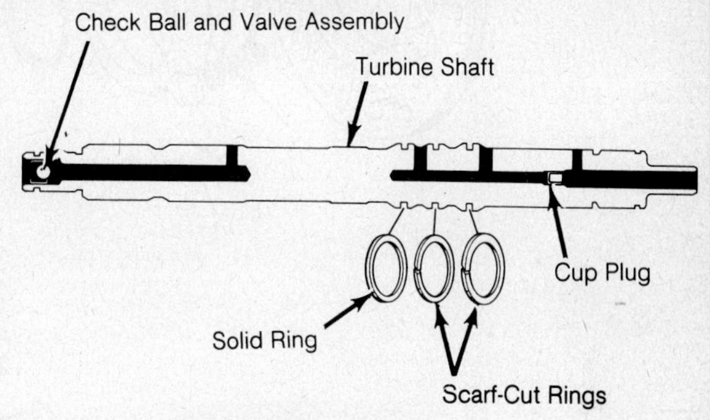

OVERRUN CLUTCH & OVERDRIVE CARRIER ASSEMBLY

Reassembly

1) Install overdrive sun gear on overrun clutch hub with groove up. Center clutches in overrun clutch housing. Position overdrive carrier in overrun clutch with pinion side of carrier facing up. It may be necessary to rotate carrier counterclockwise to seat it.

2) Position clutch and carrier assembly (clutch up) over hole in work bench. Install turbine shaft, ring grooved spline first, into carrier assembly. Turn assembly sideways and install NEW turbine shaft snap ring.

CAUTION: A new turbine shaft snap ring must be installed as damage to unit may occur if old snap ring is used.

PUMP ASSEMBLY

Disassembly

1) Remove pump-to-case seal ring. Remove pump cover-to-pump body attaching bolts and separate cover from body. Remove stator shaft-to-overrun selective thrust washer.

2) Push in on T.V. boost valve bushing, compressing pressure regulator spring, and remove retaining snap ring. Release spring tension slowly and remove valve train.

3) Push in on converter clutch stop valve, compressing converter clutch valve spring and remove snap ring. Release spring tension slowly and remove stop valve and converter clutch valve. Using a punch, remove pressure relief spring retaining pin. Remove relief spring and ball.

4) If replacement of stator shaft and flange assembly is required, remove attaching screws and press stator shaft until it is removed from pump cover bore.

5) Place shop towel over pump slide spring (spring is under high pressure) and using a screwdriver, remove spring from pump body. Remove pump slide, slide-to-wear plate oil seal and back-up "O" ring seal, rotor, rotor guide, 7 vanes and 2 vane rings, pump slide seal support and seal. Remove pivot slide pin and spring.

GENERAL MOTORS TURBO HYDRA-MATIC 200-4R (Cont.)

Fig. 30: Exploded View of Pump Assembly

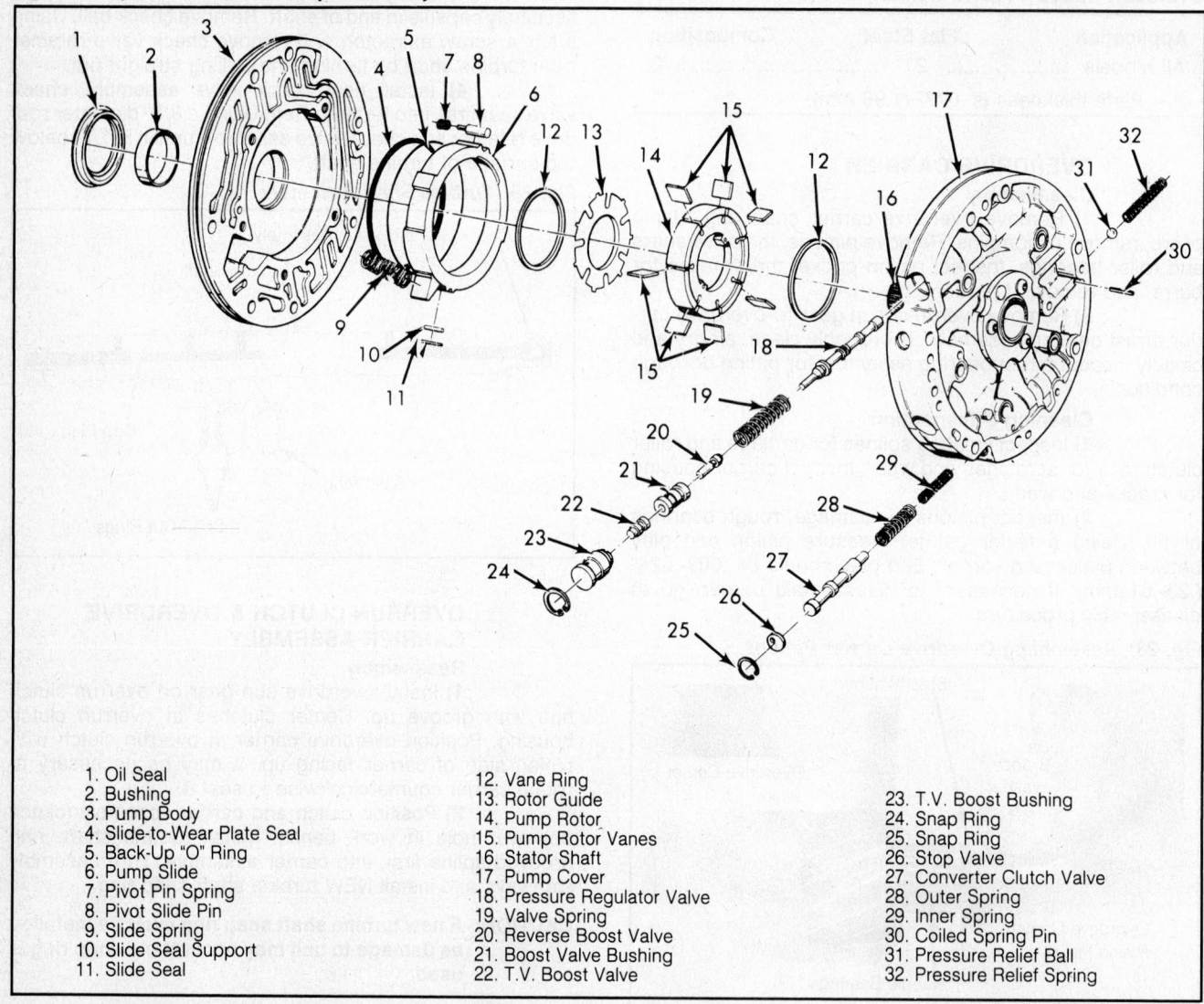

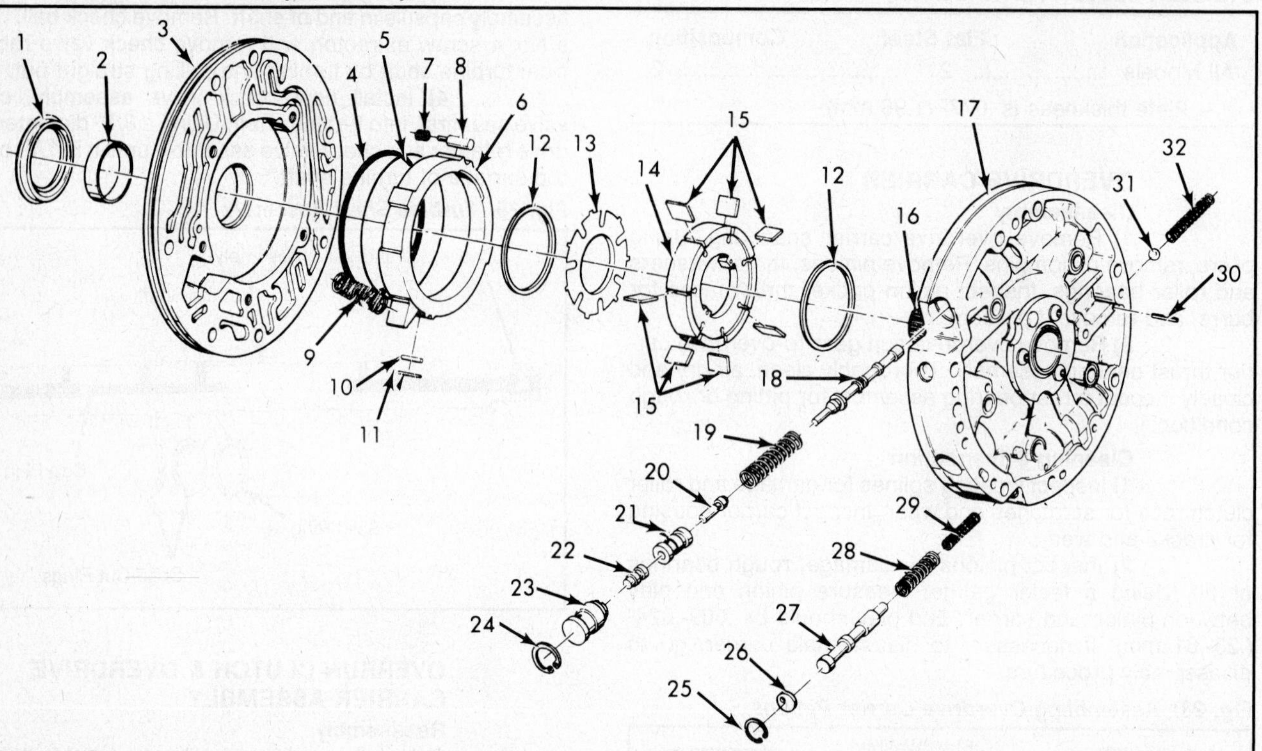

1. Oil Seal
2. Bushing
3. Pump Body
4. Slide-to-Wear Plate Seal
5. Back-Up "O" Ring
6. Pump Slide
7. Pivot Pin Spring
8. Pivot Slide Pin
9. Slide Spring
10. Slide Seal Support
11. Slide Seal
12. Vane Ring
13. Rotor Guide
14. Pump Rotor
15. Pump Rotor Vanes
16. Stator Shaft
17. Pump Cover
18. Pressure Regulator Valve
19. Valve Spring
20. Reverse Boost Valve
21. Boost Valve Bushing
22. T.V. Boost Valve
23. T.V. Boost Bushing
24. Snap Ring
25. Snap Ring
26. Stop Valve
27. Converter Clutch Valve
28. Outer Spring
29. Inner Spring
30. Coiled Spring Pin
31. Pressure Relief Ball
32. Pressure Relief Spring

Cleaning & Inspection

1) Inspect pump-to-case seal ring groove in pump body for damage. Inspect stator shaft-to-overrun selective washer for wear and damage. Wash pump body, springs, pump slide, rotor, vanes, vane rings and rotor guide. Do not put pump seals in solvent.

2) Inspect pump pocket and pump body for damage or scoring. Check pump body bushing for wear or scoring. Inspect springs for damage or distortion and pump slide for damage, cracks or wear. Check rotor for damage, cracks or wear. Inspect vanes and vane rings for damage, cracks or wear. Inspect pump body face for nicks and overall flatness and open oil passages.

3) Inspect T.V. boost valve, reverse boost valve, stop valve and converter clutch valve for nicks or damage. Check valves for free operation in bushing or cover bore. Inspect all springs for damage or distortion. Inspect stator shaft and flange assembly for damaged splines or bushing. Check stator shaft for damaged or missing orifice cup plug in dowel pin. Do not remove cup plug unless damaged.

4) Inspect pump cover for open oil passages. Check pump cover face for nicks and overall flatness. Inspect for chips in pressure regulator, pressure relief and converter clutch bores. Inspect cup plugs and orifice plugs in cover and if damaged, replace plugs.

Pump Cover Cup Plug Replacement

If cup plug is missing, drive a new plug to 1/32" below top of hole, using a 9/32" diameter rod on the 2 smaller plugs, a 5/16" rod on the line-to-case cup plug, and a 7/16" rod on the large plug. Stake top of hole in 2 places, directly opposite each other, to retain plug.

Pump Cover Orifice Plug Replacement

If plugs require replacement, place new plug, orifice end first, into plug hole from rough casting side of cover. Drive new plug flush to .100" (2.8 mm) below top of hole, on rough casting side. Stake top of hole in 2 places to retain plug.

Reassembly

1) Turn pump body so that pump pocket side is up. Install slide "O" ring and slide-to-wear plate oil seal in slide and retain with petrolatum. Install slide into pump pocket with seal side down. Install slide seal support and pump slide seal. *See Fig. 32.* Retain with petrolatum. Install pivot pin and spring into bore in pump body (opposite pivot pin and spring).

GENERAL MOTORS TURBO HYDRA-MATIC 200-4R (Cont.)

Fig. 31: View of Pump Cover and Body Showing Hydraulic Passages

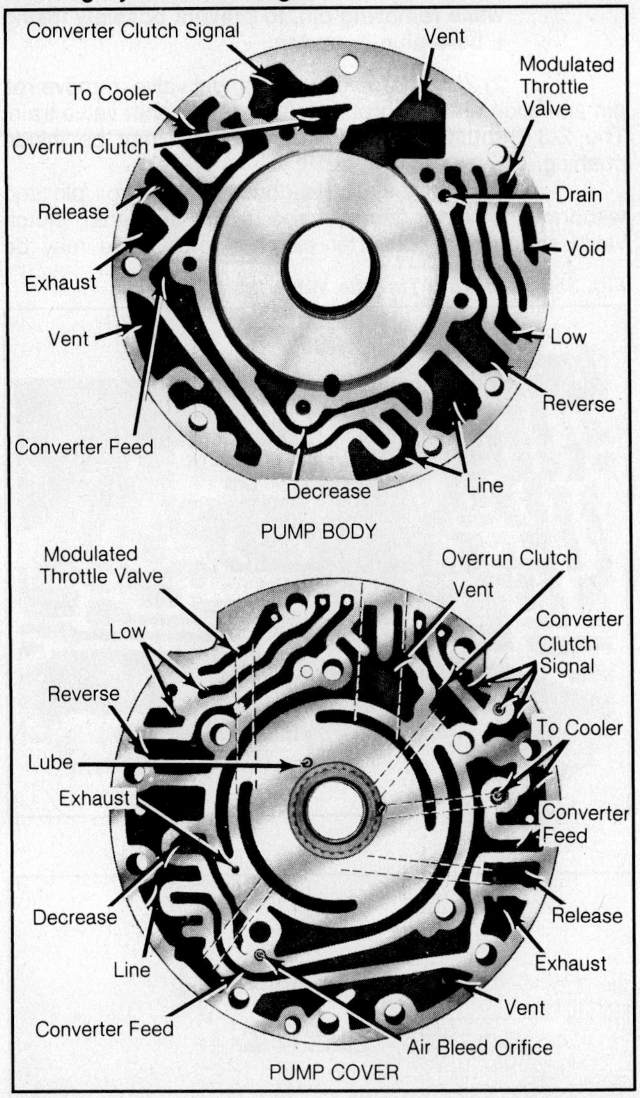

2) Install a vane ring in pump pocket. Install rotor guide in pump rotor, then install rotor into pump pocket. Center and seat rotor on guide so rotor is flush with pump slide. Install 7 vanes into pump. Ensure vane pattern is installed against vane ring. Install top vane ring. Install pump slide spring.

3) If stator shaft and flange assembly was removed from pump cover, install as follows: Align dowel pin of stator shaft with hole in pump cover. Using a press, press stator shaft into cover until fully seated on cover. Install stator shaft and flange assembly attaching bolts.

4) Install all valve trains in reverse order of removal. *See Fig. 2.* Assemble pump cover to pump body and install attaching bolts finger tight. Align cover to body using Alignment Strap (J-25015), and tighten attaching bolts. Install pump-to-case seal ring, chamfered side out, making sure seal is not twisted. Install stator shaft-to-overrun clutch selective thrust washer and retain with petroleum jelly.

Fig. 32: Installing Slide Seal and Support

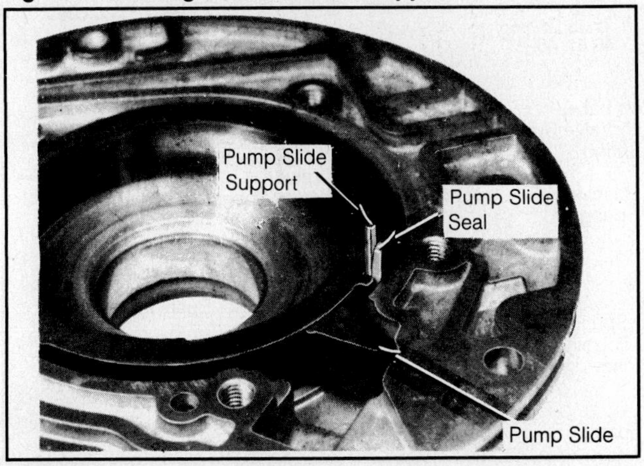

GOVERNOR ASSEMBLY

Cleaning & Inspection

1) Inspect governor cover for damage, plugged oil passage, scored or worn bore. Inspect governor driven gear for nicks or damage. If replacement is necessary, remove retaining ring and slide gear and thrust washer from shaft.

CAUTION: Care must be taken after removing driven gear to keep governor in a vertical position to retain governor weight pin in its holding position.

2) Inspect governor shaft seal ring for cuts, damage and free fit in groove. Inspect for free operation of weights. Weights must operate freely and independently of each other. Check spring for damage and correct installation. Check for presence of 2 check balls. Inspect shaft for damage.

INTERMEDIATE SERVO ASSEMBLY

Disassembly

Using a small screwdriver, remove intermediate pin-to-retainer snap ring. Separate band apply pin, spring and washer from servo pistons.

Cleaning & Inspection

Inspect pin oil seal rings for damage and replace if necessary. Inspect pin for damage and fit in case. Inspect inner and outer piston seal rings for damage and free fit in grooves; do not replace unless damaged. Inspect spring for damage and distortion.

Fig. 33: Exploded View of Intermediate Servo

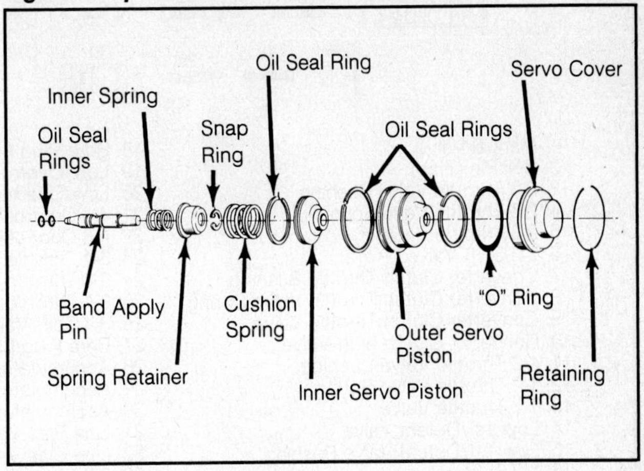

GENERAL MOTORS TURBO HYDRA-MATIC 200-4R (Cont.)

Reassembly

1) Install retainer on band apply pin, then install snap ring. Install apply pin, retainer end first, through servo pistons. If removed, install new inner and outer piston seal rings, making sure cut ends are assembled in same relationship as cut, and retain with petrolatum.

2) Lubricate with petrolatum and install new seal ring on intermediate servo cover. Install servo piston into servo cover.

CAUTION: Intermediate servo cover seal rings must be well lubricated to prevent damage or cutting of ring.

CONTROL VALVE ASSEMBLY

NOTE: As valve trains are removed from each valve body bore, place individual parts in correct order in relative position to valve body to ease reassembly. Valves, bushings and springs are not interchangeable, and all parts must be installed in correct order in proper valve body bore. Remove all roll pins and spring retaining sleeves by pushing through from rough case surface side of valve body, except for the blind hole roll pins.

Disassembly

1) Lay control valve assembly with machined face up and manual valve at upper left corner. If not removed at Transmission Disassembly, remove 3 check balls from cored passages of valve body. From upper left corner bore, remove manual valve.

CAUTION: Some roll pins in valve body have pressure against them. Hold a shop towel over bore while removing pin, to prevent possibly losing a bore plug or spring.

2) From bore beneath manual valve, remove roll pin and slide out 2-3 throttle valve and 2-3 shift valve train. The 2-3 throttle valve spring and valve may be inside bushing.

3) From next bore down, remove roll pin and withdraw converter clutch valve train. Converter clutch valve spring and converter clutch throttle valve may be

Fig. 35: Removing Throttle Valve Inner Roll Pin

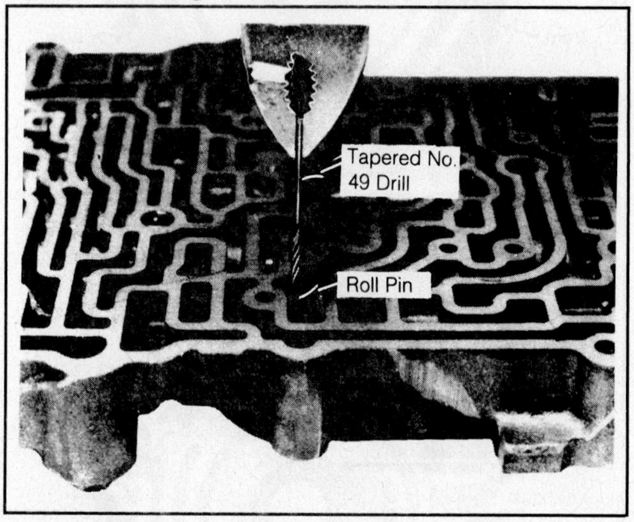

Fig. 34: Exploded View of Control Valve Assembly

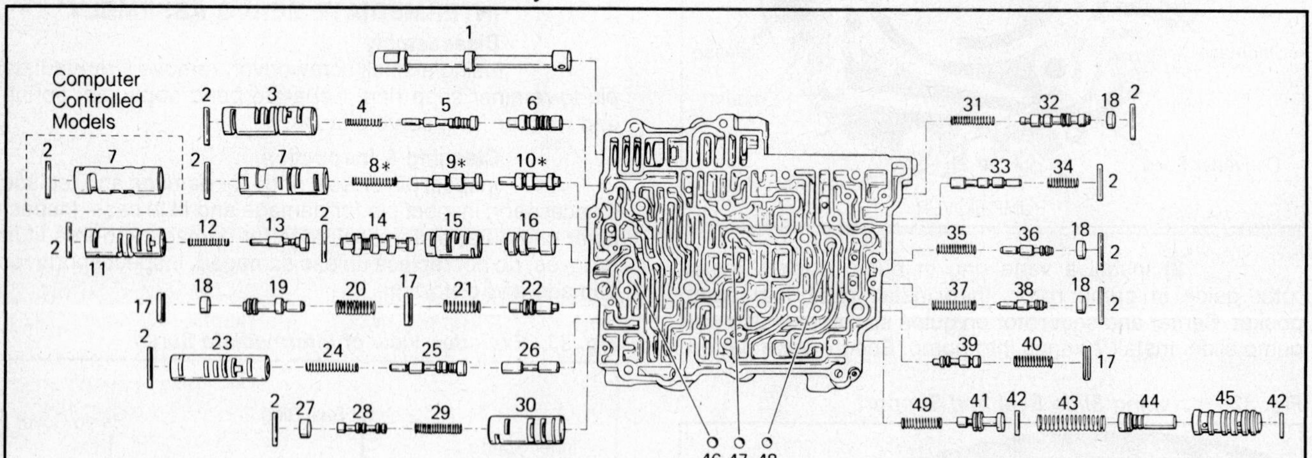

1. Manual Valve
2. Roll Pin (Zinc)
3. 2-3 Throttle Valve Bushing
4. 2-3 Throttle Vave Spring
5. 2-3 Throttle Valve
6. 2-3 Shift Valve
7. Converter Clutch Throttle Bushing
8. Converter Clutch Throttle Valve Spring
9. Converter Clutch Throttle Valve
10. Converter Clutch Shift Valve
11. 1-2 Throttle Valve Bushing
12. 1-2 Throttle Valve Spring
13. 1-2 Throttle Valve
14. Low 1st/Detent Valve
15. Low 1st/Detent Valve Bushing
16. 1-2 Shift Valve
17. Spring Retaining Sleeve
18. Bore Plug (.50")
19. Low/Overrun Clutch Valve
20. Low/Overrun Clutch Valve Spring
21. 4-3 Control Valve Spring
22. 4-3 Control Valve
23. 3-4 Throttle Valve Bushing
24. 3-4 Throttle Valve Spring
25. 3-4 Throttle Valve
26. 3-4 Shift Valve
27. Bore Plug (.560")
28. Accumulator Valve
29. Accumulator Valve Spring
30. Accumulator Valve Bushing
31. Line Bias Valve Spring
32. Line Bias Valve
33. 3-2 Control Valve
34. 3-2 Control Valve Spring
35. T.V. Modulator Upshift Valve Spring
36. T.V. Modulator Upshift Valve
37. T.V. Modulator Downshift Valve Spring
38. T.V. Modulator Downshift Valve
39. T.V. Limit Valve
40. T.V. Limit Valve Spring
41. Throttle Valve
42. Roll Pin (Black)
43. Throttle Valve Spring
44. Throttle Valve Plunger
45. Throttle Valve Plunger Bushing
46. "D3" Check Ball
47. 1-2 Shift Check Ball
48. Low/1st Check Ball

* Items 8, 9 & 10 are not used on diesel models.

inside bushing. On Computer Command Control models, clutch throttle valve and spring have been eliminated.

4) From next bore down, remove outer roll pin and remove 1-2 throttle valve train and low 1st/detent valve. Remove inner roll pin and slide out low 1st/detent valve bushing and 1-2 shift valve.

5) Cover the next bore down to prevent loss of spring, then remove outer spring retaining sleeve. Remove bore plug and 4-3 control valve and spring. Remove inner spring retaining sleeve and withdraw low/overrun clutch valve spring and valve.

6) From next bore down, remove roll pin and slide out 3-4 throttle valve train. From last bore down, remove roll pin and bore plug and withdraw accumulator valve train.

7) From upper right corner, remove roll pin and remove line bias valve train. From next bore down, remove roll pin and 3-2 control valve train.

8) From next bore down, remove roll pin, then remove T.V. modulator upshift valve train. From next bore down, remove roll pin and T.V. modulator downshift valve train.

9) Cover the next bore down to prevent loss of spring, then remove spring retaining sleeve and withdraw T.V. limit valve train.

10) From last bore, remove outer roll pin, then remove throttle valve bushing, plunger and spring. Remove inner pin as follows: Grind a taper to end of a No. 49 drill. Lightly tap tapered end of drill into roll pin, then pull drill and roll pin out. Remove throttle valve.

Cleaning & Inspection

1) Wash control valve body, springs, valves and other parts in clean solvent and air dry. Inspect valves for scoring, cracks and free movement in their bores.

2) Inspect bushings for cracks and scored bores. Inspect valve body for cracks, damage or scored bores. Inspect springs for distortion or collapsed coils. Inspect bore plugs for damage.

Reassembly

Reassembly is the reverse of disassembly procedure. Reassemble control valve assembly using exploded view as a guide. Note the following:

- Install all flared roll pins (zinc coated) flared end out and from machined face of valve body.
- Install the 2 tapered roll pins (Black finish) that retain throttle valve and throttle valve bushing, tapered end first.
- Roll pins do not fit flush on rough casting face. Ensure all roll pins are flush at machined face or damage to transmission will occur.
- Ensure all spring retaining sleeves are installed from machined face and that they are level with or below machined surface.
- Install all bore plugs with hole out.
- Install all valve sleeves so that slot in sleeve aligns with roll pin hole in valve body.

TRANSMISSION REASSEMBLY

MANUAL SHAFT & PARKING PAWL PARTS

1) Turn transmission to horizontal position with oil pan side up. If removed, install new manual shaft seal with lip facing into case using a 9/16" socket to seat seal. Install parking pawl and spring into case with tooth toward inside of case and spring under pawl tooth with spring ends toward inside of case. Ensure spring ends locate against case pad.

2) Align parking pawl and spring with case shaft hole, then install parking pawl shaft, tapered end first. Using a 3/8" diameter rod, install new parking pawl cup plug, open end out, past retaining pin hole. Install retaining pin.

Fig. 36: Manual Shaft and Parking Parts

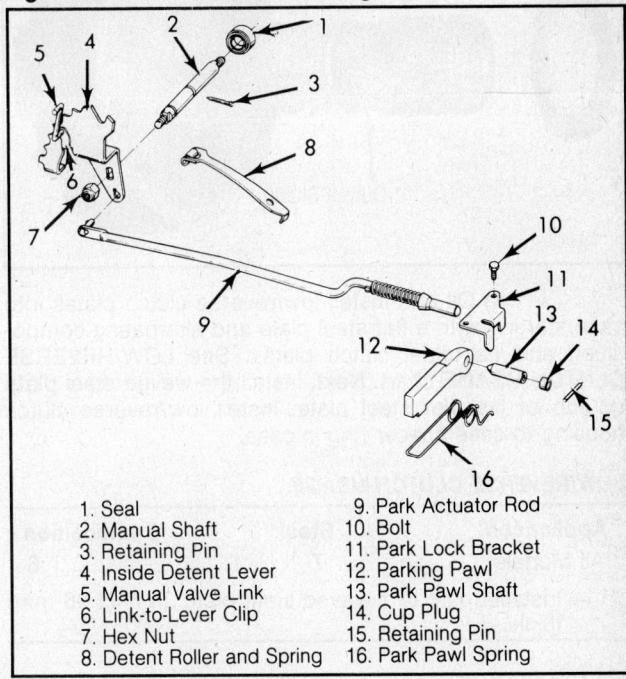

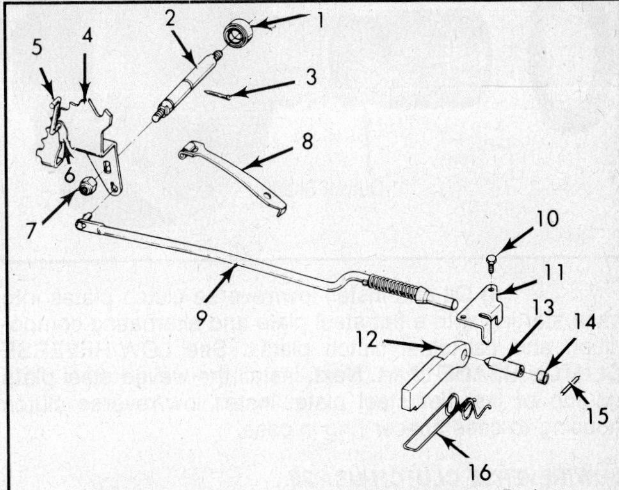

1. Seal
2. Manual Shaft
3. Retaining Pin
4. Inside Detent Lever
5. Manual Valve Link
6. Link-to-Lever Clip
7. Hex Nut
8. Detent Roller and Spring
9. Park Actuator Rod
10. Bolt
11. Park Lock Bracket
12. Parking Pawl
13. Park Pawl Shaft
14. Cup Plug
15. Retaining Pin
16. Park Pawl Spring

3) While holding parking pawl toward center of transmission, install parking lock bracket and tighten attaching bolts. Assemble parking actuator rod on pin side of inside detent lever, locating lever between actuator rod tangs. Install rod and detent lever into case with detent lever pin toward center of transmission and actuator plunger between parking pawl and parking lock bracket.

NOTE: **File any burrs or raised edges off manual shaft that could damage manual shaft seal during installation of shaft.**

4) Install manual shaft, small identification ring groove first, through case. Align inside detent lever with flats on shaft, then install detent lever on manual shaft. Install hex nut on manual shaft and tighten. Install manual shaft retaining pin, indexing with large groove on shaft.

REAR GEAR PARTS

1) Install rear internal gear, hub end first, onto output shaft. Install rear internal gear-to-rear thrust bearing assembly, inside diameter race against gear, over output shaft and into internal gear.

2) Install roller clutch and rear carrier assembly into rear internal gear. Install output shaft loading fixture and support sleeve into rear of case. *See Fig. 8.* Turn case to vertical position, pump end up. Install rear unit parts into case, indexing internal gear parking pawl lugs to pass by parking pawl tooth.

3) Using adjusting screw on output shaft loading fixture, adjust height of rear internal gear parking pawl lugs to align flush with parking pawl tooth.

GENERAL MOTORS TURBO HYDRA-MATIC 200-4R

***Fig. 37:* Installing Rear Internal Gear & Thrust Bearing**

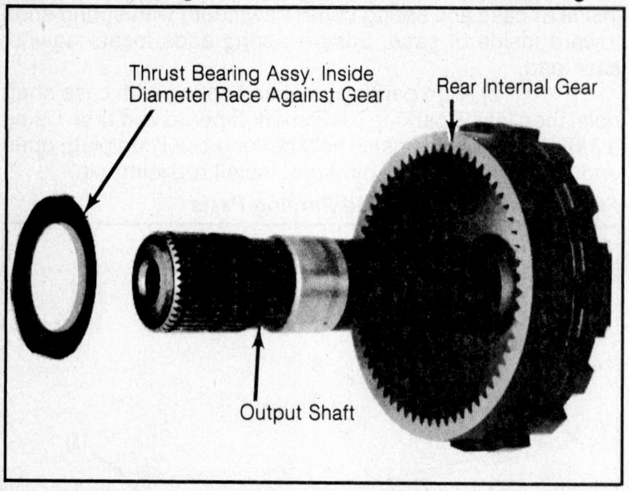

4) Oil and install low/reverse clutch plates into case starting with a flat steel plate and alternating composition and flat steel clutch plates. See LOW/REVERSE CLUTCH USAGE chart. Next, install the waved steel plate on top of last flat steel plate. Install low/reverse clutch housing-to-case spacer ring in case.

LOW/REVERSE CLUTCH USAGE

Application	Steel	Composition
All Models	7 [1]	6

[1] – Installed last is 1 waved steel plate .077" (1.96 mm) thick.

5) Install low/reverse clutch housing into case, aligning feed hole in housing with reverse clutch feed passage in case. If clutch housing does not seat past case snap ring groove, install input drum and rear sun gear into case.

6) Rotate sun gear back and forth, tapping lightly with input drum to align roller clutch race with low/reverse clutch hub splines. Remove input drum and rear sun gear assembly.

7) Install low/reverse clutch-to-case snap ring with flat side against clutch (beveled side up). Position snap ring groove on opposite side of parking pawl rod.

***Fig. 38:* Installing Low/Reverse Clutch Housing Cup Plug and Seal Assembly**

NOTE: **It may be necessary to loosen adjusting screw on output shaft loading fixture to install clutch-to-case snap ring.**

8) If removed, install new low/reverse clutch housing-to-case cup plug and seal. Use a 3/8" diameter rod to drive cup plug and seal assembly into case until it seats against clutch housing. *See Fig. 38.*

FRONT GEAR PARTS

1) Install 4-tanged thrust washer on input drum over sun gear end; align tangs into input drum and retain with petrolatum. Install rear sun gear and input drum assembly into case.

2) Install front sun gear into case and input drum with face of gear having identification groove against input drum. Install front sun gear-to-front carrier thrust bearing and race assembly into case with needle bearings against sun gear.

3) Install front carrier-to-front internal gear thrust bearing assembly on carrier with small diameter race against carrier. Install front carrier and thrust bearing assembly into transmission.

4) Install thrust washer on front internal gear and retain with petrolatum. Install front internal gear and thrust washer into case. Install rear unit end play selective washer into case with identification number on washer toward front of transmission. Install wide retaining snap ring. *See Fig. 13.*

NOTE: **At this point, recheck rear unit end play to verify that correct selective thrust washer has been installed. See REAR UNIT END PLAY.**

5) Install output shaft-to-forward clutch shaft selective thrust washer into case and position washer. *See Fig. 39.*

***Fig. 39:* Installing Front Selective Washer**

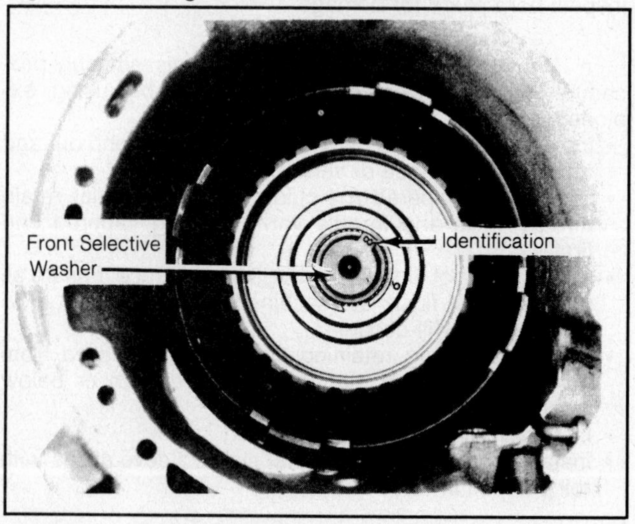

FRONT UNIT PARTS

1) Install intermediate band into case, locating band apply lug and anchor pin lug in case slot. Install band anchor pin.

2) Position direct clutch assembly, clutch plate end up, over hole in work bench. Align teeth of composition plates in direct clutch, then install forward clutch assembly, shaft first, into direct clutch assembly. Hold direct clutch and rotate forward clutch back and forth until fully seated.

NOTE: **When forward clutch is fully seated, it will be approximately 5/8" from tang end of direct clutch housing to end of forward clutch drum.**

3) Install direct and forward clutch assemblies into case and rotate into position. When assemblies are correctly installed, it will be approximately 4 1/8" from pump face in case to direct clutch housing.

4) Install center support-to-direct clutch thrust washer on center support. Visually align center support with case bolt holes and install center support into case. Install, but do not tighten, center support attaching bolts. Install center support-to-case snap ring with beveled side up. Tighten center support attaching bolts.

NOTE: **At this point, recheck input shaft end play to verify that correct front selective washer has been installed. See INPUT SHAFT END PLAY.**

OVERDRIVE UNIT PARTS

1) Install 4th clutch outer and inner seals on center support with lips facing down, apply petrolatum to seals. Install 4th clutch piston into case, aligning piston tab with wide case spline. Position return spring and retainer assembly on piston, then compress retainer assembly and install support-to-4th clutch spring snap ring.

NOTE: **The 4th clutch inner seal, installed on center support, is identified by a white stripe.**

2) Install internal gear-to-support thrust washer into case with tangs down. Install overdrive internal gear, hub end first, on forward clutch shaft. Install overdrive carrier-to-sun gear thrust bearing assembly into overdrive internal gear with large diameter race against carrier.

3) Grasp turbine shaft and lower overrun clutch and overdrive carrier assembly into case and rotate into position. Select proper 4th clutch plates. See 4th CLUTCH PLATE USAGE chart. Oil and install 4th clutch plates into case. *See Fig. 40.* Install clutch pack retaining snap ring. Install oil deflector plate into case with tangs facing up.

Fig. 40: Fourth Clutch Plate Installation Sequence

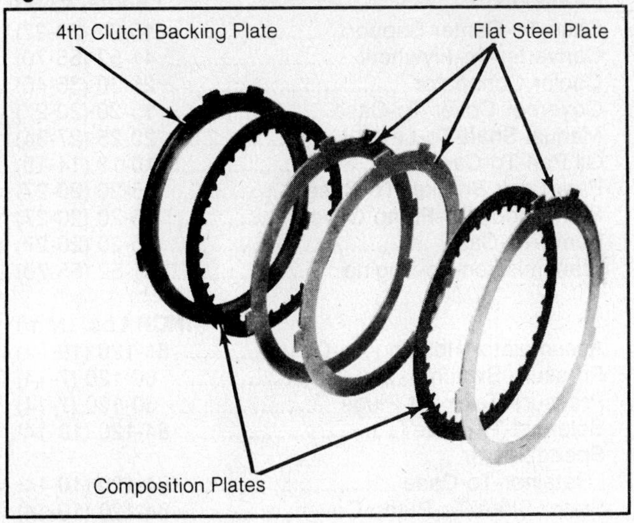

CAUTION: **Note installation order of 4th clutch plates. The center has 2 steel plates together and the thick plate is on top. Incorrect installation sequence will cause damage.**

4) Install a new pump-to-case gasket on pump and retain with petrolatum. Install 2 alignment pins into pump attaching bolt holes opposite each other. Install pump assembly in case. Install pump attaching bolts with NEW washers. Remove alignment pins and install remaining bolts and washers. Tighten oil pump attaching bolts.

NOTE: **At this point, recheck overdrive unit end play to verify that correct overdrive end play thrust washer has been installed. See OVERDRIVE UNIT END PLAY.**

EXTERNAL PARTS

1) Remove output shaft loading fixture and support sleeve from rear of transmission case. Turn transmission to horizontal position with oil pan side up. If removed, install new oil seal ring on governor shaft. Install governor assembly into case, then install governor cover and tighten attaching bolts.

CAUTION: **Ensure governor shaft is piloted in governor cover before tightening cover attaching bolts.**

2) With correct band apply pin installed, as determined during Transmission Disassembly, install intermediate servo assembly into case. Ensure tapered end of apply pin is properly located against band apply lug. Install servo cover retaining ring and align ring gap with end showing in case slot.

NOTE: **Intermediate servo cover seal rings must be well lubricated with petrolatum to prevent damage or cutting of ring.**

Fig. 41: Installing 3/4 Accumulator Assembly

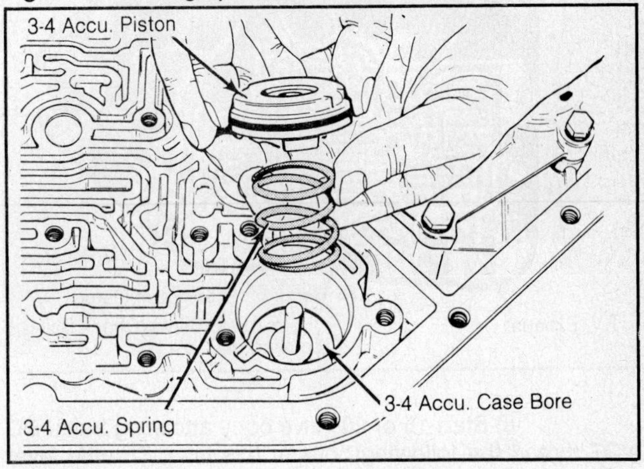

On "OG" & "OJ" models, invert piston, then install piston first and spring second.

4th CLUTCH PLATE USAGE

Application	Steel	Composition
All Models	3	2

GENERAL MOTORS TURBO HYDRA-MATIC 200-4R (Cont.)

3) Lubricate with petrolatum and install new "O" rings on case electrical connector. Install electrical connector with lock tabs facing into case, positioning locator tab in notch on side of case.

4) Install a new Teflon seal on 3-4 accumulator piston. Install accumulator pin in case, then install accumulator piston and spring. *See Fig. 41.*

NOTE: **On "OG" & "OJ" model transmissions, invert piston, install piston first, and install spring second. On "OZ" models, spring is not used. On all other models, install as shown. See Fig. 45.**

5) Install 9 check balls into locations in case. *See Fig. 42.* Install 2 valve body alignment pins into opposing bolt holes. Install spacer plate-to-case gasket (marked "C") on case, then install spacer plate.

6) Install valve body assembly-to-spacer plate gasket (marked "VB") on spacer plate. Position 1-2 accumulator plate and gasket in place on case, install accumulator spring on plate. Install a new teflon seal on 1-2 accumulator piston, install piston in accumulator housing with dome up. Install 1-2 accumulator assembly, then install and tighten 5 attaching bolts.

7) Position remaining 3 check balls in valve body. *See Fig. 35.* Retain with petrolatum. Remove alignment pins. Install valve body assembly making sure to align manual valve with detent lever.

CAUTION: **It is possible during reassembly to position manual valve too far into valve body and still connect the selective lever link to it. This will prevent valve body from fitting properly in case.**

Fig. 42: Location of Check Balls in Bottom of Case

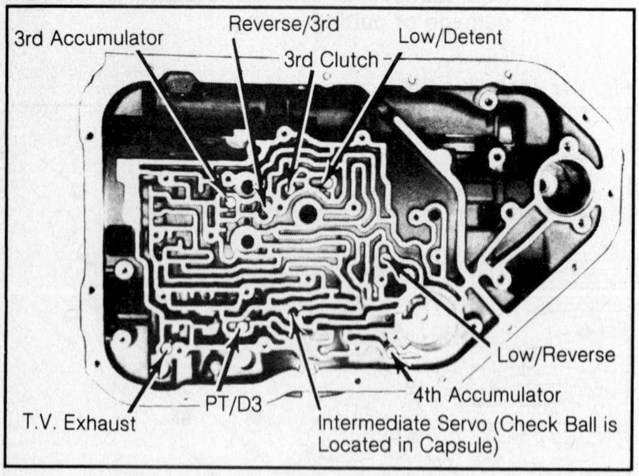

8) Start 15 of 20 valve body attaching bolts. DO NOT thread the following bolts at this time: Throttle lever and bracket assembly, manual detent roller and spring assembly and clip retaining bolts. Install signal oil pipe in valve body assembly.

9) Install manual detent roller and spring assembly, locating tang in valve body and roller on inside detent lever. If removed, install throttle and bracket assembly spring on top of lifter. Install link on throttle. Ensure link is hooked. *See Fig. 44.* Install throttle lever and bracket assembly, locating slot in bracket with roll pin and aligning lifter through valve body hole and link through T.V. linkage case bore. Install retaining bolt.

Fig. 43: Proper Positioning of Manual Valve and Selective Lever Link in Valve Body

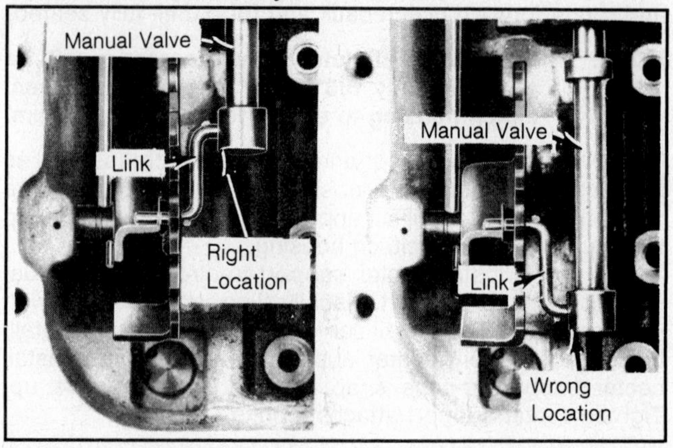

10) With locating pipe in hole, install 4-3 pressure switch (on non Computer Command Control models only) and attaching bolt. Install filter intake pipe "O" ring on pipe and coat with petrolatum. Install filter in pump bore. Install oil pan using a new gasket and tighten attaching bolts.

Fig. 44: Throttle Lever and Bracket Installation

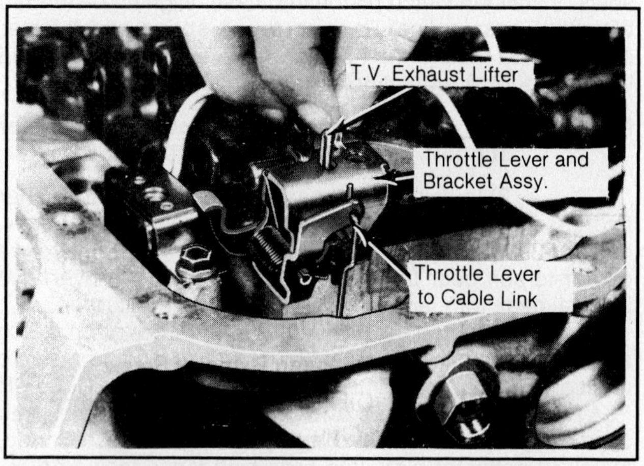

TIGHTENING SPECIFICATIONS

Application	Ft. Lbs. (N.m)
Case-To-Center Support	15-20 (20-27)
Converter-To-Flywheel	41-52 (55-70)
Cooler Connector	26-30 (35-40)
Governor Cover-To-Case	15-20 (20-27)
Manual Shaft-To-Lever Nut	20-25 (27-34)
Oil Pan-To-Case	10-13 (14-18)
Park Lock Bracket-To-Case	15-20 (20-27)
Pump Body-To-Pump Cover	15-20 (20-27)
Pump-To-Case	15-20 (20-27)
Transmission-To-Engine	41-52 (55-70)
	INCH Lbs. (N.m)
Accumulator Housing-To-Case	84-120 (10-14)
Pressure Switch	60-120 (7-14)
Pressure Take Off Plugs	60-120 (7-14)
Solenoid-To-Case	84-120 (10-14)
Speedometer Retainer-To-Case	84-120 (10-14)
Stator Shaft-To-Pump Cover	84-120 (10-14)
Valve Body-To-Case	84-120 (10-14)

GENERAL MOTORS TURBO HYDRA-MATIC 350C

Chevrolet, GMC

IDENTIFICATION

The Turbo Hydra-Matic 350C transmission can be identified by the two letter code stamped near the dipstick tube on the right hand side. See TRANSMISSION MODEL CODES for a list of the two letter codes used.

TRANSMISSION MODEL CODES

Application	Model Code
All Models	XA, XX

DESCRIPTION

The Turbo Hydra-Matic 350C transmission is a fully automatic unit consisting primarily of a 4-element torque converter and 2 planetary gear sets. Four multiple-disc clutches, 2 roller clutches and an intermediate overrun band provide the friction elements required to obtain the desired function of the 2 planetary gear sets.

A hydraulic system pressurized by a gear type pump provides the working pressure required to operate the friction elements and automatic controls. The torque converter clutch assembly consists of a 3-element torque converter with the addition of a converter clutch.

The converter clutch is splined to the turbine assembly, and when operated, applies against the converter cover, providing mechanical direct drive coupling of the engine to the transmission planetary gears. When the converter clutch is released, the assembly operates as a normal torque converter.

NOTE: **See GENERAL MOTORS TORQUE CONVERTER CLUTCH (TCC) SYSTEM article in this section for information on the torque converter clutch system used in the THM 350C transmission.**

LUBRICATION & ADJUSTMENTS

See appropriate AUTOMATIC TRANSMISSION SERVICING article in DOMESTIC GENERAL SERVICING section.

TESTING

ROAD TEST

Drive Range

With selector lever in "D", accelerate vehicle from zero MPH. A 1-2 and 2-3 shift should occur at all throttle openings. (Shift points will vary with throttle openings.) As vehicle speed decreases to zero MPH, 3-2 and 2-1 shifts should occur.

"2" – Forward Range (L2)

Place selector lever in "2" and accelerate vehicle from zero MPH. A 1-2 shift should occur at all throttle openings. No 2-3 shift can be obtained in this range. The 1-2 shift point will vary with throttle opening. As vehicle speed decreases to zero MPH, a 2-1 shift should occur. The 1-2 shift in intermediate range may be somewhat firmer than in Drive range; this is normal.

Fig. 1: Sectional View of Turbo Hydra-Matic 350C Automatic Transmission

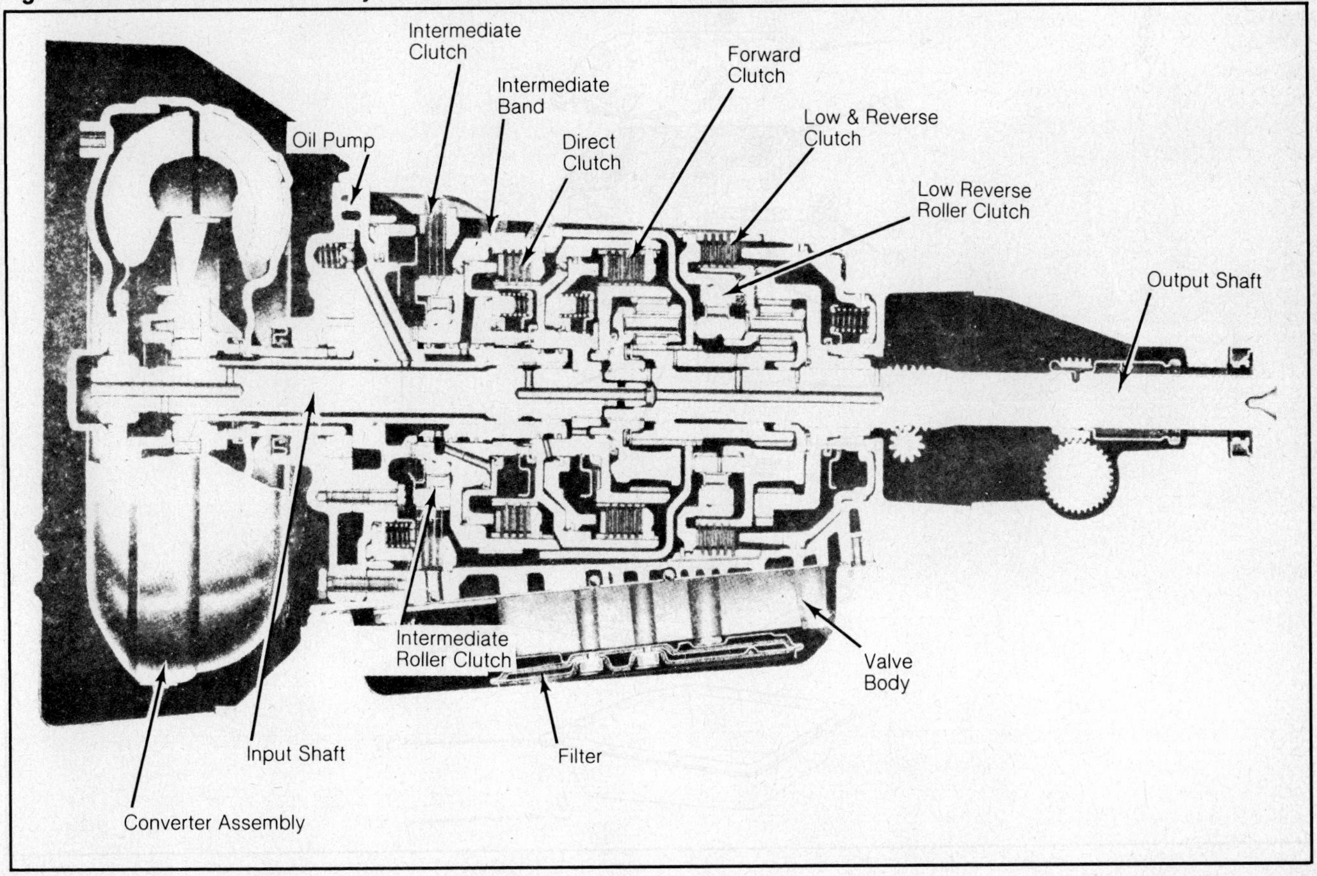

GENERAL MOTORS TURBO HYDRA-MATIC 350C (Cont.)

Fig. 2: Exploded View of Turbo Hydra-Matic 350C External Parts

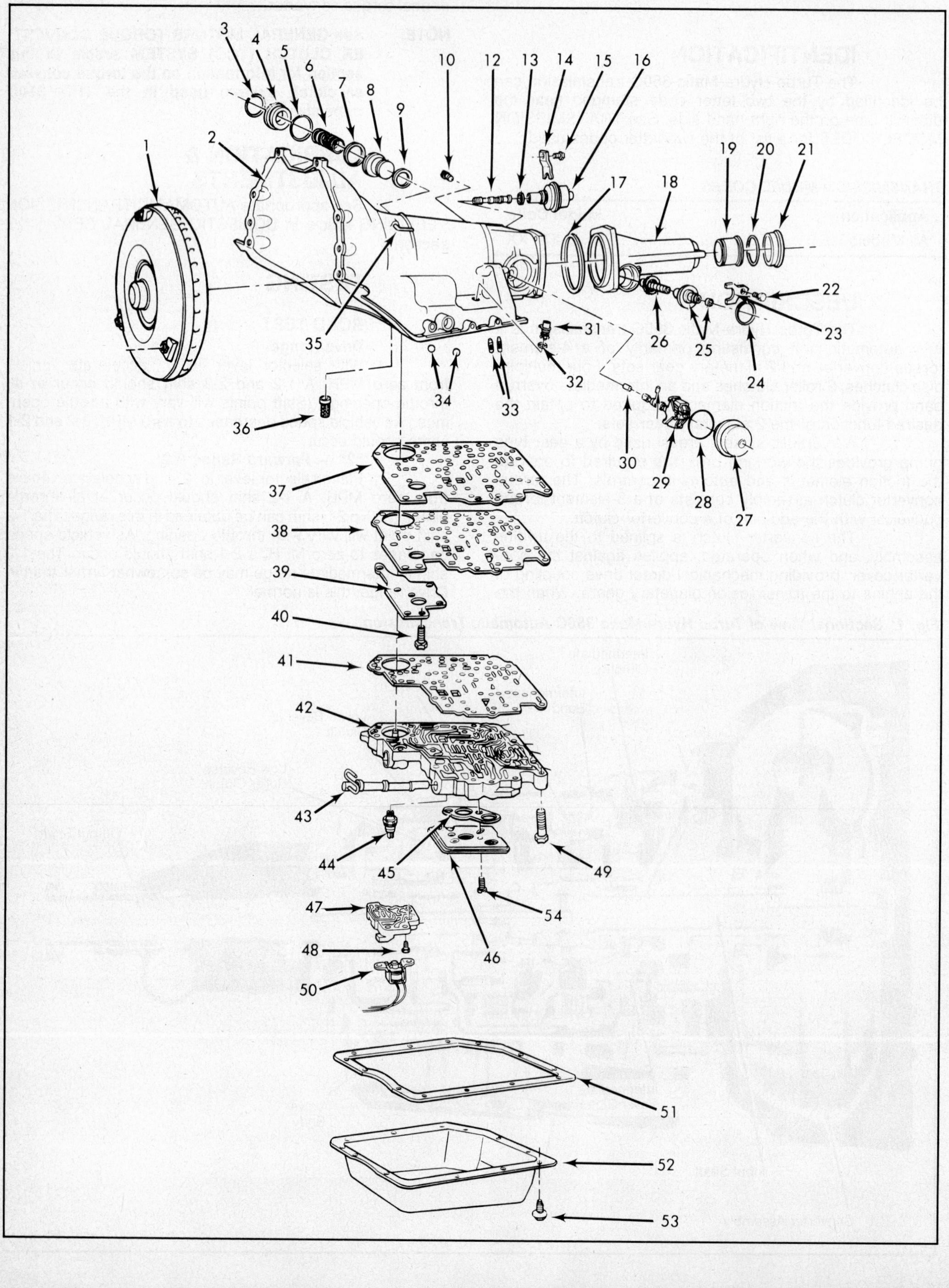

GENERAL MOTORS TURBO HYDRA-MATIC 350C (Cont.)

Turbo Hydra-Matic 350C External Parts (Use With Fig. 2)

1. Torque Converter
2. Case
3. Intermediate Clutch Accumulator Piston Cover Retainer
4. Intermediate Clutch Accumulator Piston Cover
5. Intermediate Clutch Accumulator Piston Cover Seal
6. Intermediate Clutch Accumulator Piston Spring
7. Intermediate Clutch Accumulator Piston Seal Ring
8. Intermediate Clutch Accumulator Piston
9. Intermediate Clutch Accumulator Piston Seat Ring
10. Line Pressure Check Plug
12. Vacuum Modulator Valve
13. Vacuum Modulator-to-Case Seal
14. Vacuum Modulator Retainer
15. Vacuum Modulator Retainer-to-Case Bolt
16. Vacuum Modulator
17. Case Extension-to-Case Seal
18. Extension Housing
19. Extension Housing Bushing
20. Output Yoke Sleeve Seal
21. Extension Housing Oil Seal
22. Sleeve Retainer Bolt
23. Speedometer Driven Gear Sleeve Retainer
24. Speedometer Driven Gear Sleeve-to-Housing Seal
25. Speedometer Driven Gear Sleeve
26. Speedometer Driven Gear
27. Governor Cover
28. Governor Cover-to-Case Seal
29. Governor Assembly
30. Dowel Pin
31. Case Electrical Connector
32. Case Electrical Connector Seal
33. Governor Pressure Hole Screen
34. Check Valve Ball
35. Vent Pipe
36. Oil Pump Pressure Hole Screen
37. Upper Valve Body Gasket
38. Valve Body Spacer Plate
39. Valve Body Spacer Plate Support
40. Support-to-Case Bolt
41. Lower Valve Body Gasket
42. Valve Body
43. Manual Valve Assembly
44. Oil Pressure Switch
45. Oil Pump Filter Gasket
46. Oil Filter Screen
47. Auxiliary Valve Body
48. Auxiliary Valve Body-to-Valve Body Bolt
49. Valve Body-to-Case Bolt
50. Torque Converter Clutch Solenoid
51. Oil Pan Gasket
52. Oil Pan
53. Oil Pan-to-Case Bolt
54. Oil Screen-to-Valve Body Bolt

Low Range (L1)

Place selector in "L" and accelerate vehicle from zero MPH. No upshift should occur in this range.

2nd Gear (L2) – Overrun Braking

With selector lever in "D" and vehicle speed at approximately 35 MPH with foot off accelerator, move selector lever to "2" position. Transmission should downshift to second gear. An increase in engine RPM and an engine braking effect should be noticed.

1st Gear (L-1) – Overrun Braking

With selector lever in "2" position, throttle closed, and vehicle speed at approximately 30 to 50 MPH, move selector lever to "L". A 2-1 downshift should occur in speed range of approximately 30 to 45 MPH, depending on axle ratio and valve body calibration. The 2-1 downshift at closed throttle will be accompanied by increased engine RPM and an engine braking effect should be noticed.

CONTROL PRESSURE CHECK

1) Connect tachometer to engine and 0-300 psi pressure gauge at line pressure take-off point. *See Fig. 3.* With transmission fluid at correct level and normal operating temperature, perform test as follows:

2) With vehicle stationary and service brakes set, test with vacuum gauge attached in line with modulator and tachometer hooked to engine. Check oil pressures with those found in the CONTROL PRESSURE SPECIFICATIONS table.

CONTROL PRESSURE RESULTS

Control Pressure Too High

- Vacuum leak or improper engine vacuum.
- Vacuum modulator valve stuck; water in modulator; modulator valve damaged or not operating properly.
- Detent valve or cable stuck in detent position.
- Valve body pressure regulator and/or boost valve stuck;

CLUTCH AND BAND APPLICATION CHART (ELEMENTS IN USE)

Selector Lever Position	Intermed. Clutch	Direct Clutch	Forward Clutch	Low & Reverse Clutch	Intermed. Overrun Roller Clutch	Low & Reverse Roller Clutch	Intermed. Overrun Band
D - DRIVE							
First Gear			X			X	
Second Gear	X		X		X		
Third Gear	X	X	X				
2 - INTERMEDIATE							
Second Gear	X		X		X		X
1 - LOW (First)			X	X		X	
R - REVERSE		X		X			

NEUTRAL OR PARK – All clutches and bands released and/or ineffective.

GENERAL MOTORS TURBO HYDRA-MATIC 350C (Cont.)

boost valve sleeve broken or defective; incorrect pressure regulator valve spring; 2-3 shift control valve and sleeve installed in pressure regulator bore; pressure regulator exhaust hole blocked or not drilled.

Control Pressure Too Low

- Low transmission fluid level.
- Defective vacuum modulator assembly.
- Oil screen blocked or restricted; gasket omitted or damaged.
- Incorrect oil pump gear clearance; pump gears damaged, worn or installed backward; pump-to-case gasket out of position; defective pump body and/or cover; bottom seal ring on pump cover hub omitted or damaged; priming valve in pump omitted.
- Valve body pressure regulator or boost valve stuck; pressure regulator valve spring too weak; No. 1 check ball omitted from valve body; loose valve body bolts; valve body spacer plate support omitted; reverse and modulator boost valve stuck.
- Internal leak in forward clutch circuit (pressure low in Drive, normal in Neutral and Reverse); check pump oil seal rings and forward clutch seals.
- Internal leak in direct clutch circuit (pressure low in Reverse, normal in other ranges); direct clutch outer seal and 1-2 and 2-3 accumulator pistons and rings damaged or missing.
- Intermediate servo piston seal ring broken or omitted.
- Check ball missing from cored passage in transmission case face.

No Control Pressure

- Flashing blocking suction cavity in case.
- Priming valve in pump omitted.
- Front pump drive gear lugs sheared off.
- Vacuum modulator valve omitted.
- Pump-to-case gasket incorrectly installed.

GOVERNOR PRESSURE CHECK

1) With vehicle on a hoist (rear wheels off ground), disconnect vacuum line to modulator, then install a tachometer to engine and a pressure gauge to line pressure take-off point on transmission case. *See Fig. 3.*

2) Start engine. Keeping foot off brake, move shift lever to Drive range and check line pressure with

Fig. 3: Pressure Take-Off Points

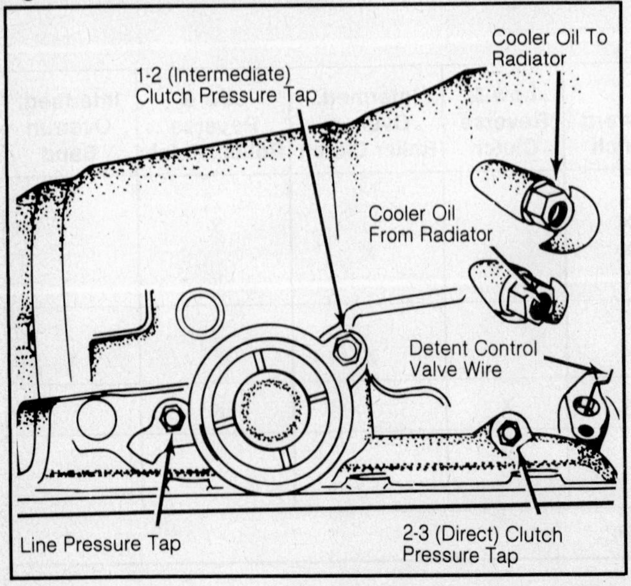

engine speed at 1000 RPM. Slowly increase engine speed to 3000 RPM and determine if a pressure drop occurs (7 psi or more).

3) If no pressure drop takes place, inspect governor for a stuck valve, weight or restricted orifice in governor valve. Check governor feed system for plugged or restricted screen in control valve assembly, restrictions in feed line or scored governor bore.

VACUUM MODULATOR CHECK

See procedure given in GENERAL MOTORS TURBO HYDRA-MATIC 400 article in this section.

TORQUE CONVERTER CLUTCH CHECK

See Testing in GENERAL MOTORS TORQUE CONVERTER CLUTCH (TCC) SYSTEM article in this section.

SERVICE (IN VEHICLE)

The following components can be removed from transmission without removing transmission from vehicle:

- Governor Assembly
- Intermediate Servo Cover and Seals
- Oil Pan and Oil Screen
- Valve Body Assembly
- Auxiliary Valve Body Assembly
- Check Balls and Valve Body Spacer Plates and Gaskets
- Pressure Regulator Parts
- Inside Detent Lever
- Manual Detent Roller and Spring Assembly
- Detent Cable and "O" Ring
- Parking Pawl, Actuator Rod and Bracket
- Manual Shaft and Seal
- Extension Housing, Gasket and Seal
- 1-2 Accumulator Housing, Gasket and Spring
- Vacuum Modulator
- Cooler Fittings
- Oil Filler Pipe and "O" Ring
- Speedometer Driven and Drive Gears
- Converter Clutch Solenoid
- Solenoid Wire Clips
- Electrical Connectors
- Governor Feed and Pump Pressure Screens
- Modulator Valve

For removal and installation of these components, see TRANSMISSION DISASSEMBLY and TRANSMISSION REASSEMBLY procedures.

REMOVAL & INSTALLATION

See appropriate AUTOMATIC TRANSMISSION REMOVAL article in DOMESTIC GENERAL SERVICING Section.

TORQUE CONVERTER

NOTE: **Torque converter is a sealed unit and cannot be disassembled for service.**

LEAKAGE CHECK

See procedure given in GENERAL MOTORS TURBO HYDRA-MATIC 400 article in this section.

GENERAL MOTORS TURBO HYDRA-MATIC 350C (Cont.)

Fig. 4: Turbo Hydra-Matic 350C Hydraulic Circuits Diagram

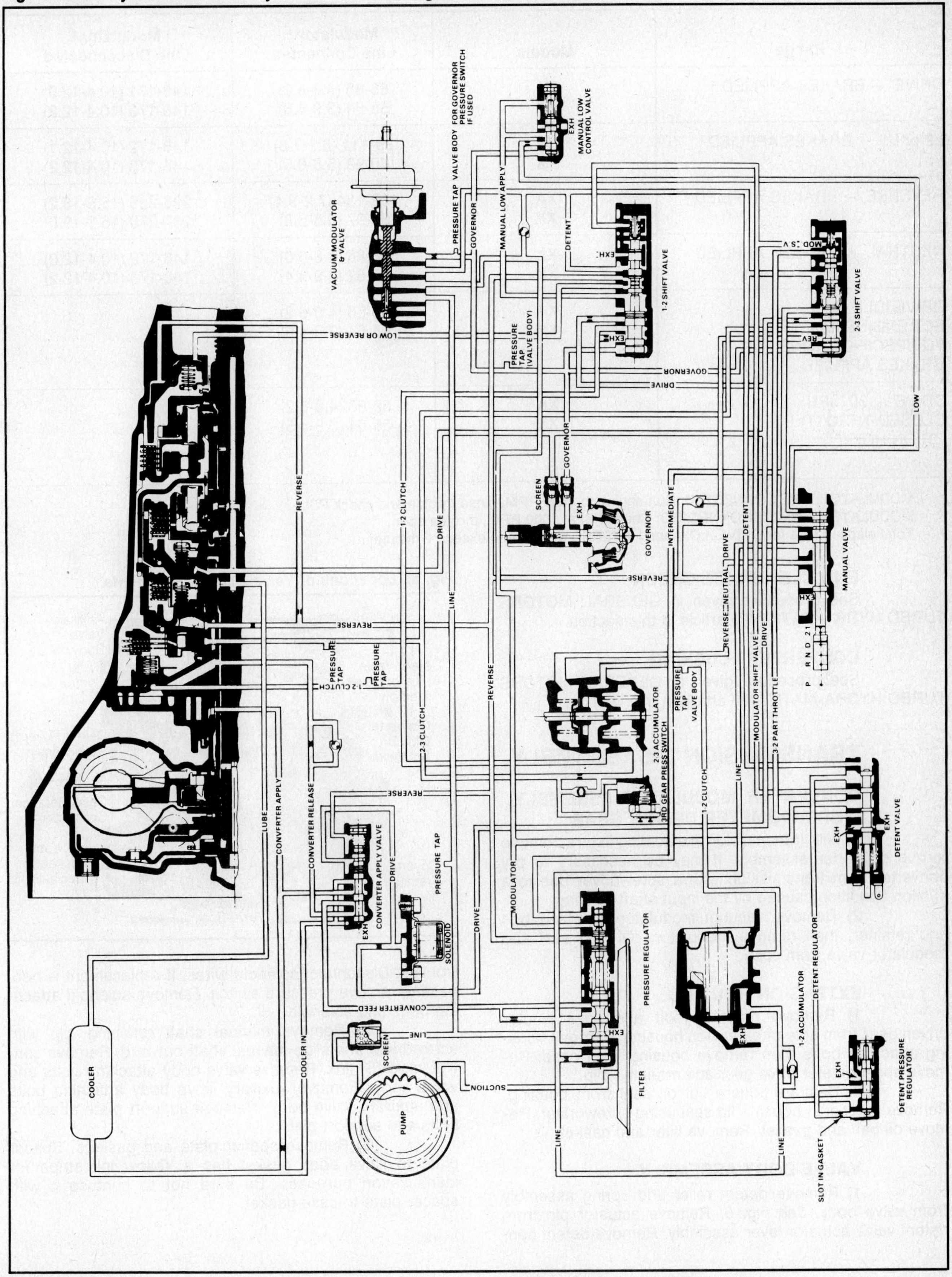

GENERAL MOTORS TURBO HYDRA-MATIC 350C (Cont.)

CONTROL PRESSURE SPECIFICATIONS – psi (kg/cm²)

Range	Models	Modulator [1] Line Connected	Modulator [2] Line Disconnected
DRIVE - BRAKES APPLIED [3]	XA XX	68-88 (4.8-6.2) 55-64 (3.9-4.5)	148-171 (10.4-12.0) 148-173 (10.4-12.2)
L2 or L1 - BRAKES APPLIED [3]	XA XX	89-111 (6.3-7.8) 80-93 (5.6-6.5)	148-172 (10.4-12.1) 148-173 (10.4-12.2)
REVERSE - BRAKES APPLIED [3]	XA XX	102-134 (7.2-9.4) 83-97 (5.8-6.8)	226-259 (15.9-18.2) 237-270 (16.7-19.0)
NEUTRAL - BRAKES APPLIED	XA XX	68-86 (4.8-6.0) 55-62 (3.9-4.4)	148-170 (10.4-12.0) 148-173 (10.4-12.2)
DRIVE IDLE SET ENGINE IDLE TO SPECIFICATIONS BRAKES APPLIED	XA XX	68-88 (4.8-6.2) 55-64 (3.9-4.5)	....
DRIVE - 30 MPH CLOSED THROTTLE OR ON HOIST	XA XX	68-88 (4.8-6.2) 55-64 (3.9-4.5)	....

[1] – MODULATOR LINE CONNECTED: Run engine to 1000 RPM, close throttle and check PSI.
[2] – MODULATOR LINE DISCONNECTED: Check PSI at 1000 RPM, throttle open.
[3] – Total elapsed time for DRIVE, LOW and REVERSE tests not to exceed 2 minutes.

END CLEARANCE CHECK

See procedure given in GENERAL MOTORS TURBO HYDRA-MATIC 400 article in this section.

CONVERTER FLUSHING

See procedure given in GENERAL MOTORS TURBO HYDRA-MATIC 400 article in this section.

TRANSMISSION DISASSEMBLY

CONVERTER, MODULATOR ASSEMBLY, & SPEEDOMETER DRIVEN GEAR

1) With transmission in a holding fixture, remove torque converter assembly. It may be necessary to pry converter from transmission with a screwdriver due to a suction condition caused by the input shaft "O" ring.

2) Remove vacuum modulator attaching bolt and retainer, then remove modulator, "O" ring seal and modulator valve from case.

EXTENSION HOUSING

1) Remove retaining bolt and speedometer driven gear from side of extension housing. Remove housing attaching bolts then remove housing from case. Remove speedometer drive gear and retaining clip.

2) Remove square cut oil seal from housing. Remove extension housing lip seal using screwdriver. Remove oil pan and gasket. Remove filter and gasket.

VALVE BODY ASSEMBLY

1) Remove detent roller and spring assembly from valve body. *See Fig. 5.* Remove actuator pin from detent valve actuator lever assembly. Remove detent control link. Disconnect solenoid wires. If replacement is necessary, remove pressure switch. Remove solenoid attaching bolts and solenoid.

Fig. 5: Locations of Valve Body Components

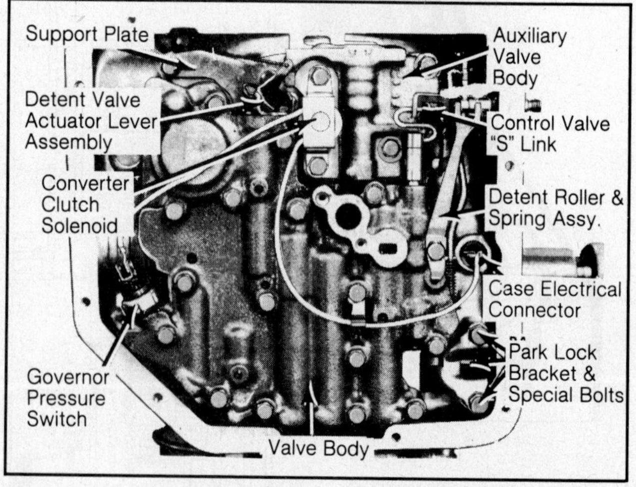

2) Remove manual shaft retaining clip with screwdriver and slide manual shaft outward. Remove control valve "S" link. Remove valve body attaching bolts and valve body. Remove auxiliary valve body attaching bolts and auxiliary valve body. Remove support plate attaching bolts and support plate.

3) Remove spacer plate and gaskets. Spacer plate to valve body gasket has a Yellow ink stripe for identification purposes. Be sure not to confuse it with spacer plate-to-case gasket.

GENERAL MOTORS TURBO HYDRA-MATIC 350C (Cont.)

4) Remove 5 check balls, noting locations for reference at reassembly. *See Fig. 6.* Remove park lock bracket and special bolts. Remove oil pump pressure screen from the case. Remove governor screen from case. Remove case electrical connector and the "O" ring by depressing tabs.

Fig. 6: Location of Check Balls

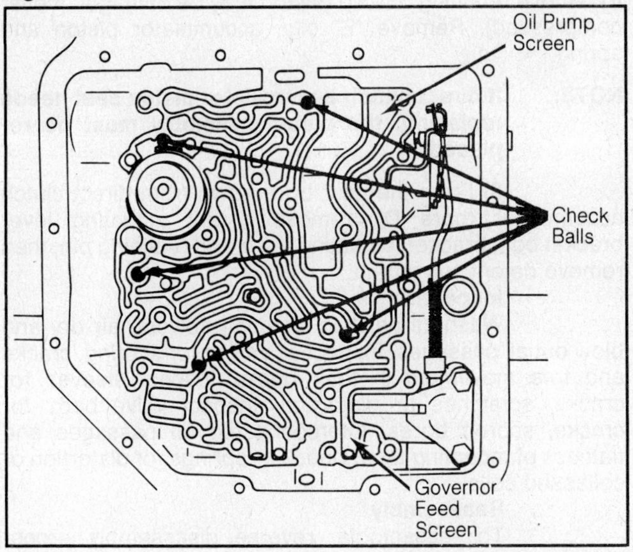

MANUAL SHAFT & PARKING PAWL

1) Remove jam nut holding range selector lever inner lever to manual shaft. Remove manual shaft from case. Remove range selector inner lever and parking pawl actuating rod. Remove manual shaft to case lip seal, if necessary.

Fig. 7: Bottom View of Parking Pawl Assembly

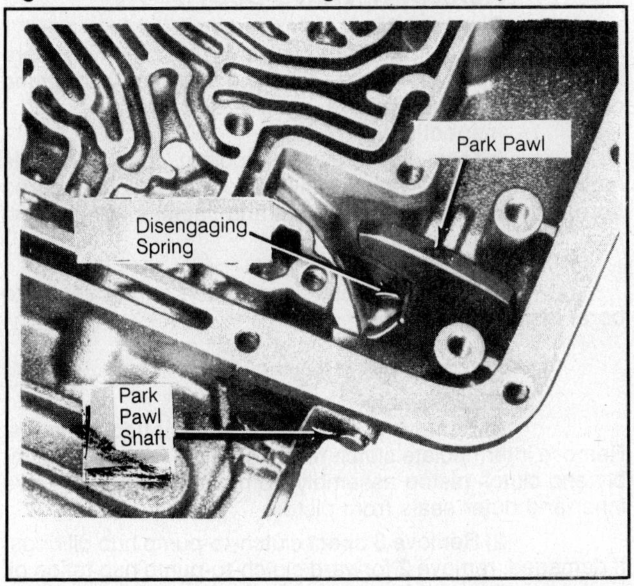

2) Remove parking pawl retaining plug, parking pawl shaft, parking pawl and disengaging spring. *See Fig. 7.* Remove intermediate servo piston, washer, spring seat, and apply pin. *See Fig. 8.* If piston or seal need replacement, both will have to be replaced as an assembly.

Fig. 8: Intermediate Servo Removal

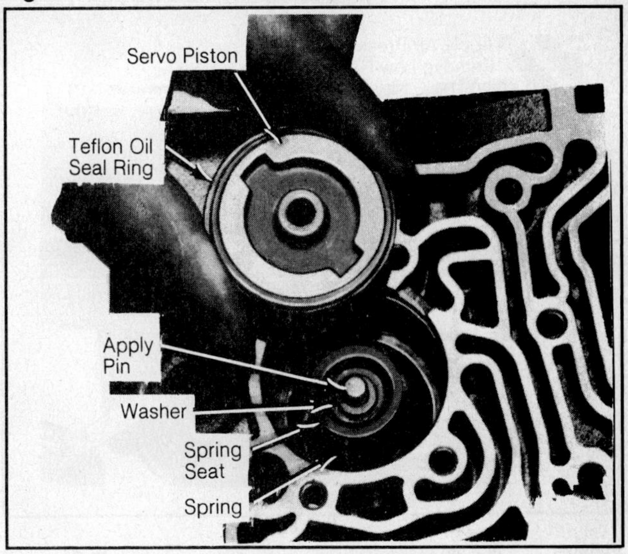

OIL PUMP & INTERNAL COMPONENTS

1) Remove oil pump-to-case attaching bolts with washer type seals, then discard seals. Install 2 slide hammers into threaded holes in pump body, tighten jam nuts and remove pump from case. Remove and discard gasket.

2) Remove intermediate clutch cushion spring, faced clutch plates, steel separator plates, wave spring and pressure plate from case. Remove intermediate overrun brake band. Grasp input shaft and pull direct and forward clutches from case as an assembly.

3) Remove forward clutch housing-to-input ring gear front thrust washer. Remove input ring gear and ring gear-to-output carrier needle thrust bearing. Remove output carrier-to-output shaft snap ring and remove output carrier.

4) Remove sun gear driving shell assembly. Remove low and reverse roller clutch support-to-case snap ring. Grasp output shaft and pull up until low and reverse roller clutch and support assembly clear retainer spring. Then remove support assembly from case. Remove retainer (anti-clunk) spring.

5) Remove low and reverse clutch faced plates and steel separator plates, noting number and position of plates used for reassembly reference. Remove reaction carrier assembly from output ring gear and shaft assembly, then remove output ring gear and shaft assembly from case. Remove reaction carrier-to-output ring gear needle thrust bearing.

6) Remove output ring gear to case needle bearing assembly from output shaft assembly or case. If necessary, remove ring gear to output shaft snap ring, then remove output ring gear from ouput shaft. Using a compressor tool, compress low and reverse clutch piston spring retainer.

7) Remove piston retaining ring, spring retainer and springs. Remove low and reverse clutch piston assembly by applying air pressure to oil passage in case. *See Fig. 9.* Remove seals from low and reverse clutch piston.

8) Using Compressor (J-23069), compress intermediate clutch accumulator piston cover and remove retaining ring. Remove cover, "O" ring seal, accumulator piston spring and piston assembly.

GENERAL MOTORS TURBO HYDRA-MATIC 350C (Cont.)

Fig. 9: Removing Low-Reverse Clutch Piston

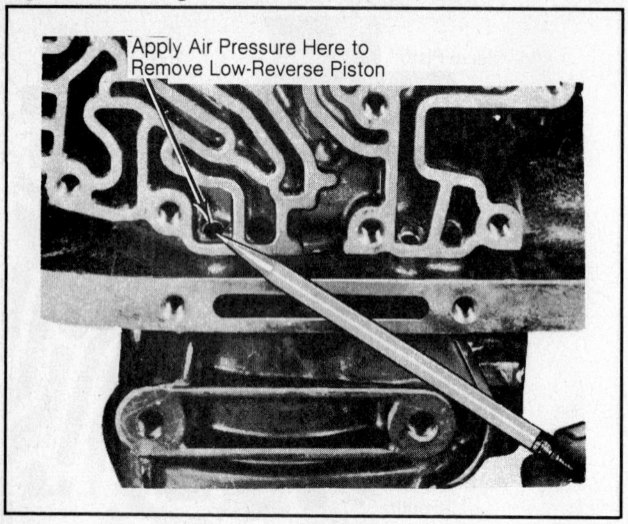

NOTE: **Do not remove accumulator piston Teflon oil seal rings. If seal rings are damaged, the piston assembly must be replaced.**

Fig. 10: Exploded View of Intermediate Accumulator Assembly

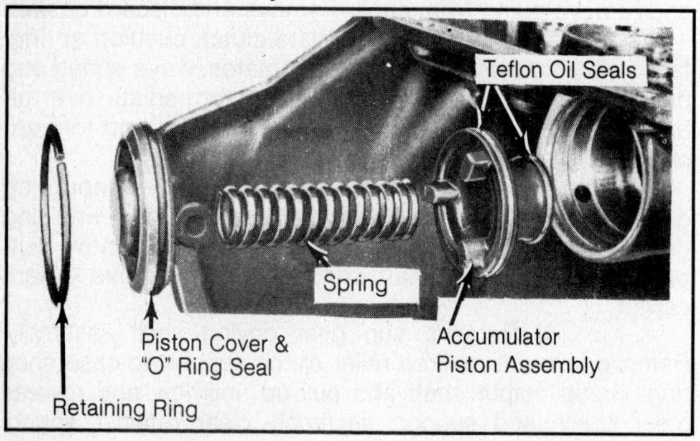

COMPONENT DISASSEMBLY & REASSEMBLY

VALVE BODY

NOTE: **As valve trains are removed from each valve body bore, place individual parts in correct order and in relative position to valve body to simplify reassembly. Valves and springs are not interchangeable, and all parts must be installed in correct order in proper valve body bore. *See Fig. 11.***

Disassembly

1) Position valve body assembly with cored face up. Position direct clutch accumulator piston pocket at upper left. Remove manual valve from lower left-hand bore (bore J).

2) From lower right-hand bore (bore A) remove retaining pin, then remove pressure regulator valve train.

3) From next bore up (bore B), remove retaining pin, then remove 2-3 shift valve train.

4) From next bore up (bore C), remove retaining pin, then remove 1-2 shift valve train.

5) From the next bore up (bore E), remove retaining pin, plug manual low control valve spring and manual low control valve.

6) From the next bore up (bore F), remove retaining pin, spring seat and detent regulator valve.

7) Install a compressor tool on direct clutch accumulator piston (G), then compress piston only enough to remove retaining "E" clip (piston may be damaged if over compressed). Remove "E" clip, accumulator piston and spring.

NOTE: **If direct clutch accumulator piston seal needs replacing, the piston assembly must be replaced.**

8) From the next bore down from direct clutch accumulator (bore D), remove detent actuating lever bracket bolt, bracket, actuating lever and retaining pin, then remove detent valve train.

Inspection

Wash all parts in cleaning solvent, air dry and blow out all passages. Inspect all valves for scoring, cracks and free movement in their bores. Inspect sleeves for cracks, scratches or distortion. Inspect valve body for cracks, scored bores, interconnected oil passages and flatness of mounting face. Check all springs for distortion or collapsed coils.

Reassembly

To reassemble, reverse disassembly procedure. Align piston and oil seal ring when installing direct clutch accumulator piston spring and piston with same tool used at disassembly and secure with retaining ring.

CAUTION: **When installing direct clutch accumulator piston into valve body, compress piston only enough to install retaining "E" clip. Piston may be damaged if over compressed.**

AUXILIARY VALVE BODY

Disassembly

Position auxiliary valve body assembly core face up. From bore, remove retaining pin, seat, spring and converter clutch apply valve.

Inspection

Inspect apply valve for scoring, cracks and free movement in bore. Check valve body for cracks, scored bore, interconnected oil passage and flatness of mounting face. Check spring for distortion.

Reassembly

Install apply valve, spring and spring seat into bore. Install retaining pin.

OIL PUMP

Disassembly

1) Remove pump cover-to-body attaching bolts. Remove intermediate clutch return springs, retainer assembly and clutch piston assembly from pump cover. Remove inner and outer seals from piston.

2) Remove 3 direct clutch-to-pump hub oil rings. If damaged, remove 2 forward clutch-to-pump hub teflon oil seal rings. Remove pump cover-to-direct clutch drum needle thrust bearings and, if equipped, remove input shaft end play adjusting shim.

NOTE: **If replacement of forward clutch-to-pump hub Teflon oil seal rings is necessary, use 2 metal hook-type service replacement rings.**

GENERAL MOTORS TURBO HYDRA-MATIC 350C (Cont.)

Fig. 11: Exploded View of Valve Body Assembly

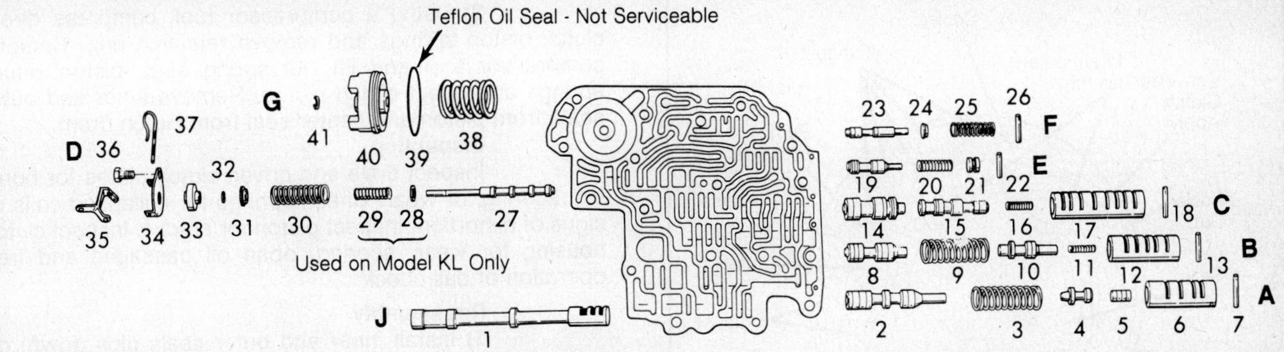

1. Manual Valve
2. Pressure Regulator Valve
3. Spring
4. Reverse/Modulator Boost Valve
5. Intermediate Boost Valve
6. Boost Valve Sleeve
7. Retaining Pin
8. 2-3 Shift Valve
9. Spring
10. 2-3 Shift Control Valve
11. Spring
12. Sleeve
13. Retaining Pin
14. 1-2 Shift Valve
15. 1-2 Shift Control Valve
16. Spring
17. Sleeve
18. Retaining Pin
19. Manual Low Control Valve
20. Spring
21. Plug
22. Retaining Pin
23. Detent Regulator Valve
24. Spring Seat
25. Spring
26. Retaining Pin
27. Detent Valve
28. Washer
29. Inner Spring (Detent Valve)
30. Outer Spring (Detent Valve)
31. Outer Spring Seat
32. Spring Retainer
33. Detent Valve Stop
34. Detent Valve Actuating Lever Bracket
35. Detent Valve Actuating Lever
36. Retaining Bolt
37. Retaining Pin
38. Spring
39. Oil Seal Ring
40. Direct Clutch 2-3 Accumulator
41. Retaining "E" Clip

Fig. 12: Auxiliary Valve Body Exploded View

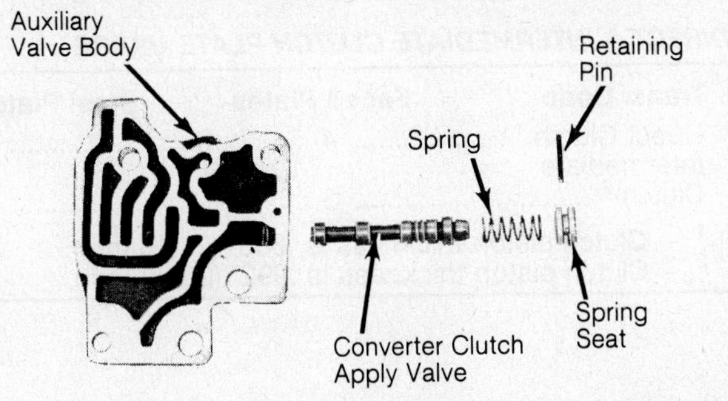

3) Check steady ring. If cut or frozen in groove, remove and replace with a new ring of the same color. The different colors compensate for groove depth. ALWAYS replace this ring with a new ring of the same color.

4) Separate pump cover and stator shaft assembly from pump body. Remove pump drive gear and driven gear from pump body. Remove pump to case square cut "O" ring seal. If required, remove pump body-to-converter hub lip seal.

Inspection

1) Wash all parts in cleaning solvent, blow out all passages and air dry. Do not use rags to dry parts. Inspect pump drive and driven gears, gear packet and crescent for nicks, scoring or other damage. Inspect pump body and cover for nicks or scoring.

2) Inspect pump cover hub outer diameter for nicks or burrs which might damage direct clutch drum bushing. Check pump cover and hub lubrication holes for restrictions. If replacement of forward clutch teflon seal rings is necessary, replace with 2 metal hook-type rings.

Reassembly

1) If pump body oil seal was removed, place pump body on wood blocks, coat outside diameter of new

Fig. 13: Oil Pump Body Oil Passages

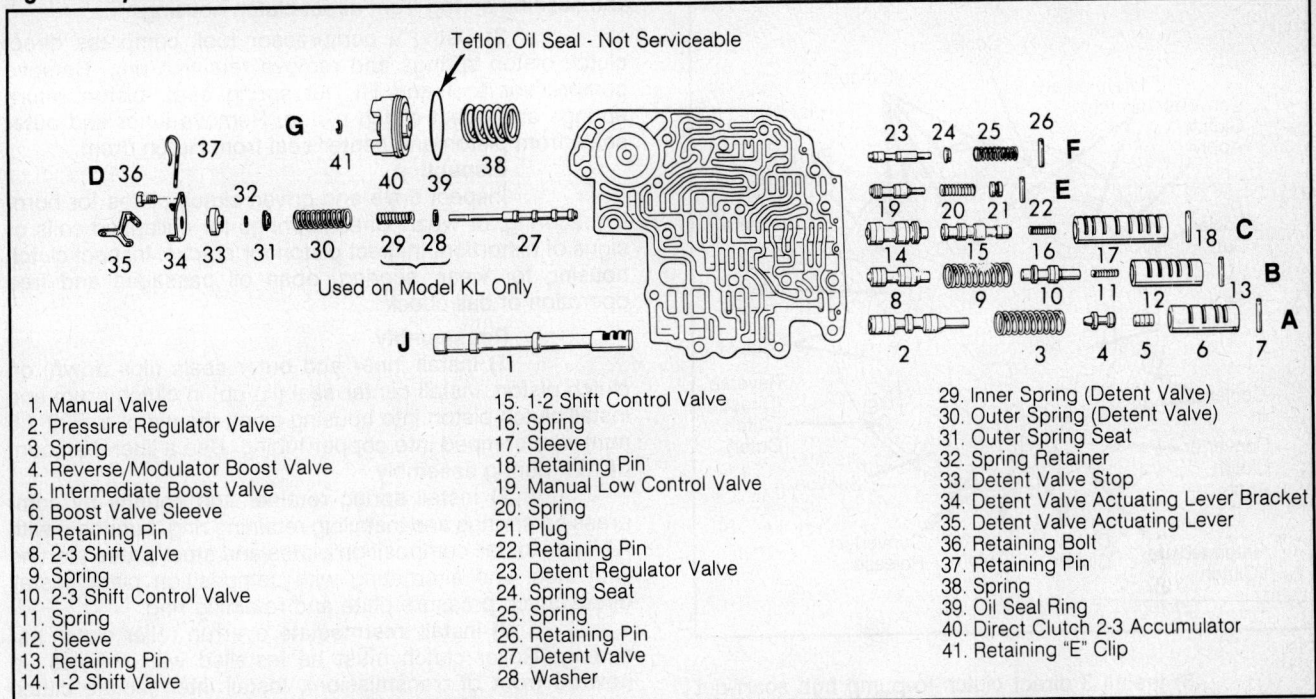

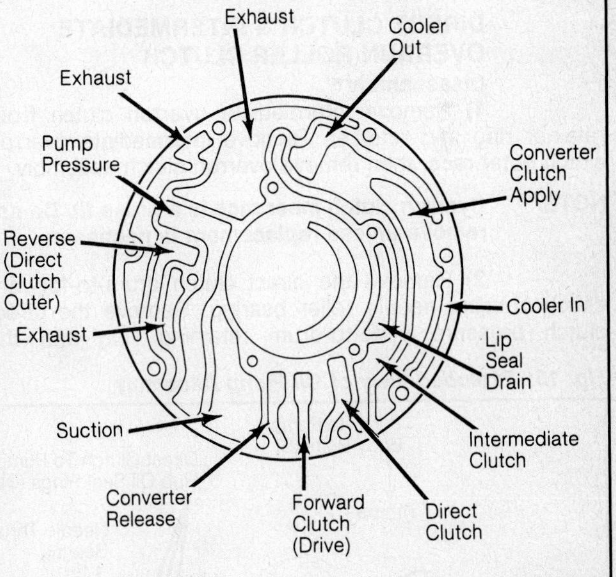

seal with a non-hardening sealer, then install seal fully into its counterbore.

2) Install pump drive and driven gear. Drive gear has offset tangs. Assemble with tang face up to prevent damage to converter. Assemble pump cover to pump body.

3) Install new inner and outer seals on intermediate clutch piston, then install piston assembly into pump cover, using care not to damage seals. Install spring retainer on clutch piston.

4) Install pump cover-to-body attaching bolts finger tight. Place Alignment Strap (J-21368) over cover and body, then tighten attaching bolts. Remove alignment strap. Install pump outside diameter square-cut "O" ring.

GENERAL MOTORS TURBO HYDRA-MATIC 350C (Cont.)

Fig. 14: Pump Cover Oil Passages

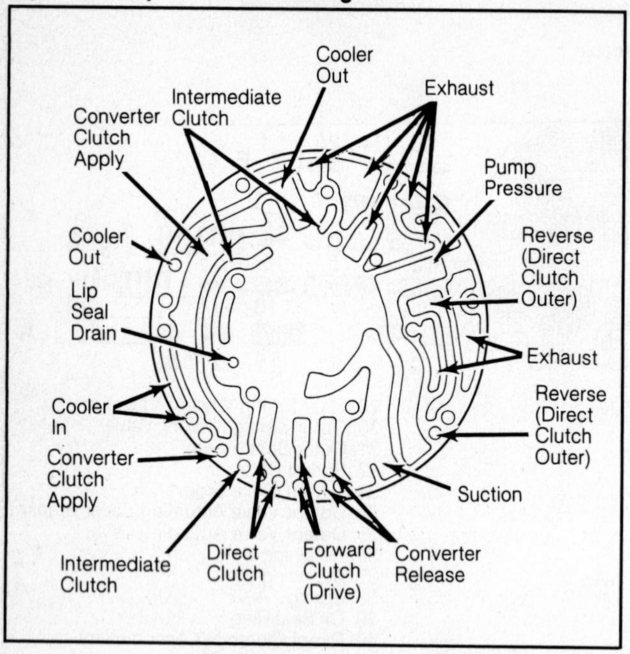

5) Install 3 direct clutch-to-pump hub scarf-cut oil seal rings. If removed, install 2 new forward clutch-to-pump hub hook-type seal rings. Check that 3 pump cover oil holes are not restricted.

DIRECT CLUTCH & INTERMEDIATE OVERRUN ROLLER CLUTCH

Disassembly

1) Remove intermediate overrun clutch front retainer ring and retainer. Remove intermediate overrun clutch outer race, then remove overrun clutch assembly.

NOTE: **Overrun clutch inner race is a press fit. Do not remove unless replacement is necessary.**

2) Remove the direct clutch drum-to-forward clutch housing needle roller bearing. Remove the direct clutch pressure plate-to-drum retaining ring and the pressure plate. Withdraw composition plates, steel plates and cushion spring from direct clutch housing.

3) Using a compressor tool, compress direct clutch piston springs and remove retaining ring. Remove compressor tool and lift out spring seat, piston return springs and direct clutch piston. Remove inner and outer seals from piston and center seal from clutch drum.

Inspection

Inspect drive and driven clutch plates for burning, scoring, or wear. Check springs for collapsed coils or signs of distortion. Inspect piston for cracks. Inspect clutch housing for wear, scoring, open oil passages and free operation of ball check.

Reassembly

1) Install inner and outer seals (lips down) on clutch piston. Install center seal (lip up) in clutch drum and install clutch piston into housing using the aid of a .020" (.5 mm) wire crimped into copper tubing. Use a liberal amount of ATF during assembly.

2) Install spring retainer and springs by compressing springs and installing retaining ring. Lubricate with ATF and install composition plates and steel plates starting with steel and alternating with composition plate. Install direct clutch pressure plate and retaining ring.

3) Install intermediate overrun roller clutch assembly. Roller clutch must be installed with 4 holes up (toward front of transmission). Install intermediate clutch overrun outer race. When properly installed, it should free-wheel in the counterclockwise direction only. Install intermediate overrun clutch retainer and retaining ring.

DIRECT & INTERMEDIATE CLUTCH PLATE USAGE

Trans. Code	Faced Plates	Steel Plates
Direct Clutch [1]	4	4
Intermediate Clutch [2]	3	3

[1] – Clutch piston thickness is .833" (21.16 mm).
[2] – Clutch piston thickness is .992" (25.20 mm).

Fig. 15: Exploded View of Oil Pump Assembly

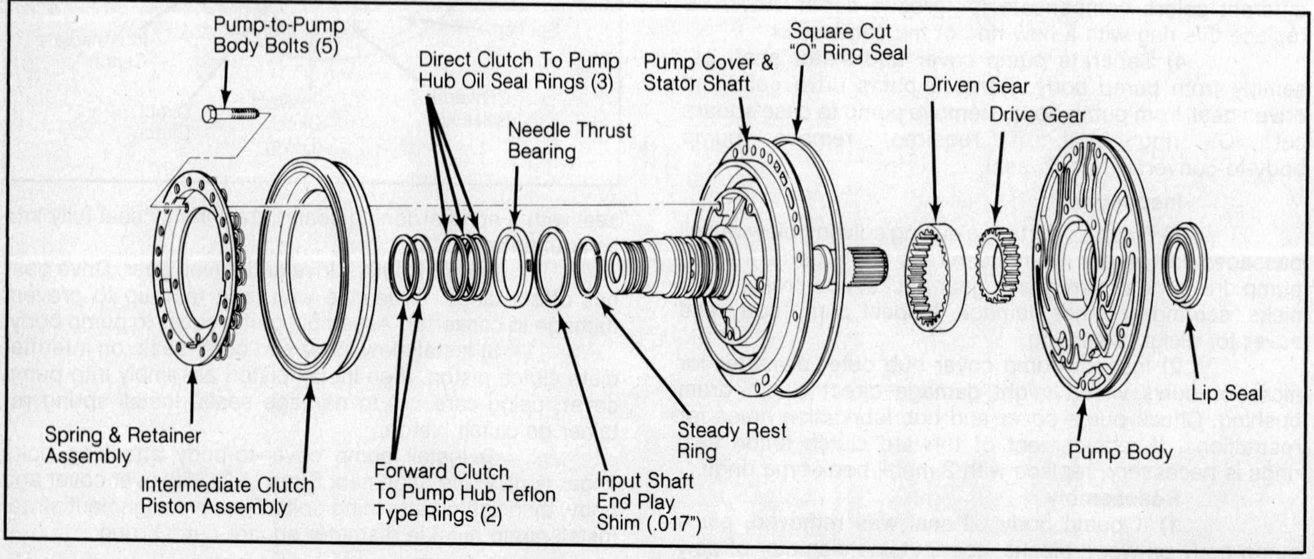

GENERAL MOTORS TURBO HYDRA-MATIC 350C (Cont.)

Fig. 16: Exploded View of Direct Clutch Assembly

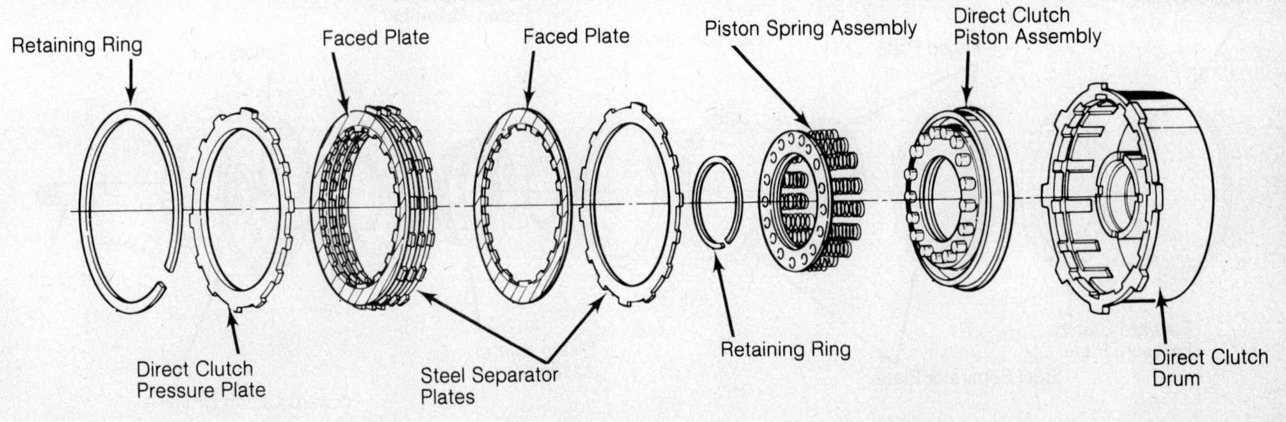

Fig. 17: Exploded View of Intermediate Overrun Roller Clutch Assembly

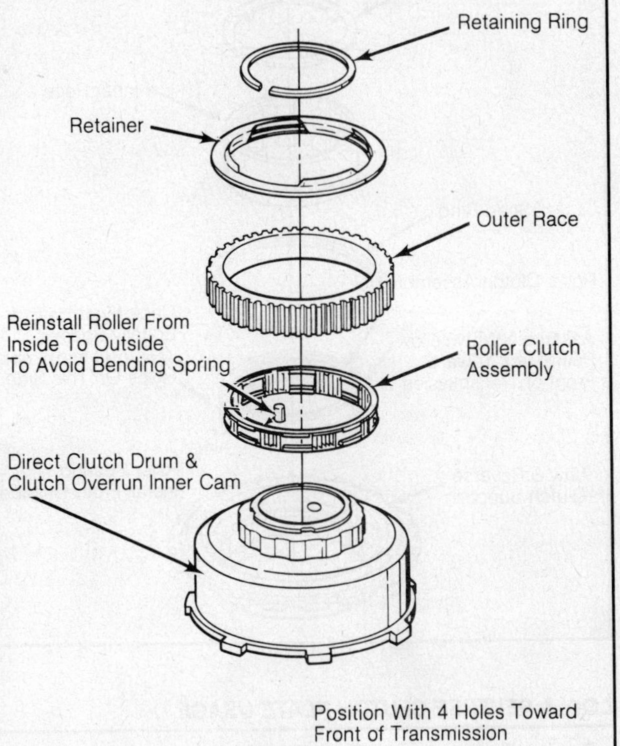

FORWARD CLUTCH

Disassembly

1) Remove forward clutch drum-to-pressure plate retaining ring, then remove pressure plate. Remove faced plates, steel separator plates and cushion spring, noting position and number used.

2) Using a ram compressor, compress forward clutch piston return spring and seat assembly and remove retaining ring. Remove tool, and lift out return springs, seat assembly, and forward clutch piston assembly.

3) Remove inner and outer seals from piston. If required, use wood blocks for support and press input shaft out of forward clutch housing.

NOTE: **When pressing the input shaft into the forward clutch housing, care must be taken not to place excessive force on the input shaft as damage may result.**

Inspection

1) Inspect lined and steel separator plates for signs of burning, scoring or wear. Inspect piston return springs for collapsed coils or signs of distortion or over-heating. Inspect piston for cracks. Inspect clutch housing for wear, scoring, open oil passages and free operation of exhaust check ball.

2) Inspect input shaft for open lubrication passages at ends, damaged splines, damaged ground bushing journals and cracks or distortion.

Reassembly

1) Install forward clutch inner piston seal and outer piston seal, (if removed). Install the forward clutch piston assembly using a thin feeler gauge. Install spring retainer and springs. Compress spring retainer with an arbor or ram press.

2) Lubricate with ATF and install cushion spring, faced spring, faced plates and steel separator plates, starting with cushion spring and alternating steel and faced plates.

FORWARD CLUTCH PLATE USAGE

Trans. Code	Faced Plates	Steel Plates
XX [1]	5	5
XA [2]	5	5

[1] - Clutch piston thickness is 1.223" (31.06 mm).
[2] - Clutch piston thickness is 1.405" (35.68 mm).

3) Using a feeler gauge, check clearance between forward clutch pressure plate and faced plate. Desired clearance is .011-.082" (.27-2.08 mm). Three thicknesses of pressure plates are available, identified by the number of tangs having markings. If necessary, select a replacement plate to give the desired clearance.

GENERAL MOTORS TURBO HYDRA-MATIC 350C (Cont.)

Fig. 18: Exploded View of Foward Clutch Assembly

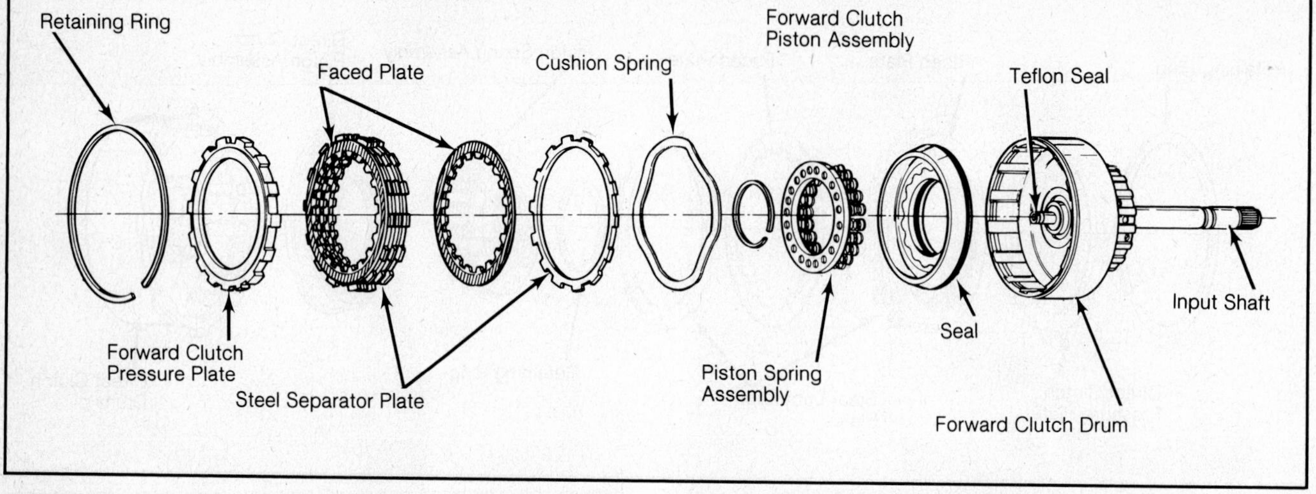

FORWARD CLUTCH PRESSURE PLATE IDENTIFICATION MARK & THICKNESS SPECIFICATIONS

No. of Marks	In. (mm)
None	.245-.255 (6.22-6.47)
1 Mark	.275-.285 (6.98-7.23)
2 Marks	.306-.316 (7.77-8.02)

SUN GEAR & SUN GEAR DRIVE SHELL

Disassembly

Remove and discard sun gear-to-sun gear drive shell rear retaining ring. Remove sun gear-to-drive shell flat rear steel thrust washer. Remove sun gear assembly from drive shell, then remove and discard front retaining ring.

Reassembly

Install new front retaining ring on sun gear. Install sun gear into sun gear shell. Install sun gear-to-drive shell flat steel thrust washer. Install new sun gear-to-sun gear shell drive retaining ring.

NOTE: **Do not overstress front and rear sun gear retaining rings when installing.**

LOW & REVERSE ROLLER CLUTCH ASSEMBLY

Disassembly

Remove low-reverse clutch-to-sun gear shell thrust washer. Remove low-reverse overrun clutch inner race. Remove low-reverse roller clutch retaining ring. Remove low reverse roller clutch assembly.

Reassembly

1) Install low and reverse roller clutch assembly to inner race. Install overrun roller clutch assembly and inner race into low and reverse clutch support with 4 holes down or to rear of transmission. When properly installed, inner race should freewheel in clockwise direction only.

2) Install low and reverse clutch-to-cam retaining ring. Install low and reverse-to-sun gear driving shell thrust washer.

Fig. 19: Exploded View of Low and Reverse Clutch Support and Overrun Roller Clutch Assembly

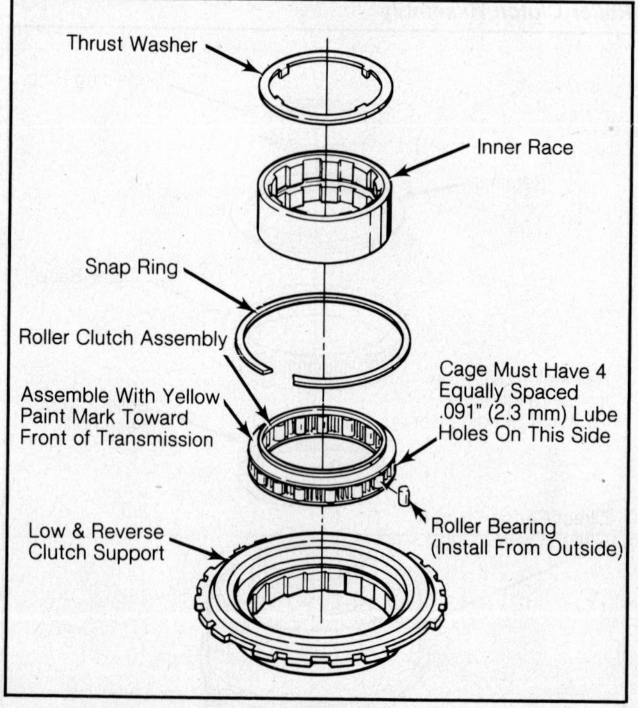

LOW & REVERSE CLUTCH PLATE USAGE

Trans. Code	Faced Plates	Steel Plates
XX [1]	5	5
XA [2]	5	5

1 – Clutch piston thickness 2.921" (74.19 mm).
2 – Clutch piston thickness 3.106" (78.89 mm).

GOVERNOR ASSEMBLY

Governor, including driven gear, is serviced as a complete assembly. Driven gear, however, may be serviced separately. Disassembly is necessary to replace a driven gear. Disassembly may also be necessary due to improper operation.

GENERAL MOTORS TURBO HYDRA-MATIC 350C (Cont.)

Disassembly

Cut off one end of each governor weight pin and remove pins, thrust cap, weights and springs. Remove governor valve from governor sleeve.

NOTE: **Governor weights are interchangeable from side to side and need not be identified.**

Inspection

1) Wash all parts, air dry and blow out all passages. Inspect governor sleeve for nicks, burrs, scoring or galling. Check governor sleeve for free operation in bore of case. Inspect valve for nicks, burrs, scoring, galling and free operation in bore of governor sleeve.

2) Inspect driven gear for nicks, burrs, damage or looseness on governor sleeve. Inspect springs for distortion or damage. Check weights for free operation in their retainers. Check valve opening at entry and exhaust. It should be .020" (.5 mm) minimum.

Fig. 20: Exploded View of Governor Assembly

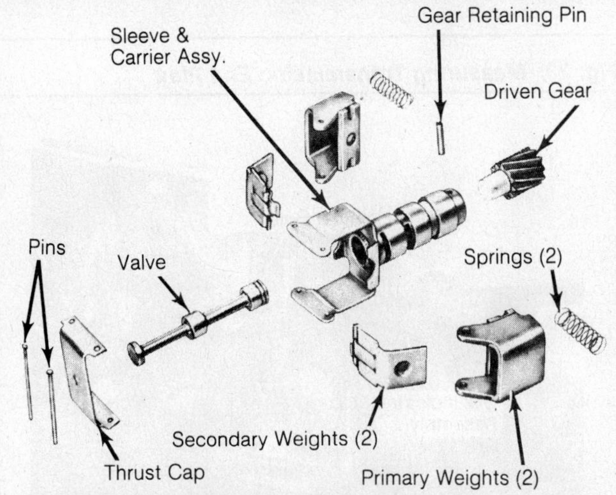

Driven Gear Replacement

1) Drive split retaining pin out of gear. Support governor on 3/16" plates installed in exhaust slots of governor sleeve. Place in an arbor press. With a long punch, press gear out of sleeve. Wash all parts to remove metal chips.

2) Support governor on 3/16" plates installed in exhaust slots of sleeve. Position new gear in sleeve. Using a socket, press gear into sleeve until nearly seated. Remove any chips that may have shaved off gear hub, then press gear in until it bottoms on shoulder.

3) Locate a new pin hole position 90° from existing hole. Make hole with center punch and while supporting governor in press, drill a new 1/8" hole through sleeve and gear. Install split retaining pin. Wash governor assembly thoroughly to remove any metal chips.

Reassembly

1) Install governor valve in bore of sleeve (large land end first). Install weights and springs and thrust cap on governor sleeve. Align pin holes in thrust cap, weight assemblies and governor sleeve.

2) Install new pins and crimp both ends of pins to keep them from falling out. Check weight assemblies for free operation on pins. Check governor valve for free movement in governor sleeve.

TRANSMISSION REASSEMBLY

NOTE: **When reassembling transmission, use only transmission fluid or petrolatum as lubricants to retain bearings or races. Lubricate all bearings, bushings, seal rings and clutch plates prior to reassembly.**

INTERNAL COMPONENTS

1) Install inner, outer and center seals on low and reverse clutch piston. Install piston into transmission case with notch on piston adjacent to parking pawl. Install piston return springs and spring retainer. Compress retainer and install retaining snap ring.

NOTE: **As spring retainer is compressed, make sure inner edge of retainer does not hang up in snap ring groove.**

2) Install output ring on output shaft and retain with a new snap ring. Install reaction carrier-to-output ring gear needle thrust bearing with lip side face up. Install output ring gear-to-case needle thrust bearing assembly with lip on inner race pointing toward rear of transmission.

3) Install reaction carrier assembly into output ring gear and shaft assembly. Install output shaft and reaction carrier assembly into case. Oil and install low and reverse clutch plates, starting with a steel plate and alternating with faced plates.

4) Make sure notches in steel plates are placed toward bottom of case. Install low and reverse clutch support retainer (anti-clunk) spring. *See Fig. 22.* Install low and reverse clutch support assembly into case, pushing firmly until support assembly is seated past top of low and reverse support retainer spring. Install support-to-case retaining ring.

NOTE: **Make sure splines on inner race of roller clutch align with splines on reaction carrier.**

5) Install low-reverse clutch support inner race-to-sun gear drive shell thrust washer and install drive shell. Install output carrier assembly. Install input ring gear-to-output carrier needle thrust bearing (lip side face down), then install a new output carrier-to-output shaft snap ring.

6) Install input ring gear into case, then install forward clutch-to-input ring gear front thrust washer. Washer has 3 tangs. Install direct clutch drum-to-forward clutch housing needle roller bearing. Install direct clutch assembly to forward clutch assembly.

7) Install assemblies into case making sure forward clutch faced plates are positioned over input ring gear and tangs on direct clutch housing are installed into slots on sun gear drive shell. Install intermediate overrun brake band with anchor lug and apply lug positioned properly. Install intermediate clutch pressure plate.

8) After lubricating with transmission fluid, install intermediate clutch plates, starting with a faced plate, then alternating steel and faced plates. Install intermediate clutch cushion spring.

9) Install .017" (.43 mm) shim and needle thrust bearing face down on pump cover hub. Before installation, coat both sides of shims and bearing with petrolatum. Lubricate oil pump bore in case, then install a new pump-to-case gasket. Install guide pins to case.

10) Install pump into case bore. Remove guide pins and install 4 pump-to-case attaching bolts. Using new washer type seals, tighten bolts. If input shaft cannot be

GENERAL MOTORS TURBO HYDRA-MATIC 350C (Cont.)

Fig. 21: Exploded View of Planetary Gear Train

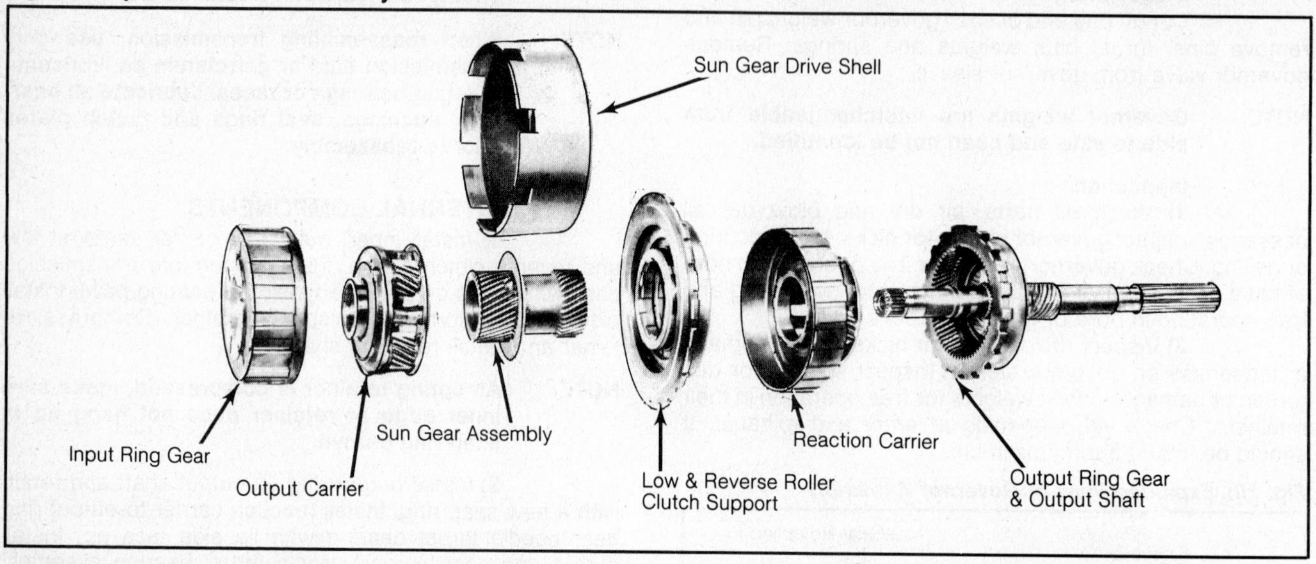

Fig. 22: Installing Low and Reverse Clutch Support Retainer (Anti-Clunk) Spring

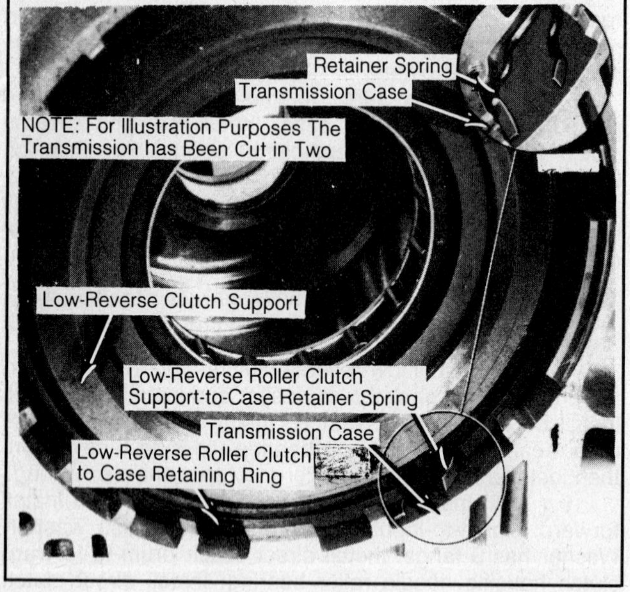

Fig. 23: Measuring Transmission End Play

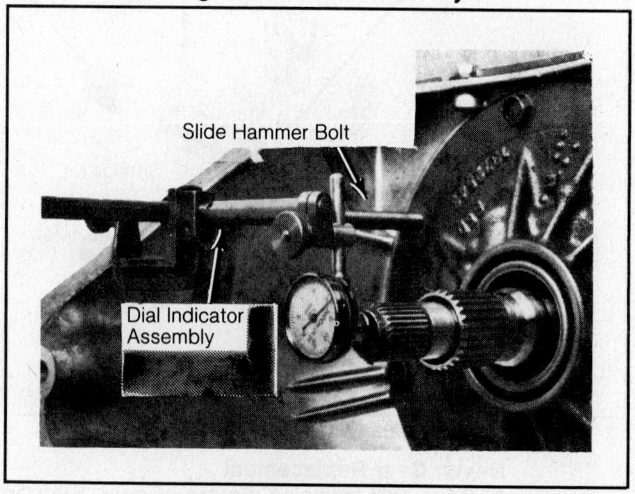

rotated as the pump is being pulled into place, the direct and forward clutch housings have not been properly installed to index the composition plates with their respective parts. Correct this condition before proceeding.

11) Install a slide hammer bolt into threaded hole in pump, then push input shaft rearward. Attach a dial indicator to slide hammer bolt, place indicator pointer on end of input shaft and zero dial indicator. Push on end of output shaft and read resulting end play on indicator.

12) End play should be .010-.044" (.25-1.12 mm). If end play is not within specifications, add or subtract .017" (.43 mm) adjusting shims, located between pump-to-direct clutch needle thrust bearing and oil pump.

13) Remove pump assembly and install correct thickness adjusting shim(s). Install a new square cut "O" ring on oil pump. Install guide pins into case, then install oil pump and tighten attaching bolts.

SPEEDOMETER GEARS & EXTENSION HOUSING

1) Place speedometer drive gear retaining clip into hole in output shaft. Align slot in speedometer drive gear with retaining clip and install.

2) Position square-cut "O" ring seal on extension housing, mount extension housing to case and install and tighten attaching bolts. Install speedometer driven gear and retainer. Install and tighten retainer bolt.

MANUAL LINKAGE

1) Install parking pawl into case with tooth toward inside of case. Install parking pawl shaft into case through disengaging spring. Install spring on parking pawl and slide shaft through parking pawl.

2) Using a 3/8" diameter rod, drive a new shaft retaining plug into case until plug is flush to .010" (.25 mm) below face of case. Stake plug in 3 places to retain in case.

3) Install parking lock bracket and tighten bolts. Install actuator rod under parking lock bracket and parking pawl. If removed, install a new manual shaft-to-case lip seal. Install manual shaft through case and range selector inner lever. Install and tighten manual shaft jam nut. Install manual shaft-to-case spacer clip.

GENERAL MOTORS TURBO HYDRA-MATIC 350C (Cont.)

Fig. 24: Exploded View of Manual Shaft and Parking Pawl Components

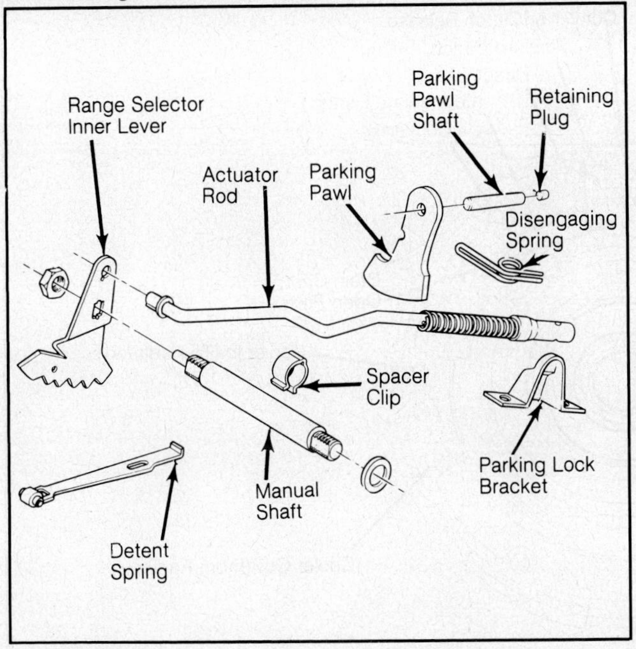

VALVE BODY & OIL PAN

1) Install intermediate servo piston, apply pin, spring and spring seat. Install check balls into correct transmission case pockets. *See Fig. 6.* Clean and install oil pump pressure screen (open end toward front of case) and governor feed screen into case pockets. *See Fig. 6.*

NOTE: **If number "1" check ball is omitted or incorrectly positioned, transmission failure will result due to minimum line pressure.**

2) Install valve body spacer plate-to-case gasket, valve body spacer plate and spacer plate-to-valve body gasket (Yellow stripe). Install spacer plate support plate and tighten attaching bolts. Install auxiliary valve body and tighten attaching bolts.

3) On all models, install valve body. Connect manual control valve link to range selector inner lever. Install manual shaft retaining clip. Tighten valve body attaching bolts in random sequence leaving detent roller and spring bolt loose.

NOTE: **When handling valve body assembly do not touch sleeves as retainer pins may fall into transmission.**

Fig. 25: Bottom View of Transmission Case Showing Oil Passages

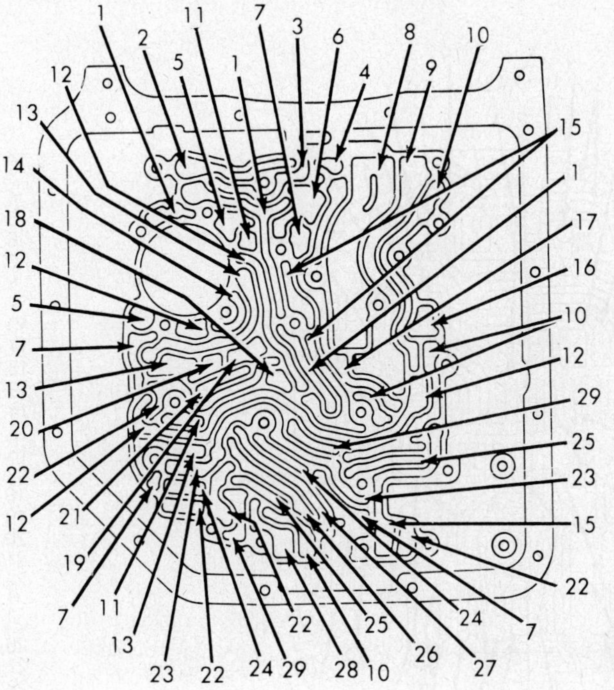

1. Direct Clutch (2-3)
2. Cooler In
3. Converter Apply
4. Converter Release
5. Intermediate Clutch (1-2)
6. Drive Forward Clutch
7. Drain
8. Suction
9. Pump Pressure
10. Reverse
11. Void
12. Intermediate Servo Release (R, N, D)
13. Line
14. 2-3 Clutch
15. Drive
16. Exhaust
17. Converter Feed
18. Exhaust Feed
19. Modulator or Detent Regulator
20. Exhaust Intermediate Clutch
21. Detent Regulator
22. Governor
23. Modulator
24. Detent 2
25. Low
26. Detent Modulator
27. Modulator Thru Detent Valve
28. Low Reverse Clutch
29. Manual Low Control

GENERAL MOTORS TURBO HYDRA-MATIC 350C (Cont.)

Fig. 26: Front View of Transmission Case Showing Oil Passages

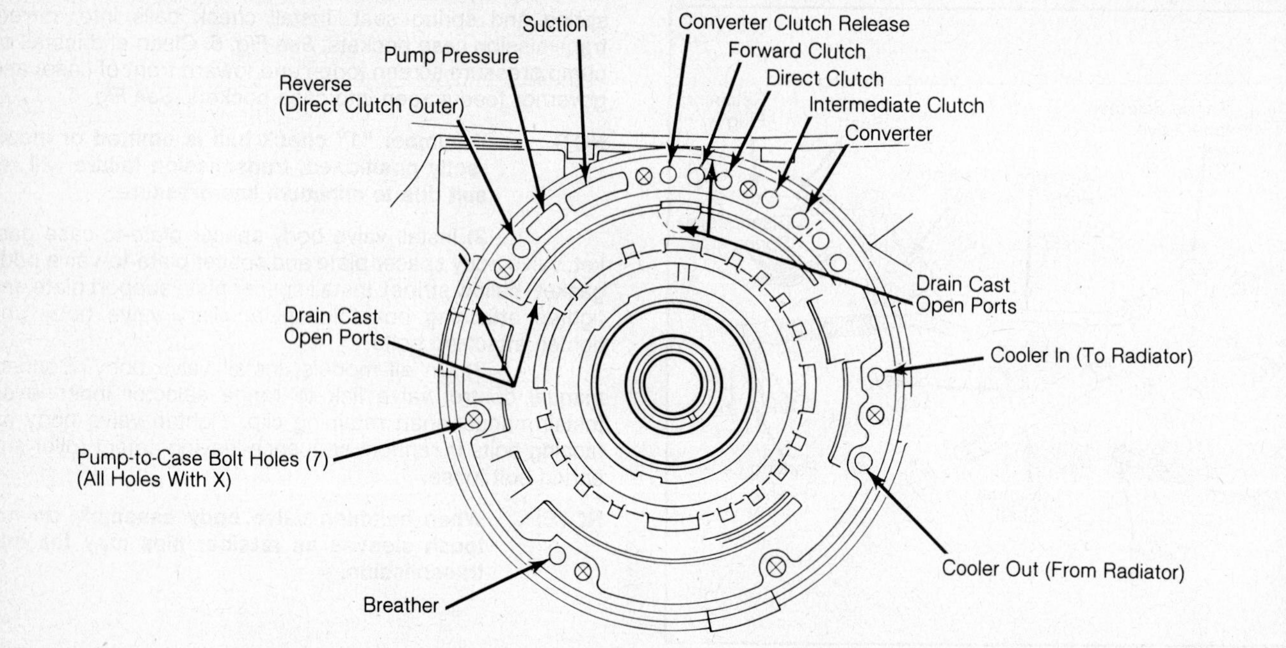

Fig. 27: Valve Body Oil Passages

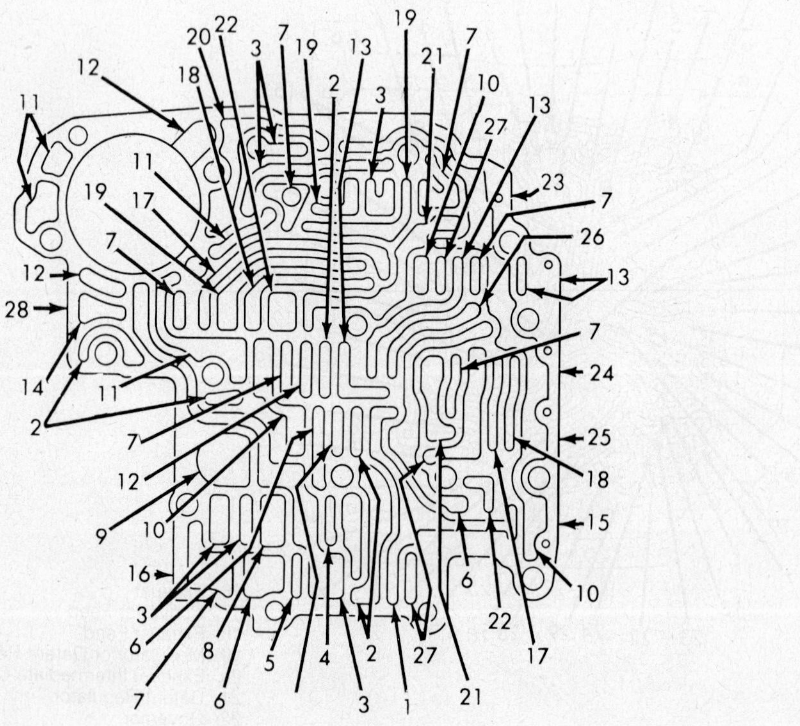

1. Intermediate (L2)
2. Drive
3. Line
4. Converter Feed
5. Speed Release
6. Reverse
7. Exhaust
8. Exhaust Open to Sump
9. Suction
10. Governor
11. 2-3 Clutch
12. 1-2 Clutch
13. Manual Low Control
14. Void
15. Pressure Regulator
16. Manual
17. Detent 1
18. Modulator or Detent Regulator
19. Detent Regulator
20. Intermediate Servo Release
21. Detent 2
22. Modulator
23. Detent Pressure Regulator
25. 1-2 Shift
26. Low or Reverse
27. Low
28. Detent

GENERAL MOTORS TURBO HYDRA-MATIC 350C (Cont.)

4) Install detent control valve wire to detent valve actuating lever, then attach lever to valve body. Install detent roller and spring to valve body and tighten attaching bolt. Install torque converter clutch solenoid and connect wires. If removed, install governor pressure switch.

5) Align lube holes in strainer with those in valve body and install strainer assembly gasket and strainer. Lubricate new "O" ring seal with petrolatum and install on case electrical connector. Install connector (with tabs facing into case) and connect solenoid wire. Install oil pan using a new gasket and tighten attaching bolts.

GOVERNOR & VACUUM MODULATOR

1) Install governor assembly, and uniformly apply sealant (Loctite Cup Plug Sealant II) to governor cover outside diameter. Install by gently tapping into place with plastic or rawhide hammer.

NOTE: If governor cover is damaged, it must be replaced.

2) Install vacuum modulator valve and modulator. Position vacuum modulator retainer with tangs pointing toward modulator. Lubricate "O" ring seal to prevent damage, then install retaining clip and tighten bolt to specifications.

INTERMEDIATE CLUTCH ACCUMULATOR

Install intermediate clutch accumulator piston assembly and spring into case bore. Install new "O" ring seal on accumulator piston cover. Install cover into case. Compress cover with a Compressor (J-23069). Install retaining ring and remove tool.

Fig. 28: Installing Intermediate Clutch Accumulator Retaining Ring

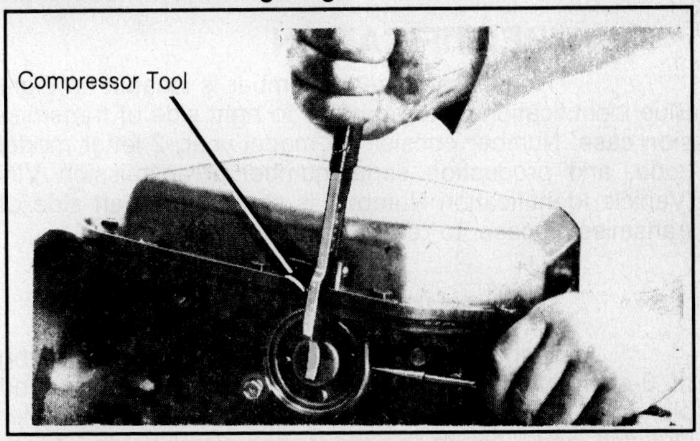

TIGHTENING SPECIFICATIONS

Application	Ft. Lbs. (N.m)
Oil Pan-to-Case	13 (18)
Pump-to-Case	20 (27)
Modulator-to-Case	12 (16)
Valve Body-to-Case	13 (18)
Oil Channel Support Plate-to-Case	13 (18)
Pump Body-to-Pump Cover	15 (20)
Extension Housing-to-Case	35 (48)
Inside Shift Nut	30 (41)
External Test Plugs	8 (11)
Manual Shift Nut	20 (27)
Converter-to-Flywheel	35 (48)
Transmission-to-Engine	35 (48)

GENERAL MOTORS TURBO HYDRA-MATIC 400

Chevrolet, GMC

IDENTIFICATION

Transmission serial number is located on Light Blue identification plate attached to right side of transmission case. Number consists of model year, 2 letter model code, and production serial number. Transmission VIN (Vehicle Identification Number) is stamped on left side of transmission case, to rear of manual lever shaft.

DESCRIPTION

Transmission is fully automatic unit consisting of 3-element hydraulic torque converter and compound planetary gear set. Three multiple disc clutches, 2 roller clutches, and 2 bands provide friction elements necessary to control functions of planetary gear set. Hydraulic system pressurized by gear-type pump provides pressure required to operate friction elements and automatic controls.

LUBRICATION & ADJUSTMENT

See AUTOMATIC TRANSMISSION SERVICING article in DOMESTIC GENERAL SERVICING section.

TESTING

ROAD TEST

1) Connect portable tachometer to engine. Place selector lever in Drive range and accelerate vehicle from standstill at minimum throttle opening. Changes in engine RPM will identify shift points.

2) Upshifts 1-to-2 and 2-to-3 should occur as vehicle reaches correct speed ranges. As vehicle speed decreases, 3-to-2 and 2-to-1 downshifts should occur. Increase in engine RPM and engine braking effect should be noticed. See SHIFT POINT SPECIFICATIONS table.

3) Stop vehicle and place selector lever in "2" (Intermediate) range. Accelerate from standstill. Upshift 1-to-2 should occur at all throttle openings (shift point will vary with throttle opening). No 2-to-3 upshift should occur. Stop vehicle and place selector lever in "1" (Low) range. Accelerate from standstill. No upshift should occur regardless of throttle opening.

4) With selector lever in Drive range and vehicle speed at 35 MPH, move selector lever to "2" (Intermediate) range. Transmission should downshift to 2nd gear. Increase in engine RPM and engine braking effect should be noticed.

5) With selector lever in "2" (Intermediate) range and vehicle speed at 25-35 MPH (not over 40 MPH), move selector lever to "1" (Low) range. Throttle must be in closed position for this test. Transmission should downshift to 1st gear. Increase in engine RPM and engine braking effect should be noticed.

6) Stop vehicle. Place selector lever in Reverse range and check for reverse operation.

SHIFT POINT SPECIFICATIONS

Application	Speed (MPH)
Upshift	Minimum
1-2	15
2-3	30
Detent Downshift	Minimum
3-2	68-73
2-1	28-32
Upshift	Maximum
1-2	44-48
2-3	77-83

CLUTCH AND BAND APPLICATION CHART (ELEMENTS IN USE)

Selector Lever Position	Forward Clutch	Direct Clutch	Front Band	Intermed. Clutch	Intermed. Roller Clutch Or Sprag	Low Roller Clutch	Rear Band
D - DRIVE							
First Gear	X					X	
Second Gear	X			X	X		
Third Gear	X	X		X			
2 - INTERMEDIATE							
First Gear	X					X	
Second Gear	X		X	X	X		
1 - LOW							
First Gear	X					X	X
Second Gear	X		X	X	X		
R - REVERSE		X					X

NEUTRAL OR PARK – All clutches and bands released and/or ineffective.

GENERAL MOTORS TURBO HYDRA-MATIC 400 (Cont.)

Fig. 1: Cutaway View of Turbo Hydra-Matic 400 Automatic Transmission

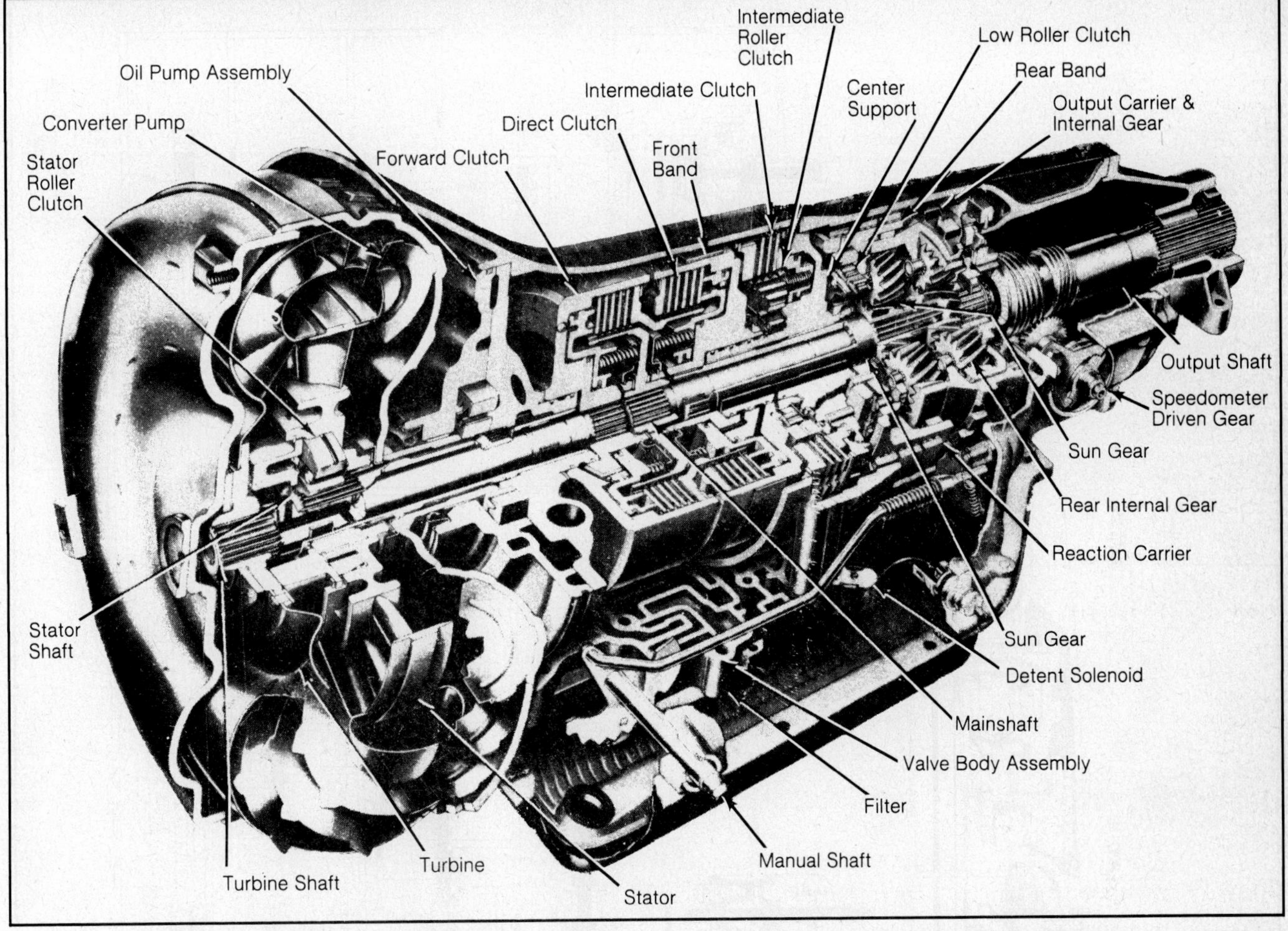

CONTROL PRESSURE CHECK

1) Install 0-300 psi (0-21 kg/cm^2) oil pressure gauge (J-5907) at pressure take-off point at left side of transmission to rear manual lever. Place gauge where it can be seen from driver's seat. Connect tachometer to engine.

2) With transmission fluid at correct level and operating temperature, hydraulic pressures can be checked. Check pressures with vehicle stationary and brakes applied as noted. See HYDRAULIC PRESSURES table.

CAUTION: For control pressure tests, total running time in Drive and Reverse ranges with brake applied must not exceed 2 minutes. Damage to transmission may result.

HYDRAULIC PRESSURES

Range @ RPM	psi (kg/cm^2)
Neutral [1] @ 1000	55-70 (4-5)
Drive @ Idle	60-85 (4.2-6)
Drive [1] @ 1000	60-90 (4.2-6.3)
Low or "2" [1] @1000	135-160 (9.5-11.2)
Reverse [1] @1000	95-150 (6.7-10.5)
Drive [1] [2] @1000	90-110 (6.3-7.7)

1 – Brakes applied.
2 – Downshift switch activated.

3) On vehicles equipped with Exhaust Gas Recirculation, throttle is open enough in Drive range at 1000 RPM to cause EGR valve to open. This allows exhaust gas to enter intake manifold and lower manifold vacuum. Transmission line oil pressure rises with lower intake manifold vacuum. Line pressure may go above upper limit.

4) If high line pressures are obtained, disconnect and plug vacuum line at EGR valve. Recheck line pressure. If high pressures are still found, check engine vacuum. If low intake vacuum is found, use hand operated vacuum pump and apply 20 in. Hg vacuum to modulator.

5) Recheck pressures according to table. If line pressures are normal with external vacuum applied, check engine vacuum and vacuum systems for leaks. If high line pressures are found, refer to CONTROL PRESSURE RESULTS for possible causes.

6) When stationary testing is complete, drive vehicle at 30 MPH and allow throttle to close completely. Read pressure on gauge. This test may also be conducted on hoist. Run engine at 3000 RPM with driving wheels off ground, selector in Drive, and brakes released. Close throttle and read pressure between 2000 and 1200 RPM. Pressure should read 55-70 psi (3.8-4.9 kg/cm^2).

CONTROL PRESSURE RESULTS

Line Pressure Too Low

- Transmission fluid level low, faulty vacuum modulator assembly. Oil filter blocked or restricted, "O" ring on filter

Automatic Transmissions

GENERAL MOTORS TURBO HYDRA-MATIC 400 (Cont.)

Fig. 2: Turbo Hydra-Matic 400 Hydraulic Circuits Diagram

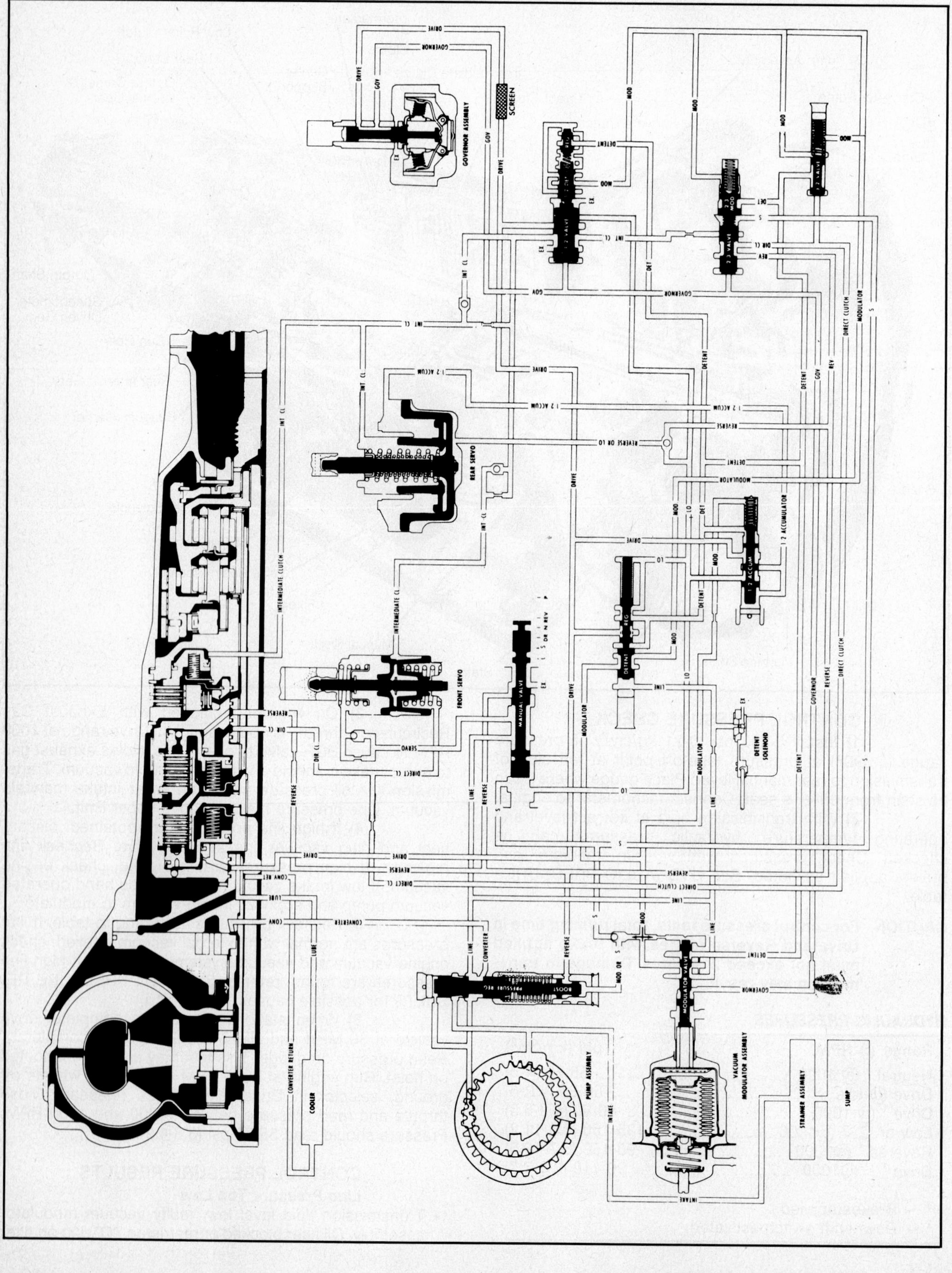

GENERAL MOTORS TURBO HYDRA-MATIC 400 (Cont.)

Fig. 3: View of Case Showing Pressure Take-Off Point

intake pipe omitted or damaged, intake pipe split or leaking, or incorrect filter.

- Oil pump assembly damaged, worn, or mismatched parts. Oil pump gear clearance damaged or worn. Pressure regulator spring too weak or not enough spacers in pressure regulator.
- Internal leak in direct clutch circuit (pressure normal in Neutral, Low, Intermediate and Drive, but low in Reverse). Internal leak in forward clutch circuit (pressure normal in Neutral and Reverse, low in Drive).
- Case assembly porous in intake bore area. Missing plug or leak at intermediate clutch plug. Low-Reverse check ball installed wrong or missing (causing loss of Reverse and no engine braking in low).

Line Pressure Too High

- Vacuum system leak or improper engine vacuum. Water in vacuum modulator. Modulator valve not operating properly or defective. Defective EGR valve.
- Detent switch actuated or shorted, detent solenoid stuck open. Detent feed orifice in spacer plate blocked, detent solenoid loose. Detent valve bore plug damaged. Detent regulator valve pin too short.
- Oil pump pressure regulator and/or boost valve stuck. Incorrect pump pressure regulator spring. Pressure boost valve installed backward. Too many pressure regulator valve spacers. Oil pump casting defective. Aluminum bore plug has hole or not working. Pressure boost bushing broken or not working.
- Control valve assembly-to-spacer gasket out of proportion, control valve assembly gaskets switched.

GOVERNOR CHECK

1) Raise vehicle on hoist (rear wheels off ground). Disconnect vacuum line to modulator. Connect pressure gauge to transmission and tachometer to engine.

2) Start engine, keep foot off brake pedal, move selector lever to Drive range, and check line pressure at 1000 RPM. Slowly increase engine speed to 3000 RPM and determine if line pressure drop of 10 psi (.7 kg/cm^2) or more occurs.

3) If no pressure drop occurs, inspect governor for stuck valve or weight, or restricted orifice in valve. Make sure that governor valve entry and exhaust has .020" (.51 mm) minimum opening.

4) Check governor feed system. Check control valve assembly or case screen. Check governor pipe for restrictions and proper fit in case holes. Control valve assembly should be disassembled, cleaned, and inspected if pressure drop of 10 psi (.7 kg/cm^2) or more occurs (with transmission malfunction).

VACUUM MODULATOR CHECK

Vacuum Diaphragm Leak Check

Insert pipe cleaner into vacuum connector pipe as far as possible and check for presence of transmission oil. If oil is found, replace modulator. Gasoline or water vapor may settle in vacuum side of modulator. If this is found without presence of oil, modulator should not be changed. If vehicle is to be exposed to temperatures 10°F or below, modulator MUST be replaced.

Atmospheric Leak Check

1) Apply liberal coating of soap bubble solution to vacuum connector pipe seam (crimped upper-to-lower housing seam).

2) Using short piece of rubber hose, apply air pressure to vacuum pipe by blowing into hose and check for leak bubbles. If bubbles appear, replace modulator.

CAUTION: **Do not use any method other than human lung power for applying air pressure. Pressures over 6 psi (.4 kg/cm^2) may damage modulator.**

Bellows Comparison Check

1) Using Comparison Gauge (J-24466), compare load of vacuum modulator in question with known good modulator of same type. Part number is stamped on modulator dome.

2) Install good modulator on either end of gauge. Install modulator in question on opposite end of gauge. Holding modulators in horizontal position, bring them slowly together under pressure.

3) If modulator in question is bad, gauge line will remain Blue. If modulator in question is good, gauge line will be White.

Sleeve Alignment Check

Roll main body of modulator on flat surface and observe sleeve for concentricity to can. If sleeve is concentric and plunger is free, modulator is acceptable.

VACUUM REGULATOR VALVE (DIESEL MODELS ONLY)

1) Attach vacuum regulator valve to fuel injection pump. Valve body must be securely attached but free to rotate on pump. Attach vacuum source of 9.0-10.4 psi (.6-.7 kg/cm^2) to bottom vacuum nipple. Attach vacuum gauge to upper nipple.

2) Insert vacuum regulator gauge bar between gauge boss on injection pump and wide open stop screw on throttle lever. Rotate throttle shaft and hold lever against gauge bar. Slowly rotate vacuum regulator valve body clockwise.

3) Setting will only be valid if performed with clockwise rotation. When vacuum gauge reads 5.3-5.9 psi (.37-.41 kg/cm^2), tighten valve body mounting screws. Check setting by releasing throttle lever to idle stop position.

4) Rotate throttle shaft back until lever rests against gauge bar again. Check vacuum gauge reading to make sure it is still 5.3-5.9 psi (.37-.41 kg/cm^2). If outside limits, reset valve and check setting again.

DOWNSHIFT SOLENOID CHECK

1) Place selector lever in "Park". Turn ignition to "ON", but do not start engine. From under hood, slowly move throttle linkage to wide open position. One click should be heard from transmission.

2) Allow throttle to return to closed position. One click should be heard from transmission. If clicks are heard, downshift solenoid is operating properly. If solenoid does not perform as described, go to step **3)**.

3) Use test light to check Brown wire at connector on side of transmission case. Test light should light with throttle wide open and go out when throttle is released.

4) If test light operates as described, but solenoid did not click during tests, replace solenoid after first checking to see that internal wiring is operational.

5) If test light fails to light with throttle open, solenoid circuit is open. If light lights with throttle closed, solenoid circuit is shorted. Check transmission control fuse in fuse panel. Check solenoid circuit and repair open or short (Orange wire with Black stripe).

SERVICE (IN VEHICLE)

The following components may be removed from transmission without removing transmission from vehicle.

- Governor Cover and Seals
- Governor Assembly
- Governor Pipes
- Intermediate Servo Piston Assembly
- Rear Servo Assembly
- Front Servo Assembly
- Oil Pan and Oil Screen (Intake Pipe) Assembly
- Valve Body Assembly
- Check Balls and Valve Body Spacer Plates and Gaskets
- Pressure Regulator Parts
- Manual Detent Roller and Spring Assembly
- Parking Pawl Actuator Rod
- Parking Pawl Bracket and Parking Pawl
- Manual Shaft and Seal
- Manual Valve and Valve Link
- Extension Housing and Gasket
- Rear Seal
- 1-2 Accumulator Assembly
- Vacuum Modulator
- Oil Filter Pipe and "O" Ring
- Speedometer Driven Gear Assembly
- Cooler Fittings
- Downshift Solenoid
- Electrical Connectors
- Governor Feed Screen
- Pump Pressure Screen
- Modulator Valve

TRANSMISSION REMOVAL & INSTALLATION

See appropriate article in AUTOMATIC TRANSMISSION REMOVAL section.

TORQUE CONVERTER

LEAKAGE CHECK

Install Pressure Test Plug (J-21369-B) into converter hub and tighten tool to expand it. Install safety strap to prevent tool from blowing out when air pressure is applied. Apply 80 psi (5.6 kg/cm^2) air pressure to air valve in tool. Submerge converter in water and check for leaks.

CAUTION: After leak checking converter, bleed air pressure from test tool before removing tool from converter.

Fig. 4: Assembling Pressure Test Plug to Converter

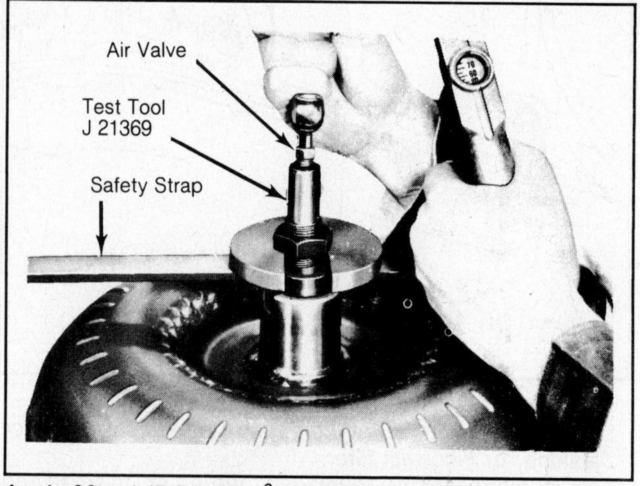

Apply 80 psi (5.6 kg/cm^2) to check for leakage.

CLEARANCE CHECK

1) Release collet end of End Play Checker (J-21371). Install end play checking tool into converter hub until collet end of tool bottoms. Expand collet by tightening cap nut to 60 INCH lbs. (6.7 N.m). Install Support Collar (J-21371-3) of checking tool on converter hub.

2) Tighten hex nut to 36 INCH lbs. (4 N.m). Install dial indicator on support collar so that indicator plunger rests against test tool cap nut. Zero dial indicator. *See Fig. 5.* Loosen hex nut while holding cap nut stationary.

Fig. 5: Assembling Measuring Tools to Converter

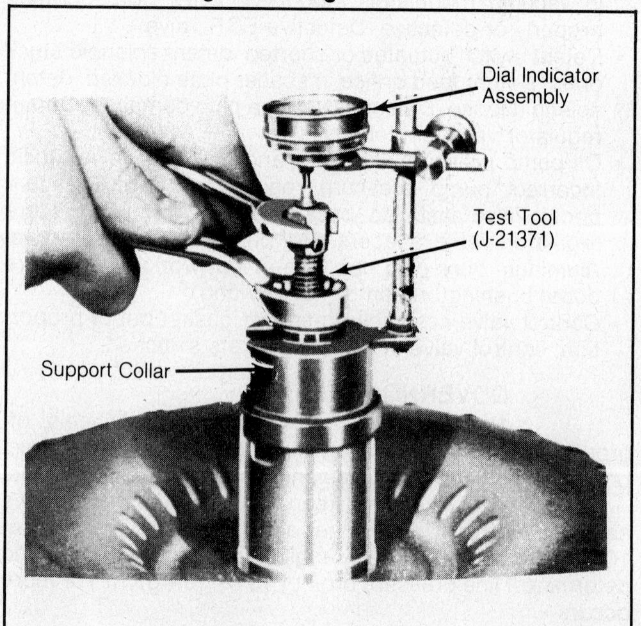

Assembly is used to check converter end clearance.

3) With hex nut loose and Support (J-21371-3) firmly against converter hub, reading obtained on indicator will be converter end clearance. Converter end clearance should be less than .050" (1.27 mm). If clearance is greater than specified, replace torque converter assembly.

TRANSMISSION DISASSEMBLY

VACUUM MODULATOR & VALVE

Disconnect vacuum hose from modulator stem. Remove vacuum modulator attaching screw and retainer. Remove modulator and "O" ring seal from case. Discard "O" ring. Remove modulator valve from case bore.

GOVERNOR

Remove attaching screws, cover, and "O" ring, being careful not to distort cover. Remove governor assembly by pulling straight out of case.

SPEEDOMETER DRIVEN GEAR

Disconnect speedometer cable. Remove attaching screw and retainer. Apply slight pressure to remove speedometer driven gear assembly and "O" ring from case.

INTAKE PIPE, FILTER & OIL PAN

Remove pan attaching bolts and remove oil pan. Remove filter retaining bolt, withdraw intake pipe and filter assembly, then discard filter and "O" ring seal from intake pipe.

Fig. 6: Removing Intake Pipe and Filter Assembly

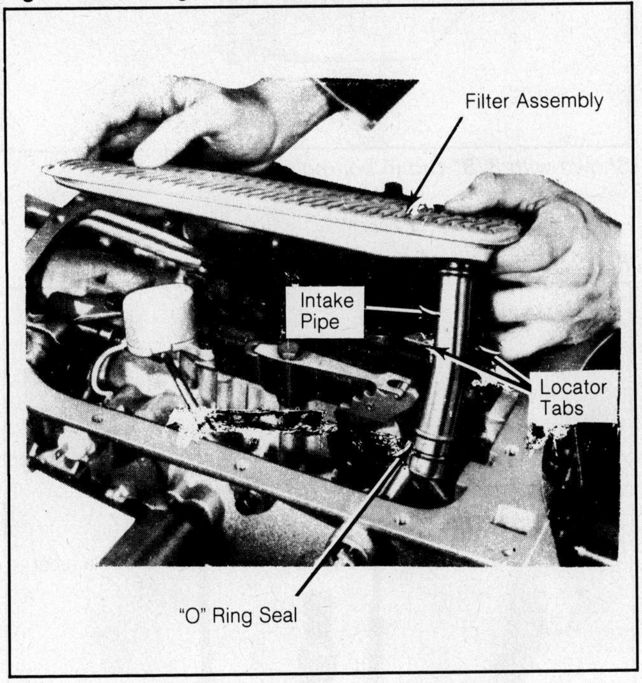

CONTROL VALVE ASSEMBLY

1) Disconnect lead wire from pressure switch assembly. Remove control valve assembly attaching bolts and detent roller spring assembly (do not remove solenoid attaching screws).

NOTE: **If transmission is in vehicle, front servo parts may drop out as control valve assembly is removed.**

2) Remove control valve assembly and governor pipes, using care not to drop manual valve as control valve assembly is removed. Remove governor screen assembly from governor feed pipe hole in case or from end of feed pipe.

3) Remove governor pipes from control valve assembly. Governor pipes are interchangeable and need not be identified. Disconnect detent solenoid wire from electrical connector.

REAR SERVO

Remove servo cover and gasket and discard gasket. Remove servo assembly and accumulator spring. Make band apply pin selection check at this time to determine correct pin for use at reassembly. This is equivalent to band adjustment.

Band Apply Pin Selection Check

1) Position Band Apply Pin Selection Gauge (J-21370-6) on transmission case over rear servo bore. *See Fig. 7.* Hex nut on side of gauge faces toward parking brake linkage. End of Gauge Pin (J-21370-5) with smaller diameter fits in servo pin bore.

2) Secure gauge with 2 attaching screws. Tighten screws to 18 ft. lbs. (24 N.m). Make sure stepped gauge pin is free to move up and down in both tool and servo pin bore. Stepped side of pin must face front of transmission case.

Fig. 7: Using Gauge to Select Rear Band Apply Pin

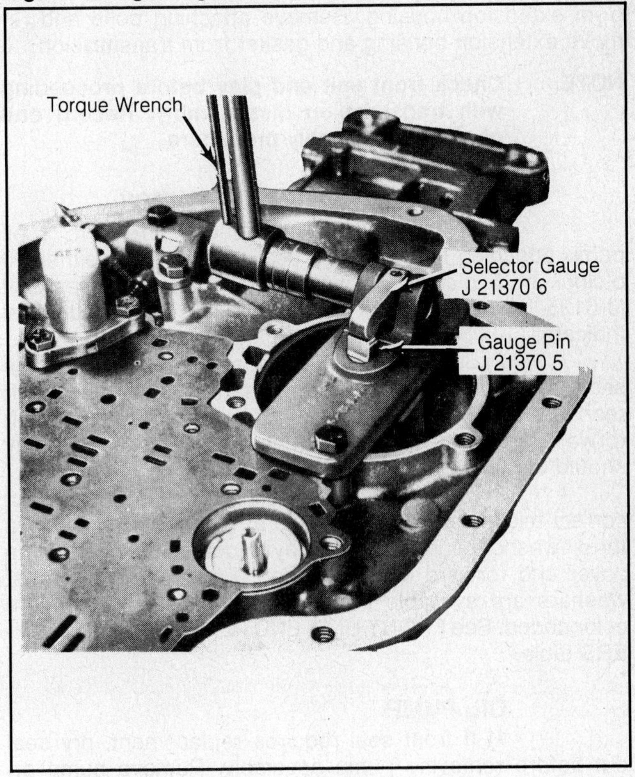

3) Apply 25 ft. lbs. (34 N.m) of force to hex nut on side of gauge. This will cause lever on top of gauge to depress stepped gauge pin into servo pin bore, simulating actual operating conditions. Note relation of steps on gauge pin and machined surface on top of gauge. To determine proper size pin, go to step **4)**.

GENERAL MOTORS TURBO HYDRA-MATIC 400 (Cont.)

4) If machined surface on top of gauge is even with or above upper step on gauge pin, long size (3 rings) pin must be installed. If machined surface is between upper and lower steps on pin, medium size (2 rings) pin must be installed. If machined surface is even with or below bottom step on pin, short size (1 ring) pin must be installed.

5) If new band apply pin is required, make note of pin size for reassembly reference. Remove selection gauge from transmission case.

DETENT SOLENOID, CONTROL VALVE SPACER & FRONT SERVO

Compress connector tabs. Withdraw connector and "O" ring seal. Remove attaching screws and lift off detent solenoid assembly and gasket. Remove control valve spacer plate and gasket. Remove 6 check balls from cored passages in case. Remove front servo piston, retainer ring, pin, spring retainer, and spring from case.

CAUTION: If transmission is installed in vehicle, be careful when detent solenoid is removed to prevent spacer plate, gasket, and check balls from dropping out. Make sure to keep control valve spacer plate level when removing so check balls do not fall.

REAR OIL SEAL & EXTENSION HOUSING

If replacement is necessary, pry rear oil seal from extension housing. Remove attaching bolts and remove extension housing and gasket from transmission.

NOTE: Check front unit end play before proceeding with transmission disassembly. Record end play for reassembly procedure.

FRONT UNIT END PLAY CHECK

1) With transmission removed, remove 1 oil pump attaching bolt and bolt sealing washer at either 10 o'clock or 5 o'clock position. Install Slide Hammer Bolt (J-6125-1) and Adapter (J-6125-2) into bolt hole. Mount Dial Indicator (J-8001-02) on bolt. *See Fig. 8.*

2) Set indicator tip to register with end of turbine shaft. Hold output shaft forward and push turbine shaft rearward until it stops. Zero dial indicator, pull turbine shaft forward, and read resulting end play on indicator. End play should be .003-.024" (.08-.61 mm).

3) If end play is not within specified limits, select correct thickness washer for use at reassembly. Selective thrust washer controlling end play is located between pump cover and forward clutch housing. Front end play thrust washers are available in varying thicknesses which are color coded. See FRONT UNIT END PLAY THRUST WASHERS table.

OIL PUMP

1) If front seal requires replacement, pry seal out before removing pump assembly. Remove pump attaching bolts. Install 2 Slide Hammers (J-6125-1) and Adapters (J-6125-2), 1 in 10 o'clock bolt hole and 1 in 5 o'clock bolt hole.

2) Operate both hammers at same time to avoid cocking pump assembly. Remove pump assembly from case. Remove slide hammer assemblies from pump. Remove and discard pump-to-case seal ring and gasket.

FRONT UNIT END PLAY THRUST WASHERS

Washer Thickness	I.D. Number	Color Code [1]
.060-.064"	0	Yellow
.071-.075"	1	Blue
.082-.086"	2	Red
.093-.097"	3	Brown
.104-.108"	4	Green
.115-.119"	5	Black
.126-.130"	6	Purple

[1] – Oil soaked washers may discolor. Measure such washers for actual thickness.

Fig. 8: Measuring Front Unit End Play

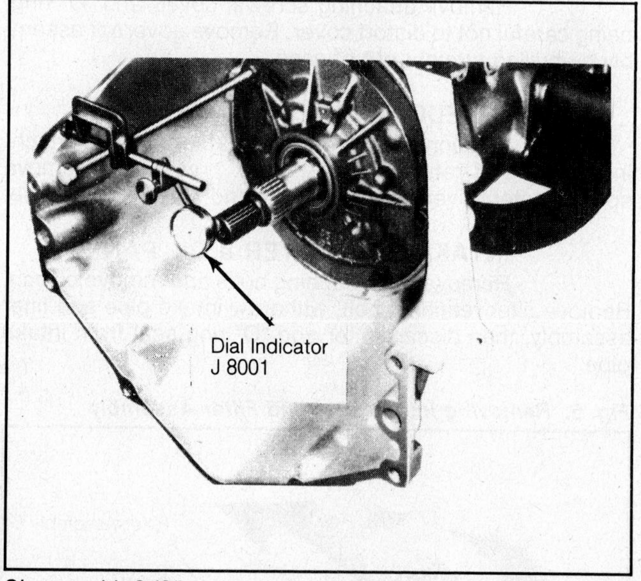

Shown with 3/8" rod in bolt hole.

Fig. 9: Using Slide Hammers to Remove Oil Pump

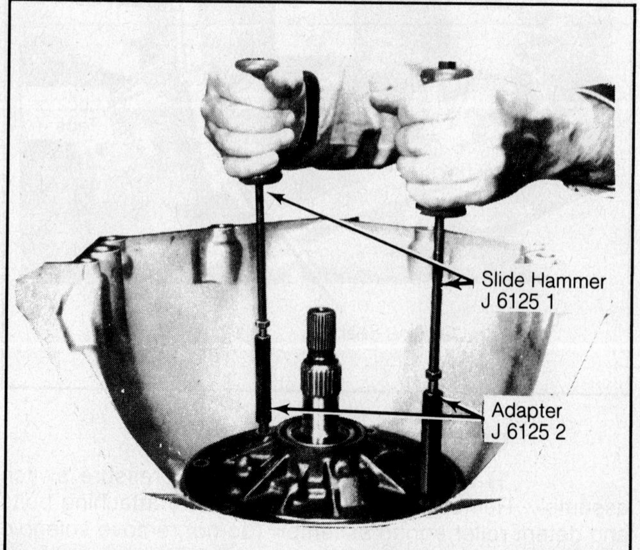

Operate hammers together with equal force to avoid cocking pump.

GENERAL MOTORS TURBO HYDRA-MATIC 400 (Cont.)

DETENT LEVER, MANUAL LEVER, SHAFT & PARKING LINKAGE

1) If necessary for parts replacement, remove manual linkage. Loosen lock nut holding inside detent lever to manual shaft. Remove pin holding manual shaft to case. Remove lock nut and inside detent lever from manual shaft. Remove manual shaft. *See Fig. 10.*

2) Remove parking actuator rod and detent lever from case. Remove attaching bolts and parking lock bracket. Remove parking pawl return spring. Remove parking pawl shaft spring retainer. Remove parking pawl shaft cup plug. Pry outward to remove plug. Remove parking pawl shaft and parking pawl.

Fig. 10: Exploded View of Manual Linkage

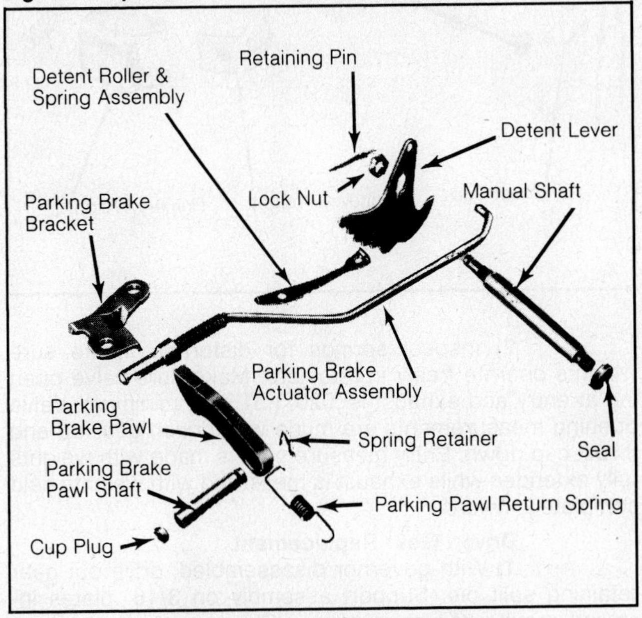

TURBINE SHAFT, FORWARD & DIRECT CLUTCH ASSEMBLIES, SUN GEAR SHAFT & FRONT BAND

Remove forward clutch and turbine shaft assembly from case. Remove forward clutch hub-to-direct clutch housing thrust washer if not removed with forward clutch. Remove direct clutch and intermediate roller assembly. Remove sun gear shaft if it did not come out with direct clutch. Remove front band assembly.

REAR UNIT END PLAY CHECK

1) Transmission must be out of vehicle. Extension housing must be removed to check rear unit end play. Install Speedometer Puller Bolt (J-21797) in one of extension housing bolt holes in rear of case. Install dial indicator on bolt with tip touching flat surface on end of output shaft.

2) Zero indicator dial, move output shaft in and out, and note end play reading. End play should be .007-.019" (.18-.48 mm). If end play needs adjustment, select thrust washer that will bring end play within specifications.

3) Selective washer controlling rear unit end play is steel washer having 3 tabs. It is located between output shaft thrust washer and rear face of transmission case. Notches and/or numerals on tabs of washer identify thickness. See REAR UNIT SELECTIVE WASHERS table.

Fig. 11: Measuring Rear Unit End Play

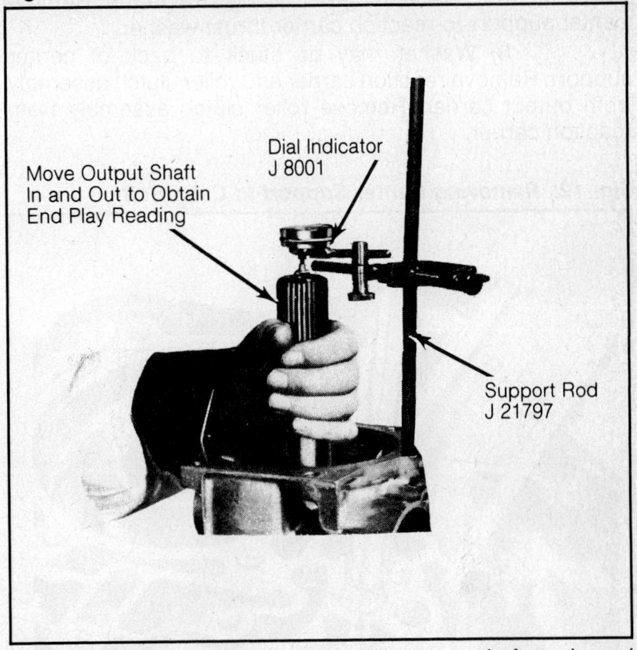

Set dial indicator at zero then pull up on shaft and read indicator.

REAR UNIT SELECTIVE WASHER

Washer Thickness	I.D. Notches	I.D. Numeral
.074-.078"	None	1
.082-.086"	Side 1 Tab	2
.090-.094"	Side 2 Tabs	3
.098-.102"	End 1 Tab	4
.106-.110"	End 2 Tabs	5
.114-.118"	End 3 Tabs	6

CENTER SUPPORT, REAR BAND, & GEAR UNIT ASSEMBLIES

1) Remove center support bolt from case using 3/8", 12-point thin wall deep socket. Remove intermediate clutch backing plate-to-case snap ring. Withdraw backing plate and 6 clutch plates (3 composition and 3 steel).

2) Remove center support-to-case snap ring. Install Remover (J-21795) on end of mainshaft so that tangs engage groove in shaft. Tighten screw on tool to secure tool on shaft. This will prevent roller clutch movement during gear unit removal.

NOTE: **Install piece of pipe over output shaft for use as handle and to prevent spline damage to case bushing when removing gear unit, center support, and reaction carrier.**

3) Loosen transmission holding fixture pivot pin slightly so gear unit assembly will not bind during removal from case. With transmission case in horizontal position, shift complete assembly forward and remove from case.

4) Remove output shaft-to-case thrust washer from shaft or case. Place gear unit assembly in Holding Fixture (J-6116 01) using Adapter (J-21364) with mainshaft pointing up. Remove rear unit selective washer from transmission case. Remove center support-to-case spacer.

5) Rotate rear band lugs away from pins and pull band assembly from case. Remove center support

GENERAL MOTORS TURBO HYDRA-MATIC 400 (Cont.)

assembly from reaction carrier, lifting straight up. Remove center support-to-reaction carrier thrust washer.

6) Washer may be stuck to back of center support. Remove reaction carrier and roller clutch assembly from output carrier. Remove roller clutch assembly from reaction carrier.

Fig. 12: Removing Center Support-to-Case Bolt

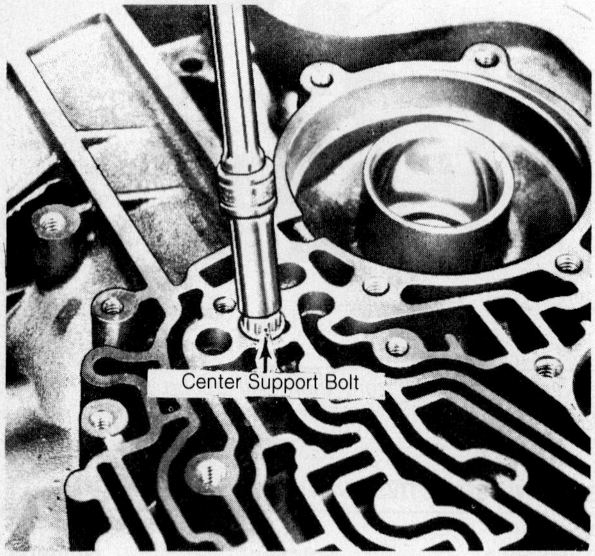

COMPONENT DISASSEMBLY & REASSEMBLY

NOTE: **When reassembling transmission units, lubricate all bushings, seals, thrust bearings, and mating surfaces with transmission fluid. Use petroleum jelly to lubricate and retain thrust washers.**

GOVERNOR

NOTE: **Governor, including driven gear, is serviced as complete assembly. Driven gear may be serviced separately and requires disassembly of governor for gear replacement.**

Disassembly

Governor weights are interchangeable from side to side and need not be identified for reassembly. Cut off one end of each governor weight pin and remove pins, governor thrust cap, governor weights and springs. Remove governor valve from governor sleeve using care not to damage valve. *See Fig. 13.*

Inspection

1) Wash all parts in solvent and air dry. Blow out all passages. Inspect sleeve for wear or damage and check for free operation in case bore. Inspect valve for wear or damage and for free operation in sleeve bore. Check driven gear for wear or damage and for looseness on sleeve.

Fig. 13: Exploded View of Governor Assembly

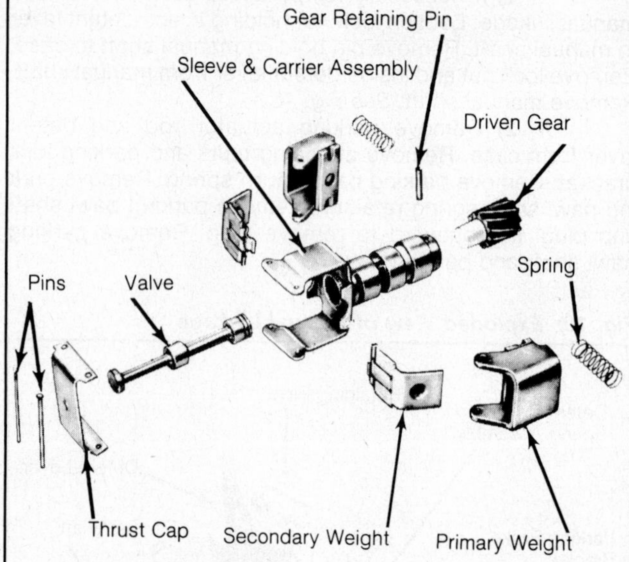

2) Inspect springs for distortion. Make sure weights operate freely in retainers. Make sure valve open ing at entry and exhaust is .020" (.51 mm) minimum. Valve opening measurements are made with driven gear up and thrust cap down. Entry measurement is made with weights fully extended while exhaust is measured with weights held completely inward.

Driven Gear Replacement

1) With governor disassembled, drive out gear retaining split pin. Support assembly on 3/16" plates installed in exhaust slots of sleeve. Place assembly in press. Press gear out of sleeve with long punch. Carefully clean governor sleeve of chips that remain from original gear installation.

2) To install new gear, support governor assembly in same manner as for gear removal. Press gear into sleeve until nearly seated. Remove any chips that may have been shaved off gear. Press gear in until bottomed on shoulder.

3) New pin hole must be drilled through sleeve and gear. Support governor in press. Locate hole position 90° from existing hole. Center punch and drill new hole through sleeve and gear with 1/8" drill. Install retaining split pin.

Reassembly

Install valve in bore of sleeve, then install weights, springs, and thrust cap on sleeve. Align pin holes in thrust cap, weight assemblies, and sleeve. Install new pins. Crimp both ends of pin to prevent them from falling out. Check weight assemblies for free operation in sleeve. Make sure valve is free in sleeve.

CONTROL VALVE ASSEMBLY

NOTE: **As each valve is removed, place individual valve in separate location relative to its position in valve body. None of valves or springs are interchangeable.**

GENERAL MOTORS TURBO HYDRA-MATIC 400 (Cont.)

Fig. 14: Disassembled View of Front Accumulator

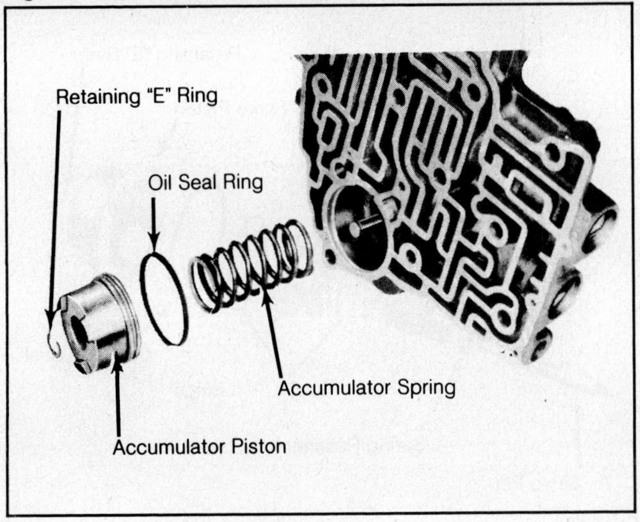

Disassembly

1) Position control valve assembly with gasket surface up and accumulator pocket at bottom. Remove manual valve from upper bore. Install Compressor Tool (J-21885 or J-22269-01) on accumulator piston. Compress piston and remove "E" retaining ring. Remove piston and spring.

2) Remove all retaining pins (except grooved pin in lower left bore) from bores with pin punch. Drive pins from outer side of valve body. When removing pins, hold hand over bore end in case spring forces components out of bore. *See Fig. 15.* Pry grooved pin from lower left bore with long nose pliers.

3) Remove 1-2 valve train from upper right bore. Remove 2-3 valve train from center right bore. From lower right bore, remove 3-2 valve train. From upper left bore, remove detent valve train. From lower left bore, remove 1-2 accumulator valve train.

Inspection

1) Wash all parts in clean solvent. Inspect all valves and bushings carefully to make sure they are free from dirt and are not damaged in any way. If burrs are present, remove with fine stone or fine grade crocus cloth and light oil.

CAUTION: When removing burrs from valves, use care not to round off shoulders of valves.

2) Test all valves and bushings in their bores to make sure they slide freely of their own weight. Only manual valve can be serviced separately. If other valves require replacement, complete valve body assembly should be replaced.

Fig. 15: Exploded View of Control Valve Assembly

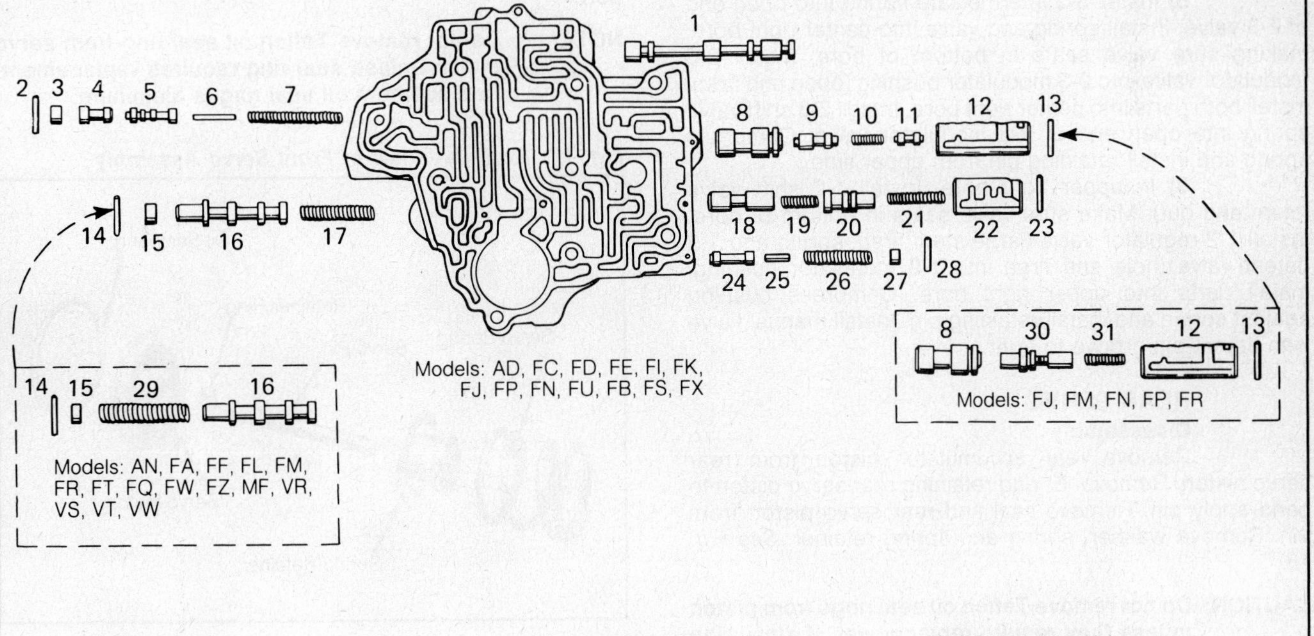

1. Manual Valve
2. Retaining Pin
3. Bore Plug
4. Detent Valve
5. Detent Regulator Valve
6. Spacer
7. Detent Regulator Valve Spring
8. 1-2 Shift Valve
9. 1-2 Detent Valve
10. 1-2 Regulator Valve Spring
11. 1-2 Regulator Valve
12. 1-2 Modulator Bushing
13. Retaining Pin
14. Retaining Pin
15. Bore Plug
16. 1-2 Accumulator Valve
17. 1-2 Accumulator Pri. Spring
18. 2-3 Shift Valve
19. 3-2 Intermediate Spring
20. 2-3 Modulator Valve
21. 2-3 Shift Valve Spring
22. 2-3 Modulator Bushing
23. Retaining Pin
24. 3-2 Valve
25. Spacer
26. 3-2 Valve Spring
27. Bore Plug
28. Retaining Pin
29. 1-2 Accumulator Sec. Spring
30. 1-2 Modulator Valve
31. 1-2 Modulator Valve Spring

GENERAL MOTORS TURBO HYDRA-MATIC 400 (Cont.)

3) Inspect valve body for cracks or scored bores. Check all springs for distortion or collapsed coils. Inspect accumulator piston and oil ring for damage.

NOTE: Do not remove Teflon oil seal from front accumulator piston unless seal ring needs replacing. Service oil seal ring is cast iron.

Reassembly

1) Install front accumulator spring and piston into valve body. Compress piston and spring and install retaining "E" clip. In lower left bore, install 1-2 accumulator primary spring and 1-2 accumulator valve, stem end out, then install bore plug. Some control valve assemblies use secondary spring on 1-2 accumulator valve.

2) Secondary spring should be installed between valve and bore plug. It will be necessary to compress secondary spring to install retaining pin. Install retaining pin from cast surface side of valve body, with grooved end of pin installed last. Tap pin in until flush with cast surface of valve body.

3) Install spacer inside detent regulator spring. Install spring and spacer in upper left bore, making sure spring seats in bottom of bore. Compress spring and retain in place with small screwdriver. Install detent regulator valve (stem end out) and detent valve (narrow land first).

4) Install bore plug with open end out. Press in plug and remove screwdriver. Install retaining pin from upper side of valve body. Install 3-2 valve in lower right bore, then install valve spring with spacer inside. Install bore plug (open end out) and drive in retaining pin from upper side.

5) Install 3-2 intermediate spring into open end of 2-3 valve. Install spring and valve into center right bore, making sure valve seats in bottom of bore. Install 2-3 modulator valve into 2-3 modulator bushing (open end first). Install both parts into center right bore. Install 2-3 shift valve spring into open end of 2-3 modulator valve. Compress spring and install retaining pin from upper side.

6) In upper right bore, install 1-2 shift valve (stem end out). Make sure valve seats in bottom of bore. Install 1-2 regulator valve (large stem first), spring and 1-2 detent valve (hole end first) into 1-2 modulator bushing. Install parts into upper right bore. Compress bushing against spring and install retaining pin. Install manual valve with detent pin groove to right.

REAR SERVO

Disassembly

Remove rear accumulator piston from rear servo piston. Remove "E" ring retaining rear servo piston to band apply pin. Remove seal and rear servo piston from pin. Remove washer, spring and spring retainer. *See Fig. 16.*

CAUTION: Do not remove Teflon oil seal rings from piston unless they require replacement. If small ring requires replacement, use aluminum oil seal ring. If large ring requires replacement, use only Teflon oil seal ring as groove is machined for it.

Inspection

Check freedom of oil seal rings in grooves of piston. Inspect fit of band apply pin in servo piston. Inspect band apply pin for scores or cracks. Make sure band apply pin is proper size as selected during disassembly. See BAND APPLY PIN SELECTION CHECK in this article.

Fig. 16: Exploded View of Rear Servo Assembly

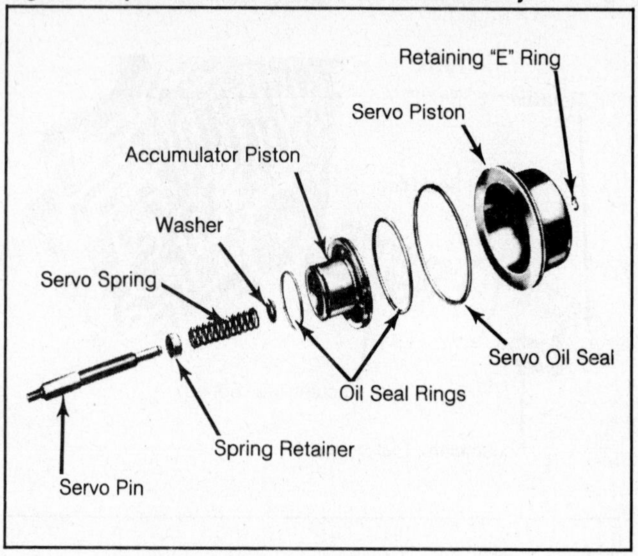

Reassembly

To reassemble, reverse disassembly procedure.

FRONT SERVO

Inspection

Inspect servo pin, piston and oil seal ring for wear or damage. Check fit of servo pin in piston and in case bore.

NOTE: Do not remove Teflon oil seal ring from servo piston unless seal ring requires replacement. Replacement oil seal ring is aluminum.

Fig. 17: Exploded View of Front Servo Assembly

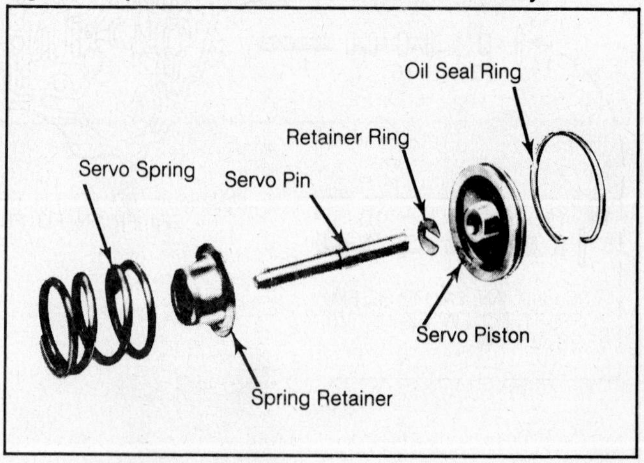

OIL PUMP

Disassembly

1) Place pump assembly in holding fixture (Adapter J-21364 and Rear Unit Holding Fixture J-6116) with stator shaft pointing down. Compress regulator boost valve bushing against pressure regulator spring. Remove snap ring.

CAUTION: Pressure regulator spring is very tightly compressed.

GENERAL MOTORS TURBO HYDRA-MATIC 400 (Cont.)

2) Withdraw regulator boost valve bushing and valve, then pressure regulator spring. Remove regulator valve, spring retainer, and spacer(s) if present. Remove 5 pump cover attaching bolts (noting different lengths and relative positions). Separate cover from body. Index mark drive and driven gears for reassembly reference and remove from pump body.

3) Reassembly of pump gears in same position will ensure quietest possible operation of oil pump. Remove retaining pin and bore plug from end of regulator bore. Remove 2 oil seal rings from cover. Remove pump-to-forward clutch housing thrust washer.

Fig. 18: Exploded View of Oil Pump Cover

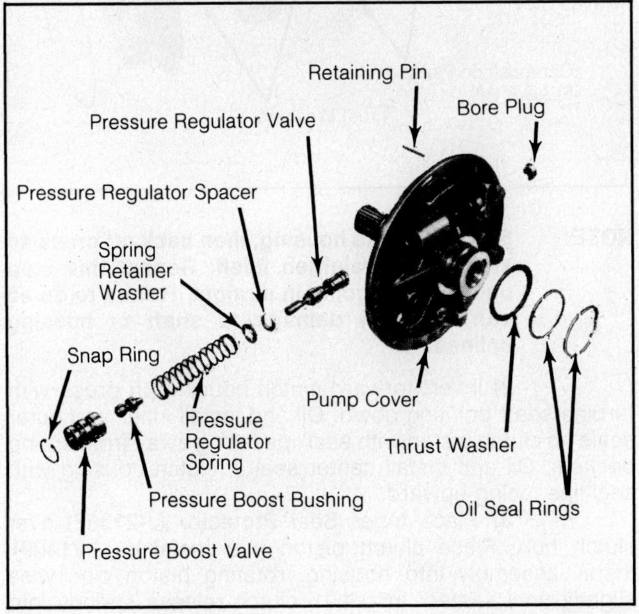

Inspection

1) Inspect all parts for scoring, galling, or other damage. Install pump gears in pump body. Check pump body face-to-gear face clearance with feeler gauge and straightedge. Clearance should be .0008-.0035" (.020-.089 mm). Check overall flatness of pump body and cover faces.

2) Check oil ring grooves and stator shaft for damage or wear. Make certain oil passages are clear and nonporous. Make sure pressure regulator and boost valves are free in bore. Install pump cover oil seal rings in counterbore of forward clutch housing and check for proper fit. Make sure 1/8" breather hole in pump cover is open.

NOTE: Several different pump covers are used in service. Solid valve must be used ONLY in pump cover with squared-off pressure regulator boss (at boost bushing end). Previous pressure regulator valve (with oil holes and orifice cup plug) may be used with either type pump cover.

Reassembly

1) Reverse disassembly procedure. When installing front unit thrust washer, make sure it is proper thickness as determined at disassembly. See FRONT UNIT END PLAY CHECK. Install gears in pump body with index marks made at disassembly aligned.

2) If correct, driving tangs on drive gear should face upward. Install pump cover attaching bolts, making sure to install correct length bolts in corresponding holes. Leave bolts one turn loose.

3) Install Alignment Strap (J-21368) to align cover and body. Tighten attaching bolts and remove alignment band. Install new square-cut "O" ring on pump. Install new pump oil seal on front of pump using Installer (J-21359).

Fig. 19: Current Type Pump Cover

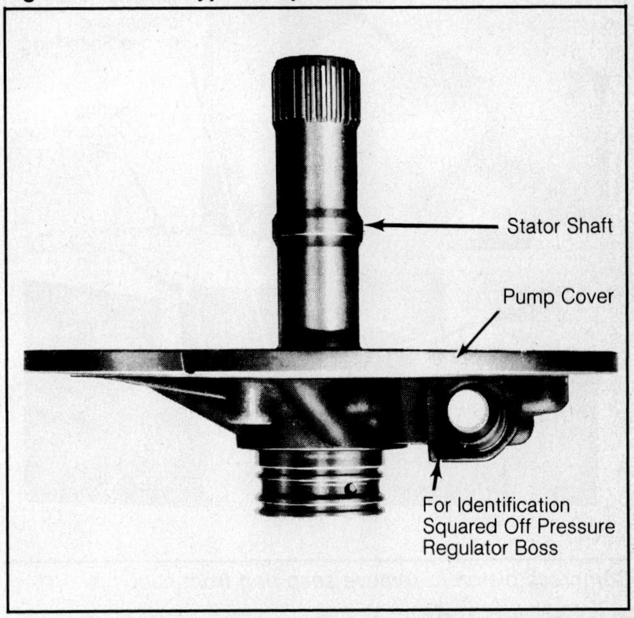

Solid pressure regulator valve must be installed in this type of cover.

Bushing Replacement

1) To replace oil pump body bushing, disassemble pump and remove front seal. Support pump body on wood blocks. Drive bushing from body with Remover/Installer (J-8092 and J-21465-17). Clean pump bushing bore. Drive bushing squarely into bore until flush or .010" (.25 mm) below gear pocket face.

2) To replace stator shaft rear bushing, mount pump cover in vise with stator shaft held in brass jaws. Assemble Remover (J-21465-15) to slide hammer and Adapter (J-2619 and J-2619-4). Thread remover into bushing. Use slide hammer to remove bushing.

3) Clean any shavings from stator bore. Place pump cover in vise with stator shaft resting on block of wood. Place new bushing on shoulder of Installer (J-21465-2). Bushing should be driven squarely into bore to depth of 19/32".

4) To replace stator shaft front bushing, mount pump cover in vise with stator shaft held in brass jaws. Attach bushing Remover (J-21465-15) to slide hammer and Adapter (J-2619 and J-2619-4). Thread removal tool into front bushing.

5) Remove bushing with slide hammer. Clean shavings from stator shaft. Assemble installer with Drive Handle (J-21465-3 and J-8092). Support hub of pump cover on soft material to protect ring lands. Place bushing on installer and drive squarely into bore with lead or brass hammer.

FORWARD CLUTCH

Disassembly

1) Place forward clutch assembly in Adapter and Holding Fixture (J-21364 and J-6116-01) with turbine shaft

GENERAL MOTORS TURBO HYDRA-MATIC 400 (Cont.)

Fig. 20: Compressing Forward Clutch Piston

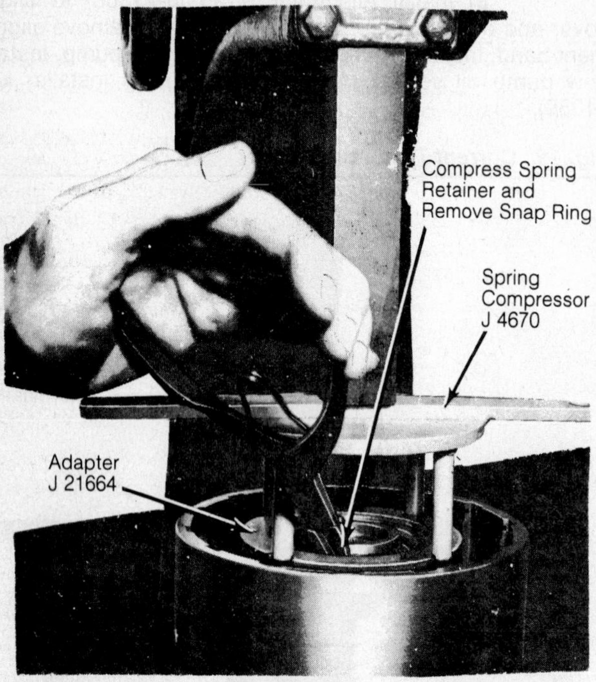

Compress piston to remove snap ring from hub.

pointing down. Do not damage turbine shaft. Remove forward clutch housing-to-direct clutch hub snap ring and withdraw hub. Remove forward clutch hub and one thrust washer from each side of hub.

2) Remove composition and steel clutch plates. Place forward clutch assembly in press with turbine shaft pointing down. Using Clutch Spring Compressor and Adapter (J-4670-01 and J-21664), compress spring retainer and remove snap ring. Remove tools. Lift out spring retainer and 16 clutch release springs.

NOTE: **Keep forward clutch release springs separate from direct clutch release springs.**

3) Remove forward clutch piston from housing. Remove inner and outer seals from piston. Remove center piston seal from clutch housing. If turbine shaft or housing is damaged, place housing in press with shaft facing down. Using 3" driver, press turbine shaft out of forward clutch housing.

Inspection

Inspect clutch plates for burning, scoring, or wear. Check release springs for distortion or collapsed coils. Inspect clutch hubs for worn splines and thrust faces. Check for clear lubrication passages in housing, hub, and turbine shaft. Check piston for cracks. Check turbine shaft and clutch housing for wear, scoring, or other damage. Make sure ball check in housing moves freely.

Reassembly

1) If turbine shaft was removed, place forward clutch housing in press with flat side up. Align shorter splined end of turbine shaft with splines in forward clutch housing. Carefully press shaft into housing until shaft bottoms out.

Fig. 21: Exploded View of Forward Clutch Assemby

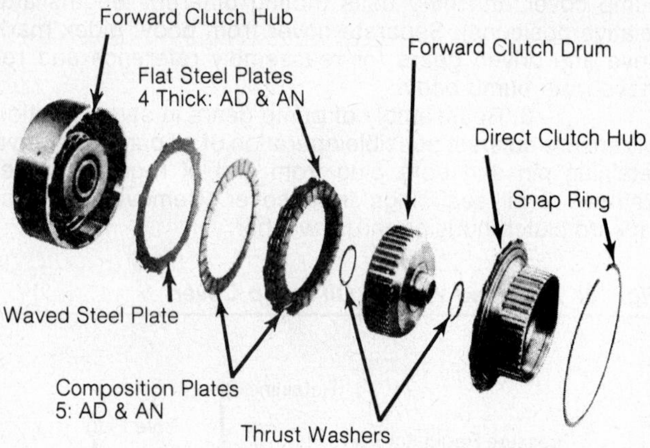

NOTE: **Start shaft into housing, then back off press so shaft can straighten itself. Repeat this step until shaft is going in straight. Failure to do so can result in damage to shaft or housing splines.**

2) Invert forward clutch housing on press with turbine shaft pointing down. Oil and install inner and outer seals on clutch piston with seal lips facing away from spring pockets. Oil and install center seal in clutch housing with seal lips facing upward.

3) Place Inner Seal Protector (J-21362) over clutch hub. Place clutch piston into Installer (J-21409). Install assembly into housing, rotating piston clockwise slightly until seated. Install 16 clutch release springs into piston pockets.

4) Place spring retainer over springs and compress springs with Compressor and Adapter (J-4670-01 and J-21664). Use care to avoid catching retainer in snap ring groove. Install snap ring. Remove tools and make certain all release springs are standing straight.

NOTE: **New type of forward clutch housing center seal is being used. It has beveled edge and is interchangeable with old type seal, which has lip edge. Old type seal cannot be used in later model transmissions. Make sure correct seal is installed.**

5) Install forward clutch hub thrust washers. Make sure bronze washer is installed on side of hub facing forward clutch housing. Retain washers in place with petroleum jelly. Place forward clutch hub in clutch housing.

6) Lubricate clutch plates with transmission fluid. Install clutch plates, starting with waved steel plate (plate with "U" notch), then alternating composition and flat steel plates (plate with "V" notch) until all clutch plates are installed. See FORWARD CLUTCH PLATE USAGE CHART.

FORWARD CLUTCH PLATE USAGE

Steel Plate Thickness	Flat Steel	Composition
.077" (1.96 mm)	3	4
.091" (2.31 mm)	4	5

GENERAL MOTORS TURBO HYDRA-MATIC 400 (Cont.)

7) Install direct clutch hub and retaining snap ring. Place forward clutch housing on oil pump delivery sleeve. Check operation of forward clutch by applying air through forward clutch passage in pump to actuate piston and move forward clutch. *See Fig. 22.*

Fig. 22: Checking Operation of Forward Clutch

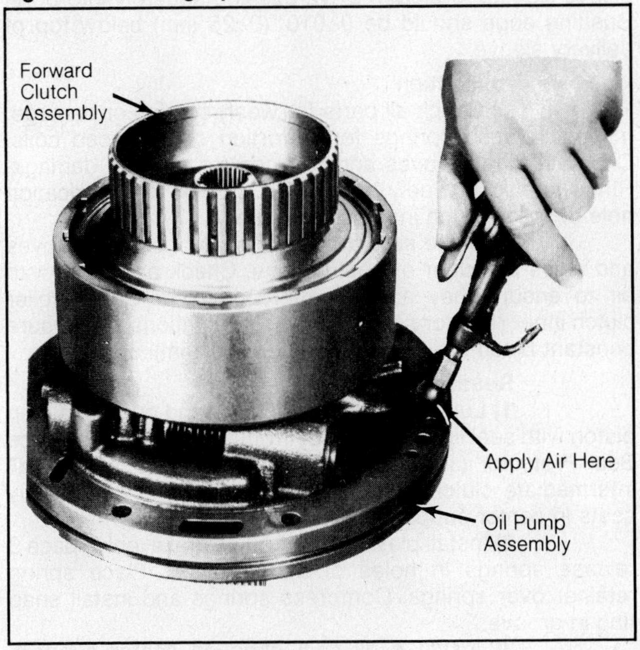

Compressed air must be clean and dry.

DIRECT CLUTCH & INTERMEDIATE ROLLER ASSEMBLY

Disassembly

1) Remove roller retainer snap ring. Remove clutch retainer. Remove roller outer race and roller assembly. Turn unit over and remove direct clutch backing plate-to-clutch housing snap ring. Remove direct clutch backing plate and clutch pack of steel and composition plates.

2) Compress spring retainer and remove snap ring. Use either Clutch Spring Compressor (J-4670), Rear Clutch Spring Compressor (J-6129), or press and Adapter (J-21664) to compress spring retainer. Remove tools, retainer, and 14 clutch release springs.

NOTE: Keep direct clutch release springs separate from forward clutch release springs.

3) Remove direct clutch piston from clutch housing. Remove inner and outer seals from piston. Remove center piston seal from direct clutch housing.

Inspection

1) Inspect roller assembly for damaged rollers, cage, or springs. Inspect cam and outer race for scratches or wear. Inspect clutch housing for cracks, wear, proper opening of oil passages or wear on clutch plate drive lugs.

Fig. 24: Checking Operation of Direct Clutch Assembly

Compressed air must be clean and dry.

Fig. 23: Exploded View of Direct Clutch and Intermediate Roller Clutch Assembly

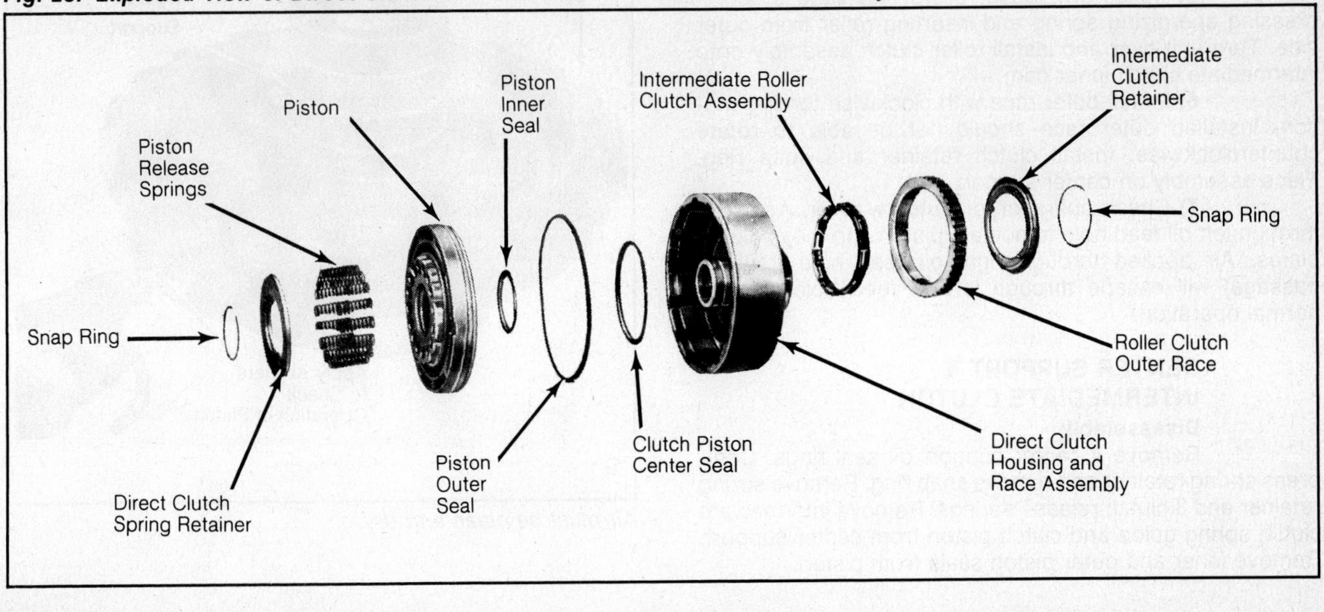

GENERAL MOTORS TURBO HYDRA-MATIC 400 (Cont.)

2) Inspect clutch plates for wear or burning. Inspect backing plate for scratches or damage. Inspect clutch piston for cracks. Ensure free operation of check ball in clutch housing. Check release springs for collapsed coils and distortion.

Reassembly

1) Lubricate piston seals and grooves with transmission fluid. Install new inner and outer seals on clutch piston with seal lips facing away from spring pockets. Install new center seal in clutch housing with seal lip facing upward.

2) Place Seal Protector (J-21362) over clutch hub. Place clutch piston in Installer (J-21409) and insert assembly into clutch housing. Install clutch piston by rotating slightly in clockwise direction.

3) If original clutch release springs are being used, install 14 springs into spring pockets of piston. Leave 2 opposite pockets with no springs. If replacement springs are used, install 16 springs and use all spring pockets. Place spring retainer on top of springs. Compress springs and retainer with same tool used during disassembly.

4) Install snap ring. Make sure that springs are standing straight. Lubricate clutch plates with transmission fluid. Install plates into clutch housing starting with waved steel plate (if used) or flat steel plate. Alternate composition and flat steel plates until all plates are installed. See DIRECT CLUTCH PLATE USAGE chart. Install backing plate and backing plate snap ring.

NOTE: Do not use radially grooved composition plates in direct clutch. All flat steel plates used in direct clutch are .091" (2.31 mm) thick.

DIRECT CLUTCH PLATE USAGE

Model	Flat Steel Plates	Composition Plates
AA, AB, AC, AE, AH	4	4
AM	6	6
AD [1]	4	5

[1] – Install waved ("U" notch) steel plate first.

5) Install any loose rollers into cage by compressing energizing spring and inserting roller from outer side. Turn unit over and install roller clutch assembly onto intermediate clutch inner cam.

6) Install outer race with clockwise turning motion. Installed outer race should not be able to rotate counterclockwise. Install clutch retainer and snap ring. Place assembly on center support.

7) Check operation of clutch with air. Apply air through left oil feed hole to actuate piston and move clutch plates. Air applied through right oil feed hole (reverse passage) will escape through left oil feed hole. This is normal operation.

CENTER SUPPORT & INTERMEDIATE CLUTCH

Disassembly

Remove 4 center support oil seal rings. Compress spring retainer and remove snap ring. Remove spring retainer and 3 clutch release springs. Remove intermediate clutch spring guide and clutch piston from center support. Remove inner and outer piston seals from piston.

CAUTION: DO NOT remove 3 screws holding roller clutch inner race to center support.

Bushing Replacement

If center support bushing requires replacement, use Driver (J-21465-6) and remove bushing. To install new bushing, align slot in bushing with drilled hole in oil delivery sleeve closest to piston. Drive bushing squarely into bore. Bushing edge should be 0-.010" (0-.25 mm) below top of delivery sleeve.

Inspection

1) Check all parts for wear, scoring or damage. Inspect release springs for distortion or collapsed coils. Check oil ring grooves and oil rings for wear or damage. Rings should fit freely in grooves. Check that lubrication hole of roller clutch inner race is open.

2) Make sure all passages, lubrication grooves and holes are clear of obstructions. Check passages with air to ensure they are not interconnected. Check roller clutch inner race for scratches and indentations. Make sure constant bleed orifice is open .020" (.51 mm).

Reassembly

1) Lubricate and install inner and outer seals on piston with seal lips facing away from spring pockets. Place Seal Protector (J-21363) over center support hub. Install intermediate clutch piston. Make certain that piston fully seats in center support.

2) Install plastic spring guide and evenly space 3 release springs in holes of spring guide. Place spring retainer over springs. Compress springs and install snap ring in groove.

3) Install 4 oil seal rings on center support. Apply air through center oil feed hole to actuate clutch piston. Check operation of clutch piston. *See Fig. 25.*

NOTE: All replacement center support oil seal rings are cast iron with overlapping hook ends. Make sure to fit correctly.

Fig. 25: Checking Operation of Intermediate Clutch Piston

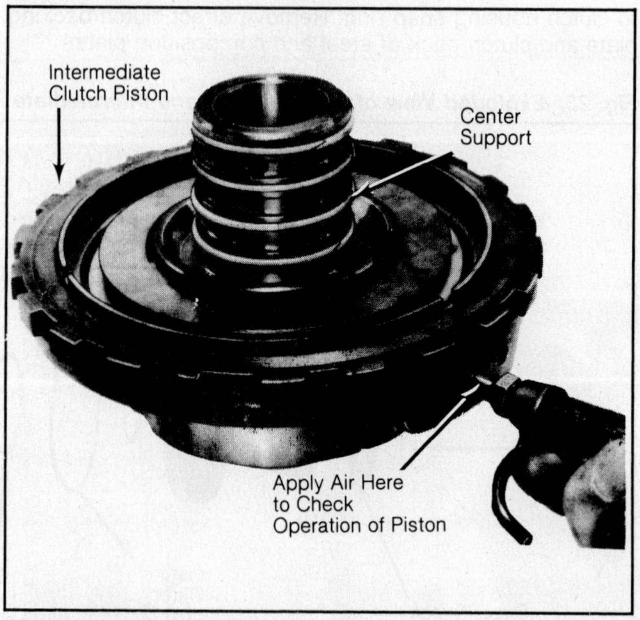

Air must be clean and dry.

GENERAL MOTORS TURBO HYDRA-MATIC 400 (Cont.)

GEAR UNIT

Disassembly

1) Mount gear unit in Holding Fixture (J-6116-01) using Adapter (J-21364). Output shaft must point downward. Remove center support-to-sun gear races and thrust bearing. Outer race may have remained with center support during removal. Remove sun gear from output carrier.

2) Remove reaction carrier-to-output carrier thrust washer. Remove front internal gear ring from output carrier assembly. Turn gear unit over in fixture so main shaft is pointing downward. Remove and discard "O" ring from output shaft. Remove output shaft-to-output carrier snap ring. Remove output shaft.

3) Remove output shaft-to-rear internal gear thrust bearing with both races. Remove rear internal gear and mainshaft from output carrier. Remove rear internal gear-to-sun gear thrust bearing with both races from inner face of rear internal gear. Remove rear internal gear-to-mainshaft snap ring to remove mainshaft.

Inspection

1) Inspect output shaft. Look for galling, damage to lugs or splines, worn thrust washer or bearing surfaces, and rough or damaged teeth on speedometer and governor drive gears.

2) Inspect main shaft. Look for cracks or distortion, damage to splines or snap ring grooves, or ground bushing journal damage. Make sure that lubrication holes are open. Inspect rear internal gear. Check teeth and bearing surfaces for damage or wear. Inspect splines and gear for cracks or damage.

3) Inspect output carrier assembly. Check front internal gear and pinion gears for tooth damage, rough bearings, flaking, cracks, or tilt. Pinion end play range is .009-.024" (.23-.61 mm). Check parking gear lugs for cracks. Check output shaft locating splines for wear.

4) Inspect for burning or scoring on reaction carrier band surface, on roller clutch outer cam, and on thrust washer surfaces. If bushing is damaged, carrier must be replaced. Check pinion gears for damage, rough bearings, or excessive tilt. Pinion end play range is .009-.024" (.23-.61 mm).

5) Check roller clutch assembly for damage to rollers, springs, or clutch cage. Inspect sun gear and sun gear shaft for damage or wear to splines, teeth, and bushings. Make sure oil lubrication holes are open on shaft and gear.

Speedometer Drive Gear Replacement

1) Use Puller and Gear Remover (J-8433 and J-21427-01) to remove speedometer drive gear. Attach tools on output shaft so puller bolt indexes with end of shaft. Flat face of remover must be under front face of drive gear. Tighten bolt on puller until gear is free on shaft.

2) To install new gear, support output shaft and drive gear on with pipe. Select pipe that does not contact gear teeth, as gear would be damaged during installation. Drive speedometer gear onto shaft until distance from rear face of gear to end of output shaft is 5 21/32" (83.34 mm).

Output Shaft Bushing Replacement

If bushing is worn or galled, thread Bushing Remover (J-21465-16) into bushing. Attach slide hammer and withdraw bushing. Place new bushing on Driver (J-21465-1) and drive into place until tool bottoms. Output flange bushing must be installed so oil hole in flange is aligned with oil hole in hub. Notch in bushing must face outward.

Sun Gear Shaft Bushing Replacement

Support sun gear shaft in soft-jawed vise. Thread Bushing Remover (J-21465-15) into bushing, attach slide hammer, and remove bushing. Place new bushing on Driver (J-21465-5) and drive into place until tool bottoms.

Fig. 26: Exploded View of Center Support Assembly

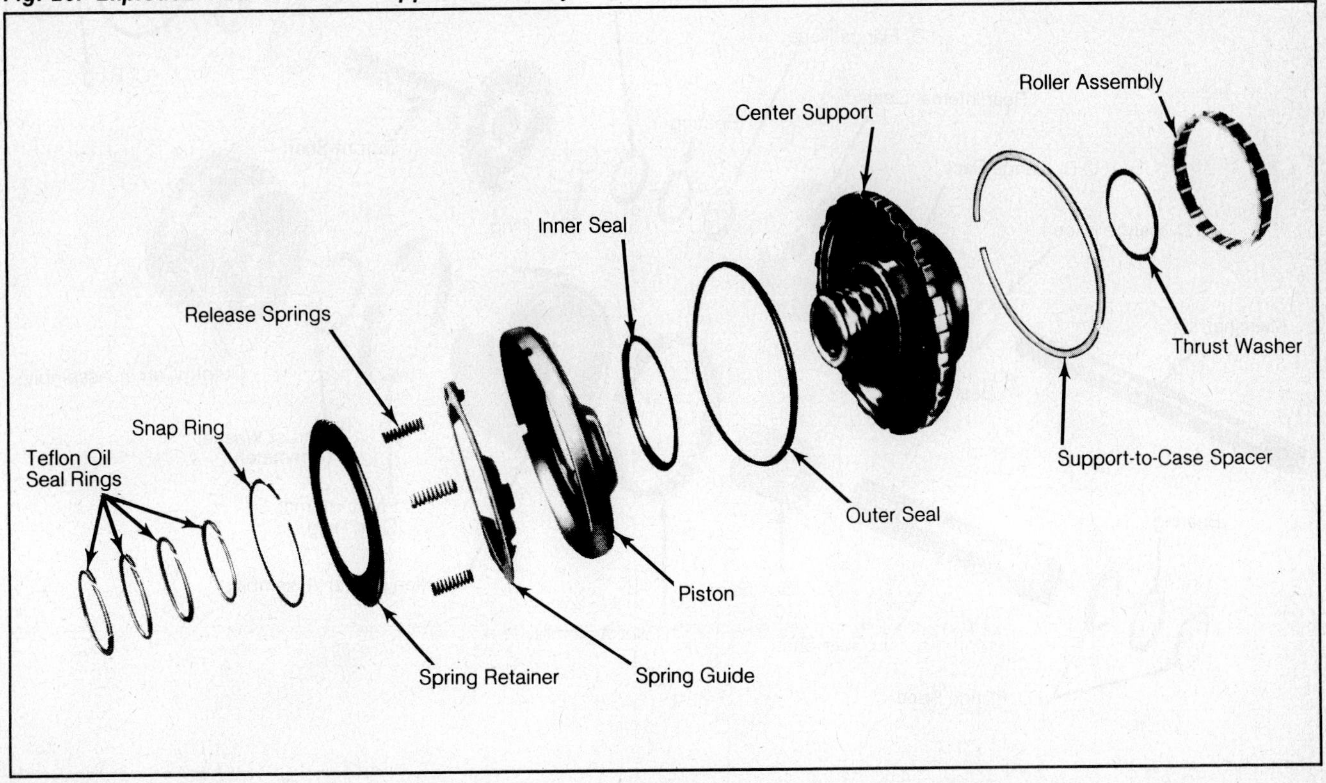

GENERAL MOTORS TURBO HYDRA-MATIC 400 (Cont.)

Pinion Gear Replacement

1) Support carrier assembly on front face. Using 1/2" drill, remove stake marks from end of pinion pin(s) to be replaced. This reduces possibility of cracking carrier when pressing out pins. Do not remove any material from carrier as it will be weakened and tend to crack.

2) Using tapered punch, drive or press pinion pins out of carrier. Remove pinion gears, thrust washers and roller needle bearings. Inspect pinion pocket thrust faces for burrs. Remove if present.

Fig. 27: Exploded View of Pinion Assembly

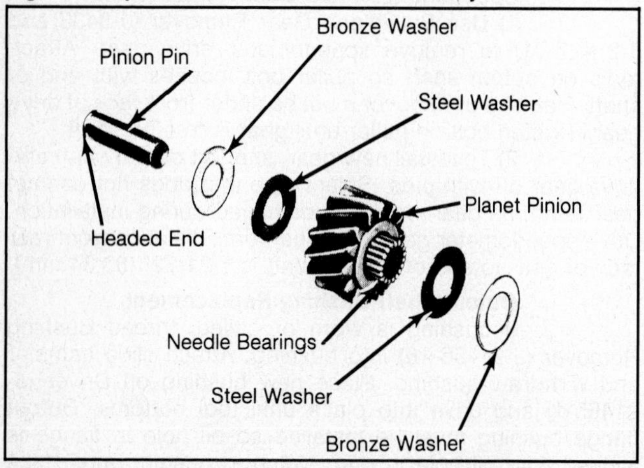

3) Install 18 needle bearings into each pinion. Use pinion pin as guide and petroleum jelly to hold bearings in place. Place 1 bronze and 1 steel washer on each side of pinion so steel washer is against pinion. Use petroleum jelly to hold washers in place.

4) Place pinion gear assembly in carrier and install pilot shaft through rear face of assembly to hold parts in place. Drive in new pinion pin from front while rotating pinion gear.

5) Make sure headed end is flush or below face of carrier. Use punch held in bench vise for an anvil. Place carrier over punch and stake pinion pin in 3 places with blunt radius chisel.

NOTE: **Both ends of pinion pins must lie below face of carrier or interference may occur.**

Reassembly (Complete Gear Assembly)

1) Install rear internal gear on end of mainshaft with snap ring groove. Install snap ring. Install sun gear-to-internal gear thrust races and bearing against inner face of rear internal gear. Retain with petroleum jelly.

2) Place large race against internal gear with flange facing forward or upward. Place thrust bearing in race. Place small race against bearing with inner flange into bearing or downward.

3) Oil output carrier pinion gears with transmission fluid. Install output carrier on mainshaft so pinion gears mesh with rear internal gear. Install assembly in Holding Fixture (J-6116-01). Mainshaft must point down. Install rear

Fig. 28: Exploded View of Planetary Gear Unit

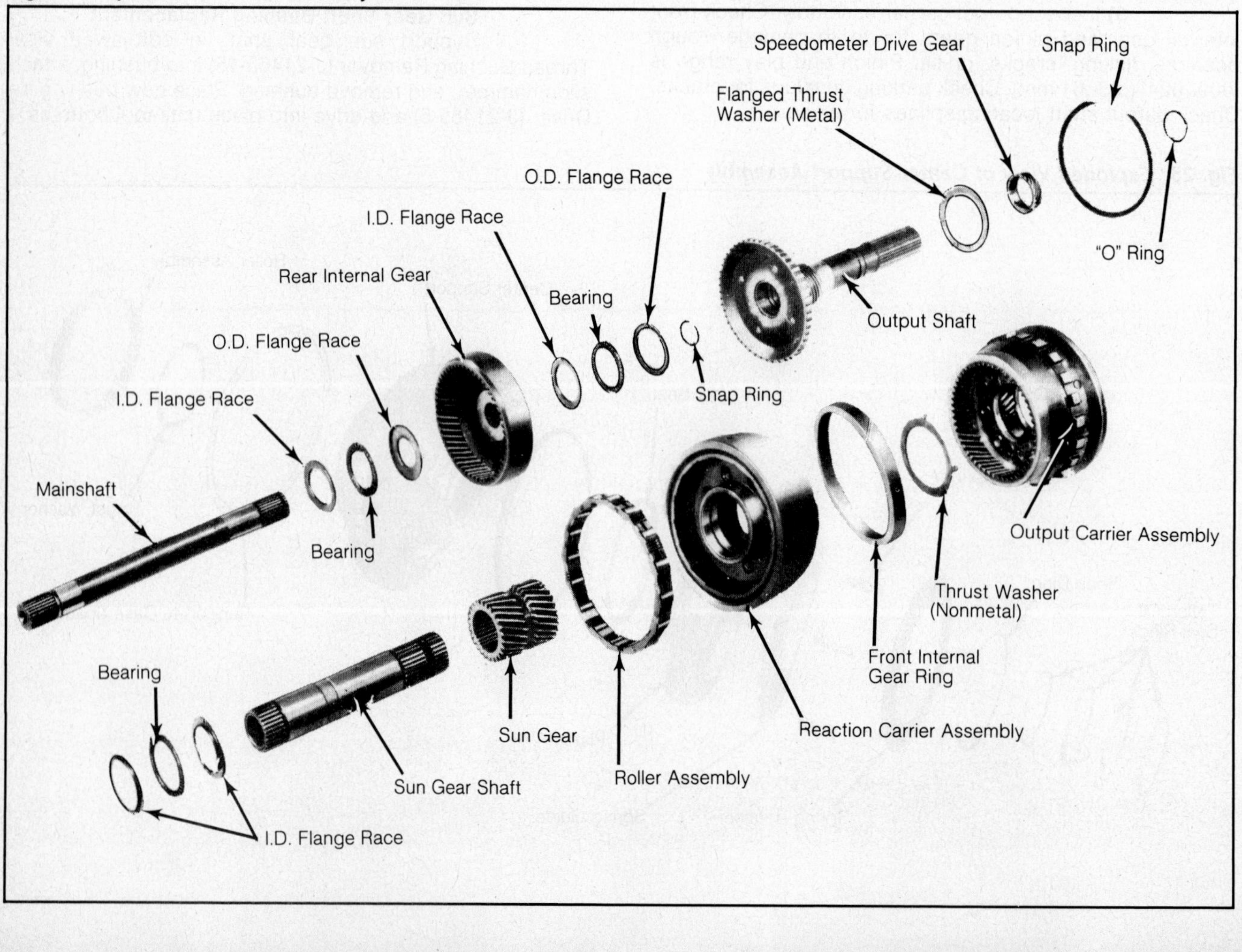

GENERAL MOTORS TURBO HYDRA-MATIC 400 (Cont.)

internal gear-to-output shaft thrust races and bearings. Retain with petroleum jelly.

4) Place small diameter race against internal gear with inner diameter flange facing up. Place thrust bearing in race. Place large diameter race on bearing with outer flange cupped over bearing. Install output shaft into output carrier assembly. Install snap ring holding output shaft into output carrier.

5) Install new output shaft "O" ring. Invert assembly in holding fixture so output shaft faces down. Install reaction carrier-to-output carrier thrust washer with tabs inserted into pockets. Retain with petroleum jelly.

6) Install sun gear so inner chamfer faces down. Install sun gear shaft with longer splined end down. Install gear ring over output carrier. Oil pinion gears in reaction carrier with transmission fluid. Install reaction carrier on output carrier so reaction pinion gears mesh with front internal gear.

NOTE: **If front internal gear ring prevents assembly of carrier when new output carrier and/or reaction carrier is being installed, replace front internal gear ring with service gear ring. Front internal gear ring is selective fit at factory but not in service.**

7) Install center support-to-sun thrust races and bearing (retain with petroleum jelly). Install large race on sun gear with flange facing up against sun gear shaft. Install thrust bearing on race. Lubricate smaller race with petroleum jelly and install on center support with flange facing toward lower end.

8) Coat reaction carrier-to-center support thrust washer with petroleum jelly. Install thrust washer in recess of center support. Install any rollers that may have come out of roller case by compressing energizing spring with forefinger and inserting roller from outer side.

9) Make sure that roller clutch springs are not distorted. Curved end leaf of spring should be against roller. Install roller clutch assembly into reaction carrier. Install center support-to-reaction carrier thrust washer into recess in center support. Retain with petroleum jelly. Install center support into roller clutch in reaction carrier.

NOTE: **With reaction carrier held stationary, center support should rotate counterclockwise only.**

10) Install Holding Tool (J-21795-02) so tangs engage groove in mainshaft. Tighten set screw on tool to prevent movement of roller clutch during installation of gear unit assembly. Remove gear unit from holding tool. Place unit on side. Install output shaft-to-case metal thrust washer (bent tabs in pockets). Retain with petroleum jelly.

TRANSMISSION CASE

Inspection

Inspect case for cracks, porosity, or interconnected passages. Check governor and modulator valve bores for scratches or scoring. Check band anchor pins for retention. Inspect intermediate clutch driven plate lugs for damage. Inspect snap ring grooves for damage. Ensure that parking pawl shaft cup plug is properly staked and sealed.

CAUTION: **If case assembly requires replacement, make sure that center support-to-case spacer and name plate are removed from old case and installed on new case.**

Case Bushing Replacement

1) With converter end of transmission case downward, use Bushing Driver (J-21465-8) and soft-faced hammer to drive bushing out of case. Invert case to install new bushing from front of case. Use Drive Handle and Adapters (J-8092, J-21465-13, J-21465-8, and J-21465-9) to install new bushing.

2) Lubrication passage of bushing should face Adapter Ring (J-21465-9). Drive bushing squarely into bore until adapter ring bottoms. Bushing should be .040-.055" (1.02-1.4 mm) above selective thrust washer surface. Stake bushing in place with Staker (J-21465-10). Staking marks must be in bushing groove.

EXTENSION HOUSING

Inspection

Check housing for cracks or porosity. Inspect gasket mounting face for burrs or other damage. Make sure rear seal drain-back part is not obstructed. Check rear bushing for wear or damage. Replace as necessary.

Bushing Replacement

Remove rear seal and stand extension housing seal end up. Using driver tool, drive or press bushing from extension housing. Use same tool to drive or press bushing into housing. Bushing should be 0-.010" (0-.25 mm) below oil seal counterbore surface. Stake bushing in place using Staker (J-21465-10). Stake marks must be in lube grooves.

NOTE: **Staking in production bushings may not be in lubrication groove. Production equipment does not distort bushing surface, making location of stakes optional.**

Fig. 29: Front View of Transmission Case Showing Oil Passages

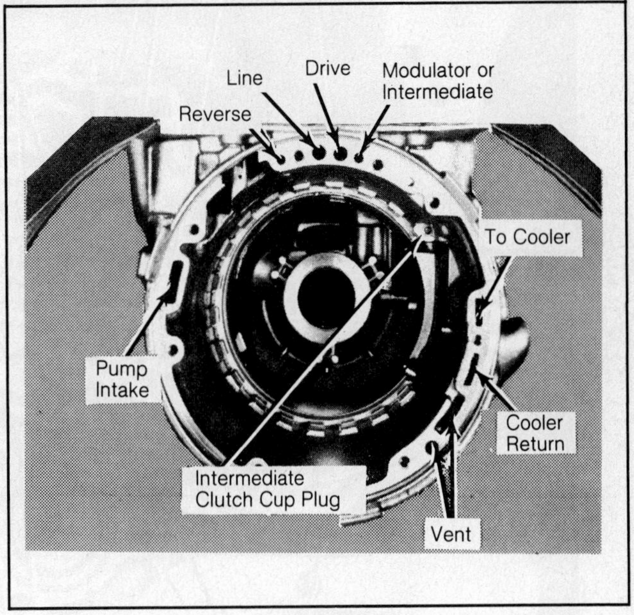

TRANSMISSION REASSEMBLY

PARKING PAWL

Install parking pawl with tooth toward center of transmission. Install parking pawl shaft and shaft retainer clip. Install new shaft cup plug using 3/8" diameter rod.

GENERAL MOTORS TURBO HYDRA-MATIC 400 (Cont.)

Drive plug into case until shaft bottoms on case rib. Install parking pawl return spring with square end hooked on pawl. Install parking pawl bracket guides over parking pawl.

REAR BAND & GEAR UNIT

1) Install rear band assembly so that 2 lugs index with 2 anchor pins. Make sure band is seated on lugs. Install support-to-case spacer against shoulder at bottom of case splines and with gap in spacer adjacent to band anchor pin.

NOTE: Support-to-case spacer is .040" (1.02 mm) thick and both sides are flat. Do not confuse this spacer with either center support-to-case snap ring, which has one side beveled, or intermediate clutch backing plate-to-case snap ring, which is .093" (2.36 mm) thick and flat on both sides.

2) Install previously selected rear unit end play washer into slots provided inside rear of case. See REAR UNIT END PLAY. Retain washer with petroleum jelly. Place transmission case in horizontal position in holding tool.

3) Install complete gear unit assembly into case by lining up slots. Carefully guide assembly into case. Make sure center support bolt hole is aligned with hole in case.

4) Position transmission vertically with front end of case up. Install center support-to-case snap ring with beveled side up and flat side against center support. Locate gap adjacent to front band anchor pin. Expand snap ring until center support is against shoulder of case.

5) Install case-to-center support bolt by placing locating tool into direct clutch passage of case. *See Fig. 31.* Handle of tool should be pointing to right (viewed from front of transmission) and parallel to bellhousing mounting face.

6) Apply pressure downward on tool handle. This will rotate center support counterclockwise (viewed from front of transmission). Hold center support firmly counterclockwise against case splines and tighten case-to-center support bolt.

CAUTION: Use care not to burr case valve body mounting surface when using locating tool.

7) Lubricate intermediate clutch plates with transmission fluid. Start with waved steel plate. Alternate

Fig. 30: Bottom View of Transmission Case Showing Oil Passages

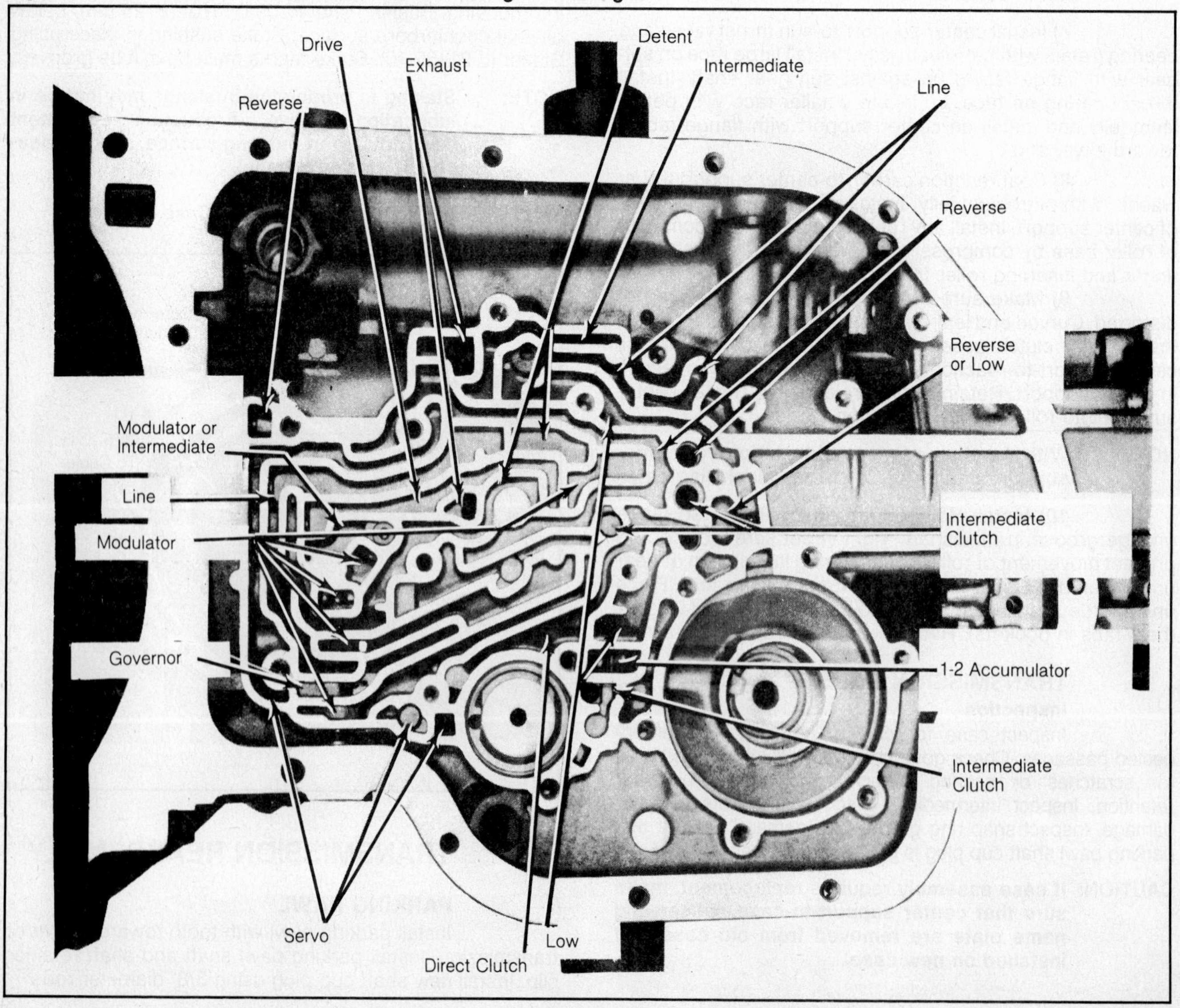

Fig. 31: Using Locating Tool to Install Center Support-to-Case Bolt

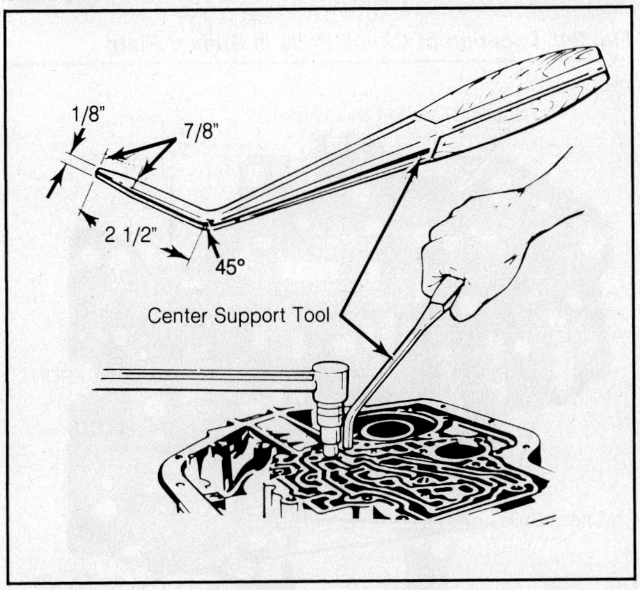

composition and flat steel plates until all clutch plates are installed.

8) Install intermediate clutch backing plate with flat machined surface against clutch plates. Install backing plate-to-case snap ring with end gap on side of case opposite front band anchor pin. Before proceeding with transmission reassembly, recheck rear unit end play.

NOTE: **Both sides of intermediate backing plate-to-case snap ring are flat. Ring is .093" (2.36 mm) thick.**

FRONT BAND & CLUTCH ASSEMBLIES

1) Install front band with band anchor hole over band anchor pin. Apply lug faces servo hole. Install direct clutch housing and intermediate roller assembly. Be certain that clutch housing hub bottoms on sun gear shaft. Splines on forward end of sun gear shaft must be flush with splines in direct clutch housing.

NOTE: **It will be necessary to rotate housing to allow roller outer race to index with composition clutch plates.**

2) Install forward clutch hub-to-direct clutch housing thrust washer on forward clutch hub. Retain with petroleum jelly. With transmission in horizontal position, install forward clutch and turbine shaft. Be sure that end of mainshaft goes completely into forward clutch hub.

3) Rotate clutch housing so that direct clutch driving hub can index with direct clutch composition plates. When forward clutch is seated, it will be 1 1/4" (32 mm) from pump mounting face in case. Be sure to verify this distance by measuring.

NOTE: **Missing internal splines in forward clutch hub are lubrication passages and do not have to be indexed with any particular spline on mainshaft.**

OIL PUMP

1) Lubricate turbine shaft journals with transmission fluid. Lubricate Teflon oil seal rings with petroleum jelly. Place Slide Hammer Bolts (J-6125-1) into 2 opposing unthreaded holes in pump assembly to use as guide pins. Align pump-to-case gasket on case mounting face.

2) Thread slide hammer bolts into holes in transmission case. Install pump assembly into case. Do not remove slide hammer bolts until final 2 pump attaching bolts are installed. Install 6 pump attaching bolts with new rubber coated washers. Leave 1 bolt (at either 5 o'clock or 10 o'clock position) out to recheck front unit end play. Tighten bolts evenly.

CAUTION: **If turbine shaft cannot be rotated as pump is being pulled into place, forward or direct clutch housings have been installed improperly and are not indexing with all clutch plates. This condition MUST be corrected before pulling pump fully into place.**

3) Recheck front unit end play. Adjust if necessary. See FRONT UNIT END PLAY. Install remaining pump attaching bolt with washer. Apply nonhardening sealer to outside of new front oil seal. Install seal into pump using Driver (J-21359).

PARKING LINKAGE, DETENT LEVER & MANUAL SHAFT

Install new manual shaft seal in transmission case using 3/4" diameter rod to seat seal. Install actuator rod into manual detent lever from side opposite pin. Install actuator rod plunger under parking bracket and over parking pawl. Install manual shaft through case and detent lever. Install lock nut on manual shaft and tighten. Install retaining pin, indexing with groove in manual shaft.

NOTE: **If work is being done with transmission installed, it may be necessary to bend manual shaft retaining pin. Straighten pin after installation.**

Fig. 32: View of Oil Pump Cover Passages

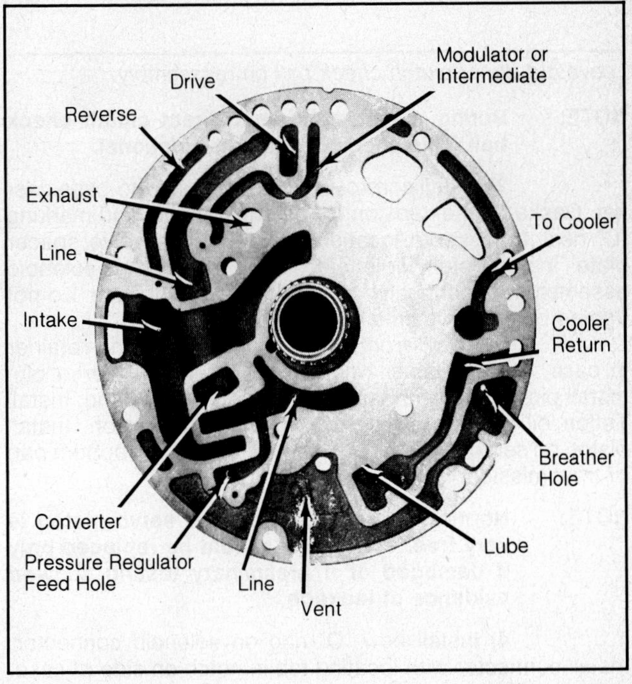

GENERAL MOTORS TURBO HYDRA-MATIC 400 (Cont.)

EXTENSION HOUSING

1) Install new gasket on extension housing and retain with petroleum jelly. Check "O" ring on output shaft for any nicks or flattening and replace ring. Install housing on transmission case and tighten attaching bolts.

2) Apply non-hardening sealer to outside diameter of rear oil seal. Position seal on extension housing and seat in housing with driver.

CONTROL VALVE SPACER DETENT SOLENOID, & FRONT SERVO

1) Install 2 guide pins opposite each other into 2 control valve assembly attaching bolt holes. Install 5 check balls into ball seat pockets in case. If transmission is in vehicle, install check balls in pockets of spacer plate. *See Figs. 33 and 34.*

Fig. 33: Location of Check Balls in Transmission Case

Leave out direct clutch check ball on reassembly.

NOTE: **During reassembly, omit direct clutch check ball. This check ball is non-functional.**

2) Install control valve spacer plate-to-case gasket. Gasket has extension for detent solenoid and marking "C" near front servo location. Install control valve spacer plate. Install detent solenoid gasket and detent solenoid assembly with connector facing outer edge of case. Do not tighten bolts at this time.

3) Install front servo spring and spring retainer in case. Place retainer ring in groove of front servo pin. Install pin in case with tapered end contacting band. Install Teflon oil seal ring, if removed, on servo piston. Install piston on servo pin with flat side of piston facing bottom pan of transmission.

NOTE: **Normal fit of Teflon ring and servo piston is very free. Teflon ring should be replaced only if damaged or if preliminary testing showed evidence of leakage.**

4) Install new "O" ring on solenoid connector. Install connector with locating tab in notch on side of case. Lock tabs point into case. Connect solenoid lead to terminal on connector.

Fig. 34: Location of Check Balls in Spacer Plate

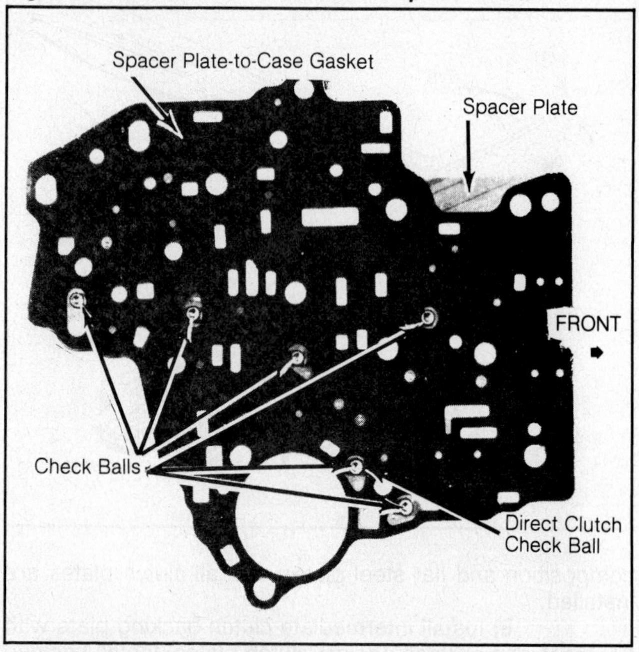

Use this method when transmission is in vehicle.

REAR SERVO

1) Before installing servo, check band apply pin. See BAND APPLY PIN SELECTION CHECK. Make certain that rear band apply lug is aligned with servo pin bore in transmission case.

2) Lubricate inner and outer rear servo bores in case with transmission fluid. Install rear accumulator spring in servo inner bore. Install rear servo assembly. Press down on rear servo assembly and make sure it seats properly in bore. With servo depressed, install gasket and cover. Tighten attaching bolts.

CONTROL VALVE BODY ASSEMBLY

1) Install control valve-to-spacer gasket (gasket marked "VB" near front servo location). Install interchangeable governor pipes on control valve assembly. Install governor screen assembly (open end first) into governor feed pipe hole in case (hole nearest center of transmission).

NOTE: **If transmission is installed in vehicle, insert governor screen (closed end first) into governor feed pipe before installing control valve assembly and governor pipes. Feed pipe locates in hole in case nearest center of transmission.**

2) Using 2 guide pins, install control valve assembly and governor pipes on transmission. Be careful when aligning governor feed pipe over screen. Make sure gasket and spacer plate are not moved out of position, that manual valve is indexed properly with pin on detent lever, and that governor pipes are properly seated in case holes.

3) Start control valve body-to-case bolts. Remove guide pins. Install detent roller and spring assembly. Install and tighten remaining attaching bolts. Tighten solenoid attaching screws. These screws should be zinc plated to ensure good electrical contact.

GENERAL MOTORS TURBO HYDRA-MATIC 400 (Cont.)

Fig. 35: Installing Detent Roller and Spring

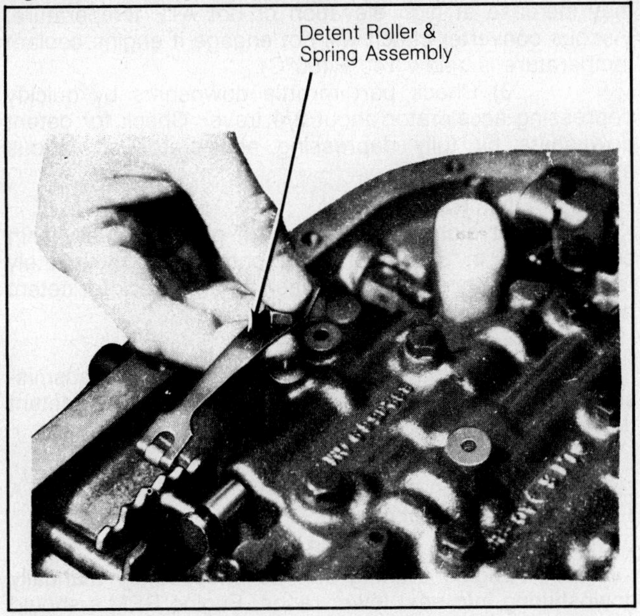

GOVERNOR

Install governor assembly into case. Install cover with new gasket and tighten attaching bolts.

SPEEDOMETER DRIVEN GEAR

CAUTION: Speedometer driven gears come in 3 different tooth sizes. Driven gear and matching sleeve must correspond to axle ratio. Never turn sleeve in transmission case as gear damage will result. Shaft center line is eccentric to outside diameter of sleeve.

Install driven gear into sleeve. Install driven gear assembly into case. Install retainer with tangs in sleeve positioning bosses. Install and tighten attaching bolt.

INTAKE PIPE, FILTER & OIL PAN

Install new intake pipe "O" ring seal. Install pipe into new filter assembly. Place filter and intake pipe in case bore. Install filter retaining bolt and tighten. Install oil pan with new gasket. Install and tighten attaching screws.

VACUUM MODULATOR & VALVE

Install modulator valve into case with stem end out. Install new "O" ring seal on vacuum modulator. Install modulator into case with vacuum hose pipe facing front and angled 5° toward top of case. Install modulator retainer with curved side of tangs inboard. Tighten attaching bolt.

CONVERTER ASSEMBLY

Install converter onto turbine shaft. Make sure converter hub drive slots are fully engaged with pump drive gear tangs. Install converter fully toward rear of transmission.

TIGHTENING SPECIFICATIONS

Application	Ft. Lbs. (N.m)
Center Support Bolts	25 (34)
Extension Housing-to-Case Bolts	23 (32)
Transmission-to-Engine Bolts	35 (48)
Converter-to-Drive Plate Bolts	35 (48)
Pump Cover Bolts	20 (27)
Parking Pawl Bracket Bolts	20 (27)
Pump-to-Case Bolts	20 (27)
Rear Servo Cover Bolts	20 (27)
Oil Pan Bolts	12 (16)
Modulator Retainer Bolts	20 (27)
Governor Cover Bolts	20 (27)
Manual Lever-to-Detent Lever	20 (27)
Line Pressure Take-Off Plug	10 (14)
Filter Retainer Bolt	10 (14)
	INCH Lbs. (N.m)
Detent Solenoid Bolts	84 (10)
Control Valve Body Bolts	96 (11)
Manual Lever-to-Manual Shaft Nut	96 (11)

GENERAL MOTORS TURBO HYDRA-MATIC 440-T4 TRANSAXLE

Buick
  Century, Electra
Cadillac
  DeVille, Fleetwood
Chevrolet
  Celebrity
Oldsmobile
  Cutlass Ciera, Ninety-Eight
Pontiac
  6000

IDENTIFICATION

The transaxle identification code is located on a stamped metal tag on the rear face of transaxle case adjacent to right axle opening.

Fig. 1: THM 440-T4 Transaxle Identification

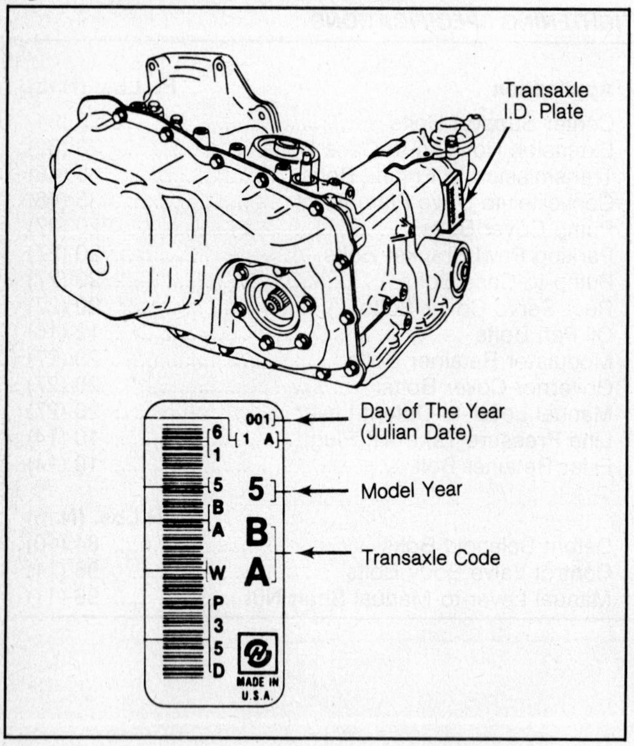

REMOVAL & INSTALLATION

TRANSAXLE

See appropriate AUTOMATIC TRANSMISSION REMOVAL article in DOMESTIC GENERAL SERVICING section.

TESTING

ROAD TEST

Drive Range

1) From stationary position, accelerate vehicle with selector lever in "D" range. Check 1-2, 2-3 and 3-4 shifts. Shift points will vary depending on throttle opening.

2) Check viscous converter clutch engagement on Cadillac models. Engagement should occur at about 25 MPH at minimum throttle. Engagement speed threshold may increase at high elevation or hot ATF temperature. Viscous converter clutch will not engage if engine coolant temperature is below 140°F (60°C).

3) Check part throttle downshifts by quickly depressing accelerator about 3/4 travel. Check for detent downshifts by fully depressing accelerator at various speeds.

"3" Range

At highway speed in 4th gear, manually shift selector lever in "3". Transmission should shift immediately to 3rd gear. It should not shift back to 4th. Check for detent downshifts by fully depressing accelerator.

"2" Range

While in range "3", shift to range "2". Transmission should shift immediately to "2". Check for 2-1 detent downshift by fully depressing accelerator.

"1" (Low) Range

Position selector lever in "1" and accelerate. A 1-2 upshift should not occur.

Overrun (Engine) Braking

Engine braking can be checked by manually downshifting into next lower range. Engine RPM's should increase and a braking effect should be noticed.

TRANSAXLE IDENTIFICATION CODES

Application	Code
Celebrity & 6000	CM, CN, HJ
Century	BA, BC, BS, BV, CN, HJ
Ciera	BA, BC, BS, CM, CN, HJ
DeVille & Fleetwood	
Electra	BA, BC, BS, CN,HJ
Ninety-Eight	BA, BC, CM, CN, HJ

DESCRIPTION

The THM 440-T4 transaxle is a 4-speed automatic unit that provides 4 forward speeds, including overdrive. The transaxle assembly consists of a torque converter with clutch, a sprocket and drive link assembly, 1-2 and reverse band assemblies, an input, 2nd, 3rd and 4th multiple-disc clutch assemblies, an input sprag and 3rd roller clutch, a compound planetary gear set, a differential and final drive.

A variable vane type oil pump supplies the transaxle with oil pressure. Oil pressure is regulated by vacuum modulation. Transaxle shift points are controlled by throttle opening through the throttle valve cable.

LUBRICATION & ADJUSTMENTS

See appropriate AUTOMATIC TRANSMISSION SERVICING article in DOMESTIC GENERAL SERVICING section.

TROUBLE SHOOTING

See appropriate AUTOMATIC TRANSMISSION TROUBLE SHOOTING article in DOMESTIC GENERAL SERVICING section.

GENERAL MOTORS TURBO HYDRA-MATIC 440-T4 TRANSAXLE (Cont.)

Fig. 2: Cross Section of Turbo Hydra-Matic 440-T4 Automatic Transaxle

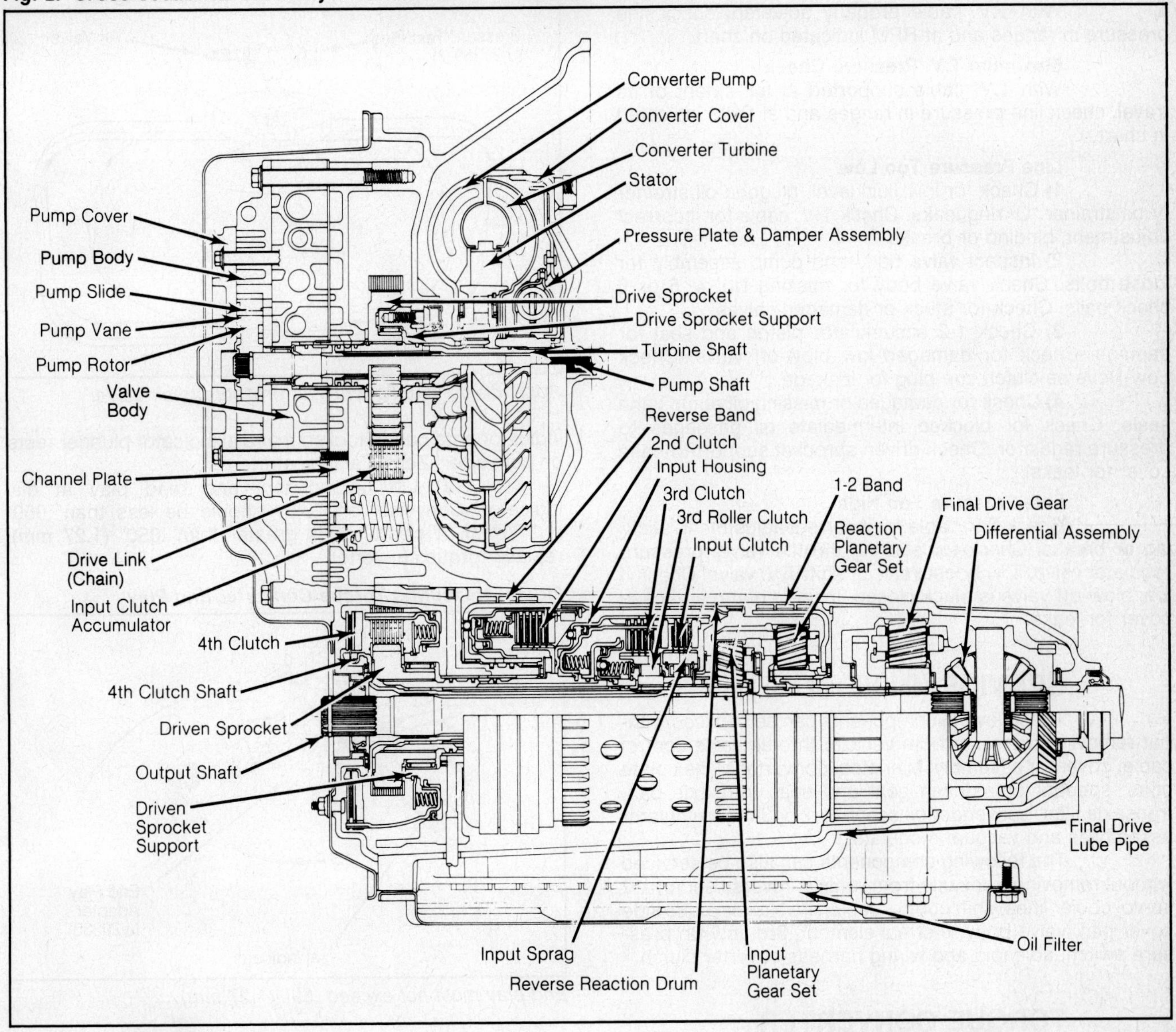

Reverse

Check reverse operation.

HYDRAULIC PRESSURE TESTS

CAUTION: Parking and service brakes must be applied at all times during test. Total time for tests with selector in driving ranges should not exceed 2 minutes.

1) Before making hydraulic pressure tests, check ATF for proper fluid level and condition. Check T.V. (throttle valve) and manual control linkages for correct adjustment. Ensure engine is properly tuned.

2) Check transaxle code *See Fig. 1.* and refer to chart for correct pressure range and engine RPM. Connect a tachometer to engine and an oil pressure gauge to transaxle. *See Fig. 3.*

NOTE: Hydraulic pressure is controlled by pump output and pressure regulator valve. Line pressure is boosted in Reverse, "2" and "1" by reverse boost valve. In Neutral, "D" and Reverse positions, line pressure should increase with throttle opening.

Fig. 3: Hydraulic Pressure Test

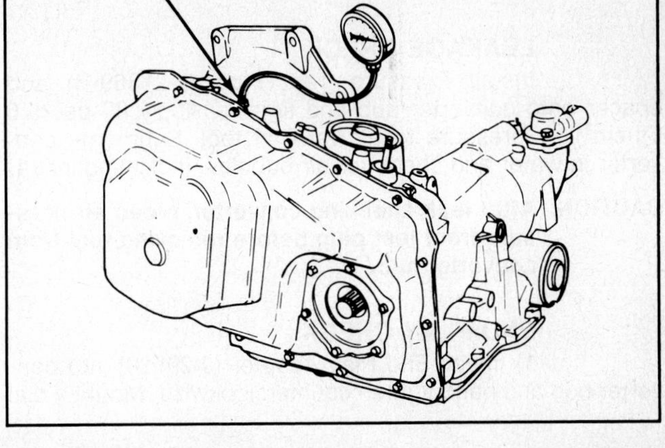

GENERAL MOTORS TURBO HYDRA-MATIC 440-T4 TRANSAXLE (Cont.)

Minimum T.V. Pressure Check

With T.V. cable properly adjusted, check line pressure in ranges and at RPM indicated on chart.

Maximum T.V. Pressure Check

With T.V. cable supported at full extent of its travel, check line pressure in ranges and at RPM indicated in chart.

Line Pressure Too Low

1) Check for low fluid level, plugged oil strainer or oil strainer "O" ring leaks. Check T.V. cable for incorrect adjustment, binding or breaks.

2) Inspect valve body and pump assembly for loose bolts. Check valve body for missing No. 4, 5 or 6 check balls. Check for stuck or damaged valves.

3) Check 1-2 accumulator piston and seal for damage. Check for damaged low blow-off valve. Check Low-Reverse clutch cup plug for leakage.

4) Check for damaged or missing oil pump vane seals. Check for blocked intermediate oil passages to pressure regulator. Check driven sprocket support-to-case cover for leaks.

Line Pressure Too High

Check T.V. cable for incorrect adjustment, sticking or breaks. Check for sticking throttle valve, pressure regulator valve, T.V. boost valve or shift T.V. valve. Check if low blow-off valve is stuck closed. Inspect pump and case cover for leaks.

SERVICE (IN VEHICLE)

The following components can be serviced without removing transaxle from vehicle: throttle valve control cable, governor assembly, filler pipe, converter-to-flex plate bolts, speedometer driven gear and seal, transaxle pan, transaxle filter, scavenger oil scoop, 1-2 or 3-4 accumulator assemblies and vacuum modulator.

The following components can also be serviced without removing transaxle from vehicle: reverse servo, 1-2 servo, cooler lines, shift control cable, drive axles, case side cover pan, valve body, thermal element, 3rd and 4th pressure switch, solenoid and wiring harness-coverter clutch.

TORQUE CONVERTER

NOTE: **Torque converter is a sealed unit and cannot be disassembled for service or repair. Cadillac models with the 4.3L V6 Diesel engine use a Viscous Converter Clutch. See General Motors Viscous Converter Clutch (VCC) System article in this section.**

LEAKAGE CHECK

Install Pressure Test Plug (J-21369-B) and spacer onto converter hub and tighten. Apply 80 psi (5.6 kg/cm^2) air pressure to air valve in tool. Submerge converter in water and check for air bubbles, indicating leaks.

CAUTION: **After leak checking converter, bleed air pressure from test plug before removing tool from converter hub.**

Fig. 4: Installing Converter Pressure Test Plug

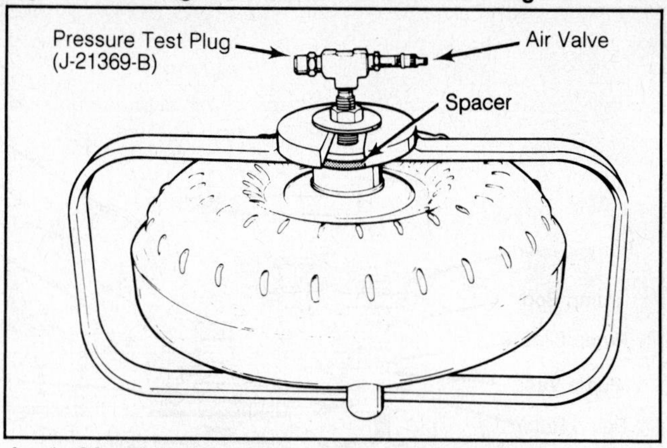

Apply 80 psi (5.6 kg/cm²) air pressure to air valve.

END PLAY CHECK

1) Install End Play Adapter (J-29830) into converter hub and hand tighten counterclockwise. Mount a dial indicator onto hub of tool so that dial indicator plunger rests on converter. Zero dial indicator.

2) Lift up on tool and read play at dial indicator. Converter end play should be less than .050" (1.27 mm). If clearance is greater than .050" (1.27 mm), replace torque converter.

Fig. 5: Measuring Torque Converter End Play

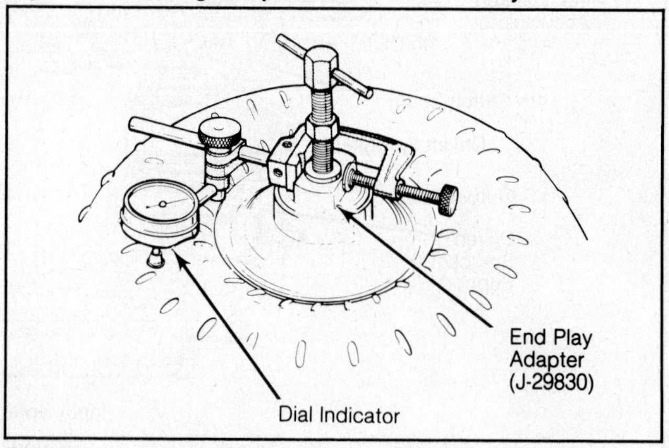

End play must not exceed .50" (1.27 mm).

TRANSAXLE DISASSEMBLY

Thoroughly clean transaxle exterior. Remove torque converter. Place transaxle in holding fixture and drain fluid from transaxle.

SPEEDOMETER DRIVE GEAR, GOVERNOR ASSEMBLY & MODULATOR

Remove speedometer driven gear attaching bolt and retainer. Remove speedometer sleeve and driven gear assembly from governor cover. Remove governor cover and oil seal. Lift out governor and speedometer drive gear as an assembly. Remove modulator retainer bolt and retainer. Remove modulator and "O" ring. Using a magnet, remove modulator valve.

REVERSE & 1-2 SERVO ASSEMBLIES

1) Position transaxle so oil pan is up. Remove oil pan and oil strainer from lower case. Remove accumulator cover bolts and governor control body bolts.

GENERAL MOTORS TURBO HYDRA-MATIC 440-T4 TRANSAXLE (Cont.)

THROTTLE VALVE LINE PRESSURE CHECK

Model	Range	MINIMUM T.V. psi	MINIMUM T.V. kg/cm²	MAXIMUM T.V. psi	MAXIMUM T.V. kg/cm²
AA, AU	P @ 1250	61-69	4.27-4.83	61-69	4.27-4.83
AF, AM, AR, BA, BB, BC, BD, BH BL, BM, BP, BT, CM, CN, HJ	P @ 1250	61-69	4.27-4.83	61-69	4.27-4.83
BZ	P @ 1250	66-74	4.62-5.18	66-74	4.62-5.18
AA, AU	N,4,3,2 @ 1250	61-69	4.27-4.83	150-184	10.50-12.88
AF, AM, AR, BA, BB, BC, BD, BH BL, BM, BP, BT, CM, CN, HJ	N,4,3,2, @ 1250	61-69	4.27-4.83	167-202	11.69-14.14
BZ	N,4,3,2, @ 1250	66-74	4.62-5.18	172-207	12.04-14.49
AA, AU	LOW @ 1250	137-192	9.59-13.44	137-192	9.59-13.44
AF, AM, AR, BA, BB, BC, BD, BH BL, BM, BP, BT, CM, CN, HJ,	LOW @ 1250	145-185	10.15-12.95	145-185	10.15-12.95
BZ	LOW @ 1250	161-203	11.27-14.21	161-203	11.27-13.21
AA, AU	R @ 1250	61-69	4.27-4.83	209-257	14.63-17.99
AF, AM, AR, BA, BB, BC, BD, BH BL, BM, BP, BT, CM, CN, NJ	R @ 1250	61-69	4.27-4.83	209-257	14.63-17.99
BZ	R @ 1250	66-74	4.62-5.18	235-283	16.45-19.81

2) Remove accumulator oil pipes, cover body and gasket as an assembly. Remove accumulator cover gaskets and spacer plate. Remove lube oil pipe, retainer, "O" ring and spring. Remove accumulator assemblies. Do not interchange springs. Remove oil scavenging scoop.

3) Remove servo cover snap ring, cover and "O" ring. Remove servo assembly. *See Fig. 6.* Keep reverse and 1-2 servo assemblies separate. Reverse servo apply pin is longer than 1-2 servo apply pin.

NOTE: **Make band apply pin selection check at this time to determine correct pin to use during reassembly.**

Band Apply Pin Selection Check

Install Band Apply Pin Gauge (J-33382) with reverse servo pin. *See Fig. 7.* Apply 20 ft. lbs. (27 N.m) of torque to hex nut on gauge. Check pin length using band apply pin gauge. See REVERSE AND 1-2 BAND APPLY PIN TABLE. If gauge "GO" side will slide under head and "NO-GO" side will not, pin is correct size.

OIL PUMP ASSEMBLY

Remove case side cover and gaskets. Disconnect wiring harness from solenoid pressure switches and case connector. Remove T.V. lever, bracket and link from valve body assembly. Remove pump from valve body assembly.

CLUTCH AND BAND APPLICATION CHART (ELEMENTS IN USE)

Selector Lever Position	4th Clutch	Reverse Band	2nd Clutch	3rd Clutch	3rd Roller Clutch	Input Clutch	Input Sprag	1-2 Clutch
D - DRIVE								
First Gear						X	[1]	X
Second Gear			X			[2]	[3]	X
Third Gear			X	X	[1]			
Overdrive	X		X	[2]	[3]			
3 - MANUAL THIRD			X	X	[1]	X	[1]	
2 - MANUAL SECOND			X			[2]	[3]	X
1 - MANUAL LOW				X	[1]	X	[1]	X
R - REVERSE		X				X	[1]	
NEUTRAL or PARK						[2]	[2]	

[1] – Holding. [2] – Applied but not effective. [3] – Overrunning.

Automatic Transmissions

GENERAL MOTORS TURBO HYDRA-MATIC 440-T4 TRANSAXLE (Cont.)

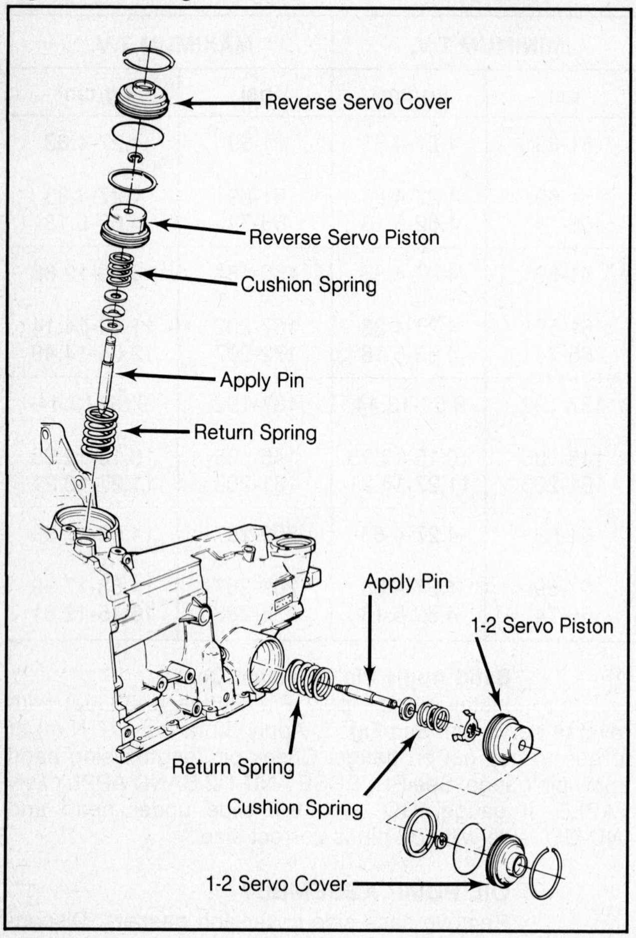

Fig. 6: Removing Reverse & 1-2 Servo Assemblies

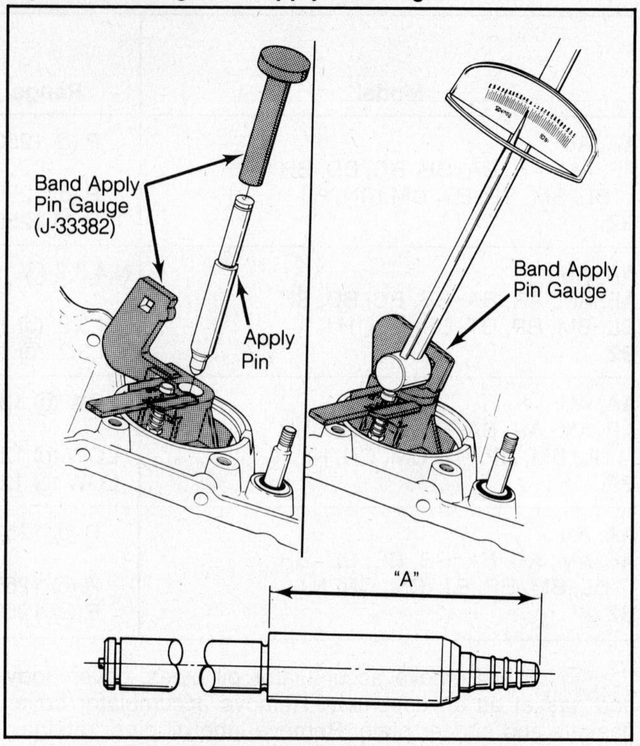

Fig. 7: Checking Band Apply Pin Length

REVERSE AND 1-2 BAND APPLY PIN TABLE

Apply Pin Identification	Dimension "A" In. (mm)
Reverse Apply Pin	
2 Wide Bands	2.79-2.80 (70.9-71.1)
3 Grooves & Wide Band	2.83-2.84 (71.9-72.1)
2 Grooves & Wide Band	2.87-2.88 (72.9-73.1)
1 Groove & Wide Band	2.91-2.92 (74.0-74.2)
No Groove	2.95-2.96 (75.0-75.2)
1 Groove	2.99-3.00 (76.0-76.2)
2 Grooves	3.03-3.04 (77.1-77.3)
3 Grooves	3.07-3.08 (78.1-78.3)
4 Grooves	3.11-3.12 (79.2-79.3)
1-2 Apply Pin	
1 Ring & Wide Band	2.21-2.22 (56.2-56.4)
1 Ring	2.25-2.26 (57.2-57.4)
2 Rings	2.29-2.30 (58.3-58.4)
3 Rings	2.33-2.34 (59.3-59.5)
Wide Band	2.37-2.38 (60.3-60.5)
2 Rings & Wide Band	2.41-2.42 (61.3-61.5)

VALVE BODY

Remove valve body bolts and remove valve body assembly from channel plate. Remove 4 check balls from spacer plate. Remove spacer plate and gaskets. Remove 8 check balls from channel plate. Remove converter clutch screen.

CHANNEL PLATE

Remove oil pump shaft. Place detent lever in "P" position and remove manual valve clip. Remove channel plate from case. Remove modulator port gasket, upper and lower gaskets from channel plate. Remove input accumulator piston and spring. Remove converter clutch accumulator piston and spring.

4TH CLUTCH, OUTPUT SHAFT & DRIVE LINK ASSEMBLIES

1) Before removing (chain) drive link assembly, measure drive link wear. Midway between sprockets and at right angles to chain, push down on lower chain strand until all slack is removed.

2) Mark chain position on case using bottom side of chain links as a guide. Push up on chain until all slack is removed and place a second mark on case, making sure that both marks are made from same point on chain.

3) Maesure the distance between the 2 marks. If the distance exceeds 1 1/6" (27 mm), replace drive link. Remove 4th clutch plates and apply plate from output shaft. Remove thrust bearing. Remove 4th clutch hub and shaft assembly.

4) Rotate output shaft until "C" ring opening is visible. Push "C" ring partially off shaft, then rotate shaft and remove "C" ring with needle-nose pliers. Pull output shaft from transaxle. *See Fig. 10.*

5) Remove turbine shaft "O" ring. Remove sprockets and link assembly from case, noting position of colored link (should face up). Remove thrust washers. Remove chain scavenging scoop and oil reservoir baffle from driven sprocket support. Remove driven sprocket support and thrust washer.

GENERAL MOTORS TURBO HYDRA-MATIC 440-T4 TRANSAXLE (Cont.)

2ND, INPUT & ROLLER CLUTCHES & SPRAG ASSEMBLY

1) Using Final Drive/Clutch Remover (J-33381), remove 2nd and input clutches, sprag and roller clutch assembly and sun gear. *See Fig. 8.*

Fig. 8: Removing 2nd Clutch, Input Housing and Shaft

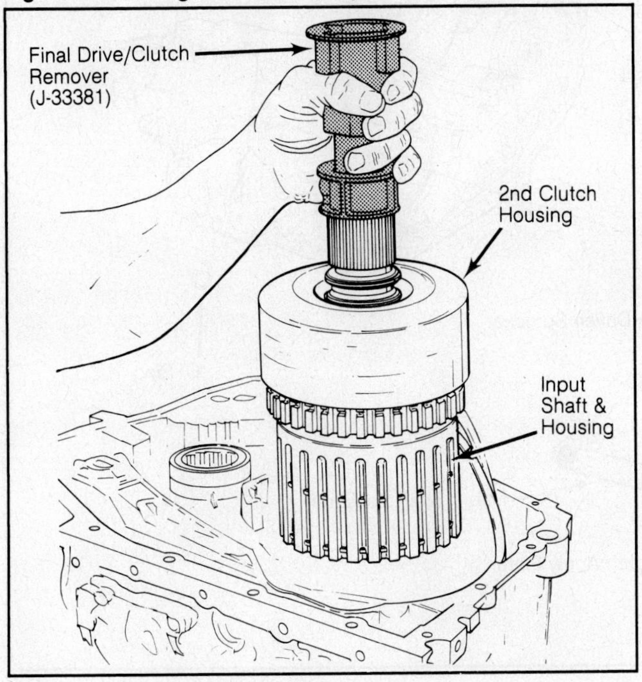

2) Remove reverse band if it did not come out with 2nd clutch. Remove reverse reaction drum. Remove input carrier assembly. Remove thrust bearing, reaction carrier and other thrust bearing.

3) Remove reaction sun gear/drum assembly. Remove 1-2 band. DO NOT clean band in solvent. Remove reaction sun gear/internal gear bearing. Remove final drive sun gear shaft.

FINAL DRIVE UNIT

Remove final drive internal gear-to-case snap ring. Using Final Drive/Clutch Installer (J-33381), remove final drive unit. *See Fig. 9.*

MANUAL SHAFT/DETENT LEVER & ACTUATOR ROD

NOTE: **Do not remove these parts unless replacement is necessary**

Remove pin and lock nut from manual shaft. Remove actuator rod from detent lever. Remove retaining pin from case. Remove actuator rod assembly from case. Remove "O" ring from actuator rod guide. Parking lock pawl assembly cannot be removed from final drive internal gear.

COMPONENT DISASSEMBLY & REASSEMBLY

NOTE: **During reassembly, lubricate bushings, seals, thrust bearings and internal mating surfaces with transmission fluid. Use petroleum jelly to lubricate and retain thrust washers.**

Fig. 9: Removing Final Drive Unit

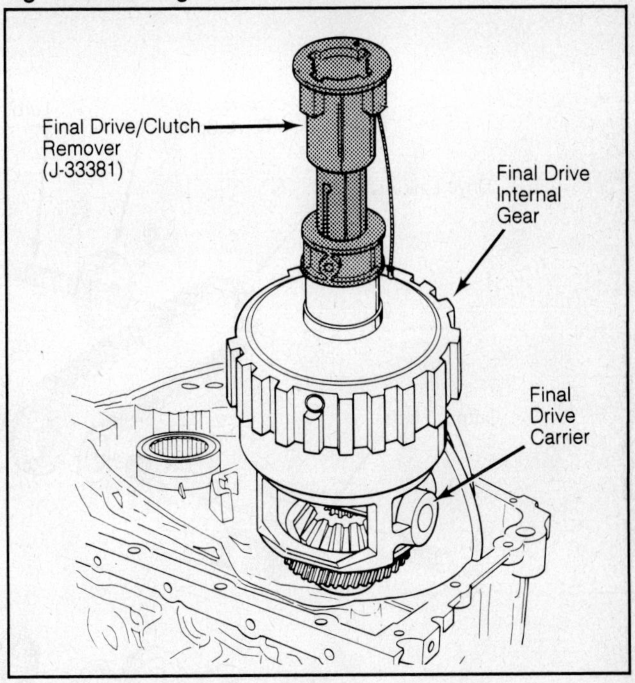

CASE

Cleaning & Inspection

1) Clean case in solvent and air dry. Do not use rags to dry. Inspect case assembly for damage, cracks, porosity or interconnected oil passages. Check for servo bore damage or stripped threads in bolt heads.

2) Inspect case lugs, intermediate servo bore and snap ring grooves for damage. Inspect case bushings for wear or scoring. Check vent assembly for damage. Check converter and axle seals.

3) Inspect drive sprocket support bearing for damage. If needed, replace bearing using bearing puller, slide hammer and adapter. Install bearing with identification mark facing up.

4) Inspect drive sprocket support for spline, journal or bushing damage. Check for blocked converter drain holes.

Disassembly

1) Remove drive sprocket support. Remove 1-2 servo pipes from case. Inspect pipes, seals and ball capsule assembly for damage. If necessary, remove 1-2 servo pipe seals with a modified screw extractor.

2) To remove check ball and spring, flatten dimples that retain check ball and spring in capsule. Remove check ball and spring with magnet. Remove capsule from case with screw extractor.

Reassembly

1) Install new capsule assembly into case with a 1/2" (13 mm) diameter steel rod. Position capsule slot so it opens into servo bore. Install new 1-2 servo pipe seals into case. Install servo pipes.

2) Install drive sprocket support with attaching screws. Install new converter and axle seals, if removed.

Reassembly

1) Install new capsule assembly into case with a 1/2" (13 mm) diameter steel rod. Position capsule slot so it opens into servo bore. Install new 1-2 servo pipe seals into case. Install servo pipes.

Fig. 10: Exploded View of 4th Clutch, Output Shaft and Drive Link Assemblies

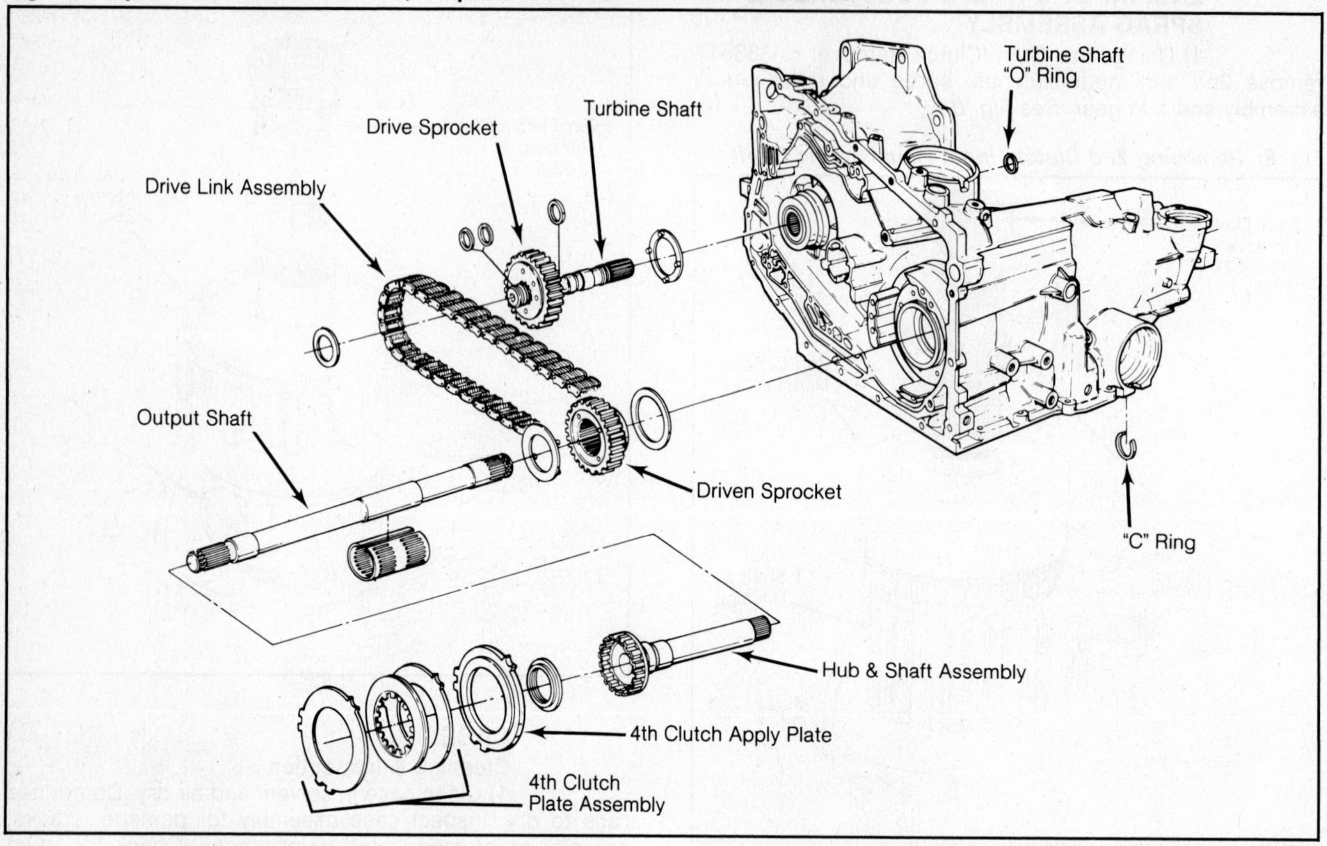

2) Install drive sprocket support with attaching screws. Install new converter and axle seals, if removed.

FINAL DRIVE UNIT

Disassembly & Inspection

1) Remove final drive internal gear and thrust bearing. Remove parking gear and sun gear. Inspect final drive pinions for damage and excessive end play. *See Fig. 11.* End play should be .009-.025" (.23-.64 mm).

Fig. 11: Checking Final Drive Pinion End Play

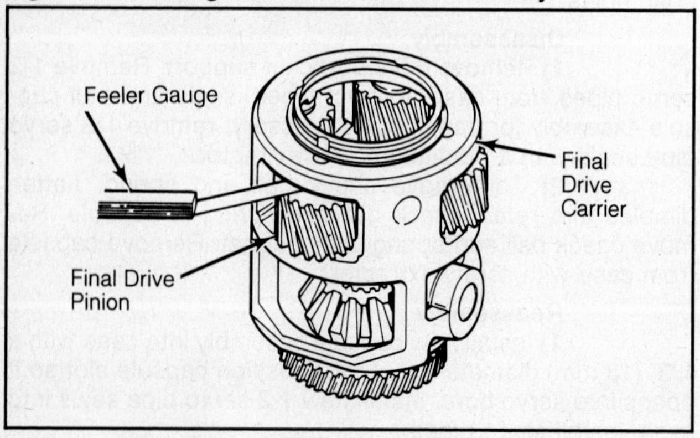

2) Inspect internal gear for damaged teeth, scored bearing surfaces or damaged parking pawl or spring. Inspect sun gear for damaged teeth. Inspect parking gear for damaged lugs or splines.

3) Inspect thrust bearings for damage. Sun gear/carrier thrust bearing cannot be removed from carrier. Inspect governor drive gear for wear or damage. If damaged, place a thick washer on hub and remove governor drive gear with gear remover. *See Fig. 12.*

Fig. 12: Removing Governor Drive Gear

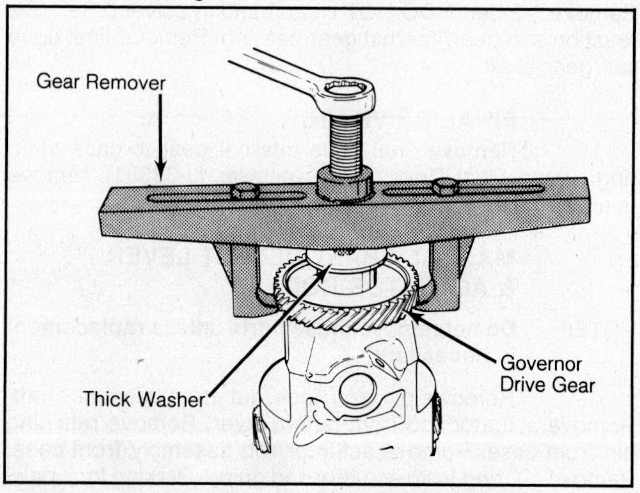

4) Inspect differential pinion gears and side gears for damage. If gears are damaged, remove pinion retaining pin with a punch. Remove pinion shaft, pinion gears, side gears and thrust washers. Inspect thrust washers and final drive carrier for damage.

Reassembly

1) Assemble differential side gears and thrust washers into carrier. Using petroleum jelly, stick thrust washers onto pinion gears. Assemble pinion gears and washers into carrier.

2) Slide pinion shaft through both pinion gears for alignment, then remove shaft. Rotate pinion gears into position, then install pinion shaft. Tap retaining pin into position using a plastic mallet.

3) Tap governor drive gear into position using plastic mallet. Install sun gear with stepped side facing out. Assemble parking gear into sun gear. Assemble thrust bearing into internal gear. Install internal gear onto carrier.

Fig. 13: Measuring Final Drive End Play

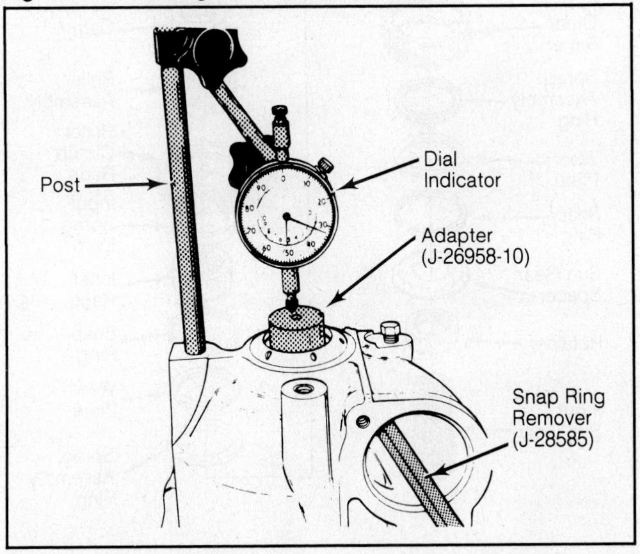

4) Inspect carrier-to-case selective thrust washer for damage. Install thrust washer onto carrier hub and retain washer with petroleum jelly. Install thrust bearing onto thrust washer and retain with petroleum jelly.

5) Move detent lever out of "P" position. Use pin to hold parking pawl in place and install final drive assembly into case using Final Drive/Clutch Installer (J-33381).

6) Install snap ring into case. To measure final drive end play, install dial indicator so pointer contacts Adapter (J-26958-10). *See Fig. 13.* Lift governor drive gear with Snap Ring Remover (J-28585) and read dial indicator.

7) Correct end play is .005-.025" (.12-.62 mm). If needed, adjust end play with selective carrier-to-case thrust washer. See Carrier-to-Case Selective Thrust Washer Sizes table.

CARRIER-TO-CASE SELECTIVE THRUST WASHER SIZES

Washer Identification	Thickness In. (mm)
1	.059-.062 (1.5-1.6)
2	.062-.066 (1.6-1.7)
3	.066-.070 (1.7-1.8)
4	.070-.074 (1.8-1.9)
5	.074-.078 (1.9-2.0)
6	.078-.082 (2.0-2.1)

SUN GEAR SHAFT

Inspection & Reassembly

Inspect final drive sun gear shaft for damaged splines or journals. Install final drive sun gear shaft into final drive, ensuring splines engage with parking gear and sun gear.

1-2 BAND ASSEMBLY

Inspection & Reassembly

DO NOT wash 1-2 band in solvent. Inspect 1-2 band assembly for heat damage, lining cracks and separation. Check band stop for damage and replace as required. Assemble 1-2 band into case, making sure band anchor pins engage band.

REACTION SUN GEAR & DRUM

Inspection

Inspect reaction sun gear and drum assembly for damaged teeth and bushings and scored or warped drum. Check thrust bearings for damage. Using a feeler gauge, check reaction carrier pinion end play. End play should be .009-.024" (.23-.61 mm). Check for damaged pinion and internal gear.

Fig. 14: Exploded View of Differential and Final Drive Unit

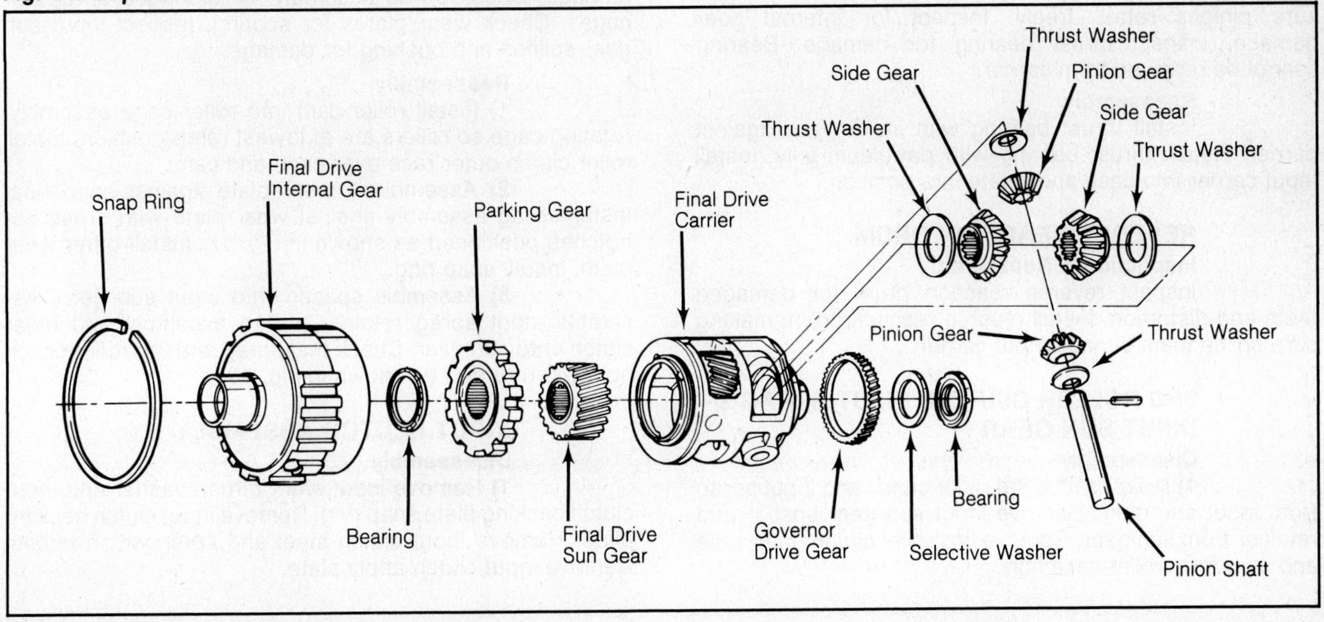

GENERAL MOTORS TURBO HYDRA-MATIC 440-T4 TRANSAXLE (Cont.)

Fig. 15: Exploded View of Input and Reaction Carriers

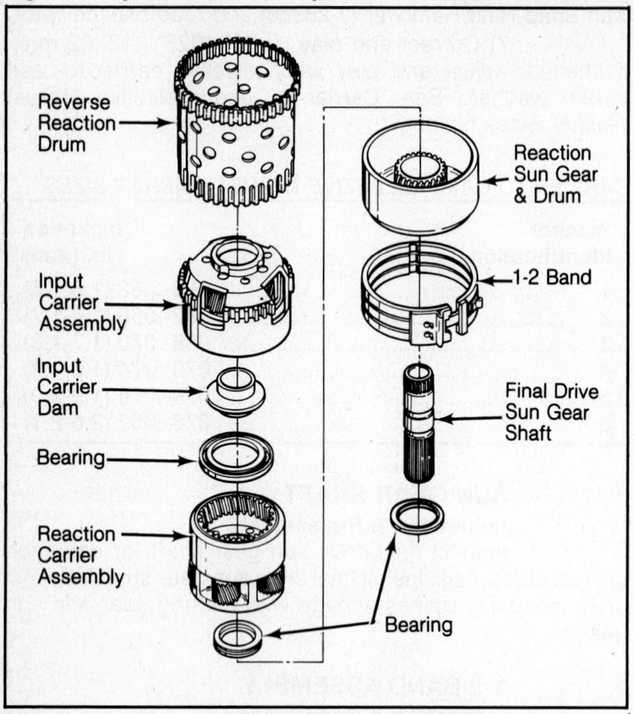

Input carrier dam is not used in some models.

Reassembly

1) Install reaction sun gear-to-final drive internal gear bearing, positioning inside race against internal gear. Assemble sun gear and drum assembly into case.

2) Install reaction carrier-to-sun gear thrust bearing, positioning inside race against reaction carrier. Retain bearing with petroleum jelly. Install reaction carrier, rotating carrier until pinions engage sun gear.

INPUT CARRIER ASSEMBLY

Inspection

Check input carrier end play with a feeler gauge. Correct end play is .009-.024" (.23-.61 mm). Make sure pinions rotate freely. Inspect for internal gear damage. Inspect thrust bearing for damage. Bearing cannot be removed from carrier.

Reassembly

Install thrust bearing with inside race against carrier. Retain thrust bearing with petroleum jelly. Install input carrier into case and rotate into position.

REVERSE REACTION DRUM

Inspection & Reassembly

Inspect reverse reaction drum for damaged teeth and distortion. Install reverse reaction drum, making sure spline teeth engage input carrier.

3RD ROLLER CLUTCH, INPUT SPRAG & INPUT SUN GEAR

Disassembly

1) Disassemble 3rd roller clutch and input sprag from input sun gear. Remove input sun gear spacer and retainer from sun gear. Remove 3rd roller clutch outer race and cam from roller assembly.

2) Remove inner race from input sprag assembly. Remove 1 input sprag snap ring. Disassemble input sprag and wear plate.

Fig. 16: Exploded View of 3rd Roller Clutch, Input Sprag and Input Sun Gear

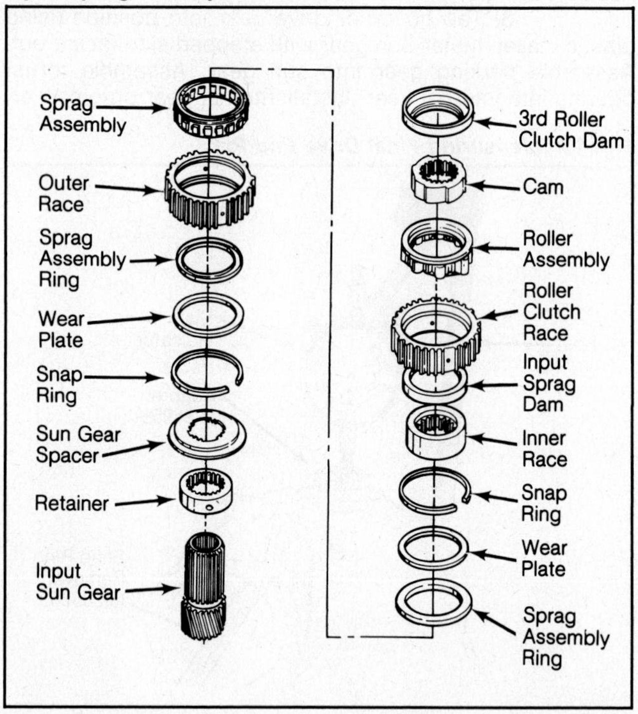

Input sprag and 3rd roller clutch dams are not used in some models.

Inspection

1) Inspect 3rd roller clutch outer race for scoring and wear. Inspect roller cam for cracks and damage. Inspect roller assembly for damaged rollers and springs. Install any loose roller by depressing spring and inserting roller.

2) Inspect input sprag inner and outer races for damage. Check sprag assembly for damaged sprags or cages. Check wear plates for scoring. Inspect input sun gear splines and bushing for damage.

Reassembly

1) Install roller cam into roller cage assembly, rotating cage so rollers are at lowest ramp position. Install roller clutch outer race over cage and cam.

2) Assemble 1 wear plate against snap ring. Install sprag assembly against wear plate with cross bar notches positioned as shown in *Fig. 17.* Install other wear plate. Install snap ring.

3) Assemble spacer onto input sun gear. Assemble input sprag retainer, sprag assembly and roller clutch onto sun gear. Check that sprag and 3rd roller clutch hold when turned as shown in *Fig. 18.*

INPUT CLUTCH ASSEMBLY

Disassembly

1) Remove input shaft thrust washer and input clutch backing plate snap ring. Remove input clutch backing plate. Remove input clutch steel and composition plates. Remove input clutch apply plate.

Fig. 17: Proper Input Sprag Reassembly

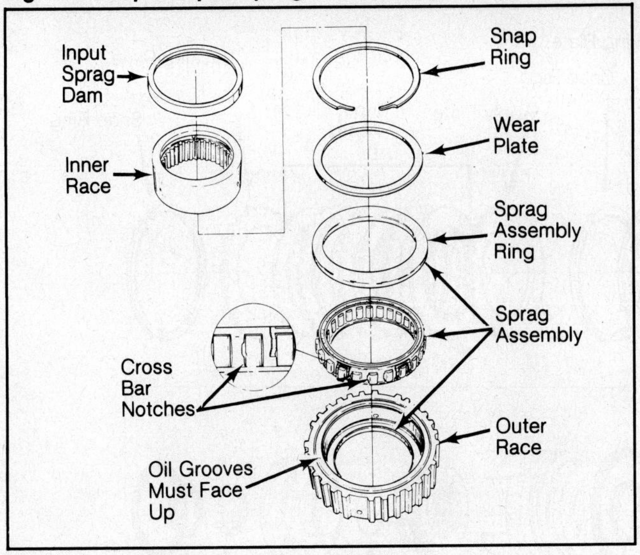

Input sprag dam is not used in some models.

Fig. 18: Checking Sprag and Roller Clutch

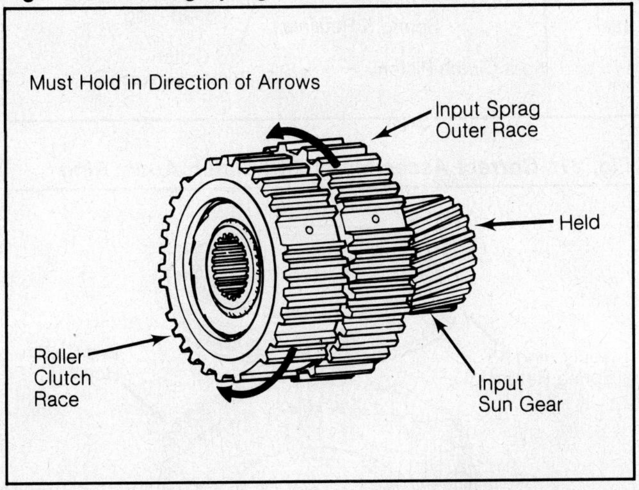

Sprag and roller clutch must hold in directions shown.

2) Remove 3rd clutch backing plate snap ring and backing plate. Remove 3rd clutch steel and composition plates. Remove 3rd clutch spring snap ring. Using Clutch Spring Compressor (J-23327) and Adapter (J-25018-A), compress and remove spring retainer.

3) Remove 3rd clutch piston from housing. Remove 3rd clutch piston inner seal from shaft. Compress piston housing and remove snap ring. Remove "O" ring. Remove spring and retainer assembly. Remove input clutch piston and inner seal.

Inspection

Inspect all clutch plates for cracks, wear, lining separation, pitting or other damage. Inspect thrust washer for damage. Inspect input clutch housing and shaft for interconnected oil passages, damaged clutch hub, worn bushings, damaged 4th clutch shaft seal or oil seal rings.

4th Clutch Shaft Seal Replacement

1) Using Bushing Remover (J-29369-2) and slide hammer, remove lock-up sleeve. Expand bushing remover just enough to contact lock-up sleeve.

2) Install new seal into input shaft, aligning seal tab with shaft slot. Install lock-up sleeve into shaft with Bushing Installer (J-25019-6) and bench press.

Input Shaft Seal Replacement

1) Cut solid oil seal rings from input shaft. Inspect seal ring grooves for nicks or burrs. Lubricate oil seal ring and position it on Seal Protector (J-34741-1).

2) Quickly slide seal into position with Seal Driver (J-34741-2) over seal protector. Size seal with Seal Sizer (J-34741-3), gently twisting sizer over seal.

Retainer & Ball Assembly Replacement

Remove retainer and ball assembly from housing using a 3/8" (9.5 mm) drift. Tap in new retainer using drift.

Piston Seal Replacement

Remove seals from input clutch piston or 3rd clutch piston. Lubricate new seals with ATF and install seals.

Reassembly

1) Lubricate input clutch piston inner seal with ATF and install seal using Seal Driver (J-34093) and Protector (J-34092). Assemble input piston into input housing. Assemble "O" ring seal onto input shaft.

2) Install spring retainer into piston. Install 3rd clutch piston housing into input housing. Using Clutch Compressor (J-23327), compress 3rd clutch housing and install snap ring.

3) Install 3rd clutch inner seal. Install 3rd clutch piston into housing. Compress 3rd clutch spring retainer and install snap ring.

4) Install wave plate. Assemble 3rd clutch plates, starting with steel, then alternating composition and steel. Install 3rd clutch backing plate with stepped side facing up. Install snap ring.

5) Assemble input clutch plates, starting with composition, then alternating steel and composition. Install input clutch backing plate with identification mark facing up.

6) Install snap ring. Apply air pressure to oil passages in input shaft and check for proper operation of clutch. Air pressure must not exceed 90 psi (6.3 kg/cm^2).

2ND CLUTCH ASSEMBLY

Disassembly

Remove 2nd clutch housing support, snap ring and backing plate. Remove clutch plates, waved plate and snap ring. Remove apply ring and spring return assembly. Remove apply piston.

Inspection

1) DO NOT soak composition plates in solvent. Inspect steel and composition plates for wear, lining separation, pitting or damage. Inspect apply ring and spring return for damage. Inspect piston and seal for damage.

2) Inspect 2nd clutch housing for damaged inner piston seal. Inspect for damaged bushings and spline teeth. Check for scored band surface. Check retainer and ball assembly for damage. Inspect housing for warpage.

Piston Seal Replacement

Remove seal from 2nd clutch piston. Lubricate new seal with ATF and install.

Retainer & Ball Assembly Replacement

Remove retainer and ball assembly from housing with a 3/8" (9.5 mm) drift. Tap in new retainer using drift.

Reassembly

Assemble piston into housing. Install apply ring and spring return. *See Fig. 21.* Install wave plate and snap

Automatic Transmissions

GENERAL MOTORS TURBO HYDRA-MATIC 440-T4 TRANSAXLE (Cont.)

Fig. 19: Exploded View of Input Clutch Assembly

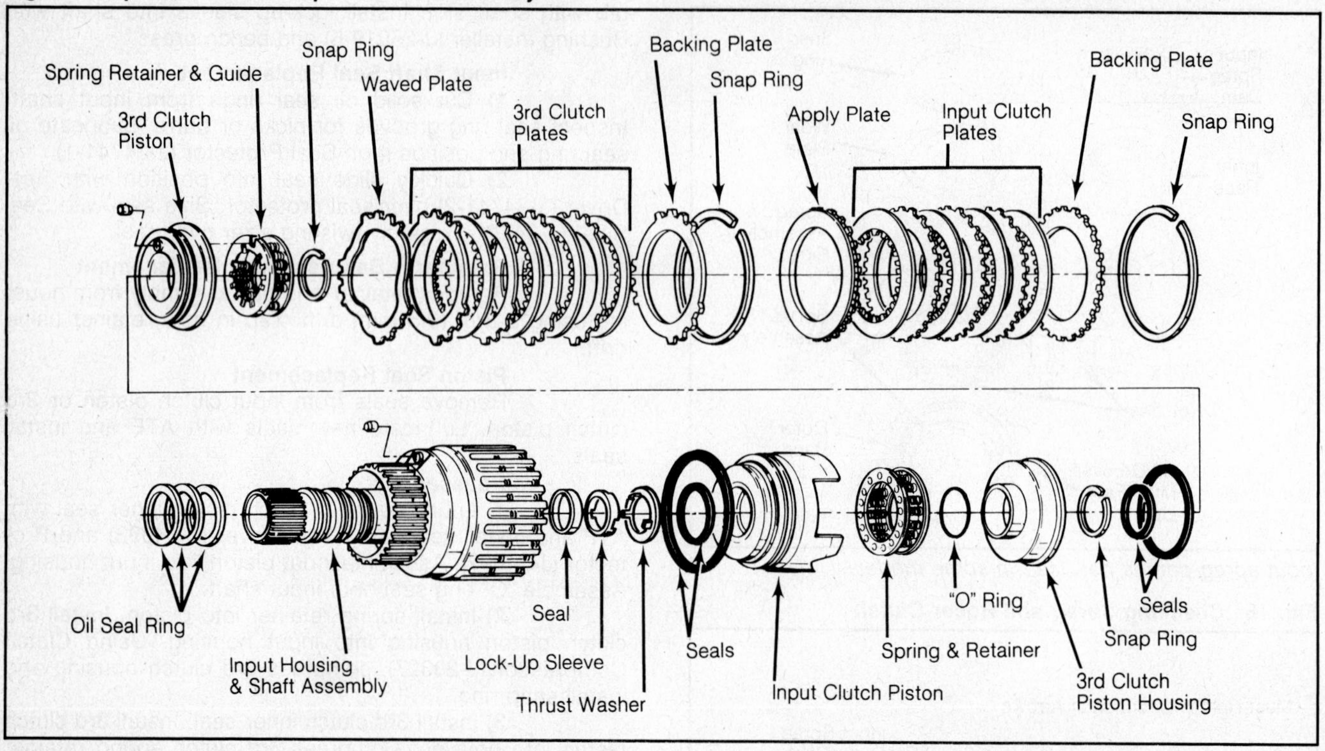

Fig. 20: Reverse Band & Second Clutch Exploded View

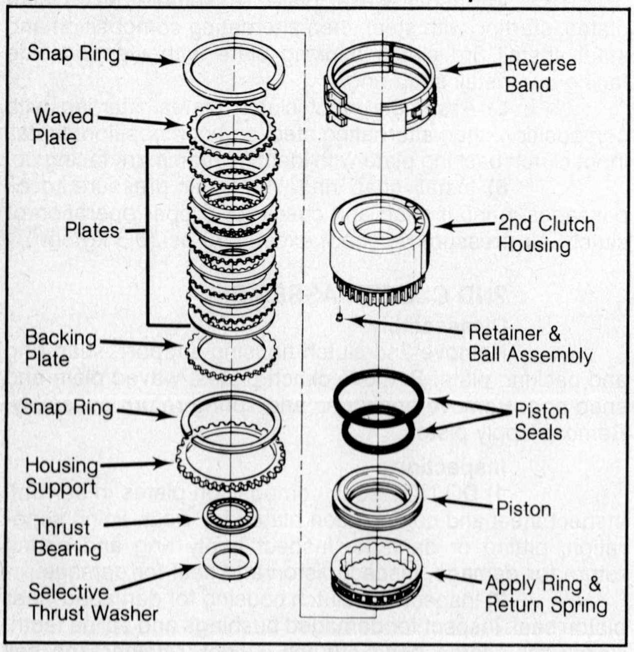

Fig. 21: Correct Assembly of 2nd Clutch Apply Ring

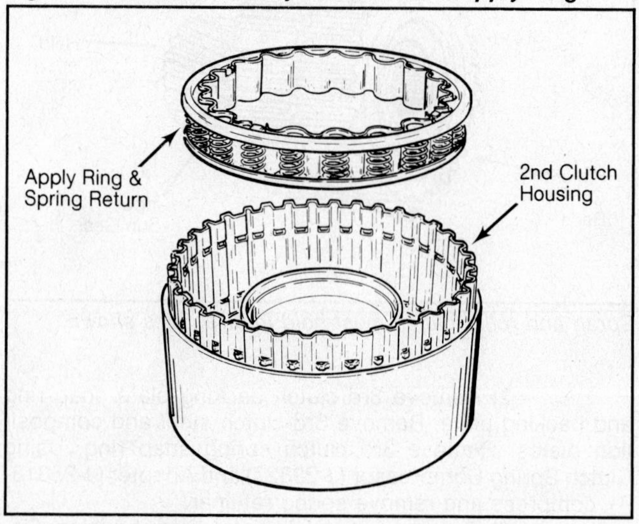

ring. Assemble clutch plates, starting with steel, then alternating composition and steel. Install backing plate and snap ring. Install support and stake into place.

DRIVEN SPROCKET SUPPORT

Disassembly

Compress spring return with a press and remove snap ring. Remove retainer and piston from sprocket support.

Inspection

1) Inspect driven sprocket support for worn or damaged oil seal rings. Check for damaged or scored bushing or piston seal surface. Check for blocked or interconnected oil passages or cup plug.

2) Check chain scavenging scoop and baffle for cracks. Inspect piston, seals and thrust washer for damage. Check spring retainer for distorted springs. Inspect driven sprocket bearing for damage.

Sprocket Support Bearing Replacement

Tap out old bearing with Driver (J-34129-B). Press in new bearing with Installer (J-34126) until seated.

GENERAL MOTORS TURBO HYDRA-MATIC 440-T4 TRANSAXLE (Cont.)

Reassembly

Press piston into driven sprocket support using arbor press. Install spring retainer onto piston. Compress spring retainer with arbor press and install snap ring.

OUTPUT SHAFT

Inspection

Inspect output snap ring groove, splines, journal, and bearings for damage. Replace as necessary.

DRIVE LINK ASSEMBLY & SPROCKETS

Inspection

Inspect drive and driven sprockets for damaged or chipped teeth. Check sprockets for damaged bearings surfaces or spline damage. Check thrust washers and drive link for excessive wear or damage. Inspect 4th clutch shaft and turbine shaft for damaged bushings, splines or seals.

VALVE BODY

Disassembly

1) Thoroughly clean and air dry valve body. Remove valve trains, beginning with upper left hand corner. Cover bores when removing roll pins because some valves are under pressure.

2) Remove blind hole roll pins with a modified drill bit. Lay valves, springs and bushings on a clean surface exactly as removed. Remove servo pipe lip seals. Clean valves, springs and bushings in solvent. Do not use shop rags to clean valve body components.

Inspection

Inspect valves and bushings for scoring, nicks and scratches. Inspect springs for damaged or distorted coils. Inspect valve body casting for porosity, interconnected oil passages and damaged machined surfaces.

Reassembly

Assemble valve body assembly as shown in *Fig. 24.* Install new servo pipe lip seals.

OIL PUMP ASSEMBLY

Disassembly

Clean and air dry oil pump. Remove oil pump cover bolts. Remove vane ring, vanes and rotor. Remove seal and springs. Remove slide, slide seal support and slide seal. Remove pivot pin and roll pin. Remove 3-2 coast-down valve, spring and bore plug.

Inspection

Inspect pump body for porosity, interconnected oil passages, pump pocket damage or damaged machine face. Check slide, springs, rotor and vanes for damage. Inspect slide seal, slide support and seals for damage.

NOTE: **Oil pump components are matched sets. Do not switch parts with another pump as damage may occur.**

Reassembly

1) Assemble 3-2 coast-down valve train into pump body. Install vane ring onto pump pocket. Install pump slide into pump body. Install seal and support into slide.

2) Install inner priming spring into outer priming spring. Press springs into pump body. Install seal onto slide. Install rotor into pump body. Install vanes into rotor, ensuring vanes are flush with top of rotor.

3) Install pump cover onto body with cover bolts. Install pump pressure screen into pump. (Screen has one-way tab for locating.) Install pump onto valve body assembly. Install pump attaching bolts.

Fig. 22: Exploded View of Oil Pump Assembly

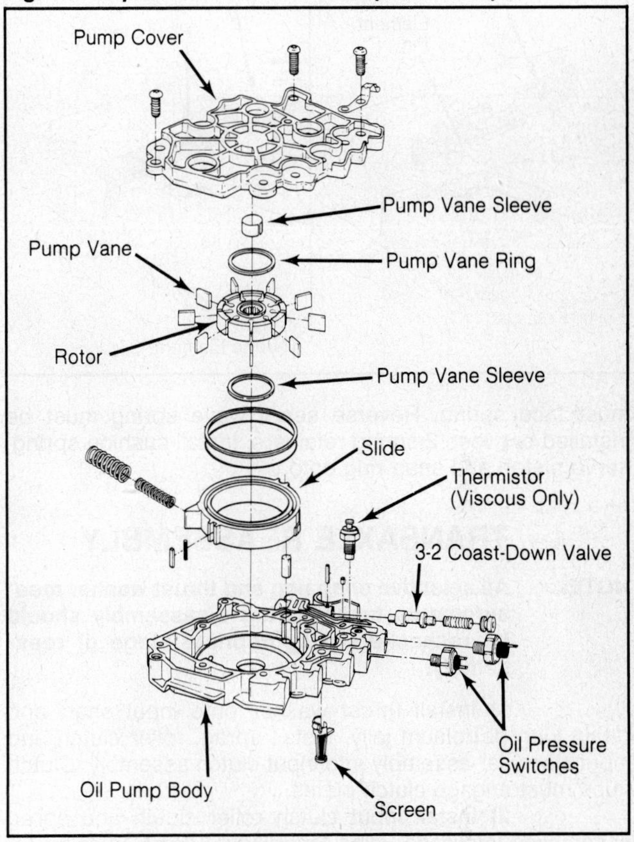

1-2 & 3-4 ACCUMULATORS & GOVERNOR CONTROL BODY

Disassembly

Remove oil pipes from accumulator cover and governor retainer. Remove governor screen from pipe.

Inspection

Inspect governor pipes, orifice cup plug and lube oil pipes for damage. Inspect accumulator cover for damage or porosity. Inspect accumulator pistons, seals and springs for damage. Inspect lube pipe retainer and thermo element for damage.

Thermo Element Replacement

Remove washers, pins and thermo element. Remove plate element. For new element, set thermo pin height with Height Gauge (J-34094). *See Fig. 23.* Install element plate. Install pin and washer assemblies, and set height with gauge. Install new thermo element.

Reassembly

Assemble oil pipe into accumulator cover. Install governor screen (closed end first) into governor feed pipe. Install oil pipes into governor retainer.

1-2 & REVERSE SERVOS

Inspection

Inspect servo pistons and seals for damage or cracks. Do not remove seals unless replacement is required. Inspect springs for damaged coils.

Reassembly

DO NOT interchange servo parts. Assemble spring retainer onto pin. The 1-2 servo spring retainer step

GENERAL MOTORS TURBO HYDRA-MATIC 440-T4 TRANSAXLE (Cont.)

Fig. 23: Installing Thermo Element

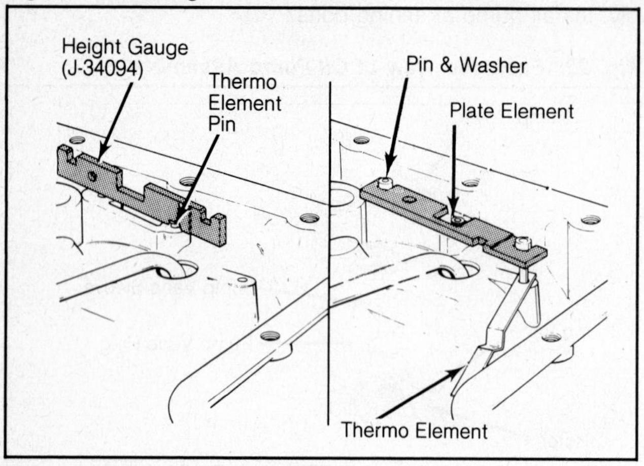

must face spring. Reverse servo wave spring must be installed between 2 spring retainers. Install cushion spring, servo piston and snap ring onto pin.

TRANSAXLE REASSEMBLY

NOTE: **All selective snap ring and thrust washer measurements taken during disassembly should be rechecked at appropriate stage of reassembly.**

1) Install thrust washer onto input shaft and retain with petroleum jelly. Install sprag, roller clutch and input sun gear assembly into input clutch assembly. Clutch hubs must engage clutch plates.

2) Install input clutch roller clutch and sprag assemblies into case using Final Drive/Clutch Installer (J-33381). DO NOT install 2nd clutch, thrust bearing or thrust washer yet.

3)Check input shaft end play. *See Fig, 25.* Install and tighten loader (J-26958). Install End Play Gauge (J-33386), then measure with selective thruse washer. If a .006" (.152 mm) feeler gauge can be inserted between thrust washer and tool, use next larger washer.

INPUT SHAFT THRUST WASHER SELECTION GUIDE

Washer Color	Thickness In. (mm)
Orange/Green	.114-.118 (2.90-3.00)
Orange/Black	.120-.124 (3.05-3.15)
Orange	.126-.130 (3.20-3.30)
White	.132-.136 (3.35-3.45)
Blue	.138-.142 (3.50-3.60)
Pink	.144-.148 (3.65-3.75)
Brown	.150-.154 (3.80-3.90)
Green	.155-.159 (3.95-4.05)
Black	.161-.165 (4.10-4.20)
Purple	.167-.171 (4.25-4.35)
Purple/White	.173-.177 (4.40-4.50)
Purple/Blue	.179-.183 (4.55-4.65)
Purple/Pink	.185-.189 (4.70-4.80)
Purple/Brown	.191-.195 (4.85-4.95)
Purple/Green	.197-.201 (5.00-5.10)

4) Install reverse reaction plate and thrust washer. Install thrust bearing with large race facing down. Install 2nd clutch assembly onto input clutch assembly. Clutch plates must engage input clutch hub and clutch housing must engage reverse reaction drum splines.

5) Install reverse band into case, locating band on anchor pins. Install thrust washer to driven sprocket support and retain washer with petroleum jelly. Install driven sprocket support into case, ensuring support lube hole aligns with hole in bottom of case.

6) Install output shaft into case. Install "C" ring onto output shaft through bottom of case. Push "C" ring onto output shaft.

7) Coat Seal Installer (J-29569-1 and J-29829-1) with petroleum jelly and place installer over turbine shaft. Slide oil ring seals into position. Size seals using Seal Sizer (J-29569-2 and J-29829-1) by gently twisting sizer over seal.

8) Install thrust washer onto drive sprocket and retain washer with petroleum jelly. Install sprockets and drive link onto case. Ensure colored link faces up.

9) Install thrust washer onto driven sprocket and retain with petroleum jelly. Insert 4th clutch shaft through driven sprocket and install clutch apply plate with identification mark down. Install 4th clutch plates.

10) If necessary, pry out axle seal and tap new seal into place. Install pistons and pins into channel plate. Install springs into case. Install channel plate gaskets and modulator port gasket. Install thrust washer onto channel plate.

11) Install channel plate onto case. Channel plate lugs must align with tangs on 4th clutch plates and apply plate. *See Fig. 26.* Install sleeve into channel plate. Install oil reservoir baffle, detent spring and roller.

12) Install and tighten channel plate bolts. Install check balls in channel plate, using petroleum jelly to retain check balls. *See Fig. 27.* Install converter clutch screen. Install detent spring and roller assembly.

13) Install new spacer plate/channel plate gasket onto channel plate, using alignment pins. Install spacer plate onto gasket. Install new spacer plate/valve body gasket onto spacer plate.

14) Install oil pump drive shaft and converter clutch solenoid screen. Install check balls into valve body assembly, using petroleum jelly to retain check balls. *See Fig. 28.*

15) Install valve body assembly onto channel plate, using alignment pins. Install servo pipes into valve body with retainer and bolt.

16) Install gaskets onto case and channel plate. Install side cover. Install accumulator pins into case. Install accumulator springs into case. (Larger spring is for 3-4 accumulator.)

17) Install lube oil pipe retainer spring into pocket. Install lube oil pipe retainer onto lube oil pipe and "O" ring onto retainer. Install lube oil pipe into case. Ensure pipe is installed into driven sprocket support lube hole.

18) Install spacer plate and new gaskets onto case. Install oil scavenger scoop. Install accumulator cover, pipes and governor retainer as an assembly onto case. Ensure lube oil pipe is installed into final drive internal gear.

19) Install new filter lip seal, filter and gasket into case. Install magnet over dimple in bottom of pan. *See Fig. 29.* Install bottom pan.

20) Install 1-2 and reverse servo return springs into respective servo bore. Assemble each servo, then install into case. Install new oil seal ring onto each servo cover. Install 1-2 and reverse servo covers into case. Install snap rings.

Automatic Transmissions

GENERAL MOTORS TURBO HYDRA-MATIC 440-T4 TRANSAXLE (Cont.)

Fig. 24: Exploded View of Valve Body Assembly

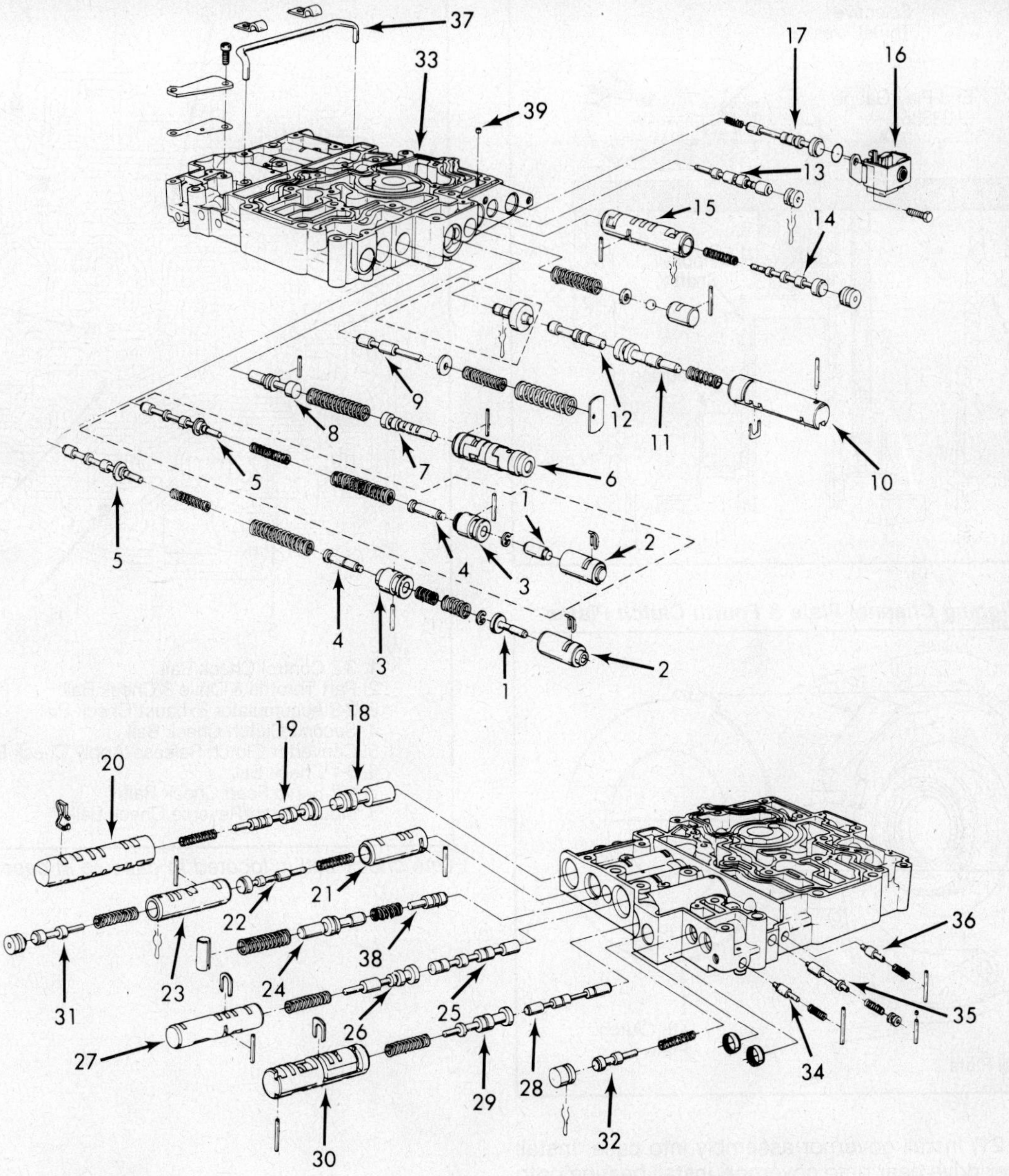

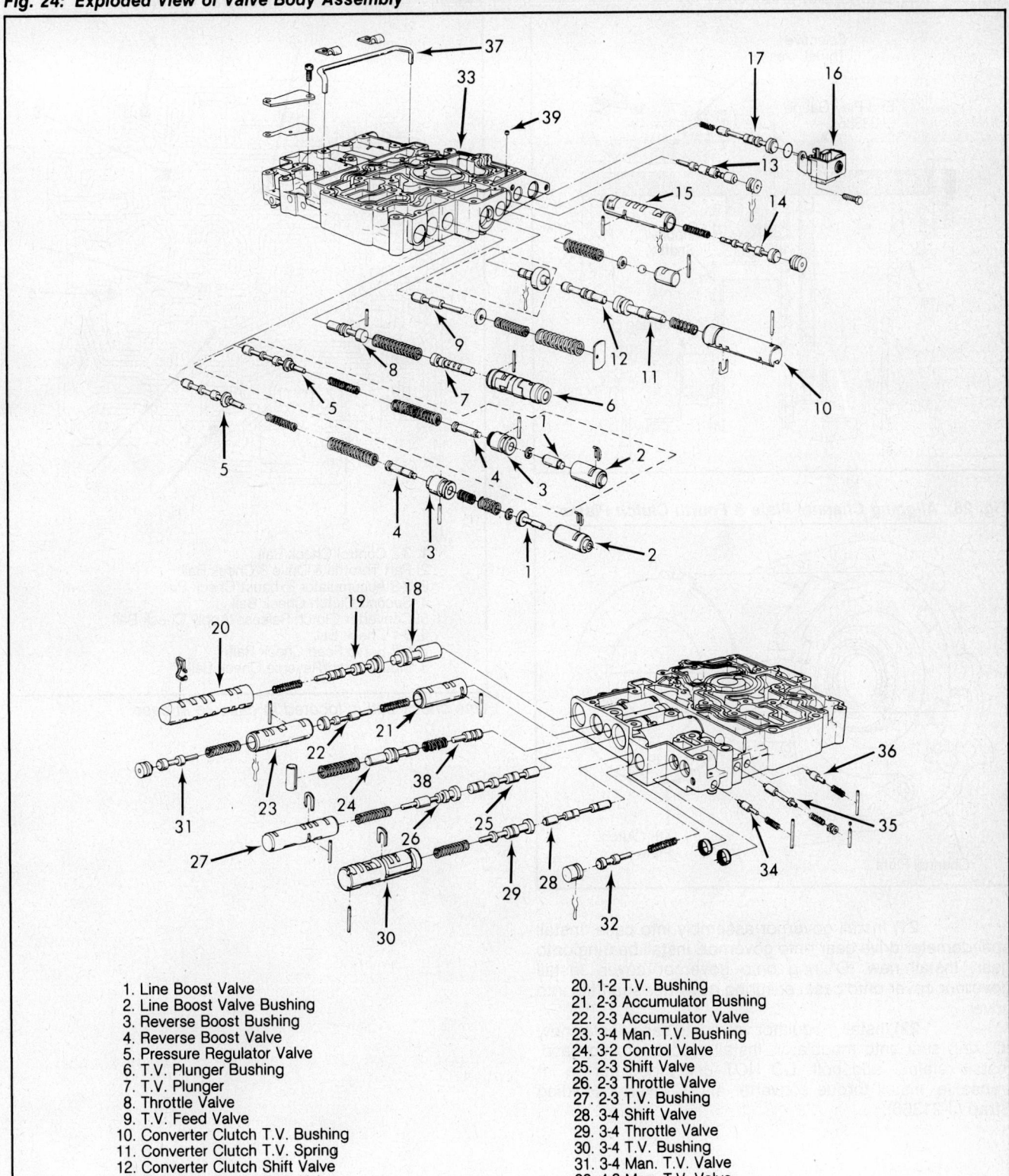

1. Line Boost Valve
2. Line Boost Valve Bushing
3. Reverse Boost Bushing
4. Reverse Boost Valve
5. Pressure Regulator Valve
6. T.V. Plunger Bushing
7. T.V. Plunger
8. Throttle Valve
9. T.V. Feed Valve
10. Converter Clutch T.V. Bushing
11. Converter Clutch T.V. Spring
12. Converter Clutch Shift Valve
13. Converter Clutch Reg. Valve (NOTE: Some models use a spring on inner end of valve.)
14. 1-2 Accumulator Valve
15. 1-2 Accumulator Bushing
16. Solenoid
17. Converter Clutch Valve
18. 1-2 Shift Valve
19. 1-2 Throttle Valve
20. 1-2 T.V. Bushing
21. 2-3 Accumulator Bushing
22. 2-3 Accumulator Valve
23. 3-4 Man. T.V. Bushing
24. 3-2 Control Valve
25. 2-3 Shift Valve
26. 2-3 Throttle Valve
27. 2-3 T.V. Bushing
28. 3-4 Shift Valve
29. 3-4 Throttle Valve
30. 3-4 T.V. Bushing
31. 3-4 Man. T.V. Valve
32. 4-3 Man. T.V. Valve
33. Valve Body
34. Reverse Servo Boost Valve
35. 1-2 Servo Control Valve
36. 1-2 Servo Boost Valve
37. 2nd Clutch Pipe
38. 3-2 Isolator Valve
39. Plug, Orificed (NOTE: AC & AY models only.)

Automatic Transmissions

GENERAL MOTORS TURBO HYDRA-MATIC 440-T4 TRANSAXLE (Cont.)

Fig. 25: Measuring Input Shaft End Play

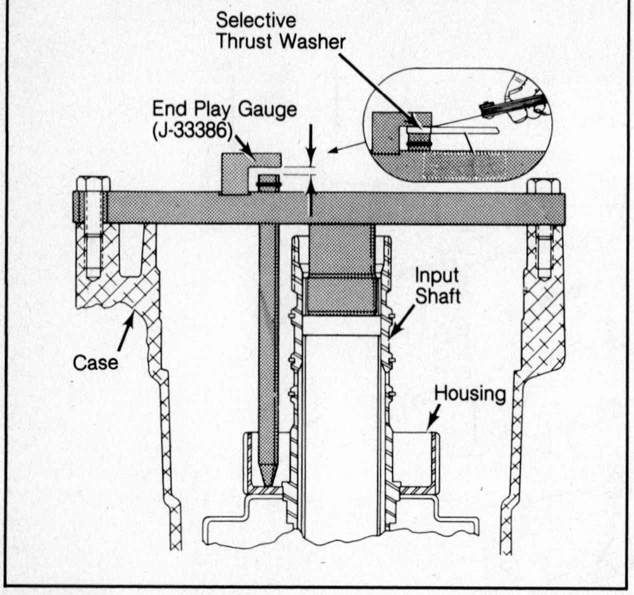

Fig. 26: Aligning Channel Plate & Fourth Clutch Plates

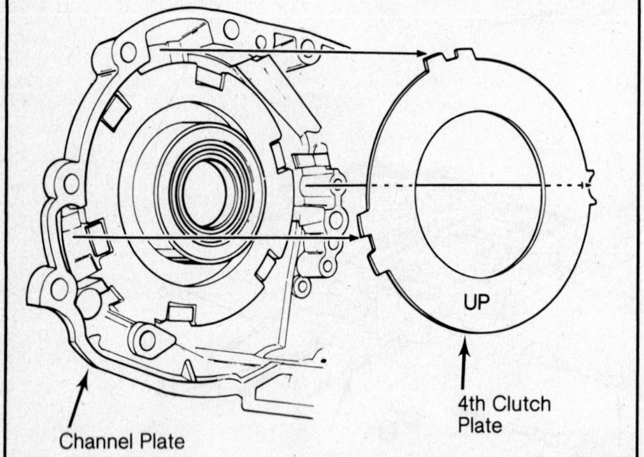

21) Install governor assembly into case. Install speedometer drive gear onto governor. Install bearing onto gear. Install new "O" ring onto governor cover. Install governor cover onto case, ensuring governor shaft fits into cover.

22) Install modulator valve into case. Install new "O" ring seal onto modulator. Install modulator into case. Install retainer and bolt. DO NOT use modulator to lift transaxle. Install torque converter and Converter Holding Strap (J-21366).

Fig. 27: Channel Plate Check Ball Locations

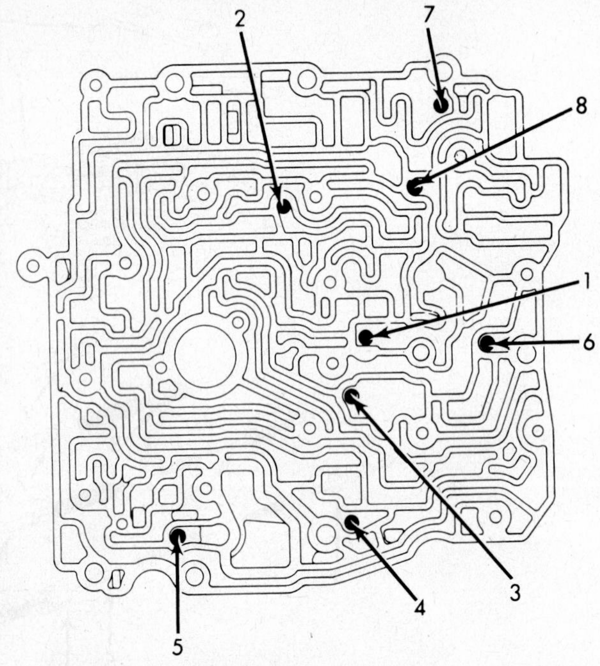

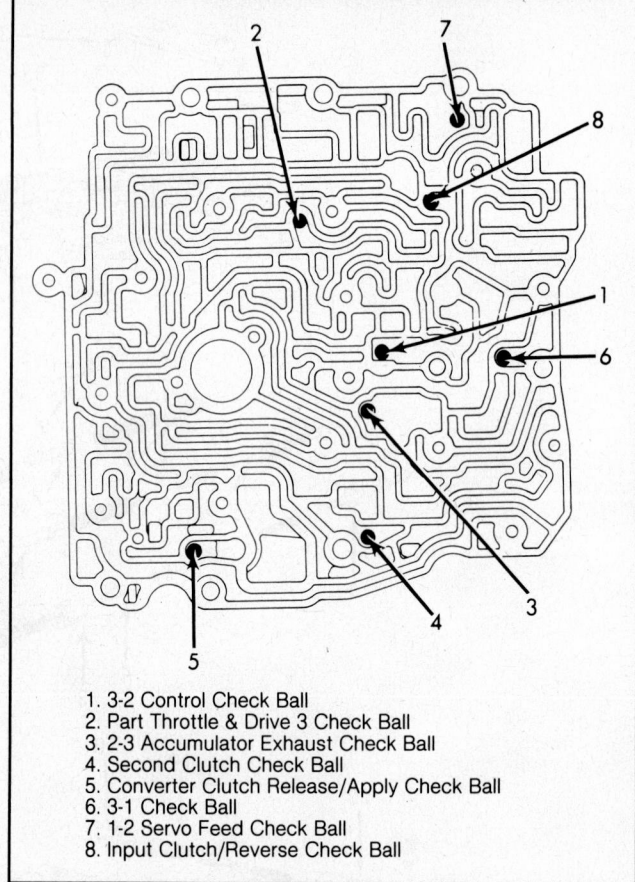

1. 3-2 Control Check Ball
2. Part Throttle & Drive 3 Check Ball
3. 2-3 Accumulator Exhaust Check Ball
4. Second Clutch Check Ball
5. Converter Clutch Release/Apply Check Ball
6. 3-1 Check Ball
7. 1-2 Servo Feed Check Ball
8. Input Clutch/Reverse Check Ball

One check ball is located in capsule in case.

GENERAL MOTORS TURBO HYDRA-MATIC 440-T4 TRANSAXLE (Cont.)

Fig. 28: Valve Body Check Ball Locations

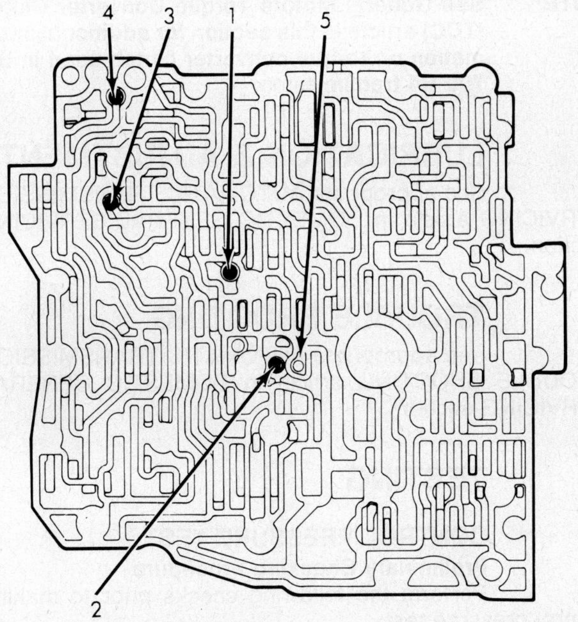

1. Fourth Clutch Check Ball
2. Third Clutch Check Ball
3. 2-3 Accumulator Feed Check Ball
4. Reverse Servo Feed Check Ball
5. Screen, Third Clutch Exhaust

One check ball is located in capsule in case.

Fig. 29: Location of Bottom Pan Magnet

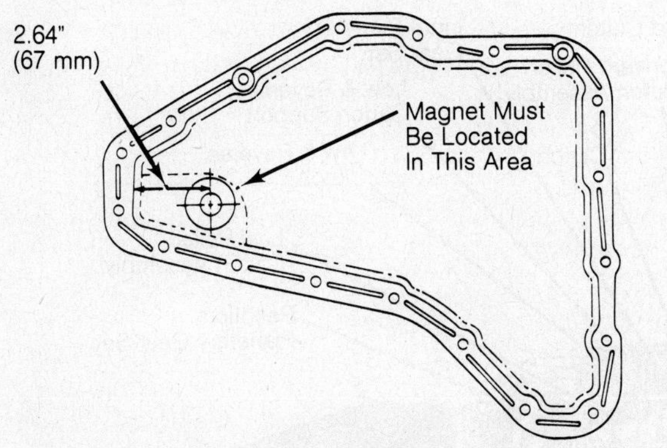

Fig. 30: Installing Governor and Modulator

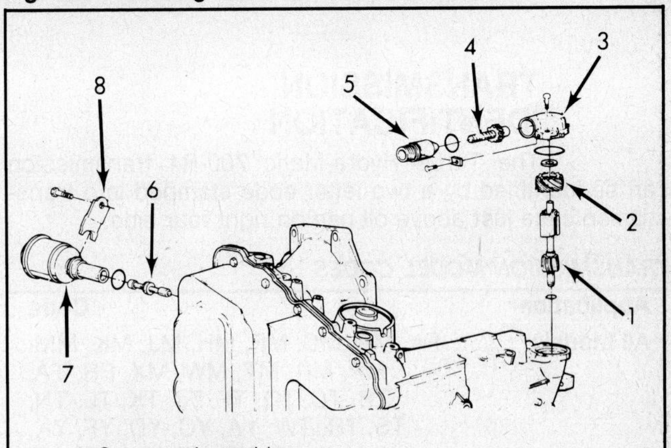

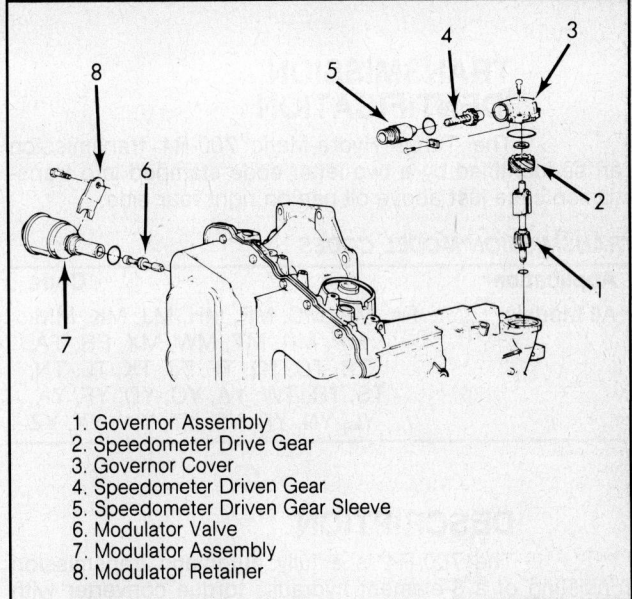

1. Governor Assembly
2. Speedometer Drive Gear
3. Governor Cover
4. Speedometer Driven Gear
5. Speedometer Driven Gear Sleeve
6. Modulator Valve
7. Modulator Assembly
8. Modulator Retainer

TIGHTENING SPECIFICATIONS

Application	Ft. Lbs. (N.m.)
Accumulator Cover-to-Case	20 (27)
Case-to-Drive Sprocket Support	20 (27)
Case Side Cover-to-Channel Plate	10 (14)
Channel Plate-to-Case	20 (27)
Channel Plate-to-Driven Sprocket Support	20 (27)
Connector Cooler Fitting	30 (41)
Governor-to-Case	20 (27)
Governor Control Body-to-Cover	20 (27)
Governor Oil Pipe Retainer	10 (14)
Hub & Bearing Assembly Bolts	
Celebrity, Century, Cutlass Ciera & 6000	63 (85)
DeVille, Electra, Fleetwood & Ninety-Eight	70 (95)
Hub Nut	
Celebrity, Century, Cutlass Ciera & 6000	192 (260)
DeVille, Electra, Fleetwood & Ninety-Eight	180 (245)
Manual Detent Spring-to-Valve Body	10 (14)
Manual Shaft-to-Detent Lever	25 (34)
Modulator-to-Case	20 (27)
Oil Scoop-to-Case	10 (14)
Pipe Plug	10 (14)
Pressure Switch	10 (14)
Pump Body-to-Case	20 (27)
Pump Cover-to-Channel Plate	10 (14)
Pump Cover-to-Pump Body	20 (27)
Pump Cover-to-Valve Body	10 (14)
Servo Pipe Bracket-to-Valve Body	10 (14)
Solenoid-to-Valve Body	10 (14)
Side Cover-to-Case	10 (14)
Valve Body-to-Case	20 (27)
Valve Body-to-Channel Plate	10 (14)

GENERAL MOTORS TURBO HYDRA-MATIC 700-R4

Chevrolet, GMC, Pontiac

TRANSMISSION IDENTIFICATION

The Turbo Hydra-Matic 700-R4 transmission can be identified by a two letter code stamped into transmission case just above oil pan on right rear side.

TRANSMISSION MODEL CODES

Application	Code
All Models	FA, MA, MC, MF, MH, MJ, MK, MM, MP, MR, MT, MW, MX, PR, TA, TB, TC, TD, TF, TJ, TK, TL, TN, TS, TR, TW, YA, YC, YD, YF, YK, YL, YN, YP, YS, YT, YW, YX, YZ

DESCRIPTION

The 700-R4 is a fully automatic transmission consisting of a 3-element hydraulic torque converter with the addition of a converter clutch. Two planetary gear sets, 5 multiple-disc clutches, 2 roller clutches and a band are used to provide the friction elements necessary to produce 4 forward speeds, the last of which is overdrive.

The torque converter, through oil, couples engine power to gear sets and provides additional torque multiplication when required. The converter clutch drive and driven members operate as one unit when applied, providing mechanical drive from engine through transmission. A hydraulic system, pressurized by a variable capacity vane type pump, provides working pressure required to operate friction elements and automatic controls.

NOTE: **See General Motors Torque Converter Clutch (TCC) article in this section for additional information on torque converter clutch used in the 700-R4 transmission.**

LUBRICATION & ADJUSTMENT

See appropriate AUTOMATIC TRANSMISSION SERVICING article in DOMESTIC GENERAL SERVICING section.

TROUBLE SHOOTING

See appropriate AUTOMATIC TRANSMISSION TROUBLE SHOOTING article in DOMESTIC GENERAL SERVICING section.

TESTING

CONTROL PRESSURE TEST

Preliminary Checking Procedure

Perform the following checks prior to making control pressure test:

- Check transmission fluid level.
- Check and adjust throttle valve cable.
- Check and adjust linkage.
- Check engine operating condition.
- Install oil pressure gauge to transmission.
- Connect tachometer to engine.

Fig. 1: Cutaway View of General Motors 700-R4 Automatic Transmission

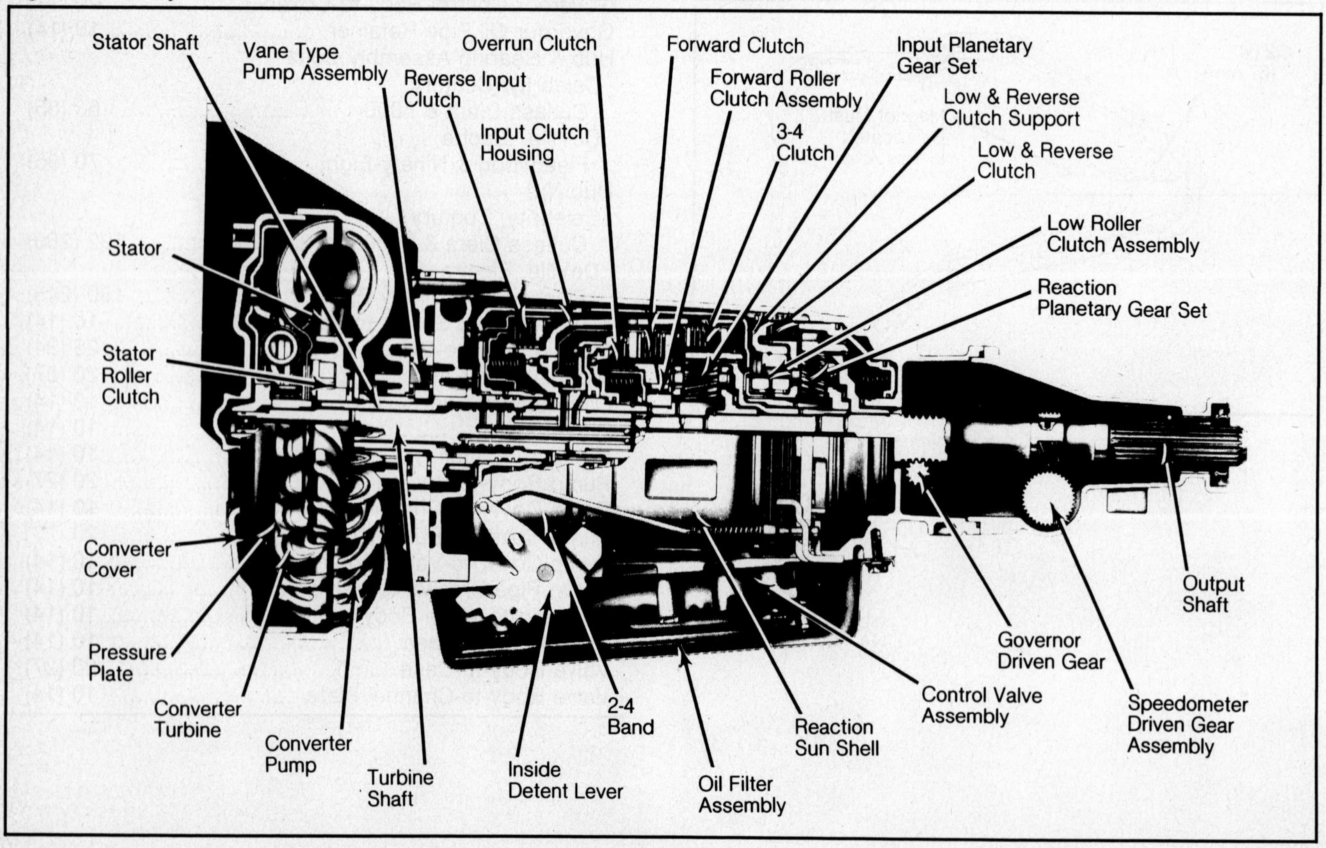

GENERAL MOTORS TURBO HYDRA-MATIC 700-R4 (Cont.)

Minimum Throttle Valve Pressure Check

With throttle valve cable properly adjusted and brakes applied, check line pressure in appropriate range at specified engine RPM. See CONTROL PRESSURE SPECIFICATIONS chart.

Full Throttle Valve Pressure Check

With throttle valve cable held at full extent of its travel and brakes applied, check line pressure in appropriate range at specified engine RPM. See CONTROL PRESSURE SPECIFICATIONS chart.

Pressure Differential Check

Check oil pressure differential between line pressure and 2nd, 3rd and 4th clutch pressure while driving vehicle. If pressure differential between line pressure and any of the clutch circuits is more than 10 psi (0.7 kg/cm^2) there is a possible leak in that clutch oil circuit. *See Fig. 2.*

Fig. 2: Oil Pressure Tap Locations

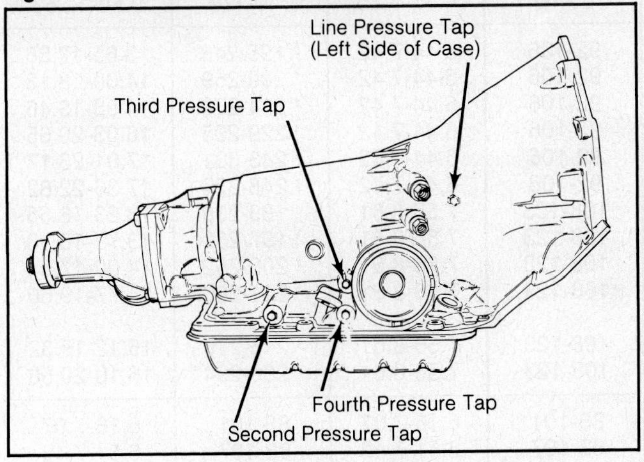

CONTROL PRESSURE TEST RESULTS

High or Low Oil Pressures

- Pump assembly pressure regulator valve binding, dirty or broken spring.
- Pump assembly throttle valve and reverse boost plugs and bushings dirty, sticking, damaged or assembled incorrectly.
- Pump assembly pressure relief ball not seated or damaged.
- Pump assembly slide sticking.
- Pump assembly not regulating.
- Pump assembly excessive rotor clearance.
- Manual valve not engaged or damaged.
- Throttle valve exhaust valve binding or damaged.
- Throttle lever and bracket assembly binding, damaged, incorrectly assembled or check valve missing.
- Throttle valve or plunger sticking in valve body.
- Throttle valve limit valve sticking in valve body.
- Throttle link not engaged, damaged, incorrect link, burr on upper end or hanging on throttle valve sleeve.
- Oil filter restricted, missing "O" ring or hole in intake pipe.

REMOVAL & INSTALLATION

See appropriate AUTOMATIC TRANSMISSION REMOVAL article in DOMESTIC GENERAL SERVICING section.

TORQUE CONVERTER

NOTE: **Torque converter is a sealed unit and cannot be disassembled for service or repair.**

LEAKAGE CHECK

See G.M. TURBO HYDRA-MATIC 400 article.

END CLEARANCE CHECK

See G.M. TURBO HYDRA-MATIC 400 article.

CONVERTER FLUSHING

See G.M. TURBO HYDRA-MATIC 400 article.

NOTE: **For additional information on Torque Converter Clutch (TCC), see General Motors Torque Converter Clutch article in this section.**

TRANSMISSION DISASSEMBLY

VALVE BODY & WIRING HARNESS PARTS

1) Mount transmission in a holding fixture and remove torque converter. Rotate transmission so that oil pan is facing up. Remove oil pan and gasket. Remove oil filter intake pipe and "O" rings which may be located in pump bore.

Fig. 3: Valve Body Bolt Locations

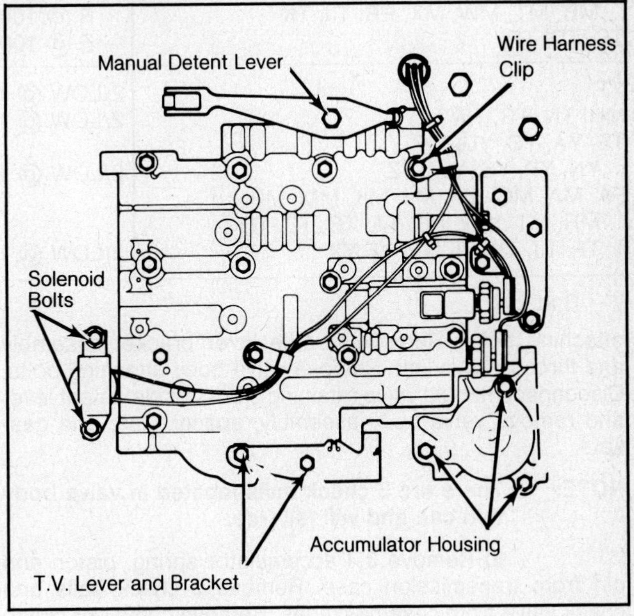

2) Disconnect inner harness connector at transmission case. Remove outside connector and "O" ring seal from transmission case. Remove solenoid and attaching bolts, and "O" ring from case and pump. Disconnect all wires from pressure switches and remove complete wiring harness and solenoid assembly.

3) Remove 1-2 accumulator housing, attaching bolts, 1-2 accumulator spring, piston, gasket and plate. Remove oil passage cover and attaching bolts from transmission case.

4) Remove manual detent roller assembly and attaching bolt. Remove wire harness retaining clips and

GENERAL MOTORS TURBO HYDRA-MATIC 700-R4 (Cont.)

THROTTLE VALVE LINE PRESSURE CHECK

Model	Range	MINIMUM T.V.		MAXIMUM T.V.	
		psi	kg/cm²	psi	kg/cm²
YT	P @ 1000	56-64	3.92-4.48	119-151	8.33-10.57
YL	P @ 1000	56-64	3.92-4.48	122-157	8.54-10.99
YK, YN, YP	P @ 1000	56-64	3.92-4.48	130-169	9.10-11.83
TS	P @ 1000	56-64	3.98-4.48	140-179	9.80-12.53
YS	P @ 1000	56-64	3.92-4.48	148-201	10.36-14.07
YA, YC, YD, YW, YZ	P @ 1000	56-64	3.92-4.48	151-199	10.57-13.93
TA, TB	P @ 1000	65-75	4.55-5.25	115-145	8.05-10.15
FA, MH, TN, TR, TW	P @ 1000	65-75	4.55-5.25	120-158	8.40-11.06
YX	P @ 1000	65-75	4.55-5.25	122-153	8.54-10.71
TL, YF	P @ 1000	65-75	4.55-5.25	128-171	8.39-11.97
MA, MC, MF, MJ, MK, MM, MP MR, MT, MW, MX, PR, TJ, TK	P @ 1000	65-75	4.55-5.25	131-168	9.17-11.76
TC, TD, TF	P @ 1000	65-75	4.55-5.25	140-179	9.80-12.53
YT	R @ 1000	92-106	6.44-7.42	[1] 195-248	13.65-17.36
YL	R @ 1000	92-106	6.44-7.42	[1] 200-259	14.00-18.13
YK, YN, YP	R @ 1000	92-106	6.44-7.42	[1] 214-278	14.98-19.46
TS	R @ 1000	92-106	6.44-7.42	[1] 229-295	16.03-20.65
YS	R @ 1000	92-106	6.44-7.42	[1] 243-331	17.01-23.17
YA, YC, YD, YW, YZ	R @ 1000	92-106	6.44-7.42	[1] 248-326	17.36-22.82
TB, TB	R @ 1000	108-123	7.56-8.61	[1] 189-238	13.23-16.66
FA, MH, TN, TR, TW	R @ 1000	108-123	7.56-8.61	[1] 197-259	13.79-18.13
YX	R @ 1000	108-123	7.56-8.61	[1] 200-252	14.00-17.64
TL, YF	R @ 1000	108-123	7.56-8.61	[1] 211-280	14.77-19.60
MA, MC, MF, MJ, MK, MM, MP MR, MT, MW, MX, PR, TJ, TK	R @ 1000	108-123	7.56-8.61	[1] 216-276	15.12-19.32
TC, TD, TF	R @ 1000	108-123	7.56-8.61	[1] 230-294	16.10-20.58
YT	2/LOW @ 1000	88-101	6.16-7.07	88-101	6.16-7.07
MH, TN, TR, TW	2/LOW @ 1000	93-107	6.51-7.49	93-107	6.51-7.49
TS, YA, YC, YD, YK, YL YN, YP, YS, YW, YZ	2/LOW @ 1000	102-118	7.14-8.26	102-118	7.14-8.26
FA, MA, MC, MF, MJ, MK, MM, MP MR, MT, MW, PR, TA, TB, TC, TD TF, TJ, TK, TL, T2, YF,YX	2/LOW @ 1000	103-117	7.21-8.19	103-117	7.21-8.19

[1] – R at 2000.

attaching bolts. Remove throttle lever bracket assembly and throttle valve link. Remove valve body attaching bolts. Disconnect manual valve retaining clip at inside detent lever and remove valve body assembly, spacer plate and gaskets.

NOTE: **There are 3 check balls located in valve body that can and will fall free.**

5) Remove 3-4 accumulator spring, piston and pin from transmission case. Remove 5 check balls and check valve from case passages. Remove converter clutch and governor screens from case.

GOVERNOR & EXTERNAL PARTS

1) Remove governor and cover. If rear seal requires replacement, remove with a screwdriver and install a new seal using a seal driver. Remove extension housing and attaching bolts. Remove sleeve and "O" ring from output shaft, then remove speedometer gear and clip.

2) Compress 2-4 servo cover and remove retaining ring. Remove servo cover and "O" ring by applying compressed air to servo apply hole in case. Remove 4th gear apply piston and "O" ring. Remove 2nd servo piston assembly. Remove inner servo piston assembly, oil seal ring and release spring.

NOTE: **Before continuing with transmission disassembly, check for correct 2-4 servo apply Pin.**

2-4 Servo Apply Pin Selection

1) Install servo apply pin Selection Gauge (J-33037) into servo bore and retain in place with snap ring, locating snap ring gap in case slot. Dissemble 2-4 servo assembly. Insert servo pin into selection gauge. Locate end of pin on band anchor lug.

2) Apply 100 INCH Lbs. (11 N.m) torque to hex nut on selection gauge. If any part of White line on servo pin appears in window of gauge, correct pin is installed. If White line cannot be seen, select another pin until correct pin is obtained.

NOTE: **Apply pin for 2-4 servo is available in 4 different lengths.**

TRANSMISSION END PLAY CHECK

1) Position transmission with oil pump facing up. Remove one oil pump attaching bolt and washer and install

GENERAL MOTORS TURBO HYDRA-MATIC 700-R4 (Cont.)

Fig. 4: General Motors 700-R4 Hydraulic Circuits Diagram

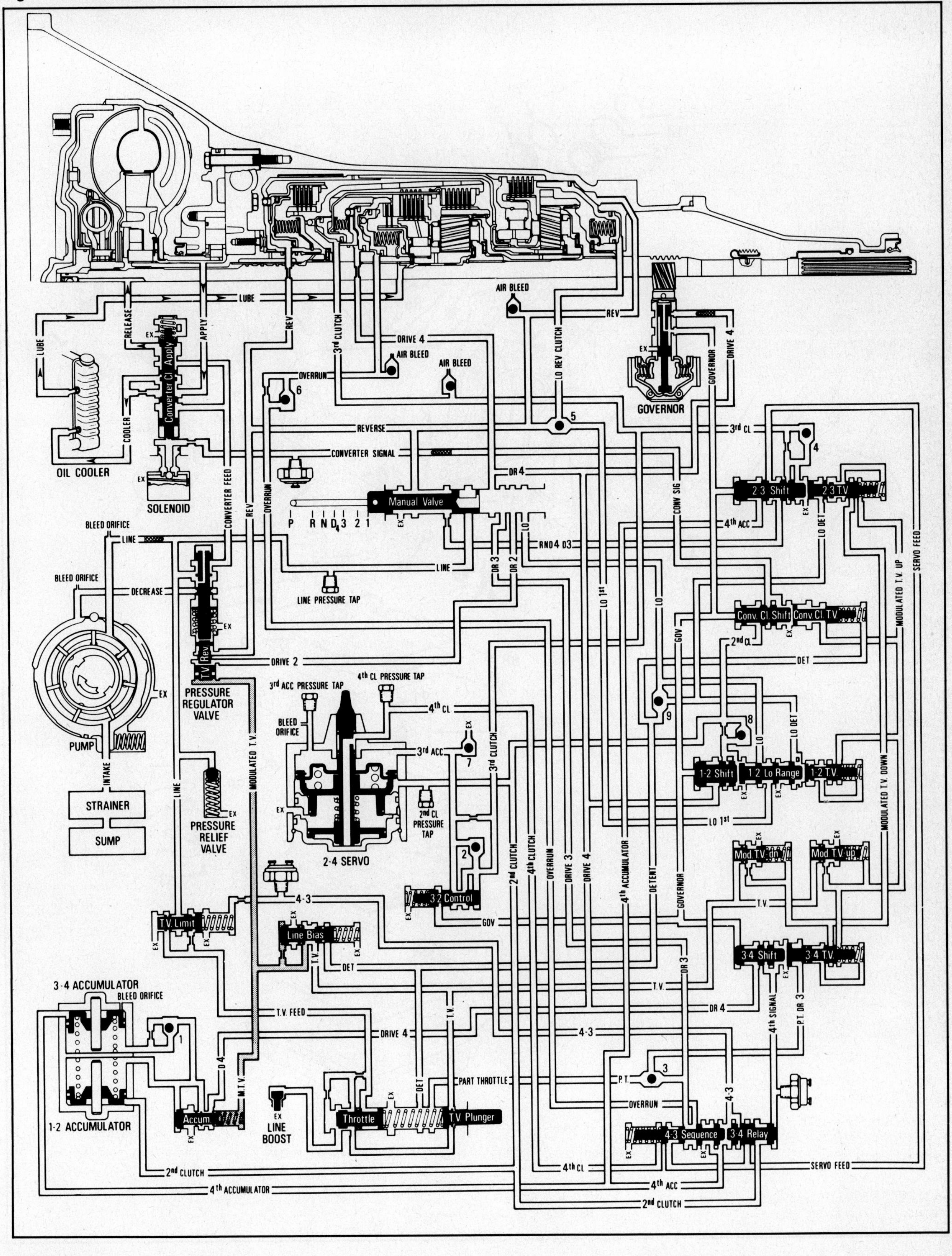

GENERAL MOTORS TURBO HYDRA-MATIC 700-R4 (Cont.)

Fig. 5: Exploded View of Turbo Hiydra-Matic 700-R4 External Parts

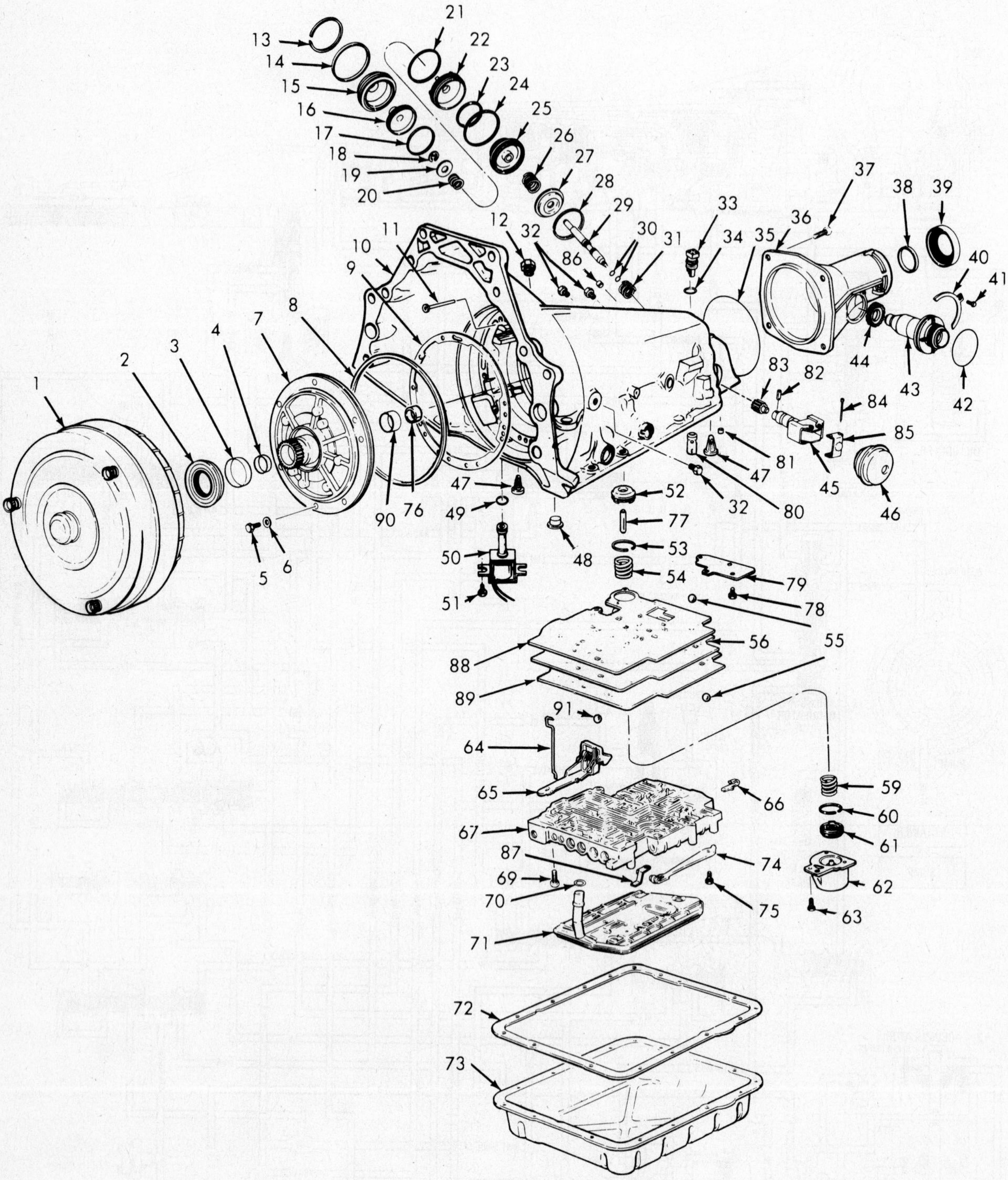

GENERAL MOTORS TURBO HYDRA-MATIC 700-R4 (Cont.)

Turbo Hydra-matic 700 R4 External Parts (Use With Fig. 5)

1. Converter Assembly
2. Oil Seal Assembly
3. Oil Pump Body Bushing
4. Stator Shaft Front Bushing
5. Pump-to-Case Bolt
6. Pump-to Case Bolt Washer
7. Oil Pump Assembly
8. Pump-to-Case Oil Seal
9. Pump Cover-to-Case Gasket
10. Transmission Case
11. Transmission Case Vent
12. Oil Cooler Pipe Connector
13. Servo Cover Retaining Ring
14. 2-4 Servo Cover "O" Ring
15. 2-4 Servo Cover
16. 4th Apply Piston
17. 4th Apply Piston Oil Seal Outer Ring
18. Apply Pin Retainer Ring
19. Servo Apply Pin Washer
20. Servo Apply Pin Spring
21. "O" Ring Seal
22. Servo Piston Inner Housing
23. 2nd Apply Piston Oil Seal Inner Ring
24. 2nd Apply Piston Oil Seal Outer Ring
25. 2nd Apply Piston
26. Servo Cushion Spring
27. Servo Cushion Spring Retainer
28. 2nd Apply Piston Retainer Ring
29. 2nd Apply Piston Pin
30. 2nd Apply Piston Pin Seal
31. Servo Return Spring
32. Pressure Plug
33. Electrical Connector
34. Electrical Connection "O" Ring Seal
35. Case Extension-to-Case Seal
36. Extension Housing
37. Extension Housing-to-Case Bolt
38. Extension Housing Bushing
39. Extension Housing Oil Seal
40. Speedo Driven Gear Fitting Retainer
41. Bolt & Washer Assembly
42. Speedo Adapter-to-Extension "O" Ring
43. Speedo Adapter Assembly
44. Speedo Driven Gear
45. Governor Assembly
46. Governor Cover
47. Converter & Governor Oil Pressure Screen
48. Band Anchor Pin
49. Solenoid "O" Ring Seal
50. Solenoid Assembly
51. Solenoid Hex Washer Head Bolt
52. 3-4 Accumulator Piston
53. 3-4 Accumulator Piston Oil Seal Ring
54. 3-4 Accumulator Spring
55. .25 Diameter Ball
56. Valve Body Spacer Plate
59. 1-2 Accumulator Spring
60. 1-2 Accumulator Piston Oil Seal Ring
61. 1-2 Accumulator Piston
62. 1-2 Accumulator Cover & Pin Assembly
63. Accumulator Cover Bolt
64. Throttle Lever-to-Cable Link
65. Throttle Lever & Bracket Assembly
66. Electrical Wire Clip
67. Valve Body
69. Valve Body Bolt
70. Oil Filter "O" Ring Seal
71. Oil Filter Assembly
72. Oil Pan Gasket
73. Oil Pan
74. Manual Detent Spring Assembly
75. Manual Detent Spring Bolt
76. Case Bushing
77. Accumulator Piston Pin
78. Oil Passage Cover Bolt
79. Oil Passage Cover
80. 3rd Accumulator Retainer & Ball Assembly
81. Case Accumulator Bleed Plug
82. Governor Gear Retainer Pin
83. Governor Driven Gear
84. Governor Weight Pin
85. Governor Thrust Cap
86. Case Servo Plug
87. Filter Retainer Clip
88. Spacer Plate-to-Case Gasket
89. Spacer Plate-to-Valve Body
90. Rear Stator Shaft Bushing
91. Carbon Steel Throttle Valve Exhaust Ball

GENERAL MOTORS TURBO HYDRA-MATIC 700-R4 (Cont.)

Fig. 6: Valve Body Check Ball Locations

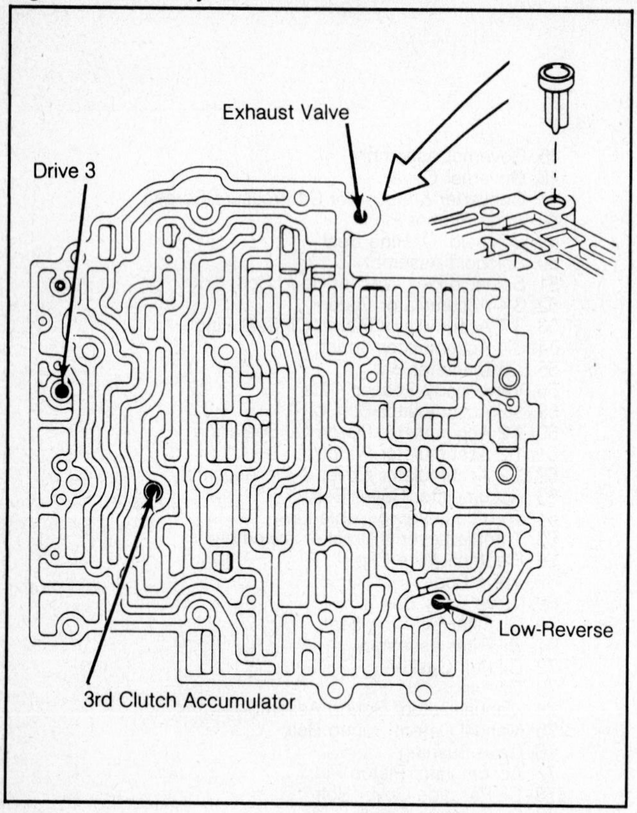

an 11" bolt and lock nut in its place. Position Oil Pump Remover (J-24773-A) and End Play Checking Fixture (J-25022) on end of turbine shaft. *See Fig. 10.*

2) Clamp a dial indicator on long bolt and position indicator point cap nut on top of pump remover. Zero dial indicator. Pull up on pump remover and read resulting end play.

3) Transmission end play should be .005-.036" (.13-.91 mm). The selective thrust washer controlling transmission end play is located between input housing and thrust washer on pump hub. If end play is not within specifications, select proper thrust washer from TRANSMISSION END PLAY WASHER SELECTION table. Remove dial indicator and fixture.

TRANSMISSION END PLAY WASHER SELECTION TABLE

I.D. Number	Washer Thickness In. (mm)
67	.074-.078 (1.88-1.98)
68	.080-.084 (2.03-2.13)
69	.087-.091 (2.21-.231)
70	.094-.098 (2.39-2.49)
71	.100-.104 (2.54-2.64)
72	.107-.111 (2.72-2.82)
73	.113-.118 (2.87-3.00)
74	.120-.124 (3.05-3.15)

OIL PUMP, REVERSE CLUTCH & INPUT CLUTCH

CAUTION: The filter and solenoid must be removed before pump can be removed.

Fig. 7: Model 700-R4 Case Attaching Parts

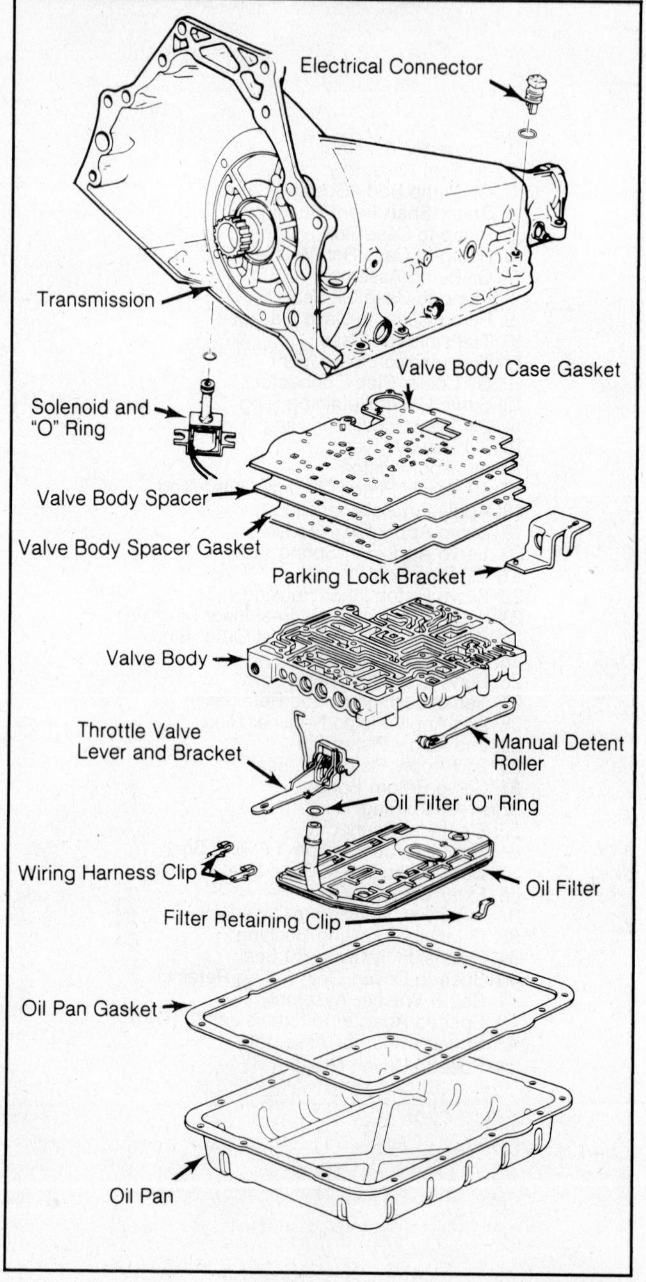

1) If required, remove oil pump seal using a screwdriver. Remove pump-to-case attaching bolts and washers. Using Oil Pump Remover (J-24773-A), pull pump assembly from case. Remove pump-to-case gasket.

2) Remove reverse input drum-to-pump washer from pump. Remove reverse and input clutch assemblies by lifting out with turbine shaft.

NOTE: Do not remove Teflon oil seal rings on turbine shaft unless required.

2-4 BAND & INPUT GEAR SET

1) Remove 2-4 band assembly from case. Remove band anchor pin from case. Remove input sun gear.

NOTE: To prevent the possibility of the output shaft falling free, install Output Shaft Support (J-29837) on case, to hold output shaft in place.

GENERAL MOTORS TURBO HYDRA-MATIC 700-R4 (Cont.)

Fig. 8: 1-2 and 3-4 Accumulator Assembly

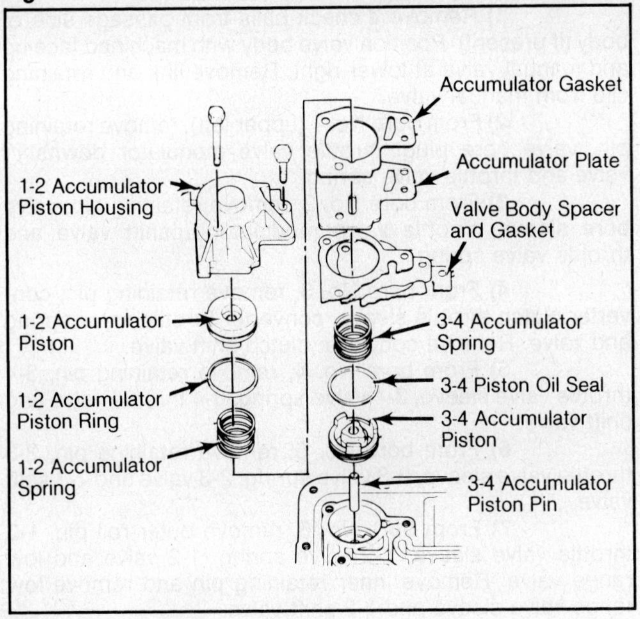

Fig. 9: 2-4 Apply Pin Selection

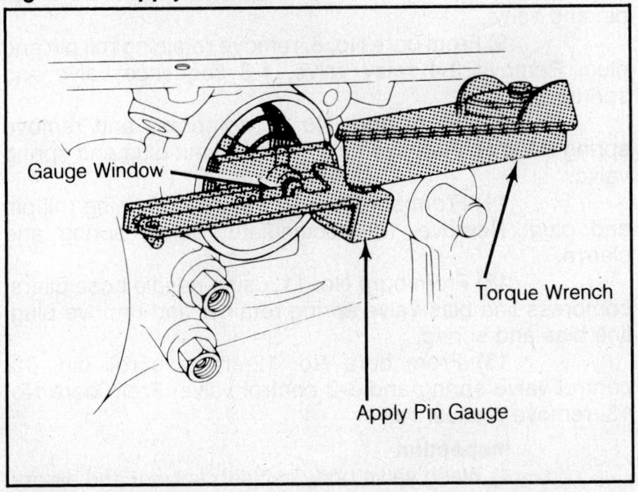

If White line on servo pin appears in gauge window, correct apply pin is installed.

2) Remove input carrier to output shaft snap ring with narrow snap ring pliers. If free, remove output shaft. Remove input carrier and thrust washer. Remove reaction shaft thrust bearing from input internal gear.

REACTION GEAR SET

1) Remove reaction shaft-to-reaction sun gear washer and reaction shell. Remove reaction shell-to-inner race washer. Remove low and reverse support-to-case retaining ring and support spring. Remove reaction sun gear.

2) Remove low and reverse inner race, roller assembly, support assembly and reaction carrier assembly. Remove low and reverse clutch composition plates and steel plates. Remove reaction internal gear, output shaft (if not previously removed) and bearing assembly. Remove support bearing assembly from case hub.

Fig. 10: Checking Transmission End Play.

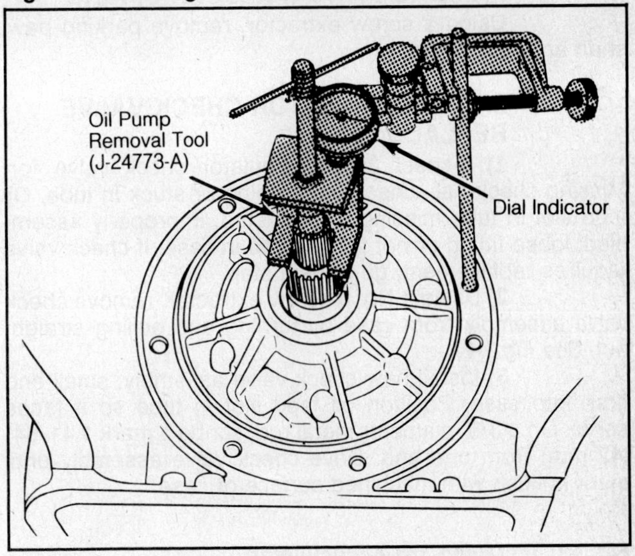

End play should be .005-.036" (.13-.92 mm).

Fig. 11: Installing Output Shaft Support Tool

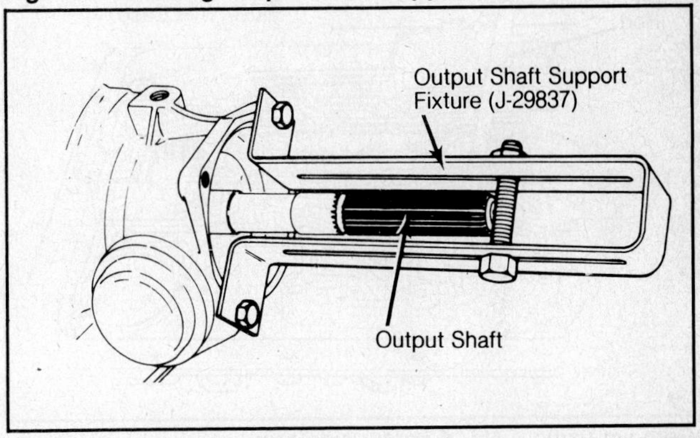

LOW/REVERSE CLUTCH

1) Remove parking lock bracket and 2 attaching bolts. Position parking lock pawl inboard. Using Clutch Spring Compressor (J-23327), compress low/reverse clutch spring retainer.

2) Remove spring retaining ring and low/reverse spring assembly. Remove compressor. Remove low/reverse clutch piston by applying air pressure in case apply passage.

INNER MANUAL LINKAGE

1) Rotate transmission to a horizontal position, loosen manual shaft retaining nut and move manual shaft inboard. Move inner detent lever, connected actuator rod assembly and manual shaft retainer, inboard.

2) Tap manual shaft outboard until retaining nut is free. If necessary, install a retaining nut on outside end of manual shaft. Using a screwdriver, remove manual shaft retainer and connect inner detent lever and actuator rod. Remove manual shaft and nut.

3) If necessary, remove inside detent lever from actuator rod by rotating rod and indexing notches in rod with hole in lever. If required, remove manual shaft seal by driving outward from case.

GENERAL MOTORS TURBO HYDRA-MATIC 700-R4 (Cont.)

PARKING PAWL & RETURN SPRING

Using a screw extractor, remove parking pawl shaft and return spring.

3RD ACCUMULATOR CHECK VALVE REPLACEMENT

1) Inspect 3rd accumulator check valve for: Missing check ball, check ball binding or stuck in tube. Oil feed slot in tube missing or restricted, improperly assembled, loose fitting or not fully seated in case. If check valve requires replacement, go to next step.

2) Using a No. 4 screw extractor, remove check valve assembly from case by turning and pulling straight out. *See Fig. 12.*

3) Install new check valve assembly, small end first, into case. Position oil feed slot in tube so it faces servo. On a 3/8" diameter metal rod, scribe a mark 1 41/64" (42 mm) from one end. Drive check valve assembly until mark is flush with machined surface of case.

Fig. 12: Installing 3rd Accumulator Check Valve Assembly

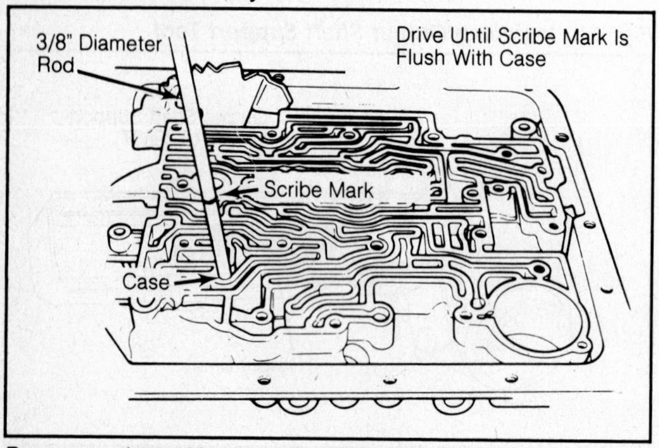

Remove using a No. 4 screw extractor.

COMPONENT DISASSEMBLY & REASSEMBLY

VALVE BODY ASSEMBLY

NOTE: As valve trains are removed from each valve body bore, place individual parts in correct order and in relative position to valve body to simplify reassembly. Valves and springs are not interchangeable and all parts must be installed in correct order in proper valve body bore.

During disassembly, remove all outside roll pins by pushing through from rough casting side of valve body.

- Remove inner roll pins by grinding a taper on one end of a 1/16" drill, then tap drill into pin and pull straight out.
- Some roll pins are spring loaded and care should be taken when removing to prevent losing them.
- Remove spring retaining sleeves by compressing with needle-nose pliers and moving upward through exposed hole.
- Do not remove pressure switches unless they require replacement.

Disassembly

1) Remove 3 check balls from passage side of body (if present). Position valve body with machined face up and manual valve at lower right. Remove link and retaining clip from manual valve.

2) From bore No. 1 (upper left), remove retaining pin, valve bore plug, throttle valve modulator downshift valve and throttle valve spring.

3) From bore No. 2, remove retaining pin, valve bore sleeve, throttle valve modulator upshift valve and throttle valve spring.

4) From bore No. 3, remove retaining pin, converter clutch throttle sleeve, converter throttle valve spring and valve. Remove converter clutch shift valve.

5) From bore No. 4, remove retaining pin, 3-4 throttle valve sleeve, 3-4 valve spring, 3-4 throttle valve and shift valve.

6) From bore No. 5, remove retaining pin, 2-3 throttle valve sleeve, 2-3 valve spring, 2-3 valve and 2-3 shift valve.

7) From bore No. 6, remove outer roll pin, 1-2 throttle valve sleeve, 1-2 valve spring, 1-2 valve and low range valve. Remove inner retaining pin and remove low range valve sleeve and 1-2 shift valve.

8) From bore No. 7 (upper right), remove outer roll pin from rough casting side, throttle valve plunger sleeve, throttle plunger and valve spring. Remove inner roll pin and valve.

9) From bore No. 8, remove retaining roll pin and plug. Remove 3-4 relay valve, 4-3 sequence valve and spring.

10) From bore No. 9, compress and remove spring retainer. Remove throttle valve limit plug and spring valve.

11) From bore No. 10, remove retaining roll pin and plug. Remove 1-2 accumulator valve, spring and sleeve.

12) From bore No. 11, using needle nose pliers, compress line bias valve spring retainer and remove plug, line bias and spring.

13) From bore No. 12, remove roll pin, 3-2 control valve spring and 3-2 control valve. From bore No. 13, remove manual valve.

Inspection

1) Wash valve body in clean solvent and air dry. Clean valve train parts one at a time and place in same order as they were removed.

2) Inspect valves for scoring, cracks and free movement in their bores. Inspect all bushings for cracks or scored bores.

3) Inspect valve body for cracks, damage or scored bores. Lands should be flat with no cross leaks.

Reassembly

1) Install all parts in reverse order of removal. Assemble all bore plugs against retaining pins with recessed holes outboard. All roll pins must be installed so they do not extend above flat machined face of valve body pad.

2) Install all flared coiled pins with flared end out. Ensure all retaining or roll pins are installed into proper slots in sleeves, not in oil passage holes.

NOTE: The bushing for the 1-2 accumulator valve train must be assembled with small hole for roll pin facing rough casting side of valve body.

GENERAL MOTORS TURBO HYDRA-MATIC 700-R4 (Cont.)

Fig. 13: Exploded View of Model 700-R4 Valve Body Assembly

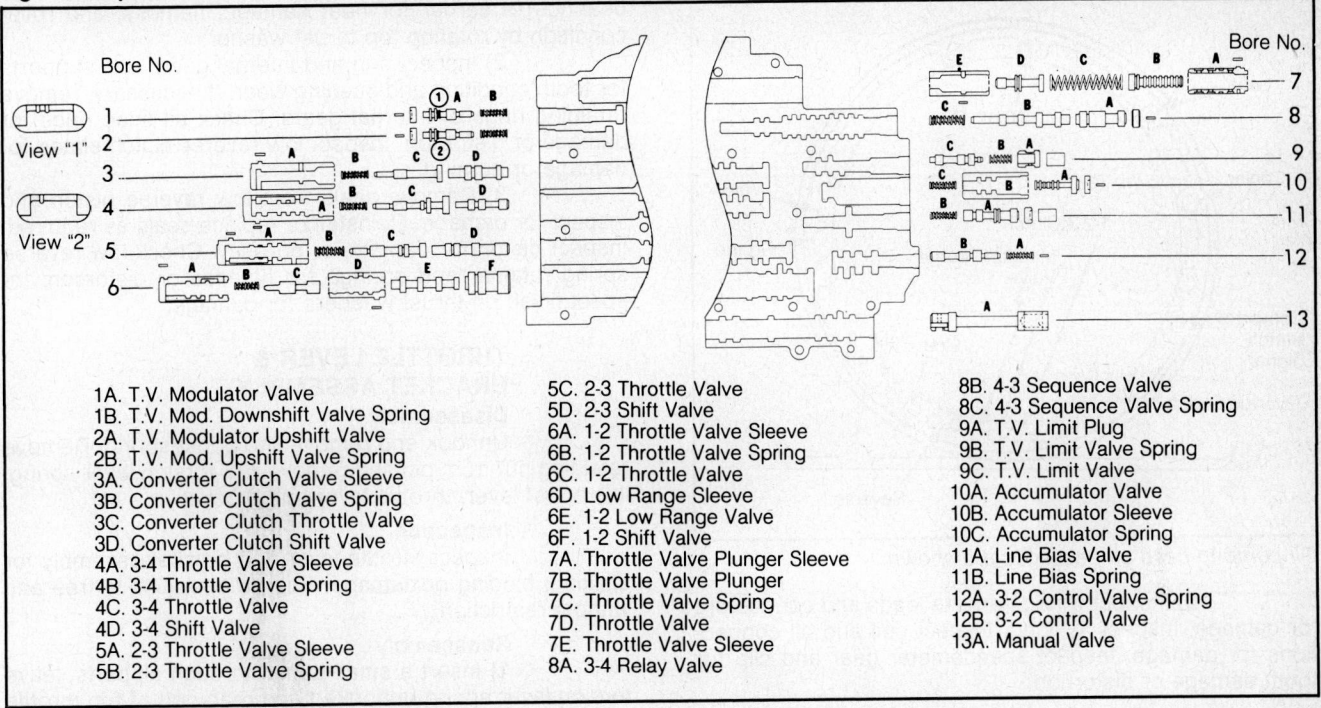

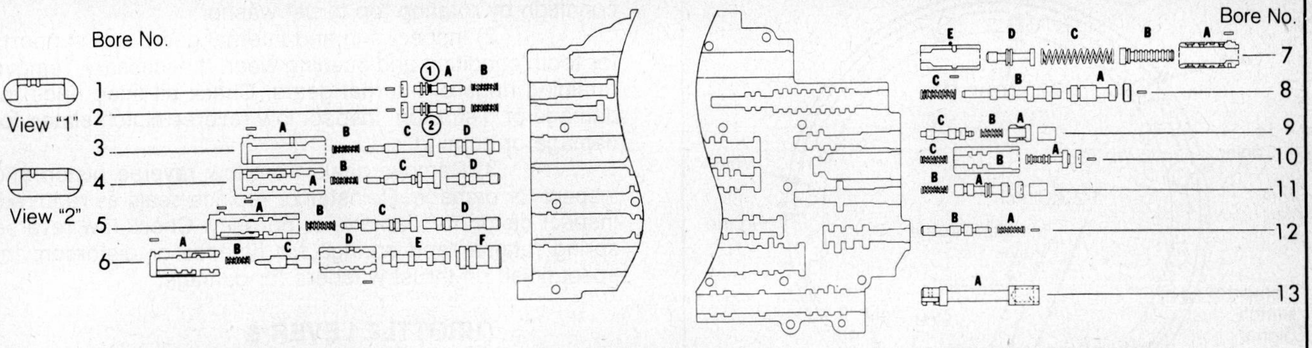

1A. T.V. Modulator Valve
1B. T.V. Mod. Downshift Valve Spring
2A. T.V. Modulator Upshift Valve
2B. T.V. Mod. Upshift Valve Spring
3A. Converter Clutch Valve Sleeve
3B. Converter Clutch Valve Spring
3C. Converter Clutch Throttle Valve
3D. Converter Clutch Shift Valve
4A. 3-4 Throttle Valve Sleeve
4B. 3-4 Throttle Valve Spring
4C. 3-4 Throttle Valve
4D. 3-4 Shift Valve
5A. 2-3 Throttle Valve Sleeve
5B. 2-3 Throttle Valve Spring
5C. 2-3 Throttle Valve
5D. 2-3 Shift Valve
6A. 1-2 Throttle Valve Sleeve
6B. 1-2 Throttle Valve Spring
6C. 1-2 Throttle Valve
6D. Low Range Sleeve
6E. 1-2 Low Range Valve
6F. 1-2 Shift Valve
7A. Throttle Valve Plunger Sleeve
7B. Throttle Valve Plunger
7C. Throttle Valve Spring
7D. Throttle Valve
7E. Throttle Valve Sleeve
8A. 3-4 Relay Valve
8B. 4-3 Sequence Valve
8C. 4-3 Sequence Valve Spring
9A. T.V. Limit Plug
9B. T.V. Limit Valve Spring
9C. T.V. Limit Valve
10A. Accumulator Valve
10B. Accumulator Sleeve
10C. Accumulator Spring
11A. Line Bias Valve
11B. Line Bias Spring
12A. 3-2 Control Valve Spring
12B. 3-2 Control Valve
13A. Manual Valve

Valves and springs are not interchangeable.

GOVERNOR ASSEMBLY

Disassembly

Cut off one end of each governor weight pin and remove pins, primary weights and secondary weights. Remove governor valve from sleeve.

Inspection

1) Wash all parts in clean solvent, air dry and blow out passages. Inspect governor body and valve for free operation, nicks, burrs, scoring or galling. Inspect springs for distortion.

2) Inspect driven gear for nicks, damage, or excessive looseness and replace as necessary.

Governor Driven Gear Replacement

1) Drive out driven gear retaining pin using a small punch. Support governor assembly on plates installed in exhaust slots of governor sleeve.

Fig. 14: Governor Assembly Exploded View

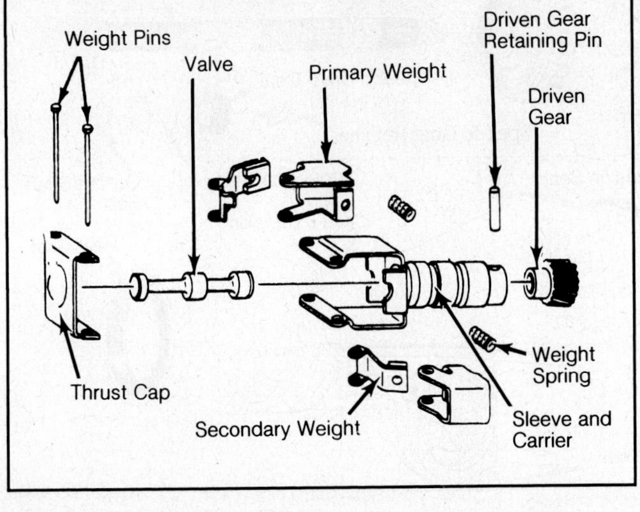

2) Place assembly in an arbor press. With a long punch, press driven gear out of sleeve. Clean sleeve of any chips that may be present.

3) To install new gear, support governor on plates installed in exhaust slots. Position new gear on sleeve and press gear into sleeve until seated against shoulder.

4) Locate a new pin hole 90 degrees from existing hole. Center punch new hole, then drill a new hole through sleeve and gear using a standard 1/8" drill. Install new retaining pin and stake in 2 locations. Thoroughly wash governor assembly to remove any chips or shavings.

Reassembly

To assemble, reverse disassembly procedure.

TRANSMISSION CASE

Inspection

1) Inspect case assembly for damage, cracks, porosity or interconnected oil passages. Inspect valve body case pad for flatness or land damage. Air check case passages for restrictions or blockage. Inspect case internal clutch plate lugs for damage or wear.

2) Inspect speedometer, servo and accumulator bores for damage and clearance relative to mating parts. Inspect all bolt holes for damaged threads. Inspect cooler line connectors. Inspect all snap ring grooves for damage. Inspect governor locating pin for proper length. An incorrect length results in a damaged governor gear.

CASE ATTACHING PARTS

Inspection

1) Check 1-2 and 3-4 accumulator parts for porosity or damage to pistons, housing or oil seal rings. Inspect for flatness and condition of accumulator and oil passage plate and gasket.

GENERAL MOTORS TURBO HYDRA-MATIC 700-R4 (Cont.)

Fig. 15: Front View of Transmission Case

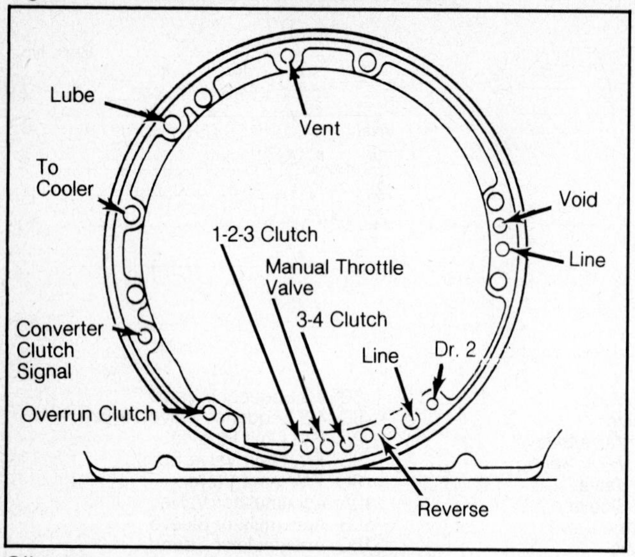

Oil pump-to-case oil passages are shown.

2) Inspect wiring harness leads and connectors for damage. Inspect "O" ring. Inspect coil and all connections for damage. Inspect speedometer gear and clip for tooth damage or distortion.

REACTION & INPUT GEAR SETS, LOW REVERSE CLUTCH & SUPPORT

Inspection

1) Check reaction and input carriers for pinion gear damage, excessive wear, incorrect number of pinion pin washers and proper staking of pinion pins. Inspect bearings of carrier for heat damage, flatness, and roller condition by rotating top thrust washer.

2) Inspect sun and internal gears and supports for tooth condition and bushing wear. If necessary, remove retaining rings of internal gears. Check all snap rings for damage or distortion. Inspect low reverse clutch plates for damage or burning.

3) Remove seals from low reverse piston and inspect for damage. Reinstall or replace seals as required. Inspect piston for damage or porosity. Check low reverse spring retainer and springs for flatness or distortion. Inspect finish on thrust washers for damage.

THROTTLE LEVER & BRACKET ASSEMBLY

Disassembly

Unhook and remove line boost spring. Remove retaining nut from pin and remove pin, torsion lever spring, line boost lever, throttle lever and bracket.

Inspection

Inspect throttle lever and bracket assembly for sticking, binding or damage. Ensure operation is free and without restriction.

Reassembly

1) Insert a small punch through all parts, leave torsion lever spring unhooked and rearward of top throttle lever to ease reassembly. Install pin through assembly and, at same time, remove punch.

2) Position short end of torsion spring under bracket and locate in notch. Install retaining nut on end of pin.

Fig. 16: Exploded View of Input, Reaction and Case Extension Parts

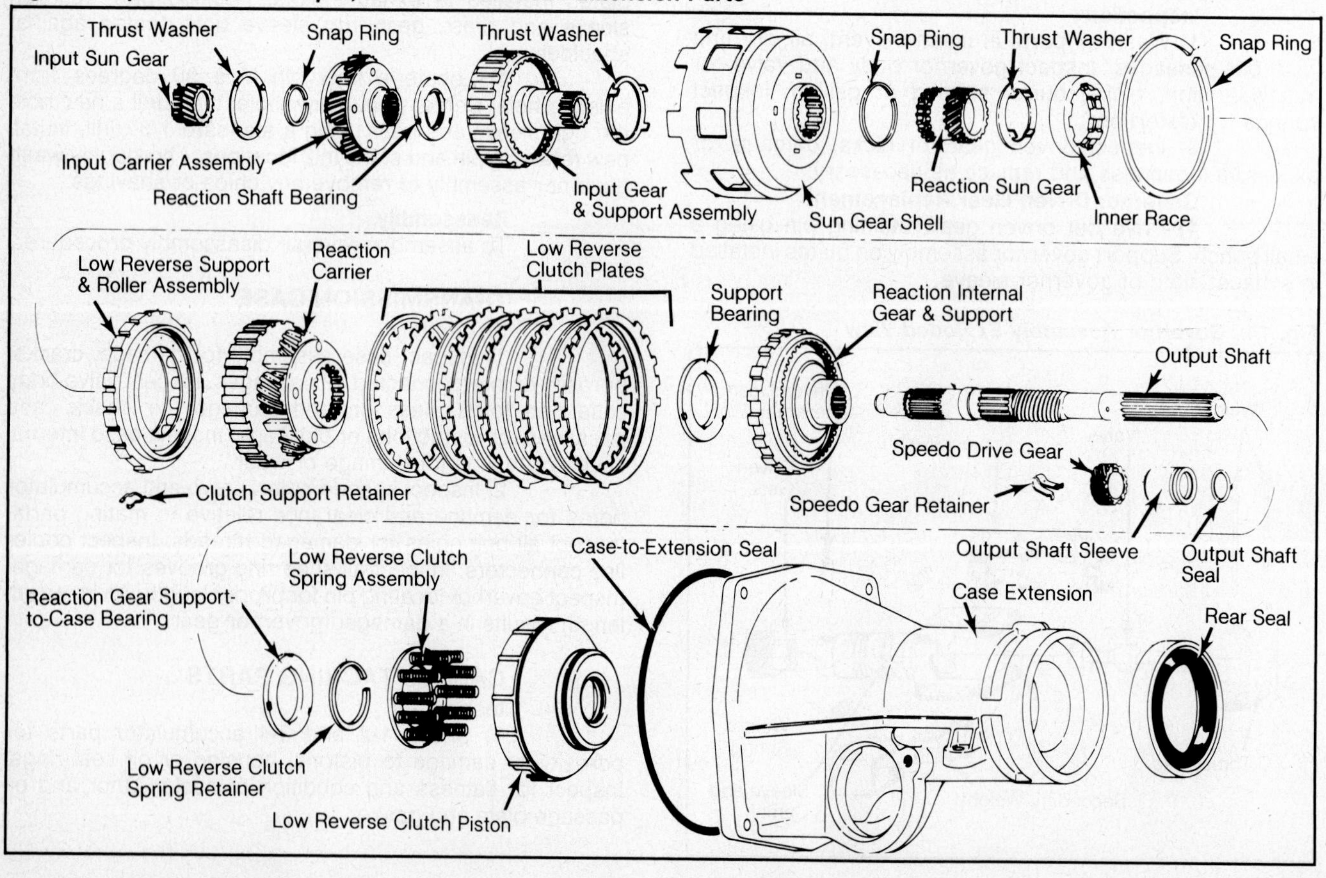

GENERAL MOTORS TURBO HYDRA-MATIC 700-R4 (Cont.)

Fig. 17: Exploded View of Throttle Lever and Bracket Assembly

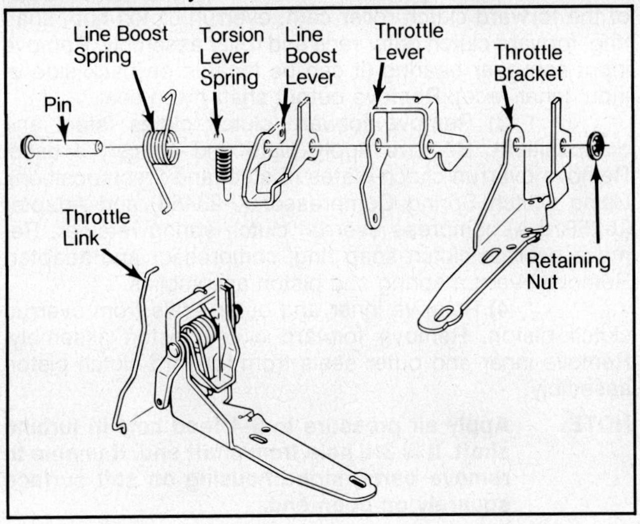

LOW REVERSE SUPPORT ASSEMBLY

Disassembly

With low reverse inner race removed, remove snap ring retaining roller assembly to support. Remove roller assembly.

Fig. 18: Low Reverse Clutch Support Assembly

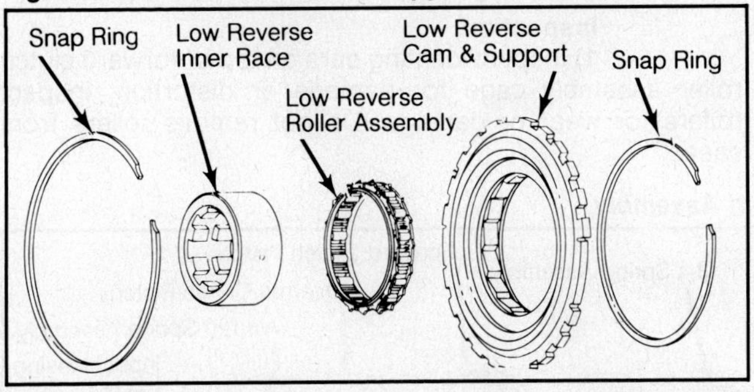

Inspection

Check inner and outer races for damage and surface finish. Inspect roller and springs for damage or distortion.

Reassembly

1) Position low reverse support on bench with chamfered side up. Install low reverse roller assembly into support with oil lube hole down (rearward).

CAUTION: Care should be taken to ensure roller and springs are not damaged and that rollers do not become dislodged.

2) Install low reverse inner race into roller assembly by rotating clockwise. When installed, the inner race should rotate in a clockwise direction and lock up in a counterclockwise direction.

REVERSE INPUT CLUTCH

Disassembly

1) Remove snap ring from reverse input housing. Remove reverse input clutch backing plate. Remove reverse input steel and composition clutch plates. Using Clutch Spring Compressor (J-23327), compress reverse input spring assembly and remove snap ring.

2) Remove compressor. Remove reverse input clutch release spring assembly. Remove reverse input clutch piston and remove inner and outer seals.

Inspection

1) Inspect reverse input clutch backing plate for damage, distortion, flatness and burred edges on clutch plate face. Inspect reverse plates. Inspect reverse input composition plates. Check release spring retainer for distortion and damage. Check reverse input clutch piston and seals for damage or distortion.

2) Inspect reverse input housing and drum for cracks. Check surface finish on hub and for worn or damaged bushings. Check freeness and condition of ball check. The ball must move freely with applied air pressure.

Reassembly

1) Lube and install inner and outer seals on clutch piston with seal lips facing away from hub. Install

Fig. 19: Exploded View of Reverse Input Clutch Assembly

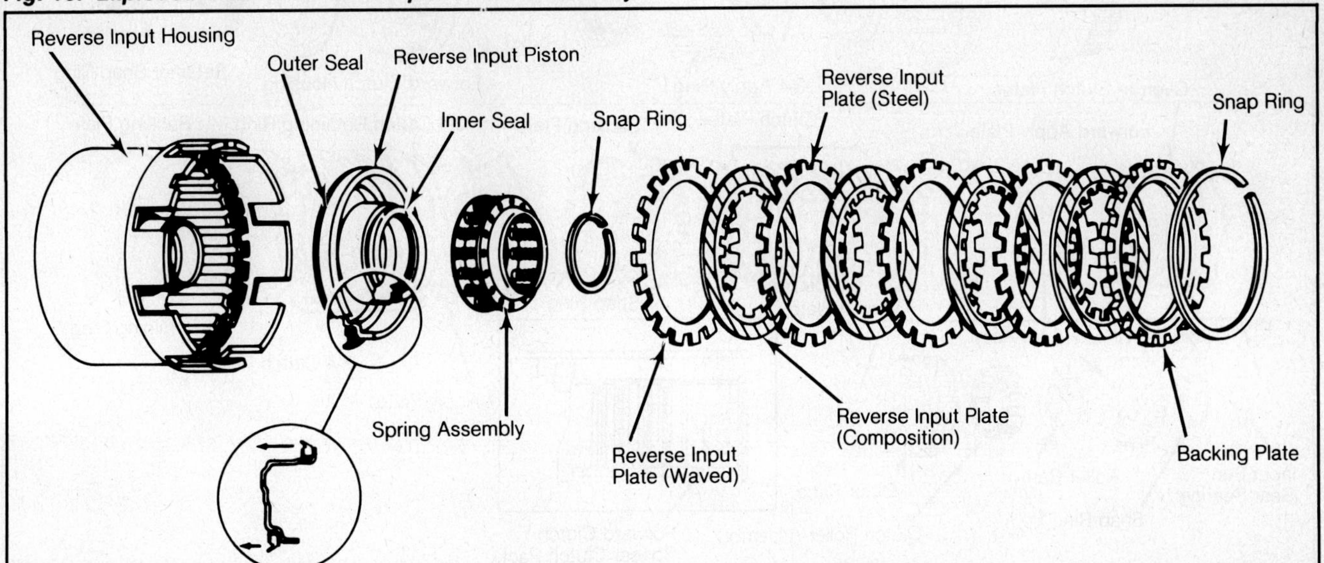

GENERAL MOTORS TURBO HYDRA-MATIC 700-R4 (Cont.)

piston into reverse input clutch housing with hub upwards, using an .031" (.8 mm) feeler gauge to position seals. Install spring assembly, large opening first, onto clutch piston.

2) Using Clutch Spring Compressor (J-23327) and Adapter (J-250I8-A) on spring retainer, compress spring retainer and install retaining snap ring. Remove compresor and adapter.

3) Install waved steel reverse plate. No indexing is necessary. Install a composition plate, followed by remaining plates, alternating composition faced and flat steel plates. Install reverse input backing plate with chamfered side up. Install backing plate snap ring.

NOTE: The reverse clutch plates are the largest plates with equally spaced tangs.

REVERSE INPUT CLUTCH PLATE USAGE CHART

Application	Flat Steel [1]	Composition [1]
MC, MJ, MP, MT, PL, PR, TA, TB, TS, YF, YX	2 [2]	3 [2]
All Others	3 [2]	4 [2]

1 - Plate thickness is .077" (1.97 mm).
2 - Plus one waved steel plate .079" (2.03 mm) thick installed first.

INPUT CLUTCH & FORWARD CLUTCH CAM ASSEMBLY

Disassembly

1) Position input clutch assembly on bench with turbine shaft located in hole on bench and resting on turbine shaft housing. Remove snap ring retaining 3-4 clutch backing plate and remove plate. Remove 3-4 clutch plates and 3-4 apply plate. Remove retaining apply ring. Remove forward clutch backing plate and backing plate snap ring.

2) Remove forward clutch cam assembly and outer race by pulling up. The complete assembly will consist of the forward clutch roller cam, overrun clutch hub, snap ring, forward clutch outer race and roller assembly. Remove input sun gear bearing (it can be located on back side of input inner race). Remove output shaft nylon seal.

3) Remove forward clutch plates (steel and composition). Remove apply plate and spacer, if used. Remove overrun clutch plates (2 steel and 2 composition). Using Clutch Spring Compressor (J-23456) and Adapter (J-25018-A) compress overrun clutch spring retainer. Remove overrun clutch snap ring, compressor and adapter. Remove overrun spring and piston assemblies.

4) Remove inner and outer seals from overrun clutch piston. Remove forward clutch piston assembly. Remove inner and outer seals from forward clutch piston assembly.

NOTE: Apply air pressure to 3-4 feed hole in turbine shaft. It is 3rd hole from shaft end. If unable to remove parts, strike housing on soft surface squarely on open end.

5) Remove forward clutch housing assembly. Remove 3-4 spring assembly. Remove 3-4 apply ring and piston. Remove "O" ring from input housing. Inspect Teflon oil seal rings on turbine shaft for damage or distortion. Remove and replace only if necessary.

6) Remove overrun clutch hub snap ring and overrun hub. Remove forward clutch cam (inner race). Remove roller assembly from forward clutch cam. Be careful not to dislodge any rollers from roller cage.

Inspection

1) Inspect locating ears on top of forward clutch roller assembly cage for damage or distortion. Inspect rollers for wear or damage. Do not remove rollers from case.

Fig. 20: Exploded View of Input Clutch and Forward Clutch Cam Assembly

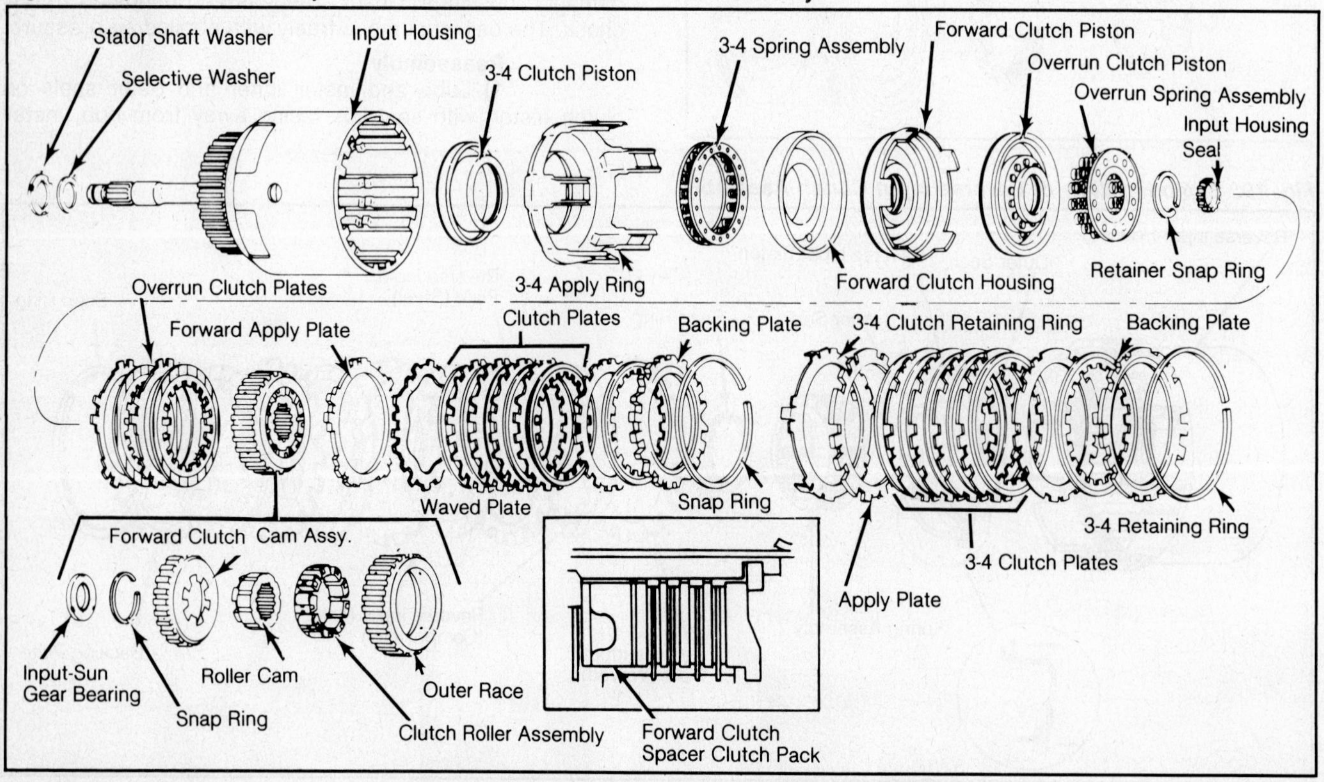

GENERAL MOTORS TURBO HYDRA-MATIC 700-R4 (Cont.)

2) Inspect overrun clutch hub for spline damage, excessive wear and open oil passages. Inspect forward clutch cam for wear to splines, tangs and roller cam surface. Check forward clutch outer race surface finish.

3) Inspect input clutch housing for spline damage, wear and open feed passages. Check rear end of turbine shaft for presence of 3 sealing balls (1 hole is an open feed hole and is not sealed). Inspect Teflon seals on turbine shaft for wear and correct installation. *See Fig. 21.*

Fig. 21: View of Turbine Shaft Showing Correct Installation of Teflon Oil Seals

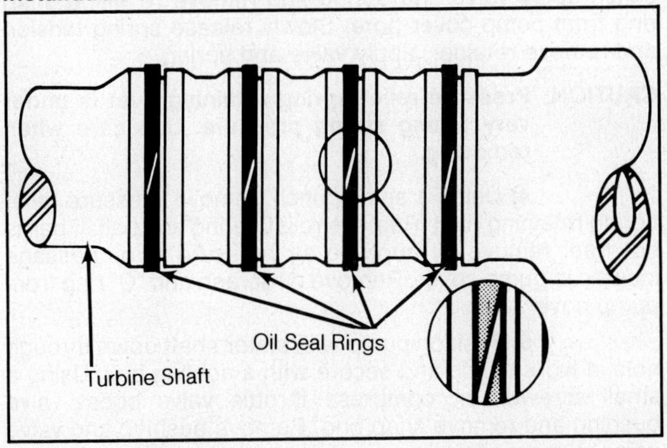

NOTE: **Do not remove turbine shaft Teflon oil seals unless damaged.**

4) Inspect converter check ball on front end of turbine shaft for restrictions and free operation. Ball must move with air pressure. If damaged, replace check ball as follows:

- Straighten tangs of retainer and check ball capsule and remove check ball.
- Using a No. 4 screw extractor, remove check valve retainer from shaft by turning and pulling straight out.
- Position new check valve assembly, check valve seat first, into turbine shaft.
- Using a 3/8" (9.5 mm) diameter rod, drive retainer and check valve assembly into shaft until it is 1/8" (3 mm) below top surface of shaft.

5) Check 3-4 check ball in input housing for free operation. Inspect all clutch pistons for wear, damage or porosity. Check piston seals for wear or damage.

6) Inspect all clutch release springs for damage, distortion and spring retainer for flatness and damage. Inspect steel clutch plates for damaged tang ends, high or burned spots, excessive wear, or distortion caused by heat. Inspect composition clutch plates for damaged tang ends, burning, flaking or excessive wear (thickness).

7) Inspect all snap rings for distortion and damage. Check backing plates for flatness, distortion and sharpness or burrs on inside edge. Inspect clutch apply rings for distortion and damaged apply tangs.

8) Inspect forward clutch housing ball check for proper operation. Inspect housing for distortion or damage. Inspect needle bearings for excessive wear, flatness, damage or flat rollers.

Reassembly

1) Position forward clutch cam with tangs facing upward. Install forward clutch roller assembly over cam, indexing roller cage to engage tangs in ramps of forward clutch cam. When properly seated, the square ears will be flush with inner race.

2) Position overrun clutch hub assembly or cam and roller assembly and install snap ring. Install assembled hub, cam and roller assembly into forward clutch outer race by rotating clockwise. When assembled, the forward clutch hub must rotate freely in a clockwise direction and lockup in a counterclockwise direction.

3) If removed, install Teflon oil seal rings on turbine shaft. *See Fig. 21.* Assemble with long edge and large "O" ring on inside of housing. If removed, install small "O" ring on end of turbine shaft.

4) Position input clutch housing over bench hole with turbine shaft downward. Install inner and outer seals on 3-4 piston, with lips facing away from hub. Install 3-4 piston in input housing, rotate and gently push downward making sure piston is properly seated. Install inner and outer seals on forward clutch piston with lips facing away from tangs.

5) Lube and install forward clutch piston into forward clutch housing. Install 3-4 spring retainer into 3-4 clutch apply ring. Install assembled forward clutch housing and piston on spring retainer in 3-4 apply ring. Notches of forward clutch piston must be indexed with long apply tangs of 3-4 apply ring. Install Seal Protector (J-29883) on input shaft.

6) Hold 3-4 apply ring and assembled parts by tangs and install into input clutch housing and firmly seat forward clutch piston. Do not let pistons separate. Install Seal Protector (J-29882) on input housing shaft and install overrun clutch piston with hub facing upward. Remove protector.

7) Overrun piston should be 3/16" below snap ring groove on input housing hub. If not seated properly, install Clutch Spring Compressor (J-23327) and tap until all parts are fully seated. Install overrun clutch spring retainer on overrun clutch piston locating release springs on piston tabs. Use Clutch Spring Compressor (J-23456) and Adapter (J-25018) on overrun spring assembly and compress spring retainer.

NOTE: **Do not over compress springs as distortion to the retainer can occur.**

8) With springs compressed, install retaining snap ring. Remove compressor. Install splined nylon output shaft seal, with seal lip facing up. On forward clutch piston in input housing, install 4 overrun clutch plates. Starting with steel plate and positioning so that long recessed slot is indexed with wide notch in housing. Install remaining clutch plates alternating steel and composition.

9) Install input sun gear bearing assembly on input clutch hub on top of nylon seal positioning outside "L" race in downward position. Make sure bearing is centered. Using a screwdriver, align and center inside drive tangs of 2 overrun clutch plates (composition).

10) Install assembled forward clutch cam assembly and outer race clutch hub, indexing overrun clutch plates. Install forward clutch spacer (thick steel) into input clutch housing, indexing lug on spacer with large slot in input housing.

NOTE: **A 5 plate forward clutch will use a single thick apply plate. A 4 plate clutch will use a thick spacer and a thin apply plate and must be assembled with thin apply plate first and spacer with holes facing thin apply plate.**

GENERAL MOTORS TURBO HYDRA-MATIC 700-R4 (Cont.)

11) Install waved steel forward clutch plate into input housing, indexing wide slot with 2 small ears with wide notch in housing. Install forward clutch plate assembly (composition) on forward clutch hub. Install remaining forward clutch plates alternating composition and steel. The last plate installed will be composition.

12) Install forward clutch backing plate into input housing, with chamfered side up. Install snap ring into input clutch housing (smaller ring with larger gap). Install 3-4 gear ring retaining plate (flat plate with legs) into clutch housing indexing each apply lug with ends of 3-4 gear apply ring.

13) Install 3-4 gear apply plate (thick steel) into input housing indexing long wide gear of plate with wide slot in housing. Install 3-4 assembly (composition), then install remaining plates alternating steel and composition indexing long wide ear of plate with wide slot in housing. The last plate installed will be composition.

14) Install 3-4 gear backing plate with chamfered side up. Install 3-4 retaining ring into input housing assembly. Using feeler gauges, measure end clearance between backing plate and first composition plate. If end clearance is not within specifications, select proper backing plate from chart. Air check all clutches by applying air pressure at feed holes in turbine shaft.

3-4 BACKING PLATE SELECTION CHART

Application	Backing Plate Travel In. (mm)	Backing Plate Diameter/I.D. In. (mm)
MC, MJ, MP, MT PL, PR, TA, TB TC, TS, YX	.055-.109 (1.39-2.78)	.278/1 (7.125)
		.239/2 (6.125)
All Others	.049-.113 (1.25-2.87)	.200/3 (5.125)
		.161/4 (4.125)

CLUTCH PLATE USAGE CHART

Application	Flat Steel	Composition
Overrun Clutch		
All Models	2 [1]	2 [2]
Forward Clutch		
MC, MJ, MP, MT, PL, PR, TA, TB, TC, TS, YF, YX	3 [3] [4]	[2] 4
All Others	4 [3] [4]	5 [2]
3-4 Clutch		
MC, MJ, MP, MT, PL, PR, TA, TB, TC, TS, YF, YX	4 [4]	5 [2]
All Others	5 [4]	6 [2]

[1] – Plate thickness is .091" (2.31 mm).
[2] – Plate thickness is .079" (2.03 mm).
[3] – Plus 1 waved steel plate .079" (2.03 mm).
[4] – Plate thickness is .077" (1.97 mm).

OIL PUMP ASSEMBLY

Disassembly

1) Remove reverse input clutch drum-to-pump thrust washer, pump-to-case gasket and pump-to-case oil seal ring from pump assembly. Do not remove Teflon oil seal rings from pump hub unless replacement is necessary. Remove attaching bolts and separate pump cover from pump body.

CAUTION: Pump slide spring is under very high pressure. Place a shop towel over spring when removing to prevent possible injury.

2) Using needle-nose pliers, compress pump slide spring and remove from pump by pulling straight out. Remove pump guide rings, pump vanes, pump rotor and rotor guide from pump body pocket. Remove slide from pump pocket. Remove slide seal and support seal from pocket or slide. Remove pivot slide pin and spring. Remove slide seal ring and backup seal from slide pocket.

3) Push in on retainer to compress converter clutch apply valve and spring and remove retaining snap ring from pump cover bore. Slowly release spring tension and remove retainer, apply valve and spring.

CAUTION: Pressure relief spring retaining rivet is under very strong spring pressure. Use care when removing.

4) Using a small punch, remove pressure relief spring retaining rivet. Remove relief spring and ball. If ball is not free, remove by applying air pressure to oil passage located in pump cover. Remove oil screen and "O" ring from pump cover.

5) Position pump with stator shaft down through hole in work bench and secure with a holding bolt. Using a small screwdriver, compress throttle valve boost valve bushing and remove snap ring. Remove bushing and valve using a magnet. Using same procedure, remove reverse boost valve and sleeve and pressure regulator valve and spring.

Inspection

1) Inspect all valves, springs, sleeves and bushings for chips, burrs, distortion and freeness in bores. Check pressure relief ball and spring for damage or distortion. Inspect pump cover screen and "O" ring for wear or damage.

2) Clean pump body and cover and check all bores for obstructions. Inspect mating sides of cover and body for scoring, flatness, porosity or voids between channels. Check channels for dirt, interconnected passages or damage.

3) Inspect rotor and slide for scoring, cracks or damage. Check rotor guide and pump vane rings for excessive wear or damage. Inspect all seals for damage. Inspect front seal for damage or excessive wear and seal retaining spring for proper location.

Reassembly

1) Install "O" ring and flat steel ring into groove on back side of pump slide and retain in place with petroleum jelly. Install small pivot pin and spring into small hole located in pump body pocket.

2) Install slide into pump body, indexing notch in slide with pivot pin hole and with flat oil seal ring facing down into pocket. Install slide seal and support into slide adjacent to rotor.

NOTE: Position pump slide seal (composition) against outer diameter of pump pocket.

3) Install a vane ring into pump pocket, centering on stator hole. Install composition rotor guide into deep pocket or rotor, indexing notches. Retain with petroleum jelly. Install rotor and guide into pump pocket with guide positioned downward.

4) Install vanes into rotor, positioning so they are flush with rotor and with full wear pattern against slide.

GENERAL MOTORS TURBO HYDRA-MATIC 700-R4 (Cont.)

Fig. 22: Exploded View of Model 700-R4 Oil Pump Assembly

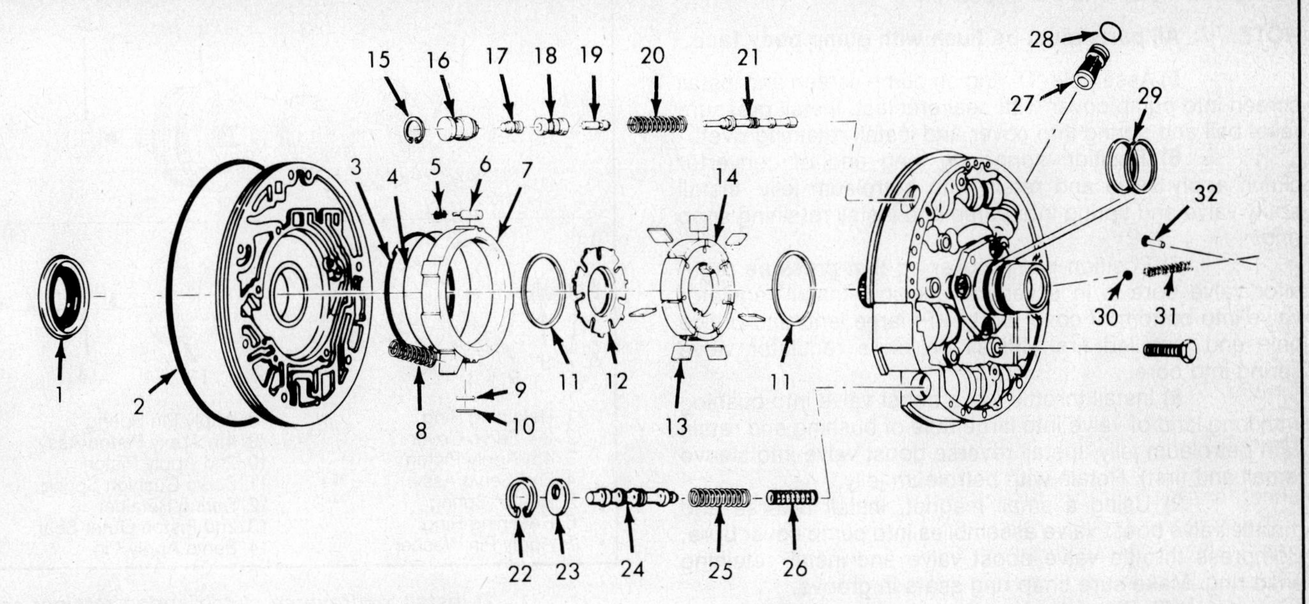

1. Front Seal
2. Pump-to-Case Seal
3. Slide Seal Ring
4. Slide Backup Seal
5. Pivot Pin Spring
6. Pivot Pin
7. Slide
8. Slide Spring
9. Support Seal
10. Slide Seal
11. Vane Ring
12. Rotor Guide
13. Vane
14. Rotor
15. Snap Ring
16. Bushing
17. T.V. Boost Valve
18. Sleeve
19. Reverse Boost Valve
20. Pressure Regulator Spring
21. Pressure Regulator Valve
22. Snap Ring
23. Converter Valve Stop
24. Conv. Clutch Apply Valve
25. Apply Valve Spring
26. Inner Apply Valve Spring
27. Pump Screen
28. Screen Seal
29. Stator Shaft Oil Seal
30. Pressure Relief Ball
31. Pressure Relief Spring
32. Ball Retainer

Fig. 23: Oil Pump Cover and Body Oil Passages

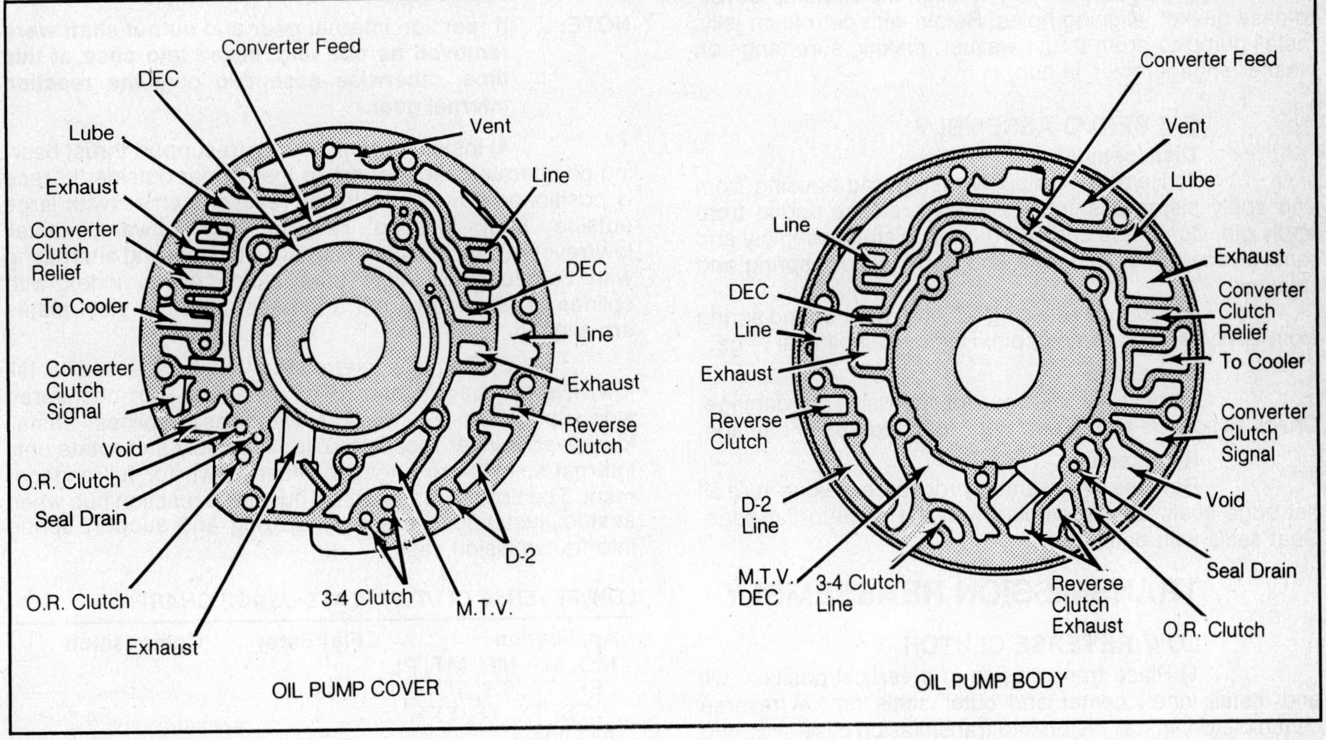

GENERAL MOTORS TURBO HYDRA-MATIC 700-R4 (Cont.)

Install vane guide ring into rotor. Compress pump slide spring and install into pump pocket.

NOTE: All parts must be flush with pump body face.

5) Assemble "O" ring on pump screen and install screen into pump cover with seal end last. Install pressure relief ball and spring into cover and install retaining rivet.

6) Position spring on long end of converter clutch apply valve and retain with petroleum jelly. Install apply valve and spring into pump and install retaining snap ring.

7) Position pump cover so that pressure regulator valve bore is in a vertical position. Install regulator valve into bottom of cover bore with large land and orifice hole end installed first. Install pressure regulator valve spring into bore.

8) Install throttle valve boost valve into bushing with long land of valve into large hole of bushing and retain with petroleum jelly. Install reverse boost valve into sleeve (small end first). Retain with petroleum jelly.

9) Using a small magnet, install reverse and throttle valve boost valve assemblies into pump cover bore. Compress throttle valve boost valve and install retaining snap ring. Make sure snap ring seats in groove.

10) Place body assembly over hole in work bench with stator shaft downward. Assemble pump cover to body and install attaching bolts finger tight. Align pump body and cover using Alignment Strap (J-21368), and place a holding bolt or screwdriver through pump-to-case bolt hole and hole in bench. Remove strap and tighten cover-to-body bolts.

11) Position new pump-to-case gasket on pump and retain with petroleum jelly. If removed, install Teflon oil seal rings on stator hub. Install new pump-to-case oil seal on cover; do not twist seal and make sure it is properly located. Apply petroleum jelly to seal. Install pump cover-to-case gasket, aligning holes. Retain with petroleum jelly. Install pump-to-drum thrust washer, making sure tangs on washer engage holes in hub.

2-4 SERVO ASSEMBLY

Disassembly

1) Remove 4th apply piston and housing from 2nd apply piston assembly. Remove release spring from apply pin. Compress 2nd servo apply piston assembly and remove snap ring. Separate 2nd apply piston, spring and retainer.

2) Remove retaining "E" ring, washer and spring from apply pin and remove pin. Remove all oil seal rings.

Inspection

Inspect all pistons for porosity or damage. Check all springs and oil seal rings for distortion or damage.

Reassembly

Reverse disassembly procedure making sure all flat edge seals are assembled with flat edge-to-flat edge. Coat seals with petrolatum.

Fig. 24: Exploded View of 2-4 Servo Assembly

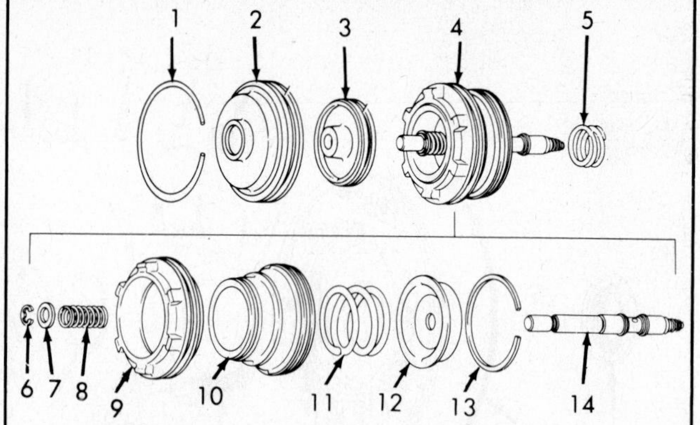

1. Retaining Ring
2. 2-4 Servo Cover
3. 4th Apply Piston
4. 2nd Servo Assy.
5. Return Spring
6. Retaining Ring
7. Apply Pin Washer
8. Apply Pin Spring
9. 4th Apply Piston Assy.
10. 2nd Apply Piston
11. Servo Cushion Spring
12. Spring Retainer
13. 2nd Piston Outer Seal
14. Servo Apply Pin

TRANSMISSION REASSEMBLY

LOW/REVERSE CLUTCH

1) Place transmission in a vertical position. Oil and install inner, center and outer seals on low/reverse clutch piston. Install piston into transmission case, indexing piston with notch at bottom of case and hub facing down. Make sure piston is fully seated and parking pawl will index into opening in piston wall.

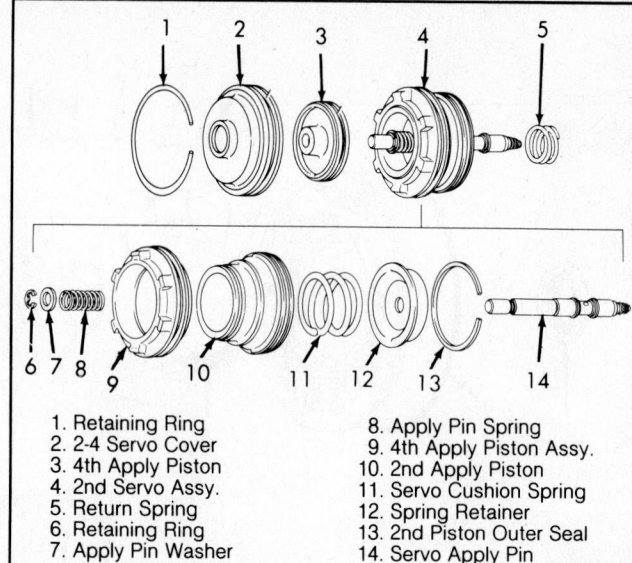

2) Install low/reverse clutch spring retainer assembly into case with flat side of retainer upward. Install Clutch Spring Compressor (J-23327) and compress springs, indexing retaining plate so that compressor is free to slide over case hub. Install low/reverse clutch snap ring. Remvoe compressor.

3) Install reaction internal gear support bearing on case hub so that longer inside "L" race is positioned downward. Install reaction internal gear and output shaft on bearing assembly in case. When gear is properly seated it will be centered with long slot in case and parking pawl can be engaged with external teeth of internal gear.

NOTE: If reaction internal gear and output shaft were removed as one unit, install into case at this time, otherwise assemble only the reaction internal gear.

4) Install reaction carrier-to-support thrust bearing on internal gear support so that longer outside "L" race is positioned downward. Install reaction carrier (with large outside hub) locating reverse hub upward. Install low/reverse clutch plates, starting with steel and alternating with composition. Make sure clutch plates index with splines of reaction carrier and case, and that steel plates are aligned.

5) Remove low/reverse inner race and install low/reverse support and roller assembly with chamfered side up in case, indexing with case splines. Install low/reverse inner race into roller assembly and rotate until internal splines are engaged. Push down for full engagement. The bottom tangs will be flush with reaction hub when seated. Install low/reverse snap ring and support spring into transmission case.

LOW/REVERSE CLUTCH PLATE USAGE CHART

Application	Flat Steel	Composition
MC, MJ, MP, MT, PL PR, TA, TB, TC TS, TX, YF, YX	4 [1]	4 [2]
All Others	5 [1]	5 [2]

[1] – Plate thickness is .069" (1.77 mm).
[2] – Plate thickness is .088" (2.25 mm).

GENERAL MOTORS TURBO HYDRA-MATIC 700-R4 (Cont.)

REACTION & INPUT GEAR SETS

1) If removed, install snap ring on reaction sun gear. Install sun gear into reaction carrier, indexing pinions. Install nylon thrust washer with 4 locating ears on low/reverse clutch inner race. Install reaction sun gear shell (large housing with end slots and holes), engaging splines of shell shaft and sun gear.

2) Install reaction shaft-to-shell thrust washer (bronze washer with wide thrust face), indexing tangs in shell. Install input internal gear and shaft (shaft end first). If output shaft and reaction gear were removed as separate parts during disassembly, go to step **3)**.

3) Position output shaft into transmission, indexing with all parts. Install Output Shaft Support (J-29837) and adjust so that output shaft is positioned upward as far as possible. *See Fig. 11.*

4) Install input carrier-to-reaction shaft thrust bearing with long "L" race on outside. Install input carrier assembly, with hub end down. Install new snap ring on output shaft. Install input sun gear, indexing gear end with input carrier pinions. Install input carrier thrust washer on input carrier.

REVERSE INPUT ASSEMBLY & INPUT CLUTCH

1) Install selective washer on turbine housing. Install oil pump hub bearing on selective washer with black finish side up.

2) Position reverse input assembly on bench hole with clutch plates facing upward. Align and center clutch plates with screwdriver and install input clutch assembly with turbine shaft downward. Index reverse clutch plates with hub of input housing. Make certain all clutch plates are fully engaged.

REVERSE & INPUT CLUTCHES

Install reverse and input clutch assemblies into case as an assembly, indexing 3-4 clutch plates of input assembly with input internal gear. Complete assembly is properly seated when reverse housing is just below pump face of case. Make sure all clutch plates are fully engaged.

2-4 BAND & SERVO ASSEMBLY

1) Position 2-4 band in case, indexing anchor pin end with case pin hole. Install band achor pin in case and index with 2-4 band end.

2) Install 2-4 servo assembly into case and index apply pin on band end. Check for proper engagement of apply pin on band end. Recheck 2-4 servo apply pin selection to ensure correct pin is installed.

3) Install servo cover and "O" ring. Install Servo Cover Compressor (J-29714) and compress cover. Install cover retaining ring, indexing ring ends with slot in case.

OIL PUMP ASSEMBLY

1) Install aligning pins into 2 opposing pump attaching bolt holes in case. Install pump into case, aligning filter and pressure regulator holes with holes in case. Install and tighten pump attaching bolts.

2) Rotate transmission to a horizontal position and rotate turbine or output shaft by hand. If shaft will not rotate, loosen pump attaching bolts and attempt to rotate

Fig. 25: View of Transmission Case Showing Oil Passages and Check Ball Locations

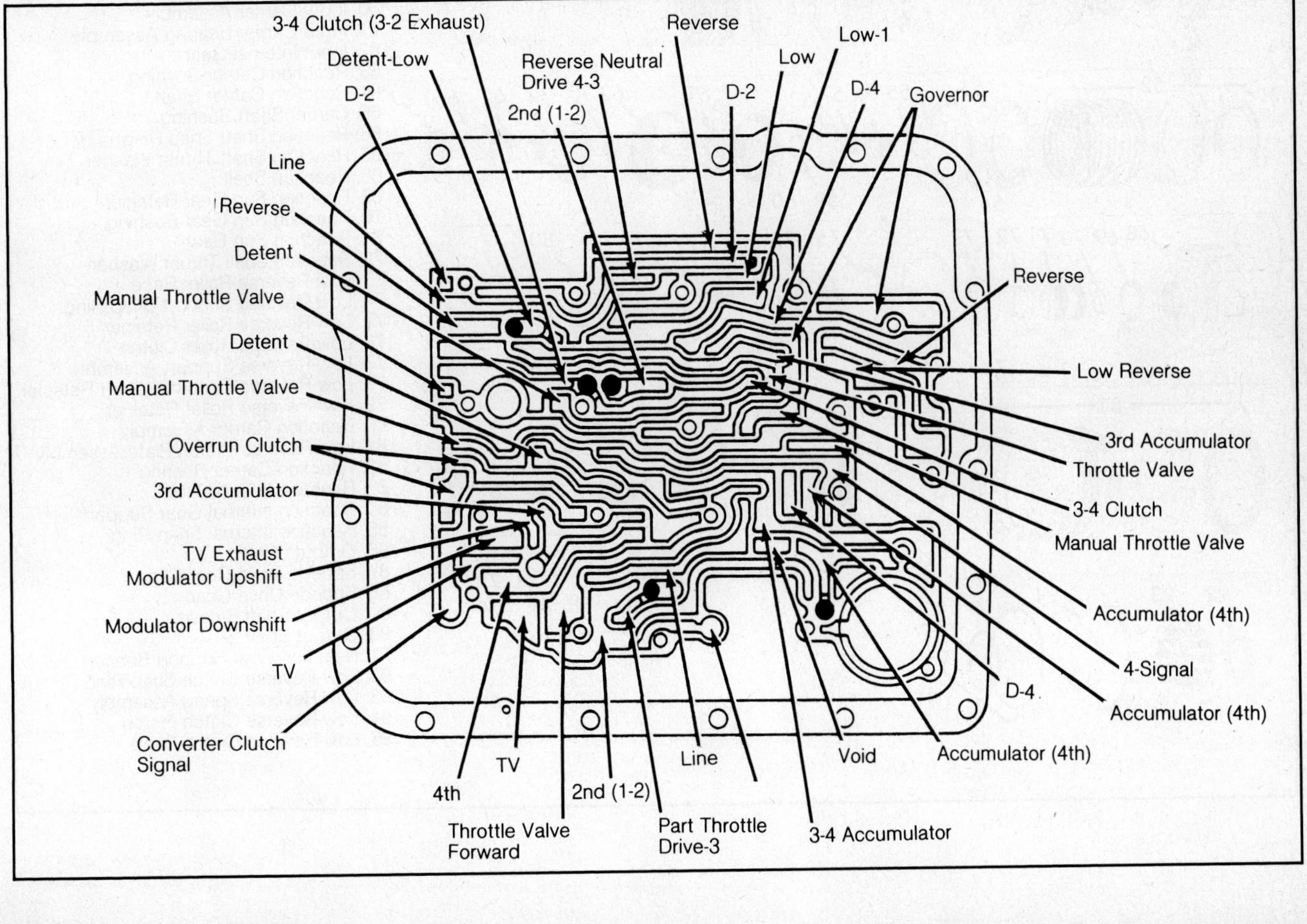

Automatic Transmissions

GENERAL MOTORS TURBO HYDRA-MATIC 700-R4 (Cont.)

Fig. 26: Exploded View of Transmission Internal Components

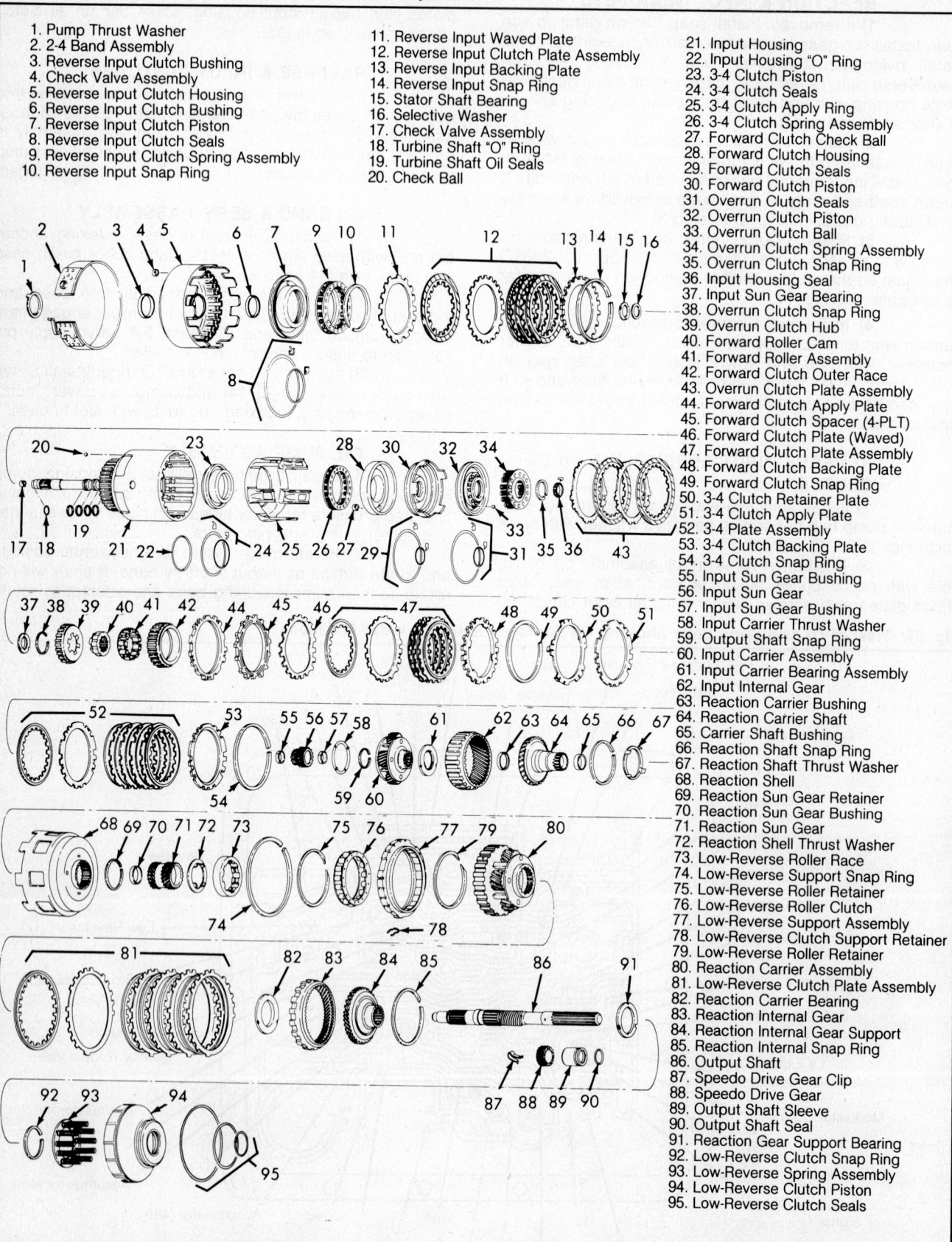

1. Pump Thrust Washer
2. 2-4 Band Assembly
3. Reverse Input Clutch Bushing
4. Check Valve Assembly
5. Reverse Input Clutch Housing
6. Reverse Input Clutch Bushing
7. Reverse Input Clutch Piston
8. Reverse Input Clutch Seals
9. Reverse Input Clutch Spring Assembly
10. Reverse Input Snap Ring
11. Reverse Input Waved Plate
12. Reverse Input Clutch Plate Assembly
13. Reverse Input Backing Plate
14. Reverse Input Snap Ring
15. Stator Shaft Bearing
16. Selective Washer
17. Check Valve Assembly
18. Turbine Shaft "O" Ring
19. Turbine Shaft Oil Seals
20. Check Ball

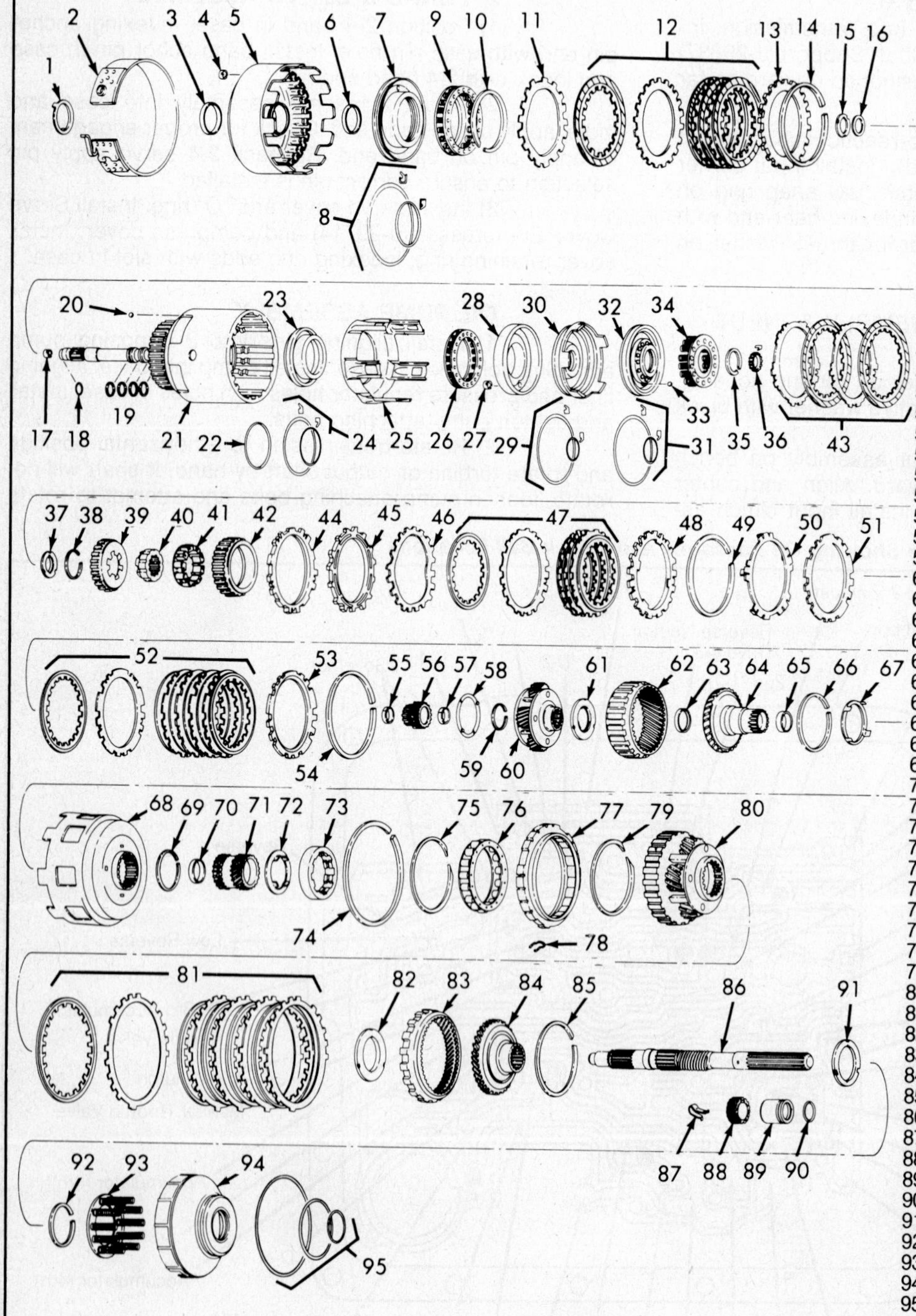

21. Input Housing
22. Input Housing "O" Ring
23. 3-4 Clutch Piston
24. 3-4 Clutch Seals
25. 3-4 Clutch Apply Ring
26. 3-4 Clutch Spring Assembly
27. Forward Clutch Check Ball
28. Forward Clutch Housing
29. Forward Clutch Seals
30. Forward Clutch Piston
31. Overrun Clutch Seals
32. Overrun Clutch Piston
33. Overrun Clutch Ball
34. Overrun Clutch Spring Assembly
35. Overrun Clutch Snap Ring
36. Input Housing Seal
37. Input Sun Gear Bearing
38. Overrun Clutch Snap Ring
39. Overrun Clutch Hub
40. Forward Roller Cam
41. Forward Roller Assembly
42. Forward Clutch Outer Race
43. Overrun Clutch Plate Assembly
44. Forward Clutch Apply Plate
45. Forward Clutch Spacer (4-PLT)
46. Forward Clutch Plate (Waved)
47. Forward Clutch Plate Assembly
48. Forward Clutch Backing Plate
49. Forward Clutch Snap Ring
50. 3-4 Clutch Retainer Plate
51. 3-4 Clutch Apply Plate
52. 3-4 Plate Assembly
53. 3-4 Clutch Backing Plate
54. 3-4 Clutch Snap Ring
55. Input Sun Gear Bushing
56. Input Sun Gear
57. Input Sun Gear Bushing
58. Input Carrier Thrust Washer
59. Output Shaft Snap Ring
60. Input Carrier Assembly
61. Input Carrier Bearing Assembly
62. Input Internal Gear
63. Reaction Carrier Bushing
64. Reaction Carrier Shaft
65. Carrier Shaft Bushing
66. Reaction Shaft Snap Ring
67. Reaction Shaft Thrust Washer
68. Reaction Shell
69. Reaction Sun Gear Retainer
70. Reaction Sun Gear Bushing
71. Reaction Sun Gear
72. Reaction Shell Thrust Washer
73. Low-Reverse Roller Race
74. Low-Reverse Support Snap Ring
75. Low-Reverse Roller Retainer
76. Low-Reverse Roller Clutch
77. Low-Reverse Support Assembly
78. Low-Reverse Clutch Support Retainer
79. Low-Reverse Roller Retainer
80. Reaction Carrier Assembly
81. Low-Reverse Clutch Plate Assembly
82. Reaction Carrier Bearing
83. Reaction Internal Gear
84. Reaction Internal Gear Support
85. Reaction Internal Snap Ring
86. Output Shaft
87. Speedo Drive Gear Clip
88. Speedo Drive Gear
89. Output Shaft Sleeve
90. Output Shaft Seal
91. Reaction Gear Support Bearing
92. Low-Reverse Clutch Snap Ring
93. Low-Reverse Spring Assembly
94. Low-Reverse Clutch Piston
95. Low-Reverse Clutch Seals

GENERAL MOTORS TURBO HYDRA-MATIC 700-R4 (Cont.)

Fig. 27: Cutaway View of Transmission Showing Thrust Washer, Bearing and Oil Seal Locations

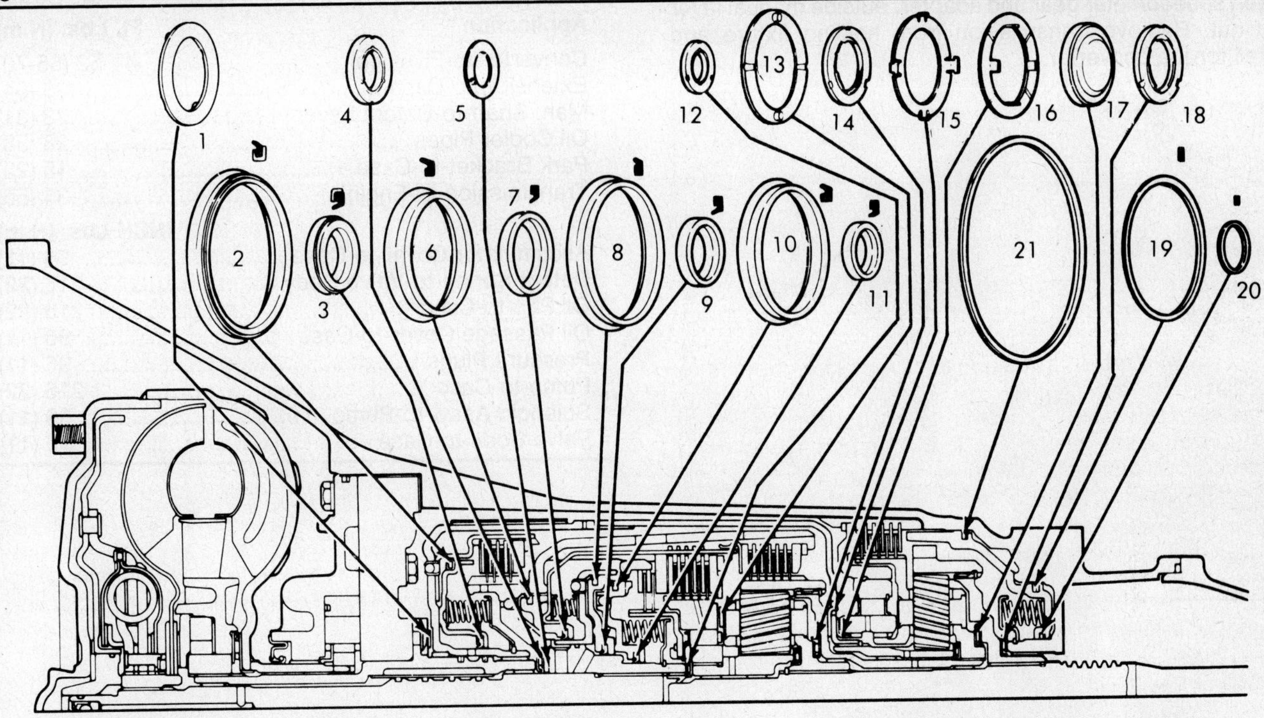

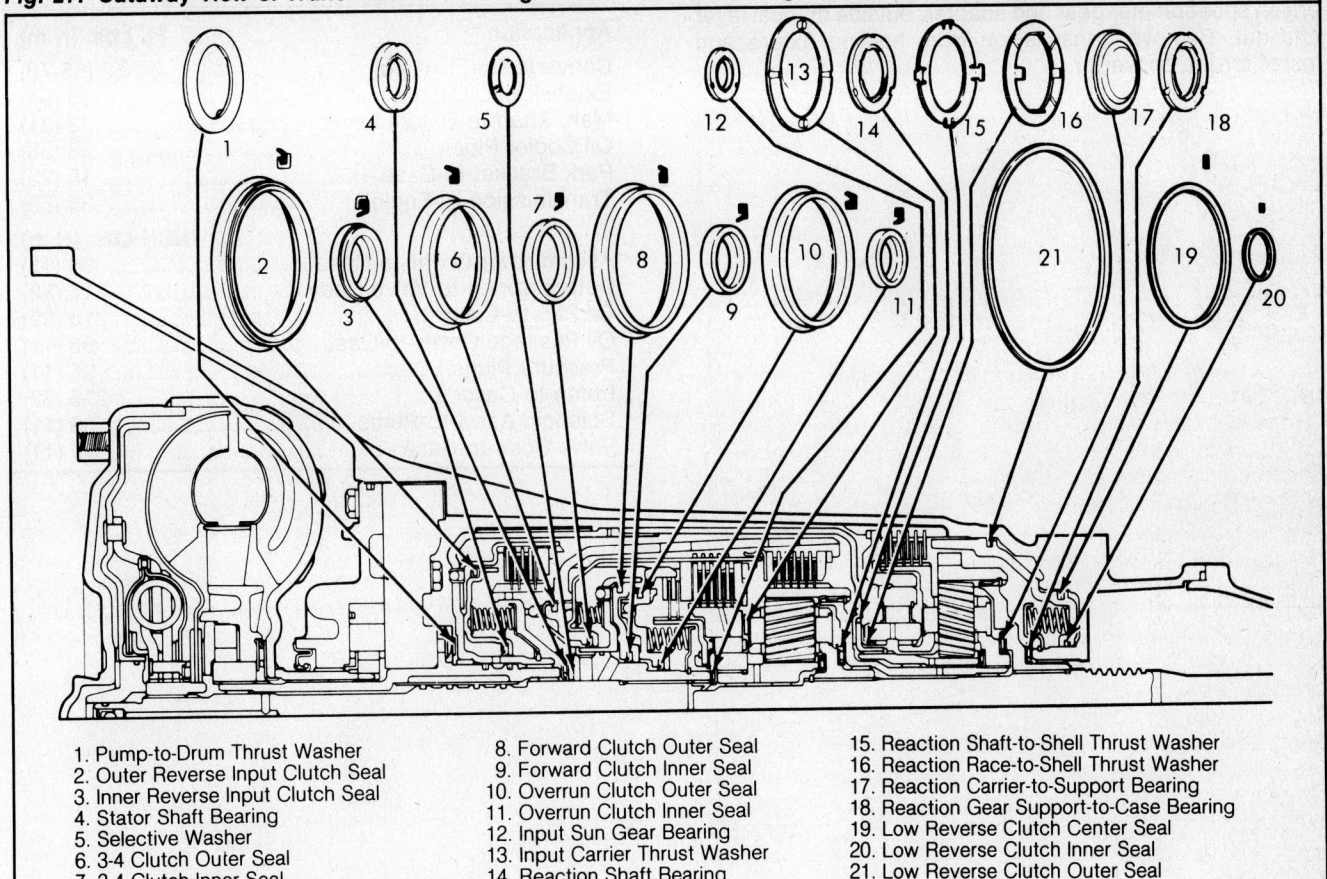

1. Pump-to-Drum Thrust Washer
2. Outer Reverse Input Clutch Seal
3. Inner Reverse Input Clutch Seal
4. Stator Shaft Bearing
5. Selective Washer
6. 3-4 Clutch Outer Seal
7. 3-4 Clutch Inner Seal
8. Forward Clutch Outer Seal
9. Forward Clutch Inner Seal
10. Overrun Clutch Outer Seal
11. Overrun Clutch Inner Seal
12. Input Sun Gear Bearing
13. Input Carrier Thrust Washer
14. Reaction Shaft Bearing
15. Reaction Shaft-to-Shell Thrust Washer
16. Reaction Race-to-Shell Thrust Washer
17. Reaction Carrier-to-Support Bearing
18. Reaction Gear Support-to-Case Bearing
19. Low Reverse Clutch Center Seal
20. Low Reverse Clutch Inner Seal
21. Low Reverse Clutch Outer Seal

shaft again. If shaft now turns, reverse and input assemblies have not been indexed properly or some other assembly problem has occurred, such as a mispositioned thrust washer. Rotate transmission to a vertical position.

VALVE BODY & WIRING HARNESS

1) Install 1-2 accumulator pin into case. Install accumulator piston and seal over pin with lug end up. Install spring on accumulator piston.

2) Install governor and converter clutch oil screens into case. Install 5 check balls into case pockets. *See Fig. 25.* Install valve body alignment pins, then install spacer plate-to-case gasket (identified with a small "c") on case. Install valve body spacer on case, aligning holes.

3) Install valve body-to-spacer gasket (identified with a "V") on spacer plate. Install 3 exhaust check balls and check valve into valve body pockets. *See Fig. 6.* Retain with petroleum jelly. Install valve body and connect link to inside detent lever. Remove aligning pins and install and tighten valve body-to-case bolts.

4) Attach retaining clip to manual valve link and inside detent lever. Install throttle lever, bracket and throttle valve link, locating slot in bracket with roll pin on valve body top face. Align link through throttle valve linkage case bore. Attach assembly with 2 valve body attaching bolts.

5) Install valve body attaching bolt and harness clip. Install parking pawl bracket. Install manual detent spring and roller assembly. Install "O" ring on solenoid. Install assembly into pump, locating attaching wire harness toward transmission. Install wiring harness and connect to all pressure switches.

NOTE: Each pressure switch is color coded. Match color of switch with same color of wire.

6) Install "O" ring on outside electrical connector and install into case by compressing inside tang. Locate tab with case notch. Attach inside connector terminal to outside connector. Install oil passage cover on transmission with 3 bolts and tighten.

7) Install 3-4 accumulator piston into housing with lug end up. Install 3-4 piston spring into housing on piston. Position 3-4 accumulator plate and gasket on transmission placing gasket on top. Install housing, spring and piston on transmission case and secure with 3 bolts and tighten.

8) Install speedometer gear and retaining clip on output shaft, positioning large notch on speedometer gear rearward. Install output shaft seal in output shaft sleeve and install on output shaft with Seal Installer (J-25016).

9) Install oil seal ring on case extension and install on case. Position so speedometer hole is located on same side as governor. Install governor assembly. Apply sealant to edge of cover, then install cover. Install "O" ring on filter and install.

10) Position new oil pan gasket on transmission case. Install oil pan and pan attaching bolts. Tighten attaching bolts.

GENERAL MOTORS TURBO HYDRA-MATIC 700-R4 (Cont.)

11) Install remaining outside connectors such as driven speedometer gear and adapter, outside manual lever and nut. Remove transmission from holding fixture and install torque converter.

TIGHTENING SPECIFICATIONS

Application	Ft. Lbs. (N.m)
Converter-to-Flywheel	41-52 (55-70)
Extension-to-Case	26 (34)
Man. Shaft-to-Detent Lever	23 (31)
Oil Cooler Pipes	28 (38)
Park Bracket-to-Case	18 (22)
Transmission-to-Engine	35 (50)
	INCH Lbs. (N.m)
Accumulator Cover-to-Case	96 (11)
Detent Spring-to-Valve Body	216 (22)
Oil Pan-to-Case	216 (22)
Oil Passage Cover-to-Case	96 (11)
Pressure Plugs	96 (11)
Pump-to-Case	216 (22)
Solenoid Assy.-to-Pump	96 (11)
Valve Body-to-Case	96 (11)

SECTION 3

DOMESTIC MANUAL TRANSMISSIONS

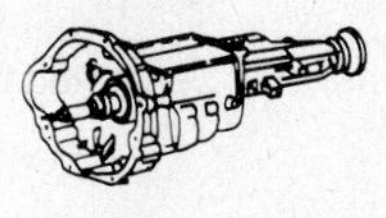

NOTE: ALSO SEE GENERAL INDEX.

AMC/RENAULT 4 & 5-SPEED JB SERIES TRANSAXLE

Alliance, Encore

IDENTIFICATION

The JB series manual transaxles can be identified by a plate affixed to the top of the transaxle by one of the clutch housing bolts. Top line of plate identifies transaxle model and date codes. Bottom line on plate is the transaxle fabrication number.

Fig. 1: JB Series Transaxle Identification Plate

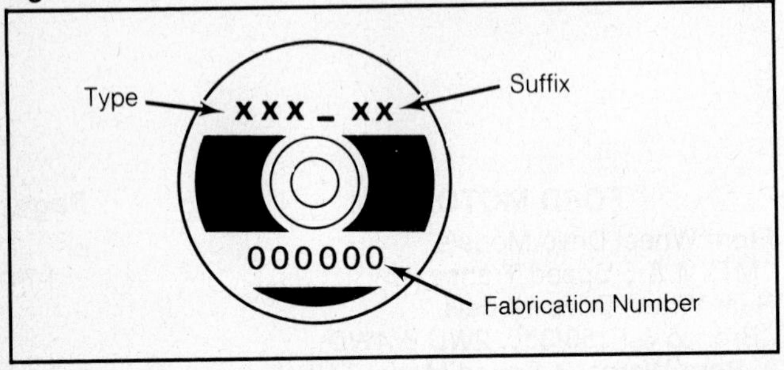

DESCRIPTION

The manual transaxle combines a 4-speed (JB 0) or 5-speed (JB 1, JB 3) manual transmission and differential into a single component designed for front drive applications. The transmission and differential are housed in a 2-piece, light weight aluminum alloy housing which is bolted to the back of the engine.

The synchro-mesh mechanism is designed by Borg-Warner. The transaxle is fully synchronized in all forward gears with reverse provided by a separate shaft and gear. All gears, except reverse, are helically cut for quiet operation. Both the input shaft and mainshaft are supported in the case by roller bearings.

The differential assembly is supported by 2 opposed roller bearings. Side plates are used to hold ends of axle shafts in place. The left side uses a constant velocity joint on the end of the axle. The right side has splines to engage with the transaxle.

LUBRICATION & ADJUSTMENT

See appropriate MANUAL TRANSMISSION SERVICING article in DOMESTIC GENERAL SERVICING section.

TROUBLE SHOOTING

See MANUAL TRANSMISSION TROUBLE SHOOTING article in DOMESTIC GENERAL SERVICING section.

REMOVAL & INSTALLATION

See appropriate MANUAL TRANSMISSION REMOVAL article in DOMESTIC GENERAL SERVICING section.

SERVICE (IN VEHICLE)

DRIVE AXLE SHAFTS

See appropriate DRIVE AXLE SHAFT article in DOMESTIC AXLE SHAFTS & TRANSFER CASES section.

GEARSHIFT LEVER & LINKAGE

Removal

Shift transaxle to 2nd gear, and prevent input lever from moving. Disconnect spring and rod beneath vehicle. Remove boot, console and gearshift lever housing. Place gearshift lever in a vise and remove components. *See Fig. 2.*

Fig. 2: Exploded View of Gearshift Lever and Linkage

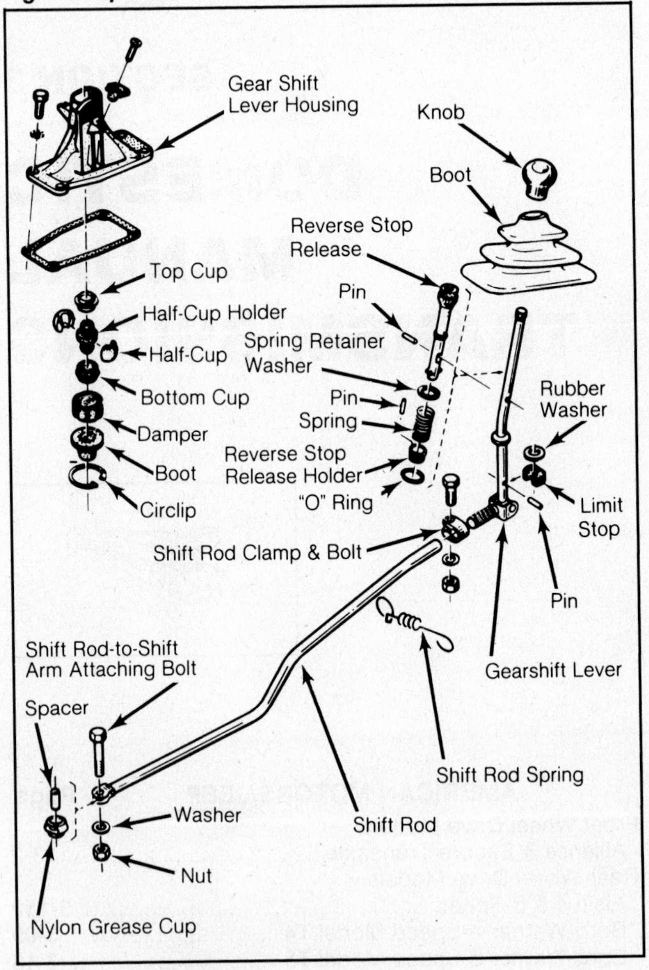

Installation

Install components and gearshift lever housing. Connect rod to gearshift lever and tighten clip. Connect spring, adjust shift rod and install console and boot.

FIFTH GEAR ASSEMBLY

CAUTION: Place the gear shift lever in 3rd or 4th position to prevent the interlocking ball from falling into the transaxle case.

Removal

1) Remove nuts from front and rear mounting pads at chassis end. Place a drain pan under the rear cover and remove cover and "O" ring.

AMC/RENAULT 4 & 5-SPEED JB SERIES TRANSAXLE (Cont.)

2) Slightly raise transmission. Insert a block of wood between 5th gear fork and gear. Tap out roll pin with Punch Set (B.Vi.31-01), or a 3/16" pin punch.

3) Shift transaxle into 1st gear with shift lever and slide 5th speed fork and hub collar rearward. Remove input shaft 5th speed nut and shift transaxle into Neutral. *See Figs. 3 and 4*.

Fig. 3: Exploded View of Shift Fork Assemblies

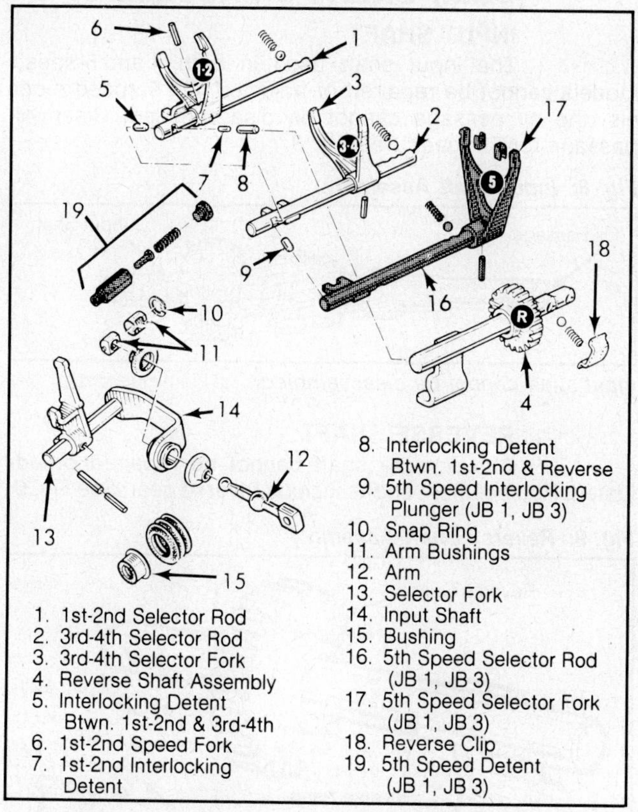

Fig. 4: Exploded View of 5th Gear Assembly

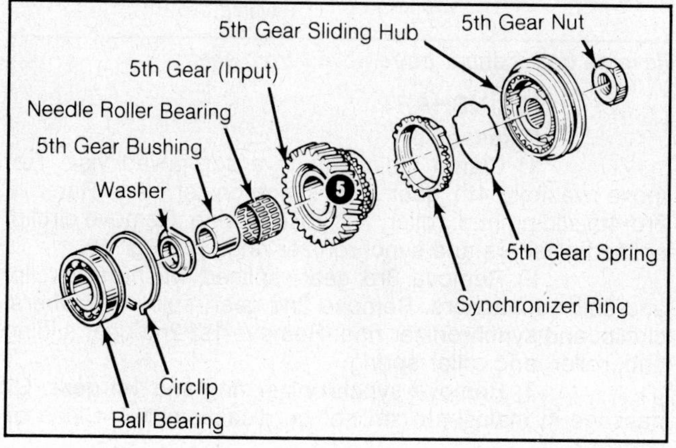

4) Inspect input shaft 5th (idling) gear. If gear is camfered, remove gear according to step **5)**. If gear is not camfered, remove gear according to step **6)**. *See Fig. 5*.

5) Using Puller Jaws (B.Vi.1007) under 5th gear, install Puller (B.Vi.28-01) on jaws and remove gear by sliding hub and fork as an assembly. Remove washer, bushing, bearing and synchronizer ring at the same time.

6) Using Puller Jaws (B.Vi.1003) in recesses of 5th gear sliding hub, remove shift fork and hub as an assembly. Remove washer, bushing, bearing and synchronizer ring at the same time.

7) Remove mainshaft bolt, washers, spacer and circlip. Inspect mainshaft 5th (fixed) gear. If gear is camfered, remove gear according to step **8)**. If gear is not camfered, remove gear according to step **9)**.

8) Remove fixed gear the same method as step **5)**, using puller jaws and Puller (B.Vi.28-01).

9) Remove fixed gear using Puller Body (B.Vi.22-01), and Puller (B.Vi.1000). Install 1/2 shell from puller and mount puller body. Install remaining half of shell and puller collar.

Fig. 5: Removing 5th Idling and Fixed Gears

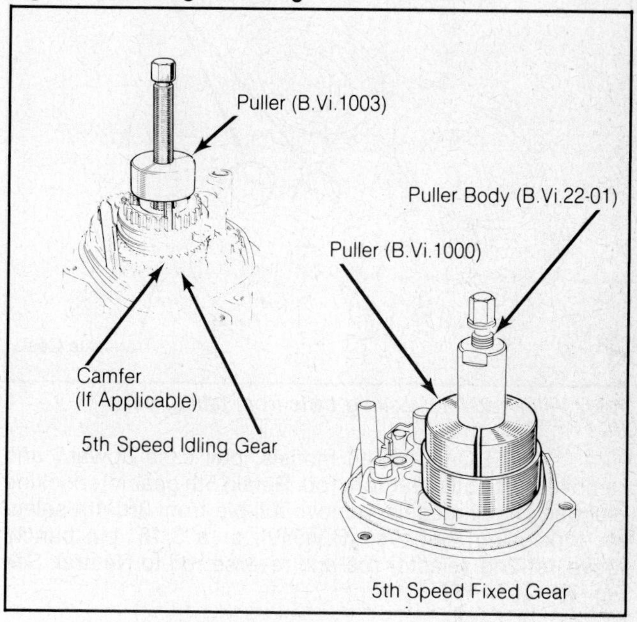

Installation

1) Apply 3 evenly spaced drops of Loctite 271 in gear bore and install gear on mainshaft. Install spacer and bolt. Tighten 10 mm bolt to 59 Ft. Lbs. (80 N.m), or 8 mm bolt to 15 Ft. Lbs. (20 N.m), depending on application.

2) Remove bolt and spacer. Install washer and circlip using Installer (B.Vi.948). Install spacer, bolt and washer. Tighten bolt as described in step **1)**. Install washer, bushing, bearing, 5th idling gear and synchronizer onto input shaft.

3) Apply 3 evenly spaced drops of Loctite 271 in 5th gear sliding hub bore. Assemble hub and shift fork and install them on input shaft. Be sure synchronizer is seated in hub.

4) Lock transaxle into two gears by shifting into 1st gear with shift lever and sliding 5th gear fork and hub collar rearward. Do not move the hub; move fork and collar only. Install new 5th gear input shaft nut and tighten to 100 Ft. Lbs. (136 N.m).

OIL SEAL

Cover side gear splines using Installer (B.Vi945). Install lip-type oil seal.

TRANSAXLE DISASSEMBLY

1) Remove rear cover. On 4-speed models, remove input shaft and mainshaft circlips and washers. On 5-speed models, engage 1st gear with gear selector lever and 5th gear with shift lock.

AMC/RENAULT 4 & 5-SPEED JB SERIES TRANSAXLE (Cont.)

2) Remove 5th gear retaining nut. To remove 5th gear components see FIFTH GEAR ASSEMBLY section in this article.

3) To remove clutch housing, remove case bolts holding clutch housing and remove reverse clip. On 4-speed models, remove threaded limit stop. On 5-speed models, remove 5th gear detent.

4) On all models, remove fork control rod. Insert 2 dummy rods at rear of case to prevent interlocking balls for 4 forward gears from falling out. *See Fig. 6.*

Fig. 6: Placement of 2 Dummy Rods in Transaxle

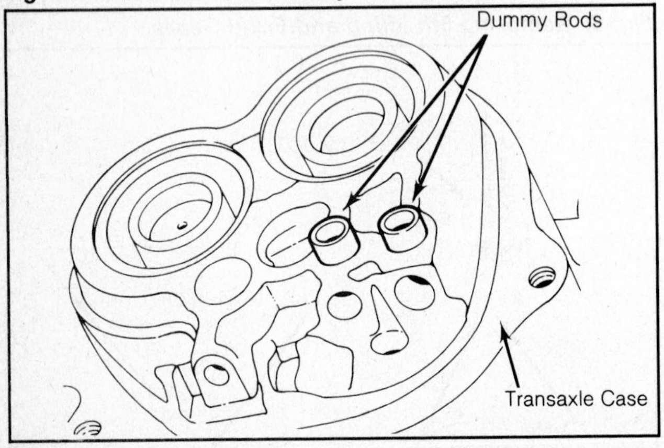

Rods will keep interlocking balls from falling out.

5) On 5-speed models, pull case upward and remove it with 5th gear fork rod. Retain 5th gear interlocking plunger. On all models, remove roll pin from 3rd-4th selector fork using Remover (B.Vi949), or a 3/16" pin punch. Move 1st-2nd selector rod and reverse rod to Neutral. *See Fig. 7.*

Fig. 7: Removing Input Shaft, Mainshaft and Reverse Shafts as an Assembly

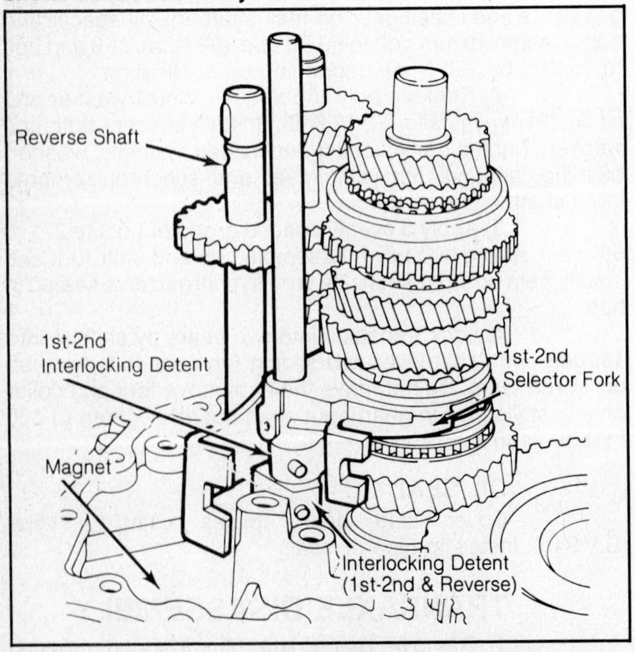

6) To remove mainshaft, remove 3rd-4th selector rod, fork, and retaining detent. Remove roll pin from 1st-2nd gear rod using remover or a 3/16" pin punch. Reverse shaft must be in Neutral. Remove 1st-2nd selector rod. Remove fork and retaining detent from rod. Push interlocking detent toward 3rd-4th selector rod.

7) Remove input shaft, mainshaft and reverse shafts together. Hold mainshaft vertical with 1st gear at bottom. Remove magnet, clean it and reinstall in case.

COMPONENT DISASSEMBLY

INPUT SHAFT

The input shaft used in both 4 and 5-speed models cannot be repaired or adjusted. On 5-speed models, the oil passage cannot be disassembled. Clean oil passage for 5th gear. *See Fig. 8.*

Fig. 8: Input Shaft Assembly

Input shaft cannot be disassembled.

REVERSE SHAFT

The reverse shaft cannot be repaired or adjusted. Replacement shafts include reverse gear. *See Fig. 9.*

Fig. 9: Reverse Shaft Assembly

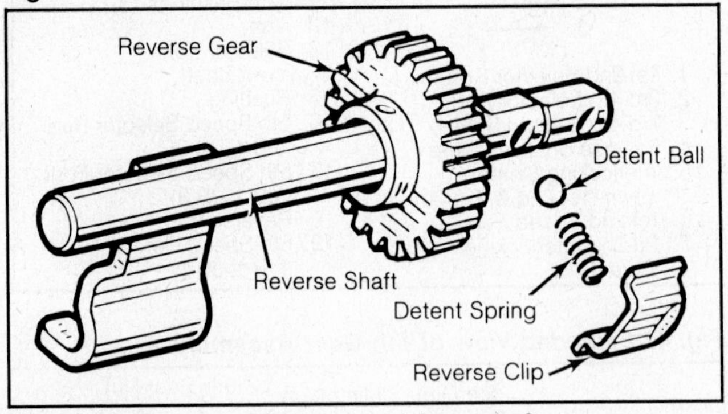

Reverse gear cannot be removed from shaft.

MAINSHAFT

Disassembly

1) Clamp mainshaft in a soft-jawed vise. Remove washer, 4th gear and synchronizer ring. Remove 3rd-4th sliding hub, roller, and roller spring. Remove circlip, splined washers and synchronizer ring. *See Fig. 10.*

2) Remove 3rd gear, splined washers, circlip, and splined washers. Remove 2nd gear, splined washers, circlip, and synchronizer ring. Remove 1st-2nd gear sliding hub, roller, and roller spring.

3) Remove synchronizer ring and 1st gear. Oil passage in mainshaft can not be disassembled. Clean oil passage.

DIFFERENTIAL

Disassembly

1) Remove "O" ring and tilt oil seal using a pin punch and a small hammer. Remove oil seal using pliers. Do not damage side gear splines.

2) On Type I and Type II, light duty differentials, use arbor press to move clutch housing and differential and free snap ring. Place a wood block under differential housing before applying press force. Remove snap ring.

AMC/RENAULT 4 & 5-SPEED JB SERIES TRANSAXLE (Cont.)

Fig. 10: Exploded View of Shaft and Gear Clusters

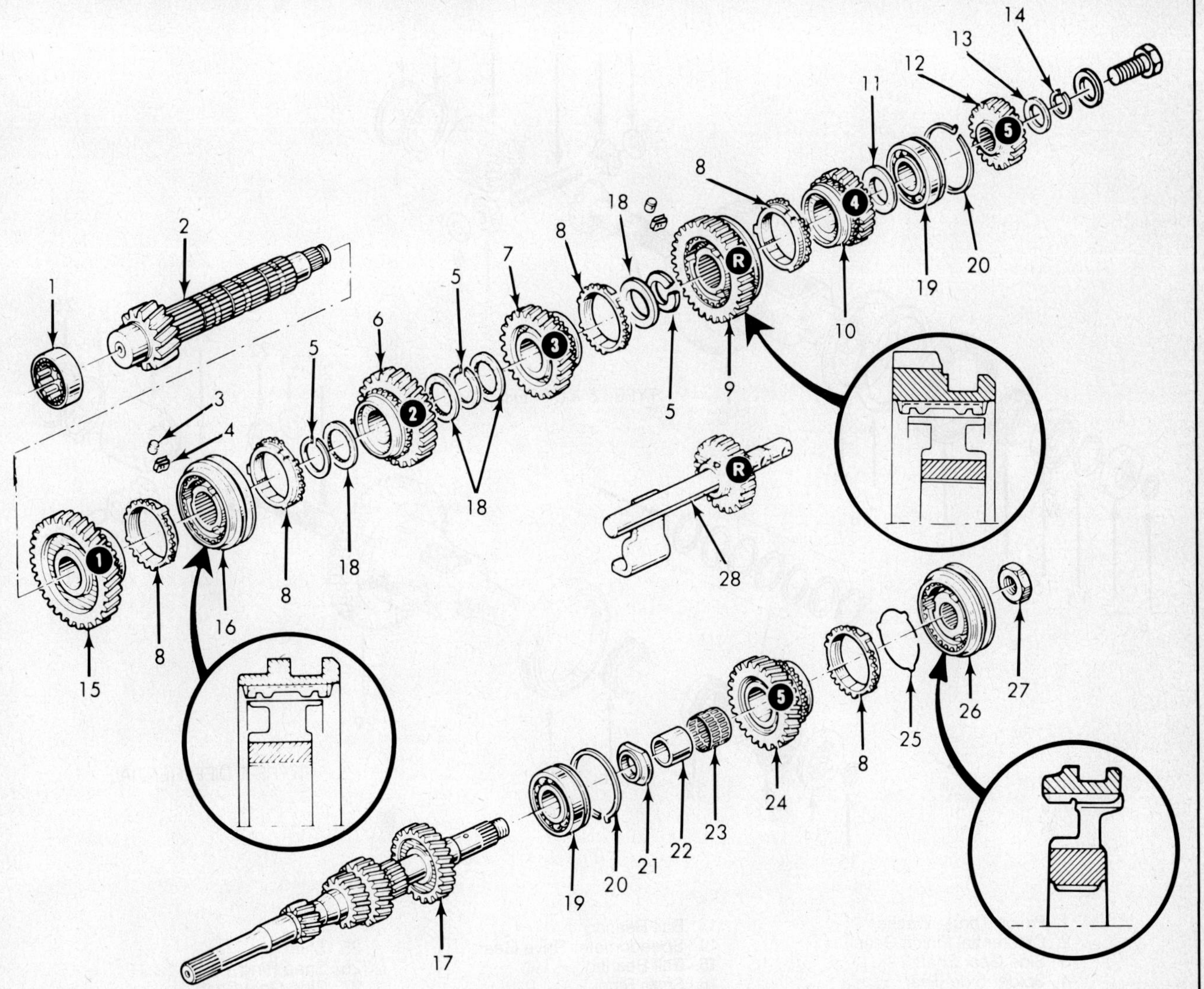

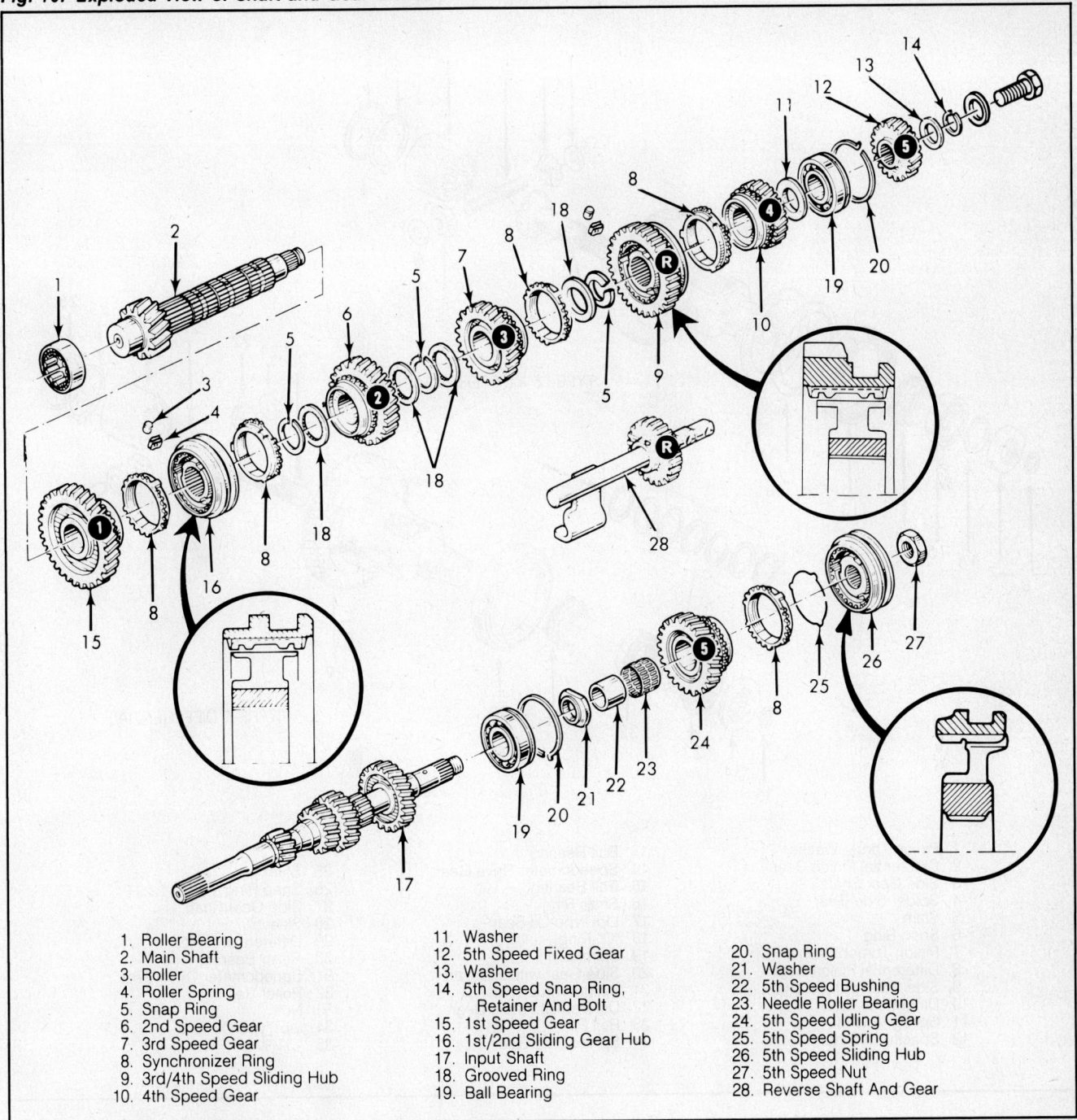

1. Roller Bearing
2. Main Shaft
3. Roller
4. Roller Spring
5. Snap Ring
6. 2nd Speed Gear
7. 3rd Speed Gear
8. Synchronizer Ring
9. 3rd/4th Speed Sliding Hub
10. 4th Speed Gear
11. Washer
12. 5th Speed Fixed Gear
13. Washer
14. 5th Speed Snap Ring, Retainer And Bolt
15. 1st Speed Gear
16. 1st/2nd Sliding Gear Hub
17. Input Shaft
18. Grooved Ring
19. Ball Bearing
20. Snap Ring
21. Washer
22. 5th Speed Bushing
23. Needle Roller Bearing
24. 5th Speed Idling Gear
25. 5th Speed Spring
26. 5th Speed Sliding Hub
27. 5th Speed Nut
28. Reverse Shaft And Gear

3) On Type III, heavy duty differentials, remove and discard nut. Except for snap ring, press out differential assembly as described in step **2)**.

4) On all models, turn assembly over. Mount differential housing in a soft-jawed vise. Remove snap ring, shim and spider side gear. *See Fig. 11.*

NOTE: Attach pinion thrust washer to its matching differential pinion gear for reassembly.

5) On Type I and Type II differentials, remove side gear shaft, differential pinion gears, pinion thrust washers and side gear with tail shaft.

6) On Type III differentials, remove roll pin, side gear shaft, sleeve, differential pinion gears, pinion thrust washers and side gear with tail shaft.

BEARINGS

Transaxle Case Bearing

Remove circlips using snap ring pliers and tap bearings down inside case using a hammer.

Mainshaft Bearing

The bearing is staked in position. Using a grinder or sharp chisel, remove case material which retains the bearing. Using a universal bearing puller, remove caged roller bearing.

AMC/RENAULT 4 & 5-SPEED JB SERIES TRANSAXLE (Cont.)

Fig. 11: Exploded View of Differential Assemblies

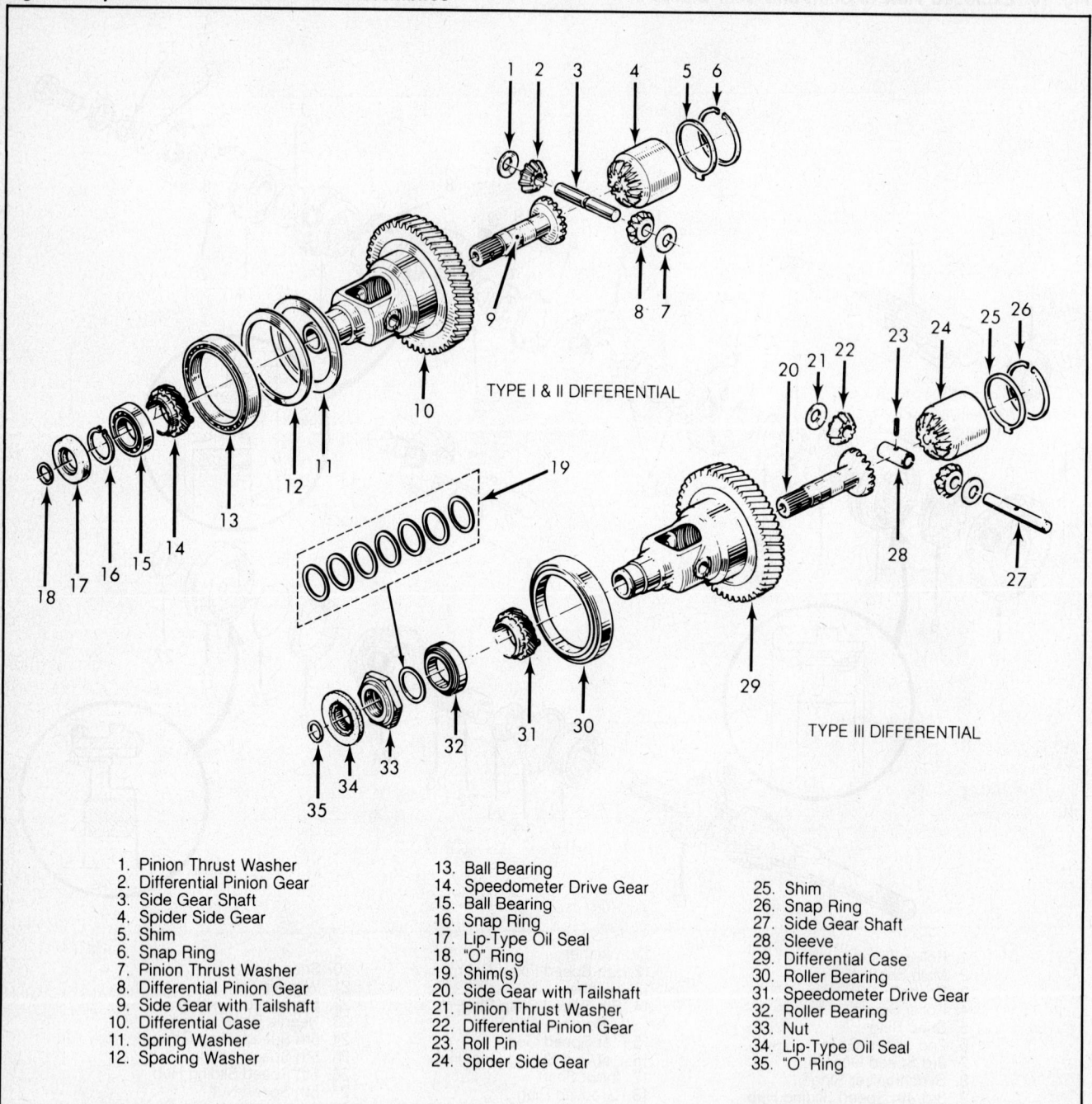

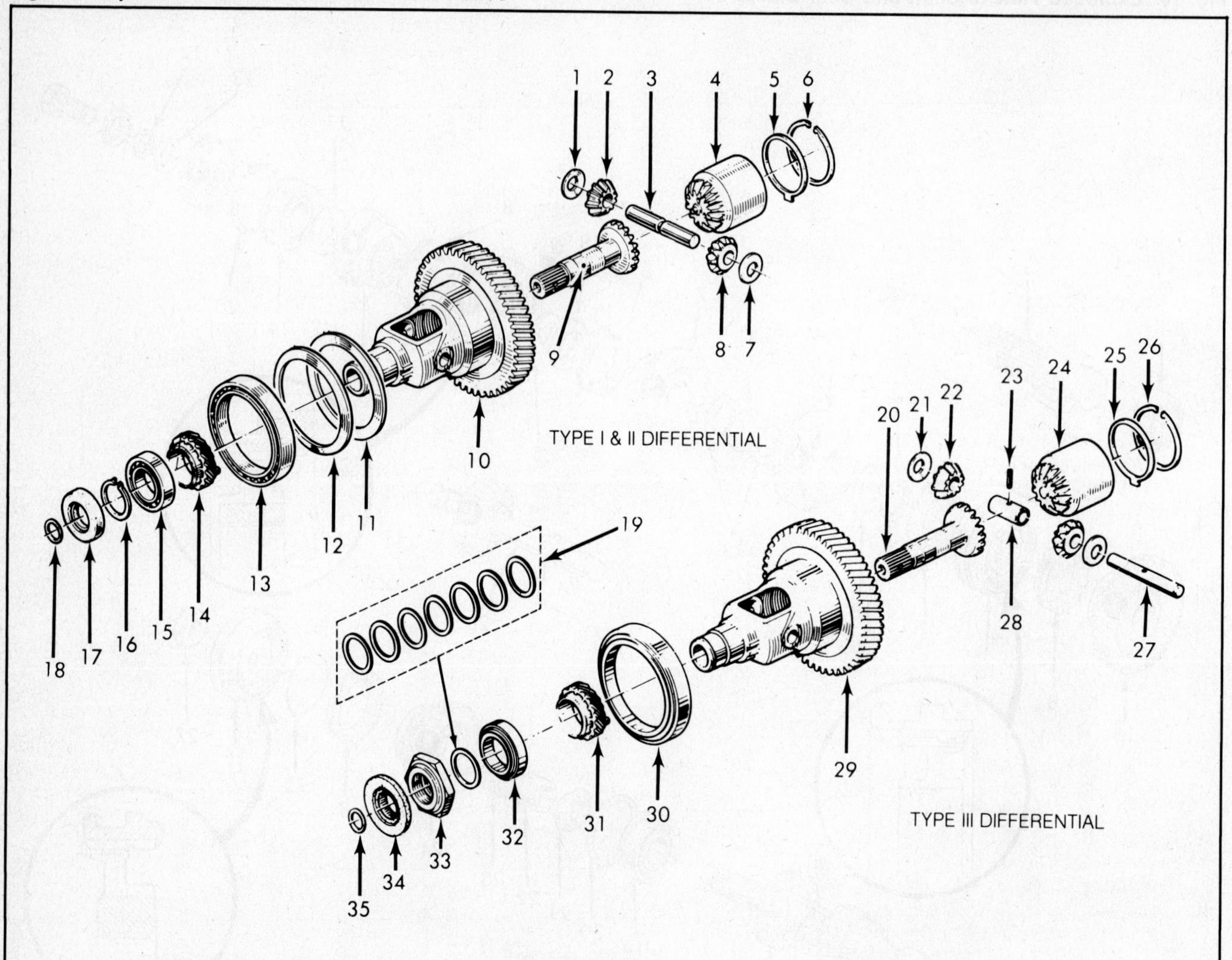

1. Pinion Thrust Washer
2. Differential Pinion Gear
3. Side Gear Shaft
4. Spider Side Gear
5. Shim
6. Snap Ring
7. Pinion Thrust Washer
8. Differential Pinion Gear
9. Side Gear with Tailshaft
10. Differential Case
11. Spring Washer
12. Spacing Washer
13. Ball Bearing
14. Speedometer Drive Gear
15. Ball Bearing
16. Snap Ring
17. Lip-Type Oil Seal
18. "O" Ring
19. Shim(s)
20. Side Gear with Tailshaft
21. Pinion Thrust Washer
22. Differential Pinion Gear
23. Roll Pin
24. Spider Side Gear
25. Shim
26. Snap Ring
27. Side Gear Shaft
28. Sleeve
29. Differential Case
30. Roller Bearing
31. Speedometer Drive Gear
32. Roller Bearing
33. Nut
34. Lip-Type Oil Seal
35. "O" Ring

Differential Bearings

On Type I and Type II differentials, remove and discard snap ring holding the bearing. Using a 1.97" (50 mm) tube and arbor press, remove small bearing. Press bearing into the case.

To remove large bearing, insert a steel bar into case and place it flat on bearing. Use a piece of tube and an arbor press to remove large bearing.

SELECTOR CONTROL ARM & BUSHING

Remove control arm snap ring. *See Fig. 2.* Remove arm bushing and control arm. Remove roll pin from selector fork using a 1/4" (7 mm) punch. Remove input shaft selector fork. Remove lip-type oil seal and bushing.

SPEEDOMETER DRIVEN GEAR

Transaxle must be disassembled and speedometer gear shaft must be broken to remove drive gear.

CLEANING & INSPECTION

1) Wash all parts, except oil seals, in cleaning solvent. Brush or scrape all foreign matter from parts, using care not to damage any part with scraper. Do not clean, wash, or soak transaxle seals in cleaning solvent. Dry all parts with compressed air.

AMC/RENAULT 4 & 5-SPEED JB SERIES TRANSAXLE (Cont.)

CAUTION: **Hold roller bearing assembly to prevent it from rotating when drying it with compressed air.**

2) Lubricate all bearings with approved transmission lubricant and wrap them in a clean, lint free cloth or paper until ready to use.

3) Inspect transaxle case and clutch housing case for cracks, worn, or damaged bearing bores. Check for damaged threads or any other damage. Inspect mating surfaces on cases for small nicks or burrs that could cause misalignment of the 2 halves. Remove all small nicks or burrs with a fine stone or file.

4) Check reverse gear and sliding gears for chipped, broken, or bent teeth. Check wear of reverse gear shaft. It is normal for front of teeth to show wear, this does not interfere with proper function.

5) Check teeth, splines and journals of mainshaft for damage. Check all other gears for chipped, broken, or worn teeth. Check for eroded clutching teeth and damaged bearing surfaces. Clutching teeth will usually show rounding of the points which does not interfere with normal operation.

6) Check synchronizer sleeves for free movement on hubs. Make sure index marks are properly aligned. Check for damaged clutching teeth. Check for proper positioning of springs.

7) Inspect synchronizer blocker rings for wear marks on spline end back face which indicates ring was bottoming on gear face due to excessive blocker ring wear.

8) Inspect differential pinion and side gears for scoring, excessive wear, nicks, and chips. Worn, scored, and damaged gears must be replaced.

NOTE: **When a scored or chipped gear is replaced, transaxle case must be cleaned thoroughly to make sure all chips are removed.**

9) Make sure differential case bearing journals are smooth. Inspect case bearing shoulders for damage caused by bearing removal. Check fit (free rotation) of side gears in their cavities.

10) Check differential bearings and bearing races for wear or other damage. Check bearings for smooth rotation in races. Examine bearing roller ends for step wear.

NOTE: **If inspection reveals either a damaged bearing or race, both parts must be replaced as they are a matched set.**

COMPONENT REASSEMBLY

SPEEDOMETER DRIVEN GEAR

The gear and gear shaft must be installed by hand. Position shaft in relation to locking notches in gear.Install gear on gear shaft by striking it with a soft hammer.

BEARINGS

Differential Bearings

Position small bearing over opening and install using an arbor press and piece of 2.56" (65 mm) diameter tube. Install new retaining snap ring. Press large bearing into housing using arbor press and a 5.12" (130 mm) long steel bar.

Mainshaft Bearing

Clean bearing seat using emery cloth and compressed air. Using an arbor press, install bearing flush with the inside face of the case. Stake the bearing in place using a chisel. Depth of stake must be within .04-.05" (.9-1.3 mm).

Transaxle Case Bearings

Install snap rings in case with open ends facing each other. Spread the snap ring in the case using Installer (B.Vi.947), and install bearings withgroove on opposite side of entry chamber. Ensure circlips are fully engaged in grooves.

NOTE: **Install new selector fork pads to avoid damage to aliminum selector fork. Replace oil flow giude if necessary.**

SELECTOR CONTROL ARM & BUSHING

To reassemble, reverse disassembly procedures. *See Fig. 2.*

DIFFERENTIAL

NOTE: **Type I and Type II differential cases are not interchangeable. New bearings should be used in Type I differentials, especially when replacing differential bearings to correct a noise condition.**

1) To install new bearings on Type I differential case, remove old bearings and spring washer. Install three 4 mm Spacers (7703 053 561), 1.4 mm Spring Washer (7700 723 384), large Bearing (7703 090 324), and small Bearing (7703 090 316), on case.

2) On Type I and Type II transaxles, lubricate components with 75W-90 lubricant and reassemble by reversing disassembly procedures. Install differential in clutch and differential case. Place a wood block under differential housing for support.

3) Install new snap ring using Installer (B.Vi946), or snap ring pliers over end of side gear with tailshaft. Apply force using an arbor press until snap ring slips into place. Remove tool.

4) On Type III transaxles, no spring washer or spacers are used. Shims are used to set bearing preload. To reassemble, reverse disassembly procedures. Lubricate components with 75W-90 lubricant and assemble into differential case. Install clip and roll pin. Install assembly into housing.

5) Select a shim which will acheive correct rotating torque when retaining nut is tightened to 95 Ft. Lbs. (130 N.m). A shim pack is available consisting of different sized shims. One shim from the pack will be used in a differential assembly.

6) Rotating torque on new bearings is 14-28 In. Lbs. (1.6-3.2 N.m), and rotating torque on used bearings is 0-14 In. Lbs. (0-1.6 N.m).

NOTE: **If differential case is equipped with an electronic speedometer trigger wheel, inspect wheel for damage and replace if necessary.**

MAINSHAFT

To reassemble mainshaft, reverse disassembly procedures. *See Fig. 10*

TRANSAXLE REASSEMBLY

NOTE: **Ensure shafts and components are lubricated. Use new circlips during reassembly.**

AMC/RENAULT 4 & 5-SPEED JB SERIES TRANSAXLE (Cont.)

1) On JB 1 transaxles, two types of input shafts and mainshafts are used. Identify type of shaft used during service. Either straight or tapered splines are used for the 5th fixed gear and sliding hub. To identify spline type, install 5th fixed gear on mainshaft or sliding hub on input shaft.

2) Note how far down splines the gear and/or hub can be installed. If the shaft has tapered splines, the gear and/or shaft will not slide down the full length of the splines. If the shaft has straight splines, the gear and/or hub will slide down the full length of the splines.

3) On all models, install input shaft, mainshaft and reverse shaft as an assembly into clutch and differential case. Tilt mainshaft to simplify installation. Install 1st-2nd-reverse interlocking detent. Install 1st-2nd selector fork with shift rod fingers facing gear. Install 1st-2nd selector rod in fork and install small plunger.

4) The interlocking ball recesses face the shafts. Lift reverse shift rod. Lower 1st-2nd shift rod. Ensure 1st-2nd-reverse interlocking detent is in recess in reverse shift rod.

5) Be sure that reverse shift rod is locked in place. Install medium sized interlocking shift detent between 1st-2nd and 3rd-4th shift rods. Install 3rd-4th fork with thicker side toward gear.

6) Install 3rd-4th shift rod with interlocking detent recesses facing shift rods. Install fork roll pins using Installer (B.Vi.949), or a 3/16 pin punch.

NOTE: **Roll pin slots must face longitudinal axis of each rod. New roll pins must be used whenever transaxle is disassembled.**

7) Apply Permatex 2 Form "A" Gasket onto joint faces of rear case and clutch case. On 4-speed models, ensure washer is installed on mainshaft. On 5-speed models, install 5th gear interlocking ball and spring in rear case. Install 5th gear selector fork.

8) On all models, pull selector control outward and center input shaft, mainshaft, and selector fork shift rods. Install rear case. Remove dummy rods used during disassembly. Tap rear case with soft mallet to seat input shaft and mainshaft in bearings.

9) Using a piece of wire in the shape of a hook, lift up reverse shaft and install interlocking ball, spring, and clip. *See Fig. 12.* Install 2 case bolts and operate shift mechanism to ensure transaxle shifts correctly.

Fig. 12: Using Wire Hook To Lift Reverse Gear

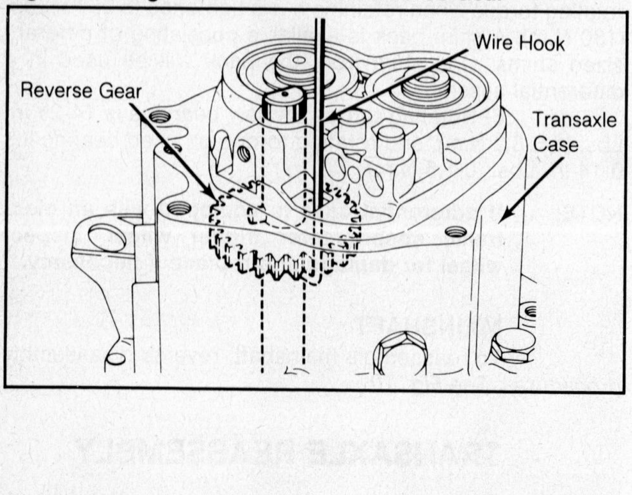

10) Install threaded limit stop, or 5th speed detent, and tighten to specification. On 4-speed models, install new mainshaft circlip using Installer (B.Vi902-01). On all models, install new circlip on input shaft using installer and hammer.

11) Support shaft on clutch spline side with screw from Installer Plate (B.Vi.902-01). Shaft may also be supported by using wood blocks on workbench. Ensure circlip is secure in groove. Install and tighten to specification remaining case bolts.

12) On 5-speed models, install 5th speed fixed gear, washer, 5th gear circlip, retainer, and bolt using Installer (B.Vi.948). Ensure 5th gear circlip is seated in groove by observing slots. Tighten bolt to specification.

NOTE: **On JB 1 and JB 3 transaxles, a new and shorter 27 mm bolt is used to attach fifth fixed gear to mainshaft.**

13) To install 5th gear assembly see 5TH GEAR ASSEMBLY section in this article. Install rear cover and a new rear cover "O" ring. Be sure to align oil channel and oil feed tube. Install transaxle assembly in vehicle and fill with lubricant.

TIGHTENING SPECIFICATIONS

Application	Ft. Lbs. (N.m)
Input Shaft Bolt	100 (136)
Mainshaft Bolt	
8 mm	15 (20)
10 mm	59 (80)
Mounting Pad Nuts	26 (35)
Rear Case Bolts	18 (24)
Shift Rod-to-Yoke Clamp Assembly, Bolt & Nut (8 mm)	20 (27)
Starter Motor Mount Bolts	32 (44)
Starter Rear Brace Bolt	16 (22)
Transaxle Housing-to-Block Bolts	31 (42)
5th Speed Detent Stop	14 (19)
5th Speed Mainshaft Bolt	18 (24)
	INCH Lbs. (N.m)
Gearshift Rod-to-Transmission Shift Arm, Bolt & Nut	80 (9)

Manual Transmissions

BORG-WARNER 4-SPEED MODEL T4

Jeep CJ-7

IDENTIFICATION

Transmission identification tag is attached to right side of the adapter housing by an adapter housing-to-transmission case bolt.

DESCRIPTION

The Borg-Warner 4-speed model T-4 transmission is a constant-mesh, fully synchronized unit which provides synchromesh in all 4 forward gears. The forward gears are helically cut. The reverse gears are spur cut and are not in constant mesh. An interlock system prevents accidental engagement of reverse gears when selecting any of the forward gears.

LUBRICATION & ADJUSTMENT

See appropriate MANUAL TRANSMISSION SERVICING article in DOMESTIC GENERAL SERVICING section.

TROUBLE SHOOTING

See MANUAL TRANSMISSION TROUBLE SHOOTING article in DOMESTIC GENERAL SERVICING section.

REMOVAL & INSTALLATION

See appropriate MANUAL TRANSMISSION REMOVAL article in DOMESTIC GENERAL SERVICING section.

TRANSMISSION DISASSEMBLY

NOTE: **All threaded holes and bolts, except for gear-shift lever attaching bolts and fill plug, are metric.**

CAUTION: **Do not attempt to remove offset lever while adapter housing is still bolted in place. Positioning lug prevents moving lever far enough rearward for removal.**

1) Remove drain plug and drain lubricant. Using pin punch, remove roll pin attaching offset lever to shift rail. Remove extension/adapter housing-to-transmission case bolts.

2) Remove housing and offset lever as an assembly. *See Fig. 2.* Remove detent ball and spring from offset lever and remove roll pin from extension/adapter housing or offset lever. *See Fig. 1.*

3) Remove and retain countershaft rear thrust bearing and bearing race. Remove transmission cover, shift fork assembly attaching bolts and remove cover. Note positions of the 2 dowel-type shift control cover bolts for reassembly.

4) Remove "C" clip attaching reverse lever to reverse lever pivot bolt. Remove bolt and remove reverse lever and lever fork as an assembly. Matchmark front bearing cap and transmission case with a punch and remove front bearing cap bolts and cap.

Fig. 1: Removing Offset Lever Spring and Detent Ball

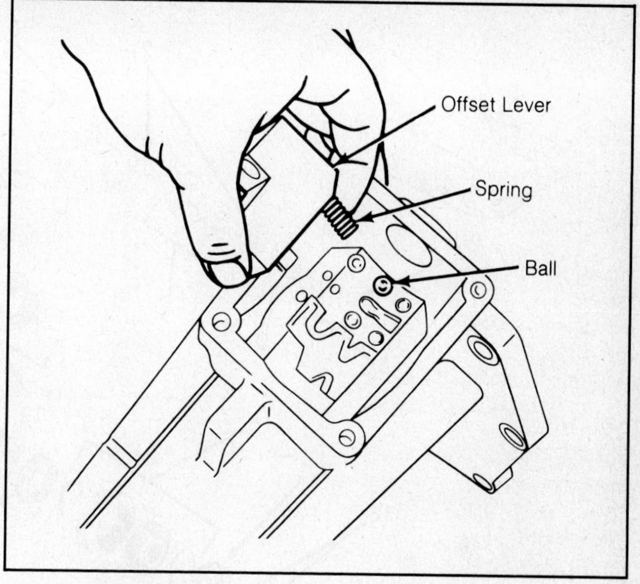

5) Remove front bearing race, shims and oil seal from bearing cap. Rotate clutch shaft until flat on gear teeth is facing countershaft and remove shaft. Remove thrust bearing and 15 roller bearings from clutch shaft.

6) Remove mainshaft bearing race. If necessary, tap mainshaft with soft hammer to remove bearing race. Tilt mainshaft assembly upward and remove from transmission case. Remove countershaft rear bearing with a drift and arbor press.

7) Note position of bearing for reassembly. Bearing number should face outward when correctly installed. Move countershaft rearward, tilt upward and remove shaft from case.

8) Note position of washer for reassembly. Remove countershaft rear bearing spacer. Remove reverse idler shaft and gear, noting position for reassembly.

9) Remove countershaft front bearing using arbor press. Using Bearing Remover (J-2972, J-22912), remove clutch shaft front bearing. Remove rear extension/adapter housing seal with drift and hammer. Remove back-up light switch from transmission case.

CLEANING & INSPECTION

1) Clean all parts in solvent and dry with compressed air except front and rear bearings. Wipe front and rear bearings dry with a clean shop rag or air dry them. To clean needle and roller bearings, submerge bearings in a shallow pan of solvent or wipe with a clean shop rag.

2) Inspect transmission case, cover and extension housing. Replace if there are cracks in bores, sides, bosses or bolt holes. Replace components if there are stripped bolt holes, nicks, burrs or rough surfaces in shaft bores or on gasket surfaces.

3) Inspect gear train and shift mechanism. Replace any parts that show wear, chips, galling, distortion or bending. Check for worn bearings and bores. Check for weak snap rings and a stripped offset lever.

Manual Transmissions

BORG-WARNER 4-SPEED MODEL T4 (Cont.)

Fig. 2: Exploded View of Borg-Warner 4-Speed Model T4 Transmission

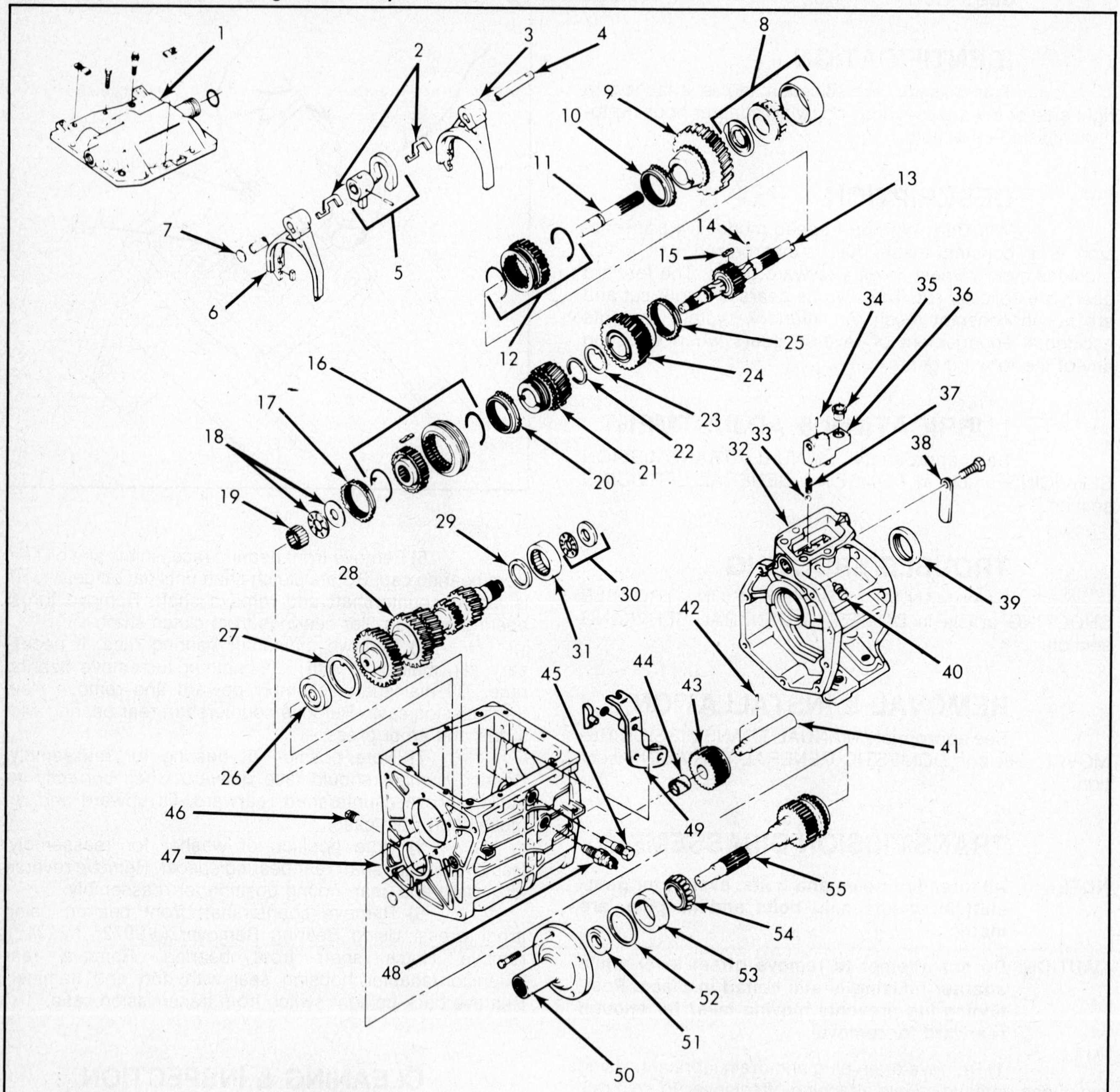

1. Transmission Cover
2. Selector Plate
3. 1st-2nd Shift Fork
4. Shift Rail
5. Selector Arm Interlock Plate & Pin
6. 3rd-4th Shift Fork
7. Plug
8. Thrust Washer, Rear Bearing & Cup
9. 1st Gear
10. Blocking Ring
11. Output Shaft
12. Reverse Sliding Gear & Insert Spring
13. Output Shaft
14. 1st Gear Pin
15. Synchro Insert
16. 3rd-4th Synchro Spring, Hub Insert & Sleeve
17. Blocking Ring
18. Needle Thrust Bearing & Race
19. Clutch Shaft Needle Roller Bearing
20. 3rd-4th Blocking Ring
21. 3rd Gear
22. Snap Ring
23. Thrust Washer
24. 2nd Speed Gear
25. Blocking Ring
26. Front Countershaft Bearing
27. Front Countershaft Thrust Washer
28. Countershaft Gear
29. Rear Countershaft Spacer
30. Needle Thrust Bearing & Race
31. Rear Countershaft Bearing
32. Adapter Housing
33. Detent Ball
34. Pin
35. Damper Sleeve
36. Offset Lever
37. Detent Spring
38. Identification Tag
39. Adapter Housing Seal
40. Breather
41. Reverse Idler Gear Shaft
42. Pin
43. Reverse Idler Gear
44. Bushing
45. Reverse Lever Pivot Bolt
46. Drain Plug
47. Transmission Case
48. Reverse Light Switch
49. Reverse Lever Fork
50. Front Bearing Cap
51. Oil Seal
52. Shim
53. Front Bearing Cup
54. Front Bearing
55. Clutch Shaft

BORG-WARNER 4-SPEED MODEL T4 (Cont.)

COMPONENT DISASSEMBLY & REASSEMBLY

MAINSHAFT ASSEMBLY

Disassembly

1) Remove thrust bearing washer from front end of mainshaft. Scribe alignment marks on 3rd-4th synchronizer hub and sleeve for reassembly.

2) Remove 3rd-4th synchronizer blocking ring, sleeve and hub as an assembly. Remove 3rd-4th synchronizer, insert springs, and remove inserts and sleeve from hub.

3) Remove 3rd gear from shaft. Remove 2nd gear retaining snap ring and remove tabbed 2nd gear thrust washer and 2nd gear. Using Puller (J-29721), and Adapters (J-293-39), remove mainshaft bearing.

NOTE: Do not remove 1st-2nd hub from mainshaft. Hub and mainshaft are machined and assembled as a matched set.

4) Remove 1st gear thrust washer and using diagonal cutters, remove 1st gear roll pin. Remove 1st gear and blocking ring. Scribe alignment marks on 1st-2nd gear synchronizer sleeve and hub for reassembly.

5) Remove insert springs and inserts from 1st-reverse sliding gear and remove gear from mainshaft hub.

Reassembly

1) Coat mainshaft, gear needle bearings and bores with transmission lubricant. Install and align 1st-2nd synchronizer sleeve on mainshaft hub using index marks. Install 3, 1st-2nd synchronizer inserts, and 2 insert springs in 1st-reverse synchronizer sleeve.

2) Engage tang end of each insert spring in same synchronizer insert but position open ends of springs to face 180° away from each other. *See Fig. 3*. Align sleeve hub with index marks. Install blocking ring and 2nd gear on mainshaft.

3) Install tabbed thrust washer and 2nd gear snap ring on mainshaft. Ensure washer tab is correctly seated in mainshaft notch. Install blocking ring, 1st gear and 1st gear roll pin on mainshaft.

Fig. 3: Installing Synchronizer Insert Springs

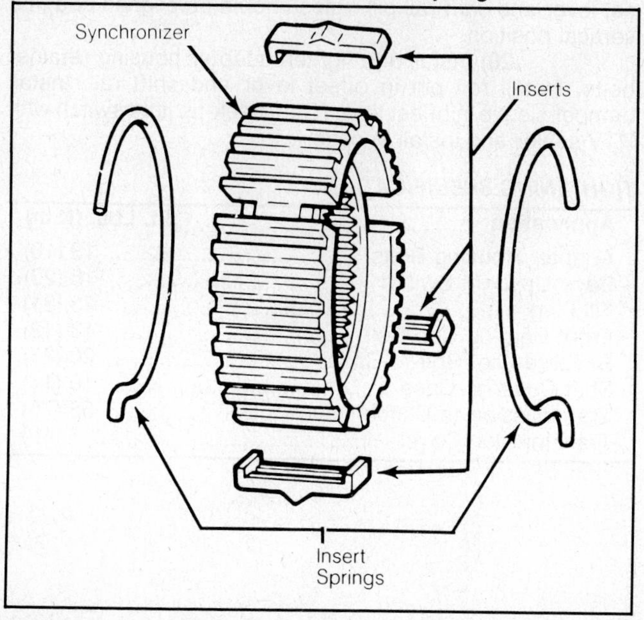

4) Using arbor press and Bearing Installer (J-2995), install rear bearing. Install 1st gear thrust washer. Install 3rd gear, 3rd and 4th gear synchronizer hub inserts, and sleeve on mainshaft. Hub offset must face forward. Install thrust bearing washer on forward end of mainshaft.

TRANSMISSION COVER ASSEMBLY

Disassembly

1) Place selector arm plates and shift rail in Neutral position. Rotate shift rail counterclockwise until selector arm disengages from selector arm plates and selector arm roll pin is accessable. *See Fig. 4*. Pull rail rearward until selector contacts 1st-2nd shift fork.

2) Using a 3/16" pin punch, remove roll pin. Remove shift rail, shift forks, selector arm plates, selector arm and roll pin assembly, and interlock plate. Using a screwdriver, remove shift rail oil seal and "O" ring.

3) Remove shift rail plug with hammer and punch. Remove nylon inserts and selector arm plates from shift forks, noting positions for reassembly.

Fig. 4: Exploded View of Transmission Cover Assembly

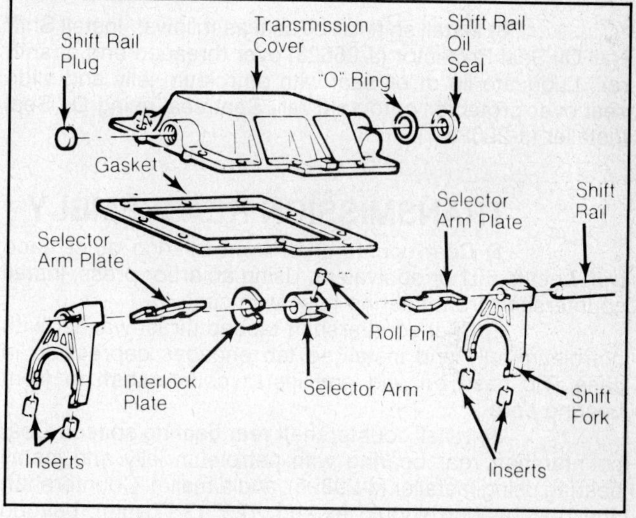

Reassembly

1) Install nylon inserts and selector arm plates in shift forks. *See Fig. 5*. Coat edge of shift rail plug with sealer and install. Coat shift rail and shift rail bores with petroleum jelly and insert shift rail in cover.

2) Install rail until end of rail is flush with inside edge of cover. Position 1st-2nd shift fork in cover with fork offset facing rear of cover and push shift rail through fork. First-2nd shift fork is the larger of the 2 shift forks.

3) Position selector arm and "C" shaped interlock plate in cover and insert shift rail through selector arm. Widest part of interlock plate must face away from cover and selector arm roll pin must face downward and toward rear of cover.

4) Position 3rd-4th shift fork in cover with fork offset facing rear of cover. The 3rd-4th shift fork selector arm plate must be positioned under 1st-2nd shift fork selector arm plate. Insert shift rail through 3rd-4th shift fork and into front shift rail bore in cover.

5) Rotate shift rail until selector arm plate at forward end of rail faces away from but is parallel to cover. Align selector arm and and shift rail roll pin holes and install roll pin. Ensure roll pin is flush with selector arm surface. Install "O" ring in groove of shift rail oil seal.

BORG-WARNER 4-SPEED MODEL T4 (Cont.)

Fig. 5: Assembling Shift Fork and Selector Arm Plates

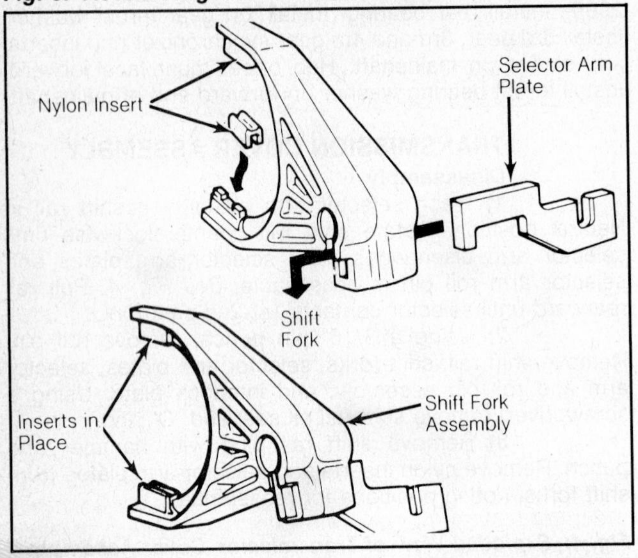

6) Install shift rail oil seal as follows: Install Shift Rail Oil Seal Protector (J-26628) over threaded end of shift rail. Lubricate lip of oil seal with petroleum jelly and slide seal over protector onto shift rail. Seat seal using Oil Seal Installer (J-22628-1).

TRANSMISSION REASSEMBLY

1) Coat countershaft front bearing outer cage with Loctite 601 or equivalent. Using an arbor press, install countershaft front bearing flush with case.

2) Coat countershaft tabbed thrust washer with petroleum jelly and install so tab engages depression in case. Tip case on end and install countershaft in front bearing bore.

3) Install countershaft rear bearing spacer. Coat countershaft rear bearing with petroleum jelly and install bearing using Installer (J-29895), and a mallet. Countershaft and rear bearing should extend .125" (3.17 mm), beyond case surface.

4) Position reverse idler gear in case with shift lever groove facing rear of case. Install reverse idler shaft from rear of case and install retaining roll pin in shaft. Install assembled mainshaft in case.

5) Install front clutch shaft bearing on clutch shaft housing using Installer (J-2995), and arbor press. Coat 15 pilot roller bearings with petroleum jelly and install in clutch shaft. Install thrust bearing and race in clutch shaft.

6) Install 4th gear blocking ring on mainshaft. Install rear mainshaft bearing race. Install clutch shaft in case and engage shaft in 3rd-4th synchronizer sleeve and blocking ring.

7) Using Seal Installer (J-26625), install replacement oil seal in front bearing cap. Using Seal Installer (J-29184), install replacement oil seal in rear adapter housing.

8) Install front bearing race in front bearing cap, but do not install shims. Install front bearing cap. Do not install sealer at this time. Install reverse lever, pivot pin and retaining "C" clip.

9) Coat countershaft rear bearing race and thrust bearing with petroleum jelly and install in extension/adapter housing. Temporarily install extension/adapter housing. Do not seal housing to case or tighten case bolts.

10) Turn transmission case on end and mount dial indicator on extension adapter housing with indicator stylus on end of mainshaft. Rotate clutch and mainshaft until end play is removed.

11) To completely eliminate mainshaft and clutch shaft end play, bearings must be preloaded from .001-.005" (.03-.13 mm). Read end play dimension on dial indicator.

12) Select shim pack measuring .001-.005" (.03-.13 mm), thicker than end play measurement. Place transmission horizontally on workbench. and remove front bearing cap and front bearing race.

13) Add shims to bearing cap to obtain necessary preload and install clutch shaft bearing race in cap. Apply bead of RTV sealant on case mating surface on front bearing cap.

14) Install front cap using index marks. Tighten retaining bolts and recheck end play. There should be no end play. Remove extension/adapter housing.

15) Move shift forks on transmission cover and synchronizer rings (inside transmission), to Neutral position. Apply bead of RTV sealant to cover mating surface. Lower cover assembly (slightly off center), onto case while aligning shift forks and synchronizer sleeves.

16) Center cover on case to engage reverse relay lever and install 2 dowel bolts in cover. Install and tighten remaining bolts. The offset lever-to-shift lever rail pin hole is in a vertical when steps **15)** and **16)** are performed correctly.

17) Apply a bead of RTV sealant to extension/adapter housing-to-transmission case mating surface. Install extension/adapter housing over mainshaft and shift rail to a position where shift rail enters shift cover opening.

18) Install detent spring into offset lever. Place detent ball in neutral guide plate detent. *See Fig. 1.* Apply pressure on detent ball with detent spring and offset lever.

19) Slide offset lever on shift rail and seal extension/adapter housing against transmission case. Offset lever and shift rail pin holes should be aligned and in a vertical position.

20) Install and tighten adapter housing retainer bolts. Install roll pin in offset lever and shift rail. Install damper sleeve in offset lever. Coat back-up light switch with RTV sealer and install in case.

TIGHTENING SPECIFICATIONS

Application	Ft. Lbs. (N.m)
Adapter Housing Bolts	13 (18)
Back-Up Light Switch	15 (20)
Fill Plug	23 (31)
Front Bearing Cap Bolt	13 (18)
Reverse Pilot Bolt-to-Case	20 (27)
Shift Cover-to-Case	10 (14)
Transmission-to-Clutch Housing Bolt	55 (75)
Transmission Cover	7 (10)

BORG-WARNER 5-SPEED MODEL T5

AMC
Eagle
Ford Motor Co.
Capri, Cougar, Mustang
Thunderbird
Jeep
CJ-7

IDENTIFICATION

AMC - An identification tag is attached to the rear of the transmission. For certain models, special identification numbers are stamped on a boss on the left side of transmission case.

Ford Motor Co. - Identification code is located on extension bolt on left-hand side of transmission.

Jeep - An identification tag displaying model part number is attached to right side of adapter housing by an adapter housing-to-transmission case bolt.

DESCRIPTION

The Borg-Warner 5-speed model T5 overdrive transmission is a constant-mesh, fully synchronized unit which provides synchromesh engagement in all forward gear ranges. The reverse gear is spur-cut and is not in constant mesh.

The transmission utilizes an internal-type non-adjustable shift mechanism with a reverse gear lock-out. The lock-out feature prevents accidental engagement in reverse when selecting any of the forward gears. On some Ford vehicles there is a top gear sensing switch attached to the transmission case cover.

LUBRICATION & ADJUSTMENT

See appropriate MANUAL TRANSMISSION SERVICING article in DOMESTIC GENERAL SERVICING section.

TROUBLE SHOOTING

See MANUAL TRANSMISSION TROUBLE SHOOTING article in DOMESTIC GENERAL SERVICING section.

REMOVAL & INSTALLATION

See appropriate MANUAL TRANSMISSION REMOVAL article in DOMESTIC GENERAL SERVICING section.

SERVICE (IN VEHICLE)

GEAR SHIFT LEVER

Removal & Installation

1) On AMC and Jeep models, remove screws attaching transmission shift lever boot to floorpan. Slide boot upward on lever. Remove bolts attaching transmission shift lever housing to transmission and remove lever and housing. To install, reverse removal procedure.

2) On Ford models, remove four bolts attaching shift boot to floor pan. Remove two bolts attaching shift lever to transmission. To install, reverse removel procedure.

TOP GEAR SENSING SWITCH FORD MODELS ONLY

Using a 22 mm wrench, remove top gear sensing switch and pigtail connector, located at front right side of transmission cover. Remove top gear and neutral sensing switch pins using a pencil magnet. To install, reverse removal procedure.

TRANSMISSION DISASSEMBLY

CAUTION: If bolts are replaced, use only those of the same size and length as the originals.

1) Remove drain bolt on transmission case to drain lubricant. Do not reuse lubricant when transmission is reassembled. Use only recommended lubricant.

2) On Ford models, use a 13 mm socket and position shift lever in Neutral. Remove turret cover attachig bolts. Using a pry bar, break turret cover-to-extension housing seal and remove turret cover.

3) On all models, do not remove offset lever while extension/adapter housing is bolted in place. Using a pin punch and hammer, remove roll pin attaching offset lever to shift rail. Remove damper sleeve. Remove extension or adapter housing-to-transmission bolts and remove housing and offset lever as an assembly.

4) On AMC and Jeep models remove plastic funnel, thrust bearing race and thrust bearing from rear of countershaft, found on end of countershaft or inside adapter housing. On Ford models, remove offset lever, roll pin detent spring and detent ball from extension housing detent plate.

5) Remove bolts attaching cover and shift fork assembly to transmission and remove cover assembly. Remove back-up light switch. Remove roll pin from 5th gear shift fork. Place a wood block under 5th gear shift fork during roll pin removal to prevent damage to 5th gear-reverse shift rail. *See Fig. 1.*

6) Remove 5th gear synchronizer snap ring, shift fork, 5th gear synchronizer sleeve, blocking ring and 5th speed drive gear from rear of countershaft. Remove 5th gear synchronizer insert retainer springs and inserts from sleeve and hub. Mark position of hub and sleeve for assembly reference.

7) Remove snap ring and 5th speed driven gear from rear of output shaft using Puller (J-25215), or equivalent. Mark front bearing cap for assembly reference. Remove front bearing cap bolts and bearing cap. Remove front bearing race, end play shims and oil seal from bearing cap.

8) Rotate input shaft until flat surface on main drive gear faces countershaft and remove 4th gear blocking ring from 3rd-4th synchronizer. Remove input shaft from transmission. Remove input shaft needle bearings, thrust bearing and race. Remove output shaft rear bearing race, then tilt output shaft upward and remove through top of transmission case. *See Fig. 2.*

9) Unlock overcenter link spring from transmission case. Remove "C" clip that retains reverse lever and fork assembly to reverse lever pivot pin. Rotate 5th-reverse gear shift rail clockwise to disengage rail from reverse lever

BORG-WARNER 5-SPEED MODEL T5 (Cont.)

Fig. 1: Removing 5th Gear Shift Fork Roll Pin

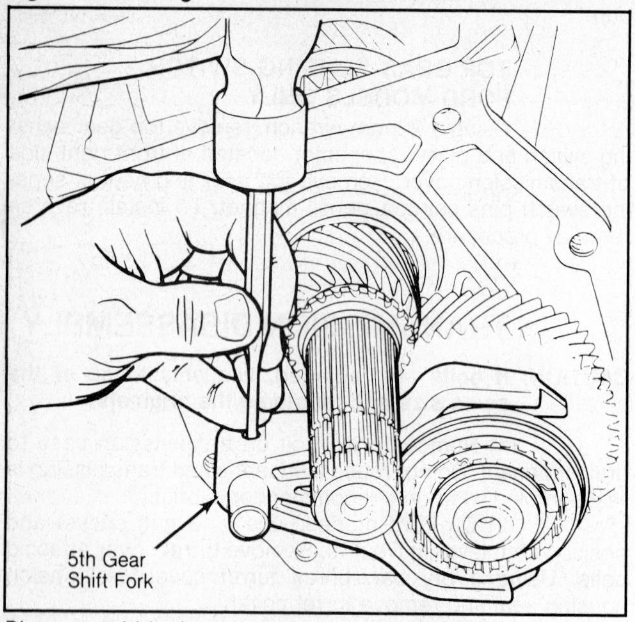

Place wood block under gear during removal.

Fig. 2: Removing & Installing Output Shaft

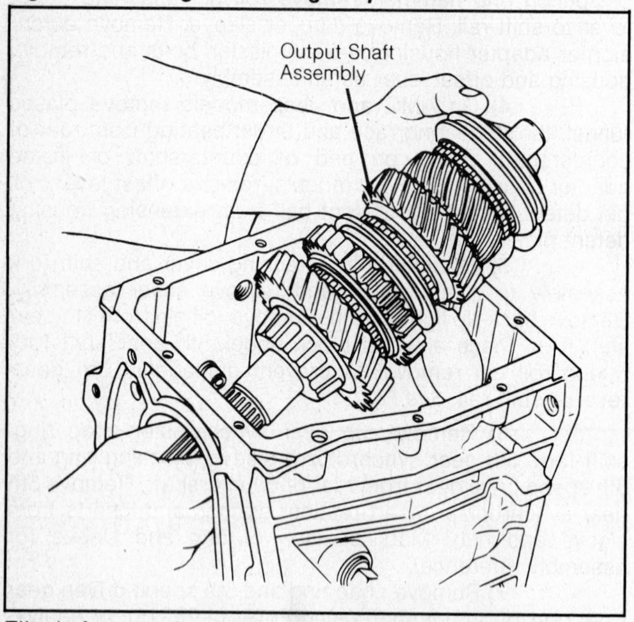

Tilt shaft upward and remove through top of case.

assembly. Remove shift rail from rear of transmission. *See Fig. 3.*

10) Remove snap ring and spacer from rear of countershaft. Insert a brass drift through clutch shaft opening in front of transmission case and press countershaft assembly rearward, using arbor press to remove rear countershaft bearing.

11) Slide countershaft assembly rearward, tilt assembly upward and remove from case. Note position of front countershaft thrust washer in case for reassembly reference. Remove countershaft front thrust washer and rear bearing spacer.

12) Remove roll pin from front end of reverse idler shaft, then remove reverse idler shaft and gear from transmission case. Note position of reverse idler gear for reassembly reference.

Fig. 3: Removing & Installing Reverse Shift Rail

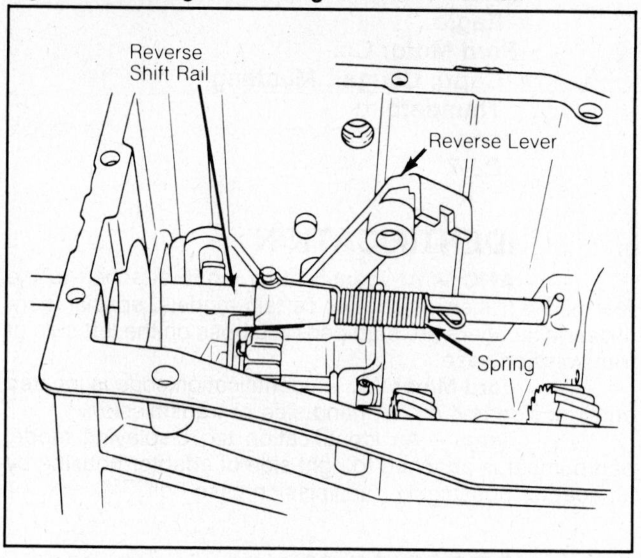

13) Using an arbor press, remove countershaft front bearing from transmission case. Remove bearing from front of clutch shaft. Using a flat drift and hammer, remove rear extension or adapter housing seal.

COMPONENT DISASSEMBLY & REASSEMBLY

OUTPUT SHAFT

Disassembly

1) Remove thrust bearing washer from front of output shaft. Scribe alignment mark on 3rd-4th synchronizer hub and sleeve for reassembly reference. Remove 3rd-4th gear synchronizer blocking ring, sleeve, hub and 3rd gear as an assembly.

2) Remove snap ring that retains 2nd gear on shaft, then remove tabbed 2nd gear thrust washer and 2nd gear. Using Puller (J-22912), Universal Press Plate (D79L-4621-A), or equivalent and arbor press, remove 5th gear. Slide rear bearing off mainshaft.

3) Remove 1st gear thrust washer, 1st gear roll pin (using diagonal cutters), 1st gear and blocking ring. Scribe alignment marks on 1st-2nd gear synchronizer sleeve and hub for reassembly reference.

4) Remove insert springs and insert from 1st-reverse sliding gear and remove gear from output shaft hub. Do not attempt to remove 1st-2nd-reverse hub from output shaft. Hub and shaft are machined as a matched set.

Reassembly

1) Coat ouput shaft and gear bores with transmission lubricant. Install and align 1st-2nd gear synchronizer sleeve on output shaft hub using reference marks made at disassembly. Install 1st-2nd synchronizer inserts and springs in 1st-reverse synchronizer sleeve.

2) Engage tang end of each insert spring in same synchronizer insert, but position open ends of springs to face 180° from each other. Be sure that reference marks are aligned. *See Fig. 5.*

BORG-WARNER 5-SPEED MODEL T5 (Cont.)

Fig. 4: Exploded View of Borg-Warner 5-Speed Model T5 Transmission

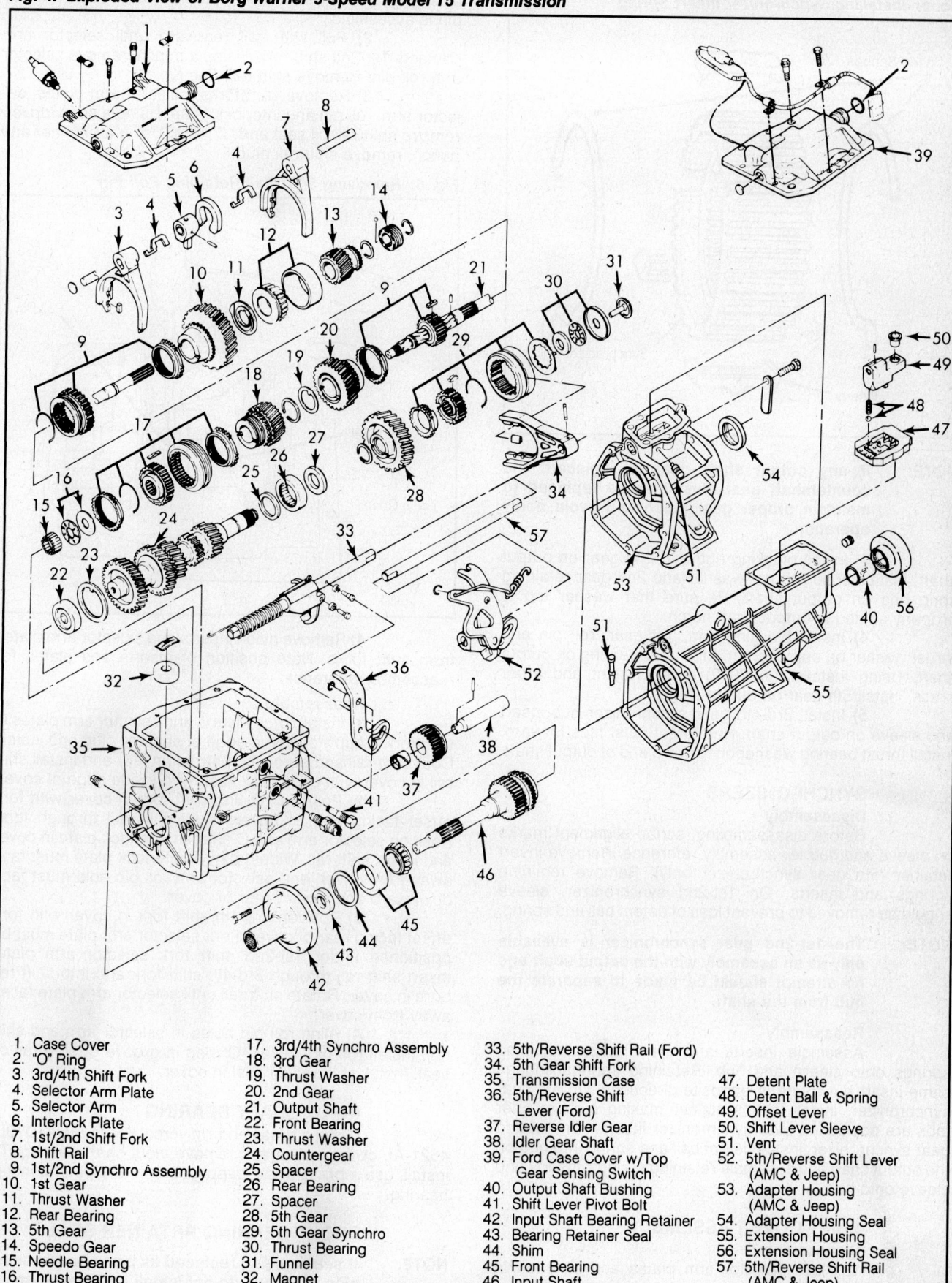

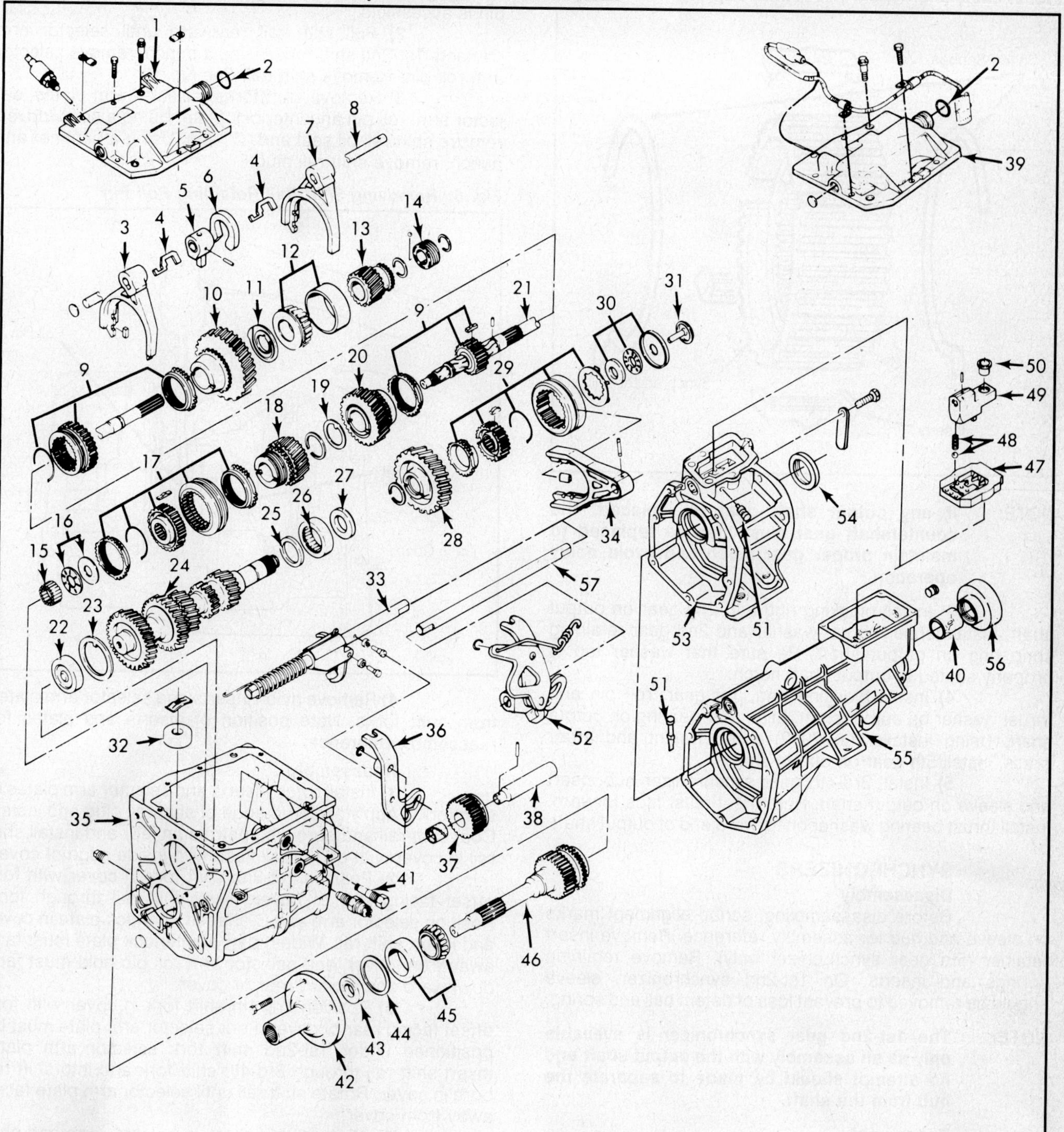

1. Case Cover
2. "O" Ring
3. 3rd/4th Shift Fork
4. Selector Arm Plate
5. Selector Arm
6. Interlock Plate
7. 1st/2nd Shift Fork
8. Shift Rail
9. 1st/2nd Synchro Assembly
10. 1st Gear
11. Thrust Washer
12. Rear Bearing
13. 5th Gear
14. Speedo Gear
15. Needle Bearing
16. Thrust Bearing
17. 3rd/4th Synchro Assembly
18. 3rd Gear
19. Thrust Washer
20. 2nd Gear
21. Output Shaft
22. Front Bearing
23. Thrust Washer
24. Countergear
25. Spacer
26. Rear Bearing
27. Spacer
28. 5th Gear
29. 5th Gear Synchro
30. Thrust Bearing
31. Funnel
32. Magnet
33. 5th/Reverse Shift Rail (Ford)
34. 5th Gear Shift Fork
35. Transmission Case
36. 5th/Reverse Shift Lever (Ford)
37. Reverse Idler Gear
38. Idler Gear Shaft
39. Ford Case Cover w/Top Gear Sensing Switch
40. Output Shaft Bushing
41. Shift Lever Pivot Bolt
42. Input Shaft Bearing Retainer
43. Bearing Retainer Seal
44. Shim
45. Front Bearing
46. Input Shaft
47. Detent Plate
48. Detent Ball & Spring
49. Offset Lever
50. Shift Lever Sleeve
51. Vent
52. 5th/Reverse Shift Lever (AMC & Jeep)
53. Adapter Housing (AMC & Jeep)
54. Adapter Housing Seal
55. Extension Housing
56. Extension Housing Seal
57. 5th/Reverse Shift Rail (AMC & Jeep)

Manual Transmissions

BORG-WARNER 5-SPEED MODEL T5 (Cont.)

Fig. 5: Installing Synchronizer Insert Spring

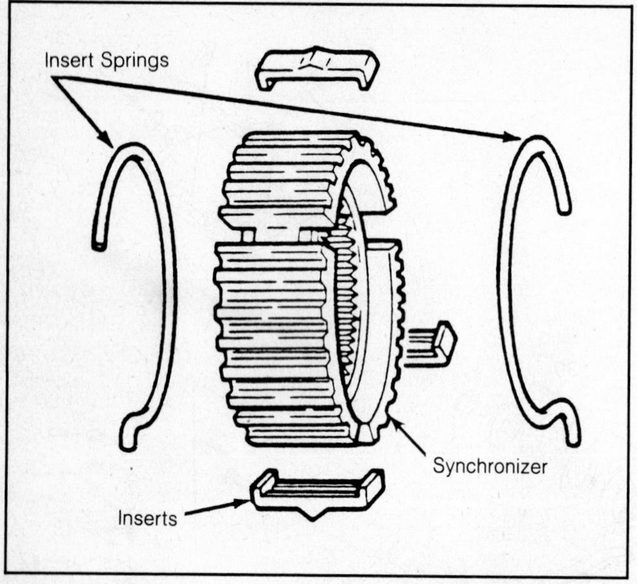

NOTE: **If any output shaft gear is replaced, the countershaft gear must also be replaced to maintain proper gear mesh and avoid noisy operation.**

3) Install blocking ring and 2nd gear on output shaft. Install tabbed thrust washer and 2nd gear retaining snap ring on output shaft. Be sure that washer tab is properly seated in output shaft notch.

4) Install blocking ring, 1st gear, roll pin and thrust washer on output shaft. Slide rear bearing on output shaft. Using Installer (J-22912) or equivalent and arbor press, install 5th gear on output shaft.

5) Install 3rd-4th gear synchronizer hub insert and sleeve on output shaft. Hub offset must face forward. Install thrust bearing washer on forward end of output shaft.

SYNCHRONIZERS

Disassembly

Before disassembling, scribe alignment marks on sleeve and hub for assembly reference. Remove insert retainer (5th gear synchronizer only). Remove retaining springs and inserts. On 1st-2nd synchronizer, sleeve should be removed to prevent loss of detent ball and spring.

NOTE: **The 1st-2nd gear synchronizer is available only as an assembly with the output shaft and no attempt should be made to separate the hub from the shaft.**

Reassembly

Assemble inserts and synchronizer retaining springs onto sleeve and hub. Retaining springs engage same insert but rotate in opposite directions. On 5th gear synchronizer, install insert retainer making sure retainer tabs are positioned over synchronizer inserts. On 1st-2nd gear synchronizer, install detent ball and spring into hub on the output shaft and assemble retaining springs, inserts and sleeve onto hub.

SHIFT COVER ASSEMBLY

Disassembly

1) Place selector arm plates and shift rail in Neutral. Rotate shift rail counterclockwise until selector arm disengages from selector arm plates and selector arm roll pin is accessible.

2) Pull shift rail rearward until selector arm contacts 1st-2nd shift fork. Using a punch, remove selector arm roll pin. Remove shift rail. *See Fig. 6.*

3) Remove shift forks, selector arm plates, selector arm, roll pin and interlock plate. Using a screwdriver, remove shift rail oil seal and "O" ring. Using a hammer and punch, remove shift rail plug.

Fig. 6: Removing Shift Rail Retaining Roll Pin

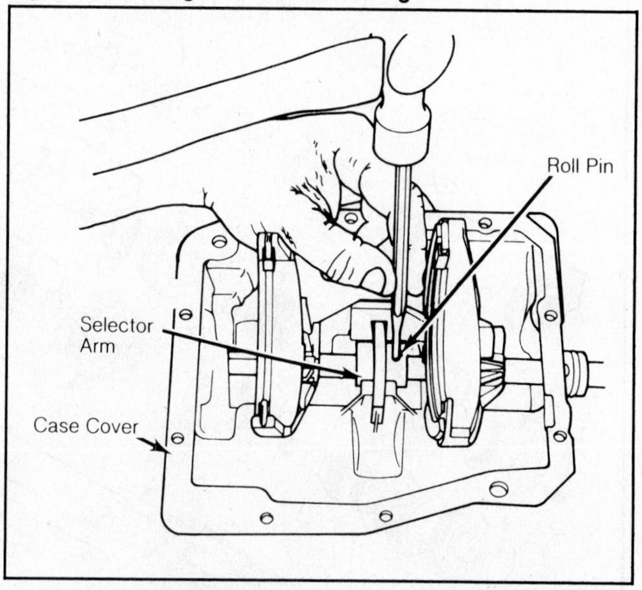

4) Remove nylon inserts and selector arm plates from shift forks. Note position of inserts and plates for reassembly reference.

Reassembly

1) Install nylon inserts and selector arm plates in shift forks. Apply sealer to edge of shift rail plug and install. Coat shift rail and bore with petroleum jelly and install shift rail in cover with end of rail flush with inside edge of cover.

2) Position 1st-2nd shift fork in cover with fork offset facing rear of cover. Push shift rail through fork. Position selector arm and C-shaped interlock plate in cover and insert shift rail. Widest part of interlock plate must face away from cover, and selector arm roll pin hold must face downward and toward rear of cover.

3) Position 3rd-4th shift fork in cover with fork offset facing rear of cover. Fork selector arm plate must be positioned under 1st-2nd shift fork selector arm plate. Insert shift rail through 3rd-4th shift fork and into shift rail bore in cover. Rotate shift rail until selector arm plate faces away from cover.

4) Align roll pin holes in selector arm and shift rail. Install roll pin. Install "O" ring in groove of shift rail oil seal. Install shift rail oil seal in cover.

INPUT SHAFT BEARING

Using a press and Universal Press Plate (D79L-4621-A), or equivalent and remove input shaft bearing. To install, use a press and a capped length of pipe and install bearing.

FRONT BEARING RRTAINER SEAL

NOTE: **If seal is being replaced as part of a transmission overhaul, do not install end play shim.**

BORG-WARNER 5-SPEED MODEL T5 (Cont.)

Remove bearing race and end play shim. using a screwdriver, carefully pry out seal from bearing retainer. To install, use Bearing Retainer Seal Installer (T77F-4220-A), or equivalent and install new seal. Install end play shim and bearing race.

CLEANING & INSPECTION

1) Wash all parts in solvent and dry all parts, except bearings, with compressed air. Allow bearings to air dry or wipe dry with a clean shop cloth. Clean needle thrust and roller bearings.

2) Inspect transmission case, cover and extension or adapter housing. Replace if there are cracks in bores, sides, bosses or bolt holes. Replace case if there are stripped bolt holes, nicks, burrs, or rough surfaces in shaft bores or on gasket surfaces.

3) Inspect gear train and shift mechanism. Replace any parts exhibitiing wear, chips, galling, distortion or bending. Check for worn bearings and bores. Check for weak snap rings and stripped offset lever.

TRANSMISSION REASSEMBLY

1) Coat countershaft front bearing outer cage with Loctite 601, or equivalent. Using an arbor press, install countershaft front bearing flush with case. Coat tabbed countershaft thrust washer with petroleum jelly and install with tab engaged with depression in case.

CAUTION: Failure to properly support countershaft during bearing installation can result in permanent damage to the case.

2) Place transmission case on end and install countershaft in front bearing. Install countershaft rear bearing spacer. Coat rear bearing with petroleum jelly and install using Bearing Installer (J-29895, T83P-7025-AH), or equivalent.

3) Use sleeve tool to prevent needle bearings from catching on countershaft shoulder. When properly installed, bearing should extend .125" (3.17 mm) beyond surface of case.

4) Place reverse idler gear in case with shift lever groove facing rearward. Install reverse idler shaft from rear of case and install retaining roll pin. Install assembled output shaft in transmission case.

5) Install output shaft rear bearing race in case. Install 4th gear in case and engage 3rd-4th synchronizer sleeve and blocking ring on output shaft. Install front bearing race in front bearing cap without shims.

6) Temporarily install front bearing cap. Install 5th speed/reverse lever, pivot bolt and retaining "C" clip. Coat pivot bolt threads with RTV sealer. Be sure to engage reverse lever fork in reverse idler gear.

7) Install front bearing race in front bearing cap without shims. Temporarily install front bearing cap. Install 5th speed driven gear and retaining snap ring on rear of output shaft. Install 5th speed gear on countershaft.

8) Insert 5th gear-reverse rail through rear of case and install 5th-reverse gear lever. To simplify engagement with lever, rotate rail during installation. Install 5th-reverse gear lever over center spring.

9) Assemble 5th gear synchronizer sleeve, insert springs and insert retainer using marks made at disassembly. Install plastic inserts in notches on each side of 5th gear shift fork. Place 5th gear synchronizer sleeve on 5th gear shift fork and slide onto countershaft and 5th-reverse gear rail.

10) Align roll pin hole in 5th-reverse gear rail and 5th gear shift fork. Place assembled 5th-reverse gear rail and shift fork on block of wood and install retaining roll pin. Install thrust race against 5th gear synchronizer hub and install retaining snap ring.

11) Install needle thrust bearing against thrust race on countershaft. Coat thrust bearing and race with petroleum jelly. Install lipped thrust race over needle thrust bearing and install plastic funnel into hole in end of countershaft gear.

12) Temporarily install extension or adapter housing. Turn transmission case on end and mount dial indicator on extension or adapter housing with indicator stylus on end of output shaft. Rotate clutch and output shaft and zero dial indicator. Pull upward on output shaft and read end play on dial indicator. *See Fig. 7.*

Fig. 7: Measuring Output Shaft End Play

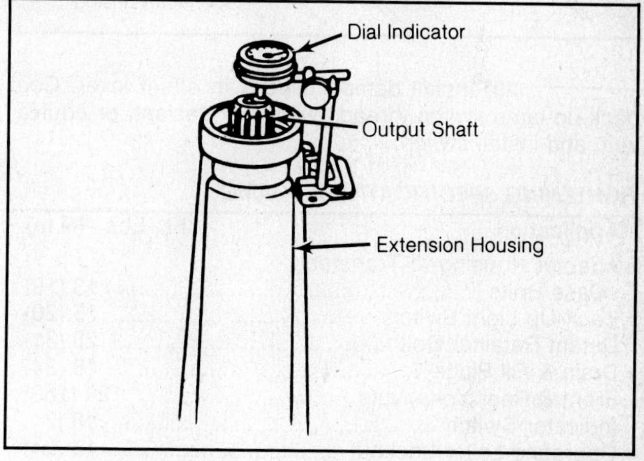

13) Select a shim pack measuring .001-.005" (.03-.13 mm) thicker than end play measured in step **12)**. Horizontally place transmission on bench and remove front bearing cap and race.

14) Add shims to cap and install clutch shaft bearing race in cap. Apply RTV sealant, or equivalent, to front bearing cap and install on transmission case. Tighten bolts. Recheck end play. There should be no end play.

15) Remove extension or adapter housing and install extension or adapter housing seal using a seal installer. Move transmission shift fork to place transmission in neutral.

16) Apply RTV sealant, or equivalent, to cover. Install cover assembly onto case while aligning shift forks and synchronizer sleeves. Install cover attaching bolts and tighten. Be sure that reverse relay lever is engaged.

17) Apply RTV sealant, or equivalent, to extension or adapter housing and install housing over output shaft and shift rail into position where shift rail just enters shift cover opening.

18) Install detent spring into offset lever and place steel ball in neutral guide plate detent. *See Fig. 8.* Apply pressure to steel ball with detent spring and offset lever.

19) Slide offset lever onto shift rail and seat extension or adapter housing to transmission case. Install and tighten housing attaching bolts. Install roll pin in offset lever and shift rail.

BORG-WARNER 5-SPEED MODEL T5 (Cont.)

Fig. 8: Offset Lever, Ball & Spring Location

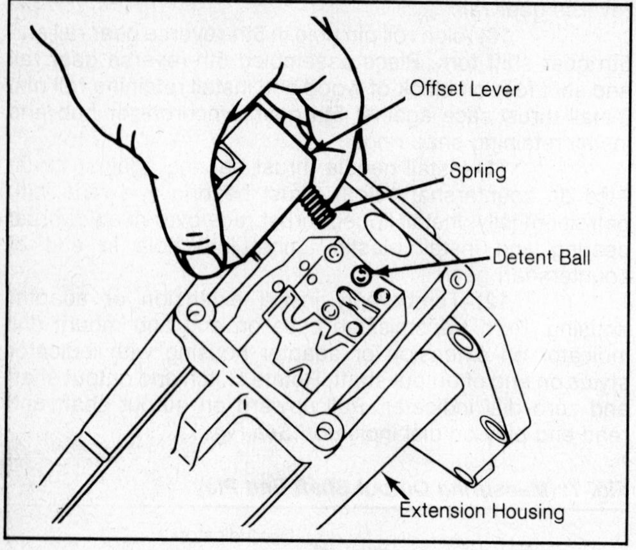

20) Install damper sleeve in offset lever. Coat back-up lamp switch threads with RTV sealant, or equivalent, and install switch.

TIGHTENING SPECIFICATIONS - AMC

Application	Ft. Lbs. (N.m)
Adapter Housing-to-Transfer Case Bolts	13 (18)
Back-Up Light Switch	15 (20)
Detent Retainer Bolt	23 (31)
Drain & Fill Plugs	18 (24)
Front & Rear Yoke Nuts	120 (163)
Indicator Switch	18 (24)
Operating Lever Locknut	18 (24)
Rear Case-to-Front Case Bolts	23 (31)
Retainer Bolts	23 (31)
Transfer Case Mounting Nuts	26 (35)

TIGHTENING SPECIFICATIONS - FORD MOTOR CO.

Application	Ft. Lbs. (N.m)
Back-Up Light Switch	12-18 (17-24)
Bearing Retainer	11-20 (15-27)
Cluster Gear Rear Bearing Retainer	10-15 (15-20)
Drain Plug	15-30 (20-41)
Extension Housing	20-45 (27-61)
Neutral Sensing Switch	12-18 (17-24)
Shift Cover	6-11 (8-15)
Shift Lever-to-Transmission	23-32 (31-43)
Shift Tower-to-Extension Housing	23-32 (31-43)
Top Gear Sensing Switch	12-18 (17-24)
Turret Cover	11-15 (15-20)
Transmission Housing Extension Bolts	28-36 (38-48)
Transmission Support	36-50 (48-68)
Transmission-to-Flywheel Housing	35-55 (61-88)

TIGHTENING SPECIFICATIONS - JEEP

Application	Ft. Lbs. (N.m)
Adapter Housing-to-Transfer Case Bolts	13 (18)
Back-Up Light Switch	15 (20)
Fill Plug	23 (31)
Front Bearing Cap Bolt	13 (18)
Shift Cover-to-Case	10 (14)
Reverse Pilot Bolt-to-Case	20 (27)
Transmission-to-Clutch Housng Bolt	13 (18)

BORG-WARNER 4-SPEED MODEL T18

Bronco and
F150/F350, 2WD & 4WD

IDENTIFICATION

An identification tag is located on the left front side of the transmission case.

DESCRIPTION

Transmission is a 4-speed unit, synchronized in 2nd, 3rd, and 4th gears only. First and reverse gears are spur type, while 2nd, 3rd, and 4th gears are helical type. The input shaft is supported with a ball bearing. The mainshaft is supported at the front by a pilot bearing in input shaft and at the rear by a ball bearing pressed onto shaft and into case. All other gears are supported by needle bearings.

LUBRICATION & ADJUSTMENT

See appropriate MANUAL TRANSMISSION SERVICING article in DOMESTIC/IMPORT GENERAL SERVICING section.

TROUBLE SHOOTING

See MANUAL TRANSMISSION TROUBLE SHOOTING article in DOMESTIC GENERAL SERVICING section.

REMOVAL AND INSTALLATION

SHIFT LEVER

NOTE: **Remove shift ball, boot and lever as an assembly. Disassemble only if individual component replacement is required.**

Removal

Remove plastic insert from shift ball. Warm ball with heat gun to 140-180°F (60-82°C). Using wooden block and hammer, carefully drive ball from lever. Remove rubber boot and floor pan cover. Shift unit into 2nd gear, remove lock pin and remove lever from housing.

Installation

Install lever in housing, making certain slot in lever aligns with tab in housing. Install lock pin. Install rubber boot and floor pan cover. Warm ball with heat gun. Using 7/16 socket and mallet, tap ball on lever. Install plastic insert.

TRANSMISSION

See appropriate MANUAL TRANSMISSION REMOVAL article in DOMESTIC GENERAL SERVICING section.

TRANSMISSION DISASSEMBLY

1) Mount transmission in holding fixture and drain lubricant. Position shift lever in 2nd gear and remove shift control housing. Lock transmission in 2 gears, then remove companion flange and oil seal.

2) Remove speedometer driven gear and bearing assembly. Remove mainshaft bearing retainer or extension housing. Remove speedometer drive gear snap ring, retainer and drive gear.

3) Remove the mainshaft bearing snap ring retainers and remove bearing spacer. Using puller and attachments (T75L-7025-B, F, H and J), remove mainshaft bearing. *See Fig. 1.*

Fig. 1: Removing Mainshaft Bearing

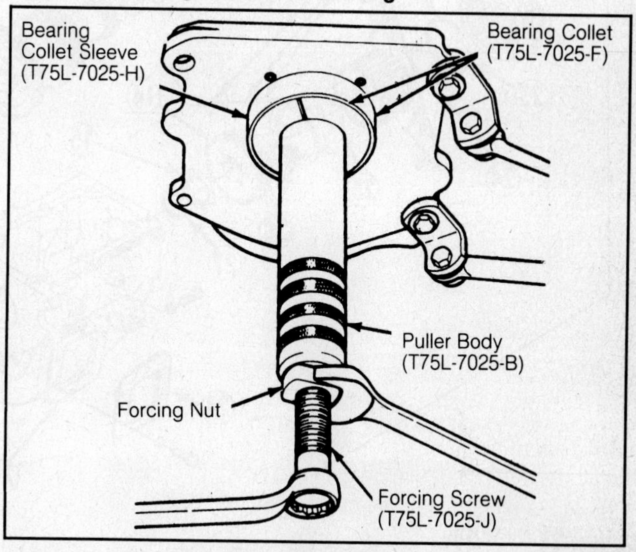

4) Remove input shaft bearing retainer. Using same puller, remove input shaft bearing. Remove input shaft oil baffle. Carefully remove input shaft assembly from case by pushing rearward and removing from inside case.

5) Remove lock plate from countershaft and reverse idler shaft. Using slide hammer and adapter (T50T-100-A and T50T-7140-C), remove reverse idler gear shaft. *See Fig. 3.* Remove reverse idler gear from case.

6) Using same tool combination, remove countershaft. Insert proper O.D. dummy shaft, about 10" long, into countershaft. Remove countershaft gear assembly from case, ensuring countershaft needle bearings and spacers remain in place.

CLEANING & INSPECTION

1) All parts should be thoroughly cleaned in solvent and air dried. If any transmission gear requires replacement, also replace gear with which it meshes. Replace gaskets, oil seals and snap rings.

2) Inspect transmission case for cracks, worn or scored bearing bosses. Examine bearings for cracked races, excessive wear and improper fit in case bores.

3) Inspect gear teeth for cracks or chips. Check countershaft and reverse idler shaft for pitting, wear, scores, nicks, cracks and flat spots. Replace shafts if worn or damaged. Replace parts as required.

COMPONENT DISASSEMBLY & REASSEMBLY

COUNTERSHAFT GEAR

Disassembly

Remove dummy shaft, roller bearings, spacers and center spacer from countershaft gear.

Manual Transmissions

BORG-WARNER 4-SPEED MODEL T18 (Cont.)

Fig. 2: Exploded View of Warner Model T 18 4-Speed Transmission

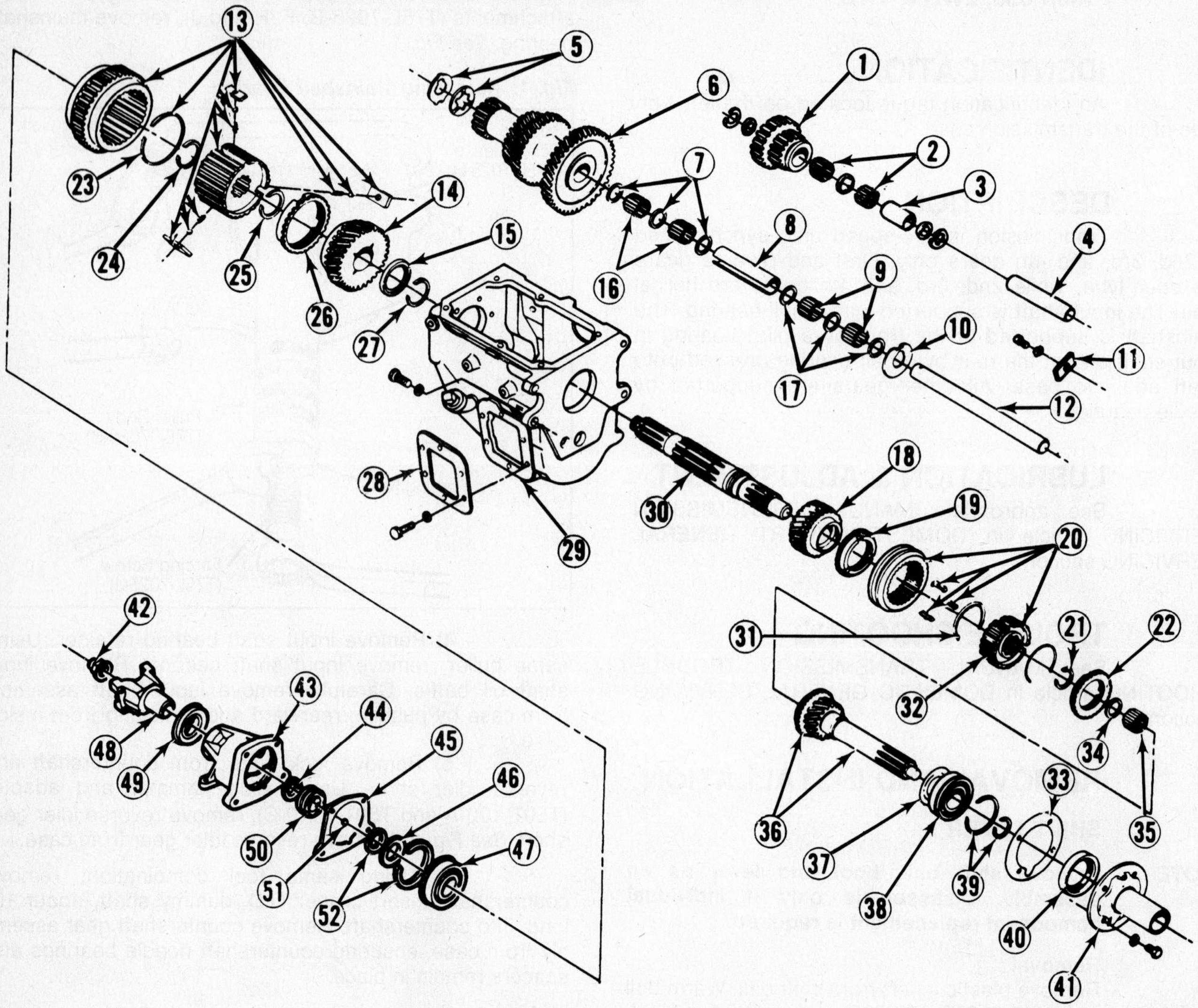

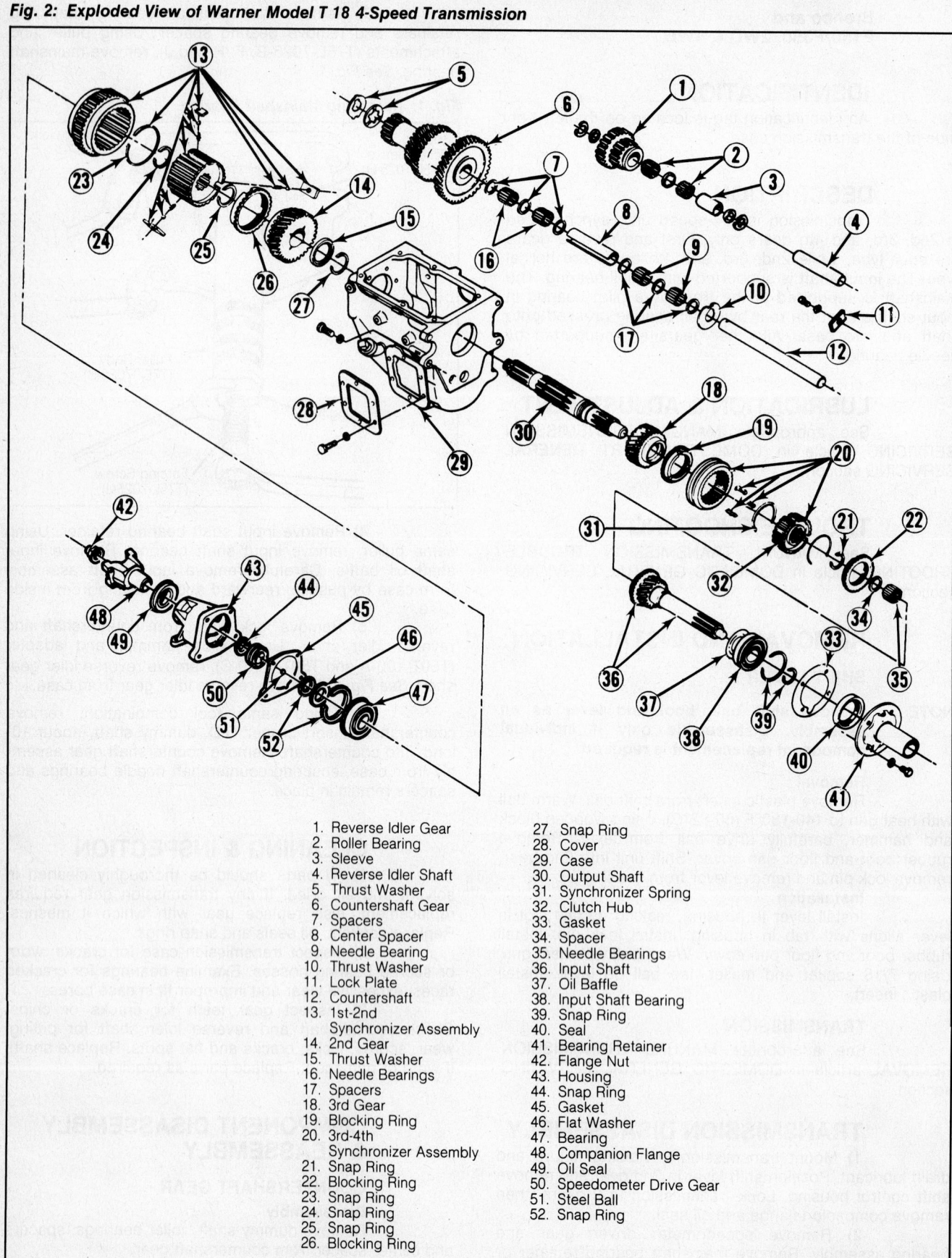

1. Reverse Idler Gear
2. Roller Bearing
3. Sleeve
4. Reverse Idler Shaft
5. Thrust Washer
6. Countershaft Gear
7. Spacers
8. Center Spacer
9. Needle Bearing
10. Thrust Washer
11. Lock Plate
12. Countershaft
13. 1st-2nd Synchronizer Assembly
14. 2nd Gear
15. Thrust Washer
16. Needle Bearings
17. Spacers
18. 3rd Gear
19. Blocking Ring
20. 3rd-4th Synchronizer Assembly
21. Snap Ring
22. Blocking Ring
23. Snap Ring
24. Snap Ring
25. Snap Ring
26. Blocking Ring
27. Snap Ring
28. Cover
29. Case
30. Output Shaft
31. Synchronizer Spring
32. Clutch Hub
33. Gasket
34. Spacer
35. Needle Bearings
36. Input Shaft
37. Oil Baffle
38. Input Shaft Bearing
39. Snap Ring
40. Seal
41. Bearing Retainer
42. Flange Nut
43. Housing
44. Snap Ring
45. Gasket
46. Flat Washer
47. Bearing
48. Companion Flange
49. Oil Seal
50. Speedometer Drive Gear
51. Steel Ball
52. Snap Ring

Manual Transmissions

BORG-WARNER 4-SPEED MODEL T18 (Cont.)

Fig. 3: Removing Reverse Idler Shaft

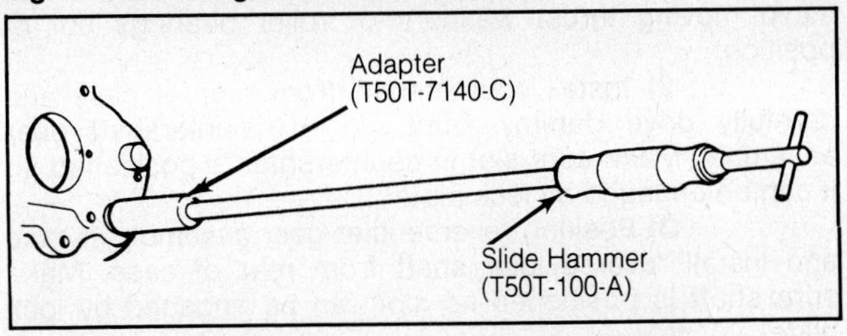

Remove countershaft using same tool combination.

Reassembly

1) Insert center spacer into bore of countershaft gear. Insert dummy shaft into center of spacer. Lightly coat bore of countershaft with petroleum jelly. Install 1 bearing spacer and 22 roller bearings in bore.

2) Position spacer on top of rollers, install 22 more rollers and another spacer. Repeat same operation at opposite end of countershaft gear. Leave dummy shaft installed in gear.

MAINSHAFT

Disassembly

1) Remove 3rd-4th synchronizer snap ring from mainshaft and slide 3rd-4th synchronizer assembly and 3rd gear from mainshaft. Remove synchronizer sleeve and inserts from hub.

2) Check end play of 2nd gear, it should be .005-.024" (.127-.609 mm). Remove snap rings from end of hub. Slide 1st-2nd gear from hub, being careful not to loose any balls, springs, inserts or anti-rattle spring and ball.

3) Remove snap ring from behind synchronizer hub. Pull synchronizer hub from shaft and remove blocking ring. Remove snap ring from 2nd gear and remove gear and thrust washer from mainshaft.

Reassembly

1) Place mainshaft in soft-jaw vise with threaded end up. Install snap ring in 3rd groove from threaded end of shaft. Place 2nd gear thrust on shaft with recessed end over snap ring.

2) Position 2nd gear against washer and install snap ring. Place blocking ring on 2nd gear. Assemble 2nd gear synchronizer assembly over splines of mainshaft while aligning blocking ring cut-outs with inserts.

3) Install snap ring in mainshaft groove behind clutch hub. Turn mainshaft over and place 3rd gear against shoulder of mainshaft. Install 3rd gear blocking ring.

4) Install 3rd-4th synchronizer assembly over mainshaft splines. Align blocking ring slots with inserts and position end of hub with long chamfer to front of transmission. Install snap ring and spacer.

Fig. 4: Exploded View of Shift Control Housing

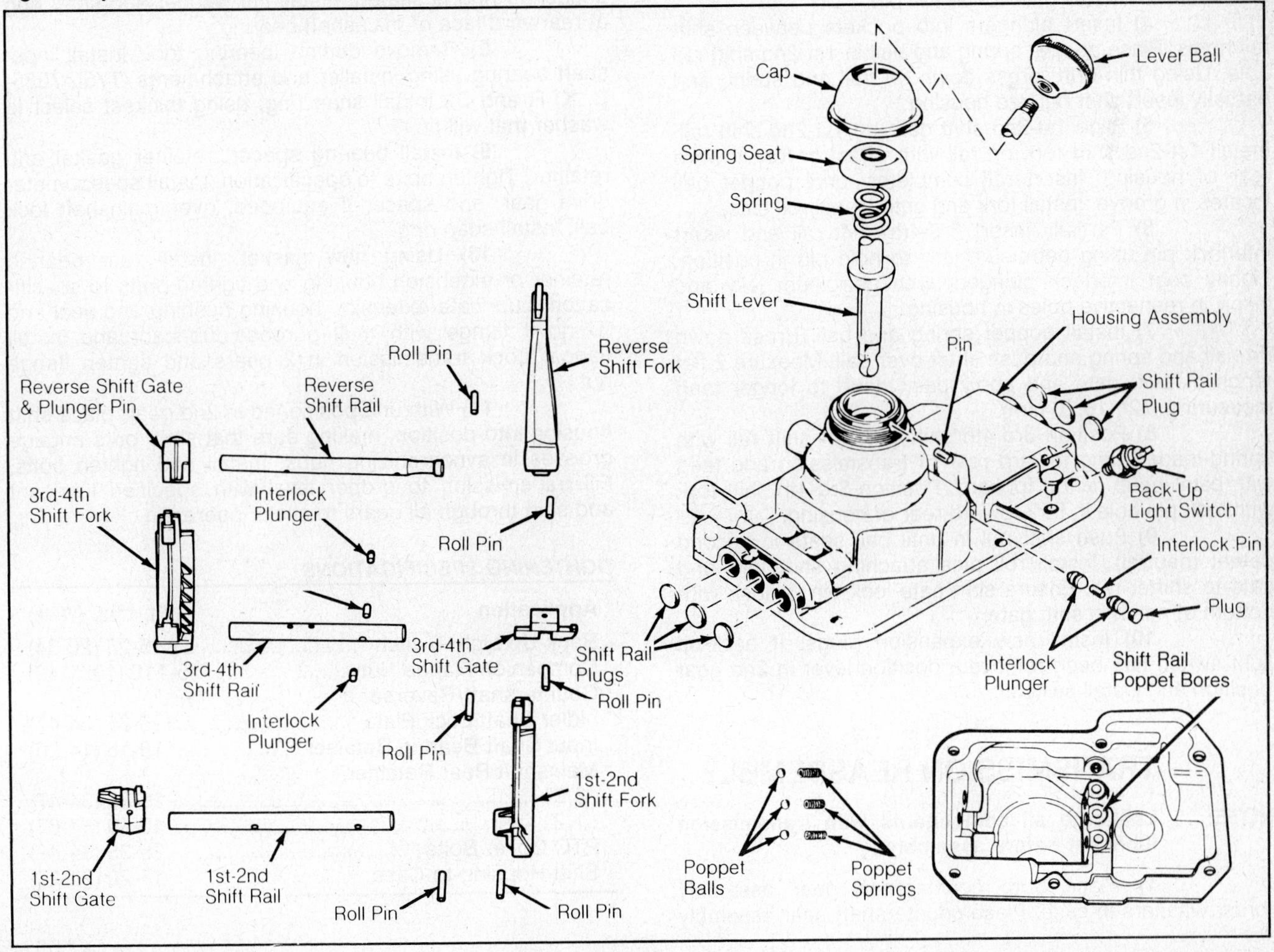

BORG-WARNER 4-SPEED MODEL T18 (Cont.)

SHIFT CONTROL HOUSING

Disassembly

1) Place housing in soft-jawed vise with shift forks facing upward. Remove back-up light switch. Using a hammer and a punch, remove shift rail expansion plugs from forward end of housing.

2) Using pin punch, drive out roll pins securing shift forks and shift gates. Tap shift rails out front of housing while holding shop towel over poppet springs and balls to prevent losing them.

3) Remove interlock pin from 3rd-4th shift rail. Remove shift forks and shift gates. Note location of forks and gates for reassembly. Remove poppet balls and springs from housing.

4) Remove interlock plungers from housing. If required, remove retaining clip, spring and plunger from reverse shift gate.

Reassembly

1) Replace breather in housing if damaged or restricted. If reverse shift gate is disassembled, install spring and plunger, compress spring and install retaining clip.

2) Position spring and ball in reverse shift rail hole in housing. Partially insert shift rail into housing and install reverse shift fork on rail. Using long thin drift, push down on poppet ball and spring.

3) Position reverse shift ball notch so it does not pass over ball. Slide reverse gate onto rail with long end forward. Drive rail into housing until ball locates in groove in rail. Install gate-to-rail roll pin.

4) Insert plungers into pockets between shift rail holes. Place poppet spring and ball in 1st-2nd shift rail hole. Using thin drift, press down on ball and spring and partially insert shift rail into housing.

5) Slide 1st-2nd shift gate on 1st-2nd shift rail. Install 1st-2nd shift fork on rail with offset in fork toward rear of housing. Insert rail completely until poppet ball locates in groove. Install fork and gate-to-rail roll pins.

6) Partially insert 3rd-4th shift rail and insert interlock pin using petroleum jelly to hold pin in position. Lightly coat interlock plungers with petroleum jelly and insert in respective holes in housing.

7) Install poppet spring and ball. Press down on ball and spring and push shaft over ball. Measure 2 flat tangs of shift gate and apply paint daub to longer tang measuring .72" (18.26 mm).

8) Position 3rd-4th shift gate on shift rail with spring-loaded tang toward rear of transmission and tang with paint daub facing forward. Position 3rd-4th shift fork with lock pin hole in fork toward rear of housing.

9) Push shift rail in until ball seats in second detent (neutral). Install roll pins attaching shift fork and gate to shifter rail. Ensure shift gate lock pin is flush with bottom of notch in shift gate.

10) Install new expansion plugs. If back-up light switch has been removed, position lever in 2nd gear position and install switch.

TRANSMISSION REASSEMBLY

NOTE: **Lubricate all components with transmission lubricant before assembly.**

1) Place both countershaft gear assembly thrust washers in case. Place countershaft gear assembly into position, with dummy shaft still installed. Use care to avoid moving thrust washers or roller bearings out of position.

2) Install countershaft from rear of case and carefully drive dummy shaft out of countershaft gear assembly. Make sure slot in countershaft is positioned so it can be engaged by lock plate.

3) Position reverse idler gear assembly in case and install reverse idler shaft from rear of case. Make sure shaft is positioned so slot can be engaged by lock plate.

4) Install countershaft and reverse idler gear shaft lock plate. Install 22 pilot roller bearings in end of input shaft. Use petroleum jelly to hold bearings in place.

5) Place input shaft in case. Place 4th gear synchronizer blocking ring on input shaft. Install mainshaft in transmission case, taking care not to move pilot roller bearings out of position.

6) Install input shaft oil baffle. Install dummy bearing (T75L-7025-Q) on transmission input shaft to hold input shaft and mainshaft in place while installing mainshaft bearing.

NOTE: **If dummy bearing is not used, slide a protector over 3rd-4th synchronizer to prevent wedging 4th blocking ring onto tapered seat.**

7) Install snap ring on mainshaft bearing. Using installer set (T75L-7025-B and L), install bearing into case until snap ring is seated. Install flat washer and snap ring at rearward face of mainshaft bearing.

8) Remove dummy bearing tool. Install input shaft bearing using installer and attachments (T75L-7025-B, K, R and S). Install snap ring, using thickest select fit washer that will fit.

9) Install bearing spacer, retainer gasket and retainer. Tighten bolts to specification. Install speedometer drive gear, and spacer if equipped, over mainshaft lock ball. Install snap ring.

10) Using new gasket, install rear bearing retainer or extension housing and tighten bolts to specification. Lubricate extension housing bushing and seal and "U" joint flange with multi-purpose lubricant and install flange. Lock transmission in 2 gears and tighten flange nut.

11) With unit positioned in 2nd gear, place shift housing into position, making sure that shift forks engage grooves in synchronizing hubs. Install and tighten bolts. Fill transmission to proper level with specified lubricant and shift through all gears to check operation.

TIGHTENING SPECIFICATIONS

Application	Ft. Lbs. (N.m)
Back-Up Light Switch	15-25 (20-34)
Companion Flange Nut	75-110 (102-149)
Countershaft/Reverse Idler Shaft Lock Plate	25-35 (34-47)
Input Shaft Bearing Retainer	10-15 (14-20)
Mainshaft Rear Retainer	
3/8"	25-35 (34-47)
1/2"	40-50 (54-67)
PTO Cover Bolts	25-35 (34-47)
Shift Housing-to-Case	17-20 (24-27)

BORG-WARNER 4-SPEED MODEL T19B/D

F250/350 HD (2WD & 4WD)

IDENTIFICATION

The transmission identification code can be found on the Vehicle Compliance Certification Label located on the driver's door lock pillar. The code for a Borg-Warner 4-speed model T19B/D is "P". There is also a service identification tag located on the left middle cover-to-case transmission bolt. *See Fig. 1.*

Fig. 1: Transmission Identification Tag

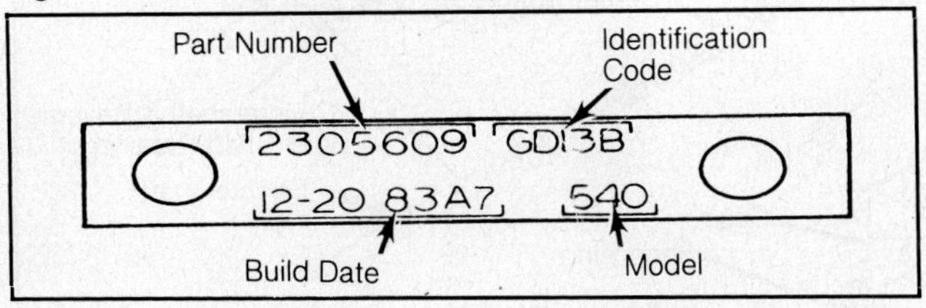

DESCRIPTION

The 4-speed fully synchronized model T19B/D transmission is equipped with a center, floor mounted gear shift lever. The reverse and 1st, 2nd, 3rd, and 4th gears are helical cut for quiet running. The input shaft is supported by a ball bearing. Front end of the output shaft is supported by a pilot bearing installed in the input shaft. The rear end of the output shaft is supported by a ball bearing. The ball bearing and shaft are retained in the case by a snap ring.

LUBRICATION & ADJUSTMENT

See appropriate MANUAL TRANSMISSION SERVICING article in DOMESTIC GENERAL SERVICING section.

REMOVAL & INSTALLATION

TRANSMISSION

See appropriate MANUAL TRANSMISSION REMOVAL article in DOMESTIC GENERAL SERVICING section.

SERVICE (IN VEHICLE)

GEAR SHIFT LEVER

NOTE: Remove shift ball only if shift ball, boot, or lever is to be replaced. If either the ball, boot, or lever is not being replaced, remove the ball, boot, and lever as an assembly.

Removal

1) Remove plastic insert from shift ball. Warm ball with heat gun to 140-160°F (60-82°C), knock ball off lever with a block of wood and a hammer, taking care not to damage finish on shift lever.

2) Remove rubber boot and floor pan cover. Shift transmission into 2nd gear, remove lock pin, and shift lever from shift lever housing.

Installation

1) Install shift lever in shifter housing, making sure that slot in lever aligns with tab in housing. Install lock pin. Install rubber boot and floor pan cover.

2) Warm ball with heat gun to 140-180°F (60-82°C) and tap ball on lever with a 7/16" socket and mallet. Install plastic shift pattern insert.

TRANSMISSION DISASSEMBLY

1) Install transmission in bench mounted holding fixture. Remove drain plug and drain lubricant from transmission. Remove bolts retaining gear shift housing to case and remove housing.

2) Lock transmission in two gears and remove U-joint flange and oil seal. Remove speedometer driven gear and bearing assembly. Remove output shaft bearing retainer or extension housing and gasket.

3) Remove speedometer drive gear snap ring retainer. Slide drive gear off output shaft. Remove output shaft bearing snap ring from output shaft and snap ring from bearing. Remove bearing spacer.

4) Install tools (T75L-7025-B, F, H & J) on output shaft and over output shaft bearing. Remove output shaft bearing. Remove input shaft bearing retainer and gasket. Remove input shaft bearing snap ring from input shaft and snap ring from bearing.

5) Install remover tube on input shaft and over input shaft bearing. Remove input shaft bearing. Remove input shaft oil baffle. Baffle is installed in an offset position away from bearing.

6) Remove spring clip from reverse shifter arm pivot screw. Remove pivot screw from shifter arm and case. Lift shifter arm and shoe assembly out of case by prying with screwdriver.

7) Remove input shaft (with flat facing upward) assembly from case. DO NOT lose the 22 pilot bearing rollers from inner end of shaft. Remove thrust spacer. Remove output shaft and gear assemblies from case.

8) Use dummy countershaft (T83T-7111-B) to drive out countershaft (from the front). Keep dummy shaft in contact with countershaft to avoid dropping rollers. The dummy shaft should be 9.379-9.380" (238.23-238.25 mm) long and 1.133-1.135" (28.78-28.83 mm) in diameter.

9) Remove countershaft and cluster gear. Make sure front and rear thrust washers are removed from case. Be careful not to lose any rollers.

10) Remove idler shaft (from front of transmission) using shaft remover (T50T-7140-C) and slide hammer. Remove reverse idler gear, and thrust washers, being careful not to lose any rollers.

CLEANING & INSPECTION

1) Wash all parts (except bearings) in cleaning solvent and dry with compressed air. Brush or scrape all foreign matter from parts. Wash bearings in clean solvent, hold bearings and dry with compressed air. Inspect transmission case for cracks, damaged bearing bores, and/or threads.

2) Check operation and condition of shift levers, forks and side rails. Ensure that vent hole in the case is open.

3) Remove all small nicks or burrs from front and/or rear of case. Check bearings for excessive wear or roughness by slowly turning race by hand.

4) Inspect needle bearing rollers, shafts, and washers for wear and/or damage. Check all other parts for wear, damage, chipped, and/or broken teeth. Replace parts as necessary.

BORG-WARNER 4-SPEED MODEL T19B/D (Cont.)

Fig. 2: Exploded View of Borg-Warner T19B 4-Speed Transmission

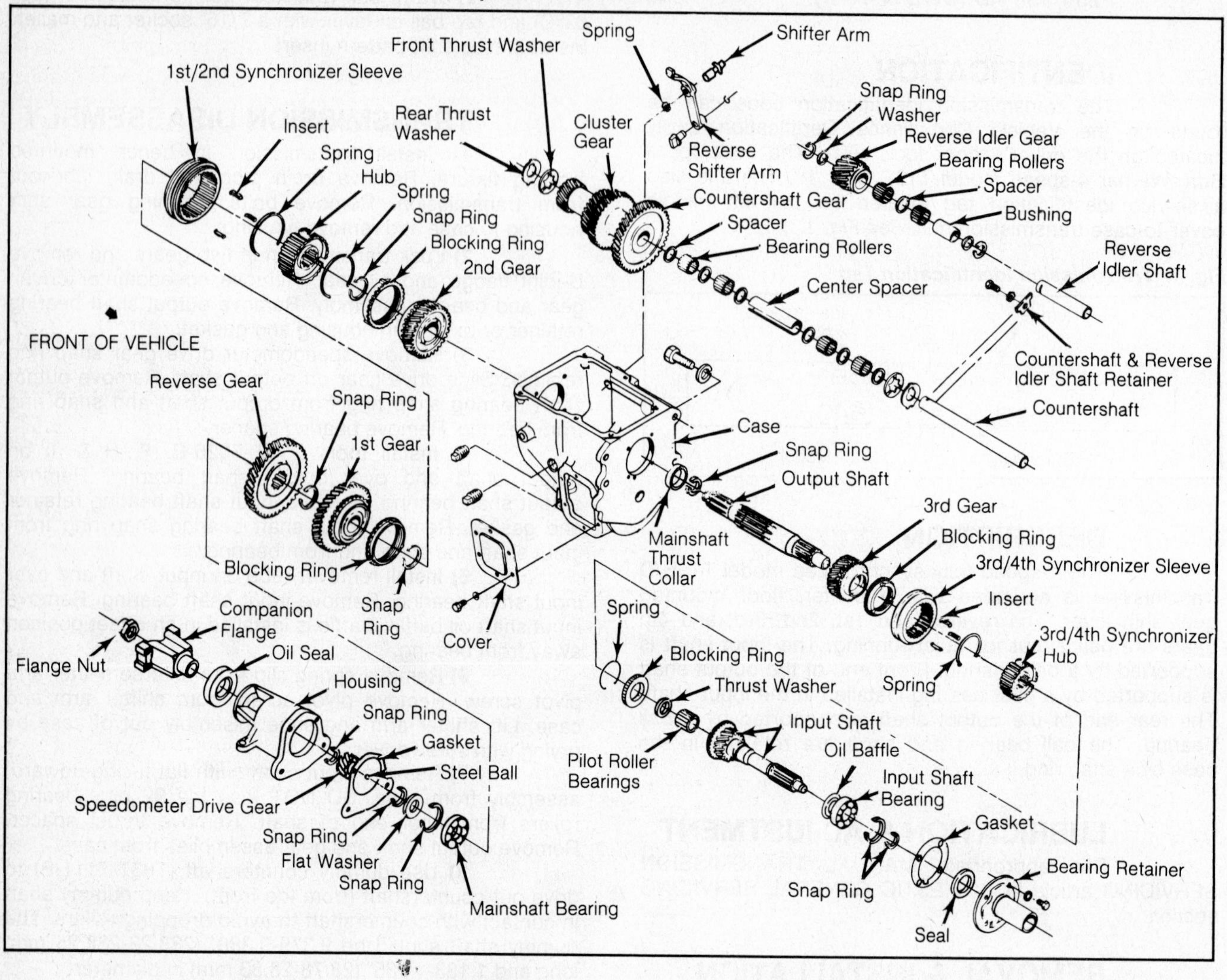

COMPONENT DISASSEMBLY & REASSEMBLY

INPUT SHAFT

Disassembly

Remove thrust spacer and pilot rollers from gear bore. Using a puller, remove input shaft ball bearing. Remove oil baffle.

Reassembly

Press ball bearing and oil baffle onto input shaft and against gear. Coat bore of gear with grease, and place 22 pilot rollers in bore. Install thrust spacer in bore against rollers. Use grease to hold it in position.

OUTPUT SHAFT

Disassembly

1) Remove snap ring. Slide 3rd/4th synchronizer assembly, blocking ring, and 3rd gear off shaft. Place output shaft in an arbor press and press reverse gear off shaft or pull reverse gear off shaft with puller.

2) Remove 1st gear selective snap ring. Slide 1st gear and blocking ring off output shaft. Remove 1st/2nd gear synchronizer snap ring. Slide synchronizer off shaft.

3) Remove snap ring from rear of 2nd gear. Remove blocking ring and synchronizer gear from output shaft.

Reassembly

1) Hold shaft in a vertical position with front of shaft down, and slide 2nd gear onto shaft (gear cone toward rear). Install selective snap ring of .092-.094" (2.34-2.39 mm) onto output shaft at rear of 2nd gear.

2) Place a blocking ring in 1st/2nd synchronizer assembly next to side of hub with counterbore. Make sure that ring slots are aligned with insert.

3) Hold blocking ring in 1st/2nd synchronizer assembly (with ring slots aligned with inserts) on side with hub counterbore and install assembly on output shaft. The hub counterbore must be toward 2nd gear. Install thickest selective snap ring that can be fit into groove.

4) Install second blocking ring in synchronizer assembly, making sure that ring slots are aligned with inserts. Install 1st gear (coned portion toward 1st/2nd synchronizer assembly) and .101-.103" (2.57-2.61 mm) thick snap ring on shaft.

5) Mount output shaft in a press and press reverse gear (longer hub toward 1st gear) on shaft. Press rear bearing cone on output shaft. If output shaft bearing

BORG-WARNER 4-SPEED MODEL T19B/D (Cont.)

is to be replaced, be sure it is a maximum load-rated bearing.

6) Remove output shaft from press. Install 3rd gear (cone toward front). Place a blocking ring in 3rd/4th synchronizer assembly on side with larger hub diameter. Make sure that slots are aligned with inserts.

7) Hold blocking ring in position, and slide synchronizer assembly onto output shaft. Blocking ring and large hub diameter must be toward 3rd gear. Install thrust race on shaft against synchronizer hub. The flange must be toward front. Install thrust bearing against race.

8) Apply grease to face of blocking ring and install it on shaft and in 3rd/4th synchronizer assembly.

COUNTERSHAFT

Disassembly

Remove dummy shaft, bearing rollers, bearing spacers, and center spacer from countershaft gear.

Reassembly

1) Slide long bearing spacer into countershaft bore and insert dummy shaft in spacer. Dummy shaft should be lubricated liberally with grease.

2) Hold gear in a vertical position and install one of the bearing spacers. Position the 22 pilot bearing rollers in gear bore. *See Fig. 3.*

Fig. 3: Countershaft Gear Bearing Rollers Installation

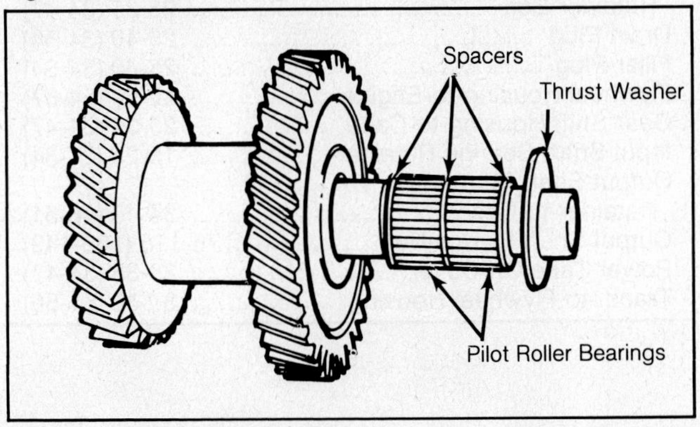

Install 22 rollers, a spacer, and 22 more rollers.

3) Place a spacer on top of rollers and install 22 pilot bearing rollers and another spacer. Coat face of large thrust washer with grease.

4) Hold a large thrust washer against the end of countershaft gear to prevent rollers from dropping out and turn assembly over. Install rollers, spacers, and thrust washer in the other end of gear.

REVERSE IDLER GEAR

Disassembly

1) Check idler gear roller bearings for roughness by holding bushing to prevent its turning while rotating gear. The gear should then be installed on shaft to check for roughness between shaft and bushing.

2) If gear turns freely and smoothly, disassembly of unit is not necessary. If any roughness is noticed, disassemble unit by removing snap ring from one end of gear.

3) Remove idler gear bearing rollers, thrust washers, bearing spacer, bushing, and remaining snap ring from gear.

Reassembly

1) Install snap ring in one end of idler gear and set gear on end, with snap ring at bottom. Position a thrust washer in gear on top snap ring. Coat outside of bushing with grease and install bushing on top of washer.

2) Insert 37 bearing rollers between bushing and gear bore. Install a spacer on top of rollers and install 37 more rollers. Place remaining thrust washer on rollers and install snap ring.

1ST/2ND & 3RD/4TH SYNCHRONIZER HUBS

Disassembly

Remove spring from each side of assembly, and remove the 3 inserts. Slide hub out of sleeve.

Reassembly

1) Install gear clutch hub in sleeve. On 1st/2nd synchro, hub counterbore should be on the same side as sleeve chamfer. On 3rd/4th synchro, the 2 grooves on chamfered portion of clutch sleeve can be assembled in either direction on hub. Place 3 inserts in hub slots. *See Fig. 4.*

Fig. 4: Synchronizer Hub and Sleeve Assembly

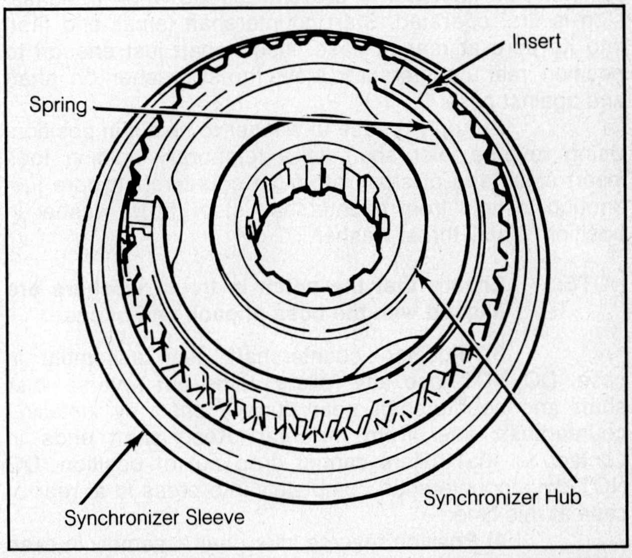

Hub counterbore should be on the side as sleeve chamfer.

2) Hook end of spring under an insert and position spring around hub and under each inserts. Turn assembly over and hook end of second spring over the other end of insert used for hooking first spring.

3) Position spring around hub and under each insert, but on opposite direction of first spring.

GEAR SHIFT HOUSING

Disassembly

1) Remove gear shift lever housing cap and lift lever out of housing. Be sure all shafts are in neutral before disassembly. Remove spring pins from shift forks and shift rail ends. Remove expansion plugs from ends of housing.

2) Tap shift rails out of housing while holding one hand over holes in housing to prevent loss of poppet springs and balls. Remove shift rail ends and forks. Lift the 2 shaft interlock plungers and pin out of housing.

3) To disassemble reverse shift rail end, remove circlip to release plunger and spring. Remove cotter pin, spring, and ball.

BORG-WARNER 4-SPEED MODEL T19B/D (Cont.)

with a spring pin. Slide rail to neutral position (center poppet).

6) Install interlock plunger and make sure it is positioned in notch in 3rd/4th shift rail. Assemble reverse plunger and spring in reverse shift rail end. Retain with a circlip inserted in plunger groove.

7) Assemble ball, spring, and cotter pin in shift rail end. Install reverse shift rail (notched end toward front), reverse shift rail end, poppet spring, and ball in housing.

8) Note that the 2 poppet notches are towards the housing top. Secure shift rail end to rail with a spring pin. Slide rail to neutral position. Install expansion plugs into the 3 shift rail openings at each end of housing.

9) Install gear shift lever, spring, spring seat, and lever housing cap.

TRANSMISSION REASSEMBLY

1) Coat all parts, especially bearings, with transmission lubricant to prevent scoring when transmission is first operated. Start countershaft (small end first) into its bore at rear of case. Insert shaft just enough to position rear countershaft steel thrust washer on shaft and against case.

2) Apply grease to washer to hold it in position. Using reverse idler shaft as a temporary holding tool, insert small end of shaft into front countershaft bore just enough to hold front countershaft steel thrust washer in position. Install thrust washer.

NOTE: **Ensure that the notch in thrust washers are aligned with the boss at each end of case.**

3) Position countershaft gear assembly in case. DO NOT lose any rollers. Slide out reverse idler shaft and countershaft gear dummy shaft by installing countershaft gear from the rear. Keep shaft ends in contact so that rollers cannot drop out of position. DO NOT drive countershaft completely into press fit at rear of case at this time.

4) Position reverse idler gear assembly in case and install idler (small end of shaft toward front). Shift fork groove of gear should be toward front of case. DO NOT drive shaft completely into position.

5) Make sure that countershaft and reverse idler gear shaft are properly aligned so that retainer can be positioned in shaft slots. Drive shafts into position in case. Install retainer and bolt. Install output shaft assembly in case.

6) With output shaft shifted slightly to the right, position reverse shifter arm and shoe assembly on reverse idler gear. Install pivot screw through hole in left side of case and into shifter arm hole. Install clip to retain shifter arm to pivot. Center output shaft to case bore.

7) Install input shaft through front bore with flats on shaft facing upward. When past countershaft, turn input shaft so flats are facing downward. Guide input shaft onto output shaft. Install input shaft oil baffle.

8) Install dummy bearing tool (T75L-7025-Q) on transmission input shaft. This tool is necessary to keep input and output shafts in alignment when installing output shaft bearing.

9) Assemble locating snap ring to outer race of output shaft bearing in groove provided. Using tools (T75L-7025-B & L) install output shaft bearing. Install flat washer against rearward face of output shaft bearing.

NOTE: **The properly installed washer will be external to the main body of transmission.**

10) Install snap ring at rearward surface of washer in output shaft groove provided. Remove dummy bearing from input shaft. Install input shaft bearing. Install snap ring. Use the thickest select fit snap rings which will fit on bearing.

11) Install input shaft bearing spacer, retainer gasket and retainer. Tighten bolts. Position speedometer drive gear and spacer (if used) on output shaft over lock ball. Install speedometer drive gear retaining snap ring.

12) Using a new gasket install output shaft bearing retainer (or extension housing). Tighten bolts. Lubricate retainer, bushing, seal, and U-joint flange with grease. Install U-joint flange. Lock transmission in 2 gears and tighten retaining nut.

13) Install gear shift housing assembly (with housing assembly and unit shifted into second gear). Fill transmission to proper level. Add 1/2 pint (1/4L) of lubricant through speedometer cable hole in rear transmission extension housing.

TIGHTENING SPECIFICATIONS

Application	Ft. Lbs. (N.m)
Countershaft and Reverse Idler Shaft Retainer Bolt	25-35 (34-47)
Drain Plug	25-40 (34-54)
Filler Plug	25-40 (34-54)
Flywheel Housing-to-Engine	40-50 (54-67)
Gear Shift Housing-to-Case	25-35 (34-47)
Input Shaft Bearing Retainer	15-25 (21-34)
Output Shaft Bearing Retainer-to-Case	34-45 (46-61)
Output Shaft Flange Nut	75-115 (102-149)
Power Take Off Cover	25-35 (34-47)
Trans.-to-Flywheel Housing	37-42 (51-56)

BORG-WARNER 4-SPEED MODEL T19B/D (Cont.)

Fig. 5: Exploded View of Gear Shift Housing and Shift Rail Locations

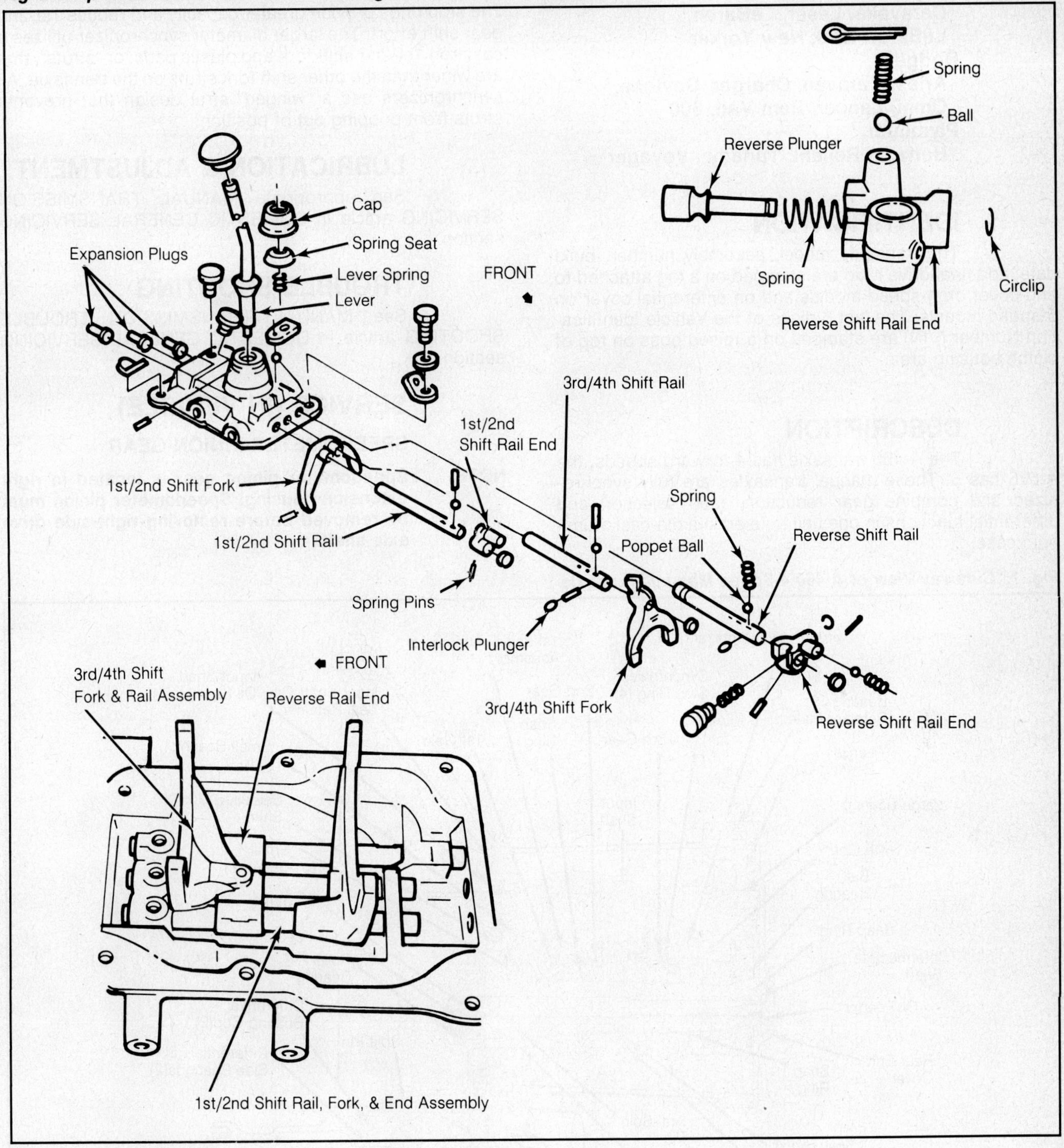

Reassembly

1) Position notched end of 1st/2nd shift rail through rear bore of housing. Slide 1st/2nd shift fork (use outer hole) onto shift rail. DO NOT slide shaft into its bore at front end at this time.

2) The 3 poppet notches should face the top of housing. Slide 1st/2nd shift rail end into rail. Place poppet spring and ball in hole at front of cover. Depress ball and spring, and slide rail into its bore over ball.

3) Drive a spring pin through hole in 1st/2nd shift rail end and into hole in rail. Secure shift fork to rail with spring pin. Slide shift rail to its neutral position (center poppet).

4) Install interlock plunger in housing making sure that end of plunger is in the side notch of 1st/2nd shift rail. Install 3rd/4th shift rail (notched end toward front) in center bore of housing, and assemble shift fork, interlock pin, and poppet spring and ball.

5) Note that 3rd/4th shift rail passes through a second hole in 1st/2nd shift fork and that poppet notches are toward housing top. Secure 3rd/4th shift fork to rail

Manual Transmissions

CHRYSLER A-460 & A-525 TRANSAXLES

Chrysler
Caravelle, Laser, LeBaron, LeBaron GTS, New Yorker
Dodge
Aries, Caravan, Charger, Daytona, Omni, Lancer, Ram Van, 600
Plymouth
Horizon, Reliant, Turismo, Voyager

IDENTIFICATION

The transaxle model, assembly number, build date, and final-drive ratio are stamped on a tag attached to end-cover on 4-speed models and on differential cover on 5-speed models. The last 8 digits of the Vehicle Identification Number (VIN) are stamped on a raised boss on top of clutch housing area.

DESCRIPTION

The A-460 transaxle has 4 forward speeds, the A-525 has 5. These manual transaxles are fully synchronized and combine gear reduction, ratio selection and differential functions in one unit housed in a die-cast aluminum case.

Larger diameter 1st-2nd synchronizers and 1st-2nd stop rings provide greater capacity and reduce 1st-2nd gear shift effort. The larger diameter synchronizer utilizes a cast iron 1st-2nd shift fork and plastic pads, or "struts", that are wider than the other shift fork struts on the transaxle. All synchronizers use a "winged" strut design that prevents struts from popping out of position.

LUBRICATION & ADJUSTMENT

See appropriate MANUAL TRANSMISSION SERVICING article in DOMESTIC GENERAL SERVICING section.

TROUBLE SHOOTING

See MANUAL TRANSMISSION TROUBLE SHOOTING article in DOMESTIC GENERAL SERVICING section.

SERVICE (IN VEHICLE)

SPEEDOMETER PINION GEAR

NOTE: **Speedometer pinion gear is located in right extension housing. Speedometer pinion must be removed before removing right-side drive axle shaft.**

Fig. 1: Cutaway View of A-460 4-Speed Manual Transaxle

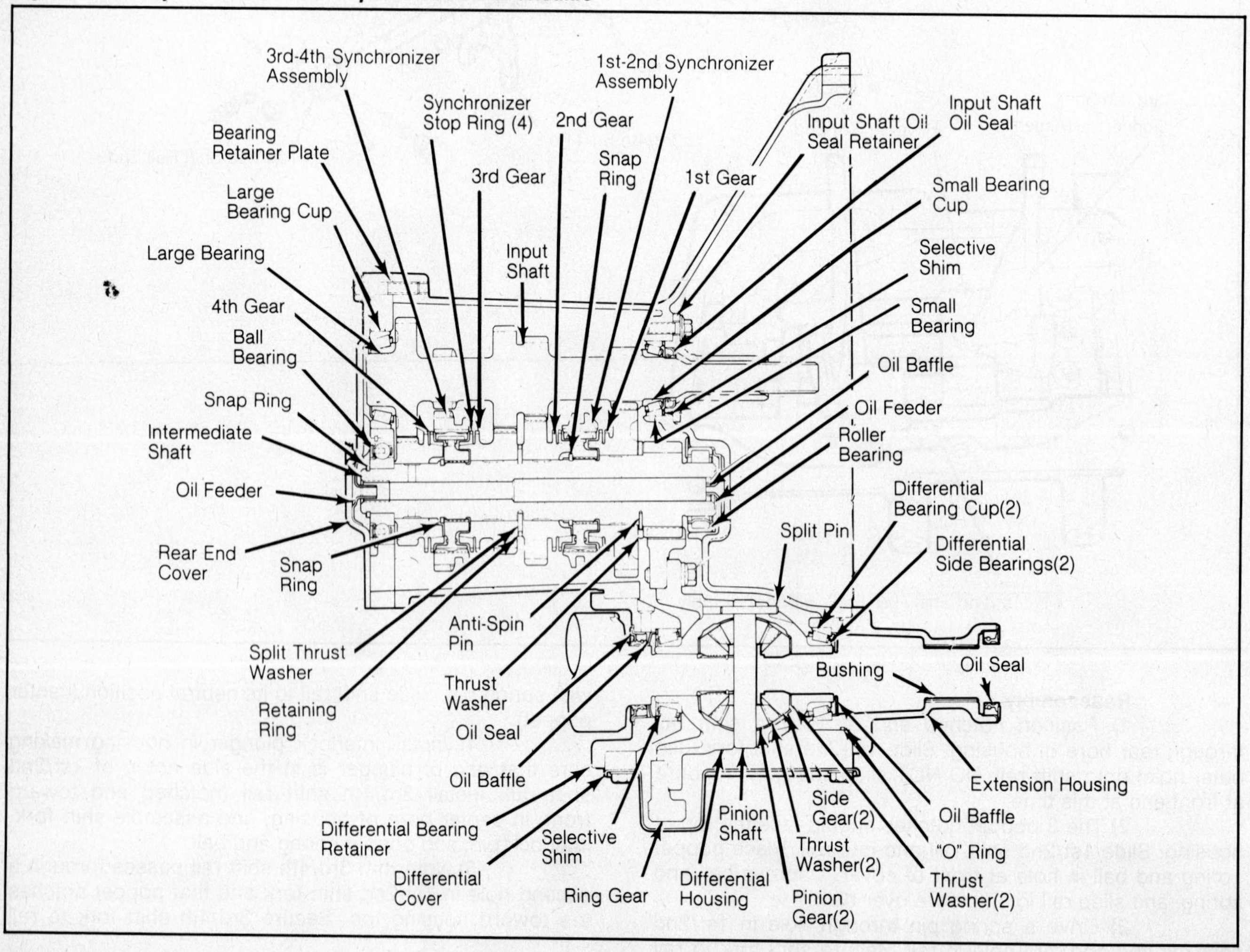

CHRYSLER A-460 & A-525 TRANSAXLES (Cont.)

Removal

Remove bolt and washer securing speedometer pinion adapter in extension housing. With cable housing connected, carefully work adapter and pinion out of extension housing. Remove retainer and remove pinion from adapter.

Seal Replacement

If transmission oil is found in cable housing, install a new speedometer pinion and seal assembly. If oil is found between cable and adapter, replace small "O" ring on cable.

Installation

Before installing pinion, adapter and cable assembly, ensure adapter flange and its mating areas on extension housing are clean. Dirt or sand will cause misalignment, resulting in speedometer pinion gear damage. Install and tighten bolt.

DRIVE AXLE SHAFTS

See appropriate DRIVE AXLE SHAFT article in DOMESTIC FWD AXLE SHAFTS & TRANSFER CASES section.

TRANSAXLE MOUNTS

Removal & Installation

Support engine-transaxle assembly. Remove transaxle mount through bolt from inside wheelwell. Remove transaxle mount from transaxle. To install, reverse removal procedure.

INTERNAL TRANSMISSION PARTS

NOTE: **The selector shaft housing, all synchronizers, intermediate shaft and gears, 5th gear, input shaft, reverse idler gear and shaft, shift forks and pads, shift fork rail and speedometer pinion can be removed without removing transaxle from vehicle.**

Removal

1) Disconnect negative battery cable. On Charger, Horizon, Omni and Turismo models, loosen left motor mount. On all models, remove nut attaching shift lever to selector shaft. Remove shift lever.

2) Remove selector shaft housing bolts. Note position of 2 pilot bolts. Remove selector shaft housing. On 5-speed models, remove 5th gear shifter pin, fill plug, end cover, 5th gear synchronizer, and input and intermediate shaft 5th gears as described in TRANSAXLE DISASSEMBLY in this article, steps **3)** through **5)**.

3) Raise vehicle on hoist. Remove left front wheel and tire assembly. Remove left splash shield. Place drain pan under transaxle and remove end cover (if not already removed). Remove bearing retainer plate.

4) Remove shift rail. Remove reverse idler gear assembly. Rotate both shift forks to the left (toward front of vehicle). Rotate 5th gear shifter to the right (toward rear of vehicle). Firmly grasp input and intermediate shaft assemblies and pull gear set out of transaxle.

NOTE: **Differential assembly can only be serviced by removing complete assembly from vehicle because bearing preload must be reset.**

Installation

To install, reverse removal procedure. Fill transaxle with ATF to bottom of fill hole in end cover.

REMOVAL & INSTALLATION

See appropriate MANUAL TRANSMISSION REMOVAL article in DOMESTIC GENERAL SERVICING section.

TRANSAXLE DISASSEMBLY

1) Place transaxle in holding fixture. Remove differential cover bolts and differential cover. Remove 8 differential bearing retainer bolts. Using Spanner (L-4435), rotate differential bearing retainer to remove retainer.

2) Remove extension housing bolts. Remove extension housing and differential assembly. DO NOT damage bearing cups. Remove 6 selector shaft housing bolts and housing assembly.

Fig. 2: Removing Differential Bearing Retainer

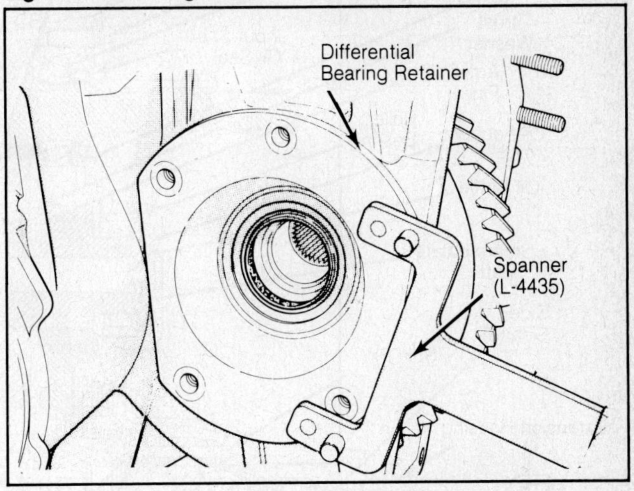

3) Remove rear end cover bolts and nuts. Using a screwdriver, pry up on cover (at notch on A-460 models) and remove end cover. On 5-speed models, remove 5th gear synchronizer strut retainer plate snap ring. Remove 5th gear shift fork set screw using an Allen wrench.

4) Remove 5th gear synchronizer sleeve and shift fork. *See Fig. 4*. Using Puller (C-4693) and Adapter (C-4621-1), remove 5th gear synchronizer hub and struts from intermediate shaft. *See Fig. 5*. Remove 5th gear from intermediate shaft.

5) Remove input shaft 5th gear snap ring. Remove 5th gear with Pulley Puller (C-4333). Remove 2 bearing support plate bolts and pry off support plate. On all models, remove intermediate shaft rear bearing snap ring. Remove bearing retainer plate (tap with plastic hammer as needed).

6) On 5-speed models, remove 5th gear shifter guide pin. On all models, remove 1st-2nd shift fork set screw. Remove shift fork rail. Remove reverse idler gear shaft, idler gear and plastic stop as an assembly.

7) Grasp intermediate shaft assembly and input shaft assembly together and remove from transaxle case. Remove shift forks and pads from intermediate shaft assembly.

8) Remove clutch release shaft "E" clip with screwdriver and remove shaft from housing. Separate shaft from release lever by removing "E" clip from end of shaft. Disassemble components. Remove release bearing, fork and bushings from housing.

CHRYSLER A-460 & A-525 TRANSAXLES (Cont.)

Fig. 3: Cutaway View of A-525 5-Speed Transaxle

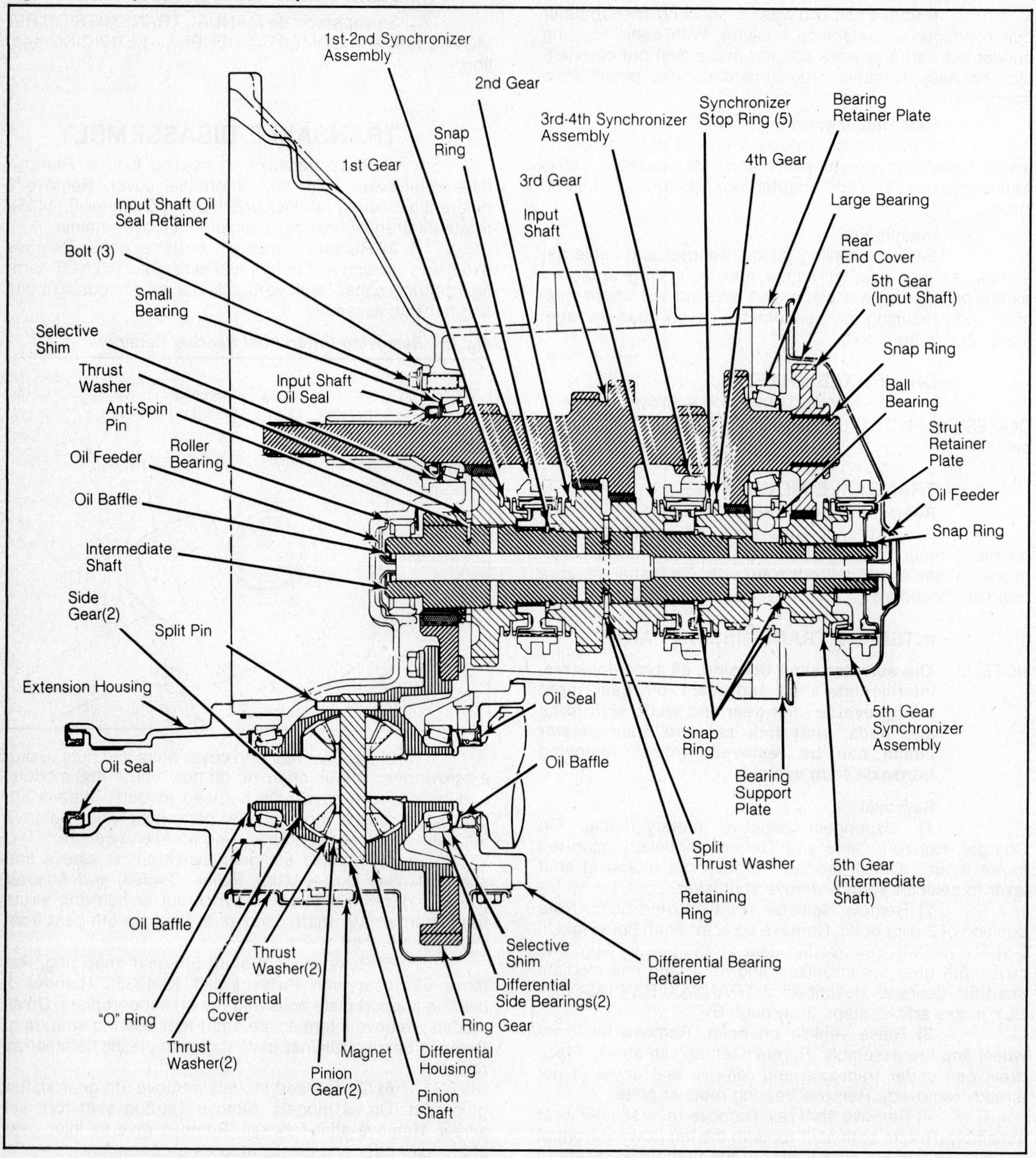

9) Remove input shaft seal retainer bolts. Remove seal retainer and selective shim. Measure shim thickness for transaxle reassembly reference. Remove reverse shift lever "E" clip. Remove flat washer, wave washer and reverse shift lever.

CLEANING & INSPECTION

1) All parts should be thoroughly washed in cleaning solvent and dried with compressed air. Do not spin bearings with compressed air. Remove gaskets with stiff brush or scraper.

2) Clean bearings separately from other parts. Hold bearing races so bearings will not rotate and use soft brush to remove all foreign material. Inspect all bearings, rollers, races and spacers for galling or flat spots.

3) Lubricate bearings with a light grade oil and check for roughness by slowly turning race by hand. If bearings are okay, wrap them in clean paper until ready to install.

Fig. 4: Removing 5th Gear Synchronizer Sleeve Assembly

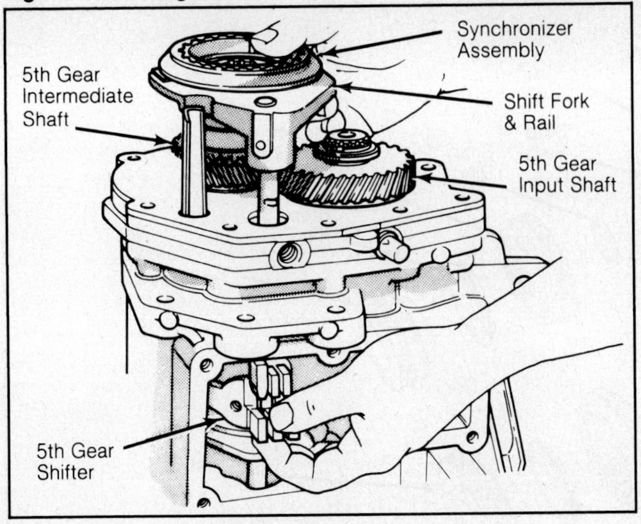

Fig. 5: Removing 5th Gear Synchronizer

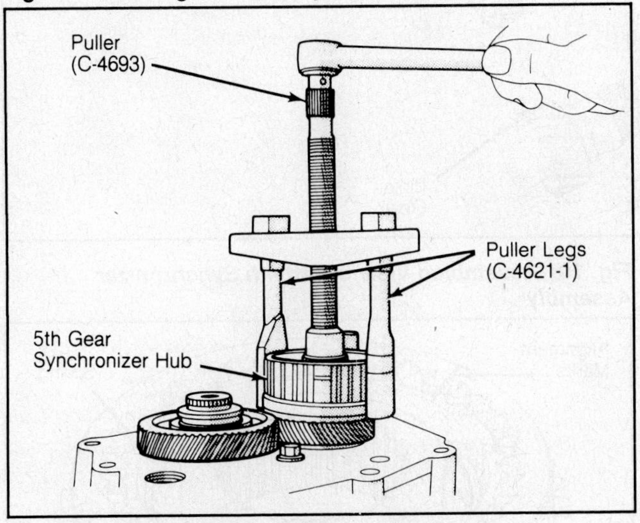

Synchronizer is on intermediate shaft.

Fig. 6: Removing Reverse Idler Gear Assembly

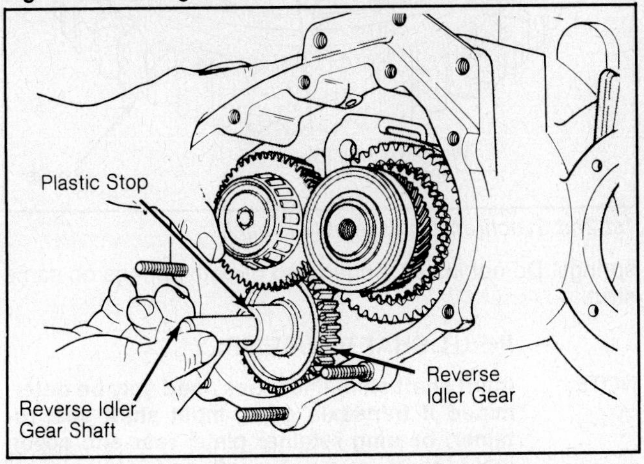

3) Lubricate bearings with a light grade oil and check for roughness by slowly turning race by hand. If bearings are okay, wrap them in clean paper until ready to install.

Fig. 7: Removing Input Shaft Seal Retainer

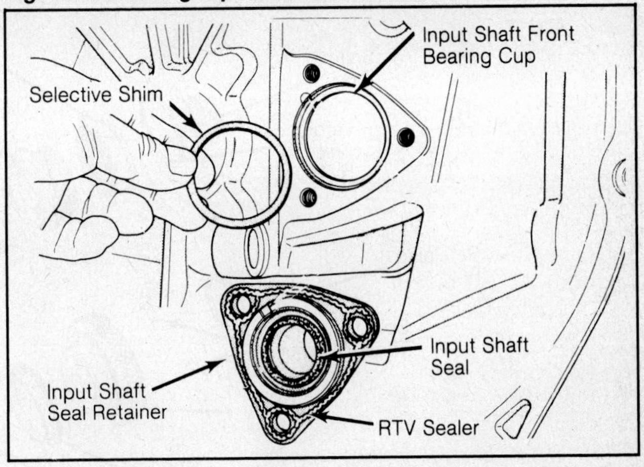

4) Examine all gear teeth and splines for chips, wear, breaks or nicks. Examine case, housing, retainers and covers for cracks, distortion or other damage. Inspect thrust washers, snap rings and snap ring grooves for wear or damage.

5) Check all synchronizers for wear, damage and proper fit. Coat all moving parts with oil before installation. Always use new gaskets, oil seals and snap rings. Replace parts as required.

COMPONENT DISASSEMBLY & REASSEMBLY

INTERMEDIATE SHAFT ASSEMBLY

NOTE: **Synchronizer stop rings are NOT interchangeable. The 1st-2nd synchronizer rings are larger diameter than other rings.**

Disassembly

1) Remove intermediate shaft rear bearing snap ring. Using a bearing puller, remove rear bearing and 4th gear as an assembly. Remove 3rd-4th synchronizer hub snap ring. Using a puller, remove 3rd-4th synchronizer hub and 3rd gear as an assembly.

2) Remove 2nd gear retaining ring, split thrust washer, 2nd gear and 2nd gear synchronizer stop ring. Remove 1st-2nd synchronizer hub snap ring. Using a press and Sleeve (C-4621-3), press shaft out of synchronizer assembly.

3) Remove 1st-2nd synchronizer assembly, 1st gear stop ring and 1st gear. Remove 1st gear thrust washer and anti-spin pin.

Reassembly

1) To reassemble, reverse disassembly procedure. Install 1st gear thrust washer with chamfered edge toward pinion gear. When assembling 1st-2nd synchronizer assembly and intermediate shaft, fit a 1 7/8" (47.6 mm) diameter, 8 1/2" (21.6 mm) long pipe over shaft, and press against end of pipe.

2) Relief on 1st-2nd synchronizer assembly faces toward 2nd gear. Ensure that all gears turn freely and have a minimum end play of .003" (.076 mm). Use arbor press and Installer (C-4672 for A-460 and L-4507 for A-525) to install rear bearing.

CHRYSLER A-460 & A-525 TRANSAXLES (Cont.)

Fig. 8: Disassembled View of Intermediate Shaft Assembly

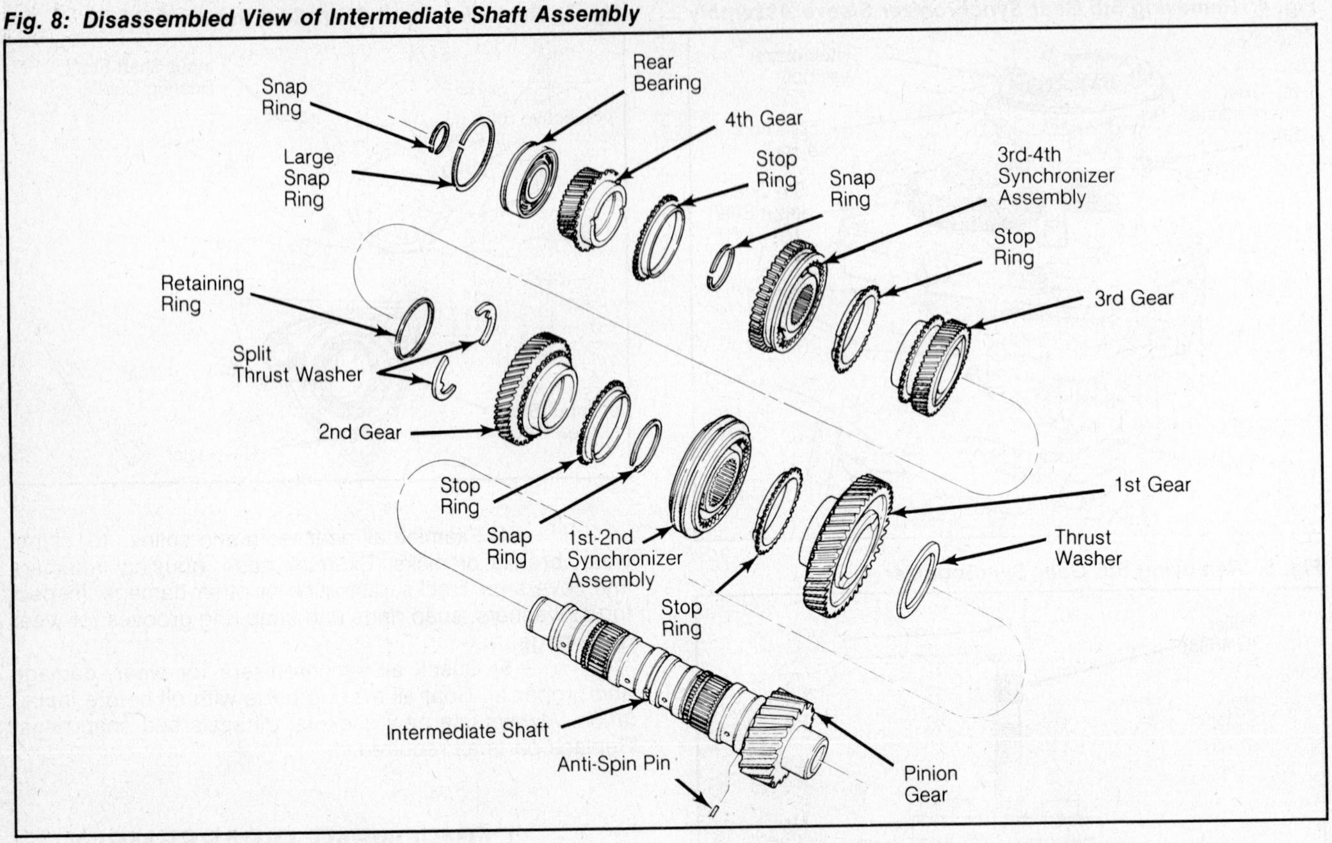

Fig. 9: Removing 1st-2nd Synchronizer Assembly

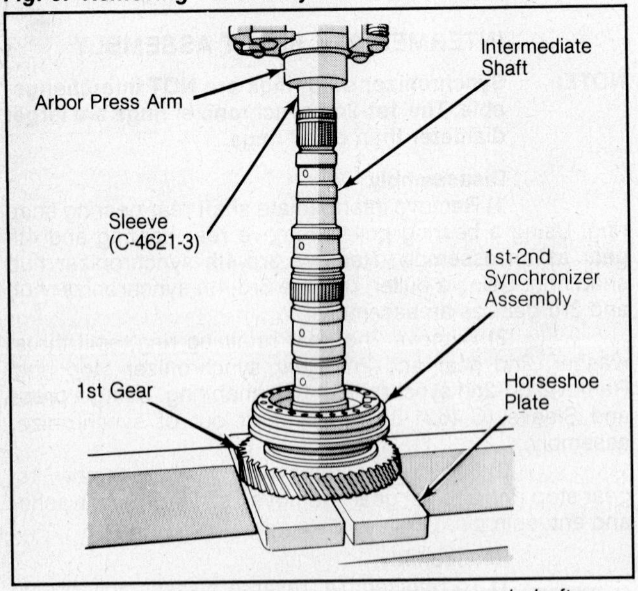

Use Adapter (C-4621-3) between press ram and shaft.

Fig. 10: Assembled View of 3rd-4th Synchronizer Assembly

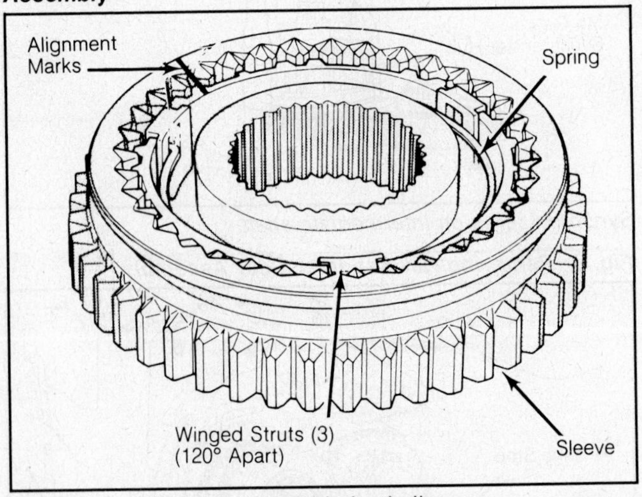

1st-2nd Synchronizer assembly is similar.

SYNCHRONIZERS

Disassembly

Mark hubs and sleeves for reassembly reference. Using care, pry out both synchronizer springs. Separate hubs, sleeves and 3 winged struts, noting their positions. Clean, inspect and replace parts, as needed.

Reassembly

Align marks made during disassembly. Assemble hub to sleeve. Install winged struts, then carefully install springs. Do not install tanged end of both springs on same strut.

INPUT SHAFT ASSEMBLY

NOTE: **Input shaft shim thickness need only be determined if transaxle case, input shaft seal retainer, bearing retainer plate, rear end cover, input shaft or input shaft bearings are replaced.**

Disassembly

Using a bearing puller and Adapters (C-293-45 rear and C-293-50 front), remove input shaft rear bearing

CHRYSLER A-460 & A-525 TRANSAXLES (Cont.)

Fig. 11: Disassembled View of 5th Gear Assembly

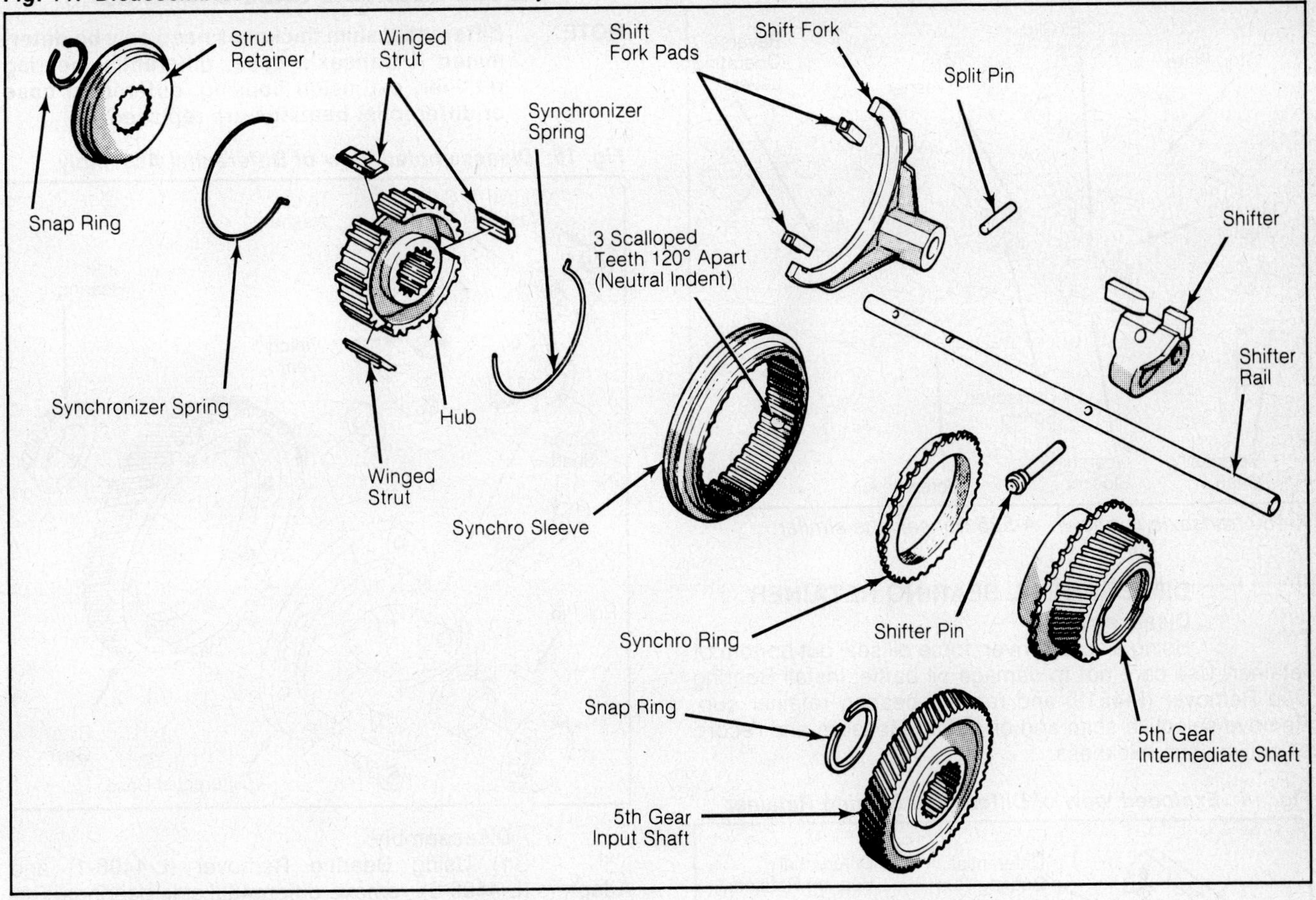

and front bearing. Place bearing retainer plate on wooden blocks. Using an arbor press and Remover (L-4520), press out rear bearing cup.

Reassembly

Press front and rear bearings onto input shaft. Install rear cover (4-speed) or bearing support plate (5-speed) on bearing retainer plate. *See Fig. 12*. Press bearing cup into plate until cup bottoms on cover.

Fig. 12: Installing End Cover on Bearing Retainer Plate

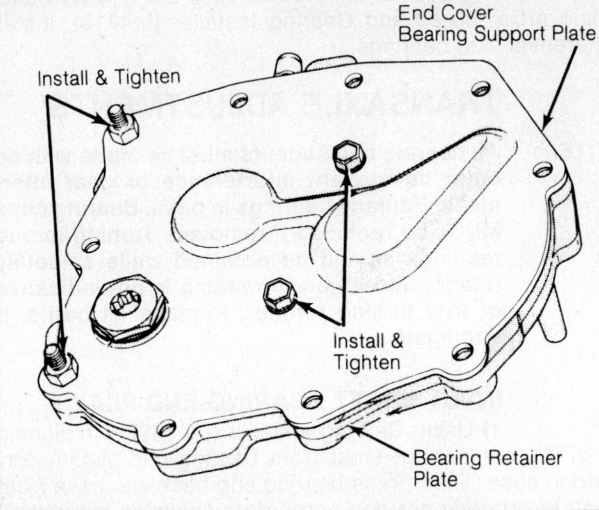

Install bearing support plate on 5-speed models.

TRANSAXLE CASE

Disassembly

Using an arbor press and Remover (C-4656), press out input shaft front bearing cup. Remove intermediate shaft front bearing retaining strap bolts and strap. Using Remover (C-4660), press intermediate shaft front bearing from case. Remove bearing and oil feeder.

Reassembly

Install oil feeder and intermediate shaft front bearing in case. Press bearing into position with letters on bearing facing upward. Install bearing retaining strap and bolts. Using press and Installer (C-4655), install input shaft front bearing cup.

SELECTOR SHAFT HOUSING

Disassembly

1) Remove dust boot snap ring and dust boot. Using a screwdriver, pry oil seal off selector shaft. Remove lock pin, back-up light switch and gasket.

2) Hold reverse operating lever away from housing. Using a screwdriver, remove "E" clip. Carefully remove selector shaft from shaft housing bore. With selector shaft removed, remove reverse operating lever, crossover spring, flat washer (A-460), gearshift block assembly and gearshift selector.

Reassembly

Reverse disassembly procedure to assemble. Use plastic hammer and Seal Installer (C-4662) to install selector shaft oil seal.

CHRYSLER A-460 & A-525 TRANSAXLES (Cont.)

Fig. 13: Removing "E" Clip from Selector Shaft

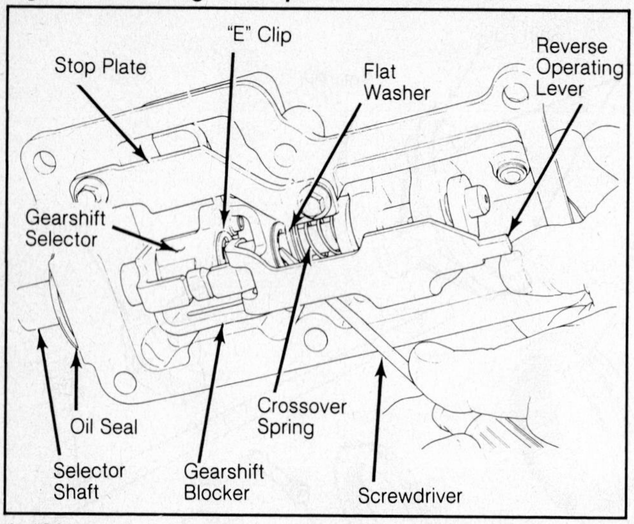

A-460 transaxle is shown. A-525 transaxle is similar.

DIFFERENTIAL BEARING RETAINER

Disassembly

Using a screwdriver, force oil seal out bottom of retainer. Use care not to damage oil baffle. Install Bearing Cup Remover (L-4518) and remove bearing retainer cup. Remove selective shim and oil baffle. Measure and record selective shim thickness.

Fig. 14: Exploded View of Differential Bearing Retainer

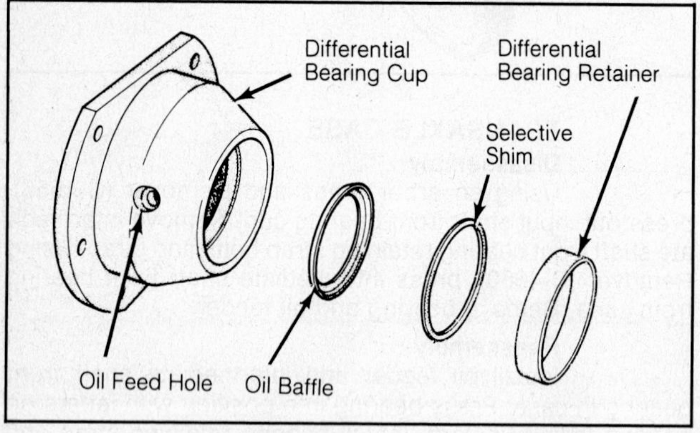

Reassembly

Using an arbor press and Installer (L-4520), press oil baffle into bearing retainer (installer must be inverted to prevent damage to baffle). Turn installer over (cone facing down) and press in selective shim and bearing retainer cup. Turn bearing retainer over, invert installer (cone facing up) and press in oil seal.

EXTENSION HOUSING

Disassembly

Using a screwdriver, remove extension housing oil seal. Using Remover (L-4518), remove bearing cup without damaging oil baffle. Remove oil baffle and "O" ring.

Reassembly

Install "O" ring. Using Installer (L-4520), with cone facing up, press oil baffle into housing. Turn installer over and press bearing cup into housing. Install new oil seal in housing using same installer and hammer.

DIFFERENTIAL CASE & RING GEAR

NOTE: **Differential shim thickness need only be determined if transaxle case, differential bearing retainer, extension housing, differential case or differential bearings are replaced.**

Fig. 15: Disassembled View of Differential Assembly

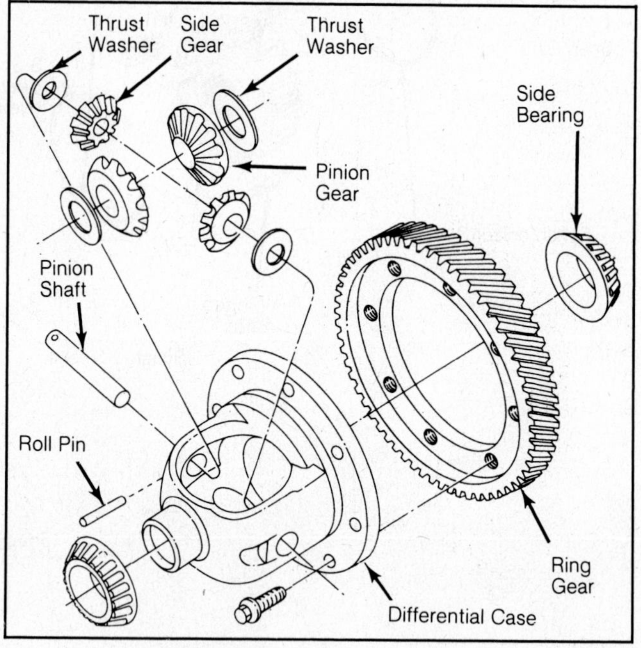

Disassembly

1) Using Bearing Remover (L-4406-1) and Adapters (L-4406-3), remove differential side bearings. Remove 8 ring gear attaching bolts and separate ring gear from differential case.

2) Using a small punch, drive out pinion shaft split pin. Remove pinion shaft. Roll gears around and remove pinion gears, side gears and thrust washers through case opening. Clean and inspect all parts, replace as necessary.

Reassembly

Install thrust washers, side gears and pinion gears in differential case. Install pinion shaft and insert split pin. Install ring gear on differential case using NEW bolts. Using arbor press and Bearing Installer (L-4410), install differential side bearings.

TRANSAXLE ADJUSTMENTS

NOTE: **All bearing adjustments must be made with no other component interference or gear intermesh. Replace bearings in pairs. Bearing cups MUST be replaced if removed. Turning torque readings should be obtained while smoothly rotating (break-away reading is not indicative of true turning torque). Replace oil baffle, if damaged.**

INPUT SHAFT BEARING END PLAY

1) Using Bearing Installer (L-4656) with Handle (C-4171), press input shaft front bearing cup slightly forward in case. Then press bearing cup back into case from front, to properly position cup before checking input shaft end play.

CHRYSLER A-460 & A-525 TRANSAXLES (Cont.)

NOTE: This step is not necessary if Installer (L-4655) was used during reassembly of input shaft front bearing and no input shaft selective shim has been installed since pressing cup into case.

2) Select a gauging shim which will give .001-.010" (.025-.25 mm) end play. A shim .010" (.25 mm) thinner than original selective shim should give this reading. Install gauging shim on bearing cup and install input shaft seal retainer. Alternately tighten input shaft seal retainer bolts until retainer is bottomed against case.

NOTE: Input shaft seal retainer is used to draw input shaft front bearing cup the proper distance into case bore during this step.

3) Oil input shaft bearings with ATF and install input shaft in case. Install bearing retainer plate with input shaft rear bearing cup pressed in and end cover (A-460) or bearing support plate (A-525) installed. Tighten all bolts and nuts to 21 ft. lbs. (28 N.m).

4) Mount dial indicator on transaxle case with plunger touching end of input shaft. *See Fig. 16.* Apply moderate pressure, by hand, to input shaft splines. Push input shaft toward rear of case while rotating shaft back and forth several times to seat bearings.

Fig. 16: Measuring Input Shaft Bearing End Play

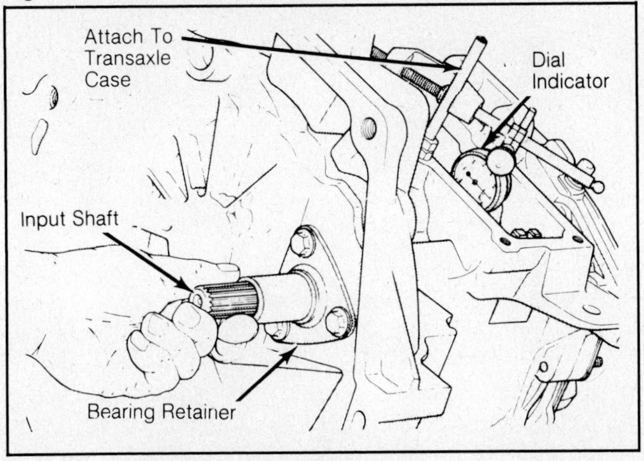

5) Zero dial indicator. Pull input shaft toward front of case while rotating shaft back and forth several times to seat bearings. Record end play.

6) The required shim for proper input shaft end play is total of gauging shim thickness, plus end play reading recorded in step **5)**, MINUS .002" (.050 mm). Combine shims (as required) to obtain a shim within .0016" (.040 mm) of required shim thickness. Shims are available in 30 thicknesses ranging from .024-.069" (.60-1.75 mm). Remove dial indicator.

7) Remove input shaft seal retainer and gauging shim. Install required shim(s). Apply a 1/16" bead of RTV sealer to input shaft seal retainer and install. Tighten bolts alternately until retainer is bottomed against case.

NOTE: Do not allow RTV sealant to get in oil slot.

8) Using Adapter (L-4508) and an INCH lb. torque wrench, check input shaft turning torque. Turning torque for new bearings should be 1-5 INCH lbs. (.11-.56 N.m). Turning torque for old bearings should be 1 INCH lb. (.11 N.m) minimum. If turning torque is too high, install a .0016" (.040 mm) THINNER shim. If torque is too low, install a .0016" (.040 mm) THICKER shim.

9) If shims require replacement after initial torque reading check, repeat step **1)** to assure that input shaft front bearing cup is properly seated. Repeat step **8)** until proper bearing turning torque is obtained.

DIFFERENTIAL BEARING PRELOAD

1) Remove bearing cup and existing shim from differential bearing retainer. Select a gauging shim which will give .001-.010" (.025-.25 mm) end play. A shim .015" (.38 mm) thinner than original selective shim should give this reading. Install gauging shim in differential bearing retainer and press in bearing cup.

NOTE: Do not install oil baffle when checking differential end play.

2) Oil differential bearings with ATF and install differential assembly in transaxle case. Install extension housing and bearing retainer. Tighten bolts to 21 ft. lbs. (28 N.m). Mount transaxle case on workbench with "C" clamps (clutch housing facing down). Mount dial indicator with plunger touching differential case. *See Fig. 17.*

3) Apply medium pressure to ring gear, by hand, in downward direction while rolling differential assembly back and forth several times to seat bearings. Zero dial indicator. Apply medium pressure, by hand, in upward direction while rotating differential several times to seat bearings. Record end play.

Fig. 17: Measuring Differential Bearing End Play

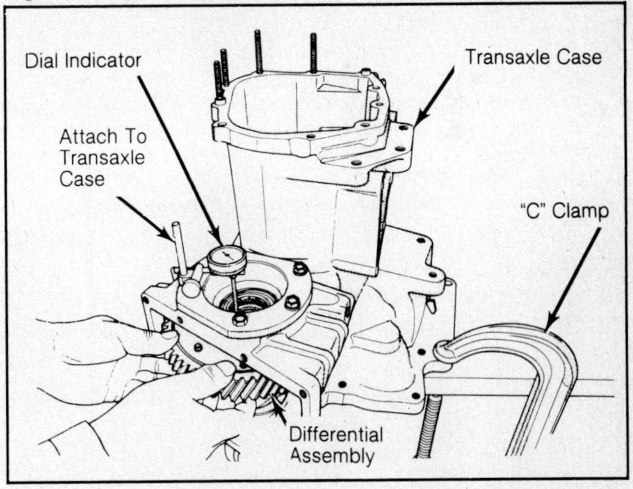

4) The required shim to obtain proper bearing preload is the total of gauging shim thickness, plus end play reading recorded in step **3)**, PLUS .010" (.25 mm). Combine shims (as required) to obtain a shim within .002" (.05 mm) of required shim thickness. Shims are available in 29 thicknesses ranging from .020-.083" (.50-2.10 mm). Remove dial indicator.

5) Remove differential bearing retainer. Remove bearing cup and gauging shim. Install oil baffle, using care not to damage baffle. Install required shim(s). Press bearing cup into differential bearing retainer.

6) Check bearing retainer "O" ring for damage and replace if necessary. Apply 1/16" bead of RTV sealer to bearing retainer and install. Install extension housing and tighten bolts.

7) Using Adapter (L-4436) and an INCH lb. torque wrench, check rotating torque of differential assembly. Rotating torque should be 9-14 INCH lbs. (1.0-1.6 N.m) for new bearings or 6 INCH lbs. (.67 N.m) mimimum for used bearings. If rotating torque is too high, install a .002" (.05 mm) THINNER shim. If torque is too low, install a .002" (.05 mm) THICKER shim. Recheck rotating torque and repeat procedure unitl proper torque is obtained.

TRANSAXLE REASSEMBLY

1) To assemble transaxle, reverse disassembly procedure. Use RTV sealer on components as indicated in TRANSAXLE REASSEMBLY RTV USAGE table. Install new seal in input shaft seal retainer.

2) When installing reverse idler gear assembly, align roll pin on idler gear with notch in transaxle case. Press 5th gear onto input shaft with Installer (C-4810). Press 5th gear synchronizer assembly onto intermediate shaft with Installer (C-4888).

TRANSAXLE REASSEMBLY RTV USAGE

Component	Bead Size
Bearing Retainer Plate	1/8"
Extension Housing	1/16"
Input Shaft Differential Cover	1/8"
Rear Cover	1/8"
Seal Retainer	1/16"
Selector Shaft Housing	1/16"

TIGHTENING SPECIFICATIONS

Application	Ft. Lbs. (N.m)
Anti-Rotational Strut Bracket	17 (23)
Axle Shaft (Hub) Nut [1]	180 (245)
Differential Bearing Retainer Bolts	21 (28)
Differential Extension Bolts	21 (28)
Differential Oil Pan Nut & Screw	15 (20)
End Cover-to-Bearing Retainer Bolts	21 (28)
End Cover-to-Case Bolts & Stud Nuts	21 (28)
Fill Plug	24 (33)
Gearshift Housing-to-Case	21 (28)
Gearshift Operating Lever Attaching Nut [1]	21 (28)
Input Shaft Seal Retaining Bolt	21 (28)
Mount-to-Block & Case	70 (95)
Ring Gear Bolts	70 (95)
Steering Knuckle Clamp Bolt	70 (95)
Strut-to-Block & Case Bolts	70 (95)
Transaxle Case-to-Engine Block	70 (95)
	INCH Lbs. (N.m)
Intermediate Shaft Bearing Strap Screw	108 (7)
Shift Linkage Adjusting Pin	108 (7)

[1] – Always replace with new nut.

FORD MOTOR CO. 3.03 3-SPEED

E150, E350, F150, F250

IDENTIFICATION

The transmission identification code can be found on the Vehicle Compliance Certification Label located on the driver's door lock pillar. There is also a service identification tag located on the right front side of transmission case. The code for a 3-Speed 3.03 transmission is "C". *See Fig. 1.*

Fig. 1: Transmission Identification Tag

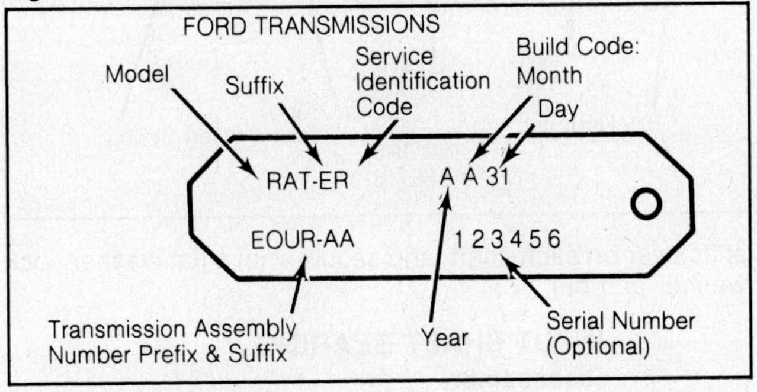

DESCRIPTION

Transmission is a 3-speed, fully synchronized unit. All forward gears are constant mesh helical type. Forward speed changes are accomplished through use of synchronizer sleeves. Synchronizers allow quicker shifts and reduce gear clash.

Reverse gears are spur type and are not synchronized. Transmission uses a system of detents and interlocks within the case, which maintains gear position and prevents selection of more than one speed at a time.

LUBRICATION & ADJUSTMENT

See appropriate MANUAL TRANSMISSION SERVICING article in DOMESTIC GENERAL SERVICING section.

TROUBLE SHOOTING

See MANUAL TRANSMISSION TROUBLE SHOOTING article in DOMESTIC GENERAL SERVICING section.

REMOVAL & INSTALLATION

See appropriate MANUAL TRANSMISSION REMOVAL article in DOMESTIC GENERAL SERVICING section.

TRANSMISSION DISASSEMBLY

1) With transmission in a sturdy holding fixture, remove lower extension bolt and drain transmission lubricant. Remove cover-to-case capscrews. Remove cover and gasket from case. Remove long spring and detent plug using a magnet.

2) Remove extension housing-to-case bolts. Remove extension housing retainer and gasket. Remove front bearing retainer-to-case bolts and withdraw front bearing retainer and gasket.

Fig. 2: Exploded View of Transmission Case Assembly

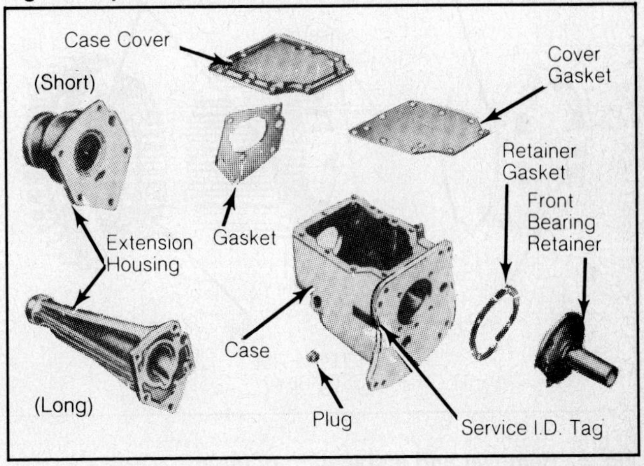

3) Remove filler plug from right side of case. Working through opening, drive roll pin out of case and countershaft using a 1/4" (6.35 mm) punch. Hold countershaft gear with hook, and with dummy shaft tool, drive countershaft out rear of case. *See Fig. 3.* Lower countershaft gear and washers to bottom of case.

Fig. 3: Removing Countershaft

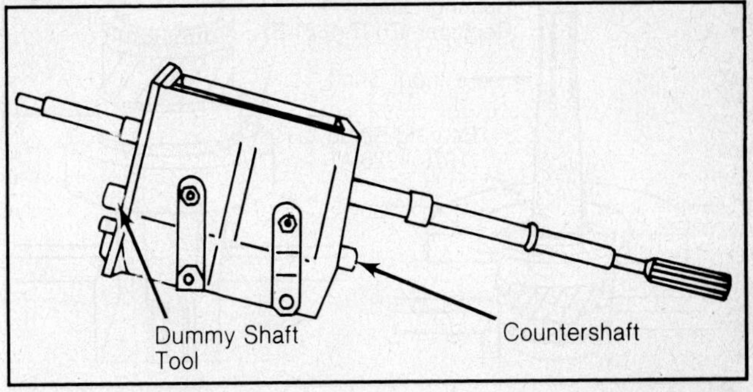

4) Remove speedometer drive gear snap ring and slide gear off shaft. Remove gear lock ball from shaft. Remove output shaft bearing snap ring. Using pullers (T75L-7025-B, C, E, G, and J) remove bearing from shaft. Place shift levers in center (neutral) position.

5) Remove set screw that secures 1st-Reverse shift fork to shift rail. Slide shift rail out through rear of case. Slide 1st-Reverse synchronizer as far forward as possible and rotate shift fork upward and remove.

6) Move 2nd-3rd shift fork to second speed position and remove set screw from fork. Rotate shift rail 90° and lift interlock plug from case with a magnet.

7) Tap on inner end of 2nd-3rd shift rail to remove expansion plug from front of case. Remove shift rail. Remove 2nd-3rd speed shift rail detent plug and spring from detent bore using a magnet.

8) Pull input gear shaft blocking ring, bearing and snap ring from case. Rotate 2nd-3rd shift fork upward and lift from case.

9) Carefully lift output shaft assembly out through top of case. Remove roll pin and reverse idler gear shaft and lift idler gear and 2 thrust washers from case. Lift out countershaft gear, thrust washer and dummy shaft tool from case.

FORD MOTOR CO. 3.03 3-SPEED (Cont.)

Fig. 4: Exploded View of Synchronizer Assemblies

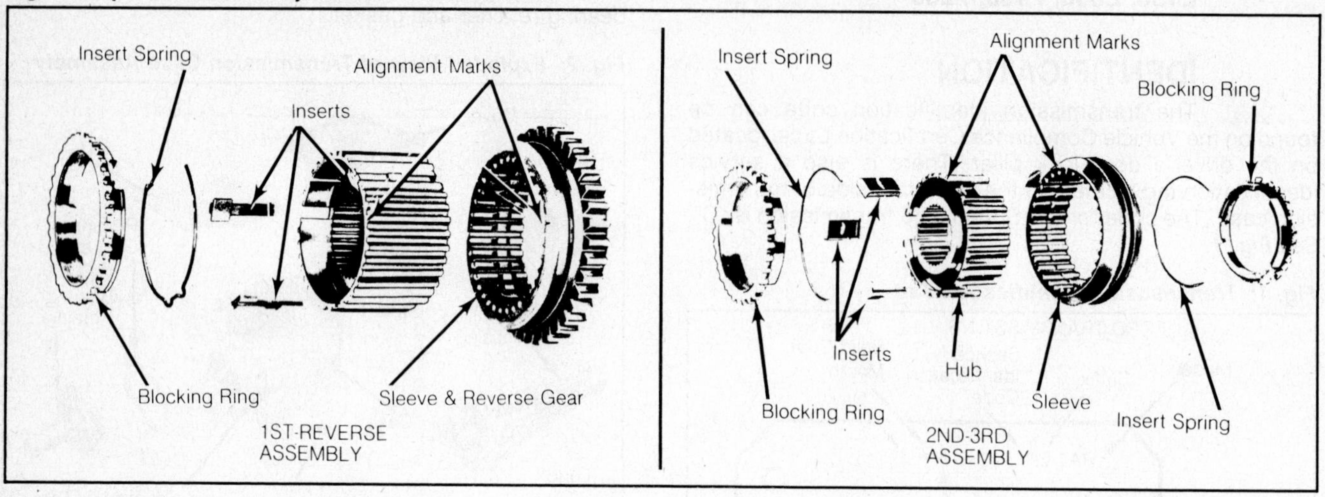

Fig. 5: Removal and Installation of Input Shaft Bearing

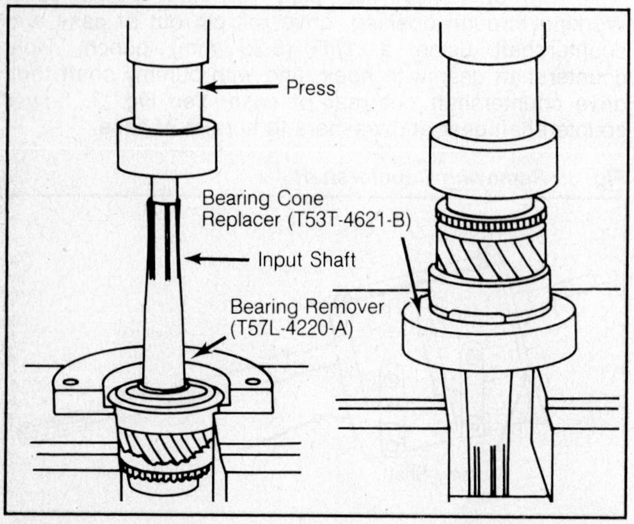

10) Remove snap ring from front of output shaft and slide 2nd-3rd speed synchronizer and 2nd speed gear off shaft. Remove snap ring and tabbed thrust washer from output shaft and withdraw first gear and blocking ring.

11) Remove next snap ring from output shaft. Using an arbor press, withdraw synchronizer hub assembly from shaft. Do not remove hub by hammering or prying. Remove rail pin from bottom of case. *See Fig. 9.*

COMPONENT DISASSEMBLY & REASSEMBLY

SHIFT LEVERS & SEALS

Disassembly

Remove nut, flat washer and lock washer securing each shift lever to lever and shaft in case. Lift off shift lever and slide each lever and shaft out of case. Discard "O" ring from each shaft.

Reassembly

Lubricate new seals with transmission fluid and install on shafts. Install lever and shafts in case. Position shift lever on each shaft, and secure with a flat washer, lock washer and nut.

INPUT SHAFT BEARING

Disassembly

Remove snap ring securing input shaft bearing and press out shaft using Remover (T57L-4220-A). *See Fig. 5.*

Reassembly

Press input shaft bearing onto shaft using press Attachment (T53T-4621-B). Install snap ring on shaft. *See Fig. 5.*

SYNCHRONIZERS

Disassembly

Mark synchronizer hub position before disassembly. Push synchronizer hub from sleeve. Separate inserts and springs from hubs. Do not interchange parts between 2 synchronizers.

Reassembly

1) Install spring in hub of 1st-Reverse synchronizer. Spring should cover all insert grooves. Start hub into sleeve. Be sure hub marks are aligned. Position 3 inserts in hub, making sure that the wide offset end is on inside of hub. Slide sleeve and reverse gear onto hub. *See Fig. 4.*

2) Install one spring into groove of 2nd-3rd synchronizer hub, making sure that all 3 insert slots are fully covered. With alignment marks on hub and sleeve aligned, start hub into sleeve. Place 3 inserts on top of retaining spring and push assembly together. Install remaining insert spring. Do not stagger springs. Place synchronizer blocking ring on each end of synchronizer sleeve. *See Fig. 4.*

COUNTERSHAFT GEAR BEARINGS

Disassembly

Remove dummy shaft tool, 50 needle bearings and 2 bearing retainer washers from countershaft gear.

Reassembly

1) Coat bore in each end of countershaft gear with grease. Hold dummy shaft tool in the gear and install 25 needle bearings and a retainer washer in each end of the gear. *See Fig 7.* Position countershaft gear, dummy shaft tool, needle bearings, retainers, and thrust washers in case.

2) Place case in vertical position. Align gear bore and thrust washers with bores in case and install

FORD MOTOR CO. 3.03 3-SPEED (Cont.)

Fig. 6: Disassembled View of Ford 3.03 3-Speed Manual Transmission

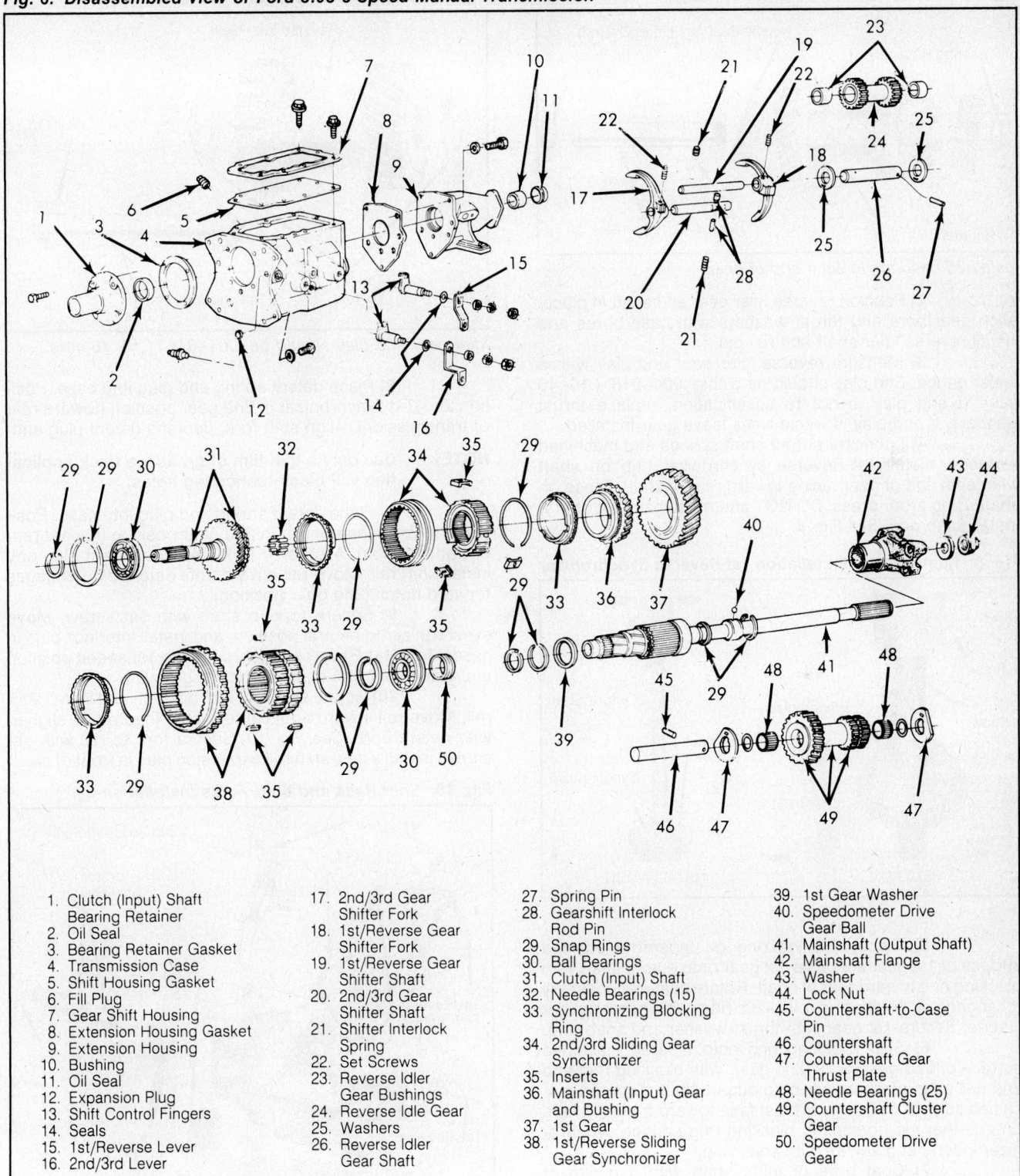

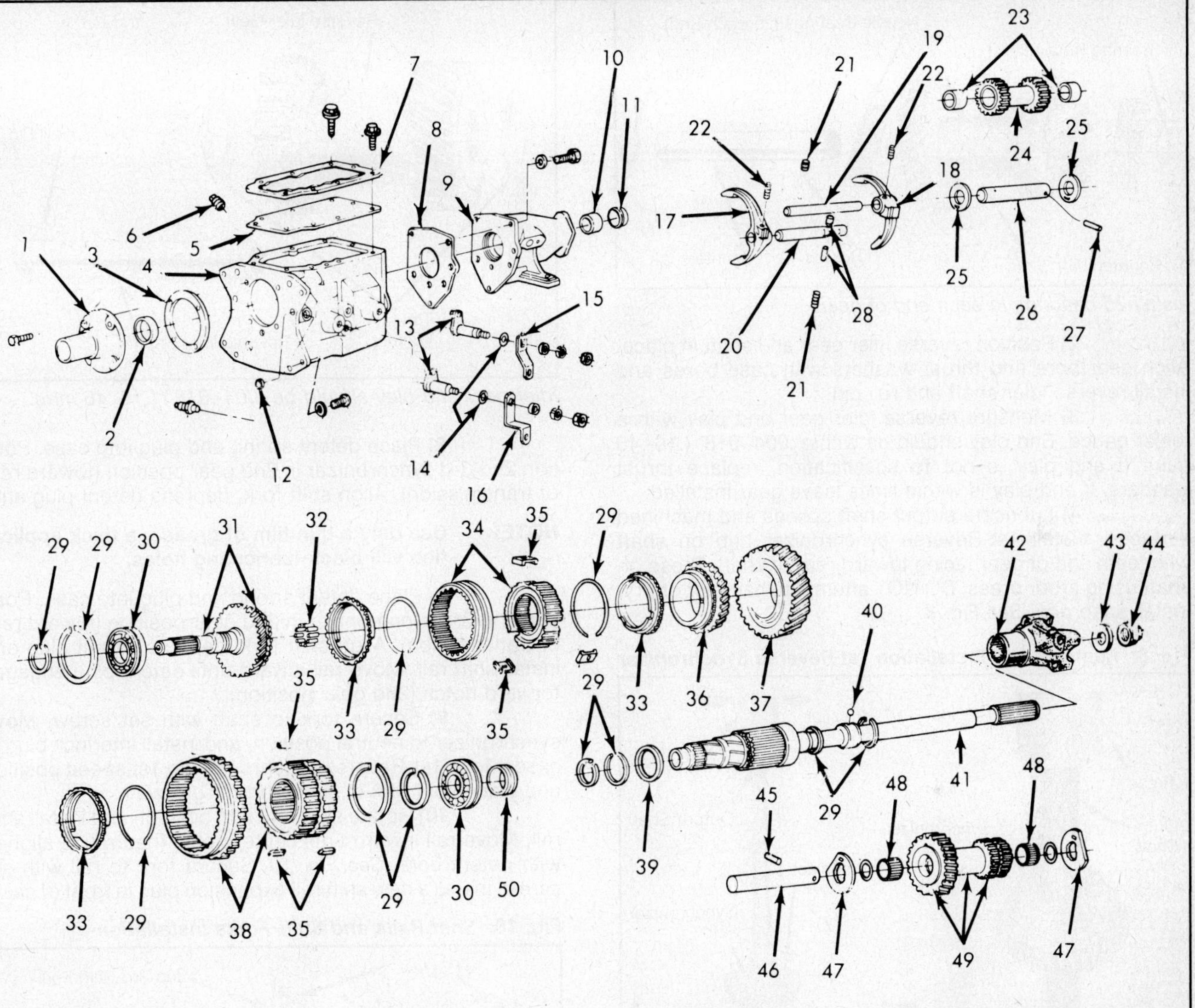

1. Clutch (Input) Shaft Bearing Retainer
2. Oil Seal
3. Bearing Retainer Gasket
4. Transmission Case
5. Shift Housing Gasket
6. Fill Plug
7. Gear Shift Housing
8. Extension Housing Gasket
9. Extension Housing
10. Bushing
11. Oil Seal
12. Expansion Plug
13. Shift Control Fingers
14. Seals
15. 1st/Reverse Lever
16. 2nd/3rd Lever
17. 2nd/3rd Gear Shifter Fork
18. 1st/Reverse Gear Shifter Fork
19. 1st/Reverse Gear Shifter Shaft
20. 2nd/3rd Gear Shifter Shaft
21. Shifter Interlock Spring
22. Set Screws
23. Reverse Idler Gear Bushings
24. Reverse Idle Gear
25. Washers
26. Reverse Idler Gear Shaft
27. Spring Pin
28. Gearshift Interlock Rod Pin
29. Snap Rings
30. Ball Bearings
31. Clutch (Input) Shaft
32. Needle Bearings (15)
33. Synchronizing Blocking Ring
34. 2nd/3rd Sliding Gear Synchronizer
35. Inserts
36. Mainshaft (Input) Gear and Bushing
37. 1st Gear
38. 1st/Reverse Sliding Gear Synchronizer
39. 1st Gear Washer
40. Speedometer Drive Gear Ball
41. Mainshaft (Output Shaft)
42. Mainshaft Flange
43. Washer
44. Lock Nut
45. Countershaft-to-Case Pin
46. Countershaft
47. Countershaft Gear Thrust Plate
48. Needle Bearings (25)
49. Countershaft Cluster Gear
50. Speedometer Drive Gear

countershaft. Place case in horizontal position and check countershaft gear end play with feeler gauge.

3) End play should be .004-.018" (.10-.46 mm). If not to specification, replace thrust washers. Install dummy shaft tool and allow countershaft gear to lay in bottom of case until output and input shafts have been installed.

TRANSMISSION REASSEMBLY

1) Coat countershaft gear and reverse idler gear thrust surfaces in case with lubricant and position thrust washers in place. Position countershaft gear with bearings, retainers and dummy shaft tool in the bottom of case. DO NOT install at this time.

FORD MOTOR CO. 3.03 3-SPEED (Cont.)

Fig. 7: Countershaft and Gear Assembly

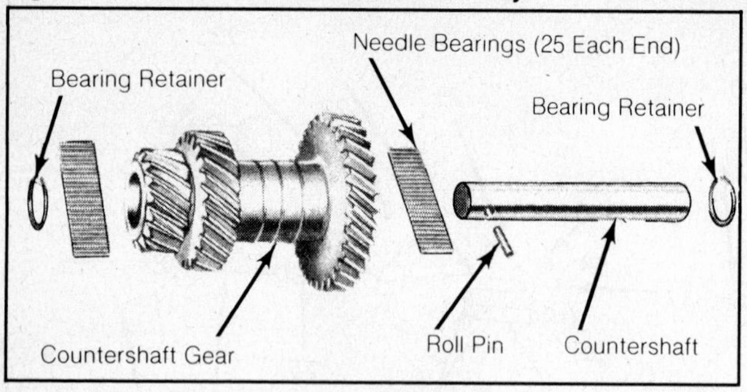

Install 25 bearings in each end of gear.

2) Position reverse idler gear and shaft in place. Align gear bore and thrust washers with case bores and install reverse idler shaft and roll pin.

3) Measure reverse idler gear end play with a feeler gauge. End play should be within .004-.018" (.10-.46 mm). If end play is not to specification, replace thrust washers. If end play is within limits leave gear installed.

4) Lubricate output shaft splines and machined surfaces. Install 1st-Reverse synchronizer hub on shaft with teeth end of gear facing toward rear of shaft. Press on shaft using arbor press, DO NOT attempt to hammer or pry. Install snap ring. *See Fig. 8.*

Fig. 8: Removal and Installation 1st-Reverse Synchronizer

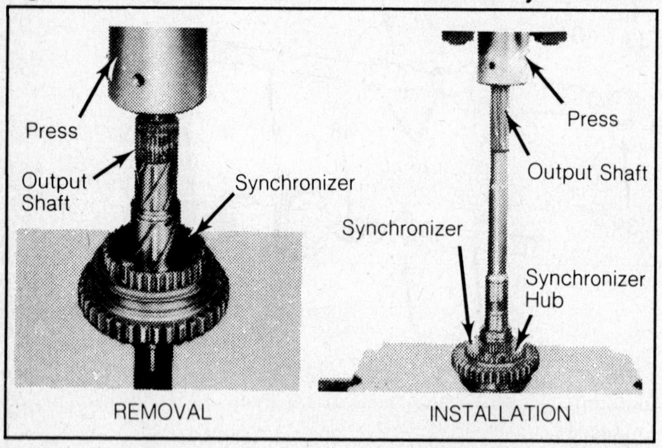

5) Place blocking ring on tapered machined surface of 1st gear and slide 1st gear onto output shaft with blocking ring toward rear of shaft. Rotate gear as necessary to engage 3 notches in blocking ring with synchronizer inserts. Secure 1st gear with thrust washer and snap ring.

6) Slide blocking ring onto tapered machined surface of 2nd gear. Slide 2nd gear, with blocking ring and 2nd-3rd gear synchronizer onto output shaft. Tapered machined surface of 2nd gear must face toward front of shaft. Ensure that the notches in blocking ring engage synchronizer inserts and secure with snap ring.

7) Coat bore of input shaft with thin film of grease and install 15 roller bearings. Install input shaft and blocking ring through front of transmission and install snap ring in bearing groove. Position output shaft assembly in case, and place shift fork on 2nd-3rd synchronizer assembly.

NOTE: **Use only a thin film of grease; a thick application will block lubricating holes.**

Fig. 9: Reverse Idler Gear and Shaft Assembly

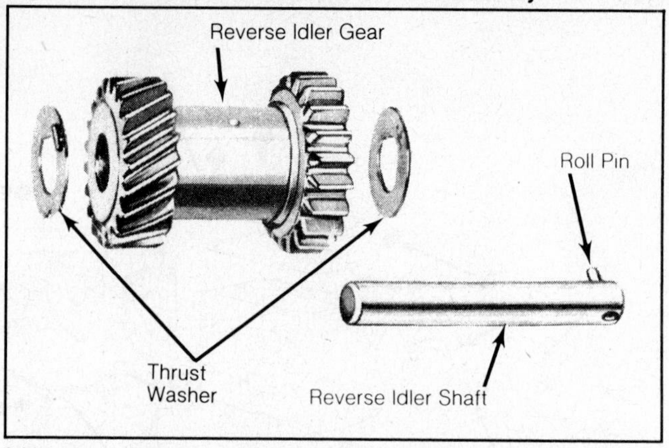

Idler gear end play should be .004-.018" (.10-.46 mm).

8) Place detent spring and plug into case. Position 2nd-3rd synchronizer in 2nd gear position (toward rear of transmission). Align shift fork, depress detent plug and

NOTE: **Use only a thin film of grease; a thick application will block lubricating holes.**

8) Place detent spring and plug into case. Position 2nd-3rd synchronizer in 2nd gear position (toward rear of transmission). Align shift fork, depress detent plug and install shift rail. Move rail inward until detent plug engages forward notch (2nd gear position).

9) Secure fork to shaft with set screw. Move synchronizer to neutral position, and install interlock plug in case. Move 1st-Reverse synchronizer to 1st speed position and place shift fork in synchronizer groove.

10) Rotate shift fork into position and install shift rail. Move rail inward until center notch (neutral) is aligned with detent bore. *See Fig. 10.* Secure fork to rail with set screw. Install a new shift rail expansion plug in front of case.

Fig. 10: Shift Rails and Shift Forks Installation

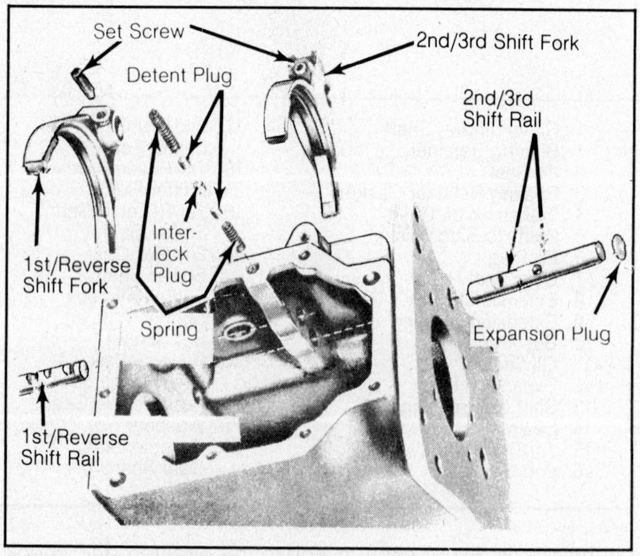

Rotate shift rail 90° to remove.

11) Hold input shaft and blocking ring in position. Move output shaft forward to seat pilot in roller bearings of input gear. Tap input gear bearing into place. Hold output shaft to prevent roller bearings from dropping.

Manual Transmissions

FORD MOTOR CO. 3.03 3-SPEED (Cont.)

12) Install front bearing retainer with new gasket. Ensure that oil return slot is at the bottom of case. Install and tighten retainer-to-case attaching screws.

Fig. 11: Input Shaft and Gear Assembly

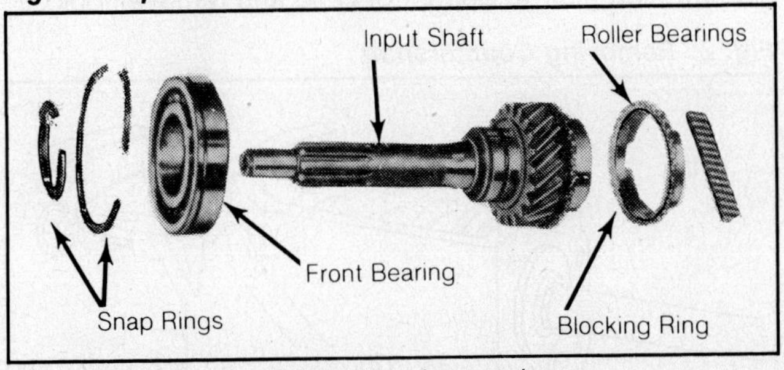

See Fig. 2 for view of front bearing retainer.

13) Install large snap ring on rear bearing and place bearing on output shaft with snap ring toward rear of shaft. Using bearing Installer (T75L-7075-B, K & P) press bearing into place. Secure bearing to shaft with snap ring.

14) Hold speedometer drive gear lock ball in detent and slide speedometer drive gear into place. Secure gear with snap ring. Place transmission in vertical position. Working with screwdriver through bottom drain hole, align bore of countershaft gear with bore of case.

15) Working from rear of case, push dummy shaft tool out of countershaft gear with countershaft. Be sure roll pin hole is aligned with hole in case before inserting countershaft. Drive shaft into place and install roll pin.

16) Place output shaft bearing retainer into front of extension housing. Coat new extension housing gasket with sealer and install. Install lock washers on 5 attaching screws and dip threads in sealer.

17) Bolt housing to case and tighten to specification. Place transmission in gear and pour approved lubricant over entire gear train while rotating either input or output shaft.

18) Install remaining detent plug and long spring into case. Coat new cover gasket with sealer. Position gasket and cover on transmission case, and install and tighten attaching screws. Check operation of transmission in all gear positions. Fill transmission to the bottom of fill hole with approved lubricant.

TIGHTENING SPECIFICATIONS

Application	Ft. Lbs. (N.m)
Cover-to-Case	20-25 (27-33)
Extension Housing-to-Case	42-50 (57-67)
Filler Plug	10-20 (14-27)
Front Bearing Retainer-to-Case	30-36 (41-48)
Outer Shift Lever Nut	18-23 (24-31)
Reverse Lamp Switch	8-12 (11-16)
Shift Fork-to-Shift Rail	10-18 (14-24)
Transmission-to-Clutch Housing	42-50 (57-67)

Manual Transmissions

FORD MOTOR CO. 4-SPEED OVERDRIVE

E150 & E350

IDENTIFICATION

The transmission identification code can be found on the Vehicle Compliance Certification Label located on the driver's door lock pillar. There is also a service identification tag located on the right front side of transmission case. The code for a 4-speed overdrive transmission is "B". *See Fig. 1.*

Fig. 1: Transmission Identification Tag

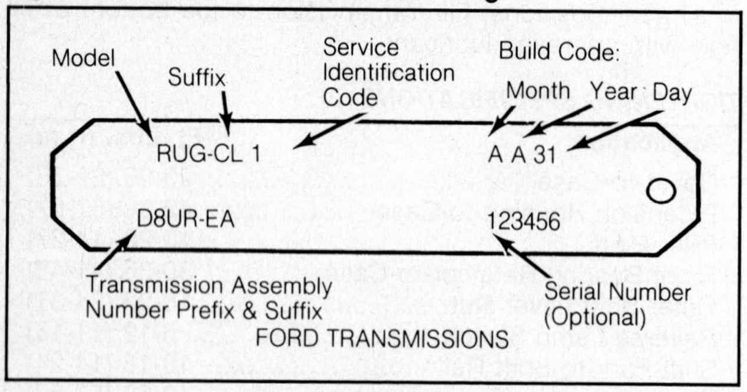

DESCRIPTION

The 4-speed overdrive transmission is fully synchronized with all gears except the reverse sliding gear being in constant mesh. All forward speed changes are accomplished with synchronizer sleeves. All forward speed gears are helical type. Reverse sliding gear and the external teeth of the 1st and 2nd speed synchronizer sleeve are spur type.

LUBRICATION

See Lubrication in MANUAL TRANSMISSION SERVICING section.

TROUBLE SHOOTING

See Manual Transmission Trouble Shooting in MANUAL TRANSMISSION SERVICING section.

REMOVAL & INSTALLATION

See appropriate MANUAL TRANSMISSION REMOVAL article in DOMESTIC GENERAL SERVICING section.

REMOVAL & INSTALLATION

See appropriate article in MANUAL TRANSMISSION REMOVAL section.

TRANSMISSION DISASSEMBLY

1) Mount transmission in a holding fixture. Drain lubricant by removing lower extension housing attaching bolt. Remove cover and gasket from case. Remove long spring which retains detent plug in case and remove detent plug using small magnet.

2) Remove extension housing bolts and washers. Remove extension housing from case and discard gasket. Remove input shaft bearing retainer screws and slide retainer off input shaft. Support countershaft gear with wire hook. With Dummy Shaft (T64P-7111-A) push countershaft out rear of case. *See Fig. 2.* Lower countershaft gear to bottom of case and remove hook.

Fig. 2: Removing Countershaft

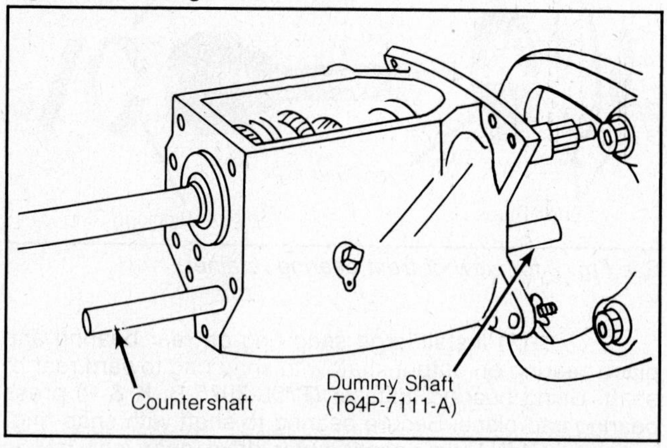

3) Remove set screw from 1st-2nd shift fork. Slide 1st-2nd shift rail out rear of case. Using magnet, remove interlock detent from between 1st-2nd and 3rd-Overdrive shift rails. *See Fig. 3.* Shift transmission into overdrive position.

4) Remove set screw from 3rd-Overdrive shift fork. Remove the side detent bolt, plug and spring. Rotate 3rd-Overdrive shift rail 90° clockwise, and tap it out through front of case. Remove interlock pin from top of case with magnet.

Fig. 3: Exploded View of Shift Rails & Forks

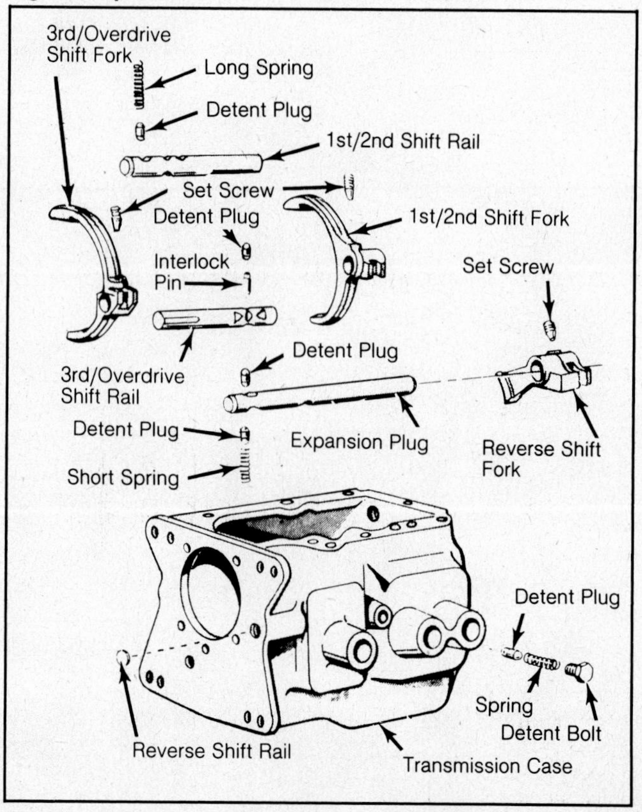

Manual Transmissions

FORD MOTOR CO. 4-SPEED OVERDRIVE (Cont.)

5) Remove snap ring securing speedometer drive gear on output shaft. Slide gear off shaft and remove speedometer gear drive ball. Remove snap ring securing output shaft bearing to shaft. *See Fig. 8.* Remove snap ring from outside diameter of bearing. Using bearing puller, pull output shaft bearing from shaft.

6) Remove snap ring securing input shaft bearing to shaft. Remove snap ring from outside diameter of bearing. Remove retaining ring. Use bearing puller to remove bearing from input shaft and transmission case. Remove input shaft and blocking ring from front of case. Move output shaft to right side of case, and rotate shift forks up and out of case.

7) Support thrust washer and 1st gear to prevent them from sliding off shaft. Lift output shaft assembly from case. Remove reverse gear shift fork set screw. Rotate shift rail 90° and slide rail out rear of case. Lift reverse shift fork from case. Remove reverse detent plug and spring from case with magnet. *See Fig. 4.*

Fig. 4: Reverse Shift Rail Removal

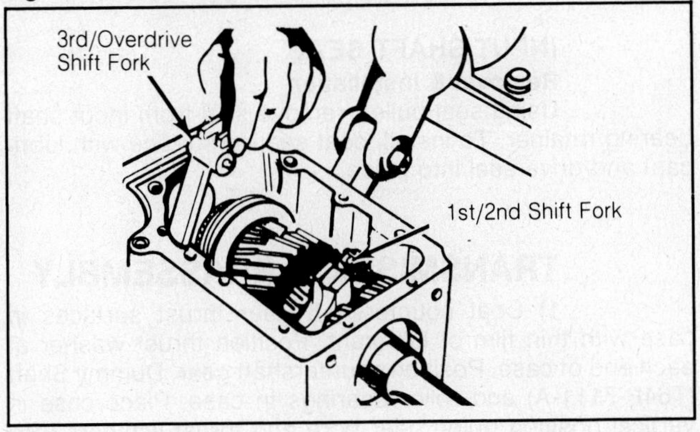

Rotate shift rail 90°.

8) Remove reverse idler gear shaft from case using Dummy Shaft (T64P-7140A). *See Fig. 5.* Lift countershaft gear and thrust washers out of case being careful not to drop bearings and Dummy Shaft (T64P-7140A) from countershaft gear. Lift reverse idler gear and thrust washer from case.

9) Remove snap ring from front of output shaft. Slide 3rd-Overdrive synchronizer blocking ring and gear from shaft. Remove next snap ring from output shaft. Slide 2nd gear thrust washer, 2nd gear and blocking ring off shaft. Remove remaining snap ring from output shaft. Remove thrust washer, 1st gear and blocking ring from rear of shaft.

CLEANING & INSPECTION

1) Wash all parts in cleaning solvent and dry with compressed air (except bearings). Brush or scrape all foreign matter from parts. Let bearings air dry in clean shop cloth. Inspect transmission case for cracks, damaged bearing bores, or threads.

2) Remove all small nicks or burrs from front or rear of case. Check bearings for roughness by slowly turning race by hand.

3) Inspect needle bearing rollers, shafts, and washers for wear or damage. Check all other parts for wear, damage, chipped, or broken teeth. Replace parts as necessary.

Fig. 5: Removing Reverse Idler Gear Shaft

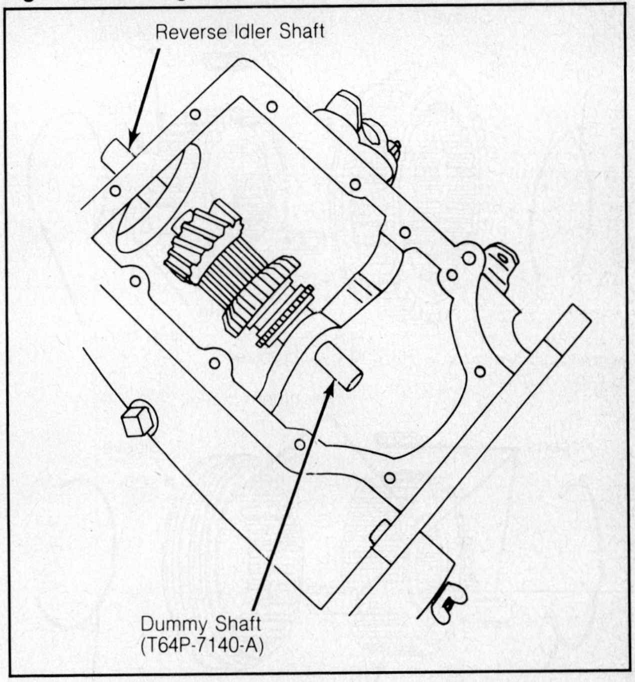

COMPONENT DISASSEMBLY & REASSEMBLY

SHIFT LEVERS AND SEALS

Disassembly

Remove nut, lock washer and flat washer. Lift shift levers off shafts. Slide each lever and shaft from case. Remove and discard "O" ring seal from each lever and shaft.

Reassembly

Lubricate new "O" ring seals with transmission lubricant and install seals on shafts. Install levers and shafts into case. Position shift lever on each shaft and secure with flat washer, lock washer and nut.

SYNCHRONIZER ASSEMBLY

Disassembly

Put alignment marks on hub and sleeve of synchronizer before disassembly. Push hub from each synchronizer sleeve. Separate inserts and insert springs from hubs. Do not mix the parts of 1st-2nd synchronizer with 3rd-Overdrive synchronizer.

Reassembly

Install hub in sleeve. Ensure that alignment marks are properly indexed. Place 3 inserts into place on hub. Install insert springs. Ensure that irregular surface (hump) is seated in one of the inserts. DO NOT stagger springs. *See Fig. 6.*

COUNTERSHAFT GEAR BEARINGS

Disassembly

Remove Dummy Shaft (T64P-7111-A), 2 bearing retainer washers and 21 roller bearings from each end of countershaft gear. *See Fig. 7.*

Reassembly

Coat bore in each end of gear with grease. Hold Dummy Shaft (T64P-7111-A) in gear and install 21 roller bearings and a retainer washer in each end of gear.

FORD MOTOR CO. 4-SPEED OVERDRIVE (Cont.)

Fig. 6: Exploded View of Synchronizer Assemblies

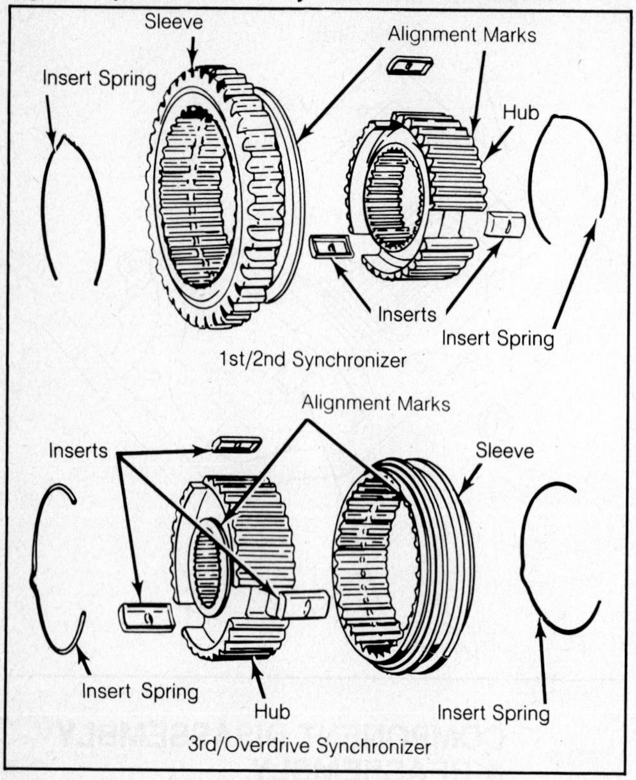

Fig. 7: Exploded View of Countershaft Gear

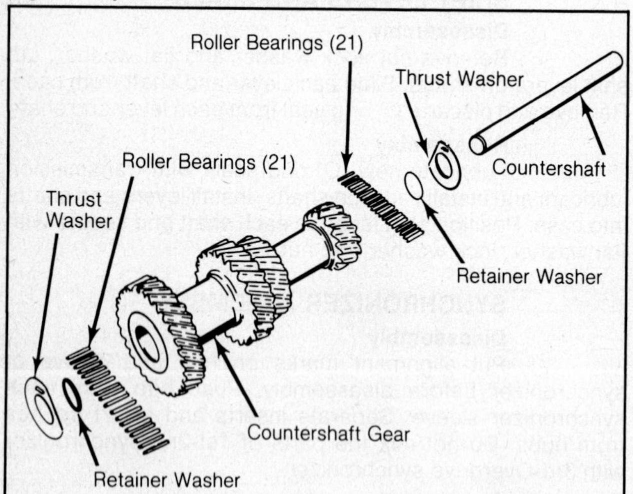

REVERSE IDLER GEAR BEARINGS

Disassembly

Slide reverse idler sliding gear off reverse idler gear. Remove Dummy Shaft (T64P-7140A), 2 bearing retainer washers and 44 roller bearings from reverse idler gear. *See. Fig. 8.*

Reassembly

Coat bore in each end of idler gear with grease. Hold Dummy Shaft (T64P-7140A) in gear and install 22 roller bearings and a retainer washer in each end of gear. Install sliding gear on reverse idler gear. Ensure that shift fork groove faces toward front.

Fig. 8: Exploded View of Reverse Idler Gear Assembly

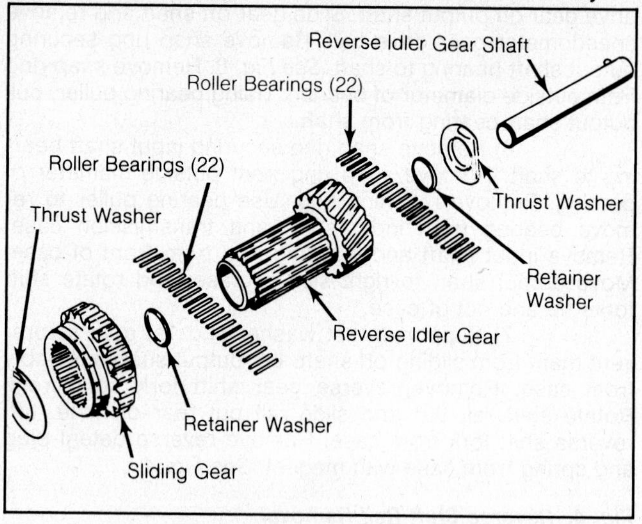

INPUT SHAFT SEAL

Removal & Installation

Using seal puller, remove seal from input shaft bearing retainer. To install, coat sealing surface with lubricant and drive seal into place.

TRANSMISSION REASSEMBLY

1) Coat countershaft gear thrust surfaces in case with thin film of lubricant. Position thrust washer at each end of case. Position countershaft gear, Dummy Shaft (T64P-7111-A) and roller bearings in case. Place case in vertical position. Align gear bore and thrust washers with bores in case and install countershaft.

2) Place case horizontal and check countershaft gear end play with feeler gauge. End play should be .004-.018" (.101-.457 mm). If not within limits, replace thrust washers. With end play correctly set, install Dummy Shaft (T64P-7140A) in countershaft gear and allow gear to remain at bottom of case.

3) Coat reverse idler gear thrust surfaces with lubricant and install 2 thrust washers. Position reverse idler gear, sliding gear, Dummy Shaft (T64P-7140A) and roller bearings in place. Ensure that shift fork groove in sliding gear faces toward front of case. Align gear bore and thrust washers with case bores and install reverse idler shaft.

4) Measure reverse idler gear end play with feeler gauge. End play should be .004-.018" (.101-.457 mm). If not within limits, replace thrust washers. Position reverse gear shift rail detent spring and plug in case. Hold reverse shift fork in place on reverse idler sliding gear. Install shift rail from rear of case. Secure fork to rail with set screw.

5) Install 1st-2nd synchronizer into front of output shaft. Ensure that shift fork groove faces toward rear of shaft. Install synchronizer hub with gear teeth facing toward rear of shaft. Position blocking ring on 2nd gear. Slide gear onto front of shaft, making sure inserts in synchronizer engage notches in blocker ring.

6) Install 2nd gear thrust washer and snap ring. Lubricate overdrive gear journal. Slide overdrive gear onto shaft with synchronizer coned surface toward front. Place blocking ring on overdrive gear. Slide 3rd-Overdrive synchronizer onto shaft.

FORD MOTOR CO. 4-SPEED OVERDRIVE (Cont.)

Fig. 9: Exploded View of Output Shaft Assembly

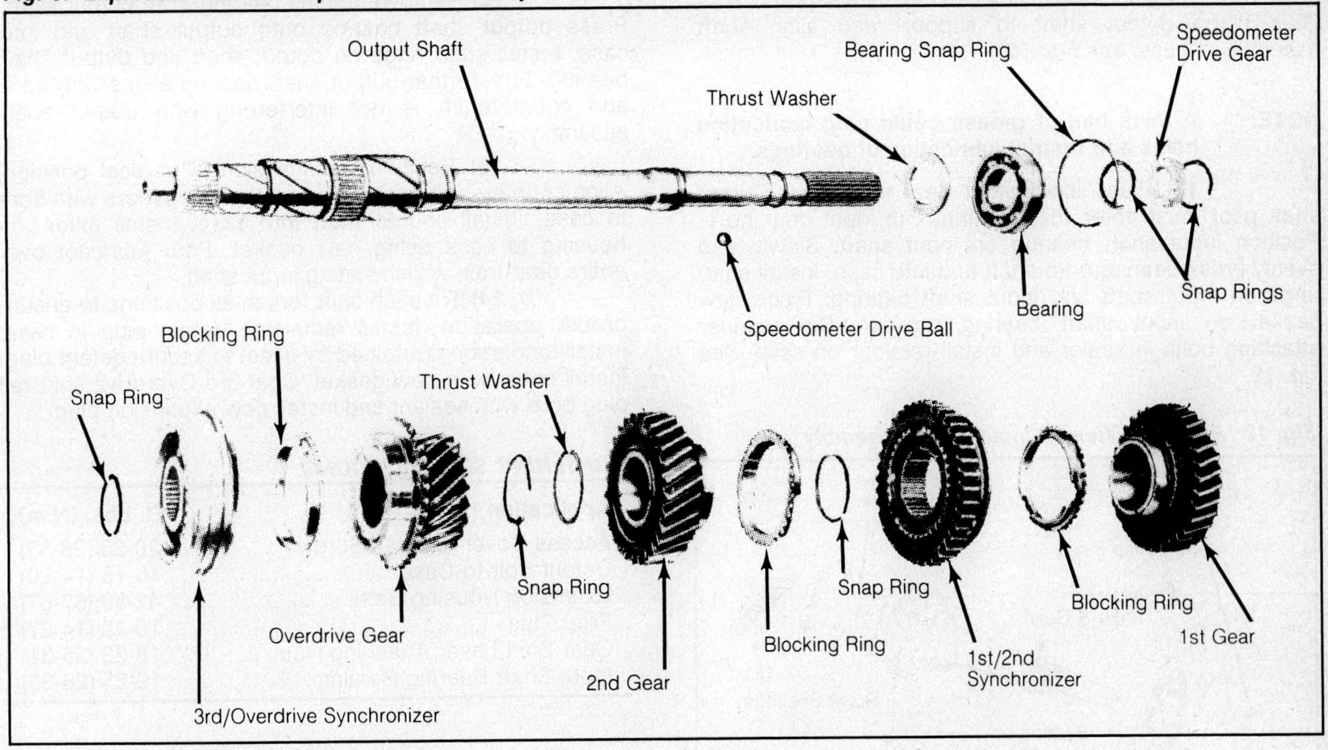

Fig. 10: Installation Dummy Bearing

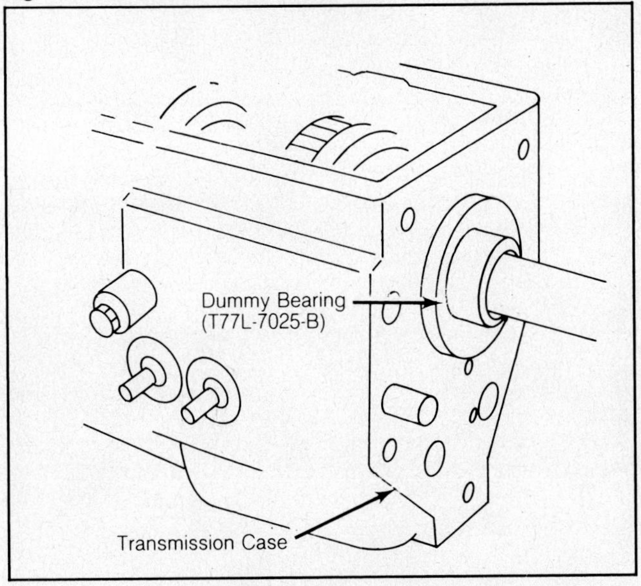

Be sure inserts engage notches in blocking ring and thrust surface faces overdrive gear.

7) Install snap ring on front of output shaft. Position blocking ring on 1st gear. Slide 1st gear onto rear of output shaft. Be sure notches of blocking ring engage synchronizer inserts. Install heavy thrust washer on rear of output shaft. Support thrust washer and 1st gear to prevent them from sliding. Carefully lower output shaft assembly into case.

8) Position 1st-2nd shift fork and 3rd-Overdrive shift forks on proper gears and rotate them into place. Install spring and detent plug into detent bore. Place reverse shift rail into neutral position. *See Fig. 11.*

Fig. 11: Output Shaft Assembly Installation

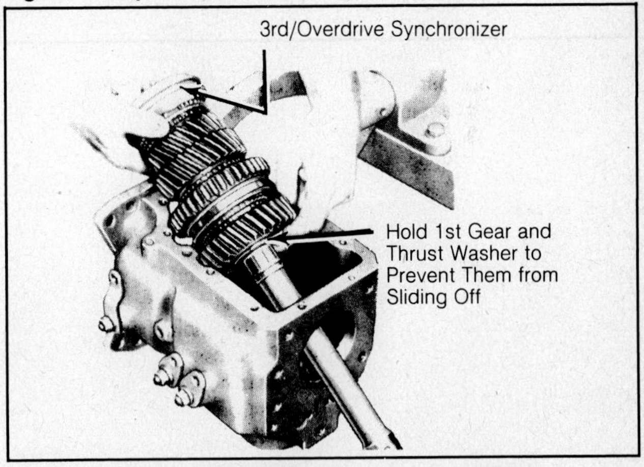

Hold 1st gear and thrust washer to prevent sliding.

9) Coat 3rd-Overdrive shift rail interlock pin (tapered ends) with grease and position in shift rail. Align 3rd-Overdrive shift fork with shift rail bores and slide rail into place. Be sure 3 detents face toward outside of case. Place front synchronizer into overdrive position and install set screw in 3rd-Overdrive shift fork. Move synchronizer to neutral position. Install 3rd-Overdrive detent plug, spring and bolt in left side of case. Place detent plug (tapered ends) in detent bore in case.

NOTE: **A missing or improperly installed interlock pin could allow the transmission to be shifted into 1st and Reverse gear at the same time.**

10) Align 1st-2nd shift fork with case bores and slide shift rail into place, securing shift fork with set screw. Coat input gear bore with thin film of grease. Install 15 roller bearings into bore. Place front blocking ring in

Manual Transmissions

FORD MOTOR CO. 4-SPEED OVERDRIVE (Cont.)

3rd-Overdrive synchronizer. Place Dummy Bearing (T77L-7025-B) on output shaft to support and align shaft assembly in case. *See Fig. 10.*

NOTE: A thick film of grease could plug lubrication holes and restrict lubrication of bearings.

11) Place input shaft gear into case. Output shaft pilot must enter roller bearings in input gear bore. Position input shaft bearing on input shaft. Slowly and evenly press bearing onto shaft and into case. Install snap rings on input shaft and input shaft bearing. Place new gasket on input shaft bearing retainer. Dip retainer attaching bolts in sealer and install retainer on case. *See Fig. 12.*

Fig. 12: Exploded View of Input Shaft Assembly

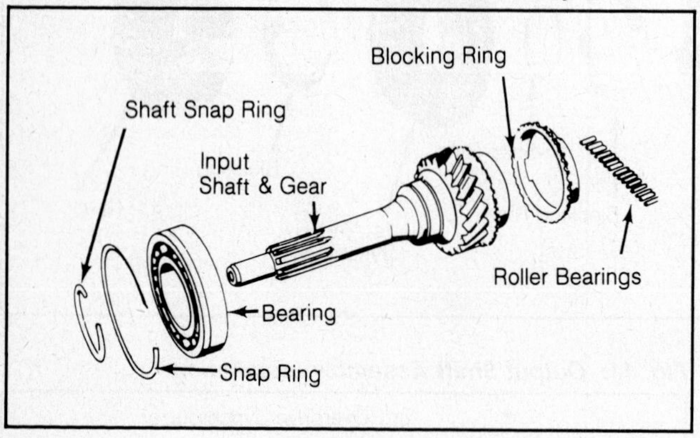

12) Remove dummy bearing from output shaft. Press output shaft bearing onto output shaft and into case. Install snap rings on output shaft and output shaft bearing. Ensure that output shaft bearing aligns with bore and countershaft is not interferring with output shaft assembly.

13) Position transmission in vertical position. Align countershaft gear bore and thrust washers with bore in case. Install countershaft into case. Install extension housing to case using new gasket. Pour lubricant over entire gear train while rotating input shaft.

14) Try each shift fork in all positions to ensure proper operation. Install remaining detent plug in case. Install long spring (retained by case) to secure detent plug. Install cover with new gasket. Coat 3rd-Overdrive shift rail plug bore with sealant and install new expansion plug.

TIGHTENING SPECIFICATIONS

Application	Ft. Lbs. (N.m)
Access Cover-to-Case Screw	20-25 (28-33)
Detent Bolt-to-Case	10-15 (14-20)
Extension Housing Bolts	42-50 (57-67)
Filler Plug	10-20 (14-27)
Gear Shift Lever Attaching Nuts	18-23 (25-31)
Input Shaft Bearing Retainer	19-25 (26-33)

FORD MOTOR CO. TOD 4-SPEED OVERDRIVE

Bronco, F150/F250

IDENTIFICATION

The transmission identification code can be found on Vehicle Compliance Certification Label located on driver's side of door lock pillar. There is also a service identification tag located on right side of case at front. First line on tag will show transmission model and service identification code when required. Lower line on tag shows transmission serial number. A serial number is stamped on top side of flange on transmission case for further identification.

DESCRIPTION

Top mounted shifter 4-speed overdrive transmission (TOD) is fully synchronized in all gears, except reverse sliding gear, being in constant mesh. All forward speed changes are accomplished with synchronizer sleeve. All forward speed gears are helical type. Reverse sliding gear and external teeth of the 1st and 2nd speed synchronizer sleeve are spur type.

LUBRICATION

See Lubrication in MANUAL TRANSMISSION SERVICING section.

TROUBLE SHOOTING

See Manual Transmission Trouble Shooting in MANUAL TRANSMISSION SERVICING section.

REMOVAL & INSTALLATION

See REMOVAL & INSTALLATION in MANUAL TRANSMISSION REMOVAL section.

TRANSMISSION DISASSEMBLY

1) Mount transmission in a holding fixture. Remove ball, boot and lever as an assembly. Remove retaining screws from boot and pad. Shift transmission into Neutral. Remove boot from cap. Place oil filter wrench (D79L-6731-A or B) around gearshift housing cap and twist off cap. Remove shift lever.

2) Insert a screwdriver into 2nd gear and shift transmission into 2nd gear. Force shift bias spring over and engage slot in 1st-2nd fork and move fork forward. *See Fig. 2.*

3) Remove 6 gear shift housing assembly-to-transmission bolts. Remove housing assembly from case by inserting a screwdriver under bosses on housing and prying up gently. Remove all gasket material.

4) Shift transmission into Neutral position. With a drain pan under extension housing, remove 5 extension housing-to-transmission case bolts. Separate housing from case and drain transmission fluid into pan. Remove all gasket material. If installed, remove shipping seal and discard.

5) Remove snap ring securing speedometer drive gear to output shaft. Slide gear off shaft, then remove .025" (.64 mm) speedometer gear drive ball. Use a punch and drive out roll pin that secures 3rd-4th shift fork to 3rd-4th shift rail.

6) Position a .375" (9.53 mm) diameter rod against 3rd-4th shift rail in case. Use rod to push shift rail through front of case. Position Dummy Shaft (T64P-7111-A) over countershaft bore in front of case. Drive dummy shaft into case and countershaft gear bore until countershaft is removed. Lower countershaft to bottom of case.

NOTE: **It is not necessary to remove roll pins from end of countershaft.**

7) Remove snap rings from output shaft and from groove in output shaft rear bearing. Remove and discard output shaft rear bearing. Remove 4 input shaft retainer-to-case bolts and remove retainer by prying in 2 notches located at 11 and 1 o'clock. Remove all gasket material.

8) Remove snap rings securing input shaft bearing to shaft and snap ring from groove in bearing. Remove retainer from input shaft ball bearing. Remove front input shaft ball bearing from case and discard.

NOTE: **Remove front bearing only if replacement is necessary.**

9) Rotate input shaft until flat on synchronizer teeth align with teeth on countershaft gear. *See Fig. 1.* Remove input shaft from case, be careful not to drop 15 roller bearings. Remove 3rd-4th blocking ring from rear of input shaft. Mark blocking ring to ensure position during reassembly.

Fig. 1: Placing 1st-2nd Shift Fork in 2nd Gear

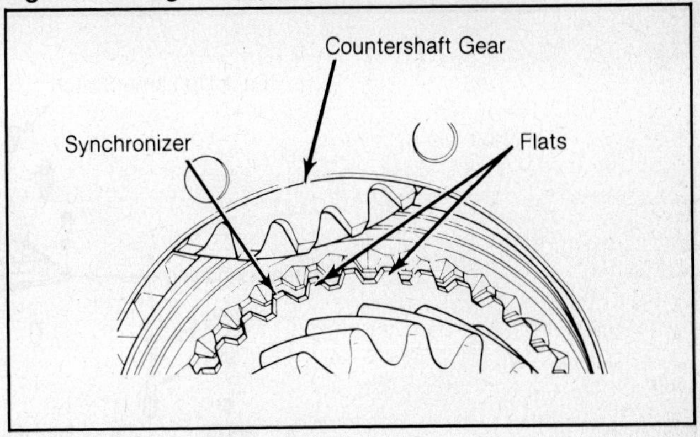

Fig. 2: Aligning Teeth on Countershaft Gear

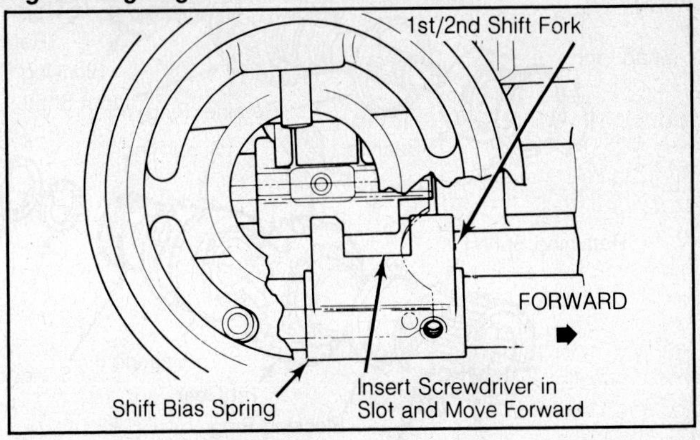

10) Remove 3rd-4th shift fork from intermediate and high clutch sleeve. Tilt output shaft and gear train

Manual Transmissions

FORD MOTOR CO. TOD 4-SPEED OVERDRIVE (Cont.)

Fig. 3: Exploded View of T.O.D. 4-Speed Transmission Assembly

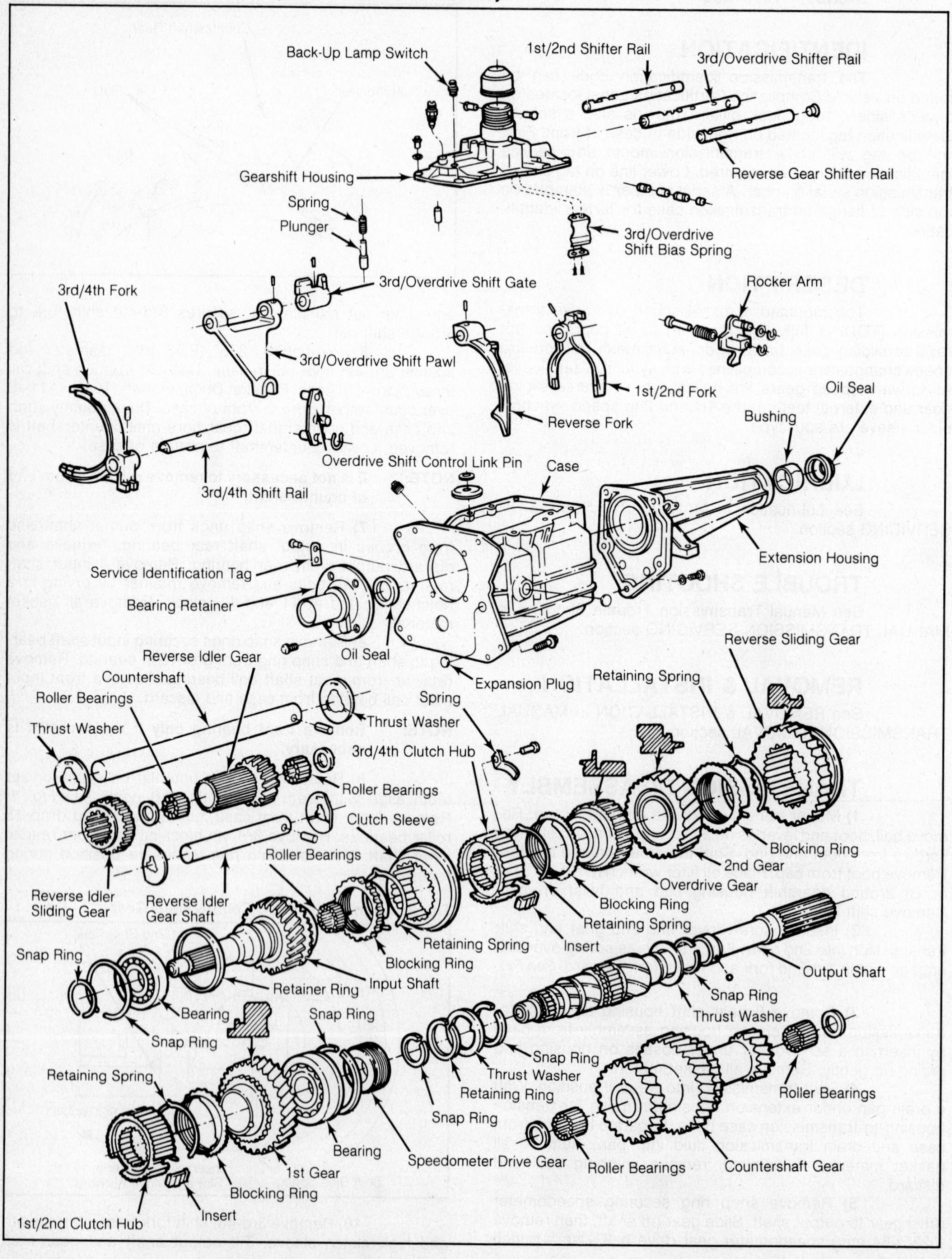

assembly upwards and remove from case. Lift countershaft gear (with dummy shaft tool still inside) from bottom of transmission case. Be careful not to drop 21 roller bearings in each end of countershaft gear assembly.

11) Remove countershaft nylon thrust washers from each end of case. Using a brass drift from inside case, drive reverse idler gear shaft out from rear of case.

12) Remove reverse idler bronze thrust washers. Remove reverse idler gear, reverse idler sliding gear 2 flat washers and idler shaft roller bearings (22 in each end) from case. Remove overdrive shift control link and pin assembly from case.

CLEANING & INSPECTION

1) Wash all parts in cleaning solvent and dry with compressed air (except bearings). Brush or scrape all foreign matter from parts. Let bearings air dry in clean shop cloth. Inspect transmission case for cracks, damaged bearing bores, or threads.

2) Remove all small nicks or burrs from front or rear of case. Check bearings for roughness by slowly turning race by hand.

3) Inspect needle bearing rollers, shafts, and washers for wear or damage. Check all other parts for wear, damage, chipped, or broken teeth. Replace parts as necessary.

COMPONENT DISASSEMBLY & REASSEMBLY

GEAR SHIFT HOUSING ASSEMBLY

Disassembly

1) With gearshift housing in vise, drive out roll pins that retain 3rd-Overdrive shift pawl and 3rd-Overdrive shift gate making sure not to strike bias spring.

2) Slide 3rd-Overdrive shift pawl to front of housing. Insert a punch in exposed roll pin hole in rail and rotate rail 90°, this will prevent meshlock plunger from locking rail in place.

3) Position a screwdriver in slots provided in housing and pry plugs from housing. Discard plugs. Using a brass drift drive 3rd-Overdrive shift rail from housing.

4) Remove each interlock plunger from housing through rear 3rd-Overdrive rail bore. By tilting housing, plungers should fall out. Drive out roll pin retaining 1st-2nd shift fork to rail, be careful not to drive pin into inner wall of housing.

5) Slide 1st-2nd shift fork to front of case. Insert a punch into exposed roll pin hole and rotate rail 90°, this will prevent meshlock plunger from locking rail in place. Use a brass drift to drive 1st-2nd shift rail from housing.

CAUTION: Cover plunger and spring bore to prevent plunger and spring from flying out after rail is removed.

6) Remove 1st-2nd shift fork from housing. Slide reverse fork and rail assembly forward so it is in Reverse position. Drive out reverse fork roll pin. Slide reverse fork rearward, insert a punch in roll pin hole and rotate rail 90°, this will prevent meshlock plunger from locking rail in place.

7) Drive reverse rail from housing using a brass drift. Remove reverse fork from housing. Remove 3 meshlock plungers and interlock springs from bores in housing.

CAUTION: Cover plunger and spring bore to prevent plunger and spring from flying out after rail is removed.

8) Remove clip retaining reverse rocker arm assembly to housing. Force shift bias spring outward only enough to remove reverse rocker arm assembly. Remove assembly from housing. DO NOT disassembly reverse rocker arm assembly. If necessary, remove back-up lamp switch and gasket from housing.

Reassembly

1) Coat all shift rails with transmission lubricant. Install back-up lamp switch in gearshift housing, if it was removed. Lubricate "O" ring and shaft on reverse rocker arm assembly with multi-purpose lubricant.

2) Force shift bias spring outward only enough to install reverse rocker arm assembly in housing. Install clip that retains reverse rocker arm assembly.

3) Drop an interlock spring and meshlock plunger in each bore in front of housing. Position reverse shift rail in housing.

4) Detent slots in rail must be inserted into housing first with slots facing meshlock plunger. *See Fig. 5.* Install reverse shift fork so it engages reverse rocker arm assembly and fork pad faces inside. Slide rail through fork bore and up to meshlock plunger.

5) Use a small punch to force meshlock plunger down into bore. Push rail forward until it blocks plunger. Withdraw punch and push rail through bore. Align roll pin holes in fork and rail. Install roll pin.

Fig. 4: Exploded View of Gearshift Housing Assembly

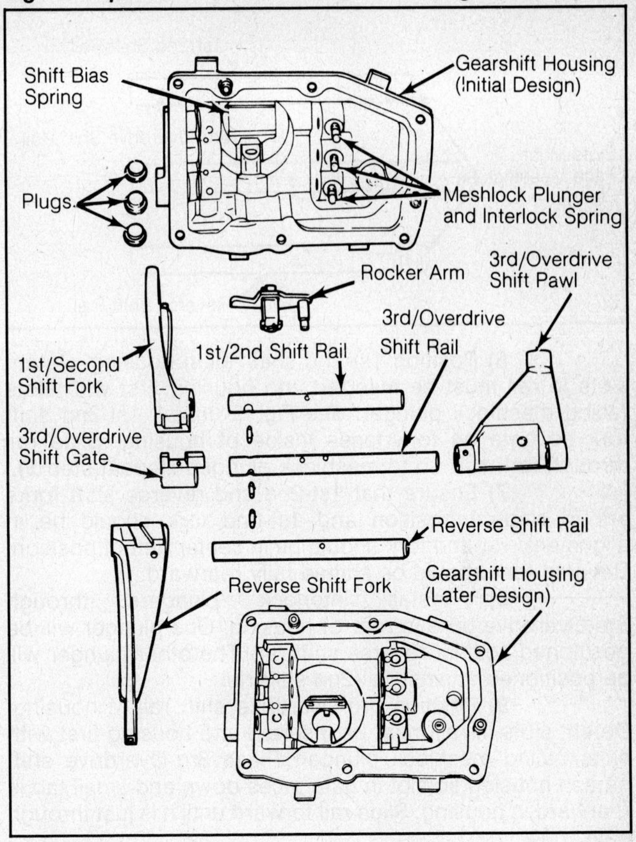

FORD MOTOR CO. TOD 4-SPEED OVERDRIVE (Cont.)

Fig. 5: Shift Rails Showing Detent Slots

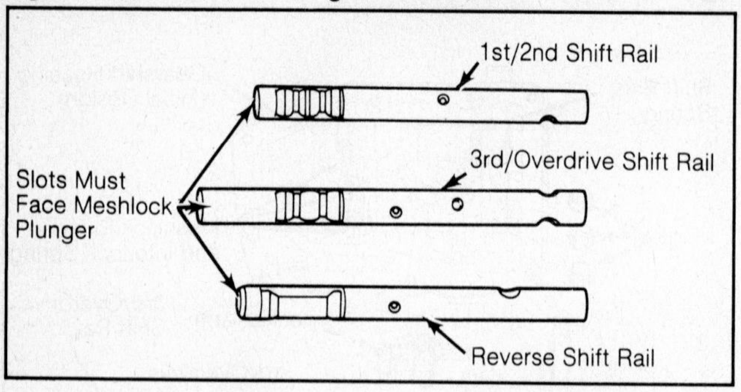

6) Position 1st-2nd shift rail in housing. Detent slots in rail must be inserted into housing first with slots facing meshlock plunger. *See Fig. 5.* Install 1st-2nd shift fork so gate on fork faces inside of housing. Slide rail through fork and up to meshlock plunger. Repeat step **5)**.

7) Ensure that 1st-2nd and reverse shift forks are in Neutral position and 1st-2nd fork should be in alignment. 1st-2nd fork should be in center detent position. Reverse fork should be shifted fully rearward.

8) Install interlock plungers through 3rd-Overdrive bore in rear of housing. One plunger will be positioned against reverse shift rail. The other plunger will be positioned against 1st-2nd shift rail.

9) Position 3rd-Overdrive shift rail in housing. Detent slots in rail must be inserted into housing first with slots facing meshlock plunger. Place 3rd-Overdrive shift gate in housing so slot in gate faces down and small tab is rearward in housing. Slide rail forward until it is just through gate.

10) Install interlock pin to rear of 3rd-Overdrive shift rail. Place 3rd-Overdrive shift pawl in housing. Position pawl so that slot is on reverse rail side of housing. Slide rail through pawl up to plunger.

11) Repeat step **5)**. Align roll pin holes in pawl, gate and rail. Install roll pin. Apply stud and bearing mount sealer to outside diameter of shift rail cup plugs. Drive cups into bores located in rear of housing. Place gearshift housing assembly in 2nd gear for installation.

SYNCHRONIZER ASSEMBLY

Disassembly

Scribe alignment marks on hub and sleeve of synchronizer before disassembly. Push synchronizer hub from each synchronizer sleeve. Separate inserts and insert springs from hubs. DO NOT mix parts of 1st and 2nd synchronizer with 3rd and Overdrive synchronizer.

Reassembly

Position hub in sleeve, ensure that alignment marks are properly indexed. Place 3 inserts into place on hub. Install insert springs making sure that tab is located in a common insert rotating in opposite directions. DO NOT stagger springs.

OUTPUT SHAFT AND GEAR TRAIN

Disassembly

1) Before disassembling output shaft and gear train assembly, end play of 1st, 2nd and Overdrive gears must be checked. *See Fig. 7.* End play is measured with 1st gear thrust washer clamped tight against shoulder of output shaft. If measurements exceed specifications, rebuild assembly with new components. See END PLAY SPECIFICATION CHART.

Fig. 6: Exploded View of Synchronizers

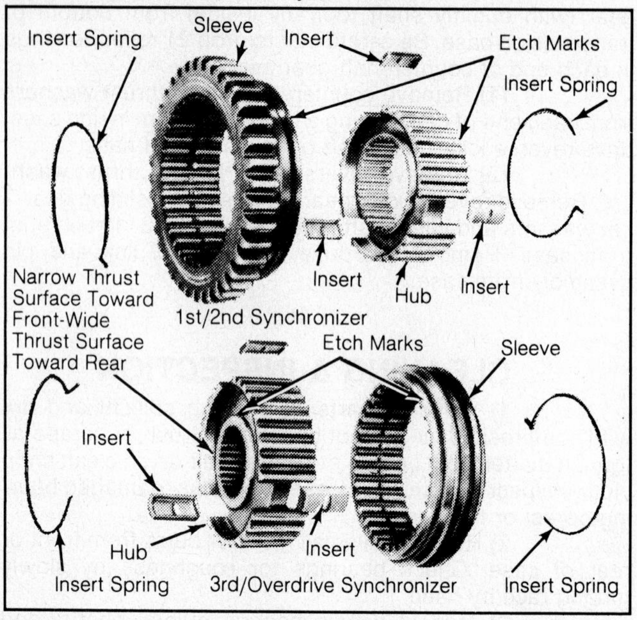

Fig. 7: Checking Gear Train End Play

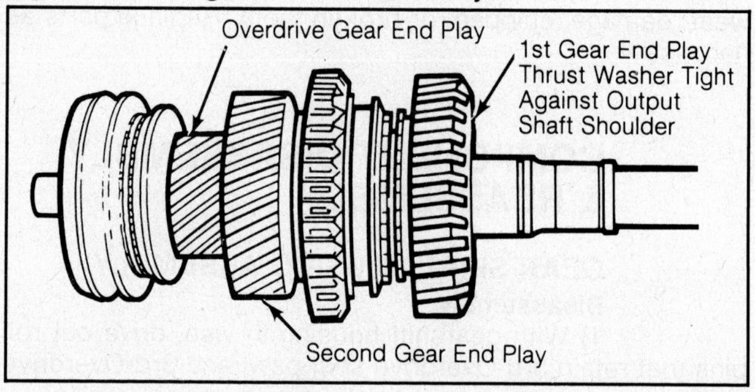

END PLAY SPECIFICATIONS

Application	End Play In. (mm)
1st Gear	.005-.024 (.127-.609)
2nd Gear	.003-.021 (.076-.553)
Countershaft Gear	.004-.018 (.10-.46)
Overdrive Gear	.009-.023 (.228-.584)
Reverse Idler Gear	.005-.023 (.127-.584)

2) Remove snap ring from front of output shaft. Remove 3rd-4th synchronizer assembly. Remove Overdrive gear from shaft. Remove next snap ring and second gear thrust washer from shaft. Slide 2nd gear and blocking ring from shaft.

3) Remove next snap ring. Using a press, remove 1st-2nd synchronizer assembly. Synchronizer assembly is a press fit on output shaft.

Reassembly

1) Lubricate 1st gear journal with multi-purpose lubricant. Press 1st-2nd synchronizer assembly onto front of output shaft, making sure shift fork groove is facing towards rear of shaft. Install 1st gear and blocking ring on rear of shaft.

2) Install snap ring in front of 1st-2nd synchronizer assembly. Position blocking ring on 2nd gear. Lubricate 2nd gear journal on output shaft with multi-purpose lubricant. Slide 2nd gear with blocking ring onto front of

FORD MOTOR CO. TOD 4-SPEED OVERDRIVE (Cont.)

shaft. Ensure that inserts in synchronizer engage notches in blocking ring.

3) Install 2nd gear thrust washer and snap ring. Lubricate Overdrive gear journal with multi-purpose grease. Slide overdrive gear onto shaft with coned synchronizer surface facing towards front.

4) Slide 3rd-4th synchronizer assembly onto shaft making sure inserts in synchronizer engage notches in blocking ring and small thrust surface is facing forward. Install snap ring on front of output shaft.

TRANSMISSION REASSEMBLY

1) Reverse disassembly procedures, noting the following: coat all moving parts with a multi-purpose grease. Use anaerobic sealer (gasket eliminator) to form a mating surface gasket instead of using a gasket. Coat bolts with threadlock and sealer prior to installation.

2) Ensure that square shouldered pin is positioned towards bottom of case. Align tabs on reverse idler gear thrust washer with slots in case. There are 22 roller bearings on each end of reverse idler shaft. Grooved portion of sliding gear for reverse fork must face front of case when installed.

3) There are 21 roller bearings on each end of countershaft. Countershaft gear must be at bottom of case with countershaft removed in order to obtain required clearance to install input shaft, output shaft and gear train assembly.

4) Install 3rd-4th shift fork with slot facing down. There are 15 roller bearings for bore of input shaft. Tighten extension housing bolts in proper sequence. *See Fig. 8.*

Fig. 8: Tightening Extension Housing Bolts

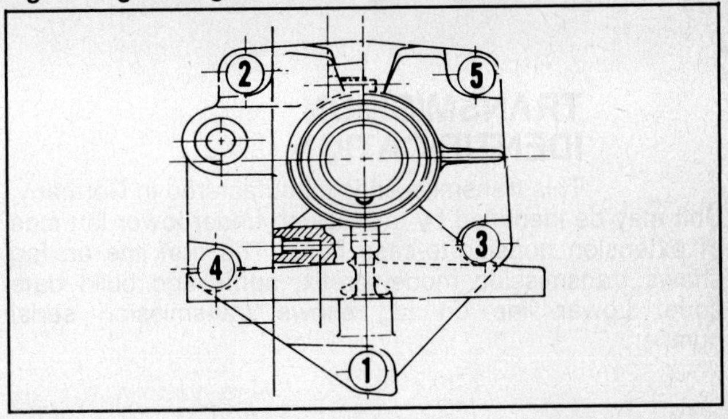

5) Welch plug must not protrude above face of case or more than .06" (1.52 mm) below face. Position 3rd-4th shift rail so that flat on rail faces front and bottom of case. Install gearshift housing assembly in 2nd gear position. Ensure that reverse idler gear is positioned rearward.

TIGHTENING SPECIFICATIONS

Application	Ft. Lbs. (N.m)
Back-Up Lamp Switch	8-12 (11-16)
Extension Housing Bolts	42-50 (54-67)
Filler Plug	10-20 (14-27)
Gearshift Housing-to-Case Bolts	18-22 (25-29)
Input Shaft Bearing Retainer	12-16 (16-21)

FORD MOTOR CO. 83ET 4-SPEED

Capri, Mustang

TRANSMISSION IDENTIFICATION

This transmission is manufactured in Germany. Unit may be identified by tag located under lower left side of extension housing-to-case bolts. The first line on tag shows transmission model prefix, suffix and build date code. Lower line on tag shows transmission serial number.

DESCRIPTION

Four speed fully synchronized, except reverse. Forward gears are in constant mesh. Gear changes are through forged blocker ring synchronized units. Engagement of two gears at once is prevented by means of a selector interlock plate pivoted in the transmission case. This plate engages with selector forks which are not in use and holds them positively in disengaged position.

Selective snap rings compensate for tolerances which must be allowed in manufacture. Whenever overhauling the gear case where snap ring removal is required, ensure correct size new snap ring is properly installed.

LUBRICATION & ADJUSTMENT

See the appropriate article in MANUAL TRANSMISSION SERVICING Section.

REMOVAL & INSTALLATION

See the appropriate article in MANUAL TRANSMISSION REMOVAL Section.

TRANSMISSION DISASSEMBLY

1) With transmission case mounted in Holding Fixture (T57L-500-B), remove clutch release bearing and lever. Remove flywheel housing mounting bolts. Separate housing from transmission case.

Fig. 1: Removing Detent Plunger Assembly from Case

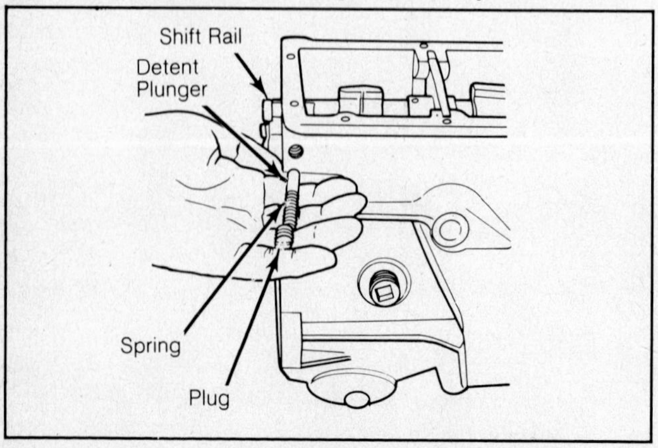

2) Remove cover mount bolts. Remove cover, discard gasket and drain gear oil. Remove threaded plug, spring and shift rail detent plunger from upper left front side of transmission case. *See Fig. 1*.

3) Working from inside transmission case, drive access plug from rear of case using proper size drift and hammer. *See Fig. 2*.

Fig. 2: Removing Access Plug from Case

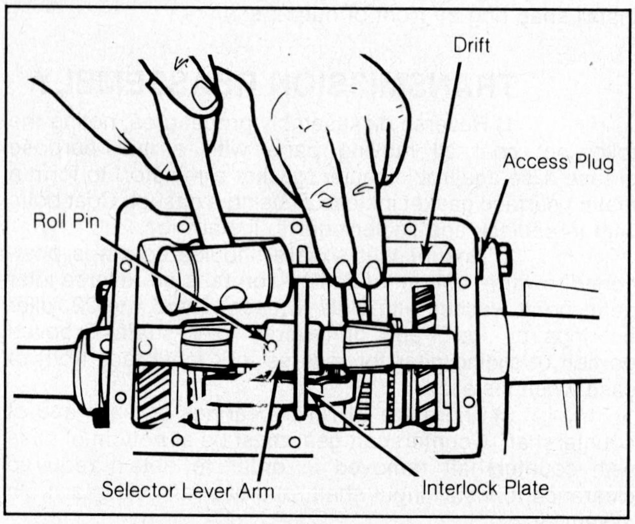

4) Working through access plug hole, drive retaining pin from case. Remove interlock plate. *See Fig. 3*.

Fig. 3: Removing Interlock Retaining Pin

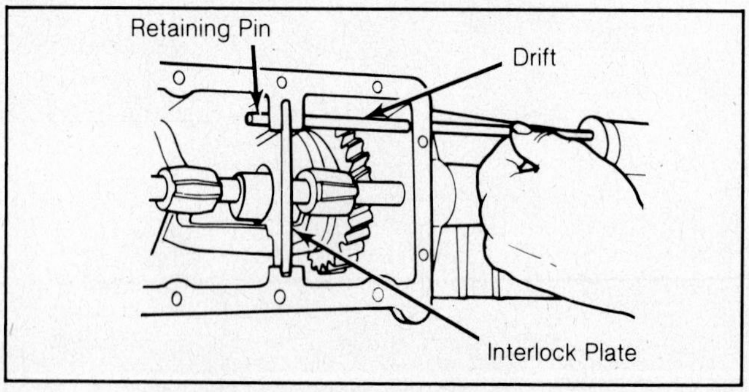

5) Remove roll pin from selector lever arm. Tap front end of shift rail to displace plug at rear of extension housing. Remove shift rail from extension housing and case. *See Fig. 4*. Lift selector arm and shift forks from case.

Fig. 4: Removing Shift Rail from Extension Housing

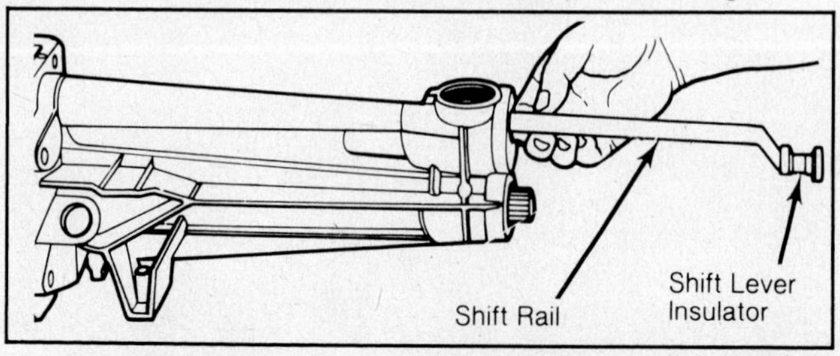

6) Remove 4 extension housing mount bolts. Tap housing with plastic mallet to loosen it from case.

FORD MOTOR CO. 83ET 4-SPEED (Cont.)

Rotate housing until countershaft is aligned with cutaway in housing flange.

7) With brass drift, drive countershaft rearward until it just clears front of case. Install Dummy Shaft (T71P-7111-B or equivalent) into case and gear until countershaft gear can be lowered to bottom of case.

8) Lower dummy shaft and countershaft gear to bottom of case. Lift extension housing and mainshaft from transmission case as an assembly.

Fig. 5: Assembled View of Extension Housing & Mainshaft Assembly

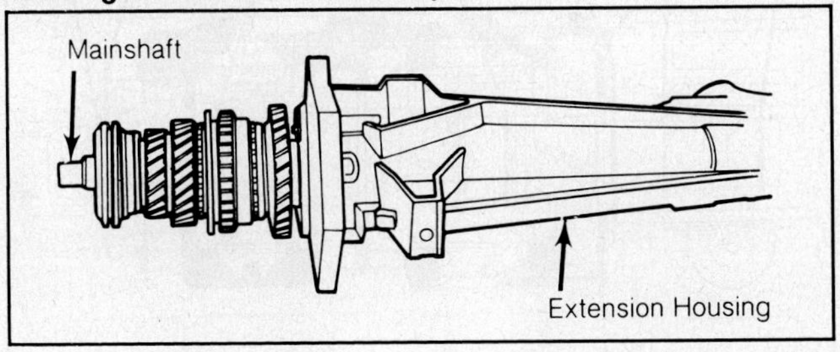

9) Remove 4 input shaft bearing retainer mounting bolts (10 mm). Remove input shaft bearing and retainer from case as an assembly. Remove reverse idler gear shaft from rear of case using Slide Hammer (T50T-100-A) and Adapter (T71P-7140-A). Remove reverse idler gear and spacer.

10) Remove countershaft gear and dummy shaft from bottom of case. Separate bearing retainer washers, bearings and dummy shaft from countershaft gear. Remove bearing retainer and pilot bearing from input shaft gear. Pry oil seal from bearing retainer.

CAUTION: Do not remove ball bearing from input shaft unless replacement is required. To remove bearing, remove retaining snap ring and press bearing from shaft.

11) Lift 4th gear blocker ring from front of output shaft. Remove and discard snap ring from forward end of output shaft. Slide 3rd-4th gear synchronizer assembly and 3rd gear from output shaft. Remove and discard snap ring. Slide thrust washer, 2nd gear and blocker ring off of output shaft.

NOTE: Scratch or etch alignment marks on hub and sleeve of synchronizer before disassembly.

12) Disassemble synchronizer assembly by pulling sleeve off hub. Renove inserts and springs. Remove and discard snap ring retaining output shaft bearing in extension housing. Press or tap output shaft assembly from housing with plastic hammer.

13) Remove snap ring which retains bearing on output shaft. Press speedometer gear from output shaft. Position Support Plate (T71P-4621-B) behind 1st Gear. Place output shaft assembly in press. Press 1st gear, spacer and bearing from output shaft.

CAUTION: The 1st-2nd gear synchronizer and hub is serviced as an assembly with the output shaft. DO NOT separate hub from shaft. Remove sleeve, springs and inserts from hub after scribing alignment marks on hub and sleeve. Only springs and inserts are serviceable.

14) Inspect shift rail bushing and, if necessary for replacement, drive bushing from rear of extension housing with 9/16" socket and extension. Do not remove bushing if serviceable. Pry shift rail seal from extension housing. Remove remaining shift linkage from case.

15) Check extension housing oil seal (lower) for wear or damage. If necessary, remove seal using Oil Seal Remover (T71P-7657-A). Install new seal using Oil Seal Installer (T71P-7095-A) and adapter. Ensure adapter shoulder faces away from seal when installing.

CLEANING & INSPECTION

Wash all parts except seals, "O" rings and ball bearings in cleaning solvent and dry with compressed air. Rotate ball bearings in solvent until lubricant is removed. Hold bearing assembly to prevent rotation and blow dry. Dip bearings in transmission lubricant and wrap in clean, lint-free cloth until ready for installation.

If equipped, clean magnet in bottom of transmission case with kerosene. Inspect case for cracks, wear, damaged bearing bores or damaged threads. Remove all small nicks or burrs from front of case. Check all gears for wear, chipped or broken teeth and damage. Replace parts as necessary. Inspect speedometer gear for stripped teeth or other damage. Replace with correct size gear as necessary.

TRANSMISSION REASSEMBLY

1) With 3/4" socket, drive new shift rail seal into rear of transmission case. If shift rail bushing was removed from extension housing, drive new one into place with 9/16" socket and extension.

2) If 1st-2nd gear synchronizer was disassembled, slide synchronizer sleeve over hub. Ensure alignment marks made at disassembly are aligned and shift fork groove is toward front of shaft.

3) Locate an insert in each of 3 slots cut in hub. Install an insert spring inside synchronizer sleeve beneath inserts. The tab on end of spring must locate in "U" section of insert. Fit other spring on opposite face making sure tab is in same recess and spring is in opposite rotational direction. *See Fig. 6.*

Fig. 6: Synchronizer Spring Installation

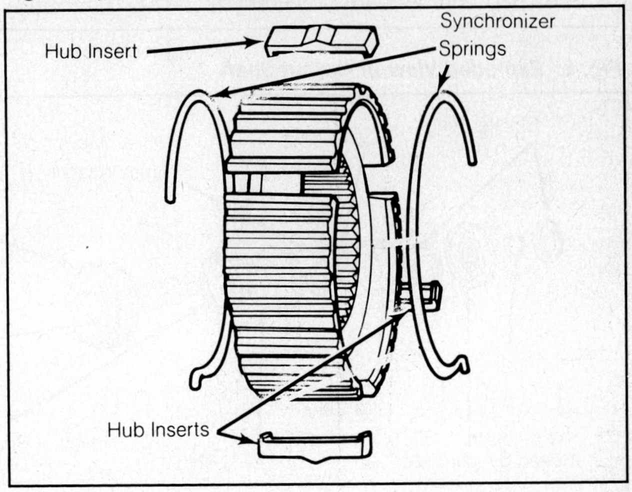

FORD MOTOR CO. 83ET 4-SPEED (Cont.)

4) Assemble a blocker ring on 1st gear side of 1st-2nd gear synchronizer. Apply lubricant to cone surface of first gear and all output shaft gear journals before installing gear onto shaft. Slide 1st gear onto output shaft so cone surface engages blocker ring.

5) Install spacer on shaft. Ensure large diameter is toward rear of shaft. Place Master Spacer (T70P-7154) in output shaft bearing bore of extension housing. *See Fig. 7*. Measure width of output shaft bearing outer race with micrometer.

Fig. 7: Using Special Gauge to Determine End Play Snap Ring Thickness

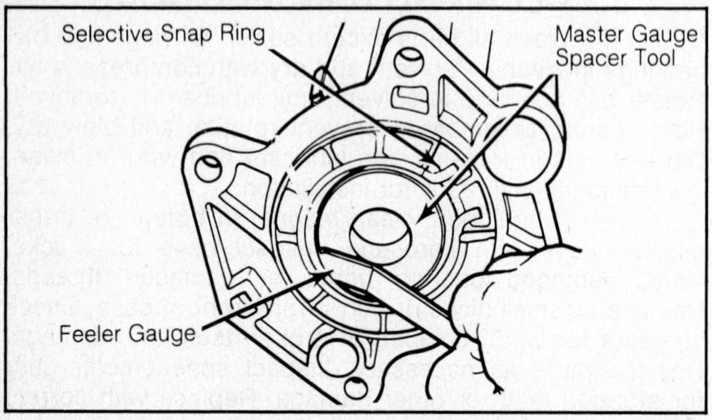

6) The difference in thickness between Master Gauge and bearing outer race will determine thickness of selective snap ring required to eliminate end play. If bearing race thickness is more than that stamped on Master Gauge, decrease snap ring thickness. If thickness is less, increase snap ring thickness to remove end play.

OUTPUT SHAFT BEARING-TO-CASE SNAP RING TABLE

Part No. [1]	Identification (Color or Letter)	Thickness In. (mm)
A	Copper	.0679 (1.725)
B	W	.0689 (1.750)
C	V	.0699 (1.775)
D	U	.0709 (1.801)
E	None	.0719 (1.826)
F	Blue	.0728 (1.849)
G	Black	.0738 (1.875)
H	Brown	.0748 (1.899)

1 - All part numbers are preceded by "D1FZ-7030-".

7) Position selected snap ring and output shaft bearing on shaft. Place assembly in hydraulic press. Press bearing into place and secure with thickest snap ring that will fit groove in output shaft.

Fig. 9: Cutaway View of Transmission Showing Snap Ring Locations

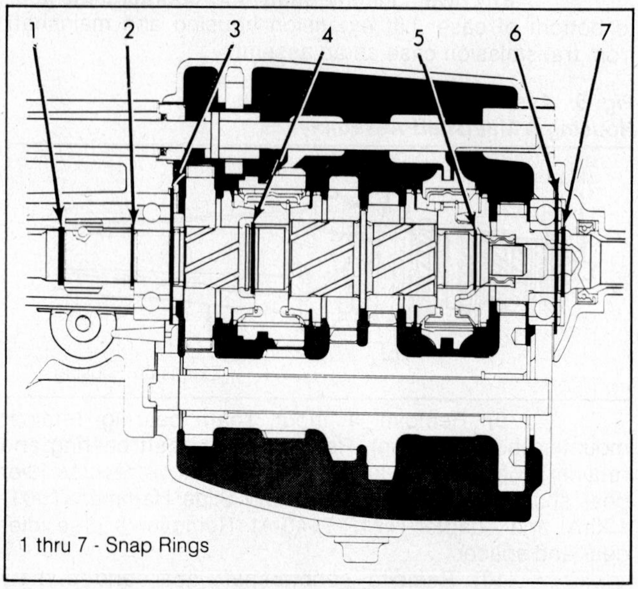

8) Install 2nd gear and blocker ring on output shaft so that dog teeth face rearward. Install washer and snap ring. Install 3rd gear on output shaft so that dog teeth face forward. Install blocker ring on 3rd gear cone.

NOTE: **Apply lubricant to cones of all gears and output shaft gear journals before installation of gears. Ensure new snap rings are used in all positions.**

9) Install 3rd-4th gear synchronizer assembly on output shaft with hub boss (small diameter) facing forward. Retain 3rd-4th gear synchronizer assembly with snap ring. Pull up on synchronizer assembly so snap ring is tight in its groove. Install 4th gear blocker ring on input shaft gear cone.

10) Press speedometer drive gear onto shaft using Speedometer Drive Gear Installer (T71P-17271-A). Press until dowels on tool just contacts bearing outer race

Fig. 8: Exploded View of Output Shaft

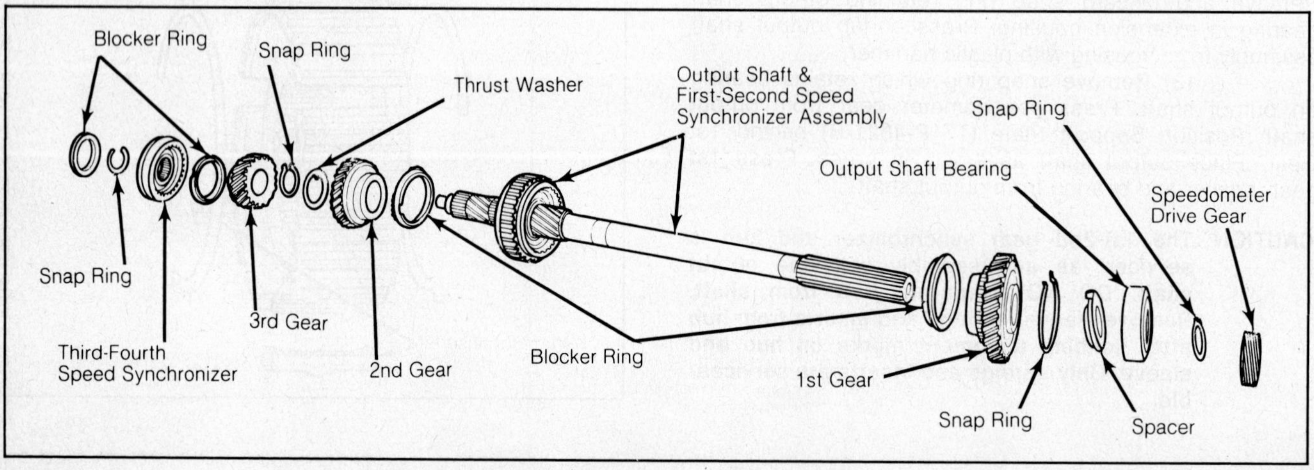

FORD MOTOR CO. 83ET 4-SPEED (Cont.)

to properly locate speedometer drive gear on shaft. *See Fig. 10.*

Fig. 10: Installing Speedometer Drive Gear

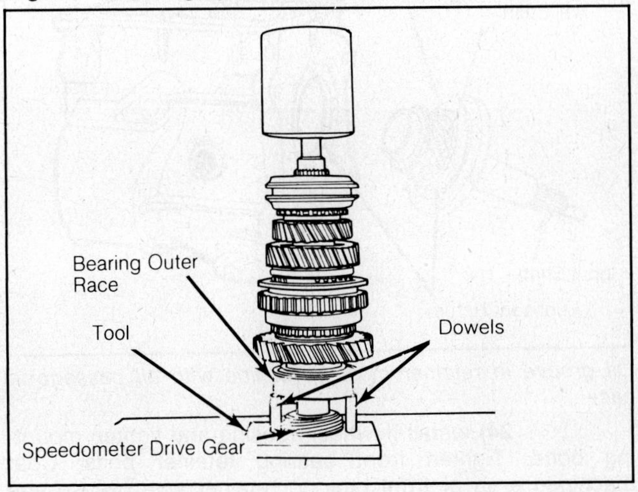

11) Coat bearing bore of extension housing with grease. Install output shaft in housing. It may be necessary to tap shaft with plastic hammer while holding the 2 synchronizer sleeves to prevent sleeve separation from hubs. Secure it to extension housing with selected snap ring that was previously installed.

12) Press bearing on input shaft. Ensure snap ring groove is toward front end of shaft. Retain with thickest snap ring that will fit groove in input shaft. Slide spacer and dummy shaft into countershaft gear. Install bearing retainer washer at each end of dummy shaft. Lubricate and load long roller bearings in small end of gear and short roller bearings in large end of gear.

13) Install retaining washer over each end of dummy shaft. Coat thrust washers with grease and install 1 on each end of dummy shaft. Make sure tabs are in same relative position so they may engage slots in case when gear is lowered into place.

14) Loop piece of rope or wire around each end of gear. Carefully install gear through rear end of case. Lower gear into place. Do not to disturb thrust washers. Ensure tabs engage slots in case. If reverse selector relay lever was removed, install it on pivot pin and secure with spring clip.

Fig. 11: Reverse Idler Gear Assembly

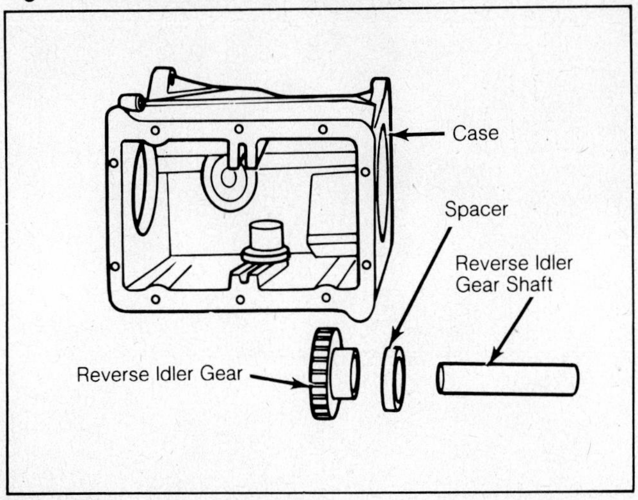

15) Hold reverse idler gear in lever with long hub toward rear of case. Slide reverse idler gear shaft into place and install spacer. *See Fig. 11.* Seat shaft into case with soft face hammer. Assemble and install input shaft into transmission case. If necessary, tap outer race of bearing with soft hammer alternately and evenly until outer snap ring seats against case.

CAUTION: Do not tap on input shaft or load will pass through bearings and may damage races and/or bearings.

16) Position new gasket on extension housing. Ensure input shaft pilot bearing is lubricated and installed in shaft. Slide extension housing and output shaft into place. Do not disturb 3rd-4th gear synchronizer.

17) Align cutaway in extension housing flange with countershaft bore in rear of transmission case. Lift countershaft gear into place. Install countershaft while making sure both thrust washers are in place.

Fig. 12: Exploded View of Countershaft Gear

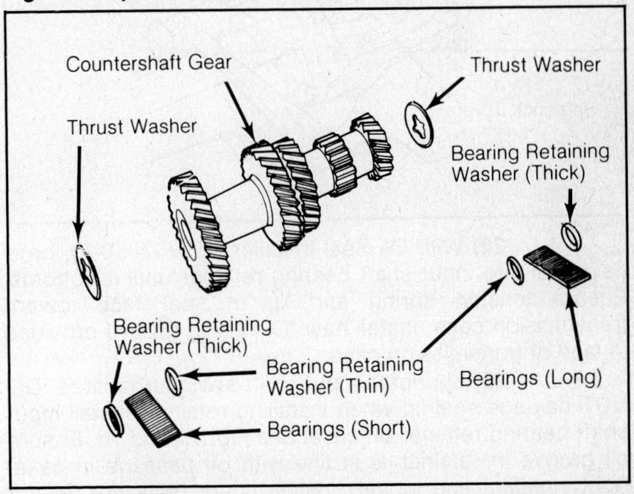

18) Make sure that flat on countershaft is toward top of case and in a horizontal position. *See Fig. 13.* Tap countershaft into case with brass hammer until front of shaft is flush with case. Rotate extension housing to align bolt holes. Coat bolts with sealer and install them loosely.

Fig. 13: Installing Countershaft into Case

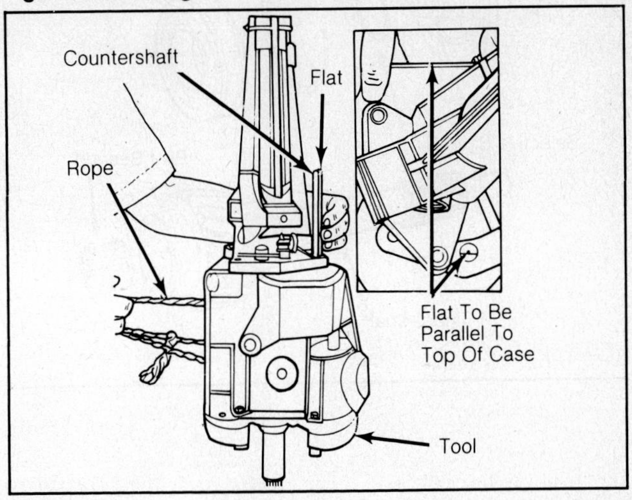

FORD MOTOR CO. 83ET 4-SPEED (Cont.)

19) Before tightening housing bolts, ensure shift rail slides freely in bore. If it binds, rotate housing slightly to free rail, then push housing into case. Tighten bolts after making sure housing does not interfere with reverse idler or countershafts.

20) Install shift forks in synchronizer sleeves. Install interlock lever with new retaining pin. Lubricate shift rail oil seal. Slide shift rail through extension housing, transmission case and 1st-2nd shift fork. Install selector arm on rail. Slide rail through 3rd-4th gear shift fork.

21) Slide rail through front of case until center detent is aligned with detent plunger bore. Install new retaining pin in selector arm. Install detent plunger, spring and plug (apply sealant to plug threads). Install new interlock lever access plug in rear of case. *See Fig. 14.*

Fig. 14: Installing Interlock Access Plug

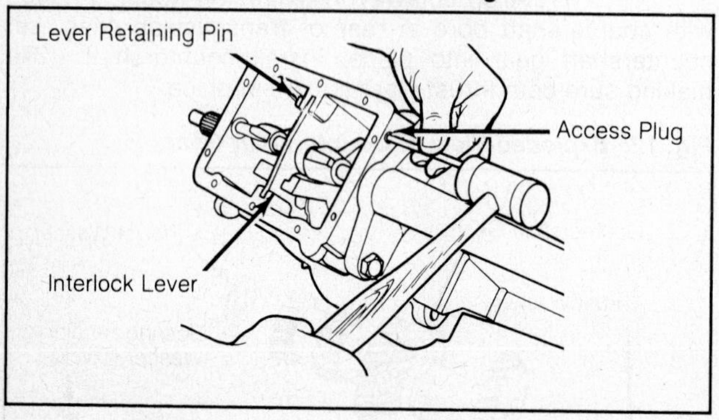

22) With Oil Seal Installer (T71P-7050-A), drive new seal into input shaft bearing retainer until it bottoms. Ensure tension spring and lip of seal face toward transmission case. Install new "O" ring in groove provided in face of transmission case.

23) Lubricate input shaft seal journal area. DO NOT damage seal lip when installing retainer. Install input shaft bearing retainer on case. *See Fig. 15 and 16*. Ensure oil groove in retainer is in line with oil passage in case. Apply sealant and loosely install mount bolts but do not tighten at this time.

Fig. 15: Exploded View of Input Shaft Assembly

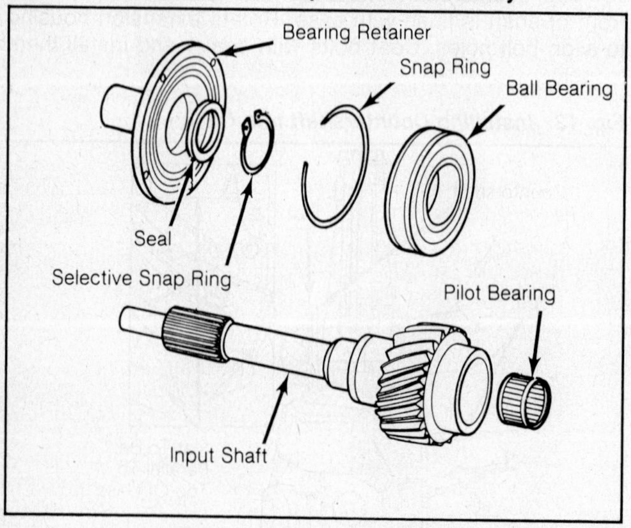

Fig. 16: Installing Input Shaft Gear

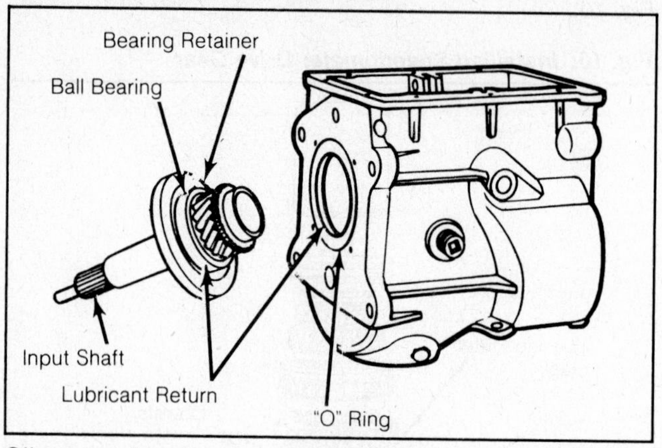

Oil groove in retainer must be in line with oil passage in case.

24) Install flywheel housing and tighten mounting bolts. Tighten front bearing retainer bolts. Coat machined area of front bearing retainer with grease and install clutch release arm and bearing. Apply sealant to new extension housing plug. Using Plug Installer (T70P-6011-A), install plug in extension housing, behind shift rail.

25) Place new cover gasket on case. Install cover with vent toward rear. Apply sealant to threads of left front cover bolt to seal bolt hole that aligns with detent plunger hole. Install and tighten 10 cover mounting bolts. Fill transmission with 2.8 pts. (1.3L) of gear oil until level is to the bottom of filler hole.

TIGHTENING SPECIFICATIONS

Application	Ft. Lbs. (N.m)
Detent Plug	12-14 (16-18)
Extension Housing-to-Case Bolt	33-36 (45-48)
Filler Plug-to-Case	24-27 (33-36)
Flywheel Housing-to-Engine Block	38-55 (52-75)
Flywheel Housing-to-Transmission Case	35-45 (47-61)
Shift Lever Bolts	17-25 (24-33)
	INCH Lbs. (N.m)
Cover-to-Case Screw	96-120 (11-13)
Input Shaft Bearing Retainer	96-120 (11-13)
Shift Lever Boot Mount Bolt	35-80 (4-9)

FORD MOTOR CO. 5-SPEED – GASOLINE

Aerostar, Bronco II, Ranger

IDENTIFICATION

Aerostar, Bronco II and Ranger 5-speed overdrive transmissions have service identification tags located at right front side of case. *See Fig. 1*. Identification code for 5-speed overdrive transmission is 5.

Fig. 1: Transmission Identification Tag

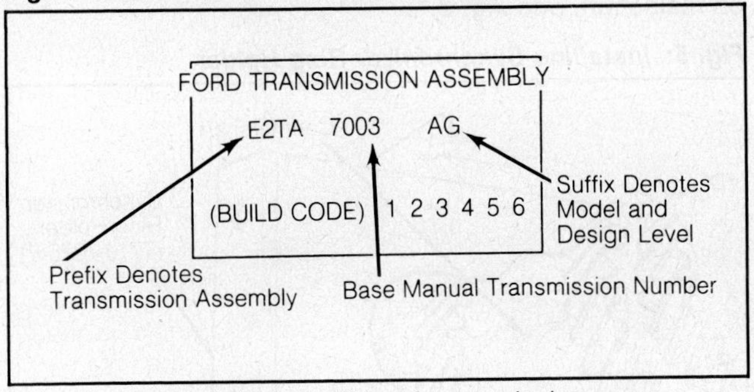

Tag is found at right front side of transmission case.

DESCRIPTION

On all models, forward gears are synchronized. Reverse gear is a constant mesh type. All forward gears are helical-cut for quiet running. Reverse gear and reverse idler gear are spur-cut.

Transmission case is of light metal construction with removable clutch and extension housing. Gearshift mechanism is a direct control with a floor shift. Floor shift mechanism is built into the extension housing.

LUBRICATION & ADJUSTMENT

See appropriate MANUAL TRANSMISSION SERVICING article in DOMESTIC GENERAL SERVICING section.

TROUBLE SHOOTING

See MANUAL TRANSMISSION TROUBLE SHOOTING article in DOMESTIC GENERAL SERVICING section.

REMOVAL & INSTALLATION

TRANSMISSION

See appropriate MANUAL TRANSMISSION REMOVAL article in DOMESTIC GENERAL SERVICING section.

SERVICE (IN VEHICLE)

GEAR SHIFT LEVER

Removal

1) Place gear shift lever in Neutral position. Detach boot retainer screws. Remove bolts attaching retainer cover to gearshift lever retainer.

2) Pull gear shift lever assembly, shim and bushing straight up and away from gear shift lever retainer. Cover shift tower opening in extension housing with a cloth to avoid dirt falling into transmission.

Installation

Install gear shift lever assembly by reversing removal procedure.

TRANSMISSION DISASSEMBLY

TRANSMISSION CASE & COMPONENTS

Disassembly

1) Detach clutch bellhousing-to-transmission case nuts. Remove clutch housing gasket and discard. Detach drain plug and drain lubricant. Clean metal filings from drain plug magnet, then reinstall.

2) Position Bench Mount Holding Fixture (T57L-500-B) onto studs on right side of transmission housing. Secure in place with Bench Holding Fixture Adapter (T77J-7025-D) to prevent damage to metric studs.

3) Place transmission in Neutral. Remove speedometer sleeve and driven gear assembly from extension housing. Remove 3 bolts (14 mm) and 4 nuts (14 mm) retaining extension housing to case.

4) Raise control lever to left and slide towards rear of transmission. Slide extension housing off mainshaft, being careful not to damage oil seal. Pull control lever and rod out front end of extension housing. *See Fig. 2*. If necessary, remove back-up light switch from extension housing.

Fig. 2: Removing Control Lever & Rod

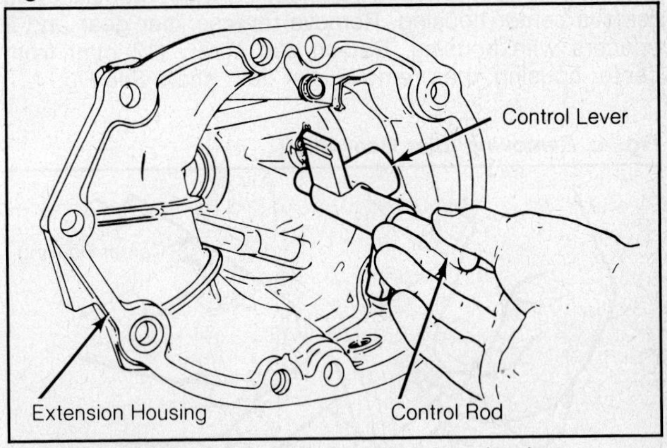

Remove lever and rod once extension housing is detached from transmission.

5) Remove anti-spill seal from mainshaft and discard. The seal is not necessary for reassembly. Detach snap ring from mainshaft, then remove speedometer drive gear. Use magnet to remove lock ball from mainshaft.

6) Evenly loosen 14 retaining bolts (10 mm) from case cover. Remove cover and discard gasket. Mark shift rails and fork for reassembly reference. Remove roll pins attaching shift rod ends to shift rod. Remove shift rod ends.

7) Gently pry bearing housing away from transmission case, being careful not to damage housing or case. Slide bearing housing off mainshaft. Remove snap ring and washer retaining mainshaft rear bearing to mainshaft.

8) Assemble Bearing Puller Ring (T77J-7025-J), Bearing Puller (T77J-7025-H) and Forcing Screw (T84T-7025-B) on Remover/Installer Tube (T75L-7025-B). Slide

FORD MOTOR CO. 5-SPEED – GASOLINE (Cont.)

tool assembly over mainshaft and engage puller jaws behind rear bearing. *See Fig. 3.*

Fig. 3: Removing Mainshaft Rear Bearing

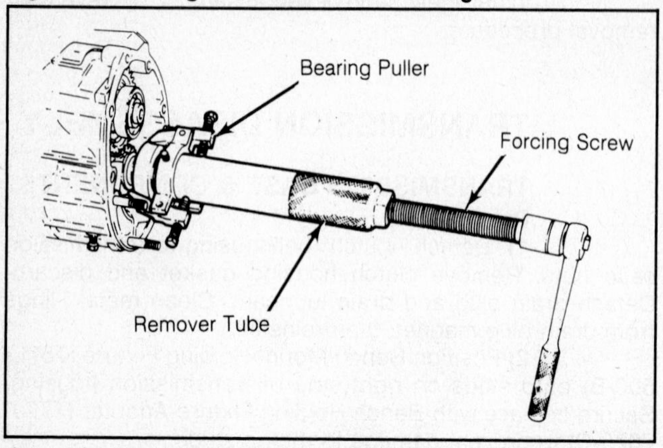

Jaws of puller must be fully behind bearing before removing.

9) Tighten jaws evenly onto bearing with wrench. Turn forcing screw to remove mainshaft rear bearing. Remove snap ring from rear end of countershaft. Assemble bearing puller, bearing puller ring and forcing screw onto remover tube.

10) Slide tool assembly over countershaft and engage puller jaws behind countershaft rear bearing. Tighten jaws evenly onto bearing with wrench. Turn forcing screw to remove bearing.

11) Remove countershaft 5th gear and spacer from rear of countershaft. Tap housing with soft mallet and remove center housing. Remove reverse idler gear and 2 spacers with housing. Detach cap screw (12 mm) from center housing, then remove idler gear shaft. *See Fig. 4.*

Fig. 4: Removing Idler Gear Shaft

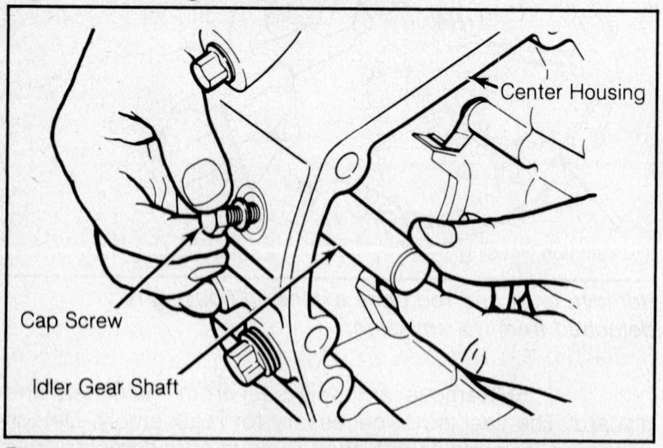

Remove cap screw from side of case and pull out shaft.

12) Remove 3 spring cap bolts. The 2 bolts on case upper portion are 17 mm and the bolt on case side is 14 mm. Using a magnet, remove detent springs and balls from case.

13) Remove 4 bolts (10 mm) retaining blind covers to case. Remove blind covers and discard gaskets. Remove roll pin from 5th-Reverse shift fork. Slide 5th/Reverse shift fork shaft out of case.

14) Shift transmission into 4th gear to provide space to drive out roll pin. Through hole in side of case, drive out roll pin from 3rd-4th shift fork. Slide 3rd-4th shift fork shaft out of rear of case.

15) Through other hole in side of case, drive out roll pin for 1st-2nd shift fork. Slide 1st-2nd shift fork shaft assembly out rear of case. Remove both interlock pins. Remove snap ring securing 5th gear to mainshaft.

16) Remove thrust washer, lock ball, 5th gear and synchronizer ring from rear of mainshaft. Install Synchronizer Ring Holder/Countershaft Spacer (T77J-7025-E) between 4th gear synchronizer ring and synchromesh gear on mainshaft. *See Fig. 5.*

Fig. 5: Installing Synchronizer Ring Holder

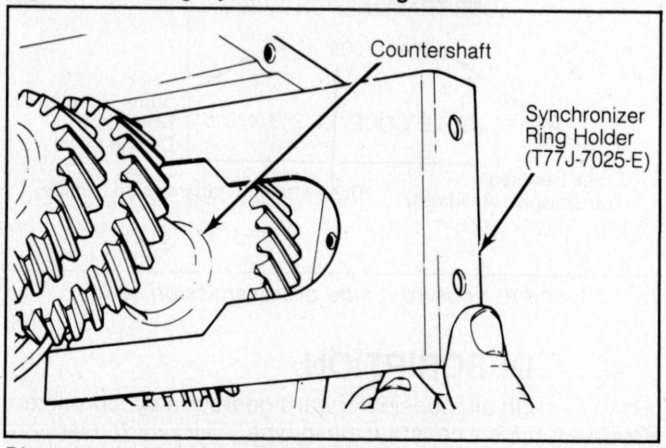

Place holder behind 3rd-4th clutch hub.

17) Shift transmission into 2nd gear to lock mainshaft and prevent assembly from rotating. Straighten staked portion of mainshaft bearing lock nut with Staking (T77J-7025-F). Using Lock Nut Wrench (T77J-7025-C), remove mainshaft bearing lock nut.

18) Slide reverse gear and clutch hub assembly off mainshaft. Remove countershaft reverse gear from countershaft. If installed, remove transmission from holding fixture and set on workbench. Detach bolts (12 mm) retaining mainshaft center bearing cover to transmission. Remove bearing cover.

19) Remove countershaft center bearing using Puller (T77J-7025-H), Puller Rings (T77J-7025-J), Remover Tube (T77J-7025-B) and Forcing Screw (T84T-7025-B) on countershaft. Squarely insert jaws of puller behind center bearing retainer ring in 2 recessed areas of case. Turn forcing screw to remove bearing. *See Fig. 6.*

CAUTION: Do not distort retainer ring during mainshaft, countershaft and input shaft bearing removal. If necessary, before puller is installed, turn retainer ring to position split in ring midway between recessed areas of case.

20) Remove mainshaft center bearing using Puller (T77J-7025-H), Puller Rings (T77J-7025-J), Long Remover Tube (T75L-7025-C) and Forcing Screw (T84T-7025-B). Squarely insert jaws of puller behind rear mainshaft bearing retainer ring in 2 recessed areas of case. Turn forcing screw clockwise to remove bearing.

21) Remove shim and spacer from behind mainshaft rear bearing along with bearing. Remove front cover by first removing 4 studs attaching cover to case. Remove each stud by installing 2 nuts (10 x 1.5 mm) on stud, lock nuts together and drawing stud out of case. Detach 4 retaining bolts (14 mm) and remove cover. Save shim found on inside of cover.

FORD MOTOR CO. 5-SPEED – GASOLINE (Cont.)

Fig. 6: Removing Countershaft Center Bearing

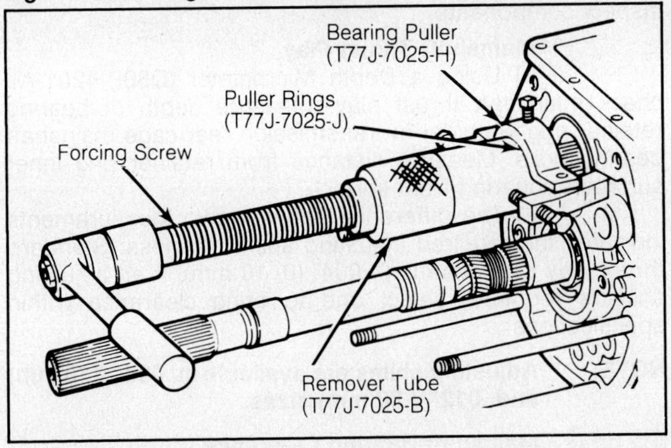

22) Remove snap ring from input shaft. Using same pullers and remover tube, remove input shaft bearing. Rotate both shift forks so that main gear train will fall to bottom of case. Remove shift forks. Rotate input shaft so that one of two flats on input shaft faces upward.

23) Remove snap ring from front of countershaft. Remove Synchronizer Ring Holder (T77J-7025-E) from front of case and insert between first gear on countershaft and rear of case. Install Forcing Screw (T84T-7025-B), Press Frame (T77J-7025-N) and Press Frame Adapter (T82T-7003-BH) against countershaft assembly. *See Fig. 7.*

Fig. 7: Pressing Countershaft Rearward

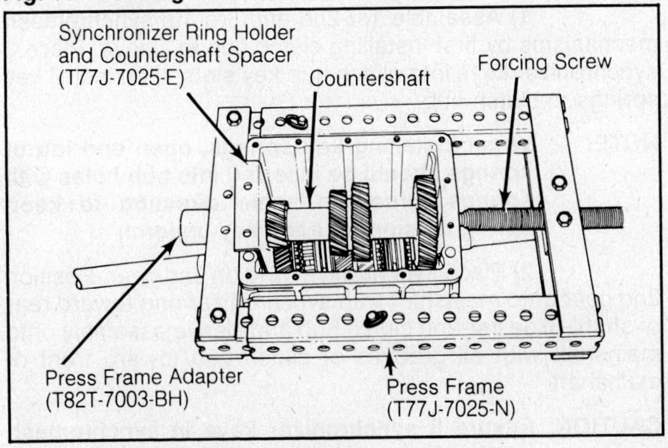

Press countershaft about 3/16".

24) Turn forcing screw clockwise to press countershaft rearward. Press countershaft about 3/16" (4.8 mm), until it contacts synchronizer ring holder/countershaft spacer.

25) Remove press frame. To remove countershaft front bearing, install puller, puller rings, remover tube and forcing screw. Squarely insert jaws of puller behind front bearing retainer ring in 2 recessed areas in case.

26) Turn forcing screw clockwise to remove bearing. Remove shim from behind countershaft front bearing. Remove countershaft from case. Remove input shaft from case.

27) Remove synchronizer ring and caged bearing from mainshaft. Remove mainshaft and gear assembly from case. Disassembly mainshaft and countershaft as necessary. Clean and inspect gears, bearings, shafts and transmission case.

CLEANING & INSPECTION

1) Wash all parts (except oil seals) in cleaning solvent and dry with compressed air (except bearings). Let bearings air dry, then lubricate with gear oil and wrap in clean, lint-free shop cloth until ready to install.

2) Inspect transmission case and extension housing for cracks, worn or damaged bearing bores or threads. Remove any small nicks or burrs from front and/or rear machined mating surfaces of case with fine stone.

3) Check bearings for roughness by first lubricating lightly with oil, then slowly turning race by hand. Inspect needle bearing rollers, shafts and washers for wear or damage. Check gears for wear, damage or chipped and/or broken teeth. Replace parts as necessary.

4) Inspect mainshaft for excessive runout. Mount mainshaft between "V" blocks and check runout (in several places) using a dial indicator. Standard runout is .0012" (.030 mm). If runout exceeds specification, straighten mainshaft in a press or replace component.

5) Inspect input shaft for damaged splines, worn or rough needle bearing bore surface and/or damaged cone surface. Replace shaft as necessary. Check countershaft gear for worn or damaged gear teeth. Check countershaft for excessive runout. Replace countershaft if bent, scored or worn.

6) Inspect contact surface of shift fork (with detent ball) for wear or damage. Check contact surface of shift fork shaft (with control lever) for wear using a feeler gauge. Clearance between shift fork shaft and control lever must be less than .031" (.80 mm). Replace parts as needed.

7) Check contact surface of shift forks with clutch sleeve for wear or damage. Clearance between shift fork and clutch sleeve must be less than .020" (.50 mm). Replace parts if worn beyond specification.

8) Inspect synchronizer gear for chipped or worn teeth. Check synchronizer ring for wear by fitting ring evenly to gear cone. Measure clearance between side faces of synchronizer ring and gear with feeler gauge. If less than .031" (.80 mm), replace ring and/or gear.

9) Check contact between inner surface of synchronizer ring and cone surface of gear. To inspect, apply a thin coat of "Prussian Blue" on cone surface of gear and fit it into the ring. If contact pattern is poor, correct by applying compound and lapping surfaces together.

10) Check synchronizer inserts (keys), inner surface of clutch sleeve and insert groove on clutch hub for wear. Check synchronizer insert spring for tension. Replace any worn or damaged parts.

11) Inspect extension housing oil seal for wear or damage and replace as needed. Remove seal using Oil Seal Remover (T71P-7657-A) and install using Oil Seal Installer (T71P-7095-A). If removed, install new oil seal after extension housing is installed on transmission.

12) If extension housing rear bushing needs replacement, remove using Bushing Remover (T72J-7697). Check speedometer shaft and drive and driven gears for wear or damage. Replace parts as needed.

COMPONENT DISASSEMBLY & REASSEMBLY

CAUTION: **Before beginning component and transmission reassembly procedures, 3 measurements must be performed: Mainshaft thrust play, countershaft thrust play and mainshaft bearing clearance.**

FORD MOTOR CO. 5-SPEED – GASOLINE (Cont.)

NOTE: When measuring mainshaft and countershaft thrust play and mainshaft bearing clearance, ensure micrometer probe touches retainer ring shoulder (second step of bore) and micrometer rests on case outer surface. Measure bearing height from where retainer ring inner surface contacts bore shoulder to bearing outer surface.

COUNTERSHAFT

Disassembly

Remove inner race of countershaft center bearing from countershaft in press frame using Axle Bearing Seal Plate (T75L-1165-B) and Pinion Bearing Cone Remover (D79L-4621-A). *See Fig. 8.*

Fig. 8: Removing Countershaft Bearing Inner Race

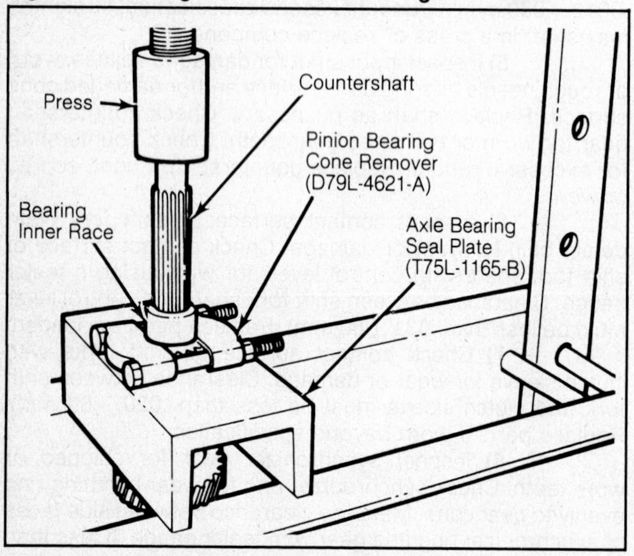

Countershaft Thrust Play

1) Check countershaft thrust play by measuring depth of countershaft front bearing bore in case (from case surface to retainer ring shoulder), using a Depth Micrometer (D80P-4201-A).

2) Measure countershaft front bearing height (from where retainer ring inner surface contacts bore shoulder to bearing outer surface).

NOTE: The difference between two measurements indicates required thickness of adjusting shims.

3) The standard thrust play is 0-.004" (0-.10 mm). Adjusting shims are available in .004" (.10 mm) and .012" (.30 mm) sizes.

Reassembly

Press inner race of countershaft rear bearing onto countershaft using Center Bearing Installer (T77J-7025-K).

MAINSHAFT

Disassembly

1) Remove 1st gear and 1st-2nd synchronizer ring. Remove snap ring retainer from mainshaft. Do not mix synchronizer rings. Install Bearing Remover (T71P-4621-B) between 2nd-3rd gear.

2) Press mainshaft out of 3rd gear and 3rd-4th clutch hub sleeve. Press 1st-2nd clutch hub and sleeve assembly and 1st gear sleeve from mainshaft. Clean and inspect components.

Mainshaft Thrust Play

1) Using a Depth Micrometer (D80P-4201-A), check mainshaft thrust play. Measure depth of bearing retainer ring shoulder in transmission rear cage mainshaft bearing bore. Measure distance from retainer ring inner surface to bearing front surface.

2) The difference between two measurements indicates the required adjusting shim thickness. Standard thrust play clearance is 0-.004" (0-.10 mm). If an adjusting shim is required, select one to bring clearance within specifications.

NOTE: Adjusting shims are available in .004" (.10 mm) and .012" (.30 mm) sizes.

Mainshaft Bearing Clearance

1) Using a Depth Micrometer (D80P-4201-A), check mainshaft bearing clearance. Measure depth of bearing retainer ring shoulder to clutch adapter plate mainshaft bearing bore. Measure distance from retainer ring inner surface to bearing front surface.

2) The difference between two measurements indicates required adjusting shim thickness. Standard thrust play clearance is 0-.004" (0-.10 mm). If an adjusting shim is required, select one to bring clearance to within specifications.

NOTE: Adjusting shims are available in .004" (.10 mm) and .012" (.30 mm) sizes.

Reassembly

1) Assemble 1st-2nd and 3rd-4th synchromesh mechanisms by first installing clutch hub to sleeve. Place 3 synchronizer keys into clutch hub key slots, then install key springs to clutch hub.

NOTE: When installing key springs, open end tab of springs should be inserted into hub holes with springs turned in same direction to keep spring tension on each key uniform.

2) Place synchronizer ring on 2nd gear. Position 2nd gear onto mainshaft with synchronizer ring toward rear of shaft. Slide 1st-2nd clutch hub and sleeve assembly onto mainshaft with oil grooves of clutch hub toward front of mainshaft.

CAUTION: Ensure 3 synchronizer keys in synchromesh mechanism engage notches in 2nd synchronizer ring.

3) Press 2nd gear and 1st-2nd gear clutch hub and sleeve assembly into position using press and Pinion Bearing Cone Replacer Set (T53T-4621-C, T57L-4621-B, T62F-4621-A and T75L-7025-Q).

4) Insert 1st gear sleeve on mainshaft. Place synchronizer ring on 3rd gear along with caged roller bearing. Slide 3rd gear onto front of mainshaft, with synchronizer ring toward front.

5) Using press and Replacer Tube (T77J-7025-B), press 3rd-4th clutch hub and sleeve assembly onto front of mainshaft. Ensure 3 synchronizer keys in synchromesh mechanism engage notches in synchronizer ring. Install snap ring onto front of mainshaft.

6) Slide needle bearing for 1st gear onto mainshaft. Place synchronizer ring on 1st gear. Slide 1st gear onto mainshaft with synchronizer ring facing front of shaft. Rotate 1st gear, as necessary, to engage 3 notches in

FORD MOTOR CO. 5-SPEED – GASOLINE (Cont.)

Fig. 9: Exploded View of 5-Speed Transmission Mainshaft

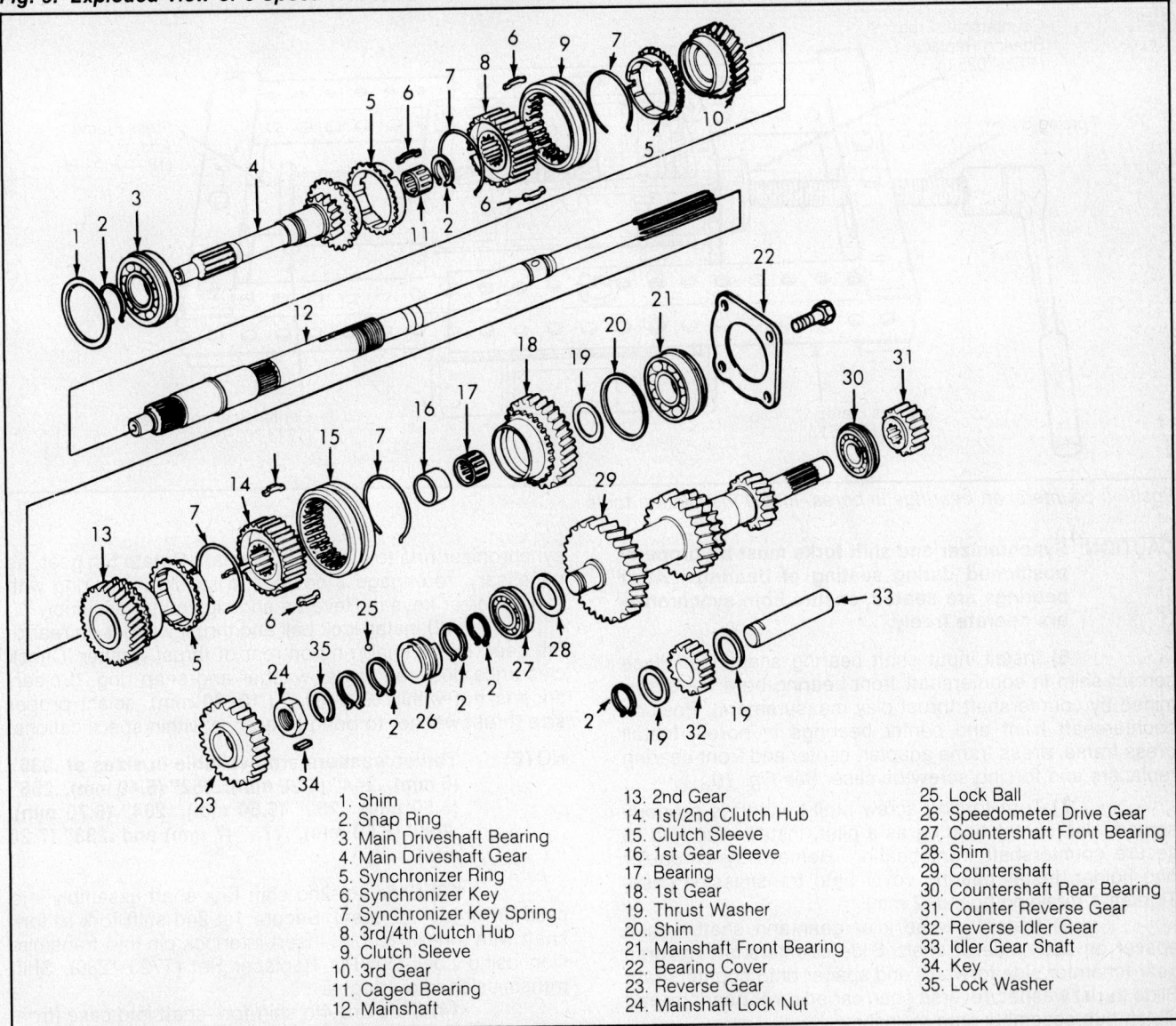

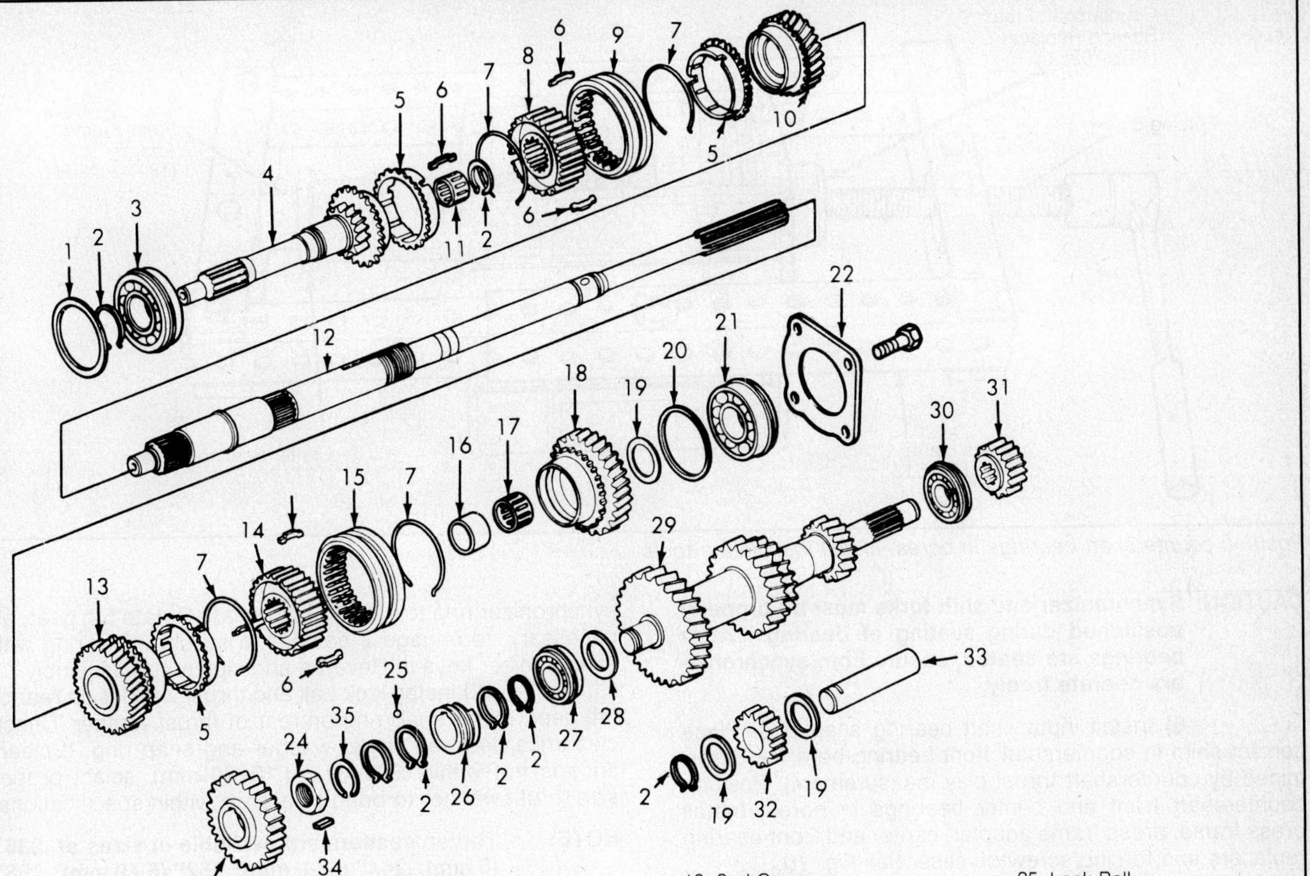

1. Shim
2. Snap Ring
3. Main Driveshaft Bearing
4. Main Driveshaft Gear
5. Synchronizer Ring
6. Synchronizer Key
7. Synchronizer Key Spring
8. 3rd/4th Clutch Hub
9. Clutch Sleeve
10. 3rd Gear
11. Caged Bearing
12. Mainshaft
13. 2nd Gear
14. 1st/2nd Clutch Hub
15. Clutch Sleeve
16. 1st Gear Sleeve
17. Bearing
18. 1st Gear
19. Thrust Washer
20. Shim
21. Mainshaft Front Bearing
22. Bearing Cover
23. Reverse Gear
24. Mainshaft Lock Nut
25. Lock Ball
26. Speedometer Drive Gear
27. Countershaft Front Bearing
28. Shim
29. Countershaft
30. Countershaft Rear Bearing
31. Counter Reverse Gear
32. Reverse Idler Gear
33. Idler Gear Shaft
34. Key
35. Lock Washer

synchronizer ring with synchronizer keys. Install original thrust washer onto mainshaft.

TRANSMISSION REASSEMBLY

TRANSMISSION CASE & COMPONENTS

NOTE: **Transmission case is made of aluminum alloy. To prevent damaging case, all nuts, bolts and/or lock washers contacting case must have a flat washer placed next to case so that turning attaching bolt or nut will not damage aluminum surface.**

Reassembly

1) Position mainshaft and gear assembly in case. Position 1st-2nd shift fork and 3rd-4th shift fork in groove of clutch hub and sleeve assembly. Position caged bearing in front end of mainshaft.

2) Place synchronizer ring on input shaft (4th gear) and install input shaft onto front end of mainshaft. Ensure 3 synchronizer keys in 3rd-4th synchromesh mechanism engage notches in synchronizer ring.

3) Press inner race of countershaft rear bearing onto countershaft using Center Bearing Replacer (T77J-7025-K). Position countershaft gear in case. Ensure countershaft gear engages each gear of mainshaft assembly.

4) Install correct shim on mainshaft center bearing (as determined by mainshaft thrust play measurement). Position input shaft bearing and mainshaft center bearing into proper bearing bores. Ensure synchronizer and shift forks have not been moved out of position.

5) Install Synchronizer Ring Holder (T77J-7025-E) between 4th synchronizer ring and synchromesh gear on mainshaft. Install Dummy Bearing Replacer (T75L-7025-Q), Input Shaft Bearing Replacer (T82T-7003-DH), Replacer Tube (T77J-7025-M) and Press Frame (T77J-7025-N) on case. Turn forcing screw on press frame until both bearings are properly seated.

FORD MOTOR CO. 5-SPEED – GASOLINE (Cont.)

Fig. 10: Countershaft Front Bearing Installation

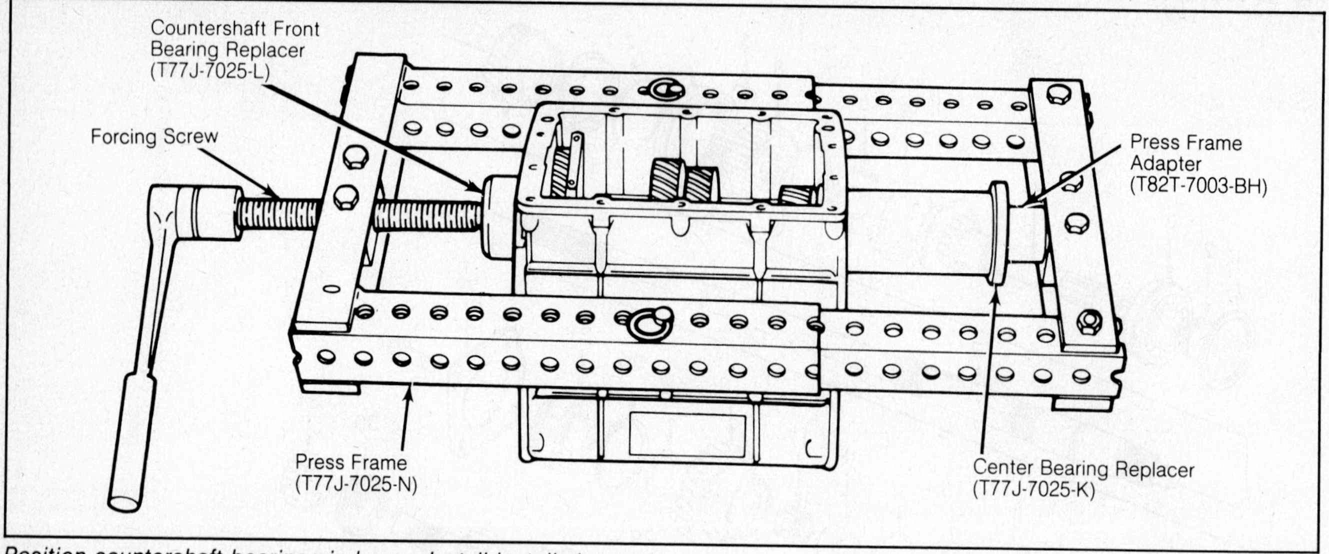

Position countershaft bearings in bores. Install installation tools.

CAUTION: Synchronizer and shift forks must be properly positioned during seating of bearings. After bearings are seated, ensure both synchronizers operate freely.

6) Install input shaft bearing snap ring. Place correct shim in countershaft front bearing bore (as determined by countershaft thrust play measurement). Position countershaft front and center bearings in bores. Install press frame, press frame adapter, center and front bearing replacers and forcing screw on case. *See Fig. 10.*

7) Turn forcing screw until bearing is properly seated. Use center bearing as a pilot. Install snap ring to secure countershaft front bearing. Remove synchronizer ring holder. Install bearing cover onto transmission case. Tighten 4 retaining bolts (12 mm).

8) Install reverse idler gear and shaft with a spacer on each side of shaft. Slide countershaft Reverse gear (chamfer side forward) and spacer onto countershaft. Slide thrust washer, reverse gear, caged roller bearings and clutch hub assembly onto mainshaft.

9) Install a new lock nut onto mainshaft (hand-tight). Shift into 2nd gear and reverse gear to lock rotation of mainshaft. Tighten lock nut using Lock Nut Wrench (T77J-7025-C). Stake lock nut into mainshaft keyway using Staking (T77J-7025-F). Place 4th-3rd clutch sleeve in 3rd gear using synchronizer ring holder and Countershaft Spacer (T77J-7025-E).

10) If new synchronizers have been installed, check clearance between synchronizer key and exposed edge of synchronizer ring with a feeler gauge. If measurement is greater than .079" (2 mm), synchronizer key can pop out of position. To correct this condition, change selective fit thrust washer between mainshaft center bearing and 1st gear.

NOTE: Thrust washers are available in sizes of .098" (2.50 mm), .118" (3 mm) and .138" (3.50 mm).

11) If thrust washer was changed, recheck clearance again with feeler gauge. If clearance is within specifications, bend lock washer tab. Position 5th synchronizer ring on 5th gear. Slide 5th gear onto mainshaft with synchronizer ring toward front of shaft. Rotate 5th gear, as necessary, to engage 3 notches in synchronizer ring with synchronizer keys in Reverse and clutch hub assembly.

12) Install lock ball and thrust washer on rear of 5th gear. Install snap ring on rear of thrust washer. Check clearance between thrust washer and snap ring. If clearance is not within .004-.012" (.10-.30 mm), select proper size thrust washer to bring clearance within specifications.

NOTE: Thrust washers are available in sizes of .236" (6 mm), .244" (6.20 mm), .252" (6.40 mm), .256" (6.50 mm), .260" (6.60 mm), .264" (6.70 mm), .268" (6.80 mm), .275" (7 mm) and .283" (7.20 mm).

13) Slide 1st-2nd shift fork shaft assembly into case (front rear of case). Secure 1st-2nd shift fork to fork shaft with a new roll pin. Insert interlock pin into transmission using Lock-Out Pin Replacer Set (T72J-7280). Shift transmission into 4th gear.

14) Slide 3rd-4th shift fork shaft into case (from rear of case). Secure 3rd-4th shift fork to fork shaft with a new roll pin. Insert interlock pin. Shift synchronizer hub into 5th gear (if equipped). Position Reverse-5th fork on clutch hub and slide Reverse-5th fork shaft into case (from rear of case). Secure Reverse-5th shift fork to fork shaft with new roll pin.

15) Install 2 blind covers and new gaskets. Install and tighten retaining bolts (10 mm) on blind covers. Position 3 detent balls and 3 springs into case, then install spring cap bolts (12 mm and 17 mm). Apply a thin coat of gasket sealer to contacting surfaces of center housing and case.

16) Position center housing on case. Align reverse idler gear shaft boss with center housing retaining bolt boss. Install and tighten idler shaft cap screw (12 mm). Slide countershaft 5th gear onto countershaft. Position countershaft rear bearing on countershaft.

17) Press into position using Adjustable Press Frame (T77J-7025-N) and Forcing Screw (T84T-7025-B). Install thrust washer and snap ring onto rear of countershaft rear bearing. Check clearance between thrust washer and snap ring using a feeler gauge.

FORD MOTOR CO. 5-SPEED – GASOLINE (Cont.)

18) If clearance is not within 0-.006" (0-.15 mm), select proper size thrust washer to bring clearance within specifications. Thrust washers are available in sizes of .0748" (1.90 mm), .0787" (2 mm), .0827" (2.10 mm) and .0866" (2.20 mm).

19) If installed, remove filler plugs. Position mainshaft rear bearing on mainshaft. Press into place using Adjustable Press Frame (T77J-7025-N), Dummy Bearing (T75L-7025-Q1) and Forcing Screw (T84T-7025-B).

20) Install thrust washer and snap ring onto rear of mainshaft rear bearing. Check clearance between thrust washer and snap ring. Clearance should be 0-.004" (0-.10 mm). If clearance is not within specifications, replace thrust washer with selective thrust washer.

NOTE: Thrust washers are available in sizes of .0787" (2 mm), .0846" (2.15 mm) and .0906" (2.30 mm).

21) Apply a thin coat of gasket sealer to contacting surfaces of bearing housing and center housing. Position bearing housing on center housing. Install each shift fork end onto proper shift fork shaft. Match up reassembly reference marks made during disassembly. Secure with new roll pins.

22) Install lock ball, speedometer drive gear and snap ring onto mainshaft. If removed, install control lever and rod in extension housing. Apply a thin coat of gasket sealer to contacting surfaces of bearing housing and extension housing.

23) Position extension housing in bearing housing with gearshift control lever end laid down to left as far as it will go. Tighten (2 long outer and 1 short center) retaining bolts (14 mm) and nuts (14 mm). If removed, insert speedometer driven gear assembly into extension housing and secure it with retaining bolt.

24) Check to ensure gear shift lever operates properly. Install new transmission case cover gasket and cover (drain plug toward rear). Install and tighten 14 retaining bolts (10 mm) to cover. Install correct size shim on second step of front cover (as determined by mainshaft bearing clearance measurement).

25) Coat new front cover gasket with sealer, then install cover and gasket to transmission case. Tighten 4 bolts and 4 studs. Fill transmission with 3 pts. (1.4L) of gear oil. If removed, install filler plugs and tighten.

NOTE: Manual transmission gear oil used must be equivalent to Ford Manual Transmission Lube D8DZ-19C547-A (ESP-M2C83-C).

TIGHTENING SPECIFICATIONS

Application	Ft. Lbs. (N.m)
Back-Up Light Switch	22-29 (30-39)
Blind Cover Mounting Bolt	23-34 (32-46)
Clutch Release Lever Pivot	23-34 (32-46)
Drain Plug	29-43 (39-58)
Extension Housing	
Mounting Bolt/Nut	60-80 (82-108)
Filler Plug	18-29 (25-39)
Idler Shaft Cap Screw	41-59 (56-79)
Mainshaft Lock Nut	115-172 (156-233)
Shift Rail Detent Spring Cap	29-43 (39-58)
Transmission Case	
Cover Mounting Bolt	23-34 (32-46)
Nut/Bolt Size	
8 mm	12-17 (17-23)
10 mm	23-34 (32-45)
12 mm	41-59 (56-79)
	INCH Lbs. (N.m)
Interlock Pin Bore Plug	97-132 (11-14)
Nut/Bolt Size	
6 mm	62-97 (7-11)

FORD MOTOR CO. 5-SPEED – DIESEL

Ranger

IDENTIFICATION

Manual transmissions have a service identification tag to identify transmissions for servicing. Tag is found at right front side of case. Transmission I.D. code for 5-speed transmission is "D". *See Fig. 1.* This transmission (Model FM145) is used on 4 x 4 models only.

Fig. 1: Transmission Identification Tag

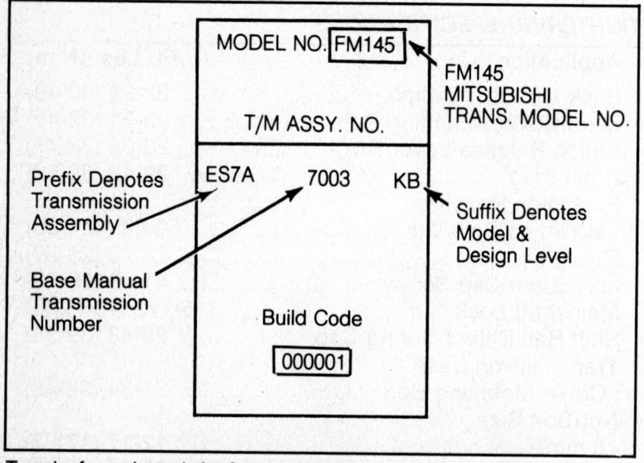

Tag is found at right front side of transmission case.

DESCRIPTION

The 5-speed manual transmission is fully synchronized in all forward gears. The 5th gear is an overdrive gear. All gear changes are accomplished with synchronizer sleeves. Reverse gear uses a reverse idler gear which is in constant mesh with countershaft gear.

Top mounted shifter operates shift rails through a set of shift forks. Shift forks mounted on rails operate synchronizer sleeves, allowing shifts of 1st-2nd, 3rd-4th and Overdrive-Reverse. A shift interlock system, located in side of transmission case, prevents shift rails from engaging 2 gears at a time.

Transmission is composed of 3 main components, a front bearing retainer, transmission case and transfer case adapter. All components are made of aluminum.

LUBRICATION & ADJUSTMENT

See appropriate MANUAL TRANSMISSION SERVICING article in DOMESTIC GENERAL SERVICING section.

TROUBLE SHOOTING

See MANUAL TRANSMISSION TROUBLE SHOOTING in MANUAL TRANSMISSION SERVICING section.

REMOVAL & INSTALLATION

See appropriate MANUAL TRANSMISSION REMOVAL article in DOMESTIC GENERAL SERVICING section.

SERVICE (IN VEHICLE)

GEAR SHIFT LEVER ASSEMBLY

NOTE: **Remove shift ball only if shift ball, boot or lever is to be replaced. If either ball, boot or lever is not being replaced, remove the ball, boot and lever as an assembly.**

Removal

1) To remove shift lever ball, first remove plastic insert. Warm ball with heat gun to 140-180°F (60-82°C), knock ball off lever with a block of wood and a hammer, taking care not to damage finish on shift lever.

2) Remove rubber boot. Detach bolts retaining shift lever to transfer case adapter, then remove gear shift lever assembly.

Installation

1) Lubricate shift lever with multi-purpose grease. Position lever in in transfer case adapter. Ensure selector ball on lever is in socket in adapter. Install bolts and tighten to 71-89 INCH lbs. (8-14 N.m).

2) Install rubber boot and floor pan cover. Warm ball with heat gun to 140-180°F (60-82°C), then tap ball onto lever with a 7/16" socket and mallet. Install plastic shift pattern insert.

TRANSMISSION DISASSEMBLY

TRANSMISSION CASE & TRANSFER CASE ADAPTER

NOTE: **During disassembly, all gaskets must be removed and discarded. Thoroughly clean all traces of gasket material from mating surfaces of transfer case adapter, input shaft front bearing retainer and transmission case.**

Disassembly

1) With transmission removed from vehicle and in Neutral position, detach nuts retaining clutch bellhousing to transmission case. Remove housing. If not removed, pull clutch slave cylinder from input shaft.

2) Remove back-up light switch, neutral position switch (2.3L E.F.I. engine only) and shift indicator switch from transfer case adapter. Remove drain plug from pan and drain gear oil.

3) Detach bolts retaining pan to transmission case, then remove pan and discard gasket. Remove all traces of gasket from pan and case mating surfaces. With shift lever assembly removed, detach bolts retaining top cover to transfer case adapter.

4) Remove cover (with stopper bracket inside) and discard gasket. Clean all traces of gasket from cover and adapter mating surfaces. Remove detent spring and ball from adapter.

5) Using a 6 mm Allen-head wrench, remove 3 shift gate roll pin access plugs (2 on side and 1 on bottom). Using a punch, drive roll pins from shift gates (through access holes).

6) From right side of adapter, remove bolt, neutral return spring and plunger. *See Fig. 2.* Note that plunger has a slot in center for detent ball.

7) From left side of adapter, remove bolt, neutral return spring and plunger. Note that this plunger has no ball slot. From top of adapter, lift gate selector lever out of shift

Fig. 2: Exploded View Of Transfer Case Adapter & Components

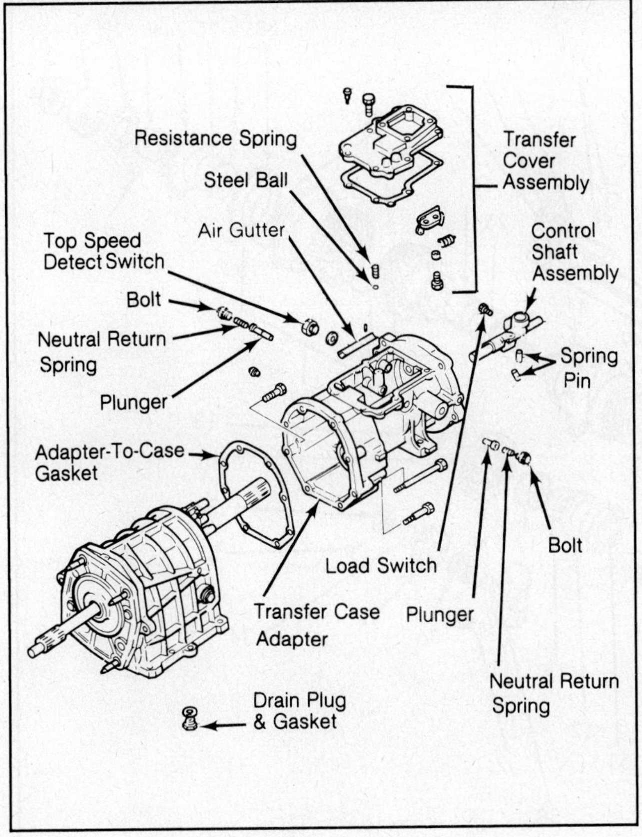

gates. Move lever as far to rear of adapter as it will go. This will allow clearance to remove adaptor from case.

8) Detach bolts retaining transfer case adapter to transmission case. Mark bolt holes for 3 different length bolts used (35 mm, 55 mm and 110 mm). Remove adapter from case and discard gasket.

NOTE: When detaching adapter from case, ensure shift gates do not bind in adapter during removal. Rotate gates on rails as needed.

9) Clean all traces of gasket from case and adapter mating surfaces. Identify and mark each shift rail and gate, then remove gates from rails. From inside transmission case, drive out roll pins retaining 1st-2nd and 3rd-4th shift forks to rails.

CAUTION: Roll pin in switch actuator does not need to be removed to disassemble transmission.

10) Drive out Overdrive/Reverse shift fork roll pin. Note installed depth of .24" (6.1 mm), then remove poppet spring set screw (on top of case). Remove one poppet spring and one steel ball from bore. Detach 2 bolts (on side of case) and remove 2 poppet springs and 2 steel balls. *See Fig. 4*.

11) Pull Overdrive/Reverse shift rail and 3rd-4th shift rail from case. Remove Overdrive/Reverse shift fork. When 2 shift rails are removed, the interlock pins can be removed from case.

CAUTION: Do not attempt to remove 1st-2nd shift rail at this time.

12) Using Mainshaft Lock Nut Staking (T77J-7025-F), unstake lock nuts on mainshaft and countershaft. To remove lock nuts, first position 2 synchronizers to engage transmission in 2 gears (to lock-up gear sets).

13) Using a 30 mm socket, remove and discard countershaft lock nut. Using Mainshaft Lock Nut Wrench (T77J-7025-C), remove and discard mainshaft lock nut. Using Tube (T77J-7025-B), Forcing Screw (T84T-7025-B), Bearing Puller (T77J-7025-H) and Puller Ring (T77J-7025-J), pull rear bearing off mainshaft and discard it.

14) Slide spacer off mainshaft and, using a magnet if necessary, remove lock ball from bore. Using Puller (T77J-4220-B1), with jaws of puller behind gear, turn forcing screw to remove countershaft overdrive gear and ball bearing from countershaft. While removing gear, pull 1st-2nd shift rail from case.

15) Remove 1st-2nd shift forks from case. Remove Overdrive gear, caged needle bearing, spacer and synchronizer ring from mainshaft. Detach overdrive synchronizer sleeve from synchronizer hub on mainshaft.

CAUTION: When separating synchronizer sleeve from hub, do not lose 3 keys (located in hub) and/or 2 springs (one on each side of hub).

16) Pull overdrive synchronizer hub and overdrive gear bearing sleeve from mainshaft with previously used forcing screw, tube, bearing puller and puller ring. *See Fig. 3*. Slide Reverse gear and caged needle bearing assembly off mainshaft.

Fig. 3: Removing Rear Mainshaft Bearing, Overdrive Synchronizer Hub & Overdrive Gear Bearing Sleeve

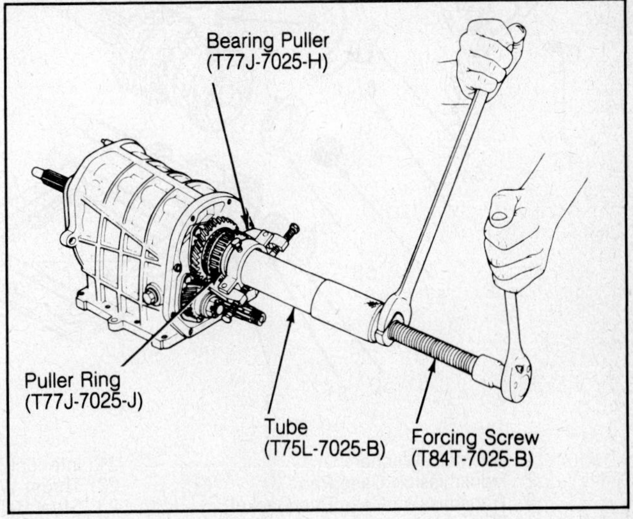

17) Slide countershaft reverse gear and distance spacer off countershaft. Remove cotter pin and detach nut from reverse idler shaft. Remove thrust washer, reverse idler gear and 2 sets of caged needle bearings. *See Fig. 5*.

18) Detach Allen-head bolts (6 mm) attaching mainshaft rear bearing retainer to case. Remove retainer and discard gasket. Clean gasket surfaces. Detach Allen-head bolts retaining reverse idler gear shaft assembly to case.

19) Using Slide Hammer (T50T-100-A) and Reverse Idler Gear Shaft Remover (T85T-7140-A), pull reverse idler gear shaft out of case. Remove 4 studs retaining input shaft front bearing retainer to case.

FORD MOTOR CO. 5-SPEED – DIESEL (Cont.)

Fig. 4: Exploded View Of Transmission Case & Components

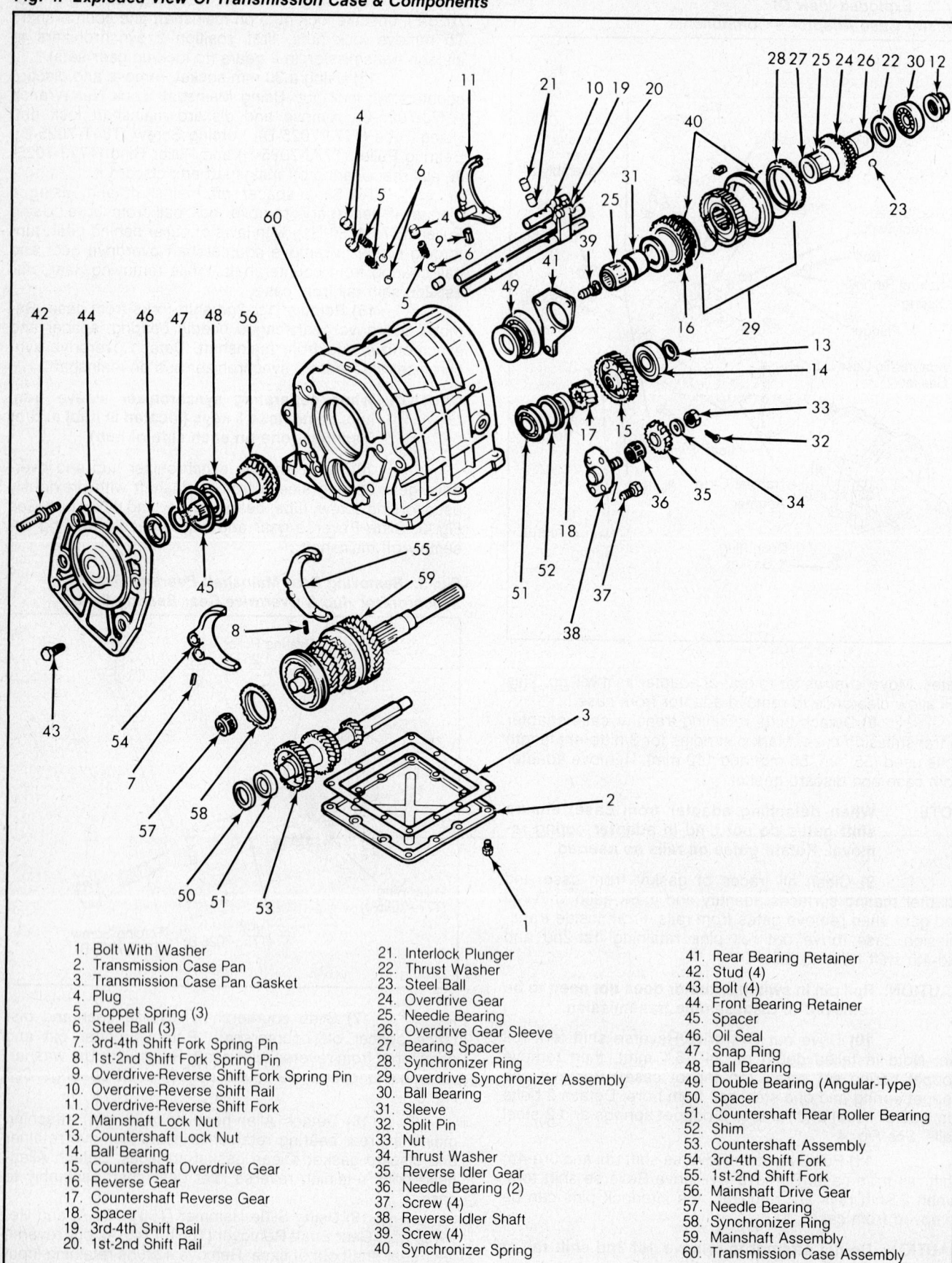

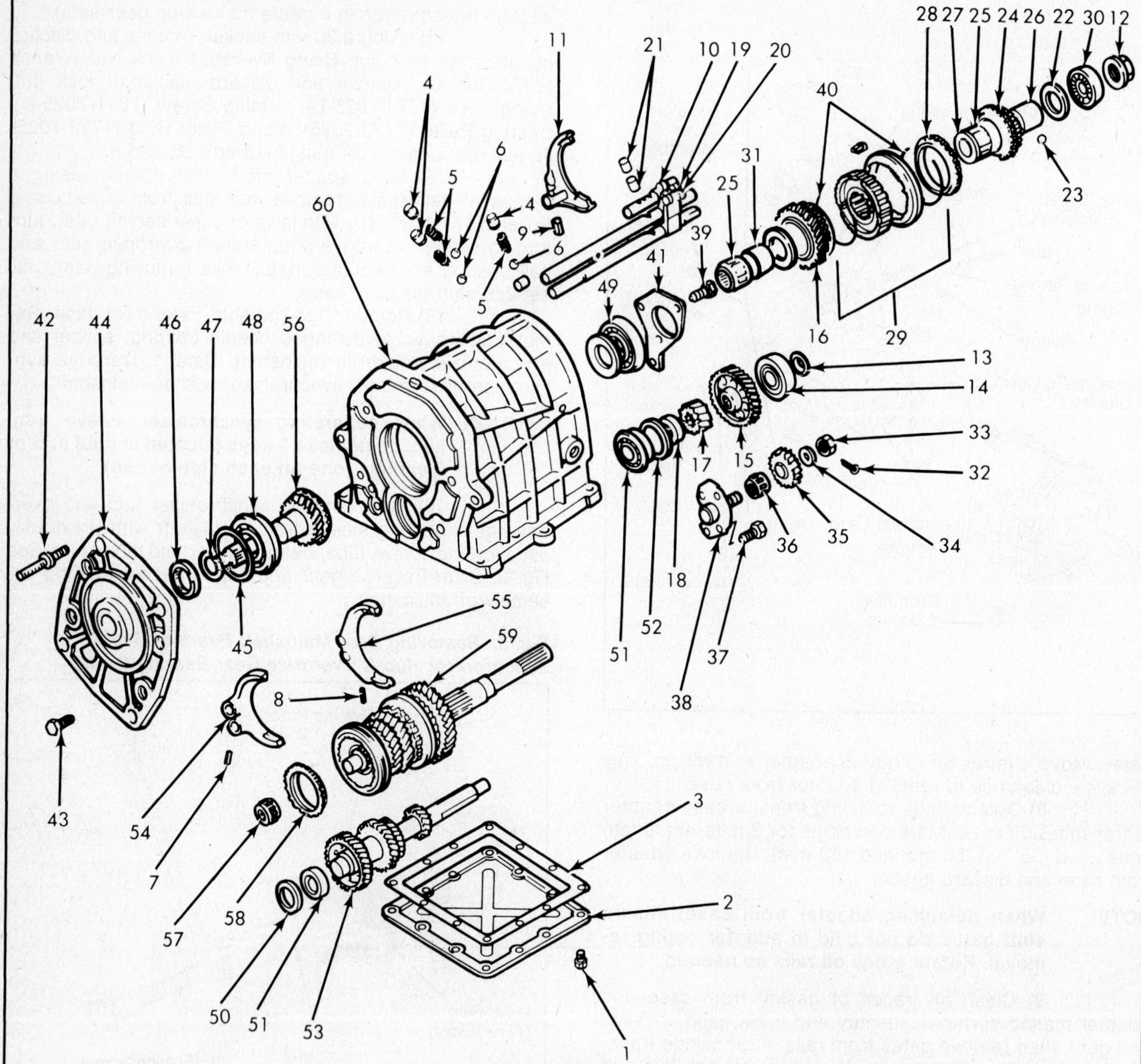

1. Bolt With Washer
2. Transmission Case Pan
3. Transmission Case Pan Gasket
4. Plug
5. Poppet Spring (3)
6. Steel Ball (3)
7. 3rd-4th Shift Fork Spring Pin
8. 1st-2nd Shift Fork Spring Pin
9. Overdrive-Reverse Shift Fork Spring Pin
10. Overdrive-Reverse Shift Rail
11. Overdrive-Reverse Shift Fork
12. Mainshaft Lock Nut
13. Countershaft Lock Nut
14. Ball Bearing
15. Countershaft Overdrive Gear
16. Reverse Gear
17. Countershaft Reverse Gear
18. Spacer
19. 3rd-4th Shift Rail
20. 1st-2nd Shift Rail
21. Interlock Plunger
22. Thrust Washer
23. Steel Ball
24. Overdrive Gear
25. Needle Bearing
26. Overdrive Gear Sleeve
27. Bearing Spacer
28. Synchronizer Ring
29. Overdrive Synchronizer Assembly
30. Ball Bearing
31. Sleeve
32. Split Pin
33. Nut
34. Thrust Washer
35. Reverse Idler Gear
36. Needle Bearing (2)
37. Screw (4)
38. Reverse Idler Shaft
39. Screw (4)
40. Synchronizer Spring
41. Rear Bearing Retainer
42. Stud (4)
43. Bolt (4)
44. Front Bearing Retainer
45. Spacer
46. Oil Seal
47. Snap Ring
48. Ball Bearing
49. Double Bearing (Angular-Type)
50. Spacer
51. Countershaft Rear Roller Bearing
52. Shim
53. Countershaft Assembly
54. 3rd-4th Shift Fork
55. 1st-2nd Shift Fork
56. Mainshaft Drive Gear
57. Needle Bearing
58. Synchronizer Ring
59. Mainshaft Assembly
60. Transmission Case Assembly

FORD MOTOR CO. 5-SPEED – DIESEL (Cont.)

Fig. 5: Removing Reverse Gears, Reverse Idler Gear, Spacer & Bearings

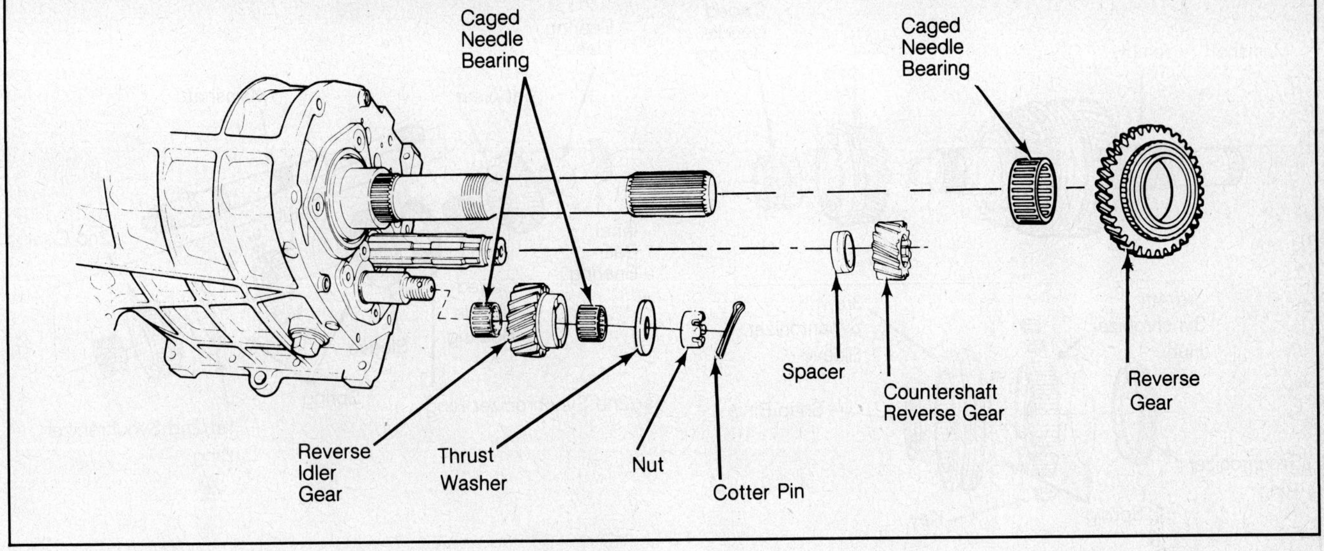

20) Remove input shaft front bearing retainer from case. Remove and discard gasket. Clean gasket surfaces. Remove selective shim from inside of retainer. Do not discard selective shim. Detach small selective snap ring retaining input shaft to bearing. Do not discard selective snap ring.

21) Detach large selective snap ring retaining input shaft bearing to case. Remove bearing from input shaft using Tube (T75L-7025-B), Bearing Collets (T75L-7025-D), Bearing Collet Sleeve (T75L-7025-G) and Forcing Screw (T84T-7025-B). Remove and discard bearing.

22) Rotate input shaft so flats on shaft face countershaft (to provide clearance to remove input shaft). Remove input shaft. If necessary, pull mainshaft toward rear of case. Remove small caged needle bearing from input gear I.D.

23) Remove snap ring from mainshaft outer bearing race. Remove outer mainshaft bearing race, ball bearing and bearing sleeve using tube, Mainshaft Bearing Collet Remover (T85T-7065-A), Bearing Collet Sleeve (T77F-7025-C) and forcing screw. Inner front bearing race will remain on mainshaft. Discard outer bearing race and ball bearing.

24) Remove countershaft front spacer and bearing race. Move mainshaft assembly slightly to side, if necessary, to allow clearance for countershaft assembly removal. Remove countershaft assembly from bottom of case. Remove mainshaft assembly from case.

MAINSHAFT ASSEMBLY

Disassembly

1) Detach and discard selective snap ring retaining 3rd-4th synchronizer assembly to mainshaft (a new snap ring will be used during assembly). *See Fig. 6 and 7.*

NOTE: **Ensure position of synchronizer hub and sleeve is noted during disassembly for reassembly reference.**

2) Remove 3rd-4th synchronizer assembly (hub, sleeve, spring and keys), synchronizer ring, 3rd gear and caged needle bearing from front of mainshaft. *See Fig. 6 and 7.*

Fig. 6: Cutaway View Of Mainshaft Assembly

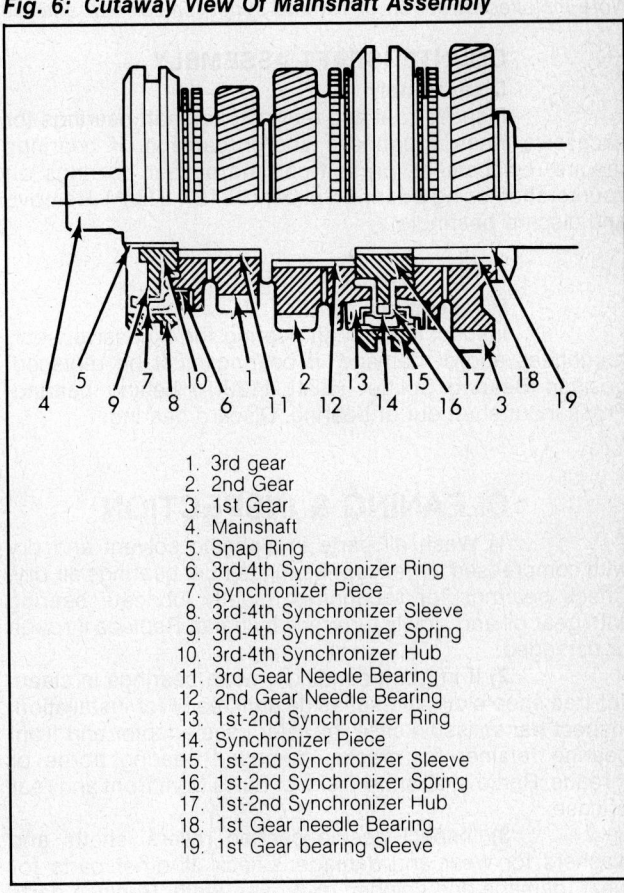

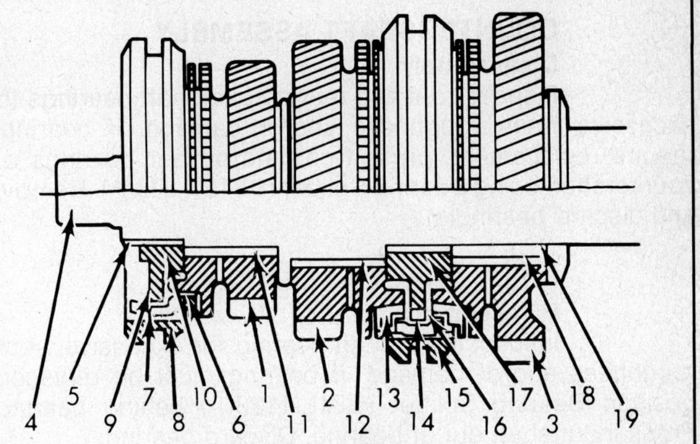

1. 3rd gear
2. 2nd Gear
3. 1st Gear
4. Mainshaft
5. Snap Ring
6. 3rd-4th Synchronizer Ring
7. Synchronizer Piece
8. 3rd-4th Synchronizer Sleeve
9. 3rd-4th Synchronizer Spring
10. 3rd-4th Synchronizer Hub
11. 3rd Gear Needle Bearing
12. 2nd Gear Needle Bearing
13. 1st-2nd Synchronizer Ring
14. Synchronizer Piece
15. 1st-2nd Synchronizer Sleeve
16. 1st-2nd Synchronizer Spring
17. 1st-2nd Synchronizer Hub
18. 1st Gear needle Bearing
19. 1st Gear bearing Sleeve

3) Position mainshaft assembly in press so 2nd gear is supported by press bed. Press mainshaft down and out from 1st and 2nd gear assembly. Separate inner ball bearing, bearing sleeve, 1st gear, caged needle bearing, 1st-2nd synchronizer assembly (hub, sleeve, 2 rings and 3 keys), 2nd gear and caged needle bearing. *See Fig. 7.* Discard inner ball bearing.

Fig. 7: Exploded View Of Mainshaft Assembly

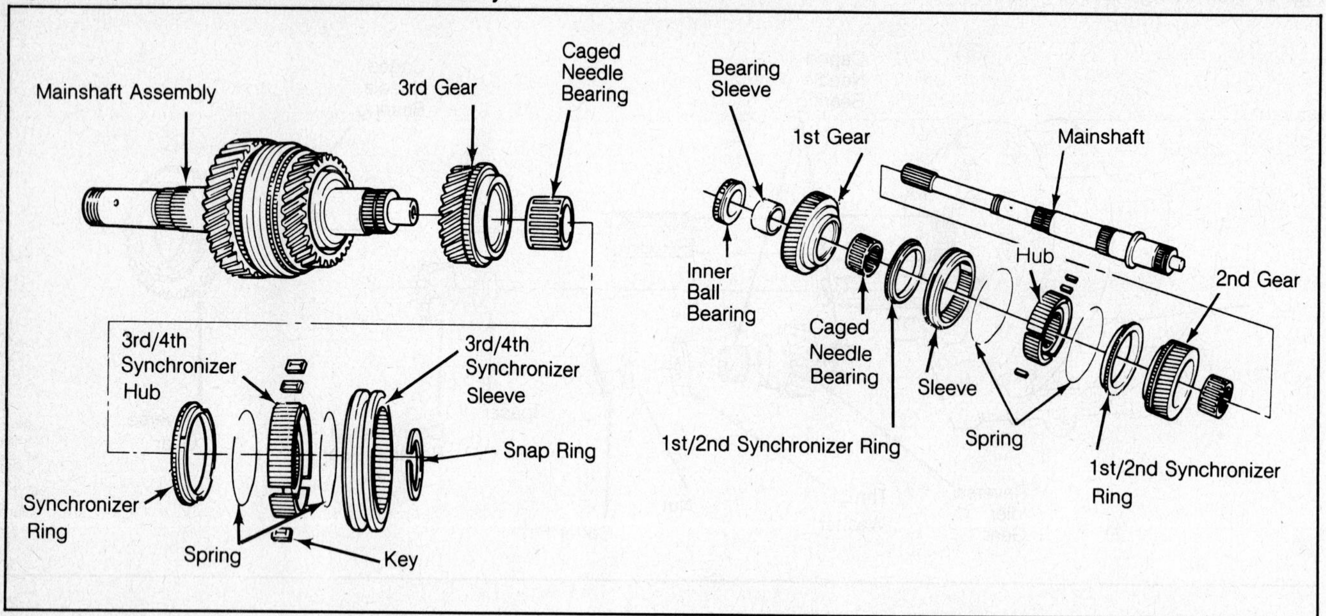

Note installed direction of 1st-2nd synchronizer hub and sleeve during disassembly for reassembly reference.

COUNTERSHAFT ASSEMBLY
Disassembly

Inspect front and rear countershaft bearings for excessive wear, roughness and/or damage. If bearings require replacement, press front and/or rear bearings off countershaft using Bearing Splitter (D84L-1123-A). Remove and discard bearing(s).

INPUT SHAFT ASSEMBLY
Disassembly

Inspect input shaft bearing for excessive wear, roughness and/or damage. If bearing must be replaced, position Bearing Splitter (D84L-1123-A) behind bearing. Press input shaft out of bearing. Discard bearing.

CLEANING & INSPECTION

1) Wash all parts in cleaning solvent and dry with compressed air (except bearings). Let bearings air dry. Check bearings for roughness. Lightly lubricate bearing with gear oil and slowly turn race by hand. Replace if rough or damaged.

2) If in good condition, wrap bearings in clean, lint-free shop cloth and set aside until ready for installation. Inspect transmission case, transfer case adapter and front bearing retainer for cracks, damaged bearing bores or threads. Remove all small nicks or burrs from front and rear of case.

3) Inspect needle bearing rollers, shafts and washers for wear and damage. Check all other parts for wear, damage and chipped or broken teeth. Replace parts as necessary.

4) Inspect synchronizer blocking rings for widened index slots, rounded clutch teeth and smooth internal surfaces (must have machined grooves). With blocker ring on cone, distance between face of gear clutching teeth and face of blocking ring must not be less than .009" (.23 mm).

5) Check synchronizer sleeves for free movement on hubs. Ensure alignment marks (etched or painted marks) are properly indexed. Replace synchronizer components as necessary. Replace seal in input shaft bearing retainer.

TRANSMISSION REASSEMBLY

INPUT SHAFT ASSEMBLY
Reassembly

Position new bearing on input shaft. Press bearing onto shaft using Tube (T75L-7025-B) with Replacing Shaft Sleeve (T75L-7025-K) and Shaft Coller (T75L-7025-M) inside tube and Rack Bushing Holder (T81P-3504-D) or an appropriate size washer against bearing.

COUNTERSHAFT ASSEMBLY
Reassembly

If bearing must be replaced, install bearing splitter on end of countershaft opposite bearing being installed. Position countershaft assembly upright, with bearing splitter resting on press bed. Press new bearing onto countershaft using hydraulic press and Countershaft Bearing Replacer (T85T-7121-A).

MAINSHAFT ASSEMBLY
Reassembly

1) Check clearance between synchronizer rings and gears. Install ring on gear, then insert feeler gauge between ring teeth and gear. If clearance is less than .009" (.23 mm), replace synchronizer ring and/or gear. *See Fig. 8.*

2) Install caged needle bearing for 2nd gear (from rear of mainshaft). Position 2nd gear on mainshaft with synchronizer ring surface facing rear of shaft. Install synchronizer ring on 2nd gear.

3) Position 1st-2nd synchronizer assembly on rear of mainshaft. Ensure mainshaft splines and synchronizer are properly aligned. Rear of 1st-2nd hub is identified by a ridge machined on rear surface. *See Fig. 10.* Ridge must face front of mainshaft.

Fig. 8: Checking Synchonizer Ring-To-Gear Clearance

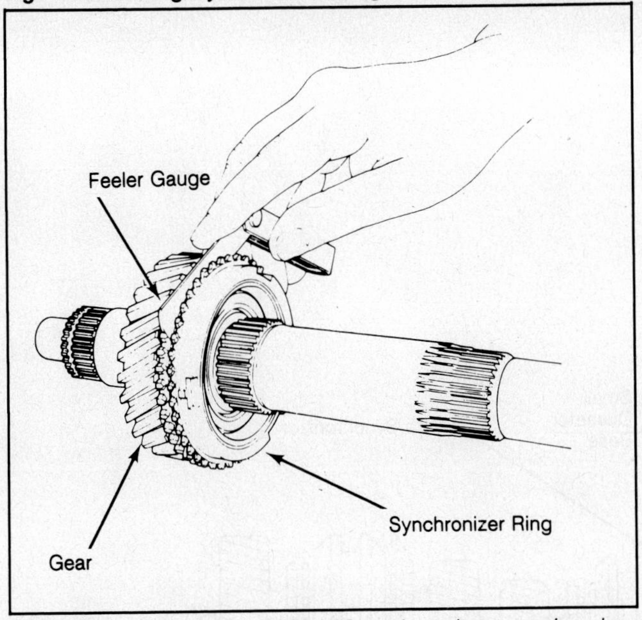

If clearance is less than .009" (.23 mm), replace synchronizer ring and/or gear.

4) Install sleeve with large bevel angle facing front of mainshaft. Synchronizer sleeve has a tooth missing at 6 positions. Assemble hub to sleeve so single tooth, between 2 missing portions, will touch synchronizer key. *See Fig. 10.*

NOTE: When synchronizer keys and springs are properly installed, the open ends of spring do not face each other.

5) Press 1st-2nd synchronizer assembly into position on mainshaft using Replacing Shaft Sleeve (T75L-7025-K), Shaft Collar (T75L-7025-M) and Tube (T75L-7025-C). If properly installed, 2nd gear should rotate freely.

6) Position 1st gear bearing sleeve on mainshaft. Press sleeve on shaft using replacing shaft sleeve, shaft collar, Rack Bushing Holder (T81P-3504-D) and tube. When properly installed, sleeve should be against synchronizer hub. Ensure gears rotate freely.

7) Install synchronizer ring on 1st-2nd synchronizer assembly. Install caged needle bearing and 1st gear. Slide a new inner ball bearing into position on mainshaft. Press bearing onto mainshaft usng rack bushing holder, tube, replacing sleeve shaft and shaft collar. After installation, ensure gears rotate freely.

8) Install 3rd gear and caged needle bearing over front of mainshaft. Install synchronizer ring against 3rd gear. When installing 3rd-4th synchronizer assembly, ensure mainshaft splines and synchronizer are properly aligned. Small diameter hub boss and small bevel angle of sleeve faces front of mainshaft. *See Fig. 9.*

NOTE: Synchronizer sleeve has a tooth missing at 6 positions. Assemble hub to sleeve so single tooth, between 2 missing portions, will touch synchronizer key. When synchronizer keys and springs are properly installed, the open ends of spring do not face each other.

9) Install 3rd-4th synchronizer assembly onto front of mainshaft. Install a new selective snap ring that

Fig. 9: Installing 3rd-4th Synchronizer Assembly Onto Mainshaft

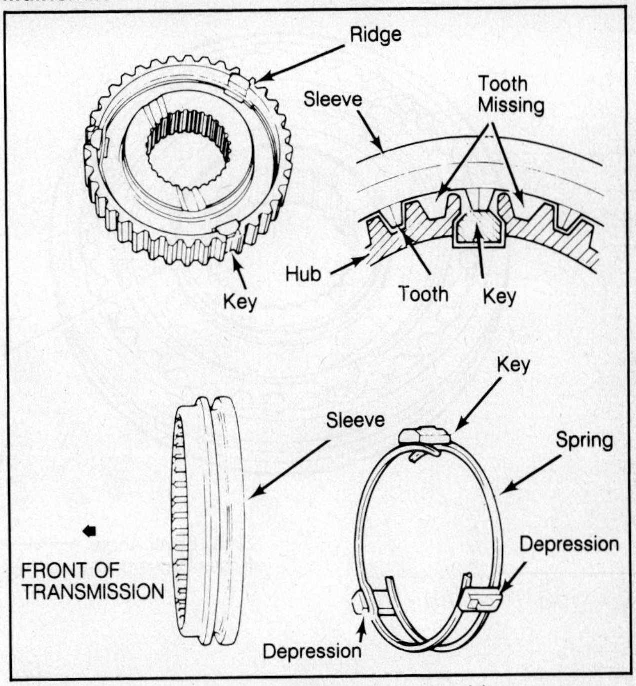

When installing 3rd-4th synchronizer assembly, ensure mainshaft splines and synchronizer are properly aligned.

retains 3rd-4th synchronizer assembly to mainshaft. Select thickest snap ring that will fit in groove. See MAINSHAFT SELECTIVE SNAP RING table.

MAINSHAFT SELECTIVE SNAP RING

Identification Color	Thickness In. (mm)
White	.091 (2.30)
Brown	.093 (2.35)
None	.094 (2.40)
Blue	.096 (2.45)
Yellow	.098 (2.50)

TRANSMISSION CASE & TRANSFER CASE ADAPTER

Reassembly

1) Install mainshaft assembly into transmission case. Install 1st-2nd and 3rd-4th shift forks into their respective synchronizer sleeves. Ensure roll pin bosses on forks face each other. Install countershaft assembly into case.

NOTE: If necessary, move mainshaft to 1 side in order to ease countershaft installation.

2) Choose and install a new selective snap ring in front of input shaft bearing. Select thickest snap ring that will fit in groove. See INPUT SHAFT SELECTIVE SNAP RING table for available sizes and identification colors.

NOTE: If necessary, move mainshaft to 1 side in order to ease countershaft installation.

2) Choose and install a new selective snap ring in front of input shaft bearing. Select thickest snap ring that

FORD MOTOR CO. 5-SPEED – DIESEL (Cont.)

Fig. 10: Installing 1st-2nd Synchronizer Assembly On Mainshaft

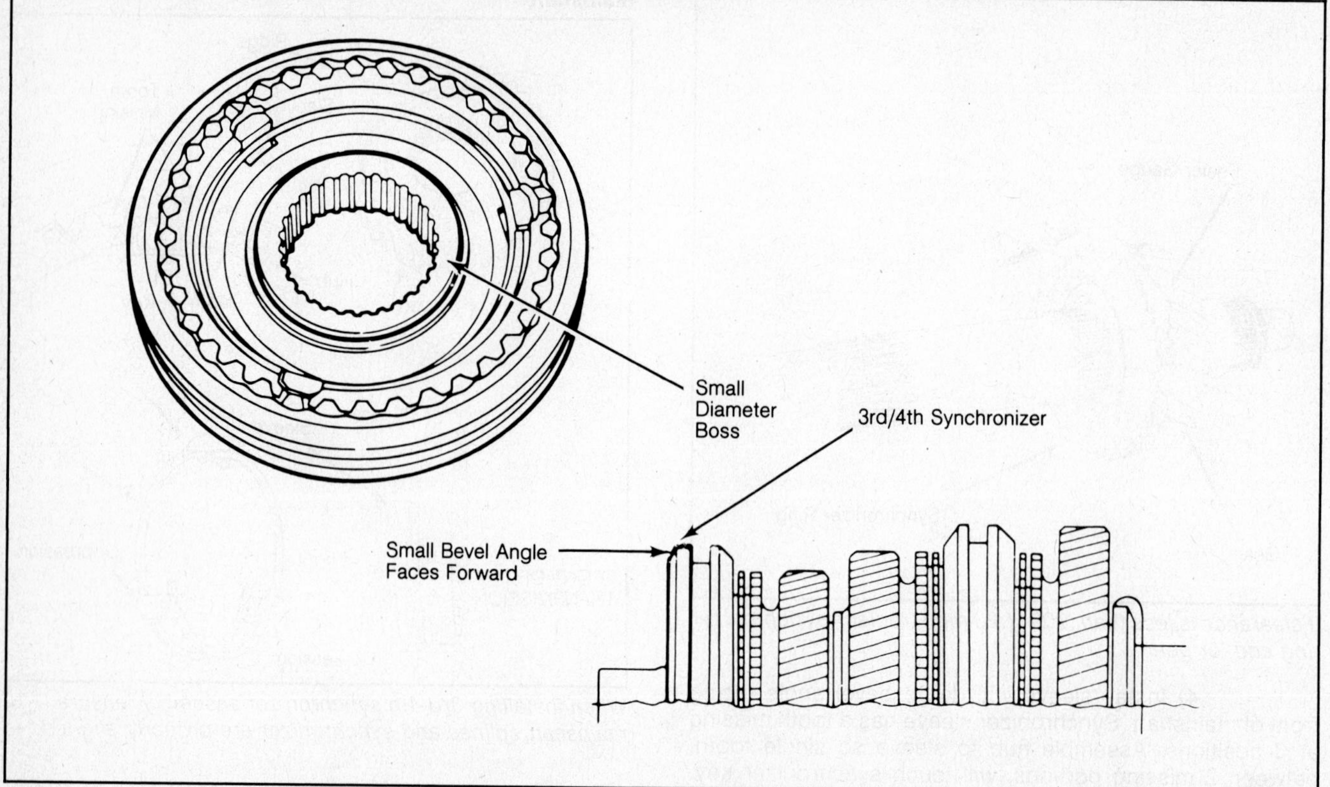

Ensure ridge machined on rear of 1st-2nd synchronizer hub faces rear of mainshaft.

will fit in groove. See INPUT SHAFT SELECTIVE SNAP RING table for available sizes and identification colors.

INPUT SHAFT SELECTIVE SNAP RING

Identification Color	Thickness In. (mm)
Blue	.085 (2.15)
None	.087 (2.22)
Brown	.090 (2.29)
White	.093 (2.36)

3) Install small caged needle bearing inside input gear. Install synchronizer ring on input shaft. Check clearance between ring and gear. If clearance is less than .009" (.23 mm), replace ring and/or input shaft.

4) Install synchronizer ring and input shaft in case. Rotate input shaft so flats face countershaft (to provide installation clearance). If necessary, tap input shaft into position with brass hammer.

5) Install a new snap ring on new outer bearing race, then install race in case. Ensure longest portion of race is installed toward case. Slide new outer ball bearing onto mainshaft.

6) Press bearing on mainshaft and in race using previously used tube, replacing shaft sleeve and shaft collar. After pressing into position, ensure all gears rotate freely.

7) Using Oil Seal Installer (T85T-7011-A) and Driver Handle (T80T-4000-W), drive new oil seal into input shaft front bearing retainer. Install large snap ring that retains input shaft bearing to case.

8) Check input shaft front bearing retainer-to-bearing clearance. Remove front bearing retainer selective shim. Using a depth micrometer, measure distance between top machined surface to spacer surface (second landing) of front bearing retainer. *See Fig. 11.* Record reading.

9) Bottom input shaft bearing so snap ring is flush against transmission case. Using depth micrometer, measure distance from top of outer front bearing race to machined surface of case. *See Fig. 11.*

10) Subtract distance of bearing-to-case from retainer dimensions. This will give required maximum shim size to obtain a 0-.004" (0-.10 mm) clearance. Measure and install appropriate size selective shim in front bearing retainer. Refer to INPUT SHAFT FRONT BEARING RETAINER-TO-BEARING SELECTIVE SHIM table for available shim sizes and identification colors.

INPUT SHAFT FRONT BEARING RETAINER-TO-BEARING SELECTIVE SHIM

Identification Color	Thickness In. (mm)
Black	.033 (.84)
None	.037 (.93)
Red	.040 (1.02)
White	.044 (1.11)
Yellow	.047 (1.20)
Blue	.051 (1.29)
Green	.054 (1.38)

11) Install countershaft front outer bearing race and non-selective spacer. Install countershaft rear outer bearing race. Install new gasket between front bearing retainer and case. Position retainer on case (with selective

Fig. 11: Checking Input Shaft Front Bearing Retainer-To-Bearing Clearance

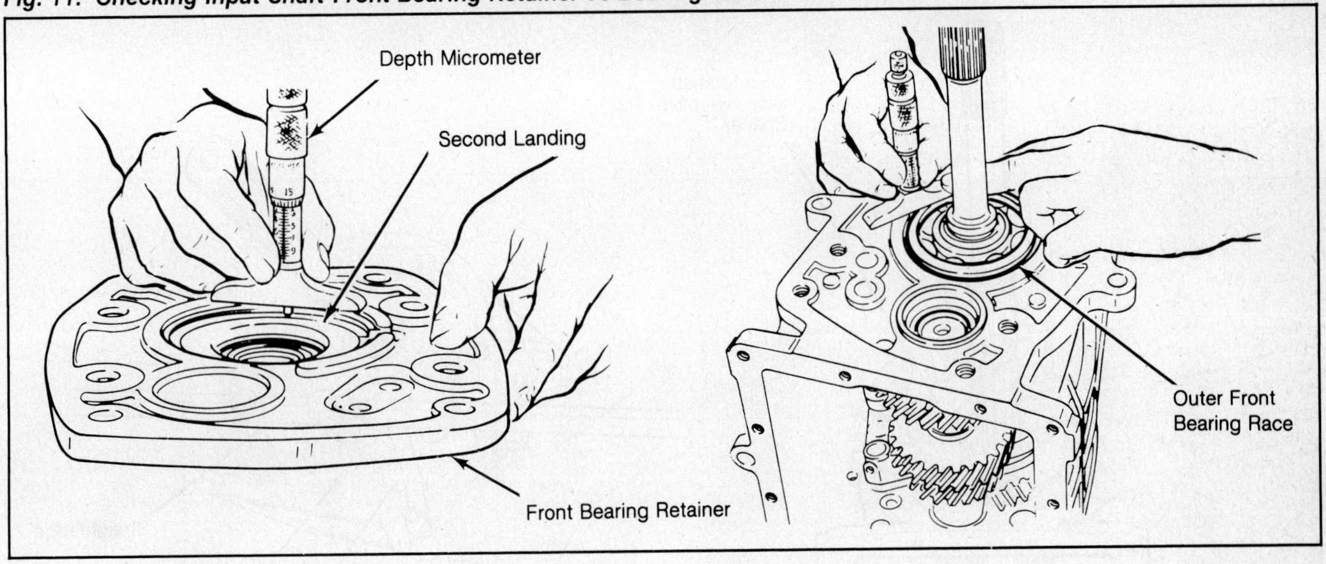

shim installed). Install 4 bolts and 4 studs, then tighten to 22-30 ft. lbs. (30-41 N.m).

12) Check and adjust countershaft end play. Place transmission so rear of mainshaft and countershaft face upward. Install countershaft rear selective spacer. *See Fig. 12*. Force countershaft downward so it bottoms against front bearing retainer.

13) Place straightedge across rear countershaft selective spacer in case. *See Fig. 12*. Try to turn spacer. If spacer turns lightly, replace spacer with next larger size.

14) Install a spacer so clearance between spacer and straightedge is 0-.002" (0-.05 mm). Refer to COUNTERSHAFT END PLAY SELECTIVE SPACER table for available sizes and identification markings on spacer. Install correct size spacer over countershaft rear bearing race.

15) Install and tighten rear bearing retainer onto case with 4 Allen-head bolts (6 mm). Ensure spacer installed in step **14)** does not fall out of place when installing rear bearing retainer.

16) Position reverse idler gear shaft assembly on case. Install Allen-head Bolts (6 mm) to act as a pilot. Install Reverse Idler Gear Shaft Remover (T85T-7140-A) on shaft and drive assembly into place. Tighten bolts to 11-16 ft. lbs. (15-21 N.m).

17) Install 2 caged needle bearings, reverse idler gear and thrust washer on idler shaft. Boss on idler gear faces away from transmission. Install lock nut and tighten to 15-42 ft. lbs. (20-58 N.m). If necessary, advance nut to next castillation and install new cotter pin.

CAUTION: When installed, ensure cotter pin does not cause interference with countershaft overdrive gear. Bend and/or cut end of cotter pin if necessary.

18) Install spacers and countershaft reverse gear on mainshaft. Press reverse gear sleeve onto mainshaft using Tube (T85T-7025-A), Shaft Sleeve Replacer (T75L-7025-K), Shaft Collar (T75L-7025-M) and Forcing Screw (T84T-7025-B).

19) Install caged needle bearing and reverse gear onto mainshaft. Assemble overdrive synchronizer hub and sleeve by first installing hub into sleeve. Ensure recessed boss on sleeve faces front of transmission. Large boss on hub must also face front of transmission.

20) When installing hub in sleeve and 3 keys, ensure single tooth between 2 spaces will touch key. Install springs so open ends do not face each other. Install overdrive synchronizer on mainshaft with recessed boss of sleeve facing front of transmission.

COUNTERSHAFT END PLAY SELECTIVE SPACER

Identification Mark	Thickness In. (mm)
84	.0724 (1.840)
87	.0736 (1.870)
90	.0748 (1.900)
93	.0760 (1.930)
96	.0772 (1.960)
99	.0783 (1.990)
02	.0795 (2.020)
06	.0807 (2.050)
08	.0819 (2.080)
11	.0831 (2.110)
14	.0843 (2.140)
17	.0854 (2.170)
20	.0866 (2.200)
23	.0878 (2.230)
26	.0890 (2.260)
29	.0902 (2.290)
32	.0913 (2.320)
35	.0925 (2.350)
38	.0937 (2.380)
41	.0949 (2.410)
44	.0961 (2.440)
47	.0972 (2.470)
50	.0984 (2.500)
53	.0996 (2.530)
56	.1008 (2.560)
59	.1020 (2.590)
62	.1031 (2.620)
65	.1043 (2.650)
68	.1055 (2.680)

Manual Transmissions

FORD MOTOR CO. 5-SPEED – DIESEL (Cont.)

Fig. 12: Checking Countershaft End Play

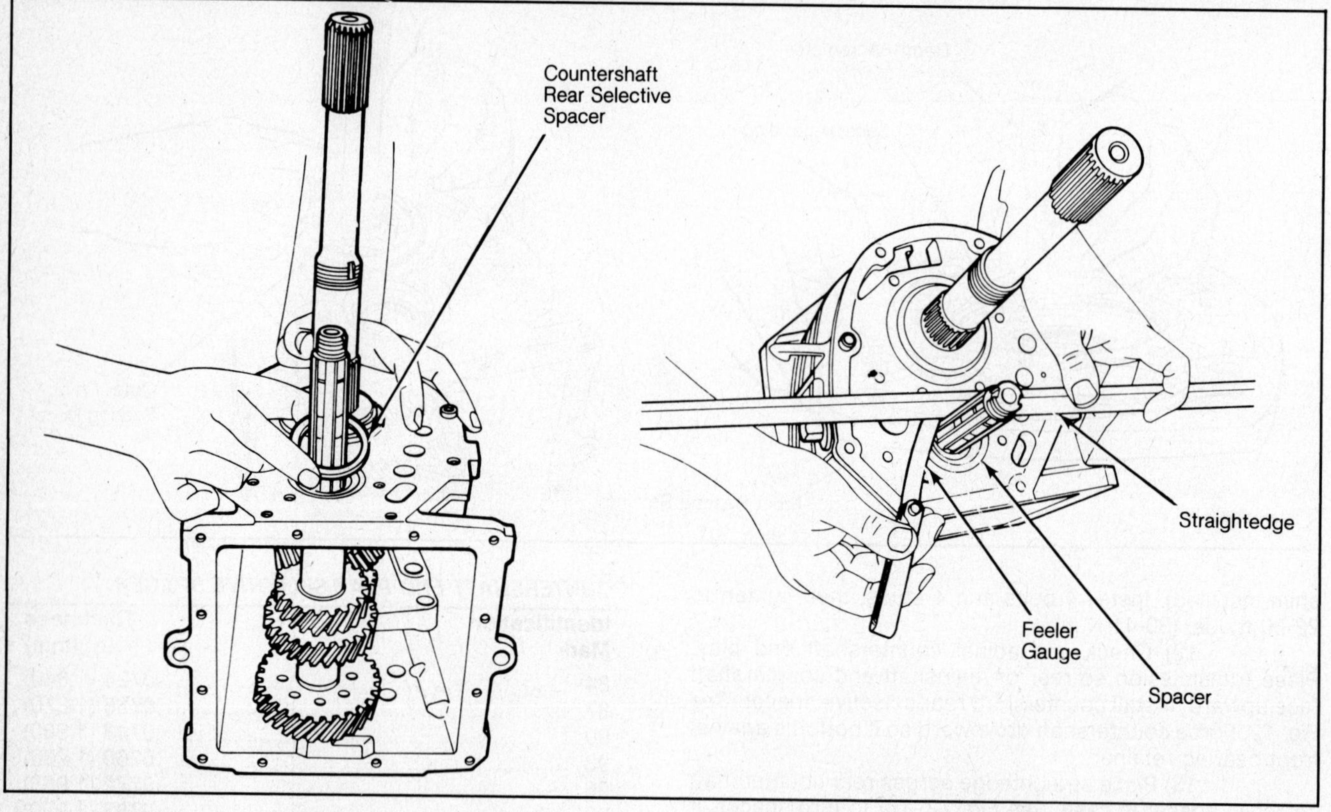

21) Press overdrive gear sleeve onto mainshaft using previously used tube, shaft sleeve replacer, shaft collar and Overdrive Gear Bearing Replacer (T85T-7061-A). Install ring onto overdrive synchronizer.

22) Slide small spacer, caged needle bearing and overdrive gear onto mainshaft. Check clearance between overdrive gear and synchronizer ring. If clearance is less than .009" (.23 mm), replace ring and/or overdrive gear.

23) Install countershaft overdrive gear and ball bearing onto countershaft along with 1st-2nd shift rail. Seat bearing into position using Countershaft Bearing Replacer Collet (T85T-7121-A), Rear Countershaft Bearing Installer Adapter (T85T-7111-A) and Remover/Replacer Tube (T77J-7025-B). Ensure rail engages forks.

24) Install lock ball and spacer onto mainshaft. Place rear bearing over mainshaft. Press bearing into position using Rack Bushing Holder (T81P-3504-D), tube, shaft sleeve replacer and shaft collar.

25) Install new lock nuts on countershaft and mainshaft. Double engage transmission in 2 gears to prevent shafts from turning. Tighten mainshaft lock nut to 180-195 ft. lbs. (245-265 N.m) using Mainshaft Lock Nut Wrench (T77J-7025-C).

26) Tighten countershaft lock nut to 115-137 ft. lbs. (157-168 N.m) using 30 mm socket. Disengage transmission. Stake lock uts on mainshaft and countershaft usng Lock Nut Staking (T77J-7025-F).

27) Install and interlock plunger in bore between 1st-2nd and 3rd-4th shift rails. Reposition 1st-2nd shift rail so flats for poppet ball and spring and interlock plunger are in correct position. Ensure roll pin holes for shift forks are in alignment.

28) Install Overdrive/Reverse shift fork on synchronizer sleeve. Slide 3rd-4th shift rail through Overdrive/Reverse shift fork, into case and into 3rd-4th shift fork (inside case). Position shift rail flats to accept poppet balls and interlock plunger.

29) Insert interlock plunger in bore between 3rd-4th shift rail and Overdrive/Reverse shift rail. Ensure roll pin holes in fork are in alignment. Insert Overdrive/Reverse shift rail so it engages forks in case. Check that roll pin holes in fork and rail are in alignment.

30) Insert Poppet ball and spring in 1st-2nd (upper) bore in case. Ensure small end of spring is installed toward ball. Install set screw and tighten until set screw head is .24" (6 mm) below top of bore.

31) Insert poppet springs and balls into 3rd-4th and Overdrive/Reverse bore (2 bores on side of case). Ensure small end of each spring faces its ball. Install and tighten bolts.

32) Install roll pins in shift forks. If removed, install switch actuator and roll pin. Install shift gates on appropriate shift rails. Move 1st-2nd gate to rear of rail. Position new gasket between transmission case and transfer case adapter.

33) Ensure selector arm is out of gates and change shifter is at rear of adapter. Position adapter on case (ensure shift gate clears adapter). Check that shift rails and rear bearings line up with bores in adapter.

34) Install 3 different sizes of bolts in appropriate holes in adapter, then tighten to 11-16 ft. lbs. (15-21 N.m). *See Fig. 13.* Install neutral return plungers, springs and bolts in adapter. Longer plunger (with slot for detent ball) is installed on right side of adapter.

35) Position shift gates so roll pin holes in gates and rails are in alignment. Install roll pins through access holes. Install access hole plugs. Position pan and new gasket on case. Install and tighten mounting bolts. Do not overtighten. Install drain plug (if necessary) and tighten.

FORD MOTOR CO. 5-SPEED – DIESEL (Cont.)

Fig. 13: Transfer Case Adapter Mounting Bolt Hole Locations

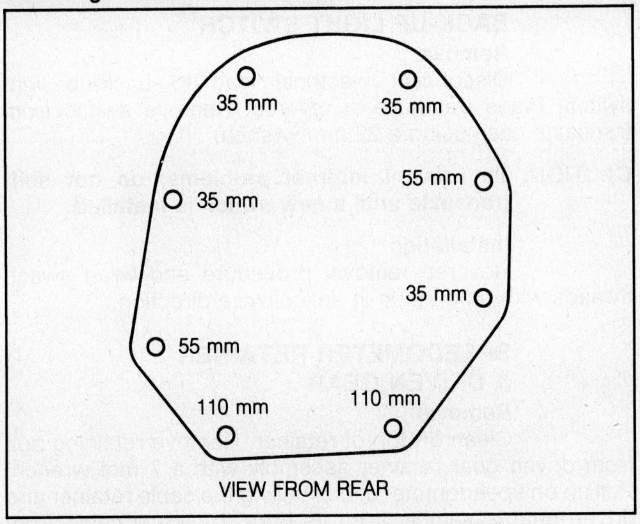

Install 3 different sizes of bolts in appropriate holes shown in adapter, then tighten to specification.

36) Insert plunger detent ball and spring in hole above neutral return plunger in adapter case. Ensure stopper bracket assembly on cover (for transfer case adapter) moves smoothly. Position new gasket on adapter and install housing cover. Install and tighten mounting bolts.

37) Install back-up light switch and shift indicator light switch in adapter. Remove filler plug and fill transmission to bottom of fill hole with SAE 80W gear oil (fluid capacity is 9 pts).

38) Install filler plug and tighten. Position clutch slave cylinder on input shaft. Position clutch bell housing on transmission case, then install and tighten mounting bolts.

TIGHTENING SPECIFICATIONS

Application	Ft. Lbs. (N.m)
Clutch Bell Housing	
To-Engine Mounting Bolt	28-38 (38-51)
To-Trans. Case Mounting Bolt	30-40 (41-54)
Countershaft Lock Nut	115-137 (157-186)
Damper-To-Insulator Nut	71-94 (97-127)
Drain Plug	25-32 (35-44)
Filler Plug	22-25 (30-34)
Front Bearing Retainer	
To-Trans. Case Mounting Bolt	22-30 (30-41)
Housing Cover	
To-Transfer Case Adapter Bolt	11-16 (15-21)
Insulator-To-Transmission Bolt	60-80 (81-108)
Mainshaft Lock Nut	180-195 (245-265)
Output Shaft Lock Nut	94-152 (127-210)
Pan-To-Trans. Case Mounting Bolt	11-16 (15-21)
Rear Bearing-To-Case Mounting Bolt	22-30 (30-41)
Reverse Idler Gear Nut	15-42 (20-58)
Rever Idler Gearshaft Assembly	
To-Transmission Case Mounting Bolt	11-16 (15-21)
Shift Lever Assembly	
To-Transfer Case Adapter Bolt	6-10 (8-14)
Starter Motor	
To-Clutch Housing Mounting Bolt	15-20 (21-27)
Stud-To-Front Retainer & Case	22-30 (30-41)

FORD MOTOR CO. MTX 4 & 5-SPEED TRANSAXLES

Escort, EXP, Lynx, Taurus, Tempo, Topaz, Sable

IDENTIFICATION

The MTX 4 and 5-speed manual transaxles can be identified by a tag affixed to top of transaxle case. Top line of tag identifies transaxle model, next line identifies transaxle assembly, third line shows build date code, and bottom line is transaxle serial number. Transaxle axle ratios are shown in TRANSAXLE RATIO table.

TRANSAXLE RATIO

Application	Model	Axle Ratio
4-Speed		
1.9L	RGS-AB	3.27:1
1.9L	RGT-AY	3.39:1
5-Speed		
Diesel Engine	RWB-AE, BH	3.52:1
Diesel Engine	RWB-AD, BK	3.73:1
Gas Engine	RWB-AC, BJ	3.33:1
Gas Engine	RWB-AB, BF	3.73:1

DESCRIPTION

The MTX transaxle combines a 4 or 5-speed manual transmission and differential into a single component designed for front wheel drive applications. The transmission and differential are housed in a 2-piece, light weight aluminum alloy housing which is bolted to the back of the engine.

The transaxle is fully synchronized in all forward gears with reverse provided by a sliding gear. All gears, except reverse, are helical cut for quiet operation. The 5-speed transaxle has a third shaft which carries the 5th gear. All shafts, input cluster, main, and 5th gear drive shaft are supported in the case on tapered roller bearings. Preload is maintained on bearings by a shim located behind each bearing race in transaxle housing. The differential assembly is supported by 2 opposed tapered roller bearings and preload is maintained by means of a selective shim.

The inboard constant velocity (CV) joints are positively connected with the differential side gears by means of splines and secured in case with 2 snap rings. The ring gear is riveted to the differential case (bolted on after service).

LUBRICATION & ADJUSTMENT

See appropriate MANUAL TRANSMISSION SERVICING article in DOMESTIC GENERAL SERVICING section.

TROUBLE SHOOTING

See MANUAL TRANSMISSION TROUBLE SHOOTING article in DOMESTIC GENERAL SERVICING section.

SERVICE (IN VEHICLE)

BACK-UP LIGHT SWITCH

Removal

Disconnect electrical lead to back-up light switch. Place transaxle in reverse. Remove switch from transaxle case using a 22 mm wrench.

CAUTION: **To prevent internal problems, do not shift transaxle until a new switch is installed.**

Installation

Reverse removal procedure and wrap switch threads with teflon tape in a clockwise direction.

SPEEDOMETER RETAINER & DRIVEN GEAR

Removal

Clean off top of retainer. Remove retaining bolt from driven gear retainer assembly with a 7 mm wrench. Pull up on speedometer cable, pulling the cable retainer and driven gear assembly from its bore. Unscrew cable from retainer.

Installation

Clean and inspect case bore and all parts. Lightly grease "O" ring on retainer. Using a 13/16" deep-well socket, gently tap retainer and gear assembly into case bore while lining up groove in retainer with hole in case. Install and tighten retaining bolt.

DRIVE AXLE SHAFTS

See appropriate DRIVE AXLE SHAFT article in DOMESTIC AXLE SHAFTS & TRANSFER CASES section.

REMOVAL & INSTALLATION

TRANSMISSION

See appropriate MANUAL TRANSMISSION REMOVAL article in DOMESTIC GENERAL SERVICING section.

DISASSEMBLY

TRANSAXLE

1) Using a drift inserted into input shaft hole, pull or push input shaft into center detent position (neutral). Remove filler plugs from transaxle case and drain transmission fluid.

2) Remove reverse idler shaft retaining bolt. Remove detent plunger retaining screw. Remove detent spring and detent plunger with a magnet.

CAUTION: **Label detent plunger and spring as they are similar to input shift shaft plunger and spring contained in clutch housing.**

3) Remove shift fork interlock sleeve retaining pin. Remove 15 case-to-clutch housing retaining bolts. Separate case from housing by tapping on case with a soft mallet. Be careful not to drop bearing races or shims from case. Remove case magnet from transaxle case.

CAUTION: **Do not insert pry bars or screwdrivers between case and housing.**

FORD MOTOR CO. MTX 4 & 5-SPEED TRANSAXLES (Cont.)

Fig. 1: Sectional View of MTX 4-Speed Manual Transaxle Assembly

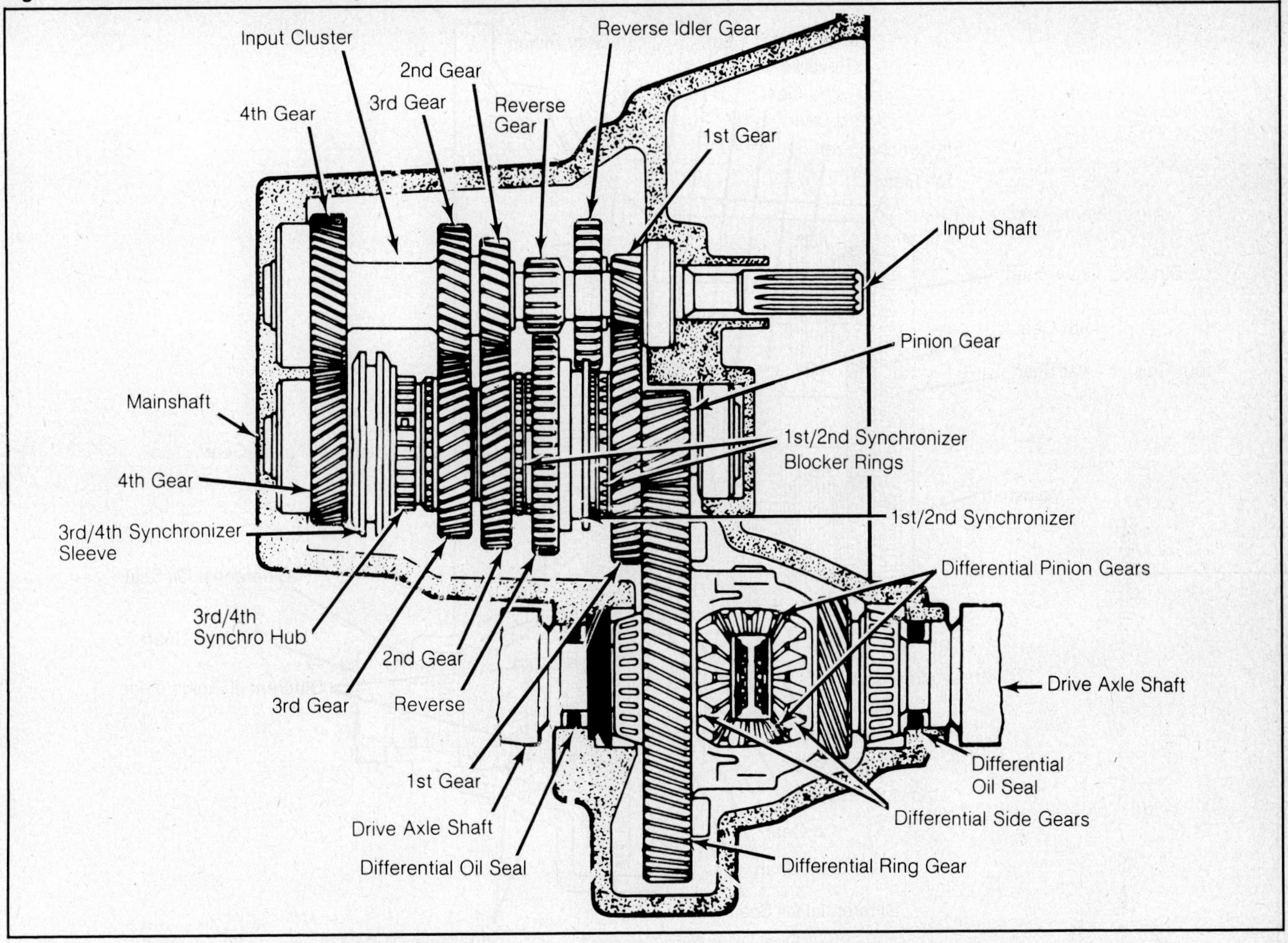

4) On 5-speed models, remove "C" clip retaining ring from 5th gear shift relay lever pivot pin. Remove 5th gear shift relay lever. On all models, remove reverse idler shaft and reverse idler gear from case by lifting straight up.

5) Use punch to drive roll pin from shift lever shaft. Gently pry on shift lever shaft to move it out of case, so that hole in shaft is exposed.

6) On vehicles equipped with diesel engines, remove 2 screws holding shift lever cover to shift lever and remove the inhibitor ball and spring.

7) On all other models hold a rag over hole in lever to prevent inhibitor ball and spring from shooting out and remove shaft using a drift in exposed shaft hole. *See Fig. 2.*

8) Remove inhibitor ball and spring from hole in lever using a pencil magnet. Remove shift lever, kickdown spring and 3-4 bias spring.

9) Lift mainshaft assembly, input cluster shaft assembly, and main shift control shaft assembly from case as a single unit. Be careful not to drop bearings or gears (slip fit).

10) On 4-speed models, remove reverse actuator arm and shaft assembly from bore in case by rotating shaft.

11) On 5-speed models, remove 5th gear shaft assembly and 5th gear fork assembly from their bores in case.

Fig. 2: Shift Lever Shaft Removal

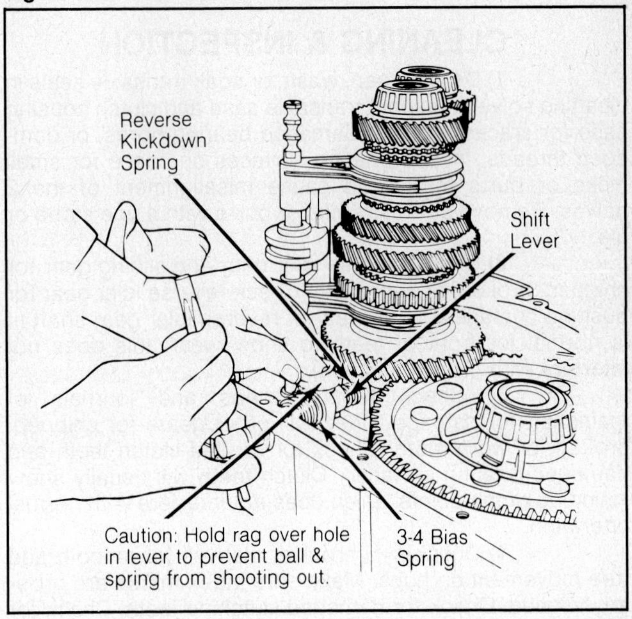

12) On all models, lift differential and final drive assembly from clutch housing case. Remove 2 bolts retaining shift relay lever support bracket assembly. Remove assembly.

FORD MOTOR CO. MTX 4 & 5-SPEED TRANSAXLES (Cont.)

Fig. 3: Sectional View of MTX 5-Speed Manual Transaxle Assembly

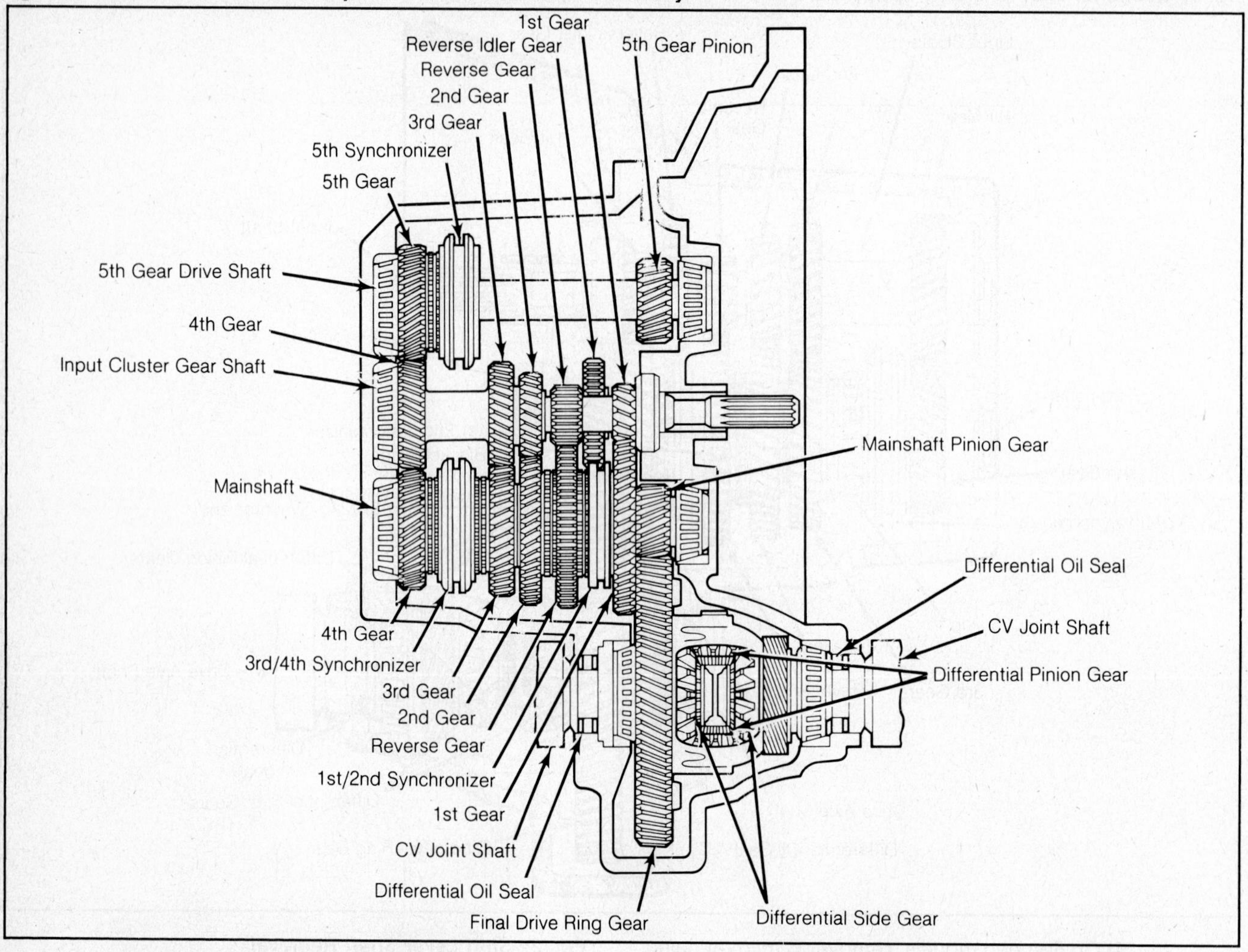

CLEANING & INSPECTION

1) Do not clean, wash, or soak transaxle seals in cleaning solvent. Inspect transaxle case and clutch housing case for cracks, worn or damaged bearing bores, or damaged threads. Inspect mating surfaces on cases for small nicks or burrs that could cause misalignment of the 2 halves. Remove all small nicks or burrs with a fine stone or file.

2) Check reverse idler gear and sliding gear for chipped, broken, or bent teeth. Check reverse idler gear for bushing damage. Check wear of reverse idler gear shaft (it is normal for front of teeth to show wear; this does not interfere with proper function).

3) Check teeth, splines and journals of mainshaft for damage. Check all other gears for chipped, broken, or worn teeth. Check for eroded clutch teeth and damaged bearing surfaces. Clutch teeth will usually show rounding of the points which does not interfere with normal operation.

4) Check synchronizer sleeves for smooth and free movement on hubs. Make sure index marks are properly aligned. Check for damaged clutching teeth. Check for proper positioning of springs.

5) Inspect synchronizer blocker rings for wear marks on spline end back face which indicates ring was bottoming on gear face due to excessive blocker ring wear.

COMPONENT DISASSEMBLY & REASSEMBLY

MAINSHAFT & SYCHRONIZER ASSEMBLIES

Mainshaft Disassembly

NOTE: All components should be identified for reassembly when removed from mainshaft.

1) Remove the slip fit tapered roller bearing from 4th gear end of shaft. Slide 4th gear and synchronizer blocker ring from mainshaft. Remove 3-4 synchronizer retaining ring. Slide synchronizer assembly, blocker ring, and 3rd gear from shaft.

2) Remove 2-3 thrust washer retaining ring and 2-piece thrust washer. Remove 2nd gear and blocker ring. Remove 1-2 synchronizer retaining ring. Slide 1-2 synchronizer assembly, blocker ring, and 1st gear from shaft.

3) Press tapered roller bearing from pinion end of mainshaft using an arbor press. Remove only if damaged.

Sychronizer Disassembly

Note position of index marks. Remove springs with a small screwdriver. Do not compress the springs any more than necessary. Remove the 3 hub inserts. Slide hub and sleeve apart.

FORD MOTOR CO. MTX 4 & 5-SPEED TRANSAXLES (Cont.)

Fig. 4: Exploded View of 4 & 5-Speed Transaxle Case, Clutch Housing & Differential Assembly

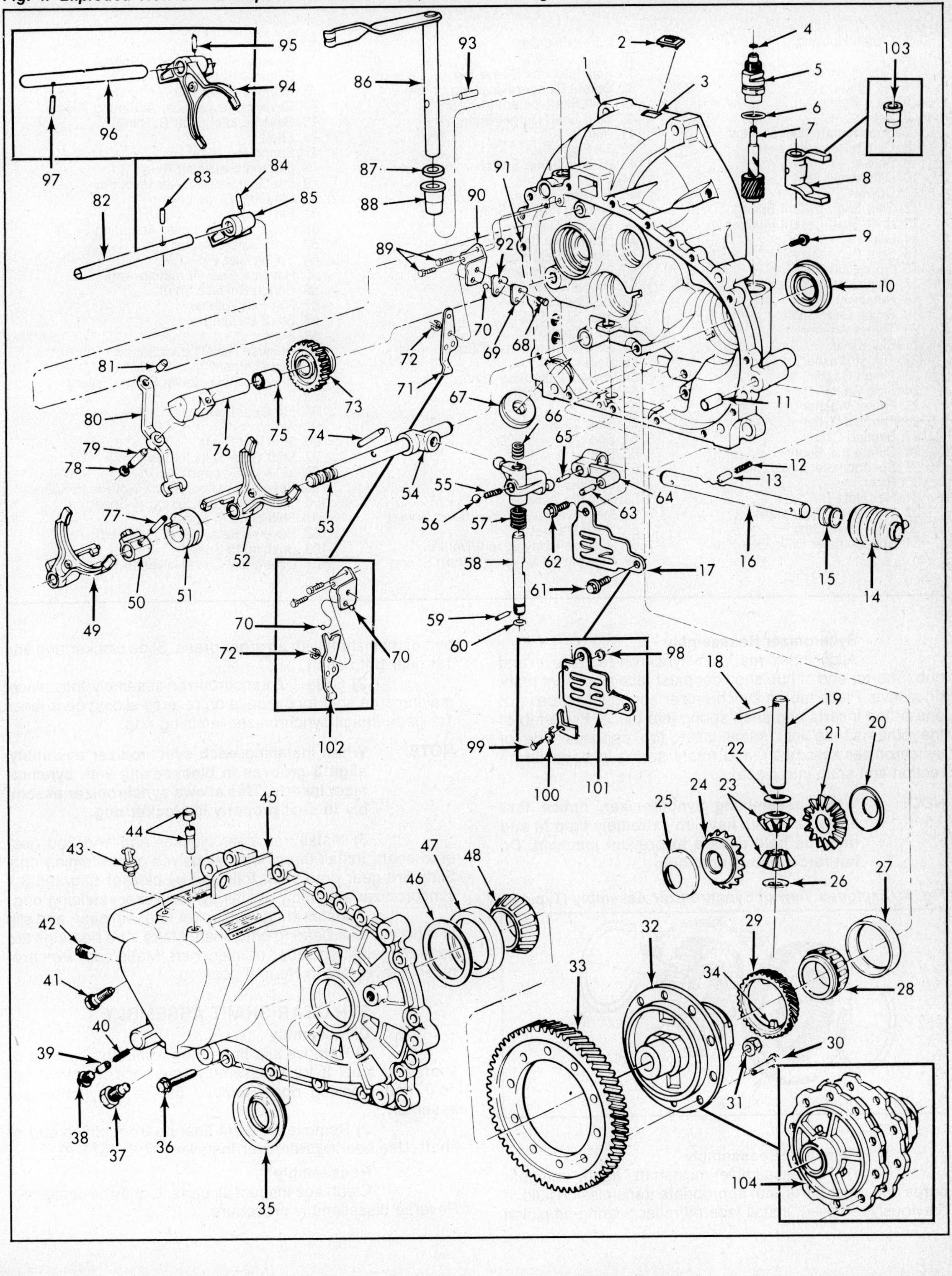

FORD MOTOR CO. MTX 4 & 5-SPEED TRANSAXLES (Cont.)

MTX 4 & 5-Speed Transaxle Components (Use With Fig. 4)

1. Clutch Housing
2. Plug
3. Timing Window
4. "O" Ring
5. Gear Retainer
6. Seal
7. Speedometer Driven Gear
8. Clutch Release Lever
9. Screw
10. Differential Seal
11. Dowel
12. Shift Shaft Detent Spring
13. Shift Shaft Detent Plunger
14. Boot
15. Seal
16. Input Shift Shaft
17. Shift Gate (4-Speed)
18. Retaining Pin
19. Pinion Gear Shaft
20. Thrust Washer
21. Side Gear
22. Thrust Washer
23. Pinion Gears
24. Side Gear
25. Thrust Washer
26. Thrust Washer
27. Bearing Cup
28. Differential Bearing
29. Speedometer Drive Gear
30. Rivet
31. Hex Nut
32. Differential Gear Case
33. Final Drive Gear
34. Speedometer Drive Gear Lock
35. Differential Seal
36. Case Bolt
37. Fork Interlock Sleeve Pin
38. Detent Plunger Retaining Screw
39. Shift Shaft Detent Plunger
40. Shift Shaft Detent Spring
41. Bolt
42. Fill Plug
43. Backup Lamp Switch
44. Vent Cap
45. Transaxle Case
46. Bearing Preload Shim
47. Bearing Cup
48. Differential Bearing
49. 3rd/4th Gear Fork
50. Fork Selector Arm
51. Fork Interlock Sleeve
52. 1st/2nd Gear Fork
53. Main Shift Shaft
54. Fork Control Block
55. 5th/Reverse Inhibitor Spring
56. Ball
57. 3rd/4th Gear Bias Spring
58. Shift Lever Shaft
59. Pin
60. Shaft Seal
61. Bolt
62. Bolt
63. Selector Pin
64. Selector Arm
65. Selector Arm Pin
66. 5th/Reverse Gear Kickdown Spring
67. Case Magnet
68. Reverse Relay Lever Pivot Pin
69. Reverse Relay Lever Return Spring
70. Ball
71. Reverse Relay Lever (4-Speed)
72. External Retaining Ring
73. Reverse Idler Gear
74. Reverse Relay Lever Actuating Pin
75. Reverse Idler Gear Bushing
76. Shaft
77. Spring Pin
78. External Retaining Ring
79. 5th Gear Relay Lever Pivot Pin
80. 5th Gear Relay Lever
81. Pin
82. Reverse Relay Lever Actuating Shaft
83. Shift Gate Selector Pin
84. Spring Slot Pin
85. Reverse Gear Actuating Arm
86. Clutch Release Shaft
87. Flat Felt Washer
88. Shaft Bushing
89. Bolts
90. Reverse Relay Lever Support Bracket
91. Dowel Mount
92. Reverse Relay Lever Return Spring
93. Pin
94. 5th Gear Fork
95. Pin
96. 5th Gear Shaft
97. Shift Gate Selector Pin
98. "C" clip (5-Speed)
99. Reverse Lockout Pawl Pivot Pin (5-Speed)
100. Shift Gate Pawl Spring (5-Speed)
101. Shift Gate (5-Speed)
102. Reverse Relay Lever (5-Speed)
103. Bushing (5-Speed)
104. Differential Case Halves (5-Speed)

Sychronizer Reassembly

Align index mark on synchronizer sleeve and hub. Shorter end of hub shoulder must face alignment mark on sleeve. Place tab on synchronizer spring into groove of one of the inserts and snap spring into place. Place tab of the other spring into same insert (on opposite side of synchronizer assembly), and rotate spring in opposite direction and snap into place.

NOTE: **When assembling synchronizer, notice that sleeve and hub have an extremely tight fit and must be held square to prevent jamming. Do not force sleeve onto hub.**

Fig. 5: Exploded View of Synchronizer Assembly (Typical)

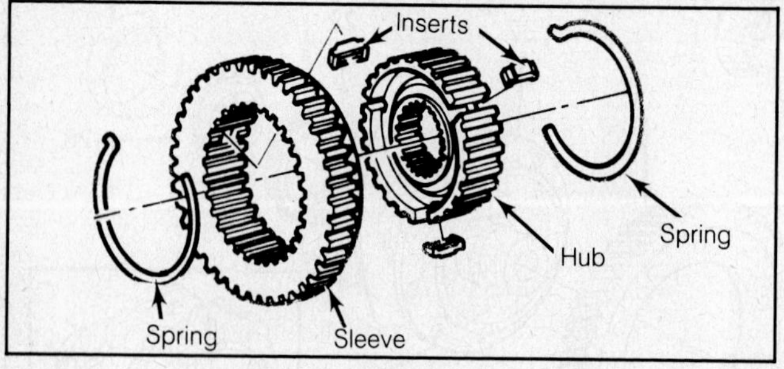

Mainshaft Reassembly

1) To reassemble mainshaft, lightly oil gear bores and other parts with appropriate transmission fluid. If previously removed, install tapered roller bearing on pinion end of mainshaft with an arbor press. Slide blocker ring and 1st gear onto shaft.

2) Slide 1-2 synchronizer assembly into place, making sure shift fork groove on reverse sliding gear faces 1st gear. Install synchronizer retaining ring.

NOTE: **When installing each synchronizer assembly, align 3 grooves in blocker ring with synchronizer inserts. This allows synchronizer assembly to seat properly in blocker ring.**

3) Install 2nd gear blocker ring and 2nd gear onto shaft. Install thrust washer halves and retaining ring. Slide 3rd gear onto shaft followed by blocker ring and 3-4 synchronizer assembly. Install synchronizer retaining ring.

4) Install 4th gear blocker ring, 4th gear, and slip fit tapered roller bearing onto shaft. Make sure bearings are seated against shoulder of mainshaft. Make sure synchronizer sleeves are in Neutral position.

5TH GEAR SHAFT ASSEMBLY

Disassembly

1) Remove slip fit bearing from 5th gear end of shaft and label it for reassembly reference. Remove 5th gear and blocking ring. Remove 5th gear synchronizer assembly.

2) Remove press fit bearing from pinion end of shaft. Use bearing Remover/Installer (D79L-4621-A).

Reassembly

Clean and inspect all parts. Lightly oil gear bore. Reverse disassembly procedure.

FORD MOTOR CO. MTX 4 & 5-SPEED TRANSAXLES (Cont.)

Fig. 6: Exploded View of Mainshaft Assembly

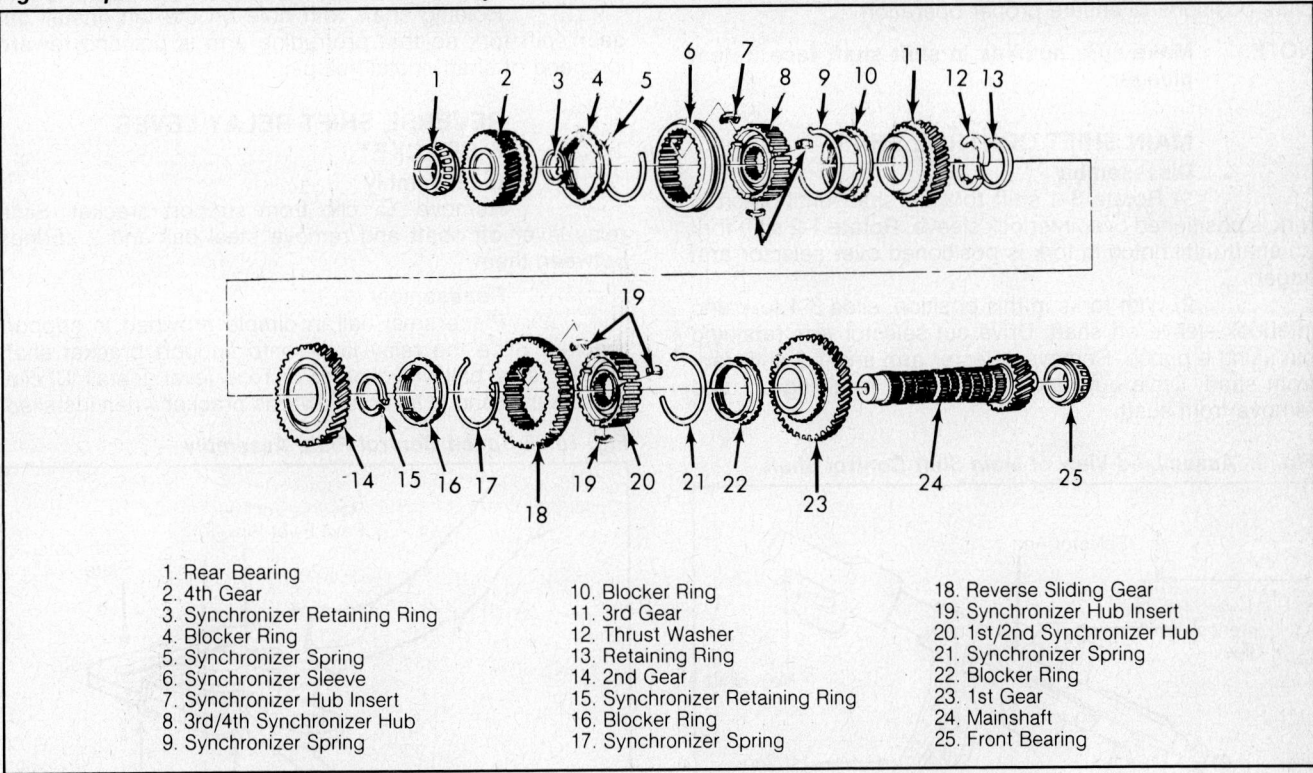

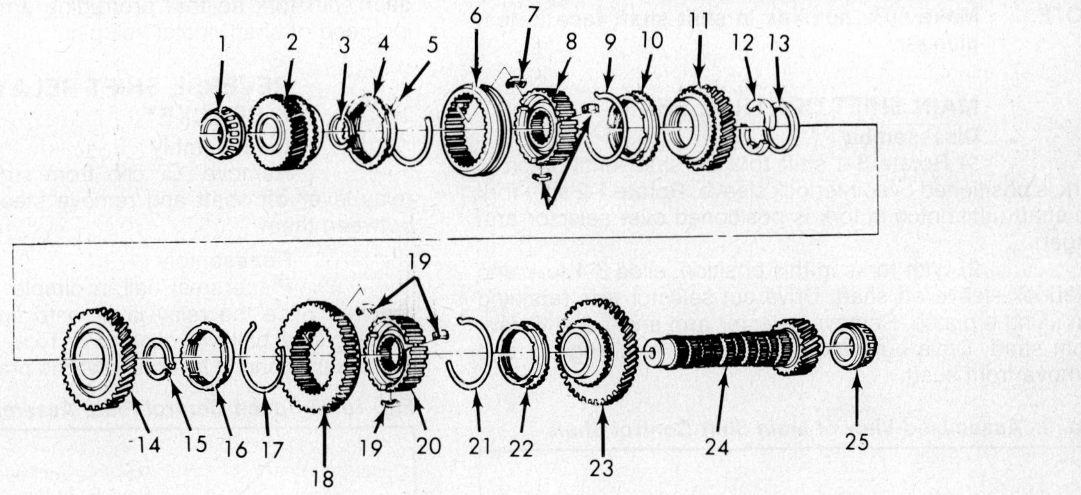

1. Rear Bearing
2. 4th Gear
3. Synchronizer Retaining Ring
4. Blocker Ring
5. Synchronizer Spring
6. Synchronizer Sleeve
7. Synchronizer Hub Insert
8. 3rd/4th Synchronizer Hub
9. Synchronizer Spring
10. Blocker Ring
11. 3rd Gear
12. Thrust Washer
13. Retaining Ring
14. 2nd Gear
15. Synchronizer Retaining Ring
16. Blocker Ring
17. Synchronizer Spring
18. Reverse Sliding Gear
19. Synchronizer Hub Insert
20. 1st/2nd Synchronizer Hub
21. Synchronizer Spring
22. Blocker Ring
23. 1st Gear
24. Mainshaft
25. Front Bearing

Fig. 7: Exploded View of 5th Gear Synchronizer

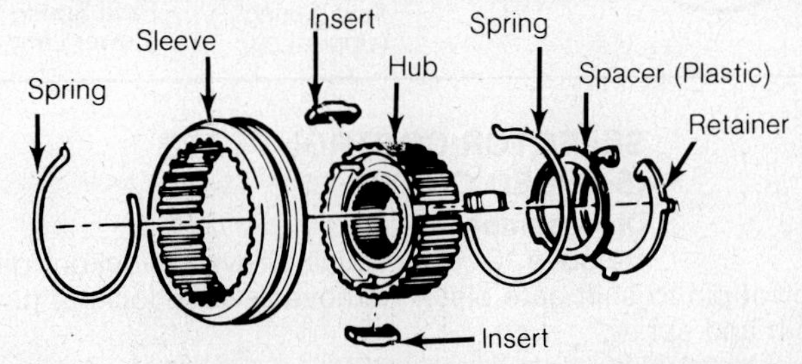

NOTE: **The 5th gear synchronizer assembly is positioned on shaft with plastic spacer and retainer facing 5th drive gear.**

INTERNAL SHIFT LINKAGE

Disassembly

1) Remove 2 control selector plate retaining bolts and remove plate from case. Place input shift shaft in center detent position. Drive roll pin through selector plate arm assembly and through shift shaft into recess in clutch housing case. Remove shift shaft boot.

2) Using a drift, rotate input shift shaft 90°. Depress detent notches inside housing and pull shift shaft out. Remove shift shaft selector plate arm assembly and spring pin. Place a rag over plunger bore to prevent detent plunger and spring from flying out. *See Fig. 8.*

3) Using a magnet, remove input shift shaft detent plunger and spring from case. Label for proper reassembly. Remove input shift shaft oil seal with Remover (T77F-7288-A) and a slide hammer.

Fig. 8: Input Shift Shaft Removal

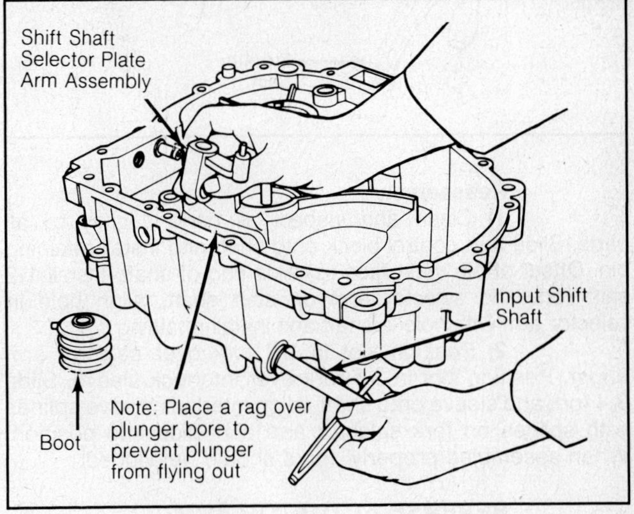

Reassembly

1) Coat seal lip with grease and install new input shift shaft oil seal in case. Install shift shaft detent spring and plunger in clutch housing case bore.

2) Using a small drift, compress spring and plunger. Slide input shift shaft into its bore and over plunger. Be careful not to cut the seal when installing shift shaft.

3) Install selector plate arm in its working position and slide shaft through selector plate arm. Align hole in arm with hole in shaft and install roll pin. Install input shift shaft boot.

4) Install control selector plate and tighten retaining bolts. Pin in selector arm must ride in cut-out of gate

FORD MOTOR CO. MTX 4 & 5-SPEED TRANSAXLES (Cont.)

in selector plate. Move input shift shaft through selector plate positions to ensure proper operation.

NOTE: **Make sure notches in shift shaft face detent plunger.**

MAIN SHIFT CONTROL SHAFT

Disassembly

1) Rotate 3-4 shift fork on shaft until notch in fork is positioned over interlock sleeve. Rotate 1-2 shift fork on shaft until notch in fork is positioned over selector arm finger.

2) With forks in this position, slide 3-4 fork and interlock sleeve off shaft. Drive out selector arm retaining pin using a punch. Remove selector arm and 1-2 shift fork from shaft. Drive out fork control block retaining pin and remove from shaft.

Fig. 9: Assembled View of Main Shift Control Shaft

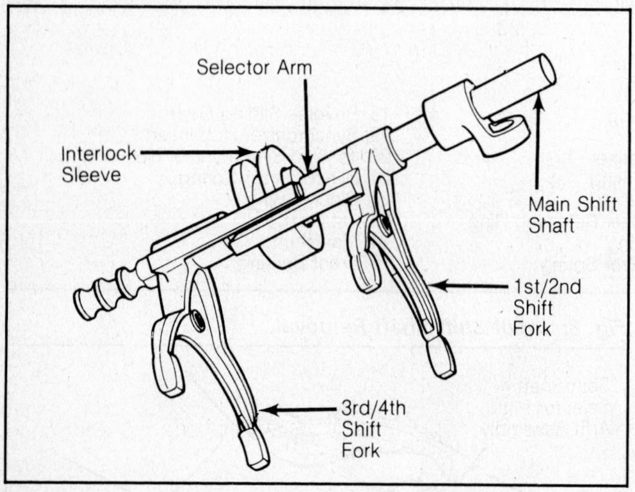

Reassembly

1) Clean and inspect all parts. Lightly oil all parts. Slide fork control block onto shaft and install retaining pin. Offset of pin must face towards end of shaft. Install 1-2 shift fork and selector arm on shift shaft. Align hole in selector arm with hole in shaft and install retaining pin.

2) Position slot in 1-2 fork over selector arm finger. Position slot in 3-4 fork over interlock sleeve. Slide 3-4 fork and sleeve onto shaft. Align interlock sleeve splines with splines on fork selector arm and slide into position. When assembled properly, forks should be aligned.

REVERSE ACTUATOR ARM (4-SPEED ONLY)

Disassembly

Using a punch, remove roll pin. Slide arm from shaft.

Reassembly

Holding shaft with hole on the left, install the reverse actuator arm so that protruding arm is pointing towards long end of shaft. Install roll pin.

5TH GEAR SHIFT CONTROL SHAFT

Disassembly

Using a punch, remove roll pin. Slide fork from shaft.

Reassembly

Holding shaft with hole on the left, install 5th gear shift fork so that protruding arm is pointing toward long end of shaft. Install roll pin.

REVERSE SHIFT RELAY LEVER & BRACKET

Disassembly

Remove "C" clip from support bracket. Slide relay lever off shaft and remove steel ball and 2 springs between them.

Reassembly

Place steel ball in dimple provided in support bracket. Slide the relay lever onto support bracket shaft aligning steel ball with dimples on relay lever. Install "C" clip. Make sure bend in lever is towards bracket when installed.

Fig. 10: 5-Speed Control Plate Assembly

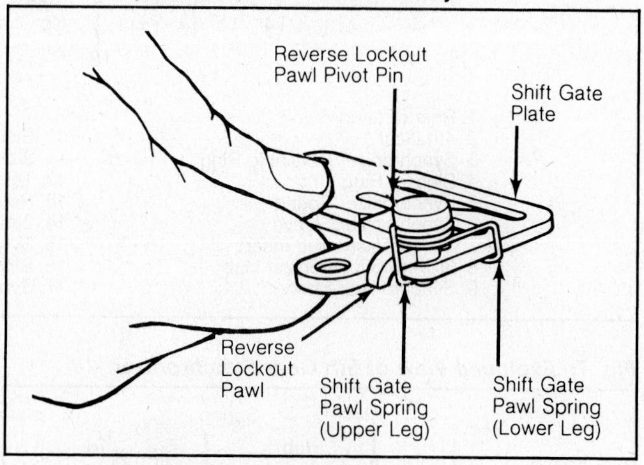

SELECTOR CONTROL PLATE (5-SPEED ONLY)

Disassembly

Remove "C" clip retaining reverse lockout pawl pivot pin to shift gate plate. Remove reverse lockout pawl, pin and spring.

Reassembly

Reverse disassembly procedures. *See Fig. 10* for correct assembly position. Install "C" clip.

DIFFERENTIAL ASSEMBLY

4-Speed (Disassembly)

1) Using a puller, remove differential side bearings from differential case. Remove speedometer drive gear from case.

2) Remove side gears and thrust washers from differential case by rotating gears toward case windows. Using a punch, drive out differential pinion gear shaft retaining pin. Remove pinion shaft, pinion gears and thrust washers from case.

3) If necessary, remove ring gear from differential case as follows: Mount differential assembly in a vise, and using a 5/16" (8 mm) drill bit, drill formed side of attaching rivets. Remove heads of rivets with a chisel. Using a punch, drive remaining rivet shank from case and remove ring gear.

4-Speed (Reassembly)

1) To reassemble differential, reverse disassembly procedures. Lubricate all thrust washers and thrust surfaces on gears and in case with automatic transmission fluid. Install speedometer gear on case with chamfer on inside diameter facing ring gear.

2) If removed, press ring gear onto differential case and secure to case with special service replacement bolts and nuts. Special service parts MUST be used to provide proper clearance with transmission case. Install bolts with heads on ring gear side of case and nuts on differential side (opposite of 5-speed). Partially tighten the nuts. Using a standard circular pattern sequence, tighten only the nuts to specification.

NOTE: **Differential side gears must be aligned in case. This alignment must be held while installing differential in transaxle case. Failure to maintain alignment will make it impossible to install axle drive shafts through side gears.**

5-Speed (Disassembly)

1) Use a 1/2" (12 mm) drill and drill through each final drive gear rivet. Using a chisel remove rivet heads. With differential assembly mounted in a vise, use a punch to drive out rivet shanks. Repeat procedure until all 10 rivet shanks are driven out.

2) Use an arbor press to press off final drive gear. Separate differential case halves by inserting a 9/16" (15 mm) deep-well socket into final drive gear left side bearing journal. Install bearing Remover (T77F-4220-B1 or T57L-4220-A) and step plate. As bearing is being removed, case halves will separate before bearing unseats.

3) Do not remove final drive gear left side bearing unless it needs to be replaced. Bearing in right half must be removed for further differential disassembly. Use bearing Remover (T57L-4220-A or T77F-4220-B1) and step plate to remove either bearing.

4) Remove speedometer gear. Remove left side gear from case. Rotate right side gear around pinions and remove. Using a 3/32" drill, drill through center of pinion shaft retaining roll pin and case wall.

NOTE: **On some differential cases, the pinion shaft retaining pin may be set in a blind hole. A through-hole must be drilled to facilitate pin removal.**

5) Using drilled hole in case as a pilot, use special Drill (T83P-4204-A) to drill through case to roll pin. Drive roll pin out of pinion shaft with a 5/32" (4 mm) drift. Remove pinion shaft, pinion gears and thrust washers.

5-Speed (Reassembly)

1) Clean and inspect all parts for wear and damage. Lubricate back face of gears and thrust surfaces on differential case with Grease (ESA-M1C75B). Assemble pinion gears and thrust washers on pinion shaft as shaft is being installed in right case half.

2) Align hole in pinion shaft with hole in case. Drive roll pin into hole, approximately 3/8" (9.5 mm) below case flange mating surface. Position side gear and thrust washer on pinions. Ensure proper tooth mesh and rotate toward right bearing journal.

NOTE: **Ensure proper alignment of side gear splines to right bearing journal. In not properly aligned, case must be disassembled to align gear splines for later CV shaft installation. Install left side gear and thrust washer. Check for correct engagement.**

3) Assemble case halves, aligning retaining pin hole in right case half with retaining pin access hole in left differential case half. Install speedometer drive gear so tangs are positioned on upper side of gear.

4) Press differential bearings on case using Installers (T83-4220-BH or T83P-4220-CH). If final drive gear has been removed, position machined surface of gear toward case with holes in gear aligned with holes in case flange. Contact final drive gear in at least 2 opposite points and press onto case.

5) Special service bolts and nuts replace rivets for ring gear-to-case assembly. Special service parts MUST be used to provide proper clearance with transmission case. Install bolts with heads on differential side of case and nuts on ring gear side (opposite of 4-speed). Partially tighten the nuts. Using a standard circular pattern sequence, tighten only the nuts to specification.

ADJUSTMENTS

DIFFERENTIAL BEARING PRELOAD

1) Differential bearing preload is set at the factory and need not be checked or adjusted unless one of the following components is replaced: transaxle case, differential case, differential side bearings or clutch housing.

2) To check and adjust preload, remove differential seal from transaxle case. Drive differential bearing outer race from case and remove preload adjusting shim located under race.

3) Position differential assembly in clutch housing. Install height Gauge Spacers (T81P-4451-B) on clutch housing dowels. Position bearing outer race removed from transaxle case on differential bearing. Install Shim Selector (T81P-4451-B) over race. *See Fig. 11.*

Fig. 11: Positioning Differential Preload Measuring Tools

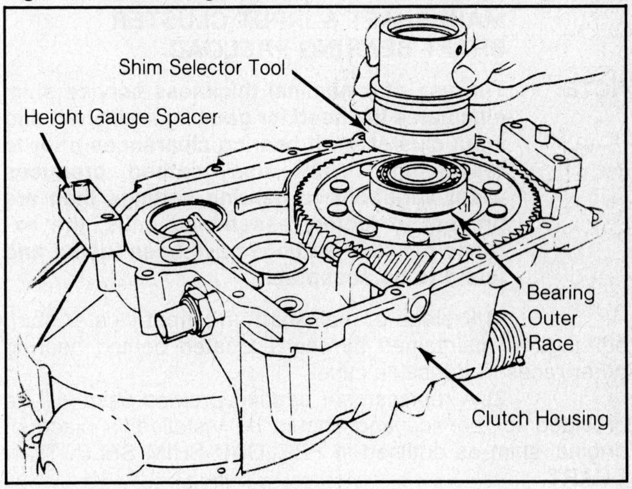

Use 4 retaining bolts supplied with measuring tool.

4) Place transaxle case in position on clutch housing and install 4 retaining bolts supplied with preload checking tools. Tighten retaining bolts to 17-21 ft. lbs. (23-28 N.m). Rotate differential several times to ensure setting of differential bearing.

5) Place Gauge Bar (T80L-77003-A) across shim selector tool. Using a feeler gauge or depth micrometer, measure clearance between gauge bar and shim selector tool. Obtain measurements from 3 positions around tool and take average of the readings. *See Fig. 12.*

FORD MOTOR CO. MTX 4 & 5-SPEED TRANSAXLES (Cont.)

Fig. 12: Measuring Differential Bearing Preload

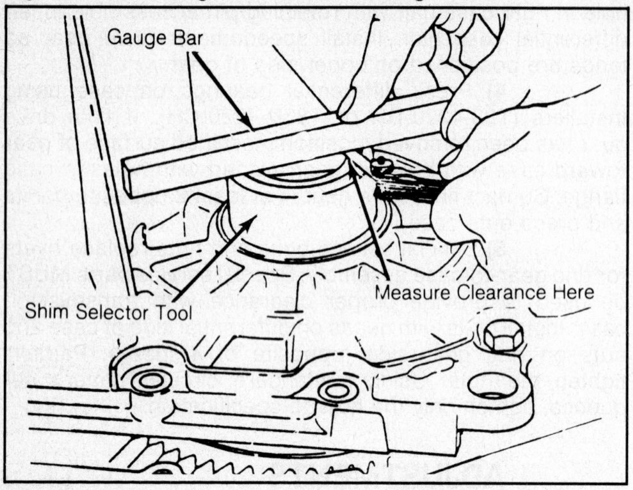

Use feeler gauge to measure bearing preload.

6) Average measurement obtained in preceding step is thickness of shim needed to obtain specified differential bearing preload. Differential bearing preload shims are available in thicknesses of .012" to .049" (.30 to 1.24 mm) in .002" (.05 mm) increments.

NOTE: **If preload adjusting shim required is not available, always use next thinner shim.**

7) Separate transaxle case from clutch housing and remove measuring tools. Install selected preload shim in transaxle case. Lubricate gearing bores and press outer race into case until fully seated. Install new differential oil seal in transaxle case.

MAIN SHAFT & INPUT CLUSTER SHAFT BEARING PRELOAD

NOTE: **The use of a nominal thickness service shim eliminates the need for gauging mainshaft and input cluster shaft bearing clearances prior to reassembly. While this method produces wider variations of bearing settings than are present in factory assembled units, the extreme possible settings have been tested and found to be acceptable.**

1) Preload of mainshaft and input cluster shaft bearings is maintained by shims located behind bearing outer races in transaxle case.

2) A replacement bearing preload shim will be provided for service and should be installed in place of original shim as outlined in PRELOAD SHIM SELECTION CHART.

3) The following points should be noted when replacing shaft bearing preload shims. When repairs require use of service replacement shim, discard original shim. DO NOT use more than 1 shim per shaft.

4) If parts are replaced other than parts shown in selection chart, original shim should be re-used. Preload shims must be installed only under bearing races at transaxle case end of both shafts.

CAUTION: **If bearing outer races are removed from case for any reason, it is very important to keep the race and its matching shim together. It is also important to label bearing races as they are removed from transaxle case or clutch housing. Maintaining proper race-to-shim relationship and proper race labeling will ensure correct bearing preload when transaxle is assembled.**

PRELOAD SHIM SELECTION CHART

	Shims Replaced with Service Shims		
Parts Replaced	**Input Cluster Shaft**	**Main Shaft**	**5th Gear Shaft**
1 Input Cluster Bearing	Yes	No	No
2 Input Cluster Bearings	Yes	No	No
1 Input Cluster Bearing 1 Mainshaft Bearing 1 5th Gear Shaft Bearing	Yes Yes Yes	Yes Yes Yes	Yes Yes Yes
2 Input Cluster Bearings 2 Mainshaft Bearings 2 5th Gear Shaft Bearings	Yes Yes Yes	Yes Yes Yes	Yes Yes Yes
1 Mainshaft Bearing	No	Yes	No
2 Mainshaft Bearings	No	Yes	No
1 5th Gear Shaft Bearing	No	No	Yes
2 5th Gear Shaft Bearings	No	No	Yes
Clutch Housing Assembly	Yes	Yes	Yes
Transaxle Case Assembly	Yes	Yes	Yes

REASSEMBLY

TRANSAXLE

1) Install reverse relay lever support bracket assembly to case with 2 bolts. Position differential assembly in clutch housing case. Align differential gears for later installation of the half shafts. On 5-speed models, install 5th gear shaft assembly and fork shaft assembly in case. On 4 and 5-speed models, place main shift control shaft assembly on mainshaft so that shift forks engage in respective slots in synchronizer sleeves. *See Fig. 13.*

2) Mesh mainshaft assembly with input cluster shaft. Hold shaft assemblies together in their respective working positions and lower them into bores in clutch housing case as a unit. Use care not to damage input shaft oil seal or mainshaft oil funnel.

3) Position shift lever, 3-4 bias spring and kickdown spring in their working positions. One shift lever ball should be in socket of input shift shaft selector plate arm assembly. The other ball should be in socket of main shift control shaft block.

4) Install inhibitor spring and ball in 5th and reverse inhibitor shaft lever hole. Depress inhibitor ball and spring using a drift and slide shift lever shaft (notch down) through shift lever. Tap shift shaft into its bore in clutch housing. Align shift shaft bore with case bore and tap in roll pin. Ensure that roll pin is slightly below case surface.

FORD MOTOR CO. MTX 4 & 5-SPEED TRANSAXLES (Cont.)

Fig. 13: Assembling Main Shift Control Shaft Assembly to Mainshaft Assembly

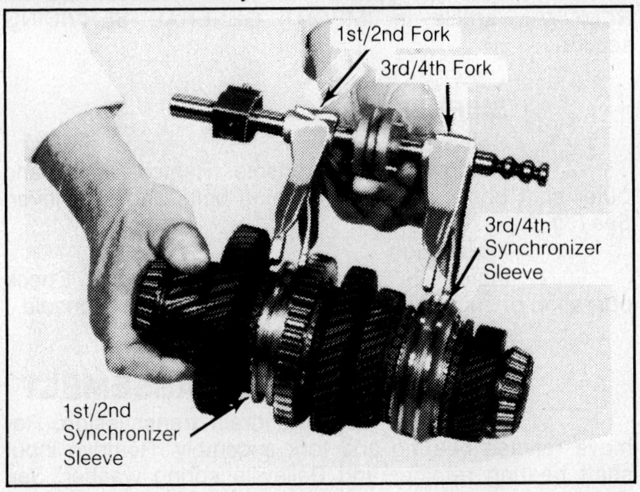

5) Before proceeding with transaxle reassembly verify the following: Selector pin should be in neutral gate of control selector plate. Finger of fork selector arm should be partially engaged with 1-2 shift fork and 3-4 shift fork. *See Fig. 14.*

Fig. 14: Checking Selector Pin Position

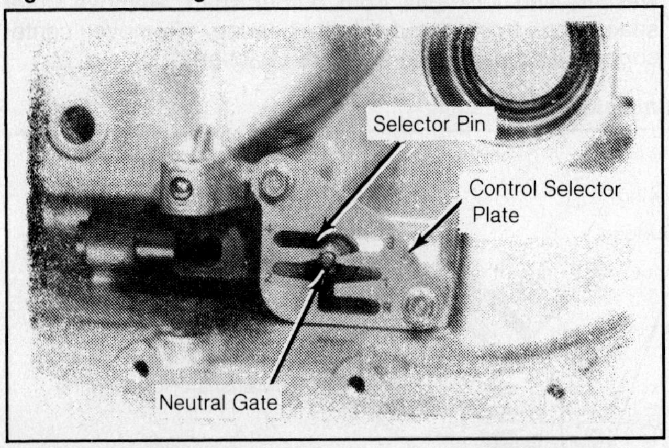

Pin selector should be in neutral gate (4-speed shown).

6) Place groove in reverse idler gear in engagement with pin at end of reverse relay lever. Slide shaft through gear and into bore. Clean and install magnet in pocket of clutch housing case.

7) On 4-speed models, install the reverse relay lever onto reverse idler shaft. Align it with the fork interlock spring and fork slot. Install retaining ring.

8) On 5-speed models, install 5th shift relay lever onto reverse idler shaft. Align it with 5th gear fork interlock sleeve and fork slot and install retaining ring.

9) Install detent spring and plunger in their bore in case. Apply a 1/16" wide bead of Sealer (E1FZ-19562-A) to clutch housing-to-transaxle case mounting surface.

10) Carefully lower transaxle case over clutch housing case. Gently lower case until shift control shaft, mainshaft, input cluster shaft, and 5th gear shaft (if equipped) align with bores in transaxle case.

11) Gently slide transaxle case over dowels. Case should sit flush on clutch housing, without binding on magnet. Apply Teflon tape to threads of interlock sleeve retaining pin. Align slot in interlock sleeve with hole in transaxle case using a drift. Install and tighten retaining pin.

NOTE: **If hole in case does not align with slot in interlock sleeve, remove case half and check for proper installation of interlock sleeve.**

12) Install and tighten transaxle case-to-clutch housing retaining bolts. Use a drift to align bore in reverse idler shaft with retaining screw hole in transaxle case. Install and tighten reverse idler shaft retaining bolt.

13) Apply Teflon tape to threads of detent plunger retaining screw. Install and tighten screw. Install differential oil seal. Place transaxle upright and position drift through hole in input shift shaft. Shift transaxle through all gears to ensure proper installation.

NOTE: **On 5-speed models, transaxle will not shift directly into reverse from 5th gear.**

TIGHTENING SPECIFICATIONS

Application	Ft. Lbs. (N.m)
Back-Up Light Switch	[1] 12-15 (16-20)
Differential Bearing Retainer-to-Case	15-19 (20-26)
Fork Interlock Sleeve Pin	[1] 12-15 (16-20)
Reverse Idler Shaft-to-Case	16-20 (21-27)
Ring Gear-to-Differential Case	
4-Speed	55-70 (75-95)
5-Speed	80-100 (108-136)
Trans. Case-to-Clutch Hsg.	13-17 (18-23)
Transaxle-to-Gas Engine	[2] 25-35 (34-47)
Transaxle-to-Diesel Engine	[3] 65-75 (88-102)
	INCH Lbs. (N.m)
Control Selector Plate	72-96 (8-11)
Detent Plunger Retainer Screw	[1] 72-96 (8-11)
Transaxle Filler Plug	108-168 (12-19)
Relay Lever Bracket-to-Case	72-96 (8-11)

[1] – Coat threads with Teflon tape prior to installation and tightening.
[2] – Models RWB-AB, AC, BF & BJ.
[3] – Models RWB-AD, AE, BK & BH. Tighten hex flange head bolt (M10x1.5x50) to 25-35 ft. lbs (34-47 N.m).

GENERAL MOTORS 5-SPEED – 69.5 MM

Chevrolet Chevette

IDENTIFICATION

Transmission can be identified by a 2 letter code, stamped on machined pad centered on right side of case. Clutch housing and gearbox are a single piece casting.

DESCRIPTION

The transmission is a 5-speed fully synchronized unit with blocker ring synchronizers and a constant mesh reverse gear. First through 4th gears are housed within the case. Reverse and 5th gears are contained in the extension housing.

The input-output shaft and the countershaft are supported by 3 ball bearings. The bearings are located in the front wall of the case, the center support and the extension housing. All forward gears are helical cut.

LUBRICATION & ADJUSTMENT

See appropriate MANUAL TRANSMISSION SERVICING article in IMPORT GENERAL SERVICING section.

TROUBLE SHOOTING

See Manual Transmission Trouble Shooting in MANUAL TRANSMISSION SERVICING section.

REMOVAL & INSTALLATION

See appropriate MANUAL TRANSMISSION REMOVAL article in IMPORT GENERAL SERVICING section.

SHIFT LEVER

Removal

Removal shifter console. Remove inner and outer shift boots. Remove retaining bolts and shift lever. *See Fig. 2.*

Installation

Install shift lever and retaining bolts. Check operation of shifter. Install outer boot and shifter console.

TRANSMISSION DISASSEMBLY

1) Remove plug and drain transmission. Remove release bearing and fork assembly. Remove input shaft bearing retainer and Belleville spring washer. *See Fig. 3.*

2) Remove speedometer driven gear and back-up light switch. Remove shift control box from extension housing. Remove extension housing from transmission case. *See Fig. 2.*

3) Remove snap rings, speedometer drive gear and retainer clip, and bearing. Remove snap ring, thrust washer, and lock ball from output shaft. Remove outer snap ring from input shaft bearing. Remove center support from case with all gears attached.

Fig. 1: Cutaway View of General Motors 69.5 mm 5-Speed Transmission

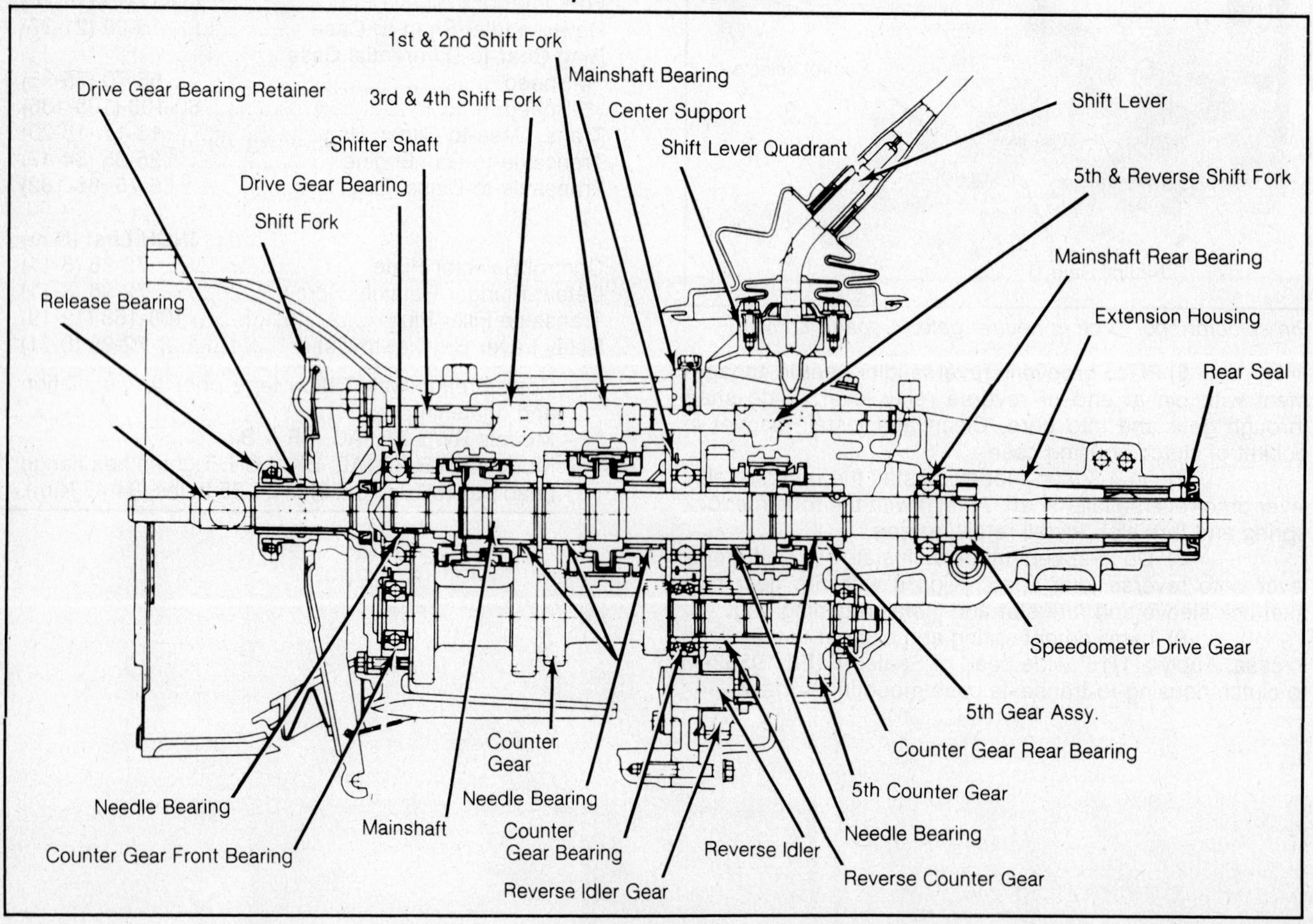

GENERAL MOTORS 5-SPEED – 69.5 MM (Cont.)

Fig. 2: Exploded View of Shifter

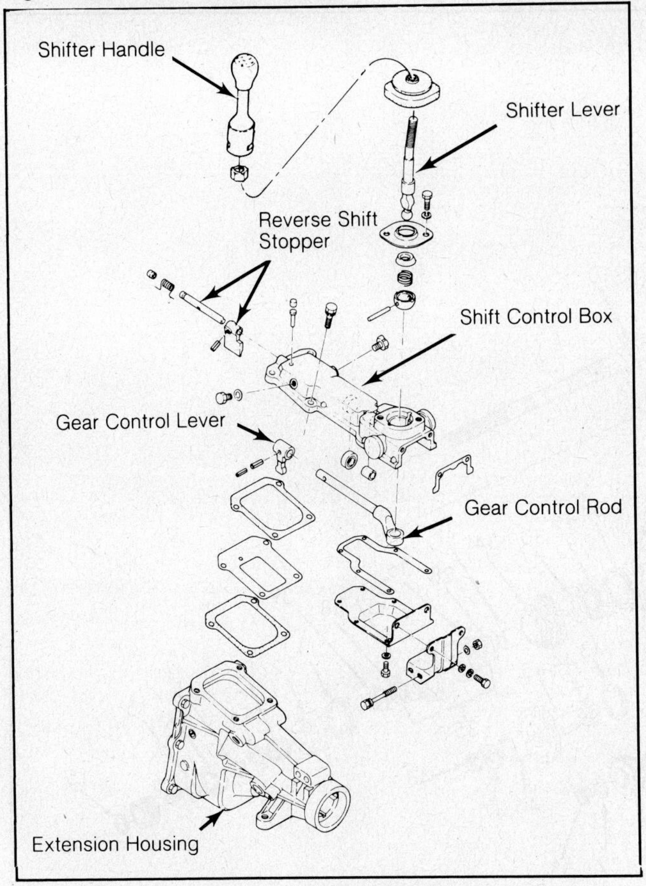

Shift box must be removed to disassemble transmission.

4) Using a punch, drive pins out of shift forks, making sure to support ends of shift shafts. Remove detent spring plate, springs, and detent balls. Remove shift shafts from center support. Remove shift forks from synchronizer sleeves. Remove interlock pins. *See Fig. 4.*

Fig. 3: Input Shaft Bearing Retainer

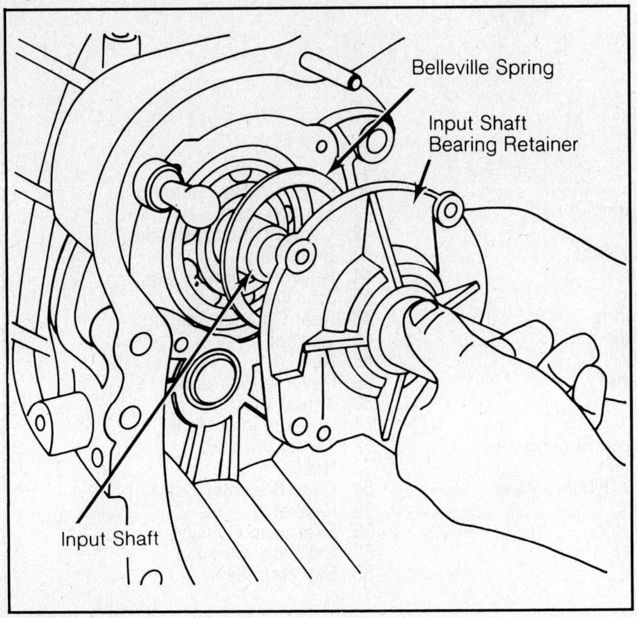

Dished side of spring faces bearing.

Fig. 4: Exploded View of Shift Shaft Assembly

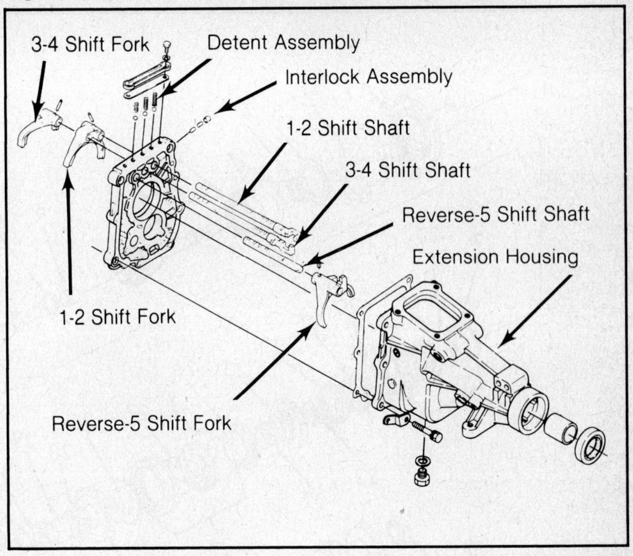

5) Engage 1st and 3rd gears to prevent rotation of countershaft. Install holding fixture (J-29768) onto front of gear assembly. Remove self-locking nut from countergear. Using a puller, remove 5th gear together with ball bearing.

6) Remove 5th gear, needle bearings, and blocker ring from output shaft. Remove thrust washers, reverse idler gear, and retaining nut from reverse idler shaft. Remove output shaft nut, retainer, and reverse-5th synchronizer assembly.

7) Remove reverse gear, collar, needle bearings, and thrust washer from rear of output shaft. Remove reverse gear from countergear and remove holding fixture.

8) Return synchronizers to neutral position. Expand countergear center bearing snap ring. Gently tap on front of center support to remove countershaft.

9) Expand output shaft center bearing snap ring. Remove output shaft from center support. Remove input shaft, needle bearings, and 4th gear blocker ring from output shaft.

CLEANING & INSPECTION

Wash case and all internal parts in solvent. Dry with compressed air. Check all parts for damage or excessive wear. Check bearings and synchronizers for rough operation. File off any burrs on mating surfaces.

COMPONENT DISASSEMBLY & REASSEMBLY

OUTPUT SHAFT

Disassembly

1) Using a press, remove output shaft center bearing. Remove thrust washer, 1st gear, needle bearings, and spacer. Remove 1st-2nd synchronizer, 2nd gear, and needle bearings.

2) Remove snap ring from front of output shaft. Remove 3rd-4th synchronizer and 3rd gear blocker ring. Remove 3rd gear and needle bearing.

GENERAL MOTORS 5-SPEED – 69.5 MM (Cont.)

Fig. 5: Exploded View of 69.5 mm 5-Speed Transmission

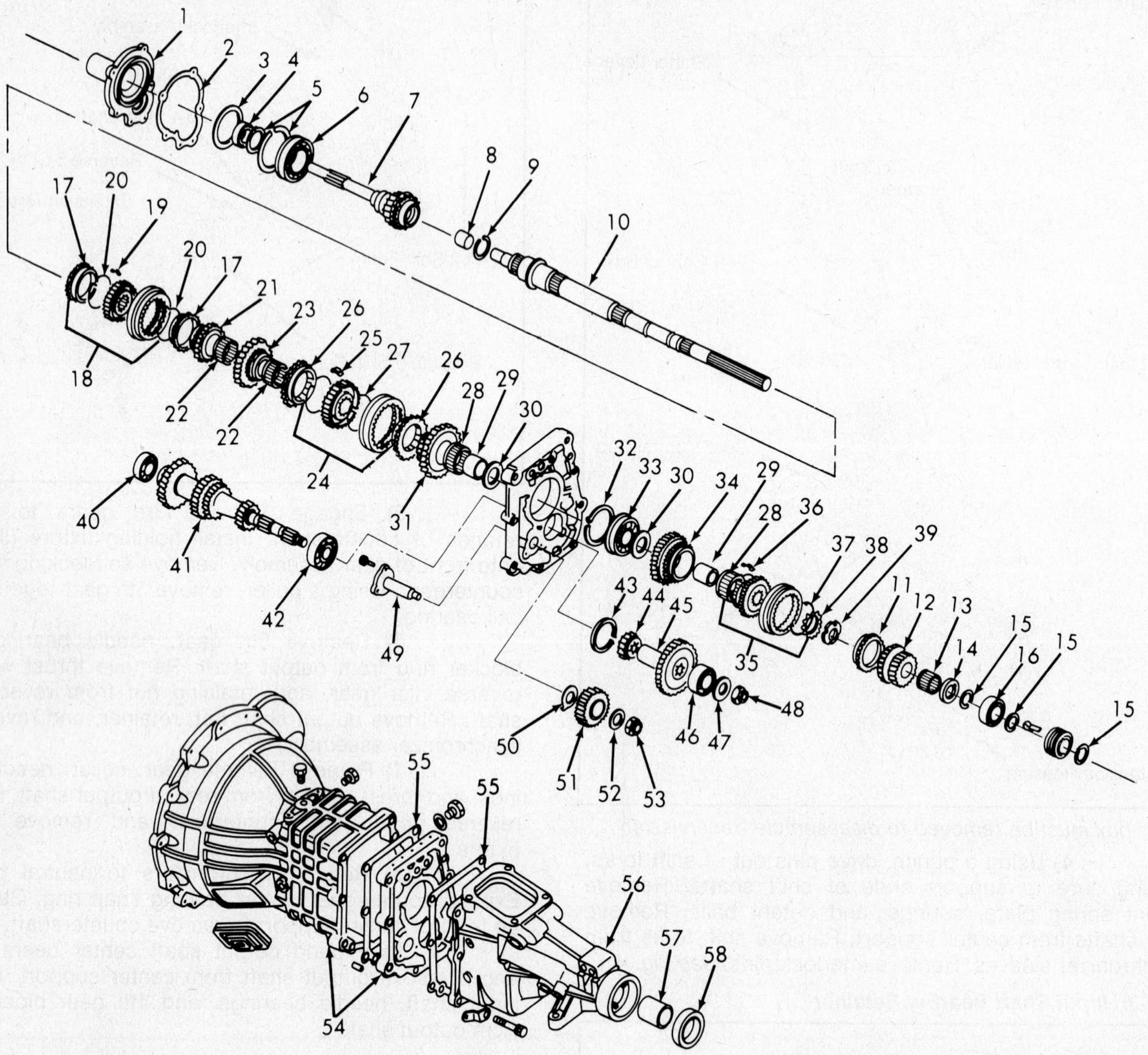

1. Input Bearing Retainer
2. Gasket
3. Belleville Spring
4. Seal
5. Snap Ring
6. Input Bearing
7. Input Shaft
8. Needle Bearing
9. Snap Ring
10. Output Shaft
11. 5th Gear Blocker Ring
12. 5th Gear
13. Needle Bearing
14. Thrust Washer
15. Snap Ring
16. Rear Output Bearing
17. Blocker Ring
18. 3-4 Synchro Assy.
19. Synchro Key
20. Synchro Spring
21. 3rd Gear
22. Needle Bearing
23. 2nd Gear
24. 1-2 Synchro Assy.
25. Synchro Key
26. Blocker Ring
27. Synchro Spring
28. Needle Bearing
29. Collar
30. Thrust Washer
31. 1st Gear
32. Snap Ring
33. Center Output Bearing
34. Reverse Gear
35. Reverse-5th Synchro Assy.
36. Synchro Key
37. Synchro Spring
38. Lock Washer
39. Nut
40. Front Counter Bearing
41. Countershaft
42. Center Counter Bearing
43. Snap Ring
44. Reverse Countergear
45. 5th Countergear
46. Rear Counter Bearing
47. Washer
48. Nut
49. Reverse Idler Shaft
50. Thrust Washer
51. Reverse Idler Gear
52. Thrust Washer
53. Nut
54. Case & Center Support
55. Gasket
56. Extension Housing
57. Ext. Hsg. Bushing
58. Ext. Hsg. Seal

GENERAL MOTORS 5-SPEED – 69.5 MM (Cont.)

Reassembly

1) Install 3rd gear and needle bearing, onto front of output shaft with coned side facing forward. Install 3rd-4th synchronizer with large chamfered end facing forward. Retain synchronizer with selective fit snap ring.

2) Measure clearance between snap ring and 3rd-4th synchronizer. Clearance should be .002" (.05 mm). Adjust clearance using selective thickness snap ring. Identification number is stamped on side of snap ring.

SELECTIVE SNAP RING THICKNESS

Identification Number	Thickness In. (mm)
1	.059 (1.50)
2	.061 (1.55)
3	.063 (1.60)
4	.065 (1.65)

3) Install 2nd gear and needle bearings on rear of output shaft with coned end facing rearward. Install 1st-2nd synchronizer on rear of shaft with large chamfered end facing rearward. Install 2nd collar using installer (J-33851) and press.

4) Install 1st gear thrust washer with slots facing gear. With snap ring groove facing front of transmission, use installer (J-33851) and press rear bearing onto shaft. Install thrust washer with oil groove facing rearward. Press on reverse collar using same installer.

INPUT SHAFT (DRIVE GEAR)

Disassembly & Reassembly

Remove snap ring and press bearing off shaft. Remove needle bearing from rear of shaft. Press on bearing and retain with snap ring. Install needle bearing into rear of shaft and lubricate with petroleum jelly.

COUNTERSHAFT

Disassembly & Reassembly

Countershaft bearing is removed and installed using bearing separator (J-22912-01) and press. Groove on bearing faces toward rear of transmission.

OIL SEALS

Removal & Installation

Remove seals by prying with a screwdriver or small chisel. Coat outside of new extension housing seal with sealer (Permatex No. 2). Install seals with seal drivers (J-21426 for Ext. Hsg. and J-26540 for Input Shaft).

TRANSMISSION REASSEMBLY

1) If removed, install center support snap rings and reverse idler shaft. Tighten reverse idler shaft retaining bolts. Install input shaft onto front of output shaft and engage with countergear.

2) Install center support onto gear assemblies while expanding snap rings until bearing grooves seat in snap rings. Engage 1st and 3rd gears to prevent rotation. Install reverse gear on countergear.

3) Install needle bearing and reverse gear on output shaft. Install reverse-5th synchronizer so side of clutch hub with raised face is toward front (reverse gear side).

4) Install locking retainer and nut with chamfered side of nut facing toward front of transmission. Tighten nut and bend down retainer to secure. Install reverse idler gear and thrust washers onto idler shaft. Tab on inner thrust washer engages hole in center support.

5) Install new self-locking nut and tighten. Install blocker ring, needle bearing and 5th gear onto output shaft. Install 5th countergear, bearing, and new self-locking nut onto countershaft.

6) Remove assembly from holding fixture. Shift synchronizers to neutral position. Grease interlock pins and install in center support. Install shift forks onto synchronizer sleeves.

7) Insert shift shafts through center support and shift forks. Install detent balls and springs in center support. Install gasket and detent plate. Support shift shafts and replace shift fork retaining pins.

8) Place a new gasket on rear of transmission case. Install center support and gear assembly into case. Install outer snap ring on input shaft bearing. Install lock ball, thrust washer, and snap ring onto rear of output shaft.

NOTE: **Be careful not to bend or distort thrust washer snap ring. Replace if found to be defective.**

9) Check clearance between 5th gear and thrust washer with a feeler gauge. Clearance should be .004-.012" (.10-.30 mm). Adjust clearance with selective thickness thrust washers.

SELECTIVE THRUST WASHERS

Part Number	Thickness In. (mm)
94027215	.307 (7.8)
94027216	.311 (7.9)
94027217	.315 (8.0)
94027218	.319 (8.1)
94027219	.323 (8.2)
94027220	.327 (8.3)

10) Install snap ring and rear bearing onto output shaft. Install speedometer drive gear with retainer clip. Install gasket on rear of center support. Install extension housing. Install speedometer drive gear and back-up light switch.

11) Install Belleville spring washer over input shaft, with dished side toward bearing. Install bearing retainer with gasket. Apply sealer (Permatex No. 2) to threads of 3 lower retainer bolts. Install retainer bolts and tighten. Install release bearing and fork assembly.

TIGHTENING SPECIFICATIONS

Application	Ft. Lbs. (N.m)
Countergear Nut	80 (108)
Extension Housing Bolts	27 (37)
Input Shaft Bearing Retainer	14 (19)
Mainshaft-to-Center Support	94 (127)
Output Shaft Nut	94 (127)
Reverse Idler Shaft Retaining Bolts	14 (19)
Reverse Idler Shaft Nut	80 (108)
Shift Box Bolts	14 (19)

GENERAL MOTORS 4-SPEED – 70 MM

Chevrolet Chevette
Pontiac 1000

TRANSMISSION IDENTIFICATION

Transmission can be identified by a 2 letter code, stamped on machined pad centered on right side of case.

DESCRIPTION

Transmission is a 4-speed unit, synchronized in all forward gears. Reverse gear is not synchronized. Helical gears are used throughout transmission and, with the exception of reverse gears, all transmission gears are in constant mesh.

All gears are carried on shafts inside transmission case, except reverse gears, which are mounted on outside of rear case face, inside extension housing. Transmission utilizes single rail shift linkage, supported on one end by extension housing, and on opposite end by clutch housing.

LUBRICATION & ADJUSTMENT

See appropriate MANUAL TRANSMISSION SERVICING article in IMPORT GENERAL SERVICING section.

REMOVAL & INSTALLATION

See appropriate MANUAL TRANSMISSION REMOVAL article in IMPORT GENERAL SERVICING section.

TRANSMISSION DISASSEMBLY

1) Place transmission on clean bench with clutch housing facing downward. Drive roll pin from shifter shaft arm assembly and shifter shaft. *See Fig. 14*. Remove shifter shaft arm assembly.

2) Remove 5 mount bolts attaching extension housing to case. Withdraw extension housing. Press down on speedometer gear retainer and slide gear and retainer off mainshaft. Remove shifter shaft snap rings. Remove reverse shifter shaft cover, shifter shaft detent cap, spring with ball and interlock lock pin. *See Fig. 2*.

Fig. 1: Cross Sectional View of General Motors 70 MM 4-Speed Transmission Assembly

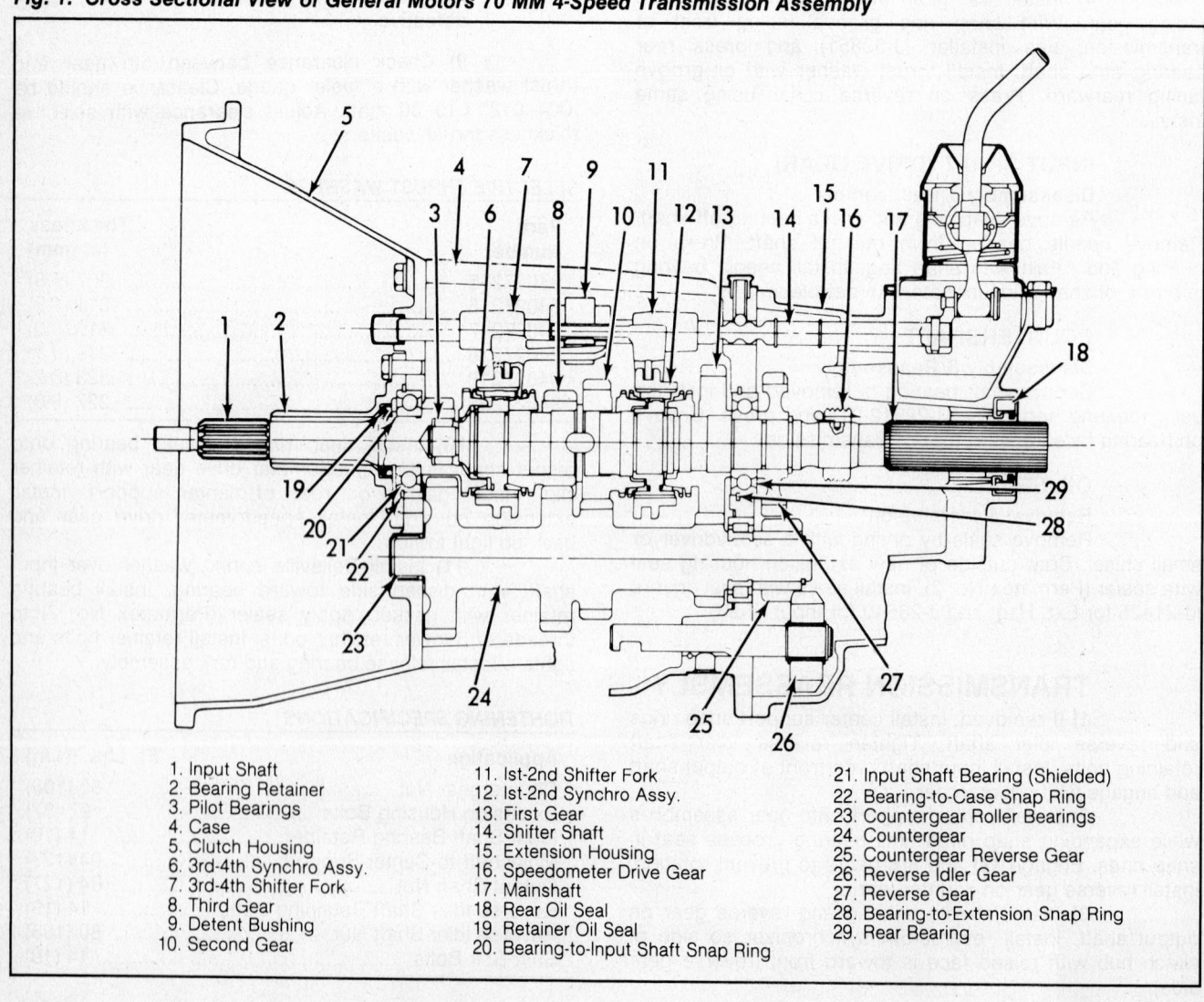

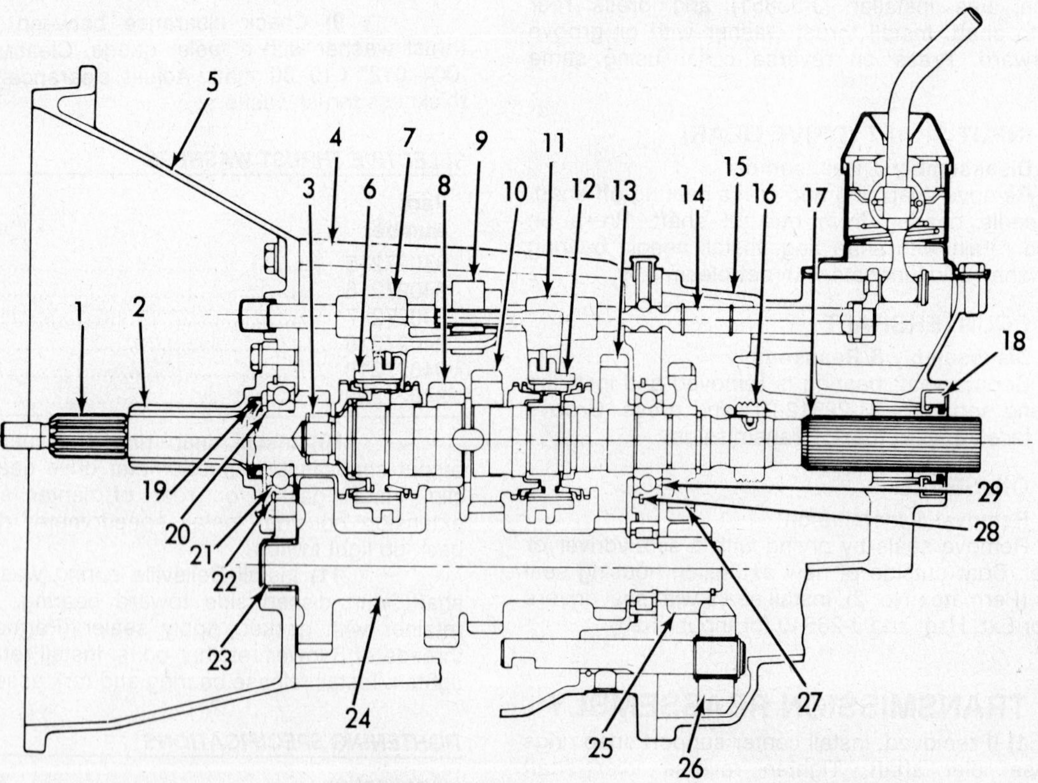

1. Input Shaft
2. Bearing Retainer
3. Pilot Bearings
4. Case
5. Clutch Housing
6. 3rd-4th Synchro Assy.
7. 3rd-4th Shifter Fork
8. Third Gear
9. Detent Bushing
10. Second Gear
11. Ist-2nd Shifter Fork
12. Ist-2nd Synchro Assy.
13. First Gear
14. Shifter Shaft
15. Extension Housing
16. Speedometer Drive Gear
17. Mainshaft
18. Rear Oil Seal
19. Retainer Oil Seal
20. Bearing-to-Input Shaft Snap Ring
21. Input Shaft Bearing (Shielded)
22. Bearing-to-Case Snap Ring
23. Countergear Roller Bearings
24. Countergear
25. Countergear Reverse Gear
26. Reverse Idler Gear
27. Reverse Gear
28. Bearing-to-Extension Snap Ring
29. Rear Bearing

GENERAL MOTORS 4-SPEED – 70 MM (Cont.)

Fig. 2: View of Transmission Case Showing Location of Cover, Detent Cap and Interlock Pin

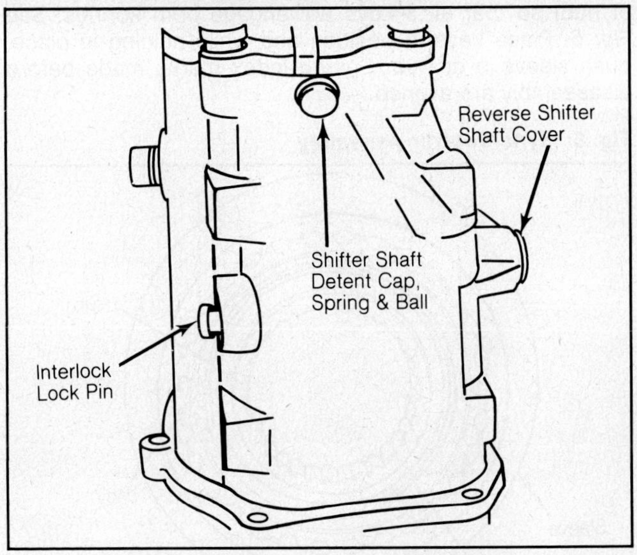

3) Using pliers, pull exposed end of reverse shifter shaft outward to disengage reverse lever from idler shaft. Remove idler shaft with gear attached. Remove snap rings retaining mainshaft reverse gear and countershaft reverse gear. *See Fig. 3*. Remove gears.

Fig. 3: Removing Reverse Countergear Snap Ring

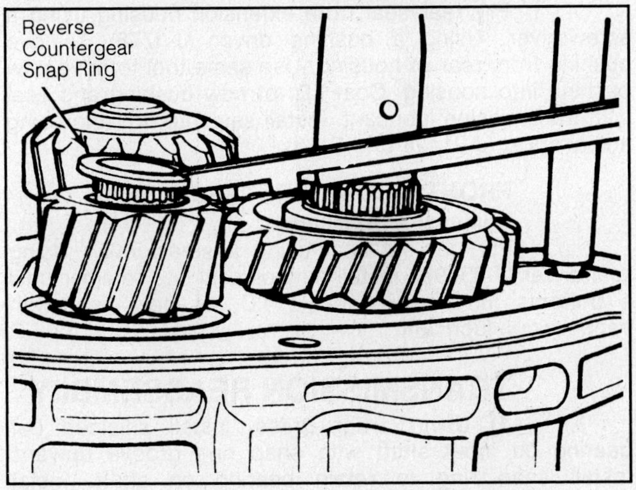

Use snap ring pliers to remove the snap ring.

4) Position transmission on its side and remove input shaft bearing retainer bolts, retainer and gasket. Remove snap ring retaining input shaft bearing to clutch housing. *See Fig. 4*.

5) Remove 6 bolts attaching clutch housing to case. Position transmission so it is resting on clutch housing. Expand snap ring in mainshaft bearing opening.

6) Remove transmission case by lifting it off the mainshaft. It may be necessary to tap case with a plastic mallet to free it from mainshaft assembly. Lift mainshaft (with shift forks attached) and countergear from clutch housing as an assembly.

NOTE: Ensure mainshaft assembly, countergear and shifter shaft assembly remains with clutch housing when case is removed.

Fig. 4: Removing Bearing-to-Clutch Housing Snap Ring

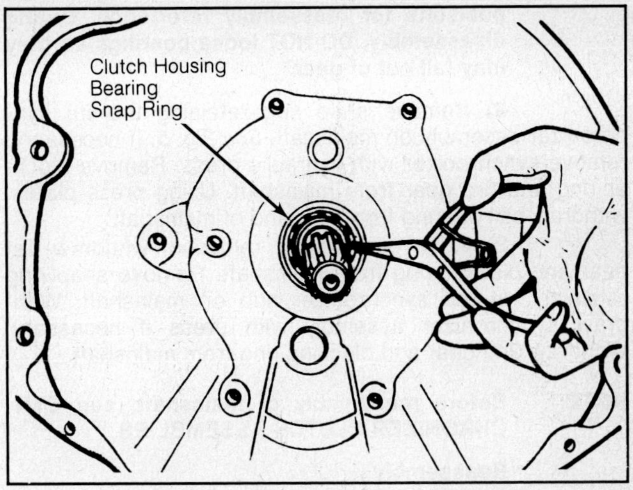

INSPECTION

1) Wash all parts thoroughly in solvent and blow dry with compressed air. DO NOT spin bearings with air. Inspect transmission case for cracks. Check front and rear case faces for burrs. Remove burrs with fine mill file.

2) After washing, check all ball bearings for wear or damage by lubricating with light oil and rotating by hand to check for roughness. Check roller bearings and contact surfaces of countergear and reverse idler shaft for wear. Replace parts as necessary.

3) Inspect all gears for excessive wear, chips and cracks. Check reverse idler gear bushing, and if worn or damaged, replace entire gear (bushing is not serviced separately). Inspect both synchronizer assemblies, making sure sleeves slide freely on hubs.

COMPONENT DISASSEMBLY & REASSEMBLY

MAINSHAFT

Disassembly

1) Separate shifter shaft and countergear assemblies from mainshaft. Withdraw input shaft (with bearings) and blocker ring from front of mainshaft.

Fig. 5: Removing/Installing 3rd-4th Synchronizer Snap Ring

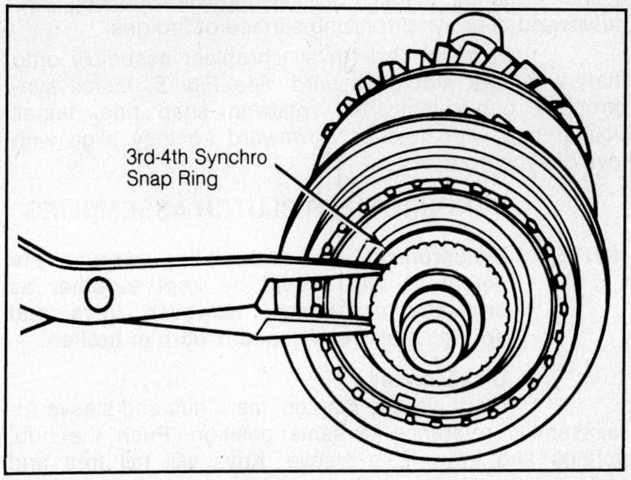

GENERAL MOTORS 4-SPEED – 70 MM (Cont.)

NOTE: **Input shaft has 15 roller bearings. Note positions for reassembly referrence. During disassembly, DO NOT loose bearings as they may fall out of gear.**

2) Remove snap ring retaining 3rd-4th synchronizer assembly on mainshaft. *See Fig. 5*. If necessary, remove synchronizer with hydraulic press. Remove blocker ring and 3rd gear from mainshaft. Using press plates, withdraw ball bearing from rear end of mainshaft.

3) With rear bearing removed, withdraw 1st gear and blocker ring from mainshaft. Remove snap ring retaining 1st-2nd synchronizer hub on mainshaft. Withdraw synchronizer assembly with press if necessary. Withdraw 2nd gear and blocking ring from mainshaft.

NOTE: **Before reassembly of mainshaft, see SYNCHRONIZER CLUTCH ASSEMBLIES.**

Reassembly

1) With rear end of mainshaft upward, install 2nd gear (clutching teeth upward) so rear face of gear butts against mainshaft flange. Install a blocker ring with clutching teeth downward over synchronizing surface of 2nd gear.

NOTE: **All 4 blocker rings used in this transmission are identical.**

2) Install 1st-2nd synchronizer assembly with fork slot downward over mainshaft. Press assembly onto mainshaft splines until it bottoms out. Ensure notches of blocker ring align with keys of synchronizer assembly.

3) Install synchronizer hub-to-mainshaft retaining snap ring. Install a blocker ring with notches downward so they align with keys of 1st-2nd synchronizer assembly.

4) Install 1st gear over end of mainshaft with clutching teeth downward. Position rear bearing over end of mainshaft with snap ring groove downward. Press bearing into position.

NOTE: **There are two ball bearings used in this transmission. A shielded input shaft bearing and a non-shielded mainshaft bearing. DO NOT interchange.**

5) Turn mainshaft so front faces upward. Install 3rd gear over shaft with clutching teeth upward. Move into place so front face of gear butts against mainshaft flange. Install a blocker ring with clutching teeth downward over synchronizing surface of 3rd gear.

6) Install 3rd-4th synchronizer assembly onto shaft with fork slot downward. *See Fig. 5*. Install synchronizer hub-to-mainshaft retaining snap ring. Install blocker ring with notches downward so they align with keys of synchronizer.

SYNCHRONIZER CLUTCH ASSEMBLIES

NOTE: **Synchronizer hub and sliding sleeves are select fit and should be kept together as originally assembled. However, keys and springs may be replaced if worn or broken.**

Disassembly

If not already marked, mark hub and sleeve for reassembly reference in same position. Push the hub, springs and keys from sleeve. Keys will fall free and springs should be easily removed.

Reassembly

Place 2 springs in position (one on each side of hub) so that all 3 keys will engage both springs. *See Fig. 6*. Place keys in position and while holding in place, push sleeve over hub. Ensure index marks made before disassembly are aligned.

Fig. 6: Synchronizer Assembly

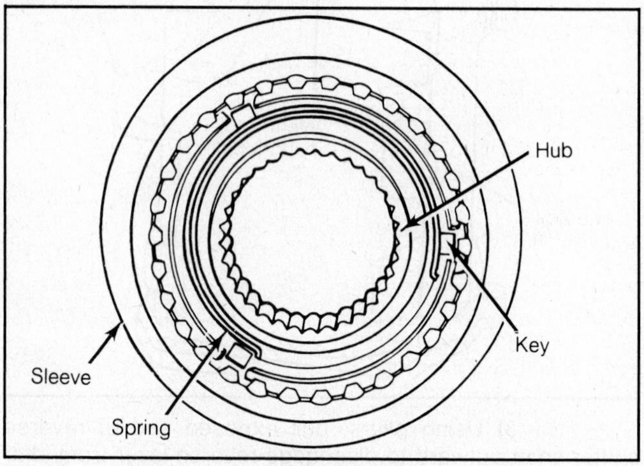

Mark the relative position of the hub to the sleeve for reassembly reference.

EXTENSION HOUSING SEAL & BUSHING

Removal & Installation

Pry rear seal from extension housing using a screwdriver. Using a bushing driver (J-5778), remove bushing from rear of housing. Use same tool to drive new bushing into housing. Coat I.D. of new bushing and seal with transmission lubricant. Install seal into housing using a seal driver (J-21426 or J-5154).

FRONT BEARING RETAINER SEAL

Removal & Installation

Pry out old seal using a screwdriver. Using seal driver (J-23096), install new oil seal into retainer until it bottoms in bore. Lubricate I.D. of new seal with transmission lubricant.

TRANSMISSION REASSEMBLY

1) Using arbor press, install shielded ball bearing on input shaft with snap ring groove upward. Install snap ring to retain bearing on shaft. Install mainshaft pilot roller bearings into input shaft cavity, using heavy grease to hold them in place.

2) Carefully assemble input shaft to mainshaft assembly. Install detent lever to shifter shaft and retain with roll pin. From rear of shifter shaft, slide 1st-2nd shifter fork onto shaft so fork arm engages detent lever.

3) Assemble 3rd-4th shifter fork to detent bushing. From front of shifter shaft, slide 3rd-4th fork and detent bushing onto shaft, locating 3rd-4th fork arm below the 1st-2nd fork arm. *See Fig. 8*.

4) With front of clutch housing resting on 2 wood blocks, place thrust washer over hole for countergear. Index washer tabs with holes provided in clutch housing. Place both synchronizers in neutral.

5) Mate shifter shaft assembly with mainshaft assembly. Index shifter forks into synchronizer sleeve grooves. Mesh countergear with mainshaft gears and install complete assembly onto clutch housing as a unit. *See Fig. 9*.

GENERAL MOTORS 4-SPEED – 70 MM (Cont.)

Fig. 8: Assembling Shift Forks on Shifter Shaft

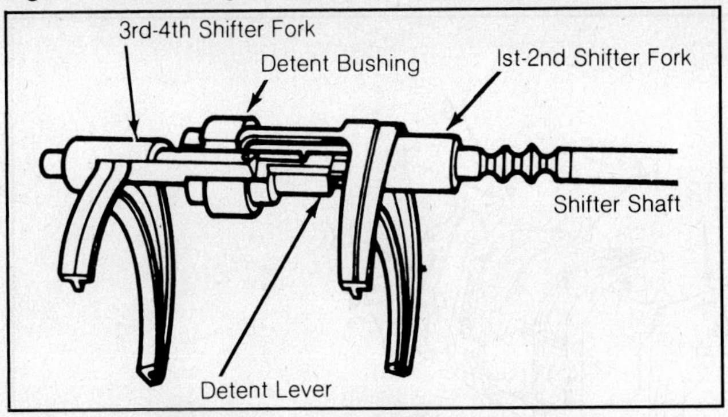

Fig. 9: Installed View of Mainshaft, Countergear and Shifter Shaft

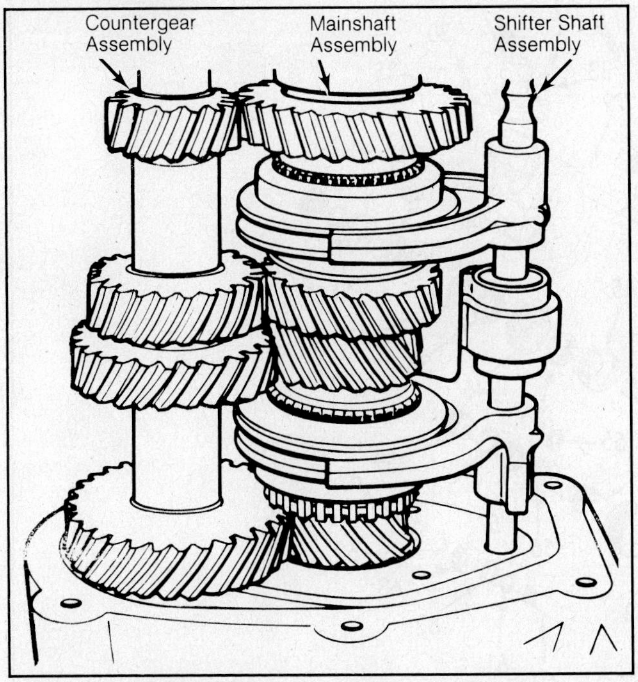

6) Place clutch housing on its side and install snap ring to ball bearing on input shaft. Install gasket and bearing retainer onto clutch housing, using sealer on retainer bolts.

7) Turn clutch housing case so it sets on wood blocks. If removed, install reverse lever into case, using grease to hold it in place. *See Fig. 10*. Ensure screwdriver slot for reverse lever is parallel with front of case. Install reverse lever snap ring.

8) Install roller bearing into countergear opening with snap ring groove inside of case (snap ring will be assembled to roller bearing). Install case-to-clutch housing gasket on clutch housing using rubber cement to hold it in place.

NOTE: **Before installing case, ensure synchronizers are in neutral, detent bushing slot is facing outward and reverse lever is flush with inside wall of case.**

9) Install case onto assembly, and at same time, expand snap ring in mainshaft opening of case to allow ring to pilot over mainshaft bearing. Use a plastic hammer if necessary to seat parts.

Fig. 10: View of Installed Reverse Lever

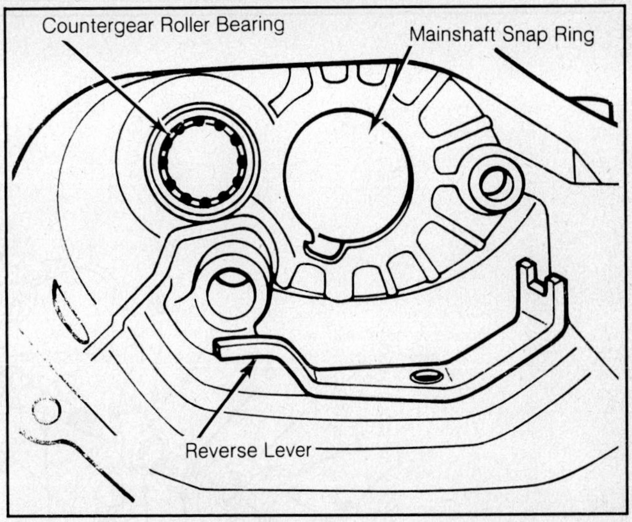

Ensure screwdriver slot for reverse lever is parallel with the front of the transmission case.

10) Install interlock lock pin to hold shifter shaft in place. Use sealer cement. Install idler shaft so it will engage with reverse lever inside of case. Install cover over reverse shifter shaft to hold the reverse lever in place.

11) Install the detent ball, spring and cap into case. Position reverse gear over end of mainshaft, with chamfer on gear teeth upward. Push gear onto splines of mainshaft and secure with snap ring.

12) Install smaller reverse gear onto countergear shaft with shoulder resting against countergear bearing. Secure snap ring. If removed, install snap ring, thrust washer and reverse idler gear (chamfer of gear teeth downward) onto idler shaft. Secure parts with thrust washer and snap ring. *See Fig. 11*.

Fig. 11: Installing Reverse Idler Gear

Position the reverse idler gear with the chamfer on the gear teeth facing upward.

13) Install snap rings on shifter shafts. *See Fig. 12*. Be sure they are tight in grooves. Position speedometer gear retainer in mainshaft hole. With retainer loop facing forward, slide speedometer gear over mainshaft and into position. Heat gear to 175°F (80°C) with heat lamp or oven prior to installation.

GENERAL MOTORS 4-SPEED – 70 MM (Cont.)

Fig. 7: Exploded View of General Motors 70 mm 4-Speed Transmission Assembly

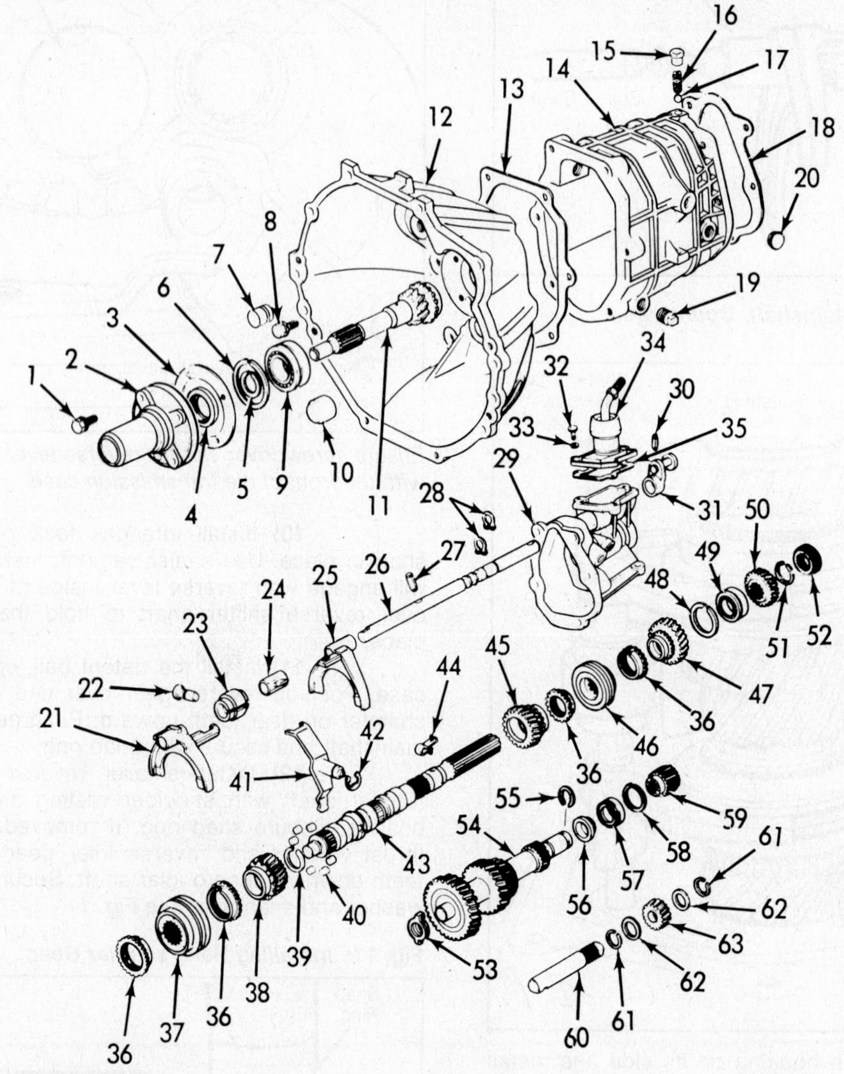

1. Bearing Retainer Bolt
2. Bearing Retainer
3. Retainer Gasket
4. Retainer Seal
5. Snap Ring
6. Bearing Outer Snap Ring
7. Shifter Shaft Stop Plug
8. Clutch Housing-to-Case Bolt
9. Input Shaft Bearing
10. Countergear Front Needle Bearings
11. Input Shaft
12. Clutch Housing
13. Housing-to-Case Gasket
14. Case
15. Shifter Shaft Detent Cap
16. Shifter Shaft Detent Spring
17. Shifter Shaft Detent Ball
18. Case-to-Extension Gasket
19. Magnet Plug
20. Reverse Lever Cap
21. 3rd-4th Shift Fork
22. Interlock Lock Pin
23. Detent Bushing
24. Detent Lever
25. Ist-2nd Shift Fork
26. Shifter Shaft
27. Detent Lever Pin
28. Shifter Shaft Snap Rings
29. Extension Housing
30. Shifter Shaft Arm Roll Pin
31. Shifter Shaft Arm
32. Shift Lever-to-Extension Bolt
33. Washer
34. Shift Lever Assembly
35. Shift Lever Gasket
36. Blocker Rings
37. 3rd-4th Synchro Assembly
38. Third Speed Gear
39. Synchro Hub-to-Shaft Snap Ring
40. Input Shaft Roller Bearings
41. Reverse Lever Assy.
42. Reverse Lever Snap Ring
43. Mainshaft
44. Speedometer Gear Retainer
45. Second Speed Gear
46. Ist-2nd Synchro Assembly
47. First Speed Gear
48. Bearing Outer Snap Ring
49. Rear Bearing
50. Reverse Gear
51. Reverse Gear Snap Ring
52. Speedometer Gear
53. Countergear Thrust Washer
54. Countergear
55. Snap Ring
56. Inner Bearing Race
57. Countergear Bearing
58. Bearing Outer Snap Ring
59. Countergear Reverse Gear
60. Idler Gear Shaft
61. Idler Gear Thrust Washer
62. Snap Ring
63. Reverse Idler Gear

GENERAL MOTORS 4-SPEED – 70 MM (Cont.)

Fig. 12: Installing Shifter Shaft Snap Rings

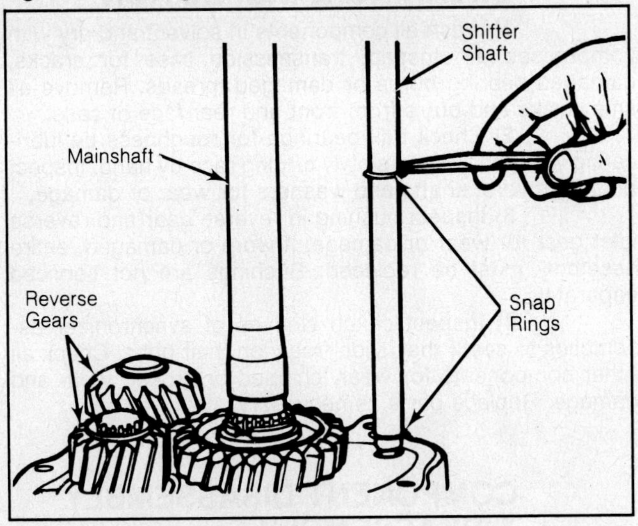

14) Position extension housing and gasket on case and install 2 partially threaded pilot bolts. *See Fig. 13.* Install other 3 remaining bolts. Ensure pilot bolts are installed in upper right corner and lower left corner of case.

CAUTION: If pilot bolts are installed in wrong holes, splitting of case may occur.

Fig. 13: Extension Housing Pilot Bolt Locations

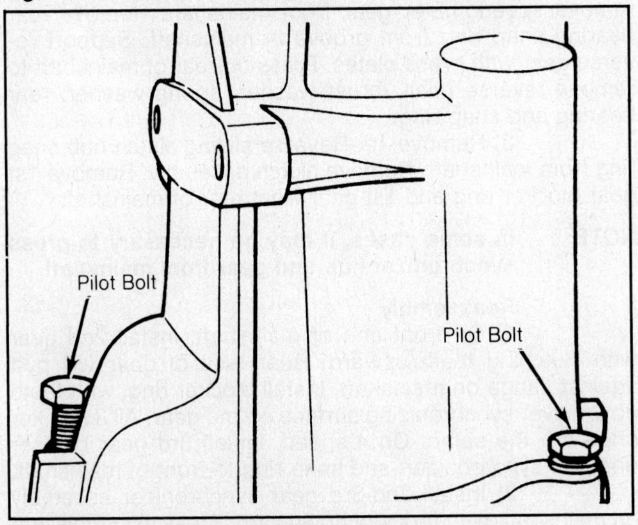

The pilot bolts are located in the top right and the bottom left corners of transmission case.

15) Install shifter shaft arm over shifter shaft. Move to a position aligned with drilled hole near end of shaft. Drive roll pin into shifter shaft arm and shaft to retain parts. *See Fig. 14*

16) Place transmission on its side. Install 2 pilot bolts before installing other 4 attaching bolts to clutch housing and case. *See Fig. 15.*

NOTE: Pilot bolts are partially threaded and are installed in upper right and lower left holes in clutch housing.

Fig. 14: Installing Shifter Shaft Arm and Roll Pin

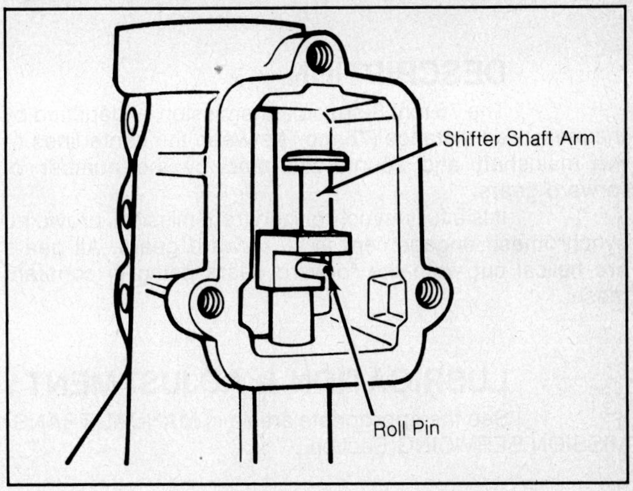

Fig. 15: Location of Pilot Bolts in Clutch Housing

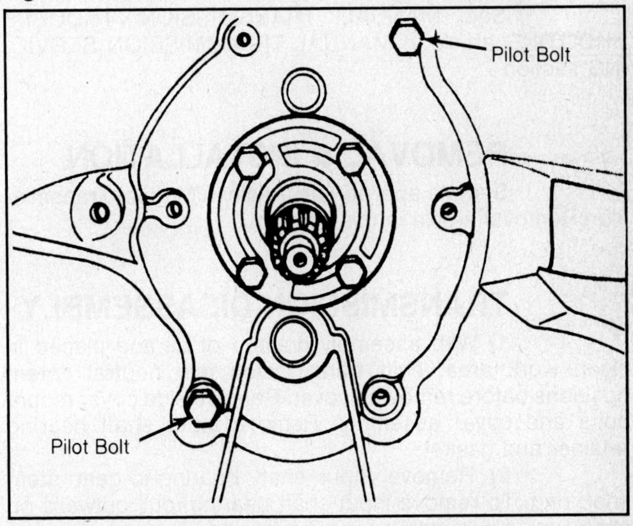

The pilot bolts are located in the top right and the bottom left corners.

TIGHTENING SPECIFICATIONS

Application	Ft. Lbs. (N.m)
Back-up Lamp Switch	25 (34)
Clutch Cover-to-Flywheel	18 (24)
Clutch Fork Ball Stud Lock Nut	24 (33)
Clutch Housing-to-Case	26 (35)
Clutch Housing-to-Engine	25 (34)
Crossmember-to-Frame	40 (55)
Crossmember-to-Transmission	
Center Nut	33 (45)
End Nut	21 (28)
Extension Housing-to-Case	26 (35)
Rear Support-to-Transmission	32 (43)
Shift Lever Retaining Bolts	10 (14)
	INCH Lbs. (N.m)
Bearing Retainer-to-Clutch Housing	105 (12)
Clutch Cable Lock Nut	53 (6)
Clutch Housing Lower Cover Bolts	90 (10)
Converter Bracket-to-Rear Support	150 (17)
Speedometer Driven Gear Retainer Bolt	44 (5)

GENERAL MOTORS 3 & 4-SPEED – 76MM

Chevrolet, GMC

DESCRIPTION

The 76 mm 3-speed transmission is identified by the measured distance (76 mm) between the centerlines of the mainshaft and countergear and by the number of forward gears.

It is a fully-synchronized transmission, providing synchromesh engagement in all forward gears. All gears are helical cut, with the forward gears being in constant mesh.

LUBRICATION & ADJUSTMENT

See the appropriate article in MANUAL TRANSMISSION SERVICING Section .

TROUBLE SHOOTING

See MANUAL TRANSMISSION TROUBLE SHOOTING article in MANUAL TRANSMISSION SERVICING section .

REMOVAL & INSTALLATION

See the appropriate article in Manual Transmission Removal article in this section.

TRANSMISSION DISASSEMBLY

1) With assembly drained of oil and placed in clean work area, shift transmission into neutral detent positions before removing cover. Remove side cover mount bolts and cover assembly. Remove input shaft bearing retainer and gasket.

2) Remove input shaft bearing-to-gear stem snap ring. To remove input shaft bearing, pull outward on shaft until a screwdriver can be inserted between bearing snap ring and case to complete removal.

NOTE: **The input shaft bearing is a slip fit on the gear and into the case bore.**

3) To remove speedometer driven gear, detach lock plate-to-housing mount bolt and washer. Remove lock plate. Insert screwdriver into lock plate slot of fitting. Pry fitting, gear and shaft from housing. Remove and discard "O" ring.

4) Remove extension housing-to-case mount bolts. Remove "E" clip from reverse idler shaft. Remove input shaft, mainshaft and extension assembly through rear of case.

5) Remove drive gear, input shaft needle bearings and synchronizer ring from mainshaft. Expand snap ring, in extension housing, retaining mainshaft rear bearing. Remove extension housing.

6) Using Dummy Countershaft (J-22246), drive countershaft and its Woodruff key out rear of case. Dummy shaft will hold roller bearings in position in gear.

7) Remove countergear, bearings and thrust washers. Using a long drift through front bearing case bore, drive reverse idler shaft and Woodruff key out rear of case. Lift out reverse idler gear.

CLEANING & INSPECTION

1) Wash all components in solvent and dry with compressed air. Inspect transmission case for cracks, damaged bearing bores or damaged threads. Remove all small nicks and burrs from front and rear face of case.

2) Check ball bearings for roughness by lubricating with light oil and slowly turning race by hand. Inspect bearing rollers, shafts and washers for wear or damage.

3) Inspect bushing in reverse gear and reverse idler gear for wear or damage. If worn or damaged, entire assembly must be replaced. Bushings are not serviced separately.

4) Inspect clutch sleeves of synchronizer assemblies to see if they slide freely on their hubs. Check all other components for wear, chipped or broken teeth and damage. Replace parts as necessary.

COMPONENT DISASSEMBLY & REASSEMBLY

MAINSHAFT

Disassembly

1) Remove 2nd-3rd gear sliding clutch snap ring from mainshaft. Remove clutch assembly, 2nd gear blocker ring and 2nd gear from front of mainshaft. *See Fig. 1.* On 4-speed, remove snap ring , slide 4-3 synchronizer off remove 3rd gear blocker ring and 3rd gear. *See Fig. 2.*

2) Depress speedometer gear retaining clip and remove speedometer gear from mainshaft. Remove rear bearing snap ring from groove in mainshaft. Support reverse gear with press plates. Press on rear of mainshaft to remove reverse gear, thrust washer, spring washer, rear bearing and snap ring.

3) Remove 1st-Reverse sliding clutch hub snap ring from mainshaft. Remove clutch assembly. Remove 1st gear blocker ring and 1st gear from rear of mainshaft.

NOTE: **In some cases, it may be necessary to press synchronizer hub and gear from mainshaft.**

Reassembly

1) On front end of mainshaft, install 2nd gear with clutching teeth upward. Rear face of gear will butt against flange on mainshaft. Install blocker ring, with teeth down, over synchronizing surface of 2nd gear. All 3 blocker rings are the same. On 4-speed, install 3rd gear blocker ring, 4-3 synchronizer, and snap ring to front of mainshaft.

2) Install 2nd-3rd gear synchronizer assembly on mainshaft, with fork slot downward. Press assembly into place until it bottoms out. Both synchronizer assemblies used in transmission are the same. *See Fig. 3.*

NOTE: **If sleeve is removed from 2nd-3rd gear hub, (3rd-4th on 4-speed) notches on hub O.D. face toward front of mainshaft. Ensure notches on blocker ring align with keys on synchronizer assembly.**

3) Install synchronizer hub snap ring. Both synchronizer snap rings are identical. Install 1st gear on rear end of mainshaft, with clutching teeth up. Front face of gear will butt against flange on mainshaft. Install blocker ring with teeth downward over 1st gear.

4) Install 1st-Reverse (1st-2nd on 4-speed) synchronizer assembly on mainshaft splines, with fork slot

GENERAL MOTORS 3 & 4-SPEED – 76MM (Cont.)

Fig. 1: Exploded View of General Motors 3-Speed 76 MM Transmission

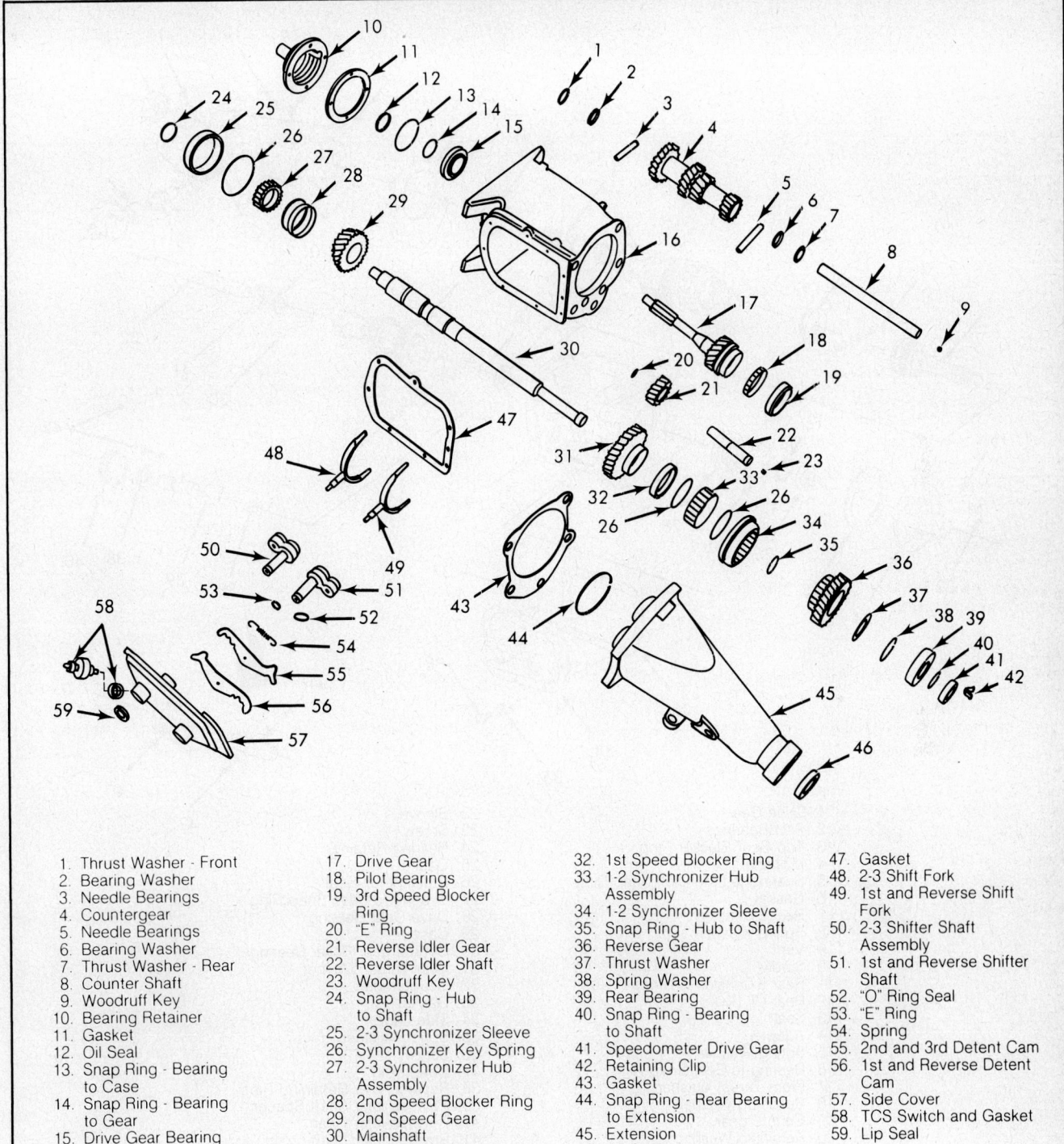

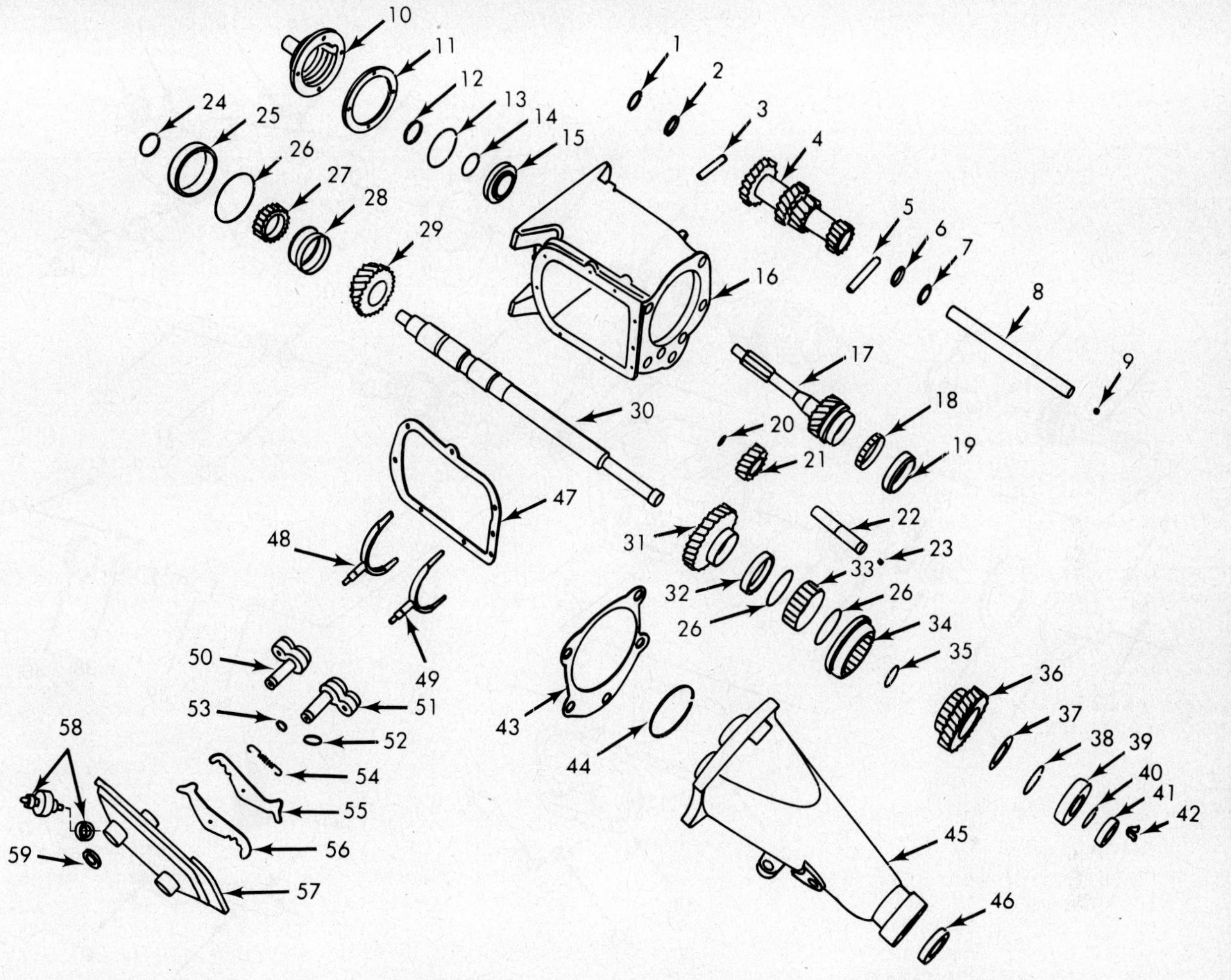

1. Thrust Washer - Front
2. Bearing Washer
3. Needle Bearings
4. Countergear
5. Needle Bearings
6. Bearing Washer
7. Thrust Washer - Rear
8. Counter Shaft
9. Woodruff Key
10. Bearing Retainer
11. Gasket
12. Oil Seal
13. Snap Ring - Bearing to Case
14. Snap Ring - Bearing to Gear
15. Drive Gear Bearing
16. Case
17. Drive Gear
18. Pilot Bearings
19. 3rd Speed Blocker Ring
20. "E" Ring
21. Reverse Idler Gear
22. Reverse Idler Shaft
23. Woodruff Key
24. Snap Ring - Hub to Shaft
25. 2-3 Synchronizer Sleeve
26. Synchronizer Key Spring
27. 2-3 Synchronizer Hub Assembly
28. 2nd Speed Blocker Ring
29. 2nd Speed Gear
30. Mainshaft
31. 1st Speed Gear
32. 1st Speed Blocker Ring
33. 1-2 Synchronizer Hub Assembly
34. 1-2 Synchronizer Sleeve
35. Snap Ring - Hub to Shaft
36. Reverse Gear
37. Thrust Washer
38. Spring Washer
39. Rear Bearing
40. Snap Ring - Bearing to Shaft
41. Speedometer Drive Gear
42. Retaining Clip
43. Gasket
44. Snap Ring - Rear Bearing to Extension
45. Extension
46. Oil Seal
47. Gasket
48. 2-3 Shift Fork
49. 1st and Reverse Shift Fork
50. 2-3 Shifter Shaft Assembly
51. 1st and Reverse Shifter Shaft
52. "O" Ring Seal
53. "E" Ring
54. Spring
55. 2nd and 3rd Detent Cam
56. 1st and Reverse Detent Cam
57. Side Cover
58. TCS Switch and Gasket
59. Lip Seal

downward. Assembly should be a sliding fit onto mainshaft. Install synchronizer hub snap ring. Ensure blocker ring notches align with synchronizer keys.

5) Install reverse gear with teeth downward. Install reverse gear thrust washer (steel) and spring washer. Using hydraulic press if necessary, press rear bearing on mainshaft with snap ring slot down. Install bearing snap ring. Install speedometer drive gear and retaining clip.

SYNCHRONIZER CLUTCH ASSEMBLIES

NOTE: **Clutch hubs and sliding sleeves are a selected assembly and should be kept together as originally assembled. Keys and 2 springs may be replaced if worn or broken.**

GENERAL MOTORS 3 & 4-SPEED – 76MM (Cont.)

Fig. 2: Exploded View of General Motors 4-Speed 76 MM Transmission

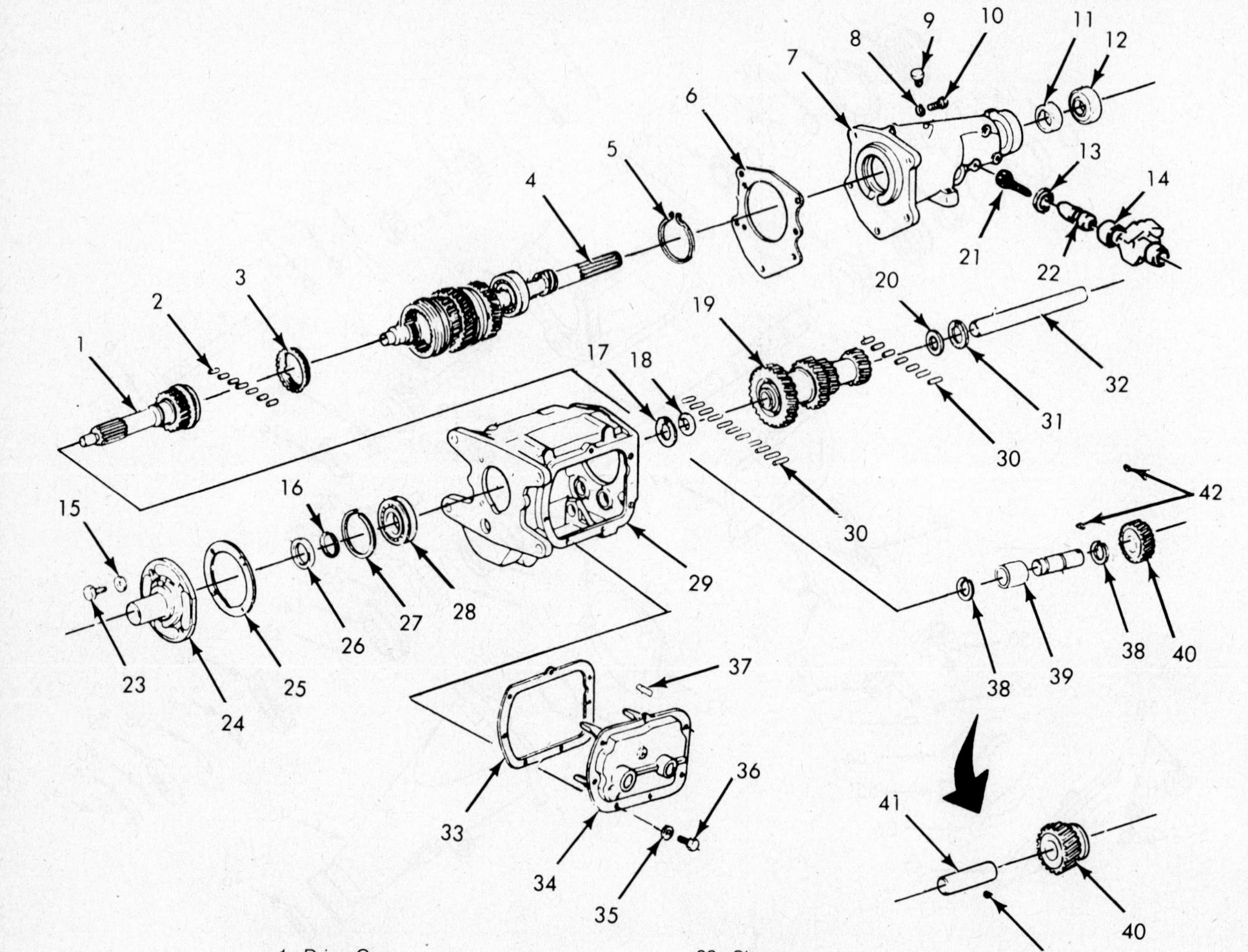

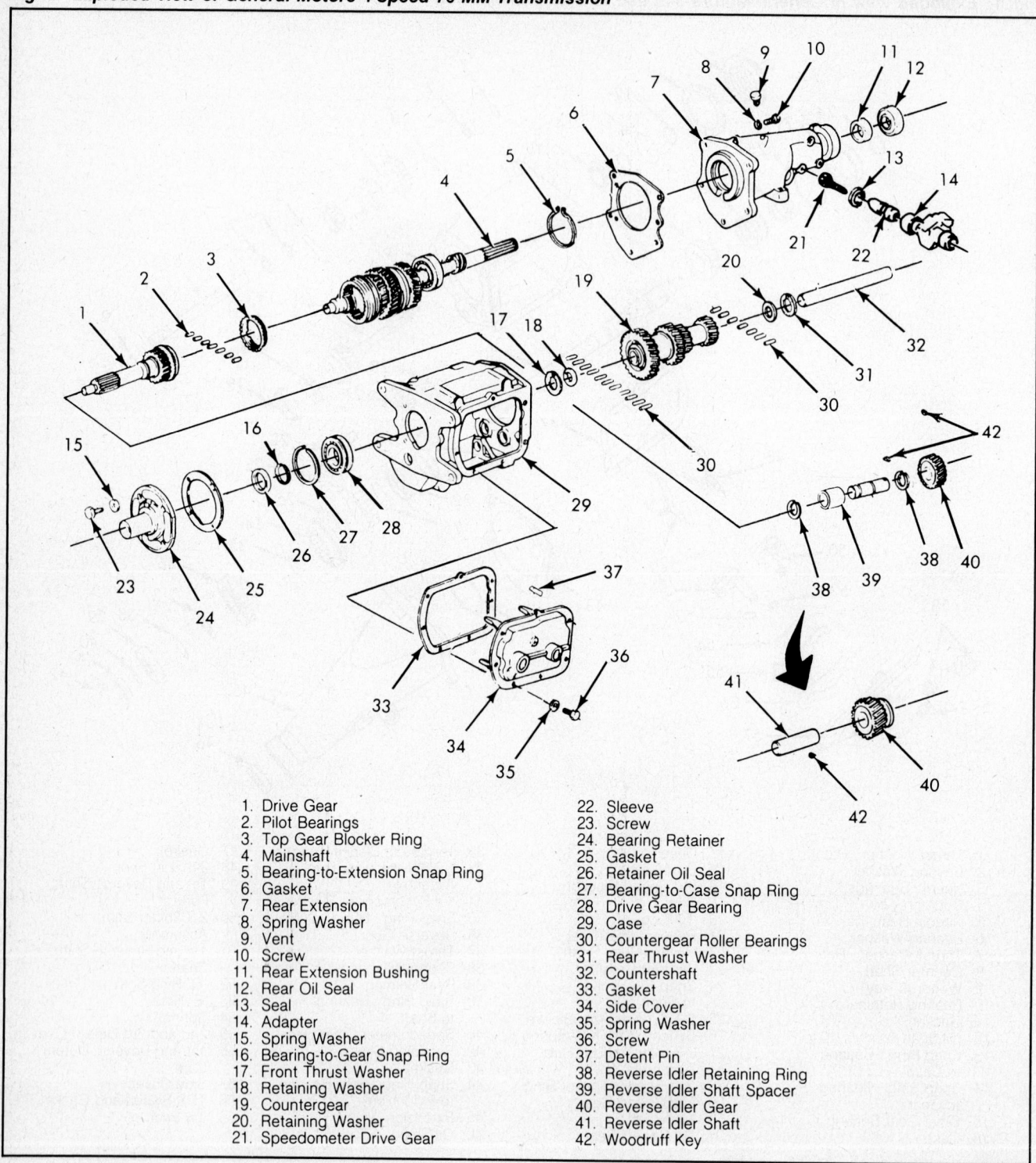

1. Drive Gear
2. Pilot Bearings
3. Top Gear Blocker Ring
4. Mainshaft
5. Bearing-to-Extension Snap Ring
6. Gasket
7. Rear Extension
8. Spring Washer
9. Vent
10. Screw
11. Rear Extension Bushing
12. Rear Oil Seal
13. Seal
14. Adapter
15. Spring Washer
16. Bearing-to-Gear Snap Ring
17. Front Thrust Washer
18. Retaining Washer
19. Countergear
20. Retaining Washer
21. Speedometer Drive Gear
22. Sleeve
23. Screw
24. Bearing Retainer
25. Gasket
26. Retainer Oil Seal
27. Bearing-to-Case Snap Ring
28. Drive Gear Bearing
29. Case
30. Countergear Roller Bearings
31. Rear Thrust Washer
32. Countershaft
33. Gasket
34. Side Cover
35. Spring Washer
36. Screw
37. Detent Pin
38. Reverse Idler Retaining Ring
39. Reverse Idler Shaft Spacer
40. Reverse Idler Gear
41. Reverse Idler Shaft
42. Woodruff Key

Disassembly

Mark hub and sleeve, so they can be aligned upon reassembly. Push hub from sliding sleeve, then remove keys and springs.

Reassembly

1) Place 3 keys and 2 springs in position, 1 on each side of hub, so all 3 keys are engaged by both springs. The tanged end of each synchronizer spring should be installed into different key cavities on either side.

2) A groove around outside of synchronizer hub identifies end that must be opposite fork slot in sleeve when assembled. *See Fig. 4.* Groove indicates end of hub with greater recess depth. Slide sleeve onto hub, aligning marks before assembly.

EXTENSION HOUSING OIL SEAL OR BUSHING

1) If bushing in rear of extension housing requires replacement, remove seal. Using Driver (J-21465 or

GENERAL MOTORS 3 & 4-SPEED – 76MM (Cont.)

Fig. 3: 4-Speed Mainshaft Assembly

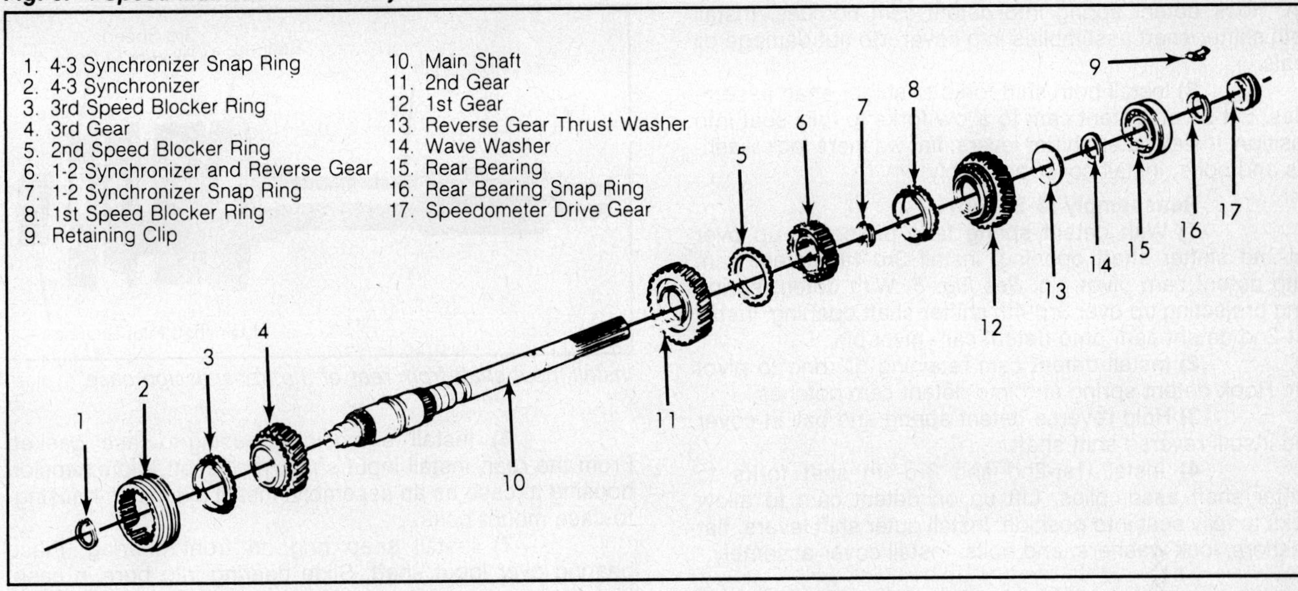

Fig. 4: Synchronizer Clutch Assembly

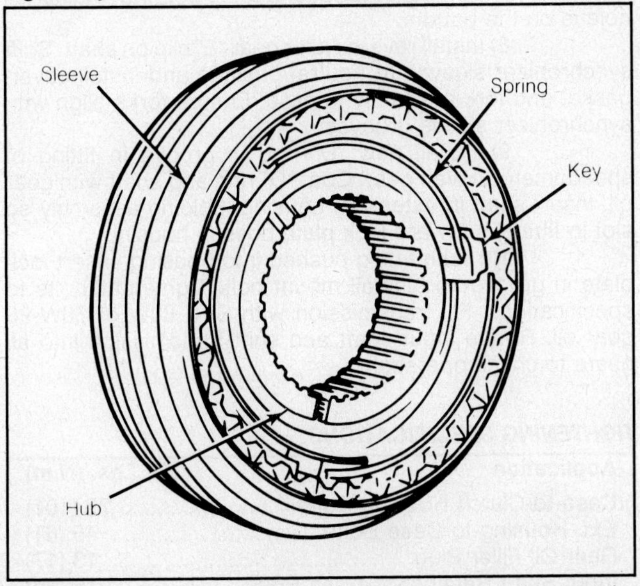

The groove around outside of synchronizer hub must be opposite fork slot in sleeve during assembly.

J-23062-14), drive bushing from its bore into extension housing. Remove old bushing.

2) Using same tool, drive new bushing into housing from rear. Coat I.D. of bushing and new seal with transmission lubricant. Coat O.D. of seal with sealant. Using Oil Seal Installer (J-21426 or J-21359), install seal into housing.

INPUT SHAFT RETAINER OIL SEAL

If seal in retainer requires replacement, pry out old seal. Using Installer (J-23096), drive new seal into retainer until seal seats in bore. During installation, make sure seal lip faces rear of transmission.

TRANSMISSION CASE COVER

Disassembly

1) With cover removed from transmission, remove outer shifter levers. Remove both shift forks from shifter shaft assemblies. Remove both shifter shaft assemblies from cover.

2) If damaged, replace seals around shifter shaft by prying out. Remove detent cam spring and pivot retainer "C" ring. Remove both detent cams. *See Fig. 5.* Inspect and replace damaged parts as necessary.

Fig. 5: 4-Speed Transmission Case Cover Assembly

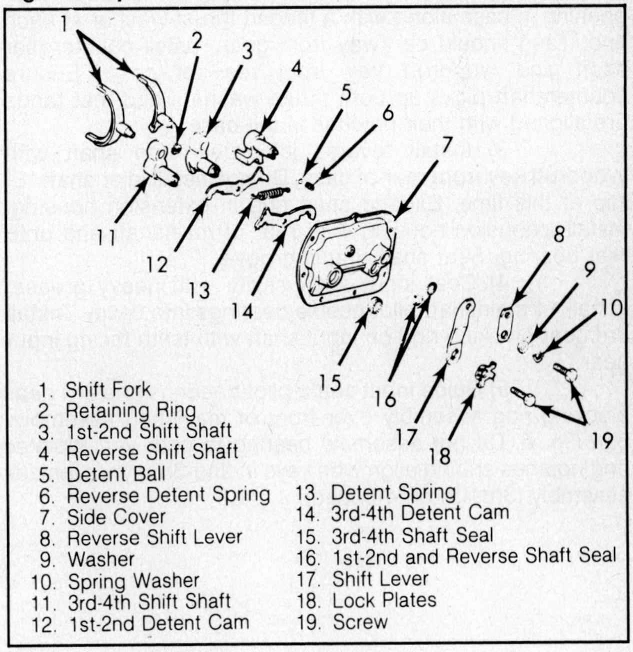

Shift the transmission into its neutral detents before removing or installing side cover assembly.

Reassembly (3-Speed)

1) With detent spring tang projecting up over 2nd-3rd shifter shaft cover opening, install 1st-Reverse detent cam onto detent cam pivot pin. With detent spring tang projecting up over the 1st-Reverse shifter shaft cover hole, install the 2nd-3rd detent cam onto detent cam pivot pin.

GENERAL MOTORS 3 & 4-SPEED – 76MM (Cont.)

2) Install detent cam retaining "C" ring to pivot pin. Hook detent spring into detent cam notches. Install both shifter shaft assemblies into cover. Do not damage oil seals.

3) Install both shift forks to shifter shaft assemblies. Lift up on detent cam to allow forks to fully seat into position. Install outer shifter levers, flat washers lock washers and bolts. Install cover assembly.

Reassembly (4-Speed)

1) With detent spring tang projecting up over 1st-2nd shifter shaft opening, install 3rd-4th detent cam onto detent cam pivot pin. *See Fig. 5.* With detent spring tang projecting up over 3rd-4th shifter shaft opening, install 1st-2nd detent cam onto detent cam pivot pin.

2) Install detent cam retaining "C" ring to pivot pin. Hook detent spring and into detent cam notches.

3) Hold reverse detent spring and ball in cover and install reverse shift shaft.

4) Install 1st-2nd and 3rd-4th shift forks to shifter shaft assemblies. Lift up on detent cam to allow forks to fully seat into position. Install outer shift levers, flat washers, lock washers, and bolts. Install cover assembly.

TRANSMISSION REASSEMBLY

NOTE: **Apply sealant to all through-bolts used during reassembly.**

1) Coat countershaft bore with heavy grease. Insert dummy countershaft into countergear. Install 27 needle bearings and a thrust washer in each end of gear.

2) Place countergear assembly through rear opening in case along with a tanged thrust washer at each end. Tang should be away from gear. Install countergear shaft and woodruff key from rear of case. Ensure countershaft picks up both thrust washers and that tangs are aligned with their notches in the case.

3) Install reverse idler gear and shaft with Woodruff key from rear of case. Do not install idler shaft "E" clip at this time. Expand snap ring in extension housing. Install extension housing over rear of mainshaft and onto rear bearing. Seat snap ring in groove.

4) Coat input shaft cavity with heavy grease. Install 14 mainshaft pilot needle bearings into cavity. Install 3rd gear blocking ring on input shaft with teeth facing input gear.

5) Guide input shaft, pilot bearings and 3rd gear blocking ring assembly over front of mainshaft assembly. *See Fig. 6.* Do not assemble bearing to gear yet. Blocker ring notches should align with keys in 2nd-3rd synchronizer assembly (3rd-4th on 4-speed).

Fig. 6: Input Shaft Assembly

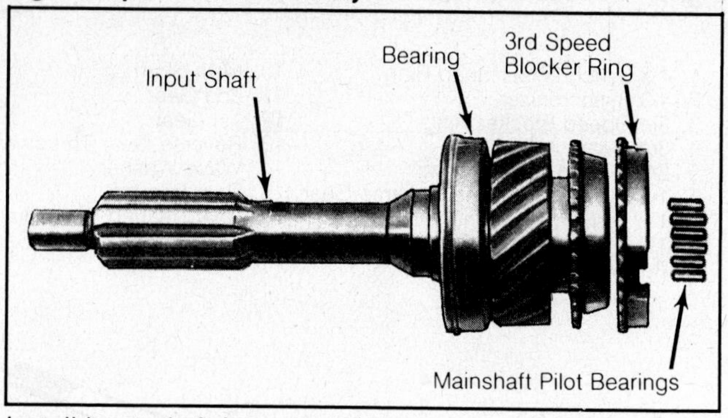

Install input shaft from rear of the transmission case.

6) Install extension housing-to-case gasket. From the rear, install input shaft, mainshaft and extension housing to case as an assembly. Install extension housing-to-case mount bolts.

7) Install snap ring on front bearing. Place bearing over input shaft. Slide bearing into bore in case. Install snap ring on input shaft. Install input shaft bearing retainer and new gasket to case. Ensure bearing retainer oil hole is on the bottom.

8) Install reverse idler gear "E" clip on shaft. Shift synchronizer sleeves to neutral position and install cover, gasket and fork assembly to case. Ensure forks align with synchronizer sleeve grooves.

9) Install new "O" ring in groove in fitting of speedometer driven gear. Coat "O" ring and shaft with gear oil. Insert shaft in extension housing, holding assembly so slot in fitting is toward lock plate boss in housing.

10) With fitting pushed into housing, insert lock plate in groove and install mount bolt. Tighten all bolts to specifications. Fill transmission with SAE 80W or 80W-90 gear oil. Rotate input shaft and shift transmission into all gears to check operation.

TIGHTENING SPECIFICATIONS

Application	Ft. Lbs. (N.m)
Case-to-Clutch Housing Bolts	75 (101)
Ext. Housing-to-Case Bolts	45 (61)
Gear Oil Filler Plug	13 (17)
Input Shaft Retainer-to-Case Bolts	15 (20)
Mount-to-Transmission Bolt	40 (54)
Shift Lever-to-Shifter Shaft Bolts	25 (32)
Side Cover-to-Case Bolts	15 (20)

GENERAL MOTORS 4-SPEED TRANSAXLES – 76 MM

Buick Skyhawk, Skylark, Chevrolet Cavalier, Celebrity, Oldsmobile Firenza, Pontiac Fiero, Sunbird

IDENTIFICATION

Transaxle may be identified by code stamped on a machined pad on forward side of transaxle case (clutch housing) next to middle transaxle-to-engine retaining bolt.

DESCRIPTION

Final drive and 4-speed transmission are mounted in a common 2-piece aluminum case. Transmission is fully synchronized in all forward gears. Forward gears are helically cut and in constant mesh. Reverse gears are spur cut and are engaged by sliding reverse idler gear. Fourth gear is indirect (overdrive).

The input gear, output gear and differential assembly are all supported by preloaded tapered roller bearings. Final output gear with its integral shaft, turns ring gear and differential assembly, drive axles and front wheel assemblies. *See Fig. 1.*

Gears are shifted by 2 cable assemblies, the trans-selector and trans-shifter cables.

SERVICE (IN VEHICLE)

TRANSAXLE MOUNTS

To check mounts, raise vehicle on hoist. Push up and pull down on transaxle case, observing mounts as you do. If rubber separates from metal plate or mount, or if case moves up but not down, replace mount.

DRIVE AXLE SHAFTS

See appropriate DRIVE AXLE SHAFT article in IMPORT FWD AXLE SHAFTS, OVERDRIVES & TRANSFER CASES section.

REMOVAL & INSTALLATION

See appropriate MANUAL TRANSMISSION REMOVAL article in DOMESTIC/IMPORT GENERAL SERVICING section.

Fig. 1: Cutaway View of General Motors 4-Speed Manual Transaxle

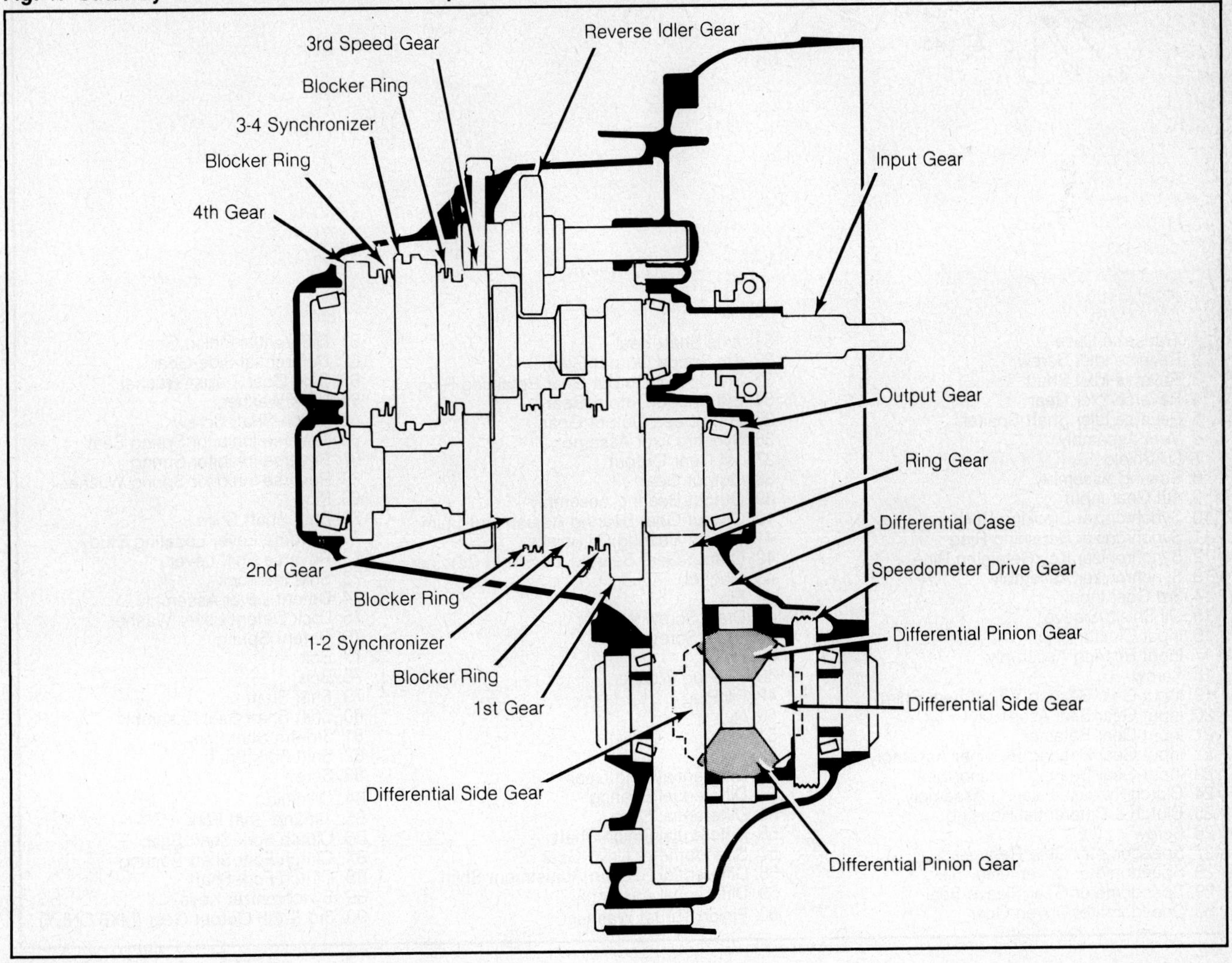

GENERAL MOTORS 4-SPEED TRANSAXLES – 76 MM (Cont.)

Fig. 2: Exploded View of General Motors 4-Speed Manual Transaxle

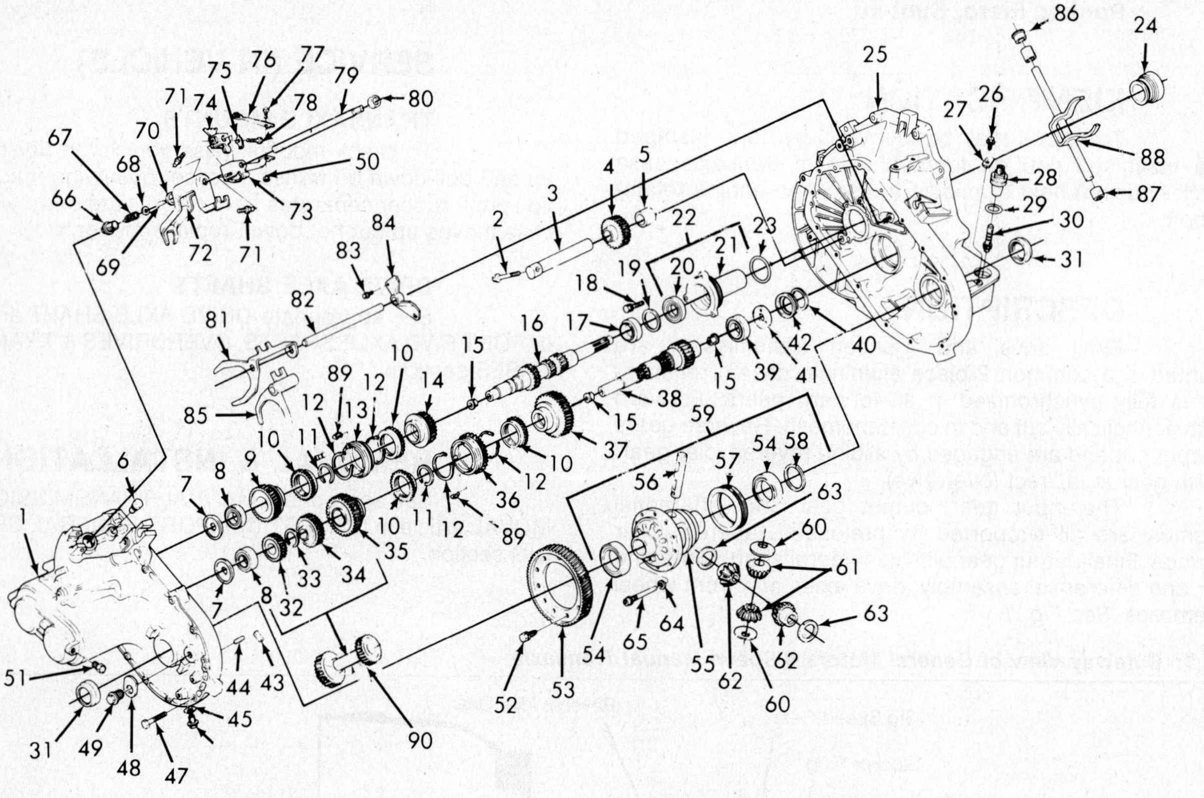

1. Transaxle Case
2. Reverse Idler Screw
3. Reverse Idler Shaft
4. Reverse Idler Gear
5. Reverse Idler Shaft Spacer
6. Vent Assembly
7. Oil Shield
8. Bearing Assembly
9. 4th Gear Input
10. Synchronizer Blocking Ring
11. Synchronizer Retaining Ring
12. Synchronizer Key Retaining Ring
13. Synchronizer Assembly
14. 3rd Gear Input
15. Oil Shield Sleeve
16. Input Cluster Gear
17. Input Bearing Assembly
18. Screw
19. Input Gear Bearing Adjustment Shim
20. Input Gear Seal Assembly
21. Input Gear Retainer
22. Input Gear Bearing Retainer Assembly
23. Input Gear Bearing Retainer Seal
24. Clutch Release Bearing Assembly
25. Clutch & Differential Housing
26. Screw
27. Speedometer Gear Retainer
28. Speedometer Driven Gear Sleeve
29. Speedometer Gear Sleeve Seal
30. Speedometer Driven Gear
31. Axle Shaft Seal
32. 4th Speed Output Gear
33. 3rd Speed Output Gear Retaining Ring
34. 3rd Speed Output Gear
35. 2nd Speed Output Gear
36. Synchronizer Assembly
37. 1st Gear Output
38. Output Gear
39. Output Bearing Assembly
40. Output Gear Bearing Adjustment Shim
41. Output Bearing Oil Shield
42. Output Gear Bearing Oil Shield Retainer
43. Magnet
44. Pin
45. Drain Screw Washer
46. Drain Screw
47. Bolt
48. Fill Plug Washer
49. Fill Plug
50. Nut
51. Plug
52. Bolt
53. Differential Ring Gear
54. Differential Bearing
55. Differential Case
56. Differential Pinion Shaft
57. Speedometer Drive Gear
58. Differential Bearing Adjustment Shim
59. Differential Assembly
60. Pinion Thrust Washer
61. Differential Pinion Gear
62. Differential Side Gear
63. Side Gear Thrust Washer
64. Lock Washer
65. Pinion Shaft Screw
66. Reverse Inhibitor Spring Seat
67. Reverse Inhibitor Spring
68. Reverse Inhibitor Spring Washer
69. Pin
70. Shift Shaft Shim
71. Reverse Lever Locating Stud
72. Reverse Shift Lever
73. Shift Interlock
74. Detent Lever Assembly
75. Lock Detent Lever Washer
76. Detent Spring
77. Bolt
78. Bolt
79. Shift Shaft
80. Shift Shaft Seal Assembly
81. 3rd-4th Shift Fork
82. Shift Fork Shaft
83. Screw
84. Oil Guide
85. 1st-2nd Shift Fork
86. Clutch Fork Shaft Seal
87. Clutch Fork Shaft Bearing
88. Clutch Fork Shaft
89. Synchronizer Keys
90. 3rd & 4th Output Gear (MX6 ONLY)

GENERAL MOTORS 4-SPEED TRANSAXLES – 76 MM (Cont.)

DISASSEMBLY

TRANSAXLE

1) Place transaxle assembly into Work Stand (J-28408) to prevent assembly from falling over. Remove 15 bolts retaining clutch cover.

2) Using soft mallet, tap clutch cover from case. *See Fig. 3.* Remove ring gear and differential assembly.

Fig. 3: Transaxle with Clutch Cover Removed

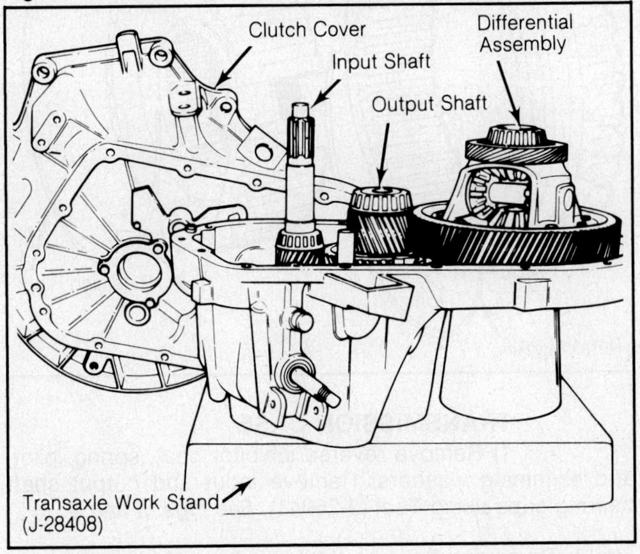

3) Position shifter shaft in neutral position, so shifter moves easily and is not engaged in any drive gear. Remove bolt from shifter shaft. Remove shaft and shift forks from synchronizer forks.

4) Remove reverse shift fork by disengaging it from guide pin and interlock bracket. Remove the lock bolt securing the reverse idler gear shaft. Remove the gear, shaft and spacer assembly.

5) Remove detent shift lever and interlock assembly. Leave shift forks engaged with synchronizers. Grasp input and output shafts and lift them from transaxle case as an assembly. *See Fig. 4.* After noting shift fork positions for reassembly reference, remove shift forks.

Fig. 4: Input and Output Shafts With Shift Forks

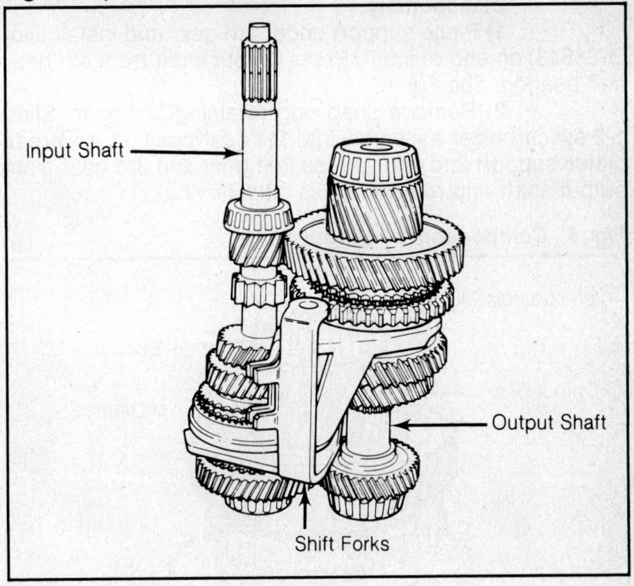

COMPONENT DISASSEMBLY & REASSEMBLY

INPUT SHAFT

Disassembly

1) Support 4th gear with bearing remover (J-22912-01). Press on end of shaft furthest from clutch in normal installed position. Remove 4th gear and outer bearing from shaft.

2) Remove brass blocker ring and snap ring from 3-4 synchronizer. Supporting 3rd gear, press 3rd gear and 3-4 synchronizer from shaft. *See Fig. 5.*

3) Using Bearing Remover (J-26946) to hold bearing, press shaft from bearing nearest clutch end.

Reassembly

1) Lubricate all parts and install on clutch end of shaft, using Bearing Installer (J-28406). Turn shaft end for end in press and install 3rd gear. Install brass blocker ring onto gear cone and install 3-4 synchronizer.

Fig. 5: Components of Input Shaft

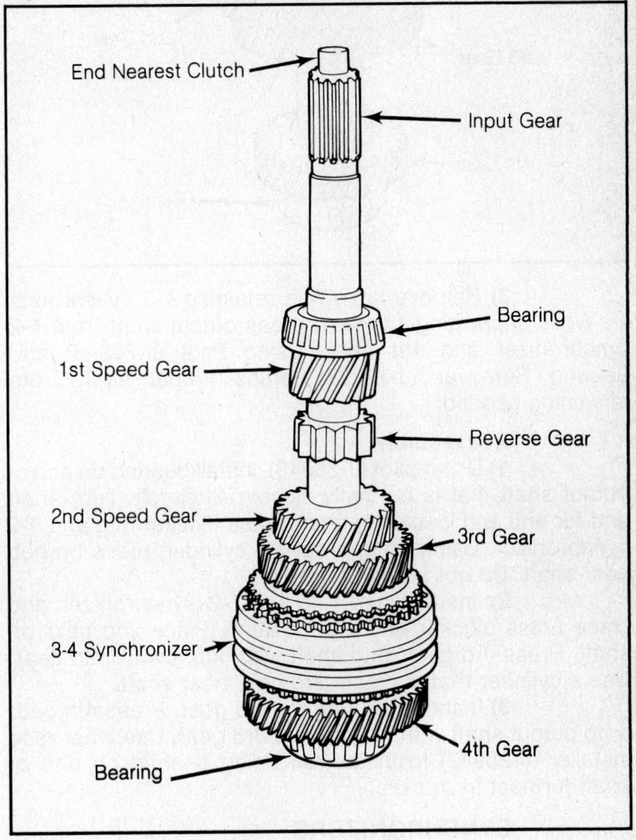

NOTE: **Use an appropriate cylinder to contact hub near shaft. Do not press on sleeve portion. Both synchronizers are press fits to shaft.**

2) Install snap ring to hold 3-4 synchronizer, making sure beveled edge of ring is away from synchronizer. Install blocker ring. Install 4th gear onto shaft, and using Inner Race Installer (J-26942), install bearing furthest from clutch end onto shaft.

GENERAL MOTORS 4-SPEED TRANSAXLES – 76 MM (Cont.)

OUTPUT SHAFT

Disassembly

1) Place support under 4th gear and install pilot (J-26943) on end of shaft. Press output shaft from 4th gear and bearing. *See Fig. 6.*

2) Remove snap ring retaining 3rd gear. Slide 1-2 synchronizer assembly into 1st gear position, so press plates support 2nd gear. Press 2nd gear and 3rd gear from output shaft and remove brass blocker ring.

Fig. 6: Components of Output Shaft

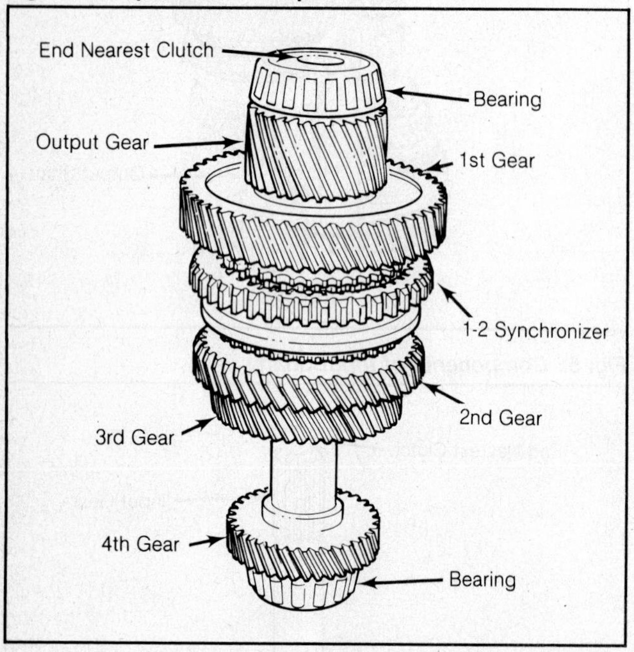

3) Remove snap ring retaining 1-2 synchronizer. While supporting 1st gear, press output shaft from 1-2 synchronizer and 1st gear. Using Pilot (J-26943) and Bearing Remover (J-22227), press output shaft from remaining bearing.

Reassembly

1) Using pilot (J-26943), install bearing on end of output shaft that is normally closest to clutch. Turn shaft end for end and install 1st gear, brass blocker ring and 1-2 synchronizer. Using an appropriate cylinder, press on hub near shaft. Do not press on sleeve.

2) Install snap ring for 1-2 synchronizer and place brass blocker ring into position. Place 2nd gear on shaft. Press 3rd gear onto shaft with hub toward 4th gear. Use a cylinder that contacts 3rd gear near shaft.

3) Install snap ring for 3rd gear. Press 4th gear onto output shaft with hub toward 3rd gear. Use inner race installer (J-26942) to install remaining bearing on end of shaft furthest from clutch.

SYNCHRONIZERS

Disassembly

Using care, pry out both synchronizer retaining rings. Separate hub, sleeve, and 3 keys, noting their position. *See Fig. 7.* Scribe hub to sleeve location and separate. Clean, inspect, and replace parts, as necessary.

Reassembly

1) Assemble hub to sleeve with lip of hub away from shift fork groove in sleeve. Align scribe marks. Carefully install retaining ring, prying it back to insert keys one at a time.

2) Flats on retaining ring should hold keys in place. Install retaining ring on opposite side of hub, so open end of ring does not align with open end of first ring.

Fig. 7: Components of Synchronizer Assemblies

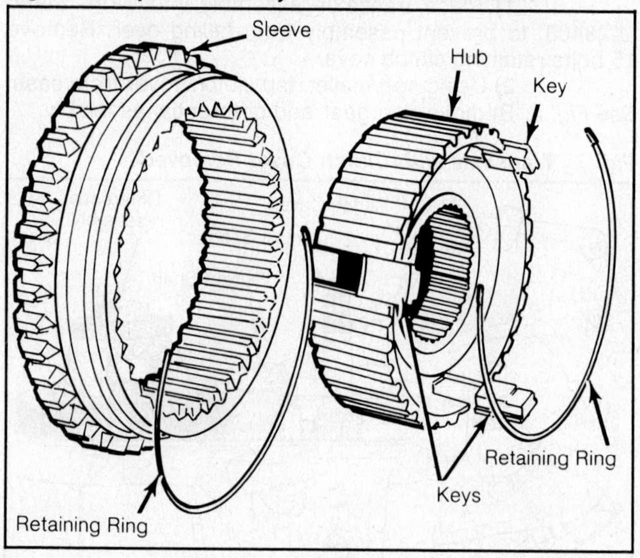

TRANSMISSION CASE

1) Remove reverse inhibitor seat, spring, pilot, and shimming washers. Remove input and output shaft bearing cups using Tool (J-26941). *See Figs. 8 and 9.*

Fig. 8: Removing Reverse Inhibitor Assembly

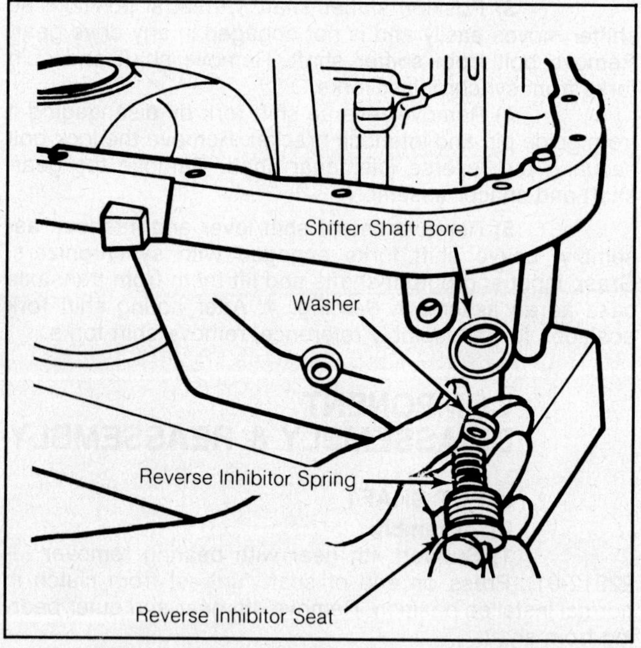

2) Remove oil slingers. Using bearing cup remover (J-26941), remove differential side bearing cup. Turn tool's set screw counterclockwise to insert tool below bearing cup. Then turn clockwise to grasp cut.

3) Inspect 2 guide pins for interlock bracket and reverse shift fork. Also check magnet. Remove sealant from transmission case surface that mates with clutch cover.

4) Take care not to gouge mating surfaces, as leaks could result. Clean all parts. Replace parts, as necessary, after careful inspection.

GENERAL MOTORS 4-SPEED TRANSAXLES – 76 MM (Cont.)

Fig. 9: Removing Bearing Cups

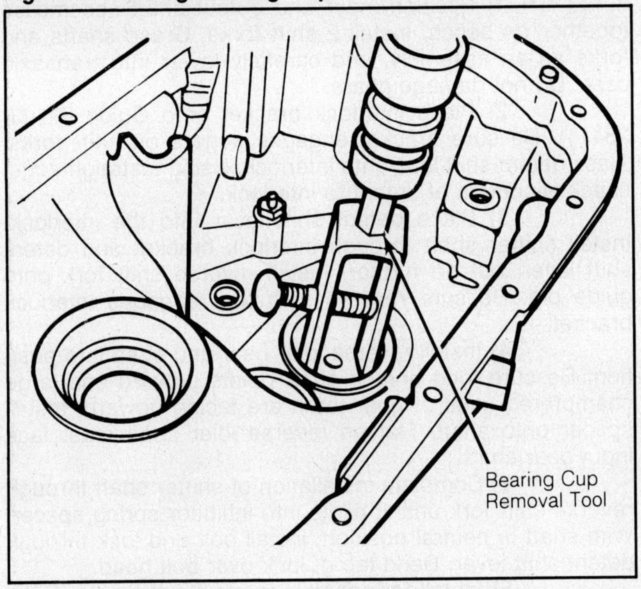

Use Bearing Cup Remover (J-26941). When installing cups, use Bearing Cup Installer (J-26938).

CLUTCH COVER

Disassembly

1) Using Bearing Cup Remover (J-26941), remove differential side bearing cup and shim from cover. Remove input and output shaft bearing cups with same tool. Remove oil shield, shim, and retainer from under output shaft bearing cup.

2) Remove input gear bearing retainer (release bearing sleeve). Tap carefully, if necessary, to remove. Remove external oil ring and internal oil seal from sleeve. Remove plastic oil scoop.

3) If replacement of clutch fork shaft or bushing is necessary, use Bushing Remover/Installer (J-28412) for both removal and installation. Always replace seal after installing clutch fork shaft or bushing. *See Fig. 10.*

Fig. 10: Replacing Clutch Fork Shaft and Bushings

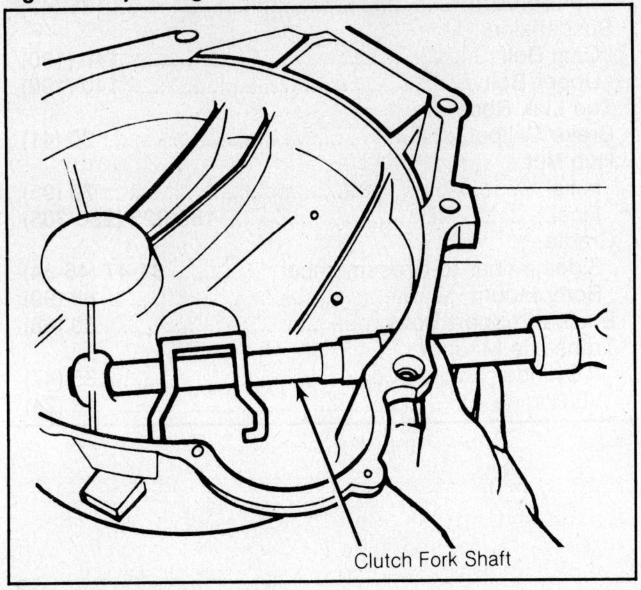

4) Remove sealant from cover mating surfaces, using care not to damage surfaces. Clean and inspect all parts, replacing those that are damaged.

Reassembly

Install plastic oil scoop, replace external square cut oil ring on sleeves. Install input bearing retainer (release bearing sleeve). Using bearing cup installer (J-26936), install internal oil seal. Reverse remainder of disassembly procedures.

DIFFERENTIAL CASE & RING GEAR

Disassembly

1) Separate ring gear from differential case. Remove pinion shaft lock bolt and pinion shaft. Roll gears and thrust washers out through opening in case.

2) If differential side bearings are to be replaced, use puller (J-22888 and J-22888-30). Use cone installer (J-22919) when installing bearings. Clean and inspect all parts. Replace parts, where necessary.

Reassembly

Install gears and thrust washers into case. Install pinion shaft and lock bolt. Attach ring gear to differential case using appropriate lock compound on bolts. Torque to specifications.

REASSEMBLY

TRANSAXLE

Shim Selection

NOTE: **Shims may be selected for proper preload as soon as input and output shaft assemblies and differential assembly are reassembled and ready for installation in transaxle case.**

1) Place transaxle case into holding fixture (J-28408). *See Fig. 3.* Install 3 bearing races into case, and install input, output and differential assemblies in position. Install remaining 3 bearing races onto their respective bearings.

2) Install Gauges over each bearing (J-26935-2 for input shaft; J-26935-4 for output shaft; and J-26935-3 for differential shaft). *See Fig. 11.* Be sure bearing races fit smoothly in bores of gauges.

3) Install metal oil shield retainer into bore on top of Output Shaft Gauge (J-26935-4). Carefully assemble clutch cover over gauges and onto transaxle case, using 7 spacers evenly around case mating surfaces.

4) Install bolts supplied and tighten bolts alternately to gradually draw clutch cover to transaxle case. Tighten bolts to 10 ft. lbs. (14 N.m) to compress gauge sleeves.

5) Rotate each gauge to seat bearings. Rotate differential case 3 revolutions in each direction. With gauges compressed, measure gap between outer sleeve and base pad of each shaft. This will provide the shim thickness required for proper bearing preloading at each shaft. *See Fig. 12.*

6) On the output and differential shafts use one size smaller than the largest shim that can be placed into the gap and drawn through without binding. On the input shaft, use a shim 2 sizes smaller. When shims are selected, remove clutch cover, spacers and gauges.

GENERAL MOTORS 4-SPEED TRANSAXLES – 76 MM (Cont.)

Fig. 11: Installing Gauges Over Shaft Bearings

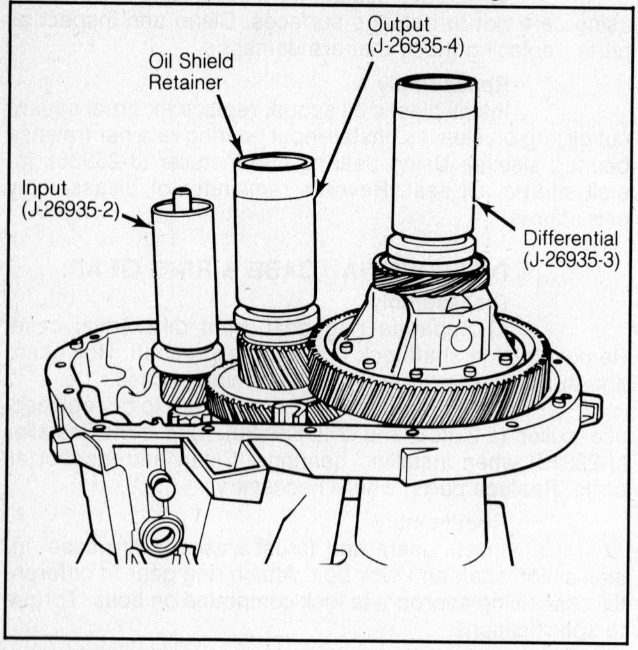

Fig. 12: Measuring Gap to Determine Preload Shim Requirements

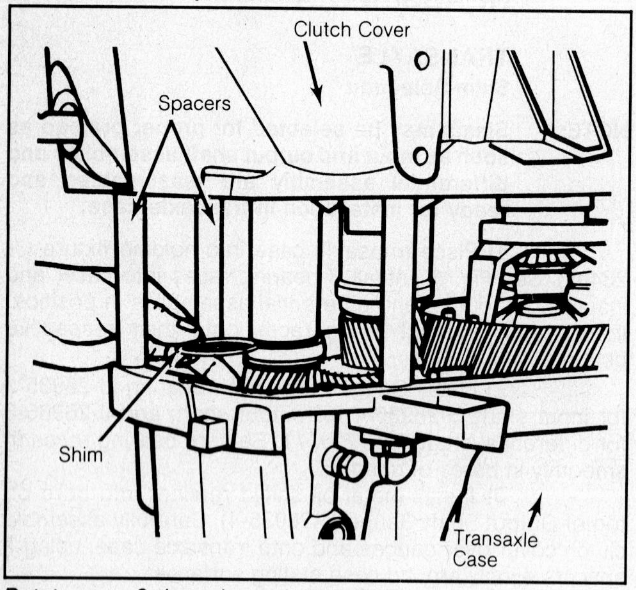

Rotate case 3 times in each direction.

7) Install shims into their respective bores in clutch cover. Add metal shield, and install bearing cups, using Cup Installer (J-26936 on input shaft; J-23423-A on output shaft; and J-26938 on differential bearing cup).

Case

1) Position input and output shaft assemblies together on bench. Install 2 shift forks. Grasp shafts and

Case

1) Position input and output shaft assemblies together on bench. Install 2 shift forks. Grasp shafts and forks as an assembly, and carefully lower into transaxle case. Do not damage gears.

2) Place interlock bracket onto Guide Pin (J-28411). Be sure bracket engages fingers on shift forks. Place detent shift lever into interlock. Using a straightedge, check alignment of detent to interlock.

3) Place detent shift lever into the interlock. Install shifter shaft through interlock bracket and detent shift lever, but no further. Install reverse shift fork onto guide pin. Be sure reverse shift fork engages interlock bracket.

4) Install reverse idler gear and shaft into position. Be sure long end of shaft points upward and large champfered ends of gear tooth are facing upward. Install spacer onto shaft. Flat on reverse idler shaft must face input gear shaft.

5) Complete installation of shifter shaft through reverse shift fork until it pilots into inhibitor spring spacer. With shaft in neutral position, install bolt and lock through detent shift lever. Bend tab of lock over bolt head.

6) Install fork shaft through synchronizer forks and into bore in case. Carefully install ring gear and differential case assembly. Install magnet.

7) Apply a thin bead of sealant to clutch cover and carefully install cover onto transaxle case. Use dowel pins to guide cover into position. Tap clutch cover lightly with soft mallet to seat parts securely.

8) Install 15 retaining bolts and tighten idler shaft retaining bolt in case. Shift through gear ranges to test that all parts move freely.

TIGHTENING SPECIFICATIONS

Application	Ft. Lbs. (N.m)
Case-to-Clutch Cover	
Shim Selection	10 (14)
Final Assembly	16 (22)
Engine-to-Transaxle	55 (75)
Stabilizer Bar Bushing Retainer	
Crossmember	40 (54)
Control Arm	35 (47)
Suspension	
Cam Bolt	140 (190)
Upper Bolt	140 (190)
Toe Link Rod-	
Brake Caliper	30 (41)
Hub Nut	
Initial	70 (95)
Final	185-225 (250-305)
Cradle	
Sidemember-to-Crossmember	34-47 (46-64)
Body Mount	66 (90)
Engine Support Bolts	50 (68)
Transaxle Mounts	
4-Cylinder Engine	35 (47)
V6 Engine	18 (24)

GENERAL MOTORS 5-SPEED MANUAL TRANSAXLE

Buick Skyhawk, Cadillac Cimarron, Chevrolet Cavalier, Oldsmobile Firenza, Pontiac Sunbird

IDENTIFICATION

Transaxle may be identified by code stamped on a machined pad on forward side of transaxle case (clutch housing) next to middle transaxle-to-engine retaining bolt.

DESCRIPTION

Final drive and 5-speed transmission are mounted in a common 2-piece aluminum case. Transmission is fully synchronized in all forward gears. Forward gears are helically cut and in constant mesh. Reverse gears are spur cut and are engaged by sliding reverse idler gear.

The input gear, output gear and differential assembly are all supported by preloaded tapered roller bearings. Final output gear with its integral shaft, turns ring gear and differential assembly, drive axles, and front wheel assemblies. *See Fig. 1.*

Gears are shifted by 2 cable assemblies, the trans-selector and trans-shifter cables.

SERVICE (IN VEHICLE)

TRANSAXLE MOUNTS

To check mounts, raise vehicle on hoist. Push up and pull down on transaxle case. If rubber separates from metal plate or mount, or if case moves up but not down, replace mount.

DRIVE AXLE SHAFTS

See appropriate DRIVE AXLE SHAFT article in DOMESTIC AXLE SHAFTS & TRANSFER CASES section.

REMOVAL & INSTALLATION

See appropriate MANUAL TRANSMISSION REMOVAL article in DOMESTIC GENERAL SERVICING section.

DISASSEMBLY

TRANSAXLE

1) Attach transaxle assembly to Holding Fixture (J-33366) and attach fixture to Base Plate (J-3389-20). Remove 7 bolts retaining clutch cover.

Fig. 1: Sectional View of General Motors 5-Speed Manual Transaxle

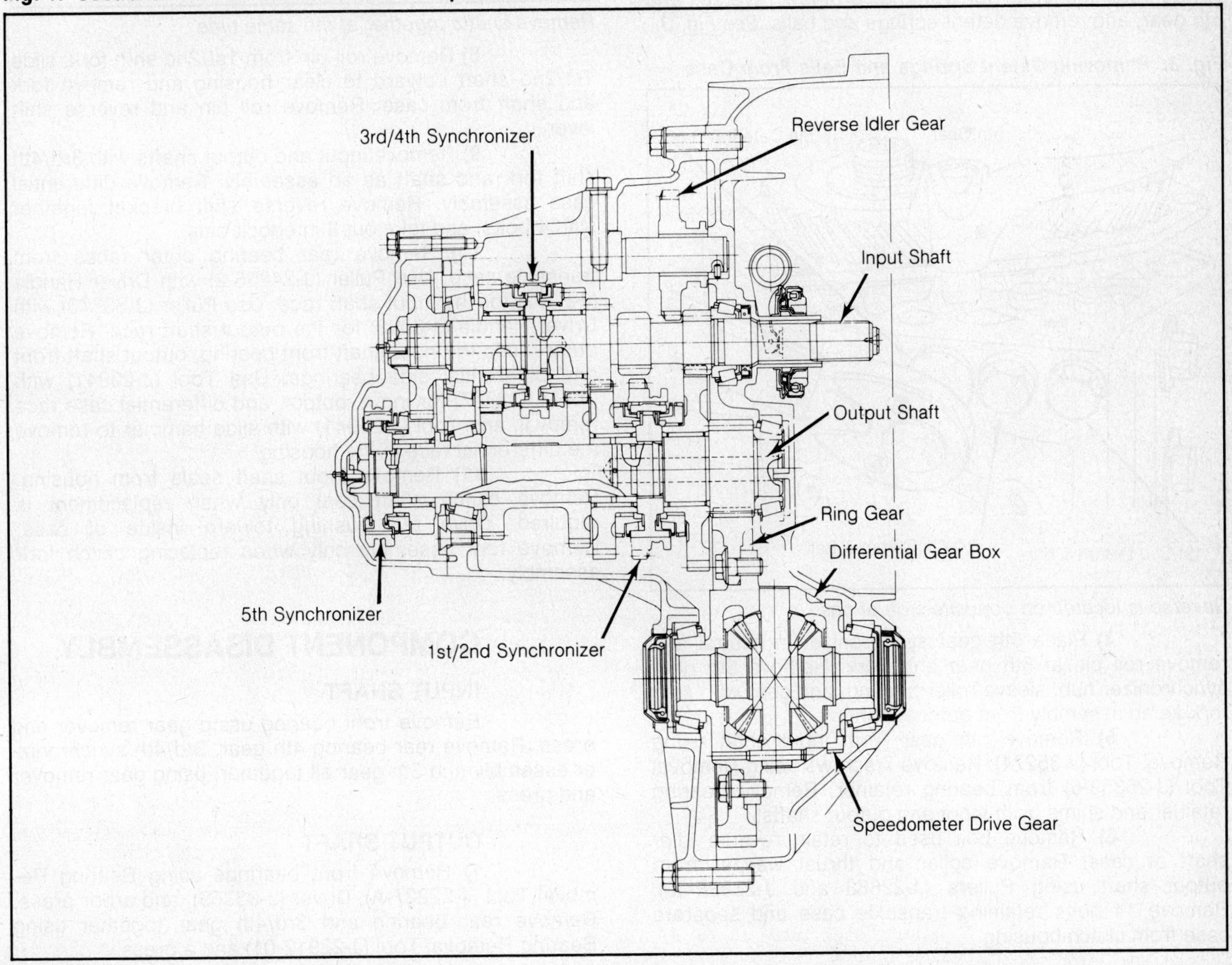

GENERAL MOTORS 5-SPEED MANUAL TRANSAXLE (Cont.)

2) Remove control box assembly together with 4 bolts from transaxle case. Shift transaxle into gear and remove 5th gear drive and driven gear retaining nuts from input and output shaft. *See Fig. 2.*

Fig. 2: Removing 5th Gear Retaining Nut

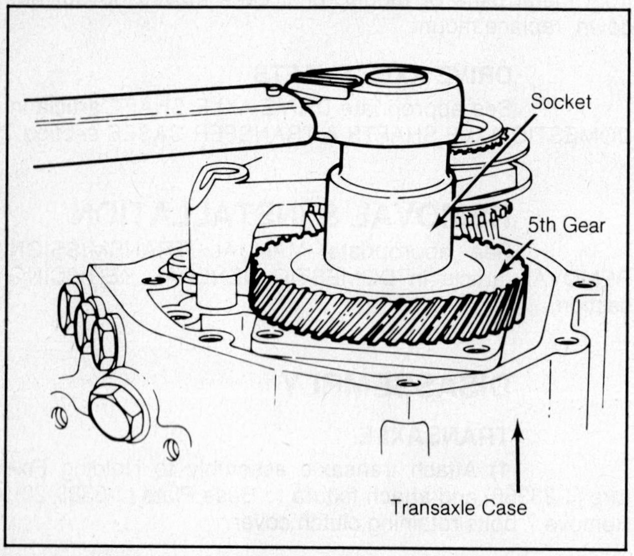

3) Shift transaxle to neutral. Remove detent spring retaining bolts for 1st/2nd, 3rd/4th, reverse, and 5th gear, and remove detent springs and balls. *See Fig. 3.*

Fig. 3: Removing Detent Springs and Balls From Case

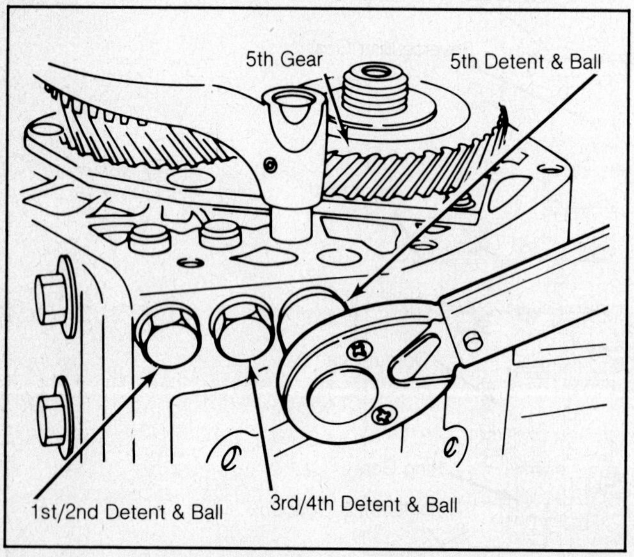

Reverse is located on opposite side of case.

4) Place 5th gear synchronizer in neutral and remove roll pin at 5th gear shift fork. Remove 5th gear synchronizer hub, sleeve roller bearing, and gear with shift fork as an assembly from output shaft.

5) Remove 5th gear from input shaft using Removal Tool (J-35274). Remove 7 screws using Removal Tool (J-25359-6) from bearing retainer. Remove bearing retainer and shims from input and output shafts.

6) Remove bolt used to retain reverse idler shaft at case. Remove collar and thrust washer from output shaft using Pullers (J-22888 and J-22888-30). Remove 14 bolts retaining transaxle case and separate case from clutch housing.

7) Remove reverse idler gear and reverse idler shaft. Lift 5th gear shaft. With detent aligned facing the same way and remove 5th and reverse shafts at the same time. *See Fig. 4.*

Fig. 4: Proper Position to Remove 5th and Reverse Shifter Shafts

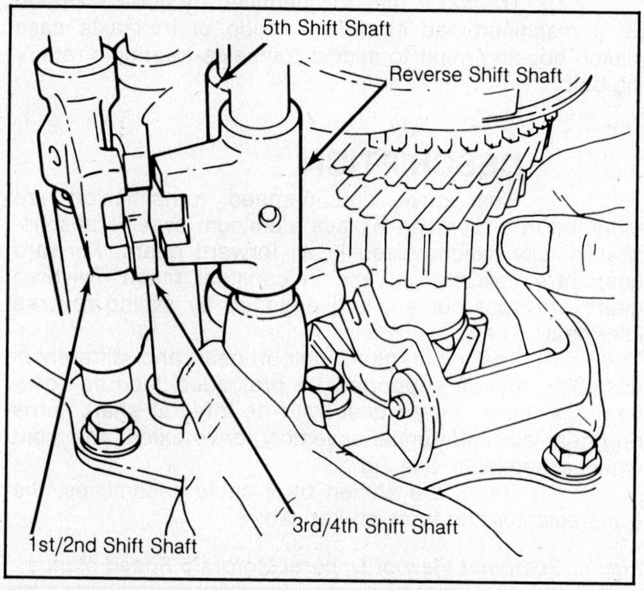

Remove shafts together at the same time.

8) Remove roll pin from 1st/2nd shift fork, slide 1st/2nd shaft upward to clear housing and remove fork and shaft from case. Remove roll pin and reverse shift lever.

9) Remove input and output shafts with 3rd/4th shift fork and shaft as an assembly. Remove differential case assembly. Remove reverse shift bracket together with 4 bolts, and take out 3 interlock pins.

10) Remove rear bearing outer races from transaxle case. Use Puller (J-24256-2) with Driver Handle (J-8092) for the input shaft race. Use Puller (J-33370) with Driver Handle (J-8092) for the output shaft race. Remove outer races for input shaft front bearing, output shaft front and differential side bearings. Use Tool (J-26941) with Tool (J-33367) for input, output, and differential case race removal, and Tool (J-26941) with slide hammer to remove the differential race in the housing.

11) Remove input shaft seals from housing. Remove clutch shaft seal only when replacement is required. Drive out bushing toward inside of case. Remove fork assembly only when replacing clutch fork assembly.

COMPONENT DISASSEMBLY

INPUT SHAFT

Remove front bearing using gear remover and press. Remove rear bearing 4th gear, 3rd/4th synchronizer assembly and 3th gear all together, using gear remover and press.

OUTPUT SHAFT

1) Remove front bearings using Bearing Removal Tool (J-22227-A), Driver (J-33369), and arbor press. Remove rear bearing and 3rd/4th gear together using Bearing Removal Tool (J-22912-01) and a press.

GENERAL MOTORS 5-SPEED MANUAL TRANSAXLE (Cont.)

Fig. 5: Exploded View 5-Speed Manual Transaxle Gear Assemblies

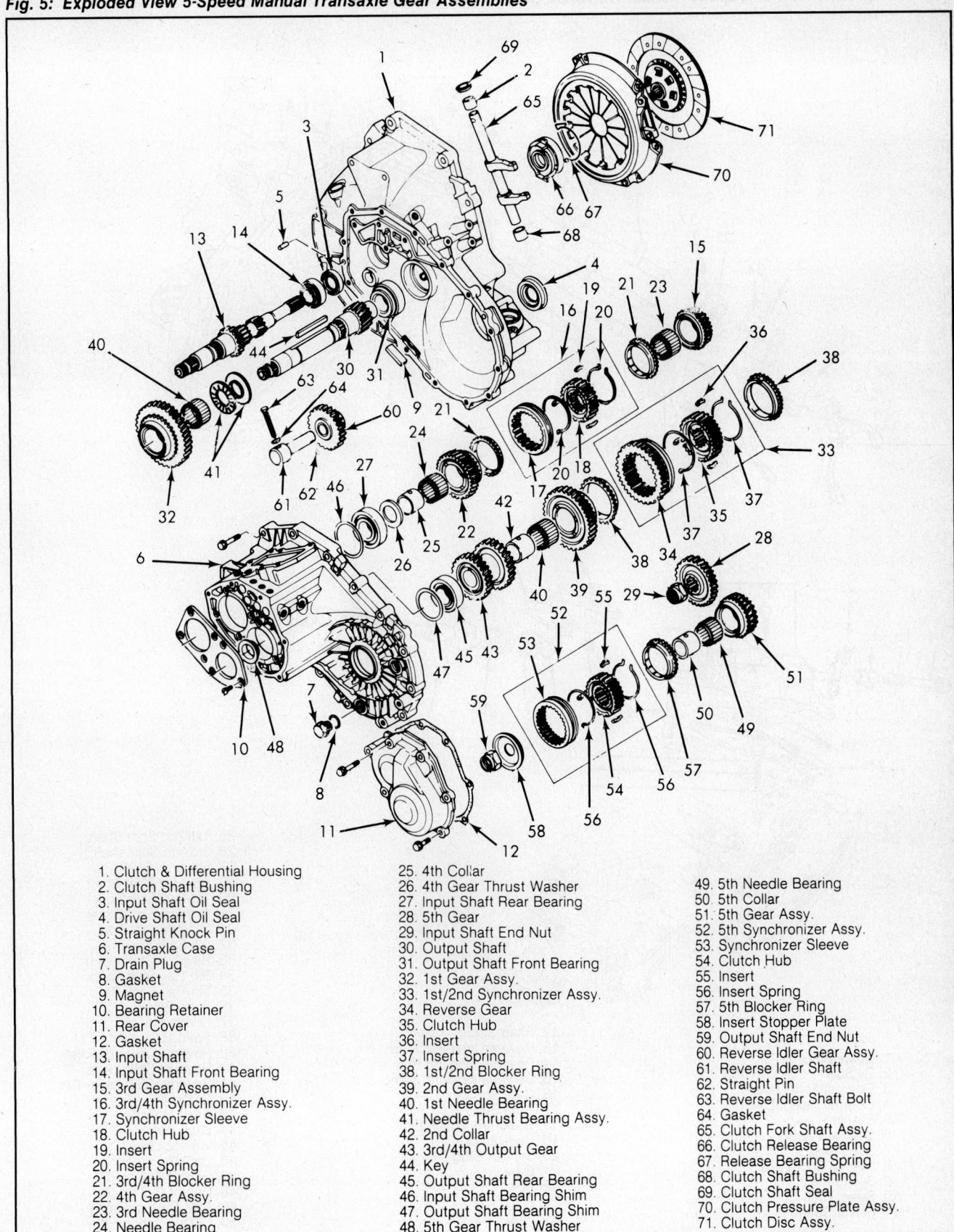

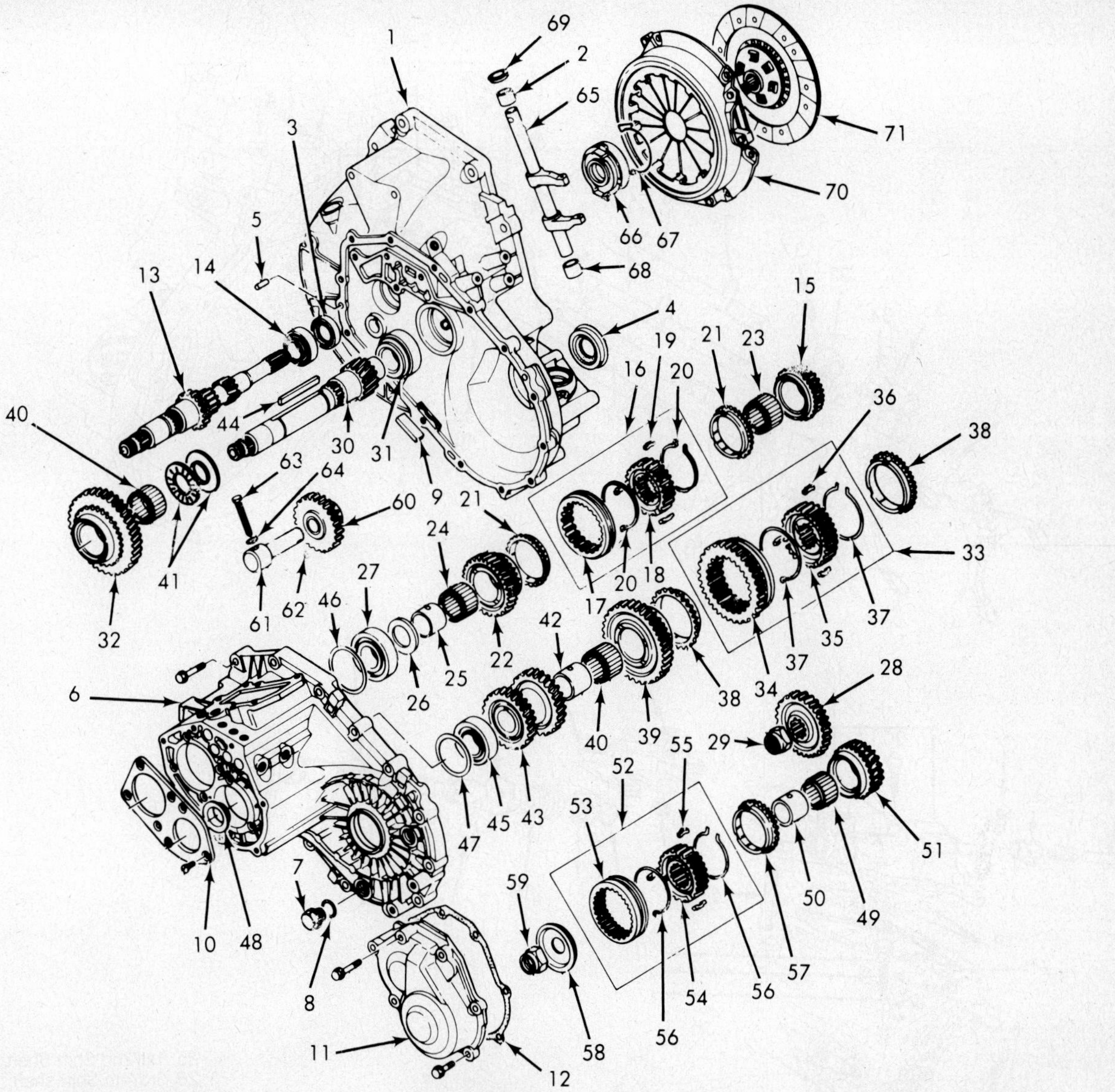

1. Clutch & Differential Housing
2. Clutch Shaft Bushing
3. Input Shaft Oil Seal
4. Drive Shaft Oil Seal
5. Straight Knock Pin
6. Transaxle Case
7. Drain Plug
8. Gasket
9. Magnet
10. Bearing Retainer
11. Rear Cover
12. Gasket
13. Input Shaft
14. Input Shaft Front Bearing
15. 3rd Gear Assembly
16. 3rd/4th Synchronizer Assy.
17. Synchronizer Sleeve
18. Clutch Hub
19. Insert
20. Insert Spring
21. 3rd/4th Blocker Ring
22. 4th Gear Assy.
23. 3rd Needle Bearing
24. Needle Bearing
25. 4th Collar
26. 4th Gear Thrust Washer
27. Input Shaft Rear Bearing
28. 5th Gear
29. Input Shaft End Nut
30. Output Shaft
31. Output Shaft Front Bearing
32. 1st Gear Assy.
33. 1st/2nd Synchronizer Assy.
34. Reverse Gear
35. Clutch Hub
36. Insert
37. Insert Spring
38. 1st/2nd Blocker Ring
39. 2nd Gear Assy.
40. 1st Needle Bearing
41. Needle Thrust Bearing Assy.
42. 2nd Collar
43. 3rd/4th Output Gear
44. Key
45. Output Shaft Rear Bearing
46. Input Shaft Bearing Shim
47. Output Shaft Bearing Shim
48. 5th Gear Thrust Washer
49. 5th Needle Bearing
50. 5th Collar
51. 5th Gear Assy.
52. 5th Synchronizer Assy.
53. Synchronizer Sleeve
54. Clutch Hub
55. Insert
56. Insert Spring
57. 5th Blocker Ring
58. Insert Stopper Plate
59. Output Shaft End Nut
60. Reverse Idler Gear Assy.
61. Reverse Idler Shaft
62. Straight Pin
63. Reverse Idler Shaft Bolt
64. Gasket
65. Clutch Fork Shaft Assy.
66. Clutch Release Bearing
67. Release Bearing Spring
68. Clutch Shaft Bushing
69. Clutch Shaft Seal
70. Clutch Pressure Plate Assy.
71. Clutch Disc Assy.

GENERAL MOTORS 5-SPEED MANUAL TRANSAXLE (Cont.)

Fig. 6: Exploded View of 5-Speed Manual Transaxle Gear Shifter Assemblies

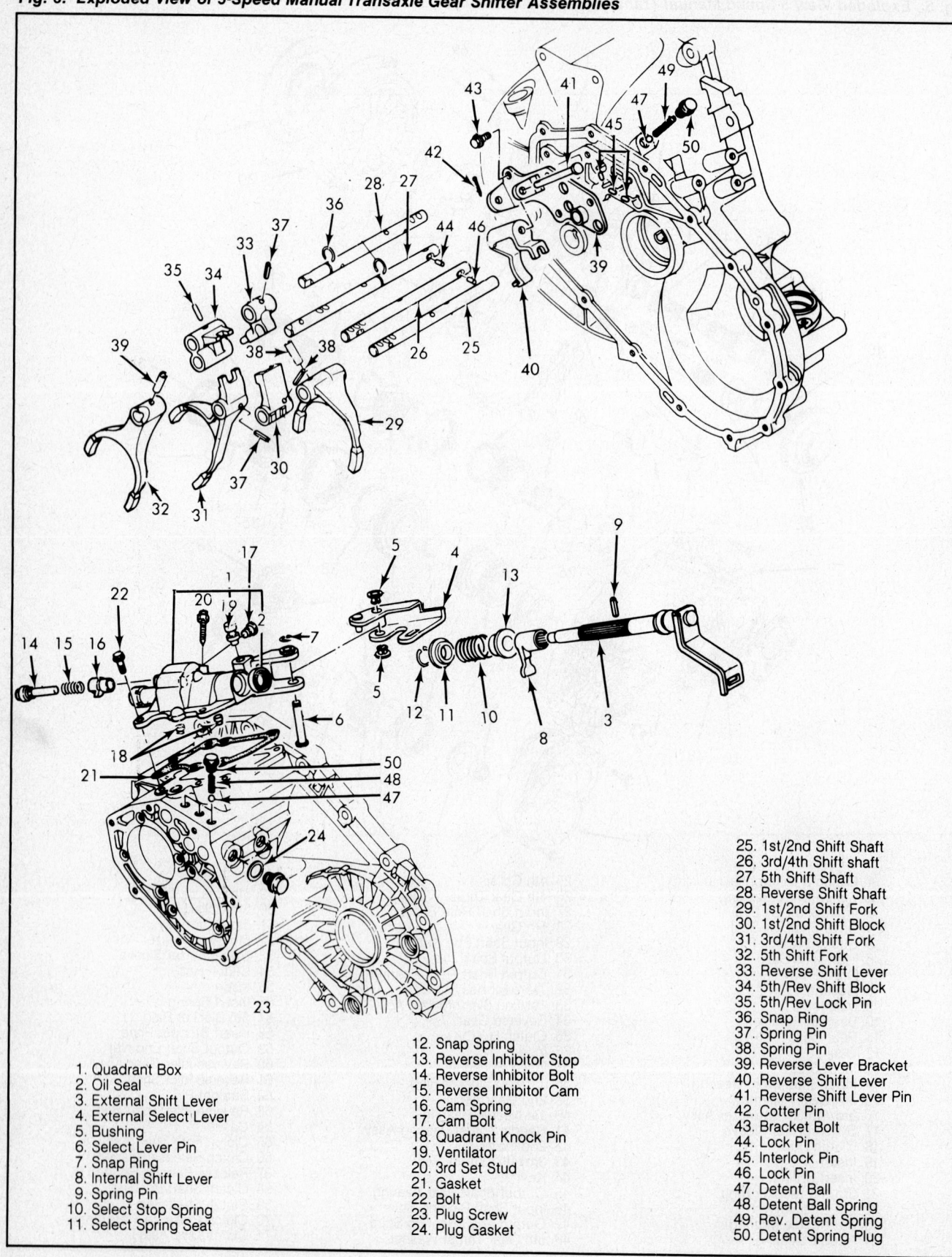

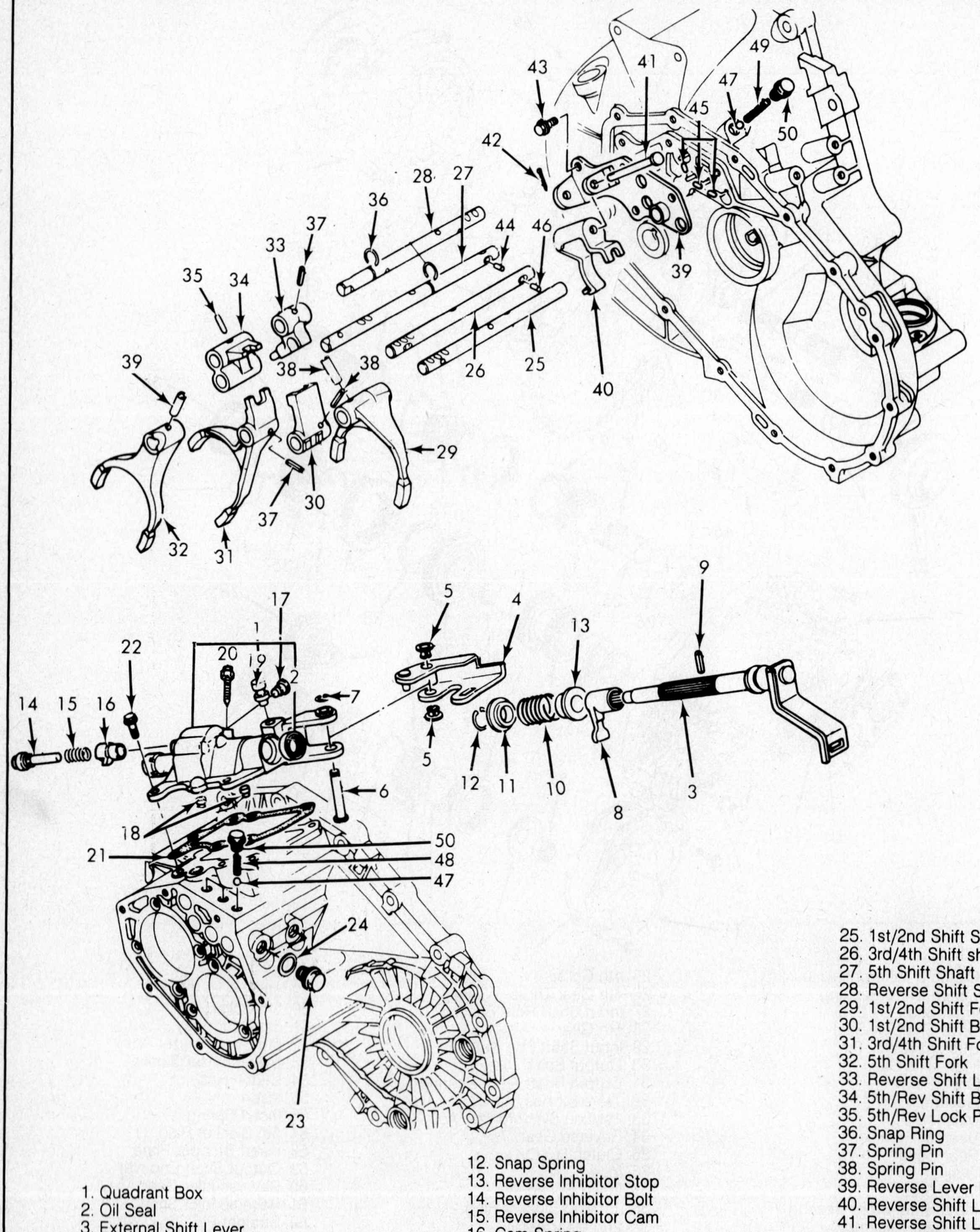

1. Quadrant Box
2. Oil Seal
3. External Shift Lever
4. External Select Lever
5. Bushing
6. Select Lever Pin
7. Snap Ring
8. Internal Shift Lever
9. Spring Pin
10. Select Stop Spring
11. Select Spring Seat
12. Snap Spring
13. Reverse Inhibitor Stop
14. Reverse Inhibitor Bolt
15. Reverse Inhibitor Cam
16. Cam Spring
17. Cam Bolt
18. Quadrant Knock Pin
19. Ventilator
20. 3rd Set Stud
21. Gasket
22. Bolt
23. Plug Screw
24. Plug Gasket
25. 1st/2nd Shift Shaft
26. 3rd/4th Shift shaft
27. 5th Shift Shaft
28. Reverse Shift Shaft
29. 1st/2nd Shift Fork
30. 1st/2nd Shift Block
31. 3rd/4th Shift Fork
32. 5th Shift Fork
33. Reverse Shift Lever
34. 5th/Rev Shift Block
35. 5th/Rev Lock Pin
36. Snap Ring
37. Spring Pin
38. Spring Pin
39. Reverse Lever Bracket
40. Reverse Shift Lever
41. Reverse Shift Lever Pin
42. Cotter Pin
43. Bracket Bolt
44. Lock Pin
45. Interlock Pin
46. Lock Pin
47. Detent Ball
48. Detent Ball Spring
49. Rev. Detent Spring
50. Detent Spring Plug

GENERAL MOTORS 5-SPEED MANUAL TRANSAXLE (Cont.)

2) Remove key, 2nd gear, needle bearing, and blocker ring. Remove collar, reverse gear assembly, and 1st gear all together by using arbor press.

DIFFERENTIAL

1) Remove side bearings using bearing puller. Remove 10 bolts from ring gear and discard. Remove gear. Remove speedometer drive gear and discard.

2) Drive out lockpin, and pull out cross pin. Remove pinion gears and thrust washers. Remove side gears and thrust washers.

SYNCHRONIZERS

Using care, pry out both synchronizer retaining rings. Separate hub, sleeve, and 3 keys, noting their position. *See Fig. 7.* Scribe hub to sleeve location and separate. Clean, inspect, and replace parts, as necessary.

Fig. 7: Components of Synchronizer Assemblies

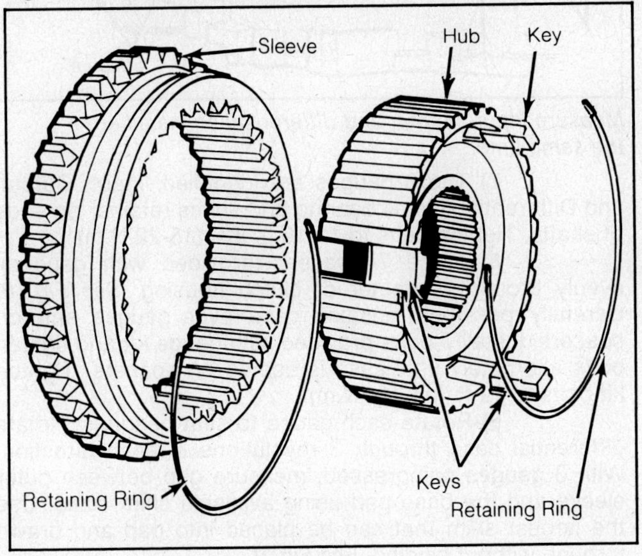

CLEANING & INSPECTION

1) Wash all parts, except oil seals, in cleaning solvent. Brush or scrape all foreign matter from parts, using care not to damage any part with scraper. Do not clean, wash, or soak transaxle seals in cleaning solvent. Dry all parts with compressed air.

CAUTION: Hold roller bearing assembly to prevent it from rotating when drying it with compressed air.

2) Lubricate all bearings with approved transmission lubricant and wrap them in a clean, lint free cloth, or paper until ready to use.

3) Inspect transaxle case and clutch housing case for cracks, worn, or damaged bearing bores. Check for damaged threads or any other damage. Inspect mating surfaces on cases for small nicks or burrs that could cause misalignment of the 2 halves. Remove all small nicks or burrs with a fine stone or file.

4) Check reverse idler gear and sliding gear for chipped, broken, or bent teeth. Check reverse idler gear for bushing damage. Check wear of reverse idler gear shaft (it is normal for front of teeth to show wear, this does not interfere with proper function).

5) Check teeth, splines, and journals of mainshaft for damage. Check all other gears for chipped, broken, or worn teeth. Check for eroded clutching teeth and damaged bearing surfaces. Clutching teeth will usually show rounding of the points which does not interfere with normal operation.

6) Check synchronizer sleeves for free movement on hubs. Make sure index marks are properly aligned. Check for damaged clutching teeth. Check for proper positioning of springs.

7) Inspect synchronizer blocker rings for wear marks on spline end back face which indicates ring was bottoming on gear face due to excessive blocker ring wear.

8) Inspect differential pinion and side gears for scoring, excessive wear, nicks, and chips. Worn, scored, and damaged gears must be replaced.

NOTE: When a scored or chipped gear is replaced, transaxle case must be cleaned thoroughly to make sure all chips are removed.

9) Make sure differential case bearing journals are smooth. Inspect case bearing shoulders for damage caused by bearing removal. Check fit (free rotation) of side gears in their cavities.

10) Check differential bearings and bearing races for wear or other damage. If races are not damaged, do not remove from transaxle case or clutch housing case. Check bearings for smooth rotation in races. Examine bearing roller ends for step wear.

NOTE: If inspection reveals either a damaged bearing or race, both parts must be replaced as they are a matched set.

COMPONENT REASSEMBLY

SYNCHRONIZERS

1) Assemble hub to sleeve with lip of hub away from shift fork groove in sleeve. Align scribe marks. Carefully install retaining ring, prying it back to insert keys one at a time.

2) Flats on retaining ring should hold keys in place. Install retaining ring on opposite side of hub, so open end of ring does not align with open end of first ring.

INPUT SHAFT

1) Install needle bearing, 3th gear, and block ring onto shaft. Match inserts of 3rd/4th sleeve and hub assembly with grooves of blocker ring. Press on sleeve, hub assembly and collar. Apply oil to collar and hub before and after installation. Use Driver (J-33374) and press.

2) Install blocker ring and needle bearing. Install 4th gear and thrust washer. Install thrust washer with recessed area facing 4th gear. Install front and rear bearings using Driver (J-33374) and press.

OUTPUT SHAFT

NOTE: Before assembly apply oil to all thrust surfaces of gears, synchronizer interiors, and to bearing races.

1) Install thrust washer, thrust needle bearing, 1st gear and blocker ring. Match the inserts of the sleeve

GENERAL MOTORS 5-SPEED MANUAL TRANSAXLE (Cont.)

and hub assembly with grooves in blocker ring and press assembly together with the collar using Support (J-8853-01) and Pilot (J-33369).

2) Install blocker ring needle bearing and 2nd gear, and install key on key groove. Apply oil to 3th/4th gear interior, match key with key groove, and fit key together with rear bearing. Using Driver (J-33374) and press, press bearing on shaft. Press front bearing on shaft using Driver (J-33368) and press.

DIFFERENTIAL

NOTE: Before assembly apply oil to bearing interiors and race surfaces.

1) Install 2 side gears on differential case together with thrust washers. Position 2 thrust washers and pinion gears opposite each other, and install them in to position by turning side gear.

2) Insert cross pin, and ensure backlash is within rated range of .0012-.0031" (.03-.08 mm). Install lock pin and stake it. Heat speedometer drive gear to about 203°F (95°C), and install it on differential.

3) Apply oil to cross pin, differential gears, thrust portion, side gear shaft portion, side gear spline portion before installation. Install ring gear on differential case. Install 10 ring gear bolts and tighten.

4) Install the side bearings on the differential case using Tool (J-22919) and press, install bearings.

REASSEMBLY

TRANSAXLE

1) Place transaxle case in holding fixture. Using Seal Installer (J-26540), drive input shaft seal into case. Install front outer bearing races for input shaft, output shaft, and differential into clutch housing.

2) Apply oil to bearing races before installation. Using Tool (J-33371) with Driver (J-8092), press input race into housing. Using Tool (J-7817) with Driver (J-8092), press output race into housing. Using Tool (J-8611-01) with Driver (J-8092), press differential race into housing. Apply grease to 3 interlock pins, and install them on clutch housing.

3) Install reverse shift bracket on clutch. Use 3rd/4th shaft rod to align bracket to housing. Make sure rod operates smoothly after installation. Install retaining bolts and torque to specifications. Install differential assembly first, then install input and output shaft with 3rd/4th shift fork and shaft together as an assembly into clutch housing.

4) The 3rd/4th shift shaft is installed into raised collar of reverse shift lever bracket. Install 1st/2nd shift fork onto synchronizer sleeve and insert shifter shaft into reverse shift lever bracket.

5) Align hole in fork with shaft and install roll pin. Install reverse lever on shift bracket. Install reverse and 5th gear shifter shaft and at the same time, engage reverse shaft with reverse shift lever. Install reverse idler shaft together with gear into clutch housing. Make sure reverse lever is engaged in collar of gear.

6) Measure and determine shim size using the 7 spacers and Shim Selector Gauges (J-33373). Position outer bearing races on input, output, and differential bearings. Position shim selection gauges on bearing races. *See Fig. 8.*

Fig. 8: Shim Gauges Sets Used to Measure Shims

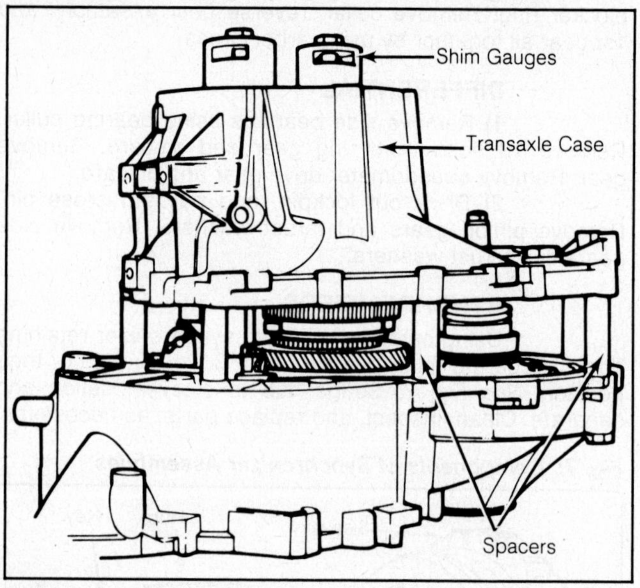

Measure input, output, and differential shims all at the same time.

7) The 3 gauges are identified: Input, Output, and Differential. Install bearing and shims retainer on ends of shafts. Tighten bolts to 11-16 ft. lbs. (15-22 N.m).

8) Place 7 spacers (provided with gauges), evenly around perimeter of clutch housing. *See Fig. 8.* Carefully position transaxle case over gauges and on spacers. Install 7 bolts provided with gauge kit and tighten bolts alternately until case is seated on spacers. Tighten kit bolts to 10 ft. lbs. (14 N.m).

9) Rotate each gauge to seat bearings. Rotate differential case through 3 revolutions in each direction. With 3 gauges compressed, measure gap between outer sleeve and the base pad using available shim sizes. Use the largest shim that can be placed into gap and drawn through without binding. *See Fig. 9.*

Fig. 9: Checking Shim Size Using Gauge Kit (J-33373)

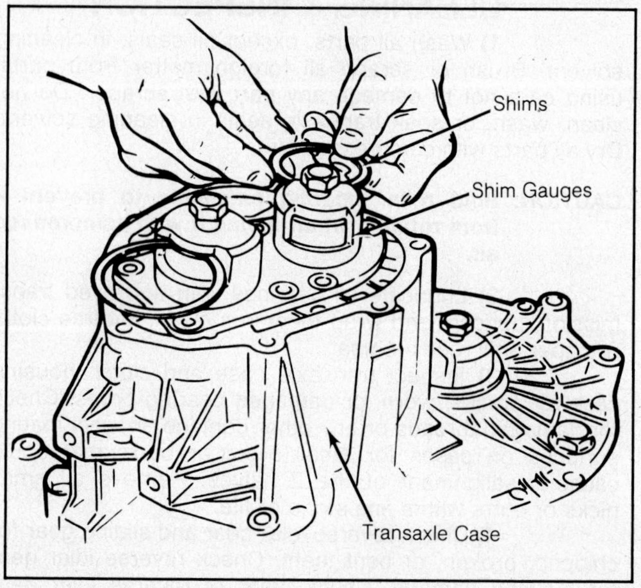

Use largest shim without binding in gauge.

GENERAL MOTORS 5-SPEED MANUAL TRANSAXLE (Cont.)

10) Preload shims for input shaft are available in thicknesses of .0394" to .0977" (1.00 to 2.48 mm) in .0016" (.04 mm) increments. Preload shims for output shaft are available in thicknesses of .0457" to .0961" (1.16 to 2.44 mm) in .0031" (.08 mm) increments. Preload shims for differential are available in thicknesses of .0426" to .0788" (1.08 to 2.00 mm) in .0016" (.04 mm) increments. The input shaft shim should be one size smaller than the largest shim that will fit in the gap. The differential should use a shim three sizes larger than that which will smoothly fit in the gap. The output shaft should use the largest shim that can be placed into the gap and drawn through without binding.

11) When each of the 3 shims have been selected, remove transaxle case, the 7 spacers, and 3 gauges. Position shims selected for input shaft, output shaft, and differential into bearing race bores in transaxle-case. Install rear input shaft bearing race using Installer (J-24256-A) and Driver (J-8092).

12) Press bearing until seated in its bore. Install rear output shaft bearing race using Installer (J-33370) and Driver (J-8092). Press bearing until seated in its bore. Install rear differential case bearing race using Installer (J-8611-01) and Driver (J-8092). Press bearing until seated in its bore.

13) Apply a 1/8" bead of sealant to the mating surfaces of clutch housing and transaxle case. Be sure magnet is installed in transaxle case. Install transaxle case on clutch housing.

14) Install reverse idle shaft bolt into transaxle case. Install 14 case bolts and tighten in diagonal sequence. Install drive axle seals. Install thrust washer and collar to output shaft.

15) Install 5th gear to input shaft. Install needle bearing, 5th gear, blocker ring, hub/sleeve assembly with shift fork in its groove and back plate on output shaft.

16) Apply Locktite No. 262 or equivalent to threads of the input and output shafts, do not allow Locktite to flow on splines of 5th gear and input shaft. Install new retaining nuts.

17) Align shift fork on shifter shaft and install roll pin. Install detent balls and detent springs for reverse, 1st/2nd, 3rd/4th, and 5th gears. Install retaining bolts and tighten. Stake nuts after reaching final torque.

18) Install gasket and control box assembly on transaxle case, and tighten 4 bolts. Make sure transaxle shifts properly before installing rear cover. Install gasket and rear cover with 7 bolts, and tighten bolts.

19) Install clutch fork assembly if it has been removed. Lubricate and install bushing into upper hole using Bushing Installer (J-28412). Install oil seal. Install the clutch release bearing.

TIGHTENING SPECIFICATIONS

Application	Ft. Lbs. (N.m)
Brake Caliper	30 (41)
Control Box-to-Case Bolts	11-16 (15-22)
Cradle	
Sidemember-to-Crossmember	34-47 (46-64)
Body Mount	66 (90)
Detent Spring Retaining Bolts	15-21 (21-29)
Engine Support Bolts	50 (68)
Engine-to-Transaxle	55 (75)
Hub Nut	
Initial	70 (95)
Final	185-225 (250-305)
Input/Output Shaft Nuts	87-101 (118-137)
Rear Cover Bolts	11-16 (15-22)
Reverse Idler Shaft Bolt	22-33 (30-45)
Ring Gear Bolts	73-79 (98-107)
Stabilizer Bar Bushing Retainer	
Crossmember	40 (54)
Control Arm	35 (47)
Suspension	
Cam Bolt	140 (190)
Upper Bolt	140 (190)
Transaxle Mounts	
4-Cylinder Engine	35 (47)
V6 Engine	18 (24)
Transaxle-to-Clutch Hsg. Bolts	22-33 (30-45)

GENERAL MOTORS 5-SPEED – 77 MM

Chevrolet
Camaro, Chevette, S10/15
Pontiac
Firebird, 1000

IDENTIFICATION

Transmission may have an identification plate on side of case or be ink stamped on bellhousing.

DESCRIPTION

The 5-speed 77 mm transmission is fully synchronized unit with blocker ring synchronizers and a sliding mesh reverse gear. It has an aluminum case and extension housing. The gearshift lever assembly is floor-mounted and is located on top the extension housing. The shift mechanism does not require adjustment and can be serviced independently of the transmission.

LUBRICATION & ADJUSTMENT

See appropriate MANUAL TRANSMISSION SERVICING article in DOMESTIC GENERAL SERVICING section.

TROUBLE SHOOTING

See appropriate MANUAL TRANSMISSION TROUBLE SHOOTING article in DOMESTIC GENERAL SERVICING section.

SERVICE (IN VEHICLE)

GEAR SHIFT LEVER

Removal & Installation

Remove screws from transmission shift lever boot retainer. Slide boot up lever. Remove shift lever attaching bolts at transmission and remove lever. To install shift lever, reverse removal procedure.

REMOVAL & INSTALLATION

TRANSMISSION

See appropriate MANUAL TRANSMISSION REMOVAL article in DOMESTIC GENERAL SERVICING section.

TRANSMISSION DISASSEMBLY

1) Drain lubricant from transmission. Clean exterior of transmission. Using pin punch and hammer, remove roll pin attaching offset lever to shift rail.

2) Remove extension housing-to-transmission case bolts. Remove housing and offset lever as an assembly.

CAUTION: Do not remove offset lever while extension housing is bolted in place. Lever has a positioning lug engaged in the housing detent plate which prevents moving the lever far enough for removal.

3) Remove detent ball and spring from offset lever. Remove roll pin from extension housing or offset lever. Remove plastic funnel, thrust bearing race and thrust bearing from rear of countershaft.

4) Remove transmission cover attaching bolts and lift off cover. Note location of 2 alignment-type dowel bolts for reassembly.

5) Support end of 5th-reverse shift rail with a wood block. Drive roll pin from 5th gear shift fork.

6) Remove 5th gear synchronizer snap ring, shift fork, 5th gear synchronizer sleeve, blocking ring and 5th speed drive gear from rear of countershaft. Remove snap ring from 5th speed driven gear on output shaft.

7) Using a hammer and punch, place mating marks on bearing cap and case for reassembly reference. Remove front bearing cap bolts and lift off bearing cap. Lift off front bearing race and end play shims from bearing cap.

8) Rotate drive gear until flat surface faces countershaft. Remove input shaft with drive gear from case.

9) Remove reverse lever "C" clip and pivot bolt. *See Fig. 1*. Remove mainshaft rear bearing race. Tilt output shaft assembly upward and remove from case.

Fig. 1: Removing Reverse Lever Retaining Clip and Bolt

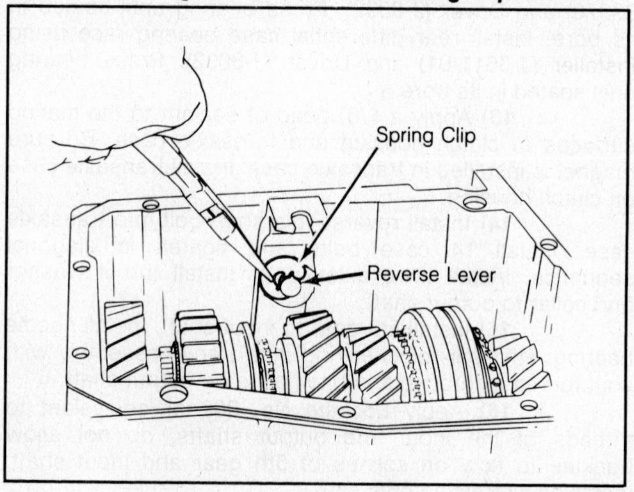

10) Unhook overcenter link spring from front of case. Rotate 5th-reverse shift rail to disengage rail from reverse lever assembly. Remove shift rail from rear of transmission case. *See Fig. 2*.

Fig. 2: Removing 5th-Reverse Shift Rail

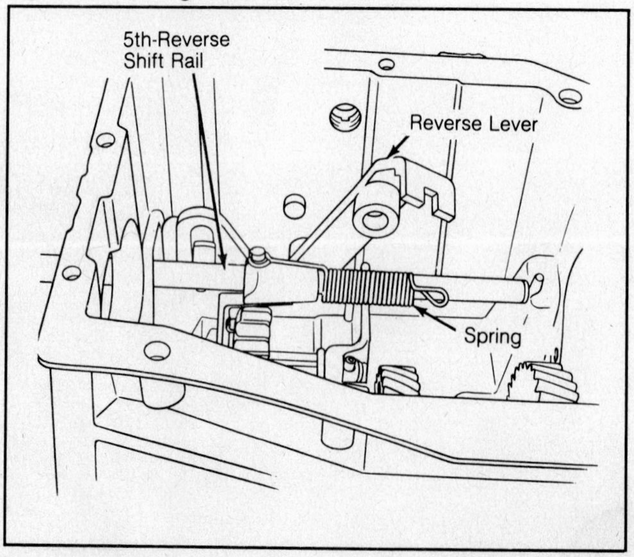

GENERAL MOTORS 5-SPEED – 77 MM (Cont.)

Fig. 3: Exploded View of 77mm 5-Speed Transmission

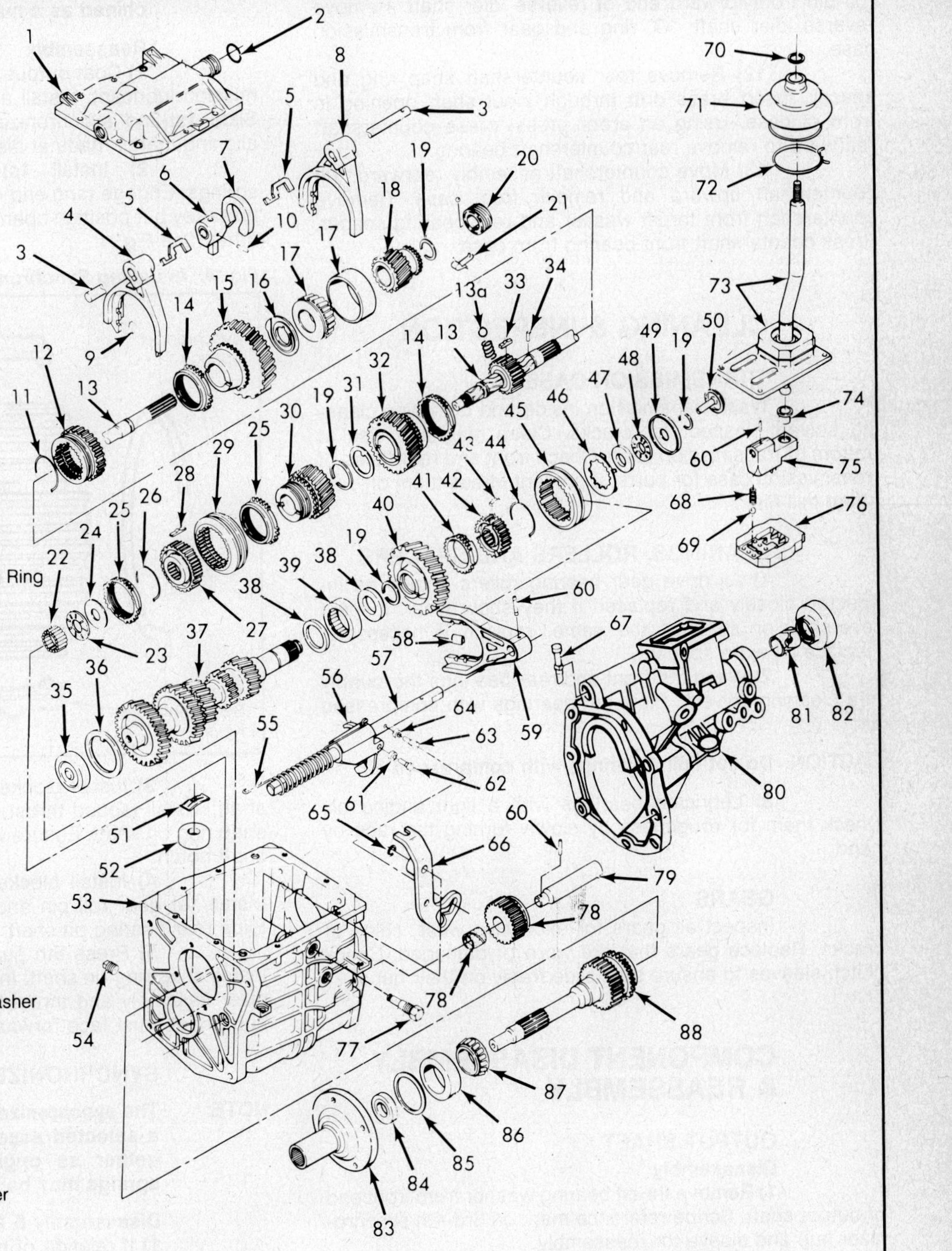

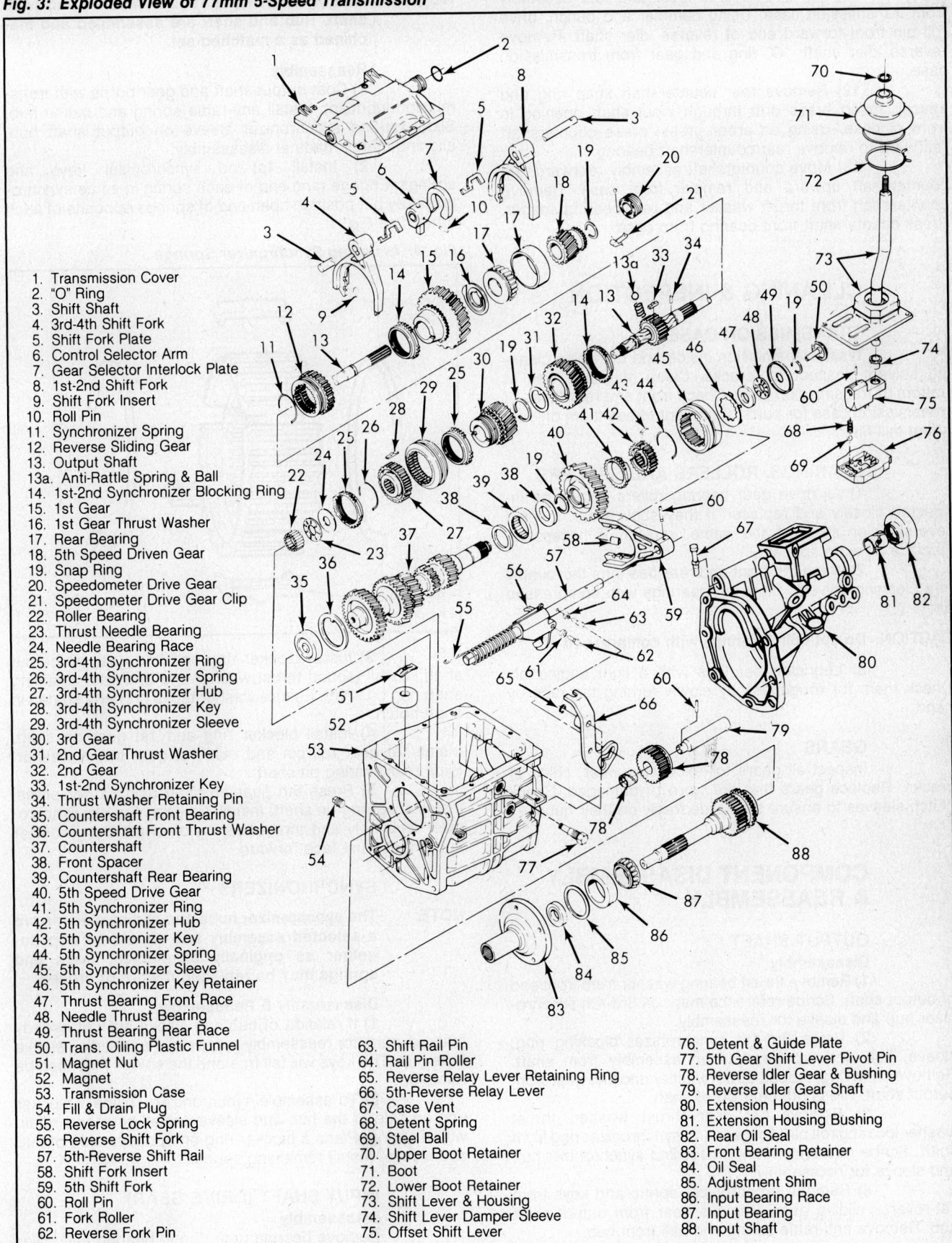

1. Transmission Cover
2. "O" Ring
3. Shift Shaft
4. 3rd-4th Shift Fork
5. Shift Fork Plate
6. Control Selector Arm
7. Gear Selector Interlock Plate
8. 1st-2nd Shift Fork
9. Shift Fork Insert
10. Roll Pin
11. Synchronizer Spring
12. Reverse Sliding Gear
13. Output Shaft

13a. Anti-Rattle Spring & Ball

14. 1st-2nd Synchronizer Blocking Ring
15. 1st Gear
16. 1st Gear Thrust Washer
17. Rear Bearing
18. 5th Speed Driven Gear
19. Snap Ring
20. Speedometer Drive Gear
21. Speedometer Drive Gear Clip
22. Roller Bearing
23. Thrust Needle Bearing
24. Needle Bearing Race
25. 3rd-4th Synchronizer Ring
26. 3rd-4th Synchronizer Spring
27. 3rd-4th Synchronizer Hub
28. 3rd-4th Synchronizer Key
29. 3rd-4th Synchronizer Sleeve
30. 3rd Gear
31. 2nd Gear Thrust Washer
32. 2nd Gear
33. 1st-2nd Synchronizer Key
34. Thrust Washer Retaining Pin
35. Countershaft Front Bearing
36. Countershaft Front Thrust Washer
37. Countershaft
38. Front Spacer
39. Countershaft Rear Bearing
40. 5th Speed Drive Gear
41. 5th Synchronizer Ring
42. 5th Synchronizer Hub
43. 5th Synchronizer Key
44. 5th Synchronizer Spring
45. 5th Synchronizer Sleeve
46. 5th Synchronizer Key Retainer
47. Thrust Bearing Front Race
48. Needle Thrust Bearing
49. Thrust Bearing Rear Race
50. Trans. Oiling Plastic Funnel
51. Magnet Nut
52. Magnet
53. Transmission Case
54. Fill & Drain Plug
55. Reverse Lock Spring
56. Reverse Shift Fork
57. 5th-Reverse Shift Rail
58. Shift Fork Insert
59. 5th Shift Fork
60. Roll Pin
61. Fork Roller
62. Reverse Fork Pin
63. Shift Rail Pin
64. Rail Pin Roller
65. Reverse Relay Lever Retaining Ring
66. 5th-Reverse Relay Lever
67. Case Vent
68. Detent Spring
69. Steel Ball
70. Upper Boot Retainer
71. Boot
72. Lower Boot Retainer
73. Shift Lever & Housing
74. Shift Lever Damper Sleeve
75. Offset Shift Lever
76. Detent & Guide Plate
77. 5th Gear Shift Lever Pivot Pin
78. Reverse Idler Gear & Bushing
79. Reverse Idler Gear Shaft
80. Extension Housing
81. Extension Housing Bushing
82. Rear Oil Seal
83. Front Bearing Retainer
84. Oil Seal
85. Adjustment Shim
86. Input Bearing Race
87. Input Bearing
88. Input Shaft

GENERAL MOTORS 5-SPEED – 77 MM (Cont.)

11) Remove reverse lever and fork assembly from transmission case. Using hammer and punch, drive roll pin from forward end of reverse idler shaft. Remove reverse idler shaft, "O" ring and gear from transmission case.

12) Remove rear countershaft snap ring and spacer. Insert brass drift through input shaft opening in front of case. Using an arbor press, press countershaft rearward to remove rear countershaft bearing.

13) Move countershaft assembly rearward. Tilt countershaft upward and remove from case. Remove countershaft front thrust washer and rear bearing spacer. Press countershaft front bearing from case.

CLEANING & INSPECTION

TRANSMISSION CASE

Wash transmission inside and out using cleaning solvent. Inspect for cracks. Clean magnetic disc at bottom of transmission case. Check front and rear faces of transmission case for burrs. If present, dress them off with a fine mill file.

BEARINGS, ROLLERS AND SPACERS

1) All drive gear bearing rollers should be inspected closely and replaced if they show wear. Inspect reverse idler shaft at the same, replace if necessary. Replace all worn spacers.

2) Wash the front and rear bearings thoroughly in a cleaning solvent. Blow out bearings with compressed air.

CAUTION: Do not spin bearings with compressed air.

3) Lubricate bearings with a light engine oil. Check them for roughness by slowly turning the race by hand.

GEARS

Inspect all gears for excessive wear, chips or cracks. Replace gears that are worn or damaged. Check clutch sleeves to ensure they slide freely on their hubs.

COMPONENT DISASSEMBLY & REASSEMBLY

OUTPUT SHAFT

Disassembly

1) Remove thrust bearing washer from front end of output shaft. Scribe reference mark on 3rd-4th synchronizer hub and sleeve for reassembly.

2) Press 3rd-4th synchronizer blocking ring, sleeve, hub and 3rd gear as an assembly from shaft. Remove snap ring, tabbed thrust washer and 2nd gear from output shaft. Press 5th gear off of shaft.

3) Remove 1st gear thrust washer, thrust washer locating roll pin, 1st gear and synchronizer ring from shaft. Scribe reference mark on 1st-2nd synchronizer hub and sleeve for reassembly.

4) Remove synchronizer spring and keys from 1st-reverse sliding gear. Remove gear from output shaft hub. Remove anti-rattle spring and ball from hub.

NOTE: Do not remove the 1st-2nd-reverse hub from shaft. Hub and shaft are assembled and machined as a matched set.

Reassembly

1) Coat output shaft and gear bores with transmission lubricant. Install anti-rattle spring and ball in hub. Slide 1st-2nd synchronizer sleeve on output shaft hub, aligning marks made at disassembly.

2) Install 1st-2nd synchronizer keys and springs. Engage tang end of each spring in same synchronizer key but position open end of springs opposite of each other. *See Fig. 4.*

Fig. 4: Installing Synchronizer Springs

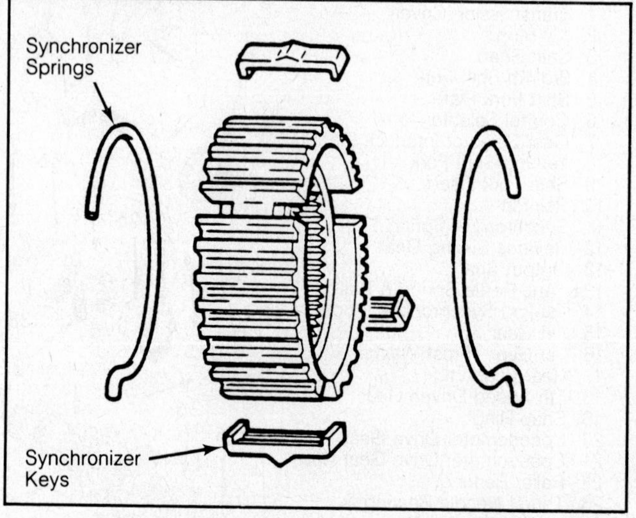

3) Install blocker ring and 2nd gear on output shaft. Install tabbed thrust washer and 2nd gear retaining snap ring on shaft. Ensure washer tab is properly seated in shaft notch.

4) Install blocker ring and 1st gear on shaft. Install 1st gear roll pin and then 1st gear thrust washer. Slide rear bearing on shaft.

5) Press 5th gear on shaft using arbor press. Install snap ring on shaft. Install 3rd gear, 3rd-4th synchronizer assembly and thrust bearing on shaft. Synchronizer hub offset must face forward.

SYNCHRONIZERS

NOTE: The synchronizer hubs and sliding sleeves are a selected assembly and should be kept together as originally assembled. Keys and springs may be replaced if worn or broken.

Disassembly & Reassembly

1) If relation of hub and sleeve are not already marked, mark for reassembly purposes. Push sliding sleeve from hub. The keys will fall free and the spings may then be removed.

2) To assemble synchronizers, place a blocker ring on side of the hub and sleeve. Install keys and retain with a spring. Place a blocker ring on opposite side of hub and sleeve. Install remaining spring.

INPUT SHAFT (DRIVE GEAR)

Disassembly

Remove bearing race, thrust bearing and roller bearings from cavity of drive gear. Press bearing from input

GENERAL MOTORS 5-SPEED – 77 MM (Cont.)

Fig. 5: Exploded View of Synchronizer Assemblies

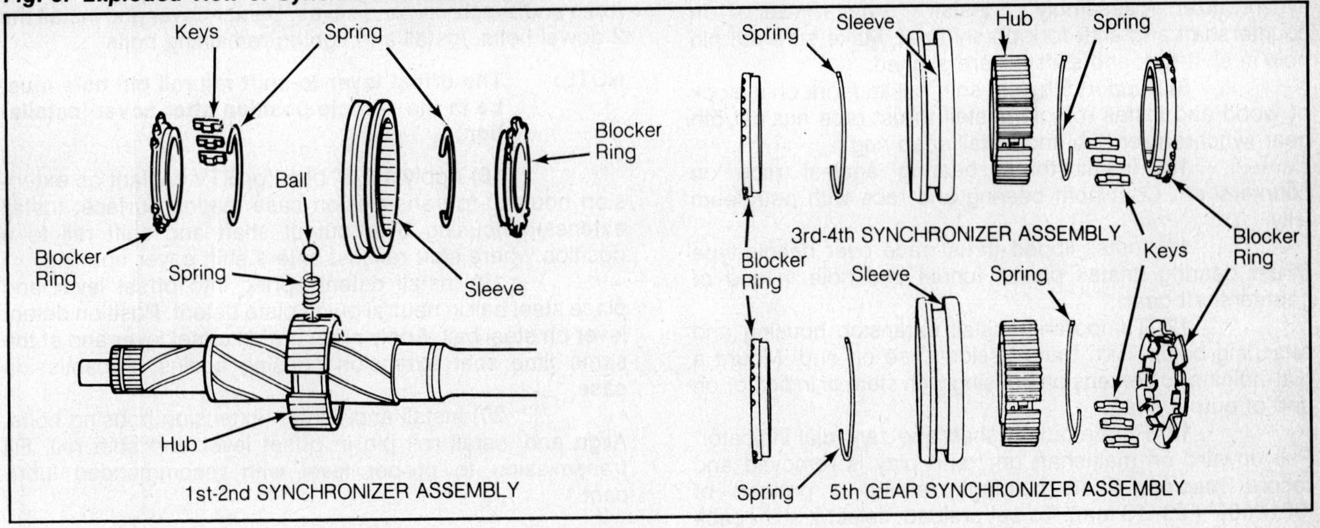

shaft. Clean all parts in solvent. Inspect gear teeth and drive shaft pilot for wear.

Reassembly

Pressing on inner race only, install bearing on input shaft. Coat roller bearings and drive gear bearing bore with grease. Install roller bearings into bore of drive gear. Install thrust bearing and race in drive gear.

EXTENSION HOUSING BUSHING

1) Pry oil seal out of extension housing, using a screwdriver or small chisel. Drive bushing out of housing using Remover/Installer (J-8092 and J-23062-14).

2) Use same tool to install bushing. Coat outer diameter of new oil seal with sealant. Install new oil seal into extension housing. Lubricate I.D. of seal with transmission lubricant.

TRANSMISSION COVER

Disassembly

1) Place selector arm plates and shift rail in neutral (centered) position. Rotate shift rail until selector arm disengages from selector arm plates and roll pin is accessible.

2) Remove selector arm roll pin using a pin punch and hammer. Remove shift rail, shift forks, selector arm plates, selector arm, interlock plate and roll pin.

3) Remove shift cover-to-extension housing "O" ring seal. Remove nylon inserts and selector arm plates from shift forks. Note position of inserts and plates for reassembly reference.

Reassembly

1) Install nylon inserts and selector arm plates in shift forks. If removed, install shift rail plug. Coat edges of plug with sealant before installing.

2) Coat shift rail and rail bores with lightweight grease and insert shift rail in cover. Install rail until flush with inside edge of cover.

3) Place 1st-2nd shift fork in cover with fork offset facing rear of cover and push shift rail through fork. The 1st-2nd shift fork is the larger of the 2 forks.

4) Position selector arm and "C" shaped interlock plate in cover and insert shift rail through arm. Widest part of interlock plate must face away from cover. Selector arm roll pin must must face downward and toward rear of cover.

5) Position 3rd-4th shift fork in cover with fork offset facing rear of cover. The 3rd-4th shift fork selector arm plate must be under 1st-2nd shift fork selector arm plate.

6) Push shift rail through 3rd-4th shift fork and into front bore in cover. Rotate shift rail until selector arm plate at forward end of rail faces away from, but is parallel to cover.

7) Align roll pin holes in selector arm and shift rail. Install roll pin. Roll pin must be flush with surface of selector arm to prevent pin from contacting selector arm plates during shifts.

8) Install a new shift cover to extension housing "O" ring seal. Coat "O" ring seal with transmission lubricant.

TRANSMISSION REASSEMBLY

1) Coat countershaft front bearing bore with Loctite 601. Install front counterhsaft bearing flush with facing of case using an arbor press.

2) Coat countershaft tabbed thrust washer with grease and install washer so tab engages depression in case. Tip transmission case on end. Install countershaft in front bearing bore.

3) Install countershaft rear bearing spacer. Coat countershaft rear bearing with grease. Install bearing using Installer Tool (J-29895). When correctly installed, bearing will extend .125" (3.0 mm) beyond case surface.

4) Position reverse idler gear in case with shift lever groove facing rear of case. Install reverse idler shaft from rear of case. Install roll pin in idler shaft.

5) Install assembled output shaft in case. Install rear output shaft bearing in case. Install drive gear in case. Engage in 3rd-4th synchronizer sleeve and blocker ring.

6) Install front bearing race in front bearing cap. Do not install shims in front bearing cap at this time. Temporarily install front bearing cap.

7) Install 5th gear-reverse shift rail in case. Engage with 5th gear-reverse shift lever. Rotate rail during installation to simplify engagement with lever. Connect spring to front of case.

GENERAL MOTORS 5-SPEED – 77 MM (Cont.)

8) Position 5th gear shift fork on 5th gear synchronizer assembly. Install synchronizer on countershaft and shift fork on shift rail. Make sure roll pin hole in shift fork and shift rail are aligned.

9) Support 5th gear shift rail and fork on a block of wood and install roll pin. Install thrust race against 5th gear synchronizer hub and install snap ring.

10) Install thrust bearing against race on countershaft. Coat both bearing and race with petroleum jelly.

11) Install lipped thrust race over needle-type thrust bearing. Install plastic funnel into hole in end of countershaft gear.

12) Temporarily install extension housing and attaching bolts. Turn transmission case on end. Mount a dial indicator on extension housing with stem of indicator on end of output shaft.

13) Rotate output shaft and zero dial indicator. Pull upward on mainshaft until end play is removed and record reading. Shaft bearings require a preload of .001-.005" (.03-.13 mm). To set preload, select a shim pack measuring .001-.005" (.03-.13 mm) greater than recorded dial indicator reading.

14) Remove front bearing cap and front bearing race. Install necessary shims to obtain preload and reinstall bearing race.

15) Apply a 1/8" bead of RTV sealant on case-to-front bearing cap mating surface. Install bearing cap aligning marks made during disassembly. Tighten bolts to specification.

16) Remove extension housing. Move shift forks on transmission cover and synchronizer sleeves inside transmission to the neutral position. Apply a 1/8" bead of RTV sealant on cover mating surface of transmission.

17) Lower cover onto case while aligning shift forks and synchronizer sleeves. Center cover and install the 2 dowel bolts. Install and tighten remaining bolts.

NOTE: The offset lever-to-shift rail roll pin hole must be in the verticle position after cover installation.

18) Apply a 1/8" bead of RTV sealant on extension housing-to-transmission case mating surface. Install extension housing over output shaft and shift rail to a position where shift rail just enters shift cover opening.

19) Install detent spring into offset lever and place steel ball in neutral guide plate detent. Position detent lever on steel ball. Apply pressure on offset lever and at the same time seat extension housing against transmission case.

20) Install and tighten extension housing bolts. Align and install roll pin in offset lever and shift rail. Fill transmission to proper level with recommended lubricant.

TIGHTENING SPECIFICATIONS

Application	Ft. Lbs. (N.m)
Crossmember-to-Frame Bolts	35 (50)
Extension-Housing-to-Case Bolts	25 (30)
Fill Plug	20 (27)
Front Bearing Cap-to-Case	15 (20)
Reverse Pivot Bolt	20 (27)
Shift Cover-to-Case Bolts	10 (13)
Trans.-to-Engine Bolts	55 (75)
Trans. Mount-to-Trans. Bolts	35 (50)
Trans. Mount-to-Crossmember Bolts	35 (50)

GENERAL MOTORS (ISUZU) 4-SPEED – 77.5 MM

Chevrolet & GMC, "S" Trucks

IDENTIFICATION

Transmission identification tag is attached to transmission by an extension housing mounting bolt. Transmission can also be identified by the measured distance (3.05", 77.5 mm) between centerlines of main-shaft and countershaft.

DESCRIPTION

The 4-speed 77.5 MM transmission is a floor shifted, fully synchronized unit with blocker ring synchronizers and a sliding mesh type reverse gear. Unit consists of a case with integral clutch housing, center support and an extension housing that holds the various gears and bearings.

LUBRICATION & ADJUSTMENT

See appropriate article in MANUAL TRANSMISSION SERVICING section.

TROUBLE SHOOTING

SEE MANUAL TRANSMISSION TROUBLE SHOOTING in DOMESTIC GENERAL SERVICING.

SERVICE (IN VEHICLE)

SHIFT CONTROL LEVER

Removal & Installation

Remove screws from transmission shift lever boot retainer. Slide boot up lever and remove bolts attaching lever to transmission. Remove lever. To install shift lever, reverse removal procedure.

EXTENSION HOUSING OIL SEAL

Removal

Raise vehicle. Disconnect propeller shaft. Using a screwdriver, pry oil seal from extension housing.

Installation

Install new oil seal in extension housing using seal installer tool (J-33035). Connect propeller shaft. Check transmission fluid level and add fluid as necessary. Lower vehicle.

REMOVAL & INSTALLATION

See appropriate article in MANUAL TRANSMISSION REMOVAL section.

TRANSMISSION DISASSEMBLY

1) Disconnect retaining springs from bearing side of clutch release bearing. Remove bearing, boot and clutch fork. Remove drain plug and drain lubricant from transmission. Remove bearing retainer bolts, retainer and gasket. Remove snap rings, bearing, and drive gear shaft. Remove ball stud, if necessary.

2) Remove speedometer driven gear and back-up light switch. Remove 4 shift cover bolts, cover and gasket. Remove rear extension bolts, rear extension and gasket. Remove speedometer drive gear from mainshaft.

3) Using a punch, remove pin from reverse shift block while supporting end of shaft with bar or wood block. Remove reverse block retaining bolts. Remove reverse shifter shaft, shift block, shift fork and reverse gear as an assembly. *See Fig. 1.* Remove retaining rings from drive gear shaft bearing outer race and countershaft front bearing outer race.

Fig. 1: Removing Reverse Shifter Assembly

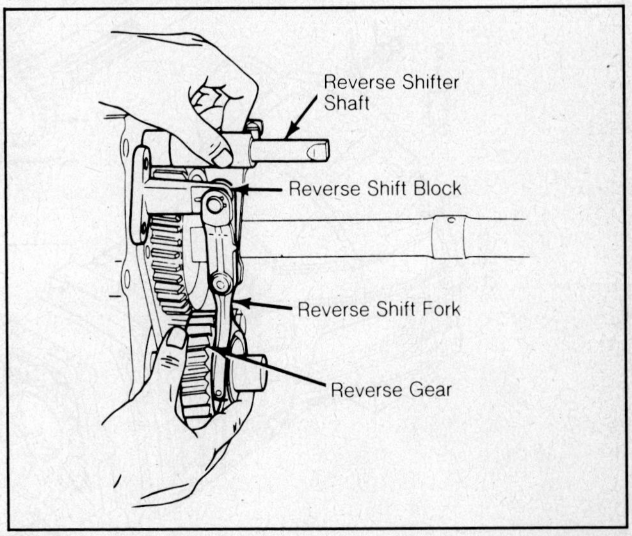

Remove shifter shaft, block, fork and gear as an assembly.

4) Remove support assembly from transmission case. Drive pins from 1st-2nd and 3rd-4th shift forks using a punch. *See Fig. 2.* Support ends of shafts during removal. Loosen retaining bolts and remove plate, gasket and springs.

Fig. 2: Removing Pin From Shifter Shafts

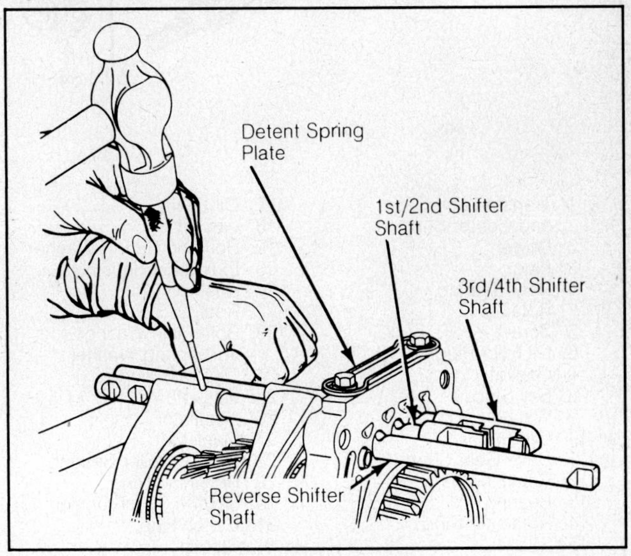

Remove pins from shift fork using a punch.

5) Position 3 shifter shafts into neutral position. Remove reverse shaft, 1st-2nd shaft and 3rd-4th

Manual Transmissions

GENERAL MOTORS (ISUZU) 4-SPEED – 77.5 MM (Cont.)

Fig. 3: Exploded View of General Motors (Isuzu) 77.5 MM 4-Speed Transmission

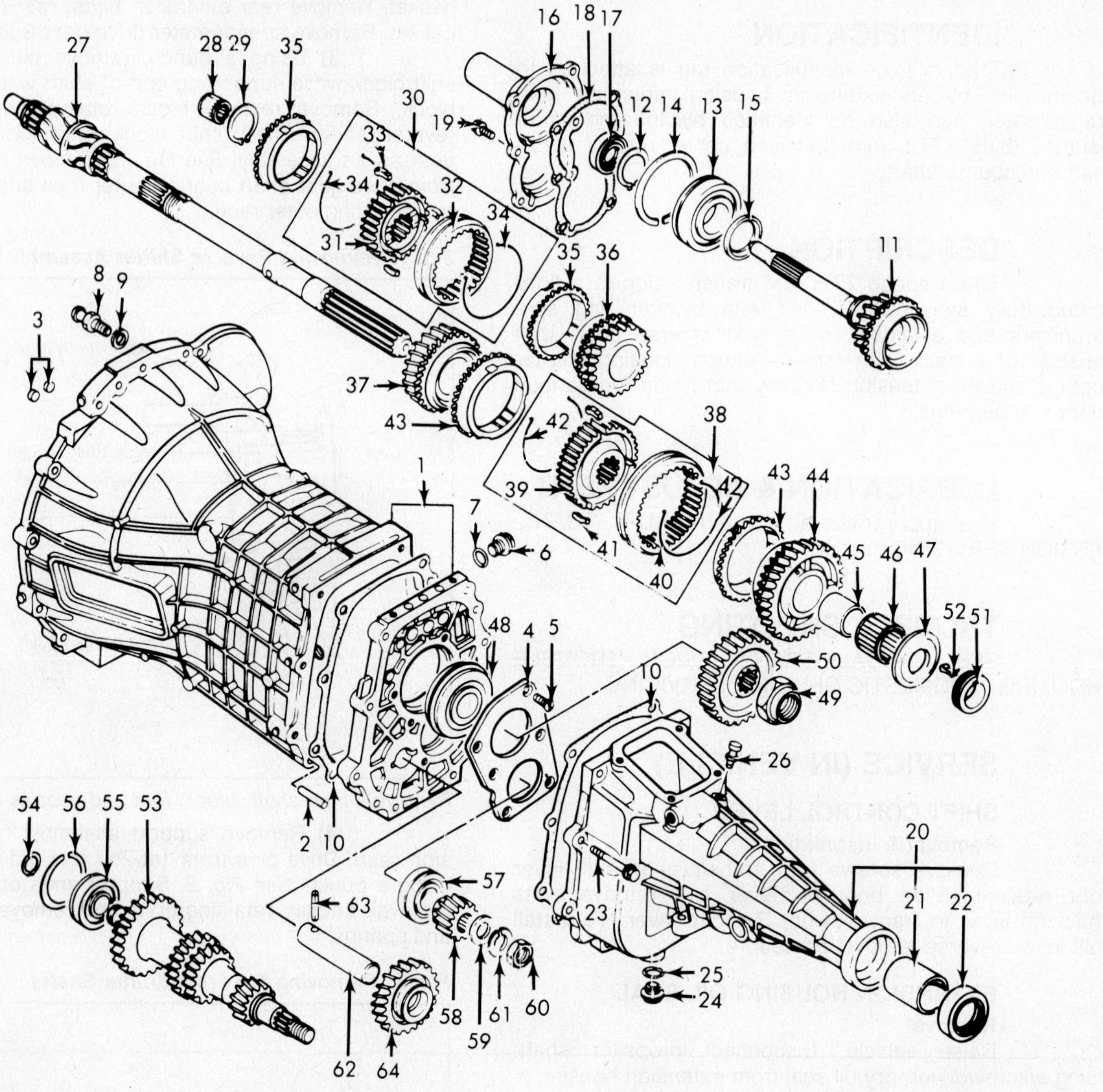

1. Transmission Case and Center Support
2. Dowel
3. Plug
4. Rear Bearing Retainer
5. Screw
6. Oil Filler Plug
7. Gasket
8. Ball Stud
9. Washer
10. Gasket
11. Drive Gear Shaft
12. Retaining Ring
13. Bearing
14. Retaining Ring
15. Spacer
16. Front Bearing Retainer
17. Oil Seal
18. Gasket
19. Bolt and Spring Washer
20. Extension Housing
21. Bushing
22. Rear Oil Seal
23. Bolt, Plain Washer and Spring Washer
24. Oil Drain Plug
25. Gasket
26. Ventilator
27. Mainshaft
28. Needle Roller Bearing
29. Retaining Ring
30. 3rd/4th Synchronizer
31. Clutch Hub
32. Sleeve
33. Insert
34. Spring
35. Blocker Ring
36. 3rd Gear
37. 2nd Gear
38. 1st/2nd Synchronizer
39. Clutch Hub
40. Sleeve
41. Insert
42. Spring
43. Blocker Ring
44. 1st Gear
45. Needle Roller Bearing
46. Bearing Collar
47. Thrust Washer
48. Bearing
49. Nut
50. Reverse Gear
51. Speedometer Drive Gear
52. Clip
53. Counter Shaft
54. Retaining Ring
55. Bearing
56. Retaining Ring
57. Bearing
58. Reverse Gear
59. Plain Washer
60. Nut
61. Spring Washer
62. Reverse Idler Shaft
63. Spring Pin
64. Reverse Idler Gear

GENERAL MOTORS (ISUZU) 4-SPEED – 77.5 MM (Cont.)

shifter shaft in that order. Remove 3 detent balls and 2 interlock pins. *See Fig. 7.* Remove shift forks. Engage synchronizers, and temporarily install transmission case to center support.

6) Raise staking on mainshaft rear nut using screwdriver or punch and remove nut. Remove reverse gear from mainshaft. Remove countershaft nut, spring washer, plain washer and reverse gear. Remove case from center support. Set synchronizers in neutral position.

Fig. 4: Exploded View of Shifter Assemblies

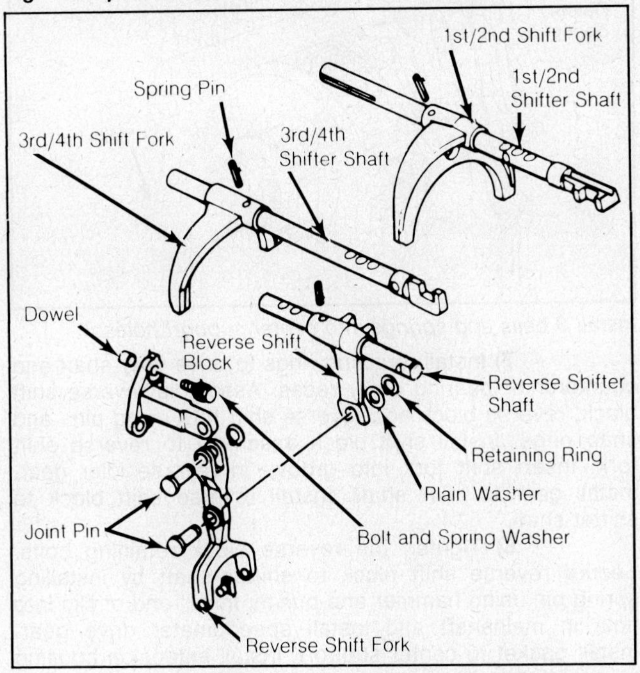

7) Remove rear bearing retainer from center support. *See Fig. 5.* Slide rear bearing outer race rearward by moving countershaft back and forth. Remove outer race using screwdrivers or equivalent. Remove countershaft and drive gear shaft. Remove 4th blocker ring and needle roller bearing.

Fig. 5: Removing Rear Bearing Retainer

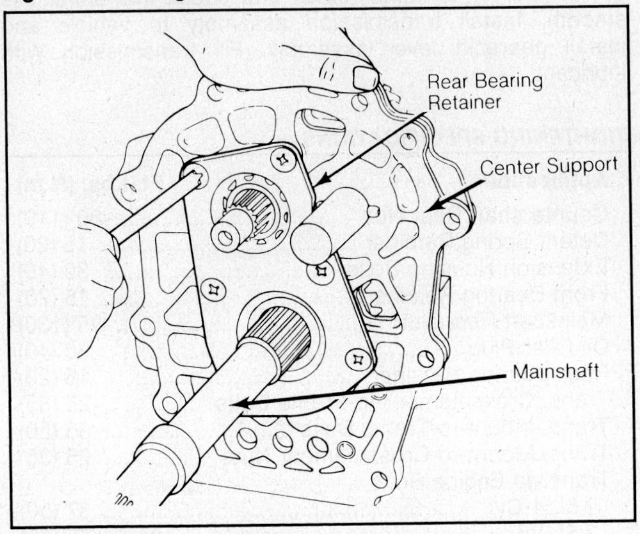

Remove retainer from center support.

COMPONENT DISASSEMBLY & REASSEMBLY

MAINSHAFT

Disassembly

1) Position support tool (J-22912-01) at rear face of 2nd gear on mainshaft. Remove mainshaft from center support using arbor press. *See Fig. 6.* Remove 2nd gear, 1st-2nd synchronizer and 1st and 2nd blocker rings. Remove 1st gear needle roller bearing, bearing collar and thrust washer. Remove mainshaft rear bearing from center support.

Fig. 6: Removing Mainshaft From Center Support

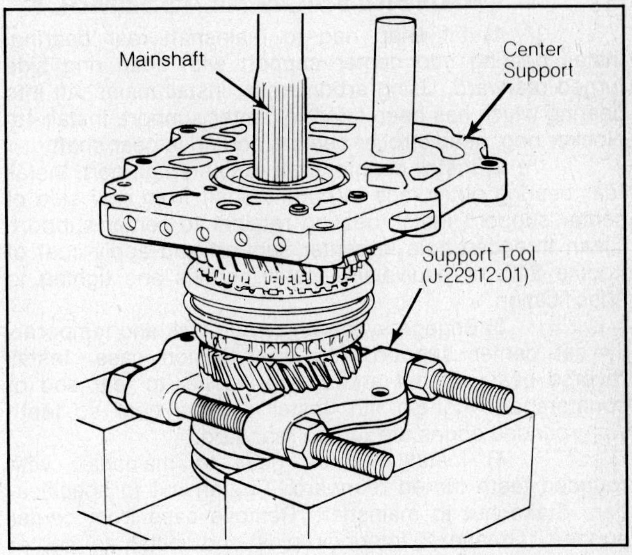

Use arbor press to remove mainshaft from support.

2) Remove snap ring from front of mainshaft. Set rear face of 3rd gear in blocks and remove mainshaft using arbor press. Remove 3rd gear, 3rd blocker ring and 3rd-4th synchronizer.

Reassembly

1) Install 3rd gear and 3rd gear blocker ring to front of mainshaft. Install 3rd-4th synchronizer assembly to mainshaft using arbor press. Install retaining ring to front of mainshaft. Install 2nd gear and 2nd gear blocker ring to rear of mainshaft.

2) Install 1st-2nd synchronizer assembly to mainshaft using arbor press. Install 1st gear bearing collar to mainshaft using installer (J-8853-01) and arbor press. Install 1st blocker ring, needle roller bearing and 1st gear.

3) Install thrust washer with oil grooves turned toward gear. If reverse idler shaft has been removed, reinstall shaft into center support with press. Be sure spring pin is fitted to shaft.

CLEANING & INSPECTION

1) Wash parts in solvent and dry all parts, except front and rear bearings, with compressed air. Wipe front and rear bearings with a clean cloth or air dry. Do not allow bearings to spin. Turn them slowly by hand. Spinning may damage race and balls. Lubricate bearings with light oil and check for roughness by slowly turning race by hand.

GENERAL MOTORS (ISUZU) 4-SPEED – 77.5 MM (Cont.)

2) Inspect transmission case, cover and extension housing. Replace if there are cracks in bores, sides, bosses or bolt holes. Replace case if there are stripped bolt holes, nicks burrs, or rough surfaces in shaft bores or on gasket surfaces. Inspect gear train and shift mechanism.

3) Replace any parts exhibiting wear, chips, galling, distortion or bending. Check for worn bearings and bores. Check for weak snap rings and stripped offset lever. Synchronizer hubs and sliding sleeves are a selected assembly. Keep together as originally assembled. Keys and springs may be replaced if worn or broken.

TRANSMISSION REASSEMBLY

1) Fit snap ring to mainshaft rear bearing. Install bearing into center support with snap ring side turned rearward. Using arbor press, install mainshaft into bearing which has been fitted to center support. Install 4th blocker ring, needle roller bearing and drive gear shaft.

2) Install countershaft to center support. Install rear bearing outer race to countershaft from rear side of center support. Install bearing retainer to center support. Clean threaded hole in center support and apply coat of Loctite 242, or equivalent. Install screws and tighten to specification.

3) Engage synchronizers in lock and temporarily set center support into transmission case. Install reverse gear, washer and spring washer to rear end of countershaft. Tighten nut. Install reverse gear so teeth with rounded edges are turned rearward.

4) Install reverse gear to mainshaft with rounded teeth turned rearward. Tighten nut to specification. Stake nut to mainshaft. Remove case from center support. Grease 2 interlock pins and install to center support. *See Fig. 7.* Install shift fork to synchronizers.

Fig. 7: Installing Interlock Pins

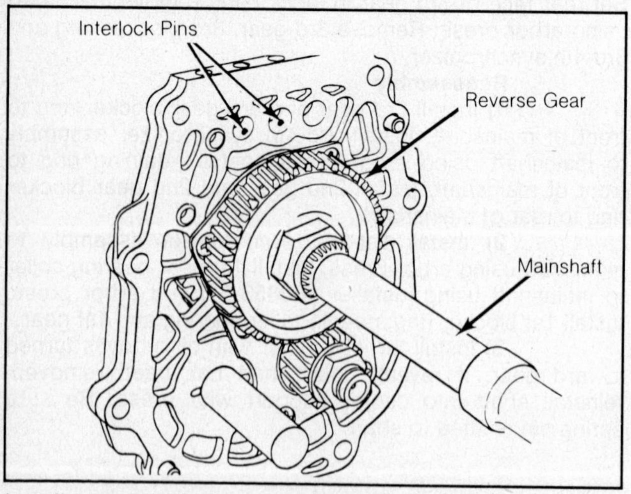

Install greased pins to center support.

5) Install 3rd-4th shifter shaft to center support and shift fork. Bring shaft into neutral position. Install 1st-2nd shifter shaft and reverse shifter shaft to center support. Drive spring pin into 1st-2nd and 3rd-4th shift forks. Support shaft end when installing spring pin.

6) Install 3 detent balls and springs into holes in center support. *See Fig. 8.* The spring for reverse is shorter in length than others. Install gasket and plate. Tighten bolts to specification. Install gasket to transmission case. Install center support by aligning it with dowels on case.

Fig. 8: Installing Detent Balls and Springs

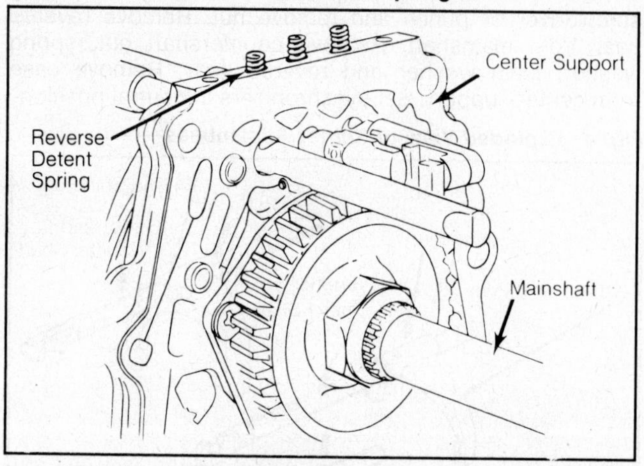

Install 3 balls and springs into center support holes.

7) Install retaining rings to drive gear shaft and countershaft bearing outer races. Assemble reverse shift block, reverse block and reverse shift fork using pins and snap rings. Install shift block assembly to reverse shift fork. Insert shift fork into groove in reverse idler gear. Install gear to idler shaft. Install reverse shift block to shifter shaft.

8) Tighten the reverse block retaining bolts. Secure reverse shift block to shifter shaft by installing spring pin using hammer and punch. Insert end of clip into hole in mainshaft and install speedometer drive gear. Install gasket to center support. Install extension housing to support by aligning it with dowels. Tighten bolts.

9) Install back-up light switch. Install gasket to upper face of extension housing. Install shifter cover. Install speedometer driven gear. Install ball stud, if removed. Install gasket to transmission case. Apply Permatex 2, or equivalent, to thread of bolts. Install and tighten bolts.

10) Install bearing, boot and clutch fork. Install gearshift lever to shifter cover and check that shifting is smooth. Install transmission assembly to vehicle and install gearshift lever assembly. Fill transmission with lubricant.

TIGHTENING SPECIFICATIONS

Application	Ft. Lbs. (N.m)
Countershaft Rear Nut	80 (110)
Detent Spring Retainer	15 (20)
Extension Housing Bolts	30 (40)
Front Bearing Retainer	15 (20)
Mainshaft Rear Nut	95 (130)
Oil Filler Plug	30 (40)
Rear Bearing Retainer	15 (20)
Trans. Crossmember-to-Frame Bolts	25 (35)
Trans. Mount-to-Trans. Bolts	35 (50)
Trans. Mount-to-Crossmember Nuts	25 (35)
Trans.-to-Engine Bolts	
2.5L 4-Cyl.	37 (50)
2.8L V6	55 (75)

GENERAL MOTORS 83 MM 4-SPEED AUTOMATIC OVERDRIVE – TRANSMISSION

Corvette

DESCRIPTION

The 83 MM 4-Speed transmission is a synchronized constant-mesh design. The input shaft has an integral main drive gear and rotates when the clutch is engaged. The drive gear is in constant mesh with the countershaft drive gear. The gears are helical designed and are used with synchronizers for all forward speeds. The transmission is identified by the distance between centerlines of the mainshaft and the countergear (83 MM).

LUBRICATION & ADJUSTMENT

See the appropriate article in MANUAL TRANSMISSION SERVICING section.

TROUBLE SHOOTING

See the appropriate article in MANUAL TRANSMISSION TROUBLE SHOOTING section.

SERVICE (IN VEHICLE)

SIDE COVER

Removal

1) Shift transmission into 2nd gear. Raise vehicle on hoist. Disconnect electrical leads at side cover switches. Remove switches.

2) Remove shift levers from shifter shafts. Remove cover attaching bolts, remove cover assembly and allow transmission to drain.

Disassembly

1) Remove outer shifter lever nuts and lockwashers. Pull levers from shafts. Carefully push shifter shafts into cover, allowing detent balls to fall free, then remove both shifter shafts.

2) Remove interlock sleeve, interlock pin and poppet spring. Clean and inspect components and replace damaged parts.

Reassembly

To reassemble, reverse disassembly procedure.

Installation

1) Move shifter levers into 2nd gear position. Position cover gasket on case. Carefully position side cover into place making sure shift forks are aligned with their respective mainshaft synchronizer sliding sleeves.

2) Install cover attaching bolts and tighten evenly. Install switches and connect electrical leads at side cover. Connect shift levers to shifter shafts. Remove filler plug and add lubricant to level of filler plug hole. Lower and remove vehicle from hoist.

SHIFTER ASSEMBLY

Removal

1) Disconnect battery negative cable. Remove left seat from vehicle. If equipped with power seats, disconnect electrical leads. Remove knob from shift lever. Remove console cover. Remove glove box lock.

2) Remove left side panel from console. Remove shifter cover. Disconnect 3 rods at shifter. Disconnect park lock cable from shifter. Remove shifter cross bolt. Remove shifter mounting bracket. Remove shifter mounting bolt at body panel and remove shifter assembly from vehicle.

Installation

1) Position shifter to body. Install mounting bolt and tighten. Position mounting bracket to shifter. Install bracket bolts and tighten. Install shifter cross bolt and tighten. Connect 3 rods to shifter. Adjust shift linkage.

2) Connect park lock cable to shifter and adjust as follows: Place steering column lock lever in "Lock Park Position", shift transmission into reverse gear and push down on lock tab on park lock cable.

3) Install shifter cover, left side panel from console, glove box lock and console cover. Install shift lever knob. Reconnect electrical leads on power seat equipped vehicles. Replace left seat. Reconnect negative battery cable.

REMOVAL & INSTALLATION

See the appropriate article in MANUAL TRANSMISSION REMOVAL section.

DISASSEMBLY

TRANSMISSION

1) With transmission removed from vehicle and separated from overdrive unit, remove drain plug from lower right side of case and drain lubricant. Shift transmission into 2nd gear. Remove shift cover attaching bolts, cover, gasket and both shift forks.

2) Remove backup switch from reverse housing. Rotate reverse shifter shaft and remove shift fork and gear from mainshaft. Remove lock pin from reverse shift lever boss and pull shaft from housing. Remove drive gear bearing retainer bolts, retainer and gasket from front of transmission.

3) Remove front bearing snap ring, selective fit snap ring and spacer washer. Using Puller (J-6654-01 and J-8433-1), pull drive gear bearing from transmission. *See Fig. 2.* Remove 6 bolts attaching reverse housing to case. Using a small drift and hammer, tap locating pin for reverse housing into case.

4) Rotate reverse housing on mainshaft until hole for reverse idler gear shaft in housing lines up with countergear shaft. Using Driver (J-24658), drive countergear shaft rearward out of gear and through reverse housing. Countergear will drop to bottom of case allowing clearance for removal of mainshaft.

5) Remove mainshaft with reverse housing and drive gear from case. Remove front reverse idler gear and thrust washer from case. Remove countergear and 2 tanged thrust washers from case. Check bottom of case for loose pilot bearings. Remove locating pin for reverse housing and any other loose components.

MAINSHAFT & COUNTERGEAR

1) Using Snap Ring Pliers, remove 3-4 synchronizer assembly retaining ring at front of mainshaft. Slide washer, synchronizer assembly, synchronizer ring and 3rd speed gear from mainshaft. Spread rear bearing retainer snap ring and slide retainer from mainshaft.

Manual Transmissions

GENERAL MOTORS 83 MM 4-SPEED AUTOMATIC OVERDRIVE – TRANSMISSION (Cont.)

Fig. 1: Exploded View of General Motors 83 MM 4-Speed Manual Transmission

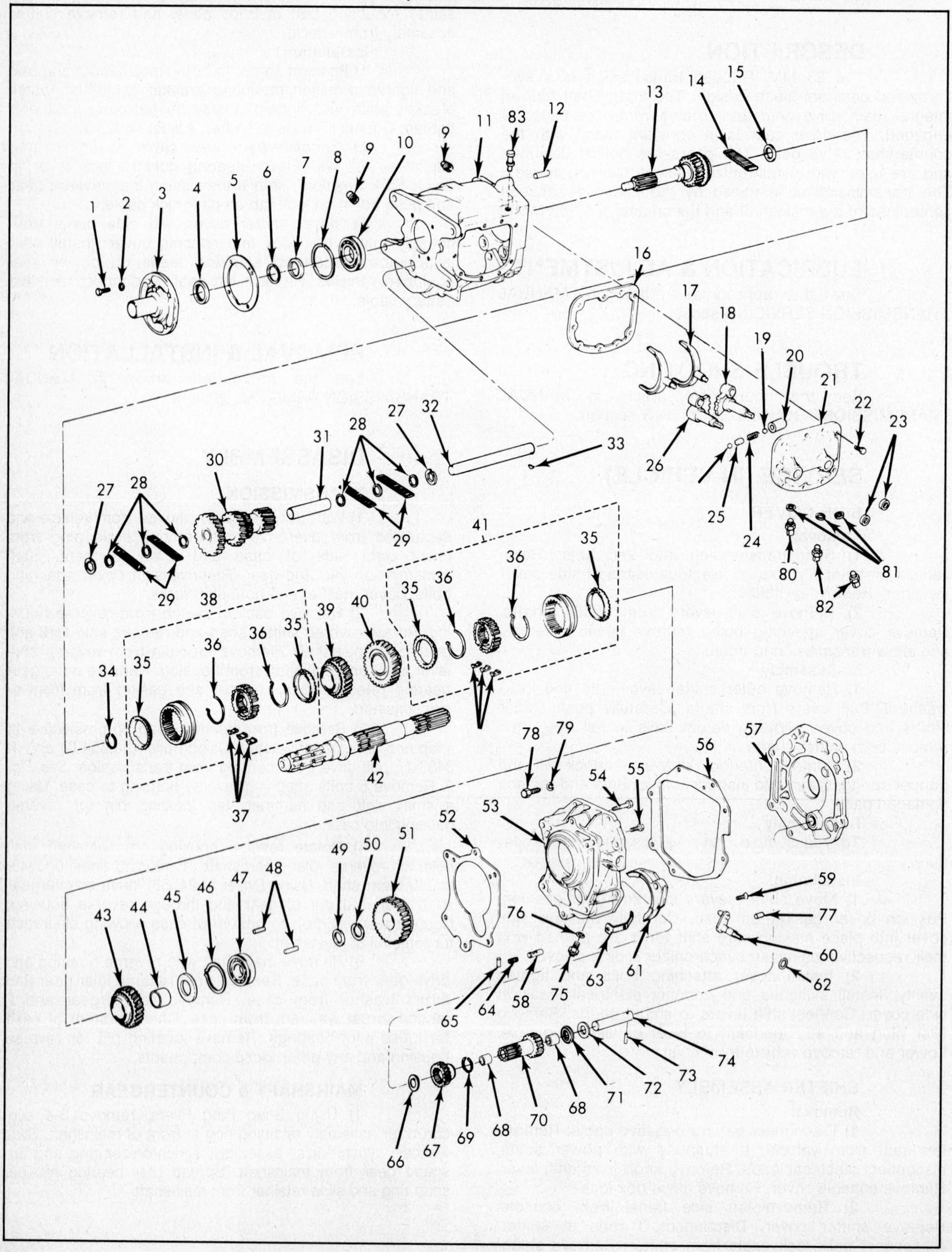

Manual Transmissions

GENERAL MOTORS 83 MM 4-SPEED AUTOMATIC OVERDRIVE – TRANSMISSION (Cont.)

General Motors 83 MM Manual Transmission Components (Use With Fig. 1)

1. Bolt
2. Lock Washer
3. Main Drive Gear Bearing Front Retainer
4. Main Drive Gear Bearing Front Oil Seal
5. Main Drive Gear Bearing Retainer Gasket
6. Main Drive Gear Bearing Retainer Snap Ring
7. Main Drive Gear Bearing Spacer
8. Main Drive Gear Bearing Lock Ring
9. Magnetic Drain Plug
10. Main Drive Gear Bearing
11. Transmission Case
12. Dowel Pin
13. Main Drive Gear
14. Main Drive Gear Pilot Rear Roller
15. Mainshaft Pilot Bearing Spacer
16. Side Cover Gasket
17. Shift Forks (1-2, 3-4)
18. 1st & 2nd Shift Shaft
19. Steel Ball
20. Interlock Sleeve
21. Side Cover
22. Transmission Cover Bolt
23. Shift Lever Shaft Oil Seals (1-2, 3-4)
24. Shift Lever Poppet Spring
25. Interlock Pin
26. 3rd & 4th Shift Shaft
27. Countergear Rear Washer
28. Countershaft Bearing Roller Washer
29. Countergear Bearing Roller
30. Countergear
31. Countergear Bearing Spacer
32. Countergear Shaft
33. Woodruff Key
34. Mainshaft Snap Ring
35. Synchronizer Blocking Ring
36. Synchronizer Spring
37. Synchronizer Key
38. Synchronizer (3rd & 4th)
39. 3rd Speed Gear
40. 2nd Speed Gear
41. Synchronizer (1st & 2nd)
42. Mainshaft
43. 1st Speed Gear
44. 1st Speed Gear Sleeve
45. 1st Speed Gear Thrust Washer
46. Rear Bearing Snap Ring
47. Mainshaft Rear Bearing
48. Dowel Pin
49. Main Drive Gear Bearing Spacer
50. Mainshaft Snap Ring
51. Reverse Gear
52. Rear Bearing Retainer-to-Transmission Case Gasket
53. Rear Bearing Retainer
54. Rear Bearing Retainer Bolt
55. Rear Bearing Retainer Bolt
56. Adapter Plate Gasket
57. Adapter Plate
58. Reverse Detent Pin
59. Rear Bearing Retainer Screw
60. Reverse Shift Shaft
61. Reverse Shift Fork
62. Reverse Shift Shaft Oil Seal
63. Harness Clip Bracket
64. Reverse Detent Pin Poppet Spring
65. Reverse Detent Spring Pin
66. Front Reverse Idler Gear Thrust Washer
67. Reverse Idler Front Gear
68. Reverse Idler Bushing
69. Reverse Idler Gear Retainer Ring
70. Reverse Idler Rear Gear
71. Reverse Idler Thrust Bearing
72. Rear Reverse Idler Gear Thrust Washer
73. Spring Pin
74. Reverse Idler Shaft
75. Overdrive Override Reverse Gear Switch
76. Reverse Gear Switch Seal
77. Solid Tapper Pin
78. Transmission-to-Overdrive Bolt
79. Transmission-to-Overdrive Bolt Lock Washer
80. Overdrive Override (3-4) Switch
81. Overdrive Override Switch Seal
82. Overdrive Override (1-2) Switch
83. Transmission Ventilator

Fig. 2: Removing Front Bearing

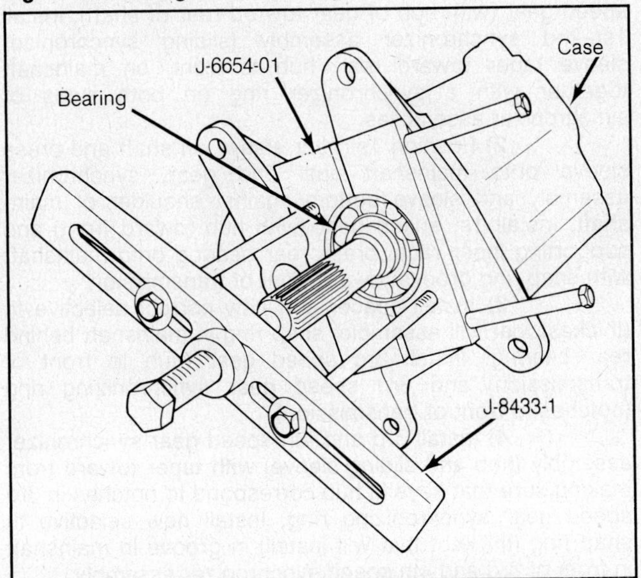

2) Remove rear bearing-to-mainshaft snap ring. Support mainshaft under 2nd gear and press mainshaft from rear bearing, 1st gear and sleave, 1-2 synchronizer assembly and 2nd gear. Remove Driver (J-24658) from countergear. Tip countergear on end and let 6 spacers, 112 rollers and roller sleeve out from gear.

CLEANING & INSPECTION

1) Wash transmission thoroughly inside and outside with cleaning solvent, then inspect case for cracks. Check front and rear faces for burrs, and if present, dress them off with a fine mill file.

2) All main drive gear and countergear bearing rollers should be inspected closely and replaced if they show wear. Inspect countershaft and reverse idler shaft at same time. Replace if necessary. Replace all worn spacers.

3) Inspect all gears for excessive wear, chips or cracks and replace any that are worn or damaged. Inspect reverse gear bushing and if worn or damaged, replace entire gear (reverse gear bushing is not serviced separately). Check both synchronizer sleeves to see that they slide freely on their hubs.

4) Wash front and rear ball bearings thoroughly in a cleaning solvent. Blow out bearing with compressed air. Do not allow bearing to spin. Turn them slowly by hand. Spinning bearing may damage race and balls.

GENERAL MOTORS 83 MM 4-SPEED AUTOMATIC OVERDRIVE – TRANSMISSION (Cont.)

COMPONENT DISASSEMBLY & REASSEMBLY

SYNCHRONIZER KEYS & SPRINGS

NOTE: The synchronizer hubs and sliding sleeves are a selected assembly and should be kept together as originally assembled, but keys and 2 springs may be replaced if worn or broken.

If relation of hub and sleeve are not already marked, mark for assembly purposes. Push hub from sliding sleeve, keys will fall free and springs may be easily removed. Place 2 springs in position (one on each side of hub) so all 3 keys are engaged by both springs. Place keys in position and while holding them in place, slide sleeve onto hub. Align marks made before disassembly.

DRIVE GEAR BEARING RETAINER OIL SEAL

Pry out old seal. Using a Seal Installer, install a new seal into retainer until it bottoms in bore. Lubricate inside diameter of seal with transmission fluid.

REVERSE SHIFTER SHAFT AND SEAL

1) With reverse housing removed from transmission, reverse shifter shaft lock pin will already be removed. Carefully drive shifter shaft into reverse housing allowing ball detent to drop into case. Remove shaft and ball detent spring. Remove "O" ring seal from shaft.

2) Place ball detent spring into detent spring hole and start reverse shifter shaft into hole in boss. Place detent ball on spring and while holding ball down, push shifter shaft into place and turn until ball drops into place in detent on shaft detent plate.

3) Install "O" ring seal on shaft. Install shift fork. Do not drive shifter shaft lock pin into place until reverse housing has been installed on transmission case.

REVERSE IDLER SHAFT

Place a small punch into hole in front cover of overdrive unit and drive pin into shaft until shaft can be pulled from front cover. Insert new idler shaft into cover until hole in shaft lines up with hole in boss. Insert roll pin into boss opening and drive pin into cover until shaft is securely locked in place.

REASSEMBLY

COUNTERGEAR

1) Install roller spacer in countergear (if removed). Insert Countergear Loader (J-24658) into countergear. Using heavy grease to retain rollers, install spacer, 28 rollers, spacer, 28 rollers, and spacer in either end of countergear. Repeat in other end of countergear.

2) Rest transmission case on its side with side cover opening toward assembler. Put countergear tanged thrust washers in place, retaining them with heavy grease, making sure tangs are resting in notches of case.

3) Set countergear in place in bottom of transmission case, making sure that tanged thrust washers are not knocked out of place. Lubricate and insert countergear (pushing Loading Tool out front of case) until Woodruff key slot is in its relative installed position (do not install key).

4) Attach a dial indicator and check end play of countergear. If end play is greater than .025" (.64 mm), a new thrust washer must be installed. *See Fig. 3.*

Fig. 3: Measuring Countergear End Play

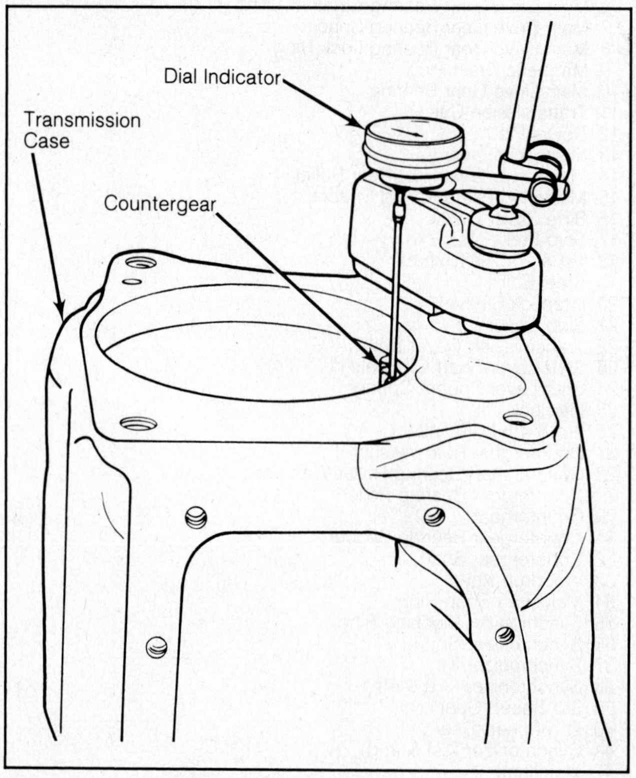

MAINSHAFT

1) From rear of mainshaft, assemble 2nd speed gear (with hub of gear toward rear of shaft). Install 1st-2nd synchronizer assembly (sliding synchronizer sleeve taper toward rear, hub to front) on mainshaft together with a synchronizer ring on both sides of synchronizer assemblies.

2) Position 1st gear sleeve on shaft and press sleeve onto mainshaft until 2nd gear, synchronizer assembly and sleeve bottom against shoulder of mainshaft. Install 1st speed gear (with hub toward front) and supporting inner race, press rear bearing onto mainshaft with snap ring groove toward front of transmission.

3) Install spacer and new correct selective fit (thickest that will assemble) snap ring in mainshaft behind rear bearing. Install 3rd speed gear (hub to front of transmission) and 3rd speed gear synchronizing ring (notches to front of transmission).

4) Install 3rd and 4th speed gear synchronizer assembly (hub and sliding sleeve) with taper toward front making sure that keys in hub correspond to notches in 3rd speed gear synchronizing ring. Install new selective fit snap ring (thickest that will install) in groove in mainshaft in front of 3rd and 4th speed synchronizer assembly.

5) Install rear bearing retainer (reverse housing) over end of mainshaft. Spread snap ring to drop around rear bearing. Release snap ring when it aligns with groove in rear bearing.

GENERAL MOTORS 83 MM 4-SPEED AUTOMATIC OVERDRIVE – TRANSMISSION (Cont.)

TRANSMISSION

1) Place transmission case on its side with shift cover opening toward assembler. Position countergear tanged washers in place, using a heavy grease to retain them. Be sure tangs are in notches of thrust face. Position countergear in bottom of case.

2) Install front reverse idler gear (teeth forward) and thrust washer in case. Use a heavy grease to hold thrust washer in position. Using a heavy grease, install 16 roller bearings and washer into main drive gear. Mate main drive gear with mainshaft assembly.

3) Position 3rd-4th synchronizer sliding sleeve forward. This will provide clearance for installation as well as hold assembly together. Position a new reverse housing to case gasket on rear of case. Install mainshaft and drive gear assembly into case.

4) Place bearing snap ring on front main bearing. Position front main bearing at case opening and with a hollow shaft, tap bearing into case. Install spacer washer and selective fit snap ring to secure main drive bearing.

5) Raise countergear in case, aligning holes in case with center of gear. With thrust washers in place, slide countershaft through rear of case. Install woodruff key and tap shaft into case, until flush with rear face of transmission case.

6) Align reverse housing and gasket with transmission case. Install locating pin for reverse housing. Tap pin in until flush with housing. Install 6 bolts attaching reverse housing to case. Tighten bolts to specifications. Install reverse shift shaft and "O" ring into housing. Install retaining pin.

7) Install reverse gear and shift fork. Slide gear and fork forward on mainshaft until shift fork and shifter shaft can be indexed into position. Position drive gear bearing retainer and gasket at front of case. Apply sealer to bolts. Install bolts and tighten to specifications.

8) Install rear reverse idler gear. Align splines on rear gear with front gear and slide together. Assemble overdrive unit to reverse housing. Guide idler shaft on overdrive unit into idler gears and align splines on mainshaft with splines in input sun gear. Slide units together and install retaining bolts. Tighten bolts to specifications.

9) Slide 1-2 synchronizer forward into 2nd gear. Install shift forks into grooves of synchronizers. Place side cover with a gasket on transmission. Guide shift forks into cover and install retaining bolts. Tighten bolts to specifications. Check operation of transmission by manually shifting transmission into all gears.

TIGHTENING SPECIFICATIONS

Application	Ft. Lbs. (N.m)
Drive Gear Bearing Retainer	15-20 (20-27)
Side Cover	15-20 (20-27)
Rev. Gear Housing-to-Case (1) Bolt	30-40 (40-54)
Rev. Gear Housing-to-Case (2) Bolts	40-50 (54-67)
Rev. Gear Housing-to-Case (3) Bolts	35-45 (47-61)
Drain Plug	15-25 (20-33)
Filler Plug	25-35 (33-47)
Transmission-to-Bell Housing	45-60 (60-80)

Manual Transmissions

GENERAL MOTORS 83 MM 4–SPEED AUTOMATIC OVERDRIVE – OVERDRIVE

Corvette

DESCRIPTION

The overdrive unit is a 2-Speed overdrive system electronically controlled by the ECM which operates with a 1:1 or 0.68:1 ratio. It is mounted to the rear of the manual transmission. By combining these 2 transmissions, the complete unit is actually capable of operating with 7 separate gear ratios. One of which is an overdrive.

The 2-Speed overdrive unit performs its function using a planetary gear system in combination with 2 sets of clutch packs. The output shaft from the manual unit is linked to a 40-tooth input sun gear in the overdrive unit. This in turn, is meshed with 4 double planet gears which mesh with a 34-tooth output shaft gear.

The overdrive mode cannot occur when 4-Speed transmission is in first gear. It can, however, occur in the remaining 3 gears. Rapid acceleration will cause a shift from overdrive to direct mode. Overdrive is automatically engaged at speeds above 110 MPH. Overdrive mode can be turned off by a switch on the vehicle's console.

LUBRICATION & ADJUSTMENT

See the appropriate article in MANUAL TRANSMISSION SERVICING section.

TROUBLE SHOOTING

See the appropriate article in MANUAL TRANSMISSION TROUBLE SHOOTING section.

SERVICE (IN VEHICLE)

COOLER LINE FLUSHING

NOTE: **If replacement of transmission steel tubing cooler lines is required, use only double wrapped and brazed steel tubing meeting GM specification 123M. Steel tubing should be flared using the double flare method.**

CAUTION: **Under no condition should copper or aluminum tubing be used to replace steel tubing. These materials do not have satisfactory fatigue durability to withstand normal vehicle vibrations.**

NOTE: **In a major transmission failure, where particles of metal have been carried with oil throughout units of transmission, it will be necessary to flush out oil cooler and connecting lines.**

1) Disconnect both cooler lines from transmission. Place a hose over end of cooler inlet line (from bottom of cooler) and insert hose into an empty container.

2) Flush clean solvent through return line (from top of cooler) using an oil suction gun until clean solvent comes out of hose. This will "backflush" cooler. Remove hose from inlet cooler line and place it on return line.

3) Flush clean solvent through inlet line until clean solvent comes out of return line. Remove remaining solvent from cooler with compressed air applied to return line and flush with transmission fluid. Reconnect oil cooler lines and tighten nuts.

Fig. 1: Hydraulic Circuit Diagram

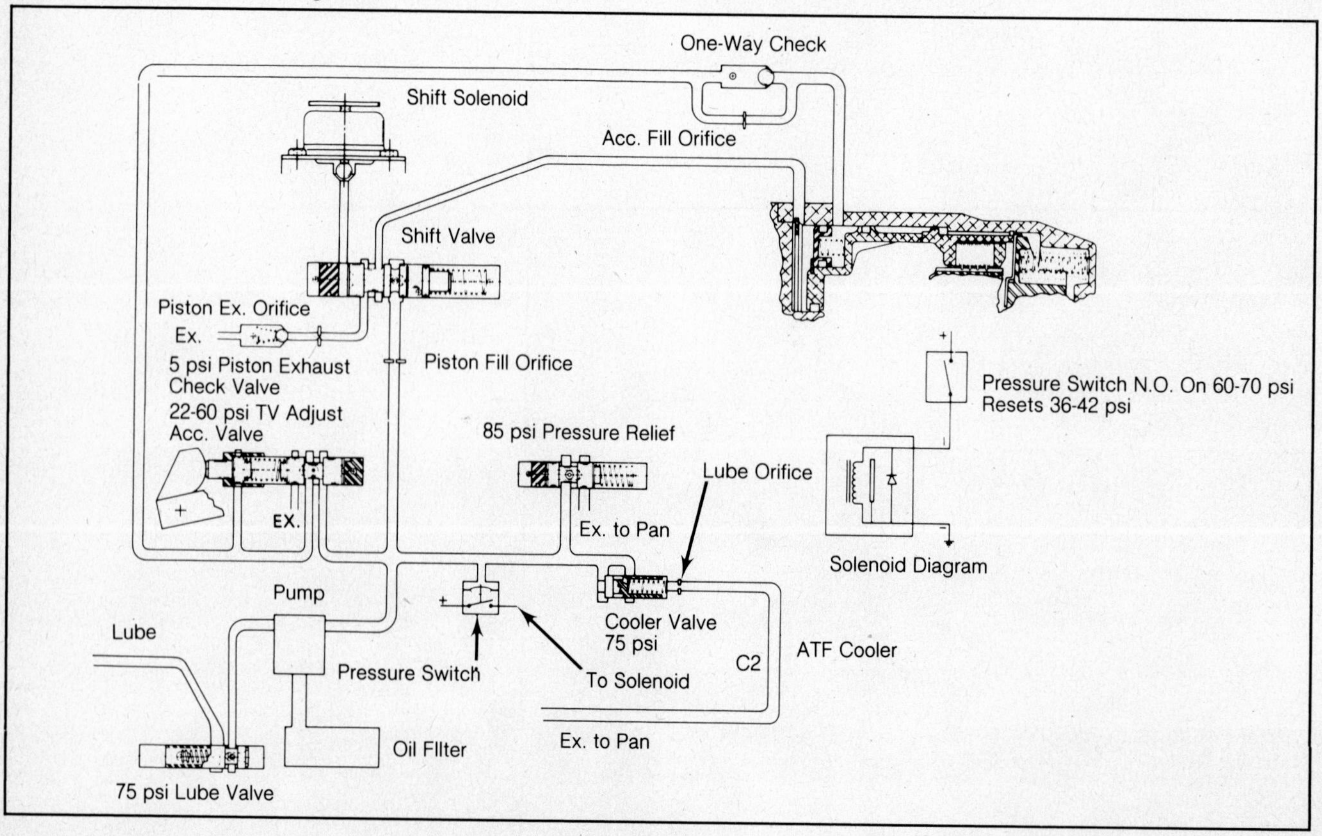

GENERAL MOTORS 83 MM 4-SPEED AUTOMATIC OVERDRIVE – OVERDRIVE (Cont.)

Fig. 2: Cross Section View of Overdrive Unit

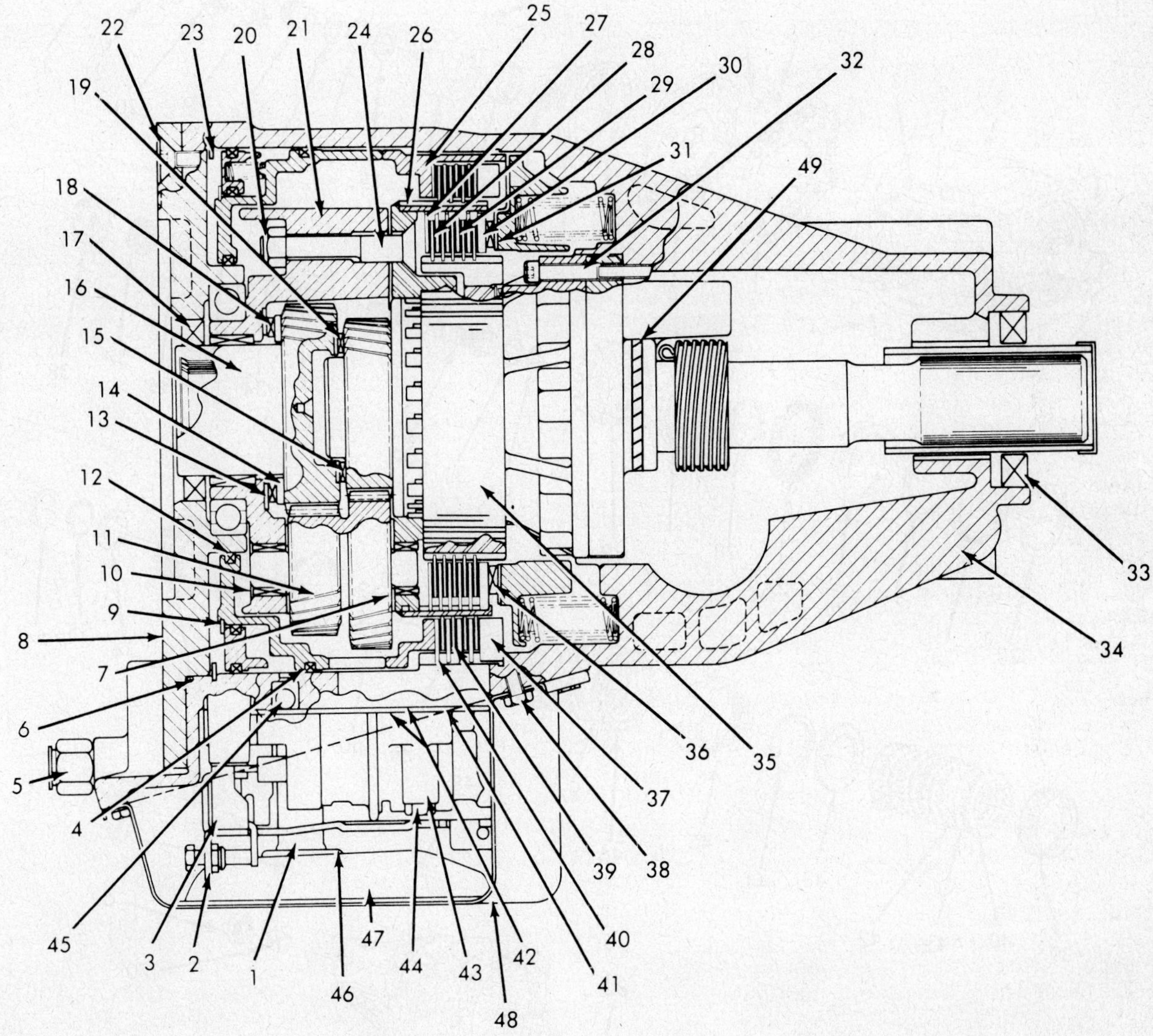

1. Pickup Tube
2. Lever Arm Assembly
3. Lever Cam
4. Quad Seal
5. Fitting
6. "O" Ring Seal
7. Thrust Plate
8. Adapter Plate
9. Piston-Accumulator Assembly
10. Thrust Washer
11. Planet Gear
12. Quad Seal
13. Thrust Washer
14. Thrust Washer
15. Thrust Washer
16. Sun Gear
17. Input Seal
18. Thrust Bearing
19. Thrust Bearing
20. Lock Nut
21. Carrier Bearing Assembly
22. Screw
23. Retaining Ring
24. Screw
25. Finger Pressure Plate
26. Clutch Hub Assembly
27. Clutch Plate
28. Clutch Disc
29. Clutch Plate
30. Bearing Plate
31. Thrust Washer
32. Allen Screw (6 mm x 40 mm)
33. Output Seal
34. Housing Assembly
35. Shaft Assembly
36. Thrust Bearing
37. Stop Clutch
38. Screw (6 mm x 12 mm)
39. Clutch Disc
40. Clutch Plate
41. Valve Plate
42. Valve Gasket
43. Valve Body Assembly
44. Screw (6 mm x 45 mm)
45. 5/16" Steel Ball
46. Grommet
47. Oil Filter
48. Oil Pan
49. Pump Seal

GENERAL MOTORS 83 MM 4-SPEED AUTOMATIC OVERDRIVE – OVERDRIVE (Cont.)

Fig. 3: Exploded View of Automatic Overdrive Unit

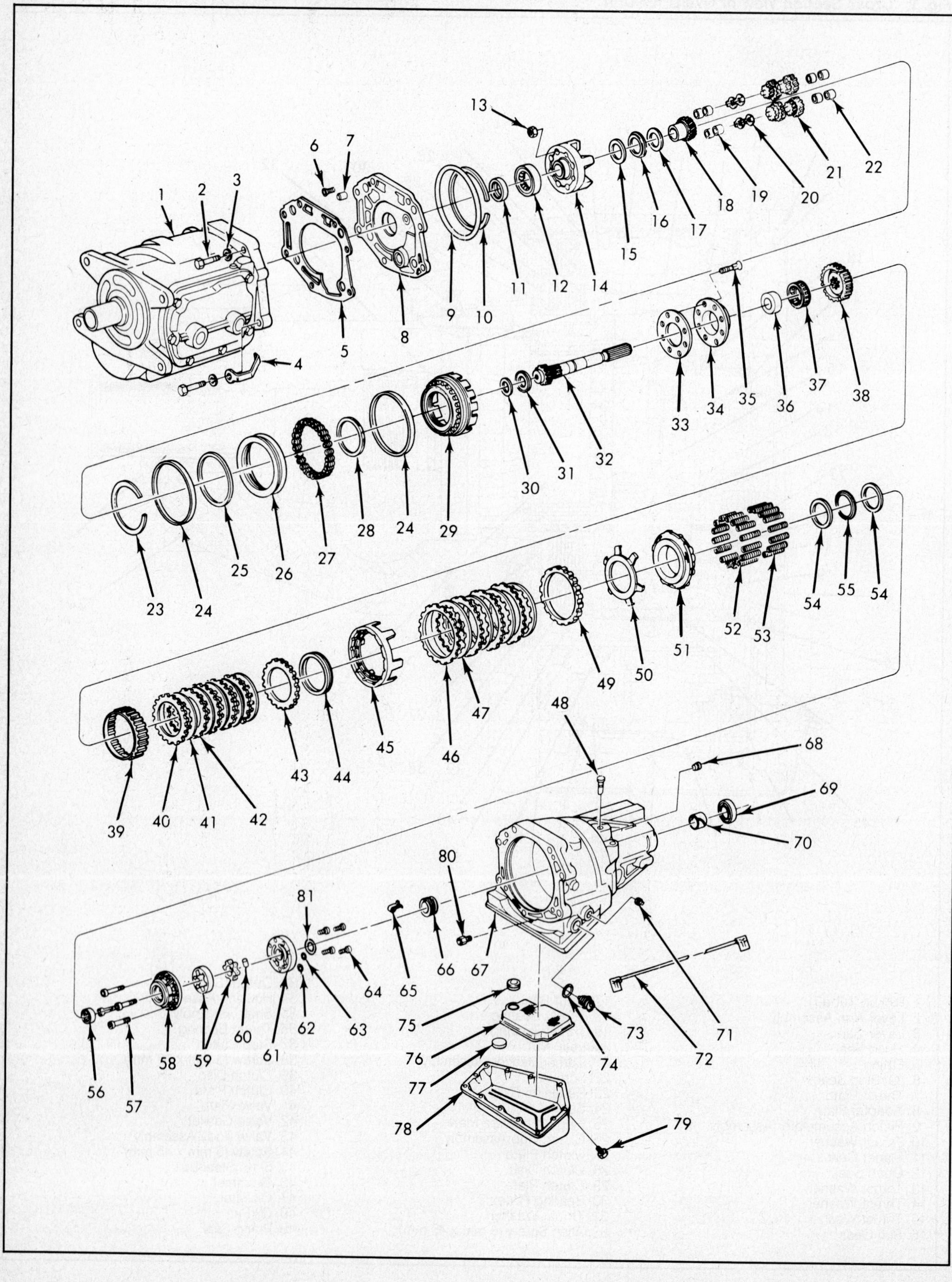

GENERAL MOTORS 83 MM 4-SPEED AUTOMATIC OVERDRIVE – OVERDRIVE (Cont.)

Automatic Overdrive Unit Components (Use With Fig. 3)

1. Transmission (Less Overdrive Unit)
2. Transmission-to-Overdrive Bolt
3. Transmission-to-Overdrive Bolt Lock Washer
4. Harness Clip Bracket
5. Adapter Plate Gasket
6. Adapter Plate Screw
7. Dowel Pin
8. Adapter Plate
9. Adapter Plate "O" Ring
10. Accumulator Piston Retaining Ring
11. Input Sun Gear Oil Seal
12. Annular Bearing
13. Carrier Bearing Lock Nut
14. Planetary Gear Carrier
15. Input Sun Gear Thrust Washer
16. Input Sun Gear Thrust Bearing
17. Input Sun Gear Thrust (Selective) Washer
18. Input Sun Gear
19. Bearing Cup
20. Planetary Gear Thrust Washer
21. Planetary Gear
22. Bearing Cup
23. Accumulator Piston Retaining Ring
24. Accumulator Piston Seal
25. Accumulator Piston Seal
26. Accumulator Cushion Piston
27. Accumulator Piston Spring
28. Accumulator Piston Seal
29. Accumulator Piston
30. Output Shaft Thrust Washer
31. Output Shaft Thrust Bearing
32. Output Shaft
33. Planetary Gear Thrust Plate
34. Clutch Drum Plate
35. Clutch Drum Bolt
36. Inner Race
37. Direct Clutch Sprag
38. Direct Clutch Hub
39. Direct Clutch Drum
40. Direct Clutch Inner Driven (Selective) Plate
41. Direct Clutch Plate
42. Direct Clutch Driven Plate
43. Direct Clutch Pressure Plate
44. Direct Clutch Bearing
45. Overdrive Clutch Piston
46. Overdrive Clutch Driven Plate
47. Overdrive Clutch Plate
48. Overdrive Vent Tube
49. Overdrive Clutch Pressure Plate
50. Direct Clutch Thrust Washer
51. Overdrive Direct Clutch Piston
52. Overdrive Direct Clutch Outer Spring
53. Overdrive Direct Clutch Inner Spring
54. Overdrive Direct Clutch Hub Thrust Washer
55. Overdrive Direct Clutch Hub Thrust Bearing
56. Pump Bearing Cup
57. Overdrive Pump & Output Shaft Screw
58. Overdrive Pump (Gerotor) Housing, with Bearing
59. Overdrive Oil (Gerotor) Pump
60. Oil Pump Drive Pin
61. Pump (Gerotor) Spool
62. Overdrive Oil Pump "O" Ring
63. Overdrive Oil Pump "O" Ring
64. Overdrive Pump Spool (Gerotor) Screw
65. Speedometer Drive Gear Clip
66. Speedometer Drive Gear
67. Overdrive Case
68. Headless Slotted Plug
69. Overdrive Output Shaft Oil Seal
70. Case Bushing
71. Overdrive Valve Body Pressure Switch Wire
72. Square Head Filler Plug
73. Overdrive Solenoid Electrical Connector
74. Overdrive Solenoid Electrical Connector "O" Ring
75. Overdrive Oil Screen Tube Grommet
76. Overdrive Oil Screen
77. Overdrive Oil Pan Magnet
78. Overdrive Oil Pan
79. Overdrive Oil Pan Bolt
80. Oil Cooler Fitting
81. Pump Seal

REMOVAL & INSTALLATION

See the appropriate article in MANUAL TRANSMISSION REMOVAL section

PRESSURE SWITCH

Removal

Remove oil pan and filter. Disconnect 2 electrical leads at switch. Unscrew switch from valve body.

Installation

To install, reverse removal procedures. Fill transmission with Dexron II automatic transmission fluid.

O/D UNIT OUTPUT SHAFT SEAL

Removal

Remove drive shaft. Pry out old seal using a Seal Removal tool.

Installation

Coat lip of new seal with automatic transmission fluid. Place a new seal on Seal Installer (J-21426), and install seal. Install drive shaft. Replace lost fluid.

O/D SOLENOID

Removal

Remove transmission oil pan and filter. Disconnect T.V. cable at throttle body lever. Remove valve body. Using Spring Compressor (J-34529), compress shift valve spring and remove pin. Using same tool, compress relief valve springs and remove pin. Remove bolts attaching solenoid valve to valve body. Remove solenoid and check ball from valve body.

Installation

To install, reverse removal procedure. Fill overdrive unit with Dexron II automatic transmission fluid.

DISASSEMBLY

OVERDRIVE UNIT

1) Remove fill plug and drain oil from case. Remove retaining bolt and bracket for speedometer sensor and driven gear. Remove sensor and gear. Remove 1/8" pipe plugs (3) from rear of unit. Install 3 pressure plate retaining bolts until flush with case. Turn bolts 2 additional turns, by rotating each bolt 1 turn at a time.

NOTE: **This sequence must be followed in order to prevent pressure plate from cocking and causing damage to unit.**

2) Remove 4 Allen head bolts retaining adapter plate to case. Remove adapter plate, using a plastic hammer and screwdriver. Tap adapter plate to separate from case.

NOTE: **Do not pry between case and adapter plate, damage to sealing surfaces may occur.**

GENERAL MOTORS 83 MM 4-SPEED AUTOMATIC OVERDRIVE – OVERDRIVE (Cont.)

3) Mount overdrive unit in a holding fixture. Remove large snap ring from overdrive unit forward of accumulator piston.

CAUTION: If pressure is felt at snap ring, do not remove. Check to ensure pressure plate retaining bolts are installed. If bolts are installed, tighten each bolt one additional turn until pressure is relieved. The pressure plate is under a 1200 lb (544 kg.) spring load. If 3 retaining bolts are not installed, personal injury could occur.

4) Remove piston and accumulator assembly. Using an Allen wrench, pry assembly up evenly by lifting under flange. *See Fig. 4.* Do not pry at or near seal surface. Remove carrier and bearing assembly (includes input sun and pinion gears) as an assembly.

Fig. 4: Removing Piston & Accumulator Assembly

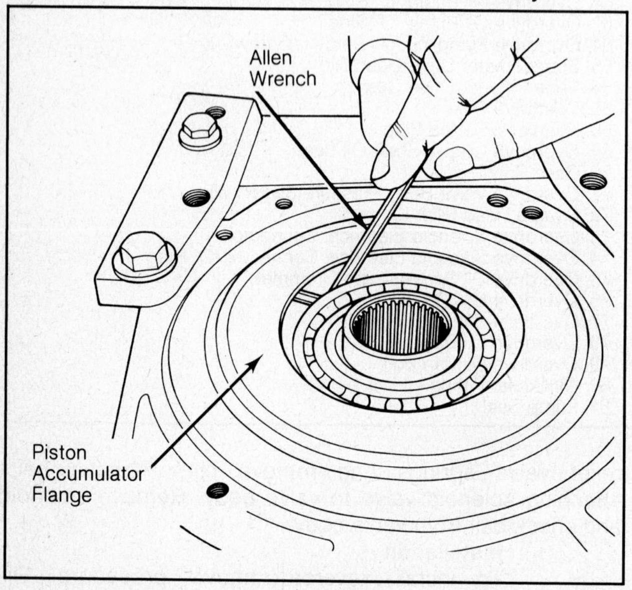

5) Remove finger pressure plate from clutch pack. Remove overdrive clutches (4 composition, 4 steel and 1 clutch stop plate). Remove direct clutch plates (5 composition, 5 steel and 1 steel bearing plate).

6) Measure each selective clutch plate in direct clutch pack and record readings. Selective clutch plates are used to control clutch pack clearance. When replacing clutch plates, replace each selective clutch plate with one of the same size.

7) Inspect overdrive and direct clutch plates as follows: Dry composition plates and inspect for pitting, flaking wear, glazing, cracking, charring and chips or metal particles imbedded in lining. If a compositioned plate shows any of these signs, replacement is required.

8) Wipe steel plate dry and check for discoloration. If surface is smooth and an even color smear is indicated, plate should be reused. If severe heat spot discoloration or surface scuffing is indicated, plate must be replaced.

9) Remove thrust washer and bearing from output sun gear. Thrust washer may stick to input sun gear hub. Remove 4 Allen head pump housing retaining bolts by rotating hub to gain access to bolts. Remove output shaft assembly (Includes: output sun gear, sprag clutch, clutch hub, gerotor pump and speedometer drive gear).

10) Remove pressure plate and springs by positioning Clutch Spring Compressor Pilot (J-21420-2) on pressure plate with bolt from Clutch Spring Compressor (J-23327) through center of plate. Position (J-23327) on rear of case and install retaining nut. *See Fig. 5.* Remove 3 retaining bolts from rear of case. Loosen retaining nut on (J-23327) bolt to relieve spring pressure.

Fig. 5: Removing Pressure Plate & Springs

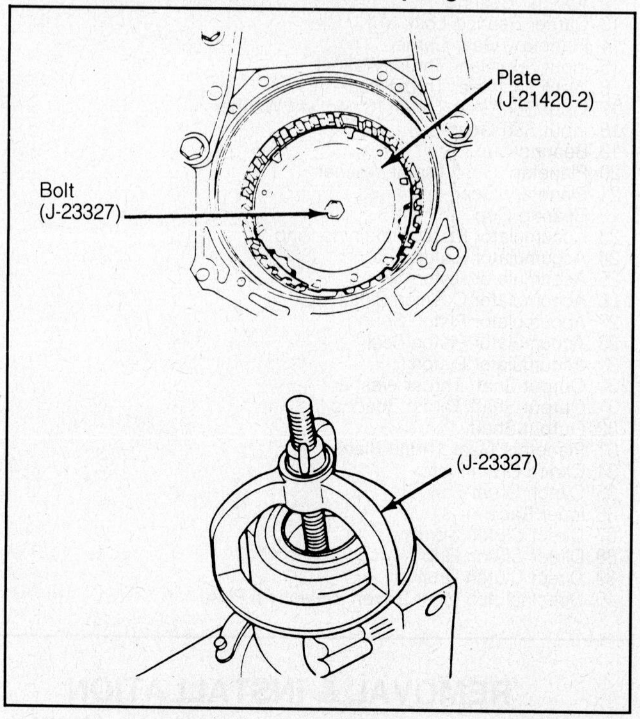

11) Remove cooler valve assembly by loosening 2 nuts on tube and then removing 2 bolts holding valve to case. Remove 12 oil pan retaining bolts and pry pan from case. Remove oil filter and tube from valve body.

12) Disconnect T.V. cable from lever. Remove cable retaining bolt and remove cable assembly. Remove T.V. lever retaining bolt and then lever from valve body. Remove remaining valve body bolts and remove valve body with spacer plate.

NOTE: There are 2 check balls, one on each side of spacer plate. One ball is located in case and the other is spring loaded in valve body.

COMPONENT DISASSEMBLY & REASSEMBLY

VALVE BODY

Disassembly

1) Using Valve Body Spring Compressor (J-34529), relieve pressure on shift valve and remove pin, spring and valve. Relieve pressure on relief valve and remove pin, spring and valve. Relieve pressure on accumulator valve and remove pin, spring, valve, plug, sleeve and plunger.

2) Disconnect solenoid electrical lead at pressure switch. Remove solenoid attaching bolts. Remove solenoid and checkball. Disconnect the other electrical lead at pressure switch. Remove switch from valve body.

Reassembly

To reassemble, reverse removal procedures. Coat all components with clean Dexron II automatic transmission fluid before reassembling.

OUTPUT SHAFT

Disassembly

1) Remove speedometer gear retaining clip and gear. Remove 4 Allen head bolts retaining pump cover to pump housing. Remove cover. Mark pump gears with a grease pencil. Gears must be installed in same direction as removed.

2) Position output shaft with splines down. Rotate pump housing until gears slide out. Remove drive pin from output shaft. Remove pump housing from output shaft. Remove thrust washer from pump housing. Remove thrust bearing and washer from clutch hub.

3) Remove clutch hub from output shaft. Note direction of hub on shaft. Oil grooves face sprag clutch or forward on shaft. Remove sprag clutch from output shaft. Note direction of sprag clutch. Lip on sprag clutch cage goes toward oil grooves on clutch hub.

Reassembly

1) Coat all parts with clean Dexron II automatic transmission fluid before reassembling. Install sprag clutch on output shaft. Lip on sprag clutch cage faces rearward or toward oil grooves on clutch hub. Install clutch hub on output shaft. Oil grooves on hub face sprag clutch or forward on shaft.

2) Install thrust washer, then thrust bearing on clutch hub. Install thrust washer on pump housing. Use petrolatum to retain thrust washer to housing. Install pump housing on output shaft. Install pin in output shaft. Install pump gears in housing. Gears must be installed in same direction as removed. Install oil pump seal in cover.

3) Place pump cover on housing. Align 4 bolt holes in cover with pump housing. Install bolts and tighten to specifications. Install speedometer gear on output shaft. Install retaining clip. Install new "O" rings on pump. Use petrolatum to retain "O" rings to cover.

CARRIER ASSEMBLY

Disassembly

1) Remove 4 nuts retaining carrier cover and remove cover. Remove thrust washer, thrust bearing, selective washer and input sun gear. Remove 4 pinion gears.

2) Remove steel thurst plate from carrier. Clean and inspect parts. Replace any parts that are cracked, chipped or show excessive wear.

Reassembly

Carrier assembly must be reassembled in transmission case.

PISTON & ACCUMULATOR ASSEMBLY

Disassembly

Remove snap ring retaining accumulator to piston. Remove accumulator and 24 springs from piston. Remove 2 "O" rings from accumulator. Remove 2 "O" rings from piston.

Reassembly

To reassemble, reverse removal procedures. Coat "O" rings with clean Dexron II automatic transmission fluid before installing.

REASSEMBLY

OVERDRIVE UNIT

1) Install pressure plate springs into pockets of transmission case as shown in *Fig 6.* Place pressure plate on top of springs. Seat springs into pockets of pressure plate.

Fig. 6: Pressure Plate Spring Installation

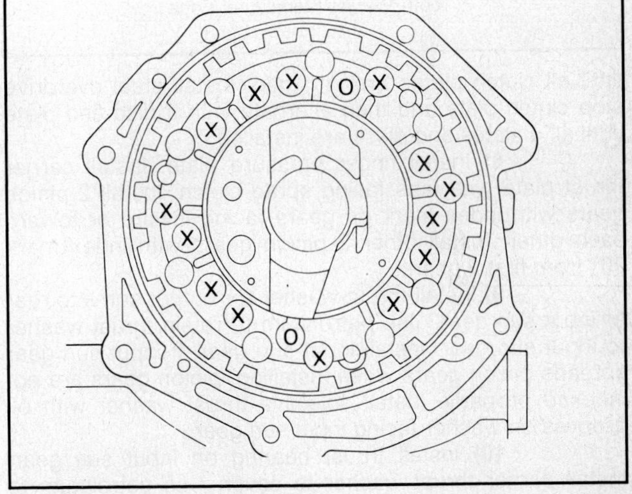

2) Position Plate Tool (J-21420-2) on top of pressure plate with bolt from Plate Tool (J23327) through center of plate. Next position Plate Tool on rear of case. Install retaining nut. Tighten nut until pressure plate is drawn approximately 1/8" below step for overdrive clutch plates. Install 3 pressure plate retaining bolts. Remove tools from case. *See Fig. 5.*

3) Install output shaft assembly into transmission case. Be sure "O" rings are positioned properly on pump cover before installing output shaft assembly. Install 4 pump retaining bolts. Tighten to specification.

4) Install thrust bearing on output sun gear. Install tanged direct clutch thrust washer with tangs facing pressure plate. Tang with hole in it should be positioned at bottom of case (6 o'clock position). Ensure tabs on back of washer are seated in pressure plate. Install direct clutch thrust bearing.

5) Install direct clutch thrust washer. Thrust washer will have tooth missing from its outer edge. Side of thrust washer with circular grind pattern must face thrust bearing. Side with grind pattern can be identified by notch ground into tooth. *See Fig. 7.*

6) Install 1 composition clutch disc and a selective clutch plate. Selective clutch plates come in 5 sizes from .080-.120" (2.03-3.05) and are used to control clutch pack clearance. Direct clutch pack clearance is .050-.070" (1.27-1.78). Incorrect clutch travel will cause failure to clutch plates and discs.

7) Alternate remaining clutch discs and plates until all 5 plates and discs are installed. Install lower half of carrier assembly onto direct clutch pack. Index carrier

GENERAL MOTORS 83 MM 4–SPEED AUTOMATIC OVERDRIVE – OVERDRIVE (Cont.)

Fig. 7: Thrust Washer Identification

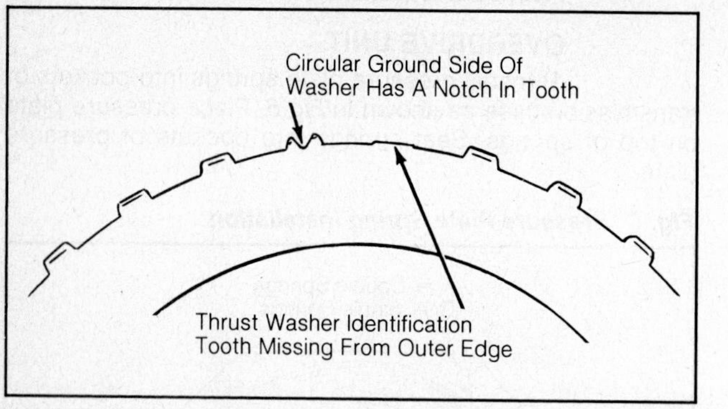

until all clutch plates are engaged. Install steel overdrive stop clutch plate and then alternate with a disc and plate until all 4 plates and discs are installed.

8) Install finger pressure plate. Install carrier thrust plate with tabs facing sprag clutch. Install 2 pinion gears with index mark on gears facing inward or toward each other. Install other 2 pinion gears with index mark 90° from first 2 gears.

9) Install thrust washer for output sun into rear of input sun gear. Use petrolatum to retain thrust washer to input sun gear. Install input sun gear. If input sun gear spreads pinion gears when installing, pinion gears are not indexed properly. Install selective thrust washer with oil grooves on washer facing input sun gear.

10) Install thrust bearing on input sun gear. Install carrier thrust washer to cover. Use petrolatum to retain thrust washer to cover. Install 4 pinion gear thrust washers onto carrier cover. Use petrolatum to retain washers to cover.

11) Install carrier cover. If pinion gears are not indexed properly, 4 bolt holes in cover will not align with bolts in lower half of carrier. Install 4 new retaining nuts and tighten to specifications.

12) Measure end play for overdrive unit as follows. Place Straightedge (J-34673) across face of overdrive unit as shown in *Fig. 8*. Use Depth Micrometer (J-34672) and measure distance from bearing to top of bar (S_1). Next, measure thickness of Straightedge (S_2) with a 0-1" Outside Micrometer and subtract (S_2) from (S_1) and record this reading (S_3).

13) Place Straightedge across rear of adapter plate as shown in *Fig. 8*. Use Depth Micrometer and measure distance from top of bar to adapter plate mounting surface and record reading (S_4).

14) Next measure distance from top of bar to bearing seat in adapter plate as shown in *Fig. 8* and record reading (S_5). Subtract S_5 from S_4 and record difference (S_6).

15) Subtract S_6 from S_3 and record reading (S_7). S_7 is the end play. End play S_7 should be .000-.003". If S_7 is not within specifications, it will be necessary to remove carrier cover and change input sun selective thrust washer.

16) Install accumulator and piston assembly. Coat lips of seals with clean Dexron II automatic transmission fluid before installing. Install large snap ring that goes in front of overdrive unit. Snap ring must be installed as shown in *Fig. 9*.

17) Install a new seal in adapter plate. Place seal on seal installer and install from front side of adapter plate. Place seal protector on input sun gear. Install

Fig. 8: Measuring End Play

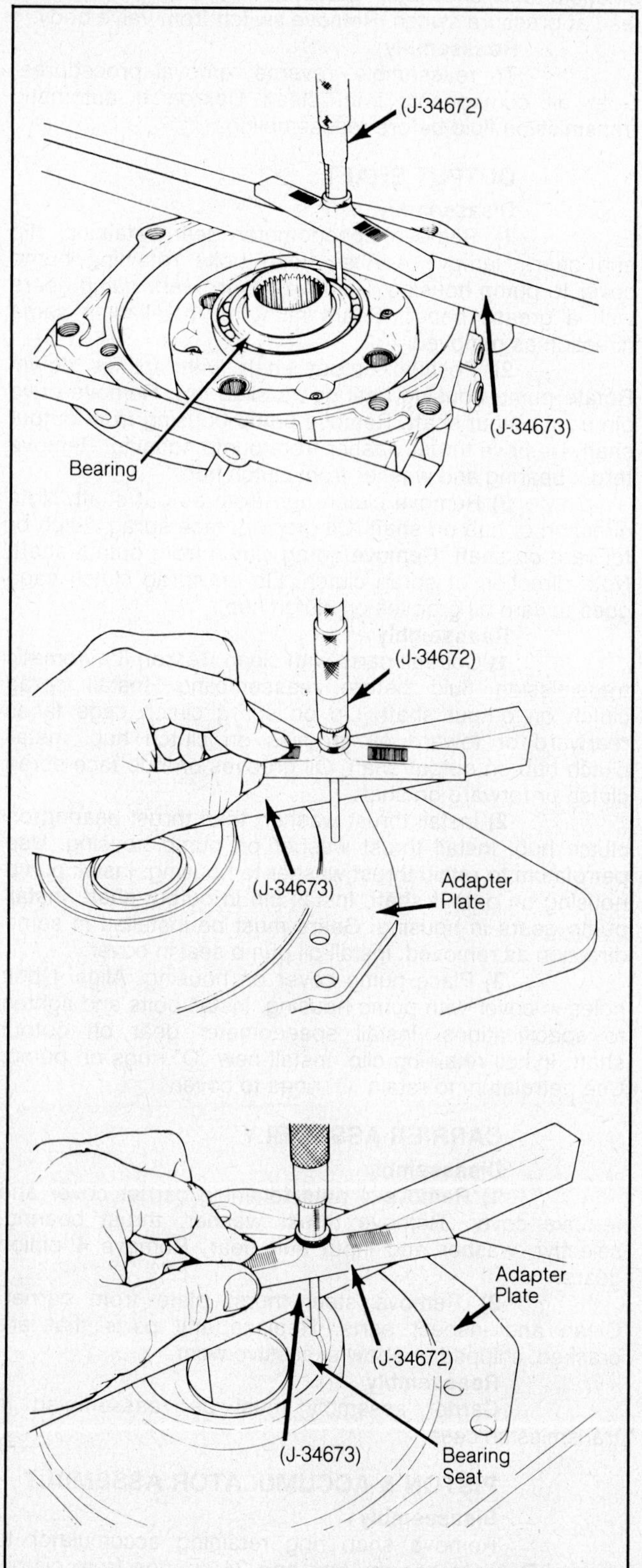

adapter plate. Apply a light coating of RTV sealant around heads of adapter plate bolts.

18) Install 4 adapter plate bolts and tighten to specifications. Remove seal protector. Remove first 1/8"

GENERAL MOTORS 83 MM 4-SPEED AUTOMATIC OVERDRIVE – OVERDRIVE (Cont.)

Fig. 9: Snap Ring Installation

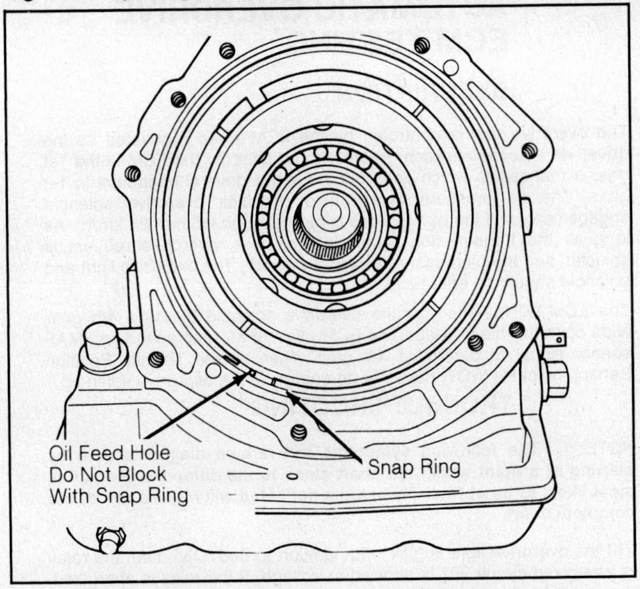

pipe plug from left side of overdrive unit. Install Air Line Adapter (J-34742) into plug hole and tighten.

19) Measure clutch pack clearance as follows. Loosen 3 pressure plate retaining bolts evenly until spring pressure is released. Assemble Dial Indicator (J-8001) to rear of overdrive unit as shown in *Fig. 10*.

Fig. 10: Checking Clutch Pack Clearance

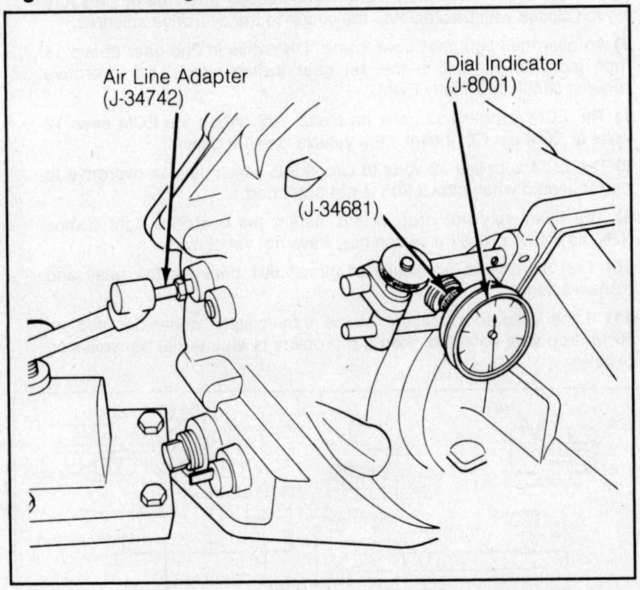

20) Apply a minimum of 100 psi (7.0 kg/cm²) to Air Line Adapter (J-34742) and read Dial Indicator. Reading should be between .050-.070". If reading is different, it will be necessary to disassemble overdrive unit to change direct clutch selective clutch plates.

21) Selective clutch plates are available in 5 sizes from .080-.120" in .010" increments. If clutch pack clearance is within specification, remove 3 clutch pack retaining bolts. Coat 3 pipe plugs (1/8") with anti-sieze compound and install plugs. Tighten plugs to specifications.

22) Remove air line adapter. Coat plug with anti-sieze compound and install plug. Tighten to specification. Install speedometer gear and sensor. Install a new output seal using a seal installer. Coat lip of seal with Dexron II automatic transmission fluid.

Fig. 11: Location of Check Ball

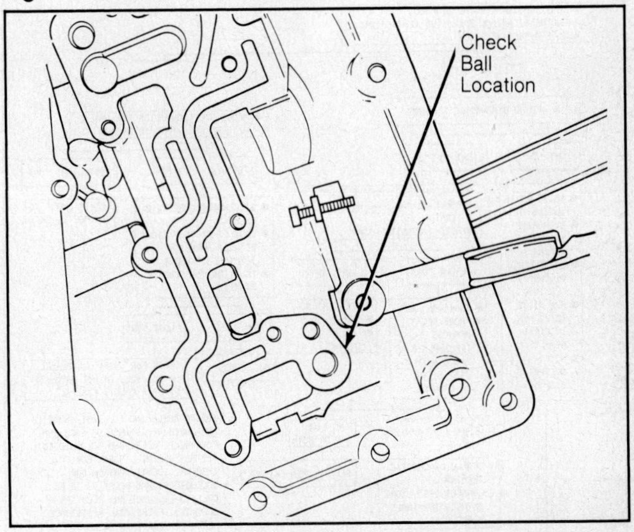

23) Install valve body as follows. Install check ball into case as shown in *Fig. 11*. Position 2 gaskets, one on each side of separator plate. Position separator plate on valve body. Position valve body to case and install retaining bolts and tighten to specifications.

24) Install T.V. cable and install retaining clip and bolt. Tighten bolt to specifications. Install T.V. lever and tighten bolt to specification. Connect T.V. cable to lever. Install Throttle Setting Guage (J-34671-1) into T.V. cable bore on side of case. *See Fig. 12.*

25) Set hook on T.V. cable onto high step of gauge. Place cam stop on valve body as close to lever as possible and install retaining bolt. Tighten to specifications. Set hook on T.V. cable onto lower step of gauge. Place Gauge (J-34671-2) between piston and solenoid bracket.

26) Adjust screw/bolt on T.V. lever until bolt makes contact with stop on cam. After removing tools, install pickup tube and oil filter on valve body. Apply a bead of RTV sealant to oil pan flange and assemble wet.

27) Install magnet in oil pan. The bead of RTV should be applied around inside of bolt holes. Install pan bolts and tighten to specifications.

TIGHTENING SPECIFICATIONS

Application	Ft. Lbs. (N.m)
Cooler Block-to-Case	6-8 (8-10)
Pressure Tap Plugs	7-9 (9-12)
Pressure Plate Access Plugs	7-9 (9-12)
Valve Body-to-Case	6-8 (8-10)
Adapter Plate-to-Case	18-20 (24-27)
Oil Pan-to-Case	6-8 (8-10)
Pump Housing-to-Case	6-8 (8-10)
Pump Cover-to-Pump Cavity	10-12 (13-16)
O/D Case-to-Reverse Housing	34-36 (46-48)

GENERAL MOTORS 83 MM 4-SPEED AUTOMATIC OVERDRIVE – OVERDRIVE (Cont.)

1986 CHART C-8A AUTOMATIC OVERDRIVE

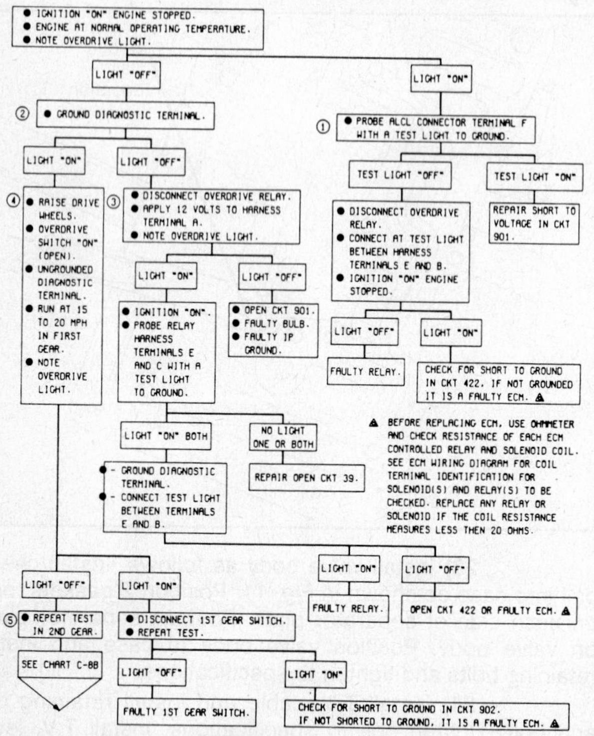

1986 CHART C-8B AUTOMATIC OVERDRIVE

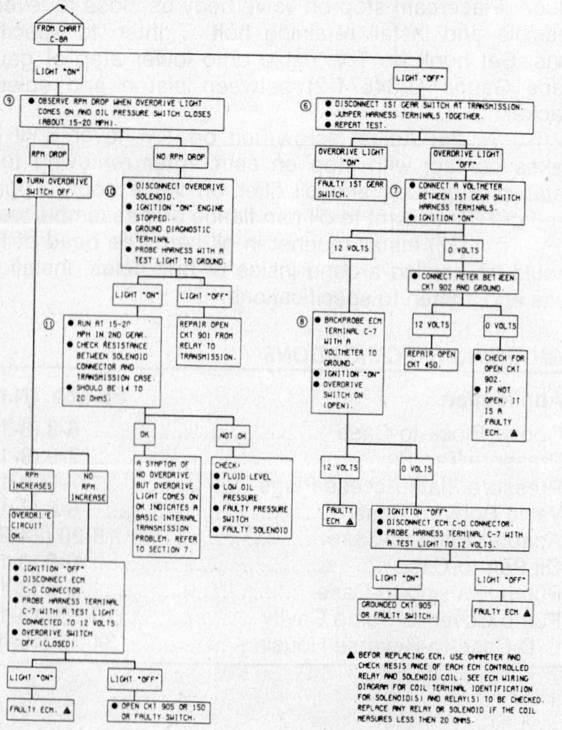

AUTOMATIC OVERDRIVE ECM TESTING

DESCRIPTION

The overdrive unit is controled by the ECM when requested by the driver via a console switch. Another input used by the ECM is the 1st gear signal switch which does not allow overdrive engagement in 1st gear. The oil pressure switch also prohibits overdrive solenoid engagement until the oil pressure is high enough (15mph 24 km/h). As long as the transmission is not in first gear, overdrive request is selected and the oil pressure switch is closed . The overdrive light and solenoid should be energized.

The ECM will de-energize the overdrive solenoid during a 4th gear wide open throttle situation.The ECM uses RPM, road speed,and MAF sensor signal to determine 4th gear. Then as the Throttle Position Sensor indicates WOT, the ECM de-energizes the overdrive solenoid.

TROUBLE SHOOTING

NOTE: The following symptoms will reduce diagnosis time by starting at a point within the chart close to the component which is most likely to be at fault. Symptoms not listed will require use of the complete chart.

1)If the overdrive light is "ON" with ignition turned "ON", then the relay is energized circuit 901 is shorted to voltage. If the relay is energized, the test light should not light at this point.

2) Grounding the diagnostic terminal with ignition "ON" should energize the relay and turn "ON" the overdrive light.

3) Connecting 12 volts to circuit 901 will check the continuity of the bulb circuit.

4) The 1st gear switch input (open) should not allow the overdrive to be energized.

5) With the vehicle in 2nd gear and above 15 mph, the overdrive light should be "ON". An RPM drop should be noticed when the oil pressure switch closes which completes the circuit to the overdrive solenoid.

6) An overdrive light that does come "ON" while in 2nd gear above 15 mph indicates a fault in the 1st gear switch circuit, the overdrive request circuit or a faulty ECM.

7) The ECM supplies 12 volts on circuit 902. When the ECM sees 12 volts at ECM pin C8, it thinks the vehicle is in 1st gear.

8) The ECM supplies 12 volts to circuit 905 which causes overdrive to be requested when circuit 905 is not grounded.

9) The RPM may not drop at the instant the overdrive light comes "ON" as the oil pressure switch may have not yet closed.

10) Test 10 checks continuity of circuit 901 between the relay and transmission.

11) If the voltage is present at the transmission connector and no RPM drop was detected, then the problem is an internal transmission problem.

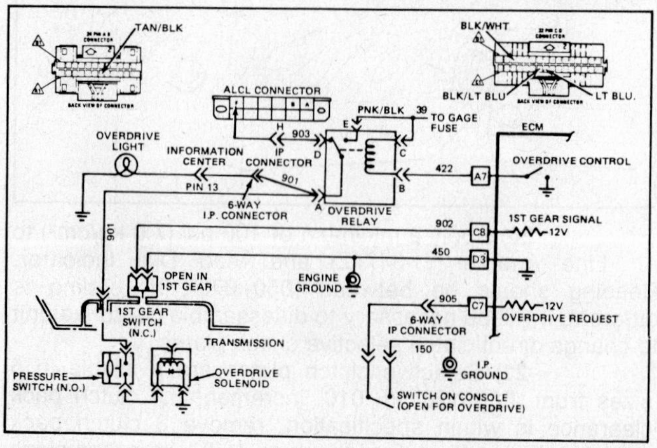

GENERAL MOTORS 4-SPEED – 117 MM

Chevrolet & GMC 10-30 Series Truck

IDENTIFICATION

Transmission can be identified by a 2 letter code, stamped on a machined pad, on right side of case.

DESCRIPTION

The 117 MM 4-speed transmission is identified by the measured distance (117 mm) between centerlines of mainshaft and countergear and also by the number of forward gears. The 1st gear is a constant mesh type that engages with the 2nd gear synchronizer sleeve. The 2nd, 3rd, and 4th gears are synchronized.

LUBRICATION & ADJUSTMENT

See the appropriate article in MANUAL TRANSMISSION SERVICING section.

TROUBLE SHOOTING

See MANUAL TRANSMISSION TROUBLE SHOOTING in DOMESTIC GENERAL SERVICING section.

SERVICE (IN VEHICLE)

SHIFT LEVER

Removal

1) On 4WD models, remove transfer case shift lever boot retaining screws and retainer from compartment floor.

2) On all models, remove transmission shift lever boot retaining screws. Slide boot and retainer up on shift lever and remove shift lever.

Installation

1) Install transmission shift lever. Slide boot and retainer down shift lever and install attaching screws.

2) On 4WD models, install transfer case shift lever boot, retainer and attaching screws.

EXTENSION HOUSING OIL SEAL

Removal

1) Raise vehicle and support with safety stands. Drain lubricant from transmission. Disconnect propeller shaft and secure out of way. Disconnect speedometer cable and remove speedometer driven gear.

2) Using flange/yoke holding tool, remove output yoke/companion flange nut. Pull output yoke and companion nut off mainshaft. Support transmission while removing mounting bolts and bearing retainer bolts.

3) Remove bearing retainer and gasket. Discard gasket. Remove and discard oil seal.

Installation

1) Clean gasket surfaces. Coat outer diameter of new oil seal with sealing cement. Install oil seal using Driver (J-22834-2). Install retaining bolts and tighten.

2) Install output yoke on mainshaft. Using a flange/yoke holding tool, install retaining nut. Tighten nut to specifications. Install speedometer driven gear, and connect speedometer cable.

3) Connect propeller shaft to transmission. Fill transmission with lubricant and lower vehicle.

REMOVAL & INSTALLATION

COVER & SHIFT FORK ASSEMBLY

Removal

1) Mount transmission in holding fixture and remove cover bolts. Move reverse shifter fork so reverse idler gear is partially engaged before removing cover.

2) Forks must be set so rear edge of slot in reverse fork is in line with front edge of slot in forward forks as viewed through tower opening.

3) If necessary, insert 2 bolts in cover flange threaded holes and turn evenly to raise cover dowel pins from case.

Installation

1) Move transmission gears to neutral except reverse idler gear which should be engaged about 3/8". Install cover with new gasket.

2) Shift forks must slide into their proper positions on clutch sleeves and reverse idler gear. Forks must be positioned as in removal. Install cover bolts and tighten.

DRIVE GEAR OIL SEAL

Removal & Installation

Remove retainer, oil seal assembly and gasket. Pry oil seal from retainer. Install new seal using Installer (J-22833), with lip of seal toward flange of installer tool. Install retainer with new gasket.

TRANSMISSION

See the appropriate article in MANUAL TRANSMISSION REMOVAL section.

TRANSMISSION DISASSEMBLY

1) Mount transmission in holding fixture and remove cap screws retaining transmission cover assembly to case. If required, insert two 5/16" x 18 bolts in cover flange threaded holes and turn evenly to raise cover dowel pin from case.

2) Move reverse shifter fork so that reverse idler gear is partially engaged before attempting to remove cover. Forks must be positioned so rear edge of slot in reverse fork is in line with front edge of slot in forward forks as viewed throught tower opening.

3) Place transmission in 2 gears at once to lock gears. Remove universal joint flange and brake drum assembly. On 4WD models, use Main Bearing Lock Nut Remover/Installer (J-23070) to remove mainshaft rear lock nut. *See Fig. 2.*

4) If equipped, remove parking brake and brake flange plate assembly. On all models, remove rear bearing retainer and gasket. Slide speedometer drive gear off mainshaft.

5) Remove drive gear bearing retainers and gasket. Remove countergear front bearing cap and gasket. Pry countergear front bearing out, by inserting a Two-Pronged Puller (J-28509) through cast slots in case.

6) Remove countergear rear bearing snap ring from shaft and bearing. Using Puller (J-8433-1) with Bearing Puller (J-22832), remove countergear rear bearing. *See Fig. 3.* Let countergear assembly rest on bottom of case.

7) Remove drive gear bearing outer race to case retaining ring. Remove drive gear and bearing by tapping gently on bottom side of drive gear shaft and

GENERAL MOTORS 4-SPEED – 117 MM (Cont.)

Fig. 1: Exploded View of General Motors 117 MM Manual Transmission

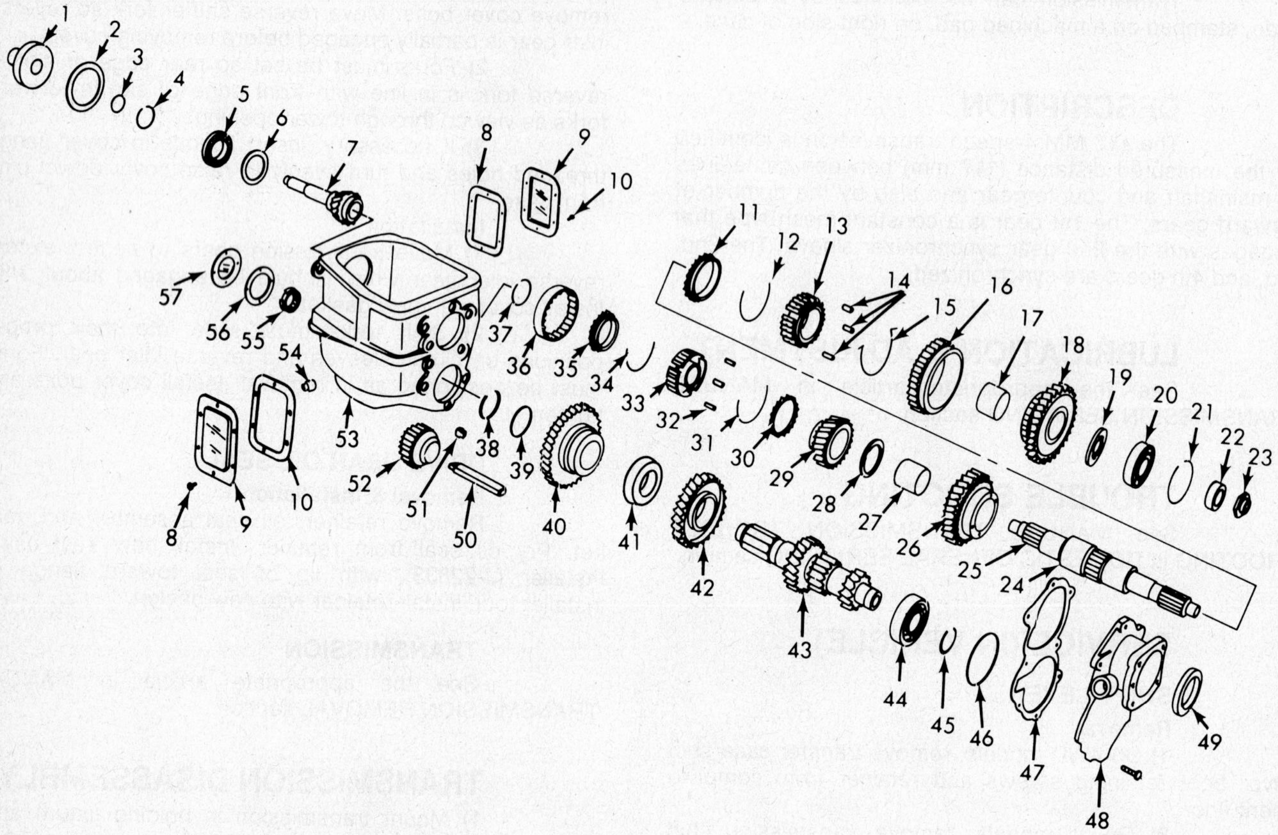

1. Drive Gear Bearing Retainer
2. Retainer Gasket
3. Lip Seal
4. Snap Ring
5. Drive Gear Bearing
6. Oil Slinger
7. Drive Gear & Pilot Bearings
8. Power Take-Off Cover Gasket
9. Power Take-Off Cover
10. Retaining Screws
11. 1st-2nd Gear Blocker Ring
12. Synchronizer Spring
13. 1st-2nd Gear Synchronizer Hub
14. Synchronizer Keys
15. Synchronizer Spring
16. Reverse Driven Gear
17. 1st Gear Bushing
18. 1st Gear
19. Thrust Washer
20. Rear Main Bearing
21. Bearing Snap Ring
22. Speedometer Gear
23. Rear Mainshaft Lock Nut
24. 2nd Gear Bushing (On Shaft)
25. Mainshaft
26. 2nd Gear
27. 3rd Gear Bushing
28. Thrust Washer
29. 3rd Gear
30. 3rd Gear Blocker Ring
31. Synchronizer Spring
32. Synchronizer Keys
33. 3rd-4th Synchronizer Hub
34. Synchronizer Spring
35. 3rd-4th Gear Blocker Ring
36. 3rd-4th Gear Synchronizer Sleeve
37. Snap Ring
38. Snap Ring
39. Thrust Washer
40. Clutch Countergear
41. Spacer
42. 3rd Gear Countergear
43. Countergear Shaft
44. Bearing
45. Snap Ring
46. Snap Ring
47. Rear Retainer Gasket
48. Rear Retainer
49. Lip Seal
50. Reverse Idler Shaft
51. Drain Plug
52. Reverse Idler Gear
53. Case
54. Fill Plug
55. Countergear Front Bearing
56. Gasket
57. Front Cover

GENERAL MOTORS 4-SPEED – 117 MM (Cont.)

prying directly opposite against case and bearing snap ring groove at the same time.

Fig. 2: Removing 4WD Mainshaft Rear Bearing Lock Nut

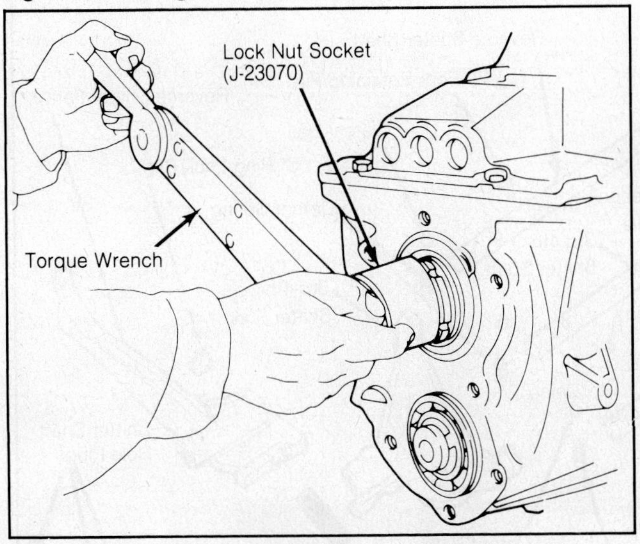

Fig. 3: Removing Rear Countergear Bearing

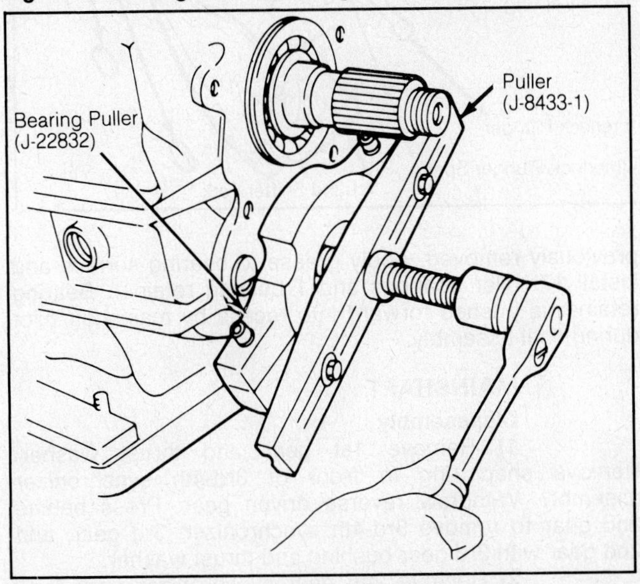

Let countergear rest on case for mainshaft removal.

8) Remove 4th gear synchronizer ring. Index cut-out section of drive gear in down position with countergear to obtain clearance for removing clutch gear. Remove rear mainshaft bearing retainer ring and using bearing remover, remove bearing from case.

9) Slide 1st gear thrust washer off mainshaft. Raise rear of mainshaft assembly and push rearward in case bore, swing front end and lift from case. Remove synchronizer cone from shaft.

10) Slide reverse idler gear rearward and move countergear rearward until front end is free of case, then lift to remove from case. Remove reverse idler gear, drive reverse idler gear shaft out of case from front to rear using a driver. Remove reverse idler gear from case.

11) Remove mainshaft rear bearing snap ring. Using Puller (J-8433-1) and Bearing Remover (J-22832), remove bearing from case. Slide 1st gear thrust washer off mainshaft. Raise rear of mainshaft and move rearward.

12) Lift front of shaft up and out of case. Remove synchronizer cone from shaft. Slide reverse idler gear rearward and move countergear back until front end is free of case. Remove assembly. Drive reverse idler gear shaft out of case from front to rear, using a drift. Remove reverse idler gear.

CLEANING & INSPECTION

Wash case and all internal parts in solvent. Dry with compressed air. Check all parts for damage or excessive wear. Check bearings and synchronizers for rough operation. File off any burrs on mating surfaces. Replace damaged parts as necessary.

COMPONENT DISASSEMBLY & REASSEMBLY

COVER & SHIFT FORK ASSEMBLY

Disassembly

1) Drive out pins retaining 1st-2nd and 3rd-4th gear shifter forks to shifter shafts. Remove shaft expansion plugs. Note that pin retaining 3rd-4th gear shifter must be removed before removing shifter head pin. With shifter shafts in neutral position, drive shafts out of cover to remove shifter forks.

2) Ensure that detent balls, springs, and interlock pins are not lost as shifter shafts are removed. Drive out pin holding reverse shifter head and drive out shaft. Ensure that detent balls are not lost as they are under spring tension in rear rail boss holes.

Reassembly

1) Install shifter shafts in correct order. *See Fig. 4.* Install reverse shaft, 3rd-4th shaft, and 1st-2nd shaft. Place fork detent ball springs and balls in hole positions in cover. Start shafts into cover, depressing yoke detent balls with a small punch, and push shaft on over balls.

2) Starting with reverse shifter shaft, hold fork in position and push shaft through yoke. Install split pin in fork and shaft, position fork in neutral position.

3) Hold 3rd-4th fork in position and push shaft through yoke, but not through front support bore. Place 2 interlock balls between reverse and 3rd-4th shifter shafts in cross bore of front support boss. Install interlock pin in 3rd-4th shaft hole and grease to hold in place.

4) Push 3rd-4th shaft through fork and cover bore, keeping both balls and pin in fork and shaft. Position fork in neutral position. Place 2 interlock balls between 1st-2nd shaft and 3rd-4th shaft in cross bore of front support boss.

5) Hold 1st-2nd fork in position and push shaft through cover bore and fork until retainer hole and fork line up with hole in shaft. Install retainer pin and move to neutral position. Install new shaft hole expansion plugs.

DRIVE GEAR (INPUT SHAFT)

Disassembly

1) Remove mainshaft pilot bearing rollers (17) from drive gear if not already removed, and remove roller retainer. Do not remove snap ring on inside of drive gear.

2) Remove snap ring securing bearing on stem of drive gear. To remove bearing, position bearing support tool under bearing and using an arbor press, press gear and shaft out of bearing.

GENERAL MOTORS 4-SPEED – 117 MM (Cont.)

Fig. 4: Exploded View of Cover and Shift Assembly

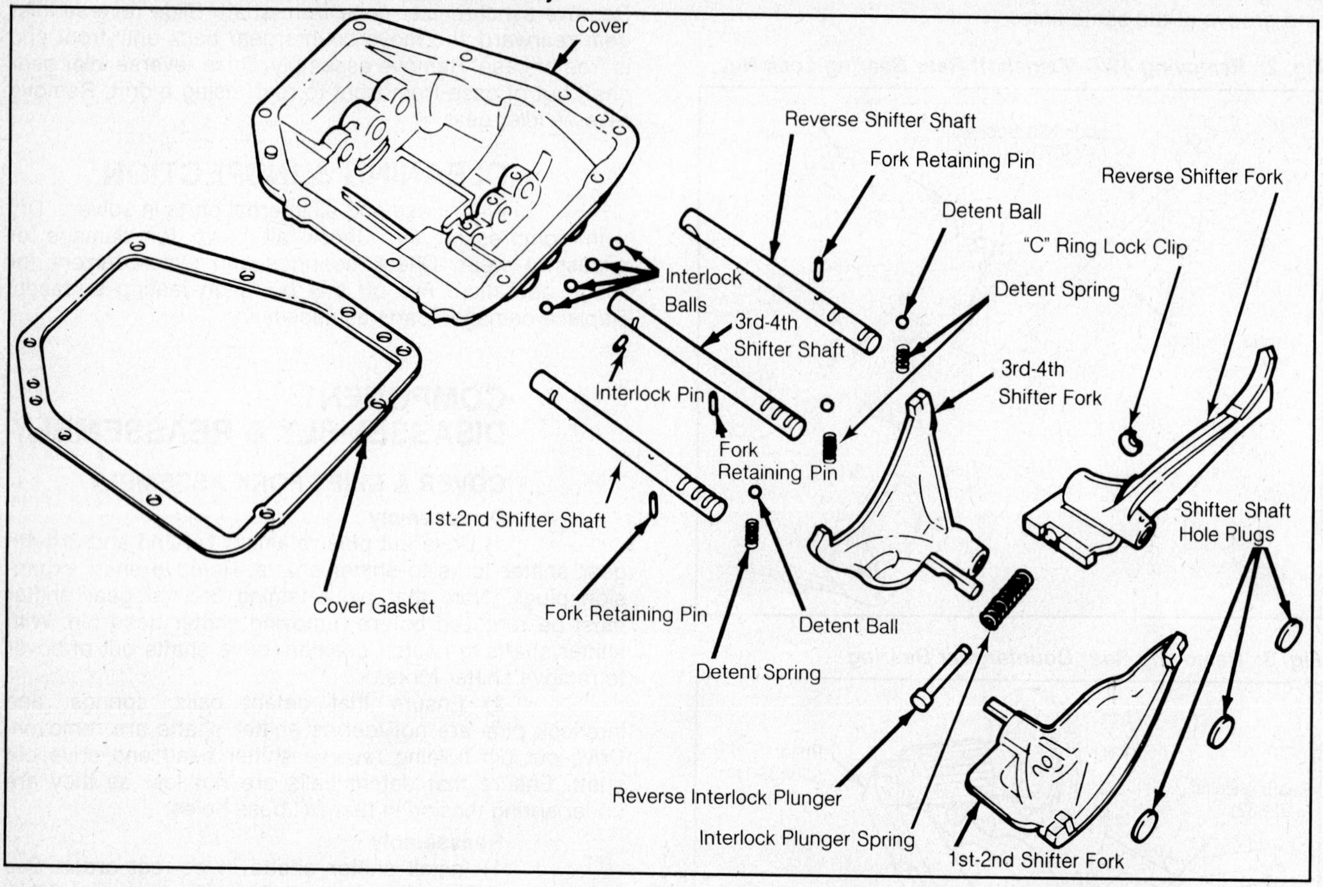

Reassembly

1) Press bearing and new oil slinger onto drive gear shaft. Slinger should be flush with bearing shoulder on drive gear. Install snap ring on shaft to secure bearing. Install bearing retainer ring in O.D. bearing groove. *See Fig. 5.*

2) Ensure bearing turns freely after installed on shaft. Install snap ring in mainshaft pilot bearing bore, if previously removed. Apply grease to bearing surface and install 17 roller bearings and 1 bearing retainer. Bearing retainer is pushed forward into recess by mainshaft pilot during final assembly.

Fig. 5: Installing Drive Gear Bearing

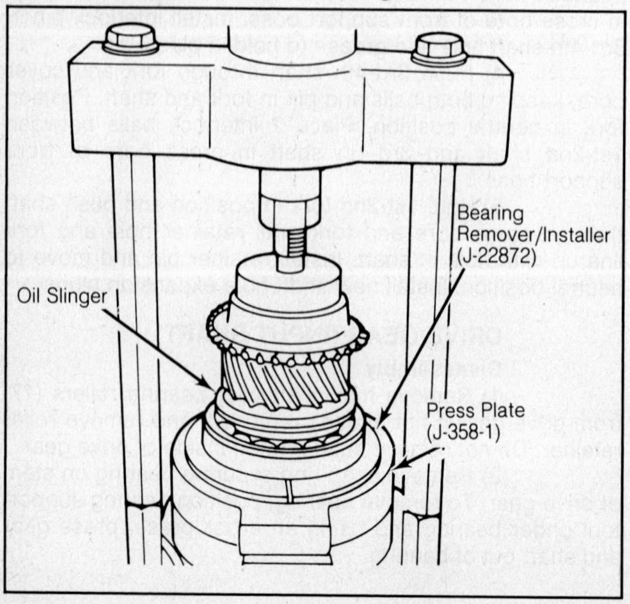

MAINSHAFT

Disassembly

1) Remove 1st gear and thrust washer. Remove snap ring in front of 3rd-4th synchronizer assembly. Withdraw reverse driven gear. Press behind 2nd gear to remove 3rd-4th synchronizer, 3rd gear, and 2nd gear with 3rd gear bushing and thrust washer.

2) Remove 2nd gear synchronizer ring. Support 2nd gear synchronizer hub on front face and press mainshaft through, removing 1st gear bushing and 2nd gear synchronizer hub. Split 2nd gear bushing with a chisel and remove bushing from shaft.

Reassembly

1) Bushing for 1st, 2nd, and 3rd gears are sintered iron and care should be taken when installing to prevent damaged. Lubricate all bushings with oil before installing gears. Press 2nd gear onto mainshaft until it bottoms on shoulder.

2) Press 1st-2nd synchronizer hub onto mainshaft until it bottoms on shoulder. Install 1st-2nd synchronizer keys and springs, if removed. Using Arbor press and Driver (J-22873), press 1st gear bushing on mainshaft until it bottoms against hub.

3) Install synchronizer blocker ring and 2nd gear on mainshaft, against synchronzier hub. Index synchronizer key slots with keys in hub. Install 3rd gear thrust washer on mainshaft with tang in slot on shaft and

GENERAL MOTORS 4-SPEED – 117 MM (Cont.)

Fig. 6: Disassembling Mainshaft

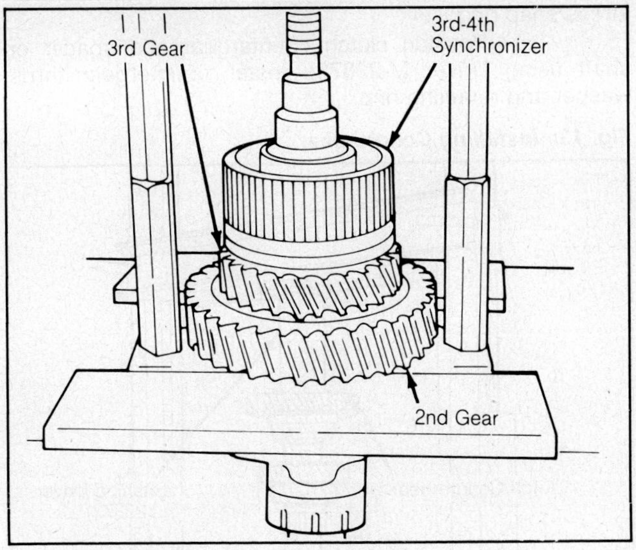

The 3rd gear should be a running fit on mainshaft.

Fig. 7: Installing 2nd Gear Bushing

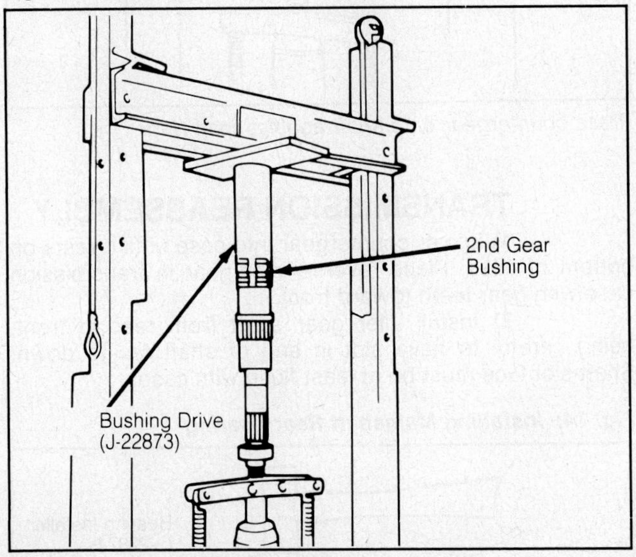

Bushing should bottom on mainshaft shoulder.

Fig. 8: Installing 1st Gear Bushing

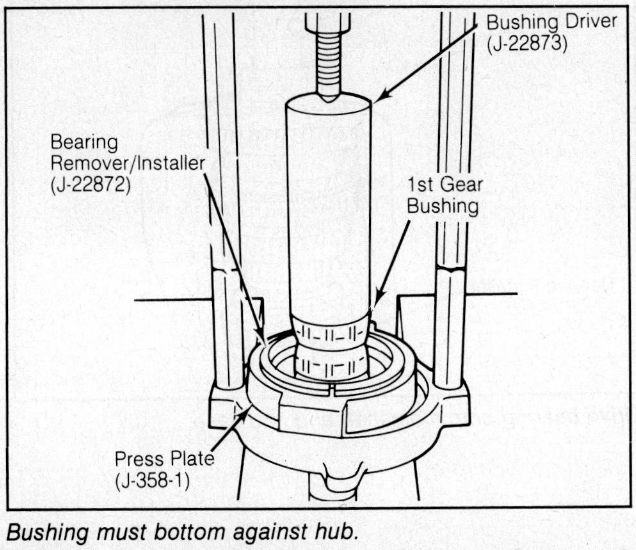

Bushing must bottom against hub.

against 2nd gear bushing. Press 3rd gear bushing on mainshaft using Arbor press and Driver (J-22875), until it bottoms thrust washer. *See Fig. 9* .

Fig. 9: Installing 3rd Gear Bushing

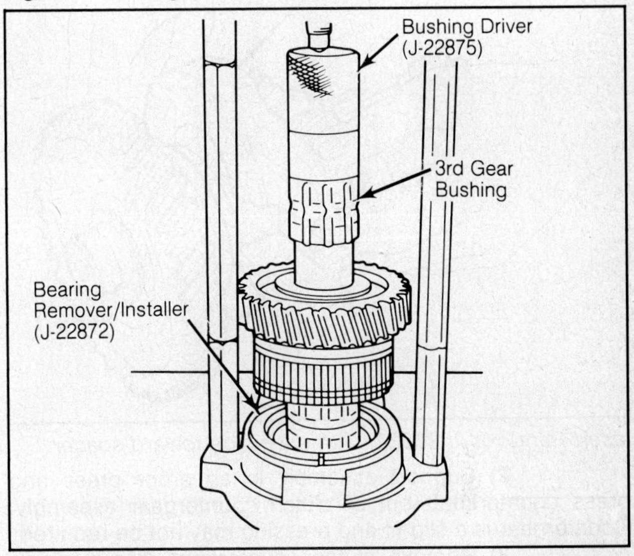

Bushing must bottom on thrust washer.

4) Install 3rd gear and 3rd synchronizer blocker ring on mainshaft, against 3rd gear thrust washer. Index synchronizer ring key slots with keys. Using arbor press and Driver (J-22875), press 3rd-4th synchronizer hub assembly onto mainshaft and against 3rd gear with bushing thrust face toward 3rd gear.

5) Retain synchronizer assembly with snap ring. Install reverse driven gear with fork groove toward rear. Install 1st gear on mainshaft and against 1st-2nd synchronizer hub. Install 1st gear thrust washer.

Fig. 10: Installing 3rd-4th Synchronizer

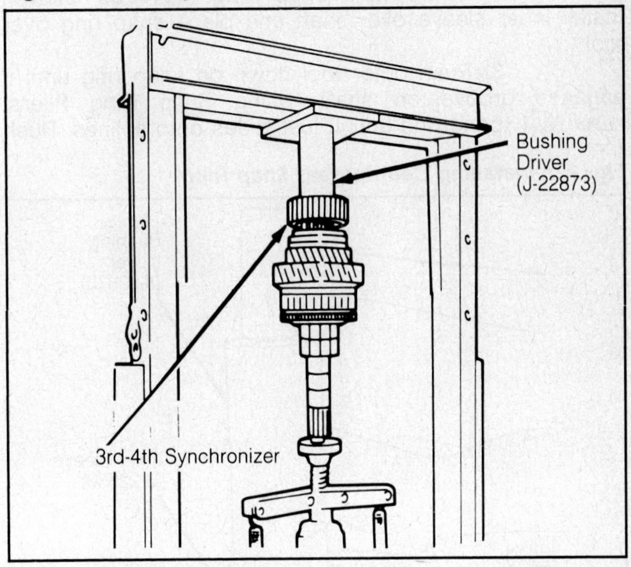

Press assembly onto mainshaft using driver (J-22875).

COUNTERSHAFT

Disassembly

1) Remove front countergear shaft snap ring and thrust washer. Discard snap ring. Install Press Plates (J-22832) on countershaft with open side to spacer. *See Fig. 11.*

Manual Transmissions

GENERAL MOTORS 4-SPEED – 117 MM (Cont.)

Fig. 11: Removing Countergear

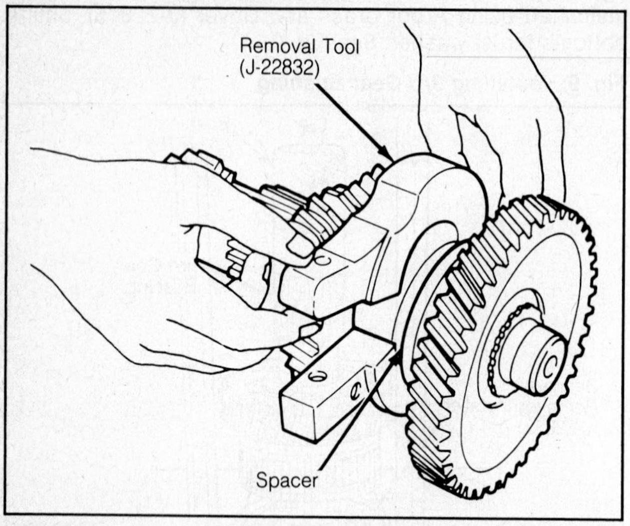

Insert Remover (J-22832) with open side toward spacer.

2) Support assembly in an arbor press and press countershaft out of clutch countergear assembly. Countergear is a slip fit and pressing may not be required.

3) Remove clutch countergear rear retaining ring and discard. Remove and discard 3rd gear countergear retaining ring. Position assembly on an arbor press and press shaft from 3rd speed gear.

Reassembly

1) Position 3rd gear countergear on shaft with undercut surface toward front of shaft. Press gear on shaft with arbor press using a minimum force of 1500 lbs. (680 kg). If gear can be installed with less than 1500 lbs. (680 kg), replace gear.

2) Install spacer and press front gear on countershaft. Using snap ring pliers, install snap ring. Install new countergear rear snap ring using Sleeve Tools (J-22830 & J-22873) and Snap Ring Pliers as follows: Install inner sleeve over shaft and place snap ring over tool.

3) Push outer tool down on snap ring until it engages groove on shaft. Using Snap Ring Pliers, carefully expand ring until it just slides onto splines. Push ring down until it engages groove on shaft. Do not overstress snap ring.

Fig. 12: Installing Countergear Snap Ring

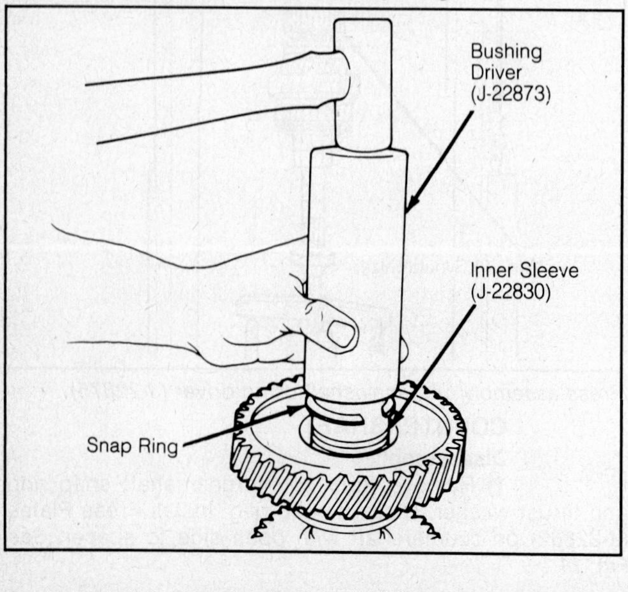

4)Position clutch countergear and spacer on shaft using Driver (J-22873). Install countergear thrust washer and retaining ring.

Fig. 13: Installing Countergear

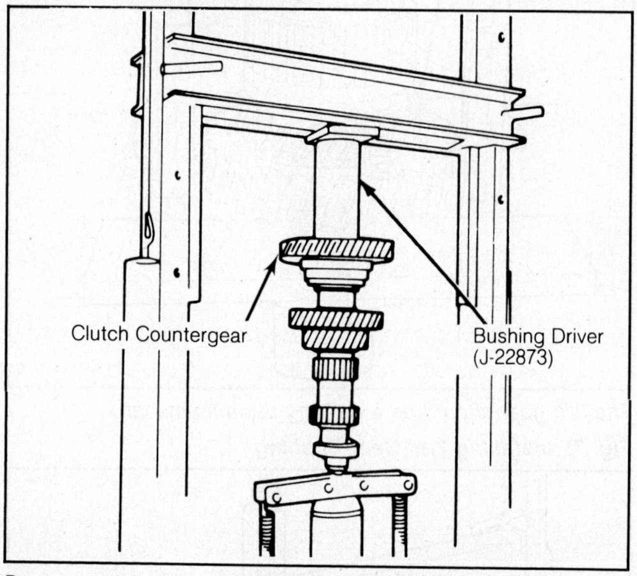

Press countergear onto shaft against snap ring.

TRANSMISSION REASSEMBLY

1) Lower countergear into case until it rests on bottom of case. Place reverse idler gear in transmission case with gear teeth toward front.

2) Install idler gear shaft from rear to front, being careful to have slot in end of shaft facing down. Shaft slot face must be at least flush with case.

Fig. 14: Installing Mainshaft Rear Bearing

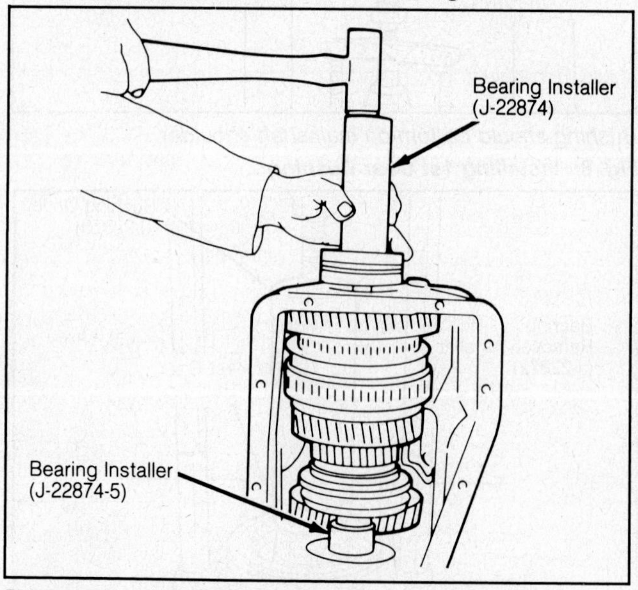

Drive bearing onto mainshaft and into case.

GENERAL MOTORS 4-SPEED – 117 MM (Cont.)

3) Install mainshaft assembly into case with rear of shaft protruding out rear bearing hole in case. Position Installer Tool (J-22874) in clutch gear case opening and engage front mainshaft. Rotate case onto front end. *See Fig. 14.*

4) Install 1st gear thrust washer on shaft, if not previously installed. Install snap ring on bearing outside diameter and position rear mainshaft bearing on shaft.

5) Using Driver (J-22874-1), seat bearing on shaft and into case. Rotate case and remove tool. Install synchronizer cone on pilot end of mainshaft and slide rearward to clutch hub.

6) Make sure the 3 cut-out sections of 4th gear synchronizer cone align with 3 clutch keys in clutch assembly. Install snap ring on drive gear bearing outside diameter.

7) Index cut-out portion of drive gear teeth to obtain clearance over countershaft drive gear teeth. Start clutch gear, then tap bearing outer race with mallet.

8) Install drive gear bearing retainer using a new gasket. Install and tighten bolts. Install Countergear Front Support (J-22874-10) into countergear front bearing opening in case. Rotate case onto front end. *See Fig. 15.*

Fig. 15: Installing Rear Countergear Bearing

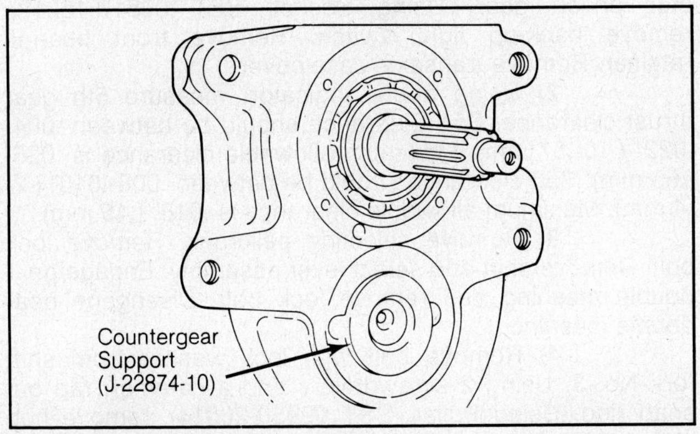

Use bearing support to secure front of countergear shaft when installing rear countergear bearing.

9) Install snap ring on O.D. of countergear rear bearing. Position bearing on countergear and using Driver (J-22874-1), seat bearing. *See Fig. 16.* Rotate case, install snap ring on countershaft at rear bearing and remove tool.

10) Tap countergear front bearing assembly into case. Install countergear front bearing cap and new gasket. Slide speedometer drive gear over mainshaft to bearing.

11) Install rear bearing retainer with new gasket. Be sure snap ring ends are in lube slot and cut-out in bearing retainer. Install bolts and tighten. Install brake backing plate assembly on models equipped with propeller shaft brake.

12) On 4WD models, install rear lock nut and washer using Lock Nut Remover/Installer (J-23070). *See Fig. 2.* Tighten lock nut and bend washer tangs to fit slots in nut.

13) Install parking brake drum and/or universal joint flange. Apply light coat of oil to seal surface. Lock transmission in 2 gears at once. Install universal joint flange lock nut and tighten.

Fig. 16: Installing Rear Countergear Bearing

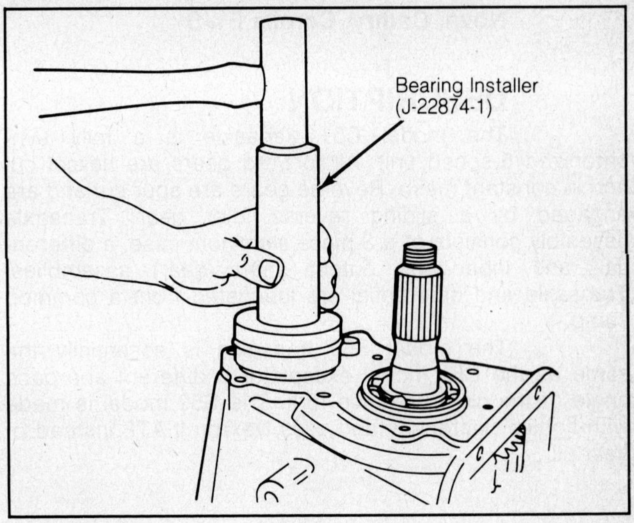

TIGHTENING SPECIFICATIONS

Application	Ft. Lbs. (N.m)
Cover-to-Case Bolts	20 (27)
Crossmember-to-Frame Nuts	55 (75)
Crossmember-to-Mount Bolts	40 (55)
Drain & Filler Plug	30 (40)
Drive Gear Bearing	
Retainer-to-Case Bolts	25 (34)
Extension and Retainer-to-Case Bolts	
Upper	20 (27)
Lower	30 (40)
Main Shaft Lock Nut	100 (135)
Parking Brake Flange Plate Bolts	30 (41)
Power Takeoff Cover Bolts	17 (23)
Shift Lever-to-Shifter Shaft Nut	20 (27)
Universal Joint Flange Nut	100 (135)

GENERAL MOTORS NOVA/TOYOTA C51 & S50 5-SPEED TRANSAXLE

Nova, Camry, Corolla FWD

DESCRIPTION

The model C51 transaxle is a fully synchronized 5-speed unit. All forward gears are helical cut and in constant mesh. Reverse gears are spur cut and are engaged by a sliding reverse idler gear. Transaxle assembly consists of a 3-piece aluminum case, a differential, and input and output shaft (gear) assemblies. Transaxle and differential are lubricated from a common sump.

The model S50 transaxle is essentially the same as the C51 model except for a different approach angle of the clutch release fork. The S50 model is made with tighter clearances and uses Dexron II ATF instead of gear oil.

LUBRICATION & ADJUSTMENT

See appropriate MANUAL TRANSMISSION SERVICING article in IMPORT GENERAL SERVICING section.

TROUBLE SHOOTING

EXCESSIVE NOISE

Transaxle or differential faulty. Wrong oil grade. Low oil level.

OIL LEAKAGE

Oil level too high. Oil seal, "O" ring, or gaskets worn or damaged.

HARD TO SHIFT OR WILL NOT SHIFT

Control cable faulty. Transaxle faulty.

JUMPS OUT OF GEAR

Transaxle faulty.

SERVICE (IN VEHICLE)

DRIVE AXLE SHAFTS

See appropriate DRIVE AXLE SHAFT article in IMPORT AXLE SHAFTS, OVERDRIVES & TRANSFER CASES section.

SHIFTER ASSEMBLY

Removal

Disconnect battery cable, remove console and shifter boot. If necessary, disconnect shift cables, mounting screws and assembly.

Inspection

Using feeler gauge, measure clearance between shim and shift lever retainer. Clearance should be 0-.004" (0-.10mm). See SHIFT LEVER SHIM CHART for appropriate size shim.

Reassembly

Reverse removal proceedure.

SHIFTER ASSEMBLY SHIM CHART (ALL MODELS)

Inches	(mm)	Inches	(mm)
.5	(.020)	.9	(.035)
.6	(.024)	1.0	(.039)
.7	(.028)	1.1	(.043)
.8	(.031)	1.2	(.047)

TRANSAXLE MOUNTS

Information not available from manufacturer.

REMOVAL & INSTALLATION

TRANSAXLE

See appropriate MANUAL TRANSMISSION REMOVAL article in IMPORT GENERAL SERVICING section.

TRANSAXLE DISASSEMBLY

1) Remove release fork, bearing and speedometer driven gear. Using Socket (SST 09817-16010), remove back-up light switch. Remove front bearing retainer. Remove transaxle case cover.

2) Using a dial indicator, measure 5th gear thrust clearance. C51 Clearance should be between .004-.022" (.10-.57 mm). Maximum allowable clearance is .026" (.65 mm). S50 clearance should be between .008-.016" (.2-.4 mm). Maximum allowable clearance is .018" (.45 mm).

3) Remove selecting bellcrank. Remove lock bolt. Remove shift and select lever assembly. Engage gear double meshing and remove lock bolt. Disengage gear double meshing.

4) Remove bolt with lock washer from shift fork No. 3. Using 2 screwdrivers and a hammer, tap out snap ring. Using Puller (SST 09950-20014), remove hub sleeve No. 3 assembly and shift fork No. 3. For S50 models, use three case bolts in No. 3. hub sleeve. Tighten bolts evenly to remove sleeve.

5) Remove 5th gear, synchronizer ring, needle roller bearing and spacer. Using Puller (SST 09950-20014), remove 5th gear driven gear. Remove rear bearing retainer. Using snap ring pliers, remove 2 bearing snap rings.

6) Remove reverse idler gear shaft lock bolt. Using 2 screwdrivers and hammer, tap out and remove snap ring from No. 2 shift fork shaft. Using Socket (SST 09313-30021), remove 4 transaxle plugs. Using a magnetic pick-up tool, remove 4 springs and balls.

7) Remove transaxle case cover bolts (16) and tap case apart with a plastic hammer. Remove 2 bolts and pull out reverse shaft arm bracket. Pull out reverse idler gear and shaft. For S50 model, Useing Socket (SST 09313-30021), remove interlock pin screw. Drive out pin with pin punch and pull out interlock pin.

8) Using 2 screwdrivers and a hammer, tap out 3 snap rings. Pry out lock washer and remove 3 set bolts. Remove fork shaft No. 2 and shift head. Using a magnetic pick-up tool, remove 2 balls. Remove fork shaft No. 3 and reverse shift fork.

9) Pull out shift fork shaft No. 1. Remove shift forks No. 1 and No. 2. Remove input and output shafts as an assembly. Remove differential assembly. Remove magnet and oil receiver.

GENERAL MOTORS NOVA/TOYOTA C51 & S50 5-SPEED TRANSAXLE (Cont.)

Fig. 1: Exploded View of Front Transaxle Case

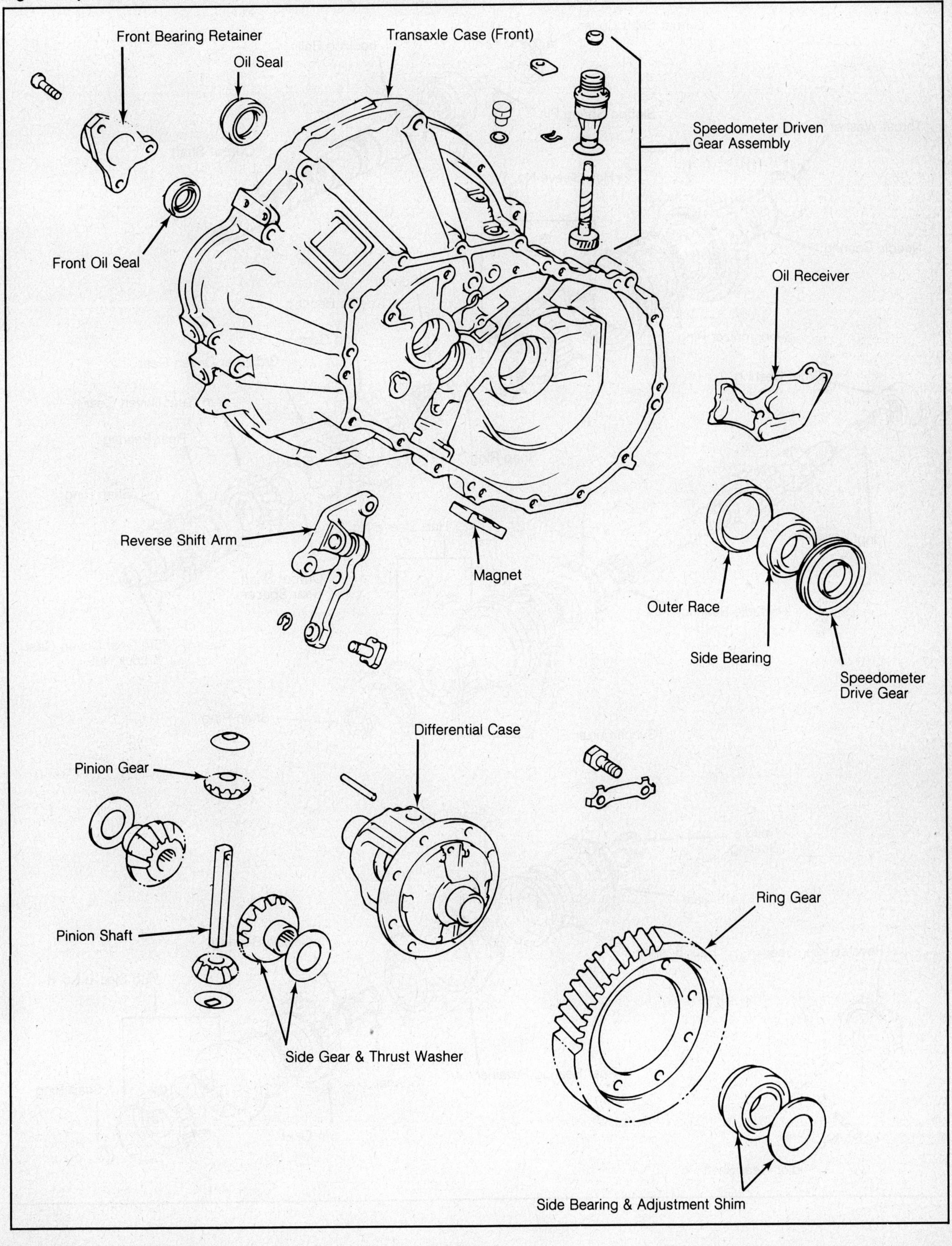

GENERAL MOTORS NOVA/TOYOTA C51 & S50 5-SPEED TRANSAXLE (Cont.)

Fig. 2: Exploded View of Input & Output Shaft Assemblies

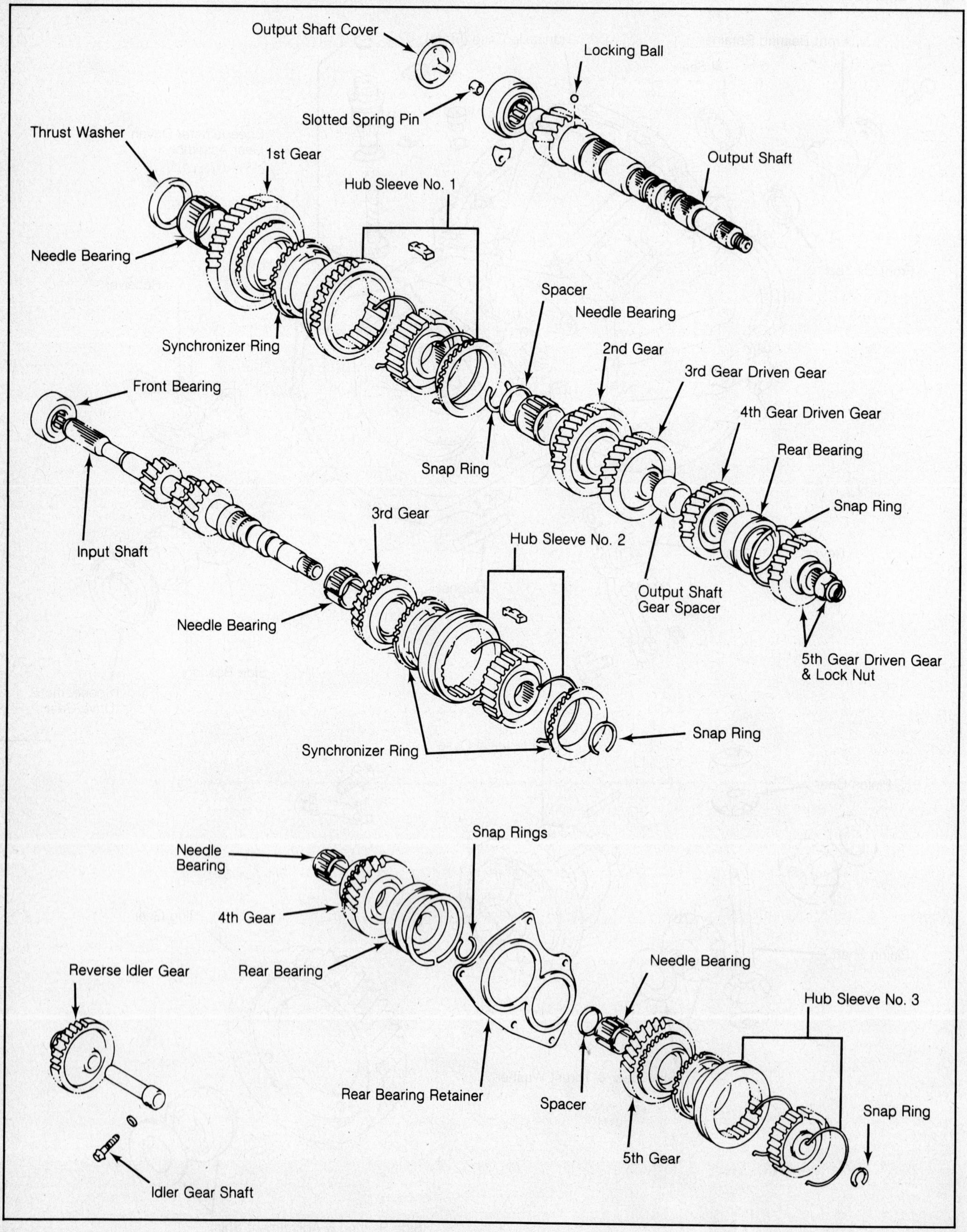

Manual Transmissions

GENERAL MOTORS NOVA/TOYOTA C51 & S50 5-SPEED TRANSAXLE (Cont.)

Fig. 3: Exploded View of Rear Transaxle Case & Cover

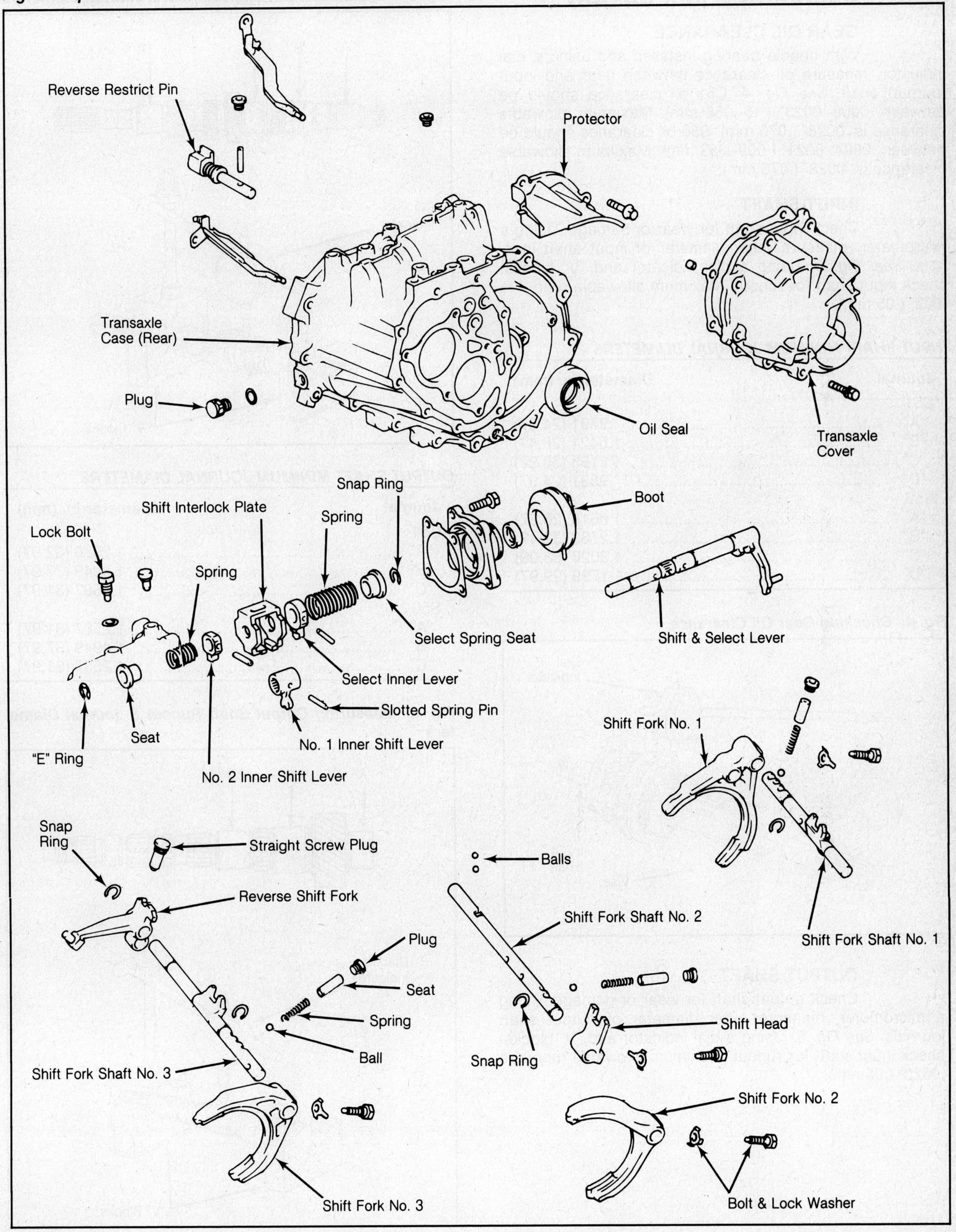

GENERAL MOTORS NOVA/TOYOTA C51 & S50 5-SPEED TRANSAXLE (Cont.)

CLEANING & INSPECTION

GEAR OIL CLEARANCE

With needle bearing installed and using a dial indicator, measure oil clearance between gear and input (output) shaft. *See Fig. 4.* C51 oil clearance should be between .0006-.0023" (.15-.058 mm). Maximum allowable clearance is .0028" (.070 mm). S50 oil clearance should be between .0004-.0021" (.009-.053 mm). Maximum allowable clearance is .0028" (.070 mm).

INPUT SHAFT

Check input shaft for wear or damage. Using a micrometer, measure outer diameter of input shaft journals. *See. Fig. 5.* Using a dial indicator and "V" blocks, check input shaft for runout. Maximum allowable runout is .002" (.05 mm).

INPUT SHAFT MINIMUM JOURNAL DIAMETERS

Journal	Diameter In. (mm)
C51	
"A"	.9791 (24.87)
"B"	1.0421 (26.47)
"C"	1.2193 (30.97)
"D"	.9831 (24.97)
S50	
"A"	1.0618 (26.97)
"B"	1.2783 (32.47)
"C"	1.3028 (33.09)
"D"	1.1799 (29.97)

Fig. 4: Checking Gear Oil Clearance

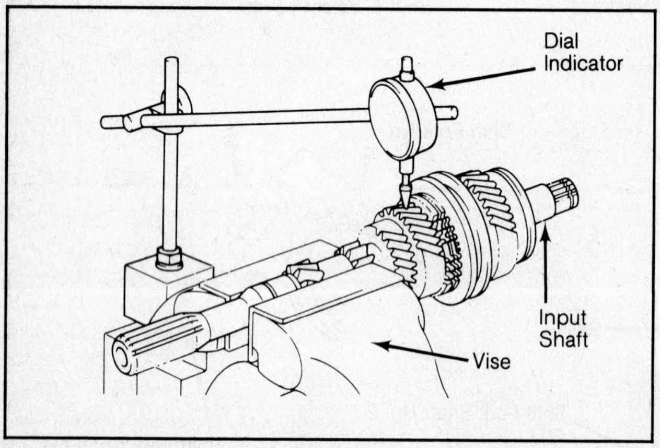

OUTPUT SHAFT

Check output shaft for wear or damage. Using a micrometer, measure outer diameter of output shaft journals. *See Fig. 6.* Using a dial indicator and "V" blocks, check input shaft for runout. Maximum allowable runout is .0020" (.05 mm).

Fig. 5: Measuring Input Shaft Runout & Journal Diameters

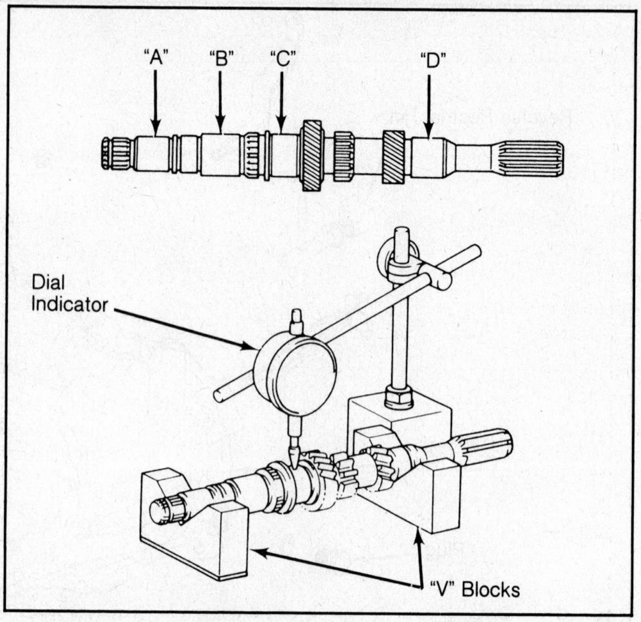

OUTPUT SHAFT MINIMUM JOURNAL DIAMETERS

Journal	Diameter In. (mm)
C51	
"A"	1.2980 (32.97)
"B"	1.4949 (37.97)
"C"	1.2587 (31.97)
S50	
"A"	1.2587 (31.97)
"B"	1.4949 (37.97)
"C"	1.2587 (31.97)

Fig. 6: Measuring Output Shaft Runout & Journal Diameters

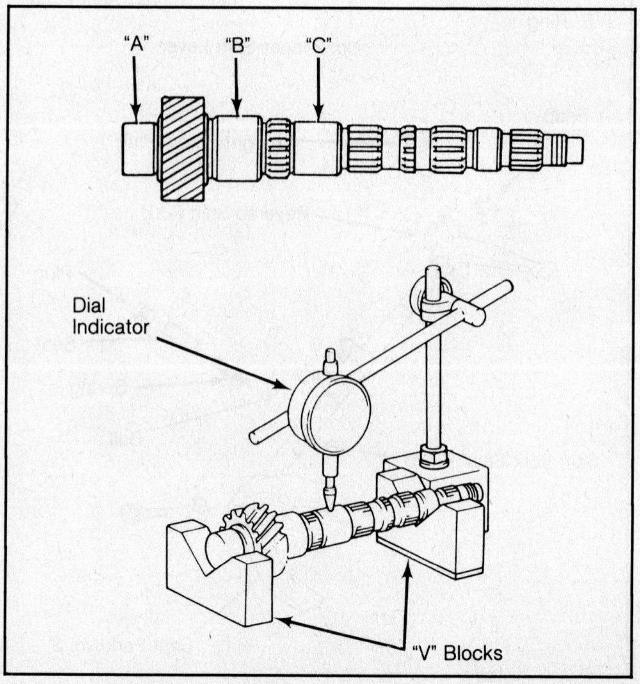

GENERAL MOTORS NOVA/TOYOTA C51 & S50 5-SPEED TRANSAXLE (Cont.)

SYNCHRONIZER RINGS, SHIFT FORKS & HUB SLEEVES

1) Check synchronizer for wear and damage. Turn ring to check locking action. Measure clearance between synchronizer ring back and gear spline end. *See. Fig. 7.* Maximum allowable clearance is .024" (.6 mm).

2) Using a feeler gauge, measure clearance between hub sleeve and shift fork. Maximum allowable clearance is .04" (1 mm).

COMPONENT DISASSEMBLY & REASSEMBLY

NOTE: **When working on C51 transaxle be sure to use a suitable gear oil during reassembly. When working on S50 transaxle be sure to use a suitable ATF fluid during reassembly.**

INPUT SHAFT

Disassembly

1) Using a feeler gauge, measure 3rd and 4th gear thrust clearance. C51 clearance on 3rd gear should be between .004-.014" (.10-.35 mm). Maximum allowable clearance is .016" (.40 mm). S50 clearance on 3rd gear should be between .004-.010" (.10-.25 mm). Maximum allowable clearance is .012" (.30 mm).

2)C51 clearance on 4th gear should be between .004-.022" (.10-.55 mm). Maximum allowable clearance is .024" (.60 mm). S50 clearance on 4th gear should be between .008-.018" (.20-.45 mm). Maximum allowable clearance is .020" (.50 mm).

3) Using 2 screwdrivers and a hammer, tap out and remove snap ring from input shaft. Press ball bearing and 4th gear out of input shaft. Remove needle bearing and synchronizer ring.

4) Using snap ring pliers, remove hub sleeve No. 2 snap ring. Press hub sleeve No. 2, 3rd gear, synchronizer ring and needle bearing out of input shaft.

Fig. 7: Checking Synchronizer Rings, Shift Forks and Hub Sleeve Clearance

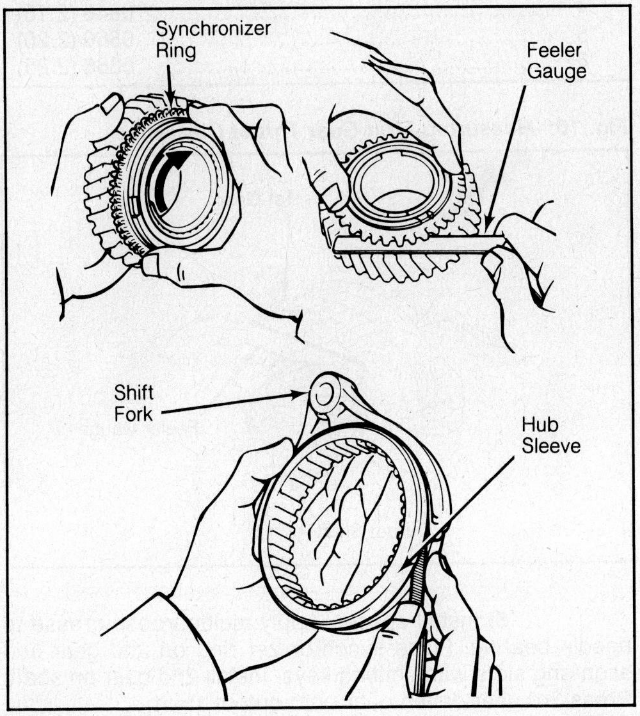

Reassembly

1) Install clutch hub and shifting keys onto hub sleeve No. 2. Install shifting key springs under shifting keys. Ensure that key spring end gaps are not in line.

2) Apply multipurpose grease to needle bearing. Place syncronizer ring on 3rd gear and align ring slots with shifting keys. Press 3rd gear and hub sleeve No. 2 onto input shaft.

3) Select 3rd gear snap ring that will allow minimum axial play on shaft. Install snap ring. Using a feeler gauge, measure 3rd gear thrust clearance. C51 maximum allowable clearance is .004" (.10 mm). S50 3rd gear maximum allowable clearance is .020" (.30 mm).

THIRD GEAR SNAP RING SELECTION

I.D. Mark	Thickness In. (mm)
C51	
0	.0906 (2.30)
1	.0929 (2.36)
2	.0953 (2.42)
3	.0976 (2.48)
4	.1000 (2.54)
5	.1024 (2.60)
S50	
1	.0787 (2.00)
2	.0807 (2.05)
3	.0827 (2.10)
4	.0846 (2.15)
5	.0866 (2.20)
6	.0886 (2.25)

Fig. 8: Measuring Third Gear Thrust Clearance

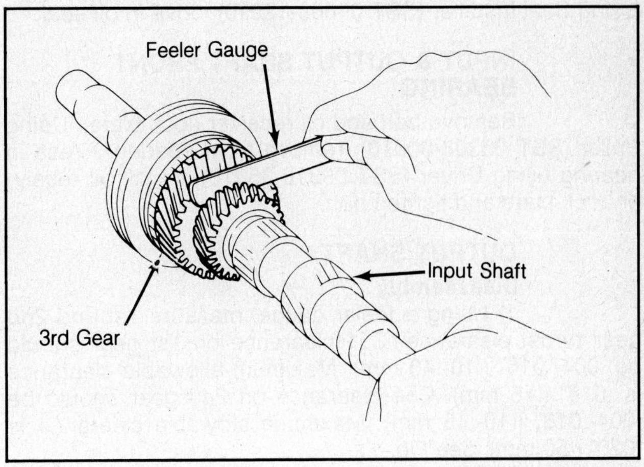

4) Apply multipurpose grease to needle bearing. Place synchronizer ring on 4th gear and align ring slots withshifting keys. Install assembly on input shaft. Press ball bearing onto input shaft.

5) Select 4th gear snap ring that will allow minimum axial play on shaft. Install snap ring. Using a feeler gauge, measure 4th gear thrust clearance. C51 maximum allowable clearance is .004" (.10 mm). S50 maximum allowable clearance is .020" (.5 mm).

GENERAL MOTORS NOVA/TOYOTA C51 & S50 5-SPEED TRANSAXLE (Cont.)

FOURTH GEAR SNAP RING SELECTION

I.D. Mark	Thickness In. (mm)
C51	
"A"	.0902 (2.29)
"B"	.0925 (2.35)
"C"	.0949 (2.41)
"D"	.0972 (2.47)
"E"	.0996 (2.53)
"F"	.1020 (2.59)
S50	
"A"	.0866 (2.20)
"B"	.0886 (2.25)
"C"	.0906 (2.30)
"D"	.0925 (2.35)
"E"	.0945 (2.40)

Fig. 9: Measuring Fourth Gear Thrust Clearance

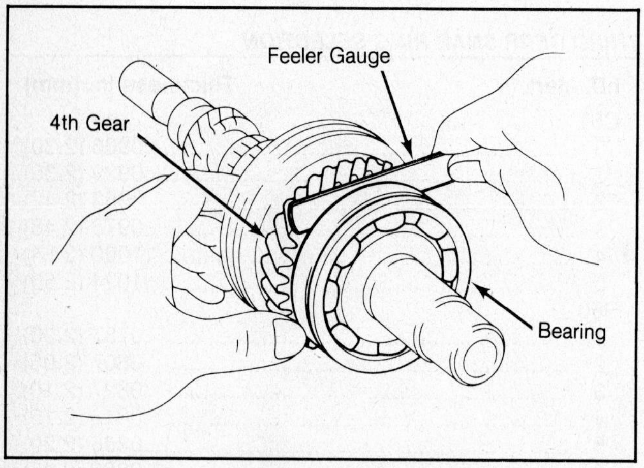

INPUT SHAFT FRONT OIL SEAL

Using a screwdriver, pry oil seal out of case. Using Seal Installer (SST 09608-12010), drive in oil seal.

INPUT & OUTPUT SHAFT FRONT BEARING

Remove bolt and oil receiver (lock plate). Using Puller (SST 09308-00010), remove front bearing. Press in bearing using Driver (SST 09310-35010). Install oil receiver, lock plate and tighten bolt.

OUTPUT SHAFT

Disassembly

1) Using a feeler gauge, measure 1st and 2nd gear thrust clearance. C51 clearance on 1st gear should be .004-.016" (.10-.40 mm). Maximum allowable clearance is .018" (.45 mm). C51 clearance on 2nd gear should be .004-.018" (.10-.45 mm). Maximum alowable clearance is .020" (.50 mm). *See Fig. 11.*

2) S50 clearance on 1st gear should be .004-.011" (.10-.29 mm). Maximum allowable limit is .014" (.35 mm). S50 clearance on 2nd gear should be .008-.017" (.20-.44 mm). Maximum allowable limit is .020" (.50 mm).

3) Press ball bearing and 4th gear driven gear out of output shaft. Remove spacer. Shift hub sleeve No. 1 into 1st gear. Press 3rd gear driven gear and 2nd gear out of output shaft. Remove needle bearing, spacer and synchronizer ring.

4) Using 2 screwdrivers and a hammer, tap out and remove hub sleeve No. 1 snap ring. Press hub sleeve No. 1, 1st gear and synchronizer ring out of output shaft. Remove needle bearing, thrust washer and lock ball.

Reassembly

1) If input shaft was replaced, drive slotted spring pin in end of output shaft to a depth of .24" (6 mm). Install clutch hub and shifting keys on hub sleeve.

2) Install shifting key springs under shifting keys. Ensure that key spring end gaps are not in line. Install locking ball in output shaft. Install thrust washer on shaft and fit thrust washer groove securely over locking ball.

3) Apply multipurpose grease to needle bearing. Place synchronizer ring on 1st gear and align ring slots with shifting keys. Press 1st gear and hub sleeve No. 1 onto output shaft.

4) Select 1st gear snap ring that will allow minimum axial play on shaft. Install snap ring. Using a feeler gauge, measure 1st gear thrust clearance. C51 maximum allowable clearance is .004" (.10 mm). S50 maximum allowable clearance is .014" (.35 mm).

FIRST GEAR SNAP RING SELECTION

I.D. Mark	Thickness In. (mm)
C51	
"A"	.0984 (2.50)
"B"	.1008 (2.56)
"C"	.1031 (2.62)
"D"	.1055 (2.68)
"E"	.1079 (2.74)
"F"	.1102 (2.80)
S50	
"1"	.0787 (2.00)
"2"	.0807 (2.05)
"3"	.0827 (2.10)
"4"	.0846 (2.15)
"5"	.0866 (2.20)
"6"	.0886 (2.25)

Fig. 10: Measuring First Gear Thrust Clearance

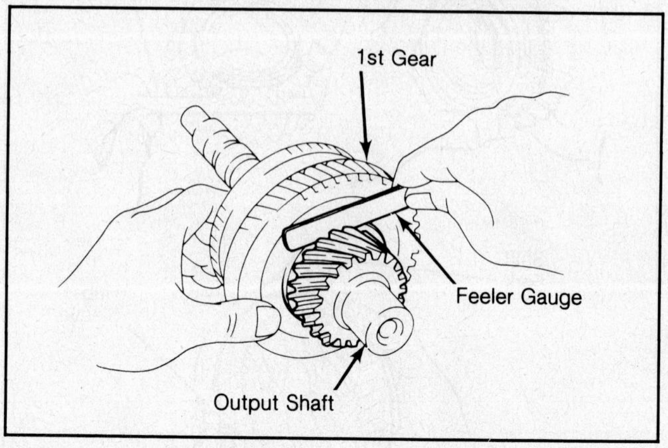

5) Install spacer. Apply multipurpose grease to needle bearing. Place synchronizer ring on 2nd gear and align ring slots with shifting keys. Install 2nd gear on shaft. Press 3rd gear driven gear onto output shaft.

GENERAL MOTORS NOVA/TOYOTA C51 & S50 5-SPEED TRANSAXLE (Cont.)

Fig. 11: Measuring Second Gear Thrust Clearance

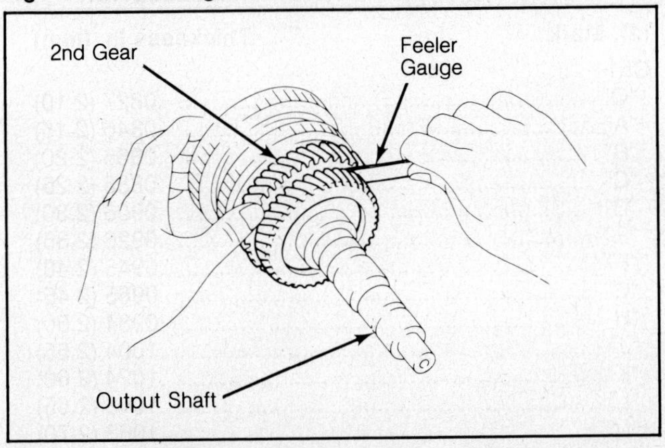

6) Using a feeler gauge, measure 2nd gear thrust clearance. C51 clearance should be .004-0.018" (.10-.45 mm). Maximum allowable clearance is .020" (.50 mm). S50 clearance should be .008-.017" (.20-.40 mm). Maximum allowable clearance is .020" (.50 mm).

7) Install output gear spacer onto shaft. Using Bearing Installer (SST 09608-12010), press 4th gear driven gear and bearing onto output shaft.

SHIFT & SELECT LEVER ASSEMBLY

Disassembly

1) Remove "E" clip and compression spring. Using a pin punch and a hammer, drive out slotted spring from No. 1 and No. 2 inner shift levers. Remove No. 2 inner lever. Remove No. 1 inner shift lever and shift interlock plate.

2) Using a pin punch and a hammer, drive out the slotted spring pin from select inner lever. Remove select lever, compression spring and spring seat. Using 2 screwdrivers and a hammer, tap out and remove snap ring from lever shaft. Remove lever shaft and boot.

Fig. 12: Disassembly of Shift & Select Lever Assembly

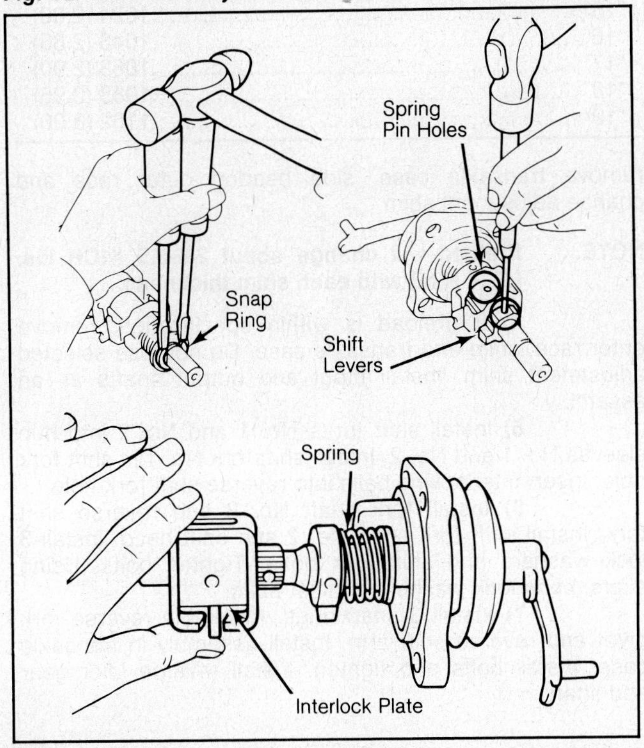

Reassembly

1) Apply multipurpose grease to lever shaft. Install boot and shaft on control shaft cover. Ensure that air bleed on boot is downward. Install snap ring and spring seat.

2) Using a hammer and punch, drive in slotted spring pin. Align interlocking plate with No. 1 inner shift lever and install. Install No. 2 inner shift lever. Using a hammer and punch, drive in slotted spring pin. Install compression spring, seat and "E" clip.

DIFFERENTIAL

Disassembly

1) Using Puller (SST 09502-10012), remove bearings from differential case. Remove speedometer drive gear. Mark ring gear and case for reassembly reference. Bend locking tabs on ring gear bolts. Remove 8 bolts and locking tabs. Using a copper hammer, tap ring gear and remove from case.

2) While holding 1 pinion against case, measure side gear backlash. *See Fig. 13.* Backlash should be between .002-.008" (.05-.20 mm). If backlash is incorrect, drive out pinion shaft lock pin from ring gear side of case. Remove pinion shaft, pinion gears, side gears and 4 thrust washer from each gear.

Fig 13: Measuring Side Gear Backlash

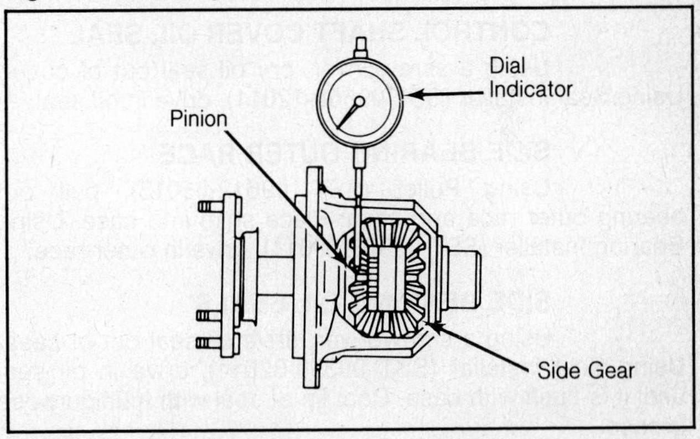

Reassembly

1) If backlash is incorrect, select thrust washers that will ensure correct backlash. If backlash is correct, use thrust washer removed during disassembly. Install thrust washers, side gears, pinion gears and pinion shaft in case.

2) Whild holding 1 pinion gear against case, check side gear backlash. Backlash should be between .002-.008" (.05-.20 mm). If backlash is incorrect, disassemble case once more and install thrust washer of a different thickness. Try to install washer of equal size.

NOTE: **Side gear thrust washers for C51 and S50 are available in the following thickness variations: .037" (.95 mm), .039" (1.00 mm), .041" (1.05 mm), .043" (1.10 mm), .045" (1.15 mm) and .047" (1.2 mm).**

3) Using a hammer and punch, drive lock pin through case and into pinion shaft. Stake differential case to hold pin in place. Clean ring gear contact surface of case. Heat ring gear to 212°F (100°C) in an oil bath.

GENERAL MOTORS NOVA/TOYOTA C51 & S50 5-SPEED TRANSAXLE (Cont.)

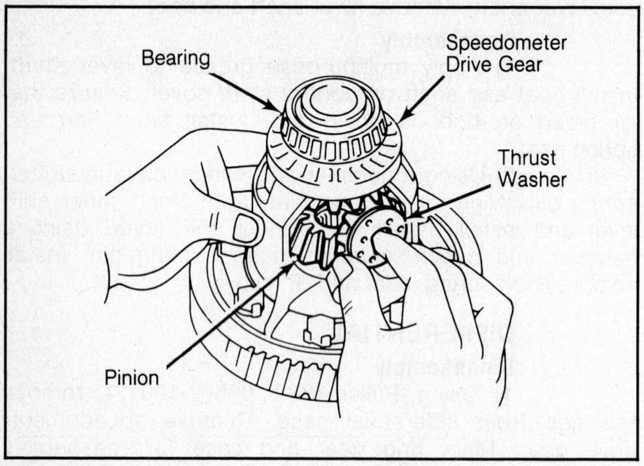

Fig. 14: Installing Side Gear & Thrust Washer

4) Clean contact surface of ring gear with cleaning solvent. Align ring gear with differential case and quickly install ring gear on case. Install locking tabs and bolts. Tighten bolts evenly and a little at a time. Tighten ring gear bolts.

5) Using a hammer and punch, bend locking tabs. Stake 1st tab flush with flat surface of nut. Stake 2nd tab against corner of nut. Install speedometer drive gear. Using Bearing Installer (SST 09350-32011), press bearings onto case.

CONTROL SHAFT COVER OIL SEAL

Using a screwdriver, pry oil seal out of cover. Using Seal Installer (SST 09608-12011), drive in oil seal.

SIDE BEARING OUTER RACE

Using Puller (SST 09612-65013), pull out bearing outer race and shim. Place shim into case. Using Bearing Installer (SST 09608-20011), drive in outer race.

SIDE BEARING OIL SEALS

Using a screwdriver, drive oil seal out of case. Using Seal Installer (SST 09350-32011), drive in oil seal until it is flush with case. Coat lip of seal with multipurpose grease.

SPEEDOMETER DRIVEN GEAR OIL SEAL

Using Puller (SST 09921-00010), pull out oil seal. Using Seal Installer (SST 09201-60011), drive oil seal .8" (20 mm) into bore.

TRANSAXLE REASSEMBLY

1) Install magnet on transaxle case. Install oil receiver and 2 bolts. Install thinnest shim into transaxle case. Using Bearing Installer (SST 09608-20011), drive in side bearing outer race. Install differential on transaxle case.

2) Install transaxle case and tighten bolts. Using Differential Preload Adapter (SST 09564-32011) and an INCH Lb. torque wrench, measure differential side bearing preload.

3) Starting preload should be between 6.9-13.9 INCH lbs. (.8-1.6 N.m) for a new bearing; 4.3-8.7 INCH lbs. (.5-1.0 N.m) for a used bearing. If preload is incorrect, remove transaxle case, side bearing outer race and change adjustment shim.

DIFFERENTIAL BEARING PRELOAD SHIM SELECTION

I.D. Mark	Thickness In. (mm)
C51	
"Q"	.0827 (2.10)
"A"	.0846 (2.15)
"B"	.0866 (2.20)
"C"	.0886 (2.25)
"D"	.0906 (2.30)
"E"	.0925 (2.35)
"F"	.0945 (2.40)
"G"	.0965 (2.45)
"H"	.0984 (2.50)
"J"	.1004 (2.55)
"K"	.1024 (2.60)
"L"	.1043 (2.65)
"M"	.1063 (2.70)
"N"	.1083 (2.75)
"P"	.1102 (2.80)
"Q"	.1122 (2.85)
"R"	.1142 (2.90)
"S"	.1161 (2.95)
"T"	.1181 (3.00)
S50	
"1"	.0748 (2.10)
"2"	.0768 (2.15)
"3"	.0787 (2.20)
"4"	.0807 (2.25)
"5"	.0827 (2.30)
"6"	.0846 (2.35)
"7"	.0866 (2.40)
"8"	.0886 (2.45)
"9"	.0906 (2.50)
"10"	.0925 (2.55)
"11"	.0945 (2.60)
"12"	.0965 (2.65)
"13"	.0984 (2.70)
"14"	.1004 (2.75)
"15"	.1024 (2.80)
"16"	.1043 (2.85)
"17"	.1063 (2.90)
"18"	.1083 (2.95)
"19"	.1102 (3.00)

NOTE: Preload will change about 2.6-3.5 INCH lbs. (.3-.4 N.m) with each shim thickness.

4) If preload is within specification, remove outer race, shim and transaxle case. Do not lose selected adjustment shim. Install input and output shafts as an assembly.

5) Install shift forks No. 1 and No. 2 into hub sleeves No. 1 and No. 2. Install shift fork No. 1 in shift fork hole. Insert interlocking balls into reverse shift fork hole.

6) Install fork shaft No. 3 and reverse shift fork. Install shift fork shaft No. 2 and shift head. Install 3 lock washers and shift fork bolts. Tighten bolts. Using pliers, bend lock washers against bolts.

7) Install 3 snap rings. Assemble reverse fork pivot and reverse shift arm. Install assembly in transaxle case. Install bolts and tighten. Install reverse idler gear and shaft.

GENERAL MOTORS NOVA/TOYOTA C51 & S50 5-SPEED TRANSAXLE (Cont.)

8) Apply sealant to transaxle case, install cover and tighten bolts. Insert balls, springs and seats into holes. Apply sealant to plugs. Using Socket (SST 09313-30021), tighten 4 transaxle plugs.

9) Install and tighten reverse idler gear shaft lock bolt. Install 2 bearing snap rings. Install snap ring on fork shaft No. 2. Install rear bearing retainer and tighten bolts.

10) Using Installer (SST 09309-12020), press 5th gear driven gear onto shaft. Install spacer. Apply grease to needle bearing. Install 5th gear, needle bearing and synchronizer ring.

11) Install clutch hub and shifting keys on hub sleeve No. 3. Ensure tht key spring end gaps are not in line. Align synchronizer ring slots with shifting keys. Using Installer (SST 09612-22011), drive in hub sleeve No. 3 with shift fork onto shaft.

12) Using a dial indicator, measure 5th gear thrust clearance. Maximum allowable clearance is .004" (.10 mm). Select 5th gear snap ring that will allow minimum axial play on shaft and install snap ring.

Fig. 15: Measuring Differential Bearing Preload

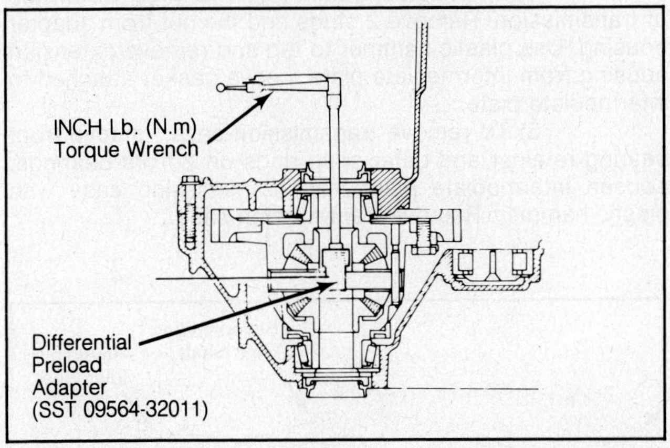

FIFTH GEAR SNAP RING SELECTION (C51 ONLY)

I.D. Mark	Thickness In. (mm)
"A"	.0886 (2.25)
"B"	.0909 (2.31)
"C"	.0933 (2.37)
"D"	.0957 (2.43)
"E"	.0980 (2.49)
"F"	.1004 (2.55)
"G"	.1028 (2.61)

13) Engage gear double meshing. Install lock nut and tighten. Disengage gear double meshing. Stake lock nut. Install shift fork lock washer and bolt. Tighten bolt and bend lock washer against bolt.

14) Install gasket on shift and select lever assembly control shaft cover. Install assembly on transfer case and tighten bolts. Install bellcrank on case. Install and tighten lock bolt.

15) Install transaxle cover and tighten bolts. Install front bearing retainer and tighten bolts. Using Socket (SST 09817-16010), install and tighten back-up light switch. Install speedometer driven gear.

TIGHTENING SPECIFICATIONS

Application	Ft. Lbs. (N.m)
C51	
Back-Up Light Switch	30 (41)
Differential Ring Gear	71 (96)
Drain & Fill Plugs	29 (39)
Lock Ball Assembly	29 (39)
Rear Bearing Retainer	14 (19)
Reverse Idler Shaft Lock Bolt	17 (23)
Reverse Shift Arm Bracket	13 (18)
Shift Fork Screw Plugs	18 (24)
Shift & Select Lever Assembly	14 (19)
Transaxle Case	22 (30)
Transaxle Case Cover	13 (18)
Transaxle Screw Plugs	29 (39)
5th Gear Driven Gear Lock Nut	87 (118)
S50	
Back-Up Light Switch	33 (44)
Differential Ring Gear	71 (96)
Drain & Fill Plugs	36 (49)
Lock Ball Assembly	27 (37)
Rear Bearing Retainer	13 (18)
Reverse Idler Shaft Lock Bolt	18 (25)
Reverse Shift Arm Bracket	13 (18)
Side Bearing Cap	36 (49)
Shift & Select Lever Assembly	13 (18)
Transaxle Case	22 (30)
Transaxle Case Cover	22 (29)
5th Gear Driven Gear Lock Nut	90 (123)
	INCH Lbs. (N.m)
C51	
Clutch Release Bearing Retainer	65 (7.4)
Front Bearing Retainer	96 (11)
Oil Receiver	65 (7.4)
Output Shaft Bearing Lock Plate	96 (11)
Shift Fork & Lock Bolts	108 (13)
Shift Fork Screw Plugs	108 (13)
Speedometer Driven Gear Lock Plate	48 (5.4)
Straight Screw Plug	108 (13)
S50	
Front Bearing Retainer	96 (11)
Oil Receiver	96 (11)
Output Shaft Bearing Lock Plate	96 (11)
Shift Fork & Lock Bolts	108 (12)
Speedometer Driven Gear Lock Plate	96 (11)

JEEP AISIN 4 & 5-SPEED MODELS AX 4 & AX 5

Cherokee, Comanche, Wagoneer

IDENTIFICATION

Two separate identification codes are used on AX 4 and AX 5 units. Model number and coded shipping date are found to rear of shift tower. Second code, which shows build date and serial number, is stamped on bottom of case next to intermediate plate.

First number of 2nd code is year of manufacture, while 2nd and 3rd numbers are month of manufacture. Five numbers remaining indicate serial number in sequence of building.

DESCRIPTION

Model AX 4 is a 4-speed unit and AX 5 is a 5-speed unit. Both transmissions have synchro-mesh engagement in all forward gears controlled by a floor shift mechanism integrated into the transmission top cover.

LUBRICATION & ADJUSTMENT

See appropriate MANUAL TRANSMISSION SERVICING article in DOMESTIC GENERAL SERVICING section.

TROUBLE SHOOTING

See MANUAL TRANSMISSION TROUBLE SHOOTING article in DOMESTIC GENERAL SERVICING section.

REMOVAL & INSTALLATION

See appropriate MANUAL TRANSMISSION REMOVAL article in DOMESTIC GENERAL SERVICING section.

TRANSMISSION DISASSEMBLY

1) To remove clutch housing, remove release fork and bearing. Remove back-up light switch. Remove shift lever retainer and restrict pins. Note restrict pins are different, with left side being Black. Remove clutch housing-to-transmission case attaching bolts.

2) Seperate the clutch housing from transmission case. To remove detent ball, remove screw plug, spring, and detent ball. Use Torx bit to remove screw plug and magnetic finger to remove the spring and ball. *See Figs. 1 and 2.*

3) To remove adapter housing, remove 5 bolts and the nut holding adapter housing to intermediate plate. Remove shift lever housing set bolt and lock plate. Remove plug from back of shift fork shaft. Remove large magnet and withdraw shaft.

4) While rotating shift lever, remove it from top of transmission. Remove 2 studs and the nut from adapter housing. Use plastic hammer to tap and remove extension housing from intermediate plate. Leave gasket attached to intermediate plate.

5) To remove transmission case, remove front bearing retainer and outer snap rings on 2 front bearings. Loosen intermediate plate from transmission case with plastic hammer. Remove transmission case.

Fig. 1: Exploded View of AX4 & AX5 Transmissions

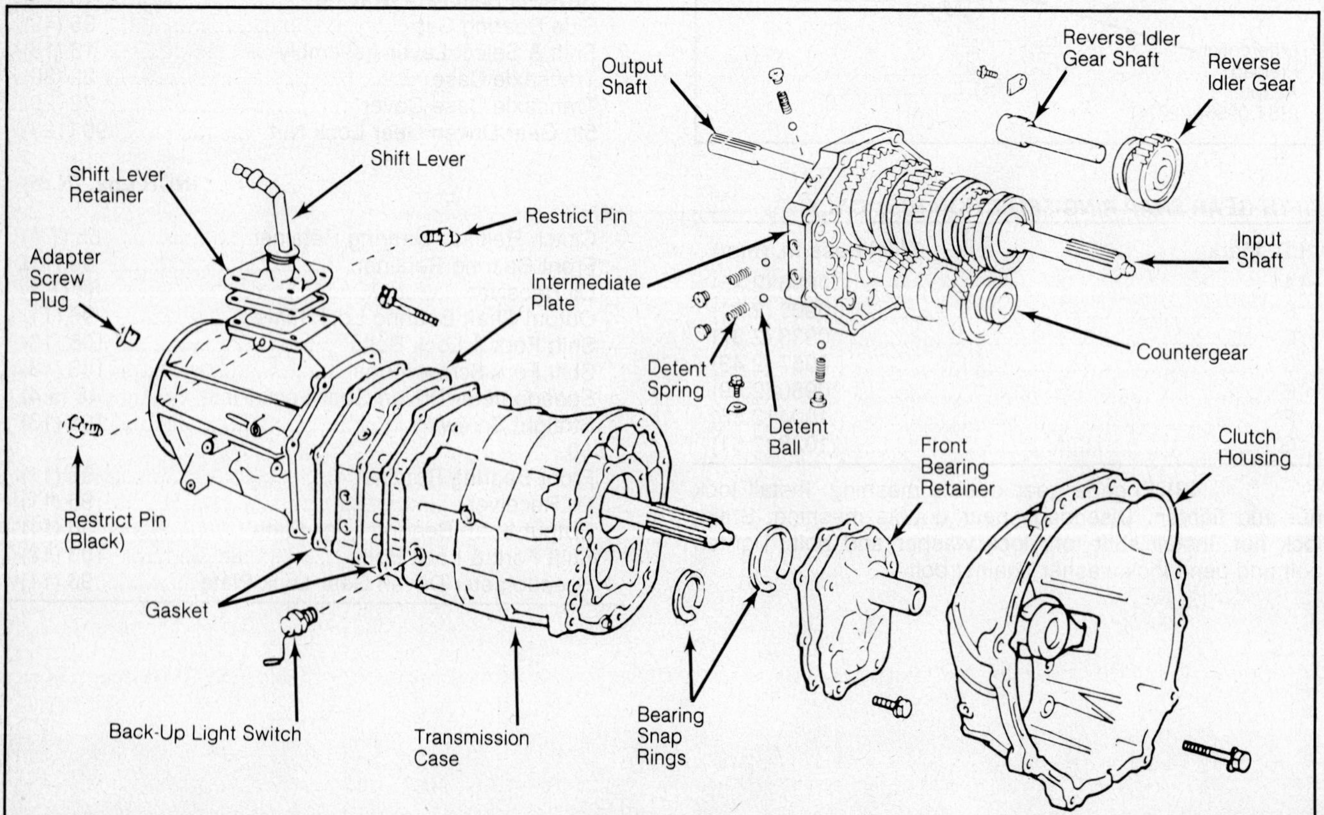

JEEP AISIN 4 & 5-SPEED MODELS AX 4 & AX 5 (Cont.)

Fig. 2: Location of Switches and Detent Ball Plug

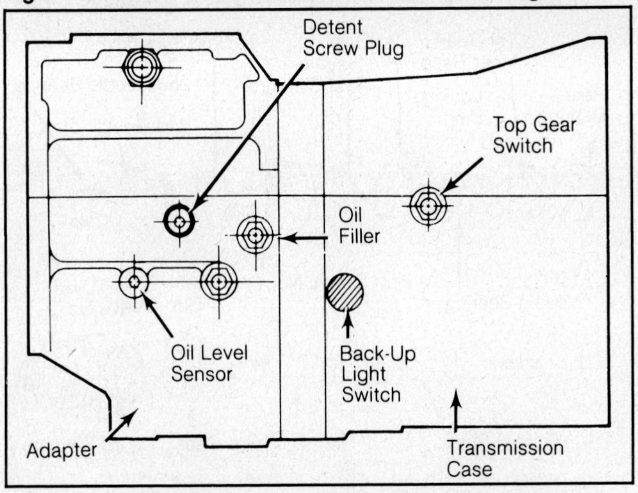

Use Torx bit and magnet to remove plug, ball and spring.

COMPONENT DISASSEMBLY

SHIFT MECHANISM

NOTE: **Detent balls in intermediate housing will usually fall out when plugs or shift fork shafts are removed. Be careful to retain all detent balls, springs, and interlock pins. Magnet should be used to remove parts that do not come out easily.**

1) Place intermediate plate in vise using 2 clutch housing bolts, washers and suitable nuts. Increase or decrease number of washers used so that bolt tip and outer surface of nut are aligned.

2) Make sure that machined surfaces of intermediate plate are protected from damage to sealing surfaces with soft jaws or by other means. Using a Torx bit and magnetic finger, remove screw plugs, detent balls, and springs from side and bottom of intermediate plate.

3) Using a hammer and punch, drive out 5 slotted spring pins and remove 2 "E" rings from the shift rails. Pull shift fork shaft No. 4 from intermediate plate and catch detent ball. Remove shift fork shaft No. 4 and 5th gear fork. *See Fig. 3.*

4) Remove shift fork shaft No. 5 from intermediate plate with reverse shift head attached. Remove shift fork shaft No. 3 from intermediate plate, catching interlock pins if necessary. Remove shift fork shaft No. 1 from intermediate plate.

5) Remove shift fork shaft No. 2 along with shift forks No. 2 and No. 1. Remove reverse idler gear shaft stopper, reverse idler gear and reverse gear shaft. Remove reverse shift arm from reverse shift arm bracket.

GEARS & SHAFTS

1) On AX 5 models, before removing gears and shafts from intermediate plate, thrust clearance between fifth gear on countershaft and rear counter gear bearing spacer should be measured. Standard clearance is .004-.012" (.10-.30 mm). If clearance is not correct, check parts for wear or damage.

2) Engage any 2 gears so that output shaft is locked up. Loosen staked part of nut on countershaft. Remove locknut and disengage gears. Using Puller (J-

Fig. 3: Shift Shafts and Forks

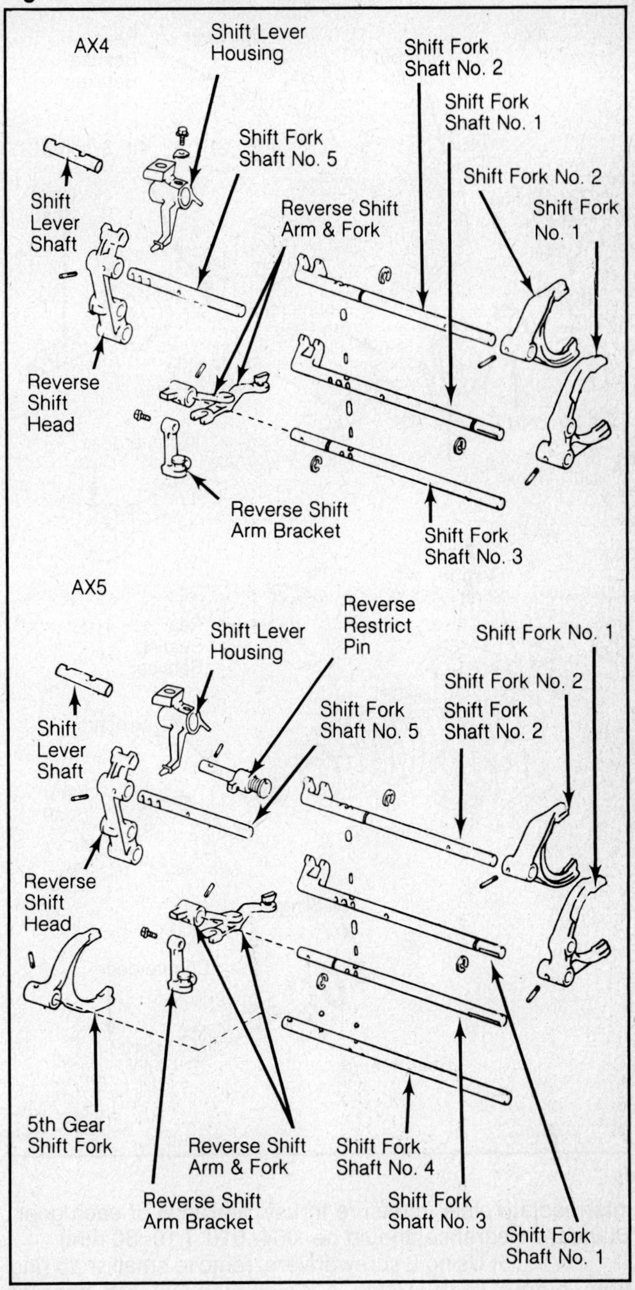

Use care to avoid losing parts when disassembling shift mechanisms.

22888), remove countershaft 5th gear, needle bearing, synchro ring, and gear spline piece No. 5. Remove spacer and ball underneath spacer. Remove reverse shift arm bracket.

3) On both models, remove bolts with Torx bit from rear output shaft bearing retainer. With snap ring pliers, remove snap ring from rear output shaft bearing after retainer is removed. Remove output shaft, counter gear, and input shaft as unit by tapping on intermediate plate while holding counter gear.

4) Remove input shaft, with 14 needle roller bearings, from output shaft. Remove countergear rear bearing from intermediate plate. With shaft removed from

Fig. 4: Exploded Views of Intermediate Plates and Shafts

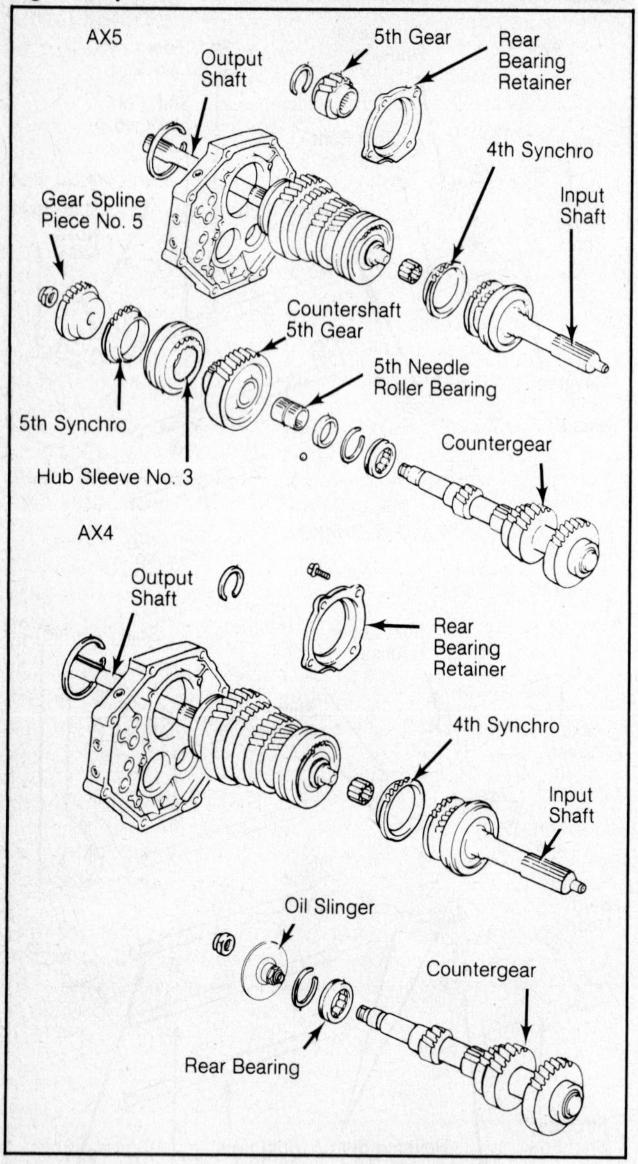

intermediate plate, measure thrust clearance of each gear. Standard clearance should be .004-.010" (.10-.30 mm).

5) Using 2 screwdrivers, remove small snap ring from output shaft. Using a press, remove 5th gear (if applicable), rear bearing first gear and inner race off output shaft. Remove needle roller bearing. Remove synchro ring and locking ball.

6) Using a press, remove hub sleeve No. 1, synchro ring and 2nd gear. Remove needle roller bearing. Using snap ring pliers, remove snap ring. Using press, remove hub sleeve No. 2, synchro ring and 3rd gear. Remove needle roller bearing.

INSPECTION

1) Check output shaft and 1st gear inner race for wear or damage. Measure flange thickness on both output shaft and inner race with vernier caliper. Minimum thickness of output shaft flange is .189" (4.80 mm). Minimum thickness of inner race flange is .157" (3.99 mm).

Fig. 5: Exploded View of Output Shaft

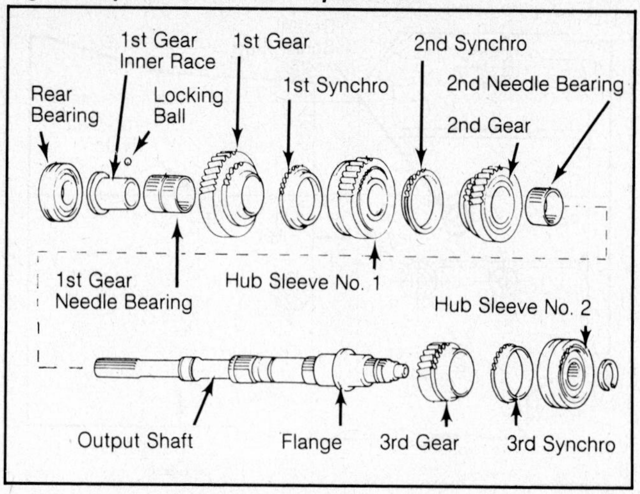

2) Measure outer diameter of output shaft journals for 2nd and 3rd gears. Minimum diameter for 2nd gear journal is 1.495" (37.96 mm). Minimum diameter for 3rd gear journal is 1.377" (34.98 mm). Measure outer diameter of 1st gear inner race. Minimum diameter for inner race is 1.535" (38.99 mm).

3) Mount output shaft in "V" blocks or lathe. Mount dial indicator with tip on portion of shaft where 1st gear inner race sears. Rotate output shaft and measure runout. Maximum runout allowed is .002" (.05 mm).

4) Oil clearance between gears and bearing races must be measured with dial indicator. Install 1st gear needle bearing and inner race into 1st gear. With tip of indicator on inner race and gear held securely, move race up and down to measure oil clearance. *See Fig. 6.* Standard clearance range is .0004-.0013" (.009-.032 mm).

Fig. 6: Measuring 1st Gear Oil Clearance

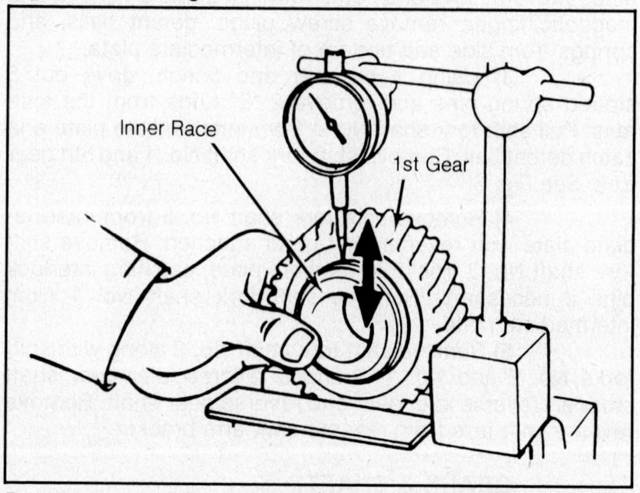

Procedure is similar for other gears with needle roller bearings.

5) Measure oil clearance of 2nd, 3rd, and countershaft 5th gears. Install gear on shaft with needle roller bearing in place. Position dial indicator tip on tooth of gear to be measured.

6) With shaft held securely, move gear up and down to measure clearance. Standard clearance range for 2nd and 3rd gears is .004-.0013" (.009-.033 mm). Standard clearance range for countershaft 5th gear is .0004-.0013" (.009-.032 mm).

7) Check synchro ring braking action by pushing in and turning ring on tapered cone of gear. Measure synchro-to-gear face clearance with feeler gauge. This measurement should be made while ring is firmly pushed toward gear on cone. Standard clearance is .040-.078" (1.0-2.0 mm) while wear limit is .031" (.80 mm).

8) Measure clearance between inner edge of hub sleeve and face of shift fork. Maximum clearance between sleeve and fork is .039" (1.0 mm). Check input shaft for wear or damage. To remove bearing, snap ring must be removed and bearing pressed off input shaft.

9) Check countergear and bearing for wear or damage. If necessary, remove snap ring and press bearing off countergear with Bearing Remover (J-22912-01). Check front bearing retainer and adapter housing for any damage or wear.

COMPONENT REASSEMBLY

NOTE: **Manufacturer recommends replacing all lip type oil seals, lock nuts, roll pins and snap rings when overhauling transmission. Use of Loctite Thread Lock or Loctite 242 Sealer is recommended when liquid sealer is required.**

GEARS & SHAFTS

1) If input shaft bearing is replaced, use Installer (J-34603) and press to install new bearing. Select snap ring that allows minimum axial play of bearing. There are 6 snap rings available, marked zero (0) through 5, in different thicknesses. See BEARING SNAP RING SIZES table.

BEARING SNAP RING SIZES

Input Mark	Countergear Mark	Thickness In. (mm)
0	1	.0807-.0827 (2.05-2.10)
1	2	.0827-.0846 (2.10-2.15)
2	3	.0846-.0866 (2.15-2.20)
3	4	.0866-.0886 (2.20-2.25)
4	5	.0886-.0906 (2.25-2.30)
5	6	.0906-.0925 (2.30-2.35)

2) If countergear front bearing is to be replaced, use Installer (J-28406) to press new bearing and inner race. Select snap ring which will allow minimal axial play. There are 6 snap rings available, marked 1 through 6, in different thicknesses. See BEARING SNAP RING SIZES table.

3) Press new seal into front bearing retainer with Installer (J-34602). Oil seal should be installed so that top edge of seal is .441-.480" (11.18-12.19 mm) from bearing retainer-to-transmission mating surface.

4) On AX 5 models, reverse restrict pin must be replaced if worn or damaged. Remove screw plug and drive out roll pin. Remove lever housing and slide out shaft. Install lever housing with new reverse restrict pin. Install new roll pin and tighten screw plug. On all models, replace adapter housing oil seal using Driver (J-29184).

5) Install hub No. 1 and hub No. 2 into hub sleeves along with the shift keys. Install key springs so that the gaps are not in line. Install shift springs under shift keys. *See Fig. 7.*

Fig. 7: Assembling Synchronizer Hubs & Shift Sleeves

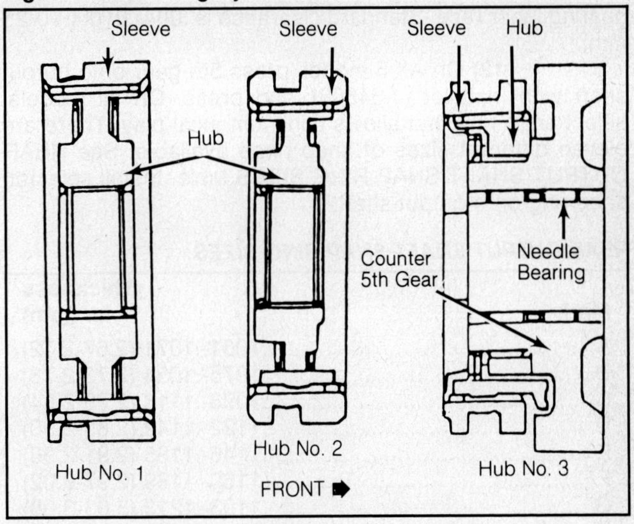

Make sure to stagger end gaps of key springs.

6) Put gear oil on output shaft and 3rd gear needle roller bearing. Place 3rd gear synchro ring on gear. Ensure ring slots align with shift keys. Install needle roller bearing into 3rd gear and hub sleeve No. 2.

7) Press gear and synchro hub assembly onto output shaft. Install new snap ring selected to allow minimal axial play. Snap rings are available in 7 thicknesses. See 3RD GEAR SNAP RINGS SIZES table.

3RD GEAR SNAP RING SIZES

Mark	Thickness In. (mm)
C-1	.0689-.0709 (1.75-1.80)
D	.0709-.0728 (1.80-1.85)
D-1	.0728-.0748 (1.85-1.90)
E	.0748-.0768 (1.90-1.95)
E-1	.0768-.0787 (1.95-2.00)
F	.0788-.0807 (2.00-2.05)
F-1	.0807-.0827 (2.05-2.10)

8) Measure 3rd gear thrust clearance between face of gear and flange on output shaft. Standard clearance range is .004-.010" (.10-.25 mm). Lightly coat output shaft and 2nd gear needle bearing with gear oil. Put 2nd gear synchro ring on 2nd gear. Align slots in ring with keys in hub.

9) Install needle roller bearing into 2nd gear. Press 2nd gear and hub sleeve No. 1 onto output shaft. Install 1st gear locking ball into output shaft. Lightly coat 1st gear needle roller bearing with gear oil. Assemble 1st gear, synchro ring, needle roller bearing, and bearing inner race.

10) Install assembly on output shaft and align shynchro ring slots with shift keys. Turn inner race so that it aligns with locking ball. Install rear output shaft bearing using Installer (J-34603), and press. Ensure snap ring groove of outer race facing toward rear of shaft. Hold 1st gear inner race to keep it from falling during assembly.

11) Measure thrust clearance of both 1st and 2nd gears. Thrust of 2nd gear is measured between face of gear and flange on output shaft. Thrust of 1st gear is

JEEP AISIN 4 & 5-SPEED MODELS AX 4 & AX 5 (Cont.)

measured between face of gear and flange of needle bearing inner race. Standard clearance is .004-.010" (.10-25 mm).

12) On AX 5 model, press 5th gear onto output shaft with Installer (J-34603), and press. On all models, select snap ring that allows minimum axial play. There are eleven different sizes of snap rings available. See REAR OUTPUT SHAFT SNAP RING SIZES table. Install selected snap ring onto output shaft.

REAR OUTPUT SHAFT SNAP RING SIZES

Mark	Thickness In. (mm)
A	.1051-.1071 (2.67-2.72)
B	.1075-.1094 (2.73-2.78)
C	.1098-.1118 (2.79-2.84)
D	.1122-.1142 (2.85-2.90)
E	.1146-.1165 (2.91-2.96)
F	.1169-.1189 (2.97-3.02)
G	.1193-.1213 (3.03-3.08)
H	.1217-.1236 (3.09-3.14)
J	.1240-.1260 (3.15-3.20)
K	.1264-.1283 (3.21-3.26)
L	.1287-.1307 (3.27-3.32)

13) Apply multipurpose grease to 14 needle roller bearings which were removed from input shaft. Install bearings into input shaft. Install output shaft into intermediate plate. Tap on intermediate plate while pulling on output shaft. Install input shaft to output shaft, using care to avoid cocking bearings in input shaft.

14) Ensure synchro ring slots on input shaft are aligned with shift keys. Install countergear into intermediate plate. With intermediate plate securely clamped and countergear held in place, drive rear countergear bearing into intermediate plate.

15) Install small snap ring for rear countergear bearing. Ensure snap ring is flush with intermediate plate surface. Using a Torx bit, install and tighten screws to 13 Ft Lbs. (18 N.m). Install reverse shift arm bracket and tighten bolts to 13 Ft. Lbs. (18 N.m).

16) On AX 5 models, install ball and spacer on countergear. Install shift keys and hub sleeve No. 3 onto countershaft 5th gear. Make sure key springs are positioned so end gaps are staggered and install key springs under shift keys.

17) Apply light coating of gear oil to needle roller bearing. Install countershaft 5th gear with hub sleeve No. 3 needle roller bearing. Install synchro ring on gear spline piece No. 5. Drive gear spline piece No. 5 onto countergear, using Driver (J-28406). Make sure synchro ring slots line up with shift keys.

NOTE: **When driving gear spline piece No. 5 onto countergear, support front of countergear with hammer or other solid object.**

18) Engage 2 gears to lock output shaft. Install lock nut on countergear and tighten to 90 Ft. Lbs. (122 N.m). Stake lock nut and disengage gears. Measure thrust clearance of countergear 5th gear between spacer and face of gear. Standard clearance should be .004-.012" (.10-.30 mm).

SHIFTING MECHANISM

1) Install reverse shift arm on pivot of reverse shift arm bracket. Put reverse idler gear onto shaft. Align reverse shift fork in groove of reverse idler gear. Install reverse idler gear shaft into intermediate plate. Install reverse idler shaft stop and tighten bolt to 13 Ft. Lbs. (18 N.m).

2) Insert shift forks No. 1 and No. 2 into groove of hub sleeves No. 1 and No. 2. Install fork shaft No. 2 through intermediate plate to shift forks No. 1 and No. 2. Lightly coat detent balls and interlock pins with multipurpose grease. Using a magnetic finger and screwdriver, install detent ball into intermediate plate. Make sure that interlock pins and balls are installed in correct locations. *See Fig. 8.*

Fig. 8: Installation of Detents and Interlocks

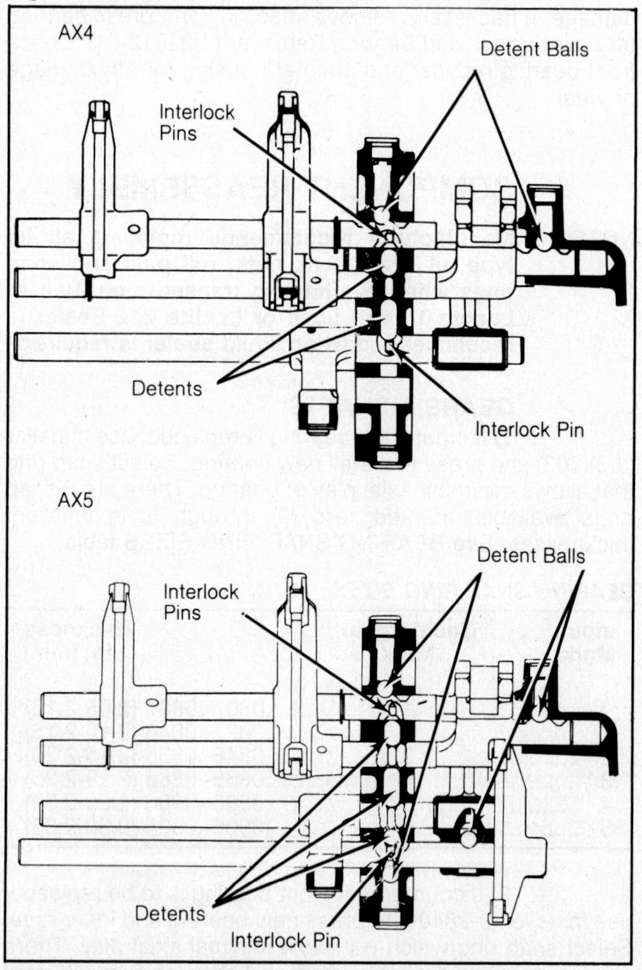

Note position by size and shape of balls and pins.

3) Install interlock pin into shaft hole. Install fork shaft No. 1 to shift fork No. 1 through intermediate plate. Using magnetic finger and screwdriver, install interlock pin into intermediate plate. Install interlock pin into shaft hole. Install fork shaft No. 3 to reverse shift arm through intermediate plate.

4) Install reverse shift head on shift fork shaft No. 5. Insert fork shaft No. 5 into intermediate plate while sliding reverse shift head onto shift fork No. 3.

5) On AX 5 models, install detent ball into reverse shift head hole. Shift hub sleeve No. 3 to 5th speed position. Place shift fork No. 3 into groove of hub sleeve No. 3 and install fork shaft No. 4 to shift fork No. 3 and reverse shift arm.

6) Using magnetic finger and screwdriver, install detent ball into intermediate plate. Slide shift fork shaft No. 4 into intermediate plate. On all models, check the interlock by positioning shift fork shaft No. 1 to the 1st speed position.

7) Remaining shift fork shafts should not move. Using a pin punch and hammer, drive new slotted springs into each shift fork, reverse shift arm, and reverse shift head. Install 2 fork shaft "E" rings. Apply liquid sealer to new screw plugs.

8) With Torx bit, install locking balls, springs, and screw plugs to intermediate plate. Tighten screws to 14 Ft. Lbs. (19 N.m). Short spring goes into top hole on intermediate plate. Remove intermediate plate from vise. Remove bolts, nuts washers and gasket.

TRANSMISSION REASSEMBLY

NOTE: Manufacturer recommends replacing all lip type oil seals, lock nuts, roll pins and snap rings when overhauling transmission. Use of Loctite Thread Lock or Loctite 242 Sealer is recommended when liquid sealer is required.

1) Place new gasket on front of intermediate plate. Align bearing outer races, shift fork shaft ends, and reverse idler gear with holes in transmission case. Install case against intermediate plate, tapping on case with plastic hammer if necessary.

2) Install 2 new bearing snap rings outside transmission housing. Install front bearing retainer with new gasket. Apply liquid sealer to retainer-to-transmission bolts and tighten retainer plate to transmission. Install new gasket on back of intermediate plate. Install adapter housing.

3) Tighten adapter-to-intermediate plate bolts. Install shift lever housing. Insert shift lever into adapter and shift lever housing. Tighten shift lever housing bolt, using lock plate. Lock plate in place. Install and tighten adapter screw plug.

4) Apply liquid sealer to detent plug. Install detent ball, spring, and plug into adapter housing. Tighten plug and make sure that input and output shafts rotate smoothly. Make sure that shifting can be done smoothly into all gears.

5) Install Black restrict pin on reverse gear-5th gear side. Install remaining pin and tighten pins to 20 Ft. Lbs. (27 N.m). Install shift lever retainer with new gasket. Install back-up light switch. Install clutch housing and tighten bolts evenly.

TIGHTENING SPECIFICATIONS

Application	Ft. Lbs. (N.m)
Adapter Housing-to-Transmission Case	27 (37)
Back-Up Lamp Switch	27 (37)
Clutch Housing-to-Transmission Case	27 (37)
Countergear Locknut	90 (122)
Fill & Drain Plugs	27 (37)
Front Bearing Retainer-to-Transmission Case	12 (16)
Oil Level Sensor	13 (18)
Rear Bearing Retainer-to-Intermediate Plate	13 (18)
Reverse Restrict Pin-to-Adapter Housing	27 (37)
Reverse Shift Arm Bracket-to-Intermediate Plate	13 (18)
Reverse Idle Gear Shaft-to-Stopper	13 (18)
Shift Lever Housing	27 (37)
Top Gear Switch	27 (37)
4th Gear Switch	27 (37)

NEW PROCESS 435

Chrysler Corp. Ramcharger,
D & W100/350,
Ford Bronco, F150/F350

IDENTIFICATION

Chrysler Corp. 4-speed manual transmissions use aluminum identification tag secured by 2 bolts on power take-off cover. Information on tag includes part number, model and build date.

Ford 4-speed manual transmissions have service identification tag found on 2 bolts retaining power take-off cover to case. *See Fig. 1.*

Fig. 1: Ford Motor Company Identification Tag

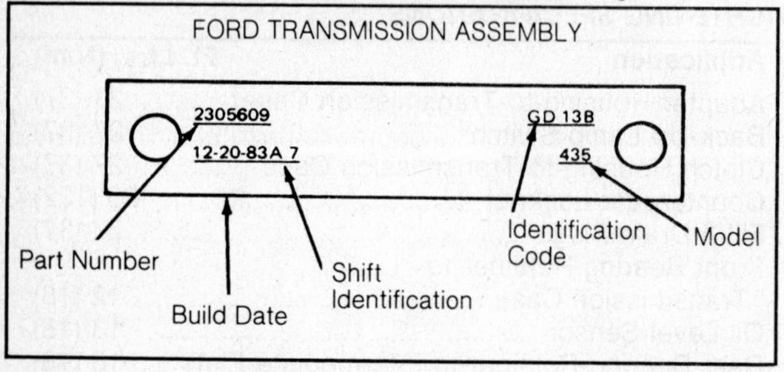

DESCRIPTION

New Process 435 4-speed transmission uses top-mounted shift lever and cover. Spur cut gears are used for 1st and Reverse speeds. Helical cut gears, synchronized for easier shifting, are used for 2nd, 3rd, and 4th speeds.

Input shaft is supported at front by tapered roller bearing. End play is controlled by gasket thickness between case and bearing retainer. Front of mainshaft is supported by pilot roller bearing in input shaft. Rear of mainshaft is supported by ball bearing that is pressed onto shaft and held in case by snap ring.

Countershaft and gears are integral one-piece design. Countershaft gear is supported by caged roller bearings at each end. Roller-type thrust bearing and race are provided at rear of countershaft gear, with thrust washer at front of gear.

Reverse idler gear uses bronze bushing. The 3rd-4th speed synchronizer is mounted at front of mainshaft. The 2nd speed synchronizer and 1st speed sliding gear is mounted at rear of mainshaft.

LUBRICATION & ADJUSTMENT

See appropriate MANUAL TRANSMISSION SERVICING article in DOMESTIC GENERAL SERVICING section.

TROUBLE SHOOTING

See MANUAL TRANSMISSION TROUBLE SHOOTING article in DOMESTIC GENERAL SERVICING section.

REMOVAL & INSTALLATION

See appropriate MANUAL TRANSMISSION REMOVAL article in DOMESTIC GENERAL SERVICING section.

SERVICE (IN VEHICLE)

GEAR SHIFT LEVER

NOTE: **Following gear shift lever procedure applies to Ford vehicles only. Remove shift ball only if shift ball, boot or lever is to be replaced. If either ball, boot or lever is not being replaced, remove ball, boot, and lever as assembly.**

Removal

1) Remove plastic insert from shift ball. Warm ball with heat gun to 140-180°F (60-80°C). Knock ball off lever with block of wood and hammer, taking care not to damage finish on shift lever.

2) Remove rubber boot and floor pan cover. Shift into 2nd gear. Remove lock pin and remove shift lever from shifter housing.

Installation

1) Lubricate shift lever. Install shift lever in shifter housing, making sure that slot in lever aligns with tab in housing. Install lock pin. Install rubber boot and floor pan cover.

2) Remove shift pattern insert from ball. Warm ball with heat gun to 140-180°F (60-80°C) and tap ball on lever with 7/16" socket and mallet. Install insert.

TRANSMISSION DISASSEMBLY

1) Mount transmission assembly in holding fixture and remove drain and filler plugs. Place gearshift lever in Neutral position. Remove shift control cover bolts.

2) Remove cover by lifting and rotating slightly counterclockwise to provide clearance for shift forks. Remove cover and discard gasket. *See Fig. 9.*

3) Lock transmission in 2 gears. Remove mainshaft flange nut and mainshaft flange. Remove extension housing and slide speedometer drive gear off mainshaft.

4) Measure and record synchronizer outer stop ring and 3rd gear end play for reference during reassembly. *See Fig. 15.*

5) Remove input shaft bearing retainer and gasket. Rotate gear to align notch in input shaft gear clutch teeth with countershaft drive gear teeth.

6) Remove input shaft assembly and tapered roller bearing. Remove snap ring, washer, and pilot roller bearing from recess in rear of input shaft. *See Fig. 2.*

7) Place brass drift in front center of mainshaft and drive mainshaft to rear. Remove rear bearing with puller. Move mainshaft to rear and tilt front of mainshaft upward.

8) Remove roller-type thrust bearing. Remove synchronizer and stop rings separately. Remove mainshaft assembly. *See Figs. 3 and 4.*

9) Remove Reverse idler lock screw and lock plate. Use brass drift, held at angle, to drive idler shaft to rear. Remove shaft. Lift Reverse idler gear from case.

Manual Transmissions

NEW PROCESS 435 (Cont.)

Fig. 2: Input Shaft Assembly

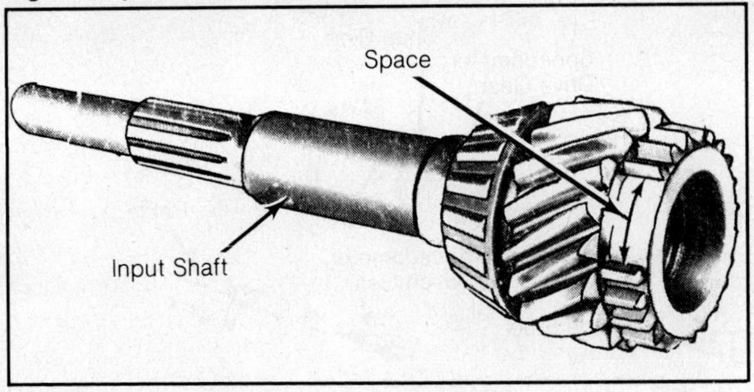

Align space in input gear clutch teeth with countershaft gear teeth.

10) Remove bearing retainer from rear of countershaft. Roller bearing remains with retainer. Tilt cluster gear assembly and work out of case. Use driver to remove front bearings from case.

Fig. 3: Removing Rear Mainshaft Bearing

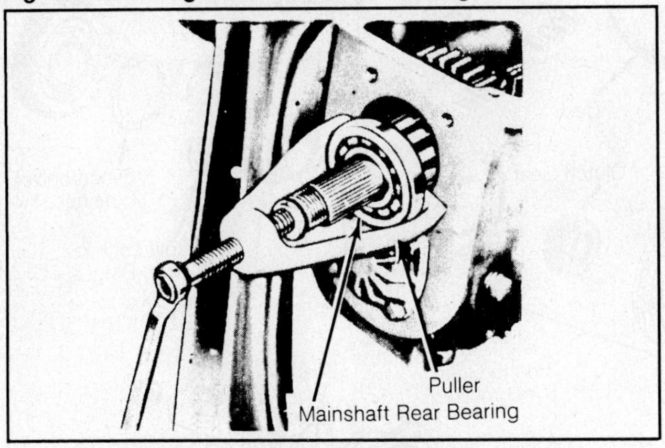

Attach puller to rear bearing and remove bearing.

Fig. 4: Removing Mainshaft from Case

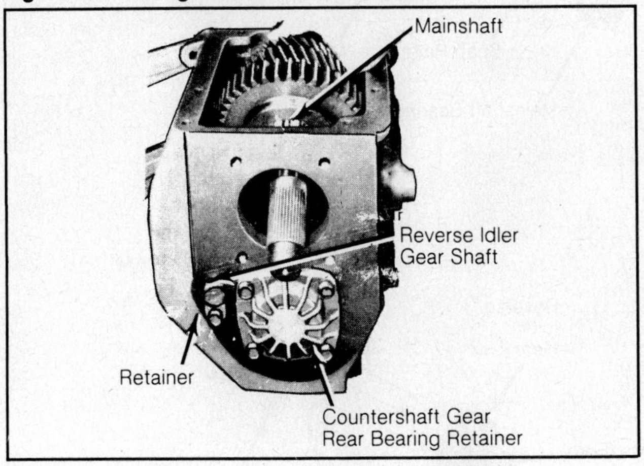

Move mainshaft to rear and tilt front upward.

CLEANING & INSPECTION

1) All parts should be thoroughly washed in cleaning solvent and air dried. Remove portions of old gaskets with stiff brush or scraper. Clean bearings separately from other parts. Hold bearing races so bearings will not rotate and brush with soft brush to remove all foreign material.

2) Loose particles may be removed by striking bearing flat against wood block. Rinse bearings in clean solvent and air dry. Lubricate with light grade oil and wrap in clean paper until ready to reinstall. Do not spin bearings.

3) Examine all gear teeth and splines for chips, wear, breaks, or nicks. Examine case, housing, retainers, and covers for cracks or other damage. Inspect thrust washers, snap ring grooves, and spacers for wear or damage.

4) Check all bearings and synchronizers for wear, damage, and proper fit. Coat all moving parts before installation with lubricant and always use new gaskets, oil seals, and snap rings.

COMPONENT DISASSEMBLY & REASSEMBLY

SHIFT CONTROL COVER

NOTE: **Gearshift housing should be disassembled only if it is necessary to replace rails, poppets, interlock plungers, broken springs or if shift forks or cover itself need replacing.**

Disassembly

1) Using No. 2 screw extractor, remove roll pins from 1st-2nd shift fork and gate. Push shift rail out through front to force plug out of housing. *See Fig. 6.* Cover detent ball hole to prevent ball and spring from flying out. Remove rail, fork and gate.

2) Remove back-up light switch. Remove remaining shift rails in same manner. Compress Reverse gear plunger and remove retaining clip. Withdraw plunger and spring from gate.

Cleaning & Inspection

1) Examine housing for cracks or other damage. Inspect shift forks for wear and/or distortion. Check detent ball springs for distortion or collapsed coils.

2) Examine detent balls for corrosion and wear. If shift lever shaft detents show signs of wear, replace them. Replace all gaskets, expansion plugs, and roll pins. *See Fig. 9.*

Reassembly

1) Place spring on Reverse gear plunger, install and compress assembly in Reverse shift gate. Install retaining clip. Start Reverse shift rail in cover. Place detent spring and ball in position, depress ball and slide shift rail over it.

2) Install gate and shift fork on rail and install new roll pins. Apply film of sealer to plug seat at front of cover. Install new plug in Reverse shift rail bore.

3) Place Reverse fork in Neutral position and install 2 interlock plungers in bores. Insert interlock pin in 3rd-4th shift rail. Install remaining rails in same manner as Reverse rail, making sure that interlock plunger in 1st-2nd shift rail is in place.

4) Install back-up light switch. Install new expansion plugs and rail interlock hole plug.

INPUT SHAFT DRIVE GEAR

Disassembly

Remove tapered roller bearing from pinion shaft with puller. Remove snap ring, pilot roller bearing washer

Manual Transmissions

NEW PROCESS 435 (Cont.)

Fig. 5: Exploded View of New Process 435 4-Speed Transmission

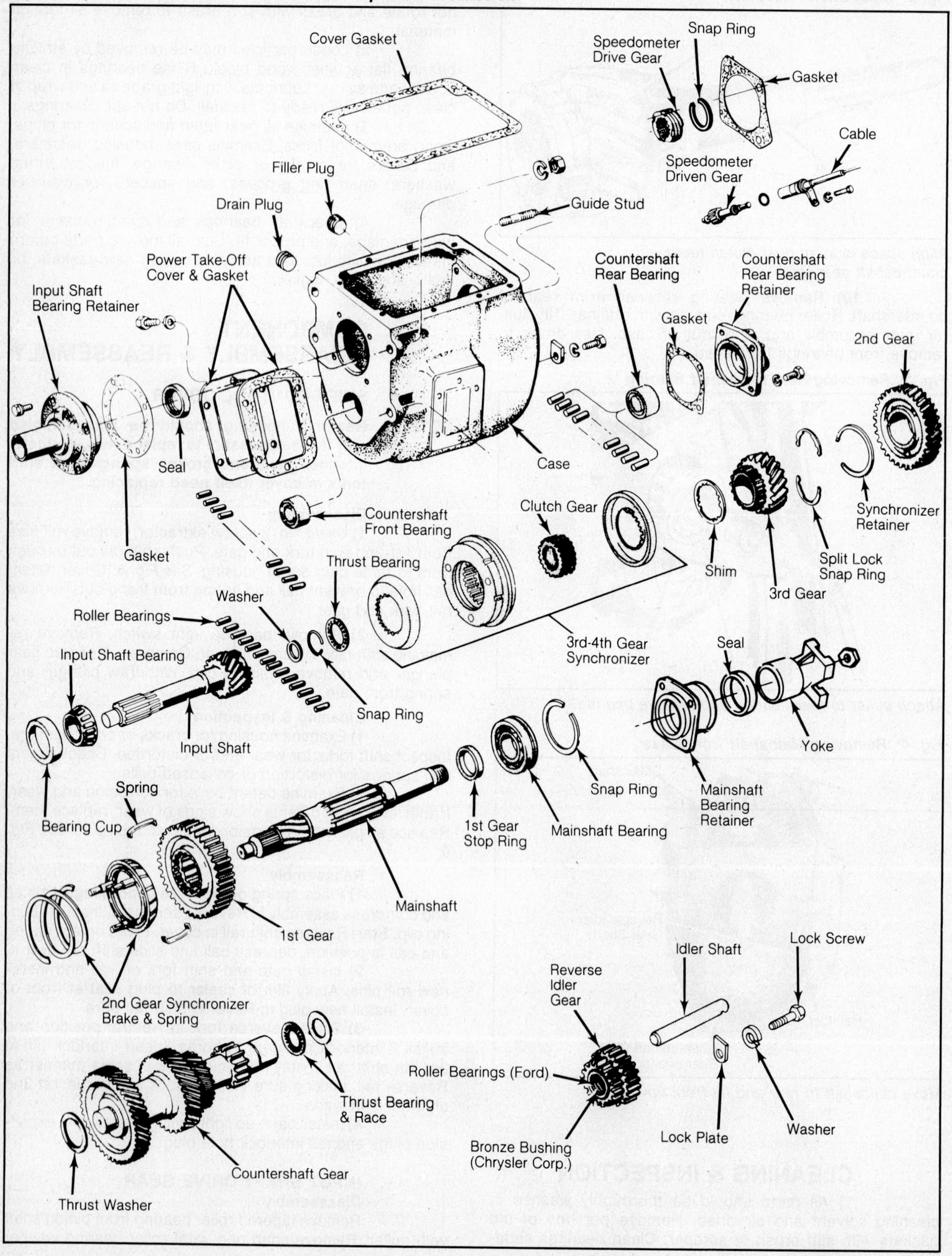

Manual Transmissions

NEW PROCESS 435 (Cont.)

Fig. 6: Removing Shift Rail Roll Pins

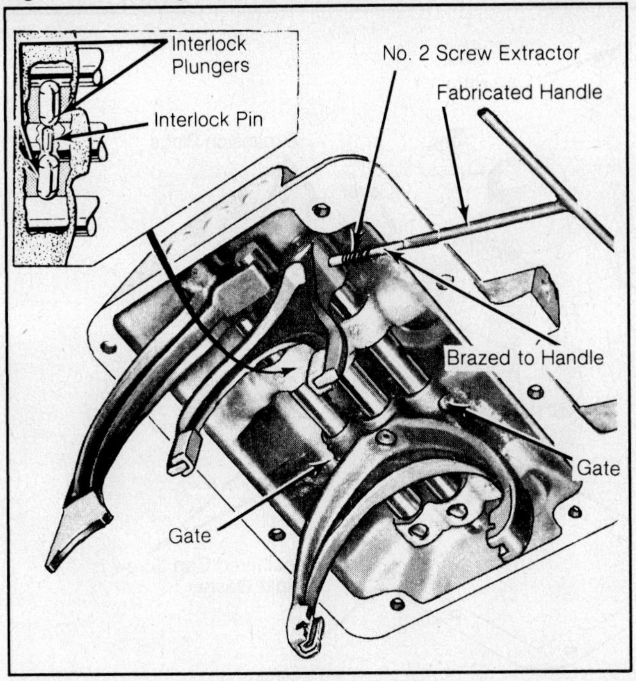

Remove pins using No. 2 screw extractor.

and pilot bearing rollers from gear. Remove bearing race from front bearing retainer with puller. Remove pinion shaft seal.

Reassembly

Position drive pinion in arbor press. Place wooden block on pinion gear and press bearing until it contacts bearing inner race. *See Fig. 7.* Lubricate pilot bearing rollers with light grease and insert in cavity at rear of drive pinion gear. Install washer and snap ring. Press new seal into place with lip of seal toward mounting surface. Press bearing race into retainer.

Fig. 7: Installing Tapered Roller Bearing on Input Shaft

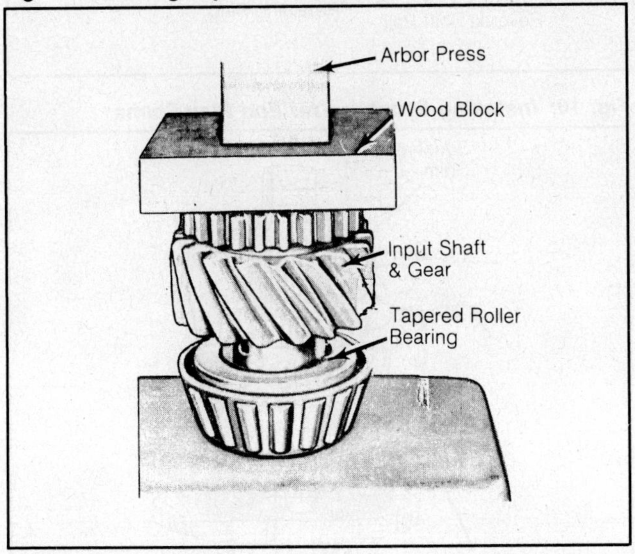

Place block on input gear and press gear into bearings.

INPUT SHAFT BEARING RETAINER

Roller Bearing Race

Bearing race is installed in bearing retainer. Use puller to remove race from retainer. Press new race squarely into retainer. *See Fig. 8.*

Fig. 8: Installing Input Shaft Bearing Race

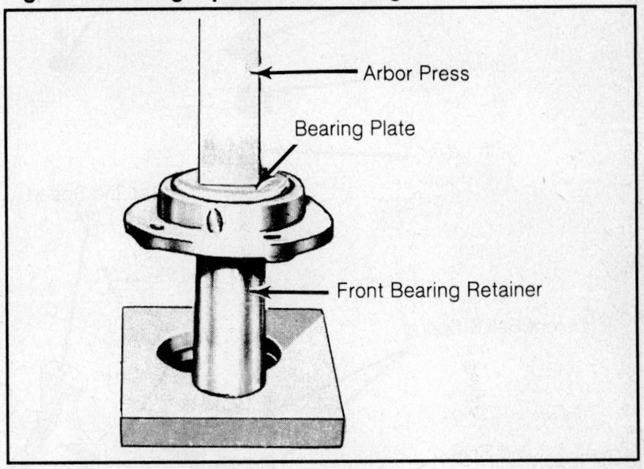

Oil Seal Replacement

Pry oil seal out of retainer and press new seal into place using sleeve. Lip of oil seal should point toward gasket surface of retainer.

MAINSHAFT

Disassembly

Remove clutch gear snap ring. Remove clutch gear, synchronizer outer stop ring-to-3rd gear shim(s), and 3rd gear. Remove split lock ring with 2 screwdrivers. Withdraw 2nd gear and synchronizer assembly. Remove 1st-Reverse sliding gear from shaft.

Reassembly

1) Place mainshaft assembly in soft-jawed vise with rear end up. Install 1st-Reverse gear making sure 2 spline springs are in place inside gear as it is installed on shaft.

2) Move mainshaft in vise so that forward end is up. Install synchronizer spring and synchronizer on 2nd gear. Secure with snap ring, making sure snap ring tangs are away from gear.

3) Slide 2nd gear assembly onto mainshaft making sure synchronizer is toward rear. Secure gear to shaft with split lock snap rings, then install 3rd gear.

NOTE: **Synchronizer clutching gear must be installed with BOTH oil slots facing 3rd gear. Oil slots must NOT face thrust bearing.**

4) Install correct shim(s) between 3rd gear and 3rd-4th synchronizer stop ring. Refer to end play measurement obtained during disassembly to bring end play within specification. Exact determination of end play will be made after mainshaft and main drive gear are installed in case.

REVERSE IDLER GEAR

Gear is serviced by replacement only. Replacement gear is equipped with integral bearings rather than bushing as on original gear.

Manual Transmissions

NEW PROCESS 435 (Cont.)

Fig. 9: Exploded View of Shift Control Cover Assembly

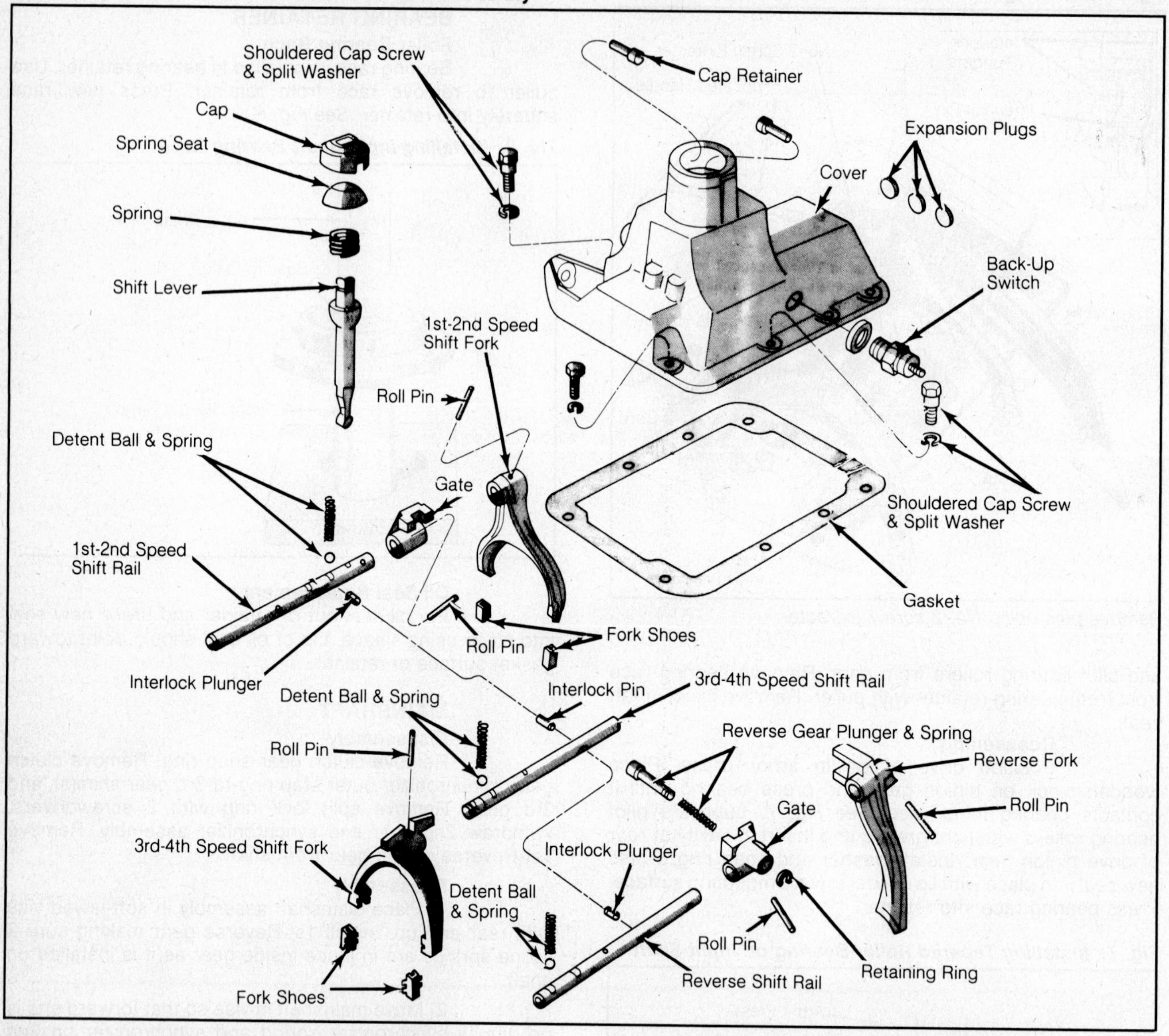

NOTE: **Do not attempt to disassemble roller bearing assembly. Bearing lock ring cannot be removed without damaging gear or bearing.**

COUNTERSHAFT

Front Bearing

Press or drive old bearing out of case and discard. Install new bearing, pressing bearing cage into case until flush with front of case. Coat roller bearings with multi-purpose grade 2 grease or equivalent.

Rear Bearing

Using puller, remove rear bearing from retainer and discard. Position new bearing squarely in retainer bore and press into place until bearing bottoms in retainer. Coat roller bearings with multi-purpose grade 2 grease or equivalent.

TRANSMISSION REASSEMBLY

1) Press front countershaft roller bearing into case until cage is flush with front of case. Lubricate roller

Fig. 10: Installing Synchronizer End Play Shims

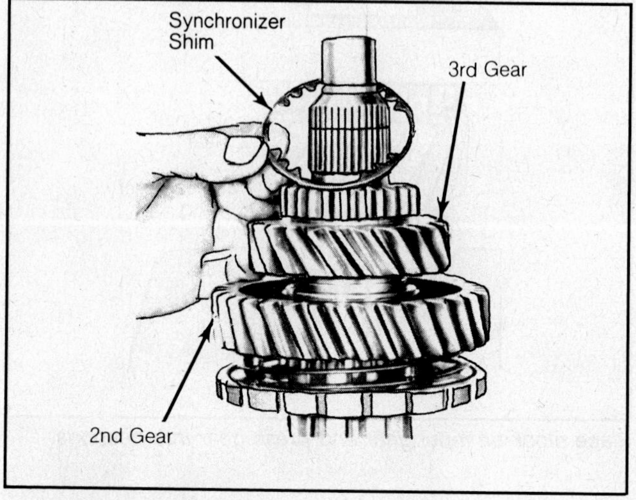

Manual Transmissions

NEW PROCESS 435 (Cont.)

bearings with light coating of grease. Place transmission with front of case facing down. If uncaged bearings are re-used, hold loose rollers in place with light film of grease.

2) Lower countershaft assembly into case placing thrust washer tangs in slots in case, and inserting front end of shaft into bearing. Install countershaft gear rear thrust bearing and race on pilot diameter of countershaft. *See Fig. 11.*

Fig. 11: Installing Rear Countershaft Bearing

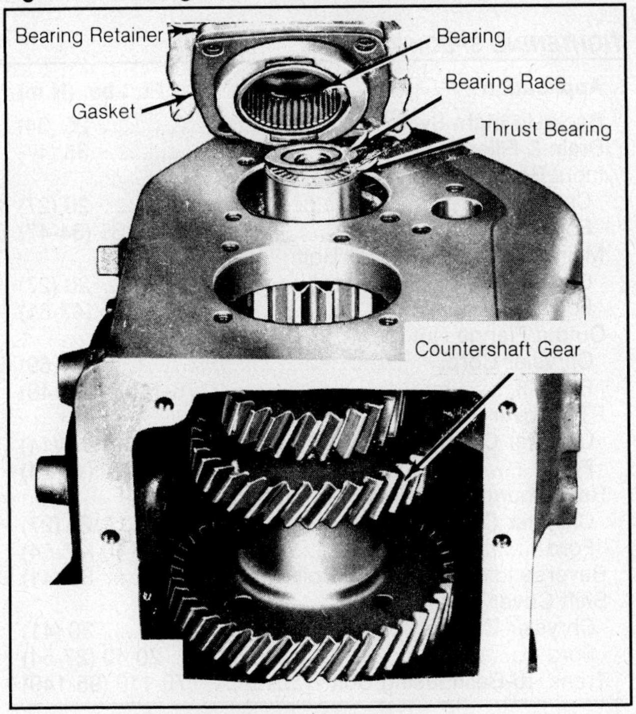

Install bearing and race on countergear.

3) Install new rear bearing retainer gasket, rear bearing retainer and bearing assembly. Install bolts and tighten.

4) Install Reverse idler gear assembly in transmission case. Align Reverse idler shaft so lock plate groove in shaft is in proper alignment to install lock plate.

5) Hold gear in position and tap shaft through case and gear. Install lock plate and washer. Tighten bolt. Ensure that gear turns freely on shaft.

6) Lower rear end of mainshaft into case (holding 1st gear on shaft) and maneuver through rear bearing opening. Ensure that synchronizer and shims remain in position on mainshaft. Install roller thrust bearing. *See Fig. 12.*

7) Place block of wood between front end of mainshaft and front of case. Install rear bearing on mainshaft and drive into case until bearing snap ring is flush with case.

8) Install drive pinion shaft and bearing assembly. Ensure that pilot rollers remain in place. Install rear bearing retainer and gasket. Install drive pinion bearing retainer (without gasket).

9) While holding bearing retainer tight against bearing, measure clearance between retainer and face of case with feeler gauge. *See Fig. 13.*

10) Remove bearing retainer. Install gasket shim pack .010-.015" (.254-.381 mm) thicker than measured

Fig. 12: Installing Rear Mainshaft Bearing

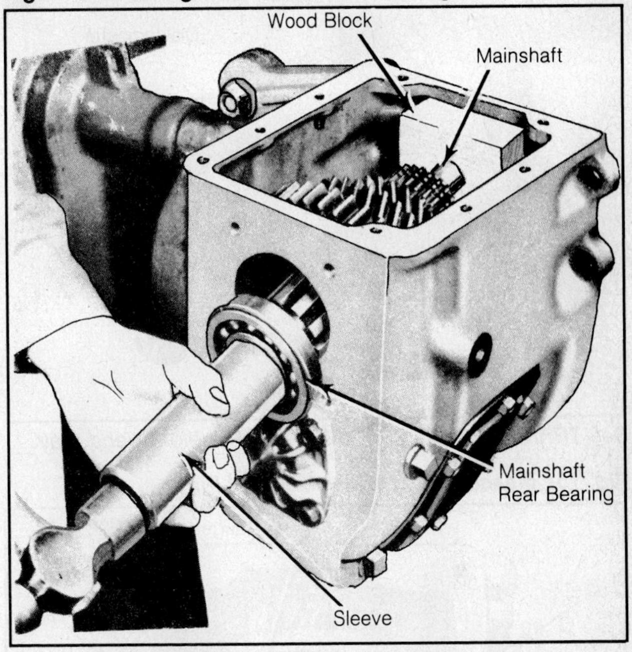

Place wood block between front of mainshaft and case.

Fig. 13: Measuring Bearing Retainer Clearance

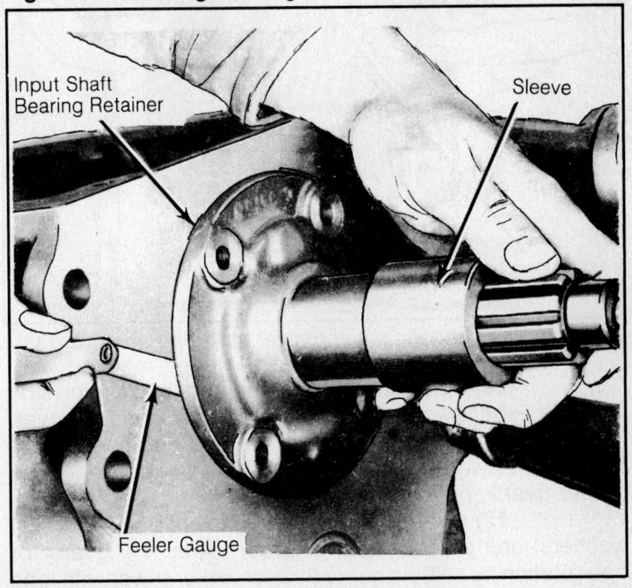

Measure clearance between retainer and case.

clearance between retainer and case. Reinstall and tighten retainer. Recheck end play.

11) Using dial indicator, measure input shaft and gear end play. *See Fig. 14.* End play of input shaft and gear is necessary to allow for normal heat expansion of parts during operation.

12) Check synchronizer end play after all mainshaft components are in position and properly tightened. Two equal size feeler gauges are used to measure synchronizer end play.

13) Keep feeler gauges as close as possible to both sides of mainshaft. Disassemble mainshaft and add or subtract shims to bring end play within specification. *See Fig. 15.* Shift gears into all gear positions and check for free rotation.

Manual Transmissions

NEW PROCESS 435 (Cont.)

Fig. 14: Measuring Input Shaft Drive Gear End Play

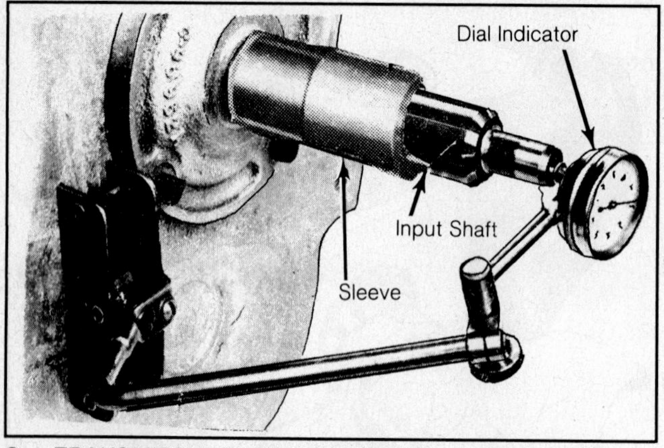

See TRANSMISSION SPECIFICATIONS table for end play.

Fig. 15: Measuring Synchronizer End Play

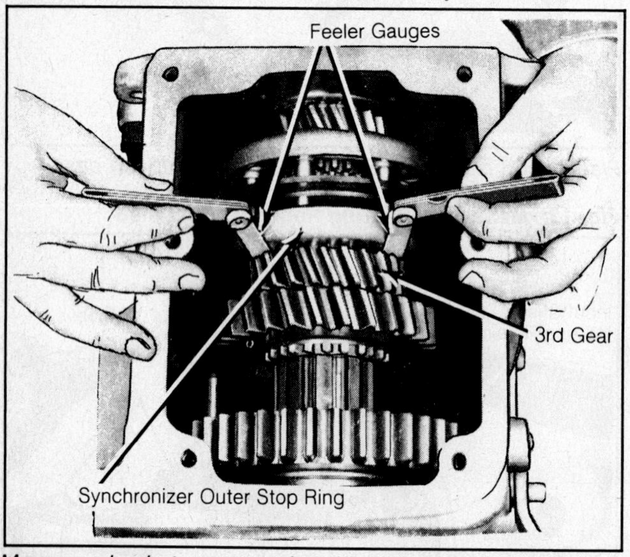

Measure play between synchronizer stop ring and 3rd gear.

14) Make sure all internal parts of transmission are well lubricated before installing shift control cover. Place all transmission gears in Neutral position. Install cover with new gasket on case. Carefully engage forks into proper gears and lower cover into place.

15) Install shouldered alignment bolts and split washers, one on each side of cover tower. Try gears for free rotation by shifting gears through cover tower with long screwdriver. Install remaining bolts and washers.

TRANSMISSION SPECIFICATIONS

Application	Inches (mm)
Input Shaft & Gear End Play	
Chrysler Corp.	.007-.017 (.177-.432)
Ford	.007-.014 (.177-.355)
Synchronizer End Play	
Chrysler Corp.	.050-.070 (1.27-1.77)
Ford	.063-.081 (1.60-2.06)

TIGHTENING SPECIFICATIONS

Application	Ft. Lbs. (N.m)
Back-Up Light Switch	25 (34)
Drain & Filler Plugs	35 (47)
Input Shaft Bearing Retainer Screw	
Chrysler Corp.	20 (27)
Ford	25-35 (34-47)
Mainshaft Rear Retainer Bolt	
Chrysler Corp.	20 (27)
Ford	35-45 (47-61)
Output Flange Nut	
Chrysler Corp.	125 (169)
Ford	75-110 (102-149)
PTO Cover Bolt	
Chrysler Corp.	10 (14)
Ford	12-18 (16-24)
Rear Countershaft Retainer Bolt	
Chrysler Corp.	20 (27)
Ford	20-40 (27-54)
Reverse Idler Shaft Lock Bolt	30 (41)
Shift Cover Screw	
Chrysler Corp.	30 (41)
Ford	20-40 (27-54)
Trans.-to-Bellhousing Bolt	70-110 (95-149)

Manual Transmissions

NEW PROCESS A833 OVERDRIVE

Chrysler Corp., General Motors

IDENTIFICATION

Transmission may be identified by number stamped on machined pad on right side of case. First two letters of code identify manufacturing plant, next three numbers designate transmission type (833), next four numbers indicate manufacturing date, and last four numbers are production sequence series.

DESCRIPTION

Transmission is 4-speed unit providing clash-free shifting in all forward gears due to use of 2 synchronizer assemblies. Drive pinion (input shaft) is supported by ball bearing in front of transmission case and oilite bushing pressed in rear of crankshaft.

Front end of mainshaft is supported by roller bearings in end of drive pinion and by ball bearing in front of extension housing.

Rear end of mainshaft is supported by sliding yoke of propeller shaft, which is supported by bushing in extension housing. Countershaft gear is supported by double row of needle-type roller bearings at each end.

Gear thrust is taken up by means of thrust washers located between ends of gear and case. Reverse idler gear is supported on bronze bushing, pressed into gear.

LUBRICATION & ADJUSTMENT

See appropriate MANUAL TRANSMISSION SERVICING article in DOMESTIC GENERAL SERVICING section.

TROUBLE SHOOTING

See MANUAL TRANSMISSION TROUBLE SHOOTING article in DOMESTIC GENERAL SERVICING section.

SERVICE (IN VEHICLE)

SPEEDOMETER PINION GEAR

Removal

Place drain pan under speedometer adapter. Remove bolt and retainer securing pinion adapter to extension housing. With cable housing connected, work adapter and pinion out of extension housing.

NOTE: **General Motors models use "O" ring on adapter but do not use internal oil seal. SEAL REPLACEMENT procedure is for Chrysler Corp. models only.**

Seal Replacement

1) If transmission fluid is found in cable housing, replace seal in adapter. Start new seal and retainer ring in adapter, then push into adapter with Seal Installer (C-4004) until installer bottoms.

2) Be sure adapter flange and mating area on extension housing are clean and lubricated. Dirt or sand will cause misalignment and pinion gear damage.

Fig. 1: Exploded View of Chrysler Corp. Speedometer Pinion & Adapter Assembly

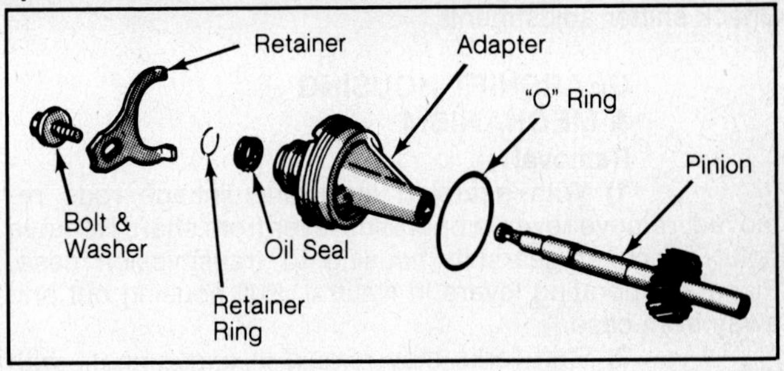

General Motors models do not use oil seal.

Installation

1) On Chrysler Corp. models, note number on adapter. This number corresponds to correct number of teeth on gear. Count gear teeth and install correct speedometer pinion gear into adapter. Rotate pinion gear and adapter assembly so that number on adapter is in 6 o'clock position.

2) Install assembly in housing. Install retainer with tangs in adapter positioning slots. Tap adapter firmly into extension housing and tighten retaining bolt. Check fluid level in transmission.

3) On General Motors models, place assembly in housing so slot in adapter is toward retainer boss on housing. Push adapter into housing until retainer fits into groove on adapter. Tighten bolt holding retainer to housing. Check fluid level in transmission.

Fig. 2: Installed View of Chrysler Corp. Speedometer Pinion & Adapter

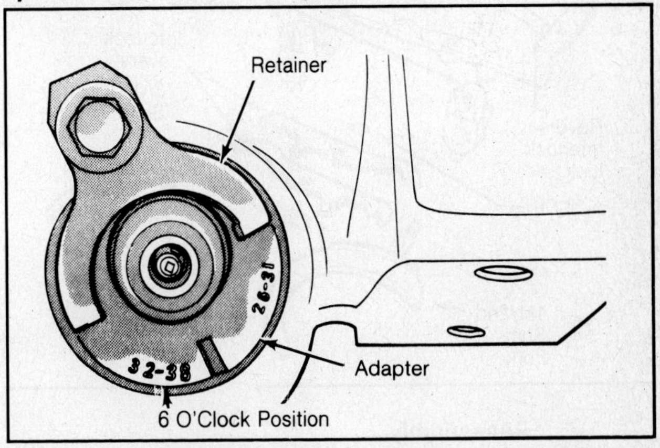

Secure pinion adapter in extension housing with retainer.

GEARSHIFT LEVER & LINKAGE

Removal

1) Disconnect battery ground cable. Remove floor pan boot, sliding it up and off shift lever. Slide .010" (.25 mm) feeler gauge down left side of shift lever into floor shift assembly to release gearshift lever.

2) Pull up on lever to remove it from floor shift assembly. Remove clips, washers and control rods from shift unit levers. Remove 2 bolts holding shift unit to mounting plate on extension housing. Remove shift unit.

Installation

Attach shift unit to mounting plate. Tighten bolts to 24 ft. lbs. (32 N.m). Install shift rods, washers and clips.

NEW PROCESS A833 OVERDRIVE (Cont.)

Install shift lever in shift assembly. Slide boot down shift lever and attach to floor. Reconnect battery ground cable. Check shifter adjustments.

GEARSHIFT HOUSING & MECHANISM

Removal

1) With gearshift lever and linkage rods removed, remove reverse operating lever from shaft. Remove bolts attaching gearshift housing to transmission case. Place all operating levers in Neutral. Pull housing out and away from case.

2) Shift forks may remain in engagement with synchronizer sleeves. If so, work forks out of sleeves and remove from case. Remove reverse detent spring and ball from bore in side of case.

Disassembly

1) If oil leakage is visible around lever shafts or if interlock levers are cracked, remove shift levers and shafts. Make sure shafts are free of burrs before removing to avoid damaging housing bores.

2) Remove "O" ring retainers and "O" rings from housing. Remove "E" clip from interlock lever pivot pin. Remove interlock levers and spring from housing.

Fig. 3: Exploded View of Gearshift Housing & Mechanism

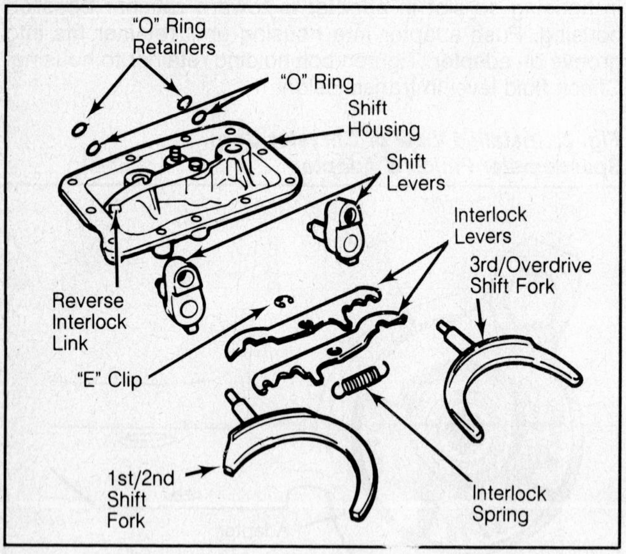

Reassembly

1) Install interlock levers on pivot pin and fasten with "E" clip. Use pliers to install spring on interlock lever hangers. Coat new oil seal "O" rings and "O" ring retainers with multipurpose grease.

2) Lubricate shift shaft bores in cover and install each shift lever shaft, followed by "O" ring and "O" ring retainer. Install operating levers and retaining nuts. Make sure 3rd/Overdrive operating lever points downward.

Installation

1) Rotate each shaft fork bore to Neutral (straight up). Install 3rd/Overdrive shift fork into bore under both interlock levers. Set both synchronizer sleeves in Neutral. Place 1st/2nd shift fork in groove of 1st/2nd synchronizer sleeve.

2) Slide reverse idler gear to Neutral. Place transmission on right side. Position gearshift housing gasket on case using grease to retain gasket. Install reverse detent ball and spring into bore in side of case.

3) Lower shift housing into place. Guide 3rd/Overdrive shift fork into 3rd/Overdrive synchronizer groove. Place shaft of 1st/2nd shift fork into bore of 1st/2nd shift lever. Hold reverse interlock link against 1st/2nd shift lever to provide clearance while cover is lowered.

4) Using screwdriver, raise interlock lever against spring tension to allow 1st/2nd shift fork shaft to slip under levers. Ensure that reverse detent spring is positioned in cover bore. Cover should seat against case gasket.

5) Install housing bolts finger tight and shift transmission through all gears to ensure proper operation. Grease reverse shaft. Install operating lever and retaining nut. Shift transmission into each gear to check for correct shift travel and smooth action.

NOTE: Eight shift housing bolts are shoulder bolts for locating shift mechanism. One bolt has longer shoulder and acts as locating dowel into case in center rear hole of flange. Two bolts at lower rear of cover are standard.

EXTENSION HOUSING YOKE SEAL

Removal

Place drain pan under seal. Mark propeller shaft for reassembly and remove propeller shaft. Remove oil seal from housing using seal remover or screwdriver.

Installation

Drive new seal into opening of extension housing with Seal Installer (C-3972 on Chrysler Corp. models; J-21426 on General Motors models). Install propeller shaft, aligning marks made at removal. Check transmission fluid level.

REMOVAL & INSTALLATION

TRANSMISSION

See appropriate MANUAL TRANSMISSION REMOVAL article in DOMESTIC GENERAL SERVICING section.

TRANSMISSION DISASSEMBLY

1) Remove speedometer pinion and adapter from extension housing. Remove bolts attaching extension housing to transmission case. Rotate extension housing on output shaft to expose rear of countershaft. Install 1 extension housing bolt to hold extension housing in this position.

2) With center punch or drill, make hole in countershaft expansion plug at front of case. Working through hole, drive countershaft forward and remove Woodruff key. Push countershaft forward until expansion plug is driven out of case.

3) Using Arbor Adapter (C-3938 on Chrysler Corp. models; J-29793 on General Motors models), push countershaft out rear of case. Lower countershaft gear to bottom of case. Rotate extension housing back to normal position. Remove drive pinion bearing retainer and gasket from transmission.

Manual Transmissions

NEW PROCESS A833 OVERDRIVE (Cont.)

Fig. 4: Exploded View Of A833 Overdrive Transmission

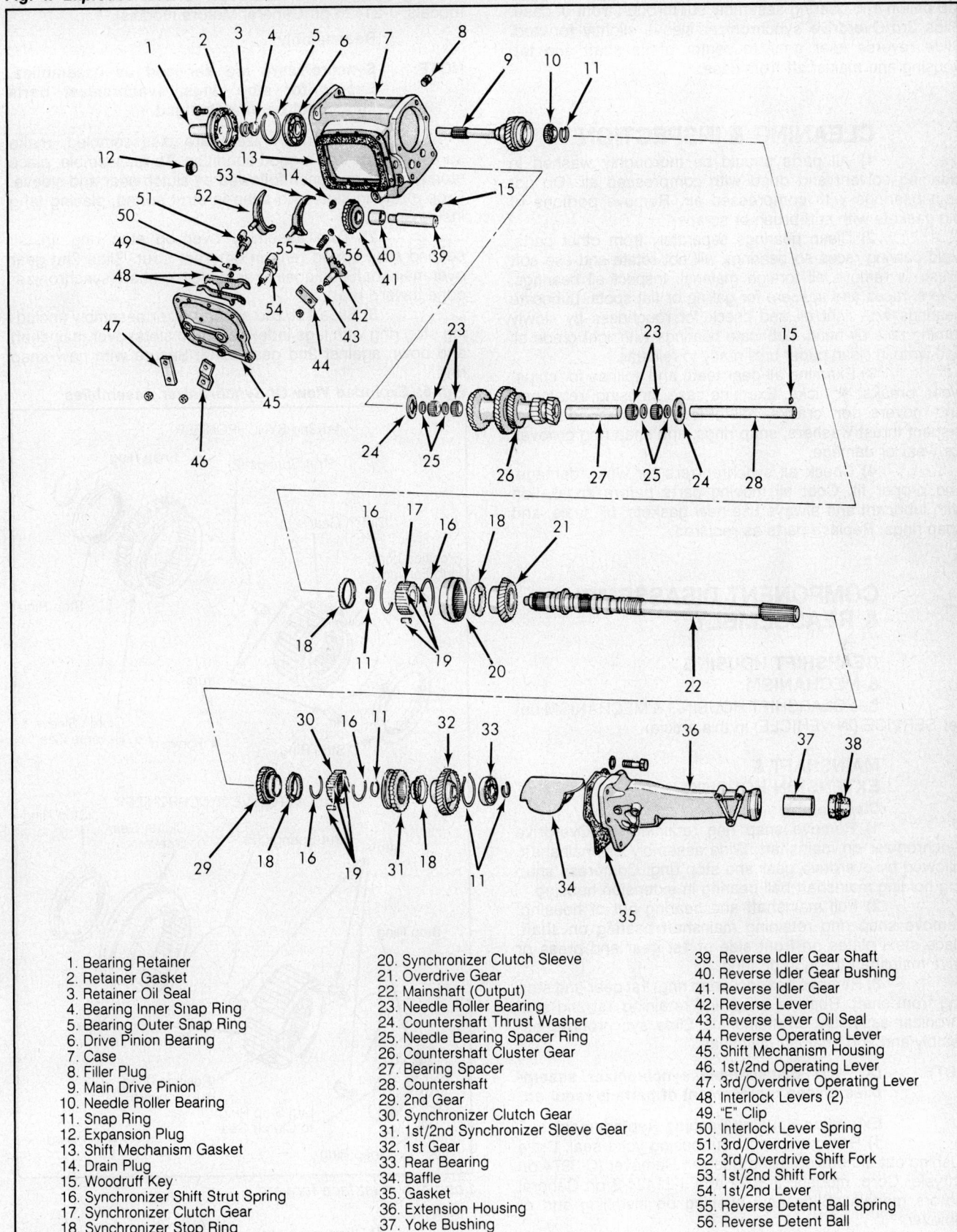

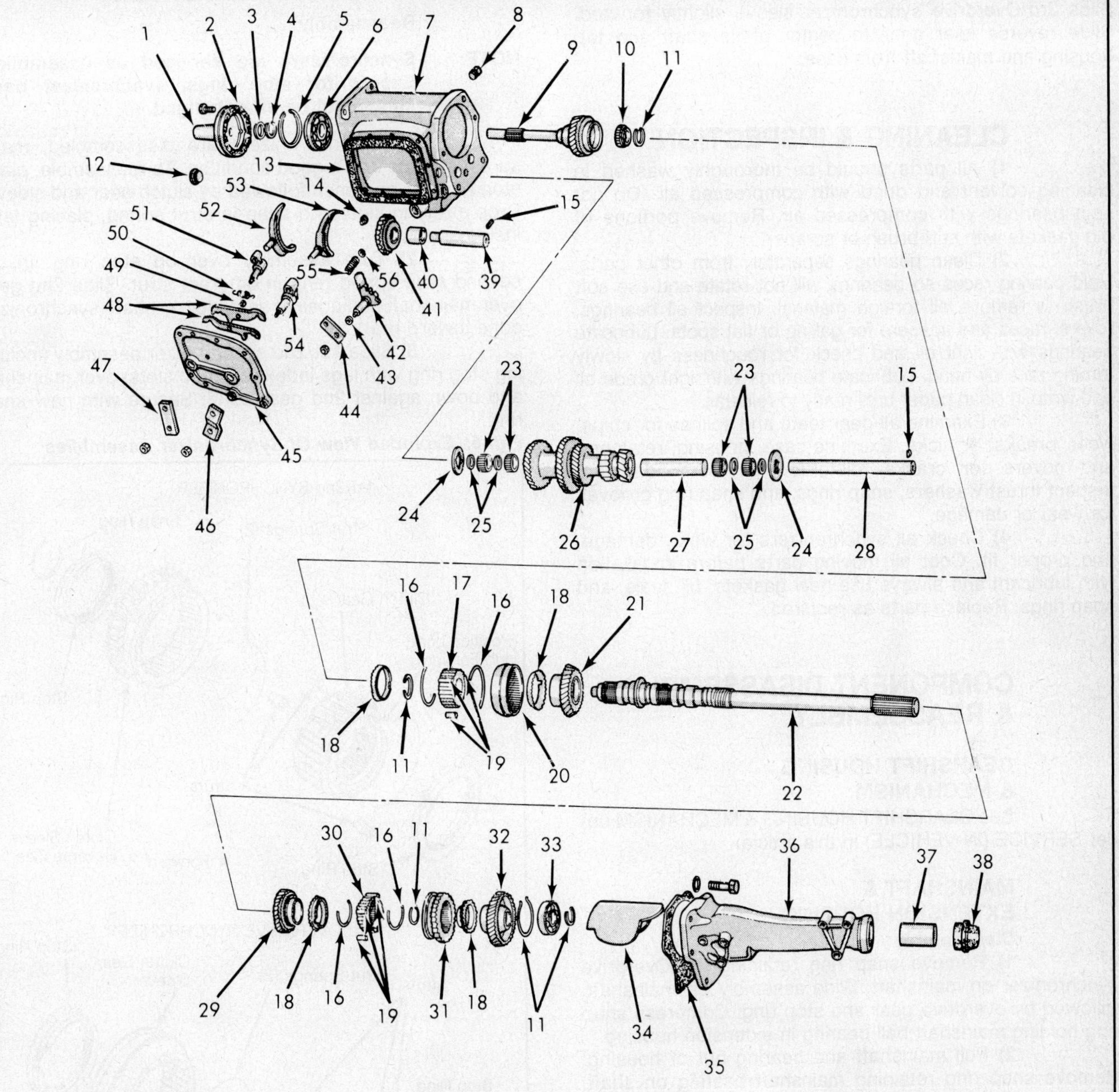

1. Bearing Retainer
2. Retainer Gasket
3. Retainer Oil Seal
4. Bearing Inner Snap Ring
5. Bearing Outer Snap Ring
6. Drive Pinion Bearing
7. Case
8. Filler Plug
9. Main Drive Pinion
10. Needle Roller Bearing
11. Snap Ring
12. Expansion Plug
13. Shift Mechanism Gasket
14. Drain Plug
15. Woodruff Key
16. Synchronizer Shift Strut Spring
17. Synchronizer Clutch Gear
18. Synchronizer Stop Ring
19. Synchronizer Shift Struts
20. Synchronizer Clutch Sleeve
21. Overdrive Gear
22. Mainshaft (Output)
23. Needle Roller Bearing
24. Countershaft Thrust Washer
25. Needle Bearing Spacer Ring
26. Countershaft Cluster Gear
27. Bearing Spacer
28. Countershaft
29. 2nd Gear
30. Synchronizer Clutch Gear
31. 1st/2nd Synchronizer Sleeve Gear
32. 1st Gear
33. Rear Bearing
34. Baffle
35. Gasket
36. Extension Housing
37. Yoke Bushing
38. Yoke Seal
39. Reverse Idler Gear Shaft
40. Reverse Idler Gear Bushing
41. Reverse Idler Gear
42. Reverse Lever
43. Reverse Lever Oil Seal
44. Reverse Operating Lever
45. Shift Mechanism Housing
46. 1st/2nd Operating Lever
47. 3rd/Overdrive Operating Lever
48. Interlock Levers (2)
49. "E" Clip
50. Interlock Lever Spring
51. 3rd/Overdrive Lever
52. 3rd/Overdrive Shift Fork
53. 1st/2nd Shift Fork
54. 1st/2nd Lever
55. Reverse Detent Ball Spring
56. Reverse Detent Ball

4) Remove seal from retainer. Using brass drift, tap pinion and bearing assembly out through front of case. Slide 3rd/Overdrive synchronizer sleeve slightly forward. Slide reverse idler gear to center of its shaft and tap housing and mainshaft from case.

CLEANING & INSPECTION

1) All parts should be thoroughly washed in cleaning solvent and dried with compressed air. Do not spin bearings with compressed air. Remove portions of old gaskets with stiff brush or scraper.

2) Clean bearings separately from other parts. Hold bearing races so bearings will not rotate and use soft brush to remove all foreign material. Inspect all bearings, rollers, races and spacers for galling or flat spots. Lubricate bearings with light oil and check for roughness by slowly turning race by hand. Lubricate bearings with light grade oil and wrap in clean paper until ready to reinstall.

3) Examine all gear teeth and splines for chips, wear, breaks, or nicks. Examine case, housing, retainers, and covers for cracks, distortion, or other damage. Inspect thrust washers, snap rings, and snap ring grooves for wear or damage.

4) Check all synchronizers for wear, damage, and proper fit. Coat all moving parts before installation with lubricant and always use new gaskets, oil seals, and snap rings. Replace parts as required.

COMPONENT DISASSEMBLY & REASSEMBLY

GEARSHIFT HOUSING & MECHANISM

See GEARSHIFT HOUSING & MECHANISM under SERVICE (IN VEHICLE) in this article.

MAINSHAFT & EXTENSION HOUSING

Disassembly

1) Remove snap ring retaining 3rd/Overdrive synchronizer on mainshaft. Slide assembly off mainshaft, followed by overdrive gear and stop ring. Compress snap ring holding mainshaft ball bearing in extension housing.

2) Pull mainshaft and bearing out of housing. Remove snap ring retaining mainshaft bearing on shaft. Place steel plates on front side of 1st gear and press or drive mainshaft through bearing.

3) Remove bearing, snap ring, 1st gear and stop ring from shaft. Remove snap ring retaining 1st/2nd synchronizer assembly on mainshaft. Slide synchronizer assembly and 2nd gear off mainshaft.

NOTE: DO NOT disassemble synchronizer assemblies unless replacement of parts is required.

Extension Housing Bushing Replacement

1) Remove extension housing yoke seal. Drive bushing out of housing using Bushing Remover (C-3974 on Chrysler Corp. models; J-8092 and J-21424-9 on General Motors models). Slide new bushing on installing end of remover.

2) Align oil hole in bushing with oil slot in housing and drive bushing into place. Drive new oil seal into housing using Seal Installer (C-3972 on Chrysler Corp. models; J-21426 on General Motors models).

Reassembly

NOTE: Synchronizers are serviced as assemblies. Except for stop rings, synchronizer parts should not be interchanged.

1) If synchronizers are disassembled, make sure that parts are in good condition. To reassemble, place stop ring flat on bench followed by clutch gear and sleeve. Drop struts in slots and snap in strut spring, placing tang inside one strut.

2) Turn assembly over on stop ring. Install second strut spring tang in different strut. Slide 2nd gear over mainshaft and against shoulder on shaft (synchronizer cone toward rear).

3) Slide 1st/2nd synchronizer assembly (including stop ring with lugs indexed in hub slots) over mainshaft and down against 2nd gear cone. Secure with new snap ring.

Fig. 5: Exploded View Of Synchronizer Assemblies

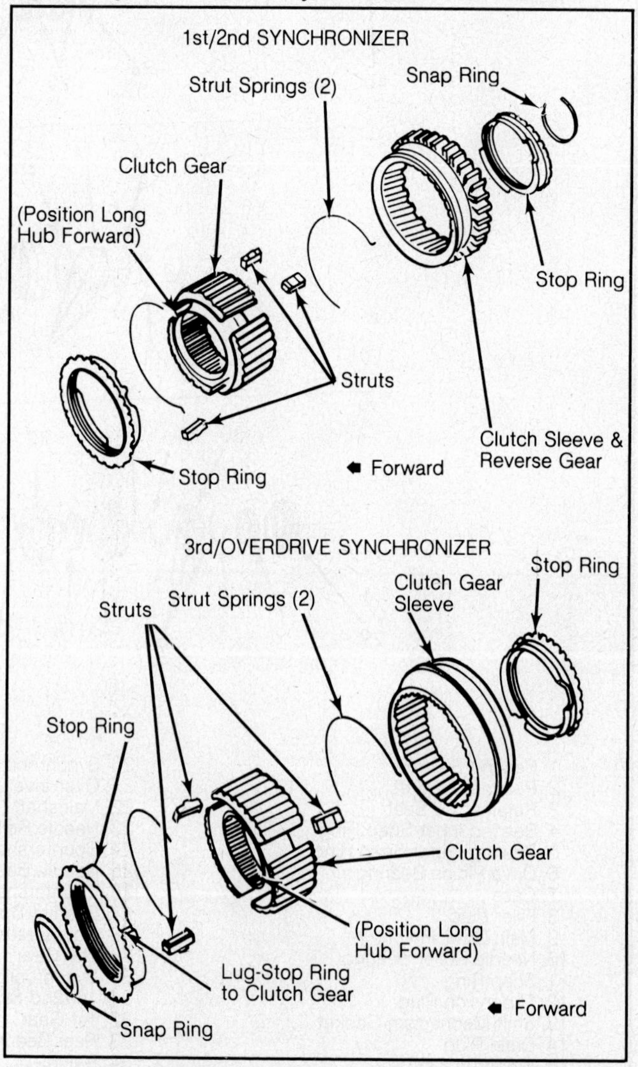

Long hub must face forward.

4) Slide next stop ring over shaft and index lugs into clutch hub slots. Slide 1st gear into position over mainshaft, against clutch sleeve gear. Install mainshaft bearing retaining ring and mainshaft rear bearing.

5) Using arbor and driving tool, press bearing into position. Install new snap ring on shaft to secure bearing. Snap ring is selective fit for minimum end play.

6) Install partially assembled mainshaft into extension housing far enough to engage bearing retaining ring in slot in housing. Compress ring with pliers so that mainshaft ball bearing can bottom against thrust shoulder in housing. Release ring and ensure that it is completely seated in groove in housing.

7) Slide overdrive gear over mainshaft with synchronizer cone toward front. Install stop ring. Install 3rd/Overdrive synchronizer assembly on mainshaft with shift fork slot toward rear.

8) Ensure that stop ring is indexed with shift struts. Install retaining ring. Grease front stop ring and install on synchronizer, indexing ring lugs with shift struts.

DRIVE PINION & COUNTERSHAFT GEAR

Disassembly

1) Remove pinion bearing inner snap ring. Using arbor press, remove ball bearing from pinion. Remove snap ring and 16 bearing rollers from cavity in pinion. Remove countershaft gear from bottom of case.

2) Remove arbor adapter. Remove thrust washers, spacers and 76 needle bearings from center of countershaft gear.

Reassembly

1) Coat inner bore of countershaft gear with light film of grease. Install roller bearing spacer with arbor into gear. Center spacer and arbor in gear. Coat needle bearings with grease. At each end of gear, install 19 rollers, followed by spacer ring, then 19 more roller bearings and another spacer ring.

2) Coat thrust washers with grease. Install thrust washers over arbor with tang side toward case boss. Place countershaft assembly on bottom of case, making sure thrust washers stay in place.

Fig. 6: Assembled View of Drive Pinion

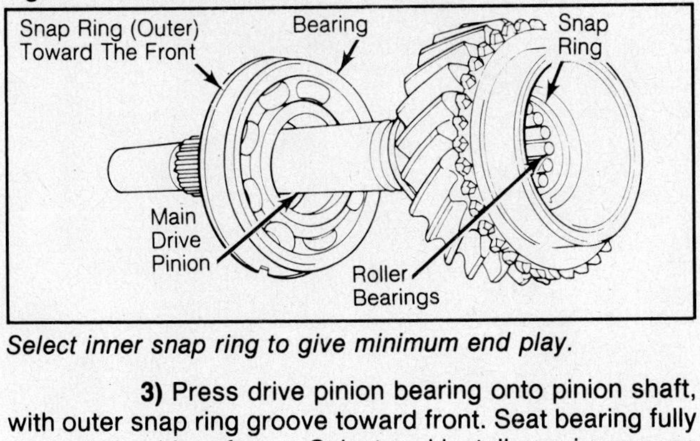

Select inner snap ring to give minimum end play.

3) Press drive pinion bearing onto pinion shaft, with outer snap ring groove toward front. Seat bearing fully against shoulder of gear. Select and install new inner snap ring on shaft to retain bearing and give minimum end play. Be sure snap ring is fully seated.

4) Place pinion shaft in soft-jawed vise and install 16 bearing rollers in cavity of shaft. Coat rollers with grease and install retaining snap ring. Using Seal Installer (C-3789 on Chrysler Corp. models; J23096 on General Motors models), drive new oil seal into gear retainer bore until installer bottoms out.

REVERSE GEAR, LEVER & FORK

Disassembly

1) Remove reverse idler gear shaft using 3/8" X 3 1/2" bolt with free spinning nut and 7/16" deep socket. Place bolt and socket in case with socket against end of shaft and head of bolt against case. Press shaft out of case using nut to extend tool. Remove Woodruff key from shaft. *See Fig. 7.*

Fig. 7: Removing Reverse Idler Gear Shaft

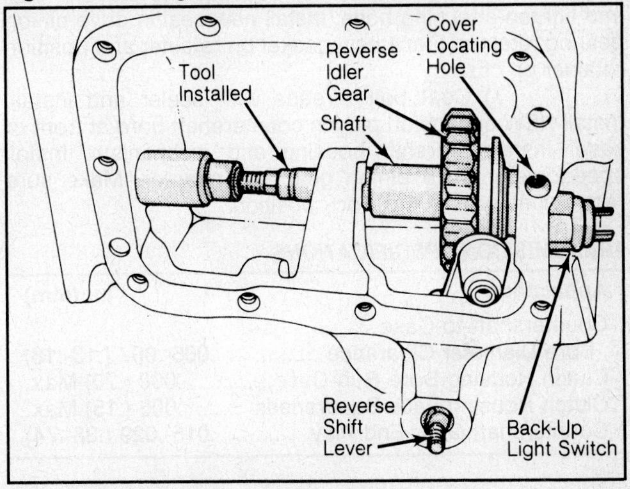

Use locally made tool to press shaft from case.

2) Remove back-up light switch and gasket. If oil leakage is visible around reverse gearshift lever shaft, remove burrs from shaft. Push shaft inward and remove from case. Remove "O" ring and "O" ring retainer from case bore.

Reassembly

1) Coat oil seal "O" ring and "O" ring retainer with multipurpose grease. Install reverse shift lever in case bore followed by "O" ring and "O" ring retainer.

2) Place reverse idler gear shaft in end of case. Drive shaft in far enough to position reverse idler gear on shaft with fork slot toward rear. Engage slot with reverse shift fork.

3) When reverse idler gear is correctly positioned, drive shaft further into case and install Woodruff key. Press shaft in until flush with end of case. Install back-up light switch and gasket.

TRANSMISSION REASSEMBLY

1) Install countershaft gear in bottom of case. Make sure thrust washers remained in place. Coat new extension housing-to-case gasket with grease. Install gasket on extension housing. Slide reverse idler gear to center of its shaft. Move 3rd/Overdrive synchronizer sleeve as far forward as possible without losing struts.

2) Insert mainshaft assembly into case, tilting it to clear idler and cluster gears. Place 3rd/Overdrive synchronizer in Neutral. Rotate extension housing on output shaft to expose rear of countershaft. Install 1 extension housing bolt to hold extension housing in inverted position.

3) Install drive pinion and bearing assembly into case. Position it in front bore. Install outer snap ring in drive pinion bearing groove. Tap lightly into position with soft-faced hammer. Snap ring should bottom on case. If not, internal parts are not in correct position.

NEW PROCESS A833 OVERDRIVE (Cont.)

4) Turn transmission upside down while holding countershaft gear assembly to prevent damage. Lower countershaft gear assembly into position (teeth meshed with drive pinion gear). Make sure thrust washers remain in position and tangs are aligned with slots in case.

5) Install countershaft into bore from rear of case and push forward until installed approximately half-way. Install Woodruff key. Push shaft forward until end is flush with rear of case face. Remove arbor tool.

6) Rotate extension housing into place. Install and tighten attaching bolts. Install new seal in drive pinion bearing retainer. Place new gasket on retainer and position retainer on case.

7) Coat bolt threads with sealer and install. Install NEW expansion plug in countershaft bore at front of case. Install gearshift housing and mechanism. Install speedometer drive pinion gear and adapter. Make sure range number is in 6 o'clock position.

TRANSMISSION SPECIFICATIONS

Application	In. (mm)
Countershaft-to-Case	
Bore Diameter Clearance	.005-.007 (.13-.18)
Clutch Housing Bore Run-Out	.008 (.20) Max.
Clutch Housing Face Squareness	.006 (.15) Max.
Countershaft Gear End Play	.015-.029 (.38-.74)

TIGHTENING SPECIFICATIONS

Application	Ft. Lbs. (N.m)
Back-Up Light Switch	15 (20)
Drain Plug	
Chrysler Corp.	25 (34)
General Motors	15 (20)
Extension Hsg.-to-Case Bolts	50 (68)
Gearshift Mount-to-Ext. Hsg. Bolts	12 (16)
Gearshift Mount-to-Plate Bolts	24 (32)
Input Bearing Retainer Bolts	30 (41)
Shift Cover Housing Bolts	15 (20)
Shift Lever Nuts	18 (24)
Transmission-to-Bellhousing Bolts	
Chrysler Corp.	50 (68)
General Motors	75 (100)

Manual Transmissions

TREMEC 4-SPEED MODEL T-176

Jeep
CJ-7, J10 Pickup,
Fleet Grand Wagoneer

IDENTIFICATION

Transmission identification tag showing Jeep part number is bolted to transmission shift control lever housing, near left rear corner.

DESCRIPTION

The Tremec model T-176 transmission is a 4-speed constant mesh unit, fully synchronized in all forward gears. Forward gears are helical cut type and speed changes are accomplished through use of blocker type synchronizer assemblies. Clutch shaft and mainshaft are supported by ball bearings in front and rear of case. All other gears are supported by needle type roller bearings.

LUBRICATION & ADJUSTMENT

See appropriate MANUAL TRANSMISSION SERVICING article in DOMESTIC GENERAL SERVICING section.

TROUBLE SHOOTING

See MANUAL TRANSMISSION TROUBLE SHOOTING article in DOMESTIC GENERAL SERVICING section.

REMOVAL & INSTALLATION

See appropriate MANUAL TRANSMISSION REMOVAL article in DOMESTIC GENERAL SERVICING section.

TRANSMISSION DISASSEMBLY

1) Remove transfer case if not already removed. Remove shift control housing, noting positions of 2 dowel-type alignment bolts for reassembly reference. Using Arbor (J-29342), remove countershaft through rear of case.

2) Remove locating ring and retaining snap ring from rear bearing. Remove rear bearing using Puller Set (J-25152). Matchmark front bearing retainer and case for reassembly reference. Remove front bearing retainer cap and gasket.

3) Remove and discard front bearing retainer cap oil seal. Remove locating ring and retaining snap ring from front bearing. Remove clutch shaft and front bearing using puller set and Adapter (J-29344). *See Fig. 1.*

4) Remove 4th gear synchronizer ring from clutch shaft or synchronizer hub. Remove mainshaft pilot bearing rollers from clutch shaft. Remove sliding gear from idler gear noting position for reassembly. *See Fig. 2.* Remove mainshaft and geartrain assembly.

5) Move 3rd-4th synchronizer sleeve rearward to Neutral position. Tilt rear end of mainshaft downward and lift front end of mainshaft upward and out of case. Remove countershaft gear, arbor tool, thrust washers and any needle bearing rollers that may have fallen into case.

Fig. 1: Removing Clutch Shaft and Front Bearing

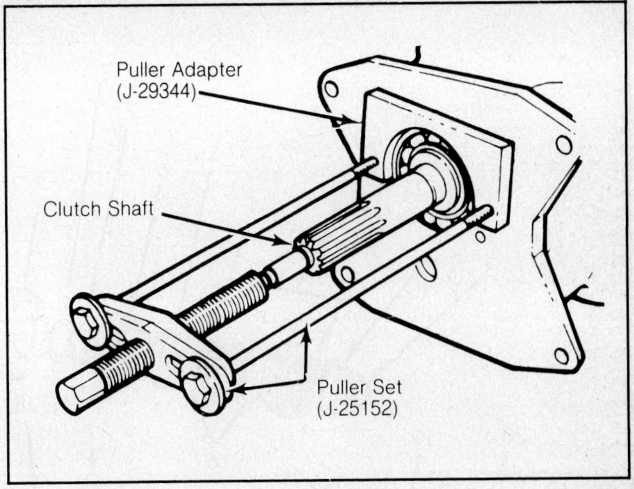

Fig. 2: Clutch Shaft and Bearing Assembly

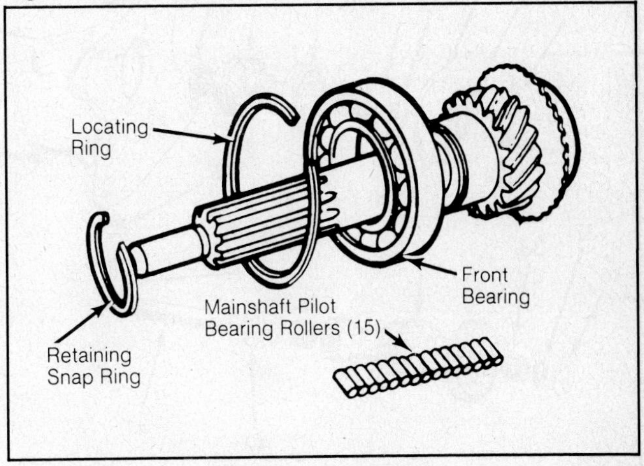

6) Tap reverse idler shaft out rear of case. Remove reverse idler gear and thrust washers from case. Remove needle bearings and bearing retainers from gear assembly.

7) Remove sliding gear from idler gear noting position for reassembly. Remove arbor from countershaft gear and remove needle bearings and bearing retainers.

CLEANING & INSPECTION

1) Wash all parts in cleaning solvent. Dry all parts, except bearings, with compressed air. Let bearings air dry in clean shop cloth. Inspect transmission case for cracks, damaged bearing bores or damaged threads. Remove all small nicks or burrs from front or rear of case.

2) Clean needle and clutch shaft roller bearings by wrapping in clean cloth and submerging cloth in solvent, or place them in a shallow parts cleaning tray and cover with solvent.

3) Check ball bearings for roughness by slowly turning race by hand. Inspect needle bearing rollers, shafts and washers for wear or damage. Check all other parts for wear, damage, chipped or broken teeth. Replace parts as necessary.

TREMEC 4-SPEED MODEL T-176 (Cont.)

Fig. 3: Exploded View of Tremec 4-Speed Model T-176 Transmission

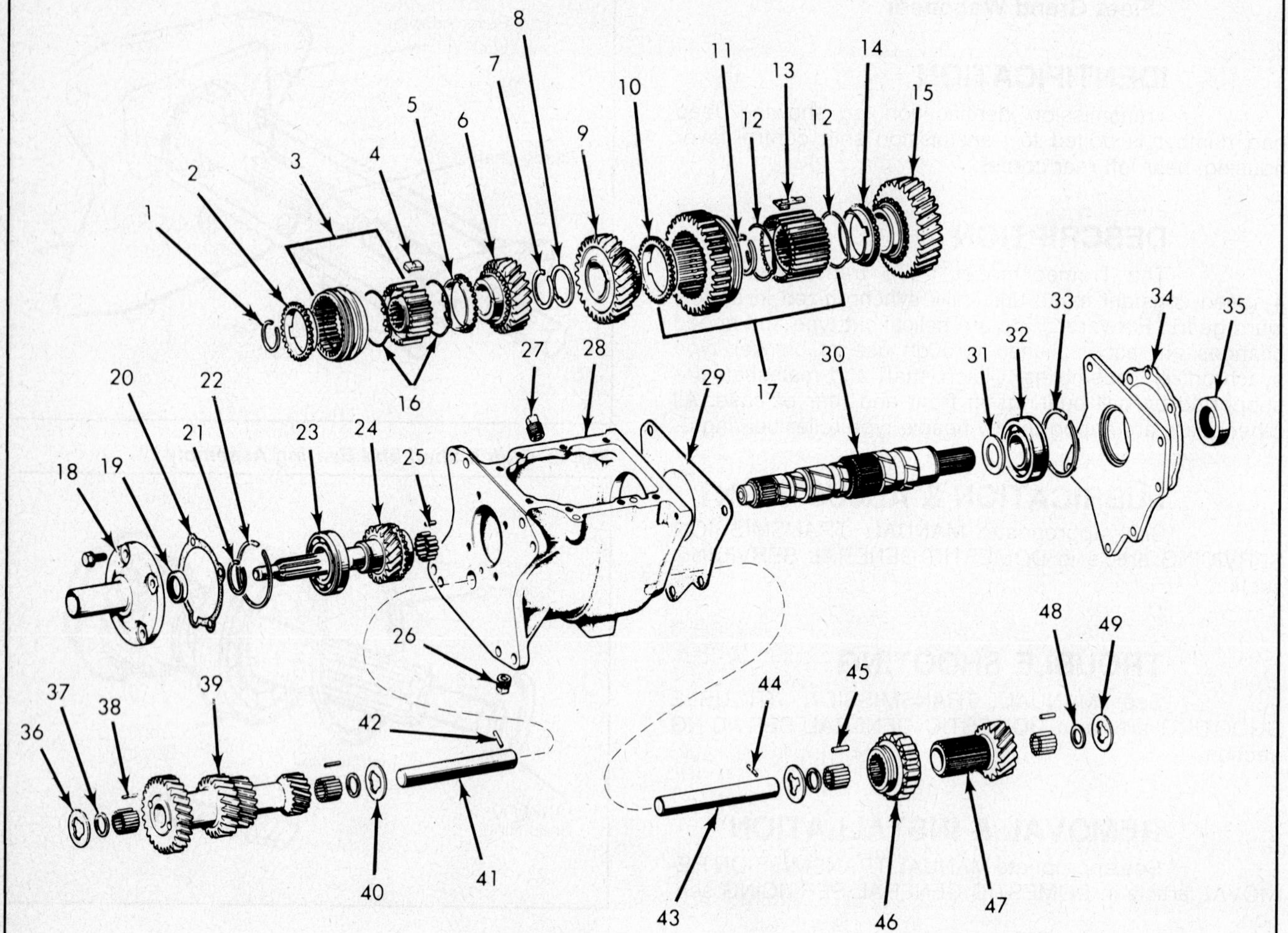

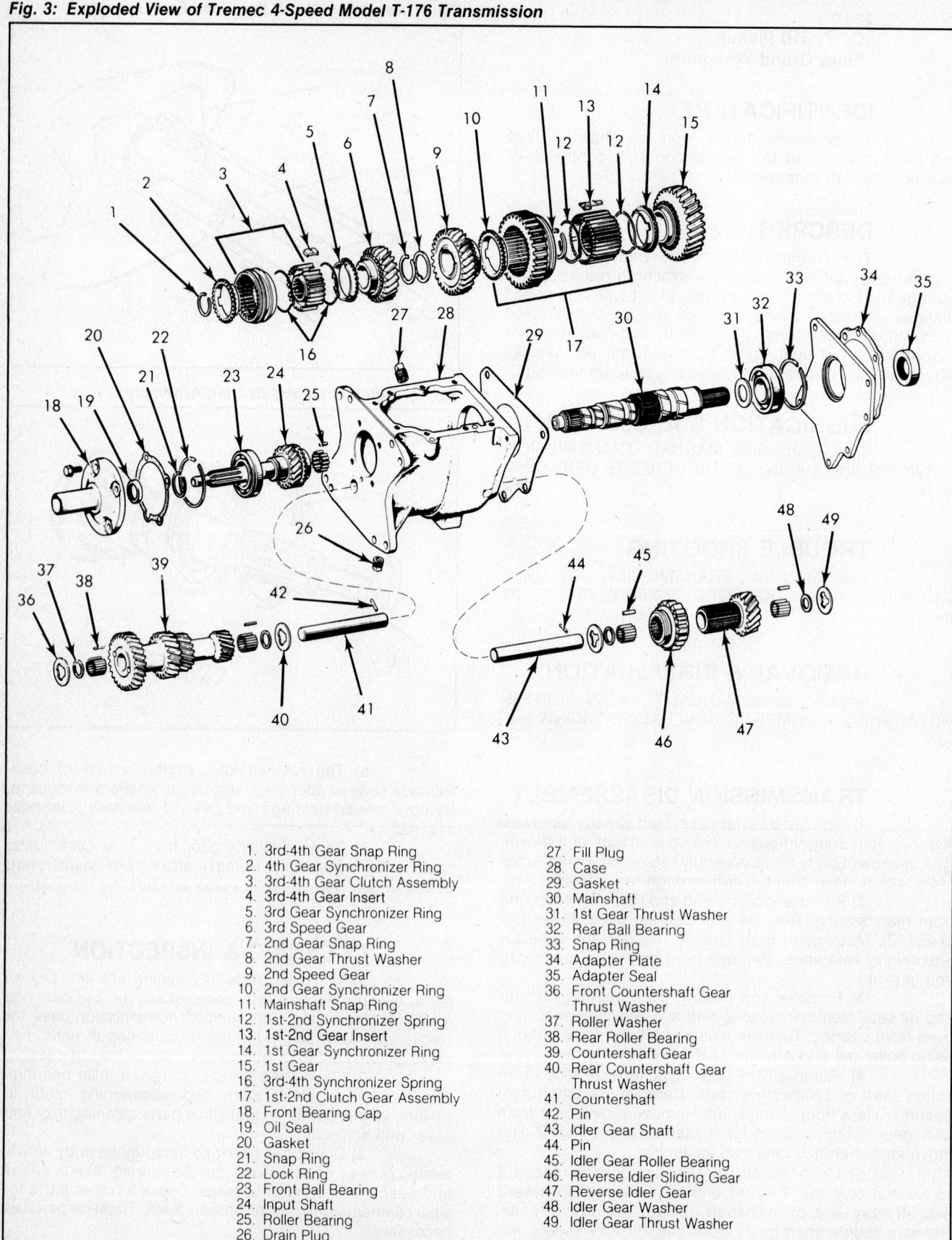

1. 3rd-4th Gear Snap Ring
2. 4th Gear Synchronizer Ring
3. 3rd-4th Gear Clutch Assembly
4. 3rd-4th Gear Insert
5. 3rd Gear Synchronizer Ring
6. 3rd Speed Gear
7. 2nd Gear Snap Ring
8. 2nd Gear Thrust Washer
9. 2nd Speed Gear
10. 2nd Gear Synchronizer Ring
11. Mainshaft Snap Ring
12. 1st-2nd Synchronizer Spring
13. 1st-2nd Gear Insert
14. 1st Gear Synchronizer Ring
15. 1st Gear
16. 3rd-4th Synchronizer Spring
17. 1st-2nd Clutch Gear Assembly
18. Front Bearing Cap
19. Oil Seal
20. Gasket
21. Snap Ring
22. Lock Ring
23. Front Ball Bearing
24. Input Shaft
25. Roller Bearing
26. Drain Plug
27. Fill Plug
28. Case
29. Gasket
30. Mainshaft
31. 1st Gear Thrust Washer
32. Rear Ball Bearing
33. Snap Ring
34. Adapter Plate
35. Adapter Seal
36. Front Countershaft Gear Thrust Washer
37. Roller Washer
38. Rear Roller Bearing
39. Countershaft Gear
40. Rear Countershaft Gear Thrust Washer
41. Countershaft
42. Pin
43. Idler Gear Shaft
44. Pin
45. Idler Gear Roller Bearing
46. Reverse Idler Sliding Gear
47. Reverse Idler Gear
48. Idler Gear Washer
49. Idler Gear Thrust Washer

Manual Transmissions

TREMEC 4-SPEED MODEL T-176 (Cont.)

COMPONENT DISASSEMBLY & REASSEMBLY

MAINSHAFT ASSEMBLY

Disassembly

1) Remove 3rd-4th synchronizer snap ring from front of mainshaft and slide 3rd-4th synchronizer assembly from shaft. Slide hub out of sleeve. Remove insert springs, 3 inserts and blocking ring, noting positions for reassembly reference.

2) Remove 3rd gear from mainshaft. Remove snap ring holding 2nd gear. Remove 2nd gear and blocking ring from shaft. Remove tabbed thrust washer from mainshaft. Remove snap ring retaining 1st-2nd synchronizer hub.

3) Remove hub, reverse gear and sleeve as an assembly. Matchmark hub and sleeve for reassembly. Remove insert springs, 3 inserts, sleeve and gear from hub. Remove 1st gear thrust washer from rear of shaft and remove 1st gear and blocking ring.

Reassembly

1) Lubricate mainshaft, synchronizer assemblies and gear bores with transmission lubricant. Align matchmarks and assemble 1st-2nd synchronizer hub and reverse gear and sleeve. Install gear and sleeve on hub and place assembly on flat surface.

2) Place inserts into hub slots. Install insert spring with loop end in one insert. Compress spring ends and insert spring ends under lips of 2 remaining inserts. Ensure spring is under lip of each insert.

3) Turn assembly over and install 2nd spring in the same manner. Install 2nd spring so that open end faces 180° opposite the first spring. *See Fig. 4.*

Fig. 4: Exploded View of Synchronizer Assembly

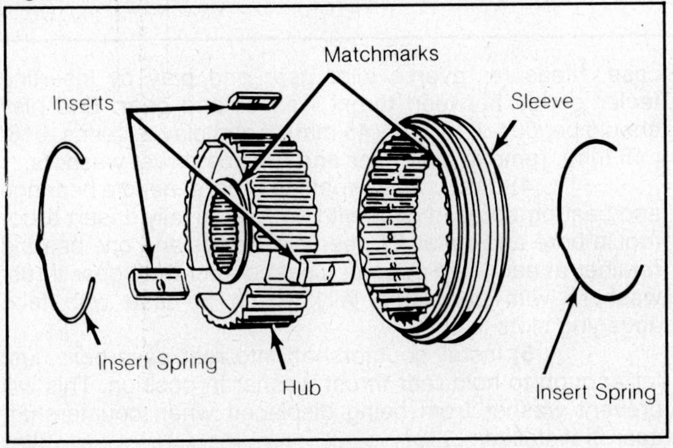

Ensure spring is under lip of each insert.

4) Install 1st-2nd synchronizer assembly, hub, reverse gear, sleeve and new snap ring on mainshaft. Install 1st gear and blocking ring on rear of mainshaft. Install first gear thrust washer. Install new tabbed thrust washer on mainshaft. Ensure washer tab is seated in mainshaft tab bore with the sharp edge facing outward.

5) Install 2nd gear and blocking ring on mainshaft and install new tabbed thrust washer and second gear snap ring. Install 3rd gear and blocking ring. Align matchmarks and assemble 3rd-4th synchronizer hub and sleeve. Place assembly on flat surface and install inserts and springs as described in steps **2)** and **3)**.

6) Install 3rd-4th synchronizer assembly and new snap ring on mainshaft. Measure end play between hub and snap ring with feeler gauge. End play should be .004-.014" (.10-.35 mm). Replace mainshaft thrust washers and snap rings if end play is excessive. *See Fig. 5.*

Fig. 5: Measuring Mainshaft End Play

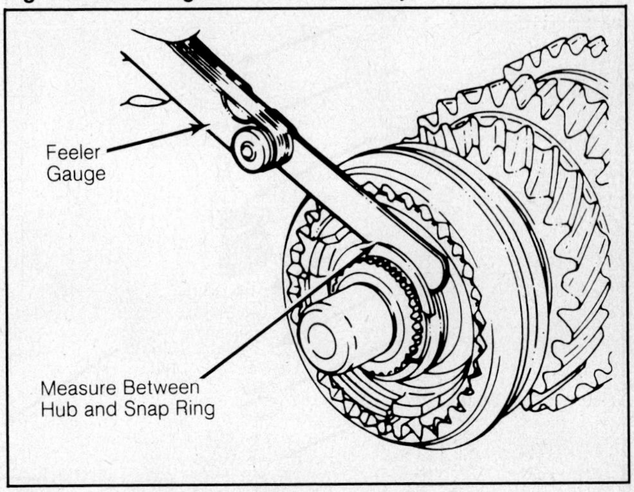

Clearance should be .004-.014" (.10-.35 mm).

SHIFT CONTROL HOUSING

Disassembly

1) Remove shift lever cover, control housing cap, retainer, shift lever and spring. *See Fig. 6.* Position transmission case cover in vise so shift forks are facing upward. Use wooden blocks to protect cover.

2) Place shift rails in Neutral. Remove shift plate attaching bolts and tabbed washers. Remove support plates, 1st-2nd shift rail, 3rd-4th shift rail, shift lug, interlock pins and reverse shift rail.

3) Remove poppet balls, shifter interlock rings, poppet springs, fulcrum pins and reverse rocker arm assembly. Remove cover from vice. Note position of components for reassembly.

Cleaning & Inspection

1) Clean all components in solvent and dry using compressed air. Inspect all compponents for wear, replacing any that are nicked, cracked, broken or excessively worn.

2) Do not discard spacer on reverse gear shift rail. This spacer is provided to prevent reverse gear overtravel and must remain in place on shift rail.

Reassembly

1) With transmission case cover in vise, install fulcrum pins in cover. Install replacement "O" ring seal on reverse rocker arm assembly. Install assembly and clip.

2) Lubricate shift rails and shift rail grooves in cover with petroleum jelly. Install poppet springs and balls (one on each spring), in transmission case cover bores.

3 Position reverse gear shift rail and fork on reverse rocker arm in cover. Be sure notch on shift rail is over reverse poppet ball and reverse rocker arm is engaged in reverse fork slot.

4) Install 3rd-4th shift rail and shift fork assembly. Be sure interlock pin is in position in shift rail. Install 1st-2nd shift rail and shift fork assembly. Be sure rail notch is over poppet ball. Install shifter interlock rings in cover and between poppet balls.

Manual Transmissions

TREMEC 4-SPEED MODEL T-176 (Cont.)

Fig. 6: Exploded View of Shift Control Housing Assembly

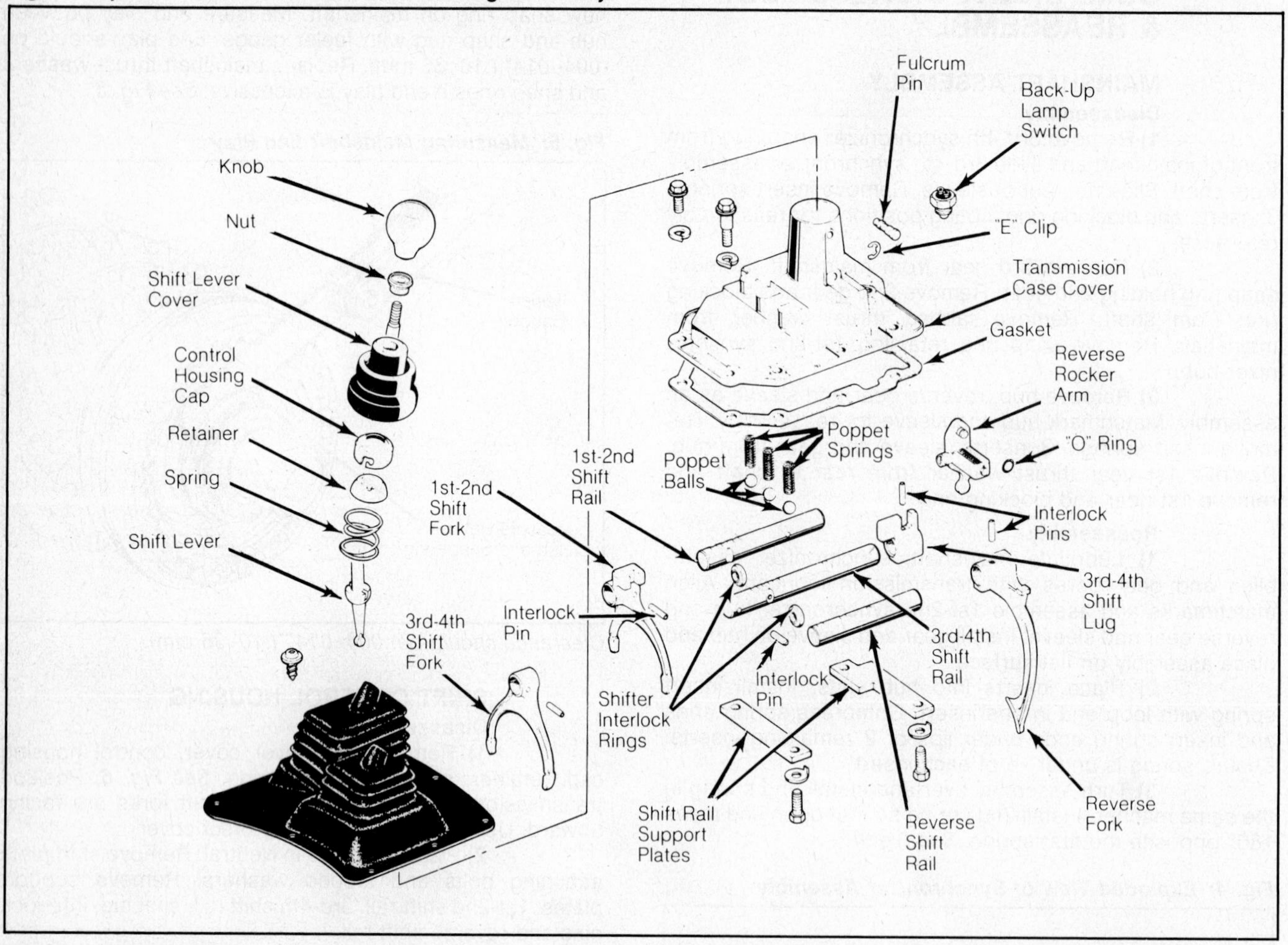

5) Press downward evenly on rails to compress poppet balls and springs. Position shift rail retaining plates on housing and secure with bolts and tabbed washers.

6) Tighten bolts to 12-15 Ft. Lbs. (16-19 N.m). Check tabbed washer position before bending over tabs. Check shift rail operation. After checking, place forks in third gear position.

7) Install shift lever, spring, spring retainer and control housing cap. Push cap downward and turn lever retainer clockwise to install and seat.

TRANSMISSION REASSEMBLY

CAUTION: Do not use chassis grease or a similar heavy grease in clutch shaft bore. Use petroleum jelly only.

1) Lubricate reverse idler gear shaft bore and sliding gear with transmission lubricant. Install sliding gear on reverse idler gear. Using Arbor (J-29394) in reverse idler gear, install 22 needle bearings and one bearing retainer at each end of gear.

2) Coat reverse idler gear thrust washers with petroleum jelly and install in case. Place gear in case with flats of washers facing mainshaft and tabs engaging slots in case. Install reverse idler gear assembly. Align gear bore, thrust washers and case bores.

3) Install reverse idler gear shaft from rear of case. Make sure shaft roll pin is aligned with counterbore in case. Measure reverse idler gear end play by inserting feeler gauge between thrust washer and gear. End play should be .004-.018" (.10-.45 mm). If end play exceeds .018" (.45 mm), remove idler gear and replace thrust washers.

4) Coat countershaft gear bore, needle bearings and bearing bores in gear with petroleum jelly. Insert arbor tool in bore and install 21 needle bearings and one bearing retainer at each end of gear. Coat countershaft gear thrust washers with petroleum jelly. Place in case with tabs engaging slots in case.

5) Install countershaft into rear case bore, just far enough to hold rear thrust washer in position. This will prevent washer from being displaced when countershaft gear is installed.

6) Install countershaft gear and align gear bore, thrust washers and case bores and install countershaft part way into case. Make sure arbor tool enters shaft bore at front of case.

7) Measure countershaft gear end play by inserting feeler gauge between thrust washer and gear. End play should be .004-.018" (.10-.45 mm). If end play exceeds .018" (.45 mm), remove gear and replace thrust washers.

8) After correct end play is obtained, push arbor tool back into countershaft gear and allow gear to remain at bottom of case. Leave countershaft in rear case bore to hold rear thrust washer in place.

9) Allow countershaft gear to lie at bottom of case to provide clearance for installation of mainshaft and

TREMEC 4-SPEED MODEL T-176 (Cont.)

clutch shaft assemblies. Leave countergear at bottom of case to provide clearance for installation of mainshaft assembly.

10) To assemble mainshaft, see MAINSHAFT ASSEMBLY (Reassembly) section of this article. Install mainshaft assembly in case. Make sure synchronizers are in neutral position. Install locating snap ring on front bearing and install front bearing part way onto clutch shaft.

11) Do not install bearing completely as the shaft will not clear the countershaft gear. Coat bearing bore in clutch shaft and mainshaft pilot roller bearings with petroleum jelly. Install 15 roller bearings in clutch shaft bearing bore.

12) Coat blocking ring surface of clutch shaft with transmission lubricant and position blocking ring on shaft. Support mainshaft assembly and insert clutch shaft through front bearing bore in case. Align and seat mainshaft pilot hub in clutch shaft roller bearings and tap front bearing and clutch shaft into case using a soft mallet.

13) Install front bearing retainer cap and hand-tighten bolts. Position rear bearing on mainshaft and install into case using Bearing Installer (J-29345). Remove tool and complete installation using soft mallet. When bearing is fully seated, install bearing retaining snap ring.

14) Remove front bearing retainer cap and seat front bearing fully on clutch shaft. Install bearing retaining snap ring. Apply sealer to front bearing retainer cap gasket and position on case. Ensure gasket notch is aligned with oil return hole in case.

15) Remove front bearing cap oil seal using a screwdriver and install replacement oil seal using Installer (J-25233). Install front bearing cap and tighten cap bolts to 12 Ft. Lbs. (16 N.m).

16) Install locating ring on rear bearing and reseat bearing if necessary. Position case on end with clutch shaft facing downward. Align countershaft gear bores with thrust washers. Install shaft from rear and tap into place being careful not to damage thrust washers.

17) Shift synchronizer sleeves through all gear positions, making sure no binding exists. If clutch shaft and mainshaft appear to bind in Neutral, check synchronizer rings for sticking on tapered portion of gears. Use a screwdriver to free any sticking blocking rings.

18) Fill transmission with 3.5 pts. (1.7L) of AMC/Jeep Manual Transmision Fluid (8983 000 000), or equivalent. Install new shift control housing gasket on case and install control housing assembly. Tighten housing bolts to specification.

TIGHTENING SPECIFICATIONS

Application	Ft. Lbs. (N.m)
Back-Up Lamp Switch	15 (20)
Detent Retainer Bolt	23 (31)
Drain & Fill Plugs	15 (20)
Front Bearing Cap Bolts	13 (18)
Rear Case-to-Front Case Bolts	23 (31)
Shift Control Housing	13 (18)
Shift Housing-to-Transmission Case Bolts	13 (18)
Support Plate Bolts	18 (24)
Transfer Case-to-Transmission Nuts	26 (35)

SECTION 4

DOMESTIC AXLE SHAFTS & TRANSFER CASES

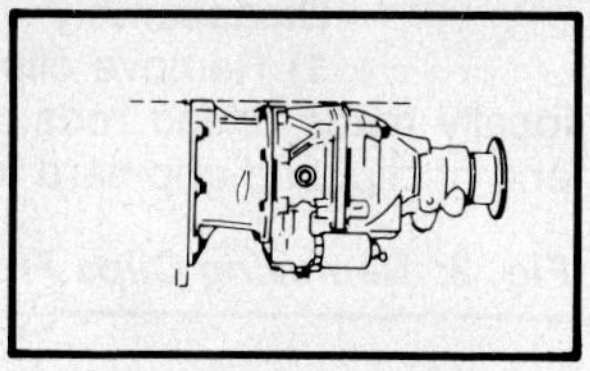

NOTE: ALSO SEE GENERAL INDEX.

Axle Shafts

AMERICAN MOTORS

1986 FWD Models Only

DESCRIPTION

Axle shafts transfer power from transaxle to driving wheels. The left axle shaft is held in the transaxle by the CV joint on the end of the axle. Right axle shaft is connected to transaxle by a spline. Each axle shaft is splined to the wheel hub and secured by a spindle nut.

SERVICE (IN VEHICLE)

HUB BEARINGS

Removal

1) Raise and support vehicle with safety stands. Remove wheel and caliper assemblies. Support caliper up out of the way. Remove spindle nut using Holder (Rou. 604-01) attached to lug nuts.

2) Remove steering arm ball joint nut. Disconnect ball joint assembly using Extractor (T.AV. 476). Remove shock absorber bottom mounting bolts. Install Puller (J-25109-01) to hub. Using slide hammer, remove hub.

NOTE: **Slide hammer must be used to remove hub to avoid damaging bearings and seals inside hubs. Do not use "knock-out type" pullers, or any puller that attaches to outer circumference of hub.**

3) Remove hub-to-rotor Torx head bolts (male hex T40). Mount hub in vise. Mount Puller (T.AR. 65) around inner bushing. Install Bolts (B.TR. 02) in puller. Alternately turn bolts to remove inner bushing from hub.

4) Remove snap ring from inside hub. Press bearing assembly out of hub. Bearings must be replaced as complete assemblies. Bearings are always damaged during removal and should not be reused.

Installation

1) Remove protection covers from each end of new bearing. Turn hub over in vise. Using cylinder with 2.5" (63 mm) outside diameter and 2.3" (59 mm) inside diameter, press in complete bearing assembly with plastic sleeve holding both inner races in position. Apply pressure on outer race only. Remove plastic sleeve from inside bearing.

2) Install snap ring against face of bearing outer race. Coat each seal lip of SNR bearings with Mobilux EP2. If Timken bearings are being installed, DO NOT lubricate seal lips. Only SNR bearings are to be lubricated.

3) Install shock absorber bottom mounting nuts to stub axle carrier, with nuts toward caliper. Install steering arm ball joint and nut. Tighten nuts and install holding tool to spindle using lug nuts. Tighten stub axle nut.

4) Install calipers. Install wheel assemblies and lower vehicle. Press brake pedal several times to push caliper piston into contact with brake pads.

AXLE SHAFTS

Removal

1) Raise and support vehicle with safety stands. Remove wheel and caliper asssemblies. Support caliper up out of the way. Remove spindle nut using Holder (Rou. 604-01) attached to lug nuts.

2) On left side, drain oil from transaxle. Remove 3 mounting bolts. Remove boot and axle shaft.

CAUTION: **During removal of left shaft, ensure that 3 rollers on CV joint are not dislodged. Tape CV joint to prevent components from falling apart.**

Fig. 1: Axle Shaft Assembly

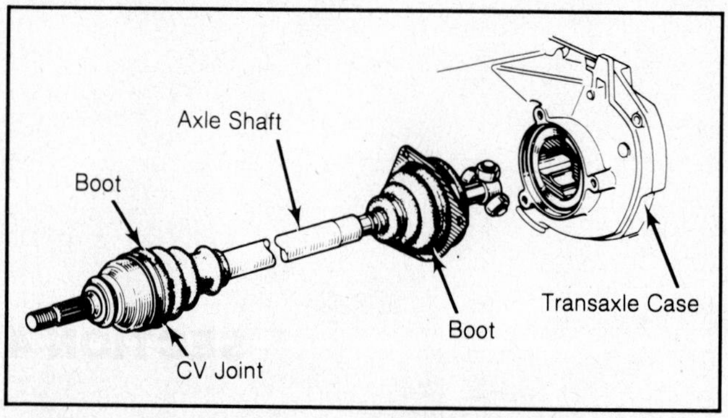

3) On right side, remove roll pins using a pin punch. On both sides, remove steering arm ball joint nut. Disconnect ball joint assembly using Extractor (T.AV. 476). Remove shock absorber bottom mounting bolts.

4) Tilt stub axle carrier. Remove axle shaft from transaxle at the same time. Install impact tool on hub. Remove axle shaft. Tilt stub axle carrier. Remove axle shaft from its sunwheel at the same time.

OUTER CV JOINT

Disassembly

1) Remove clip ring from around boot using 2 locally made drilled rods. Install the rods, one over each end of clip, and grip hard to expand clip and remove.

Fig. 2: Removing Clips From Axle Shaft Boots

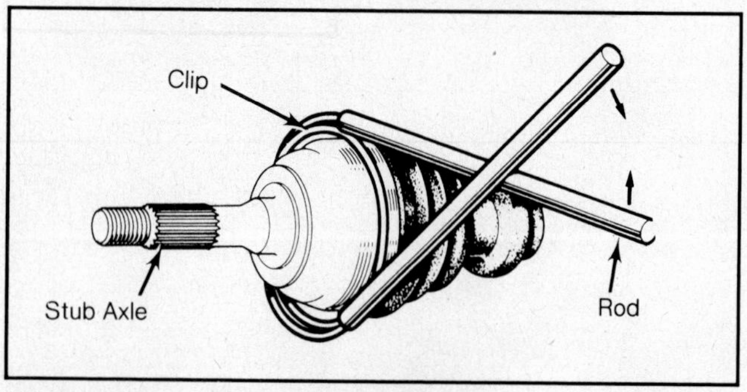

Use 2 pieces of rod to remove clips.

2) Remove as much grease from CV joint as possible. Remove bell-shaped stub axle from axle shaft by raising starplate arms one by one (DO NOT twist starplate arms).

Reassembly

1) Place and hold axle shaft at a convenient angle in a vise equipped with soft jaws. Install Expander (T.AV. 537-02) on end of yoke. Lubricate the whole expander, inside the boots, and the neck in particular.

2) Place a thumb over bottom hole of boot and pour some oil into boot and spread it around inside. Slip boot over end of expander. Wrap a piece of clean rag around one hand and grip boot so that the first fold will stretch when slid on.

AMERICAN MOTORS (Cont.)

Fig. 3: Sectional View of Axle Shaft Assembly

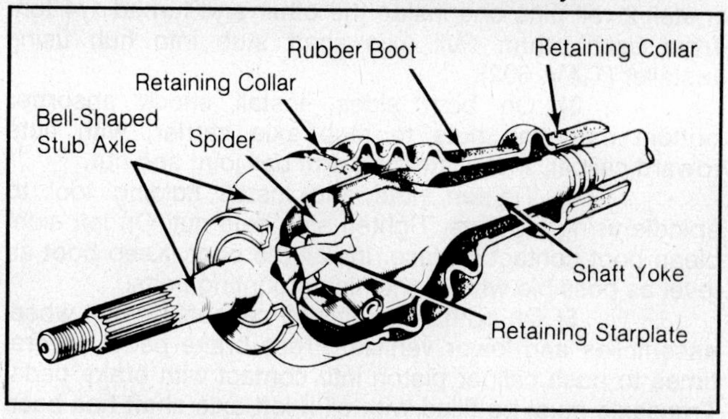

3) Firmly place expander against vise and, using one hand over the other to obtain a firm grip, pull boot down over expander. Pull boot along expander as far as possible, then let it return half-way. Repeat the above 2 or 3 times. Ensure that first fold stretches and does not "double back" on itself.

4) Lubricate stems before final positioning. Pull boot firmly and continuously up to circular portion of the tool in one motion. Install spring and thrust ball in spider. Move roller cages toward center.

5) Position retaining starplate so that each arm is centered between each spider trunnion. Insert axle shaft yoke in bell-shaped stub axle. Tilt shaft to fit 1 starplate arm into its slot, then press it in to locate it.

6) The other 2 arms may be installed easily by using a screwdriver with tip ground to fit end of arm. Make sure that each starplate arm is located in slot. Check that spider coupling moves freely by hand in all directions.

7) Distribute grease evenly between boot and bell-shaped stub axle. Position boot lips in grooves in stub axle and axle shaft. Insert a smooth round-ended piece of rod between boot and stub axle to restrict the amount of air inside. Install retaining collars over boot using the 2 fabricated rods.

INNER CV JOINT

Disassembly

1) On right side joint, remove boot retaining springs. Cut and remove boot. Remove grease and spider retaining plate.

Fig. 4: Pressing Spider From Axle Shaft

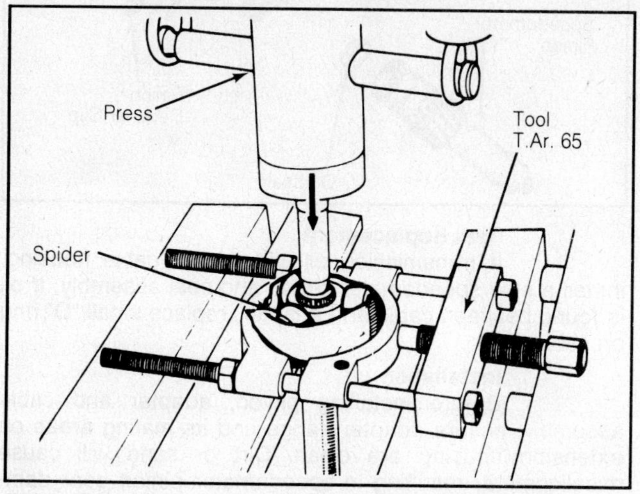

Puller (T.Ar. 65) is also used to press left axle boot.

2) On both side joints, wrap spider with tape or use plastic collar supplied with replacement spider kit to hold roller cages. Remove snap ring. Support spider with Puller (T.Ar. 65). Press spider from axle shaft.

3) To remove boot on left axle shaft, use Puller (T.Ar. 65) to press boot with bearing frorn shaft.

Reassembly

1) To install boot on left axle shaft, use Mandrel (T.Av. 944) or fabricate a pipe 5.85" (148.5 mm) long. Press boot with seal onto axle shaft until mandrel or pipe is flush with end of shaft. To install boot on right side, oil axle shaft and install retaining springs with boot onto axle shaft.

2) On both CV joints, install spider and secure with snap ring. On right side joint, spread 5 ounces (135 grams) of grease inside boot and on spider. Fabricate a shim made from .10" (2.5 mm) stock. *See Fig. 5.* Install the spider and spider retaining plate in the housing. Use shim to hold spider in place while installing retaining plate. Remove the shim. *See Fig. 6.*

Fig. 5: Diagram of Spider Installation Shim

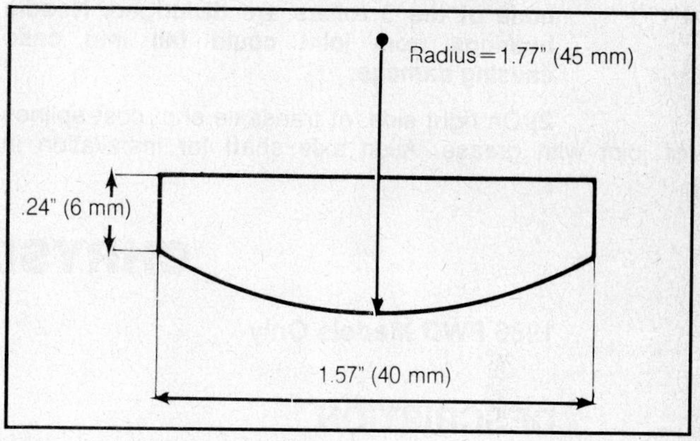

Fig. 6: Position of Installation Shim

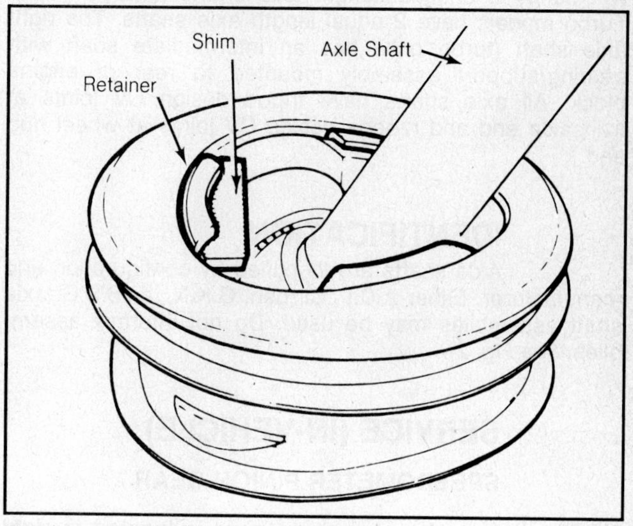

Remove shim after installing spider.

3) Position boot on the right axle shaft. Insert a small blunt rod between the boot and housing. Position the housing to obtain 6" (153.5 mm) from end of boot to large end of joint housing. *See Fig. 7.* Remove the rod. Install the boot retaining springs.

Axle Shafts

AMERICAN MOTORS (Cont.)

Fig. 7: Positioning Right Axle Boot

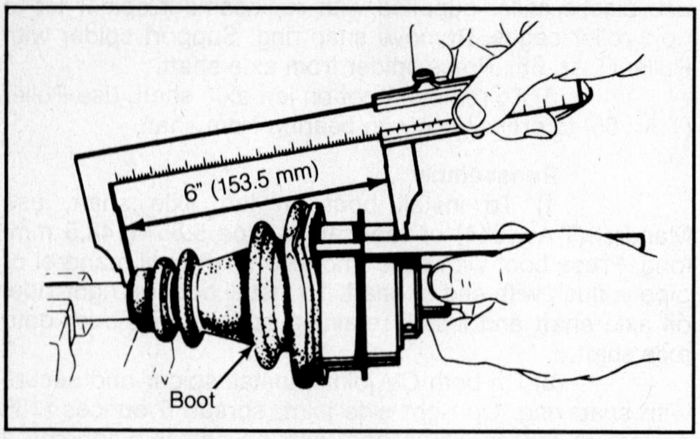

Axle Shaft Installation

1) On left side, remove tape securing CV joint components. Install axle shaft in sunwheel. Pull it into hub using Installer (T.AV. 602).

CAUTION: During installation of left shaft, be sure that none of the 3 rollers are dislodged. Needle bearings from joint could fall into case causing damage.

2) On right side, at transaxle end, coat splines of joint with grease. Align axle shaft for installation in transaxle (roll pin holes). Use 3/16" punch to align holes. Install 2 roll pins one inside the other and turned 1/4 turn from each other. Pull axle shaft stub into hub using Installer (T.AV. 602).

3) On both sides, install shock absorber bottom mounting nuts to stub axle carrier, with nuts toward caliper. Install steering arm ball joint and nut.

4) Tighten nuts and install holding tool to spindle using lug nuts. Tighten stub axle nut. On left side, clean boot contact surface. Install the boot. Keep boot as level as possible while tightening mounting bolts.

5) On both sides, install calipers. Install wheel assemblies and lower vehicle. Press brake pedal several times to push caliper piston into contact with brake pads. Transaxle must be filled with oil if left axle shaft has been removed.

TIGHTENING SPECIFICATIONS

Application	Ft. Lbs. (N.m)
Ball Joint Nut	25 (35)
Caliper Mounting Bolt	26 (36)
Inner Left Boot Retainer	17 (23)
Spindle Nut	154 (210)

CHRYSLER CORP.

1986 FWD Models Only

DESCRIPTION

Power from transaxle is transferred to driving wheels by 2 unequal length axle shafts (except turbo). Turbo models have 2 equal length axle shafts. The right axle shaft (turbo only) has an intermediate shaft with bearing/support assembly mounted to rear of engine block. All axle shafts have tripod design CV joints at transaxle end and rzeppa design CV joints at wheel hub end.

IDENTIFICATION

Axle shafts are identified by configuration and manufacturer. Either A.C.I., Citroen, G.K.N., or S.S.G. axle shaft assemblies may be used. Do not intermix assemblies. *See Fig. 2.*

SERVICE (IN-VEHICLE)

SPEEDOMETER PINION GEAR

NOTE: Speedometer pinion gear is located in right extension housing and must be removed before removing right axle shaft.

Removal

Remove bolt and washer securing speedometer pinion adapter in extension housing. With cable housing connected, carefully work adapter and pinion out of extension housing. Remove retainer and separate pinion from adapter. *See Fig. 1.*

Fig. 1: Exploded View Of Speedometer Pinion & Adapter

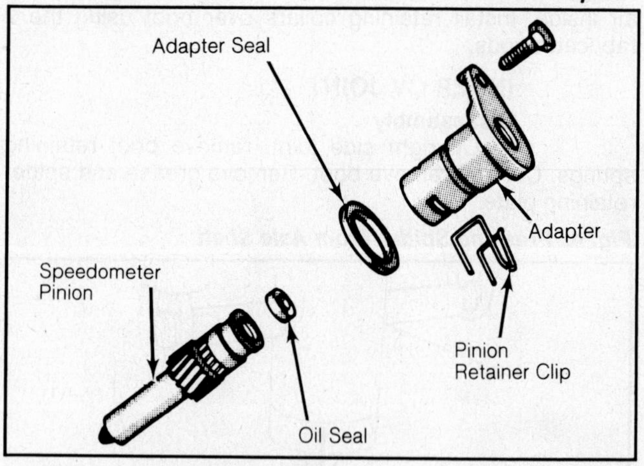

Seal Replacement

If transmission oil is found in cable housing, install a new speedometer pinion and seal assembly. If oil is found between cable and adapter, replace small "O" ring on cable.

Installation

Before installing pinion, adapter and cable assembly, ensure adapter flange and its mating areas on extension housing are clean. Dirt or sand will cause misalignment, resulting in speedometer pinion gear damage. Install components and tighten bolt.

CHRYSLER CORP. (Cont.)

Fig. 2: Axle Shaft Identification

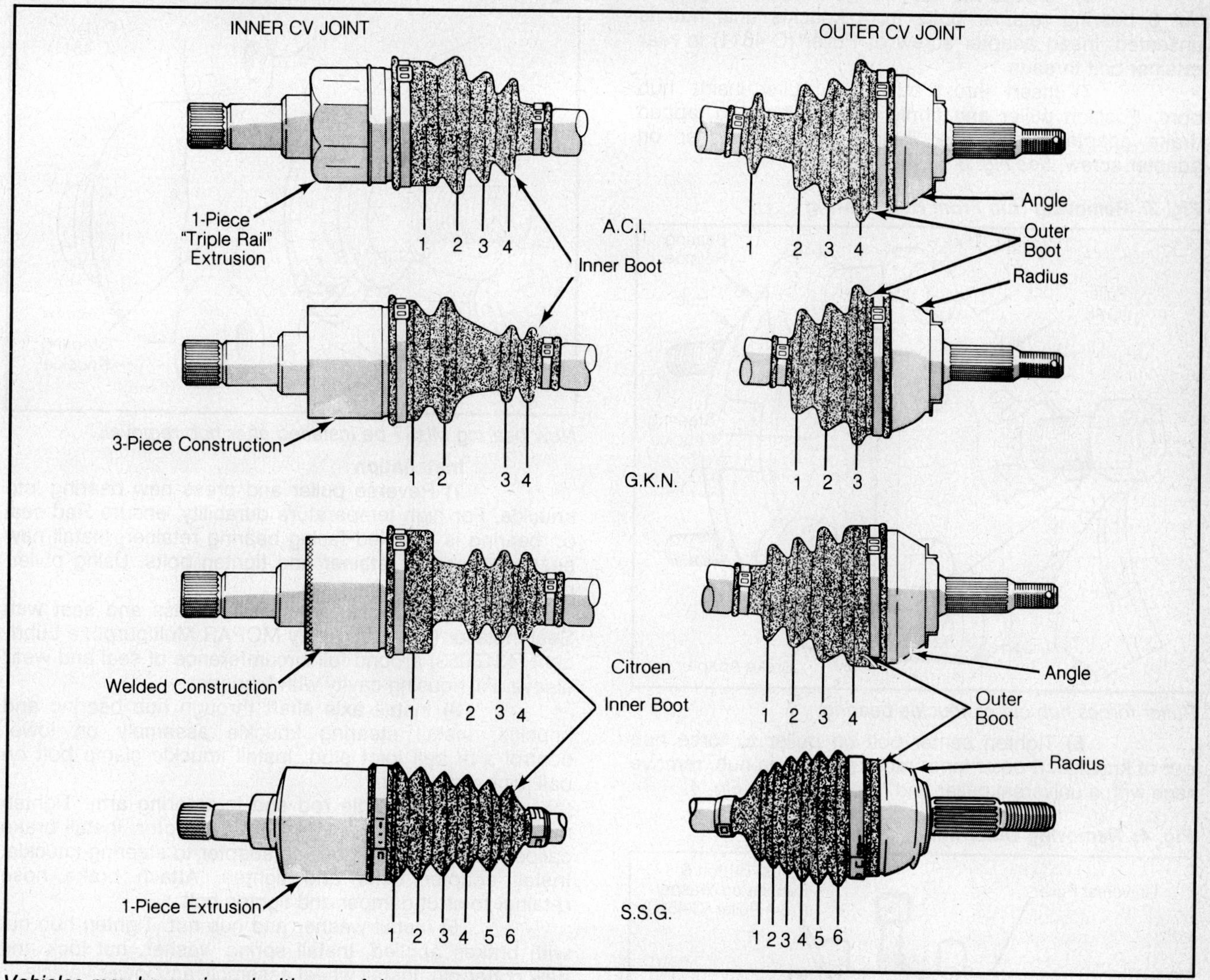

Vehicles may be equipped with any of the assemblies shown. Never intermix axle shaft assemblies.

HUB BEARINGS

NOTE: **Hub and axle shaft is splined together through knuckle hub bearing and retained by hub nut. New bearing MUST be installed whenever hub is removed.**

Removal

1) Remove cotter pin and nut lock. With vehicle on ground and brakes applied, loosen hub nut and wheel nuts. Raise and support vehicle. Remove hub nut, washer and wheel assembly.

NOTE: **Ensure splined shaft is "free" to separate from spline in hub during knuckle removal. A pulling force on shaft can separate inner CV joint. If necessary, tap lightly using soft brass punch.**

2) Remove tie rod end cotter pin and nut. Using Tie Rod Remover (C-3894-A), disconnect tie rod end from steering arm. Disconnect brake hose retainer from strut damper.

3) Remove clamp bolt securing ball joint stud to steering knuckle. Remove brake caliper adapter bolts and washers. Wire caliper up out of the way with wire. Do not allow caliper to hang by brake hose.

4) Remove brake rotor. Separate ball joint stud from steering knuckle by prying against knuckle leg and control arm. Do not damage ball joint or CV joint boots. Do not pry on or otherwise damage wear sleeve on outer CV joint. On equal length axle shafts, do not pry on or otherwise damage slinger on right inner CV joint.

NOTE: **If axle shaft must be removed, pull outward on inner joint housing while supporting outer joint housing. Do not pull on shaft. Ensure speedometer pinion gear is removed before removing right axle shaft.**

5) Separate outer CV joint splined shaft from hub by holding CV housing while moving knuckle/hub assembly away. Support axle shaft assembly at CV joint housing. Ensure speedometer pinion gear is removed before removing right axle shaft.

NOTE: **Whenever knuckle and axle shaft are separated, thoroughly clean seal and wear sleeve with solvent. Relubricate both components before reassembly.**

CHRYSLER CORP. (Cont.)

6) To separate hub from knuckle bearing, back out 3 bearing retainer bolts from knuckle until hub is unseated. Insert adapter screw of Puller (C-4811) in rear retainer bolt threads.

7) Insert thrust button of puller inside hub bore. Position puller and firmly install 2 bolts in tapped brake adapter extensions. Install nut and washer on adapter screw. *See Fig. 3.*

Fig. 3: Removing Hub From Hub Bearing

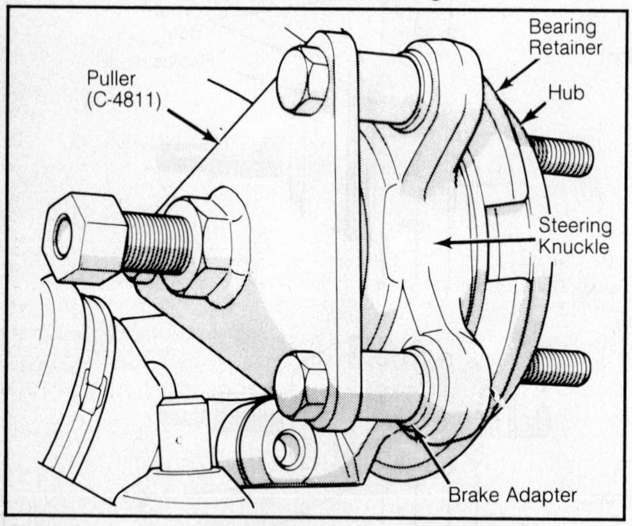

Puller forces hub out of knuckle bearing.

8) Tighten center bolt on puller to force hub out of knuckle. If outer inner race remains on hub, remove race with a universal puller and "C" clamp. *See Fig. 4.*

Fig. 4: Removing Outer Inner Race From Hub

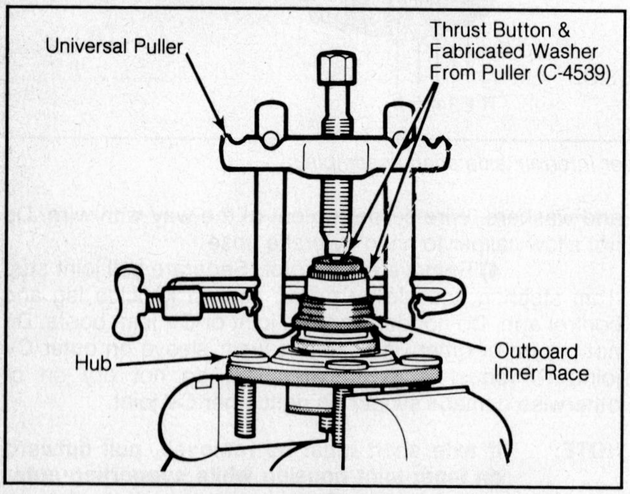

The thrust button from Puller (C-4539) and a fabricated washer must be used during race removal.

9) Remove puller and attaching bolts from steering knuckle. Remove 3 bolts and bearing retainer from knuckle. Carefully pry bearing seal from knuckle recess and clean recess.

10) Using Puller (C-4811), press bearing out of knuckle. *See Fig. 5.* Discard bearing and seal. Inspect hub/bearing interface surfaces for damage before installing new bearing. If damage has occured, replace hub.

Fig. 5: Removing Hub Bearing From Knuckle

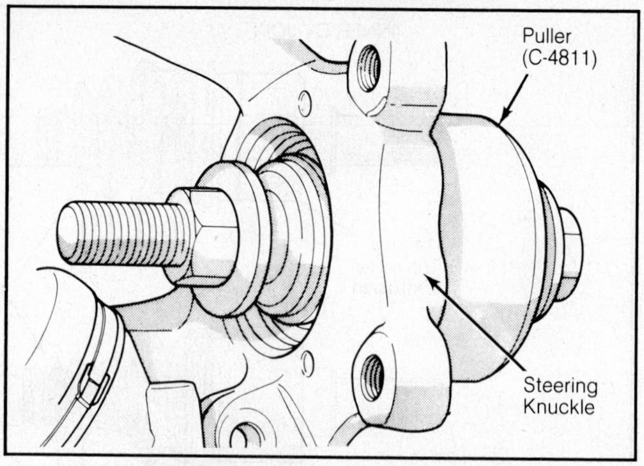

New bearing MUST be installed after hub removal.

Installation

1) Reverse puller and press new bearing into knuckle. For high temperature durability, ensure Red seal on bearing is installed facing bearing retainer. Install new seal and bearing retainer and tighten bolts. Using puller, press hub into knuckle.

2) Position new seal in recess and seat with Seal Installer (C-4698). Apply MOPAR Multipurpose Lubricant (4318063) around full circumference of seal and wear sleeve. Fill housing cavity with lubricant.

3) Install axle shaft through hub bearing and knuckle. Install steering knuckle assembly on lower control arm ball joint stud. Install knuckle clamp bolt on ball joint and tighten.

4) Install tie rod end in steering arm. Tighten nut and install cotter pin. Install brake rotor. Install brake caliper assembly and position adapter to steering knuckle. Install adapter bolts and tighten. Attach brake hose retainer to strut damper and tighten bolt.

5) Install washer and hub nut. Tighten hub nut with brakes applied. Install spring washer, nut lock and new cotter pin. Install wheel assembly and lower vehicle.

AXLE SHAFTS

NOTE: **Axle shafts are retained in differential side gears by spring-loaded inner CV joint that maintains constant engagement with transaxle. This design allows axle shaft removal without dismantling part of transaxle.**

Removal

Separate axle shaft from hub as previously outlined under HUB BEARINGS. Support shaft assembly at CV joint housings. Remove shaft by pulling outward on inner joint housing. DO NOT pull on shaft. On equal length axle shafts, do not pry on or otherwise damage slinger on right inner CV joint.

CAUTION: **When installed, axle shaft acts as a bolt, securing hub/bearing assembly. If vehicle is to be supported or moved on its wheels, install a bolt through hub to ensure hub bearing assembly cannot loosen.**

Installation

1) Thoroughly clean seal and wear sleeve with solvent and relubricate. Support outer joint housing. Hold

Axle Shafts

CHRYSLER CORP. (Cont.)

Fig. 6: Exploded View Of Axle Shaft Assembly

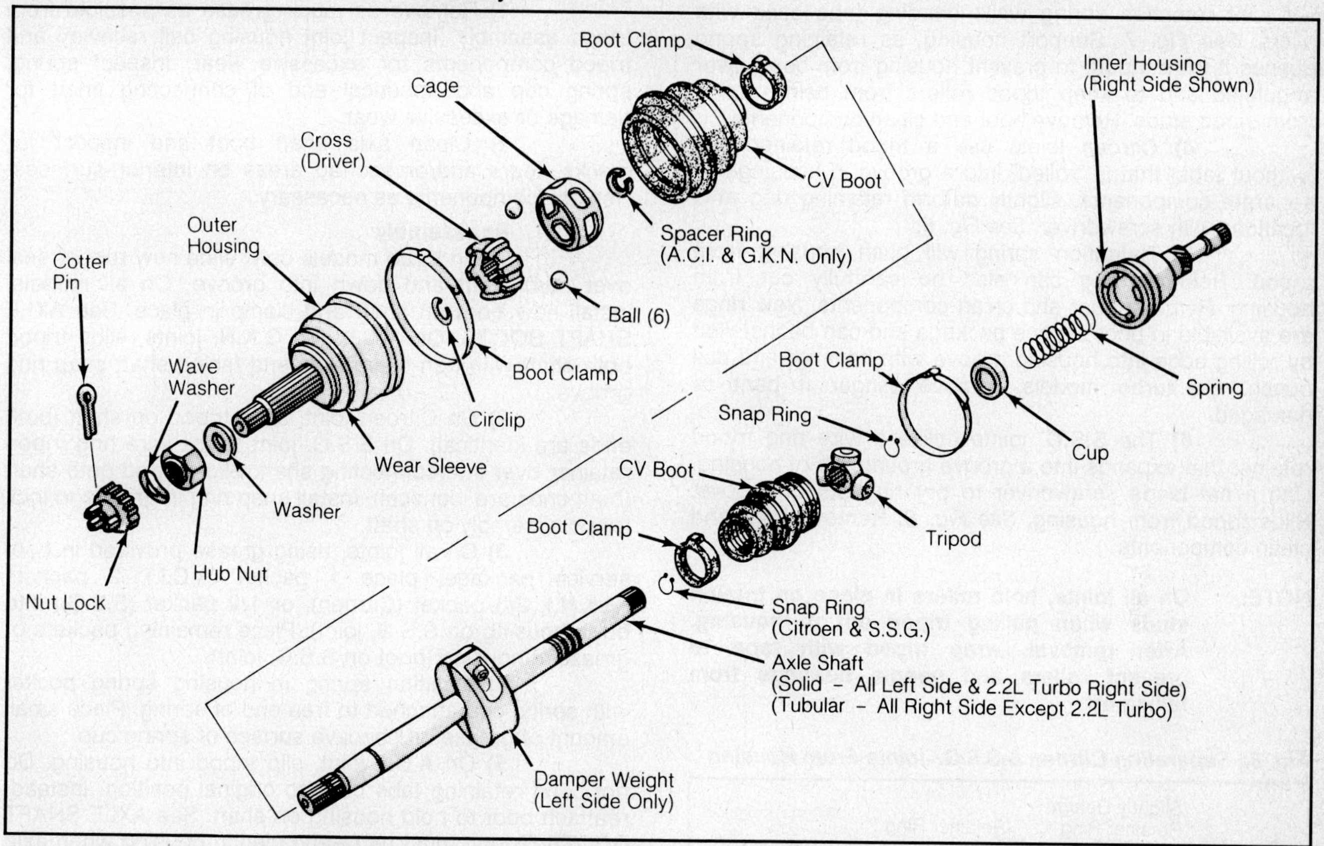

Due to different axle shaft manufacturers, components may vary between vehicles, engines and transaxles.

inner joint assembly at housing while aligning and guiding inner joint splines into transaxle or intermediate shaft assembly.

CAUTION: When installing A.C.I. axle shaft assembly, ensure tripod is engaged in housing and boot is not twisted.

2) Push knuckle/hub assembly out and install splined outer CV joint shaft into hub bearing. Reinstall knuckle assembly on ball joint stud. Install and tighten clamp bolt.

3) Install speedometer pinion gear. Check and fill differential as required. Install hub nut assembly. If after installing axle shaft assembly, inboard boot appears collapsed or deformed, vent boot by inserting round tipped, small diameter rod between boot and shaft.

4) If necessary, massage boot to remove all deformation. Do not allow dirt to enter, or grease to leave boot cavity. If a rubber clamp is used to retain boot, it need not be removed to perform venting operation. If a metal clamp is used, remove and discard clamp. After venting, install NEW clamp.

INNER CV JOINT

Disassembly

1) With axle shaft assembly removed from vehicle, identify shaft type and remove boot clamps. *See Fig. 2.* Slide boot back to gain access to tripod retention system (prevents accidental separation from CV joint housing).

2) On A.C.I. joints, tripod retaining tabs are an integral part of "staked" boot retaining collar. On G.K.N. joints, the tripod retaining tabs are an integral part of housing cover.

Fig. 7: Separating A.C.I. & G.K.N. Joints From Housing

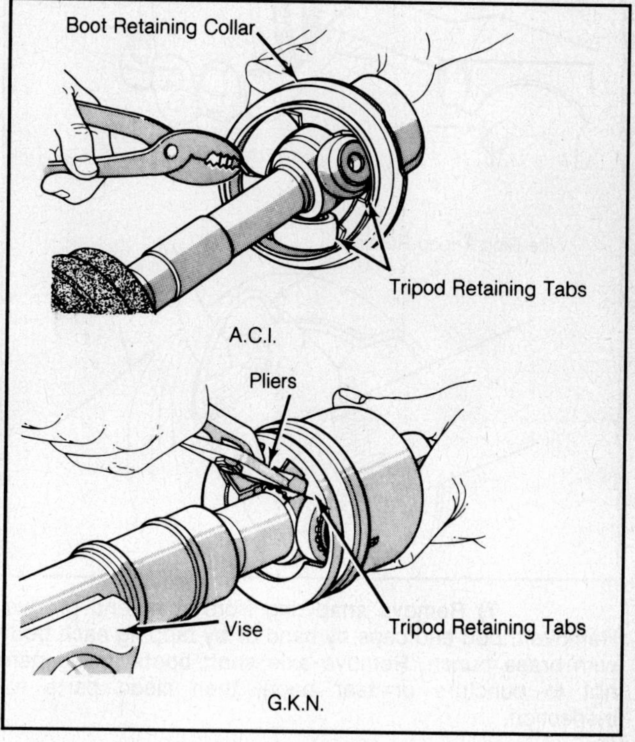

Axle Shafts

CHRYSLER CORP. (Cont.)

3) To separate components, lightly compress CV joint retention spring while bending tabs back with pliers. *See Fig. 7*. Support housing, as retaining spring pushes it from tripod, to prevent housing from being over angulated and to keep tripod rollers from being pulled from tripod studs. Remove boot and clean components.

4) Citroen joints use a tripod retainer ring (without tabs) that is "rolled" into a groove in housing. To separate components, slightly deform retaining ring at 3 locations with screwdriver. *See Fig. 8*.

5) Retention spring will push housing from tripod. Retainer ring can also be carefully cut from housing. Remove boot and clean components. New rings are available in boot service package and can be installed by rolling edge into housing groove with hammer and dull punch. On turbo models, remove slinger if bent or damaged.

6) The S.S.G. joints utilize a wire ring tripod retainer that expands into a groove around top of housing. Use a flat blade screwdriver to pry ring out of groove. Slide tripod from housing. *See Fig. 8*. Remove boot and clean components.

NOTE: **On all joints, hold rollers in place on trunion studs when pulling tripod out of housing. After removal, wrap tripod with tape to prevent rollers and needle bearings from falling off.**

Fig. 8: Separating Citroen & S.S.G. Joints From Housing

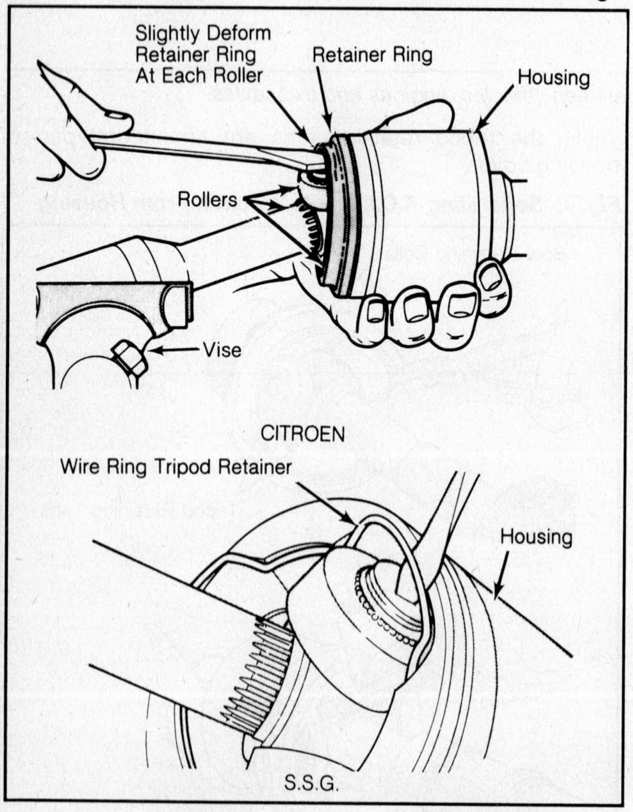

7) Remove snap ring from shaft end groove. Remove tripod end caps by hand or by tapping each body with brass punch. Remove axle shaft boots (using care not to puncture or tear boot), then clean parts for inspection.

Inspection

1) Remove as much grease as possible from tripod assembly. Inspect joint housing ball raceway and tripod components for excessive wear. Inspect spring, spring cup and spherical end of connecting shaft for damage or excessive wear.

2) Clean axle shaft boot and inspect for cracks, tears and/or scuffed areas on interior surfaces. Replace components as necessary.

Reassembly

1) On turbo models only, slide new rubber seal over stub shaft and down into groove. On all models, install new boot on shaft and clamp in place. See AXLE SHAFT BOOTS. On A.C.I. and G.K.N. joints, slide tripod onto shaft with non-chamfered end facing shaft snap ring groove.

2) On Citroen joint, slide tripod on shaft (both ends are identical). On S.S.G. joint, place wire ring tripod retainer over interconnecting shaft. Slide tripod onto shaft (both ends are identical). Install snap ring in groove to lock tripod assembly on shaft.

3) On all joints, using grease provided in boot service package, place 1 packet (A.C.I.), 2 packets (G.K.N.), 2/3 packet (Citroen), or 1/2 packet (S.S.G.) into boot (housing on S.S.G. joint). Place remaining packets of grease in housing (boot on S.S.G. joint).

4) Position spring in housing spring pocket with spring cup attached to free end of spring. Place small amount of grease on concave surface of spring cup.

5) On A.C.I. joint, slip tripod into housing. Do not bend retaining tabs back to original position. Instead, reattach boot to hold housing on shaft. See AXLE SHAFT BOOTS. Tripod must be re-engaged in housing when axle shaft is installed in vehicle.

6) On G.K.N. joint, slip tripod into housing. Bend retaining tabs down to original positions. Check ability of retaining tabs to hold tripod in housing. Install boot and attach clamp. See AXLE SHAFT BOOTS.

7) On Citroen joint, remove tape from tripod assembly. While holding rollers and needle bearings in place, slide tripod assembly into housing. Reform or install new retaining ring to secure rollers in housing.

8) If new retaining ring is installed, hold retaining collar in place with 2 "C" clamps. Do not overtighten clamps. Roll edge of ring into groove with hammer and dull punch.

9) Check ability of retaining ring to hold tripod assembly in housing. Position boot over housing and install clamp. See AXLE SHAFT BOOTS.

10) On S.S.G. joint, slip tripod assembly into housing. Install tripod wire retaining ring in position. Ensure spring is centered in housing spring pocket when tripod is installed and seated in spring cup. Ensure retaining ring will hold tripod in housing. Position boot over boot retaining groove in housing and clamp in place. See AXLE SHAFT BOOTS.

OUTER CV JOINT

Disassembly

1) Remove and discard boot clamps. Slide boot back and wipe grease away to expose joint. On S.S.G. joint, a circlip located in groove on cross locks it to axle shaft. Loosen damper weight bolts. Slide it and boot toward inner joint. Expand snap ring and slide joint off shaft.

2) On all other joints, support axle shaft in a soft-jawed vise. Using soft-faced mallet, sharply tap top of joint body to dislodge joint from internal circlip installed in groove at outer end of shaft.

3) On all joints, carefully pry wear sleeve from CV joint machined ledge if bent or damaged. Remove and discard circlip from shaft groove. Unless shaft is damaged and requires replacement, DO NOT remove heavy lock ring from inner side of A.C.I. or G.K.N. joint shafts.

4) With joint separated, proceed as follows: If outer CV joint was operating properly and grease does not appear to be contaminated, only replace boot. DO NOT disassemble any further. If outer joint is noisy or badly worn, replace entire unit, including boot.

5) Wipe off surplus grease and mark relative position of inner cross, cage and housing with spot of paint. Hold joint vertically in soft-jawed vise by clamping on splined shaft. Press down on one side of inner race to tilt cage and remove ball from opposite side.

6) If joint is tight, use hammer and brass drift to tap inner race. DO NOT hit cage. Repeat this procedure until all 6 balls are removed. If necessary, a screwdriver may be used to pry balls loose.

7) Tilt cage and inner race assembly vertically. Position 2 opposing elongated cage windows in area between ball grooves. *See Fig. 9*. Pull up and away from housing to remove cage and inner race assembly.

8) Turn inner cross (driver) 90° to cage and align 1 spherical land of race with elongated cage window. Raise land into cage window and remove inner race by swinging it out of cage.

Fig. 9: Removing Cage & Cross Assembly From Outer CV Joint Assembly

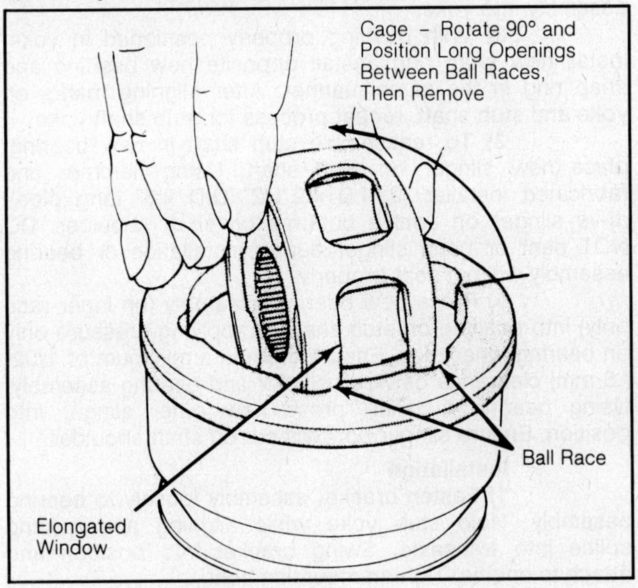

Inspection

1) Check grease for contamination. Wash all parts in solvent and dry with compressed air. Inspect housing ball races for defects, excessive wear and scoring. Check splined shaft and nut threads for damage.

2) Inspect all 6 balls for pitting, cracks, scoring and wear (dulling of surface is normal). Inspect cage for excessive wear on inside and outside spherical surfaces, heavy brinelling (surface ripples) of cage window, cracks and chipping.

3) Inspect inner race (cross) for excessive wear or scoring of ball races. If any of the preceding conditions are found, complete CV joint must be replaced. Polished areas in races (cross and housing) and on cage spheres are normal and do not indicate need for joint replacement, unless they are suspected of causing noise and/or vibration.

Fig. 10: Exploded View Of Outer CV Joint

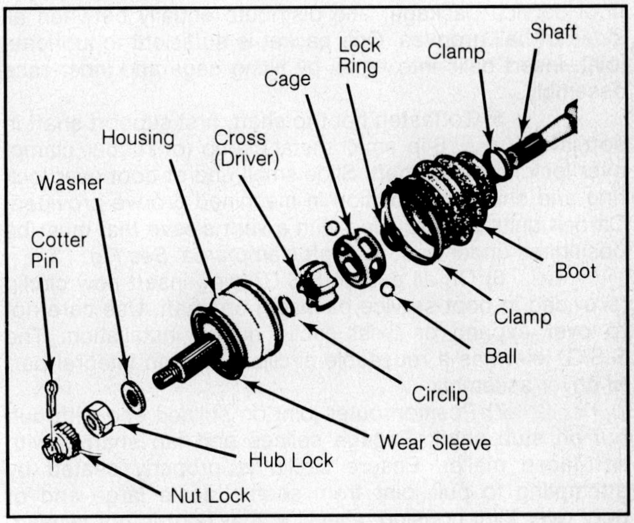

Reassembly

1) If removed, position new wear sleeve on joint housing machined ledge. Install with Driver (C-4698). Lightly oil all components before reassembling outer joint. Align parts according to paint markings made during disassembly.

2) Insert 1 inner race (cross) land into cage window and feed race into cage. Pivot cross 90° to complete cage assembly. Align opposing cage window with housing land and feed race assembly into housing. Pivot cage 90° to complete installation.

Fig. 11: Cutaway View Showing Correct Cage & Cross Installation

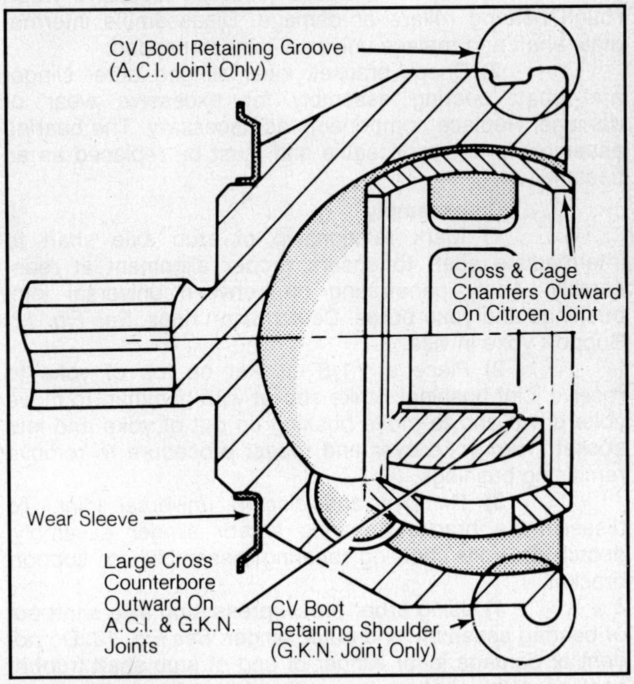

Different cage and cross installation positions are used depending on manufacturer.

3) When A.C.I. and G.K.N. joints are properly assembled, large cross counterbore should face outward from joint. On Citroen joint, cross and cage chamfers will face outward from joint. On S.S.G. joint, internal circlip in cross will face outward from housing. *See Fig. 11*.

4) Apply lubricant to ball races (from packet in boot service package) and distribute equally between all sides of ball grooves. One packet is sufficient to lubricate joint. Insert balls into races by tilting cage and inner race assembly.

5) To fasten boot to shaft, first support shaft in soft-jawed vise. Slip small metal clamp (or rubber clamp) over lock ring and shaft. Slide small end of boot over lock ring and shaft and position in machined groove provided. Citroen units are provided with a vent sleeve that must be positioned under boot-to-shaft clamp area. *See Fig. 13*.

6) On all except S.S.G. joint, insert new circlip (provided in boot service package) on shaft. Use care not to over expand or twist circlip during installation. The S.S.G. joint has a reuseable circlip that is an integral part of driver assembly.

7) Position outer joint on splined end with hub nut on stub shaft. Engage splines and tap sharply with soft-faced mallet. Ensure circlip is properly seated by attempting to pull joint from shaft. Locate large end of boot over joint housing, checking that boot is not twisted. To complete boot installation, see AXLE SHAFT BOOTS.

INTERMEDIATE SHAFT, BRACKET, BEARING & SLINGER ASSEMBLY

Removal

Remove speedometer pinion from extension housing and right axle shaft from vehicle, as previously outlined. Remove 2 bolts mounting intermediate shaft bearing assembly bracket to engine block. Remove assembly from transaxle extension by pulling outward on yoke.

Inspection

1) Inspect universal joint for excessive wear, rough bearing rollers or damage. Disassemble intermediate shaft and replace universal joint as needed.

2) Check bracket, inner slinger, outer slinger and shaft bearing assembly for excessive wear or damage. Replace components as necessary. The bearing assembly is not serviceable and must be replaced as an assembly.

Disassembly

1) Mark relationship of stub axle shaft to intermediate shaft to ensure proper alignment at reassembly. Apply penetrating oil between universal joint bushings and yoke bores. Detach snap rings. *See Fig. 12*. Support yoke in vise.

2) Place a 1 1/8" socket on top of yoke to receive joint bushing. Strike socket with hammer, to move yoke down and to move bushing up out of yoke and into socket. Turn yoke over and repeat procedure to remove remaining bushings.

3) Remove and discard universal joint. To disassemble bracket, bearing and/or slinger assembly, detach 2 bolts holding bearing assembly to support bracket.

4) Using arbor press, press stub axle shaft out of bearing assembly and outer slinger. *See Fig. 12*. Do not dent or damage inner slinger or end of stub shaft (rubber seal on right shaft mates with this surface). Excessive wear to rubber seal will result and allow moisture to enter, corroding internal splines.

5) If inner slinger is damaged, carefully press shaft out through slinger. Discard slinger.

Fig. 12: Exploded View Of Intermediate Shaft, Bracket, Bearing & Slinger Assembly

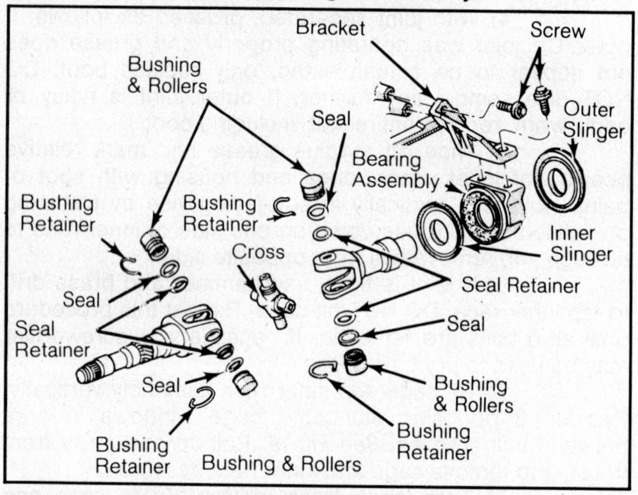

Only turbo models use intermediate shaft assembly.

Reassembly

1) Hold new joint cross in position between intermediate shaft yoke ears with one hand. Start new bushing and roller assembly into yoke bore with other hand. While holding cross in position, tap bushing assembly into yoke.

2) With bushing properly positioned in yoke, install new snap ring. Install opposite new bushing and snap ring in the same manner. After aligning marks on yoke and stub shaft, repeat process for stub shaft yoke.

3) To reassemble stub shaft in new bearing, place new slinger on stub shaft. Using hammer and fabricated installer (2" I.D. x 2 1/2" O.D. x 3" long pipe), drive slinger on until it bottoms on shaft shoulder. DO NOT dent or bend slinger during installation or bearing assembly will not seat properly.

4) Press new bearing assembly (on inner race only) into position on stub shaft by applying pressure only on bearing inner race. Ensure there is a minimum of 1/32" (.8 mm) clearance between slinger and bearing assembly. Using bearing installer, press new outer slinger into position. Ensure slinger bottoms out on shaft shoulder.

Installation

1) Fasten bracket assembly loosely to bearing assembly. Hold stub yoke while aligning and guiding spline into transaxle. Swing bracket into position and attach to engine. Tighten mounting bolts.

2) Push intermediate shaft assembly into transaxle as far as it will travel. Hold in this position and tighten bolts on bracket (bracket-to-bearing bolts). Apply liberal amount of Mopar Multipurpose Lubricant (4318063) inside spline and pilot bore, on bearing end of intermediate shaft. Install speedometer pinion and right axle shaft.

AXLE SHAFT BOOTS

Clamp Selection

1) Different boot clamping methods are used by various manufacturers. A.C.I. and G.K.N. joints general-

CHRYSLER CORP. (Cont.)

ly use metal "ladder" type clamps. Two alternate clamps used are a small rubber clamp on inner CV joint shaft and a large metal spring clamp for housing.

2) "Ladder" type clamps with 3 tangs and 3 slots are used on S.S.G. joints. Citroen joints use a 2-piece strap and buckle clamp for all attachment points. This clamp may also be used on A.C.I. and G.K.N. joints.

3) During any service procedures requiring boot handling, DO NOT puncture or tear boot by overtightening clamps, by misuse of tools or by pinching boot. Pinching can occur by rotating CV joints (especially tripod) beyond normal working angles.

CAUTION: Axle shaft boots are NOT compatable with oil, gasoline or solvents. The only acceptable cleaning agent is soap and water. After washing, boot must be thoroughly rinsed and dried before reusing.

Reassembly

1) To install new A.C.I. or G.K.N. axle shaft boot, first slide small rubber clamp onto shaft (if equipped). Slide small end of boot over shaft. On right inner CV joint boot, position small end of boot lip face in-line with mark on shaft.

2) On left inner and outer CV joint boots, position small end of boot in retaining groove. *See Fig. 13*. Fasten small end of boot by placing rubber clamp over boot groove, or fit metal clamp in boot groove. Ensure boot is properly located on shaft and housing, without being twisted.

Fig. 13: CV Joint Boot Positioning

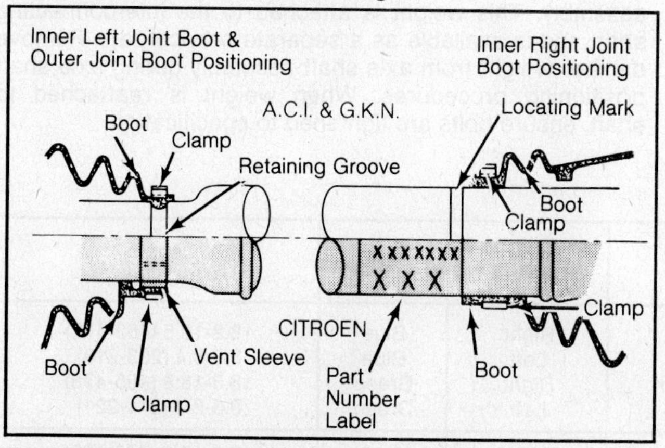

Boot location grooves may not be exactly as shown.

3) Locate clamp tangs in slot, making clamp as tight as possible by hand. Using Clamp Installer (C-4124), clamp bridge and squeeze to complete tightening. *See Fig. 14*. Use care not to cut or damage boot.

4) After attaching boot to shaft, install CV joint. See INNER CV JOINT or OUTER CV JOINT. With CV joint installed, locate large end of boot in housing groove or over retaining shoulder. Do not twist boot. Install metal spring clamp or fit metal ladder clamp in boot groove and locate clamp tangs in slots. Make clamp as tight as possible by hand.

5) Clamp bridge using Clamp Installer (C-4124) and squeeze to complete tightening. Use care not to cut or damage boot. *See Fig. 14*. Apply a 1/4" (1 mm) wide bead of MOPAR Multipurpose Lubricant (4318063) to full circumference of wear sleeve and seal contact surfaces. Install axle shaft assembly. See AXLE SHAFTS.

Fig. 14: Clamping Bridge On A.C.I. & G.K.N. CV Joint Assemblies

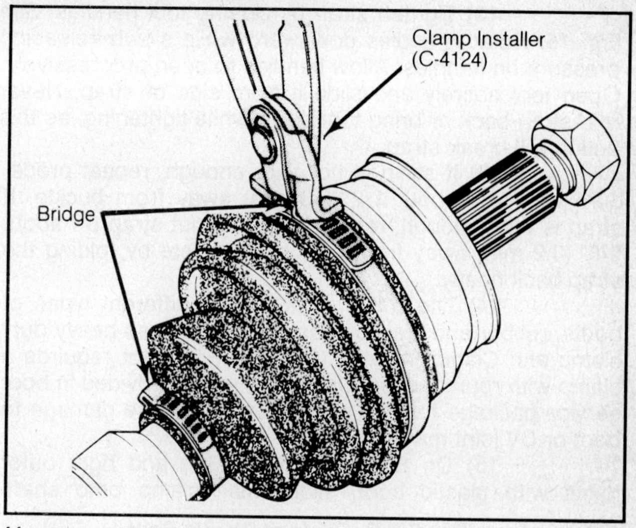

Use care not to cut through clamp bridge or damage boot.

6) To install new Citroen axle shaft boot, position small end of boot over shaft. If installing an outer CV joint boot, position vent sleeve under boot clamp groove.

7) On right inner CV joint boot, align boot lip face with inboard edge of part number label. If part number label is no longer attached, align edge of new boot with mark remaining on shaft where old boot was attached. *See Fig. 14*.

8) On left inner and outer CV joint boots, position boot between locating shoulders and align edge of boot lip with mark left from previous boot. *See Fig. 13*.

9) Wrap binding strap around boot twice, plus an additional 2 1/2" (63.5 mm). Pass strap through buckle and fold it back about 1 1/8" (28.6 mm) on inside of buckle. Place strap around boot with eye of buckle toward you.

10) Wrap strap around boot once and pass it through buckle. Wrap strap around boot a second time, also passing it through buckle. Fold strap back slightly to prevent it from slipping backward.

11) Open Clamp Installer (C-4653) and place strap in narrow slot about 1/2" (13 mm) away from buckle. Hold strap with left hand and push clamp installer forward

Fig. 15: Tightening Boot Strap On Citroen CV Joint Assemblies

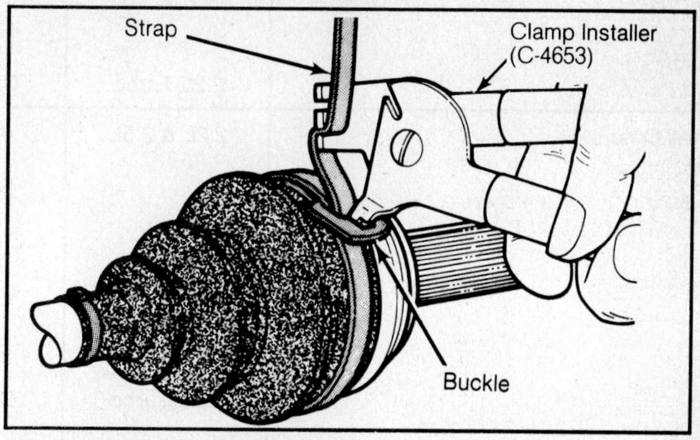

Axle shaft boot clamping procedures are the same for attachment to the axle shafts or CV joints.

Axle Shafts

CHRYSLER CORP. (Cont.)

and slightly upward. Fit hook of clamping tool into eye of buckle.

12) Tighten strap by closing tool handles. *See Fig. 15.* Rotate handles downward while slowly releasing pressure on handles. Allow handles to open progressively. Open tool entirely and slide it from side of strap. Never fold strap back or bring tool down while tightening, as this action will break strap.

13) If strap is not tight enough, repeat procedure with tool about 1/2" (13 mm) away from buckle. If strap is tight enough, remove tool and cut strap off about 1/8" (3.2 mm) away from buckle. Complete by folding the strap back neatly.

14) The S.S.G. joint uses 2 different types of boots, rubber and plastic. Plastic boot requires heavy duty clamp and Clamp Installer (C-4975). Soft boot requires a clamp with round edges. Use only clamps provided in boot service package for this application, otherwise damage to boot or CV joint may occur.

15) On S.S.G. left inner, left and right outer joints with plastic boot, slide small clamp onto shaft. Position small end of boot over shaft with lip of boot in third groove, toward center of shaft. *See Fig. 16.*

Fig. 16: Installing S.S.G. CV Joint Plastic Boot

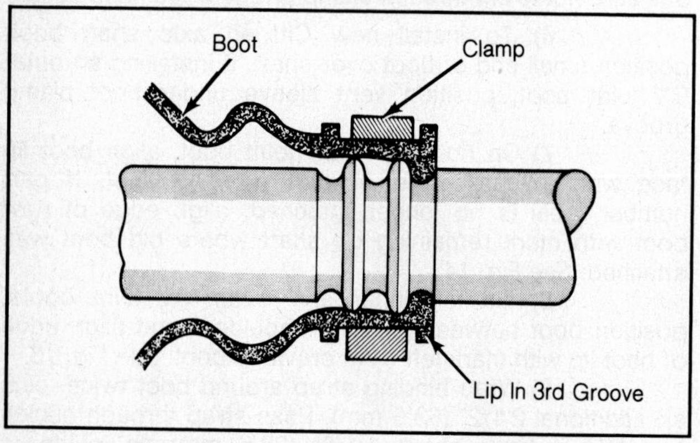

16) Position clamp evenly over boot. Place Clamp Installer (C-4975) over bridge of clamp and tighten nut until tool jaws are completely closed, face-to-face. Remove tool.

17) On right inner joint with rubber boot, slide small clamp onto shaft. Install boot onto shaft and position on flat between locating shoulders. *See Fig. 17.* Position clamp on boot and crimp bridge of clamp using Clamp Installer (C-3250). Remove tool and install CV joint.

Fig. 17: Installing S.S.G. CV Joint Rubber Boot

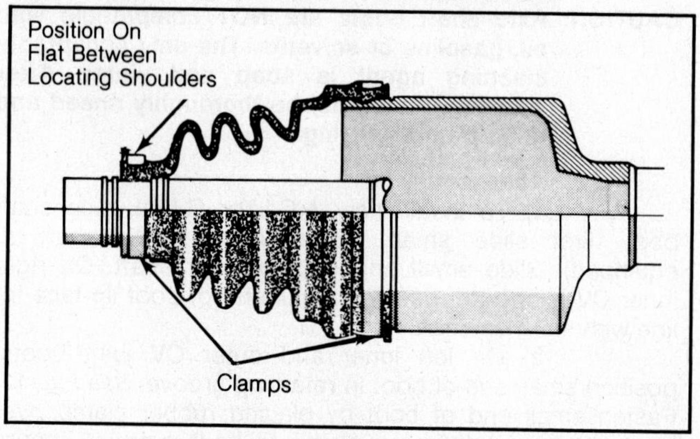

DAMPER WEIGHTS

A damper weight is used on left axle shaft assembly. This weight is attached to the interconnecting shaft and is available as a separate service part. Remove damper weight from axle shaft assembly during axle shaft positioning procedures. When weight is reattached to shaft, ensure bolts are tightened to specification.

AXLE SHAFT LENGTH SPECIFICATIONS

Application	Engine	Shaft Type	Side of Vehicle	Tape Color	Length In. (mm)
Omni GLH	2.2L	A.C.I.	Right	Blue	18.2-18.6 (462-472)
			Left	Blue	8.0-8.4 (203-213)
		Citroen	Right	Green	18.3-18.8 (465-478)
			Left	Green	8.3-8.7 (211-221)
Charger, Horizon, Omni, Turismo	1.6L & 2.2L	A.C.I.	Right	Red	18.5-19.0 (470-483)
			Left	Red	8.2-8.6 (208-218)
		G.K.N.	Right	Yellow	19.6-20.0 (498-508)
			Left	Yellow	9.5-10.0 (241-254)
	2.2L Turbo	Citroen	Both	Orange	8.3-8.7 (211-221)
All Others	2.2L & 2.5L	A.C.I.	Right	Green	18.8-19.1 (478-485)
			Left	Green	9.0-9.6 (229-244)
		G.K.N.	Right	Blue	19.9-20.3 (506-516)
			Left	Blue	10.2-10.9 (259-277)
		A.C.I./G.K.N.	Right	Orange	19.4-19.7 (493-500)
			Left	Orange	9.6-10.2 (244-259)
		Citroen	Right	White	18.9-19.4 (480-493)
			Left	White	9.4-10.0 (239-254)
		S.S.G.	Right	Gold	17.9-18.5 (455-470)
			Left	Gold	8.5-9.1 (216-231)
	2.2L Turbo	Citroen	Right	Red	9.5-9.9 (241-252)
			Left	Yellow	9.4-10.0 (239-254)
		G.K.N.	Right	Tan	10.1-10.4 (257-264)
			Left	Silver	10.0-10.6 (254-269)

CHRYSLER CORP. (Cont.)

AXLE SHAFT POSITIONING

1) Engine mounts on FWD vehicles have slotted holes to allow side-to-side positioning of engine. If the vertical bolts on right or left upper engine mounts have been loosened for any reason, or if vehicle has sustained front structural damage, axle shaft lengths must be checked and corrected as required.

2) A shorter than required shaft can result in objectionable noise. A longer than required shaft can result in potential damage. When checking and/or performing axle shaft positioning, vehicle should be on a platform hoist or front end alignment rack.

3) Vehicle must be completely assembled with front wheels properly aligned and in straight-ahead position. Full vehicle weight must be on all 4 wheels. Remove damper weight from left axle shaft.

4) Using a tape measure, measure direct distance from inner edge of outboard boot to inner edge of inboard boot on both shafts. Measure at bottom of axle shaft (six o'clock position). *See Fig. 18.* Compare the measurements with those in the AXLE SHAFT LENGTH SPECIFICATIONS table.

NOTE: **Axle shaft lengths vary between manufacturers. If length of both shafts are within specified range, no further action is required.**

Fig. 18: Measuring Axle Shaft Length

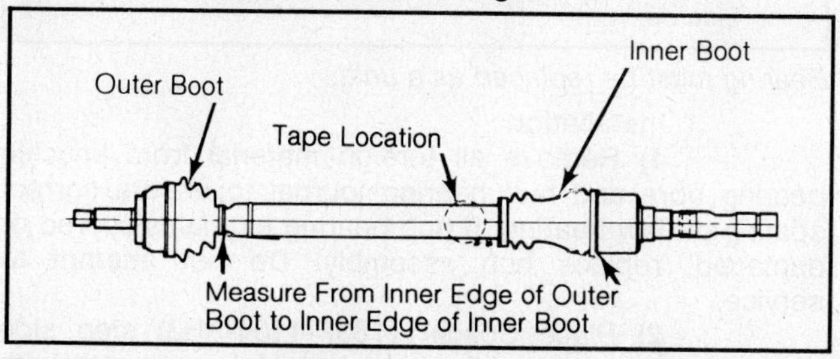

Compare this measurement with AXLE SHAFT LENGTH SPECIFICATIONS table.

5) If either shaft length is not within specified range, adjust engine position. If proper axle shaft length cannot be achieved within travel limits of engine mounts, check for any condition that could affect side-to-side position of measuring points. After achieving correct axle shaft positioning, adjust transmission shift linkage.

TIGHTENING SPECIFICATIONS

Application	Ft. Lbs. (N.m)
Ball Joint Stud Clamp Bolt	70 (95)
Brake Caliper Adapter Bolt	160 (217)
Brake Hose Retainer Bolt	10 (14)
Damper Weight Fastener	
A.C.I.	8 (11)
Citroen & S.S.G	21 (28)
G.K.N.	23 (31)
Differential Cover Bolt	21 (28)
Hub Bearing Retainer Bolt	20 (27)
Hub Nut	180 (244)
Inner CV Joint Flange	36 (49)
Intermediate Shaft	
Bracket-to-Bearing Bolts	21 (28)
Bracket-to-Engine Bolts	40 (54)
Tie Rod End Nut	35 (47)
Wheel Lug Nut	95 (129)
	INCH Lbs. (N.m)
Speedometer Pinion Gear	
Adapter Mounting Bolt	60 (7)

FORD MOTOR CO.

1986 FWD Models Only

DESCRIPTION

Power from transaxle is transferred to driving wheels by 2 unequal length axle shafts. Both axle shafts use CV joints at inboard and outboard ends. On Sable and Taurus models with ATX or MTX transaxle, the right axle shaft is connected to an intermediate shaft. The intermediate shaft is splined in differential and held in place by circlip. All other inner CV joints are splined in the transaxle differential and held by circlips. The outboard ends are splined to the wheel hubs and secured by spindle nuts.

SERVICE (IN-VEHICLE)

HUB BEARINGS

NOTE: **Hub bearings are a cartridge design and are pre-greased, sealed, and require no maintenance. They are also preset and cannot be adjusted. If bearing is disassembled for any reason, complete bearing unit must be replaced.**

Removal

1) Loosen lug nuts. Remove hub nut/retainer and washer without unstaking. Use of a chisel may damage spindle threads. Discard hub nut when removed; it must NOT be reused. On Sable and Taurus models, loosen but do not remove, 3 top mount-to-inner fender panel nuts.

2) Raise and support vehicle on safety stands. Remove tire and wheel assembly. Remove brake caliper by loosening caliper locating pins and rotating caliper off rotor. Start from lower end of caliper and lift upward. Do not remove caliper pins from caliper assembly. Lift caliper off rotor and hang out of way with wire.

3) Remove rotor from hub by pulling it off hub bolts. If rotor will not pull off, apply rust penetrating liquid to inner and outer rotor/hub mating surfaces. Install 3-jaw

Axle Shafts

FORD MOTOR CO. (Cont.)

puller and remove rotor by pulling on rotor outside diameter and pushing on hub center. If excessive force is required for removal, check rotor for lateral runout.

4) Remove cotter pin from tie rod end stud and remove slotted nut. Using Tie Rod Remover and Adapter (3290-C and T81P-3504-W), remove tie rod end from knuckle. Remove stabilizer link, if equipped.

5) Remove lower control arm-to-steering knuckle pinch bolt and nut, using drift punch to remove bolt if required. Discard bolt and nut. Using a screwdriver, slightly spread knuckle-to-lower arm pinch joint and remove lower arm from knuckle.

NOTE: Make sure steering column is in unlocked position. DO NOT use a hammer to separate ball joint from knuckle.

6) Remove shock absorber strut-to-steering knuckle pinch bolt. Using a large screwdriver, slightly spread knuckle-to-strut pinch joint. On all except Sable and Taurus models, loosen but do not remove, 2 strut top mount-to-apron nuts. DO NOT allow axle shaft to move outward because over extension could result in separation of internal CV joint components, causing CV joint failure.

7) Remove rotor splash shield, if equipped. Install Hub Remover/Installer (T81P-1104-C), Adapter (T81P-1104-A), and Wheel Bolt Adapter (T83P-1104-BH) and remove hub, bearing and knuckle assembly by pushing outer CV joint and stub shaft out of knuckle assembly. Support knuckle with wire and remove strut bolt. Slide hub/knuckle assembly off strut.

NOTE: Never use a hammer to separate outer CV joint from hub. Damage to CV joint internal components may result.

8) Carefully remove support wire and carry hub/knuckle assembly to work bench. Install Front Hub Puller (D80L-1002-L) and Shaft Protector (D80L-625-L) with puller jaws on knuckle bosses, and remove hub. Ensure shaft protector just clears I.D. of bearing and rests on face of hub journal. *See Fig. 1.*

Fig. 1: Separating Hub From Steering Knuckle

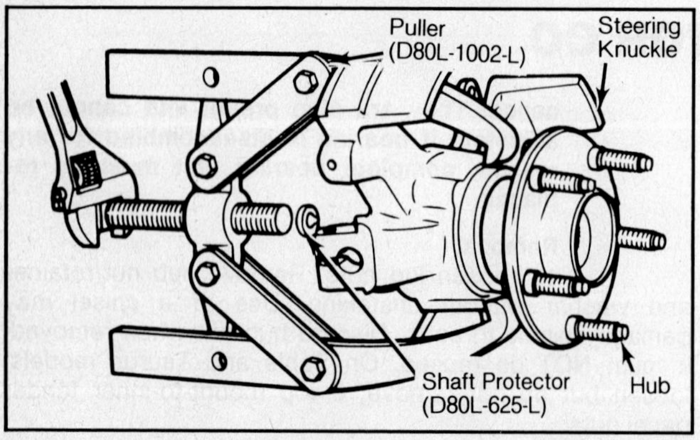

9) Remove and discard bearing retaining snap ring. Using hydraulic press, place Spacer (T83P-1104-AH3) step side up on press plate. Place knuckle on spacer with outboard side up. Install Bearing Remover (T83P-1104-AH2) on bearing inner race and press bearing out of knuckle. Discard bearing. *See Fig. 2.*

Fig. 2: Removing Hub Bearing from Knuckle

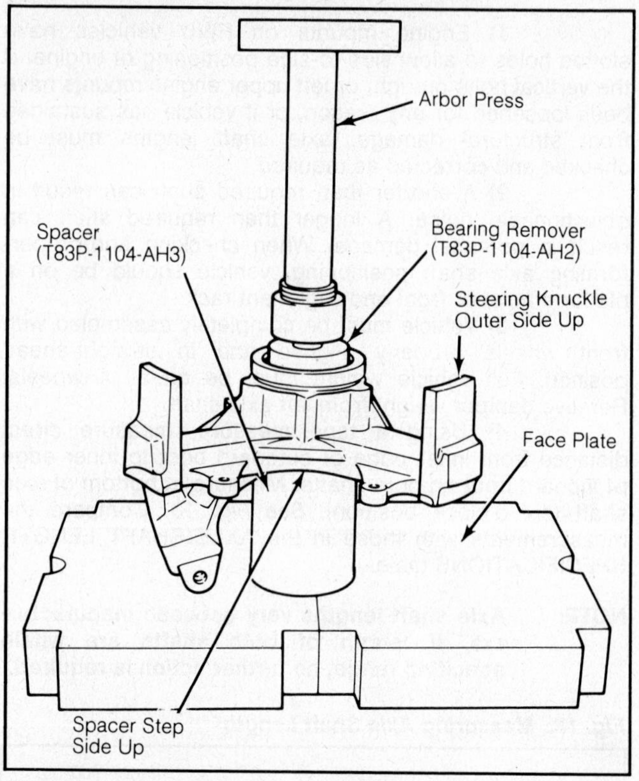

Bearing must be replaced as a unit.

Installation

1) Remove all foreign material from knuckle bearing bore and hub bearing journal to ensure correct seating of new bearing. If hub bearing journal is scored or damaged, replace hub assembly. Do not attempt to service.

2) Place Spacer (T83P-1104-AH3) step side down on press plate. Position knuckle on spacer with outboard side down. Position new bearing in inboard side of knuckle. Install Bearing Installer (T83P-1104-AH1) on bearing outer race with undercut side facing bearing. Press bearing in until it seats against knuckle bore shoulder. *See Fig. 3.*

3) Using snap ring pliers, install new bearing retaining snap ring (part of bearing kit) in knuckle groove. Install Spacer (T83P-1104-AH3) on arbor press plate. Position hub on spacer with lugs facing downward. Position knuckle assembly on hub barrel with outboard side down.

4) Insert bearing remover/installer on inner race of bearing. Press on remover/installer until bearing is fully seated on hub. Hub should rotate freely in knuckle after installation.

5) Before hub/knuckle installation, replace bearing dust seal on outer CV joint with new seal from bearing kit. Mount CV joint in vise and remove seal by tapping uniformly on seal with screwdriver and light hammer. Turn CV joint in vise. Using Flange Installer (T83P-3425-AH) and hammer, install dust seal on CV joint with seal flange toward bearing. *See Fig. 4.*

FORD MOTOR CO. (Cont.)

Fig. 3: Installing Hub Bearing in Knuckle

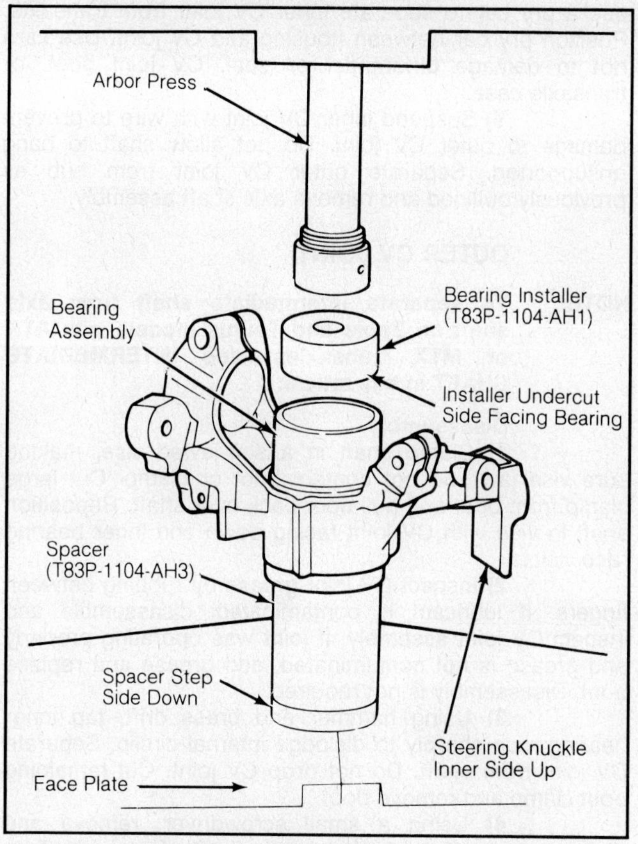

Bearing installer must be installed with undercut side facing bearing to prevent damage to bearing.

Fig. 4: Installing Bearing Dust Seal

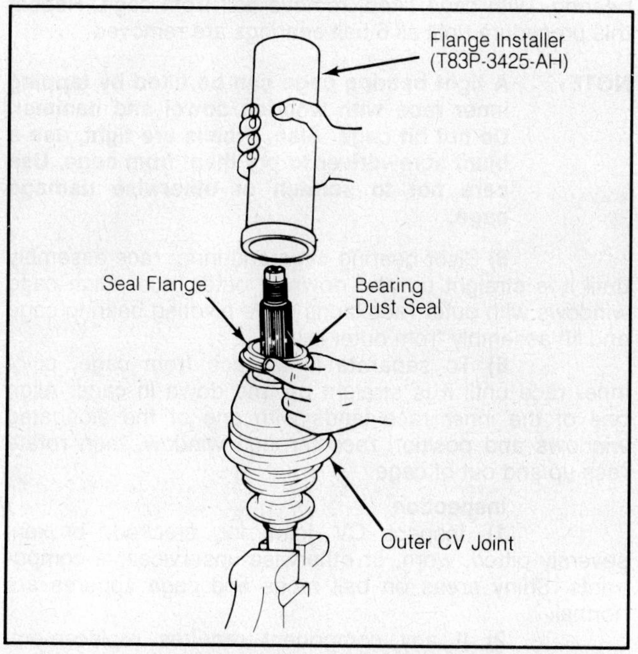

Dust seal must be replaced when hub bearing is replaced.

6) Install rotor splash shield on knuckle, if equipped. Suspend hub/knuckle assembly on vehicle with wire and attach strut loosely to knuckle. Lubricate CV joint stub shaft splines with 30-weight motor oil. Install shaft into hub splines as far as possible with hand pressure only. Check that splines are properly engaged.

7) On Sable and Taurus models, temporarily mount rotor to hub with 2 washers and lug nuts. Insert steel rod into rotor and rotate clockwise to lock rotor in position. Install hub nut washer and NEW hub nut. Turn nut clockwise to seat CV joint. Tighten nut to specifications. Remove steel rod, washers and lug nuts.

8) On all other models, install Hub Remover/Installer (T81P-1104-C), Adapter (T81P-1104-A), and Wheel Bolt Adapter (T83P-1104-BH) to hub and stub shaft. Tighten installer to 120 ft. lbs. (163 N.m) to make sure that hub is fully seated. Remove remover/installer and install washer and new hub nut/retainer. Install retainer finger tight.

9) On all models, install steering knuckle on shock absorber strut. Install new pinch bolt in knuckle to retain strut. Tighten bolt. Install axle shaft. Install lower control arm to knuckle, ensuring that stud groove is properly positioned. Install new nut and bolt and tighten.

10) Install rotor on hub assembly. Install caliper over rotor. Make sure that outer brake shoe spring hook is seated under upper arm of knuckle. Position tie rod end in knuckle and install new slotted nut. Tighten nut, advancing nut to align slots and install cotter pin. Install stabilizer link, if equipped.

11) Install wheel assembly and tighten lug nuts finger tight. Lower vehicle and block wheels. Tighten lug nuts. Manually tighten hub nut/retainer on axle shaft as far as possible.

12) Tighten hub nut/retainer using a 1 3/16" (30 mm) socket. During tightening, "clicking" sound will indicate proper ratchet function of nut/retainer. As nut/retainer tightens, ensure that 1 of the 3 locking tabs is in slot of axle shaft. If nut/retainer is damaged or more than 1 tab is missing, replace nut/retainer.

NOTE: **Do not use power or impact-type tools to tighten hub nut/retainer. Do not move vehicle without tightening hub nut/retainer. Do not back-off nut/retainer to meet tightening specifications. If specification is exceeded, replace nut/retainer.**

AXLE SHAFTS

NOTE: **Prior to removing axle shafts, note the following:**

1) When removing both axle shafts, shipping plugs (T81P-1177-B) must be installed in differential case. Failure to install these plugs may result in differential side gears becoming misaligned. Should this happen, differential must be removed from transaxle to realign gears.

2) Axle shafts should not be removed unless new hub nut/retainer, new lower control arm-to-steering knuckle retaining bolt and nut, and new inner CV joint stub shaft circlip are available. These parts must not be reused. Once removed, their torque holding ability is destroyed.

Removal

1) Before raising vehicle, remove wheel hub dust cap and loosen hub/retainer and lug nuts. Raise and support vehicle on safety stands. Remove tire and wheel assembly. Remove hub nut/retainer and washer without unstaking. Use of a chisel may damage spindle threads. Discard hub nut when removed; it must NOT be reused.

Axle Shafts

FORD MOTOR CO. (Cont.)

2) Disconnect brake hose retaining clip at suspension strut. Remove ball joint-to-steering knuckle bolt. Drive bolt from knuckle using a punch and hammer. Discard bolt and nut; once removed they cannot be reused.

3) To separate ball joint from steering knuckle, bend plastic disc brake shield back away from ball joint. Position pry bar with end outside bushing pocket to prevent damage to bushing. Do not allow pry bar to contact lower control arm to prevent damage to ball joint boot.

NOTE: **On models with ATX transaxle, right axle shaft must be removed first. Insert driver through differential to drive left axle shaft from transaxle.**

4) To remove right axle shaft on Sable and Taurus models with ATX and MTX transaxle, remove 2 bolts attaching bearing support to bracket. Slide intermediate shaft out of transaxle. Suspend inner CV joint with wire. Do not allow inner joint to hang freely as damage to outer CV joint can occur. Separate outer CV joint from hub as previously outlined and remove axle shaft and intermediate shaft assembly.

5) To remove left axle shaft on Sable and Taurus models with ATX transaxle, remove and support right axle shaft first. Insert Driver (T81P-4026-A) in transaxle case and drive left axle shaft out of transaxle. Suspend inner CV joint with wire to prevent damage to outer CV joint. Separate outer CV joint from hub as previously outlined and remove axle shaft assembly.

6) To remove left axle shaft (MTX transaxle) and both axle shafts (AXOD transaxle) on Sable and Taurus models, turn steering knuckle out of way or wire strut out of way. Install CV Joint Puller (T86P-3514-A1) between inner CV joint and transaxle case.

7) Screw Extension (T86P-3514-A2) into puller and hand tighten. Attach Slide Hammer (D79P-100-A) onto extension. Pull inner CV joint from transaxle case. *See Fig. 5.* Suspend inner CV joint with wire to prevent damage to outer CV joint. Separate outer CV joint from hub as previously outlined and remove axle shaft assembly.

Fig. 5: Removing Inner CV Joint On Sable & Taurus

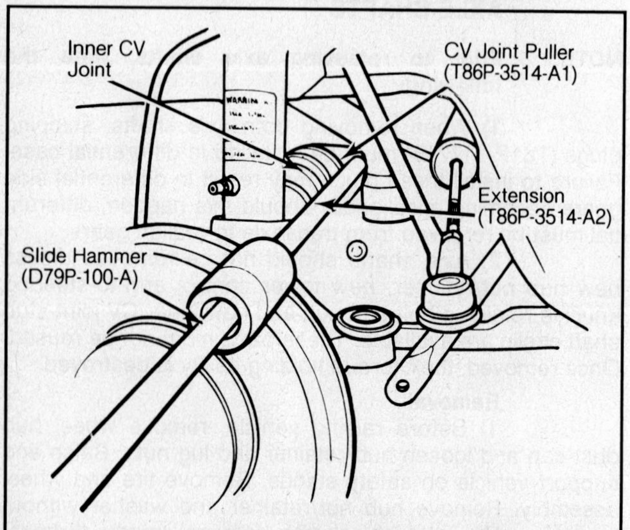

These tools must be used to remove left axle shaft on MTX transaxle and both shafts on AXOD transaxle.

8) To remove axle shafts on all other models, use a pry bar to separate inner CV joint from transaxle. Position pry bar between housing and CV joint. Use care not to damage differential oil seal, CV joint boot, or transaxle case.

9) Suspend inner CV joint with wire to prevent damage to outer CV joint. Do not allow shaft to hang unsupported. Separate outer CV joint from hub as previously outlined and remove axle shaft assembly.

OUTER CV JOINT

NOTE: **To separate intermediate shaft from axle shaft on Sable and Taurus models with ATX or MTX transaxles, see INTERMEDIATE SHAFT in this article.**

Disassembly

1) Clamp shaft in a soft-jawed vise, making sure vise jaws do not contact boot or clamp. Cut large clamp from boot and pull boot back over shaft. Reposition shaft in vise with CV joint facing down and inner bearing race visible.

2) Inspect CV joint grease by rubbing between fingers. If lubricant is contaminated, disassemble and inspect CV joint assembly. If joint was operating properly and grease is not contaminated, add grease and replace boot. Disassembly is not required.

3) Using hammer and brass drift, tap inner bearing race sharply to dislodge internal circlip. Separate CV joint from shaft. Do not drop CV joint. Cut remaining boot clamp and remove boot.

4) Using a small screwdriver, remove and discard circlip at end of axle shaft. Replace stop ring, located just below circlip, only if damaged or worn. Clamp CV joint stub shaft in vise with bearing facing up. Press down on inner race until it tilts enough to remove a ball bearing. With cage tilted, remove ball from cage. Repeat this procedure until all 6 ball bearings are removed.

NOTE: **A tight bearing cage can be tilted by tapping inner race with wooden dowel and hammer. Do not hit cage. Also, if balls are tight, use a blunt screwdriver to pry them from cage. Use care not to scratch or otherwise damage cage.**

5) Pivot bearing cage and inner race assembly until it is straight up and down in outer race. Align cage windows with outer race lands while pivoting bearing cage and lift assembly from outer race.

6) To separate inner race from cage, pivot inner race until it is straight up and down in cage. Align one of the inner race lands with one of the elongated windows and position race through window, then rotate race up and out of cage.

Inspection

1) Inspect CV joint for cracked, broken, severely pitted, worn, or otherwise unserviceable components. Shiny areas on ball races and cage spheres are normal.

2) If any component requires replacement, entire CV joint must be replaced. DO NOT intermix components from other CV joints. CV joint components are matched during assembly by manufacturer.

Axle Shafts

FORD MOTOR CO. (Cont.)

Fig. 6: Exploded View of Axle Shaft and CV Joint Assembly

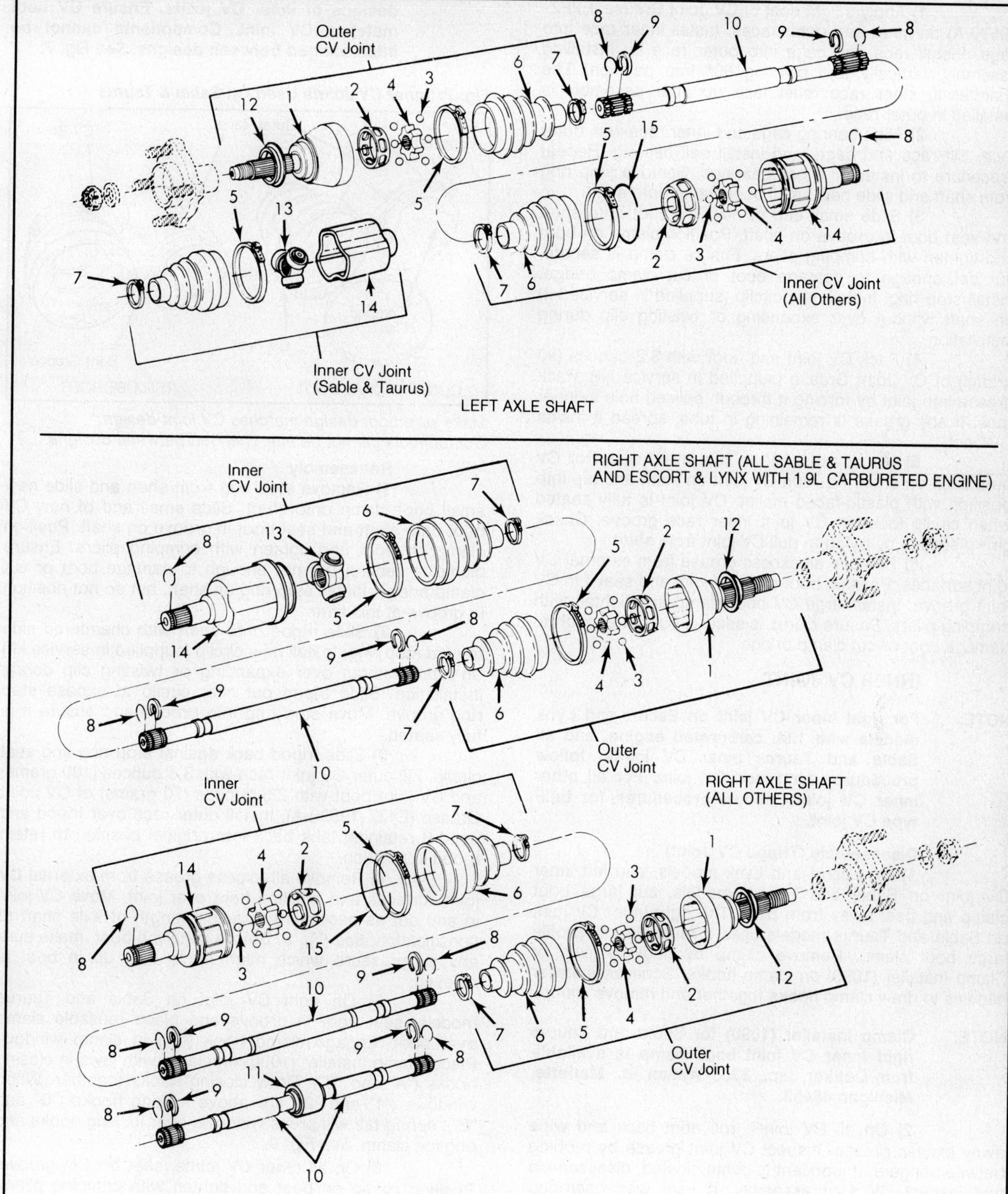

1. Outer CV Joint Outer Race & Stub Shaft
2. Bearing Cage
3. Ball Bearings (6)
4. Inner Bearing Race
5. Large CV Boot Clamp
6. CV Boot
7. Small CV Boot Clamp
8. Circlip
9. Stop Ring
10. Axle Shaft
11. Rubber Damper (Tempo & Topaz 2.3L Only)
12. Dust Shield
13. Tripod Assembly
14. Inner CV Joint Outer Race & Stub Shaft
15. Wire Ring Ball Retainer

Axle Shafts

FORD MOTOR CO. (Cont.)

Reassembly

1) Apply a light coat of CV Joint Grease (E2FZ-19590-A) on inner and outer races. Install inner race into cage. Install race and cage into outer race by installing assembly vertically and pivoting 90° into position. The chamfer in inner race must face up after assembly is installed in outer race.

2) Align bearing cage and inner race with outer race. Tilt race and cage, and install ball bearing. Repeat procedure to install all 6 ball bearings. Remove stop ring from shaft and slide new small boot clamp onto shaft.

3) Slide small end of new CV boot onto shaft and seat boot in groove on shaft. Position clamp on boot and tighten with crimping pliers. Ensure clamp is secure, but not enough to damage boot or cut clamp bridge. Install stop ring. Install new circlip (supplied in service kit) on shaft without over expanding or twisting clip during installation.

4) Pack CV joint and boot with 3.2 ounces (90 grams) of CV Joint Grease (supplied in service kit). Pack grease into joint by forcing it through splined hole in inner race. If any grease is remaining in tube, spread it inside CV boot.

5) Mount axle shaft in soft-jawed vise. Roll CV boot back on shaft. Position CV joint on shaft and tap into position with plastic-faced mallet. CV joint is fully seated when circlip locks in CV joint inner race groove. Check circlip seating by trying to pull CV joint from shaft.

6) Remove all excess grease from external CV joint surfaces. Position boot over CV joint and seat it in CV joint groove. Install large CV boot clamp and tighten with crimping pliers. Ensure clamp is secure, but not enough to damage boot or cut clamp bridge.

INNER CV JOINT

NOTE: **For right inner CV joint on Escort and Lynx models with 1.9L carbureted engine, and all Sable and Taurus inner CV joints, follow procedures for tripod CV joint. For all other inner CV joints, follow procedures for ball-type CV joint.**

Disassembly (Tripod CV Joint)

1) On Escort and Lynx models, and left inner CV joint on Sable and Taurus models, cut large boot clamp and peel away from boot. The right inner CV joint on Sable and Taurus models uses a reusable low profile large boot clamp. Remove clamp by hooking jaws of Clamp Installer (1090) on clamp hooks. Squeeze installer handles to draw clamp hooks together and remove clamp.

NOTE: **Clamp Installer (1090) for Sable and Taurus right inner CV joint boot clamp is available from Oetiker, Inc., 3305 Wilson St., Marlette, Michigan 48453.**

2) On all CV joints, roll boot back and wipe away excess grease. Inspect CV joint grease by rubbing between fingers. If lubricant is contaminated, disassemble and inspect CV joint assembly. If joint was operating properly and grease is not contaminated, add grease and replace boot. Disassembly is not required.

3) Using needle nose pliers, bend retaining rings back inside outer race and slide outer race off tripod. Using snap ring pliers, move stop ring back on shaft. Move tripod back on shaft. Remove and discard circlip. Remove tripod. Remove small CV boot clamp and remove CV boot.

NOTE: **Sable and Taurus models use 2 similar designs of inner CV joints. Ensure CV boot matches CV joint. Components cannot be interchanged between designs. *See Fig. 7.***

Fig. 7: Inner CV Joints Used On Sable & Taurus

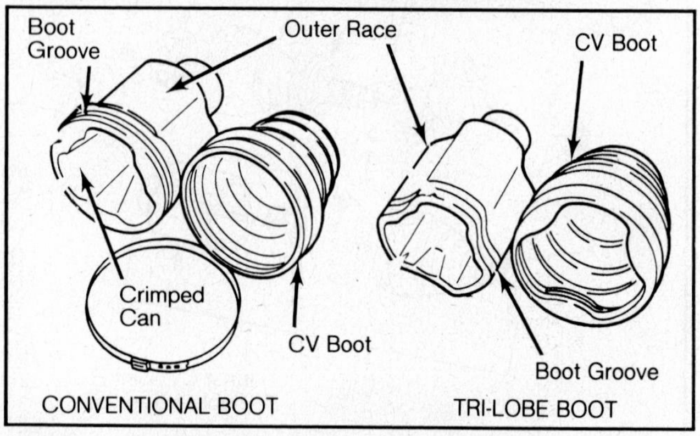

Make sure boot design matches CV joint design. Components cannot be interchanged between designs.

Reassembly

1) Remove stop ring from shaft and slide new small boot clamp onto shaft. Slide small end of new CV boot onto shaft and seat boot in groove on shaft. Position clamp on boot and tighten with crimping pliers. Ensure clamp is secure, but not enough to damage boot or cut clamp bridge. Install stop ring on shaft, but do not position in groove at this time.

2) Slide tripod onto shaft with chamfered side toward stop ring. Install new circlip (supplied in service kit) on shaft without over expanding or twisting clip during installation. Slide tripod out over circlip to expose stop ring groove. Move stop ring into groove and ensure it is fully seated.

3) Slide tripod back against stop ring and seat circlip. Fill outer CV joint race with 3.5 ounces (100 grams) and CV joint boot with 2.5 ounces (70 grams) of CV Joint Grease (E43Z-19590-A). Install outer race over tripod and bend 6 retaining tabs back into original position to retain tripod in position.

4) Remove all excess grease from external CV joint surfaces and position boot over joint. Move CV joint in and out as necessary to adjust length of axle shaft to specification. *See Fig. 8*. Before installing boot, make sure any air pressure which might have built up in boot is relieved.

5) On right CV joint on Sable and Taurus models, seat boot in groove and place reusable clamp over boot. Engage clamp hook ("C") in clamp window. Place Clamp Installer (1090) on clamp with jaws in closing hooks ("A" and "B"). Draw closing hooks together. When windows ("1" and "2") are above locking hooks ("D" and "E"), spring tab will press windows over locking hooks and engage clamp. *See Fig. 9*.

6) On all other CV joints, seat boot in groove. Position clamp on boot and tighten with crimping pliers. Ensure clamp is secure, but not enough to damage boot or cut clamp bridge. Install new circlip (supplied in service kit) on shaft without over expanding or twisting clip during installation.

Disassembly (Ball-Type CV Joint)

1) Clamp shaft in a soft-jawed vise, making sure vise jaws do not contact boot or clamp. Cut large

Axle Shafts

FORD MOTOR CO. (Cont.)

Fig. 8: Axle Shaft Assembled Lengths

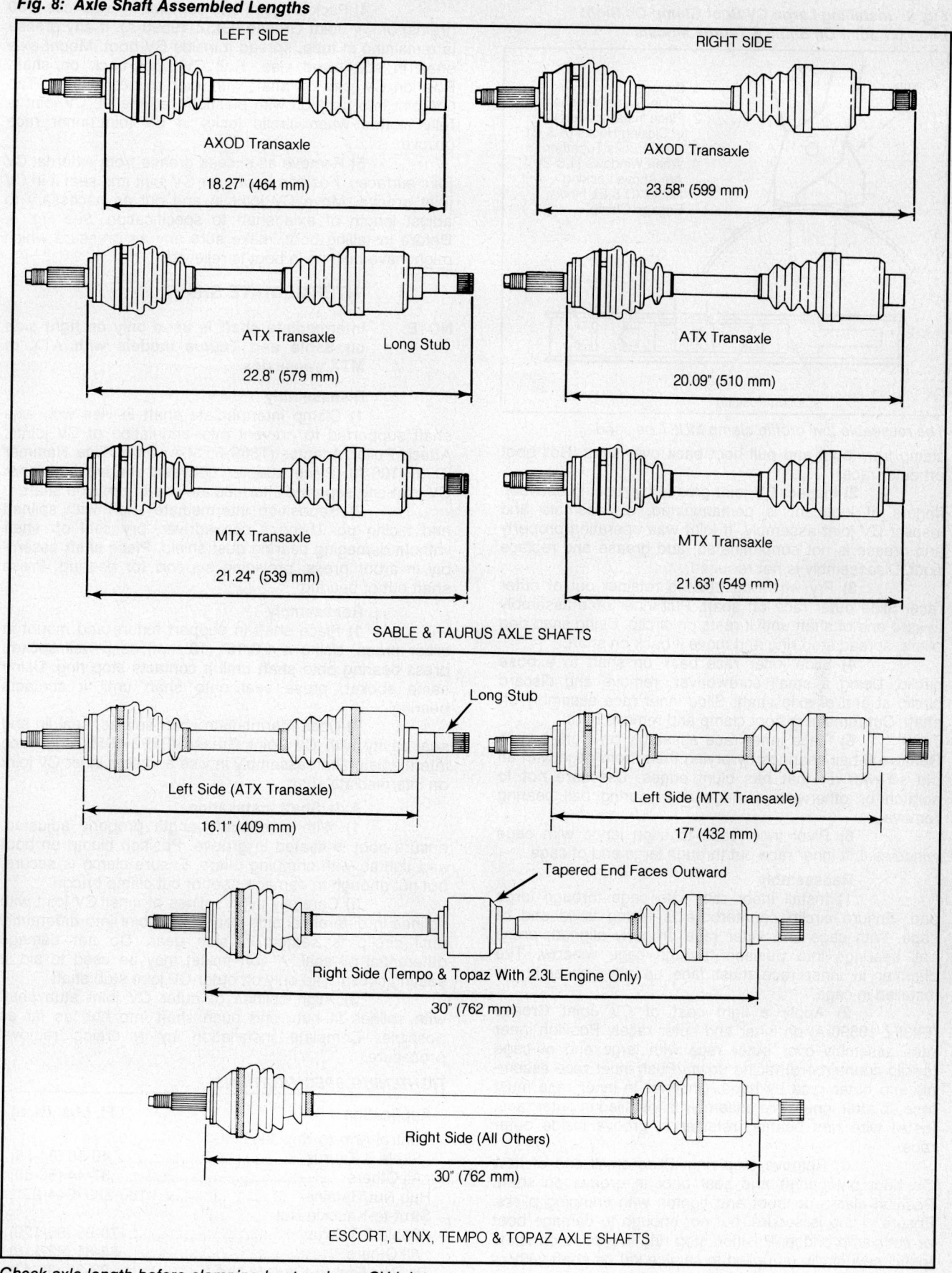

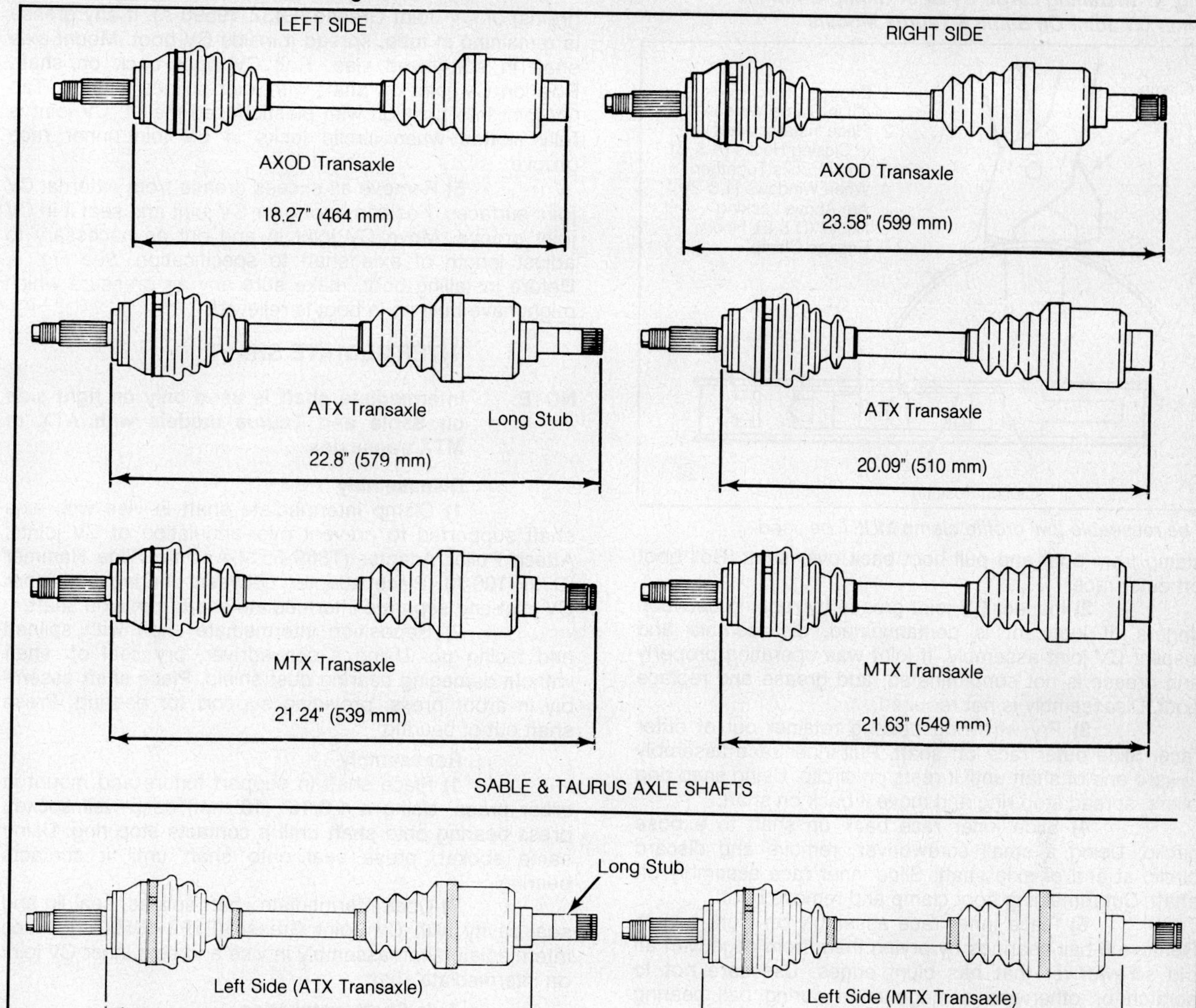

Check axle length before clamping boot on inner CV joint.

Axle Shafts

FORD MOTOR CO. (Cont.)

Fig. 9: Installing Large CV Boot Clamp On Right Inner CV Joint On Sable & Taurus Models

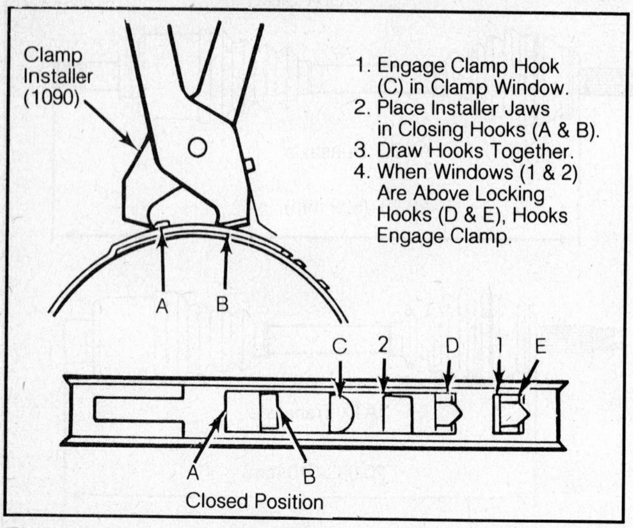

Clamp Installer (1090)
1. Engage Clamp Hook (C) in Clamp Window.
2. Place Installer Jaws in Closing Hooks (A & B).
3. Draw Hooks Together.
4. When Windows (1 & 2) Are Above Locking Hooks (D & E), Hooks Engage Clamp.
A
B
C
2
D
1
E
A
B
Closed Position

The reuseable low profile clamp MUST be used.

clamp from boot and pull boot back over shaft. Roll boot off outer race.

2) Inspect CV joint grease by rubbing between fingers. If lubricant is contaminated, disassemble and inspect CV joint assembly. If joint was operating properly and grease is not contaminated, add grease and replace boot. Disassembly is not required.

3) Pry wire ring bearing retainer out of outer race. Slide outer race off shaft. Pull inner race assembly toward end of shaft until it rests on circlip. Using snap ring pliers, spread stop ring and move it back on shaft.

4) Slide inner race back on shaft to expose circlip. Using a small screwdriver, remove and discard circlip at end of axle shaft. Slide inner race assembly off shaft. Cut remaining boot clamp and remove boot.

5) Place inner race assembly on work bench. Remove 6 ball bearings by prying them from cage with an old screwdriver that has blunt edges. Use care not to scratch or otherwise damage cage during ball bearing removal.

6) Pivot inner race to align lands with cage windows. Lift inner race out through large end of cage.

Reassembly

1) Install inner race into cage through large end. Ensure circlip counterbore is facing large end of cage. With cage and inner race properly aligned, press ball bearings into position through cage window. The chamfer in inner race must face up after assembly is installed in cage.

2) Apply a light coat of CV Joint Grease (E43FZ-19590-A) on inner and outer races. Position inner race assembly over outer race with large end of cage (circlip counterbore) facing down. Push inner race assembly into outer race by hand. Chamfer in inner race must face up after inner race assembly is installed in outer race. Install wire ring bearing retainer in groove inside outer race.

3) Remove stop ring. Slide small end of new CV boot onto shaft and seat boot in groove on shaft. Position clamp on boot and tighten with crimping pliers. Ensure clamp is secure, but not enough to damage boot or cut clamp bridge. Position stop ring in groove on shaft. Install new circlip (supplied in service kit) on shaft without over expanding or twisting clip during installation.

4) Pack CV joint and boot with 4.6 ounces (130 grams) of CV Joint Grease (E43Z-19590-A). If any grease is remaining in tube, spread it inside CV boot. Mount axle shaft in soft-jawed vise. Roll CV boot back on shaft. Position CV joint on shaft with joint splines aligned. Tap CV joint into position with plastic-faced mallet. CV joint is fully seated when circlip locks in CV joint inner race groove.

5) Remove all excess grease from external CV joint surfaces. Position boot over CV joint and seat it in CV joint groove. Move CV joint in and out as necessary to adjust length of axle shaft to specification. *See Fig. 8*. Before installing boot, make sure any air pressure which might have built up in boot is relieved.

INTERMEDIATE SHAFT

NOTE: **Intermediate shaft is used only on right side on Sable and Taurus models with ATX or MTX transaxles.**

Disassembly

1) Clamp intermediate shaft in vise with axle shaft supported to prevent over-angulation of CV joints. Attach Puller Adapter (T86P-3514-A) onto Slide Hammer (D79P-100-A). Place adapter between bearing and inner CV joint and separate intermediate shaft from axle shaft.

2) Reposition intermediate shaft with splined end facing up. Using a screwdriver, pry seal off shaft without damaging bearing dust shield. Place shaft assembly in arbor press, providing support for bearing. Press shaft out of bearing.

Reassembly

1) Place shaft in support fixture and mount in arbor press. Using a 1 3/16" (13 mm) deep-well socket, press bearing onto shaft until it contacts stop ring. Using same socket, press seal onto shaft until it contacts bearing.

2) Coat intermediate shaft splines, seal lip and seal cavity with CV Joint Grease (E2FZ-19590-A). Place intermediate shaft assembly in vise and seat inner CV joint on intermediate shaft.

Axle Shaft Installation

1) With axle shaft length properly adjusted, ensure boot is seated in groove. Position clamp on boot and tighten with crimping pliers. Ensure clamp is secure, but not enough to damage boot or cut clamp bridge.

2) Carefully align splines of inner CV joint with splines in differential side gear. Push joint into differential until circlip is seated in side gear. Do not damage differential oil seal. A soft mallet may be used to aid in seating circlip. Tap only on outer CV joint stub shaft.

3) Align splines of outer CV joint stub shaft with splines in hub, and push shaft into hub as far as possible. Complete installation by reversing removal procedure.

TIGHTENING SPECIFICATIONS

Application	Ft. Lbs. (N.m)
Control Arm-to-Knuckle Nut	
Sable & Taurus	40-55 (54-75)
All Others	37-44 (50-60)
Hub Nut/Retainer	180-200 (244-271)
Strut-to-Knuckle Nut	
Sable & Taurus	70-95 (95-129)
All Others	68-81 (92-110)
Tie Rod End-to-Knuckle Nut	23-35 (31-47)

GENERAL MOTORS

"A" Body - Buick Century, Chevrolet Celebrity, Oldsmobile Cutlass Ciera, Pontiac 6000
"C" Body - Buick Electra, Cadillac DeVille & Fleetwood, Oldsmobile Ninety-Eight
"E" Body - Buick Riviera, Cadillac Eldorado, Oldsmobile Toronado
"H" Body - Buick LeSabre, Oldsmobile Delta 88
"J" Body - Buick Skyhawk, Cadillac Cimarron, Chevrolet Cavalier, Oldsmobile Firenza, Pontiac Sunbird
"K" Body - Cadillac Seville
"N" Body - Buick Skylark & Somerset, Oldsmobile Calais, Pontiac Grand Am
"P" Body - Pontiac Fiero
"S" Body - Chevrolet Nova

DESCRIPTION

Power is transferred from transaxle to drive wheels by 2 axle shafts. The CV joints are of 2 designs, all outer joints are double-offset design and inner joints are tripod design or double-offset design. All outer CV joints are splined (helical splines) to the wheel bearing hub and are secured by a spindle nut. The right axle shaft on "C, E, H, K" bodies incorporates a damper.

All inner axle shafts, except left inner joint of automatic transaxles, use male splines and interlock with transaxle gears by barrel-type snap rings. The left inner joint of automatic transaxles use female splines and installs over stub shaft of transaxle.

SERVICE (IN-VEHICLE)

CAUTION: Whenever vehicle is on hoist, provide additional support for vehicle at opposite end from which components are being removed. This will reduce the possibility of vehicle falling off hoist.

HUB & BEARING ASSEMBLY

NOTE: Hub and bearing must be replaced as an assembly.

Removal ("S" Body)

1) Loosen hub and lug nuts. Raise and support vehicle. Remove wheel and tire. Remove brake hose retaining clip on strut and disconnect flex hose from brake line. Remove brake caliper and support out of way with wire. Remove rotor. Remove hub cotter pin, cap, nut and washer.

2) Using Hub Remover/Installer (J-25287), turn bolt to push axle shaft from steering knuckle. Using Tie Rod Remover (J-24319-01), separate tie rod from knuckle after removing cotter pin and nut. Remove ball joint-to-control arm bolts.

3) Sribe alignment mark on upper cam adjusting bolt and strut damper clamp. Remove 2 strut-to-knuckle bolts. Support outer end of axle shaft and remove steering knuckle. Support axle shaft up out of way with wire. Mount steering knuckle in vise and remove dust seal from rear of knuckle.

4) Using Seal Remover (J-26941) and slide hammer, remove inner grease seal. Remove inner bearing snap ring and brake dust shield. Using Adapter (J-35378) and Puller (J-25287), push hub assembly out of knuckle. Using same adapter and puller, remove outer bearing race from hub.

5) Remove outer grease seal from hub with seal remover and slide hammer. Place knuckle assembly on Spacer (J-35399) and use Driver (J-35379) to remove hub bearing assembly from knuckle.

Fig. 1: Exploded View of "S" Body Hub & Bearing Assembly

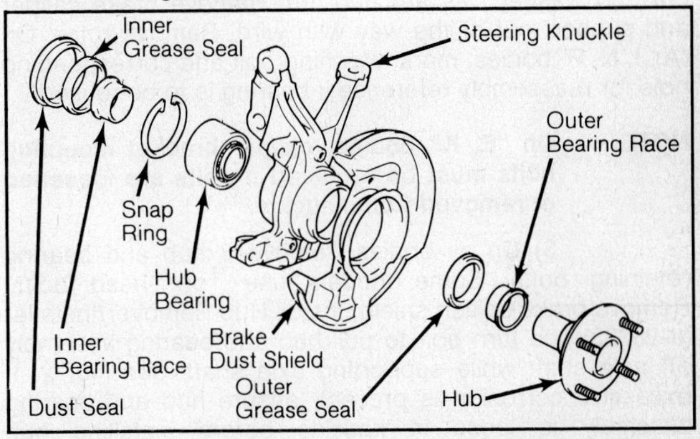

Do not use hammer or apply heat to remove hub and bearing assembly.

Installation

1) Using Bearing Installer (J-35411) and Driver (J-8092), drive hub bearing into knuckle. Install NEW outer grease seal with Installer (J-35737). Apply sealer to brake dust shield and mount on knuckle. Install outer bearing race on hub.

2) Apply multipurpose grease to lip of outer grease seal, seal and hub bearing. Using Installer (J-35399) and Driver (J-8092), press knuckle onto hub. Install inner bearing race and snap ring.

3) Mount steering knuckle in vise with hub facing down. Using Installer (J-35737), install NEW inner grease seal. Using Driver (J-35379), install dust seal with open end down. Mount lower ball joint on steering knuckle. Install old nut and tighten to 14 ft. lbs. (19 N.m). Remove and discard old nut. Install new nut and tighten to specification.

4) Mount steering knuckle on strut assembly. Install upper strut-to-knuckle bolt, aligning mark on upper cam adjusting bolt made during removal. Rotate knuckle assembly downward and position ball joint in lower control arm. Install and tighten nuts finger tight. Install remaining strut-to-knuckle bolt and tighten both bolts.

5) Tighten lower control arm-to-ball joint nuts. Position tie rod in steering knuckle. Install and tighten nut. Install cotter pin. Do not back off nut to install cotter pin. Install rotor and brake caliper. Reconnect flex hose to brake line and install retaining clip.

6) Install wheel and tire. Lower vehicle and tighten lug nuts. Install hub washer and nut. Tighten nut. Install cap and cotter pin. If cotter pin holes are not aligned, bend tangs on cap enough to align holes. DO NOT back off nut. Bleed and adjust brakes.

Removal (All Other Bodies)

1) On "P" body with aluminum wheels, set parking brake, raise vehicle and remove wheel. On all

GENERAL MOTORS (Cont.)

other bodies, loosen hub and lug nuts. On all bodies, raise and support vehicle. If twin-post hoist is used, place jack stands under frame and lower front post of hoist. Remove wheel assembly. Install CV Joint Boot Protectors (J-28712 on outer joints and J-33162 on inner joints).

NOTE: **Boot protectors are only required on silicone (Gray) boots, generally right inner CV joint. All other boots are made of thermoplastic material (Black) and do not require boot protectors. Not all models use Gray boots.**

2) Clean stub shaft of dirt and oil. Remove hub nut and washer. Discard hub nut. Remove brake caliper and support out of the way with wire. Remove rotor. On "A, J, N, P" bodies, mark attaching bolt and corresponding hole for reassembly reference if bearing is to be reused.

NOTE: **On "E, K" bodies, caliper bracket mounting bolts must be replaced if bolts are loosened or removed from knuckle.**

3) On all bodies, remove 3 hub and bearing retaining bolts. Some models use Torx head bolts. Remove brake splash shield. Install Hub Remover/Installer (J-28733) and turn bolt to pull hub and bearing assembly off axle shaft while supporting axle shaft. *See Fig. 2.* If excessive corrosion is present, ensure hub and bearing assembly is loose in knuckle before installing hub remover/installer.

NOTE: **Do not move vehicle with axle shaft out of hub and bearing assembly or until hub nut is installed and tightened. Do not use a hammer or apply heat to remove hub and bearing assembly to avoid internal bearing damage.**

Fig. 2: Removing Hub & Bearing Assembly From Axle Shaft on All Except "S" Body

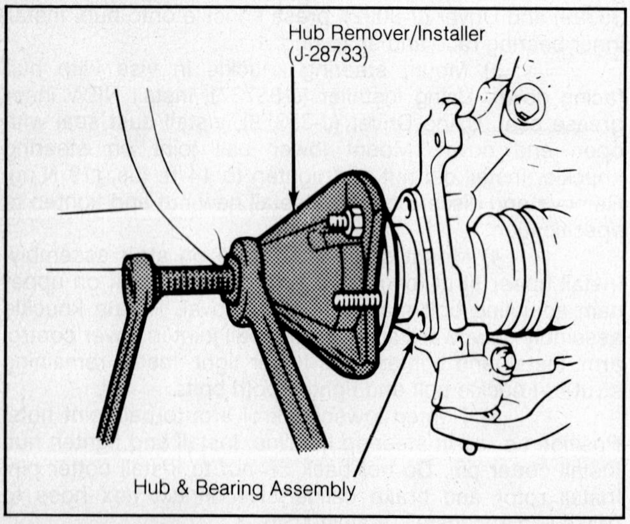

Do not use hammer or apply heat to remove hub and bearing assembly.

4) If hub and bearing assembly is being replaced, separate stabilizer bar from control arm, if equipped. Separate tie rod from steering knuckle. Remove lower ball joint nut and separate lower ball joint from steering knuckle with Ball Joint Separator (J-35315).

5) Sribe alignment mark on upper cam adjusting bolt and strut damper clamp. Remove 2 strut-to-knuckle bolts. Support outer end of axle shaft and remove steering knuckle. Separate axle shaft from steering knuckle and support out of way. Pry seal out of knuckle.

NOTE: **Some models do not require the complete removal of steering knuckle to replace bearing seal. Drive seal out of knuckle with punch and cut it off axle shaft. Install service seal from wheel side of knuckle.**

Fig. 3: Exploded View of Hub & Bearing Assembly on All Except "S" Body

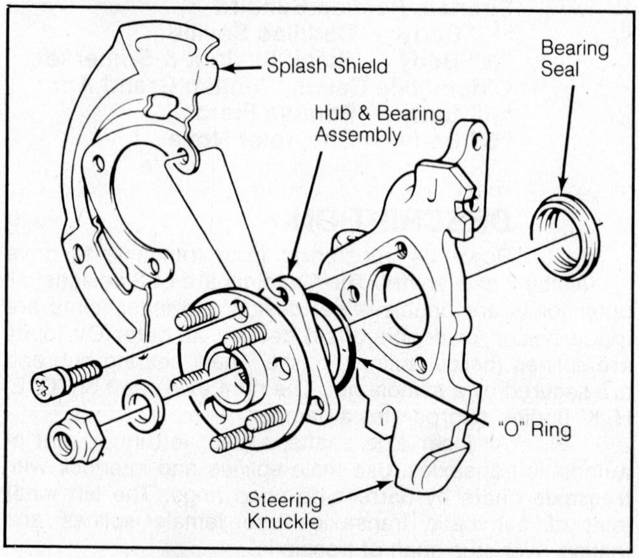

Installation

1) Clean and inspect bearing mating surfaces and knuckle bore for dirt, knicks and burrs. If hub and bearing assembly is being replaced, lubricate new seal and knuckle bore with grease. Install new seal with Seal Installer (J-28671 on "P" body; J-22388 on "J, N" bodies; J-34657-A on "A" bodies with heavy duty brakes and "C, H" bodies; J-34658 on all others).

2) Install new "O" ring on hub and bearing assembly. If removed, position knuckle, aligning marks made on cam adjusting bolt during removal. Bolt heads must face front of vehicle. Install lower ball joint. Tighten nuts. Install tie rod end and tighten nut. Do not back off nut to install cotter pin. Install stabilizer bar,if equipped, and tighten nut.

3) Install splash shield and position hub and bearing assembly in knuckle. Install and tighten retaining bolts (Torx head bolts), aligning marks made during removal on "A, J, N, P" bodies, if bearing is being reused.

4) Install rotor and brake caliper. Install new caliper mounting bracket bolts on "E, K" bodies. On "A, C, J, N" bodies set caliper-to-bracket clearance. See CALIPER-TO-BRACKET SPECIFICATIONS chart.

CALIPER-TO-BRACKET SPECIFICATIONS [1]

Application	Clearance In. (mm)
"A, J, N" Bodies	.005-.012 (.13-.30)
"C" Bodies	.010-.024 (.25-.61)

[1] – Total for top and bottom of caliper.

GENERAL MOTORS (Cont.)

Fig. 4: Removing Axle Shafts From Transaxle Assembly

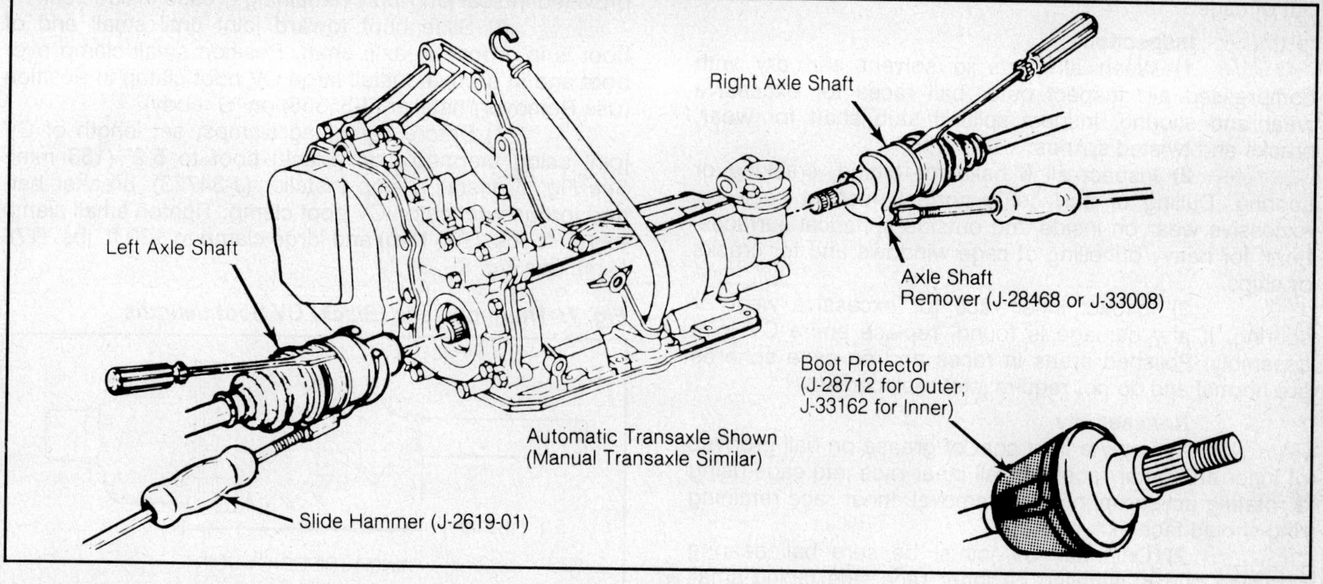

Fig. 5: Exploded View of Double-Offset Axle Shaft Assembly

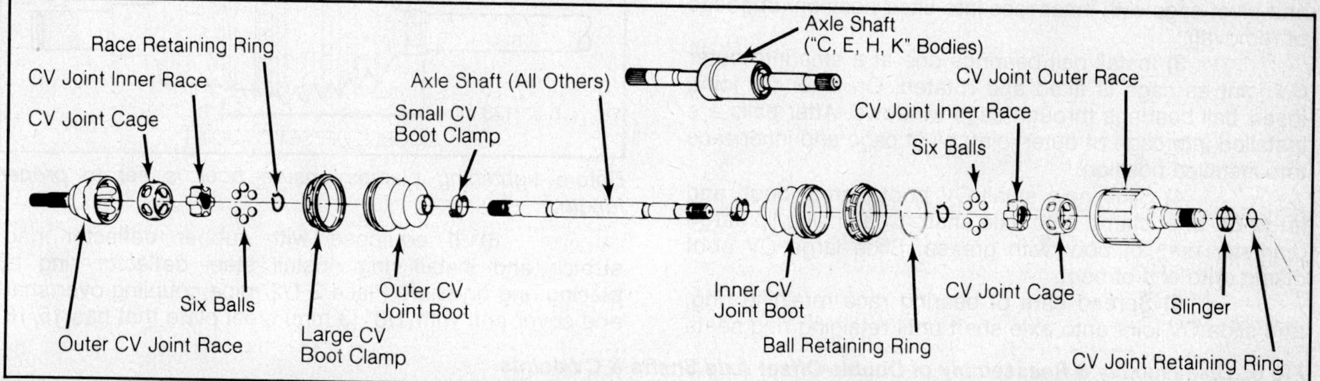

5) Install washer and new hub nut. Prevent rotor from turning and tighten hub nut. Do not back off hub nut to install cotter pin, if equipped. Remove CV boot protectors. Install wheel assemblies and lower vehicle. Tighten lug nuts.

AXLE SHAFTS

Removal

1) Install CV Joint Boot Protectors (J-28712 on outer joints and J-33162 on inner joints). Boot protectors are only required on silicone (Gray) boots, generally right inner CV joint. All other boots are made of thermoplastic material (Black) and do not require boot protectors. Not all models use Gray boots.

2) Remove steering knuckle as previously outlined. See HUB & BEARING ASSEMBLY. Support outer CV joint with wire. Using Axle Shaft Remover (J-28468 or J-33008) and slide hammer, separate inner CV joint from transaxle. Remove support wire from outer CV joint and remove axle shaft from vehicle.

DOUBLE-OFFSET CV JOINTS

CAUTION: Models equipped with Anti-Lock Braking System have speed sensor ring that is an integral part of each outer CV joint. Sensor ring and joint must be replaced as a unit. When CV joint is removed from vehicle, speed sensor ring adjustment must be checked.

Disassembly

1) Disassembly procedures are similar for inner and outer CV joints. Remove rubber or steel deflector ring, if equipped. Remove CV boot clamp protectors, if equipped, by prying up on tabs on both sides of clamp halves.

2) On "S" body, use Remover/Installer (J-35566) to remove large CV boot clamp. On all other CV joint clamps, cut and remove clamps. Roll boot back on shaft to expose joint assembly. Using Snap Ring Pliers (J-8059), spread retaining ring at inner race and pull shaft from joint assembly. Slide boot off shaft.

3) For outer CV joint, use brass drift to tap lightly on bearing cage until it tilts enough to remove 1 ball bearing. Rotate cage and repeat procedure to remove remaining balls from cage.

4) On inner CV joint, remove ball retaining ring. Balls will come out when cage and inner race are removed from outer race.

5) On outer CV joint, pivot cage and inner race until 90° to normal installed position (cage windows will align with lands of outer race). *See Fig. 6*. Lift cage and

Axle Shafts

GENERAL MOTORS (Cont.)

inner race from outer race. Rotate inner race upward and out of cage.

Inspection

1) Wash all parts in solvent and dry with compressed air. Inspect outer ball races for excessive wear and scoring. Inspect splined stub shaft for wear, cracks and twisted splines.

2) Inspect all 6 balls for pitting, cracking or scoring. Dulling of surface is normal. Inspect cage for excessive wear on inside and outside spherical surfaces. Look for heavy brinelling of cage windows and for cracks or chips.

3) Inspect inner race for excessive wear or scoring. If any damage is found, replace entire CV joint assembly. Polished areas in races and on cage spheres are normal and do not require joint replacement.

Reassembly

1) Apply a light coat of grease on ball grooves of inner and outer races. Install inner race into cage using a rotating action opposite of removal. Inner race retaining ring should face axle side.

2) On inner CV joints, be sure ball bearing retaining ring is installed on inner race side facing small end of cage. Align windows of cage with outer race lands, and pivot cage with inner race into tilted position (opposite of removal).

3) Install ball bearings one at a time into outer CV joint as cage is tilted and rotated. On inner CV joint, insert ball bearings through cage windows. After balls are installed into cage of outer joint, pivot cage and inner race into installed position.

4) Slide new small CV boot clamp, boot, and large CV boot clamp onto axle shaft. Coat inside lip (large diameter end) of boot with grease. Slide large CV boot clamp onto end of boot.

5) Spread ears of bearing race retaining ring, and slide CV joint onto axle shaft until retaining ring seats in groove. Pack joint with approximately one-half grease provided in seal kit. Apply remaining grease inside seal.

6) Slide boot toward joint until small end of boot is in groove in axle shaft. Position small clamp over boot and in groove. Install large CV boot clamp in position (use Remover/Installer (J-35566) on "S" body).

7) Before tightening clamps, set length of CV joint using thermoplastic (Black) boot to 5.2" (133 mm). *See Fig. 7*. Install Clamp Installer (J-34773), breaker bar, and torque wrench on CV boot clamp. Tighten small clamp to 100 ft. lbs. (136 N.m) and large clamp to 130 ft. lbs. (176 N.m). *See Fig. 6*.

Fig. 7: Thermoplastic (Black) CV Boot Lengths

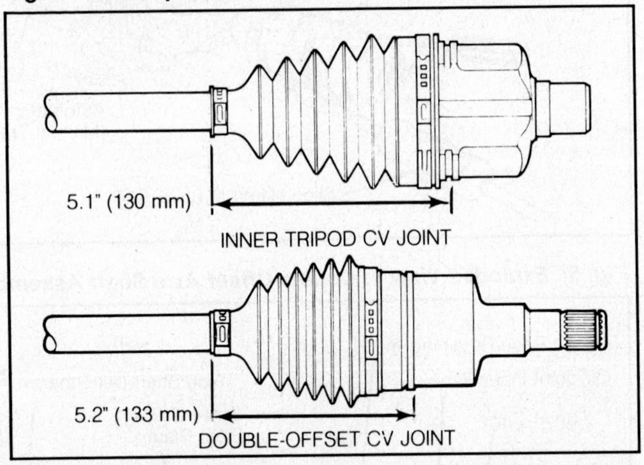

Before tightening clamps ensure boot is set to proper length.

8) If equipped with rubber deflector ring, stretch and install ring. Install steel deflector ring by placing ring on shaft. Place 2 1/2" pipe coupling over shaft and cover end with 1/8" (3 mm) steel plate that has 15/16"

Fig 6: Disassembly & Reassembly of Double-Offset Axle Shafts & CV Joints

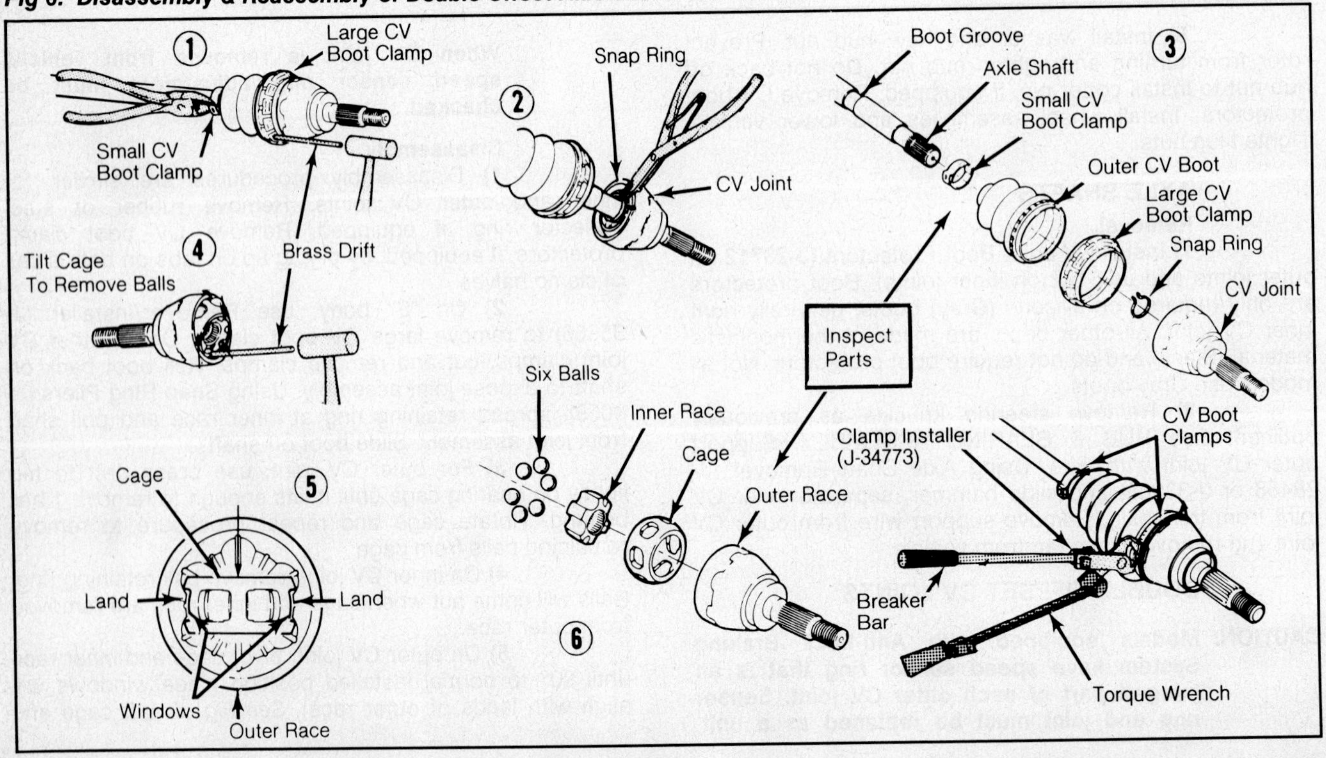

GENERAL MOTORS (Cont.)

(24 mm) hole in the center. Install hub nut and tighten to press steel plate against coupling to seat deflector. *See Fig. 8.*

Fig. 8: Installing Steel Deflector Ring

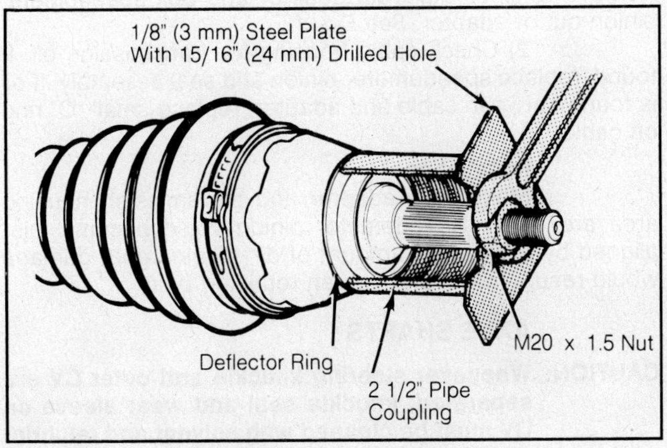

Use only for double-offset joints equipped with steel ring.

INNER TRIPOD CV JOINT

Disassembly

1) Remove CV boot clamp protectors, if equipped, by prying up on tabs on both sides of clamp halves. On "S" body, use Remover/Installer (J-35566) to remove large CV boot clamp. On all other CV boot clamps, cut and remove clamps. Roll boot back on shaft and slide tripod housing off spider assembly.

2) Wrap spider bearings with tape or install Retainer (J-33165). Slide spacer ring away from spider. Slider spider assembly back on shaft and remove spider retaining ring. Slide spider assembly off axle shaft. Remove CV boot. Clean assembly and inspect for wear or damage.

Reassembly

1) Install spider with counterbore facing end of axle shaft. Install retaining ring and slide spider assembly toward end of shaft. Install spacer ring and seat it in its groove. Slide spider assembly back into position and seat retaining ring.

Fig. 9: Exploded View of Inner Tripod CV Joint

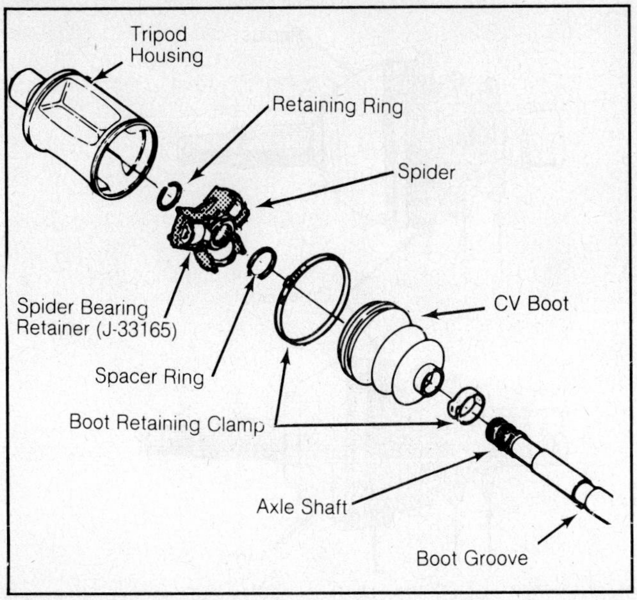

2) Repack CV boot with half of grease supplied in service kit. Repack tripod housing with remaining grease. Reverse removal procedure to complete reassembly. On "S" body, use Remover/Installer (J-35566) to install large CV boot clamp.

3) Before tightening clamps, set length of CV joint using thermoplastic (Black) boot to 5.1" (130 mm). *See Fig. 7.* Install Clamp Installer (J-34773), breaker bar, and torque wrench on CV boot clamp. Tighten small clamp to 100 ft. lbs. (136 N.m) and large clamp to 130 ft. lbs. (176 N.m). *See Fig. 6.*

Axle Shaft Installation

1) Install steering knuckle as previously outlined. See HUB & BEARING ASSEMBLY. With CV boot protectors installed, position axle shaft loosely into steering knuckle. Support axle shaft in position with wire.

2) Seat axle shaft in transaxle by using a screwdriver in the groove provided on the large CV boot clamp. *See Fig. 1.* Tap screwdriver until shaft is seated. Complete installation as previously outlined under HUB & BEARING ASSEMBLY.

TIGHTENING SPECIFICATIONS

Application	Ft. Lbs. (N.m)
Ball Joint	
To Control Arm Nuts	
"P" Body	13 (18)
All Other Bodies	50 (68)
To Steering Knuckle Nut	
"A" Body	33 (45)
"J, N" Bodies	45 (61)
"P" Body	50 (68)
"S" Body	82 (111)
All Other Bodies	[1]
Brake Caliper Bolts	
"C" Body	38 (51)
"E, K" Bodies	63 (85)
"P" Body	35 (47)
"S" Body	65 (88)
All Other Bodies	28 (38)
Hub & Bearing Assembly Bolts	
"A" Body	[2] 63 (85)
"P" Body	62 (84)
"J, N" Bodies	40 (54)
All Other Bodies	70 (95)
Hub Nut	
"C, E, H, K" Bodies	180 (244)
"P" Body	200 (271)
"S" Body	137 (186)
All Other Bodies	185 (251)
Tie Rod End Nut	
"C, E, H, K" Bodies	[3]
All Other Bodies	35 (47)
Wheel Lug Nuts	
"S" Body	76 (103)
All Other Bodies	100 (136)

[1] – Tighten to 7 ft. lbs. (9 N.m), then turn nut additional 1/2 turn. Minimum torque of 37 ft. lbs. (50 N.m) must be obtained.

[2] – "A" body with heavy duty brakes – 70 ft. lbs. (95 N.m).

[3] – Tighten to 7 ft. lbs. (9 N.m), then turn nut additional 1/3 turn. Minimum torque of 33 ft. lbs. (45 N.m) must be obtained.

Axle Shafts

CHRYSLER CORP. – LIGHT TRUCKS

Caravan, Mini Ram Van, Voyager

DESCRIPTION

Power from transaxle is transmitted to drive wheels by 2 axle shafts of unequal length. Both shafts use tripod type CV joints on inner end and Rzeppa type CV joints on outer end. Tripod joints are splined to transaxle while Rzeppa joint has stub axle splined to hub. Drive axle assemblies are of 2 different types, either G.K.N. or Citroen. *See Fig. 2.*

REMOVAL & INSTALLATION

SPEEDOMETER PINION GEAR

NOTE: **Speedometer pinion gear is located in extension housing on right side of transaxle. Pinion must be removed before removing right axle shaft assembly.**

Fig. 1: Speedometer Pinion and Adapter

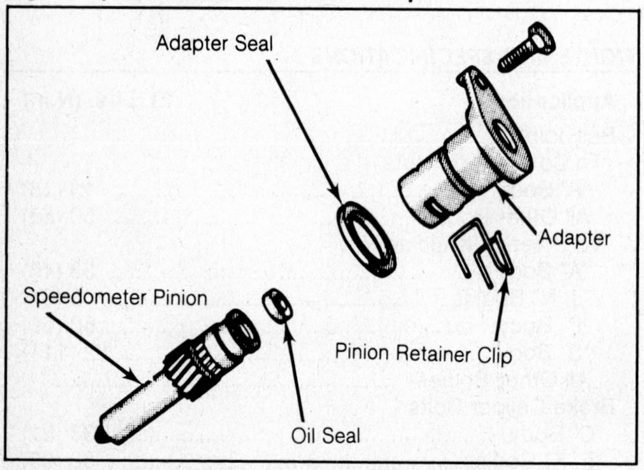

Remove pinion before removing right axle shaft.

Removal

1) Remove clamp retaining bolt which holds pinion assembly into extension housing. Leaving cable connected, gently remove adapter and pinion from housing. Remove retainer clip from adapter and pull speedometer pinion out of adapter. *See Fig. 1.*

2) Check cable housing for transmission oil. If found, replace speedometer pinion and seal assembly. If oil is found between cable and adapter, replace small "O" ring on cable.

Installation

Make sure adapter and transmission housing area are clean. Speedometer pinion could become misaligned by even small amount of dirt. Pinion gear damage would result. Install and tighten retaining bolt.

AXLE SHAFTS

CAUTION: **Whenever steering knuckle and outer CV are separated, knuckle seal and wear sleeve on CV must be cleaned with solvent and relubricated before reassembly. Do not allow solvent to contact CV boot. Cover seal contact area of wear sleeve with 1/4" bead of multipurpose grease. Fill in lip-to-housing cavity of seal and lightly coat entire seal face and lip with multipurpose grease.**

Removal

1) Remove cotter key and hub nut lock from end of axle shaft. Loosen hub and lug nuts. Raise vehicle. Remove hub nut and wheel. Remove lower ball joint clamping bolt at steering knuckle. Pry against knuckle and control arm to separate ball joint from knuckle.

2) Separate outer CV joint from hub by holding CV joint and pushing out on knuckle assembly. DO NOT pry on CV joint. Support drive axle shaft at CV joints. Pull out on inner CV joint, holding inner joint at housing.

NOTE: **Outer CV joint stub axle holds hub and bearing assembly together when installed. If vehicle must be moved, install bolt through hub assembly so assembly cannot loosen.**

Fig. 2: Chrysler Corp. Axle Shaft Identification

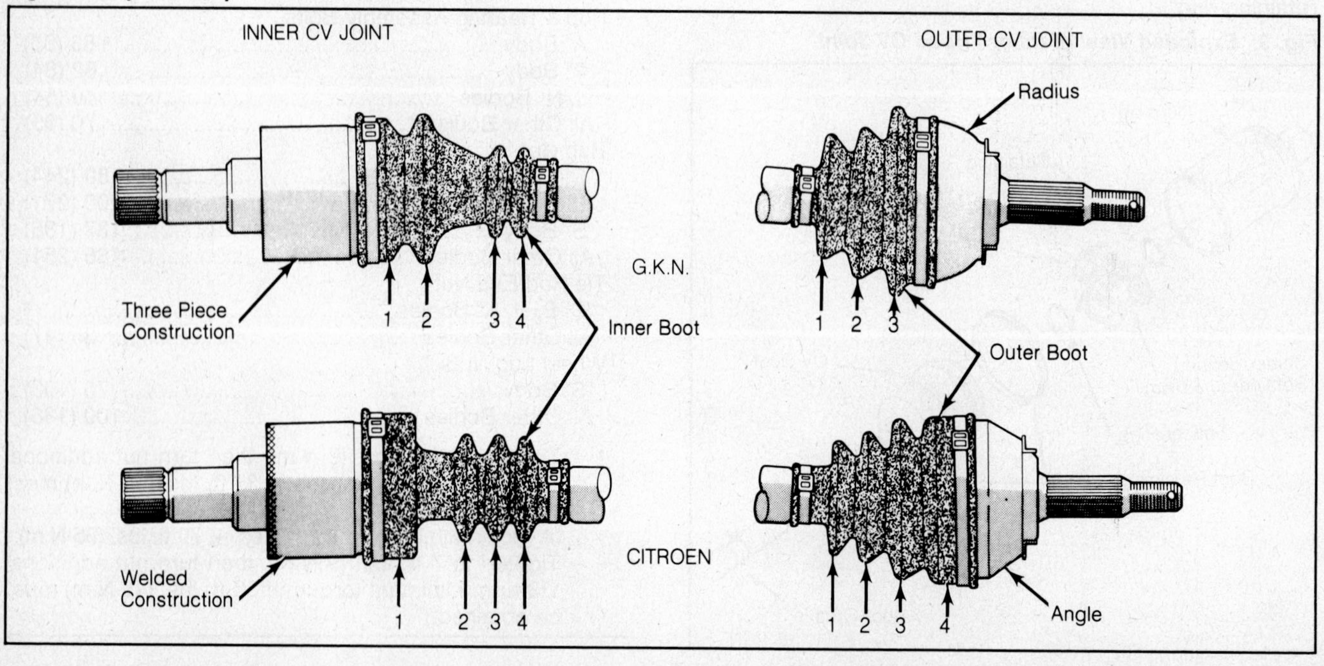

CHRYSLER CORP. – LIGHT TRUCKS (Cont.)

Fig. 3: Exploded View of Axle Shaft Assembly

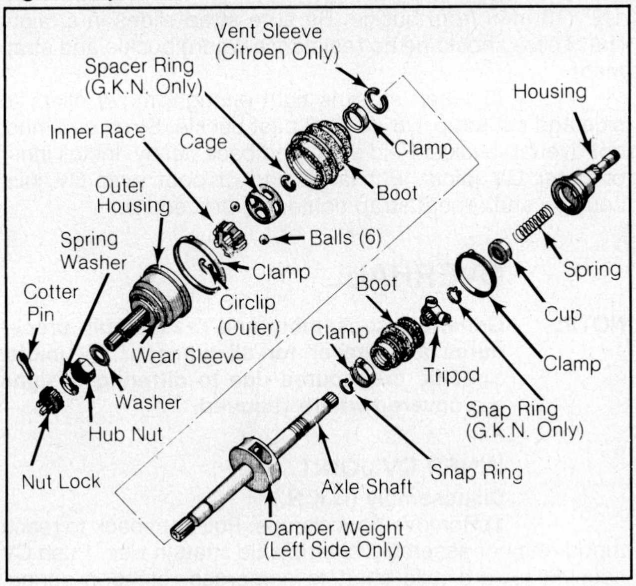

Fig. 4: CV Boot Clamps

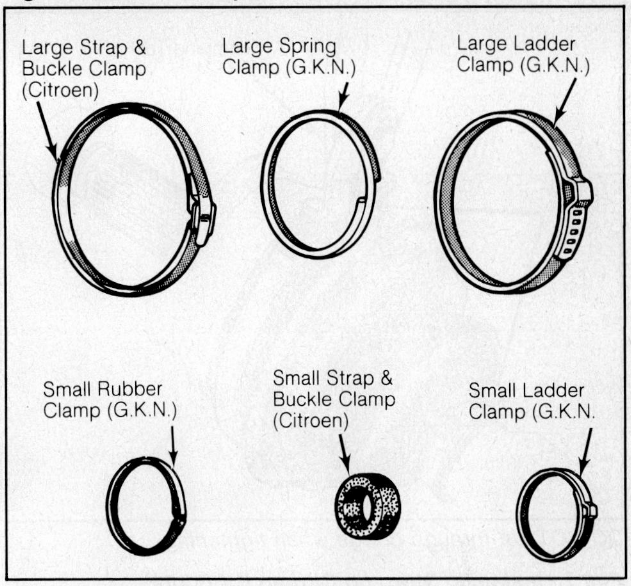

Citroen clamps may be found on G.K.N. type joints.

Fig. 5: CV Joint Boot Placement

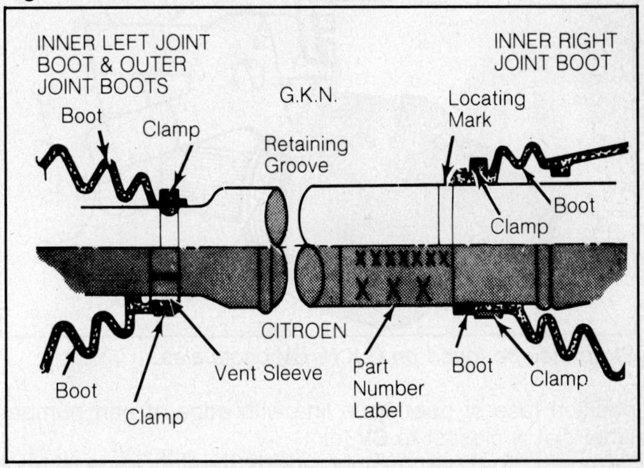

Use prior boot location if markings are unclear.

Installation

1) Hold inner CV at housing and guide splines into transaxle or intermediate shaft assembly. Push knuckle assembly outward and install outer CV stub axle. Reinstall knuckle on lower ball joint. Use original bolt or same grade as original for clamping ball joint to arm. Tighten clamping bolt to 70 ft. lbs. (95 N.m).

2) If inner CV boot appears twisted or distorted, vent it by inserting blunt rod between boot and shaft. If boot is held by rubber clamp, leave it clamped. If held by metal clamp, clamp must be removed and replaced with new clamp after venting operation is complete. Use correct clamp and clamping procedure as described in CV boot installation in this article.

3) Install speedometer pinion. Fill differential. Install hub nut and tighten to 180 ft. lbs. (243 N.m). Install lock, spring washer, and new cotter pin. Wrap opened ends of cotter pin tightly around nut lock. Install wheel and tighten lug nuts to 95 ft. lbs. (129 N.m).

CV BOOTS

CAUTION: When using Clamping Pliers (C 4124) on G.K.N. boots, use care to avoid cutting bridge of clamp or damaging boot.

Removal (All Models)

Remove drive axle from vehicle. Remove clamps holding boot to CV joint and shaft. Remove CV joint from axle shaft. Use procedures described in drive axle overhaul and CV disassembly in this article. Remove boot from axle shaft.

Installation (G.K.N.)

1) Several different types of clamps are used on G.K.N. boots. Metal ladder type is most common. On inner CV joints, small rubber clamp may be used to hold small end of boot to axle shaft. Large metal spring clamp may be used to hold large end of boot to inner CV housing. *See Fig. 4.*

2) If equipped, slide small rubber clamp onto axle shaft. Slide inner CV boot onto shaft and position correctly. Right inner boot lip should line up with locating mark on axle shaft. Small end of left inner boot and both outer boots should fit in groove on axle shaft. *See Fig. 5.*

3) Fasten small end of boot either by placing rubber clamp over groove in boot or by fitting metal clamp in groove on boot. Make sure boot is properly located and locate metal clamp tangs in slots. Make clamp as tight as possible by hand.

4) Close bridge of metal clamp with Clamp Pliers (C 4124). *See Fig. 6.* Install correct CV joint as described in CV assembly procedure in this article. Fit large end of boot in groove on housing or over retaining shoulder. Make sure boot does not get twisted.

5) Install metal spring clamp or metal ladder clamp in groove on boot. Locate ladder clamp tangs in slots, making clamp as tight as possible by hand. Close bridge with Clamp Pliers (C 4124) and squeeze tightly.

Installation (Citroen Type)

1) Citroen type CV joint boot uses 2-piece clamp consisting of strap and buckle. *See Fig. 4.* Clamp Installer (C 4653) is used to tighten and cut strap clamps. *See Fig. 7.*

2) Slide small end of boot onto axle shaft. If installing outer CV joint boot, place vent sleeve under boot clamp groove. *See Fig. 5.* On right inner CV joint boot,

CHRYSLER CORP. – LIGHT TRUCKS (Cont.)

Fig. 6: Installing Ladder Clamps on G.K.N. CV Boots

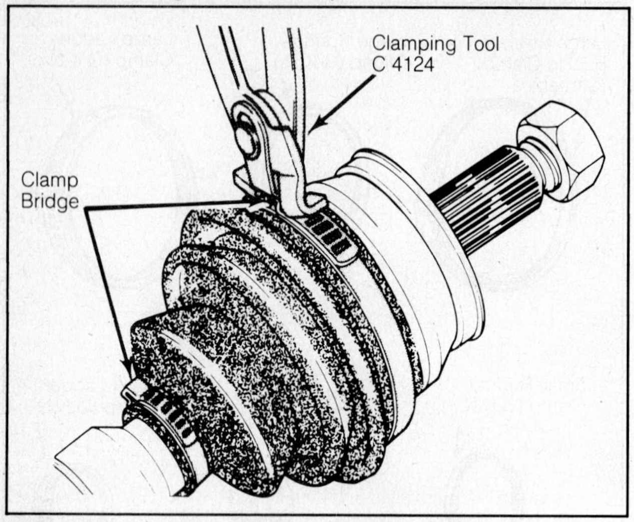

DO NOT cut through bridge when tightening.

Fig. 7: Installing Strap on Citroen CV Boots

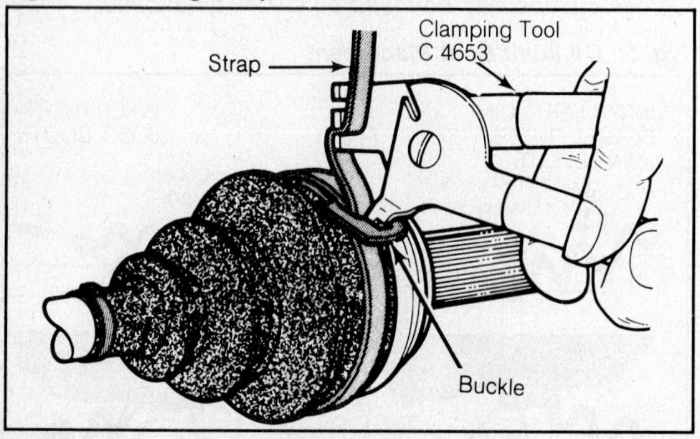

Strap may be found on G.K.N. CV boots also.

position face of boot lip in line with edge of part number label that is closest to CV joint.

3) If part number label is missing, edge of boot lip should be placed in same position as previous boot was installed. Use mark left on shaft as reference for this location.

4) On left inner and both outer CV joint boots, edge of boot lip should be aligned with mark on shaft left by previous boot. This mark should be between shoulders of shaft.

5) Wrap binding strap around small end of boot twice. Add free length of two 1/2" (64 mm) straps. Cut strap and remove from boot. Pass end of strap through buckle and fold it back about 1 1/8" (29 mm) on inside of buckle. Put strap around boot with inside of buckle toward boot.

6) Wrap strap around boot once. Thread strap through buckle and wrap strap around boot again. Run strap through buckle again and fold it slightly to keep strap from slipping backward. Open Clamp (C 4653) and put strap in narrow slot about 1/2" (13 mm) from buckle.

7) Hold strap with one hand. Push clamping pliers forward and slightly upward. Fit hook of tool into eye of buckle. Tighten strap by closing handles of pliers. Rotate handle end of tool down while slowly releasing pressure on handles. Allow handles to open as end of pliers is rotated.

8) Open pliers completely and remove from strap and buckle. If strap is not tight, repeat tightening procedure once or twice, if necessary. Always grasp strap 1/2" (13 mm) from buckle. Be sure strap slides in straight line. There should be no resistance where buckle and strap meet.

9) When strap is tight enough, move pliers to side and cut strap 1/8" (3 mm) past buckle. Strap end must not overlap buckle. Fold strap end back neatly. Install inner or outer CV joints. Put large end of boot over CV joint housing and repeat strap tightening procedure.

OVERHAUL

NOTE: General disassembly and reassembly procedures are similar for all types of CV joints. Specific procedures due to differing designs are covered where required.

INNER CV JOINT

Disassembly (G.K.N.)

1) Remove boot clamps. Pull boot back to reach tripod retainer assembly. Clamp axle shaft in vise. Push CV housing toward axle shaft to compress retention spring. Bend retaining tabs (part of housing) back with pliers while spring is compressed.

2) Support housing in horizontal plane while retention spring pressure forces housing off tripod. Remove outer snap ring from axle shaft groove. Remove tripod by hand. Use brass punch to tap tripod body if necessary.

Disassembly (Citroen Type)

1) Remove boot clamps and pull boot back. Tripod retainer ring (no tabs) is rolled into groove in outer housing. Spread retainer ring out at each tripod roller, using chisel or small pry tool. Retention spring will push housing from tripod.

NOTE: Hold tripod rollers in place on trunion studs while removing housing. Secure rollers in place with tape when out of housing. Rollers and needle bearings could fall if not held in place.

2) Retainer ring can also be cut out from housing. DO NOT damage housing or groove when cutting ring. New rings come with boot kit.

Inspection (All Types)

Clean grease from assembly. Check housing races and tripod components for wear or pitting. Inspect spring, spring cup, and rounded end of axle shaft. Replace parts if worn, galled, or pitted.

Reassembly (G.K.N. Type)

1) Install new axle boot on axle shaft. Slide tripod onto axle shaft, chamfered side first. Flat side of tripod should be next to retaining ring groove. Using grease found in boot kit, put 2 of 3 packets provided into boot. Third packet goes into CV housing.

2) Position retention spring in housing spring pocket. Install spring cup onto exposed end of spring. Lubricate concave surface of spring cup with grease.

NOTE: Make sure that spring stays centered in housing spring pocket as tripod seats in spring cup.

3) Install housing over tripod and bend retaining tabs into original position. Make sure tabs can hold tripod in housing. Place boot over retaining groove in housing. Clamp boot in position.

CHRYSLER CORP. – LIGHT TRUCKS (Cont.)

Reassembly (Citroen Type)

1) Fasten new boot to shaft. Install inner snap ring. Slide tripod onto shaft. Both sides are identical, so either side can go onto shaft first. Install outer snap ring in groove on shaft, locking tripod in position.

2) Using grease provided in boot kit, place 2/3 of one packet into boot. Rest of grease goes into housing. Position spring in housing spring pocket with spring cup in place over exposed end of spring. Lightly grease concave surface of spring cup.

NOTE: **Make sure that spring stays centered in housing spring pocket as tripod seats in spring cup.**

3) Remove tape holding tripod rollers and needle bearings in place on tripod studs. Hold rollers and needle bearings while installing tripod into housing. Roll edge of new retaining ring into machined groove in housing. Use hammer and dull punch to roll ring.

4) Hold retaining collar in place with 2 "C" clamps while rolling retainer ring into groove. Make sure retaining collar will hold tripod in housing. Position boot over retaining groove in housing. Clamp boot in place.

OUTER CV JOINT

Disassembly

1) Remove and discard boot clamps. Wipe away grease so CV joint body edge is visible. Hold axle shaft in soft jaws of vise. Support joint body. Using soft hammer, give top of CV joint body sharp blow to break joint loose from internal circlip in groove at end of shaft.

2) The wear sleeve on outer CV housing is a wiping surface for hub bearing seal. If sleeve is bent or damaged, pry wear sleeve away from machined ledge of CV joint. Remove and discard circlip from shaft groove. New circlip comes with replacement boot kit. *See Fig. 8.*

Fig. 8: Exploded View of Outer CV Joint

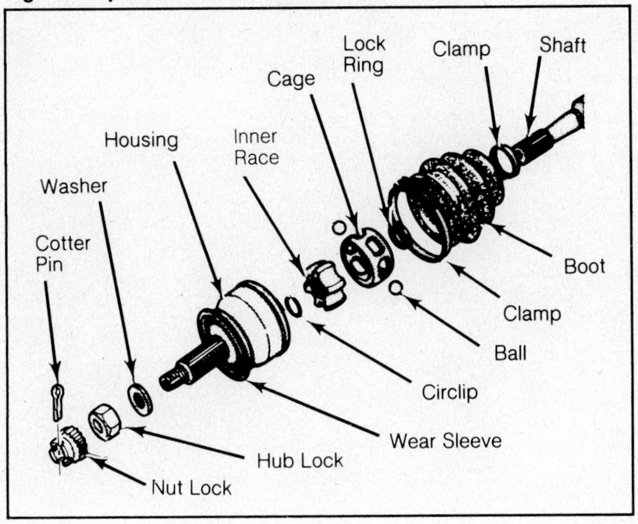

3) If shaft is damaged, remove heavy spacer ring from inner groove of G.K.N. type axle. If joint was operating properly, replace only the boots. If joint was noisy or badly worn, replace complete joint. Manufacturer recommends boot replacement whenever joint is replaced.

4) Wipe grease off outer CV joint and index mark inner race (cross), cage, and housing with dab of paint. Position joint vertically in vise, using soft jaws to clamp on splined shaft. Press down on one side of inner race to tilt cage and remove ball from opposite side. Repeat until all 6 balls are out.

CAUTION: **DO NOT hit cage when using hammer and drift to loosen CV joint.**

5) If joint is very tight, use brass drift and hammer to tap inner race and remove balls. Tilt cage and inner race assembly to vertical. Place 2 opposing, elongated cage windows in area between ball grooves in outer race. Citroen type joints alternate 2 short and one long cage window while G.K.N. type joints alternate long and short windows or have all identical cage windows.

6) Remove inner race and cage assembly by pulling upward away from housing. Turn inner race 90° to cage. Align elongated cage window with one of spherical lands on race. Raise land to cage window and remove inner race by swinging it out of cage.

Inspection

Check grease for contamination. Wash all parts in solvent and dry with compressed air. Inspect races for excessive wear and scoring. Check splined shaft and nut threads for damage. Check 6 balls for pitting, cracks, scoring, and wear. Inspect cage for excessive wear on spherical surfaces, surface ripples on cage window, cracks, or chipping. Inspect inner race (cross) for excessive wear or scoring of ball races.

NOTE: **Any defects found justify replacing CV assembly as unit. Some polishing is normal, especially in ball races and in cage spheres. Replace polished parts only if they cause noise and vibration.**

Reassembly

1) Position new wear sleeve on joint housing machined ledge. Assemble Installer (C 4698) and install wear sleeve. Lightly oil all components before reassembly. Align parts according to paint markings.

2) Insert one inner race (cross) into cage window and feed race into cage. Pivot inner race to fully assemble cage and race. Align opposing elongated cage windows with housing land. Feed cage assembly into housing. Pivot cage 90° to complete installation.

3) On properly assembled G.K.N. units, counterbore of inner race should face outward from joint. On properly assembled Citroen units, inner race and cage chamfers will face outward from joint. On all types, apply lubricant to ball races from packet in boot kit. *See Fig. 9.*

4) Distribute grease equally between all sides of ball grooves. Each joint uses one packet. Insert balls into raceways by tilting cage and inner race assembly. Fasten boot to shaft. Insert new circlip from shaft groove kit.

5) Position outer joint on splined end of axle shaft. Put hub nut on stub axle. Engage splines and tap sharply with mallet. Check that circlip is properly seated by trying to pull joint off shaft. Install large end of boot over joint housing making sure that boot is not twisted. Attach boot to housing.

TIGHTENING SPECIFICATIONS

Application	Ft. Lbs. (N.m)
Axle Hub Nut	180 (244)
Ball Joint Clamp Nut	70 (95)
Wheel Lug Nut	95 (129)

CHRYSLER CORP. – LIGHT TRUCKS (Cont.)

Fig. 9: Cutaway Views of Outer CV Joints

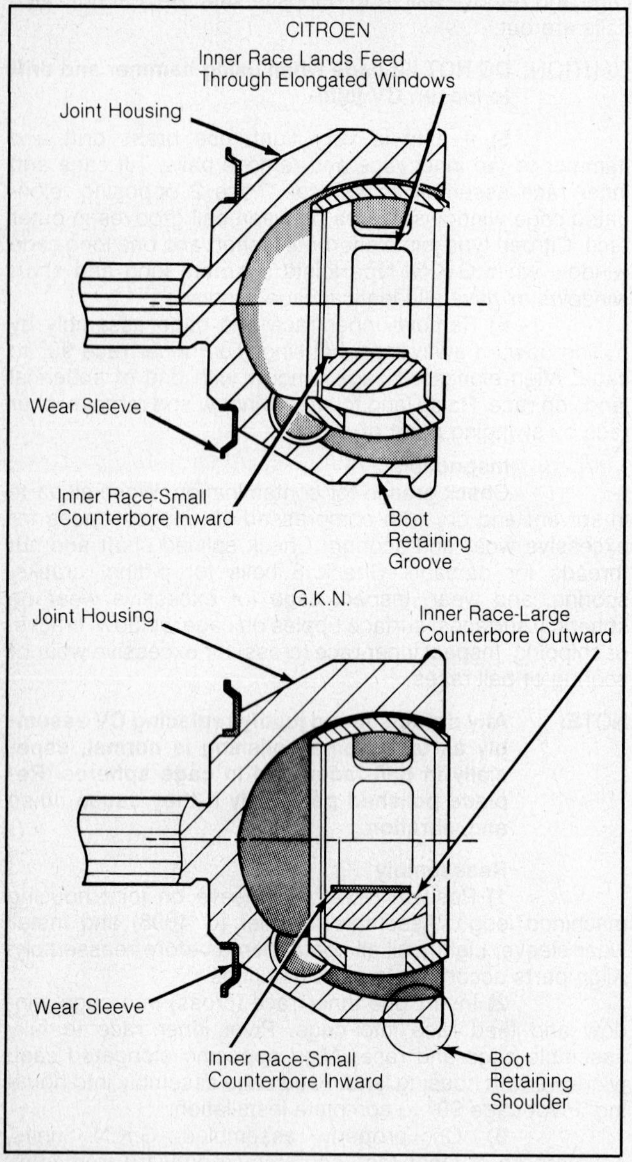

Note correct cage and inner race installation.

GENERAL MOTORS "S" TRUCKS

DESCRIPTION

Chevrolet and GMC "S" series 4WD models use an independent front drive axle which incorporates constant velocity (CV) joints. The inner CV joints uses a "Tri-Pot" design, and outer CV joints are a "Double Offset" design.

The inner CV joint is completely flexible, plus it has capability of in and out movement. The outer CV joint is also flexible, but cannot move in and out.

REMOVAL & INSTALLATION

AXLE SHAFTS

Removal & Installation

1) Raise and support vehicle on safety stands. Remove wheel and brake caliper and flex hoses at brackets. Remove tie rods at steering knuckle using Puller (J-24319). Remove shock lower bolts and push shocks out of way.

2) Remove drive axle-to-axle tube bolts. Remove axle shaft cotter pin, nut and washer. Position inner part of drive axle forward and support away from frame. Remove shaft from hub using Puller (J-28733). Remove axle shaft from vehicle.

3) Install axle shaft into hub. Tighten nut and washer to specifications. Install retainer and install cotter pin. To complete installation, reverse the remaining removal procedure.

Fig. 2: Removing Front Drive Axle

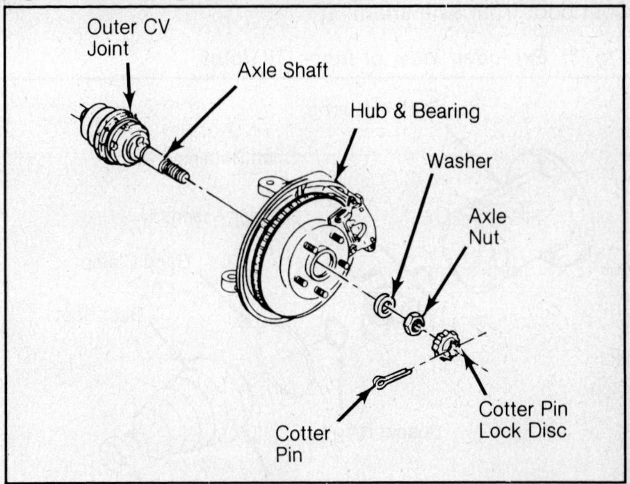

OVERHAUL

DISASSEMBLY

Inner CV Joint

1) Using side cutter pliers, cut dust boot band clamps. Pull boot from tri-pot housing and separate tri-pot housing from spider assembly. Wrap tape around spider assembly to retain needle bearings.

2) Using snap ring pliers, remove axle shaft retaining ring and separate spider assembly from axle shaft. Note position of counter bore of spider for reas-

Fig. 1: Exploded View of Chevrolet & GMC "S" Series Drive Axle

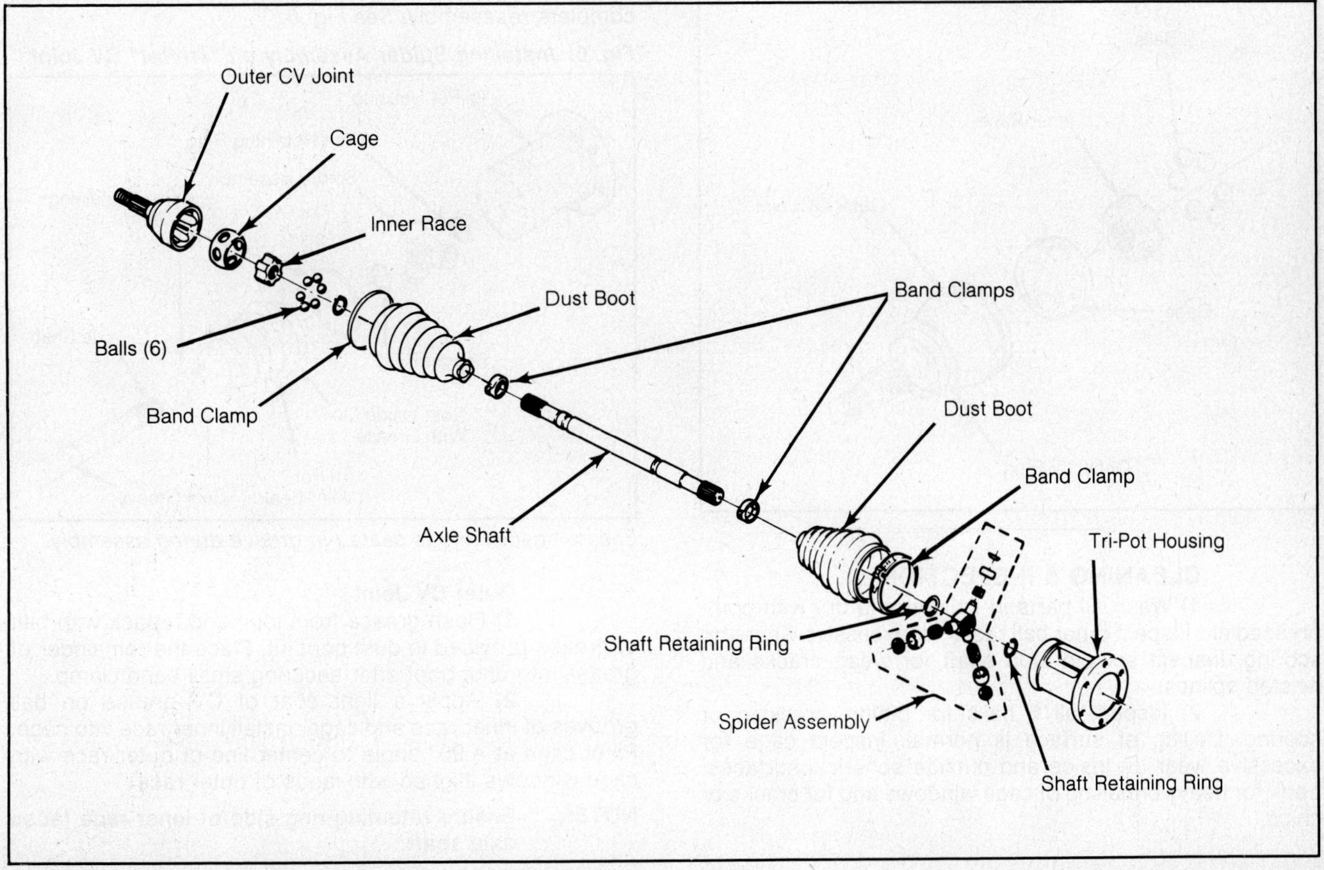

GENERAL MOTORS "S" TRUCKS (Cont.)

sembly purposes. Remove spacer ring if necessary. Slide dust boot from axle shaft.

Fig. 3: Exploded View of Inner CV Joint

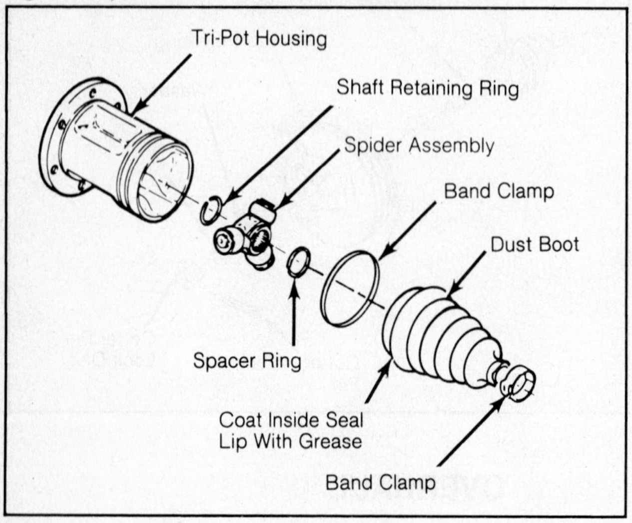

Outer CV Joint

1) Using side cutter pliers, cut dust boot clamps. Pull boot back from CV joint. Using Snap Ring Pliers (J-8059), spread retaining ring ears apart and pull axle shaft out of CV cage.

2) Using a brass drift and hammer, gently tap on cage until its tilted enough to remove the first ball. Repeat procedure to remove the remaining balls. Rotate inner race at a 90° angle to cage and remove race. *See Fig. 5*

Fig. 4: Exploded View of Outer CV Joint

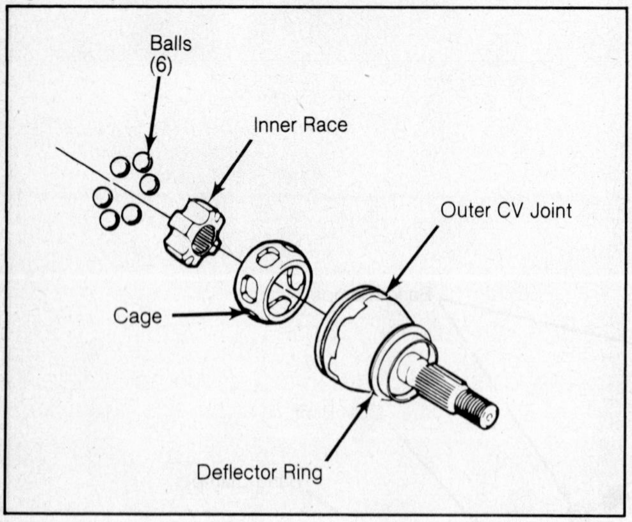

CLEANING & INSPECTION

1) Wash all parts in solvent and dry with compressed air. Inspect outer ball races for excessive wear and scoring. Inspect splined stub shaft for wear, cracks and twisted splines.

2) Inspect all 6 balls for pitting, cracking or scoring. Dulling of surface is normal. Inspect cage for excessive wear on inside and outside spherical surfaces. Look for heavy brinelling of cage windows and for cracks or chips.

Fig. 5: Removing Outer CV Joint Cage

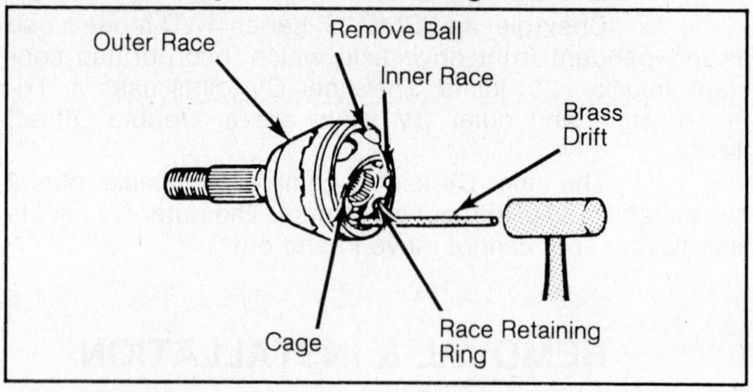

3) Inspect inner race for excessive wear or scoring. If any damage is found, replace entire CV joint assembly. Polished areas in races and on cage spheres are normal and do not require joint replacement.

REASSEMBLY

Inner CV Joint

1) Flush grease from tri-pot housing. Repack housing using half of grease supplied in dust boot kit. Place the remainder of grease into dust boot after securing small band clamp.

2) Position small band clamp to dust boot. Slide boot onto axle shaft. Ensure boot seats into groove on axle shaft and secure clamp using side cutter pliers. Install spacer ring, if previously removed. Ensure ring seats into groove properly.

3) Install spider with counter bore facing end of axle shaft. Install snap ring to retain spider assembly. Position large band clamp onto dust boot. Coat inner lip with grease and seat boot into groove on tri-pot housing. Secure band clamp. Reverse disassembly procedures to complete reassembly. *See Fig. 6.*

Fig. 6: Installing Spider Assembly on "Tri-Pot" CV Joint

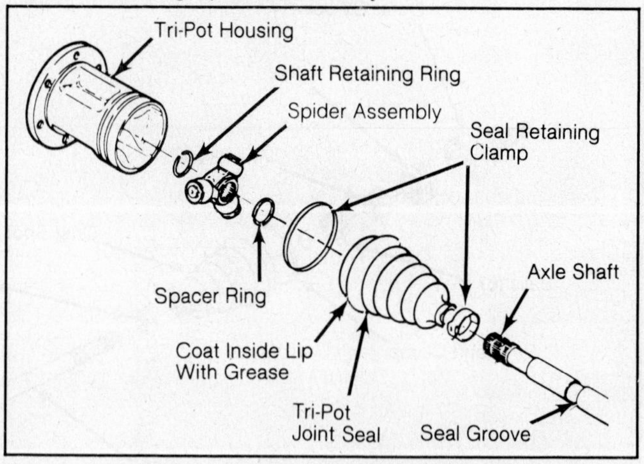

Ensure spacer ring is seated in groove during assembly.

Outer CV Joint

1) Flush grease from joint and repack with half of grease provided in dust boot kit. Place the remainder of grease into dust boot after securing small band clamp.

2) Apply a light coat of CV grease on ball grooves of inner race and cage. Install inner race into cage. Pivot cage at a 90° angle to center line of outer race with cage windows aligned with lands of outer race.

NOTE: **Ensure retaining ring side of inner race faces axle shaft.**

GENERAL MOTORS "S" TRUCKS (Cont.)

3) Install ball bearings one at a time into outer CV joint as cage is tilted and rotated. After balls are installed into cage, pivot cage and inner race into installed position.

4) Position band clamp onto boot and slide boot onto axle shaft. Secure clamp using side cutter pliers. Coat inside lip (large diameter end of seal with CV grease) and slide large band camp onto dust boot.

5) Install snap ring onto axle shaft, and slide CV joint onto axle shaft until snap ring seats in groove. *See Fig. 7.* Slide dust boot toward joint until dust boot is in groove in axle shaft. Secure large band clamp. Reverse remaining disassembly procedure.

Fig. 7: Installing Outer CV Joint to Axle Shaft

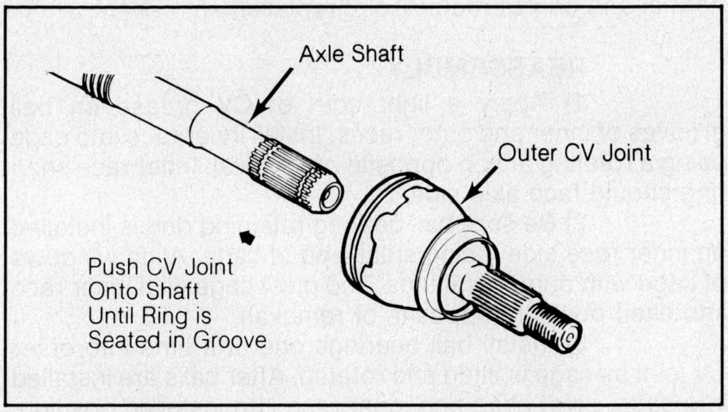
Axle Shaft
Outer CV Joint
Push CV Joint
Onto Shaft
Until Ring is
Seated in Groove

TIGHTENING SPECIFICATIONS

Application	Ft. Lbs. (N.m)
Drive Axle Nut-to-Hub and Bearing	174 (235)
Drive axle Flange to Differential Flange	63 (85)
Hub-to-Knuckle Assembly	77 (105)
Wheel Lug Nuts	75 (102)

JEEP CHEROKEE, COMANCHE & WAGONEER

DESCRIPTION

Jeep 4WD Cherokee, Comanche and Wagoneer models use a front drive axle which incorporates constant velocity (CV) joints. The CV joints are a "Double Offset" design. The CV joints are flexible, but cannot move in and out.

REMOVAL & INSTALLATION

AXLE SHAFTS

Removal

1) Raise and support vehicle. Remove wheel and brake caliper. Wire caliper out of way. Remove cotter key, cotter key lock disc, axle nut and washer. Remove 3 bolts holding hub to steering knuckle. Remove hub assembly and splash shield from steering knuckle.

2) On left side, remove axle shaft. On right side, disconnect vacuum harness from shift motor. Remove shift motor from axle housing and remove axle shaft.

Installation

To install axle shaft, reverse removal procedure. On right side, ensure shift collar is in position on intermediate shaft and that axle shaft is fully engaged over end of intermediate shaft. Install shift motor with fork engaged with collar.

OVERHAUL

DISASSEMBLY

1) Cut and remove both outer boot clamps. Slide boot off outer CV joint.

2) Using a block of wood seated on inner race, tap joint from shaft. If shaft is clamped in a vise, be sure to use protective vise jaws.

3) Tap outer CV cage with a brass punch until cage is tilted out far enough to remove first ball bearing. Remove remaining ball bearings in same manner.

4) Rotate outer CV joint cage outward until it is at a 90° angle to installed position. Align 2 oblong holes in outer joint cage with slots in interior wall of spindle housing and remove cage and inner race.

5) Remove inner race from cage by aligning shoulder between race grooves with inside of oblong cage holes. Rotate inner race out of cage using larger of 2 openings in cage.

6) Remove retaining ring and spacer ring from shaft and remove outer boot.

CLEANING & INSPECTION

1) Wash all parts in solvent and dry with compressed air. Inspect outer ball races for excessive wear and scoring. Inspect splined stub shaft for wear, cracks and twisted splines.

2) Inspect all 6 balls for pitting, cracking or scoring. Dulling of surface is normal. Inspect cage for excessive wear on inside and outside spherical surfaces. Look for heavy brinelling of cage windows and for cracks or chips.

3) Inspect inner race for excessive wear or scoring. If any damage is found, replace entire CV joint assembly. Polished areas in races and on cage spheres are normal and do not require joint replacement.

REASSEMBLY

1) Apply a light coat of CV grease on ball grooves of inner and outer races. Install inner race into cage using a rotating action opposite of removal. Inner race snap ring should face axle side.

2) Be sure ball bearing retaining ring is installed on inner race side facing small end of cage. Align windows of cage with outer racelands, and pivot cage with inner race into tilted position (opposite of removal).

3) Install ball bearings one at a time into outer CV joint as cage is tilted and rotated. After balls are installed into cage, pivot cage and inner race into installed position.

4) Slide new seal clamp for small end of boot seal, boot seal and seal retainer onto axle shaft. Coat inside lip (large diameter end of seal) with CV grease. Slide seal retainer on end of seal.

5) Spread ears of bearing race snap ring, and slide CV joint onto axle shaft until snap ring seats in groove. Pack joint with approximately 1/2 of grease provided in seal kit. Apply remaining grease inside seal.

6) Slide seal toward joint until small end of seal is in groove in axle shaft. Position small clamp over small end of seal and into groove and tighten.

TIGHTENING SPECIFICATIONS

Application	Ft. Lbs. (N.m)
Drive Axle Nut-to-Hub and Bearing	175 (237)
Hub-to-Knuckle Assembly	75 (101)
Wheel Lug Nuts	75 (101)

Fig. 1: Exploded View of Jeep Cherokee, Comanche & Wagoneer Drive Axle

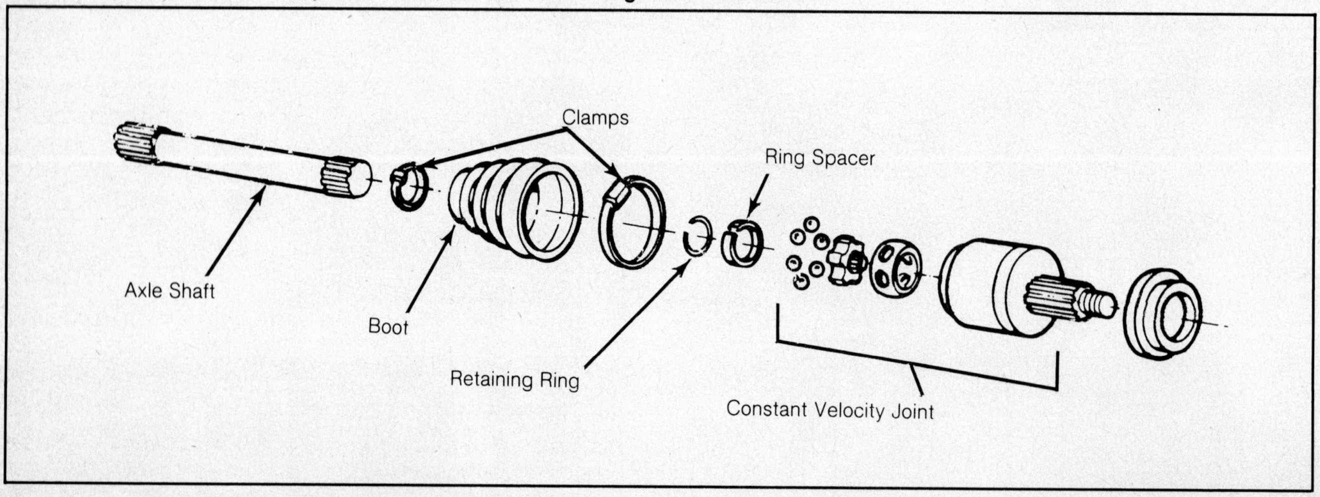

AMERICAN MOTORS MODEL 128

Eagle

DESCRIPTION

Eagle models are equipped with model 128 full-time 4-wheel drive transfer case. This unit provides fully differentiated 4-wheel drive under all operating conditions. The model 128 is a single range unit. Selection of 4-wheel drive is automatic and can be engaged while moving. This system does not require any external linkage to achieve 4-wheel operation.

The Select Drive system consists of a dash mounted switch, vacuum actuated shift lever in transfer case and vacuum actuated front axle disconnect.

Select Drive provides drive train selection appropriate for road conditions. Selection of 2WD mode activates transfer case shift lever to provide torque to rear propeller shaft only. Selection of 4WD mode activates transfer case shift lever to provide torque to both front and rear propeller shafts. *See Fig. 1.*

Differentiated operation occurs through a coupling connected to an open differential. Torque is distributed to the front and rear propeller shafts through 2 drive sprockets and drive chain. Case assembly is cast aluminum. Case consists of front and rear halves and a rear retainer.

LUBRICATION

SERVICE INTERVAL

Check transfer case fluid level at first 5 month or 5,000 mile interval. Change fluid every 30,000 miles.

FLUID TYPE

Use Dexron II automatic transmission fluid or equivalent.

CAPACITY

About 7 pints (3.3L) or up to bottom edge of fill plug hole.

TROUBLE SHOOTING

LUBRICANT LEAKS PAST YOKE OR OUT OF VENT

Overfilled condition or vent may be closed or restricted. Yoke seal may be worn or damaged.

NOISY OPERATION

Incorrect or insufficient lubrication. Incorrect tire pressure. Mismatched or unequal tire sizes and type.

TESTING

WILL NOT ENGAGE 2WD

NOTE: **Select Drive Vacuum Diagram and related component diagrams are at the end of this article. These diagrams may aid in diagnosing vacuum related problems of the Select Drive system.**

1) Raise vehicle so all 4 wheels are free to rotate. Start engine. Disconnect mode selector vacuum harness at steel tube connection. Check for vacuum at

Fig. 1: Eagle Select Drive Transfer Case

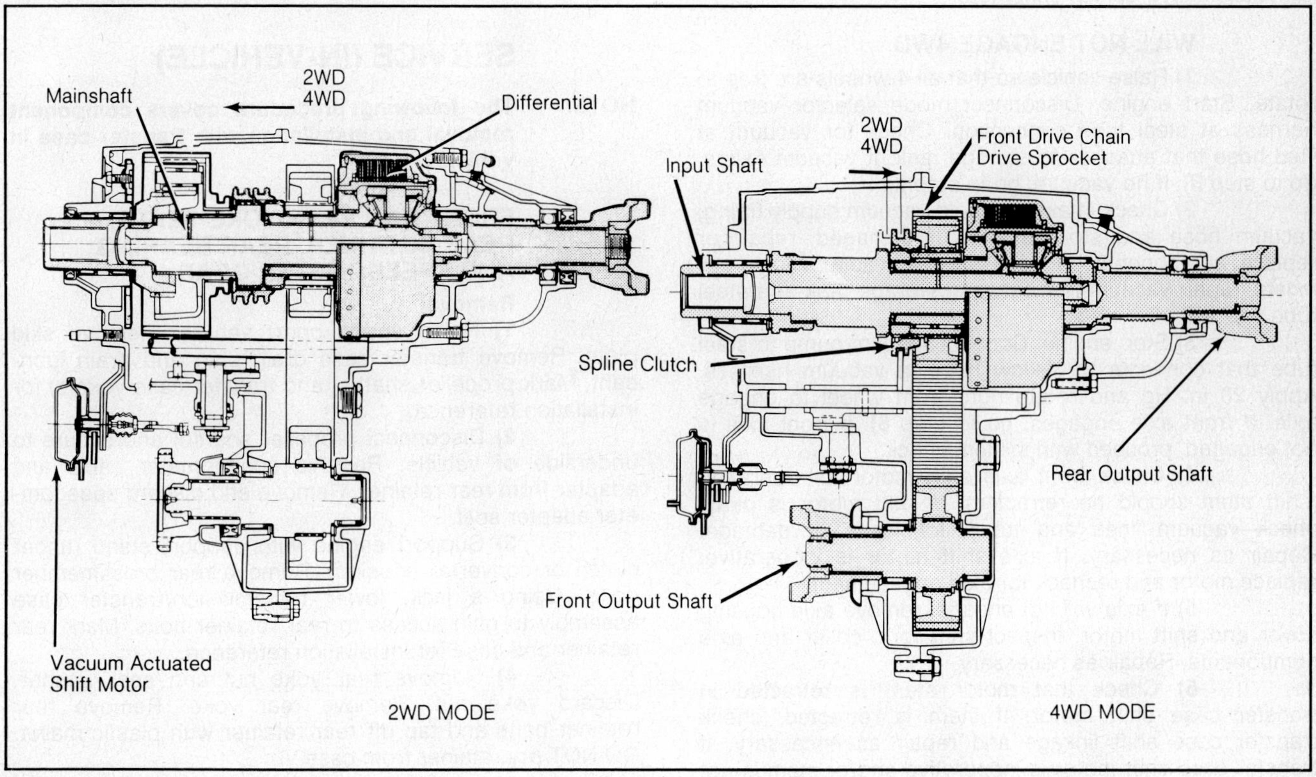

Red hose that attaches to storage tank. If vacuum exists, go to step **3)**. If no vacuum, go to step **2)**.

2) Check intake manifold vacuum supply fitting, vacuum hose and storage tank. If damaged, repair or replace components as necessary. If vacuum leak still exists, repair vacuum line between storage tank and steel tube. If vacuum exists at Red hose, proceed with system check.

3) Stop engine. Connect vacuum pump to steel tube that connects to Green hose in vacuum harness. Apply 20 in. Hg and rotate propeller shaft to engage transfer case. Shift transmission into "P" or first gear. If transfer case engages, go to step **7)**. If transfer case does not engage, go to step **4)**.

4) Check transfer case shift motor. Motor stem should be extended. If stem is not extended, check vacuum tubes for leaks and/or damage. Repair as necessary. If transfer case shift motor is still inoperative, check shift motor function. Replace shift motor if found defective. If shift motor is operative, go to step **5)**.

5) If transfer case will not engage in 2WD, check transfer case shift linkage and repair as necessary. If linkage is okay and transfer case will not shift into 2WD, repair case.

6) If transfer case now engages in 2WD, check axle for 2WD mode engagement (disconnected). If front axle is not in 2WD mode, check axle shaft motor and replace as necessary.

7) If front axle shift motor is okay, check the shift mode selector switch and vacuum harness. Repair as necessary. If front axle shift motor will not disengage, check vacuum lines and repair as necessary.

8) If vacuum lines are okay and axle will not disengage, remove axle housing cover and shift motor. Inspect shift fork, collar and axle components. If components are okay, replace shift motor.

WILL NOT ENGAGE 4WD

1) Raise vehicle so that all 4 wheels are free to rotate. Start engine. Disconnect mode selector vacuum harness at steel tube connection. Check for vacuum at Red hose that attaches to storage tank. If vacuum exists, go to step **3)**. If no vacuum, go to step **2)**.

2) Check intake manifold vacuum supply fitting, vacuum hose and storage tank. If damaged, repair or replace components as necessary. If vacuum leak still exists, repair vacuum line between storage tank and steel tube.

3) Stop engine. Connect vacuum pump to steel tube that connects to Yellow hose in vacuum harness. Apply 20 in. Hg and rotate right front wheel to engage axle. If front axle engages, go to step **6)**. If front axle is not engaged, proceed with system check.

4) Check front axle shift motor for operation (shift stem should be retracted). If shift motor is okay, check vacuum lines and tubes for leaks or damage. Repair as necessary. If axle shift motor is inoperative, replace motor and recheck for axle engagement.

5) If axle will not engage, remove axle housing cover and shift motor. Inspect shift fork, collar and axle components. Repair as necessary.

6) Check that motor stem is retracted in transfer case shift motor. If stem is retracted, check transfer case shift linkage and repair as necessary. If transfer case shift motor is inoperative and/or stem is not retracted, check vacuum hoses and repair as necessary.

7) If transfer case motor is still inoperative, test motor operation with a vacuum pump. If vacuum motor is defective, replace motor and retest.

8) If transfer case motor is okay and transfer case does not engage in 4WD, check axle shift linkage and repair as necessary. If linkage is okay, repair transfer case as necessary.

VACUUM SHIFT MOTOR TEST

1) Disconnect vacuum harness from shift motor. Connect vacuum pump to front port and apply 15 in. Hg to motor. On transfer case, rotate rear propeller shaft to engage transfer case in 4WD mode. On front axle, rotate right wheel to fully disengage axle.

2) Shift motor should maintain vacuum applied for at least 30 seconds. If motor does not hold vacuum, replace motor. If motor does hold vacuum, go to step **3)**.

3) Disconnect vacuum pump from front port of vacuum motor. Connect pump to rear port of motor and plug connecting port. Apply 15 in. Hg to motor. Shift transmission into "P" or first gear. Vacuum should hold for 30 seconds. If vacuum is not maintained, replace motor.

4) If motor maintains vacuum, remove plug from connecting port and check for vacuum at this port. If vacuum is not present, rotate rear propeller shaft on transfer case or right wheel on rear axle, to ensure full engagement of shift motor.

5) If no vacuum exists at connecting port, pull back boot on stem and measure distance that stem has extended. Stem should extend a distance of 5/8" (16 mm), as measured from the edge of shift motor housing to "E" ring on stem.

6) If stem does not extend the specified distance or if stem extends the specified distance but no vacuum is present at the connecting port, replace motor.

SERVICE (IN-VEHICLE)

NOTE: **The following procedure covers component removal and installation with transfer case in vehicle.**

FRONT AND REAR YOKE SEALS, REAR RETAINER, REAR BEARING AND SPEEDOMETER GEAR

Removal

1) Raise and support vehicle. Remove skid plate. Remove transfer case drain plug and drain lubricant. Mark propeller shaft(s) and transfer case yoke(s) for installation reference.

2) Disconnect propeller shaft(s) and secure to underside of vehicle. Remove speedometer cable and adapter from rear retainer. Remove and discard speedometer adapter seal.

3) Support engine with support stand (under clutch or converter housing). Remove rear crossmember bolts. Using a jack, lower transmission/transfer case assembly to gain access to rear retainer bolts. Mark rear retainer and case for installation reference.

4) Remove rear yoke nut and seal washer. Discard yoke nut. Remove rear yoke. Remove rear retainer bolts and tap off rear retainer with plastic mallet. DO NOT pry retainer from case.

AMERICAN MOTORS MODEL 128 (Cont.)

5) Remove differential shim(s) and speedometer gear from output shaft. Remove bearing snap ring (if equipped), bearing and rear yoke seal from retainer.

Installation

1) Install rear output bearing in rear retainer with shielded side facing case interior. Install bearing snap ring (if equipped). Install yoke seal. Install speedometer gear and differential shim(s).

2) Coat rear retainer mating surface with Loctite 515, align marks made during removal and install rear retainer. Tighten retainer bolts. Install yoke(s), NEW seal washer(s) and nut(s). Tighten nut(s).

3) Install transfer case drain plug and fill transfer case. Raise transmission/transfer case and rear crossmember. Install and tighten crossmember attaching bolts.

4) Remove engine support and jack. Connect propeller shaft(s) after aligning marks made during removal. Install new seal on speedometer adapter. Install adapter and speedometer cable in rear retainer. Install skid plate and lower vehicle.

REMOVAL & INSTALLATION

TRANSFER CASE

Removal

1) Raise and support vehicle. Support engine and transmission with transmission jack or support stand. Disconnect catalytic converter support bracket at adapter housing. Remove skid plate, stiffening brace (if equipped), speedometer cable and adapter. Remove and discard adapter seal.

2) Mark propeller shafts and transfer case yokes for installation reference. Remove vacuum motor harness. Disconnect propeller shafts at yokes and secure to underside of vehicle.

3) Disconnect gearshift and throttle linkage at transmission. Remove rear crossmember and transfer case-to-adapter housing nuts. Lower and remove transfer case from vehicle.

Installation

To install transfer case, reverse removal procedure and note the following: Always replace speedometer adapter seal.

OVERHAUL

TRANSFER CASE

Disassembly

1) Drain lubricant from transfer case. Remove shift motor bracket and motor as an assembly. Remove front and rear yoke nuts. Remove and discard seal washers. Remove yokes. Mount transfer case on wooden blocks ("V" notch blocks to clear front case mounting studs).

2) Mark rear retainer and rear case for reassembly reference, then remove retainer bolts. Using 2 screwdrivers inserted in retainer and case slots, pry retainer loose. Remove retainer.

3) Remove differential shim(s) and speedometer drive gear from output shaft. Remove bolts attaching rear case to front case. Using 2 screwdrivers inserted in slots at each end of rear case, loosen case halves. Remove rear case.

CAUTION: Do not attempt to wedge case halves apart. Case mating surfaces may be damaged.

Fig. 2: Speedometer Gear and Differential Shim

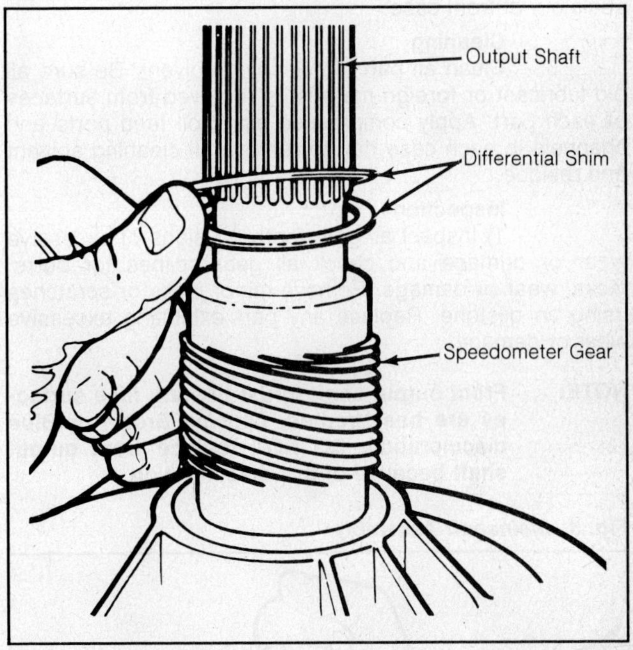

4) Remove thrust bearing and races from front output shaft, noting position of bearing and races for reassembly reference. Remove oil pump from rear output shaft, noting position of pump for reassembly reference (recessed side faces case interior). Remove rear output shaft from mainshaft.

5) Remove 15 mainshaft pilot bearing rollers from shaft or from differential, if rollers dropped off during removal of rear output shaft. Remove mainshaft "O" ring from end of shaft. Remove differential from mainshaft and side gear.

6) Lift front output shaft, sprocket and drive chain upward as an assembly. Tilt front shaft toward mainshaft, slide chain off drive sprocket and remove assembly.

7) Remove front output shaft front thrust bearing assembly from front case or shaft, if bearing and races remained on shaft during removal. Remove drive chain from front output shaft and sprocket.

8) Remove snap ring retaining driven sprocket on front output shaft. Mark sprocket and shaft for reassembly reference and remove sprocket. Remove mainshaft, side gear, drive sprocket and spline gear as an assembly. Place assembly aside on clean surface.

9) Remove shift fork, rail and clutch sleeve as an assembly. Mark sleeve and fork for reassembly reference. Separate sleeve from fork. Drive roll pin out of fork and rail. Remove rail from fork.

10) Remove mainshaft thrust washer from input gear. Remove input gear, input gear thrust bearing and race. Remove shift rail detent bolt, spring and plunger. Remove range sector shaft retaining nut and washer. Remove range lever.

11) Remove range sector. Tap sector shaft with plastic mallet to remove shaft from case bore. Remove range sector shaft "O" ring and seal retainer from case shaft bore.

Transfer Cases

AMERICAN MOTORS MODEL 128 (Cont.)

12) Remove rear output bearing and rear yoke seal from rear retainer. Note position of bearing for reassembly reference (bearing is shielded on one side). Remove input gear. Using a screwdriver, pry front yoke seals out of front case.

Cleaning

Clean all parts in cleaning solvent. Be sure all old lubricant or foreign material is removed from surfaces of each part. Apply compressed air to oil feed ports and channels in each case half to remove all cleaning solvent and residue.

Inspection

1) Inspect all gear teeth for signs of excessive wear or damage and check all gear splines for burrs, nicks, wear or damage. Remove minor nicks or scratches using an oilstone. Replace any part exhibiting excessive wear or damage.

NOTE: **Front output shaft thrust bearing race surfaces are heat treated, causing Brown or Blue discoloration. DO NOT replace front output shaft because of this discoloration.**

Fig. 3: Mainshaft Assembly

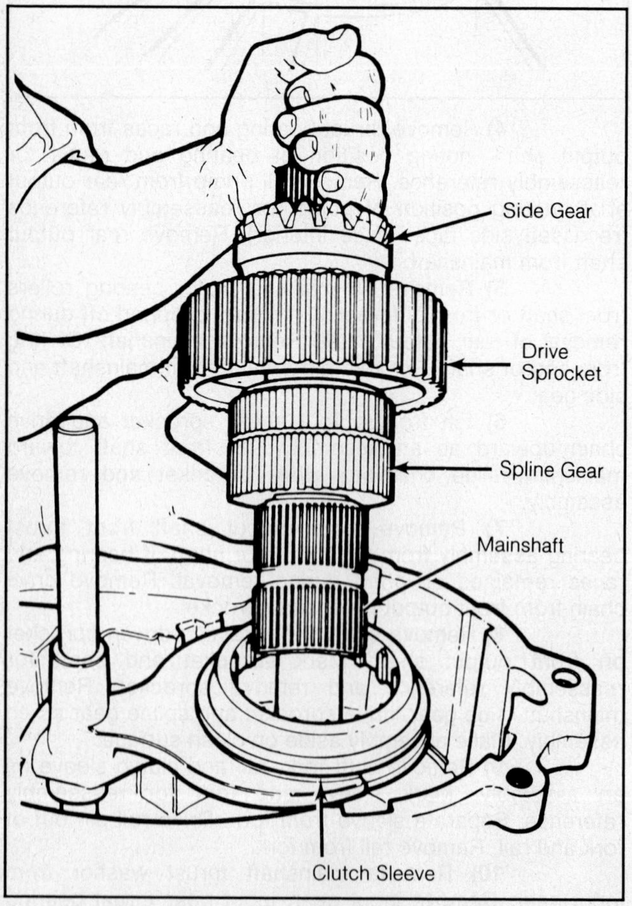

2) Inspect case halves and rear retainer for cracks, porosity, damaged mating surfaces, stripped bolt threads or distortion.

3) Inspect the condition of all bearings. Also check the condition of all bearing bores. Replace any part that exhibits signs of wear or damage.

4) Inspect differential pinions. If the pinions or carrier are damaged or worn excessively, replace the differential as an assembly.

CAUTION: **All bearings and bushings used in transfer case halves must be correctly positioned to avoid blocking oil feed holes. After replacing bearing and/or bushings, check that feed hole is not covered.**

MAINSHAFT

Disassembly

1) Grasp drive sprocket and lift sprocket and side gear up and off mainshaft. Remove mainshaft needle bearings (82) and bearing spacers (3) from mainshaft. Note spacer position for reassembly reference. *See Fig. 4.*

2) Remove spline gear and thrust washer from mainshaft. Remove side gear and thrust washer from sprocket carrier and sprocket. Remove thrust washer from side gear.

3) Remove 1 sprocket carrier snap ring and remove drive sprocket from carrier. Mark sprocket and carrier for reassembly reference. Remove 3 bearing spacers and all sprocket carrier needle bearings (120) from carrier.

NOTE: **The sprocket carrier and mainshaft needle bearings are different sizes. DO NOT intermix needle bearings.**

Fig. 4: Removing Drive Sprocket, Side Gear & Sprocket Carrier from Mainshaft

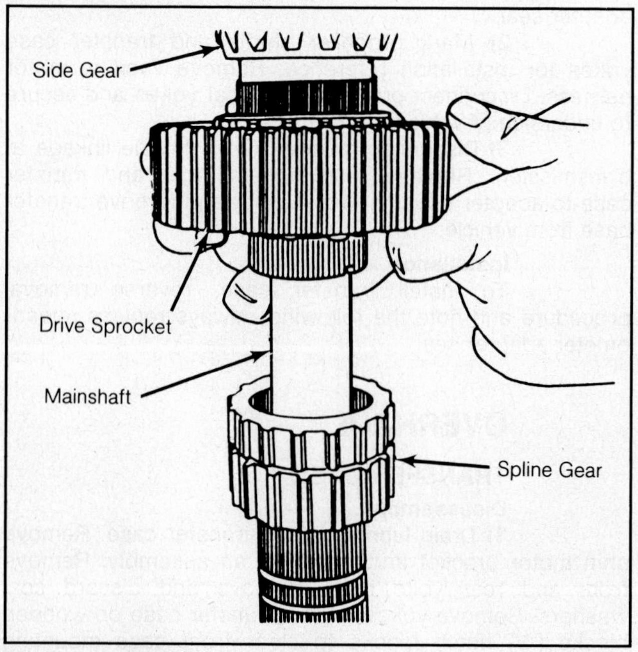

Reassembly

1) Install thrust washer, new "O" ring, needle bearings and bearing spacers on mainshaft. Coat shaft bearing surfaces and all needle bearings with petroleum jelly. Install short bearing spacer on shaft and install first 41 needle bearings.

2) Install long bearing spacer, remaining 41 needle bearings and remaining short spacer. Be careful to avoid displacing bearings as spacers are installed. Use

AMERICAN MOTORS MODEL 128 (Cont.)

Fig. 5: American Motors Model 128 Transfer Case

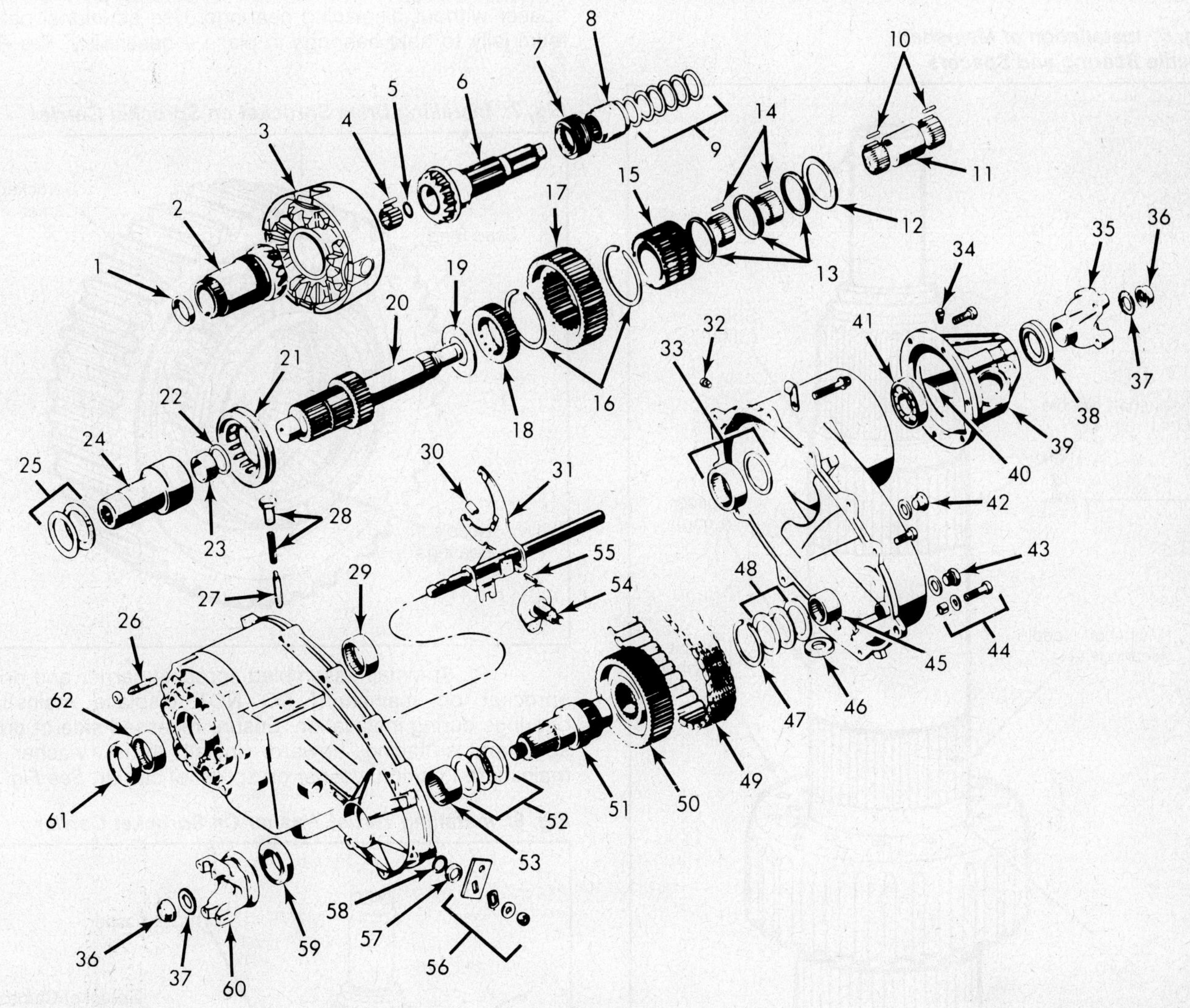

1. Mainshaft Bearing Spacers (Short - 2)
2. Side Gear
3. Differential
4. Mainshaft Pilot Bearings (15)
5. Mainshaft "O" Ring
6. Rear Output Shaft
7. Oil Pump
8. Speedometer Drive Gear
9. Differential Shims
10. Mainshaft Needle Bearings (82)
11. Mainshaft Bearing Spacer (Long - 1)
12. Thrust Washer
13. Sprocket Carrier Needle Bearing Spacers (3)
14. Sprocket Carrier Needle Bearings (120)
15. Sprocket Carrier
16. Sprocket Carrier Snap Rings
17. Drive Sprocket
18. Spline Gear
19. Mainshaft Thrust Washer
20. Mainshaft
21. Clutch Sleeve
22. Mainshaft Thrust Washer
23. Mainshaft Bushing
24. Input Gear
25. Input Gear Thrust Bearing & Race
26. Case Stud
27. Detent Plunger
28. Detent Spring & Bolt
29. Input Gear Rear Bearing
30. Shift Fork Pad
31. Shift Fork & Rail
32. Plug
33. Rear Output Shaft Bearing & Seal
34. Vent
35. Rear Yoke
36. Yoke Nut
37. Yoke Washer
38. Yoke Seal
39. Rear Retainer
40. Vent Chamber Seal
41. Rear Output Bearing
42. Fill Plug & Washer
43. Drain Plug & Washer
44. Alignment Dowel, Washer & Bolt
45. Front Output Shaft Rear Bearings
46. Magnet
47. Driven Sprocket Retaining Snap Ring
48. Front Output Shaft Rear Thrust Bearing & Races
49. Drive Chain
50. Driven Sprocket
51. Front Output Shaft
52. Front Output Shaft Front Thrust Bearing & Races
53. Front Output Shaft Front Bearing
54. Range Sector
55. Shift Fork Retaining Pin
56. Range Lever & Collar
57. Range Lever Retainer
58. Range Lever "O" Ring
59. Front Yoke Seal
60. Front Yoke
61. Input Gear Oil Seal
62. Input Gear Front Bearing

additional petroleum jelly to hold bearings in place, if required. Install spline gear on mainshaft without displacing bearings.

Fig. 6: Installation of Mainshaft Needle Bearing and Spacers

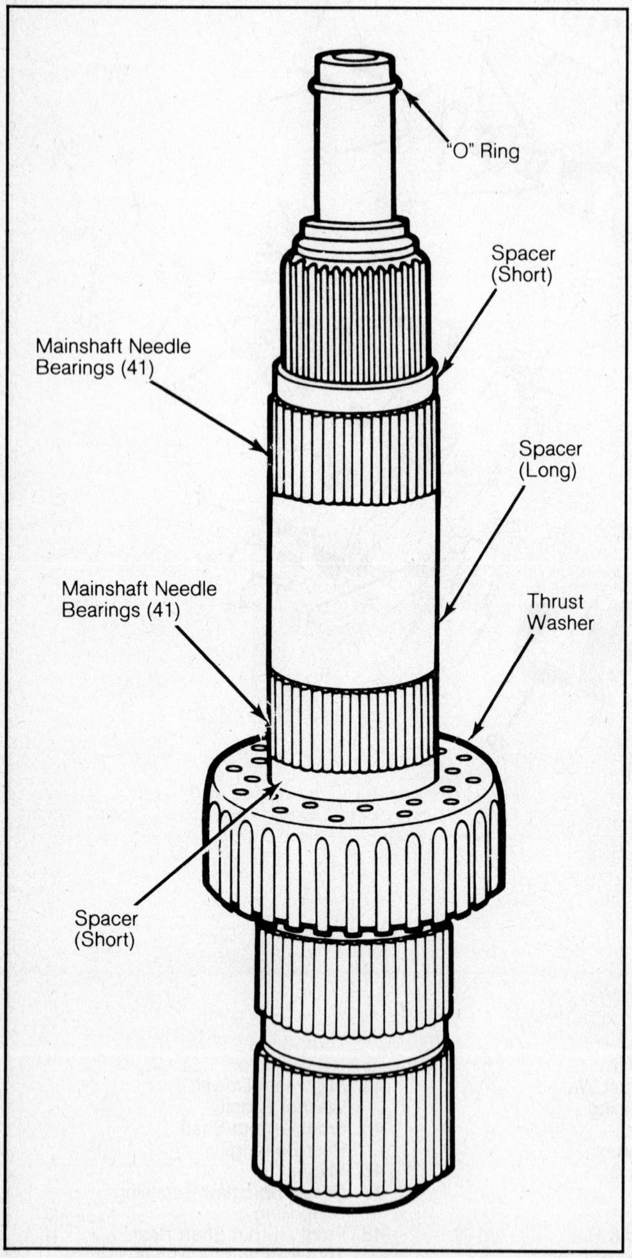

3) Install sprocket carrier in drive sprocket, aligning carrier and sprocket reference marks made during disassembly. Install sprocket carrier snap rings. *See Fig. 7.*

NOTE: **The sprocket carrier teeth are tapered on one side. The drive sprocket has a deep recess on one side. Assemble these components so carrier tapered teeth and sprocket recess are on the same side.**

4) Install sprocket carrier bearings and spacers. Coat carrier bore and all 120 carrier needle bearings with petroleum jelly. Install first spacer in sprocket, then install 60 bearings. Install second (center) bearing spacer and remaining 60 needle bearings. Install remaining spacer without displacing bearings. Use additional petroleum jelly to hold bearings in place if necessary. *See Fig. 7.*

Fig. 7: Installing Drive Sprocket on Sprocket Carrier

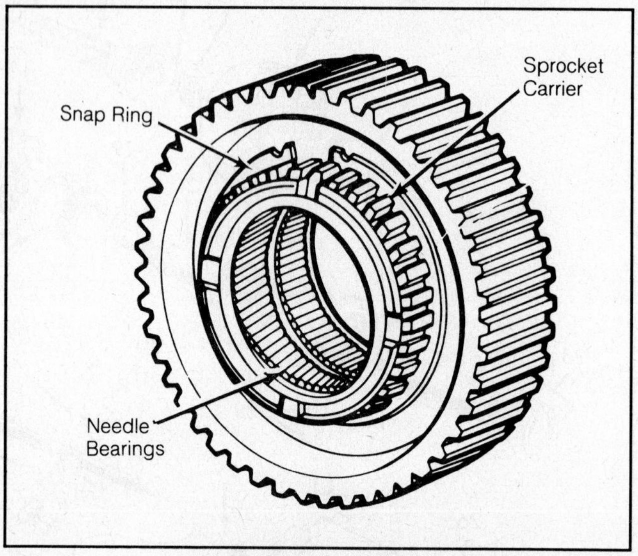

5) Install assembled sprocket carrier and drive sprocket on mainshaft. DO NOT displace mainshaft bearings during installation. Ensure recessed side of drive sprocket is facing upward. Install thrust washer in mainshaft. Position washer on sprocket carrier. *See Fig. 8.*

Fig. 8: Installing Thrust Washer On Sprocket Carrier

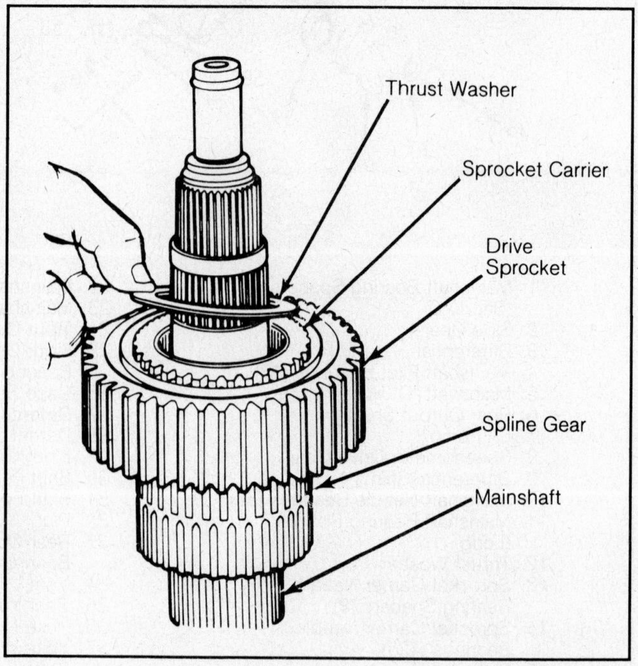

6) Install side gear on mainshaft, ensuring side gear is fully seated in sprocket carrier. Avoid displacing any carrier or mainshaft needle bearings while installing side gear.

AMERICAN MOTORS MODEL 128 (Cont.)

Fig. 9: Select Drive System Vacuum Diagram

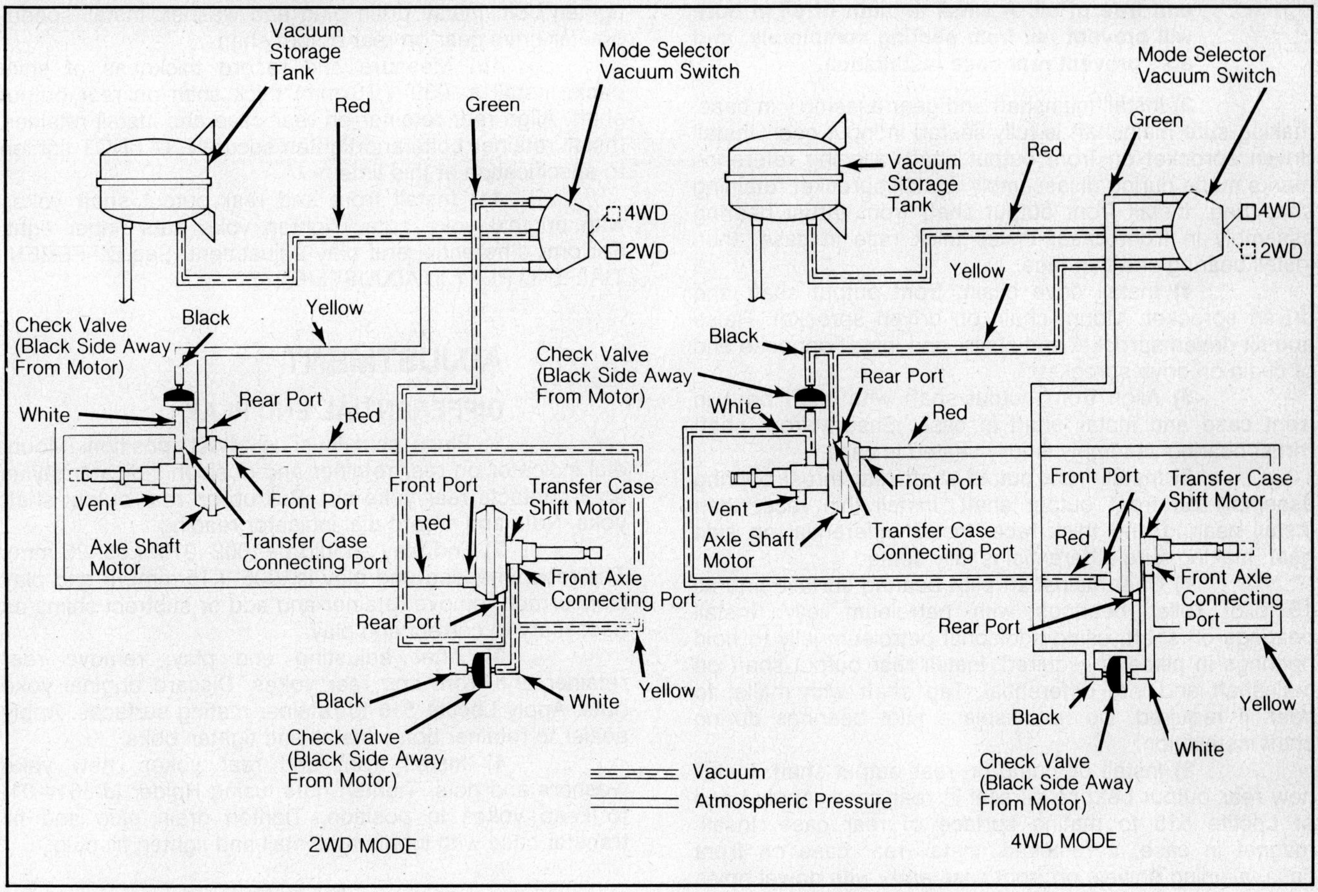

Fig. 10: Select Drive Vacuum Shift Motor

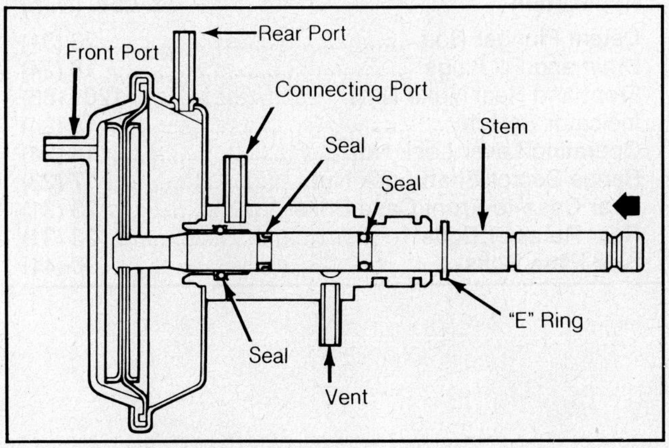

Fig. 11: Select Drive Switch Assembly

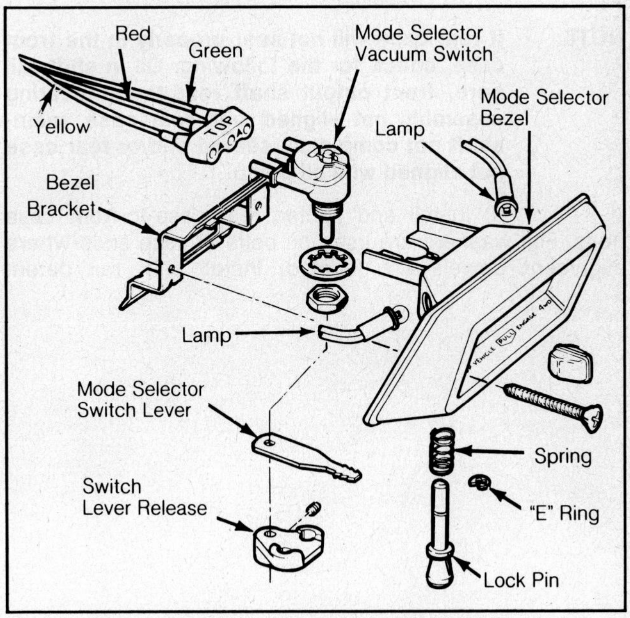

Connecting port is supplied with air when stem is extended. Stem is shown in retracted position.

TRANSFER CASE

NOTE: **During reassembly, lubricate all the transfer case components with automatic transmission fluid (Dexron II), or petroleum jelly where specified.**

Reassembly

1) Install new input gear and front yoke oil seals with Installer (J-29162). Install new range sector shaft "O" ring and retainer in case shaft bore. Install range sector. Install "O" ring seal, retainer, range lever, washer and lock nut on sector shaft. Tighten lock nut.

2) Install thrust bearing and race on input gear. Install input gear in front case. Install mainshaft thrust washer in input gear. Assemble range fork, rail and clutch sleeve. Install assembly in case, making sure rail is fully seated in case bore.

AMERICAN MOTORS MODEL 128 (Cont.)

NOTE: **Rail bore in front case must be absolutely dry and free of oil. A small amount of oil in bore will prevent rail from seating completely, and also prevent rear case installation.**

3) Install mainshaft and gear assembly in case, making sure mainshaft is fully seated in input gear. Install driven sprocket on front output shaft, aligning reference marks made during disassembly. Install sprocket retaining snap ring. Install front output shaft front thrust bearing assembly in front case. Install thick race in case, then install bearing and thin race.

4) Install drive chain, front output shaft and driven sprocket. Mount chain on driven sprocket. Raise and tilt driven sprocket and chain, and install opposite end of chain on drive sprocket.

5) Align front output shaft with shaft bore in front case and install shaft in case. Ensure front shaft thrust bearing assembly is fully seated in case.

6) Install front output shaft rear thrust bearing assembly on front output shaft. Install thin race, then install bearing and thick race. Install differential on side gear, making sure differential is fully seated.

7) Coat mainshaft pilot bearing surface and all 15 pilot roller bearings with petroleum jelly. Install bearings on shaft, using additional petroleum jelly to hold bearings in place, if required. Install rear output shaft on mainshaft and into differential. Tap shaft with mallet to seat, if required. Do not displace pilot bearings during shaft installation.

8) Install oil pump on rear output shaft. Install new rear output bearing oil seal in rear case. Apply bead of Loctite 515 to mating surface of rear case. Insall magnet in case, if removed. Install rear case on front case, aligning dowels on front case ends with dowel holes in rear case. Ensure rear case is fully seated on front case.

NOTE: **If rear case will not seat properly in the front case, check for the following: Oil in shift rail bore, front output shaft rear thrust bearing assembly not aligned with rear case, mainshaft not completely seated and/or rear case not aligned with oil pump.**

9) Install and tighten rear case-to-front case bolts. Flat washers are used on bolts at case ends where alignment dowels are located. Install shift rail detent plunger and spring. Apply sealer to bolt and install and tighten bolt. Install drain plug and washer. Install speedometer drive gear on rear output shaft.

10) Measure and record thickness of shim pack. Install a .030" (.76 mm) thick shim on rear output shaft. Align rear retainer on rear case and install retainer. Install retainer bolts and tighten securely. DO NOT tighten to specification at this time.

11) Install front and rear output shaft yokes with original yoke nuts. Tighten yoke nuts finger tight. Perform differential end play adjustment. See DIFFERENTIAL END PLAY in ADJUSTMENTS.

ADJUSTMENT

DIFFERENTIAL END PLAY

1) Place shift lever in "4WD" position. Mount dial indicator on rear retainer and position indicator stylus so it contacts rear yoke nut. Pull up on rear output shaft yoke. Note and record dial indicator reading.

2) End play should be .002-.010" (.05-.25 mm). The recommended end play is .006" (.15 mm). If end play is incorrect, remove retainer and add or subtract shims as necessary to correct end play.

3) After adjusting end play, remove rear retainer and front and rear yokes. Discard original yoke nuts. Apply Loctite 515 to retainer mating surfaces. Apply sealer to retainer bolts. Install and tighten bolts.

4) Install front and rear yokes, new yoke washers and nuts. Tighten nuts, using Holder (J-8614-01) to keep yokes in position. Tighten drain plug and fill transfer case with lubricant. Install and tighten fill plug.

TIGHTENING SPECIFICATIONS

Application	Ft. Lbs. (N.m)
Detent Plunger Bolt	23 (31)
Drain and Fill Plugs	18 (24)
Front and Rear Yoke Nuts	120 (163)
Indicator Switch	18 (24)
Operating Lever Lock Nut	18 (24)
Range Sector Shaft Lock Nut	17 (23)
Rear Case-to-Front Case Bolts	23 (31)
Rear Retainer Bolts	23 (31)
Skid Plate Bolts	30 (41)

AMERICAN MOTORS MODEL 228

Jeep

DESCRIPTION

Model 228 transfer case with Selec-Trac is full-time/part-time 4WD unit with integral low range. Selec-Trac is only available with automatic transmission and includes: Model 44 front axle with 2WD disconnect, a vacuum control system, Model 228 transfer case, and a 2/4WD mode selector on the instrument panel. This unit provides 4 driving ranges: 4WD high, 4WD low, 2WD high and Neutral.

The vacuum control system consists of 2 vacuum shift motors, a vacuum storage tank, lines and hoses, check valves and a 2/4WD mode selector. *See Fig. 1.* This system will allow for low range operation only after 4WD mode has been selected. The design of the vacuum motors allows for sequential engagement of the vacuum controlled components. *See Fig. 2.* When shifting into 4WD, the axle is shifted first. When shifting into 2WD, the transfer case is shifted first.

LUBRICATION

SERVICE INTERVALS

Check fluid every 5 months or 5000 miles. Replace as necessary. Drain and refill transfer case every 30 months or 30,000 miles.

FLUID TYPE

Use only Jeep Automatic Transmission fluid or equivalent labeled Dexron II.

CAPACITY

Capacity is 6 pints (2.8L).

Fig. 1: Drive Mode Selector on Instrument Panel

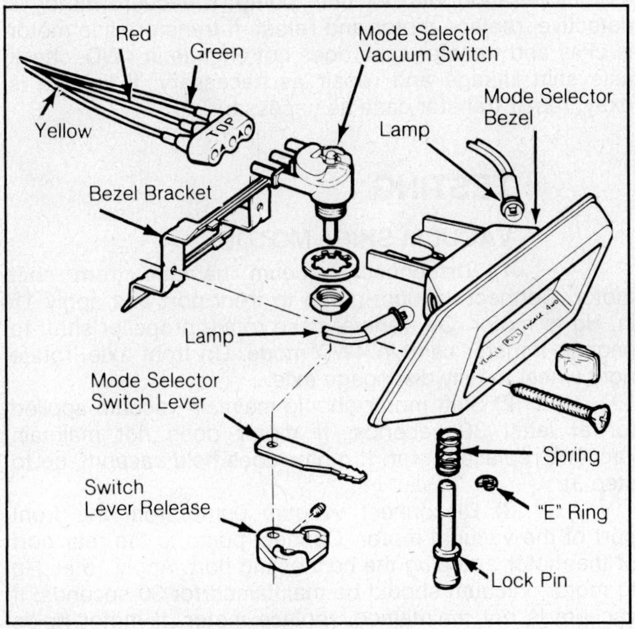

LO range can only be selected when operating in 4WD mode.

Fig. 2: Vacuum Shift Motor

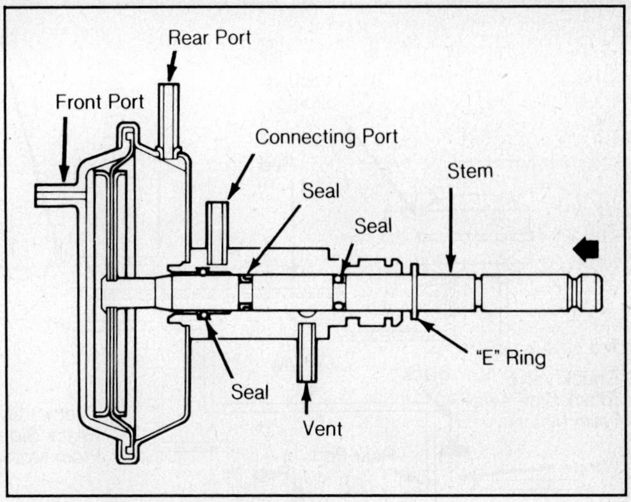

Vacuum at connecting port only when stem is fully extended.

TROUBLE SHOOTING

WILL NOT ENGAGE IN 2WD

1) Raise vehicle so that all 4 wheels are free to rotate. Start engine. Disconnect mode selector vacuum harness at steel tube connection. Check for vacuum at Red hose that attaches to canister. If vacuum exists, go to step **3)**. If no vacuum, go to step **2)**.

2) Check intake manifold vacuum supply fitting, vacuum hose and storage tank. If damaged, repair or replace components as necessary. If vacuum leak still exists, repair vacuum line between canister and steel tube. If vacuum exists at Red hose, proceed with system check.

3) Stop engine. Connect vacuum pump to steel tube that connects to Green hose in vacuum harness. Apply 20 in. Hg and rotate propeller shaft to engage transfer case. Shift transmission into park or first gear. If transfer case engages, go to step **6)**. If transfer case does not engage, go to step **4)**.

4) Check transfer case shift motor. Motor stem should be extended. If stem is not extended, check vacuum tubes for leaks and damage. Repair as necessary. If transfer case shift motor is still inoperative, check shift motor function. If shift motor is defective, replace motor. If shift motor is operative go to step **5)**.

5) If transfer case will not engage in 2WD, check transfer case shift linkage and repair as necessary. If linkage is okay and transfer case will not shift into 2WD, repair case. If transfer case now engages in 2WD, check axle for 2WD mode engagement (disconnected). If front axle is not in 2WD mode, check axle shift motor and replace as necessary.

6) If front axle shift motor is okay, check the shift mode selector switch and vacuum harness. Repair as necessary. If front axle shift motor will not disengage, check vacuum lines and repair as necessary.

7) If vacuum lines are okay and axle will not disengage, remove axle housing cover and shift motor. Inspect shift fork, collar and axle components. Repair as necessary.

AMERICAN MOTORS MODEL 228 (Cont.)

Fig. 3: Selec-Trac System Vacuum Diagram

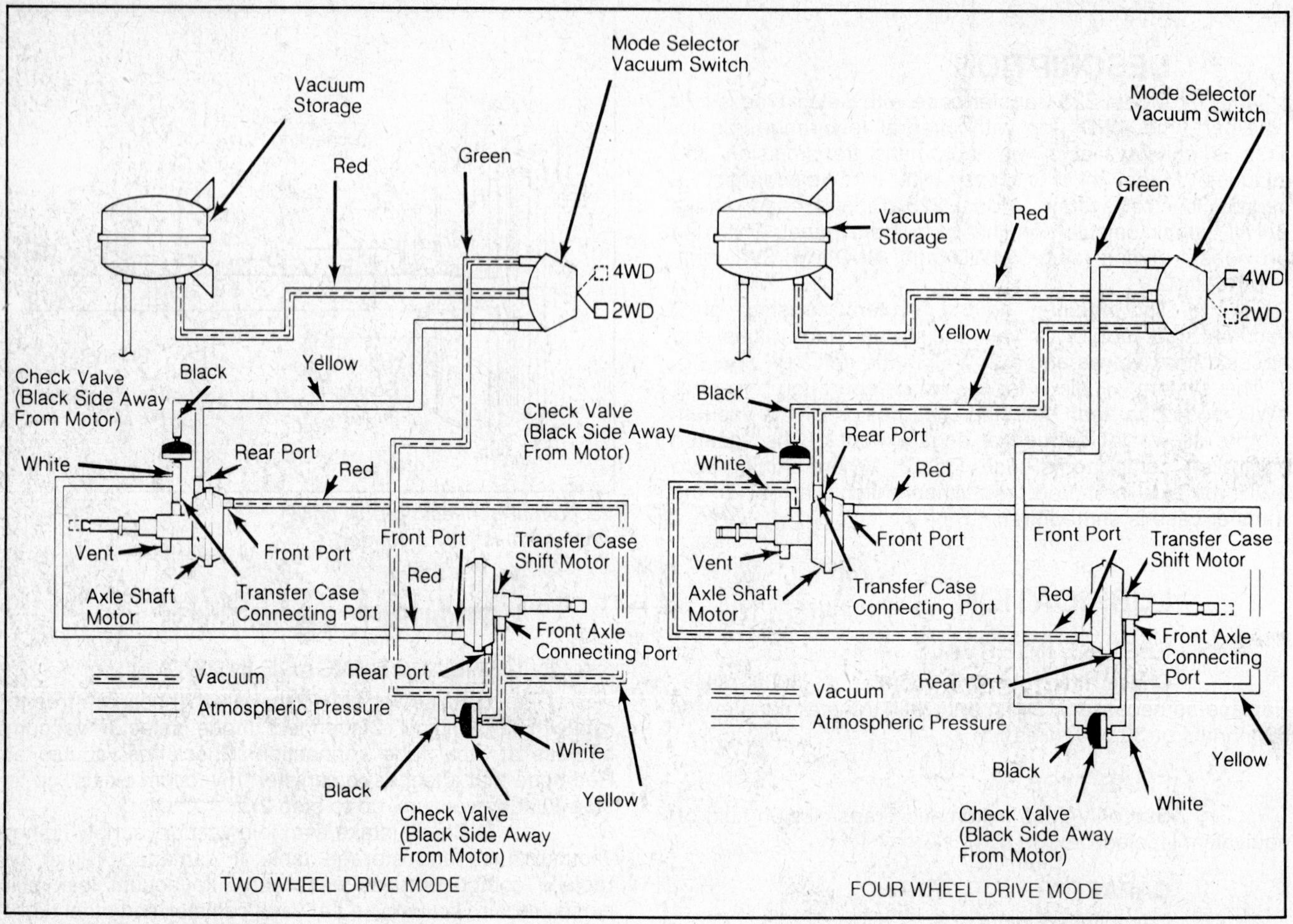

WILL NOT ENGAGE IN 4WD

1) Raise vehicle so that all 4 wheels are free to rotate. Start engine. Disconnect mode selector vacuum harness at steel tube connection. Check for vacuum at Red hose that attaches to canister. If vacuum exists, go to step **3)**. If no vacuum, go to step **2)**.

2) Check intake manifold vacuum supply fitting, vacuum hose and storage tank. If damaged, repair or replace components as necessary. If vacuum leak still exists, repair vacuum line between canister and steel tube. If vacuum exists at Red hose, proceed with system check.

3) Stop engine. Connect vacuum pump to steel tube that connects to Yellow hose in vacuum harness. Apply 20 in. Hg and rotate right front wheel to engage axle. If front axle is engaged, go to step **6)**. If front axle is not engaged proceed with system check.

4) Check front axle shift motor for operation. If shift motor is okay, check vacuum lines and tubes for leaks or damage. Repair as necessary. If axle shift motor is inoperative, replace motor and recheck for axle engagement.

5) If axle will not engage, remove axle housing cover and shift motor. Inspect shift fork, collar, and axle components. Repair as necessary.

6) Check that transfer case shift motor stem is retracted. If so, check transfer case shift linkage and repair as necessary. If not, check vacuum hoses and repair as necessary.

7) If transfer case motor is still inoperative, test motor operation with vacuum pump. If vacuum motor is defective, replace motor and retest. If transfer case motor is okay and transfer case does not engage in 4WD, check axle shift linkage and repair as necessary. If linkage is okay, repair transfer case as necessary.

TESTING

VACUUM SHIFT MOTOR

1) Disconnect vacuum harness from shift motor. Connect vacuum pump to front port and apply 15 in. Hg to motor. On transfer case rotate propeller shaft to engage transfer case in 4WD mode. On front axle, rotate right wheel to fully disengage axle.

2) Shift motor should maintain vacuum applied for at least 30 seconds. If motor does not maintain vacuum, replace motor. If motor does hold vacuum, go to step **3)**.

3) Disconnect vacuum pump from the front port of the vacuum motor. Connect pump to the rear port of the motor and plug the connecting port. Apply 15 in. Hg to motor; vacuum should be maintained for 30 seconds. If vacuum is not maintained, replace motor. If motor holds vacuum, go to step **4)**.

4) Remove plug from connecting port and check for vacuum at this port. If vacuum is not present,

AMERICAN MOTORS MODEL 228 (Cont.)

rotate propeller shaft on transfer case or right wheel on front axle, to ensure full engagement of shift motor.

5) If no vacuum exists at connecting port, pull back boot on stem and measure distance that stem has extended. Stem should extend a distance of 5/8" (15.9 mm) as measured from the edge of shift motor housing to "E" ring on stem. If stem does not extend the specified distance or if stem extends the specified distance but no vacuum is present at the connecting port, replace motor.

ADJUSTMENTS

NOTE: **Coupling Torque Bias Check must be performed during reassembly of transfer case.**

COUPLING TORQUE BIAS CHECK

In Vehicle

1) Shift into 4 HI range and place vehicle on a level surface. Stop engine. Place transmission shift lever in neutral and transfer case shift lever in 4 HI.

2) Raise one front wheel off floor and remove hubcap. Assemble socket and torque wrench and install on any lug nut on the wheel just raised.

3) Rotate wheel using torque wrench and measure torque required to rotate wheel. If coupling is operating properly, MINIMUM torque required is 45 ft. lbs. (34 N.m). If coupling is below minimum torque, perform torque bias test on bench.

On Bench

1) Bench test is performed with transfer case disassembled. Install clutch gear on side gear. Install assembled clutch gear and side gear in viscous coupling. Mount assembled viscous coupling and gears in vise which has wood blocks installed to prevent gear damage. Firmly clamp assembly on side gear.

2) Check engagement of clutch gear in viscous coupling. Clutch gear must be fully engaged in coupling. If necessary, reposition wood blocks so they support gear in coupling. Install rear output shaft and install yoke retaining nut. Install torque wrench on yoke nut.

3) Rotate output shaft and measure torque required to rotate shaft in coupling. Rotating torque should be 25 ft. lbs. (34 N.m) MINIMUM. If rotating torque is less than specified, replace coupling. If torque is at or above specification, coupling is operating properly.

REMOVAL & INSTALLATION

TRANSFER CASE

Removal

1) Raise vehicle and drain transfer case lubricant. Disconnect speedometer cable, indicator switch and transfer case shift lever link at operating lever. Disconnect parking brake cable guide from pivot located on right frame rail, if necessary.

2) Place support stand under transmission and remove rear crossmember. Mark the output shaft yokes for reassembly reference. Mark the yokes and the propeller shafts.

3) Disconnect front and rear propeller shafts, support them in vehicle with wire. Do not allow shafts to hang on universal joint as damage to joint may result. Disconnect shift motor vacuum lines and transfer case shift linkage.

4) Remove bolts attaching exhaust pipe support bracket-to-transfer case, if necessary. Remove transfer case-to-transmission bolts. Move transfer case assembly rearward until it is free of transmission output shaft and lower assembly out of vehicle. Remove all gasket material from transmission housing and transfer case.

Installation

1) Align and install transfer case assembly on transmission. Be sure transfer case input gear splines are aligned with transmission output shaft. Align splines by rotating transfer case rear output shaft yoke.

NOTE: **Do not install any transfer case-to-transmission bolts until transfer case is fully seated on transmission.**

2) Install transfer case attaching bolts and tighten to specified torque. Attach exhaust pipe support to transfer case, if removed. Align and connect propeller shafts. Connect parking brake cable guide to pivot bracket on frame rail, if removed.

3) Connect speedometer cable and indicator switch wires. Connect transfer case shift lever link to operating lever. Install rear crossmember and remove transmission support stand. Fill transfer case with Dexron II or equivalent.

4) Connect shift motor vacuum hoses and transfer case shift linkage. Lower vehicle.

DISASSEMBLY

TRANSFER CASE

1) Remove drain and fill plugs, front and rear yoke nuts and seal washers. Discard washers. Mark front and rear yokes and drive shafts for assembly alignment reference. Remove front and rear yokes, using puller if necessary.

2) Mount transfer case on wood blocks. Cut V-notches in blocks to clear front case mounting studs.

Fig. 4: Separating Rear and Front Cases

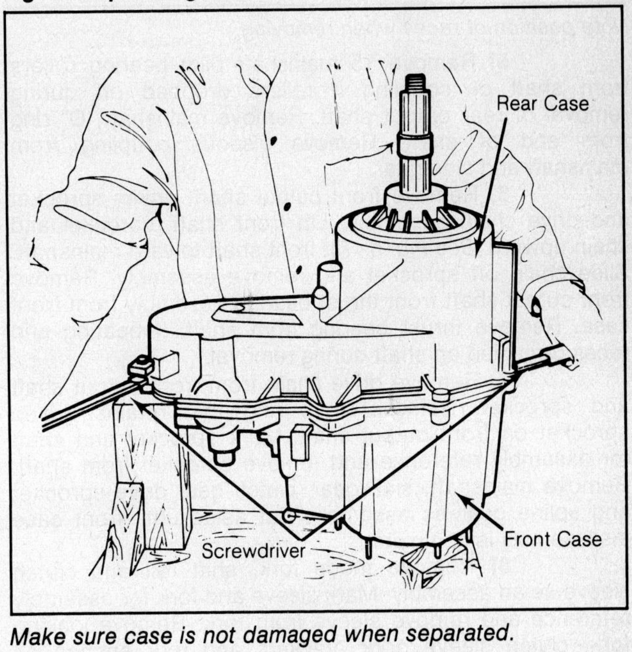

Make sure case is not damaged when separated.

Transfer Cases

AMERICAN MOTORS MODEL 228 (Cont.)

Mark rear retainer and rear case for assembly reference. Remove rear retainer bolts and retainer. Use 2 screw drivers to pry retainer off case. Position screwdrivers in slots in retainer and case to pry retainer loose.

3) Remove differential shims and speedometer gear from rear output shaft. Remove bolts attaching rear case to front case. Remove rear case from front case by prying with screwdriver. *See Fig. 4.*

CAUTION: Insert screwdrivers in the slots at each end of the rear case to loosen it. Do not attempt to wedge the case halves apart. The case mating surfaces will be damaged.

4) Remove thrust bearing and races from front output shaft. Note position of bearing and races for assembly reference. *See Fig. 5.* Remove oil pump from rear output shaft. Note that the recessed side of the pump faces case interior. Remove rear output shaft from the viscous coupling.

Fig. 5: Thrust Bearing and Races on Front Output Shaft

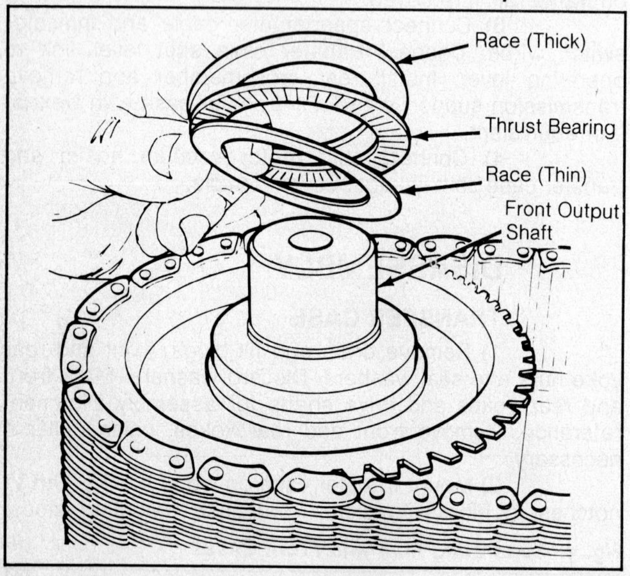

Note position of races when removing.

5) Remove 15 mainshaft pilot bearing rollers from shaft or coupling if rollers dropped off during removal of rear output shaft. Remove mainshaft "O" ring from end of shaft. Remove viscous coupling from mainshaft and side gear.

6) Remove front output shaft, driven sprocket and drive chain assembly. Lift front shaft, sprocket and chain upward. *See Fig. 6.* Tilt front shaft toward mainshaft. Slide chain off sprocket and remove assembly. Remove front output shaft front thrust bearing assembly from front case. Remove thrust bearing from shaft, if bearing and races remained on shaft during removal.

7) Remove drive chain from front output shaft and sprocket. Remove snap ring that retains driven sprocket on front output shaft. Mark sprocket and shaft for assembly reference and remove sprocket from shaft. Remove mainshaft, side gear, clutch gear drive sprocket and spline gear as assembly. Set aside until front case disassembly is completed.

8) Remove mode fork, shift rail and clutch sleeve as an assembly. Mark sleeve and fork for assembly reference and remove sleeve from fork. Remove locking fork, clutch sleeve, fork brackets and fork springs as

Fig. 6: Removing Front Output Shaft, Chain and Driven Sprocket

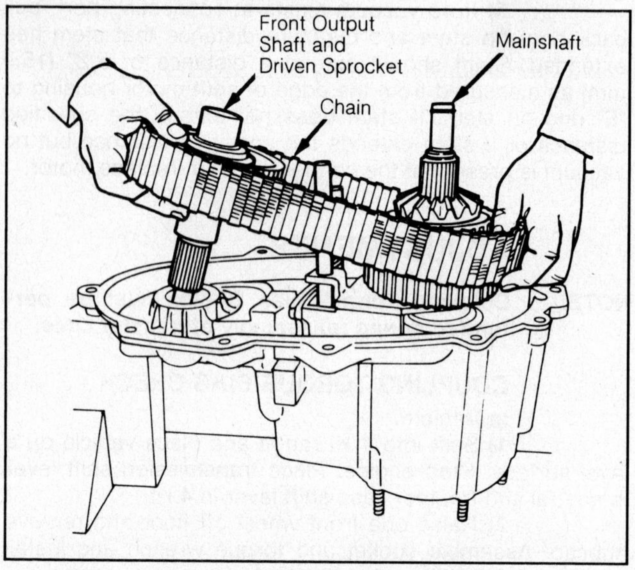

Slide chain off sprocket and remove assembly.

assembly. Note position of components for reassembly. Disassemble components for cleaning and inspection.

9) Remove range selector detent screw and remove detent spring, plunger and ball. *See Fig. 7.* Move range operating lever downward to last detent position. Disengage low range fork lug from range sector slot. Remove planetary assembly by grasping hub and lifting it upward.

Fig. 7: Removing Detent Ball, Spring, Retainer and Screw

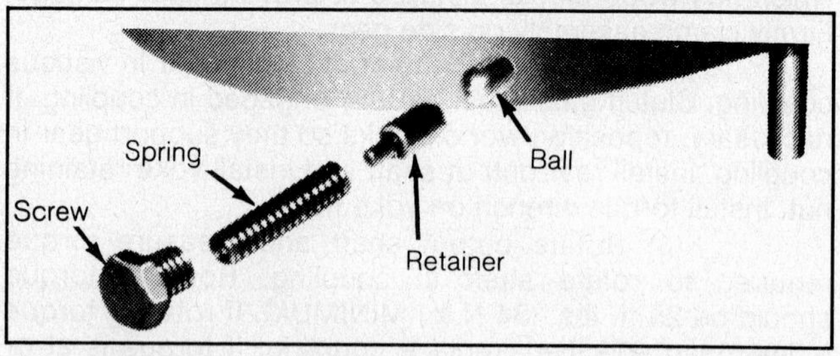

Note order for reassembly.

10) Remove mainshaft thrust bearing from input gear. Remove input gear and remove input gear thrust bearing and race. Remove range sector and operating lever attaching nut and lock washer and remove lever. Remove range sector and shaft from front case. Remove range sector "O" ring and retainer.

11) Remove rear output bearing and rear yoke seal from rear retainer. The bearing is shielded on one side. Note bearing position for reassembly. Remove input gear and front yoke seals from front case. Use screwdriver to pry seals out of case.

MAINSHAFT & GEARS

1) Grasp drive sprocket and lift sprocket clutch gear and side gear upward and off mainshaft. *See Fig. 8.* Remove mainshaft needle bearings and 2 bearing spacers from mainshaft. A total of 82 bearings are used. Note spacer position for reassembly.

Transfer Cases

AMERICAN MOTORS MODEL 228 (Cont.)

Fig. 8: Removing Mainshaft and Gear Assembly

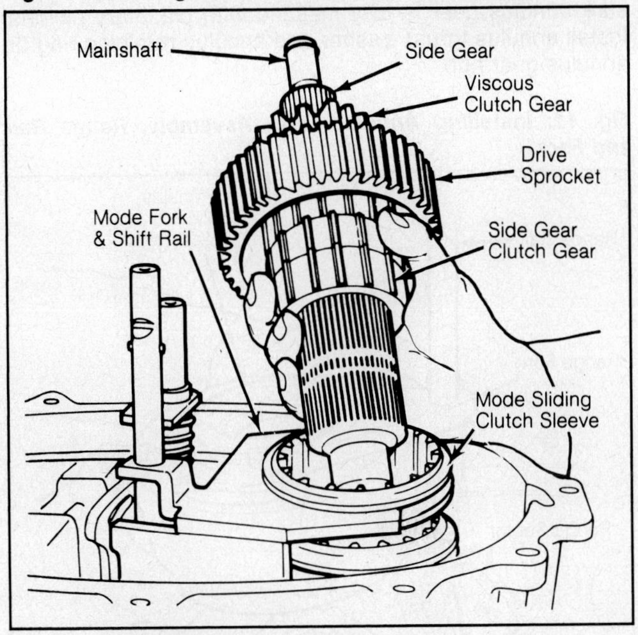

Note order for reassembly.

2) Remove spline gear and thrust washer from mainshaft. Remove side gear, clutch gear and clutch gear thrust washer from sprocket carrier and sprocket. Remove clutch gear and thrust washer from side gear.

3) Remove one sprocket carrier snap ring and remove drive sprocket from carrier. Mark for assembly references. Remove 3 bearing spacers and all sprocket carrier needle bearings from carrier. A total of 120 needle bearings are used.

SUB-ASSEMBLY OVERHAUL

BEARING/BUSHING REPLACEMENT

CAUTION: All bearings used in the transfer case must be correctly positioned to avoid blocking the bearing oil feed holes. After replacing any bearing, check the bearing position to be sure the feed hole is not covered by the bearing.

Rear Output Shaft Bearing

1) Remove bearing using slide hammer and bearing remover (J-26941). Remove rear output lip seal using a small screwdriver.

2) Install new lip seal. Install new bearing using driver J-29166. After bearing installation, check that bearing does not cover oil feed hole.

Front Output Shaft Front Bearing

Drive front output shaft front bearing out of case using driver (J-29168). Install bearing using same tool, check that bearing does not cover oil passage.

Front Output Shaft Rear Bearing

1) Support front case so that it will not be damaged. Using slide hammer and puller (J-26941), remove front output shaft rear bearing.

2) Install new bearing using driver (J-29163). Remove installer tool and check that bearing does not block oil passage.

Input Gear Front/Rear Bearing

1) Remove both bearings simultaneously using driver (J-29169). Install new bearings one at a time, rear bearing first. Use same tool for installation.

2) Remove bearing installer and check that bearing does not block oil passage. Check that bearings are flush with case. Install new oil seal using seal installer (J-29162).

Mainshaft Pilot Bushing

1) After carefully supporting input gear to prevent damage, remove bushing using slide hammer and remover tool (J-29369-1).

2) Install new bushing using driver (J-29174). Check that bushing is clear of oil passage.

Rear Output Bearing & Rear Yoke Seal

1) Remove bearing using brass drift and hammer. Remove seal from retainer using brass drift and hammer.

2) Install new bearing using driver (J-7818). Install bearing so that shielded side is facing the case interior after installation. Install seal in retainer using driver (J-29162).

CLEANING & INSPECTION

Cleaning

Clean all parts in cleaning solvent. Be sure all old lubricant or foreign material is removed from surfaces of every part. Apply compressed air to blow dry parts.

Inspection

1) Inspect all gear teeth for signs of excessive wear or damage and check all gear splines for burrs, nicks, wear or damage. Remove minor nicks or scratches using an oilstone. Replace any part exhibiting excessive wear or damage.

NOTE: Front output shaft thrust bearing race surfaces are heat treated, causing Brown or Blue discoloration. Do not replace front output shaft because of this discoloration.

2) Inspect case halves and rear retainer for cracks, porosity, damaged mating surfaces, stripped bolt threads or distortion.

3) Inspect the condition of all bearings. Also check the condition of all bearing bores. Replace any part that exhibits signs of wear or damage.

4) Inspect the viscous coupling and differential drive pinions. If the pinions or carrier are damaged or worn excessively, replace the coupling as an assembly only. If the coupling is cracked, leaking or damaged, replace the coupling as an assembly only.

REASSEMBLY

TRANSFER CASE

NOTE: During assembly, prelubricate all transfer case internal components with Jeep Dexron II automatic transmission fluid or petroleum jelly where indicated. Do not use chassis lubricant or other "heavy" grease.

1) Install new input gear and rear output shaft bearing oil seals. Seat seals flush with edge of seal bore

AMERICAN MOTORS MODEL 228 (Cont.)

or in groove in case. Coat seal lips with petroleum jelly after installation. Install input gear thrust bearing race in case counterbore.

2) Install input gear thrust bearing on input gear and install gear and bearing in case. *See Fig. 9.* Install mainshaft thrust bearing in bearing recess in input gear. Install planetary assembly on input gear. Be sure planetary pinion teeth mesh fully with input gear. Install planetary thrust washer on planetary hub. *See Fig. 10.*

Fig. 9: Installing Input Gear and Thrust Bearing in Centerbore

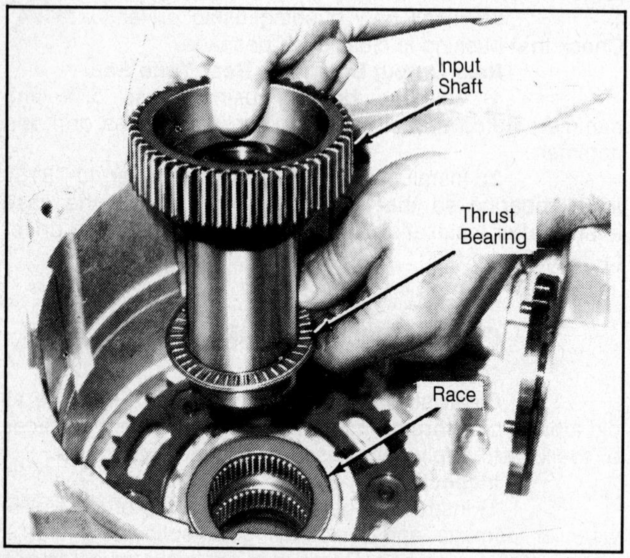

Install gear and bearing as an assembly.

3) Install new sector shaft "O" ring and install retainer in shaft bore in case. Install "O" ring on mode sector shaft and install mode sector through range sector. Install range sector in front case. Install operating lever and snap ring on range sector shaft.

Fig. 10: Installing Planetary Gear Assembly

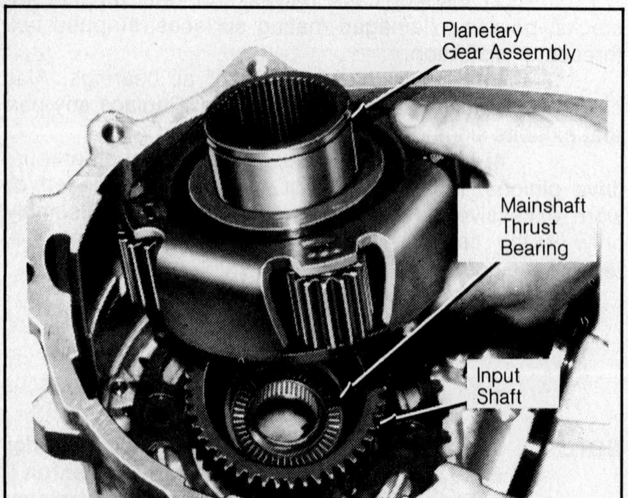

Be sure planetary pinion teeth mesh fully with input gear.

4) Install lever attaching washer and lock nut on mode sector shaft. Tighten lock nut to specified torque. Assemble annulus gear, range fork, and rail. *See Fig. 11.* Install assembled fork on and over planetary assembly. Be sure annulus gear is fully meshed with planetary pinions. Install annulus thrust washer and annulus retaining ring on annulus gear hub.

Fig. 11: Installing Annulus Gear Assembly, Range Rail and Fork

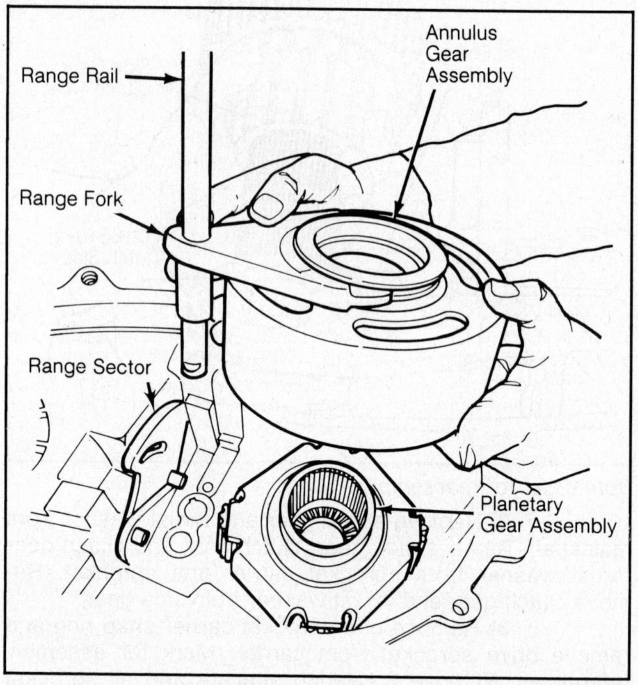

Be sure annulus gear is fully meshed with planetary pinions.

5) Install detent spring plunger ball and retainer screw in front case detent bore. *See Fig. 7.* Torque bolt to specifications. Assemble and install locking fork, fork brackets, fork springs and clutch sleeve. Be sure lug on fork is seated in range sector detent slot.

6) Install range fork lug in range sector detent notch. Move range sector to high range position. Assemble and install mode fork, shift rail and mode clutch sleeve. Install thrust washer and new "O" ring on mainshaft.

7) Install needle bearings and bearing spacers on mainshaft. *See Fig. 12.* Coat shaft bearing surface and all needle bearings with petroleum jelly. Install first 41 needle bearings. Install long bearing spacer, remaining 41 needle bearings and remaining short spacer. Be careful to avoid displacing bearings as spacers are installed. Use additional petroleum jelly to hold bearings in place if necessary.

8) Install spline gear on mainshaft. Take care to avoid displacing bearings while installing gear. Install sprocket carrier in drive sprocket and install sprocket carrier snap rings. Be sure to align carrier and sprocket according to reference marks made during disassembly. Be sure that the tapered teeth on the drive sprocket carrier and the recess on the sprocket are on the same side.

9) Install sprocket carrier bearings and spacers. Coat carrier bore and all 120 carrier needle bearings with petroleum jelly. Install center spacer. Install 60 bearings in each end of carrier and install remaining 2

AMERICAN MOTORS MODEL 228 (Cont.)

Fig. 12: Installing Needle Bearings and Spacers on Mainshaft

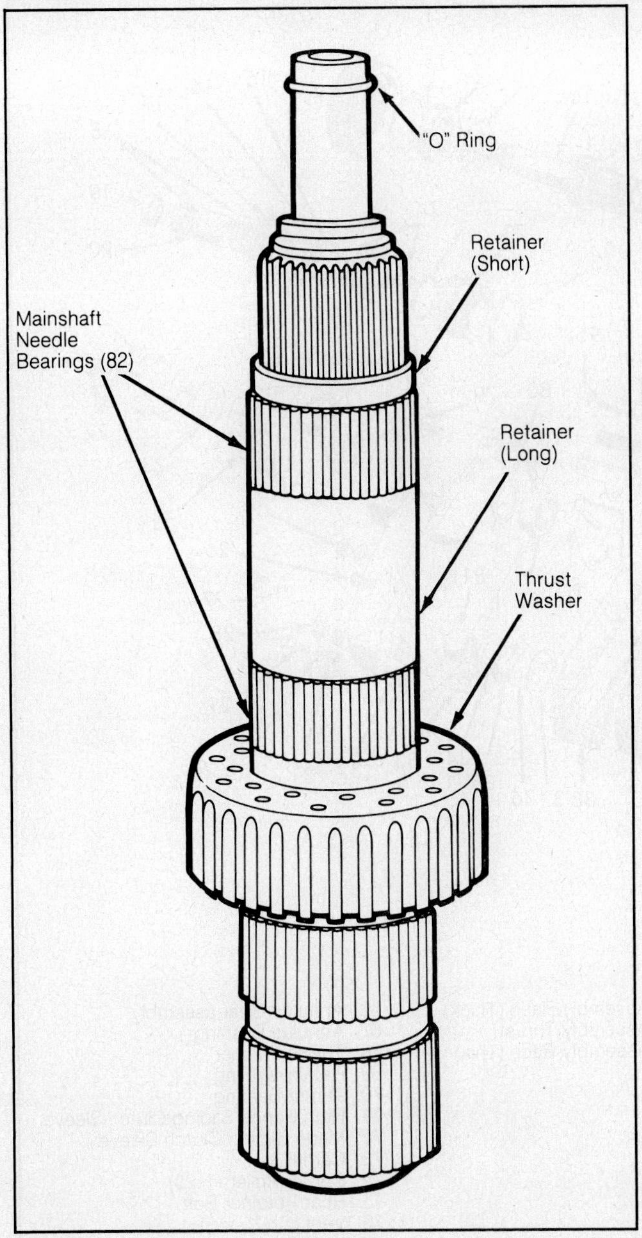

Use new "O" ring.

Fig. 13: Installing Side Gear on Clutch Gear

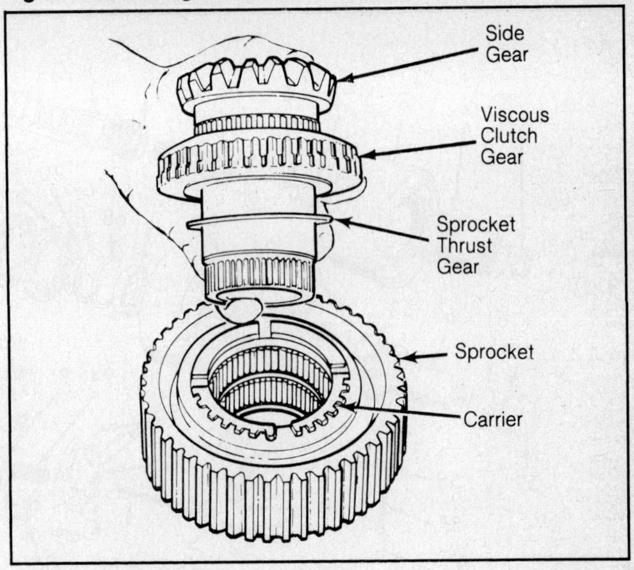

Note position of thrust washer.

spacers, one at each side of carrier. Use additional petroleum jelly to hold bearings in place if necessary.

10) Install assembled sprocket carrier and drive sprocket on mainshaft. Do not displace mainshaft bearings during installation. Be sure recessed side of drive sprocket is facing downward. Install clutch gear thrust washer in mainshaft. Position washer on sprocket carrier.

11) Install clutch gear on side gear. *See Fig. 13.* Be sure tapered edge of clutch gear faces side gear teeth. Install assembled side gear and clutch gear on mainshaft. Be sure side gear is fully seated in sprocket carrier. Take care to avoid displacing any of the carrier or mainshaft needle bearings.

12) Install mainshaft and gear assembly in case. Be sure mainshaft is fully seated in input gear. Install driven sprocket on front output shaft and install sprocket retaining snap ring. Be sure sprocket is installed according to reference marks made during disassembly.

13) Install front output shaft front thrust bearing assembly in front case. Install thick race in case, then install bearing and thin race. *See Fig. 5.* Install drive chain, front output shaft and driven sprocket. Install chain on driven sprocket. Raise and tilt driven sprocket and chain and install opposite end of chain on drive sprocket. *See Fig. 6.*

14) Align front output shaft with shaft bore in front case and install shaft in case. Be sure front shaft thrust bearing assembly is seated in case. Install front output shaft rear thrust bearing assembly on front output shaft. Install thin race first; then install bearing and thick race. *See Fig. 5.*

15) Install viscous coupling on side gear and clutch gear. Be sure coupling is fully seated on clutch gear. Clutch gear should be flush with coupling and gear teeth should be visible. See Coupling Torque Bias Check. Coat mainshaft pilot bearing surface and all 15 pilot roller bearings with petreoleum jelly and install bearings on shaft. Use additional petroleum jelly to hold bearings in place if necessary.

16) Install rear output shaft on mainshaft and into viscous coupling. Be sure shaft is completely seated in coupling. Tap shaft with plastic mallet or brass punch to seat it if necessary. Do not displace pilot bearings during shaft installation. Install oil pump on rear output shaft. Install new rear output shaft bearing oil seal in rear case.

17) Apply suitable sealer to mating surface of rear case. Install magnet in case, if removed. Install rear case on front case. Be sure alignment dowels are aligned with bolt holes in rear and seat rear case on front case.

NOTE: **If the rear case will not seat completely in the front case, check for the following: oil in the range fork rail bore, front output shaft rear thrust bearing assembly is not aligned with the rear case, mainshaft is not completely seated, rear case not aligned with oil pump.**

18) Install rear case-to-front bolts and torque to specifications. Be sure that flat washers are used on

AMERICAN MOTORS MODEL 228 (Cont.)

Fig. 14: Exploded View of Model 229 Transfer Case

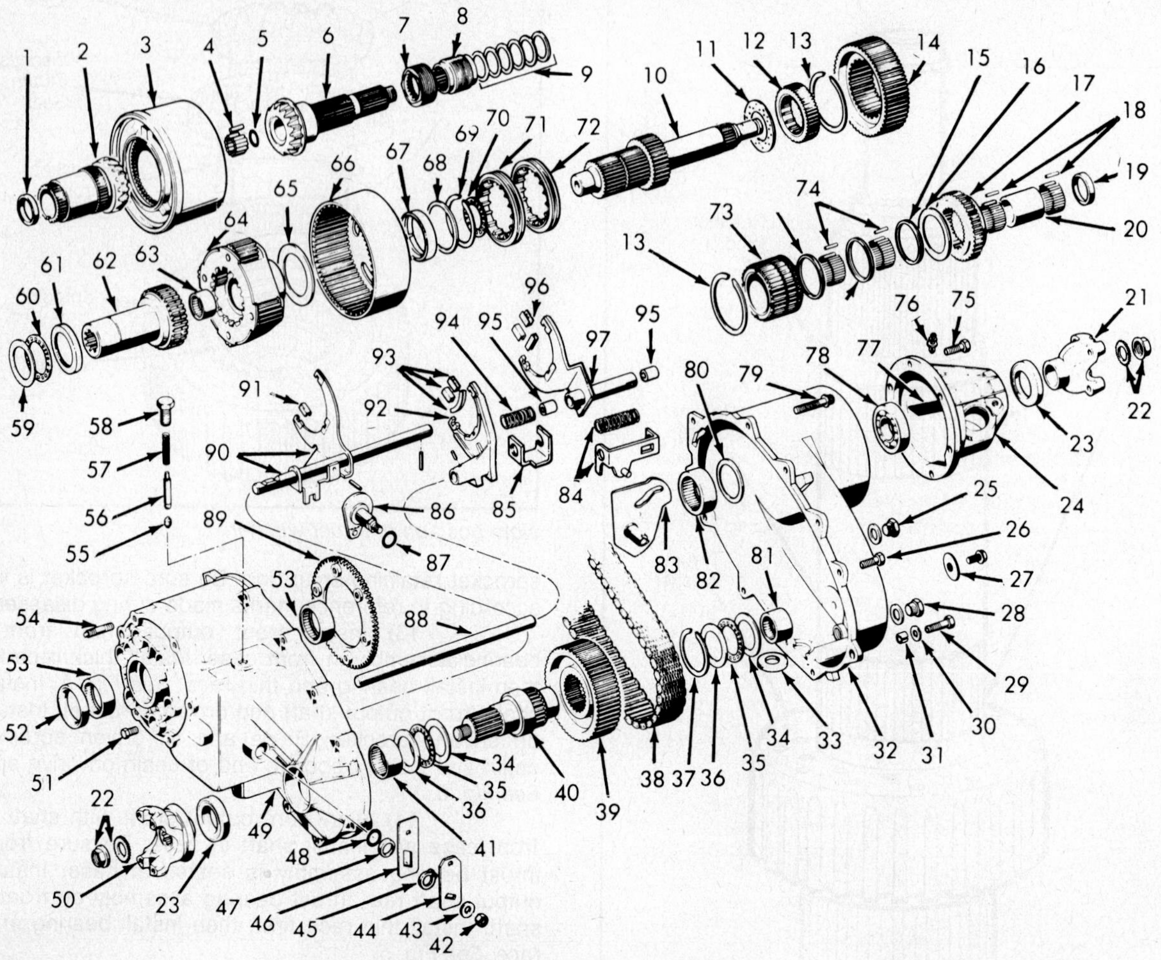

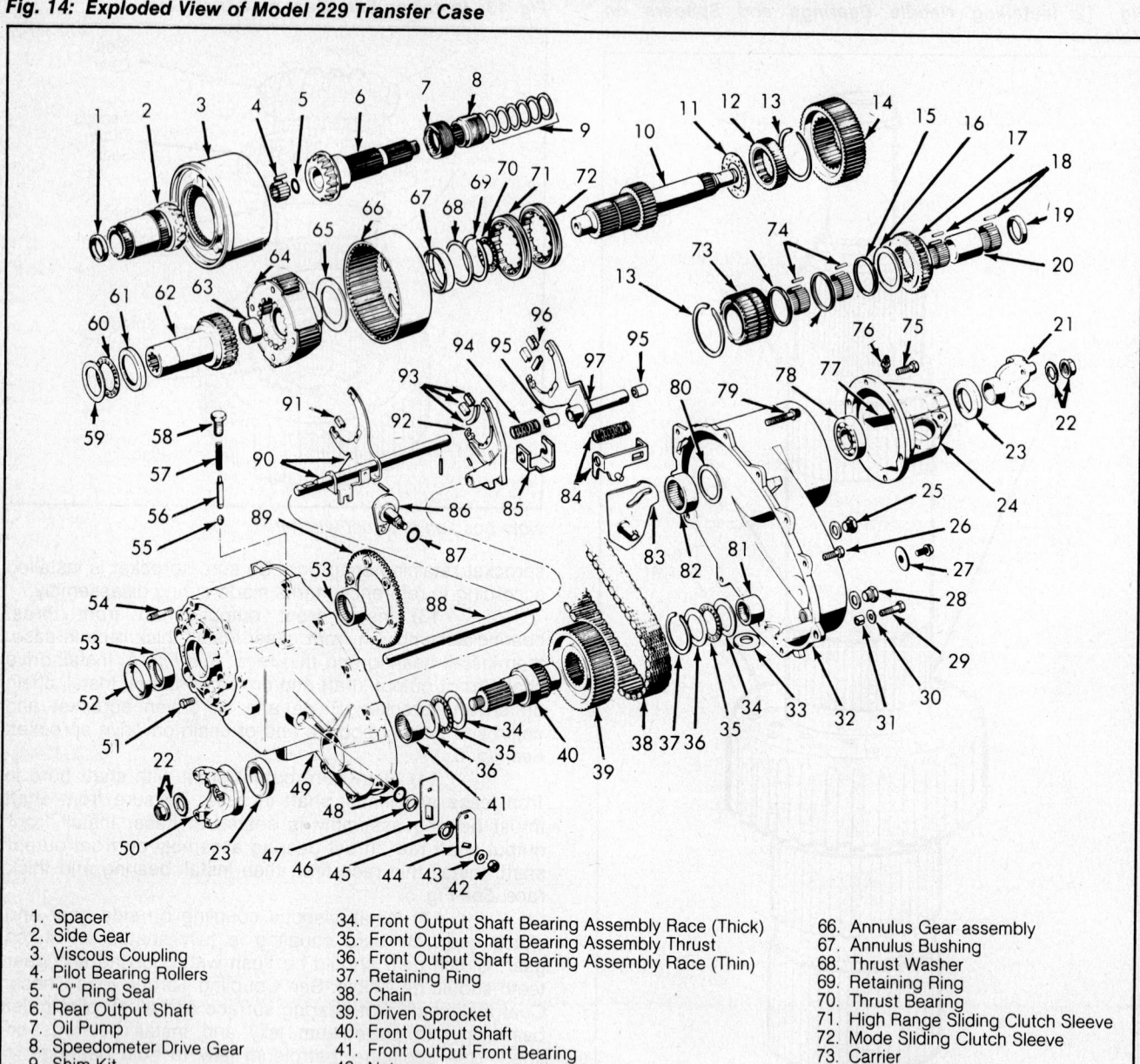

1. Spacer
2. Side Gear
3. Viscous Coupling
4. Pilot Bearing Rollers
5. "O" Ring Seal
6. Rear Output Shaft
7. Oil Pump
8. Speedometer Drive Gear
9. Shim Kit
10. Mainshaft
11. Manishaft Thrust Washer
12. Side Gear Clutch Gear
13. Retaining Ring
14. Sprocket
15. Spacer
16. Sprocket Thrust Washer
17. Viscous Clutch Gear
18. Side Gear Roller
19. Spacer (Short)
20. Spacer (Long)
21. Rear Yoke
22. Nut & Seal Washer
23. Seal
24. Rear Retainer
25. Plug Assembly
26. Bolt
27. Identification Tag
28. Plug Assembly
29. Dowel Bolt
30. Dowel Bolt Washer
31. Case Half Dowel
32. Rear Half Case
33. Magnet
34. Front Output Shaft Bearing Assembly Race (Thick)
35. Front Output Shaft Bearing Assembly Thrust
36. Front Output Shaft Bearing Assembly Race (Thin)
37. Retaining Ring
38. Chain
39. Driven Sprocket
40. Front Output Shaft
41. Front Output Front Bearing
42. Nut
43. Washer
44. Mode Lever
45. Snap Ring
46. Range Lever
47. "O" Ring Retainer
48. "O" Ring Seal
49. Front Half Case
50. Front Output Yoke
51. Low Range Plate Bolt
52. Input Shaft Oil Seal
53. Input Shaft Bearing
54. Stud
55. Ball
56. Plunger
57. Plunger Spring
58. Screw
59. Input Race
60. Input Thrust Bearing
61. Input Race (Thick)
62. Input Shaft
63. Input Bearing
64. Planetary Gear Assembly
65. Input Gear Thrust Washer
66. Annulus Gear assembly
67. Annulus Bushing
68. Thrust Washer
69. Retaining Ring
70. Thrust Bearing
71. High Range Sliding Clutch Sleeve
72. Mode Sliding Clutch Sleeve
73. Carrier
74. Carrier Rollers (120)
75. Rear Retainer Bolt
76. Vent
77. Vent Seal
78. Output Bearing
79. Bolt
80. Seal
81. Front Output Rear Bearing
82. Output Shaft Inner Bearing
83. Range Sector
84. Range Bracket (Outer) and Spring
85. Range Bracket (Inner)
86. Mode Sector
87. "O" Ring Seal
88. Range Rail
89. Low Range Lockout Plate
90. Mode Fork, Rail and Pin
91. Mode Fork Pad
92. Range Fork
93. Range Fork Pads
94. Range Bracket Spring (Inner)
95. Locking Fork Bushing
96. Locking Fork Pads
97. Locking Fork

AMERICAN MOTORS MODEL 228 (Cont.)

Fig. 15: Checking Differential End Play

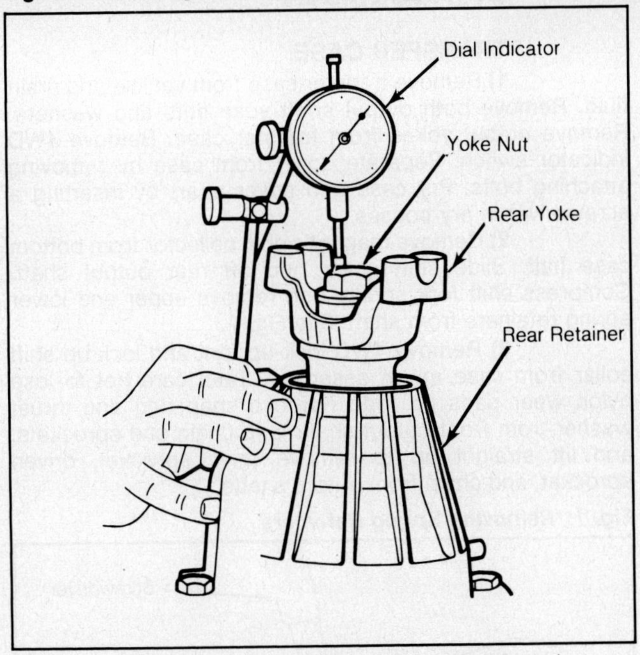

Indicator reading should be .002"-.010" (.05-.25 mm).

bolts at case ends where alignment dowels are located. Install speedometer drive gear and differential shims on rear output shaft. Align rear retainer on rear case and install retainer. Install retainer bolts securely but not to specified torque.

19) Install front and rear output shaft yokes with original yoke nuts. Tighten nuts finger tight only. Check differential end play with dial indicator. Mount dial indicator on rear retainer and position stylus so it contacts rear yoke nut. *See Fig. 15.*

20) Rotate front output shaft 10 to 12 revolutions and zero dial indicator. Rotate front shaft one more revolution and note dial indicator reading. Dial indicator should read .002"-.010" (.05-.25 mm). If end play is correct go to step **21)**. If end play is incorrect, remove retainer, add or subtract differential shims as necessary to correct end play and recheck end play.

21) After checking or adjusting end play, remove front and rear yokes. Discard original yoke nuts. Remove rear retainer and apply a suitable sealer to retainer mating surface and bolts. Install retainer and torque bolts to specification. Install front and rear yokes using new yoke seal washers and yoke nuts. Torque yoke nuts to specification

22) Install detent ball, spring and bolt if not installed previously. Use sealer on bolt and torque bolt to specification. Install drain plug and washer and fill case with specified amount of Dexron II. Install filler plug and washer and torque to specification.

TIGHTENING SPECIFICATIONS

Application	Ft. Lbs. (N.m)
Detent Retainer Bolt	23 (31)
Drain & Fill Plugs	18 (24)
Front & Rear Yoke Nuts	120 (163)
Operating Lever Lock Nut	18 (24)
Rear Case-to-Front Case Bolts	23 (31)
Rear Retainer Bolts	23 (31)

Transfer Cases

BORG-WARNER 1345

Ford Motor Co.

DESCRIPTION

Transfer case is a 2-piece, part-time unit using planetary gearing, a chain drive, and an aluminum case. The unit is lubricated by a positive-displacement oil pump that channels oil flow through drilled holes in rear output shaft. Pump turns with the rear output shaft, permitting towing of the vehicle for extended distances without disconnecting rear propeller shaft.

LUBRICATION

SERVICE INTERVALS

Check fluid level whenever malfunction is suspected or when fluid leakage or contamination is observed. Also check after operation in water.

FLUID TYPE

Use Dexron II ATF.

CAPACITY

Refill capacity is 6.5 pints (3.1L).

ADJUSTMENTS

Adjust shift linkage so that all positions may be selected without interference or binding. Inspect all swivels, rods and mountings for wear or damage. Replace as necessary.

REMOVAL & INSTALLATION

TRANSFER CASE

Removal

1) Raise vehicle. Remove drain plug and drain fluid from transfer case. Replace plug. Disconnect 4WD indicator switch connector at transfer case. If equipped, remove skid plate.

2) Disconnect front and rear propeller shafts from transfer case output shaft yokes, and wire out of way. Do not allow shafts to hang free as damage to universal joints may result.

3) Disconnect speedometer driven gear from rear bearing retainer. Remove retaining clips and shift rod from transfer case control and transfer case shift levers. Disconnect vent hose from case.

4) Remove heat shield. Support transfer case with transmission jack. Remove transfer case-to-transmission adapter bolts and slide transfer case off of transmission output shaft (toward rear). Lower transfer case and remove gasket from between transfer case and adapter.

Installation

Reverse removal procedure to install transfer case. Fill case with 6.5 pints (3.1L) of Dexron II type ATF.

DISASSEMBLY

TRANSFER CASE

1) Remove transfer case from vehicle and drain fluid. Remove both output shaft yoke nuts and washers. Remove output yokes from transfer case. Remove 4WD indicator switch. Separate cover from case by removing attaching bolts. Pry case and cover apart by inserting a screwdriver in pry bosses.

2) Remove magnetic chip collector from bottom case half. Slide shift collar hub off rear output shaft. Compress shift fork spring, and remove upper and lower spring retainers from shaft. *See Fig. 1.*

3) Remove 4WD lock-up fork and lock-up shift collar from case as an assembly. Take care not to lose nylon wear pads on fork. Remove snap ring and thrust washer from front output shaft. Grip chain and sprockets, and lift straight up to remove drive sprocket, driven sprocket, and chain from output shafts.

Fig. 1: Removing Spring Retainers

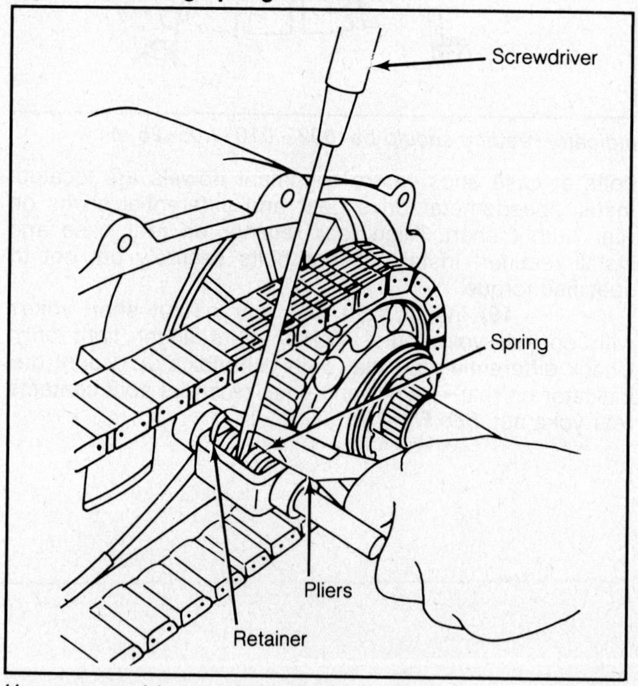

Use a screwdriver and needle nose pliers.

4) Remove thrust washer from rear output shaft. Remove front output shaft from case. Remove oil pump attaching bolts and remove oil pump rear cover, pick-up tube, pump body and filter, 2 pump pins, pump spring and oil pump front cover from rear output shaft. Disconnect oil pick-up tube from pump body.

5) Remove bearing retainer snap ring from inside case. Lift out rear output shaft, while tapping on bearing retainer with a plastic hammer. Lift rear output shaft and bearing retainer from case, noting that 2 dowel pins will fall into case.

6) Remove rear output shaft from bearing retainer. If necessary, press needle bearing assembly from bearing retainer. Remove "C" clip holding shift cam to shift actuating lever inside the case. Remove shift lever retaining screw and remove lever from case. *See Fig. 3.*

Transfer Cases

BORG-WARNER 1345 (Cont.)

Fig. 2: Exploded View of Borg-Warner 1345 Transfer Case

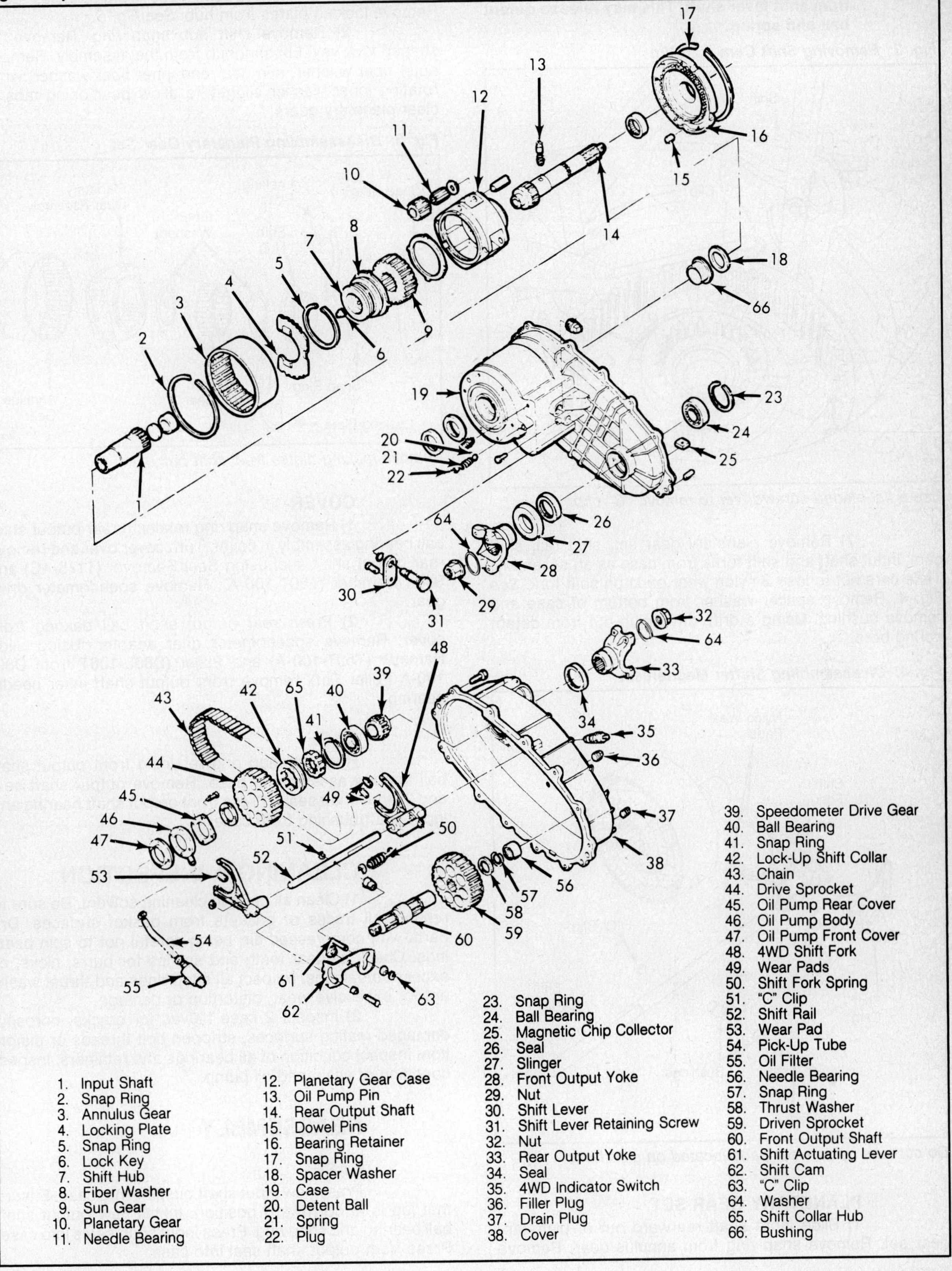

1. Input Shaft
2. Snap Ring
3. Annulus Gear
4. Locking Plate
5. Snap Ring
6. Lock Key
7. Shift Hub
8. Fiber Washer
9. Sun Gear
10. Planetary Gear
11. Needle Bearing
12. Planetary Gear Case
13. Oil Pump Pin
14. Rear Output Shaft
15. Dowel Pins
16. Bearing Retainer
17. Snap Ring
18. Spacer Washer
19. Case
20. Detent Ball
21. Spring
22. Plug
23. Snap Ring
24. Ball Bearing
25. Magnetic Chip Collector
26. Seal
27. Slinger
28. Front Output Yoke
29. Nut
30. Shift Lever
31. Shift Lever Retaining Screw
32. Nut
33. Rear Output Yoke
34. Seal
35. 4WD Indicator Switch
36. Filler Plug
37. Drain Plug
38. Cover
39. Speedometer Drive Gear
40. Ball Bearing
41. Snap Ring
42. Lock-Up Shift Collar
43. Chain
44. Drive Sprocket
45. Oil Pump Rear Cover
46. Oil Pump Body
47. Oil Pump Front Cover
48. 4WD Shift Fork
49. Wear Pads
50. Shift Fork Spring
51. "C" Clip
52. Shift Rail
53. Wear Pad
54. Pick-Up Tube
55. Oil Filter
56. Needle Bearing
57. Snap Ring
58. Thrust Washer
59. Driven Sprocket
60. Front Output Shaft
61. Shift Actuating Lever
62. Shift Cam
63. "C" Clip
64. Washer
65. Shift Collar Hub
66. Bushing

Transfer Cases

BORG-WARNER 1345 (Cont.)

NOTE: **When removing lever, shift cam will disengage from shift lever shaft. This may release detent ball and spring.**

Fig. 3: Removing Shift Cam "C" Clip

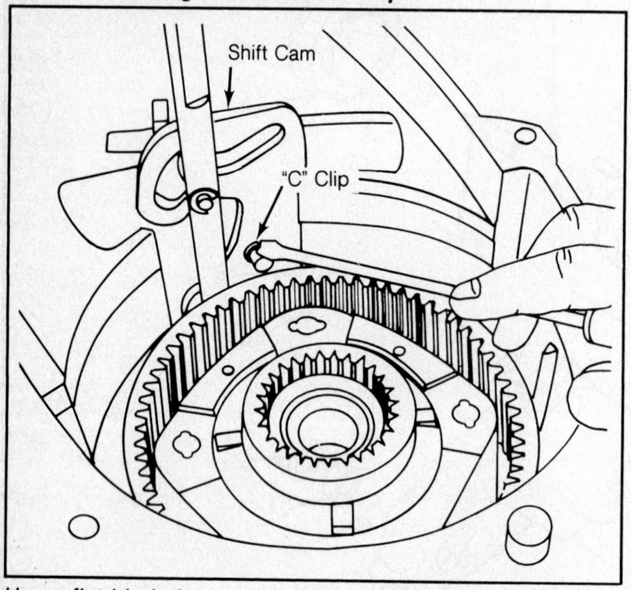

Use a flat-bladed screwdriver to remove "C" clip.

7) Remove planetary gear set, shift rail, shift cam, input shaft and shift forks from case as an assembly. Take care not to lose 2 nylon wear pads on shift fork. *See Fig. 4*. Remove spacer washer from bottom of case and remove bushing. Using a drift, drive plug out from detent spring bore.

Fig. 4: Disassembling Shifter Mechanism

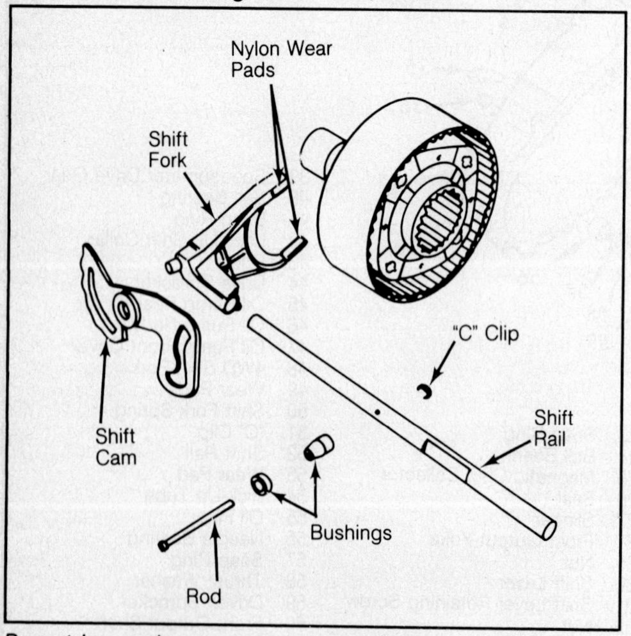

Do not lose nylon wear pads located on shift forks.

PLANETARY GEAR SET

1) Slide input shaft rearward out of planetary gear set. Remove snap ring from annulus gear. Remove shift hub and planetary gear case from annulus gear. Remove locking plates from hub. *See Fig. 5*.

2) Remove shift hub snap ring. Remove "T" shaped lock key. Lift shift hub from the assembly. Remove outer fiber washer, sun gear and inner fiber washer, while rotating inner washer slightly to allow positioning tabs to clear planetary gears.

Fig. 5: Disassembling Planetary Gear Set

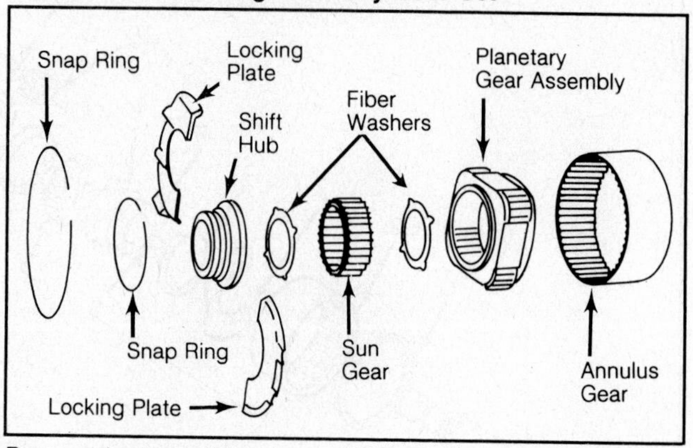

Remove locking plates from shift hub.

COVER

1) Remove snap ring retaining rear output shaft ball bearing assembly in cover. Turn cover over and remove rear output shaft seal using Seal Remover (1175-AC) and Slide Hammer (T50T-100-A). Remove speedometer drive gear.

2) Press rear output shaft ball bearing from cover. Remove speedometer gear adapter. Using Slide Hammer (T50T-100-A) and Puller (D80L-100T from D80-100-A Puller Set), remove front output shaft inner needle bearing.

CASE

Remove snap ring retaining front output shaft ball bearing assembly in case. Remove output shaft seal and 2 input shaft seals. Press front output shaft bearing and input shaft bushing from case.

CLEANING & INSPECTION

1) Clean all parts in cleaning solvent. Be sure to remove all traces of gaskets from gasket surfaces. Dry parts with compressed air, being careful not to spin bearings. Check all gear teeth and splines for burrs, nicks, or excessive damage. Inspect all snap rings and thrust washers for excessive wear, distortion or damage.

2) Inspect 2 case halves for cracks, porosity, damaged mating surfaces, stripped bolt threads or distortion. Inspect condition of all bearings and retainers. Inspect condition of chain and oil pump.

REASSEMBLY

CASE

Press new input shaft bushing into case. Ensure that lug is in downward position. Install new output shaft ball bearing and snap ring. Press input shaft seals into case. Press front output shaft seal into case.

Transfer Cases

BORG-WARNER 1345 (Cont.)

COVER

Press a new needle bearing into cover. Using Bearing Installer (T80T-7127-B), press new ball bearing into cover and install snap ring. Turn cover over and install speedometer drive gear. Install new output shaft seal. Install speedometer gear adapter.

PLANETARY GEAR ASSEMBLY

1) Place a new inner fiber washer into the planetary gear housing. Install sun gear. Coat new outer fiber washer with petroleum jelly, and install on hub. *See Fig. 5.* Place hub in planetary gear cage, and install "T" shaped lock key and snap ring.

2) Install locking plates on shift hub, with dished side toward planetary gear set. Lower planetary assembly into annulus gear. Be sure tabs on locking plate engage annulus gear teeth. Install snap ring.

TRANSFER CASE

1) Lubricate all parts with Dexron II ATF. Assemble planetary gear set, shift rail, shift cam, input shaft, and shift fork together as an assembly. *See Fig. 6.* Ensure that the boss on the shift cam is installed toward the case. *See Fig. 7.* Install spacer washer on input shaft.

2) Place rear output shaft in planetary gear set, making sure shift cam engages shift fork actuating pin. Lay case on its side. Insert rear output shaft and planetary gear set into case. Be sure spacer washer remains on input shaft.

3) Install shift rail into hole in case. Install outer roller bushing into guide in case. Remove rear output shaft, and position shift fork in Neutral. Place shift control lever shaft through cam, and install clip ring. Ensure shift control lever is pointed downward and parallel to front face of case.

Fig. 6: Installing Planetary Gear Set and Shifter Mechanism

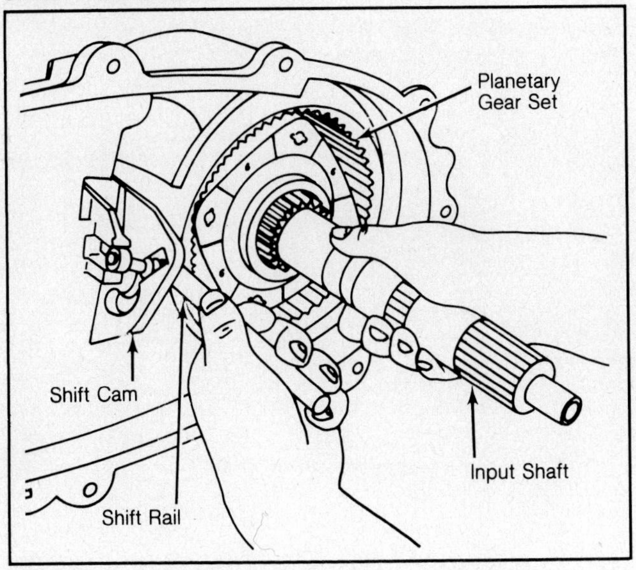

Install components as an assembly.

4) Check shift fork and planetary gear engagement. Unit should operate freely without binding. Using Bearing Installer (T80T-7127-C), press new needle bearing into bearing retainer (if removed).

5) Insert output shaft through bearing retainer from the bottom side outward. Insert rear output shaft pilot into the input shaft rear bushing. Align dowel holes, and lower bearing into position. Install dowel pins. Install bearing retainer snap ring.

6) Insert detent ball and spring in detent bore in case half. Coat seal plug with RTV sealant. Drive plug into case until plug lip is 1/32" (.79 mm) below surface of case. Stake the plug to case in 2 places. Install oil pump front cover over the output shaft with flanged side down. The word "TOP" must face the top of the transfer case as it is positioned for installation in the vehicle.

7) Install oil pump spring and 2 pump pins, with flat side outward in the hole in output shaft. Install oil pump body, pick-up tube and filter, and push in pins. The word "REAR" on pump body must face upward. Prime oil pump with Dexron II ATF.

8) Place oil pump rear cover onto output shaft, with flanged side outward. The words "TOP REAR" must face the top of the transfer case as it is positioned for installation in the vehicle. Apply Loctite to oil pump bolts, install to pump cover, and tighten while rotating pump.

NOTE: Pump will rotate freely on output shaft when correctly installed.

9) Install thrust washer to rear output shaft near oil pump. Install chain on drive and driven sprockets. Lower chain and sprockets into position in case. The driven sprocket is installed over front output shaft and the drive sprocket is placed over rear output shaft.

10) Install washer and snap ring behind driven sprocket. Engage 4WD shift fork on shift collar. Slide shift fork over shift shaft. Install shift collar over rear output shaft. Ensure nylon wear pads are installed on shift fork

Fig. 7: Installing and Engaging Shift Cam

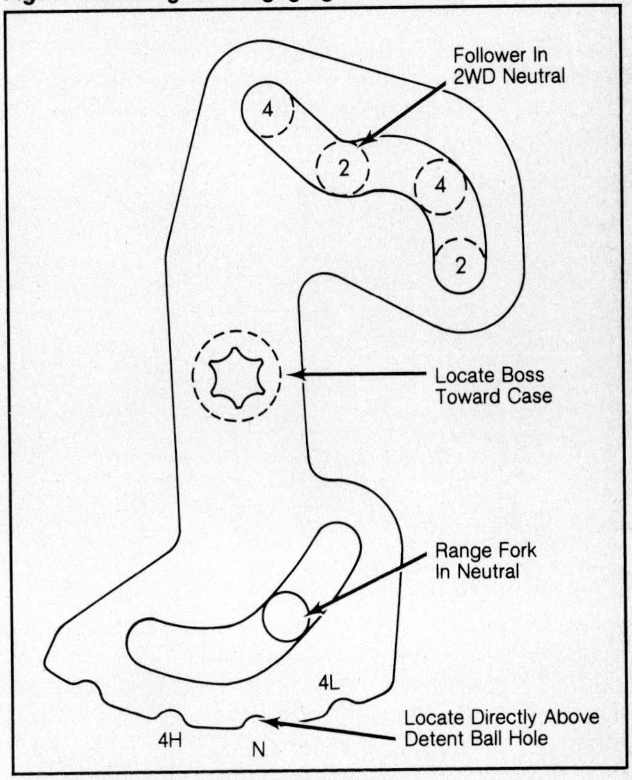

Install shift cam with boss toward case.

Transfer Cases

BORG-WARNER 1345 (Cont.)

tips, and that necked down portion of shift collar is facing rearward.

11) Push 4WD shift spring downward and install upper spring retainer. Push spring upward and install lower spring retainer. Install shift collar hub on rear output shaft.

12) Apply RTV sealant to the case mounting surface. Lower the cover over rear output shaft. Align shift rail with blind hole in cover. Ensure the front output shaft is seated in support bearing. Install bolts and tighten. Install 4WD indicator switch.

13) Press oil slinger on front yoke. Install front and rear output shaft yokes. Apply Loctite to threads of output shafts and faces of yoke nuts, then tighten. Refill transfer case, install in vehicle, and test for correct operation.

TIGHTENING SPECIFICATIONS

Application	Ft. Lbs. (N.m)
Case Half Attaching Bolts	35-40 (47-54)
Drain Plug	14-22 (19-29)
Fill Plug	15-25 (20-34)
Front Propeller Shaft-to-Front Output Yoke	8-15 (11-20)
Heat Shield-to-Transfer Case	40-45 (54-61)
Output Yokes-to-Transfer Case	120-150 (163-203)
Rear Propeller Shaft-to-Rear Output Yoke	20-28 (27-38)
Skid Plate-to-Frame	15-20 (20-27)
Transfer Case-to-Transmission Adapter	25-43 (34-58)
4WD Indicator Switch	8-12 (11-16)

Transfer Cases

BORG-WARNER 1350

Bronco II, Ranger

DESCRIPTION

The Borg-Warner 1350 is a chain driven, part time 4WD unit. It provides 4 driving modes. This unit offers 2WD and 4WD high ranges, 4WD low range and Neutral. The 1350 has a 3 piece aluminum case, an internal oil pump driven off the rear output shaft and an angular front output shaft with a cardan joint. Floor mounted shift levers or overhead mounted pushbuttons select the driving ranges, high and low, and the driving modes, 2WD and 4WD. The oil pump is driven by the rear output shaft. This allows the vehicle to be towed for long distances without disconnecting propeller shafts.

LUBRICATION

SERVICE INTERVALS

Check and refill transfer case when malfunction is suspected, fluid leakage or contamination is observed or after axle is submerged in water.

FLUID TYPE

Use Dexron II ATF.

CAPACITY

Refill capacity is 3 pts. (1.4L).

SERVICE (IN VEHICLE)

FRONT OUTPUT SHAFT OIL SEAL

Removal

1) Raise vehicle on hoist. Remove front drive shaft from axle input yoke. Loosen clamp retaining drive shaft boot to transfer case. Pull drive shaft and boot assembly out of transfer case front output shaft.

2) Place a drain pan under transfer case, remove drain plug and drain fluid from case. Remove oil seal from front output housing bore with Seal Remover (1175-AC) and Slide Hammer (T50T-100-A).

Installation

1) Make sure housing face and bore are free from nicks and burrs. Coat oil seal with multipurpose grease. Position oil seal into front output housing bore, making sure oil seal is not cocked in bore. Drive oil seal into bore with Driver (T80T-4000-W) and Output Shaft Seal Installer (T83T-7065-B).

2) Clean transfer case front output female spline and apply small amount of multipurpose grease. Insert front drive shaft male spline. Connect front drive shaft to axle input yoke and tighten bolts.

3) Push drive shaft boot to engage external groove on transfer case front output shaft. Secure boot with clamp. Install drain plug and tighten. Remove fill plug and fill transfer case with Dexron II ATF to bottom of fill hole. Install fill plug and tighten. Lower vehicle from hoist.

REAR OUTPUT SHAFT OIL SEAL

Removal

1) Raise vehicle on hoist. Remove rear drive shaft from transfer case output shaft yoke. Wire drive shaft out of the way.

2) Remove output shaft yoke by removing retaining nut, steel washer, and rubber seal from rear of output shaft. Remove oil seal from rear output housing bore with Seal Remover (1175-AC) and Slide Hammer (T50T-100-A).

Installation

1) Make sure output housing bore and face are free from nicks and burrs. Coat oil seal with a small amount of multipurpose grease. Position oil seal into rear output housing bore. Make sure oil seal is not cocked in bore. Drive seal into bore with Driver (T80T-4000-W) and Output Shaft Seal Installer (T83T-7065-B).

2) Install yoke, rubber seal, steel washer, and nut on output shaft. Tighten nut. Connect rear drive shaft to transfer case output shaft yoke and tighten bolts. Lower vehicle from hoist.

REMOVAL & INSTALLATION

TRANSFER CASE

Removal

1) Raise vehicle on hoist. Remove skid plate, if used. Remove drain plug and drain transfer case lubricant. Disconnect 4WD indicator switch wire at transfer case. On electric shift models, disconnect wiring harness plug at rear of transfer case. Disconnect front drive shaft from axle input yoke.

2) Loosen clamp retaining front drive shaft boot to transfer case. Pull drive shaft and front boot assembly out of transfer case front output shaft. Disconnect rear drive shaft from transfer case output yoke. Disconnect speedometer driven gear from case rear cover.

3) Disconnect vent hose from control lever. Loosen or remove large bolt and small bolt retaining shifter to extension housing. Pull on control lever until bushing slides off transfer case shift lever pin. If necessary, unscrew shift lever from control lever. Remove heat shield from transfer case.

4) Support transfer case with a transmission jack. Remove bolts retaining transfer case to transmission and extension housing. Slide transfer case rearward off transmission and lower case from vehicle. Remove gasket from between transfer case and extension housing.

Installation

1) Place a new gasket between transfer case and extension housing. Raise transfer case with jack and position it so splines on transfer case input shaft align with transmission output shaft. Slide case forward onto transmission output shaft and dowel pin.

2) Install bolts that retain transfer case to transmission. Tighten bolts evenly and in a clockwise sequence from locating pin as viewed from front of vehicle.

3) Remove jack from transfer case. Install heat shield on transfer case and tighten bolts. Move control lever until bushing is in position over transfer case shift lever pin. Install both attaching bolts by hand. Tighten large bolt retaining shifter to extension housing first. Tighten small bolt next.

4) Install vent assembly so White marking on hose is in position in notch on shifter. Vent hose should be positioned so that upper end of hose is 2" above top of shifter and inside shift boot. Connect speedometer gear to transfer case rear cover and tighten screw.

Transfer Cases

BORG-WARNER 1350 (Cont.)

Fig. 1: Exploded View of Borg-Warner 1350 Transfer Case

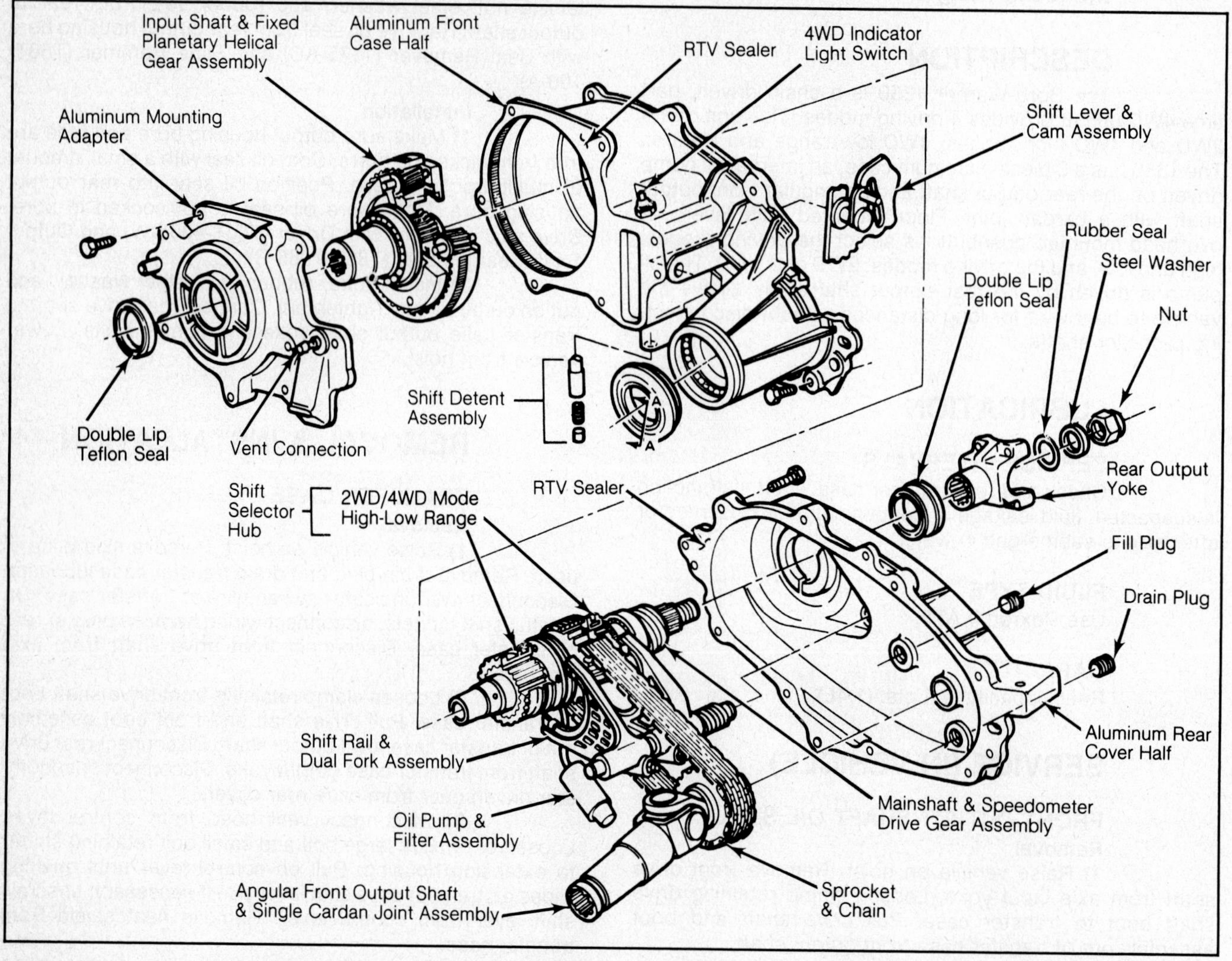

5) Connect rear drive shaft to transfer case output shaft yoke and tighten bolts. Clean transfer case front output shaft female splines. Apply a small amount of multipurpose grease to splines. Insert front drive shaft male spline.

6) Connect front drive shaft to axle input yoke and tighten bolts. Push drive shaft boot to engage external groove on transfer case front output shaft. Secure boot with clamp. Connect 4WD indicator switch wire connector at transfer case. Install drain plug and tighten.

7) Remove fill plug. Fill transfer case with 3 pts. (1.4L) of Dexron II ATF. Install fill plug. Install skid plate to frame and tighten bolts, if used. Lower vehicle from hoist.

DISASSEMBLY

TRANSFER CASE

1) Drain transfer case and remove from vehicle. Place transfer case on bench. Remove 4WD indicator switch and breather vent. Remove rear output shaft yoke by removing retaining nut, steel washer and rubber seal from output shaft.

2) Fabricate tool by forming small hook at tip of paperclip or safety pin. Remove locking sleeve from connector by hooking with tool and pulling from bottom. *See Fig.2* Remove brown wire (center), green (#4) and blue (#5) by pulling from back of connector.

3) Remove speed sensor retaining bracket screw, bracket and sensor. Remove 3 electric motor mount bolts and motor. Note position of triangular shaft in case and triangular slot in electric motor. *See Fig. 3.*

4) Remove 9 bolts retaining front case to rear cover. Insert a 1/2" drive breaker bar between 3 pry bosses to separate front case and rear cover. Remove all traces of RTV gasket sealer from mating surfaces.

5) If speedometer drive gear or ball bearing assembly is to be replaced, remove output shaft oil seal. Seal can be removed from inside of rear cover with a brass drift and hammer. Remove speedometer drive gear assembly. Note that round end of speedometer gear clip faces inside of rear cover.

6) Remove internal snap ring retaining output shaft ball bearing rear in bore. Remove ball bearing with Driver (T80T-4000-W) and Output Shaft Bearing Replacer (T83T-7025-B) from outside of case.

7) If necessary, remove front output shaft caged needle bearing from rear cover using Puller (D80L-100-S) and slide hammer. On electric models, remove 3 nuts retaining clutch coil to rear cover. Remove coil assembly,

Transfer Cases

BORG-WARNER 1350 (Cont.)

Fig. 2: Electric Shift Harness Connector

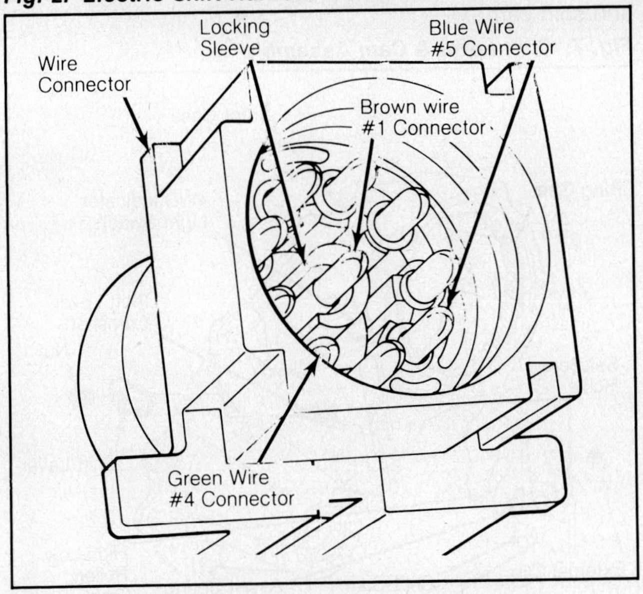

Fig. 3: View of Motor and Shift Cam Alignment.

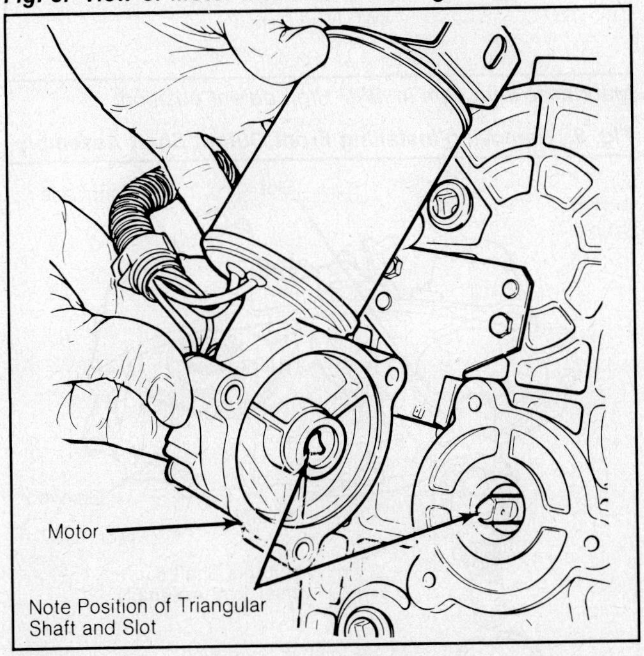

"O" rings and brown wire from cover. Remove 2WD/4WD shift fork from boss in rear cover.

8) Remove shift collar hub from output shaft. Remove 2WD/4WD lock-up assembly and 2WD/4WD shift fork as an assembly. Remove 2WD/4WD lock-up assembly from 2WD/4WD shift fork. *See Fig. 4*. If necessary, remove external clip and roller bushing assembly from 2WD/4WD shift fork.

9) If disassembly of 2WD/4WD lock-up assembly is necessary, remove internal snap ring and pull lock-up hub and spring from lock-up collar. Remove external snap ring and thrust washer that retains driven sprocket to front output shaft.

10) On electric models, remove camshaft assembly from front case. If necessary, remove helical cam, torsion spring and sleeve from camshaft.

Fig. 4: Removing Shift Collar Hub & Drive Chain

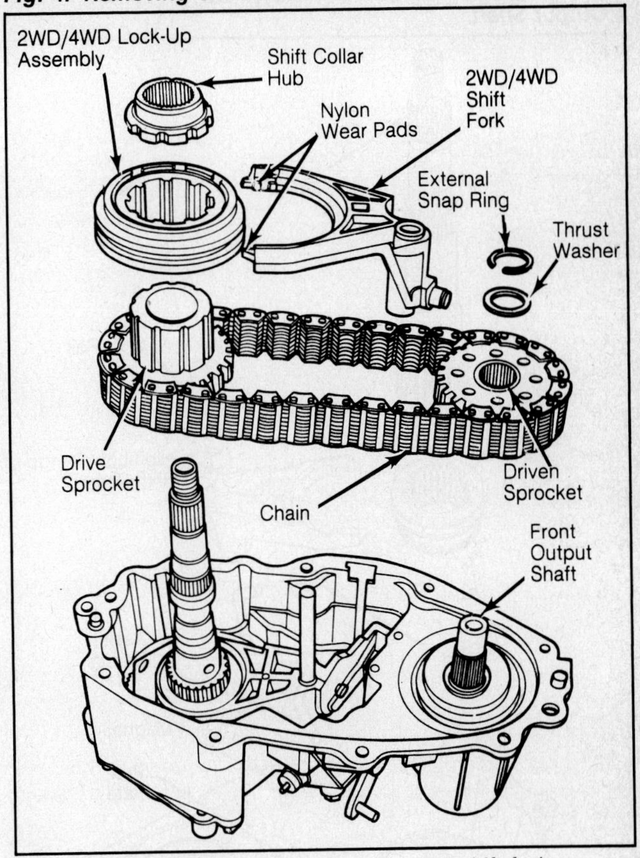

Remove 2WD/4WD lock-up assembly and shift fork as an assembly.

11) Remove chain, driven sprocket, and drive sprocket as an assembly. Remove collector magnet from notch in bottom of front case. If disassembly of oil pump is necessary, remove bolts from pump body. Note position and markings of front cover, body, pins, rear cover, and pump retainer.

12) Pull out shift rail. Slip the high-low range shift fork out of inside track of shift cam. If required, remove external clip and roller bushing assembly (bushing, shaft and external clip) from high-low range shift fork. Remove high-low shift hub from planetary gear set in front case. *See Fig. 5*.

13) Push and pull out anchor end of assist spring from locking post in front case half. Remove spring and roller out of shift cam. Turn case over and remove 6 bolts retaining mounting adapter to front case. Remove mounting adapter, input shaft and planetary gear set as an assembly.

14) If required, remove the ring gear from front case using a press. Note relationship of serrations to chamfered pilot diameter during removal. Expand tangs of large snap ring in mounting adapter and pry under planetary gear set with screwdrivers. Separate input shaft and planetary gear set from mounting adapter.

15) If required, remove oil seal from mounting adapter with Seal Remover (1175-AC) and slide hammer. Remove internal snap ring from planetary carrier and separate planetary gear set from input shaft assembly. Remove external snap ring from input shaft. *See Fig. 6*.

16) Place input shaft assembly in a press and remove ball bearing from input shaft with Bearing Splitter

Transfer Cases

BORG-WARNER 1350 (Cont.)

Fig. 5: High-Low Range Shift Assembly & Output Shaft

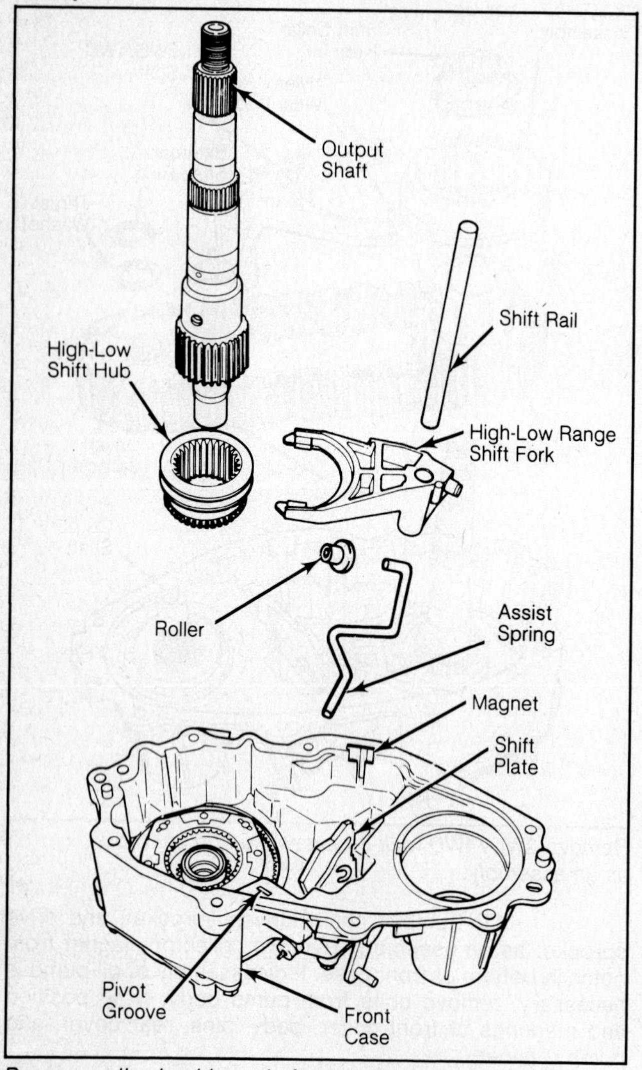

Remove roller bushing, shaft and clip as an assembly.

Fig. 6: Exploded View of Planetary Gear Set

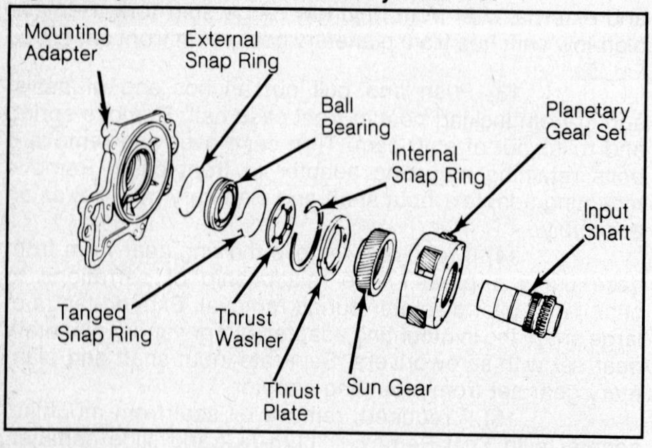

(D79L-4621-A). Remove thrust washer, thrust plate and sun gear off input shaft.

17) Move shift lever by hand until shift cam is in 4WD-High detent position. Scribe a line on outside of front case using the side of shift lever and a grease pencil. *See Fig. 7.* Remove 2 Phillips head set screws from front case and shift cam.

Fig. 7: Shift Lever & Cam Assembly

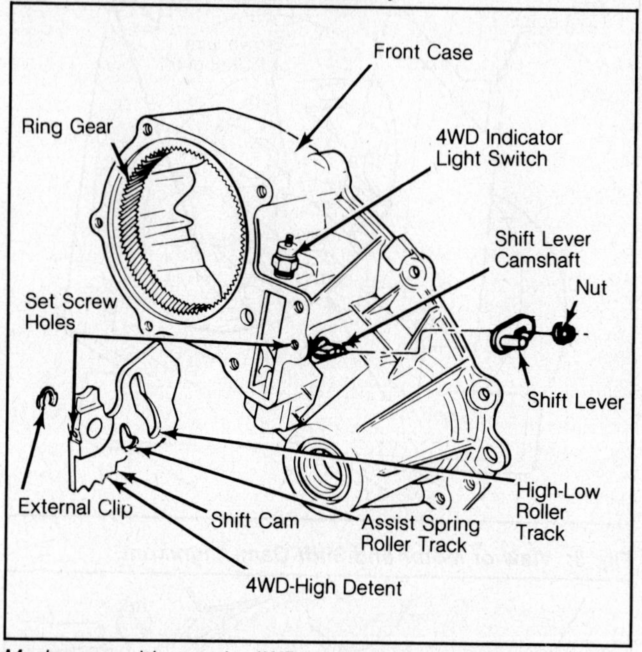

Mark case with cam in 4WD-High detent position.

Fig. 8: Removing/Installing Front Output Shaft Assembly

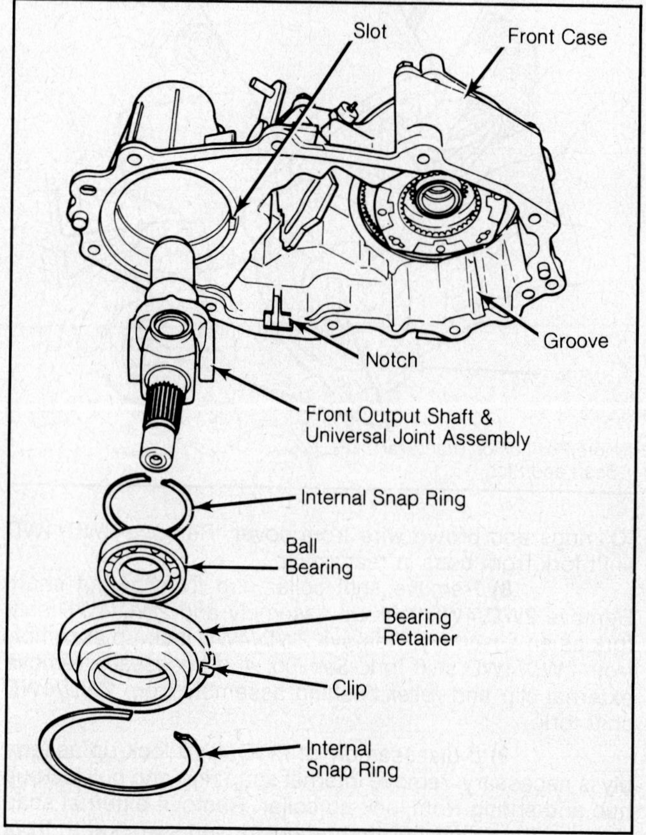

Do not discard clip.

18) Turn front case over and remove external clip. Pry shift lever out of front case and shift cam. Do not pound on external clip during removal. Remove "O" ring from 2nd groove in shift lever shaft. Remove detent plunger and compression spring from inside of front case.

19) Remove internal snap ring and ball bearing retainer from front case by tapping on face of front output shaft and universal joint assembly using a plastic hammer. Remove internal snap ring and drive ball bearing out of bearing retainer using Driver (T80T-4000-W) and Output Shaft Bearing Replacer (T83T-7025-B). *See Fig. 8*.

NOTE: **The clip on bearing retainer is required to prevent bearing retainer from rotating. Do not discard clip.**

20) Remove front output shaft and universal joint assembly from front case. If necessary, remove oil seal with Seal Remover (1175-AC) and slide hammer. If necessary, remove internal snap ring and drive ball bearing out of front case bore. Use driver and output shaft replacer.

21) If required, place front output shaft and universal joint assembly in a vise. Use copper or wood vise jaws to prevent damage to assembly. Remove internal snap rings that retain bearings in shaft.

22) Position "U" Joint Remover/Installer (T74P-4635-C) over shaft and press bearing out. If bearing cannot be pressed all the way out, remove it with a pair of vise grips or channel lock pliers. Reposition tool on spider to remove opposite bearing. Repeat procedure until all bearings are removed.

REASSEMBLY

TRANSFER CASE

1) Lubricate all parts with Dexron II ATF. Support front output shaft in a vise equipped with copper or wood jaws. If removed, start a new bearing into end of a shaft. Position spider into bearing and press bearing below snap ring groove using "U" joint installer. Remove tool and install a new internal snap ring in groove.

2) Start new bearing into opposite end of shaft. Using "U" joint installer, press bearing until opposite bearing contacts snap ring. Remove tool and install new internal snap ring in groove. Reposition front output shaft assembly and install other 2 bearings in same manner.

3) Check universal joint for freedom of movement and binding. If universal joint shows any sign of binding, tap both shafts sharply to relieve bind. Do not install front output shaft assembly if universal joint shows any sign of binding.

4) If removed, drive ball bearing into front output case bore using Driver (T80T-4000-W) and Output Shaft Bearing Replacer (T83T-7025-B). Make sure bearing is not cocked in bore. Install internal snap ring that retains ball bearing to front case. If removed, install front output oil seal in front case bore. Use Driver (T80T-4000-W) and Output Shaft Seal Installer (T83T-7065-W).

5) If removed, install ring gear in front case. Align serrations on outside diameter of ring gear to serrations previously cut in front case bore. Using a press, start piloted chamferred end of ring gear first and press in until it is fully seated. Make sure ring gear is not cocked in bore.

6) If removed, install ball bearing in bearing retainer bore. Drive bearing into retainer using driver and output shaft bearing replacer. Make sure ball bearing is not cocked in bore. Install internal snap ring that retains ball bearing to retainer. Install front output shaft and universal joint assembly through front case seal.

7) Position ball bearing and retainer assembly over front output shaft and install in front case bore. Make sure clip on bearing retainer aligns with slot in front case. Tap bearing retainer into place with a plastic hammer. Install internal snap ring that retains ball bearing and retainer assembly to front case. *See Fig. 8*.

8) Install compression spring and detent plunger into bore from inside of front case. If disassembled, install shift lever cam shaft to shift lever and tighten nut. Install a new "O" ring in second groove of shift lever shaft. Coat shaft and "O" ring with a small amount of multipurpose grease. Use a rubber band to fill the first groove so as not to cut "O" ring. Discard rubber band.

9) With shift cam, shift lever and snap ring installed in front case, position shift lever in 4WD-High detent position (line scribed during disassembly). Place assist spring roller on the 90° bend tang of assist spring and insert roller into assist spring roller slot of shift cam. *See Fig. 9*.

10) Position middle section of assist spring into the groove of front case pivot boss. Push in and lock the upper end of assist sping behind the front case spring anchor tab. *See Fig. 9*.

11) Install 2 Phillips head screws in front case and in shift cam. Tighten screws. Make sure set screw in front case is in first groove of shift lever shaft and not bottomed out against shaft itself. Shift lever should be able to move freely to all detent positions.

12) Slide sun gear, thrust plate and thrust washer over input shaft. Press ball bearing over input shaft. Install external snap ring to input shaft. Install planetary gear set to sun gear and install input shaft assembly. Install internal snap ring to planetary carrier.

NOTE: **The sun gear recessed face and ball bearing snap ring groove should be toward rear of transfer case. The stepped face of thrust washer should face toward the ball bearing.**

13) Drive oil seal into bore of mounting adapter with Driver (T80T-4000-W) and Input Shaft Seal Installer (T83T-7065-A). Place tanged snap ring in mounting adapter groove. Position input shaft and planetary gear set in mounting adapter and push inward until planetary assembly and input shaft assembly are seated in adapter. When properly seated, the snap ring will snap into place.

14) Check installation of snap ring by holding mounting adapter by hand and tapping face of input shaft against a wooden block to ensure that snap ring is engaged. Apply RTV sealer to mating surface of front case and mounting adapter. Position adapter on case, install retaining bolts and tighten.

15) Position roller on 90° bend tang of assist spring. The larger diameter end of spring must be installed first. Install roller into assist spring roller track of shift cam while at the same time locating center of spring in pivot groove in front case. *See Fig. 5 and 7*. Push anchor end of assist spring behind locking post adjacent to ring gear face.

16) Position high-low shift hub into planetary gear set. Slip high-low shift fork bushing into high-low roller track of shift cam and groove of high-low shift hub. *See Fig. 5 and 7*. Install shift rail through high-low fork and make sure shift rail is seated in bore in front case.

NOTE: **Make sure nylon wear pads are installed on shift fork and dot on pad is installed in fork hole.**

Transfer Cases

BORG-WARNER 1350 (Cont.)

Fig. 9: Assist Spring Installation

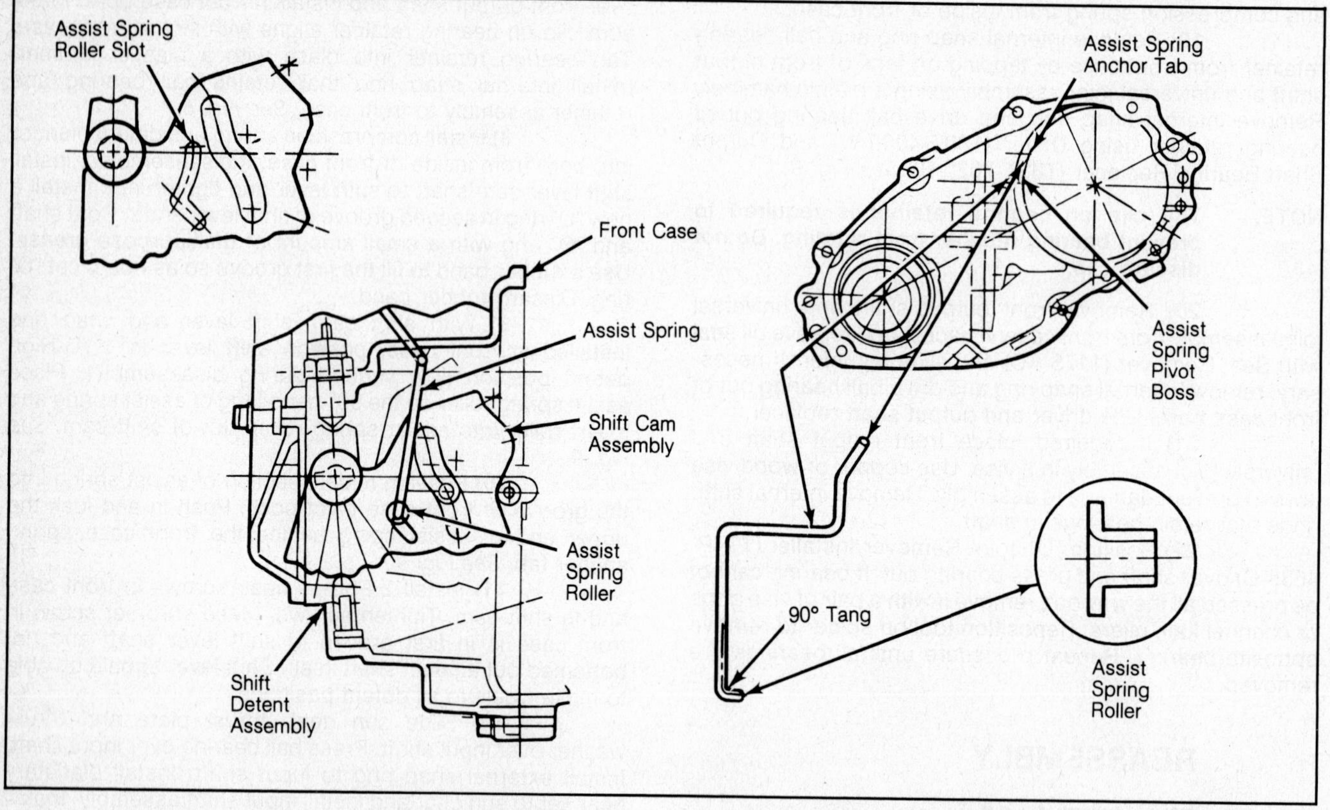

17) Place oil pump cover with word "TOP" facing front of front case. Install 2 pump pins (flats facing upward) with spring between pins and place assembly in oil pump bore in output shaft. Place oil pump body and pick-up tube assembly over shaft. Make sure pins are riding against inside of pump body.

18) Place oil pump rear cover with words "TOP REAR" facing rear of front case. The word "TOP" on front and rear covers should be on the same side. Install pump retainer, 4 bolts and rotate output shaft while tighening bolts to prevent pump from binding. The output shaft must turn freely within oil pump. If binding occurs, loosen 4 bolts and retighten.

19) Install output shaft and oil pump assembly in input shaft. Make sure external splines of output shaft engage internal splines of high-low shift hub. Make sure oil pump retainer and oil filter leg are in groove and notch of front case. Install collector magnet in notch in front case.

20) Install chain, drive sprocket and driven sprocket as an assembly over shafts. Install thrust washer on front output shaft and external snap ring over thrust washer to retain driven sprocket.

21) If disassembled, assemble 2WD/4WD lock-up assembly. Install spring in lock-up collar. Place lock-up hub over spring and engage lock-up hub in notches in lock-up collar. Retain lock-up hub to lock-up collar with an internal snap ring. *See Fig. 10*.

22) Install 2WD/4WD shift fork to 2WD/4WD lock-up assembly. If removed, make sure nylon wear pads are installed on fork and dot on pad is installed in hole in fork. Install 2WD/4WD lock-up collar and hub assembly over output shaft and onto shift rail. *See Fig. 4*.

23) If removed, install shaft, bushing and external clip to 2WD/4WD lock-up fork. Install shift collar hub to output shaft. If removed, drive caged needle bearing into

Fig. 10: Exploded View 2WD/4WD Lock-Up Assembly

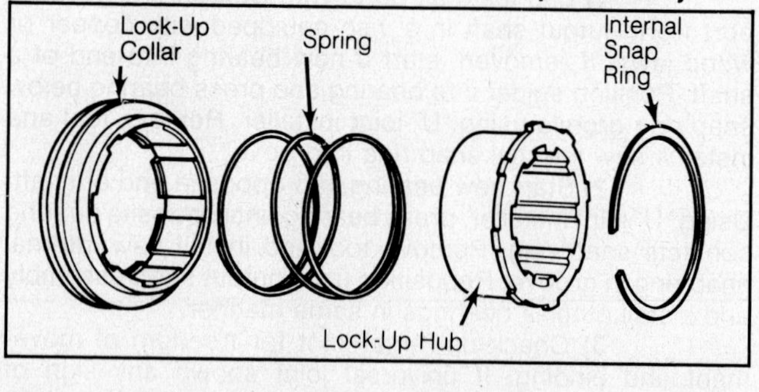

rear cover bore with Driver (T80T-4000-W) and Needle Bearing Replacer (T83T-7127-A).

24) If disassembled, assemble camshaft assembly on electric models. Slide spring spacer then spring onto camshaft. Position 1st spring tang to left side of drive tang. Wind 2nd spring tang back to right side of drive tang. Slide spring and spacer in as far as possible. Install helical cam onto camshaft with cam tang in between spring tangs. *See Fig. 11.*

25) Install camshaft assembly over alignment pin in front case. Camshaft assembly tangs should point toward top of case and rest on high-low shift fork assembly.

26) If removed, install ball bearing in rear cover bore. Drive bearing into rear cover bore with driver and Output Shaft Bearing Replacer (T83T-7025-B). Make sure ball bearing is not cocked in bore. Install internal snap ring that retains ball bearing to rear cover.

27) On electric models install new "O" rings on clutch coil assembly studs and grommet. Install clutch coil assembly making sure brown wire exits case and is not pinched.

BORG-WARNER 1350 (Cont.)

Fig. 11: Attaching Spring Tangs to Camshaft Tangs.

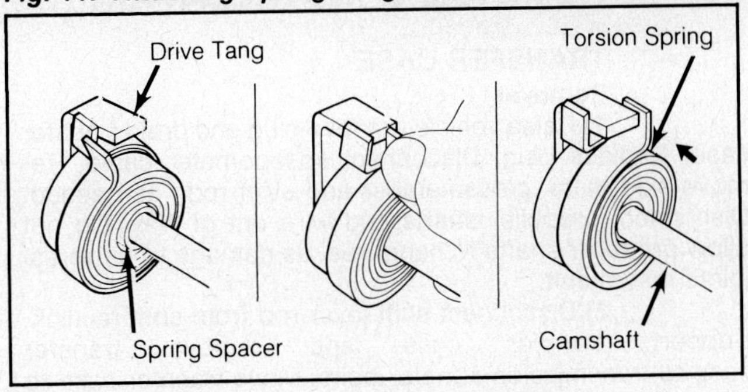

28) Install speedometer drive gear assembly into rear cover bore with round end of speedometer gear clip facing toward inside of rear cover. Drive oil seal into rear cover bore with driver and output shaft seal installer (T83T-7065-B).

29) Prior to final assembly of rear cover to front case half, transfer case shift lever assembly should be shifted into 4WD-High detent position to assure positioning of shift rail to rear cover.

30) Coat mating surface of front case with a bead of RTV sealer. Install 2WD/4WD shift fork spring on shift rail and shift fork with spring mounted in vertical position.

31) Position rear cover on front case so that spring boss engages 2WD/4WD shift fork spring and shift rod. Install bolts and tighten. If rear cover assembly does not seat properly, move rear cover up and down slightly to permit end of shift rail to enter shift rail hole in rear cover boss.

32) Noting position of triangular shaft on electric shift models, install motor and 3 screws. Install 4WD indicator switch, speed sensor and retaining bracket. Reconnect brown, green and blue wires into connector. Install locking sleeve into connector.

31) Position rear cover on front case so that spring boss engages 2WD/4WD shift fork spring and shift rod. Install bolts and tighten. If rear cover assembly does not seat properly, move rear cover up and down slightly to permit end of shift rail to enter shift rail hole in rear cover boss.

32) Noting position of triangular shaft on electric shift models, install motor and 3 screws. Install 4WD indicator switch, speed sensor and retaining bracket. Reconnect brown, green and blue wires into connector. Install locking sleeve into connector.

33) Install rear yoke on output shaft. Install rubber seal, washer, and nut. Tighten nut. Install 4WD indicator switch and breather plug. Install drain plug. Remove fill plug and fill transfer case with 3 pts. (1.4L) of Dexron II ATF. Install fill plug and install transfer case.

TIGHTENING SPECIFICATIONS

Application	Ft. Lbs. (N.m)
Breather Vent	6-14 (8-19)
Case-to-Cover Bolts	23-30 (31-41)
Drain & Fill Plug	14-22 (19-30)
Front & Rear Drive Shaft Bolts	12-15 (16-20)
Shift Control Bolts (Large)	70-90 (95-122)
Shift Control Bolts (Small)	31-42 (42-57)
Shift Lever Nut	19-26 (25-35)
Skid Plate-to-Frame Bolt	22-30 (30-41)
Transfer Case-to-Transmission	25-35 (34-47)
Upper Shift Control Lever & Heat Shield Bolts	27-37 (37-50)
Yoke Nut	120-150 (163-203)
4WD Indicator Switch	25-35 (34-47)
	INCH Lbs. (N.m)
Oil Pump Bolts	36-40 (4.0-4.5)
Clutch Coil Assembly Nuts	72-96 (8.1-10.8)
Shift Shaft & Shift Cam Set Screw	60-84 (6.8-9.5)
Speedometer Screw	20-25 (2.3-2.8)

Transfer Cases

NEW PROCESS MODEL 205

Chrysler Corp., General Motors

DESCRIPTION

Transfer case provides two gears, high (1:1) for highway driving and low (1.96:1) for off-road or heavy duty operation. With this transfer case, direct drive is available in both 2WD and 4WD.

Sliding clutch gears are used in controlling the various selections of gear combinations. The transfer case contains constant-mesh helical cut gears with shafts mounted on ball and roller bearings. When driving in a 4WD mode, hubs on the front wheels must be turned to the "LOCKED" position.

LUBRICATION

SERVICE INTERVALS

Chrysler Corp.

Check fluid level and fill as necessary. Drain and refill transfer case every 37,500 miles.

General Motors

Check fluid level and fill as necessary every 4 months or 7500 miles.

FLUID TYPE

Chrysler Corp.

Use multipurpose gear lubricants meeting API specification GL-5 or engine oils labeled "SE" and "CC".

If multipurpose gear lubricant is used and the minimum anticipated air temperature is:

- Above 90°F (32°C), use SAE 140.
- Below 90°F (32°C) but above -10°F (-23°C), use SAE 90.
- Below -10°F (-23°C), use SAE 80.

If engine oil is used and the air temperature is:

- Above 32°F (0°C), use SAE 50.
- Below 32°F (0°C), use SAE 30.

General Motors

Use Dexron II Automatic Transmission Fluid.

CAPACITY

Chrysler Corp.

Capacity is 4.5 pints (2.1L).

General Motors

Capacity is 5.1 pints (2.4L).

ADJUSTMENTS

SHIFT LINKAGE

Chrysler Corp.

Install lower shift lever to bracket. Loosely install bracket on adapter. Install shift rod. Position bracket as far forward as possible and tighten bracket bolts. Place lever in all positions to ensure that linkage operates properly.

General Motors

Adjust shift linkage so that all positions may be selected without interference or binding.

REMOVAL & INSTALLATION

TRANSFER CASE

Removal

1) Raise vehicle, remove plug and drain transfer case. Replace plug. Disconnect speedometer cable. Remove skid plate, crossmember and strut rods as needed. Disconnect propeller shafts and wire out of way. Do not allow propeller shafts to hang free, as damage to universal joints may result.

2) Disconnect shift lever rod from shift rail link. Support transfer case and remove transfer case-to-transmission adapter bolts. Move transfer case to rear until input shaft clears adapter. Lower transfer case from vehicle.

Installation

Reverse removal procedure to install transfer case. Ensure that all attaching bolts are tight. Fill transfer case with lubricant.

DISASSEMBLY

REAR OUTPUT SHAFT & YOKE ASSEMBLY

1) Loosen rear output shaft yoke nut. Remove rear output shaft housing bolts and remove housing and retainer from case. Remove retaining nut and yoke from shaft. Then remove shaft assembly from housing. Remove snap ring and discard.

2) Remove thrust washer and washer pin. Remove tanged bronze washer. Remove gear and gear needle bearings (32 per row). Remove spacer and 2nd row of needle bearings. Remove tanged bronze thrust washer from shaft.

3) Remove needle bearings from shaft (15 per row). Remove retainer ring and washer. Discard retainer ring. Remove oil seal retainer, ball bearing, speedometer gear and spacer. Discard all gaskets. Press out bearing and remove oil seal.

FRONT OUTPUT SHAFT ASSEMBLY

1) Remove lock nut, washer and yoke. Remove front bearing retainer attaching bolts and retainer. Remove front output shaft rear bearing retainer attaching bolts.

2) Using a soft-faced hammer, tap on output shaft and remove shaft, gear assembly and rear bearing retainer from case. *See Fig. 1.* Remove the sliding clutch from output high gear. Remove washer and bearing remaining in case.

3) Remove gear retaining snap ring from shaft. Discard retaining snap ring. Remove thrust washer and pin from shaft. Remove gear, needle bearings (32 per row) and spacer.

4) If necessary to replace front output shaft rear bearing, support cover and press bearing from cover. Position new bearing to outside face of cover and using a pipe or piece of wood, press bearing into cover until flush with opening. Use a new retainer when replacing bearing.

SHIFT RAIL & FORK ASSEMBLIES

1) Remove 2 poppet nuts and springs on top of case. Using a magnet, remove the poppet balls. Drive cup plugs into case using a 1/4" (6.35 mm) punch. Position both shift rails in Neutral. Using a long, narrow punch, drive shift fork pins through shift rails into case.

NEW PROCESS MODEL 205 (Cont.)

Fig. 1: Removing Front Output Shaft Assembly

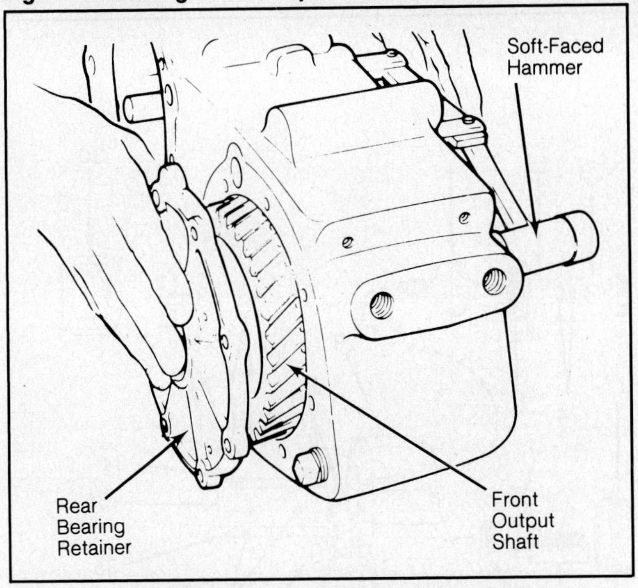

Using a soft-faced hammer, tap shaft of transfer case.

2) Remove clevis pins and shift rail link. Remove shift rails, upper range rail, then lower (4WD) rail. Remove shift forks and sliding clutch from case. Remove front output high gear, washer, and bearing from case.

3) Remove shift rail cup plugs and pins from case. Remove snap ring in front of bearing. Using a soft-faced hammer, tap shaft out rear of case. Tap bearing out front of case. Tip case on PTO and remove 2 interlock pins from inside case.

IDLER GEAR

Remove idler gear shaft nut. Remove idler shaft rear cover. Remove idler gear shaft using a soft-faced hammer and a driver. Tilt case at 45° angle and roll idler gear to front output shaft hole and remove from case. Remove 2 bearing cups from idler gear.

CLEANING & INSPECTION

1) Clean all parts with solvent, and blow parts dry with compressed air. Direct air across bearings, ensuring that they do not spin. Remove all traces of gaskets from surfaces where used.

2) Examine all bearings for wear or evidence of chipping or cracks. Replace bearings as necessary. Bearings are nonadjustable. If they are worn or damaged, they must be replaced.

3) Inspect teeth of all gears for excessive wear or damage. Replace any gear where these conditions exist. Sliding clutch wear occurs on engagement side, if wear is present, use opposite side of clutch in reassembly. Both sides of clutch are identical.

4) Carefully examine splines and shaft for scoring or evidence of wear. Sliding clutch gears must move freely on splines. Parts should be replaced if spline or shaft is scored or heavily worn.

REASSEMBLY

IDLER GEAR

1) If removed, press 2 bearing cups in idler gear. Assemble 2 bearing cones, spacer, shims and idler gear on dummy shaft with bore up. Check end play; limits are .001-.002" (.025-.050 mm). *See Fig. 2.*

Fig. 2: Checking Idler Gear End Play

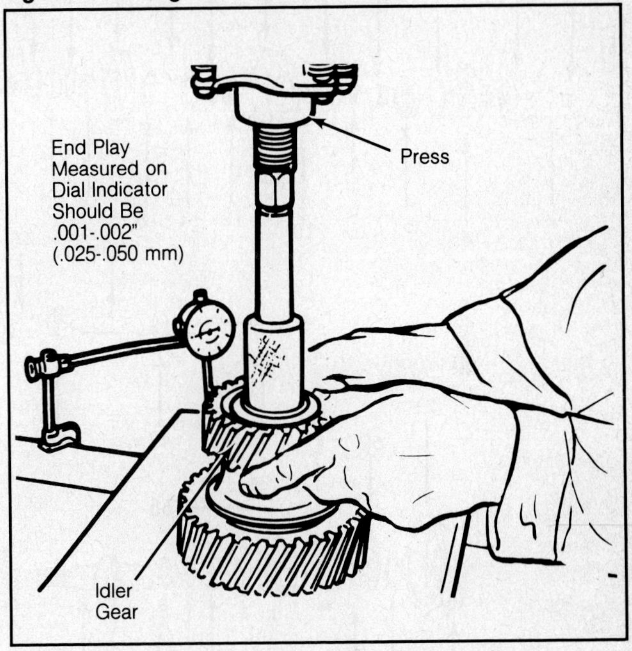

Install idler gear with dummy shaft, large end first.

2) Install idler gear assembly with dummy shaft into case. Install through front output bore, large end first. Install idler shaft from large bore side and drive through using soft-faced hammer.

3) Install washer and new lock nut. Check for end play and free rotation. Tighten lock nut. Install idler shaft cover, flat spot on cover must be located toward front output shaft rear cover. Install gasket and tighten bolts.

SHIFT RAIL & FORK ASSEMBLIES

1) Press 2 rail seals into case. Seals should be installed with metal lip outward. Install interlock pins through large bore or PTO opening. Start front output drive shift rail into case from back, slotted end first with poppet notches up.

2) Install shift fork into rail with long end inward. Push rail through to Neutral position. Install input shaft bearing and shaft into case. Start range rail into case from front with poppet notches up.

3) Install sliding clutch onto fork, placing clutch over input shaft in case. Position to receive range rail and push rail through to Neutral position. Install new lock pins through holes at top of case and drive them into forks. Tip case on PTO opening when installing range rail lock pin.

FRONT OUTPUT SHAFT & GEAR ASSEMBLY

1) Install 2 rows of needle bearings (32 each), separated by spacer, in front low output gear. Use grease to retain bearings. Place front output shaft in a soft-jawed

NEW PROCESS MODEL 205 (Cont.)

Fig. 3: New Process Model 205 Transfer Case

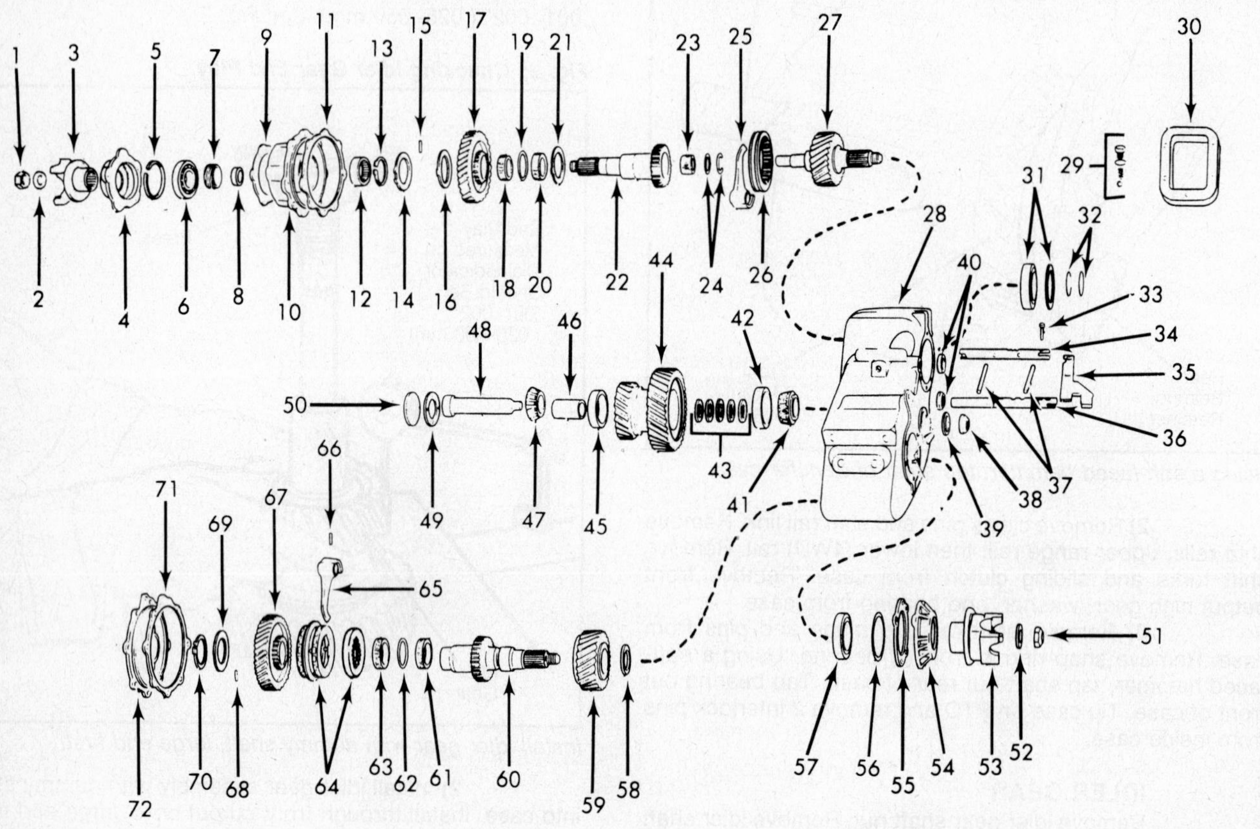

1. Rear Output Shaft Lock Nut
2. Washer
3. Rear Output Shaft Yoke
4. Bearing Retainer & Seal
5. Snap Ring
6. Bearing
7. Speedometer Gear
8. Spacer
9. Gasket
10. Rear Output Shaft Housing
11. Gasket
12. Bearing
13. Snap Ring
14. Thrust Washer
15. Thrust Washer Lock Pin
16. Thrust Washer (Tanged)
17. Low Speed Gear
18. Needle Bearings
19. Spacer
20. Needle Bearings
21. Thrust Washer (Tanged)
22. Rear Output Shaft
23. Needle Bearings
24. Washer & Retainer
25. Shift Fork
26. Sliding Clutch
27. Input Shaft
28. Transfer Case
29. Poppet Plug, Spring & Ball
30. PTO Gasket & Cover
31. Input Shaft Bearing & Snap Ring
32. Snap Ring & Rubber "O" Ring (General Motors Only)
33. Shift Link Clevis Pin
34. Range Shift Rail
35. Shift Rail Connector Link
36. 4WD Shift Rail
37. Interlock Pins
38. Rear Idler Lock Nut
39. Washer
40. Shift Rail Seals
41. Idler Shaft Bearing
42. Bearing Cup
43. Shims
44. Idler Gear
45. Bearing Cup
46. Spacer
47. Idler Shaft Bearing
48. Idler Shaft
49. Cover Gasket
50. Rear Cover
51. Front Output Shaft Lock Nut
52. Washer
53. Yoke
54. Bearing Retainer & Seal
55. Gasket
56. Snap Ring
57. Front Bearing
58. Thrust Washer
59. 4WD-High Gear
60. Front Output Shaft
61. Needle Bearing
62. Spacer
63. Needle Bearing
64. Sliding Clutch Gear
65. Shift Fork
66. Roll Pin
67. Front Output Low Gear
68. Thrust Washer Lock Pin
69. Thrust Washer
70. Snap Ring
71. Rear Cover Gasket
72. Rear Cover & Bearing

Transfer Cases

NEW PROCESS MODEL 205 (Cont.)

vise, splined end down. Install front low gear over shaft with clutch gear facing down.

2) Install thrust washer pin, thrust washer, and new snap ring. Position snap ring so opening is opposite the pin. Position front wheel high gear and washer in case. Install sliding clutch in fork, then put shift fork and rail in 4WD position with clutch teeth meshed with teeth of front wheel high gear.

3) Line up washer, high gear and sliding clutch with bearing bore. Insert front output shaft and low gear assembly through high gear assembly. Using seal driver, install new seal in bearing retainer. Install front output bearing and retainer in case.

4) Clean and grease rollers in front output rear bearing retainer. Install onto case using 1 gasket. Dip bolts into sealant. Install bolts and tighten. Install front output yoke, washer, and lock nut. Tighten nut.

REAR OUTPUT SHAFT ASSEMBLY

1) Install 2 rows of needle bearings (32 each), separated by spacer. Use grease to retain bearings. Install thrust washer onto rear output shaft, with tang down in clutch gear groove. Install output low gear onto shaft with clutch teeth facing down.

2) With tab pointing up and away from gear, install thrust washer over gear. Install washer pin and large thrust washer over shaft and pin. Rotate washer until tab fits into slot, approximately 90° away from pin. Install new snap ring and check end play. End play should be within .002-.027" (.051-.686 mm).

3) Grease pilot bore of rear output shaft and install needle bearings (15 each). Install thrust washer and new snap ring. Clean, grease and install new bearing in retainer housing.

4) Install housing onto output shaft assembly. Install spacer and speedometer gear. Using 1 or 2 gaskets depending on clearance, install bearing, rear bearing retainer seal, and bearing retainer onto housing. Tighten bolts. Install yoke, washer, and lock nut on output shaft.

5) Position range rail in high gear and install output shaft and retainer assembly on transfer case. Tighten bolts. Install PTO cover and gasket. Install and seal cup plugs at rail pin holes. Install drain and fill plug. Install shift rail cross link, clevis pins and lock pins.

Fig. 4: Rear Output Spacer and Speedometer Gear

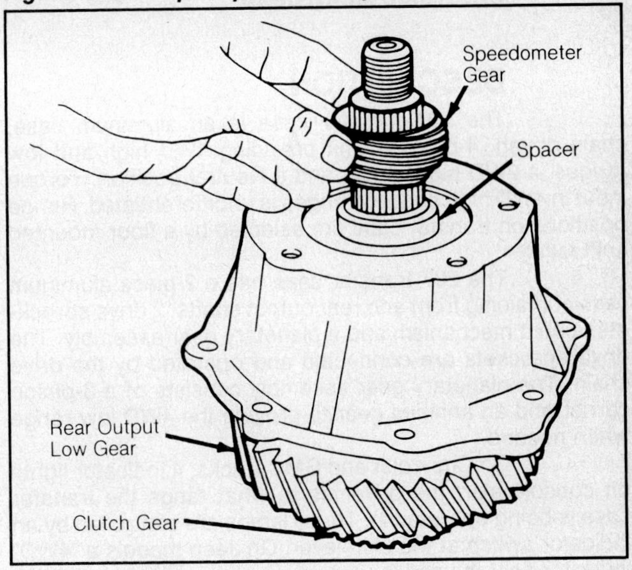

Install housing onto output shaft assembly

TIGHTENING SPECIFICATION

Application	Ft. Lbs. (N.m)
Drain & Fill Plugs	30 (41)
Idler Shaft Cover Bolts	20 (27)
Idler Shaft Lock Nut	150 (203)
Input & Output Bearing Retainer Bolts	30-35 (41-47)
Output Yoke Lock Nuts	150 (203)
PTO Cover Bolts	15 (20)
Transfer Case-to-Adapter Bolts	45 (61)

Transfer Cases

NEW PROCESS MODEL 207

Chevrolet, GMC, Jeep

DESCRIPTION

The 207 transfer case is an aluminum case, chain driven, 4-position unit providing 4WD high and low ranges, a 2WD high range, and a Neutral position. Torque input in 4WD high and low ranges is undifferentiated. Range positions on transfer case are selected by a floor mounted shift lever.

The 207 transfer case has a 2-piece aluminum case containing front and rear output shafts, 2 drive sprockets, a shift mechanism and a planetary gear assembly. The drive sprockets are connected and operated by the drive chain. The planetary gear assembly consists of a 3-pinion carrier and an annulus gear to provide the 4WD low range when needed.

On Chevrolet and GMC trucks, 4 indicator lights on console alert the driver as to what range the transfer case is being operated in. These lamps are controlled by an indicator switch at the shift lever. On Jeep models a "4WD" indicator light is used.

LUBRICATION

SERVICE INTERVALS

Check fluid and refill as necessary every 12 months or 7500 miles.

FLUID TYPE

Use Dexron II ATF.

CAPACITY

Refill capacity is 2.3 quarts (2.2L).

REMOVAL & INSTALLATION

TRANSFER CASE

Removal

1) Shift transfer case into 4WD high range and disconnect battery negative cable. Raise vehicle and remove skid plate, if used. Drain lubricant from transfer case.

2) Mark front and rear output shaft yokes and front and rear propeller shafts for reassembly reference. Remove propeller shafts. Disconnect speedometer cable and vacuum (hoses) harness at transfer case. Remove shift lever or linkage rod from case.

3) On Jeep trucks, remove shift lever bracket bolts. Support transfer case and remove transfer case attaching bolts. Remove transfer case from vehicle. On Chevrolet or GMC trucks, remove catalytic converter hanger bolts at converter. Raise transmission and transfer case and remove mount attaching bolts.

4) Remove transmission mount and catalytic converter hanger. Lower transmission and transfer case. Support transfer case and remove transfer case attaching bolts.

5) On vehicles equipped with automatic transmissions, it will be necessary to remove shift lever bracket mounting bolts from case in order to remove the upper left transfer case attaching bolt. Remove transfer case from vehicle.

Installation

1) On Jeep trucks, reverse removal procedure to complete installation. Road test vehicle. On Chevrolet or GMC trucks, clean all old gasket material from transmission and transfer case mating surfaces.

2) Position new gasket on transfer case with orientation tab at upper left bolt hole. *See Fig. 1.* Install transfer case, aligning splines of input shaft with transmission. Slide transfer case forward until seated against transmission.

Fig. 1: Assembling Transfer Case to Transmission

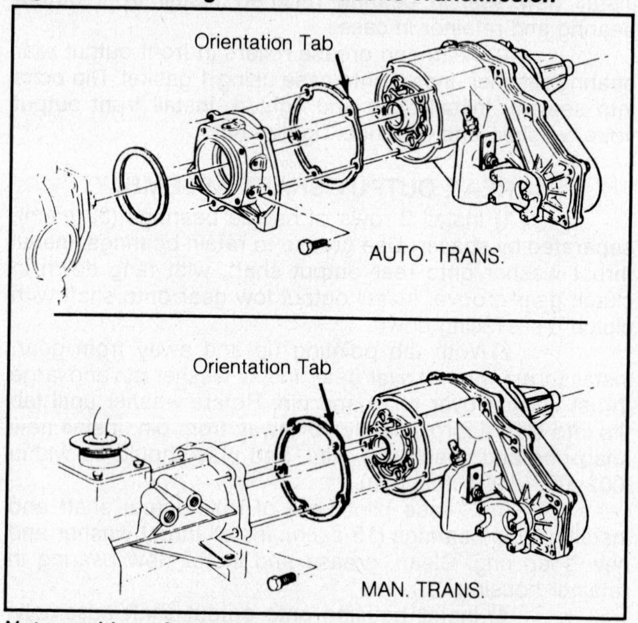

Note position of orientation tab.

3) Install transfer case attaching bolts and tighten. On vehicles equipped with automatic transmission, install shift lever bracket. Raise transmission and transfer case and install mount and hanger bracket. Install attaching bolts and tighten.

4) Install catalytic converter hanger bolts. Attach shift lever, connect speedometer and vacuum harness at transfer case. Using reference marks, made during removal, reinstall front and rear propeller shafts. Refill transfer case. Install skid plate and lower vehicle. Connect negative battery cable. Road test vehicle.

DISASSEMBLY

TRANSFER CASE

1) Remove drain and fill plugs. Remove front yoke. Discard seal washer and yoke nut. Turn transfer case on end and position transfer case on wood blocks. Shift transfer case to 4WD low.

2) Remove extension housing bolts and, using a hammer, tap shoulder on housing to break sealer loose. Remove rear bearing snap ring from mainshaft and discard. Remove rear retainer attaching bolts and, using a hammer, tap shoulder on retainer to break sealer loose.

3) Remove rear retainer and pump housing from transfer case. Remove pump seal from pump housing and discard seal. Remove speedometer drive gear and pump gear from mainshaft.

NEW PROCESS MODEL 207 (Cont.)

Fig. 2: Exploded View of New Process 207 Transfer Case

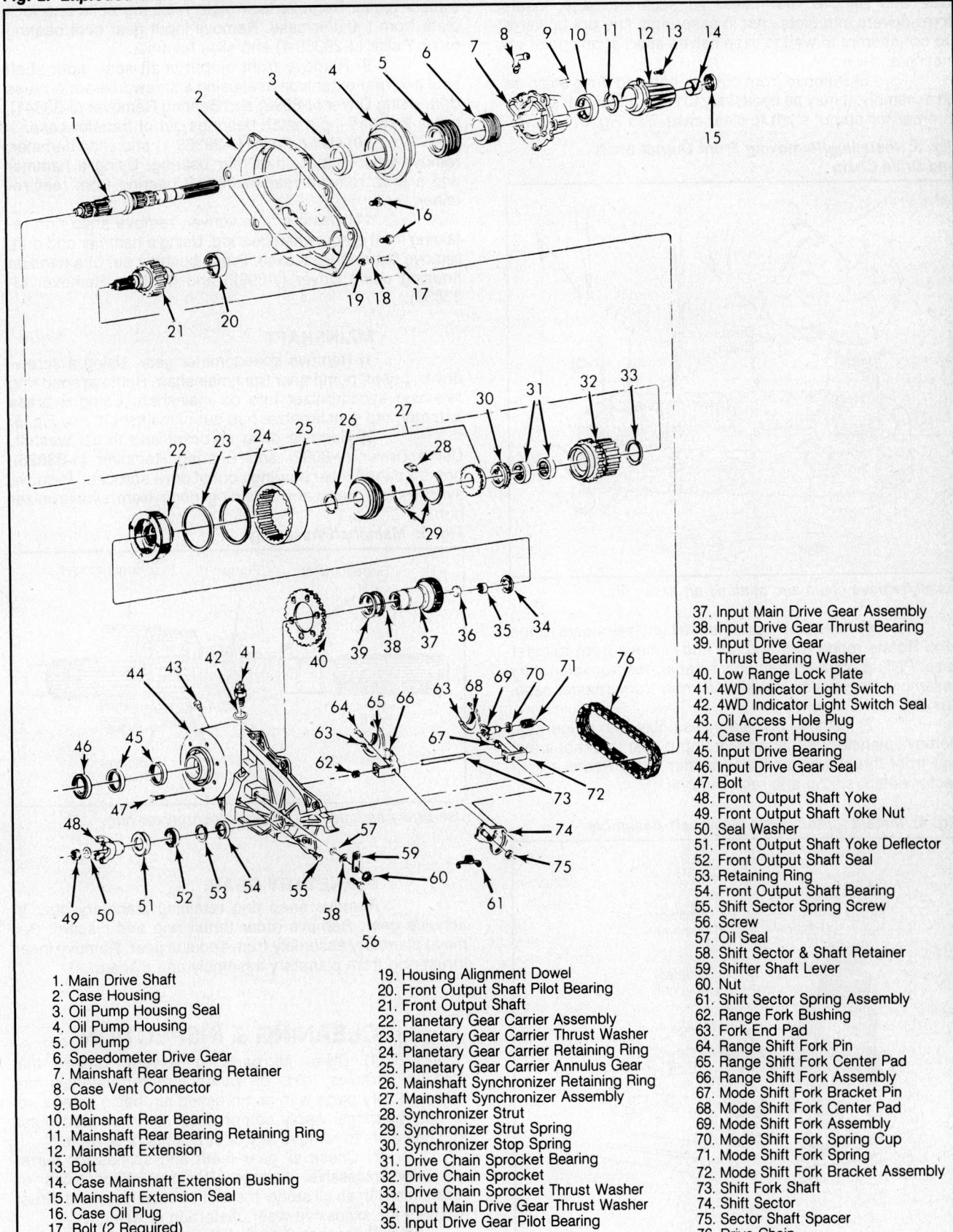

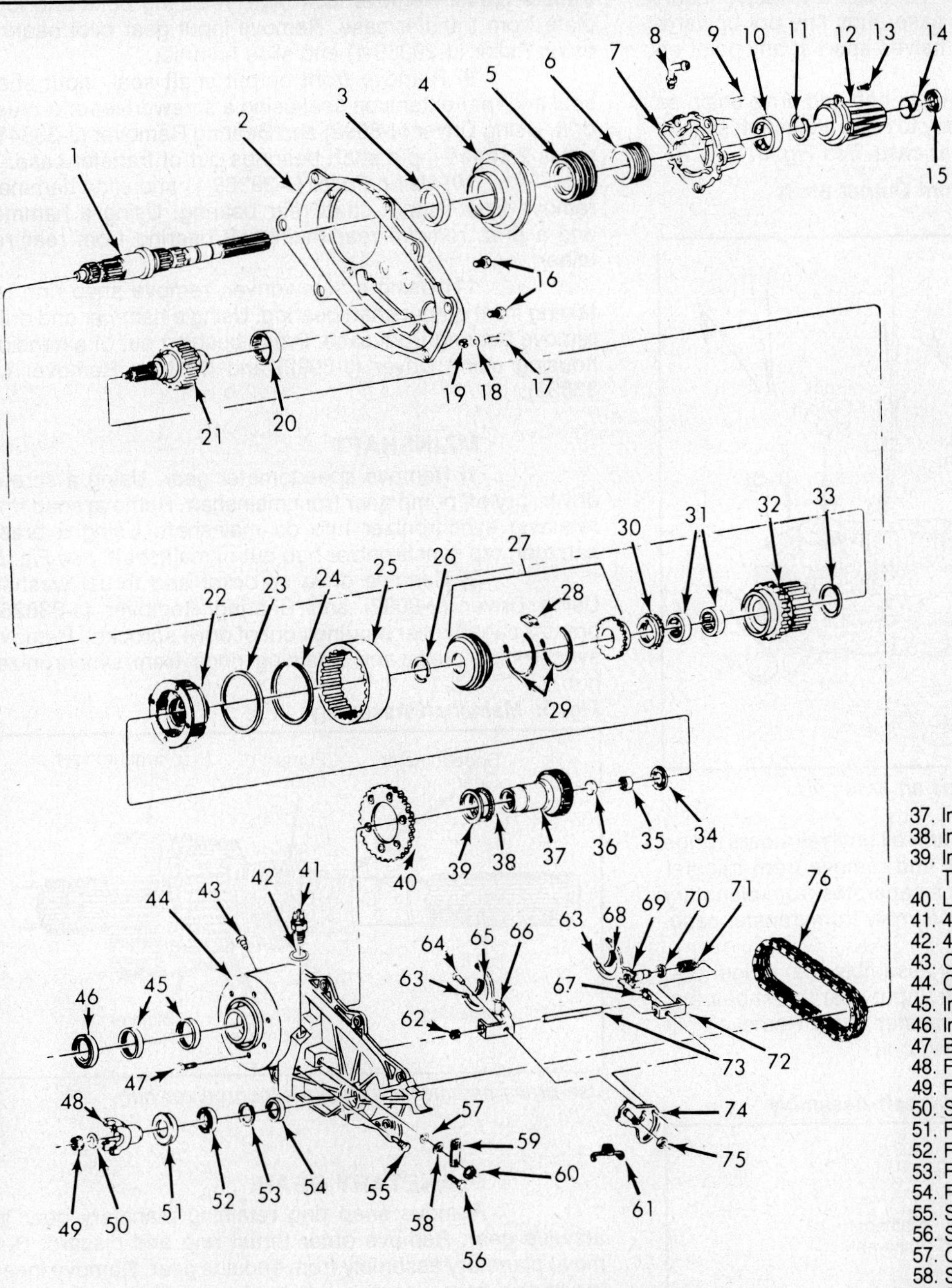

1. Main Drive Shaft
2. Case Housing
3. Oil Pump Housing Seal
4. Oil Pump Housing
5. Oil Pump
6. Speedometer Drive Gear
7. Mainshaft Rear Bearing Retainer
8. Case Vent Connector
9. Bolt
10. Mainshaft Rear Bearing
11. Mainshaft Rear Bearing Retaining Ring
12. Mainshaft Extension
13. Bolt
14. Case Mainshaft Extension Bushing
15. Mainshaft Extension Seal
16. Case Oil Plug
17. Bolt (2 Required)
18. Housing Alignment Dowel Washer
19. Housing Alignment Dowel
20. Front Output Shaft Pilot Bearing
21. Front Output Shaft
22. Planetary Gear Carrier Assembly
23. Planetary Gear Carrier Thrust Washer
24. Planetary Gear Carrier Retaining Ring
25. Planetary Gear Carrier Annulus Gear
26. Mainshaft Synchronizer Retaining Ring
27. Mainshaft Synchronizer Assembly
28. Synchronizer Strut
29. Synchronizer Strut Spring
30. Synchronizer Stop Spring
31. Drive Chain Sprocket Bearing
32. Drive Chain Sprocket
33. Drive Chain Sprocket Thrust Washer
34. Input Main Drive Gear Thrust Washer
35. Input Drive Gear Pilot Bearing
36. Plug
37. Input Main Drive Gear Assembly
38. Input Drive Gear Thrust Bearing
39. Input Drive Gear Thrust Bearing Washer
40. Low Range Lock Plate
41. 4WD Indicator Light Switch
42. 4WD Indicator Light Switch Seal
43. Oil Access Hole Plug
44. Case Front Housing
45. Input Drive Bearing
46. Input Drive Gear Seal
47. Bolt
48. Front Output Shaft Yoke
49. Front Output Shaft Yoke Nut
50. Seal Washer
51. Front Output Shaft Yoke Deflector
52. Front Output Shaft Seal
53. Retaining Ring
54. Front Output Shaft Bearing
55. Shift Sector Spring Screw
56. Screw
57. Oil Seal
58. Shift Sector & Shaft Retainer
59. Shifter Shaft Lever
60. Nut
61. Shift Sector Spring Assembly
62. Range Fork Bushing
63. Fork End Pad
64. Range Shift Fork Pin
65. Range Shift Fork Center Pad
66. Range Shift Fork Assembly
67. Mode Shift Fork Bracket Pin
68. Mode Shift Fork Center Pad
69. Mode Shift Fork Assembly
70. Mode Shift Fork Spring Cup
71. Mode Shift Fork Spring
72. Mode Shift Fork Bracket Assembly
73. Shift Fork Shaft
74. Shift Sector
75. Sector Shaft Spacer
76. Drive Chain

NEW PROCESS MODEL 207 (Cont.)

4) Remove bolts attaching rear case to front case and remove rear case. To separate case, insert screwdrivers into slots cast in case ends and pry upward. Do not attempt to wedge case halves apart at any point on mating surface.

5) Remove front output shaft and drive chain as an assembly. It may be necessary to raise mainshaft slightly in order for output shaft to clear case. *See Fig. 3.*

Fig. 3: Installing/Removing Front Output Shaft and Drive Chain

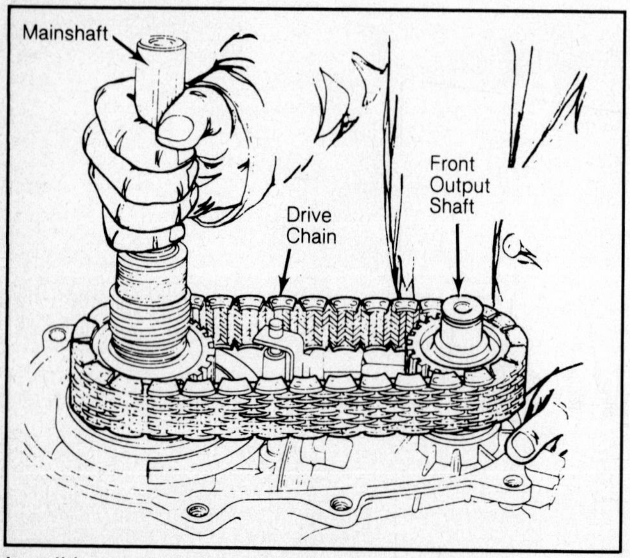

Install/remove chain and shaft as an assembly.

6) Pull up on mode fork rail until rail clears range fork. Rotate mode fork and rail and remove from transfer case. Pull up on mainshaft until it separates from planetary assembly. Remove mainshaft assembly from transfer case. *See Fig. 4.*

7) Remove planetary assembly with range fork. Remove planetary thrust washer, input gear thrust bearing, and front thrust washer from transfer case. Remove shift sector detent spring and retaining bolt.

Fig. 4: Installing/Removing Mainshaft Assembly

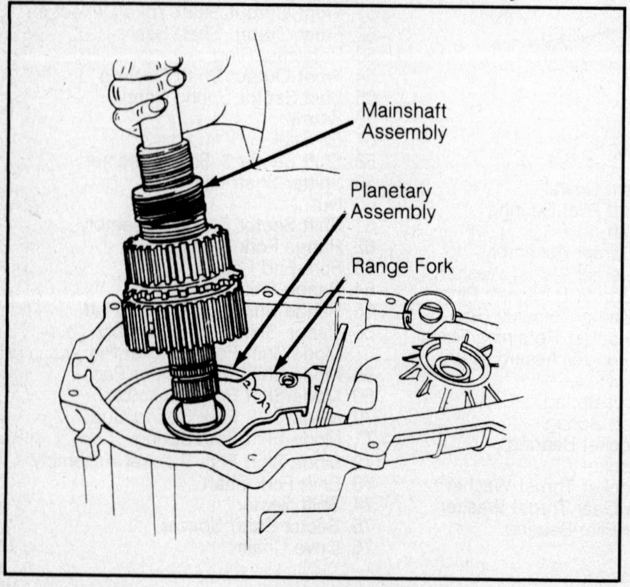

8) Remove shift sector, shaft, and spacer from transfer case. Remove lock plate retaining bolts and lock plate from transfer case. Remove input gear pilot bearing using Puller (J-29369-1) and slide hammer.

9) Remove front output shaft seal, input shaft seal and rear extension seal using a screwdriver or a brass drift. Using Driver (J-8092) and Bearing Remover (J-33841), press 2 caged input shaft bearings out of transfer case.

10) Using Puller (J-29369-1) and slide hammer, remove front output shaft rear bearing. Using a hammer and a drift, remove rear mainshaft bearing from rear retainer.

11) Using a screwdriver, remove snap ring retaining front output shaft bearing. Using a hammer and drift, remove bearing from case. Press bushing out of extension housing using Driver (J-8092) and Bushing Remover (J-33839).

MAINSHAFT

1) Remove speedometer gear. Using a screwdriver, pry off pump gear from mainshaft. Remove snap ring retaining synchronizer hub on mainshaft. Using a brass hammer, tap synchronizer hub out of mainshaft. *See Fig. 5.*

2) Remove drive sprocket and thrust washer. Using Driver (J-8092) and Bearing Remover (J-33826), press 2 caged roller bearings out of drive sprocket. Remove synchronizer keys and retaining rings from synchronizer hub.

Fig. 5: Mainshaft Assembly

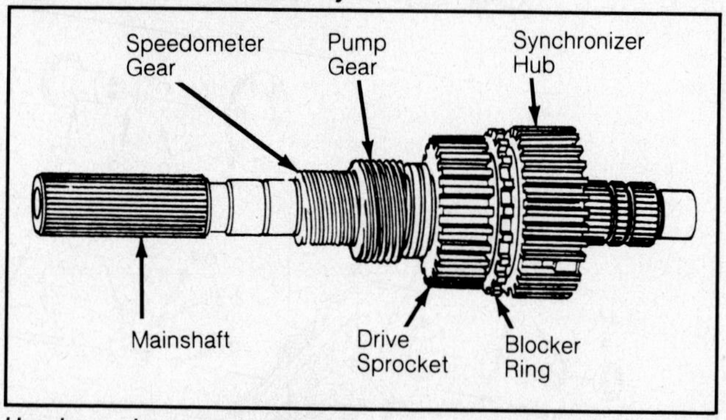

Use brass hammer to remove synchronizer hub.

PLANETARY GEAR

Remove snap ring retaining planetary gear in annulus gear. Remove outer thrust ring and discard. Remove planetary assembly from annulus gear. Remove inner thrust ring from planetary assembly and discard.

CLEANING & INSPECTION

1) Clean all parts in solvent. Ensure that metallic particles, dirt, or other foreign materials are removed. Dry parts with compressed air, being careful not to spin bearings. Apply compressed air to oil feed holes and channels to remove any obstructions or solvent.

2) Check all gear teeth and splines for burrs, nicks, or excessive damage. Remove minor nicks or scratches with an oil stone. Inspect all snap rings and thrust washers for excessive wear, distortion or damage.

3) Inspect 2 case halves for cracks, porosity, damaged mating surfaces, stripped bolt threads or distor-

NEW PROCESS MODEL 207 (Cont.)

tion. Inspect condition of all bearings and retainers. Inspect condition of chain and oil pump. Replace parts as necessary.

REASSEMBLY

PLANETARY GEAR

Install inner thrust ring on planetary assembly. Install planetary assembly into annulus gear. Install outer thrust ring and then snap ring. *See Fig. 6.*

Fig. 6: Installing Thrust Washers in Planetary Assembly

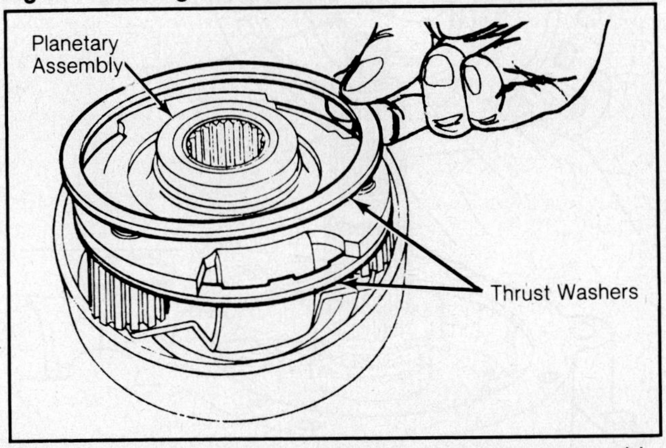

Install one thrust washer on each side of planetary assembly.

MAINSHAFT

1) Using Driver (J-8092) and Bearing Installer (J-33828), install front drive sprocket bearing. Press bearing until tool bottoms. Bearing should be flush with front surface.

2) Reverse installer on driver and press rear bearing into sprocket until tool bottoms. Rear bearing should be recessed after installation. Install thrust washer and drive sprocket on mainshaft.

3) Install blocker ring and synchronizer assembly on mainshaft. Install new snap ring. Install pump gear on mainshaft. Tap gear with hammer to seat it on mainshaft. Install speedometer gear on mainshaft.

TRANSFER CASE

CAUTION: All bearings used in transfer case must be correctly positioned to avoid covering bearing oil feed holes. After installation of bearings, check bearing position to be sure feed hole is not blocked by bearing.

1) Install lock plate in transfer case. Coat case and lock plate surfaces around bolt holes with Loctite 515. Position lock plate on case and align bolt holes with case. Install attaching bolts and tighten.

2) Install roller bearings for input shaft into case using Driver (J-8092) and Bearing Installer (J-33830). Press bearings until tool bottoms. Using Driver (J-8092) and Bearing Installer (J-33832), install front output shaft rear bearing. Press bearing until tool bottoms.

3) Install front output shaft front bearing using Driver (J-8092) and Bearing Installer (J-33833). Press bearing until tool bottoms. Install snap ring that retains front output shaft bearing in case. Install front output and input shaft seals using Seal Installers (J-33831 and J-33834).

4) Install spacer on shift sector shaft and install sector in case. Install shift lever and retaining nut. Tighten nut. Install shift sector detent spring and retaining bolt. Using Driver (J-8092) and Bearing Installer (J-33829), press pilot bearing onto input gear. Press bearing until tool bottoms.

5) Install input gear front thrust bearing and input gear in case. Install planetary gear thrust washer on input gear. Position range fork on planetary assembly and install planetary assembly into case.

6) Ensure that thrust washer is aligned with input gear and planetary assembly. Install mainshaft into case. Install mode fork on synchronizer sleeve and rotate until mode fork is aligned with range fork. Slide mode fork rail down through range fork until rail seats in bore of case.

7) Position drive chain on front output shaft and install chain on drive sprocket. Install front output shaft in case. It may be necessary to slightly raise mainshaft to seat output shaft in case. Install magnet into pocket of transfer case.

8) Apply 1/8" bead of Loctite 515 to mating surface of front case. Install rear case on front case aligning dowel pins. Install and tighten bolts. Install 2 bolts with washers into dowel pin holes.

9) Install output bearing into rear retainer using Driver (J-8092) and Bearing Installer (J-33833). Press bearing until seated in bore. Install pump seal using Seal Installer (J-33835). Apply petroleum jelly to pump housing tabs and install housing in rear retainer.

10) Apply Loctite 515 sealer to mating surface of rear retainer. Align retainer with case. Install retaining bolts and tighten. Install a new snap ring on mainshaft. Pull up on mainshaft and seat snap ring in groove.

11) Install bushing in extension housing using Driver (J-8092) and Bushing Installer (J-33826). Press bushing until tool bottoms. Install new seal in extension housing using Seal Installer (J-33843).

12) Apply Loctite 515 to mating surface of extension housing. Align housing with rear retainer. Install attaching bolts and tighten. Install front yoke on output shaft. Install a new yoke seal washer and nut. Tighten nut. Install drain and fill plugs.

TIGHTENING SPECIFICATIONS

Application	Ft. Lbs. (N.m)
Adapter-to-Transfer Case Bolt	19-29 (26-39)
Drain/Fill Plug	30-40 (41-54)
Extension Housing Bolt	20-25 (27-34)
Front Output Yoke Nut	90-130 (122-176)
Indicator Light Switch	15-25 (20-34)
Lock Plate-to-Transfer Case	20-30 (27-41)
Rear Retainer Bolt	15-20 (20-27)
Shift Bracket Bolt	47-62 (64-84)
Shift Lever Adjustment Bolt	25-35 (34-47)
Shift Lever Nut	15-20 (20-27)
Shift Lever Pivot Bolt	88-103 (119-140)
Transfer Case Bolt	20-25 (27-34)

Transfer Cases

NEW PROCESS MODEL 208

Chevrolet, Chrysler Corp., Ford, GMC, Jeep

DESCRIPTION

The Model 208 is a part-time 4WD unit having an integral 4WD-Low range. This model is a 4-position unit, providing 2 gear ratios in 4WD (High and Low), a 2WD-High and Neutral.

A chain drive is used with front and rear output shafts mounted in ball and roller bearings. Two drive sprockets and a planetary gear assembly, consisting of a 4-pinion carrier and annulus gear are housed in a 2-piece aluminum case. All models have manual locking hubs as standard equipment and 4WD indicator lamps. These lamps inform the driver of the operating mode of the vehicle.

LUBRICATION

SERVICE INTERVALS

Check fluid level. Case should be filled to edge of fill plug opening. Add fluid as necessary every 4 months or 6,000 miles. Drain and refill transfer case every 36,000 miles.

FLUID TYPE

All Models

Use Dexron II ATF.

CAPACITY

Chrysler Corp. & Jeep

Capacity is 6 pints (2.8L).

Ford

Capacity is 9 pints (4.3L).

General Motors

Capacity is 10 pints (4.7L).

ADJUSTMENTS

Adjust shift linkage so that all positions may be selected without interference or binding. Inspect all swivels, rods and mountings for wear or damage. Replace as necessary.

REMOVAL & INSTALLATION

See approriate article in MANUAL TRANSMISSION REMOVAL section.

DISASSEMBLY

TRANSFER CASE

1) Remove fill and drain plugs. Remove front and rear yokes. Discard yoke seal washers and nuts. Place transfer case on end and position front case on wood blocks. It may be necessary to cut "V" notches in wooden blocks to clear mounting studs in front case.

2) Remove lock mode indicator switch and washer. Remove detent bolt, spring and ball. Mark rear retainer and case for assembly alignment reference. Remove rear bearing retainer and pump housing as an assembly. Use mallet to remove retainer from case. Do not pry on retainer. *See Fig. 1.*

Fig. 1: Rear Retainer Case Removal & Installation

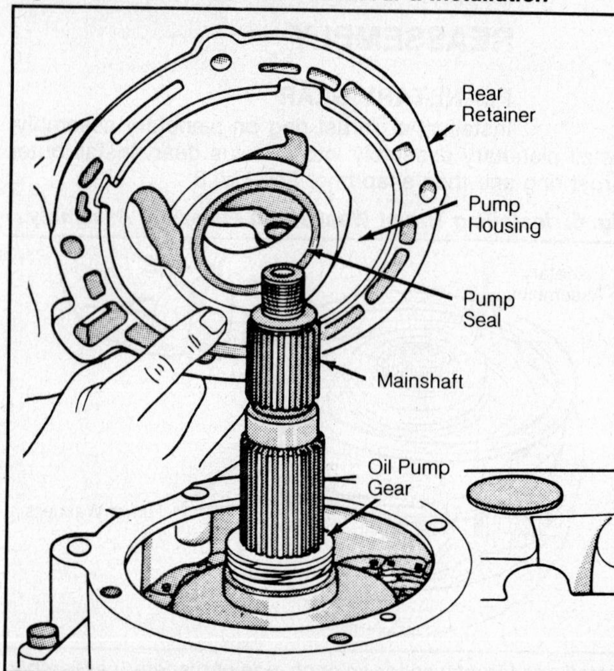

Tap retainer from case using plastic mallet.

3) Remove pump housing from retainer and pump seal from housing. Discard pump seal. Remove speedometer drive gear from mainshaft. Remove oil pump from mainshaft. Mark position of pump for reassembly. Side of oil pump facing case interior is recessed. Remove bolts attaching rear case to front case. Remove rear case.

NOTE: To remove rear case, insert screwdrivers into slots in case ends and gently pry upward. Do not pry case halves apart at any point on mating surface.

4) Remove front output shaft rear thrust bearing assembly. Mark position of bearing and races for reassembly. Remove driven sprocket retaining snap ring, drive sprocket retaining snap ring, and thrust washers.

5) Remove sprockets and drive chain as an assembly. Lift evenly on both sprockets to remove. On Chrysler Corp. and General Motors models, do not lose needle bearings (120 each) from within drive sprocket.

6) On all models, remove front output shaft front thrust bearing assembly. On Chrysler Corp. and General Motors models, remove blocker ring and synchronizer. *See Fig. 3.* On Ford and Jeep models, remove sprocket carrier stop ring and clutch spring. *See Fig. 4 and 5.*

7) On all models, remove sliding clutch, mode fork, mode fork spring and bracket as an assembly. Remove shift rail. On Ford and Jeep models, remove snap ring, sprocket carrier, thrust washer and mainshaft needle bearings as an assembly. Do not lose bearings (120 each).

8) On all models, remove mainshaft. Remove annulus gear retaining ring and thrust washer. Remove annulus gear and range fork as an assembly. Turn fork counterclockwise to disengage fork lug from range sector, and lift assembly out of case. Remove planetary thrust washer, and remove planetary assembly.

NEW PROCESS MODEL 208 (Cont.)

Fig. 2: Sprocket & Chain Removal & Installation

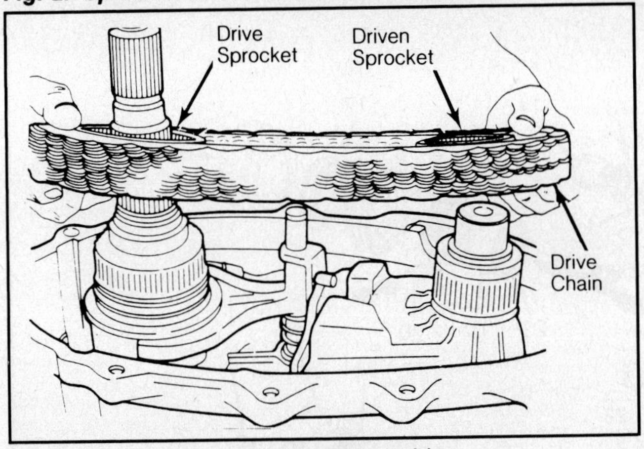

Remove sprocket and chain as assembly.

9) Remove mainshaft thrust bearing from input gear. Remove input gear by lifting straight up and out of case. Remove input gear thrust bearing and race. Note position of bearing and race for reassembly. Remove range sector operating lever nut and washer.

10) Remove lever, sector shaft seal and seal retainer. Remove range sector. Inspect lock plate. If lock plate is loose, worn or cracked, remove lock plate. See SUB-ASSEMBLY OVERHAUL in this article. Remove output shaft seals from front and rear case seal bores.

CLEANING & INSPECTION

1) Wash all parts in cleaning solvent. Be sure to remove all traces of gasket from surfaces where used. Apply compressed air to each oil feed port and channel in each case half to remove any obstruction or residue.

2) Check all gear teeth and splines for burrs, nicks, excessive wear or damage. Inspect all snap rings and thrust washers for excessive wear, distortion or damage.

3) Inspect both case halves for cracks, porosity, damaged mating surfaces, stripped bolt threads or distortion. Check lock plate teeth and hub for cracks, chips or excessive wear.

4) Inspect condition of all bearings in both case halves and input gear. Check condition of bearing bores in both case halves, input gear, rear output shaft, side gear and rear retainer. Replace bearings as required.

SUB-ASSEMBLY OVERHAUL

NOTE: **All of the bearings used in the trasnfer case must be correctly positioned to avoid covering bearing oil feed holes. After replacing any bearing check the bearing position to be sure that oil feed is not blocked by bearing.**

ANNULUS GEAR BUSHING

On Jeep, remove bushing using Driver (J-8092) and Bushing Remover/Installer (J-29185) Install new bushing and remove any chips generated by bushing replacement. On Chrysler Corp., if annulus gear bushing requires replacement, replace annulus gear.

LOCK PLATE

1) Remove and discard lock plate attaching bolts. Remove lock plate from case. Coat case and lock plate surfaces around bolt holes with RTV sealant.

2) Position new lock plate in case and align bolt holes in lock plate with case. Coat new lock plate attaching bolts with Loctite. Install and tighten lock plate bolts.

REAR OUTPUT BEARING & REAR SEAL

Remove rear seal using screwdriver or brass drift. Remove bearing retaining snap ring. Remove bearing using brass drift. Install new bearing. Ensure that shielded side of bearing faces interior of case. Install bearing retaining snap ring. Install new rear seal.

FRONT OUTPUT SHAFT FRONT BEARING

Remove bearing. Install new front bearing and check bearing position to ensure that oil feed hole is not blocked.

FRONT OUTPUT SHAFT REAR BEARING

Remove bearing. Install new front bearing and check bearing position to ensure that oil feed hole is not blocked. Ensure that bearing is flush with case.

INPUT GEAR FRONT & REAR BEARING

Remove both bearings at the same time. Install new bearings one at a time. Install rear bearing first; then install front bearing. Remove installer and check bearing position to ensure that oil feed holes are not covered. Ensure that bearings are flush with case.

MAIN SHAFT PILOT BEARING

Remove pilot bearing and plug. Install new bearing and check bearing position to ensure that oil feed hole is not blocked. Ensure that bearing is flush with edge of bearing bore. Install bearing plug.

REASSEMBLY

TRANSFER CASE

NOTE: **During assembly, lubricate all components with Dexron II type oil or petroleum jelly where indicated only. Do not use any other type of lubricants.**

1) Install input gear race and thrust bearing in front case. Install input gear. Install mainshaft thrust bearing in input gear. Install range sector shaft seal and seal retainer. Install range sector.

2) Install operating lever on range sector shaft. Install and tighten shaft washer and lock nut. Install planetary assembly over input gear making sure planetary set is fully seated and meshed with gear. Install planetary thrust washer on planetary hub.

3) If removed, install inserts in range fork. Engage range fork in annulus gear. Install annulus gear over planetary assembly. Install annulus gear thrust washer and retaining snap ring. Align shift rail bores in case and range fork. Install shift rail.

NOTE: **Ensure shift rail bore is completely dry and contains no oil. Oil may prevent rail from seating completely and also prevent front case installation.**

Transfer Cases

NEW PROCESS MODEL 208 (Cont.)

Fig. 3: Exploded View of Chrysler Corp. & General Motors Model 208 Transfer Case

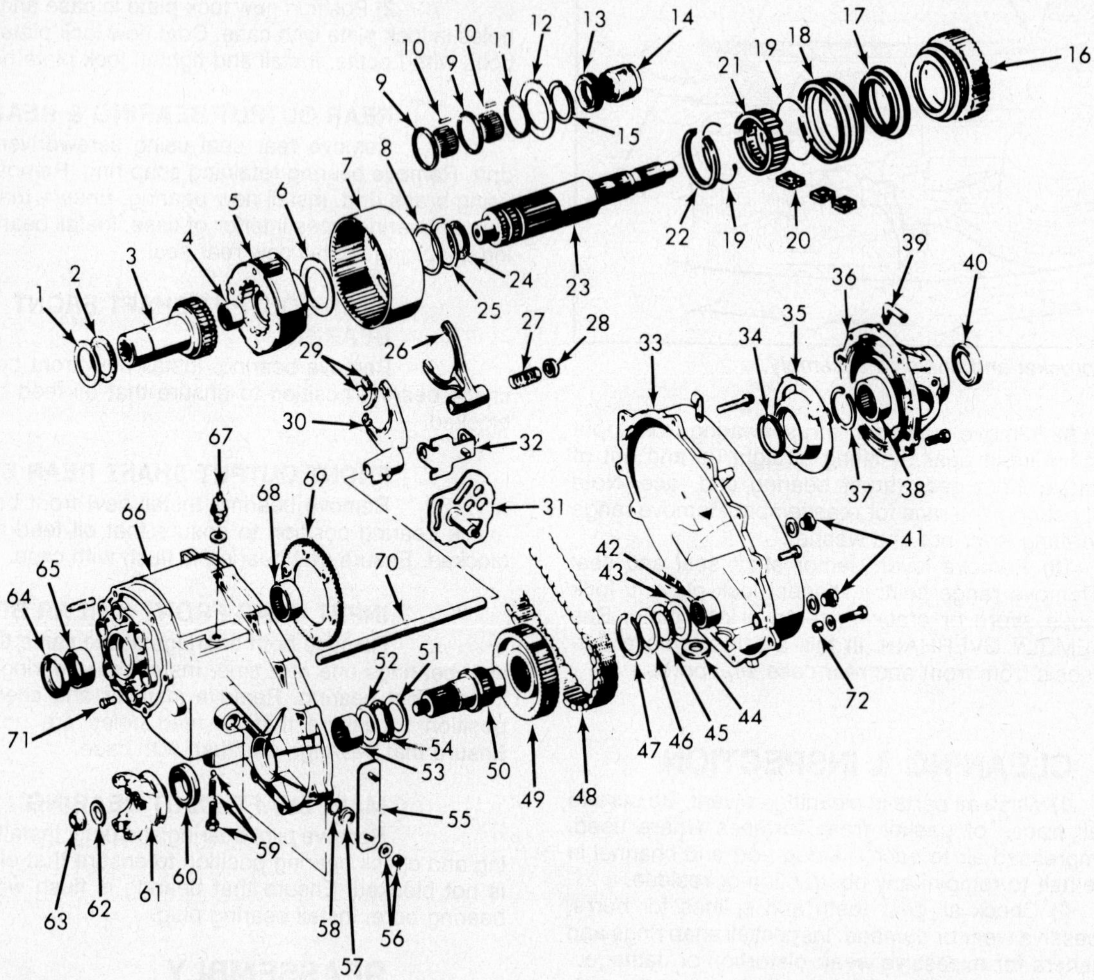

1. Input Gear Thrust Washer
2. Input Gear Thrust Bearing
3. Input Gear
4. Mainshaft Pilot Bearing
5. Planetary Assembly
6. Planetary Thrust Washer
7. Annulus Gear
8. Annulus Gear Thrust Washer
9. Needle Bearing Spacers
10. Mainshaft Needle Bearings (120)
11. Needle Bearing Spacer
12. Spacer Washer
13. Oil Pump Gear
14. Speedometer Gear
15. Drive Sprocket Snap Ring
16. Drive Sprocket
17. Blocker Ring
18. Synchronizer Sleeve
19. Synchronizer Spring
20. Synchronizer Key
21. Synchronizer Hub
22. Synchronizer Hub Snap Ring
23. Mainshaft
24. Mainshaft Thrust Bearing
25. Internal Gear Snap Ring
26. Mode Fork
27. Spring
28. Spring Retainer
29. Range Fork Pads
30. Range Fork
31. Range Sector
32. Mode Fork Bracket
33. Rear Case
34. Seal
35. Oil Pump Housing
36. Rear Retainer
37. Bearing Snap Ring
38. Rear Output Bearing
39. Vent Tube
40. Rear Seal
41. Drain & Fill Plugs
42. Front Output Shaft Rear Bearing
43. Front Output Shaft Rear Thrust Bearing Race (Thick)
44. Magnet
45. Front Output Shaft Rear Thrust Bearing
46. Front Output Shaft Rear Thrust Bearing Race (Thin)
47. Driven Sprocket Retaining Ring
48. Drive Chain
49. Driven Sprocket
50. Front Output Shaft
51. Front Output Shaft Front Thrust Bearing Race (Thin)
52. Front Output Shaft Front Thrust Bearing Race (Thick)
53. Front Output Shaft Front Bearing
54. Front Output Shaft Front Bearing Thrust Race
55. Operating Lever
56. Washer & Lock Nut
57. Range Sector Shaft Seal Retainer
58. Range Sector Shaft Seal
59. Detent Ball, Spring & Retainer Bolt
60. Front Seal
61. Front Yoke
62. Yoke Seal Washer
63. Yoke Nut
64. Input Gear Oil Seal
65. Input Gear Front Bearing
66. Front Case
67. 4WD Indicator Light Switch & Washer
68. Input Gear Rear Bearing
69. Lock Plate
70. Shifter Fork Shaft
71. Lock Plate Bolts
72. Alignment Dowels

NEW PROCESS MODEL 208 (Cont.)

Fig. 4: Exploded View of Ford Model 208 Transfer Case

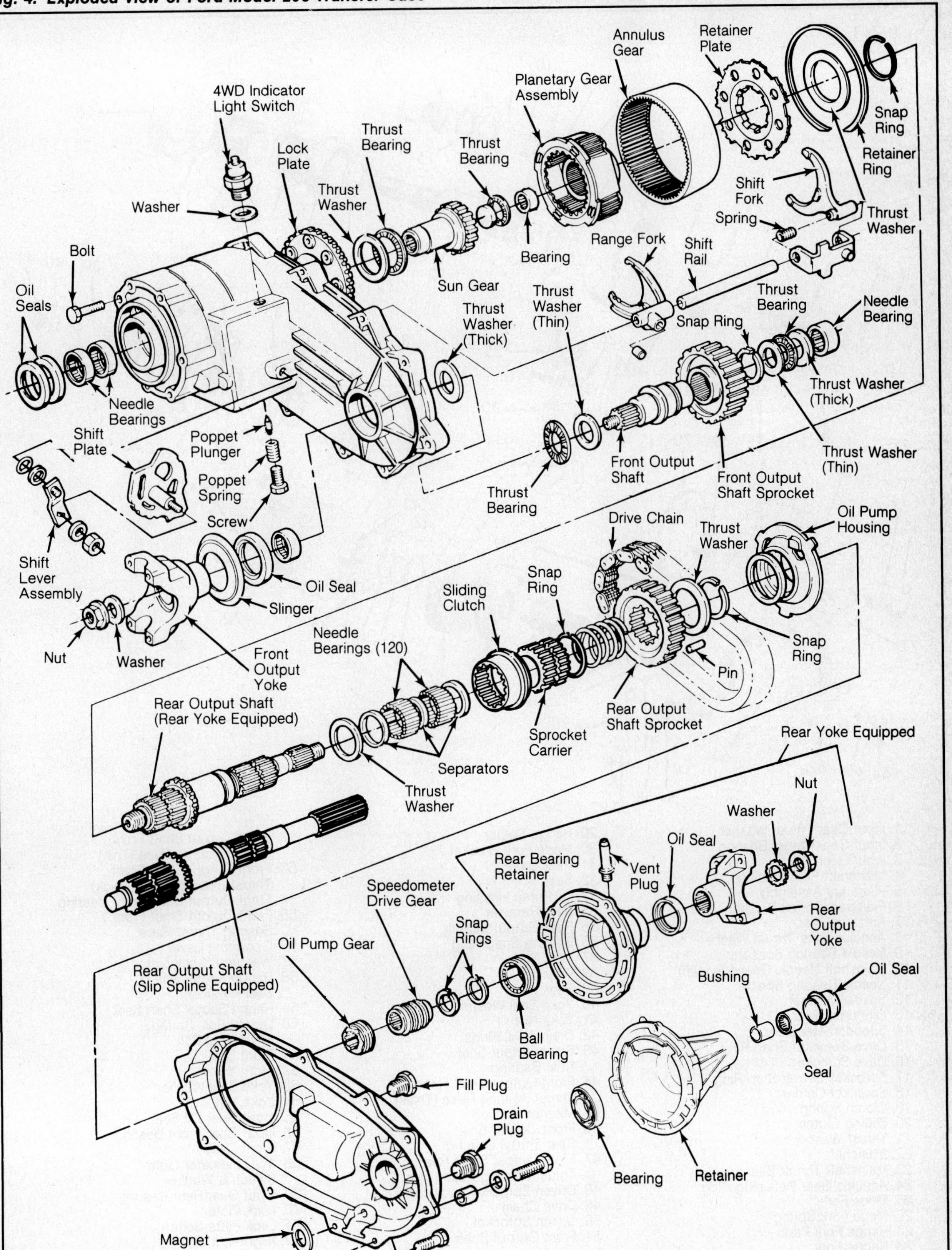

Transfer Cases

NEW PROCESS MODEL 208 (Cont.)

Fig. 5: Exploded View of Jeep Model 208 Transfer Case

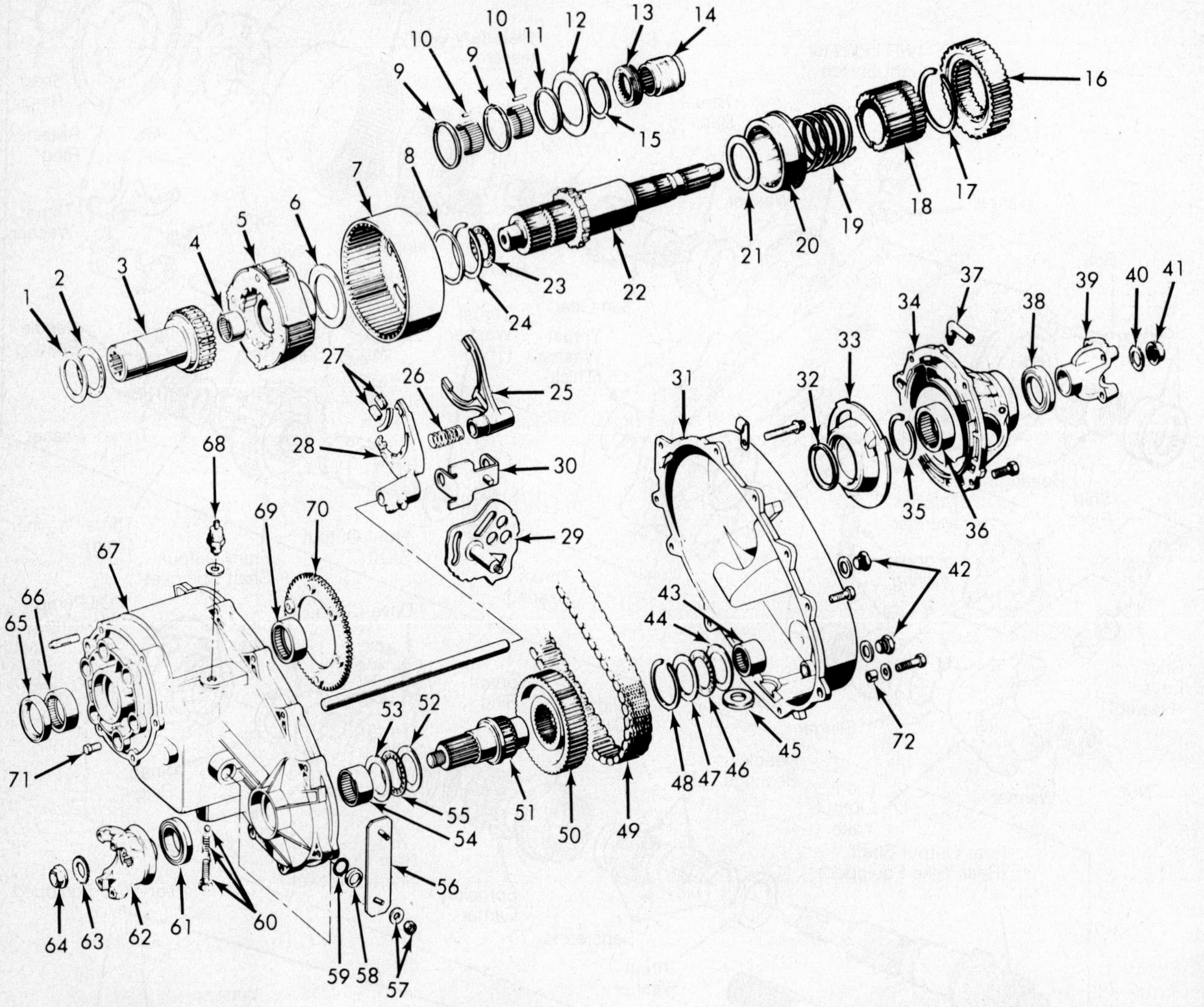

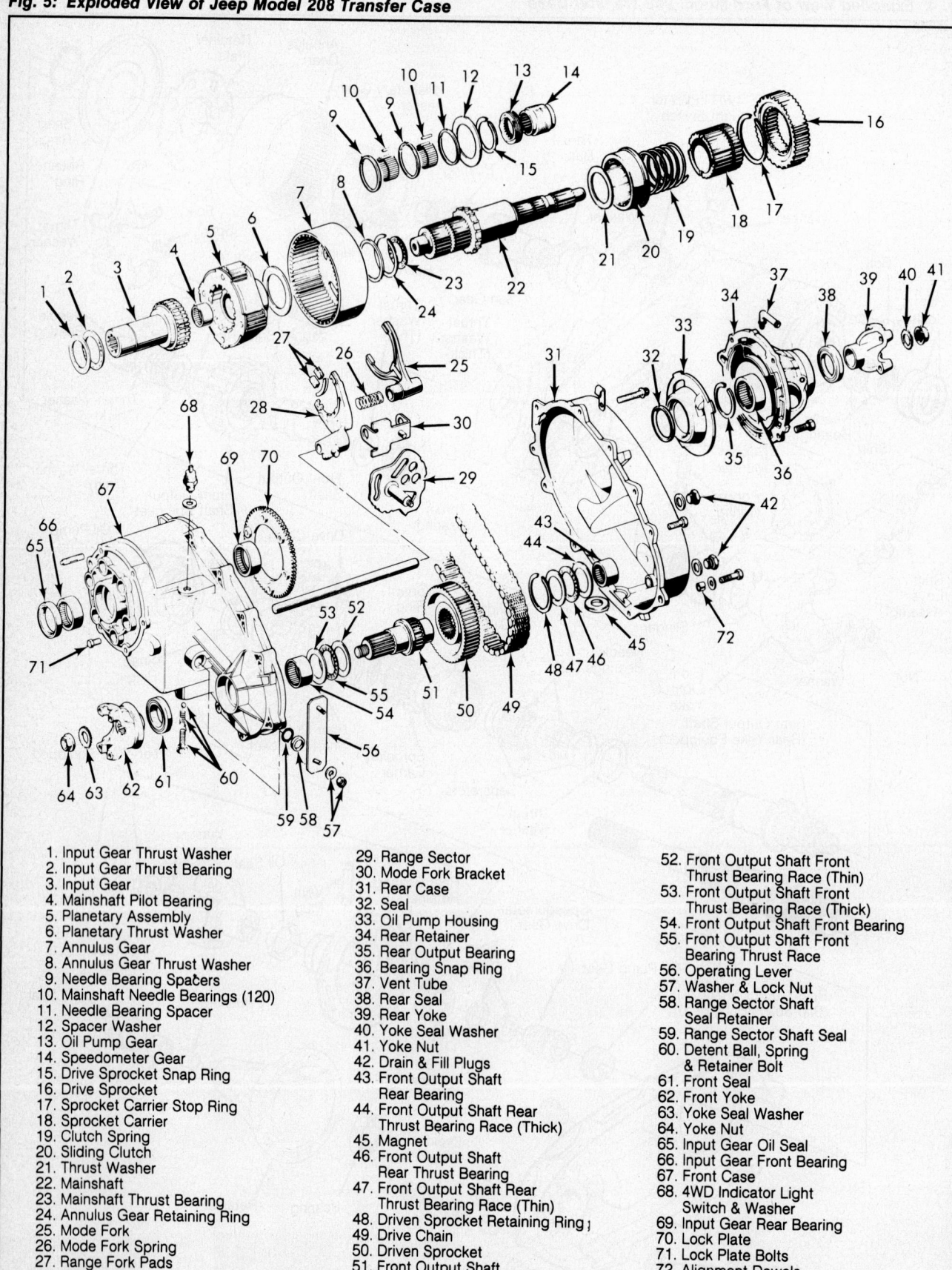

1. Input Gear Thrust Washer
2. Input Gear Thrust Bearing
3. Input Gear
4. Mainshaft Pilot Bearing
5. Planetary Assembly
6. Planetary Thrust Washer
7. Annulus Gear
8. Annulus Gear Thrust Washer
9. Needle Bearing Spacers
10. Mainshaft Needle Bearings (120)
11. Needle Bearing Spacer
12. Spacer Washer
13. Oil Pump Gear
14. Speedometer Gear
15. Drive Sprocket Snap Ring
16. Drive Sprocket
17. Sprocket Carrier Stop Ring
18. Sprocket Carrier
19. Clutch Spring
20. Sliding Clutch
21. Thrust Washer
22. Mainshaft
23. Mainshaft Thrust Bearing
24. Annulus Gear Retaining Ring
25. Mode Fork
26. Mode Fork Spring
27. Range Fork Pads
28. Range Fork
29. Range Sector
30. Mode Fork Bracket
31. Rear Case
32. Seal
33. Oil Pump Housing
34. Rear Retainer
35. Rear Output Bearing
36. Bearing Snap Ring
37. Vent Tube
38. Rear Seal
39. Rear Yoke
40. Yoke Seal Washer
41. Yoke Nut
42. Drain & Fill Plugs
43. Front Output Shaft Rear Bearing
44. Front Output Shaft Rear Thrust Bearing Race (Thick)
45. Magnet
46. Front Output Shaft Rear Thrust Bearing
47. Front Output Shaft Rear Thrust Bearing Race (Thin)
48. Driven Sprocket Retaining Ring
49. Drive Chain
50. Driven Sprocket
51. Front Output Shaft
52. Front Output Shaft Front Thrust Bearing Race (Thin)
53. Front Output Shaft Front Thrust Bearing Race (Thick)
54. Front Output Shaft Front Bearing
55. Front Output Shaft Front Bearing Thrust Race
56. Operating Lever
57. Washer & Lock Nut
58. Range Sector Shaft Seal Retainer
59. Range Sector Shaft Seal
60. Detent Ball, Spring & Retainer Bolt
61. Front Seal
62. Front Yoke
63. Yoke Seal Washer
64. Yoke Nut
65. Input Gear Oil Seal
66. Input Gear Front Bearing
67. Front Case
68. 4WD Indicator Light Switch & Washer
69. Input Gear Rear Bearing
70. Lock Plate
71. Lock Plate Bolts
72. Alignment Dowels

NEW PROCESS MODEL 208 (Cont.)

4) Install mainshaft making sure thrust bearing is properly seated in input gear. On Chrysler Corp. and General Motors models, position synchronizer keys and install synchronizer and mode fork as an assembly. Install blocker ring.

5) Coat sprocket carrier with petroleum jelly and position bearing retainer at center of carrier bore bore. Coat needle bearings with petroleum jelly and install 60 needle bearings in each end of drive sprocket bore; a total of 120 bearings are used. Install bearing retainer in each end of sprocket, and position thrust washer on bottom of drive sprocket.

6) Align assembled carrier and needle bearings with mainshaft and install on mainshaft. Do not displace needle bearings during installation. Assemble mode fork, fork spring and bracket. Engage sliding clutch and install assembly on shift rail and mainshaft.

7) On Ford and Jeep models, install clutch spring and stop ring in sprocket carrier. On all models, install front output shaft thrust bearing assembly in front case. Correct sequence is: thick race, thrust bearing, thin race. Install front output shaft.

8) Position sprockets in chain, align sprockets with shafts and install as an assembly. Make sure drive sprocket recessed side is facing into case. Install spacer and thrust washer on drive sprocket. Install snap ring.

9) Install driven sprocket retaining snap ring. Install front output shaft rear thrust bearing assembly on front output shaft. Correct sequence is: thin race, thrust bearing, thick race.

10) Install oil pump on mainshaft. Make sure recessed side of pump faces into case. Install speedometer drive gear. Install magnet in front case, if removed. Apply RTV silicone or equivalent sealant to 1 side of case and mate rear case on front case.

11) Make sure front output shaft rear thrust bearing assembly is seated in rear case. Align bolt holes and dowels. Install flat washers on 2 bolts installed at opposite ends of case. Install all bolts and tighten.

12) Install seal in pump housing. Coat pump housing tabs with petroleum jelly and install housing in rear retainer. Apply sealer to mating surface of rear retainer, align with case index marks, install retainer and bolts.

13) Install oil seal in rear retainer bore. Coat seal lip with petroleum jelly before installation. Install indicator switch and washer. Apply small amount of sealer to detent retainer bolt and install detent ball, spring and bolt.

14) Install drain plug and gasket. Install oil seal in front case output shaft bore. Install front and rear yokes. Be sure yoke with collar is on front output shaft. Install yoke seal washers and nuts. Fill transfer case and install fill plug.

TIGHTENING SPECIFICATIONS

Application	Ft. Lbs. (N.m)
Detent Retainer Bolt	20-25 (27-34)
Drain & Fill Plugs	
Chrysler	15-20 (20-27)
All Others	30-40 (41-54)
Indicator Switch	15-20 (20-27)
Lock Plate Bolts	30 (41)
Operating Lever Lock Nut	15-20 (20-27)
Rear Case-to-Front Case Bolts	20-25 (27-34)
Rear Retainer Bolts	20-25 (27-34)
Sector Shaft Nut	20-25 (27-34)
Yoke Nuts	120 (163)

SPICER (DANA) MODEL 300

Jeep

DESCRIPTION

The Model 300 is a 4-position, dual range, part-time 4WD unit with integral low range. It provides 4-wheel undifferentiated high and low ranges, a Neutral position and 2-wheel high range. The 300 is used with both manual and automatic transmission applications. Locking front hubs are standard equipment.

LUBRICATION

SERVICE INTERVALS

Check fluid level every 5 months or 5000 miles and refill as necessary. Change fluid every 30 months or 30,000 miles.

FLUID TYPE

Use SAE 85W-90, API grade GL-5 gear lubricant.

CAPACITY

Refill capacity is 4.0 pints (1.9L).

REMOVAL & INSTALLATION

TRANSFER CASE

Removal

1) On models with manual transmission, remove shift lever knob, trim ring and boot from transmission and transfer case shift levers. Remove floor covering, if equipped, and remove transmission access cover. Raise vehicle and drain transfer case.

2) Support transmission and remove rear crossmember. Mark propeller shaft yokes for reassembly. Disconnect propeller shafts at transfer case. Disconnect speedometer cable at transfer case.

3) Disconnect parking brake cable at equalizer. Disconnect exhaust pipe support bracket at transfer case, if equipped. Remove bolts attaching transfer case to transmission. Remove transfer case.

Installation

1) Shift transfer case to "4L" position. Rotate transfer case output shaft by turning yoke until transmission output shaft engages transfer case input shaft. Move transfer case forward until case seats against transmission.

NOTE: Do not install transfer case attaching bolts until case is completely seated against transmission as damage to transfer case will occur.

2) Install transfer case attaching bolts and tighten. Install drain plug and refill case. Connect speedometer driven gear to case. Connect shift lever and control links to shift rods.

3) Align reassembly marks and connect propeller shafts to transfer case. Install rear crossmember and remove support. Install parking brake cable at equalizer and connect exhaust pipe support bracket at transfer case, if disconnected.

4) Lower vehicle and install transmission access cover and floor covering, if equipped. Install shift lever boot, trim ring, levers, and shift knob.

DISASSEMBLY

TRANSFER CASE

1) Remove shift lever assembly. Remove bottom cover, using a putty knife to break seal. Use Puller (J-8614-01) to remove front and rear yokes, discard lock nuts.

2) Remove screws attaching input shaft support to case. Remove support, rear output shaft gear and input shaft as an assembly, using a putty knife to break seal. *See Fig. 1.*

Fig. 1: Rear Output Shaft Gear & Input Assembly

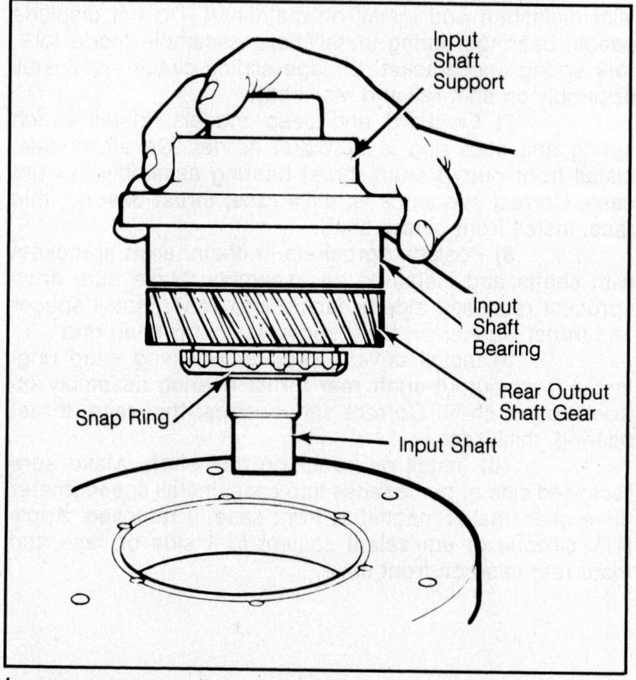

Loosen support using a putty knife.

3) Remove rear output shaft clutch sleeve from case. Remove and discard snap ring holding rear output shaft gear on input shaft. Remove gear. Remove and discard input shaft bearing snap ring.

4) Remove input shaft and bearing from support using a plastic mallet to tap shaft loose. Remove bearing and shims from input shaft using an arbor press. Remove and discard seal from input shaft support. Remove intermediate shaft lock plate bolt and lock plate.

5) Tap intermediate shaft out of case using a brass punch and plastic mallet. Remove and discard intermediate shaft seal. Remove thrust washers and intermediate gear assembly. Note location of tabs on thrust washers for reassembly.

6) Remove 48 needle bearings and 3 bearing spacers from intermediate gear. Remove rear bearing cap bolts. Remove rear bearing cap using a putty knife to break seal and a plastic mallet to tap output shaft loose. Remove end play shims and speedometer drive gear from rear output shaft.

7) Remove and discard rear output shaft oil seal. Remove bearings and races from rear bearing cap. Remove set screws retaining front and rear output shaft shift forks from shift rods.

8) Using a punch, inserted in pin holes in rods, rotate rods to remove them from case. Take care not to lose poppet balls and springs. Remove shift forks from case.

9) Remove bolts attaching front bearing cap-to-case. Remove front cap using a putty knife to break seal. Remove front output shaft from front cap. Remove and discard shift rod oil seals from front cap.

10) Remove bearing race from front cap using Bearing Remover (J-29168) and Driver (J-8092). Remove cover plate and shims from case. Keep shims together for reassembly. Move front output shaft toward front of case and remove rear bearing race from case.

11) Remove rear output shaft front bearing. Position case on wood blocks to allow for rear output shaft removal clearance. Seat clutch gear on case interior surface and tap shaft out of bearing using a rawhide mallet.

12) Remove rear output shaft front bearing, thrust washer, clutch gear and output shaft from case. Using an arbor press and press tool, remove front output shaft rear bearing. Remove case from arbor press and remove front output shaft, clutch gear, sleeve, and shaft rear bearing from case.

13) Remove front output shaft using arbor press and Bearing Remover (J-22912-01). Support rear output shaft in a vise and using Bearing Puller (J-29369-1), remove input shaft rear needle bearing from shaft. Use a 3/8" drive, 7/16" socket and extension to tap shift rod thimbles out of case.

CLEANING & INSPECTION

1) Clean all parts in cleaning solvent and dry with compressed air. Be sure to remove all traces of gasket from surfaces where used. Do not dry bearings with compressed air. Use clean shop towels only.

2) Inspect all bearing surfaces for wear, brinelling, pitting, scoring, chipping or cracking. Inspect teeth of all gears for excessive wear or damage. Replace as necessary.

3) Replace any shaft that has damaged splines, threads or bearing surfaces. Check shift rods and rod bores for wear or damage. Minor scratches or nicks on rods may be cleaned with crocus clotch. Replace as necessary.

REASSEMBLY

TRANSFER CASE

1) Apply sealant (Loctite 220) to shift rod thimbles and install parts. Install front output shaft gear on front output shaft. Make sure that gear clutch teeth face shaft gear teeth.

2) Install front bearing on front output shaft using arbor press and press tool. *See Fig. 2.* Make sure bearing is seated against gear. Install front output shaft in case and install clutch sleeve and gear on shaft.

3) Install front output shaft rear bearing using arbor press and press tool. Install input shaft rear needle bearing in rear output shaft using bearing installer.

4) Position rear output shaft clutch gear in case and insert rear output shaft into gear. Install thrust washer and front bearing on rear output shaft. Install shims and bearing on input shaft. Use arbor press and press tool to install parts.

Fig. 2: Installing Front Output Shaft Rear Bearing

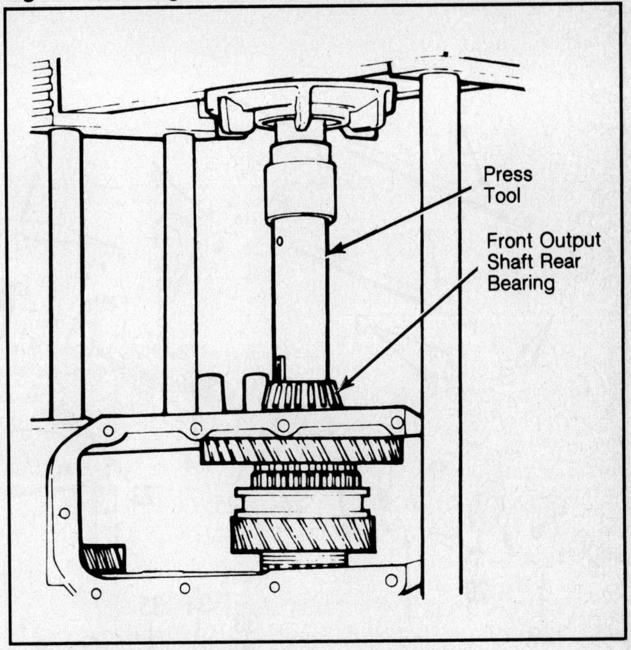

Be sure bearing is seated against gear.

5) Install new oil seal in input shaft support using Seal Installer (J-29184). Install input shaft, bearing and new snap ring in support. Install rear output shaft gear and new snap ring on input gear.

6) Measure clearance between input gear and gear retaining snap ring using a feeler gauge. If clearance exceeds 0.003" (0.076 mm), disassemble input shaft and add shims between input shaft and shaft bearing until proper measurement is obtained.

7) Install clutch sleeve on rear output shaft. Apply sealant to mating surface of input shaft support. Install assembled support, shaft, and gear in case. Using 2 support bolts to align support on case, tap support into position with a plastic mallet.

8) Install and tighten support socket head screws. Install rear bearing cap front bearing race using Bearing Installer (J-9276-3) and Driver (J-8092). Install rear bearing cap rear bearing race using Bearing Installer (J-29182) and driver.

9) Position rear output shaft rear bearing in rear bearing cap. Install rear output shaft yoke oil seal using Seal Installer (J-25160). Install speedometer gear and end play shims on rear output shaft. Install rear bearing cap.

10) Apply sealant to mating surface of rear bearing cap. Align bolt holes with 2 cap bolts and tap rear bearing cap into position using a plastic mallet. Tighten cap bolts.

11) Install rear output shaft yoke. Tighten yoke nut while holding yoke with Holder (J-8614-01). Clamp dial indicator onto bearing cap. Position indicator stylus so it contacts end of shaft. *See Fig. 4.*

12) Pry rear output shaft back and forth to check end play. End play should be 0.001-0.005" (0.025-0.127 mm). If end play is not correct, remove or add shims between speedometer drive gear and output shaft rear bearing.

13) Install front output shaft rear bearing race. Install front output shaft end, shims and cover plate. Apply

Transfer Cases

SPICER (DANA) MODEL 300 (Cont.)

Fig. 3: Exploded View of Model 300 Transfer Case

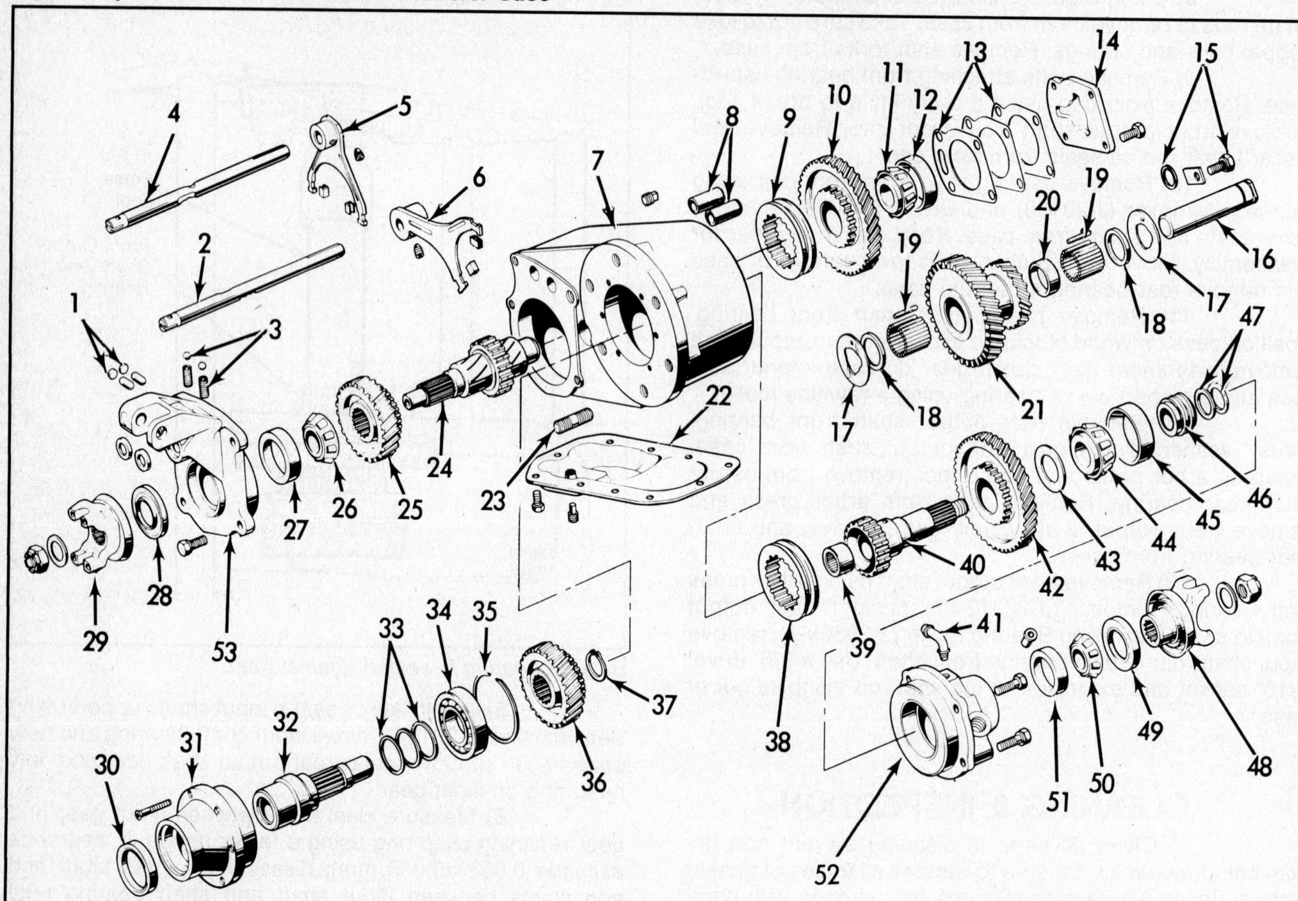

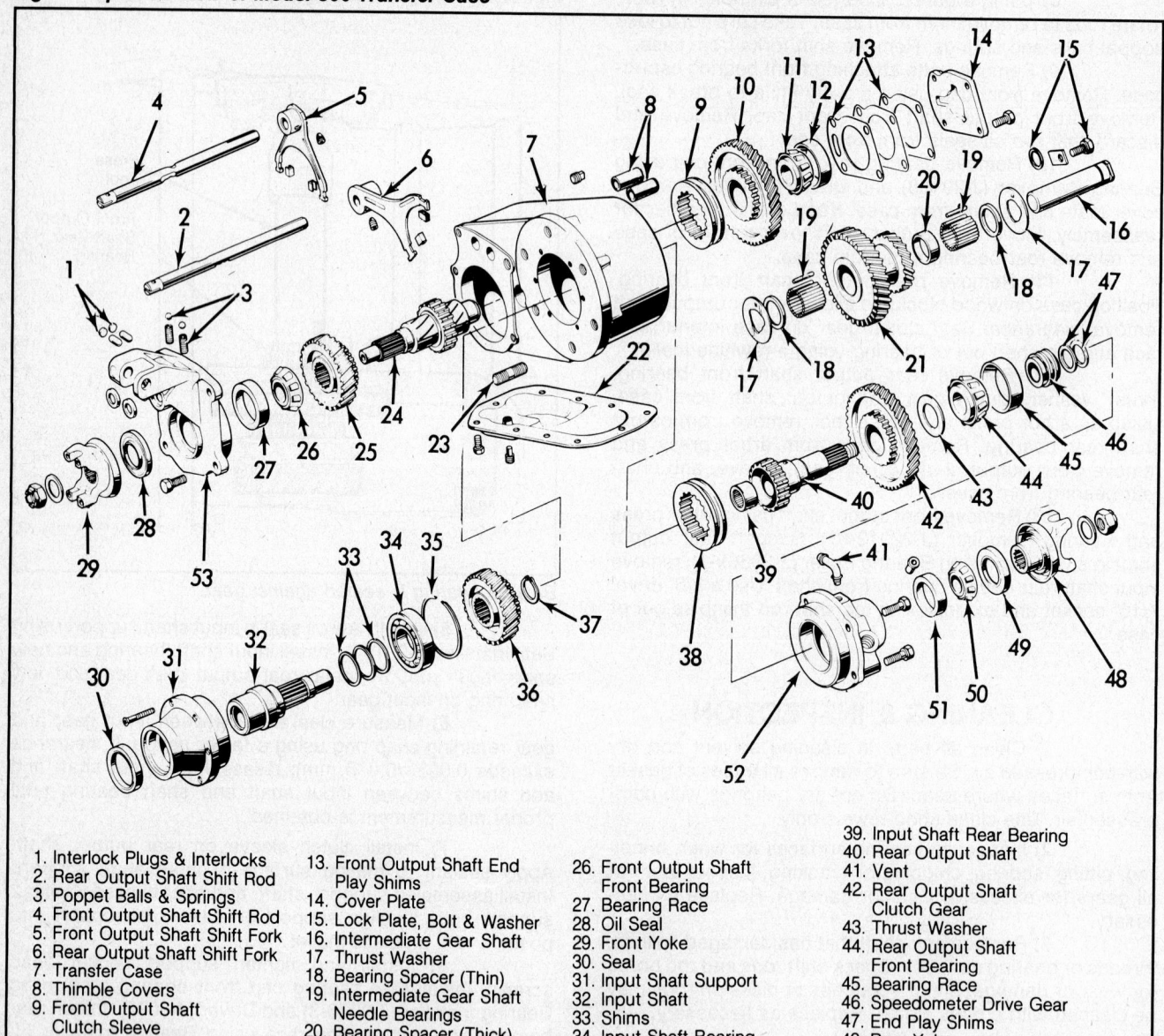

1. Interlock Plugs & Interlocks
2. Rear Output Shaft Shift Rod
3. Poppet Balls & Springs
4. Front Output Shaft Shift Rod
5. Front Output Shaft Shift Fork
6. Rear Output Shaft Shift Fork
7. Transfer Case
8. Thimble Covers
9. Front Output Shaft Clutch Sleeve
10. Front Output Shaft Clutch Gear
11. Front Output Shaft Rear Bearing
12. Bearing Race
13. Front Output Shaft End Play Shims
14. Cover Plate
15. Lock Plate, Bolt & Washer
16. Intermediate Gear Shaft
17. Thrust Washer
18. Bearing Spacer (Thin)
19. Intermediate Gear Shaft Needle Bearings
20. Bearing Spacer (Thick)
21. Intermediate Gear
22. Bottom Cover
23. Case-to-Transmission Stud
24. Front Output Shaft
25. Front Output Shaft Gear
26. Front Output Shaft Front Bearing
27. Bearing Race
28. Oil Seal
29. Front Yoke
30. Seal
31. Input Shaft Support
32. Input Shaft
33. Shims
34. Input Shaft Bearing
35. Bearing Snap Ring
36. Rear Output Shaft Gear
37. Snap Ring
38. Rear Output Shaft Clutch Sleeve
39. Input Shaft Rear Bearing
40. Rear Output Shaft
41. Vent
42. Rear Output Shaft Clutch Gear
43. Thrust Washer
44. Rear Output Shaft Front Bearing
45. Bearing Race
46. Speedometer Drive Gear
47. End Play Shims
48. Rear Yoke
49. Rear Output Shaft Oil Seal
50. Rear Output Shaft Rear Bearing
51. Bearing Race
52. Rear Bearing Cap
53. Front Bearing Cap

sealant (Loctite 220) to cover plate bolt threads and install bolts. Install front output shaft front bearing race using Bearing Installer (J-29181) and Driver (J-8092).

14) Install front output shaft yoke oil seal using Seal Installer (J-25160). Install shift rod oil seals using Seal Installer (J-25167). Install front bearing cap. Apply sealant to mating surface of front bearing cap. Use 2 bolts to align cap with case bolt holes and tap front bearing cap into position.

15) Install and tighten bearing cap bolts. Seat rear bearing cup against cover plate by tapping end of front output shaft with plastic mallet. Mount dial indicator on front bearing cap and postion indicator stylus against end of output shaft.

16) Pry front output shaft back and forth to check end play. End play should be 0.001-0.005" (0.025-0.127 mm). If end play is not correct, remove or add shims between cover plate and case. If shims are added, reseat rear bearing cup before checking end play again.

17) Install front output shaft yoke. Install new lock nut. Tighten yoke nut while holding yoke. Insert front and rear output shaft shift forks into case. Install front output shaft shift rod poppet ball and spring in front bearing cap.

18) Compress poppet ball and spring. Install front output shaft shift rod part way in case. Insert shift rod through shift fork. Align set screw hole in shift fork and rod. Install and tighten set screw.

SPICER (DANA) MODEL 300 (Cont.)

Fig. 4: Checking Rear Output Shaft End Play

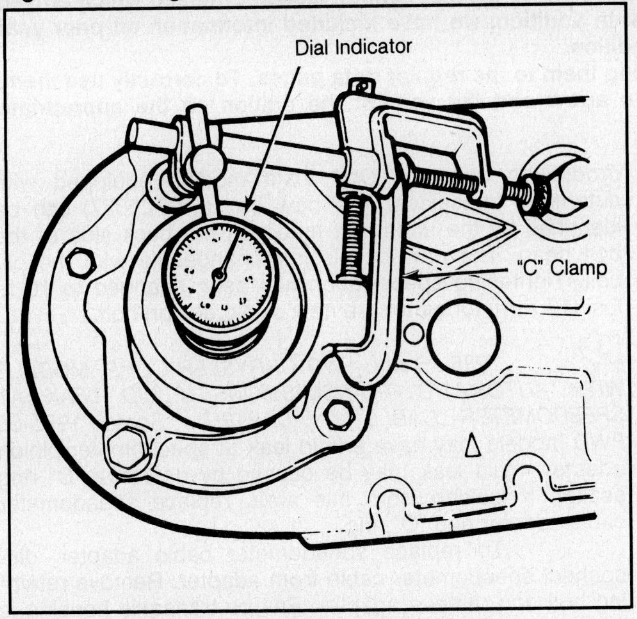

End play should be .001-.005" (.025-.129 mm).

19) Compress and install remaining poppet ball and spring in front bearing cap. Install rear output shaft shift rail part way in case, through shift fork, and align set screw hole on fork and rod. Install and tighten set screws.

20) Insert Dummy Shaft (J-25142) in intermediate gear and install needle bearings and spacers in gear. Install intermediate gear thrust washers in case. Make sure washer tangs align with grooves in case.

21) Install new "O" ring on intermediate shaft. Position intermediate gear in case. Install intermediate shaft in case bore. Using plastic mallet, tap intermediate shaft into gear until shaft forces dummy shaft out of case and shaft is in place.

22) Install intermediate shaft lock plate. Install and tighten lock plate bolt. Apply sealant to mating surface of bottom cover. Install and tighten bottom cover bolts.

TIGHTENING SPECIFICATIONS

Application	Ft. Lbs. (N.m)
Bottom Cover Bolts	15 (20)
Cover Plate Bolts	35 (47)
Front/Rear Bearing Cap Bolts	35 (47)
Front/Rear Yoke Lock Nuts	120 (163)
Input Shaft Support Screws	10 (14)
Lock Plate Bolt	23 (31)
Shift Fork Set Screws	14 (19)

Latest Changes & Corrections

FOR 1986 & EARLIER DOMESTIC MODELS

NOTE: **The Latest Changes and Corrections represent a collection of the last minute 1986 information which arrived to late to be included into the regular data pages. In addition, we have included information on prior year models which we have received since last year's edition.**
This information is numbered to assist you in relating them to the regular data pages. To correctly use them, simply write the corresponding number within the arrow and the year of the edition on the appropriate page(s) of the text.

AUTOMATIC TRANSMISSIONS

CHRYSLER CORP.

1

1981-86 "D" PICKUPS AND 1984-86 DIPLOMAT, GRAN FURY AND 5TH AVENUE MODELS WITH A904/A999 TRANSMISSIONS: MOAN OR DRONE AT 1600-2100 RPM – Some Chrysler Corp. vehicles equipped with A904/A999 transmissions may exibit a "moan" or "drone" at approximately 1600 RPM (V8 engines) or 2100 RPM (6-cylinder engines) in any/all gears. On pickup models, the addition of a new transmission mount insulator may reduce "moan". The insulator can be used on all A727, A904 and A999 transmissions.

1) On passenger cars, remove original damper weight from transmission extension housing. Install new damper weight. Ensure spacers and washers are installed as shown in illustration. Tighten bolts to 150 INCH lbs.

2) On pickup models, raise vehicle on hoist. Raise rear of transmission and engine slightly using a transmission jack. Remove rear mount through-bolt. Remove original insulator spacers and assembly from the bottom of the transmission extension housing.

3) Install new insulator assembly on transmission extension housing. Place spacers between bolts and insulator bracket. Use new bolts and tighten to 50 ft. lbs. (70 N.m). Reinstall rear mount through-bolt. Remove transmission jack.

4) Position damper weight assembly and plate on mounting pad at rear end of transmission extension housing. Spacer must be placed between weight and extension housing. Install mounting bolts and tighten to 150 INCH lbs.

Installing Damper Weight Assembly on 1984-86 Chrysler Corp. RWD Cars & 1981-86 "D" Pickups

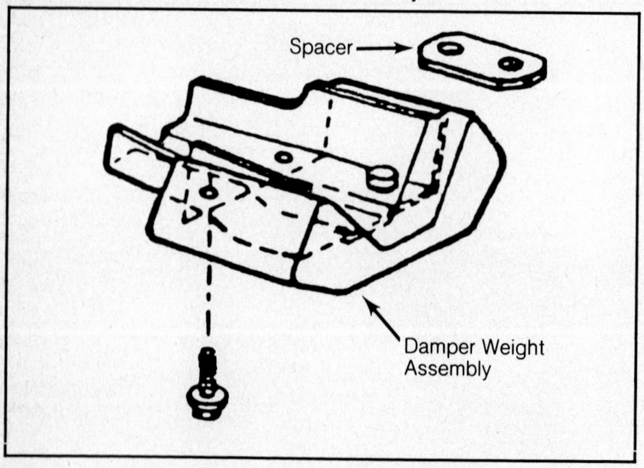

2

1985 COLT VISTA MODELS WITH AUTOMATIC TRANSMISSIONS: NEW CARRIER PLANET BOLT – A new design planet carrier bolt has been introduced into production on 1985 Colt Vista models equipped with automatic transaxles. The new bolt (MD720857) can be identified by the under-cut made on the back side of the bolt head. The new bolt is interchangeable with the old bolt. Tightening specification has been changed to 10 ft. lbs. (13 N.m) for either the new or old design bolt.

3

1985-86 ALL FWD CHRYSLER CORP. MODELS WITH AUTOMATIC TRANSMISSIONS: FLUID LEAK AT SPEEDOMETER CABLE & ADAPTER – Some 1985-86 FWD models may have a fluid leak at speedometer pinion adapter. Fluid leak may be caused by defective "O" ring seal(s). If leaking from this area, replace speedometer cable adapter and "O" ring.

To replace speedometer cable adapter, disconnect speedometer cable from adapter. Remove retaining bolt and remove adapter. Ensure transaxle housing is clean and there are no burrs. Install new speedometer cable adapter and "O" ring(s). Reconnect speedometer cable.

FORD MOTOR CO.

4

1985 FORD MOTOR CO. VEHICLES WITH AUTOMATIC OVERDRIVE (AOT) TRANSMISSION: LINKAGE ADJUSTMENT USING THROTTLE VALVE CONTROL PRESSURE (NEW CABLE SYSTEM) – Adjust cable using the following procedure:

1) Attach 0-60 psi TV pressure gauge to TV port on transmission. Remove air cleaner cover and inlet tube from the throttle body inlet for easier access to throttle lever. Insert tapered end of TV Gauge (T86L-70332-A) between crimped slug on end of cable and plastic cable fitting that attaches to throttle lever. Push in gauge forcing crimped slug away from plastic fitting. Ensure gauge is pushed in completely.

2) Run engine until normal operating temperature is reached. Transmission fluid temperature should be approximately 100-150°F. Set parking brake and place shift selector in Neutral. With TV gauge in place and engine idling in Neutral, TV pressure should be 30-40 psi. Do not check or set TV pressure in Park.

3) For best transmission function, set TV pressure as close as possible to 35 psi. Using a screwdriver pry up White toggle lever on cable adjuster located directly behind throttle body cable mounting bracket. The adjuster preload spring should cause adjusting slider to move away from throttle body and TV pressure should increase. Toggle lever must be completely up to allow slider to move freely.

4) Push on slider from behind bracket until TV pressure is 35 psi. While still holding slider, push down on toggle lever, locking slider in position. Remove gauge, allowing cable to return to its normal idle position. With engine still idling in Neutral, TV pressure must be at or near 0 psi or less than 5 psi.

Latest Changes & Corrections

FOR 1986 & EARLIER DOMESTIC MODELS (Cont.)

5) If not, reinstall TV gauge. Repeat steps **3)** and **4)**, but set TV pressure less than 35 psi but not less than 30 psi. Remove gauge block and check TV pressure to determine if it is at or near 0 psi.

GENERAL MOTORS

5 *ALL GENERAL MOTORS VEHICLES WITH THM 700-R4: REMOVAL AND INSTALLATION OF LOW/REVERSE PISTON* – When removing or installing the low/reverse piston on THM 700-R4 transmissions, always remove the parking pawl before removing the piston. The parking pawl may interfere with piston removal or installation if left in place, damaging the piston outer seal. Damaging the seal may cause slipping in Reverse or no Reverse gear. DO NOT grind on the parking pawl in an attempt to remove the interference point.

6 *1984-86 CADILLAC CIMARRON MODELS WITH 125C/CJC TRANSAXLE: THROTTLE VALVE BUZZ* – Some 1984-86 Cimarron models equipped with 125C/CJC transaxles may have a "buzz" noise coming from the throttle valve. This condition is noticeable at idle and decreases as vehicle speed increases.

A revised valve body-to-case cover eliminates the "buzz" by reducing the diameter of the 1-2 accumulator valve bleed orifice. The reduction of the bleed orifice prevents rapid oscillation of the valve.

This oscillation, when transmitted to the throttle pressure valve, causes the "buzz". Replace the original valve body-to-case cover with spacer plate (8660569).

7 *1985 PONTIAC FIERO, GRAND AM, SUNBIRD AND 6000 MODELS WITH THM 125/125C TRANSAXLES: REVISED TRANSAXLE CASE* – Beginning April 15, 1985, THM 125/125C transaxles are being produced using a revised case. The new case is produced without the intermediate servo bleed orifice. Either case can be used for all applications in service.

8 *1986 PONTIAC 6000 WITH THM 440-T4 TRANSAXLE: TORQUE CONVERTER CLUTCH (TCC) SHUDDER AT 45-55 MPH* – Some 1986 Pontiac 6000 models with THM 440-T4 transaxles built before January 27, 1986, may exibit torque converter clutch apply shudder at 45-55 MPH. This condition may be caused by the torque converter. If TCC apply shudder exists, replace torque converter with service replacement unit.

REPLACEMENT TORQUE CONVERTER

Model Application	Replacement Part No.
BAH, BCH, BSH	8653959
BHH	8653939
BDH, BLH, BMH, BTH, BYH, BZH	8644936
BBH	8644938
CFH, CMH, CNH, CBH,CJH	8644932

9 *1980-86 PONTIAC FIERO, PHOENIX, SUNBIRD 2000 AND 6000 MODELS WITH THM 125/125C TRANSAXLES: TRANSAXLE SLIPS IN ALL RANGES* – Some 1980-86 Fiero, Phoenix, Sunbird, 2000 and 6000 models with THM 125/125C transaxles may exibit a condition where the transaxle slips in all gear ranges when under heavy acceleration.

This condition may be caused by a drop in oil pressure due to a cut or improperly seated oil strainer seal. A revised oil strainer and seal kit (8652910) may be used on models that exhibit this slip condition.

If replacement of the oil strainer is necessary during transaxle service, remove original seal from transaxle case and replace with new seal provided in service kit. Always install seal in case prior to installing replacement oil strainer and seal assembly.

Always use correct seal based on design of oil strainer filler neck. Use "O" ring seal on short-shouldered filter neck and lip seal on long-shouldered filter neck.

10 *1984-86 PONTIAC BONNEVILLE, GRAND PRIX AND PARISENNE WITH THM 200-C TRANSMISSION: ENGINE STALLS IN REVERSE* – Some 1984-86 Bonneville, Grand Prix and Parisenne models equipped with THM 200-C transmission may stall the engine when the transmission selector is placed in reverse. This condition may be caused by a partial torque converter clutch engagement in reverse range. A new design pressure regulator valve and installation kit (8638951) is now available to correct this condition.

Revised THM 200-C Pressure Regulator Valve

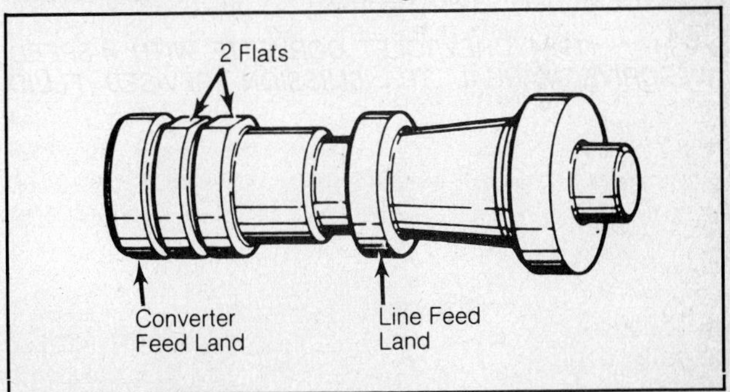

JEEP

11 *1986 JEEP CHEROKEE, COMANCHE AND WAGONEER WITH 4-CYLINDER ENGINES: EARLY SHIFT POINTS* – Some 1986 Cherokee, Comanche and Wagoneer models equipped with 4-cylinder engines may develope early shift points. This condition may be caused by a loose pivot bolt at the throttle valve linkage bellcrank.

Inspect pivot bolt and bellcrank spring for correct tightness and position. If necessary, remove pivot bolt and apply Loctite (271) to the bolt threads. Align bellcrank spring and tighten pivot bolt to 16 ft. lbs. (22 N.m). Check and adjust throttle linkage as necessary.

FOR 1986 & EARLIER DOMESTIC MODELS (Cont.)

View Of Bellcrank Spring & Pivot Bolt

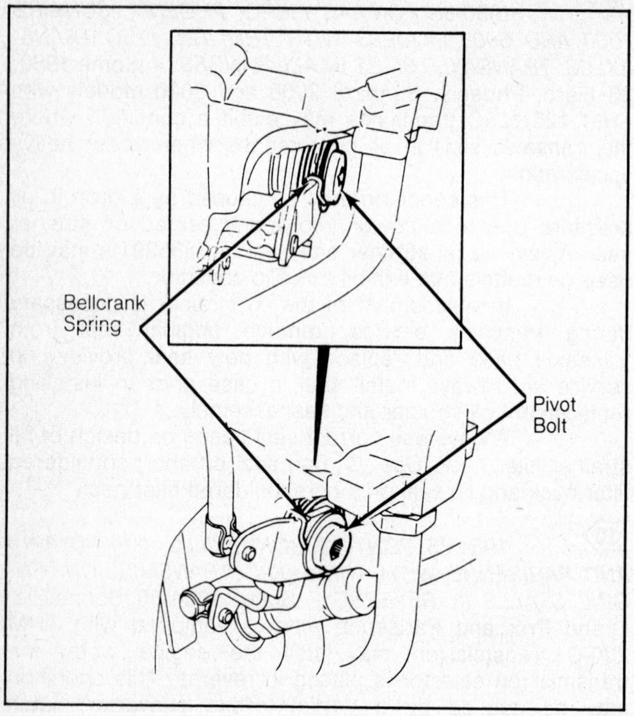

MANUAL TRANSMISSIONS

GENERAL MOTORS

12 *1984 CHEVROLET CORVETTE WITH 4-SPEED OVERDRIVE MANUAL TRANSMISSION: REVISED FLUID CHANGE INTERVAL* – The fluid used in the overdrive portion of the 1984 Corvette manual transmission should be changed every 30,000 miles. During 30,000 mile service, check manual transmission fluid level at the filler plug, located on passenger side of transmission.

If necessary, add gear oil (SAE 80W GL-5) to the bottom of the filler plug. No fluid change interval is required for the manual transmission portion of the transmission. Drain the overdrive fluid. Refill it to the level of the filler plug, located on driver side of transmission, with ATF Dextron II.

13 *1984 CAVALIER, CELEBRITY AND CITATION MODELS WITH MANUAL TRANSAXLE: CHANGE IN TRANSAXLE LUBRICANT* – Engine oil (5W-30) is now recommended for use in 1984 Cavalier, Celebrity and Citation models equipped with 4-speed transaxles. This replaces the ATF that was previously used in service on these models.

PROPELLER SHAFT

FORD MOTOR CO.

14 *1984-86 FORD MOTOR CO. AEROSTAR, E-SERIES VANS & F-SERIES PICKUPS: PROPELLER SHAFT SERVICE* – Some 1984-86 Aerostar, E-series vans and F-series pickups may be equipped with aluminum or graphite propeller shafts. DO NOT clamp the tube in a standard vise during "U" joint or yoke replacement. If repairs are necessary, use caution to prevent damage to propeller shaft tube. If the tube is dented or fractured, the propeller shaft may fail during vehicle operation.

1985 IMPORT GENERAL INDEX

The first step in using these pages is to locate the listed components that you require information on. Go down the list under the specific component heading to the model or transmission type of the vehicle you are working on. On the right-hand side of the column is the number of the article you require.

1985 Import General Index

A

1985 Import General Index

1985 Import General Index

1985 Import General Index

B

C

D

F

G

1985 Import General Index

1985 Import General Index

SECTION 5

IMPORT GENERAL SERVICING

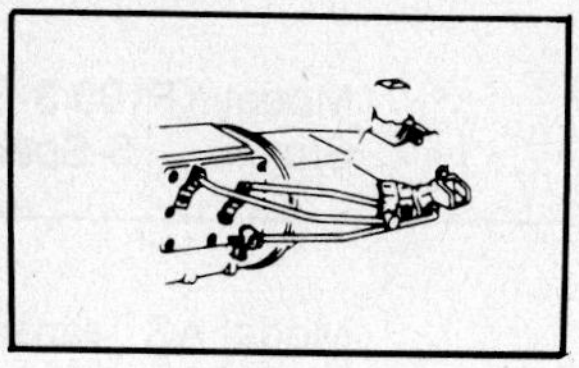

TRANSMISSION APPLICATIONS — Page

AUTOMATIC TRANSMISSION SERVICING

AUTOMATIC TRANSMISSION REMOVAL — Page

MANUAL TRANSMISSION SERVICING

MANUAL TRANSMISSION REMOVAL

GENERAL SERVICING

NOTE: ALSO SEE GENERAL INDEX.

Transmission Application

AUTOMATIC TRANSMISSIONS – IMPORTED CARS & TRUCKS

MANUFACTURER & MODEL	TRANSMISSION MODEL
AUDI	
Coupe GT	Model 087 Transaxle
4000S	Model 089 Transaxle
5000S Series	Model 087 Transaxle
BMW	
318i	Model ZF 3 HP-22
All Others	Model ZF 4 HP-22
CHRYSLER CORP. IMPORTS	
Colt	Mitsubishi – Model KM171 Transaxle
Colt Vista	Mitsubishi – Model KM172 Transaxle
Conquest	Mitsubishi – Model MR600
Ram-50 Pickup	2WD – Torqueflite Model MA-904A
	4WD – Mitsubishi Model KM146
FORD MOTOR CO. IMPORTS	
Merkur	
XR4Ti	Ford – Model C-3
GENERAL MOTORS IMPORTS	
Spectrum	Model KF100 3-Speed Transaxle
Sprint	Suzuki – 3-Speed Transaxle
HONDA	
Accord & Prelude	Model AS Transaxle
Civic	Model AW Transaxle
ISUZU	
I-Mark (FWD)	Model KF100 3-Speed Transaxle
I-Mark (RWD) & P'UP	Model AW03-55
Impulse	Model AW03-70 or AW03-72L
JAGUAR	
XJ6	Borg-Warner – Model 66
XJS HE	GM Turbo Hydra-Matic – Model 400
MAZDA	
GLC & 626	Mazda – Model F3A Transaxle
RX7	Jatco – Model L4N71B
MERCEDES-BENZ	
190 Series & 300 Series (Calif.)	MB – Model W4A020 4-Speed
300 Series (Fed.), 380 Series & 500 Series	MB – Model W4A040 4-Speed
MITSUBISHI	
Cordia & Tredia	Mitsubishi – Model KM172 Transaxle
Galant	Mitsubishi – Model ELC-4 Transaxle
Mirage	Mitsubishi – Model KM171 Transaxle
Pickup	2WD – Torqueflite Model MA-904A
Pickup & Montero	4WD – Mitsubishi Model KM146
Starion	Mitsubishi – Model MR600

AUTOMATIC TRANSMISSIONS – IMPORTED CARS & TRUCKS (Cont.)

MANUFACTURER & MODEL	TRANSMISSION MODEL
NISSAN	
Maxima	Jatco – Model RL4F02A Transaxle
Pickup	Jatco – Model L3N71B
Pulsar NX, Sentra & Stanza	Jatco – Model RL3F01A Transaxle
200SX & 200SX Turbo	Jatco – Model L4N71B
300ZX & 300ZX Turbo	Jatco – Model E4N71B
PEUGEOT	
505	Model ZF 3 HP-22
PORSCHE	
928S	Model A28.01 Transaxle
944	Model 087 Transaxle
RENAULT	
Fuego & Sportwagon	Renault – Model 4139-65 Transaxle
SAAB	
900 Series	Borg-Warner – Model 37 Transaxle
SUBARU	
All Models	3-Speed Transaxle
TOYOTA	
Camry	Model A140E Transaxle
Celica	Model A40D
Corolla FWD	Model A130L, A131L or A240L Transaxle
Corolla RWD	Model A42L
Cressida & Supra	Model A43DE
Pickup	Model A43D
Tercel	2WD – Model A55 Transaxle 4WD – Model A55F Transaxle
Van	Model A43DL
VOLKSWAGEN	
Cabriolet, Golf, GTI, Jetta	Model 010 Transaxle
Quantum	Model 087, 089 or 089-E Transaxle
Vanagon	Model 090 Transaxle
VOLVO	
740/760 Turbo Diesel & 760 GLE	Model ZF22
All Other Models	Borg-Warner Model AW70 or AW71

Transmission Application

MANUAL TRANSMISSIONS – IMPORTED CARS & TRUCKS

MANUFACTURER & MODEL	TRANSMISSION MODEL
ALFA ROMEO	
Graduate & Spider 2.0 Veloce	5-Speed – Model Alfa Romeo
GTV-6 2.5L	5-Speed – Model Alfa Romeo Transaxle
AUDI	
Quattro	5-Speed – Model 5H Transaxle
Coupe GT, 4000S	5-Speed – Model 013 or 093 Transaxle
5000S Series	5-Speed – Model 016 Transaxle
BMW	
318i	5-Speed – Getrag 240 or ZFS5-16
All Others	5-Speed – Getrag 260 or 265
CHRYSLER CORP. IMPORTS	
Colt	5-Speed – Model KM162 Transaxle (1.5L)
	5-Speed – Model KM163 Transaxle (1.6L)
Colt Vista (2WD)	5-Speed – Model KM163 Transaxle
Colt Vista (4WD)	5-Speed – Model KM182 Transaxle
Conquest	5-Speed – Model KM132
Ram-50 Pickups (2WD)	4-Speed – Model KM130
	5-Speed – Model KM132
Ram-50 Pickups (4WD)	5-Speed – Model KM145
FORD MOTOR CO. IMPORTS	
Merkur XR4Ti	5-Speed – Model Ford German Design
GENERAL MOTORS IMPORTS	
Spectrum	5-Speed – Model GM (76 mm) Transaxle
Sprint	5-Speed – Model MV2 Transaxle
HONDA	
Accord & Prelude	5-Speed – Model GM or GS Transaxle
Civic	4-Speed – Model GV Transaxle
	5-Speed – Model GW Transaxle
	6-Speed – Model GW-SL 4WD Transaxle
ISUZU	
I-Mark (RWD), Impulse & P'UP (2WD)	4 or 5-Speed – Model MSG-4K or MSG-5K
I-Mark (FWD)	5-Speed – Model G.M. (76 mm) Transaxle
P'UP (4WD) & Trooper II	4-Speed – Model MSG-4ET
MAZDA	
B2000 Pickup & RX7	5-Speed
GLC	4 or 5-Speed Transaxle
626	5-Speed Transaxle
MERCEDES-BENZ	
190D	5-Speed – Model GL 68/20 A-5
190E	5-Speed – Model GL 68/20 B-5
MITSUBISHI	
Cordia & Tredia	5-Speed – Model KM163 Transaxle
Pickup (2WD)	4-Speed – Model KM130
	5-Speed – Model KM132
Mirage	5-Speed – Model KM162 (1.5L) Transaxle
	5-Speed – Model KM163 (1.6L) Transaxle
Pickup (4WD) & Montero	5-Speed – Model KM145
Starion	5-Speed – Model KM132

MANUAL TRANSMISSIONS – IMPORTED CARS & TRUCKS (Cont.)

MANUFACTURER & MODEL	TRANSMISSION MODEL
NISSAN	
Maxima	5-Speed – Model RS5F50A Transaxle
Pickup (2WD & 4WD)	5-Speed – Model FS5W71B
Pulsar NX	5-Speed – Model RS5F30A Transaxle
Sentra	4-Speed – Model RN4F30A Transaxle 5-Speed – Model RS5F30A Transaxle
Stanza	5-Speed – Model RS5F31A Transaxle
200SX & 200SX Turbo	5-Speed – Model FS5W71B
300ZX & 300ZX Turbo	5-Speed – Model Borg-Warner T-5 5-Speed – Model FS5W71C
PEUGEOT	
505 Series	4 or 5-Speed – Model Peugeot
PORSCHE	
911 Carrera	5-Speed – Model 915/68 or 915/73 Transaxle
928S	5-Speed – Model G28.11 Transaxle
944	5-Speed – Model 016 K Transaxle
RENAULT	
Fuego & Sportwagon	5-Speed – Model NG1 Transaxle
SAAB	
900 & Turbo	5-Speed – Model GM-45606
Turbo (16 Valve)	5-Speed – Model GM-45706
SUBARU	
Brat & Hatchback (4WD)	4-Speed Transaxle
Hatchback (2WD), Sedan (2WD), Station Wagon (2WD) & XT Coupe (2WD)	4 or 5-Speed Transaxle
Sedan (4WD), Station Wagon (4WD) XT Coupe (4WD) & XT Turbo Coupe (2WD)	5-Speed Transaxle (Single or Dual Range)
TOYOTA	
Camry & Corolla (FWD)	5-Speed – Model C51 or S50 Transaxle
Celica, Cressida, & Supra	5-Speed – Model W58
Corolla RWD	5-Speed – Model T50
Land Cruiser	4-Speed – Model H42
MR2	5-Speed – Model G52 Transaxle
Pickup (Diesel)	5-Speed – Model G40 or G52
Pickup (2WD Gas)	4-Speed – Model W46 5-Speed – Model W55
Pickup (4WD Gas)	5-Speed – Model G52 or W56
Tercel (2WD)	4-Speed – Model Z45 Transaxle 5-Speed – Model Z53 Transaxle
Tercel (4WD)	5-Speed – Model Z54F Transaxle
Van	5-Speed – Model G53
VOLKSWAGEN	
Quantum	5-Speed – Model 013 or 093 Transaxle
Cabriolet, Golf, GTI, Jetta & Scirocco	5-Speed – Model 020 Transaxle
Vanagon	4-Speed – Model 091/1 Transaxle 5-Speed – Model 094 Transaxle
VOLVO	
All Models	5-Speed – Model M46

AUDI

IDENTIFICATION

TRANSMISSION CODES

Application	Code
Coupe, 4000S (5-Cyl.) & 5000 Series	087
4000S (4-Cyl.)	089

LUBRICATION

SERVICE INTERVALS

Check fluid level every 15,000 miles. Change transaxle fluid every 30,000 miles under normal conditions, or every 15,000 miles under severe conditions.

CHECKING FLUID LEVEL

At normal operating temperature, park vehicle on level surface. Place selector lever in "P", apply parking brake and allow engine to idle. Ensure fluid level is between marks on dipstick. Raise vehicle. Remove fill plug. Oil level should be even with bottom of hole.

RECOMMENDED FLUID

Dexron II automatic transmission fluid. Use Hypoid SAE 90 (API GL-5) in final drive.

FLUID CAPACITIES

TRANSMISSION REFILL CAPACITIES

Application	Refill	Dry Fill
All Models		
Transaxle	3.2 qts. (3.0L)	6.4 qts. (6.0L)
Final Drive		.80 qts. (.75L)

DRAINING & REFILLING

1) Remove transaxle protection plate. Remove rear pan bolts and loosen front pan bolts. Carefully lower pan and drain as much fluid as possible. Remove oil pan and pour out remaining fluid. Remove filter. Clean oil pan in solvent and dry.

2) Install new filter and tighten screws to 27 INCH lbs. (3 N.m). Install oil pan, using a new gasket. Tighten oil pan bolts to 15 ft. lbs. (20 N.m). Install protection plate, tighten bolts to 18 ft. lbs. (25 N.m). Add 3.2 qts. (3.0L) of transaxle fluid and check fluid level.

ADJUSTMENTS

BRAKE BAND

Adjust brake band with transaxle in a horizontal position only. Loosen adjustment screw lock nut. Tighten brake band adjustment screw to 90 INCH lbs. (10 N.m). Loosen adjustment screw once more, then tighten to 45 INCH lbs. (5 N.m). Back off screw 2 turns on 087 or 2 1/2 turns on 089 transaxles. Tighten lock nut to 15 ft. lbs. (20 N.m).

Fig. 1: Brake Band Adjustment

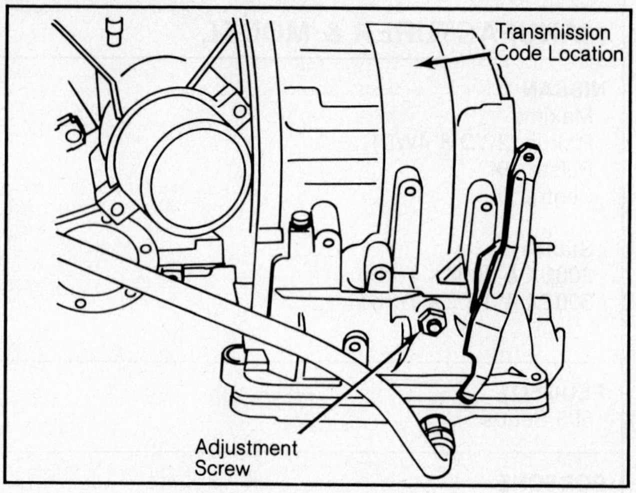

SELECTOR LEVER CABLE

Place shift selector lever in "P". Loosen clamping nut. Press shift lever on transaxle to park. Tighten nut on cable to 72 INCH lbs. (8 N.m).

THROTTLE CABLE

087 Transaxle

1) Disconnect both rods at relay control lever (near distributor). Remove cruise control linkage. Hold relay control lever at closed throttle position stop. Turn throttle rod socket until it centers over ball stud and install.

2) Loosen lock nut at transaxle operating lever. Slide operating lever apart until both ends are at stops. Tighten lock nut. Remove transaxle operating lever at transaxle.

3) Push accelerator pedal to stop on floor. Loosen accelerator cable pinch bolt near transaxle. Push transaxle shift lever up to kickdown stop. Using needle-nose pliers, pull accelerator cable and tighten pinch bolt. Attach transaxle lever control rod at transaxle lever.

4) Depress accelerator pedal until resistance is felt at full throttle position (no kickdown), throttle lever must contact stop. Depress accelerator pedal to full throttle stop. Linkage spring must be compressed 5/16" and operating lever on transaxle must contact stop (kickdown). Reconnect cruise control.

089 Transaxle

1) Loosen accelerator cable adjusting nut near transaxle. Loosen lock nuts on cylinder head cover. Pull sleeve of throttle cable until resistance is felt. Turn adjustment nut against bracket and lock using second nut.

2) Loosen accelerator cable lock nut near transaxle. Depress accelerator pedal to pedal stop. Turn transaxle throttle cable adjustment nut until transaxle lever begins to move. Tighten lock nut.

3) Depress accelerator pedal until resistance is felt at full throttle position (no kickdown), throttle lever must contact stop. Depress accelerator pedal to full throttle stop. Linkage spring must be compressed 5/16" and operating lever on transaxle must contact stop (kickdown).

NEUTRAL SAFETY SWITCH

Neutral safety switch is located in shift console. Remove console cover and adjust switch so that it engine starts in "P" and "N" positions only.

BMW

IDENTIFICATION

TRANSMISSION CODES

Application	Code
318i	ZF 3 HP-22
All Other Models	ZF 4 HP-22

LUBRICATION

SERVICE INTERVALS

Check fluid level at least at every oil change. Drain and refill transmission every 30,000 miles.

CHECKING FLUID LEVEL

Check fluid with transmission at normal operating temperature. Vehicle on level surface, engine idling and gear selector in "P". Ensure fluid level is between "MAX" and "MIN" marks on the dipstick. Distance between marks represents .42 qts. (.40L).

RECOMMENDED FLUID

Use Dexron or Dexron II fluid.

FLUID CAPACITY

TRANSMISSION REFILL CAPACITES

Application	Refill Quantity	Dry Quantity
318i	2.3 qts. (2.2L)	6.4 qts. (6.0L)
All Others	3.2 qts. (3.0L)	8.0 qts. (7.5L)

DRAINING & REFILLING

With transmission at operating temperature, remove drain plug. Remove oil pan bolts and tap on pan to break seal loose. Remove oil screen and clean or replace as necessary. Clean oil pan. Reinstall filter screen and oil pan. Fill with fluid.

ADJUSTMENTS

SHIFT LINKAGE

ZF 3 HP-22

1) Check tightness of shift console lever before adjusting. Disconnect selector rod from lever at adjustment pin. Move transmission shifter lever to "N". Press shifter against shift gate stop.

2) Move selector rod with adjusting pin until adjusting pin aligns with hole in selector lever. Shorten selector rod by 1 turn of adjusting pin. Reattach selector rod, adjusting pin and selector lever.

ZF 4 HP-22

1) Move selector lever to "P". Loosen cable attaching nut on shift lever at transmission. Push lever forward to park and push cable rod the opposite forward direction.

2) Tighten shift cable rod nut to 7-9 ft. lbs. (10-12 N.m). Check proper operation of shifter in each gear selection, readjust if necessary.

Fig. 1: BMW Shift Linkage Adjustment

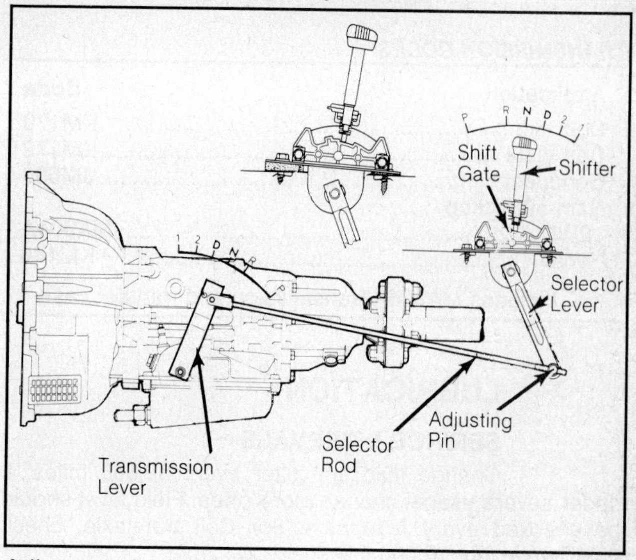

Adjustment for 318i shown.

THROTTLE CABLE & KICKDOWN STOP

Adjust cable play to .010-.030" (.25-.75 mm). *See Fig. 2.* Check kickdown stop. If necessary to adjust, loosen lock nut and screw in kickdown stop. Push down accelerator pedal to transmission pressure point. Unscrew kickdown stop in this position, until it contacts the accelerator pedal. Push down accelerator pedal to kick-down position. Distance from lead seal to end of sleeve must be at least 1.73" (44 mm).

Fig. 2: Throttle Cable & Kickdown Stop Adjustment

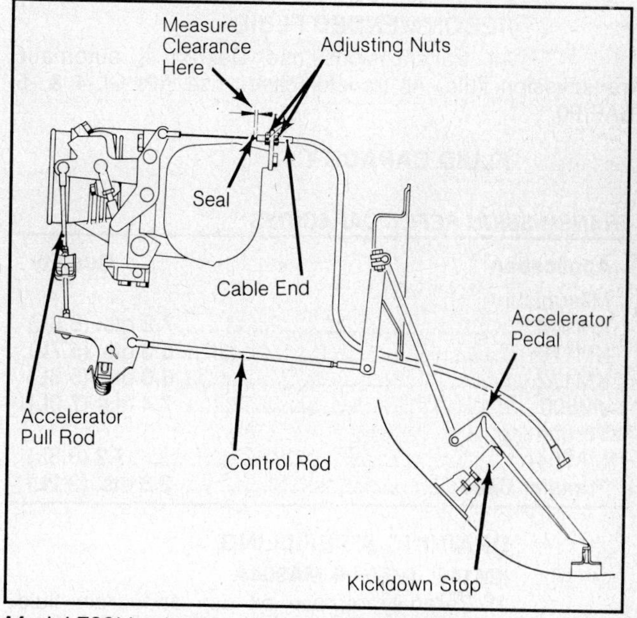

Model 733i is shown; other models are similar.

NEUTRAL SAFETY SWITCH

Neutral safety switch is connected with selector lever and a relay. If not operating properly, check relay and selector adjustment.

Automatic Transmission Servicing

CHRYSLER CORP. IMPORTS

IDENTIFICATION

TRANSMISSION CODES

Application	Code
Colt	KM170
Colt Vista	KM172
Conquest	JM600
Ram-50 Pickup	
2WD	MA904A
4WD	[1] KM146

[1] – Includes MA904A transmission and transfer case.

LUBRICATION

SERVICE INTERVALS

Change fluid and filter every 30,000 miles; if under severe usage, change more often. Fluid level should be checked every 6 months. For Colt transaxle, check fluid level every 15,000 miles.

CHECKING FLUID LEVEL

1) Park vehicle on level area. Oil must be at normal operating temperature, parking brake engaged and engine at idle. Shift transmission selector through each position, stopping briefly in each position.

2) Place selector in "N" position and clean area around dipstick tube. Ensure that fluid level is between lower and upper marks, but never over upper mark. Add or drain fluid as necessary.

CAUTION: If severe darkening of the fluid and a strong odor is noted, fluid and filter should be changed and bands adjusted.

RECOMMENDED FLUID

All transmissions use Dexron II automatic transmission fluid. All transfer cases use API GL-4 & -5 SAE 90.

FLUID CAPACITY

TRANSMISSION REFILL CAPACITIES

Application	Quanity
Mitsubishi	
KM146	7.2 qts. (6.8L)
KM170	6.0 qts. (5.7L)
KM172	6.0 qts. (5.6L)
JM600	7.4 qts. (7.0L)
Torqueflite	
MA904A	7.2 (6.8L)
Transfer Case	2.3 qts. (2.2L)

DRAINING & REFILLING

KM146, JM600 & MA904A

1) Carefully remove oil pan and drain fluid. Install new filter on bottom of valve body. Clean oil pan, replace gasket and install oil pan. Pour 4 qts. (3.8L) of specified fluid through filler tube. Start engine and allow to idle for 2 minutes.

2) Shift transmission into each position, ending in "N" position. Check fluid level with engine running at idle and add sufficient fluid to bring level to "ADD 1 PINT" mark. Recheck fluid level after transmission is at normal operating temperature.

KM170 & KM172

1) Remove drain plug from differential and drain fluid. *See Fig. 1.* If replacing filter, remove bolts and lower oil pan. Install new filter on bottom of valve body. Replace pan gasket and install pan.

2) Tighten differential plug to 22-25 ft. lbs. (30-34 N.m). Ensure that dipstick hole area is clean and pour in approximately 4.2 qts. (4.0L) of "DEXRON II" fluid.

3) Run engine for 2 minutes at idle. Shift transmission to each position, ending in "N" position. Add sufficient fluid to reach lower mark. After reaching normal operating temperature, fluid should be between upper and lower marks of "HOT" range.

Fig. 1: KM170 & KM172 Drain Plug Locations

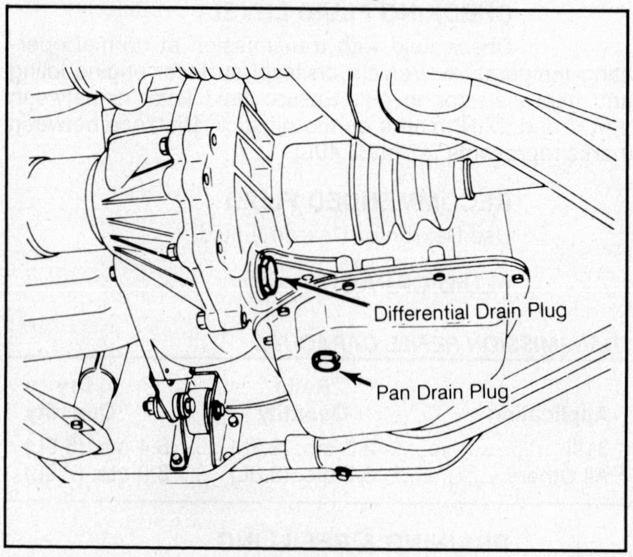

ADJUSTMENTS

FRONT (KICKDOWN) BAND

KM146 & MA904A

1) Front (kickdown) band adjuster screw is located on left side of transmission case. To adjust band, loosen and back off lock nut about 5 turns. Check that adjuster screw turns freely.

2) Using wrench (C-3380-A) with adapter (C-3705), tighten band adjuster screw to 52 INCH lbs. (5.9 N.m). *See Fig. 2.*

3) If adapter (C-3705) is not used, tighten adjuster screw to 51 INCH lbs. (5.8 N.m), which is the true torque. Back off adjusting screw 3 1/2 turns, hold adjuster screw and tighten lock nut to 37 ft. lbs. (50 N.m).

CHRYSLER CORP. IMPORTS (Cont.)

Fig. 2: KM146 & MA904A
Front (Kickdown) Band Adjusting Screw Location

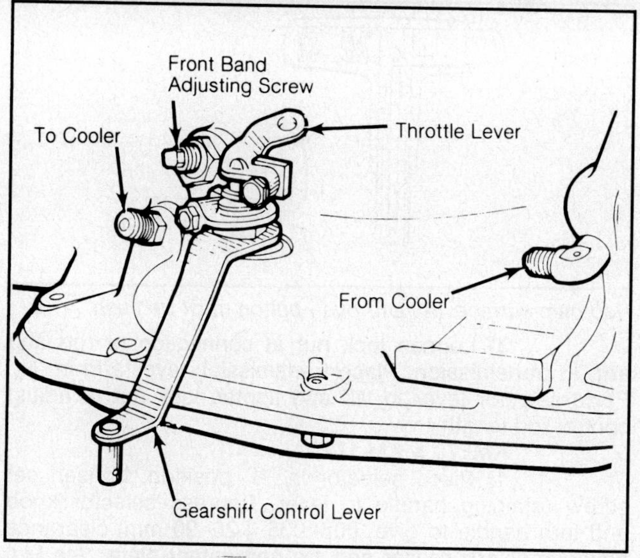

KM170 & KM172

1) Clean all dirt from kickdown servo cover and remove snap ring. Remove cover and loosen lock nut. Hold servo piston from turning and tighten adjusting screw to 88 INCH lbs. (10 N.m) and back it off.

2) Repeat torquing twice to seat kickdown band against drum. Tighten adjusting screw to 44 INCH lbs. (5 N.m) and back off 3 1/2 turns. Hold screw and tighten lock nut. Install cover and snap ring.

NOTE: **Install new seal ring with "D" shaped section to outside of cover. If reusing old seal ring, make certain it is not distorted.**

Fig. 3: KM170 & KM172 Kickdown Band Adjustment

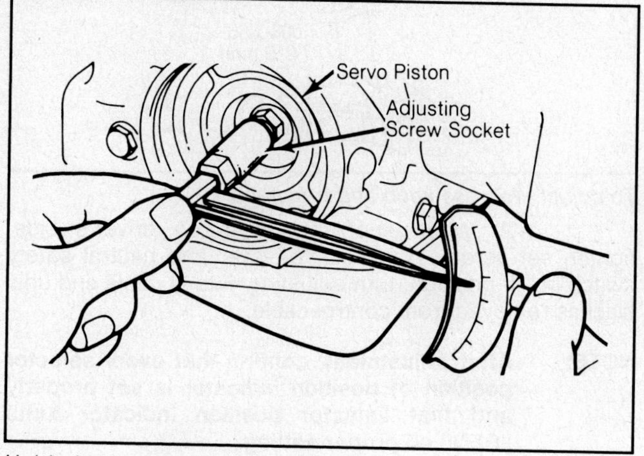

Hold piston and turn adjusting screw.

REAR BAND

KM146 & MA904A

1) Remove oil pan. Loosen lock nut and adjusting screw at servo end of lever and tighten screw to 43 INCH lbs. (4.9 N.m) of torque.

2) Back off screw 7 turns. Hold adjusting screw and tighten lock nut to 29 ft. lbs. (40 N.m). Reinstall oil pan.

Fig. 4: KM146 & MA904A
Rear Band Adjusting Screw Location

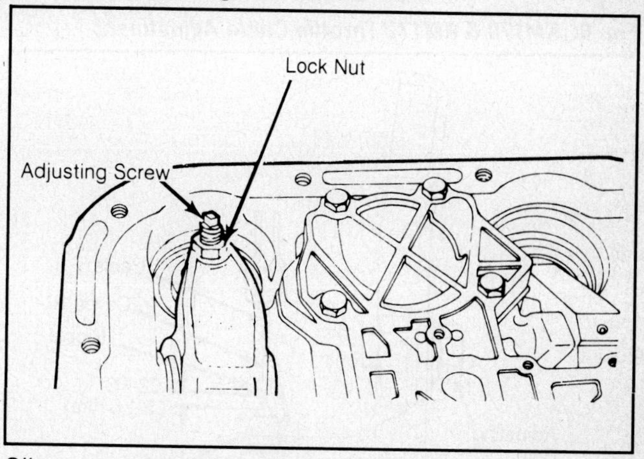

Oil pan must be removed for adjustment.

TRANSMISSION THROTTLE CONTROL

KM146 & MA904A

1) With engine at normal operating temperature and idle speed set correctly, loosen bolt retaining throttle rod "C" to "B". Lightly push throttle rod "A" or transmission throttle lever and rod toward idle stop and set rods to "IDLE" position.

2) Tighten bolt retaining rod "B" to "C". Open throttle to "WIDE OPEN" position. Make sure that transmission lever moves from "IDLE" to "WIDE OPEN" position (total movement 47.5° to 54°). Some play should still exist in throttle lever stroke at wide open throttle.

Fig. 5: KM146 & MA904A Throttle Rod Adjustment

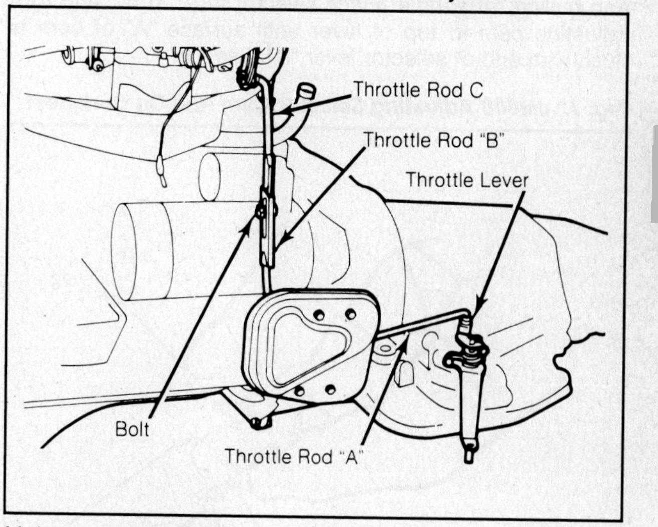

Make sure that transmission lever moves from "IDLE" to "WIDE OPEN" position.

KM170 & KM172

1) Ensure that carburetor throttle lever is at "CURB IDLE" position, engine is at operating temperature, and fast idle condition has been reset. Raise cover "B" and loosen cable bracket mounting bolt.

2) Move lower cable bracket until distance between nipple and top cover "A" of throttle cable is adjusted to .02-.06" (.5-1.5 mm). *See Fig. 6.* Tighten lower cable bracket mounting bolt.

CHRYSLER CORP. IMPORTS (Cont.)

3) With throttle lever in "WIDE OPEN" position, pull cable upward to ensure freedom of cable movement.

Fig. 6: KM170 & KM172 Throttle Cable Adjustment

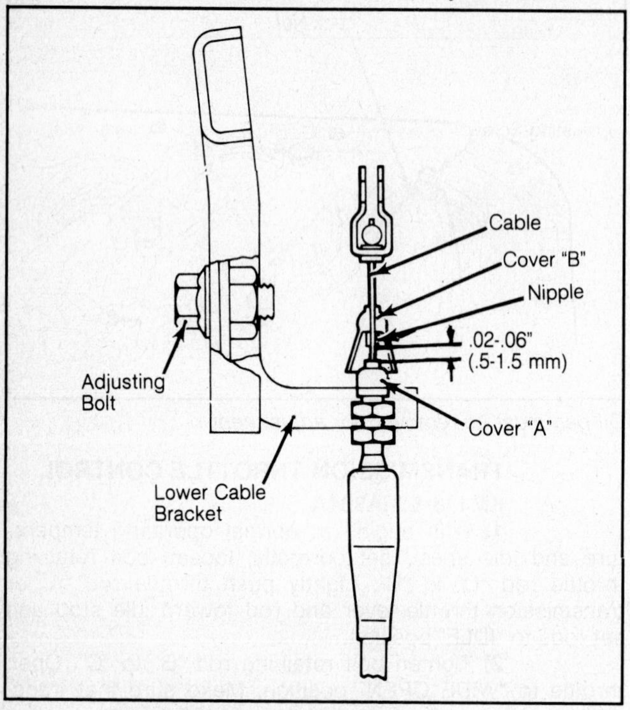

SHIFT LINKAGE

KM146, MA904A & JM600

1) Remove shift handle by loosening set screw and pulling off handle. Place selector lever in "N" and turn adjusting cam in top of lever until surface "A" of cam is flush with end of selector lever "B". *See Fig. 7.*

Fig. 7: JM600 Adjusting Selector Cam Rod On Conquest

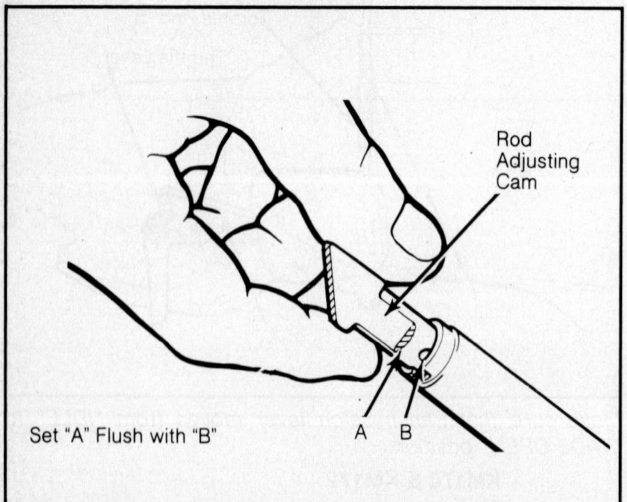

Adjust surface "A" flush with surface "B".

2) For Pickups, place selector lever in "N" and turn adjusting cam in top of lever until surface "A" of cam is flush with push button. *See Fig. 8.*

Fig. 8: KM146 & MA904A
Adjusting Selector Cam Rod On Pickups

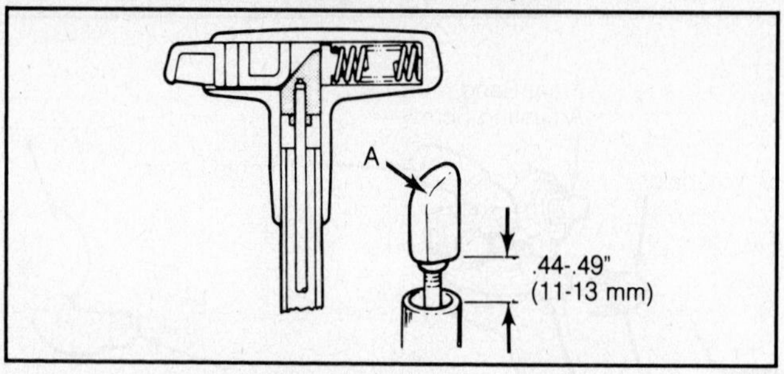

Rod cam surface "A" and push button must be flush.

3) Loosen lock nut at connection of rod and arm at transmission. Place transmission lever arm in "N". Place selector lever in "N" and tighten lock nut to adjust control rod length.

KM170 & KM 172

1) Place selector in "N" position. Loosen set screw retaining handle to lever. Depress selector knob and turn handle to give .008-.035" (.20-.90 mm) clearance between selector lever end pin and detent plate. *See Fig. 9.*

Fig. 9: Adjusting Selector Lever
On KM170 & KM172 Transaxle

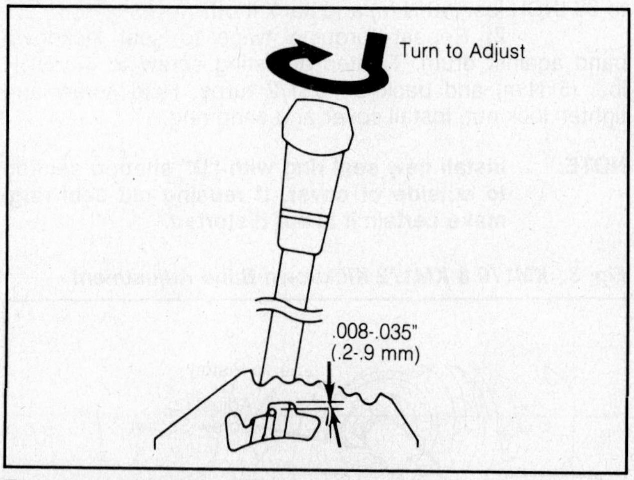

To adjust, depress knob and turn handle.

2) When knob button is on driver's side, tighten set screw. With selector lever and neutral safety switch in "N" position, turn adjusting nuts at cable end until slack is removed from control cable.

NOTE: **After adjustment, confirm that every selector position of position indicator is set properly and that selector position indicator turns "RED" on proper setting.**

NEUTRAL SAFETY SWITCH

KM146 & MA904A

NOTE: **Safety switch is located under shift lever console and is operated by shift lever. In addition to the neutral safety switch function, switch also operates back-up lights and seat belt warning system.**

CHRYSLER CORP. IMPORTS (Cont.)

1) To adjust switch, remove console, loosen switch attaching screws, and place selector lever in "N" position. Slide switch back and forth to measure contact range of "N" position. *See Fig. 11.*

Fig. 10: Positioning Neutral Safety Switch On KM146 & MA904A

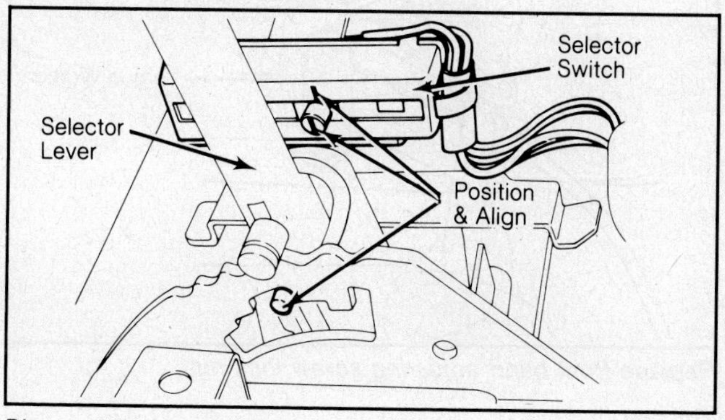

Place shift lever in "N" and align switch mark with rod indicator.

Fig. 11: Adjusting Neutral Safety Switch Movement On KM146 & MA904A

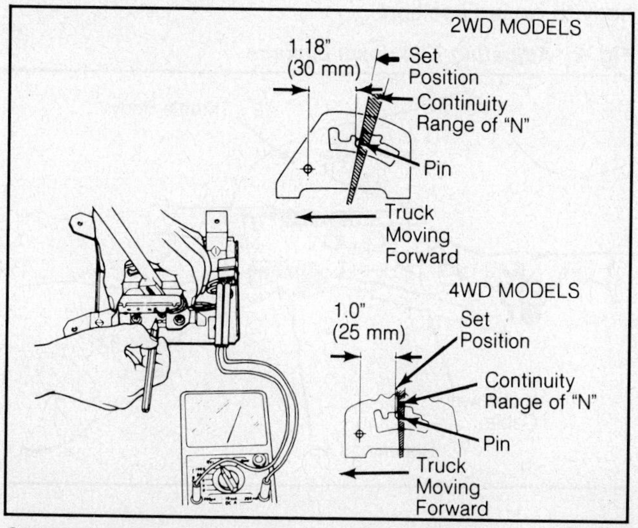

Connect tester to switch terminals (BY-BY) and move switch back and forth to check continuity.

Fig. 12: Adjusting Neutral Safety Switch On KM146 & MA904A

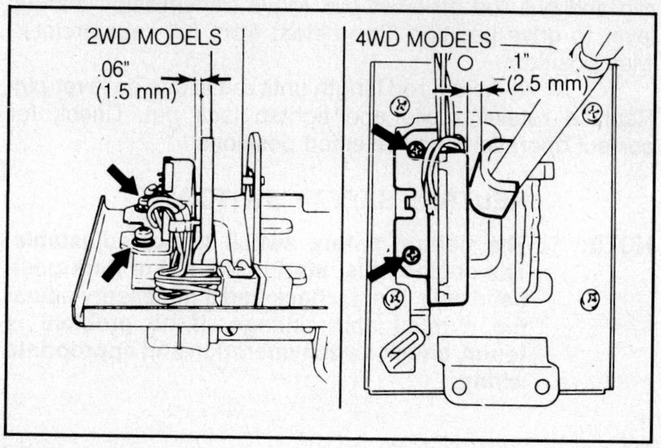

2) Temporarily install switch and adjust so there is .06" (1.5 mm) for 2WD Pickup, .1" (2.5 mm) for 4WD Pickup, side clearance between selector lever and switch. *See Fig. 12.* Set selector lever in "P", "R", and "N" positions and check continuity of terminals. After confirming continuity, tighten switch attaching screws and reinstall console.

NOTE: **If correct continuity cannot be achieved, reposition safety switch.**

KM170, KM172 & JM600

Place transmission control lever in "N" position and loosen switch retaining bolts. Turn switch body so that aligning hole end of lever overlaps switch body flange (on JM600 insert alignment pin) and tigthten bolts. *See Fig. 13.*

Fig. 13 Adjusting Neutral Saftry Switch On KM170 & KM172 Transaxle

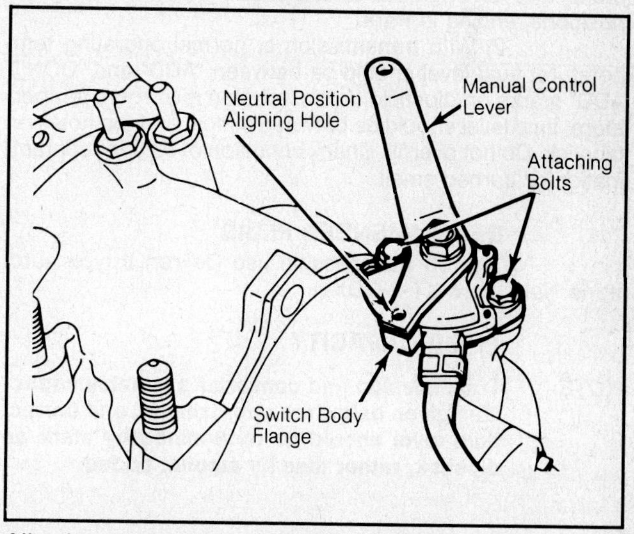

Align lever hole with housing hole. JM600 is similar.

VACUUM DIAPHRAGM ROD

JM600

Disconnect vacuum hose at vacuum diaphragm and remove diaphragm from transmission case. Using depth gauge, measure depth "L". Be sure vacuum throttle valve is pushed into valve body as far as possible. See VACUUM DIAPHRAGM ROD SELECTION table.

VACUUM DIAPHRAGM ROD SELECTION

Depth "L" in. (mm)	Rod Length in. (mm)	Part No.
Under 1.0059 (25.55)	1.142 (29.0)	MD610614
1.0098-1.0256 (25.67-26.05)	1.161 (29.5)	MD610615
1.0295-1.0453 (26.15-26.55)	1.181 (30.0)	MD610616
1.0492-1.0650 (26.65-27.05)	1.201 (30.5)	MD610617
Over 1.0689 (27.15)	1.220 (31.0)	MD610618

FORD MOTOR CO. IMPORTS

IDENTIFICATION

TRANSMISSION CODES

Application	Code
Merkur XR4Ti	C3

LUBRICATION

SERVICE INTERVALS

Check fluid level at every engine oil change. Fluid, filter changes and band adjustments are not required under normal operation. Under heavy duty (severe service), change fluid every 30 months or 30,000 miles. Adjust band when fluid is changed.

CHECKING FLUID LEVEL

1) With transmission at normal operating temperature, place vehicle on level ground. Apply parking brake, and run engine at curb idle. Shift selector through all positions, ending in Park.

2) With transmission at normal operating temperature, fluid level should be between "ADD" and "DON'T ADD" marks on dipstick. If transmission is at room temperature, fluid level should be between middle and top holes on dipstick. Do not overfill. Check condition of fluid for contamination or burned smell.

RECOMMENDED FLUID

The C3 transmission use Dexron II type auto. trans. fluid (Ford XT-2-QDX).

FLUID CAPACITY

NOTE: **Transmission and converter assembly capacities given below are approximate, and correct fluid level should be determined by mark on dipstick, rather than by amount added.**

TRANSMISSION REFILL CAPACITIES

Application	Quantity
C-3	16.0 pts. (8.5L)

DRAINING & REFILLING

Loosen oil pan attaching bolts to drain fluid. Remove oil pan and filter screen. Install new filter and gasket. Clean oil pan, and install pan with new gasket. Pour 3 qts. (2.8L) of fluid through filler tube. Check fluid level.

ADJUSTMENTS

INTERMEDIATE BAND (FRONT)

1) Clean all dirt from band adjusting screw area. Remove and discard lock nut. Install a new lock nut on band adjusting screw.

2) Tighten band adjusting screw to 10 ft. lbs. (14 N.m). Back off screw EXACTLY 2 turns. Hold adjusting screw in this position and tighten lock nut.

Fig. 1: Adjusting Front Band

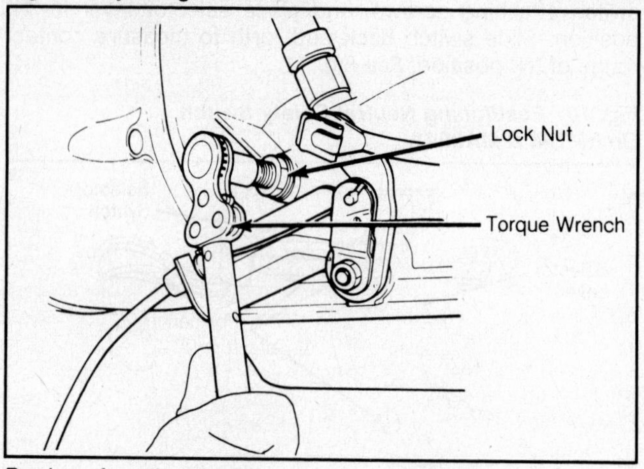

Replace front band adjusting screw lock nut.

KICKDOWN CONTROL

Open and hold throttle body at wide open position. Using pliers, remove cable retaining clip. Allow cable to set itself. Replace cable retaining clip and return throttle body to closed position.

Fig. 2: Adjusting Kickdown Linkage

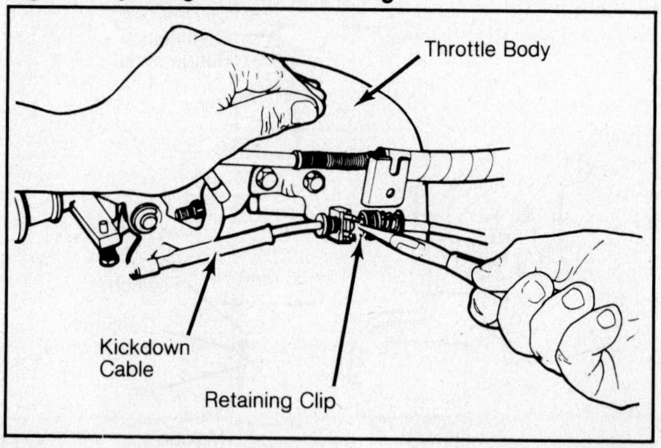

SHIFT LINKAGE

1) Move selector lever rearward against stop in Drive position. Raise vehicle. Loosen manual lever-to-control rod lock nut. Remove control rod retaining clip and pull rod off lever pin. Move transmission manual lever to drive position (2nd detent from full counterclockwise position).

2) Adjust rod length until rod slides on lever pin. Replace retaining clip and tighten lock nut. Check for correct operation in all selected positions.

NEUTRAL SAFETY SWITCH

NOTE: **The neutral safety switch is not adjustable. The engine must start in Neutral or Park positions only. If not, check and if necessary adjust the manual shift linkage. If no problem is found, check switch operation and appropriate wiring.**

GENERAL MOTORS IMPORTS

IDENTIFICATION

TRANSMISSION CODES

Application	Code
Spectrum	KF100
Sprint	MXI

LUBRICATION

SERVICE INTERVALS

Check transaxle lubricant each time engine oil is changed or every 7,500 miles. Replace lubricant and sump filter every 30,000 miles on Spectrum or 100,000 miles on Sprint.

CHECKING FLUID LEVEL

1) Park vehicle on level surface and apply parking brake. Place selector lever in Park, start engine and allow engine to idle for 2 minutes. Apply brakes, shift through all gears and return selector lever to Park.

2) Remove dipstick and carefully touch dipstick end to determine temperature of fluid. If fluid is cool or warm, fluid level should be between "COLD" range dimples. If fluid is too hot to touch, fluid level should be between "HOT" range dimples.

RECOMMENDED FLUID

Dexron II ATF.

FLUID CAPACITY

TRANSMISSION REFILL CAPACITIES

Application	Quantity
All	12.5 pts. (6.0L)

DRAINING & REFILLING

1) On Spectrum, remove drain plug located on lower part of differential and drain lubricant. Remove oil pan and discard pan gasket. Remove (3) bolts retaining sump filter to valve body. Remove filter and discard.

2) Install new sump filter and tighten bolts to 26-35 INCH lbs. (3-4 N.m). Install oil pan using a new gasket. Install drain plug, fill transaxle and check fluid level.

ADJUSTMENTS

SPECTRUM

Shift Control Cable

Loosen adjustment nuts at control rod link. With transaxle in Neutral detent, place selector lever in "N". Rotate link assembly clockwise to remove slack in cable. Tighten rear adjustment nut until it makes contact with link, then tighten front adjustment nut until it makes contact with link. *See Fig. 1.*

Park Lock Cable

Place ignition key in "LOCK" position and selector lever in Park. Pull park cable forward at shifter bracket. Tighten forward nut until it makes contact with bracket. Tighten rear nut until it makes contact with bracket.

Fig. 1: Adjusting Spectrum Shift Control Cable

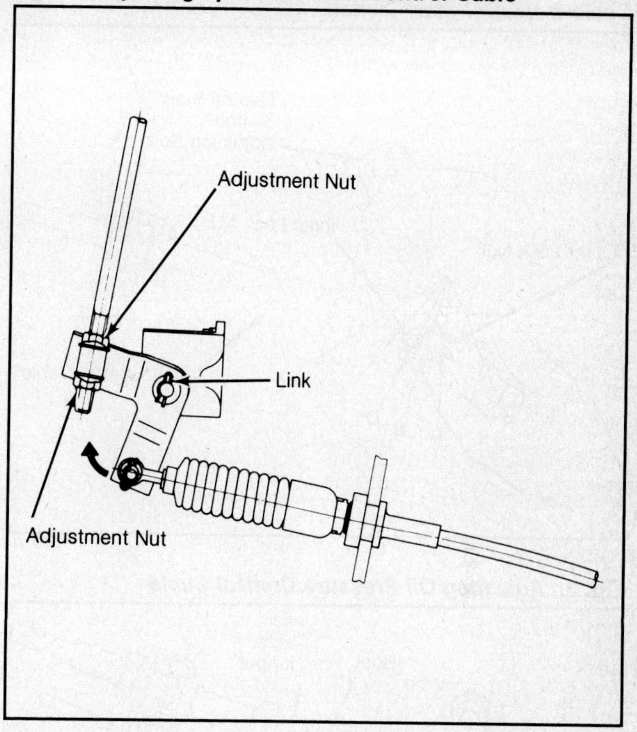

SPRINT

Shift Control Cable

1) Move trans. selector in Neutral. Loosen both control cable lock nuts. Shift trans. control lever to Neutral. By hand, tighten outer control cable lock nut until it contacts the lever joint. *See Fig. 2.*

2) Using a wrench, tighten the inner control cable lock nut. Ensure the transmission operates in all range positions. Shift trans. selector lever to Park and ensure vehicle will not move.

Neutral Start Switch

Shift trans. selector to Neutral. Loosen adjusting bolt. *See Fig. 2.* Slide the neutral start switch back and forth until a click is heard. Tighten the adjusting bolt to 14 ft. lbs. (18 N.m). Ensure starter operates in "P" or "N" position only.

Oil Pressure Control Cable

Ensure accelerator cable is adjusted. Operate engine until off fast idle speed. Remove the oil pressure control boot. Check gap between boot-to-inner cable stop.

2) If clearance is not .000-.002" (.00-.05 mm), loosen upper cable adjusting lock nuts and adjust cable length. If necessary, loosen lower cable adjusting lock nuts. *See Fig. 3.* Tighten all lock nuts.

GENERAL MOTORS IMPORTS (Cont.)

Fig. 2: Adjusting Sprint Shift Control Cable & Neutral Start Switch

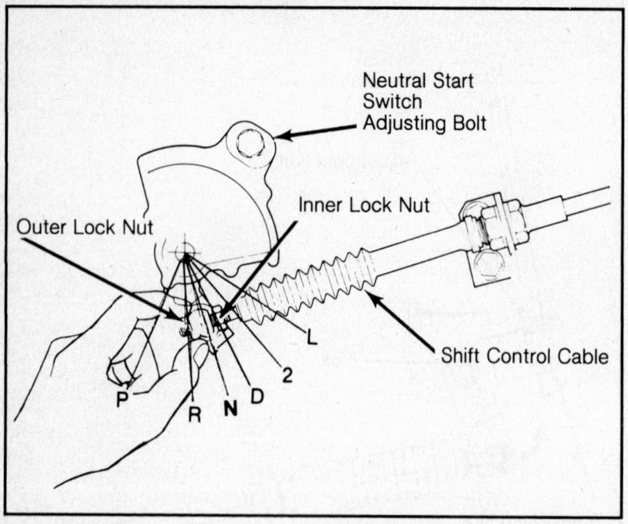

Fig. 3: Adjusting Oil Pressure Control Cable

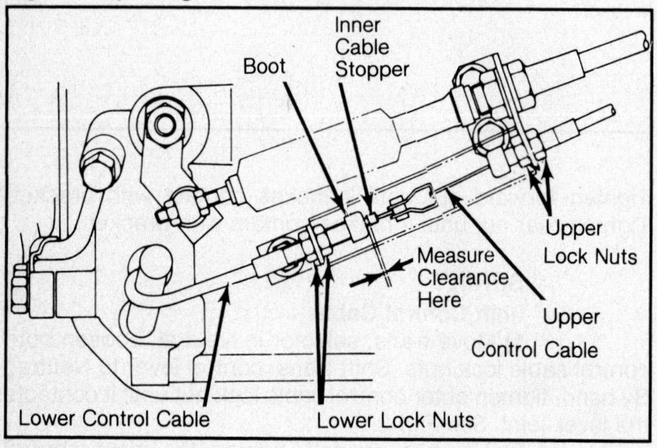

Start Inhibit Cable

1) Remove center console cover. Shift trans. selector lever to "P" position. Loosen cable sheath lock nuts. Pull cable sheath forward until all slack is removed. *See Fig. 4.*

2) Hand tighten outer lock nut. Tighten inner lock nut. Check tightness of outer lock nut. Ensure ignition key will operate column lock in the "P" position.

3) Move trans. selector lever to any other position. Ensure ignition key cannot be turned from "ACC" to "LOCK" position. If so, readjust start inhibit cable.

Fig. 4: Adjusting Start Inhibit Cable

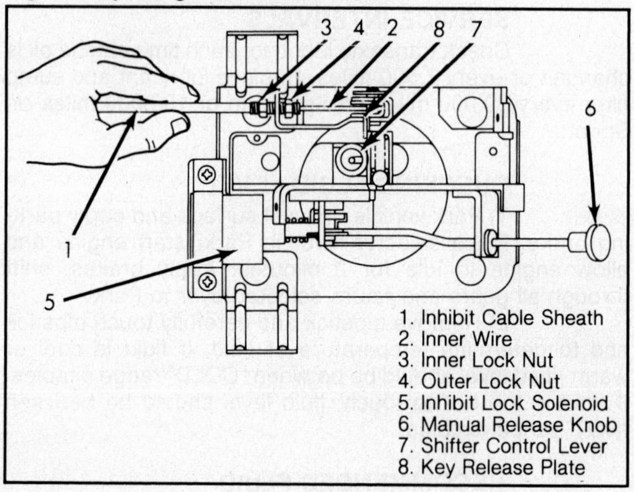

HONDA

IDENTIFICATION

TRANSMISSION CODES

Application	Code
Accord & Prelude	Model AS Transaxle
Civic	Model AW Transaxle

LUBRICATION

SERVICE INTERVALS

Check fluid level at every oil change. Transmission fluid should be changed at 15,000 miles, then every 30,000. No filter service or band adjustment is required.

CHECKING FLUID LEVEL

1) With vehicle on level floor and at normal operating temperature, stop engine. Clean area around dipstick and unscrew dipstick. Remove dipstick and wipe clean, then insert into hole but do not screw down.

2) Remove dipstick and check level. Fluid should be between upper and lower marks. Add fluid as necessary. After Checking fluid level, screw the dipstick in securly. DO NOT use a wrench.

RECOMMENDED FLUID

All models use Dexron type automatic transmission fluid (ATF).

FLUID CAPACITY

TRANSMISSION REFILL CAPACITIES

Application	Refill Quantity	Dry Fill Quantity
Accord & Prelude	3.0 qts. (2.8L)	6.1 qts. (5.8L)
Civic	2.9 qts. (2.8L)	5.6 qts. 5.4L)

DRAINING & REFILLING

1) Ensure that operating temperature is up to normal and remove transmission drain plug. Use new gasket and replace drain plug when fluid is drained.

2) Fill with about 2 qts. (1.9L) of fluid through dipstick hole and check level. Add fluid to bring to upper mark on dipstick.

NOTE: **Refill capacity will always be slightly less than specified capacity due to fluid remaining in recesses of housing and converter.**

ADJUSTMENTS

SHIFT CONTROL CABLE

1) Ensure that reverse gear engages. Remove center console. Place shift lever in "D" position. Remove lock clip and control cable pin. Check that hole in cable end is perfectly aligned with holes in selector lever arm.

2) If not, loosen lock nuts on control cable and adjust as required. Tighten lock nuts and install pin with lock clip. If pin does not go in easily, further adjustment is required. Check gear operation. *See Fig. 1.*

Fig. 1: Shift Control Cable Alignment

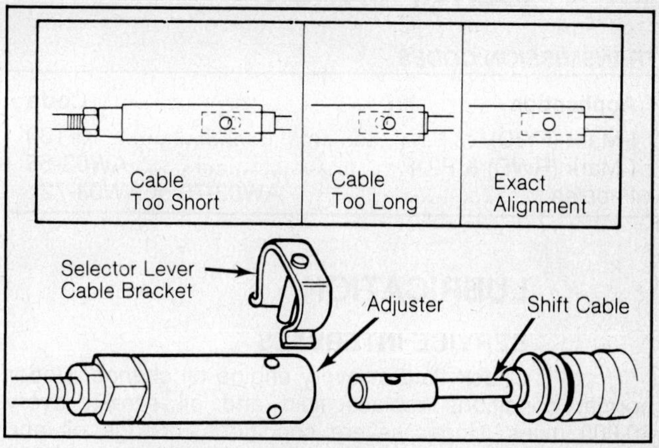

THROTTLE CONTROL CABLE & BRACKET

1) Ensure that engine is warmed to normal operating temperature and cable securing clamps are in position. Disconnect control cable from lever and lay end on top of shock absorber tower.

2) Using throttle gauge (07974-6890300), adjust cable control bracket so that distance between bracket and lever is 3.29" (83.5 mm). Depress accelerator until there is no slack in carburetor throttle cable.

3) Adjust distance between control cable end and nut "A" to 3.3" (84.5 mm). Install cable and tighten lock nut "B", ensuring that lock nut "A" does not turn. *See Fig. 2.*

Fig. 2: Throttle Cable & Bracket Adjustment

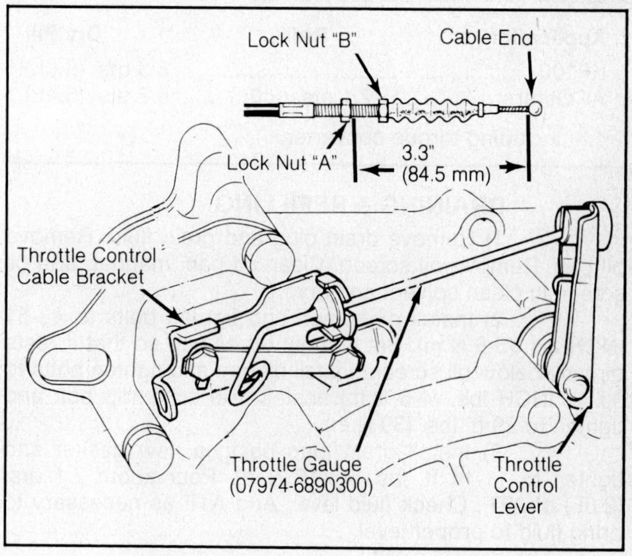

NEUTRAL SAFETY SWITCH

Move selector lever to "P", "R" and "N" to check switch continuity. On all models, continuity between Black/White and Black/White terminals should be present in "P" and "N". On Accord and Prelude models, continuity between Green/Black and Green/Black terminals should be present when in "R". On Civic models, continuity between Yellow and Green/Black should be present when in "R".

ISUZU

IDENTIFICATION

TRANSMISSION CODES

Application	Code
I-Mark (FWD)	KF100
I-Mark (RWD) & P'UP	AW03-55
Impulse	AW03-70 or AW03-72L

LUBRICATION

SERVICE INTERVALS

Check fluid at every engine oil change. Under normal conditions replace fluid and oil screen every 30,000 miles. Under severe conditions, change oil and screen at 15,000 mile intervals.

CHECKING FLUID LEVEL

1) Park vehicle on level surface, place selector lever in "P" position, set parking brake and run engine to operating temperature. Apply brake pedal. Move shift lever through each gear. Place shift lever in "P" position.

2) With engine idling, clean dipstick and insert. Remove dipstick and check level reading. Fluid level should be between dimples of "HOT" range.

RECOMMENDED FLUID

Dexron II automatic transmission fluid.

FLUID CAPACITY

TRANSMISSION REFILL CAPACITIES

Application	Refill	[1] Dry Fill
KF100	....	6.3 qts. (6.0L)
All Others	2.1 qts. (2.0L)	6.7 qts. (6.4L)

[1] – Including torque converter.

DRAINING & REFILLING

1) Remove drain plug and drain fluid. Remove oil pan. Remove oil screen. Clean oil pan, magnet, and oil screen in clean solvent and dry.

2) Install oil screen and tighten bolts to 43-51 INCH lbs. (5-6 N.m). Set magnet on oil pan so that it rests directly below oil screen. Install oil pan and tighten bolts to 35-41 INCH lbs. (4-5 N.m). Install filler tube clip bolt and tighten to 29 ft. lbs. (39 N.m).

3) Install drain plug using a new gasket and tighten to 11-14 ft. lbs. (15-19 N.m). Pour about 2.1 qts. (2.0L) of ATF. Check fluid level. Add ATF as necessary to bring fluid to proper level.

ADJUSTMENTS

PARK LOCK CABLE

I-Mark FWD

Place ignition key in "LOCK" position and selector lever in "P" position. Pull park cable forward at shifter bracket. Tighten forward nut until it makes contact with bracket. Tighten rear nut until it makes contact with bracket.

THROTTLE VALVE CABLE

Gasoline Engines (Except FWD)

1) Loosen throttle valve cable adjusting nuts. Ensure carburetor throttle adjusting screw is in contact with idle stop.

2) Adjust setting of outer cable. Ensure distance between upper face of rubber boot on outer cable and inner cable stopper is .032-.059" (0.8-1.5 mm). *See Fig. 1.*

Fig. 1: Gasoline Throttle Valve Cable Adjustment

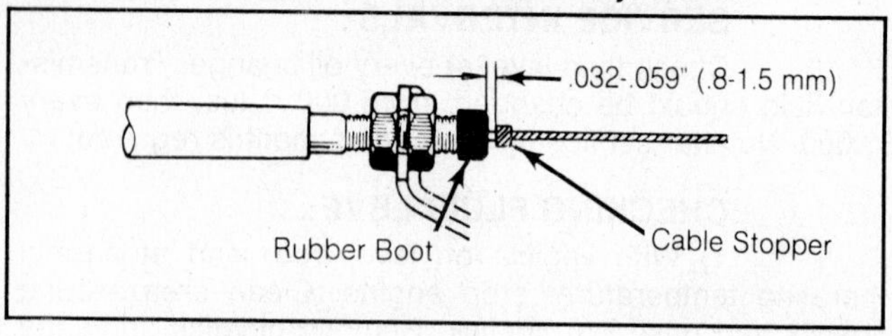

3) Tighten adjusting nuts. Ensure stroke of inner cable from normal idling position to wide open throttle is 1.30-1.36" (32.0-34.5 mm).

Diesel Engines (Except FWD)

1) Loosen throttle valve cable adjusting nuts. With accelerator pedal fully depressed, ensure injection pump lever is in contact with maximum speed adjust screw.

2) Hold lever in this position. Adjust setting of outer cable so distance between end of rubber boot on outer cable and inner cable stopper is 0-.04" (0-1 mm). *See Fig. 2.*

Fig. 2: Diesel Throttle Valve Cable Adjustment

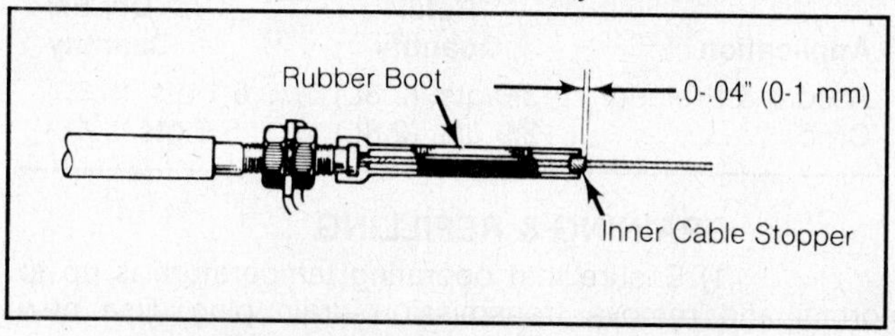

3) Tighten adjusting nuts. Check that stroke of inner cable from normal idling position to wide open throttle is 1.30-1.36" (32.0-34.5 mm).

SHIFT LINKAGE

1) Loosen shift control rod adjusting nuts on transmission. Turn manual shaft fully clockwise as viewed from right side (left side on P'UP) of transmission. Turn back to 3rd stop and set shaft in "N" position.

2) On all models, place transmission in "N", ensure manual shift lever is in vertical position. Hold manual shaft in this position and place shift lever in "N".

3) To remove play, tighten adjusting nuts with control shaft lever pushed rearward together with shift control lever. Road test vehicle. Ensure shift lever moves properly and transmission operates smoothly.

NEUTRAL SAFETY SWITCH

Loosen switch retaining screws (near base of selector lever). Place selector lever in "N". Bring center of switch moving piece into alignment with line scribed on steel case of switch. Tighten retaining screws. Ensure vehicle will only start in "P" or "N" position.

JAGUAR

IDENTIFICATION

TRANSMISSION CODES

Application	Code
XJ6	Borg-Warner 66
XJS	GM THM 400

LUBRICATION

SERVICE INTERVALS

Check fluid level at first 1,000 miles and then every 7,500 miles. Change fluid and filter at 30,000 mile intervals.

CHECKING FLUID LEVEL

1) Park vehicle on level ground. Apply hand brake and run engine at 750 RPM for several minutes. Place selector lever in all ranges and return to "P" position.

2) With engine idling, withdraw and wipe off dipstick. Replace dipstick in filler tube, withdraw it and check fluid level. If necessary, add fluid to reach "MAX" level on "COLD" side of dipstick. After adding fluid, repeat checking procedure to ensure overfilling has not occurred.

RECOMMENDED FLUID

XJ6

Type G automatic transmission fluid.

XJS

Dexron II automatic transmission fluid.

FLUID CAPACITY

TRANSMISSION REFILL CAPACITIES

Application	[1] Quantity
Borg-Warner 66	8.4 qts. (8.0L)
GM THM 400	19.2 pts. (9.1L)

[1] – Dry fill.

DRAINING & REFILLING

Borg-Warner 66

1) Disconnect dipstick/filler tube at oil pan and drain oil. Remove oil pan bolts and pan. Remove screws securing suction tube to valve body. Lower suction tube, discard gasket and remove filter.

2) Install oil filter and suction tube, using a new gasket. Clean and install oil pan. Connect dipstick/filler tube, add transmission fluid and check fluid level.

GM THM 400

1) Remove vacuum capsule clamp and bolt. Disconnect capsule and drain oil. Remove oil pan bolts, carefully lower pan and drain remaining oil. Remove oil filter bolt and filter.

2) Install oil filter. Clean and install oil pan, using a new gasket. Connect capsule, install clamp and tighten using bolt. Add transmission fluid and check fluid level.

ADJUSTMENTS

FRONT BAND

Borg-Warner 66

Remove nut securing selector lever to selector shaft and remove lever. Loosen lock nut retaining band adjustment screw and loosen screw 2 or 3 turns. Tighten screw to 60 INCH lbs. (7 N.m). Back off screw 3/4 of a turn. Tighten lock nut while holding screw in place.

REAR BAND

Borg-Warner 66

Loosen lock nut securing band adjustment screw and loosen screw 2 or 3 turns. Tighten screw to 60 INCH lbs. (7 N.m). Back off 3/4 of a turn. Tighten lock nut while holding screw in place.

DOWNSHIFT CABLE

Borg-Warner 66

1) Engine must be correctly tuned before attempting downshift cable adjustment. Using Allen wrench, remove plug from transmission and connect pressure gauge to transmission with adapter.

2) Feed gauge hose through passenger window, keeping hose clear of exhaust pipe. Block wheels and apply hand and foot brakes. Run engine to normal operating temperature.

3) With transmission selector in "D" position, pressure gauge should read 60-75 psi (4.2-5.3 kg/cm²) at idle speed. Increase engine speed to 1200 RPM. Gauge should now read 75-115 psi (5.3-8.1 kg/cm²).

4) If correct pressures are not obtained, turn engine off and place transmission in "N". Loosen lock nut on downshift cable, and turn adjustment nut on outer cable to alter pressure. *See Fig. 1.*

5) Increasing length of cable increases pressure. Decreasing length decreases pressure. When pressures are correct, tighten cable lock nut, install plug and road test vehicle.

Fig. 1: Downshift Cable Adjustment

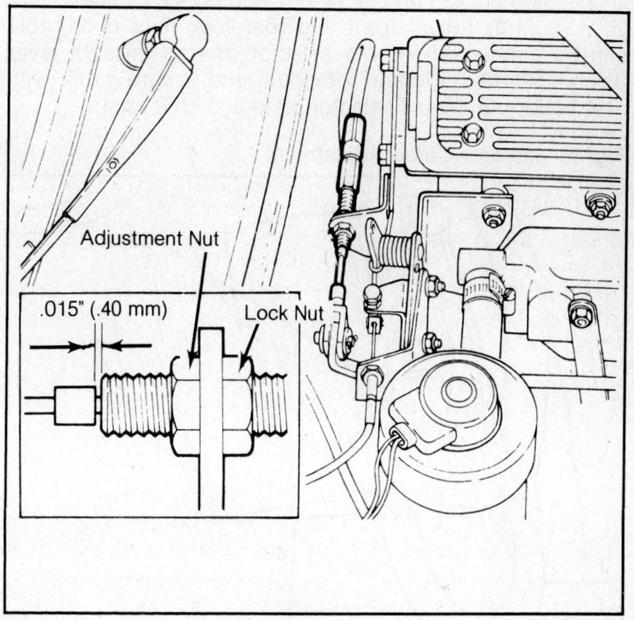

Ferrule crimped on inner cable should be 0.015" (0.4 mm) from threaded portion of outer cable.

JAGUAR (Cont.)

KICKDOWN SWITCH

GM THM 400

1) With ignition on, check that power is available at input terminal (Green wire). With one lead of test lamp grounded, connect other lead to output terminal (Green/White wire).

2) Fully depress accelerator pedal, test lamp should light. If test lamp fails to light, release accelerator pedal and gently depress switch arm. If test lamp still does not light, replace kickdown switch.

3) If test lamp lights when switch arm is depressed, loosen switch screws and move switch toward cable until at full throttle opening test lamp lights. Tighten switch screws and recheck.

Fig. 2: Kickdown Switch Adjustment

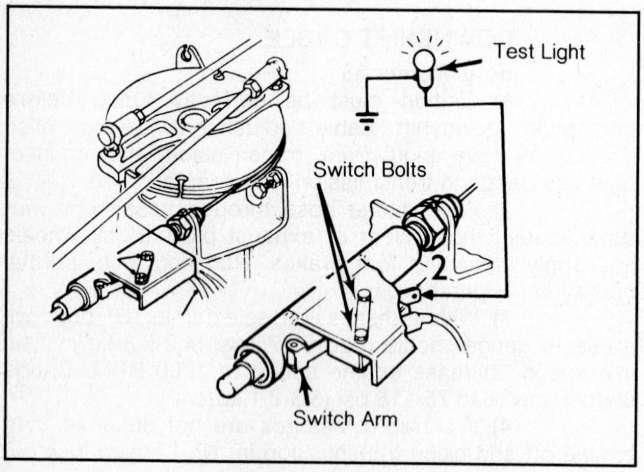

SELECTOR CABLE

1) Remove console and place selector lever in "1" position on XJ6 models, and in "N" position on XJS models. Unscrew shift knob and remove indicator plate.

2) Remove cotter pin and washer retaining cable to bracket on lever. Ensure transmission lever is in "1" position on XJ6 and in "N" position on XJS models.

3) Adjust front and rear lock nuts until cable can be connected without selector or transmission lever being disturbed. Tighten lock nuts and secure cable with new cotter pin. Install selector plate and shift knob.

Fig. 3: Selector Cable Adjustment

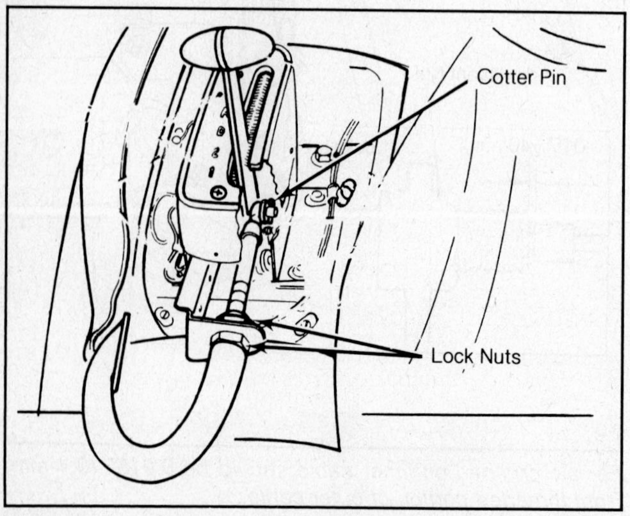

NEUTRAL SAFETY SWITCH

1) Remove selector indicator and position electric window switch panel away from console. Move control panel to gain access to cigar lighter wiring and door lock switch wiring. Note position of wires and disconnect.

2) Remove control panel. Disconnect feed wire to switch and connect self-powered test light to terminal. Place selector lever in "N" position and loosen lock nuts which secure the switch. Adjust switch until test lamp lights.

3) Tighten switch lock nuts and check that light remains on with lever in "P", and goes off with lever in any driving position. Remove test lamp, reconnect feed wire, and install all removed parts.

Fig. 4: Neutral Safety Switch Adjustment

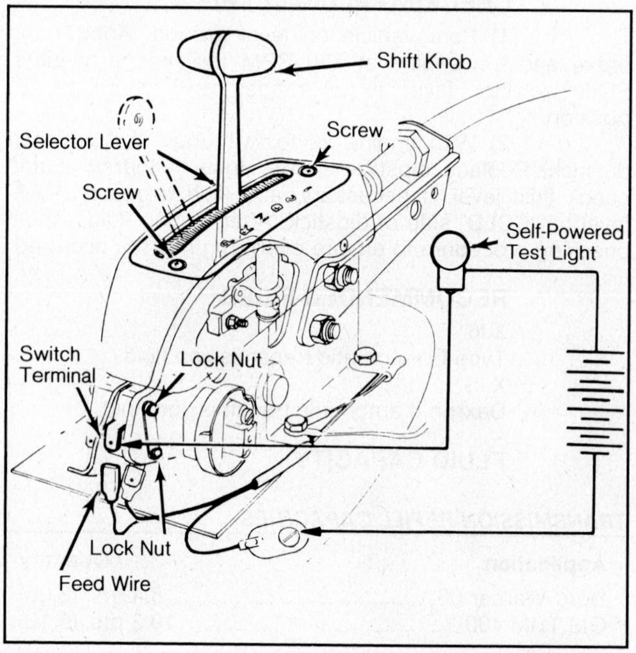

MAZDA

IDENTIFICATION

TRANSMISSION CODES

Application	Codes
GLC & 626	F3A
RX7	L4N71B

LUBRICATION

SERVICE INTERVALS

Check fluid level every 7,500 miles or every 8 months, whichever occurs first.

CHECKING FLUID LEVEL

Park vehicle on level ground. Apply parking brake and run engine at idle for 2 minutes. Briefly place selector lever in all gears and return to "P". Clean dipstick and insert in tube. Remove dipstick. Level should be between "L" and "F" marks. If necessary, add fluid.

RECOMMENDED FLUID

Type F automatic transmission fluid.

FLUID CAPACITY

TRANSMISSION REFILL CAPACITIES

Application	Quantity
RX7	6.6 qts. (6.2L)
GLC & 626	6.0 qts. (5.7L)

DRAINING & REFILLING

RX7

Remove oil pan bolts and drain fluid. Remove oil pan and discard gasket. Clean oil pan and install, using a new gasket. Tighten oil pan bolts to 43-72 INCH lbs. (5-8 N.m). Add fluid and check fluid level. Do not overfill.

GLC & 626

Remove drain plug on bottom of differential and drain fluid. If transaxle is to be completely drained, remove oil pan bolts and drain remaining fluid. Remove oil pan and discard gasket. Clean oil pan and install, using a new gasket. Tighten oil pan bolts to 43-72 INCH lbs. (5-8 N.m). Add fluid and check fluid level. Do not overfill.

ADJUSTMENTS

BRAKE BAND

GLC & 626

NOTE: **Make this adjustment with oil pump installed. Apply sealant to anchor bolt threads.**

Loosen lock nut on brake band anchor bolt. Tighten brake band anchor bolt to 108-132 INCH lbs. (12-15 N.m), then back off bolt 2 turns. Hold brake band anchor bolt and tighten lock nut to 41-59 ft. lbs. (56-80 N.m).

Fig. 1: GLC & 626 Brake Band Adjustment

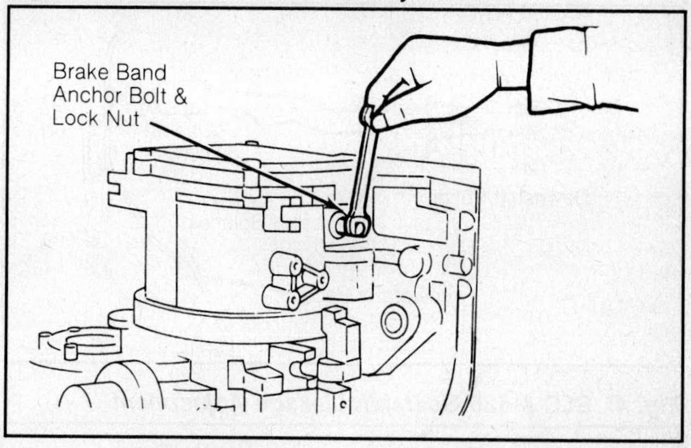

RX7

1) Remove overdrive brake band servo cover to adjust overdrive brake band. Remove oil pan to adjust 2nd gear brake band. Loosen overdrive brake band and 2nd gear brake band servo piston stem lock nuts.

2) Tighten overdrive brake band servo piston stem to 61-86 INCH lbs. (7-10 N.m). Back off piston stem 2 turns. Hold piston stem in this position and tighten lock nut to 11-29 ft. lbs. (15-39 N.m).

3) Tighten 2nd gear brake band servo piston stem to 108-132 INCH lbs. (12-15 N.m). Back off piston stem 3 turns. Hold piston stem in this position and tighten lock nut to 11-29 ft. lbs. (15-39 N.m).

Fig. 2: RX7 Brake Band Adjustment

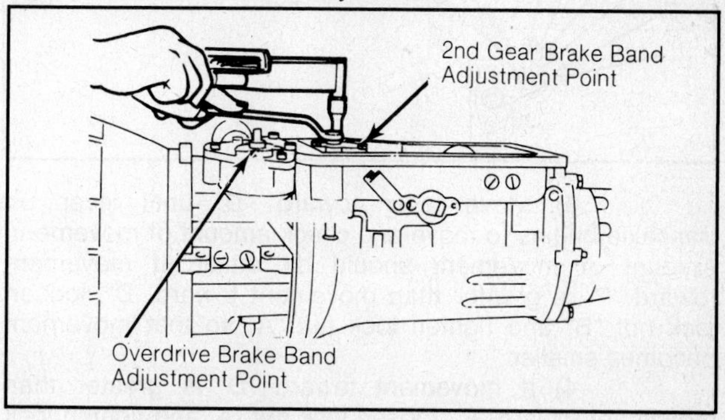

KICKDOWN SWITCH & DOWNSHIFT SOLENOID

1) Depress accelerator pedal to limit. Listen for a click from solenoid. Switch must operate at or after 7/8 of pedal travel.

2) If not, loosen switch retaining nut. Adjust switch to engage when pedal is 7/8 of its full travel. Tighten retaining nut and check solenoid.

GEARSHIFT LINKAGE

GLC & 626

1) Loosen lock nuts "A" and "B" at "T" joint and place selector lever in "N". Move transaxle lever to neutral, fourth detent position away from transaxle.

2) Turn lock nut "A" until it comes in contact with "T" joint. Tighten lock nut "B". Move selector lever toward "P" until lever on transaxle begins to move and check amount of movement.

MAZDA (Cont.)

Fig. 3: Kickdown Switch & Downshift Solenoid

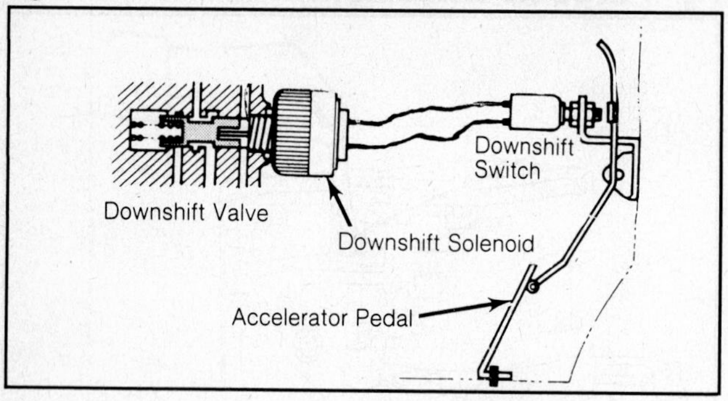

Fig. 4: GLC & 626 Gearshift Linkage Adjustment

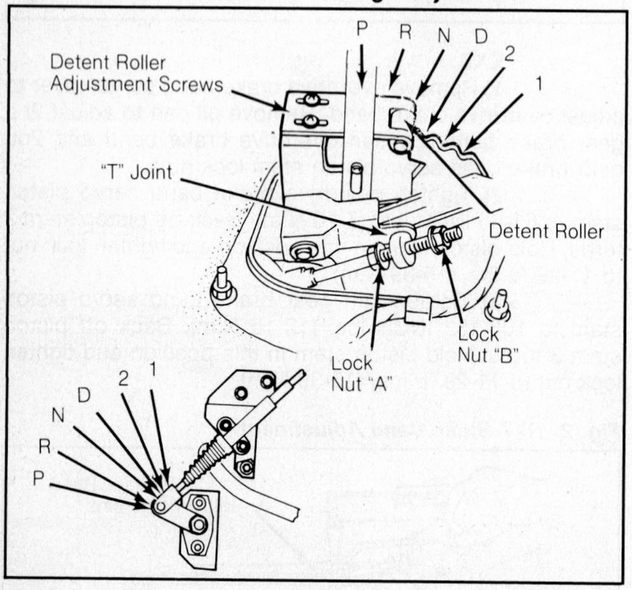

3) Move lever toward "D" until lever on transaxle begins to move and check amount of movement. Amount of movement should be equal. If movement toward "P" is greater than movement toward "D", loosen lock nut "B" and tighten lock nut "A" so that movement becomes smaller.

4) If movement toward "D" is greater than movement toward "P", loosen lock nut "A" and tighten lock nut "B" so that movement becomes smaller. Shift selector lever from "P" to "1". Ensure that a "click" can be felt in each position and gear corresponds to position plate.

5) Ensure that lever can be shifted between "D" and "N" without depressing push button. If lever can be shifted from "D" to "R" without depressing push button, or if push button is loose, adjust selector lever handle.

RX7

1) Remove boot plate. Place selector lever in "P". Loosen selector lever plate adjustment bolt. Raise vehicle and support with safety stands. Move transmission selector rod to "P" position (first detent from rear of transmission).

2) Tighten selector lever plate adjustment bolt to 23-34 ft. lbs. (32-47 N.m). Lower vehicle. Place selector lever in each position to ensure that selector lever functions properly.

SELECTOR LEVER HANDLE

NOTE: **No adjustment is necessary for RX7 models.**

GLC & 626

1) Place selector lever in "P". Loosen lock nut below selector lever handle and turn nut and handle until they bottom. Unscrew selector lever handle 1 full turn until button is on driver's side. Tighten lock nut to 11-15 ft. lbs. (15-20 N.m).

2) Ensure that selector lever functions properly. If button does not operate smoothly, set lever in "P" and loosen detent roller adjustment screws and adjust by moving detent roller.

NEUTRAL SAFETY SWITCH

RX7

1) Place transmission lever in neutral. Place selector lever in "N". Loosen neutral safety switch attaching bolts and remove screw from alignment pin hole from bottom of switch. Rotate switch and insert a .08" (2.0 mm) alignment pin through alignment holes.

2) Tighten attaching bolts and remove alignment pin. Install alignment pin hole screw and check operation of switch. Vehicle should start in "P" and "N" positions only.

GLC & 626

NOTE: **The following instructions are for checking neutral safety switch. No adjustments are possible.**

1) Ensure vehicle starts in "P" and "N" only. Ensure back-up lights illuminate with selec-tor lever in "R". If switch is faulty, disconnect it and check continuity between each terminal.

2) With selector lever in "P" or "N", continuity should exist between terminals "A" and "B". With lever in "R", continuity should exist between terminals "C" and "D".

Fig. 5: Neutral Safety Switch Continuity Check

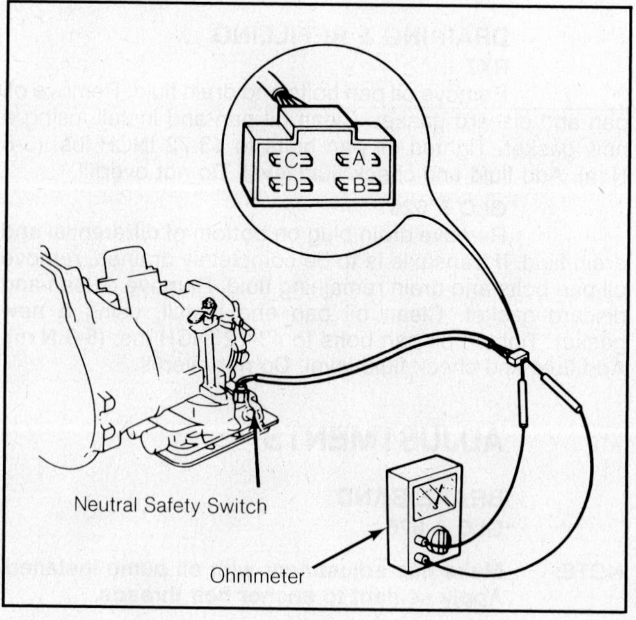

MERCEDES-BENZ

IDENTIFICATION

TRANSMISSION CODES

Application	Code (Model)
190D	722.403 (W4A020)
190E	722.400 (W4A020)
300 Series (Calif.)	722.416 (W4A020)
300 Series (Federal) [1]	722.315 (W4A040)
380SE	722.310 (W4A040)
380SL	722.312 (W4A040)
500 Series	722.311 (W4A040)

[1] - The 300SD uses automatic transmission 722.303 (W4A040).

LUBRICATION

SERVICE INTERVALS

Check fluid level at first 800-1000 miles and every 15,000 miles thereafter. Change fluid and filter every 30,000 miles. Under severe service conditions, change fluid every 15,000 miles.

CHECKING FLUID LEVEL

With transmission fluid at normal operating temperature 176°F (80°C), park vehicle on level surface. Place selector lever in "P" position and set parking brake. Allow engine to idle for 2 minutes. Measure fluid level with dipstick completely inserted and locking lever released.

RECOMMENDED FLUID

Dexron II automatic transmission fluid.

FLUID CAPACITY

TRANSMISSION REFILL CAPACITIES

Application	Refill	Dry Fill
190 Series	5.8 qts. (5.5L)	7.0 qts. (6.6L)
300 Series	6.6 qts. (6.2L)	7.7 qts. (7.3L)
380 & 500 Series	8.1 qts. (7.7L)	9.1 qts. (8.6L)

DRAINING & REFILLING

1) Disconnect fill tube from oil pan and drain fluid. Rotate engine until torque converter drain plug is at bottom of torque converter housing. Remove plug and drain fluid. Install plug, using a new sealing ring. Remove oil pan and filter.

2) Install filter and oil pan, using a new gasket. Attach fill tube, using new sealing rings on hollow screw. Add 4.2 qts (4.0L) of automatic transmission fluid.

3) Apply parking brake and start engine. Place selector lever in "P" position. Run engine at idle and gradually add fluid. Mometarily place selector lever in each gear, and then return to "P" position. Check fluid level and adjust if necessary. Do not overfill.

ADJUSTMENTS

SHIFT LINKAGE

Disconnect control rod from selector lever. Place transmission lever in "N" (vertical) position. Loosen lock nut at and of control rod and adjust rod length so that a .04" (1 mm) clearance exists between selector lever and "N" stop on gate plate. Connect control rod, secure and tighten lock nut.

Fig. 1: Shift Linkage Adjustment

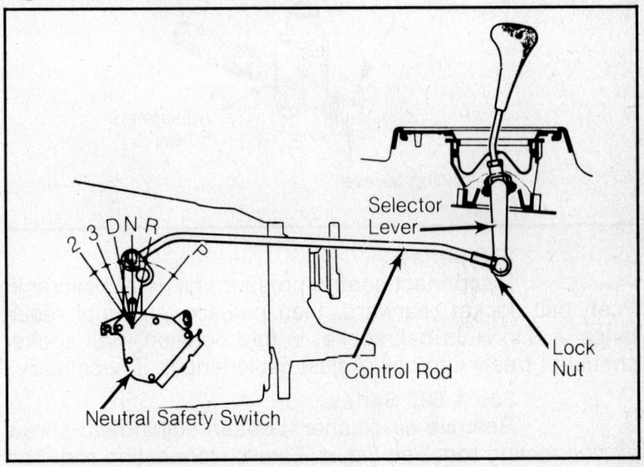

Series 190 linkage shown, others are similar.

CONTROL PRESSURE CABLE

190D

Disconnect control cable at bellcrank. Extend telescoping rod to maximum length. *See Fig. 2.* Pull control cable forward until a slight resistance is felt. Hold ball socket in this position. Ball socket should fit freely into ball. Adjust rod length, if necessary.

Fig. 2: 190D Control Pressure Cable Adjustment

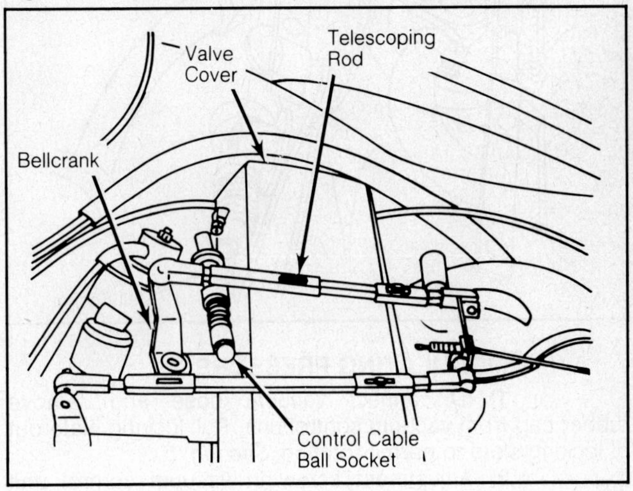

190E

Turn adjustment screw inward until compression nipple on spacing sleeve has a .04" (1 mm) free play. Turn adjustment screw until tip of pointer rests directly above groove of adjustment screw. *See Fig. 3.*

MERCEDES-BENZ (Cont.)

Fig. 3: 190E Control Pressure Cable Adjustment

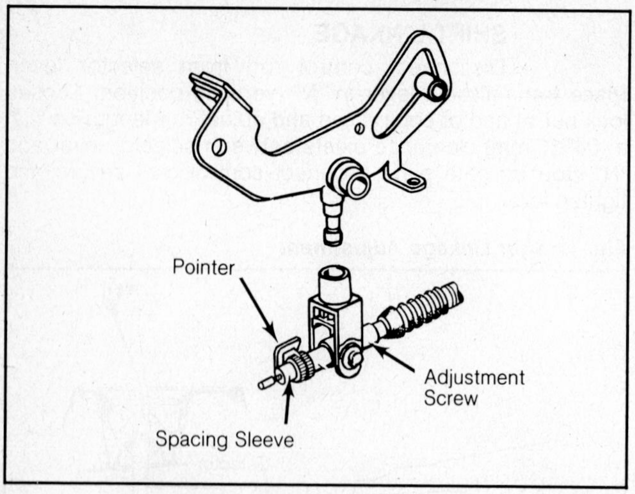

300 Series

Disconnect control pressure cable at bellcrank. Push ball socket rearward, then pull forward until resistance is felt. Hold ball socket in this position. Ball socket should fit freely into ball. Adjust cable lenght, if necessary.

380 & 500 Series

Remove air cleaner. Loosen adjustment screw on connecting rod. *See Fig. 4*. Extend connecting rod then retract, until resistance is felt. Tighten adjustment screw and install air cleaner.

Fig. 4: 380 & 500 Series Control Pressure Cable Adjustment

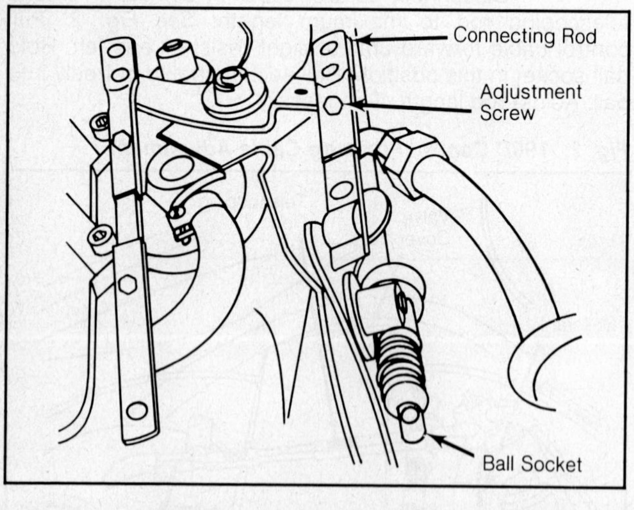

MODULATING PRESSURE

1) Disconnect vacuum hose and remove rubber cap from vacuum control unit. Pull locking plate out of locking slots to permit rotation. *See Fig. 5*.

2) Adjustment screw in vacuum control unit can now be adjusted by means of locking plate. One turn of adjusting screw results in pressure change of 6 psi (.4 kg/cm²).

3) After turning adjustment screw, push locking plate back into locking slots. Put rubber cap back on vacuum control unit. Connect vacuum hose and check modulating pressure again. Install screw on vacuum line holder (if equipped).

Fig. 5: Modulating Pressure Adjustment

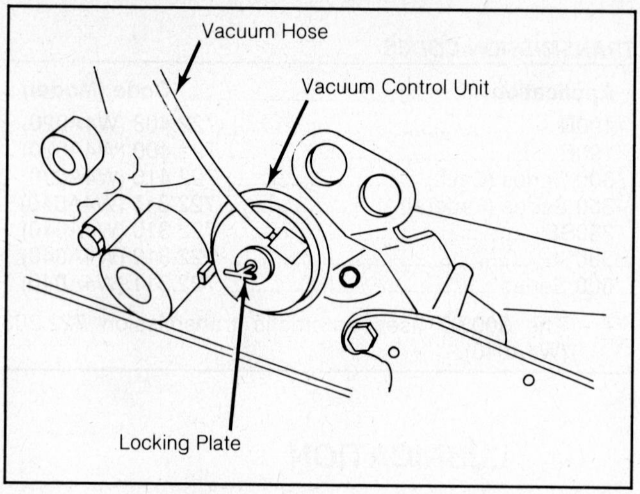

VACUUM CONTROL VALVE

190 Series

1) On 190D, remove air cleaner and air distributor housing. On all models, loosen vacuum control valve Allen head screws. Turn vacuum control valve clockwise as far as possible and hold in this position. *See Fig. 6*.

2) Apply full throttle until throttle lever of injection pump rests against full throttle stop, this will turn vacuum control valve back (counterclockwise).

Fig. 6: Series 190 Vacuum Control Valve Adjustment

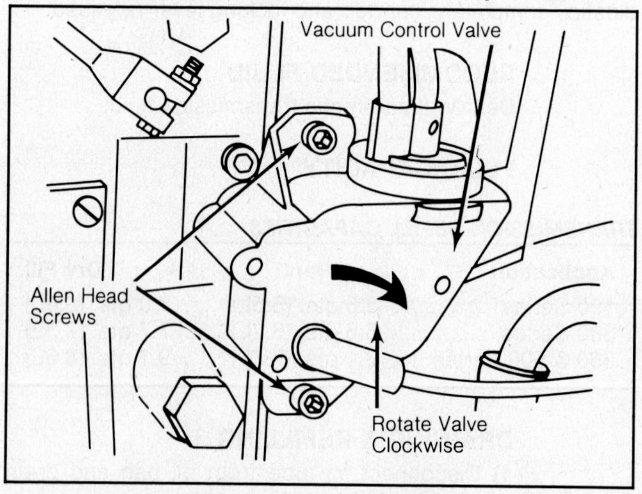

NEUTRAL SAFETY SWITCH

Loosen neutral safety switch screws and insert a 5/32" (4 mm) drill through adjustment hole and into hosuing. Tighten screws and remove drill. Ensure that vehicle starts in "P" and "N" positions only.

MITSUBISHI

IDENTIFICATION

TRANSMISSION CODES

Application	Codes
Cordia & Tredia	KM172
Galant	KM175
Mirage	KM171
Montero 4WD	[1] KM146
Pickup 2WD	MA904A
Starion	MR600

[1] - Includes MA904A transmission and transfer case.

LUBRICATION

SERVICE INTERVAL

Check oil level every 15,000 miles. Change oil and filter every 30,000 miles or if under severe usage, change every 15,000 miles.

CHECKING FLUID LEVEL

1) Position vehicle on a level surface and set parking brake. Run engine at idle. Move selector lever through all positions, ending in "N".

2) With engine at normal operating temperature, remove dipstick and wipe with a clean cloth, and check oil level. Oil level must be between "FULL" and "ADD" mark of dipstick.

CAUTION: If severe darkening of the fluid and a strong odor is noted, fluid and filter should be changed and bands adjusted.

RECOMMENDED FLUID

All transmissions use Dexron or Dexron II automatic transmission fluid. Transfer Case uses API GL-4 SAE 90.

FLUID CAPACITY

TRANSMISSION REFILL CAPACITIES

Application	Quantity
Mitsubishi	
KM171, KM172 & KM175	6.1 qts. (5.8L)
MR600	7.4 qts. (7.0L)
Torqueflite	
KM146 & MA904A	7.2 qts. (6.8L)
Transfer Case	2.3 qts. (2.2L)

DRAINING & REFILLING

KM146, MR600 & MA904A

1) Carefully remove oil pan and drain fluid. Install new filter on bottom of valve body. Clean oil pan, replace gasket and install oil pan. Pour 4 qts. (3.8L) of specified fluid through filler tube. Idle engine for 2 minutes.

2) Shift transmission into each position, ending in "N" position. Check fluid level with engine running at idle and add sufficient fluid to bring level to "ADD 1 PINT" mark. Recheck fluid level after transmission is at normal operating temperature. See CHECKING FLUID LEVEL.

KM171, KM172 & KM175

1) Remove drain plug from differential and drain fluid. Carefully remove oil pan bolts and lower oil pan. Install new filter on bottom of valve body. Replace pan gasket and install pan.

2) Tighten differential plug to 22-25 ft. lbs. (30-34 N.m). Ensure that dipstick hole area is clean and pour in approximately 4.2 qts. (4.0L) of "DEXRON II" fluid.

3) Run engine for 2 minutes at idle. Shift transmission to each position, ending in "N" position. After reaching normal operating temperature, fluid should be between upper and lower marks of "HOT" range.

ADJUSTMENTS

BRAKE BAND

JM600

Remove oil pan. Loosen lock nut. Tighten adjustment screw to 72 INCH lbs. (8.5 N.m). Back off adjustment screw 2 turns. Hold adjusting screw and tighten lock nut to 20 ft. lbs. (24 N.m). *See Fig. 1.*

Fig. 1: Adjusting JM600 Brake Band

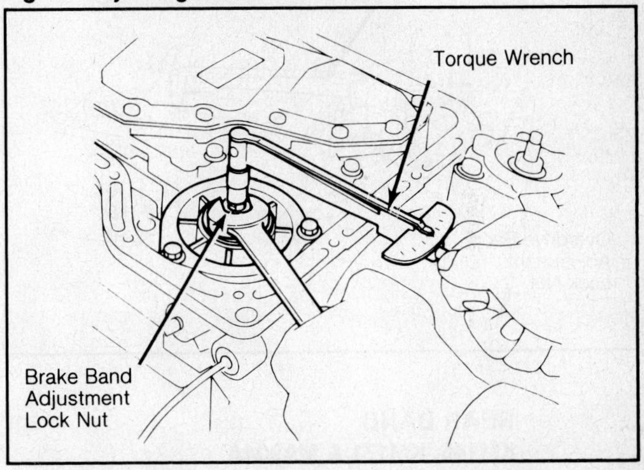

FRONT (KICKDOWN) BAND

KM146, KM171 & MA904A

1) Front (kickdown) band adjuster screw is located on left side of transmission case. To adjust band, loosen and back off lock nut about 5 turns.

2) Using wrench (C-3380-A) with adapter (C-3705), tighten band adjuster screw to 52 INCH lbs. (5.9 N.m). *See Fig. 2.*

3) If adapter (C-3705) is not used, tighten adjuster screw to 51 INCH lbs. (5.8 N.m). Back off adjusting screw 3 1/2 turns, hold adjuster screw and tighten lock nut to 37 ft. lbs. (50 N.m).

OVERDRIVE BAND

JM600

Loosen lock nut. Tighten adjustment screw to 72 INCH lbs. (8.5 N.m). Back off adjustment screw 2 turns. Hold adjusting screw and tighten lock nut to 20 ft. lbs. (24 N.m). *See Fig. 3.*

MITSUBISHI (Cont.)

Fig. 2: KM146, KM171 & MA904A
Front (Kickdown) Band Adjusting Screw Location

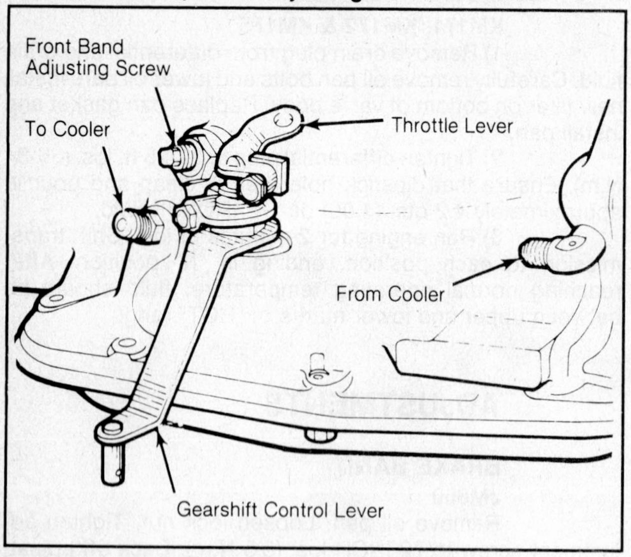

Fig. 3: Adjusting JM600 Overdrive Band

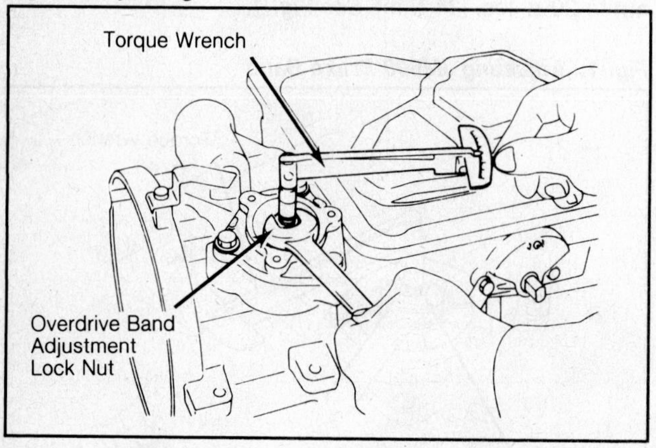

REAR BAND

KM146, KM171 & MA904A

1) Remove oil pan. Loosen lock nut and adjusting screw at servo end of lever and tighten screw to 43 INCH lbs. (4.9 N.m) of torque.

2) Back off screw 7 turns. Hold adjusting screw and tighten lock nut to 29 ft. lbs. (40 N.m). *See Fig. 4.* Reinstall oil pan.

Fig. 4: KM146, KM171 & MA904A
Rear Band Adjusting Screw Location

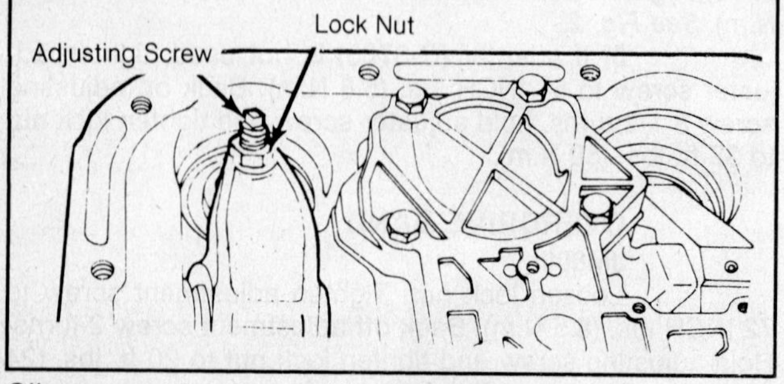

Oil pan must be removed for adjustment.

TRANSMISSION THROTTLE CONTROL

KM146 & MA904A

1) With engine at normal operating temperature and idle speed set correctly, loosen bolt retaining throttle rod "C" to "B". Lightly push throttle rod "A" toward idle stop and set rods to "IDLE" position.

2) Tighten bolt retaining rod "B" to "C". Open throttle to "WIDE OPEN" position. Ensure transmission lever moves from "IDLE" to "WIDE OPEN" position (total movement 47.5° to 54°). Some play should still exist in throttle lever stroke at wide open throttle.

Fig. 5: KM146 & MA904A Throttle Rod Adjustment

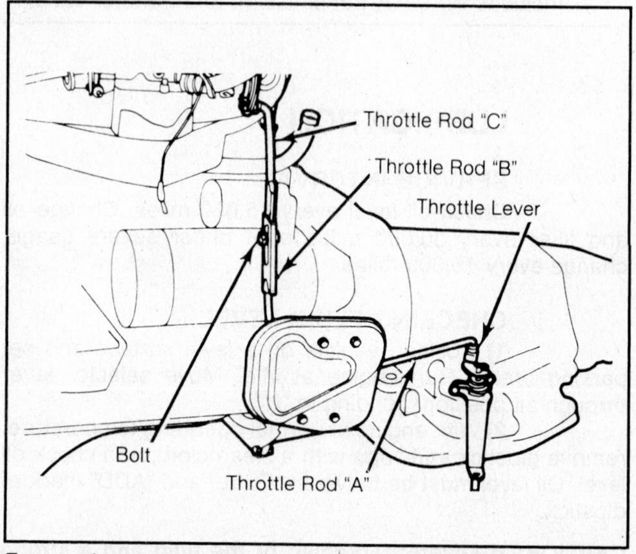

Ensure that transmission lever moves from "IDLE" to "WIDE OPEN" position.

KM171 & KM172

1) Ensure that carburetor throttle lever is at "CURB IDLE" position, engine is at operating temperature, and fast idle condition has been reset. Raise cover "B" and loosen cable bracket mounting bolt.

2) Move lower cable bracket until distance between nipple and top cover "A" of throttle cable is adjusted to .02-.06" (.5-1.5 mm). *See Fig. 6.* Tighten lower cable bracket mounting bolt.

3) With throttle lever in "WIDE OPEN" position, pull cable upward to ensure freedom of cable movement.

SHIFT LINKAGE

KM146, KM171, KM175, MR600 & MA904A

1) Remove shift handle by loosening set screw and pulling off handle. Place selector lever in "N". Turn rod adjusting cam in top of lever until surface "A" of cam is flush with push button. *See Fig. 7.*

2) Loosen lock nut at connection of rod and arm or connecting lever and crossshaft or end of shift cable and bracket at transmission. Place transmission lever arm in "N". Place selector lever in "N" and tighten lock nut to adjust control rod length or secure shift cable to bracket.

MITSUBISHI (Cont.)

Fig. 6: KM172 Throttle Cable Adjustment

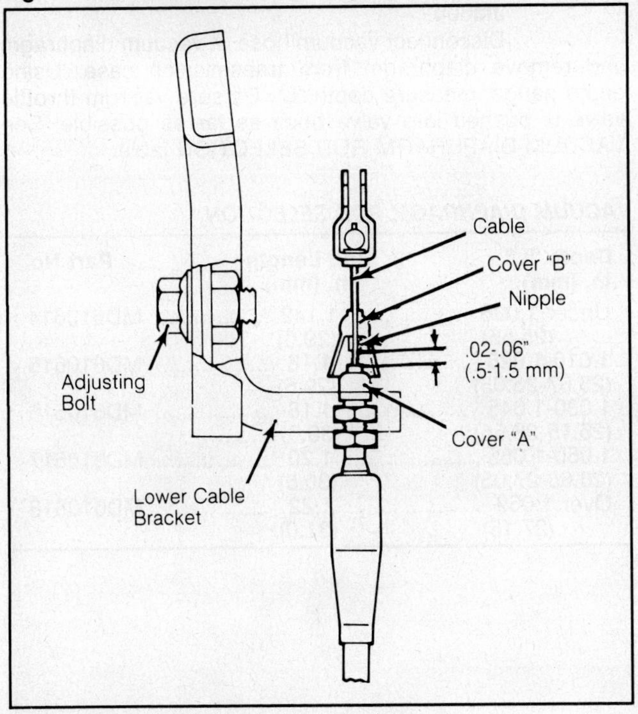

Pull back cover "B" to loosen bracket nut.

Fig. 7: Adjusting Selector Rod Cam On KM146 & MA904A

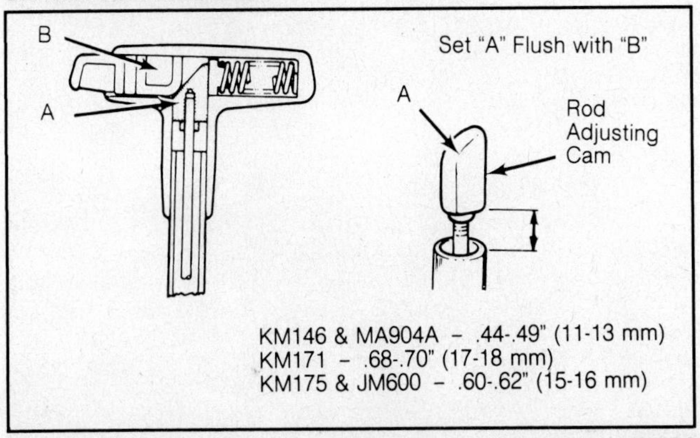

Rod cam surface "A" and push button must be flush. MR600 is similar.

KM172

1) Place selector in "N" position. Loosen set screw retaining handle to lever and remove handle. Turn rod adjusting cam in top of lever until surface "A" is flush with surface "B". *See Fig. 8.*

2) When knob button is on driver's side, tighten set screw. With selector lever and neutral safety switch in "N" position, turn adjusting nuts at cable end until slack is removed from control cable.

NOTE: **After adjustment, confirm that every selector position of position indicator is set properly.**

NEUTRAL SAFETY SWITCH

KM146 & MA904A

NOTE: **Safety switch is located under shift lever console and is operated by shift lever. This switch also operates back-up lights and seat belt warning system.**

Fig. 8: Adjusting KM172 Selector Lever

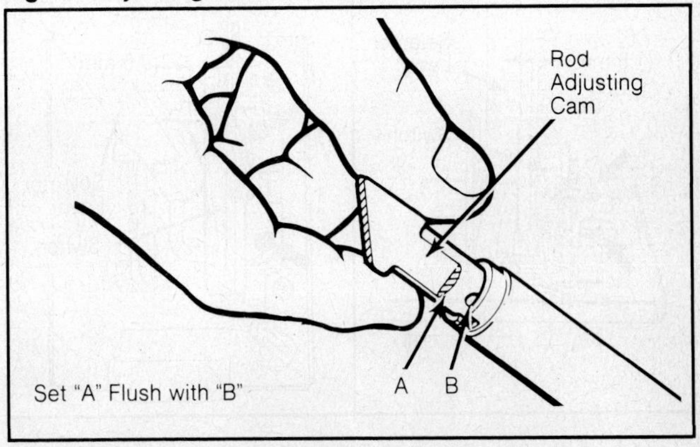

Wedge must face driver's side after adjustment. Adjust surface "A" flush with surface "B".

1) To adjust switch, remove console, loosen switch attaching screws, and place selector lever in "N" position. Slide switch back and forth to measure contact range of "N" position. *See Fig. 9.*

Fig. 9: Adjusting Neutral Safety Switch Movement On KM146 & MA904A

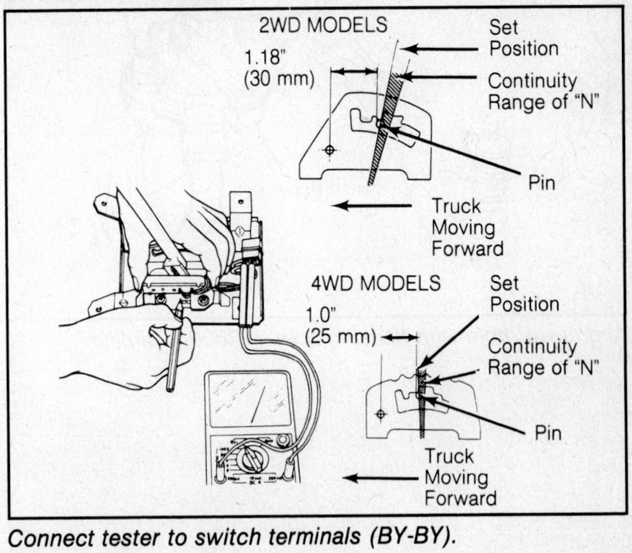

Connect tester to switch terminals (BY-BY).

2) Install switch and adjust so there is .06" (1.5 mm) for 2WD Pickup and .1" (2.5 mm) for 4WD Montero, side clearance between selector lever and switch. *See Fig. 10.* Set selector lever in "P", "R", and "N" positions and check continuity of terminals. After confirming continuity, tighten switch attaching screws and reinstall console.

NOTE: **If correct continuity cannot be achieved, reposition safety switch.**

KM171, KM172, KM175 & MR600

Place transmission control lever in "N" position and loosen switch retaining bolts. Turn inhibitor switch body so that aligning hole end of lever overlaps switch body flange (insert alignment pin on JM600) and tighten bolts. *See Fig. 11.*

MITSUBISHI (Cont.)

Fig. 10: Adjusting Neutral Safety Switch On KM146 & MA904A

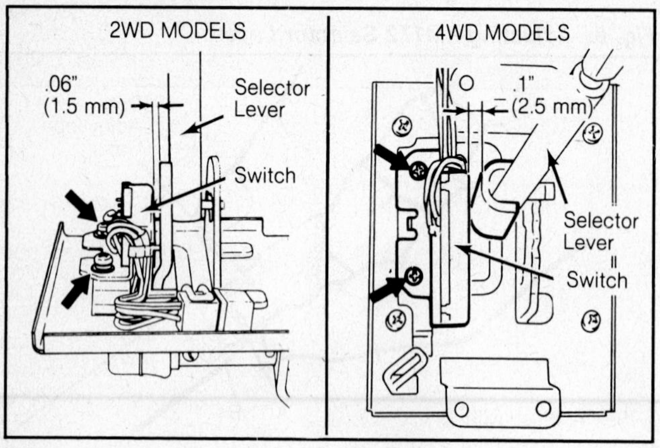

Fig. 11: Adjusting Neutral Safety Switch On KM171, KM172 & KM175 Transaxle

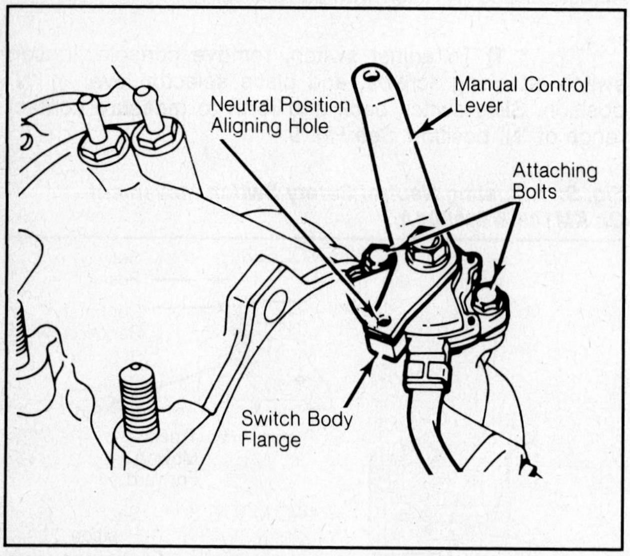

Align lever hole with housing hole. MR600 is similar.

VACUUM DIAPHRAGM ROD

JM600

Disconnect vacuum hose at vacuum diaphragm and remove diaphragm from transmission case. Using depth gauge, measure depth "L". Be sure vacuum throttle valve is pushed into valve body as far as possible. See VACUUM DIAPHRAGM ROD SELECTION table.

VACUUM DIAPHRAGM ROD SELECTION

Depth "L" in. (mm)	Rod Length in. (mm)	Part No.
Under 1.006 (25.55)	1.142 (29.0)	MD610614
1.010-1.025 (25.67-26.05)	1.16 (29.5)	MD610615
1.030-1.045 (26.15-26.55)	1.18 (30.0)	MD610616
1.050-1.065 (26.65-27.05)	1.20 (30.5)	MD610617
Over 1.069 (27.15)	1.22 (31.0)	MD610618

NISSAN

IDENTIFICATION

TRANSMISSION CODES

Application	Code
FWD	
Maxima	RL4F02A
Pulsar NX, Sentra & Stanza	RL3F01A
RWD	
Pickup	L3N71B
200SX & 200SX Turbo	L4N71B
300ZX	E4N71B

LUBRICATION

SERVICE INTERVAL

Inspect fluid level every 15,000 miles or 12 months. If under severe usage, change every 30,000 miles or 24 months.

CHECKING FLUID LEVEL

Transaxle & Transmission

1) Check fluid with transmission at operating temperatures. Place vehicle on level ground and engine at idle. Shift through all gears and return to "P".

2) Remove dipstick and clean. Insert and withdraw. Level should be between "H" and "L" marks. If not, add as necessary.

NOTE: **Normal fluid should be clear with a Pink color and should not have a strong odor.**

Transfer Case

Oil level should be at bottom of fill hole.

RECOMMENDED FLUID

All transmissions use Dexron or Dexron II Automatic Transmission Fluid (ATF). All transfer cases use SAE 80W/90 (API GL-4).

FLUID CAPACITY

TRANSMISSION REFILL CAPACITIES

Application	Quantity
FWD	
RL3F01A	6.5 qts. (6.0L)
RL4F02A	7.5 qts. (7.0L)
RWD	
E4N71B	7.5 qts. (7.0L)
L3N71B	6.5 qts. (6.0L)
L4N71B	7.5 qts. (7.0L)
Transfer Case	1.5 qts. (1.4L)

DRAINING & REFILLING

Transaxle & Transmission

Loosen oil pan bolts and allow ATF to drain. Remove oil pan and clean pan and screen. Install pan using a new gasket and add fluid. Run engine at idle speed for about 2 minutes. Operate at fast idle (1200 RPM) for several more minutes. Shift transmission through all gears and return to "P". Check fluid level and add to obtain appropriate level.

ADJUSTMENTS

BRAKE BAND

Pickup

Loosen piston stem lock nut. Tighten piston stem to 106-133 INCH lbs. (12-15 N.m). Back off piston stem 2 turns. While holding servo piston stem stationary, tighten lock nut to 14 ft. lbs. (20 N.m).

200SX & 300ZX (2nd Brake Band)

1) To gain access to 2nd brake band adjustment stem, drain transmission fluid and remove pan. Loosen and back off lock nut 5 turns.

2) Tighten piston stem to 106-133 INCH lbs. (12-15 N.m). Back off adjusting stem 3 turns. Hold adjuster stem and tighten lock nut.

200SX & 300ZX (Overdrive Band)

Loosen lock nut. Tighten adjustment stem to 62-88 INCH lbs. (7-10 N.m). Back off adjustment stem 2 turns. Hold adjustment stem and tighten lock nut.

Transaxle

Remove transmission oil pan. On Maxima, remove electrical harness grommet from case. Loosen brake band adjuster lock nut. Torque anchor end pin to 36-48 INCH lbs. (4-6 N.m). Back off anchor end pin 4 1/2 turns on Maxima or 2 1/2 turns on all others. Tighten lock nut (while holding anchor pin) to 12-16 ft. lbs. (16-22 N.m).

SHIFT LINKAGE

RWD

1) Starting in "P", shift through all positions to "1". If detents cannot be felt or pointer is improperly aligned, linkage must be adjusted.

2) Place shift lever in "N" and loosen lock nuts on rod. Turn lock nuts until pointer aligns properly and all detents can be felt. Tighten lock nuts and recheck positions. Ensure full detent is felt in "N".

NOTE: **If unable to adjust, grommets at ends of rod may be worn or damaged.**

FWD

1) Place control lever in "P". Connect control cable end to manual lever of transaxle unit and tighten control cable retaining bolts. Move control lever from "P" to "1".

2) Ensure control lever can move smoothly and without any sliding noise. Place control lever in "P" and check that control lever locks in "P". If necessary, remove lock nut at control cable and loosen adjusting nut. Connect control cable to trunnion. Adjust and tighten adjusting nut. Install and tighten lock nut.

KICKDOWN SWITCH

RWD

Kickdown switch is located at top of accelerator pedal post. A "click" should be heard just before accelerator

NISSAN (Cont.)

bottoms out when depressed. If not, loosen switch lock nut and adjust.

NOTE: Do not allow switch to close too soon, or downshift will occur at part throttle.

THROTTLE WIRE

FWD

1) Loosen both throttle wire adjustment nuts near throttle plate lever. Turn throttle lever to full throttle opening. Push cable sheath down to remove all play.

2) Tighten lower adjustment nut until it contacts support bracket. Turn lower adjustment nut back 1 turn. Tighten upper adjustment nut. Road test vehicle and note kickdown range and operation. If no kickdown occurs, lower the cable sheath. If kickdown occurs too early, raise the cable sheath.

NEUTRAL SAFETY SWITCH

1) Switch operates back-up lights and prevents starting except in "P" or "N". To adjust, ensure transmission is in "N" with lever at transmission in vertical position.

2) Remove alignment hole screw at bottom of switch and loosen retaining bolts. Secure an alignment pin of .08" (2.0 mm) for RWD, .16" (4.0 mm) for Maxima or .098" (2.5 mm) diameter for all other FWD. Move switch until alignment pin can be inserted in rotor. Tighten retaining bolts and replace alignment hole screw.

Fig. 1: Adjusting Neutral Safety Switch

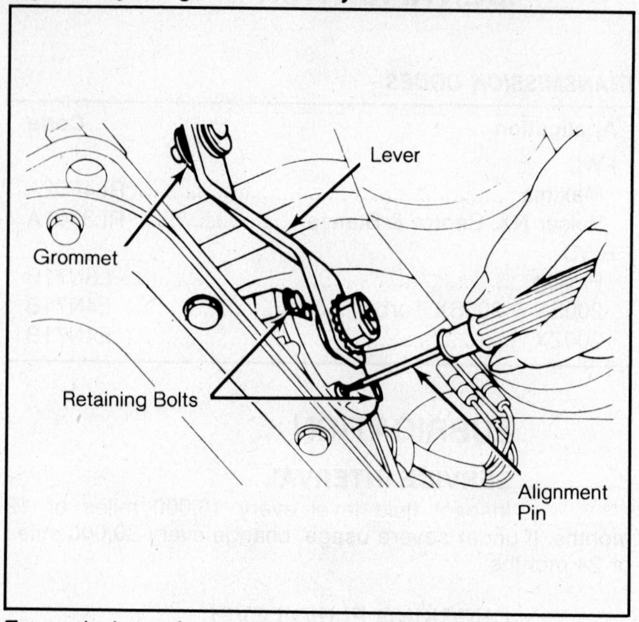

Transmission safety switch shown; transaxle is similar.

PEUGEOT

IDENTIFICATION

TRANSMISSION CODES

Application	Codes
505	ZF 3HP-22

LUBRICATION

SERVICE INTERVALS

Check transmission level at every oil change. Drain and refill transmission every 30,000 miles or 2 years, whichever comes first. In severe driving conditions change fluid at 12,500 miles.

CHECKING FLUID LEVEL

1) Position vehicle on level floor and have engine at operating temperature. Apply parking brake, move selector lever through all positions ending in "P".

2) Remove dipstick and wipe with a clean lint free cloth. Reinstall dipstick and check fluid level. "MAX" mark is maximum hot level. "MIN" mark is minimum cold level. "MIDDLE" mark is minimum hot level or maximum cold level.

RECOMMENDED FLUID

All transmissions use Dexron "B" or "D" automatic transmission fluid.

FLUID CAPACITY

TRANSMISSION REFILL CAPACITIES

Application	Refill Quantity	Dry Fill Quantity
All Modles	1.7 qts. (1.6L)	5.4 qts. (5.2L)

DRAINING & REFILLING

1) Have engine at normal operating temperature. Remove drain plug from transmission oil pan, allow all fluid to drain and install drain plug. Pour approximate amount of fluid as listed in Fluid Capacity chart.

2) Start and run engine at normal idle. Shift selector lever through all positions, check fluid level, add fluid as needed. DO NOT overfill.

ADJUSTMENTS

KICKDOWN CABLE

With throttle control drum in normal hot idle position, adjust cable housing to give maximum clearance of .020" (.5 mm) between end of cable housing and clip on cable.

SHIFT LINKAGE

Disconnect selector rod at transmission lever. Place transmission lever in "N" position. Place gear selector lever in "N" and adjust rod length to fit both levers without tension.

NEUTRAL SAFETY SWITCH

Engine should start in "N" or "P" positions only. To adjust, install or remove shims at base of switch until proper operation is achieved.

PORSCHE

IDENTIFICATION

TRANSMISSION CODES

Application	Code
928S	A28.01
944	087

LUBRICATION

SERVICE INTERVALS

Check fluid level every 15,000 miles. Change fluid and filter every 30,000 miles.

CHECKING FLUID LEVEL

Check fluid level through transparent reservoir, located at rear end of transaxle housing. Fluid must be at operating temperature. Place vehicle on a level surface, with engine idling and selector lever in neutral. Fluid level should be between "MIN" and "MAX" marks. Do not overfill.

RECOMMENDED FLUID

Dexron B automatic transmission fluid.

FLUID CAPACITY

TRANSMISSION REFILL CAPACITIES

Application	Refill	Dry Fill
928S	3.0 qts. (2.8L)	6.3 qts. (6.0L)
944	5.8 qts. (5.5L)	6.3 qts. (6.0L)

DRAINING & REFILLING

1) Remove drain plug. Turn crankshaft until torque converter drain plug is at bottom opening of torque converter housing. Remove drain plug. Remove oil pan and filter.

2) Install new oil filter. Install oil pan and a new gasket. Tighten bolts to 6 ft. lbs. (8 N.m). Install drain plugs, using new seals. Add approximately 5.3 qts. (5.0L) of fluid.

3) Start engine with selector lever in "P" and run engine at idle. Check fluid level in reservoir and add more fluid. Apply brake pedal and momentarily place selector lever in each gear. Check fluid level.

ADJUSTMENTS

SELECTOR LEVER

928S

Place selector lever in "N". Detach cable from operating lever on transmission. Place transaxle lever in "N". Adjust cable so that socket attaches to operating lever without tension and attach cable to lever. *See Fig. 1.*

944

1) Place selector lever in "P". Loosen nut on clamping sleeve for selector lever cable. Place operating lever on transaxle in "P" (against stop). *See Fig. 2.*

Fig. 1: 928S Selector Lever Adjusting Point

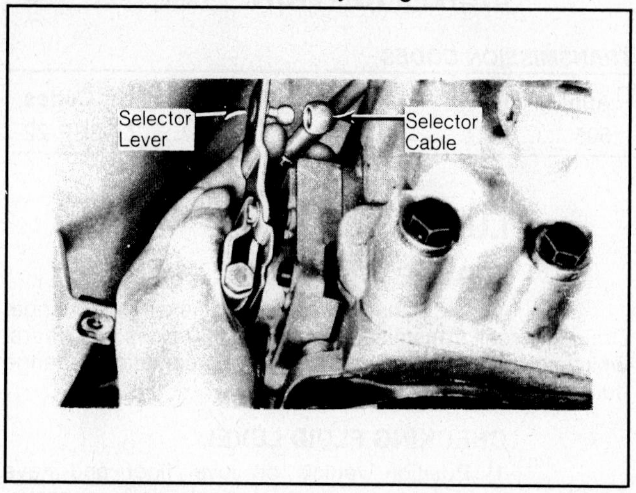

2) Tighten nut on clamping sleeve. Move selector through all positions with engine running. Engagement should be felt after 5 seconds.

Fig. 2: 944 Selector Lever Adjusting Point

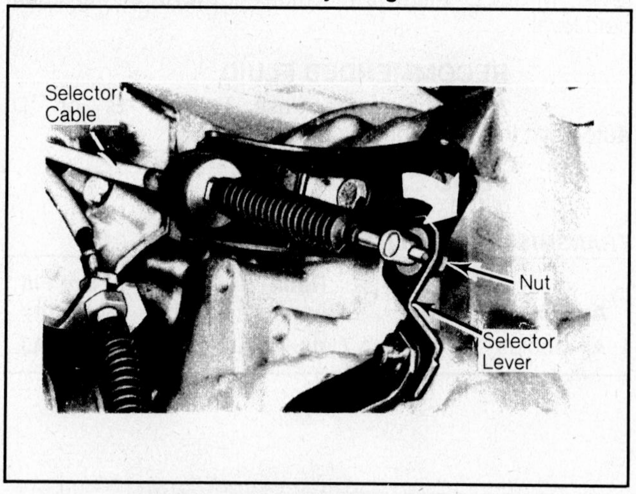

THROTTLE CABLE

928S

Detach cable at transaxle lever. Adjust lever with adjusting bolt "A" after loosening bolt "B" so that cable can be attached without tension or free play. *See Fig. 3.*

944

1) Completely screw in mounting nut for cable sleeve on transaxle bracket, and ball socket for transaxle lever and mount. Relax cable sleeve on firewall and long cable sleeve on cam plate bracket.

2) Position cable around cam plate. Adjust long cable sleeve until clamping nipple is positioned in opening without tension. Adjust accelerator pedal cable to sleeve control without tension.

3) When cable is adjusted correctly, accelerator pedal will be in idle position, throttle will be closed, and transaxle operating lever will be on lower step.

BRAKE BAND

1) Loosen lock nut. Tighten adjusting screw to 84 INCH lbs. (10 N.m). Back off adjusting screw and tighten to 48 INCH lbs. (5 N.m). Loosen adjusting screw 1 3/4 turns and tighten lock nut.

Fig. 3: 928S Throttle Cable Pressure Adjustment

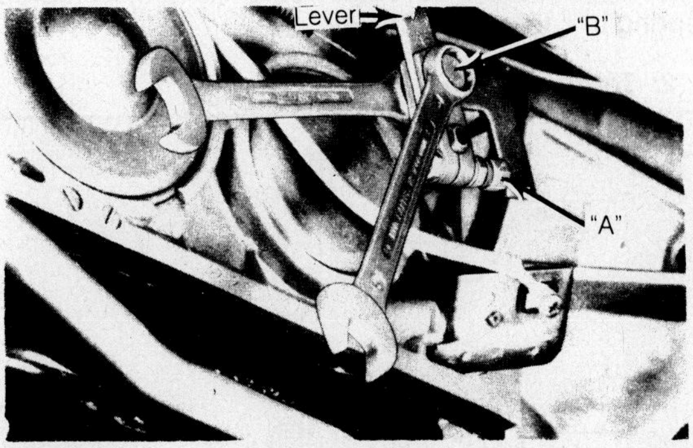

2) On 928S models, there are 2 additional bands to adjust. Measure distance of free play for piston No. 2 by applying air pressure to No. 2 release port. Check distance at "B", apply air pressure to No. 2 apply port and recheck distance at "B". Difference between measurements equals free play.

3) Brake band No. 1 is checked by measuring distance at "A". Apply air pressure to No. 1 apply port, and recheck distance "A". Difference between measurements equals free play. Free play of both bands should be .118-.157" (3-4 mm). Adjustments are made using new pins.

NEUTRAL SAFETY SWITCH

928S

Place selector lever in "N". Loosen adjusting screw and insert a .157" (4 mm) pin through drive dog into hole in case. Tighten adjusting screw and remove locating pin. Check that engine starts in "N" or "P" positions only.

Fig. 4: 928S Brake Band Measurement

944

Starter should operate only in "P" or "N" positions. If starter operates in any other position, remove selector lever gate and loosen retaining bolts on safety switch. Adjust switch as necessary.

RENAULT

IDENTIFICATION

TRANSMISSION CODES

Application	Code
Fuego & Sportwagon	4139-65

LUBRICATION

SERVICE INTERVALS

Check fluid every 6,000 miles. Change fluid at first 1,000 miles and every 30,000 miles thereafter.

CHECKING FLUID LEVEL

1) With vehicle on level floor, place selector lever in "P" position. Apply parking brake and start engine. Allow engine to idle. Remove dipstick, wipe clean, replace, and remove again.

2) With engine at normal operating temperature, fluid level should be between "MINI HOT" and "MAXI HOT" marks. With fluid level at ambient temperatures, level should be between "MINI COLD" marks.

RECOMMENDED FLUID

Dexron II automatic transmission fluid.

FLUID CAPACITY

TRANSMISSION REFILL CAPACITIES

Application	Refill Quantity	Dry Fill Quantity
All	2.7 qts. (2.6L)	5.2 qts. (5.0L)

ADJUSTMENTS

KICKDOWN SWITCH

Make sure that throttle cable has sufficient play to allow a 0.12-0.16" (3-4 mm) movement in stop sleeve when accelerator pedal is completely depressed. Make sure that cover is in position to prevent tarnishing of contacts. *See Fig. 1.*

Fig. 1: Kickdown Switch Adjustment

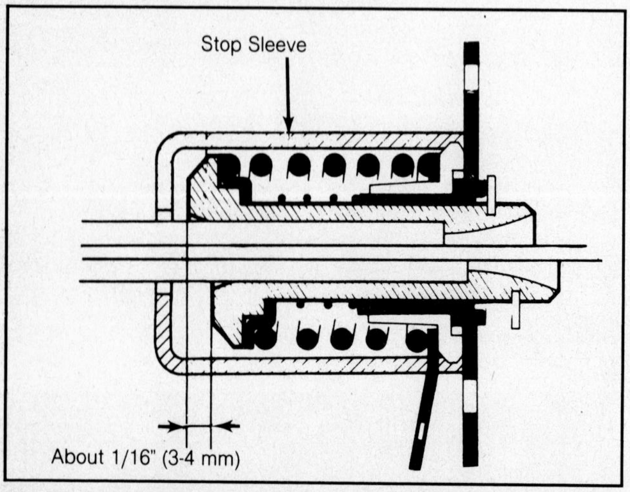

Adjust kickdown switch before adjusting other components.

THROTTLE CABLE

Depress accelerator fully to wide open throttle. Adjust throttle cable to obtain 0.08" (2 mm) compression of spring in cable stop. *See Fig. 2.*

Fig. 2: Throttle Cable Adjustment

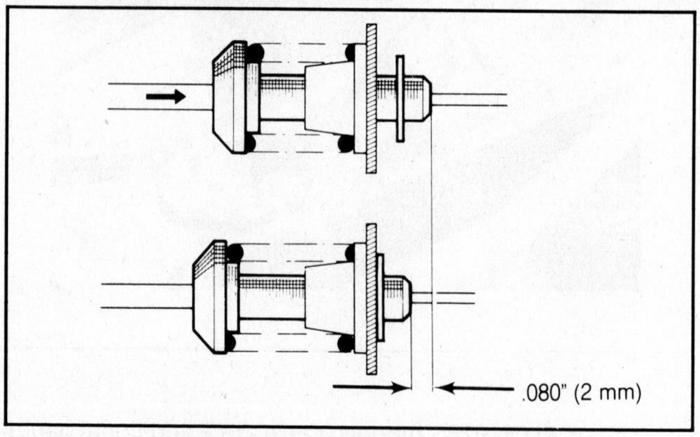

Make sure kickdown switch is functioning correctly.

GOVERNOR CABLE

Adjust cable adjusters on both governor and throttle sides to midway. Adjust cable stop to obtain a clearance of .008-.028" (.20-.70 mm). *See Fig. 3.*

Fig. 3: Governor Cable Adjustment

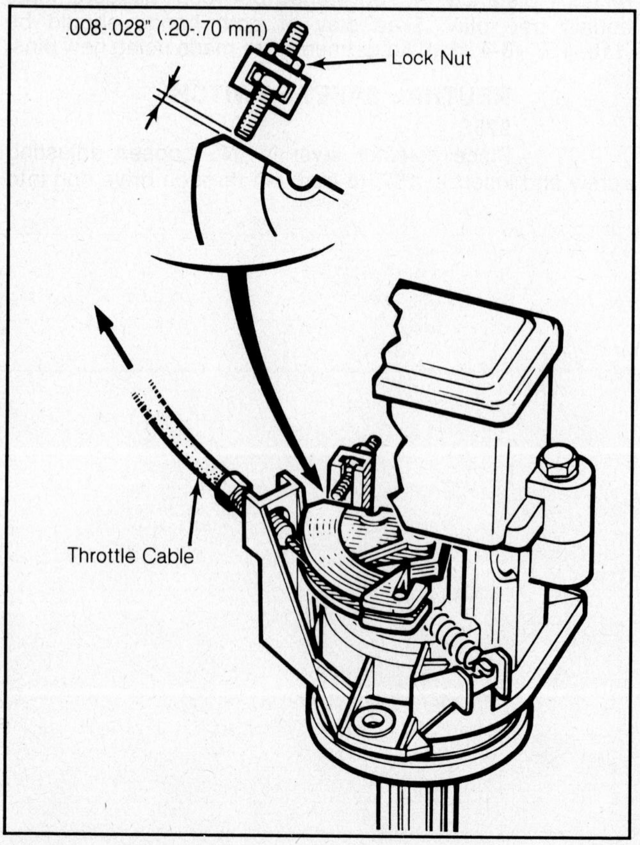

All other components must be operating properly before adjusting governor.

SAAB

IDENTIFICATION

TRANSMISSION CODES

Application	Code
All (Borg-Warner)	37

LUBRICATION

SERVICE INTERVALS

Check fluid level every 7,500 miles, change every 30,000 miles.

CHECKING FLUID LEVEL

1) Park vehicle on level surface and apply hand brake. Allow engine to idle. Place selector lever in all gear positions. Return to "P".

2) Remove dipstick, wipe and check fluid level. Fluid level should be between maximum and minimum marks. Use hot or cold markings on dipstick, depending on transaxle oil temperature. Do not overfill.

RECOMMENDED FLUID

Type F automatic transmission fluid.

FLUID CAPACITY

TRANSMISSION REFILL CAPACITIES

Application	Quantity
All	8.5 qts. (8.0L)

DRAINING & REFILLING

Transaxle drain plug is 13 mm across flats. Remove drain plug. Replace drain plug, add fluid and check fluid level. Do not overfill.

ADJUSTMENTS

THROTTLE CABLE

1) Connect a pressure gauge to transaxle. Place selector lever in "P", block wheels and apply hand brake. Start engine. Idle should be 850 RPM.

2) Disconnect throttle cable from throttle lever, ensure throttle is not binding. Withdraw cable to obtain maximum line pressure and return it to original position. Pressure should return to initial pressure. If pressure stays above 69 psi (4.9 bar), throttle must be cleaned or adjusted.

3) Connect throttle cable to throttle lever. Place selector lever in "D". Check that cable is released, to obtain lowest pressure. Increase pressure to 1.4 psi (0.1 bar) by adjusting throttle cable. Place selector lever in "P". Pressure should be between 59-69 psi (4.1-4.9 bar).

SELECTOR LEVER

1) Place selector lever in "N". Depress pawl button and move selector lever slightly back and forth, increased resistance should be felt in both directions. Hold lever mid-way between positions in which resistance is felt.

2) Disconnect gear selector cable from lever, using an Allen wrench. Release pawl button and move lever to "N". Tighten gear selector cable set screw.

Fig. 1: Selector Lever Adjustment

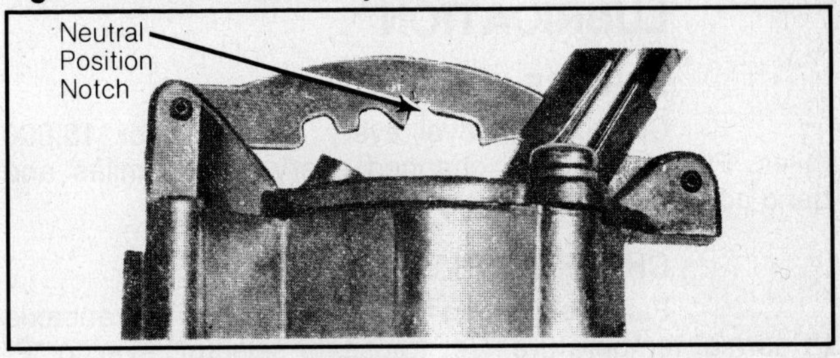

FRONT BAND

Drain fluid and remove oil pan. Loosen lock nut. On transaxles with No. ending in 008, 009, 010 or 011, place a .31" (7.8 mm) spacer. On all others, place a .35" (8.9 mm) spacer (87 91 030) between adjustment screw and rod on servo piston. Tighten adjustment screw to 10 INCH lbs. (1 N.m). Hold screw in position and tighten lock nut to 15-20 ft. lbs. (20-27 N.m). Do not back off adjustment screw.

Fig. 2: Front Band Adjustment

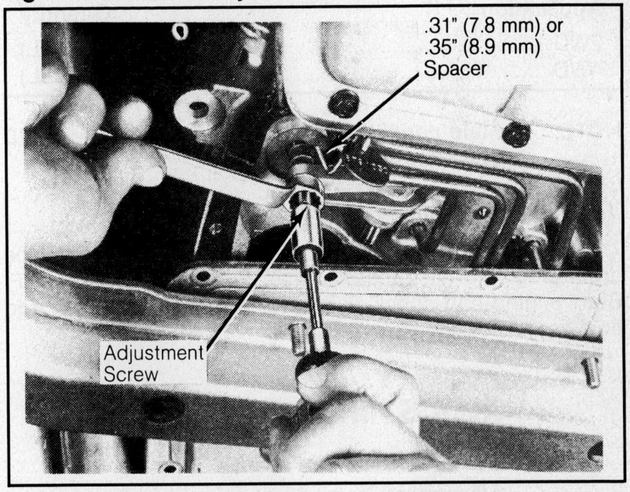

Oil pan must be removed to adjust front band.

REAR BAND

Loosen lock nut (located on left side of case) a few turns and tighten adjustment screw to 114-124 INCH lbs. (13-14 N.m). Back screw off 1 1/4 turn and while holding in position, tighten lock nut to 29-40 ft. lbs. (39-54 N.m).

NEUTRAL SAFETY SWITCH

Place selector lever in "N". Loosen securing screws. Rotate switch housing to line up lever with mark on switch housing. Tighten securing screws.

SUBARU

IDENTIFICATION

TRANSMISSION CODES

Application	Transmission (Code)
1800 2WD	Model Gunma (C)
1800 4WD & Turbo	Model Gunma (F)

LUBRICATION

SERVICE INTERVALS

Check fluid level every 5 months or 15,000 miles. Fluid should be changed every 30,000 miles and band adjusted as necessary.

CHECKING FLUID LEVEL

Park vehicle on level floor. Operate transaxle to normal temperature. Set transaxle selector lever in "P" position with engine idling. Remove dipstick and clean. Insert, note fluid level and add fluid to full mark. Do not overfill.

RECOMMENDED FLUID

Use Dexron ATF.

FLUID CAPACITY

TRANSMISSION REFILL CAPACITIES

Application	Quantity
2WD	6.3-6.8 qts. (6.0-6.4L)
4WD	7.2-7.6 qts. (6.8-7.2L)

NOTE: **Fluid capacity of transfer case is part of 4WD specification.**

DRAINING & REFILLING

Remove drain plug and drain fluid. Replace drain plug and fill transaxle with about 4 quarts of ATF. Start engine and check fluid level with engine idling. Add fluid as necessary. Do not overfill.

ADJUSTMENTS

REAR BAND

Adjustment is made at left side of transaxle. Loosen lock nut on band adjusting screw and tighten screw to 78 INCH lbs. (9 N.m). Loosen screw 2 turns and hold in position while tightening lock nut.

KICKDOWN SWITCH & DOWNSHIFT SOLENOID

Switch ignition on and fully depress accelerator. A click should be heard just as accelerator bottoms out. Adjust switch inward or outward for proper operation.

If kickdown failure occurs infrequently, it may be due to malfunction of the solenoid. Remove and wash the inside of solenoid while moving the pushrod. After washing, carefully check the operation of the solenoid.

NOTE: **If switch operates too soon, downshift will occur at part throttle.**

SHIFT LINKAGE

1) Move selector lever from "P" to "1". Lever should set into each position with a click and selector dial indicate correct gear position.

2) If linkage is out of adjustment, set selector lever to "N". Loosen the linkage adjusting nut, adjust until the "N" is aligned within 1/4".

3) Adjust rod until the "N" mark of the guide plate is aligned correctly with the detent position. Recheck in all positions.

4) If indicator needle is not aligned with guide plate marking, remove console box, loosen mounting screws and adjust as required.

Fig. 1: Shift Linkage Adjustment

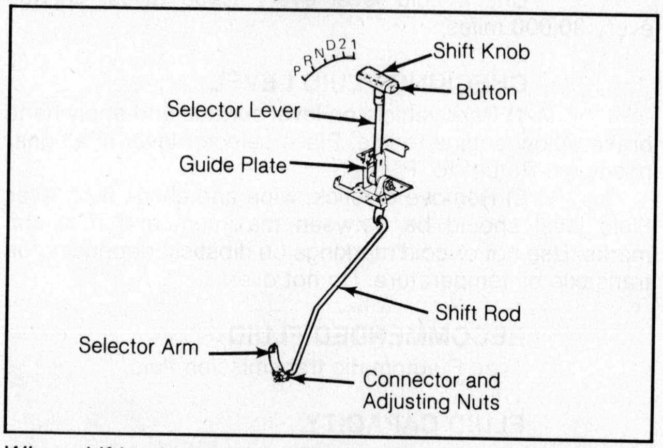

When shifting into each position, a click should be heard.

NEUTRAL SAFETY SWITCH

1) Switch is mounted on right side of selector lever plate. To adjust, remove switch from plate and insert .08" (2.0 mm) diameter pin in alignment hole on switch.

2) Ensure selector lever is in "N". Push selector lever lightly toward "P". Match locator to bracket hole and moving plate pin to arm hole. Tighten retaining bolts in position and remove alignment pin.

Fig. 2: Neutral Safety Switch Adjustment

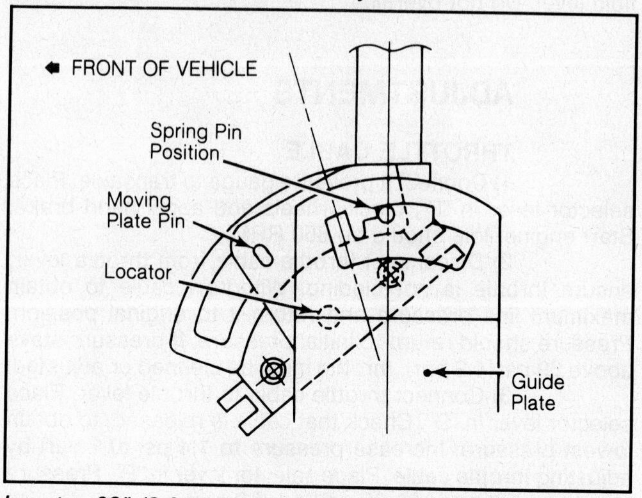

Insert a .08" (2.0 mm) diameter pin to align hole in switch.

TOYOTA

IDENTIFICATION

TRANSMISSION CODES

Application	Code
Front Wheel Drive	
Camry	A140E
Corolla	A130L, A131L or A240L
Tercel	
2WD	A55
4WD	A55F
Rear Wheel Drive	
Celica	A40D
Corolla	A42L
Cressida & Supra	A43DE
Pickup	A43D
Van	A43DL

LUBRICATION

SERVICE INTERVALS

Check fluid every 15,000 miles. In severe conditions change fluid every 15,000 miles.

CHECKING FLUID LEVEL

Check fluid level with engine idling. Shift each gear from "P" through "L" and back to "P". Fluid level should be within ranges marked on dipstick. Do not overfill.

RECOMMENDED FLUID

Use Dexron II automatic transmission fluid.

FLUID CAPACITY

TRANSMISSION REFILL CAPACITIES

Application	Refill Quantity	Dry Fill Quantity
Camry	2.5 qts. (2.4L)	6.3 qts. (6.0L)
Celica	2.5 qts. (2.4L)	6.7 qts. (6.3L)
Corolla FWD		
Diesel	2.5 qts. (2.4L)	6.2 qts. (5.9L)
Gas	2.4 qts. (2.3L)	5.8 qts. (5.5L)
Corolla RWD	2.5 qts. (2.4L)	6.0 qts. (5.7L)
Cressida, Pickup & Supra	2.5 qts. (2.4L)	6.9 qts. (6.5L)
Tercel		
2WD	2.3 qts. (2.2L)	4.8 qts. (4.5L)
4WD	4.4 qts. (4.2L)	6.9 qts. (6.5L)
Van	2.6 qts. (2.5L)	6.9 qts. (6.5L)

DRAINING & REFILLING

1) Remove drain plug and drain fluid. Replace drain plug and fill transmission with approximate amount of ATF fluid. See TRANSMISSION REFILL CAPACITIES table.

2) Start engine and shift through all gears. Shift into "P" and check fluid level. Add fluid as necessary. DO NOT overfill.

ADJUSTMENTS

FLOOR SHIFTER LINKAGE

Place transmission shift lever in "N" and adjust shift rod until shift lever indicates "N" correctly. Holding shift selector lightly toward "R", tighten lock nuts. Check that all ranges engage correctly.

Fig. 1: Floor Shift Linkage Assembly

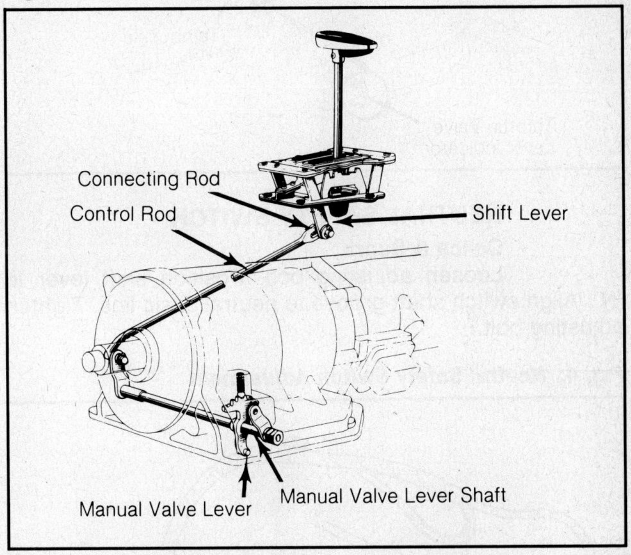

THROTTLE CABLE

Remove air cleaner. Check throttle cable bracket and linkage for looseness or bending. Depress accelerator to wide open throttle position. Adjust cable housing so distance between rubber boot end and inner cable stopper is .04" (1.0 mm). Tighten lock nut.

Fig. 2: Adjusting Throttle Cable

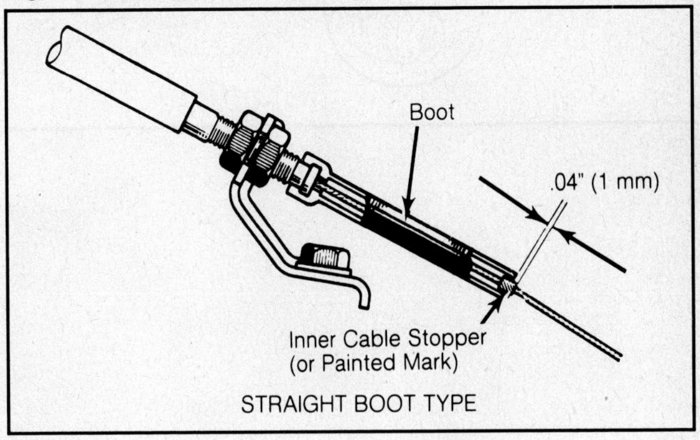

THROTTLE LINK

Tercel

1) Remove air cleaner. Check throttle cable bracket and linkage for looseness or binding. Depress accelerator to wide open throttle position, and check that throttle opens fully. If not, adjust throttle cable.

2) Fully depress accelerator pedal and hold. Adjust linkage by turning turnbuckle until throttle valve lever indicator lines up with mark on transmission case. Tighten lock nut.

TOYOTA (Cont.)

Fig. 3: Tercel Throttle Link Adjustment

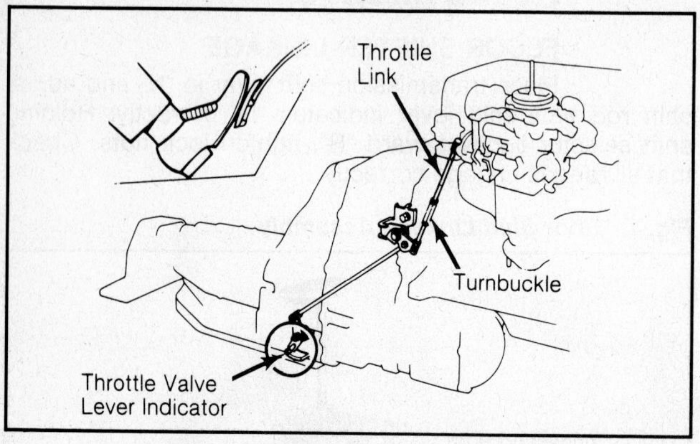

NEUTRAL SAFETY SWITCH

Celica & Supra

Loosen adjusting bolt. Position shift lever in "N". Align switch shaft groove to neutral basic line. Tighten adjusting bolt.

Fig. 4: Neutral Safety Switch Adjustment

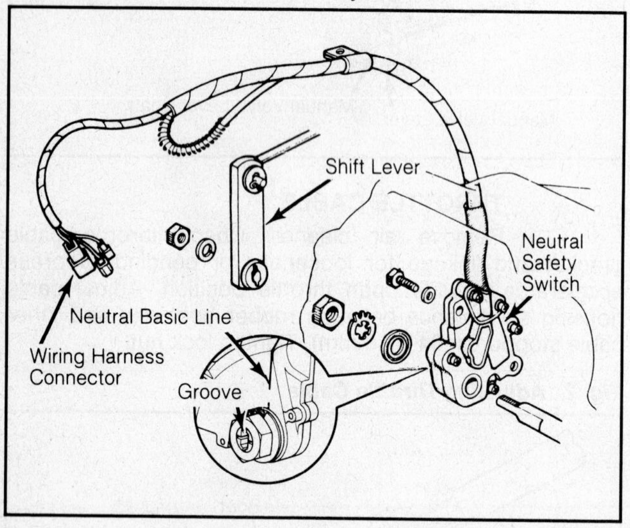

All Other Models

Disconnect switch connector. Connect an ohmmeter between terminals and adjust switch to the point where there is continuity between terminals. Tighten screws and connect switch connector.

Fig. 5: Neutral Safety Switch Test Terminals

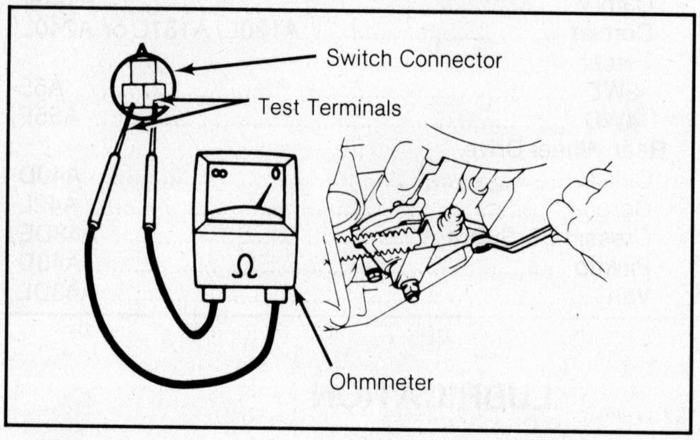

VOLKSWAGEN

IDENTIFICATION

TRANSMISSION CODES

Application	Code
Cabriolet, Golf, GTI, Jetta & Scirocco	010
Quantum	087, 089 or 089-E
Vanagon	090

LUBRICATION

SERVICE INTERVALS

Check fluid level every 15,000 miles. Change fluid every 30,000 miles under normal conditions, or every 15,000 miles under severe conditions.

CHECKING FLUID LEVEL

With transaxle at operating temperature, park vehicle on level surface. Place selector lever in "P" or "N", apply parking brake and allow engine to idle. Remove dipstick, clean and insert. Ensure fluid level is between marks.

RECOMMENDED FLUID

Dexron II automatic transmission fluid.

FLUID CAPACITY

TRANSMISSION REFILL CAPACITIES

Application	Refill	Dry Fill
All Models	3.2 qts. (3.0L)	6.4 qts. (6.0L)

DRAINING & REFILLING

1) Remove transaxle protection plate. Remove rear pan bolts and loosen front pan bolts. Drain as much fluid as possible. Remove oil pan and finish draining fluid. Remove filter. Clean oil pan in solvent and dry.

2) Install new filter and tighten screws to 27 INCH lbs. (3 N.m). Install oil pan, using a new gasket. Tighten oil pan bolts to 15 ft. lbs. (20 N.m). Install protection plate, tighten bolts to 18 ft. lbs. (25 N.m). Add 3.2 qts. (3.0L) of fluid and check fluid level.

ADJUSTMENTS

BRAKE BAND

Loosen adjustment screw lock nut. Tighten brake band adjustment screw to 90 INCH lbs. (10 N.m). Loosen adjustment screw. Retighten to 45 INCH lbs. (5 N.m). Back off screw 2 turns on 5-cyl. engines or 2 1/2 turns on all others. Tighten lock nut to 178 INCH lbs. (20 N.m).

SELECTOR LEVER CABLE

Vanagon

Place transaxle lever in "P". Loosen bolt retaining shift rod to operating lever on transaxle. Ensure selector lever and operating lever are in "P". Push shift rod to rear and tighten bolt.

All Others

Place transaxle in "P". Loosen nut for clamping pin which retains selector cable to operating lever on transaxle. Ensure selector lever and operating lever are in "P". Tighten cable clamping nut to 72 INCH lbs. (8 N.m).

THROTTLE CABLE

Cabriolet, Golf, GTI, Jetta & Scirocco

NOTE: **Accelerator linkage must be adjusted so that the operating lever on transaxle is against stop when throttle valve is closed.**

Warm engine to operating temperature. Place gear selector in "P". Loosen throttle cable adjusting nuts. Push cable housing away from transaxle until all slack is taken up. Throttle valve must remain closed. Tighten adjusting nuts at this point. Check adjustment.

Fig. 1: Quantum Throttle Control Cable

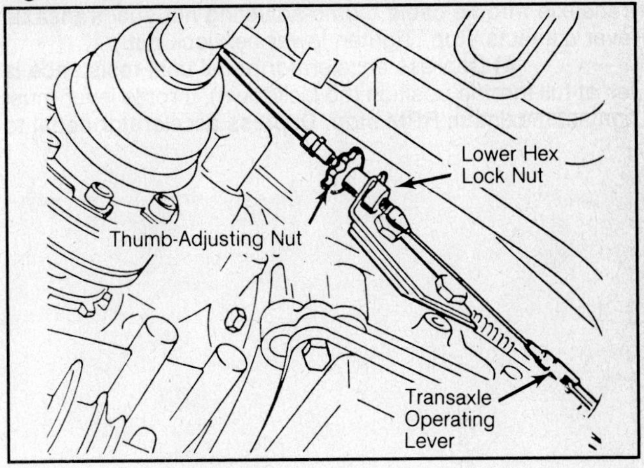

Quantum 087 Transaxle

1) Loosen accelerator cable thumb-adjusting nut near transaxle. Disconnect both rods at relay control lever (near distributor). Remove cruise control linkage. Hold relay control lever at closed throttle position stop. Turn throttle rod socket until it centers over ball stud and install.

2) Loosen lock nut at transaxle operating lever. Slide operating lever apart until both ends are at stops. Tighten lock nut. Remove transaxle operating lever at transaxle.

3) Loosen accelerator cable lower hex lock nut near transaxle. Push accelerator pedal to stop on floor. Turn thumb-adjusting nut down until transaxle lever begins to move. Tighten lower hex lock nut.

4) Depress accelerator pedal until resistance is felt at full throttle position (no kickdown), throttle lever must contact stop. Depress accelerator pedal to full throttle stop. Linkage spring must be compressed 5/16" and transaxle operating lever must contact stop (kickdown). Reconnect cruise control.

Quantum 089 Transaxle

1) Loosen accelerator cable thumb-adjusting nut near transaxle. Loosen throttle cable lock nuts on cylinder head cover. Pull sleeve of throttle cable until resistance is felt. Turn outer-adjusting nut against bracket and tighten inner-adjusting nut.

2) Loosen accelerator cable lower hex lock nut near transaxle. Depress accelerator pedal to pedal stop.

VOLKSWAGEN (Cont.)

Turn transaxle throttle cable thumb-adjusting nut until transaxle lever begins to move. Tighten lower hex lock nut.

3) Depress accelerator pedal until resistance is felt at full throttle position (no kickdown), throttle lever must contact stop. Depress accelerator pedal to full throttle stop. Linkage spring must be compressed 5/16" and transaxle operating lever must contact stop (kickdown).

Quantum 089-E Transaxle

1) Loosen accelerator cable thumb-adjusting nut near transaxle. Remove throttle cable at transaxle control lever. Ensure injector lever travel from idle-to-full throttle opening is 1.56" (32 mm). Measure throttle travel at ball stud.

2) Pull sleeve of throttle cable until resistance is felt. Turn outer-adjusting nut against bracket and tighten inner-adjusting nut. Install throttle cable at transaxle control lever.

3) Loosen accelerator cable lower hex lock nut near transaxle. Depress accelerator pedal to floor. Turn transaxle throttle cable thumb-adjusting nut until transaxle lever contacts stop. Tighten lower hex lock nut.

4) Depress accelerator pedal until resistance is felt at full throttle position (no kickdown), throttle lever must contact maximum RPM stop. Depress accelerator pedal to full throttle stop. Linkage spring must be compressed 5/16" and transaxle operating lever must contact stop (kickdown).

Vanagon

1) Loosen adjustment nut and remove override spring. Start engine, adjust idle speed to 800-1000 RPM and turn engine off. Push throttle lever forward until it stops.

2) Using a screwdriver, turn adjustment rod until it contacts throttle lever pivot. Install override spring, start engine and check idle speed. If necessary, adjust idle speed by turning rod. Tighten lock nut on adjustment rod.

3) Depress accelerator pedal to floor. Transaxle kickdown lever must be in kickdown position with 1/32-3/32" free play between lever and stop. Release accelerator pedal, kickdown lever must return to idle position. If necessary, adjust throttle cable at clamping bolt.

NEUTRAL SAFETY SWITCH

Neutral safety switch is located in shift console. Remove console cover and adjust switch so that engine starts in "P" and "N" only.

VOLVO

IDENTIFICATION

TRANSMISSION CODES

Application	Code
740/760 Turbo & 760 GLE	AW70 or AW71
All Others	ZF 4 HP-22

LUBRICATION

SERVICE INTERVAL

Check fluid every 7,500 miles or twice a year. Change fluid every 25,000 miles.

CHECKING FLUID LEVEL

1) Position vehicle on level floor. Apply parking brake and shift selector lever to "P". Start engine and let idle. Shift selector lever through all gears pausing 4-5 seconds for engagement at each position.

2) Return selector lever to "P". Wait 2 minutes and remove dipstick. Wipe dipstick and insert. Withdraw dipstick and check reading. Level must be between "MIN" and "MAX" marks.

RECOMMENDED FLUID

Use DEXRON II automatic transmission fluid.

FLUID CAPACITY

TRANSMISSION REFILL CAPACITIES

Application	Refill Quantity	Dry Fill Quantity
AW70 & AW71	....	8.0 qts. (7.5L)
ZF 4 HP-22	....	6.5 qts. (6.0L)

ADJUSTMENTS

THROTTLE & KICKDOWN CABLES

1) Transmission cable should be stretched in idle position. Distance between clip and sheath should be .010-.040" (.25-1.0 mm). *See Fig. 1.*

Fig. 1: Checking Throttle Controls

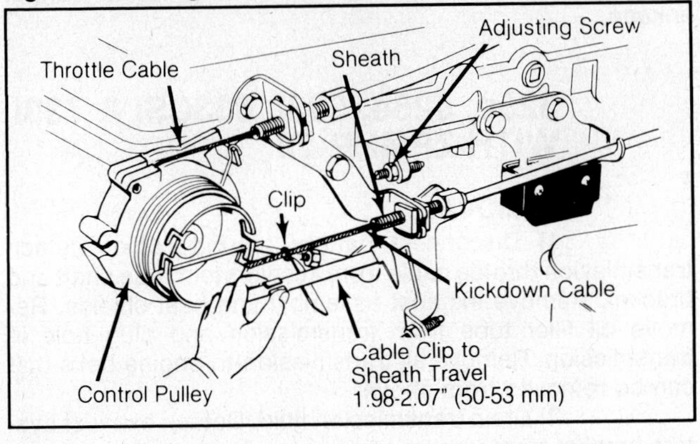

2) Pull transmission cable out by hand approximately .39-.59" (10-15 mm), and release. A distinct "click" should be heard from transmission, indicating cable moves freely and throttle cam returns to initial position.

3) Depress accelerator pedal completely. The transmission cable should travel 1.98-2.07" (50-53 mm), from idle position to full throttle position. *See Fig. 1.*

GEAR SELECTOR

1) Press on gear selector and check that clearance from "D" to stop is about the same as from "2" to stop. If clearance is incorrect, control rod needs adjustment.

2) Adjustment is made by turning clevis in or out on control rod. Maximum visible thread length permitted is 1.1" (28 mm).

3) Increasing rod length reduces position "D" clearance. Decreasing rod length increases position "D" clearance. Shift to "1" then to "P" for recheck. *See Fig. 2.*

Fig. 2: Gear Selector Adjustment

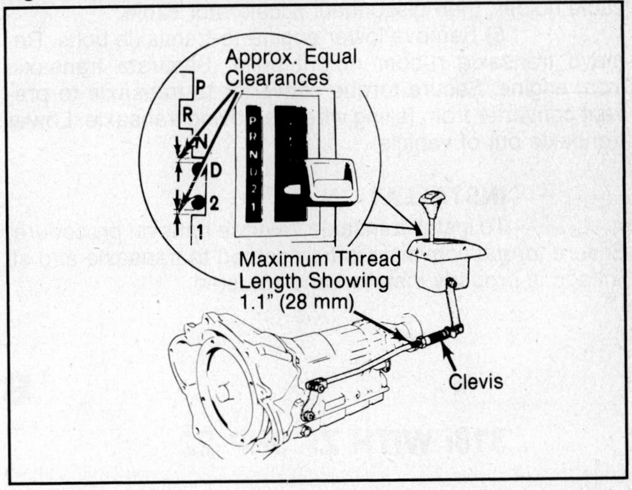

NEUTRAL SAFETY SWITCH

1) Switch is located at and directly controlled by the shift control lever. Place selector lever in "P". Adjust neutral safety switch to set "P" mark at center of switch lever.

2) Place selector lever in "N". Confirm "N" mark is at center of switch lever. Move selector lever from "P" to "1" and back again.

3) Ensure control pin does not slide out of switch lever. *See Fig. 3.* Ensure engine only starts in "P" and "N", and back-up lights illuminate in "R" only.

Fig. 3: Adjusting Neutral Safety Switch

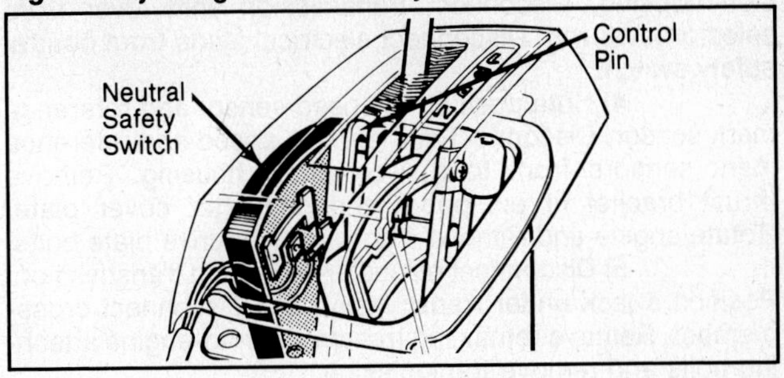

Automatic Transmission Removal

AUDI

AUDI COUPE & 4000

REMOVAL

1) Disconnect battery ground cable. Disconnect accelerator linkage rod. Disconnect speedometer cable. Remove upper engine-to-transaxle bolts.

2) Support engine from above. Disconnect automatic transaxle cooler lines. Disconnect exhaust pipe from manifold. Disconnect exhaust pipe bracket at transaxle.

3) Unbolt exhaust pipe from catalytic converter. Remove axle shaft guard plate, then disconnect axle shafts from transaxle flanges. Wire axle shafts back out of way. Remove starter. Remove 3 bolts securing torque converter to drive plate.

4) Remove subframe rear mounting bolts and loosen front bolts (do not remove). Disconnect linkage rod from transaxle. Remove selector cable holder and circlip. Disconnect cable and "O" ring. Place transaxle jack under transaxle and raise transaxle slightly. Remove accelerator cable holder, then disconnect accelerator cable.

5) Remove lower engine-to-transaxle bolts. Remove transaxle rubber mount bolts. Separate transaxle from engine. Secure torque converter to transaxle to prevent converter from falling when removing transaxle. Lower transaxle out of vehicle.

INSTALLATION

To install transaxle, reverse removal procedure. Ensure torque converter is fully seated to transaxle and all linkage is properly installed and adjusted.

5000

REMOVAL

1) Disconnect battery ground cable. Disconnect hoses from transaxle cooler. Disconnect accelerator linkage and speedometer cable. Support engine from above. Remove upper engine-to-transaxle bolts. Remove guard plate from subframe and remove exhaust pipe.

2) Remove right guard plate at right axle drive shaft and remove drive shaft bolts. Mark left ball joint position on control arm. Remove bolts attaching ball joints to control arm. Remove starter, selector lever cable holder and selector lever cable at transaxle lever.

3) Disconnect lower accelerator linkage rod and accelerator cable from transaxle lever. Remove right side guard plate from subframe. Remove torque converter-to-drive plate bolts.

4) Support transaxle with jack and raise slightly. Remove lower engine-to-transaxle bolts and rear subframe bolts. Position drive shafts to rear of vehicle. Separate transaxle from engine, secure torque converter in place and lower transaxle from vehicle.

INSTALLATION

To install, reverse removal procedure. When attaching torque converter to drive plate use new bolts and lock washers. After transaxle installation, check and adjust accelerator cable and throttle linkage (if necessary).

BMW

318i WITH ZF 3HP-22

REMOVAL

1) Disconnect battery ground cable. Detach transmission throttle cable from accelerator cross shaft and bracket. Remove oil filler tube from transmission and plug hole in transmission. Remove all transmission-to-engine bolts that can be removed from above.

2) Drain transmission fluid. Detach exhaust system bracket from transmission extension housing. Disconnect exhaust pipe from exhaust manifold. Turn steering wheel to full left lock to provide clearance for removal. Disconnect propeller shaft from transmission output flange by removing 3 bolts and nut.

3) Remove bolts from center support to body. Position propeller shaft out of way. Remove retaining bolt and withdraw speedometer cable from transmission extension housing. Disconnect transmission shift lever from selector lever rod. Disconnect electrical leads from neutral safety switch.

4) Note position of speed sensor and reference mark sensor. Disconnect and remove speed and reference mark sensors from torque converter housing. Remove thrust bracket (if equipped) and converter cover plate. Rotate engine and remove 4 converter-to-drive plate bolts.

5) Disconnect oil cooler lines from transmission. Position a jack under transmission and disconnect crossmember. Remove remaining transmission-to-engine attaching bolts and remove transmission.

INSTALLATION

1) To install, reverse removal procedure. Check for correct engagement of torque converter in transmission by measuring distance from front of transmission case to torque converter-to-drive plate lugs. Distance should be about .50" (12 mm).

2) Coat speed and reference mark sensors with anti-seize compound prior to installation. When installing speed and reference mark sensors, Black plug of speed sensor faces ring gear and Gray plug of reference mark sensor faces flywheel.

3) When installing oil cooler lines, check condition of line-to-case gaskets and replace if necessary. Fill transmission with fluid and adjust transmission control linkage.

325e, 528e, 533i, 633CSi & 733i WITH ZF 4HP-22

REMOVAL

1) Disconnect battery ground cable. Detach transmission throttle cable from accelerator cross shaft and bracket. Remove exhaust assembly and heat shields. Remove oil filler tube from transmission and plug hole in transmission. Remove all transmission-to-engine bolts that can be removed from above.

2) Drain transmission fluid. Detach exhaust system bracket from transmission extension housing. Discon-

BMW (Cont.)

nect exhaust pipe from exhaust manifold. Turn steering wheel to full left lock to provide clearance for removal. Disconnect propeller shaft from transmission output flange by removing 3 bolts and nut.

3) Remove bolts from center support to body. Position propeller shaft out of way. Disconnect transmission shift lever from selector lever rod. Disconnect electrical leads from neutral safety switch.

4) Note position of speed sensor and reference mark sensor. Disconnect and remove speed and reference mark sensors from torque converter housing. Remove thrust bracket (if equipped) and converter cover plate. Rotate engine and remove 4 converter-to-drive plate bolts.

5) Disconnect oil cooler lines from transmission. Position a jack under transmission and disconnect crossmember. Remove remaining transmission-to-engine attaching bolts and remove transmission.

INSTALLATION

1) To install, reverse removal procedure, noting the following: Clean out all transmission oil cooler lines. Check for correct engagement of torque converter in transmission by measuring distance from front of transmission case to torque converter-to-drive plate lugs. Distance should be about .50" (12 mm).

2) Coat speed and reference mark sensors with anti-seize compound prior to installation. When installing speed and reference mark sensors, Black plug of speed sensor faces ring gear and Gray plug of reference mark sensor faces flywheel.

3) When installing oil cooler lines, check condition of line-to-case gaskets and replace if necessary. Fill transmission with new fluid and adjust transmission control linkage.

CHRYSLER CORP. IMPORTS

CONQUEST & RAM-50 PICKUP

REMOVAL

NOTE: **Transmission and converter must be removed as an assembly to prevent damage to drive plate, pump bushing, and oil seal. Do not allow weight of transmission to rest on drive plate at any time during removal or installation.**

1) Disconnect battery ground cable. Remove oil cooler lines at transmission. Remove starter motor and cooler line bracket. Loosen pan to drain transmission.

2) Mark converter and drive plate for reassembly reference. Using socket wrench on crankshaft vibration damper bolt, rotate engine clockwise to position converter attaching bolts for removal. Remove bolts and propeller shaft.

3) Disconnect electrical leads. Disconnect gearshift rod and torque shaft assembly, throttle rod lever from left side of transmission, and linkage bellcrank (if so equipped) from transmission.

4) Remove oil filler tube and speedometer cable. Support rear of engine with engine support fixture. With a transmission support on a service jack, support transmission. Raise transmission slightly to relieve load on supports.

5) Remove bolts securing transmission mount to crossmember and crossmember to frame, then remove crossmember. Remove all converter housing bolts, then carefully work transmission and converter assembly rearward off engine block dowels and disengage converter hub from end of crankshaft.

6) Attach a small "C" clamp to edge of converter housing to hold converter in place during transmission removal. Lower transmission and remove from under vehicle. To remove converter assembly, remove "C" clamp from edge of converter housing and carefully slide assembly from transmission.

INSTALLATION

1) To install, reverse removal procedure. To install converter, rotate pump rotors with Front Pump Aligner (C-3756) until 2 small holes in handle are vertical. Carefully slide converter over input shaft and reaction shaft. Ensure converter hub slots are also vertical and fully engage pump inner rotor lugs.

2) Test for full engagement by placing straight edge on face of converter housing. Surface of converter front cover lug should be at least 1/2" from rear of straightedge when converter is pushed all the way into transmission. Attach a small "C" clamp to converter housing to hold converter in place during transmission installation.

Fig. 1: Using Front Pump Aligner to Align Pump Rotors for Torque Converter Installation

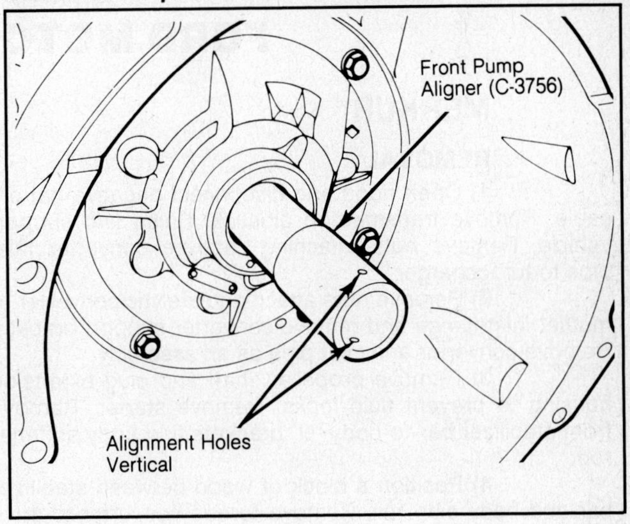

3) Inspect converter drive plate for distortion or cracks and replace if necessary. Coat converter hub hole in crankshaft with multi-purpose grease. When drive plate replacement has been necessary, ensure both transmission dowel pins are in engine block and they are protruding far enough to hold transmission in alignment.

4) Place transmission and converter assembly on a jack and position under vehicle for installation. Raise or tilt as necessary to align transmission to engine. Rotate

CHRYSLER CORP. IMPORTS (Cont.)

Fig. 2: Measuring for Full Converter Engagement

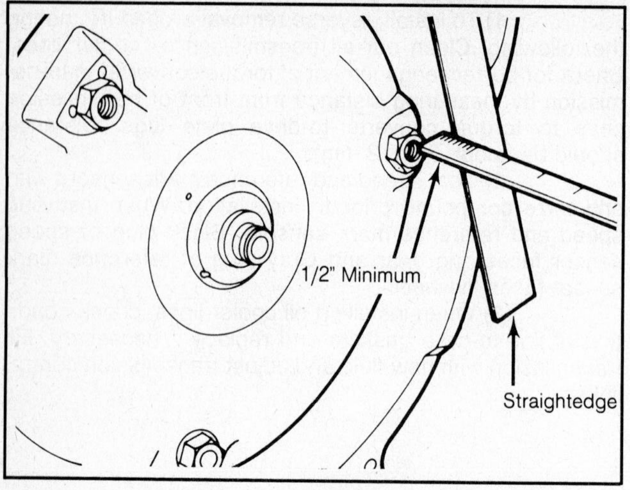

converter so that mark on converter (made during removal) will align with mark on drive plate.

5) Carefully work transmission assembly forward over engine block dowels with converter hub entering crankshaft opening. After transmission is in position on engine, install and tighten all bolts. Adjust shift and throttle linkage, then refill transmission with DEXRON II type automatic transmission fluid.

COLT & COLT VISTA

REMOVAL

1) Disconnect negative battery cable. Disconnect throttle cable at carburetor and manual control cable at transaxle. On Colt Vista models, remove battery, battery tray, reservior tank and air cleaner housing.

2) On all models, remove inhibitor switch connector, cooler hoses and 4 top engine-to-transaxle mounting bolts. Raise vehicle and remove front wheels. Remove under cover and drain transaxle fluid. Remove strut and stabilizer bars from lower control arm.

3) Remove both drive shafts from transaxle case. Remove starter and disconnect speedometer cable from transaxle. Remove converter housing. Remove 3 special bolts attaching converter to drive plate. Ensure torque converter is loose from engine and will come out with transmission.

4) Install an engine support. Place transmission jack under transaxle assembly. Remove remaining bolts holding engine-to-transaxle assembly. Remove transaxle mounting bolts. Lower transaxle assembly (with torque converter) out of vehicle.

INSTALLATION

To install transaxle assembly, reverse removal procedure. Install torque converter to transaxle, not to engine. Install new drive shaft retainer rings on reassembly. Ensure transaxle assembly is filled with fluid and all cables are properly connected and adjusted.

FORD MOTOR CO. IMPORTS

MERKUR

REMOVAL

1) Open hood and disconnect negative battery cable. Remove transmission dipstick. Raise and support vehicle. Remove nuts attaching catalytic converter inlet pipe to turbocharger.

2) Remove nuts attaching catalytic converter to muffler inlet flange and remove converter support bracket. Remove converter and inlet pipe as an assembly.

3) Remove propeller shaft and plug extension housing to prevent fluid leaks. Remove starter. Remove front stabilizer bar-to-body "U" brackets and body stiffener rod.

4) Position a block of wood between stabilizer bar and body side rail. Remove torque converter-to-drive plate nuts through starter opening. Use a ratchet and socket on crankshaft pulley bolt to bring nuts into position.

NOTE: **Turn crankshaft only in a clockwise direction, turning crankshaft counterclockwise may cause timing belt to jump time.**

5) Support transmission. Remove bolts attaching rear mount to transmission support bracket. Remove rear mount nuts and mount. Lower transmission. Disconnect speedometer cable and wiring to neutral/safety switch.

6) Disconnect shift rod and cable from shift levers. Disconnect vacuum hose at modulator. Using Quick Disconnect Remover (T82L-9500-AH), disconnect transmission cooler lines.

7) Loosen engine mount attaching nuts until only 2 or 3 threads are visible on end of studs. Position a block of wood against engine oil pan and raise engine until stud nuts contact crossmember. As engine tilts downward, lower transmission.

8) Remove top torque converter housing attaching bolts. Remove remaining torque converter housing attaching bolts and transmission filler tube. Pull transmission rearward and lower out of vehicle.

INSTALLATION

1) Before installing transmission, make sure that torque converter hub is fully engaged in transmission

FORD MOTOR CO. IMPORTS (Cont.)

pump gear. Raise transmission into position and rotate torque converter to align studs with holes on drive plate. Push transmission against engine.

2) Install trnsmission filler tube and converter housing bolts. Tighten bolts to 28-38 ft. lbs. (38-51 N.m). Connect transmission cooler lines and vacuum hose. Connect downshift cable, shift rod, neutral/safety switch, and speedometer cable.

3) Remove stand and block of wood supporting engine. Tighten engine mount nuts to 50-70 ft. lbs. (68-95 N.m). Install rear mounts and install attaching bolts. Tighten mount bolts to 25-35 ft. lbs. (34-47 N.m).

4) Install rear mounts to transmission support bracket. Tighten rear mount bolts to 50-70 ft. lbs. (68-95 N.m). Remove transmission support. Install torque converter-to-drive plate nuts. Tighten nuts to 12-16 ft. lbs. (16-22 N.m).

5) Install starter. Remove plug from extension housing and install propeller shaft. Install catalytic converter. Tighten nuts to 20-30 ft. lbs. (27-41 N.m) at converter outlet, tighten nuts at turbocharger to 25-35 ft. lbs. (34-47 N.m).

6) Check and adjust shift rod and downshift cable. Lower vehicle and connect battery. Start engine. Make sure engine cranks only in Neutral or Park positions. Check and adjust transmission fluid level. Raise vehicle and check for leaks.

NOTE: **If transmission is empty due to overhaul, add 2 quarts of automatic transmission fluid before starting engine, and 5 more quarts immediately after engine start-up.**

GENERAL MOTORS IMPORTS

SPECTRUM

REMOVAL

1) Disconnect negative cable at battery. Remove air intake hose from air cleaner. Disconnect shift cable from transaxle. Disconnect speedometer cable. Disconnect vacuum hose at vacuum diaphragm.

2) Disconnect engine wiring harness clamp at transaxle. Disconnect ground cable at transaxle. Disconnect inhibitor switch wire connector at left fender. Disconnect kickdown solenoid wire connector at left fender.

3) Disconnect transaxle cooler lines. Remove 3 upper transaxle to engine attaching bolts. Raise vehicle. Remove both front wheel and tire assemblies. Remove splash shield at left front fender.

4) Disconnect both tie rod ends at steering knuckle. Remove both front tension rod brackets. Disconnect both tension rods from control arms. Disengage both drive axle shafts from transaxle. Remove flywheel dust cover.

5) Remove converter to flywheel attaching bolts. Remove rear mount thru bolts at transaxle. Disconnect starter motor. Support transaxle. Remove lower transaxle to engine attaching bolts. Remove transaxle from vehicle.

INSTALLATION

To install, reverse removal procedure. Adjust shift linkage. Fill transaxle with Dexron II automatic transmission fluid.

SPRINT

REMOVAL

1) Disconnect air suction guide from air cleaner. Disconnect negative and positive cables from battery. Remove battery and tray. Disconnect negative cable at transaxle. Disconnect solenoid wire coupler and shift lever switch wire couplers. Disconnect wire harness and speedometer cable from transaxle.

2) Disconnect oil pressure control cable from accelerator cable, and then, accelerator cable from transaxle. Disconnect select cable from transaxle. Remove starter motor. Drain transaxle fluid.

3) Disconnect oil outlet and inlet hoses from oil pipes. After disconnecting, plug 2 oil hoses to prevent fluid in hoses and oil cooler from draining. Raise vehicle. Disconnect exhaust No. 1 pipe. Remove clutch housing lower plate.

4) Remove 6 drive plate bolts. To lock drive plate, engage a screwdriver with drive plate gear through notch provided at under side of transaxle case. Remove left front drive axle. Detach inner CV joint of right axle from differential. Remove transaxle mounting member.

5) Securely support transaxle with a suitable jack for removal. Disconnect transaxle left mounting. Remove bolts fastening engine and transaxle. Disconnect transaxle from engine by sliding toward left side, and then, carefully lower jack.

6) When removing transaxle assembly from engine, move it in parallel with crankshaft and use care so

GENERAL MOTORS IMPORTS (Cont.)

as not to apply excessive force to drive plate and torque converter. After removing transaxle assembly, be sure to keep it so oil pan is at bottom. If transaxle is tilted, fluid in it may flow out.

INSTALLATION

1) To install, reverse removal procedure. Before installing, apply grease around cup at center of torque converter. When installing transaxle, guide right drive axle into differential side gear as tranaxle is being raised.

2) After inserting inner CV joints of right and left axles into differential side gears, push inner joints into side gears until snap rings on drive axles engage side gears. After connecting oil pressure control cable to accelerator cable, check oil pressure control cable play and adjust if necessary.

HONDA

ALL MODELS

REMOVAL

1) Disconnect battery ground cable and ground strap at transmission. Release steering lock and place selector lever in "N". Disconnect battery cable from starter and wires from starter solenoid. Disconnect wire from water temperature sender and wire from ignition timing thermosensor.

2) Disconnect cooler hoses and wire them up out of way, making sure they won't drain. Remove starter mounting bolt, on transmission side, and top transmission mounting bolt. Raise and support front of vehicle. Remove wheels. Remove fender well shield from right front wheel well on Accord models only.

3) On all models, drain transmission and reinstall plug. Remove throttle control cable from transmission. Remove speedometer cable from transmission. Do not remove speedometer cable holder or speedometer gear may fall into transmission housing.

4) On Accord models only, remove starter side mounting bolt and remove 2 upper transmission mounting bolts. Place a jack under transmission and attach an engine support to engine. Remove crossbeam. Disconnect radius rods, then disconnect axle shafts from transmission.

5) Remove remaining starter bolt and remove starter. Remove transmission damper bracket, located in front of torque converter cover plate, then remove cover plate. Remove center console and shift indicator. Place selector lever in "R" and remove shift cable from shift lever. Loosen nuts and pull shift cable out of transmission housing.

6) Remove torque converter-to-drive plate bolts. Remove 3 engine-to-transmission mounting bolts and lower transmission mounting bolt. Pull transmission rearwards, then lower transmission out of vehicle.

7) On Civic and Prelude models only, remove splash shields, stabilizer bar nuts, mounting brackets and then remove stabilizer bar. Remove axle shafts from transmission. Remove engine torque rods and brackets. Remove engine side starter mounting bolt, then remove starter.

8) Attach engine support to engine and place a jack under transmission. Remove nuts from front and rear engine mounts. Remove crossbeam bolts and crossbeam. Remove torque converter cover plate and center damper bracket.

9) Remove center console and shift indicator. Place selector lever in "R" and remove shift cable from selector lever. Loosen "U" bolt nuts and pull shift cable out of transmission housing. Remove torque converter-to-drive plate bolts. Remove remaining transmission mounting bolts and pull transmission rearward. Lower transmission out of vehicle.

INSTALLATION

1) To install, reverse removal procedures. Be sure ignition is off when connecting ground cable to battery and transmission.

2) With installation complete and transmission filled with oil, start engine and shift through all gear ranges. Check shift cable adjustment. Road test vehicle. With engine at operating temperature, check fluid level.

ISUZU

NOTE: **For I-Mark FWD models, see GENERAL MOTORS IMPORTS SPECTRUM.**

I-MARK (RWD)

REMOVAL

1) Disconnect negative battery cable. Disconnect throttle valve control cable from engine. Remove transmission oil dipstick and tube. Raise vehicle on hoist and drain transmission.

2) Remove starter attaching hardware. Remove starter by moving it toward front of vehicle. Remove propeller shaft. Disconnect shift control rod from shifter lever. Disconnect speedometer cable from transmission. Remove exhaust pipe bracket.

3) Remove transmission oil cooler lines from transmission and position aside to avoid damage. Remove under cover on front of engine. Remove converter housing cover. Remove 6 bolts attaching converter to drive plate. Access to bolts is obtained by rotating crankshaft pulley.

4) Remove bolt from center part of rear mounting frame bracket. Raise engine and transmission assembly. Support rear of engine with a jack. Remove 4 nuts (gas engine) or 4 bolts (diesel engine) attaching rear mounting frame bracket to frame. Remove bracket.

5) Lower transmission and engine slightly. Remove transmission-to-engine bolts. Remove transmission from vehicle by moving it toward rear of vehicle.

ISUZU (Cont.)

INSTALLATION

Reverse removal procedure and note the following: Tighten all nuts and bolts evenly. After installation, fill transmission with fluid. Adjust throttle linkage and shift control linkage.

IMPULSE

REMOVAL

1) Drain transmission fluid. Disconnect throttle cable at engine side. Disconnect negative battery cable. Remove transmission oil dipstick and tube. Raise vehicle on hoist.

2) Remove starter attaching hardware. Remove starter by moving it toward front of vehicle. Remove propeller shaft. Disconnect shift control rod from shifter lever. Disconnect speedometer cable from transmission. Remove exhaust pipe.

3) Loosen joint nut on transmission side. Disconnect by-pass pipe and wire aside to avoid damage. Remove dust cover and under cover on front of engine. Remove 6 bolts attaching converter to drive plate. Access to bolts is obtained by rotating crankshaft pulley.

4) Remove bolt from center part of rear mounting frame bracket. Remove housing bolt. Raise engine and transmission assembly. Support rear of engine with a jack.

5) Lower transmission and engine slightly. Remove transmission-to-engine bolts. Remove transmission from vehicle by moving it toward rear of vehicle. Do not let torque converter slip out of transmission.

INSTALLATION

Reverse removal procedure and note the following: Tighten all nuts and bolts evenly. Check that distance from end of converter housing to front face of converter is about 1.4" (35 mm). After installation, fill transmission with fluid. Adjust throttle linkage and shift control linkage.

P'UP

REMOVAL

1) Disconnect negative battery cable. Detach throttle valve cable from bracket on carburetor. Remove air cleaner and transmission dipstick. Remove dipstick tube upper mounting bolt.

2) Raise and support vehicle. Remove dust cover from lower side of converter housing. Remove starter mounting bolts, then move starter assembly forward.

3) Mark propeller shaft for reassembly reference and remove. Disconnect speedometer cable, and oil cooler lines from transmission. Disconnect shift control linkage.

4) Support transmission with jack and remove rear transmission support bolt and mount. Remove exhaust pipe bracket.

NOTE: Mark converter and flywheel for reassembly to same position.

5) Remove torque converter bolts under pan. Lower transmission until jack barely supports it and remove transmission-to-engine attaching bolts. Raise transmission to normal position. Support engine with jack. Slide transmission away from engine and lower out of vehicle.

NOTE: Use converter holder to prevent converter from sliding out of transmission during removal.

INSTALLATION

1) Reverse removal procedure and note the following: Before installing drive plate-to-converter bolts, ensure welded brackets on converter are flush with drive plate. Check that converter rotates freely by hand in this position.

2) Hand start all 3 bolts and finger tighten before final tightening to ensure correct converter alignment. After installation, adjust shift linkage and downshift cable. Fill transmission with fluid.

JAGUAR

XJS

REMOVAL

1) Drive vehicle onto ramp. Remove transmission dipstick. Unscrew and remove bolt securing dipstick upper tube to lifting eye bracket. Remove dipstick upper tube.

2) Loosen fender supports to firewall securing bolt. Remove fender support-to-fender attaching bolts. Remove support from fender clamps. Secure fender supports away from fenders.

3) Unscrew and remove handles from Engine Lifting Hooks (MS 53 A). Attach hooks to rear lifting eyes. Attach engine support. Attach and tighten handles. Raise ramp.

4) Unscrew and remove nuts and bolts holding intermediate exhaust pipes, rotating flanges for access. Disconnect exhaust pipes and remove sealers. Remove intermediate and rear heat shields.

5) Secure exhaust pipes aside. Remove front heat shields. Remove rear mount center nut and spacer. Put block of wood between jack and transmission rear mount. Remove rear mount bolts and spacers. Lower jack. Remove rear mounts, wooden block and jack.

6) Remove crossmember. Remove propeller shaft and set aside. Working from above engine compartment, loosen hooks 10 turns only. From beneath vehicle, disconnect speedometer cable from transmission.

7) Unscrew nut holding selector pin to lever and disconnect cable. Unscrew bolt holding selector cable to support bracket and secure cable aside. Disconnect kickdown solenoid feed wire and remove clamp bolt holding feed wire to transmission.

8) Disconnect modulator capsule vacuum tube. Remove bolt and clamp plate holding modulator. Place container under modulator, remove modulator and partially drain transmission fluid. Remove and discard modulator "O" ring.

9) Unscrew cooler pipe union nuts from unions. Unscrew bolt holding cooler pipe bracket to engine sump. Remove spacer. Disconnect and plug cooler pipes. Remove access cover.

JAGUAR (Cont.)

10) Remove bolts holding converter to drive plate. Turn drive plate for access. Remove right side heat shield. Remove and secure catalytic converter from manifold.

11) Remove all engine-to-transmission attaching bolts except 2 lower left side bolts and lower starter attaching bolt. Remove dipstick tube and position tube/vacuum pipe mounting bracket along the vacuum pipe.

12) Using an Epco Lift (V1000), remove front and rear clamps. Attach lift to transmission and remove weight from transmission. Adjust tilt angle and side clamps. Tighten clamps.

13) Fit chain to right side arm, fit securing peg and pass chain over transmission into front arm. Tighten chain adjuster. Remove remaining securing bolts, lower unit and remove transmission from beneath vehicle.

INSTALLATION

1) With lift unit attached, position speedometer cable, selector cable, kickdown solenoid feed wire and vacuum pipe. Align transmission mating flange over locating dowels.

2) Install and tighten 3 lower left transmission bolts. Install starter. Loosen lift chain and remove pin from left side arm. Remove chain assembly. Lower and remove lift. Tighten remaining securing bolts.

3) Place dipstick pipe clamp on torque converter housing and fit lower dipstick tube. Connect dipstick tube to transmission and pull vacuum pipe through bracket. Install, but do not tighten, 2 accessible torque converter/drive plate bolts.

4) Install remaining drive plate bolts. Turn drive plate and tighten first 4 bolts. Install torque converter cover plate. Loosen left side nut attaching strap to cover and position strap aside.

5) Remove plugs from cooler pipes and connect pipes to transmission. Position cooler pipe mounting bracket, fit spacer and bolt and secure bracket to engine sump.

6) Fit new "O" ring to modulator capsule and fit modulator to transmission with clamp plate and bolt. Connect vacuum pipe to modulator. Connect kickdown solenoid feed wire to transmission.

7) Install selector cable bracket to mount and connect cable to lever. Fit and tighten selector pin securing nut. Working from above engine, tighten hook handles to raise engine.

8) Working from beneath vehicle, connect propeller shaft to transmission flange. Position and align crossmember and install attaching bolts. Place ramp jack under rear mount with wooden block. Raise jack and align attachment holes.

9) Install rear spacers and bolts. Remove jack and wooden block. Install rear mounting spacer and center nut. Install right side catalyst to manifold. Attach converter cover strap to catalyst.

10) Install exhaust pipes and heat shields. Lower ramp. Remove support hook handles and support. Install dipstick upper tube and fender stays. Fill transmission with fluid.

XJ6

REMOVAL

1) Disconnect battery cable. Remove transmission dipstick from tube and bolts securing tube to manifold. Remove upper fan shroud and disconnect kickdown cable from throttle bellcrank.

2) Raise vehicle on hoist. Remove transmission fill tube, exhaust intermediate pipe and heat shields. Secure transmission jack-to-transmission, and raise enough to support weight of transmission. Remove rear transmission support plate. Remove mount-to-transmission securing bolts and remove mount.

3) Remove drive shaft from vehicle as a unit. Lower transmission jack to position required to remove transmission, but do not remove transission at this time. Remove rubber pad from top of transmission.

4) Position Engine Support (MS 53A) and attach to rear lifting eye on engine. Turn adjusting nut to support weight of engine. Take care not to damage water heater valve.

5) From transmission unit selector lever, remove nut to release ball peg on inner selector cable. Remove set screw and spring washer securing outer selector cable clamp. Disconnect speedometer cable from transmission.

6) Remove dipstick tube and cover on front of converter housing. Remove 4 bolts retaining torque converter to drive plate. Disconnect oil cooler lines from transmission case and plug lines.

7) Remove all converter housing-to-engine bolts. Move starter out of way. Separate and lower transmission from engine.

INSTALLATION

Secure transmission to jack, fit torque converter to transmission and reverse removal procedure to complete installation.

MAZDA

GLC & 626

REMOVAL

1) Drain all fluid from tranxaxle assembly (oil pan must be removed to completely drain transaxle as drain plug alone will not drain all fluid). Disconnect negative cable from battery. Disconnect speedometer cable, inhibitor switch connector, neutral switch connector and kickdown solenoid connector.

2) Remove vacuum diaphragm line. Raise front end of vehicle and support. Remove wheels, disconnect lower control arm ball joints and pull drive shafts out of transaxle. Use care when removing drive shafts to avoid stressing outer constant velocity joint to its limit, as this will damage the joint. Remove engine undercover.

3) Attach engine support to engine hanger and support engine. Remove shift linkage from transaxle assembly. Remove crossmember. Disconnect oil hose from oil pipe and plug ends of hose and pipe. Remove rear

MAZDA (Cont.)

transmission mount. Remove starter, end cover and torque converter-to-drive plate retaining bolts.

4) Support transaxle with jack and remove transaxle-to-engine retaining bolts. Lower transaxle assembly out of vehicle. Use care when removing transaxle so that torque converter does not fall out.

INSTALLATION

To install, reverse removal procedure.

RX-7

REMOVAL

1) Disconnect negative battery cable. Remove air cleaner, converter housing upper and side covers, and top bolts attaching transmission to engine. On models so equipped, disengage torsion shaft from accelerator linkage. Raise vehicle and support with safety stands.

2) Drain fluid from transmission. Remove propeller shaft. Use output shaft plug to prevent oil leakage from rear of transmission. Remove any exhaust mounts attached to transmission. Disconnect exhaust pipe from manifold. Disconnect shift linkage from manual shaft on transmission.

3) Disconnect all electrical and vacuum leads from transmission. Disconnect speedometer cable. Remove oil filler tube from transmission, then disconnect both oil cooler pipes.

4) Disconnect governor tube from converter housing and transmission case (if equipped). Support transmission with wood block between oil pan and transmission jack.

5) Remove converter inspection plate. Mark converter and flywheel for realignment reference during installation. Remove torque converter-to-flywheel attaching bolts.

6) Remove rear mount and crossmember mounting bolts. Remove starter (lower transmission as needed to gain access to starter bolts). Remove transmission-to-engine bolts and slowly lower transmission out of vehicle.

INSTALLATION

Reverse removal procedure to install transmission, noting the following: When installing torque converter, ensure notch in converter lines up with notch in oil pump. When bolting converter to flywheel, align mark made during removal to ensure proper alignment. After transmission is installed, rotate crankshaft several times to be sure that transmission rotates freely without binding.

MERCEDES-BENZ

190 SERIES

REMOVAL

NOTE: To avoid damaging compartment wall (firewall), attach a sheet metal panel to vehicle's compartment wall to protect insulating mat during all jobs where the transmission is lowered at the rear. Disconnect exhaust assembly at rear mounting bracket and fasten by means of a wire approximately 2 inches lower than bracket.

1) Disconnect negative cable on battery. Unscrew holder for oil filler pipe on cylinder head. Force off ball socket. Disconnect cable control for control pressure.

2) Pull out lock and loosen cable control. Unscrew drain plug on oil pan and torque converter. Drain fluid. Screw back drain plugs with new seals and tighten.

3) Remove 6 torque converter bolts. Remove crossmember with rear engine mount. Remove exhaust support. Remove companion plate on universal flange of transmission.

MERCEDES-BENZ (Cont.)

NOTE: Loosen soft companinon plate installed at transmission end by using a mandrel.

4) Disconnect exhaust system at rear mount. Remove shielding plate. Loosen propeller shaft clamping nut and push propeller shaft together as much as possible.

5) Pull cable from kickdown solenoid valve. Loosen tachometer shaft. Disconnect control rod on floor shift. Remove fastening clip for tachometer shaft.

6) Swivel locking bracket in upward direction and pull plug from starter lockout switch. Pull vacuum line from vacuum control unit. Pull out filler pipe in upward direction.

7) Remove oil cooler lines and clamps. Remove all transmission-to-engine mounting bolts. Slightly lift transmission with mounting. Slide transmission to the rear and carefully let dowm.

Installation

1) Place transmission on removing and installing fixture, turn torque converter so that one of 3 threaded plates is in alignment with bottom of bell housing. Lightly grease centering pin on torque converter. Connect control rod to transmission and secure.

2) Lift transmission, slide forward at engine level until converter housing rests against engine. Bolt transmission to engine. Fasten control pressure cable control and vacuum line to holder.

3) Fasten grounding strap by means of lower bolt. Connect oil cooler lines with new sealing rings. Bolt on fastening clamps. Insert oil filler pipe. Connect oil cooler line with new sealing rings.

4) Push plug on starter lockout switch and fold locking bracket in downward direction. Plug cable to kickdown solenoid valve. Slip in tachometer shaft and secure.

5) Attach control rod to floor shift and secure with clip. Install companion plate to universal flange of transmission. Install crossmember with rear engine mount, fasten cable for kickdown solenoid valve.

6) Fasten tachometer shaft with clip. Tigthen propeller shaft clamping nut. Install shielding plate under propeller shaft intermediate bearing. Install exhaust system. Attach cable control for control pressure insert lock. Push on ball socket.

300, 380 & 500 SERIES

REMOVAL

1) Disconnect negative battery cable. Remove transmission oil filler pipe clamp from cylinder head. Force off ball socket on control wire linkage pivot. Pull out wire lock and loosen control wire. Compress tabs on plastic clip and pull retainer control wire from bracket.

2) Raise vehicle on hoist. Remove cross yoke center body support. Remove oil pan drain plug and drain oil from transmission. Remove drain plug from torque converter and drain. Reinstall drain plugs. Remove torque converter cover plates. Remove 6 bolts that secure torque converter-to-drive plate.

3) Place a block of wood between engine oil pan and front crossmember. Disconnect exhaust pipes at coupler at rear of transmission and remove exhaust pipes. Remove rear crossmember and rear transmission mount as an assembly. Remove cable strap and unscrew kickdown solenoid valve cable. Remove impulse transmitter retaining screws and remove transmitter.

4) Remove bolts attaching transmission companion flange to propeller shaft 3-arm flange. Remove exhaust shielding plate. Loosen propeller shaft clamping nut and slide propeller shaft as far rearward as possible. Turn starter lock-out switch plug retainer ring in upward direction. Carefully remove plug with 2 screwdrivers.

5) Disconnect shift control rod from range selector lever. Unscrew holder and remove vacuum line from vacuum control unit. Disconnect oil cooler lines from transmission. Remove oil filler tube retainer bolt and push tube upward to remove.

6) Remove all engine-to-transmission attaching bolts except for 2 bottom bolts. Slightly raise transmission with transmission jack. Remove 2 bottom engine-to-transmission bolts. Push transmission and jack toward rear of vehicle as far as possible. Remove transmission from vehicle. Place transmission in vertical position. Install Converter Handles (065) and lift converter from transmission.

INSTALLATION

Reverse removal procedures and note the following: When installing torque converter to transmission, coat converter tangs, turbine and stator shaft with assembly lubricant. Be sure that converter is fully seated in transmission before installing in vehicle.

MITSUBISHI

ALL FWD MODELS

REMOVAL

1) Remove battery and battery tray. Remove reservoir tank and windshield washer tank. Remove air cleaner case. Disconnect throttle control cable from carburetor.

2) Disconnect control cable from transaxle. Disconnect inhibitor switch connector, oil cooler hoses and speedometer from transaxle. Plug oil cooler hoses. Disconnect starter harness and remove starter.

3) Lift vehicle and remove wheels. Drain transmission fluid. Remove strut bars and stabilizer bars from lower control arms. Remove right and left drive shafts from transaxle and set them aside.

4) Remove bell housing cover. Remove 3 special bolts (3 pieces) connecting converter with drive plate. Turn engine for access to all 3 bolts. Push torque converter into transaxle after bolt removal.

5) Remove upper 5 bolts connecting transaxle to engine. Support a wide area of lower part of transaxle with transmission jack. Remove remaining engine connecting bolts. Remove transaxle mount insulator bolts.

6) Remove blank cap from inside right fender shield and remove installation bolts. Remove transaxle insulator and mounting brackets. Slide transaxle assembly to the right and lower it to remove.

MITSUBISHI (Cont.)

INSTALLATION

Reverse removal procedures and note the following: Be sure to install torque converter first to transaxle and then to engine. Refill transaxle fluid to specified level. Adjust control cables. Ensure that inhibitor switch harness does not contact transaxle insulator bracket.

MONTERO & PICKUP

REMOVAL

1) Drain transmission. Raise and support vehicle. Disconnect control rod, throttle linkage and cooler lines to transmission fittings. Remove starter motor. Remove converter to drive plate bolts.

2) Mark propeller shaft and universal joints for reassembly reference. Remove propeller shaft. Disconnect control rod from manual control lever. Disconnect throttle rod from transmission throttle lever.

3) Support transmission with hydraulic jack. Remove oil filter tube and speedometer cable. Remove extension housing mount from rear insulator, raise transmission and remove rear engine support bracket from body. Lower and remove transmission from vehicle.

INSTALLATION

Reverse removal procedures and note the following: Tighten converter housing bolts to 31-40 ft. lbs. (42-54 N.m). Align reference marks before connecting propeller shaft.

STARION

REMOVAL

1) Disconnect battery ground cable. Remove oil cooler lines at transmission. Remove starter motor and cooler line bracket. Loosen pan to drain transmission.

2) Mark converter and drive plate for reassembly reference. Using socket wrench on crankshaft vibration damper bolt, rotate engine clockwise to position converter attaching bolts for removal. Remove bolts and propeller shaft.

3) Disconnect electrical leads. Disconnect gearshift rod and torque shaft assembly, throttle rod lever from left side of transmission, and linkage bellcrank (if so equipped) from transmission.

4) Remove oil filler tube and speedometer cable. Support rear of engine with engine support fixture. With a transmission support on a service jack, support transmission. Raise transmission slightly to relieve load on supports.

5) Remove bolts securing transmission mount to crossmember and crossmember to frame, then remove crossmember. Remove all converter housing bolts, then carefully work transmission and converter assembly rearward off engine block dowels and disengage converter hub from end of crankshaft.

6) Attach a small "C" clamp to edge of converter housing to hold converter in place during transmission removal. Lower transmission and remove from under vehicle. To remove converter assembly, remove "C" clamp from edge of converter housing and carefully slide assembly from transmission.

INSTALLATION

1) To install, reverse removal procedure. Install converter and test for full engagement by placing straight edge on face of converter housing. Surface of converter front cover lug should be at least 1/2" from rear of straightedge when converter is pushed all the way into transmission.

2) Attach a small "C" clamp to converter housing to hold converter in place during transmission installation. Inspect converter drive plate for distortion or cracks and replace if necessary.

3) Coat converter hub hole in crankshaft with multi-purpose grease. When drive plate replacement has been necessary, ensure both transmission dowel pins are in engine block and they are protruding far enough to hold transmission in alignment.

4) Place transmission and converter assembly on a jack and position under vehicle for installation. Raise or tilt as necessary to align transmission to engine. Rotate converter so that mark on converter (made during removal) will align with mark on drive plate.

5) Carefully work transmission assembly forward over engine block dowels with converter hub entering crankshaft opening. After transmission is in position on engine, install and tighten all bolts. Adjust shift and throttle linkage, then refill transmission with DEXRON II type automatic transmission fluid.

NISSAN

REAR WHEEL DRIVE MODELS

REMOVAL

1) On models so equipped, disengage torsion shaft from accelerator linkage. Raise vehicle and support with safety stands. Drain fluid from transmission. Remove propeller shaft.

2) Use output shaft plug to prevent oil leakage from rear of transmission. Remove any exhaust mounts attached to transmission. Disconnect exhaust pipe from manifold. Disconnect shift linkage from manual shaft on transmission.

3) Disconnect all electrical and vacuum leads from transmission. Disconnect speedometer cable. Remove oil filler tube from transmission, then disconnect both oil cooler pipes.

4) Disconnect governor tube from converter housing and transmission case (if equipped). Support transmission with wood block between oil pan and transmission jack. On Maxima and 200SX models, remove gussets from front of transmission.

NISSAN (Cont.)

5) On all models, remove converter inspection plate. Mark converter and flywheel for realignment reference during installation. Remove torque converter-to-flywheel attaching bolts.

6) Remove rear mount and crossmember mounting bolts. Remove starter (lower transmission as needed to gain access to starter bolts). Remove transmission-to-engine bolts and slowly lower transmission out of vehicle.

INSTALLATION

1) Reverse removal procedure to install transmission, noting the following: Check flywheel runout with dial indicator before installing transmission. Runout must not exceed .02" (.5 mm).

2) When installing torque converter, ensure that notch in converter lines up with notch in oil pump. Measure distance from front of converter housing to flywheel bolt mounting surface on converter. If distance is less than 1.38" (35.0 mm), converter or other components are incorrectly assembled.

FRONT WHEEL DRIVE MODELS

REMOVAL

1) Disconnect battery ground cable. Raise and support vehicle. Remove wheels and tires. Drain transaxle fluid. Remove left fender protector. Remove brake caliper and pry cotter pin out of hub. Loosen, do not remove, wheel hub nut from axle shaft while preventing hub from turning.

2) Remove tie rod end from steering knuckle. Remove lower ball joint and discard nut. Remove axle shaft from transaxle and discard axle shaft snap ring. Do not damage oil seal during axle shaft removal. Insert a bar or equivalent tool into each side of differential case to prevent dropping of side gear.

3) Remove knuckle attaching bolts and remove hub, knuckle and axle shaft as an assembly. Disconnect speedometer cable, throttle cable and control linkage. Remove fluid dipstick and tube assembly. Place transmission jack under engine and transaxle assembly. DO NOT place jack under oil pan drain plug.

4) Disconnect oil cooler lines. Remove inspection plate from torque converter. Rotate crankshaft and remove torque converter-to-drive plate bolts. Mark position of torque converter in relation to housing for installation reference. Remove engine mount bolts. Remove starter motor.

5) Remove transaxle-to-engine bolts. Gradually move jack to rear until transaxle can be removed. Carefully remove transaxle from vehicle by taking out through left wheel housing.

INSTALLATION

1) To install, reverse removal procedure. Measure drive plate runout with a dial indicator before installing torque converter. Runout should not exceed .020" (.5 mm). After installing torque converter to transaxle, ensure distance from converter housing surface to converter face ring is more than .83" (21 mm).

2) Apply sealant to torque converter bolts prior to installation. Align reference marks made during removal when installing converter. After converter is installed, rotate crankshaft several times and make sure transaxle rotates freely without binding.

PEUGEOT

ALL MODELS

REMOVAL

1) Open hood as far as possible without forcing and support open with block placed under safety hook. Disconnect negative battery cable. Remove air duct between metering unit and butterfly housing. Remove 2 bolts from control pressure regulator.

2) Remove upper and lower radiator mounts and fan shroud. Place a piece of cardboard between radiator and fan to protect radiator from damage during transmission removal. Disconnect kickdown control cable at throttle linkage.

3) Remove exhaust-to-manifold nuts. Disconnect all exhaust system hangers. Remove heat shield from above muffler. Remove front seat stiffener located above muffler.

4) Remove vibration damper from propeller shaft tube. Remove extension housing bracket bolts. Disconnect differential from its mount. Mark position of lower steering column flange coupling and remove bolts.

5) On models with power steering, remove front crossmember-to-front mount bolts and replace with 2" (50 mm) bolts. Remove remaining crossmember bolts. Lower crossmember about 2" (50 mm) by unscrewing 2 bolts in crossmember. On all other models, remove steering box mounting bolts and lower steering gear without disconnecting links.

6) On all models, drain transmission fluid. Disconnect and plug cooler lines at transmission. Remove starter motor bolts. Disconnect filler tube from transmission. Remove torque converter cover plate and sensor from bellhousing. DO NOT alter sensor adjustment.

7) Remove torque converter-to-flywheel bolts. Using a retainer, secure torque converter in housing so it will not fall out during transmission removal. Place jack under transmission and remove 4 propeller shaft-to-transmission bolts.

8) Separate transmission from tube about .8" (20 mm) and install Retaining Plate (8.0403SZ) between the 2 units. Install 2 bolts to hold plate in place.

9) Pull differential and propeller shaft assembly to the rear of vehicle and allow front of tube to rest on rear crossmember. Disconnect gear shift linkage, speedometer and electrical connections from transmission. Lower and tilt transmission as far as possible.

10) Install engine lift equipment to front of engine. Lift engine far enough to gain access to upper transmission-to-engine bolts. Remove bolts and remove transmission from vehicle.

INSTALLATION

Reverse removal procedure to install, noting the following: Apply grease to torque converter pilot bushing. Adjust shift and throttle linkage as needed. Fill transmission with fluid and check for leaks.

Automatic Transmission Removal

PORSCHE

944

REMOVAL

1) Remove heat shield and rear muffler bracket. Detach axle shafts at transaxle. Suspend axle shafts in horizontal position to prevent damage to dust covers. Remove transaxle oil filter shield.

2) Detach selector and transaxle lever cables. Remove converter bolts through hole in torque converter housing. Support transaxle with jack and remove transaxle-to-engine bolts and transaxle mounts. Slide transaxle toward rear of vehicle and remove.

INSTALLATION

Reverse removal procedures to install, noting the following: Ensure pump shaft and torque converter are fully seated in transaxle or damage to internal components may result during installation.

928S

REMOVAL

1) Disconnect and remove battery. Remove self-locking nuts from spring struts in trunk. Disconnect multiple plug in spare wheel well and pull toward rear. Disconnect parking brake cable and lock. Remove rear wheels and splash shield. Drain torque converter and transmission oil sump. Remove oil filler tube. Disconnect transmission oil cooler lines.

2) Remove lower body brace. Disconnect exhaust pipe from catalytic converter. Remove exhaust pipe heat shields. Remove battery box. Remove rubber cap from inspection hole in front converter housing and turn crankshaft to position coupling so that socket head screw can be removed. Disconnect brake calipers and suspend with wire. Disconnect axle shafts and swing out of the way. Remove rear reinforcement plate. Disconnect stabilizer bar from lower control arm.

3) Support transaxle with Support (9164) and remove 2 bolts from transaxle mounts. Remove 2 bolts holding rear axle crossmember to frame. Mark position of eccentric bolts and remove bolts. Mark position of rear axle crossmember for reinstallation. Place jack under transaxle crossmember and remove mounting bolts from crossmember.

4) Lower rear axle carefully and take care that spring struts, crossmember and bearing brackets do not tilt. Mount Special Tool (9163) on adjustable floor jack. Lift transaxle and remove Special Tool (9164). Lower transaxle slightly and remove selector lever. Disconnect modulator vacuum line. Remove 6 bolts from central tube. Pull transaxle out of coupling splines and lower carefully.

NOTE: **Transaxle has to be lowered as far as possible to gain access to all tube bolts.**

INSTALLATION

To install, reverse removal procedure and check rear end alignment.

RENAULT

FUEGO & SPORTWAGON

REMOVAL

1) Raise and support vehicle. Disconnect battery. Drain transmission fluid. Disconnect vacuum capsule hose from intake manifold. Disconnect transaxle wiring connectors and remove support. Insert Spacer (T. Av. 509-01) between lower shock mounting base and lower control arm pivot shaft on each side.

Fig. 1: Location of Spacer in Front Suspension

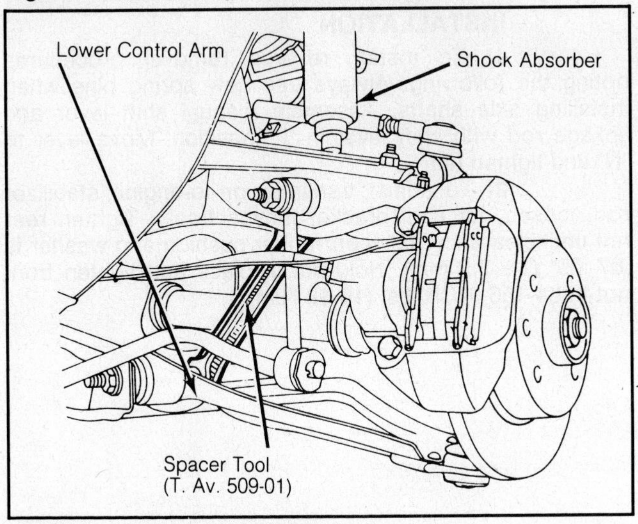

Install tool between lower shock mount and lower control are pivot shaft.

2) Remove drive shaft retaining roll pins with drift. Separate tie rod end ball joints and upper control arm ball joints from steering knuckle using puller. Tilt axle carriers away from transaxle to separate drive shafts from side gears.

3) With shift lever in neutral position, disconnect shift rod at entry to transaxle and at the shift lever. Remove dipstick and inspection plate. Remove 3 torque converter retaining bolts. Remove exhaust pipe bracket nut at transaxle.

4) Position Transmission Jack (Desvil 701 ST) under rear of transaxle and raise until assembly is supported on the 4 studs. Remove transaxle mounts. Lower assembly enough to remove speedometer and governor cables. Remove engine-to-transaxle retaining bolts. Lower transaxle from vehicle. Attach Torque Converter Retaining Strap (B. Vi. 465 Ref. D) to hold torque converter in place in case.

INSTALLATION

1) Reverse removal procedures to install, noting the following: Lightly lubricate axle shaft splined ends before installing. Tilt stub axle carrier as needed to line up roll pin holes. If equipped with TDC sensor, make sure it is adjusted correctly when installed.

2) If a new TDC sensor is used, install into position until pegs (3) on sensor contact flywheel. Tighten retaining screw. If reusing an old sensor, install until it contacts flywheel, mark position with a fine line on sensor body, and back sensor out about .04" (1 mm). Tighten retaining screw.

3) Adjust selector lever and governor cable. Check computer and governor connections and make sure ground wire is connected.

Automatic Transmission Removal

SAAB

ALL MODELS

REMOVAL

NOTE: **Engine and transaxle must be removed as an assembly.**

1) Disconnect positive battery terminal from battery. Drain radiator. Disconnect windshield washer hose from hood. Remove hood.

2) Disconnect all engine or transaxle electrical connections as needed for engine removal. Remove air cleaner, preheater hose and crankcase ventilation hose.

3) Disconnect fuel line and plug. Disconnect choke, throttle cable, hose to expansion tank and brake servo vacuum hose. Remove clamps from drivers side inner universal joint.

4) Place special tool 83 93 209 between the upper control arm underside and frame (insert tool from engine compartment side). Raise and support vehicle.

5) Remove lower control arm-to-ball joint bolts. Pull control arm assembly from control arm and support with jack stand.

6) Remove gear selector cable screw at transaxle. Pull cable out of transaxle and slide back spring loaded sleeve, then disconnect from control lever. Disconnect speedometer cable from transaxle. Remove rear engine mounting bolts.

7) Loosen front engine mounting nut so mount can be lifted from bracket. Attach engine lifting device on 2 engine lifting lugs and raise engine slightly. Move engine assembly side to side to free universal joints. Lift assembly from vehicle and place on engine stand.

8) To separate transaxle from engine, drain engine oil and remove inspection cover. Remove starter. Disconnect throttle cable. Remove engine-to-transaxle bolts. Remove 4 converter-to-flex plate bolts. Turn flex plate until plate angles are horizontal and lift engine off of transaxle.

INSTALLATION

1) To install, reverse removal procedure and note the following: Mating surfaces of transaxle and engine must be thoroughly clean. Use gasket sealer on new gasket when assembling transaxle and engine. Apply sealer to bolts indicated in *Fig. 1* of SAAB MANUAL TRANSAXLE REMOVAL procedure.

2) Pack inner universal joints with grease, adjust shift cable if necessary and check cooling system for leaks.

SUBARU

ALL MODELS

REMOVAL

1) Remove spare tire from engine compartment. Disconnect negative battery cable. Remove spare tire mount. Disconnect transmission diaphragm vacuum hose. Disconnect speedometer cable from transmission and unfasten clip on cable.

2) Disconnect back-up light switch connector from transmission, ground cable from body and starter harness. Remove torque converter-to-drive plate retaining bolts (4) through hole in torque converter housing (timing hole). Be careful that bolts do not fall into housing. Disconnect transmission fluid lines from transmission and drain transmission fluid.

3) Remove starter (cable still attached) and set aside. Remove upper transmission-to-engine retaining bolts and loosen lower nuts. Loosen retaining nut on transmission-to-engine stabilizer rod (transmission side of bracket) not more than .4" (10 mm). Tighten nut on opposite side by an equal amount. Tilt engine back slightly.

4) Disconnect oxygen sensor harness and unclamp. Raise front of vehicle and remove exhaust pipe assembly. Use care not to damage oxygen sensor during exhaust removal. Drain transmission fluid and disconnect oil supply pipe. With shift lever in "P" position, mark location of connector nut on manual lever. Separate manual lever from linkage rod.

5) Remove suspension stabilizer bar and transverse link-to-front crossmember retaining bolts (both sides). Lower transverse links. Drive out left and right axle shaft retaining spring pins. Push wheels toward outside of vehicle to separate axle shafts from transmission drive shafts.

6) Remove transmission mount-to-crossmember attaching nut and support transmission on a jack. Remove the crossmember. Remove 2 transmission-to-engine retaining nuts that were loosened in step **3)**. Pull transmission away from engine and lower out of vehicle.

INSTALLATION

1) To install, reverse removal procedures noting the following: Always use new spring pins when installing axle shafts. Assemble manual shift lever and linkage rod with shift lever in "P" position. Move lever to "N" and tighten nut.

2) To adjust transmission-to-engine stabilizer rod, loosen nut until bracket moves freely. Tighten rear nut until clearance between rubber cushion and washer is .07-.09" (1.8-2.2 mm). Hold nut in place and tighten front nut to 84-156 INCH lbs. (10-18 N.m).

Automatic Transmission Removal

TOYOTA

CAMRY

REMOVAL

1) Remove front and rear mounts. Remove left dust cover and mounting bracket. Remove side gear shaft, intermediate shaft and universal joint from transaxle. Remove control cable bracket and stiffener plate. Remove torque converter dust cover and locking plate.

2) Remove 6 torque converter mounting bolts. Turn crankshaft to gain access to each bolt. Hold crankshaft pulley nut with a wrench. Remove starter. Remove transaxle mounting bolts.

3) Install guide pin in one of the torque converter bolt holes. Pry on end of guide pin to begin moving transmission with converter. Remove transaxle assembly from engine.

INSTALLATION

1) Install torque converter in transmission. Using calipers and a straightedge, measure from installed surface to front surface of transmission housing. Correct distance should be .51" (13 mm).

2) Install guide pin in torque converter. Align guide pin with one of the drive plate holes. Align 2 knock pins on block with the converter housing. Temporarily install one bolt.

3) Install transmission housing mounting bolts. Tighten 12 mm bolts to 47 ft. lbs. (64 N.m) and 10 mm bolts to 25 ft. lbs. (34 N.m). Install starter. Remove guide pin. Install 6 torque converter bolts finger tight. Turn crankshaft to gain access. Tighten bolts evenly to 13 ft. lbs. (18 N.m).

4) Install torque converter dust cover. Lock transaxle mounting bolt near differential with the locking plate and one dust cover mounting bolt. Tighten bolts to 18 ft. lbs. (24 N.m).

5) Install stiffener plate and tighten bolts to 27 ft. lbs. (37 N.m). Install control cable bracket. Install side gear shaft and universal joint. Install left dust cover. Install front and rear mounts.

CELICA

REMOVAL

1) Disconnect negative battery cable. Drain coolant. Disconnect upper radiator hose. Remove air intake connector. Disconnect transmission throttle cable. Raise vehicle and drain transmission.

2) Disconnect wiring connectors to neutral start and back-up light switches. Remove intermediate shaft with center bearing from propeller shaft. Disconnect manual shift linkage. Disconnect speedometer cable.

3) Remove sliding yoke from gear housing and shift. Disconnect 2 oil cooler lines. Disconnect front exhaust pipe from rear pipe. Remove pipe clamp from transmission housing. Disconnect pipe from exhaust manifold and remove exhaust pipe from vehicle.

4) Remove power steering oil cooler clamp. Remove automatic transmission oil cooler pipe clamp at left of cylinder block. Remove power steering pressure line clamp.

5) Using Remover (SST09611-22012), disconnect both tie rod ends. Remove gear housing and suspend at crossmember. Remove both stiffener plates from transmission housing. Jack up transmission slightly to take weight off rear crossmember.

6) Remove rear support member, removing rubber exhaust hanger and ground strap if equipped. Remove engine under cover to gain access to crankshaft pulley. Lower transmission on wood piece. Pry out rubber plugs from service holes for torque converter.

7) Turn crankshaft as necessary to gain access to torque converter bolts and remove bolts. Install guide pin or cut off bolt in a torque converter bolt hole. Remove transmission housing mounting bolts. Pry on end of guide pin to start transmission movement to rear of vehicle.

8) Move transmission toward rear of vehicle, being careful not to catch throttle cable or neutral start switch cable. Keep oil pan positioned down. Place pan under converter housing and remove converter, pulling straight off and allowing fluid to drain into pan. If not already removed, remove filter tube and rear transmission support with ground strap.

INSTALLATION

1) Measure drive plate runout with dial indicator. If runout exceeds .0079" (.20 mm), or if ring gear is damaged, replace drive plate. If installing new drive plate, note positioning of spacers and tighten with new bolts.

2) Measure torque converter sleeve runout. If runout exceeds .012" (.30 mm), try to correct by repositioning converter. If runout cannot be corrected in this manner, torque converter must be replaced. Be sure to mark position of converter to ensure correct installation.

3) Install filler tube. Apply grease to center hub of torque converter and pilot hole in drive plate. Install torque converter in transmission. Refill with fresh ATF. Check torque converter installation.

4) Using calipers and straightedge, check that distance from center of hub to front surface of transmission housing is .79" (20 mm). Install guide pin in torque converter. Install transmission assembly. Align guide pin with a drive plate hole.

5) Align upper starter stud with hole on engine plate. Align 2 sleeves on block with converter housing. Tighten transmission housing mounting bolts. Install and tighten torque converter bolts.

6) To complete installation, reverse removal procedure. Fill transmission with automatic transmission fluid. Road test vehicle for proper operation of all functions.

COROLLA

REMOVAL

1) Disconnect negative battery cable. Drain coolant. Disconnect upper radiator hose. Remove air cleaner. Disconnect transmission throttle cable. Raise vehicle and drain transmission.

2) Disconnect wiring connectors to neutral start and back-up light switches. Remove propeller shaft. Remove front exhaust pipe. Disconnect 2 oil cooler lines. Remove power steering gear housing.

3) Disconnect manual shift linkage. Disconnect speedometer cable. Remove both stiffener plates from transmission housing. Jack up transmission slightly. Remove rear support member, rubber exhaust hanger and ground strap.

4) Remove engine under cover. Pry out rubber plug from service hole at rear of engine. Turn crankshaft

TOYOTA (Cont.)

to gain access to each torque converter mounting bolt. Remove 6 mounting bolts.

5) Install guide pin or cut off bolt in a torque converter bolt hole. Remove transmission housing mounting bolts. Pry on end of guide pin to start transmission movement to rear of vehicle.

6) Move transmission toward rear of vehicle, being careful not to catch throttle cable or neutral start switch cable. Keep oil pan positioned down.

7) Place pan under converter housing and remove converter, pulling straight off and allowing fluid to drain into pan. Remove filter tube and rear transmission support with ground strap.

INSTALLATION

1) Measure drive plate runout with dial indicator. If runout exceeds .0079" (.20 mm), or if ring gear is damaged, replace drive plate. If installing new drive plate, note positioning of spacers and tighten with new bolts.

2) Measure torque converter sleeve runout. If runout exceeds .012" (.30 mm), try to correct by repositioning converter. If runout cannot be corrected in this manner, torque converter must be replaced. Be sure to mark position of converter to ensure correct installation.

3) Install rear transmission mount on extension housing. Install filler tube. Apply grease to center hub of torque converter and pilot hole in drive plate. Install torque converter in transmission. Refill with fresh ATF. Check torque converter installation.

4) Ensure that distance from center of hub to front surface of transmission housing is .91" (23 mm). Install guide pin in torque converter. Install transmission assembly. Align guide pin with a drive plate hole.

5) Align upper starter stud with hole on engine plate. Align 2 sleeves on block with converter housing. Tighten transmission housing mounting bolts. Install and tighten torque converter bolts.

6) To complete installation, reverse removal procedure. Fill transmission with automatic transmission fluid. Road test vehicle for proper operation of all functions.

CRESSIDA & SUPRA

REMOVAL

1) Disconnect negative battery cable. Drain coolant. Disconnect upper radiator hose. Remove air intake connector. Disconnect transmission throttle cable. Raise vehicle and drain transmission.

2) Disconnect wiring connectors to neutral start and back-up light switches. Remove intermediate shaft with center bearing from propeller shaft. Disconnect exhaust pipe at rear side of converter. Remove 2 rubber hangers and pipe clamp from transmission case.

3) Disconnect 2 oil cooler lines. Disconnect manual shift linkage and speedometer cable. Remove exhaust pipe bracket and converter cover stiffener plates from transmission housing and cylinder block.

4) Remove sliding yoke from gear housing. Using Remover (SST09611-22012), disconnect both tie rod ends. Remove fluid line clamps. Remove 4 bolts and remove 2 brackets and rubber insulator. Remove gear housing from crossmember and suspend it from frame.

5) Jack up transmission enough to remove weight from rear support member. Remove ground cable from rear support member. Install a wooden block between cowl panel and cylinder head rear end to prevent damage to heater hose. Remove rear support member.

6) Remove engine under cover. Remove 6 torque converter mounting bolts. Turn crankshaft to gain access to each bolt. Install guide pin in one of the torque converter bolt holes.

7) Remove starter and transmission housing mounting bolts. Pry on end of guide pin to start transmission movement to rear of vehicle. Move transmission toward rear of vehicle, being careful not to catch throttle cable or neutral start switch cable.

8) Keep oil pan positioned down. Place pan under converter housing and remove converter, pulling straight off and allowing fluid to drain into pan. If not already removed, remove filter tube and rear transmission support with ground strap.

INSTALLATION

1) Measure drive plate runout with dial indicator. If runout exceeds .0079" (.20 mm), or if ring gear is damaged, replace drive plate. If installing new drive plate, note positioning of spacers and tighten with new bolts.

2) Measure torque converter sleeve runout. If runout exceeds .012" (.30 mm), try to correct by repositioning converter. If runout cannot be corrected in this manner, torque converter must be replaced. Be sure to mark position of converter to ensure correct installation.

3) Install rear transmission mount on extension housing. Install filler tube. Apply grease to center hub of torque converter and pilot hole in drive plate. Install torque converter in transmission. Refill with fresh ATF. Check torque converter installation.

4) Ensure that distance from center of hub to front surface of transmission housing is 1.02" (26 mm). Install guide pin in torque converter. Install transmission assembly. Align guide pin with a drive plate hole.

5) Align upper starter stud with hole on engine plate. Align 2 sleeves on block with converter housing. Tighten transmission housing mounting bolts. Install and tighten torque converter bolts.

6) To complete installation, reverse removal procedure. Fill transmission with automatic transmission fluid. Road test vehicle for proper operation of all functions.

PICKUP

REMOVAL

1) Disconnect negative battery cable. Remove air cleaner. Loosen transmission throttle cable adjusting nuts. Disconnect cable housing from bracket. Remove clip from cable guide and disconnect guide grommet. Disconnect cable from carburetor linkage.

2) Remove upper monuting nut on starter. Raise vehicle and drain transmission. Disconnect wiring connectors to neutral start and back-up light switches. Remove starter. Remove propeller shaft. Disconnect speedometer cable. Disconnect manual shift linkage.

3) Disconnect 2 oil cooler lines. Disconnect exhaust pipe clamp and remove oil filler tube. Jack up

Automatic Transmission Removal

TOYOTA (Cont.)

transmission slightly. Remove rear engine mount with bracket. Remove engine under cover.

4) Insert wooden block between engine oil pan and crossmember. Lower transmission and rest engine on crossmember. Pry out rubber plugs from service holes at rear of engine. Turn cranksahft to gain access to each bolt and remove 6 torque converter mounting bolts.

5) Install guide pin in one of the torque converter bolt holes. Remove transmission housing mounting bolts. Pry on end of guide pin to start transmission movement to rear of vehicle.

6) Move transmission toward rear of vehicle, being careful not to catch throttle cable or neutral start switch cable. Keep oil pan positioned down. Place pan under converter housing and remove converter, pulling straight off and allowing fluid to drain into pan.

INSTALLATION

1) Measure drive plate runout with dial indicator. If runout exceeds .0079" (.20 mm), or if ring gear is damaged, replace drive plate. If installing new drive plate, note positioning of spacers and tighten with new bolts.

2) Measure torque converter sleeve runout. If runout exceeds .012" (.30 mm), try to correct by repositioning converter. If runout cannot be corrected in this manner, torque converter must be replaced. Be sure to mark position of converter to ensure correct installation.

3) Apply grease to center hub of torque converter and pilot hole in drive plate. Install torque converter in transmission. Refill with fresh ATF. Check torque converter installation.

4) Using calipers and a straightedge, measure from center hub to front surface of transmission housing. Ensure that distance is .79" (20 mm). Install guide pin in torque converter. Install transmission assembly. Align guide pin with a drive plate hole.

5) Align upper starter stud with hole on engine plate. Align 2 sleeves on block with converter housing. Tighten transmission housing mounting bolts. Install and tighten torque converter bolts.

6) To complete installation, reverse removal procedure. Fill transmission with automatic transmission fluid. Road test vehicle for proper operation of all functions.

TERCEL

REMOVAL

1) Disconnect battery ground cable and neutral safety switch. Partially drain radiator, then disconnect upper radiator hose at engine. Remove air cleaner. Disconnect throttle linkage, transmission cooler pipes and clamps. Disconnect cooler pipes from transmission.

2) Remove transmission-to-engine top bolts. Remove drive axle assemblies. Raise and support vehicle. Disconnect exhaust pipe from manifold. Remove 2 right side stiffener plate bolts. Disconnect shift control link bolt and speedometer cable (from transmission).

3) Remove engine under cover. Remove torque converter cover and torque converter-to-drive plate bolts. Hold crankshaft from turning when removing bolts. Disconnect oil cooler outlet pipe.

4) Place transmission jack under transmission and remove remaining transmission-to-engine bolts. Disconnect rear bond cable. Remove rear transmission support. Pull transmission to the rear to separate torque converter from drive plate. Lower transmission out of vehicle.

INSTALLATION

1) Before installing transmission, apply grease to torque converter shaft and crankshaft pilot hole. Install Guide Pin (SST09350-12010) in outside converter mounting hole. Align guide pin with 1 of the drive plate holes.

2) Be careful not to tilt transaxle forward or torque converter will slide out. Install transaxle to engine so that tip of converter goes into crankshaft hole. Remove guide pin. Temporarily insert 2 bolts about 3/8" (10 mm) and tighten evenly a little at a time.

3) Install 4 transaxle-to-engine bolts and install exhaust pipe bracket and throttle link bracket on the right side of the transaxle case. Install rear transaxle support member and tighten to 26-36 ft. lbs. (35-48 N.m). Remove temporarily installed bolts from torque converter and install 6 bolts finger tight.

4) Turn crankshaft to gain access. Tighten bolts evenly to 11-15 ft. lbs. (15-20 N.m). Install torque converter cover and connect bond cable. Connect cooler outlet pipe and tighten to 15-21 ft. lbs. (20-28 N.m). Install engine under cover. Install 2 right side stiffener plate bolts. Install exhaust pipe. Connect speedometer and rear bond cable.

5) Align shift lever and control link at neutral position. Connect control link. Lower vehicle. Install both drive shafts. Connect oil cooler inlet pipe. Install cooler pipe clamp. Connect throttle linkage. Connect all wiring connectors. To complete installation, reverse removal procedure.

6) Check and adjust wheel alignment, throttle link rod and selector lever if necessary. Fill transmission with automatic transmission fluid Type F. Fill differential with 1 quart of SAE 80W-90 gear oil.

VAN

REMOVAL

1) Disconnect negative battery cable. Loosen transmission throttle cable adjustment nuts. Disconnect cable housing from bracket. Disconnect cable from throttle body.

2) Disconnect Neutral start switch, back-up light and overdrive solenoid connectors. Raise vehicle and drain transmission. Remove propeller shaft. Disconnect exhaust pipe clamp from transmission housing. Remove exhaust pipe clamp.

3) Disconnect shift cable from transmission. Disconnect speedometer and bond cables. Loosen oil cooler nuts. Remove clamps and disconnect oil cooler lines. Remove starter.

4) Support transmission with jack. Remove 2 fuel tank mount bolts and support fual tank. Remove transmission mount through bolt. Remove stiffner plates from transmission housing.

5) Remove access cover from lower rear side of engine. Remove 6 torque converter attaching bolts. Install guide pin in torque converter. If necessary, a guide pin can be made by cutting off the head of a bolt.

6) Remove transmission mount bolts. Pry on end of guide pin to begin moving transmission and torque converter toward rear. Remove transmission and torque converter.

Automatic Transmission Removal

TOYOTA (Cont.)

NOTE: Position transmission down and toward rear. Do not catch throttle cable or Neutral safety switch cable. Keep oil pan positioned downward.

7) Place pan under converter housing and remove converter. Drain converter. Remove filler tube. Remove transmission mount.

INSTALLATION

1) Measure drive plate runout with dial indicator. If runout exceeds 0.0079" (0.20 mm), or if ring gear is damaged, replace drive plate. If installing a new drive plate, note position of spacers and tightn with new bolts.

2) Measure torque converter sleeve runout, If runout exceeds 0.012" (0.30 mm), try to correct by repositioning converter. If runout cannot be corrected in this manner, replace torque converter. Mark torque converter for correct installation.

3) Install rear transmission mount on extension housing. Install filler tube. Apply grease to center hub of torque converter and pilot hole in drive plate. Fill torque converter with ATF. Install torque converter in transmission.

4) Check torque converter installation by measuring the distance between transmission case and torque converter bolt hole pad. Correct distance is 1.02" (26 mm). Install guide pin in torque converter.

5) Aling guide pin with a hole in drive plate. Install transmission assembly and align upper starter stud with hole on engine plate. Align 2 sleeves on block with converter housing.

6) Tighten transmission housing mount bolts. Install and tighten torque converter bolts. To complete installation, reverse removal procedure. Fill transmission with ATF. Road test vehicle.

VOLKSWAGEN

GOLF, JETTA & SCIROCCO

REMOVAL

1) Disconnect battery ground strap and starter cable at battery. Disconnect speedometer cable from transmission. Remove 2 upper engine-to-transmission attaching bolts. Loosen left side transmission mount. Install Support Fixture (10-222).

2) Remove 5 rear transmission mounting bolts. Mark axle drive shafts for reassembly reference, and disconnect from final drive flanges. Remove starter bolts and position starter out of the way.

3) Remove transmission protection plate and converter cover plate, then remove drive plate-to-torque converter bolts. Place selector lever in "P" position and disconnect selector cable from transmission lever. Remove cable bracket from transmission, then disconnect accelerator and pedal cables from bracket.

4) Support transmission with Fixture (US 4470) attached to engine hoist. Remove left side engine/transmission mount. Detach side carrier and mount from transmission. Remove front mount. Remove lower transmission-to-engine bolt. Remove remaining transmission-to-engine bolts. Lift transmission slightly and, taking care not to allow converter to drop, lower transmission from vehicle.

INSTALLATION

1) Reverse removal procedure and note the following: Ensure that torque converter is fully seated on one-way clutch support. Adjust selector lever cable.

2) To check converter installation, lay a straight edge across converter housing and measure distance from straight edge to center converter hub. If distance is less than 1.2" (30 mm), converter is not fully engaged.

QUANTUM

REMOVAL

1) Disconnect negative battery cable. Disconnect accelerator linkage rod. Disconnect speedometer cable then remove upper engine-to-transaxle bolts.

2) Support engine from above. Disconnect automatic transaxle cooler lines. Disconnect exhaust pipe from manifold, exhaust pipe bracket at transaxle and unbolt exhaust pipe from catalytic converter.

3) Remove axle shaft guard plate, then disconnect axle shafts from transaxle flanges. Wire axle shafts back out-of-way. Remove starter. Remove 3 bolts securing torque converter-to-drive plate.

4) On 089 transaxle, mark left ball joint position on control arm. Remove ball joint-to-control arm bolts. On all models, remove sub-frame rear mounting bolts and loosen front (do not remove).

5) Disconnect linkage rod from transaxle. Remove selector cable holder and circlip, then disconnect cable and "O" ring.

6) Place transaxle jack under transaxle and raise slightly. Remove accelerator cable holder, then disconnect accelerator cable. Remove lower engine-to-transaxle bolts. Remove transaxle rubber mount bolts. Separate transaxle from engine. Lower transaxle out of vehicle.

CAUTION: Secure torque converter to transaxle to prevent converter from falling out when removing transaxle.

INSTALLATION

To install transaxle, reverse removal procedures. Ensure torque converter is fully seated in transaxle and all linkage is properly installed and adjusted.

VOLKSWAGEN (Cont.)

VANAGON

REMOVAL

1) Disconnect battery ground and remove fan housing grill. Remove torque converter bolts. To gain access to bolts, rotate engine until each bolt is visible in hole at top of transmission housing.

NOTE: When turning crankshaft, use "T" handle and adapter 3052. This adapter has a pin that must engage recess on cooling fan hub.

2) Disconnect both drive shafts from transmission. Disconnect wires from starter, remove starter. Loosen bracket for automatic transmission filler tube. Disconnect accelerator linkage, accelerator cable and selector lever cable from operating lever.

3) Install engine support and disconnect engine ground wire. Support transmission with jack. Remove mounting bracket bolts, then disconnect rear transmission mount from body. Remove lower engine-to-transmission bolts and lower transmission out of vehicle.

NOTE: When lowering transmission from vehicle, torque converter must be secured to transmission so it will not slide off transmission.

INSTALLATION

To install transaxle assembly, reverse removal procedures. Make sure torque converter is fully seated on one-way clutch support or damage to oil pump could occur when assembly is bolted to engine.

VOLVO

ALL MODELS

REMOVAL

NOTE: Removal and installation information on 760 GLE with ZF 4 HP22 automatic transmission was not available from manufacturer.

1) Remove air cleaner. Disconnect throttle cable at pulley and cable sheath at bracket. Remove 2 upper transmission-to-engine bolts. Remove transmission oil dipstick.

2) Raise and support vehicle. Disconnect oil filler pipe from oil pan and drain transmission fluid. Remove vehicle splash guard.

3) Disconnect muffler from hanger. Disconnect propeller shaft from transmission rear drive flange. Remove exhaust pipe clamps from bracket. Remove transmission support member attaching bolts. Pull support member back, twist and lift out. Remove rear transmission mount and exhaust pipe bracket.

4) Disconnect speedometer cable from transmission. Disconnect oil cooler lines from transmission and oil cooler, then remove from vehicle. Disconnect gear shift control rod from transmission.

5) Remove torque converter cover plate. Remove starter motor attaching bolts and starter motor cover. Remove 4 torque converter-to-drive plate attaching bolts.

6) Support transmission with transmission jack. Remove 2 lower transmission-to-engine attaching bolts. Using a screwdriver, separate torque converter from drive plate. Lower transmission from vehicle.

INSTALLATION

Reverse removal procedure and note the following: Tighten all nuts and bolts evenly. After installation, fill transmission with fluid. Adjust throttle linkage and shift control linkage.

ALFA ROMEO

LUBRICATION

SERVICE INTERVALS

Inspect transmission lubricant level every 30,000 miles. Lubricant does not have to be changed.

CHECKING FLUID LEVEL

Check lubricant level at fill hole. Lubricant should be level with bottom of fill hole.

RECOMMENDED FLUID

Hypoid SAE 85W/90.

FLUID CAPACITY

TRANSMISSION REFILL CAPACITIES

Application	Quantity
GTV-6	6.0 pts. (2.7L)
Graduate & Spider Veloce	4.0 pts. (1.8L)

ADJUSTMENTS

LINKAGE

No external adjustment is possible.

AUDI

LUBRICATION

SERVICE INTERVALS

Check transmission lubricant level when vehicle is serviced. Lubricant never requires changing.

CHECKING FLUID LEVEL

Check fluid level at fill hole. Lubricant should be slightly below bottom of fill hole.

RECOMMENDED FLUID

Hypoid oil SAE 80 or SAE 80W/90 (API GL-4).

FLUID CAPACITY

TRANSMISSION REFILL CAPACITY

Application	Quantity
093	[1] 5.0 pts. (2.4L)
013	[1] 4.2 pts. (2.0L)
016	[2] 7.0 pts. (3.3L)

[1] – Includes differential.
[2] – Includes front and center differential.

ADJUSTMENTS

GEARSHIFT LEVER

1) Place gearshift lever in 1st gear, push to left stop and release. Lever must spring back 1/4-3/8" to right. Place lever in 5th gear position, push shift lever to right stop and release. Lever must spring back 1/4-3/8" to left. Lever must spring back approximately same distance in both directions.

2) If gearshift lever does not spring back as indicated, loosen gearshift lever housing (stop plate) bolts and move housing slightly sideways in slots. If this adjustment does not correct hard shifting, perform GEARSHIFT LINKAGE ADJUSTMENT.

GEARSHIFT LINKAGE

Coupe GT & 4000S Except 4WD

1) Place gearshift lever in neutral. Loosen shift rod clamp so that shift finger slides freely on shift rod. Remove shift lever knob and rubber boot.

2) Loosen gearshift lever housing bolts, align centering holes and tighten bolts. Install Linkage Adjustment Gauge (3057) with locating pin toward front. Push shift lever to 5/R gear position of gauge. Tighten lower knurled knob on gauge.

Fig. 1: Gearshift Linkage Adjustment

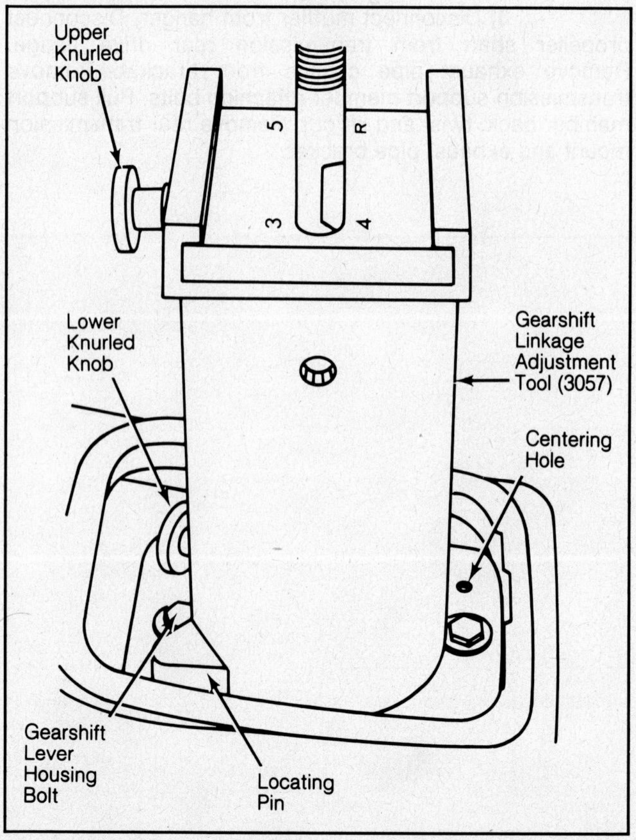

Manual Transmission Servicing

AUDI (Cont.)

3) Move shift lever and slide to right stop. Tighten upper knurled knob on gauge. Push shift lever into 3/4 gear position of gauge. Adjust shift rod and finger. Tighten clamp nut and remove gauge.

4) Place shift lever in 1st gear, press to left stop and release. Shift lever must spring back to right. Place lever in 5th gear, push shift lever to right stop and release. Shift lever must spring back to left.

5) If gearshift lever does not spring back as indicated, move gearshift lever housing slightly sideways in slots. Ensure all gears engage easily and without jamming, particularly reverse gear stop. Install shift boot and lever knob.

NOTE: All 4WD transaxle linkage adjustment should be performed only when gearshift lever adjustment cannot be corrected or after a repair which involved loosening shift rod clamp.

5000S Series & 4WD

1) Place gearshift lever in neutral. Measure linkage rod length and adjust to 5 9/32", if necessary. Remove shift lever knob and rubber boot. Loosen stop plate bolts, align centering holes and tighten bolts.

2) Loosen shift rod clamp between front and rear rods, so that rods move freely. Install Linkage Adjustment Gauge (3048) by inserting locating pins (right side pins first) into centering holes of stop plate.

3) Ensure gearshift rod remains in neutral, tighten shift rod clamp and remove adjustment gauge. Ensure all gears engage easily and without jamming, particularly reverse gear safety catch. Adjust stop plate, if necessary. Install shift lever knob and rubber boot.

Fig. 2: Linkage Rod Length Adjustment

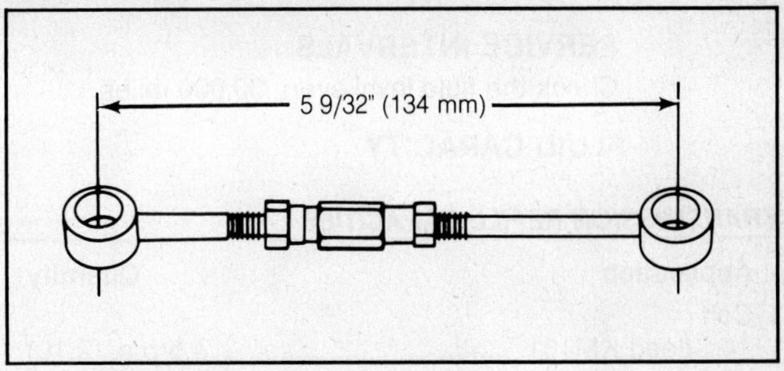

Adjust rod length to 5 9/32" (134 mm).

Fig. 3: Gearshift Linkage Adjustment

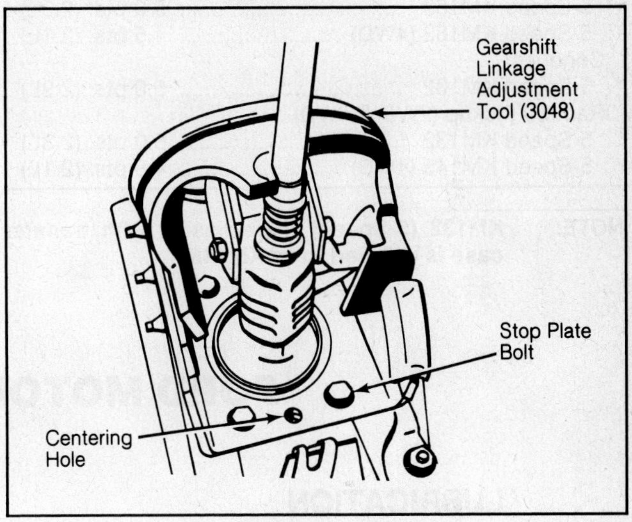

BMW

LUBRICATION

SERVICE INTERVALS

Inspect fluid level when vehicle is serviced. Change oil every 30,000 miles.

CHECKING FLUID LEVEL

Check lubricant at fill hole. Lubricant should be at bottom of fill plug hole.

RECOMMENDED FLUID

SAE 80W (API GL-4). In cold climates use HD.

FLUID CAPACITY

TRANSMISSION REFILL CAPACITIES

Application	Quantity
318i	3.0 pts. (1.2L)
All Others	3.5 pts. (1.6L)

ADJUSTMENTS

LINKAGE

No external adjustment is provided.

CHRYSLER CORP. IMPORTS

LUBRICATION

SERVICE INTERVALS

Check the fluid level every 30,000 miles.

FLUID CAPACITY

TRANSMISSION REFILL CAPACITIES

Application	Quantity
Colt	
4-Speed KM161	4.5 pts. (2.1L)
5-Speed KM162 (1.5L)	4.5 pts. (2.1L)
5-Speed KM163 (1.6L)	5.0 pts. (2.3L)
Colt Vista	
5-Speed KM163	5.0 pts. (2.3L)
5-Speed KM182 (4WD)	4.5 pts. (2.1L)
Conquest	
5-Speed KM132	5.0 pts. (2.3L)
Ram-50 Pickup (2WD & 4WD)	
5-Speed KM132	5.0 pts. (2.3L)
5-Speed KM145 (4WD)	4.5 pts. (2.1L)

NOTE: KM132 (5-Speed) transmission with transfer case is referred to as KM145.

CHECKING FLUID LEVEL

Check lubricant level at fill hole. Lubricant must be at bottom of fill hole.

RECOMMENDED FLUID

Transaxle - SAE 75W/85W (API GL-4).
Transmission - SAE 80W (API GL-4).

ADJUSTMENTS

LINKAGE

No external linkage adjustment is possible.

FORD MOTOR CO. IMPORTS

LUBRICATION

SERVICE INTERVALS

Inspect fluid level when vehicle is serviced. Change oil every 30,000 miles.

CHECKING FLUID LEVEL

Check lubricant at fill hole. Lubricant should be 1 INCH below bottom of fill plug hole.

RECOMMENDED FLUID

Use FORD E5RY-19C547-A (semisynthetic).

FLUID CAPACITY

TRANSMISSION REFILL CAPACITIES

Application	Quantity
Merkur XR4Ti	2.5 pts. (1.3L)

ADJUSTMENTS

LINKAGE

No external linkage adjustment is provided.

GENERAL MOTORS IMPORTS

LUBRICATION

SERVICE INTERVALS

Check fluid each time engine oil is changed or every 7500 miles. Replace every 30,000 miles on Spectrum or 15,000 miles on Sprint.

CHECKING FLUID LEVEL

Spectrum

Remove speedometer cable assembly located on driver's side of case, above drive shaft. Ensure fluid level is between "L" and "H" marks on speedometer cable bushing. If needed, add oil to bring fluid level up to "L" mark. Install speedometer cable.

Sprint

1) Remove fluid level gauge from side case of transaxle. Insert fluid level gauge through opening until threaded part of gauge rests on top of side case.

2) Remove gauge and check oil level. Fluid level should be between "FULL" and "LOW" lines. If fluid level is below "LOW" line, add fluid until it reaches "FULL" line.

NOTE: During fluid change on Sprint models, clean drain plug and apply sealant (GM 1052080) to thread portion of plug. After draining, install gasket and drain plug. If transaxle is cold, tighten drain plug to 18-22 ft. lbs. (24-30 N.m). If transaxle is warm, tighten drain plug to 15-18 ft. lbs. (20-24 N.m).

GENERAL MOTORS IMPORTS (Cont.)

RECOMMENDED FLUID

Spectrum
SAE 5W/30 SF rated engine oil.
Sprint
Hypoid oil SAE 80W or 80W/90 (API GL-5).

FLUID CAPACITY

TRANSMISSION REFILL CAPACITIES

Application	Quantity
Spectrum	5.4 pts. (2.7L)
Sprint	4.5 pts. (2.3L)

ADJUSTMENTS

GEARSHIFT LINKAGE

Spectrum

Place transaxle and lever in neutral. Turn adjustment nuts, one cable at a time, until shift lever is in vertical position. Tighten adjustment nuts. *See Fig. 1.*

NOTE: Sprint gearshift adjustment should be performed only when each shift stroke is short or when gears are not in complete mesh.

Sprint

1) Loosen gearshift housing nuts and guide plate bolts. Adjust guide plate by moving it from front to rear so that base of gearshift control lever is brought to middle of guide plate and at a right angle.

Fig. 1: Spectrum Gearshift Linkage Adjustment

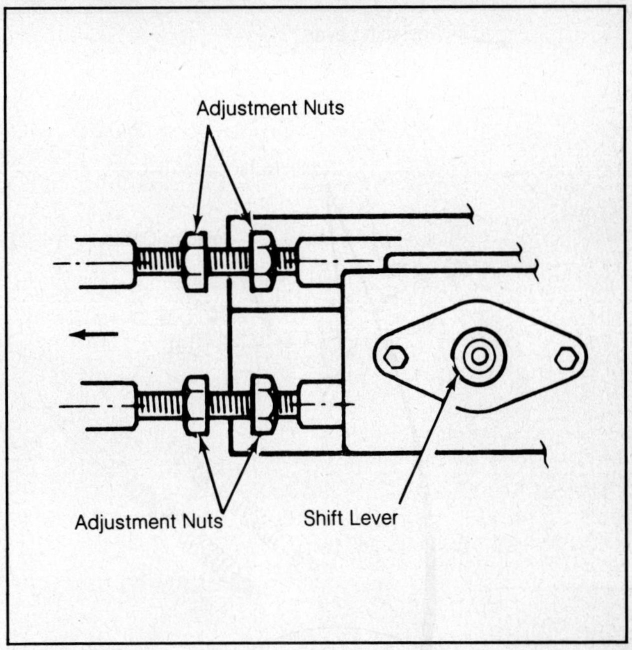

2) With guide plate in position, tighten guide plate bolts to 72-84 INCH lbs. (8-9 N.m). Tighten left front and right rear housing nut to 11-14 ft. lbs. (15-19 N.m). Tighten right front and left rear housing nut to 36-48 INCH lbs. (4-5 N.m).

HONDA

LUBRICATION

SERVICE INTERVALS

Change lubricant every 30,000 miles.

CHECKING FLUID LEVEL

Ensure fluid level is at bottom of fill hole.

RECOMMENDED FLUID

SAE 10W/40 engine oil rated SE or SF.

FLUID CAPACITY

TRANSMISSION REFILL CAPACITIES

Application	Quantity
All Models	5.3 pts. (2.5L)

ADJUSTMENTS

LINKAGE

2WD Models
No external adjustments are required.

4WD Models (Selector Cable)

Remove center console. Place transaxle in neutral. Ensure groove in lever bracket is aligned with index mark on selector cable. *See Fig. 1.* If not, loosen lock nuts and turn adjuster as necessary.

NOTE: After adjustment, check operation of gearshift lever. Threads of the cables must not extend out of cable adjuster more than 3/8".

4WD Models (Gearshift Cable)

Remove center console. Place gear seletor in 4th. Measure clearance between gearshift lever bracket and stopper while pushing the lever forward. *See Fig. 2.* If clearance is not okay, loosen lock nuts and turn adjuster until clearance is correct.

NOTE: After adjustment, check operation of gearshift lever. Threads of the cables must not extend out of cable adjuster more than 3/8".

HONDA (Cont.)

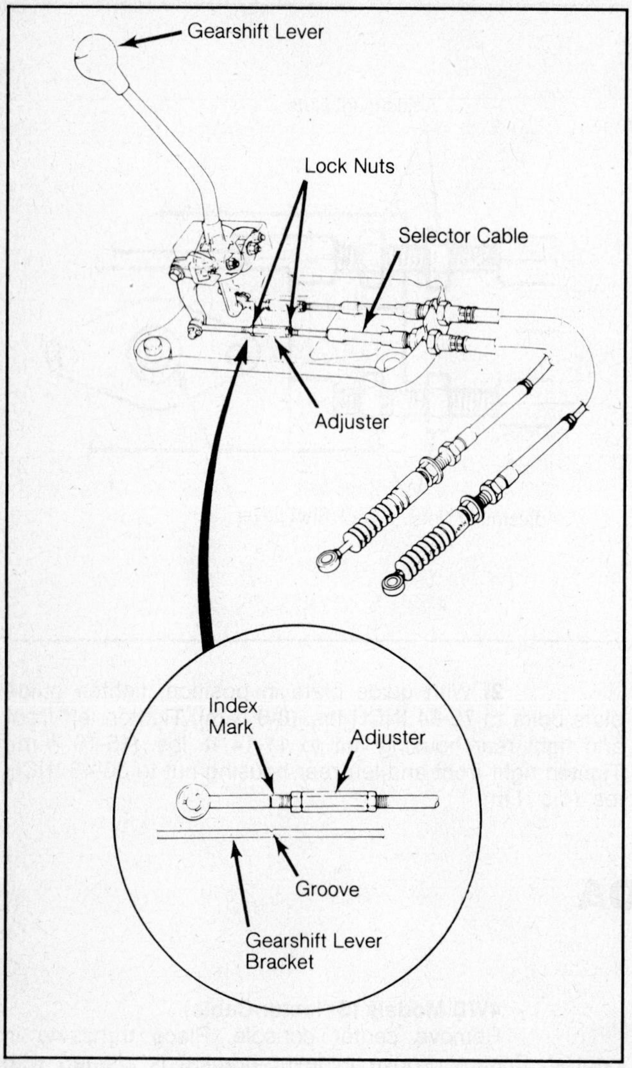

Fig. 1: Checking Selector Cable Adjustment

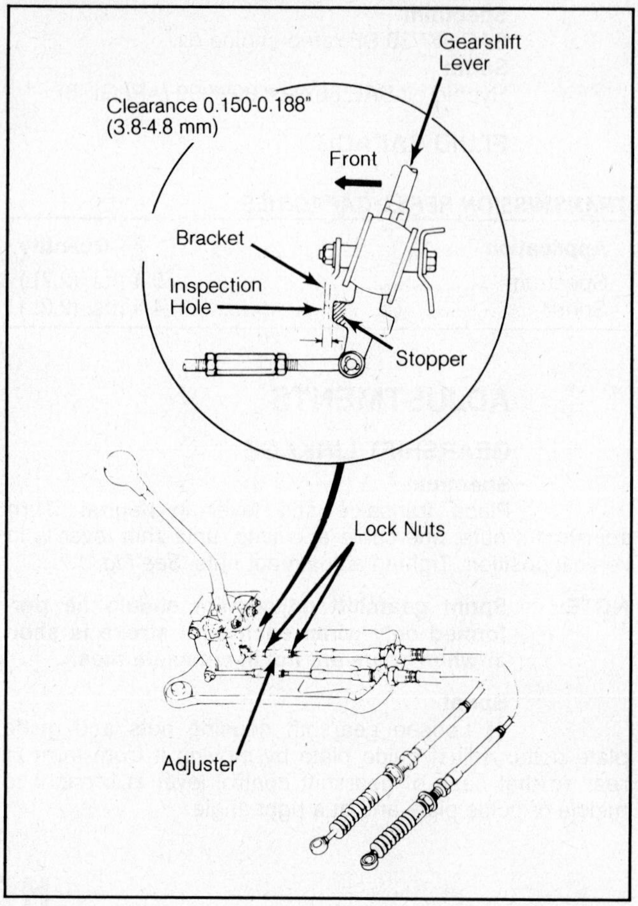

Fig. 2: Checking Gearshift Cable Adjustment

ISUZU

LUBRICATION

SERVICE INTERVALS

Check fluid every 7500 miles or 12 months. Replace fluid after first 7500 miles and every 30,000 miles thereafter.

CHECKING FLUID LEVEL

FWD I-Mark

Remove speedometer cable assembly located on driver's side of case, above drive shaft. Ensure fluid level is between "L" and "H" marks on speedometer cable bushing. If needed, add oil to bring fluid level up to "L" mark. Install speedometer cable.

All Other Models

Ensure fluid level is at bottom edge of fill hole.

RECOMMENDED FLUID

Impulse & I-Mark

0°-90°F (-18°-32°C) SAE 5W/30 engine oil.
Above 90°F (32°C) SAE 40 engine oil.

P'UP & Trooper II

Below 50°F (10°C) SAE 10W/30 engine oil.
0°-90°F (-18°-32°C) SAE 30 engine oil.
Above 50°F (10°C) SAE 40 engine oil.

Manual Transmission Servicing

ISUZU (Cont.)

FLUID CAPACITY

TRANSMISSION REFILL CAPACITIES

Application	Quantity
FWD	
I-Mark 5-Speed	5.4 pts. (2.8L)
RWD	
4-Speed MSG-4K	2.7 pts. (1.3L)
4-Speed MSG-4ET (4WD)	[1] 5.3 pts. (2.5L)
5-Speed MSG-5K	3.3 pts. (1.6L)

[1] – Including transfer case.

ADJUSTMENTS

LINKAGE

FWD I-Mark

Place transaxle and lever in neutral. Turn adjustment nuts, one cable at a time, until shift lever is in vertical position. Tighten adjustment nuts. *See Fig. 1.*

All Other Models

Shift linkage is integral with transmission housing and requires no external adjustment.

Fig. 1: FWD I-Mark Gearshift Linkage Adjustment

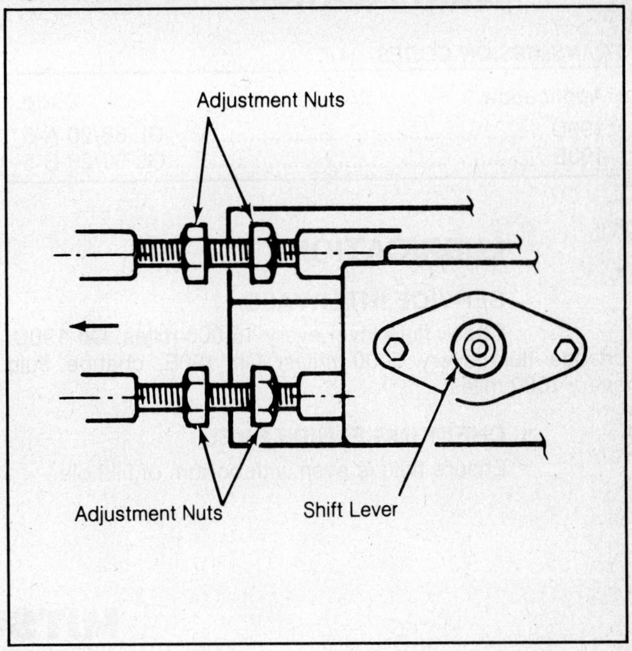

MAZDA

LUBRICATION

SERVICE INTERVALS

Replace fluid every 30,000 miles.

CHECKING FLUID LEVEL

B2000 (1986) & RX7

Fluid should be up to bottom of fill hole.

GLC & 626

Remove speedometer cable and driven gear from transaxle case. Use "L" and "F" marks on driven gear to determine fluid level. If necessary, add oil through driven gear opening.

RECOMMENDED FLUID

Hypoid SAE 80W/90 (API GL-4 or GL-5).

FLUID CAPACITY

TRANSMISSION REFILL CAPACITIES

Application	Quantity
B2000 & RX7	3.6 pts. (1.7L)
GLC	6.8 pts. (3.2L)
626	7.2 pts. (3.4L)

Fig. 1: GLC & 626 Oil Level Gauge

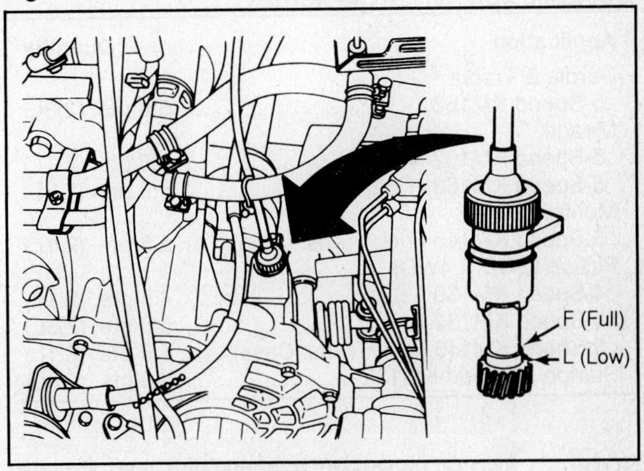

GLC location shown; 626 is similar.

ADJUSTMENTS

LINKAGE

No external linkage adjustment is required.

MERCEDES-BENZ

IDENTIFICATION

TRANSMISSION CODES

Application	Code
190D	GL 68/20 A-5
190E	GL 68/20 B-5

LUBRICATION

SERVICE INTERVALS

Check fluid level every 15,000 miles. On 190D, change fluid every 5000 miles. On 190E, change fluid every 7500 miles.

CHECKING FLUID LEVEL

Ensure fluid is even with bottom of fill hole.

RECOMMENDED FLUID

Type A Suffix A, automatic transmission fluid.

FLUID CAPACITY

TRANSMISSION REFILL CAPACITIES

Application	Quantity
All	3.2 pts. (1.5L)

ADJUSTMENTS

LINKAGE

Place transmission in neutral. Disconnect rods at transmission and align levers by inserting a centering pin at shift bracket. Adjust rods to fit freely in transmission levers. Install rounded locking clips. Remove centering pin and check for proper operation.

MITSUBISHI

LUBRICATION

FLUID CAPACITY

TRANSMISSION REFILL CAPACITIES

Application	Quantity
Cordia & Tredia	
5-Speed KM163	5.0 pts. (2.3L)
Mirage	
5-Speed KM162 (1.5L)	4.5 pts. (2.1L)
5-Speed KM163 (1.6L)	5.0 pts. (2.3L)
Montero	
5-Speed KM145 (incl. Trans. Case)	4.5 pts. (2.1L)
Pickup (2WD & 4WD)	
4-Speed KM130	4.5 pts. (2.1L)
5-Speed KM132	5.0 pts. (2.3L)
5-Speed KM145 (incl. Trans. Case)	4.5 pts. (2.1L)
Starion 5-Speed KM132	5.0 pts. (2.3L)

NOTE: KM132 (5-Speed) transmission with transfer case is referred to as KM145.

SERVICE INTERVALS

Check fluid every 30,000 miles.

CHECKING FLUID LEVEL

Fluid should be up to bottom of fill hole.

RECOMMENDED FLUID

Hypoid SAE 75W/85W or 80W (API GL-4).

ADJUSTMENTS

LINKAGE

No external adjustments are possible on either transaxles or transmissions.

NISSAN

LUBRICATION

SERVICE INTERVALS

Add or replace oil level every 15,000 miles.

CHECKING FLUID LEVEL

Fluid level should be to bottom of fill hole.

RECOMMENDED FLUID

Hypoid SAE 80W/90 (API GL-4).

FLUID CAPACITY

TRANSMISSION REFILL CAPACITIES

Application	Quantity
Maxima 5-Speed RS5F50A	10.0 pts. (4.7L)
Pickup (2WD & 4WD)	
5-Speed FS5W71B	4.5 pts. (2.1L)
Transfer Case T100-L	3.0 pts. (1.4L)
Pulsar 5-Speed RS5F30A	5.4 pts. (2.5L)
Sentra	
4-Speed RN4F30A	4.8 pts. (2.3L)
5-Speed RS5F30A	5.7 pts. (2.7L)
Stanza 5-Speed RS5F31A	5.7 pts. (2.7L)
200SX 5-Speed FS5W71B	4.5 pts. (2.1L)
300ZX & 300ZX Turbo	
5-Speed FS5W71C	4.0 pts. (1.9L)
5-Speed FS5R90A	4.0 pts. (1.9L)

ADJUSTMENTS

LINKAGE

NOTE: **All RWD models do not have external linkage and require no adjustment.**

Pulsar, Sentra & Stanza

1) Loosen selector stopper bolts. Place trans-axle in first gear. Slide selector stopper to establish clearance of .040" (1.0 mm) between control lever and select stopper. *See Fig. 1.*

Fig. 1: Control Lever Adjustment

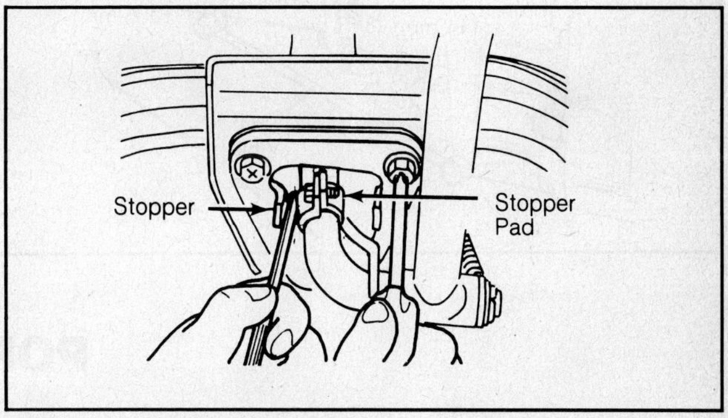

Place shifter in first gear.

2) Tighten bolts. After adjustment, inspect shift control lever to be sure no binding or dragging exists.

PEUGEOT

LUBRICATION

SERVICE INTERVALS

Check fluid level every 7500 miles. Change fluid every 22,500 miles.

CHECKING FLUID LEVEL

Fluid should be at bottom edge of hole.

RECOMMENDED FLUID

SAE 10W/40 engine oil (API grade CC).

FLUID CAPACITY

TRANSMISSION REFILL CAPACITIES

Application	Quantity
505 5-Speed	3.6 pts. (1.7L)

ADJUSTMENTS

LINKAGE

1) Install Shift Lever Gauge (00315) and place shift lever in correct position. *See Fig. 1.* Loosen reverse plunger bolts and place reverse plunger against selector lever. Tighten 2 bolts and remove gauge.

2) Lubricate ball sockets. Install shift link with center-to-center dimension "B" of 11.0". *See Fig. 1.* Adjust gate selector link with center-to-center dimension "A" to 4.37" (111 mm). Holding ball sockets in proper directions, tighten lock nut. Install gate selector link with fixed ball socket side mounted to gearshift lever.

NOTE: **Gearshift lever dimension "C" is 4.13" (105 mm).**

PEUGEOT (Cont.)

Fig 1: Shift Lever Adjustment

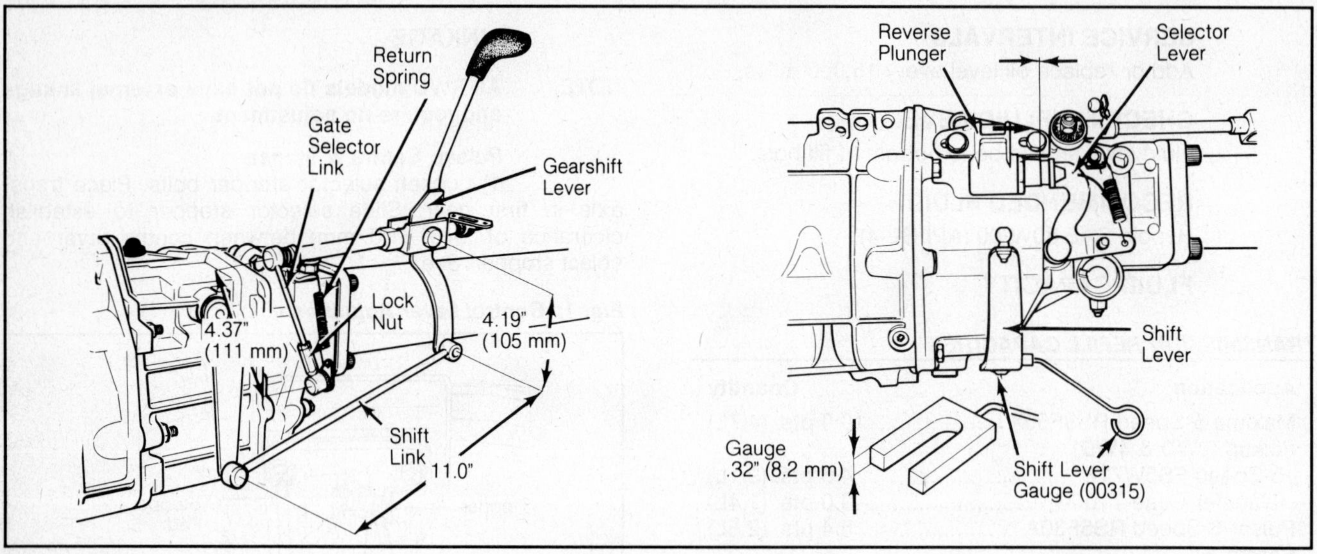

PORSCHE

LUBRICATION

SERVICE INTERVALS

Check fluid level every 15,000 miles and replace every 30,000 miles.

CHECKING FLUID LEVEL

Fluid should be level with bottom of fill hole.

RECOMMENDED FLUID

911 Carrera
Hypoid SAE 90W (API GL-5).
928S
Hypoid SAE 75W/90 (API GL-5).
944
Hypoid SAE 80 (API GL-5).

FLUID CAPACITY

TRANSMISSION REFILL CAPACITIES

Application	Quantity
911 Carrera	6.4 pts. (3.0L)
928S	8.0 pts. (3.8L)
944	5.6 pts. (2.6L)

ADJUSTMENTS

LINKAGE

No adjustment is required.

RENAULT

LUBRICATION

SERVICE INTERVALS

Change fluid every 12,000 miles.

CHECKING FLUID LEVEL

Fluid should be even with bottom of fill hole.

RECOMMENDED FLUID

Hypoid SAE 80 (API GL-5).

FLUID CAPACITY

TRANSMISSION REFILL CAPACITIES

Application	Quantity
All	4.4 pts. (2.0L)

ADJUSTMENTS

LINKAGE

1) Place shift lever in neutral. Loosen lock nut on yoke so shift linkage turns freely. Put lever at transaxle case exit, against 3rd-4th gear line.

2) Place a .40" (10 mm) shim between end piece of shift linkage and surface of housing. Tighten yoke nut. Ensure clearance between end piece and lever housing equals size of shim.

SAAB

LUBRICATION

SERVICE INTERVALS

Check fluid level every 5,000 miles on 900 Turbo, every 7500 miles on other models.

CHECKING FLUID LEVEL

Check oil level with dipstick, located on right side of engine. Oil level should be between "MIN" and "MAX" marks.

RECOMMENDED FLUID

SAE 10W/30 engine oil.

FLUID CAPACITY

TRANSMISSION REFILL CAPACITIES

Application	Quantity
All Models 5-Speed	6.3 pts. (3.0L)

ADJUSTMENTS

LINKAGE

1) Select reverse gear. Loosen clamp on gear shift rod joint, so that gear shift rod can be moved in joint. Remove gear lever console cover. Lock gear lever in reverse by inserting a 1/4" drift pin into locking holes of gear shift lever housing and gear shift rod.

2) Check that reverse gear at transmission is fully engaged. Tighten clamp on gear shift rod joint to 12-16 ft. lbs. (16-22 N.m). After adjustment, ensure gear shift lever is in alignment with 3rd-4th gear gate, when placed in neutral.

3) If lever adjustment is required, remove driver's seat and fold back carpeting enough to allow heating duct to be dismantled. Select 3rd gear and remove bolts holding control unit to gear shift lever housing.

4) Adjust control unit so that rollers reach bottom of plunger groove, and spring is at its shortest length. Tighten control unit, return gear shift lever to neutral. Check that spring moves gear shift lever in alignment with 3rd-4th gear gate. Fit carpeting and install seat.

SUBARU

LUBRICATION

SERVICE INTERVALS

Check fluid level every 15,000 miles. Replace fluid every 30,000 miles.

CHECKING FLUID LEVEL

Check fluid level at dipstick located in engine compartment. Transmission and differential (transaxle) are lubricated through a common oil supply.

FLUID CAPACITY

TRANSMISSION REFILL CAPACITIES

Application	Quantity
2WD 4 & 5-Speed	5.5 pts. (2.6L)
4WD 5-Speed & Turbo	7.0 pts. (3.3L)
4WD 5-Speed (Dual Range)	7.0 pts. (3.3L)

RECOMMENDED FLUID

Hypoid SAE 80W/90.

ADJUSTMENTS

LINKAGE

All models use shift linkage which does not require external adjustment. If equipped with dual-range, confirm that lower surface of drive selector grip is approximately 1.57" (40 mm) from rod cover surface. If not, readjust positioning plate.

Manual Transmission Servicing

TOYOTA

LUBRICATION

SERVICE INTERVALS

Check fluid level every 15,000 miles.

CHECKING FLUID LEVEL

Fluid should be to bottom of fill hole.

FLUID CAPACITY

TRANSMISSION REFILL CAPACITIES

Application	Quantity
Camry	5.4 pts. (2.6L)
Celica, Cressida & Supra	5.0 pts. (2.4L)
Corolla FWD	5.4 pts. (2.6L)
Corolla RWD	3.6 pts. (1.7L)
Land Cruiser	6.6 pts. (3.1L)
MR2	4.8 pts. (2.3L)
Pickup	
2WD	
4-Speed & 5-Speed	5.0 pts. (2.4L)
4WD	
5-Speed G52	8.0 pts. (3.9L)
5-Speed W56	6.4 pts. (3.0L)
Transfer Case	3.4 pts. (1.6L)
Tercel 2WD	7.0 pts. (3.3L)
Tercel 4WD	8.0 pts. (3.9L)
Van	4.6 pts. (2.2L)

RECOMMENDED FLUID

Camry

Type ATF Dexron II transmission fluid.

Land Cruiser

Type SAE 90W (API GL-4 or GL-5) transmission fluid.

Tercel

Above 0° F (-18° C) – SAE 80W/90 or 90W (API Hypoid GL-5) transmission fluid.

Below 0° F (-18° C) SAE 80W/90 or 80W (API Hypoid GL-5) transmission fluid.

All Others

Type SAE 75W/90 (API GL-4 or GL-5) or SAE 80W/90 (API GL-4 or GL-5) transmission fluid.

ADJUSTMENTS

LINKAGE

NOTE: **Models not listed do not require adjustment.**

Corolla FWD

Remove shifter console. Check clearance between bottom of lower shift lever pivot seat and top plate of shifter control mount. If clearance is not .04" (1.0 mm), change shims at shift lever pivot seat to shifter control mounting bolts.

Van

1) Remove shifter console box. Loosen shift cable adjusting nut at the cable to shifter connection. Place the transmission in neutral.

2) Insert a .20" (5 mm) guide pin through shifter base and shift lever to hold the position. Lengthen or shorten cable as needed to obtain the proper cable stroke. Tighten adjusting nut, remove guide pin and install console box.

VOLKSWAGEN

LUBRICATION

SERVICE INTERVALS

Check oil every 15,000 miles.

CHECKING FLUID LEVEL

Fluid should be up to bottom of fill hole.

RECOMMENDED FLUID

Hypoid SAE 80W or 80W/90 (API GL-4).

FLUID CAPACITY

TRANSMISSION REFILL CAPACITIES

Application	Quantity
Cabriolet, Golf, GTI, Jetta, Quantum & Scirocco	
5-Speed	
4-Cyl. Engine	4.2 pts. (2.0L)
5-Cyl. Engine	4.6 pts. (2.3L)
Vanagon	
4-Speed	5.4 pts. (3.5L)
5-Speed	8.4 pts. (4.0L)

ADJUSTMENTS

LINKAGE

Cabriolet & Scirocco

1) Adjust gearshift lever as described in this article. Loosen lever housing bolts. Pull boot off housing. Loosen shift rod clamp bolt so lever moves freely on shift rod. Adjust shift finger in center of lock-out plate so that an equal distance is obtained on both sides of shift finger. *See Fig. 1.*

2) Pivot gearshift lever until stop finger on shift lever is as far away as possible from stop plate area on shifter plate housing. Adjust shift rod end so that 5/8" exists between shift finger and stop plate. Tighten shift rod clamp. Shift through all gears and check operation.

VOLKSWAGEN (Cont.)

Fig. 1: Cabriolet & Scirocco Linkage Adjustment

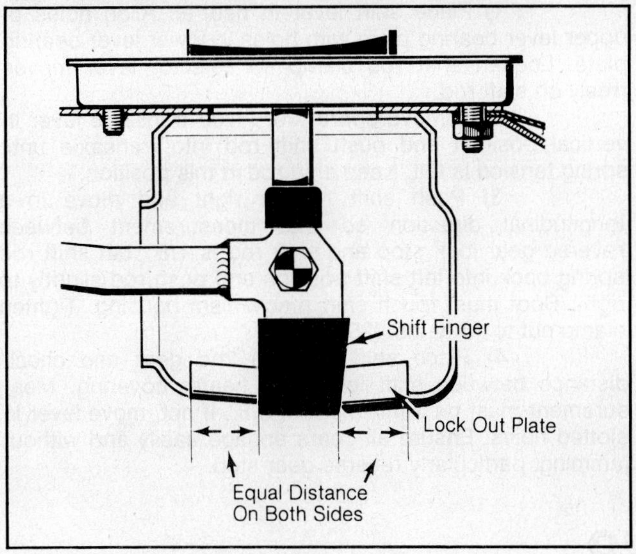

Golf, GTI & Jetta

1) Place shift lever in neutral. Loosen shifter rod clamp. *See Fig. 2.* Selector lever must move freely on shifter rod.

Fig. 2: Shift Rod Clamp Location

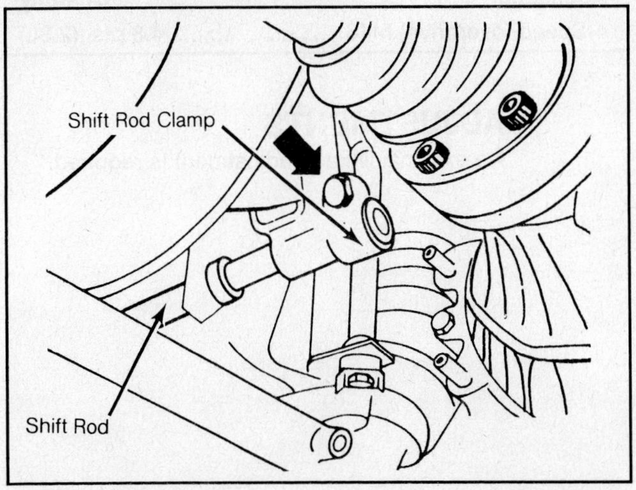

2) Remove gearshift knob and boot. Position Adjustment Gauge (3104) over shift rod. *See Fig. 3.* With transaxle in neutral, align shift rod with selector lever. Tighten shifter rod clamp to 19 ft. lbs. (26 N.m).

3) Move gearshift lever through entire range of gear selection, including reverse. Gears must engage smoothly and without jamming. Reinstall gearshift knob and boot.

Vanagon

1) Place shift lever in neutral. Align holes of upper lever bearing plate with holes in lower lever bearing plate.

2) Loosen shift rod clamp so selector lever moves freely on shift rod. Remove spare tire. Move shift finger of front shift rod to center of rubber stop in housing.

3) Adjust shift rod end so that a distance of 7/8" exists between shift rod end and stop plate. Check for proper operation.

Fig. 3: Adjustment Gauge Location

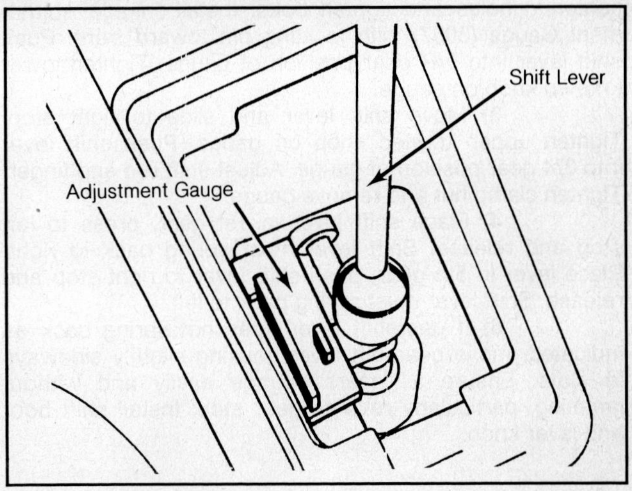

GEARSHIFT

Cabriolet & Scirocco

1) Remove gearshift lever boot. Loosen bolts through elongated holes on shift lever bearing assembly. Position shift lever bearing assembly until round holes are aligned with round holes in lever housing.

2) Ensure bolts through elongated holes are centered in holes. If not, remove bolts and turn shift lever bearing assembly 180°. Install bolts, adjust plates and tighten bolts.

Quantum

1) Place gearshift lever in neutral. Loosen shift rod clamp so that shift finger slides freely on shift rod. Remove shift lever knob and rubber boot.

Fig. 4: Quantum Gearshift Lever Adjustment

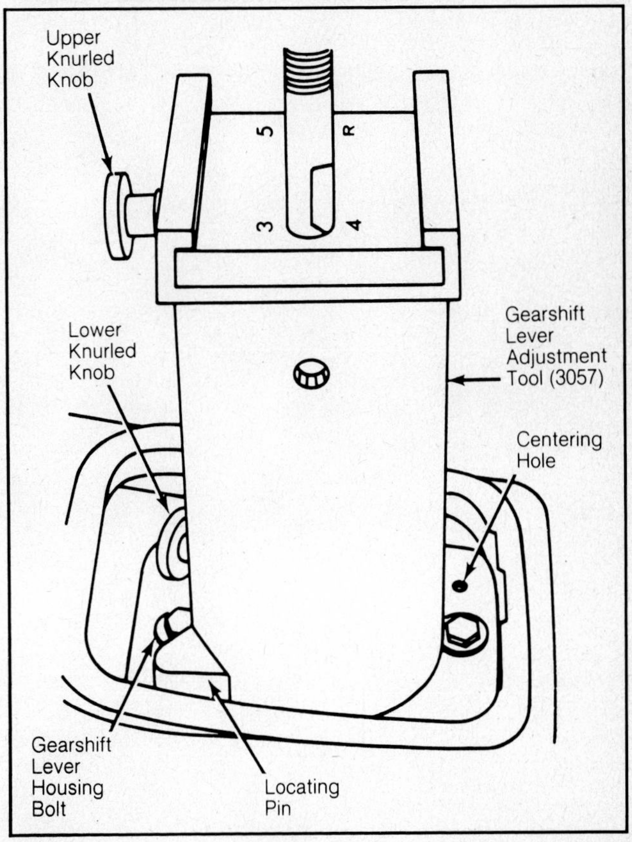

VOLKSWAGEN (Cont.)

2) Loosen gearshift lever housing bolts, align centering holes and tighten bolts. Install linkage Adjustment Gauge (3057) with locating pin toward front. Push shift lever into 5/R gear position of gauge. Tighten lower knurled knob on gauge.

3) Move shift lever and slide to right stop. Tighten upper knurled knob on gauge. Push shift lever into 3/4 gear position of gauge. Adjust shift rod and finger. Tighten clamp nut and remove gauge.

4) Place shift lever in 1st gear, press to left stop and release. Shift lever must spring back to right. Place lever in 5th gear, push shift lever to right stop and release. Shift lever must spring back to left.

5) If gearshift lever does not spring back as indicated, move gearshift lever housing slightly sideways in slots. Ensure all gears engage easily and without jamming, particularly reverse gear stop. Install shift boot and lever knob.

Vanagon

1) Place shift lever in neutral. Align holes of upper lever bearing plate with holes in lower lever bearing plate. Loosen shift rod clamp so selector lever moves freely on shift rod.

2) Remove spare tire. Place transaxle lever in vertical position and push shift rod into transaxle until spring tension is felt. Keep shift rod in this position.

3) Push shift rod to right and move in a longitudinal direction so that measurement between reverse gear lock stop and shift rod is 1/8". Let shift rod spring back into left shift position and push rod slightly to right. Boot must touch shift mechanism housing. Tighten clamp nut to 18 ft. lbs. (25 N.m).

4) Place shift lever in 2nd gear and check distance between shift lever and heater covering. Measurement must be a minimum of 5/8". If not, move lever in slotted holes. Ensure all gears engage easily and without jamming, particularly reverse gear stop.

VOLVO

LUBRICATION

SERVICE INTERVALS

Check fluid every 7500 miles.

CHECKING FLUID LEVEL

Fluid should be up to bottom of fill hole. When adding oil, allow sufficient time for oil to flow into overdrive unit.

RECOMMENDED FLUID

F or G Automatic Transmission Fluid (FLM).

FLUID CAPACITY

TRANSMISSION REFILL CAPACITIES

Application	Quantity
4-Speed (overdrive) M46	4.8 pts. (2.3L)

ADJUSTMENTS

No external linkage adjustment is required.

Manual Transmission Removal

AUDI

4000

REMOVAL

1) Disconnect battery ground strap. Disconnect exhaust pipe from transaxle bracket and engine. Remove square bolt and press shifter coupling from rear of transaxle shifting shaft. Unhook clutch cable and disconnect speedometer. On models equipped with a 5-cylinder engine, support front of engine when transaxle is removed.

2) Disconnect CV joints at inner drive flanges. Support axle shafts from vehicle with wire. Remove starter, front mounting plate and transaxle mounting bolts. Disconnect back-up light switch connector. Support transaxle on floor jack and remove crossmember mount. Remove transaxle from engine and lower from vehicle.

INSTALLATION

1) Install crossmember to transaxle. Raise transaxle up to vehicle and install crossmember bolts finger tight. Slide transaxle up to engine and install mounting bolts. Install front mounting plate and starter. Install inner CV joint mounting bolts into CV joint and drive flange. Tighten crossmember mounting bolts.

2) Install shift rod coupling bolt and lock with safety wire. Connect exhaust pipe, allowing 3/8" (10 mm) clearance between pipe and floor. Reconnect all wires, cables and linkages that were removed during removal procedure.

NOTE: **Always use longer hex head bolt when replacing shift rod coupling instead of original square head bolt. Secure with safety wire.**

5000

REMOVAL

1) Remove air cleaner (diesel only). Disconnect battery ground cable. Remove windshield washer reservoir. Remove upper engine-to-transaxle bolts. Disconnect speedometer cable.

2) Remove right side guard plate. Disconnect drive axle shafts from drive flanges and support on top of subframe. Disconnect wire from back-up light switch. Disconnect shift linkage from transaxle case.

3) Remove lower engine-to-transaxle bolts, starter and guard plate from subframe. Lift transaxle slightly and remove transaxle supports. Remove rear subframe mounting bolts. Remove right transaxle bracket, then remove transaxle from below.

INSTALLATION

Reverse removal procedure and note the following: Lubricate mainshaft splines lightly with grease. Make sure transaxle seats on engine dowels. Adjust shift linkage as necessary.

QUATTRO

REMOVAL

1) Disconnect battery ground strap and RPM sensor. Remove upper engine-to-transmission bolts. Disconnect speedometer cable with wrench (#3016). Disconnect tie rod coupling from steering rack. Always remove self-locking nuts (below tie rod coupling) first, then mounting bolts.

2) Drive out clutch slave cylinder lock pin. Remove clutch slave cylinder (leave hydraulic line connected). Disconnect backup light switch and shift linkage. Install engine support tool (#10-222). Remove deflector for axle shaft and right transmission mount.

3) Remove right transmission mount. Disconnect exhaust pipe at flange. Disconnect right axle shaft at transmission. Remove left transmission mount. Disconnect left axle shaft at transmission and drive shaft at rear of transmission.

4) Disconnect cable for differential lock. Remove transmission cover plate. Turn spindle of engine support tool (#10-222) to raise engine slightly. Place hoist (VWAG-1383) under transmission. Remove the lower engine-to-transmission bolts and push transmission back.

INSTALLATION

To install transmission, reverse removal procedure and note the following: Check that the engine-to-transmission mounts are free of tension. Readjust shift linkage. Clean drive shaft and axle flanges and lightly coat with MoS_2 grease or spray. If pickup eye is still in place on transmission (near starter), remove with hacksaw to gain easier access to exhaust pipe.

BMW

ALL MODELS

REMOVAL

1) Push up shift lever boot and foam ring, then remove circlip from shift lever ball socket. Remove exhaust bracket from transmission and exhaust pipe from manifold. Remove upper clutch housing bolts.

2) Remove propeller shaft from transmission (coupling or flexible disc remains with shaft). Remove propeller shaft center support bearing, pull shaft downward and away from centering pin.

3) Remove shift lever bearing pin and push shift lever upward. Remove clutch linkage and slave cylinder as required. Loosen angle support and remove transmission front cover plate.

4) Support engine using a block between engine and front axle subframe. Remove speedometer shaft and electrical connections. Loosen crossmember and turn steering to full right lock position.

5) On 325e models, remove remaining bolts securing transmission to engine and frame; remove transmission. On all other models, remove transmission-to-clutch housing bolts and separate transmission from clutch housing.

INSTALLATION

Reverse removal procedure and note the following: Use new lock nuts on propeller shaft; tighten nuts on propeller shaft only, never bolts; use shims under shift lever circlip to remove play in shift lever; preload center bearing .079" (2 mm); adjust clutch pedal free play.

Manual Transmission Removal

CHRYSLER CORP. IMPORTS

ALL FWD MODELS

REMOVAL

1) Disconnect battery negative cable. Remove the following parts from transaxle: Clutch cable, speedometer cable, back-up light switch harness, starter, and 4 top engine-to-transaxle mounting bolts.

2) Raise vehicle and remove wheels. Remove shift rod and extension. Drain transaxle fluid. Remove drive shafts. Disconnect gear selector cable. Remove engine rear cover.

3) Connect engine to hoist and remove remaining transaxle-to-engine bolts. Remove transaxle mount insulator bolt. Lower and remove transaxle.

INSTALLATION

To install, reverse removal procedure and note the following: The coupling bolt at each end of front roll rod should be temporarily tightened at installation. After the transaxle has been installed, tighten bolts to specifications.

ALL RWD MODELS - 4-SPEED

REMOVAL

1) In engine compartment, disconnect negative battery cable. Remove air cleaner and starter. Remove 2 upper transmission mounting bolts.

2) Inside vehicle, take out console box (if equipped) and carpet. Remove dust cover retainer plate at base of shift lever. Lift up dust cover and remove attaching bolts at lower part of extension housing and remove gearshift lever.

NOTE: **Make sure gearshift lever is in 2nd speed position before removing.**

3) With vehicle raised and supported, drain transmission. Remove bolts from rear of propeller shaft and draw shaft out of transmission.

4) Disconnect speedometer and back-up light switch harness at transmission side. Disconnect front exhaust pipe. From clutch control lever, disconnect clutch cable.

5) Support rear of engine with jack, place transmission jack under transmission and remove rear supports and crossmember.

6) Remove clutch housing inspection cover and bolts attaching clutch housing to engine block. Pulling rearward and downward, remove transmission from vehicle.

INSTALLATION

1) To install, reverse removal procedure and note the following: When installing control lever assembly, place shift lever in 2nd gear position so that nylon bushing hole is vertical.

CAUTION: **During this operation, use care that dirt does not enter through opening.**

2) When installing clutch housing inspection cover, make sure that it is not bent. When installing shift lever dust boot, make sure cover is tightly installed to prevent noise entry into vehicle. After installing transmission, refill with SAE 80 gear oil.

RAM-50 (2WD) 5-SPEED

REMOVAL

1) In engine compartment, disconnect negative battery cable. Remove air cleaner and starter. Remove 2 upper transmission mounting bolts.

2) Inside vehicle, take out console box (if equipped), and carpet. Remove dust cover retainer plate at base of shift lever. Lift up dust cover and remove attaching bolts at lower part of extension housing and remove gearshift lever.

NOTE: **Make sure gearshift lever is in 2nd speed position before removing.**

3) With vehicle raised and supported, drain transmission. Remove bolts from rear of propeller shaft and draw shaft out of transmission.

4) Disconnect speedometer and back-up light switch harness at transmission side. Disconnect front exhaust pipe. From clutch control lever, disconnect clutch cable.

5) Support rear of engine with jack, place transmission jack under transmission and remove rear supports and crossmember.

6) Remove clutch housing inspection cover and bolts attaching clutch housing to engine block. Pulling rearward and downward, remove transmission from vehicle.

INSTALLATION

1) To install, reverse removal procedure and note the following: When installing control lever assembly, place shift lever in 2nd gear position so that nylon bushing hole is vertical.

CAUTION: **During this operation, use care that dirt does not enter through opening.**

2) When installing clutch housing inspection cover, make sure that it is not bent. When installing shift lever dust boot, make sure cover is tightly installed to prevent noise entry into vehicle. After installing transmission, refill with SAE 80 gear oil.

RAM-50 (4WD)

REMOVAL

1) Inside vehicle, take out console box (if equipped), and carpet. Remove dust cover retainer plate at base of shift lever. Lift up dust cover and remove attaching bolts at lower part of extension housing and remove gearshift lever. Shift levers should be in neutral position (transmission) and "4H" position (transfer case).

2) Raise and support vehicle. Remove drain plugs and drain transission and transfer case fluid. Remove front and rear propeller shafts.

3) Disconnect speedometer cable, back-up light switch wiring and 4WD indicator light switch harness from transmission. Disconnect front exhaust pipe. Disconnect clutch cable from clutch control lever.

4) Support rear of engine with safety stand. Support transmission with transmission jack. Disconnect plate and remove transfer case mounting bracket. Remove second crossmember.

Manual Transmission Removal

CHRYSLER CORP. IMPORTS (Cont.)

5) Remove clutch housing cover, then remove remaining transmission mounting bolts. Pull transmission assembly back and lower out of vehicle.

INSTALLATION

Reverse removal procedure to install, noting the following: Shift lever assembly must be installed with transmission lever in neutral position and transfer case lever in "4H" position.

FORD MOTOR CO. IMPORTS

MERKUR

REMOVAL

1) Wedge a wooden block 7" long under clutch pedal. Holding pedal above its normal position will disengage clutch cable self-adjuster. Open hood and disconnect negative battery cable. Raise and support vehicle.

2) Remove nuts attaching catalytic converter inlet pipe to turbocharger. Remove nuts attaching catalytic converter to muffler inlet flange and remove converter support bracket. Remove converter and inlet pipe as an assembly.

3) Remove propeller shaft and plug extension housing to prevent fluid leaks. Remove starter. Remove front stabilizer bar-to-body "U" brackets and body stiffener rod.

4) Position a block of wood between stabilizer bar and body side rail. Support transmission. Remove bolt attaching rear mount to transmission. Remove rear mount bolts and mount.

5) Loosen engine mount attaching nuts until only 2 or 3 threads are visible on end of studs. Position a block of wood against engine oil pan and raise engine until stud nuts contact crossmember. As engine tilts downward, lower transmission.

6) Disconnect wiring at neutral/safety and back-up light switch. Using a No. 40 Torx bit, remove shift lever attaching bolts. Remove lever out of extension housing. Remove snap ring and pull speedometer cable out of extension housing.

7) Remove clutch release lever cover. Pull rearward on clutch release cable and disengage it from release lever. Remove speedometer cable attaching clips and position cable out of way.

8) Remove bolt attaching engine rear cover plate to bell housing. Remove bell housing attaching bolts. Pull transmission rearward until bell housing contacts body. Raise rear of transmission and pull rearward to clear body. Lower rear of transmission and continue to pull rearward. Remove transmission.

INSTALLATION

1) Align transmission input shaft with pressure plate and push transmission forward until bell housing contacts body. Raise rear of transmission until it clears body.

2) Lower rear of transmission and push forward into position. Rock transmission slightly to align input shaft and clutch disc splines. Install and tighten bell housing bolts to 28-38 ft. lbs. (38-51 N.m).

3) Install and tighten engine rear cover bolt to 28-38 ft. lbs. (38-51 N.m). Remove stand and block of wood supporting engine. Raise transmission until it is in its normal position. Tighten engine mount nuts to 50-70 ft. lbs. (68-95 N.m).

4) Lower transmission. Position shift lever and install attaching bolts. Connect wiring at neutral/safety and back-up light switch. Install speedometer cable clips.

5) Raise transmission and install rear transmission mount. Tighten mount bolts to 25-35 ft. lbs. (34-47 N.m). Remove wood block and install stabilizer bar "U" brackets and body stiffener rod. Tighten bolts to 33-41 ft.lbs. (45-56 N.m).

6) Connect clutch cable to release lever and install cover. Install starter. Remove plug from extension housing and install propeller shaft. Install catalytic converter. Reverse removal procedure to complete installation.

GENERAL MOTORS IMPORTS

NOTE: **For Spectrum, see ISUZU I-MARK (FWD).**

SPRINT

REMOVAL

1) Disconnect ground cable from battery and transaxle. Remove air cleaner and heat pipe. Remove clutch cable from clutch release lever. Remove starter.

2) Disconnect speedometer cable at transaxle. Disconnect all wires from transaxle. Remove front and rear torque rod bolts from transaxle. Raise and support vehicle.

3) Drain transaxle oil. Disconnect exhaust pipe at exhaust manifold and at the first exhaust hanger. Remove clutch housing lower plate. Disconnect gear shift control shift and extension rod at transaxle.

4) Remove left front wheel. Detach the snap rings on right hand and left hand drive axles from the differential side gears. To detach the snap ring fitted on the spline of differential side joint (inboard joint) from differential side gear, pry the inboard joint out by using a pry bar.

5) Remove stabilizer bar mount bolts and ball stud bolt on left side. After removing these bolts, detach ball stud from the steering knuckle by pushing down on the stabilizer bar.

6) Draw out the inboard joint of the lift drive axle from the transaxle. Remove front torque rod. Securely support the transaxle caes with a jack for removal.

7) Remove mounting member bolts from the body and transaxle. Remove bolts and nuts fastening transaxle to the engine. Disconnect transaxle from engine by silding towards the left side and carefully lowering the jack.

INSTALLATION

To install, reverse removal procedure and note the following: Guide the right drive axle into the transaxle as the transaxle is being raised. Push the R and L drive axles into differential side gears until the snaprings on drive axles ingage side gears. Refill transaxle with new oil.

Manual Transmission Removal

HONDA

ACCORD & PRELUDE

REMOVAL

1) Disconnect ground cable from battery and transaxle. Release steering lock and place shift selector lever in neutral. Disconnect the following electrical leads: Positive battery cable at starter, starter solenoid and backup light switch.

2) Disconnect clutch cable at release arm. Remove starter mounting bolt from transaxle and upper transaxle mounting bolts. Raise and support vehicle, drain transaxle and remove front wheels.

3) Support transaxle with jack. Remove speedometer drive holder retaining bolt and pull assembly out of transaxle. Disconnect torque rod from clutch housing. Remove shift rod clevis bolt.

4) Disconnect and remove tie-rod ball joints. Remove lower arm ball joint pinch bolts and free arms by tapping downward with soft (brass) hammer. Turn steering knuckle to outward-most position, pry CV joint out about 1/2" and pull axle shaft out of transaxle housing. Repeat on other side.

5) Remove right-side radius rod. Remove torque arm brackets from clutch housing. Remove damper bracket from center beam. Remove clutch housing bolts at both transaxle mounting brackets. Remove clutch cover.

6) Remove remaining starter mounting bolt and remove starter. Remove front transaxle mounting bolt. Pull transaxle back until it clears dowel pins and lower assembly out of vehicle.

INSTALLATION

Reverse removal precedures to install transaxle, noting the following: Clean and lightly grease release bearing sliding surface. Always use spring clips when installing axle shafts.

CIVIC

REMOVAL

1) Disconnect ground cable from battery and transaxle. Release steering lock and place gear shift in neutral Position. Disconnect the following electrical leads: Starter motor, starter solenoid, temperature sending unit, ignition timing thermosensor and back-up light switch.

2) Remove speedometer cable and clip without disassembling speedometer gear holder. Remove clutch cable at release arm. Remove tannsaxle-side starter mounting bolt and top transaxle mounting bolt. Remove forward bolt from rear torque arm bracket.

3) Raise and support vehicle on hoist. Drain transaxle fluid and remove wheels. Remove engine shields, (if equipped). Remove stabilizer bar and brackets. Disconnect tie rod ends and lower ball joints from suspension arms. Remove CV joints from transaxle and remove axle shafts.

4) Disconnect shift lever torque rod from clutch housing. Slide pin retainer back and drive out spring with punch. Disconnect shift rod. Remove bolt from shift rod. Raise engine slihgtly and remove engine torque rods and brackets. Remove engine damper bracket from center beam. Remove transaxle and rear engine mount and bracket.

5) Place 1" x 2" x 4" wooden board between engine oil pan and center beam. Lower engine until it rests on beam. Remove engine-side starter mounting bolt and starter. Place transmisson jack under transaxle and remove remaining transaxle mounting bolts. Raise transaxle just enough to remove weight from engine and pull assembly away from engine until mainshaft clears clutch pressure plate. Lower transaxle out of vehicle.

INSTALLATION

To install, reverse removal procedure and note the following: When connecting axle shafts to transaxle, ensure they are fully seated in transaxle case. After insatllation, refill transaxle with fluid and adjust shift linkage as needed.

ISUZU

I-MARK (FWD)

REMOVAL & INSTALLATION

1) Disconnect negative battery cable. Remove hood. Remove air duct. Disconnect wiring connectors from transaxle. Disconnect speedometer cable at transaxle. Disconnect clutch and shift cables from transaxle. Drain transaxle lubricant.

2) Raise and support front of vehicle with jack stands. Disconnect right control arm at knuckle. Remove left strut rod with bracket. Disconnect both outer tie rod ends from knuckles. Pry drive axles from transaxle using a large screwdriver. Be careful to avoid damaging seals when removing drive axles.

3) Support engine with a hoist. Support transaxle with a floor jack. Remove center crossmember-to-frame mounting bolts. Lower transaxle side of engine. Remove transaxle-to-engine mounting bolts. Lower floor jack and remove transaxle assembly.

4) To install, reverse removal procedure.

I-MARK (RWD) 4-SPEED & 5-SPEED, P'UP 5-SPEED

REMOVAL & INSTALLATION

1) Disconnect negative battery cable. From inside vehicle, remove shift lever assembly. Loosen clutch cable adjusting nuts at lift side of engine compartment. Disconnect upper starter mounting nut and starter wiring.

2) Raise and support vehicle. Disconnect speedometer cable and clutch cable. Remove propeller shaft. Remove lower starter mounting bolt and remove starter. Disconnect exhaust pipe from manifold. Remove exhaust pipe bracket.

3) Remove flywheel inspection cover. Remove rear support mounting bolt. Support transmission under case and remove rear support. Lower transmission about 4" from normal position and remove any wires connected to transmission. Remove transmission-to-engine bolts. Remove transmission by sliding straight back and lowering from vehicle.

4) To install, reverse removal procedure.

Manual Transmission Removal

ISUZU (Cont.)

IMPULSE 5-SPEED

REMOVAL & INSTALLATION

1) Remove magnetic plug and drain oil. Disconnect negative battery cable. Remove gearshift lever boot. Remove console assembly. Raise vehicle on hoist and remove exhaust hanger at transmission.

2) Disconnect speedometer cable, ground cable and propeller shaft. Remove propeller shaft. Remove slave cylinder assembly.

3) Remove transmission rear mounting bolts and nuts at clutch cover plate. Remove bolts for shift quadrant cover, lever attaching bolts and lever. Remove control box assembly.

4) Lower engine and transmission and support rear of engine. Disconnect back-up light switch. Remove transmission-to-engine bolts. Pull transmission back until disengaged from clutch. Remove transmission.

5) To install, reverse removal procedure.

P'UP 4-SPEED (2WD)

REMOVAL & INSTALLATION

1) Disconnect negative battery terminal. Slide gearshift boot up on lever and remove lever attaching bolts, then withdraw lever. Remove starter attaching bolts and place starter out of way.

2) Raise vehicle on hoist. Disconnect exhaust pipe hanger at transmission, speedometer cable at extension housing, battery ground cable at transmission and propeller shaft from rear axle. Remove propeller shaft and either drain transmission fluid or install plug in extension housing to prevent fluid loss.

3) Remove return spring from clutch fork. Remove bolts attaching flywheel cover and remove frame bracket-to-transmission rear mount bolts. Raise engine and transmission as required and remove crossmember-to-frame bracket bolts. Remove rear mounting from extension housing.

4) Lower engine and transmission assembly and support rear of engine with support stand. Disconnect electrical connectors at back-up light and "coasting richer solenoid" (Federal models) switches. Remove transmission-to-engine attaching bolts. Pull transmission straight back until disengaged from clutch. Tip front of transmission down and remove transmission from vehicle.

5) To install, reverse removal procedure.

P'UP & TROOPER II 4-SPEED WITH TRANSFER CASE (4WD)

REMOVAL & INSTALLATION

1) Disconnect negative battery terminal. Slide gearshift boot up on lever and remove lever attaching bolts. Disconnect transfer gear shift lever return spring. Remove both gear shift levers.

2) Remove starter attaching bolts and lay starter out of way. Raise vehicle on hoist. Disconnect exhaust pipe from manifold and at hanger on transmission. Disconnect speedometer cable at transfer case, ground cable at transmission and propeller shaft from rear axle. Disconnect front propeller shaft and remove both shafts from vehicle.

3) Disconnect clutch fork return spring, then remove clutch cable from hooked portion of fork. Pull cable forward through stiffener bracket. Remove the lower 2 bolts attaching transmission rear mount-to-frame.

4) Raise engine and transmission just enough so that the 4 crossmember-to-frame bolts can be removed. Remove the 2 transfer case rear mounting bolts, then remove bolts attaching transfer side case to transfer case and remove transfer side case.

NOTE: **DO NOT lose shift rod detent spring and ball from transfer side case.**

5) Remove stud bolt from transfer case then lower engine and transmission, supporting rear of engine. Disconnect electrical connectors at back-up light and "coasting richer solenoid" (Federal models) switches. Remove 4 bolts holding shift cover to transfer case and remove cover and gasket.

6) Remove all bolts attaching transmission to engine then remove transmission with transfer case. To ease removal, turn transfer case side of transmission downward, slide transmission backward until clear of clutch, then tilt front of transmission down and slide forward and out of vehicle.

7) To install, reverse removal procedure.

MAZDA

GLC

REMOVAL

1) Disconnect negative battery cable, speedometer cable and any wires or connectors that may be connected to transaxle. Remove 2 clutch brackets and disconnect clutch cable from release lever. Remove water pipe bracket and harness clips.

2) Raise and support vehicle. Drain fluid from transaxle. Remove wheels and any shields or grards that may interfere with transmission removal. Remove ball joint from lower control arm. Disconnect drive shaft from differential by pulling outward on knuckle.

3) Support drive shaft out of the way. Support rear of engine with a support beam. Separate shift control rod and extension bar from transaxle.

4) Remove transaxle support crossmember and separate mount. Remove starter. Support transaxle with a jack. Remove transaxle-to-engine bolts. Lower transaxle out of vehicle.

INSTALLATION

Reverse removal procedure and note the following: Refill transaxle with lubricant. Check operation of shifter and clutch linkages and adjust as needed.

626

REMOVAL

1) Disconnect negative battery cable, speedometer cable and any wires or connectors that may be connected to transaxle. Remove 2 clutch cable bracket bolts

MAZDA (Cont.)

and disconnect clutch cable from release lever. Remove ground wire installation bolt and harness clips.

2) Remove starter. Mount engine support (49-G030-025), and attach the support hook to the engine hanger. Remove transaxle-to-engine attaching bolts. Raise vehicle and support with safety stands. Drain fluid from transaxle. Remove wheels and any shields or guards that may interfere with transmission removal.

3) Remove control link of stabilizer bar. Remove the under cover (if equipped). Remove ball joint from lower control arm by pulling arm downward. Remove left drive shaft from transaxle by inserting a lever between the drive shaft and the transaxle case and tap the end of the lever to uncouple the drive shaft and the differential side gear. Pull front hub forward and disconnect drive shaft from differential by pulling outward on knuckle.

NOTE: In order not to mark the oil seal, hold the joint at the differential side with one hand and pull the shaft straight out.

4) Remove the right drive shaft and the joint shaft by inserting a lever between them. Pull the front hub forward and separate the drive shaft from the joint shaft and set it aside. Remove joint shaft bracket mounting bolts and remove joint shaft and shaft bracket assembly from transaxle as an assembly.

5) Remove transaxle mounting bracket nuts at the crossmember. Remove the crossmember and the left lower arm as an assembly. Separate change control rod from change rod. Remove extension bar from transaxle. Remove transaxle under cover. Attach a rope to transaxle mount bracket at 2 places and over the engine support. Place a board on a floor jack and use this to support the transaxle as it is lowered from the vehicle.

CAUTION: Because the transaxle is not well balanced, be careful concerning the point of support.

6) Remove transaxle-to-engine attaching bolts (2). Seprate transaxle from engine. Loosen rope while lowering transaxle on jack. Remove transaxle mount brackets from the transaxle.

INSTALLATION

Reverse removal procedure and note the following: Install new clips on ends of drive shafts. After installing drive shafts, pull outward on shaft to ensure that shaft doesn't come out. Refill transaxle with lubricant. Check operation of shifter and clutch linkages and adjust as necessary.

ALL RWD MODELS

REMOVAL

1) Disconnect negative battery cable. Place gearshift lever in neutral position, and remove gearshift knob. Remove console box (if equipped) and gearshift lever. B2000 gearshift lever components include a wave washer, shim and bushing.

2) On RX7, remove air cleaner and upper transmission-to-engine bolts. On all models, raise and support vehicle and drain transmission. Disconnect and remove propeller shaft. Disconnect and/or remove under cover, exhaust components and emission control components as required.

3) On all models, reomve clutch slave cylinder and place out of the way without removing line. On all models, disconnect and remove starter, speedometer cable, back-up light wires and other electrical connections.

4) Place jack under rear of engine, protecting oil pan with wooden block. Position transmission jack under transmission and remove transmission-to-engine mounting bolts. If equipped, remove transmission-to-crossmember bolts, crossmember-to-frame bolts and crossmember. Slide transmission back until input shaft is cleared. Remove from vehicle.

INSTALLATION

To install, reverse removal precedure, ensureing that splines in input shaft align with those in clutch disc.

MERCEDES-BENZ

190 SERIES

REMOVAL

1) Disconnect negative battery cable. Cover damping mat with a piece of sheet metal to prevent damage to engine compartment firewall when lowering transmission.

2) Raise and support vehicle. Remove engine splash shield. Support engine and transmission. Remove transmission mount nut from rear transmission cover. Remove transmission crossmember. *See Fig. 1.*

3) Disconnect exhaust bracket from transmission, paying attention to location of washers. Remove shielding plate above propeller shaft intermediate bearing. Loosen propeller shaft nut. Loosen bolts from propeller shaft intermediate bearing, but DO NOT remove bolts.

4) Disconnect propeller shaft from transmission so that companion plate stays on propeller shaft. Using a 3/8" (10 mm) diameter mandrel, loosen fitted sleeves on transmission universal joint flange. Push companion plate away from universal joint flange.

5) Pull propeller shaft toward rear axle as far as possible. Hang propeller shaft out of way. Disconnect exhaust pipe at rear suspension. Carefully lower pipe and hang pipe out of way.

6) Disconnect speedometer cable from transmission and remove clip from holder. Disconnect clutch slave cylinder line. Remove clips and disconnect shift rods. Remove starter.

7) Remove transmission attaching bolts, removing the 3 upper bolts last. Pull transmission out until it clears dowel pins, turn transmission 45° to left and continue to pull transmission rearward until input shaft clears clutch. Lower transmission.

Manual Transmission Removal

MERCEDES-BENZ (Cont.)

Fig. 1: Removing 190 Series Manual Transmission

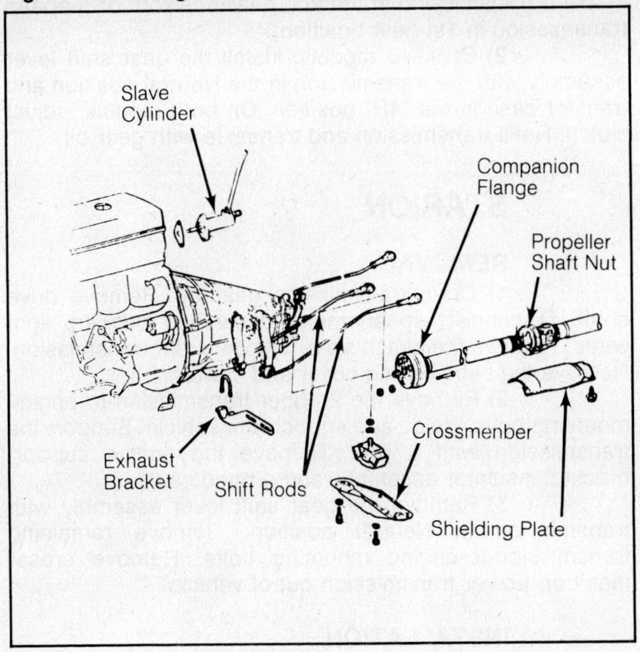

NOTE: On vehicles with auxiliary heater, make sure that heater hose is not damaged when transmission is lowered.

INSTALLATION

1) Apply grease to input shaft splines and bushing. Engage transmission in one gear and rotate it back and forth until input shaft and clutch disc splines align. Make sure to connect engine ground cable when installing transmission bolts.

2) After connecting clutch slave cylinder, bleed hydraulic system. Using Crow's Foot (201 589 00 01 00), tighten propeller shaft nut to 22-30 ft. lbs. (30-41 N.m). Reverse removal procedure to complete installation.

MITSUBISHI

ALL FWD MODELS

REMOVAL

1) Remove the battery, battery tray, windshield washer reservoir, and air cleaner. Disconnect the clutch cable, speedometer cable, and back-up light harness from transaxle. Disconnect starter motor harness.

2) Remove upper 5 transaxle-to-engine bolts. Remove stater. Raise and support vehicle. Remove wheels. Drain transaxle oil. Remove the extension, shift control rod, and range selector control cable from under the engine compartment.

3) Disconnect the stabilizer bar and strut rod from the lower control arm. Remove drive axle shafts. See appropriate Mitsubishi article in MANUAL TRANSMISSIONS section. Support the transaxle with a jack. Do not compress the oil pan.

4) Remove bell housing cover. Remove transaxle-to-engine bolts, transaxle mount insulator bracket, and transaxle mount bracket. Lower transaxle from under vehicle.

INSTALLATION

To install, reverse removal procedure. Fill transaxle with Hypoid gear oil. Adjust clutch cable. Adjust linkage as necessary.

MONTERO

REMOVAL

Transmission & Transfer Case

1) Disconnect negative battery cable. Place transmission gearshift lever in Neutral position and transfer case lever in 4WD high range position. Remove both gearshift lever assemblies.

2) Raise and support vehicle. Remove skid plate. Drain transmission and transfer case oil. Remove front and rear drive shafts. Disconnect speedometer cable, back-up light switch harness, and 4WD indicator light harness.

3) Detact clutch slave cylinder from case. Remove bell housing cover, starter, and front exhaust pipe mounting bracket. Remove rear transmission mount bolts. Support transmission with a jack and remove the crossmember. Remove transfer case mount.

4) Remove transmission-to-engine mounting bolts. Pull transmission and transfer case away from engine and remove from vehicle.

INSTALLATION

To install, reverse removal procedure. Fill transaxle with Hypoid gear oil. Adjust clutch cable. Adjust linkage as necessary.

MITSUBISHI (Cont.)

PICKUP

REMOVAL

4 & 5-Speed (2WD & 4WD)

1) Disconnect negative battery cable. Remove air cleaner, starter and upper 2 transmission-to-engine mounting bolts. From inside passenger compartment, remove console box or carpeting covering transmission access plate.

2) Remove the shift lever assembly from the extension housing. Raise and support vehicle. Drain all gear oil. Remove drive shaft(s). Disconnect the speedometer cable.

3) On 2WD models, disconnect the back-up lights harness. On 4WD models, disconnect back-up light and indicator light harnesses. On both models, disconnect front exhaust pipe. Remove clutch slave cylinder or disconnect clutch release cable.

4) Support rear of engine with a jack. On 4WD models, remove the transfer case mounting bracket. On both models, place jack under transmission. Do not crush oil pan. Remove crossmember.

5) Remove bell housing cover and remaining transmission-to-engine bolts. Slide transmission away from engine and remove from vehicle.

INSTALLATION

1) To install, reverse removal procedure. On 2WD models, install the gear shift lever assembly in the 4-speed transmission in the 2nd gear position, or 5-speed transmission in 1st gear position.

2) On 4WD models, install the gear shift lever assembly with the transmission in the Neutral position and transfer case in the "4H" position. On both models, adjust clutch. Refill transmission and transaxle with gear oil.

STARION

REMOVAL

1) Drain transmission gear oil. Remove drive shaft. Disconnect speedometer cable and back-up light wires. Remove the clutch slave cylinder from transmission. Remove the bell housing cover and starter.

2) Remove the 2 upper transmission-to-engine mounting bolts. Raise and support the vehicle. Support the transmission with a jack. Remove the engine support bracket, insulator assembly, and ground cable.

3) Remove the gear shift lever assembly with transmission in Neutral position. Remove remaining transmission-to-engine mounting bolts. Remove crossmember. Lower transmission out of vehicle.

INSTALLATION

To install, reverse removal procedure. Fill transaxle with Hypoid gear oil. Adjust linkage as necessary.

NISSAN

ALL RWD MODELS

REMOVAL

1) Disconnect negative battery cable. Remove console (if equipped) and shift lever boot. Place transmission in neutral. Remove snap ring or nut from control lever pin. Remove control lever pin and control lever.

2) Raise vehicle and remove exhaust pipe. Disconnect wiring at back-up light switch, high gear switch, neutral switch (if equipped) and overdrive switch (210 5-speed). Disconnect speedometer cable.

3) On 4WD pickups, disconnect wires from 4WD indicator switch. Disconnect propeller shaft between transmission and transfer case. Remove front differential carrier crossmember. Disconnect propeller shaft between transfer case and front differential carrier.

4) On all other models, disconnect propeller shaft from transmission. On all models, remove clutch cylinder from transmission case. Support engine and transmission. Remove rear transmission mounting bolts and crossmember bolts. Remove starter. Remove transmission-to-engine mounting bolts.

5) Slide transmission to rear away from engine. Remove transmission from vehicle. Use care when removing transmission to avoid striking any adjacent parts or main drive shaft.

INSTALLATION

Reverse removal procedures to install transmission, noting the following:

- Clean mating surfaces of engine rear plate and transmission case. Apply a light coat of grease to splined parts of clutch disc, input shaft and moving surfaces of control lever and striking rod.
- Lubricate oil seal lip and bushing of extension housing before installing propeller shaft.
- Fill transmission with gear oil to level of filler hole.

ALL FWD MODELS

REMOVAL

1) Remove battery and battery holding plate. Remove radiator reservoir tank. Remove drive shafts from transaxle without damaging oil seals. Insert a shaft into each side of differential to prevent side gears from falling into differential case.

2) Remove wheel well protector. Separate shifter control rod and support rod from transaxle. Remove exhaust pipe securing nuts and bolts. Remove engine gusset bolts and transmission protector. Remove clutch control cable from withdraw lever.

3) Disconnect speedometer cable. Disconnect wires from reverse and neutral switches. Support engine with a jack and a block of wood placed under the oil pan. Spuuort the transaxle with a jack.

4) Remove starter motor. Remove engine mount securing bolts. Remove bolts securing transaxle to engine. Separate teansaxle from engine and remove transaxle from under vehicle.

Manual Transmission Removal

NISSAN (Cont.)

INSTALLATION

To install, reverse removal procedure and note the following: Clean mating surface between engine and clutch housing. Apply grease to splines on input shaft and clutch disc. Remove filler plug and fill transaxle with recommended amount and type of gear lube.

PEUGEOT

ALL MODELS

REMOVAL

1) Open hood as far as possible and support with wooden blocks under safety hooks. Disconnect battery cable and fan shroud. Remove header pipe bolts and disconnect oxygen sensor (if equipped). Remove heat shield and air injection hose.

2) Remove front seat track floor brace. Remove rear tailpipe brackets. Remove rear axle mounts. Mark position of strap on steering column flange and remove bolts.

3) On each side of crossmember, remove bolt and install bolt 2" longer than original. Remove 2 remaining bolts. Lower crossmember by backing off new bolts about 2 inches.

4) Place transmission jack under transmission and remove propeller shaft tube bolts. Separate propeller shaft from transmission by 13/16" (20 mm). Insert transmission shaft retaining plate (80403-SZ) to clear transmission output shaft.

5) Remove front mount for gear selector rod. Remove shifting link rod, selector link rod and back-up light switch. Remove speedometer cable. Remove bolts from inspection plates on clutch housing. Remove plates

6) Remove slave cylinder circlip and flexible hose bracket. With engine suspended from hoist and hooks, lower hoist to tilt the transmission as far as possible. Remove starter. Remove clutch housing bolts and lower transmission.

INSTALLATION

To install, reverse removal procedures. Lubricate input shaft splines and clutch release bearing guide with grease (Molykote or equivalent). Prior to fully engaging transmission into place, install slave cylinder into its housing. Refill transmission to proper level. Adjust linkage as needed.

PORSCHE

911 CARRERA

REMOVAL

1) Transaxle and engine must be removed as a unit. After removal, assemblies may be separated. Vehicle must be raised and supported with safety stands to remove assembly from below vehicle.

2) Disconnect battery ground cable. Remove engine block vent hose and plug hose. On A/C equipped vehicles, detach compressor at console but leave hoses connected.

NOTE: **Air conditioning system is under pressure. DO NOT unhook hoses unless system is discharged first.**

3) Remove relay plate cover and disconnect engine wires at relay plate, adapter plug, relay, socket and ignition control unit. Remove fuel hoses at filter and return line. Disconnect accelerator linkage.

4) Remove rear center tunnel cover in passenger compartment. Remove rubber boot in tunnel by pulling forward over selector rod. Loosen shift rod coupling and pull coupling off of transmission inner shift rod.

5) Disconnect speedometer sensor wires in tunnel. Remove rubber plug with wire plug. Drain crankcase and plug hoses on engine and oil tank. Remove heater hoses at exchangers. Remove rear stabilizer.

6) Disconnect ground strap at body and battery wires at starter. Disconnect accelerator linkage at pedal and clutch cable from transmission.

CAUTION: **Be careful when jacking assembly upward not to damage secondary air injection pipes.**

7) Place a jack under engine/transmission assembly and apply a little upward pressure to relieve tension on motor mounts. Remove transmission and engine mount bolts. Lower engine/transmission assembly out of vehicle.

CAUTION: **Do not move vehicle unless drive shafts are suspended horizontally, to prevent damage to dust covers.**

INSTALLATION

To install, reverse removal procedure and note the following: Do not clamp heater hoses. Slide them onto exchangers just before engine/transmission assembly is in final installation position.

928S

TRANSAXLE ASSEMBLY

Removal

1) Remove battery from case. Loosen rear wheels and position transmission in 5th gear. Loosen screw clamping selector rod to transmission linkage at rear of tunnel.

2) Open inspection cover (rubber cap) in transmission. Turn 1 wheel and hold opposite wheel to position coupling bolt between drive and input shafts for removal. Remove bolt.

Manual Transmission Removal

PORSCHE (Cont.)

3) Position shift lever in neutral. Remove rear wheels and detach brake calipers and suspend them to relieve hoses of any tension. Disconnect axle shafts from transaxle and suspend horizontally from car to prevent damage to boots.

4) Push dust cover back and remove set screw from shift rod coupling. Detach shift rod and slide rod forward in tunnel to clear linkage at rear. Disconnect back-up light wires and speedometer pulse transmitter wires from transmission. Remove switch and pulse transmitter.

Fig. 1: Location of Input Shaft Coupling Bolt and Shift Rod Coupling Set Screw

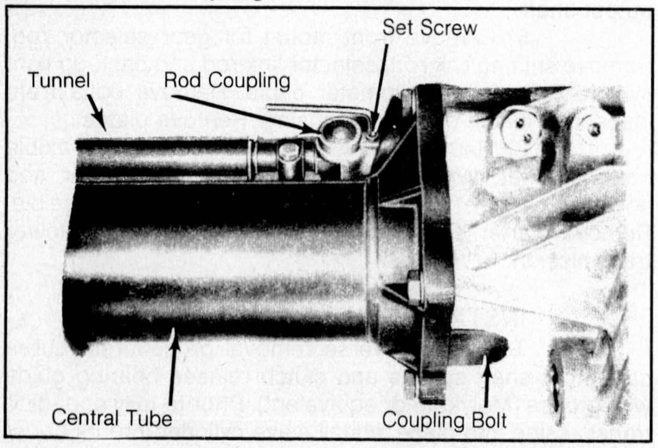

5) Detach exhaust assembly and remove entire assembly after the catalytic converter. This requires removal of 4 bolts between converter and intermediate muffler, 2 bolts on front rubber mount, 1 bolt on rear rubber mount and 2 bolts on holder for main muffler. Remove battery box.

6) Remove 2 transmission mounting bolts on rear axle crossmember and 2 bolts between rear axle crossmember and frame. Place transmission jack beneath rear axle crossmember and mark position of crossmember. Remove remaining 4 bolts on crossmember. Tilt rear axle carefully and support in tilted position taking weight off the lower control arm link pins.

7) Mount transmission support bracket to transmission with fixtures (9148 and 9149). *See Fig. 2.* Remove 6 bolts between central tube and transmission. Pull transmission back to one side and lower from vehicle.

Installation

To install, reverse removal procedure noting that propeller shaft extends .50-.53" (12.5-13.5 mm) beyond rear flange surface. Improper position may cause clutch drag due to improper engagement of spline and clutch disc. Tighten all nuts and bolts to specifications.

TRANSAXLE CENTRAL TUBE

Removal

1) With transaxle removed from vehicle, disconnect negative battery cable. Suspend engine from front eyelet with fixture (VW 10-222) and hold tightly in installation position.

2) Support tube at front tunnel reinforcing brace with a front block. Detach central tube from front clutch housing and slide back about 4".

3) Remove rear cross traverse in tunnel, then loosen rear axle mountings and lower torsion bar tube. Pull selector rod out to the rear. Remove central tube by lowering and pulling out to the rear.

Fig. 2: Installing Transmission Support Brackets

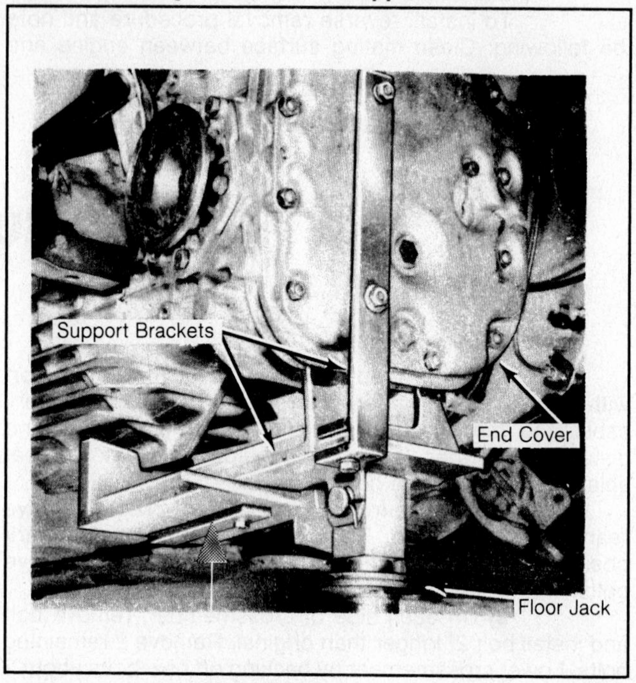

Inspection

Propeller shaft must extend .50-.53" (12.5-13.5 mm) beyond face of clutch housing flange in order to properly engage clutch disc splines. Correct shaft position by tapping end with soft faced hammer. Check free rotation of shaft turning by hand.

NOTE: **Shaft must turn easily without noise or flat spots. If bearings or shaft are damaged, entire assembly must be replaced. Separate component replacement is not possible as individual parts are not available.**

Installation

To install, reverse removal procedure.

944

TRANSAXLE

Removal

1) Detach exhaust pipe from catalytic converter and loosen exhaust system brackets at central tube. Remove muffler clamp from transaxle end plate and remove entire converter and muffler assembly.

2) Push shift linkage dust boot back and remove lock wire from shift linkage connecting bolt. Remove connecting bolt. From inside vehicle, fold back dust boot and inner cover on shift lever. Remove clamp from shift lever knob, then remove knob.

3) Remove circlip holding selector rod to shift lever. Pull shift rod and spring washer from shift lever pin. Turn shift lever 180° and tilt out to right. Press down on rubber seal between central tube and tunnel. Slide selector rod forward in tunnel about 12" to clear linkage at rear.

PORSCHE (Cont.)

4) Remove plug from rear of central tube housing. Push shift rod protective tube back far enough so shift rod tube is outside central tube housing. Remove inspection plugs (1 located at bottom of central tube housing; the other on upper left side of transmission case). Remove propeller shaft-to-mainshaft coupling screws through inspection holes. Slide coupling back toward transmission case.

5) Detach axle shafts from transaxle and suspend from vehicle in horizontal position. Disconnect wires from back-up light switch. Place a jack with transmission adapter (US 618 and 618/1) under transmission and raise slightly to release pressure from transmission suspension.

6) Remove transmission-to-central tube housing flange bolts. Remove transaxle mount bolts. Lower transaxle assembly and central tube until central tube rests on rear axle cross tube. Remove transaxle out rear.

Installation

1) To install, reverse removal procedure and note the following: Before installing transaxle, check propeller shaft protrusion at rear flange. Shaft should extend .49-.53" (12.5-13.5 mm) beyond flange lips. Make small corrections by tapping on end of shaft with soft-faced hammer.

2) After installation, adjust shift linkage as follows: Place transmission in Neutral and install intermediate shift lever with a 5° rearward offset from center of shaft. Ensure shift lever is in neutral, then move shift lever base to adjust shift lever to an 85° angle from rear of central tube.

3) With shift lever in Neutral, transverse selector shaft will be held in 3rd/4th gear (middle shift pattern) by spring pressure. With shift linkage connected and adjusted properly, shift lever will not lean to either side. If shift lever leans to either side, adjust at intermediate shift lever.

CENTRAL TUBE

Removal

1) With transaxle assembly removed from vehicle, disconnect negative battery strap. Suspend engine from front eyelet with support fixture (VW10-222) and hold tight in installation position.

2) Support tube at front tunnel reinforcing brace with locally made block. Detach central tube from clutch housing. Remove rear reinforcement strut, then loosen rear axle mountings and lower torsion bar tube. Pull selector rod rearward. Remove central tube by lowering and pulling out to rear.

Inspection

Check for free rotation of central tube bearings by turning propeller shaft by hand. Shaft must turn easily without binding. If bearings or shaft are damaged, central tube with shaft and bearings must be replaced.

Installation

To install, reverse removal procedure and check propeller shaft protrusion. Check and adjust shift linkage.

RENAULT

FUEGO

REMOVAL

1) Disconnect battery ground cable and starter wiring harness. Remove starter attaching bolts and starter. Disconnect clutch cable at release lever.

2) Remove axle shafts from transaxle. Do not disconnect outer end from hub unless outer CV joint service is required. See appropriate Renault article in MANUAL TRANSMISSIONS section. Disconnect speedometer cable, shift linkage, and any wires that are connected to transaxle.

NOTE: DO NOT remove any of the gear shift linkage ball joints from their sockets.

3) Remove clutch cover and any shields or guards that may interfere with transaxle removal. Support transaxle with a transmission jack. Remove transmission mounts. Remove engine-to-transaxle bolts. Slide transaxle rearward and remove from vehicle.

Installation

To install, reverse removal procedure. Lightly coat input shaft splines with assembly lube prior to reinstalling transaxle. Adjust and check operation of shifter and clutch linkage. Adjust Top Dead Center sensor as needed. End of sensor should be .04" (1 mm) from flywheel face.

SAAB

ALL MODELS

REMOVAL

1) Remove hood, then disconnect battery cables and lift out battery. Drain coolant from radiator and engine. Disconnect power brake unit vacuum hose from intake manifold. Remove rubber bellows between air flow sensor and intake manifold. Disconnect and plug fuel line. Disconnect air flow sensor electrical leads. Remove air cleaner and mixture control unit.

2) Remove air intake, preheater hose, crankcase ventilation hose and intake hose. Disconnect cable from oil pressure sender. On California models, disconnect all EGR system hoses. If equipped with power steering, disconnect and plug hoses at steering pump.

3) Disconnect and remove ignition coil. Disconnect the following electrical connections: Temperature sending unit, radiator fan, thermostat contact, oil pressure sender, headlights and starter leads. Disconnect and plug all fuel injection lines (if equipped). Disconnect choke and throttle cables. Disconnect all water hoses. Disconnect hose to expansion tank.

4) Remove grill and hood locking cable. Remove radiator/headlight assembly. Disconnect hose from clutch slave/cylinder and plug hose and hole in cylinder. Disconnect exhaust pipe from manifold and ground cable from

SAAB (Cont.)

Fig. 1: Installing New Transmission Housing Gasket

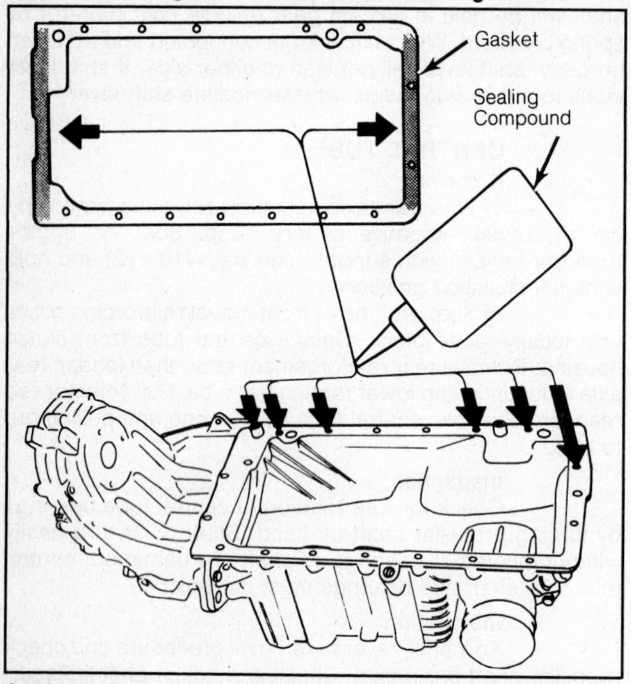

Apply sealing compound on ends of gasket and in bolt holes indicated.

transaxle. Remove bellows clamp and bellows from inner CV joints.

5) Place spacer (8393209) between upper control arm underside and body to unload suspension when vehicle is raised. Insert spacer from engine compartment side. Raise and support front of vehicle.

6) Remove lower end piece from control arm. Pull out steering knuckle assembly and support end piece against control arm outer end. Place shifter in Neutral. Remove nut and knock out taper pin in gear shift rod joint.

NOTE: Gear shift rod joints are made of steel or plastic. DO NOT knock out taper pin from plastic joints.

7) Remove rear engine mounting bolts. Loosen nut on front engine mounting so mounting can be lifted from bracket. Slightly raise engine and move engine/transaxle unit to each side to free CV joints. Lift engine/transaxle unit from vehicle.

8) To separate transaxle from engine, drain engine oil. Remove clutch cover, starter and clutch shaft. Remove 3 clutch slave cylinder retaining screws. Remove engine-to-transaxle attaching bolts and carefully lift engine off transaxle unit.

INSTALLATION

To install, reverse removal procedure. Be sure CV joints are packed with grease prior to installation. Apply sealing compound to 3 clutch slave cylinder retaining bolts. Use new gasket on transmission housing, applying sealing compound to both sides of gasket ends. Also apply sealing compound to 6 bolts shown in *Fig. 1*.

SUBARU

ALL MODELS

REMOVAL

1) Disconnect battery cables. Remove spare tire and air cleaner. Remove clutch cable return spring and clutch cable. Disconnect speedometer cable from transaxle housing. Disconnect back-up light switch, ground strap from vehicle body and starter harness. DO NOT remove battery cable from starter.

2) Remove starter and upper engine-to-transmission mounting bolts. Loosen lower mounting bolts. Loosen transmission side stabilizer bar .39" (10 mm) and tighten engine side stabilizer bar the same amount. Slightly tilt engine backward to facilitate transaxle removal.

NOTE: DO NOT tighten engine side stabilizer bar more than .39" (10 mm).

3) On 4WD vehicles, remove hand brake tray cover and brake cover. Remove the rod cover. Set the drive selector lever at 4WD position. Remove the nut connecting gear shift and drive selector rods.

4) Remove 2 nuts securing drive selector rod and drive selector to plate. Remove gearshift lever boot screws and nut connecting gearshift lever with operating lever. Remove gearshift lever and boot.

5) On all models, disconnect the oxygen sensor harness. Raise and support vehicle. Disconnect hot air intake hose. Separate front exhaust pipe from rear exhaust pipe.

6) Remove bolts front exhaust pipe-to-bracket bolts. Support the front exhaust pipe and remove nuts from exhaust port of engine. Remove exhaust pipe, being carefull not to damage oxygen sensor. Remove stove from exhaust manifold.

7) On 4WD models, remove transmission skid plate. Remove rear drive shaft from transmission. Plug open end of transmission assembly. On all models except 4WD, remove exhaust system shield. Remove gearshift retaining bolts from transmission. Free gearshift system from transmission.

8) On all models, remove stabilizer bar. Disconnect and lower transverse links from front crossmember. Drive out inner axle shaft-to-drive axle shaft retaining pin. Push wheel assembly toward outside of vehicle and separate axle shaft from drive axle. Remove clamp on left side of parking brake cable to facilitate removal of rear crossmember.

9) Remove left and right transmission mounts. Support transaxle assembly with a jack. Remove crossmember. Remove 2 nuts securing engine to transaxle. Move transaxle assembly rearward to clear mainshaft, then lower transaxle from vehicle.

INSTALLATION

To install, reverse removal procedure. Replace all lock nuts and roll pins. Tighten nut connecting control arm to crossmember only when vehicle has been lowered to floor.

Manual Transmission Removal

TOYOTA

CAMRY

REMOVAL

NOTE: **The engine and transaxle are removed as an assembly.**

1) Mark hood hinge positions. Remove hood and battery. Drain cooling system. Disconnect accelerator cable from throttle body.

2) If equipped with cruise control, remove actuator cover. Disconnect wiring connector and vacuum hose. Remove actuator with bracket. If equipped with air conditioning, disconnect main and sub fan motor connectors. Disconnect reservoir and upper and lower radiator hoses.

3) Remove radiator supports, rubber cushions, and radiator. Remove air cleaner assembly with air flow meter and hose.

4) Mark for reassembly reference and remove all electrical connectors, cables, and vacuum hoses that interfer with engine removal. Pull out EFI wire harness to right side fender apron.

5) Disconnect 2 heater hoses. Detach fuel inlet hose from filter and return hose from return pipe. Remove speedometer cable from transaxle.

6) Detach clutch slave cylinder and hose bracket. Do not disconnect hoses from the hydraulic system. Disconnect transaxle control cable. If equipped, detach A/C belt, compressor, power steering belt, and steering pump with bracket. Set assemblies aside. Do not discharge A/C system.

7) Raise and support vehicle. Drain oil from transaxle. Wrap drive axle boots with shop towels. Remove 6 nuts from each drive shaft flange while depressing brake pedal. Disconnect both front drive shafts.

8) Disconnect front exhaust pipe and remove 2 gaskets from manifold. Remove exhaust pipe stay from cylinder block. Remove 2 hole covers and disconnect front and rear engine mounts. Remove crossmember if necessary. Lower vehicle.

NOTE: **Do not damage power steering gear housing or neutral start switch during removal. Ensure all wiring, hoses, and cables are clear of engine before lifting.**

9) Attach engine hoist to lift brackets on engine. Remove engine and transaxle mounts from brackets. Remove left side transaxle mount bracket. Carefully lift engine/transaxle assembly out of vehicle.

10) Remove front and rear brackets. Remove side gear shaft and universal joint. Remove starter. Separate engine from transaxle.

INSTALLATION

1) Install mounts and starter on engine/transaxle assembly. Install side gear shaft and universal joint. With engine hoist chained to lift brackets, slowly lower engine/transaxle assembly into engine compartment.

2) Tilt transaxle down while lowering to clear neutral start switch, mount brackets, and power steering gear housing. Install engine mounts, brackets, and crossmembers.

3) To complete installation, reverse removal procedures. Connect all wiring and fuel and vacuum hoses. Adjust drive belts. Fill radiator with coolant and transaxle with gear oil.

CELICA & COROLLA (RWD)

REMOVAL

1) Drain coolant from upper portion of radiator. Remove upper radiator hose. Disconnect battery at ground terminal. Remove shift lever from inside of vehicle. Drain transmission lubricant. Mark propeller shaft and rear flange for orientation and remove propeller shaft.

2) On Celica models, disconnect exhaust pipe clamp from stiffener plate, speedometer cable and back-up light switch wire. Remove lower clutch housing cover plate. Disconnect the clutch release cylinder from clutch housing leaving hydraulic line connected. Remove starter.

3) On Corolla models, disconnect speedometer cable, back-up light switch wire and exhaust pipe clamp at clutch housing. Remove exhaust pipe at manifold. Remove lower clutch housing cover plate. Disconnect the clutch release cylinder from clutch housing leaving hydraulic line connected. Remove starter.

4) On both models, support transmission and remove rear support member. Remove remaining bolts attaching clutch housing to engine. Move transmission rearward and lower from vehicle, clear of clutch assembly.

INSTALLATION

To install, reverse removal procedure. Lightly grease friction surfaces and reverse removal procedure. Ensure propeller shaft and rear flange marks are aligned. Refill transmission lubricant.

CRESSIDA & SUPRA

REMOVAL

1) Remove negative battery terminal. Drain coolant from upper tank. Remove upper radiator hose. Remove console box and shift lever from inside of vehicle. Raise and support vehicle.

2) Drain transmission gear oil. Remove steering gear housing without disconnecting fluid hoses and suspend it. Mark drive shaft and rear flange for reassembly reference and remove drive shaft.

3) Remove exhaust pipe clamp bolt from stiffener plate. Disconnect speedometer cable and back-up light switch from transmission. Remove clutch slave cylinder. Do not disconnect hydraulic line.

4) Remove starter. Place jack under transmission and raise slightly. Remove rear transmission mount. Remove transmission-to-engine mounting bolts and remove transmission from vehicle.

INSTALLATION

To install, reverse removal procedure. Lightly grease friction surfaces and reverse removal procedure. Ensure propeller shaft and rear flange marks are aligned. Refill transmission lubricant.

COROLLA (FWD)

REMOVAL

1) Remove negative battery terminal. Drain coolant from radiator (C51). Remove air cleaner with air hose. Raise and support vehicle.

TOYOTA (Cont.)

2) Disconnect back-up light switch connector. Remove speedometer cable. Disconnect control cables. Remove water inlet from transaxle (C51).

3) Remove clip from clutch pipe bracket (S41 and 50). Disconnect bracket from the transaxle (S41 ans 50). Remove 2 bolts and clutch release cylinder.

4) Remove under cover. Remove front and rear mounting. Remove engine mounting center member. Disconnect drive shaft from transaxle.

5) Disconnect steering knuckle from the lower arm. Pull steering knuckle outward, and remove left drive shaft. Remove starter. Disconnect bond cable. Remove engine rear plate No. 2 (C51).

6) Raise transaxle and engine slightly, use wooden block between jack and engine. Disconnect left engine mount. Disconnect transaxle mount bolts from engine. Lower engine left side and remove the transaxle from the engine.

INSTALLATION

To install, reverse removal procedure. Lightly grease friction surfaces and reverse removal procedure. Refill transmission lubricant.

LAND CRUISER

REMOVAL

1) Disconnect battery cable. Raise and support vehicle. Drain gear oil from transmission and transfer cases. Remove transmission skid plate. Disconnect the drive shafts, speedometer cable, and parking brake cable from transmission/transfer case assembly.

2) From inside vehicle, remove scuff plate, side panel trim, heater duct, and carpets. Remove shift lever knobs, dust boots, and transmission shift lever.

3) Disconnect electrical wiring and vacuum hoses (if necessary) from transmission/transfer case assembly. Remove attaching bolts, then remove transmission/transfer case assembly from vehicle.

4) To separate transfer case from transmission, move transfer case lever to "4L" position. Remove back-up light switch from transmission case. Remove stake marks from transmission output shaft nut, then hold power take-off companion flange stationary and remove output shaft nut.

NOTE: **When removing transmission output shaft nut, have front drive engaged.**

5) Remove 5 transfer case-to-transmission case attaching bolts. Using a puller, separate transfer case from transmission case, holding power take-off gear to prevent it from dropping out of case.

INSTALLATION

To install, reverse removal procedure. After transfer case is attached to transmission case, stake transmission output shaft nut in place. With transmission/transfer case assembly installed in vehicle, fill transmission case and transfer case with gear oil. Adjust shift linkage.

MR2

REMOVAL

1) Disconnect negative battery cable. Drain transaxle gear oil. Disconnect back-up light switch connector. Disconnect speedometer cable. Remove bolts holding water inlet and remove water inlet from transaxle. Remove engine lower cover. Remove fuel tank protector.

2) Disconnect transaxle control cable. Remove control cable bracket and clutch release cylinder. Disconnect exhaust pipe at exhaust manifold. Remove front mounting bracket from body. Remove exhaust pipe assembly from rear bracket and remove exhaust pipe. Remove transaxle protector.

3) Disconnect drive axle shaft from side gear shaft. Disconnect and remove starter. Remove rear engine plate No. 2. Disconnect front engine mount from body. Disconnect rear engine mount from body. Raise engine-transaxle assembly slightly. Disconnect left engine mount. Disconnect transaxle from engine. Lower left side of engine and remove transaxle from engine.

INSTALLATION

To install, reverse removal procedure. Tighten all mounting bolts to specification. Refill transaxle with 2.4 qts. (2.3L) of gear oil (SAE 75-90W GL-4 or GL-5).

PICKUP

REMOVAL

1) Disconnect negative battery cable. Remove floor mat and shifter boot(s). Remove shift lever(s) and retainer from inside vehicle. Remove upper starter mounting nut.

2) Raise and support vehicle. Drain transmission (and transfer case on 4WD models). Remove clutch slave cylinder (with hydraulic line connected) and position out of way. Remove starter. Mark drive shaft and transmission yoke for reassembly reference and remove shaft.

3) Disconnect speedometer cable. Disconnect back-up light switch wire. Disconnect exhaust pipe clamp from transmission housing. Remove 4 mounting bolts from extension housing.

4) On 2WD models, raise transmission slightly by raising engine with jack and wooden block under engine. Remove the 4 bracket bolts from support member and remove rear mounting with bracket.

5) On 4WD models, jack up transmission enough to remove the weight from the rear support. Remove 8 bolts, and remove support member. On all models, remove remaining transmission housing bolts. Place a safety support with a wooden block under engine and lower jack until engine is resting on support.

6) Draw out transmission and transfer case assembly, down and toward the rear. Remove engine rear mounting. Remove transfer case from transmission.

INSTALLATION

To install, reverse removal procedure. Apply a small amount of multi-purpose grease to end of input shaft, shaft splines, release bearing and diaphragm spring contact surfaces before installation. Refill transmission and transfer case with lubricant after installation.

TOYOTA (Cont.)

TERCEL

NOTE: **Transmission assembly may be removed without removing differential assembly. Procedure given here covers removal of complete transaxle assembly.**

REMOVAL

All 2WD & 4WD Models

1) Drain coolant from upper radiator tank. Disconnect negative battery cable, air cleaner inlet duct, and upper radiator hose (from engine). Disconnect clutch cable. Remove starter motor. Remove 4 upper clutch housing-to-engine bolts.

2) On 4WD models, remove console box and shift lever from passenger compartment. On both models, raise and support vehicle. Remove axle drive shafts. See appropriate Toyota article in MANUAL TRANSMISSION section. Remove drain plugs and drain transaxle (and transfer case) fluid.

3) On 4WD models, remove drive shaft and insert tool (SST09325-12010). On both models, disconnect exhaust pipe at manifold and remove exhaust system. Remove transaxle stiffener plate on right side.

4) On 4WD models, disconnect 4WD link. Disconnect back-up light switch and 4WD switch wire. On 2WD models, disconnect gear shift rod at housing rod yoke. Disconnect and remove shift lever housing rod retaining bolt. Disconnect and remove back-up light wiring connector.

5) On both models, disconnect speedometer cable at transaxle housing. Support transaxle on jack. Remove lower transaxle-to-engine mounting bolts. Disconnect ground wire.

6) Remove engine rear support member and lower transaxle assembly out from under vehicle. Place a 1.2" (30 mm) block of wood between crossmember and oil pan to support engine for installation of transaxle assembly.

INSTALLATION (ALL MODELS)

To install transaxle assembly, reverse removal procedure. Install all drain plugs and fill transaxle assembly with gear oil (SAE 90 GL-5 or SAE 80W-90).

VAN

REMOVAL

1) Disconnect battery cable. Raise and support vehicle. Drain gear oil from transmission and transfer cases. Disconnect the drive shaft.

2) Disconnect select cable from select outer lever. Remove clip and select cable. Disconnect shift cable from shift outer lever. Remove clip and shift cable.

3) Remove clutch release cylinder. Disconnect starter wires. Remove starter bolts and starter. Disconnect bond and speedometer cable. Disconnect back-up light switch connector.

4) Remove exhaust pipe clamp and bracket. Remove stiffener plate. With hydraulic jack, raise transmission to remove the weight from rear support. Remove engine rear mount and bracket.

5) Remove the transmission mounting bolts. Remove transmission. Pull out transmission down and to the rear.

INSTALLATION

To install, reverse removal procedure. Lightly grease friction surfaces. Ensure that splines on input shaft align with those in clutch disc. Refill transmission lubricant.

VOLKSWAGEN

QUANTUM

REMOVAL

1) Disconnect battery ground strap. Disconnect exhaust pipe from transaxle bracket and engine. Remove square bolt and press shifter coupling from rear of transaxle shifting shaft. Unhook clutch cable and disconnect speedometer.

2) Disconnect CV joints at inner drive flanges. Support axle shafts from vehicle with wire. Remove starter, front mounting plate and transaxle mounting bolts. Disconnect back-up light switch connector. Support transaxle on floor jack and remove crossmember mount. Remove transaxle from engine and lower from vehicle.

INSTALLATION

1) Install crossmember to transaxle. Raise transaxle up to vehicle and install crossmember bolts finger tight. Slide transaxle up to engine and install mounting bolts. Install front mounting plate and starter. Install inner CV joint mounting bolts into CV joint and drive flange. Tighten crossmember mounting bolts.

2) Install shift rod coupling bolt and lock with safety wire. Connect exhaust pipe, allowing 3/8" (10 mm) clearance between pipe and floor. Reconnect all wires, cables and linkages that were removed during removal procedure.

NOTE: **Always use longer hex head bolt when replacing shift rod coupling instead of original square head bolt. Secure with safety wire.**

Manual Transmission Removal

VOLKSWAGEN (Cont.)

GOLF, JETTA & SCIROCCO

REMOVAL

1) Disconnect negative battery cable. Install engine support bar. Remove 3 transmission mount bolts located on left side of vehicle near battery. Disconnect speedometer cable from case and plug opening. Remove upper transaxle-to-engine bolts, electrical connection at back-up light switch and clutch cable. Remove shift linkage parts from relay lever on transaxle and rod lever.

2) Disconnect ground strap from transaxle. Remove starter and 2 engine-to-transaxle bolts on either side of starter opening. Remove exhaust pipe bracket from bottom of transaxle. Place floor jack with adapter under transaxle and raise until transaxle is supported. Remove rear transaxle mount and bracket.

3) Disconnect both axle drive shafts from drive flanges and wire up out of the way. Remove bolts attaching cover plates to transaxle. Remove small cover plate, then remove remaining transaxle-to-engine bolts and nuts. Lower transaxle and remove from under vehicle.

INSTALLATION

Reverse removal procedure to install. Fill with lubricant and adjust shift linkage.

VANAGON

REMOVAL

1) Disconnect negative battery cable. Remove upper right transmission-to-engine bolt. Disconnect clutch hydraulic line from transmission case, then remove clutch slave cylinder from bracket and suspend out of way with wire.

NOTE: Do not disconnect hydraulic line from slave cylinder.

2) Remove upper left, then lower left transmission-to-engine bolts. Remove the bolts from left axle shaft, remove axle shaft from transmission and suspend with wire. Disconnect starter cables. Remove the bolts from right axle shaft, remove axle shaft from transmission and suspend with wire.

3) Remove lower right transmission-to-engine nut. Support engine. Disconnect back-up light wires, shift linkage and ground strap from transmission. Remove front transmission support-to-body bolts and support transmission. Separate transmission from engine and remove transmission.

INSTALLATION

To install transmission, reverse removal procedures and note the following: Clean and lubricate splines with grease. Make sure air deflector plates are positioned correctly. Make sure engine compartment seals are not damaged or missing.

VOLVO

4-SPEED

REMOVAL

1) Disconnect battery ground cable. From under vehicle, disconnect gearshift lever from rod by removing lock bolt and pressing out pivot pin.

2) Working inside vehicle, lift shift lever boot and remove left side of center console. Disconnect back-up light and overdrive connectors (if equipped) and remove reverse detent plate. Remove lock ring and lift out gearshift lever. Remove plastic bushing and rubber ring.

3) From under vehicle, remove crossmember at rear of transmission and disconnect clutch fork return spring and release cable. Disconnect speedometer cable and unbolt propeller shaft from drive flange. Remove exhaust pipe attachment to clutch housing and unhook rubber supports for front muffler.

4) Remove starter from engine and take out all except 2 bottom bolts holding clutch housing to engine. Attach transmission jack and support transmission. Remove 2 bottom bolts and pull transmission to rear, turning slightly to clear tunnel while separating from vehicle.

INSTALLATION

To install, reverse removal procedure.

DRIVE AXLE GEAR TOOTH PATTERNS

INSPECTION

PRELIMINARY INSPECTION

Wipe lubricant from internal parts. Rotate gears, and inspect for wear or damage. Mount dial indicator to housing, and check backlash at several points around ring gear. Backlash must be within specifications at all points. If no defects are found, check gear tooth contact pattern.

GEAR TOOTH CONTACT PATTERN

NOTE: **Drive pattern should be well centered on ring gear teeth. Coast pattern should be centered, but may be slightly toward toe of ring gear teeth.**

1) Paint ring gear teeth with marking compound. Wrap cloth or rope around drive pinion flange to act as brake. Rotate ring gear until clear tooth contact pattern is obtained.

2) Contact pattern will indicate whether correct pinion bearing mounting shim has been installed and if drive gear backlash has been set properly. Backlash between drive gear and pinion must be maintained within specified limits, until correct tooth pattern is obtained.

ADJUSTMENTS

GEAR BACKLASH & PINION SHIM CHANGES

NOTE: **Backlash is adjusted by either shifting shims from 1 side of differential case to other or by turning adjusting nuts on which differential side bearings ride. Changing pinion shims changes distance from face of pinion to centerline of ring gear.**

1) With no change in backlash, moving pinion further from ring gear moves drive pattern toward heel and top of tooth, and moves coast pattern toward toe and top of tooth.

2) With no change in backlash, moving pinion closer to ring gear moves drive pattern toward toe and bottom of tooth, and moves coast pattern toward heel and bottom of tooth.

3) With no change in pinion shim thickness, an increase in backlash moves ring gear further from pinion. Drive pattern moves toward heel and top of tooth, and coast pattern moves toward heel and top of tooth.

4) With no change in pinion shim thickness, decrease in backlash moves ring gear closer to pinion gear. Drive pattern moves toward toe and bottom of tooth, and coast pattern moves toward toe and bottom of tooth.

Fig. 1: Drive Axle Gear Tooth Pattern

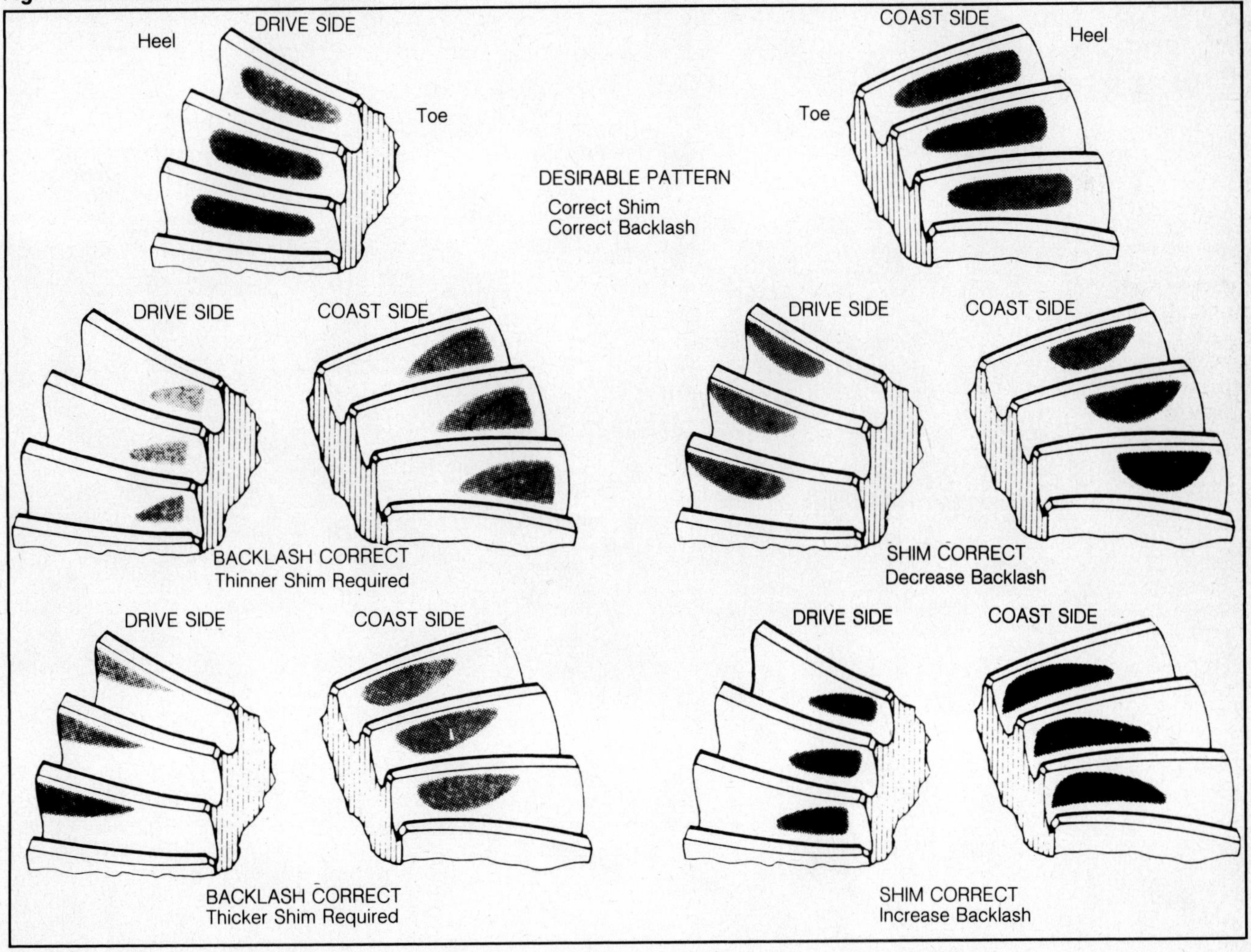

SECTION 6

IMPORT AUTOMATIC TRANSMISSIONS

NOTE: **ALSO SEE GENERAL INDEX.**

AISIN-WARNER 55, 70, 71 & BORG-WARNER 55

Isuzu I-Mark, Impulse, P'UP
Volvo DL, GL, Turbo, 740, 760 GLE

TRANSMISSION IDENTIFICATION

Transmissions are manufactured by either Aisin-Warner (AW) or Borg-Warner (BW). Units are interchangeable with exception of oil cooler pipes, which must be changed to match particular unit installed.

Transmissions may be identified by plate attached to left side of transmission case. Plate shows manufacturer (AW or BW), transmission model number, and transmission serial number.

DESCRIPTION

AW 55 and BW 55 transmissions are fully automatic 3-speed units consisting of 3-element torque converter, compound planetary gear set, 2 multiple-disc clutches, 2 one-way roller clutches, and 3 multiple-disc brakes. Clutches may use either single or multiple piston return springs.

AW 70 and AW 71 transmissions are fully automatic 4-speed units consisting of 3-element torque converter, compound planetary gear set, 3 multiple-disc clutches, 3 one-way roller clutches, and 4 multiple-disc brakes.

Hydraulic system, pressurized by gear type pump, provides working pressure required to operate automatic controls. Valve bodies will vary in different models.

AW 70 and 71 transmissions are equipped with overdrive. Overdrive is automatically engaged in 3rd gear direct drive and gives drive ratio of 0.69:1. Overdrive will not operate in kickdown 3rd gear (throttle open more than 85%).

Overdrive can be manually disengaged by depressing button on shift lever. This will illuminate "OD OFF" warning lamp on instrument panel and remove power from relay to overdrive solenoid on transmission. Relay automatically resets and returns transmission to overdrive mode when ignition is turned off.

LUBRICATION & ADJUSTMENT

See appropriate AUTOMATIC TRANSMISSION SERVICING article in IMPORT GENERAL SERVICING section.

TROUBLE SHOOTING

NOTE: **Most transmission problems will show up in one or more of following tests: Check for proper fluid level, gear selector adjustment, throttle cable adjustment, line pressure, stall speed, or governor pressure. These tests show condition of most important transmission components and should be checked to determine proper repair for reported malfunction.**

NO MOVEMENT IN "D" OR SLIPS IN "D"

Low fluid level. Manual linkage out of adjustment. Faulty direct (rear) clutch, intermediate brake, one-way clutch for planetary gear set, forward (front) clutch, secondary regulator valve or valve body assembly.

NO MOVEMENT IN "R" OR SLIPS IN "R"

Low fluid level. Manual linkage out of adjustment. Faulty direct (rear) clutch, intermediate brake, oil pump, or valve body assembly. Line pressure too low.

NO MOVEMENT IN ANY RANGE

Low fluid level. Manual linkage out of adjustment. Parking pawl jammed or defective. Faulty torque converter, valve body assembly, or oil pump. Multiple unit damage. Shaft and or spline damage. Faulty forward clutch.

Fig. 1: Mechanical System Schematic for AW 71 & BW 55 Transmissions

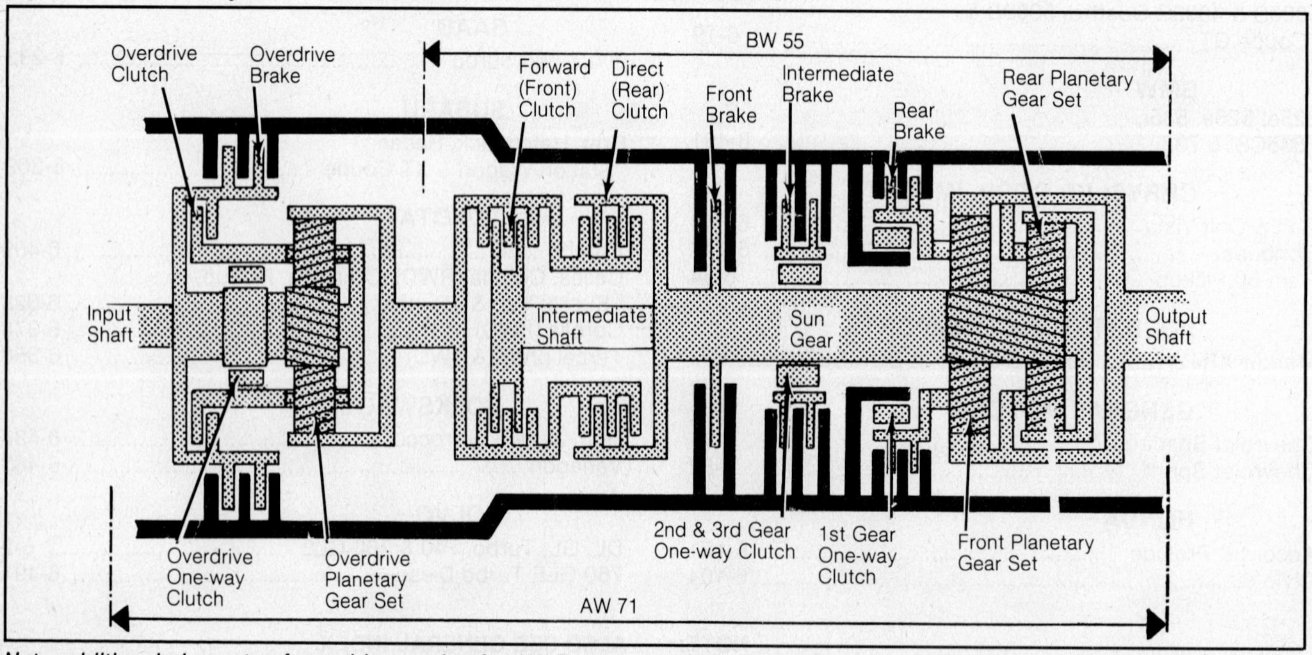

Note additional elements of overdrive portion for AW 71.

HARSH SHIFT FROM "N" TO "D" OR "R"

Manual linkage out of adjustment. Accumulator pistons for forward (front) or direct (rear) clutch seized or leaking. Defective valve bodies or accumulator pistons.

HARSH "1-2" OR "2-1" SHIFT

Second speed brake accumulator piston seized or leaking. Intermediate coast shift valve seized. Governor valve or 1-2 shift valve stuck.

HARSH "2-3" OR "3-2" SHIFT

Direct (rear) clutch accumulator piston seized or leaking. Defective governor valve body assembly. Check intermediate coast modulator valve. Governor valve or 2-3 shift valve stuck.

SLIP ON "1-2" UPSHIFT

Intermediate coast shift valve seized, thereby not engaging No. 1 brake. Defective No. 1 brake. Defective No. 2 brake. Center support one-way clutch defective.

SLIP ON "2-3" UPSHIFT

Defective direct (rear) clutch or its oil circuit. Faulty valve body assembly (2-3 shift valve, etc.).

NO ENGINE BRAKING IN "1"

Defective No. 3 brake. Low coast modulator valve seized or low coast valve frozen in top position.

NO ENGINE BRAKING IN "2"

No. 1 brake or its oil circuit defective. Intermediate coast modulator valve seized.

NO "2-1" SHIFT IN "1"

Defective No. 3 brake. Low coast modulator valve or low coast shift valve seized.

VEHICLE STARTS OUT IN "2" OR "3"

Governor pressure inaccurate (should be 0 with vehicle stationary). Defective valve body assembly, 1-2 throttle valve, 2-3 shift valve, primary throttle valve or primary regulator valve.

TRANSMISSION NOISE

Growling On Acceleration

Low fluid level, clogged oil filter or worn oil pump. Defective torque converter. Broken gears. Worn bushings.

NOTE: **If torque converter is replaced, oil cooler and lines must be cleaned.**

Gear Noise

Torque converter-to-drive plate bolts loose. Faulty coupling of one-way clutches. Faulty planetary gear sets. Worn thrust needle bearings or bushings. Partially engaged park pawl.

Whining or Humming Noise

Defective torque converter (noise may disappear in "N"). Defective oil pump (noise varies with engine speed). Low fluid level.

TESTING

ROAD TEST

1) Before road testing, ensure fluid level and condition are okay. Control linkage adjustments have been checked and corrected as necessary. During test, transmission should upshift and downshift at speed shown in SHIFT SPEED SPECIFICATIONS chart.

2) All shifts may vary somewhat due to production tolerances or tire size. Important factor is quality of shifts. All shifts should be smooth, responsive, and with no slippage or engine speed runaway.

3) Slippage or engine runaway in any gear usually indicates clutch or brake problems. Slipping unit in particular gear can usually be identified by noting transmission operation in other selector positions and comparing which internal units are applied in those positions. See CLUTCH & BRAKE APPLICATION chart.

4) This process of elimination can be used to detect any unit which slips, and to confirm proper operation of good units; however, actual cause of malfunction usually cannot be easily decided.

5) Almost any condition can be caused by leaking hydraulic circuits or sticking valves. Therefore, unless obvious condition exists, do not disassemble transmission until hydraulic pressure tests have been made.

STALL SPEED TEST

CAUTION: **Before making stall speed test, ensure that line pressure is correct. If line pressure is too low when performing stall test, transmission can be damaged. During stall test, do not hold throttle open for more than 5 seconds at time. Return transmission to neutral between stall speed tests to allow for cooling of ATF.**

Stall Test Procedure

1) Road test vehicle and warm transmission to normal operating temperature. Connect tachometer to engine. Position tachometer so that it can be read from driver's seat.

2) Set parking and service brakes. Start engine and place selector lever in "D". Depress accelerator pedal completely and note maximum RPM obtained. RPM should be approximately as shown in STALL SPEED SPECIFICATIONS chart.

3) Place selector lever in "N" and allow engine to idle to cool off transmission. Then, place selector lever in "R" and repeat stall test. Stall RPM should be approximately as shown in STALL SPEED SPECIFICATIONS chart.

Stall Test Results

1) If stall test RPM is about 600 RPM lower than specifications, torque converter one-way clutch is slipping and torque converter should be replaced. If stall RPM is about 300 RPM lower than specifications, engine performance may be unsatisfactory.

2) If stall test RPM is about 300 RPM above specifications in "R", direct (rear) clutch or 1st-Reverse brake is slipping. If RPM is about 300 RPM above specifications in "D", forward (front) clutch or rear one-way clutch is slipping.

3) If stall speed is about 300 RPM above specifications, and no clutch or brake is slipping, fluid level is incorrect, line pressure is too low or valve body oil strainer is clogged.

AISIN-WARNER 55, 70, 71 & BORG-WARNER 55 (Cont.)

CLUTCH AND BAND APPLICATION (ELEMENTS IN USE)

Selector Lever Position	Forward (Front) Clutch	Direct (Rear) Clutch	Overdrive (OD) Clutch (70 & 71 Only)	Planetary Gear	Brake	One-Way Clutch	Overdrive Brake (70 & 71 Only)
D - DRIVE							
First	Applied		Applied	Both		Rear/OD	
Second	Applied		Applied	Rear	No. 2	Front/OD	
Third	Applied	Applied	Applied	Direct [1]	No. 2	OD	
Overdrive (70 & 71 Only)	Applied	Applied		Direct/OD	No. 2		Applied
2 - SECOND							
First	Applied		Applied	Both		Rear/OD	
Second	Applied		Applied	Rear	No. 1 & No. 2	Front/OD	
1 - LOW	Applied		Applied	Both	No. 3	Rear/OD	
R - REVERSE		Applied	Applied	Front	No. 3	OD	
P - PARK			Applied [2]		No. 3 [2]		
N - NEUTRAL			Applied				

[1] – Direct means planetary gear set is locked up with 1:1 ratio.
[2] – With engine running.

STALL SPEED SPECIFICATIONS

Application	[1] Stall Speed (RPM)
Isuzu	
Impulse	2000-2300
I-Mark	
Gas Engine	1700-2000
Diesel Engine	1900-2200
P'UP	
Gas Engine	1950-2250
Diesel Engine	1900-2200
Volvo	
DL & GL	
Gas Engine	2250
Diesel Engine	2200
Turbo	2050-2500
760 GLE	
Gas Engine	2000 min.
Diesel Engine	2200-2700

[1] – Speed measured at sea level. Stall speed will drop 120 RPM for each 3200 ft. of elevation.

LINE PRESSURE TEST

1) Road test vehicle to bring transmission to normal operating temperature. Connect pressure gauge to front plug on transmission. *See Fig. 2.* Place gauge so that it is visible from driver's seat. Connect tachometer to engine.

2) Start engine and if necessary, adjust idle speed to 900 RPM (1000 RPM on I-Mark). Depress brake pedal and place selector lever in "D". Note line pressure reading on gauge. Pressure should be approximately as shown in LINE PRESSURE SPECIFICATIONS chart.

3) Repeat line pressure test with selector lever in "R". Pressure should be approximately as shown in LINE PRESSURE SPECIFICATIONS chart.

Fig. 2: Transmission Case Pressure Test Port Locations

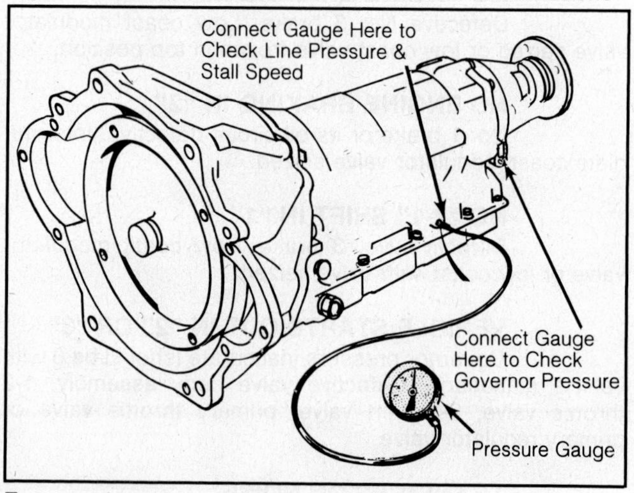

Test port locations apply to all transmissions.

LINE PRESSURE SPECIFICATIONS

Application	psi (kg/cm^2)
AW 55	
In "D"	57-64 (4.0-4.5)
In "R"	82-97 (5.8-6.8)
AW 70 & 71	
In "D"	65-77 (4.6-5.4)
In "R"	108-117 (7.6-8.2)
BW 55	
In "D"	75-90 (5.3-6.3)
In "R"	104-129 (7.3-9.1)

LINE PRESSURE TEST RESULTS

Pressure Too High

If pressure is too high, check throttle cable adjustment. If cable is correctly adjusted and pressure is still high, primary regulator valve or throttle valve may be seized.

AISIN-WARNER 55, 70, 71 & BORG-WARNER 55 (Cont.)

SHIFT SPEED SPECIFICATIONS [1]

Application	MPH
Isuzu	
I-Mark [5]	
Gas Engine	
1-2 Upshift	36-43
2-3 Upshift	67-73
3-2 Downshift	60-67
3-1 or 2-1 Downshift	22-29
Diesel Engine	
1-2 Upshift	29-35
2-3 Upshift	53-58
3-2 Downshift	49-55
3-1 or 2-1 Downshift	20-25
P'UP [5]	
Gas Engine	
1-2 Upshift	31-37
2-3 Upshift	58-64
3-2 Downshift	55-61
3-1 or 2-1 Downshift	24-30
Diesel Engine	
1-2 Upshift	23-29
2-3 Upshift	46-53
3-2 Downshift	40-46
3-1 or 2-1 Downshift	16-23
Volvo	
DL & GL	
Gas Engine [2]	
1-2 Upshift	40
2-3 Upshift	67
3-4 Upshift (3/4 Throttle)	70
4-3 Downshift (Coasting)	25
3-2 Downshift	64
2-1 Downshift	32
Diesel Engine [3]	
1-2 Upshift	36
2-3 Upshift	66
3-2 Downshift	61
3-1 Downshift	31
Turbo [4]	
1-2 Upshift	37
2-3 Upshift	62
3-4 Upshift (3/4 Throttle)	65
4-3 Downshift (Coasting)	23
3-2 Downshift	58
2-1 Downshift	30
760 GLE	
Gas Engine [4]	
1-2 Upshift	42
2-3 Upshift	70
3-4 Upshift (3/4 Throttle)	74
4-3 Downshift (Coasting)	18
3-2 Downshift	66
2-1 Downshift	33
Diesel Engine [3]	
1-2 Upshift	38
2-3 Upshift	69
3-2 Downshift	63
3-1 Downshift	38

1 – At full throttle (kick-down) unless otherwise noted.
2 – AW 70.
3 – BW 55.
4 – AW 71.
5 – AW 55.

Pressure Too Low

If line pressure is too low, check for seizing of primary regulator valve or throttle valve in valve body. If valves are not seized, check pressure relief valve and oil pump assembly for damage. Defective oil pump assembly will usually make noise.

GOVERNOR PRESSURE TEST

NOTE: **Governor pressure is "modified" line pressure. Therefore, governor pressure will be incorrect if line pressure is incorrect. Line pressure must be correct before checking governor pressure.**

Testing Procedures

Road test vehicle to warm transmission to normal operating temperature. Connect pressure gauge to rear pressure port on transmission case. *See Fig. 2.* Position gauge so it is visible from driver's seat. Test drive vehicle in "D" and note pressure readings. Pressures should be about as shown in GOVERNOR PRESSURE SPECIFICATIONS chart.

SERVICE (IN VEHICLE)

NOTE: **Following units can be replaced without removing transmission from vehicle: Oil Pan, Valve Body Assembly, Accumulator Pistons, Parking Pawl, Rear Extension Housing and Oil Seal, Speedometer Driven Gear, Overdrive Solenoid (AW 70 & 71 models only) and Governor Body. See procedures given in TRANSMISSION DISASSEMBLY and TRANSMISSION REASSEMBLY in this article.**

REMOVAL & INSTALLATION

See appropriate AUTOMATIC TRANSMISSION REMOVAL article in IMPORT GENERAL SERVICING section.

TORQUE CONVERTER

NOTE: **Torque converter is sealed unit and cannot be disassembled for service. Replace if found defective.**

TRANSMISSION DISASSEMBLY

CAUTION: **All Isuzu models use Dexron II ATF. All Volvo models except those using BW 55 transmission use Dextron II ATF. Volvo models using BW 55 transmission use Type "F" ATF. Use only specified ATF. Damage to friction linings may occur if incorrect type of ATF is used.**

1) Clean outside of transmission thoroughly before disassembly to prevent dirt or foreign material from entering transmission. Pull torque converter from transmission. Place transmission in holding fixture.

2) Remove 6 converter housing-to-transmission case bolts. Separate converter housing from case. Remove speedometer driven gear assembly retaining bolt. Using screwdriver, pry speedometer driven gear assembly from case.

AISIN-WARNER 55, 70, 71 & BORG-WARNER 55 (Cont.)

GOVERNOR PRESSURE SPECIFICATIONS

Vehicle Speed	psi (kg/cm²)
Isuzu	
I-Mark	
Gas Engine	
19 MPH	13-21 (0.9-1.5)
39 MPH	23-33 (1.6-2.3)
68 MPH	58-75 (4.1-5.3)
Diesel Engine	
18 MPH	14-23 (1.0-1.6)
37 MPH	33-43 (2.3-3.0)
64 MPH	64-81 (4.5-5.7)
P'UP	
Gas Engine	
19 MPH	13-21 (0.9-1.5)
39 MPH	23-33 (1.6-2.3)
68 MPH	58-75 (4.1-5.3)
Diesel Engine	
17 MPH	17-26 (1.2-1.8)
35 MPH	37-47 (2.6-3.3)
61 MPH	67-84 (4.7-5.9)
Volvo	
DL & GL	
Gas Engine	
19 MPH	14-18 (1.0-1.3)
37 MPH	21-27 (1.5-1.9)
68 MPH	37-65 (3.6-4.6)
Diesel Engine	
19 MPH	16-20 (1.1-1.4)
37 MPH	26-31 (1.8-2.2)
68 MPH	53-61 (3.8-4.3)
Turbo	
19 MPH	13-21 (0.9-1.5)
31 MPH	23-31 (1.6-2.2)
62 MPH	59-75 (4.1-5.3)
760 GLE	
Gas Engine	
21 MPH	15-24 (1.1-1.7)
33 MPH	24-33 (1.7-2.3)
66 MPH	54-71 (3.8-5.0)
Diesel Engine	
18 MPH	14-18 (1.0-1.3)
48 MPH	24-32 (1.7-2.2)
66 MPH	48-57 (3.4-4.0)

3) Hold output shaft drive flange stationary and remove flange bolt. Using puller, pull drive flange from output shaft. Remove extension housing-to-case bolts. Lift off extension housing.

4) If equipped, remove speedometer drive gear snap ring and slide gear and spacer ring from output shaft. If equipped, remove 2nd snap ring. Remove governor retaining clip and pull governor assembly off shaft.

5) Remove oil pan and gasket. Invert transmission. Remove attaching bolts and lift oil strainer and particle magnet from transmission case. Remove valve body-to-case bolts. Carefully lift valve body and disconnect throttle cable from valve body cam. Lift valve body assembly from case.

6) Apply low pressure, 14 psi (.98 kg/cm²), compressed air to holes under accumulator pistons to force pistons from case bores. *See Fig. 3.* Remove pistons and springs. Press out plastic throttle cable sheath, using 10

Fig. 3: Accumulator Pistons & Springs Removal

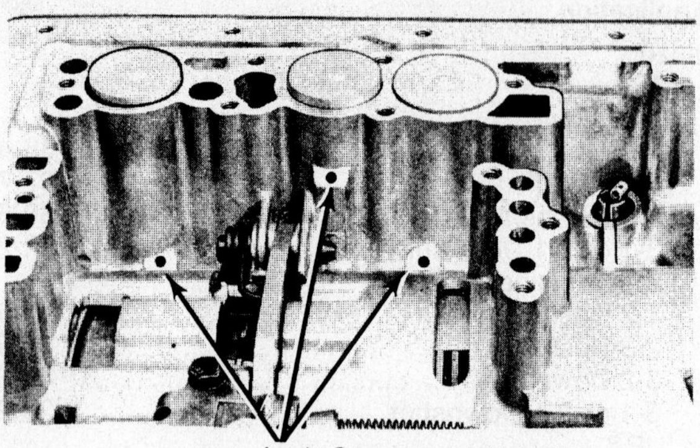

Note spring position for reassembly as sizes vary.

mm socket. Invert transmission case so oil pump faces up. Remove oil pump attaching bolts. Using puller, remove oil pump assembly from case.

7) Hold input shaft with hand and pull forward (front) clutch assembly from case. Remove thrust bearing and race from clutch. Remove direct (rear) clutch bearing and race. Pull direct (rear) clutch assembly from case. Remove center support bolts. *See Fig. 4.* Lift center support assembly from case.

Fig. 4: Location of Center Support Attaching Bolts

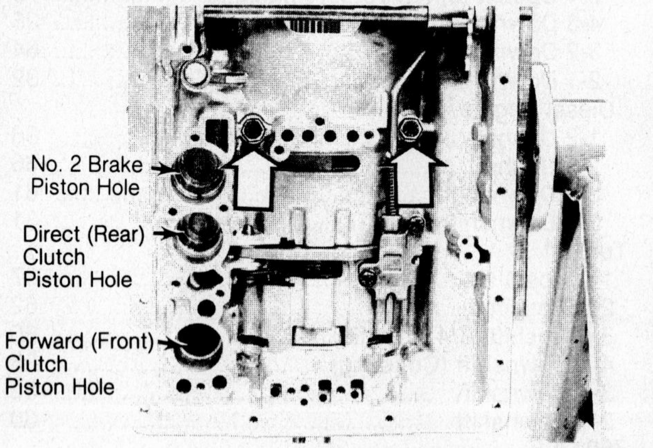

Note positions for reassembly reference.

8) Remove No. 3 brake snap ring from groove in case. Lift No. 3 brake disc pack and planetary gear assembly from case as unit. Remove brake apply tube (shell), thrust bearing and races from transmission case.

9) Turn transmission so rear face of case is up. Remove governor oil duct cover screws and cover from case. Noting position for reassembly reference, remove oil cooler line nipples from case. Remove plugs from governor and line pressure ports.

10) Turn transmission so oil pan attaching surface is up. Remove parking pawl rod plate bolts. Remove plate and rod. Using drift, drive detent lever lock pin out of lever and shaft. Pull shaft out of lever and case. Lift up parking pawl, press out shaft and spring, then lift parking pawl from case. Pry shaft oil seals out of case.

COMPONENT DISASSEMBLY & REASSEMBLY

OIL PUMP ASSEMBLY

CAUTION: Do not use punch to make matching marks on oil pump gears. High spots in metal may occur and cause binding when pump is reassembled. Make marks with paint or pen.

Disassembly

Remove 2 oil seal rings from pump cover. Remove cover bolts and separate cover from pump housing. Remove large "O" ring from housing. Mark pump drive and driven gears for reassembly in same position. Remove gears from pump housing. Pry oil seal from housing.

Fig. 5: Exploded View of Oil Pump Assembly

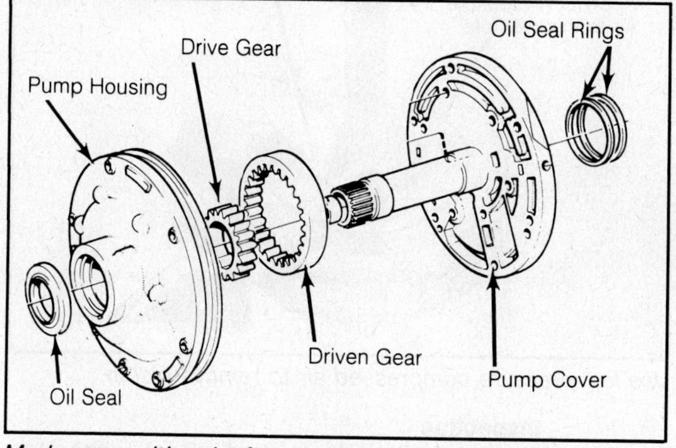

Mark gears with paint for reassembly reference. DO NOT use punch for markings.

Inspection

Clean all parts thoroughly and dry with compressed air. Inspect all parts for wear, cracks, or scoring. If pump housing, cover, drive gear or driven gear requires replacement, complete oil pump assembly must be replaced as unit.

Reassembly

1) Install drive and driven gear into housing, aligning marks made during disassembly. Measure clearance between driven (outer) gear and pump housing with feeler gauge. Clearance should be .003-.006" (.07-.15 mm) for AW models and .003-.012" (.07-.30 mm) for BW models. Replace oil pump assembly if clearance is excessive.

2) Check clearance between driven (outer) gear teeth and crescent. Clearance should be .004-.006" (.11-.14 mm) for AW models and .004-.020" (.11-.50 mm) for BW models. Replace oil pump if clearance is excessive.

3) Using straightedge and feeler gauge, check pump housing face-to-gear face clearance. Clearance should be .0008-.0020" (.020-.050 mm) for AW models and .0008-.0040" (.020-.100 mm) for BW models. Replace oil pump assembly if clearance is excessive.

4) Lubricate all parts with ATF. Press new oil seal into pump housing. Assemble pump cover to housing, then install bolts finger tight. Fit Centering Clamp (Isuzu J-25280 or Volvo 5077) around housing and cover. Tighten centering clamp screw to align housing and cover. *See Fig. 7.*

Fig. 6: Measuring Housing-to-Gear Face Clearance

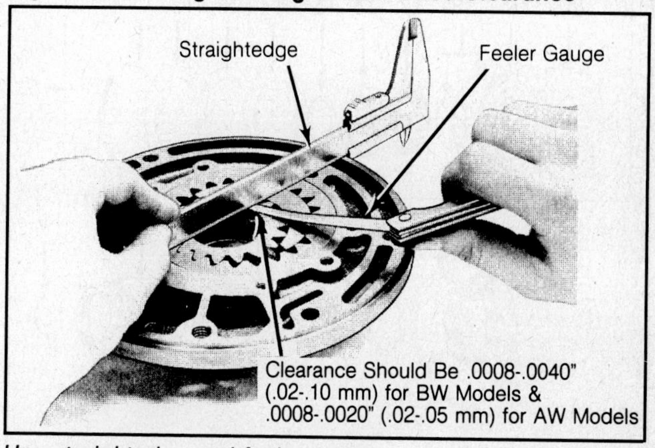

Use straightedge and feeler gauge.

Fig. 7: Aligning Oil Pump Housing & Cover

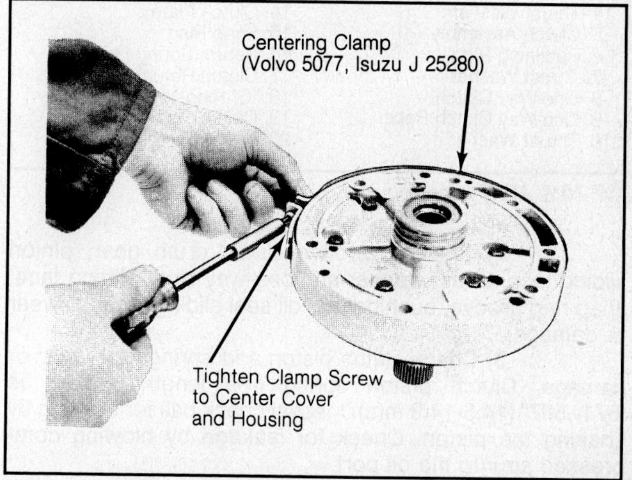

Bolts must be installed in cover finger tight.

5) Tighten bolts and remove centering clamp. Lubricate large "O" ring with ATF and install in groove on pump housing. Lubricate oil seal rings with petroleum jelly and install on pump cover.

OVERDRIVE CLUTCH ASSEMBLY

Disassembly

1) Remove snap ring and overdrive brake hub. Remove overdrive input shaft assembly and thrust washer. Remove overdrive clutch drum and clutch assembly.

2) Install clutch drum to the oil pump. Remove the clutch piston by blowing compressed air into oil pump from the oil port. Lift clutch plates and discs from drum. Note number and arrangement of plates and discs for reassembly reference.

3) Compress return spring retainer. Remove snap ring and lift out retainer and return spring(s). Remove snap ring, thrust washer, one-way clutch, one-way clutch race and thrust washer.

Inspection

1) Check the overdrive planetary gear pinion, clutch disc groove, snap ring groove and input shaft splines for wear or damage. Check one-way overdrive clutch sprag, ribbon spring and outer race for wear or damage.

AISIN-WARNER 55, 70, 71 & BORG-WARNER 55 (Cont.)

Fig. 8: Exploded View of Overdrive Clutch Assembly

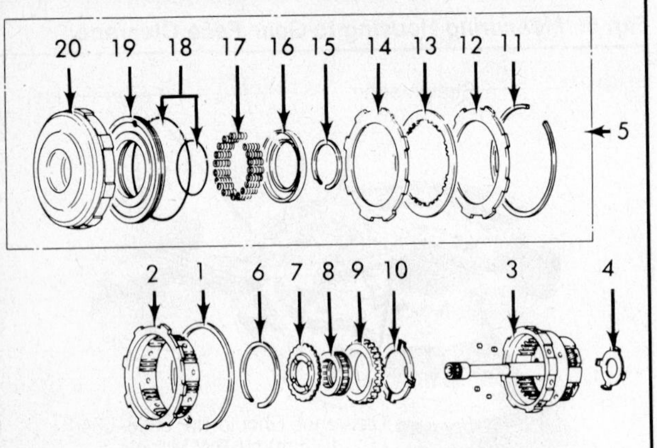

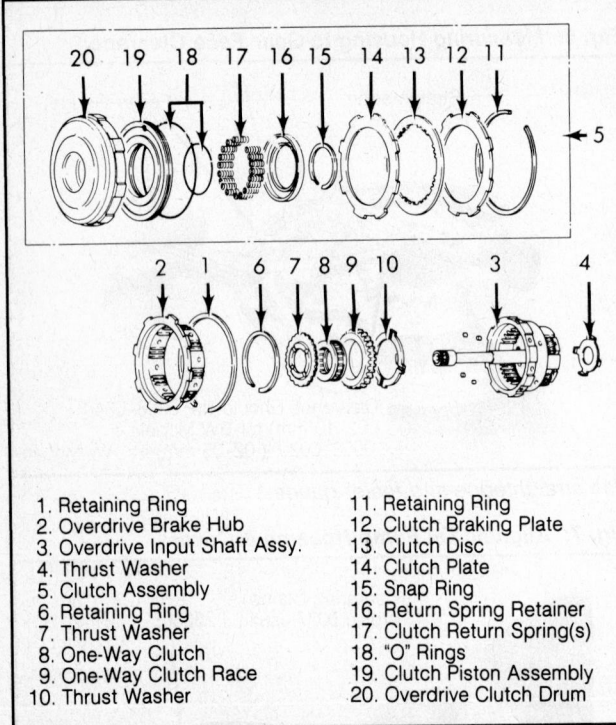

1. Retaining Ring
2. Overdrive Brake Hub
3. Overdrive Input Shaft Assy.
4. Thrust Washer
5. Clutch Assembly
6. Retaining Ring
7. Thrust Washer
8. One-Way Clutch
9. One-Way Clutch Race
10. Thrust Washer
11. Retaining Ring
12. Clutch Braking Plate
13. Clutch Disc
14. Clutch Plate
15. Snap Ring
16. Return Spring Retainer
17. Clutch Return Spring(s)
18. "O" Rings
19. Clutch Piston Assembly
20. Overdrive Clutch Drum

AW 70 & AW 71 models only.

2) Check overdrive clutch drum gear, pinion sliding face, thrust washer and one-way clutch fitting face, snap ring groove, bushing and oil seal sliding face for wear or damage.

3) Check clutch piston and springs for wear or damage. Clutch piston spring free length should be .571-.587" (14.5-14.9 mm). Inspect check ball for sticking by shaking the piston. Check for leakage by blowing compressed air into the oil port.

4) Check the overdrive brake hub clutch disc fitting face and drum fitting face for wear. Check thrust washers for excessive wear.

Reassembly

1) Assemble clutch piston, "O" rings and drum. Lubricate "O" rings with ATF before installing. Install clutch return springs, retainer and snap ring into clutch drum using Spring Compressor (J-25048).

2) Install clutch plates and discs in original order. Ensure flange is installed with the stepped face turned up. Install snap ring. Install brake hub and snap ring. Measure clutch clearance in the following manner: Install dial indicator so tip is resting on direct (rear) clutch hub lip.

3) Apply 57-114 psi (4-8 kg/cm^2) compressed air and read dial indicator. Piston stroke should be .061-.090" (1.55-2.28 mm). If stroke exceeds specification, clutch pack is excessively worn. If stroke does not meet specification, clutch components have been incorrectly installed or too much ATF was applied to clutch plates and discs.

4) Remove dial indicator. Install bearing and race on input shaft. Install thrust washer, one-way clutch race, one-way clutch assembly, thrust washer and snap ring. Install clutch assembly, planetary gear assembly and thrust washer.

FORWARD (FRONT) CLUTCH ASSEMBLY

Disassembly

1) Remove bearing and race from input shaft. Remove snap ring and lift direct (rear) clutch hub from clutch assembly. Pull forward (front) clutch hub from clutch drum, then remove bearing and races.

2) Lift clutch plates and discs from drum. Note number and arrangement of plates and discs for reassembly reference. Compress return spring retainer. Remove snap ring and lift out retainer and return spring(s).

3) Position clutch drum with input shaft facing up. Apply low pressure compressed air to one oil hole on inside of drum. Cover other hole with finger and force piston from drum. *See Fig. 9.* Remove and discard "O" rings from clutch piston.

Fig. 9: Forward (Front) Clutch Piston Removal

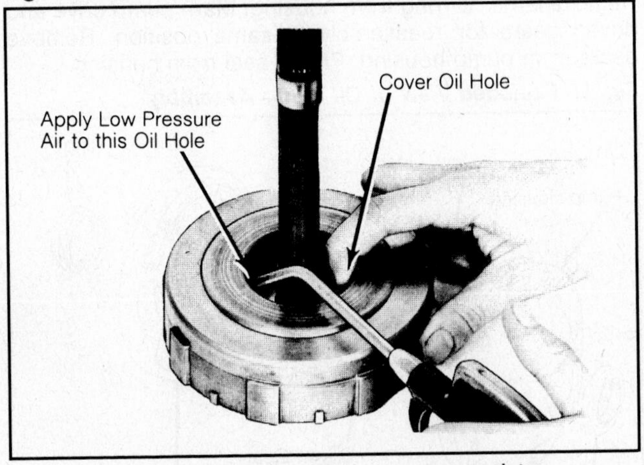

Use low pressure compressed air to remove piston.

Inspection

1) Clean all parts (except discs) with clean solvent and dry with compressed air. Inspect clutch plates and discs to ensure they are flat with no burns or cracks.

2) Minimum thickness of discs is .08" (2.1 mm). Inspect all other parts for wear or damage. Check clutch piston to ensure check ball is not stuck. Replace defective or worn parts.

Reassembly

1) Coat all friction surfaces with ATF. Install new "O" rings on clutch piston. Install piston into clutch drum with check valve toward input shaft end. Install return spring(s) and retainer.

2) Using compressor, compress return spring retainer and install snap ring. Remove compressor. Install clutch plates and discs into clutch drum. Alternate plates and discs until they are installed in same positions and amounts as found during disassembly.

3) Install bearing and races onto top of return spring retainer. Install forward (front) clutch hub and ensure hub meshes with all clutch discs. Install direct (rear) clutch hub and snap ring. Ensure snap ring fits properly in groove and that ends are not near groove which holds clutch plate lug.

4) On Isuzu applications of AW 55 model, install dial indicator so tip is resting on direct (rear) clutch hub lip. Apply compressed air and read dial indicator. Piston stroke should be .056-.092" (1.42-2.33 mm). Thin inner snap ring should be left out for this procedure.

AISIN-WARNER 55, 70, 71 & BORG-WARNER 55 (Cont.)

Fig. 10: Exploded View of Forward (Front) Clutch Assembly

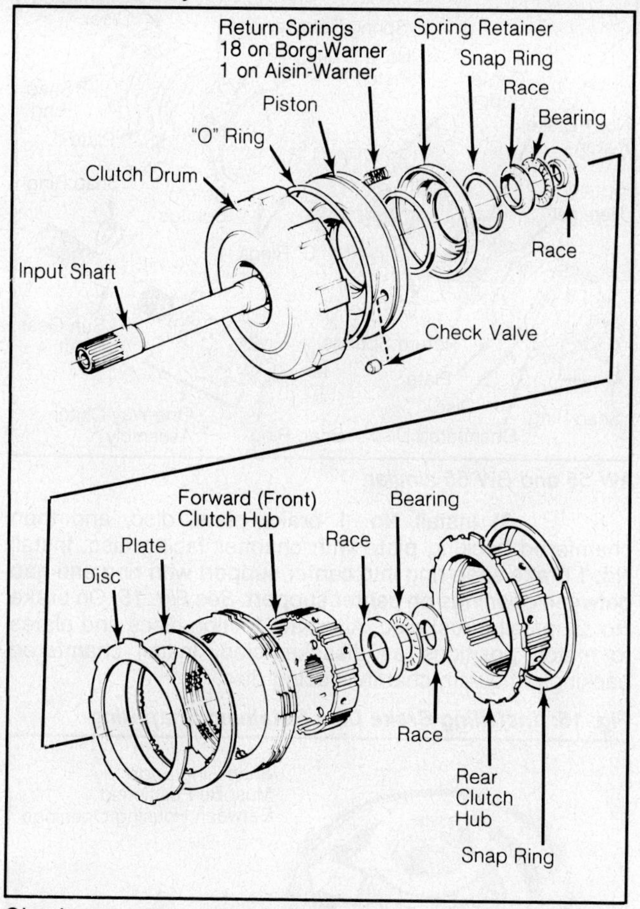

Clutch may use a single large piston return spring or 18 small piston return springs.

Fig. 11: Exploded View of Direct (Rear) Clutch Assembly

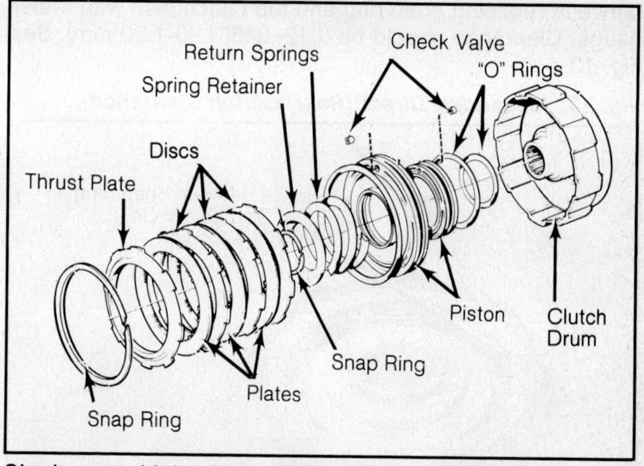

Single or multiple piston return springs may be used.

Fig. 12: Direct (Rear) Clutch Piston Removal from Drum

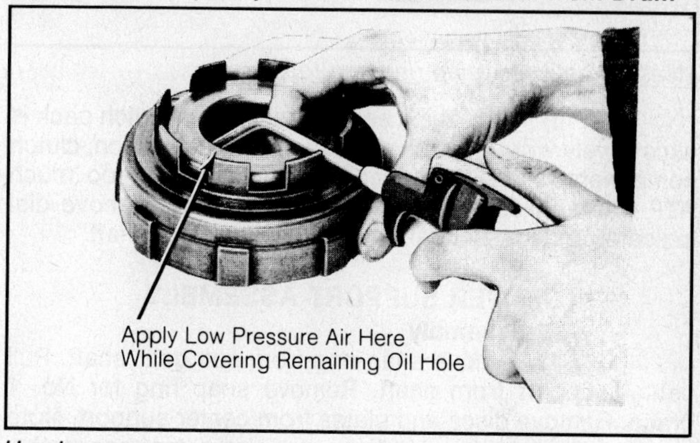

Use low pressure compressed air to remove piston.

5) On Volvo applications of BW and AW 55 models, check operation of piston by applying low pressure compressed air to one oil hole while covering other. When air is applied, distinct "plop" should be heard as piston applies. Install bearing and race on input shaft.

6) If stroke exceeds specification, clutch pack is excessively worn. If stroke does not meet specification, clutch components have been incorrectly installed or too much ATF was applied to clutch plates and discs. Remove dial indicator. Install bearing and race on input shaft.

DIRECT (REAR) CLUTCH ASSEMBLY

Disassembly

1) Using screwdriver, remove clutch disc pack snap ring. Lift out backing plate, clutch discs and plates. Note number and arrangement of discs and plates for reassembly reference.

2) Using compressor, compress return spring retainer. Remove snap ring. Remove compressor. Lift retainer and clutch return spring(s) from drum.

3) Apply low pressure compressed air to one oil hole in clutch drum while covering other oil hole. *See Fig. 12.* Force piston from drum. Remove "O" rings from piston.

Inspection

Clean all parts (except plates and discs) in clean solvent and dry with compressed air. Inspect clutch discs for signs of burning and wear. Check thickness of clutch discs. Minimum thickness is .08" (2.1 mm). Inspect all other parts for wear or damage. Shake piston to ensure check ball is free. Replace any defective part.

Reassembly

1) Lubricate all friction surfaces with ATF. Lubricate and install new "O" rings on clutch piston. Install piston into drum. Install return spring(s) on piston and install retainer over spring(s). Compress spring retainer and install snap ring.

2) Install clutch plates and discs into clutch drum. Alternate plates and discs until number and position of plates and discs are installed as they were removed. Install backing plate with bevelled side facing discs and plates. Install clutch pack snap ring with ends away from groove in which clutch plate lug is installed.

3) On BW transmissions, check operation of piston by applying compressed air to one oil hole while blocking other. When air is applied, distinct "plop" should be heard as piston applies.

4) On Isuzu applications, install direct clutch assembly on center support. Install dial indicator so tip is resting on edge of backing plate. Apply compressed air and read dial indicator. Piston stroke should be .037-.067" (.93-1.70 mm).

AISIN-WARNER 55, 70, 71 & BORG-WARNER 55 (Cont.)

5) On Volvo applications, measure clearance between retaining snap ring and top clutch disc with feeler gauge. Clearance should be .012-.048" (.30-1.20 mm). *See Fig. 13.*

Fig. 13: Measuring Direct (Rear) Clutch Clearance

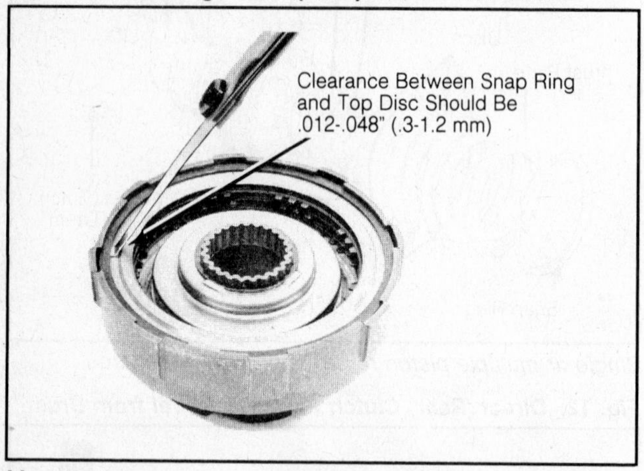

Measure between snap ring and top disc.

6) If stroke exceeds specification, clutch pack is excessively worn. If stroke is less than specification, clutch components have been incorrectly installed or too much ATF was applied to clutch plates and discs. Remove dial indicator and install bearing and race on input shaft.

CENTER SUPPORT ASSEMBLY

Disassembly

1) Remove snap ring from sun gear shaft. Pull center support from shaft. Remove snap ring for No. 1 brake. Remove discs and plates from center support. Note number and position of discs and plates for reassembly reference. Invert center support.

2) Remove snap ring for No. 2 brake. Remove discs and plates from center support. Using compressor, compress No. 2 brake return spring retainer and remove snap ring. Remove compressor and lift return springs and retainer from center support. Repeat procedure on No. 1 brake return springs.

3) Using compressed air, force No. 2 and No. 1 brake pistons from center support. Slide one-way clutch hub from sun gear shaft after noting direction of rotation. Remove 3 oil seal rings from center support hub and 2 oil seal rings from sun gear shaft. Remove "O" rings from brake pistons.

Inspection

Clean all parts (except discs) in clean solvent and dry with compressed air. Inspect all parts for wear or other damage and replace as necessary. Check thickness of all brake discs. Replace discs if thickness is less than .08" (2.1 mm).

Reassembly

1) Lubricate all moving parts with ATF. Install new oil seals and "O" rings on center support hub, sun gear shaft and brake piston. Lubricate "O" rings and install No. 2 brake piston into center support. Use care not to damage "O" rings.

2) Install return springs into position on piston, then place retainer onto return springs. Compress return springs and install snap ring. Repeat procedure for No. 1 brake piston.

Fig. 14: Exploded View of Center Support Assembly

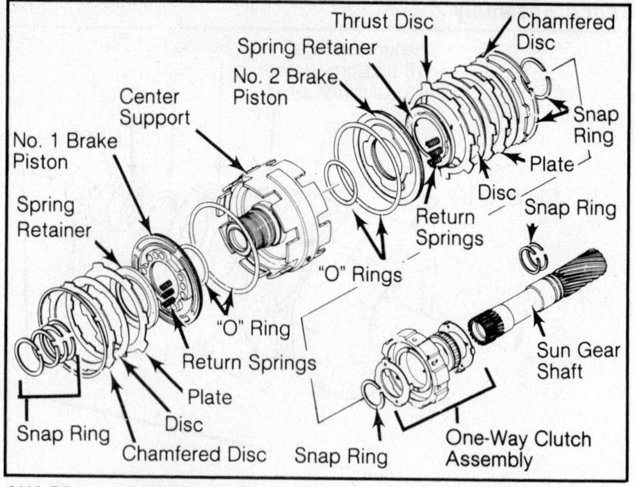

AW 55 and BW 55 similar.

3) Install No. 1 brake plate, disc, and then chamfered backing plate with chamfer facing disc. Install No. 1 brake snap ring into center support with ring end gap between openings on center support. *See Fig. 15.* On brake No. 2, install thrust disc. Alternate friction discs and plates to match positions as disassembled. Install chamfered backing plate with chamfer facing disc.

Fig. 15: Installing Brake Disc Retaining Snap Ring

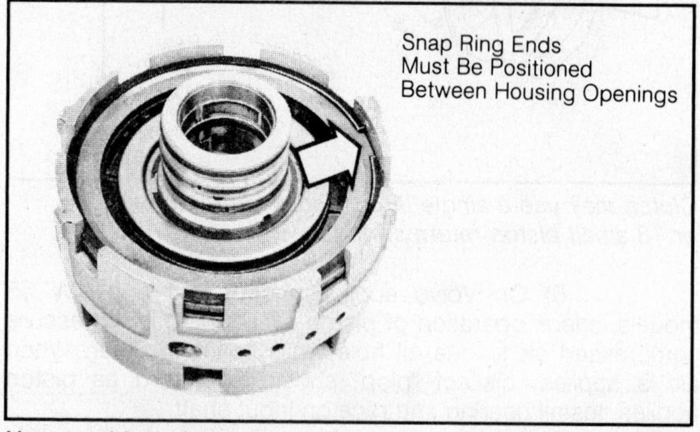

Note position of snap ring openings.

4) Install No. 2 brake snap ring. On Isuzu applications, install dial indicator so tip is resting on backing plate. Apply compressed air and record piston stroke as measured on dial indicator. Piston stroke should be .026-.051" (.65-1.30 mm) for No. 1 (front) brake and .037-.068" (.93-1.7 mm) for No. 2 (rear) brake.

5) In Volvo applications, BW 55 models use .055" (1.4 mm) snap ring on No. 2 brake while AW 55 models use .047" (1.2 mm) snap ring which has blue marking to identify it further. End clearance between snap rings and discs on both brakes should be .012-.048" (.30-1.20 mm). *See Fig. 16.*

6) Check operation of No. 1 and No. 2 brake pistons by applying compressed air to oil holes. When air is applied, distinct clicking should be heard as piston is activated. *See Fig. 17.*

7) If stroke exceeds specification, clutch pack is excessively worn. If stroke is less than specification, clutch components have been incorrectly installed or too much ATF was applied to clutch plates and discs.

Fig. 16: Measuring Center Support Brake Clearance

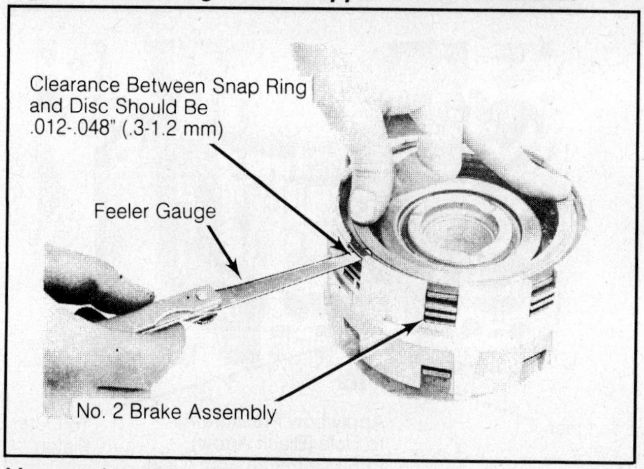

Measure between snap ring and top brake disc.

Fig. 17: Checking Brake Piston Operation

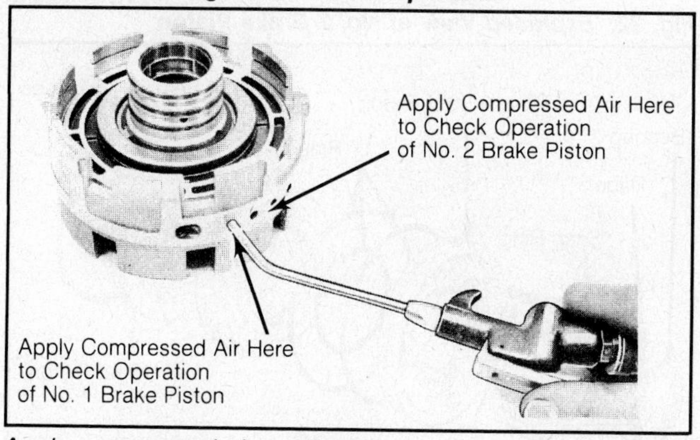

Apply compressed air as shown.

8) Install brake hub assembly on sun gear with cupped side facing splines of sun gear. Install one-way clutch on sun gear shaft. Check that one-way clutch is not loose or stiff when installed on shaft. Check one-way clutch by holding No. 2 brake hub and rotating sun gear. Sun gear should rotate counterclockwise but lock up if clockwise rotation is attempted.

9) Install one-way clutch and sun gear shaft into center support. Align grooves of brake hub with lugs on discs. Install snap ring on sun gear shaft in groove on splined portion of shaft.

PLANETARY GEAR ASSEMBLY

Disassembly

1) Separate front planetary gear set, one-way clutch, and No. 3 brake discs from output shaft assembly. Invert shaft assembly so that assembly is resting on output shaft. Compress snap ring and lift front planetary ring gear from assembly.

2) Pull intermediate shaft and rear planetary gear set from output shaft housing. Remove bearing and race from output shaft housing. Remove plastic and steel thrust washers from intermediate shaft. Pull rear planetary gear set from rear ring gear.

3) Remove bearing and race. Remove snap ring and slide rear ring gear from intermediate shaft. Slide rear bearing race from shaft. Remove oil seal rings from output shaft. Remove steel thrust plate from front planetary gear set.

4) Remove No. 3 brake discs and plates from around planetary gear set. Remove one-way clutch inner hub from front planetary gear set. Remove snap ring from one-way clutch. Remove both bearing cages, one-way clutch and plastic ring from gear set.

Fig. 18: Exploded View of Planetary Gear Set

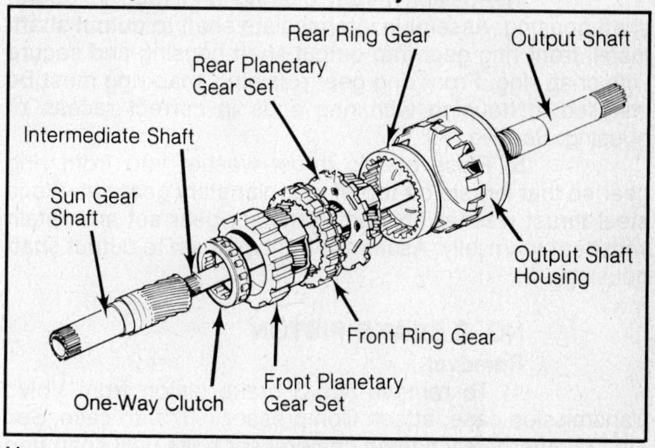

Note component position during disassembly.

Inspection

Clean all parts (except discs) with clean solvent and dry with compressed air. Inspect all parts for wear, cracks, or other damage and replace as necessary. Check thickness of each brake disc. Replace discs if thickness is less than .08" (2.1 mm).

Reassembly

1) Lubricate all moving parts with ATF. Install plastic ring and lower bearing cage into front planetary gear set. Install one-way clutch into gear set with arrow on side of clutch pointing down. Collar end of clutch should be up. Install one-way clutch upper bearing cage on top of clutch and retain with snap ring.

2) Install one-way clutch and front planetary gear set into front ring gear. With one-way clutch installed in front ring gear, front planetary gear set should rotate freely in counterclockwise direction. Front planetary gear set should be locked in clockwise direction. Assemble No. 3 brake discs to front planetary gear set.

Fig. 19: Installing Front Ring Gear Snap Ring

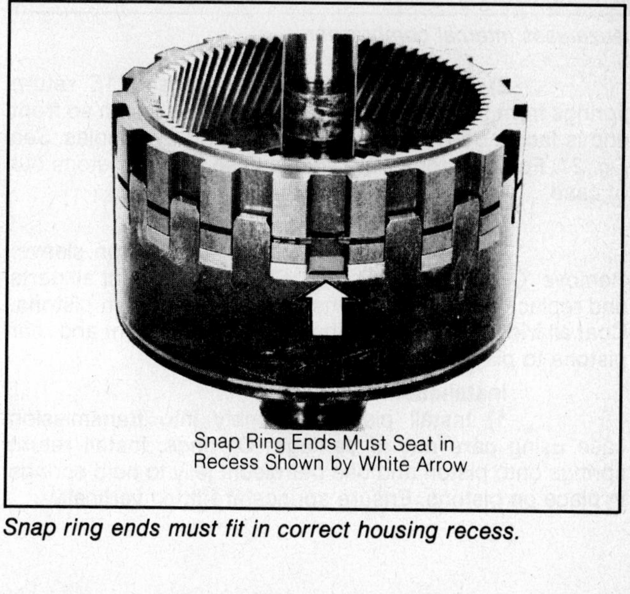

Snap Ring Ends Must Seat in Recess Shown by White Arrow

Snap ring ends must fit in correct housing recess.

3) Install new oil seal rings on output shaft and ensure that ring ends are properly hooked. Position rear race on intermediate shaft. Slide rear ring gear onto shaft. Secure with snap ring. Position bearing and front race on intermediate shaft in rear ring gear. Install rear planetary gear set into ring gear.

4) Position thrust bearing and race in output shaft housing. Assemble intermediate shaft to output shaft. Install front ring gear into output shaft housing and secure with snap ring. Front ring gear retaining snap ring must be installed in housing with ring ends in correct recess of housing. *See Fig. 19.*

5) Place plastic thrust washer into front ring gear so that it rests on top of rear planetary gear set. Place steel thrust washer on front planetary gear set and retain with petroleum jelly. Assemble front gear set to output shaft housing.

NO. 3 BRAKE PISTON

Removal

1) To remove No. 3 brake piston from Volvo transmission case, attach Compressor (5073) to case. *See Fig. 20.* Alternately tighten compressor bolts until snap ring on piston return spring retainer is free of tension. Isuzu uses Internal Compressor (J-25048). Using screwdriver, pry out snap ring. Remove compressor.

Fig. 20: Installing Volvo Compressor (5073)

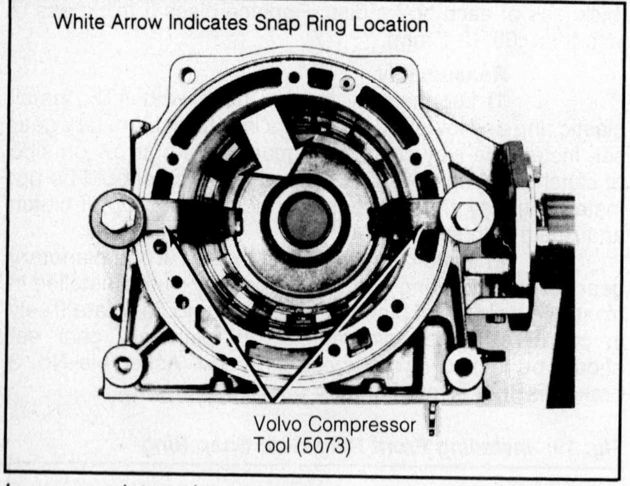

Isuzu uses internal compressor.

2) Lift return spring retainer and 16 return springs from transmission case. Turn transmission so front end is facing down. Apply compressed air to oil holes. *See Fig. 21.* Force pistons from seat in case and lift pistons out of case.

Disassembly & Reassembly

Pull front and rear pistons from piston sleeve. Remove "O" rings from pistons. Clean and inspect all parts and replace as necessary. Install new "O" rings on pistons. Coat all friction surfaces with ATF. Assemble front and rear pistons to piston sleeve.

Installation

1) Install piston assembly into transmission case using care not to damage "O" rings. Install return springs onto piston and use petroleum jelly to hold springs in place on pistons. Ensure springs are fitted vertically.

Fig. 21: Removing No. 3 Brake Piston

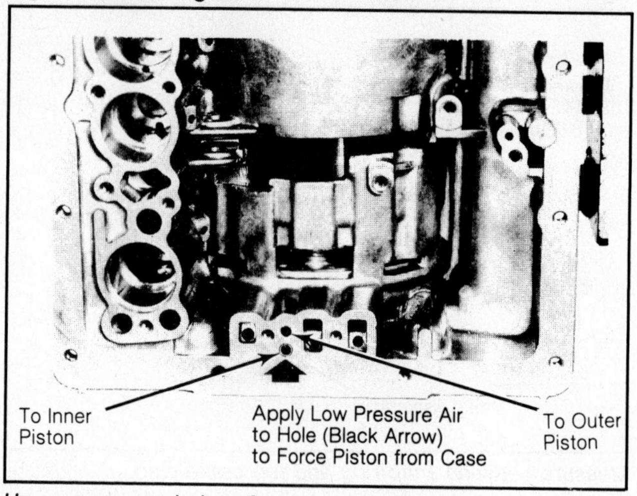

Use compressed air to force out pistons.

Fig. 22: Exploded View of No. 3 Brake Piston

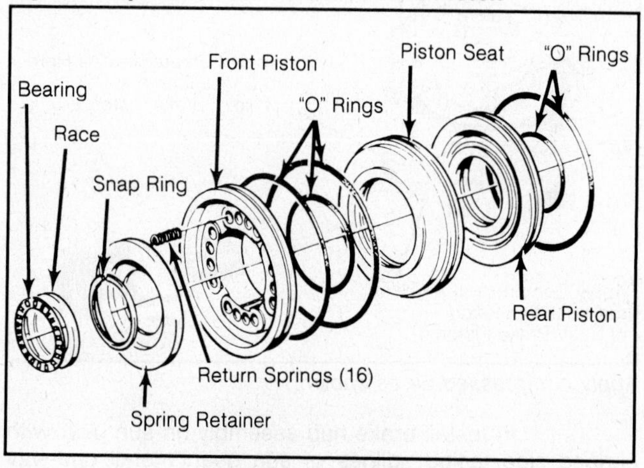

2) Install spring retainer on top of springs. Compress piston springs with compressor used at removal. Install retaining snap ring. Remove compressor.

Fig. 23: Disassembled View of Governor Assembly

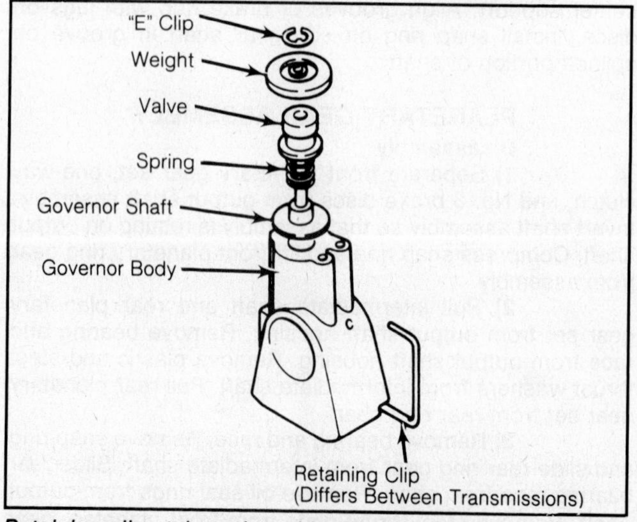

Retaining clip style varies with different models.

GOVERNOR ASSEMBLY

Disassembly

Remove retaining clip from governor assembly. Remove "E" clip from end of governor shaft. Remove shaft with governor valve, spring and weight from valve bore side of body.

Inspection

Clean all parts with solvent and dry with compressed air. Inspect all parts for wear or damage.

Reassembly

Lubricate all parts with ATF. Install spring and valve on shaft. Install shaft into governor body. Place weight on shaft. Install "E" clip to retain parts. Install retaining clip on governor housing. Install new oil seal in extension housing.

VALVE BODY ASSEMBLY

NOTE: **Valve body assemblies used on BW and AW transmissions differ slightly. These differences will be called out in following procedures.**

Disassembly

1) Remove detent spring assembly. Pull manual valve out of valve body bore. Remove front and rear upper valve body attaching bolts from top of lower valve body. Invert valve body assemblies and remove retaining bolts from bottom of lower valve body.

2) Carefully lift lower body off both upper bodies with plate and gasket. Ensure gasket does not stick to upper bodies. Place lower body aside with gasket up. To disassemble front upper valve body, place valve body upside down on work bench. Remove check ball and throttle valve retaining plate. Using screwdriver, push out cutback valve retainer. Remove cutback valve and spring.

3) Remove throttle cam, spring and spacer sleeve from front upper valve body. Pull out throttle valve, kickdown valve, springs, and spacers, noting number of spacers removed with throttle valve. Equal amount of spacers must be reinstalled for correct throttle valve adjustment.

4) Remove one secondary regulator valve cover plate bolt. Loosen other bolt while keeping tension on plate. Carefully swing plate aside without allowing spring to pop out of cavity. Remove regulator valve.

5) To disassemble rear upper valve body, place body upside down on work bench. On AW transmissions, remove 4 check balls (3 rubber and one steel). On BW transmissions, remove 2 check balls from valve body passages, if equipped. *See Fig. 27.*

6) On both models, push in intermediate coast shift valve and remove retainer. Slide coast valve and spring for 2-3 shift valve out of valve body. Remove 2-3 shift valve retainer and shift valve. Push out detent regulator valve retainer using small screwdriver. Remove detent regulator valve with spring.

7) Remove remaining cover plate from rear upper valve body. Remove following valves and springs from valve body bores, keeping valve and springs together for identification: Low coast modulator valve, governor modulator valve (if equipped), reverse clutch sequence valve, and intermediate coast modulator valve.

8) To disassemble lower valve body, lift off spacer plate and gaskets. Remove cooler by-pass valve and spring. On AW transmissions, remove 2 check balls from valve body passages. On BW transmissions, remove 4 check balls from valve body passages (if equipped). *See Fig. 27.*

9) On all transmissions, push in 1-2 shift valve and allow retainer to drop out of valve body. Remove plug, 1-2 shift valve, and spring. Remove low coast shift valve cover plate. Slide low coast shift valve, reverse gear pilot valve (or brake sequence valve), and spring from valve body.

NOTE: **Isuzu AW transmission models use brake sequence valve while Volvo AW transmission models use reverse gear pilot valve.**

10) On Isuzu AW transmissions, remove pressure relief valve (ball type) retainer. Remove relief ball and spring. Remove primary regulator valve train retainer. Slide valve train and spring out of valve body. Remove cover plate.

Inspection

1) Thoroughly clean all parts in clean solvent, then use compressed air to dry parts. Blow out all channels and passages in valve bodies.

2) Check spacer plate to ensure all holes are open. Check all valves and valve bores for wear and damage. After cleaning and lubricating valves with ATF, ensure they slide freely in bores.

Reassembly

1) Reverse disassembly procedure and note the following: Lubricate all valves and valve bores with ATF before reassembly. Ensure all check balls are installed in correct valve body passages. *See Fig. 27.*

2) When installing throttle valve in front upper valve body, install same number of spacers that were removed. This ensures correct throttle valve adjustment.

TRANSMISSION REASSEMBLY

1) Install new oil seals for manual shaft in case. Install new "O" rings on oil cooler line nipples. Install nipples in transmission case so they point in same direction as when removed. Install line pressure and governor pressure plugs with new "O" rings.

2) Install cover for governor oil ducts on transmission case. Always use new gasket. Install throttle cable in case. Assemble parking pawl, spring and shaft in case. Install detent lever and shaft, using new collar and pin. Drive new retaining pin through lever and shaft.

3) Fit parking pawl rod to pawl and detent lever. Install parking pawl cam plate. Invert transmission case so case opening is up. Install rearmost bearing and race. Install No. 3 brake apply tube into case. Lower lugs on tube go inside No. 3 brake piston bore. Parking pawl pin fits in middle of drum recess.

4) Install planetary gear and No. 3 brake disc assembly into transmission case with recess in reaction plate lug toward oil pan. Install planetary assembly retaining snap ring in groove of case. Snap ring ends must be between splines. *See Fig. 28.*

5) Check operation of No. 3 brake piston by applying low pressure compressed air to oil holes. *See Fig. 29.* When air is applied, audible "plop" noise should be heard.

6) Hold sun gear shaft and lower center support assembly into transmission case until it mates with planetary gear assembly. Install center support bolts into case by hand to avoid thread damage. DO NOT tighten bolts at this time.

AISIN-WARNER 55, 70, 71 & BORG-WARNER 55 (Cont.)

Fig. 24: Exploded View of Volvo AW 55 & BW 55 Valve Body Assemblies

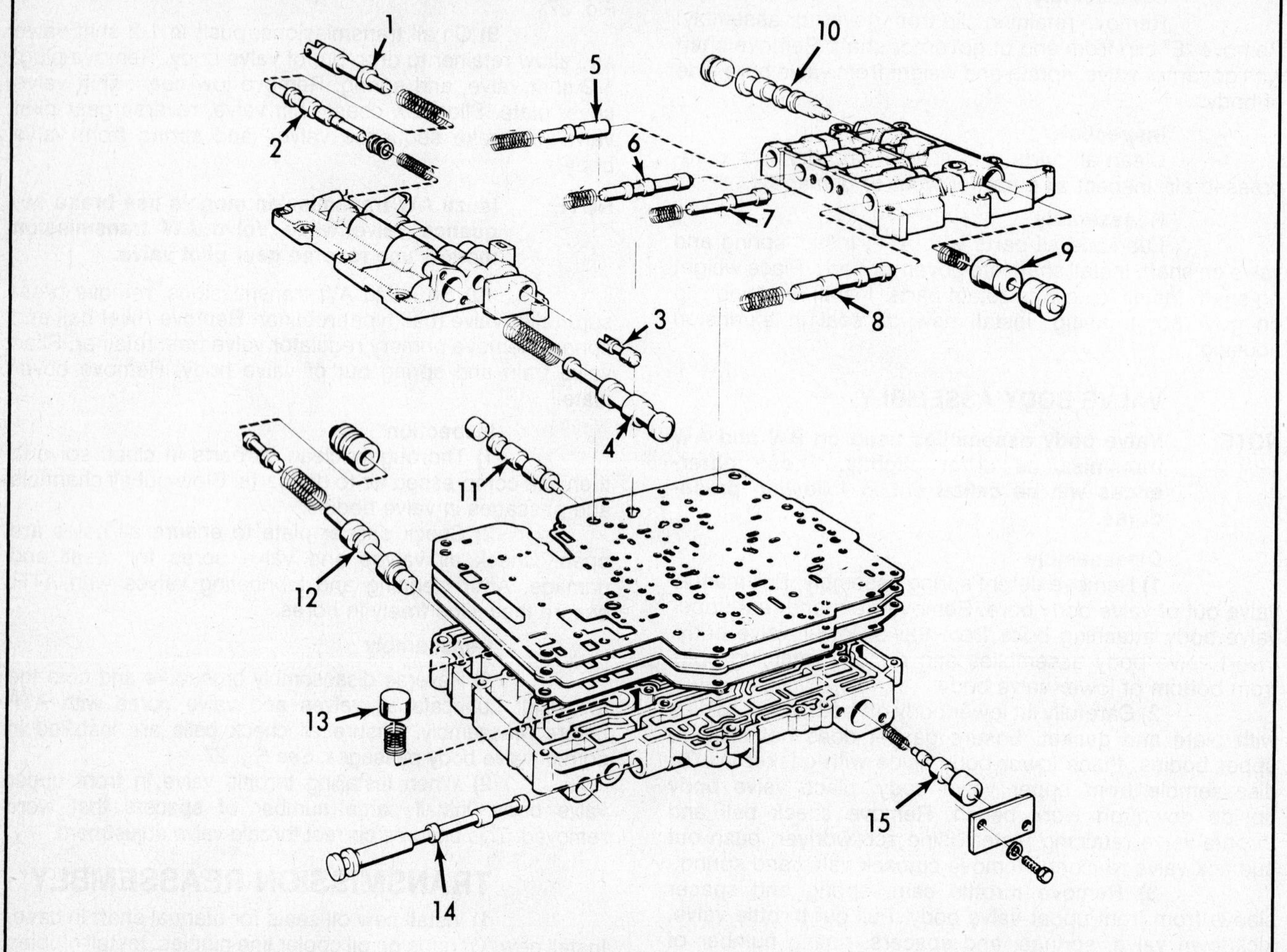

1. Secondary Throttle Valve
2. Primary Throttle Valve
3. Cutback Valve
4. Secondary Regulator Valve
5. Detent Regulator Valve
6. Intermediate Coast Modulator Valve
7. Reverse Clutch Sequence Valve
8. Low Coast Modulator Valve
9. Intermediate Coast Shift Valve
10. 2-3 Shift Valve
11. 1-2 Shift Valve
12. Primary Regulator Valve
13. Cooler Bypass Valve
14. Manual Valve
15. Low Coast Shift Valve

7) Align discs on center support and install direct (rear) clutch assembly into transmission case. If direct (rear) clutch is properly assembled, clutch splines and sun gear shaft splines should mesh. Position bearings and races on direct (rear) clutch hub.

8) Align discs and install forward (front) clutch in case, engaging lugs of direct (rear) clutch to grooves in hub of forward (front) clutch. Isuzu specifies that face of correctly installed forward (front) clutch will be about .06" (1.5 mm) from face case where oil pump attaches.

9) Install bearing and race on input shaft, with race toward oil pump. Position oil pump in case, then install and tighten attaching bolts. Tighten bolts alternately and evenly. Be careful to avoid damaging or warping of "O" rings.

10) Tighten center support bolts in 4 steps, starting with bolt next to accumulator piston bores. Check operation of brake and clutch pistons by applying low pressure compressed air to respective oil hole. *See Fig. 30.* When air is applied to each oil hole, distinct "plop" should be heard.

11) Mount dial indicator on transmission case with indicator tip touching end of input shaft. Zero dial indicator. Move input shaft up and down and note maximum dial indicator reading. This reading is input shaft end play. End play should be .009-.020" (.22-.53 mm) for BW 55 and .012-.035" (.30-.90 mm) for all others. Input shaft should rotate without binding.

12) Attach torque converter housing to transmission case and tighten bolts. Rotate transmission on holding fixture until oil pan mounting surface is up. Install accumulator piston springs into case bore. Install new "O" rings on accumulator pistons and install pistons into bores.

NOTE: **On AW 70 and 71 transmissions, No. 2 brake spring is longer than forward (front) clutch spring. On AW and BW 55 transmissions, forward (front) clutch spring is longer than No. 2 brake spring. Short spring is installed in center bore on all transmissions. Install small piston in center bore on all transmissions. Two large pistons are different sizes and cannot be incorrectly installed.**

AISIN-WARNER 55, 70, 71 & BORG-WARNER 55 (Cont.)

Fig. 25: Exploded View of Isuzu AW & BW Valve Body Assembly

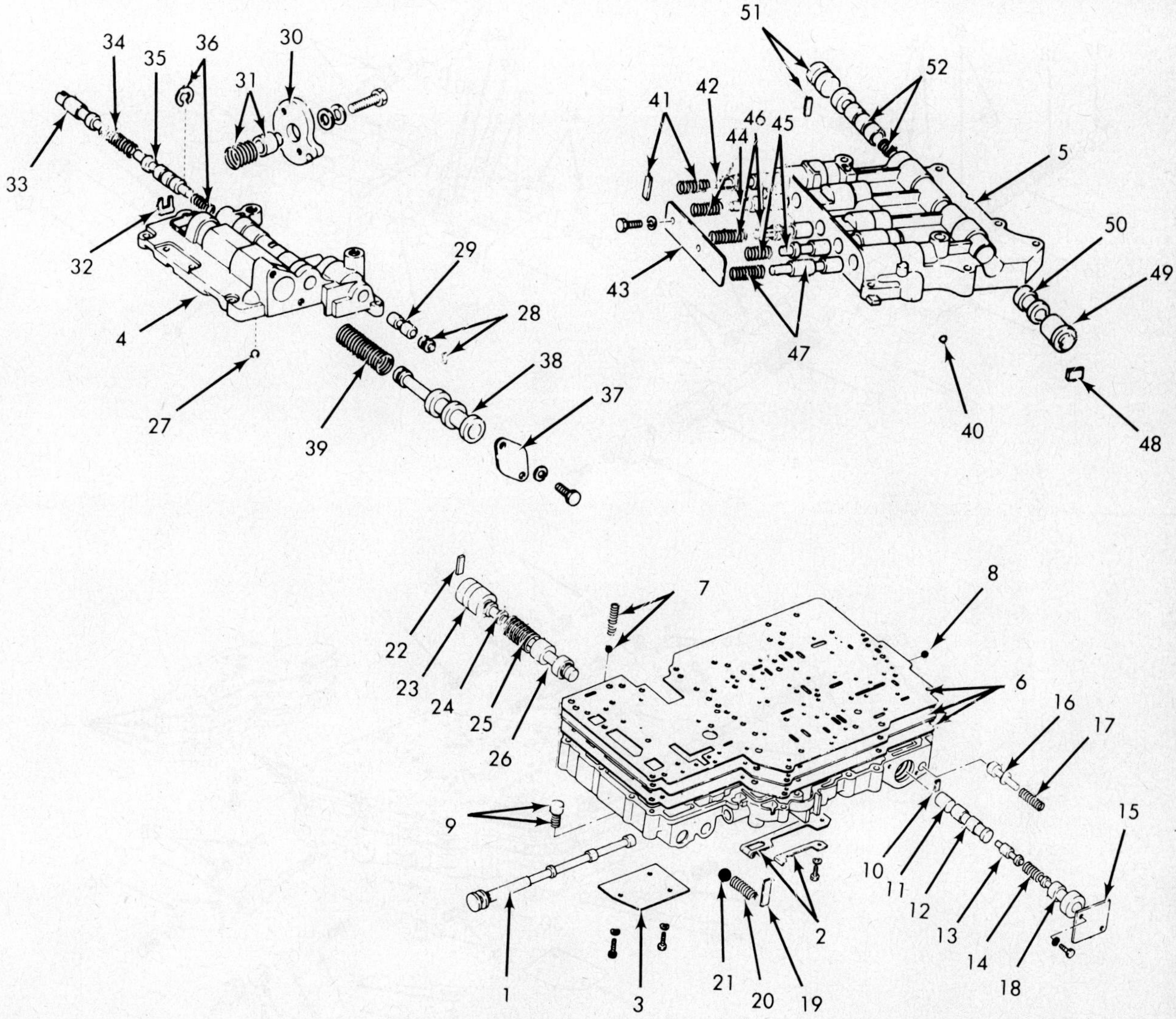

1. Manual Valve
2. Spring & Plate Assembly
3. Lower Valve Cover
4. Front Upper Valve Body
5. Rear Upper Valve Body
6. Separator Plate & Gaskets
7. Spring & 1/4" Check Ball
8. 7/32" Rubber Check Ball
9. By-pass Valve & Spring
10. Valve Retainer
11. 1-2 Shift Valve Plug
12. 1-2 Lower Shift Valve
13. 1-2 Upper Shift Valve
14. 1-2 Shift Valve Spring
15. Valve Cover
16. Reverse Valve
17. Reverse Valve Spring
18. Low Coast Shift Valve
19. Pressure Relief Valve Retainer
20. Pressure Relief Valve Spring
21. Steel Check Ball
22. Sleeve Retainer
23. Primary Regulator Valve Sleeve
24. Primary Regulator Valve Plunger
25. Primary Regulator Valve Spring
26. Primary Regulator Valve
27. 7/32" Rubber Check Ball
28. Plug & Retainer
29. Cutback Valve
30. Kickdown & Throttle Valve Cam
31. Spacer & Spring
32. Throttle Valve Plate
33. Kickdown Valve Assembly
34. Primary Throttle Valve Spring
35. Throttle Valve
36. Retaining Clip & Spring
37. Front Valve Cover
38. Secondary Valve
39. Secondary Spring
40. 7/32" Rubber Check Ball
41. Retainer & Spring
42. Detent Valve
43. Rear Valve Cover
44. Intermediate Valve & Spring
45. Reverse Clutch Valve & Spring
46. Governor Valve & Spring
47. Low Coast Valve & Spring
48. Intermediate Retainer
49. Plug
50. Intermediate Valve
51. 2-3 Shift Plug & Retainer
52. 2-3 Shift Valve & Spring

AISIN-WARNER 55, 70, 71 & BORG-WARNER 55 (Cont.)

Fig. 26: Exploded View of Isuzu Overdrive Transmission Valve Body Assembly

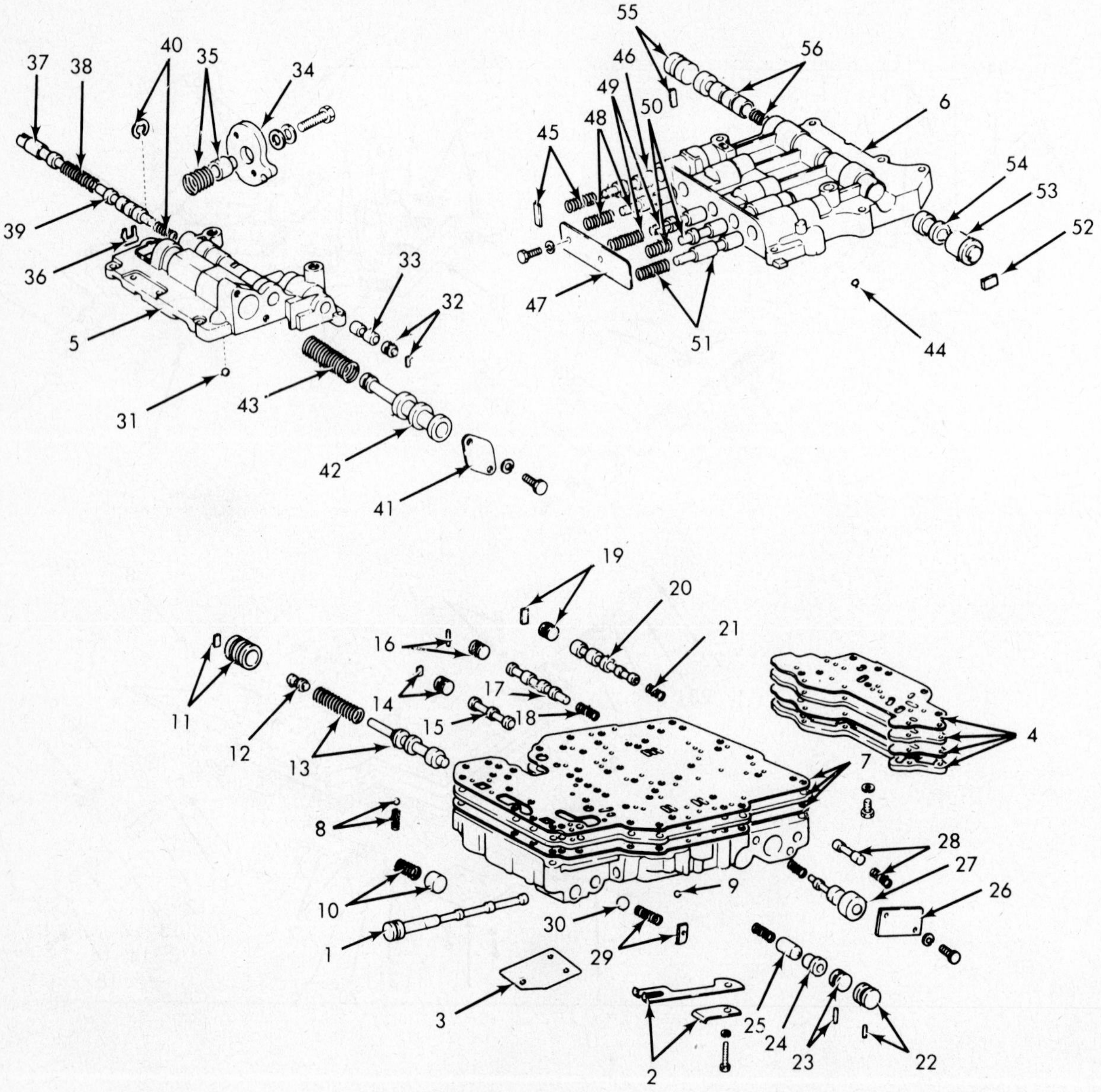

1. Manual Valve
2. Spring & Plate Assembly
3. Lower Valve Cover
4. Gasket & Cover Plate
5. Front Upper Valve Body Assy.
6. Rear Upper Valve Body Assy.
7. Plate & Gasket
8. Spring & 1/4" Rubber Check Ball
9. 7/32" Rubber Check Ball
10. By-Pass Valve & Spring
11. Sleeve & Retainer
12. Primary Regulator Valve Plunger
13. Primary Regulator Valve & Spring
14. Plug & Retainer
15. D-2 Downshift Timing Valve
16. Plug & Roll Pin
17. 3-4 Shift Valve
18. 3-4 Shift Valve Spring
19. Plug & Retainer
20. 1-2 Shift Valve
21. 1-2 Shift Valve Spring
22. Manual Valve Plug & Pin
23. 3rd Coast Shift Valve Plug & Pin
24. 3rd Coast Shift Valve
25. 3-4 Shift Control Valve
26. Valve Cover
27. Low Coast Shift Valve
28. Reverse Valve & Spring
29. Pressure Relief Valve Spring & Retainer
30. Steel Check Ball
31. 7/32" Rubber Check Ball
32. Plug & Retainer
33. Cutback Valve
34. Kickdown & Throttle Valve Cam
35. Spacer & Spring
36. Throttle Valve Plate
37. Kickdown Valve Assembly
38. Primary Throttle Valve Spring
39. Throttle Valve
40. Retaining Clip & Spring
41. Front Valve Cover
42. Secondary Valve
43. Secondary Spring
44. 7/32" Rubber Check Ball
45. Retainer & Spring
46. Detent Valve
47. Rear Valve Cover
48. Intermediate Valve & Spring
49. Reverse Clutch Valve & Spring
50. Governor Valve & Spring
51. Low Coast Valve & Spring
52. Intermediate Retainer
53. Plug
54. Intermediate Valve
55. Plug & Retainer
56. 2-3 Shift Valve & Spring

Fig. 27: Check Ball Installation in AW 55 & BW 55 Valve Bodies

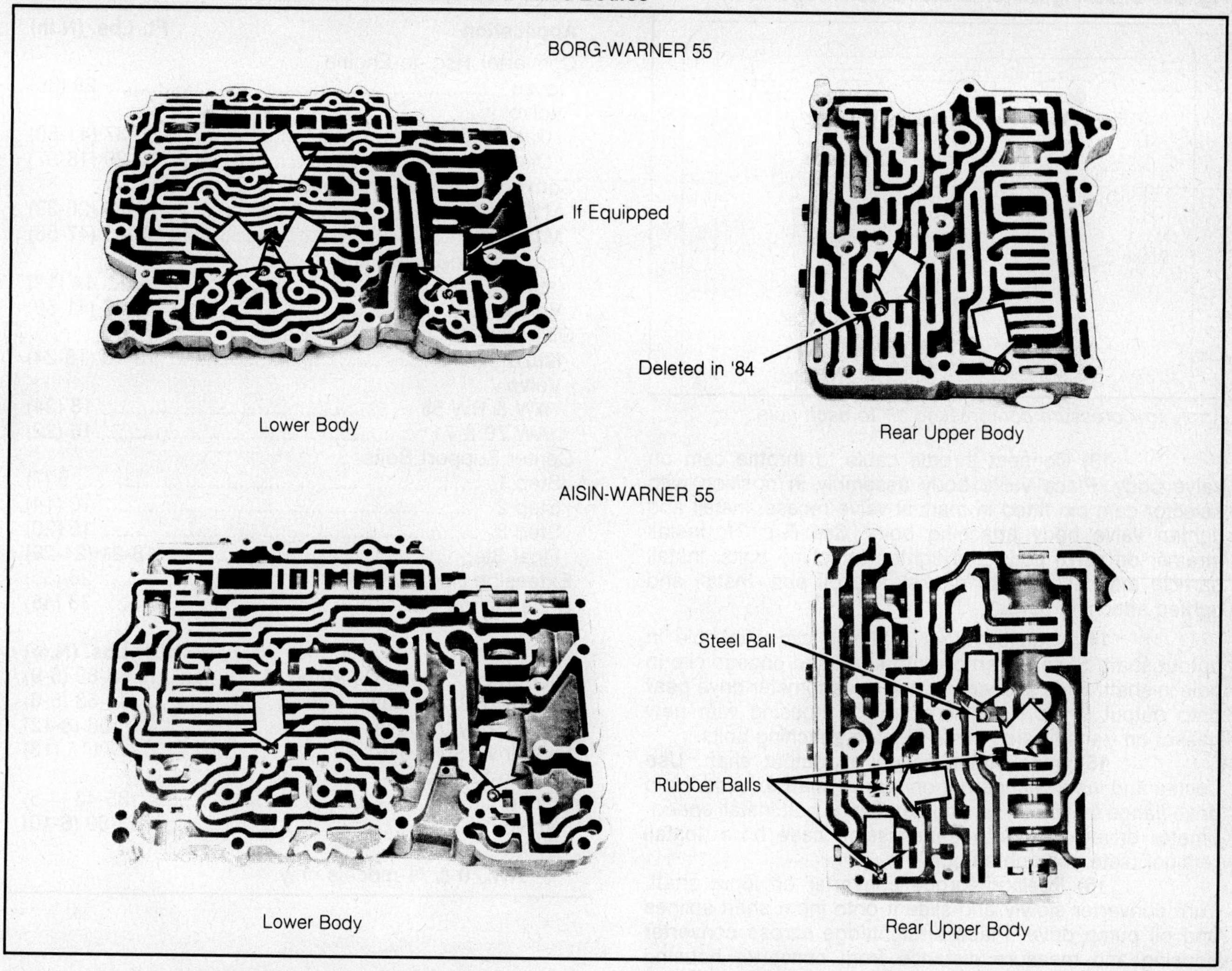

Fig. 28: Installing Planetary Assembly Snap Ring

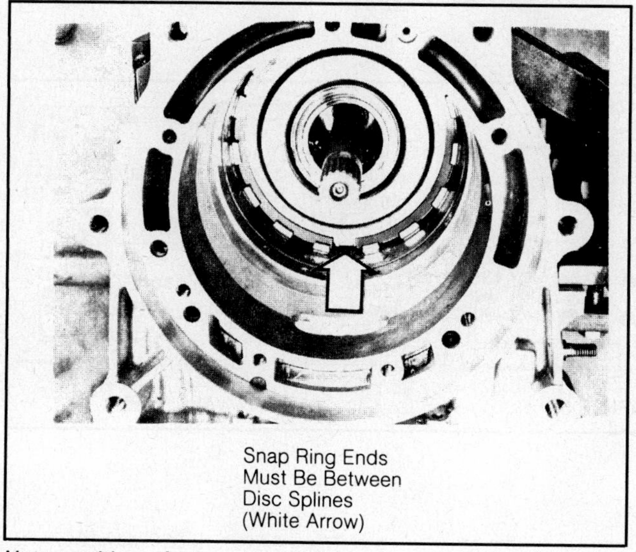

Note position of snap ring ends.

Fig. 29: Checking No. 3 Brake Piston Operation

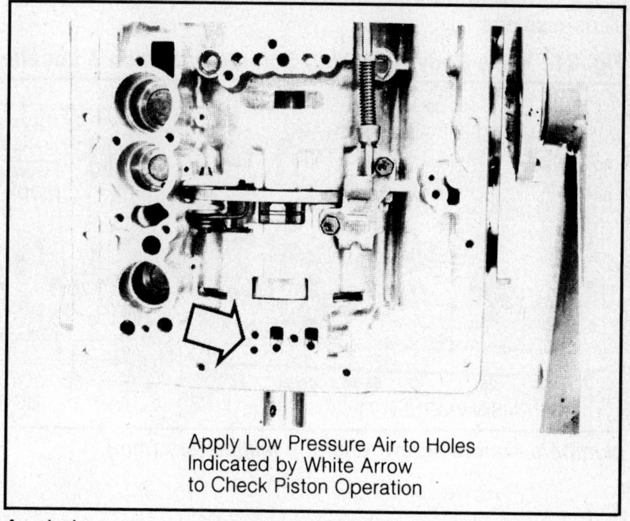

Apply Low Pressure Air to Holes
Indicated by White Arrow
to Check Piston Operation

Apply low pressure compressed air to oil hole.

AISIN-WARNER 55, 70, 71 & BORG-WARNER 55 (Cont.)

Fig. 30: Checking Clutch & Brake Piston Operation

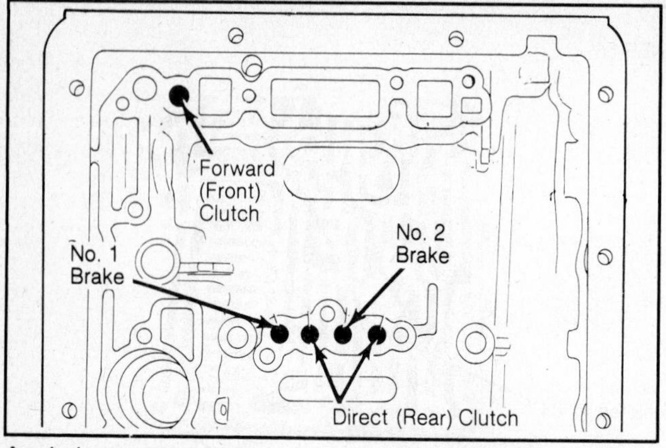

Apply low pressure compressed air to each hole.

13) Connect throttle cable to throttle cam on valve body. Place valve body assembly in position with selector cam pin fitted in manual valve recess. Install and tighten valve body attaching bolts. *See Fig. 31.* Install strainer on valve body and tighten attaching bolts. Install particle magnet, oil pan gasket and oil pan. Install and tighten attaching bolts.

14) Align governor retaining clip with hole in output shaft. Slide governor onto shaft and engage clip in hole in shaft. Slide spacer ring and speedometer drive gear onto output shaft. Position extension housing with new gasket on transmission case. Tighten attaching bolts.

15) Install drive flange on output shaft. Use Loctite and install flange nut on output shaft threads. Hold drive flange stationary and tighten flange nut. Install speedometer driven gear into transmission case bore. Install retainer plate and tighten bolt.

16) Position torque converter on input shaft. Turn converter slowly and slide it onto input shaft splines and oil pump drive. Place straightedge across converter housing and measure distance from converter housing surface to converter face ring. Distance should be .64-.77" (16.3-19.6 mm) for BW 55 and 1.24" (31.5 mm) for AW 55 transmissions.

TIGHTENING SPECIFICATIONS

Application	Ft. Lbs. (N.m)
Converter Hsg.-to-Engine	
Isuzu	29 (39)
Volvo	
Gas Engine	30-37 (41-50)
Diesel Engine	13-20 (18-27)
Converter Hsg.-to-Transmission Case	
M10 Bolts	19-29 (26-39)
M12 Bolts	35-43 (47-58)
Converter-to-Drive Plate	
Isuzu	14 (19)
Volvo	30-37 (41-50)
Oil Pump-to-Transmission Case	
Isuzu	13-18 (18-24)
Volvo	
AW & BW 55	18 (24)
AW 70 & 71	16 (22)
Center Support Bolts	
Step 1	5 (7)
Step 2	10 (14)
Step 3	15 (20)
Final Step	18-21 (24-29)
Extension Hsg.-to-Case	26 (35)
Drive Flange Nut	33 (45)
	INCH Lbs. (N.m)
Oil Pump Cover-to-Oil Pump	53-80 (6-9)
Lower-to-Upper Valve Bodies	44-53 (5-6)
Valve Body-to-Case	71-106 (8-12)
Overdrive Solenoid [1]	115 (13)
Oil Pan-to-Case	
Isuzu	35-43 (4-5)
Volvo	53-89 (6-10)

[1] – AW 70 & 71 models only.

Fig. 31: Valve Body Attaching Bolt Identification & Location

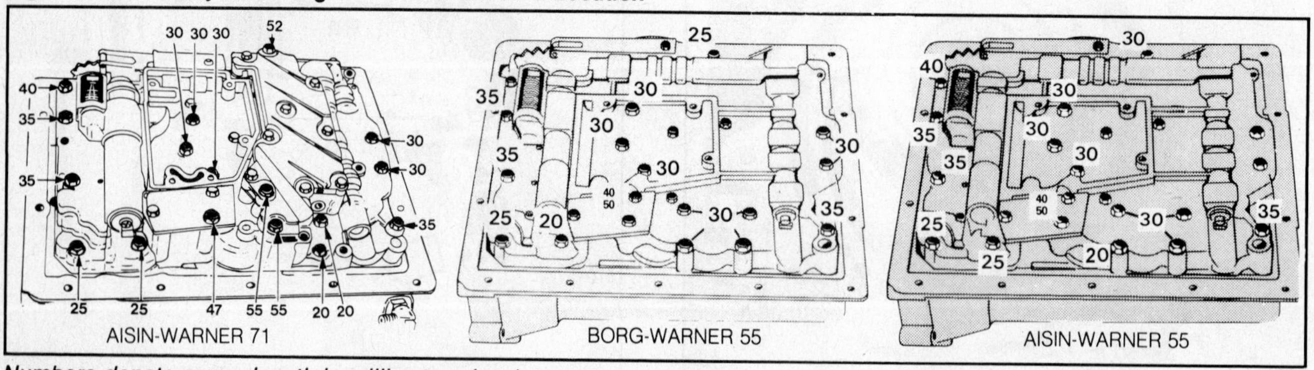

Numbers denote screw length in millimeters (mm).

Automatic Transmissions

AUDI 087, 087E, 089

Audi 4000S, 4000S Quattro, 5000S, Coupe GT
Porsche 944, Volkswagen Quantum

IDENTIFICATION

Transaxle type may be identified by group of numbers cast into top rear of case. Transaxle model code is identified by group of figures stamped into torque converter housing. These figures consist of model code and build date code. Audi uses type 087 and 089 transaxles. Volkswagen Quantum uses type 087 and 089 transaxles. Porsche 944 is equipped with type 087 transaxle. Turbine shaft length is the primary difference between the 2 transaxle types. Type 087 uses 16.71" (424.5 mm) shaft and type 089 uses 15.82" (401.7 mm) shaft. Testing, disassembly and reassembly procedures are the same for both types.

TRANSAXLE MODEL CODES

Application	Code
Audi	
Coupe GT, 4000S & 4000S Quattro	
087	RR
089	KJ
089 E-Mode	RC
5000S	
087	RY
087 E-Mode	RC
Porsche	
087	RCF
Volkswagen	
087	RBE
089	KJ/KAF
089 E-Mode	KU/KAC

DESCRIPTION

Transaxle assembly consists of automatic transmission and final drive assembly. Transmission housing contains 2 planetary gear sets, 2 multiple-disc clutches, one brake band and servo, one multiple-disc brake, one-way clutch, and hydraulic control system.

Final drive housing contains torque converter, transmission governor, ring gear, and differential carrier with pinion and side gears.

Some vehicles with diesel engines use E-Mode transaxles to improve fuel economy. When selector lever is in "E" position, transmission disengages from differential when accelerator pedal is released. In all other selector lever positions, transmission operates same as conventional model. Main modifications to E-Mode transaxle are in valve body and forward clutch.

LUBRICATION & ADJUSTMENTS

See appropriate AUTOMATIC TRANSMISSION SERVICING article in IMPORT GENERAL SERVICING section.

TROUBLE SHOOTING

NO MOVEMENT

In Any Gear

Low fluid level. Manual lever not connected to manual valve. Torque converter disconnected from drive plate. Main pressure valve sticking. Oil pump and/or pump drive shaft defective.

In Forward Gears

Forward clutch internal damage (worn plates, broken diagram spring, seals leaking, etc.). Forward planetary gears damaged.

In First Gear in "D" or "2"

One-way clutch not holding. Forward clutch internal damage.

In First Gear in "1"

First/Reverse brake plates worn or burnt. Forward clutch damage.

In Second Gear

Second gear brake band out of adjustment or burnt, or servo defective.

In Third Gear

Direct/Reverse clutch plates burnt or worn.

In Reverse

First/Reverse brake plates worn or burnt. Direct/Reverse clutch internal damage. Forward clutch seized in applied position.

NO UPSHIFT

Into Second Gear

Faulty governor drive. Governor incorrectly assembled or dirty. Loose accumulator cover plate. 1-2 gear shift valve sticking. Brake band for 2nd gear burnt or worn.

Into Third Gear

Governor or valve body dirty. 2-3 shift valve sticking. Loose oil pump bolts.

NO DOWNSHIFT

Into Second Gear

Governor dirty. 2-3 shift valve sticking.

Into First Gear

Governor dirty. 1-2 shift valve sticking.

DELAYED ENGAGEMENT ON UPSHIFTS

1-2 Upshift

Low fluid level. Dirty valve body. Second gear brake band worn, burnt or out of adjustment. Second gear servo defective, possible wrong piston.

2-3 Upshift

Low fluid level. Dirty valve body. Second gear brake band worn, burnt or out of adjustment. Second gear servo defective. Direct/Reverse clutch plates worn or burnt. Wrong Direct/Reverse clutch installed.

ERRATIC DRIVE

Low fluid level. Bushing in one-way clutch support and turbine shaft worn. Oil filter dirty. Governor dirty. Valve body dirty. Planetary gears or separation plate gasket damaged.

E-MODE

Transaxle Does Not Disengage Properly

Accelerator cable or selector lever incorrectly adjusted. Main pressure too high. Declutching valve in valve body sticking. Forward clutch damaged.

CLUTCH AND BAND APPLICATION (ELEMENTS IN USE)

Selector Lever Position	Forward Clutch	Direct/Reverse Clutch	First/Reverse Brake	Second Gear Band	One-Way Clutch
"D" - DRIVE					
1st Gear	X				Holding
2nd Gear	X			X	Overrun
3rd Gear	X	X			Overrun
"2" - INTERMEDIATE					
1st Gear	X				Holding
2nd Gear	X			X	Overrun
"1" - LOW (First)	X		X		
"R" - REVERSE		X	X		

NEUTRAL OR PARK – All clutches, brakes, and bands released and/or ineffective.

TESTING

ROAD TESTING

1) Before road testing, ensure that fluid level and condition are correct. Check control linkage adjustments and correct as necessary. During test, transmission should upshift and downshift at correct speeds. See SHIFT SPEEDS chart.

2) Shift speeds may vary slightly due to production tolerances or tire size. Quality of shifts is most important factor. All shifts should be smooth, responsive, and with no slippage or engine speed runaway.

3) Slippage or engine runaway in any gear usually indicates clutch, band, or brake problems. Slipping unit in particular gear can be identified by noting transmission operation in other selector positions and comparing which internal units are applied. See CLUTCH AND BRAKE BAND APPLICATION chart.

4) This process of elimination can be used to detect any unit which slips and to confirm proper operation of good units.

5) Practically all conditions may be caused by leaking hydraulic circuits or sticking valves. Unless definite problem exists, DO NOT disassemble transmission until hydraulic pressure test has been made.

HYDRAULIC PRESSURE TEST

1) Connect pressure gauge to main pressure test point on case (adjacent to servo cover). Transmission must be at normal operating temperature.

2) Verify that pressures obtained during each phase of test are correct. See MAIN PRESSURES TEST chart. If pressures are incorrect, check for oil leaks, defective oil pump, or sticking valves in valve body assembly.

STALL TEST

CAUTION: DO NOT hold throttle open for longer than time needed to read tachometer. Maximum stall speed test time is 5 seconds. Wait at least 20 seconds with transmission in neutral before repeating test. If engine speed exceeds limits, release accelerator immediately as clutch or band slippage is indicated.

Fig. 1: Testing Transmission Pressures

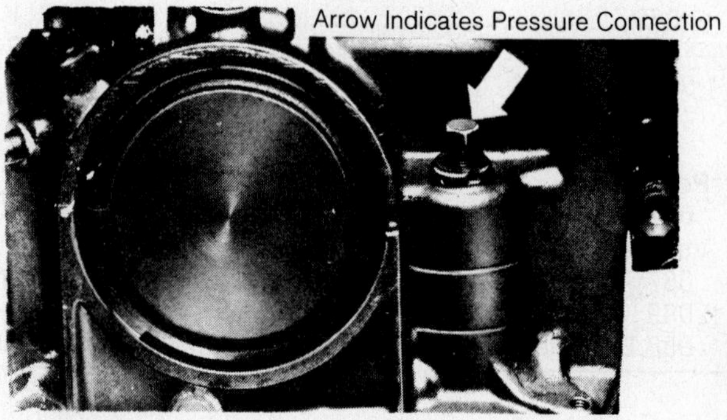

Testing Procedure

Engine must be at normal operating temperature. Connect tachometer. Start engine and set parking and service brakes. Place selector in "D". Depress accelerator briefly to full throttle and note maximum RPM obtained. Engine speed should be within limits. See STALL SPEEDS table.

Stall Speed Test Results

1) If stall speed is higher than specified, forward clutch or one-way clutch for 1st gear is slipping. If stall speed in "D" range is too high, repeat stall test in "1". If RPM is now within specification, 1st gear one-way clutch is defective. If RPM exceeds specification in "1" also, forward clutch is defective.

2) If stall speed is approximately 200 RPM below specifications, engine performance may be unsatis-

SHIFT SPEEDS (MPH)

Application	Full Throttle	Kickdown
Coupe GT, 4000S & 4000S Quattro		
087		
1-2 Upshift	19-28	40-42
2-3 Upshift	47-60	72-73
3-2 Downshift	34-47	68-70
2-1 Downshift	14-16	37-38
089		
1-2 Upshift	20-28	34-37
2-3 Upshift	48-61	66-67
3-2 Downshift	35-48	62-64
2-1 Downshift	14-16	37-38
089 E-Mode		
1-2 Upshift	23-26	37-40
2-3 Upshift	53-65	65-66
3-2 Downshift	35-48	60-62
2-1 Downshift	17-30	32-35
5000S		
087		
1-2 Upshift	19-27	38-40
2-3 Upshift	45-57	69-70
3-2 Downshift	32-45	65-67
2-1 Downshift	13-16	35-37
087 E-Mode		
1-2 Upshift	22-25	40-42
2-3 Upshift	51-63	66-67
3-2 Downshift	34-47	62-63
2-1 Downshift	27-31	35-37
944		
087		
1-2 Upshift	22-30	45-48
2-3 Upshift	52-65	81-83
3-2 Downshift	37-52	77-80
2-1 Downshift	16-17	42-44
Quantum		
087		
1-2 Upshift	19-28	40-42
2-3 Upshift	47-60	72-73
3-2 Downshift	34-47	68-70
2-1 Downshift	14-16	37-38
089		
1-2 Upshift	20-28	34-37
2-3 Upshift	48-61	66-67
3-2 Downshift	35-48	62-64
2-1 Downshift	14-16	29-31
089 E-Mode		
1-2 Upshift	23-26	37-40
2-3 Upshift	53-65	65-66
3-2 Downshift	35-48	60-62
2-1 Downshift	17-30	32-35

factory. If stall speed is more than 200 RPM below specifications, torque converter stator one-way clutch is faulty and complete converter should be replaced.

SERVICE (IN VEHICLE)

DRIVE AXLE SHAFTS

See appropriate DRIVE AXLE SHAFT article in IMPORT AXLE SHAFTS, OVERDRIVES & TRANSFER CASES section.

VALVE BODY

CAUTION: As valve body components are removed from each valve body bore, place individual parts in tray (2008) in correct order to simplify reassembly. DO NOT interchange valves or valve springs. Several valve springs have identical dimensions but different tolerances. Individual valve body components are not available. Valve bodies are available only as exchange units.

STALL SPEEDS

Application	Stall RPM [1]
Coupe GT, 4000S & 4000S Quattro	
087	2250-2500
089	2450-2700
089 E-Mode	2530-2780
5000S	
087	2250-2500
087/Turbo	3000-3400
087 E-Mode	2400
944	
087	2600-3000
Quantum	
087	2250-2500
089	2450-2700
089 E-Mode	2530-2780

[1] – Stall speeds will drop 125 RPM for each 3300 ft. increase in elevation. High ambient temperature may cause slight drop in stall speed.

Disassembly

1) Remove transfer plate-to-main valve body attaching screws. Lift transfer plate and separator plate from main valve body. Remove main valve body check balls from passeages in valve body.

NOTE: DO NOT alter settings of adjusting screws. Adjusting screws change pressures and can only be properly adjusted on test stand.

2) Remove rear end cover plate and withdraw valves, springs and adjusting screws. Remove remaining end plates one at a time and withdraw all valves, plugs, springs and adjusting screws. Tag all parts for reassembly reference or use tray (2008) to hold parts. This tray holds springs and valves in correct order and location.

Inspection

1) Wash all parts in clean solvent and dry them with compressed air only. DO NOT use rags or water. Lint from rags can cause problems in flow of ATF after reassembly. Check all parts for burrs and scores. Replace assembly if damaged.

NOTE: Valve which are slightly scored may be reused, if they slide under their own weight after cleaning and lubrication with fresh ATF. This scoring will not affect operation of transmission.

2) Check all valve body springs for damage or collapsed coils. Some transfer plates are equipped with 3 sealing balls. If transmission did not shift into 3rd gear, trouble may be caused by missing sealing ball.

3) To install new sealing balls, stick .118' (3 mm) diameter sealing ball on 8 mm diameter punch with small amount of grease and drive ball flush into hole of transfer plate.

Reassembly

1) Lubricate all parts with ATF and install into proper valve body bores in reverse order of disassemlby.

Automatic Transmissions

AUDI 087, 087E, 089 (Cont.)

MAIN PRESSURE TEST

Selector Lever Position	Accelerator Pedal Position	Main Pressure psi (kg/cm²)	Test Conditions [1]
"D" - DRIVE All Models	At Idle	42.06-43.51 (3.0-3.1)	Accelerate to 35 mph, release throttle and check pressure
"D" - DRIVE All Except E-Mode 087 (Coupe GT, 4000S, 5000S, & Quantum) 089 (Coupe GT, 4000S 5000S, & Quantum) 087 (944) All Models E-Mode [2]	W.O.T.	 81.95-83.40 (5.8-5.9) 84.85-86.30 (6.0-6.1) 105.88-107.33 (7.4-7.6) 84.85-86.30 (6.0-6.1)	Vehicle speed above 35 mph
"R" - REVERSE All Except E-Mode 087 (Coupe GT, 4000S, & 5000S) 089 (Coupe GT & 4000S) 087 & 089 (Quantum) 087 (944) All Models E-Mode	At Idle	 131.99-140.69 (9.3-9.9) 131.99-140.69 (9.3-9.9) 130.54-145.04 (9.2-10.2) 133.44-142.14 (9.4-10.0) 130.54-145.04 (9.2-10.2)	Vehicle Stationary
"R" - REVERSE 087 (944)	W.O.T.	290.0 (20.0) Min.	At stall speed

[1] – Manufacturer recommends that "D" tests be performed on chassis dynamometer.
[2] – No specifications available for Quantum E-Mode at time of publication.

DO NOT overtighten plate attaching screws. Overtightening can strip threads or distort valve body body enough to cause valve to stick.

2) Ensure all check balls are installed in proper valve body passages. Check ball "A" is .12" (3 mm) in diameter. All other check balls are .24" (6 mm) in diameter. Install transfer plate-to-main valve body screws and tighten from center outward. DO NOT tighten.

GOVERNOR ASSEMBLY

NOTE: Governor is mounted in final drive assembly.

Removal

Removal cover bolts and washers. Remove governor cover and "O" ring from final drive housing. Withdraw governor from housing with clockwise turning motion to allow governor from housing with clockwise turning motion to allow governor drive gear to disengage from drive pinion gear.

Disassembly

Remove 2 attaching screws and withdraw thrust plate and governor housing. Remove transfer plate (noting position), balance weight and oil strainer (if equipped). Remove "E" clip and pull centrifugal weight, valve, spring and dished washer from pin.

Reassembly

Reverse disassembly procedure and lubricate all parts with ATF when reassembling. Transfer plate must be reinstalled in same position. DO NOT reinstall oil strainer. Be sure angle in thrust plate is in center of housing so cover will bear against it.

Installation

Check governor oil seal and needle bearing in housing for damage or wear. Replace if necessary. Reverse removal procedure to install. Rotate governor to engage drive gear.

REMOVAL & INSTALLATION

TRANSAXLE

See appropriate AUTOMATIC TRANSMISSION REMOVAL article in IMPORT GENERAL SERVICING section.

TORQUE CONVERTER

Torque converter is a sealed unit and cannot be disassembled for service.

Torque Convertor Bushing Replacement

1) Check bushing wear using inside micrometer. Wear limit is 1.343" (34.12 mm). Maximum allowable out-of-round is .001" (.03 mm). If bushing wear exceeds limit, use Bushing Puller (US 691, VW 201 and adapter US 4452) to withdraw bushing from converter hub.

2) Press new bushing into place using Bushing Driver (VW 474). Measure inside diameter of new bushing after installation. Remove any burrs from edge of converter hub after installation of new bushing.

3) Minimum allowed inside diameter of new bushing is 1.340-1.341" (34.03-34.05 mm). Bushing may seize if inside diameter is less than minimum limit. Do not ream out bushing to fit. Repeat replacement procedure with another new bushing if necessary.

AUDI 087, 087E, 089 (Cont.)

Fig. 2: Removing Torque Converter Bushing

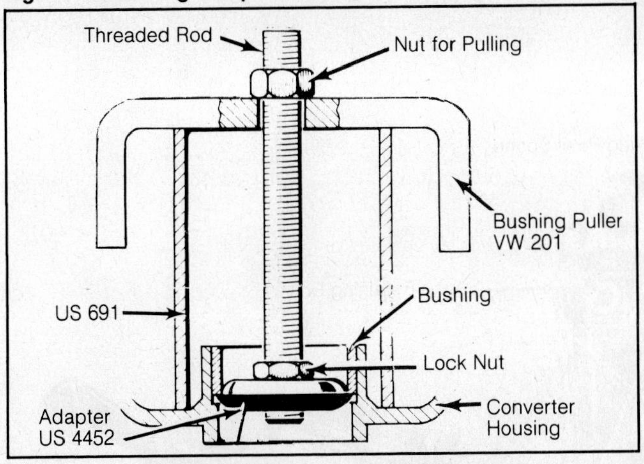

TRANSAXLE DISASSEMBLY

1) To separate transmission from final drive assembly, withdraw torque converter from final drive housing and remove oil pump shaft from center of turbine shaft. Disconnect filler pipe from oil pan. Mount transaxle assembly in holding fixture with back of transmission assembly bolted to fixture.

2) Remove nuts from studs attaching final drive to transmission. Separate final drive unit from transmission case. Withdraw turbine shaft from final drive. For final drive disassembly and reassembly, see FINAL DRIVE in this article.

Fig. 3: Installed View of One-Way Clutch Assembly Showing Location of Retaining Snap Ring

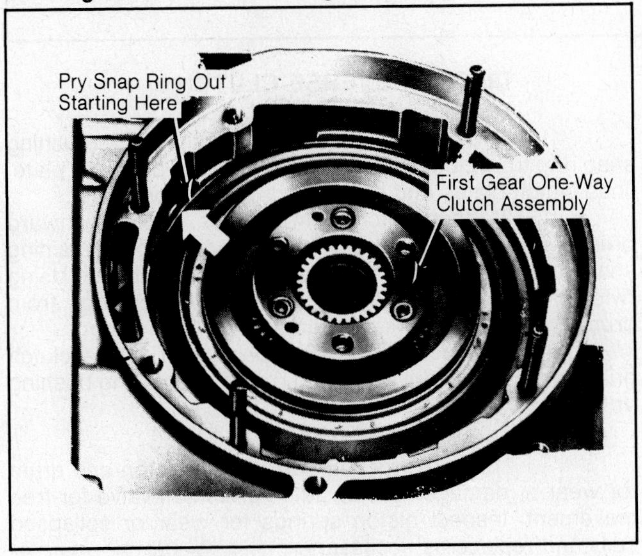

3) Remove separation plate and gasket from transmission case. Remove reverse planetary ring gear, needle bearing and thrust washer. Using screwdriver, carefully remove large snap ring retaining 1st gear one-way clutch assembly in case.

4) Lift out one-way clutch, 1st/Reverse gear brake plates, and reverse planetary gear set. Remove thrust washers, then lift following components from case as assembly: sun gear, driving shell, forward planetary gear set, and forward clutch.

5) Remove 2nd gear brake band servo cover snap ring. Use rubber mallet to tap cover until cover and piston pop out under spring pressure. Loosen 2nd gear brake band lock nut and remove adjusting screw and lock nut. Withdraw pushrod for adjusting screw.

Fig. 4: Removing Brake Band Servo Cover

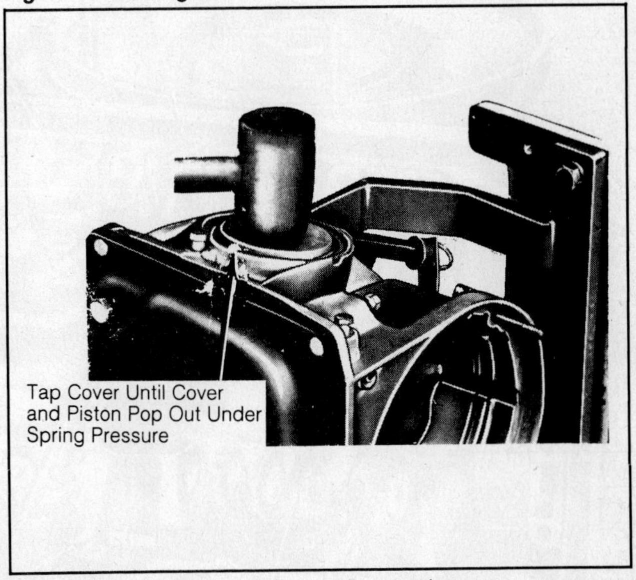

Be careful during removal as spring tension can cause servo cover to pop out.

6) Lift out remaining components that are housed in 1st/Reverse gear brake shell. Remove bolts from 1st/Reverse brake spring plate, withdraw spring plate and springs. Pull brake shell, brake piston, and oil pump from case.

7) Invert transmission so that oil pan is facing up. Remove attaching bolts and lift off oil pan and gasket. Remove oil strainer and cover from valve body. Remove 11 valve body attaching bolts.

8) Lift valve body assembly from case. DO NOT drop manual valve. Remove accumulator spring and piston from transmission case. If necessary for replacement, disassemble kickdown and selector linkage. *See Fig 5.*

COMPONENT DISASSEMBLY & REASSEMBLY

OIL PUMP ASSEMBLY

CAUTION: Pump cover is under spring tension.

Disassembly

1) Remove pump cover attaching screws and separate cover from pump housing. Remove check ball and spring from pump body. Lift out pump gears and drive plate.

2) Unhook piston ring ends and remove rings from pump body. Remove thrust washer from end of pump housing.

Automatic Transmissions

AUDI 087, 087E, 089 (Cont.)

Fig. 5: Bottom View of Transmission Housing Showing Kickdown and Selector Linkage

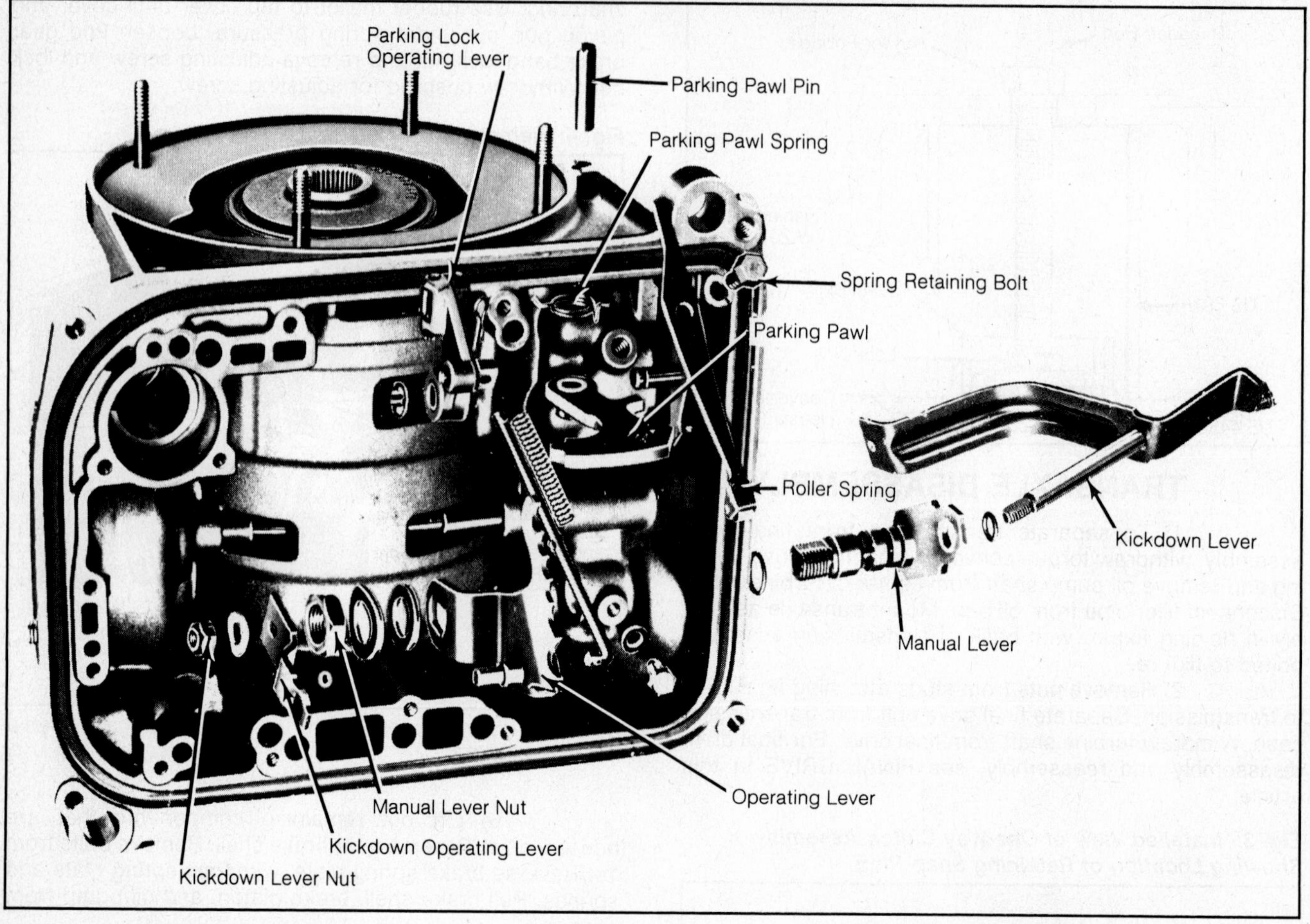

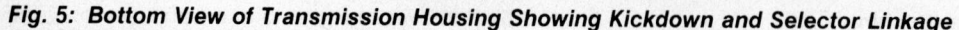

Cleaning & Inspection

Wash all parts in solvent and blow out oil passages with compressed air. Inspect all parts for wear, scoring, chipped teeth or other damage. Replace parts as necessary.

NOTE: **If either pump gear, pump housing or cover is damaged, entire oil pump assembly must be replaced. Drive plate, piston rings and thrust washer (thrust bearing and washers) may be replaced individually as needed.**

Reassembly

1) Install thrust washer on pump housing. Carefully install large piston rings and then small piston rings. Ensure ring ends are hooked together correctly. Lubricate all parts with ATF.

2) Install inner and outer gears into housing. Side of outer gear with marking (code letter) must face cover plate. Install drive plate with extended hub inserted into pump body away from cover plate. Install check ball and spring. Align cover with housing. Install and tighten attaching screws.

NOTE: **After reassembly, insert pump shaft into oil pump and ensure that gears rotate smoothly without binding. Gear movement should also be checked after pump is installed in transmission case.**

DIRECT/REVERSE CLUTCH

Disassembly

1) Using screwdriver, pry clutch pack retaining snap ring from clutch drum. Withdraw clutch pressure plate, lined clutch plates and steel clutch plates from drum.

2) Place clutch drum in press, apply downward pressure to piston spring retainer and remove retaining snap ring. Release press and remove spring retainer. Using twisting motion, remove piston with return springs from drum. Remove piston seals and springs from piston.

3) If necessary for replacement, place clutch drum in press and drive bushing out of drum using bushing driver.

Cleaning & Inspection

1) Inspect friction surfaces of piston and drum for wear or damage. Check clutch drum ball valve for free movement. Inspect piston springs for wear or collapsed coils and replace as necessary.

2) Inspect steel (externally splined) clutch plates. If plates are scored or have radial grooves, they must be replaced. Plates that are only discolored can be reused.

3) Inspect lined (internally splined) clutch plates. Replace any plate that is worn, damaged, or burned.

Reassembly

1) If removed, press new bushing into clutch drum until it is .067" (1.7 mm) below lip of drum hub on all series.

AUDI 087, 087E, 089 (Cont.)

Fig. 6: Exploded View of Transmission Case and Main Components

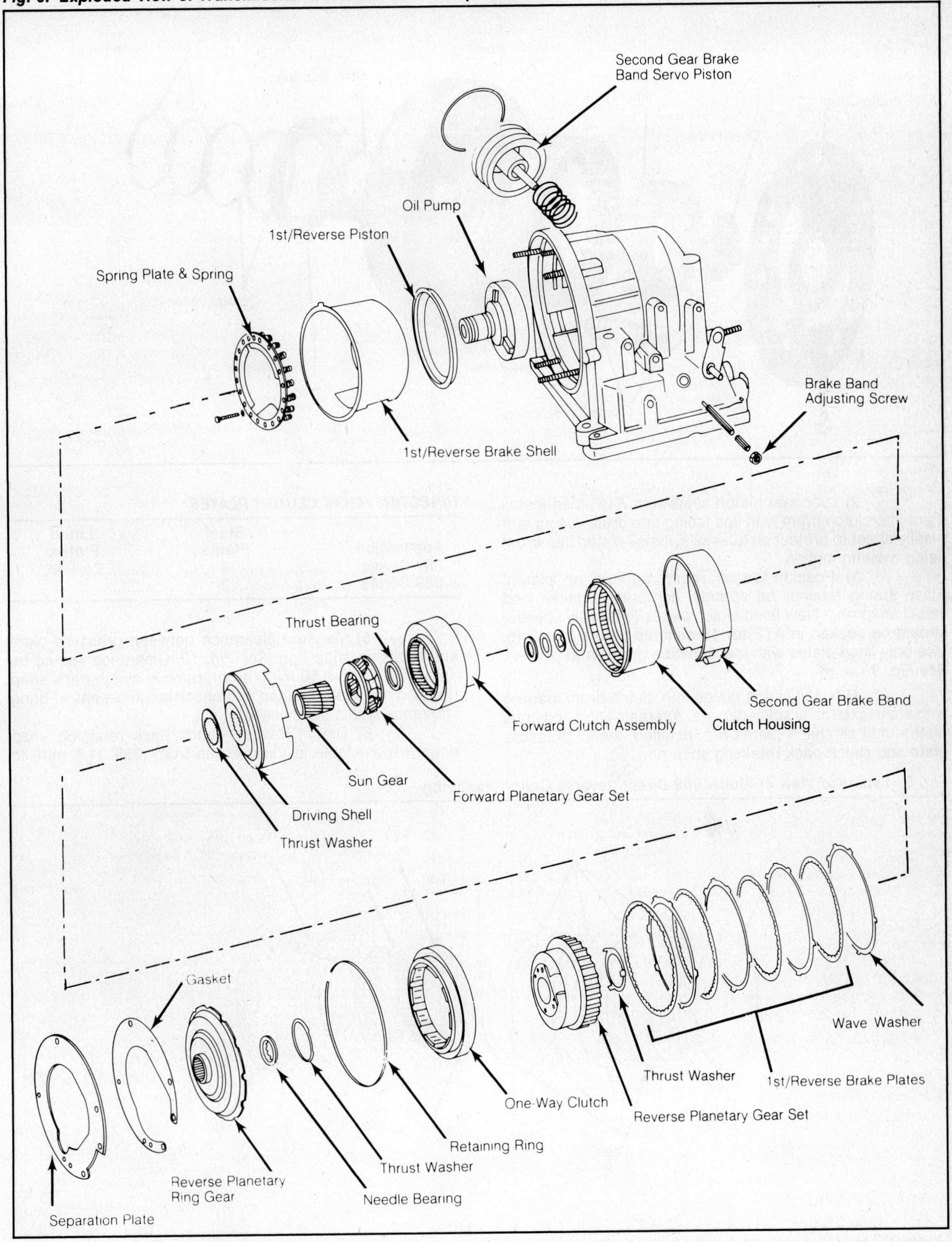

Automatic Transmissions

AUDI 087, 087E, 089 (Cont.)

Fig. 7: Exploded View of Oil Pump Assembly

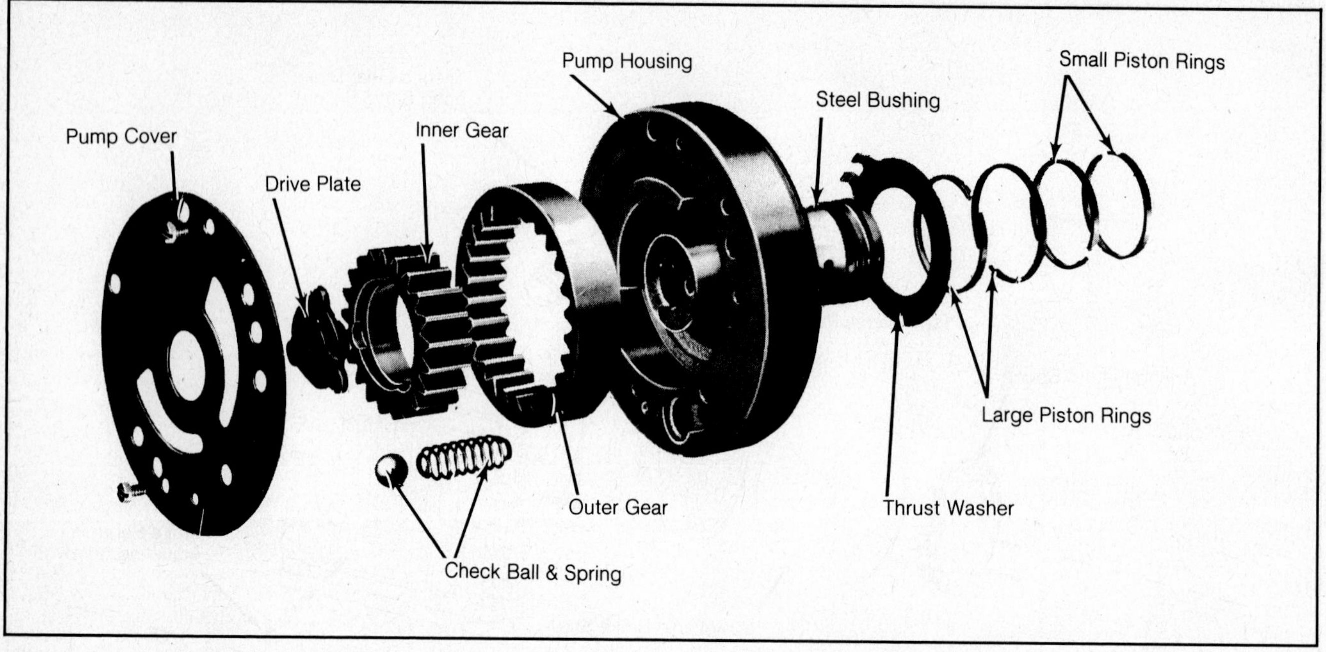

2) Lubricate piston seals with ATF, then install them into clutch drum with lips facing into drum. Using stiff plastic sheet to protect piston seals, install piston into drum using twisting motion.

3) Position piston return springs on piston. Place spring retainer on springs, compress retainer and install snap ring. New lined clutch plates (internally splined) should be soaked in ATF for 15 minutes before installing. Use only lined plates with identification grooves as shown. *See Fig. 9.*

4) Install clutch plates into clutch drum starting with steel (externally splined) plate. Alternate lined and steel plates until all clutch plates are installed. Install pressure plate and clutch pack retaining snap ring.

DIRECT/REVERSE CLUTCH PLATES

Application	Steel Plates	Lined Plates
087 Series	4	4
089 Series	3	3

5) Measure clearance between pressure plate and retaining snap ring. *See Fig. 10.* Clearance should be .081-.098" (2.05-2.50 mm). If not, remove clutch pack snap ring and replace with snap ring of correct thickness to bring clearance within specification.

6) Direct/Reverse clutch pack retaining snap rings are available in thicknesses from .059" (1.5 mm) to

Fig. 8: Exploded View of Model 089 Direct/Reverse Clutch Assembly

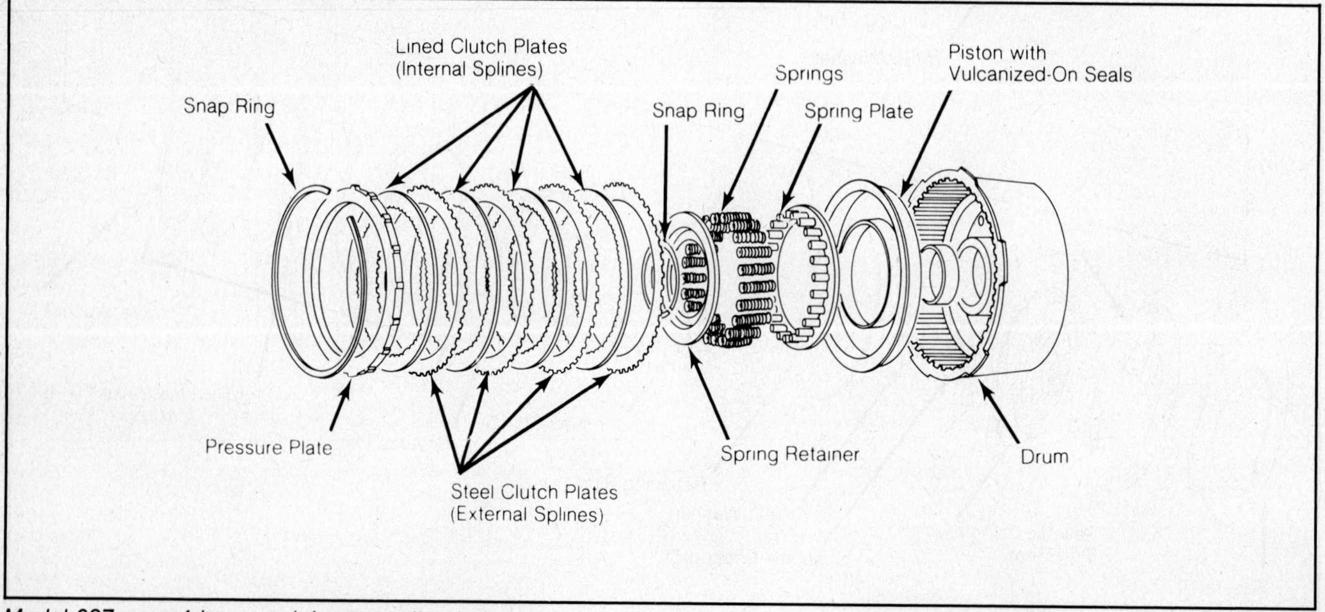

Model 087 uses 4 inner and 4 outer splined plates.

Fig. 9: Direct/Reverse Clutch Lined Plate

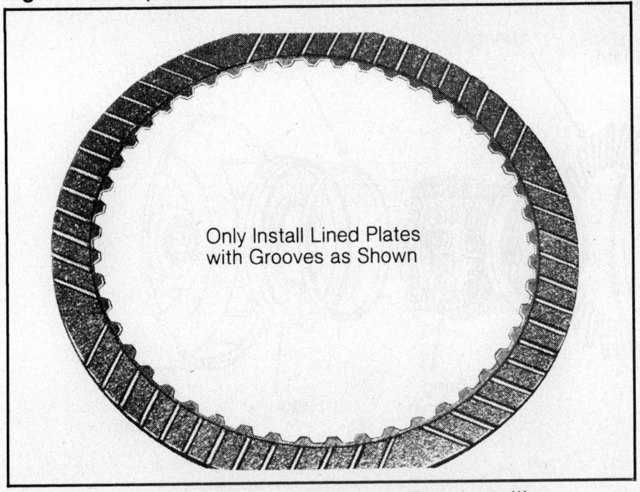

Soak new plates in ATF for 15 min. before installing.

Fig. 10: Measuring Direct/Reverse Clutch Clearance

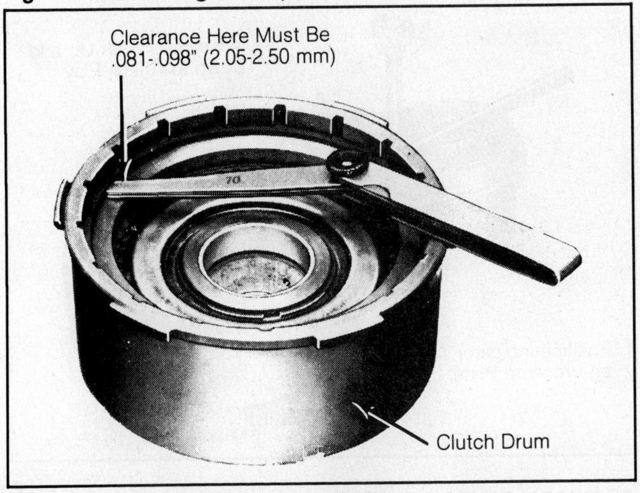

Change snap ring to adjust clearance.

.098" (2.5 mm). Install correct thickness clutch pack retaining snap ring. Recheck clutch pack clearance.

FORWARD CLUTCH

Disassembly

1) Using screwdriver, pry clutch pack retaining snap ring from clutch drum. Withdraw pressure plate, forward planetary ring gear, lined and steel clutch plates, and thrust plate.

2) On E-Mode series, remove spring washer, spring, spring plate, spring retaining ring with springs, spring support ring and snap ring. *See Fig. 12.*

3) On all other series, carefully pry out diaphragm spring snap ring. Remove diaphragm spring. Lift clutch piston. If necessary, use compressed air to force clutch piston from drum. *See Fig. 11.*

Cleaning & Inspection

1) Inspect clutch drum for scoring, wear, or other damage. Check clutch drum ball valve for free movement and ensure that drilling is clear. On E-Mode series, inspect all springs for wear or damage.

2) On all other series, inspect diaphragm spring and piston for damage. Place diaphragm spring onto piston and ensure that top of spring reaches at least to lower edge of snap ring groove. If not, replace spring.

NOTE: **Forward clutch piston sealing lips are vulcanized to piston. Replace entire piston if there is damage to sealing lip or if there is leakage past sealing lips.**

3) Use direct-reverse clutch inspection procedures to inspect lined and steel clutch plates. If new lined (internally splined) clutch plates are to be installed, soak them in ATF for 15 minutes before installing.

Reassembly

1) Lubricate piston sealing lips with ATF. Install piston into drum using twisting motion. On all series except E-Mode, install diaphragm spring, with convex side toward piston, into clutch drum. Install retaining snap ring.

2) With snap ring installed, diaphragm spring should be lightly tensioned; if not, replace spring. Install

Fig. 11: Exploded View of Standard Forward Clutch Assembly

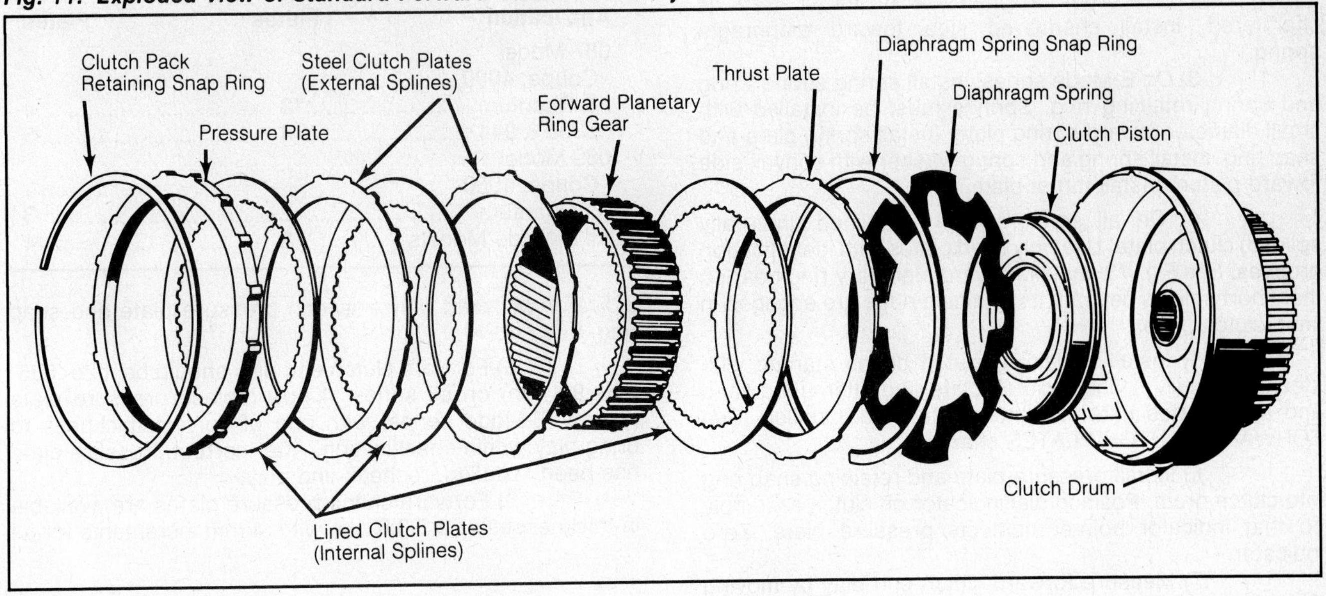

Fig. 12: Exploded View of E-Mode Forward Clutch Assembly

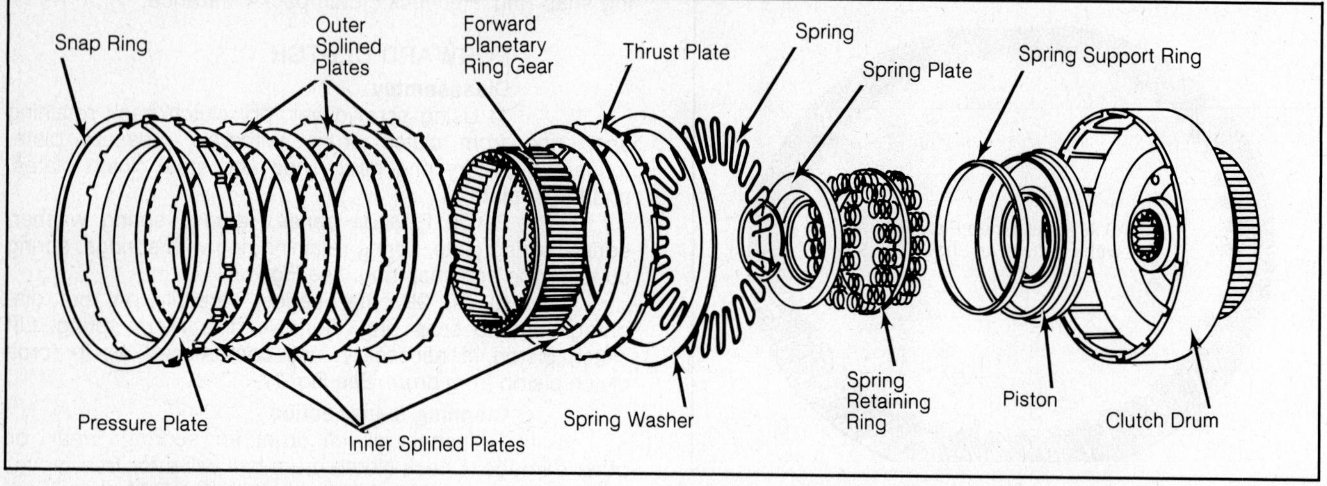

Fig. 13: Forward Clutch Lined Plate

Soak new friction plates in ATF for 15 minutes before installing.

thrust plate into drum. If one side of thrust plate is chamfered, install chamfered side toward diaphragm spring.

3) On E-Mode series, install spring support ring and spring retaining ring. Springs must be installed with small diameter toward spring plate. Install spring plate and snap ring. Install spring and spring washer with convex side toward piston. Install thrust plate.

4) On all series, install one lined (internally splined) clutch plate. Use only lined plates with identification grooves. *See Fig. 13.* Install forward planetary ring gear so that short splines beneath its retaining ridge are engaged in lined clutch plate.

5) Install remaining clutch plates starting with steel (externally splined) clutch plate and alternating lined and steel plates until all clutch plates are installed. See FORWARD CLUTCH PLATES chart.

6) Install pressure plate and retaining snap ring into clutch drum. Position dial indicator on clutch assembly so that indicator pointer contacts pressure plate. Zero indicator.

7) Measure forward clutch end play by moving forward planetary ring gear up and down so that dial indicator will read play between pressure plate and snap ring. *See Fig. 14.*

Fig. 14: Measuring Forward Clutch End Play

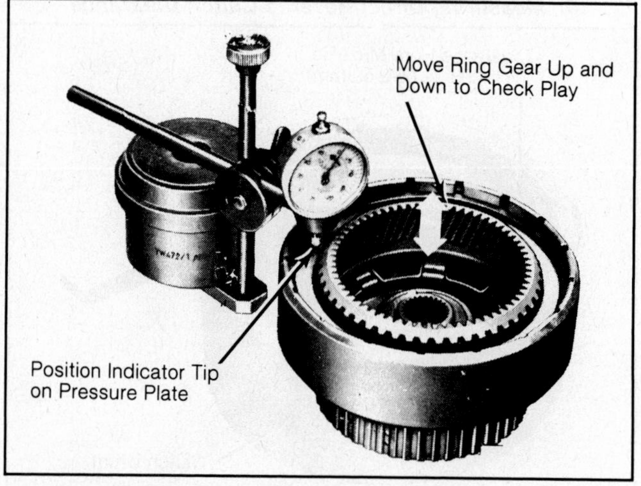

FORWARD CLUTCH PLATES

Application	Steel Plates	Lined Plates
087 Model		
Coupe, 4000 & Quantum	3	4
5000 & 944	4	5
089 Model		
Coupe, 4000 & Quantum	2	3
All E-Mode Models	3	4

8) Forward clutch end play should be .020-.035" (.50-.90 mm) on all series. If not, replace pressure plate (except E-Mode series) with one of correct thickness to bring play within specification. After correct pressure plate has been installed, recheck end play.

9) Forward clutch pressure plates are available in thicknesses of 2.3-3.9 mm with .4 mm increments for all

087 series except for those in Quantum vehicles. Quantum 087 series use pressure plates ranging from 6.0-7.6 mm with .4 mm increments.

10) On 5000S (087) series, both 2.3-3.9 mm and 6.0-7.6 mm ranges are available. On 089 series in Coupe GT, 4000S, 4000S Quattro and Quantum vehicles, forward clutch pressure plates are available in thicknesses of 6.0-7.6 mm with .4 mm increments.

11) All E-Mode transaxles adjust forward clutch end play by replacing snap ring. Snap rings are available in sizes 1.5 to 3.5 mm.

FIRST GEAR ONE-WAY CLUTCH

Disassembly

Remove one-way clutch rollers and spring. Remove snap rings. Using plastic hammer, carefully drive roller cage out of outer race.

Cleaning & Inspection

Inspect all parts for wear, scoring, or other damage and replace parts as necessary.

Reassembly

1) Install lower snap ring in groove of outer race. Heat outer race to 300-375°F (150-190°C), then place roller cage into race using 2 pair of pliers.

CAUTION: Heat from outer race will transfer quickly to roller cage, causing cage to stick inside race. If cage is not correctly positioned against lower snap ring and inside race, DO NOT attempt to press it into position after cage has stuck. Carefully knock cage out of outer race and repeat procedure again after race has cooled down.

2) Ensure short sides of retaining lugs on cage are positioned correctly against shoulders in outer ring. *See Fig. 15.* If necessary, turn cage slightly immediately after installation. Install upper snap ring, rollers, and springs.

Fig. 15: Installing Cage Into Outer Race

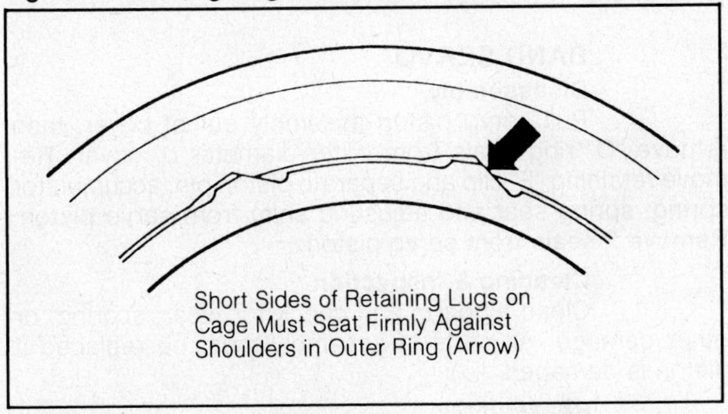
Short Sides of Retaining Lugs on
Cage Must Seat Firmly Against
Shoulders in Outer Ring (Arrow)

Heat outer race to 300°F (150°C).

REVERSE PLANETARY RING GEAR

NOTE: Disassemble reverse planetary ring gear only if replacing component part.

Disassembly, Cleaning & Inspection

Remove snap ring and lift ring gear hub from ring gear. Inspect parking lock notches on ring gear for wear. Replace if worn.

Fig. 16: Exploded View of One-Way Clutch

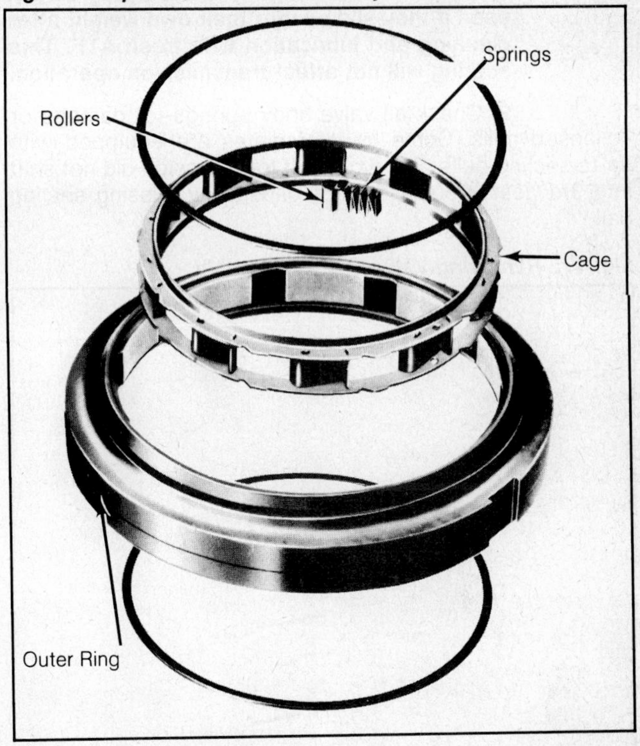
Springs
Rollers
Cage
Outer Ring

Reassembly

To reassemble, reverse disassembly procedure.

VALVE BODY ASSEMBLY

CAUTION: As valve body components are removed from each valve body bore, place individual parts in Holding Tray (2008) in correct order to simplify reassembly. This tray holds springs and valves in correct order and location. DO NOT interchange valves or valve springs. Several valve springs have identical dimensions but different tolerances. Individual valve body components are not available. Valve bodies are available only as exchange units.

Disassembly

1) Remove screws attaching transfer plate to main valve body. Lift transfer plate and separator plate from main valve body. Remove main valve body check balls from passages in valve body. *See Fig. 17.*

CAUTION: DO NOT alter settings of adjusting screws. Adjusting screws change pressures and can only be properly adjusted on test stand.

2) Remove rear end cover plate and withdraw valves, springs, and adjusting screws. Remove remaining end plates one at time and withdraw all valves, plugs, springs and adjusting screws. Tag all parts for reassembly reference or use Holding Tray (2008) to hold parts. This tray holds springs and valves in correct order and location.

Cleaning & Inspection

1) Wash all parts in clean solvent and dry them with compressed air. DO NOT use rags or water. Lint from rags can cause problems with ATF flow after reassembly. Check all parts for burrs and scores. Replace assembly if damaged.

Automatic Transmissions

AUDI 087, 087E, 089 (Cont.)

NOTE: Valves which are slightly scored may be reused if they slide under their own weight after cleaning and lubrication with fresh ATF. This scoring will not affect transmission operation.

2) Check all valve body springs for damage or collapsed coils. Some transfer plates are equipped with three sealing balls. *See Fig. 18.* If transmission did not shift into 3rd gear, trouble may be caused by missing sealing ball.

Fig. 17: Removing Valve Body Assembly

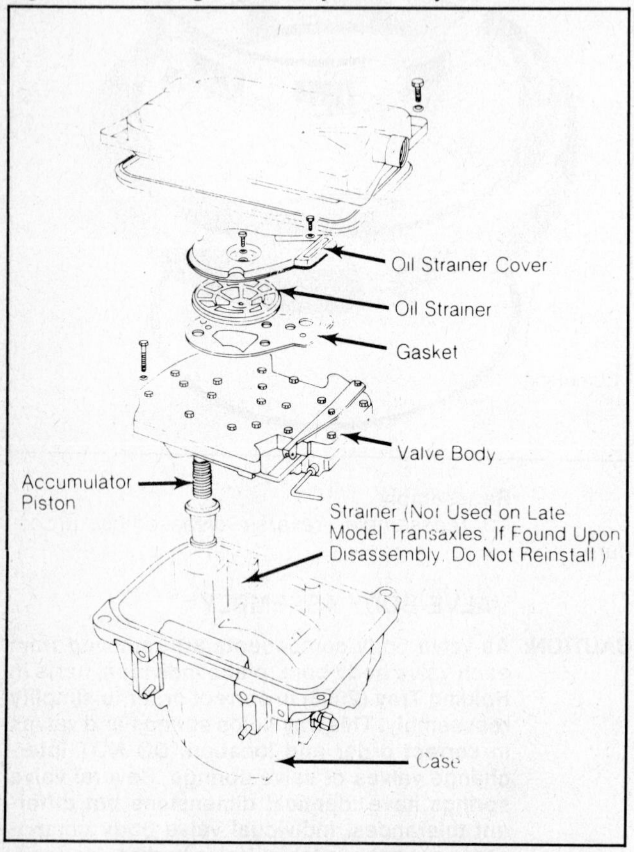

3) To install new sealing balls, stick .118" (3 mm) diameter sealing ball on 8 mm diameter punch with small amount of grease and drive ball flush into hole of transfer plate.

Reassembly

1) Lubricate all parts with ATF and install into proper valve body bores in reverse order of disassembly. DO NOT overtighten plate attaching screws. Overtightening can strip threads or distort valve body enough to cause valve to stick.

2) Ensure all check balls are installed in proper valve body passages. Check ball "A" is .12" (3 mm) in diameter. All other check balls are .24" (6 mm) in diameter. *See Fig. 17.* Install screws attaching transfer plate to main valve body, and tighten from center outward. DO NOT overtighten.

GOVERNOR ASSEMBLY

NOTE: Governor is mounted in final drive assembly.

Removal

Remove cover bolts and washers. Remove governor cover and "O" ring from final drive housing. Withdraw governor from housing with clockwise turning motion to allow governor drive gear to disengage from drive pinion gear.

Fig. 18: Sealing Balls in Valve Body Transfer Plate

Sealing Balls are Installed in Holes Indicated by Large Arrows
To Install New Sealing Balls, Drive into Hole With an 8 mm Punch

Disassembly

Remove 2 attaching screws and withdraw thrust plate and governor housing. Remove transfer plate (noting position), balance weight and oil strainer (if equipped). Remove "E" clip and pull centrifugal weight, valve, spring and dished washer from pin.

Reassembly

Reverse disassembly procedure and lubricate all parts with ATF when reassembling. Transfer plate must be reinstalled in same position. DO NOT reinstall oil strainer. Be sure angle in thrust plate is in center of housing so cover will bear against it.

Installation

Check governor oil seal and needle bearing in housing for damage or wear. Replace if necessary. Reverse removal procedure to install. Rotate governor to engage drive gear.

BAND SERVO

Disassembly

Pull servo piston assembly out of cover, then remove "O" ring seals from outer diameter of cover. Remove retaining "E" clip and separate piston pin, accumulator spring, spring seat and adjusting shim from servo piston. Remove 2 seals from servo piston.

Cleaning & Inspection

Clean all parts and check for wear, scoring, or other damage. All parts in assembly must be replaced if piston is damaged.

Reassembly

1) Position spring seat, accumulator spring and shim on piston pin. Install assembly into servo piston and install retaining "E" clip onto pin.

2) Install lip seals onto piston with smaller (upper) seal with lip facing upward into servo cover. Larger seal is positioned with lip facing downward, out of servo cover.

3) Lubricate assembly thoroughly and install piston into cover. Install "O" rings on outer diameter of servo cover.

Automatic Transmissions

AUDI 087, 087E, 089 (Cont.)

Fig. 19: Exploded View of E-Mode Valve Body

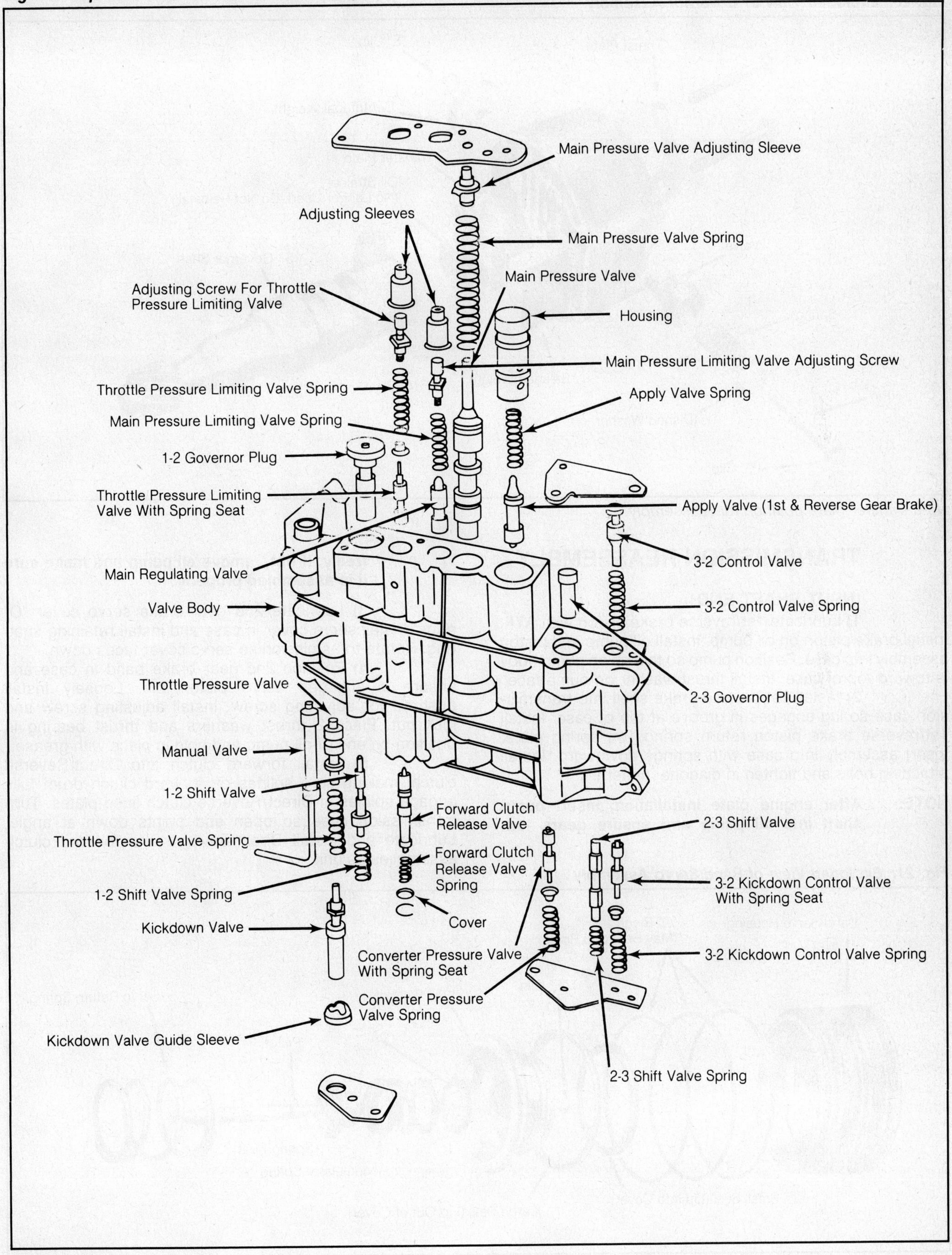

All other models are similar.

AUDI 087, 087E, 089 (Cont.)

Fig. 20: Exploded View of Governor Assembly

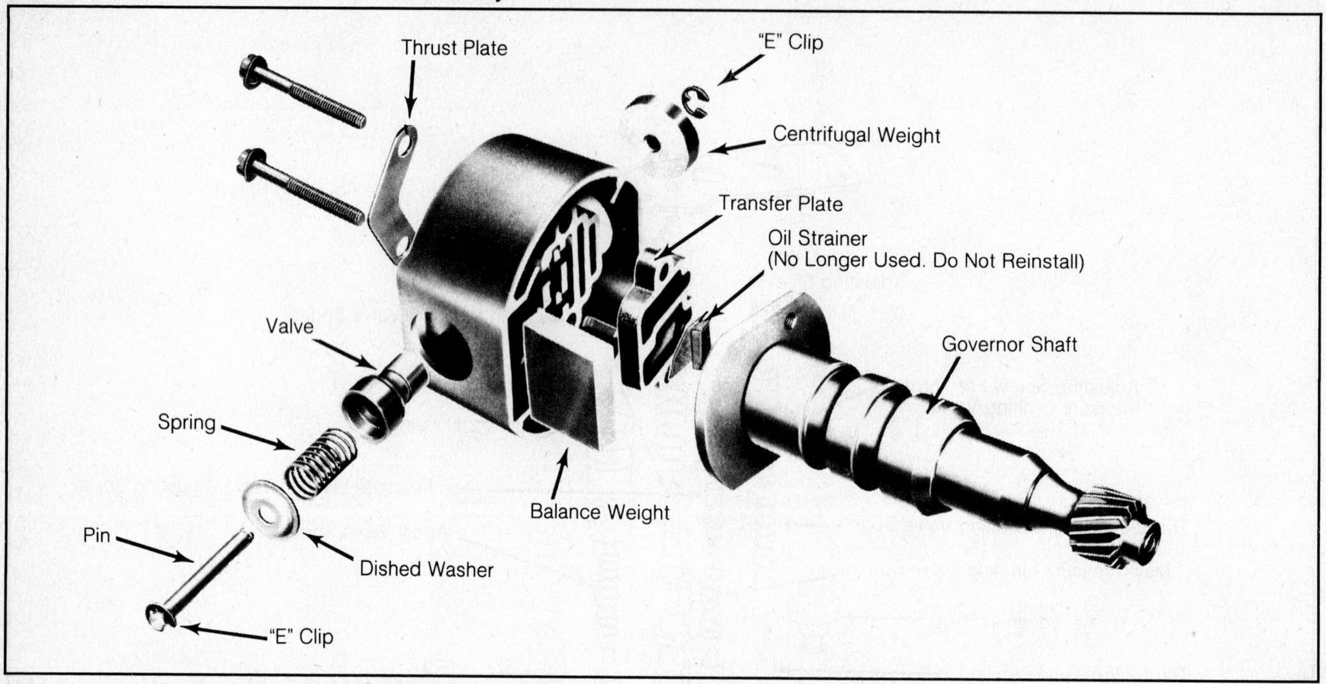

Note transfer plate position for reassembly.

TRANSMISSION REASSEMBLY

INPUT SHAFT END

1) Lubricate 1st/reverse brake piston with ATF. Install brake piston on oil pump. Install oil pump and piston assembly into case. Position pump so thin rib on pump body is toward top of case. Install thrust washer on pump face.

2) Install 1st/reverse brake shell into transmission case so lug engages in groove at top of case. Install 1st/reverse brake piston return springs on spring plate. Insert assembly into case with springs downward. Install attaching bolts and tighten in diagonal pattern.

NOTE: After engine plate installation, insert pump shaft into oil pump and ensure gears turn freely. If not, remove oil pump and make sure it is assembled properly.

3) Lubricate 2nd gear brake servo cover "O" rings. Install serve cover in case and install retaining snap ring. Rotate transmission so servo cover faces down.

4) Position 2nd gear brake band in case and ensure it engages servo piston pin. Loosely install pushrod for adjusting screw. Install adjusting screw and lock nut. Place 2 thrust washers and thrust bearing in position on end of oil pump and hold in place with grease.

5) Install forward clutch into Direct/Reverse clutch, making sure splines on forward clutch drum fully engage splines in Direct/Reverse clutch lined plates. Turn transmission case so open end points down at angle. Lubricate and install Direct/Reverse and forward clutch assemblies as unit.

Fig. 21: Exploded View of Band Servo Assembly

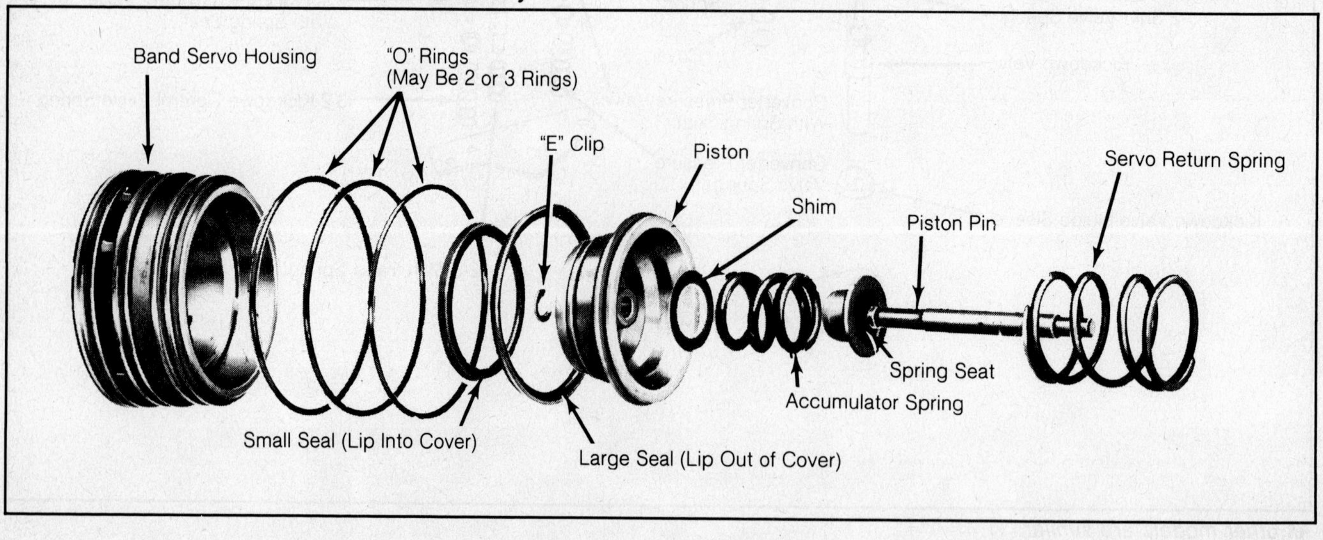

AUDI 087, 087E, 089 (Cont.)

Fig. 22: Installing Brake Shell in Transmission Case

Lug Must Engage
Groove at Top of Case

6) Slide clutch assembly unit onto oil pump neck and into 2nd gear brake band. Tighten 2nd gear brake band adjusting screw just enough to prevent band from shifting its position on direct/reverse clutch drum. Rotate transmission case so open end is up.

7) Install forward planetary-to-forward clutch needle bearing into forward clutch. Needle bearing is installed with smaller inside diameter toward forward planetary gear.

8) Install forward planetary gear set into forward planetary ring gear in forward clutch. Install sun gear (short end first) into gear set. Install driving shell and thrust washer over sun gear. Install thrust washers on underside of reverse planetary gear set and hold in place with grease.

9) Install gear set into case and onto sun gear. Install 1st/reverse brake waved washer into case. Install 1st/reverse brake plates into case, starting with steel (externally splined) brake plate. Alternate lined and steel plates until all are installed. See 1st/REVERSE BRAKE PLATES chart.

1st/REVERSE BRAKE PLATE

Application	Steel Plates	Lined Plates
087 Models	5	5
089 Models	4	4

NOTE: **New lined clutch plates must be soaked in ATF for 15 minutes before installing. Manufacturer states that new valve body must be used with new 1st/reversed lined plates.**

10) Install 1st gear one-way clutch assembly into transmission case. Insert retaining key between case and one-way clutch. Push clutch downward while rotating reverse planetary gear set to fully engage parts.

NOTE: **With one-way clutch installed, it should not be possible to rotate reverse planetary gear set counterclockwise due to locking of one-way clutch.**

11) Install one-way clutch-to-case snap ring. Snap ring opening must be opposite to retaining key. If all parts are correctly installed, one-way clutch snap ring groove will be exposed. Do not force snap ring into groove of incorrectly assembled transmission.

12) Position thrust washer and needle bearing on rear side of reverse planetary gear set. Larger inside diameter collar faces towared reversee planetary gear set. Install reverse planetary ring gear into case so it fully engages reverse planetary gear set.

13) Install new separation plate gasket over case studs and place separation plate over gasket. Install and tighten retaining screws.

NOTE: **Second gear brake band must be adjusted at this time. Transmission case must be horizontal during adjustment to prevent band from jamming.**

14) Tighten brake band adjusting screw to 87 INCH lbs. (10 N.m). Loosen screw. Retighten to 43 INCH lbs. (5 N.m). Back off adjusting screw exactly 2 1/2 turns on 089 models and on 087 models found in 5000 vehicles. Back off adjusting screw exactly 2 turns on all other 087 models. Tighten adjusting screw lock nut.

15) If case linkage was disassembled, reinstall in case. *See Fig. 5.* Install accumlator piston with seal lip pointing toward case. Install accumulator piston spring in piston.

16) Install valve body assembly into case, making sure manual valve engages manual lever and kickdown valve engages kickdown lever. Install valve body-to-case bolts and tighten from center outward.

17) Position new pan gasket on transmission case. Install oil pan and tighten oil pan bolts.

NOTE: **See FINAL DRIVE ASSEMBLY for installatin of turbine and pump shaft and measurement of play between transmission and final drive.**

FINAL DRIVE ASSEMBLY

DISASSEMBLY

NOTE: **Backlash and turning torque should be measured and recorded before final drive disassembly. If parts are used again, set backlash and turning torque to same values as measured. See Pinion Shaft Turning Torque and Pinion Depth and Bearing Preload procedures for measuring instructions.**

1) Place final drive housing in vise. Mark position of side bearing adjusting rings before removing. Remove governor assembly from final drive housing. Use slide hammer to remove governor oil seal and needle bearing together.

2) Remove ATF oil cooler from case. Remove final drive housing front cover. Use slide hammer to remove front cover if necessary. Remove pinion rear cover. Remove retaining bolt from center of each axle drive flange. Pull flanged shafts out of final drive housing.

3) Remove bolts and lock plates from adjusting rings. Remove adjusting rings with Spanner (VW 544). Pull pinion out slightly. Tilt differential case assembly with ring gear to one side and remove. Lift pinion shaft out of housing.

4) Place differential case assembly in soft jaw vise with ring gear attaching bolts up. Loosen attaching bolts and remove ring gear by tapping lightly on bolt head.

5) Remove pinion gears, side gears, thrust washers and nuts for axle shaft drive flange retaining bolts. Remove differential side bearings and speedometer drive gear (if equipped) with press or gear puller. Mark side bearings so that they may be reinstalled in same position and with matching outer race.

CAUTION: **If original shims are to be reused, note number and thickness of pinion adjusting shims on pinion shaft for reassembly reference. When pressing drive pinion bearings on or off, use extreme care to avoid damage to any teeth on shaft.**

6) Remove drive pinion bearings using press. Remove rear pinion bearing and oil sleeve together. Pinion bearing outer races and oil seals will also have to be replaced if pinion bearings are replaced. Remove torque converter seal from front cover. Remove front cover pinion seal.

7) Press pinion bearing outer race from front cover. Drive both pinion oil seals from rear cover using driver. Press pinion bearing outer race from rear cover using driver.

NOTE: **If pinion bearing outer races are being removed from both front and rear covers, be sure to keep races with their repective bearings.**

DIFFERENTIAL

Disassembly

1) Place differential case assembly in soft jaw vise with ring gear attaching bolts up. Loosen attaching bolts and remove ring gear by tapping lightly on bolt heads.

2) Remove pinion gears, side gears, thrust washers and nuts for axle shaft drive flange retaining bolts. Remove differential side bearings and speedometer drive gear (if equipped) with press or gear puller.

3) Mark side bearings so that they may be reinstalled in same position and with matching outer race.

CAUTION: **If original shims are to reused, note number and thickness of pinion adjusting shims on pinion shaft for reassembly reference. When pressing drive pinion bearings on or off, use extreme care to avoid damage to any teeth on shaft.**

TRANSAXLE REASSEMBLY & ADJUSTMENT

1) Lubricate 1st/Reverse brake piston with ATF. Install brake piston on oil pump. Install oil pump and piston assembly into case. Position pump so thin rib on pump body is toward top of case. Install thrust washer on pump face.

2) Install 1st/Reverse brake shell into transmission case so lug engages in groove at top of case. Install 1st/Reverse brake piston return springs on spring plate. Insert assembly into case with springs downward. Install attaching bolts and tighten in diagonal pattern.

NOTE: **After spring plate installation, insert pump shaft into oil pump and ensure gears turn freely. If not, remove oil pump and ensure it is assembled properly.**

3) Lubricate 2nd gear brake servo cover "O" rings. Install servo cover in case and install retaining snap ring. Rotate transmission so servo cover faces down.

4) Position 2nd gear brake band in case and ensure it engages servo piston pin. Loosely install pushrod for adjusting screw. Install adjusting screw and lock nut. Place 2 thrust washers and thrust bearing in position on end of oil pump and hold in place with grease.

5) Install forward clutch into Direct/Reverse clutch, making sure splines on forward clutch drum fully engage splines in Direct/Reverse clutch lined plates. Turn transmission case so open end points down at angle. Lubricate and install Direct/Reverse and forward clutch assemblies as unit.

6) Slide clutch assembly unit onto oil pump neck and into 2nd gear brake band. Tighten 2nd gear brake band adjusting screw just enough to prevent band from shifting its position on Direct/Reverse clutch drum. Rotate transmission case so open end is up.

7) Install forward planetary-to-forward clutch needle bearing into forward clutch. Needle bearing is installed with smaller inside diameter toward forward planetary gear.

8) Install forward planetary gear set into forward planetary ring gear in forward clutch. Install sun gear (short end first) into gear set. Install driving shell and thrust washer over sun gear. Install thrust washers on underside of reverse planetary gear set and hold in place with grease.

9) Install gear set into case and onto sun gear. Install 1st/Reverse brake waved washer into case. Install 1st/Reverse brake plates into case, starting with steel (externally splined) brake plate. Alternate lined and steel plates until all are installed. See 1st/REVERSE BRAKE PLATE chart.

1st/REVERSE BRAKE PLATE

Application	Steel Plates	Lined Plates
087 Series	5	5
089 Series	4	4

NOTE: **New lined clutch plates must be soaked in ATF for 15 minutes before installing. Manufacturer states that new valve body must be used with new 1st/Reverse lined plates.**

10) Install 1st gear one-way clutch assembly into transmission case. Insert retaining key between case and one-way clutch. Push clutch downward while rotating reverse planetary gear set to fully engage parts.

NOTE: **With one-way clutch installed, it should not be possible to rotate reverse planetary gear set counterclockwise due to locking of one-way clutch.**

11) Install one-way clutch-to-case snap ring. Snap ring opening must be opposite to retaining key. If all parts are correctly installed, one-way clutch snap ring groove will be exposed. Do not force snap ring into groove of incorrectly assembled transmission.

12) Position thrust washer and needle bearing on rear side of reverse planetary gear set. Larger inside diameter collar faces toward reverse planetary gear set. Install reverse planetary ring gear into case so it fully engages reverse planetary gear set.

13) Install new separation plate gasket over case studs and place separation plate over gasket. Install and tighten retaining screws.

AUDI 087, 087E, 089 (Cont.)

Fig. 23: Installing One-Way Clutch Snap Ring

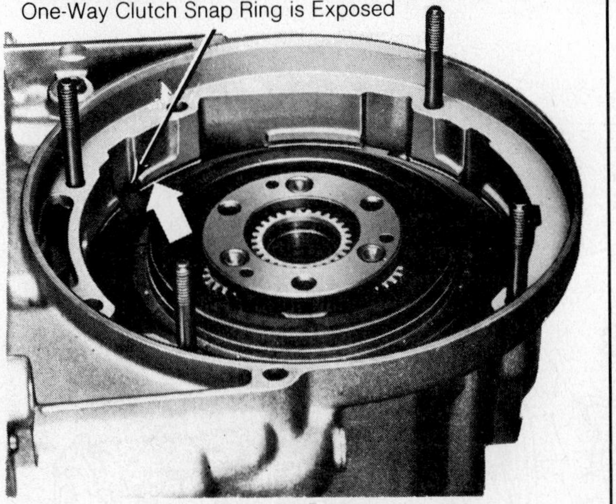

Parts are Installed Correctly if Groove for One-Way Clutch Snap Ring is Exposed

Opening of snap ring must be opposite retaining key (White arrow).

NOTE: **Second gear brake band must be adjusted at this time. Transmission case must be horizontal during adjustment to prevent band from jamming.**

14) Tighten brake band adjusting screw to 87 INCH lbs. (10 N.m). Loosen screw. Retighten to 43 INCH lbs. (5 N.m). Back off adjusting screw exactly 2 1/2 turns on 089 models and on 087 models found in 5000S vehicles. Back off adjusting screw exactly 2 turns on all other 087 models. Tighten adjusting screw lock nut.

15) If case linkage was disassembled, reinstall in case. *See Fig. 5*. Install accumulator piston with seal lip pointing toward case. Install accumulator piston spring in piston.

16) Install valve body assembly into case, making sure manual valve engages manual lever and kickdown valve engages kickdown lever. Install bolts attaching valve body to case, and tighten from center outward.

17) Position new pan gasket on transmission case. Install oil pan and tighten oil pan bolts.

NOTE: **See Final Drive Assembly for installation of turbine and pump shafts and for measurement of end play between transmission and final drive.**

FINAL DRIVE

DISASSEMBLY

NOTE: **Backlash and turning torque should be measured and recorded before final drive disassembly. If parts are used again, set backlash and turning torque to same values as measured. See Pinion Shaft Turning Torque and Pinion Depth and Bearing Preload procedures for measuring instructions.**

1) Place final drive housing in holding fixture. Mark position of side bearing adjusting rings before removing. Remove governor assembly from final drive housing. Use slide hammer to remove governor oil seal and needle bearing together.

2) Remove ATF oil cooler from case. Remove final drive housing front cover. Use slide hammer to remove front cover if necessary. Remove pinion rear cover. Remove retaining bolt from center of each axle drive flange. Pull flanged shafts out of final drive housing.

3) Remove bolts and lock plates from adjusting rings. Remove adjusting rings with Spanner (VW 544). Pull pinion out slightly. Tilt differential case assembly with ring gear to one side and remove. Lift pinion shaft out of housing.

4) Place differential case assembly in soft jaw vise with ring gear attaching bolts up. Loosen attaching bolts and remove ring gear by tapping lightly on bolt heads.

5) Remove pinion gears, side gears, thrust washers and nuts for axle shaft drive flange retaining bolts. Remove differential side bearings and speedometer drive gear (if equipped) with press or gear puller. Mark side bearings so that they may be reinstalled in same position and with matching outer race.

CAUTION: **If original shims are to be reused, note number and thickness of pinion adjusting shims on pinion shaft for reassembly reference. When pressing drive pinion bearings on or off, use extreme care to avoid damage to any teeth on shaft.**

6) Remove drive pinion bearings using press. Remove rear pinion bearing and oil sleeve together. Pinion bearing outer races and oil seals will also have to be replaced if pinion bearings replaced. Remove torque converter seal from front cover. Remove front cover pinion seal.

7) Press pinion bearing outer race from front cover. Drive both pinion oil seals from rear cover using driver. Press pinion bearing outer race from rear cover using driver.

NOTE: **If pinion bearing outer races are being removed from both front and rear covers, be sure to keep races with their respective bearings.**

REASSEMBLY & ADJUSTMENTS

Differential Assembly

1) Inspect all thrust surfaces on differential case, cover, ring gear, pinion shaft and thrust washers. Replace all worn parts. Inspect gear teeth for burrs and excessive wear. Replace as necessary.

NOTE: **If either pinion shaft or ring gear requires replacement, replace both as a set.**

2) Position differential side gears, large thrust washers, dished thrust washers and pinion gear into differential case. Align pinion gear holes with holes in case. Drive pinion shaft through pinion gears. If pinion shaft does not fit tightly, replace it.

3) Place differential cover on differential case. Install 2 centering pins in opposite ring gear attaching bolt holes. Heat ring gear to about 212°F (100°C), then position it on housing. Remove centering pins and tighten attaching bolts.

NOTE: **On 087 models with pressed on speedometer gear, new speedometer gear must be pressed onto differential case before side bearing installation.**

Automatic Transmissions

AUDI 087, 087E, 089 (Cont.)

Fig. 24: Exploded View of Final Drive Assembly

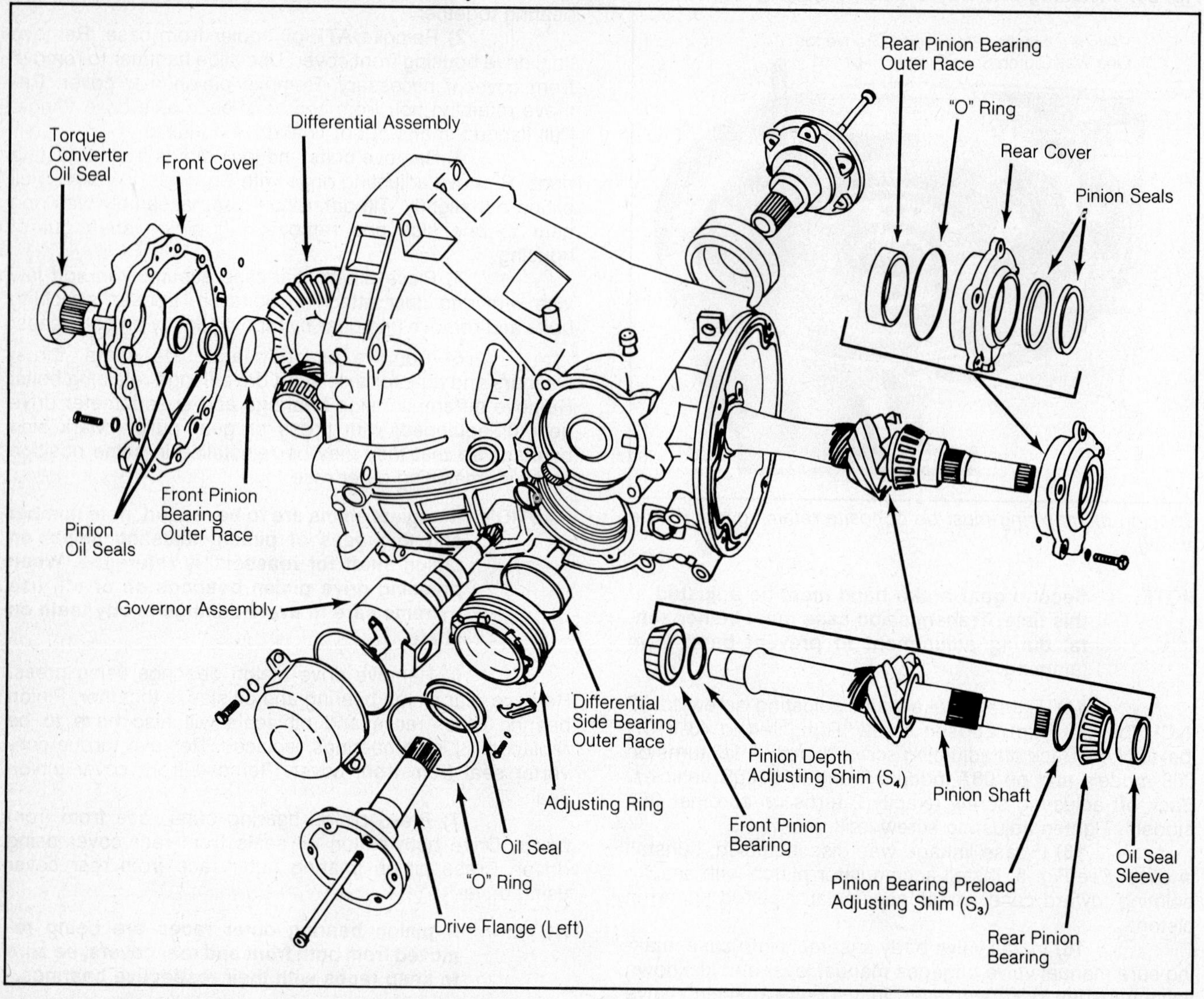

Fig. 25: Exploded View of 087 Model Differential Case Assembly

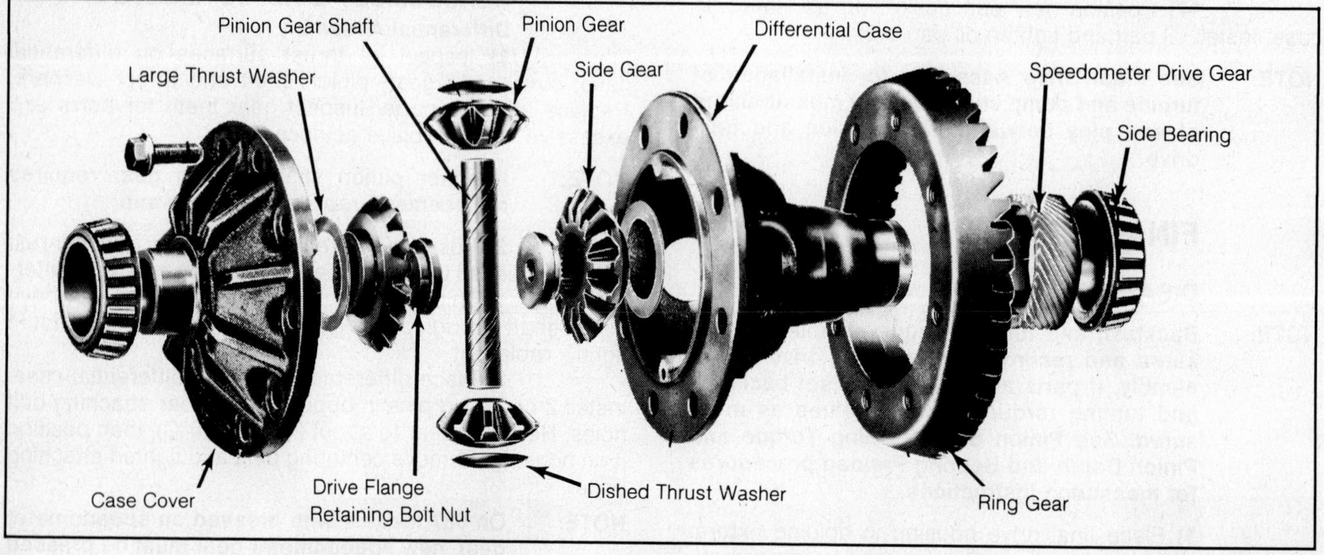

AUDI 087, 087E, 089 (Cont.)

Fig. 26: Measuring Pinion Shaft End Play

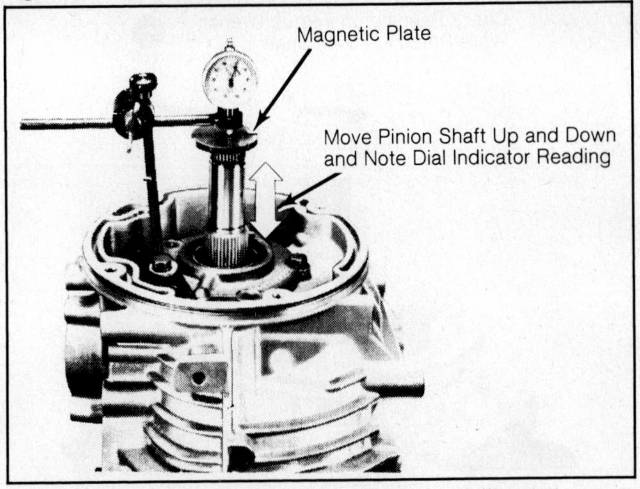

Turning drive pinion will cause incorrect reading.

4) Heat side bearings in hot oil and press them onto differential case and cover. Press side bearing outer races into position in side bearing adjusting rings.

NOTE: **If original parts are reused, use same thickness pinion depth and bearing preload adjusting shims as were removed during disassembly.**

Pinio Depth and Bearing Preload

1) Heat pinion shaft bearings to about 212°F (100°C) in oil bath. Press rear (larger) bearing onto shaft without any shim until seated at back of gear with 3 tons of pressure. Press front (smaller) bearing onto pinion shaft with 1.1 mm test shim installed behind bearing.

CAUTION: **If pinion shaft is installed into housing without this test shim installed, it will contact housing and cause incorrect reading.**

2) Install final drive housing front cover (without oil seals) and tighen attaching bolts. Position pinion shaft in place in housing. Install rear cover (without oil seals) and tighten attaching bolts.

3) Install Magnetic Plate (VW 385/17) onto rear end of pinion shaft. Attach dial indicator to final drive housing so indicator tip is touching magnetic plate on pinion shaft. Zero indicator. Move pinion shaft up and down (without turning) and note indicator setting.

CAUTION: **If pinion shaft is turned during measurement, readings will be incorrect due to settling of bearings.**

4) Add end play measured on dial indicator, plus .001" (.25 mm) for settling allowance (constant value), plus .006" (.15 mm) for bearing preload, plus .043" (1.1 mm) for thickness of test shim. Total is thickness of shims required to obtain proper pinion depth and bearing preload. Record total shim pack thickness.

5) Remove rear cover and pinion shaft from housing. Press front pinion bearing from shaft, remove test shim, and install shims equal to total thickness determined in step **4)**. Heat and press bearing back onto pinion shaft.

6) Reinstall pinion shaft in housing. Reinstall rear cover and tighten bolts. Turn pinion in both directions several times. Install Gauge Plate (VW 385/28) on pinion

Fig. 27: Installation of Measuring Tools for 089 Model Pinion Depth

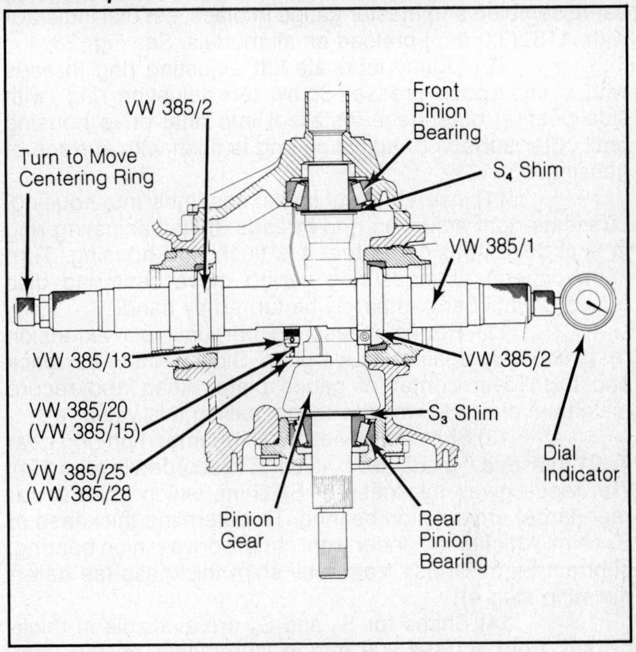

Tool numbers in parentheses are for 087 models.

shaft. *See Fig. 28.* Adjust clamp ring on Universal Measuring Bar (VW 385/1) until distance "A" is 3.23" (82 mm) for 087 models or 2.28" (58 mm) for 089 models. *See Fig. 29.*

Fig. 28: Measuring Tools for Pinion Depth Shim Selection

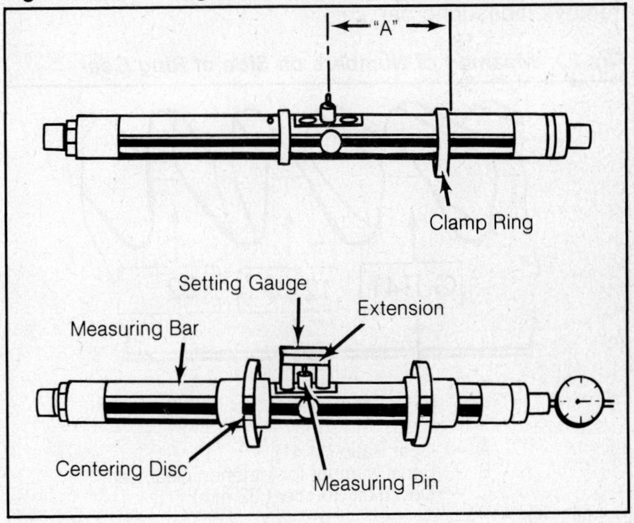

7) Assemble dial indicator, Centering Discs (VW 385/2), Measuring Pin (VW 385/13), Extension (VW 385/15 for 087 models; VW 385/20 for 089 models) and Master (Setting) Gauge to Measuring Bar (VW 385/1). Master gauge usage varies with model and is needed to adjust measuring bar. Universal Master Gauge (VW 385/30) will work for all models.

8) Universal master gauge sets measuring bar to "R_0", which is length of master gauge used in factory testing machine to measure deviation "R". Deviation "R" is found on side of ring gear and is always given in .01 mm. *See Fig. 29.* Different models have different "R_0" values.

9) All 087 models have "R_0" of 46.60 mm. All 089 models have "R_0" of 40.55 mm. Individual master gauges are available. All 087 models use Master Gauge (VW 385/26). All 089 models use Master Gauge (VW 385/5). With bar assembled and master gauge in place, set dial indicator with .118" (3.0 mm) preload on all models. *See Fig. 28.*

10) Lightly lubricate left adjusting ring threads with multipurpose grease. Screw left adjusting ring (with side bearing outer race installed) into final drive housing until outer surface of adjusting ring is flush with surface of housing.

11) Insert measuring bar assembly into housing. Lubricate right adjusting ring threads. Install adjusting ring in final drive housing so that it is flush with housing. Turn knob on end of measuring bar to move centering disc outward, until bar can barely be turned by hand.

12) Rotate measuring bar until pin extension rests squarely against gauge plate. Slowly rotate bar back and forth over center of gauge plate. Read and record maximum dial indicator deflection, calling this value "e".

13) Subtract deviation "R" (stamped on ring gear in .01 mm; *See Fig. 29.*) from value "E" (recorded in step **12)**). The result gives thickness of S_3 shim, which goes under rear (large) drive pinion bearing. To determine thickness of S_4 shim, which goes under front (small) drive pinion bearing, subtract S_3 thickness from total shim thickness (as determined in step **4)**).

14) Shims for S_3 and S_4 are available in thicknesses from 1.100-1.900 mm in increments of .025 mm. Measure selected shims at several points, and check for burrs or other damage. Install selected shims and bearings on drive pinion shaft. Install drive pinion in housing and lubricate bearings with hypoid oil.

15) Reinstall universal measuring bar and ensure indicator reading agrees with deviation "R", ±.04 mm. Remove measuring bar.

Fig. 29: Meaning of Numbers on Side of Ring Gear

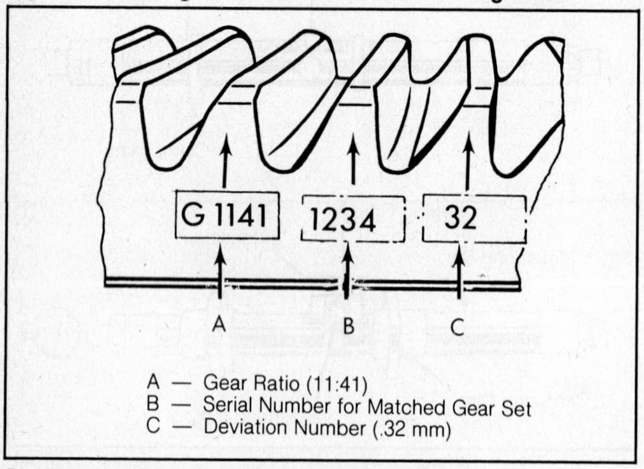

Deviation number is refered to as "R" in text.

Pinion Shaft Turning Torque

After installing correct pinion adjusting shims, check turning torque of pinion shaft. Turning torque for all models should be 22-49 INCH lbs. (2.5-5.5 Nm). If turning torque is incorrect, recheck shim thicknesses for proper bearing preload.

NOTE: Turning torque value is for new bearings only. If used bearings are reinstalled, turning torque should be same as that measured before disassembly.

Fig. 30: Checking Pinion Shaft Turning Torque

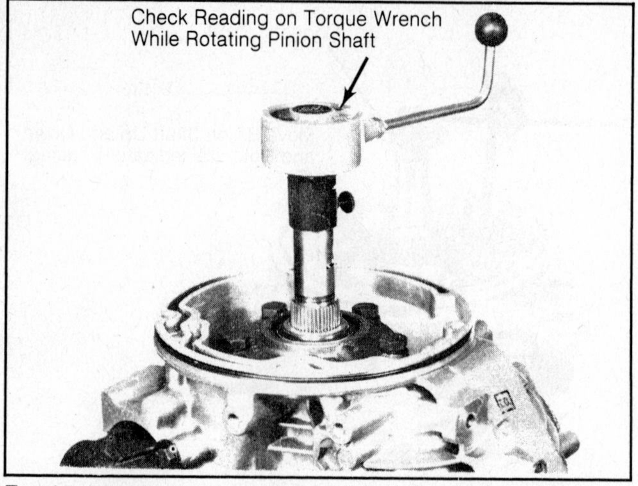

Turning torque should be 22-49 INCH lbs. (2.5-5.5 Nm) with new bearings.

Side Bearing Preload & Ring Gear Backlash

1) After adjusting pinion shaft depth and bearing preload, remove front and rear covers from final drive housing. Withdraw pinion shaft. Install differential assembly and pinion shaft into final drive housing.

2) Install new oil seals into front and rear covers. Install new "O" ring on rear cover. Lubricate "O" ring and pinion shaft bearings. Apply sealer to bolt flange of front cover. Install front and rear covers and tighten attaching bolts.

3) Install new "O" rings on differential side bearing adjusting rings. Lightly coat "O" rings and threads on adjusting rings with multi-purpose grease. Lubricate bearings with hypoid gear oil. Install each adjusting ring into housing until surfaces between tooth divisions are flush with housing surface.

4) Turn in right adjusting ring slowly until ring gear meshes fully with pinion gear without backlash. Screw in left adjusting ring (opposite ring gear) as far as possible. Preload left ring slightly to take play out of differential side bearings.

5) Turn right adjusting ring 1/2 tooth division out. Turn left adjusting ring 2 tooth divisions in. This should correctly set side bearing preload and ring gear backlash.

6) To check ring gear backlash, turn pinion shaft several times in both directions to settle bearings. Using Holding Fixture (VW 386a), clamp pinion shaft so that it cannot turn.

7) Insert Clamping Sleeve (VW 521/4) with Slotted Sleeve (VW 521/7 on 089 models; 521/8 on 087 models) into differential through adjusting ring and secure with nut. Adjust length of Backlash Measuring Bar (VW 388) to 2.44" (62 mm) on 089 models or to 2.68" (68 mm) on 087 models.

NOTE: See Fig. 32 and 33 for assembly and positioning of ring gear backlash measuring tools.

8) Attach Measuring Bar (VW 388) to Clamping Sleeve (VW 521/4). Install dial indicator with Square End Extension (VW 382/10) in Holder (VW 387) and attach holder to final drive housing.

NOTE: Dial indicator tip must be located at right angle to backlash measuring lever.

AUDI 087, 087E, 089 (Cont.)

Fig. 31: ***Adjusting Side Bearing Preload and Ring Gear Backlash***

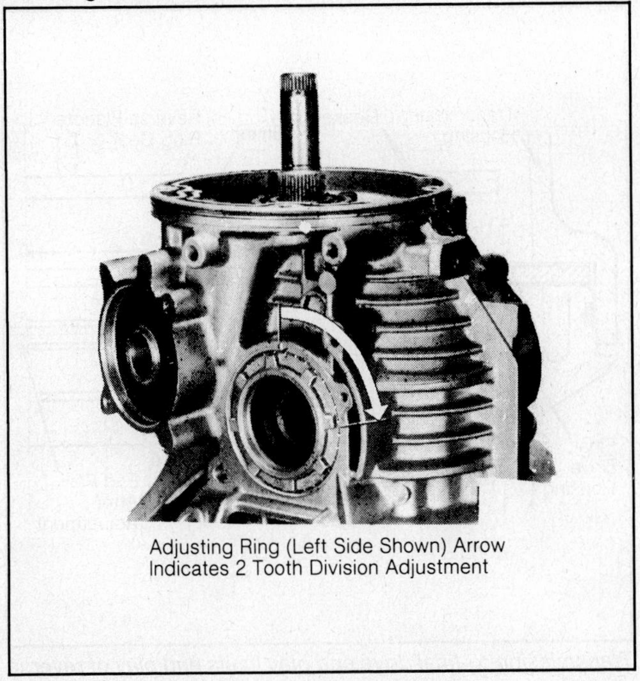

Adjusting Ring (Left Side Shown) Arrow
Indicates 2 Tooth Division Adjustment

Use Spanner (VW 544) to turn adjusting rings.

Fig. 32: ***Adjusting Measuring Bar Length for Ring Gear Backlash Check***

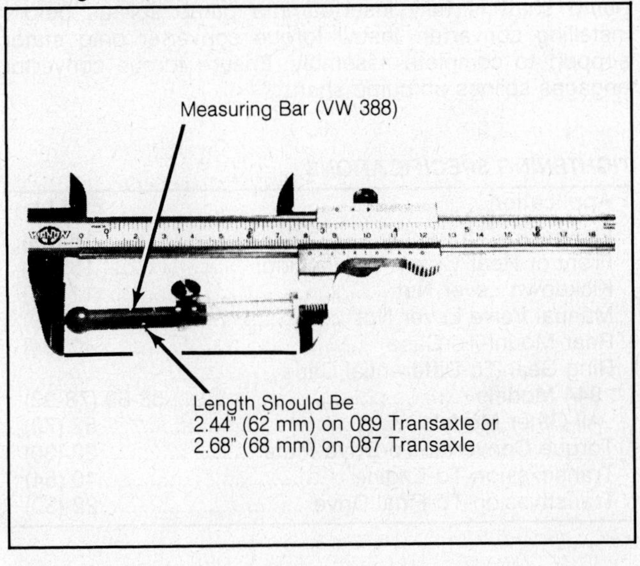

9) Turn ring gear to take up backlash. Zero dial indicator and clamp in holder. Turn ring gear in opposite direction until it touches pinion gear again and note indicator reading. This reading is ring gear backlash.

10) Check ring gear backlash at 4 locations (90° apart) around circumference of ring gear. Add 4 measurements together, then divide total by 4. Resulting figure is average ring gear backlash. Average ring gear backlash should be .006-.010" (.15-.25 mm).

NOTE: **Backlash specifications apply to new ring and pinion set. If ring and pinion are being reused, backlash should be set to same value as found prior to disassembly.**

Fig. 33: ***Positioning of Ring Gear Backlash Measuring Tools***

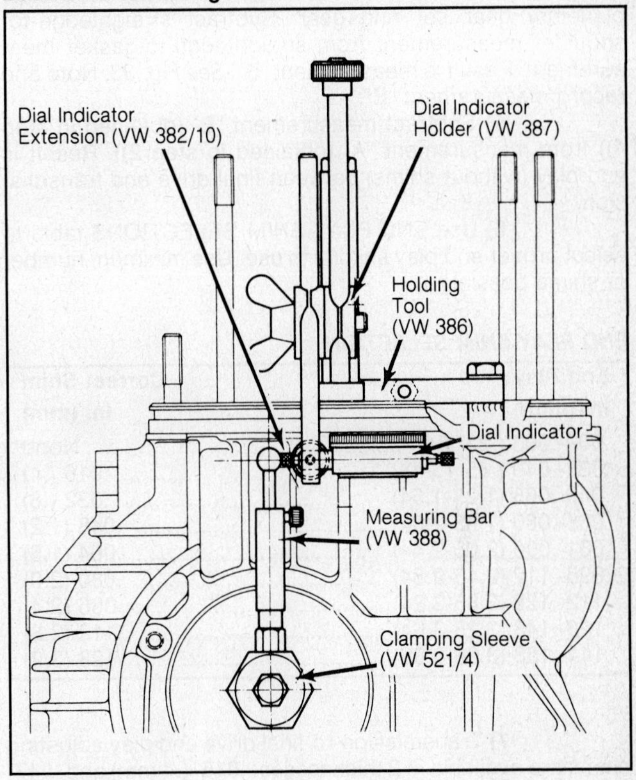

CAUTION: **Difference between individual backlash measurements must not exceed .002" (.05 mm). If measurements differ more than this, ring gear or pinion shaft is incorrectly installed.**

11) If backlash is not within specification, correct by turning both side bearing adjusting rings by equal amounts in opposite directions. Adjusting rings must be moved in equal amounts to maintain bearing preload.

NOTE: **If new differential side bearings have been installed, as well as new pinion shaft bearings, recheck pinion shaft turning torque. With differential installed, pinion shaft turning torque should be approximately 3.5-4.4 INCH lbs. (.4-.5 N.m) greater than it was when only pinion shaft was installed.**

12) Install side bearing adjusting ring lock plate. Recheck total bearing preload to ensure no alterations were made during backlash adjustment.

Final Assembly of Transaxle

1) To measure end play between final drive housing and transmission, place straightedge on transmission attaching face of final drive housing. Using depth gauge, measure distance from top surface of straightedge down to edge of pinion shaft oil seal sleeve.

2) Measure distance from top surface of straightedge to face of final drive housing. Subtract straightedge-to-face distance from straightedge-to-oil seal sleeve distance. Result is measurement "A". *See Fig. 34.* Note result for future reference.

3) With new gasket on transmission separation plate, position straightedge on transmission case. Measure distance from top surface of straightedge down to gasket surface.

4) Measure distance from top surface of straightedge down to shim surface on shoulder of reverse planetary gear set ring gear. Subtract straightedge-to-shoulder measurement from straightedge-to-gasket measurement. Result is measurement "B". *See Fig. 33.* Note and record measurement "B".

5) Subtract measurement "B" (obtained in step **4)**) from measurement "A" (obtained in step **2)**). Result is end play (without shims) between final drive and transmission.

6) Use END PLAY SHIM SELECTIONS table to select proper end play shim(s) to use. Use minimum number of shims possible.

END PLAY SHIM SELECTION

End Play In. (mm)	Correct Shim In. (mm)
.009-.003 (.23-.84)	None
.033-.049 (.85-1.24)	.016 (.4)
.049-.065 (1.25-1.64)	.032 (.8)
.065-.080 (1.65-2.04)	.048 (1.2)
.081-.096 (2.05-2.44)	.064 (1.6)
.096-.112 (2.45-2.84)	.080 (2.0)
.112-.128 (2.85-3.24)	.096 (2.4)
.128-.143 (3.25-3.64)	.112 (2.8)
.144-.153 (3.65-3.88)	.128 (3.2)

7) Transmission-to-final drive end play adjusting shims are available in 2 thicknesses: .016" (.4 mm) and .047" (1.2 mm). Combine shim thicknesses to obtain total thickness required. Install selected end play adjusting shim(s) on top of pinion shaft oil seal sleeve in final drive case.

8) Install "O" ring into groove around final drive housing. Install turbine shaft and pump shaft fully into pinion shaft of final drive. End of turbine shaft with piston rings must be toward transmission with rings inside pinion shaft.

9) Turbine shaft used in 087 models is 16.71" (424.5 mm) with 20.2" (513 mm) pump shaft. Turbine shaft used in 089 models is 15.82" (401.7 mm) with 19.32" (490.6 mm) pump shaft.

10) Join final drive case to transmission case. Install, and tighten, nuts attaching drive to transmission case. Drive governor needle bearing into final drive case until it bottoms, using Driver (VW 545). Using driver and Collar (VW 545/2), install governor oil seal with lip facing out toward governor. Place new "O" rings onto governor cover and speedometer driven gear assembly.

Fig. 34: Measuring End Play Between Transmission and Final Drive

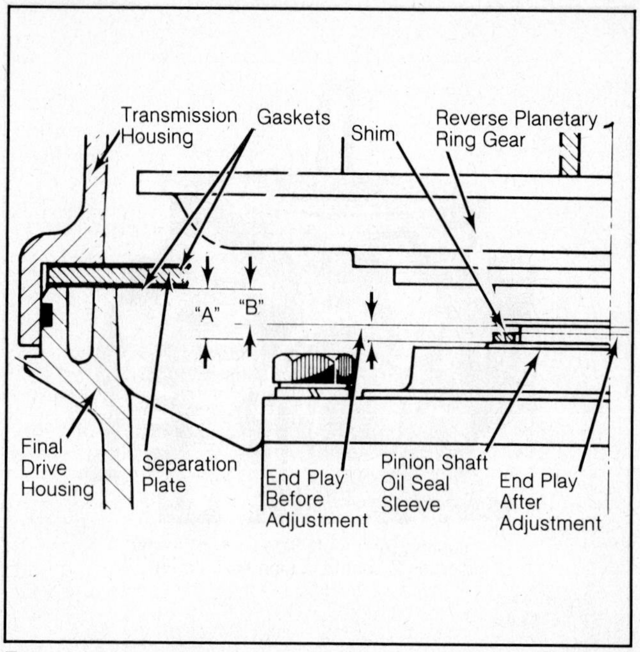

Transmission-to-final drive end play limits end play of reverse planetary ring gear.

11) Install governor, cover, and speedometer driven gear into case. Install transaxle oil cooler. Ensure pump shaft is fully inserted into pump splines before installing converter. Install torque converter onto stator support to complete assembly. Ensure torque convertor engages splines on pump shaft.

TIGHTENING SPECIFICATIONS

Application	Ft. Lbs.
Flange-To-Differential	18 (25)
Front or Rear Cover-To-Housing	18 (25)
Kickdown Lever Nut	11 (15)
Manual Valve Lever Nut	14 (19)
Rear Mount-To-Case	40 (54)
Ring Gear-To-Differential Case	
944 Models	58-69 (78-93)
All Other Models	52 (70)
Torque Converter-To-Drive Plate	22 (30)
Transmission-To-Engine	40 (54)
Transmission-To-Final Drive	22 (30)

Automatic Transmissions

BORG-WARNER MODEL 66

Jaguar XJ6

DESCRIPTION

Transmission is a fully automatic 3-speed unit consisting basically of a 3 element torque converter and a compound planetary gear set. Two multiple-disc clutches, one roller clutch, and two brake bands provide friction elements required to obtain desired function of planetary gear set. Hydraulic control system, pressurized by gear-type oil pump, provides working pressure required to operate automatic controls. Transmission kickdown is actuated by cable attached to accelerator assembly and a cam in transmission case.

LUBRICATION & ADJUSTMENTS

See appropriate AUTOMATIC TRANSMISSION SERVICING article in IMPORT GENERAL SERVICING section.

TROUBLE SHOOTING

ROUGH INITIAL ENGAGEMENT

Engine idle speed too high. Throttle cable out of adjustment. Valve body assembly faulty, valves sticking or worn.

NO ENGAGEMENT

In Any Position

Incorrect fluid level. Manual linkage out of adjustment. Throttle cable out of adjustment. Input shaft broken. Primary regulator valve sticking. Front pump worn.

In Forward Gears

Governor valve stuck or damaged. Output shaft seal rings or governor pressure tube seals worn or faulty. Also check front clutch, stator support shaft bearing, and front seal rings on sun gear shaft.

In 1st Gear in "D"

One-way clutch faulty or installed backwards.

In 2nd Gear

Front band faulty or out of adjustment. Front servo piston or seals worn or damaged. Oil pipes loose, damaged, or missing. Foreign matter or damage in valve body.

In 3rd Gear

Foreign matter in valve body or governor. Check rear clutch feed pipes, rear clutch, and piston rings in hub of intermediate shaft.

No Overrun Braking in "1"

Rear band out of adjustment or worn. Rear servo seals or feed pipes damaged or missing.

SLIPPING OR LATE SHIFTS

Throttle cable out of adjustment. Main pressure not within specifications (check oil pump and seals on pump tubes). Governor faulty. Valve body faulty. Check output

Fig. 1: Cross-Sectional View of Borg-Warner Model 66 Automatic Transmission

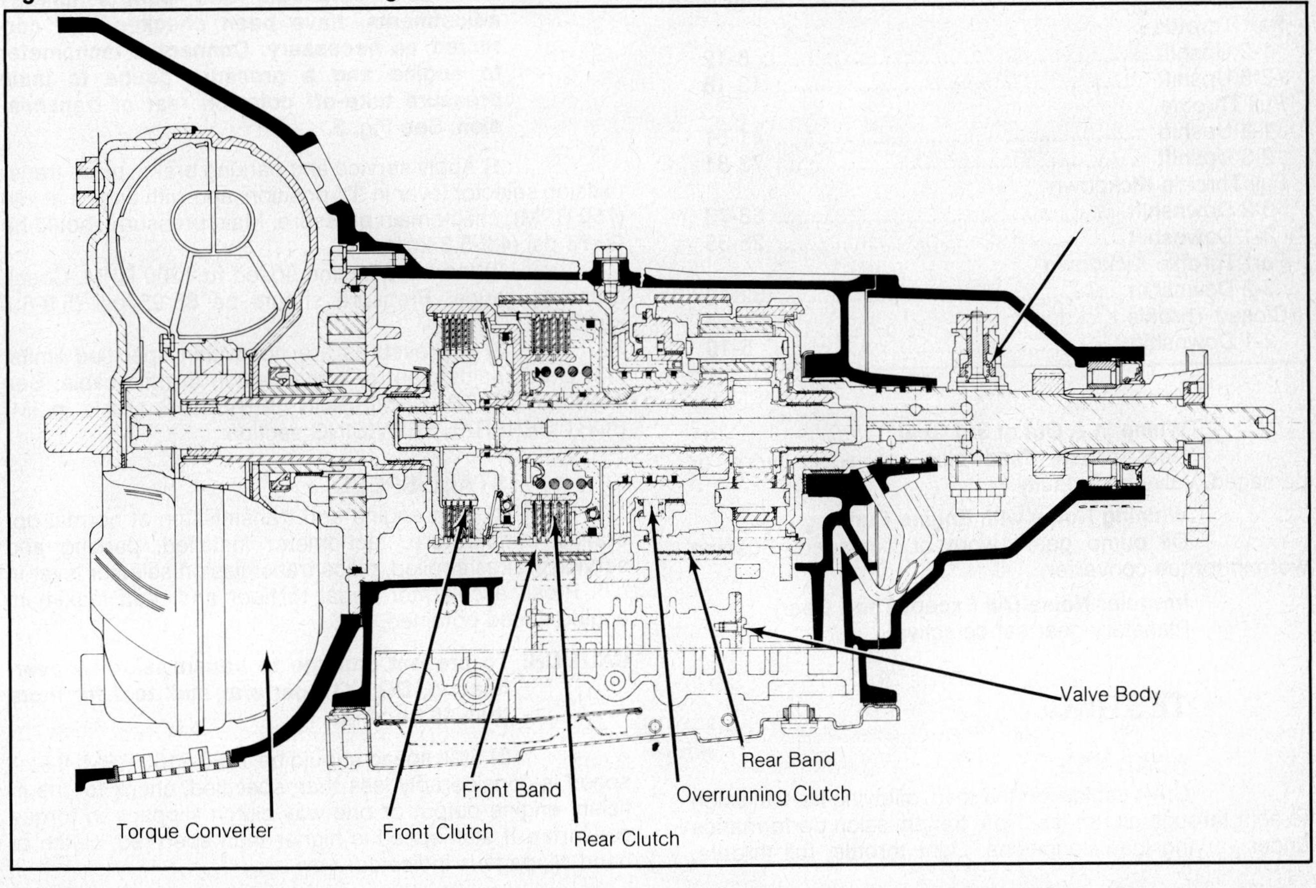

BORG-WARNER MODEL 66 (Cont.)

CLUTCH AND BAND APPLICATION CHART (ELEMENTS IN USE)

Selector Lever Position	Front Clutch	Rear Clutch	Front Band	Rear Band	One-Way Clutch
D - DRIVE					
First Gear	X				X
Second Gear	X		X		
Third Gear	X	X			
2 - INTERMEDIATE					
Second Gear	X		X		
1 - LOW	X			X	
R - REVERSE		X		X	

NEUTRAL OR PARK – All clutches, brakes, and bands released and/or ineffective.

shaft oil seal rings and governor tubes for wear or damage. Check front and rear bands and servos for wear or damage.

TRANSMISSION NOISE

Whine In & Out of 2nd Gear

Front band out of adjustment. Front servo parts worn or damaged. Oil pipes loose. Front band worn or damaged. Valve body faulty.

SHIFT SPEED SPECIFICATIONS

Shift Condition	MPH
Part Throttle	
1-2 Upshift	8-12
2-3 Upshift	13-18
Full Throttle	
1-2 Upshift	41-51
2-3 Upshift	73-81
Full Throttle Kickdown	
3-2 Downshift	63-73
3-1 Downshift	25-35
Part Throttle Kickdown	
3-2 Downshift	32-42
Closed Throttle Kickdown	
2-1 Downshift	5-10

Whine In & Out of 3rd Gear

Rear clutch, feed pipe, or seals worn or damaged. Valve body faulty.

Whining Noise with Engine Running

Oil pump gears worn or damaged. Bushing worn in torque converter.

Irregular Noise (All Except Third Gear)

Planetary gear set defective.

TESTING

ROAD TEST

Drive vehicle on the road, allowing transmission to shift through all ranges. Note transmission performance under varying load conditions: Light throttle, full throttle, and kickdown. Transmission should operate smoothly but firmly, with no apparent slipping or engine speed flare-up. Check for proper transmission shift points. See SHIFT SPEED SPECIFICATIONS table.

NOTE: **Shift speeds may vary slightly due to production tolerances, rear axle ratio, or tire size.**

HYDRAULIC PRESSURE TESTS

NOTE: **Before making pressure test, ensure fluid level and condition, and control linkage adjustments, have been checked and corrected as necessary. Connect a tachometer to engine and a pressure gauge to main pressure take-off point on rear of transmission. See Fig. 3.**

1) Apply service and parking brake, place transmission selector lever in "D" position, and with engine at idle (750 RPM), check main pressure. Main pressure should be 60-75 psi (4.2-5.3 kg/cm^2).

2) Increase engine speed to 1200 RPM. Check pressure gauge. Pressure should be 85-95 psi (5.9-6.7 kg/cm^2).

3) If pressures are not within specified limits, first check adjustment of transmission throttle cable. See AUTOMATIC TRANSMISSION SERVICING article in IMPORT GENERAL SERVICING section.

STALL SPEED

1) With engine and transmission at normal operating temperature, tachometer installed, parking and service brakes applied, place transmission selector lever in "D". Press accelerator pedal to floor and read maximum engine speed obtained.

CAUTION: **To prevent damage to transmission by overheating, DO NOT perform stall test for more than 10 seconds.**

2) Stall speed should be 1950-2100 RPM. If stall speed is considerably less than specified, check for insufficient engine output or one-way clutch slippage in torque converter. If stall speed is higher then specified, clutch or band slippage is indicated.

BORG-WARNER MODEL 66 (Cont.)

Fig. 2: Borg-Warner Model 66 Automatic Transmission Hydraulic Circuits Diagram

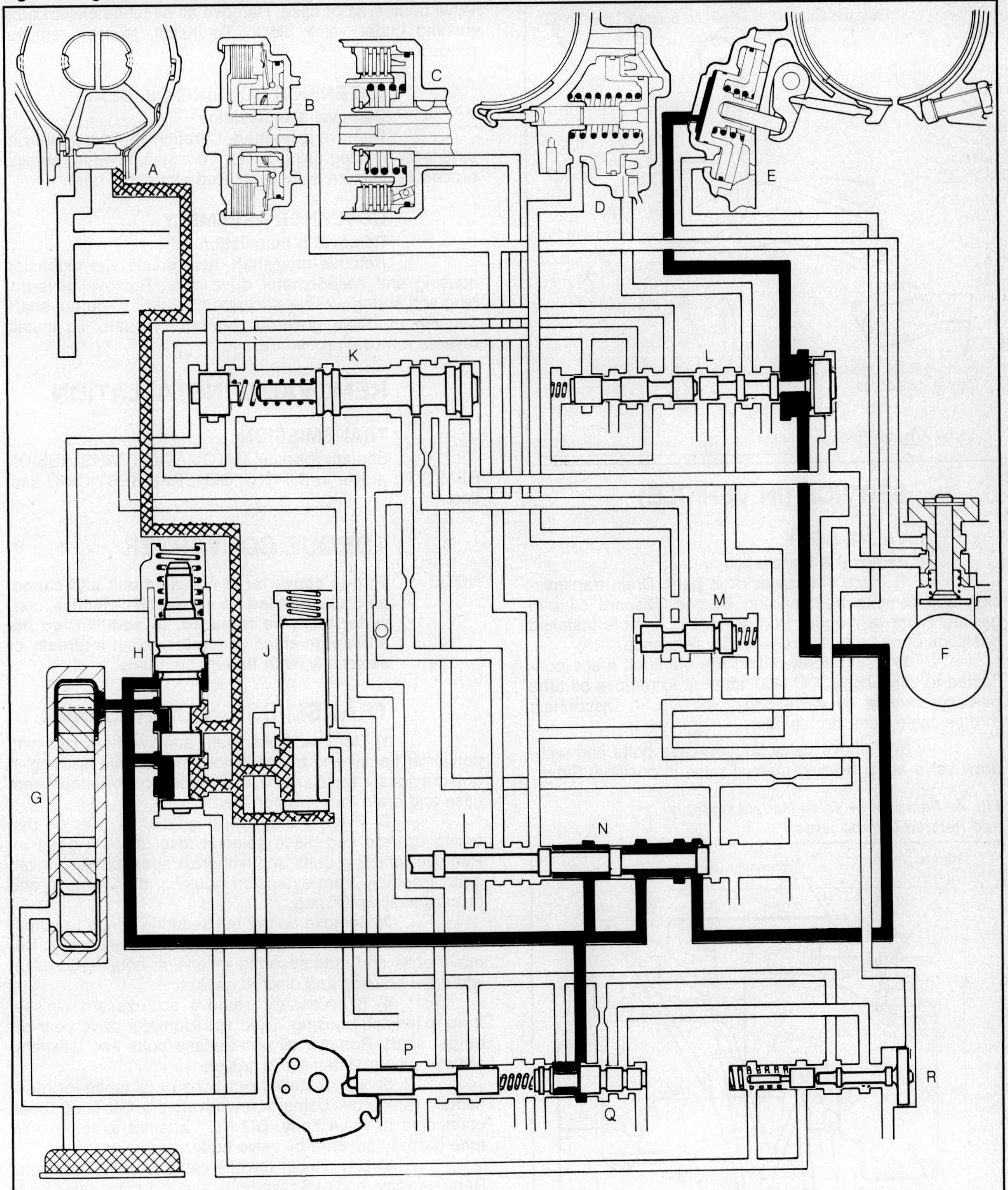

A — Torque Converter
B — Front Clutch
C — Rear Clutch
D — Front Servo
E — Rear Servo
F — Governor
G — Oil Pump
H — Primary Regulator
J — Secondary Regulator
K — 2-3 Shift Valve
L — 1-2 Shift Valve
M — Servo Orifice Control Valve
N — Manual Valve
P — Downshift Valve
Q — Throttle Valve
R — Modulator Valve

Fig. 3: Hydraulic Pressure Test Hook-Up

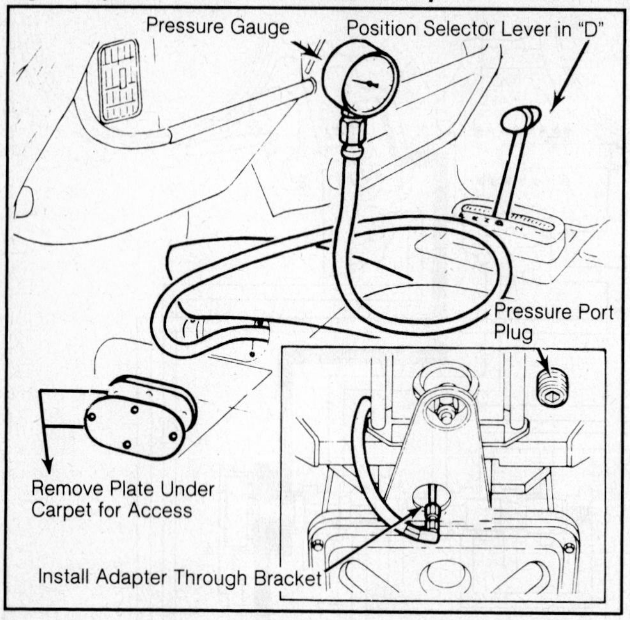

SERVICE (IN VEHICLE)

VALVE BODY

Removal & Installation

1) Place shift selector in park. Drain transmission and remove transmission oil pan. Discard oil pan gasket. Remove magnet from valve block. Note installed positions of oil tubes for reassembly reference.

2) Using screwdriver, pry out 5 oil tubes connected to valve body. DO NOT attempt to remove oil tube partially covered by valve body. *See Fig. 4.* Disconnect throttle cable from throttle cam.

3) Remove valve body-to-case bolts and withdraw valve body, holding manual valve in position. Slowly remove manual valve. Remove 2 remaining oil tubes from valve body area of case. Remove all oil tubes except tube running under valve block. To install, reverse removal procedure.

Fig. 4: Removal of Valve Body Assembly and Related Components

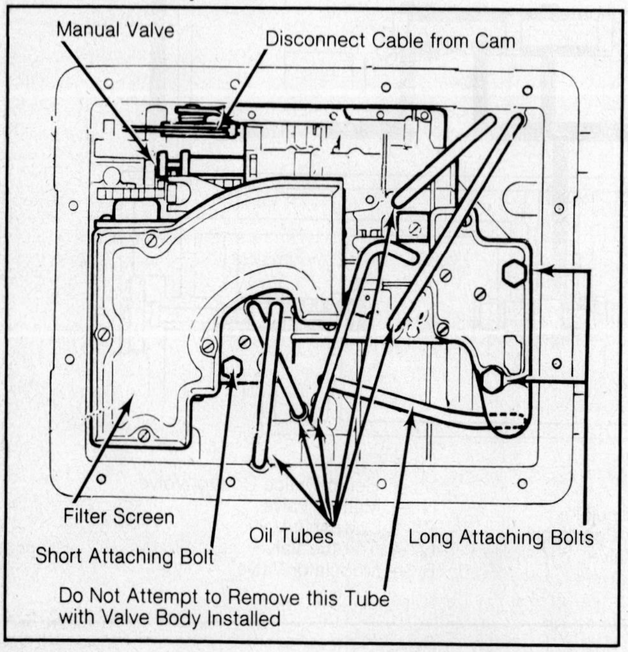

EXTENSION HOUSING OIL SEAL

Removal & Installation

Remove driveshaft. Carefully remove seal from extension housing using puller. To install, reverse removal procedure. Ensure seal is installed straight in bore.

GOVERNOR ASSEMBLY

Removal & Installation

Remove driveshaft, heat shield and extension housing and speedometer drive gear. Remove governor plug and spring washer securing governor to output shaft. *See Fig. 5.* Slide governor off output shaft. To install, reverse removal procedure.

REMOVAL & INSTALLATION

TRANSMISSION

See appropriate AUTOMATIC TRANSMISSION REMOVAL article in IMPORT GENERAL SERVICING section.

TORQUE CONVERTER

NOTE: **Torque converter is a sealed unit and cannot be disassembled for service. If defective, converter must be replaced. In addition, do not attempt to clean converter, either internally or externally, with flammable fluids.**

TRANSMISSION DISASSEMBLY

1) Remove bolts, nuts and washers retaining converter housing to transmission and remove housing. If not previously done, remove dipstick and breather from case and drain transmission fluid.

2) Place transmission on bench with oil pan facing upward and place selector lever in park position. Remove retaining bolts and withdraw speedometer driven gear assembly from extension housing, then remove and discard sealing "O" ring.

3) Remove bolt or nut securing flange to output shaft and withdraw flange using puller if necessary. Remove bolts and nuts securing extension housing to case, withdraw housing and discard gasket.

4) If necessary, remove and discard oil seal from extension housing. Slide speedometer drive gear off output shaft. Remove oil pan-to-case bolts and washers, remove oil pan and discard gasket.

5) Note installed positions of oil tubes for reassembly reference. Using screwdriver, pry out 5 oil tubes connected to valve body. DO NOT attempt to remove oil tube partially covered by valve body.

6) Disconnect throttle cable from throttle cam. Remove valve body-to-case bolts and withdraw valve body (take care not to lose manual valve). Remove 2 remaining oil tubes from valve body area of case. Remove bolts retaining oil pump tube plate and withdraw plate and tubes.

7) Scratch alignment marks on oil pump housing and transmission case. Remove pump-to-case bolts and withdraw oil pump. Remove and discard pump-to-case gasket and pump-to-front clutch thrust washer.

BORG-WARNER MODEL 66 (Cont.)

Fig. 5: Removal of Governor and Oil Tubes

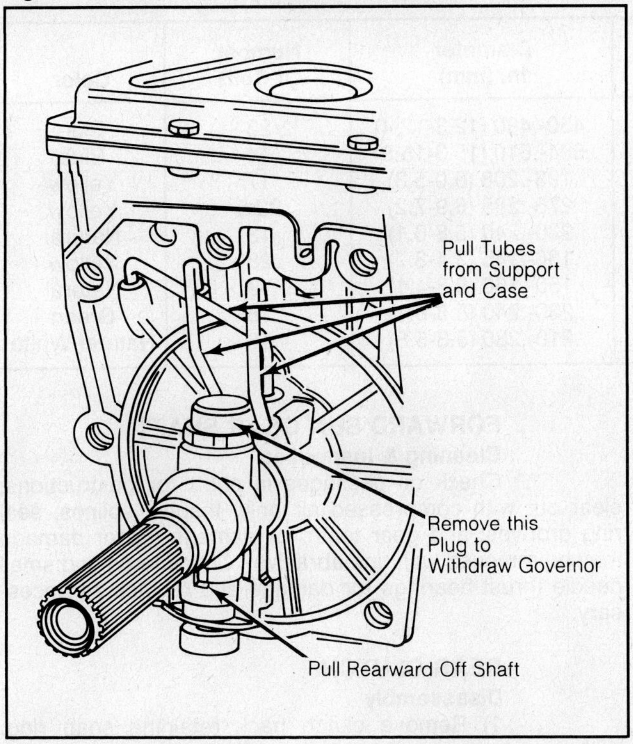

8) At rear end of transmission, remove plug and spring washer retaining governor to output shaft. Note installed position of governor, and remove from shaft. Using screwdriver, carefully pry oil tubes from case and governor support.

9) Loosen both band adjusting screw lock nuts. Remove adjusting screws from case then withdraw both band struts. Withdraw front clutch and input shaft assembly from case. Remove bronze and steel thrust washers, then withdraw rear clutch assembly.

Fig. 6: Disassembled View of Transmission Gear Train Components

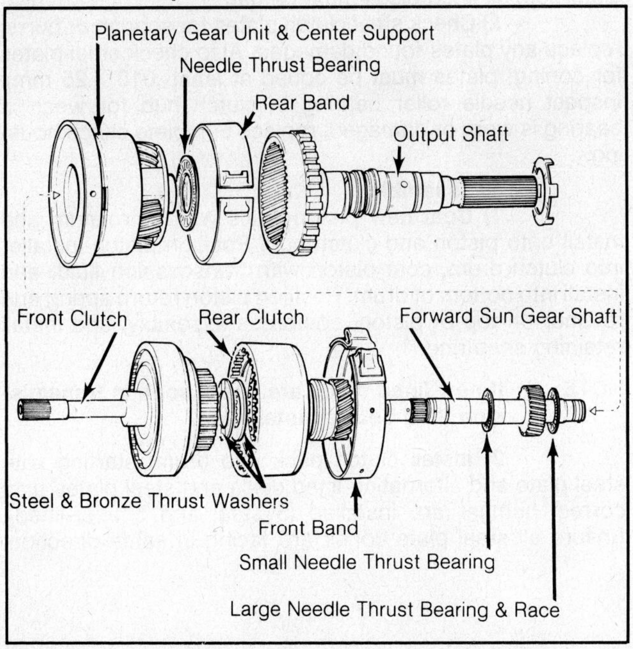

10) Compress ends of front band together and remove from case. Withdraw forward sun gear shaft from case, along with small needle thrust bearing from front end of shaft and large needle thrust bearing and race from rear end of shaft.

11) Remove bolts securing center support in case. Push forward on output shaft to break support loose, then withdraw center support and planetary assembly from case. Remove planetary-to-output shaft needle thrust bearing, then separate support and planetary.

12) Move output shaft back into original position. Compress ends of rear band together, and remove band from case. Remove output shaft assembly from case along with output shaft-to-case thrust washer.

13) Remove bolts securing front servo cover to case. Remove cover, and withdraw servo piston, rod and spring. Scribe alignment marks on rear servo cover and transmission case. Remove bolts attaching servo cover.

14) Remove rear servo cover, piston, rod and spring from case. Remove retaining bolts from plate covering parking pawl, withdraw pivot pin, and remove rear servo operating lever.

Fig. 7: Removing Rear Servo Operating Lever

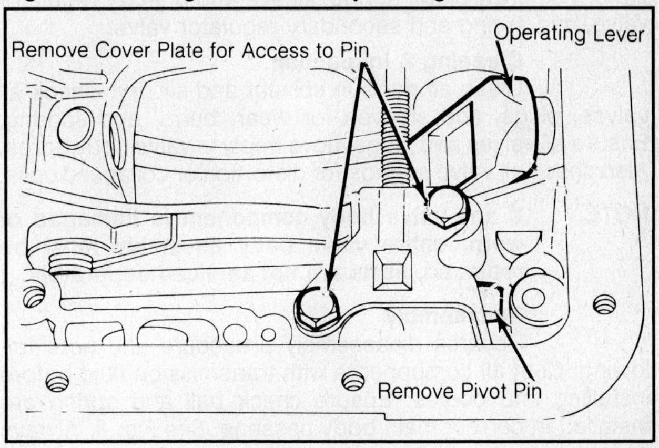

COMPONENT DISASSEMBLY & REASSEMBLY

VALVE BODY ASSEMBLY

Disassembly

1) Remove manual valve from body. Remove screws retaining filter screen (and adapter if equipped) to body and remove filter screen. Remove 6 upper valve body retaining screws from lower valve body, invert valve body, and remove 4 screws retaining upper body and cam mounting arm. Remove cam mounting arm, withdraw downshift valve and spring, then separate upper body from assembly.

2) Remove screws securing end plates to upper body and remove plates. Remove 1-2 shift valve, plunger and spring, and 2-3 shift valve, plunger and spring. Remove retaining screws and lift transfer plate off main valve body.

3) Loosen, but do not remove, governor pressure plate retaining screws. Hold separator plate in contact with main valve body, remove governor pressure plate retaining screws, and remove plate. Carefully remove separator plate from main body, noting position of ball valve and spring.

Automatic Transmissions

BORG-WARNER MODEL 66 (Cont.)

JAGUAR VALVE BODY SPRING IDENTIFICATION CHART

Valve Spring	Length In. (mm)	Diameter In. (mm)	Number Of Coils	Color
Secondary Regulator Valve	2.59 (65.8)	.480-.490 (12.3-12.4)	23	Blue
Primary Regulator Valve	2.94 (74.6)	.604-.610 (15.3-15.5)	14	Blue
Servo Orifice Control Valve	1.00 (25.5)	.198-.208 (5.0-5.3)	17	Yellow
2-3 Shift Valve	1.59 (40.4)	.275-.285 (6.9-7.2)	22.5	Yellow
1-2 Shift Valve	1.09 (27.7)	.230-.240 (5.8-6.1)	13	Natural
Throttle Return Valve	0.80 (20.5)	.136-.146 (3.4-3.7)	28	Yellow
Modulator Valve	1.07 (27.1)	.150-.160 (3.8-4.1)	19	Natural
Throttle Valve	1.18 (29.9)	.230-.240 (5.8-6.1)	18	Green
Dump Ball Valve	0.70 (17.7)	.210-.230 (5.3-5.8)	16	Natural/White

4) From main valve body, remove following parts: Retainer, spring, and servo orifice control valve; retaining pin, plug, spring, and modulator valve; 2 retainers, spring, and throttle valve. Remove retaining screw and detent roller and spring assembly.

5) Remove screws securing regulator valve retaining plate to main valve body, slowly release pressure on plate. Withdraw plate, spring, sleeve and primary regulator valve, and spring and secondary regulator valve.

Cleaning & Inspection

Clean all parts in solvent and air dry. Check all valves, plugs, and sleeves for wear, burrs, and scoring. Ensure all valves and plugs move freely in valve body bores. Also check all valve springs for distortion or collapsed coils.

NOTE: If any valve body component is damaged or worn, entire valve body assembly must be replaced; parts are not serviced separately.

Reassembly

Reverse disassembly procedure and note following: Coat all components with transmission fluid before installing into bodies. Ensure check ball and spring are installed in correct main body passage. *See Fig. 8.* Always use new strainer filter gasket when assembling.

CAUTION: Do not overtighten valve body attaching bolts and screws.

PLANETARY CARRIER & ONE-WAY CLUTCH

Cleaning & Inspection

1) Check planetary gear teeth for chipping or scoring (light scoring is acceptable). Ensure all gears rotate freely by hand, and that end play of gears is not excessive. Inspect bushing in hub of planetary carrier for wear. If any part of carrier is worn or damaged, complete carrier must be replaced.

2) Withdraw one-way clutch roller assembly from carrier and inspect for worn or broken rollers and damage to outer race. If any one-way clutch component is damaged, replace roller and outer race assembly.

NOTE: When installing roller assembly into outer race (in carrier), ensure lip of roller cage faces outward.

FORWARD SUN GEAR SHAFT

Cleaning & Inspection

Check oil passages in shaft for obstructions; clear out with compressed air only. Inspect splines, seal ring grooves, and gear teeth for damage (minor damage may be removed with fine abrasive). Check large and small needle thrust bearings for damage and replace as necessary.

REAR CLUTCH

Disassembly

1) Remove clutch pack retaining snap ring. Withdraw pressure plate, 5 steel clutch plates, and 5 line discs. Using a spring compressor, compress piston return spring.

2) Remove snap ring, then withdraw compressor, spring retainer, and piston return spring. Remove clutch piston by applying air pressure to fluid supply passage in clutch hub. Remove inner seal from clutch drum and outer seal from piston.

Cleaning & Inspection

1) Check clutch drum for scoring or wear and all fluid passages for obstructions. Clear passages with compressed air only. Inspect piston for damage and free operation of check ball. Check all lined discs for wear and distortion; all lined discs must be flat.

2) Check steel clutch plates for scoring or burrs; replace any plates found damaged. Also check steel plates for coning; plates must be coned at least .010" (.25 mm). Inspect needle roller bearing in clutch hub for wear. If bearing is worn or damaged, replace complete clutch housing.

Reassembly

1) Coat new piston seals with petrolatum and install onto piston and clutch hub. Position piston installer into clutch drum, coat piston with transmission fluid, and install into bottom of drum. Position piston return spring and retainer on top of piston, compress assembly, and install retaining snap ring.

NOTE: If new lined discs are used, soak in transmission fluid before installation.

2) Install clutch pack into drum, starting with steel plate and alternating lined discs and steel plates until correct number are installed (5 steel and 5 fiber-lined). Ensure all steel plate cones are facing in same direction.

Automatic Transmissions

BORG-WARNER MODEL 66 (Cont.)

Fig. 8: Exploded View of Valve Body Assembly

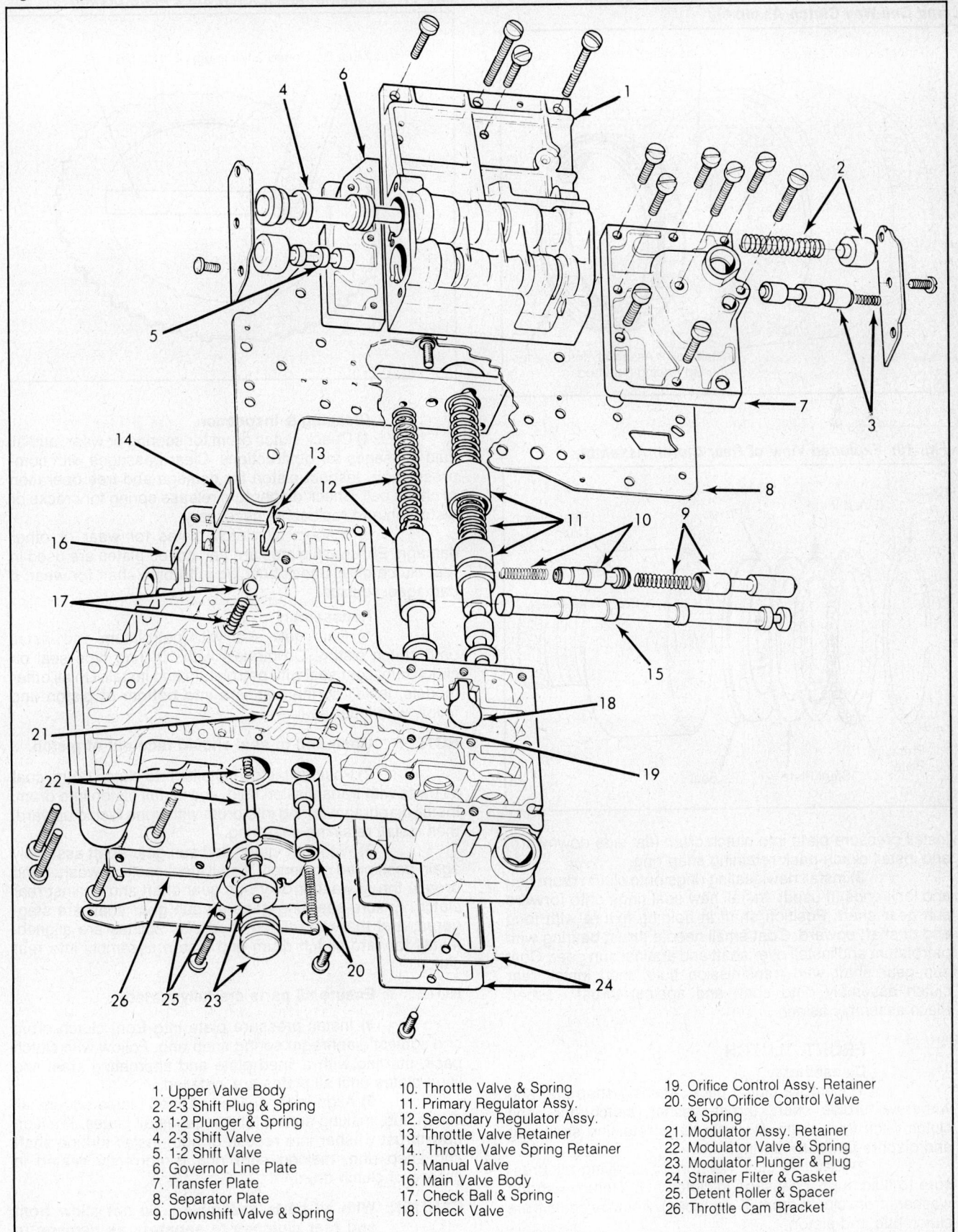

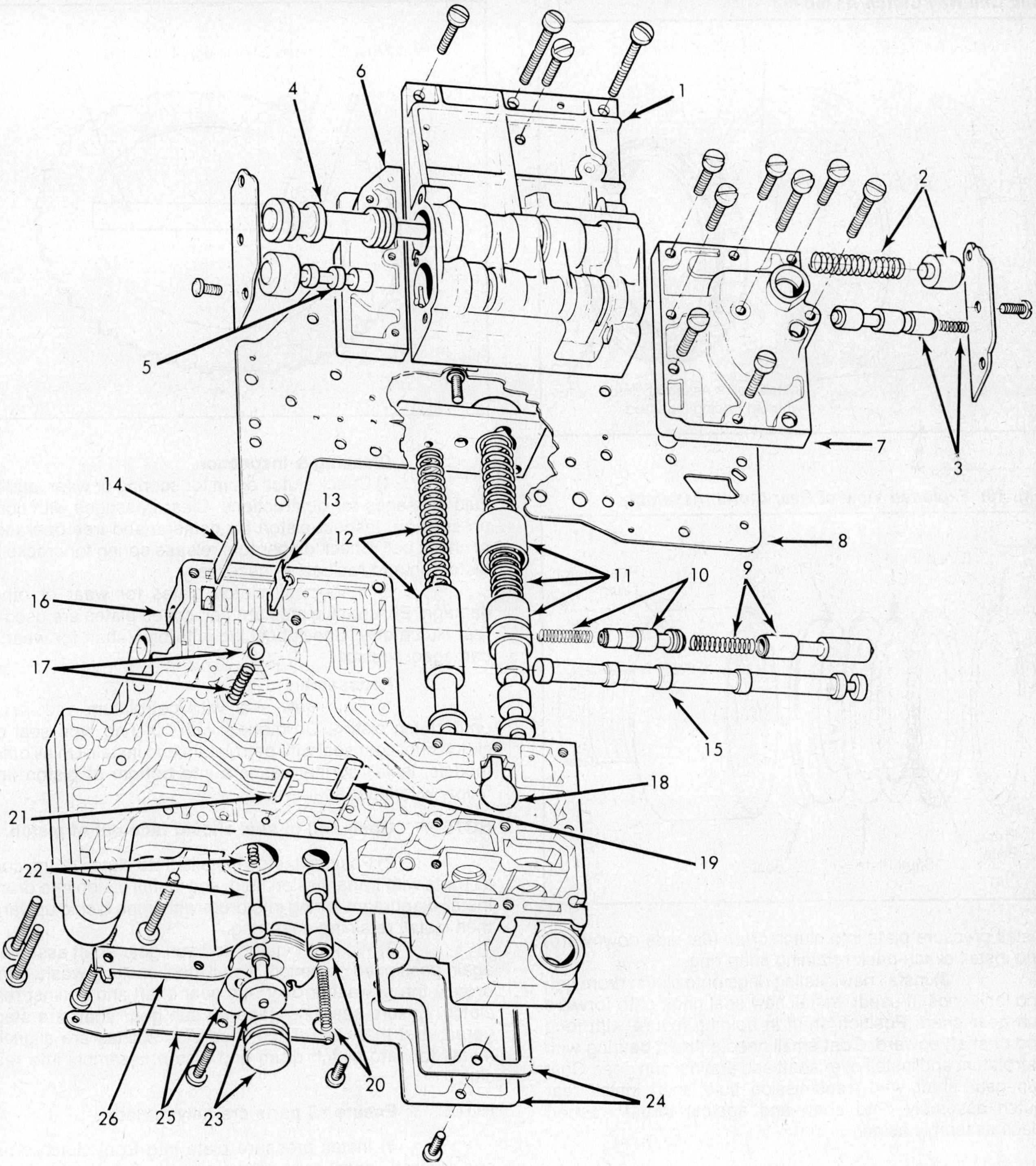

1. Upper Valve Body
2. 2-3 Shift Plug & Spring
3. 1-2 Plunger & Spring
4. 2-3 Shift Valve
5. 1-2 Shift Valve
6. Governor Line Plate
7. Transfer Plate
8. Separator Plate
9. Downshift Valve & Spring
10. Throttle Valve & Spring
11. Primary Regulator Assy.
12. Secondary Regulator Assy.
13. Throttle Valve Retainer
14.. Throttle Valve Spring Retainer
15. Manual Valve
16. Main Valve Body
17. Check Ball & Spring
18. Check Valve
19. Orifice Control Assy. Retainer
20. Servo Orifice Control Valve & Spring
21. Modulator Assy. Retainer
22. Modulator Valve & Spring
23. Modulator Plunger & Plug
24. Strainer Filter & Gasket
25. Detent Roller & Spacer
26. Throttle Cam Bracket

BORG-WARNER MODEL 66 (Cont.)

Fig. 9: Disassembled View of Planetary Carrier and One-Way Clutch Assembly

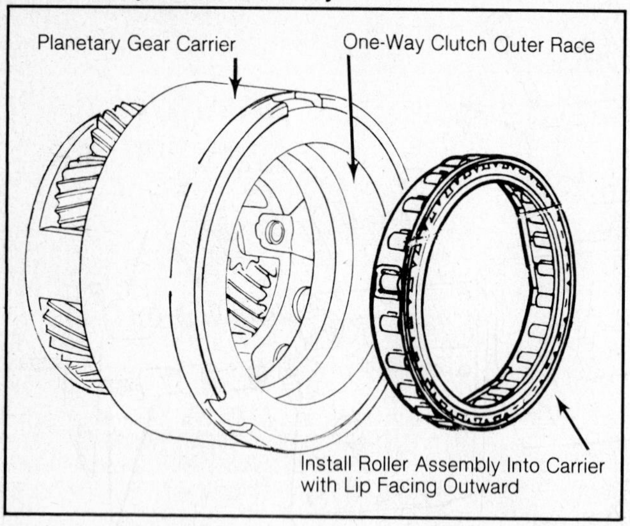

Fig. 10: Exploded View of Rear Clutch Assembly

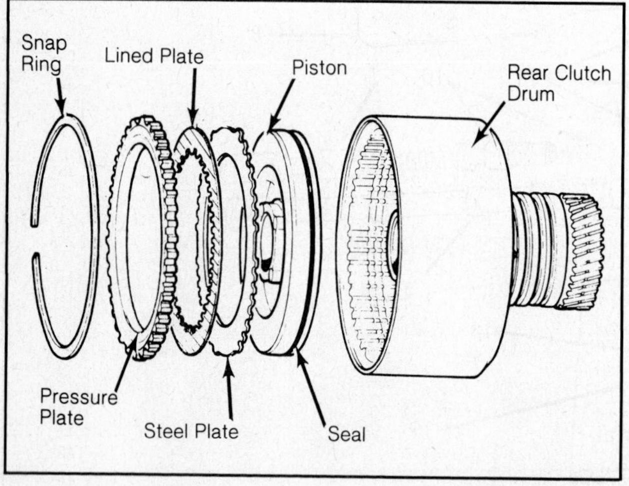

Install pressure plate into clutch drum (flat side downward) and install clutch pack retaining snap ring.

3) Install new sealing rings onto clutch drum hub and lock ends (if used). Install new seal rings onto forward sun gear shaft. Position shaft in holding fixture with long end of shaft upward. Coat small needle thrust bearing with petrolatum and install over shaft and against sun gear. Coat sun gear shaft with transmission fluid, then install rear clutch assembly onto shaft and against thrust washer. Place assembly aside.

FRONT CLUTCH

Disassembly

1) Remove clutch pack retaining snap ring and withdraw turbine shaft, thrust washer, clutch hub, and clutch pack from drum. Remove large retaining snap ring and diaphragm return spring.

2) Remove clutch piston by applying air pressure to fluid supply passage in clutch hub. Remove spring washers from clutch drum (if equipped). Remove seals from clutch hub and piston.

Fig. 11: Checking Rear Clutch Steel Plate Coning

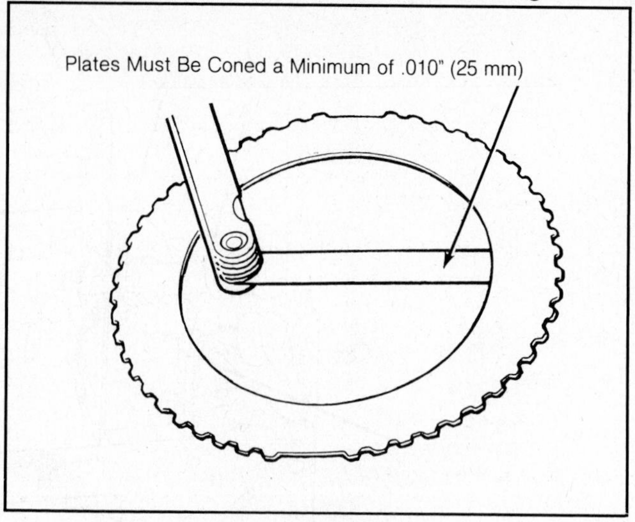

Cleaning & Inspection

1) Check clutch drum for scoring or wear, and all fluid passages for obstructions. Clear passages with compressed air. Inspect piston for damage and free operation of check ball. Check diaphragm release spring for cracks or distortion and replace as necessary.

2) Inspect all clutch plates for wear or other damage. Ensure all plates are flat; coned plates are used in rear clutch only. Check bushing in turbine shaft for wear; if damaged, replace.

Reassembly

1) Coat new seal with petrolatum and install onto clutch piston. On models with "O" ring type seal on clutch hub, coat seal with petrolatum and install. On all other models, install spring washers into bottom of piston and follow with inner seal.

NOTE: Open end of seal should face out of piston.

2) Position piston installer into clutch drum, coat all parts with transmission fluid, and install piston into drum. Install diaphragm spring into drum with cone facing upward, then install retaining snap ring.

3) With rear clutch and sun gear shaft assembly again positioned on bench, install steel backing washer and bronze thrust washer over sun gear shaft and against rear clutch. Ensure seal ring gaps on sun gear shaft are staggered, and that rear clutch lined disc splines are aligned. Install forward clutch drum and piston assembly into rear clutch.

NOTE: Ensure all parts are fully mated.

4) Install pressure plate into front clutch drum and against diaphragm spring snap ring. Follow with clutch pack, starting with a lined plate and alternating steel and lined plates until all plates are installed.

5) Align inner splines of lined plates and install clutch hub, making sure it fully engages all plates. Position new thrust washer into recess of hub. Install turbine shaft and snap ring, making sure ring is correctly seated in groove of clutch drum.

CAUTION: With all parts assembled, do not allow front and rear clutches to separate as damage to seal rings on sun gear shaft may occur.

BORG-WARNER MODEL 66 (Cont.)

Fig. 12: Exploded View of Front Clutch Assembly

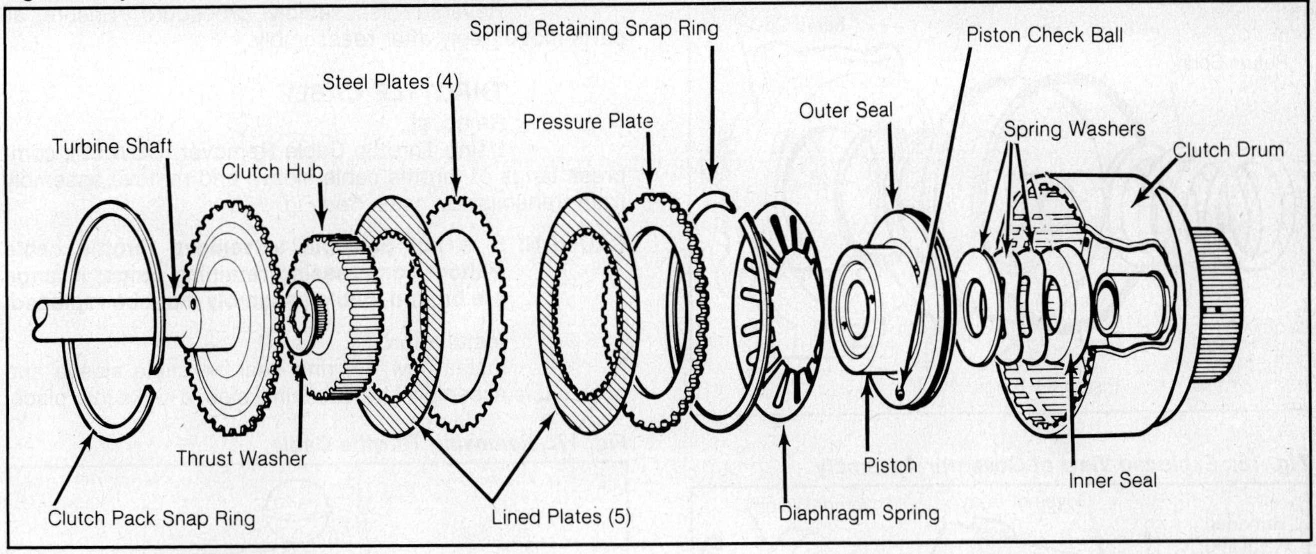

OIL PUMP

Disassembly

1) Remove bolts and screw retaining pump housing to cover. Separate cover and housing. Mark mating surfaces of pump drive and driven gears with die marker for reassembly reference.

CAUTION: Do not punch or scribe marks in gears.

2) Remove "O" ring seal from outer diameter of pump housing, and converter lip seal from front of pump housing.

Cleaning & Inspection

Check surfaces of housing and cover, gears, splines, and bushings for scoring, wear or other damage. If any part shows evidence of wear, entire assembly must be replaced; parts are not serviced separately.

Fig. 13: Exploded View of Oil Pump Assembly

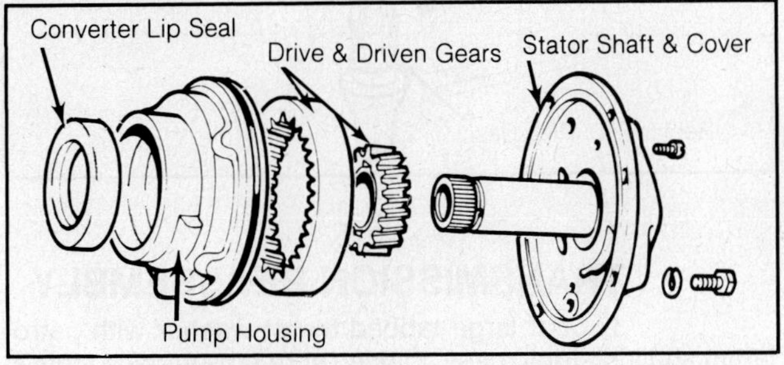

Reassembly

Soak new converter lip seal and housing "O" ring seal in transmission fluid and install into pump housing. Install drive and driven gears into housing, aligning marks made at disassembly. Install cover into housing, align bolt and screw holes, then install and tighten attaching bolts and screw. Rotate pump gears to check for freedom of movement.

FRONT & REAR SERVOS

Disassembly

Remove spring from servo piston. Remove piston from servo body. Remove seals from piston and body.

Cleaning & Inspection

Clean all parts in solvent. Blow dry with compressed air, clearing out all lubrication passages.

Fig. 14: Exploded View of Front Servo Assembly

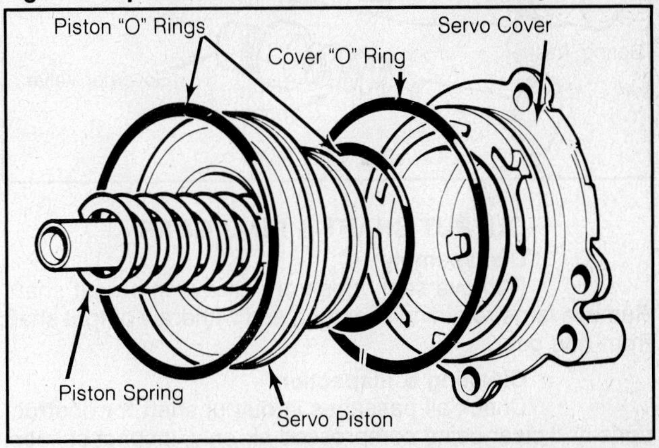

Reassembly

Coat new seals with petrolatum and install onto piston and servo body. Position spring on servo piston, then place assembly aside.

GOVERNOR

Disassembly

Depress governor shaft to expose snap ring, remove snap ring and weight from outside of assembly, withdraw governor shaft, spring, and valve from inside governor body.

Cleaning & Inspection

Wash all parts in solvent and air dry. Check all parts for wear or damage, and spring especially for distortion. If any part of governor is found to be damaged, entire governor assembly must be replaced.

Reassembly

Lubricate all parts with transmission fluid. Install governor valve, spring, and shaft into body, position weight on shaft, then install snap ring. Check all parts for freedom of movement. If governor shaft shows signs of sticking, governor assembly must be replaced.

BORG-WARNER MODEL 66 (Cont.)

Fig. 15: Exploded View of Rear Servo Assembly

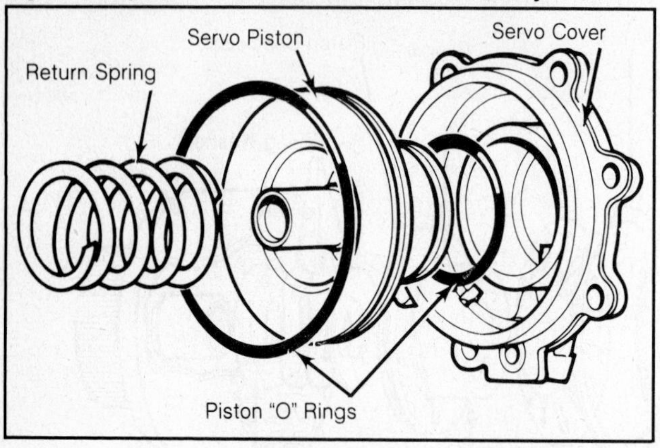

Fig. 16: Exploded View of Governor Assembly

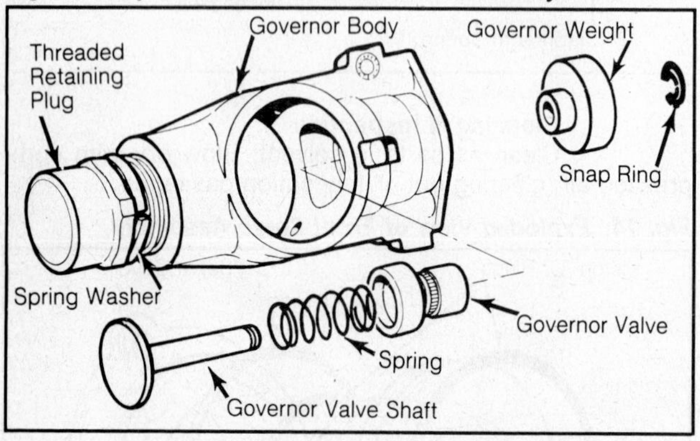

OUTPUT SHAFT & RING GEAR

Disassembly

Remove seal rings from groove in output shaft. Remove large retaining snap ring and withdraw output shaft from ring gear.

Cleaning & Inspection

Check all passages in output shaft for obstructions and clear using compressed air only. Inspect splines, seal ring grooves, and gear teeth of shaft and ring gear for burrs, scoring, or other damage (minor damage may be removed with a fine abrasive). If any part is worn or damaged, replace.

Reassembly

Position output shaft in ring gear and install retaining snap ring. Install new seal rings into grooves of output shaft, taking care to stagger ring gaps.

MANUAL LINKAGE

Disassembly

1) Note position of parking pawl spring, then detach spring from pawl. Remove parking pawl shaft from outside of case, and withdraw pawl and spring from inside case. Remove clip from manual shaft and pin retaining detent lever. Withdraw manual shaft, detent lever, spacer, and washers from case.

2) Disconnect parking rod from parking pawl. Note position of parking pawl operating lever and spring, and detach spring from lever. Using a punch, drive out operating lever pin and withdraw operating lever and spring.

Reassembly

Reverse disassembly procedure. Ensure all parts move freely after reassembly.

THROTTLE CABLE

Removal

Using Throttle Cable Remover (CBW.62), compress tangs of throttle cable sleeve and remove assembly from transmission case. *See Fig. 17.*

CAUTION: It is not possible to remove throttle cable without compressing retaining tangs; if tangs are broken, cable assembly must be replaced.

Installation

Install new "O" ring seal on cable sleeve and push cable assembly into case until sleeve locks into place.

Fig. 17: Removing Throttle Cable

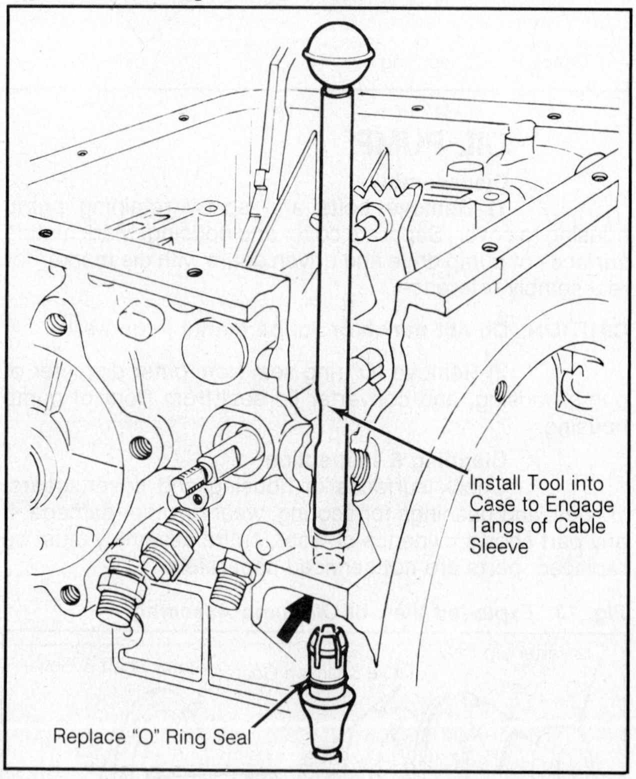

TRANSMISSION REASSEMBLY

1) Coat large tabbed thrust washer with petrolatum and install into case, making sure tabs engage slots in case. Install output shaft and ring gear assembly into case and through thrust washer. Ensure washer is positioned correctly.

2) Place front and rear bands in position in case. While holding clutch assemblies (previously assembled), install large needle thrust bearing and race onto sun gear shaft, with flange facing away from clutches.

3) Install center support, clutch and sun gear assembly into planet carrier. Rotate center support until holes on outer diameter are in approximate alignment with center support bolt holes in case, then install entire assembly (clutches, planetary carrier, and support) into transmission case.

BORG-WARNER MODEL 66 (Cont.)

Fig. 18: Exploded View of Manual Linkage Components

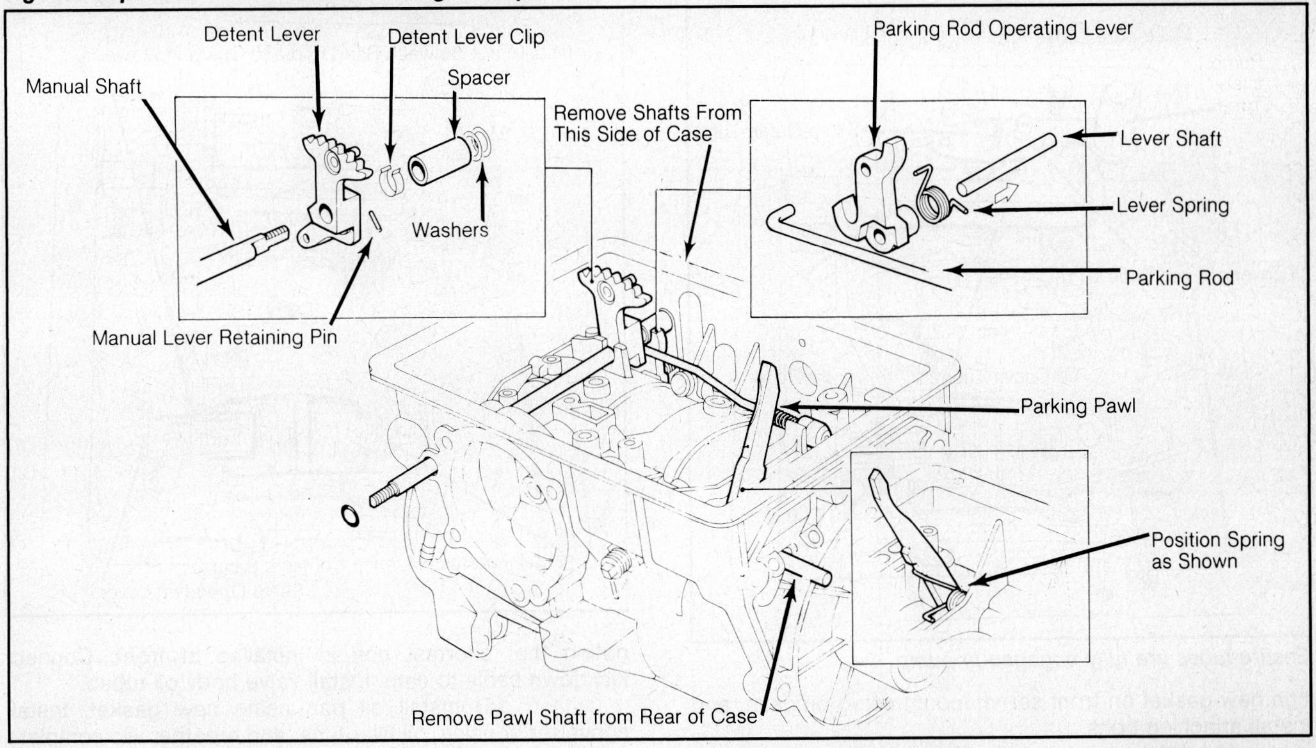

Fig. 19: Installation of Output Shaft Into Transmission Case

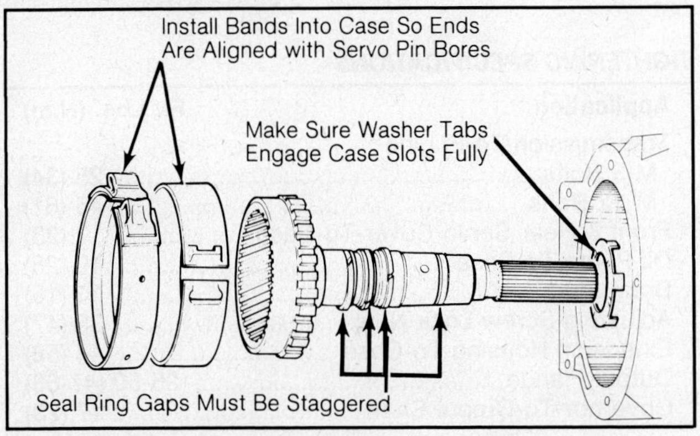

Fig. 20: Installing Oil Pump Onto Transmission Case

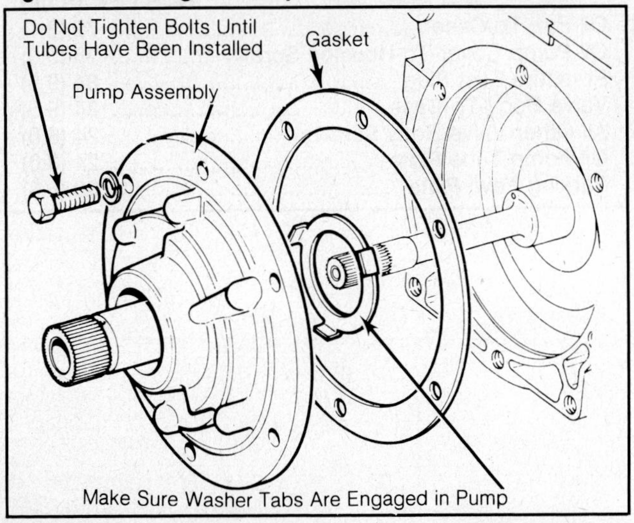

4) Position new thrust washer and gasket onto rear of oil pump. Mount oil pump to transmission case, and install but do not tighten attaching bolts. Install new "O" ring seal on pump inlet tube.

5) Install inlet tube along with outlet tube and converter feed tube into oil pump housing (inside case). Ensure tubes are correctly positioned. Install tube retaining plate and attaching bolts, then tighten oil pump-to-case bolts. At this time, also install oil cooler tube into case.

CAUTION: To prevent damage to internal parts, do not allow components to separate when installing.

6) On rear of case, install 3 oil tubes into case and governor support. Slide governor unit onto output shaft and install plug and spring washer, making sure plug enters BLIND hole in output shaft.

7) Install speedometer drive gear onto output shaft and against governor. Install new seal into extension housing, position new extension-to-case gasket, then install housing onto case, tightening nuts and bolts in a diagonal sequence.

8) Install output flange onto shaft, engage parking pawl with parking gear, then install flange attaching bolt or nut and tighten. Position dial indicator assembly on front of transmission case with button of indicator contacting turbine shaft.

9) With screwdriver inserted between front clutch and front of case, pry gear train fully rearward. Zero dial indicator. Next, with screwdriver between parking gear and rear clutch, pry gear train forward and note reading on gauge. Reading should be .008-.029" (.20-.73 mm). If not, repeat steps **4)**, **5)**, **6)**, **7)** and **8)**, installing thicker or thinner washer (as required) behind oil pump.

10) Coat new "O" ring with petrolatum and install onto speedometer driven gear housing. Install driven gear assembly into extension housing and install retainer. Posi-

Automatic Transmissions

BORG-WARNER MODEL 66 (Cont.)

Fig. 21: Installing Oil Tubes Into Case

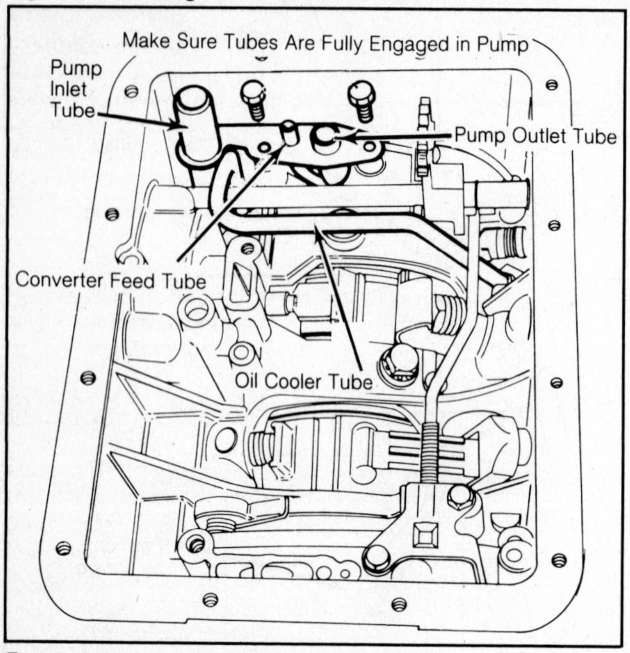
Make Sure Tubes Are Fully Engaged in Pump
Pump Inlet Tube
Pump Outlet Tube
Converter Feed Tube
Oil Cooler Tube

Ensure tubes are fully engaged in pump.

tion new gasket on front servo, mount servo on case, and install attaching bolts.

11) Install front band strut into servo rod and band. Screw in front band adjusting screw until it engages band end. Do not tighten screw or lock nut at this time. *See Fig. 22.*

Fig. 22: Installing Front Band Strut and Adjusting Screw

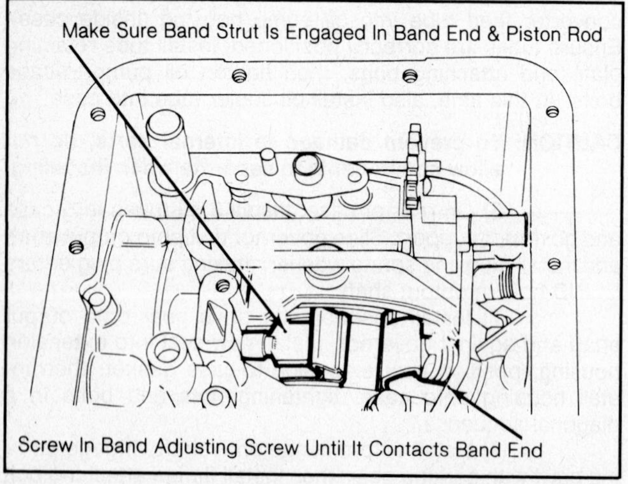
Make Sure Band Strut Is Engaged In Band End & Piston Rod
Screw In Band Adjusting Screw Until It Contacts Band End

12) If removed, install rear servo operating lever in transmission case. Install new "O" rings and gasket on rear servo body and mount servo on case. Ensure servo rod engages operating lever. Install rear band strut between band end and operating lever. *See Fig. 23.*

13) Screw in band adjusting screw until contact is just made with band, tighten servo body-to-case bolts. At this time, install oil tube "D", which will be partially covered by valve body. *See Fig. 24.*

14) Install valve body into case. Ensure manual valve engages detent lever and that valve body fully engages oil pump tubes. Install valve body-to-case bolts,

Fig. 23: Installing Rear Band Strut and Adjusting Screw

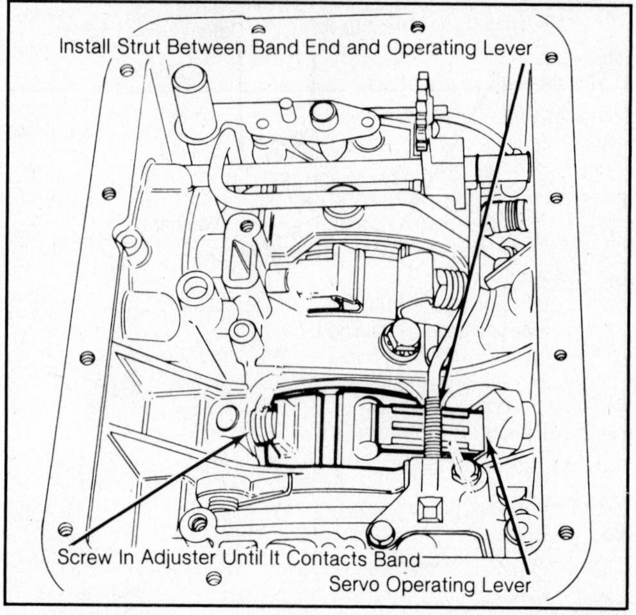
Install Strut Between Band End and Operating Lever
Screw In Adjuster Until It Contacts Band
Servo Operating Lever

noting that shortest bolt is installed at front. Connect kickdown cable to cam. Install valve body oil tubes.

15) Install oil pan using new gasket. Install converter housing, oil filler tube, and breather. To complete assembly, adjust both bands as follows: Tighten band adjusting screw to 60 INCH lbs. (7 N.m), back out screw 3/4 of a turn, hold in position and tighten adjusting screw lock nut.

TIGHTENING SPECIFICATIONS

Application	Ft. Lbs. (N.m)
Transmission-To-Engine	
M-8 Bolts	25 (34)
M-12 Bolts	45 (61)
Front & Rear Servo Cover-To-Case	17 (23)
Oil Pump-To-Case	19 (26)
Drain Plug	11 (15)
Adjusting Screw Lock Nuts	35 (47)
Extension Housing-To-Case	43 (58)
Output Flange	35-50 (47-68)
Governor-To-Output Shaft	17 (23)
	INCH Lbs. (N.m.)
Oil Pan-To-Case	72 (8.1)
Oil Pump Cover-To-Housing Screw	25 (3.0)
Pressure Test Plug	84 (9.5)
Valve Body-To-Case	84 (9.5)
All Other Valve Body Screws	24 (3.0)
Oil Pump Tube Plate	24 (3.0)
Parking Pawl Plate	60 (6.8)

BORG-WARNER MODEL 66 (Cont.)

Fig. 24: Installing Oil Tubes

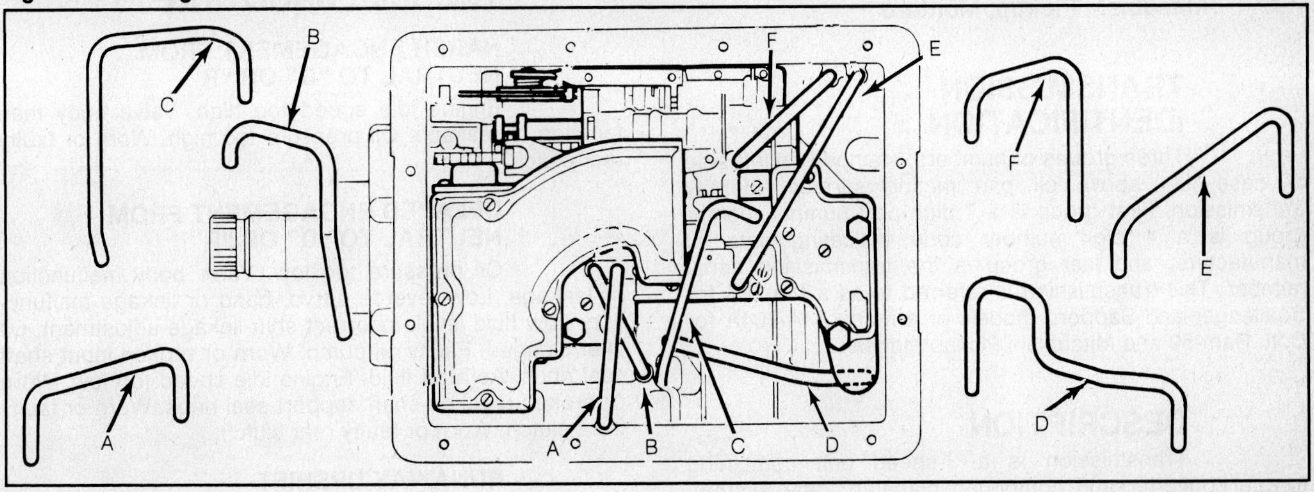

CHRYSLER CORP. & MITSUBISHI TORQUEFLITE

Chrysler Corp. Ram-50 Pickup
Mitsubishi Pickup, Montero

TRANSMISSION IDENTIFICATION

Three groups of numbers, stamped on left side of case just above oil pan mating surface, identify transmission. First group is a 7 digit part number, center group is a 4 digit number code indicating date of manufacture, and last group is the transmission serial number. This transmission is referred to as a MA-904 for Challenger and Sapporo models or a model MA-904A for Colt, Ram-50 and Mitsubishi Pickup models.

DESCRIPTION

Transmission is a 3-speed unit combining torque converter and compound planetary gear system. Transmission case and converter housing are an integral aluminum casting. Transmission consists basically of 2 multiple-disc clutches, 2 bands and servos, and overrunning clutch, 2 planetary gear sets, and a hydraulic control system.

LUBRICATION & ADJUSTMENT

See the appropriate article in AUTOMATIC TRANSMISSION SERVICING section.

TROUBLE SHOOTING

HARSH ENGAGEMENT FROM NEUTRAL TO "D" OR "R"

Engine idle speed too high. Valve body malfunction or leakage. Oil pressure too high. Worn or faulty rear clutch.

DELAYED ENGAGEMENT FROM NEUTRAL TO "D" OR "R"

Oil pressure too low. Valve body malfunction or leakage. Low-reverse servo, band or linkage malfunction. Low fluid level. Incorrect shift linkage adjustment. Oil filter clogged. Faulty oil pump. Worn or broken input shaft seal rings. Aerated fluid. Engine idle speed too low. Worn or broken reaction shaft support seal rings. Worn or faulty front clutch. Worn or faulty rear clutch.

RUNAWAY UPSHIFT

Oil pressure too low. Valve body malfunction or leakage. Low fluid level. Oil filter clogged. Aerated fluid. Incorrect throttle rod adjustment. Worn or broken reaction shaft support seal rings. Kickdown servo, band or linkage malfunction. Worn or faulty front clutch.

NO UPSHIFT

Oil pressure too low. Valve body leakage or malfunction. Low fluid level. Incorrect shift linkage adjustment. Incorrect throttle rod adjustment. Governor support

Fig. 1: Cutaway View of Torqueflite Transmission Showing Major Components

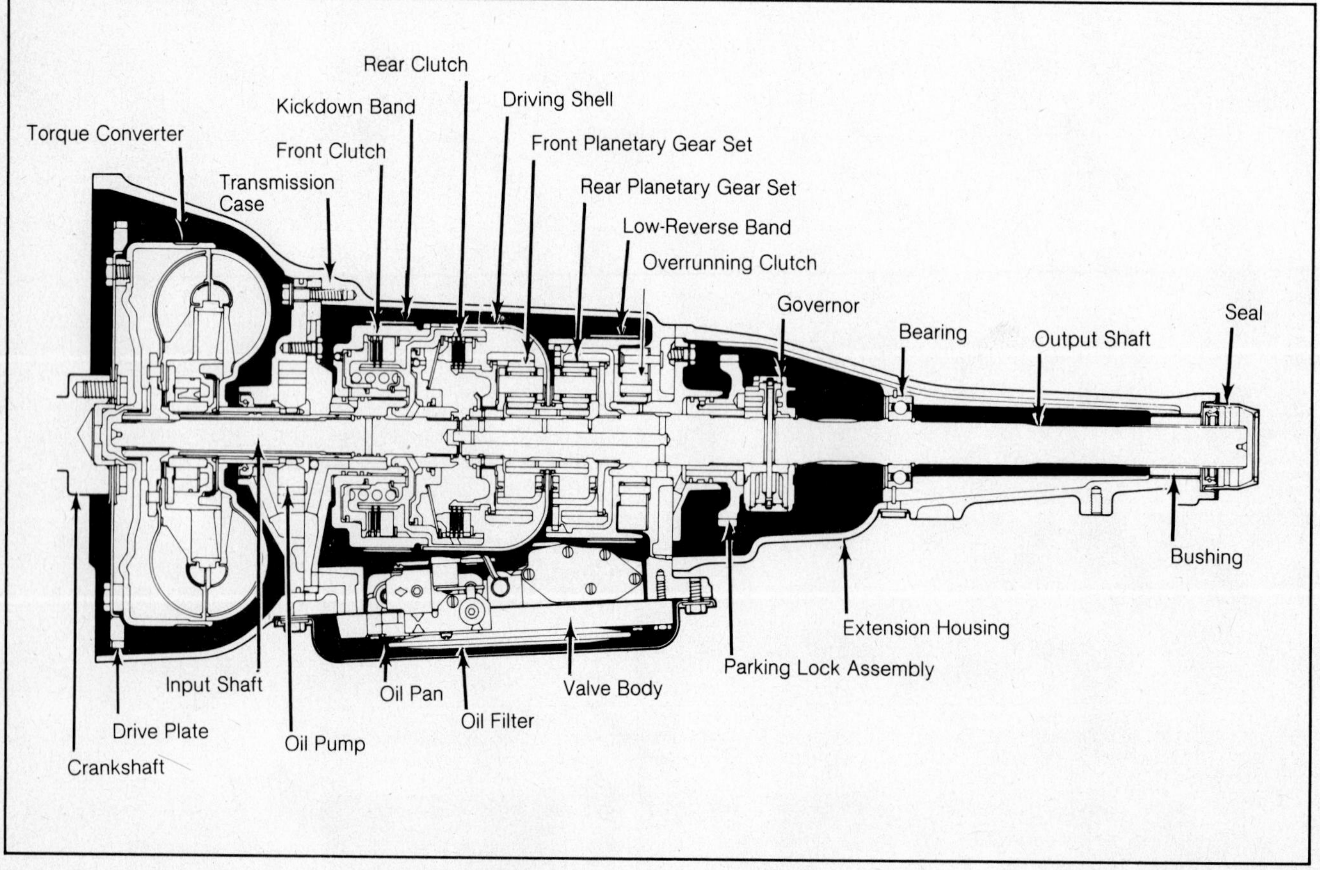

CHRYSLER CORP. & MITSUBISHI TORQUEFLITE (Cont.)

Fig. 2: Torqueflite Automatic Transmission Hydraulic Circuits Diagram

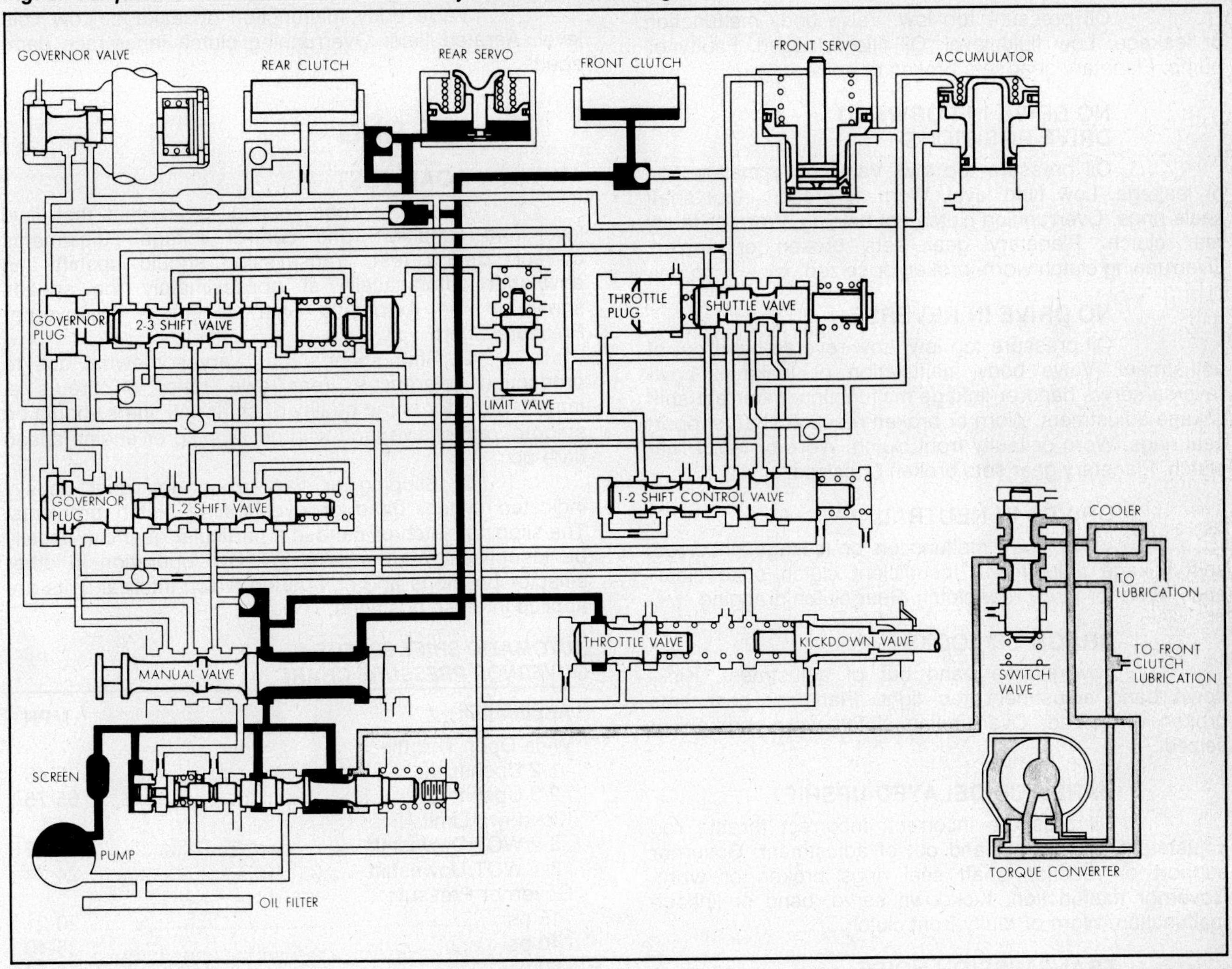

seal rings broken or worn. Worn or broken reaction shaft support seal rings. Governor malfunction. Kickdown servo, band or linkage malfunction. Worn or faulty front clutch.

3-2 KICKDOWN RUNAWAY

Oil pressure too low. Valve body malfunction or leakage. Low fluid level. Aerated fluid. Incorrect throttle rod adjustment. Kickdown band out of adjustment. Worn or broken reaction shaft support seal rings. Kickdown servo, band or linkage malfunction. Worn or faulty front clutch.

NO KICKDOWN OR NORMAL DOWNSHIFT

Valve body malfunction or leakage. Incorrect throttle rod adjustment. Governor malfunction. Kickdown servo, band or linkage malfunction.

SHIFTS ERRATIC

Oil pressure too low. Valve body malfunction or leakage. Low fluid level. Incorrect shift linkage adjustment. Oil filter clogged. Faulty oil pump. Aerated fluid. Incorrect throttle rod adjustment. Governor support seal rings broken or worn. Worn or broken reaction shaft support seal rings. Governor malfunction. Kickdown servo, band or linkage malfunction. Worn or faulty front clutch.

SLIPS IN FORWARD DRIVE POSITIONS

Oil pressure too low. Valve body malfunction or leakage. Low fluid level. Incorrect shift linkage adjustment. Oil filter clogged. Faulty oil pump. Worn or broken input shaft seal rings. Aerated fluid. Incorrect throttle rod adjustment. Overrunning clutch not holding. Worn or faulty rear clutch. Overrunning clutch worn, broken or seized.

SLIPS IN REVERSE ONLY

Oil pressure too low. Low-reverse band out of adjustment. Valve body malfunction or leakage. Low-reverse servo, band or linkage malfunction. Low fluid level. Incorrect shift linkage adjustment. Faulty oil pump. Aerated fluid. Worn or broken reaction shaft support seal rings. Worn or faulty front clutch.

SLIPS IN ALL POSITIONS

Oil pressure too low. Valve body malfunction or leakage. Low fluid level. Oil filter clogged. Faulty oil pump. Worn or broken input shaft seal rings. Aerated fluid.

CHRYSLER CORP. & MITSUBISHI TORQUEFLITE (Cont.)

NO DRIVE IN ANY POSITION

Oil pressure too low. Valve body malfunction or leakage. Low fluid level. Oil filter clogged. Faulty oil pump. Planetary gear sets broken or seized.

NO DRIVE IN FORWARD DRIVE POSITIONS

Oil pressure too low. Valve body malfunction or leakage. Low fluid level. Worn or broken input shaft seals rings. Overrunning clutch not holding. Worn or faulty rear clutch. Planetary gear sets broken or seized. Overrunning clutch worn, broken or seized.

NO DRIVE IN REVERSE

Oil pressure too low. Low-reverse band out of adjustment. Valve body malfunction or leakage. Low-reverse servo, band or linkage malfunction. Incorrect shift linkage adjustment. Worn or broken reaction shaft support seal rings. Worn or faulty front clutch. Worn or faulty rear clutch. Planetary gear sets broken or seized.

DRIVES IN NEUTRAL

Valve body malfunction or leakage. Incorrect shift linkage adjustment. Insufficient clutch plate clearance. Worn or faulty rear clutch. Rear clutch dragging.

DRAGS OR LOCKS

Low-reverse band out of adjustment. Kickdown band adjustment too tight. Planetary gear sets broken or seized. Overrunning clutch worn, broken or seized.

HARSH OR DELAYED UPSHIFT

Oil pressure incorrect. Incorrect throttle rod adjustment. Kickdown band out of adjustment. Governor support or reaction shaft seal rings broken or worn. Governor malfunction. Kickdown servo, band or linkage malfunction. Worn or faulty front clutch.

TRANSMISSION NOISE

Grating, Scraping, Or Growling

Low-reverse band out of adjustment. Output shaft bearing and/or bushing damaged. Planetary gear sets broken or seized. Overrunning clutch worn, broken or seized.

Buzzing

Valve body malfunction or leakage. Low fluid level. Aerated fluid. Overrunning clutch inner race damaged.

TESTING

ROAD TEST

1) Before road testing, be certain that fluid level and condition, and control linkage adjustments correct. During test, transmission should upshift and downshift automatically at approximately the speeds shown in the Automatic Shift Speeds and Governor Pressure Chart.

2) Shift speeds may vary somewhat due to production tolerances, rear axle ratio, or tire size. Important factor is the quality of shifts. All shifts should be smooth, responsive, and with no slipping or engine speed flare-up.

3) Slipping or flare-up in any gear usually indicated clutch, band or overrunning clutch problems. The slipping clutch or band in a particular gear can usually be identified by noting transmission operation in other selector positions and comparing which internal units are applied in those positions.

AUTOMATIC SHIFT SPEEDS & GOVERNOR PRESSURE CHART

Application	[1] MPH
Wide Open Throttle	
1-2 Upshift	35-45
2-3 Upshift	65-75
Kickdown Limit	
3-2 WOT Downshift	52-68
3-1 WOT Downshift	24-34
Governor Pressure	
15 psi	20-21
40 psi	35-40
60 psi	52-57

[1] – All speeds given are approximate. Changes in tire size or axle ratio will correspondingly raise or lower vehicle speed.

CLUTCH AND BAND APPLICATION CHART (ELEMENTS IN USE)

Selector Lever Position	Front Clutch	Rear Clutch	Over-running Clutch	Front (Kickdown) Band	Rear (Low-reverse) Band
D – DRIVE					
First		X	X		
Second		X		X	
Direct	X	X			
2 – SECOND					
First		X	X		
Second		X		X	
L – LOW (First)		X			X
R – REVERSE	X				X

NEUTRAL OR PARK – All clutches and bands released and/or ineffective.

CHRYSLER CORP. & MITSUBISHI TORQUEFLITE (Cont.)

4) For example, if transmission slips in "D" third gear, either front or rear clutch is slipping. By selecting another gear which does not use one of those units, the unit which is slipping can be identified. If transmission slips in reverse, the front clutch is slipping. If transmission does not slip in reverse, the rear clutch is slipping.

5) Although this process of elimination can be used to detect any unit which slips and to confirm proper operation of good units, the actual cause of malfunction usually cannot be decided. Practically any condition can be caused by leaking hydraulic circuits or sticking valves. Therefore, unless an obvious condition exists, transmission should never be disassembled until hydraulic pressure tests have been made.

HYDRAULIC PRESSURE TESTS

Before making pressure tests, be certain that fluid level and condition, and control linkage adjustments have been checked and corrected if necessary. Install an engine tachometer, raise vehicle on hoist which allows rear wheels to turn, and position tachometer so it can be read under vehicle. Disconnect throttle rod and shift rod from transmission levers so they can be controlled under vehicle. Make sure transmission fluid is at normal operating temperature (170°F).

Pressure Test (Selector in "L")

1) Attach 0-100 psi gauges to line and rear servo ports. Operate engine at 1000 RPM for test. Move selector lever on transmission all the way forward ("L" position). Read pressures on both gauges as throttle lever on transmission is moved from full rearward position to full forward position.

2) Line pressure should read 54-60 psi (3.8-4.2 kg/cm²) with throttle lever rearward and gradually increase, as lever is moved forward to 90-95 psi (6.3-6.7 kg/cm²). Rear servo pressure should read the same as line pressure within 3 psi (0.2 kg/cm²). This tests pump output, pressure regulation, and condition of rear clutch and rear servo hydraulic circuits.

Fig. 3: View of Right Side of Transmission Case Showing Pressure Test Ports

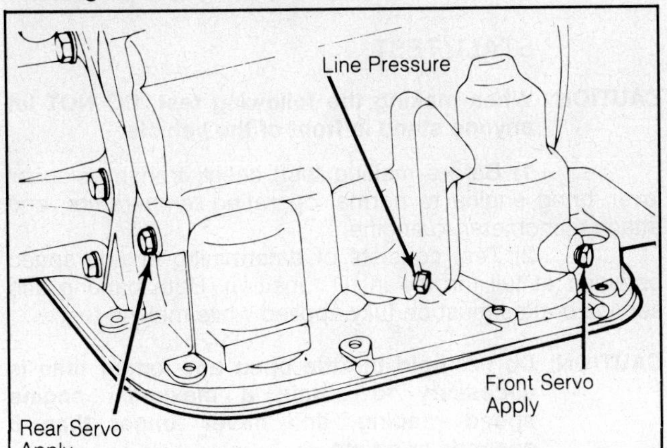

Pressure Test (Selector in "2")

1) Install "T" connection at rear cooler line fitting. Attach 0-100 psi gauges to "T" connection and line pressure port. Operate engine at 1000 RPM for test. Move selector lever on transmission 1 detent rearward from full forward position (into selector "2" position).

2) Read pressures on both gauges as throttle lever on transmission is moved from full rearward position to full forward position. Line pressure should read 54-90 psi (3.8-6.3 kg/cm²) with throttle lever rearward and gradually increase, as lever is moved forward to 90-96 psi (6.3-6.8 kg/cm²).

3) Lubrication pressure should be 6-16 psi (0.4-1.1 kg/cm²) with lever rearward, and 10-30 psi (0.7-2.1 kg/cm²) with lever forward. This tests pump output, pressure regulation, and condition of rear clutch and lubrication hydraulic circuits.

Pressure Test (Selector in "D")

1) Attach 0-100 psi gauges to line and front servo release ports. Operate engine at 1600 RPM for test. Move selector lever on transmission 2 detents rearward from full forward position (selector in "D" position).

Fig. 4: Rear View of Transmission Case Showing Pressure Test Ports

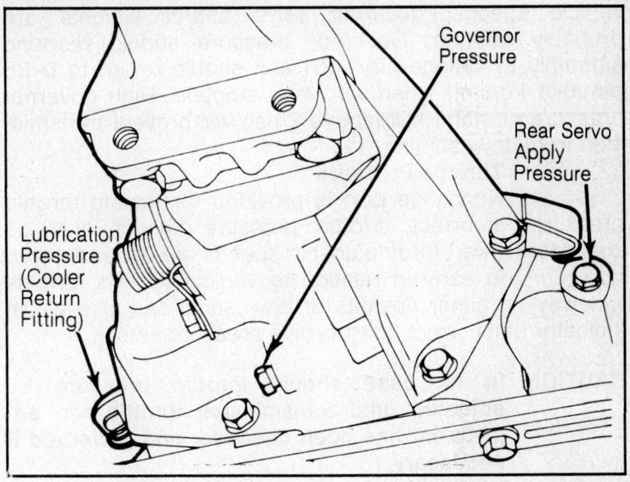

2) Read pressure on both gauges as throttle lever on transmission is moved from full rearward position to full forward position. Line pressure should rear 54-60 psi (3.8-4.2 kg/cm²) with throttle lever rearward and gradually increase, as lever is moved forward.

3) Front servo release is pressurized only in direct drive and should be same as line pressure within 3 psi (.2 kg/cm²), up to downshift point. This tests pump output, pressure regulation, and condition of rear clutch and front clutch hydraulic circuits.

NOTE: **A 0-300 psi gauge is required for the following test.**

Pressure Test (Selector in Reverse)

1) Attach gauge to rear servo apply port. Operate engine at 1600 RPM for test. Move selector lever on transmission 4 detents rearward from full forward position (into selector "R" position).

2) Rear servo pressure should read 230-260 psi (16.2-18.3 kg/cm²). This tests pump output, pressure regulation, and condition of front clutch and rear servo hydraulic circuits.

3) Move selector lever on transmission to "D" position to check that rear servo pressure drops to zero. This tests for leakage into rear servo, due to case porosity, which can cause reverse band to burn out.

Pressure Test Indication

1) If proper line pressure, minimum to maximum, is found in any one test, pump and pressure

CHRYSLER CORP. & MITSUBISHI TORQUEFLITE (Cont.)

regulator are working properly. Low pressure in "D", "L" and "2" but correct pressure in "R", indicates rear clutch circuit leakage.

2) Low pressure in "D" and "R", but correct pressure in "L", indicates front clutch circuit leakage. Low pressure in "R" and "L", but correct pressure in "2", indicates rear servo circuit leakage, low line pressure in all positions indicates defective pump, clogged filter, or stuck pressure regulator valve.

Governor Pressure

NOTE: Test only if transmission shifts at wrong vehicle speeds when throttle rod is correctly adjusted.

1) Connect 0-100 psi (0-7.0 kg/cm²) gauge to governor pressure port. Operate transmission in third gear to read pressures. See AUTOMATIC SHIFT SPEEDS and GOVERNOR PRESSURE CHART.

2) If governor pressures are incorrect at given vehicle speeds, governor valve and/or weights are probably sticking. Governor pressure should respond smoothly to changes in MPH and should return to 0-1.5 psi (0-.1 kg/cm²) when vehicle is stopped. High governor pressure at stand still (above 2 psi) will prevent transmission from downshifting.

Throttle Pressure

No gauge port is provided for testing throttle pressure. Incorrect throttle pressure should only be suspected if part throttle upshift speeds are either delayed or occur too early in relation to vehicle speeds. Engine runaway on either upshifts or downshifts can also be an indicator of incorrect (low) throttle pressure setting.

CAUTION: In no case should throttle pressure be adjusted until transmission throttle rod adjustment has been checked, and corrected if necessary.

HYDRAULIC PRESSURE ADJUSTMENTS

NOTE: An incorrect throttle pressure setting will cause incorrect line pressure readings even though line pressure adjustment is correct. Always inspect and correct throttle pressure adjustment before adjusting line pressure.

Throttle Pressure

1) Remove valve body from transmission. Insert Throttle Pressure Adjuster (C-3763) between throttle lever cam and kickdown valve.

Fig. 5: View of Valve Body Showing Throttle Pressure Adjustment

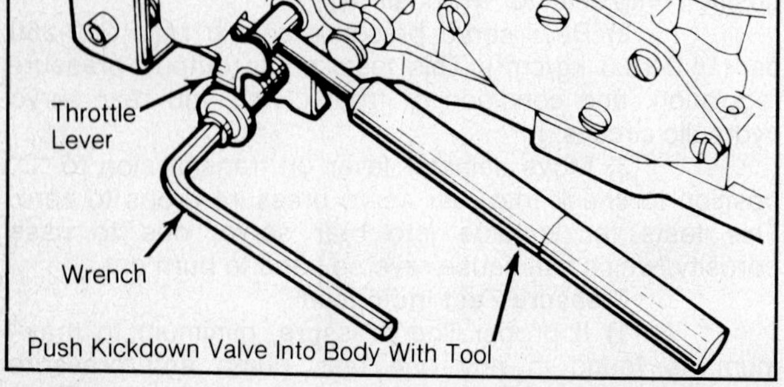

2) By pushing in on throttle pressure adjuster, compress kickdown valve against spring so valve is completely bottomed inside the valve body. As force is being exerted to compress spring, turn throttle lever stop screw with an Allen Wrench until head of screw touches throttle lever tang with throttle lever cam touching tool and throttle valve bottomed.

Line Pressure

1) Turn Allen screw in end of pressure regulator spring bracket so measurement between valve body and inner edge of adjusting nut is 1 5/16". *See Fig. 6.*

NOTE: Due to manufacturing tolerances, adjustment can be varied to obtain specified line pressure.

Fig. 6: View of Valve Body Showing Line Pressure Adjustment

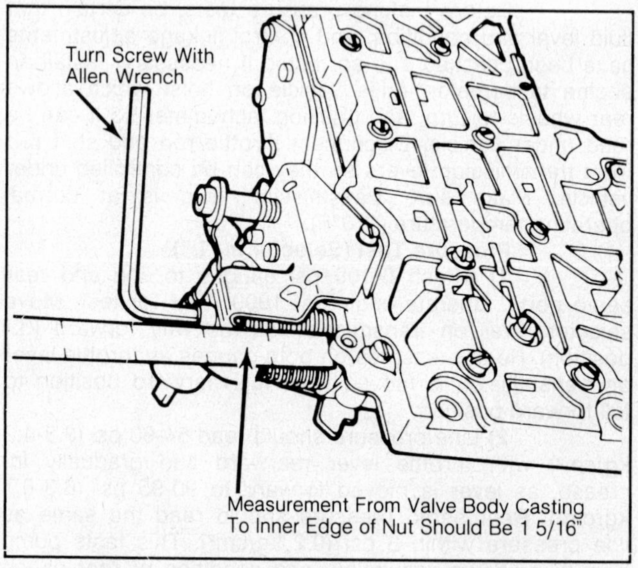

2) One complete turn of adjusting screw changes closed throttle line pressure approximately 1.4 psi (.098 kg/cm²). Turning adjusting screw counterclockwise increases pressure; clockwise decreases pressure.

STALL TEST

CAUTION: When making the following test, DO NOT let anyone stand in front of the vehicle.

1) Before making test, check transmission oil level, bring engine to normal operating temperature, and attach tachometer to engine.

2) Test consists of determining engine speed obtained at full throttle in "D" position. Both parking and service brakes must be fully applied while making test.

CAUTION: Do not hold throttle open any longer than is necessary to obtain a maximum engine speed reading, and never longer than 5 seconds at a time.

3) If more than one stall check is required, operate engine at approximately 1000 RPM in neutral for 20 seconds to cool transmission fluid between runs. If engine speed exceeds maximum limits shown, release accelerator immediately since transmission clutch slippage is indicated.

CHRYSLER CORP. & MITSUBISHI TORQUEFLITE (Cont.)

Stall Speed Above Specification

If stall speed exceeds maximum limits shown by more than 200 RPM, transmission clutch slippage is indicated. Make hydraulic pressure and air pressure checks to determine cause of slippage.

Stall Speed Below Specification

1) Low stall speeds (with a properly tuned engine) indicate torque converter stator clutch problems. A road test will be necessary to identify exact problem.

2) If stall speeds are 250-350 RPM below specifications, and vehicle operates properly at highway speeds, but has poor through-gear acceleration, stator overrunning clutch is slipping.

3) If stall speed and acceleration are normal, but abnormally high throttle opening is required to maintain highway speeds, stator clutch has seized. Both of these stator defects require replacement of torque converter.

Noise

Whining or siren-like noise due to fluid flow is normal during stall operation with some converters; however, loud metallic noises from loose parts or interference within the assembly indicate a defective converter. To be sure noise originates within the converter, raise vehicle on hoist and operate at light throttle in "D" and "N" while listening under transmission bell housing.

STALL SPEED SPECIFICATIONS

Application	Stall RPM
2.0L Engine	1950-2450
2.6L Engine	1800-2200

SERVICE (IN VEHICLE)

SPEEDOMETER PINION GEAR

Removal

Remove bolt and retainer securing speedometer pinion adapter in extension housing. With cable housing connected, carefully work adapter and pinion out of extension housing.

Fig. 7: Disassembled View of Speedometer Drive

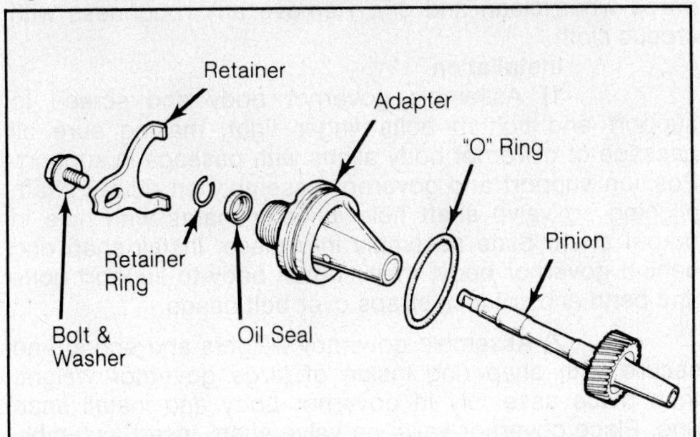

Seal Replacement

If transmission fluid is found in cable housing, replace seal in adapter. Start seal and retainer ring in adapter, then push into adapter using Seal Installer (C-4004) until tool bottoms.

Fig. 8: Speedometer Pinion Seal Installation

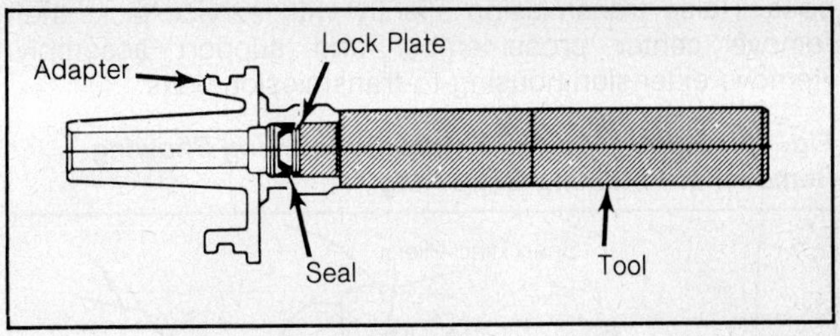

CAUTION: To avoid misalignment, make sure adapter flange and its mating area on extension housing are clean.

Installation

1) Note number of gear teeth and install speedometer pinion gear into adapter. Rotate pinion gear and adapter assembly so that number on adapter, corresponding with number of teeth on gear, is in 6 o'clock position as assembly is installed.

2) Install retainer and bolt, with tangs in adapter positioning slots. Tap adapter firmly into extension housing, then tighten retainer bolt.

Fig. 9: View of Extension Housing Showing Speedometer Pinion and Adapter Installation

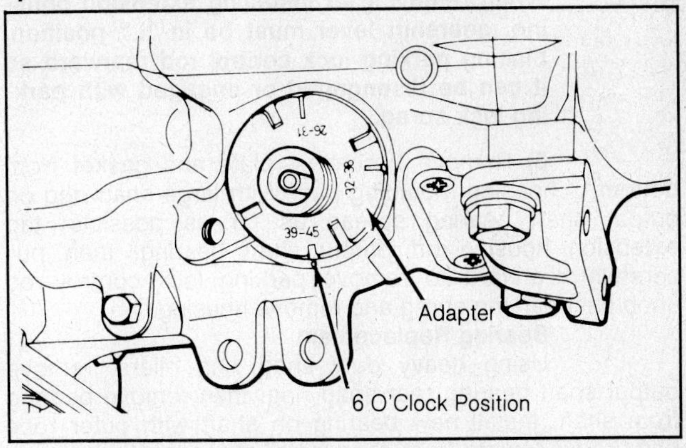

NEUTRAL SAFETY SWITCH

See AUTO. TRANS. SERVICING

EXTENSION HOUSING YOKE SEAL

CAUTION: Use care not to damage yoke and splines.

Removal

Marking parts for reassembly reference, remove propeller shaft. Cut boot end of extension housing yoke seal, then use puller to remove seal from extension housing.

Installation

Using seal installer, drive new seal into extension housing. Install propeller shaft, aligning marks made at removal.

EXTENSION HOUSING

Removal

1) Marking parts for reassembly reference, remove propeller shaft, then remove extension housing seal. Remove speedometer pinion adapter assembly, then drain approximately 2 quarts of transmission fluid.

CHRYSLER CORP. & MITSUBISHI TORQUEFLITE (Cont.)

2) Remove extension housing-to-crossmember bolts. Raise transmission slightly with service jack, then remove center crossmember and support assembly. Remove extension housing-to-transmission bolts.

Fig. 10: Bottom View of Extension Housing Showing Removal of Retaining Snap Ring

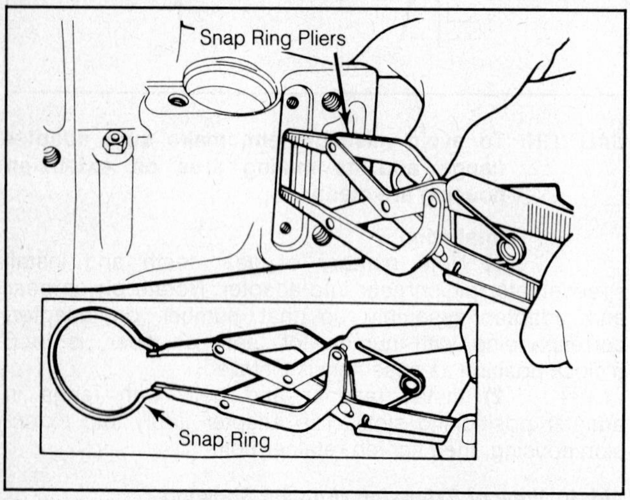

NOTE: **When removing or installing extension housing, gearshift lever must be in "L" position, placing parking lock control rod rearward so it can be disengaged or engaged with parking lock sprag.**

3) Remove 2 screws, plate and gasket from bottom of housing mounting pad. With large snap ring on output shaft bearing spread as far as possible, tap extension housing off output shaft bearing, then pull carefully rearward to remove parking lock control rod knob past parking sprag and remove housing.

Bearing Replacement

Using heavy duty snap ring pliers, remove output shaft bearing rear snap ring, then remove bearing from shaft. Install new bearing on shaft with outer race ring groove toward front, then install rear snap ring.

Bushing Replacement

Using driver, remove bushing from extension housing. Align hole in new bushing with oil slot in extension housing, drive or press bushing into housing, then install new seal.

Installation

1) Install a new gasket on transmission case. Position output shaft bearing retaining snap ring in extension housing. Slide extension housing on output shaft guiding the parking lock control rod knob past parking sprag. While spreading large snap ring in housing, carefully tap housing into place, then release snap ring.

CAUTION: **Make sure snap ring is fully seated in bearing outer race ring groove.**

2) Install and tighten extension housing-to-transmission bolts, then install gasket, plate, and screws on bottom of extension housing mounting pad. Install center crossmember and rear mount assembly, then lower transmission and install and tighten extension housing-to-support bolts.

3) Install speedometer pinion and adapter. Carefully guide front universal joint yoke into extension housing and on the output shaft splines. Align marks made at removal and connect propeller shaft to rear axle pinion shaft yoke. Adjust transmission fluid level as necessary.

Fig. 11: Rear View of Transmission Showing Output Shaft Bearing Installation

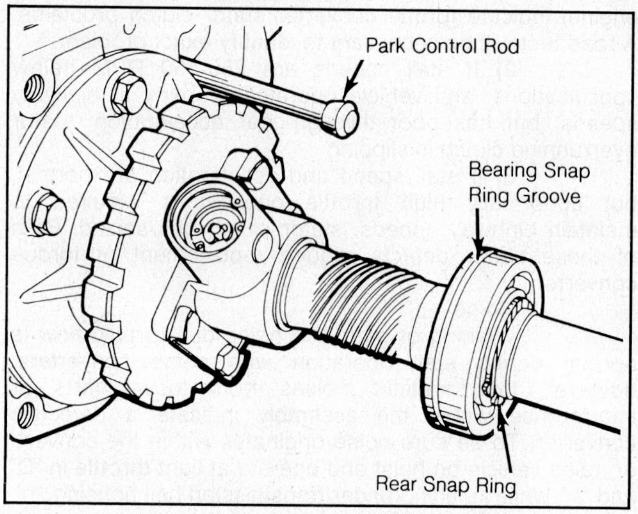

GOVERNOR & PARKING GEAR

Removal

1) Remove extension housing and output shaft bearings as previously outlined. Carefully pry snap ring from weight end of governor valve shaft, then slide valve and shaft assembly out of governor body.

2) Remove large snap ring from weight end of governor body, then lift out governor weight assembly. Remove snap ring from inside governor weight, then remove inner weight and spring from outer weight.

3) Remove snap ring from behind governor body, slide governor and support assembly off output shaft. Remove bolts and separate governor body and screen from parking gear.

Inspection

Inspect all parts for wear or damage, and spring for distortion. Weights and valve should fall freely in bores when clean and dry. Remove any roughness with crocus cloth.

Installation

1) Assemble governor body and screen to support and tighten bolts finger tight, making sure oil passage of governor body aligns with passage in support. Position support and governor assembly on output shaft, aligning so valve shaft hole in body mates with hole in output shaft. Slide assembly into place, install snap ring behind governor body, then tighten body-to-support bolts and bend ends of lock straps over bolt heads.

2) Assemble governor weights and spring and secure with snap ring inside of large governor weight, then place assembly in governor body and install snap ring. Place governor valve on valve shaft, insert assembly into body and through governor weights, then install valve shaft retaining snap ring. Inspect valve and weight assembly for free movement, then install output shaft bearing and extension housing.

CHRYSLER CORP. & MITSUBISHI TORQUEFLITE (Cont.)

Fig. 12: Installed View of Governor Assembly

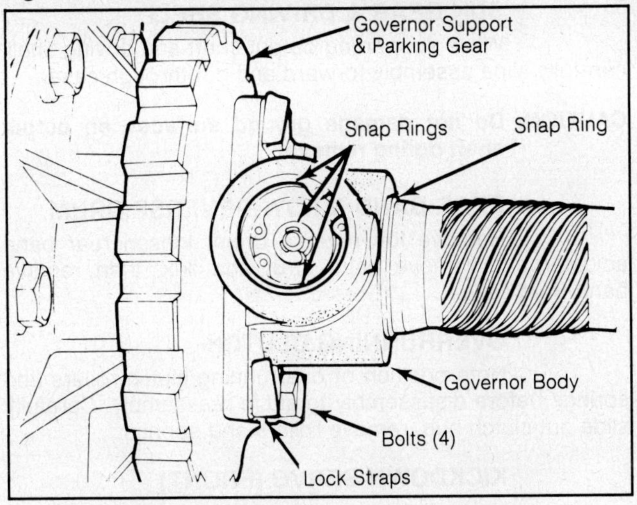

Fig. 13: Disassembled View of Governor Assembly

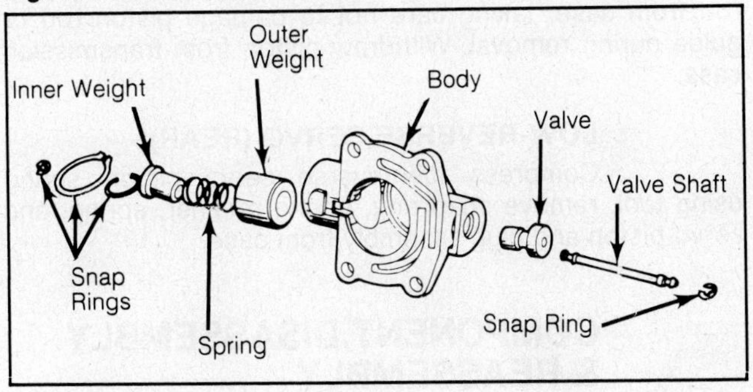

PARKING LOCK

Removal

With extension housing removed, slide shaft out of housing to remove parking sprag and spring. Remove snap ring, then slide reaction plug and pin assembly out of housing.

Installation

Install reaction plug and spring assembly in housing, then secure with snap ring. Position sprag and spring in housing then insert shaft, making sure square lug on sprag is toward parking gear, and spring is positioned so it moves sprag away from gear. Install extension housing.

Fig. 14: Disassembled View Showing Components of Parking Lock Assembly

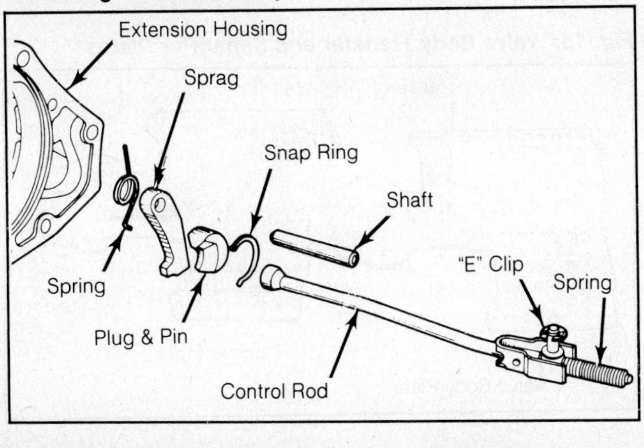

VALVE BODY ASSEMBLY & ACCUMULATOR PISTON

Removal

1) Loosen oil pan bolts, tap pan to break it loose allowing fluid to drain, then remove pan. Loosen clamp bolts, then remove throttle and shift levers from transmission.

2) Remove neutral safety switch, then remove valve body-to-transmission case bolts and lower valve body down and forward out of case. If necessary, rotate propeller shaft to align parking gear and sprag to permit knob on end of parking control rod to pass sprag.

3) Remove accumulator piston and spring from transmission case, then inspect for damage. If valve body manual lever shaft seal requires replacement, drive out of case with punch. Drive new seal into case with a 15/16" (24 mm) socket and hammer.

NOTE: **Seal may be replaced without removing valve body from case by using a small screwdriver to pry seal out of case. Take care not to damage shaft or seal bore in case.**

Installation

1) With neutral safety switch removed from case, place valve body manual lever in low position to move parking rod to rear position. Use screwdriver to push sprag into engagement with parking gear, turning output shaft to ensure engagement. This will allow knob on end of parking rod to move past sprag as valve body is installed. Install accumulator piston in case. Position accumulator spring between piston and valve body.

2) Place valve body in position, working park rod through opening and past sprag, then install retaining bolts finger tight. Install neutral safety switch. Place manual lever in neutral position, shifting valve body if necessary to center neutral finger over switch plunger.

3) Install and tighten valve body-to-case bolts evenly. Install gearshift lever and tighten clamp bolt. Move lever through all detent positions to ensure shaft does not bind in case. If binding exists, loosen valve body bolts and realign.

4) Be sure throttle shaft seal is in place, then install flat washer and throttle lever and tighten clamp bolt. Connect throttle and gearshift linkage, adjust as required. Install oil pan with new gasket, then adjust transmission fluid level.

REMOVAL & INSTALLATION

See the appropriate article in AUTOMATIC TRANSMISSION REMOVAL section.

TORQUE CONVERTER

Converter Pressure Test

Drain all oil from converter. If flushing is required, flush before checking for leakage. Install Pressure Tester (C-4102) and tighten. Apply a maximum of 100 psi (7.0 kg/cm²) air pressure to converter, then submerge in a tank of water and observe hub, ring gear and seam welds for bubbles. Five to ten minutes may be required for bubbles to appear from small leaks. If leakage occurs, converter must be replaced.

CHRYSLER CORP. & MITSUBISHI TORQUEFLITE (Cont.)

TRANSMISSION DISASSEMBLY

INPUT SHAFT END PLAY CHECK

Measuring input shaft end play before disassembly will usually indicate when thrust washer change is required (except when major parts are replaced). Thrust washer is located between input and output shafts. Attach dial indicator to transmission converter housing with plunger seated against end of input shaft. Move input shaft in and out to obtain end play reading. End play should be .022-.091" (.56-2.3 mm). Record end play reading for reassembly reference.

Fig. 15: Using a Dial Indicator to Measure Input Shaft End Play

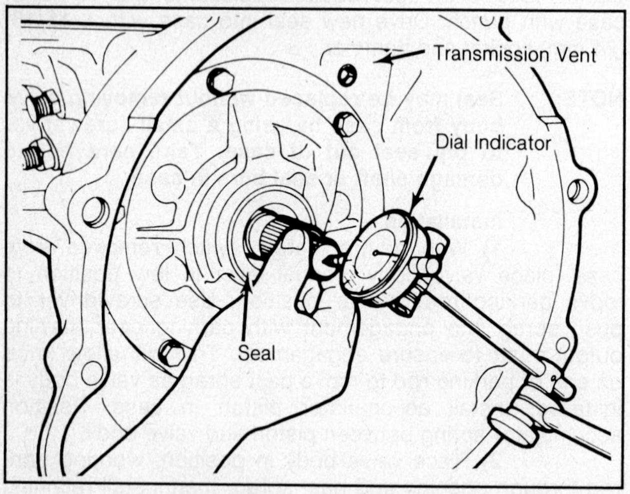

VALVE BODY ASSEMBLY & ACCUMULATOR PISTON

See SERVICE (IN VEHILCE) article.

EXTENSION HOUSING

See SERVICE (IN VEHICLE) article.

GOVERNOR

See SERVICE (IN VEHICLE) article.

OIL PUMP & REACTION SHAFT SUPPORT

Tighten front band adjusting screw until band is tight on front clutch retainer, preventing retainer from coming out with pump, damaging clutches. Remove oil pump housing retaining bolts, then install slide hammers in threaded holes in pump housing flange. Operating both hammers evenly, withdraw pump and reaction shaft support assembly from case.

FRONT BAND & FRONT CLUTCH

Loosen front band adjuster, remove band strut then slide band out of case. Slide front clutch assembly out of case.

INPUT SHAFT & REAR CLUTCH

Grasp input shaft, then slide input shaft and rear clutch assembly out of case.

CAUTION: Do not lose thrust washer located between rear end of input shaft and forward end of output shaft.

PLANETARY GEAR ASSEMBLIES, SUN GEAR & DRIVING SHELL

While supporting output shaft and driving shell, carefully slide assembly forward and out through case.

CAUTION: Do not damage ground surfaces on output shaft during removal.

REAR BAND & LOW-REVERSE DRUM

Remove low-reverse drum, loosen rear band adjuster and remove band strut and link, then remove band from case.

OVERRUNNING CLUTCH

Note position of overrunning clutch rollers and springs before disassembly to aid in reassembly. Carefully slide out clutch hub, remove rollers and springs.

KICKDOWN SERVO (FRONT)

Using tool, compress kickdown servo spring, remove snap ring. Remove rod guide, springs, and piston rod from case, taking care not to damage piston rod or guide during removal. Withdraw piston from transmission case.

LOW-REVERSE SERVO (REAR)

Compress low-reverse servo piston spring using tool, remove snap ring, spring retainer, spring, and servo piston and plug assembly from case.

COMPONENT DISASSEMBLY & REASSEMBLY

VALVE BODY DISASSEMBLY

NOTE: Tag all springs for reassembly reference as they are removed.

CAUTION: DO NOT clamp any portion of valve body or transfer plate in vise. Any distortion of valve body or transfer plate will result in sticking valves. Always place valve in repair stand when repair procedures are to be performed.

Filter, Transfer Plate & Pressure Regulators

1) Remove 3 screws from fluid filter and remove filter from valve body. Remove top and bottom screws from adjustment screw bracket. Hold bracket firmly while removing last retaining screw from side of valve body.

Fig. 16: Valve Body Transfer and Separator Plates

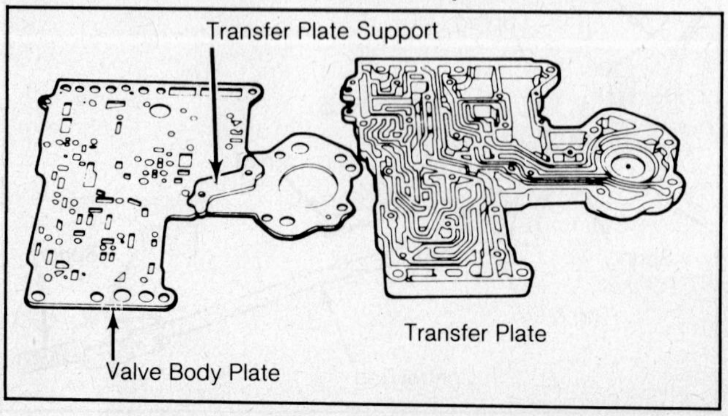

2) Remove bracket with line and throttle pressure adjusting screws (do not disturb screw settings). Also remove regulator valve and switch valve springs. Remove switch valve and regulator valve. Remove transfer plate retaining screws and remove transfer plate and valve body plate. *See Fig. 16*.

3) Remove 6 screws from transfer plate support and valve body plate and separate parts for cleaning. Remove rear clutch check ball and rear servo check ball from transfer plate. Also remove screen from valve body plate. *See Fig. 16*. Remove 7 check balls from valve body. *See Fig. 20*.

Fig. 17: Exploded View of Valve Body Showing Shuttle Valve and Governor Plugs

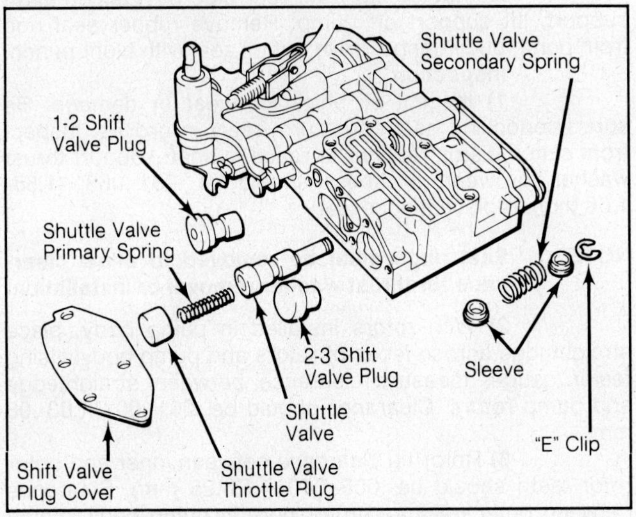

Shuttle Valve & Governor Plugs

1) Turn valve body over. Remove "E" clip and park sprag rod from manual lever. Remove shuttle valve cover plate. Remove shift valve plug cover.

2) Remove 1-2 and 2-3 shift valve plugs. Remove shuttle valve "E" clip and slide shuttle valve, along with the secondary spring and sleeve, from bore.

Manual Lever & Throttle Lever

1) Remove "E" clip and washer from throttle lever shaft. Remove any burrs from shaft. While holding manual lever detent ball and spring in bore, slide manual lever off throttle shaft.

2) Remove detent ball and spring, slide manual valve from bore. Slide out kickdown detent, kickdown valve, throttle valve spring, and throttle valve.

Shift Valves & Regulator Plugs

1) Remove regulator valve cover. Slide out sleeve, line pressure plug, throttle pressure plug, and spring. Remove limit valve body and throttle pressure plug.

2) Remove retainer, limit valve and spring. Remove each shift valve and spring. Withdraw 1-2 shift control valve out of its bore.

VALVE BODY INSPECTION

1) Wash all parts in solvent and blow dry with compressed air. Inspect all parts for nicks, burrs, scratches, or distortion. Small nicks and burrs may be removed with crocus cloth, taking care not to round off any machined sharp edges. Make sure all passages are clean and free from obstructions, and all metering holes in steel plate and valve body are open.

2) Inspect all valve springs for distortion or collapsed coils. Inspect manual and throttle valve operating levers and shafts. If lever is loose on its shaft, it may be SILVER SOLDERED ONLY, or lever and shaft assembly should be replaced. DO NOT attempt to straighten bent levers. When bores, valves and plugs are clean and dry, valves and plugs should fall freely in their bores.

VALVE BODY REASSEMBLY

Shift Valves & Regulator Plugs

1) Insert 1-2 and 2-3 shift valves and springs into proper valve body bores. Assemble limit valve body as follows: Insert limit valve and spring into proper bore. Fit spring retainer in groove in limit valve body. Place throttle plug in limit valve body. Place this assembly against shift valve spring.

2) Mount shift valve cover to valve body. Tighten screws to 26-42 INCH lbs. (2.9-4.9 N.m). Install springs, throttle pressure plug, line pressure plug and sleeve. Secure regulator valve cover to valve body.

Manual Lever & Throttle Lever

1) Install throttle valve, throttle valve spring, kickdown valve, and kickdown detent plug. Slide manual valve into bore. *See Fig. 18*. Install throttle lever on valve body. Insert detent ball and spring in bore in valve body.

2) Depress ball and spring and slide manual lever over throttle shaft so it engages manual valve and detent ball. Install seal, retaining washer, and "E" clip on throttle shaft.

Shuttle Valve & Shift Plugs

Place 1-2 and 2-3 shift valve plugs in their bores. Install shuttle valve, spring and shuttle valve throttle plug. Install shift valve end plate. Install "E" clip on end of shuttle valve, then install shuttle valve cover plate.

Fig. 18: Exploded View of Valve Body Showing Pressure Regulators and Manual Control

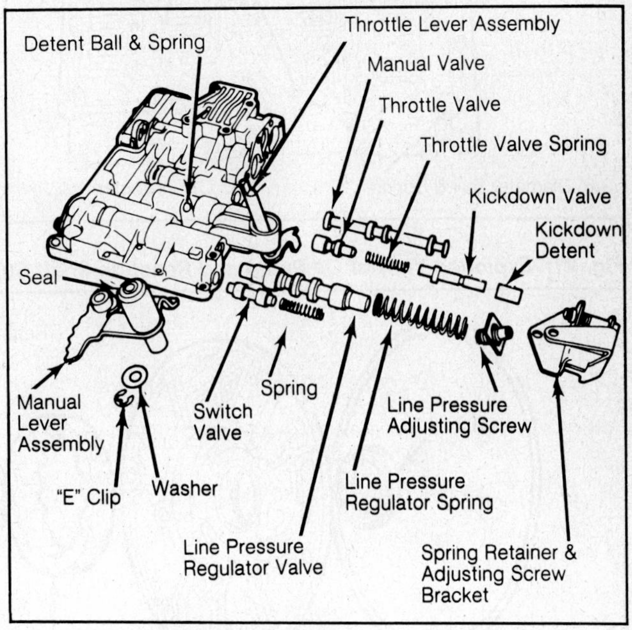

Filter, Transfer Plate, & Pressure Regulators

1) Install 7 check balls in valve body. *See Fig. 20*. Install rear clutch check ball and rear servo check ball in transfer plate. Install regulator valve screen to valve body plate.

CHRYSLER CORP. & MITSUBISHI TORQUEFLITE (Cont.)

2) Assemble transfer plate to valve body plate with 6 screws. Place transfer plate assembly on valve body and install 14 screws. Tighten screws to 26-42 INCH lbs. (2.9-4.9 N.m) working from center screws outward.

Fig. 19: Exploded View of Valve Body Showing Shift Valves and Pressure Regulator Valve Plugs

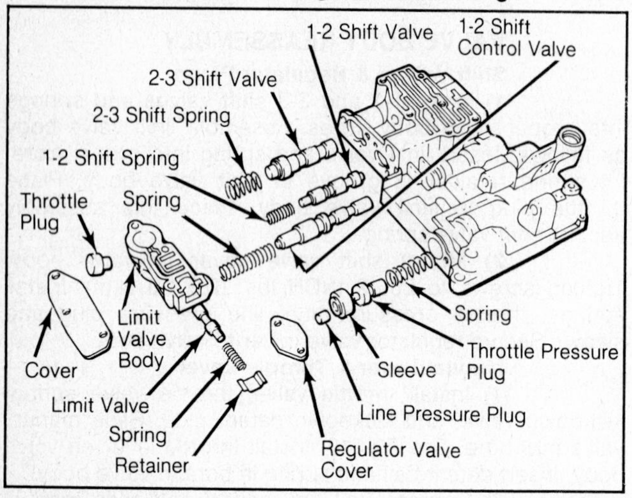

Fig. 20: View of Valve Body Showing Check Ball Locations

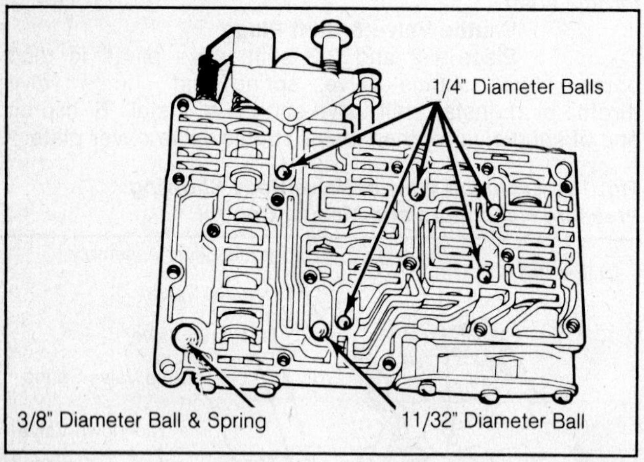

3) Place switch valve, regulator valve and spring in their respective bores. *See Fig. 18.* Place adjustment screw bracket on spring and temporarily install side mounting screw. After top and bottom screws have been installed and tightened, tighten side screw.

4) Install oil filter and tighten attaching screws. After valve body is completely assembled, measure throttle and line pressure adjustments. If pressures were satisfactory before disassembly, use original settings. Install park sprag rod and "E" clip on manual lever.

OIL PUMP & REACTION SHAFT SUPPORT

Disassembly

Remove bolts from rear side of reaction shaft support, lift support off pump. Remove rubber seal ring from pump body flange, drive out oil seal with blunt punch.

Inspection

1) Inspect all parts for wear or damage. Be sure interlocking seal rings turn freely in groves. Inspect front clutch piston retainer to reaction shaft support thrust washer for wear; thickness should be .061-.063" (1.55-1.60 mm), replace if necessary.

NOTE: Seal rings must be removed to allow clearance for thrust washer removal or installation.

2) With rotors installed in pump body, place straightedge across faces of rotors and pump body. Using feeler gauge, measure clearance between straightedge and pump rotors. Clearance should be .001-.003" (.03-.08 mm).

3) Rotor tip clearance between inner and outer rotor teeth should be .005-.010" (.13-.25 mm). Clearance between outer rotor and rotor bore in pump body should be .004-.008" (.10-.20 mm)

Pump Bushing Replacement

1) Place pump housing (seal face down) on a clean, smooth surface. Using Remover (SP-3551) and Handle (SP-3549 or C-4171), drive bushing straight down and out of bore, being careful not to cock tool in bore. Using Installing Head (SP-5117), drive new bushing into place in pump rotor housing.

2) Stake bushing in place using blunt punch or other similar tool. Using narrow bladed knife or similar tool,

Fig. 21: Exploded View of Oil Pump and Reaction Shaft Support

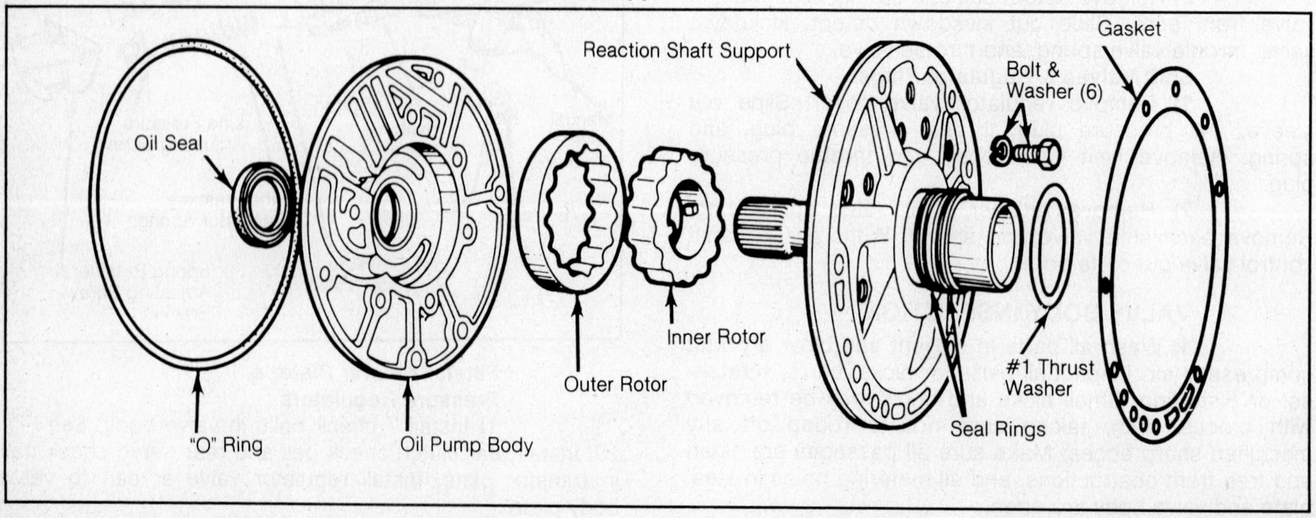

CHRYSLER CORP. & MITSUBISHI TORQUEFLITE (Cont.)

tool, remove high points or burrs around staked area. Do not use File or any tool that would remove more metal than necessary.

Fig. 22: Rear View of Oil Pump Housing Showing Staking Positions in Bushing

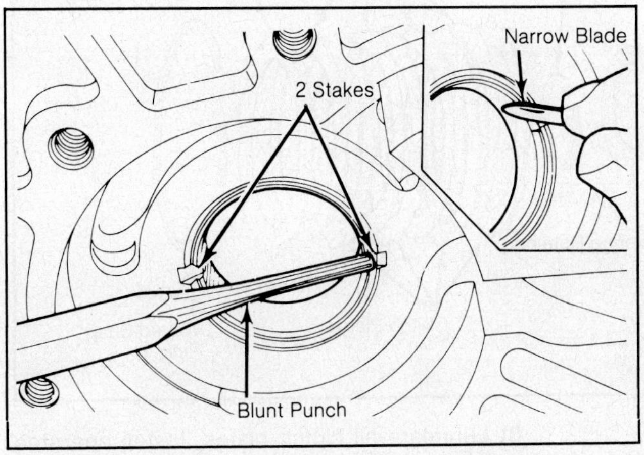

Reaction Shaft Bushing Replacement

Thread bushing remover into bushing. *See Fig. 23.* Withdraw bushing from reaction shaft. Support reaction shaft upright. Using driver, drive new bushing into place in reaction shaft.

NOTE: **If bushing failed in service, inspect support for wear from input shaft seal ring lands. If worn or grooved, replace support assembly.**

Fig. 23: Tool Set-Up for Reaction Shaft Bushing Replacement

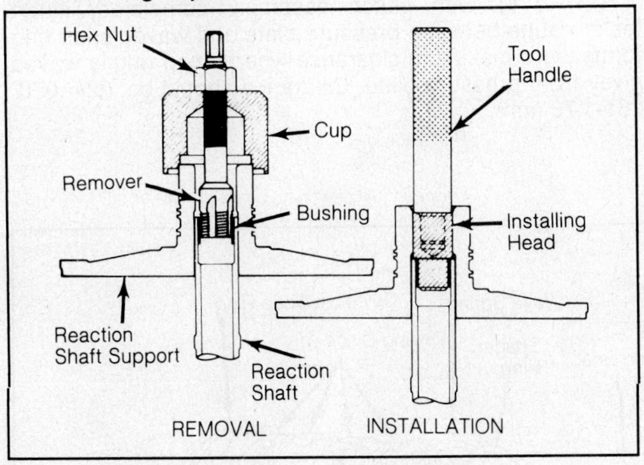

Reassembly

1) Place reaction shaft support in an Assembler (C-3759) with hub of support and tool on a smooth, flat surface. Install 2 pilot studs in threaded holes in support flange. *See Fig. 24.*

2) Assemble rotors in center of support and lower pump body over pilot studs. Using Assembler (C-3756), center rotors in pump body. With pump body firmly against reaction shaft support, tighten assembler securely.

3) Invert pump and tool assembly. Install support-to-pump bolts and tighten evenly. Remove assembler, pilot studs, and aligning tool. Using Oil Seal Installer (C-4193), install new pump oil seal.

Fig. 24: Tool Set-Up for Assembling Oil Pump and Reaction Shaft Support

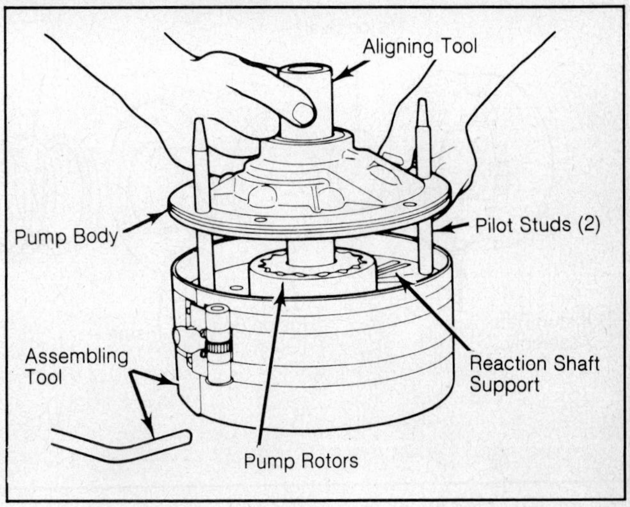

FRONT CLUTCH

Disassembly

1) Remove large waved snap ring that secures pressure plate in clutch piston retainer. Remove pressure plate, clutch discs and clutch plates from retainer. Install Compressor (C-3573-A) over piston spring retainer. Compress spring and remove snap ring.

2) Slowly release compressor until spring retainer is free from hub. Remove compressor, retainer and spring. Invert clutch retainer assembly. Bump assembly on block of wood to remove piston. Remove all seals from piston and clutch retainer hub.

Inspection

1) Inspect plates and discs for flatness; they must not be warped or cone-shaped. Inspect facing material on all driving discs, replace if damaged.

2) Inspect discs and plates for wear on splines or lugs. Check clutch retainer for damaged lug grooves, or damaged band contacting surfaces. Make sure ball check in clutch retainer moves freely.

3) Check neoprene seals for wear, hardness or deterioration. Inspect piston spring(s), retainer and snap ring for distortion.

Front Clutch Retainer Bushing Replacement

Lay clutch retainer (open end down) on a clean smooth surface. Using Head Remover (SP-3627), drive bushing straight down and out of bore, being careful not to cock tool. To install, lay clutch retainer (open end up) on clean smooth surface, using Head Installer (SP-3626), drive bushing into place in clutch retainer bore.

Reassembly

1) Lubricate and install inner seal on hub of clutch retainer, making sure lip of seal faces down and is properly seated in groove. Install outer seal on clutch piston, with lip of seal toward bottom of clutch retainer. Apply a coating of wax type lubricant to outer edge of seal. Place piston assembly in retainer and carefully seat piston in bottom of retainer.

2) Place spring on piston hub and postion spring retainer and snap ring on spring. Using Spring Compressor (C-3575-A), compress spring, seat snap ring in hub groove, remove tool.

Automatic Transmissions

CHRYSLER CORP. & MITSUBISHI TORQUEFLITE (Cont.)

Fig. 25: Exploded View of Front Clutch Assembly

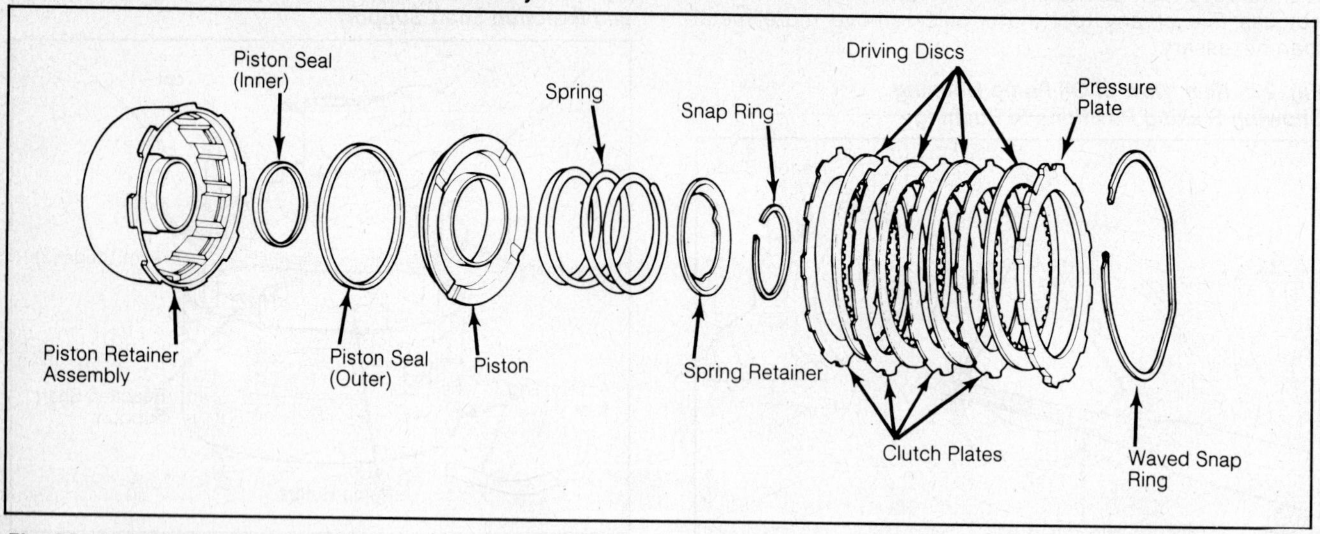

Fig. 26: Using a Feeler Gauge to Measure Front Clutch Clearance

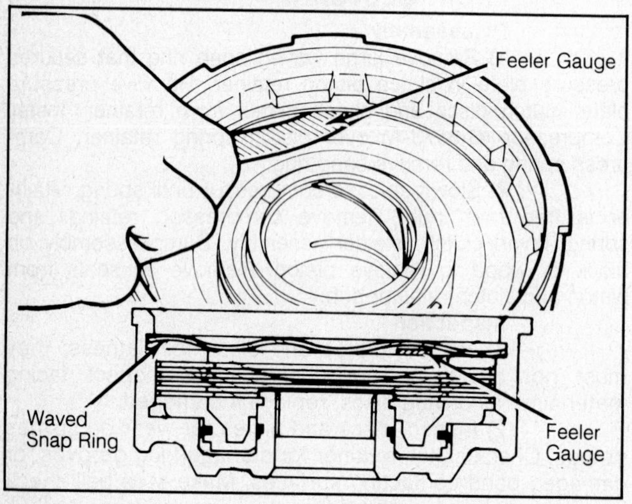

3) Lubricate all clutch plates. Install one steel plate followed by one lined disc until number given in FRONT CLUTCH CHART is installed. Install pressure plate and snap ring, making sure snap ring is properly seated. Insert feeler gauge between pressure plate and waved snap ring to measure maximum clearance where snap ring is waved away from pressure plate.

FRONT CLUTCH PLATE USAGE CHART

Application	Plates	Discs
All Models	2	2

4) With clutch assembly completed, insert feeler gauge between pressure plate and waved snap ring to measure maximum clearance where snap ring is waved away from pressure plate. Clearance should be .024-.070" (.61-1.78 mm).

Fig. 27: Exploded View of Rear Clutch Assembly

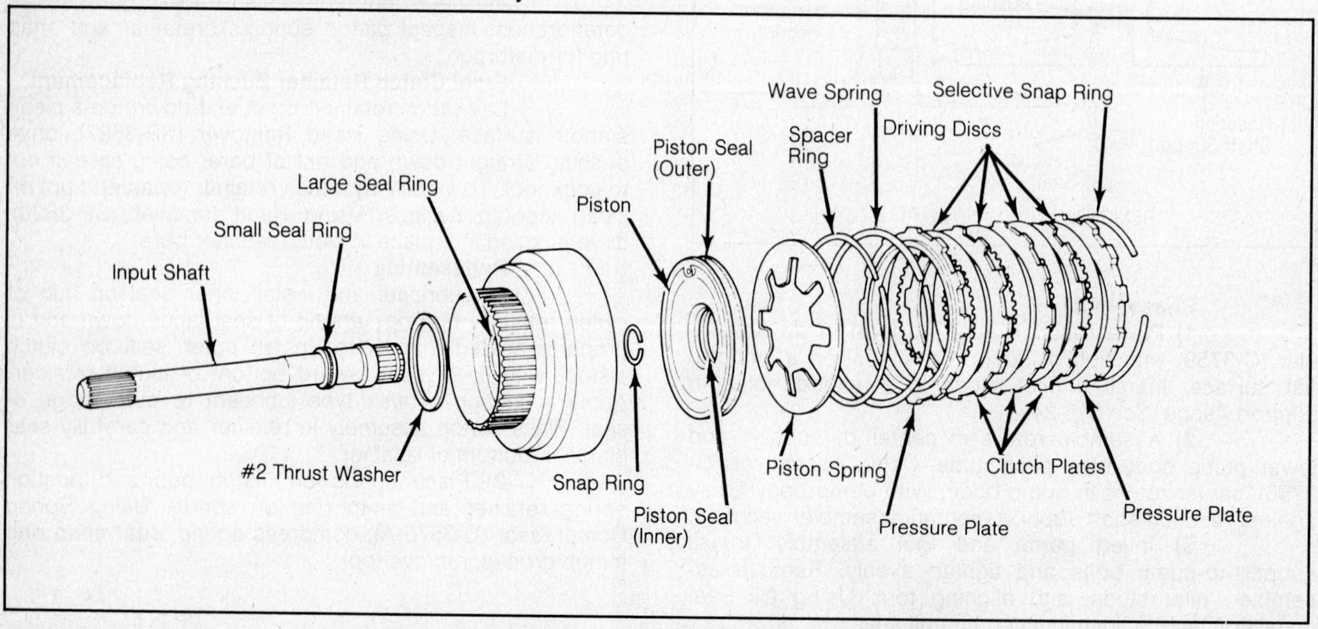

CHRYSLER CORP. & MITSUBISHI TORQUEFLITE (Cont.)

REAR CLUTCH

Disassembly

1) Remove large selective snap ring securing pressure plate in clutch piston retainer. Lift pressure plate, clutch plates, and inner pressure plate out of retainer. Carefully pry one end of wave spring out of groove in clutch retainer. Remove wave spring and clutch piston spring.

2) Invert clutch piston retainer assembly and bump it on a wood block to remove piston, then remove seals from piston. If necessary, remove snap ring and press input shaft from piston retainer.

Inspection

1) Inspect all parts for wear or damage. Plates and discs must not be warped or cone-shaped. Note ball check in clutch retainer, make sure ball moves freely. Inspect neoprene seals for deterioration, wear and hardness.

2) Inspect piston spring and wave spring for distortion or breakage. Inspect seal rings for wear or breakage, make sure they turn freely in grooves. Inspect rear clutch-to-front clutch thrust washer for wear. Thickness should be .061-.063" (1.55-1.60 mm), replace as necessary.

NOTE: **Do not remove rings unless conditions warrant. Replacement seal rings are cast iron hooked joint type.**

Reassembly

1) If removed, press input shaft into piston retainer and install snap ring. Lubricate and install inner and outer seals on clutch piston, making sure lips of seals face toward head of clutch retainer and are properly seated in grooves. Place piston assembly in retainer, with a twisting motion, seat piston in bottom of retainer.

2) Place clutch piston spring on top of piston in clutch retainer. Start one end of wave spring in retainer groove. Progressively push or tap spring into place making sure it is fully seated in groove.

3) Install inner pressure plate in clutch retainer with raised portion of plate resting on spring. Lubricate all clutch plates. Install one lined disc followed by one steel plate until all plates are installed. Install outer pressure plate and selective snap ring.

Fig. 28: Installing Piston Spring and Wave Spring in Rear Clutch Drum

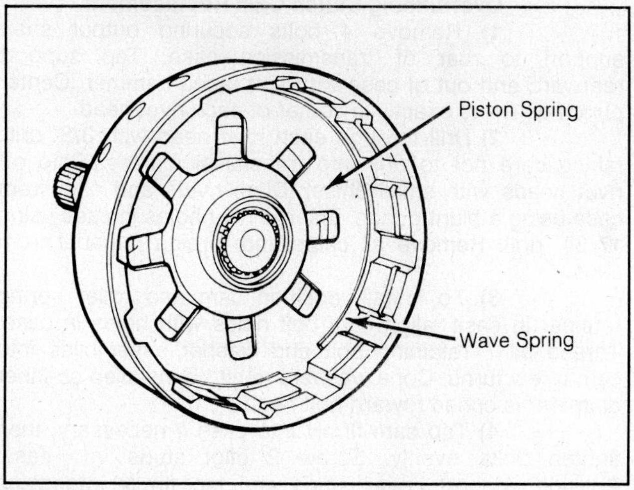

Fig. 29: Using Feeler Gauge to Measure Rear Clutch Clearance

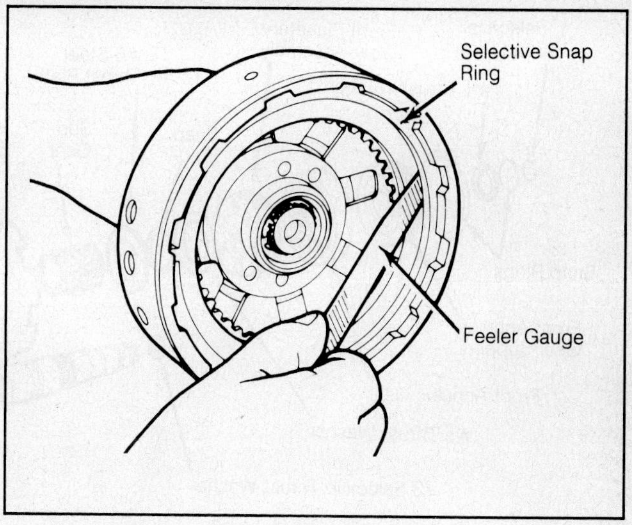

REAR CLUTCH PLATE CHART

Application	Plates	Discs
All Models	2	3

4) Measure rear clutch clearance by pressing down frimly on outer pressure plate. Inserting feeler gauge between plate and snap ring. Clearance should be .032-.055" (.82-1.39 mm), with low limit clearance desirable. Install new snap ring of proper thickness to obtain specified clearance. Snap rings are available in thicknesses of .061", .077" and .099" (1.55, 1.96 and 2.51 mm).

PLANETARY GEAR TRAIN

End Play

1) Measure end play of planetary gear assemblies, sun gear and driving shell before removing from output shaft. Stand assembly upright with forward end of output shaft on a wood block so that all parts will move forward against snap ring at front of shaft.

2) Insert feeler gauge between rear annulus gear support hub and shoulder on output shaft. Clearance should be .006-.033" (.16-.83 mm). If clearance exceeds specifications, replace thrust washers and/or necessary parts. *See Fig. 30.*

Fig. 30: Using a Feeler Gauge to Measure Planetary Gear Train End Play

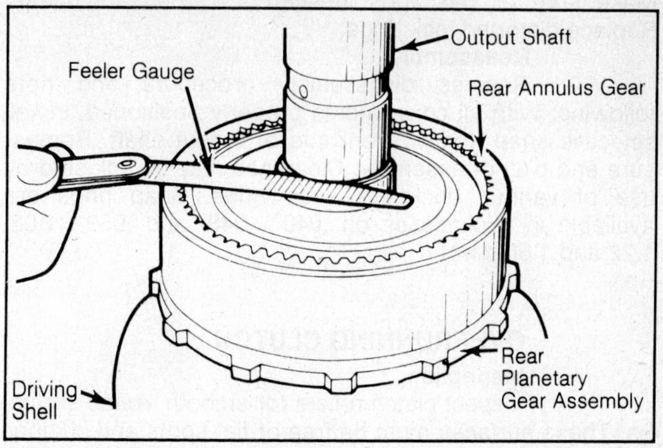

CHRYSLER CORP. & MITSUBISHI TORQUEFLITE (Cont.)

Fig. 31: Exploded View of Planetary Gear Train and Output Shaft

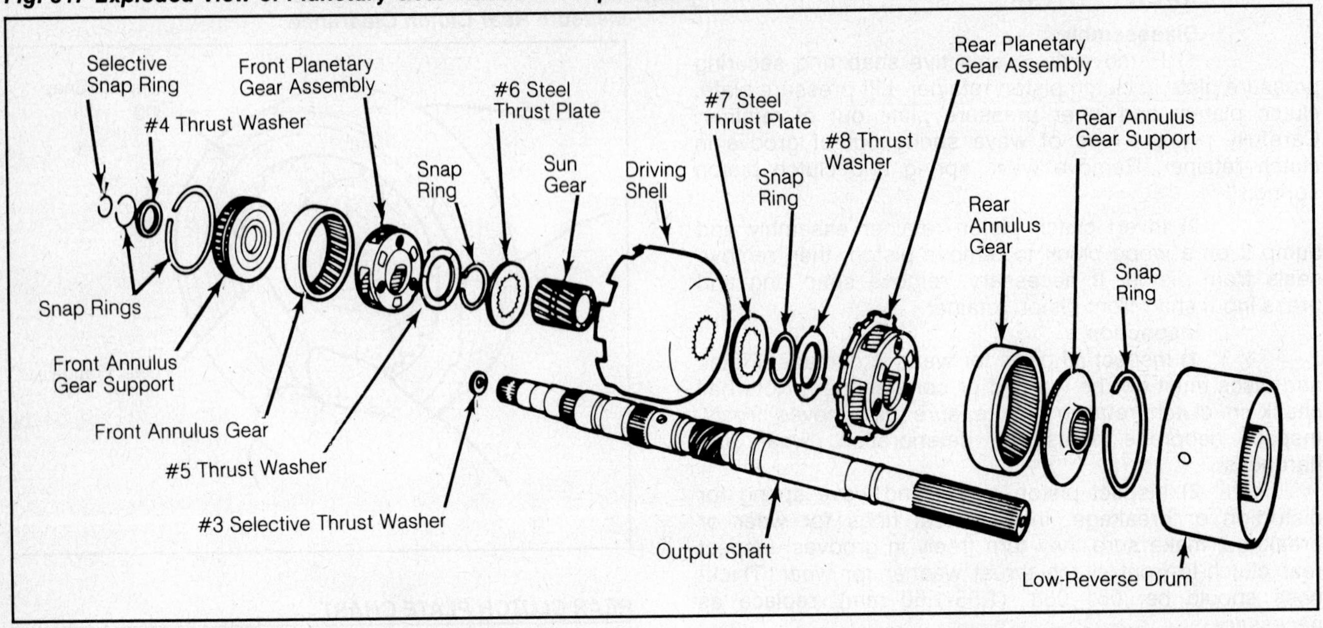

Disassembly

1) Remove selective thrust washer from forward end of output shaft. Remove selective snap ring and thrust washer from forward hub of front planetary gear assembly. Slide front annulus gear and support off planetary gear set.

2) If necessary, remove snap ring from front of annulus gear to separate support from annulus gear. Slide sun gear, driving shell and rear planetary assembly off output shaft. Lift sun gear and driving shell off rear planetary assembly. Remove snap ring and thrust plate from sun gear (rear side of driving shell).

3) Slide sun gear out of driving shell. Remove snap ring and thrust plate from opposite end of sun gear if necessary. Remove thrust washer from forward side of rear planetary assembly. Remove planetary gear set from rear annulus gear. If necessary, remove snap ring from rear of annulus gear to separate support from annulus gear.

Inspection

Inspect all parts for nicks, burrs, scores or other damage. Light scratches, small nicks or burrs can be removed with crocus cloth or fine stone. Inspect bushings in sun gear for wear or scores, replace assembly if bushings are damaged. Inspect all thrust washers for wear and scores, replace if damaged or worn. Make sure oil passages in shaft are open and clean. Replace distorted lock rings.

Reassembly

Reverse disassembly procedure and note following: With all components properly positioned, install selective snap ring on front end of output shaft. Remeasure end play of assembly. Clearance may be adjusted by use of various thickness snap rings. Snap rings are available in thicknesses on .040", .048" and .059" (1.02, 1.22 and 1.50 mm).

OVERRUNNING CLUTCH

Inspection

Inspect clutch rollers for smooth, round surfaces. These surfaces must be free of flat spots and chipped edges. Inspect roller contacting surfaces in cam and race for wear. Inspect roller springs for distortion, wear or other damage.

Fig. 32: Disassembled View of Replacement Type Overrunning Clutch Cam

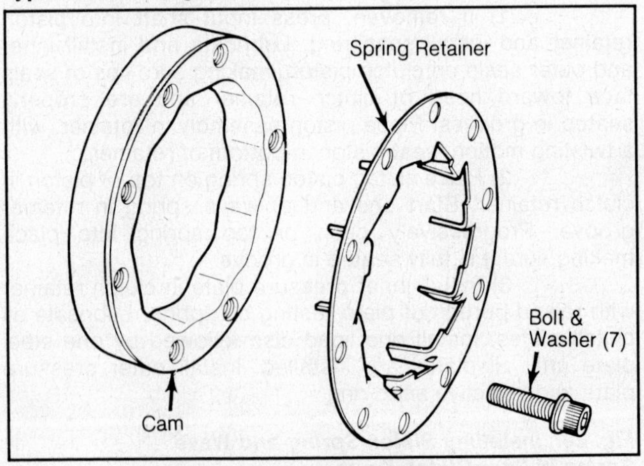

Overrunning Clutch Cam Replacement

1) Remove 4 bolts securing output shaft support to rear of transmission case. Tap support rearward and out of case with soft faced hammer. Center punch on rivets exactly in center of each rivet head.

2) Drill through each rivet head with 3/8" drill, taking care not to drill into transmission case. Chip off rivet heads with small chisel. Drive rivets and cam from case using a blunt punch. Enlarge rivet holes in case using 17/64" drill. Remove all chips and foreign material from case.

3) To install, position cam and roller spring retainer in case, align cam bolt holes with holes in case. Thread all 7 retaining bolt and washer assemblies into cam a few turns. Cone washers must be installed so inner diameter is coned toward bolt head.

4) Tap cam firmly into case if necessary, then tighten bolts evenly. Screw 2 pilot studs into case. Position support cover studs and tap firmly into place

CHRYSLER CORP. & MITSUBISHI TORQUEFLITE (Cont.)

using a soft faced hammer. Remove pilot studs, then install and tighten bolts evenly.

Fig. 33: Installed View of Overrunning Clutch Assembly

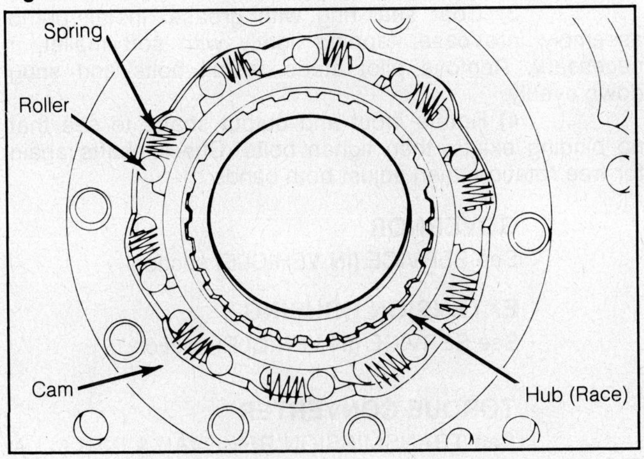

KICKDOWN SERVO & BAND

Disassembly

Disassemble servo piston by removing small snap ring from servo piston, then remove washer, spring and piston rod from servo piston.

Inspection

Inspect all parts for nicks, burrs, wear or damage. Be sure piston and guide seal rings turn freely in grooves. Do not remove seal rings unless conditions warrant. Inspect fit of guide on piston rod and piston spring for distortion. Inspect band lining for wear or damage. If lining is worn so grooves are not visible at ends or any portion of band, replace band.

Fig. 34: Exploded View of Kickdown Servo

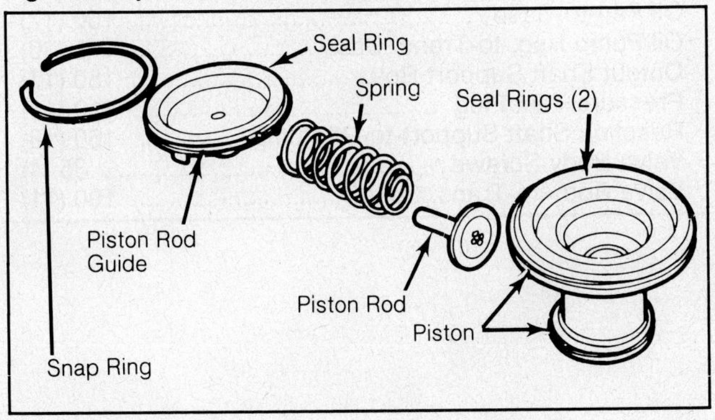

Fig. 35: Exploded View of Low-Reverse Servo

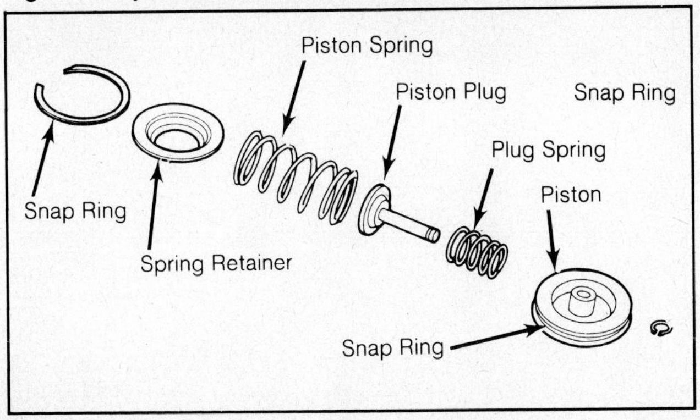

Reassembly

Carefully push servo piston into transmission case bore, then install piston rod, springs and guide. Compress kickdown servo springs with spring compressor and install snap ring.

LOW-REVERSE SERVO & BAND

Disassembly

Remove snap ring, piston, plug retainer and spring.

Inspection

Inspect seal for deterioration, wear and hardness. Inspect piston for cracks, burrs, scores and wear. Inspect piston bore for scores or damage. Check springs for distortion. Inspect band lining for wear and bond of lining to band. If lining is worn so grooves are not visible at ends or any portion of band, replace band.

Reassembly

Low-reverse servo and band are reassembled when reassembling transmission. See LOW-REVERSE SERVO & BAND under TRANSMISSION REASSEMBLY in this article.

TRANSMISSION REASSEMBLY

NOTE: Use only Dexron type Automatic Transmission Fluid to lubricate transmission parts during reassembly.

OVERRUNNING CLUTCH

With transmission case in upright position, insert clutch hub inside cam. Install overrunning clutch rollers exactly as shown in *Fig. 33*.

Fig. 36: Assembled View of Low-Reverse Band and Linkage Assembly

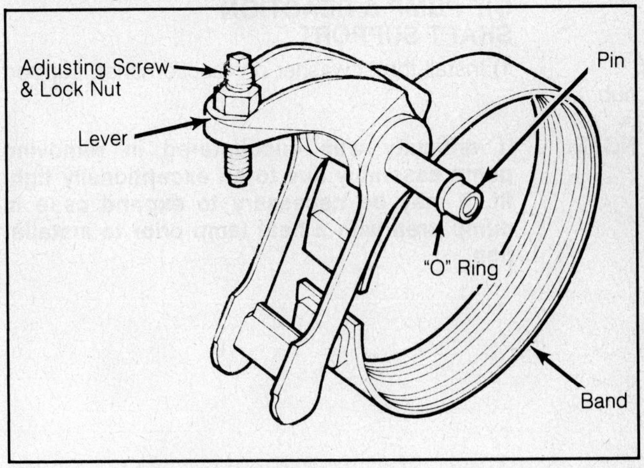

LOW-REVERSE SERVO & BAND

Low-Reverse Servo

Carefully work servo piston into transmission case with a twisting motion, then place spring, retainer and snap ring over piston. Using spring compressor, compress low-reverse servo piston and install snap ring.

Low-Reverse Band

Position rear band in transmission case, install short strut, connect long link and anchor to band. Screw in band adjuster just enough to hold strut in place, then install low-reverse drum. Make sure long link and anchor are installed so as to provide running clearance for low-reverse drum.

PLANETARY GEAR, SUN GEAR & DRIVING SHELL

While supporting assembly in case, insert output shaft through rear support. Carefully work assembly rearward, engaging rear planetary carrier lugs into low-reverse drum slots.

CAUTION: Do not damage ground surfaces on output shaft durng installation.

FRONT & REAR CLUTCH ASSEMBLIES

NOTE: Front and rear clutches, front band, oil pump and reaction shaft support are more easily installed with transmission in upright position.

1) Apply a coat of grease to selective thrust washer and install on front end of output shaft. If input shaft end play was not with in specifications, .022-.091" (.56-2.3 mm), when tested prior to disassembly, replace thrust washer with one of proper thickness.

2) Align front clutch plate inner splines. Place assembly in position on rear clutch, making sure front clutch plate splines are fully engaged on rear clutch splines.

3) Align rear clutch plate splines, grasp input shaft, lower assemblies into case. Carefully work clutch assemblies in circular motion to engage rear clutch splines over splines of front annulus gear. Make sure front clutch drive lugs are fully engaged in slots of driving shell.

FRONT (KICKDOWN) BAND

Slide front band over front clutch assembly. Install band strut, then screw in adjuster just enough to hold strut and anchor in place.

OIL PUMP & REACTION SHAFT SUPPORT

1) Install thrust washer on reaction shaft support hub.

NOTE: If difficulty was encountered in removing pump assembly due to an exceptionally tight fit, it may be necessary to expand case in pump area with a heat lamp prior to installation.

2) Screw 2 pilot studs into pump opening in case, then install new gasket over studs. Place new rubber seal ring in groove on outer flange of pump housing, making sure seal is not twisted.

3) Coat seal ring with grease. Install pump assembly into case, tapping lightly with soft mallet, if necessary. Remove pilot studs, install bolts and snug down evenly.

4) Rotate input and output shafts to see that no binding exists, then tighen bolts. Check shafts again for free rotation, then adjust both bands.

GOVERNOR

See SERVICE (IN VEHICLE) section.

EXTENSION HOUSING

See SERVICE (IN VEHICLE) section.

TORQUE CONVERTER

See TRANSMISSION REMOVAL & INSTALLATION section

TIGHTENING SPECIFICATIONS

Application	Ft. Lbs. (N.m)
Transmission Mount Bolts	31-40 (42-54)
Torque Converter-to-Drive Plate	33-36 (45-49)
Drive Plate-to-Crankshaft	83-90 (113-122)
Extension Hsg.-to-Trans. Case	24 (33)
Trans. Insulator-to-Extension Hsg.	50 (68)
Adjusting Screw Lock Nut	
Kickdown Band	35 (47)
Reverse Band	30 (41)
	INCH Lbs. (N.m)
Governor Body-to-Governor Support	100 (11)
Kickdown Lever Shaft Plug	150 (17)
Oil Pan-to-Case	150 (17)
Oil Pump Hsg.-to-Trans. Case	175 (20)
Output Shaft Support Bolt	150 (17)
Pressure Test Plug	110 (12)
Reaction Shaft Support-to-Oil Pump	160 (18)
Valve Body Screws	35 (4)
Valve Body-to-Trans. Case	100 (11)

Automatic Transmissions

GENERAL MOTORS IMPORTS & ISUZU KF100 TRANSAXLE

Chevrolet Spectrum, Izuzu I-Mark FWD

DESCRIPTION

The KF 100 automatic transaxle is designed for front wheel drive vehicles. It is a compact type transaxle consisting of the transmission and differential in one unit. The driving power is transmitted from the output gear to the ring gear through the idler gear.

The output gear, idler gear and differential gear case are supported by tapered roller bearings. The transaxle is designed so the preload on the tapered roller bearings can be adjusted by the use of shims.

The final gear in the transaxle is of a helical type design requiring no tooth contact adjustment. The unit is designed so the transmission portion and differential use the same type of lubricant (Dexron II ATF).

LUBRICATION & ADJUSTMENTS

See appropriate AUTOMATIC TRANSMISSION SERVICING article in IMPORT GENERAL SERVICING section.

TESTING

STALL TEST

1) Block wheels and set parking brake. Connect a tachometer to engine. Shift transaxle to "D". Hold down brake pedal and slowly press accelerator pedal.

2) When engine has settled to a constant speed, quickly read engine speed and release accelerator. Shift transaxle to "N" and run engine at idle for one minute.

NOTE: **Idling for more than one minute is required to cool transaxle fluid and to prevent damage from overheating.**

3) Perfrom stall test in "2", "1" and "R". Make sure operation is performed within five seconds. Be sure to provide sufficient cooling time between each stall test. Stall speed should be 2050-2350 RPM.

4) If stall speed is lower than standard, one-way clutch in torque converter is slipping. If stall speed is higher than standard, check the following:

- High in every range is caused by low line pressure.
- High in "D", "2" and "1" means rear clutch is slipping.
- High in "D" only indicates one-way clutch is slipping.
- High in "2" only shows brake band is slipping.
- High in "R" only would be low and reverse brakes or front clutch slipping.

LINE PRESSURE TEST

Connect a tachometer to engine. Install Adapter (J-25695-10) to transaxle. Connect Oil Pressure Gauge (J-21867) to adapter. Measure line pressure at stall speed while idling in each range. Provide sufficient cooling time between each pressure test.

GOVERNOR PRESSURE TEST

1) Install Adapter (J-25695-10) to transaxle. Connect Oil Pressure Gauge (J-21867) to adapter. Measure governor pressure at each speed shown in GOVERNOR PRESSURE TEST SPEEDS table.

2) When pressure does not meet specifications, check for fluid leaking from line pressure hydraulic circuit, fluid leaking from governor pressure hydraulic circuit, or faulty governor.

GOVERNOR PRESSURE TEST SPECIFICATIONS

MPH	PSI (kg/cm^2)
20	13-21 (89-147)
35	25-35 (170-240)
55	52-64 (363-441)

ROAD TEST

Road test vehicle using speeds listed in SPEED SHIFT POINTS table.

SPEED SHIFT POINTS

Application	MPH
Wide Open Throttle	
"D1" to "D2"	32-37
"D2" to "D3"	63-68
Kickdown	
"D3" to "D2"	56-62
"D2" to "D1"	25-30

SERVICE (IN VEHICLE)

SHIFT CONTROL CABLE

Removal & Installation

1) Disconnect negative cable at battery. Remove shifter handle. Remove floor console. Disconnect cable at shifter. Pull carpet rearward and remove screws attaching cable to floor.

2) Disconnect cable from transaxle. Raise vehicle and remove cable. To install, reverse removal procedure and adjust cable. To adjust, loosen 2 adjusting nuts at control rod link and connect shift cable to link on transaxle.

3) Shift transaxle into neutral detent. Place shifter lever into neutral position. Rotate link assembly clockwise to remove slack in cable. Tighten rear adjusting nut until it makes contact with link. Tighten front adjusting nut until it makes contact with link and then tighten nuts.

PARK LOCK CABLE

Removal & Installation

1) Disconnect negative cable at battery. Remove shifter handle. Remove floor console. Disconnect cable at shifter and remove adjusting nuts. Remove lower trim cover from steering column.

2) Disconnect cable from column. Pull carpet rearward and remove cable. To install, reverse removal procedure and adjust cable. To adjust cable, place ignition key in "Lock" position. Place shifter lever into park position.

3) Pull cable forward at shifter bracket and tighten forward nut until it makes contact with bracket. Tighten rear nut until it makes contact with bracket and then tighten nuts.

SHIFTER CONTROL

Removal & Installation

Disconnect negative cable at battery. Remove shifter handle. Remove floor console. Disconnect shift cable at control. Disconnect park lock cable at shifter.

Automatic Transmissions

GENERAL MOTORS IMPORTS & ISUZU KF100 TRANSAXLE (Cont.)

Fig. 1: Spectrum KF 100 Cross Section

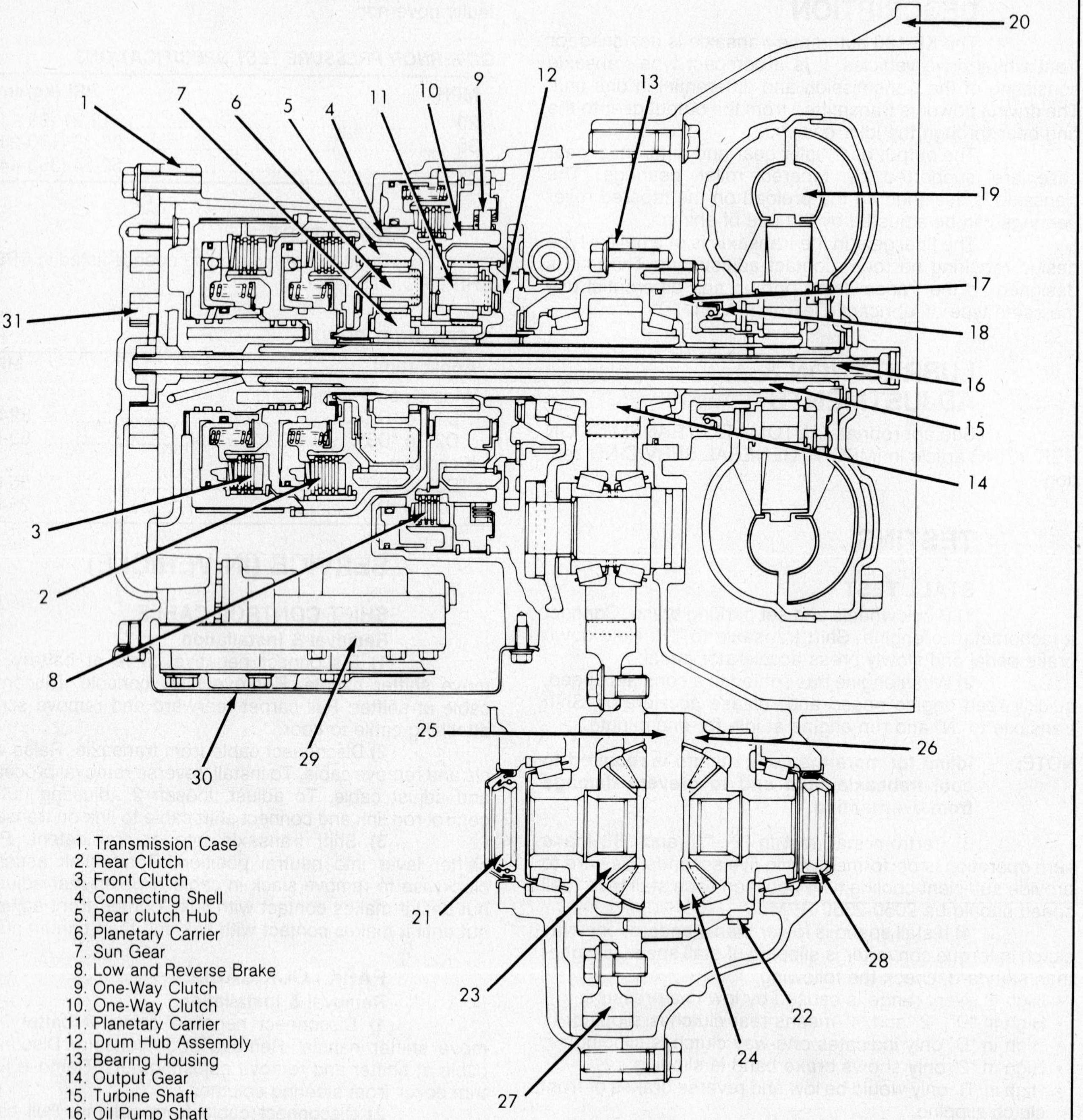

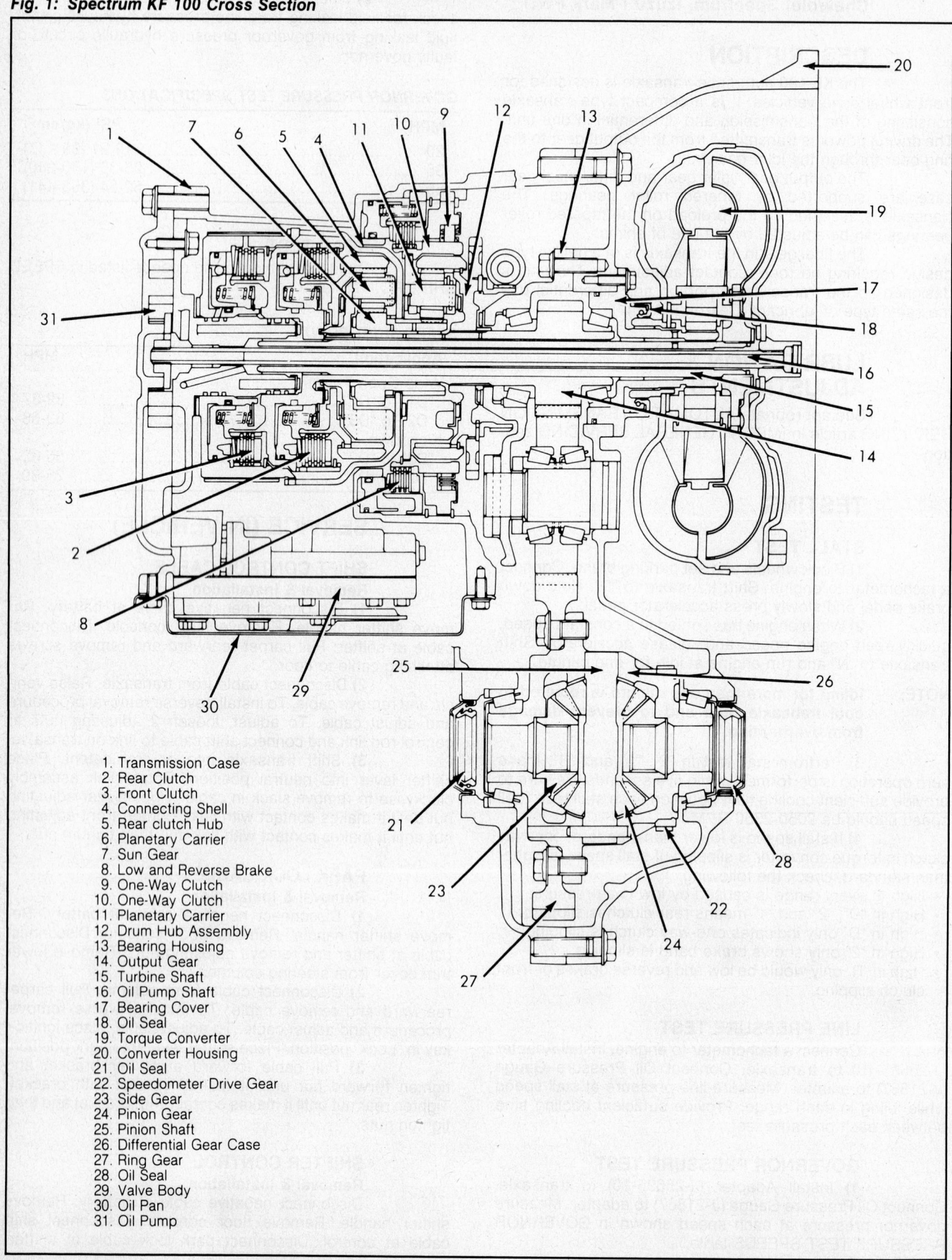

1. Transmission Case
2. Rear Clutch
3. Front Clutch
4. Connecting Shell
5. Rear clutch Hub
6. Planetary Carrier
7. Sun Gear
8. Low and Reverse Brake
9. One-Way Clutch
10. One-Way Clutch
11. Planetary Carrier
12. Drum Hub Assembly
13. Bearing Housing
14. Output Gear
15. Turbine Shaft
16. Oil Pump Shaft
17. Bearing Cover
18. Oil Seal
19. Torque Converter
20. Converter Housing
21. Oil Seal
22. Speedometer Drive Gear
23. Side Gear
24. Pinion Gear
25. Pinion Shaft
26. Differential Gear Case
27. Ring Gear
28. Oil Seal
29. Valve Body
30. Oil Pan
31. Oil Pump

Automatic Transmissions

GENERAL MOTORS IMPORTS & ISUZU KF100 TRANSAXLE (Cont.)

Fig. 2: Hydraulic Circuits Diagram

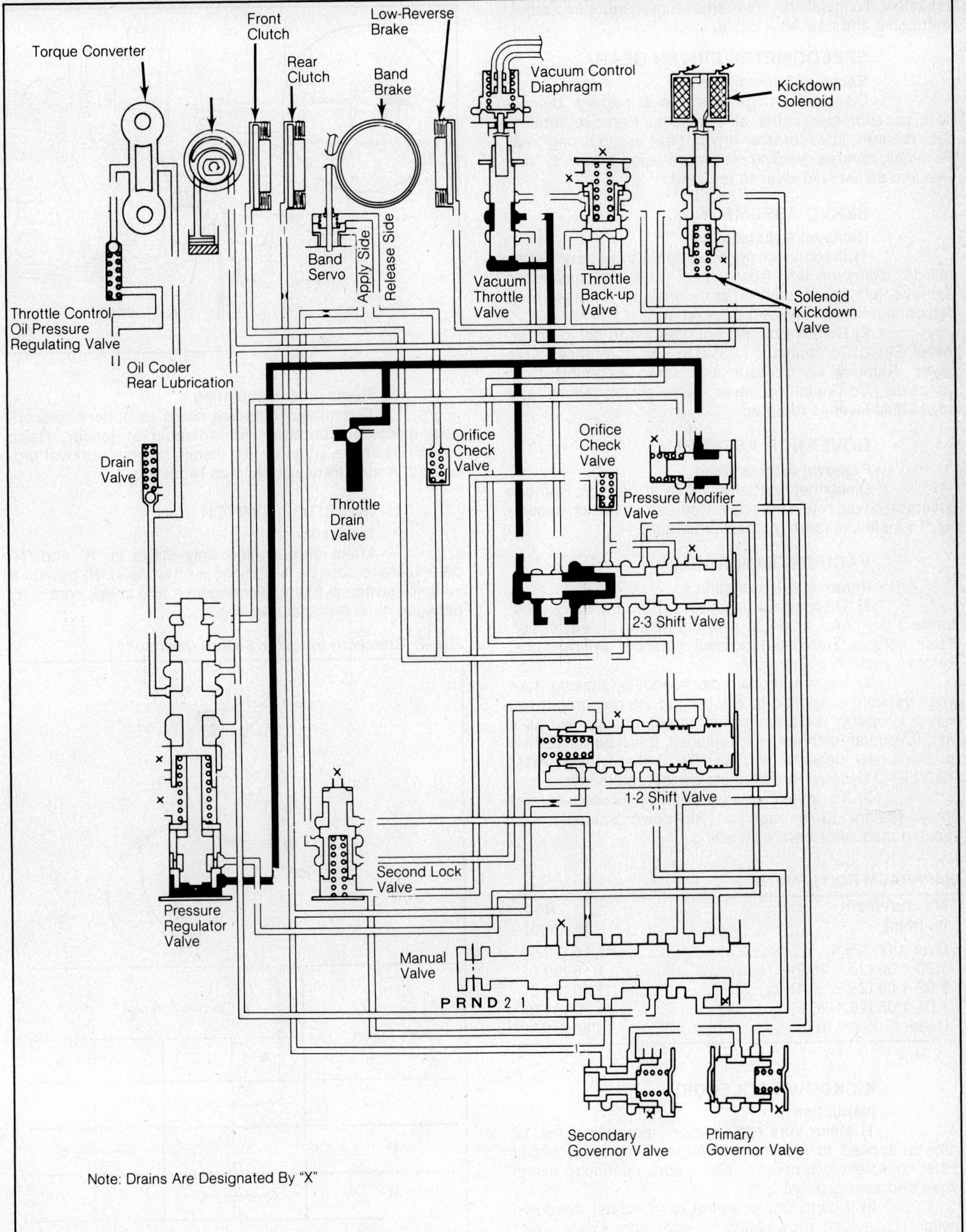

Note: Drains Are Designated By "X"

Automatic Transmissions

GENERAL MOTORS IMPORTS & ISUZU KF100 TRANSAXLE (Cont.)

Remove bolts attaching control to floor and remove control assembly. To install, reverse removal procedure and adjust shift cable and park lock cable.

SPEEDOMETER DRIVEN GEAR

Removal & Installation

Disconnect negative cable at battery. Disconnect speedometer cable at transaxle. Remove retainer bolt, retainer, speedometer driven gear and "O" ring seal. To install, reverse removal procedure using a new "O" ring seal and adjust fluid level as required.

SERVO ASSEMBLY

Removal & Installation

1) Disconnect negative cable at battery. Raise vehicle. Remove left front wheel and tire assembly. Remove left lower control arm tension rod assembly. Disconnect tie rod from left steering arm.

2) Remove oil pan bolt nearest to servo cover. Install Servo Compressor (J-35278) and compress servo cover. Remove compressor and servo assembly from transaxle. To install, reverse removal procedure and adjust fluid level as required.

GOVERNOR ASSEMBLY

Removal & Installation

Disconnect negative cable at battery. Remove governor cover retaining bolts. Remove governor assembly. To install, reverse removal procedure.

VACUUM DIAPHRAGM

Removal & Installation

1) Disconnect negative cable at battery. Disconnect kickdown solenoid wire connector at left fender. Raise vehicle. Remove kickdown solenoid at transaxle. Remove vacuum diaphragm.

2) Inspect vacuum diaphragm by making sure when vacuum is applied to diaphragm, the diaphragm rod moves properly. If diaphragm is correct, change rod as a test. If vacuum diaphragm is replaced, it will be necessary to take a new measurement. *See Fig. 3.* Use DIAPHRAGM ROD LENGTH table to determine correct rod length.

3) To install, reverse removal procedure and apply sealant to threads on kickdown solenoid and vacuum modulator before installing.

DIAPHRAGM ROD LENGTH

Measurement In. (mm)	Rod In. (mm)
Over 1.00 (25.4)	1.16 (29.5)
1.00-1.02 (25.4-25.9)	1.18 (30.0)
1.02-1.04 (25.9-26.4)	1.20 (30.5)
1.04-1.06 (26.4-26.9)	1.22 (31.0)
Under 1.06 (26.9)	1.240 (31.5)

KICKDOWN SOLENOID

Inspection

1) Make sure rod functions properly when 12 volts is applied to kickdown solenoid. Connect a circuit tester to solenoid terminals. Make sure continuity exists when depressing pedal fully

2) If continuity does not exist, adjust kickdown switch. To adjust, turn switch so continuity exists when depressing pedal more than 7/8 of its stroke.

Fig. 3: Measuring Vacuum Diaphragm Rod

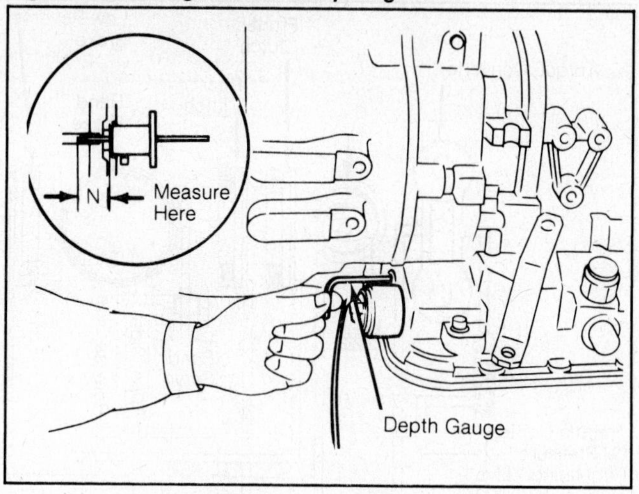

Removal & Installation

Disconnect negative cable at battery. Disconnect electrical connector for solenoid at fender. Raise vehicle. Remove solenoid. To install, reverse removal procedure. Adjust transaxle fluid as required.

INHIBITOR SWITCH

Inspection

Make sure engine only starts in "P" and "N" detent. Make sure back-up light is on while in "R" detent. If inhibitor switch is faulty, disconnect it and check continuity between each terminal. *See Fig. 4.*

Fig. 4: Checking Inhibitor Switch Continuity

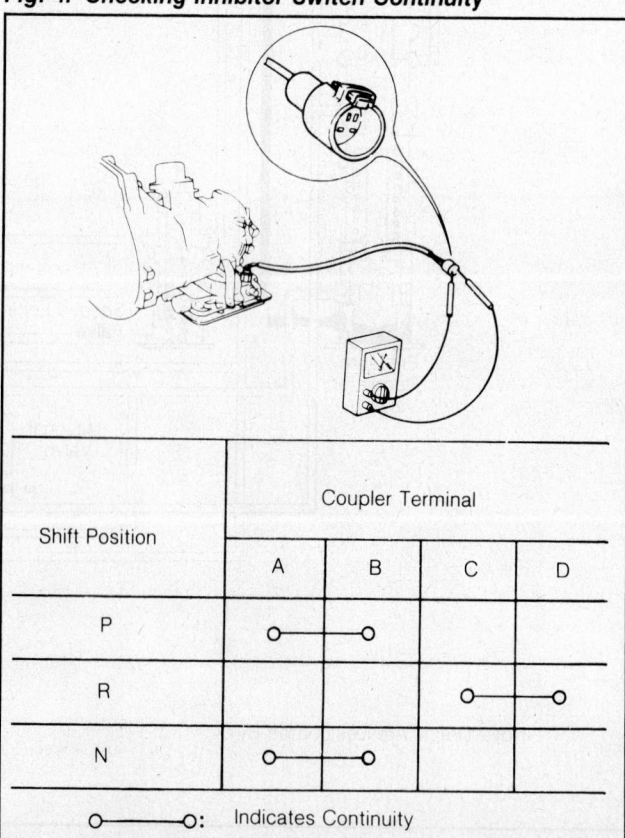

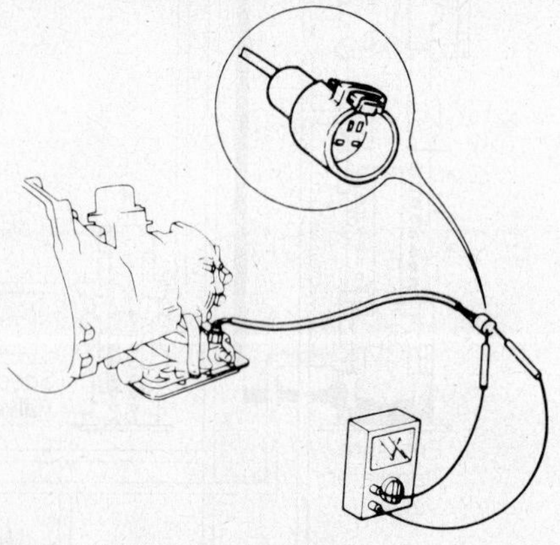

Shift Position	Coupler Terminal A	Coupler Terminal B	Coupler Terminal C	Coupler Terminal D
P	O—	—O		
R			O—	—O
N	O—	—O		

O——O: Indicates Continuity

Automatic Transmissions

GENERAL MOTORS IMPORTS & ISUZU KF100 TRANSAXLE (Cont.)

Removal & Installation

Disconnect negative cable at battery. Disconnect electrical connector for switch at left fender. Raise vehicle. Remove switch. To install, reverse removal procedure and adjust transaxle fluid as required.

REMOVAL & INSTALLATION

TRANSAXLE

See appropriate AUTOMATIC TRANSMISSION REMOVAL article in IMPORT GENERAL SERVICING section.

TORQUE CONVERTER

NOTE: **Torque converter is a sealed unit and cannot be disassembled. Replace if defective.**

TRANSAXLE DISASSEMBLY

Disassembly

1) Thoroughly clean transaxle case before disassembling. Remove torque converter. Attach Holding Fixture (J-35276) to transaxle and set it on Holding Fixture Base (J-3289-20).

2) Remove drain plug and drain fluid from transaxle. Remove inhibitor switch and kickdown solenoid. Remove vacuum diaphragm and rod. Remove oil level gauge with tube. Remove speedometer driven gear.

3) Remove oil pump shaft first and then turbine shaft by pulling outward. Remove oil pan. Remove valve body assembly. Remove spring and steel check ball from case. Remove oil pump assembly. If oil pump is difficult to remove, tighten anchor end bolt and lock front clutch with brake band.

4) Remove anchor end bolt and lock nut. Remove brake band. To avoid damage to band, use a paper clip or wire to prevent band from fully expanding. *See Fig. 5.* Remove front clutch assembly, rear clutch assembly, rear clutch hub assembly, planetary carrier, sun gear with spacer and connecting shell.

5) Attach Servo Compressor (J-35278) to case and compress servo. Remove snap ring, servo retainer and servo piston from case. Remove governor assembly. Remove converter housing to case bolts and remove housing.

6) Remove both oil pipes. See Fig. 6. Use care when prying pipes from case to prevent damage to case-to-housing surface. Remove parking pawl assembly. Remvoe differential case assembly. Remove drum hub assembly and one way clutch inner race assembly.

7) Remove snap ring retaining one-way clutch assembly. Remove one way clutch from case. Install Compressor (J-35279). Tighten bolt to compress clutch return springs. Remove snap ring from clutch return spring retainer. Remove compressor, spring retainer and springs from case.

8) Install Compressor (J-35279). Thread four small bolts included with tool through bar into piston. Tighten center bolt to pull piston from case.

9) Remove roll pin retaining manual shaft to case. Remove manual shaft from case. Remove differential side bearing outer race and shim from case using Puller Bridge (J-33367) and Bearing Race Puller (J-35280). If shim is damaged during removal, use new shims when reassembling.

10) Using a drift and hammer, remove roll pin retaining idler gear to bearing housing. Remove bolts retaining bearing housing to converter housing. Remove bearing housing. Remove output gear from housing.

11) Remove idler gear from housing. Tap idler shaft with soft face hammer from converter side of housing for removal. Remove bearing outer race from bearing housing using Puller Bridge (J-33367) with Bearing Race Puller (J-35280).

12) Remove oil seal from front bearing cover using Seal Remover (J-23129) and slide hammer. Remove bearing race from converter housing. Remove differential bearing race from converter housing. Remove front bearing cover from converter housing.

Fig. 5: Retaining Brake Band

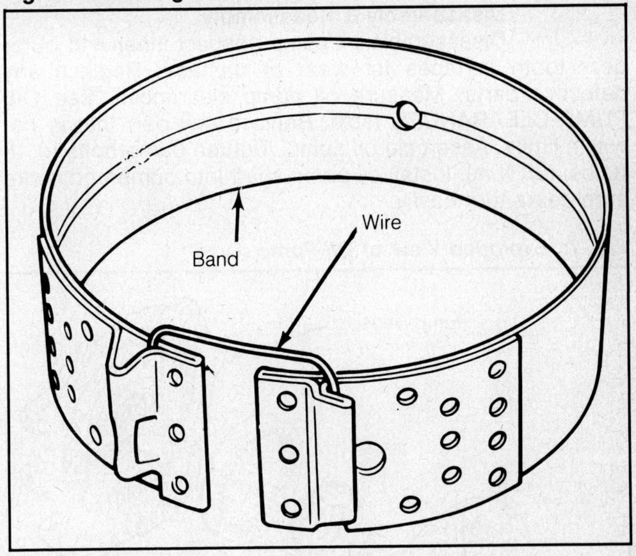

Note location of wire or paper clip.

Fig. 6: Removing Oil Pipes

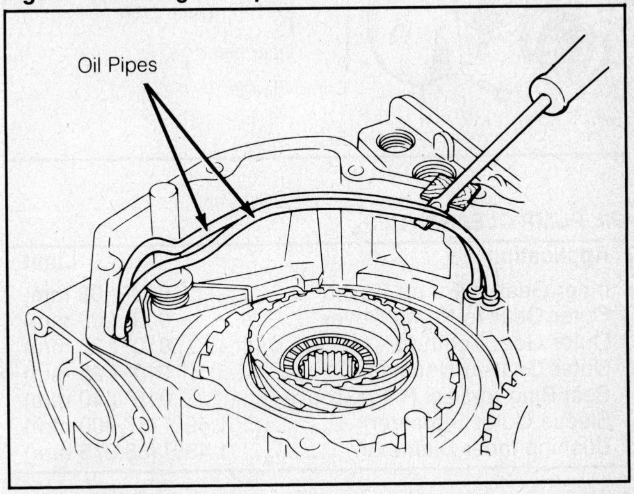

COMPONENT DISASSEMBLY & REASSEMBLY

NOTE: **When overhauling components clean parts and blow out passages, replace seal rings, roll pins and gaskets, and apply Dexron II to seals and rotating or sliding parts.**

OIL PUMP

Disassembly & Reassembly

Disassemble oil pump. Inspect inner and outer gear tooth surfaces for wear or damage. Replace any defective parts. Measure oil pump clearances. See OIL PUMP CLEARANCES table. Replace any part that is not within limits. Assemble oil pump. Tighten pump bolts to 16 ft. lbs. (23 N.m). Install oil pump shaft into pump and make sure gears turn easily.

Fig. 7: Exploded View of Oil Pump

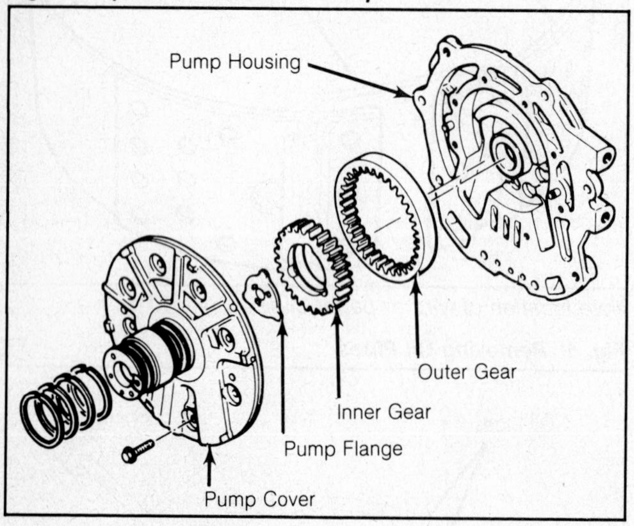

OIL PUMP CLEARANCES

Application	Limit
Inner Gear-to-Pump Cover	.003" (.08 mm)
Outer Gear-to-Pump Cover	.003" (.08 mm)
Outer Gear Teeth-to-Crescent Dam	.010" (.25 mm)
Outer Gear-to-Housing	.010" (.25 mm)
Seal Ring-to-Seal Ring Groove	.016" (.40 mm)
Sleeve Outer Diameter	1.492" (37.900 mm)
Bushing Inner Diameter	1.499" (38.075 mm)

FRONT CLUTCH

Disassembly

1) Remove large snap ring from front clutch pack. Remove clutch pack from clutch hub. Using Clutch Spring Compressor (J-23327) with a press, compress piston retaining springs. Remove snap ring from piston spring retainer.

2) Remove spring retainer and 10 springs from front clutch piston. Apply air to clutch hub to remove piston. Measure drum bushing inside diameter. Replace drum if bushing's inside diameter is greater than 1.735" (44.07 mm).

3) Remove "O" ring from clutch hub. Inspect clutch components for damaged or worn clutch plates, snap rings, or spring retainer, and replace any defective parts. Check piston spring free length. Free length should be .992-1.071" (25.2-27.2 mm).

Reassembly

1) Apply clean Dexron II automatic transmission fluid on seals and seal surfaces before assembling. Install a new seal on clutch piston. Install a new "O" ring seal on clutch hub. Install clutch piston in front clutch hub. Install 10 return springs and spring retainer in clutch hub.

Fig. 8: Exploded View of Front/Rear Clutch, Servo & Governor Assembly

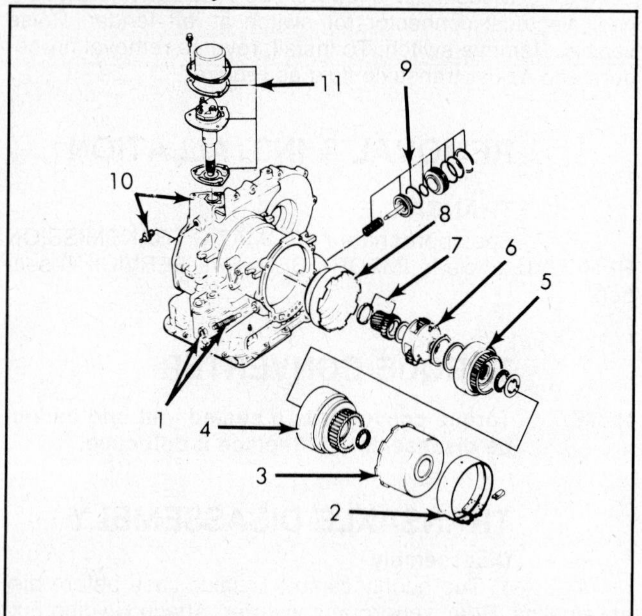

1. Anchor End-Bolt & Locknut
2. Brake Band
3. Front Clutch
4. Rear Clutch
5. Rear Clutch Hub Assy.
6. Planetary Carrier
7. Sun Gear & Spacer
8. Connecting Shell
9. Servo
10. Transcase & Neutral Switch
11. Governor

2) Compress return springs using Compressor (J-23327). Install a new snap ring on spring retainer. Install dished plate in clutch hub with concave side facing piston. Install 3 steel and 3 fiber clutch discs in clutch hub. The first disc installed on dished plate is steel.

3) Install backing plate onto clutch disc with smooth side down. Install a new snap ring in clutch hub. Place assembled front clutch on pump hub. Install a dial indicator with pin positioned on backing plate. To measure clutch pack travel, engage clutch by applying air to pump and record reading.

4) If dial indicator reading is not within .063-.071" (1.6-1.8 mm), change thickness of retaining plate. Retaining plates come in 6 sizes ranging from .205" (5.2 mm) to .244 (6.2 mm).

REAR CLUTCH

Disassembly

1) Remove large snap ring from rear clutch pack. Remove clutch pack from clutch hub. Use Compressor (J-23327) with a press and compress piston return springs. Remove snap ring from piston spring retainer.

2) Remove spring retainer and 10 springs from rear clutch piston. Apply air to clutch hub to remove piston. Remove "O" ring from clutch hub. Inspect clutch components and replace defective parts. Replace damaged or worn clutch plates, snap rings, or spring retainer. If piston spring free length is not within .992-1.071" (25.2-27.2 mm) then replace springs.

Reassembly

1) Apply clean Dexron II automatic transmission fluid on seals and seal surfaces before assembling. Install a new seal on clutch piston. Install a new "O" ring seal on clutch hub. Install clutch piston in rear clutch hub.

GENERAL MOTORS IMPORTS & ISUZU KF100 TRANSAXLE (Cont.)

2) Install 10 return springs ad spring retainers in clutch hub. Compress return springs using compresser. Install a new snap ring on spring retainer. Install dished plate in clutch hub with concave side facing piston.

3) Install 4 steel and 4 fiber clutch discs in clutch hub. The first disc installed on dished plate is steel. Install backing plate onto clutch discs with beveled edge facing clutch discs. Install a new snap ring in clutch hub. Place assembled rear clutch on front clutch .

4) Install a dial indicator with pin postioned on backing plate. To measure clutch pack travel, engage clutch by applying air to pump and record reading. If clearance is not within .031-.059" (.8-1.5 mm), replace clutch discs.

DRUM HUB

Disassembly

Remove parking gear spring. Remove parking gear from drive hub by pushing in pins protruding from dirve hub. Remove snap ring, then separate internal gear from drive hub. Inspect components for any defects like broken or worn snap ring or damaged gears.

Reassembly

Install internal gear in drive hub. Install a new snap ring to retain internal gear to drive hub. Install parking gear on drive hub. Make sure pins are seated in holes on parking gear. Install parking gear spring.

REAR CLUTCH HUB

Disassembly & Reassembly

Remove snap ring. Separate rear clutch hub from internal gear. Inspect components for broken snap ring or damaged gears. Install clutch hub in internal gear. Install a new snap ring to retain clutch hub in internal gear.

ONE-WAY CLUTCH INNER RACE

Disassembly

Remove snap ring. Separate planetary carrier from one-way clutch inner race. Inspect components for broken, damaged or worn gears, snap ring, or inner race. Clearance between pinion washer and planetary carrier should be .031" (.8 mm). Make sure that when one-way clutch is held and inner race is twisted, clutch turns smoothly in only on direction. Check for worn bushing.

Reassembly

Install planetary carrier in one-way clutch inner race. Install a new snap ring to retain planetary carrier in inner race.

LOW & REVERSE BRAKE

Inspection

Inspect components for damaged or worn drive plate facings, worn return springs. Return springs should be within 1.051-1.130" (26.7-28.7 mm). Check for damage or wear on brake band.

SERVO ASSEMBLY

Inspection

Inspect components for any defective parts like damaged or worn piston or worn return springs. The limit is 1.850-1.929" (47-49 mm).

GOVERNOR ASSEMBLY

Disassembly

1) Remove 2 bolts from governor body. Remove body and spacer from governor shaft assembly. Remove

Fig. 9: Exploded View of Low/Reverse Clutch Assy.

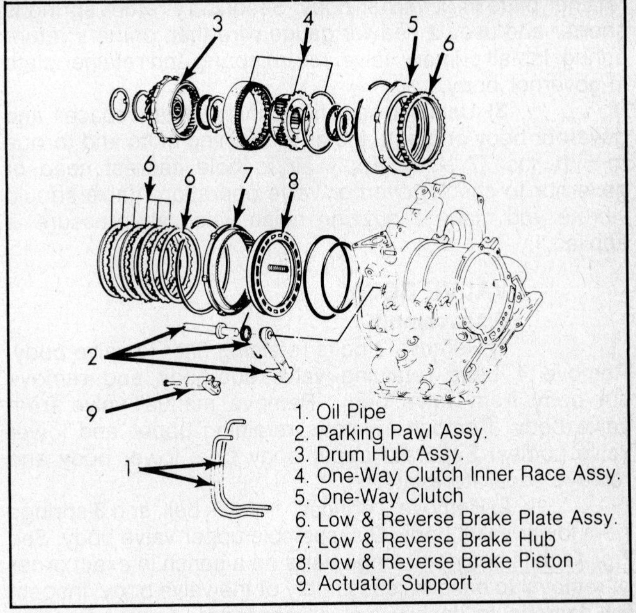

1. Oil Pipe
2. Parking Pawl Assy.
3. Drum Hub Assy.
4. One-Way Clutch Inner Race Assy.
5. One-Way Clutch
6. Low & Reverse Brake Plate Assy.
7. Low & Reverse Brake Hub
8. Low & Reverse Brake Piston
9. Actuator Support

spring retainers from governor body by pressing primary return spring. Remove secondary retainer and return spring the same way.

2) Remove roll pin from governor driven gear and remove gear from shaft. Remove governor shaft, bearing and outer race from sleeve. Inspect components for damage and replace any defective parts. Primary return spring free length should be .650-.728" (16.5-18.5 mm). Secondary return spring free length should be .488-.567" (12.4-14.4 mm)

Reassembly

1) Install 3 seal rings on shaft. Install bearing and outer race on sleeve. Install governor shaft in sleeve. Install governor driven gear on shaft and retain gear with a roll pin.

Fig. 10: Exploded View of Governor

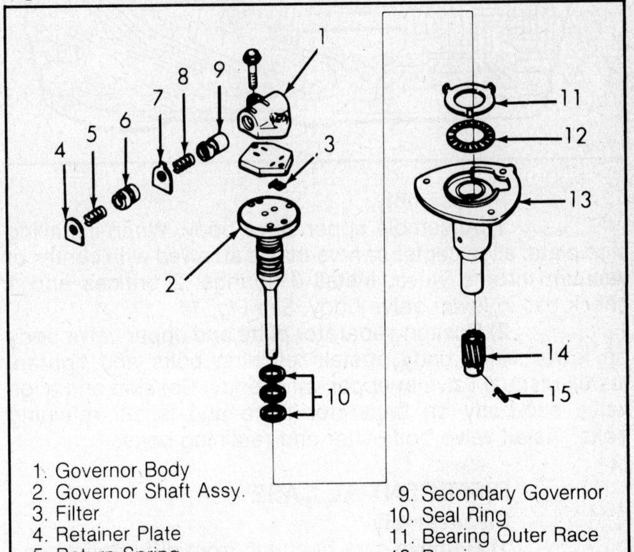

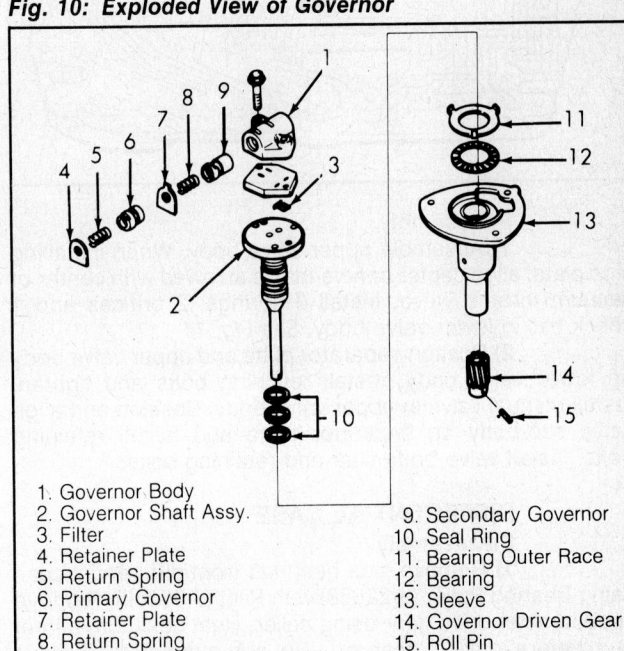

1. Governor Body
2. Governor Shaft Assy.
3. Filter
4. Retainer Plate
5. Return Spring
6. Primary Governor
7. Retainer Plate
8. Return Spring
9. Secondary Governor
10. Seal Ring
11. Bearing Outer Race
12. Bearing
13. Sleeve
14. Governor Driven Gear
15. Roll Pin

GENERAL MOTORS IMPORTS & ISUZU KF100 TRANSAXLE (Cont.)

2) Install secondary valve, return spring and retainer plate in governor body. Secondary return spring is shorter and uses a heavier gauge wire than primary return spring. Install primary valve, return spring and retainer plate in governor body.

3) Using a new filter, install filter, spacer and governor body on shaft. Install 2 retaining bolts and torque to 5 ft. lbs. (7 N.m). Apply air to hole nearest head of governor to check governor valve operation. Valve should vibrate and make a buzzing noise when air pressure is applied.

VALVE BODY

Disassembly

1) Remove 3 bolts retaining filter to valve body. Remove 4 bolts retaining valve sub-body and remove sub-body from valve body. Remove manual valve from valve body. Remove 17 bolts retaining upper and lower valve bodies. Separate upper body from lower body and remove separator plate.

2) Remove 2 orifices, 1 check ball, and 3 springs from lower valve body. Disassemble upper valve body. *See Fig. 11*. It is best to arrange parts on a bench in exact order of removal to ease in reassembly of the valve body. Inspect for damage to each valve, oil passages, valve body and valve operation.

Fig. 11: Check Ball, Springs & Orifice Locations

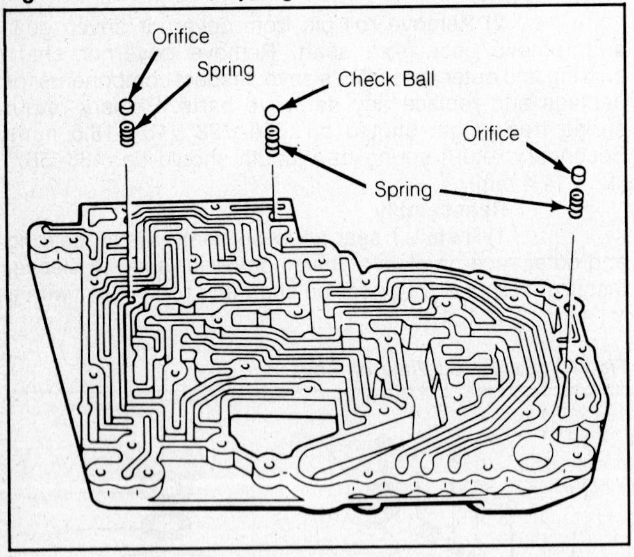

Reassembly

1) Assemble upper valve body. When installing side plate, align center of hole that is arrowed with center of vacuum throttle valve. Install 3 springs, 2 orifices and 1 check ball in lower valve body. *See Fig. 11.*

2) Positon separator plate and upper valve body on lower valve body. Install retaining bolts and tighten. Install manual valve in upper valve body. Position and align valve sub-body on separator plate and install retaining bolts. Install valve body filter and retaining bolts.

DIFFERENTIAL CASE

Disassembly

1) Remove side bearings from differential case using Bearing Puller (J-22888) with Pilot (J-35288). Remove speedometer drive gear using puller. Heat gear with a heat gun before pulling gear off. Do not attempt to remove speedometer drive gear unless it is damaged. Gear cannot be reused after removal.

2) Remove ring gear from differential case. Ring gear bolts are not reusable, discard used bolts and use new bolts during reassembly. Remove lock pin used to retain cross pin. Remove cross pin from differential case. Remove pinion gears, side gears and thrust washers from differential case.

Fig. 12: Exploded View of Final Drive Assembly

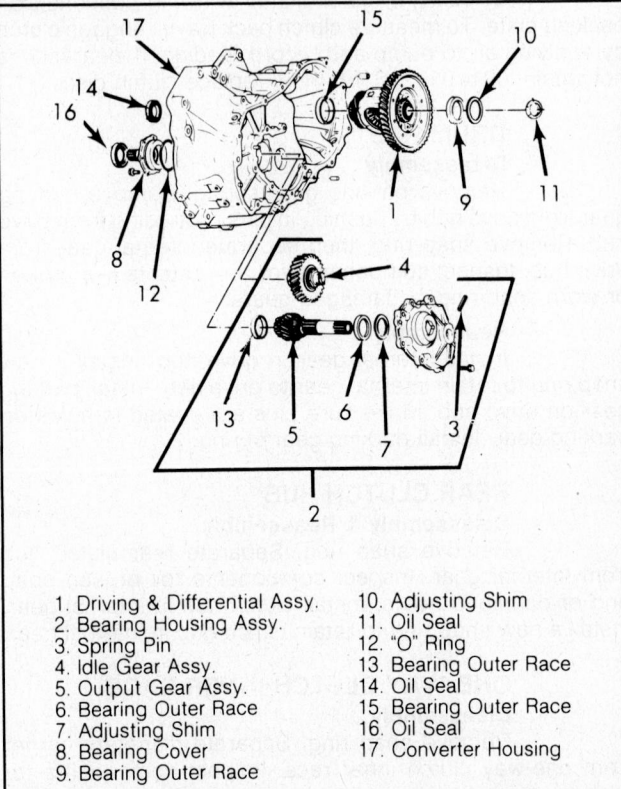

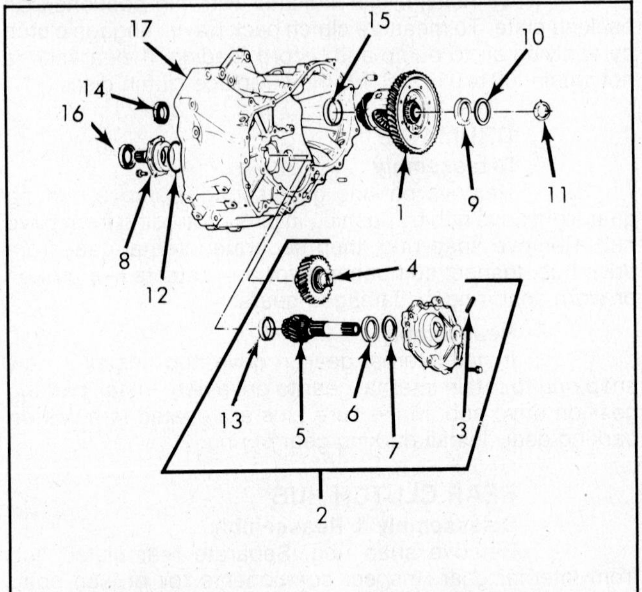

1. Driving & Differential Assy.
2. Bearing Housing Assy.
3. Spring Pin
4. Idle Gear Assy.
5. Output Gear Assy.
6. Bearing Outer Race
7. Adjusting Shim
8. Bearing Cover
9. Bearing Outer Race
10. Adjusting Shim
11. Oil Seal
12. "O" Ring
13. Bearing Outer Race
14. Oil Seal
15. Bearing Outer Race
16. Oil Seal
17. Converter Housing

Inspection

1) Measure clearance between pinion gear and cross pin. Clearance should be .08" (.2 mm). Measure clearance between differential case and side gear. Clearance should be .059" (.15 mm).

2) Measure diameter in differential case of drive axle shaft. Clearance should be 9.358" (27.35 mm). Measure backlash between side gear and pinion gear. Backlash limit is .19" (.3 mm). If backlash is beyond limit, correct by installing new thrust washers.

Reassembly

1) Install thrust washers in case. Install side gears in case. Install pinion gears in case. Align cross pin hole of pinion gear with cross pin hole in differential case. Install cross pin in case. Aligning lock pin hole in cross pin with lock pin hole in differential case.

2) Install lock pin. After install ation of pin, stake edge of lock pin hole in case with a pumch to prevent loss of lock pin. Install a new speeedometer drive gear if removed. Heat gear with a heat gun before installing. Do not use hot water to heat gear.

3) Install both differential side bearings using Installer (J-35291), Handle (J-8092) and Pilot (J-35288). Install ring gear and tighten bolts in sequence. *See Fig. 15*. Use new ring gear bolts ifring gear has been removed Apply oil to contact surface of ring gear and differential case before installing gear.

Automatic Transmissions

GENERAL MOTORS IMPORTS & ISUZU KF100 TRANSAXLE (Cont.)

Fig. 13: Exploded View of Valve Body

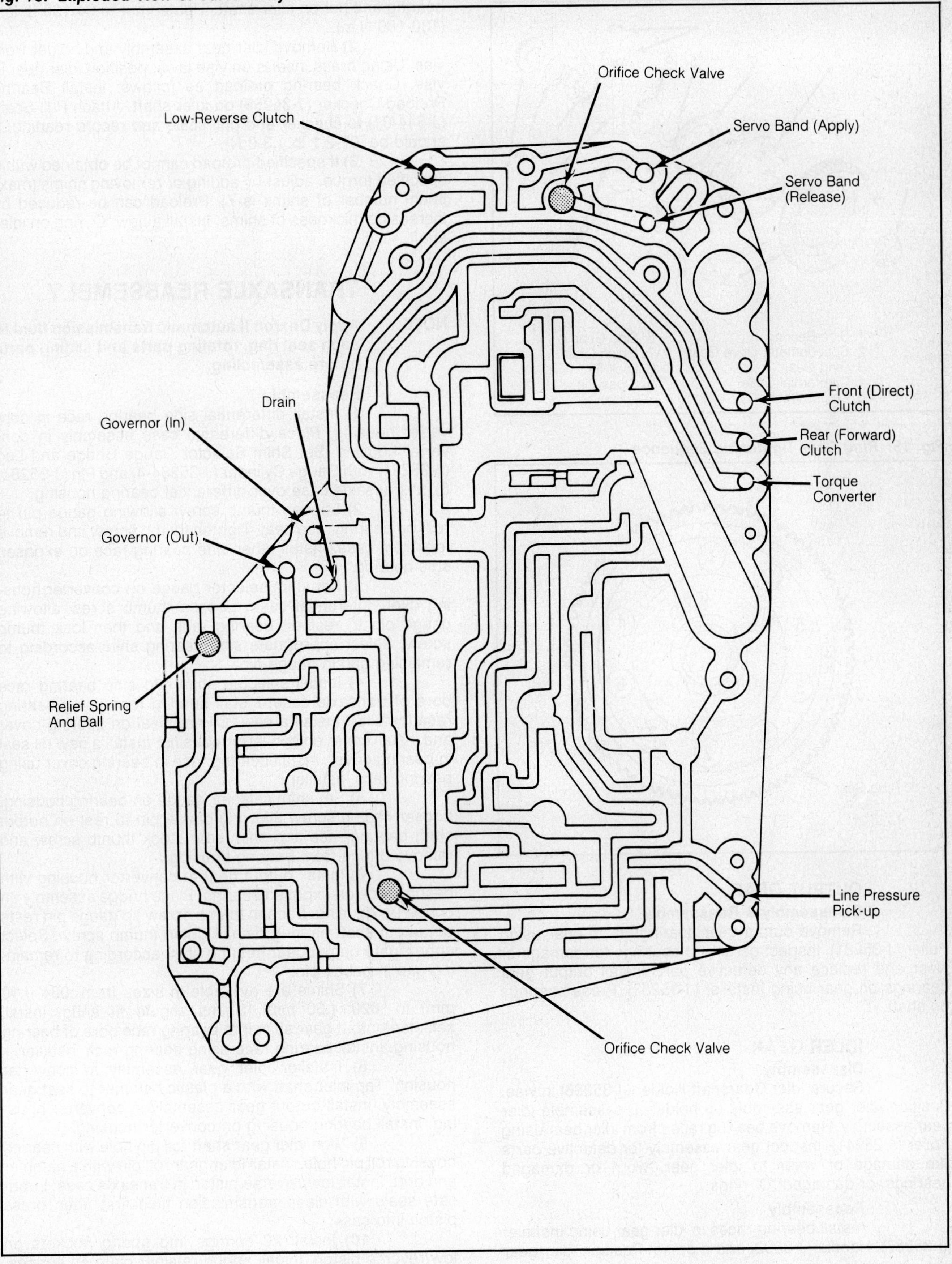

GENERAL MOTORS IMPORTS & ISUZU KF100 TRANSAXLE (Cont.)

Fig. 14: Exploded View of Differential Case

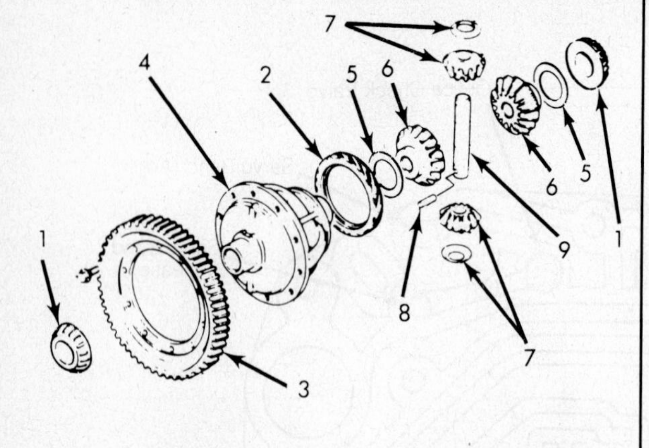

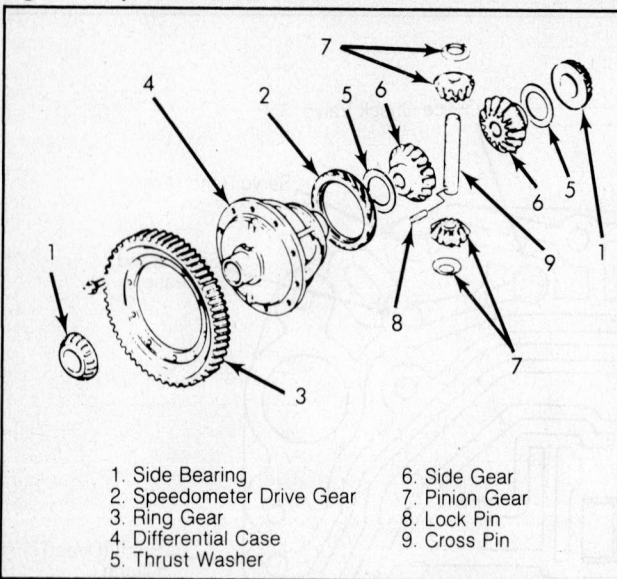

1. Side Bearing
2. Speedometer Drive Gear
3. Ring Gear
4. Differential Case
5. Thrust Washer
6. Side Gear
7. Pinion Gear
8. Lock Pin
9. Cross Pin

Fig. 15: Ring Gear Tightening Sequence

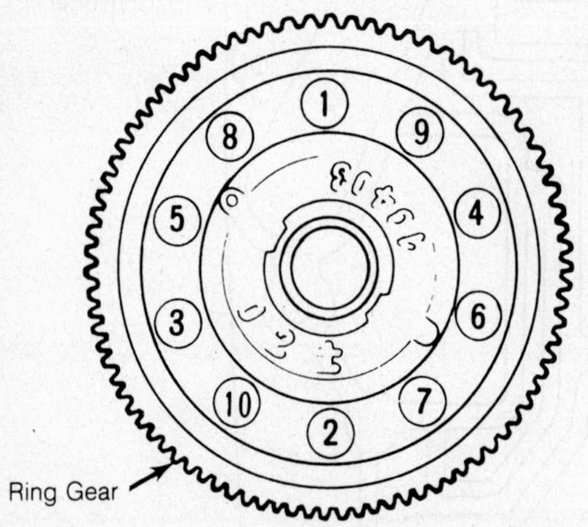

OUTPUT GEAR

Disassembly & Reassembly

Remove output gear bearings from gear using Puller (J-35281). Inspect gerar and bearings for damage or wear and replace any defective part. Install output gear bearings on gear using Installer (J-35283). Press bearings on shaft.

IDLER GEAR

Disassembly

Secure Idler Gearshaft Holder (J-35286) in vise. Position idler gear assembly on holder. Disassemble idler gear assembly. Remove bearing races from idler gear using Puller (J-26941). Inspect gear assembly for defective parts like damage or wear to idler gear, worn or damaged bearings, or damaged "O" rings

Reassembly

Install bearing races in idler gear using Installer (J-35287), Handle (J-8092) and a press. Position idler gear shaft on installer. Install bearing, idler gear, shims, spacer, bearing and nut on idler shaft. Tighten nut to 94-130 ft. lbs. (130-180 N.m).

2) Remove idler gear assembly and holder from vise. Using brass inserts on vise jaws, position idler gear in vise. Check bearing preload as follows: install Bearing Preload Checker (J-35259) on idler shaft. Attach Pull Scale (J-544-01) to checker and pull scale and record reading. It should be .07-2.1 lb. (.3-9 N).

3) If specified preload cannot be obtained within specified torque, adjust by adding or removing shims (maximum number of shims is 7). Preload can be reduced by increasing thickness of shims. Install a new "O" ring on idler shaft.

TRANSAXLE REASSEMBLY

NOTE: **Apply Dexron II automatic transmission fluid to each seal ring, rotating parts and sliding parts before assembling.**

Reassembly

1) Install differential side bearing race in converter housing. Place differential case assembly in converter housing. Set Shim Selector Gauge Bridge and Leg (J-35284) with Gauge Cylinder (J-35284-4) and Pin (J-35284-8) on transaxle case over differential bearing housing.

2) Loosen thumb screw allowing gauge pin to rest on bearing rece seat. Tighten thumb screw and remove tool from case. Install other side bearing race on exposed side bearing.

3) Set shim selector gauge on converter housing over differential case. Loosen thumb screw allowing gauge pin to rest on bearing race and then lock thumb screw. Select appropriate side bearing shim according to remaining gap in gauge pin.

4) Install selected shim into side bearing race bore of transaxle case. Install bearing race using bearing race installer. Install a new "O" ring seal on bearing cover and install cover on converter housing. Install a new oil seal in bearing cover. Install bearing race in bearing cover using bearing race installer.

5) Set shim selector gauge on bearing housing. Loosen thumb screw allowing gauge pin to rest on output shaft bearing race and shim seat. Lock thumb screw and remove bridge from bearing housing.

6) Install output gear in converter housing with bearing race on exposed bearing. Place bridge assembly on converter housing. Loosen thumb screw so gauge pin rests on output shaft bearing race. Tighten thumb screw. Select appropriate output gear bearing shim according to remaining gap in gauge pin.

7) Shims are available in sizes from .004" (.10 mm) to .020" (.50 mm). Shims should fit snug. Install selected output gear shim into bearing race bore of bearing housing. Install bearing race using bearing race installer.

8) Installer idler gear assembly in converter housing. Tap idler shaft with a plastic hammer to seat gear assembly. Install output gear assembly in converter housing. Install bearing housing on converter housing.

9) Align idler gear shaft roll pin hole with bearing housing roll pin hole. Install idler gear roll pin with a hammer and drift. Install low/reverse piston in transaxle case. Lubricate seals with clean transmission fluid first, then press piston into case.

10) Install 20 springs into spring pockets on low/reverse piston. Install spring retainer plate on springs.

GENERAL MOTORS IMPORTS & ISUZU KF100 TRANSAXLE (Cont.)

Compress piston springs and install snap ring. Make sure snap ring is seated in groove. Install multiple disc clutch pack.

11) Install dish plate first with concave side facing piston, then alternate clutch discs, 4 steel, 4 fibers starting with steel disc first. Install backing plate on clutch discs with smooth flat side facing discs. Install one-way clutch on backing plate with machined surface facing backing plate and retain with a new snap ring.

12) Measure low/reverse clutch clearance as follows: set a dial indicator on case with gauge pin on clutch plate. Apply air through oil passage to engage clutch. If dial indicator reading is not within specifications, change thickness of retaining plate. Clearance is .031-.041" (.8-1.05 mm). Retaining plate sizes come in sizes from .307" (7.8 mm) to .346" (8.8 mm).

13) Install low/reverse clutch pack spacer between case and bottom disc. Install one-way clutch inner race assembly with thrust washer. Install drum hub gear assembly with 2 thrust bearings on one-way clutch inner race assembly.

14) One thrust bearing goes between hub and one-way inner clutch. Next, install thrust washer with lip side down on thrust bearing. Install parking rod assembly in case. Install control rod assembly in case after spring and detent ball has been installed. Install locating pin.

15) Install manual shaft with a new "O" ring into case. Install manual plate lever on end of manual shaft and install retaining nut. Connect manual plate lever to parking rod assembly and install retaining clip.

16) Install actuator support in transaxle case. Install parking pawl assembly. Install 2 oil pipes in transaxle case. Install differential case assembly in case with speedometer gear facing upward.

17) Install governor assembly with a new gasket in case aligning tab on governor plate with mark on case. Install governor cover with a new gasket on governor assembly and install 3 bolts. Apply a thin bead of Loctite No. 518 on transaxle case.

18) Install converter housing on transaxle case. Install 15 retaining bolts. Install servo and spring assembly into case. Coat seals and seal surfaces with clean transmission fluid before installing.

19) Install servo cover and servo piston compressor. Use a new snap ring to retain cover. Remove low/reverse clutch pack spacer. Install thrust bearing and washer on planetary carrier. Install spacer ad sun gear into connecting shell. Install connecting shell in transaxle case.

20) Install planetary carrier assembly on sun gear. Place thrust washer and bearing on carrier. Install rear clutch hub with thrust bearing in case. Install lube oil seal in case. Install rear clutch assembly in case. Make sure tabbed thrust washer is in place on back side of clutch before installing.

21) Measure total end play in transaxle case as follows: set Shim Selector Gauge (J-35284-1), Bridge and Leg Assembly (J-35284-4) and Gauge Cylinder (J35284-10) on pump gasket surface (gasket removed) of oil pump. Loosen thumb screw to allow gauge pin to rest on pump hub, then tighten thumb screw.

22) Place bridge assembly on transaxle case. Loosen thumb screw allowing gauge pin to rest on rear clutch hub bearing. Tighten thumb screw. The remaining gap between gauge cylinder and gauge pin will be the size of selective bearing outer race to use. Bearing outer race sizes range from .047" (1.2 mm) to .087" (2.2 mm).

23) Install selective bearing outer race on pump hub. Install front clutch assembly in transaxle. Measure front clutch to pump end play as follows: set Shim Selector Gauge (J-35284-1), Bridge and Leg assembly (J-35284-4) and Gauge Cylinder (J-35284-9) with front clutch gauge pin on transaxle case.

24) Loosen thumb screw to allow gauge pin to rest on clutch hub. Tighten thumb screw and remove bridge and leg assembly from case. Place bridge and leg assembly on pump gasket surface (gasket removed). Loosen thumb screw so the gauge pin rests on pump shim surface. Tighten thumb screw.

25) Remaining gap between gauge cylinder and gauge pin will be size of selective shim. Selective shims are available in sizes from .0051" (1.3 mm) and .106" (2.7 mm). Install selective shim on oil pump. Install brake band with strut in case. Install anchor end bolt and tighten bolt to 10 ft. lbs. (14 N.m), then loosen bolt 2 full turns. Then retighten to 50 ft. lbs. (68 N.m).

27) Install pump assembly on case. Install bolts and tighetn. Install spring and check ball in transaxle case. Install valve body on transaxle case aligning manual valve with shift lever arm. Install 9 bolts and tighten. Install a new pan gasket on pan. Install gasket and pan on transaxle case and install 16 pan bolts. Install turbine shaft and then oil pump shaft.

28) Install speedometer driven gear assembly. Install oil level gauge and tube. Install rod on vacuum diaphragm and then install vacuum diaphragm in case. Before installing, apply sealant to threads of vacuum diaphragm. If valve body or vacuum diaphragm was replaced, it will be necessary to make a measurement to select proper rod length. *See Fig. 3.*

29) Install inhibitor switch in case. Apply sealant to threads of kickdown solenoid and install in case. With converter in an erect position, fill with Dexron II automatic transmission fluid. Install converter.

30) Install drive axle shaft seals using seal installer. Remove transaxle and holding fixture from holding fixture base. Remove holding fixture from transaxle.

TIGHTENING SPECIFICATIONS

Application	Ft. Lbs. (N.m)
Converter-to-Flywheel	56 (7.7)
Oil Pump Cover	10 (14)
Differential Ring Gear	83 (115)
Idler Gear Lock Nut	94-130 (130-180)
Output Gear Bearing Cover	16 (23)
Differential-to-Transmission	30 (42)
Oil Pump Assembly-to-Case	16 (23)
Transaxle-to-Torque Converter Housing	22-33 (30-45)
Reverse Idler Shaft Bolt	22-33 (30-45)
Detent Spring Retaining Bolts	15-21 (21-29)
Input/Output Shaft Retaining Nuts	87-101 (118-137)
Rear Cover Bolts	11-16 (15-22)
	INCH Lbs. (N.m.)
Front Bearing Cover	108 (1.2)
Actuator Support	120 (1.4)
Governor	60 (.7)
Valve Body-to-Case	84 (1.0)
Oil Pan	60 (.7)

GENERAL MOTORS IMPORTS/SUZUKI 3-SPEED TRANSAXLE

Sprint

DESCRIPTION

The automatic 3-speed transaxle consists of a hydraulic torque converter, a transaxle gear assembly, a countershaft, and a differential assembly. The transaxle consists of 2 planetary gears, 2 disc clutches, a brake band, one disc brake, and a one-way clutch.

LUBRICATION & ADJUSTMENT

See appropriate MANUAL TRANSMISSION SERVICING article in IMPORT GENERAL SERVICING section.

TESTING

LINE PRESSURE TEST

1) Ensure transaxle fluid is at normal operating temperature. Make sure transaxle fluid level is between "FULL HOT" and "LOW HOT" on oil level gauge. DO NOT perform this test for more than 5 seconds.

2) Remove transaxle plug and connect pressure gauge. *See Fig. 1*. Install tachometer to engine. Apply parking brake and block drive wheels. Start engine, depress brake pedal (left foot), and shift transaxle into "D" range.

3) Increase engine speed to 700-800 RPM, and then to 2000-2400 RPM. Shift transaxle into "R" range, and check line pressure using same procedure. If line pressure is within specifications, line pressure is correct.

Fig. 1: Line Pressure Test Port

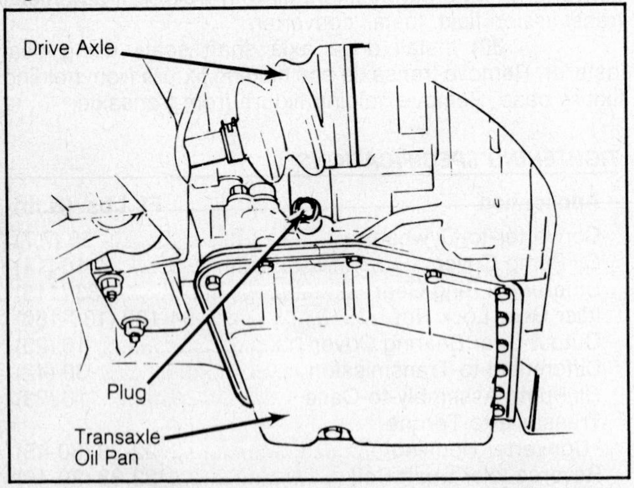

4) If line pressure is higher than specified in both "D" and "R" ranges, regulator valve or throttle valve is defective, accelerator cable or oil pressure control cables are improperly adjusted.

5) If line pressure is lower than specified in both "D" and "R" ranges, oil pump, regulator valve, or throttle valve is defective. Accelerator cable or oil pressure control cables are improperly adjusted.

6) If line pressure is lower than specified in "D" range only, forward clutch or "D" range oil system is leaking. If line pressure is lower than specified in "R" range only, direct clutch, 1st-Reverse, or "R" range oil system is leaking.

LINE PRESSURE SPECIFICATIONS

Engine RPM	psi (kg/cm²) In "D" Range	psi (kg/cm²) In "R" Range
700-800	28.5-56.8 (2.0-4.0)	78.3-113.7 (5.5-8.0)
2000-2400	56.9-85.3 (4.0-6.0)	78.3-113.7 (8.5-12.0)

ROAD TEST

1) Ensure engine is at normal operating temperature. Disconnect vacuum switch coupler. With engine at idle, shift transaxle into "D" range. Accelerate vehicle and verify 1st-2nd gear upshift. Upshift should take place at about 25 MPH.

2) Continue to accelerate engine and verify 2nd-3rd gear upshift. Upshift should take place at about 38 MPH. Stop vehicle and shift transaxle into "P" range. Connect vacuum switch coupler.

3) Start vehicle and shift transaxle into "D" range. Accelrate vehicle and verify 1st-2nd gear upshift. Upshift should take place at about 32 MPH. Continue to accelerate engine and verify 2nd-3rd gear upshift. Upshift should take place at about 60 MPH.

4) Stop vehicle. Start up vehicle and keep it running at 18 MPH. Release accelerator pedal. One or two seconds later, fully depress accelerator pedal and check if 2nd-1st gear downshift takes place.

5) Accelerate vehicle to 47 MPH. Release accelerator pedal. One or two seconds later, fully depress accelerator pedal and check if 3rd-2nd gear downshift takes place.

6) If 1st-2nd gear upshift fails to take place, 1st-2nd gear shift valve or 2nd brake band is defective. Check electric circuit for bad connections, poor terminal connections, or defective controller.

7) If 2nd-3rd gear upshift fails to take place, 2nd-3rd gear shift valve or direct clutch solenoid is defective. Check electric circuit for bad connections, poor terminal connections, or defective controller.

8) If 2nd-1st gear or 3rd-2nd gear downshifts fail to take place, accelerator switch is defective. Check electric circuit for bad connections, poor terminal connections, or defective controller.

STALL TEST

1) Ensure transaxle fluid is at normal operating temperature. Make sure transaxle fluid level is between "FULL HOT" and "LOW HOT" on oil level gauge. DO NOT perform this test for more than 5 seconds.

2) Install techometer to engine. Apply parking brake and block drive wheels. Start engine, depress brake pedal (left foot), and shift transaxle into "D" range. Fully depress accelerator pedal (right foot) and note RPM reading on tachometer.

3) Shift transaxle into "R" range, and check stall speed using same procedure. Stall speed in both instances should be 2000-2400 RPM. If stall speed is lower than specified, engine output is low or torque converter is defective.

4) If stall speed is higher than specified in "D" range only, forward clutch is slipping, or one-way clutch is defective. If stall speed is higher than specified in "R" range only, direct clutch is slipping, or 1st-Reverse brake band is slipping.

GENERAL MOTORS IMPORTS/SUZUKI 3-SPEED TRANSAXLE (Cont.)

SERVICE (IN VEHICLE)

OIL PAN & STRAINER

Removal & Installation

1) Raise and support vehicle. Drain transaxle fluid. Remove stabilizer shaft bolts. Remove transaxle crossmember. Note position of oil pan bolts, and then remove bolts. Using a plastic hammer, lightly tap on oil pan for removal. Remove oil strainer.

2) To install, reverse removal procedure. Make sure magnet is located on bottom of pan, just below oil strainer. Apply sealant to 2 cross-grooved bolts, and install them in original position.

DIRECT CLUTCH SOLENOID, 2ND BRAKE SOLENOID & WIRING

Removal

Remove oil pan. Remove couplers from direct clutch and 2nd brake solenoids. Remove 2nd brake solenoids and wire harness, including grommet.

Installation

Install solenoid wiring harness on transaxle case. Replace grommet if damaged. Install direct clutch and 2nd brake solenoids on valve body. Replace "O" rings if damaged. Connect wiring to solenoids. Install oil pan and connect solenoid wire harness. Add transaxle lubricant.

Fig. 2: Installing Transaxle Solenoids

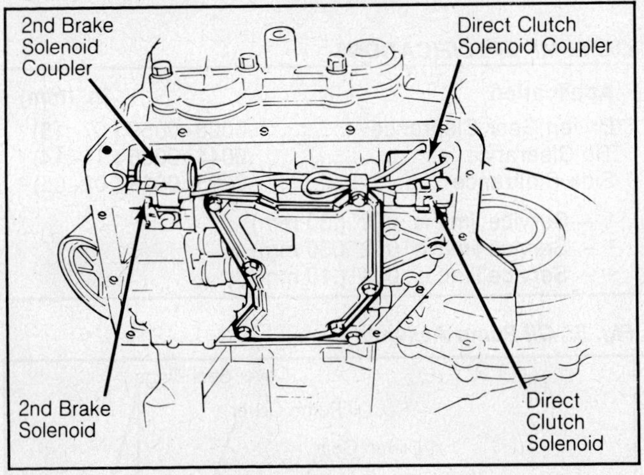

OIL PRESSURE CONTROL CABLE

Removal & Installation

1) Remove cable cover and disconnect oil pressure control cable from accelerator cable. Remove oil pan. Pull down on cable and disconnect cable from throttle valve cam. Remove oil pressure cable from transaxle.

2) To install cable, reverse removal procedure. Adjust oil pressure control cable. See AUTOMATIC TRANSMISSION SERVICING article in IMPORT GENERAL SERVICING section.

REMOVAL & INSTALLATION

TRANSMISSION

See appropriate MANUAL TRANSMISSION REMOVAL article in IMPORT GENERAL SERVICING section.

TRANSMISSION DISASSEMBLY

1) Remove torque converter. Remove rear cover bolts and solenoid wire harness clamps. Install transaxle in Holding Fixture (J-35525) and Stand (J-38920).

2) Remove oil level gauge, filler tube, and oil cooler lines. Drain transaxle fluid. Remove oil pan and gasket. Tap oil pan lightly with hammer to remove. Disconnect direct clutch solenoid and 2nd brake solenoid couplers. *See Fig. 2.*

3) Remove oil tubes from lower valve body. Disconnect oil pressure control cable from throttle cam, and then remove cable. Remove oil strainer and lower valve body.

4) Using compressed air, remove accumulator piston and spring. Position shop rag over pistons to catch each piston assembly. Remove 2nd brake band and cover.

5) Scribe mark on 2nd brake band piston rod. Apply air into 2nd brake band port and measure rod stroke. *See Fig. 3.* Rod stroke must be .06-.11" (1.5-3.0 mm). If incorrect, replace piston rod or 2nd brake band.

Fig. 3: Measuring 2nd Brake Band Piston Rod Stroke

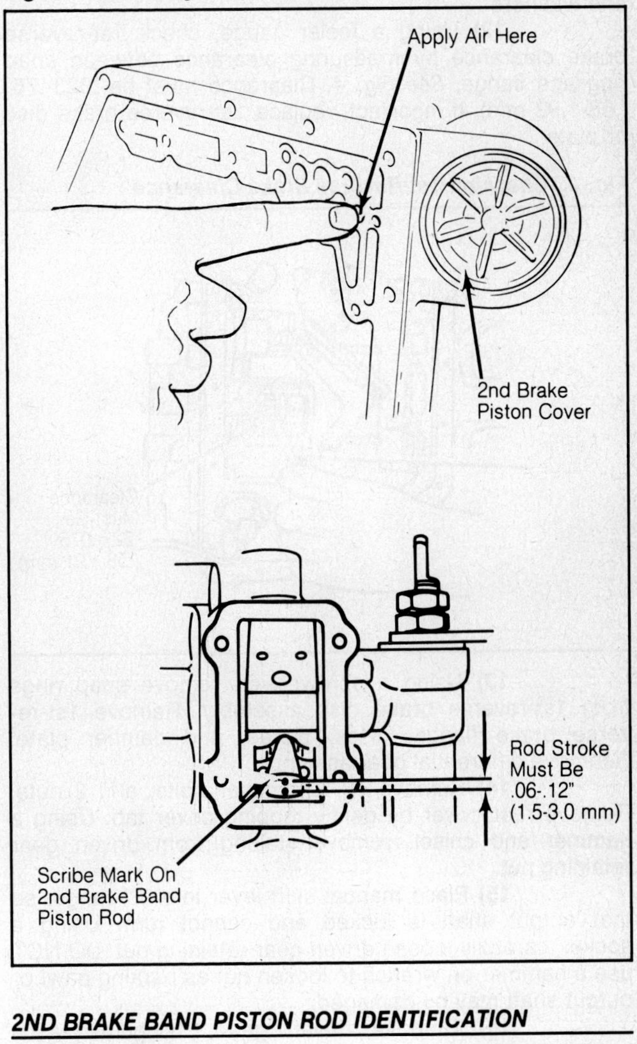

2ND BRAKE BAND PISTON ROD IDENTIFICATION

Identification	Length In. (mm)
Marked	4.83 (122.7)
Unmarked	4.77 (121.2)

GENERAL MOTORS IMPORTS/SUZUKI 3-SPEED TRANSAXLE (Cont.)

6) Install Piston Cover Depressor (J-35534) on transaxle oil pan flange to compress 2nd brake piston cover. *See Fig. 3.* Remove snap ring. Remove depressor, piston cover, piston and spring.

7) Remove wire holding plate retaining nut. Pull out solenoid wire harness. Remove 6 oil pump bolts. Using slide hammer and Adapter (J-35495), carefully remove oil pump. DO NOT drop bearing races which may stick to oil pump.

8) Remove transaxle case housing internal and external bolts. Remove transaxle housing by gently tapping it with a plastic hammer. Remove 2nd brake band pin.

9) While holding input shaft, remove direct clutch and forward clutch as an assembly. DO NOT drop ring gear bearing race or bearing which may stick to input shaft. Remove clutch assembly from input shaft.

10) Remove 2nd brake band. Remove front planetary ring gear, ring gear bearing, and front planetary gear assembly. Remove planetary sun gear and front planetary gear bearing. *See Fig. 10.*

11) Using a screwdriver, carefully remove one-way clutch snap ring. Use care not to damage transaxle case. Remove rear planetary ring gear, ring gear bearing, and washers.

12) Using a feeler gauge, check 1st-reverse brake clearance by measuring clearance between snap ring and flange. *See Fig. 4.* Clearance must be .023-.75" (.58-1.92 mm). If incorrect, replace 1st-reverse brake disc or plate.

Fig. 4: Checking 1st-Reverse Brake Clearance

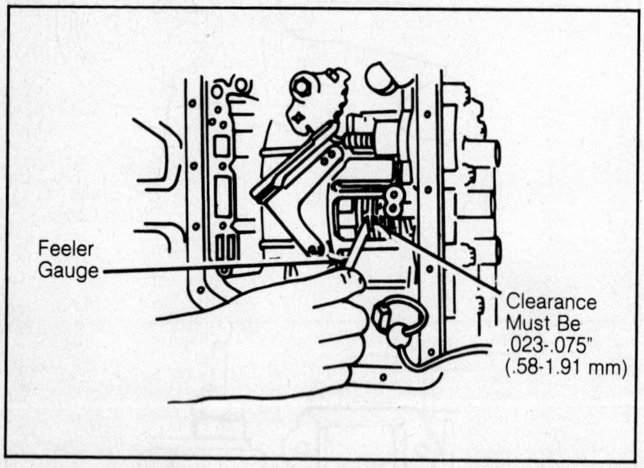

13) Using a screwdriver, remove snap rings from 1st-reverse brake disc assembly. Remove 1st-reverse brake flange, discs, plates, and damper plate. Renmove differential gear assembly.

14) Remove 10 rear cover bolts, and 2 nuts. Remove rear cover by gently tapping cover tab. Using a hammer and chisel, remove staking from driven gear retaining nut.

15) Place manual shift lever into "P" range, so that output shaft is locked and cannot turn. Using a socket, carefully loosen driven gear retaining nut. DO NOT use a hammer on wrench to loosen nut as parking pawl or output shaft may be damaged.

16) Remove driven gear. Using a plastic hammer, drive countershaft out of case. Remove output shaft by pushing outer race of internal output shaft bearing with Output Shaft Remover (J-35539) from inside of transaxle case.

NOTE: **Do not tap directly on output shaft, as output shaft or bearing will be damaged. Position output shaft remover legs in notches (4) of transaxle case.**

17) Pull out parking pawl lock shaft and spring. Remove parking lock pawl and sleeve. Remove manual detent spring assembly and manual shift shaft. Push down on 1st-reverse return spring assembly and remove snap ring.

18) Remove return spring assembly. Remove 1st-reverse brake piston by applying compressed air to port in 2-hole stack in transaxle case (oil pan) cavity.

COMPONENT DISASSEMBLY

OIL PUMP

1) Remove oil pump cover seal rings. Remove oil pump cover "O" ring. Remove 11 bolts and pump cover. *See Fig. 5.* Push driven gear to one side of pump body.

2) Using a feeler gauge, measure clearance between driven gear and body. If clearance exceeds specification, replace driven gear. Measure gear tip clearance between drive (driven) gear and cresent.

3) If clearance exceeds specification, replace drive (driven) gear. Using a straightedge and a feeler gauge, measure side clearance between drive (driven) gear and pump body. If clearance exceeds specification, replace drive (driven) gear.

OIL PUMP SPECIFICATIONS

Application	In. (mm)
Driven Gear Clearance	.0028-.0059 (.07-.15) [1]
Tip Clearance	.0044-.0055 (.11-.14) [2]
Side Clearance	.0008-.0019 (.02-.05) [3]

[1] – Service limit is .012" (.30 mm)
[2] – Service limit is .012" (.30 mm)
[3] – Service limit is .004" (.10 mm)

Fig. 5: Oil Pump Assembly

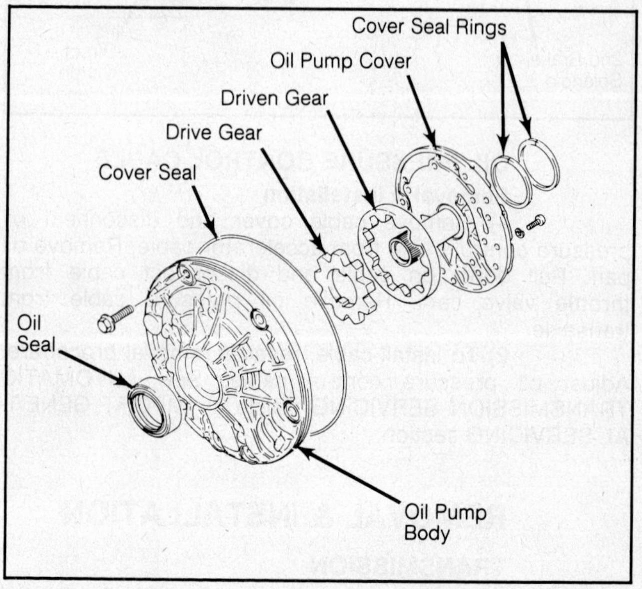

GENERAL MOTORS IMPORTS/SUZUKI 3-SPEED TRANSAXLE (Cont.)

DIRECT CLUTCH

1) Remove direct clutch snap ring. Remove clutch flange, discs, and plates. Place Clutch Spring Compressor (J-23327) on return spring seat and compress with press. Remove direct clutch plate snap ring. Remove spring seat and return spring assembly.

2) Apply compressed air to clutch drum hole to remove direct clutch piston. If piston does not pop out, lift piston out with needle nose pliers. Remove inner seal from drum and outer seal from piston.

3) Shake direct clutch piston to ensure check valve moves freely in piston. Apply compressed air to piston hole in both directions to check valve for leakage.

FORWARD CLUTCH

1) Remove forward clutch snap ring. Remove clutch flange, discs, and plates. Place Clutch Spring Compressor (J-23327) and Adapter (J-25018-A) on return spring seat and compress with press. Remove forward clutch plate snap ring. Remove spring seat and return spring assembly.

2) Apply compressed air to hole in input shaft to remove forward clutch piston. If piston does not pop out, lift piston out with needle nose pliers. Remove inner seal and outer seal from piston.

3) Shake forward clutch piston to ensure check valve moves freely in piston. Apply compressed air to input shaft hole in both directions to check valve for leakage.

VALVE BODY

Remove upper valve body from lower valve body, being careful not to drop 4 check balls. *See Fig. 7.* Remove valves and corresponding springs. Note valve and spring position as they are being removed. Keep valve and spring together. *See Fig. 6.*

COUNTERSHAFT BEARINGS

Using a screwdriver, remove output shaft bearing snap rings. Remove backing plate. Using slide hammer and Bearing Remover (J-29369-1), remove countershaft ball bearing from transaxle case. Using slide hammer and Bearing Remover (J-29369-2), remove countershaft roller bearing from transaxle case.

OUTPUT SHAFT BEARINGS

Using bench press and Bearing Puller (J-22912-01), remove output shaft bearing. DO NOT reuse bearings.

DIFFERENTIAL

1) Using Puller (J-28509-A) and Plug (J-34851), remove differential case side bearings. Using same procedure, remove speedometer drive gear.

2) Remove roll pin securing pinion shaft. Remove pinion shaft, pinion gears, and side gears from case. Remove ring gear bolts and then remove ring gear.

CLEANING & INSPECTION

1) Thoroughly wash all parts in cleaning solvent. Make sure old lubricant, metallic particles, dirt, or foreign materials are removed from surface of parts. Dry parts with compressed air.

2) Inspect case halves for porosity, cracks, damaged mating surfaces, stripped threads, or distortion. Apply compressed air to each oil feed port or channel to remove obstructions.

3) Inspect all gears for wear or damage. Check splines for burrs, nicks, wear, or other damage. Remove minor nicks or scratches with an oil stone. Inspect thrust washers for wear, distortion, or damage.

4) Inspect condition of all needle, roller, and thrust bearings. Lubricate bearings with ATF and check them for roughness while slowly rotating them by hand. Inspect shafts for wear, distortion, or damage. Replace any part showing excessive wear or damage.

COMPONENT REASSEMBLY

DIFFERENTIAL

1) Lubricate differential components before assembly. Install side washers and side gears. Install pinion washers an pinion gears. Install pinion gear shaft.

2) Using a feeler gauge, measure backlash between pinions and side gears. If backlash is not 0.004-.009" (.01-.25 mm), adjust backlash by changing thickness of side gear washers. Install pinion shaft roll pin.

3) Install ring gear and tighten retaining bolts. Using bench press, install speedometer gear. Install differential bearings with bearing seal toward differential case.

SIDE GEAR & WASHER AVAILABILITY

Application	Size In. (mm)
Side Gear	.035 (.90)
Side Gear	.037 (.95)
Side Washers	.039 (1.00)
Side Washers	.041 (1.05)
Side Washers	.043 (1.10)
Side Washers	.045 (1.15)
Side Washers	.047 (1.20)

OUTPUT SHAFT BEARINGS

Using bench press and Bearing Installer (J-35539), install bearings on output shaft.

COUNTERSHAFT BEARINGS

1) Install countershaft spacer in case. Using Bearing Installer (J-35537) and Handle (J-7079-2), install countershaft roller bearing in case. Install snap ring.

2) Using handle and reverse side of Bearing Installer (J-35537), install countershaft ball bearing in case. Install bearing backing plate and snap ring.

VALVE BODY

1) Install valves and corresponding springs. Make sure to install same number of throttle valve rings as those removed. Install check balls in upper valve body. *See Fig. 7.*

2) Carefully check valve body gaskets to ensure they match those removed. Install lower valve body cover and gasket on lower valve body. Tighten lower valve body bolts.

3) Install upper valve body on lower valve body. Install reamer bolts (finger-tight) at locations shown. *See Fig. 7.* DO NOT tighten bolts at this time.

4) Install remaining 14 valve body bolts. Tighten 4 bolts, marked with "2", to specification. Tighten 8 bolts, marked with "3", to specification. Tighten 2 bolts,

GENERAL MOTORS IMPORTS/SUZUKI 3-SPEED TRANSAXLE (Cont.)

Fig. 6: Suzuki 3-Speed Transaxle Valve Body

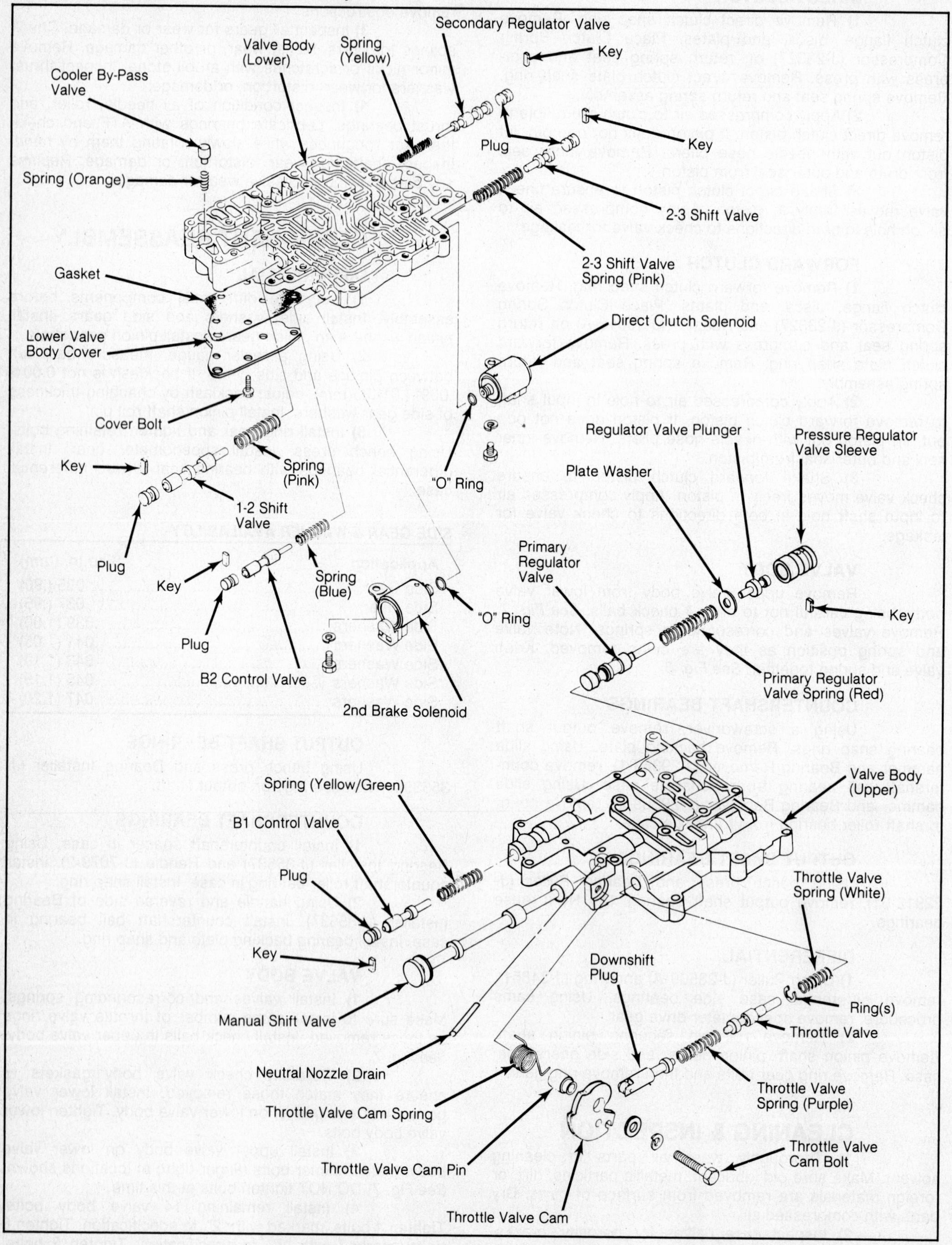

GENERAL MOTORS IMPORTS/SUZUKI 3-SPEED TRANSAXLE (Cont.)

marked with "4", to specification. Tighten reamer bolts, marked with "1", to specification.

Fig. 7: Installing Check Balls & Valve Body Bolts

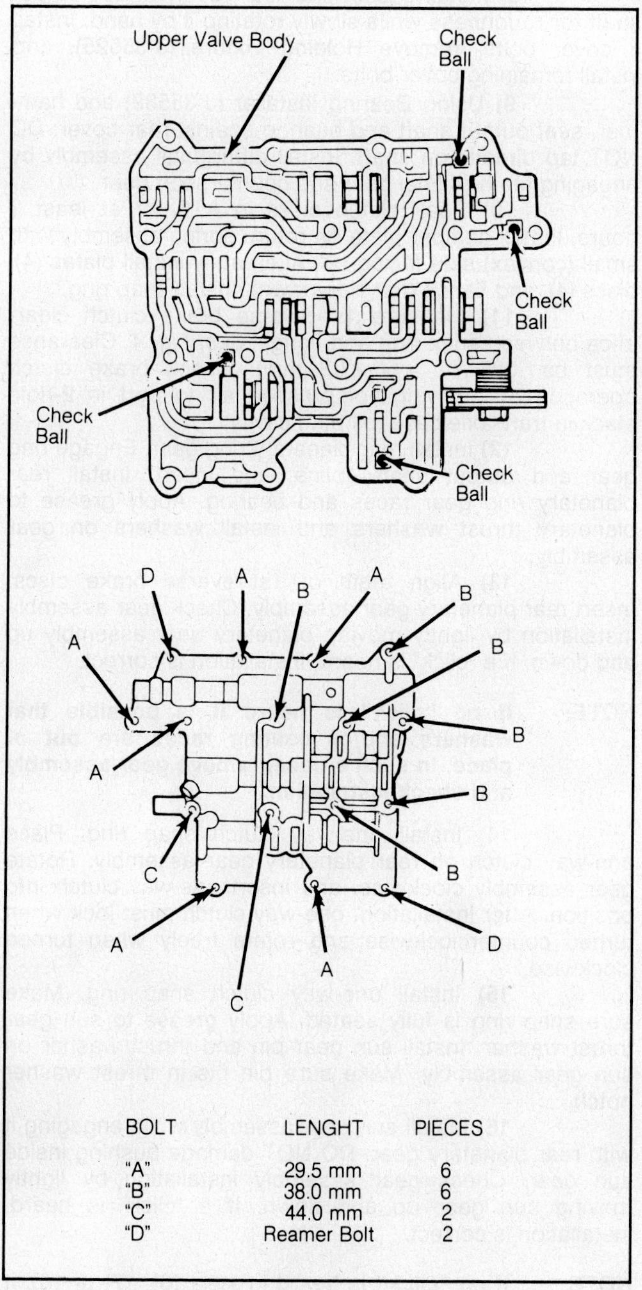

BOLT	LENGHT	PIECES
"A"	29.5 mm	6
"B"	38.0 mm	6
"C"	44.0 mm	2
"D"	Reamer Bolt	2

FORWARD CLUTCH

1) Soak clutch discs in ATF for at least 2 hours before assembly. Lubricate inner "O" ring with ATF and install in drum. Lubricate outer "O" ring and install in piston. Install piston in drum, making sure that seals do not get cut or twisted.

2) Install clutch return springs and spring seat. Using clutch spring compressor, compress spring seat and install snap ring. Make sure snap ring is securely installed.

3) Install plate, disc, plate, another plate, disc, and flange. Install clutch snap ring. Using a feeler gauge, measure clearance between snap ring and clutch flange. Clearance must be .098-.120" (2.5-3.0 mm).

4) If clearance is incorrect, replace top flange. Flange is available in .118" (3.0 mm) and .132" (3.35 mm) thicknesses. If clearance is correct, check piston for movement by applying air through hole.

Fig. 8: Forward Clutch Assembly

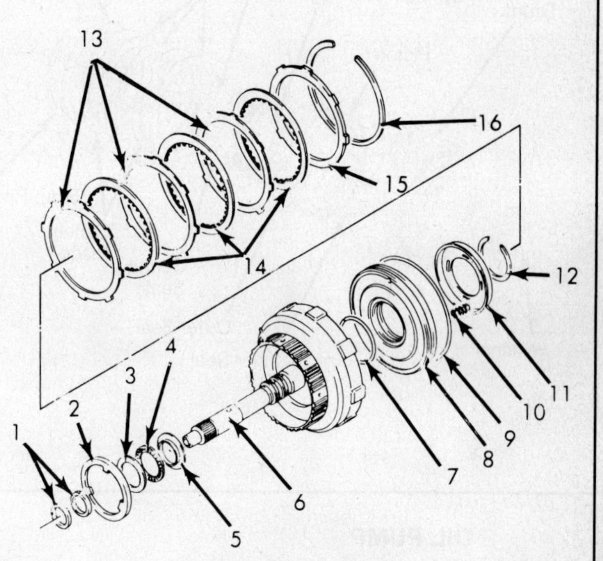

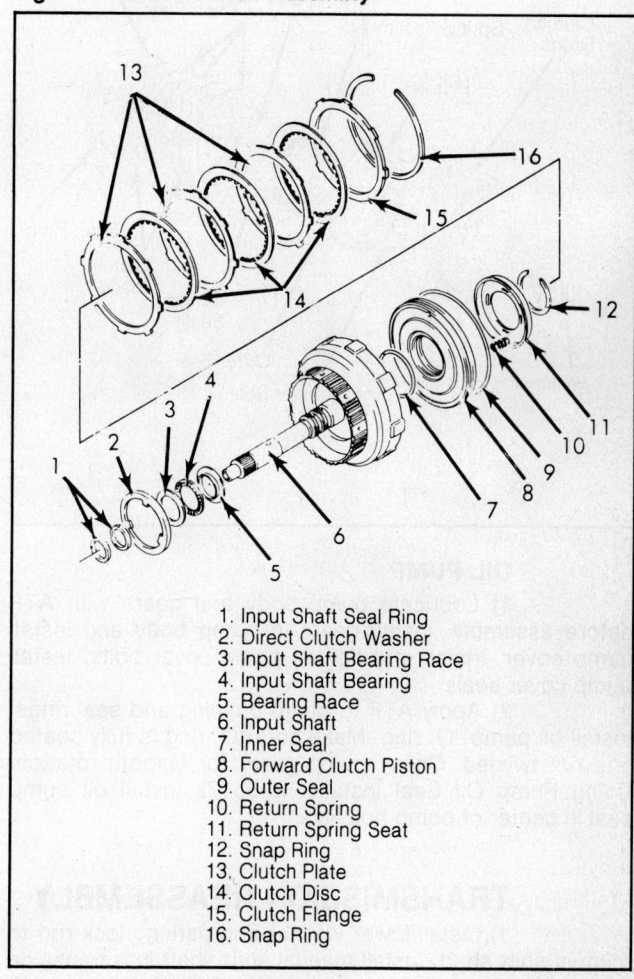

1. Input Shaft Seal Ring
2. Direct Clutch Washer
3. Input Shaft Bearing Race
4. Input Shaft Bearing
5. Bearing Race
6. Input Shaft
7. Inner Seal
8. Forward Clutch Piston
9. Outer Seal
10. Return Spring
11. Return Spring Seat
12. Snap Ring
13. Clutch Plate
14. Clutch Disc
15. Clutch Flange
16. Snap Ring

DIRECT CLUTCH

1) Soak clutch discs in ATF for at least 2 hours before assembly. Lubricate inner and outer "O" rings with ATF and install in piston. Install piston in input shaft drum, making sure that seals do not get cut or twisted.

2) Install clutch return springs and spring seat. Using clutch spring compressor and adapter, compress spring seat and install snap ring. Make sure snap ring is securely installed.

3) Install plate, disc, plate, disc, plate, disc, and flange. Install clutch snap ring. Using a feeler gauge, measure clearance between snap ring and clutch flange. Clearance must be .079-.105" (2.0-2.7 mm).

4) If clearance is incorrect, replace top flange. Flange is available in .118" (3.0 mm) and .132" (3.35 mm) thicknesses. If clearance is correct, check piston for movement by applying air through input shaft hole.

GENERAL MOTORS IMPORTS/SUZUKI 3-SPEED TRANSAXLE (Cont.)

Fig. 9: Direct Clutch Assembly

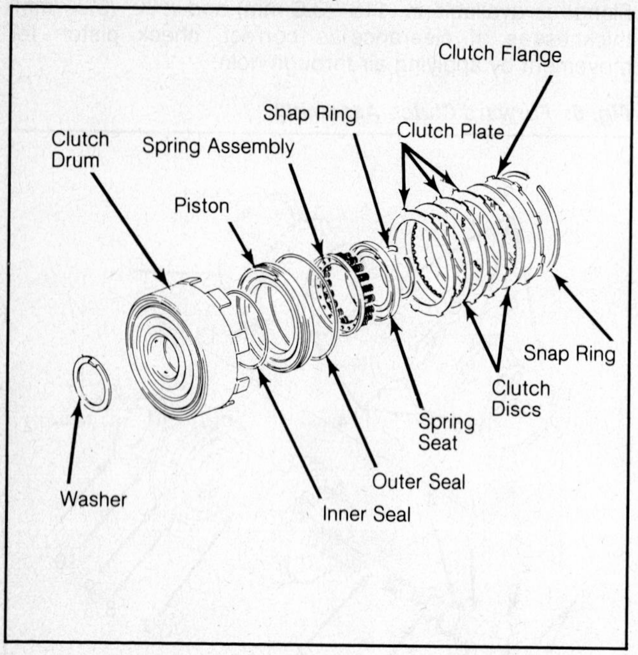

OIL PUMP

1) Lubricate pump body and gears with ATF before assembly. Install gears in pump body and install pump cover. Install and tighten pump cover bolts. Install pump cover seals.

2) Apply ATF to pump bushing and seal rings. Install oil pump "O" ring. Make sure "O" ring is fully seated and not twisted. Check pump gears for smooth rotation. Using Pump Oil Seal Installer (J-9617), install oil pump seal in center of pump housing.

TRANSMISSION REASSEMBLY

1) Install lower washer and parking lock rod to manual shift shaft. Install manual shift shaft into transaxle case, and then manual detent spring. Tighten manual shift shaft bolt.

2) Install shift shaft upper washer and shift lever on manual shift shaft. Tighten nuts and check manual shift shaft for smooth rotation. Install pin and snap ring to parking lock pawl, and then install in case.

3) Place shift lever in any position (except parking), and install parking lock pawl. Install lock pawl shaft and lock pawl spring. Move manual shift lever to ensure pawl moves smoothly.

4) Apply ATF to 1st-reverse "O" rings and install them on piston. Insert piston into case so that spring holes are at top. Make sure "O" ring is not cut or twisted.

5) Install return spring assembly on piston, making sure each spring is securely installed in corresponding hole. Push down on return spring assembly and install snap ring.

6) Using Countershaft Installer (J-35608), Handle (J-7079-2) and hammer, install countershaft. Make sure that spacer is installed on end of shaft. DO NOT hammer shaft excessively hard as snap ring or case may be damaged.

7) Place shift lever in any position (except parking). Using Bearing Installer (J-35539) and hammer, install output shaft. Place shift lever in parking position to lock output shaft. Tighten driven gear nut. Stake nut into place.

8) Install gasket and rear cover. Check output shaft for roughness while slowly rotating it by hand. Install 5 cover bolts, remove Holding Fixture (J-35525), and install remaining cover bolts.

9) Using Bearing Installer (J-35539) and hammer, seat output shaft and bearing against rear cover. DO NOT tap directly on shaft. Install differential assembly by engaging teeth of final gear and countershaft gear.

10) Soak clutch discs in ATF for at least 2 hours. Install damper plate on return spring assembly with small (convex) side facing up. Alternately install plates (4), discs (4), and flange (flat side down). Install snap ring.

11) Measure 1st-reverse brake clutch clearance between snap ring and flange. *See. Fig. 4*. Clearance must be .023-.75" (.58-1.92 mm). Check brake clutch operation by applying compressed air to port in 2-hole stack in transaxle case (oil pan) cavity.

12) Install rear planetary ring gear. Engage ring gear and output shaft spline, and insert. Install rear planetary ring gear races and bearing. Apply grease to planetary thrust washers and install washers on gear assembly.

13) Align teeth of 1st-reverse brake discs. Insert rear planetary gear assembly. Check gear assembly installation by lightly moving planetary gear assembly up and down. If a "click" is heard, installation is correct.

NOTE: **If no "click" is heard it is possible that washers and/or bearing races are out of place. In such a case, remove gear assembly and check installation.**

14) Install one-way clutch snap ring. Place one-way clutch on rear planetary gear assembly. Rotate gear assembly clockwise, and insert one-way clutch into position. After installation, one-way clutch must lock when turned counterclockwise and rotate freely when turned clockwise.

15) Install one-way clutch snap ring. Make sure snap ring is fully seated. Apply grease to sun gear thrust washer. Install sun gear pin and thrust washer on sun gear assembly. Make sure pin fits in thrust washer notch.

16) Install sun gear assembly while engaging it with rear planetary gear. DO NOT damage bushing inside sun gear. Check gear assembly installation by lightly moving sun gear up and down. If a "click" is heard, installation is correct.

NOTE: **If no "click" is heard in step 16), 17) or 18), it is possible that washers and/or bearing races are out of place. In such a case, remove gear assembly and check installation.**

17) Install planetary gear bearing and race. Install front planetary gear assembly while rotating it in both directions. Check gear assembly installation by lightly moving gear assembly up and down. If a "click" is heard, installation is correct.

18) Install ring gear bearings and races on front planetary ring gear assembly. Install front planetary ring gear assembly. Check gear assembly installation by lightly ring gear up and down. If a "click" is heard, installation is correct.

GENERAL MOTORS IMPORTS/SUZUKI 3-SPEED TRANSAXLE (Cont.)

Fig. 10: Exploded View Of Planetary Gear Assembly

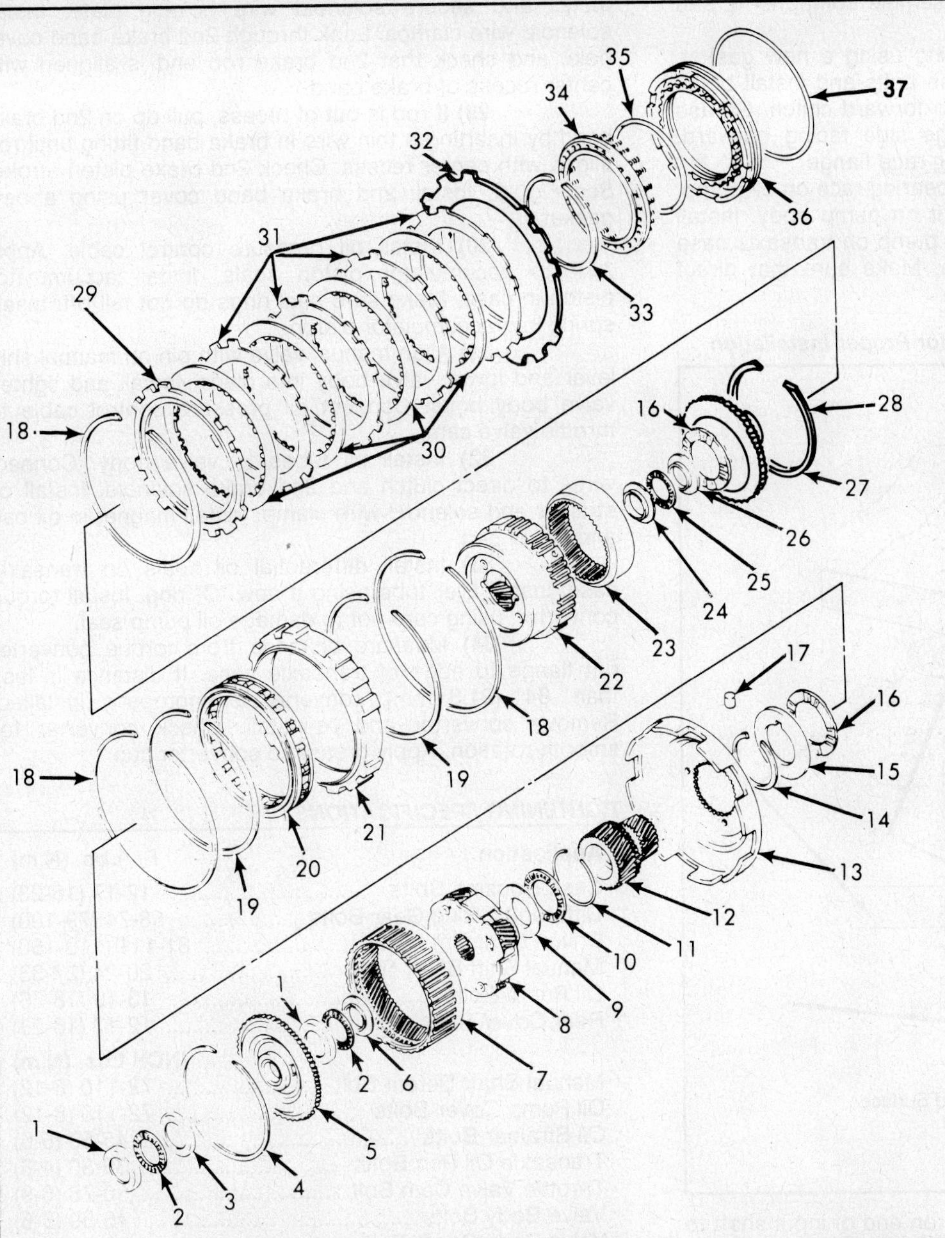

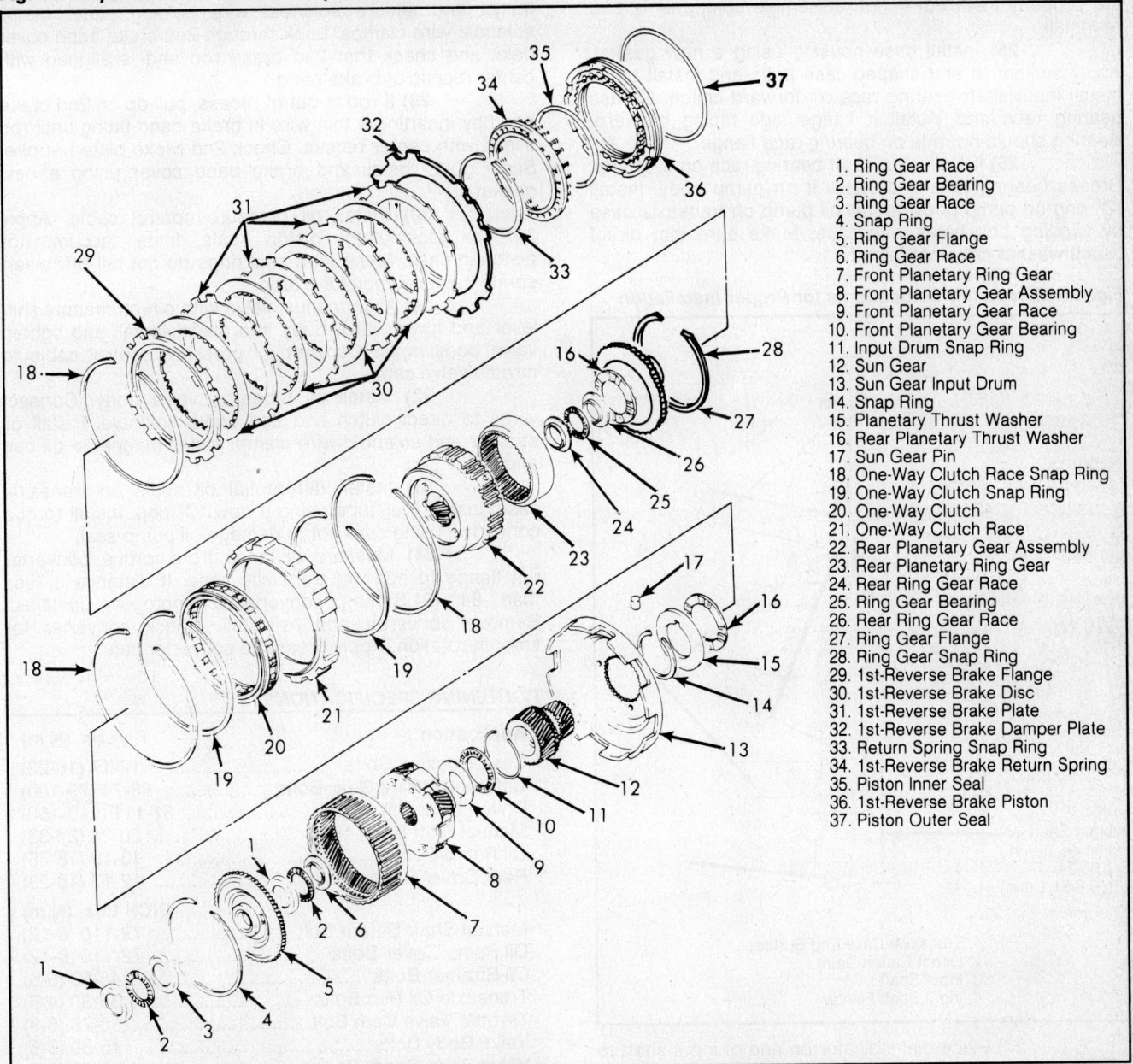

1. Ring Gear Race
2. Ring Gear Bearing
3. Ring Gear Race
4. Snap Ring
5. Ring Gear Flange
6. Ring Gear Race
7. Front Planetary Ring Gear
8. Front Planetary Gear Assembly
9. Front Planetary Gear Race
10. Front Planetary Gear Bearing
11. Input Drum Snap Ring
12. Sun Gear
13. Sun Gear Input Drum
14. Snap Ring
15. Planetary Thrust Washer
16. Rear Planetary Thrust Washer
17. Sun Gear Pin
18. One-Way Clutch Race Snap Ring
19. One-Way Clutch Snap Ring
20. One-Way Clutch
21. One-Way Clutch Race
22. Rear Planetary Gear Assembly
23. Rear Planetary Ring Gear
24. Rear Ring Gear Race
25. Ring Gear Bearing
26. Rear Ring Gear Race
27. Ring Gear Flange
28. Ring Gear Snap Ring
29. 1st-Reverse Brake Flange
30. 1st-Reverse Brake Disc
31. 1st-Reverse Brake Plate
32. 1st-Reverse Brake Damper Plate
33. Return Spring Snap Ring
34. 1st-Reverse Brake Return Spring
35. Piston Inner Seal
36. 1st-Reverse Brake Piston
37. Piston Outer Seal

19) Install 2nd brake band. Apply ATF to 2nd brake band pin and install it by aligning hole in 2nd brake band with hole in case. Apply ATF to 2nd brake piston assembly. Install 2nd brake piston spring and piston assembly in case.

20) Apply ATF to piston cover seals and install cover in case using Piston Cover Depressor (J-35534). Install output shaft seal ring. Apply grease to input shaft seal rings and install on input shaft.

21) Apply grease to direct clutch washer and install on clutch with groove facing outward. Align teeth of direct clutch discs. Install direct clutch on input shaft. Check clutch installation by lightly moving it up and down. If a "click" is heard, installation is correct.

NOTE: **If no "click" is heard it is possible that direct clutch is incorrectly installed. In such a case, remove clutch assembly and check installation.**

22) Apply grease to ring gear races and bearing. Install 1.41" (35.8 mm) diameter ring gear race on ring gear with its flange side down. Install 1.49" (37.9 mm) diameter ring gear race and bearing.

23) Align teeth of forward clutch discs. Install input shaft and forward/direct clutch assembly while rotating input shaft back and forth in case. Check input shaft installation by lightly moving it up and down. If a "click" is heard, installation is correct.

NOTE: **If no "click" is heard, input shaft is incorrectly installed. In such a case, remove input shaft assembly and check installation.**

24) Place a strightedge on transaxle case surface. Using a depth micrometer measure depth of input shaft flange. Subtract width of straightedge from reading.

GENERAL MOTORS IMPORTS/SUZUKI 3-SPEED TRANSAXLE (Cont.)

If final reading is 1.96-2.01" (49.8-51.1 mm), components are properly installed. If not, dissemble components and re-install.

25) Install case housing using a new gasket. Apply sealant to star-shaped case bolts and install bolts. Install input shaft bearing race on forward clutch. Grease bearing race and install it flange side facing outward. Bearing should not ride on bearing race flange.

26) Install input shaft bearing race on oil pump. Grease bearing race and install it on pump body. Install "O" ring on pump body. Install oil pump on transaxle case by aligning bolt holes with case. Make sure that direct clutch washer does not fall off.

Fig. 11: Measuring Components for Proper Installation

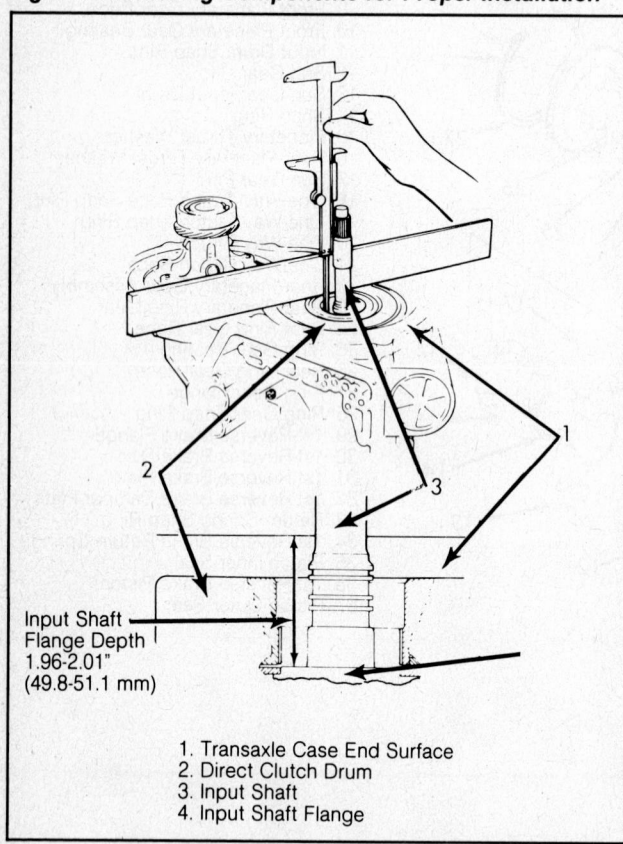

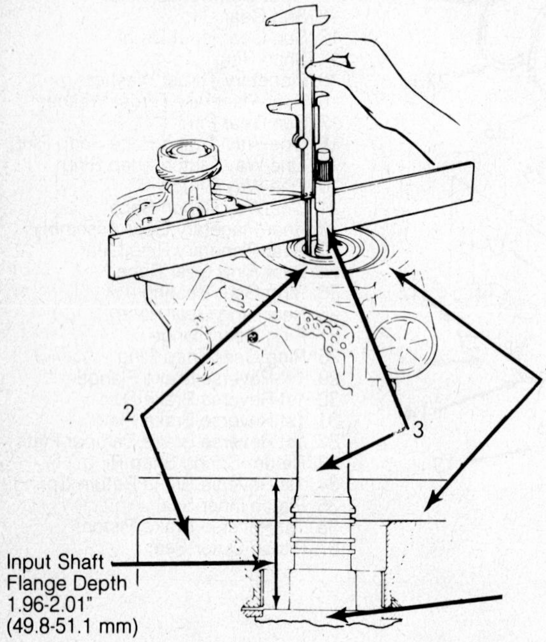

1. Transaxle Case End Surface
2. Direct Clutch Drum
3. Input Shaft
4. Input Shaft Flange

27) Place dial indicator on end of input shaft to check end play. End play must be .012-.035" (.3-.9 mm). If incorrect, remove oil pump and replace input shaft bearing race on oil pump side.

28) Install solenoid wire harness on case. Install and secure solenoid wire holding plate. Install solenoid wire clamps. Look through 2nd brake band cover hole, and check that 2nd brake rod end is aligned with center recess of brake band.

29) If rod is out of recess, pull up on 2nd brake band by inserting a thin wire in brake band fitting until rod aligns with center recess. Check 2nd brake piston stroke. *See Fig. 3*. Install 2nd brake band cover using a new gasket.

30) Install oil pressure control cable. Apply ATF to accumulator piston seals. Install accumulator piston in case. Make sure seal rings do not fall off. Insert spring into accumulator piston.

31) Align manual valve with pin on manual shift lever and lower valve body into place. Install and tighten valve body bolts. Connect oil pressure control cable to throttle valve cam.

32) Install oil tubes to valve body. Connect wires to direct clutch and 2nd brake solenoid. Install oil strainer and solenoid wire clamp. Install magnet in oil pan and install pan.

33) Install differential oil seals on transaxle case. Install filler tube using a new "O" ring. Install torque converter, using care not to damage oil pump seal.

34) Measure distance from torque converter nut flange to edge of transaxle case. If distance is less than .84" (21.3 mm), converter is improperly installed. Remove converter and re-install. Check converter for smooth rotation. Apply grease to converter cup.

TIGHTENING SPECIFICATIONS

Application	Ft. Lbs. (N.m)
Case Housing Bolts	12-17 (16-23)
Differential Ring Gear Bolts	58-74 (79-100)
Driven Gear Nut	81-111 (110-150)
Manual Shift Shaft Nuts	20-24 (27-33)
Oil Pump Bolts	13-19 (18-26)
Rear Cover Bolts	12-17 (16-23)
	INCH Lbs. (N.m)
Manual Shaft Detent Bolt	72-110 (8-12)
Oil Pump Cover Bolts	72-110 (8-12)
Oil Strainer Bolts	45-50 (5-6)
Transaxle Oil Pan Bolts	36-50 (4-6)
Throttle Valve Cam Bolt	50-78 (6-9)
Valve Body Bolts	45-50 (5-6)
Valve Body Cover Bolts	36-50 (4-6)

Automatic Transmissions

GM TURBO HYDRA-MATIC 400 – JAGUAR

XJS-HE

DESCRIPTION

Transmission is a fully automatic unit consisting primarily of a 3 element hydraulic torque converter and a compound planetary gear set. Three multiple disc clutches, 2 roller clutches, and 2 bands provide friction elements required to obtain desired function of planetary gear set. A hydraulic system pressurized by a gear-type pump provides working pressure required to operate friction elements and automatic controls.

LUBRICATION & ADJUSTMENTS

BAND ADJUSTMENT

Band Apply Selection Test

1) Raise and support vehicle. Remove oil pan and allow fluid to drain. Remove valve body assembly with governor lines attached. Remove rear servo cover and gasket, rear servo assembly and servo accumulator spring.

2) Position selection gauge and gauge of Service Set (18G-1310) in servo bore and secure with 2 bolts. Ensure gauge is free to move up and down in both selection gauge and servo bore.

3) Using 9/16" socket on torque wrench, tighten nut on gauge to 25 ft. lbs. (34 N.m). This will cause lever on top of gauge to depress stepped gauge pin into servo pin bore, simulating actual operating conditions.

4) Note letter and relation of steps on gauge pin and select appropriate size apply pin. *See Fig. 2.* If new band apply pin is required, make note of pin size. Remove selection gauge and gauge pin.

Fig. 2: Band Apply Pin Selection

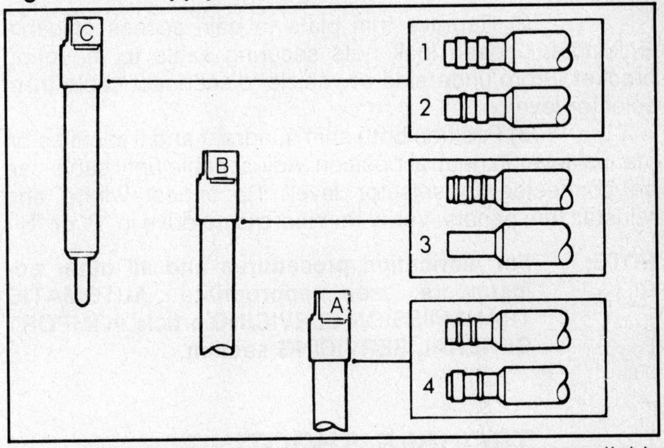

Pins 1, 2, 3 and 4 are factory installed, but are not available as replacement parts.

5) Install selected apply pin, servo accumulator spring and servo assembly. Install servo cover with new

Fig. 1: Cutaway View of Turbo Hydra-Matic 400 Automatic Transmission

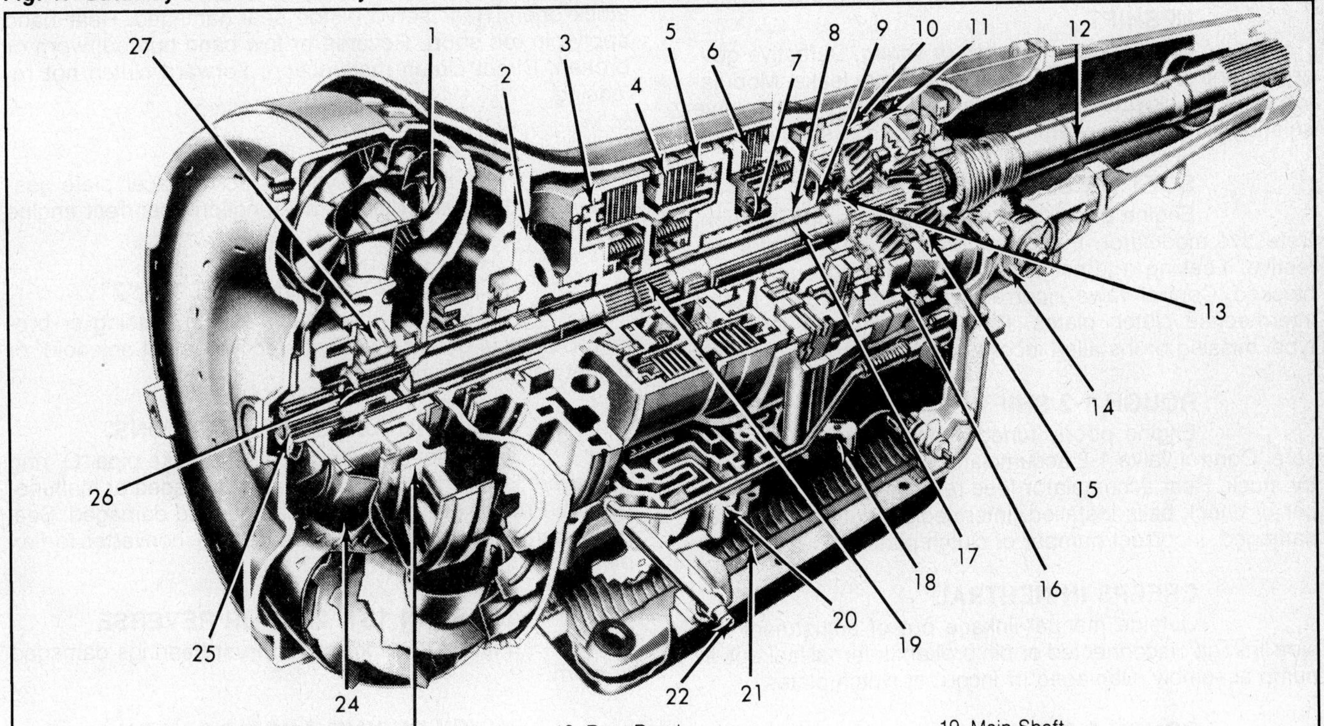

1. Converter Pump
2. Pump Assembly
3. Forward Clutch
4. Direct Clutch
5. Front Band
6. Intermediate Clutch
7. Intermediate Sprag
8. Center Support
9. Low Roller Clutch
10. Rear Band
11. Output Carrier & Internal Gear
12. Output shaft
13. Sun Gear
14. Speedometer Driven Gear
15. Rear Internal Gear
16. Reaction Carrier
17. Sun Gear Shaft
18. Detent Solenoid
19. Main Shaft
20. Control Valve
21. Filter Assembly
22. Manual Shaft
23. Stator
24. Turbine
25. Turbine Shaft
26. Stator Shaft
27. Stator Roller Clutch

gasket. Install valve body and governor pipes. Install oil pan with new gasket. Replenish transmission fuid.

SELECTOR CABLE ADJUSTMENT

1) Disconnect negative battery cable. Remove gear selector knob. Remove screws from selector trim plate, withdraw plate slightly and disconnect electrical connections.

2) Remove trim plate to gain access of cable lock nuts. Loosen lock nuts securing cable to mounting bracket. From underside of vehicle, disconnect cable from selector lever.

3) Position both shift quadrant and transmission manual lever in neutral position. Adjust cable until cable can be connected to selector lever. Reconnect wiring and reinstall trim panels. Verify that there is no drive in "P" or "N".

NOTE: **For lubrication procedures and all other adjustments, see appropriate AUTOMATIC TRANSMISSION SERVICING article in IMPORT GENERAL SERVICING section.**

TROUBLE SHOOTING

NO DRIVE IN "D"

Manual linkage out of adjustment. Low hydraulic pressures. Manual valve disconnected from lever. Forward clutch malfunction. Pump assembly feed passage blocked.

NO 1-2 UPSHIFT – OR DELAYED UPSHIFT

Short in detent switch or wiring. Defective governor control valve or feed system. Vacuum leaks. Modulator valve stuck. Leaking modulator diaphragm. Defective solenoid or detent system. Blocked orifice in spacer plate.

SOFT OR SLIPPING 1-2 SHIFT

Engine poorly tuned. Incorrect engine vacuum. Defective modulator. Pump and/or pressure regulator defective. Leaking internal seals, gaskets or circuits. Filter blocked. Control valve incorrectly torqued. Wrong type of intermediate clutch plates. Release springs of incorrect type, missing or installed incorrectly. Leaking case.

ROUGH 1-2 SHIFT

Engine poorly tuned. Incorrect hydraulic pressure. Control valve 1-2 accumulator stuck. Rear accumulator stuck. Rear accumulator feed restricted. Incorrect number of check balls installed. Intermediate clutch burned or damaged. Incorrect number of clutch plates.

CREEPS IN NEUTRAL

Outside manual linkage out of adjustment. Inside linkage disconnected or pin broken. Internal leakage in pump assembly. Damaged or incorrect clutch plates.

ROUGH 2-3 SHIFT

Defective vacuum modulator. Modulator valve stuck. Pump pressure regulator or boost valve stuck. Front servo accumulator spring damaged or missing. Front servo accumulator piston stuck. Extra waved steel plate installed in in direct clutch. Drilled controlled valve assembly blocked.

SLIPPING 2-3 SHIFT

Incorrect hydraulic pressure. Direct clutch leaking. Leaky passages or stuck valves in control valve assembly. Spacer plate damaged in control valve. Blocked direct clutch feed orifice. Servo pin leaking. Broken or missing front servo spring. Incorrect number of direct clutch plates. Damaged or missing piston seals. Broken or undersize oil rings. Case-to-center support leaking.

WILL NOT HOLD IN PARK

Misadjusted linkage. Parking pawl broken or chamfer missing.

WILL NOT RELEASE FROM PARK

Misadjusted linkage.

NO ENGINE BRAKING IN "L1"

Low/Reverse check ball missing. Rear servo oil seal ring, bore or piston damaged. Rear band apply pin to short or improperly installed. Rear band damaged.

NO ENGINE BRAKING IN "L2"

Front servo or accumulator oil rings/bore damaged. Front servo piston stuck. Front band damaged or incorrectly installed.

NO REVERSE – OR SLIPS IN REVERSE

Manual linkage incorrectly adjusted. Incorrect hydraulic pressure. Spacer plate gaskets damaged. Low/Reverse check ball missing. Two-three shift valve train stuck open. Rear servo piston seal damaged. Rear band apply pin too short. Reverse or low band burned, worn or broken. Direct clutch malfunction. Forward clutch not releasing.

NO 2-3 SHIFT

Two-three shift valve stuck. Spacer plate gaskets damaged. Direct clutch malfunction. Incorrect engine vacuum.

NO MANUAL DOWNSHIFT TO "2"

Three-two valve stuck, spring missing or broken. Defective detent switch, defective detent solenoid, or detent valve train sticking.

NOISY IN ALL GEAR POSITIONS

Incorrect or restricted filter. Intake pipe "O" ring damaged. Leaking case. Pump gears damaged or malfunctioning. Pressure regulator orifice cup plug damaged. Seal rings damaged or worn. Loose torque converter-to-flex plate bolts.

NOISY IN 1ST, 2ND, OR REVERSE

Planetary gear set or thrust bearings damaged or worn.

NOISY DURING ACCELERATION

Transmission cooler lines contacting body. Motor mounts loose.

SQUEAK AT LOW SPEEDS

Speedometer shaft seal damaged. Extension housing seal damaged.

TESTING

ROAD TEST

1) Place selector lever in "D", and accelerate vehicle from a stop. The 1-2 and 2-3 shift should occur at all throttle openings. See SHIFT SPEED SPECIFICATIONS table. As vehicle speed decreases below 10 MPH, a 3-2 and 2-1 downshift should occur.

2) Place selector lever in "2" (Intermediate) and accelerate from a stop. A 1-2 upshift should occur and no 2-3 shift should occur. See SHIFT SPEED SPECIFICATIONS table. As vehicle speed decreases below 10 MPH, a 2-1 downshift should occur.

3) Place selector lever in "1" (Low), and accelerate vehicle from a stop. No upshifts should occur below 6200 RPM. Testing for upshift is not necessary.

4) With selector lever in "D", and vehicle speed approximately 35 MPH, close throttle and move selector lever to "2" (Intermediate). Transmission should immediately downshift to 2nd gear, increase engine RPM and an engine braking effect should be noticed.

5) With selector lever in "2" (Intermediate), and vehicle speed approximately 30-40 MPH, close throttle and move selector lever to "1" (Low). Transmission should downshift to 1st gear between 40-20 MPH, increase engine RPM and an engine braking effect should be noticed.

SHIFT SPEED SPECIFICATIONS

Application	Speed (MPH) Axle Ratio 3.07 or 3.31	Speed (MPH) Axle Ratio 2.88
Upshift		
Light Throttle		
1-2	5-12	5-13
2-3	10-20	11-21
Full Throttle		
1-2	40-50	43-53
2-3	50-70	60-90
Full Throttle Kick-Down		
1-2	50-60	53-64
2-3	80-95	91-101
Kick-Down		
3-2	70-85	80-91
3-1	28-38	32-43
Downshift		
Manual		
2-1	13-18	18-25
Part Throttle Kick-Down		
3-2	40-50	43-53
Closed Throttle		
3-2	8-12	5-13
2-1	3-8	3-9

LINE PRESSURE TESTS

1) With transmission fluid at correct level and operating temperature, and pressure gauge installed as previously described, line pressure can be checked.

2) With vehicle stationary, service brakes applied (except as noted), check line pressures according to selector position and RPM conditions. See LINE PRESSURES table.

3) Total running time when performing combination of, Low or "2" at 1000 RPM and Reverse at 1000 RPM tests, must not exceed 2 minutes.

4) When stationary testing is complete, perform Drive at 30 MPH Test, with vehicle on road or with vehicle raised on hoist and brakes released. Raise engine speed to 3000 RPM. Close throttle. Read pressure between 1200-2000 RPM.

LINE PRESSURES

Range at RPM	psi (kg/cm^2)
Neutral at 1000 RPM [1]	55-70 (3.9-4.9)
Drive at Idle [1]	60-85 (4.2-6.0)
Drive at 1000 RPM [1]	[2] 60-90 (4.2-6.3)
Low or "2" at 1000 RPM [1]	135-160 (9.5-11.2)
Reverse at 1000 RPM [1]	95-150 (6.7-10.5)
Drive at 1000 RPM [3]	90-100 (6.3-7.0)
Drive at 30 MPH [4]	55-70 (3.9-4.9)

[1] - Brakes applied.
[2] - If line pressure is high, check vacuum and, if necessary check modulator.
[3] - Brakes applied and downshift swith activated.
[4] - Vehicle on hoist, driving wheels off ground, brakes released. Raise speed to 3000 RPM, close throttle and read pressure between 1200-2000 RPM.

LINE PRESSURE TESTS RESULTS

Too Low

- Transmission fluid level low. Faulty vacuum modulator assembly. Oil filter blocked or restricted, "O" ring on filter intake pipe omitted or damaged, intake pipe split or leaking.
- Not enough spacers in oil pump pressure regulator. Pressure regulator spring too weak. Oil pump gear clearance incorrect. Oil pump damaged or worn.
- Internal leak in direct clutch circuit (pressure normal in neutral, low, intermediate and drive, but low in reverse).
- Internal leak in forward clutch circuit (pressure normal in neutral and reverse, low in drive).

Too High

- Vacuum system leak or improper engine vacuum. Vacuum modulator not operating properly or defective. Stuck modulator valve. Defective EGR valve.
- Detent switch actuated or shorted, detent solenoid stuck open. Detent feed orifice in spacer plate blocked, detent solenoid loose. Detent valve bore plug damaged. Detent regulator valve pin too short.
- Oil pump pressure regulator and/or boost valve stuck. Incorrect pump pressure regulator spring. Pressure boost valve installed backward. Too many oil pump pressure regulator valve spacers. Oil pump casting defective.
- Valve body assembly-to-spacer gasket out of proportion. Valve body assembly gaskets switched.

STALL TEST

CAUTION: Test must not last longer than 10 seconds. Allow engine to idle in neutral at least 2 minutes between tests to cool transmission.

1) Install a 0-300 psi pressure gauge with extension pressure line, to pressure take-off point at left side of transmission near manual lever. Place gauge where it can be seen from driver's seat. *See Fig. 3.*

2) Ensure engine is properly tuned and engine and transmission are at operating temperature. Chock

GM TURBO HYDRA-MATIC 400 – JAGUAR (Cont.)

CLUTCH AND BAND APPLICATION CHART (ELEMENTS IN USE)

Selector Lever Position	Forward Clutch	Direct Clutch	Front Band	Intermed. Clutch	Intermed. Roller Clutch Or Sprag	Low Roller Clutch	Rear Band
"D" - DRIVE							
1st Gear	X					X	
2nd Gear	X			X	X		
3rd Gear	X	X		X			
"2" - INTERMEDIATE							
1st Gear	X					X	
2nd Gear	X		X	X	X		
"1" - LOW (First)	X					X	X
"R" - REVERSE		X					X

NEUTRAL OR PARK – All clutches and bands released and/or ineffective.

Fig. 3: Transmission Case Pressure Take-Off Point

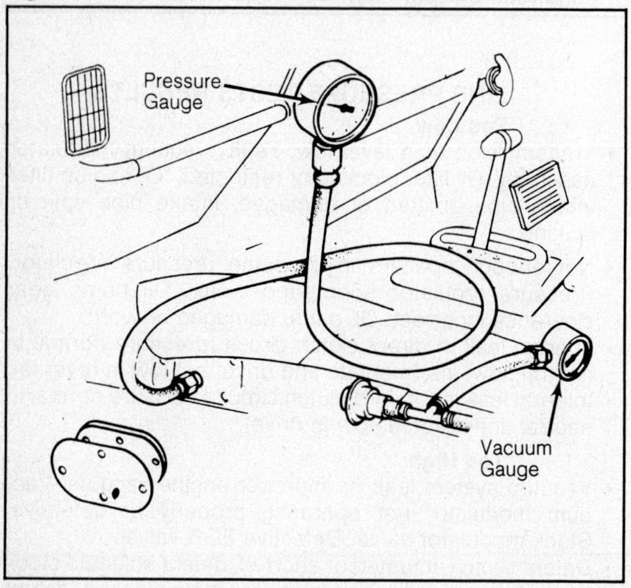

wheels, set hand brake and apply service brake. Start engine and place selector in drive.

3) Gradually apply full throttle and note maximum RPM and line pressure. If transmission slip occurs, stop engine and locate cause. Restart engine and repeat procedure with selector in reverse.

STALL SPEED SPECIFICATIONS

Selector Position	Stall Speed RPM	Stall Pressure psi (kg/cm^2)
Drive	2100-2400	145-155 (10.2-10.9)
Reverse	2100-2400	240-260 (16.8-18.2)

GOVERNOR

1) With vehicle on hoist (rear wheels off ground), disconnect vacuum line to modulator. Connect pressure gauge to transmission and tachometer to engine.

2) Start engine. Move selector lever to "D", and release brake. Check line pressure at 1000 RPM. Line

STALL SPEED RESULTS

RPM	Condition
Under 1800	Stator Slipping
1800-1900	Poorly Tuned Engine
2100-2400	Normal Stall Speed
Over 2400	Transmission Slipping

pressure should be 150 psi (10.5 kg/cm^2). Slowly increase engine speed to 3000 RPM. Check line pressure.

3) Line pressure should drop 10 psi (.7 kg/cm^2). If no pressure drop occurs, inspect governor for sticking valve or weight, restricted orifice in valve, scored or cracked bore or restricted feed pipe or screen.

VACUUM MODULATOR

Vacuum Diaphragm Leak Test

Insert a pipe cleaner into vacuum connector pipe as far as possible and check for presence of transmission oil. If oil is found, replace modulator.

NOTE: **Gasoline or water vapor may settle in vacuum side of modulator. If this is found without presence of oil, modulator should not be changed. If vehicle is to be exposed to temperatures 10°F or below, modulator MUST be changed.**

Atmospheric Leak Test

1) Apply a liberal coating of soapy solution to threaded screw seal and vacuum connector pipe seam at crimped upper-to-lower housing seam.

2) Using a short piece of rubber hose, apply air pressure to vacuum pipe by blowing into hose and check for leak bubbles. If bubbles appear, replace modulator.

CAUTION: **Do not use a compressor for applying air pressure. Pressures over 6 psi (.4 kg/cm^2) may damage modulator.**

Bellows Comparison Test

Where the vacuum bellows are suspected, substitute vacuum modulator in question with a new or good modulator.

Sleeve Alignment Test

Roll main body of modulator on a flat surface and observe sleeve for concentricity to cam. If sleeve is concentric and plunger is free, modulator is okay.

KICK-DOWN SOLENOID

1) Turn ignition to "ON", but do not start engine. From under hood, check that there is current at input terminal (Green cable) of switch. Connect a test lamp between output terminal (Green/White cable) and ground.

2) Move throttle linkage to wide open position. If test lamp fails to light, allow throttle to return to closed position. Depress the switch by hand. If lamp still fails to light, replace switch.

3) If lamp lights when operated by hand, loosen attaching bolts and adjust switch toward cable until lamp lights at full throttle. Test light should go out when throttle is released.

SERVICE (IN VEHICLE)

VALVE BODY

1) With oil pan, filter and intake tube removed, remove detent spring and roller assembly retaining bolt. Remove remaining valve body attaching bolts but leave solenoid attached.

NOTE: **Front servo parts may drop out of the transmission case as valve body assembly is removed.**

2) Remove valve body assembly with governor pipes attached, using care not to drop manual valve as valve body assembly is removed. Remove front servo piston assembly, if still in case.

3) Remove governor screen from governor feed pipe hole in case or from end of feed pipe. Remove governor pipes from valve body assembly. Governor pipes are interchangeable.

EXTENSION HOUSING OIL SEAL

1) Support engine/transmission assembly using rear engine lifting eye. Remove rear engine/transmission mount. Remove crossmember. Lower engine slightly. Remove driveshaft from gearbox output flange.

2) Remove output shaft drive flange bolt, washer and flange. Using a puller remove extension housing oil seal. To install, reverse removal procedure. Ensure seal is installed straight in bore.

GOVERNOR ASSEMBLY

1) Support engine/transmission assembly using rear engine lifting eye. Remove rear engine/transmission mount. Remove crossmember. Lower engine slightly.

2) Remove governor attaching screws, cover, and gasket, being careful not to distort cover. Discard gasket. Remove governor assembly by pulling straight out of case.

OIL PAN, FILTER & INTAKE PIPE

Remove oil pan attaching bolts and remove pan. Remove filter retaining bolt and withdraw intake pipe and filter assembly. Discard filter and "O" ring seal from intake pipe.

REAR SERVO

1) With oil pan and valve body assembly removed, remove rear servo cover and gasket, rear servo assembly and servo accumulator spring.

2) Make a band apply pin selection check at this time to determine correct pin for proper band application. This is equivalent to band adjustment.

SPEEDOMETER DRIVE PINION

Disconnect speedometer cable from drive pinion. Remove pinion clamp bolt and clamp plate. Remove pinion assembly from case. Discard seals.

REMOVAL & INSTALLATION

TRANSMISSION

See appropriate AUTOMATIC TRANSMISSION REMOVAL article in IMPORT GENERAL SERVICING section.

TORQUE CONVERTER

Remove transmission from vehicle. See appropriate AUTOMATIC TRANSMISSION REMOVAL article in IMPORT GENERAL SERVICING section. Slide torque converter off input shaft. Remove bolts attaching torque converter housing to transmission case. To install, reverse removal procedure.

TRANSMISSION DISASSEMBLY

NOTE: **Perform input shaft end play check before proceeding with transmission disassembly. Record end play for use in determining proper selective thrust washer during reassembly.**

INPUT SHAFT END PLAY

1) With transmission removed from vehicle and torque converter removed, remove 1 front pump attaching bolt and bolt seal at either 10 o'clock or 5 o'clock position.

2) Install slide hammer bolt into threaded bolt hole in front pump. Mount a dial indicator to bolt and index indicator to register with end of turbine shaft. While holding output shaft forward, push turbine shaft rearward.

FRONT UNIT END PLAY SELECTIVE THRUST WASHERS

Washer Thickness [1]	Color Code
.060-.064"	Yellow
.071-.075"	Blue
.082-.086"	Red
.093-.097"	Brown
.104-.108"	Green
.115-.119"	Black
.126-.130"	Purple

[1] – An oil soaked washer may tend to discolor, so it will be necessary to measure washer for its actual thickness.

3) Zero dial indicator. Pull turbine shaft forward and read resulting end play on indicator. End play should be .003-.025" (.08-.64 mm). If end play is not within specified limits, select correct thickness washer for use at reassembly.

4) Selective thrust washer controlling this end play is located between pump cover and forward clutch housing. Front end play selective thrust washers are available in varying thicknesses and are color coded.

VALVE BODY ASSEMBLY & SPACER PLATE

1) Invert transmission and remove oil pan, filter and intake tube. Remove bolt securing detent spring and roller assembly. Remove valve body retaining bolts and remove valve body.

2) Remove detent solenoid attaching bolts and remove solenoid. Being careful to prevent distorting, remove valve body spacer plate. Remove 6 check balls from transmission casing.

FRONT PUMP

If front seal requires replacement, pry seal out before removing pump assembly. Remove pump attaching bolts. Install 2 slide hammers into 2 opposite threaded pump bolt holes, and evenly remove pump assembly from case. Remove and discard pump-to-case seal ring and gasket.

TURBINE SHAFT, FORWARD & DIRECT CLUTCH ASSEMBLIES, SUN GEAR SHAFT & FRONT BAND

Remove forward clutch and turbine shaft assembly from case, then remove forward clutch hub-to-direct clutch housing thrust washer. Remove direct clutch and intermediate roller assembly, then remove sun gear shaft and front band.

NOTE: **Make rear end play check before removing center support or proceeding with transmission disassembly. Record end play for use in determining proper selective thrust washer.**

REAR UNIT END PLAY CHECK

1) With extension housing removed, install threaded end of a 3/8"-16 rod into one of the extension housing bolt holes in rear of case. Install dial indicator on rod with indicator pin contacting end of output shaft.

2) Zero indicator dial, then move output shaft in and out and note end play reading. End play should be .003-.019" (.08-.48 mm). If end play needs adjustment, select a thrust washer that will bring end play within specifications.

SELECTIVE THRUST WASHERS (REAR UNIT END PLAY)

Washer Thickness	I.D. Notches
.080-.082"	None
.086-.090"	Side of 1 Tab
.094-.098"	Side of 2 Tabs
.102-.106"	End of 1 Tab
.110-.114"	End of 2 Tabs
.118-.122"	End of 3 Tabs

3) Selective thrust washer controlling rear unit end play is a steel washer having 3 tabs. It is located between output shaft thrust washer and rear face of transmission case. Notches and/or numerals on tabs of washer identify thickness.

CENTER SUPPORT, INTERMEDIATE CLUTCH, GEAR CARRIER/OUTPUT SHAFT ASSEMBLY & REAR BAND

1) Using 3/8", 12 point socket, remove recessed center support retaining bolt from hole in valve body mating surface of transmission case between rear servo and detent solenoid mounting position.

2) Remove intermediate clutch backing plate-to-case snap ring. Withdraw backing plate and clutch plates. Remove center support-to-case snap ring. Install Gear Carrier Remover (J-21795) on end of main shaft so tangs engage groove in shaft.

3) Tighten screw on remover to prevent movement of roller clutch during gear carrier assembly removal. Also, cover shaft splines to prevent damaging case bushing.

4) With transmission case in horizontal position, remove complete assembly from case. Remove output shaft-to-case thrust washer and rear unit selective thrust washer. Remove rear band from case.

DETENT LEVER, MANUAL LEVER SHAFT & PARK LINKAGE

1) If necessary for parts replacement, remove manual linkage. Loosen jam nut holding detent lever to manual shaft. Remove manual shaft retaining pin from case. Remove jam nut and detent lever from manual shaft. Remove manual shaft.

2) Remove parking pawl actuator rod and detent lever assembly. Remove attaching bolts and parking bracket. Remove parking pawl return spring. Remove parking pawl shaft retainer. Remove parking pawl shaft cup plug. Pry outward to remove plug. Remove parking pawl shaft and parking pawl.

Fig. 4: Detent and Manual Levers and Parking Pawl Assembly

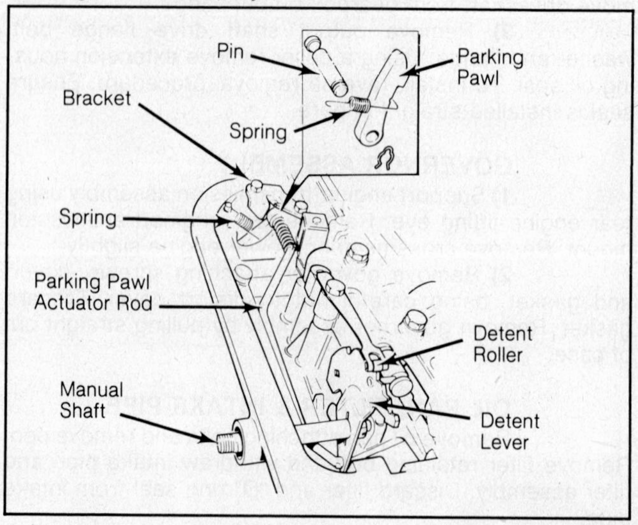

GM TURBO HYDRA-MATIC 400 – JAGUAR (Cont.)

COMPONENT DISASSEMBLY & REASSEMBLY

VALVE BODY

Disassembly

NOTE: **As each valve train is removed, place the individual valve train in a separate location relative to its position in valve body. None of valves or springs are interchangeable.**

1) Position valve body assembly with machined surface facing up, with manual valve away from you and accumulator pocket toward you. Remove manual valve from upper bore.

NOTE: **Steps 2) and 3) require using a pin punch to remove valve train retaining pins.**

2) Install Piston Spring Compressor (18G 1295) on accumulator piston. Compress spring, remove "E" ring and remove piston and spring. Remove retaining pins, and remove 1-2 valve train from upper right hand bore.

3) From center right hand bore, remove 2-3 valve train. From lower right hand bore, remove 3-2 valve train. From upper left hand bore, remove detent valve train. From lower left hand bore, remove 1-2 accumulator valve train.

Cleaning & Inspection

1) Inspect all valves and bushings carefully to make sure they are free from dirt and are not damaged in any way. If burrs are present, remove with a fine stone or fine grade crocus cloth and light oil.

CAUTION: **When removing burrs from valves, use care not to round off shoulders of valves.**

2) Test all valves and bushings in their bores to make sure they slide freely of their own weight. Manual valve is only valve that can be serviced separately. If other valves require replacement, complete valve body assembly should be replaced.

3) Inspect valve body for cracks or scored bores. Check all springs for distortion or collapsed coils. Inspect accumulator piston and oil ring for damage.

NOTE: **Do not remove Teflon oil seal from front accumulator piston unless seal needs replacing. For service, the oil seal ring is cast iron.**

Reassembly

1) Install front accumulator spring and piston into valve body, then compress piston and spring and install retaining "E" clip.

2) In lower left bore, install 1-2 accumulator primary spring (if required) and 1-2 accumulator valve, stem end out, then install bore plug.

3) Install detent regulator spring and spacer in upper left bore. Install detent regulator valve (stem end out) and detent valve (narrow land first). Install bore plug with open end out and install retaining pin.

4) Install 3-2 valve in lower right bore, then install spacer, valve spring, bore plug (open end out) and retaining pin. In next bore up, install 2-3 shift valve (hole end out) and 3-2 intermediate spring. Install 2-3 modulator valve into bushing and install both parts into valve bore. Install 2-3 valve spring, then install retaining pin.

5) In next bore, install 1-2 valve (stem end out). Install 1-2 regulator valve (large stem first), spring and 1-2 detent valve (hole end first) into 1-2 modulator bushing, aligning spring in bore of detent valve and install parts into valve body bore.

6) Compress bushing against spring and install retaining pin. Install manual valve with detent pin groove to the right.

REAR SERVO

Disassembly

Remove rear accumulator piston from rear servo piston. Remove "E" ring retaining rear servo piston to

Fig. 5: Exploded View of Valve Body Assembly

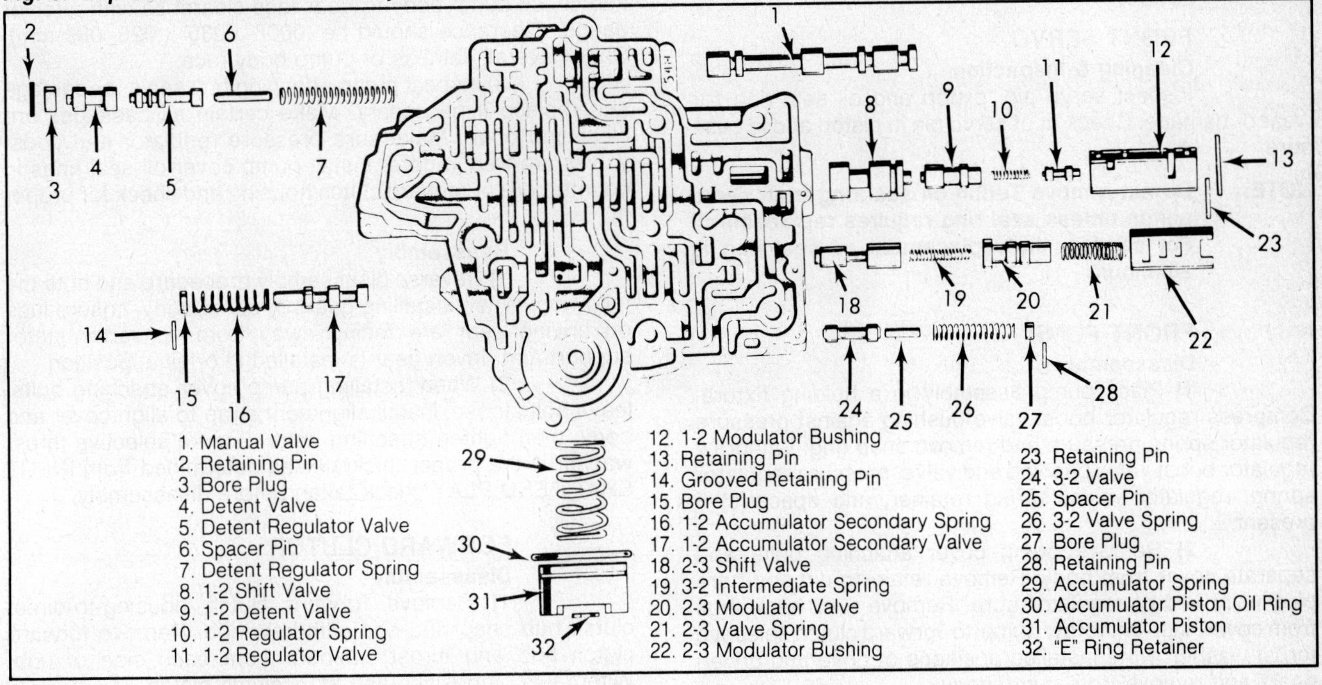

1. Manual Valve
2. Retaining Pin
3. Bore Plug
4. Detent Valve
5. Detent Regulator Valve
6. Spacer Pin
7. Detent Regulator Spring
8. 1-2 Shift Valve
9. 1-2 Detent Valve
10. 1-2 Regulator Spring
11. 1-2 Regulator Valve
12. 1-2 Modulator Bushing
13. Retaining Pin
14. Grooved Retaining Pin
15. Bore Plug
16. 1-2 Accumulator Secondary Spring
17. 1-2 Accumulator Secondary Valve
18. 2-3 Shift Valve
19. 3-2 Intermediate Spring
20. 2-3 Modulator Valve
21. 2-3 Valve Spring
22. 2-3 Modulator Bushing
23. Retaining Pin
24. 3-2 Valve
25. Spacer Pin
26. 3-2 Valve Spring
27. Bore Plug
28. Retaining Pin
29. Accumulator Spring
30. Accumulator Piston Oil Ring
31. Accumulator Piston
32. "E" Ring Retainer

band apply pin, then remove rear servo piston and seal from pin. Remove washer, spring and retainer.

CAUTION: Do not remove Teflon oil seals unless they require replacement. If small ring requires replacement, use service aluminum ring. If large ring requires replacement, use only Teflon oil ring.

Fig. 6: Exploded View of Rear Servo Assembly

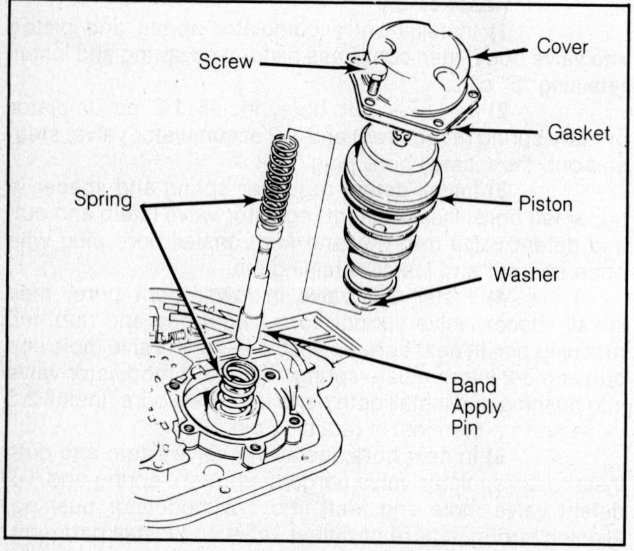

Cleaning & Inspection

Check for free movement of accumulator rings in piston and their respective bores. Inspect fit of band apply pin in servo piston and case bore. Inspect band apply pin for scores or cracks. Inspect servo piston for cracks or porosity.

Reassembly

To reassemble, reverse disassembly procedure.

FRONT SERVO

Cleaning & Inspection

Inspect servo pin, piston and oil seal ring for wear or damage. Check fit of servo pin in piston and in case bore.

NOTE: Do not remove Teflon oil seal ring from servo piston unless seal ring requires replacement. For service, the replacement oil seal ring is aluminum.

FRONT PUMP

Disassembly

1) Place pump assembly in a holding fixture. Compress regulator boost valve bushing against pressure regulator spring pressure and remove snap ring. Withdraw regulator boost valve bushing and valve, pressure regulator spring, regulator valve, spring retainer, and spacer(s) if present.

2) Remove pump cover attaching bolts and separate cover from body. Remove retaining pin and bore plug from end of regulator bore. Remove 2 oil seal rings from cover, then withdraw pump-to-forward clutch selective thrust washer. Note installed positions of drive and driven gears and remove from pump body.

Fig. 7: Exploded View of Front Servo Assembly

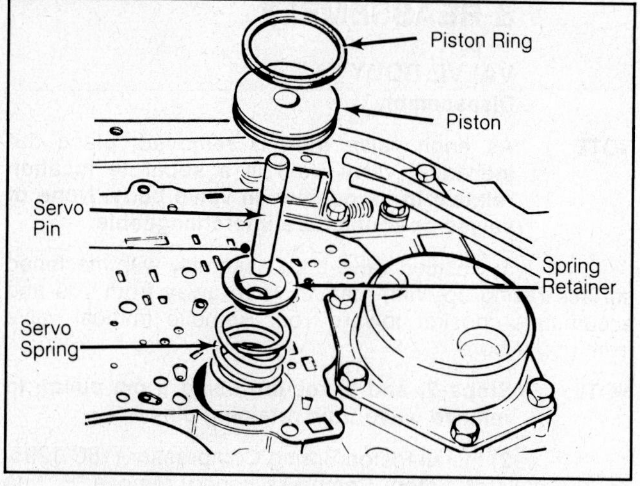

Fig. 8: Exploded View of Front Pump Cover and Pressure Regulator Valve

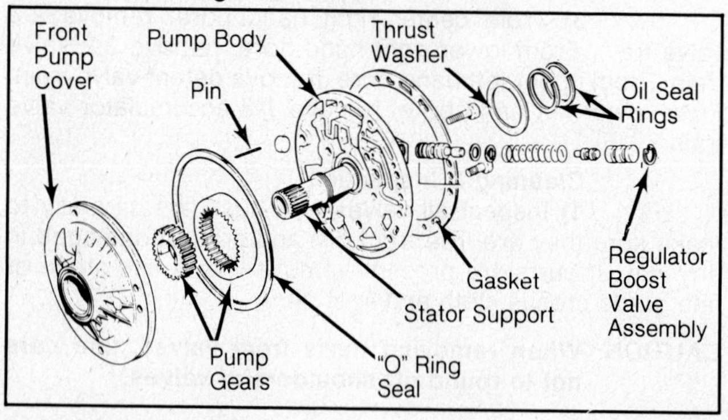

Cleaning & Inspection

1) Inspect all parts for nicks, scoring or galling, wear, or other damage. Install pump gears in pump body, and check pump body-to-gear face clearance with a feeler gauge. Clearance should be .0008-.0035" (.020-.089 mm). Check overall flatness of pump body face.

2) Inspect pump attaching bolt seals for damage and replace if necessary. Make certain all passages are clear and open. Make sure pressure regulator and boost valves are free in bore. Install pump cover oil seal rings in counterbore of forward clutch housing and check for proper fit.

Reassembly

1) Reverse disassembly procedure and note the following: When installing gears in pump body, ensure lugs on driving gear are facing away from converter stator support and driven gear is installed in original position.

2) When installing pump cover attaching bolts, leave bolts loose, install alignment strap to align cover and body, then tighten attaching bolts. Ensure selective thrust washer is the proper thickness as determined from INPUT SHAFT END PLAY check taken before disassembly.

FORWARD CLUTCH

Disassembly

1) Remove forward clutch housing-to-direct clutch hub snap ring and withdraw hub. Remove forward clutch hub and thrust washers from each side of hub. Withdraw composition and steel clutch plates.

GM TURBO HYDRA-MATIC 400 – JAGUAR (Cont.)

2) If necessary, place clutch housing in an arbor press and press turbine shaft out of housing. Using a compressor, compress spring retainer and remove snap ring.

3) Remove compressor and lift out spring retainer and 16 clutch release springs. Remove forward clutch piston from housing. Remove inner and outer seals from piston and center seal from clutch housing.

NOTE: **Keep forward clutch release springs separate from direct clutch release springs.**

Fig. 9: Exploded View of Forward Clutch Assembly

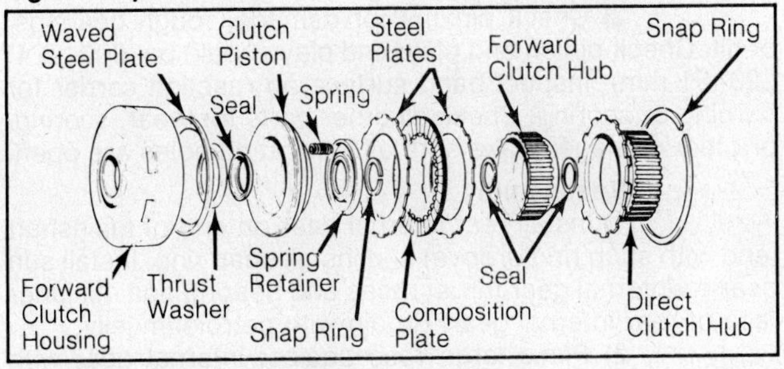

Cleaning & Inspection

1) Inspect clutch plates for burning, scoring, or wear. Check release springs for distortion or collapsed coils. Inspect clutch hubs for worn splines and thrust faces, and for clear lubrication passages.

2) Check piston for cracks or porosity. Check turbine shaft and clutch housing for wear, scoring or other damage. Make sure check ball in housing moves freely.

Reassembly

1) Oil and install inner and outer seals on clutch piston with seal lips facing away from spring pockets. Oil and install center seal on clutch housing with seal lips facing upward.

2) Place seal protectors over clutch hub and into clutch housing, then install piston into housing. Install 16 clutch release springs into piston pockets, place spring retainer and snap ring over springs, then compress springs and install snap ring into groove.

3) If turbine shaft was removed, install shaft into housing using an arbor press. Install forward clutch hub thrust washers. Make sure bronze washer is installed on side of hub facing forward clutch housing. Retain washers in place with petroleum jelly. Place forward clutch hub into clutch housing.

4) Lubricate with transmission fluid and install clutch plates, starting with a waved steel plate (plate with "U" notch), then alternating composition and flat steel plates (plate with "V" notch) until all clutch plates are installed. See FORWARD CLUTCH PLATE chart.

5) Install direct clutch hub and retaining snap ring. Place forward clutch housing on oil pump delivery sleeve. Air check operation of forward clutch by applying air through forward clutch passage in pump to actuate piston and move forward clutch.

FORWARD CLUTCH PLATE

Flat Steel	Composition	Waved Steel
5	5	1

DIRECT CLUTCH & INTERMEDIATE ROLLER ASSEMBLY

Disassembly

1) Remove intermediate roller assembly retainer snap ring and retainer. Remove roller outer race and roller assembly. Turn unit over and remove backing plate-to-direct clutch housing snap ring. Remove direct clutch backing plate and clutch pack.

2) Using a compressor, compress spring retainer in arbor press and remove snap ring. Remove retainer and piston and 16 clutch release springs. Remove direct clutch piston from clutch housing, then remove inner and outer seals from piston. Remove center piston seal from direct clutch housing.

NOTE: **Keep springs separate from forward clutch release springs.**

Cleaning & Inspection

1) Inspect roller assembly for popped or loose rollers; inner cam and outer race for scratches or wear and clutch housing for cracks, wear, proper opening of oil passages or wear on clutch plate drive lugs.

2) Inspect clutch plates for wear or burning; backing plate for scratches or damage; clutch piston for cracks; clutch housing for free operation of check ball and springs for collapsed coils and distortion.

Reassembly

1) Lubricate seals with transmission fluid and install new inner and outer seals on clutch piston with seal lips facing away from spring pockets. Install new center seals on clutch hub with seal lip facing upward.

2) Place seal protectors over clutch hub and into clutch housing, then install clutch piston into housing with a rotating motion. If production clutch release springs are being used, install 14 springs into spring pockets of piston, leaving 2 opposite pockets with no springs.

3) If service relacement springs are used, install all 16 springs into spring pockets. Place spring retainer on top of springs and snap ring on top of retainer. Using compressor used at disassembly, compress springs and install snap ring.

4) Lubricate clutch plates with transmission fluid. Install plates into clutch housing starting with a waved steel plate. Alternate composition and flat steel plates until all plates are installed. See DIRECT CLUTCH PLATES chart. Install backing plate and retaining snap ring.

5) Install rollers in case by compressing energizing spring and inserting roller from outer side. Turn unit over and install roller clutch assembly onto intermediate clutch inner cam, then install outer race with a clockwise turning motion. Install clutch retainer and snap ring. Place assembly on center support and air check operation of clutch.

DIRECT CLUTCH PLATES

Flat Steel [1]	Composition	Waved Steel
5	5	1

[1] – Four of steel plates are .077" (1.9 mm) thick. One of steel plates is .091" (2.2 mm) thick.

Fig. 10: Exploded View of Direct Clutch and Intermediate Roller Clutch Assembly

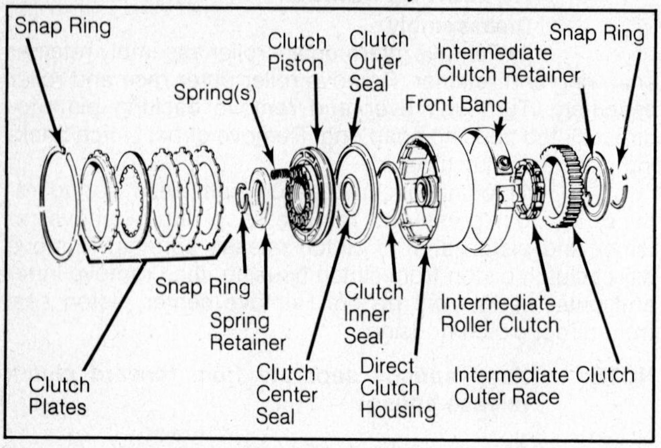

GEAR CARRIER/OUTPUT SHAFT ASSEMBLY

Disassembly

1) Remove center support-to-sun gear races and thrust bearing (1 race may have come out with center support). Remove sun gear from output carrier.

2) Remove reaction carrier-to-output carrier thrust washer and front internal gear ring from output carrier assembly. Remove output shaft-to-output carrier snap ring and remove output shaft.

3) Remove output shaft-to-rear internal gear thrust bearing and races. Remove rear internal gear and mainshaft. Remove thrust bearing and races from inner face of rear internal gear. Remove snap ring from end of main shaft and remove rear internal gear.

Fig. 11: Exploded View of Gear Carrier/Output Shaft Assembly

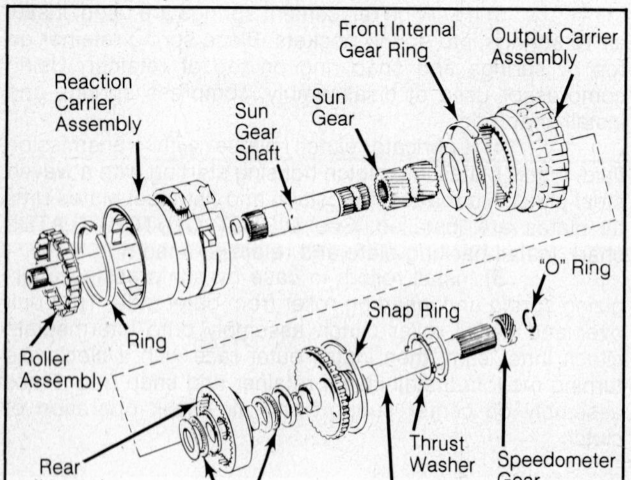

Speedometer Drive Gear Replacement

1) If equipped with a nylon speedometer gear, depress retaining clip and slide gear off shaft. To install, place retaining clip (square end toward flange of shaft) into hole in shaft, align slot in gear with clip, and install gear.

2) If equipped with a steel gear, use a puller and remove gear from shaft. To install, support output shaft on front face and use driver to drive gear onto shaft.

3) Drive speedometer gear onto shaft until distance from rear face of gear to end of output shaft is 5 21/32" (83.34 mm).

Cleaning & Inspection

1) If reaction carrier is equipped with a spacer ring in an undercut at bottom of roller cam ramps, inspect ring for wear or damage. Inspect reaction carrier bushing for damage; if bushing is damaged, carrier must be replaced.

2) Check pinions for damage, rough bearings, or tilt. Check pinion end play; end play should be .009-.024" (.23-.61 mm). Inspect band surface on reaction carrier for burning or scoring. Check all other parts for wear, scoring, or other damage. Make sure all lubrication holes are open.

Reassembly

1) Install rear internal gear on end of mainshaft (end with snap ring groove) and install snap ring. Install sun gear-to-internal gear thrust races and bearing against inner face of rear internal gear. Retain with petroleum jelly.

2) Place large race against internal gear with flange facing forward or upward, place thrust bearing against race, then place small race against bearing with inner flange into bearing or downward.

3) Install output carrier over mainshaft so pinions mesh with rear internal gear. With mainshaft in downward position, install rear internal gear to output shaft thrust races and bearings. Retain with petroleum jelly.

4) Place small diameter race against internal gear with center flange facing up. Place bearing on race, then place second race on bearing with outer flange cupped over bearing. Install output shaft into output carrier assembly. Install output shaft to output carrier snap ring.

5) Install speedometer drive gear. Install output shaft "O" ring (if required). With output shaft in a downward position, install reaction carrier to output carrier thrust washer with tabs facing down in pockets, and retain with petroleum jelly.

6) Install sun gear with chamfer down. Install gear ring over output carrier. Install sun gear shaft with long splined-end down. Install reaction carrier. Install center support-to-sun thrust races and bearing (retain with petroleum jelly).

7) Install large race over sun gear shaft with center flange upward, install thrust bearing against race, then install second race with center flange upward.

8) Install rollers that may have come out of roller case by compressing energizing spring with forefinger and inserting roller from outer side. Install roller clutch into reaction carrier outer race.

9) Install center support-to-reaction carrier thrust washer into recess in center support and retain with petroleum jelly. Install center support into reaction carrier and roller clutch assembly.

10) Install a holding fixture to keep units in place, then install output shaft-to-case thrust washers (bent tabs in pockets) and retain with petroleum jelly.

CENTER SUPPORT & INTERMEDIATE CLUTCH

Disassembly

If necessary, remove 4 center support oil seal rings. Compress spring retainer and remove snap ring. Remove spring retainer and 3 clutch release springs. Remove intermediate clutch spring guide and clutch piston from center support. Remove inner and outer piston seals from piston.

Cleaning & Inspection

1) Check all parts for wear, scoring or damage. Inspect release springs for distortion or collapsed coils. Check oil ring grooves and oil rings for wear or damage. Rings should fit freely in grooves.

2) Make sure all passages, lubrication grooves and holes are clear of obstructions. Check roller clutch inner race for scratches and indentations. Make sure constant bleed orifice is open .020" (.51 mm).

Fig. 12: Exploded View of Center Support and Intermediate Clutch

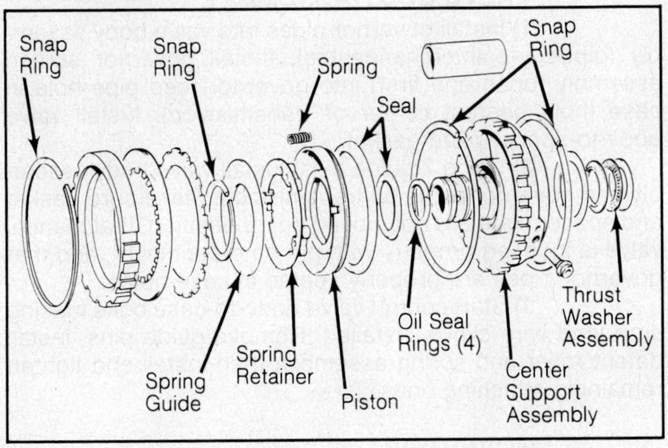

Reassembly

1) Lubricate and install inner and outer seals on piston with seal lips facing away from spring pockets. Place a seal protector over center support hub. Install piston indexing spring pockets in drum and piston.

2) Install spring guide and evenly space 3 release springs in spring guides. Place spring retainer and snap ring over springs, then compress springs and install snap ring in groove.

3) If removed, install 4 oil seal rings on center support. Air check operation of intermediate clutch piston by applying air through center oil feed hole to actuate clutch piston.

NOTE: **When installing Teflon oil seal rings on center support, be sure split ends are assembled in the same relation as cut.**

TRANSMISSION CASE

Cleaning & Inspection

Inspect case for cracks, porosity, or interconnected passages. Check governor and modulator valve bores for scratches or scoring. Check band anchor pins for retention, and intermediate clutch driven plate lugs for damage. Inspect snap ring grooves for damage. Ensure intermediate clutch cup plug is properly staked and sealed.

CAUTION: **If case assembly requires replacement, make sure that center support-to-case spacer and name plate are removed from old case and installed in new case.**

EXTENSION HOUSING

Cleaning & Inspection

Check housing for cracks or porosity. Inspect gasket mounting face for burrs or other damage. Make sure rear seal drain-back part is not obstructed. Check rear bushing for wear or damage. Replace as necessary.

TRANSMISSION REASSEMBLY

PARKING PAWL

1) Install parking pawl, tooth toward inside of case, then install parking pawl shaft and shaft retainer. Install a new cup plug using a 3/8" (9.5 mm) diameter rod, and drive plug into case until shaft bottoms on case rib.

2) Install parking pawl return spring, with square end hooked on pawl and other end on case. Install parking pawl bracket with guides over parking pawl, then install and tighten attaching bolts.

CENTER SUPPORT, INTERMEDIATE CLUTCH, GEAR CARRIER/OUTPUT SHAFT ASSEMBLY & REAR BAND

1) Install rear band so that lugs index with anchor pins. Install support-to-case spacer against shoulder at bottom of case splines and with ring gap adjacent to band anchor pin.

2) Install previously selected rear unit end play washer into slots provided inside rear of case and retain washer with petroleum jelly. Place transmission in a horizontal position and install holding fixture on output shaft.

3) Install complete gear unit assembly into case by lining up slots and carefully guiding assembly horizontally into case making sure center support bolt hole is aligned with hole in case.

4) Position transmission vertically and remove output shaft holding fixture. Install center support-to-case retaining ring, with beveled side up. Locate gap adjacent to band anchor pin.

5) Lubricate and install intermediate clutch plates, starting with a waved steel plate, then alternating composition and flat steel plates until all clutch plates are installed.

6) Install intermediate clutch backing plate with flat machined surface against clutch plates. Install backing plate-to-case snap ring, locating ring gap opposite band anchor pin. Before proceeding with transmission reassembly, recheck rear unit end play.

CLUTCH ASSEMBLIES & FRONT BAND

1) Install front band with band anchor hole over band anchor pin and apply lug facing servo hole. Install direct clutch and intermediate roller assembly. Install forward clutch hub to direct clutch housing thrust washer on forward clutch hub and retain with petroleum jelly.

NOTE: **Rotate housing to index roller outer race with composition clutch plates.**

2) Install forward clutch and turbine shaft, indexing direct clutch hub so end of mainshaft will go all the way into forward clutch hub. When forward clutch is seated, it will be 1 1/4" (25.4-31.8 mm) from pump mounting face in case.

FRONT PUMP

1) Install square cut "O" ring around outer circumference of pump body and attach new gasket to oil pump cover, retaining gasket with petroleum jelly. Lubricate turbine shaft journals and pump oil seal rings.

2) Using 2 alignment dowels, install pump assembly into case. Install pump attaching bolts with new seals (omit 1 bolt for end play check), and tighten bolts evenly.

CAUTION: **If turbine shaft cannot be rotated as pump is being pulled into place, forward or direct clutch housings have not been installed properly to index with all clutch plates. Correct this condition before pulling pump fully into place.**

3) Recheck front unit end play. If necessary, adjust end play by changing thrust washer located between pump cover and forward clutch housing. Install remaining pump attaching bolt. Apply a non-hardening sealer to outside of new front oil seal. Install seal into pump using a driver.

PARKING LINKAGE, DETENT LEVER & MANUAL SHAFT

1) If removed, install a new manual shaft seal into transmission case using a 3/4" (19 mm) diameter rod to seat seal. Install actuator rod into manual detent lever from side opposite pin.

2) Install actuator rod plunger under parking bracket and over parking pawl. Install manual shaft through case and detent lever. Install detent retaining lock nut on manual shaft and tighten. Install retaining pin, indexing with groove in manual shaft.

NOTE: **It may be necessary to bend manual shaft retaining pin to install. Straighten pin during installation.**

EXTENSION HOUSING

1) Install a new gasket on extension housing and retain with petroleum jelly. Install housing on transmission case and tighten attaching bolts. If applicable, check "O" ring on output shaft for any nicks or flattening and replace ring if necessary.

2) Apply a non-hardening sealer to outside diameter of rear oil seal, position on extension housing, then seat seal in housing using driver.

VALVE BODY SPACER PLATE & DETENT SOLENOID

1) Install 2 guide pins opposite each other into 2 valve body assembly attaching bolt holes. Install check balls into ball seat pockets in case. Install control valve spacer plate-to-case gasket, gasket with extension for detent solenoid and marked with a "C".

2) Install control valve spacer plate and control valve-to-spacer plate gasket, marked with a "VB". Install detent solenoid gasket, then install solenoid with connector facing outer edge of case. Do not tighten bolts at this time.

NOTE: **Some overhaul kits supply a solenoid gasket. This gasket must not be installed.**

3) Install "O" ring seal on solenoid connector. Compress connector tangs and install in case with locator tab in notch on side of case. Connect detent solenoid wire to connector terminal.

FRONT SERVO

1) Install front servo spring and spring retainer into transmission case. Install retainer ring in front servo pin groove and install pin in case so tapered end contacts band.

2) Make sure retainer ring is still installed in groove. Install seal ring on piston. Install piston on pin with flat side of piston positioned toward oil pan.

REAR SERVO

1) Before installing servo, check band apply pin. See Band Apply Selection Test in ADJUSTMENTS section. Ensure rear band apply lug is aligned with servo pin bore in transmission case.

2) Lubricate inner and outer rear servo bores in case with transmission fluid, then install rear accumulator spring in servo inner bore. Install rear servo assembly, install gasket and cover. Install and tighten attaching bolts.

VALVE BODY ASSEMBLY

1) Install governor pipes into valve body assembly (pipes are interchangeable). Install governor screen assembly (open end first) into governor feed pipe hole in case (hole nearest center of transmission). Install valve body-to-spacer plate gasket.

2) Using 2 guide pins, install valve body assembly and governor pipes on transmission. Make sure gasket and spacer plate are not moved out of position, that manual valve is indexed properly with pin on detent lever, and that governor pipes are properly seated in case holes.

3) Start control valve body-to-case bolts making sure lead wire clip is installed. Remove guide pins, install detent roller and spring assembly, then install and tighten remaining attaching bolts.

GOVERNOR

Install governor assembly into case. Install cover with new gasket and tighten attaching bolts.

SPEEDOMETER DRIVE PINION

Install new seals to housing. Lubricate and install pinion into housing. Install pinion assembly into case and secure with clamp plate and bolt.

OIL PAN, FILTER & INTAKE PIPE

Install case-to-intake pipe "O" ring seal on intake pipe. Install pipe into filter assembly. Place filter and intake pipe in case, install retaining bolt and tighten. Install oil pan with new gasket. Install and tighten attaching screws.

VACUUM MODULATOR & VALVE

Install modulator valve into case with stem end out. Install new "O" ring seal on vacuum modulator. Install modulator into case with vacuum hose pipe facing front and angled 5° toward top of case. Install modulator retainer with curved side of tangs inboard. Install and tighten attaching bolt.

CONVERTER ASSEMBLY

Install converter into front pump assembly. Make sure converter hub drive slots are fully engaged with pump drive gear tangs and converter is installed fully toward rear of transmission.

GM TURBO HYDRA-MATIC 400 – JAGUAR (Cont.)

TIGHTENING SPECIFICATIONS

Application	Ft. Lbs. (N.m)
Center Support Bolts	25 (34)
Converter-To-Drive Plate Bolts	35 (48)
Extension Housing-To-Case Bolts	23 (32)
Transmission-To-Engine Bolts	35 (48)
	INCH Lbs.
Detent Solenoid Bolts	84 (10)
Filter Retainer Bolt	120 (14)
Governor Cover Bolts	240 (27)
Line Pressure Take-Off Plug	120 (14)
Manual Lever-To-Detent Lever	240 (27)
Manual Lever-To-Manual Shaft Nut	96 (11)
Modulator Retainer Bolts	240 (27)
Oil Pan Bolts	144 (16)
Parking Pawl Bracket Bolts	240 (27)
Pump Cover Bolts	240 (27)
Pump-To-Case Bolts	240 (27)
Rear Servo Cover Bolts	240 (27)
Valve Body Bolts	96 (11)

HONDA 3-SPEED

Civic

IDENTIFICATION

Transaxle may be identified by a group of characters stamped in a pad on top of transaxle. First 2 characters show transaxle type. Next 7 characters are transaxle serial number.

AUTOMATIC TRANSAXLE CODE

Application	Code
Civic	AW

DESCRIPTION

The Honda 3-speed automatic transaxle is a combination of a 3-section torque converter, dual shift transmission and a differential-type final drive assembly. Transmission housing is comprised of 2 sections; the torque convertor housing and the transmission housing. Transmission is controlled by main valve body, regulator valve body and servo valve. Countershaft is in constant mesh with differential ring gear.

Fig. 1: Cutaway View of Transaxle Gears

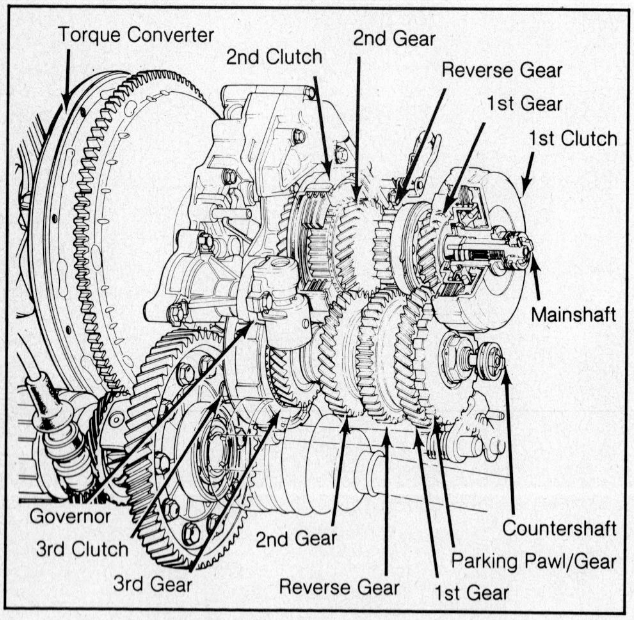

LUBRICATION & ADJUSTMENTS

See appropriate AUTOMATIC TRANSMISSION SERVICING article in IMPORT GENERAL SERVICING section.

TROUBLE SHOOTING

NO MOVEMENT

In Any Gear

Low fluid level. Faulty pump. Regulator valve stuck or damaged spring. Servo shaft stuck. Reverse hub splines stuck. Mainshaft damaged. Manual shift cable out of adjustment or broken. Damaged final drive gear. Broken flex plate. Oil filter clogged.

In "D1"; OK in Other Gears

Low fluid level. Manual shift cable out of adjustment. Worn or damaged one-way clutch. Low gear damaged. 1st clutch piston stuck, damaged "O" ring, damaged feed pipe or "O" rings, check valve stuck, worn or burnt clutch discs.

In "2"; OK in Other Gears

Low fluid level. Manual shift cable out of adjustment. Damaged 2nd gear. Faulty 2nd clutch.

In "R"; OK in Other Gears

Low fluid level. Servo shaft stuck. Faulty 2nd clutch. Damaged reverse gear.

ENGINE RACES IN "D"

Stall RPM High in "D" and "2"

Low fluid level. Faulty pump. Regulator valve stuck or spring damaged. Manual shift cable out of adjustment. Torque converter check valve.

Stall RPM High in "D" Only

Low fluid level. Faulty pump. Manual shift cable out of adjustment. 1st clutch piston stuck, damaged clutch "O" ring, clutch feed pipe or "O" ring damaged, check valve stuck, worn or burnt clutch discs.

Stall RPM High in "2"

Manual shift cable out of adjustment. Faulty 2nd clutch.

Stall RPM OK

1-2 shift valve faulty. Faulty governor valve. Fluid level too high. Faulty torque converter one-way clutch.

Stall RPM Low

Throttle cable at carburetor out of adjustment. Throttle control cable at automatic transmission out of adjustment. Engine performance not to specifications.

HARSH "D1-D2" UPSHIFT

Faulty 2nd clutch. Defective 2nd accumulator. No 2nd ball check valve.

ENGINE RACES IN "2"

Faulty 2nd clutch.

UPSHIFT SPEED TOO HIGH

Governor valve faulty. Throttle cable at carburetor out of adjustment. Defective throttle valve.

JUMPS FROM "D1" TO "D3"

Defective 2-3 shift valve.

UPSHIFT TOO EARLY

"D1-D2" and "D2-D3"

Faulty governor valve. Throttle cable at carburetor out of adjustment. Defective throttle valve. Defective modulator valve.

"D1-D2"

Faulty 1-2 shift valve.

"D2-D3"

Faulty 2-3 shift valve.

KICKDOWN TOO LOW

Faulty 1-2 shift valve or 2-3 shift valve.

HONDA 3-SPEED (Cont.)

TESTING

ROAD TEST

1) Before road testing, be certain that fluid level and condition, and control linkage adjustments have been checked and corrected as necessary. While testing, ensure that upshifts and downshifts occur at specified speeds. See SHIFT SPEED SPECIFICATIONS chart.

SHIFT SPEED SPECIFICATIONS

Application	Shift Speed (MPH)
Upshift	
Full Throttle	
1-2 Shift	36-41
2-3 Shift	60-66
Lock-Up	68-74
Half Throttle	
1-2 Shift	18-22
2-3 Shift	35-43
Closed Throttle	
1-2 Shift	11-14
2-3 Shift	21-24
Lock-Up	30-33
Downshift	
Full Throttle	
3-2 Shift	54-60
2-1 Shift	24-30
Closed Throttle	
3-2 Shift	17-21
2-1 Shift	4-7

2) Shift speeds may vary slightly due to production tolerances or tire size. The important factor is the quality of the shifts. All shifts should be smooth, responsive and with no slippage or engine speed runaway.

3) Slippage or engine runaway in any gear usually indicates clutch or sprague problems. The slipping unit in a particular gear can usually be identified by noting transmission operation in other selector positions and comparing which internal units are applied in those positions. See CLUTCH & BAND APPLICATION chart.

4) This process of elimination can be used to detect any unit which slips, and to confirm proper operation of good units; however, the actual cause of the malfunction usually cannot be easily decided.

5) Practically any condition can be caused by leaking hydraulic circuits or sticking valves. Therefore, unless an obvious condition exists, do not disassemble transmission until hydraulic pressure tests have been made.

ENGINE RACES IN "D2-D3" SHIFT

Throttle valve "B" defective. Faulty 2nd accumulator, 3rd accumulator or orifice control valve faulty. Main orifice plugged. Faulty 3rd clutch.

ENGINE VIBRATES IN "D2-D3" SHIFT

Orifice control valve faulty or second orifice plugged.

VEHICLE CREEPS IN "N"

Low fluid level. Manual shift cable out of adjustment. Faulty 1st or 2nd clutch. Throttle cable at carburetor out of adjustment. Damaged needle bearing or thrust washer. Improper clutch clearance.

DELAYED ENGAGEMENT

From "N" to "D"

Manual shift cable out of adjustment. Faulty 1st clutch. Low orifice plugged.

From "N" to "R"

Servo shaft stuck. Manual shift cable out of adjustment. Faulty 2nd clutch.

PROBLEMS AFTER REASSEMBLY

Loud Noise in All Selector Positions

Oil pump gear installed backwards. Damaged 3rd gear. Damaged ball bearings.

Vehicle Will Not Move in Any Gear

Fluid level too low. Manual shift control out of adjustment.

Movement only in Reverse

Faulty 1st clutch assembly. Counter shaft one-way clutch upside down.

Acceleration to 30 MPH Only

Stator assembled backwards in torque converter, or seized.

Vibration in All Gears

Torque converter not fully tightened or seated.

No Park Position

Manual shift control out of adjustment or binding. Parking pawl installed backward.

CLUTCH AND BAND APPLICATION CHART (ELEMENTS IN USE)

Selector Lever Position	Low Clutch	Second Clutch	Third Clutch	Sprag Clutch
D — DRIVE				
First	X			X
Second	X	X		
Third	X		X	
2 — MANUAL		X		
REVERSE		X		

NEUTRAL OR PARK — All clutch and sprag clutch released and/or ineffective.

HONDA 3-SPEED (Cont.)

Vehicle Has 3rd Gear Only
Faulty governor valve.

SERVICE (IN VEHICLE)

DRIVE AXLE SHAFTS

See appropriate DRIVE AXLE SHAFT article in IMPORT AXLE SHAFTS, OVERDRIVES & TRANSFER CASES section.

HYDRAULIC PRESSURE TESTS

1) Before performing pressure tests, be sure that fluid level and condition have been checked and corrected as necessary. With engine at normal operating temperature, connect a tachometer to engine.

2) Connect pressure gauges to the following pressure test points: line pressure port, 1st clutch pressure port, 2nd clutch pressure port and 3rd clutch pressure port. *See Fig. 2.*

Fig. 2: Pressure Test Point Locations

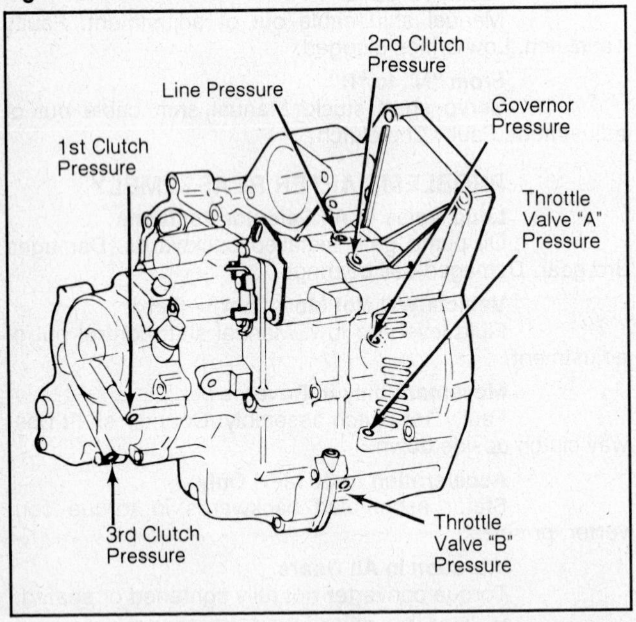

3) Raise front of vehicle so front wheels are off ground and support with safety stands. Start and run engine at 2000 RPM. Place selector lever in the following positions: "P", "N", "D", "2" and "R". Verify correct pressure readings for each selector position. See MAIN PRESSURES chart.

4) If reading in "P" or "N" is not to specifications, check torque converter, oil pump pressure regulator or torque converter check valve. If reading in "D" (high gear) is not to specifications, check 3rd clutch. If reading in "D1" is not to specifications, check 1st clutch. If reading in "2" (manual), is not to specifications. Check 2nd clutch. If reading in "R" is not to specifications, check servo valve.

NOTE: Allow engine to return to idle before changing selector positions.

5) Stop engine and remove pressure gauge connections. Connect pressure gauge to throttle pressure port and disconnect throttle cable at carburetor. Start engine, place selector lever in "D" and run engine at 1000 RPM. Depress accelerator pedal so throttle control lever is in full throttle position and note pressure reading. Verify correct reading. See MAIN PRESSURES chart.

6) If throttle pressure reading in "D" is not to specifications, check throttle valve "A" or throttle modulator valve. Stop engine and remove pressure gauge from throttle pressure port and reconnect throttle cable at carburetor.

7) Place vehicle on a chassis dynamomator or raise and support front of vehicle on safety stands. Connect pressure gauge to governor pressure port. Start engine, place selector lever in "D" and increase engine speed to 38 MPH. compare pressure reading to specifications. See MAIN PRESSURES chart.

8) If governor pressure reading was not to specifications, check governor valve.

MAIN PRESSURES

Application	psi (kg/cm²)
Line ("P", "N")	
Standard	106.7-113.7 (7.5-8.0)
Limit	99.5 (7.0)
1st & 2nd ("D", "2", "R")	
Standard	99.5-113.7 (7.0-8.0)
Limit	92.4 (6.5)
3rd ("D")	
W/Lever Released	
Standard	71 (5.0)
Limit	64 (4.5)
W/Lever @ Full Throttle	
Standard	114 (8.0)
Limit	100 (7.0)
Throttle ("D")	
Throttle Valve "A"	
W/Lever Released	0 (0)
W/Lever @ Full Throttle	
Standard	77.8-80.0 (5.45-5.60)
Limit	76 (5.4)
Throttle Valve "B"	
W/Lever Released	0 (0)
W/Lever @ Full Throttle	
Standard	106.7-113.8 (7.5-8.0)
Governor ("D")	
Standard	31.9-33.3 (2.25-2.35)
Limit	31.2 (2.20)

STALL TEST

Testing Precautions

Maximum stall speed test time is 10 seconds. Allow engine to run at idle for at least 2 minutes in "N" to cool transmission between tests. If engine speed exceeds limits, release accelerator immediately as clutch slippage is indicated. See STALL SPEEDS chart.

Testing Procedure

With engine at normal operating temperature, connect a tachometer to engine. Start engine and set parking brake and service brakes. Place selector lever in "D". Depress accelerator briefly (6 to 8 seconds) to full throttle and note maximum RPM obtained.

NOTE: Maximum stall speed test time is 10 seconds.

Allow 2 minutes for cooling and repeat test in "2" and "R". Engine speed should be within limits. See STALL SPEEDS chart.

HONDA 3-SPEED (Cont.)

STALL SPEEDS

Application	Stall RPM
Civic 3-Speed	
Standard	2700
Limit	2300-2900

TRANSAXLE REMOVAL & INSTALLATION

See appropriate AUTOMATIC TRANSMISSION REMOVAL article in IMPORT GENERAL SERVICING section.

TORQUE CONVERTER

DISASSEMBLY & REASSEMBLY

With transmission removed and torque converter pulled off stator shaft, scribe an alignment mark across edge of converter for reassembly reference. Remove drive plate and washer from converter. *See Fig. 3.* To assemble, reverse removal procedure. Tighten converter bolts in a star pattern.

Fig. 3: Exploded View of Torque Converter

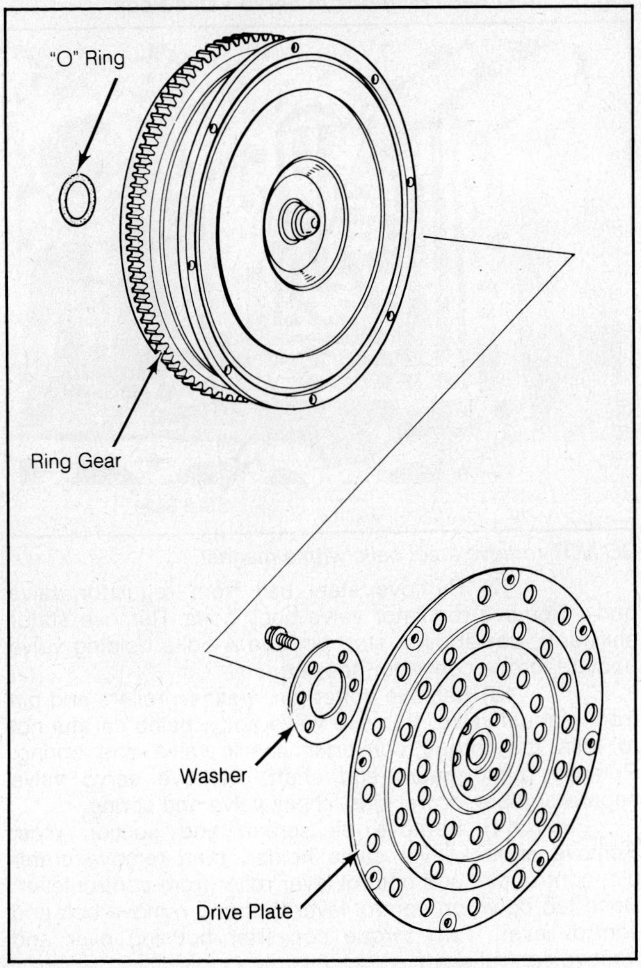

TRANSAXLE DISASSEMBLY

1) Remove dipstick. Remove bolts from end cover, then remove cover. Shift transmission to "P". Lock mainshaft using Holder (07923-6890202). *See Fig. 4.*

2) Remove end cover gasket, dowel pins and "O" rings. Pry staked edge of lock nut flange out of notch in 1st clutch. Remove mainshaft lock nut (LEFT HAND thread), then remove 1st clutch. Remove 1st clutch thrust washer, needle bearing and 1st gear. Remove bearing and thrust washer from mainshaft.

3) Pry staked edge of lock nut out of notch in parking gear. Remove coutershaft lock nut and parking pawl stop pin. Remove parking pawl, shaft and spring. Remove parking gear and countershaft 1st gear as a unit. Remove bearing and 1st gear collar from countershaft. Remove "O" ring and 1st gear collar from mainshaft.

Fig. 4: Locking Mainshaft Using Holding Tool

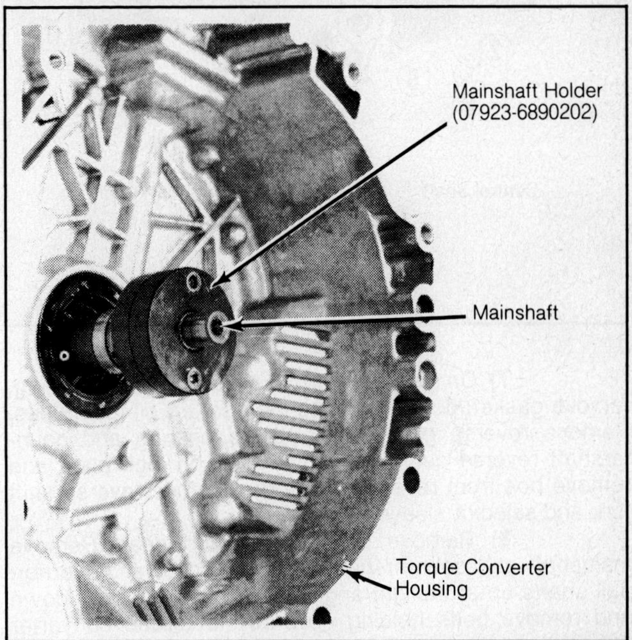

4) Remove reverse idler bearing holder. Bend down tab on lock plate under parking shift arm bolt. Remove bolt and parking shift arm. Lift out parking shift arm, then remove shift arm spring.

5) Bend down tab on throttle control lever bolt lock plate and remove bolt. Remove throttle control lever and spring from shaft. Remove torque converter housing-to-transmission housing bolts. *See Fig. 5.*

NOTE: Do not remove bolt number 1, just loosen enough so bolt threads are free of torque converter housing. If bolt is removed completely, throttle control bracket will have to be readjusted.

6) Align control shaft spring pin with cut-out in transmission housing. Install a puller (that will bolt to transmission housing and press against the countershaft) and separate transmission housing from torque converter housing. After separating housings, remove transmission housing completely.

HONDA 3-SPEED (Cont.)

Fig. 5: Location of Converter Housing to Transmission Housing Bolts

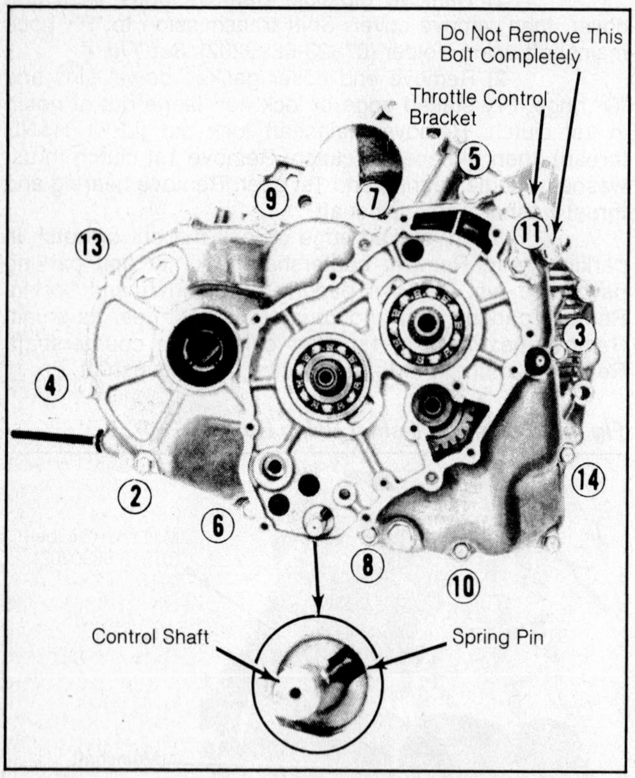

Fig. 6: Removing Accumulator Springs from Servo Valve Body

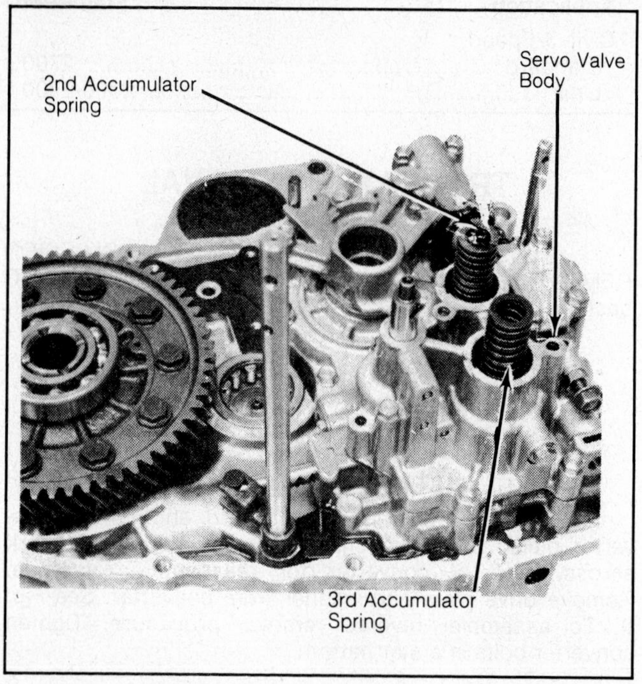

7) On gear side of torque converter housing, remove gasket, dowel pins and 1st and 3rd oil feed pipes. Remove reverse gear collar, needle bearing and countershaft reverse gear. Bend down tab on lock plate and remove bolt from reverse shift fork. Remove reverse shift fork and selector sleeve as a unit.

8) Remove countershaft 2nd gear. Remove mainshaft and countershaft together. To clear governor, pull shafts up at a slight angle. Bend governor tabs down and remove bolts holding governor to torque converter housing.

CAUTION: Accumulator cover is spring loaded. Hold cover down while removing bolts in an alternating pattern.

9) Remove accumulator cover, 2nd and 3rd accumulator springs. *See Fig. 6.* Remove 4 lock-up valve body mounting bolts. Slide the valve body away from clutch pressure control valve to remove the oil feed pipe and lock-up valve body.

10) Remove 1st gear oil feed pipe (pipe nearest clutch pressure control valve). Remove 3rd gear oil feed pipe (pipe nearest differential gear). Remove clutch pressure control valve and separator plate.

11) Remove 7 servo body bolts and servo body. Remove "E" clip from throttle control shaft and remove shaft. Remove servo valve separator plate and dowel pins. Remove steel balls from valve body oil passage. Note ball locations for reassembly reference. *See Fig. 7.*

Fig. 7: Steel Ball Locations in Servo Valve Body

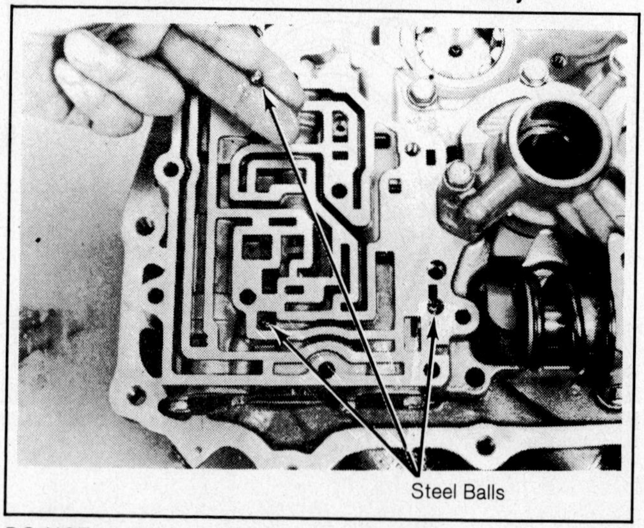

DO NOT remove steel balls with a magnet.

12) Remove steel ball from regulator valve body. Remove regulator valve body bolts. Remove stator shift arm, dowel pins, stop pin and 4 bolts holding valve body to torque converter housing.

13) Remove cotter pin, washer, rollers and pin from manual valve. Remove valve body, being careful not to lose the torque converter check valve and spring. Remove pump gears and shaft. Remove servo valve separator plate, dowel pins, check valve and spring.

14) Remove oil screen and suction pipe. Remove control lever cable holder, then remove cotter pin, control pin, and control lever roller from control lever. Bend tab down on control lever bolt and remove bolt and control lever. Turn torque converter housing over and remove control shaft.

HONDA 3-SPEED (Cont.)

Fig. 8: Exploded View of Transmission Housing and Components

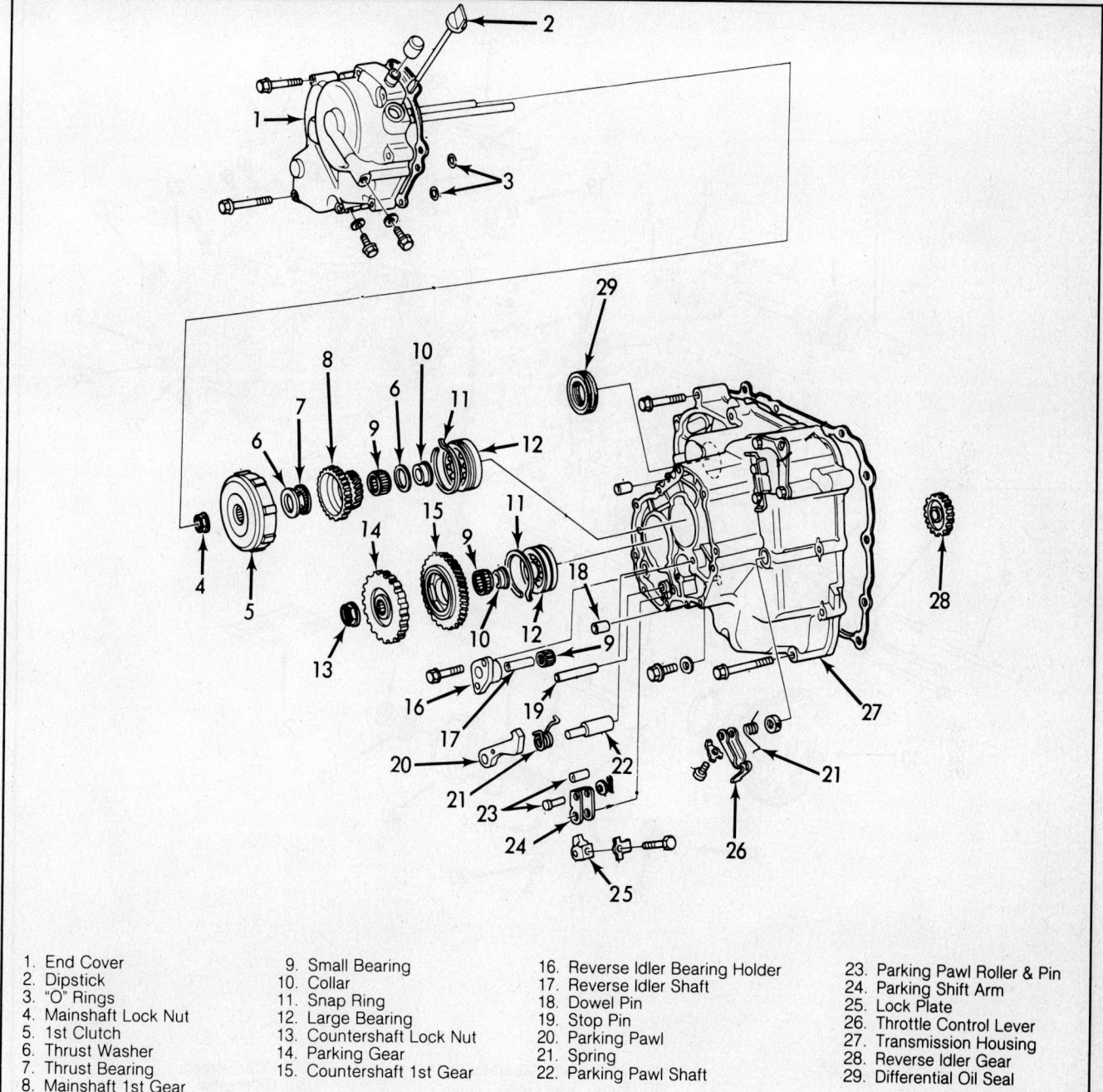

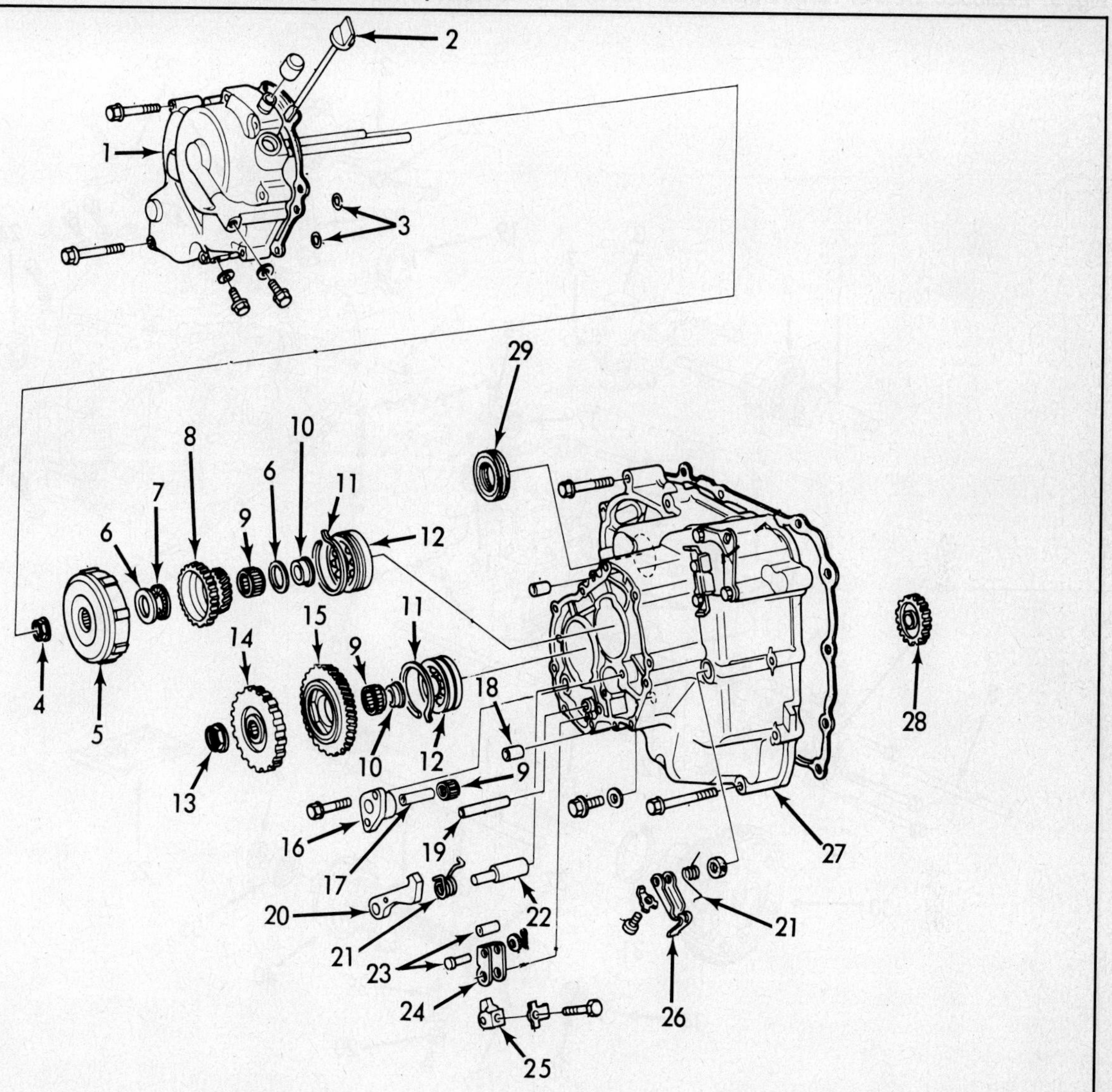

1. End Cover
2. Dipstick
3. "O" Rings
4. Mainshaft Lock Nut
5. 1st Clutch
6. Thrust Washer
7. Thrust Bearing
8. Mainshaft 1st Gear
9. Small Bearing
10. Collar
11. Snap Ring
12. Large Bearing
13. Countershaft Lock Nut
14. Parking Gear
15. Countershaft 1st Gear
16. Reverse Idler Bearing Holder
17. Reverse Idler Shaft
18. Dowel Pin
19. Stop Pin
20. Parking Pawl
21. Spring
22. Parking Pawl Shaft
23. Parking Pawl Roller & Pin
24. Parking Shift Arm
25. Lock Plate
26. Throttle Control Lever
27. Transmission Housing
28. Reverse Idler Gear
29. Differential Oil Seal

COMPONENT DISASSEMBLY & REASSEMBLY

ONE-WAY CLUTCH AND PARKING GEAR

Disassembly

Separate countershaft 1st gear from parking gear by gripping 1st gear in left hand and turning parking gear counterclockwise. Remove one-way clutch from counter 1st gear by prying out with a screwdriver. Inspect countershaft 1st gear and parking gear for wear, damage or scoring. Inspect one-way clutch for damage.

Reassembly

To reassemble one-way clutch and parking gear, reverse disassembly procedures. When reassembled, check one-way clutch for free movement in one direction only.

VALVE BODY

NOTE: **When disassembling valve body, lay out components in order of removal for reassembly reference.**

HONDA 3-SPEED (Cont.)

Fig. 9: Exploded View of Torque Converter Housing and Components

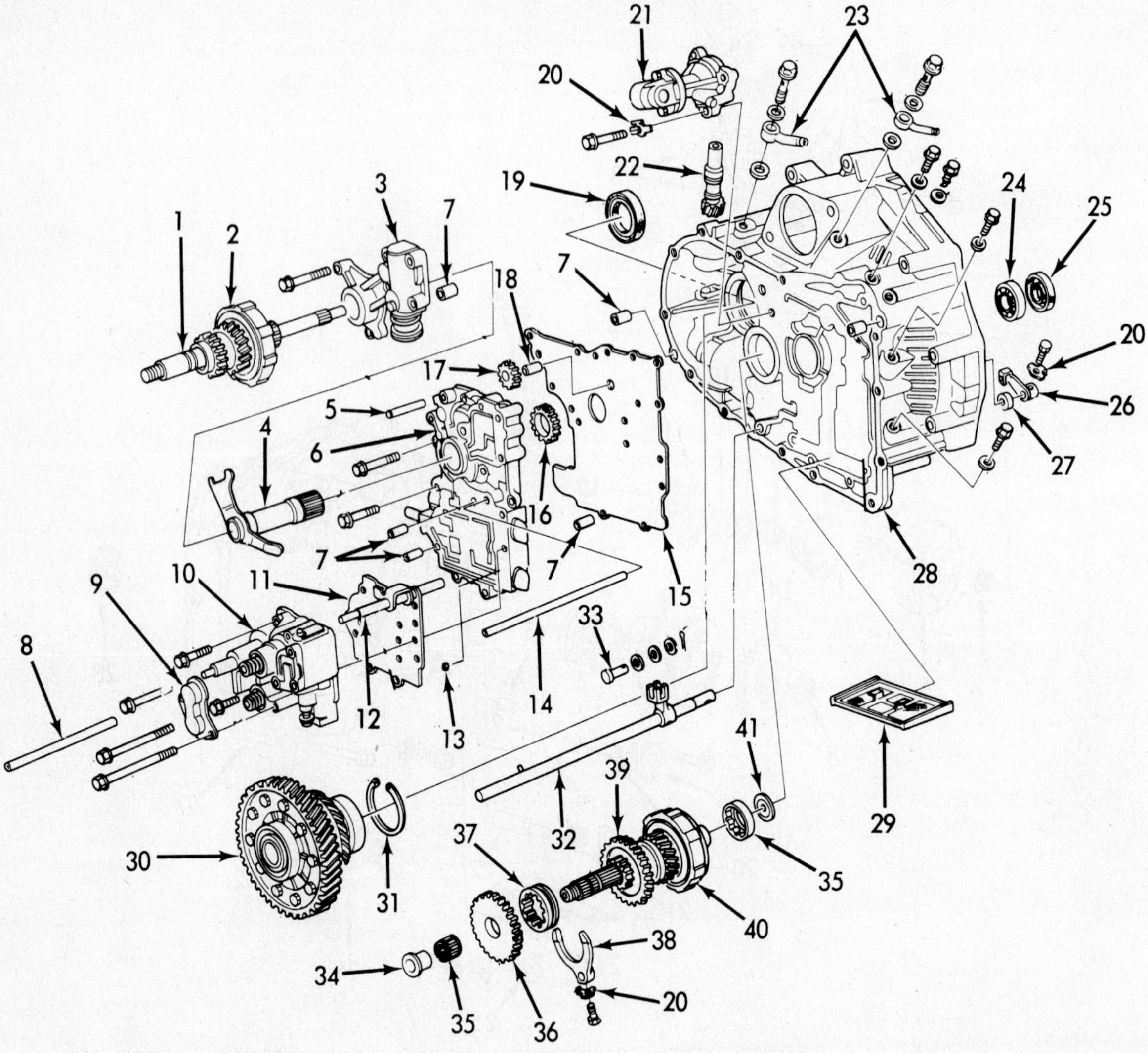

1. Mainshaft Assembly
2. 2nd Clutch
3. Regulator Assembly
4. Stator Shaft
5. Stop Pin
6. Valve Body Assembly
7. Dowel Pin
8. Feed Pipe for 1st Gear
9. Accumulator Cover
10. Servo Valve Assembly
11. Servo Separator Plate
12. Throttle Control Shaft
13. Steel Ball
14. Feed Pipe for 3rd Gear
15. Valve Body Separator Plate
16. Pump Drive Gear
17. Pump Driven Gear
18. Pump Shaft
19. Differential Oil Seal
20. Lock Plate
21. Governor Assembly
22. Speedometer Drive Gear
23. Transmission Cooler Lines
24. Mainshaft Bearing
25. Mainshaft Oil Seal
26. Shift Lever
27. Oil Seal
28. Torque Converter Housing
29. Filter Screen
30. Differential
31. Snap Ring
32. Shift Shaft
33. Manual Valve Pin
34. Reverse Gear Collar
35. Bearing
36. Countershaft Reverse Gear
37. Selector Hub
38. Reverse Shift Fork
39. Countershaft Assembly
40. 3rd Clutch
41. Oil Guide Plate

HONDA 3-SPEED (Cont.)

SPRING IDENTIFICATION CHART

Valve Spring	Length In. (mm)	Outer Diameter In. (mm)	Number Of Coils	Wire Thickness In. (mm)
Regulator Valve Outer Spring	3.28 (83.2)	.58 (14.7)	17	.07 (1.8)
Regulator Valve Inner Spring	1.73 (44.0)	.38 (9.6)	9	.07 (1.8)
Stator Reacting Spring	1.19 (30.3)	1.51 (38.4)	2	.24 (6.0)
Torque Converter Check Valve Spring	1.53 (38.9)	.35 (8.89)	15	.04 (.9)
Throttle Modulator Valve Spring	1.20 (30.5)	.37 (9.4)	8	.05 (1.2)
Relief Valve Spring	1.86 (47.2)	.33 (8.4)	15	.03 (.8)
Governor Spring	1.11 (28.3)	.74 (18.8)	3.5	.05 (1.2)
Orifice Control Spring	1.28 (32.5)	.27 (6.8)	16	.04 (.9)
Throttle Control Valve "A" Outer Spring	.84 (21.4)	.33 (8.4)	6	.04 (1.0)
Throttle Control Valve "A" Inner Spring	1.18 (29.9)	.24 (6.2)	8	.03 (1.4)
Throttle Control Valve "B" Spring	1.20 (30.5)	.33 (8.4)	8.5	.06 (1.4)
Servo Return Spring	1.24 (31.4)	1.13 (28.6)	2.4	.10 (2.5)

Fig. 10: Exploded View of Valve Body and Components

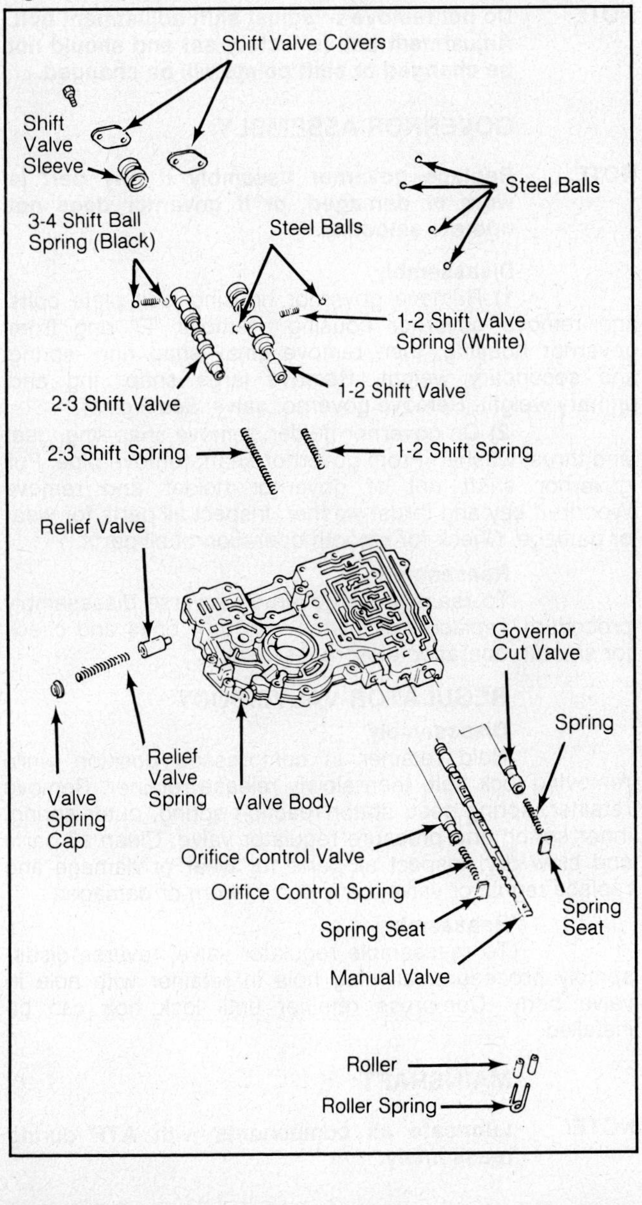

Disassembly

1) Remove torque converter check valve and spring. Remove relief valve cap, spring and valve. Remove orifice control valve plate, spring and valve. Remove detent spring and rollers. Remove manual valve.

2) Remove 1-2 shift valve plate, then carefully remove 1-2 shift valve with sleeve. Remove 1-2 shift spring. On 1-2 shift valve, carefully slide sleeve off valve, being careful to catch 2 steel balls and spring as sleeve is removed.

3) Remove and disassemble 2-3 shift valve in same manner as 1-2 shift valve. Check all components for wear or damage. Replace spring if not to specifications. See SPRING IDENTIFICATION table. Replace complete valve body assembly if valve body or any valve is worn or damaged. *See Fig. 10.*

NOTE: Coat all parts in ATF before reassembly.

Reassembly

1) Slide 1-2 shift valve spring into hole in 1-2 shift valve. Press steel balls (1 on each side of spring) into hole of shift valve and slide sleeve over shift valve and balls. Place 1-2 shift spring in valve body, then install shift valve (with sleeve) into valve body. Install 1-2 shift valve plate and bolts to valve body. *See Fig. 11.*

2) Assemble 2-3 shift valve in same manner as 1-2 shift valve and install it to valve body. Place relief spring in relief valve and install in valve body. Compress spring with a screwdriver and insert valve spring cap (with cut-out aligned with screwdriver).

3) Install manual valve into valve body, then install detent rollers and spring. Install oil pump driven gear shaft and driven gear (make sure chamfered side of gear faces away from valve body). Install oil pump drive gear.

4) Measure driven gear-to-valve body thrust clearance. Clearance should be .001-.002" (.03-.05 mm). Measure side clearance of driven and drive gears. Driven gear side clearance should be .002-.004" (.05-.10 mm), drive gear side clearance should be .004-.006" (.10-.14 mm). *See Fig. 12.* If clearance is not to specifications, check valve body for excessive wear. If wear exists, replace valve body assembly.

HONDA 3-SPEED (Cont.)

Fig. 11: Exploded View of Shift Valve Assembly

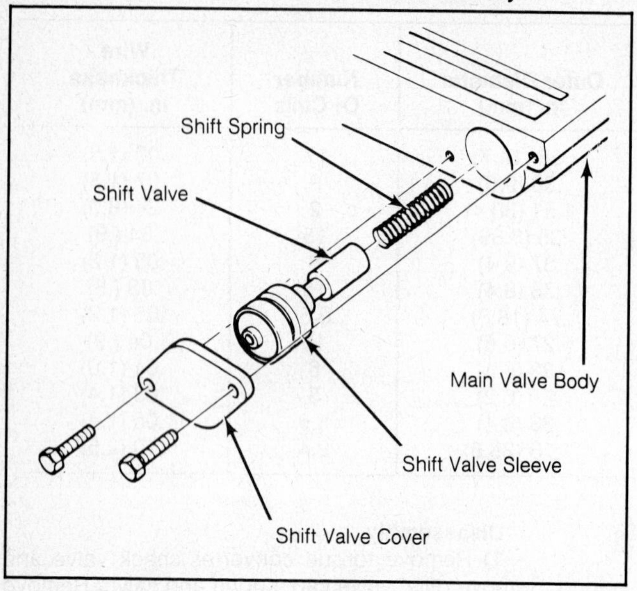

Fig. 12: Measuring Oil Pump-to-Valve Body Gear Clearance

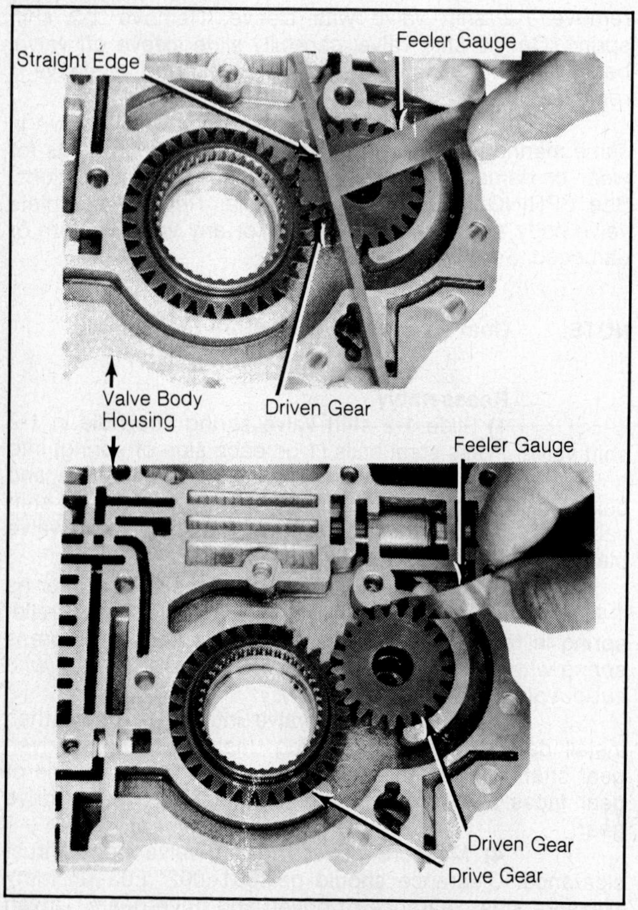

SERVO VALVE ASSEMBLY

NOTE: **Clean all parts in solvent and blow dry with air. Replace servo valve as an assembly if any parts are worn or damaged.**

Disassembly

1) Push out 2nd and 3rd accumulator pistons, then remove "O" rings. Remove servo valve and spring, then remove "O" ring from valve. Remove throttle control valve "B", then separate control valve "B" from inner and outer springs and plug. *See Fig. 13.*

2) Remove retainer bolt and retainer of throttle control valve "A". Remove plug, outside spring, throttle control valve "A" and inside spring. Remove throttle control cover, then separator plate. Remove oil passage pipe from valve body.

3) Remove plug and washer from servo valve body. Remove modulator valve retainer plate, spring and modulator valve. Inspect all components for wear or damage. verify that springs meet specifications. See SPRING IDENTIFICATION table. Replace springs that are not to specifications or complete servo assembly if any part is worn or damaged.

Reassembly

To reassemble servo valve, reverse disassembly procedure. Always replace "O" rings with new ones.

NOTE: **Do not remove or adjust shift adjustment bolt. Adjustment bolt is factory set and should not be changed or shift points will be changed.**

GOVERNOR ASSEMBLY

NOTE: **Replace governor assembly if any part is worn or damaged, or if governor does not operate smoothly.**

Disassembly

1) Remove governor housing lock plate bolts and remove governor housing. Remove "E" ring from governor housing, then remove small snap ring, spring and secondary weight. Remove large snap ring and primary weight. Remove governor valve. *See Fig. 14.*

2) On governor holder, remove snap ring, gear and thrust washer. From governor shaft, remove pipe. Pull governor shaft out of governor holder and remove Woodruff key and thrust washer. Inspect all parts for wear or damage. Check for smooth operation of all parts.

Reassembly

To reassemble governor, reverse disassembly procedure, replace lock plates with new ones and check for smooth operation after reassembly.

REGULATOR VALVE BODY

Disassembly

Hold retainer in compressed position while removing lock bolt, then slowly release retainer. Remove retainer, spring seat, stator reaction spring, outer spring, inner spring and pressure regulator valve. Clean all parts and blow dry. Inspect all parts for wear or damage and replace regulator valve if any part is worn or damaged.

Reassembly

To reassemble regulator valve, reverse disassembly procedure, aligning hole in retainer with hole in valve body. Compress retainer until lock bolt can be installed.

MAINSHAFT

NOTE: **Lubricate all components with ATF during reassembly.**

HONDA 3-SPEED (Cont.)

Fig. 13: Exploded View of Servo Valve Assembly

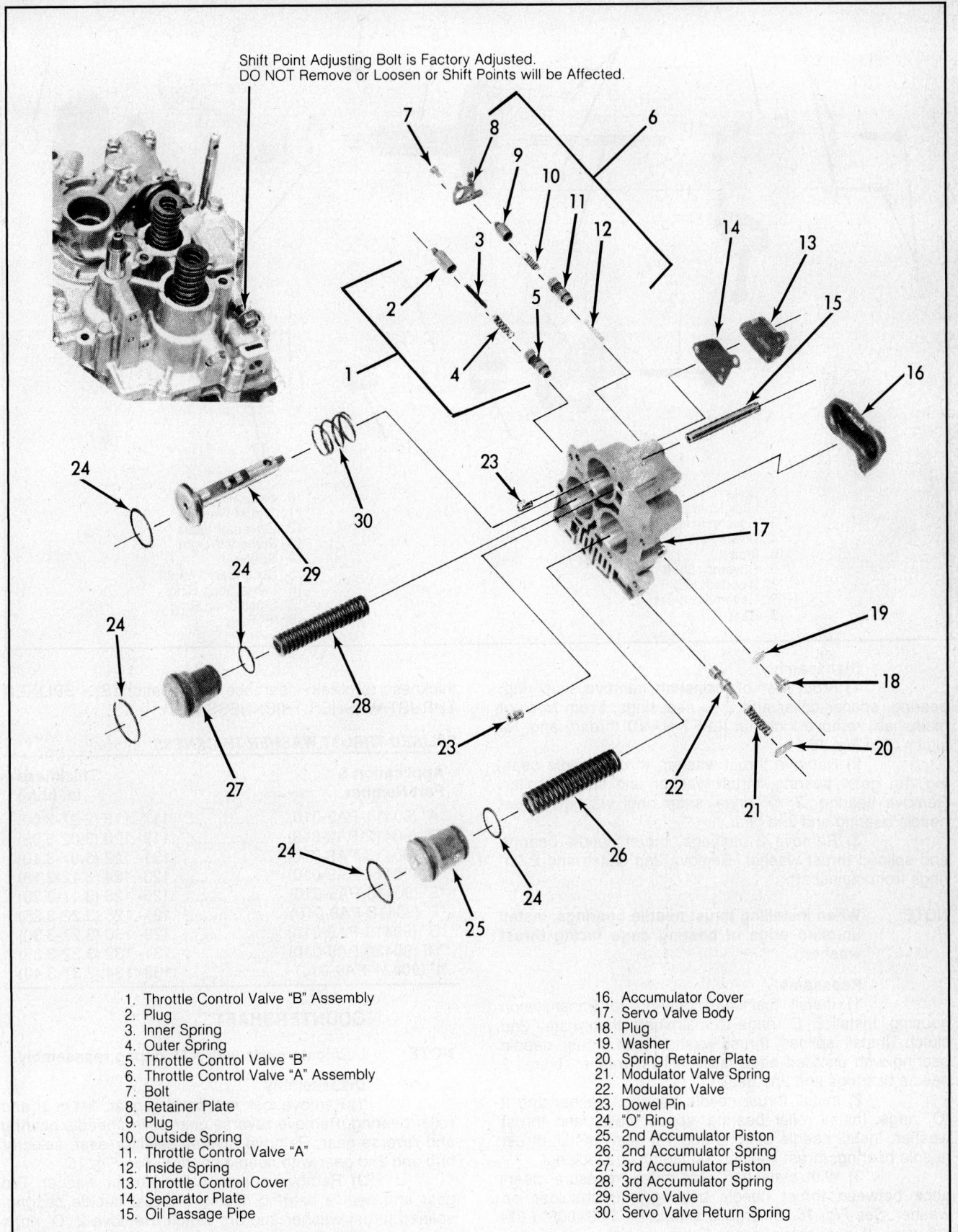

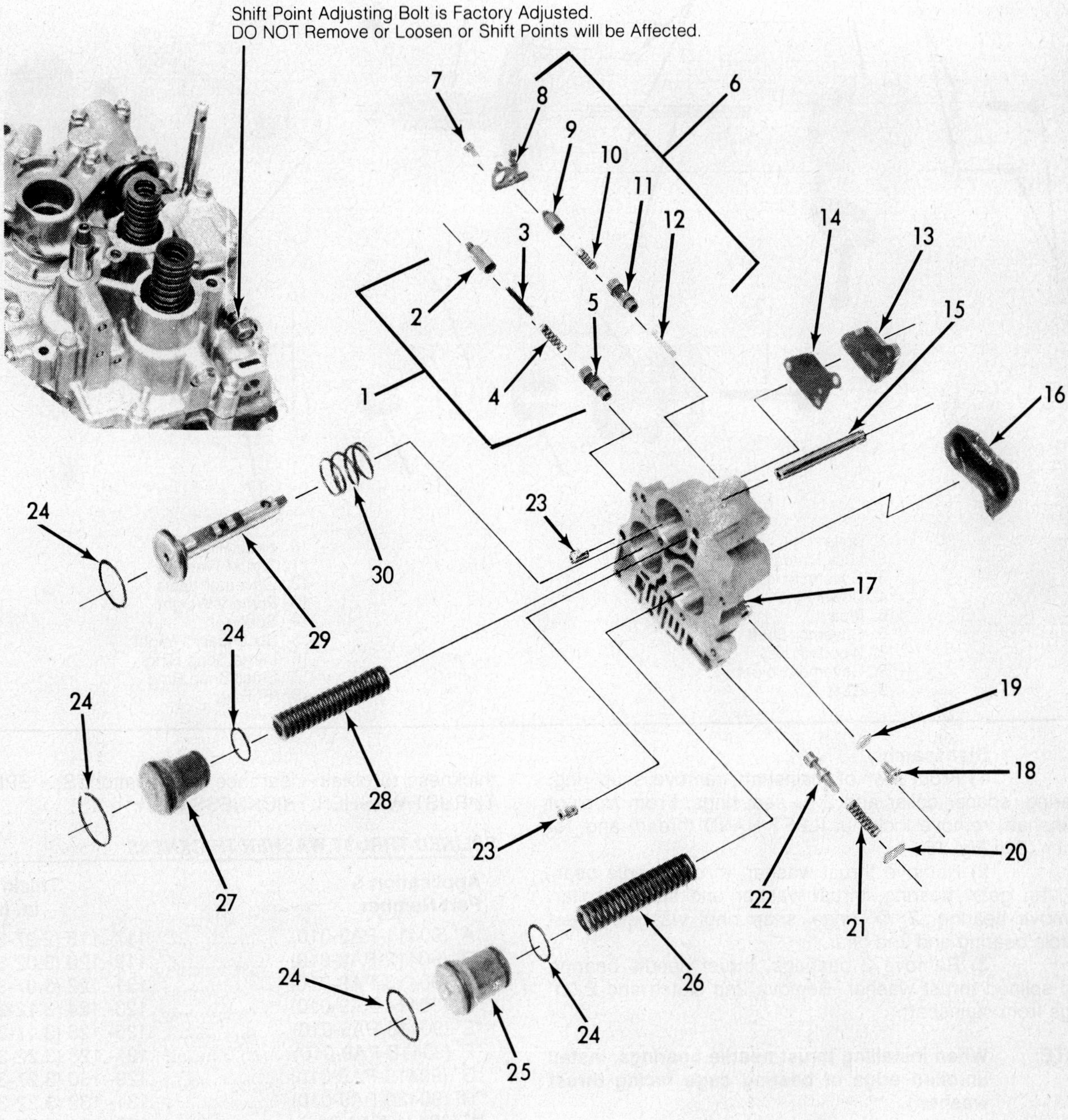

1. Throttle Control Valve "B" Assembly
2. Plug
3. Inner Spring
4. Outer Spring
5. Throttle Control Valve "B"
6. Throttle Control Valve "A" Assembly
7. Bolt
8. Retainer Plate
9. Plug
10. Outside Spring
11. Throttle Control Valve "A"
12. Inside Spring
13. Throttle Control Cover
14. Separator Plate
15. Oil Passage Pipe
16. Accumulator Cover
17. Servo Valve Body
18. Plug
19. Washer
20. Spring Retainer Plate
21. Modulator Valve Spring
22. Modulator Valve
23. Dowel Pin
24. "O" Ring
25. 2nd Accumulator Piston
26. 2nd Accumulator Spring
27. 3rd Accumulator Piston
28. 3rd Accumulator Spring
29. Servo Valve
30. Servo Valve Return Spring

HONDA 3-SPEED (Cont.)

Fig. 14: Exploded View of Governor Assembly

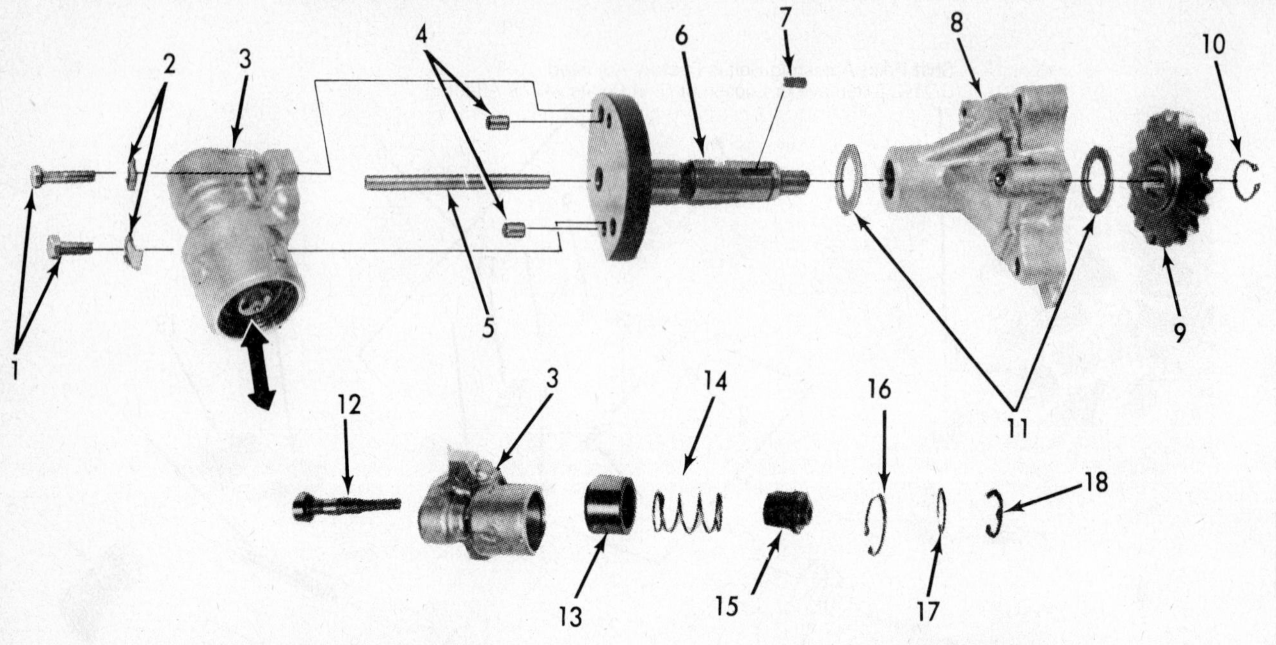

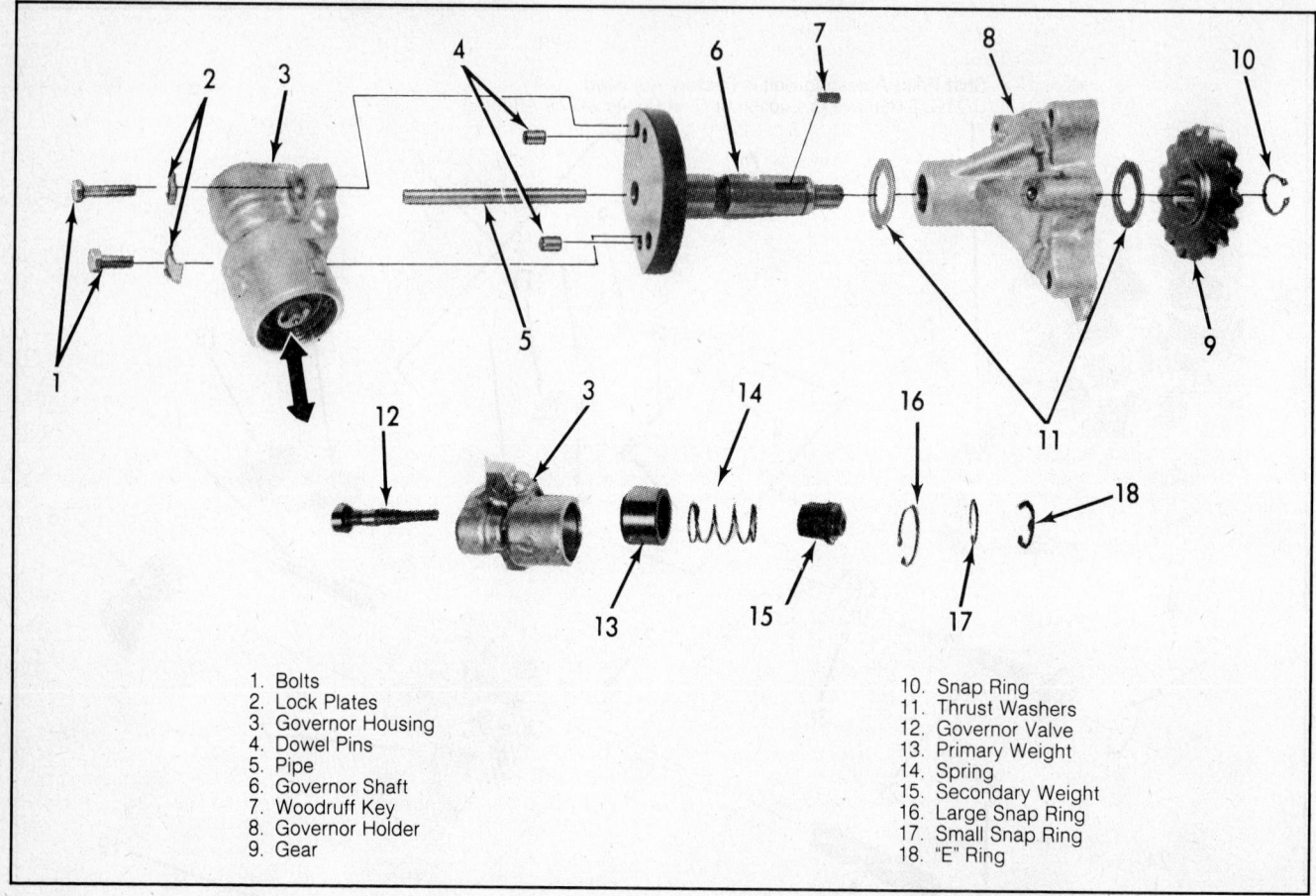

1. Bolts
2. Lock Plates
3. Governor Housing
4. Dowel Pins
5. Pipe
6. Governor Shaft
7. Woodruff Key
8. Governor Holder
9. Gear
10. Snap Ring
11. Thrust Washers
12. Governor Valve
13. Primary Weight
14. Spring
15. Secondary Weight
16. Large Snap Ring
17. Small Snap Ring
18. "E" Ring

Disassembly

1) From rear of mainshaft, remove snap ring, bearing, spacer collar and 2 oil seal rings. From front of mainshaft, remove lock nut (LEFT HAND thread) and 1st clutch. *See Fig. 15.*

2) Remove thrust washer, thrust needle bearing, 1st gear, bearing, thrust washer and spacer collar. Remove bearing, 2 "O" rings, snap ring, washer, thrust needle bearing and 2nd gear.

3) Remove 2 bearings, thrust needle bearing and splined thrust washer. Remove 2nd clutch and 2 "O" rings from mainshaft.

NOTE: When installing thrust needle bearings, install unrolled edge of bearing cage facing thrust washer.

Reassembly

1) Install mainshaft bearing to transmission housing. Install 2 "O" rings to mainshaft, then install 2nd clutch. Install splined thrust washer then thrust needle bearing with unrolled edge facing thrust washer. Install 2 needle bearings and 2nd gear.

2) Install thrust needle bearing, washer and 2 "O" rings. Install roller bearing, spacer collar and thrust washer. Install needle bearing and 1st gear. Install thrust needle bearing, thrust washer, 1st clutch and lock nut.

3) With mainshaft assembled, measure clearance between thrust needle bearing and shoulder on washer. *See Fig. 16.* Clearance should be .003-.006" (.07-.15 mm), if not, select splined thrust washer of proper thickness to obtain clearance specification. See SPLINED THRUST WASHER THICKNESS chart.

SPLINED THRUST WASHER THICKNESS

Application & Part Number	Thickness In. (mm)
"A" (90411-PA9-010)	.117-.118 (2.97-3.00)
"B" (90412-PA9-010)	.119-.120 (3.02-3.05)
"C" (90413-PA9-010)	.121-.122 (3.07-3.10)
"D" (90414-PA9-010)	.123-.124 (3.12-3.15)
"E" (90415-PA9-010)	.125-.126 (3.17-3.20)
"F" (90418-PA9-010)	.127-.128 (3.22-3.25)
"G" (90419-PA9-010)	.129-.130 (3.27-3.30)
"H" (90420-PA9-010)	.131-.132 (3.32-3.35)
"I" (90421-PA9-010)	.133-.134 (3.37-3.40)

COUNTERSHAFT

NOTE: Lubricate parts with ATF during reassembly.

Disassembly

1) Remove lock nut, parking gear, 1st gear and roller bearing. Remove reverse gear collar, needle bearing and reverse gear. Remove reverse selector gear, selector hub and 2nd gear with needle bearing. *See Fig. 16.*

2) Remove spacer collar, thrust washer, 3rd gear and needle bearing. Remove thrust needle bearing, splined thrust washer and 3rd clutch. Remove 2 "O" rings from countershaft. Remove countershaft bearing from transmission housing.

HONDA 3-SPEED (Cont.)

Fig. 15: Exploded View of Mainshaft Assembly

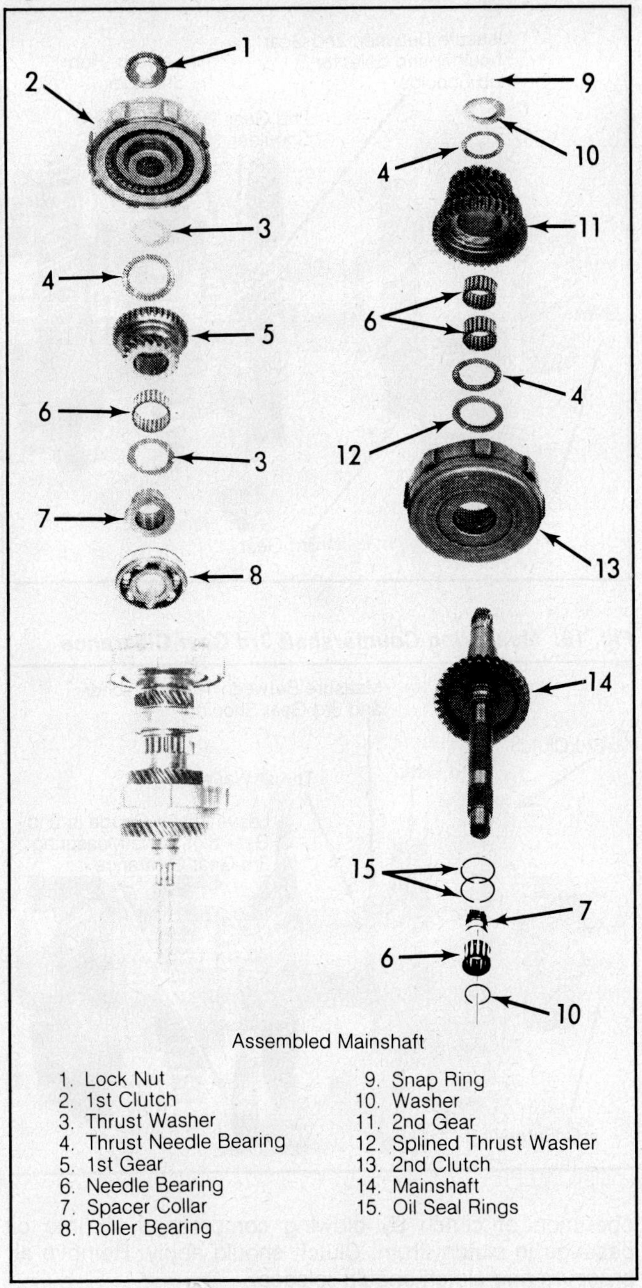

NOTE: When installing thrust needle bearing, install unrolled edge of bearing cage facing thrust washer.

Reassembly

1) Install countershaft bearing to transmission housing. Install 2 new "O" rings to countershaft. Install splined thrust washer, thrust needle bearing and 3rd gear with needle bearing. Install thrust washer, spacer collar and 2nd gear with needle bearing.

2) Install selector hub, reverse selector gear and reverse gear with needle bearing. Install reverse gear collar, roller bearing, 1st gear, parking gear and lock nut. *See Fig. 18.*

3) With countershaft assembled, measure clearance between selector hub and shoulder on 2nd

Fig. 16: Measuring Mainshaft Gear Clearance

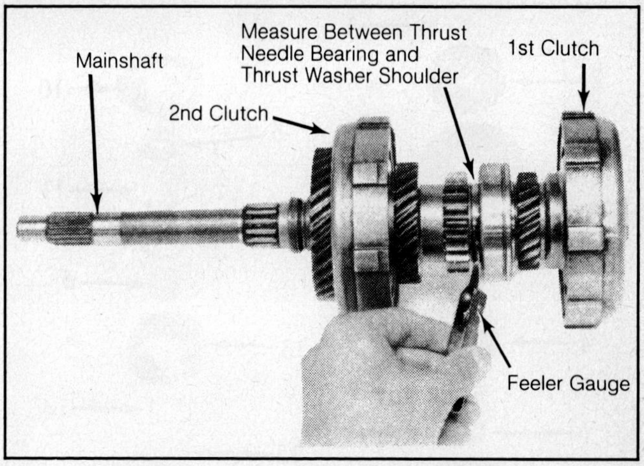

gear. Clearance should be .003-.006" (.07-.15 mm). If clearance is more than specifications, install a thrust washer of proper thickness to achieve correct clearance. See THRUST WASHER THICKNESS chart.

THRUST WASHER THICKNESS

Application & Part Number	Thickness In. (mm)
"A" (90401-PA9-010)	.089-.091 (2.27-2.30)
"B" (90402-PA9-010)	.091-.093 (2.32-2.35)
"C" (90403-PA9-010)	.093-.094 (2.37-2.40)
"D" (90404-PA9-010)	.095-.096 (2.42-2.45)
"E" (90407-PA9-010)	.097-.098 (2.47-2.50)
"F" (90408-PA9-010)	.099-.100 (2.52-2.55)
"G" (90409-PA9-010)	.101-.102 (2.57-2.60)

4) Leave feeler gauge of .003-.006" (.07-.15 mm) thickness (standard 2nd gear clearance) installed between selector hub and 2nd gear, then install another feeler gauge between thrust washer and shoulder of 3rd gear to measure 3rd gear clearance. *See Fig. 19.* Clearance should be .003-.006" (.07-.15 mm).

5) If clearance is not to specifications, install a splined thrust washer of proper thickness. See SPLINED THRUST WASHER THICKNESS chart, to determine amount of mainshaft 2nd gear clearance.

CLUTCH ASSEMBLIES

NOTE: 1st, 2nd and 3rd clutches are identical.

Disassembly

1) Remove large snap ring retaining end plate and clutches. Remove end plate and clutch pack, keep steel plates and lined plates in order removed. *See Fig. 20.*

2) Install a spring compressor that seats against clutch drum and against spring retainer. Compress spring and remove small snap ring. Slowly release spring compressor, then remove spring retainer, return spring, large "O" ring, small "O" ring and piston.

3) Check condition of piston and check valve. Check for excessive wear or scoring on steel plates and lined plates. Replace steel or lined plates if necessary. Replace clutch assembly if piston is damaged.

NOTE: If new lined plates are installed, soak in ATF before installation.

HONDA 3-SPEED (Cont.)

Fig. 17: Exploded View of Countershaft Assembly

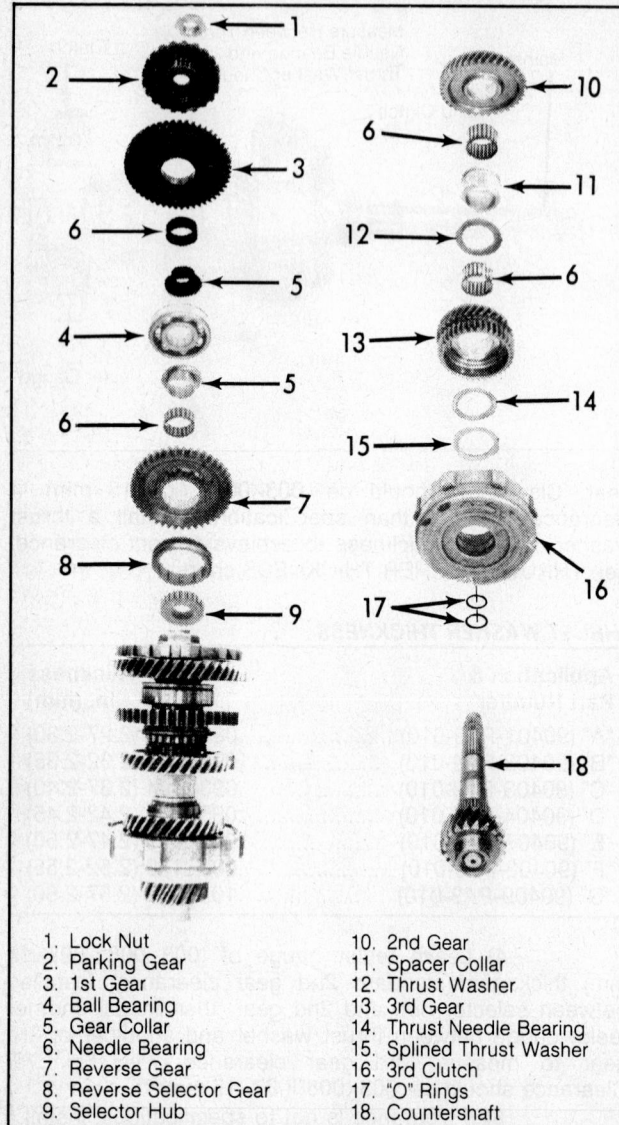

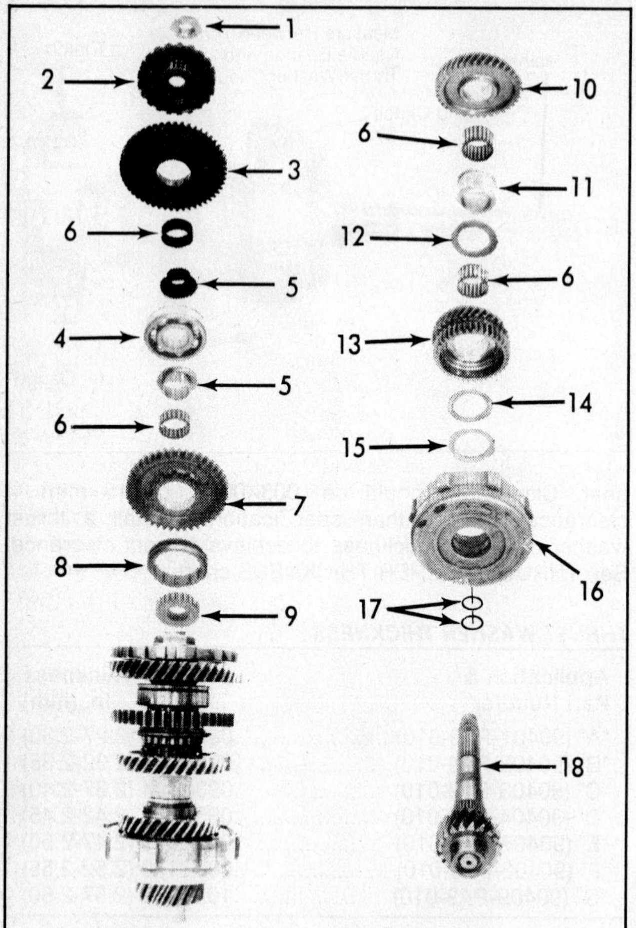

1. Lock Nut
2. Parking Gear
3. 1st Gear
4. Ball Bearing
5. Gear Collar
6. Needle Bearing
7. Reverse Gear
8. Reverse Selector Gear
9. Selector Hub
10. 2nd Gear
11. Spacer Collar
12. Thrust Washer
13. 3rd Gear
14. Thrust Needle Bearing
15. Splined Thrust Washer
16. 3rd Clutch
17. "O" Rings
18. Countershaft

Fig. 18: Measuring Countershaft 2nd Gear Clearance

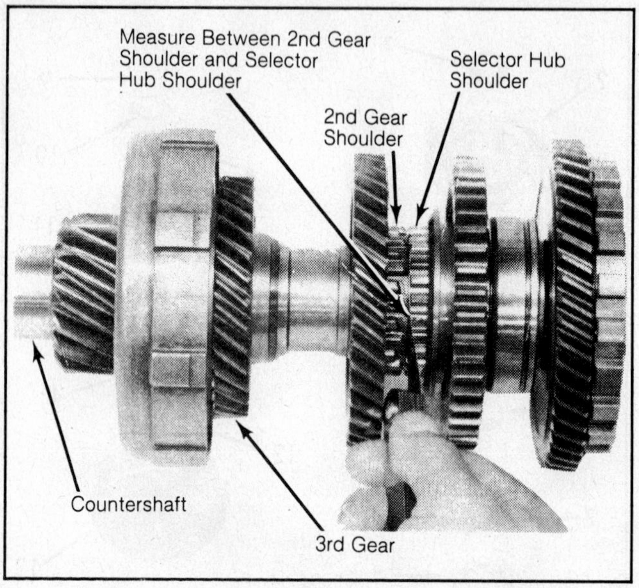

Fig. 19: Measuring Countershaft 3rd Gear Clearance

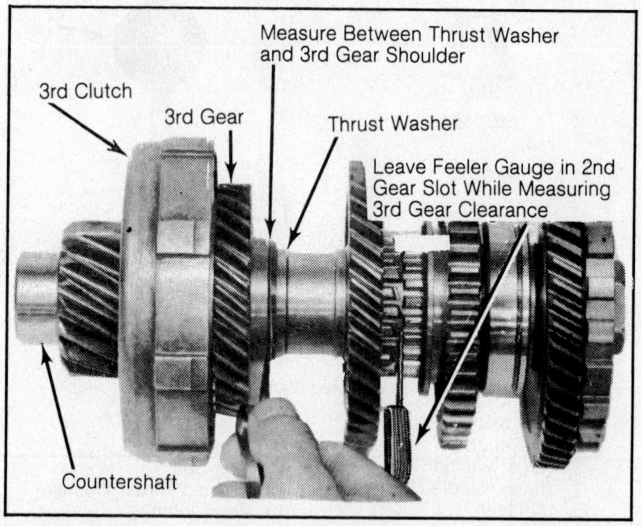

Reassembly

1) Lubricate all parts with ATF before assembling. Install new "O" ring on piston. Make sure clutch piston spring washer is installed with high side facing away from clutch drum. Install piston (lubricate "O" ring with ATF) to clutch drum. Apply pressure to piston (by hand) and rotate piston to ensure proper seating.

2) Install return spring and spring retainer. Position a new snap ring on spring retainer, then install a spring compressor to clutch drum and spring retainer. Compress spring and fit snap ring to groove. Slowly release spring compressor and make sure snap ring seats properly.

3) Install clutch pack, starting with a steel plate and alternating with lined plates, ending with the end plate. Install large snap ring to clutch drum. Measure clearance between end plate and lined plate. Clearance should be .016-.028" (.4-.7 mm).

4) If clearance is not to specifications, select an end plate to obtain correct clearance. See END PLATE THICKNESS chart. With correct end plate installed, check operation of clutch by blowing compressed air into oil passage in clutch drum. Clutch should apply. Remove air pressure and clutch should release.

END PLATE THICKNESSES

Application & Part Number	Thickness In. (mm)
"1" (22551-PA9-010)	.091-.094 (2.3-2.4)
"2" (22552-PA9-010)	.094-.098 (2.4-2.5)
"3" (22553-PA9-010)	.098-.102 (2.5-2.6)
"4" (22554-PA9-010)	.102-.106 (2.6-2.7)
"5" (22555-PA9-010)	.106-.110 (2.7-2.8)
"6" (22556-PA9-010)	.110-.114 (2.8-2.9)
"7" (22557-PA9-010)	.114-.118 (2.9-3.0)
"8" (22558-PA9-010)	.118-.122 (3.0-3.1)
"9" (22559-PA9-010)	.122-.126 (3.1-3.2)
"10" (22560-PA9-010)	.126-.130 (3.2-3.3)

HONDA 3-SPEED (Cont.)

Fig. 20: Exploded View of 1st, 2nd and 3rd Clutch Assemblies

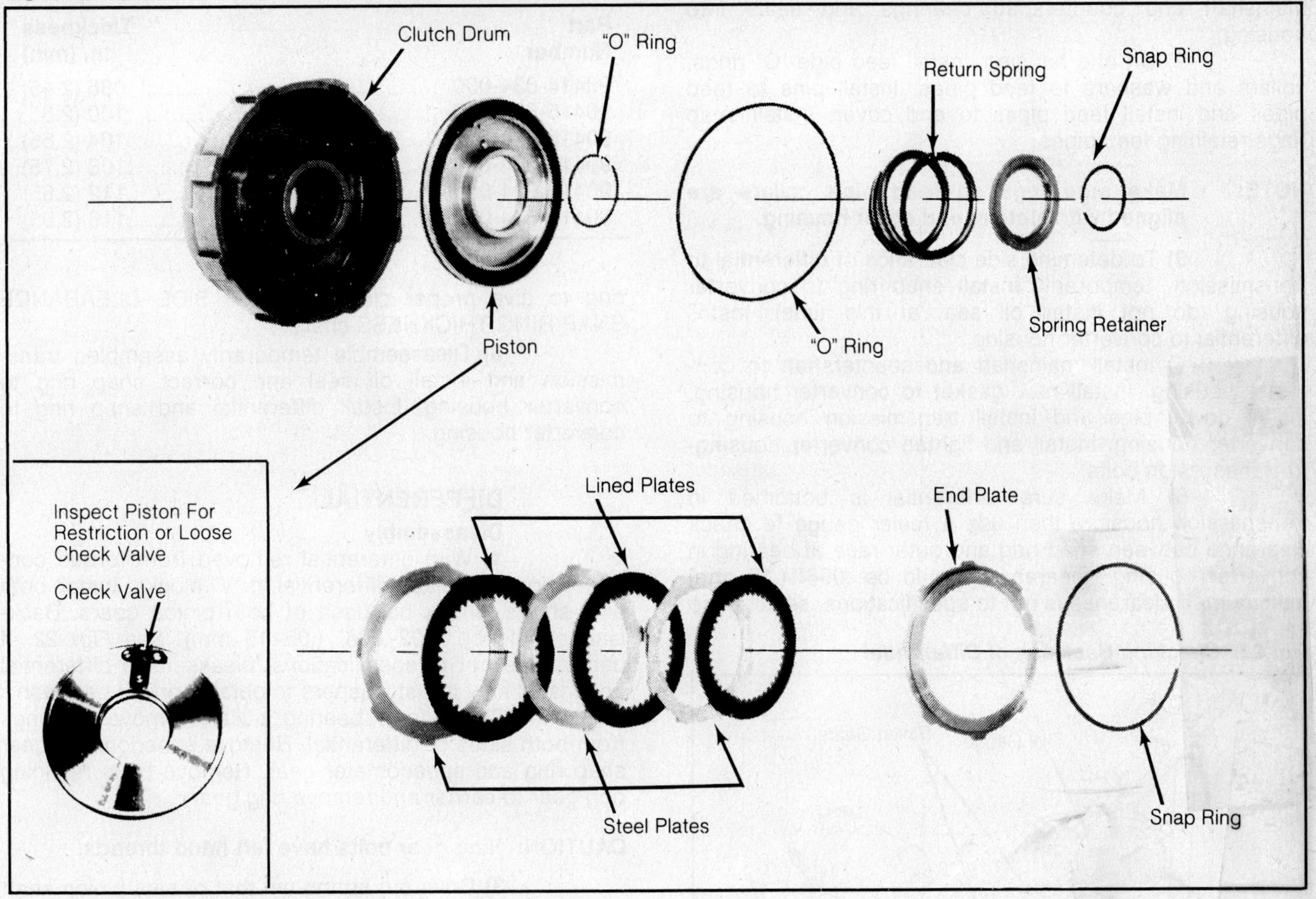

TRANSMISSION, END & TORQUE CONVERTER HOUSING

Disassembly

1) If seals are to be replaced or if differential needs repair, lift differential out of torque converter housing. Remove differential seal snap ring and drive seal out.

2) On end cover, remove snap rings to feed pipes "A" and "B". Remove feed pipes with collars, then remove pins and collars from feed pipes. *See Fig. 21*

3) On torque converter housing, drive in oil seals and bearings from mainshaft and countershaft. On transmission housing, expand snap rings (do not remove) and push bearings out by hand. Push out idler gear shaft and bearing from inside transmission housing then remove idler gear.

Reassembly

1) Install idler gear, then idler gear shaft and bearing to transmission housing. Expand mainshaft and countershaft bearing snap rings and install bearings to

Fig. 21 Exploded View of End Housing Assembly

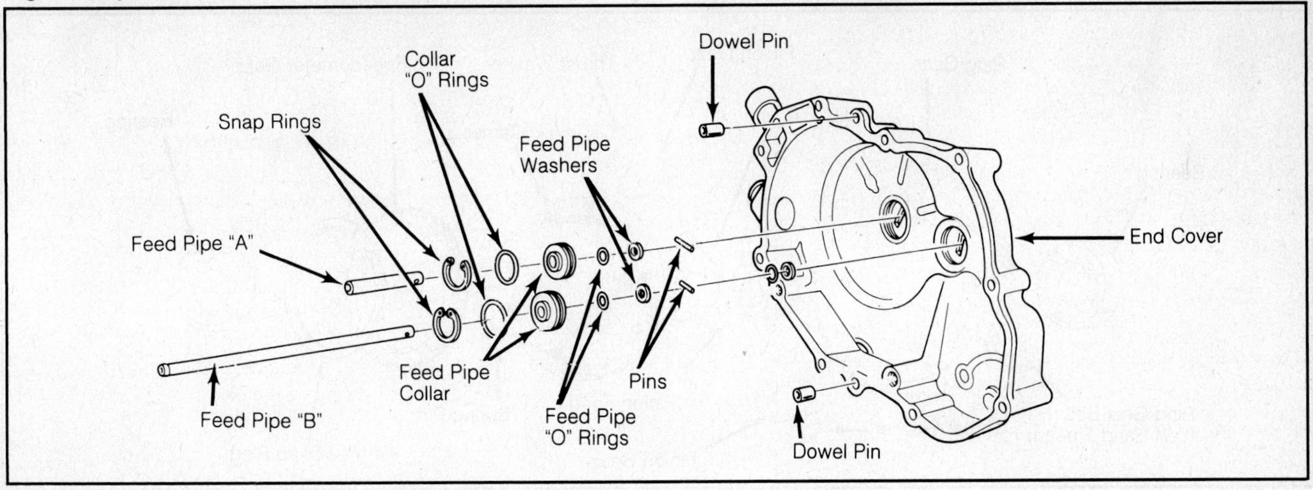

HONDA 3-SPEED (Cont.)

transmission housing. On torque converter housing, drive mainshaft and countershaft bearings and seals into housing.

2) On end housing, install feed pipe "O" rings, collars and washers to feed pipes. Install pins to feed pipes and install feed pipes to end cover. Install snap rings retaining feed pipes.

NOTE: Make sure lugs on feed pipe collars are aligned with slots in end cover housing.

3) To detemine side clearance of differential to transmission, temporarily install snap ring to converter housing (do not install oil seal at this time). Install differential to converter housing.

4) Install mainshaft and countershaft to converter housing. Install new gasket to converter housing, install dowel pins and install transmission housing to converter housing. Install and tighten converter housing-to-transmission bolts.

5) Make sure differential is bottomed in transmission housing, then use a feeler gauge to check clearance between snap ring and outer race of bearing in converter housing. Clearance should be .006" (.15 mm) maximum. If clearance is not to specifications, select snap ring to give proper clearance. See SIDE CLEARANCE SNAP RING THICKNESS chart.

Fig. 22: Checking Backlash of Differential

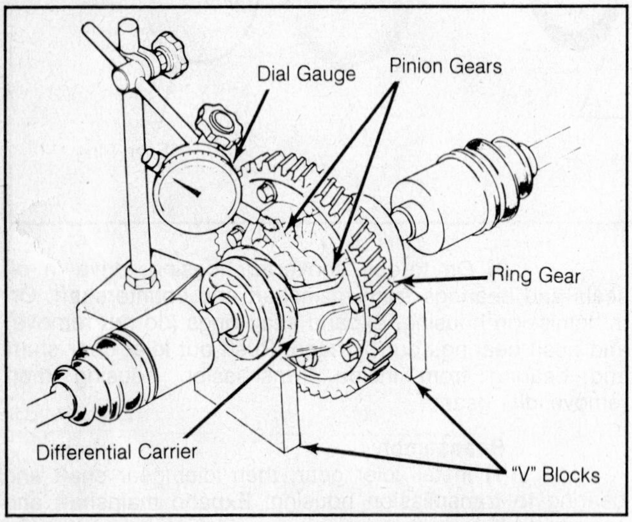

SIDE CLEARANCE SNAP RING THICKNESS

Part Number	Thickness In. (mm)
90414-634-000	.096 (2.45)
90415-634-000	.100 (2.55)
90416-634-000	.104 (2.65)
90417-634-000	.108 (2.75)
90418-634-000	.112 (2.85)
90419-634-000	.116 (2.95)

6) Disassemble temporarily assembled transmission and install oil seal and correct snap ring to converter housing. Install differential and snap ring to converter housing.

DIFFERENTIAL

Disassembly

1) With differential removed from torque converter housing, place differential in "V" blocks. Install both axle shafts, check backlash of both pinion gears. Backlash should be .002-.006" (.05-.15 mm). *See Fig. 22.* If backlash is not to specifications, disassemble differential and install new thrust washers to obtain correct backlash.

2) Using a bearing puller, remove bearings from both sides of differential. Remove speedometer gear snap ring and speedometer gear. Remove bolts retaining ring gear to carrier and remove ring gear.

CAUTION: Ring gear bolts have left hand threads.

3) Drive out spring pin that retains pinion shaft and remove pinion shaft, pinion gears, side gears and thrust washers. Wash all components and check for excessive wear or damage.

Reassembly

1) Install side gears in differential carrier. Install pinion gears and mesh with side gears. Install thrust washers of equal and proper thickness to obtain correct backlash. See THRUST WASHER THICKNESS chart. Install pinion shaft while rotating gears to align holes in gears with hole in carrier. Align hole in pinion shaft with hole in carrier and install spring pin. *See Fig. 23.*

Fig. 23: Exploded View of Differential Assembly

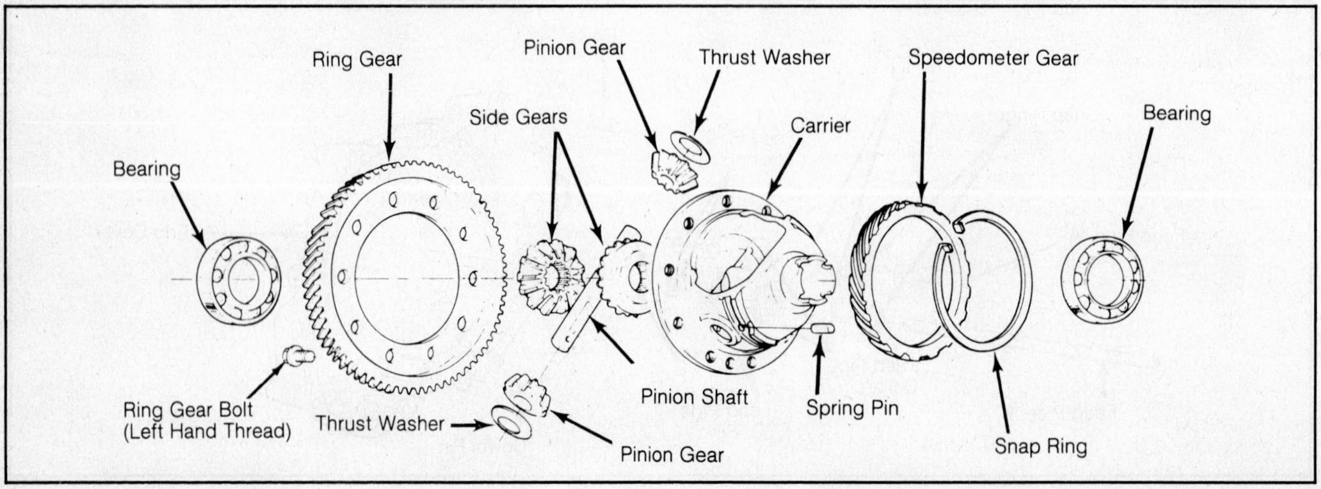

HONDA 3-SPEED (Cont.)

THRUST WASHER THICKNESS

Part Number	Thickness In. (mm)
41351-689-0000	.028 (.70)
41355-PC8-0000	.030 (.75)
41352-689-0000	.031 (.80)
41356-PC8-0000	.033 (.85)
41353-689-0000	.035 (.90)
41357-PC8-0000	.037 (.95)
41354-689-0000	.039 (1.00)

2) With differential assembled with new thrust washers, again measure backlash. If backlash is still not to specifications, replace both pinion gears and recheck backlash. If still not to specifications, replace both side gears and recheck backlash. If still out of specification, replace complete carrier assembly.

3) Install bearings to carrier. Install speedometer gear (with chamfer facing carrier) and install snap ring. Make sure snap ring ends do not align with carrier bearing support. *See Fig. 24.*

4) Install ring gear to carrier with chamfer on inside diameter of ring gear facing carrier. Install ring gear bolts (left hand threads) and tighten.

Fig. 24: Installation of Snap Ring on Differential Carrier

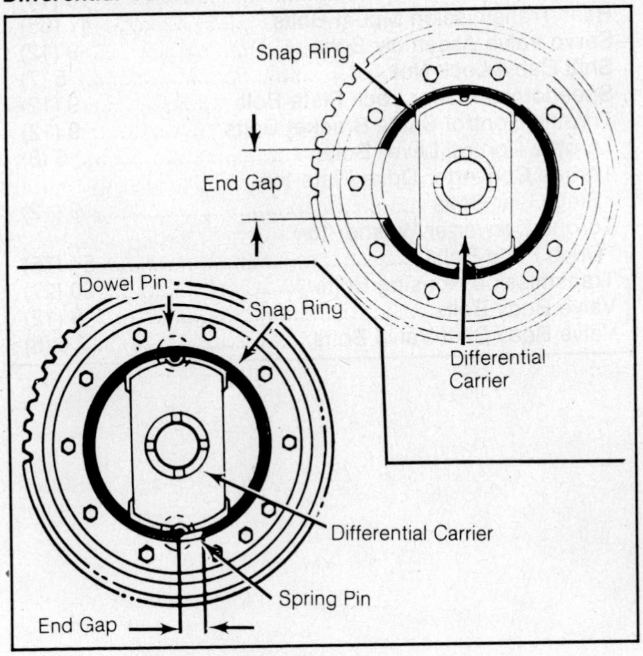

TRANSAXLE REASSEMBLY

NOTE: **Lubricate parts with ATF during reassembly.**

1) Install differential assembly. Assemble manual valve lever on control shaft, then install torque converter housing. Install control lever and new lock plate on other end of control shaft, install and tighten bolt. Bend tab of lock plate up to prevent bolt from turning.

2) Install new filter screen in converter housing. Install separator plate, dowel pin, oil pump gears and shaft. Make sure chamfered side of driven gear and shouldered side of drive gear is facing down. Install check valve and spring, then install valve body on converter housing.

3) Install and tighten valve body bolts. Install stator shaft arm, stop pin and dowel pins. Install regulator valve. Install steel balls in valve body oil passage. *See Fig. 7.* Install separator plate, throttle control shaft and dowel pins.

4) Install servo. Ensure correct length bolt is installed or servo will not seal to housing. *See Fig. 25.* Place a roller on each side of manual valve stem, then attach valve to lever with pin. Secure with cotter pin.

5) Install 2nd and 3rd accumulator spring in servo body. See VALVE BODY SPRING IDENTIFICATION chart for accumulator spring diameters and lengths. Install accumulator cover; compress accumulator springs before tightening bolts.

Fig. 25: Installation of Servo-to-Converter Housing Showing Attaching Bolt Lengths

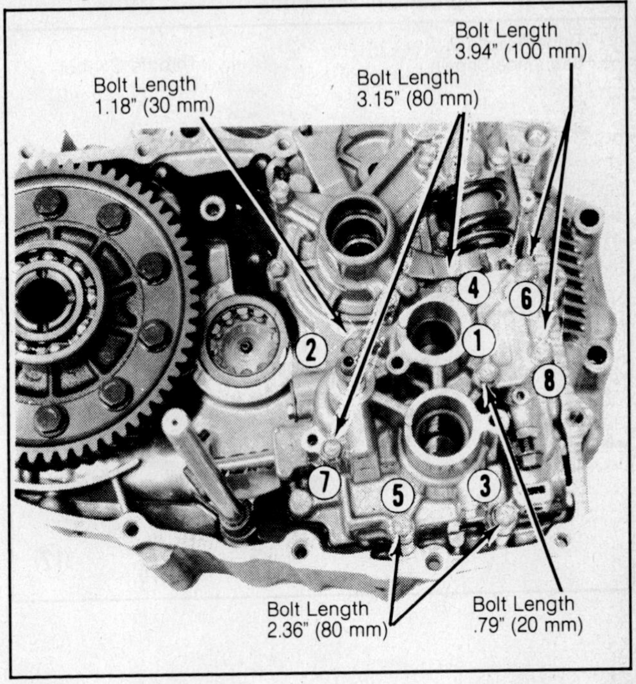

6) Install governor valve, using new lock plates, then bend lock plate tabs over so bolts will not turn. Install mainshaft and countershaft in converter housing, as an assembly.

NOTE: **Do not tap on shaft ends to force shafts to seat.**

7) Remove lock nuts from mainshaft and countershaft, if installed, then install countershaft 2nd gear and reverse selector sleeve with reverse shift fork (assembled before installation). Groove on selector sleeve faces down.

8) Install reverse shift fork over servo valve stem and align hole in stem with hole in fork. Install bolt and new lock plate. Bend tab on lock plate so bolt will not turn. Install countershaft reverse gear, needle bearing and reverse gear collar. Install gasket and 2 dowel pins in converter housing.

9) Place transmission housing on converter housing and install oil feed pipes. Make sure throttle control shaft aligns with hole in converter housing. Tighten bolts in 2 steps in order. *See Fig. 26.*

Automatic Transmissions

HONDA 3-SPEED (Cont.)

10) Install control lever and spring on control shaft, then install bolt and new lock plate. Bend tab against bolt. Install parking shift arm and spring on shift shaft, use new lock tab and bend tab against bolt.

NOTE: **Parking shift arm spring should put clockwise tension on shift arm, forcing it against stop pin.**

11) Install 1st gear collar and needle bearing on countershaft. Install reverse idler bearing holder then install "O" rings to mainshaft. Install countershaft 1st gear and parking gear on countershaft. Install stop pin, parking pawl shaft, parking pawl and pawl release spring. Spring should put clockwise tension on pawl, forcing it away from parking gear.

Fig. 26: Transmission Housing-to-Converter Housing Bolt Tightening Sequence

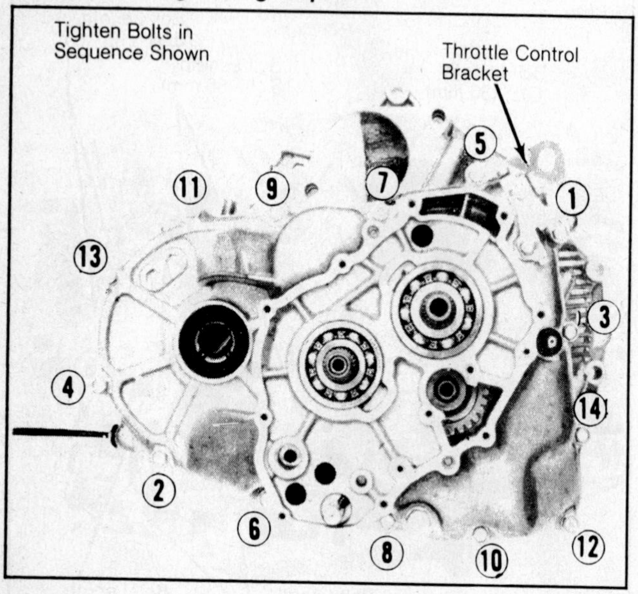

12) Shift lever to "P" and install mainshaft holder. Install new countershaft lock nut. Stake lock nut flange into gear groove. Install needle bearing and thrust washer on mainshaft. Install 1st gear, needle bearing and thrust washer on mainshaft.

13) Install 1st clutch on the mainshaft. Attach mainshaft holder from underside of converter housing, then install new mainshaft lock nut. Stake lock nut to groove in 1st clutch.

14) Install gasket, dowel pins and "O" rings on transmission housing. Install end cover and bolts. Install dipstick, coller fittings. Do not tighten cooler fittings until transmission is installed in vehicle.

TIGHTENING SPECIFICATIONS

Application	Ft. Lbs. (N.m)
Cooling Hose Fitting	21 (29)
Countershaft Lock Nut	70 (95)
Differential Carrier-to-Ring Bolts	74 (103)
Drain Plug	29 (40)
End Cover Bolts	9 (12)
Front Engine Torque Bracket Bolts	33 (45)
Governor Attaching Bolts	9 (12)
Idler Bearing Holder Retaining Bolt	20 (27)
Lock-Up Shift Valve Body Bolts	12 (18)
Mainshaft Lock Nut	70 (95)
Park Lever Bolts	10 (14)
Rear Transmission Mount Bolts	47 (65)
Servo Valve Assembly Bolts	9 (12)
Shift Cable Lock Nut	5 (7)
Speedometer Gear Lock Plate Bolt	9 (12)
Throttle Control Cable Bracket Bolts	9 (12)
Throttle Control Lever Bolts	6 (8)
Torque Converter Drive Plate-to-Ring Gear Bolts	9 (12)
Torque Converter Washer-to-Drive Plate Bolts	54 (75)
Transmission Housing Bolts	20 (27)
Valve Body Bolts	9 (12)
Valve Body Shift Valve Bolts	6 (8)

Automatic Transmissions

HONDA 4-SPEED

Accord & Prelude

IDENTIFICATION

The automatic transmission may be identified by a group of letters and numbers stamped on a pad on top of transaxle case. First 2 letters are transmission type. Next 7 numbers are transmission serial number.

TRANSMISSION MODEL CODE

Application	Code
All Models	AS

DESCRIPTION

The Honda automatic transaxle is a combination of a 3-element torque converter, dual-shaft 4-speed automatic transmission and a differential-type final drive assembly. Transmission consists of two parallel shafts; a mainshaft and a countershaft. The mainshaft is in line with crankshaft. Transmission is controlled by main valve body, regulator valve body and servo valve. Countershaft is in constant mesh with differential ring gear.

The torque converter consists of a pump, turbine and stator, assembled in a single unit. A lock-up mechanism is built into torque converter. When transmission is in 4th gear, above 43 MPH, pressurized fluid is drained from back of torque converter, through an oil passage. This causes lock-up piston to press against torque converter cover. As this takes place, the mainshaft rotates at the same speed as crankshaft.

A pressure control valve body is bolted to top of regulator body and includes the pressure control shift valve and pressure control timing valve. The pressure control shift valve controls the range of lock-up according to vehicle speed and throttle pressure. The timing valve senses when transmission is in 4th gear.

LUBRICATION & ADJUSTMENTS

See appropriate AUTOMATIC TRANSMISSION SERVICING article in IMPORT GENERAL SERVICING section.

TROUBLE SHOOTING

NO MOVEMENT

In Any Gear (With Engine Running)

Low fluid level. Faulty ATF pump. Regulator valve stuck or damaged spring. Mainshaft damaged. Manual shift cable out of adjustment. Damaged final drive gear. Torque converter not fully seated (causing flex plate to deform).

In "D3" Or "D4"; OK In 2nd (No Low Gear)

Manual shift cable out of adjustment. Worn or damaged one-way clutch. Low gear damaged. Faulty 1st clutch. Defective clutch pressure control (CPC) valve.

In 2nd (OK In "D3" or "D4")

Manual shift cable out of adjustment. Damaged 2nd gear. Faulty 1st clutch assembly.

In "R" (OK in "D3", "D4" & 2nd)

Stuck servo shaft. Manual shift cable out of adjustment (broken cable, loose end pin). Reverse gear damaged. Defective 2nd-3rd shift valve. Defective 4th clutch assembly.

POOR ACCELERATION

ENGINE RACES WHEN STARTING OFF IN "D3" & "D4"

Stall RPM High In "D3", "D4" & 2nd

Low fluid level. Faulty ATF pump. Regulator valve stuck or spring damaged. Manual shift cable out of adjustment. Oil filter clogged. Falty torque converter check valve.

Stall RPM High in "D3" & "D4"

Manual shift cable out of adjustment. Worn or damaged one-way clutch. Faulty 1st clutch.

Stall RPM High in 2nd

Manual shift cable out of adjustment. Faulty 2nd clutch.

Stall RPM OK

ATF fluid level too high.

Stall RPM Low

Burnt or seized torque converter one-way clutch. Improperly adjusted throttle cable (at carburetor). Lack of engine power.

ENGINE VIBRATES AT IDLE

Faulty ATF pump. Lack of engine power. Torque converter not fully seated (causing flex plate to deform).

UPSHIFT SPEED TOO HIGH

Governor valve faulty. Improperly adjusted throttle control cable (at automatic transmission). Defective throttle valve "A". Defective modulator valve.

JUMPS FROM 1ST-3RD IN "D3"

Defective 2nd-3rd shift valve.

JUMPS FROM 1ST-4TH IN "D4"

Defective 2nd-3rd shift valve. Defective 3rd-4th shift valve.

UPSHIFT POINTS (TO EARLY OR TO LATE)

1st-2nd, 2nd-3rd & 3rd-4th

Faulty governor valve. Throttle control cable out of adjustment (at automatic transmission). Defective throttle valve "A". Defective modulator valve.

"D1-D2" Only

Faulty governor valve or 1st-2nd shift valve.

"D2-D3" Only

Faulty governor valve or 2nd-3rd shift valve.

"D3-D4" Only

Faulty governor valve or 3rd-4th shift valve.

HARSH UPSHIFT

From 1st-2nd

Faulty 2nd clutch. Defective throttle shift valve "B" or 2nd accumulator.

Automatic Transmissions

HONDA 4-SPEED (Cont.)

From 2nd-3rd

Defective throttle shift valve "B". Defective 3rd accumulator. Defective 2nd orifice control valve. Defective 3rd clutch.

From 3rd -4th

Defective throttle shift valve "B". Defective 4th accumulator. Defective 4th clutch assembly. Lack of engine power.

HARSH DOWNSHIFT

From 2nd-1st

Defective throttle shift valve "B". Defective 2nd accumulator. Defective 2nd orifice control valve. No 2nd ball check valve.

From 3rd-2nd

Defective throttle shift valve "B". Defective 3rd accumulator. Defective 3rd orifice control valve. No 3rd ball check valve.

From 4th-3rd

Defective throttle valve "B". Defective 4th accumulator. No 4th ball check valve.

ENGINE RACES DURING SHIFT

From 2nd-3rd (Shift Timing OK)

Defective throttle valve "B", 3rd accumulator or 2nd orifice control valve. Main or 3rd orifice plugged. Defective 3rd clutch assembly.

From 3rd-4th (Shift Timing OK)

Defective throttle valve "B" or 4th accumulator. Defective 3rd orifice control valve. Defective 4th clutch assembly.

ENGINE VIBRATES DURING SHIFT

From 2nd-3rd (Shift Timing OK)

Faulty 2nd clutch assembly. Defective throttle valve "B". Defective 3rd accumulator. Plugged 2nd orifice or separator port orifice. No 3rd ball check valve.

From 3rd-4th (Shift Timing OK)

Defective 3rd orifice control valve. Defective throttle valve "B". No 4th ball check valve. Plugged separator port orifice.

VEHICLE CREEPS FORWARD IN "N"

With Shift Cable Properly Adjusted

ATF level too high. Faulty 2nd or 4th clutch assembly. Faulty 1st or 3rd clutch assembly. Damaged (burnt) needle bearing and/or thrust washer. Improper clutch clearance.

EXCESSIVE TIME LAG WHEN SHIFTING

From "N" to "D3" or "D4" (Shift Cable Adjusted Correctly)

Faulty 1st clutch assembly. Plugged 1st orifice.

From "N" to "R" (Shift Cable Adjusted Correctly)

Servo shaft stuck. Defective 4th clutch assembly. Faulty 2nd-3rd shift valve.

PROBLEMS AFTER REASSEMBLY

Loud Noise in All Selector Positions

Faulty ATF pump. Damaged 3rd gear. Damaged mainshaft ball bearings and/or countershaft bearings.

Acceleration to 30 MPH Only

Burnt or seized torque converter one-way clutch.

Vibration in All Gears

Torque converter not fully seated (causing flex plate to deform).

Shift Lever Requires Excessive Force

Manual shift cable out of adjustment or cable housing damaged.

Vehicle Has 4th Gear Only

Faulty governor valve.

No Park Position

Manual shift cable out of adjustment or cable housing damaged.

High Stall Speed, OK Pressure Readings

Faulty torque converter check valve.

IMPROPER OPERATION OF LOCK-UP CLUTCH

Lock-Up Clutch Engages Or Disengages Abnormally

Improperly adjusted throttle control cable (at automatic transmission). Defective thottle valve "B", pressure control timing valve, governor cut switch or pressure control shift valve.

Engine Vibrates When Lock-Up Clutch Engages

Defective governor cut valve, pressure control shift valve, Lock-up piston, lock-up piston damper spring or pressure control valve.

Lock-Up Clutch Slips

Stuck regulator valve or damaged spring. Faulty torque converter check valve. Defective pressure control shift valve or pressure control valve.

TESTING

ROAD TEST

NOTE: **Before testing transmission, ensure ATF level is between full and low marks on dipstick. With transmission at operating temperature, check ATF level immediately after shutting off engine. Standard ATF capacity is 3.0 qts. (2.8L) after oil change and 6.1 qts. (5.8L) after overhaul.**

Before Transmission Removal

1) Before road testing, be certain that fluid level, condition and control linkage adjustments have been checked and corrected as necessary. During test, transmission should upshift and downshift at approximately the speeds shown. See SHIFT SPEED SPECIFICATIONS table.

2) All shifts may vary somewhat due to production tolerances or tire size. The important factor is shift quality. All shifts should be smooth and responsive, with no slippage or engine speed runaway.

3) Slippage or engine runaway in any gear usually indicates clutch or sprag problems. The slipping unit in a particular gear can usually be identified by noting transmission operation in other selector positions.

4) This process of elimination can be used to detect any unit which slips and to confirm proper operation of good units; however, the actual cause of the malfunction usually cannot be easily decided.

HONDA 4-SPEED (Cont.)

5) Practically any condition can be caused by leaking hydraulic circuits or sticking valves. Therefore, unless an obvious condition exists, do not disassemble transmission until hydraulic pressure tests have been made.

SHIFT SPEED SPECIFICATIONS

Application	Shift Speed (MPH)
Full Throttle Upshift [1]	
Accord (Cabureted)	
1st-2nd Shift	37-42
2nd-3rd Shift	58-65
3rd-4th Shift	86-92
Lock-Up Clutch On	89-95
Accord SEi (Fuel Injected)	
1st-2nd Shift	39-43
2nd-3rd Shift	58-64
3rd-4th Shift	88-94
Lock-Up Clutch On	88-94
Prelude	
1st-2nd Shift	35-40
2nd-3rd Shift	59-65
3rd-4th Shift	92-98
Half Throttle [1]	
Accord (Cabureted)	
1st-2nd Shift	18-22
2nd-3rd Shift	33-42
3rd-4th Shift	50-60
Lock-Up Clutch On	50-60
Accord SEi (Fuel Injected)	
1st-2nd Shift	20-24
2nd-3rd Shift	40-45
3rd-4th Shift	58-64
Lock-Up Clutch On	60-65
Prelude	
1st-2nd Shift	18-22
2nd-3rd Shift	38-44
3rd-4th Shift	57-64
Closed Throttle [2]	
Accord (Cabureted)	
1st-2nd Shift	12-15
2nd-3rd Shift	21-24
3rd-4th Shift	23-30
Lock-Up Clutch On	31-34
Accord SEi (Fuel Injected)	
1st-2nd Shift	10-13
2nd-3rd Shift	22-25
3rd-4th Shift	26-31
Lock-Up Clutch On	31-34
Prelude	
1st-2nd Shift	11-14
2nd-3rd Shift	22-25
3rd-4th Shift	25-31

[1] – Acceleration from a stop.
[2] – Coasting down-hill from a stop.

SHIFT SPEED SPECIFICATIONS (Cont.)

Application	Shift Speed (MPH)
Full Throttle Downshift [3]	
Accord (Carbureted)	
4th-3rd Shift	77-83
3rd-2nd Shift	51-58
2nd-1st Shift	24-30
Accord SEi (Fuel Injected)	
4th-3rd Shift	77-83
3rd-2nd Shift	48-54
2nd-1st Shift	24-30
Prelude	
4th-3rd Shift	83-89
3rd-2nd Shift	53-58
2nd-1st Shift	23-28
Closed Throttle [4]	
Accord (Carbureted)	
4th-3rd Shift	....
3rd-2nd Shift	16-19
2nd-1st Shift	5-8
Accord SEi (Fuel Injected)	
4th-3rd Shift	....
3rd-2nd Shift	16-19
2nd-1st Shift	5-8
Prelude	
4th-3rd Shift	....
3rd-2nd Shift	18-21
2nd-1st Shift	5-8

[3] – When vehicle is slowed by increased grade, wind, etc.
[4] – Coasting or braking from a stop.

After Transmission Installation

1) Check floor mat to ensure it does not interfer with accelerator pedal travel. Fully depress accelerator pedal and check carburetor to ensure throttle lever is fully opened.

2) Release accelerator pedal and check both inner control cables to ensure they have slight play. Warm engine to operating temperature.

3) With transmission in "D3" and "D4" range, apply parking brake and block wheels. Move selector to "D4" while depressing brake pedal. Start engine, depress accelerator pedal, then release it suddenly. Engine should not stall.

NOTE: **Check that shift points occur at approximate speeds shown in SHIFT SPEEDS SPECIFICATION table. Also check for abnormal noise and/or clutch slippage.**

4) With transmission in "D3" and "D4" range, accelerate vehicle to about 35 MPH (transmission in 4th), then shift from "D4" to 2nd. Vehicle should immediately begin slowing down from engine braking.

CAUTION: **Do not shift from "D4" or "D3" to 2nd at speeds over 60 MPH or transmission damage may result.**

Automatic Transmissions

HONDA 4-SPEED (Cont.)

5) With vehicle in 2nd gear, accelerate from a stop at full throttle. Check for abnormal noise or clutch slippage. Upshifts and downshifts should not occur with selector in this range.

6) With vehicle in Reverse, accelerate from a stop at full throttle and check for abnormal noise and clutch slippage. With vehicle in parked on a slope (approximately 16°), apply parking brake and shift into Park. Release brake. Vehicle should not move.

HYDRAULIC PRESSURE TESTS

1) Before performing pressure tests, be sure that fluid level and condition have been checked and corrected as necessary. With engine at normal operating temperature, connect a tachometer to engine.

2) Connect Pressure Test Hoses (07406-0020201), from Pressure Gauge Set (07406-0020002), to 3 of the following pressure test points (depending on pressure readings required): line pressure port, 1st clutch pressure port, 2nd clutch pressure port, 3rd clutch pressure port and 4th clutch pressure port. *See Fig. 1.*

Fig. 1: Pressure Test Point Locations

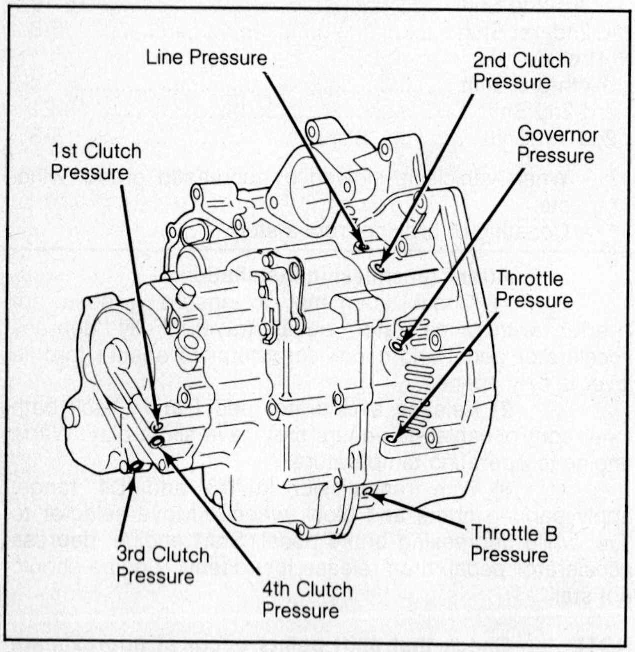

Before checking the line, clutch, governor or throttle pressures, ensure transmission is filled to proper level.

3) To test 1st-4th clutch pressures and line pressure, first apply parking brake, then raise front wheels off ground and support with safety stands. Start and run engine at 2000 RPM.

4) Place selector lever in one of the following positions: "P", "N", "2", "D3" ,"D4" or "R". Note pressure readings at each selector lever position and compare readings to FLUID PRESSURE TEST SPECIFICATIONS table.

NOTE: **Allow engine to return to idle before changing selector positions.**

5) If low or no line pressure reading (with selector in "P" or "N"), check torque converter, oil pump pressure regulator or torque converter check valve. If 1st clutch pressure reading (with selector in "D3 or D4") shows low or no pressure, check 1st clutch assembly.

6) If 2nd clutch pressure reading (with selector in "2") shows low or no pressure, check 2nd clutch assembly. If 3rd clutch pressure reading (with selector in in "D3") shows low or no pressure, check 3rd clutch assembly.

7) If 4th clutch pressure reading (with selector in "D4") shows low or no pressure, check 4th clutch assembly. If 4th clutch pressure reading (with selector in "R") shows low or no pressure, check servo valve.

8) Stop engine and remove pressure gauge hose connections from transmission. Reconnect 2 pressure gauge hoses to throttle pressure port "A" and "B". Disconnect throttle control cable (at throttle lever).

9) Start engine, place selector lever in "D3" or "D4" and run engine at 1000 RPM. Read pressure with lever released. Manually push lever up (simulating full throttle) and note pressure reading. Compare reading with FLUID PRESSURE TEST SPECIFICATIONS table.

10) If low or no throttle pressure reading in "D3" or "D4", check throttle valve "A", throttle valve "B" or throttle modulator valve. Stop engine. Remove pressure gauge from throttle pressure ports. Reconnect throttle control cable.

FLUID PRESSURE TEST SPECIFICATIONS

Pressure Application	Fluid Pressure psi (kg/cm^2)	Service Limit psi (kg/cm^2)
Line		
In "P" or "N"		
Accord	106-113 (7.5-7.9)	100 (7.0)
Accord SEi	114-121 (8.0-8.5)	100 (7.0)
Prelude	114-121 (8.0-8.5)	107 (7.5)
1st Clutch		
In "D3" or "D4"		
Accord	100-114 (7.0-8.0)	100 (7.0)
Accord SEi	107-121 (7.5-8.5)	107 (7.5)
Prelude	114-121 (8.0-8.5)	107 (7.5)
2nd Clutch		
In "2"		
Accord	78-114 (5.5-8.0) [1]	71 (5.0) [2]
Accord SEi	78- 114 (5.5-8.0) [1]	71 (5.0) [3]
Prelude	78-121 (5.5-8.5) [1]	78 (5.0) [3]
3rd Clutch		
In "D3"		
Accord	78-114 (5.5-8.0) [1]	71 (5.0) [2]
Accord SEi	78-114 (5.5-8.0) [1]	71 (5.0) [3]
Prelude	78-121 (5.5-8.5) [1]	78 (5.5) [3]
4th Clutch		
In "D4"		
Accord	78-114 (5.5-8.0) [1]	71 (5.0) [2]
Accord SEi	78-114 (5.5-8.0) [1]	71 (5.0) [3]
Prelude	78-121 (5.5-8.5) [1]	78 (5.5) [3]
4th Clutch		
In "R"		
Accord	[4]	[5]
Accord SEi	[4]	[5]
Prelude	[4]	[5]

[1] – Varies with throttle opening.
[2] – With lever released. Pressure is 100 psi (7.0 kg/cm^2) with lever in full throttle.
[3] – With lever released. Pressure is 107 psi (7.5 kg/cm^2) with lever in full throttle.
[4] – No fluid pressure specification.
[5] – No fluid pressure service limit.

HONDA 4-SPEED (Cont.)

FLUID PRESSURE TEST SPECIFICATIONS (Cont.)

Pressure Application	Fluid Pressure psi (kg/cm^2)	Service Limit psi (kg/cm^2)
Throttle Port "A" In "D3" or "D4"		
Accord	[6]	70 (4.9) [9]
Accord SEi	[7]	71 (5.0) [9]
Prelude	[8]	73 (5.1) [9]
Throttle Port "B" In "D3" or "D4"		
Accord	[10]	100 (7.0)
Accord SEi	[11]	107 (7.5)
Prelude	[11]	107 (7.5)
Governor In "D3" or "D4"		
Accord	33-34 (2.3-2.4)	32 (2.2)
Accord SEi	31-33 (2.2-2.3)	31 (2.2)
Prelude	31-33 (2.2-2.3)	31 (2.2)

[6] – Fluid pressure is 0 psi (0 kg/cm^2) with lever released. Pressure is 70-73 psi (4.9-5.1 kg/cm^2) with lever in full throttle position.

[7] – Fluid pressure is 0 psi (0 kg/cm^2) with lever released. Pressure is 72-74 psi (5.1-5.2 kg/cm^2) with lever in full throttle position.

[8] – Fluid pressure is 0 psi (0 kg/cm^2) with lever released. Pressure is 73-75 psi (5.1-5.3 kg/cm^2) with lever in full throttle position.

[9] – With lever in full throttle position.

[10] – Fluid pressure is 0 psi (0 kg/cm^2) with lever released. Pressure is 107-114 psi (7.5-8.0 kg/cm^2) with lever in full throttle position.

[11] – Fluid pressure is 0 psi (0 kg/cm^2) with lever released. Pressure is 114-121 psi (8.0-8.5 kg/cm^2) with lever in full throttle position.

11) Place vehicle on a chassis dynamometor (or raise and support front of vehicle on safety stands). Block rear wheels and set hand brake. Connect pressure gauge to governor pressure port. Start engine, place selector lever in "D3 or D4" and run vehicle at 38 MPH.

12) Note pressure reading and compare it to table. See FLUID PRESSURE TEST SPECIFICATIONS table. If low or no governor pressure reading, check governor valve.

STALL TEST

Testing Precautions

When making test, do not hold throttle open any longer than the time it takes to read tachometer. Maximum stall speed test is 10 seconds at a time. Allow engine to run at idle for at least 2 minutes in "N" to cool transmission between tests. If engine speed exceeds limits shown, release accelerator immediately as clutch slippage is indicated. See STALL SPEEDS table.

Testing Procedure

1) Connect a tachometer to engine. Set parking brake and block front wheels. With engine at normal operating temperature, start engine. Place selector lever in "D3".

2) Depress accelerator briefly (6 to 8 seconds) to full throttle and note maximum RPM obtained. Allow 2 minutes for cooling and repeat test in "D4", "2" and "R". Stall speed in "D3", "D4", "2" and "R" should be the same and within limits shown. See STALL SPEED RPM table.

STALL SPEED SPECIFICATIONS

Application	RPM	Service Limit RPM
Accord	2600	2300-2900
Accord SEi	2400	2100-2700
Prelude	2400	2100-2700

3) If stall speed RPM is high in "2", "D3", "D4", and "R", check for low ATF level, low pump output, clogged oil strainer or pressure regulator and slipping clutch assembly or slipping one-way clutch in torque converter.

4) If stall speed RPM is high in "D3" and "D4" only, check for slipping 1st clutch assembly. If stall speed RPM is low in "2", "D3", "D4" and "R", check for low engine output, misadjusted throttle control cable (at carburetor) and seized oil pump or converter thrust washer.

REMOVAL & INSTALLATION

AUTOMATIC TRANSMISSION

See appropriate AUTOMATIC TRANSMISSION REMOVAL article in IMPORT GENERAL SERVICING section.

TORQUE CONVERTER

Removal

1) Before detaching engine-to-transmission mounting bolts, remove torque converter cover plate. Detach 8 torque converter-to-drive plate mounting bolts.

2) Remove transmission from engine and lower from vehicle, then pull torque converter from transmission. Remove and discard converter "O" ring (32 x 1.9 mm).

3) If necessary, detach drive plate-to-crankshaft flange mounting bolts, then remove drive plate and washer. Inspect components for wear or damage.

Inspection

Inspect torque converter for broken and/or chipped ring gear teeth or fluid leakage. Check drive plate and washer for cracks. Replace components as necessary.

Installation

Install new "O" ring to converter. If removed, install drive plate and washer onto crankshaft flange and tighten mounting bolts in a crisscross pattern. To install torque converter, reverse removal procedure.

CONTROL SHAFT

Removal

Remove control cable holder. Detach cotter pin, control pin and control lever roller from control lever. Bend down lock plate tab under bolt in control lever, then remove bolt and lever. Turn torque converter housing over remove control shaft.

Installation

Install control shaft in reverse of removal procedure. Replace lock plate.

HONDA 4-SPEED (Cont.)

Fig. 2: Internal Views Of 4-Speed Automatic Transmission

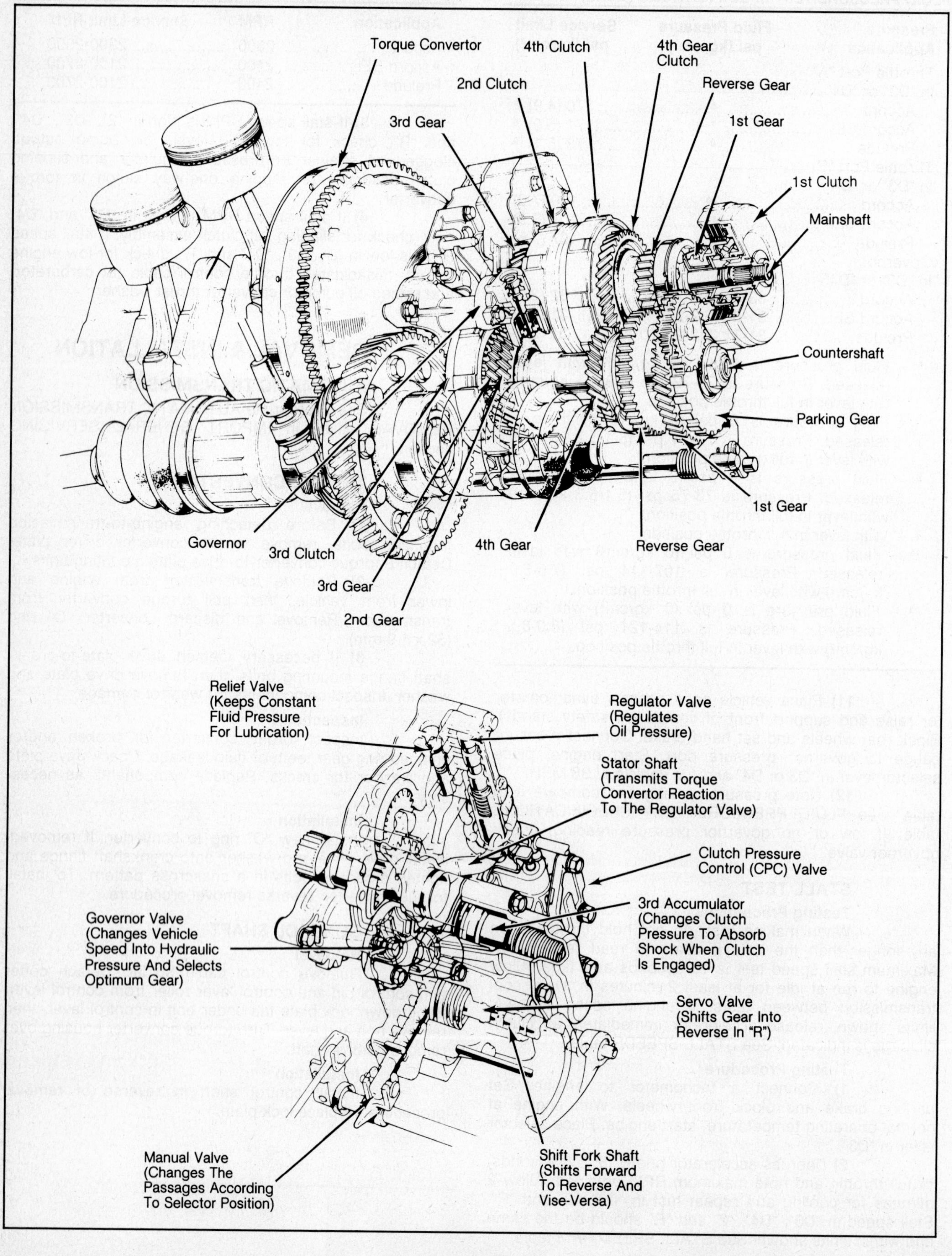
Torque Convertor
4th Clutch
4th Gear Clutch
2nd Clutch
Reverse Gear
3rd Gear
1st Gear
1st Clutch
Mainshaft
Countershaft
Parking Gear
1st Gear
Governor
3rd Clutch
4th Gear
Reverse Gear
3rd Gear
2nd Gear
Relief Valve (Keeps Constant Fluid Pressure For Lubrication)
Regulator Valve (Regulates Oil Pressure)
Stator Shaft (Transmits Torque Convertor Reaction To The Regulator Valve)
Clutch Pressure Control (CPC) Valve
3rd Accumulator (Changes Clutch Pressure To Absorb Shock When Clutch Is Engaged)
Governor Valve (Changes Vehicle Speed Into Hydraulic Pressure And Selects Optimum Gear)
Servo Valve (Shifts Gear Into Reverse In "R")
Manual Valve (Changes The Passages According To Selector Position)
Shift Fork Shaft (Shifts Forward To Reverse And Vise-Versa)

HONDA 4-SPEED (Cont.)

TRANSAXLE DISASSEMBLY

TORQUE CONVERTER

The torque converter is a sealed unit. If torque converter is full of contaminated fluid or a possible cause of transaxle problems, do not attempt disassembly and repair, replace torque converter as a unit.

TRANSMISSION HOUSING & TORQUE CONVERTER HOUSING

Disassembly

1) Remove dipstick. Detach 9 bolts from transmission housing end cover, then remove cover. If necessary, detach mounting bolts and remove 1st accumulator (Prelude only) from end cover, then disassembly unit as needed.

NOTE: **On Prelude only, 1st accumulator can be removed with end cover installed.**

2) Shift transmission to "P". Lock mainshaft using Mainshaft Holder (07923-6890201). *See Fig. 3.* Remove end cover gasket, 2 dowel pins (8 x 14 mm) and 3 "O" rings (6 x 2.3 mm). Discard "O" rings.

Fig. 3: Locking Mainshaft For Lock Nut Removal

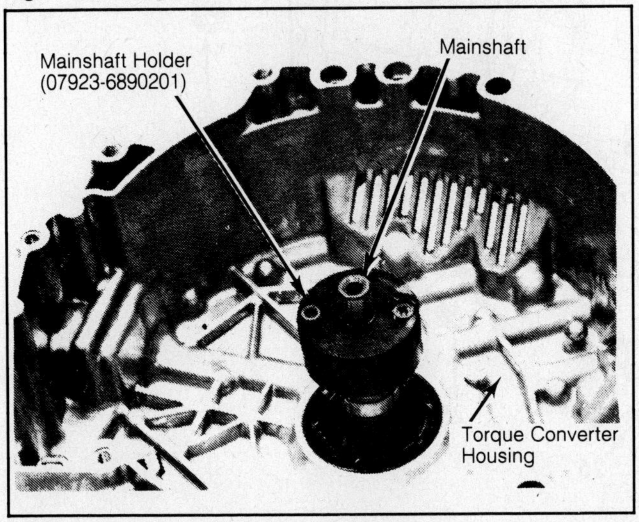

Mainshaft lock nut has left-hand threads.

3) Pry staked edge of lock nut flange out of notch in 1st clutch assembly. Using breaker bar and socket (22 mm), remove mainshaft lock nut (LEFT-HAND thread). Remove 1st clutch assembly. Remove 1st clutch thrust washer (26 mm), needle bearing (31 x 47 x 2 mm) and 1st gear. Remove 1st gear needle bearing (31 x 36 x 18.5 mm) and thrust washer from mainshaft.

4) Pry staked edge of lock nut out of notch in parking gear. Using breaker bar and socket (30 mm), remove countershaft lock nut. Remove parking pawl stop pin. Remove parking pawl, shaft and spring. *See Fig. 5.* Remove parking gear and countershaft 1st gear as a unit.

5) Remove needle bearing (30 x 35 x 11 mm) and 1st gear collar from countershaft. Remove 2 "O" rings (19.8 x 1.9 mm) and 1st gear collar (26 mm) from mainshaft. Discard "O" rings. *See Fig. 4.*

6) Detach and remove reverse idler gear shaft locating bolt (with washer and spring) and bearing holder mounting bolts. Remove reverse idler gear bearing holder. *See Fig. 4.*

7) Bend down tab on parking shift arm bolt lock plate (under bolt). Remove bolt. Lift out parking shift arm and shift arm spring. *See Fig. 4.*

NOTE: **The torque converter housing-to-transmission housing mounting bolt pattern may be slightly different between models but removal sequence is the same.**

Fig. 4: Removing Collars, Needle Bearings & "O" Rings From Mainshaft & Countershaft

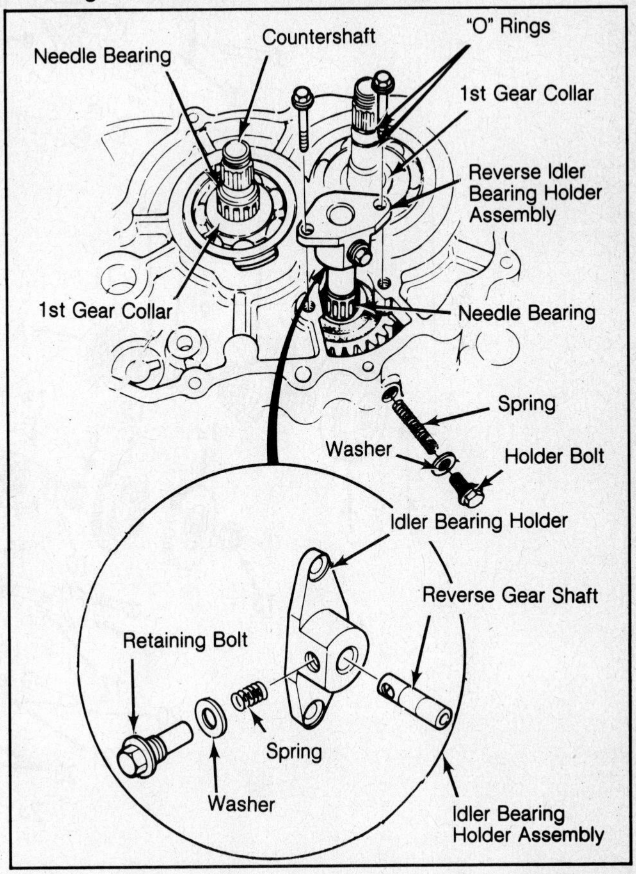

8) Bend down tab on throttle control lever bolt lock plate and remove bolt. Remove throttle control lever and spring from throttle valve shaft. Remove 15 torque converter housing-to-transmission housing mounting bolts (8 x 1.25 mm) in proper sequence. *See Fig. 6.*

NOTE: **Do not remove bolt number 1, loosen just enough so bolt threads are free of torque converter housing. If bolt is removed completely, throttle control bracket will have to be readjusted.**

9) Align control shaft spring pin with cut-out in transmission housing. Install Transmission Housing Puller (07933-6890201) onto housing with 4 bolts (6 x 1.0 x 18 mm). Screw puller bolt against end of countershaft until transmission housing comes free from torque converter housing.

10) After separating housings, remove transmission housing completely. On gear side of torque converter housing, remove gasket, one dowel pin (14 x 20 mm) and 2 dowel pins (14 x 25 mm).

HONDA 4-SPEED (Cont.)

Fig. 5: Exploded View of Transmission End Housing, End Housing Cover & Components

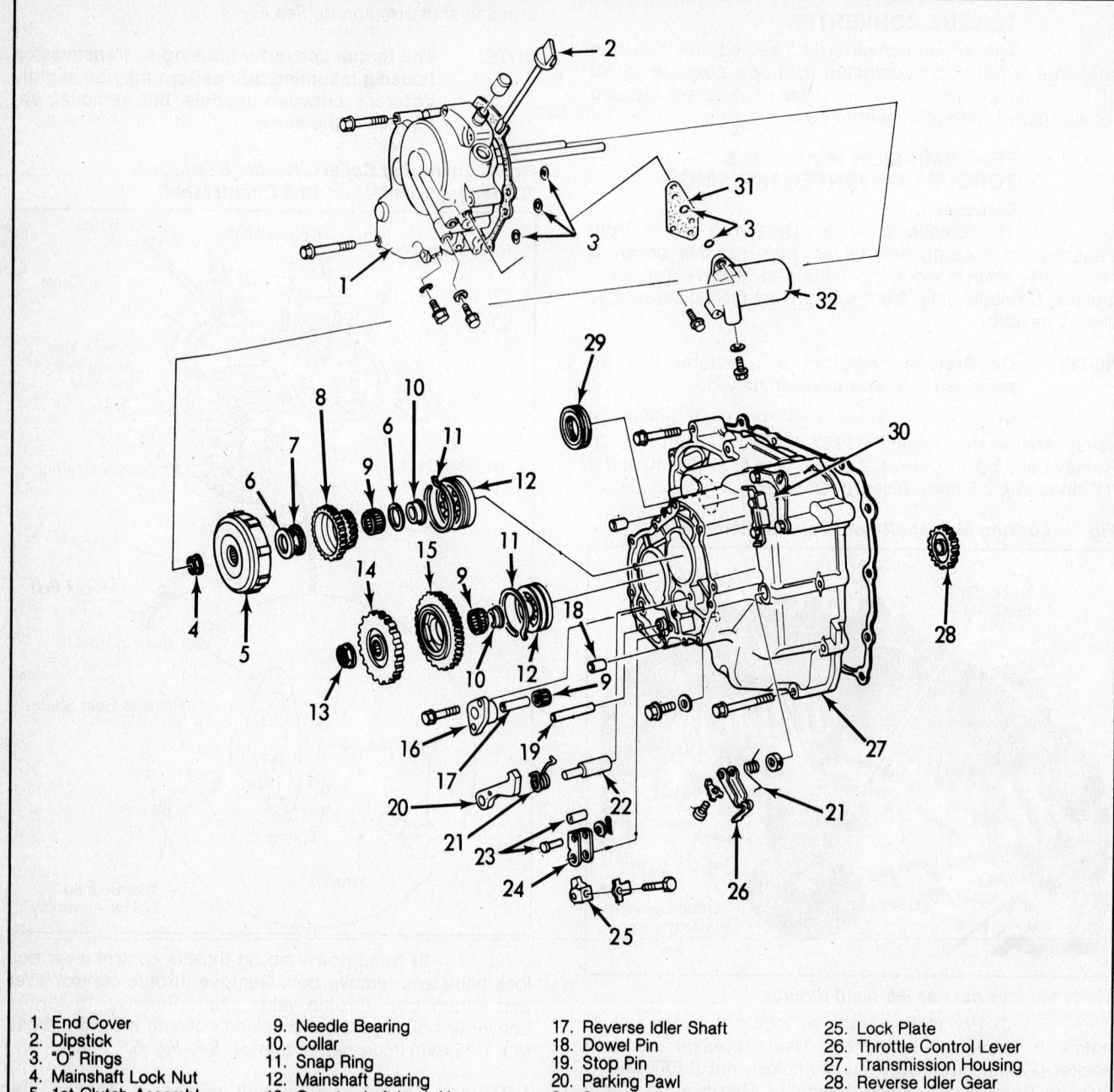

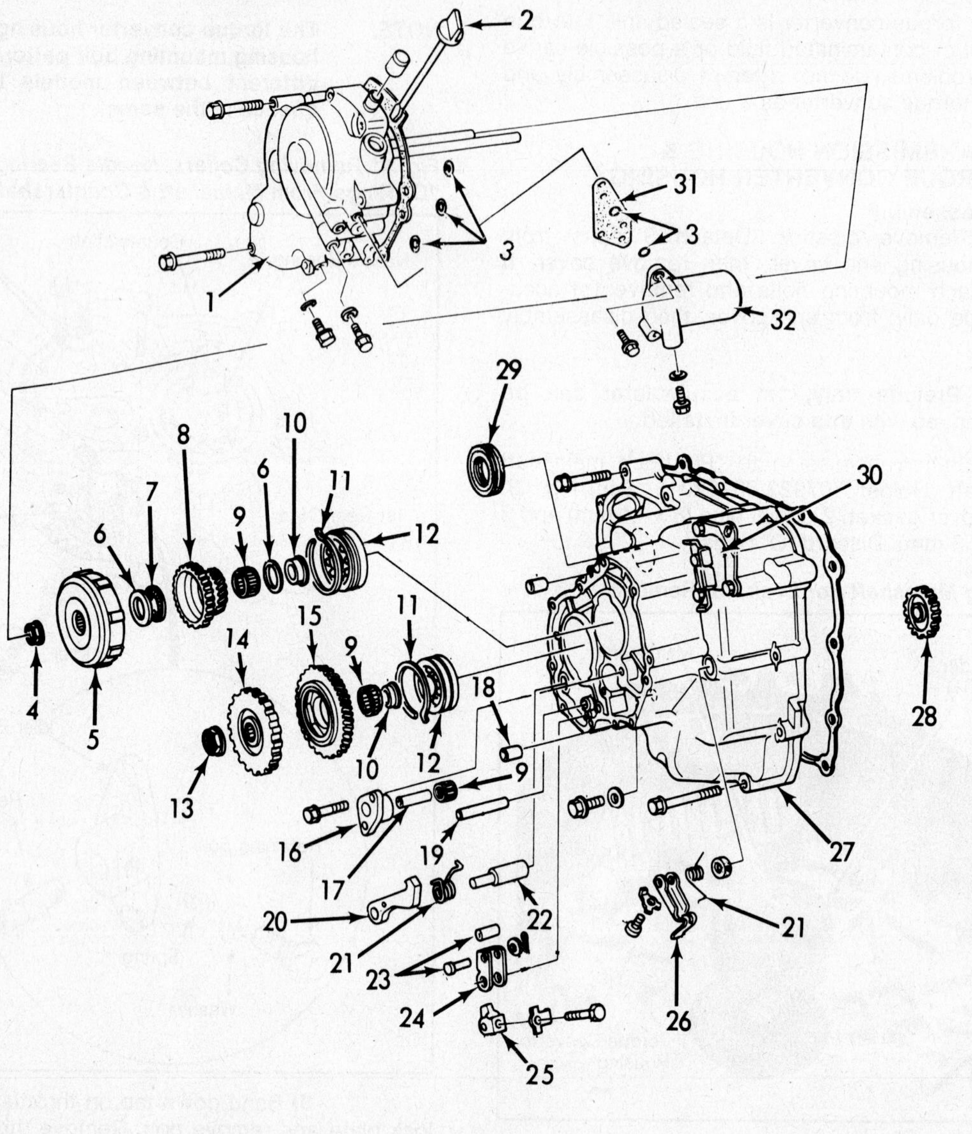

1. End Cover
2. Dipstick
3. "O" Rings
4. Mainshaft Lock Nut
5. 1st Clutch Assembly
6. Thrust Washer
7. Thrust Needle Bearing
8. Mainshaft 1st Gear
9. Needle Bearing
10. Collar
11. Snap Ring
12. Mainshaft Bearing
13. Countershaft Lock Nut
14. Parking Gear
15. Countershaft 1st Gear
16. Reverse Idler Bearing Holder
17. Reverse Idler Shaft
18. Dowel Pin
19. Stop Pin
20. Parking Pawl
21. Spring
22. Parking Pawl Shaft
23. Parking Pawl Roller & Pin
24. Parking Shift Arm
25. Lock Plate
26. Throttle Control Lever
27. Transmission Housing
28. Reverse Idler Gear
29. Differential Oil Seal
30. Throttle Control Cable Bracket
31. Gasket
32. 1st Accumulator (Prelude Only)

11) To remove mainshaft and countershaft, first remove reverse gear collar and countershaft reverse gear with needle bearing. Bend down tab on reverse shift fork bolt lock plate, then remove bolt.

12) Remove reverse shift fork and selector sleeve as a unit. Remove selector hub, countershaft 4th gear, needle bearing and spacer collar. Remove mainshaft and countershaft as an assembly.

NOTE: **When removing mainshaft and countershaft, pull countershaft up at a slight angle to clear governor.**

13) Bend governor mounting bolt lock tabs down and detach bolts holding governor to torque converter housing. Remove governor. *See Fig. 12.*

CAUTION: **Accumulator covers are spring loaded. To prevent stripping threads in torque converter housing, hold covers down while removing bolts (in a crisscross pattern).**

14) To remove main valve body assembly, first detach 2nd-3rd accumulator cover and 4th accumulator cover. Note locations and sizes, then remove 2nd, 3rd and 4th accumulator springs. *See Fig. 8.*

HONDA 4-SPEED (Cont.)

Fig. 6: Removal Sequence of Torque Converter Housing-to-Transmission Housing Mounting Bolts

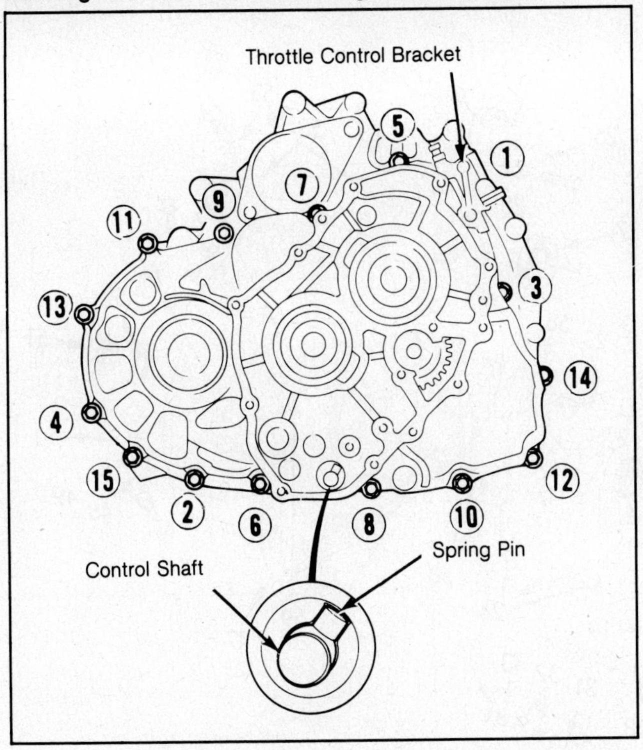

cover. Note locations and sizes, then remove 2nd, 3rd and 4th accumulator springs. *See Fig. 8*.

15) Detach 3 pressure control valve body mounting bolts. To remove 2 oil passage pipes (5 x 168 mm and 8 x 136 mm), slide pressure control valve body to the side. Remove 1st, 3rd and 4th clutch pipes. Remove clutch pressure control valve body. *See Fig. 7*.

Fig. 7: Removing Pressure Control Valve Body, Oil Passage Pipes & Clutch Pipes

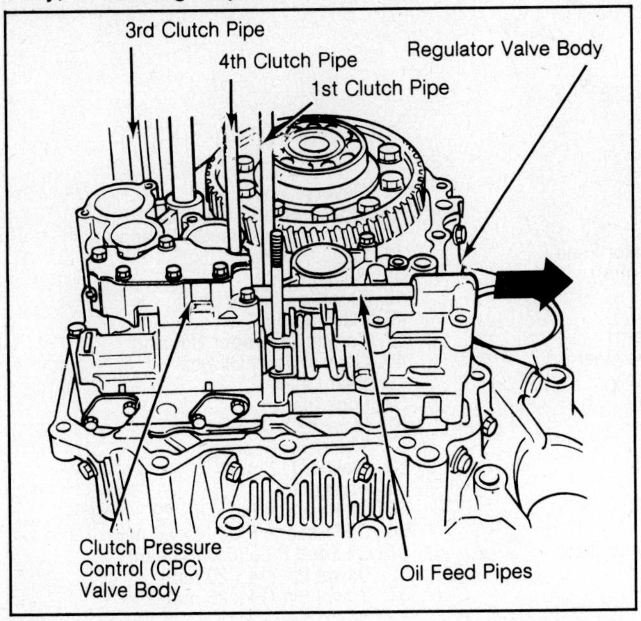

Detach oil passage pipes by moving pressure control valve body in direction of arrow.

16) Detach "E" clip from throttle control shaft. Remove shaft from servo valve body. Detach 3 servo valve body mounting bolts from main valve body, then remove servo valve body assembly.

17) Remove 2 oil pipes (8 x 50 mm and 8 x 29.5 mm). Remove servo separator plate and 2 dowel pins (8 x 14 mm). Remove all 7/32" (5.5 mm) steel balls and the spring from servo valve body oil passages in main valve body (note locations for reassembly).

CAUTION: Do not use a magnet to remove steel balls or balls may become magnetized. Note all steel ball locations for reassembly reference.

18) Remove steel ball from regulator valve (Prelude) and note location for reassembly reference. Detach 3 regulator valve body mounting bolts. Remove stator shift arm, 2 dowel pins (8 x 14 mm), stop pin and 4 mounting bolts holding main valve body to torque converter housing.

19) Remove cotter pin, washer, rollers and pin from manual valve. Remove main valve body, being careful not to lose torque converter check valve and spring. Remove pump gears and shaft. Remove separator plate, dowel pins, check valve and spring. Remove filter screen and suction pipe. Discard filter screen.

20) To remove control shaft, first remove control lever cable holder. Remove cotter pin, control pin and control lever roller from control lever. Bend tab down on control lever bolt lock plate, then remove bolt and control lever. Turn torque converter housing over and remove control shaft.

COMPONENT DISASSEMBLY & REASSEMBLY

NOTE: When disassembling any valve body, lay out components in order of removal for reassembly reference.

PARKING GEAR & ONE-WAY CLUTCH

Disassembly

Separate countershaft 1st gear from parking gear by gripping 1st gear in left hand and turning parking gear counterclockwise. Remove one-way clutch from countershaft 1st gear by prying retainer tab out of gear with a screwdriver. *See Fig. 9*. Inspect contact surfaces of countershaft 1st gear and parking gear for wear, damage or scoring. Inspect one-way clutch for damage or faulty movement.

Reassembly

To reassemble one-way clutch and parking gear, reverse disassembly procedures. When reassembled, check one-way clutch for movement in one direction (counterclockwise) only. *See Fig. 9*.

MAIN VALVE BODY

Disassembly

1) Remove torque converter check valve and spring. Remove relief valve spring cap, spring and valve. Remove 2nd gear orifice control valve, spring and seat. Remove detent spring and rollers. Remove manual valve.

2) Detach 2 shift valve sleeve cover mounting bolts (5 x .8 x 12 mm), then remove 1st-2nd shift valve cover. Carefully remove 1st-2nd shift valve with sleeve. Remove 1st-2nd shift spring (White).

Automatic Transmissions

HONDA 4-SPEED (Cont.)

Fig. 8: Exploded View of Torque Converter Housing & Components

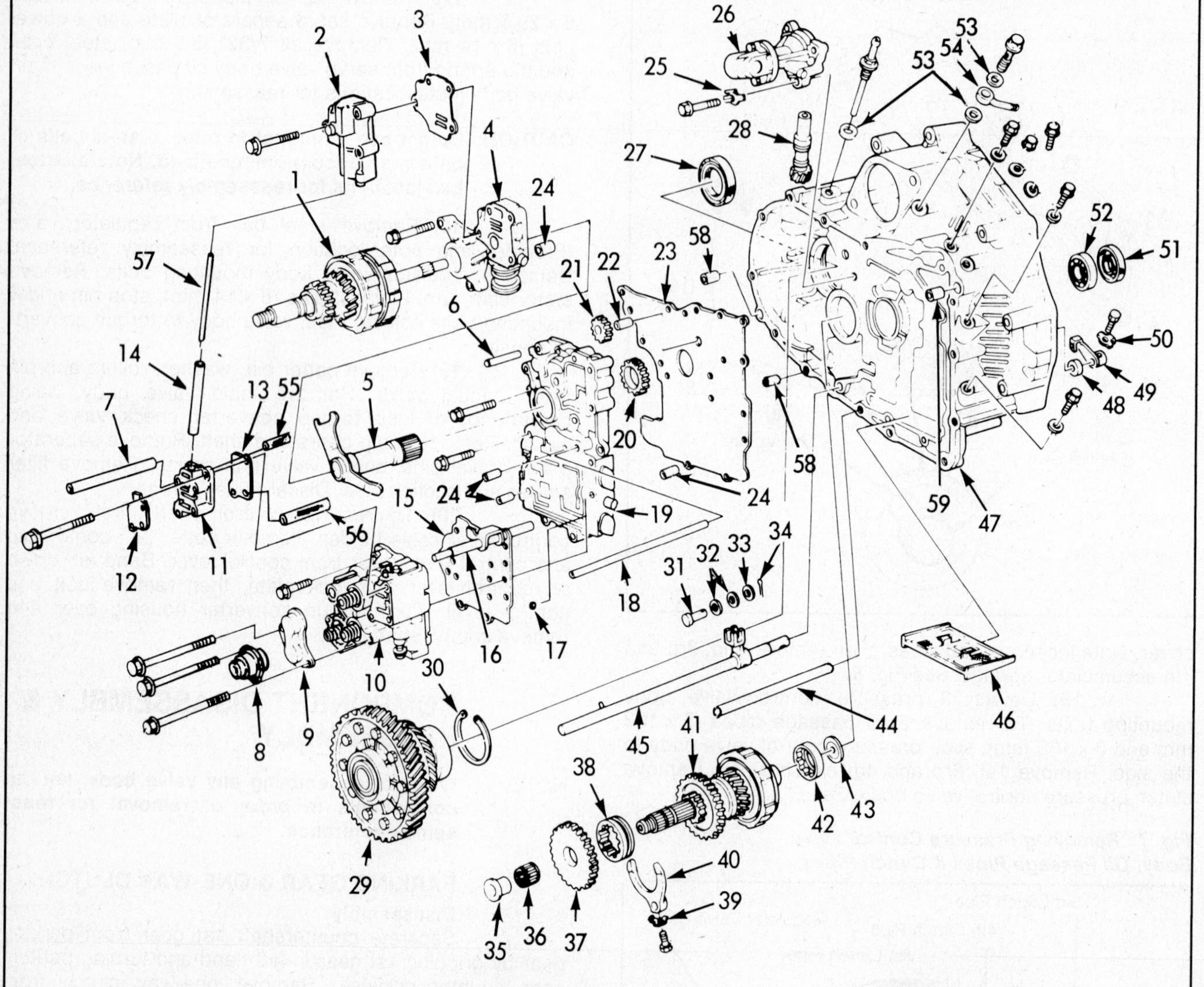

1. Mainshaft Assembly
2. Regulator Valve Cover
3. Separator Plate
4. Regulator Valve Assembly
5. Stator Shaft
6. 3rd Clutch Pipe
7. 4th Clutch Pipe
8. 4th Accumulator Cover
9. 2nd/3rd Accumulator Cover
10. Servo Valve Assembly
11. Clutch Pressure Control Valve (Prelude Similar)
12. Cover
13. Plate
14. Oil Feed Pipe (8 x 136 mm)
15. Servo Separator Plate
16. Throttle Control Shaft
17. Steel Ball (No. 6)
18. 1st Clutch Pipe
19. Main Valve Body
20. Pump Drive Gear
21. Pump Driven Gear
22. Pump Shaft
23. Main Valve Separator Plate
24. Dowel Pin (8 x 14 mm))
25. Lock Plate
26. Governor Assembly
27. Differential Oil Seal
28. Speedometer Drive Gear
29. Differential Assembly
30. Snap Ring (72 mm)
31. Manual Valve Pin
32. Rollers
33. Washer (5 mm)
34. Cotter Pin
35. Reverse Gear Collar
36. Needle Bearing
37. Countershaft Reverse Gear
38. Selector Hub
39. Lock Plate
40. Reverse Shift Fork
41. Countershaft Assembly
42. Countershaft Needle Bearing
43. Oil Guide Plate
44. Suction Pipe
45. Throttle Control Shaft
46. Filter Screen
47. Torque Convertor Housing
48. Control Shaft Oil Seal
49. Shift Lever
50. Lock Plate
51. Mainshaft Oil Seal
52. Mainshaft Bearing
53. Washer (12 mm)
54. Hose Joint
55. Oil Passage Pipe (8 x 29.5 mm)
56. Oil Passage Pipe (8 x 50 mm)
57. Oil Feed Pipe (5 x 168 mm)
58. Dowel Pin (14 x 20 mm)
59. Dowel Pin (14 x 25 mm)

HONDA 4-SPEED (Cont.)

Fig. 9: Disassembling One-Way Clutch & Parking Gear

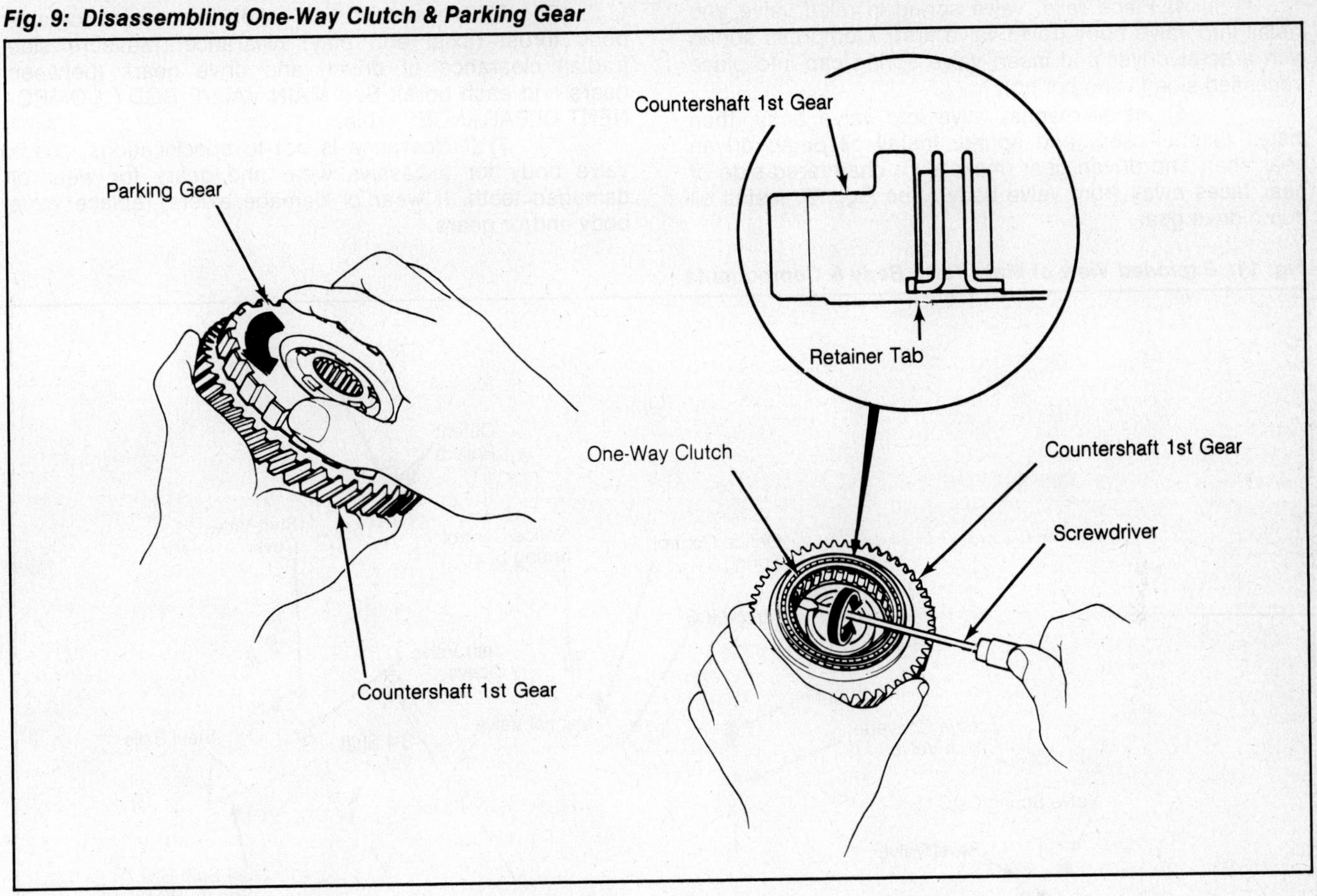

CAUTION: On 1st-2nd, 2nd-3rd and 3rd-4th shift valves, when sliding sleeve off valve, catch two .187" (4.76 mm) steel balls and spring as sleeve is removed.

3) Remove 2 shift valve sleeve cover mounting bolts (5 x .8 x 12 mm), then remove 2nd-3rd shift valve cover. Carefully remove 2nd-3rd shift valve with sleeve. Remove 2nd-3rd shift spring (Black).

4) Detach 2 shift valve sleeve cover mounting bolts (5 x .8 x 12 mm), then remove 3rd-4th shift valve cover. Carefully remove 3rd-4th shift valve with sleeve. Remove 3rd-4th shift spring (Black).

5) Clean all parts thoroughly in solvent or carburetor cleaner and blow dry with compressed air. Blow out all valve body passages. Inspect valves for scraches or scoring.

6) Replace any damaged or bent spring. Replace complete valve body assembly if valve body or any valve is worn or damaged. *See Fig. 11*. Repair valve body if one or more valves do not slide smoothly in their bores. See VALVE BODY REPAIR.

Reassembly

1) Coat all parts in ATF fluid. Slide 1st-2nd shift ball spring into hole in 1st-2nd shift valve. Press steel balls (one on each side of spring) into hole of shift valve. While holding in balls with fingers, slide sleeve over shift valve and balls.

2) Place 1st-2nd shift spring in valve body, then install shift valve assembly into valve body. Install 1st-2nd shift valve cover and mounting bolts onto main valve body.

3) Assemble 2nd-3rd and 3rd-4th shift valves, balls, springs and sleeves in same manner as 1st-2nd shift valve components. Install assembled components into valve body.

Fig. 10: Installing Oil Pump Gears & Shaft Into Main Valve Body

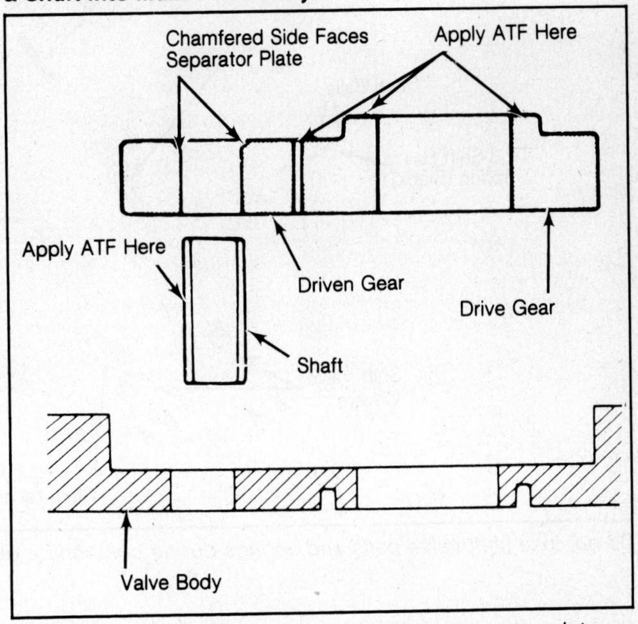

Chamfered side of driven gear must face separater plate.

HONDA 4-SPEED (Cont.)

4) Place relief valve spring in relief valve and install into valve body (relief valve first). Compress spring with a screwdriver and insert valve spring cap into place (recessed side facing spring).

5) Install manual valve into valve body, then install detent rollers and spring. Install oil pump driven gear shaft and driven gear (make sure chamfered side of gear faces away from valve body). *See Fig. 10*. Install oil pump drive gear.

6) Measure driven and drive gears-to-valve body thrust (axial end play) clearance. Measure side (radial) clearance of driven and drive gears (between gears and each bore). See MAIN VALVE BODY COMPONENT CLEARANCES table.

7) If clearance is not to specifications, check valve body for excessive wear and gears for wear or damaged teeth. If wear or damage exists, replace valve body and/or gears.

Fig. 11: Exploded View of Main Valve Body & Components

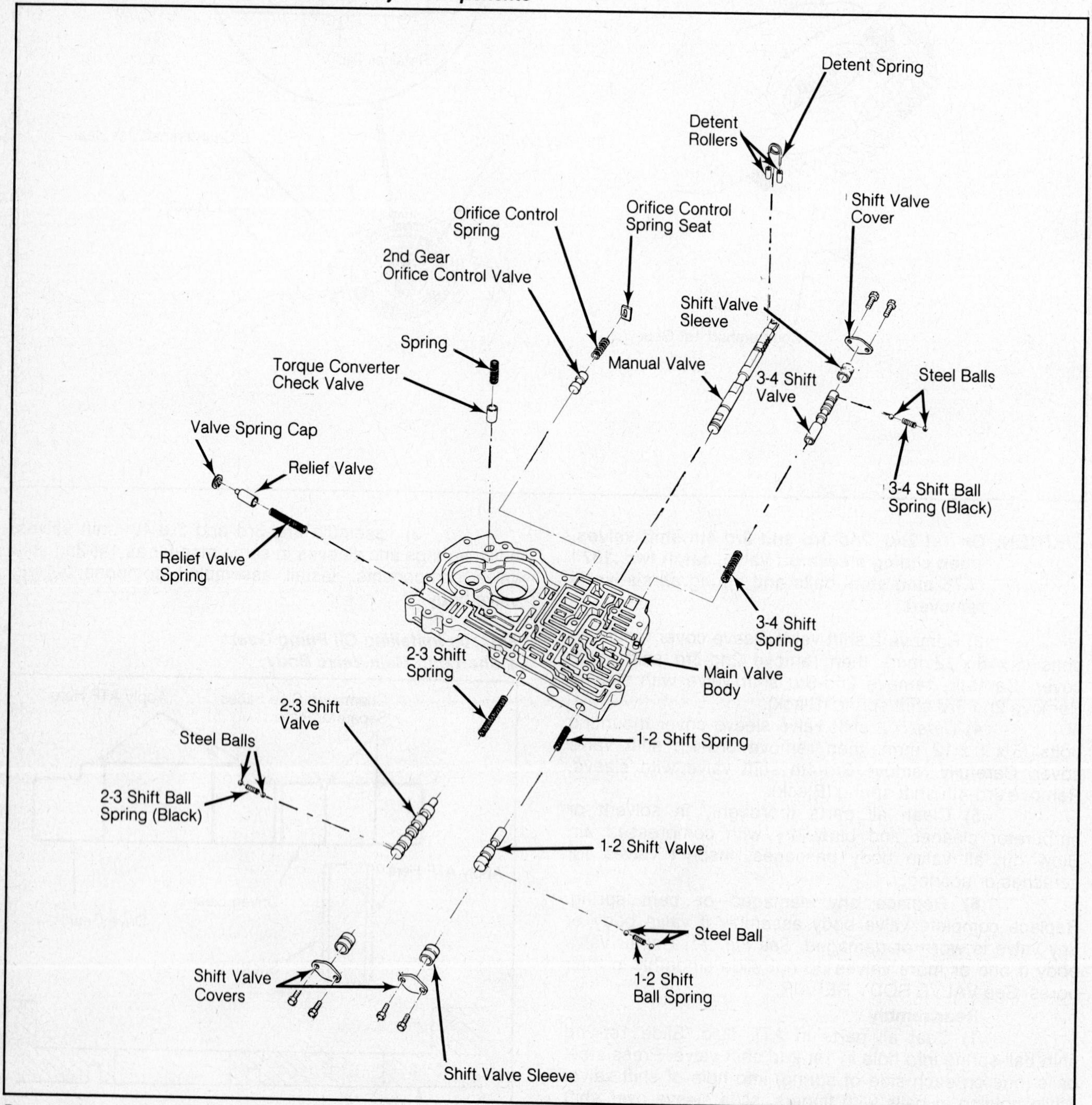

Do not lose shift valve balls and springs during component disassembly.

HONDA 4-SPEED (Cont.)

MAIN VALVE BODY COMPONENT CLEARANCES

Application	Standard (New) In. (mm)	Service Limit In. (mm)
End Play Clearance		
Drive Gear	.0012-.0020 (.03-.05)	.003 (.08)
Driven Gear	.0012-.0020 (.03-.05)	.003 (.08)
Side Clearance		
Drive Gear	.008-.011 (.20-.27)	.....
Driven Gear	.0020-.0035 (.05-.09)	.....

REGULATOR VALVE BODY

Disassembly

1) Hold retainer in place (compressed) while removing lock bolt (6 x 10 mm), then slowly release retainer. Remove retainer, spring seat, stator reaction spring, outer spring, inner spring and pressure regulator valve. *See Fig. 12.*

2) Detach roller pin (3 x 21.8 mm) and remove pressure control valve cap, spring and valve. Do not lose steel ball during component removal. Clean all parts thoroughly in carburetor cleaner and blow dry with compressed air.

3) Blow out all passages. Inspect valve for scoring or scratches and remaining parts for damage. On valve body, check sealing ring contact area diameter for proper size.

4) Standard diameter is 1.2598-1.2608" (32.000-32.025 mm). Service limit is 1.260" (32.05 mm). Replace regulator valve body and/or components if any part is worn or damaged. Repair valve body if one or more valves do not slide smoothly in their bores. See VALVE BODY REPAIR.

Reassembly

Coat all parts with ATF before reassembly. To reassemble regulator valve body components, reverse disassembly procedure. With pressure regulator valve components installed, align hole in retainer with hole in valve body. Compress retainer into valve body until lock bolt can be installed.

PRESSURE CONTROL VALVE BODY

Disassembly

1) Detach pressure control shift valve end plate mounting bolts, then remove end plate, pressure control shift valve and spring. Remove pressure control timing valve retainer, spring and valve. *See Fig. 13.*

Fig. 13: Exploded View Of Pressure Control Valve Body & Components

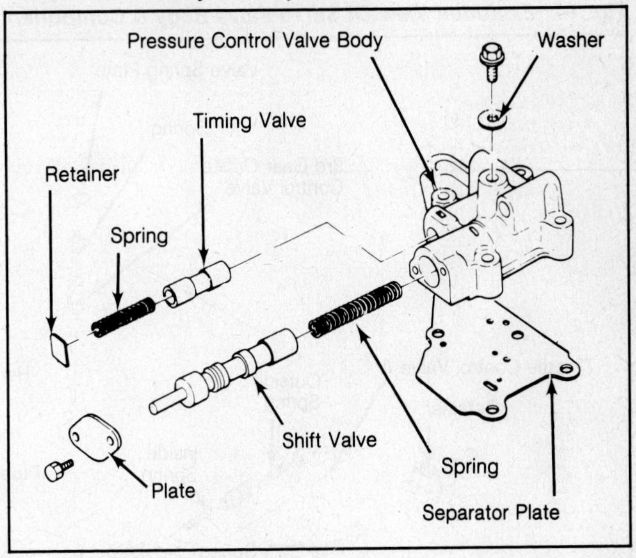

Fig. 12: Exploded View Of Regulator Valve Body & Components

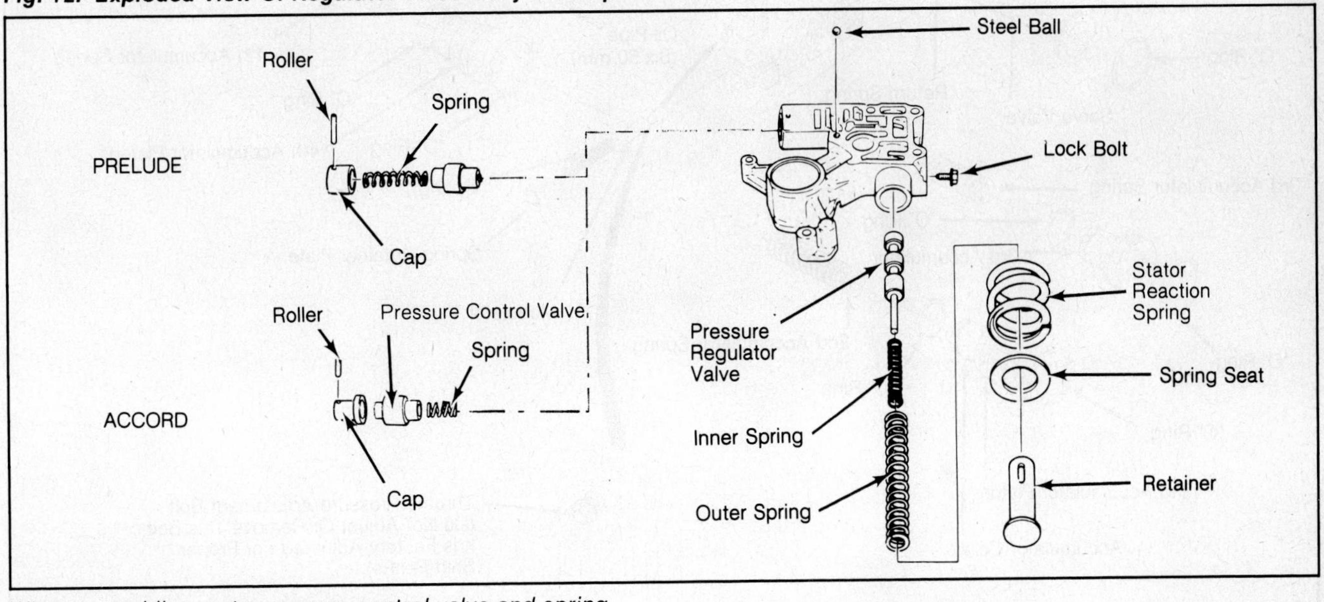

When assembling, note pressure control valve and spring location differences between Accord and Prelude.

HONDA 4-SPEED (Cont.)

2) Inspect all parts. Check valves for scoring or scratches and valve body for scoring or damage. Replace valve body and/or components as necessary. Repair valve body if one or more valves do not slide smoothly in their bores. See VALVE BODY REPAIR.

Reassembly

To reassemble pressure control valve body and components, reverse disassembly procedure.

SERVO VALVE BODY

Disassembly

1) Push out 2nd accumulator piston. Remove spring, collar (2 mm), outer "O" ring (33.2 x 2.4 mm) and inner "O" ring (23.5 x 2.1 mm). Push out 3rd accumulator piston. Remove spring, outer "O" ring (35.2 x 2.4 mm) and inner "O" ring (23.5 x 2.1 mm). Discard "O" rings.

2) Remove servo valve with "O" ring (31 x 2.7 mm) and return spring. Remove "O" ring from valve and discard. Detach throttle control valve "B" retainer mounting bolt (6 x 1.25 mm). Remove retainer and throttle control valve "B" assembly.

3) Separate control valve "B" components from spring. *See Fig. 14.* Remove throttle control valve "A" assembly from servo body and separate valve components from inner and outer springs. Detach 4th accumulator piston cover mounting bolts, then remove cover.

4) Remove "O" ring (31 x 2.7 mm) and spring from cover. Discard "O" ring. Pull 4th accumulator piston, outer "O" ring (21.2 x 2.4 mm) and inner "O" ring (29 x 2.4 mm) from servo body. Remove and discard "O" rings.

5) Detach Clutch Pressure Control (CPC) valve body mounting bolts. Remove cover, CPC valve body and

Fig. 14: Exploded View Of Servo Valve Body & Components

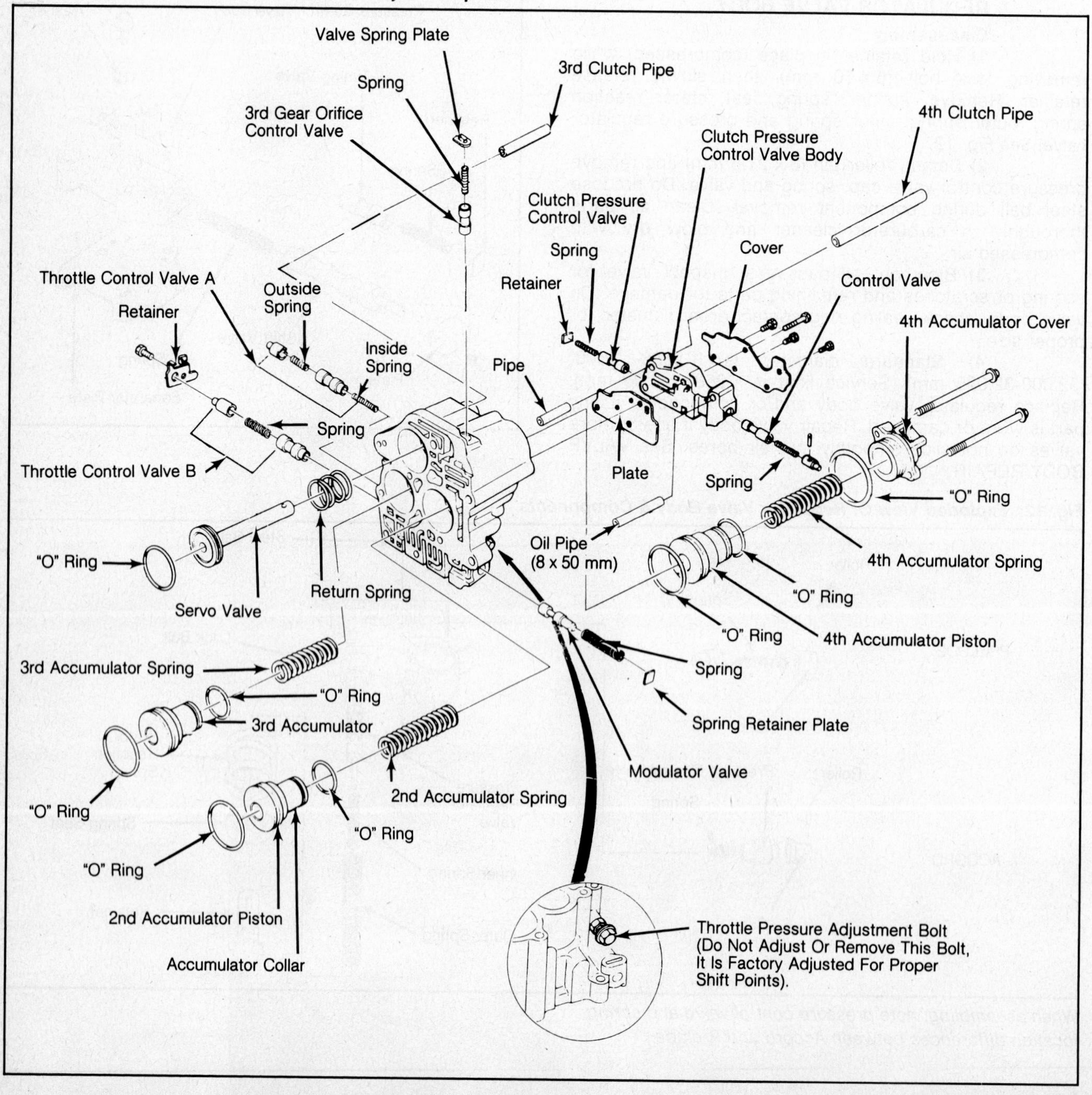

HONDA 4-SPEED (Cont.)

plate from servo valve body. Remove CPC valve retainer, spring and valve. Remove clutch oil passage pipes from valve body as necessary.

CAUTION: Do not adjust or remove throttle pressure adjustment bolt (on servo valve body). Bolt has been adjusted at factory for proper shift points.

6) Remove modulator valve retainer plate, spring and modulator valve. Clean all parts thoroughly in solvent or carbuetor cleaner, then blow dry with compressed air. Blow out all passages. Inspect all components.

7) Inspect valves for free movement, damage, scratches or scoring. Check clutch oil passage pipes for damage to ends. Replace servo valve body and/or components if any part is worn or damaged.

NOTE: When removing springs, be sure to note location, diameter and length of each spring for reassembly reference.

8) Check springs for proper length. See SERVO VALVE BODY SPRING SPECIFICATIONS table. Replace springs that are not to specifications. Repair valve body if one or more valves do not slide smoothly in their bores. See VALVE BODY REPAIR.

NOTE: Clean all parts in solvent and blow dry with compressed air. Replace servo valve as an assembly if any parts are worn or damaged. Do not remove or adjust throttle pressure adjustment bolt. Adjustment bolt is factory set for proper shift points.

SERVO VALVE BODY SPRING SPECIFICATIONS

Application	Free Lenght In. (mm)
2nd Accumulator	3.20 (81.3)
3rd Accumulator	3.41 (86.5)
4th Accumulator	3.72 (94.4)
Return Spring	1.44 (36.7)

Reassembly

To reassemble servo valve, reverse disassembly procedure. Always install new "O" rings.

VALVE BODY REPAIR

NOTE: Valve body repair is only necessary if one or more valves in valve body do not slide smoothly in their bores. This procedure may be used to free valves in main valve body, regulator valve body, pressure control valve body and servo valve body. Do not attempt to repair governor assembly, replace unit if valves are stuck.

1) With unit removed, carefully tap valve body so that sticking valve drops out of its bore. If necessary, use a small screwdriver to pry valve free. DO NOT damage bore during valve removal.

2) Soak a sheet of #600 grit sandpaper in ATF for about 30 minutes. Inspect valve for any scuff marks. Use ATF-soaked sandpaper to polish off any scuffs or burrs found on valve, then wash in solvent and blow dry with compressed air.

3) Roll up half a sheet of ATF-soaked sandpaper and insert it in bore of sticking valve. Twist paper slightly so that it unrolls and fits bore tightly, then polish bore by twisting paper as it is moved in and out.

NOTE: The aluminum valve body does not require much polishing to remove any scuffs or burrs.

4) Remove sandpaper and thoroughly wash entire valve body in solvent and blow dry with compressed air. Coat valve with ATF and drop it into its bore.

5) Valve should drop to bottom of bore under its own weight. If not, repeat step **3)**, then retest. Final clean valve and valve body in solvent and blow dry. Assemble components using ATF as a lubricant.

GOVERNOR ASSEMBLY

Disassembly

1) Bend governor housing mounting bolt lock plates away from bolt heads. Detach mounting bolts (6 x 1.0 mm) and remove governor housing from shaft. Discard lock plates.

NOTE: Push down on secondary weight to ease removal of 20 mm snap ring.

Fig. 15: Exploded View of Governor Valve & Housing Assembly

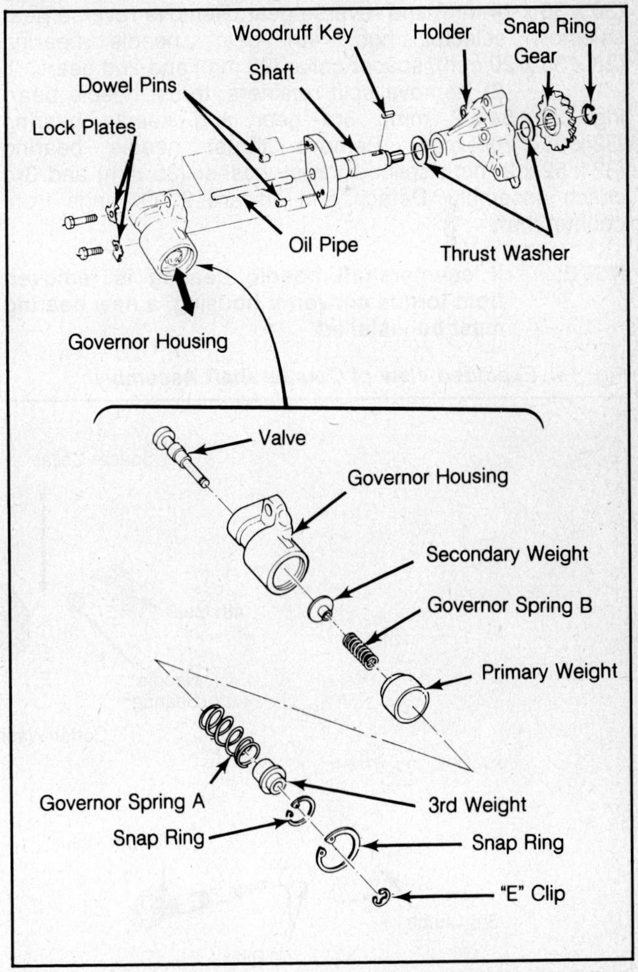

Replace governor assembly if any part is worn or damaged or unit does not operate smoothly. Do not attempt repair.

HONDA 4-SPEED (Cont.)

2) Remove "E" ring (5 mm) from end of governor valve. Slide out valve. Detach small snap ring (20 mm), then remove governor spring "A" and 3rd weight from inside of primary weight.

3) Detach large snap ring (28 mm), then remove primary weight, governor spring "B" and secondary weight from governor housing bore. *See Fig. 15.*

4) On governor holder, detach snap ring (14 mm). Remove gear and thrust washer (14 mm). Remove pipe (5 x 65 mm) from governor shaft. Pull governor shaft out of governor holder and remove Woodruff key (3 mm) and thrust washer (14 mm). Inspect all parts.

5) Check oil pipe for damaged ends. Inspect governor housing and holder for scoring or warpage. Check gear teeth for chipped teeth, damage or excessive wear. Inspect primary, secondary and 3rd weights for wear, scoring or scratches. Replace parts as needed.

Reassembly

To reassemble governor, reverse disassembly procedure. Use a new "E" clip (5 mm) when installing valve in housing. Install new lock plates when replacing governor housing onto shaft. Check governor assembly for smooth operation after reassembly.

COUNTERSHAFT ASSEMBLY

Disassembly

1) Remove reverse gear collar, needle bearing (30 x 36 x 14 mm) and reverse gear. Remove reverse gear selector, selector hub, 4th gear, needle bearing (28 x 33 x 20 mm), spacer collar (28 mm) and 2nd gear.

2) Remove split retainers, thrust needle bearing (39 x 54 x 2 mm), 3rd gear and needle bearing (32 x 38 x 20 mm). Remove thrust needle bearing (32 x 52 x 2 mm), splined thrust washer (35 mm) and 3rd clutch assembly. Detach and discard 2 "O" rings from countershaft.

NOTE: **If countershaft needle bearing is removed from torque converter housing, a new bearing must be installed.**

3) To remove countershaft needle bearing from torque converter housing, install Bearing Puller (07936-6340000) and Attachment (07936-6890101) to bearing. Tap bearing out of case. Note position of oil guide plate for reassembly reference.

4) To remove countershaft bearing from transmission case, expand bearing locating snap ring (62 mm) with snap ring pliers. Push bearing out through case (away from snap ring) by hand. Do not remove snap ring unless it is necessary to clean housing.

Inspection

Check needle bearings for galling and/or rough movement. Inspect countershaft splines for excessive wear or damage. Check bearing surfaces for scoring, scratches or excessive wear. Replace countershaft and/or components as necessary.

NOTE: **On all thrust needle bearings, ensure unrolled edge of bearing cage faces thrust washer. Lubricate all parts with ATF during reassembly.**

Reassembly

1) To install countershaft bearing to transmission housing, first expand snap ring with snap ring pliers. With part number facing out, insert new bearing part-way into housing (from snap ring side), then release pliers.

2) Push bearing down into transmission until ring snaps in place around it. Ensure snap ring is properly seated in bearing and housing grooves. To install countershaft bearing into torque converter housing, first ensure oil guide plate is in proper position.

3) Using Driver (07749-0010000) and Attachment (07746-0010400), tap bearing in until flush with case. To reassemble countershaft, first install 2 new "O" rings. Install 3rd clutch assembly, splined thrust washer, thrust needle bearing. Check splined thrust washer for proper fit. See MAINSHAFT & COUNTERSHAFT CLEARANCE MEASUREMENTS. Install 3rd gear with needle bearing.

Fig. 16: Exploded View of Countershaft Assembly

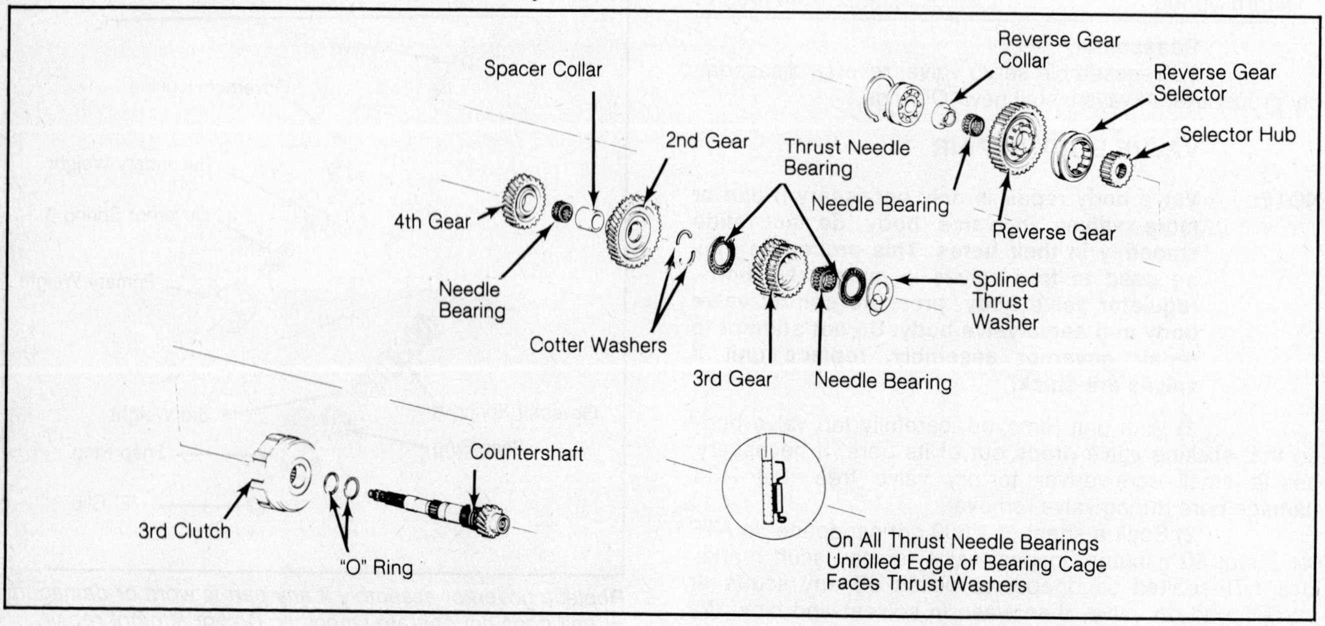

HONDA 4-SPEED (Cont.)

4) Install thrust needle bearing, split retainers and 2nd gear with space collar and needle bearing. Install 4th gear, selector hub (groove facing converter housing), reverse gear selector (chamfer toward torque converter housing) and reverse gear with needle bearing. Install reverse gear collar and ball bearing. *See Fig. 16.*

5) With countershaft assembled, measure clearance between selector collar and shoulder of 4th gear. Clearance should be .003-.006" (.07-.15 mm). Adjust clearance as necessary. See MAINSHAFT & COUNTERSHAFT CLEARANCE MEASUREMENTS.

MAINSHAFT ASSEMBLY

Disassembly

1) From rear of mainshaft, detach snap ring (20 mm), needle bearing (20 x 26 x 20 mm) and spacer washer. Detach 2 metal sealing rings (32 mm) and discard. From front of mainshaft, detach snap ring (26 mm). *See Fig. 17.*

2) Remove thrust washer (26 x 45 x 3 mm), thrust needle bearing (32 x 44 x 2 mm) and 4th gear with 2 needle bearings (32 x 38 x 20 mm). Remove thrust needle bearing (39 x 54 x 2 mm) and 4th gear collar.

3) Remove thrust washer, 2nd-4th clutch assembly and 3 oil seal "O" rings (34 x 1.9 mm). Remove thrust washer (36 mm), thrust needle bearing (36 x 52 x 2 mm), 2nd gear, needle bearing (36 x 41 x 18.3 mm) and thrust needle bearing (42 x 58 x 2 mm). Remove and discard 2 "O" rings (19.8 x 1.9 mm) from mainshaft. *See Fig. 17.*

4) Using hammer, driver and Attachment (07947-6340500), remove mainshaft bearing and seal from torque converter housing (drive out from valve body side). Discard oil seal.

5) To remove mainshaft bearing from transmission housing, expand snap ring (60 mm) with snap ring pliers. Push bearing out of housing (away from snap ring) by hand.

Inspection

Check mainshaft splines for excessive wear or damage. Inspect bearing surface for scoring, scratches or excessive wear. Check all needle bearings for galling and/or rough movement. Replace parts as needed.

NOTE: When installing thrust needle bearings, ensure unrolled edge of bearing cage faces thrust washer. Lubricate all parts with ATF fluid during reassembly.

Reassembly

1) To install new mainshaft bearing to transmission housing, expand locating snap ring with snap ring pliers and insert bearing part-way into it, then release pliers. Push bearing into housing until ring snaps in place around it. Ensure snap ring is seated in bearing and housing grooves.

2) Using hammer, driver and Attachment (07947-6340500), drive in new bearing (from torque converter side) until it bottoms in converter housing. Install new mainshaft oil seal (from torque converter side) using hammer, driver and Oil Seal Installer (07947-6340201).

3) Install 2 new "O" rings onto mainshaft. Install thrust needle bearing, needle bearing and 2nd gear. Install thrust needle bearing, thrust washer and 3 new "O" rings. Check measurement. See MAINSHAFT & COUNTERSHAFT CLEARANCE MEASUREMENTS. Install 2nd-4th clutch assembly.

4) Install thrust washer, 4th gear collar, thrust needle bearing and 4th gear (with 2 needle bearings). Install thrust needle bearing, thrust washer and snap ring onto mainshaft.

Fig. 17: Exploded View of Mainshaft Assembly

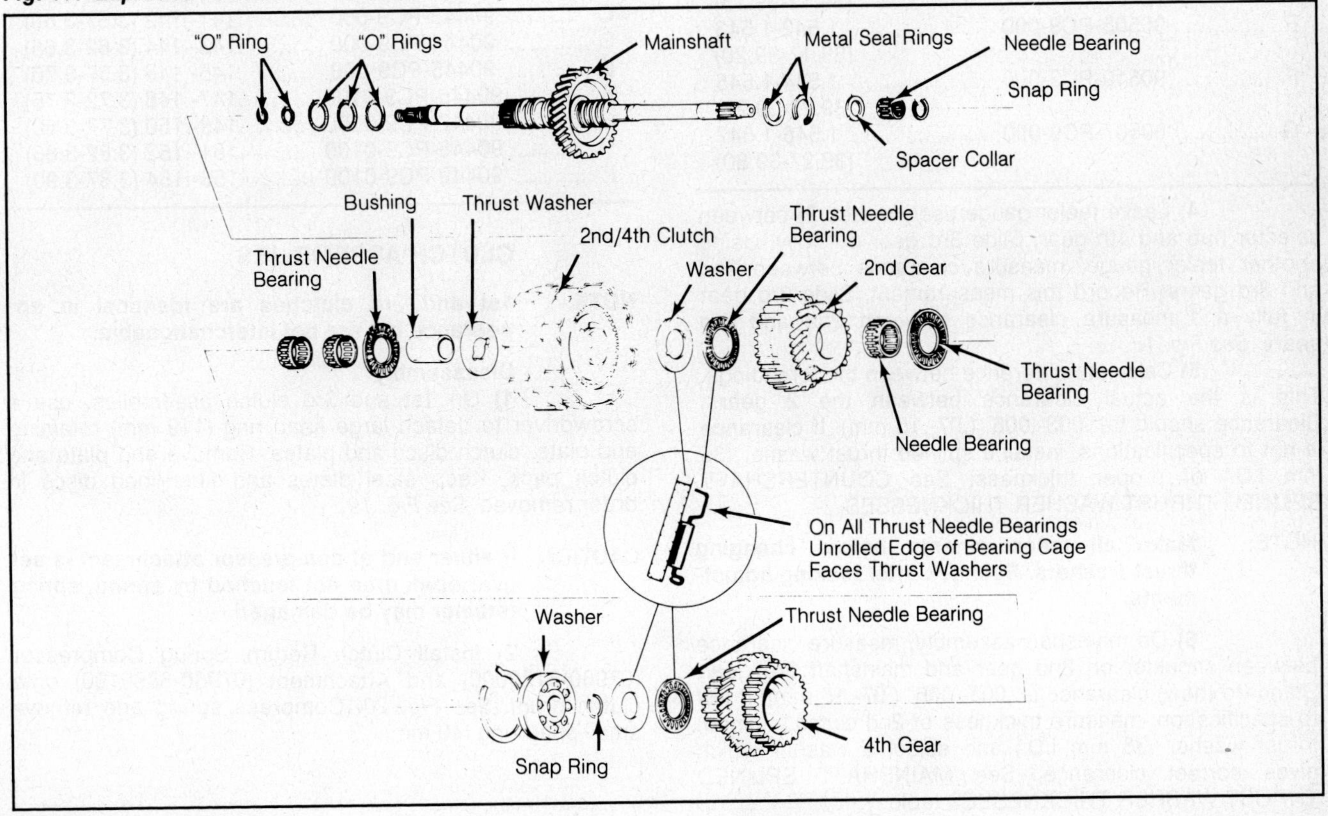

HONDA 4-SPEED (Cont.)

Install thrust needle bearing, thrust washer and snap ring onto mainshaft.

MAINSHAFT & COUNTERSHAFT CLEARANCE MEASUREMENTS.

NOTE: **To check mainshaft and countershaft clearances, both shaft assemblies must be removed from transmission housing and checked in assembled form.**

1) Install mainshaft and countershaft assemblies into torque converter housing. Install Mainshaft Holder (07923-6890201) and tighten mainshaft and countershaft lock nuts to 25 ft. lbs. (35 N.m). Remove assemblies from housing and lay each flat on work surface. Using a feeler gauge, measure clearances.

2) On countershaft, measure clearance between shoulder on gear selector hub and shoulder of 4th gear. Standard countershaft 4th gear clearance is .003-.006" (.07-.15 mm).

3) If countershaft clearance is more than specifications, measure thickness of spacer collar and select a replacement which gives proper clearance. See COUNTERSHAFT SPACER COLLAR THICKNESSES table.

COUNTERSHAFT SPACER COLLAR THICKNESSES

Class	Part Number	Thickness In. (mm)
A	90503-PC9-000	1.534-1.535 (38.97-39.00)
B	90508-PC9-000	1.536-1.537 (39.02-39.05)
C	90504-PC9-000	1.538-1.539 (39.07-39.10)
D	90509-PC9-000	1.540-1.541 (39.12-39.15)
E	90505-PC9-000	1.542-1.543 (39.17-39.20)
F	90510-PC9-000	1.544-1.545 (39.22-39.25)
G	90507-PC9-000	1.546-1.547 (39.27-39.30)

4) Leave feeler gauge used in step **2)** between selector hub and 4th gear. Slide 3rd gear out fully. Using another feeler gauge, measure clearance between 2nd and 3rd gears. Record this measurement. Slide 3rd gear in fully and measure clearance between 2nd and 3rd gears. *See Fig. 18.*

5) Calculate difference between the 2 readings. This is the actual clearance between the 2 gears. Clearance should be .003-.006" (.07-.15 mm). If clearance is not to specifications, install a splined thrust washer (35 mm I.D.) of proper thickness. See COUNTERSHAFT SPLINED THRUST WASHER THICKNESSES.

NOTE: **Make all measurements before changing thrust washers. Recheck after making adjustments.**

6) On mainshaft assembly, measure clearance between shoulder on 2nd gear and mainshaft 3rd gear. Standard (new) clearance is .003-.006" (.07-.15 mm). If not to specification, measure thickness of 2nd clutch (splined) thrust washer (36 mm I.D.) and select a washer which gives correct clearance. See MAINSHAFT SPLINED THRUST WASHER THICKNESSES table.

Fig. 18: Measuring Countershaft 2nd-3rd Gear Clearance

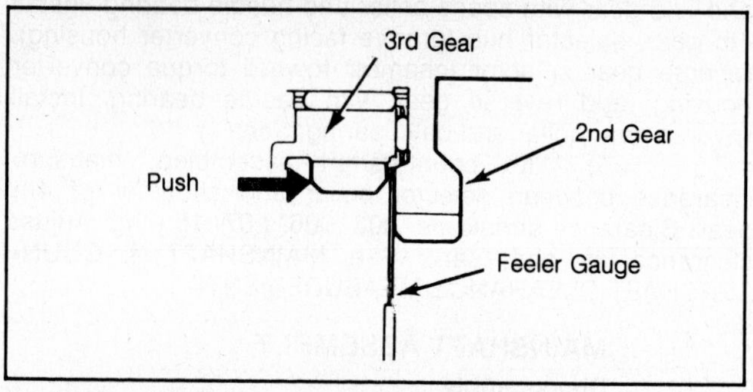

Replace splined thrust washer with one of proper thickness if measurement is not within specification.

COUNTERSHAFT SPLINED THRUST WASHER THICKNESSES

Class	Part Number	Thickness In. (mm)
A	90411-PA9-0100	.117-.118 (2.97-3.00)
B	90412-PA9-0100	.119-.120 (3.02-3.05)
C	90413-PA9-0100	.121-.122 (3.07-3.10)
D	90414-PA9-0100	.123-.124 (3.12-3.15)
E	90415-PA9-0100	.125-.126 (3.17-3.20)
F	90418-PA9-0100	.127-.128 (3.22-3.25)
G	90419-PA9-0100	.129-.130 (3.27-3.30)
H	90420-PA9-0100	.131-.132 (3.32-3.35)
I	90421-PA9-0100	.133-.134 (3.37-3.40)

MAINSHAFT SPLINED THRUST WASHER THICKNESSES

Class	Part Number	Thickness In. (mm)
A	90441-PC9-000	.137-.138 (3.47-3.50)
B	90442-PC9-000	.139-.140 (3.52-3.55)
C	90443-PC9-000	.141-.142 (3.57-3.60)
D	90444-PC9-000	.143-.144 (3.62-3.65)
E	90445-PC9-000	.145-.146 (3.67-3.70)
F	90446-PC9-0100	.147-.148 (3.72-3.75)
G	90447-PC9-0100	.149-.150 (3.77-3.80)
H	90448-PC9-0100	.151-.152 (3.82-3.85)
I	90449-PC9-0100	.153-.154 (3.87-3.90)

CLUTCH ASSEMBLIES

NOTE: **1st and 3rd clutches are identical in appearance but are not interchangeable.**

Disassembly

1) On 1st and 3rd clutch assemblies, use a screwdriver to detach large snap ring (119 mm) retaining end plate, clutch discs and plates. Remove end plate and clutch pack. Keep steel plates and fiber-lined discs in order removed. *See Fig. 19.*

CAUTION: **If either end of compressor attachment is set over open area not touched by spring, spring retainer may be damaged.**

2) Install Clutch Return Spring Compressor (07960-6120000) and Attachment (07960-6890100) onto clutch drum. *See Fig. 20.* Compress spring and remove small snap ring (40 mm).

HONDA 4-SPEED (Cont.)

Fig. 19: Exploded View of 1st & 3rd Clutch Assemblies

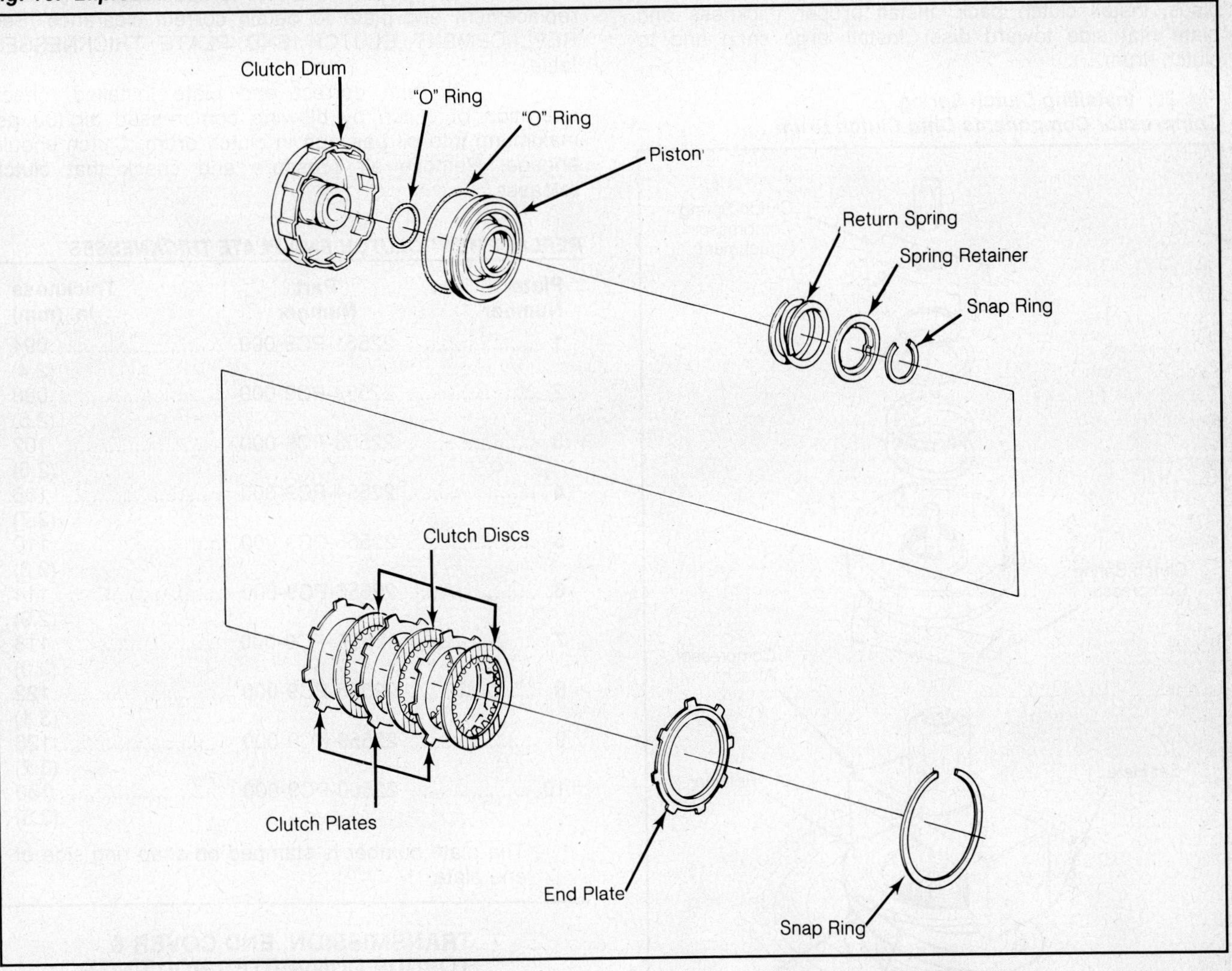

3) Slowly release spring compressor. Remove spring retainer and return spring. To remove clutch piston, first wrap shop rag around clutch drum. Carefully apply air pressure (30 psi maximum) to oil passage in clutch drum while holding finger over other passage opening.

4) Remove piston, then detach large "O" ring (104 x 2.2 mm) from piston O.D. and small "O" ring (39.8 x 2.2 mm) from piston I.D. Discard "O" rings. Inspect clutch components for damage or wear.

5) On 2nd-4th clutch assembly, disassemble components by follow steps **1)** through **4)** for each clutch assembly. *See Fig. 21.* Inspect clutch components for damage or wear.

Inspection

Clean all parts thoroughly in solvent and blow dry with compressed air. Blow out all passages. Check piston for restriction and/or loose check valve. Check for excessive wear or scoring on steel plates and lined plates. Replace steel or lined plates if necessary. Replace clutch assembly if piston is damaged.

NOTE: Soak new fiber-lined plates in ATF for 30 minutes before installation.

Reassembly

1) Lubricate all parts with ATF fluid before assembling. Install new "O" ring on piston. Make sure clutch piston spring washer is installed with high side facing away from clutch drum.

2) Install piston (lubricate "O" ring with ATF fluid) to clutch drum. Apply pressure to piston (by hand) and rotate piston to ensure proper seating. Do not pinch "O" ring by forcing piston into drum.

3) Install return spring and spring retainer. Position a new snap ring on spring retainer. Install return spring compressor to clutch drum and spring retainer. Compress spring until retainer is below groove in hub. Fit snap ring to groove. Slowly release spring compressor and ensure snap ring seats properly.

4) Before installing clutch pack, inspect clutch drum I.D. to ensure it is free of grit or other matter.

HONDA 4-SPEED (Cont.)

Starting with a steel plate and alternating with fiber-lined discs, install clutch pack. Install proper thickness end plate (flat side toward disc). Install large snap ring to clutch drum.

Fig. 20: Installing Clutch Spring Compressor Components Onto Clutch Drum

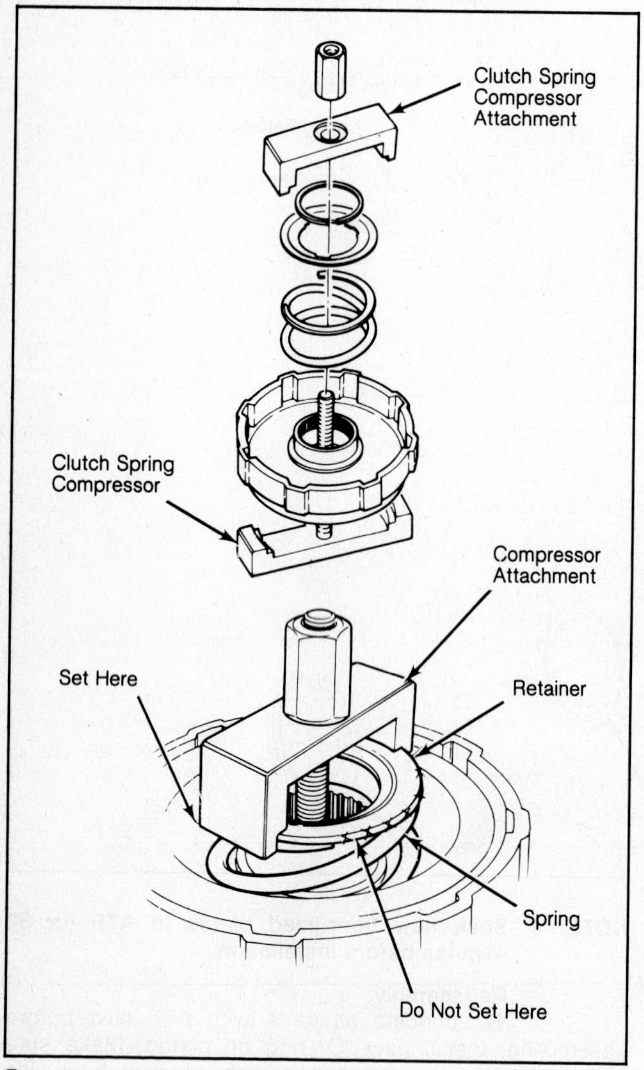

Ensure compressor attachment is properly installed or damage to spring retainer will result.

Clutch End Plate Clearance & Replacement Selection

1) Using an angled-end feeler gauge, measure clearance between each clutch pack end plate and top fiber-lined plate. See END PLATE-TO-TOP DISC CLEARANCE table. Do not damage fiber-lined disc during measurement.

END PLATE-TO-TOP CLUTCH DISC CLEARANCE

Application	Service Limit In. (mm)
1st Clutch	.016-.028 (.40-.70)
2nd Clutch	.026-.031 (.65-.80)
3rd Clutch	.016-.023 (.40-.60)
4th Clutch	.016-.023 (.40-.60)

2) If clearance is not to specification, select a replacement end plate to obtain correct clearance. See REPLACEMENT CLUTCH END PLATE THICKNESSES table.

3) With correct end plate installed, check operation of clutch by blowing compressed air (30 psi maximum) into oil passage in clutch drum. Clutch should engage. Remove air pressure and check that clutch releases.

REPLACEMENT CLUTCH END PLATE THICKNESSES

Plate Number [1]	Part Number	Thickness In. (mm)
1	22551-PC9-000	.094 (2.4)
2	22552-PC9-000	.098 (2.5)
3	22553-PC9-000	.102 (2.6)
4	22554-PC9-000	.106 (2.7)
5	22555-PC9-000	.110 (2.8)
6	22556-PC9-000	.114 (2.9)
7	22557–PC9-000	.118 (3.0)
8	22558-PC9-000	.122 (3.1)
9	22559-PC9-000	.126 (3.2)
10	22560-PC9-000	.130 (3.3)

[1] – The plate number is stamped on snap ring side of end plate.

TRANSMISSION, END COVER & TORQUE CONVERTER HOUSINGS

Disassembly

1) If differential seals are to be replaced or if differential needs repair, lift differential out of torque converter housing. Remove differential seal snap ring (72 mm) from torque converter housing.

NOTE: Seal installed depth should be noted for reassembly reference.

2) Using Driver (07749-0010000) and Attachment (07947-6340500), drive seal out through torque converter housing. Using hammer and drift, drive differential seal (away from snap ring) out of transmission housing.

CAUTION: Use care not to damage end cover components during disassembly.

3) On end cover, detach snap rings retaining 1st and 3rd clutch feed pipe assemblies. Remove feed pipe assemblies from cover, then disassemble "O" rings, guide, pin and flange from feed pipes. Discard "O" rings. *See Fig. 22.*

HONDA 4-SPEED (Cont.)

Fig. 21: Exploded View of 2nd & 4th Clutch Assemblies

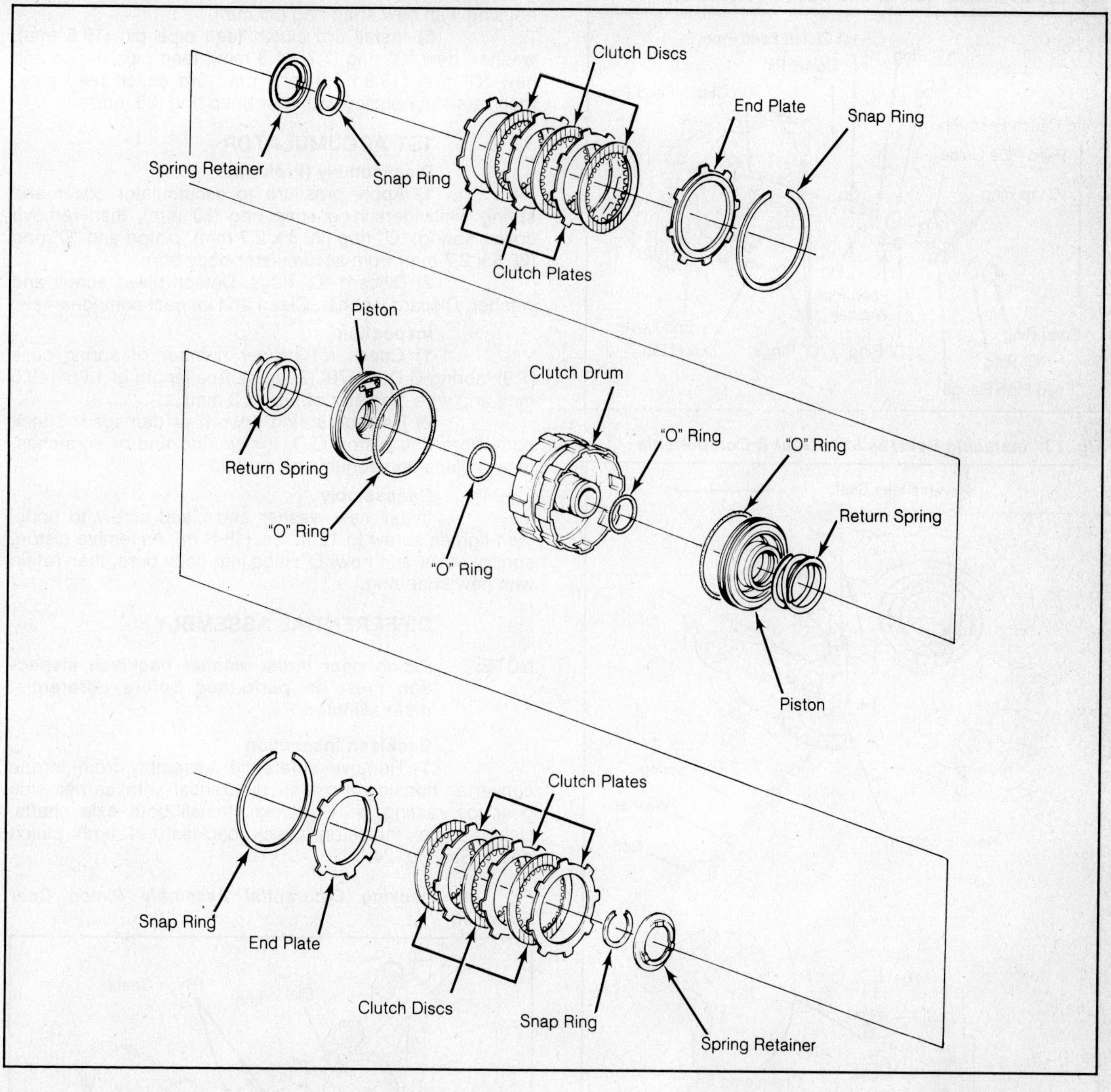

4) If not previously removed, detach reverse idler bearing holder mounting bolts and remove holder. Detach 2 idler gear shaft locating bolts and remove washers and springs.

5) Pull out reverse idler gear shaft from outside transmission housing. From inside housing, remove idler gear and needle bearing (14 x 18 x 15 mm). Inspect components and replace if worn or damaged.

Inspection

Inspect end cover components. Check 1st and 3rd clutch feed pipes for damage to ends. Check end cover for cracks, grooves and/or scoring. Ensure all passages are clear by blowing out with compressed air. Check and replace dowel pins (8 x 14 mm) if necessary.

Reassembly

1) Install reverse idler gear so that large chamfer on shaft bore faces away from transmission housing. *See Fig. 23.* Position idler gear shaft and needle bearing to transmission housing, then install shaft locating bolts, washers and springs.

2) Install reverse idler gear bearing holder and tighten mounting bolts. Expand mainshaft and countershaft bearing snap rings and install bearings to transmission housing.

3) On torque converter housing, install snap ring (72 mm) if removed. Using hammer, driver and Attachment (07947-6110500), drive new mainshaft and countershaft seals into housing.

HONDA 4-SPEED (Cont.)

Fig. 22: Exploded View of End Housing Assembly

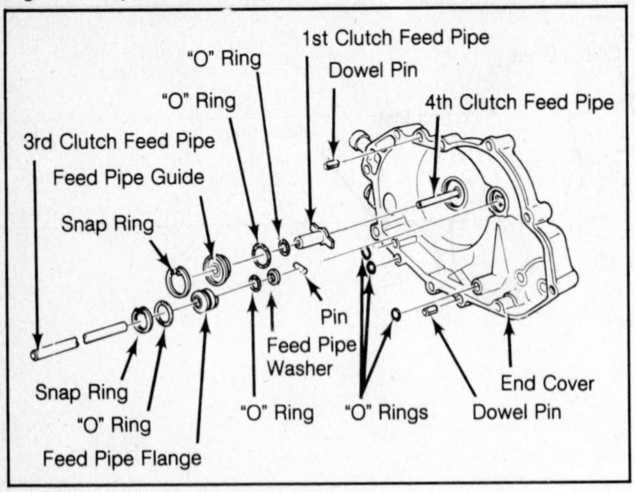

Fig. 23: Installing Reverse Idler Gear & Components

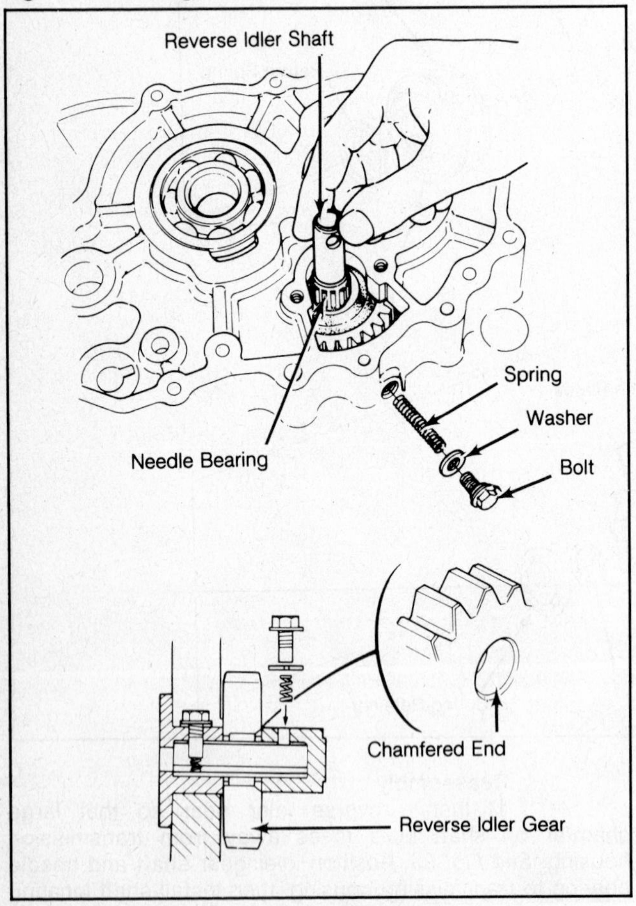

The large chamfer on the idler gear shaft bore must face toward the torque converter housing.

NOTE: With feed pipes assembled, ensure lugs on feed pipe collars are aligned with slots in end cover housing.

4) On end cover housing, install 3 new "O" rings (6 x 2.3 mm). Install new "O" ring (34 x 1.9 mm), 1st clutch feed pipe, new "O" ring (8.5 x 1.9 mm) and feed pipe guide onto 4th clutch feed pipe. Retain assembly in housing with new snap ring (38 mm).

5) Install 3rd clutch feed pipe pin (19.8 mm), washer, new "O" ring (7.7 x 1.9 mm), feed pipe flange and new "O" ring (19.8 x 1.9 mm) onto 3rd clutch feed pipe, then retain in housing with new snap ring (26 mm).

1ST ACCUMULATOR

Disassembly (Prelude)

1) Apply pressure to accumulator cover and spring while detaching snap ring (30 mm), then remove cover, spring, "O" ring (22.5 x 2.7 mm), piston and "O" ring (22.5 x 2.7 mm) from accumulator body bore.

2) Discard "O" rings. Detach bleed screw and washer. Discard washer. Clean and inspect components.

Inspection

1) Check for proper number of spring coils (7.9), spring O.D. of .79" (20 mm), free length of 1.96" (49.8 mm) and wire diameter of .09" (2.3 mm).

2) Replace spring if worn or damaged. Check body bore and piston O.D. for scoring and/or scratches, then replace components as needed.

Reassembly

Install new washer and bleed screw to body, then tighten screw to 12 ft. lbs. (18 N.m). Assemble piston, spring, cover and new "O" rings into body bore, then retain with new snap ring.

DIFFERENTIAL ASSEMBLY

NOTE: Pinion gear thrust washer backlash inspection must be performed before differential disassembled.

Backlash Inspection

1) Remove differential assembly from torque converter housing. Position differential with carrier side bearings resting in "V" blocks. Install both axle shafts. Using a dial indicator, check backlash of both pinion gears. *See Fig. 24.*

Fig. 24: Checking Differential Assembly Pinion Gear Backlash

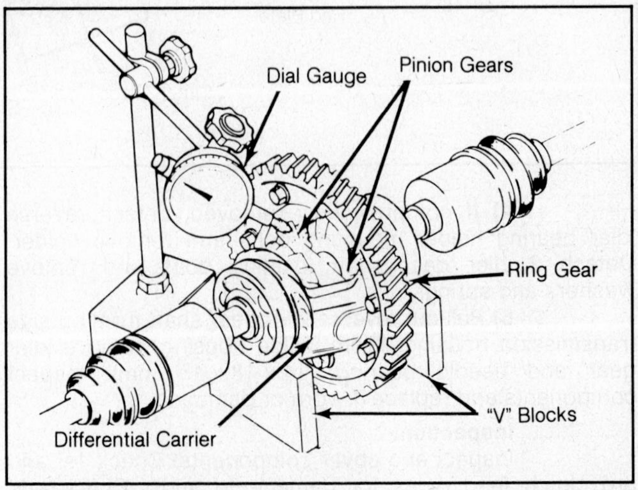

2) Standard backlash is .002-.006" (.05-.15 mm). If backlash is not to specification, disassemble differential. Measure orignal thrust washers to determine thickness. Select new pinion gear thrust washers to obtain

HONDA 4-SPEED (Cont.)

correct backlash. See DIFFERENTIAL PINION GEAR THRUST WASHER THICKESSES table.

NOTE: **New thrust washers must be of equal thickness.**

DIFFERENTIAL PINION GEAR THRUST WASHER THICKESSES

Part Number	Thickness In. (mm)
41351-689-000	.028 (.70)
41355-PC8-000	.030 (.75)
41352-689-000	.031 (.80)
41356-PC8-000	.033 (.85)
41353-689-000	.035 (.90)
41357-PC8-000	.037 (.95)
41254-689-000	.039 (1.0)

NOTE: **Before disassembly, inspect differential side bearings for wear or rough rotation. If bearings are in good condition, removal is not necessary.**

Disassembly

1) Remove differential assembly from torque converter housing and check backlash. If necessary, remove bearings from both sides of differential using a 2-jaw bearing puller. Detach 10 LEFT-HAND thread ring gear mounting bolts (10 x 1.25 mm). Remove ring gear from carrier. Inspect teeth for damage or excessive wear.

CAUTION: **The speedometer drive gear has sharp edges. Use care when handling it during disassembly and reassembly procedures.**

2) Using a screwdriver, pry snap ring (80 mm) off carrier. Carefully remove speedometer drive gear and dowel pin (5 x 10 mm). Using hammer and a 4 mm Pin Punch (07499-SA00000), drive out pinion shaft spring pin. *See Fig. 25.*

3) Remove pinion shaft, pinion gears, side gears and thrust washers. Wash all components thoroughly in solvent and blow dry with compressed air. Inspect all parts for excessive wear or damage. Check pinion shaft for scoring or burrs. Check bearings for damage or rough movement. Replace any parts that are defective.

NOTE: **Completely coat all gears with molybdenum disulfide grease before reassembly.**

Reassembly

1) Install side gears in differential carrier. Position pinion gears in place (exactly opposite each other), in mesh with side gears. Install new thrust washers (of equal and proper thickness) behind each one. See DIFFERENTIAL PINION GEAR THRUST WASHER THICKESSES table.

2) Install pinion shaft, while rotating gears, to align shaft holes in gears with shaft holes in carrier. Insert pinion shaft and align spring pin hole in one end with matching hole in carrier. Install spring pin. *See Fig. 25.*

3) If removed, install side bearings onto carrier. With differential assembled, remeasure backlash. If backlash is still out of tolerance (from initial backlash inspection), replace both pinion gears and recheck backlash.

4) If still out of tolerance, replace both side gears and recheck backlash. If still out of tolerance, replace complete carrier assembly. Install dowel pin.

5) Install speedometer drive gear. Ensure chamfer (on gear I.D.) is facing carrier. Install and align snap ring properly on carrier. *See Fig. 26.* Ensure snap ring end gap does not align with spring pin or dowel pin.

6) Install ring gear onto carrier. Check that chamfer on inside diameter of ring gear is facing carrier. Install ring gear bolts (LEFT-HAND threads) from RIGHT-HAND side of carrier and tighten.

7) Temporarily install large snap ring into torque converter housing bore. Do not install oil seal at this time. Install differential assembly into converter housing using Driver (07749-0010000) and Attachment E (07947-6340500). Tap on differental assembly with driver and attachment to seat snap ring in housing.

NOTE: **If torque converter housing, transmission housing and/or differential side bearings were replaced, differential side clearance must be checked.**

8) Install mainshaft and countershaft assemblies into converter housing. Install new gasket onto

Fig. 25: Exploded View of Differential Assembly

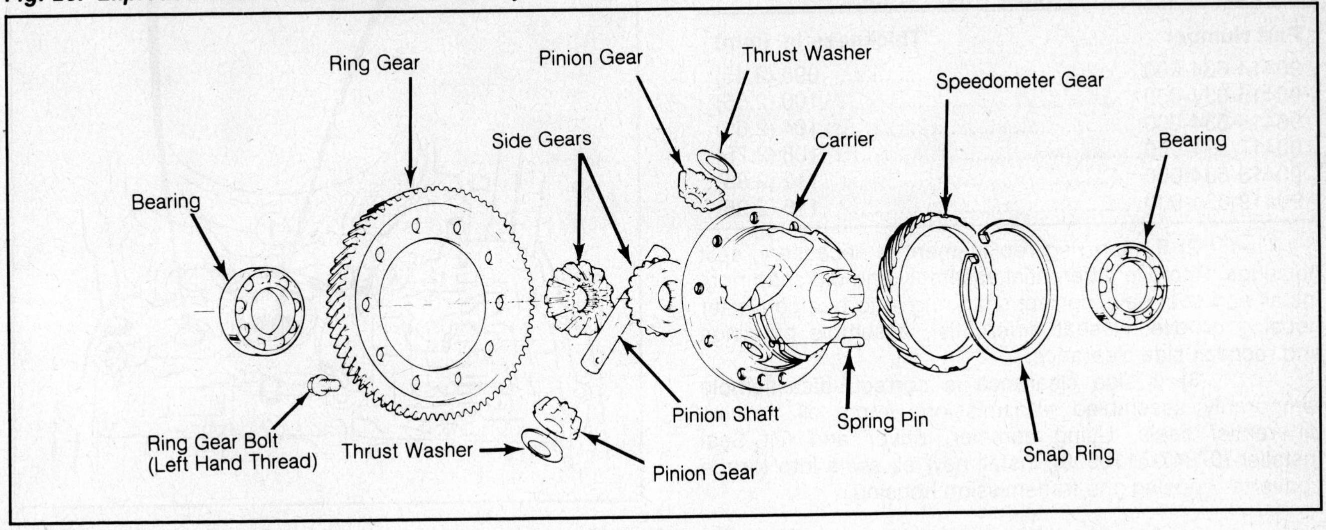

HONDA 4-SPEED (Cont.)

Fig. 26: Installation of Snap Ring On Differential Carrier

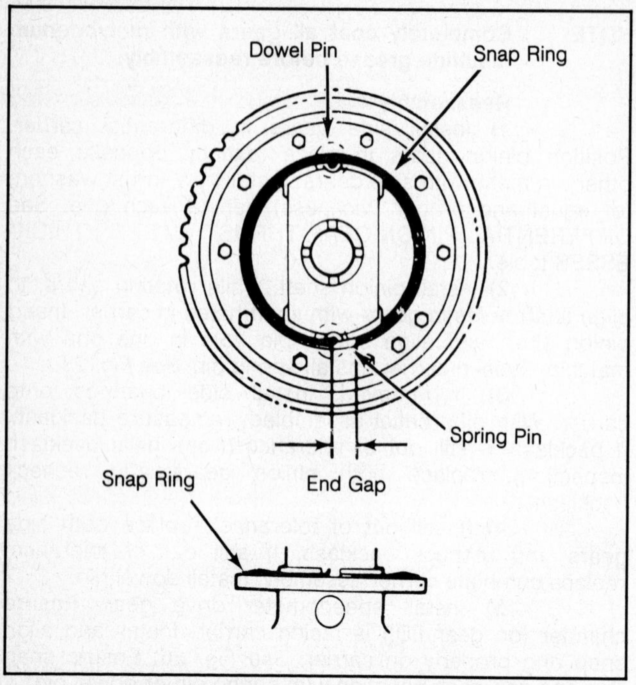

Ensure the snap ring end gap does not aligned with the pinion shaft spring pin or carrier dowel pin.

converter housing. Install dowel pins. Install transmission housing onto torque converter housing.

9) Install and tighten converter housing-to-transmission housing mounting bolts the same as removal sequence. *See Fig. 6.* Tighten mounting bolts in 2 or more steps. Check differential side clearance.

Differential Side Clearance Check

1) Ensure differential is bottomed in transmission housing. Using a feeler gauge, check clearance between snap ring and outer race of bearing in torque converter housing. Standard side clearance is .006" (.15 mm) maximum. If clearance is not to specification, select snap ring to give proper clearance. See SIDE CLEARANCE SNAP RING THICKNESSES table.

SIDE CLEARANCE SNAP RING THICKNESSES

Part Number	Thickness In. (mm)
90414-634-000	.096 (2.45)
90415-634-000	.100 (2.55)
90416-634-000	.104 (2.65)
90417-634-000	.108 (2.75)
90418-634-000	.112 (2.85)
90419-634-000	.116 (2.95)

2) If snap ring replacement is necessary, split housings. Remove differential assembly and old snap ring. Install and seat new, correct snap ring in torque converter housing groove. Reseat differential, assemble housings and recheck side clearance.

3) If side clearance is correct, disassemble temporarily assembled transmission. Apply oil to new differential seals. Using hammer, driver and Oil Seal Installer (07947-6110500), install new oil seals into torque converter housing and transmission housing.

TRANSAXLE REASSEMBLY

NOTE: Lubricate parts with ATF during reassembly.

1) Install differential assembly. Assemble manual valve lever on control shaft, then install in torque converter housing. Install control lever and new lock plate on other end of control shaft. Install and tighten bolt (6 x 10 mm). Bend tab of lock plate up to prevent bolt from turning.

2) Install suction pipe and new filter screen in converter housing. Install separator plate, dowel pin, oil pump gears and shaft. Ensure chamfered side of driven gear and shouldered side of drive gear face housing.

3) Install check valve and spring, then install main valve body onto converter housing. Install and tighten 4 valve body mounting bolts in sequence. *See Fig. 27.*

NOTE: Ensure oil pump drive gear rotates smoothly in normal operating direction and pump shaft moves smoothly in both axial and normal operating directions.

Fig. 27: Main Valve Body Mounting Bolt Tightening Sequence

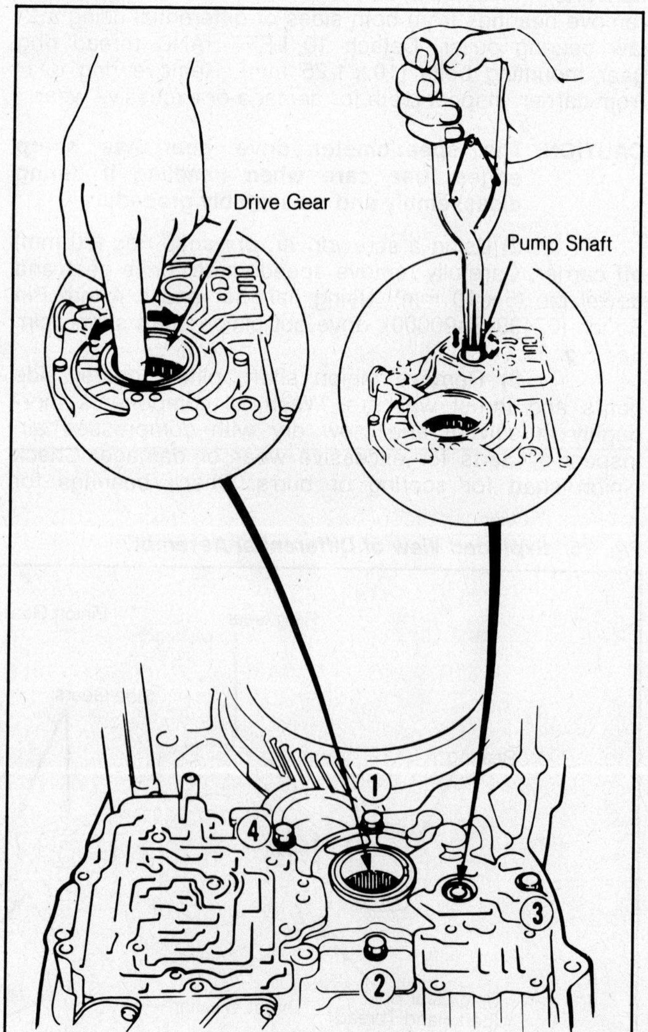

HONDA 4-SPEED (Cont.)

NOTE: **On Accord, when installing .22" (5.5 mm) steel balls, place 5 steel balls in main valve body passages. On Prelude, install one steel ball in regulator valve oil passage and 4 balls in main valve body oil passages.**

4) Install stator shaft arm, stop pin and dowel pins. Install regulator valve and tighten 3 mounting bolts. Install steel balls in oil passage(s). Install separator plate and dowel pins. On Prelude, install throttle control shaft.

5) On all models, install servo valve body. Ensure correct length bolt is installed in proper hole or servo will not seal to housing. On Accord, install 2 oil pipes and throttle control shaft. On all models, attach "E" clip to control shaft.

6) Place rollers on each side of manual valve stem. Attach valve to lever with pin and secure with cotter pin. If necessary, install 2 oil passage pipes (8 x 50 mm and 8 x 29.5 mm). Install clutch pressure control (CPC) valve body, body cover and separator plate onto servo valve body. Tighten mounting bolts.

7) Install 1st, 3rd and 4th clutch feed pipes. Install separator plate. Position 2 oil passage pipes (8 x 136 mm and 5 x 168 mm) between pressure control valve and CPC valve body. Slide pressure control valve into position (opposite of removal). *See Fig. 7.* Install pressure control valve body mounting bolts in their proper positions and tighten.

8) Install 2nd, 3rd and 4th accumulator springs in servo body. Check to ensure proper spring diameters and lengths. See SERVO VALVE BODY COMPONENTS & SPRING SPECIFICATIONS table. When installing 2nd/3rd and 4th accumulator covers, compress accumulator springs (by pushing on each cover) before tightening mounting bolts (in a crisscross pattern).

9) Install 3 governor valve mounting bolts (6 mm), with new lock plates, and tighten. Bend lock plate tabs over against bolt heads so bolts will not turn. Install mainshaft and countershaft assemblies into torque converter housing, as an assembly.

NOTE: **Do not tap on shaft ends to force shafts to seat.**

10) If installed, remove lock nuts from mainshaft and countershaft. Install selector hub, countershaft 4th gear and needle bearing. Assemble reverse selector sleeve with reverse shift fork (un-marked side up). Install as an assembly onto countershaft. Ensure flat face on selector sleeve faces up.

11) Install reverse shift fork over servo valve stem. Align hole in valve stem by turning stem so chamfered hole faces fork bolt hole. Install bolt and new lock plate. Bend lock plate tab over bolt head. Install countershaft reverse gear, needle bearing (30 x 36 x 14 mm) and reverse gear collar. Install new gasket, one dowel pin (14 x 20 mm) and 2 dowel pins (14 x 25 mm) on converter housing.

12) Place transmission housing on torque converter housing. Ensure main valve control shaft lines up with hole in housing and that reverse idler gear meshes with mainshaft and countershaft or housing will not go on. Tighten housing mounting bolts, in 2 or more steps, in the same sequence as removal.

NOTE: **When tightening transmission housing mounting bolts, ensure throttle control bracket is not distorted or damage or transmission shift points will be changed.**

13) Install throttle control lever and spring on throttle control shaft. Install bolt and new lock plate. Bend tab against bolt head. Install parking shift arm, parking lever and spring onto shift shaft. Ensure flat pad of parking lever faces closed end of shift arm. Using a new lock tab, bend tab against bolt head.

NOTE: **Parking shift arm spring should put clockwise tension on shift arm, forcing it against stop pin.**

14) Install 1st gear collar and needle bearing on countershaft. Install collar (26 mm) onto mainshaft. Install reverse idler bearing holder over shaft and onto case. Tighten mounting bolts. Install new "O" rings (19.8 x 1.9 mm) onto mainshaft.

15) Install countershaft 1st gear and parking gear on countershaft. Install stop pin, parking pawl shaft, parking pawl and pawl release spring. Ensure end of parking pawl release spring fits into hole in parking pawl. Release spring should put clockwise tension on pawl, forcing it away from parking gear.

16) Shift lever to "P" and install mainshaft holder. Using breaker bar and 30 mm socket wrench (07907-6890100), install and tighten new countershaft lock nut. Stake lock nut flange into gear groove. Install needle bearing (31 x 36 x 18.5 mm) and thrust washer on mainshaft. Install 1st gear, needle bearing (31 x 37 x 72 mm) and thrust washer (26 mm) on mainshaft.

NOTE: **When installing thrust washer and needle bearing, ensure that unrolled edge of bearing faces thrust washer.**

17) Install 1st clutch on mainshaft. Attach Mainshaft Holder (07932-6890202) from underside of converter housing, then install new mainshaft lock nut (LEFT-HAND threads). Stake lock nut flange to groove in 1st clutch. Install gasket, dowel pins and "O" rings on transmission housing.

18) Install end cover and tighten mounting bolts. If removed, install 1st accumulator (if equipped) onto end cover with new gasket and "O" rings (8.5 x 1.9 mm). Install dipstick and cooler fittings. Do not tighten cooler fittings until transmission is installed in vehicle.

HONDA 4-SPEED (Cont.)

TIGHTENING SPECIFICATIONS

Application	Ft. Lbs. (N.m)
Countershaft Lock Nut	70 (95)
Ring Gear Mounting Bolts	74 (103)
Stabilizer Bar	28 (38)
Starter Bolts	33 (45)
Drive Plate-to-Crankshaft Mounting Bolt	54 (73)
Torque Rods	54 (73)
Transmission Cooler	
Hose (Banjo) Mounting Bolt	19 (26)
Transmission Housing [1]	
To-Converter Housing Mounting Bolts	20 (27)
Transmission Mounting Bolts	33 (45)
1st Accumulator (Prelude)	
Bleed Screw	12 (18)
1st Clutch Assembly Lock Nut	70 (95)
	INCH Lbs. (N.m)
Clutch Pressure Control (CPC)	
Valve Body Mounting Bolt	106 (12)
Governor Valve Body Mounting Bolt	106 (12)
Main Valve Body	
Mounting Bolt	106 (12)
Shift Valve Cover Mounting Bolt	71 (8)
Pressure Control Valve Body Mounting Bolt	106 (12)
Pressure Regulator Valve Mounting Bolt	106 (12)
Regulator Valve Body Mounting Bolt	106 (12)
Ring Gear-to-Converter Mounting Bolt	106 (12)
Servo Valve Body Mounting Bolt	106 (12)
Throttle Control Lever	
To-Throttle Valve Shaft Mounting Bolt	71 (8)
Torque Converter	
To-Drive Plate Mounting Bolt	106 (12)
Throttle Valve "A"	
Retainer Plate Mounting Bolt	106 (12)
1st Accumulator (Prelude)	
To-End Cover Mounting Bolt	106 (12)

[1] – Tighten housing mounting bolts in 2 or more steps, in same sequence as removal.

JATCO 3N71B, E4N71B, JM600, L3N71B & L4N71B

APPLICATION

TRANSMISSION APPLICATION

Vehicle	Transmission
Chrysler Corp.	
Conquest	JM600
Mazda	
B2000 Pickup	3N71B
B2200 Pickup	3N71B
RX7	L4N71B
Mitsubishi	
Starion	JM600
Nissan	
Pickup	L3N71B
200SX & 200SX Turbo	L4N71B
300ZX & 300ZX Turbo	E4N71B

IDENTIFICATION

These transmissions are manufactured by Japan Automatic Transmission Company (JATCO). Transmission model may be identified by stamped metal plate attached to right side of transmission case. Plate lists model code on top line and serial number on bottom line.

DESCRIPTION

JATCO 3N71B and L3N71B transmissions are 3-speed units, consisting of 3-element torque converter and 2 planetary gear sets. The E4N71B and L4N71B are 4-speed units, consisting of 3-element torque converter and 3 planetary gear sets.

The L3N71B and L4N71B models use lock-up type torque converter. Model 3N71B uses conventional type converter. Model E4N71B is based on L4N71B and provides electronic control of converter lock-up in all forward gears.

The E4N71B model uses microcomputer to select shift pattern ("standard" or "power") depending upon rate at which accelerator is depressed. Shift pattern programs are set in lock-up control unit depending upon vehicle speed and throttle position.

To provide friction elements required to obtain desired function of planetary gear sets, 3N71B and L3N71B models utilize 2 multiple disc clutches, one multi-disc brake, one brake band and one-way clutch. On E4N71B and L4N71B models, 3 multiple disc clutches, one multi-disc brake, 2 brake bands and one-way clutch are used.

On all models, hydraulic system, pressurized by gear-type pump, provides working pressure required to operate friction elements and automatic controls.

LUBRICATION & ADJUSTMENT

See appropriate AUTOMATIC TRANSMISSION SERVICING article in IMPORT GENERAL SERVICING section.

TROUBLE SHOOTING

Possible causes of problem are listed in order of probability for particular malfunction.

ENGINE WILL NOT START WITH SELECTOR LEVER IN "N" OR "P"

Check ignition and starter systems. Adjust selector lever linkage. Check inhibitor switch and wiring.

ENGINE STARTS IN POSITIONS OTHER THAN "N" OR "P"

Check selector lever linkage, inhibitor switch and wiring.

SHARP SHOCK WHEN SHIFTED FROM "N" TO "D"

Engine idle RPM too high. Check vacuum diaphragm and hoses. Check transmission line pressure. Check control valve body. Check forward clutch.

VEHICLE HAS "2", "1", AND "R", BUT NO "D"

Check selector lever linkage. Check control valve body. Check one-way clutch operation.

VEHICLE HAS "R", BUT NO FORWARD GEARS. TRANSMISSION SLIPS BADLY, POOR ACCELERATION

Check ATF level and quality. Check selector lever adjustment. Check transmission line pressure. Check control valve body. Check forward clutch, oil passage leakage or high-reverse clutch.

NO MOVEMENT IN ANY RANGE

Check ATF level and quality. Check selector lever linkage adjustment. Check control valve body. Check forward clutch, oil passage leakage or park linkage failure.

SLIPPAGE OF CLUTCHES OR BRAKES WHEN STARTING AWAY

Check ATF level and quality. Check line pressure. Check vacuum diaphragm and hoses. Check oil pump or oil passage leakage.

VEHICLE MOVES IN "N"

Check selector linkage adjustment. Check ATF level and quality. Check control valve body. Check forward clutch.

POOR ACCELERATION, VEHICLE WILL NOT ATTAIN TOP SPEED

Check ATF level and quality. Check selector lever linkage adjustment. Check line pressure. Incorrect stall RPM. Check band servo. Check control valve body. Check 2nd gear band brake, low and reverse brake, forward clutch, high-reverse clutch or oil pump.

VEHICLE BRAKES WHEN SHIFTED INTO "R"

Check ATF level and quality. Check band servo. Check forward clutch, 2nd band brake or park linkage.

VEHICLE HAS EXCESSIVE "CREEP"

Adjust engine idle RPM.

VEHICLE HAS NO "CREEP"

Check ATF level and selector lever adjustment. Adjust engine idle RPM. Check control valve body. Check

JATCO 3N71B, E4N71B, JM600, L3N71B & L4N71B (Cont.)

Fig. 1: Exploded View Of L3N71B 3-Speed As Used In Nissan/Datsun Pickup

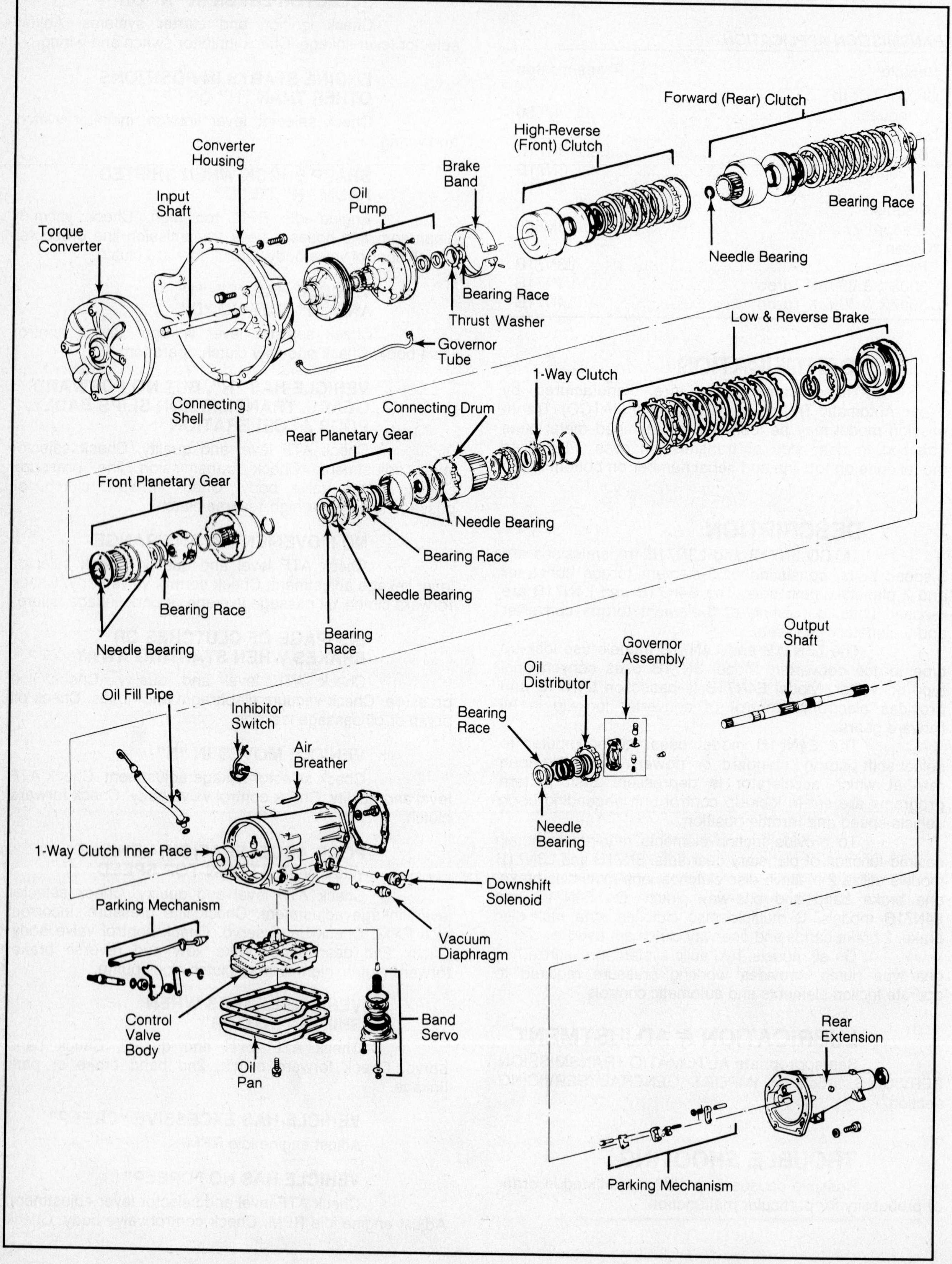

JATCO 3N71B, E4N71B, JM600, L3N71B & L4N71B (Cont.)

Fig. 2: Exploded View Of E4N71B 4-Speed As Used In Nissan/Datsun 300ZX.

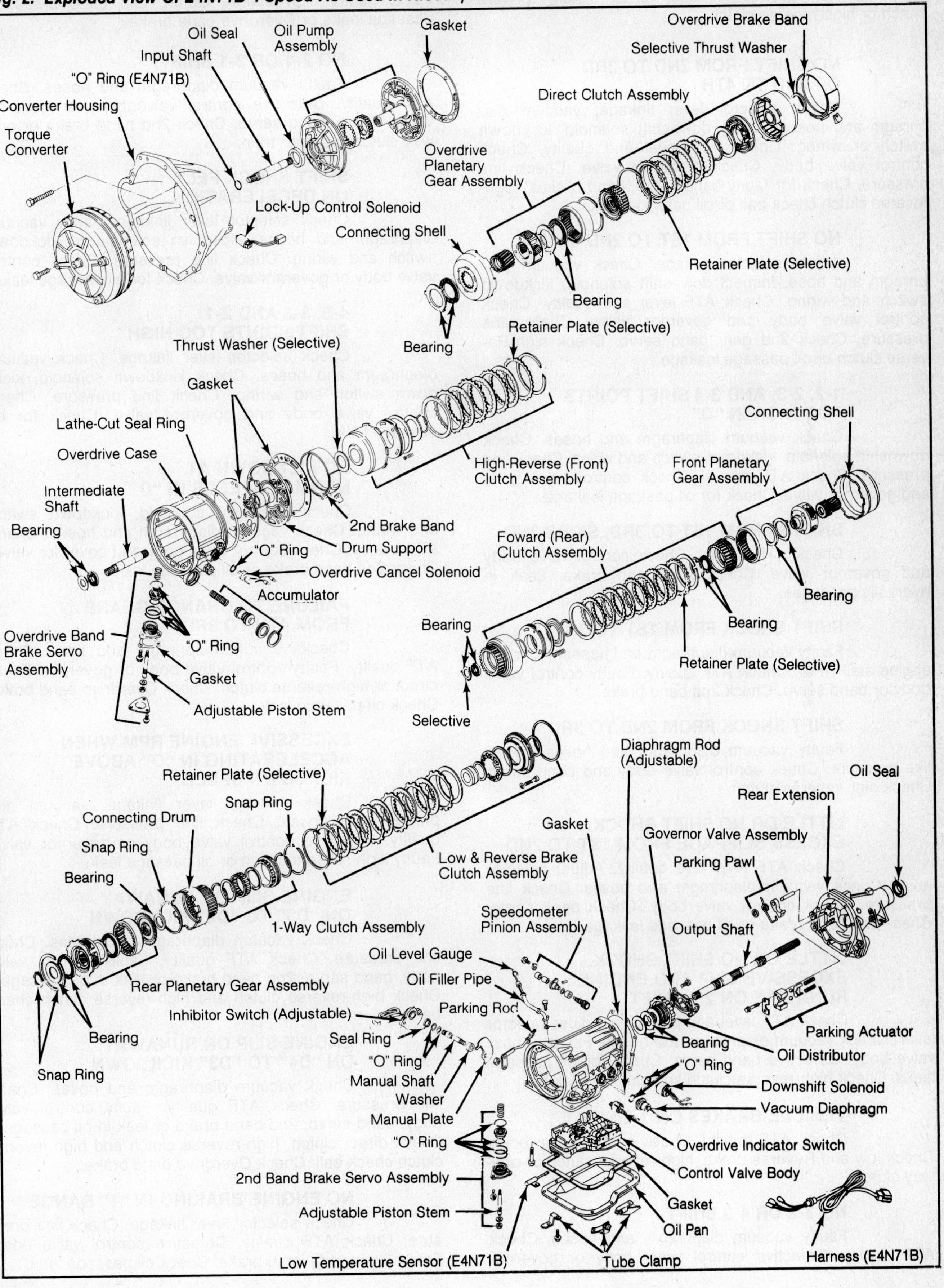

oil pump, oil passage leakage, direct clutch, forward clutch or high-reverse clutch.

NO SHIFT FROM 2ND TO 3RD OR 3RD TO 4TH

Check selector lever linkage, vacuum diaphragm and hoses. Faulty downshift solenoid, kickdown switch or wiring. Check ATF level and quality. Check control valve body. Check governor valve. Check line pressure. Check for faulty band servo, band brakes, high-reverse clutch check ball or oil passage leak.

NO SHIFT FROM 1ST TO 2ND IN "D"

Adjust selector linkage. Check vacuum diaphragm and hose. Inspect downshift solenoid, kickdown switch and wiring. Check ATF level and quality. Check control valve body and governor valve. Check line pressure. Check 2nd gear band servo. Check high-Reverse clutch or oil passage leakage.

1-2, 2-3, AND 3-4 SHIFT POINTS TOO HIGH IN "D"

Check vacuum diaphragm and hoses. Check downshift solenoid, kickdown switch and wires. Check line pressure. Check ATF quality. Check control valve body and governor valve. Check for oil passage leakage.

SHIFTS FROM 1ST TO 3RD, SKIPS 2ND

Check ATF quality. Check control valve body and governor valve. Check 2nd band brake. Leak in hydraulic passages.

SHIFT SHOCK FROM 1ST TO 2ND

Faulty vacuum diaphragm and hoses. Incorrect engine stall RPM. Check ATF quality. Faulty control valve body or band servo. Check 2nd band brake.

SHIFT SHOCK FROM 2ND TO 3RD

Faulty vacuum diaphragm and hoses. Check line pressure. Check control valve body and band servo. Check high-reverse clutch.

LITTLE OR NO SHIFT SHOCK. EXCESS SLIPPAGE FROM 1ST TO 2ND

Check ATF level and quality. Adjust selector lever. Check vacuum diaphragm and hoses. Check line pressure. Check control valve body. Check band servo. Check 2nd band brake or oil passage leakage.

LITTLE OR NO SHIFT SHOCK. EXCESSIVE SLIP AND ENGINE RUNAWAY ON 2-3 SHIFT

Check ATF level and pressure. Adjust selector lever. Check vacuum diaphragm and hoses. Faulty control valve body. Defective band servo. Check for oil passage leaks. Check high-reverse clutch and clutch check ball.

VEHICLE BRAKES ON 1-2 SHIFT

Check ATF quality. Check control valve body. Check low and Reverse brake, high-reverse clutch or one-way clutch.

NO 3-2 OR 4-2 SHIFT

Faulty vacuum diaphragm and hoses. Check ATF quality. Defective control valve body or governor valve. Faulty high-reverse clutch, 2nd band brake, oil passage leaks or Overdrive band brake.

NO 2-1 OR 3-1 SHIFT

Faulty vacuum diaphragm and hoses. Check ATF quality. Defective control valve body or governor valve. Check band servo. Check 2nd band brake or one-way clutch in power train.

SHIFT SHOCK FELT ON DECELERATION

Check selector lever linkage. Faulty vacuum diaphragm and hoses, kickdown solenoid or kickdown switch and wiring. Check line pressure. Check control valve body or governor valve. Check for oil passage leaks.

4-3, 3-2 AND 2-1 SHIFT POINTS TOO HIGH

Check selector lever linkage. Check vacuum diaphragm and hoses. Check kickdown solenoid, kickdown switch and wiring. Check line pressure. Check control valve body and governor valve. Check for oil passage leak.

NO KICKDOWN AT NORMAL SPEEDS IN "D"

Check kickdown solenoid, kickdown switch and wiring. Check vacuum diaphragm and hoses. Check ATF quality. Check control valve body and governor valve. Check 2nd band brake or oil passage leak.

FAILURE TO CHANGE GEARS FROM 4TH TO 3RD

Check vacuum diaphragm and lines. Check ATF quality. Faulty control valve body or governor. Faulty direct or high-reverse clutch. Check Overdrive band brake. Check oil passage leak.

EXCESSIVE ENGINE RPM WHEN ACCELERATING IN "D" ABOVE KICKDOWN SPEED

Check selector lever linkage, vacuum diaphragm and hoses. Check line pressure. Check ATF quality. Defective control valve body or governor valve. Faulty high-reverse clutch or oil passage leak.

ENGINE SLIP OR RUNAWAY ON "D3" TO "D2" KICKDOWN

Check vacuum diaphragm and hoses. Check line pressure. Check ATF quality. Faulty control valve body, band servo, 2nd band brake or leak in oil passages. Check high-reverse clutch and high-reverse clutch check ball.

ENGINE SLIP OR RUNAWAY ON "D4" TO "D3" KICKDOWN

Check vacuum diaphragm and hoses. Check line pressure. Check ATF quality. Faulty control valve body, band servo, 2nd band brake or leak in oil passages. Check direct clutch, high-reverse clutch and high-reverse clutch check ball. Check Overdrive band brake.

NO ENGINE BRAKING IN "1" RANGE

Check selector lever linkage. Check line pressure. Check ATF quality. Defective control valve body. Faulty low and reverse brake. Check oil passage leak.

JATCO 3N71B, E4N71B, JM600, L3N71B & L4N71B (Cont.)

TRANSMISSION OVERHEATS

Check ATF level and quality. Faulty rear lubrication or line pressure. Incorrect engine stall speed. Defective control valve body. Faulty band servo, high-reverse clutch, band brake, low and reverse brake, oil pump. Possible hydraulic passage leaks. Defective 1-way clutch in torque converter or planetary gear. Faulty torque converter.

TRANSMISSION NOISY IN "P" AND "N"

Check fluid level. Faulty line pressure. Faulty pump.

TRANSMISSION NOISY IN "R" AND ALL "D" RANGES

Check fluid level. Faulty line pressure, forward clutch, oil pump, one-way clutch in power train or planetary gear.

NOTE: **Following problems and possible causes apply ONLY to models with lock-up control and Overdrive functions. These are E4N71B, JM600, L3N71B and L4N71B transmission models.**

TORQUE CONVERTER DOES NOT LOCK UP

Governor tube disconnected or damaged. Governor faulty. Incorrect line pressure. Check "O" ring in input shaft and oil pump condition. Speed cut valve (L3N71B model only) or lock-up control valve faulty or defective. Check lock-up orifice in oil pump cover. Faulty torque converter.

CLUTCH AND BAND APPLICATION – 3N71B & L3N71B (ELEMENTS IN USE)

Selector Lever Position	High-Reverse (Front) Clutch	Forward (Rear) Clutch	Low-Reverse Brake	Brake Band	One-Way Clutch
P – PARK			X		
R – REVERSE	X		X		
N – NEUTRAL [1]					
D – DRIVE					
First		X			X
Second		X		X	
Direct	X	X			
2 – SECOND		X		X	
1 – LOW					
First		X	X		
Second		X		X	

[1] – NEUTRAL or PARK – All clutches and bands released and/or ineffective.

CLUTCH AND BAND APPLICATION – E4N71B, JM600 & L4N71B (ELEMENTS IN USE)

Selector Lever Position	Direct Clutch	Overdrive Band	High-Reverse (Ft.) Clutch	Forward (Rear) Clutch	Low & Reverse Brake	Brake Band	One-Way Clutch
P – PARK	X	X			X		
R – REVERSE	X	X	X		X		
N – NEUTRAL [1]	X	X					
D – DRIVE							
First	X	X		X			X
Second	X	X		X		X	
Direct	X	X	X	X		X	
Overdrive		X	X	X		X	
2 – SECOND	X	X		X		X	
1 – LOW							
Second	X	X		X		X	
First	X	X		X	X		X

[1] – NEUTRAL or PARK – All clutches and bands released and/or ineffective.

JATCO 3N71B, E4N71B, JM600, L3N71B & L4N71B (Cont.)

LOCK-UP PISTON SLIPS

Incorrect line pressure. Check condition of "O" ring in input shaft. Check lock-up orifice in oil pump cover. Check oil pump condition. Faulty torque converter.

LOCK-UP POINT TOO HIGH OR TOO LOW

Governor tube disconnected or damaged. Governor faulty. Check speed cut valve (L3N71B model only) and lock-up control valve condition.

ENGINE STOPPED IN ANY GEAR RANGE

Faulty lock-up control valve. Defective torque converter.

TRANSMISSION SHIFTS TO OVERDRIVE EVEN WHEN CANCEL SWITCH IS ON

Check Overdrive cancel switch and wiring. Check Overdrive cancel solenoid.

TRANSMISSION OVERHEATS

Check line pressure. Check "O" ring in input shaft. Check lock-up orifice in oil pump cover. Oil pump faulty. Torque converter faulty or damaged.

TESTING

LOCK-UP & OVERDRIVE CONTROLS

200SX Lock-Up & Overdrive Control

1) Operation of torque converter lock-up and Overdrive (D_4) is handled by ECU that senses vehicle speed. ECU will activate lock-up solenoid if conditions are correct. Overdrive control switch activates Overdrive cancel solenoid when turned off and transmission can not shift into D_4 range.

2) If lock-up or Overdrive malfunction, perform Lock-Up Control Unit Test first. See NISSAN/DATSUN 200SX LOCK-UP CONTROL UNIT TEST CHART. If ECU tests properly, proceed to lock-up control testing and 3rd/Overdrive control testing as shown in flow charts and associated text.

3) ECU is located in left side of luggage compartment on hatchback models; on coupe models, it is located behind right panel in rear seat area. Testing is to be performed with wiring harness connected to ECU. Using voltmeter, check voltage between terminal No. 5 (Ground) and each terminal as listed in test chart.

4) No. 6 terminal is not used on ECU connector. No. 1 terminal is directly above No. 6. Upper row of connector contains terminals 1 through 5, counting left to right viewed from front. Lower row contains terminals 6 through 10.

NISSAN/DATSUN 200SX LOCK-UP CONTROL UNIT TEST CHART

Terminal	Unit Tested	Test Condition	Result
1	Power Source	Meter between terminals 1 & 5	12 volts at all times
2	Overdrive Cancel Solenoid	Operate Overdrive control switch	Switch ON: O volts Switch OFF: 12 volts
3	Lock-Up Solenoid	Driving in "D"	0 volts when ON 12 volts when OFF
4	Throttle Sensor (Ground)	.....	.....
5	Ground	.....	.....
6	Not Used		
7	Speed Sensor	Check voltage variation over 3 feet at very low speed	0 volts to 5.1 (or more) volts
8	Throttle Sensor (Power Source)	Meter between terminals 8 & 5	5 volts at all times
9	Throttle Sensor	Depress and release accelerator pedal	Closed throttle: .4 volts Full throttle: 4 volts
10	Lock-Up Cancel Signal	Depress and release accelerator pedal	Coolant 149°F (65°C) or less: 12 volts at all times Coolant 158°F (70°C) or more: Full throttle: 12 volts Partial throttle: 0 volts

JATCO 3N71B, E4N71B, JM600, L3N71B & L4N71B (Cont.)

200SX LOCK-UP CONTROL INSPECTION POINTS

Inspection Item-1

Connect voltmeter between terminals No. 3 and No. 5. Check lock-up signals while running vehicle with partial throttle and Overdrive control switch on. At speeds above 48 MPH, lock-up solenoid should be ON. At speeds below 45 MPH, lock-up solenoid should be OFF.

Inspection Item-2

Check wiring between ECU and lock-up solenoid. Check connections and continuity.

Inspection Item-3

Make sure "O" ring is installed on tip of lock-up solenoid. Check that solenoid clicks when 12 volts is applied to it.

Inspection Item-4

Check wiring between ECU and following sensors: throttle and vehicle speed. Check wiring between ECU and Overdrive control switch. Check connections and continuity.

Inspection Item-5

Check signals of input sensors and switches. See NISSAN/DATSUN 200SX LOCK-UP CONTROL UNIT TEST CHART for correct results.

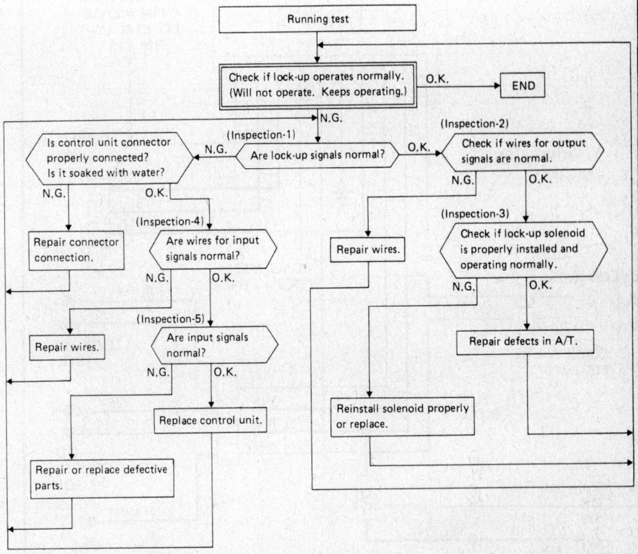

200SX 3RD/OVERDRIVE CONTROL INSPECTION POINTS

Inspection Item-1

Check operation of Overdrive solenoid by applying 12 volts to solenoid. Good solenoid will click if working.

Inspection Item-2

Check continuity between terminals of Overdrive control switch. There should be no continuity when control switch is ON. There should be continuity when control switch is OFF.

Inspection Item-3

Check wiring between ECU and vehicle speed sensor. Check wiring between ECU and terminal No. 20 on EFI control unit connector terminal. Check connections and continuity.

Inspection Item-4

Check ECU connector terminals No. 4 and No. 10 for continuity and voltage. See NISSAN/DATSUN 200SX LOCK-UP CONTROL UNIT TEST CHART for correct results of tests.

Inspection Item-5

Check wiring between ECU and Overdrive cancel solenoid. Check connections and continuity.

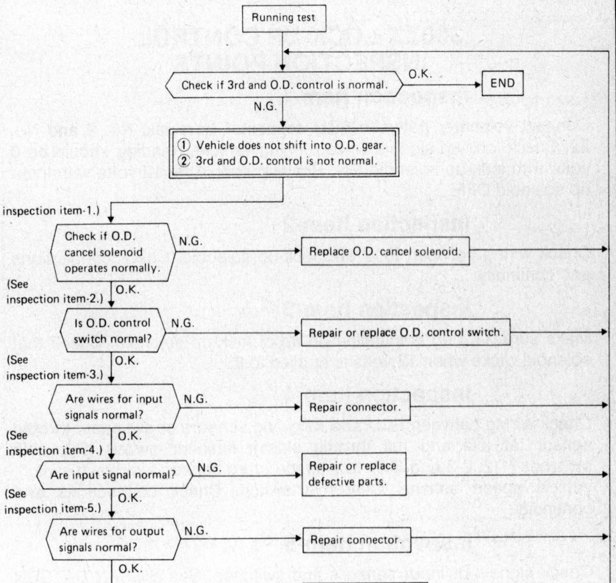

JATCO 3N71B, E4N71B, JM600, L3N71B & L4N71B (Cont.)

Fig. 3: 1985 Nissan/Datsun 200SX A/T Lock-Up Control Wiring Diagram

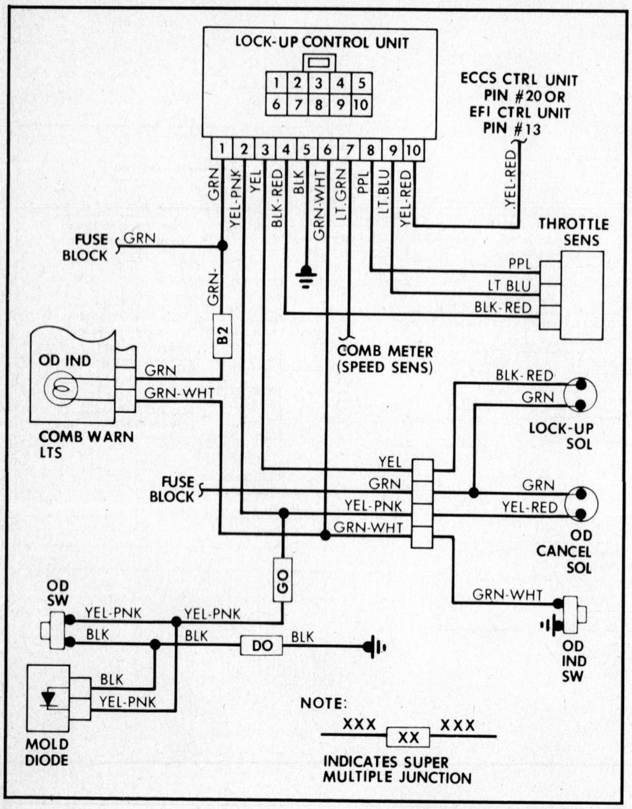

300ZX Electronic Lock-Up & Overdrive Control

1) Operation of torque converter lock-up and Overdrive (D_4) is handled by electronic control unit (ECU), located on floor near driver's seat. ECU will activate lock-up solenoid in all forward ranges if conditions are correct. Either "standard" or "power" shift pattern is selected by ECU depending upon rate at which accelerator is depressed.

2) Vehicle speed and throttle position are both inputs to ECU. Power shift switch activates Overdrive cancel solenoid when turned off and transmission will not shift into D_4 range. If lock-up or Overdrive malfunction, test lock-up control unit first. See NISSAN/DATSUN 300ZX ELECTRONIC LOCK-UP CONTROL UNIT TEST CHART.

3) Testing is to be performed with wiring harness connected to ECU. Using voltmeter, check voltage between terminal No. 22 (Ground) and each terminal as listed in test chart. If ECU tests properly, proceed to lock-up, Overdrive, downshift, shift pattern change, A.S.C.D. (Automatic Speed Control Device), and kickdown control testing as shown in flow charts and associated text.

4) Terminal No. 20 is not used on ECU connector. Terminal No. 1 is directly above No. 6. Top row of connector contains terminals 1 through 17, viewed from front. Bottom row contains terminals 6 through 22.

300ZX LOCK-UP CONTROL INSPECTION POINTS

Inspection Item-1

Connect voltmeter between ECU connector terminals No. 2 and No. 22. Check lock-up signals while running vehicle. Reading should be 0 volts with lock-up solenoid ON. Reading should be 12 volts with lock-up solenoid OFF.

Inspection Item-2

Check wiring between ECU and lock-up solenoid. Check connections and continuity.

Inspection Item-3

Make sure "O" ring is installed on tip of lock-up solenoid. Check that solenoid clicks when 12 volts is applied to it.

Inspection Item-4

Check wiring between ECU and following sensors or switches: throttle sensor (at idle and full throttle sides); inhibitor switch (D_2); shift switches (1-2, 2-3 and 3-4); low-temperature sensor; kickdown switch; vehicle speed sensor; Overdrive switch. Check connections and continuity.

Inspection Item-5

Check signals of input sensors and switches. See NISSAN/DATSUN 300ZX ELECTRONIC CONTROL UNIT TEST CHART for correct results.

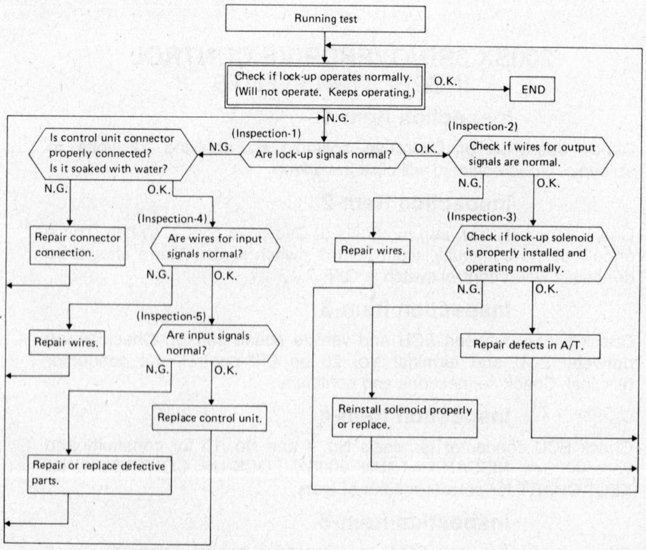

JATCO 3N71B, E4N71B, JM600, L3N71B & L4N71B (Cont.)

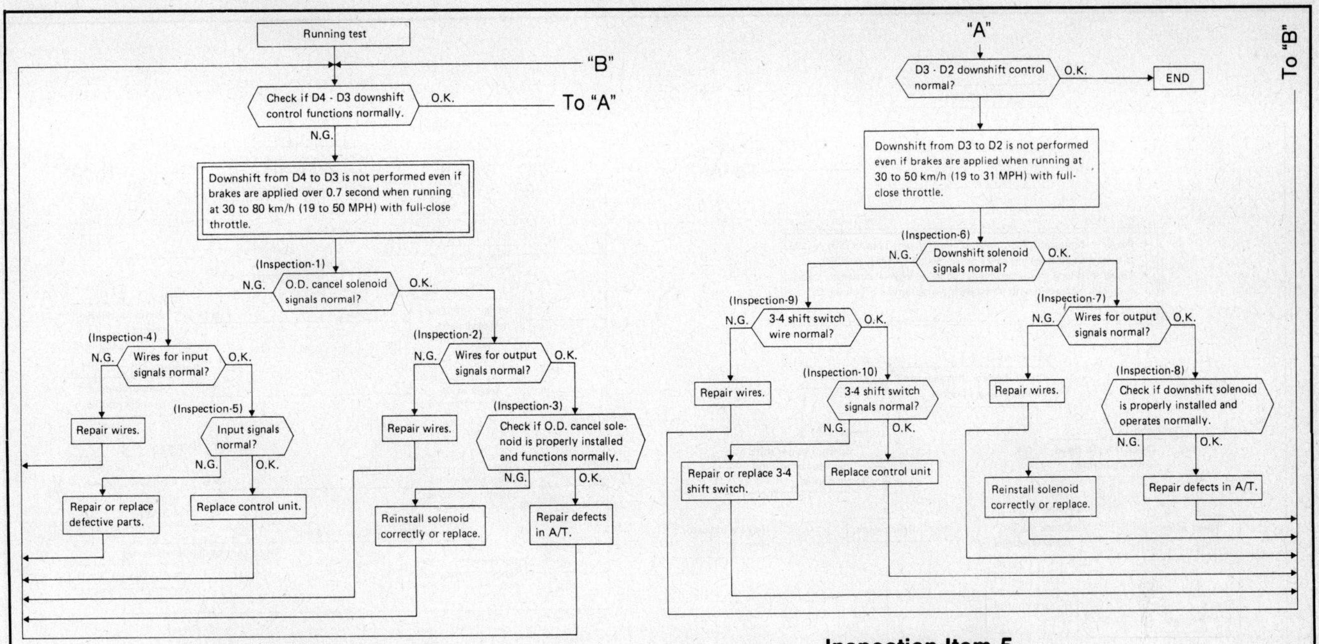

300ZX DOWNSHIFT CONTROL INSPECTION POINTS

Inspection Item-1

Jack up rear wheels. Set selector lever in "D" range. Accelerate to D_4 speed at partial throttle. When vehicle speed is in 19-50 MPH range, close throttle fully. Apply brakes for longer than .7 seconds. Check output signals to Overdrive cancel solenoid. See NISSAN/DATSUN 300ZX ELECTRONIC CONTROL UNIT TEST CHART for correct results.

Inspection Item-2

Check wiring between ECU and Overdrive cancel solenoid. Check connections and continuity.

Inspection Item-3

Apply 12 volts to Overdrive cancel solenoid. Proper operation is indicated by click from Overdrive cancel solenoid.

Inspection Item-4

Check wiring between ECU and and following sensors and switches: inhibitor switch (D_2); shift switches (1-2, 2-3 and 3-4); brake switch; idle contact switch; throttle sensor; vehicle speed sensor. Check connections and continuity.

Inspection Item-5

Check signals from input sensors and switches. See NISSAN/DATSUN 300ZX ELECTRONIC CONTROL UNIT TEST CHART for correct results.

Inspection Item-6

Jack up rear wheels. Set selector lever in "D" range. Accelerate to D_3 speed at partial throttle. When vehicle speed is in 19-31 MPH range, close throttle fully and apply brakes. See NISSAN/DATSUN 300ZX ELECTRONIC CONTROL UNIT TEST CHART to check downshift solenoid operation.

Inspection Item-7

Check wiring between ECU and downshift solenoid. Check connections and continuity.

Inspection Item-8

Apply 12 volts to downshift solenoid. Proper operation is indicated by click from downshift solenoid.

Inspection Item-9

Check wiring between ECU and 3-4 shift switch. Check connections and continuity.

Inspection Item-10

Check signals from 3-4 switch. See NISSAN/DATSUN 300ZX ELECTRONIC CONTROL UNIT TEST CHART for correct results.

300ZX KICKDOWN CONTROL INSPECTION POINTS

Inspection Item-1

Turn ignition ON and depress accelerator fully. Proper operation is indicated by click from downshift solenoid.

Inspection Item-2

Connect voltmeter to ECU connector terminals No. 21 and No. 22. Reading should be 0 volts with wide open throttle. Reading should be 5 volts at any less than full throttle.

Inspection Item-3

Check wiring between ECU and kickdown switch. Check connections and continuity.

Inspection Item-4

Check wiring between ECU and downshift solenoid. Check connections and continuity.

Inspection Item-5

Apply 12 volts to downshift solenoid. Proper operation is indicated by click from downshift solenoid.

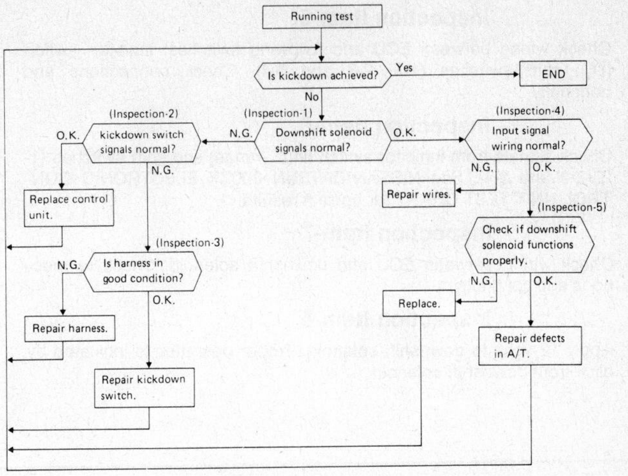

JATCO 3N71B, E4N71B, JM600, L3N71B & L4N71B (Cont.)

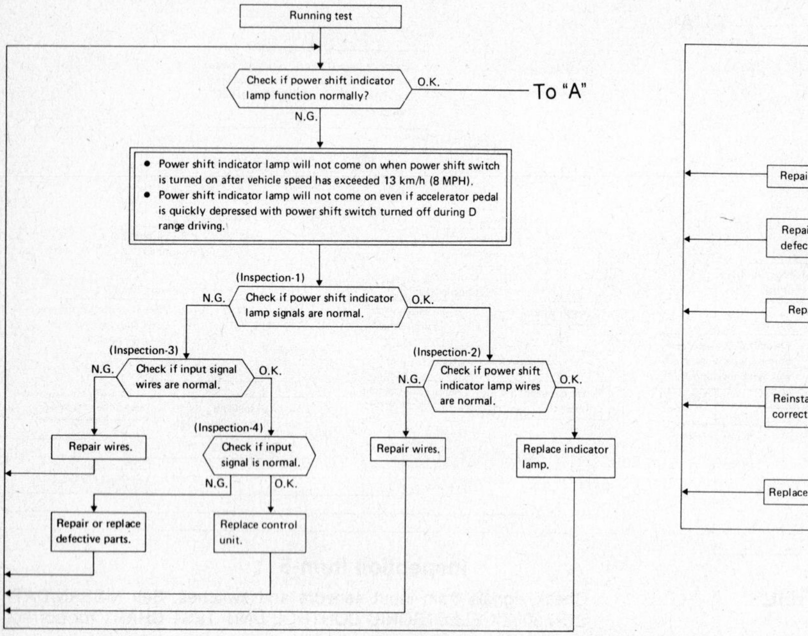

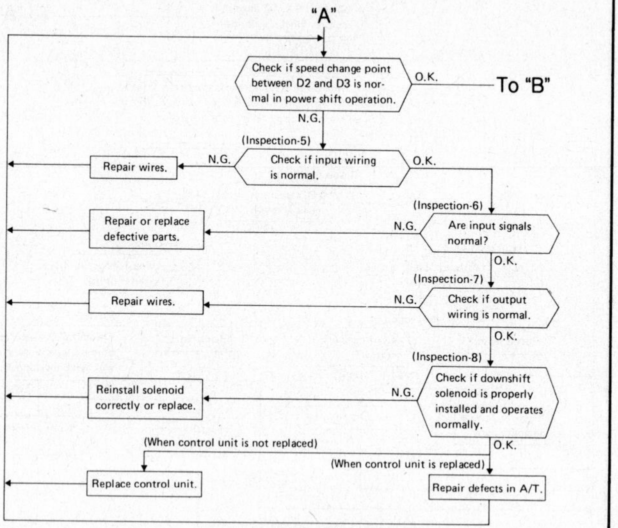

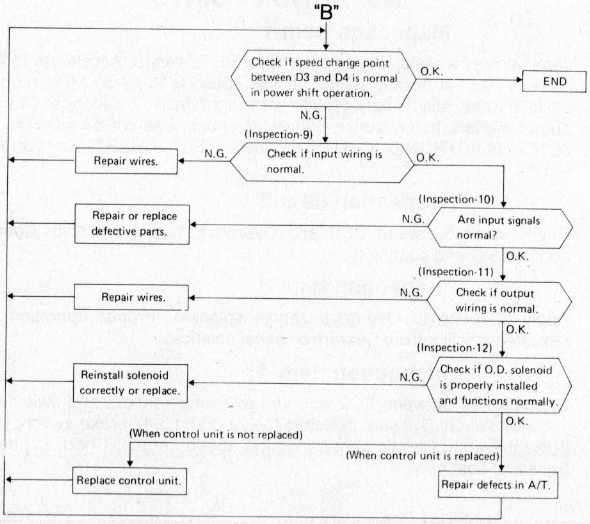

300ZX SHIFT PATTERN CHANGE CONTROL INSPECTION POINTS

Inspection Item-1

Jack up rear wheels and accelerate in "D" range. Turn on power shift switch as speed goes over 8 MPH. Depress and release accelerator pedal quickly at same time. Check power shift indicator light. See NISSAN/DATSUN 300ZX ELECTRONIC CONTROL UNIT TEST CHART for correct results.

Inspection Item-2

Check wiring between ECU and power shift indicator lamp. Check connections and continuity.

Inspection Item-3

Check wiring between ECU and following sensors and switches: power shift switch; throttle sensor; vehicle speed sensor. Check connections and continuity.

Inspection Item-4

Check signals from power shift switch, throttle sensor and vehicle speed sensor. See NISSAN/DATSUN 300ZX ELECTRONIC CONTROL UNIT TEST CHART for correct results.

Inspection Item-5

Check wiring between ECU and following switches: inhibitor switch (D_2); shift switches (1-2, 2-3 and 3-4). Check connections and continuity.

Inspection Item-6

Check signals from inhibitor switch (in D_2 range) and shift switches (1-2, 2-3 and 3-4). See NISSAN/DATSUN 300ZX ELECTRONIC CONTROL UNIT TEST CHART for correct results.

Inspection Item-7

Check wiring between ECU and downshift solenoid. Check connections and continuity.

Inspection Item-8

Apply 12 volts to downshift solenoid. Proper operation is indicated by click from downshift solenoid.

Inspection Item-9

Check wiring between ECU and 3-4 shift switch. Check connections and continuity.

Inspection Item-10

Check signals from 3-4 shift switch. See NISSAN/DATSUN 300ZX ELECTRONIC CONTROL UNIT TEST CHART for correct results.

Inspection Item-11

Check wiring between ECU and Overdrive cancel solenoid. Check connections and continuity.

Inspection Item-12

Apply 12 volts to Overdrive cancel solenoid. Proper operation is indicated by click from downshift solenoid.

JATCO 3N71B, E4N71B, JM600, L3N71B & L4N71B (Cont.)

300ZX A.S.C.D. PARTS INSPECTION POINTS

Inspection Item-1

Jack up rear wheels. Set selector lever in "D" range. Accelerate to D_4 speed at partial throttle. When vehicle speed is in 19-50 MPH range, close throttle fully. Apply brakes for longer than .7 seconds. Check output signals to Overdrive cancel solenoid. See NISSAN/DATSUN 300ZX ELECTRONIC CONTROL UNIT TEST CHART for correct results.

Inspection Item-2

Connect voltmeter to ECU connector terminals No. 13 and No. 22. Release vehicle speed setting repeatedly while driving in A.S.C.D. (Automatic Speed Control Device) mode. If A.S.C.D. is set, reading should be 12 volts. If A.S.C.D. is released, reading should be 0 volts.

Inspection Item-3

Inspect physical condition of A.S.C.D. wiring harness. Check connections and continuity.

Inspection Item-4

Test A.S.C.D. controller.

Inspection Item-5

Connect voltmeter to ECU connector terminals No. 15 and No. 22. Release vehicle speed setting repeatedly while driving in A.S.C.D. mode in D_4 range. If accelerator pedal is depressed, reading should be 0 volts. If accelerator pedal is released, reading should be 5 volts.

Inspection Item-6

Inspect physical condition of A.S.C.D. wiring harness.Check connections and continuity.

Inspection Item-7

Check wiring between ECU and Overdrive cancel solenoid. Check connections and continuity.

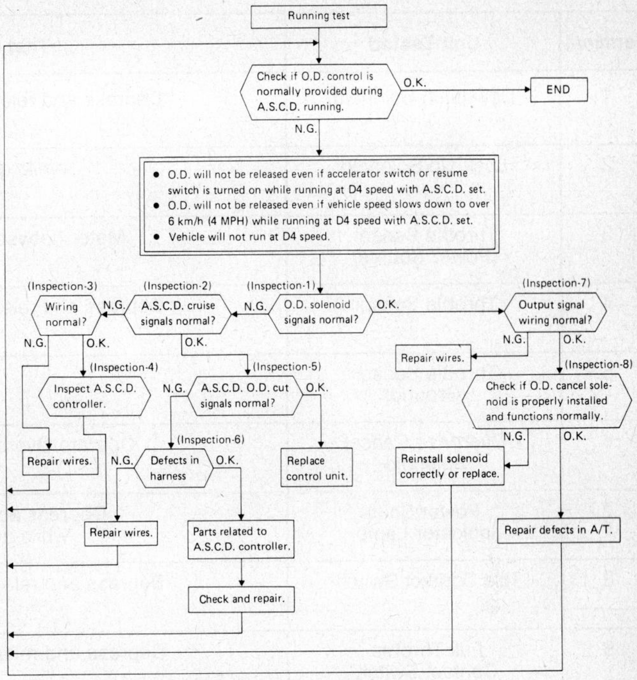

Inspection Item-8

Apply 12 volts to Overdrive cancel solenoid. Proper operation is indicated by click from Overdrive cancel solenoid.

300ZX OVERDRIVE CONTROL INSPECTION POINTS

Inspection Item-1

Turn ignition key ON. Set Overdrive switch to "Overdrive Release" position. Proper operation is indicated by click from Overdrive solenoid.

Inspection Item-2

Check signals of following input sensors and switches: shift switches (1-2, 2-3 and 3-4); vehicle speed sensor; low-temperature sensor; full throttle contact switch; kickdown switch. See NISSAN/DATSUN 300ZX ELECTRONIC CONTROL UNIT TEST CHART for correct results.

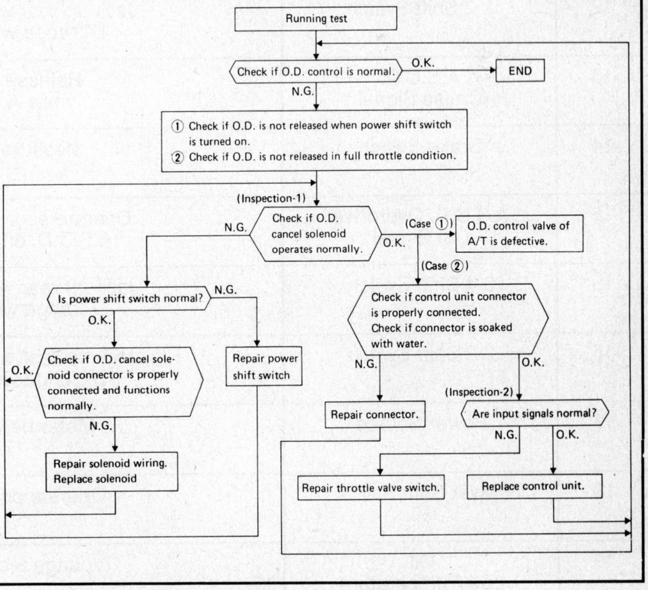

300ZX Self-Diagnosing

1) If power shift indicator flickers at intervals of 1 second up to D_2 speed (8-9 MPH), check for broken wiring between shift switch and ECU connector harness. If wiring is good, shift switch is malfunctioning.

2) If power shift indicator flickers at intervals of 1 second above D_2 speed (8-9 MPH), vehicle speed sensor is defective or wiring between vehicle speed sensor and ECU is broken.

3) To check vehicle speed sensor, connect voltmeter between terminals No. 11 and No. 22 of ECU connector. Good vehicle speed sensor will give voltage reading varying from 0 volts to over 5 volts while driving vehicle very slowly over 3 feet.

4) If power shift indicator light flickers at 1/4 second intervals, throttle sensor is defective, wiring harness is broken between throttle sensor and ECU, or ECU is malfunctioning.

5) To check throttle sensor, connect voltmeter to ECU connector terminals No. 4 and No. 22. Reading should be 0 volts in fully closed throttle position. Reading should be 4 volts in full open throttle position.

JATCO 3N71B, E4N71B, JM600, L3N71B & L4N71B (Cont.)

NISSAN/DATSUN 300ZX ELECTRONIC LOCK-UP CONTROL UNIT TEST CHART

Terminal	Unit Tested	Test Condition	Result
1	Downshift Solenoid	Depress and release accelerator pedal	0 volts when ON 12 volts when OFF
2	Lock-Up Solenoid	While driving in "D"	O volts when ON 12 volts when OFF
3	Throttle Sensor (Power Source)	Meter between terminals 3 & 5	5 volts at all times
4	Throttle Sensor	Depress and release accelerator pedal	Closed throttle: .4 volts Full throttle: 4 volts
5	Throttle Sensor (Ground)	.....	.....
6	Overdrive Cancel Solenoid	Operate Overdrive cancel switch	Switch ON: 0 volts Switch OFF: 12 volts
7	Power Shift Indicator Lamp	Depress accelerator pedal while driving in "D"	0 volts when ON 12 volts if OFF
8	Idle Contact Switch	Depress and release accelerator pedal	Closed throttle: 12 volts Partial throttle: 0 volts
9	Full Throttle Contact Switch	Depress and release accelerator pedal	Above 1/2 throttle: 12 volts Below 1/4 throttle: 0 volts
10	Inhibitor "2" Range Switch	Shift lever in "2" or other ranges	12 volts in "2" 0 volts in other ranges
11	Speed Sensor	Check voltage variation over 3 feet at very low speed	0 volts to 5.1 (or more) volts
12	1-2 Shift Switch	Jack up rear wheels, accelerate in "D" range with partial throttle	0 volts in D1 5 volts in D2, D3, D4
13	A.S.C.D. Cruise Signal	Release speed setting while A.S.C.D driving	A.S.C.D. released: 0 volts A.S.C.D. set: 12 volts
14	Brake Switch	Measure while braking	Braking: 12 volts Not braking: 0 volts
15	A.S.C.D. Overdrive Cut Signal	Operate accelerator switch while A.S.C.D. driving at D4 speed	Switch ON: 0 volts Switch OFF: 5 volts
15	3-4 Shift Switch	Jack up rear wheels, accelerate in "D" range with partial throttle	0 volts in D1, D2, D3 5 volts in D4
16	2-3 Shift Switch	Jack up rear wheels, accelerate in "D" range with partial throttle	0 volts in D1 & D2 5 volts in D3 & D4
17	Power Source	Meter between terminals 17 and 22	12 volts at all times
18	Power Shift Switch	Operate power shift switch	Switch ON: 0 volts Switch OFF: 12 volts
19	Oil Low Temperature Sensor	Voltage test while installed Continuity test while removed	Oil over 68°F (20°C): 5 volts Oil under 50°F (10°C): 0 volts 68°F (20°C) & higher: OPEN 50°F (10°C) & lower: CLOSED
20	Not Used	.....	.....
21	Kickdown Switch	Depress and release accelerator pedal	Full throttle: 0 volts Less than full throttle: 5 volts
22	Ground	.....	.....

JATCO 3N71B, E4N71B, JM600, L3N71B & L4N71B (Cont.)

Fig. 4: Nissan 300ZX Electronic A/T Lock-up Wiring Diagram.

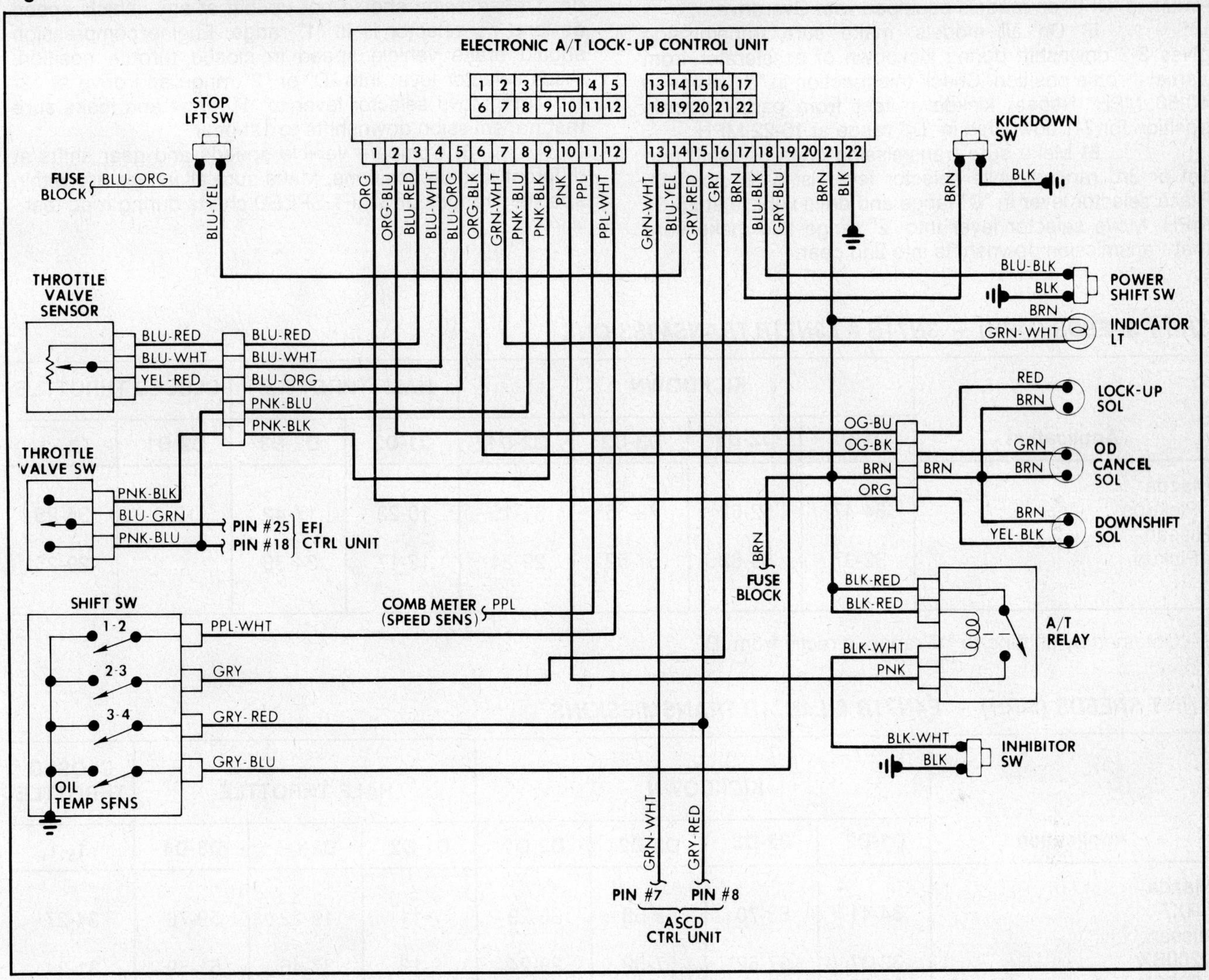

ATF CONDITION

1) Before performing road test, check color, texture and odor of ATF. Dark or Black ATF with burned odor indicates worn friction material is in ATF. Milky Pink ATF indicates water contamination, often from road water entering filler tube or breather. Leaks in lower radiator tank or in ATF lines inside tank can also cause water contamination.

2) ATF that is tacky and light-to-dark Brown (varnished) indicates oxidation. This can be caused by overfilling or underfilling. Overheating of ATF will also cause oxidation to occur.

3) If ATF leak is suspected, clean area of transmission in question. Raise vehicle, supporting it securely, and start engine. Apply foot brake and place selector lever in Drive. After several minutes, stop engine and look for fresh leakage.

4) Ensure that ATF level, shift linkage, control linkage and detent cable adjustments have been checked and adjusted as needed. Attach vacuum gauge to engine to measure intake manifold vacuum.

ROAD TEST

1) Place selector lever in "P" range and start engine. Stop engine and repeat starting procedure in all gear ranges, including Neutral. Drive vehicle to slight upgrade and park vehicle. Place selector lever in "P" and release parking brake. Make sure vehicle remains locked in place.

2) Shift from "P" to "R" range and note quality of shift engagement. Drive vehicle in Reverse long enough to detect any slippage or other problems. Shift from "R" and "D" ranges in and out of "N" range while noting shift quality. Release parking brake while vehicle is in "N" range. Make sure vehicle does not move or "creep" when accelerator is lightly depressed.

NOTE: If transmission is new or recently rebuilt, vehicle might have some slight movement. This is NOT cause for concern.

3) Move selector lever from "N" to "D" range. Check shift quality. Take vehicle on road test in "D" range. Compare actual vehicle speeds at upshift and downshift points with those listed in SHIFT SPEED charts. Note points at which shifting shock and clutch engagement occur.

4) On E4N71B models, compare shift speed as accelerator is depressed slowly or quickly. Make sure that Overdrive range cannot be selected when power shift

JATCO 3N71B, E4N71B, JM600, L3N71B & L4N71B (Cont.)

switch is "ON" (E4N71B models) or Overdrive cancel switch is "OFF" on models equipped with Overdrive.

5) On all models, make sure transmission gives 3-2 downshift during kickdown of accelerator from partial throttle position. Check this function in "D_3" range at 40-53 MPH. Repeat kickdown test from partial throttle position for 2-1 downshift in "D_2" range at 16-22 MPH.

6) Make sure transmission does not shift into 1st or 3rd ranges while selector lever is in "2" position. Place selector lever in "D" range and drive vehicle at 25-31 MPH. Move selector lever into "2" range and make sure that transmission downshifts into 2nd gear.

7) Place selector lever in "1" range and drive on. Transmission should not upshift at any vehicle speed as long as selector is in "1" range. Engine compression should brake vehicle speed in closed throttle position. Place selector lever into "D" or "2" range and drive at 12-19 MPH. Move selector lever to "1" range and make sure that transmission downshifts to 1st gear.

8) Compare vehicle speeds and gear shifts at different throttle positions. Make sure all values are within specified ranges of SHIFT SPEED charts during road test.

SHIFT SPEEDS (MPH) – 3N71B & L3N71B TRANSMISSIONS

Application	KICKDOWN				HALF-THROTTLE		CLOSED THROTTLE	
	D1-D2	D2-D3	D3-D2	D2-D1	D1-D2	D2-D3	D2-D1	[1] 1_2-1_1
Mazda								
Pickups	34-47	52-62	72-55	31-15	10-23	17-42	12-5	35-25
Nissan								
Pickup	32-37	58-62	57-52	29-24	12-17	34-39	.....	29-25

[1] – Obtained by shifting to "1" range, directly from "D".

SHIFT SPEEDS (MPH) – E4N71B & L4N71B TRANSMISSIONS

Application	KICKDOWN				HALF-THROTTLE			CLOSED THROTTLE
	D1-D2	D2-D3	D3-D2	D2-D1	D1-D2	D2-D3	D3-D4	[1] 1_2-1_1
Mazda								
RX7	34-41	63-70	65-58	36-29	7-11	19-22	59-70	34-27
Nissan								
200SX	32-37	57-62	57-52	29-24	9-19	37-46	51-59	31-24
200SX Turbo	28-32	47-51	47-42	26-22	11-18	16-32	26-38	39-34
300ZX	37-42	63-68	60-55	31-26	7-14	29-37	42-52	29-24
300ZX Turbo	37-43	64-70	58-53	34-29	10-16	13-21	25-35	34-27

[1] – Obtained by shifting to "1" range, directly from "D".

SHIFT SPEEDS (MPH) – JM600 TRANSMISSION

Application	KICKDOWN				HALF-THROTTLE			CLOSED THROTTLE
	D1-D2	D2-D3	D3-D2	D2-D1	D1-D2	D2-D3	D3-D4	[1] 1_2-1_1
Chrysler Corp.								
Conquest	14-21	42-50	31-21	12-7	10-16	12-21	25-35	32-26
Mitsubishi								
Starion	14-21	42-50	31-21	12-7	10-16	12-21	25-35	32-26

[1] – Obtained by shifting to "1" range, directly from "D".

JATCO 3N71B, E4N71B, JM600, L3N71B & L4N71B (Cont.)

HYDRAULIC PRESSURE TESTS

Line Pressure Tests

1) Make sure engine fluids and ATF are at correct levels. Connect oil pressure gauges to line pressure and 2nd servo release test ports. *See Fig. 5.* Connect vacuum gauge so intake manifold vacuum can be monitored. Warm up engine until coolant and ATF are at operating temperatures.

Fig. 5: Line Pressure Test Ports

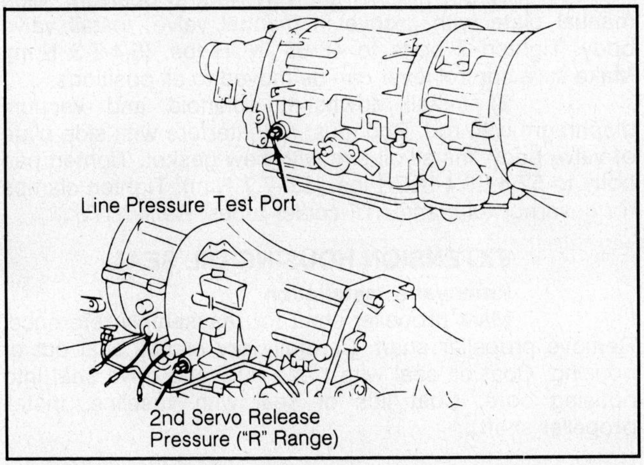

Use 2nd servo release port for measurements in "R" range.

LINE PRESSURE SPECIFICATIONS (CHRYSLER CORP./MITSUBISHI)

Application	psi (kg/cm²)
At Idle Speed	
In "R"	44-64 (3.0-4.5)
In "D"	40-54 (2.8-3.8)
In "2"	114-164 (8.0-11.5)
In "1"	40-54 (2.8-3.8)
At Stall Speed	
In "R"	284-341 (20.0-24.0)
In "D"	242-273 (17.0-19.2)
In "2"	242-259 (17.0-18.2)
In "1"	249-273 (17.5-19.2)

2) Block front and rear wheels. Set parking brake firmly. Place selector lever in range to be checked. Note pressure reading on gauge at idle. Apply brake pedal fully and check pressure reading at full throttle (stall point).

LINE PRESSURE SPECIFICATIONS (MAZDA)

Application	psi (kg/cm²)
At Idle Speed	
In "R"	57-110 (4.0-7.7)
In "D"	43-57 (3.0-4.0)
In "2"	114-171 (8.0-12.0)
In "1"	43-57 (3.0-4.0)
At Stall Speed	
In "R"	228-270 (16.0-19.0)
In "D"	128-156 (9.0-11.0)
In "2"	114-171 (8.0-12.0)
In "1"	128-156 (9.0-11.0)

3) Use readings at 2nd servo release port for testing in "R" range. All pressures should be in range shown in appropriate LINE PRESSURE SPECIFICATIONS table. Pressure readings should increase steadily as car speed increases under light load. Maximum pressure drop between shift points is 14 psi (.98 kg/cm²). Excessive pressure drop could be caused by internal leak at servo or clutch seal.

CAUTION: Do not maintain wide open throttle condition longer than 5 seconds for any reading.

LINE PRESSURE SPECIFICATIONS (NISSAN)

Application	psi (kg/cm²)
At Idle Speed	
In "R"	
200SX	60-80 (4.2-5.6)
200SX Turbo	57-71 (4.0-5.0)
300ZX	80-100 (5.6-7.0)
300ZX Turbo	48-63 (3.4-4.4)
All Others	60-80 (4.2-5.6)
In "D"	
200SX	46-54 (3.2-3.8)
200SX Turbo	43-57 (3.0-4.0)
300ZX	46-54 (3.2-3.8)
300ZX Turbo	37-51 (2.6-3.6)
All Others	46-54 (3.2-3.8)
In "2"	
200SX	85-166 (6.0-11.7)
200SX Turbo	85-171 (6.0-12.0)
300ZX	82-164 (5.7-11.5)
300ZX Turbo	85-171 (5.9-12.9)
All Others	85-166 (6.0-11.7)
In "1"	
200SX	46-54 (3.2-3.8)
200SX Turbo	43-57 (3.0-4.0)
300ZX	46-54 (3.2-3.8)
300ZX Turbo	37-51 (2.6-3.6)
All Others	46-54 (3.2-3.8)
At Stall Speed	
In "R"	
200SX	203-230 (14.2-16.2)
200SX Turbo	313-356 (22.0-25.0)
300ZX	317-344 (22.2-24.1)
300ZX Turbo	311-354 (21.8-24.8)
All Others	203-230 (14.3-16.2)
In "D"	
200SX	141-158 (9.9-11.1)
200SX Turbo	259-282 (18.2-19.8)
300ZX	168-185 (11.8-13.0)
300ZX Turbo	264-287 (18.5-20.1)
All Others	141-158 (9.9-11.1)
In "2"	
200SX	144-165 (10.1-11.6)
200SX Turbo	259-282 (18.2-19.8)
300ZX	168-185 (11.8-13.0)
300ZX Turbo	264-287 (18.5-20.1)
All Others	145-166 (10.2-11.7)
In "1"	
200SX	141-158 (9.9-11.1)
200SX Turbo	259-282 (18.2-19.8)
300ZX	168-185 (11.8-13.0)
300ZX Turbo	264-287 (18.5-20.1)
All Others	141-158 (9.9-11.1)

Governor Pressure Test

1) Governor pressure test should only be used if vehicle shift speeds are different than those indicated in SHIFT SPEED chart. Install pressure gauge in governor

JATCO 3N71B, E4N71B, JM600, L3N71B & L4N71B (Cont.)

pressure port on transmission case. Use Pipe Adapter (49 HO75 406) to connect both pressure gauge and governor pipe at same time.

2) Read pressure with vehicle running at speeds indicated in GOVERNOR PRESSURE SPECIFICATIONS table. If pressures are incorrect, disassemble and clean governor assembly. Repeat tests after reinstalling governor.

GOVERNOR PRESSURE SPECIFICATIONS

Application	psi (kg/cm²)
Chrysler Corp.	[1]
Mazda	
RX7	
At 20 MPH	11-17 (0.8-1.2)
At 35 MPH	21-32 (1.5-2.2)
At 55 MPH	46-58 (3.2-4.1)
Pickup	
At 20 MPH	11-17 (0.8-1.2)
At 35 MPH	20-28 (1.4-2.0)
At 55 MPH	38-48 (2.7-3.4)
Mitsubishi	[1]
Nissan	[1]

[1] – Information not available from manufacturer.

STALL TEST

1) Check engine and transmission for proper lubricant levels. Bring engine to normal operating temperature. Attach tachometer to engine and position so it is visible from driver's seat. Block front and rear wheels, and apply hand brake.

2) Place one foot firmly on brake pedal and place selector lever in "D" position. Gradually increase engine speed to wide open throttle. When engine speed will not increase further, note tachometer reading. Release throttle to idle position immediately.

CAUTION: Do not hold wide open throttle position for more than 5 seconds. Severe transmission damage due to heat and load may result. DO NOT test more than 2 ranges without driving vehicle to cool engine and ATF.

3) Move selector lever to "N" range and run engine at 1200 RPM for at least 1 minute to cool engine and ATF. Repeat stall test procedure with shift lever in "2", "1" and "R" ranges.

STALL SPEED SPECIFICATIONS

Application	Stall RPM
Chrysler Corp.	
Conquest	2350-2650
Mitsubishi	
Starion	2350-2650
Nissan	
Pickup	2000-2300
200SX	1900-2200
200SX Turbo	2000-2200
300ZX	2150-2450
300ZX Turbo	2500-2800
Mazda	
RX7	2400-2650
Pickups	2000-2250

SERVICE (IN VEHICLE)

VALVE BODY

Removal

Drain ATF by removing pan. Remove downshift solenoid and vacuum diaphragm with vacuum rod. Remove 7 bolts holding valve body to transmission case. Remove valve body from transmission.

Installation

1) Set manual shaft in Neutral position. Align manual plate with groove in manual valve. Install valve body. Tighten 7 bolts to 48-65 INCH lbs. (5.4-7.3 N.m). Make sure control lever can be moved to all positions.

2) Install downshift solenoid and vacuum diaphragm with rod. Rod must not interfere with side plate of valve body. Install oil pan with new gasket. Tighten pan bolts to 52.8-68.4 INCH lbs. (5.9-7.7 N.m). Tighten clamps for governor tube and ATF cooler tubes. Refill ATF.

EXTENSION HOUSING OIL SEAL

Removal & Installation

Mark propeller shaft for reassembly reference. Remove propeller shaft. Carefully pry or pull seal out of housing. Coat oil seal with clean ATF and drive seal into housing bore. Coat lips of seal with vaseline. Install propeller shaft.

PARKING COMPONENTS

Removal

1) Drain ATF while removing pan. Mark propeller shaft for reassembly reference. Remove propeller shaft. Disconnect speedometer cable from sleeve assembly. Remove sleeve assembly from housing.

2) Support weight of transmission with jack and wooden block. Remove rear extension housing and rear mount. Remove valve body. Remove parking pawl, pin, spring and washer. Note location for reassembly procedure.

Installation

Install parking pawl, pin, spring and washer, using new parts if necessary. Install valve body. Install rear extension and mounting parts. Install speedometer housing and attach cable. Install propeller shaft after aligning marks made during disassembly. Install oil pan with new gasket. Refill transmission with ATF.

GOVERNOR VALVE ASSEMBLY

Removal & Installation

Drain ATF by removing pan. Remove rear mountings and rear extension. Remove governor assembly from transmission housing. To install, reverse removal procedure.

REMOVAL & INSTALLATION

TRANSMISSION

See appropriate AUTOMATIC TRANSMISSION REMOVAL article in IMPORT GENERAL SERVICING section.

TRANSMISSION DISASSEMBLY

1) Remove torque converter. Drain ATF through end of rear extension. Mount transmission in holding fixture. Remove lock-up solenoid from E4N71B models. On all models, remove governor tube. Remove converter housing. Remove oil pan and check contents for signs of contamination or internal part damage.

2) Loosen 2nd band servo lock nut. Tighten piston stem of 2nd band servo. If more than 2 turns are required to tighten stem, band is worn out. Back off stem to release pressure. On models without Overdrive, go to step **5)**. On models with Overdrive, remove Overdrive assembly. Remove high-reverse (front) clutch thrust washer, needle bearing and race.

3) Take out input shaft and intermediate shaft. Attach slide hammers to pump and remove pump. Remove Overdrive servo cover. Loosen Overdrive band servo piston stem. Remove Overdrive planetary gear and direct clutch assembly. Remove needle bearing, race and direct clutch thrust washer.

4) Remove Overdrive brake band and strut. Remove Overdrive servo assembly by lightly tapping retainer. Remove accumulator snap ring. Apply air pressure to remove accumulator plug, piston and spring. Remove Overdrive cancel solenoid and "O" ring. Remove drum support.

5) On all models, remove downshift solenoid, vacuum diaphragm, diaphragm rod and "O" rings. Remove speedometer lock plate and speedometer pinion. Remove valve body bolts. Remove valve body from transmission. Remove manual valve from valve body to prevent it from dropping out accidentally.

6) On L3N71B and 3N71B transmissions, loosen brake band adjusting screw lock nut and tighten screw enough to prevent high-reverse clutch drum from coming out with oil pump. Remove input shaft from oil pump. Remove pump with slide hammers. Remove high-reverse clutch thrust washer and bearing race. Back off band servo piston stem to release band.

7) On all transmissions, remove brake band strut. Before removing brake band, secure ends together with clip. This will keep band from flexing enough to crack or peel. Remove brake band, high-reverse (front) clutch, forward (rear) clutch and front planetary gear set (if equipped) as assembly.

8) On 3N71B and L3N71B models, remove front pump thrust bearing and forward clutch thrust washer. Remove forward clutch hub, front planetary carrier and connecting shell. Remove forward clutch thrust bearing, front planetary carrier thrust washer and thrust bearing.

9) On all models, back out band servo attaching bolts about half-way. Carefully apply air pressure at band servo release port to loosen servo. *See Fig. 19.* Remove band servo retaining bolts and pull band servo out.

10) On E4N71B models, check one-way clutch for correct operation. On all models, remove rear planetary carrier snap ring. Remove rear planetary carrier. Remove output shaft snap ring. Remove rear connecting drum and internal annulus gear as assembly.

11) Pry off one end of low and reverse brake snap ring. Remove snap ring by gripping loose end of ring with pliers and turning it in direction away from gap in ring while pulling outward. Remove low and reverse brake clutch assembly. Remove extension housing being careful not to lose parking pawl, spring and retaining washer.

12) Remove output shaft and governor as assembly. Remove governor thrust washer and needle bearing. Remove one-way clutch inner race attaching bolts. Remove one-way clutch inner race, return thrust washer, low and reverse return spring and spring thrust ring.

13) Apply air pressure to passage in transmission case to remove low and reverse brake piston. *See Fig. 19.* Remove snap rings from both ends of parking brake lever and remove lever. Remove lock nut, manual plate and parking rod. Remove inhibitor switch and manual shaft. On Overdrive models, remove Overdrive indicator switch and "O" ring.

COMPONENT DISASSEMBLY & REASSEMBLY

OIL PUMP ASSEMBLY

Disassembly

1) Take cover off pump housing. On 3N71B and L3N71B models, remove speed cut valve and lock-up control valve. On E4N71B models, remove lock-up valve retaining pin with punch.

2) Remove lock-up control valve and spring. On all models, match mark inner and outer gears with quick-drying ink or paint for reassembly reference. Remove gears from housing.

CAUTION: Oil pump gears MUST be reinstalled in original positions. Mark gears with ink or paint before removing. NEVER use punch to mark gears.

Inspection

1) Check all parts for wear, cracks or other damage. Replace any defective parts. Check gear teeth for excessive wear or damage. Replace rubber seal ring if worn. Check clearances of oil pump.

2) Using straightedge and feeler gauge, measure pump gear face-to-cover clearance. Clearance should be .0008-.0016" (.02-.04 mm). If clearance exceeds .003" (.08 mm), replace gears.

3) Measure clearance between outer gear and crescent. Clearance should be .006-.008" (.14-.21 mm). If clearance exceeds .010" (.25 mm), replace gears.

4) Measure clearance between outer gear and pump housing. Clearance should be .002-.008" (.05-.20 mm). If clearance exceeds .010" (.25 mm), replace gears.

5) Check that oil seal rings and oil feed grooves are not damaged. Make sure that rings still have tension. Check side clearance of oil rings. Clearance should be .002-.006" (.04-.16 mm). Replace seal rings if clearance exceeds .006" (.16 mm).

Reassembly

1) Install valves and springs in cover with NEW retaining pins. On all models except JM600, place pump housing in Oil Pump Assembler (Nissan/Datsun: ST2558001; Mazda: 49 0378 405A). Fit inner and outer gears in housing in same position as when disassembled. On JM600 models, use Aligning Dowels (MD998393) to align cover with pump body.

2) On all models except JM600, check pump cover runout. Temporarily assemble pump cover and housing. DO NOT tighten bolts completely at this time. Attach dial indicator to assembler. Measure total pump cover runout. Total runout must not exceed .003" (.07 mm).

3) Runout can be adjusted by tapping cover lightly with plastic hammer. Tighten pump cover bolts. Recheck runout. On all models, install seal rings on stator

JATCO 3N71B, E4N71B, JM600, L3N71B & L4N71B (Cont.)

support and new large seal ring on pump housing outside diameter.

DRUM SUPPORT

Disassembly

Inspect drum support bushing and ring groove areas for wear. Remove drum support and gasket from Overdrive case. Stake off retaining pin using punch having .059-.071" (1.5-1.8 mm) outer diameter. DO NOT stake off from contacting face side. Remove Overdrive cancel valve and spring.

Inspection

Inspect Overdrive cancel valve and spring and all internal surfaces for faults and visible wear. Spring should have free length of .906" (23 mm) and outer coil diameter of .1949" (4.95 mm). Measure clearance between seal ring and ring groove. Clearance should be .0020-.0079" (.05-.20 mm). Replace if clearance exceeds .0079" (.2 mm).

Reassembly

1) Install Overdrive cancel valve and spring into drum support, and tap retaining pins. Install fiber lubrication plug into drum support. Install one-way plug in Overdrive case. On all models except JM600, mount oil pump assembly in oil pump assembly tool with .79" (20 mm) spacer below tool to protect oil pump. Mount Overdrive case, drum support and gasket in oil pump assembly.

2) Temporarily assemble drum support. Make sure Overdrive case is inserted properly into oil pump assembly. Insert 4.33" (110 mm) bar in oil pump at shaft location and install intermediate shaft onto it. *See Fig. 6.*

3) Set runout of drum support to less than .002" (.05 mm). On JM600 models, use aligning dowels to center drum support in Overdrive case. Tighten drum support securing bolts. Recheck runout. Replace "O" ring and gasket.

Fig. 6: Assembling Drum Support

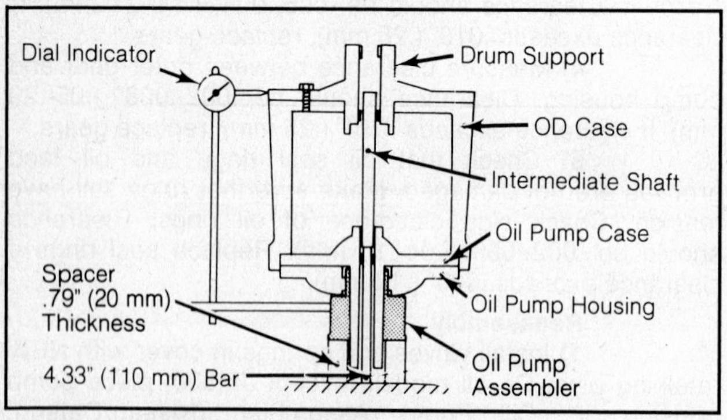

Runout should be less than .002" (.05 mm).

DIRECT CLUTCH & HIGH-REVERSE CLUTCH

Disassembly

Remove snap ring and take out retaining plate, lined plates, steel plates and dished plate. Compress and hold clutch springs. Remove coil spring retainer snap ring. Remove compressor tool. Remove spring retainer and springs. Remove high-reverse (front) clutch piston by applying compressed air into oil hole.

Inspection

Inspect lined plates for wear or fatigue. Check coil spring retainer and replace if deformed. Ensure that coil spring has not lost tension. Inspect seal around piston and "O" ring inside clutch drum for damage. Replace all parts which show undue wear or fatigue. Standard plate thickness is .059-.065" (1.50-1.65 mm). Minimum thickness is .055" (1.4 mm).

Reassembly

1) Coat new seals with clean ATF and install seals onto clutch piston and clutch drum. Install piston into drum. Position return springs and retainer on top of piston. Compress return springs and retainer and install snap ring. Install dished plate into drum.

2) Install flat steel plate, then alternate lined and steel plates until all plates are installed. See HIGH-REVERSE (FRONT) CLUTCH PLATE USAGE chart. Position retaining ring in drum and install clutch pack snap ring. Using feeler gauge, measure clearance between clutch pack retaining snap ring and retaining plate in drum.

3) Clearance should be .063-.071" (1.6-1.8 mm) for direct and high-reverse clutches on Mazda models and direct clutches on Chrysler Corp. and Mitsubishi models; .063-.079" (1.6-2.0 mm) for direct and high-reverse clutches on Nissan models and high-reverse clutches on Chrysler Corp. and Mitsubishi models.

4) If clearance is incorrect, adjust by installing retaining plate of different thickness. Retaining plates for direct clutches are available in thicknesses ranging from .197-.244" (5.0-6.2 mm). Additional retaining plates, measuring .283" (7.2 mm) and .291" (7.4 mm), are available for direct clutches used in Nissan/Datsun 300ZX Turbo model.

5) Retaining plates for high-reverse clutches used in Mazda Pickups are available in thicknesses ranging from .283-.323" (7.2-8.2 mm) in increments of .008" (.2 mm). Retaining plates for high-reverse clutches in all other models are available in thickness ranging from .197-.244" (5.0-6.2 mm). Retaining plate thicknesses change in increments of .008" (.2 mm) for all models.

DIRECT & HIGH-REVERSE CLUTCH PLATE USAGE

Application	Lined Plates	Steel Plates
High-Rev. Clutch		
Chrysler Corp		
Conquest	3	5
Mazda		
All Models	2	2
Mitsubishi		
Starion	3	5
Nissan		
Pickup	3	5
200SX	3	3
200SX Turbo	3	3
300ZX	3	5
300ZX Turbo	4	5
Direct Clutch		
Nissan		
300ZX Turbo	3	3
All Others	2	2

JATCO 3N71B, E4N71B, JM600, L3N71B & L4N71B (Cont.)

Fig. 7: Exploded View Of High-Reverse (Front) Clutch Assembly

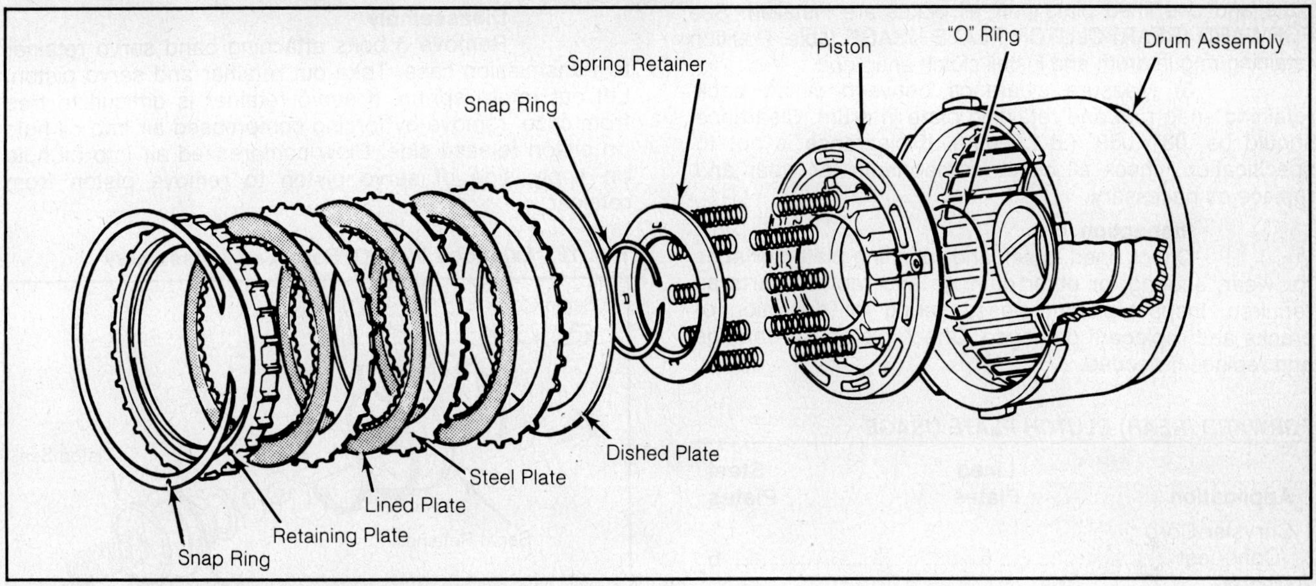

Number of clutch plates and discs varies with application.

FORWARD (REAR) CLUTCH

Disassembly

Remove snap ring, retaining plate, steel plate, lined plate, and dished plate in same order used for high-reverse (front) clutch. Remove coil spring retainer using compressing tool. Take out retainer and all springs. Remove piston by blowing compressed air into oil hole.

Inspection

Make same inspection of components as for high-reverse (front) clutch. Replace any parts showing signs of undue wear or fatigue.

Reassembly

1) Coat new seals with clean ATF and install seals on clutch piston and clutch drum. Install piston into drum. Position return springs and retainer on top of piston. Compress return springs and retainer.

Fig. 8: Exploded View Of Forward (Rear) Clutch Assembly

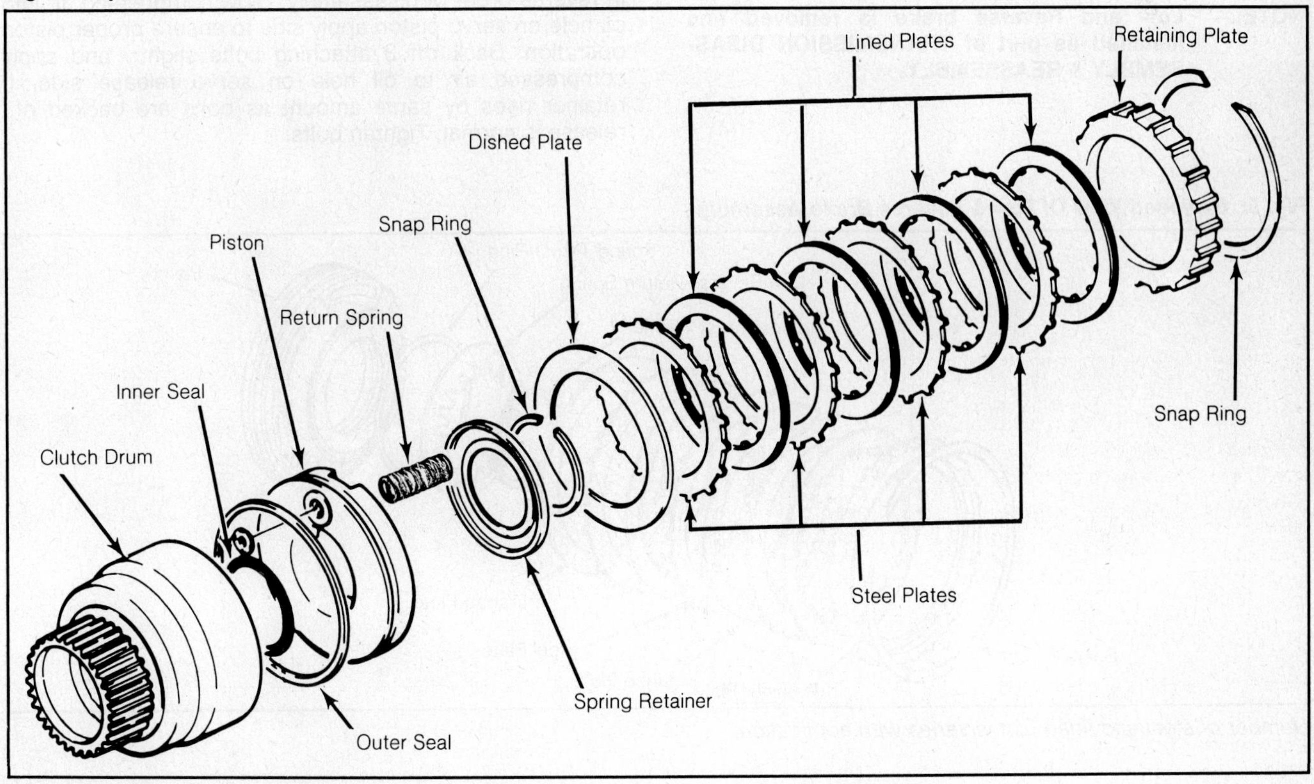

Number of lined and steel plates varies with application.

JATCO 3N71B, E4N71B, JM600, L3N71B & L4N71B (Cont.)

2) Install dished plate, then alternate one steel plate and one lined plate until all plates are installed. See FORWARD (REAR) CLUTCH PLATE USAGE table. Position retaining ring in drum and install clutch snap ring.

3) Measure clearance between clutch pack retaining snap ring and retaining plate in drum. Clearance should be .031-.059" (.8-1.5 mm). If clearance is not to specification, check all clutch components for wear and replace as necessary.

Inspection

Check lined, steel, and retaining plate surfaces for wear, scoring, or other damage and replace parts as required. Inspect piston release spring for distortion or cracks and replace if damaged. Check piston for damage and replace if needed.

FORWARD (REAR) CLUTCH PLATE USAGE

Application	Lined Plates	Steel Plates
Chrysler Corp		
Conquest	6	6
Mazda		
All Models	4	4
Mitsubishi		
Starion	6	6
Nissan		
Pickup	6	6
200SX	5	5
200SX Turbo	4	4
300ZX	6	6
300ZX Turbo	6	6

LOW AND REVERSE BRAKE

NOTE: **Low and Reverse brake is removed and installed as part of TRANSMISSION DISASSEMBLY & REASSEMBLY.**

BAND SERVO PISTON

Disassembly

Remove 3 bolts attaching band servo retainer to transmission case. Take out retainer and servo piston. Lift out return spring. If servo retainer is difficult to free from case, remove by forcing compressed air into oil hole on piston release side. Blow compressed air into oil hole on apply side of servo piston to remove piston from retainer.

Fig. 10: Exploded View Of Band Servo Assembly

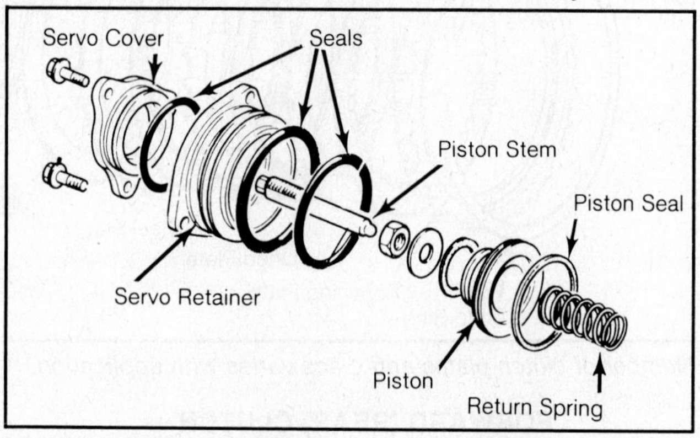

Mazda model shown. Other models are similar.

Inspection

Ensure that 2 "O" rings on servo retainer and rubber seal on servo piston are not damaged. Check all parts for undue wear or fatigue. Inspect return spring for adequate tension. Inspect brake band lining for excessive wear or damage. Replace parts as needed.

Reassembly

Coat all parts with clean ATF and reassemble in reverse order of disassembly. Blow compressed air into oil hole on servo piston apply side to ensure proper piston operation. Back off 3 attaching bolts slightly and apply compressed air to oil hole on servo release side. If retainer rises by same amount as bolts are backed off, release is normal. Tighten bolts.

Fig. 9: Exploded View Of Low & Reverse Brake Assembly

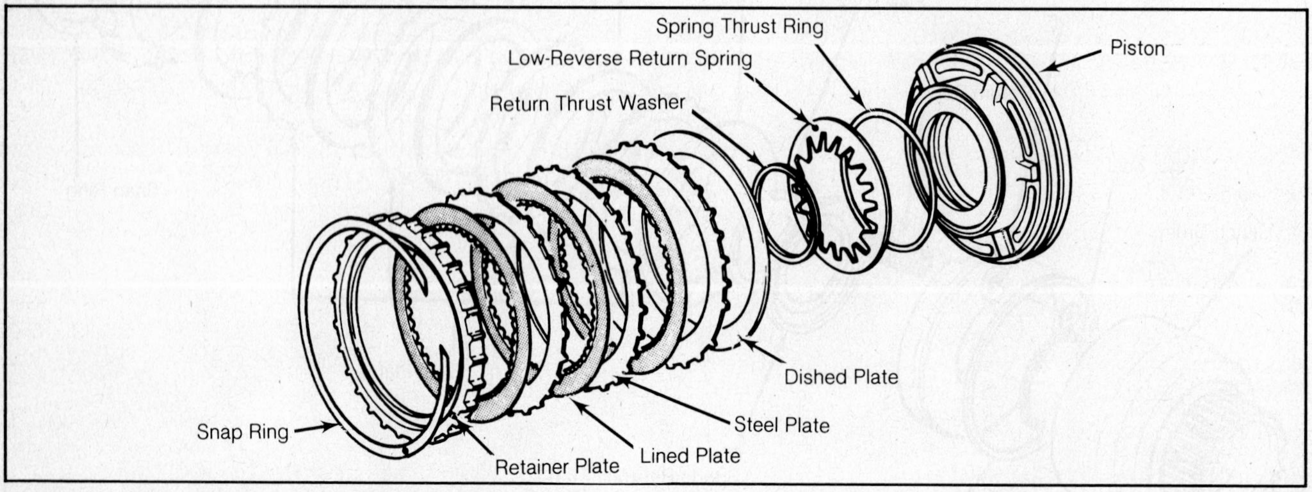

Number of steel and lined plates varies with application.

JATCO 3N71B, E4N71B, JM600, L3N71B & L4N71B (Cont.)

GOVERNOR VALVE ASSEMBLY

Disassembly

Separate governor from oil distributor by removing 4 attaching bolts. Remove secondary governor valve retainer plate. Remove spring and secondary governor valve from governor body. Remove primary governor valve spring seat, primary governor valve, spring and spring seat.

Fig. 11: Exploded View Of Governor Assembly

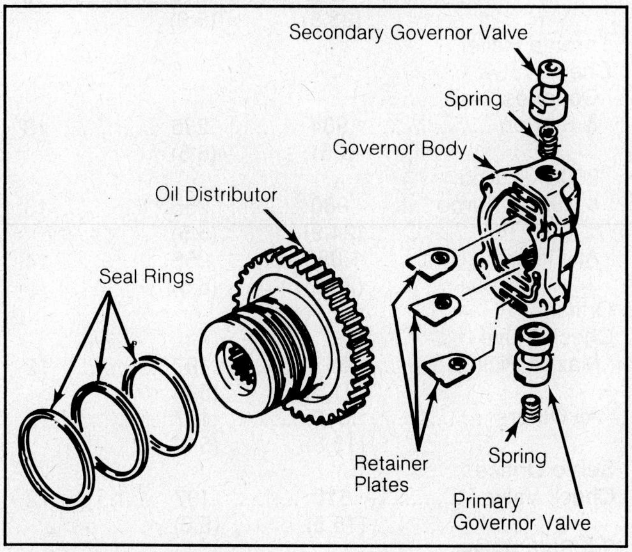

Keep primary and secondary components separate.

Inspection

Check valve and body for valve sticking or catching. Ensure that spring has not lost tension and that retainer plates are not deformed.

Reassembly

1) Coat all parts with clean ATF and reassemble in reverse order of disassembly. Be careful not to confuse primary valve and secondary valve.

2) Primary governor spring has free length of .858" (21.8 mm) and outer coil diameter of .345" (8.8 mm).

3) Secondary governor spring has free length of .783" (19.9 mm) and outer coil diameter of .362" (9.2 mm). Install and tighten governor attaching bolts.

ACCUMULATOR

Remove accumulator snap ring. Apply air pressure to remove accumulator plug, piston, spring and spacer. Check accumulator components for wear and scoring. Accumulator spring should have free length of 1.56" (39.7 mm) and outer coil diameter of .5846" (14.85 mm).

PLANETARY CARRIER

Planetary carrier is 1-piece unit. Clearance check is between pinion washer and carrier. Standard clearance is .008-.028" (.20-.70 mm). If clearance exceeds .031" (.80 mm), replace carrier.

CONNECTING DRUM & 1-WAY CLUTCH ASSEMBLY

Disassembly & Reassembly

Draw out one-way clutch by removing snap ring from each end. Remove outer race snap ring and draw outer race rearward out of drum. Inspect one-way clutch for undue wear or damage. Check contacting surfaces of inner and outer races. When reassembling one-way clutch, ensure that clutch roller cage is fitted so that arrow on side of cage points toward front of vehicle.

Fig. 12: Exploded View Of Valve Body Assembly For L3N71B & 3N71B

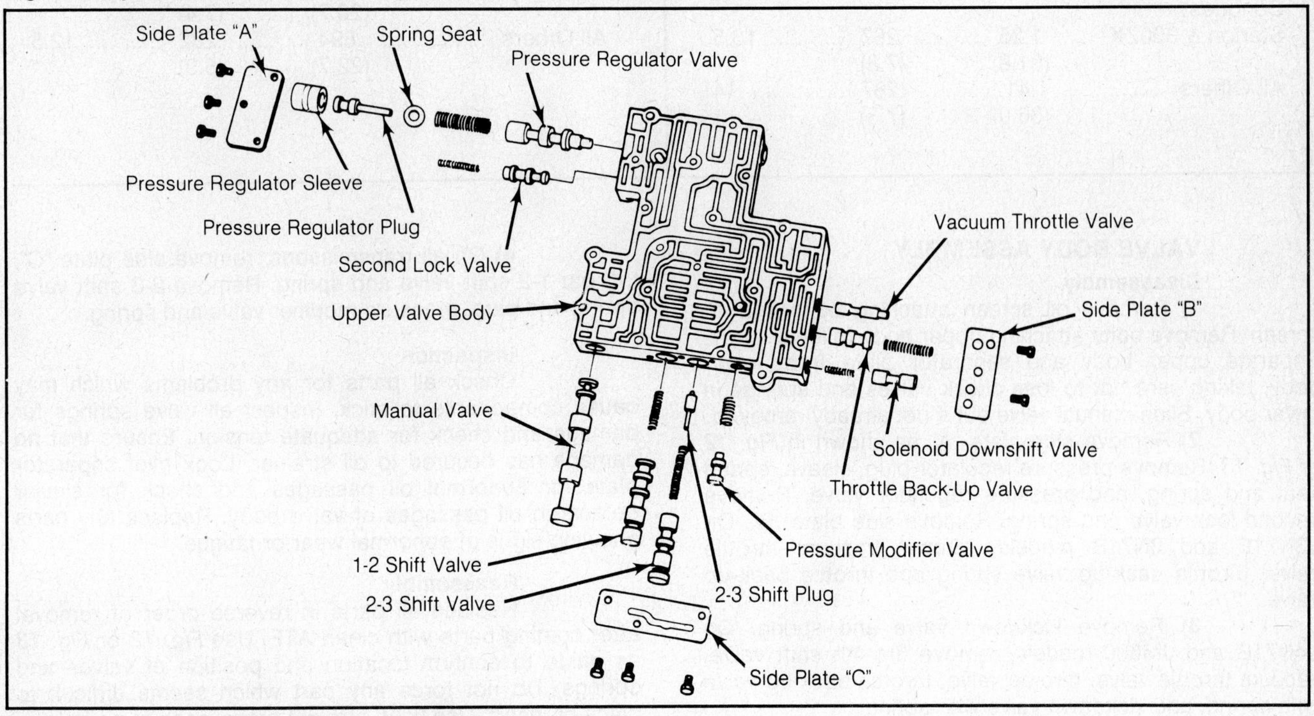

Keep all parts in rack in sequence of assembly.

JATCO 3N71B, E4N71B, JM600, L3N71B & L4N71B (Cont.)

VALVE BODY SPRING IDENTIFICATION

Application	Length In. (mm)	Diameter In. (mm)	Number of Coils
Manual Detent	1.276 (32.4)	.287 (7.3)	15
Pressure Regulator Valve			
300zx Turbo	1.53 (38.9)	.461 (11.7)	13
All Others	1.693 (43.0)	.461 (11.7)	13
Pressure Modifier Valve			
Conquest & Starion	.772 (19.6)	.339 (8.6)	5.5
300ZX Turbo	.728 (18.5)	.339 (8.6)	5.5
All Others	.728 (18.5)	.331 (8.4)	5
1-2 Shift Valve			
RX7	1.26 (32.0)	.260 (6.6)	16
Conquest, Starion & 300ZX Turbo	1.11 (28.3)	.276 (7.0)	11.8
200SX Turbo	1.11 (28.3)	.....	.....
All Others	1.39 (33.25)	.260 (6.6)	16
2-3 Shift Valve	1.614 (41.0)	.272 (6.9)	18
Throttle Back-Up Valve			
RX7	1.25 (31.8)	.287 (7.3)	14
Conquest, Starion & 300ZX	1.25 (31.8)	.287 (7.3)	13.5
All Others	1.417 (36.0)	.287 (7.3)	14

Application	Length In. (mm)	Diameter In. (mm)	Number of Coils
Solenoid Down-Shift Valve	.866 (22.0)	.219 (5.6)	12
Second Lock Valve	1.319 (33.5)	.219 (5.6)	16
Throttle Relief Check Valve			
Conquest & Starion	.984 (25)	.256 (6.5)	13
200SX Turbo & 300ZX Turbo	.980 (24.9)	.256 (6.5)	13
All Others	1.055 (26.8)	.256 (6.5)	14
Orifice Check Valve			
Mazda Pickup	.847 (21.5)	.197 (5.0)	12
All Others	.610 (15.5)	.197 (5.0)	12
Servo Orifice Check Valve	.610 (15.5)	.197 (5.0)	12
3-4 Shift Valve			
RX7	1.02 (25.8)	.287 (7.3)	.....
All Others	1.19 (30.3)	.260 (6.6)	12.6
3-2 Timing Valve			
300ZX	.815 (20.7)	.291 (7.4)	9
All Others	.894 (22.7)	.232 (5.9)	12.5

VALVE BODY ASSEMBLY

Disassembly

1) Remove oil screen attaching bolts and oil screen. Remove bolts attaching upper body to lower body. Separate upper body and separator plate from lower body, taking care not to lose check valves and springs in lower body. Slide manual valve out if not already removed.

2) Remove side plate "A" as shown in *Fig. 12* or *Fig. 13*. Remove pressure regulator plug, sleeve, spring seat and spring, and pressure regulator valve. Remove second lock valve and spring. Remove side plate "B". On L3N71B and 3N71B models, remove vacuum throttle valve, throttle back-up valve spring and throttle back-up valve.

3) Remove kickdown valve and spring. On L4N71B and JM600 models, remove 3rd-4th shift valve, vacuum throttle valve, throttle valve, throttle back-up valve with spring, and kickdown valve with spring.

4) On all transmissons, remove side plate "C". Lift out 1-2 shift valve and spring. Remove 2-3 shift valve spring and plug, pressure modifier valve and spring.

Inspection

Check all parts for any problems which may cause components to stick. Inspect all valve springs for damage and check for adequate tension. Ensure that no damage has occured to oil strainer. Look over separator plate for abnormal oil passages and check for similar defects in oil passages of valve body. Replace any parts showing signs of abnormal wear or fatigue.

Reassembly

Replace all parts in reverse order of removal after coating parts with clean ATF. Use *Fig. 12* or *Fig. 13* as guide to confirm location and position of valves and springs. Do not force any part which seems difficult to place or insert. Use light, straight pressure to fit parts.

JATCO 3N71B, E4N71B, JM600, L3N71B & L4N71B (Cont.)

Fig. 13: Exploded View Of Valve Body Assembly For E4N71B, L4N71B & JM600

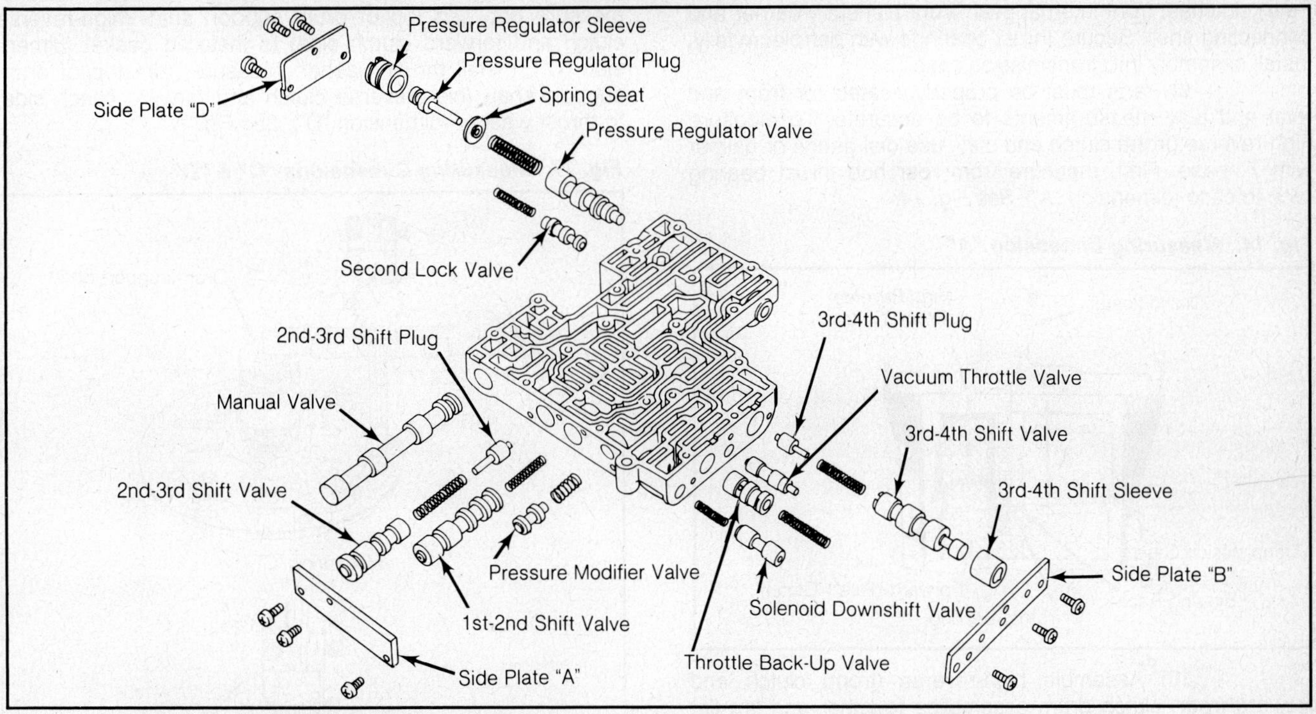

Use nothing coarser than crocus cloth to clean valves or valve bodies.

INPUT SHELL & SUN GEAR ASSEMBLY

Disassembly & Reassembly

Remove external snap ring from sun gear, withdraw thrust washer, then remove sun gear from shell. Remove internal snap ring from sun gear. To assemble, coat all parts with clean ATF and reverse disassembly procedure.

INTERNAL DRIVE FLANGE ASSEMBLY

Disassembly & Reassembly

Remove snap ring and disconnect flange from internal gear. Inspect part for wear or fatigue. Reverse disassembly procedure to assemble after coating all parts with clean ATF.

TRANSMISSION REASSEMBLY

1) Lubricate low and reverse brake piston with clean ATF and install in transmission case. Position thrust ring, piston return spring, snap ring, and one-way clutch inner race into transmission case.

2) Hold inner race in position and install one-way clutch inner race attaching bolts. Check that return spring is centered on race before tightening. Tighten bolts. Install steel dished plate, steel and friction plates. See LOW & REVERSE BRAKE PLATE USAGE table.

3) Install retaining plate and snap ring. Check clearance between retaining plate and snap ring. Clearance should be .032-.049" (.80-1.25 mm). If clearance is incorrect, it may be adjusted by installing retaining plate of different thickness.

4) Plates are available in sizes from .465" (11.8 mm) to .504" (12.8 mm) in .008" (.2 mm) increments for JM600 models. On all other models, plates are available in sizes from .307" (7.8 mm) to .346" (8.8 mm) in .008" (.2 mm) increments. Install correct plate and recheck clearance. Using air gun with tapered rubber tip, check low and reverse brake operation.

5) Install governor thrust washer and needle bearing. Slide governor distributor assembly on output shaft from front of shaft. Install shaft and governor distributor into case, using care not to damage distributor rings.

6) Install connecting drum with sprag by rotating drum clockwise using slight pressure and wobbling to align plates with hub and sprag assembly. Connecting drum should now be free to rotate clockwise only. This verifies that sprag is correctly installed and operative.

7) Install rear internal gear and snap ring on shaft. Secure thrust bearing and washer with petroleum jelly and install rear planetary carrier. Install rear planetary carrier snap ring. Note that this snap ring is thinner than clutch drum snap rings.

LOW & REVERSE BRAKE PLATE USAGE

Application	Lined Plates	Steel Plates
Chrysler Corp		
Conquest	6	6
Mazda		
All Models	4	4
Mitsubishi		
Starion	6	6
Nissan		
Pickup	5	5
200SX	5	5
200SX Turbo	5	5
300ZX	6	6
300ZX Turbo	8	8

JATCO 3N71B, E4N71B, JM600, L3N71B & L4N71B (Cont.)

8) Assemble high-reverse (front) and forward (rear) clutches, front internal gear, front planetary carrier and connecting shell. Secure thrust bearings with petroleum jelly. Install assembly into transmission case.

9) Parts must be properly seated for front and total end play measurements to be accurate. To measure high-reverse (front) clutch end play, use dial gauge or caliper with 7" base. First, measure from rear hub thrust bearing race to case (dimension "A"). *See Fig. 14.*

Fig. 14: Measuring Dimension "A"

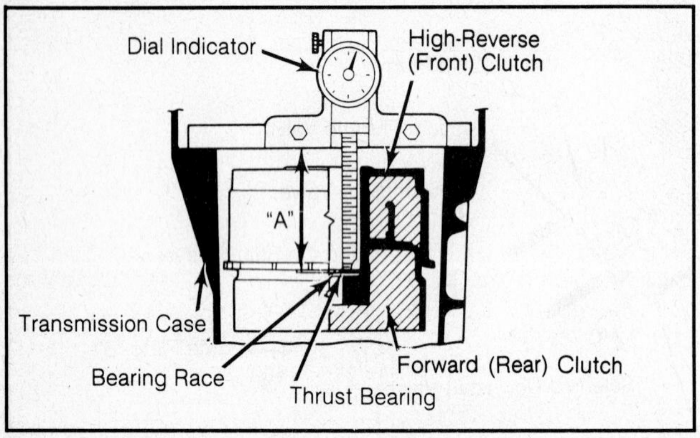

10) Assemble high-reverse (front) clutch and forward (rear) clutch drum assemblies together and lay flat on bench. Make sure rear hub thrust bearing is properly seated. Measure from front face of clutch drum to top of thrust bearing race (dimension "B"). *See Fig. 15.*

Fig. 15: Measuring Dimension "B"

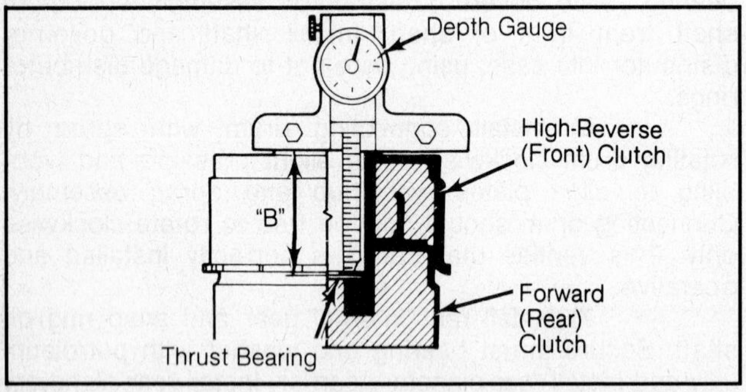

11) On L3N71B and 3N71B transmissions, measure from top of oil pump shaft to installed gasket (dimension "C"). Install thrust washer. Measure from top of oil pump shaft to thrust washer (dimension "D".) *See Fig. 16.*

Fig. 16: Measuring Dimensions "C" & "D"

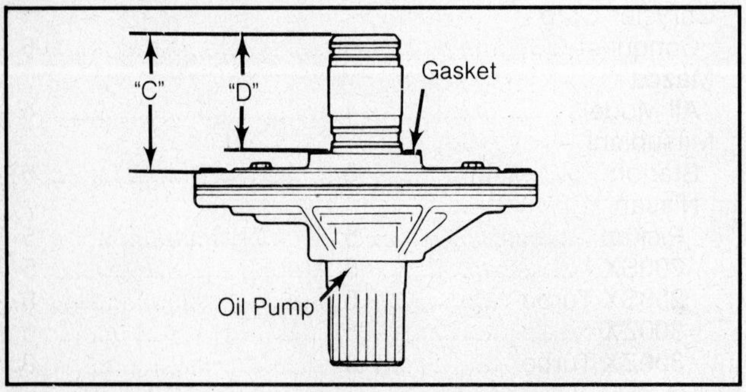

This procedure is for models 3N71B and L3N71B.

12) On L4N71B and JM600 transmissions, measure between top of drum support shaft (high-reverse clutch and forward clutch side) to installed gasket (dimension "C"). Install thrust washer. Measure from top of drum support shaft (high-reverse clutch and forward clutch side) to thrust washer (dimension "D"). *See Fig. 17.*

Fig. 17: Measuring Dimensions "C" & "D"

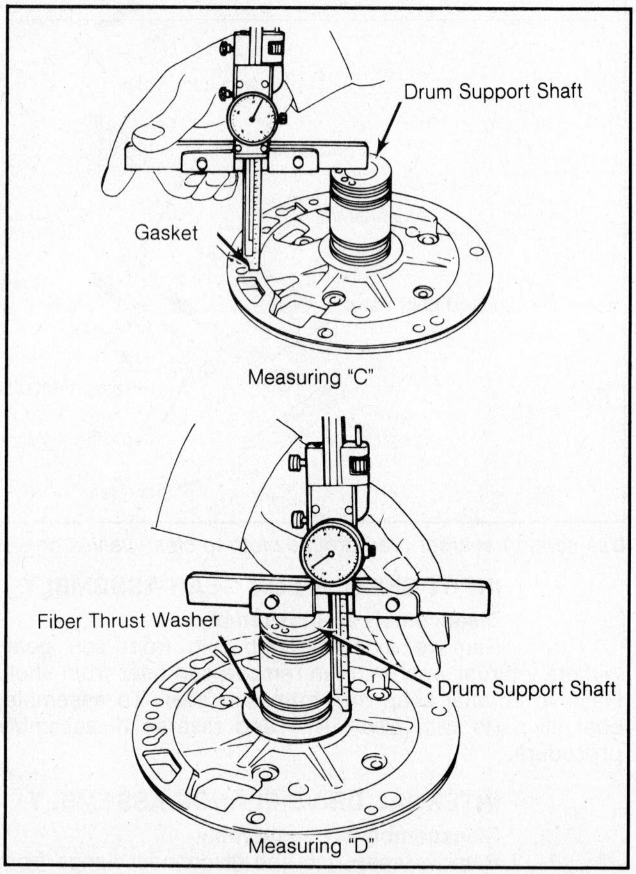

This procedure is for models E4N71B, L4N71B and JM600.

13) First, subtract .004" (.1 mm) from dimension "A". Then subtract dimension "B" from result. Note this result. Then subtract dimension "D" from dimension "C". The result of sum ("A" minus .004" (.1 mm) minus "B") less sum ("C" minus "D") is high-reverse (front) clutch end play.

14) Front end play range is .020-.031" (.5-.8 mm). Front end play can be adjusted by changing thicknesses of high-reverse (front) clutch thrust washers. These washers are available in thicknesses from .051-.106" (1.3-2.7 mm) in .008" (.2 mm) increments.

15) Total end play is result of sum ("A" minus .004" (.1 mm)) less dimension "C". Total end play range is .0098-.0197" (.25-.50 mm). Change total end play with oil pump cover bearing races of different thicknesses. Bearing races are available in thicknesses of .047-.087" (1.2-2.2 mm) in .08" (.2 mm) increments.

16) Install brake band, band strut and band servo. Lubricate servo "O" rings before installing. Install and tighten retainer bolts. Loosen piston stem. Finger tighten brake band servo piston stem enough to prevent brake band and strut from falling out.

17) DO NOT adjust at this time. On 3N71B and L3N71B models, go to step **26)**. On L4N71B, JM600 and

JATCO 3N71B, E4N71B, JM600, L3N71B & L4N71B (Cont.)

E4N71B models, apply petroleum jelly to bearing race and thrust washer and mount them to drum support. Mount drum support gasket to drum support after coating with petroleum jelly. Apply clean ATF to "O" ring of drum support.

18) Align drum support with Overdrive case to transmission case and install. Install Overdrive case and temporarily tighten it using 2 converter housing securing bolts. Insert intermediate shaft. Make sure shaft is installed in correct direction.

19) Overdrive pack end play and Overdrive total end play must be correct. To check Overdrive pack end play, assemble direct clutch assembly, Overdrive planetary gear set and connecting drum.

20) Install this assembly on Overdrive pack. Install oil pump bearing, gasket and Overdrive pack on oil pump. Measure dimensions "F" and "H". *See Fig. 18.* Attach thrust washer and needle bearing to drum support and Overdrive case. Measure dimensions "E" and "G". *See Fig. 18.*

Fig. 18: Measuring Dimensions "E", "F", "G" & "H"

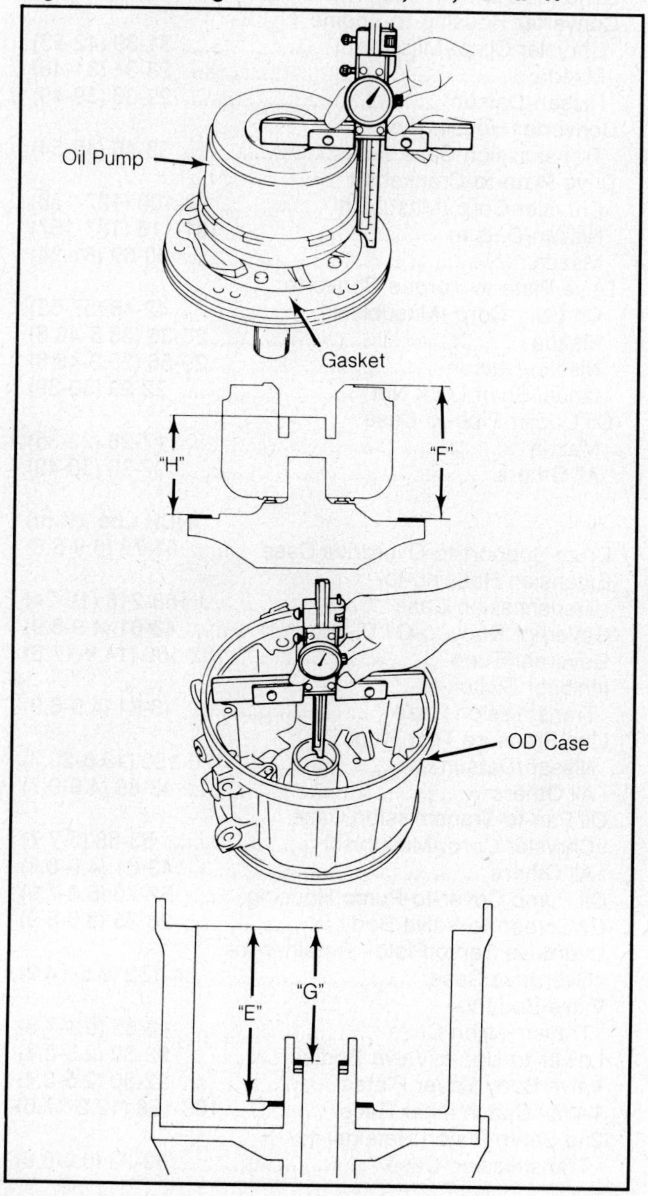

21) Result of sum ("E" minus .004" (.1 mm)) less dimension "F" is Overdrive pack end play. Overdrive pack end play range is .020-.031" (.5-.8 mm). Overdrive pack end play can be changed with Overdrive thrust washers of different thicknesses. These washers, which are same as high-reverse (front) clutch thrust washers, are available in thicknesses of .051-.106" (1.3-2.7 mm) in .008" (.2 mm) increments.

22) Result of sum ("G" minus .004" (.1 mm)) less "H" is Overdrive total end play. Total Overdrive end play range is .0098-.0197" (.25-.50 mm). Adjust total Overdrive end play with different thicknesses of Overdrive bearing race. Races are available in thicknesses from .047-.087" (1.2-2.2 mm) in .008" (.2 mm) increments.

23) Adjust band. See appropriate AUTOMATIC TRANSMISSION SERVICING article in IMPORT GENERAL SERVICING section for band adjustment procedure. Make sure brake band strut is correctly installed. Tighten piston stem to 60-84 INCH lbs. (7-10 N.m). Back off 2 full turns and tighten piston stem lock nut.

24) Lubricate Overdrive servo "O" rings with clean ATF. Install brake band, band strut and Overdrive band servo. Apply clean ATF to seal ring of direct clutch. Install Overdrive bearing and race, Overdrive thrust washer and Overdrive pack on drum support.

25) Make sure brake band strut is correctly installed. Apply clean ATF to "O" ring of oil pump. Install needle bearing, race and oil pump. Make sure oil pump housing and oil pump have been centered correctly. Adjust Overdrive band. Tighten piston stem to 61.2-86.4 INCH lbs. (7-10 N.m). Back of 2 full turns and tighten piston stem lock nut.

Fig. 19: Air Check Points

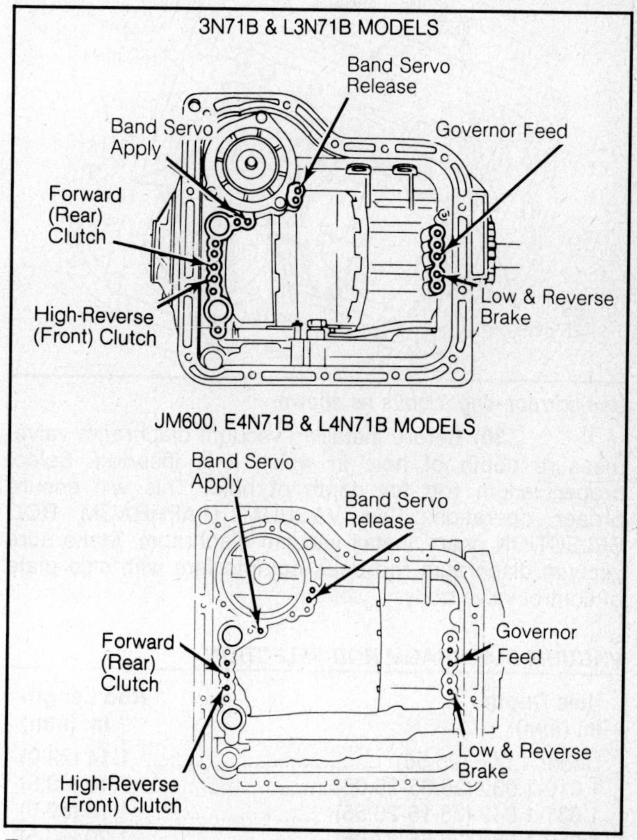

Test clutch and band functions with compressed air before installing valve body.

JATCO 3N71B, E4N71B, JM600, L3N71B & L4N71B (Cont.)

26) Using air gun with tapered rubber tip, test Overdrive band servo operation. Install accumulator parts. Install accumulator snap ring. Remove 2 converter housing bolts used to tighten Overdrive case. Apply sealant to seating surfaces of converter housing at bolt locations. Install converter housing on Overdrive case and tighten securing bolts. Install input shaft.

27) On L3N71B and 3N71B models, mount oil pump gasket on oil pump with petroleum jelly. Align pump to transmission case and install. Adjust band. See appropriate AUTOMATIC TRANSMISSION SERVICING article in IMPORT GENERAL SERVICING section for band adjustment procedure. Make sure that brake band strut is correctly installed. Tighten piston stem to 108-132 INCH lbs. (12-15 N.m). Back off 2 full turns. Tighten lock nut.

28) On all models, use air gun with tapered rubber tip to perform final air check of all assembled components. *See Fig. 19.* Do this BEFORE proceeding with installation of valve body assembly. This will ensure that all bolts are tightened and that seals have not been damaged during assembly.

29) Check that parking pawl, pin, spring and washer are assembled correctly. Install rear extension. Install control valve body with correct length attaching bolts. *See Fig. 20.* Be sure manual valve is in alignment with selector pin. Tighten control valve body attaching bolts. Make sure manual lever can be moved to all positions after control valve body attaching bolts are tightened.

Fig. 20: Control Valve Body Attaching Bolts

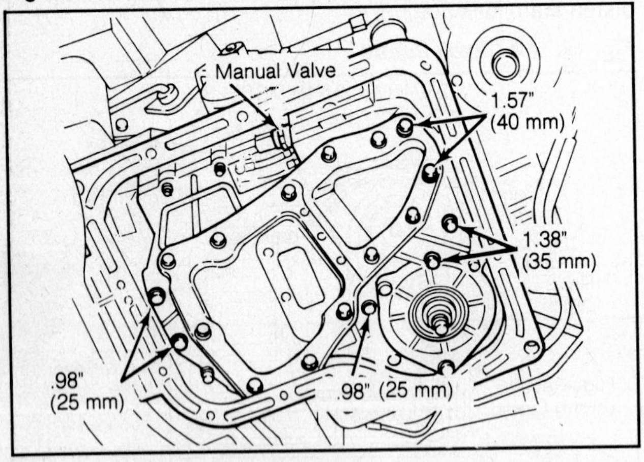

Use correct length bolts as shown.

30) Before installing vacuum diaphragm valve, measure depth of hole in which it is inserted. Select proper length rod for depth of hole. This will ensure proper operation. See VACUUM DIAPHRAGM ROD SELECTION chart. Install vacuum diaphragm. Make sure vacuum diaphragm rod does not interfere with side plate of control valve body.

VACUUM DIAPHRAGM ROD SELECTION

Hole Depth In. (mm)	Rod Length In. (mm)
Under 1.006 (25.55)	1.14 (29.0)
1.010-1.030 (25.65-26.05)	1.16 (29.5)
1.031-1.049 (26.15-26.55)	1.18 (30.0)
1.050-1.069 (26.65-27.05)	1.20 (30.5)
Over 1.070 (27.15)	1.22 (31.0)

31) Install downshift solenoid, Overdrive cancel solenoid and Overdrive indicator switch. Install inhibitor switch and check for proper operation. See appropriate AUTOMATIC TRANSMISSION SERVICING article in IMPORT GENERAL SERVICING section for checking and adjustment procedures.

32) Before installing oil pan, check alignment and operation of control lever and parking pawl engagement. Clean mechanism with compressed air. Make final check to be sure all bolts are correctly installed in control valve body. Install oil pan with new gasket.

33) Install governor tube. Carefully inspect torque converter for damage. Check converter hub for grooves caused by hardened seals. Check bushing contact area. Lubricate oil pump lip seal and converter neck before installing converter. Install converter, making sure that converter is properly meshed with oil pump drive gear.

TIGHTENING SPECIFICATIONS

Application	Ft. Lbs. (N.m)
Band Piston Stem Lock Nut	11-29 (15-39)
Converter Housing-to-Engine	
Chrysler Corp./Mitsubishi	31-39 (42-53)
Mazda	23-34 (31-46)
Nissan/Datsun	29-36 (39-49)
Converter Housing-to-Transmission Case	33-40 (45-54)
Drive Plate-to-Crankshaft	
Chrysler Corp./Mitsubishi	94-100 (127-136)
Nissan/Datsun	101-116 (137-157)
Mazda	60-69 (81-94)
Drive Plate-to-Torque Converter	
Chrysler Corp./Mitsubishi	42-46 (57-62)
Mazda	25-36 (33.8-48.8)
Nissan/Datsun	29-36 (39.3-48.8)
Manual Shaft Lock Nut	22-29 (30-39)
Oil Cooler Pipe-to-Case	
Mazda	17-26 (23-35)
All Others	22-36 (30-49)
	INCH Lbs. (N.m)
Drum Support-to-Overdrive Case	61-78 (6.9-8.8)
Extension Housing-to-Transmission Case	168-216 (19-24)
Governor Body-to-Oil Distributor	43-61 (4.9-6.9)
Governor Tube	132-156 (14.9-17.6)
Inhibitor Switch-to-Transmission Case	43-61 (4.9-6.9)
Line Pressure Test Plugs	
Nissan/Datsun	120-180 (13.6-20.3)
All Others	43-86 (4.9-9.7)
Oil Pan-to-Transmission Case	
Chrysler Corp./Mitsubishi	53-68 (6-7.7)
All Others	43-61 (4.9-6.9)
Oil Pump Cover-to-Pump Housing	52-70 (5.8-7.9)
Oil Screen-to-Valve Body	26-35 (3.0-3.9)
Overdrive Servo Piston Retainer-to-Overdrive Case	84-132 (9.5-14.9)
Valve Body-to-Transmission Case	48-65 (5.4-7.3)
Lower-to-Upper Valve Bodies	22-30 (2.5-3.4)
Valve Body Cover Plates	22-30 (2.5-3.4)
1-Way Clutch Inner Race	108-156 (12.2-17.6)
2nd Servo Piston Retainer-to-Transmission Case	60-78 (6.9-8.8)

MAZDA F3A 3-SPEED TRANSAXLE

GLC, 626 (FWD)

DESCRIPTION

The transaxle consists of 3 main units: Automatic transaxle, torque converter and differential assembly. The automatic transaxle consists of front, rear and one-way clutches, low-reverse brake assembly, oil pump and hydraulic controls (valve body and servo piston assemblies). The torque converter and differential are housed together in the torque converter housing.

LUBRICATION & ADJUSTMENTS

See appropriate AUTOMATIC TRANSMISSION SERVICING article in IMPORT GENERAL SERVICING section.

TROUBLE SHOOTING

ENGINE STARTS IN "D", "2", "1" OR "R", OR WILL NOT START IN "N" OR "P"

Check ignition and starter circuit. Shift linkage faulty or installed improperly. Leak in vacuum circuit.

Fig. 1: Exploded View of Transaxle Housing & Primary Components

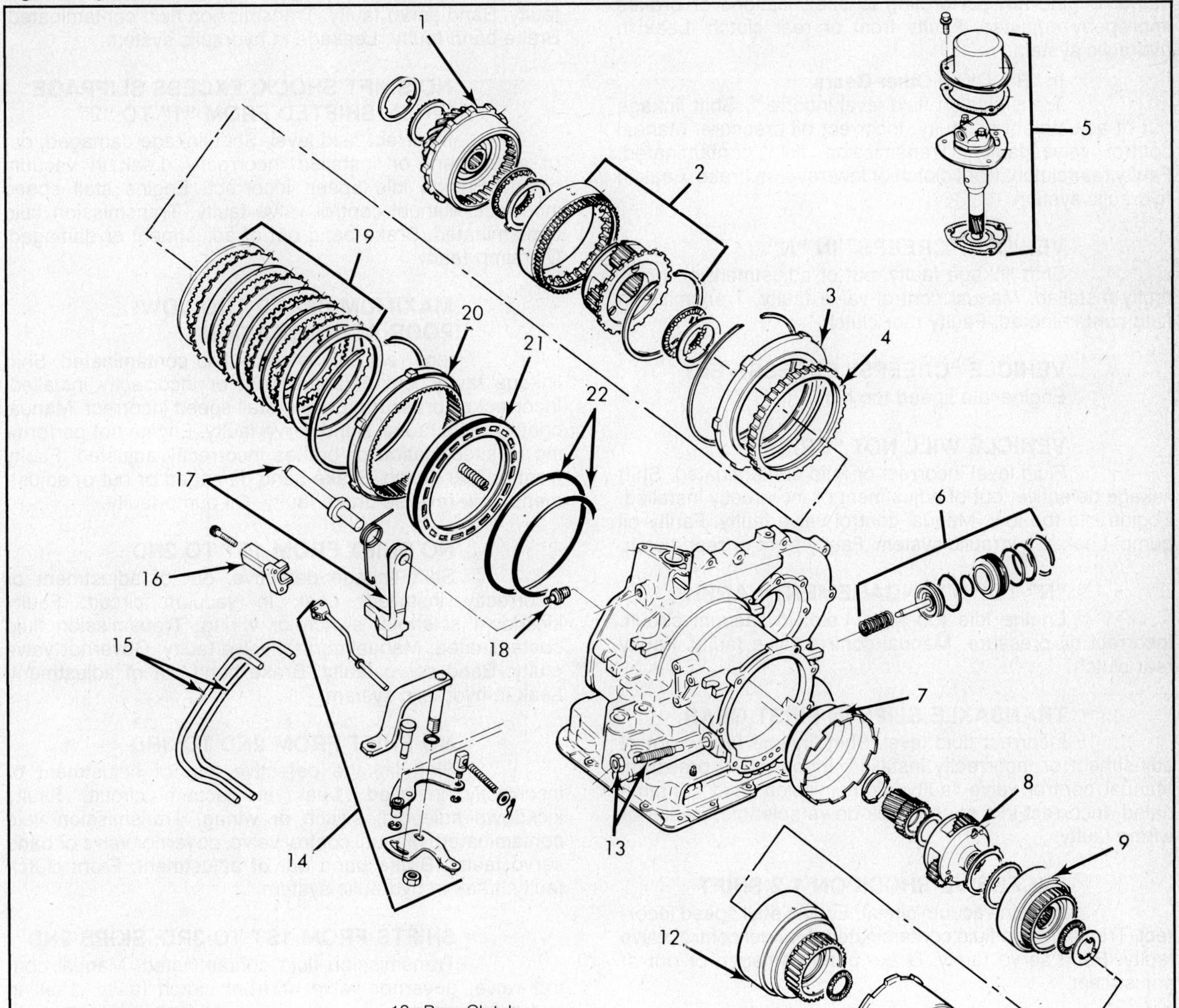

1. Drum Hub Assembly
2. One-Way Clutch Inner Race Assembly
3. One-Way Clutch
4. Low-Reverse Brake Retaining Plate
5. Governor
6. Servo Assembly
7. Connecting Shell
8. Planetary Carrier
9. Rear Clutch Hub Assembly
10. Brake Band
11. Front Clutch
12. Rear Clutch
13. Brake Band Anchor Bolt & Lock Nut
14. Control Rod Assembly
15. Oil Pipes
16. Actuator Support
17. Parking Pawl Assembly
18. Neutral Switch
19. Low-Reverse Brake Plate Assembly
20. Low-Reverse Brake Hub
21. Low-Reverse Brake Piston
22. Oil Seals

MAZDA F3A 3-SPEED TRANSAXLE (Cont.)

NO MOVEMENT

In Any Gear

Incorrect fluid level. Shift linkage faulty, out of adjustment or incorrectly installed. Incorrect oil pressure. Manual control valve faulty. Faulty oil pump. Leak in hydraulic system. Parking linkage improperly adjusted.

In "D", OK in Other Gears

Shift linkage faulty, out of adjustment or improperly installed. Incorrect oil pressure. Manual control valve faulty. Faulty one-way clutch.

In "D", "2" OR "1", OK in "R"

Incorrect fluid level. Shift linkage faulty, out of adjustment or incorrectly installed. Incorrect oil pressure. Manual control valve faulty. Transmission fluid contaminated. Engine not performing to specifications or brakes improperly adjusted. Faulty front or rear clutch. Leak in hydraulic system.

In "R", OK in Other Gears

Transmission fluid level incorrect. Shift linkage out of adjustment or faulty. Incorrect oil pressure. Manual control valve faulty. Transmission fluid contaminated. Faulty rear clutch, front clutch or low-reverse brake. Leak in hydraulic system.

VEHICLE "CREEPS" IN "N"

Shift linkage faulty, out of adjustment or incorrectly installed. Manual control valve faulty. Transmission fluid contaminated. Faulty rear clutch.

VEHICLE "CREEPS" EXCESSIVELY

Engine idle speed too high.

VEHICLE WILL NOT "CREEP"

Fluid level incorrect or fluid contaminated. Shift linkage defective, out of adjustment or incorrectly installed. Engine idle too low. Manual control valve faulty. Faulty oil pump. Leak in hydraulic system. Faulty front or rear clutch.

"N" TO "D" ENGAGEMENT HARSH

Engine idle too high. Leak in vacuum circuit. Incorrect oil pressure. Manual control valve faulty. Faulty rear clutch.

TRANSAXLE SLIPS IN FIRST GEAR

Incorrect fluid level. Shift linkage faulty, out of adjustment or incorrectly installed. Incorrect oil pressure. Manual control valve faulty. Transmission fluid contaminated. Incorrect idle speed. Kick-down solenoid, switch or wiring faulty.

EXCESSIVE SHOCK ON 1-2 SHIFT

Leak in vacuum circuit. Engine stall speed incorrect. Transmission fluid contaminated. Manual control valve faulty. Band servo faulty. Brake band damaged or out of adjustment.

EXCESSIVE SHOCK ON 2-3 SHIFT

Leak in vacuum circuit. Kickdown solenoid, switch or wiring faulty. Incorrect oil pressure. Manual control valve faulty. Band servo or front clutch faulty.

SHIFT SHOCK FELT ON DECELERATION

Shift linkage damaged, out of adjustment or incorrectly installed. Leak in vacuum circuit. Kickdown solenoid, switch or wiring faulty. Incorrect oil pressure. Manual control valve faulty. Governor valve faulty. Leak in hydraulic system.

EXCESSIVE 2-1 SHIFT SHOCK WITH LEVER IN "1" POSITION

Leak in vacuum circuit. Engine stall speed incorrect. Manual control valve faulty. Transmission fluid contaminated. Low-reverse brake faulty.

LITTLE OR NO SHIFT SHOCK; EXCESSIVE SLIPPAGE ON 1-2 SHIFT

Transmission fluid level incorrect. Shift linkage damaged, out of adjustment or incorrectly installed. Leak in vacuum circuit. Oil pressure incorrect. Manual control valve faulty. Band servo faulty. Transmission fluid contaminated. Brake band faulty. Leakage in hydraulic system.

NO SHIFT SHOCK; EXCESS SLIPPAGE WHEN SHIFTED FROM "1" TO "2"

Incorrect fluid level. Shift linkage damaged, out of adjustment or installed incorrectly. Leak in vacuum circuit. Engine idle speed incorrect. Engine stall speed incorrect. Manual control valve faulty. Transmission fluid contaminated. Brake band out of adjustment or damaged. Oil pump faulty.

MAXIMUM SPEED TOO LOW; POOR ACCELERATION

Incorrect fluid level or fluid contaminated. Shift linkage faulty, out of adjustment or incorrectly installed. Incorrect oil pressure. Engine stall speed incorrect. Manual control valve faulty. Band servo faulty. Engine not performing to specification or brakes incorrectly adjusted. Faulty front or rear clutch. Brake band damaged or out of adjustment. Low-reverse brake faulty. Oil pump faulty.

NO SHIFT FROM 1ST TO 2ND

Shift linkage defective, out of adjustment or incorrectly installed. Leak in vacuum circuit. Faulty kickdown solenoid, switch or wiring. Transmission fluid contaminated. Manual control valve faulty. Governor valve faulty. Band servo faulty. Brake band out of adjustment. Leak in hydraulic system.

NO SHIFT FROM 2ND TO 3RD

Shift linkage defective, out of adjustment or incorrectly installed. Leak in vacuum circuit. Faulty kickdown solenoid, switch or wiring. Transmission fluid contaminated. Manual control valve, governor valve or band servo faulty. Brake band out of adjustment. Front clutch faulty. Leak in hydraulic system.

SHIFTS FROM 1ST TO 3RD; SKIPS 2ND

Transmission fluid contaminated. Manual control valve, governor valve or front clutch faulty. Leak in hydraulic system.

NO 3-2 DOWNSHIFT

Leak in vacuum circuit. Manual control valve, governor valve or band servo faulty. Transmission fluid contaminated. Brake band out of adjustment or damaged. Front clutch damaged. Leak in hydraulic system.

MAZDA F3A 3-SPEED TRANSAXLE (Cont.)

NO 2-1 OR 3-1 DOWNSHIFT

Leak in vacuum circuit. Manual control valve, governor valve or band servo faulty. Transmission fluid contaminated. Brake band out of adjustment or damaged. One-way clutch faulty.

SHIFT POINTS FROM 3RD TO 2ND, 2ND TO 1ST TOO HIGH

Shift linkage damaged, out of adjustment or incorrectly installed. Kickdown solenoid, switch or wiring faulty. Leak in vacuum circuit. Incorrect oil pressure. Manual control valve or governor valve faulty. Leak in hydraulic system.

NO KICKDOWN AT NORMAL SPEEDS IN 3RD GEAR

Leak in vacuum circuit. Kickdown solenoid, switch or wiring faulty. Manual control valve or governor valve faulty. Transmission fluid contaminated. Brake band out of adjustment or damaged. Leak in hydraulic system.

1-2 OR 2-3 GEAR SHIFT IN "1"

Shift linkage damaged, out of adjustment or installed incorrectly. Manual control valve faulty. Leak in hydraulic system.

NO 2-1 SHIFT WHEN SHIFTER MOVED FROM "D" TO "1" POSITION

Incorrect oil pressure. Shift linkage damaged, out of adjustment or installed incorrectly. Transmission fluid contaminated. Manual control valve faulty. Governor valve faulty. Band servo faulty. Leak in hydraulic system. Front clutch damaged. Brake band out of adjustment or damaged.

NO 3-2 DOWNSHIFT WHEN MANUALLY SHIFTED FROM "D" TO "2"

Shift linkage damaged, out of adjustment or installed incorrectly. Incorrect oil pressure. Manual control valve faulty. Band servo faulty. Transmission fluid contaminated. Brake band out of adjustment or damaged. Leak in hydraulic system.

2-1, 2-3 SHIFTS WITH SHIFT LEVER IN "2"

Shift linkage damaged, out of adjustment or installed incorrectly. Incorrect oil pressure. Manual control valve faulty.

EXCESSIVE ENGINE RPM WHEN ACCELERATING IN 3RD GEAR ABOVE KICKDOWN SPEED

Shift linkage damaged, out of adjustment or installed incorrectly. Leak in vacuum circuit. Oil pressure incorrect. Manual control valve or governor valve faulty. Transmission fluid contaminated. Front clutch faulty. Leak in hydraulic system.

ENGINE RUNAWAY OR TRANSAXLE SLIPPAGE ON 3-2 KICKDOWN

Leak in vacuum circuit. Oil pressure incorrect. Manual valve faulty. Band servo faulty. Transmission fluid contaminated. Front clutch faulty. Brake band out of adjustment or damaged. Leak in hydraulic system.

TRANSAXLE BRAKES IN "R"

Band servo faulty. Transmission fluid contaminated. Faulty rear clutch. Brake band damaged or out of adjustment. Parking linkage damaged or improperly adjusted.

VEHICLE BRAKES ON 1-2 SHIFT

Manual control valve faulty. Transmission fluid contaminated. Front clutch or low-reverse brake faulty. One-way clutch faulty.

VEHICLE BRAKES ON 2-3 SHIFT

Manual control valve faulty. Band servo faulty. Transmission fluid contaminated. Brake band out of adjustment or damaged.

NO ENGINE BRAKING IN "1"

Shift linkage damaged, out of adjustment or installed incorrectly. Incorrect oil pressure. Manual control valve faulty. Transmission fluid contaminated. Low-reverse brake faulty. Leak in hydraulic system.

VEHICLE MOVES IN "P"; PARKING GEAR REMAINS ENGAGED WHEN SHIFTED OUT OF "P" POSITION

Shift linkage damaged, out of adjustment or incorrectly installed. Parking linkage out of adjustment or damaged.

TRANSAXLE OVERHEATS

Incorrect fluid level or oil pressure. Incorrect stall speed. Insufficient rear lubrication. Manual control valve faulty. Faulty band servo. Transmission fluid contaminated. Faulty front clutch, low-reverse brake, oil pump or torque converter one-way clutch. Brake band out of adjustment or damaged. Leak in hydraulic system. Planetary gear faulty.

TRANSAXLE NOISY

In "P" or "N"

Incorrect fluid level. Incorrect oil pressure. Faulty oil pump.

In All Other Drive Ranges

Incorrect fluid level. Incorrect oil pressure. Rear clutch, oil pump, one-way clutch or planetary gear faulty.

TESTING

ROAD TEST

1) Before road test, ensure that fluid level, condition and control linkage adjustments have been checked and corrected as necessary. During test, transaxle should upshift and downshift at approximately same speed as shown in SHIFT SPEED CHART. All shifts may vary slightly due to production tolerances or tire size. The important factor is the quality of the shifts. All shifts should be smooth, responsive and with no slippage or engine speed runaway.

2) Slippage or engine speed runaway in any gear usually indicates clutch or band problems. The slipping clutch or band in a particular gear can usually be identified by noting transaxle operation in other selector positions and comparing internal units which are applied in these positions. See CLUTCH and BAND APPLICATION CHART.

MAZDA F3A 3-SPEED TRANSAXLE (Cont.)

Fig. 2: Mazda F3A Automatic Transaxle Hydraulic Circuits Diagram

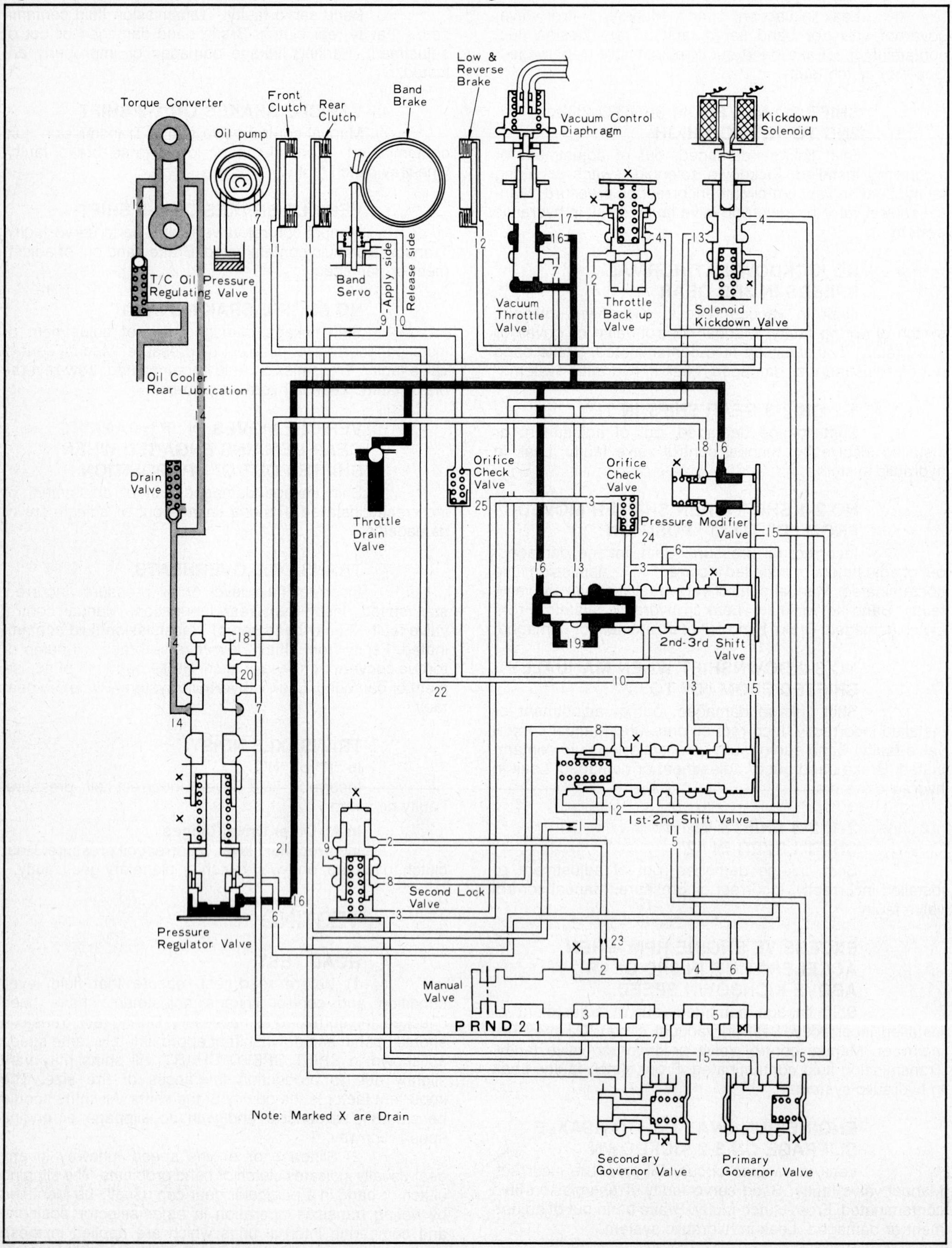

MAZDA F3A 3-SPEED TRANSAXLE (Cont.)

3) With vehicle at a standstill, accelerate under half and full throttle conditions to ensure that 1-2 and 2-3 shifts occur within specified range.

4) With shift lever in "D" position and vehicle speed at about 55 MPH, depress accelerator pedal to floor and ensure that a 3-2 downshift occurs. Slow vehicle to about 25 mph. Repeat and ensure that a 2-1 downshift occurs.

SHIFT SPEED CHART

Application	Speed (MPH) Half Throttle	Speed (MPH) Full Throttle
GLC		
1-2 Upshift	9-21	30-43
2-3 Upshift	17-38	54-74
3-2 Downshift	[1] 6-13	[2] 48-64
2-1 Downshift	[3] 23-32	[2] 13-29
626		
1-2 Upshift	10-23	34-47
2-3 Upshift	17-42	62-52
3-2 Downshift	[1] 25-35	[2] 55-72
2-1 Downshift	[3] 25-35	[2] 15-31

1 – Coastdown. Throttle fully closed.
2 – Kickdown.
3 – Shift lever in "1" position. Throttle fully closed.

STALL TEST

Testing Precautions

When making test, do not hold throttle open any longer than 5 seconds. Shift to "N" and allow engine to idle for at least 1 minute between tests to cool transaxle. If engine speed exceeds maximum limit shown in STALL SPEEDS SPECIFICATIONS table, release accelerator immediately as clutch or band slippage is indicated.

Testing Procedures

With engine at normal operating temperature, tachometer installed and parking and service brakes applied, make transaxle stall test in "D", "2", "1" and "R" ranges at full throttle and note maximum RPM obtained.

STALL SPEED SPECIFICATIONS

Application	Stall RPM
GLC	2200-2450
626	2000-2250

Stall Test Results

1) If stall speed is below specifications, engine performance is unsatisfactory or torque converter one-way clutch is faulty (slipping).

2) If stall speed is high in all drive ranges, oil pressure is incorrect. Check oil pump (weak), oil pump control valve and transaxle case for leaks. Check pressure regulator valve (sticking).

3) If stall speed is high in forward gears only, the rear clutch is slipping; in "D" only, the one-way clutch is slipping; in "2" only, the brake band is slipping. If high in "R" only, either the low-reverse brake or the front clutch is slipping.

HYDRAULIC PRESSURE TESTS

Line Pressure

1) Attach oil pressure gauge at line pressure checking plug located at rear of transaxle case on left side. *See Fig. 3.* Attach tachometer. Position gauges so that they may be observed from the driver's seat.

Fig. 3: Transaxle Assembly

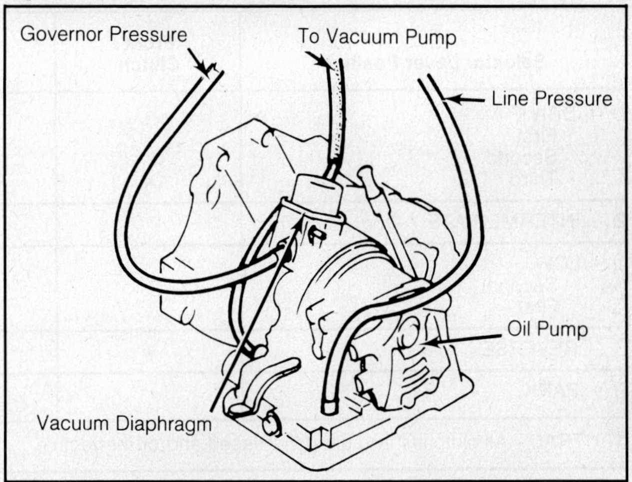

Attach lines as shown for hydraulic pressure tests.

2) With engine at normal operating temperature, transmission fluid level correct and transaxle in "D", check line pressure at idle and stall speed. Repeat test in "2" and "R", allowing sufficient time for engine and transaxle to cool between tests. Record results.

3) Disconnect line from vacuum diaphragm and connect a vacuum pump at connection. With shift lever in "D", increase engine RPM gradually and observe gauge reading. If line pressure drops abruptly, check governor pressure.

Governor Pressure Tests

1) Attach vacuum pump at vacuum diaphragm and oil pressure gauge at governor port. With gauge on pump at zero, check governor pressure and record result. Increase vacuum to 7.9 in. Hg (200 mm Hg) and record gauge reading. Pressure observed should be 14-23 psi (1.0-1.6 kg/cm^2) at zero and 6-14 psi (.4-1.0 kg/cm^2) at 7.9 in. Hg. If readings are not to specifications, check that the vacuum diaphragm rod is installed correctly and check that the manual control valve is not sticking.

LINE PRESSURES TABLE (ALL MODELS)

Gear Range	At Idle In psi (kg/cm^2)	At Stall Speed In psi (kg/cm^2)
"D"	43-57 (3.0-4.0)	128-156 (9.0-11.0)
"2"	114-171 (8.0-12.0)	114-171 (8.0-12.0)
"R"	57-110 (4.0-7.7)	228-270 (16.0-19.0)

GOVERNOR PRESSURES

Vehicle Speed (MPH)	Pressure on Gauge Psi (kg/cm^2)
GLC	
20	11-20 (.8-1.4)
35	24-34 (1.7-2.4)
55	48-64 (3.4-4.5)
626	
20	12-17 (.85-1.2)
35	20-28 (1.4-2.0)
55	38-48 (2.7-3.4)

MAZDA F3A 3-SPEED TRANSAXLE (Cont.)

CLUTCH AND BAND APPLICATION CHART (ELEMENTS IN USE)

Selector Lever Position	Front Clutch	Rear Clutch	Low-Reverse Brake	Brake Band	One-Way Clutch
D - DRIVE					
First		X			X
Second		X		X	
Third	X	X			
2 - INTERMEDIATE		X		X	
1 - LOW					
Second		X		X	
First		X	X		
R - REVERSE	X		X		
P - PARK			X		

NEUTRAL - All clutches and bands released and/or ineffective.

2) With oil pressure gauge attached as in step **1)** and shift lever in "D", accelerate vehicle smoothly and record governor pressure readings at 20, 35 and 55 MPH. If recorded results are not to specifications as given in GOVERNOR PRESSURES table, check for fluid leakage from the line pressure hydraulic circuit and/or the governor pressure hydraulic circuit. Check for faulty governor.

SERVICE (IN VEHICLE)

DRIVE AXLE SHAFTS

See appropriate DRIVE AXLE SHAFT article in IMPORT AXLE SHAFTS, OVERDRIVES & TRANSFER CASES section.

REMOVAL & INSTALLATION

See appropriate article in AUTOMATIC TRANSMISSION REMOVAL Section.

TORQUE CONVERTER

The torque converter is a sealed unit and cannot be disassembled for service. If the converter or any component thereof is found to be faulty, the entire assembly must be replaced.

TRANSAXLE DISASSEMBLY

Whenever working with transaxle, it is important that normal standards of cleanliness be observed. Complete transaxle assembly should be thoroughly steam cleaned before beginning any disassembly. Disassemble only those parts which require repair or replacement. Compressed air is preferred for drying components and oil passages, however, nylon cloth may be used. Never use fluffy rags or cloths to wipe parts dry.

1) Remove torque converter. Attach transaxle to Hanger (49 F401 495) and place on engine stand. Remove inhibitor switch, kickdown solenoid and vacuum diaphragm with rod, from transaxle case. Remove oil dipstick and tube. Remove speedometer drive gear retaining bolt and lift out gear assembly.

Fig. 4: Transaxle Outer Components

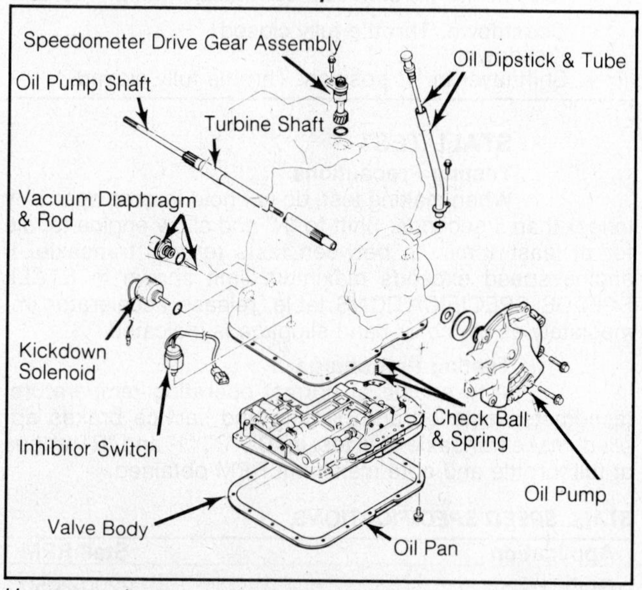

Use care when removing valve body so as not to lose check ball and spring.

2) Remove oil pump drive shaft and turbine shaft. Remove oil pan. Remove valve body, being careful not to lose check ball and spring. Measure and record front clutch drum end play. To determine front clutch drum end play, pry clutch drum toward oil pump with screwdriver and measure gap between drum and the connecting shell.

3) End play should be .020-.031" (.5-.8 mm). Determine adjusting shims required to bring end play to specifications and record for reassembly. Shims are available in thicknesses of .051" (1.3 mm) to .106" (2.7 mm) in increments of .008" (.02 mm).

4) Remove oil pump. If oil pump is difficult to remove, tighten brake band adjusting bolt until front clutch locks, then remove pump. Measure total end play. To do so, remove pump cover from oil pump. Place bearing in front brake drum. Fit bearing outer race on pump cover and install in front brake drum.

5) Place straightedge on face of transaxle case and measure distance between straightedge and pump cover or straightedge and transaxle case. Pump cover

MAZDA F3A 3-SPEED TRANSAXLE (Cont.)

Fig. 5: Measuring Front Clutch Drum End Play

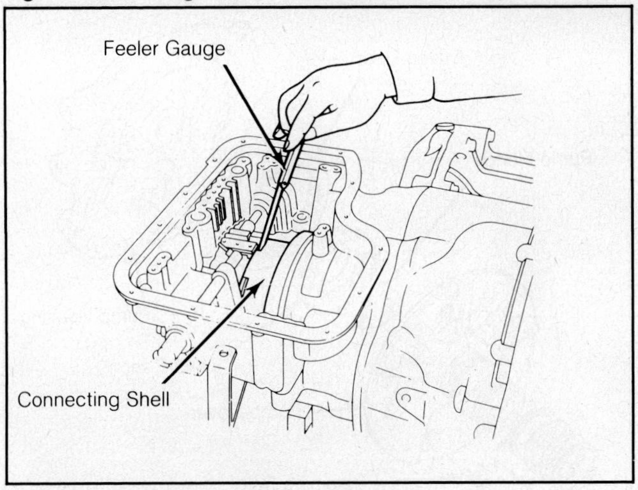

Clearance must be .020-.031" (.5-.8 mm).

should be between .004" (.10 mm) below transaxle case and .006" (.15 mm) above case. Limits are .008" (.20 mm) and .012" (.30 mm), respectively.

6) If end play is not to specifications, select new bearing race as needed to obtain correct end play. Selective bearing races are available in thicknesses of .047" (1.2 mm) to .087" (2.2 mm) in increments of .008" (.2 mm). Record race chosen for reassembly reference.

Fig. 6: Measuring Transaxle Total End Play

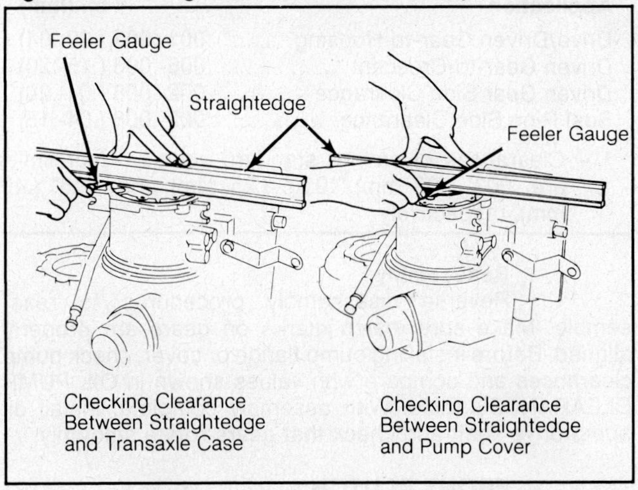

7) Remove brake band adjusting bolt and lock nut. Remove brake band. DO NOT allow brake band to rest in fully expanded state. Hold band partially closed with a piece of wire. Remove front clutch, rear clutch and rear clutch hub assembly.

8) Remove planetary gear carrier, sun gear with spacer and connecting shell. Compress servo piston with "C" clamp and remove snap ring. Release "C" clamp and remove servo piston.

9) Separate transaxle case from torque converter case. Remove Neutral switch and governor assembly from transaxle case. Remove oil pipes and parking pawl assembly. Remove drum hub assembly. Remove one-way clutch inner race assembly.

10) Attach dial indicator and measure clearance between one-way clutch and low-reverse brake assembly. With gauge pin resting on drive plate, move plate up and

Fig. 7: Removing Servo Piston

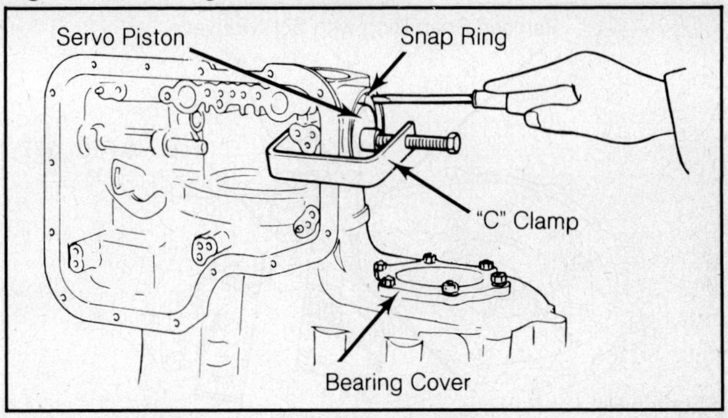

Compress piston with "C" clamp while removing snap ring.

down by hand while observing indicator dial. Clearance should be .031-.041" (.80-1.05 mm).

11) If clearance is not to specifications, select a retaining plate of different thickness to obtain correct clearance. Retaining plates are available in thicknesses of .181" (4.6 mm) to .221" (5.6 mm) in increments of .008" (.2 mm). Record plate chosen for reassembly reference.

Fig. 8: Checking Low-Reverse Brake Clearance

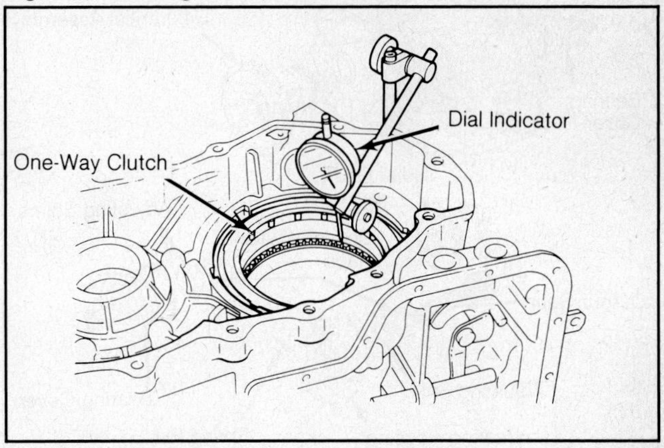

Clearance must be .031-.041" (.80-1.05 mm).

12) Remove snap ring, one-way clutch and low-reverse brake retaining plate. Remove low-reverse brake plates. Attach low-reverse brake hub and Piston Remover (49 FT01 377). Remove snap ring with screwdriver, then remove brake hub and piston.

13) Drive out manual shaft retaining spring pin and remove manual shaft assembly. Do not lose check ball and spring. Remove shift control rod assembly and assembly support. Retain all components in correct order to aid in installation procedures.

14) Remove differential assembly from torque converter housing. Remove bearing housing assembly (with idler and output gears). If necessary, strike idler shaft lightly with soft hammer to ease bearing housing removal. Drive out idler gear retaining spring pin and remove idler from bearing housing. Remove output gear assembly and press off bearing race. Save adjusting shim for reassembly.

15) Remove 6 bearing cover-to-transaxle case retaining bolts and remove bearing cover. Press off bearing race. Remove and retain adjusting shims for reassembly. Drive out oil seal. Remove bearing cover from torque converter side of torque converter housing. Press out bearing race. Drive oil seal from last bearing cover removed. Remove bearing race from differential assembly.

MAZDA F3A 3-SPEED TRANSAXLE (Cont.)

Fig. 9: Removing Low-Reverse Brake Hub & Piston

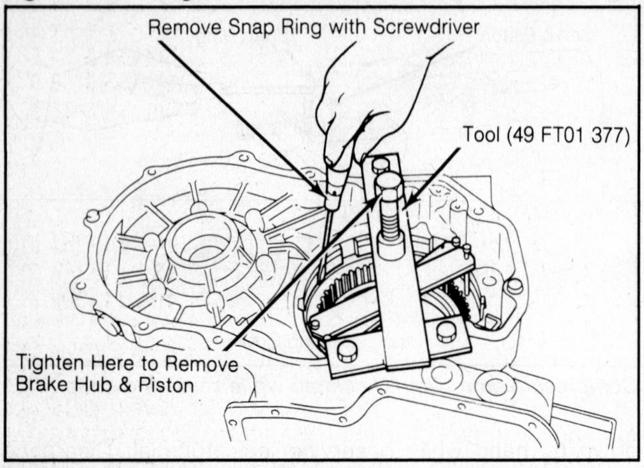

Tighten tool slowly as brake and piston assembly is removed.

Fig. 10: Torque Converter Housing Components

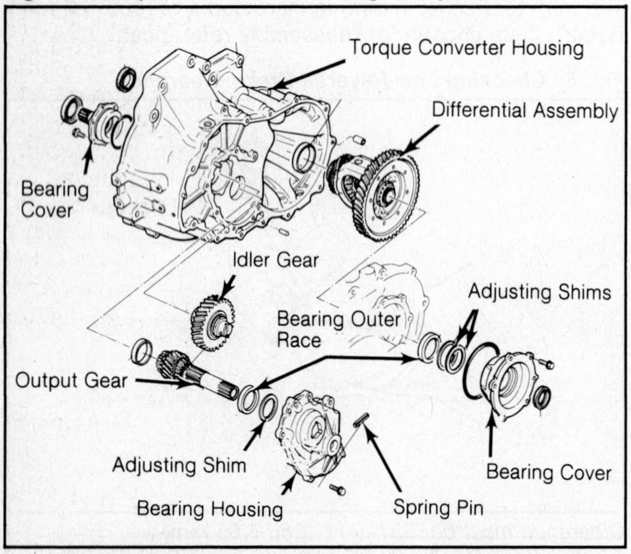

COMPONENT DISASSEMBLY & REASSEMBLY

When reassembling transaxle components, observe the following practices and precautions:

- Wash all parts thoroughly.
- Use new drive plates in all clutch assemblies.
- Soak drive plates and brake band in ATF for at least 2 hours before assembly in the transaxle.
- Use petroleum jelly as needed to hold thrust bearings and/or washers in place during installation. Do not use grease.

OIL PUMP

Disassembly

1) Remove pump cover retaining bolts and separate cover from pump body. Remove pump flange. If gears are to be reused, scribe marks on gears to ensure reassembly in same position. Remove drive and driven gears.

2) Check condition of gear teeth and surfaces. Check seal ring for cracks or breaks and replace as

Fig. 11: Exploded View of Oil Pump Assembly

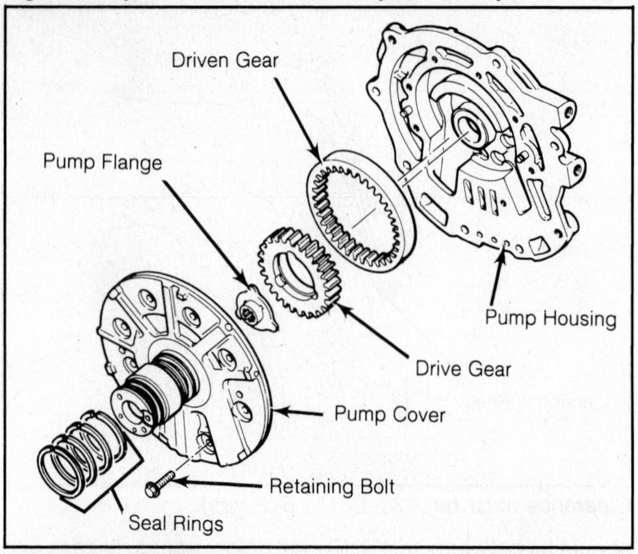

needed. Check condition of pump housing sleeve and inner gear bushing. Check sleeve outer diameter and bushing inner diameter. If sleeve diameter is less than 1.499" (38.075 mm) or bushing diameter is greater than 1.492" (37.90 mm), replace sleeve and bushing as a set.

OIL PUMP CLEARANCES (ALL MODELS)

Application	[1] In. (mm)
Drive/Driven Gear-to-Housing	.001-.002 (.02-.04)
Driven Gear-to-Crescent	.006-.008 (.15-.20)
Driven Gear Side Clearance	.002-.008 (.04-.20)
Seal Ring Side Clearance	.002-.006 (.04-.15)

1 – Clearances given are standard values. Wear limits are .003" (.08 mm), .010" (.25 mm) and .016" (.40 mm), respectively.

Reassembly

Reverse disassembly procedures to reassemble. Make sure match marks on gears are properly aligned. Before installing pump flange or cover, check pump clearances and compare with values shown in OIL PUMP CLEARANCES table. With assembly complete, install oil pump drive shaft and check that gears rotate smoothly.

FRONT CLUTCH

Disassembly

1) Before disassembling clutch, check clearance. Place front clutch on oil pump, install dial indicator so that the plunger rests on retaining plate and apply compressed air to oil hole of oil pump. Measurement shown on gauge face is front clutch clearance.

2) If clearance is not .063-.071" (1.6-1.8 mm), it may be adjusted by replacing the retaining plate with one of a different size. Retaining plates are available in thicknesses of .205" (5.2 mm) to .244" (6.2 mm) in increments of .008" (.2 mm).

3) Compress clutch assembly with Clutch Spring Compressor (49 0378 375) and remove large snap ring. Lift out retaining plate, clutch plates and dished plate. Remove small snap ring, spring retainer and clutch return springs. Apply compressed air at oil hole in clutch drum and remove piston. Remove seal rings.

MAZDA F3A 3-SPEED TRANSAXLE (Cont.)

Fig. 12: Exploded View of Front Clutch

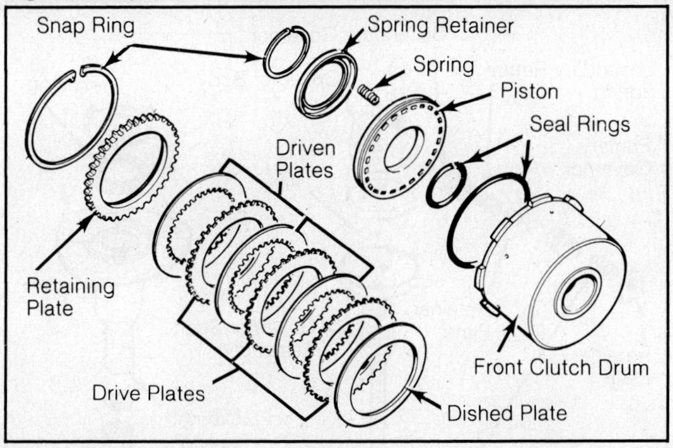

Fig. 13: Checking Clutch Clearance

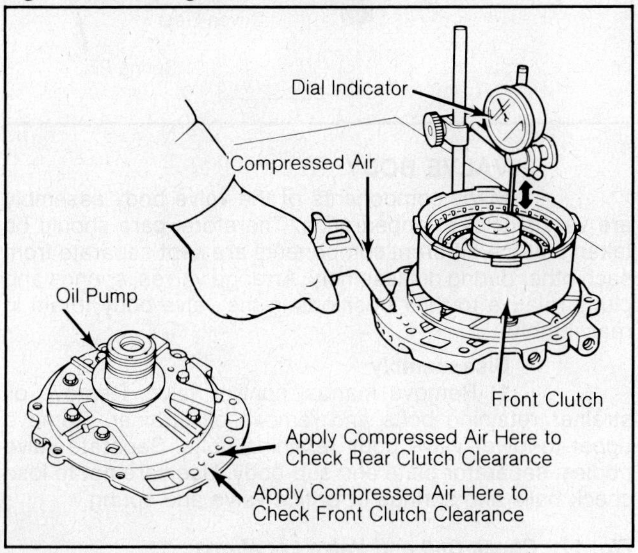

Apply compressed air at oil passages indicated.

4) Inspect all parts for wear or damage and replace as needed. Return springs must have free length of .992-1.071" (25.2-27.2 mm). If not, they are fatigued and should be replaced. Check inside diameter of clutch drum bushing. If diameter exceeds 1.735" (44.075 mm), replace bushing.

Reassembly

Reverse disassembly procedure to reassemble. Be careful to avoid damage to oil seal ring when installing clutch piston. When installing dished plate, make sure that dished face is away from piston. Install retaining plate as determined during disassembly. Place clutch assembly on oil pump and apply compressed air to oil hole to determine proper clutch operation.

REAR CLUTCH

Disassembly

1) Before disassembling clutch, check clearance. To do so, follow same procedure used for checking front clutch clearance. Clearance should be .031-.059" (.80-1.50 mm). If clearance is incorrect, adjust by selecting a new retaining plate. Available retaining plates are same as those for front clutch.

Fig. 14: Exploded View of Rear Clutch

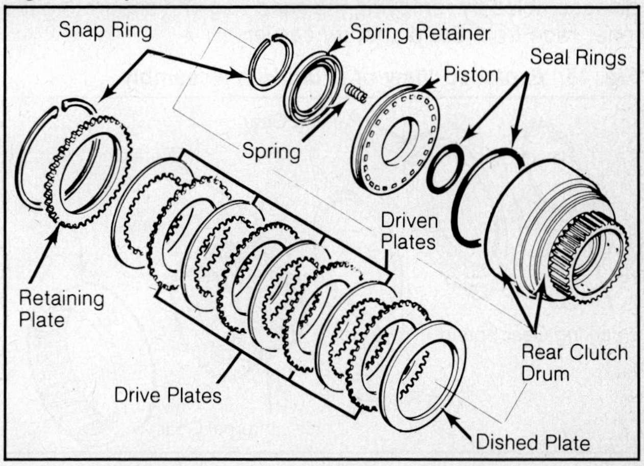

2) Compress clutch assembly with Clutch Spring Compressor (49 0378 375) and remove large snap ring. Lift out retaining plate, clutch plates and dished plate. Remove small snap ring, spring retainer and clutch return springs.

3) Apply compressed air to oil hole in clutch drum and remove piston. Remove seal rings. Inspect all parts for wear or damage and replace as needed. Return springs must have free length of .992-1.071" (25.2-27.2 mm). If not, they are fatigued and should be replaced.

CLUTCH BAND APPLICATION CHART

Application	GLC	626
Front Plates	3	3
Rear Plates	4	4
Low/"R" Plates	3	4

Reassembly

Reverse disassembly procedure to reassemble. Be careful not to damage oil seal ring when installing clutch piston. When installing dished plate, make sure that dished face is facing away from piston. Install retaining plate as determined during disassembly. Place clutch assembly on oil pump and apply compressed air at oil hole in pump to determine proper clutch operation.

DRUM HUB

Disassembly

Remove parking gear spring. Push in parking gear retaining pin with screwdriver and remove parking gear. Remove snap ring and lift internal gear assembly from drive hub. Check gears for excessive wear or damage and replace if needed.

Reassembly

Reverse disassembly procedures to reassemble drum hub.

REAR CLUTCH HUB

Disassembly & Reassembly

Remove snap ring and separate hub from internal gear. Check for worn or damaged snap ring or gear. Replace as needed. Reassemble in reverse order of disassembly.

ONE-WAY CLUTCH

Disassembly

1) One-way clutch and one-way clutch inner race are removed from transaxle case separately. The clutch requires no further disassembly. The inner race is disassembled by removing the snap ring and separating the inner race from the planetary carrier.

Fig. 15: Exploded View of Drum Hub Assembly

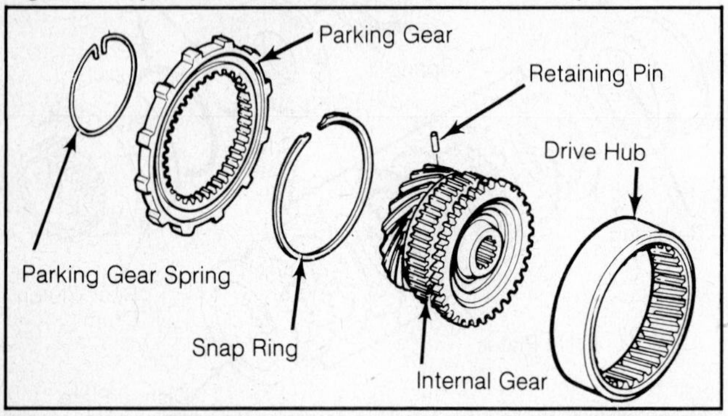

2) Check for worn or damaged gears on inner race. Check pinion operation in planetary carrier. Check clearance between the pinion washer and planetary carrier. Clearance must not exceed .031" (.8 mm).

Reassembly

Reverse disassembly procedures to reassemble. Install one-way clutch in inner race and ensure that it will turn in one direction only.

LOW-REVERSE BRAKE

Disassembly

Low-Reverse brake assembly was disassembled during transaxle disassembly. Check all components for signs of damage or excessive wear. Check return springs free length. If length is not 1.051-1.130" (26.7-28.7 mm), the spring is fatigued and should be replaced.

Reassembly

Reassembly will be accomplished when transaxle is reassembled. See TRANSAXLE REASSEMBLY.

GOVERNOR ASSEMBLY

Disassembly

Remove 2 governor housing retaining bolts and separate governor body with shaft from housing. Separate body from shaft using care not to lose filter. Disassemble governor body and retain components in correct order for reassembly. Check filter and clean if clogged. Check return springs free length and outside diameter. If not to specification, replace spring.

Reassembly

Reverse disassembly procedure to assemble. Apply compressed air at top oil hole in housing and ensure that valve is operating properly.

GOVERNOR RETURN SPRING SPECIFICATIONS (ALL MODELS)

Application	Free Length In. (mm)	Diameter In. (mm)
Primary Spring	.650-.728 (16.5-18.5)	.350-.366 (8.7-9.3)
Secondary Spring	.488-.567 (12.4-14.4)	.352-.396 (8.95-9.55)

Fig. 16: Exploded View of Governor Assembly

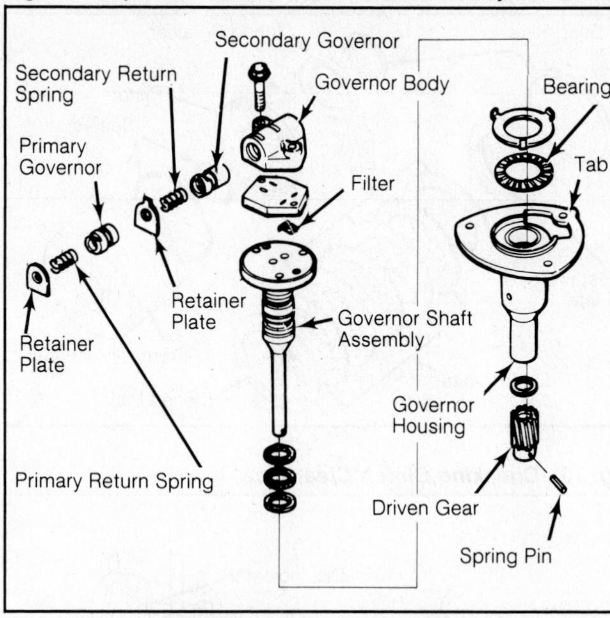

VALVE BODY

Many components of the valve body assembly are very similar in appearance. Therefore, care should be taken that the different components are kept separate from each other during disassembly. Arrange valves, springs and plugs relative to their positions in the valve body to aid in reassembly.

Disassembly

1) Remove manual control valve. Remove oil strainer retaining bolts and remove oil strainer. Remove upper-to-lower valve body retaining bolts. Separate valve bodies, separator plate and sub-body. Use care not to lose check balls and springs or orifice valve and spring.

Fig. 17: Check Ball and Valve Locations

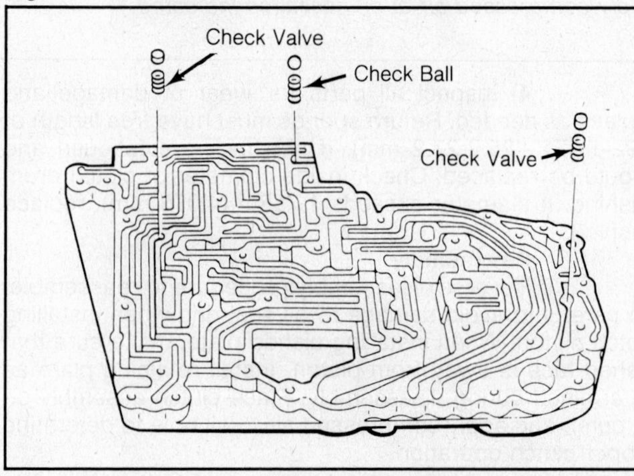

2) Remove side plate. Remove vacuum throttle valve, throttle backup valve and spring, and downshift valve and spring. Remove end plate. Remove pressure modifier valve, 2-3 shift valve, spring and plug, and 1-2 shift valve and spring.

3) Remove side plate. Remove second lock valve and spring. Remove pressure regulator valve assembly (sleeve, plug, seat, spring and valve).

MAZDA F3A 3-SPEED TRANSAXLE (Cont.)

Fig. 18: Exploded View of Valve Body and Main Controls

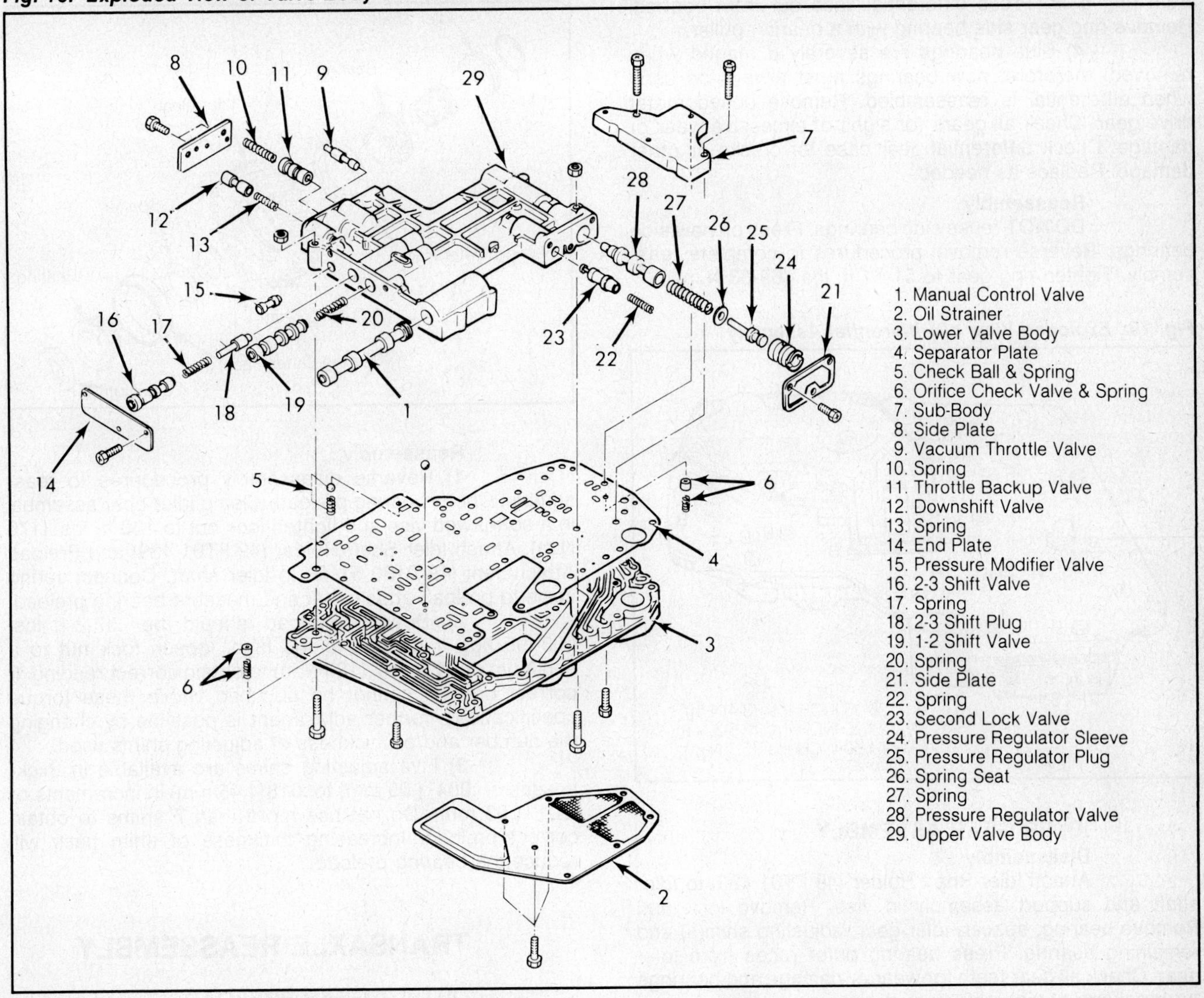

VALVE BODY SPRING IDENTIFICATION (ALL MODELS)

Spring	Outer Diameter In. (mm)	Free Length In. (mm)
Throttle Backup Valve	.287 (7.3)	1.417 (36.0)
Downshift Valve	.218 (5.55)	.866 (22.0)
2-3 Shift Valve	.272 (6.9)	1.164 (41.0)
1-2 Shift Valve	.258 (6.55)	1.260 (32.0)
Second Lock Valve	.218 (5.55)	1.319 (33.5)
Pressure Regulator Valve	.461 (11.7)	1.693 (43.0)
Steel Check Ball Spring	.256 (6.5)	1.516 (26.8)
Orifice Check Valve	.197 (5.0)	.846 (21.5)

Reassembly

1) Reverse disassembly procedures to reassemble. Coat all parts with clean transmission fluid. When tightening parts, be sure to observe the specified torque values. *See Fig. 20.* Do not force valves into position. They should push lightly into place by hand.

2) Ensure orifice check valve, check ball and springs are located correctly. Put separator plate in place and hold there with hand clamps. Install upper valve body and bolt in place.

DIFFERENTIAL

Disassembly

1) Measure side gear and pinion gear backlash before disassembling differential assembly. To do so, insert both drive shafts into differential and support by shafts in "V" blocks. Position dial indicator with plunger resting on teeth of pinion gear. Measure backlash. Repeat procedure with plunger on other pinion gear.

2) Backlash readings should be less than .004" (.1 mm). If not, adjust by changing thrust washers. There are 3 sizes of thrust washers available: .079" (2.0) mm), .083" (2.1 mm) and .087" (2.2 mm). Use thrust washers of the same thickness on both sides whenever possible.

3) Disassemble differential assembly. Remove ring gear retaining bolts, knock out locating pin and remove right gear. Push out pinion gear shaft. Remove pinion and side gears, with washers, from case. Place differential

MAZDA F3A 3-SPEED TRANSAXLE (Cont.)

housing in press and support by bearing on opposite side from ring gear. Press differential case out from bearing. Remove ring gear side bearing with a bearing puller.

4) Side bearings are severely damaged when removed, therefore, new bearings must always be used when differential is reassembled. Remove speedometer drive gear. Check all gears for signs of excessive wear or damage. Check differential gear case for cracks or other damage. Replace as needed.

Reassembly

DO NOT reuse side bearings. Press on new side bearings. Reverse removal procedures to complete reassembly. Tighten ring gear to 51-61 ft. lbs. (69-83 N.m)

Fig. 19: Exploded View of Differential Assembly

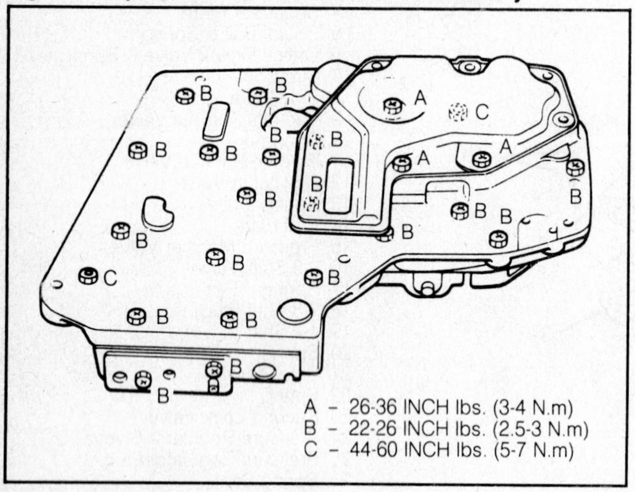

IDLER GEAR ASSEMBLY

Disassembly

Attach Idler Shaft Holder (49 FT01 439) to idler shaft and support assembly in vise. Remove lock nut. Remove bearing, spacer, idler gear, adjusting shim(s) and remaining bearing. Press bearing outer races from idler gear. Check all gear teeth for wear or damage and bearings for breakage or signs of unusual wear.

Fig. 20: Valve Body Tightening

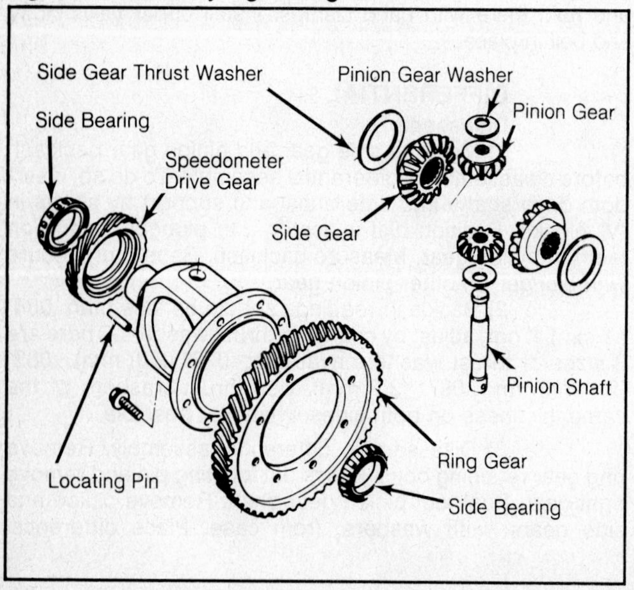

Fig. 21: Exploded View of Idler Gear Assembly

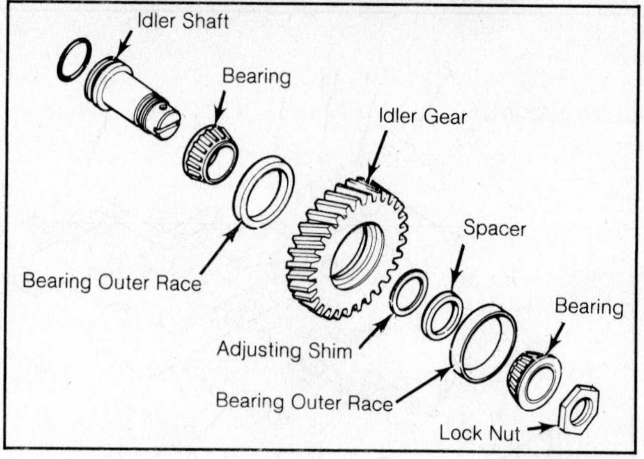

Reassembly

1) Reverse disassembly procedures to reassemble. Check bearing preload. Clamp idler gear assembly in a soft-jawed vise and tighten lock nut to 130 ft. lbs. (176 N.m). Attach Idler Shaft Holder (49 FT01 439) and Preload Attachment (49 0180 510B) to idler shaft. Connect spring scale to preload attachment and measure bearing preload.

2) Bearing preload should be .07-2.1 lbs. (.03-.95 kg). If preload is too high, loosen lock nut to a minimum of 94 ft. lbs. (127 N.m) to obtain correct reading. If correct preload cannot be obtained within these torque specifications, further adjustment is possible by changing the number and/or thickness of adjusting shims used.

3) Five adjusting shims are available in thicknesses of .004" (.09 mm) to .018" (.45 mm) in increments of .001" (.03 mm). Do not use more than 7 shims to obtain correct preload. Increasing thickness of shim pack will reduce the bearing preload.

TRANSAXLE REASSEMBLY

OUTPUT GEAR PRELOAD

1) If output gear, bearing housing, bearing cover, output gear bearings and/or converter housing is replaced, output gear bearing preload must be checked and adjusted before transaxle reassembly.

2) To check preload, the following special tools are required: Bearing Selector (49 FT01 383), Preload Adapter (49 FT01 389) and Attachment (49 0180 510B), Spacers (49 FT01 384), Bars (49 F401 385) and Bolt Set (49 FT01 386).

3) Remove bearing outer race and adjusting shims from bearing housing. Set output gear assembly in converter housing. Place outer race on bearing selector and attach selector with race to output gear assembly. Turn halves of selector to eliminate gap between them.

4) Install bearing housing on selector. Place 4 spacers between converter housing and bearing housing and install bolts through bearing housing, spacers and into converter housing. Tighten bolts to 14-19 ft. lbs. (19-26 N.m). *See Fig. 22* for proper positioning of spacers.

5) To seat bearing, insert bars in holes in each half of bearing selector. Turn halves as gap between them widens. Continue to increase gap until selector stops. Reverse direction and close gap.

MAZDA F3A 3-SPEED TRANSAXLE (Cont.)

6) Set preload adapter and attachment on output gear. Measure bearing preload while gradually increasing gap in bearing selector. When preload is 1.1-2.0 lbs. (.5-.9 kg), measure gap in selector (check at several different points). Select adjusting shims to fill gap at widest point.

7) Shims are available in thicknesses of .004" (.10 mm) to .008" (.20 mm) in .001" (.02 mm) increments, and .020" (.50 mm). Do not exceed 7 shims in the pack. Remove selector, install shims and install bearing housing. Check that preload with components properly installed is .07-.20 lbs. (.03-.09 kg).

Fig. 22: Measuring Output Gear Bearing Preload

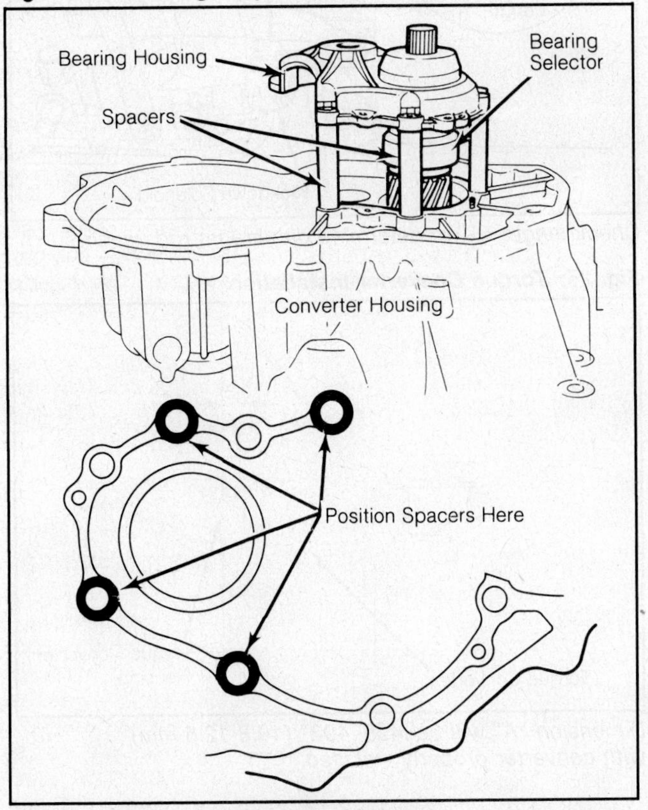

Position spacers between converter and bearing housings in positions as shown.

DIFFERENTIAL SIDE BEARING PRELOAD

1) If differential gear case, side bearing(s), bearing cover, torque converter housing and/or transaxle case is replaced, differential side bearing preload must be checked and adjusted before transaxle reassembly.

2) To check preload, the following special tools will be required: Bearing Selector (49 F401 381), Preload Adapter (49 FT01 515), Spacers (49 F401 384), Bars (49 F401 385) and Bolt Set (49 FT01 387).

3) Remove bearing outer race and adjusting shims from differential bearing cover. Place differential assembly in converter housing. Place outer race on bearing selector and place selector with race in differential assembly. Turn halves of selector to eliminate gap between them.

4) Install transaxle case on selector using 6 spacers between transaxle case and torque converter housing. Install bolts through transaxle case, spacers and into converter housing. Tighten bolts to 23-34 ft. lbs. (31-46 N.m). *See Fig. 23* for proper positioning of spacers.

Fig. 23: Measuring Differential Side Bearing Preload

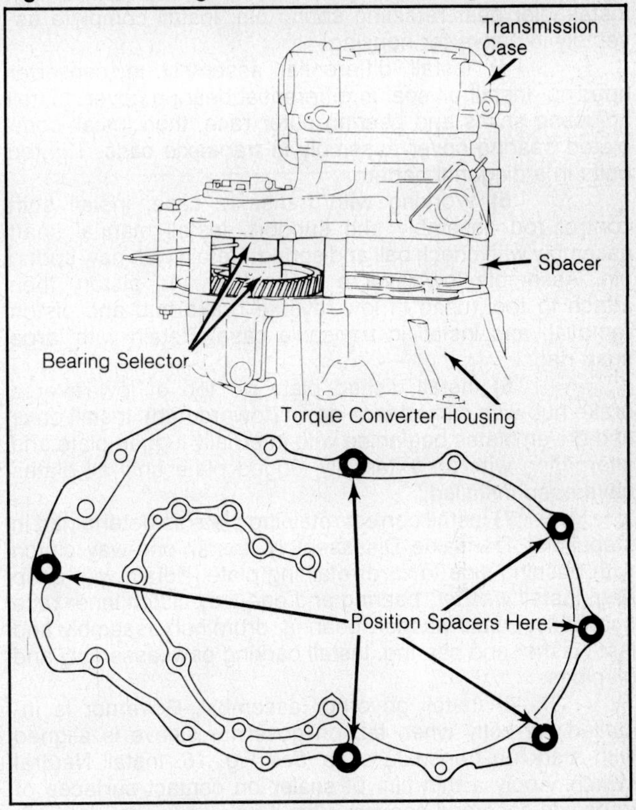

Position spacers between transaxle case and converter housing as shown.

5) To seat bearing, insert bars in holes in each half of bearing selector and turn so that gap between them widens. Continue to increase gap until selector stops. Reverse direction and close gap.

6) Set preload adapter and attachment on output gear. Measure bearing preload while gradually increasing gap in bearing selector. When preload is 1.1-2.0 lbs. (.5-.9 kg), measure gap in selector (check at several different points). Select adjusting shim to fill gap at widest point.

7) Shims are available in thicknesses of .004" (.10 mm) to .008" (.20 mm) in increments of .001" (.03 mm) and .012" (.30 mm) to .036" (.90 mm) in increments of .04" (1.0 mm). Use as few shims as possible to meet gap requirements. Remove selector, install shim pack and install transaxle case. Check that preload with components properly installed is .07-1.7 lbs. (.03-.76 kg).

TRANSAXLE REASSEMBLY

1) Throughout reassembly procedure, handle all parts carefully to avoid damaging bearing and mating surfaces. Lubricate all components with ATF fluid. Gaskets and thrust washers may be held in place with petroleum jelly where needed. DO NOT use grease. Install all new gaskets and seals.

2) Install oil seal on output gear bearing cover and in opening in converter case adjacent to differential assembly. Press differential bearing outer race into bearing cover. Press output gear bearing outer race into bearing cover. Install output gear bearing cover on torque converter housing and place housing on stand.

3) Install output gear adjusting shims in bearing housing and press in bearing outer race. Install output gear

MAZDA F3A 3-SPEED TRANSAXLE (Cont.)

assembly and idler gear assemblies in bearing housing. Install idler gear retaining spring pin. Install complete assembly in converter housing.

4) Install differential assembly in converter housing. Install oil seal in differential bearing cover. Install adjusting shims and bearing outer race, then install completed bearing cover assembly in transaxle case. Tighten bolts in a diagonal pattern.

5) Working with transaxle case, install shift control rod assembly and support. Install manual shaft assembly with check ball and spring. Retain with new spring pin. Assemble low-reverse brake hub and piston, then attach to tool (used in low-reverse brake hub and piston removal) and install in transaxle case. Retain with large snap ring.

6) Install dished plate on top of low-reverse brake hub with dished face down (toward hub). Install drive and driven plates beginning with internally lugged plate and alternating with an externally lugged plate until all plates have been installed.

7) Install correct retaining plate as determined in step **7)** of Transaxle Disassembly. Install one-way clutch with bushing side toward retaining plate. Retain with snap ring. Install washer, bearing and one-way clutch inner race assembly. Install washer, bearing, drum hub assembly and last washer and bearing. Install parking pawl assembly and oil pipes.

8) Install governor assembly. Governor is installed correctly when tab on governor sleeve is aligned with mark on transaxle case. *See Fig. 16.* Install Neutral switch. Apply a thin film of sealer on contact surfaces of transaxle case and converter housing.

9) Assemble transaxle case to torque converter housing. Place servo assembly in position in case and compress with "C" clamp. Install retaining snap ring and remove "C" clamp.

10) Install connecting hub, sun gear with spacer and planetary gear carrier assembly. Install rear clutch hub assembly, rear clutch and front clutch. Install bearing race used for end play adjustment as determined during oil pump disassembly.

11) Install brake band. Install oil pump. Install and adjust brake band adjusting bolt. Install bolt and tighten to 9-11 ft. lbs. (12-15 N.m). Loosen exactly 2 turns. Tighten lock bolt.

12) Install steel check ball and spring in case, then install valve body assembly. Install oil pan. Install turbine and oil pump shafts. Install speedometer drive gear, oil dipstick and tube, and vacuum diaphragm.

13) A check must be made to determine which rod to install. Measure dimension "A" shown in *Fig. 24,* and compare to DIAPHRAGM ROD CHART to determine which rod to install. Install kickdown solenoid and inhibitor switch hand tight.

DIAPHRAGM ROD CHART (ALL MODELS)

Dimension "A" In. (mm)	Rod Size In. (mm)
Under 1.00 (25.4)	1.16 (29.5)
1.00-1.02 (25.4-25.9)	1.18 (30.0)
1.02-1.04 (25.9-26.4)	1.20 (30.5)
1.04-1.06 (26.4-26.9)	1.22 (31.0)
Over 1.06 (26.9)	1.24 (31.5)

14) Install torque converter in torque converter housing. With converter properly installed, dimension "A" in *Fig. 24* should be .425-.492" (10.8-12.5 mm).

Fig. 24: Vacuum Diaphragm Installation

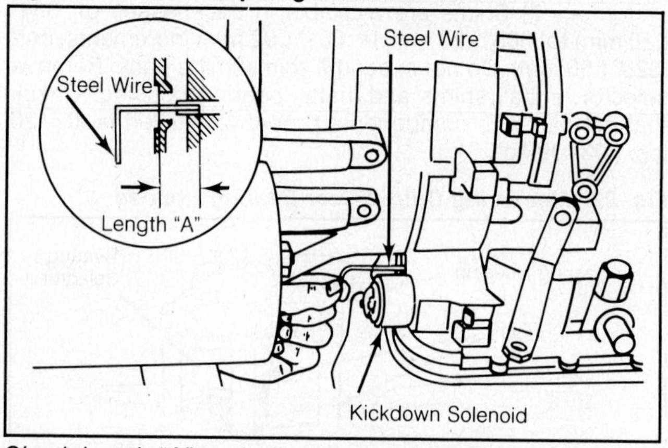

Check length "A" to determine diaphragm rod usage.

Fig. 25: Torque Converter Installation

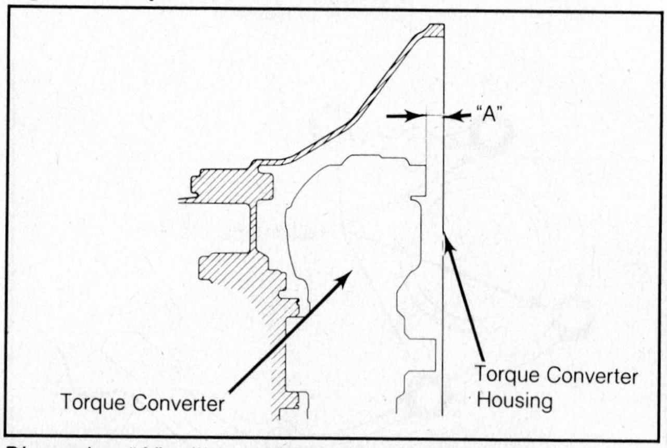

Dimension "A" will be .425-.492" (10.8-12.5 mm) with converter properly installed.

TIGHTENING SPECIFICATIONS (ALL MODELS)

Application	Ft. Lbs. (N.m)
Torque Converter-to-Drive Plate	25-36 (34-49)
Drive Plate-to-Crankshaft	60-69 (81-94)
Trans. Case-to-Converter Housing	23-34 (31-46)
Converter Housing-to-Engine	
12 mm Bolts	47-69 (64-94)
14 mm Bolts	65-87 (88-118)
Idler Gear Lock Nut	94-130 (127-176)
	INCH Lbs. (N.m)
Bearing Cover-to-Transaxle Case	168-228 (19-26)
Bearing Cover-to-Converter Housing	168-228 (19-26)
Bearing Housing-to-Converter Housing	96-120 (11-14)
Governor Cover-to-Transaxle Case	44-72 (5-8)
Oil Pan-to-Transaxle Case	44-72 (5-8)
Oil Pump Cover	96-120 (11-14)
Oil Pump-to-Transaxle Case	168-228 (19-26)

MERCEDES-BENZ W4A020

190, 300 (California) Series

IDENTIFICATION

Identification code is punched into rating plate or transmission housing. Use identification code when ordering parts.

W4A020 AUTOMATIC TRANSMISSION CODES

Application	Identification Code
190D	722.403
190E	722.400
300D	722.416
300CD	722.416
300TD	722.416
300SD	722.416

DESCRIPTION

This is a fully automatic 4-speed unit consisting primarily of a 3-element welded torque converter and 2 compound planetary gear sets. There are 2 multiple-disc clutches, 1 overrunning clutch, and 3 brake bands provide friction elements required to obtain desired function of planetary gear set. A hydraulic system, pressurized by a primary pump and a secondary piston type pump provide working pressure required to operate friction elements and automatic controls.

In order to set full load and kickdown shift points closer to maximum engine speed cut-out and electric kickdown system is used in all W4A020 transmissions. The electric circuit to kickdown solenoid is interupted about 200 RPM before maximum engine speed cut-out on the 190 series, 600 RPM before maximum engine speed cut-out on the 300 series.

On 190D models a vacuum control valve is attached to the injection pump and connected to the throttle lever by a push rod. This valve regulates vacuum (from vacuum pump) to transmission modulator in relation to throttle position. At idle, a vacuum of about 11 In. Hg is applied to modulator. Vacuum decreases as throttle opening increases, becoming zero vacuum at full throttle.

The 300 series uses an aneroid compensator, a vacuum control valve, a 122°F (50°C) coolant temperature switch, a switchover valve, and a vacuum transducer within vacuum control circuit to improve shift quality. *See Fig. 1.* When engine is running the central vacuum (VAC) connection of transducer receives full vacuum.

When engine coolant temperature is below 122°F (50°C), the switchover valve is connected to ground through temperature switch, and vacuum between control valve and the vacuum control valve (VCV) connection of transducer is cut-off.

The orifices in vacuum circuit allow vacuum pump to produce a higher vacuum than in control valve circuit. This higher vacuum is directed through switchover valve connections to the VCV connection of transducer. The higher vacuum in transducer allows full vacuum to reach modulator valve, providing a lower hydraulic modulating pressure.

A second vacuum input is applied to turbo boost pressure (PRE) connection of vacuum transducer. This input cause transducer to lower vacuum applied to modulator valve, increasing hydraulic modulating pressure.

Fig. 1: 300 Series Automatic Transmission Vacuum Control Circuit

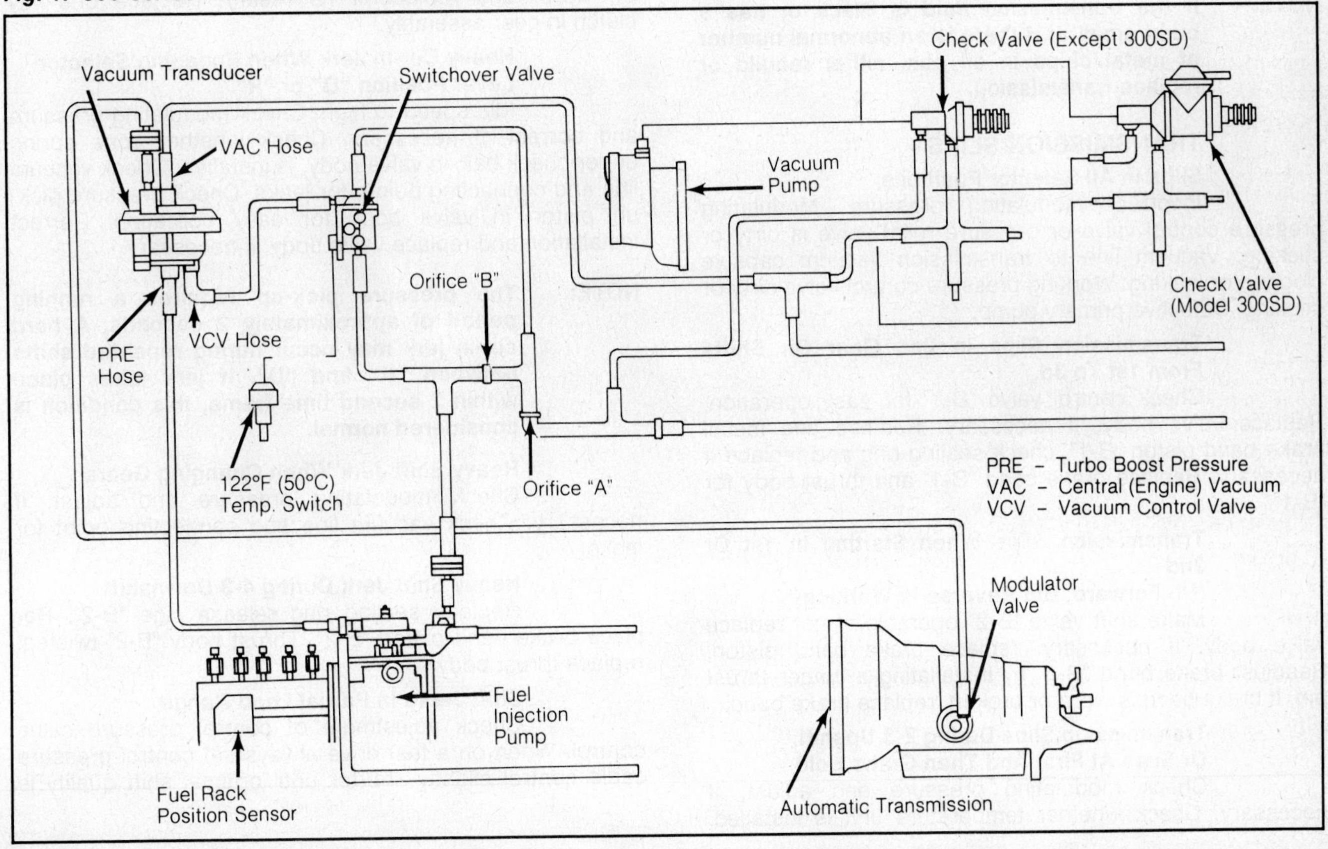

MERCEDES-BENZ W4A020 (Cont.)

OPERATION

The W4A020 automatic transmission is similar to the W4A040 transmission. The similarity applies to arrangement and layout of planetary gear sets, clutches and brake bands, as well as to shift valves of individual gears.

The 190D models start in first gear in all forward driving positions and shifts up depending on accelerator pedal position and speed. Activation for kickdown solenoid is via A/C compressor/kickdown cut-out control unit.

On 190E models, with shift lever in positions "D" and "3", transmission starts in 2nd gear when driving in lower partial load range and in 1st gear beginning in higher partial load range. When stopped, 2nd gear remains engaged at idle to prevent creeping. Activation for kickdown solenoid is routed through the fuel pump relay.

The California 300 series transmission is similar in design and operation to transmissions used in the 190 series. The transimission starts in 1st gear in all forward driving positions and downshifts to 1st gear when coasting to a stop. A torque converter having a slightly higher stall speed is used in these transmissions. Activation for kickdown solenoid is via A/C compressor/kick-down cut-out control unit.

LUBRICATION & ADJUSTMENT

See appropriate AUTOMATIC TRANSMISSION SERVICING article in IMPORT GENERAL SERVICING section.

TROUBLE SHOOTING

NOTE: **If the transmission fluid is Black or has a burnt smell or if there is an abnormal number of metal chips in oil pan, either rebuild or replace transmission.**

TRANSMISSION SLIPS

Slips In All Selector Positions

Incorrect modulating pressure. Modulating pressure control valve or pressure relief valve is dirty or sticking. Vacuum line to transmission vacuum capsule clogged or leaking. Working pressure control valve dirty or sticking. Defective primary pump.

Transmission Slips In 2nd Gear On Shifts From 1st To 3d.

Check control valve "B-1" for easy operation. Replace valve body, if necessary. Remove and install brake band piston "B-1", check sealing ring and replace if necessary. Replace brake band "B-1" and thrust body for "B-1".

Transmission Slips When Starting In 1st Or 2nd (No Forward, But Reverse Is Working)

Make shift valve "B-2" operable, if not replace valve body. If necessary, replace brake band piston. Readjust brake band "B-2" by installating a longer thrust pin. If brake band is worn or broken, replace brake band.

Transmission Slips During 2-3 Upshift, Or Slips At First And Then Grabs Hold

Check modulating pressure and adjust, if necessary. Check whether temperature unit is installed. Replace valve body, if necessary. Replace inner plate of clutch "K-1". Recondition clutch, if necessary.

Transmission Slips During 3-4 Upshift

Check modulating pressure and adjust, if necessary. Replace valve body. Replace inner plates of clutch "K-2", recondition clutch according to condition.

Transmission Shifts Hard Or Slips During Shift

On 190 series, check vacuum control valve. On 300 series, check vacuum control valve, 122°F (50°C) coolant temperature switch, switchover valve, and vacuum transducer.

OTHER SHIFTING PROBLEMS

Transmission Has No Positive Contact Following Installation Or Fails After A Short Period Of Operation

Torque converter not installed correctly. Transmission "drivers" not aligned with drive gear of primary pump. The "drivers" on torque converter and primary pump are distorted. Replace primary pump or torque converter, if necessary.

No Power Transmission In All Selector Lever Positions Immediately After Starting Engine

Torque converter has drained partially by leaking or defective lubrication pressure ring on input shaft or by leaking lubricating pressure valve in valve body.

Check lubrication pressure ring on input shaft, replace pressure ring if necessary. Check and clean lubrication pressure valve in valve body.

No Positive Contact In Reverse Gear

Check lining plates and sealing rings on piston of "LB-3" and replace if necessary. Replace one-way clutch in gear assembly.

Heavy Cut-In Jerk When Engaging Selector Lever Position "D" or "R"

Idle speed to high. Check modulating pressure and correct, if necessary. Check whether cone spring under check ball, in valve body, is installed. Check vacuum line and connecting points for leaks. Check pressure pick-up piston in valve body for easy operation. Correct installation and replace valve body, if necessary.

NOTE: **The pressure pick-up requires a running period of approximately 2 seconds. A hard cut-in jerk may occur during repeated shifts between "N" and "D". If jerk takes place within 2 second time frame, this condition is considered normal.**

Heavy Shift Jerk When Changing Gears

Check modulating pressure and adjust, if necessary. Check vacuum line and connecting point for leaks.

Heavy Shift Jerk During 4-3 Downshift

Replace sealing ring release side "B-2". Replace brake band piston "B-2". Thrust body "B-2" twisted, replace thrust body.

Shift Jerks In Partial Load Range

Check adjustment of control pressure cable control. When on a test drive always set control pressure cable control slightly shorter until optimal shift quality is

MERCEDES-BENZ W4A020 (Cont.)

obtained. Check modulating pressure and adjust, if necessary. Check vacuum line and connecting points for leaks.

NOTE: Do not set control pressure cable control too short, otherwise there will be no more brake shifts.

No Upshifts

Check regulating pressure. Clean centrifugal governor and make operable. Disassemble and clean valve body and replace, if necessary.

Upshifts In Upper Speed Range Of Gears Only

Check cable control for control pressure and adjust, if necessary. Check regulator pressure. If regulator pressure is too low, replace centrifugal governor. Make control pressure regulating valve operable.

Upshifts In Lower Speed Range Of Gears Only

Check cable control for control pressure whether disengaged, torn, or improperly adjusted. Check full throttle stop by accelerating engine and checking whether throttle valve rests against full throttle stop. Readjust throttle stop, if necessary. Check regulator pressure. If regulator pressure is too high, replace centrifugal governor.

No Kickdown Downshifts

Check magnetic valve fuse. If okay, remove magnetic valve and connect to battery and check for proper function. Replace valve if necessary. Check cable control for control pressure whether disengaged, torn, or improperly adjusted. Check kickdown regulating valve in valve body and replace valve body, if necessary.

No Brake Shifts (4-3 and 3-2)

Adjust cable control for control pressure. Check vacuum lines and connections of leaks. Make brake shift piston operable and replace valve body, if necessary.

Automatic And Unwanted Downshifts Outside Partial Throttle Downshift Range Without Actuating Kickdown Switch

1) Remove kickdown solenoid valve. Check "O" ring on kickdown solenoid valve for damage. Check whether kickdown switch sticks in pushed-in position. Replace switch, if necessary.

2) Check whether magnetic valve sticks in opened position. Replace magnetic valve, if necessary.

Poor Acceleration When Starting

Check stalling speed. If stalling speed drops by approximately 400-700 RPM below specified value, one-way clutch in torque converter will slip. Replace torque converter, if necessary.

Parking Lock Not Engaging

Check rear engine mount. Replace mount, if necessary. Check adjustment of selector rod. Adjust selector rod, if necessary.

Selector Lever Positions "R" and "P" Cannot Be Engaged

With engine running, clean centrifugal governor and make operable. With engine not running, make detent piston on lower cover operable.

Engine Cannot Be Started In Selector Lever Position "P" and "N"

Adjust shift rod and starter lock out switch. Replace starter lock out switch, if necessary.

Oil Loss With Smoke in Exhaust

Diaphragm in vacuum control unit defective. Transmission oil drawn from engine by vacuum line. Replace control unit, if necessary.

Oil Loss Between Torque Converter and Primary Pump

1) Screw in oil drain plug on torque converter with new sealing ring. Coat threads with Hylomar paste and tighten. If leak continues, go to next step.

2) Replace radial sealing ring and "O" ring of primary pump, while checking groove for "O" ring on primary pump for porous spots. Replace primary pump, if necessary.

TESTING

VACUUM CONTROL CIRCUIT

190 Series

1) Ensure engine is at normal operating temperature and that throttle linkage is adjusted properly. Pull off vacuum hose and connect Vacuum/Pressure Tester (116 589 25 21 00). *See Fig. 2.*

Fig. 2: Testing 190 Series Vacuum Control Valve

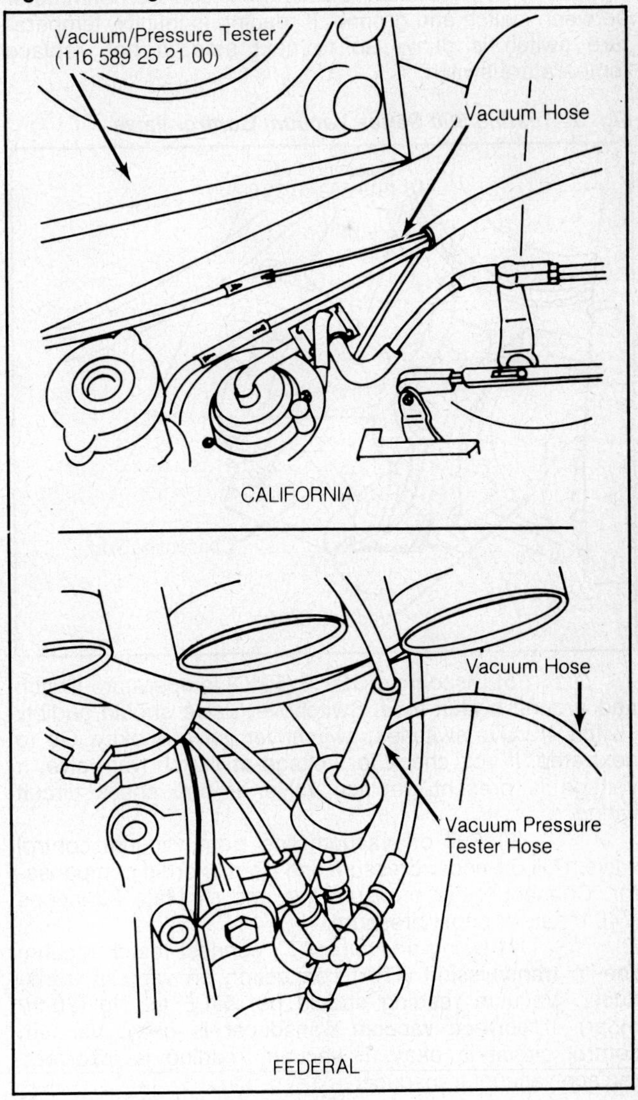

MERCEDES-BENZ W4A020 (Cont.)

2) Start engine and check vacuum at idle. Vacuum reading should be 10-11 In. Hg (360-410 mbar). Stop engine and place throttle linkage at full throttle stop. Vacuum reading should be zero.

3) If vacuum readings are correct, vacuum control valve is okay. If not, check vacuum line routing. If correct, check vacuum pump. If okay, adjust vacuum control valve and replace, if necesary.

300 Series

1) Ensure engine is at normal operating temperature and that vacuum lines are routed properly. *See Fig. 1.* Also check orifice "A" and "B" for blockage. Disconnect connecting rod at vacuum control valve.

2) Using a vacuum "T", connect Vacuum/Pressure Tester (201 589 13 21 00) behind vacuum damper of vacuum control valve. Install Adjusting Roller (916 589 00 21 00) on vacuum control valve. *See Fig. 3.*

3) Raise lever so it rests against roller. *See Fig. 3.* Vacuum reading should be 3.3-3.8 In. Hg (120-160 mbar). If correct, control valve is okay. Go to next step. If not, adjust vacuum control valve. Replace if necessary.

4) With coolant temperature above 122°F (50°C), the ground connection for switchover valve must be disconnected by 122°F (50°C) temperature switch. To test switch, disconnect switch and connect ohmmeter between switch and ground. If reading is infinity, temperature switch is okay. Go to next step. If not, replace temperature switch.

Fig. 3: Testing 300 Series Vacuum Control Valve

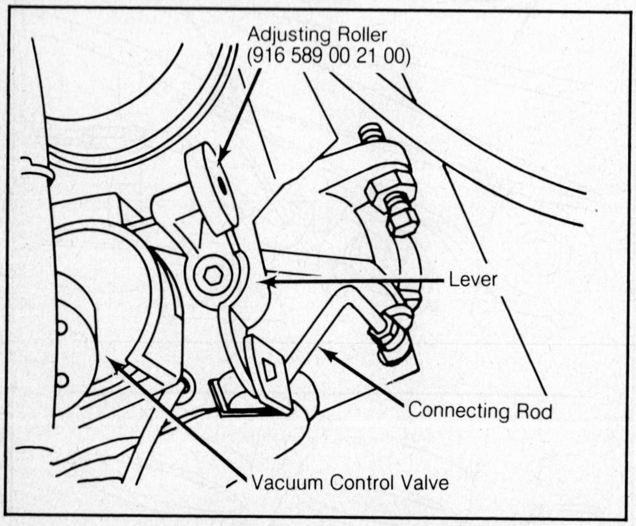

5) Disconnect 122°F (50°C) temperature switch and ground switch lead. Switchover valve should audibly switch. If valve switches, switchover valve is okay. Go to next step. If not, check for voltage at switchover valve. If voltage is present, replace valve. If not, check circuit wiring.

6) Pull off vacuum line from vacuum control valve. Pull off boost pressure line from aneroid compensator. Connect tester pressure line and simulate 20 inches (740 mbar) of boost pressure.

7) Using a vacuum "T", connect tester vacuum line to transmission (TRA) connection on vacuum transducer. Vacuum reading should be .5-1.6 In. Hg (20-60 mbar). If correct, vacuum transducer is okay. Vacuum control circuit is okay. If vacuum reading is incorrect, replace vacuum transducer.

ROAD TEST

NOTE: Before road testing, check transmission fluid level, idle speed, and control pressure cable adjustment. Correct if necessary.

1) During test drive, in addition to shift points, special attention should be paid to changeover during shift. Carefully listen for upshift at part throttle.

2) At full throttle and kickdown the gear changes are clearly heard. Make sure that shift is smooth hold and that engine RPM is stable. Sudden revving up of the engine indicates a slipping brake band or clutch. Check transmission as required.

SHIFT SPEED MPH SPECIFICATIONS

Shift Condition	Model 190D	Model 190E
Lever in "D"		
Idle [1]		
1-2 Upshift	8	.....
2-3 Upshift	13	16
3-4 Upshift	18	21
4-3 Downshift	13	17
3-2 Downshift	9	9
2-1 Downshift	.....	.....
Full Throttle		
1-2 Upshift	18	17
2-3 Upshift	35	47
3-4 Upshift	59	81
4-3 Downshift	42	53
3-2 Downshift	19	25
2-1 Downshift	11	12
Kickdown		
1-2 Upshift	22	27
2-3 Upshift	39	52
3-4 Upshift	63	85
4-3 Downshift	57	78
3-2 Downshift	34	46
2-1 Downshift	18	19
Lever in "3"		
Idle [1]		
1-2 Upshift	8	.....
2-3 Upshift	13	16
3-2 Downshift	9	9
2-1 Downshift	.....	.....
Full Throttle		
1-2 Upshift	18	17
2-3 Upshift	35	47
3-2 Downshift	19	25
2-1 Downshift	11	12
Kickdown		
1-2 Upshift	22	27
2-3 Upshift	39	52
3-2 Downshift	34	46
2-1 Downshift	18	19
Lever in "2"		
Idle [1]		
1-2 Upshift	.....	.....
2-1 Downshift	6	7
Full Throttle		
1-2 Upshift	22	27
2-1 Downshift	11	12
Kickdown		
1-2 Upshift	22	27
2-1 Downshift	18	19

[1] – At light throttle on model 190E.

MERCEDES-BENZ W4A020 (Cont.)

SHIFT SPEED MPH SPECIFICATIONS (Cont.)

Shift Condition	300 Series
Lever in "D"	
Light Throttle	
1-2 Upshift	10
2-3 Upshift	18
3-4 Upshift	23
4-3 Downshift	17
3-2 Downshift	12
2-1 Downshift	8
Full Throttle	
1-2 Upshift	24
2-3 Upshift	45
3-4 Upshift	73
4-3 Downshift	48
3-2 Downshift	25
2-1 Downshift	15
Kickdown	
1-2 Upshift	26
2-3 Upshift	46
3-4 Upshift	75
4-3 Downshift	68
3-2 Downshift	41
2-1 Downshift	22
Lever in "3" or "S"	
Light Throttle	
1-2 Upshift	10
2-3 Upshift	18
3-2 Downshift	12
2-1 Downshift	8
Full Throttle	
1-2 Upshift	24
2-3 Upshift	45
3-2 Downshift	25
2-1 Downshift	15
Kickdown	
1-2 Upshift	26
2-3 Upshift	46
3-2 Downshift	41
2-1 Downshift	22
Lever in "2" or "L"	
Light Throttle	
1-2 Upshift	....
2-1 Downshift	8
Full Throttle	
1-2 Upshift	25
2-1 Downshift	15
Kickdown	
1-2 Upshift	26
2-1 Downshift	22

3) Automatic downshifts without acceleration occur at very low speeds and will be heard only when listening very carefully (increase in engine RPM). On the other hand, downshifts under kickdown are coupled with clearly felt shifting impulse in addition to an increase in engine RPM. At certain speed ranges a downshift under part throttle to full throttle is possible.

4) Downshifts with selector lever are either acceleration downshifts (on hills) or deceleration brake shifts (downhill or during deceleration). Accelerating downshifts require only a few fractions of a second for changing gears, while deceleration brake shifts require from 1 to 2 seconds.

5) During test drive make sure that transmission, particularly under load, is not constantly shifted. While shifting, the brake bands and clutch develop considerable heat. If necessary repeat a gear shift under maximum load only once every 15 seconds.

6) During road test, transmission should upshift and downshift at approximately the speeds shown in SHIFT SPEEDS SPECIFICATION (MPH) tables. All shifts may vary somewhat due to production tolerances or tire size.

HYDRAULIC PRESSURE TESTS

Preparation For Tests

1) Before making tests, check fluid level and condition. Check throttle linkage, EGR system, and neutral safety switch. Correct as necessary. Connect Pressure Gauge (123 589 04 21 00) to pressure take-off points on transmission. *See Fig. 4.*

2) Attach pressure gauge to inside mirror in such a manner that it can be easily read from driver's seat. Run pressure hoses through passenger window.

3) Make sure that pressure hoses do not drag on pavement or contact exhaust system. After tests, run engine and check take-off points for leaks.

Fig. 4: Pressure Take-Off Points

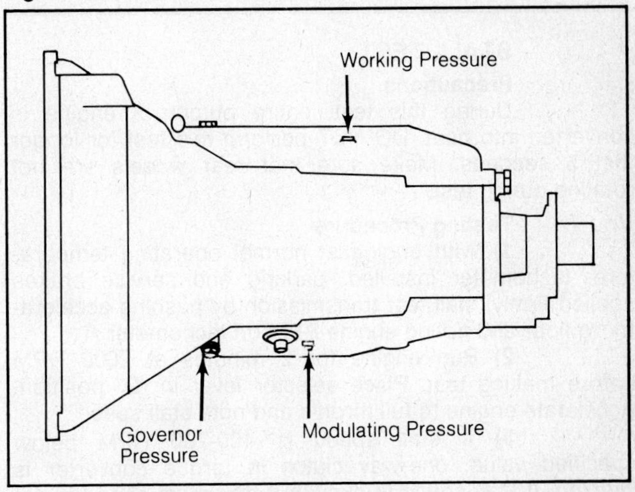

Modulating Pressure Test

Disconnect vacuum line from vacuum control unit. Place selector lever in "D" and drive at 31 MPH while reading pressure gauge. Pressure should be as shown in MODULATING PRESSURE SPECIFICATIONS table. If necessary, adjust modulating pressure.

MODULATING PRESSURE SPECIFICATIONS

Application	psi (kg/cm²)
Modulating Pressure (In "D" at 31 MPH)	
Model 190D	44 (3.1)
Model 190E	46 (3.2)
300 Series	44 (3.1)

Working Pressure Test

1) Disconnect vacuum line from vacuum control unit. Start and run engine at 1000 RPM while reading pressure. Pressure should be as shown in WORKING PRESSURE SPECIFICATIONS table.

2) Working pressure is not adjustable. Measurement simply provides information concerning operation of working pressure regulator valve in valve housing.

MERCEDES-BENZ W4A020 (Cont.)

WORKING PRESSURE SPECIFICATIONS

Application	psi (kg/cm²)
Working Pressure (In stationary "D")	
Model 190D	178-207 (12.5-14.6)
Model 190E	199-228 (14.0-16.0)
300 Series	190-219 (13.4-15.4)

Governor Pressure Test

Drive vehicle on road or on dynamometer at speeds indicated in table. Compare pressures noted on gauge with pressures given in GOVERNOR PRESSURE SPECIFICATIONS table.

NOTE: **If values are not within specifications, replace governor assembly.**

GOVERNOR PRESSURE SPECIFICATIONS

Application	psi (kg/cm²) @ 19 MPH	psi (kg/cm²) @ 56 MPH
Model 190D	22 (1.5)	46 (3.2)
Model 190E	15 (1.1)	36 (2.5)
300 Series	17 (1.2)	41 (2.9)

STALL TEST

Precautions

During this test, entire output of engine is converted into heat. DO NOT perform this test for longer that 5 seconds. Make sure that rear wheels are not rotating during test.

Testing Procedure

1) With engine at normal operating temperature, tachometer installed, parking and service brakes applied firmly, stall test transmission by pushing accelerator to floor and noting engine RPM on tachometer.

2) Run engine for 2 minutes at 2000 RPM before making test. Place selector lever in "D" position. Accelerate engine to full throttle and note stall speed.

3) If stall speed is 400-700 RPM below specified value, one-way clutch in torque converter is slipping. If stall speed is okay, but maximum speed is not attained, one-way clutch locks in both directions or is stuck. Repair or replace one-way clutch as necessary.

STALL SPEED SPECIFICATIONS

Application	Stall RPM
190D	1400-1600
190E	1650-1850
300 Series	2400-2700 [1]

[1] – Stall speed at 10-15 secods.

Stall Test Results

If stall speed is higher than specified, general transmission problems are indicated and hydraulic pressure tests should be made to locate faulty units. If stall speed is lower than specified, torque converter roller clutch is faulty.

NOTE: **Make sure engine performance is satisfactory before condemning converter assembly. Torque converter is a sealed unit and cannot be disassembled for service.**

SERVICE (IN VEHICLE)

The following units may be removed from transmission without removing transmission from vehicle: Oil Pan and Gasket, Valve Body, Vacuum Control Unit, Speedometer Driven Gear Assembly, Secondary Pump Assembly, Extension Housing, Pressure Receiving Piston, Modulating Pressure Housing, and Bi-Metallic Spring, Speedometer Drive Gear, Secondary Pump Eccentric, Governor Assembly, Parking Pawl and Parking Linkage. See procedures given in TRANSMISSION DISASSEMBLY & REASSEMBLY.

REMOVAL & INSTALLATION

See appropriate AUTOMATIC TRANSMISSION REMOVAL article in IMPORT GENERAL SERVICING section.

TORQUE CONVERTER

NOTE: **Torque converter is a sealed unit and cannot be diassembled for service. If hub of converter is scored, or if metallic particles are found in transmission fluid, replace converter assembly.**

TRANSMISSION DISASSEMBLY

1) Remove control pressure cable by pushing link toward sleeve and turning sleeve 90° in a counterclockwise direction. Pull control pressure cable out in upward direction.

2) Install transmission in Holding Fixture (116 589 06 59 00 and 126 589 10 63 00) with oil pan facing upward. Remove oil pan screws and oil pan. Remove oil filter. Remove valve body screws and valve body. Remove holder and leaf spring.

3) Remove screws and lift off lower cover with intermediate plate and oil pipe. Disassemble lower cover. Push in brake band piston cover and remove snap ring. Remove brake band piston cover. Pull out brake band piston.

4) Mount Assembly Device (126 589 00 59 00) and screw to transmission housing. Clamp assembly device and remove snap ring. Unclamp assembly device, remove brake band "B-1" piston, cover, and backpressure screws. Remove assembly device. Pull out brake band "B-1" guide.

5) Remove plug for brake band "B-1" thrust body. Remove holding plate and vacuum control unit with thrust pin. Remove screw and starter lock out switch. Remove thrust body and modulating pressure control valve.

6) Remove kickdown solenoid valve. Remove double hex collar nut and pull off universal flange. Remove rear cover washer and screws. Loosen rear cover by means of light blows with a plastic hammer. Disassemble rear cover.

7) Remove oil pipe, tachometer drive helical gear, parking lock gear, parking lock pawl, and expanding spring from output shaft. Pull out plastic guide in upward direction, and remove roller.

MERCEDES-BENZ W4A020 (Cont.)

Fig. 5: Valve Body Assembly Showing Plastic Valves And Check Ball Locations

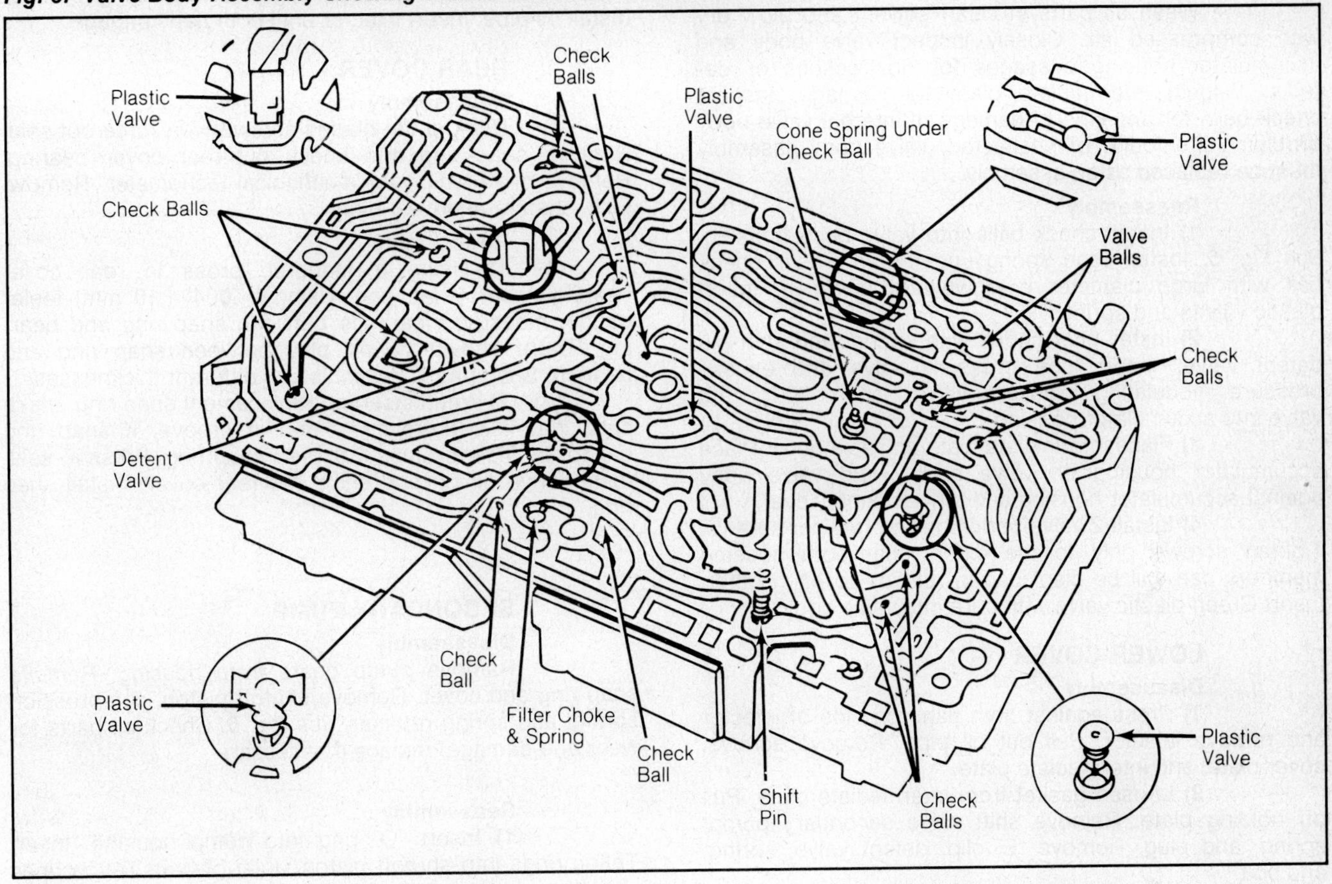

8) Remove compensating washer and spacing sleeve. Remove snap ring from output shaft and remove helical gear. Remove snap ring from output shaft. Remove screw and oil pipe. Remove secondary pump. Remove "O" ring and intermediate plate of secondary pump.

9) Push in on centrifugal governor cover and remove snap ring. Pull out cover. Compress snap ring and remove centrifugal governor. Pry off snap ring and remove linkage from detent plate.

10) Remove brake band "B-2" guide and one-way valve. Remove temperature throttle and oil deflector. Install 2 screws into threaded holes of front cover and use screws to pull off cover. Hold gear assembly at input shaft and pull out carefully in forward direction.

11) Pull clutch "K-1" with brake band "B-1" from gear assembly. Remove clutch plates of brake "B-3". Remove thrust pin. Pull out clutch "K-2". Remove screws for selector lever and remove detent plate.

12) Remove thrust washer. Remove bolts attaching support flange to case. Install 2 bolts, approximately 3 5/32" (80 mm) long, into support flange from opposite side of transmission. Loosen support flange by hitting bolts with hammer.

13) Set brake band "B-2" diagonally and remove. Pull out thrust body "B-2". Remove sealing rings and plugs still in housing. Remove transmission from holding fixture.

COMPONENT DISASSEMBLY & REASSEMBLY

VALVE BODY

Preparation

Observe particular cleanliness for all jobs on valve body. The work should be done as much as possible on a plastic surface. DO NOT use fuzzy cloth, leather would be best. Upon disassembly, wash all parts and blow out with compressed air.

NOTE: **The shift valve body has 19 steel balls. Be careful not to loose them during disassembly. Make sure of proper placement during reassembly.**

Disassembly

Remove 2 screws that attach valve body to accumulator housing. Hold assembly together and turn it over. Lift accumulator housing and intermediate plate from valve body. Remove plastic valves, shift pin, and detent valve "K-1". Note position of check balls and remove. *See Fig. 5.*

NOTE: **Plastic valves are similar in shape and dimension, they differ only by a bore in one valve holder. Keep removed valves in proper order for replacement.**

MERCEDES-BENZ W4A020 (Cont.)

Inspection

Wash all parts in clean solvent and blow dry with compressed air. Closely inspect valve body and accumulator housing passages for obstructions or defects. Inspect intermediate plate for damage. Inspect check balls for any kind of damage. If internal valve body problems are found or suspected, valve body assembly must be replaced as an assembly.

Reassembly

1) Install check balls into valve body housing. *See Fig. 5.* Install cone spring underneath plastic check ball with large diameter in downward direction. Insert plastic valves and springs.

2) Install filter choke with spring, and shift pin detent valve. Insert lube pressure valve and excess pressure modulating pressure valve. Insert "K-1" vent valve into accumulator housing.

3) Place intermidiate plate on valve body. Place accumulator housing on valve body. Hold valve body against accumulator housing and turn assembly over.

4) Install 2 valve body housing retainer screws. Tighten screws only to the extent that both housing members can still be displaced in relation to each other. Insert Green plastic valve with bore into valve body.

LOWER COVER

Disassembly

1) Press against both flaps on side of injector and remove injector. Pull out oil pipe. Remove screws, cover plate, and intermediate plate.

2) Loosen gasket from intermediate plate. Pull off holding plate. Remove shift valve secondary pump, spring, and plug. Remove "E" clip, detent valve, spring, and bolt.

Reassembly

1) Insert shift valve secondary pump, spring, and plug. Secure with holding plate. Insert detent valve, spring, and bolt. Install "E" clip. Check valve (near screen filters) for tight seat. Insert both screen filters into lower cover.

2) Place intermediate plate with gasket on lower cover. Locate gasket in relation to intermediate plate. Mount cover plate and tighten fastening screws. Install oil pipe. Insert injector until both flaps engage.

REAR COVER

Disassembly

Using a flat bladed screwdriver, force out seal. Remove snap ring and knock out rear cover bearing. Remove drive pinion for mechanical tachometer. Remove lock, shaft, and drive pinion.

Reassembly

1) Using a mandrel, press in rear cover bearing. Insert snap ring. Using a .004" (.10 mm) feeler gauge, measure clearance between snap ring and bearing. There should be no play between snap ring and bearing. Snap ring is available in 3 different thicknesses.

2) When inserting replacement snap ring, make sure that it is correctly seated in groove. If snap ring cannot be inserted, use a thinner snap ring. Press in seal. Install drive pinion and shaft into rear cover. Install snap ring.

SECONDARY PUMP

Disassembly

Remove pump gears from housing. Remove snap ring and cover. Remove shutoff piston, compression spring, and spring retainer. *See Fig. 6.* Check all parts for wear and damage, replace if necessary.

Reassembly

1) Insert "O" ring into pump housing. Insert Teflon rings into shutoff piston. Joint of both Teflon rings should completely come together. If necessary, grease rings slightly before inserting into grooves.

2) Install shutoff piston in pump housing. Install compression spring and spring retainer in shutoff piston. Install cover and snap ring. Lubricate pump gears and insert driven gear into pump housing. Insert driving pump gear so that slot faces upward.

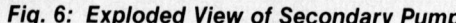

Fig. 6: Exploded View of Secondary Pump

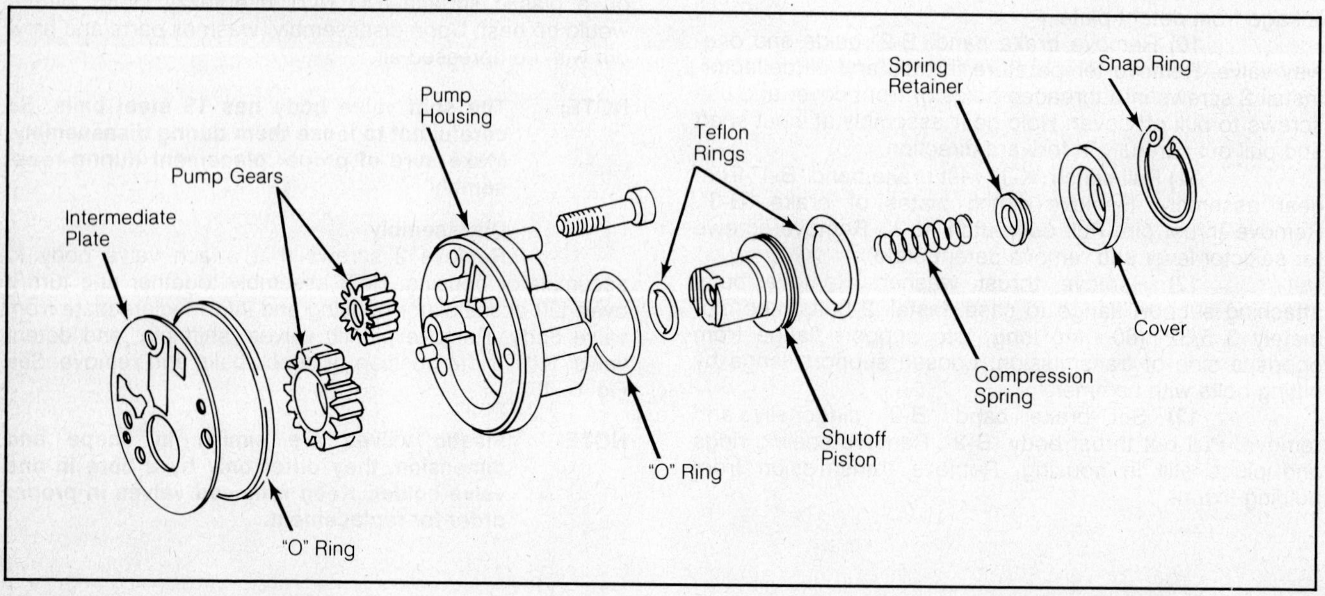

MERCEDES-BENZ W4A020 (Cont.)

Fig. 7: Installing Driven Gear

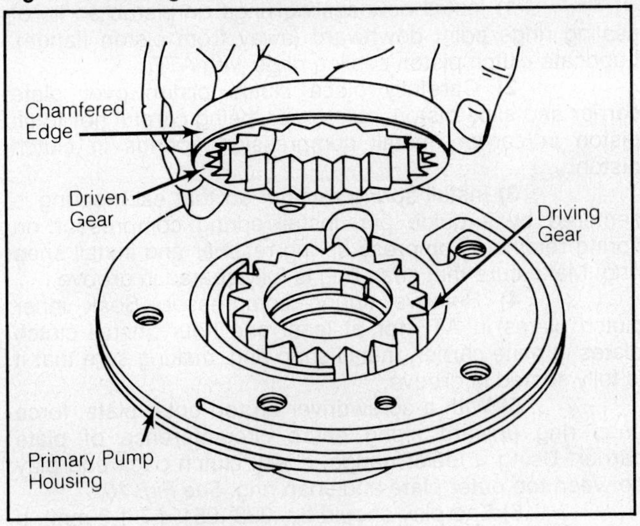

Install gear with chamfered edge down.

PRIMARY PUMP

Disassembly

1) Remove 2 Teflon rings from stator shaft. Install Spring Compressor (201 589 12 43 00) on spring retainer and compress until snap ring is exposed. Remove snap ring. Release pressure from spring compressor and remove.

2) Remove spring washer and springs for "B-3" piston. Remove "B-3" piston. Remove bolts attaching pump housing to front cover and lift pump from cover. Remove pump gears from housing. *See Fig. 7.*

Inspection

Check pump bearing and seal for damage, replace if necessary. Check that "O" ring is properly seated in groove. Check that pump gears are not scored or damaged.

Reassembly

1) Lubricate and install pump gears into pump housing. Make sure that chamfered edge of driven gear faces down in pump housing. *See Fig. 7.* Install intermediate plate on pump housing.

2) Install primary pump onto front cover being careful not to damage bearing on stator shaft. Install pump-to-front cover attaching bolts. Install sealing rings on "B-3" piston.

3) Place Insertion Sleeve (126 589 04 14 00) on front cover. Lubricate sealing rings. Install piston over insertion sleeve so that pin on piston lines up with bore in front cover. Carefully push piston down without tilting piston. Remove sleeve.

4) Install springs and spring retainer. Install spring compressor and compress spring retainer. Install snap ring. Release pressure from spring compressor and remove. Joint of both Teflon rings should completely come together. If necessary, grease rings slightly before inserting into grooves.

Fig. 8: Exploded View of Planetary Gear Set

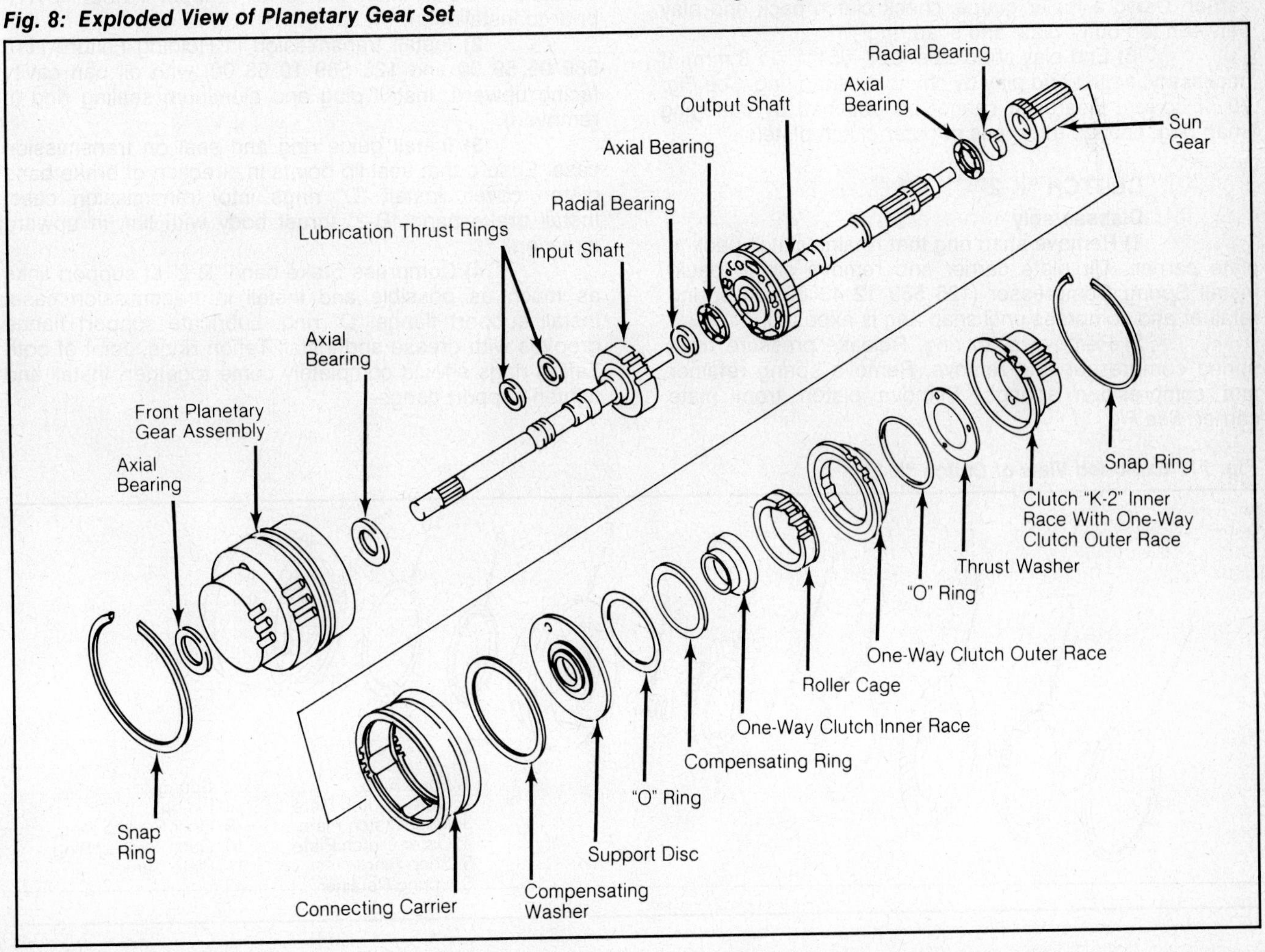

MERCEDES-BENZ W4A020 (Cont.)

Fig. 10: Checking Clutch "K-1" & Clutch "K-2" End Play

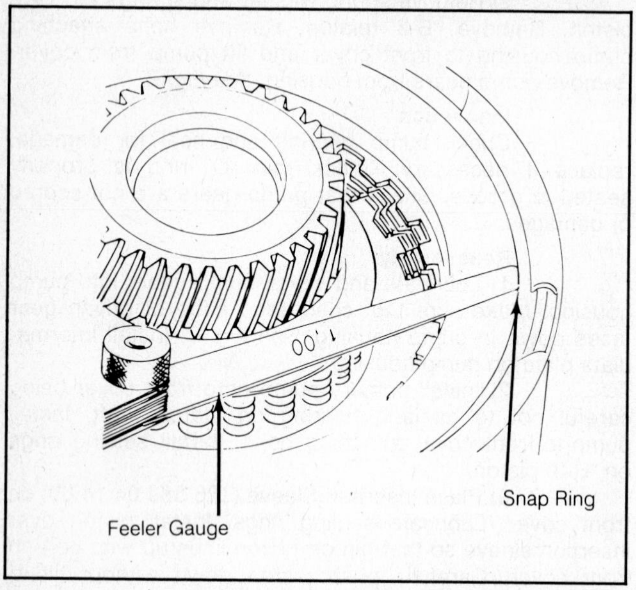

4) Soak inner clutch plates in ATF for at least one hour. Install clutch plates in plate carrier. Install snap ring, making sure that it is fully seated in groove.

5) With a screwdriver on top outer plate, force snap ring upward along entire circumference of plate carrier. Using a feeler gauge, check clutch pack end play between top outer plate and snap ring.

6) End play should be .028-.051" (.7-1.3 mm). If necessary, adjust end play by changing snap ring. *See Fig. 10*. If correct clearance cannot be obtained by changing snap ring, change thickness of outer clutch plate(s).

CLUTCH "K-2"

Disassembly

1) Remove snap ring that retains clutch pack in plate carrier. Tilt plate carrier and remove clutch pack. Install Spring Compressor (126 589 12 43 00) on spring retainer and compress until snap ring is exposed.

2) Remove snap ring. Release pressure from spring compressor and remove. Remove spring retainer and compression springs. Remove piston from plate carrier. *See Fig. 11*.

Reassembly

1) Install new sealing rings on piston so lip of sealing rings point downward (away from piston flange). Lubricate clutch piston sealing rings with ATF.

2) Carefully place clutch piston over plate carrier and slide piston into carrier, being careful not to tilt piston in carrier. Install compression springs in clutch piston.

3) Install spring retainer so that each spring is centered by a guide pin. Install spring compressor on spring retainer. Compress spring retainer and install snap ring. Make sure that snap ring is fully seated in groove.

4) Remove spring compressor. Soak inner clutch plates in ATF for at least one hour. Install clutch plates in plate carrier. Install snap ring, making sure that it is fully seated in groove.

5) With a screwdriver on top outer plate, force snap ring upward along entire circumference of plate carrier. Using a feeler gauge, check clutch pack end play between top outer plate and snap ring. *See Fig. 10*.

6) End play should be .028-.051" (.7-1.3 mm). If necessary, adjust end play by changing snap ring. If correct clearance cannot be obtained by changing snap ring, change thickness of outer clutch plate(s).

TRANSMISSION REASSEMBLY

1) During reassembly, lubricate bearing and valve body sliding surfaces with ATF. Soak new brake bands and clutch inner plates for at least 1 hour in ATF prior to installation.

2) Install transmission in Holding Fixture (116 589 06 59 00 and 126 589 10 63 00) with oil pan cavity facing upward. Install plug and aluminum sealing ring (if removed).

3) Install guide ring and seal on transmission case. Ensure that seal lip points in direction of brake band piston cover. Install "O" rings into transmission case. Install brake band "B-2" thrust body with link in upward direction.

4) Compress brake band "B-2" at support links as much as possible and install in transmission case. Install support flange "O" ring. Lubricate support flange grooves with grease and install Teflon rings. Joint of both Teflon rings should completely come together. Install and tighten support flange.

Fig. 11: Exploded View of Clutch "K-2"

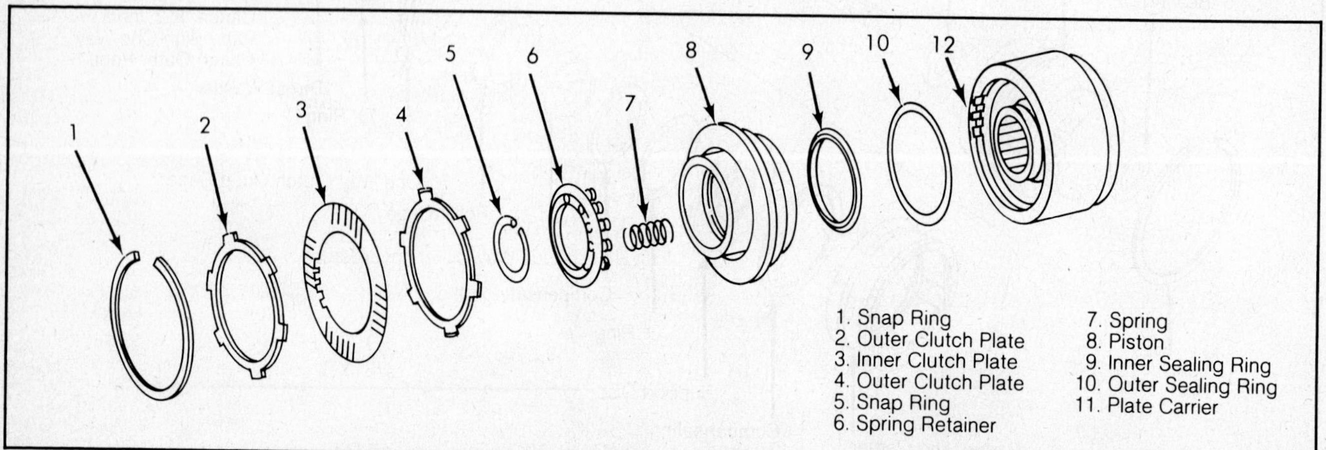

MERCEDES-BENZ W4A020 (Cont.)

PLANETARY GEAR SET

Disassembly

1) Clamp Assembly Fixture (126 589 00 35 00), with disc facing upward, in a vise. Place planetary gear assembly into assembly fixture. Remove lubrication thrust rings from input shaft. Remove snap ring.

2) Remove front planetary gear assembly. Remove axial bearing from front plantery gear assembly. Remove axial bearing and input shaft. Remove radial bearing and axial bearing. Remove output shaft. *See Fig. 8.*

3) Remove radial bearing and axial bearing from output shaft. Pull out sun gear. Remove snap ring and remove inner plate carrier with one-way clutch out of connecting carrier.

4) Remove support disc. Remove compensating ring and "O" ring. Turn one-way clutch inner race counterclockwise and pull out. Remove rollers from cage. *See Fig. 8.*

Reassembly

1) Check bearings and one-way clutch inner race for wear. If running surface of rollers on one-way clutch inner race show heavy score marks or notches, replace entire one-way clutch. Lubricate bearings with ATF during assembly.

2) Place thrust washer into inner plate carrier. Insert rollers into roller cage. Place one-way clutch outer race on inner plate carrier and insert roller cage.

3) Push rollers against compression springs and insert locking plates with offset pointing outward. Install one-way clutch inner race while rotating it in a counterclockwise direction. Pull out locking plates.

NOTE: **Install "O" ring only after one-way clutch end play has been checked.**

4) Install compensating ring. Install support disc so that pin engages hole in one-way clutch outer race. Install compensating washers into connecting carrier. Hold one-way clutch together and install into connecting carrier.

5) Install snap ring and push into groove using a screwdriver. Using a feeler gauge, check clearance between one-way clutch and connecting carrier. Clearance should be .002-.008" (.05-.2 mm).

6) If clearance is incorrect, add or remove compensating washers until specified clearance is obtained. Install "O" ring. Insert sun gear into one-way clutch assembly. One-way clutch should lock when sun gear is rotated in clockwise direction.

7) Install axial bearing and radial bearing on input shaft. Place one-way clutch on assembly fixture and insert output shaft. Install axial bearing and radial bearing on output shaft. Install input shaft and axial bearing.

8) Insert axial bearing into front planetary gear assembly. Install front gear assembly in output shaft and secure with snap ring. Using a screwdriver, push snap ring into groove. Insert lubrication thrust rings into input shaft. Lift planetary gear set out of assembly fixture.

CLUTCH "K-1"

Disassembly

1) Remove snap ring. Tilt plate carrier and remove clutch pack. Install Spring Compressor (201 589 12 43 00) on spring retainer and compress until snap ring is exposed. Remove snap ring.

2) Release pressure from spring compressor and remove. Remove spring retainer and compression springs. Pull piston out of plate carrier. *See Fig. 9.*

Reassembly

1) Install new sealing rings on piston so lip of sealing rings point downward (toward flat surface of piston). Place Installation Sleeves (126 589 02 14 00 and 126 589 03 14 00) on plate carrier.

2) Lubricate installation sleeves and sealing rings with ATF. Install piston into plate carrier being careful not to tilt piston. Remove installation sleeves.

3) Install compression springs in piston. Install spring retainer, making sure that each compression spring is centered by a guide pin. Install spring compressor and compress springs. Install snap ring and release compressor. Make sure that snap ring is properly seated in groove. Remove compressor.

NOTE: **Outer and inner plates which are bent or badly burnt must be replaced. Inner plates which are .08" (2 mm) thick or less must be replaced.**

Fig. 9: Exploded View of Clutch "K-1"

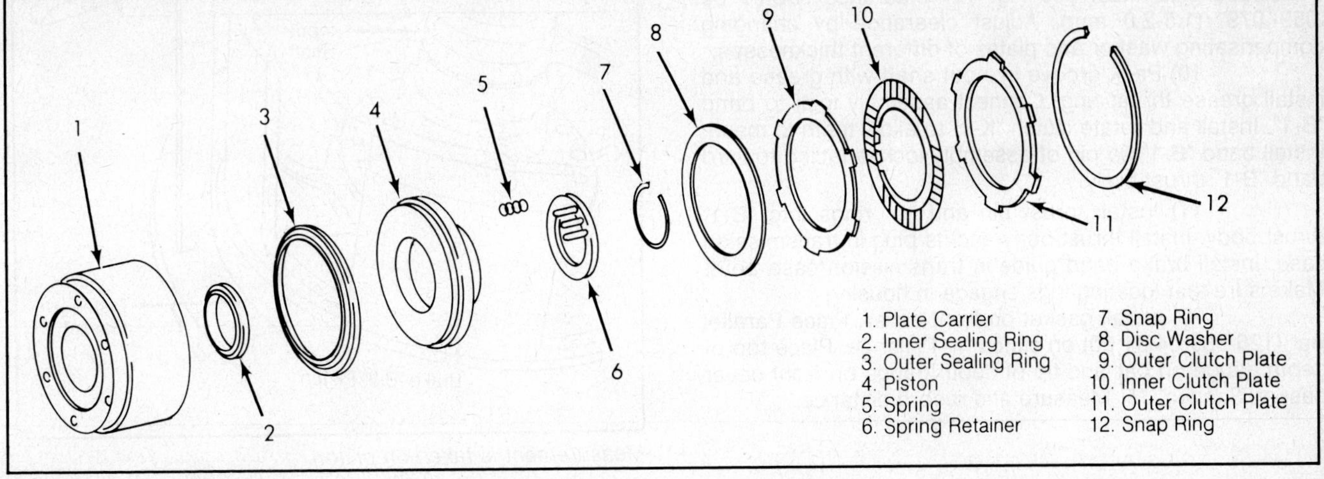

MERCEDES-BENZ W4A020 (Cont.)

5) Install thrust washer so that lug enters bore in support flange. Check support flange Teflon rings once again. Install clutch "K-2" on planetary gear assembly. Insert gear assembly into transmission case while rotating input shaft.

6) Place transmission in a vertical position so that input shaft points upward. Check installation of gear assembly. Gear assemby is correctly installed if upper edge of connection carrier is lower than support surface of outer plate. Assemble front cover with primary pump.

Fig. 12: Installing Brake "B-3" Clutch Pack

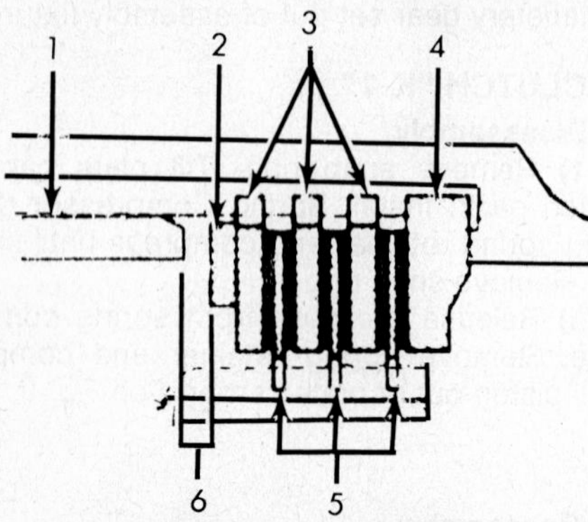

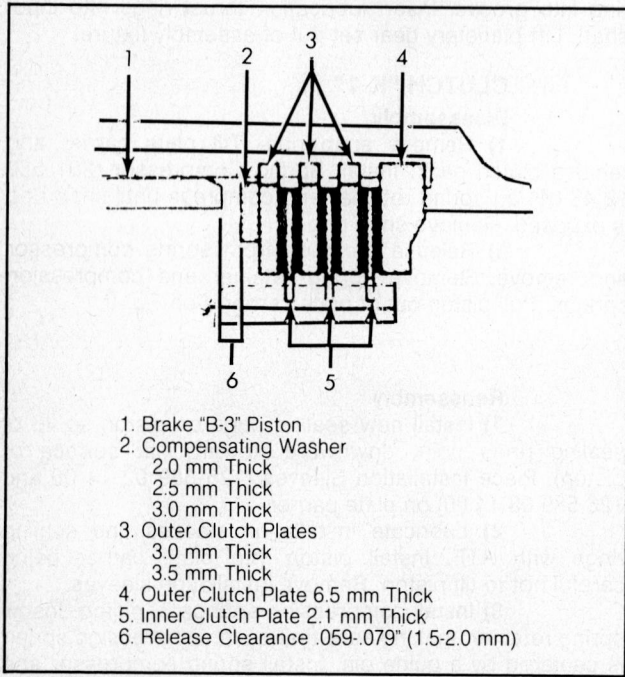

1. Brake "B-3" Piston
2. Compensating Washer
   2.0 mm Thick
   2.5 mm Thick
   3.0 mm Thick
3. Outer Clutch Plates
   3.0 mm Thick
   3.5 mm Thick
4. Outer Clutch Plate 6.5 mm Thick
5. Inner Clutch Plate 2.1 mm Thick
6. Release Clearance .059-.079" (1.5-2.0 mm)

7) Install brake "B-3" clutch pack in transmission case. *See Fig. 12*. Place Parallel Bar (126 589 04 31 00) on machined surface of transmission case. Place top of depth gauge on bar and tip of gauge on compensating washer. *See Fig. 13*. Measure and record distance.

8) Place parallel bar on top of brake "B-3" piston. Place top of depth gauge on parallel bar and tip of depth gauge on piston gasket. *See Fig. 14*. Measure and record distance.

9) Difference between clutch pack depth measurement and piston height measurement is brake "B-3" release clearance. *See Fig. 12*. Clearance should be .059-.079" (1.5-2.0 mm). Adjust clearance by changing compensating washer and plates of different thicknesses.

10) Pack groove in input shaft with grease and install grease thrust ring. Connect assembly lock to band "B-1". Install and rotate clutch "K-1" to allow teeth to mesh. Install band "B-1" so pin of assembly lock is facing toward band "B-1" thrust body.

11) Install thrust pin and "O" rings into "B-1" thrust body. Install thrust body and its plug in transmission case. Install brake band guide in transmission case bore. Make sure that locating lugs engage in housing.

12) Install gasket on front cover. Place Parallel Bar (126 589 04 31 00) on clutch "K-1" flange. Place top of depth gauge on bar and tip of depth gauge on front cover gasket. *See Fig. 15*. Measure and record distance.

Fig. 13: Measuring Brake "B-3" Clutch Pack Depth

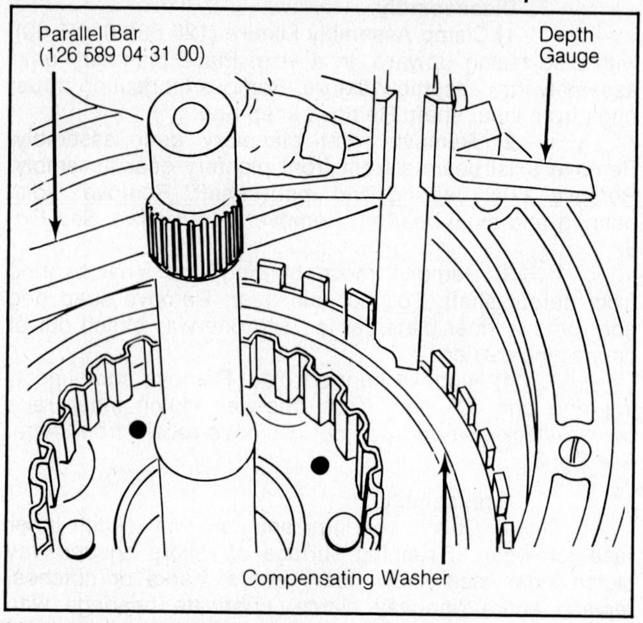

Measurement is taken in case.

13) Place parallel bar on machined surface of transmission case. Place top of depth gauge on bar and tip of depth gauge on a roller of axial bearing. *See Fig. 16*. Measure and record distance.

14) Difference between flange height measurement and axial bearing depth measurement is clutch "K-1" end clearance. Clearance should be .024" (.6 mm). Adjust clearance by inserting compensating washers under axial bearing washer.

15) Check Teflon rings on front cover and on input shaft for proper installation. Install front cover, with gasket, on transmission case. Install and tighten front cover bolts.

Fig. 14: Measuring Brake "B-3" Piston Height

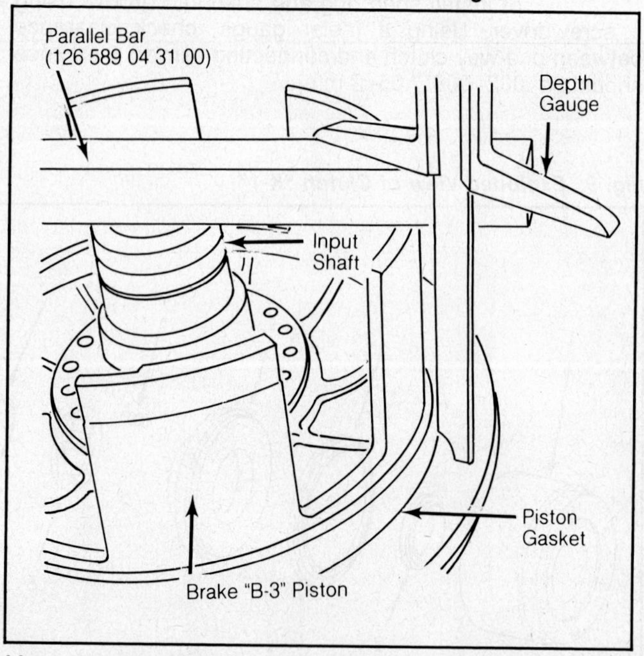

Measurement is taken on piston.

MERCEDES-BENZ W4A020 (Cont.)

16) Position transmission case so output shaft is pointing upward. Install snap ring into groove on output shaft. Install oil pipe and attaching screw. Install helical gear and snap ring on output shaft.

17) Install "O" ring in governor bore. Install governor while turning bearing ring so that lug enters groove in housing. . Install governor cover and retaining ring. Pull cover out so it rests on retaining ring. Install intermediate plate and "O" ring.

18) Install secondary pump and pump attaching bolts. Install temperature throttle and oil deflector. Install detent plate with selector lever and tighten. Insert thrust pin with large diameter toward brake band "B-2". Install brake band "B-2" guide and one-way valve.

Fig. 15: Measuring Clutch "K-1" Flange Height

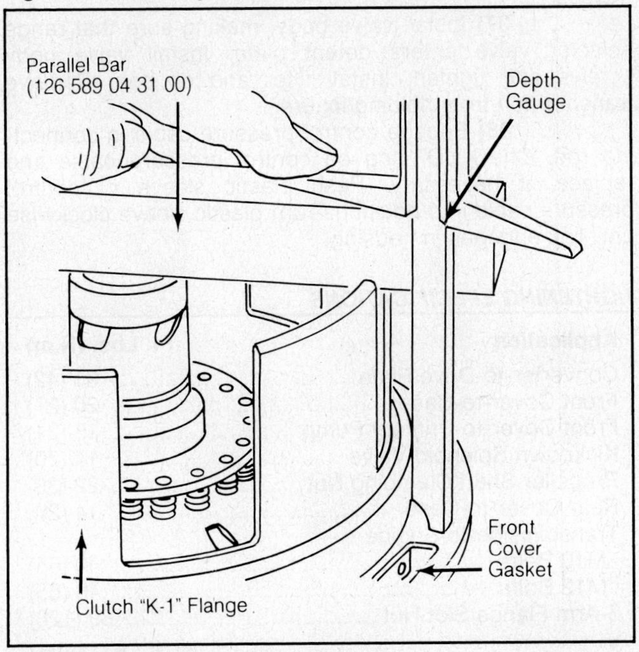

Measurement taken on clutch flange.

19) Connect linkage to detent plate and install snap ring. Install spacing sleeve and compensating washers on helical gear. Mount roller on linkage. Install plastic guide over roller and push into locating bore.

20) Install parking lock pawl, insert expanding spring, and attach spring to pawl. Install parking lock wheel. Make sure that lugs on helical gear engage holes in parking lock wheel.

21) Install Measuring Sleeve (126 589 06 14 00) over output shaft and tighten slot nut to 74 ft. lbs. (100 N.m). *See Fig. 17*. Engage parking lock pawl to keep assembly from turning. Install rear cover gasket.

22) Place Parallel Bar (126 589 04 31 00) across rear cover gasket. Measure distance from top on parallel bar to flange (lip) of measuring sleeve. *See Fig. 17*. Add .59" (15 mm) to measurement to compensate for height of parallel bar and lip of measuring sleeve. Record measurement.

23) Assemble rear cover. Using a depth gauge, measure distance from rear cover sealing surface to inner race of radial bearing. Subtract this measurement from measurement made in step **22)** to obtain output shaft end play. End play should be .004-.011" (.1-.3 mm). Adjust end play by adding or removing compensating washers under parking lock wheel.

Fig. 16: Measuring Clutch "K-1" Axial Bearing Depth

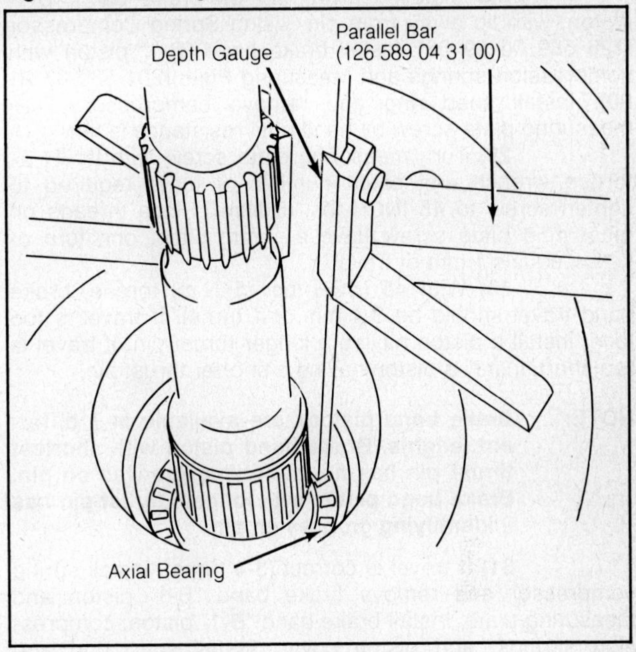

Measurement taken in transmission case.

24) Install "O" ring on tachometer oil pipe. Install tachometer oil pipe, making sure that lugs engage holes in parking lock wheel. Install rear cover and insert washer.

25) Install "O" ring into output flange. Install output flange and tighten double hex collar nut. Using a mandrel, knock collar of double hex nut into recess of output shaft. Install kickdown solenoid valve and tighten.

26) Install modulating pressure control valve and thrust pin. Install vacuum control unit and retaining plate. Install starter lock-out switch and range selector lever. DO NOT tighten screws at this time.

27) Move range selector lever into Neutral and insert a .16" (4 mm) pin through range selector lever and into bore of starter lock-out switch. Tighten starter lock-out switch screws. Remove pin.

Fig. 17: Measuring Output Shaft End Play

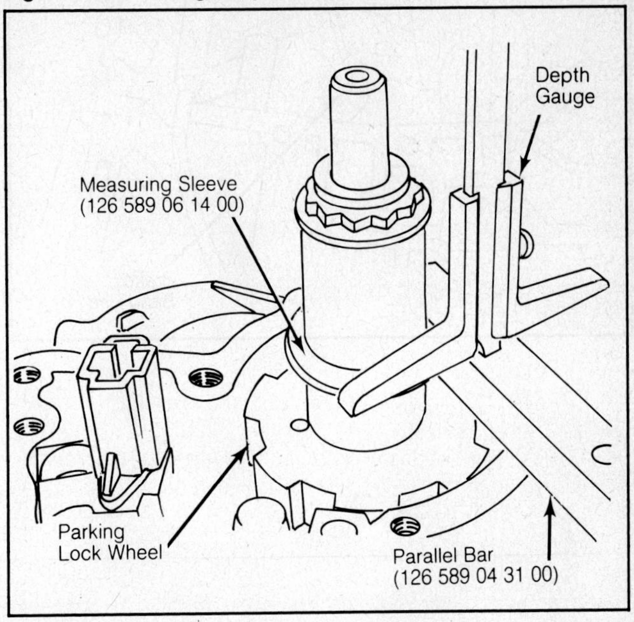

MERCEDES-BENZ W4A020 (Cont.)

28) Install sealing ring on brake band "B-1" piston, with lip away from pin. Using Spring Compressor (126 589 00 59 00), install brake band "B-1" piston with compression springs and Measuring Plate (201 589 07 21 00). Install snap ring and remove compressor. Turn measuring plate screw by hand until resistance is felt.

29) Turn measuring plate screw with INCH lb. torque wrench and count number of turns required to tighten screw to 45 INCH lbs. (5 N.m). Since threads on measuring plate screw have a 1 mm pitch, one turn of screw equals 1 mm of travel.

30) With 45 INCH lbs. (5 N.m) torque, brake band travel should be 3-4 mm (3-4 turns). If travel is too long, install a piston having a longer thrust pin. If travel is too short, install a piston having a shorter thrust pin.

NOTE: **Brake band pistons are available in 7 different lenghts. Brake band piston with shortest thrust pin has no identifying grooves on pin. Brake band piston with longest thrust pin has 6 identifying grooves on pin.**

31) If travel is correct (3-4 turns), install spring compressor and remove brake band "B-1" piston and measuring plate. Install brake band "B-1" piston, compression springs, and piston cover. Install snap ring and remove compressor.

32) Install thrust pin into brake band "B-2" piston. Install Teflon ring on piston. Install piston in transmission, making sure that thrust pin enters brake band. Install piston cover and snap ring.

33) Push brake band support lug (above thrust pin) in direction of brake band piston until piston rests against piston cover. Measure and record distance between support lug and brake band end. *See Fig. 18.*

Fig. 18: Measuring Brake Band "B-2" Free Play

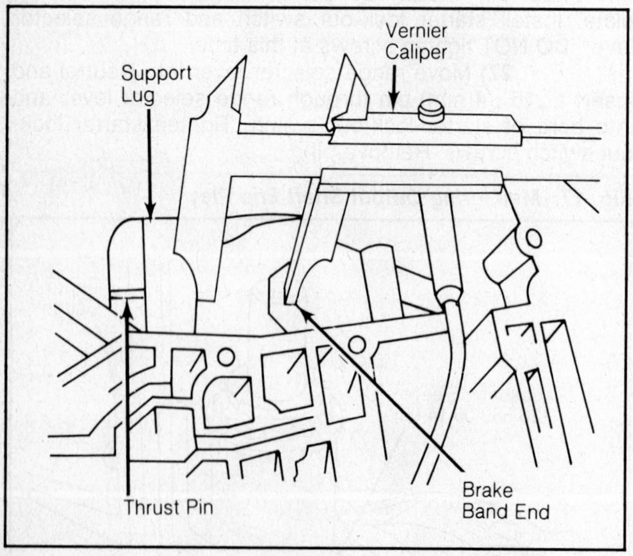

34) Push brake band support lug toward thrust body (away from thrust pin). Measure and record distance between support lug and brake band end. Difference between measurements should be .24-.28" (6-7 mm). Adjust clearance by changing thrust pin. Thrust pin is available in 5 lenghts.

35) Insert locating pin into transmission case. Assemble lower cover. Install lower cover while making sure that oil pipe is introduced into bore. Center intermediate plate by means of 2 screws. Install screws and tighten. Install leaf spring with holder and tighten.

36) Check clearance between detent piston and stop on shift linkage with selector lever in Neutral. Adjust clearance by means of plastic clip to .0016-.040" (.4-1.0 mm). Plastic clip is available in 3 different thicknesses.

37) Install valve body, making sure that range selector valve enters detent plate. Install valve body screws and tighten. Install filter and oil pan. Remove transmission from holding fixture.

38) Engage control pressure cable in connecting rod. Check "O" ring on control pressure cable and replace, if necessary. Push plastic sleeve of control pressure cable into housing. Turn plastic sleeve clockwise until link engages in housing.

TIGHTENING SPECIFICATIONS

Application	Ft. Lbs. (N.m)
Converter-to-Drive Plate	31 (42)
Front Cover-to-Case	20 (27)
Front Cover-to-Primary Pump	15 (21)
Kickdown Solenoid Valve	14 (20)
Propeller Shaft Clamping Nut	22 (30)
Rear Cover-to-Case	14 (20)
Transmission-to-Engine	
M10 Bolts	41 (55)
M12 Bolts	48 (65)
3-Arm Flange Slot Nut	89 (120)
	INCH Lbs. (N.m)
Clutch K-2 Support Flange-to-Case	96 (11)
Converter Drain Plug	120 (14)
Governor Axial Holder Nut	72 (8)
Lower Cover-to-Case	72 (8)
Oil Drain Plug	120 (14)
Oil Filter-to-Valve Body	36 (4)
Oil Pan-to-Case	72 (8)
Range Selector Lever Nut	72 (8)
Secondary Pump-to-Case	72 (8)
Vacuum Control Unit-to Case	72 (8)
Valve Body-to-Case	72 (8)

MERCEDES-BENZ W4A040

300 (Federal), 380, 500 Series

IDENTIFICATION

Identification code is punched into rating plate or transmission housing. Use identification code when ordering parts.

W4A040 AUTOMATIC TRANSMISSION CODES

Application	Identification Code
300D	722.315
300CD	722.315
300TD	722.315
300SD	722.303
380SL	722.312
380SE	722.310
500SEL	722.311
500SEC	722.311

DESCRIPTION

This is a fully automatic 4-speed unit consisting primarily of a 3-element welded torque converter and 2 compound planetary gear sets. Two multiple-disc clutches, 1 overrunning clutch, and 3 brake bands.

Brake bands provide friction elements required to obtain desired function of planetary gear set. A hydraulic system, pressurized by a primary gear type pump and a secondary piston type pump provide working pressure required to operate friction elements and automatic controls.

On 380 series, to relieve load on the vehicle's service brakes on lengthy downgrades, the engine's braking effect is utilized by providing an additional shift lever position "B" (Braking). When shift lever is placed in position "B", the solenoid valve in the transmission is energized through the switch at the shift lever. The transmission will remain in 1st gear independent of accelerator position. It will shift to 2nd gear when the regular kickdown shift point is reached.

On 500 series, the transmission is the same as 300 and 380 series except for the following: 500 series transmissions have a torque converter that is 11.4" (290 mm) in diameter. Clutches "K-1" and "K-2" have five inner discs each. The diaphragm diameter of the vacuum modulator valve is 1.08" (27.5 mm), the identifying color is White. Depending on driving style, the transmission can start in 2nd or 1st gear. The electrical circuit for the lock out and back-up light switch has an additional contact pin, which is energized in shift lever positions "3" and "2", allowing the transmission to start in 1st gear at moderate acceleration.

OPERATION

STARTING IN 1ST GEAR

In shift lever positions "3" and "2", the switching unit is activated by terminal 15 by the starter lock out and back up light switch. The switching unit then activates the kickdown valve which switches to 1st gear, while the vehicle is stationary.

Starting at a speed of approximately 7 MPH, the switching unit is activated by the cruise control connection of the speedometer. The switching unit interrupts the current flow to the kickdown valve and the transmission will shift to 2nd gear.

Fig. 1: Shift Lever Position "B" Circuit

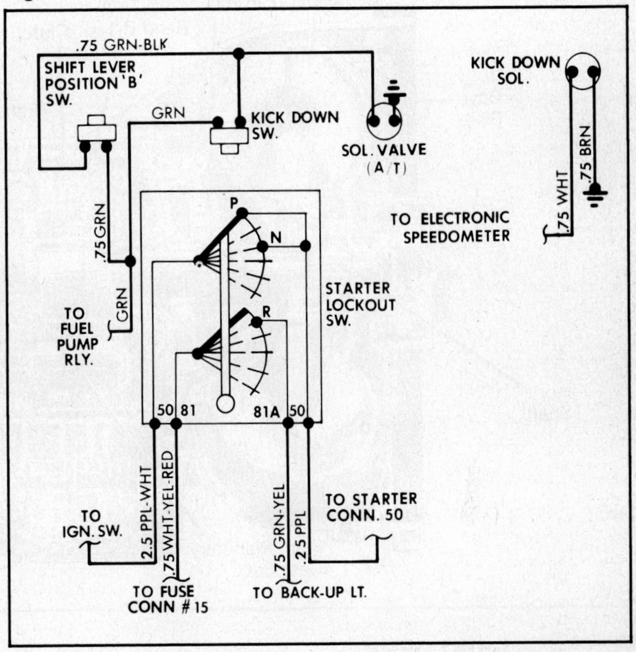

LUBRICATION & ADJUSTMENT

See appropriate AUTOMATIC TRANSMISSION SERVICING article in IMPORT GENERAL SERVICING section.

TROUBLE SHOOTING

TRANSMISSION SLIPS

Slips In All Selector Positions

Incorrect modulating pressure. Modulating pressure control valve or pressure relief valve for modulating pressure dirty or sticking. Line to transmission vacuum unit clogged or leaking. Working pressure control valve dirty or sticking. Defective primary pump.

Transmission Slips in 1st & 2nd Gear When Starting Off or Starting Off Impossible, Okay in Reverse

Band "B-2" shift valve sticking. Valve body malfunction. Band "B-2" piston worn or damaged. Band "B-2" adjustment incorrect, worn or damaged.

Transmission Slips in 2nd Gear Or Shifts From 1st to 3rd

Brake band "B-1" control valve sticking. Valve body malfunction. Brake band "B-1" piston sealing ring worn or damaged. Band "B-1" worn or damaged.

Transmission Slips During 2-3 Upshift Or During 3-4 Upshift

Governor and/or working pressure incorrect. Valve body assembly worn or damaged. Defective front or rear clutch assembly.

No Positive Engagement In Reverse

Front band out of adjustment. Sealing ring on rear band piston worn or damaged. One-way roller clutch in gear assembly worn or damaged.

MERCEDES-BENZ W4A040 (Cont.)

Fig. 2: Sectional View of Mercedes-Benz W4A040 Automatic Transmission

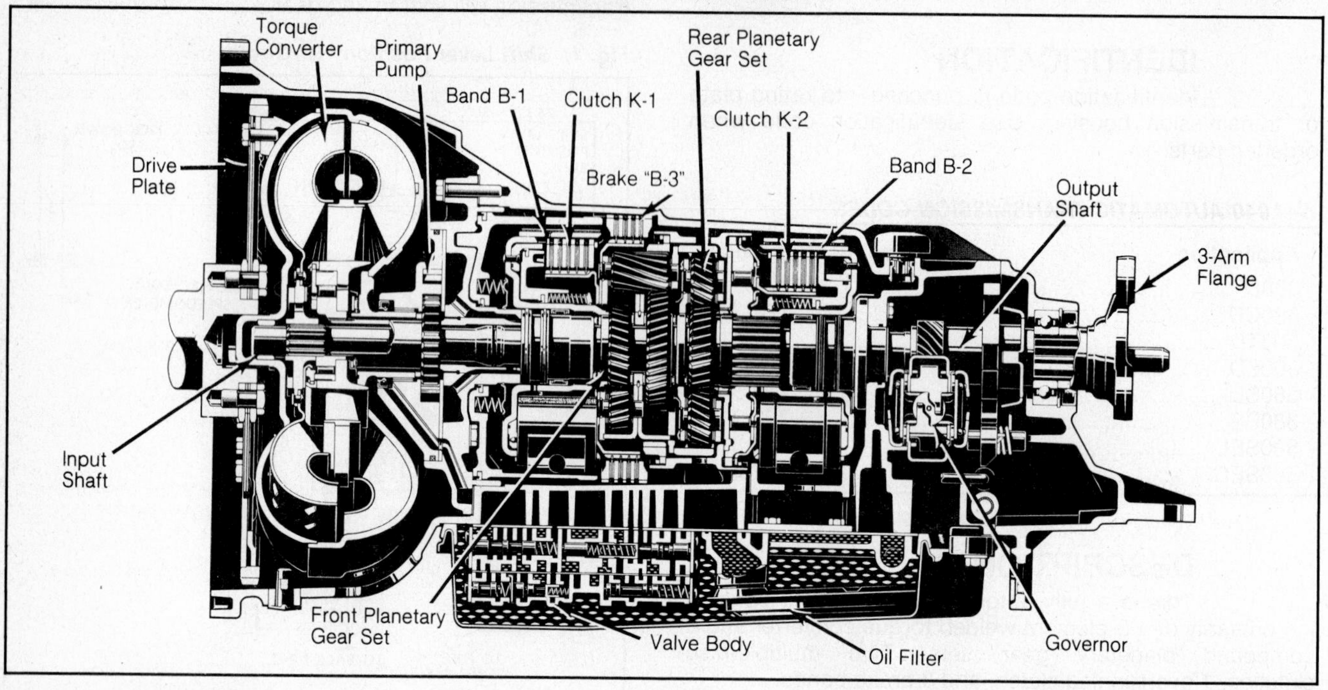

SHIFT JERK

Rough Jerk When Changing Gears

Incorrect modulating pressure. Incorrect working pressure. If working pressure is too high, replace valve body assembly. Vacuum line to modulator leaking. Control pressure cable out of adjustment. Control valve converter adjustment incorrect.

Jerk When Engaging "D" or "R"

Engine idle speed too high. Modulating and/or working pressure incorrect. Leak in vacuum modulator vacuum line. Pressure receiving piston in extension housing worn, damaged, or installed incorrectly. Feed bore in pressure receiving piston plugged.

Rough Jerk on 4-3 Downshift

Sealing ring on release end of band "B-2" worn or damaged. Band "B-2" piston worn or damaged. Band "B-2" thrust body damaged.

UPSHIFTS & DOWNSHIFTS

No Upshift

Incorrect governor pressure. Defective governor assembly. Valve body dirty or valves sticking.

Upshifts Only In Upper Speed Range Of Gears

Control pressure cable out of adjustment. Defective governor assembly. Control pressure valve inoperable.

Upshifts Only In Lower Speed Range Of Gears

Control pressure cable out of adjustment. Full throttle stop out of adjustment. Incorrect modulating pressure.

No Kickdown Shifts

Fuse for power supply to solenoid valve blown. Defective solenoid valve. Control pressure cable damaged or out of adjustment. Kickdown control valve in valve body sticking.

No Brake Shifts (4-3 & 3-2)

Control pressure cable out of adjustment. Leaking vacuum hoses and/or connections. Make brake shaft piston operable and exchange shift valve housing, if required.

TESTING

ROAD TEST

NOTE: **Before road testing, check transmission fluid level, idle speed and control pressure cable adjustment. Correct if necessary.**

1) During road test, transmission should upshift and downshift at approximately the speeds shown in SHIFT SPEEDS SPECIFICATION (MPH) tables. All shifts may vary somewhat due to production tolerances or tire size. The important factor is quality of shifts. All shifts should be smooth, responsive, and with no engine speed flare-up.

NOTE: **Shifts at full throttle and kickdown are somewhat firmer than part throttle shifts.**

2) Slipping or engine speed flare-up in any gear usually indicates clutch or band problems. The slipping clutch or band in a particular gear can usually be identified by noting transmission operation in all selector positions and comparing which internal units are applied in those positions. See CLUTCH & BAND APPLICATION CHART.

3) Although this process of elimination can be used to detect any unit which slips, and to confirm proper operation of good units, actual cause of malfunction usually cannot be decided. Practically any condition can be caused by leaking hydraulic circuits or sticking valves. Therefore, unless an obvious condition exists, transmission should never be disassembled until hydraulic pressure tests have been made.

MERCEDES-BENZ W4A040 (Cont.)

SHIFT SPEED MPH SPECIFICATIONS

Shift Condition	300 Series	Model 380SL
Shift Lever in "D"		
Idle [1]		
1-2 Upshift	10	13
2-3 Upshift	18	17
3-4 Upshift	24	25
4-3 Downshift	18	17
3-2 Downshift	12	11
2-1 Downshift	8	.....
Full Throttle		
1-2 Upshift	25	34
2-3 Upshift	45	58
3-4 Upshift	75	101
4-3 Downshift	49	65
3-2 Downshift	25	32
2-1 Downshift	15	19
Kickdown		
1-2 Upshift	29	44
2-3 Upshift	46	65
3-4 Upshift	78	106
4-3 Downshift	70	95
3-2 Downshift	41	55
2-1 Downshift	22	30
Shift Lever in "3" [2]		
Idle [1]		
1-2 Upshift	10	13
2-3 Upshift	18	17
3-2 Downshift	12	11
2-1 Downshift	8	.....
Full Throttle		
1-2 Upshift	25	34
2-3 Upshift	45	58
3-2 Downshift	25	32
2-1 Downshift	15	19
Kickdown		
1-2 Upshift	29	44
2-3 Upshift	46	65
3-2 Downshift	41	55
2-1 Downshift	22	30
Shift Lever in "2" [3]		
Idle [1]		
1-2 Upshift	.....	13
2-1 Downshift	8	29
Full Throttle		
1-2 Upshift	28	34
2-1 Downshift	15	19
Kickdown		
1-2 Upshift	29	44
2-1 Downshift	22	30
Shift Lever in "B" [4]		
Idle-to-Kickdown		
Upshift	.....	44
Downshift	.....	30

1 – At light throttle on 300 series.
2 – Lever in "S" on 300 series.
3 – Lever in "L" on 300 series.
4 – Model 380SL only.

SHIFT SPEED MPH SPECIFICATIONS (Cont.)

Shift Condition	Model 380SE	500 Series
Shift Lever in "D"		
Idle		
1-2 Upshift	13	.....
2-3 Upshift	17	18
3-4 Upshift	25	25
4-3 Downshift	17	17
3-2 Downshift	7	11
2-1 Downshift	.....	.....
Full Throttle		
1-2 Upshift	34	.....
2-3 Upshift	59	62
3-4 Upshift	100	102
4-3 Downshift	65	66
3-2 Downshift	32	32
2-1 Downshift	19	.....
Kickdown		
1-2 Upshift	45	38
2-3 Upshift	65	65
3-4 Upshift	106	106
4-3 Downshift	95	94
3-2 Downshift	55	55
2-1 Downshift	30	30
Shift Lever in "3"		
Idle		
1-2 Upshift	13	11
2-3 Upshift	17	18
3-2 Downshift	11	11
2-1 Downshift	.....	6
Full Throttle		
1-2 Upshift	34	25
2-3 Upshift	59	62
3-2 Downshift	32	32
2-1 Downshift	19	6
Kickdown		
1-2 Upshift	44	38
2-3 Upshift	66	65
3-2 Downshift	55	55
2-1 Downshift	30	30
Shift Lever in "2"		
Idle		
1-2 Upshift	13	11
2-1 Downshift	10	6
Full Throttle		
1-2 Upshift	34	25
2-1 Downshift	19	6
Kickdown		
1-2 Upshift	44	38
2-1 Downshift	30	30
Shift Lever in "B"		
Idle-to-Kickdown		
Upshift	44	38
Downshift	30	30

HYDRAULIC PRESSURE TESTS

Preparation For Tests

Before making tests, make sure fluid levels, linkage, EGR system, and neutral safety/back-up light switch have been checked and adjusted or corrected as necessary. Connect a pressure gauge test set to pressure take-off points on transmission. *See Fig. 3.*

NOTE: **Make sure pressure gauge hoses do not drag on pavement or contact exhaust system.**

MERCEDES-BENZ W4A040 (Cont.)

Fig. 3: Pressure Test Take-Off Points

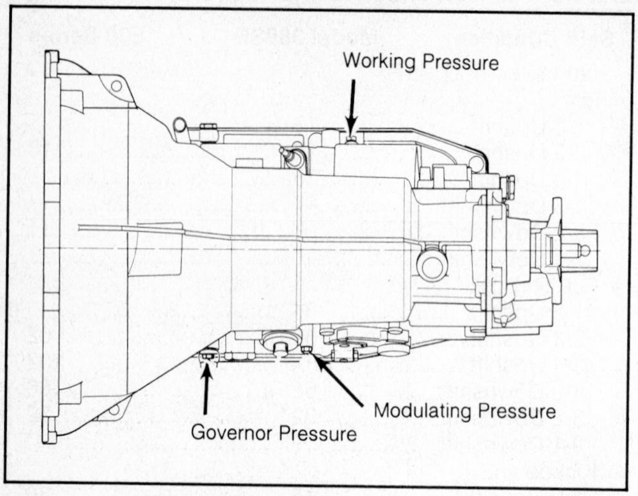

Modulating Pressure Test

1) Remove vacuum line holder and pull off vacuum line from vacuum control unit. Place transmission in "D" and drive vehicle on road or on dynamometer at 31 MPH. Run engine at full throttle, and keep speed at 31 MPH by lightly applying service brakes.

2) Read resulting pressure on gauge attached to modulating pressure take-off point on transmission. Pressure should be as shown in MODULATING PRESSURE SPECIFICATIONS table. If necessary, adjust pressure.

NOTE: **Modulating pressure must be measured (and corrected) before making working pressure and governor pressure tests.**

MODULATING PRESSURE SPECIFICATIONS

Application	psi (kg/cm²)
Modulating Pressure (In "D" at 31 MPH)	
300 Series	48 (3.4)
380 Series	54 (3.8)
500 Series	48 (3.4)

Working Pressure

1) Disconnect vacuum line from vacuum control unit. Start and run engine at 1000 RPM while reading pressure. Pressure should be as shown in WORKING PRESSURE SPECIFICATIONS table.

2) Working pressure is not adjustable. Measurement simply provides information concerning operation of working pressure regulator valve in valve housing.

WORKING PRESSURE SPECIFICATIONS

Application	psi (kg/cm²)
Working Pressure (In stationary "D")	
300 Series	199-228 (14.0-16.0)
380 Series	191-220 (13.4-15.5)
500 Series	191-220 (13.4-15.5)

Governor Pressure

Drive vehicle on road or on dynamometer at speeds indicated in table. Compare pressures noted on gauge with pressures given in GOVERNOR PRESSURE SPECIFICATIONS table.

NOTE: **Governor pressure is a part of working pressure and is controlled by centrifugal governor on output shaft. If values are not within specifications, disassemble and clean governor assembly.**

GOVERNOR PRESSURE SPECIFICATIONS

Application	psi (kg/cm²) @ 19 MPH	psi (kg/cm²) @ 56 MPH
300 Series	17 (1.2)	41 (2.9)
380 Series	9 (0.6)	29 (2.0)
500 Series	7 (0.5)	28 (1.9)

STALL TEST

Testing Precautions

Do not hold throttle open longer than 5 seconds as severe transmission damage may result from heat generated. If engine speed exceeds maximum limits shown, release accelerator immediately as this is an indication of clutch or band slippage.

Testing Procedure

With engine at normal operating temperature, tachometer installed, and parking and service brakes applied firmly, stall test transmission by pushing accelerator to floor and noting engine speed on tachometer. Engine speed should be within limits in table.

CLUTCH AND BAND APPLICATION CHART (ELEMENTS IN USE)

Selector Lever Position	Band B-1	Band B-2	Disc Brake	Clutch K-1	Clutch K-2	One-Way Clutch
First Gear		X			X	X
Second Gear	X	X				
Third Gear		X		X		
Fourth Gear				X	X	
Reverse			X		X	X

NEUTRAL OR PARK – All clutches and bands released and/or ineffective.

MERCEDES-BENZ W4A040 (Cont.)

STALL SPEED SPECIFICATIONS

Application	Stall RPM
300 Series	2400-2700 [1]
380 Series	1450-1650
500 Series	1850-2000

[1] - Stall speed at 10-15 seconds.

Stall Test Results

If stall speed is higher than specified, general transmission problems are indicated and hydraulic pressure tests should be made to locate faulty units. If stall speed is lower than specified, torque converter clutch is faulty.

NOTE: **Make sure engine performance is satisfactory before condemning converter assembly. Torque converter is a sealed unit and cannot be disassembled for service.**

SERVICE (IN VEHICLE)

The following units may be removed from transmission without removing transmission from vehicle: Oil Pan and Gasket, Valve Body, Vacuum Modulator Unit, Speedometer Driven Gear Assembly, Secondary Pump Assembly, Extension Housing, Pressure Receiving Piston, Modulating Pressure Housing and Bi-Metallic Spring, Speedometer Drive Gear, Secondary Pump Eccentric, Governor Assembly, Parking Pawl, and Parking Linkage. See procedures given in TRANSMISSION DISASSEMBLY and TRANSMISSION REASSEMBLY

REMOVAL & INSTALLATION

See appropriate AUTOMATIC TRANSMISSION REMOVAL article in IMPORT GENERAL SERVICING section.

TORQUE CONVERTER

NOTE: **Torque converter is a sealed unit and cannot be disassembled for service. If hub of converter is scored, or if metallic particles are found in transmission fluid, replace converter assembly.**

TRANSMISSION DISASSEMBLY

1) Position transmission in Holding Fixture (116 589 06 59 00 and 126 589 10 63 00) with oil pan facing upward. Remove oil pan and gasket. Remove oil filter and bolts attaching valve body to transmission case, and then lift valve body from case.

2) Remove leaf spring screw and remove leaf spring and holder as an assembly. *See Fig. 4.* Remove screws and remove lower transmission case cover along with intermediate plate and oil pipe. Remove one-way valve and band "B-2" guide and filler (if equipped). Push in band "B-2" piston cover and remove snap ring. Remove band piston cover and pull piston out of bore.

3) Attach Compressor (126 589 00 59 00) to transmission housing. Apply compressor to band "B-1" piston cover and remove snap ring. Remove compressor and withdraw band "B-1" piston cover, piston and back pressure springs. Remove guide for band "B-1". Remove closing cover for band "B-1" thrust bolt.

Fig. 4: Bottom View of Transmission Case Showing Location of Leaf Spring

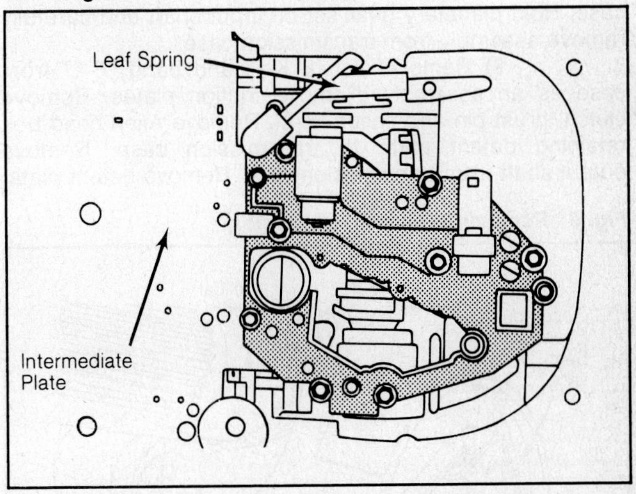

4) Remove gear selector lever. Remove starter lock-out switch. Remove retaining screws and remove vacuum control unit holding plate. Withdraw vacuum control unit from transmission case. Remove band "B-1" thrust body and modulating pressure control valve.

5) Remove kickdown solenoid valve. Remove slot nut, collar nut and 3-arm (universal) flange. Remove bolts attaching rear cover-to-transmission case. Loosen rear cover by lightly tapping cover with a plastic hammer. Remove rear cover. Remove parking lock gear and parking pawl as an assembly.

6) Remove expanding spring. Remove nut from axial holder for governor. Remove Allen head bolts that retain secondary pump and remove pump. *See Fig. 5.* Remove "O" ring and intermediate plate of secondary pump. Remove plastic guide and roller assembly from bottom of transmission case.

Fig. 5: Secondary Pump Assembly

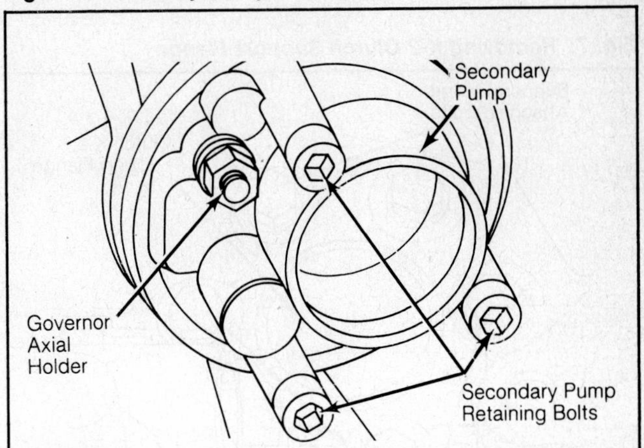

Showing location of nuts and bolts for removal.

7) Pry off snap ring and remove linkage from detent plate. Remove Allen head bolt and oil pipe as an assembly. Push in governor cover and remove retaining ring. Pull cover out of bore. Swivel axial holder back.

MERCEDES-BENZ W4A040 (Cont.)

Remove governor assembly. Remove axial holder. Remove helical gear. *See Fig. 6.*

8) Remove snap ring from output shaft. Remove bolts attaching front cover to transmission case. Install 2 long bolts into threaded holes in front cover (to serve as handles). Pull front cover from transmission case. Hold planetary gear set on input shaft and carefully remove assembly from transmission case.

9) Remove clutch "K-1" and band "B-1" from case as an assembly. Remove friction plates. Remove clutch thrust pin and clutch "K-2". Remove Allen head bolt retaining detent plate to transmission case. Remove output shaft from transmission case. Remove detent plate.

Fig. 6: Removing Governor Assembly

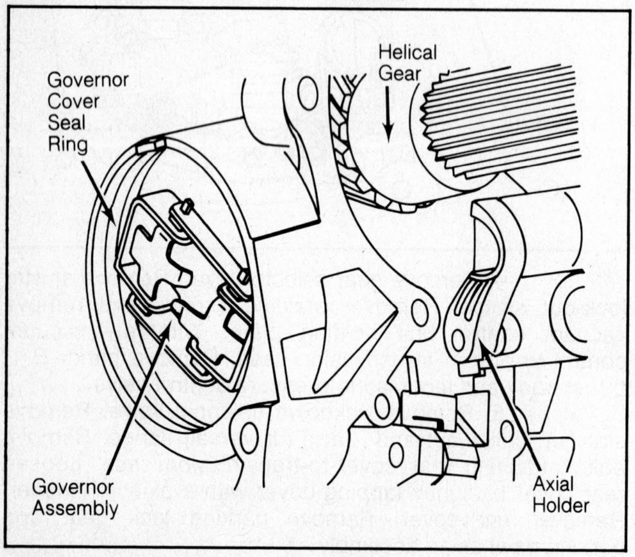

Note location of governor, axial holder and helical gear.

10) Tilt band "B-2" on an angle and remove. Remove band "B-2" thrust washer and thrust body. Remove bolts attaching clutch "K-2" support flange to case. Install 2 bolts, approximately 3 5/32" (80 mm) long, into support flange from opposite side of transmission. Loosen support flange by hitting bolts with hammer. *See Fig. 7.*

Fig. 7: Removing K-2 Clutch Support Flange

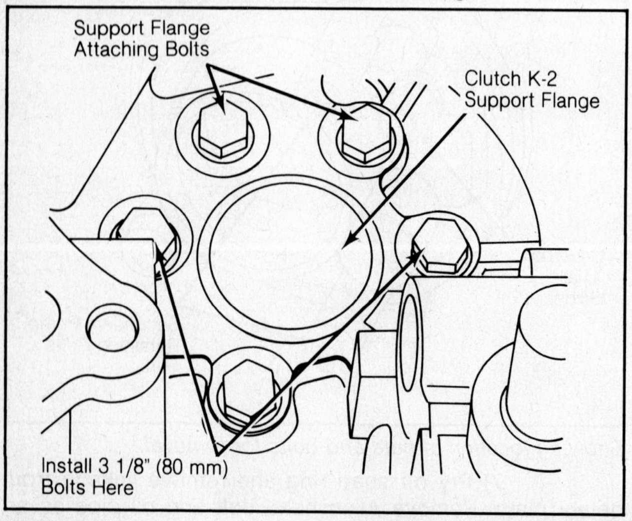

Showing location of clutch "K-2" support flange attaching bolts.

11) Release tabs on detent cable retainer from inside case. Pull detent cable out of case. Disconnect control pressure cable and remove from case.

COMPONENT DISASSEMBLY & REASSEMBLY

VALVE BODY

Disassembly

1) Remove 2 screws that attach valve body to pick-up housing. Hold assembly together and turn over. Lift pick-up housing and intermediate plate from valve body.

2) Remove modulating pressure filter screen and shift pin. Note number, size, and location of check balls for reassembly reference. *See Fig. 8.* Number of check balls used may vary by one or two. Remove all check balls.

Fig. 8: Valve Body Check Ball Locations

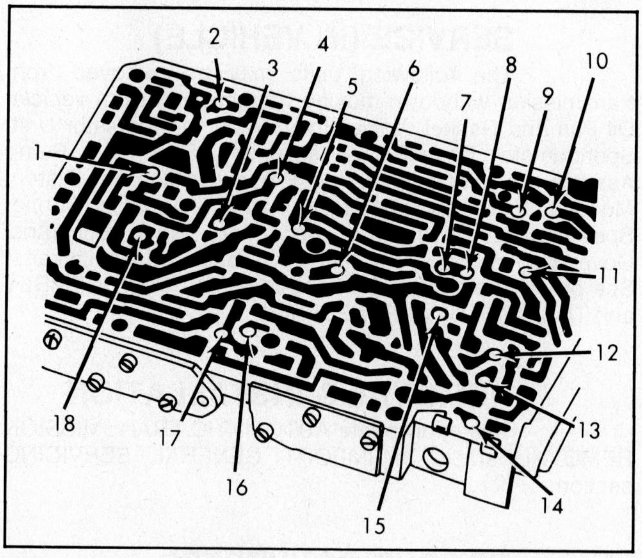

Note number, size, and location of check balls during disassembly.

Inspection

1) Wash all parts in clean solvent and blow dry with compressed air. Closely inspect valve body and pick-up housing passages for obstructions or defects.

2) Inspect intermediate plate for damage. Inspect check balls for damage. If internal valve body problems are found or suspected, valve body assembly must be replaced as an assembly.

Reassembly

1) Install check balls into pick-up housing. Install modulating pressure filter screen and shift pin. Install conical spring under check ball No. 7 with large end of spring downward. *See Fig. 9.*

2) Install intermediate plate on pick-up housing. Hold pick-up housing and intermediate plate together, turn over and place assembly on valve body. Install 2 screws that attach valve body to pick-up housing.

MERCEDES-BENZ W4A040 (Cont.)

Fig. 9: Installing Valve Body Springs

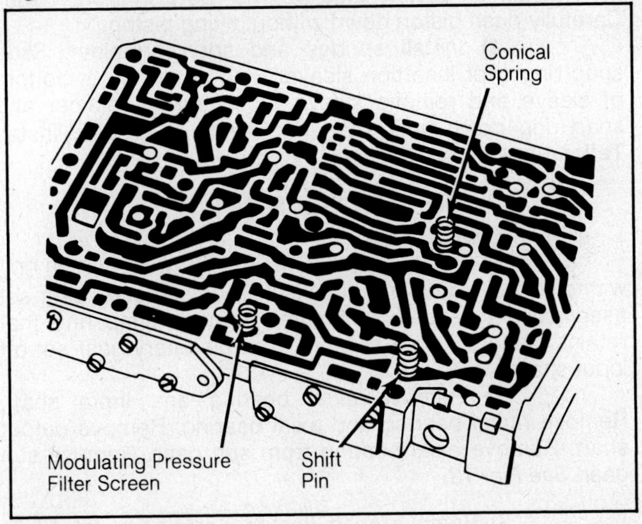

Showing location of conical spring, shift pin, and filter screen.

LOWER COVER

Disassembly

1) Turn injector in direction of arrow and remove from lower cover. *See Fig. 10.* Remove oil pipe. Remove cover plate retaining screws and remove cover plate and intermediate plate as an assembly. Remove gasket from intermediate plate.

2) Remove secondary pump shift valve plug. Remove secondary pump shift valve with spring. Remove locking valve retainer. Remove locking valve, spring and bolt.

Inspection

Check that intermediate plate is not plugged or distorted in any way. Inspect secondary pump shift valve and spring for damage or distortion. Inspect locking valve and spring for damage or distortion.

Fig. 10: Injector Located on Bottom of Lower Cover

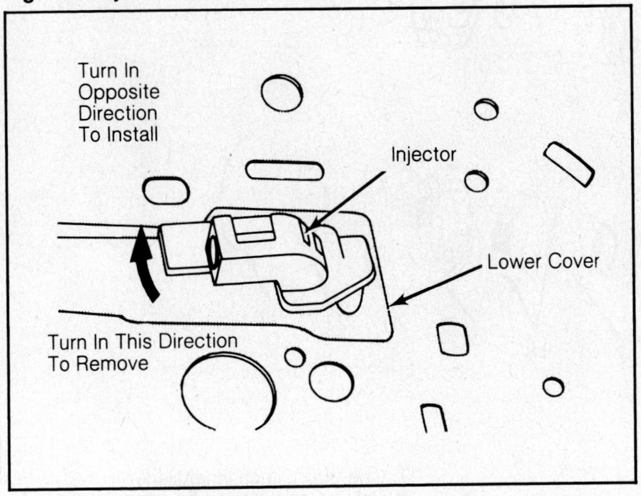

Reassembly

1) Install secondary pump shift valve, spring, and plug into lower cover. Install locking valve, spring, and bolt. Install locking valve retainer. Install intermediate plate, with a new gasket, on lower cover.

2) Install cover plate on intermediate plate and lower cover assembly. Install oil pipe. Install injector in lower cover and rotate in opposite direction of arrow. *See Fig. 10.*

SECONDARY PUMP

Disassembly

Remove gears from pump housing. Remove shutoff piston cover retaining ring and cover. Remove shutoff piston with compression spring, spring retainer, and ball from pump housing. *See Fig. 11.*

Inspection

Check gears and pump housing for damage or unusual wear. Check compression spring for distortion. Check shutoff piston and piston seal for damage and replace as necessary.

Reassembly

Install "O" ring in pump housing. Install Teflon sealing ring on shutoff piston. Install shutoff piston into pump housing. Install compression spring, spring retainer, and ball into shutoff piston. Install piston cover and piston cover retaining ring. Lubricate gears and place in pump housing. *See Fig. 11.*

Fig. 11: Exploded View of Secondary Pump

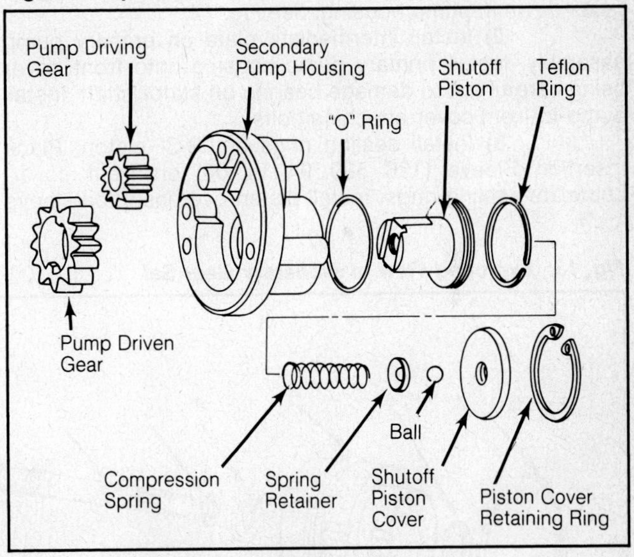

PRIMARY PUMP

Disassembly

1) Remove 2 Teflon rings from stator shaft. Push spring retainer down and remove snap ring. Remove spring retainer and springs for "B-3" piston.

2) Remove "B-3" piston. Remove bolts attaching pump housing to front cover and lift pump from cover. Remove gears from pump housing. *See Fig. 12.*

Inspection

Check bearing for scores or damage. Check seal for damage. Check that "O" ring is properly seated in groove. Check that pump gears are not scored or damaged.

MERCEDES-BENZ W4A040 (Cont.)

Fig. 12: Installing Driven Gear

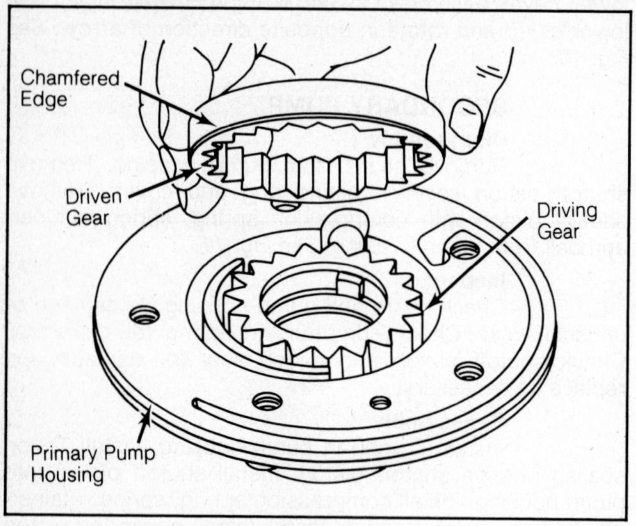

Install gear with chamfered edge down.

Reassembly

1) Lubricate and install gears into pump housing. Make sure that chamfered edge of driven gear faces down in pump housing. *See Fig. 12.*

2) Install intermediate plate on primary pump assembly. Install primary pump housing onto front cover being careful not to damage bearing on stator shaft. Install pump-to-front cover attaching bolts.

3) Install sealing rings on "B-3" piston. Place Insertion Sleeve (126 589 04 14 00) on front cover. Lubricate sealing rings. Install piston over insertion sleeve so that pin on piston lines up with bore in front cover. Carefully push piston down without tilting piston.

4) Install springs and spring retainer. Slide snap ring over insertion sleeve. Hold snap ring at bottom of sleeve and remove sleeve. Push spring retainer and snap ring down until snap ring seats in groove. Install Teflon rings on stator shaft.

PLANETARY GEAR SET

Disassembly

1) Clamp Assembly Fixture (126 589 00 35 00), with disc facing upward, in a vise. Place planetary gear set assembly into assembly fixture. Remove snap ring that retains planetary gear set. Lift front planetary gear set off input shaft.

2) Remove axial bearing and input shaft. Remove radial bearing and axial bearing. Remove output shaft. Remove axial bearing from sun gear. Remove sun gear. *See Fig. 13.*

3) Remove snap ring that retains clutch "K-2" inside plate carrier. Remove inside plate carrier with one-way clutch from connecting carrier. Remove support disc, compensating ring, and "O" ring from one-way clutch. *See Fig. 14.* Rotate inner race of one-way clutch in counterclockwise direction and pull out. Remove one-way clutch and rollers.

Inspection

Check bearing surfaces and bearing races for scoring or damage. Check one-way clutch roller bearings for scoring, roundness and extreme wear. If damage to one-way clutch rollers is noted, replace one-way clutch as an assembly.

Fig. 13: Exploded View of Planetary Gear Set

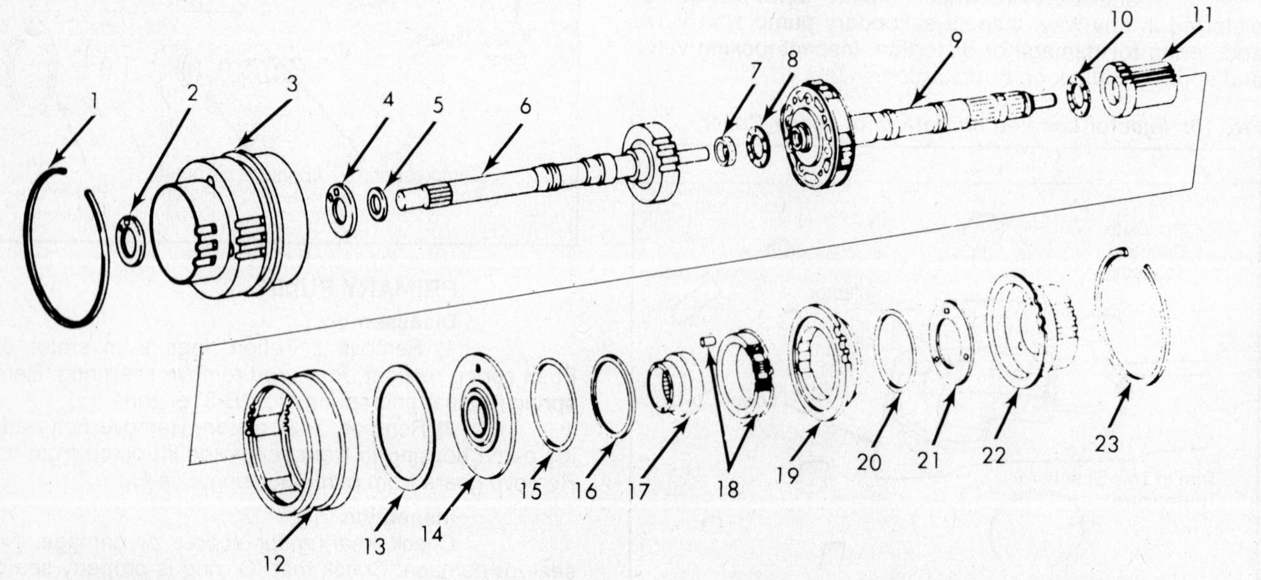

1. Snap Ring
2. Axial Bearing
3. Front Planetary Gear Set
4. Axial Bearing
5. Lube Pressure Ring
6. Input Shaft
7. Radial Bearing
8. Axial Bearing
9. Output Shaft
10. Axial Bearing
11. Sun Gear
12. Connecting Carrier
13. Compensating Washer
14. Support Disc
15. "O" Ring
16. Compensating Ring
17. One-Way Clutch Inner Race
18. Roller, Compression Springs & Roller Cage Assembly
19. Clutch Outer Race
20. "O" Ring
21. Thrust Washer
22. Clutch "K-2" Inner Plate With One-Way Clutch Outer Race

MERCEDES-BENZ W4A040 (Cont.)

Fig. 14: Installing One-Way Clutch

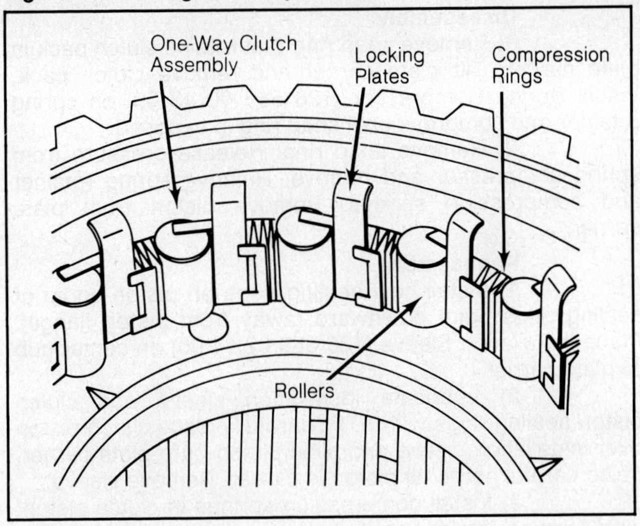

Note position of rollers, compression springs, and locking plates.

Reassembly

1) Install thrust washer and "O" ring into inner plate carrier. The "O" ring is installed only into one-way clutch having a single bearing, with clutch outer race and inner plate carrier which consists of two parts.

2) Install rollers into cage. Install one-way clutch outer race on inner plate carrier and insert roller cage. Press rollers against compression springs and insert locking plates with offset pointing outward. *See Fig. 14.*

3) Install one-way clutch inner race while rotating it counterclockwise. Pull out locking plates. Install compensating ring. Install support disc so that pin enters bore of one-way clutch outer race. *See Fig. 15.*

4) Install compensating washers into connecting carrier. Hold one-way clutch together and place assembly into connecting carrier. Install snap ring and push into groove with screwdriver.

Fig. 15: Installing One-Way Clutch Support Disc

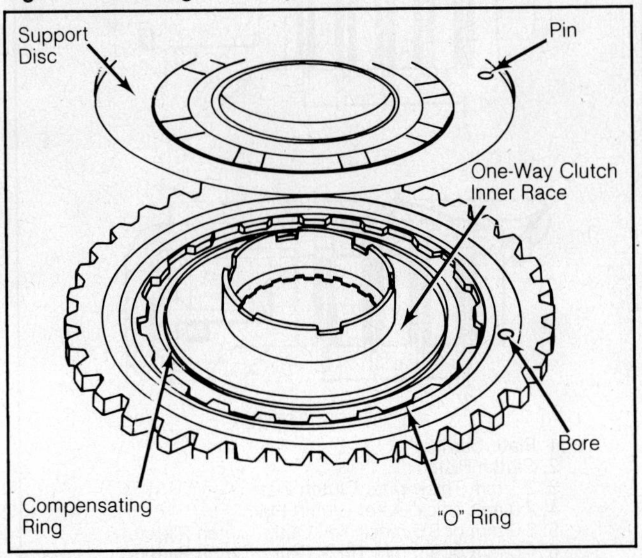

5) Check clearance between one-way clutch and connecting carrier. *See Fig. 16.* Clearance should be .002-.008" (.05-.20 mm). If clearance is incorrect, add or remove compensating washer until clearance is within limits. If clearance is correct, install one-way clutch "O" ring.

6) Insert sun gear into one-way clutch assembly. One-way clutch should lock when sun gear is rotated in clockwise direction. Install axial bearing on sun gear. Place one-way clutch on assembly fixture and install output shaft. Install axial and radial bearings on output shaft.

7) Install input shaft and axial bearing. Install front planetary gear set and secure by pushing snap ring into groove. Remove planetary gear set from assembly fixture and install axial bearing on input shaft.

Fig. 16: Measuring One-Way Clutch Clearance

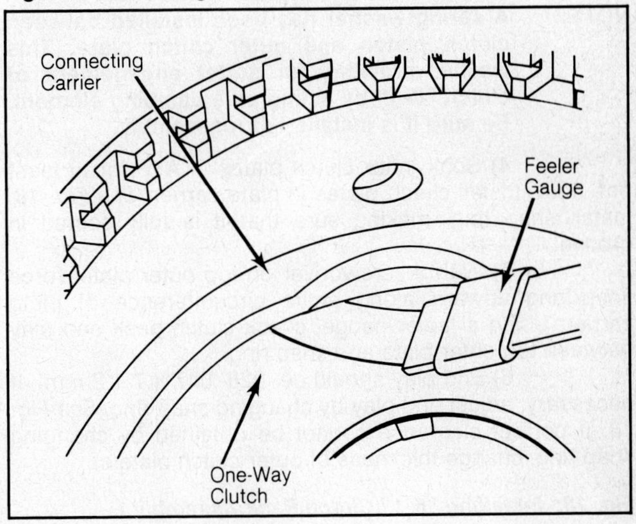

CLUTCH "K-1"

Disassembly

1) Remove snap ring that retains clutch pack in plate carrier. Tilt plate carrier, remove clutch pack, and conical spring washer. Install Spring Compressor (126 589 00 43 00) on spring retainer and compress until snap ring is exposed. Remove snap ring.

2) Release pressure from spring compressor and remove. Remove spring retainer and compression springs. Remove piston from plate carrier. *See Fig. 17.*

Fig. 17: Exploded View of Clutch "K-1" Assembly

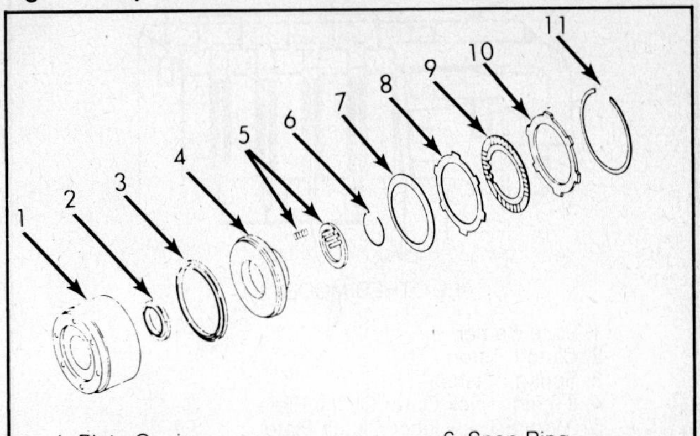

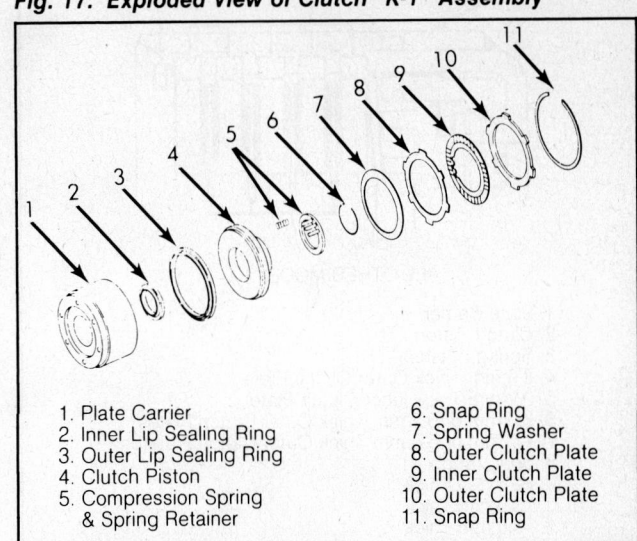

1. Plate Carrier
2. Inner Lip Sealing Ring
3. Outer Lip Sealing Ring
4. Clutch Piston
5. Compression Spring & Spring Retainer
6. Snap Ring
7. Spring Washer
8. Outer Clutch Plate
9. Inner Clutch Plate
10. Outer Clutch Plate
11. Snap Ring

MERCEDES-BENZ W4A040 (Cont.)

Reassembly

1) Install new sealing rings on piston so lip of sealing rings point downward (toward flat surface of piston). Place Installation Sleeves (126 589 02 14 00 and 126 589 03 14 00) on plate carrier.

2) Lubricate installation sleeves and sealing rings with ATF. Install piston into plate carrier being careful not to tilt piston. Remove installation sleeves.

3) Install compression springs in piston. Install spring retainer, making sure that each compression spring is centered by a guide pin. Install spring compressor and compress springs. Install snap ring and release compressor. Make sure that snap ring is properly seated in groove. Remove compressor.

NOTE: A spring washer has been installed between clutch piston and outer clutch plate. This washer provides for softer engagement of clutch "K-1" by acting as a damping element. Be sure it is installed at reassembly.

4) Soak inner clutch plates in ATF for at least one hour. Install clutch plates in plate carrier. *See Fig. 18.* Install snap ring, making sure that it is fully seated in groove.

5) With a screwdriver on top outer plate, force snap ring upward along entire circumference of plate carrier. Using a feeler gauge, check clutch pack end play between top outer plate and snap ring.

6) End play should be .028-.047" (.7-1.2 mm). If necessary, adjust end play by changing snap ring. *See Fig. 18.* If correct clearance cannot be obtained by changing snap ring, change thickness of outer clutch plate(s).

Fig. 18: Installing "K-1" Clutch Pack Assembly

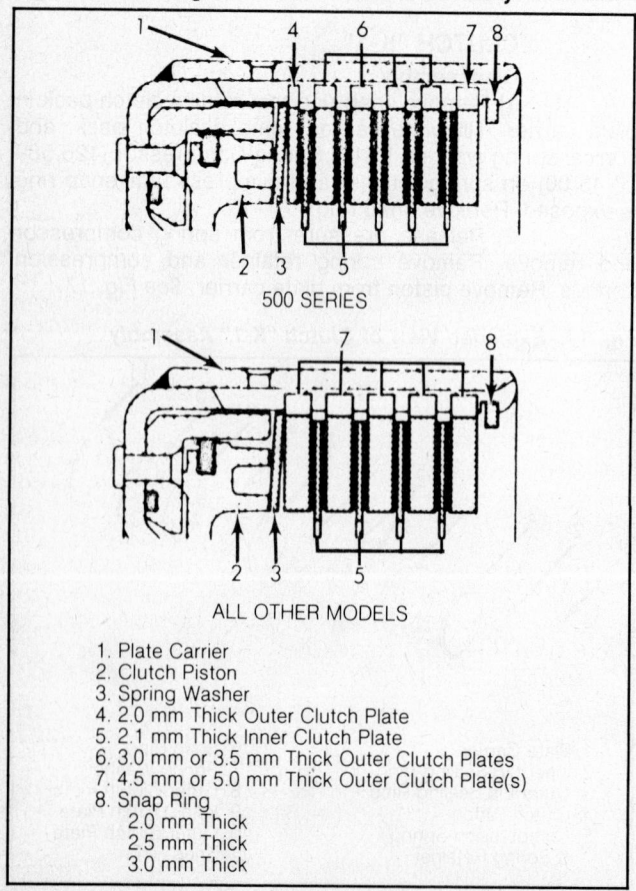

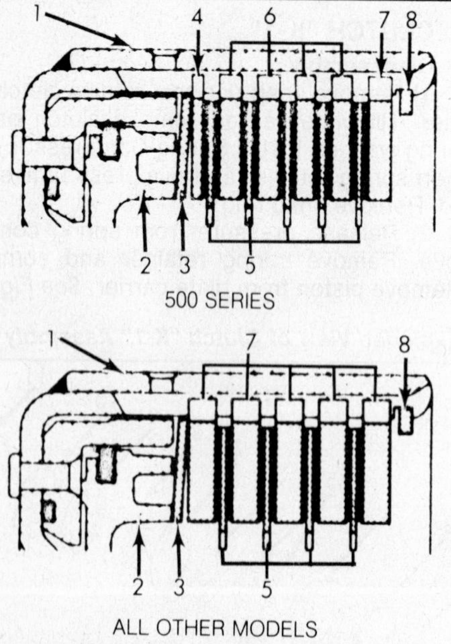

1. Plate Carrier
2. Clutch Piston
3. Spring Washer
4. 2.0 mm Thick Outer Clutch Plate
5. 2.1 mm Thick Inner Clutch Plate
6. 3.0 mm or 3.5 mm Thick Outer Clutch Plates
7. 4.5 mm or 5.0 mm Thick Outer Clutch Plate(s)
8. Snap Ring
   - 2.0 mm Thick
   - 2.5 mm Thick
   - 3.0 mm Thick

CLUTCH "K-2"

Disassembly

1) Remove snap ring that retains clutch pack in plate carrier. Tilt plate carrier and remove clutch pack. Install Spring Compressor (126 589 00 43 00) on spring retainer and compress until snap ring is exposed.

2) Remove snap ring. Release pressure from spring compressor and remove. Remove spring retainer and compression springs. Remove piston from plate carrier.

Reassembly

1) Install new sealing rings on piston so lip of sealing rings point downward (away from piston flange). Place Installation Sleeve (126 589 02 14 00) on center hub of plate carrier.

2) Lubricate installation sleeve and clutch piston sealing rings with ATF. Carefully place clutch piston over installation sleeve and slide piston onto plate carrier, being careful not to tilt piston in carrier. Remove sleeve.

3) Install compression springs in clutch piston. Install spring retainer so that each spring is centered by a guide pin. Install spring compressor on spring retainer. Compress spring retainer and install snap ring. Make sure that snap ring is fully seated in groove.

4) Remove spring compressor. Soak inner clutch plates in ATF for at least one hour. Install clutch plates in plate carrier. *See Fig. 19.* Install snap ring, making sure that it is fully seated in groove.

5) With a screwdriver on top outer plate, force snap ring upward along entire circumference of plate carrier. Using a feeler gauge, check clutch pack end play between top outer plate and snap ring.

6) End play should be .028-.047" (.7-1.2 mm). If necessary, adjust end play by changing snap ring. *See Fig. 19.* If correct clearance cannot be obtained by changing snap ring, change thickness of outer clutch plate(s).

Fig. 19: Installing "K-2" Clutch Pack Assembly

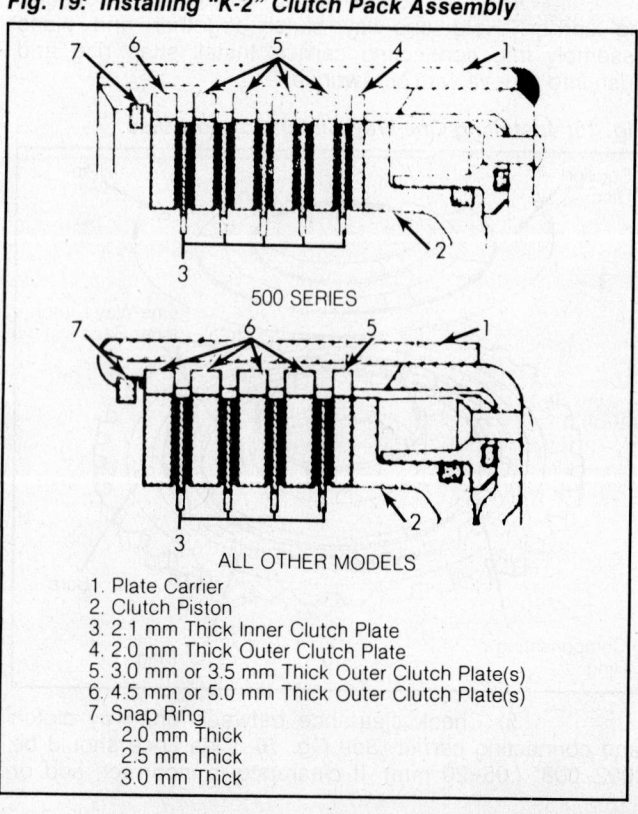

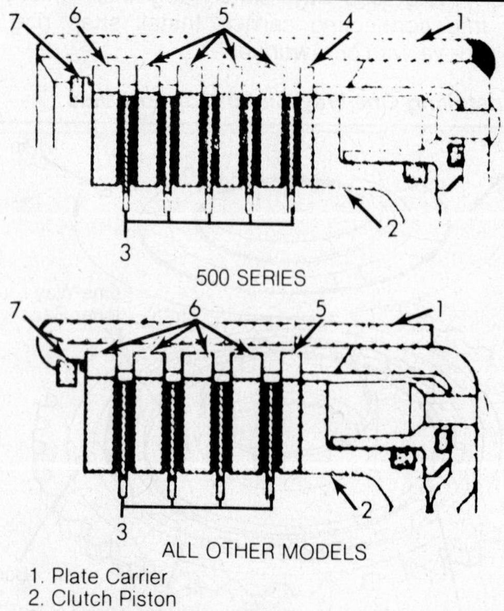

1. Plate Carrier
2. Clutch Piston
3. 2.1 mm Thick Inner Clutch Plate
4. 2.0 mm Thick Outer Clutch Plate
5. 3.0 mm or 3.5 mm Thick Outer Clutch Plate(s)
6. 4.5 mm or 5.0 mm Thick Outer Clutch Plate(s)
7. Snap Ring
   - 2.0 mm Thick
   - 2.5 mm Thick
   - 3.0 mm Thick

MERCEDES-BENZ W4A040 (Cont.)

TRANSMISSION REASSEMBLY

1) Place transmission case in holding fixture. Install guide ring and sealing ring in transmission housing. Sealing lip should face direction of brake band piston cover. Install "O" ring and radial sealing ring into selector lever shaft bores.

2) Install plug with a new aluminum sealing ring. Install "O" ring in support flange bore of transmission case. Install Teflon seals on clutch "K-2" support flange. Install band "B-2" thrust body and plate in upward direction. Install support flange and tighten attaching bolts.

3) Install clutch "K-2" thrust washer so plate for torsion lock is fixed in housing. Compress band "B-2" on supporting lugs as much as possible and install in transmission case. Install clutch "K-2" on planetary gear set. While rotating input shaft, install planetary gear set assembly into case.

4) Place transmission in a vertical position so input shaft points upward. Check that planetary gear set is properly installed. Planetary gear set is properly installed when upper edge of connecting carrier is lower than supporting surface of disc outside plate.

5) Mount front cover on primary pump. Install brake "B-3" clutch plates. Place Parallel Bar (126 589 04 31 00) on machined surface of transmission case. Place top of depth gauge on bar and tip of depth gauge on compensating washer. *See Fig. 20*. Measure and record distance.

6) Place parallel bar on top of brake "B-3" piston. Place top of depth gauge on parallel bar and tip of depth gauge on piston gasket. *See Fig. 21*. Measure and record distance.

7) Difference between clutch pack depth measurement and piston height measurement is brake "B-3" release clearance. Clearance should be .059-.079" (1.5-2.0 mm). Adjust clearance by changing compensating washer and plates of different thicknesses.

Fig. 20: Measuring Brake "B-3" Clutch Pack Depth

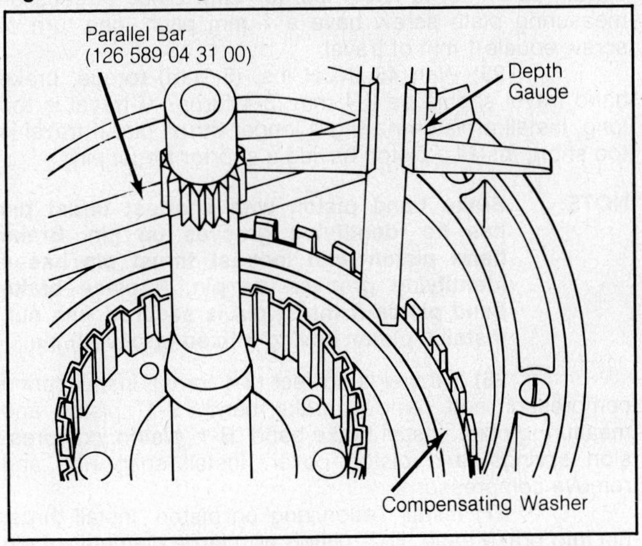

Measurement is taken in case.

8) Install axial bearing into planetary gear carrier. Pack groove in input shaft with grease and install grease pressure ring. Connect assembly lock to band "B-1". Rotate clutch "K-1" to allow teeth to mesh. Install band "B-1" so pin of assembly lock is facing toward band "B-1" thrust body.

9) Install axial bearing. Install pin and "O" rings into "B-1" thrust body. Install thrust body and its plug in transmission case. Install brake band guide in transmission case bore. Make sure that locating lugs engage in housing.

10) Install gasket on front cover. Place Parallel Bar (126 589 04 31 00) on clutch "K-1" flange. Place top of depth gauge on bar and tip of depth gauge on front cover gasket. *See Fig. 22*. Measure and record distance.

11) Place parallel bar on machined surface of transmission case. Place top of depth gauge on bar and tip of depth gauge on a roller of axial bearing. *See Fig. 23*. Measure and record distance.

12) Difference between flange height measurement and axial bearing depth measurement is clutch "K-1" end clearance. Clearance should be .031" (.8 mm). Adjust clearance by inserting compensating washers under axial bearing washer.

Fig. 21: Measuring Brake "B-3" Piston Height

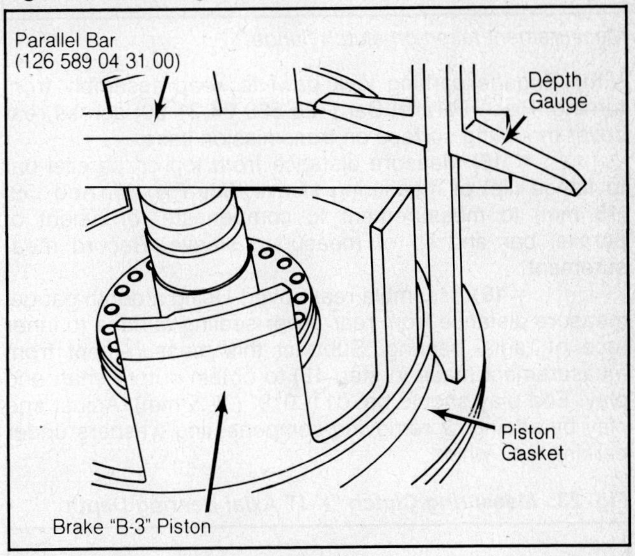

Measurement is taken on piston.

13) Check Teflon rings on front cover and on input shaft for proper installation. Install front cover, with gasket, on transmission case. Install and tighten front cover bolts. Position transmission case so output shaft is pointing upward. Install snap ring into groove on output shaft.

14) Install helical gear on output shaft. Install governor axial holder. Install "O" ring in governor bore and install governor. Swivel axial holder toward governor so it will enter groove of governor shaft. Install governor cover and retaining ring. Pull cover out so it rests on retaining ring.

15) Install intermediate plate and "O" ring. Install secondary pump and pump attaching bolts. Check that governor axial holder is properly seated. Install governor axial holder nut. Install oil pipe and attaching bolt. Install detent plate and shaft. Install detent plate attaching bolt.

16) Connect linkage to detent plate and install snap ring. Mount roller on linkage. Install plastic guide over roller. Install compensating washers on helical gear. Mount parking lock pawl, insert expanding spring, and attach spring to pawl. Install parking lock wheel.

17) Install Measuring Sleeve (126 589 06 14 00) over output shaft and tighten slot nut to 74 ft. lbs. (100

MERCEDES-BENZ W4A040 (Cont.)

Fig. 22: Measuring Clutch "K-1" Flange Height

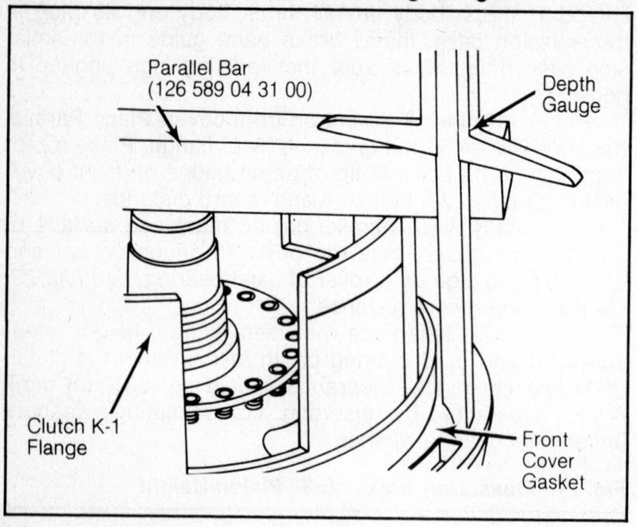

Measurement taken on clutch flange.

N.m). Engage parking lock pawl to keep assembly from turning. Place Parallel Bar (126 589 04 31 00) across rear cover mounting surface on transmission case.

18) Measure distance from top on parallel bar to flange (lip) of measuring sleeve. *See Fig. 24*. Add .59" (15 mm) to measurement to compensate for height of parallel bar and lip of measuring sleeve. Record measurement.

19) Assemble rear cover. Using a depth gauge, measure distance from rear cover sealing surface to inner race of radial bearing. Subtract this measurement from measurement made in step **18)** to obtain output shaft end play. End play should be .011-.019" (.3-.5 mm). Adjust end play by adding or removing compensating washers under parking lock wheel.

Fig. 23: Measuring Clutch "K-1" Axial Bearing Depth

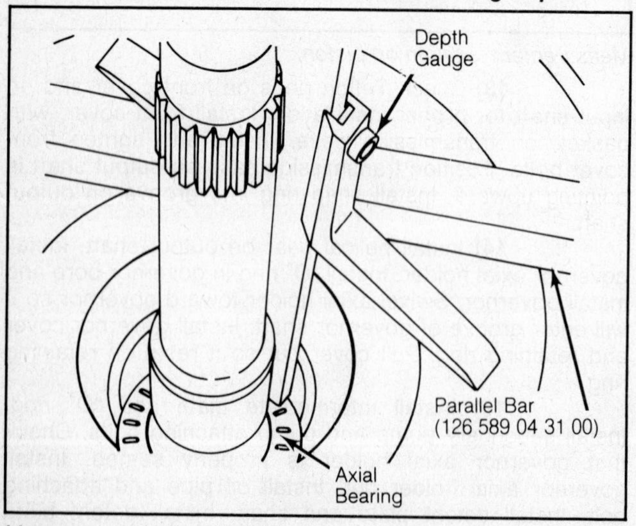

Measurement taken in transmission case.

20) Install rear cover and attaching bolts. Install washer for 3-arm flange on output shaft. Insert "O" ring into 3-arm flange. Slide 3-arm flange onto output shaft and install slot nut. Stake collar of slot nut into groove in output shaft.

21) Install kickdown solenoid valve. Install modulating pressure control valve and thrust pin. Install vacuum control unit and retaining plate. Install starter lock-out switch, but do not tighten screws. Install range selector lever.

22) Install and tighten range selector lever retaining bolt and nut. Move range selector lever into Neutral and insert a .16" (4 mm) pin through range selector lever and into bore of starter lock-out switch. Tighten starter lock-out switch screws. Remove pin.

23) Install sealing ring on brake band "B-1" piston, with lip away from pin. Using Spring Compressor (126 589 00 59 00), install brake band "B-1" piston with compression springs and Measuring Plate (126 589 06 21 00). Install snap ring and remove compressor. Turn measuring plate screw by hand until resistance is felt.

Fig. 24: Measuring Output Shaft End Play

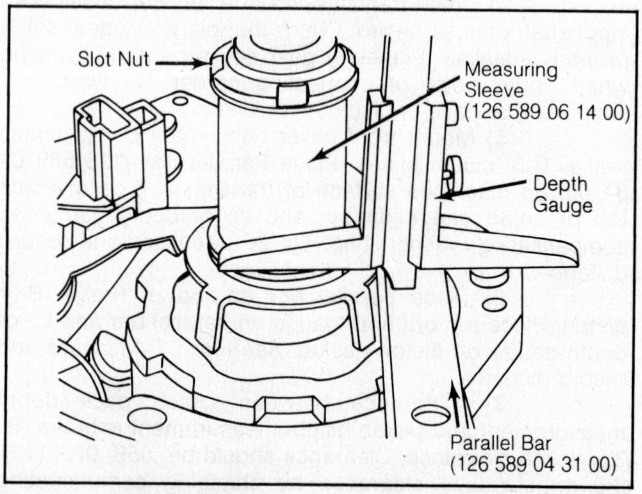

24) Turn measuring plate screw with INCH lb. torque wrench and count number of turns required to tighten screw to 45 INCH lbs. (5 N.m). Since threads on measuring plate screw have a 1 mm pitch, one turn of screw equals 1 mm of travel.

25) With 45 INCH lbs. (5 N.m) torque, brake band travel should be 3-4 mm (3-4 turns). If travel is too long, install a piston having a longer thrust pin. If travel is too short, install a piston having a shorter thrust pin.

NOTE: **Brake band piston with shortest thrust pin has no identifying grooves on pin. Brake band piston with longest thrust pin has 4 identifying grooves on pin. Replace brake band piston if thrust pin is secured with nut. Install a piston having a fixed (grooved) pin.**

26) If travel is correct (3-4 turns), install spring compressor and remove brake band "B-1" piston and measuring plate. Install brake band "B-1" piston, compression springs, and piston cover. Install snap ring and remove compressor.

27) Install Teflon ring on piston. Install thrust pin into brake band "B-2" piston with large diameter of pin toward brake band "B-2". Install piston in transmission making sure that thrust pin enters brake band.

28) Install piston cover and snap ring. Push brake band support lug (above thrust pin) in direction of brake band piston until piston rests against piston cover.

MERCEDES-BENZ W4A040 (Cont.)

Measure and record distance between support lug and brake band end. See Fig. 25.

Fig. 25: Measuring Brake Band "B-2" Free Play

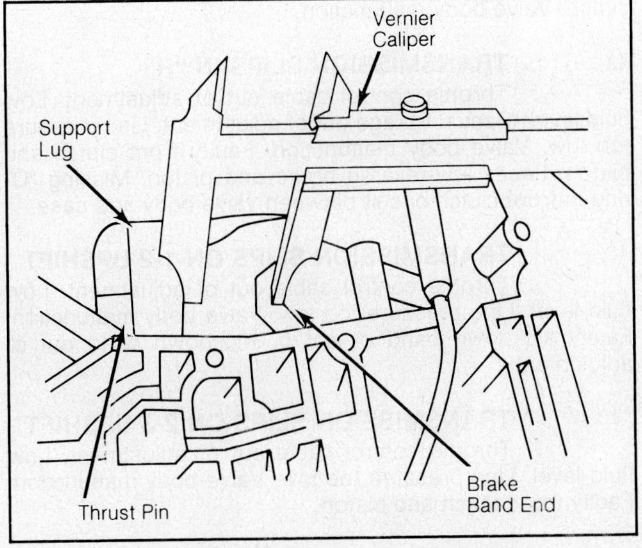

29) Push brake band support lug toward thrust body (away from thrust pin). Measure and record distance between support lug and brake band end. Difference between measurements should be .24-.28" (6-7 mm). Adjust clearance by changing thrust pin. Thrust pin is available in 4 lenghts.

30) Install one-way valve and guide for brake band "B-2". Install filler (if equipped). Connect control pressure cable to connecting rod. Push plastic sleeve of control pressure cable into transmission case.

31) Install lower cover making sure that oil pipe enters bore in transmission case. Install intermediate plate on transmission case. Install and tighten plate attaching bolts. Install leaf spring with holder and attaching bolt.

32) Check clearance between detent piston and stop on shift linkage with selector lever in Neutral. Adjust clearance by means of plastic clip to .0016-.040" (.4-1.0 mm). Plastic clip is available in 3 different thicknesses.

33) Install valve body making sure that range selector valve engages detent plate. Install and tighten valve body attaching bolts. Install oil filter and attaching bolts. Install oil pan with new gasket.

TIGHTENING SPECIFICATIONS

Application	Ft. Lbs. (N.m)
Converter Drain Plug	10 (14)
Converter-to-Drive Plate	31 (42)
Front Cover-to-Case	10 (14)
Front Cover-to-Primary Pump	15 (21)
Kickdown Solenoid Valve	14 (20)
Propeller Shaft Clamping Nut	22 (30)
Rear Cover-to-Case	10 (14)
Transmission-to-Engine	
M10 Bolts	41 (55)
M12 Bolts	48 (65)
Thrust Body Plug	52 (70)
3-Arm Flange Slot Nut	89 (120)
	INCH Lbs. (N.m)
Clutch "K-2" Support Flange-to-Case	96 (11)
Governor Axial Holder Nut	53 (6)
Intermediate Plate Bolts	72 (8)
Lower Cover-to-Case	72 (8)
Oil Filter-to-Valve Body	36 (4)
Oil Pan-to-Case	72 (8)
Range Selector Lever Nut	72 (8)
Starter Lock-Out Switch Screws	72 (8)
Secondary Pump-to-Case	72 (8)
Vacuum Control Unit-to Case	72 (8)
Valve Body-to-Case	72 (8)

Automatic Transmissions

MITSUBISHI KM171, KM172 & KM175

Chrysler Corp. Colt, Colt Vista,
Mitsubishi Cordia, Galant, Mirage, Tredia

DESCRIPTION

Mitsubishi models KM171, KM172 and KM175 automatic transaxle assemblies consist of automatic transmission, torque converter, transfer assembly and differential. The complete transaxle assembly is contained in a single housing.

The automatic transmission consists of a front and rear clutch, kickdown band, low-reverse brake, one-way clutch, valve body and a planetary gear set.

The transfer assembly consists of a drive gear, idler gear, driven gear and a transfer shaft. The differential consists of a differential case, ring gear, pinion shaft and gears, speedometer gear and 2 side gears.

The Colt Vista, Cordia and Tredia models use a lock-up torque converter.

LUBRICATION & ADJUSTMENT

See appropriate AUTOMATIC TRANSMISSION SERVICING article in IMPORT GENERAL SERVICING section.

TROUBLE SHOOTING

NO STARTER OPERATION IN "P" OR "N"

Faulty or misadjusted inhibitor switch. Manual linkage out of adjustment.

NO DRIVE IN "D"

Throttle control cable out of adjustment. Low fluid level. Manual linkage out of adjustment. Line pressure too low. Faulty rear clutch and piston. Faulty overrunning clutch. Valve body malfunction. Defective oil pump.

NO DRIVE IN "R"

Throttle control cable out of adjustment. Low fluid level. Manual linkage out of adjustment. Line pressure too low. Valve body malfunction. Faulty front clutch and piston. Faulty low reverse brake and piston. Missing "O" ring in front clutch circuit between valve and body case. Defective oil pump.

HARSH ENGAGEMENT

From "N" to "D", "2", "L" or "R"

Idle speed too high. Throttle control cable out of adjustment. Line pressure too high.

3-2 Kickdown

Throttle control cable out of adjustment. Low fluid level. Line pressure too low. Valve body malfunction. Kickdown band out of adjustment.

POOR PERFORMANCE OR OVERHEATING IN "D"

Faulty torque converter.

TRANSMISSION SLIPS IN "D"

Throttle control cable out of adjustment. Low fluid level. Manual linkage out of adjustment. Line pressure too low. Faulty rear clutch and piston. Faulty overrunning clutch. Valve body malfunction.

TRANSMISSION SLIPS IN "R"

Throttle control cable out of adjustment. Low fluid level. Manual linkage out of adjustment. Line pressure too low. Valve body malfunction. Faulty front clutch and piston. Faulty low-reverse brake and piston. Missing "O" ring in front clutch circuit between valve body and case.

TRANSMISSION SLIPS ON 1-2 UPSHIFT

Throttle control cable out of adjustment. Low fluid level. Line pressure too low. Valve body malfunction. Faulty kickdown band or servo. Kickdown band out of adjustment.

TRANSMISSION SLIPS ON 2-3 UPSHIFT

Throttle control cable out of adjustment. Low fluid level. Line pressure too low. Valve body malfunction. Faulty front clutch and piston.

TRANSMISSION SLIPS OR SHUDDERS ON STARTS IN "L"

Throttle control cable out of adjustment. Low fluid level. Manual linkage out of adjustment. Valve body malfunction.

NO DOWNSHIFT IN "D" TO "L" SHIFT

Manual shift linkage out of adjustment. Valve body malfunction. Faulty kickdown band or servo. Kickdown band out of adjustment.

NO 1-2 UPSHIFT OR WRONG SPEED 1-2 UPSHIFT

Throttle control cable out of adjustment. Low fluid level. Line pressure too low. Valve body malfunction. Governor valve malfunction. Faulty kickdown band or servo. Kickdown band out of adjustment.

NO 2-3 UPSHIFT OR WRONG SPEED 2-3 UPSHIFT

Throttle control cable out of adjustment. Low fluid level. Line pressure too low. Valve body malfunction. Faulty front clutch or piston. Governor valve malfunction.

UPSHIFT IN "L"

Manual linkage out of adjustment.

"P" WILL NOT ENGAGE

Manual linkage out of adjustment. Faulty parking mechanism.

CONVERTER NOISE

Loose converter bolts or warped flex plate. Defective oil pump. Interference of oil pump gear teeth, and wear of bushing.

Fig. 1: Cross-Sectional View of Mitsubishi KM170 Automatic Transaxle for Colt

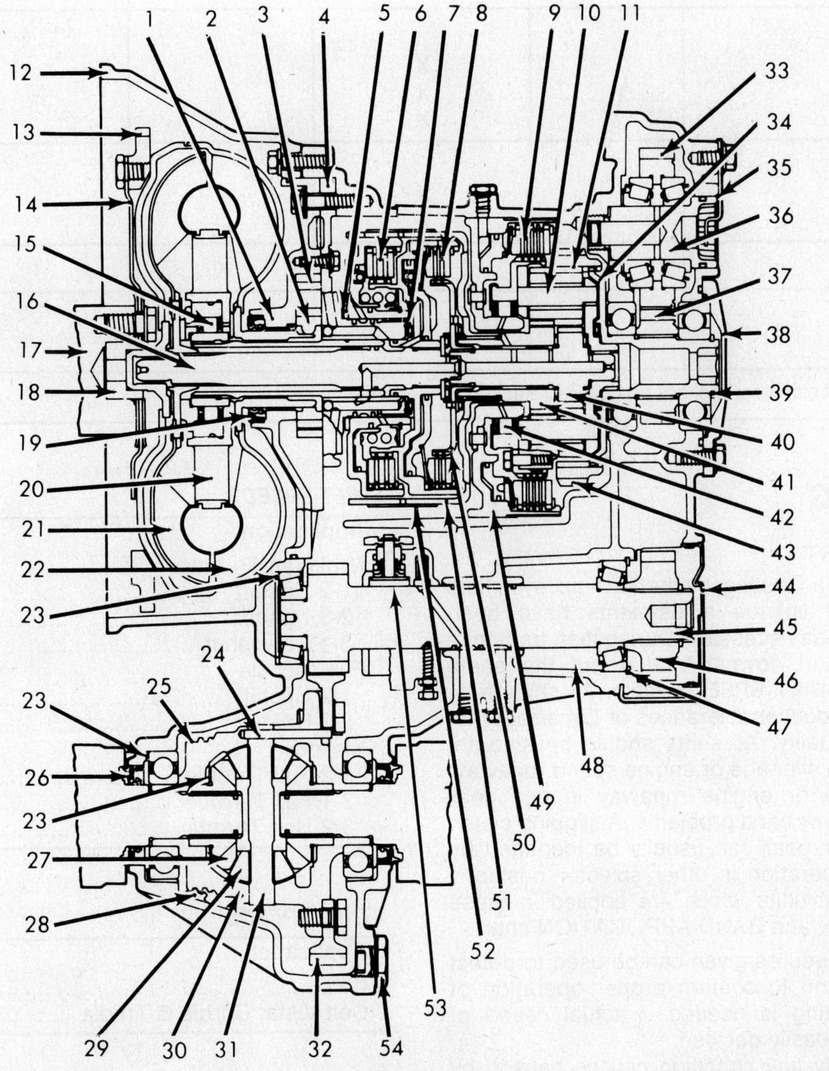

1. Oil Pump Housing
2. Oil Pump Drive Gear
3. Oil Pump Driven Gear
4. Reaction Shaft Support
5. Selective Thrust Washer
6. Front Clutch
7. Selective Thrust Race
8. Rear Clutch
9. Low-Reverse Brake
10. Planetary Gear Set
11. Annulus Gear
12. Converter Housing
13. Starter Ring Gear
14. Flexible Plate
15. One-Way Clutch
16. Input Shaft
17. Crankshaft
18. Bushing
19. Oil Seal
20. Stator
21. Turbine
22. Impeller
23. Selective Spacer
24. Pinion Shaft Lock Pin
25. Speedometer Drive Gear
26. Oil Seal
27. Side Gear
28. Speedometer Driven Gear
29. Pinion Gear
30. Differential Case
31. Pinion Shaft
32. Differential Ring Gear
33. Transfer Idle Gear
34. Output Flange
35. Lock Plate
36. Transfer Idle Shaft
37. Transfer Drive Gear
38. Bearing Retainer
39. Selective Snap Ring
40. Forward Sun Gear
41. Reverse Sun Gear
42. One-Way Clutch
43. Parking Sprag
44. Cover
45. Transfer Shaft
46. Transfer Driven Gear
47. Snap Ring
48. Transaxle Case
49. Center Support
50. Clutch Hub
51. Kickdown Drum
52. Kickdown Band
53. Governor
54. Drain Plug

Mitsubishi MK171 Automatic Transaxle is virtually the same.

MITSUBISHI KM171, KM172 & KM175 (Cont.)

CLUTCH AND BAND APPLICATION CHART (ELEMENTS IN USE)

Selector Lever Position	Forward Clutch	Direct-Reverse Clutch	First-Reverse Brake	Second Gear Band	One-Way Clutch
D - DRIVE					
First Gear		X			X
Second Gear		X		X	X
Third Gear	X	X			
2 - INTERMEDIATE					
First Gear		X			X
Second Gear		X		X	
1 - LOW (First)		X	X		
R - REVERSE	X		X		

NEUTRAL OR PARK – All clutches, brakes, and bands released or ineffective.

TESTING

ROAD TEST

1) Before road testing, be certain fluid level, fluid condition and control linkage adjustments have been checked and corrected as necessary. During test, transmission should upshift and downshift at about the same speeds as shown in SHIFT SPEEDS table. All shifts may vary slightly due to production tolerances or tire size. What is important is shift quality. All shifts should be smooth, responsive and with no slippage or engine speed runaway.

2) Slippage or engine runaway in any gear usually indicates clutch or band problems. A slipping clutch or band in a particular gear can usually be identified by noting transmission operation in other selector positions and comparing internal units which are applied in these positions. See CLUTCH and BAND APPLICATION chart.

3) The procedures given can be used to detect any unit which slips and to confirm proper operation of good units. More testing is needed if actual cause of malfunction cannot be easily decided.

4) Practically any condition can be caused by leaking hydraulic circuits or sticking valves. Unless an obvious condition exists, transmission should never be disassembled until hydraulic pressure tests have been made.

STALL TEST

Testing Precautions

When making stall test, do not hold throttle open any longer than 10 seconds to obtain steady gauge reading. After each stall test, move selector lever to "N" and run engine at 1000 RPM for at least one minute to cool down engine and transmission. If engine speed exceeds limits shown in STALL SPEEDS table, release accelerator immediately as clutch or band slippage is indicated.

Testing Procedure

With engine at normal operating temperature, tachometer installed, and parking and service brakes applied, make transmission stall test in "D" and "R" ranges at full throttle and note maximum RPM obtained. Engine speed should be within limits shown in STALL SPEEDS table.

SHIFT SPEEDS

Application	Shift Points (MPH)
Minimum Throttle	
1-2 Upshift	7-12
2-3 Upshift	11-16
3-1 Downshift	5-9
Full Throttle	
1-2 Upshift	30-37
2-3 Upshift	58-64
Kickdown	
3-2 Full Throttle	52-58
3-1 Full Throttle	24-29
3-2 Half Throttle	32-40

STALL SPEEDS

Application	Stall RPM
Colt	1650-2050
Colt Vista, Cordia & Tredia	2000-2400

Stall Speed Too High

In all ranges: general transmission problems are indicated and a control pressure test should be made to locate faulty unit(s). In "D"; Stator overrunning clutch is defective, rear clutch is slipping, line pressure is low or overrunning clutch in planetary gear is defective. In "R"; front clutch or low-reverse brake is slipping, line pressure is low or stator overrunnning clutch is defective.

Stall Speed Too Low

Torque converter is faulty, engine output is not sufficient.

NOTE: **Ensure engine performance is satisfactory before condemning converter. Converter cannot be overhauled and must be replaced if defective.**

HYDRAULIC PRESSURE TESTS

NOTE: Ensure transmission fluid level is correct, control cable is adjusted and transmission is at normal operating temperature. Connect a tachometer, disconnect throttle control cable from carburetor and raise vehicle on a hoist so front wheels are off ground.

Line Pressures

1) Connect oil pressure gauge(s) to line pressure port, low-reverse brake pressure port, front clutch pressure port, and "tee" to transmission "To Cooler" line. *See Fig. 2.*

2) Place manual control lever to "L" position (all the way rearward). Take pressure reading at idle, half throttle then with full throttle (engine speed should be at stall speed). Also note low-reverse brake pressure.

3) Place control lever to "2" position (one detent forward). Note pressures at idle, half and full throttle. Also note lubrication (from "To Cooler" line) pressure.

4) Place control lever in "D" position (2 detents forward). Note pressures at idle, half and full throttle.

5) Place control lever in "R" position (4 detents forward). With pressure gauge attached to low-reverse pressure port, note pressures at idle, half and full throttle.

Line Pressure Test Results

1) If line pressure is correct in any test, pump and pressure regulator are working properly. See HYDRAULIC PRESSURE SPECIFICATIONS table.

HYDRAULIC PRESSURE SPECIFICATIONS

Application	psi (kg/cm²)
Line Pressure in All Ranges	
Idle	58-67 (4.1-4.7)
Half Throttle	96 (6.7)
Full Throttle [1]	98-100 (6.9-7.0)
Low-Reverse Brake Pressure	
In "L"	24-33 (1.7-2.3)
In "R"	199-284 (14.0-20.0)
Lubrication Pressure	
In "2"	7-21 (.5-1.5)

[1] – Pressure should increase as cable is moved from idle to full throttle. Full throttle should be at stall speed specification.

2) A low pressure reading in "L", "2" and "D" but correct pressure in "R" indicates rear clutch circuit leakage.

3) A low pressure reading in "D" and "R" but correct pressure in "L" indicates front clutch circuit leakage.

4) A low pressure reading in "L" and "R" but correct pressure in "2" indicates low-reverse brake circuit leakage.

5) Low pressure readings in all positions indicates a defective pump, clogged filter or a stuck pressure regulator valve.

Governor Pressure Test

1) Make this test only if vehicle shifts at wrong speeds with throttle cable properly adjusted. Connect pressure gauge to governor pressure port. *See Fig. 2.*

2) Place manual control lever in "D" position and increase vehicle speed and note pressures at which transmission shifts. Transmission should shift at indicated speeds and governor pressure should be as indicated in GOVERNOR PRESSURE table. If not, governor valve is sticking, or filter in governor body is clogged.

Fig. 2: Pressure Test Hookup Locations

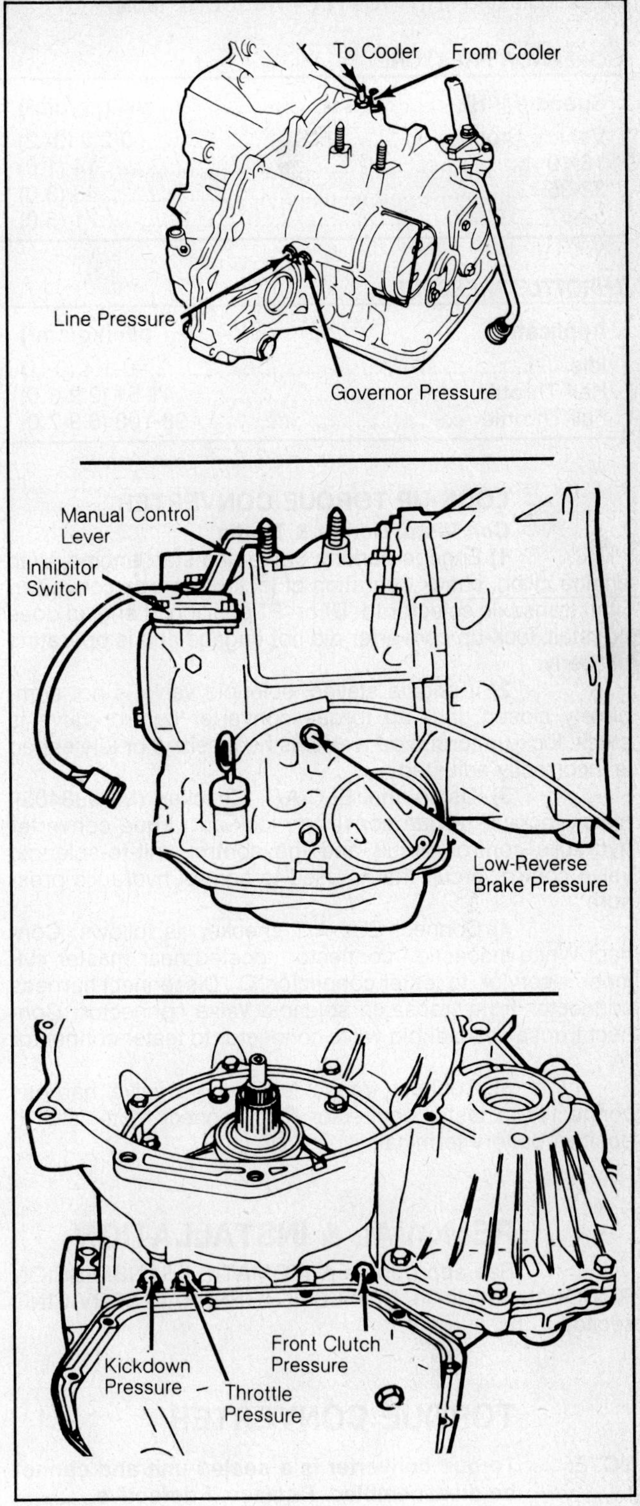

Throttle Pressure Test

Connect pressure gauge to throttle pressure port. *See Fig. 2.* Note pressure readings at idle, half throttle and at full throttle (stall speed). Pressure readings should be as indicated in THROTTLE PRESSURE table.

GOVERNOR PRESSURE

Speed (MPH)	psi (kg/cm²)
Vehicle Stopped	0-2.8 (0-.2)
16-19	14 (1.0)
32-35	43 (3.0)
53-57	71 (5.0)

THROTTLE PRESSURE

Application	psi (kg/cm²)
Idle	0-1.4 (0-.1)
Half Throttle	41-51 (2.9-3.6)
Full Throttle	98-100 (6.9-7.0)

LOCK-UP TORQUE CONVERTER

Colt Vista, Cordia & Tredia

1) Engage parking brake and start engine. With engine idling, check operation of lock-up torque converter. Shift transaxle selector to "D" or "R" position. If engine does not stall, lock-up converter did not engage and is operating properly.

2) If engine stalled, solenoid valve is not completely closed, lock-up torque converter control valve is stuck, lock-up torque converter is heat seized or idle speed is incorrectly adjusted.

3) Using the ELC-A/T Checker (MD998405), check lock-up torque converter, lock-up torque converter hydraulic control circuit and the control unit-to-solenoid valve control circuit that is used to control hydraulic pressure.

4) Connect ELC-A/T checker as follows: Connect White inspection connector, located near master cylinder reservior, to tester connector "C". Disconnect harness connector from transaxle solenoid valve connector. Connect transaxle solenoid valve connector to tester connector "A".

5) Connect transaxle solenoid valve harness connector to tester connector "B". Connect tester clip to positive battery terminal.

REMOVAL & INSTALLATION

See appropriate AUTOMATIC TRANSMISSION REMOVAL article in DOMESTIC GENERAL SERVICING section.

TORQUE CONVERTER

NOTE: **Torque converter is a sealed unit and cannot be disassembled. Replace if defective.**

TRANSAXLE DISASSEMBLY

1) Remove torque converter, speedometer pinion adapter, manual control lever and inhibitor switch. Attach dial indicator to measure input shaft end play. Record end play measurement.

2) Remove oil pan and filter. Disconnect throttle cable. Remove valve body, being careful that manual shift valve does not fall out of valve body.

NOTE: **Low-reverse brake clutch "O" ring is attached to valve body with petroleum jelly. Be careful not to misposition seal when removing or installing valve body.**

3) Remove throttle cable, accumulator and spring, being careful not to damage cable or retainer end.

4) Remove transfer shaft cover then attach dial indicator to measure transfer shaft end play. Record measurement. Rotate transaxle assembly so converter housing is up and remove converter housing.

5) Remove oil pump bolts and install Pump Remover (MD998333) into pump removing holes (located in pump housing). Pump may tilt up (side "B") when removing. If so, tap on pump side "A" with a soft mallet. *See Fig. 3.*

Fig. 3: Removing Oil Pump from Transaxle Housing

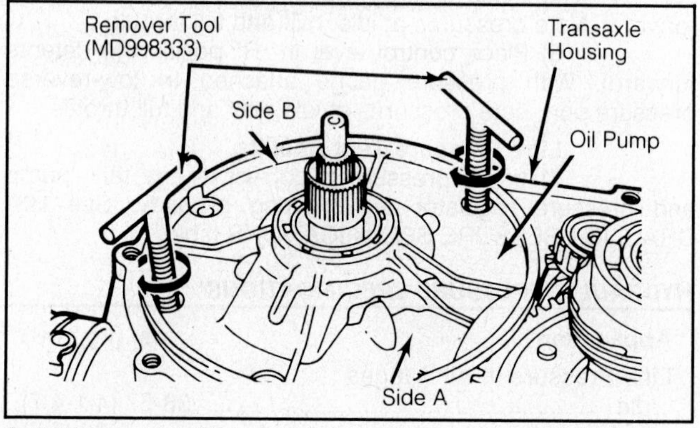

Pull pump straight up.

6) Remove differential assembly, then remove fiber thrust washer from front clutch assembly. Remove front clutch assembly and remove fiber thrust washer, 2 metal thrust races and one needle bearing. Remove rear clutch assembly, thrust washer and needle bearing. Remove clutch hub, 2 thrust washers and needle bearing. Remove kickdown drum and band.

7) Check height of planetary gear set. Long pinion should be same height as reverse sun gear. Remove center support bolts, then center support. *See Fig. 5.* Remove reverse sun gear and forward sun gear as an assembly. Remove planetary carrier assembly, thrust bearing and race.

8) Rotate transaxle assembly. Remove idler shaft lock plate, idler shaft and idler gear. Remove 2 bearing inner races and spacer from inside transaxle case.

NOTE: **For reassembly reference, note that machined groove in gear faces away from torque converter.**

9) Remove bearing cover and outer snap ring. Remove annulus gear bearing snap ring, then remove annulus gear, output flange, transfer drive gear and bearing as an assembly.

10) Remove transfer rear end snap ring. Use a brass drift to drive transfer shaft out toward engine mounting surface. Remove snap ring from transaxle case, then remove bearing inner and outer races.

Fig. 4: Lock-Up Torque Converter WIRING DIAGRAM

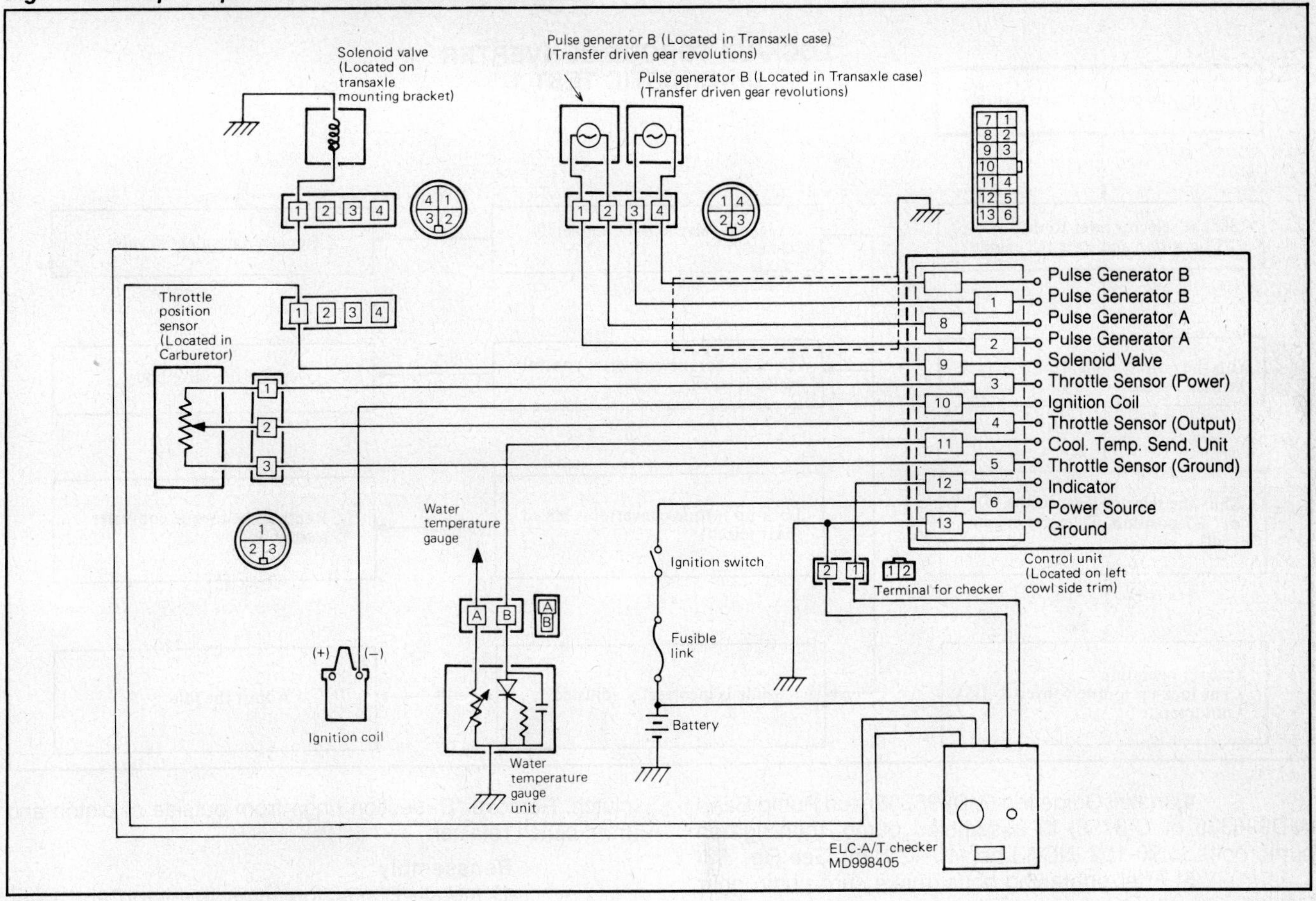

Fig. 5: Center Support Bolt Location

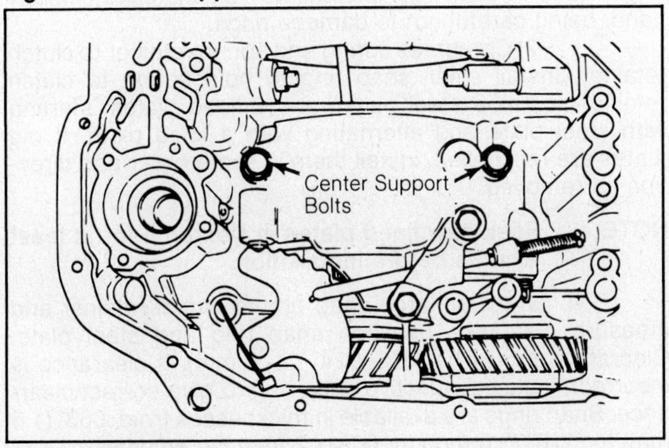

Bolt head has mark "8" on top.

COMPONENT DISASSEMBLY & REASSEMBLY

OIL PUMP

Disassembly

1) Remove bolts to separate pump housing from reaction shaft support. If pump gears are to be reused, mark gears with felt pen so they can be reinstalled in original positions.

2) Remove drive and driven gears from pump housing. Remove steel ball from pump housing. Remove 2 steel rings from reaction shaft support. Pry out pump housing oil seal.

Reassembly

1) Apply Dexron II to oil seal and install oil seal to pump housing. Lubricate pump gears with Dexron II, then install gears to pump housing. If original gears are being reinstalled, install them in original positions using marks made during disassembly.

2) Make the following measurements of pump gears to pump housing: driven gear-to-pump housing clearance, driven gear-to-crescent clearance, driven gear side clearance, drive gear-to-crescent clearance and drive gear side clearance. If clearances are incorrect, replace components as necessary.

OIL PUMP CLEARANCES

Application	In. (mm)
Driven Gear-to-Housing	.003-.006 (.08-.15)
Driven Gear-to-Crescent	.004-.009 (.11-.24)
Driven Gear Side Clearance	.001-.002 (.025-.05)
Drive Gear-to-Crescent	.009-.013 (.24-.34)
Drive Gear Side Clearance	.001-.002 (.025-.05)

3) Install steel ball in pump housing, then install 2 seal rings (coated with Dexron II) to reaction shaft support. Place reaction shaft support to pump housing, then tighten bolts finger tight.

MITSUBISHI KM171, KM172 & KM175 (Cont.)

Fig. 6: Lock-Up Torque Converter Diagnostic Test 1

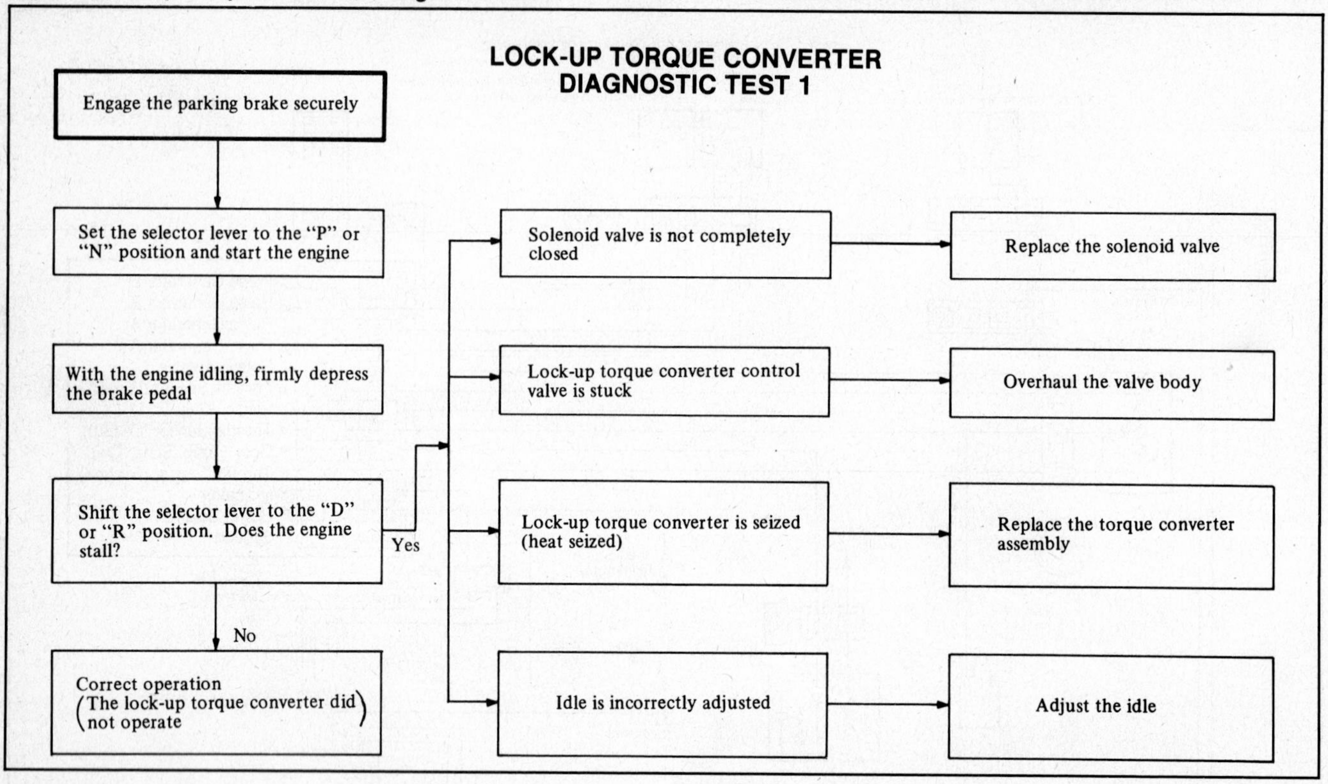

4) Install Guide Pin (MD998336) and Pump Band (MD998335 or C-3759) to assembled pump, then tighten pump bolts to 90-102 INCH Lbs. (10-12 N.m). *See Fig. 7.*

5) After tightening bolts, make sure pump gear turns freely. If not, disassemble and recheck reassembly procedures and clearances. Install a new large "O" ring to outside circumference of pump and lubricate "O" ring with petroleum jelly.

Fig. 7: Assembling Oil Pump

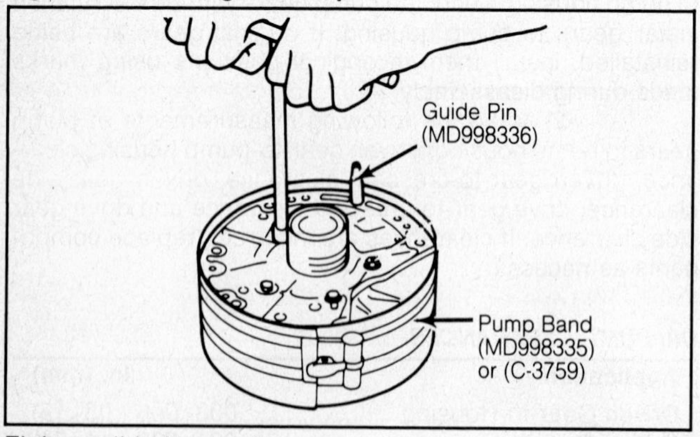

Tighten all bolts evenly.

FRONT CLUTCH

Disassembly

1) Remove snap ring, then remove 3 steel plates and 2 lined plates. If plates are to be reused, keep them in same order and direction (as removed) for reassembly. *See Fig. 12.*

2) Compress return spring, remove snap ring, spring retainer and return spring. Remove piston from front clutch. Remove "D" section rings from outside of piston and front clutch retainer.

Reassembly

1) Install "D" section rings to piston and front clutch retainer (round side of ring facing out), then lubricate rings with Dexron II. Push piston into front clutch retainer by hand, being careful not to damage rings.

2) Compress spring and spring retainer to clutch retainer. Install small snap ring to hold spring to clutch retainer. Install 3 steel plates and 2 lined plates, starting with steel plate and alternating with a lined plate. If old plates are reinstalled, install them in same order and direction as removed.

NOTE: **Soak new lined plates in Dexron II for at least 2 hours before installation.**

3) Install large snap ring to clutch retainer and measure clearance between snap ring and steel plate. Clearance should be .016-.024" (.4-.6 mm). If clearance is incorrect, install a selective snap ring to give correct clearance. Snap rings are available in thicknesses from .063" (1.6 mm) to .118" (3.0 mm) in .008" (.2 mm) increments.

REAR CLUTCH

Disassembly

1) Remove large snap ring, reaction plate, 2 lined plates, clutch plate and pressure plate from rear clutch retainer. If plates are to be reused, keep them in same order and direction (as removed) for reassembly.

2) Remove seal ring, small snap ring and thrust race. Use a press to compress piston, then remove waved snap ring. Release pressure from press and remove waved snap ring, return spring and piston. Remove 2 "D" section rings from piston.

MITSUBISHI KM171, KM172 & KM175 (Cont.)

Fig. 8: Lock-Up Torque Converter Diagnostic Test 2

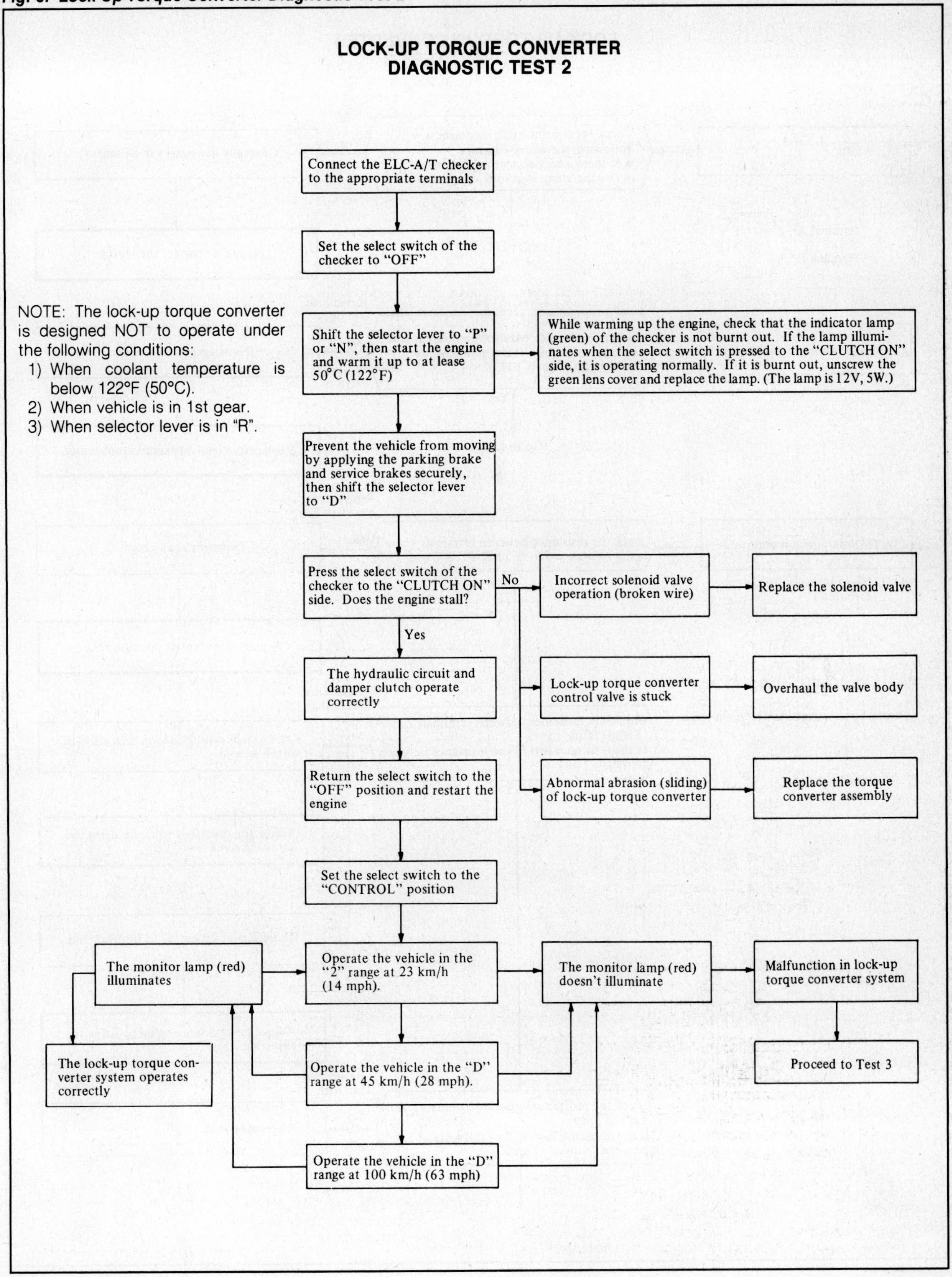

MITSUBISHI KM171, KM172 & KM175 (Cont.)

Fig. 9: Lock-Up Torque Converter Diagnostic Test 3

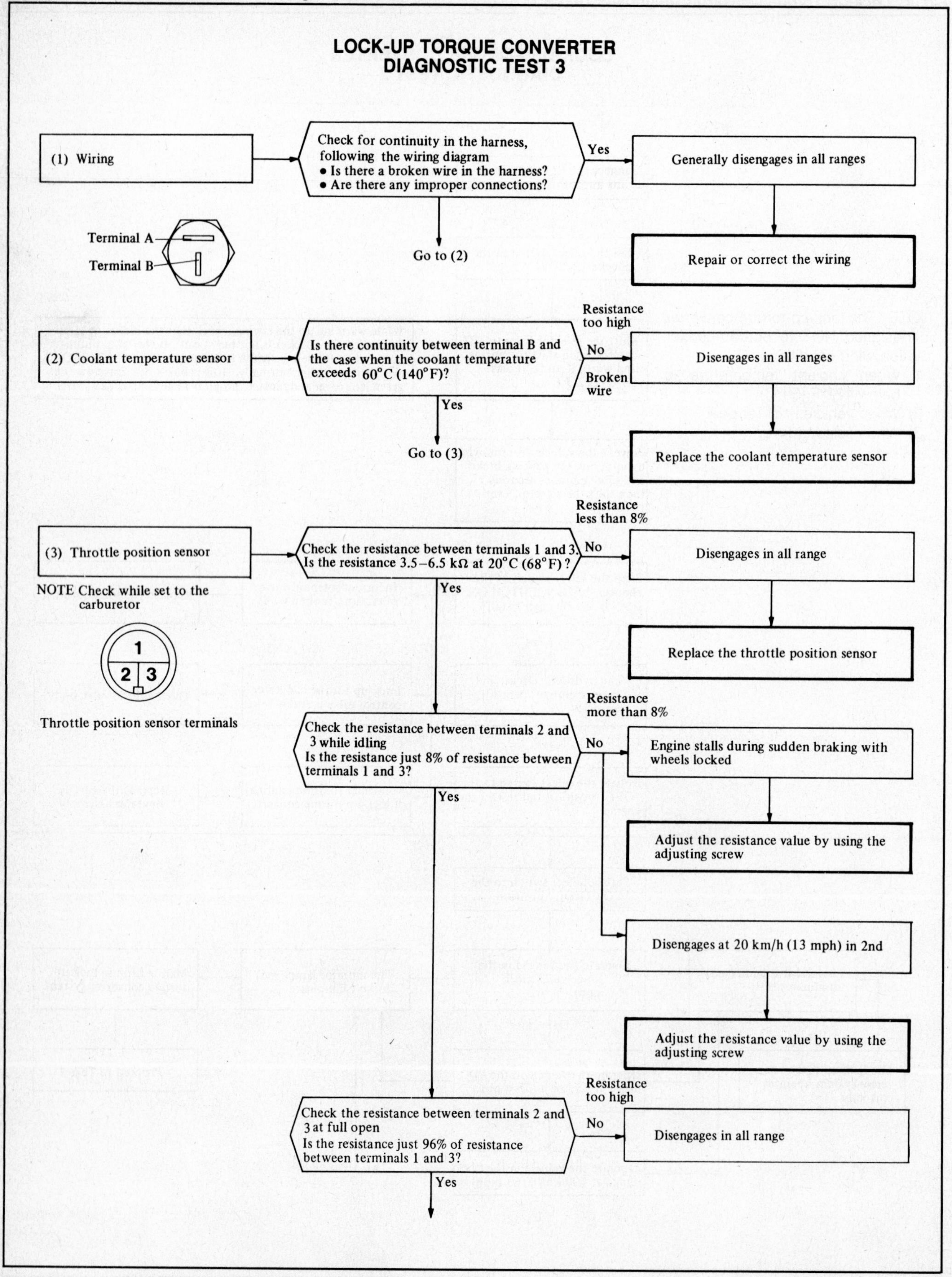

MITSUBISHI KM171, KM172 & KM175 (Cont.)

Fig. 10: Lock-Up Torque Converter Diagnostic Test 3 (Cont.)

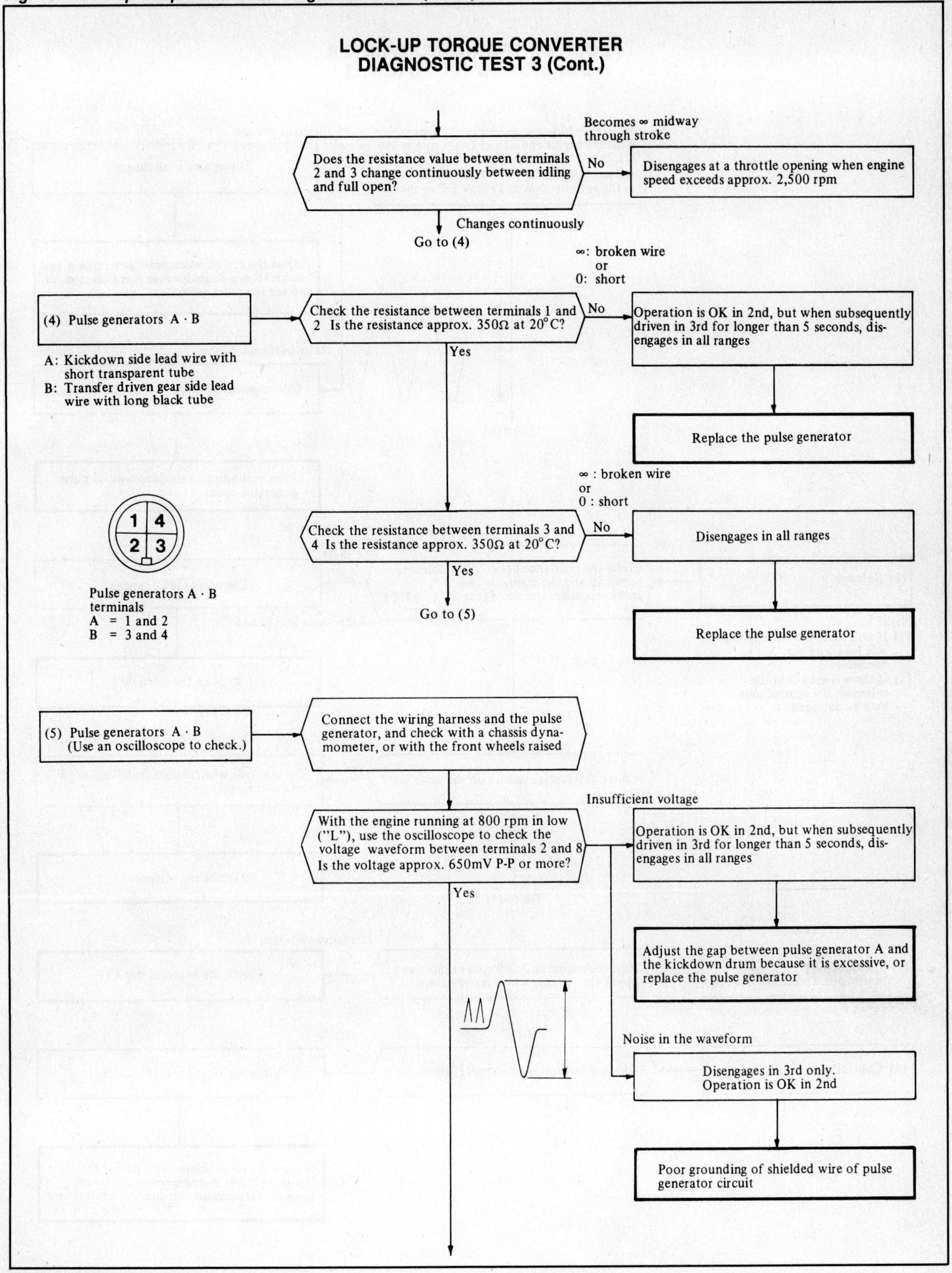

LOCK-UP TORQUE CONVERTER
DIAGNOSTIC TEST 3 (Cont.)
Does the resistance value between terminals 2 and 3 change continuously between idling and full open?
Becomes ∞ midway through stroke
No
Disengages at a throttle opening when engine speed exceeds approx. 2,500 rpm
Changes continuously
Go to (4)
(4) Pulse generators A · B
A: Kickdown side lead wire with short transparent tube
B: Transfer driven gear side lead wire with long black tube
Check the resistance between terminals 1 and 2 Is the resistance approx. 350Ω at 20°C?
∞: broken wire
or
0: short
No
Operation is OK in 2nd, but when subsequently driven in 3rd for longer than 5 seconds, disengages in all ranges
Replace the pulse generator
Yes
1 4
2 3
Pulse generators A · B terminals
A = 1 and 2
B = 3 and 4
Check the resistance between terminals 3 and 4 Is the resistance approx. 350Ω at 20°C?
∞ : broken wire
or
0 : short
No
Disengages in all ranges
Replace the pulse generator
Yes
Go to (5)
(5) Pulse generators A · B (Use an oscilloscope to check.)
Connect the wiring harness and the pulse generator, and check with a chassis dynamometer, or with the front wheels raised
With the engine running at 800 rpm in low ("L"), use the oscilloscope to check the voltage waveform between terminals 2 and 8 Is the voltage approx. 650mV P-P or more?
Insufficient voltage
Operation is OK in 2nd, but when subsequently driven in 3rd for longer than 5 seconds, disengages in all ranges
Adjust the gap between pulse generator A and the kickdown drum because it is excessive, or replace the pulse generator
Yes
Noise in the waveform
Disengages in 3rd only. Operation is OK in 2nd
Poor grounding of shielded wire of pulse generator circuit

Automatic Transmissions

MITSUBISHI KM171, KM172 & KM175 (Cont.)

Fig. 11: Lock-Up Torque Converter Diagnostic Test 3 (Cont.)

LOCK-UP TORQUE CONVERTER DIAGNOSTIC TEST 3 (Cont.)

With the engine running at 1,000 rpm in low ("L"), use the oscilloscope to check the voltage waveform between terminals 1 and 7. Is the voltage approx. 180mV P-P or more?

- Insufficient voltage → Disengages in all ranges → Adjust the gap between pulse generator A and the kickdown drum because it is excessive, or replace the pulse generator
- Noise in the waveform → Disengages in all ranges, or vibration occurs → Poor grounding of shielded wire of pulse generator circuit
- Yes → Go to (6)

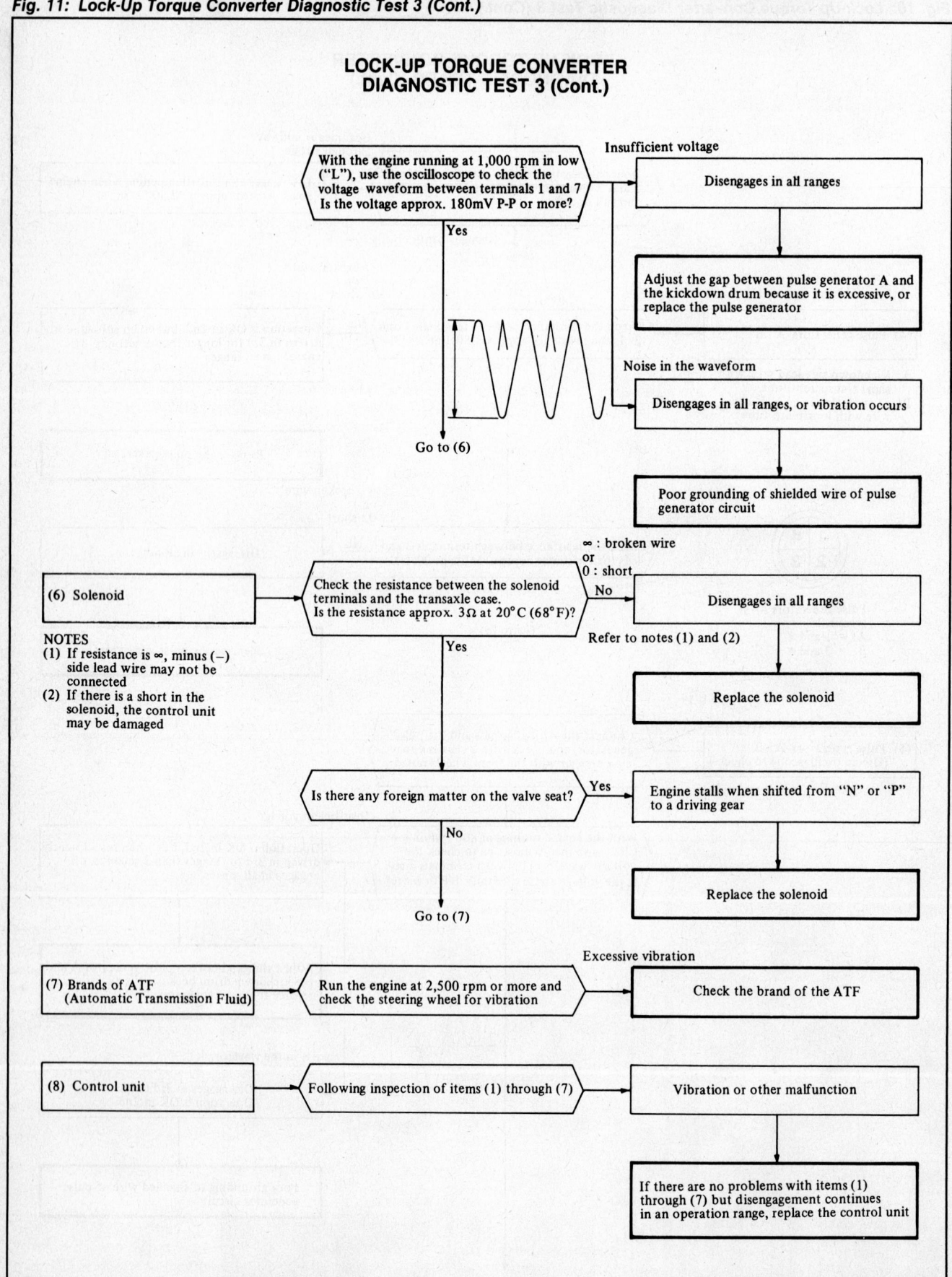

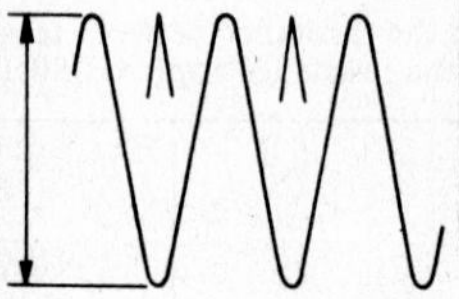

(6) Solenoid → Check the resistance between the solenoid terminals and the transaxle case. Is the resistance approx. 3Ω at 20°C (68°F)?

- No (∞ : broken wire or 0 : short) → Disengages in all ranges → Replace the solenoid. Refer to notes (1) and (2)
- Yes → Is there any foreign matter on the valve seat?
  - Yes → Engine stalls when shifted from "N" or "P" to a driving gear → Replace the solenoid
  - No → Go to (7)

NOTES
(1) If resistance is ∞, minus (–) side lead wire may not be connected
(2) If there is a short in the solenoid, the control unit may be damaged

(7) Brands of ATF (Automatic Transmission Fluid) → Run the engine at 2,500 rpm or more and check the steering wheel for vibration

- Excessive vibration → Check the brand of the ATF

(8) Control unit → Following inspection of items (1) through (7) → Vibration or other malfunction → If there are no problems with items (1) through (7) but disengagement continues in an operation range, replace the control unit

MITSUBISHI KM171, KM172 & KM175 (Cont.)

Fig. 12: Front Clutch Components

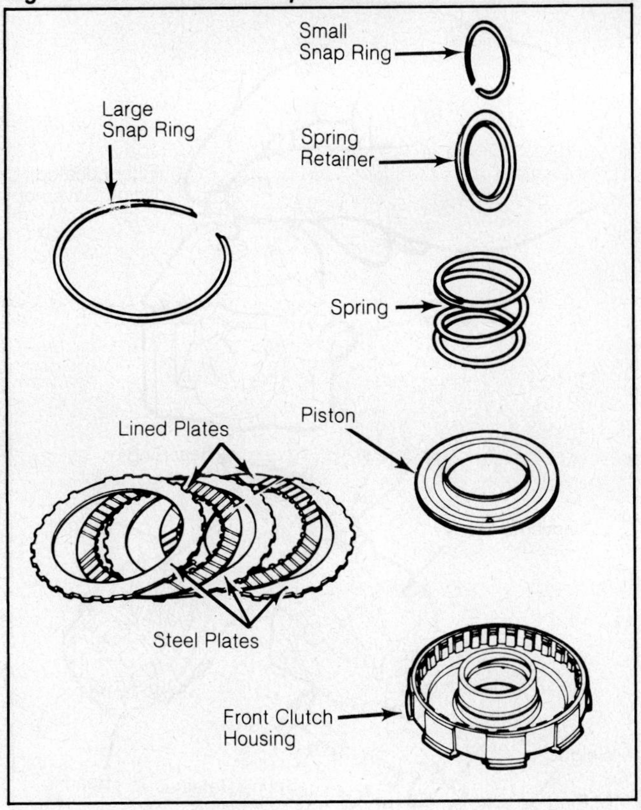

Reassembly

1) Install "D" section rings to piston with round side facing out. Lubricate rings with Dexron II and install piston in rear clutch retainer by hand. Be careful not to damage rings.

2) Install return spring with waved snap ring to clutch retainer. Use a press to compress return spring until waved snap ring seats in groove of clutch retainer. Install pressure plate, lined plate, clutch plate, lined plate and reaction plate. *See Fig. 13.*

Fig. 13: Rear Clutch Components

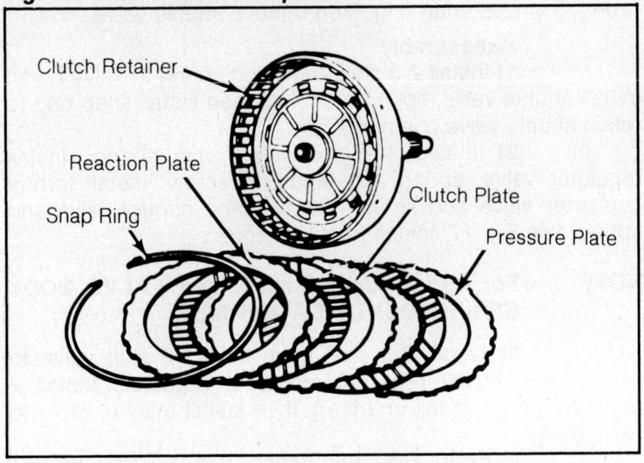

NOTE: Soak new lined plates in Dexron II for at least 2 hours before installation.

3) Install large snap ring to clutch retainer and measure clearance between reaction plate and snap ring. Clearance should be .012-.020" (.3-.5 mm). If clearance is incorrect, selective snap rings are available in thicknesses from .063" (1.6 mm) to .118" (3.0 mm) in .008" (.2 mm) increments. Install thrust race, small snap ring and new seal ring.

LOW-REVERSE BRAKE

Disassembly

1) Remove snap ring. Remove reaction plate, 4 lined plates, 3 steel plates and the pressure plates. If plates are to be reused, keep them in same order and direction (as removed) for reassembly.

2) Compress piston and remove piston snap ring, then remove return spring and waved spring. Remove piston, then remove "D" section rings from piston.

Reassembly

1) Install "D" section rings (round side out) to piston. Lubricate rings with Dexron II and install piston by hand, being careful not to damage rings. Install waved spring and return spring. Compress springs and install snap ring. Install pressure plate, then install plates starting with a lined plate and alternating with steel plates, ending with reaction plate. *See Fig. 14.*

2) Install large snap ring and measure clearance between reaction plate and snap ring. Clearance should be .031-.040" (.8-1.0 mm). If clearance is incorrect, selective snap rings are available from .063" (1.6 mm) to .118" (3.0 mm) in .008" (.2 mm) increments.

Fig. 14: Low-Reverse Brake Components

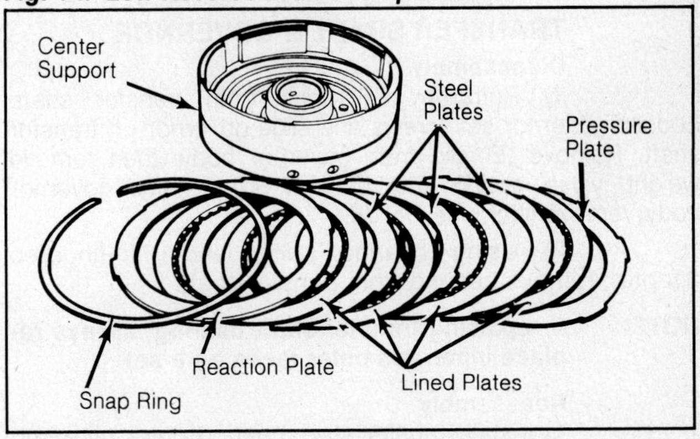

PLANETARY GEAR ASSEMBLY

Disassembly

Straighten tabs of stopper plate and remove stopper plate. Remove bearing end plates and overrunning clutch. Check overrunning clutch sprag, spring and outer race for damage. *See Fig. 15.*

Reassembly

Install end plate to overrunning clutch. Install overrunning clutch to planetary gear assembly with arrow (stamped on outside of overrunning clutch) pointing toward planetary gears. Install end plate, then stopper plate. Bend tabs of stopper plate to secure stopper plate to planetary gear assembly.

ANNULUS GEAR, OUTPUT FLANGE & TRANSFER DRIVE GEAR

Disassembly

Remove snap ring from rear of output flange. Using a bearing puller, remove bearing, transfer drive gear and bearing. Remove snap ring and separate annulus gear from output flange.

MITSUBISHI KM171, KM172 & KM175 (Cont.)

Fig. 15: Planetary Gear & Overrunning Clutch

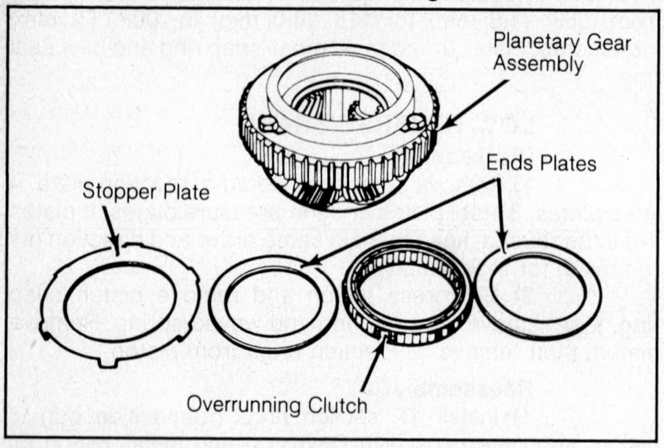

NOTE: Annulus gear and output flange are a matched set. If damaged, replace both.

Reassembly

Install annulus gear to output flange and install snap ring. Using a bearing installer, install bearing, transfer drive gear (grooved side up) and bearing. Select largest size snap ring that will fit in groove and install snap ring. Snap ring-to-bearing clearance should be 0-.002" (0-.06 mm). Snap rings are available from .074" (1.88 mm) to .081" (2.06 mm) in .002" (.06 mm) increments.

TRANSFER SHAFT & GOVERNOR

Disassembly

1) Remove seal rings from transfer shaft. Loosen governor set screws and slide governor off transfer shaft. Remove "E" clip from governor body, then remove weight, valve, spring and retainer. From inside governor body, remove filter. *See Fig. 16.*

2) Using bearing puller and thin-fingered adapter, remove bearing from transfer shaft.

NOTE: If replacing transfer shaft bearing, always replace inner and outer races as a set.

Reassembly

1) Install transfer shaft bearing outer race into converter housing. Install transfer shaft bearing inner race to transfer shaft.

2) Install spring retainer, spring, governor valve and weight to governor body. Install "E" clip to retain components in governor. Install governor filter (new filter if old filter is dirty).

3) Slide governor body onto transfer shaft in same direction as removed, then tighten set screws. Install seal rings to transfer shaft.

VALVE BODY

NOTE: When disassembling valve body, place each component in same order and relation (as removed) for reassembly reference.

Disassembly

1) Remove bolts securing throttle cam to valve body and remove throttle cam assembly. Remove bolts (one bolt is shorter than others) attaching separating plate to transfer plate, then separate plates.

2) Remove stiffener plate, then separating plate. Remove line relief and low relief steel balls with their springs. *See Fig. 17.* Remove manual valve, kickdown valve, throttle valve and 2 springs. Remove 2 regulator plugs.

Fig. 16: Transfer Gear Shaft & Governor Assembly

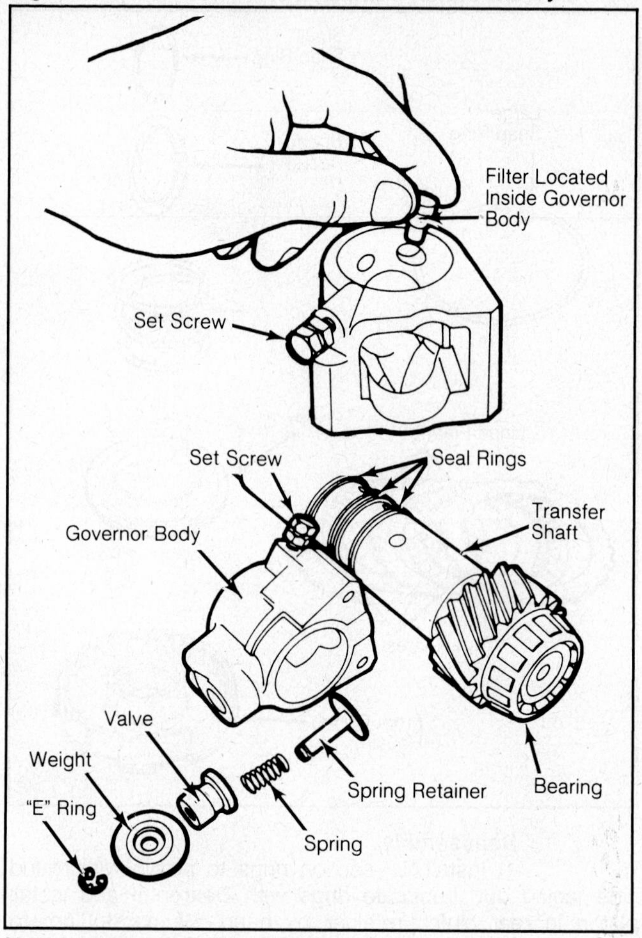

Note location of governor filter.

3) Remove rear end cover and gasket. Remove 1-2 shift valve and 2-3 shift plug. Remove front end cover. Remove all valves, springs and plugs (lay components out in order). Remove snap ring, then remove shuttle valve.

Reassembly

1) Install 2-3 shift valve and spring to valve body. Install shuttle valve, spring and plug, then install snap ring to retain shuttle valve components.

2) Install 1-2 shift plug and spring. Install regulator valve, spring and adjusting screw. Install torque converter valve and spring. Install range control valve and spring. *See Fig. 17.* Install front end cover.

NOTE: For spring identification, see VALVE BODY SPRING IDENTIFICATION table.

3) Install 2-3 shift plug, then 1-2 shift valve to valve body. Install rear end cover and gasket. Install 2 regulator plugs (small one first), then install manual valve to valve body.

4) Install kickdown spring, throttle valve, throttle spring and kickdown valve into valve body. Install stopper plate to valve body, then install 4 steel balls to valve body. *See Fig. 17.*

5) Install line relief and low relief steel balls, with their springs, to transfer plate. *See Fig. 18.* Install guide pins

MITSUBISHI KM171, KM172 & KM175 (Cont.)

Fig. 17: Exploded View of Valve Body & Components

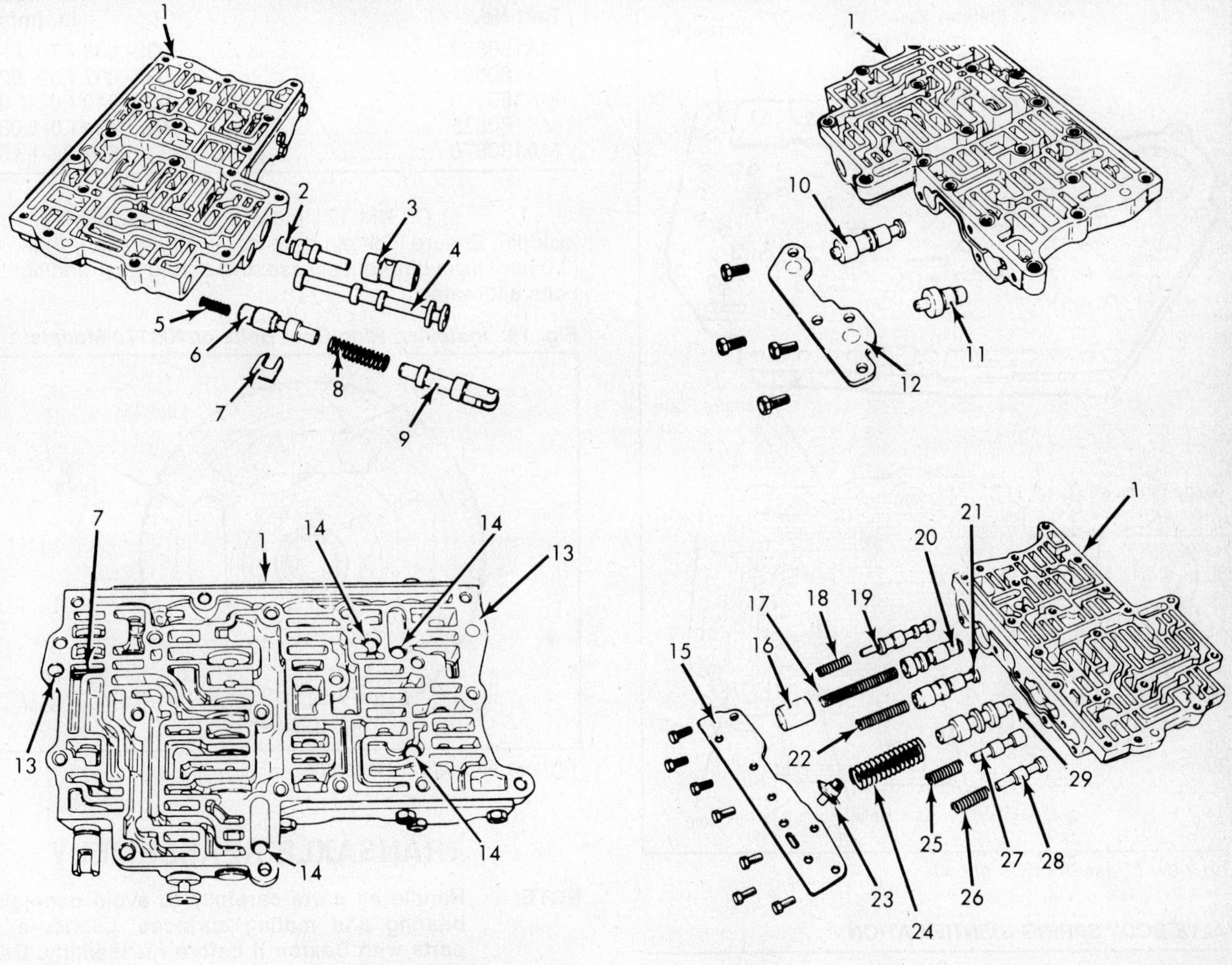

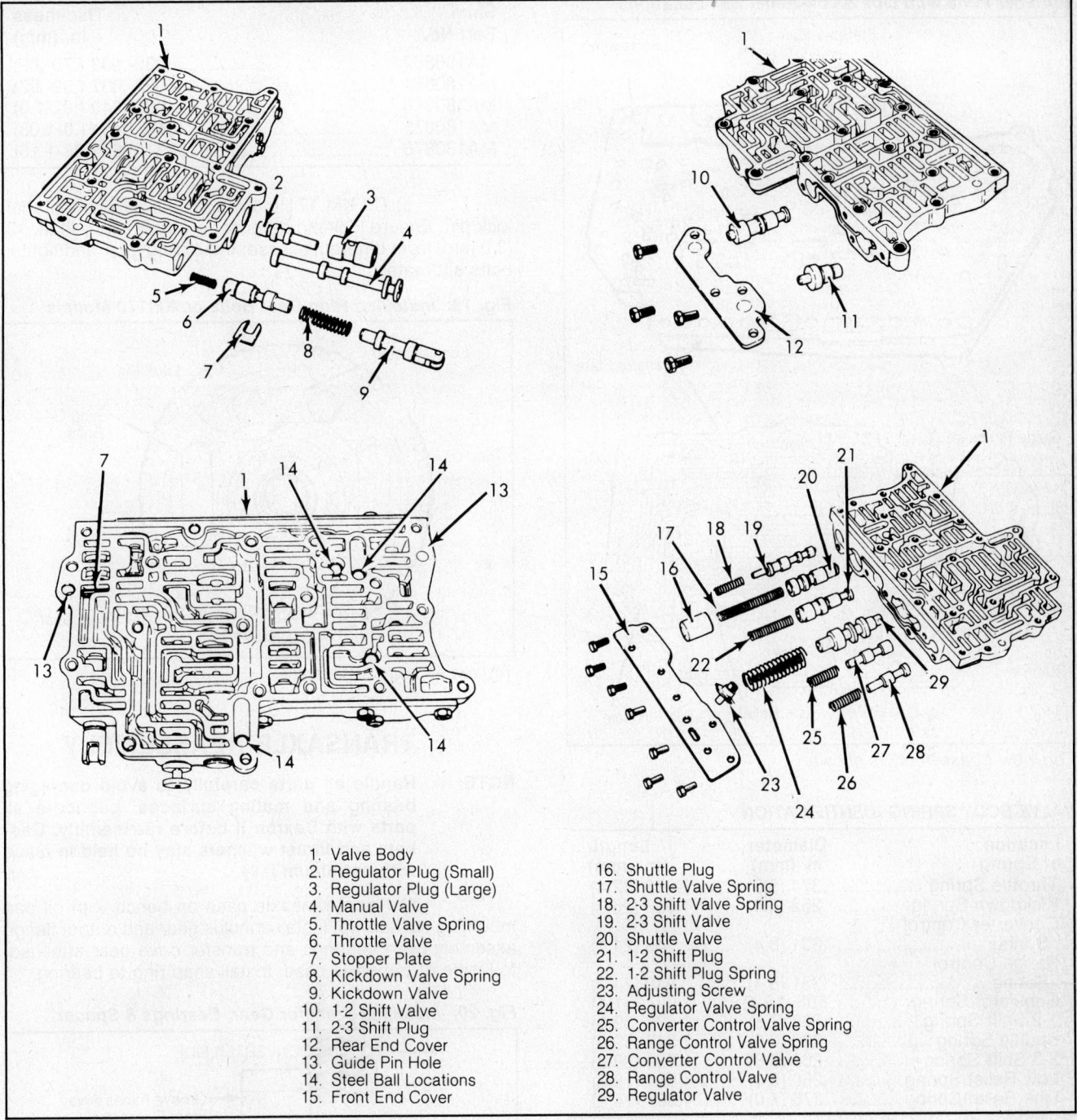

1. Valve Body
2. Regulator Plug (Small)
3. Regulator Plug (Large)
4. Manual Valve
5. Throttle Valve Spring
6. Throttle Valve
7. Stopper Plate
8. Kickdown Valve Spring
9. Kickdown Valve
10. 1-2 Shift Valve
11. 2-3 Shift Plug
12. Rear End Cover
13. Guide Pin Hole
14. Steel Ball Locations
15. Front End Cover
16. Shuttle Plug
17. Shuttle Valve Spring
18. 2-3 Shift Valve Spring
19. 2-3 Shift Valve
20. Shuttle Valve
21. 1-2 Shift Plug
22. 1-2 Shift Plug Spring
23. Adjusting Screw
24. Regulator Valve Spring
25. Converter Control Valve Spring
26. Range Control Valve Spring
27. Converter Control Valve
28. Range Control Valve
29. Regulator Valve

to transfer plate and install separating plate to transfer plate. Install stiffener plate and bolts.

6) Remove guide pins from transfer plate and install them in valve body. Using guide pins as a guide, install transfer/separating plates to valve body and install retaining bolts. Install throttle cam assembly.

NOTE: **Ensure valve body short bolt is installed in its proper location.**

DIFFERENTIAL

Disassembly

Straighten ring gear lock washers. Remove ring gear bolts and ring gear. Remove pinion shaft lock pin, pinion shaft, pinion gears and washers. Remove side gears and spacers. Keep right side gear and spacer separate from left side gear and spacer. Remove differential carrier side bearings if necessary.

Reassembly

1) Install differential carrier side bearing if removed. Install side gears and spacers. If original side gears are reused, ensure they are installed in their original positions. If new side gears are used, use new spacers of .040" (1.0 mm) thickness.

2) Place washers on back of pinion gears. Install both pinion gears at same time. Rotate pinion gears to mesh with side gears. Install pinion shaft. Measure back-

MITSUBISHI KM171, KM172 & KM175 (Cont.)

Fig. 18: Transfer Plate, Separating Plate & Stiffener Plate with Line & Low Relief Ball Locations

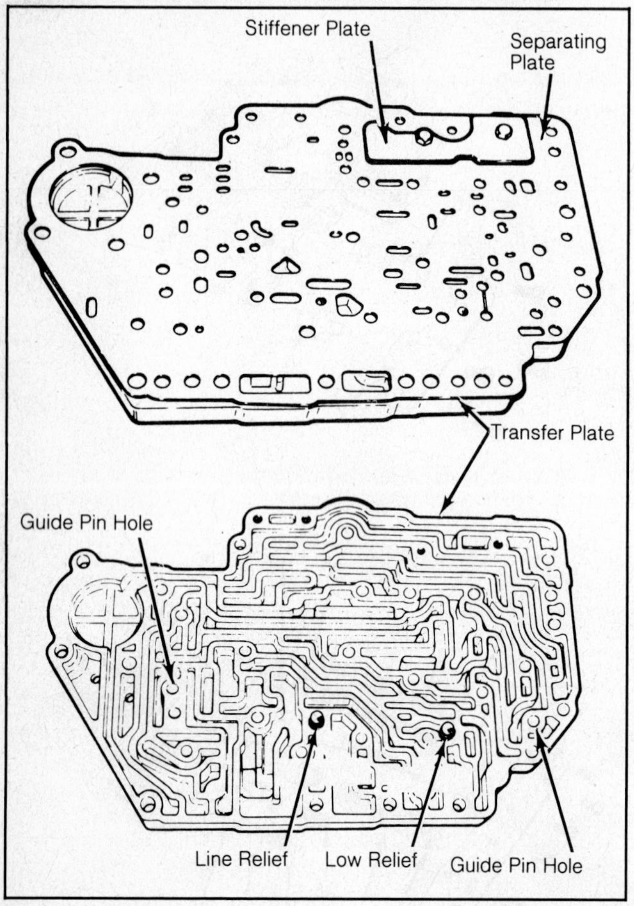

Top view of assembly is shown.

VALVE BODY SPRING IDENTIFICATION

Location of Spring	Diameter In. (mm)	Length In. (mm)
Throttle Spring	.374 (9.5)	1.276 (32.4)
Kickdown Spring	.252 (6.4)	1.028 (26.1)
Converter Control Spring	.331 (8.4)	.949 (24.1)
Range Control Spring	.331 (8.4)	.949 (24.1)
Regulator Spring	.606 (15.4)	2.024 (51.4)
1-2 Shift Spring	.299 (7.6)	1.535 (39.0)
Shuttle Spring	.260 (6.6)	2.343 (59.5)
2-3 Shift Spring	.268 (6.8)	1.189 (30.2)
Low Relief Spring	.260 (6.6)	.661 (16.8)
Line Relief Spring	.276 (7.0)	.961 (24.4)

lash between side gears and pinion gears (measure both right and left side gear backlash).

3) Backlash should be 0-.003" (0-.08 mm) on both sides. If backlash is incorrect, remove pinion and side gears and install thicker or thinner spacers behind side gears to achieve correct backlash. See SIDE GEAR SPACERS chart.

4) On KM 170 models, install ring gear and pinion shaft lock pin. Install ring gear bolts with new lock washers. Ensure one lock washer retains pinion shaft lock pin. Tighten ring gear bolts alternately and bend lock washers along a flat of ring gear bolts. Ensure lock washers are not cracked along bend. *See Fig. 19.*

SIDE GEAR SPACERS

Shim Part No.	Thickness In. (mm)
MA180862	.030-.033 (.75-.82)
MA180861	.033-.037 (.82-.92)
MA180860	.037-.040 (.92-1.0)
MA180875	.040-.043 (1.0-1.08)
MA180876	.043-.046 (1.08-1.16)

5) On KM 171 models, install new pinion shaft lock pin. Ensure lock pin does not protrude more than .12" (3.0 mm) from differential case. Install ring gear and tighten bolts alternately.

Fig. 19: Installing Ring Gear Bolts on KM170 Models

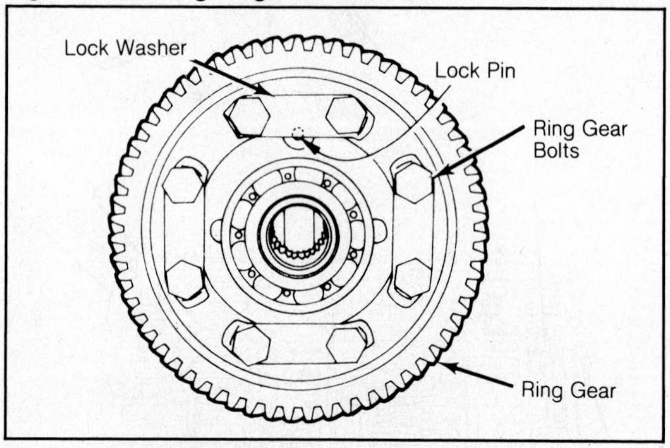

Tighten all bolts alternately.

TRANSAXLE REASSEMBLY

NOTE: **Handle all parts carefully to avoid damaging bearing and mating surfaces. Lubricate all parts with Dexron II before reassembly. Gaskets and thrust washers may be held in place with petroleum jelly.**

1) Place transaxle case on bench with oil pan mounting surface up. Install annulus gear and output flange assembly (with bearings and transfer drive gear attached) to inside of transaxle case. Install snap ring to bearing.

Fig. 20: Installing Transfer Gear, Bearings & Spacer

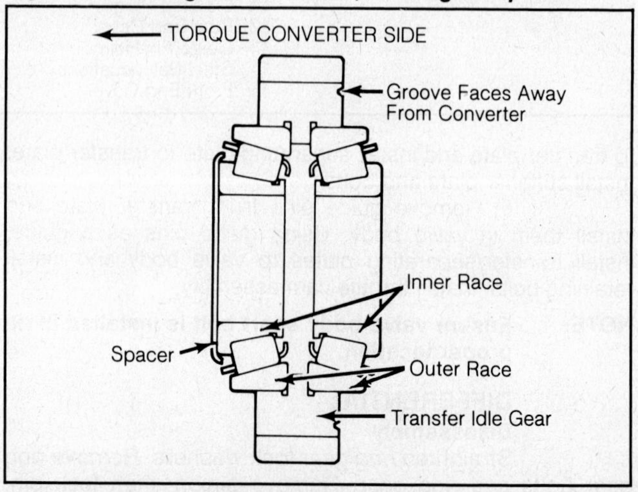

2) Install bearing outer races, inner races and spacer (in correct direction) to transfer idle gear. *See Fig. 20.* Install new "O" ring to idler shaft.

3) Install transfer idle gear assembly to transaxle case. Insert idler shaft from outside case, then screw in and tighten idler shaft to transaxle case.

4) Using a torque wrench and socket, measure output flange turning torque (preload). *See Fig. 21.* Preload should be 7 INCH Lbs. (0.8 N.m). If preload is incorrect, tighten or loosen transfer idler shaft until correct specification is obtained.

Fig. 21: Measuring Output Flange Preload

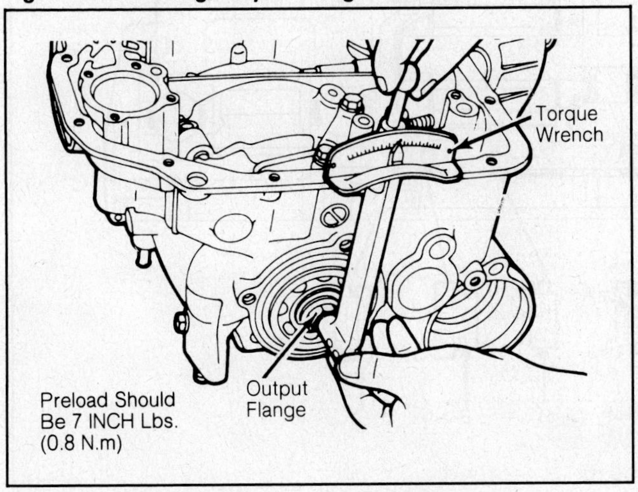

Rotate bearing several times to check preload.

5) With preload adjusted correctly, install idler shaft lock plate and tighten bolt. Install new "O" ring to groove around output flange, then install bearing retainer. Install transfer shaft, with governor, into case. Install Transfer Shaft Retainer Plate (MD998351) to converter housing mating surface (to retain transfer shaft). *See Fig. 22.*

6) Install transfer shaft bearing, inner race, outer race and snap ring to transfer shaft (end opposite retainer plate). Install transfer driven gear onto transfer shaft. Install snap ring to end of transfer shaft. Turn transaxle case so engine mating side is up.

Fig. 22: Transfer Shaft Retainer Plate

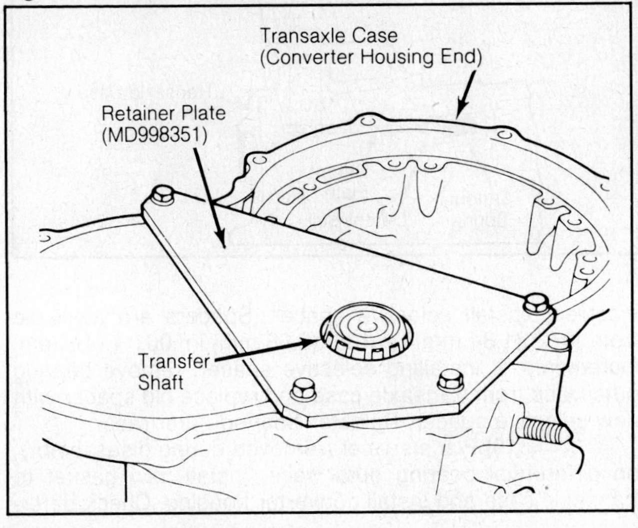

NOTE: See Fig. 23 for location of thrust bearings, thrust races and thrust washers. See THRUST BEARING, THRUST RACE & THRUST WASHER DIMENSIONS table for components available.

NOTE: Coat thrust races, thrust bearings and thrust washers with petroleum jelly to hold them in place during installation.

7) Install thrust race "E" to output flange. Attach thrust races "D" and "J" with thrust bearings "A" and "B" to front and rear of planetary gear carrier. *See Fig. 23.* Install planetary gear carrier to internal gear.

10) Insert manual control shaft to case, pushing it fully toward manual control lever. After shaft is installed, install a new "O" ring to manual control shaft. *See Fig. 24.*

NOTE: If "O" ring is installed before shaft is pushed into case, "O" ring will be damaged by set screw hole.

11) Pull manual control shaft back into case until set screw groove is aligned with set screw hole and install set screw with gasket. Install detent ball and spring when shaft is pulled back to install set screw. *See Fig. 25.*

12) Install kickdown servo spring, piston and sleeve into case. Install large and small "D" section rings to piston and a new "O" ring to sleeve before installing piston. Using spring compressor, compress piston spring and install snap ring.

13) Install kickdown band. Attach band ends to end of anchor rod and servo piston adjusting screw. Install kickdown drum, meshing splines with reverse sun gear. Place kickdown band on kickdown drum and tighten kickdown servo adjusting screw to hold band in place.

14) Install thrust race "J" and a thrust bearing "A" to kickdown drum. *See Fig. 23.* Install thrust races "I" and "G" to both ends of clutch hub. Attach thrust bearing "B" to engine side of thrust race and install clutch hub to forward sun gear splines.

15) Install rear clutch assembly. Install thrust washer "K" to rear clutch retainer. Install thrust race "J" and a thrust bearing "A" to rear clutch retainer. Install front clutch assembly and differential assembly. Install a new oil pump gasket and install thrust washer to rear end of oil pump assembly.

16) If end play (measured during disassembly) is not .028-.056" (.7-1.4 mm), install selective thrust race (E,F,G or H) to obtain correct end play. See THRUST BEARING, THRUST RACE and THRUST WASHER DIMENSIONS chart for thrust race thicknesses.

NOTE: If thrust race was replaced with one of a different thickness, also replace thrust washer between oil pump and front clutch. Replacement thrust washer should be .040" (1.0 mm) thicker than thrust race.

MITSUBISHI KM171, KM172 & KM175 (Cont.)

Fig. 23: Cross-Sectional View Showing Locations of Thrust Bearings, Thrust Races & Thrust Washers

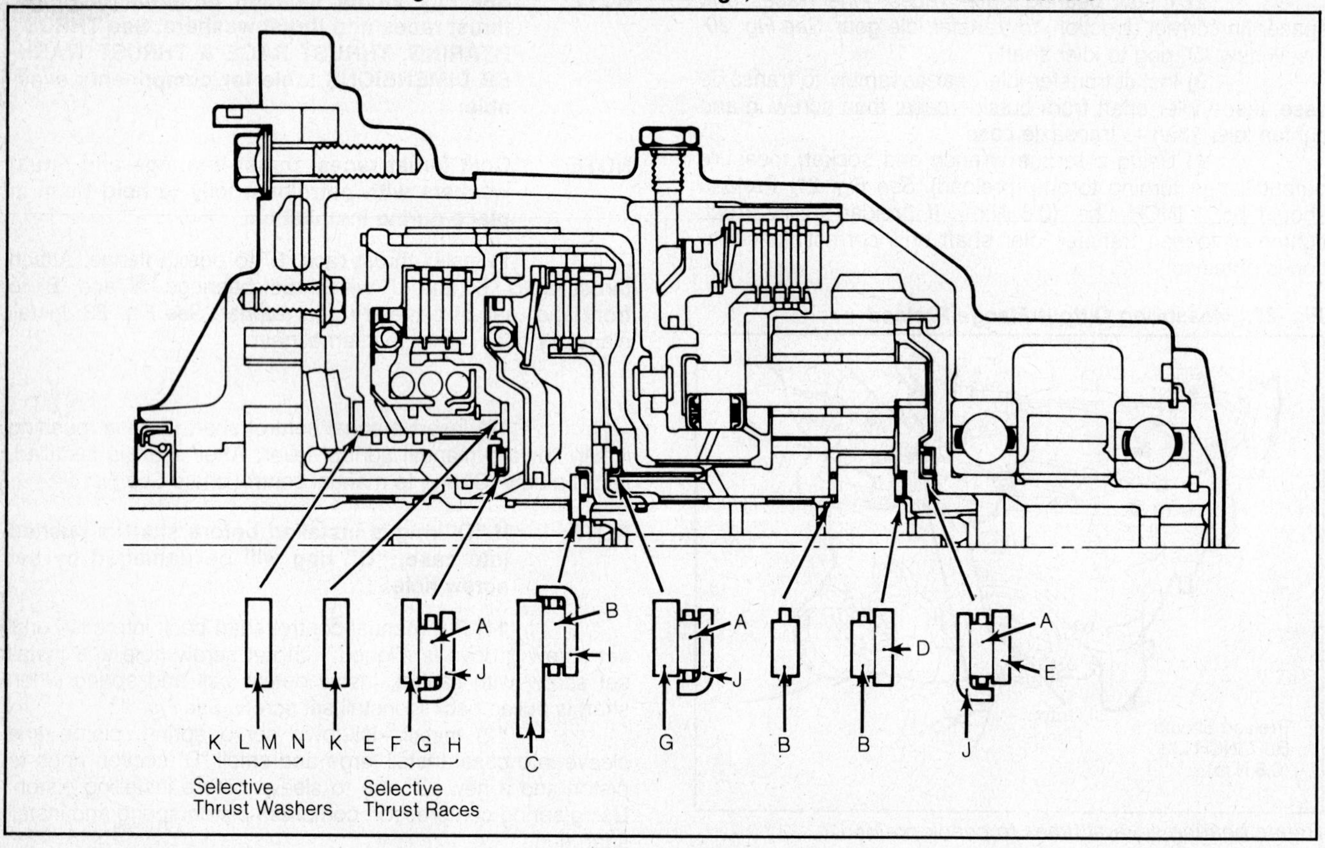

Fig. 24: Installing Manual Control Shaft

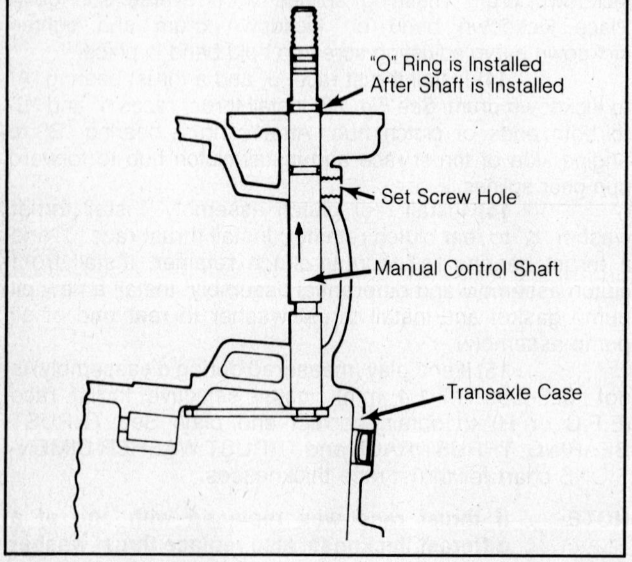

Fig. 25: Installing Set Screw, Detent Ball & Spring to Manual Control Shaft

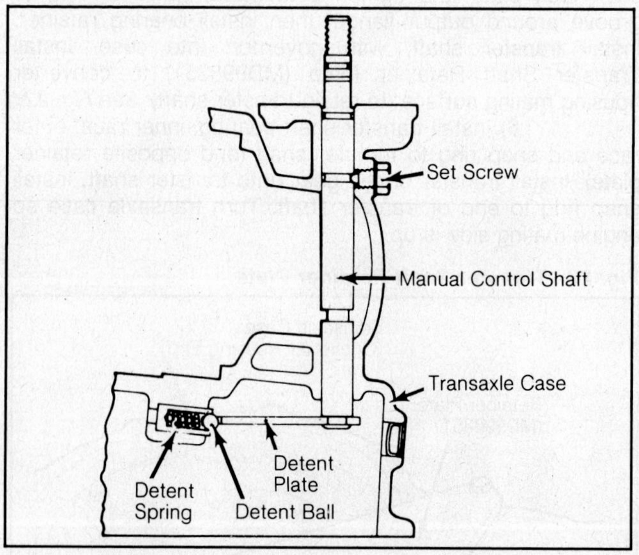

17) Install new selected thrust washer, determined in preceding step, to front clutch. Install new "O" ring to oil pump groove and lubricate "O" ring with Dexron II. Install oil pump and tighten mounting bolts. Be careful thrust washer does not drop out of place. Recheck input shaft end play.

18) Ensure transfer shaft end play (measured during disassembly) is .001" (.025 mm). If end play is incorrect, install selective spacer. Spacers are available from .072" (1.84 mm) to .106" (2.68 mm) in .001" (.025 mm) increments. If installing selective spacer, remove bearing outer race from transaxle case and replace old spacer with new selective spacer. Reinstall bearing outer race.

19) Place spacer (removed during disassembly) on differential bearing outer race. Install new gasket to transaxle case and install converter housing. Check differ-

MITSUBISHI KM171, KM172 & KM175 (Cont.)

THRUST BEARING, THRUST RACE AND THRUST WASHER DIMENSIONS

Component I.D. Mark	Outside Diameter In. (mm)	Inside Diameter In. (mm)	Thickness In. (mm)
Thrust Bearing			
A	1.894 (48.1)	1.417 (36.0)	.....
B	1.437 (36.5)	.874 (22.2)	.....
Thrust Race			
C	1.378 (35.0)	.496 (12.6)	.094 (2.4)
D	1.457 (35.0)	.925 (23.5)	.031 (.8)
E	1.925 (48.9)	1.457 (37.0)	.031 (.8)
F	1.925 (48.9)	1.457 (37.0)	.047 (1.2)
G	1.925 (48.9)	1.457 (37.0)	.063 (1.6)
H	1.925 (48.9)	1.457 (37.0)	.080 (2.0)
I	1.496 (38.0)	.925 (23.5)	.....
J	1.482 (47.0)	1.354 (34.4)	.....
Thrust Washer			
K	2.756 (70.0)	2.193 (55.7)	.071 (1.8)
L	2.756 (70.0)	2.193 (55.7)	.087 (2.2)
M	2.756 (70.0)	2.193 (55.7)	.102 (2.6)
N	2.756 (70.0)	2.193 (55.7)	.118 (3.0)

ential case end play. End play should be 0-.006" (0-.15 mm). Also recheck input shaft and transfer shaft end play. If end play measurements are incorrect, readjust.

20) Install transfer shaft cover and holder. Turn transaxle case so oil pan mounting surface is facing up. Install parking sprag rod to detent plate of manual control shaft. Install parking sprag rod and support. *See Fig. 26.*

Fig. 26: Installing Parking Sprag Rod & Support

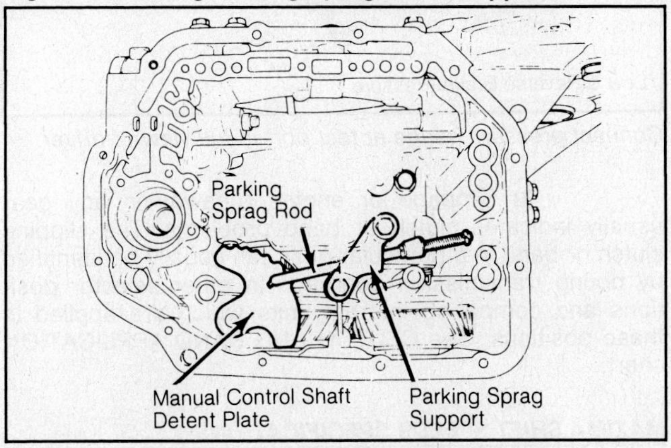

21) Install accumulator piston and spring. Install "O" ring at top center of valve body (brake oil pressure passage). Install valve body to transaxle case, fitting detent plate pin (for manual control shaft) in slot of manual valve. Install and tighten valve body bolts.

22) Insert throttle cable into transaxle case and connect throttle cable inner cable to throttle cam. Install oil filter, oil pan gasket and oil pan. Install drive shaft oil seals to transaxle.

23) Install inhibitor switch and manual lever, then adjust inhibitor switch. Lubricate torque converter surface (where converter slides into oil pump) with Dexron II fluid and carefully install converter, making sure converter meshes with oil pump drive gear.

24) After installing torque converter, measure distance from mating surface of converter housing to torque converter. If measurement is not more than .6" (15 mm), torque converter is not installed completely. Remove converter and check alignment of converter to oil pump.

TIGHTENING SPECIFICATIONS

Application	Ft. Lbs. (N.m)
Axle Shaft Nut	145-188 (196-255)
Center Support (Low-Reverse Brake)	15-19 (20-26)
Differential Carrier-to-Ring Gear	47-54 (64-73)
Drive Plate-to-Converter	26-30 (35-41)
Idler Shaft Lock Plate	15-19 (20-26)
Oil Pump Assembly	11-15 (15-20)
Rear Cover	14-17 (19-23)
Sprag Rod Support Bolts	15-19 (20-26)
Transaxle-to-Engine	
M8 Bolts	21-25 (29-34)
M10 Bolts	31-40 (42-54)
Transaxle-to-Mount Bracket	43-58 (58-78)

NISSAN MAXIMA TRANSAXLE

DESCRIPTION

The Maxima transaxle (Model RL4F02A) consists of 3 main units: Automatic transaxle, torque converter and differential assembly. The automatic transaxle consists of front, rear and one-way clutches, low-reverse brake assembly, oil pump and hydraulic controls (valve body and servo piston assemblies).

LUBRICATION & ADJUSTMENT

See appropriate article in AUTOMATIC TRANSMISSION SERVICING article in IMPORT GENERAL SERVICING section.

SERVICE (IN VEHICLE)

NOTE: The following units can be removed from transaxle without removing transaxle from vehicle: Oil Pan, Valve Body Assembly, Governor Shaft Assembly, Converter Housing Oil Seal and Governor Shaft Assembly. See procedures given in Transmission Disassembly and Transmission Reassembly.

DRIVE AXLE SHAFTS

See appropriate DRIVE AXLE SHAFT article in IMPORT AXLE SHAFTS, OVERDRIVES & TRANSFER CASES section.

TROUBLE SHOOTING

See NISSAN PULSAR, SENTRA, STANZA article TROUBLE SHOOTING section.

TESTING

NOTE: Transaxle is provided with six pressure test ports. All are useful for transaxle trouble-shooting. Ports are; Line pressure, to high clutch, Reverse clutch pressure, Lock-up pressure, Low clutch pressure, Governor pressure and Low-reverse brake pressure. *See Fig. 1.*

ROAD TEST

1) Before road testing, ensure fluid level, condition and control linkage adjustments have been checked and corrected as necessary. During test, transmission should upshift and downshift at approximately the same speeds as shown in SHIFT SPEEDS chart.

CAUTION: Do not shift transaxle into 1st gear from "D" range if car road speed is above 40 mph (65 km/h). Test when oil temperature is between 109-135°F (43-57°C). 3-4 upshift is not included in shift speed test pruceedure.

2) All shifts may vary slightly due to production tolerances or tire size. The important factor is the quality of the shifts. All shifts should be smooth and responsive with no slippage or engine speed runaway.

Fig. 1: Transaxle Case Pressure Test Port Locations

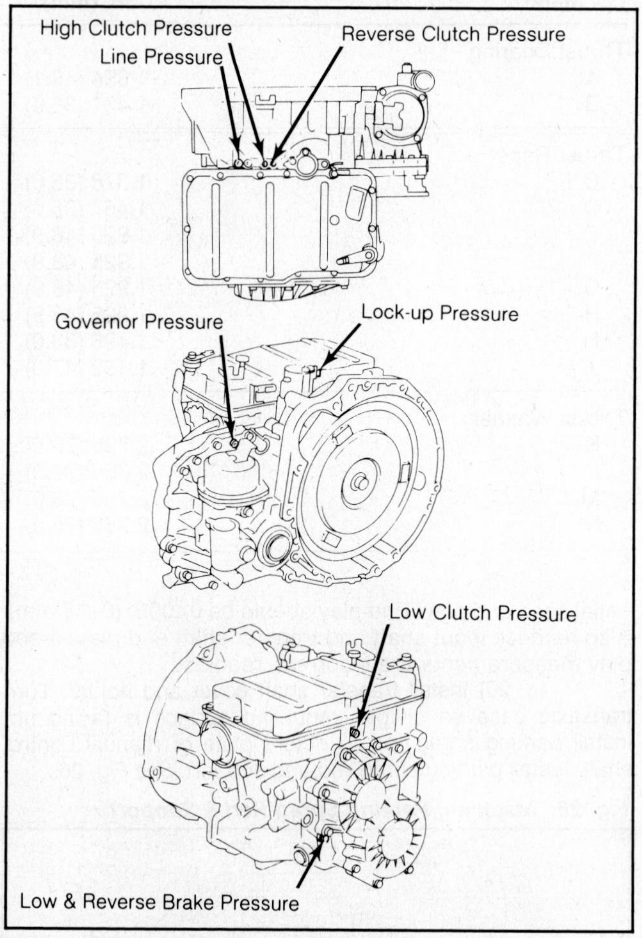

Connect pressure gauge at test port in full view of driver.

3) Slippage or engine runaway in any gear usually indicates clutch or band problems. The slipping clutch or band in a particular gear can usually be identified by noting transmission operation in other selector positions and comparing internal units which are applied in these positions. See CLUTCH AND BAND APPLICATION chart.

MAXIMA SHIFT SPEEDS SPECIFICATIONS

Application	MPH
Minimum Throttle	
1-2 Upshift	7-13
2-3 Upshift	14-20
3-2 Downshift	12-17
2-1 Downshift	7-12
Full Throttle	
1-2 Upshift	31-35
2-3 Upshift	54-65
3-2 Downshift	59-62
2-1 Downshift	22-27
Lock-Up Shift Points	
Engaged	38-45
Disengaged	36-43

NISSAN MAXIMA TRANSAXLE (Cont.)

STALL SPEED TEST

Stall Test Precautions

A stall test should only be performed as a last resort due to the high temperature it generates and the excessive load it places on the engine and transaxle. DO NOT test more than two gear ranges without driving car to cool off drivetrain.

Before making a stall speed test, ensure that line pressure is correct. If line pressure is too low when performing a stall test, transmission can be damaged. During stall test, DO NOT hold throttle open for more than 5 seconds at a time.

Stall Test Procedure

1) Road test vehicle and warm transmission to normal operating temperature. Connect tachometer to engine. Position tachometer so that it can be read from driver's seat.

2) Set parking and service brakes. Start engine and place selector lever in "D". Depress accelerator pedal completely and note maximum RPM obtained.

3) Place selector lever in "N" and allow engine to idle to cool off transmission. Then, place selector lever in "R" and repeat stall test. Stall RPM should be 2000-2300.

NOTE: **If stall test indicates proper stall RPM in "D" range, no further testing is necessary.**

Stall Test Results

1) Satisfactory results in "D" range indicate forward clutch (rear), 1-way clutch of transaxle and sprag clutch of torque converter are functioning properly.

2) If the stall RPM in "D" range (1st gear) is above the specified vehicle RPM, the forward clutch (rear) is faulty. If the stall RPM in "R" range is above the specified vehicle RPM (for "D" range), the low and reverse brakes are faulty.

3) If the stall RPM in "D' range (1st gear) is below the specified vehicle RPM, the converter 1-way clutch is faulty or the engine is not performing properly.

4) If the converter 1-way clutch is frozen, vehicle will have poor high speed performance. If converter 1-way clutch is slipping, vehicle will be sluggish up to 30-40 MPH (50-60 km/h).

LINE PRESSURE TEST

NOTE: **Measure line pressure at idling, at stall speed test and while road testing under different throttle conditions.**

1) Road test vehicle to bring transaxle to normal operating temperature of 109-135° F (43-57° C). Connect pressure gauge to appropriate test port. Place gauge so that it is visible from driver's seat.

2) Connect gauge to line pressure port . *See Fig. 1.* Connect tachometer to engine. Start engine and if necessary, adjust idle speed.

3) Depress brake pedal and place selector lever in "D". Note line pressure reading on gauge. Repeat procedure for each forward range. Pressure should be approximately as shown in LINE PRESSURE chart.

4) Connect gauge to Reverse clutch pressure port (1) to test reverse range line pressure. *See Fig. 1.* Repeat line pressure test with selector lever in "R". Pressure should be approximately as shown in LINE PRESSURE SPECIFICATIONS chart.

5) After testing at idle and during stall speed test, road test vehicle and note readings at different throttle positions. Pressure should be approximately as shown in LINE PRESSURE chart.

LINE PRESSURE SPECIFICATIONS

Application	psi (kg/cm^2)
Idle	
In All Forward Ranges	43 (3)
In "R" Range	43 (3)
At Full Throttle	
In D1, D2, D3 Ranges	121 (8.5)
At Stall Speed Test	
In All Forward Ranges	185 (13)
In "R" Range	185 (13)

LINE PRESSURE TEST RESULTS

Pressure Too High

If pressure is too high, check throttle cable adjustment. If cable is correctly adjusted and pressure is still high, regulator valve or throttle valve may be seized.

Pressure Too Low

If line pressure is too low, check for seizing of regulator valve or throttle valve in valve body. If valves are not seized, check pressure relief valve and oil pump assembly for damage. A defective oil pump assembly will usually make noise.

GOVERNOR PRESSURE TEST

NOTE: **Line pressure MUST be correct before checking governor pressure.**

Testing Procedures

Road test vehicle to warm transmission to normal operating temperature. Connect pressure gauge to governor pressure port on transmission case. *See Fig. 1.* Position gauge so it is visible from driver's seat. Test drive vehicle in "D" and note pressure readings. Governor pressure increases directly with road speed and should always be less than line pressure.

TORQUE CONVERTER LOCK-UP TEST

1) Road test vehicle to warm transmission to normal operating temperature. Connect pressure gauge to lock-up pressure port on transmission case. *See Fig. 1.*

2) Position gauge so it is visible from driver's seat. Test drive vehicle in "D" and note pressure readings. Pressure should be approximately as shown in TORQUE CONVERTER LOCK-UP PRESSURE chart.

TORQUE CONVERTER LOCK-UP PRESSURES

Lock-up Test	psi (kg/cm^2)
Lock-up "ON"	7 (.5)
Lock-up "OFF"	28 (2)

3) The torque converter lock-up pressure at idle should show a steady rise in pressure as vehicle speed increases under light load.

4) The pressure drop between shift points should not exceed 14 psi (1.0 kg/cm^2). Excessive pressure drop may indicate an internal leak at a servo or clutch seal.

NISSAN MAXIMA TRANSAXLE (Cont.)

REMOVAL & INSTALLATION

See appropriate article in AUTOMATIC TRANSMISSION REMOVAL article in IMPORT GENERAL SERVICING section.

TORQUE CONVERTER

Torque converter is a sealed unit and cannot be disassembled for service. Replace if defective.

TRANSAXLE DISASSEMBLY

1) With transaxle removed from vehicle, clean outside case thoroughly and disassemble in a clean area. When cleaning and wiping parts, use nylon cloth or paper towels. Common shop rags will leave lint that can interfere with transaxle's operation.

2) Remove control cylinder, throttle lever and valve cover. Disconnect harness connectors on control valve and remove control valve assembly. Remove terminal assembly, throttle and return spring.

3) Remove accumulator with rubber tipped air nozzel. *See Fig. 2.* Remove side cover and output gear. Using gear puller, remove idler gear. Remove parking pawl, pawl shaft, return spring and spacer. Remove speedometer case and speedometer gear. Remove governor cap, pin and assembly. Place on wooden block. Remove converter housing, final drive assembly and reduction pinion gear.

4) Remove oil strainer, lubrication tube and gutter. Loosen band brake stem lock nut, back off piston stem. Remove brake band and high-reverse clutch pack. DO NOT stretch band unnecessarily. Secure band with clip *See Fig. 3.*

Fig. 2: Removing Accumulator Piston

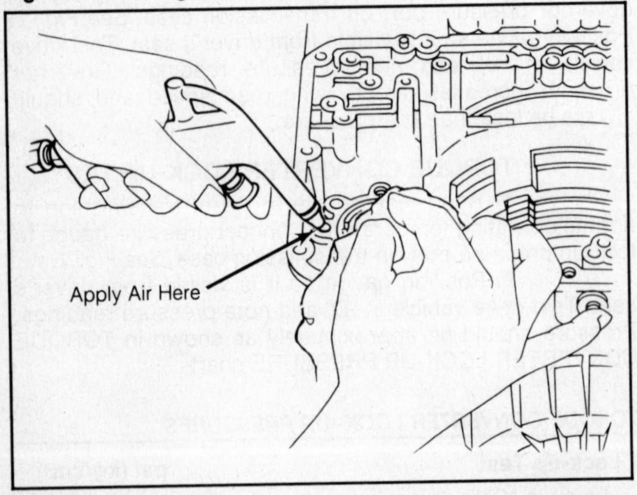

5) Remove low and reverse brake clutches. Remove low and reverse brake retainer snap ring. Apply compressed air to to oil supply hole to remove low and reverse brake piston. *See Fig. 4.* Remove bearing retaining bolts and assembly. Remove band servo snap ring, band brake servo, retainer and return spring. Loosen manual shaft lock nuts, remove manual plate. Remove retaining pin, manual plate and shaft.

Fig. 3: Brake Band Securing Clip Installation

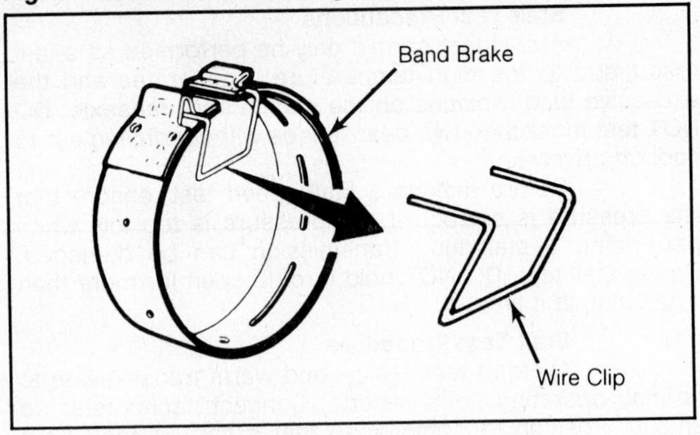

Fig. 4: Removing Low-Reverse Brake Piston

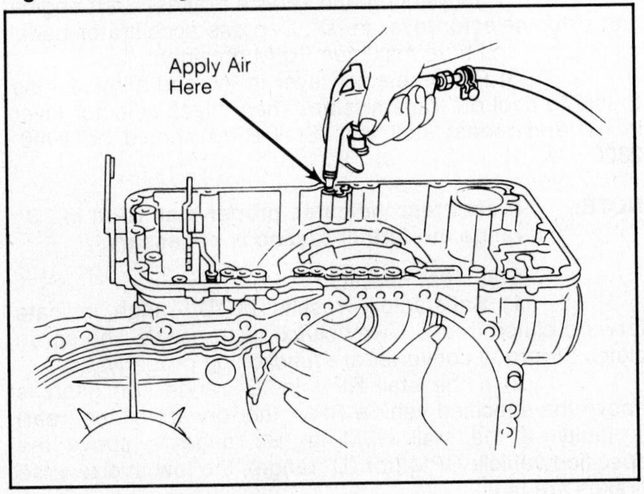

Use rubber tipped air tool.

COMPONENT DISASSEMBLY & REASSEMBLY

OIL PUMP ASSEMBLY

Dissambly

Remove oil pump cover and cam ring spring. Take care not to damage converter housing. Remove cam ring, friction ring, vane ring, and rotor. If necessary remove vanes from rotor. Take care not to damage vanes.

Cleaning & Inspection

1) Thoroughly clean all parts and dry with compressed air. Inspect parts for damage, wear, cracks or scoring. Check oil pump shaft and ring groove areas of pump housing for wear.

2) If pump housing, cover plate, shaft, inner drive gear or outer driven gear requires replacement, complete oil pump assembly must be replaced as a matched set.

NISSAN MAXIMA TRANSAXLE (Cont.)

Fig. 5: Exploded View of Oil Pump Assembly

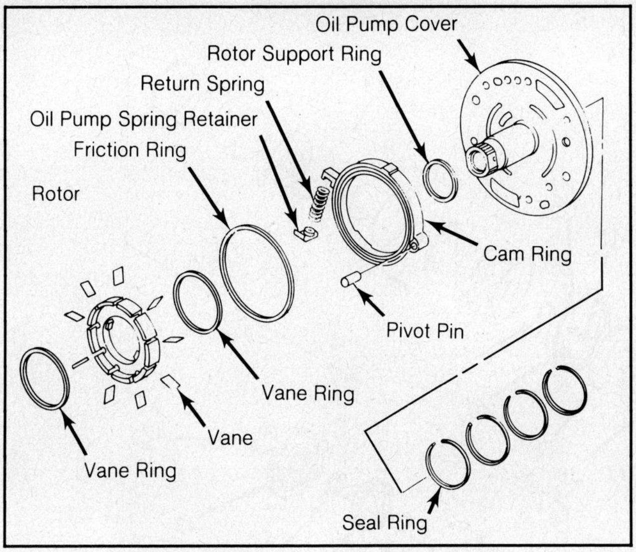

Reassembly

1) Install cam ring, oil pump spring retainer and cam ring spring. Assemble rotor, vanes, friction ring, rotor supporting ring and vanes. *See Fig. 5:*

2) Measure clearance between clutch housing and cam ring, rotor and vanes in at least four places. Clearance should be between .0004-.0009" (.01-.024 mm). If clearance exeeds .0013" (.034 mm) replace oil pump assembly. Measure clearance between seal ring and seal ring groove. Standard clearance is .0039-.0098" (.10-.25 mm).

3) Clean ring seal grooves and using petroleum jelly Install seal rings onto shaft of pump cover. Be sure to install large diameter rings near center of cover and small diameter rings at end of cover shaft.

HIGH CLUTCH ASSEMBLY

Disassembly

Using spring compressor, compress clutch springs and remove snap ring from retainer. Place clutch drum onto oil pump, remove clutch using compressed air.

Inspection

1) Check clutch discs for wear or damage. Measure plate thickness. Plate thickness should be .063" (1.6 mm). If less than .055" (1.4 mm) replace plate. Check snap ring, springs and spring retainer for damage, wear or warpage. Replace defective components as required.

Reassembly

1) Lubricate clutch drum bushing, and install inner seal and piston seal. Take care not to stretch seal during installation.

NOTE: Never assemble clutch dry. Always lubricate its components thoroughly.

2) Assemble piston taking care not to kink or damage seal. Turn piston by hand to assure there is no binding. Install clutch springs. Using spring compressor, install spring retainer and snap ring. Install driven plates, drive plates and secure with snap ring.

3) Measure minimum clearance between waved snap ring and retainer plate. Standard clearance is .071-.087" (1.8-2.2 mm). *See Fig. 7.* If clearance is greater than .118" (3 mm) replace with appropriate size retaining plate. Retaining plates are available in .008" (.2 mm) increments from .142" (3.6 mm) to .197" (5 mm).

Fig. 7: Measuring Clutch Clearance

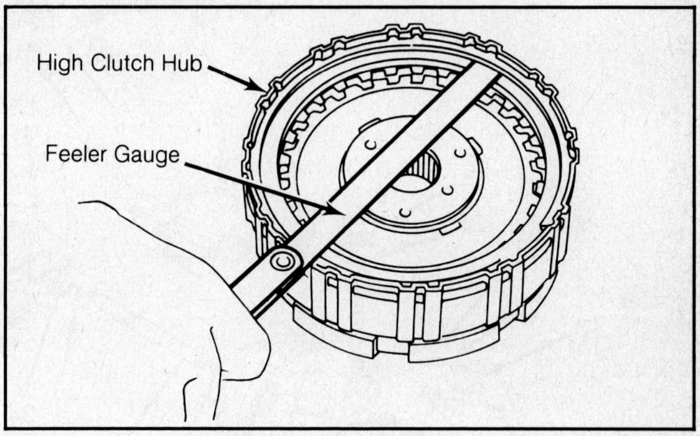

LOW CLUTCH

Service proceedures for low clutch are essentially the same as for high clutch assemblies with the exception of clearance sizes. Standard drive plate thickness for low clutch is .071-.079" (1.8-2.0 mm). Standard clearance for low clutch is .020-.031" (.5-.8 mm). Allowable limit is .079" (2.0 mm).

REVERSE CLUTCH ASSEMBLY

Service proceedures for rear clutch are essentially the same as for high and low clutch assemblies with the exception of clearance sizes. Standard drive plate thickness for rear clutch is .071-.079" (1.8-2.0 mm). Standard clearance for retainer plate is .020-.031" (.5-.8 mm). Allowable limit is .047" (1.2 mm).

LOW-REVERSE BRAKE ASSEMBLY

Disassembly

1) Using a screwdriver, remove large retaining snap ring. Remove driven and drive plates. Note number and arrangement of steel discs and fiber plates.

2) Using a spring compressor, compress springs and remove snap ring from spring retainer. Remove spring retainer and lift out springs.

Inspection

1) Check discs for wear or damage. Measure fiber plate thickness. Plate thickness should be .071-.079" (1.8-2.0 mm). Replace plate if any thickness measures less than .071" (1.8 mm).

2) Check snap ring for wear, springs for weakness or broken coils and spring retainer for warpage. Replace defective components as required.

Reassembly

1) Lubricate components with ATF. Place springs in piston and install spring retainer. Compress spring retainer and install snap ring. Install dished plate with beveled end facing piston. Assemble clutch discs and plates in proper sequence and install. *See Fig. 6.*

NISSAN MAXIMA TRANSAXLE (Cont.)

Fig. 6: Exploded View of RL4F02A Transaxle Assembly

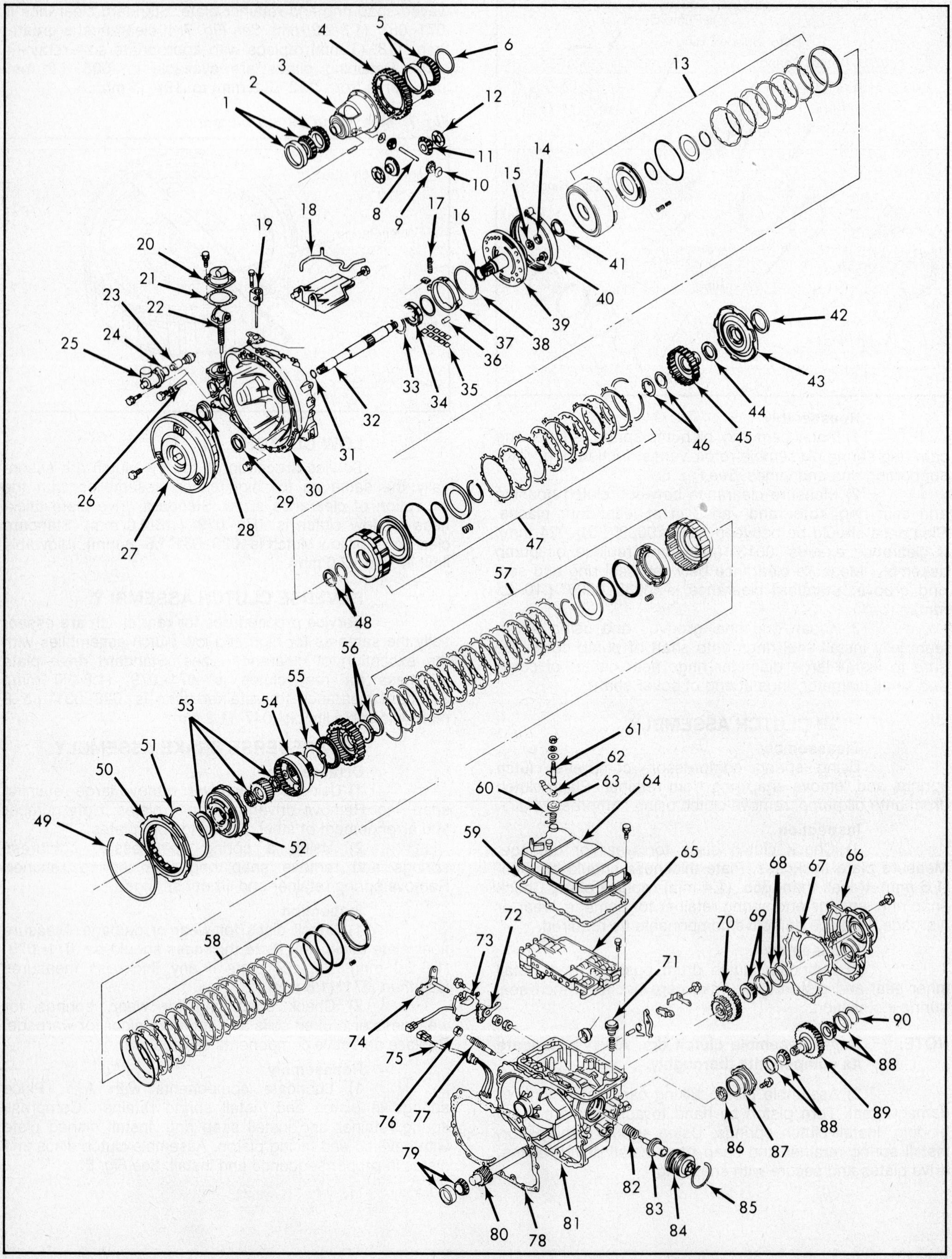

NISSAN MAXIMA TRANSAXLE (Cont.)

Fig. 7: Exploded view of RL4F02A Transaxle Assembly (Use with Fig. 6)

1. Differential Side Bearing
2. Governor Drive Gear
3. Differential Case
4. Final Gear
5. Differential Side Bearing
6. Differential Adjusting Shim
7. Lock Pin
8. Pinion Mate Shaft
9. Pinion Mate Gear
10. Pinion Thrust Washer
11. Side Gear
12. Side Gear Thrust Washer
13. Reverse Clutch Assembly
14. Bearing Race
15. Needle Bearing
16. Rotor Support Ring
17. Return Spring
18. Lubrication Tube
19. Control Cylinder
20. Governor Cap
21. Gasket
22. Governor Valve and Shaft
23. Speedometer Gear
24. Seal Ring
25. Speedometer Case
26. Pin
27. Torque Converter
28. Oil Seal
29. Oil Seal
30. Converter Housing
31. "O" Ring
32. Input Shaft
33. Vane Ring
34. Rotor
35. Vane
36. Pivot Pin
37. Cam Ring
38. Friction Ring
39. Oil Pump Cover
40. Brake Band
41. Thrust Washer
42. Seal
43. High Clutch Carrier
44. Needle Bearing
45. High Clutch Hub
46. Needle Bearing
47. High Clutch Assembly
48. Needle Bearing
49. Snap Ring
50. One Way Clutch
51. Snap Ring
52. Front Carrier
53. Needle Bearing
54. Rear Carrier
55. Needle Bearing
56. Needle Bearing
57. Low Clutch Assembly
58. Low & Reverse Brake Assembly
59. Gasket
60. Return Spring
61. Throttle Shaft
62. Throttle Lever
63. Seal
64. Valve Cover
65. Control Valve Assembly
66. Side Cover
67. Gasket
68. Idler Shaft Adjusting Shim
69. Bearing
70. Idler Gear
71. Accumulator
72. Manual Plate
73. Inhibitor Switch
74. Manual Shaft
75. Terminal Assembly
76. Lock Nut
77. Anchor Pin
78. Gasket
79. Bearing
80. Reduction Pinion Gear
81. Transmission Case
82. Return Spring
83. Band Servo Piston
84. Band Servo Assembly
85. Snap Ring
86. Needle Bearing
87. Bearing Retainer
88. Bearing
89. Output Shaft
90. Output Shaft Adjusting Shim

2) Install end retainer plate and large snap ring. Using a feeler gauge, measure clearance between end plate and snap ring. Clearance should be .087-.102" (2.2-2.6 mm) with maximum allowable limit of .157" (4 mm).

3) If clearance is not to specification, replace end retainer plate. End plates are available in thicknesses ranging from .134-.197" (3.4-5 mm) in .008" (.2 mm) increments.

BRAKE BAND & BAND SERVO

Disassembly

Loosen adjusting lock nut and back off piston stem. Remove brake band servo assembly. Remove snap ring and separate servo piston retainer from piston. Disassemble piston assembly and discard "O" rings.

Inspection

Check brake band friction material for wear. Replace band if cracked, chipped or burnt. Check band servo components and replace if worn or scored. Replace all "O" rings.

Reassembly

To reassemble, reverse disassembly procedure and note the following: Install new "O" rings and ensure snap ring is properly seated. Perform band adjustment during transaxle reassembly.

PLANETARY GEAR SET

Manufacturer does not recommend disassembly of planetary gear set. Measure clearance between planetary carrier and pinion washer. Normal clearance should be .0059-.0276" (.15-.70 mm). If clearance exceeds .0315" (.8 mm) or gear set is worn or damaged, replace planetary gear set. Heat damage is revealed by Blue discoloration of gear sets.

Fig. 8: Exploded View of Governor Assembly

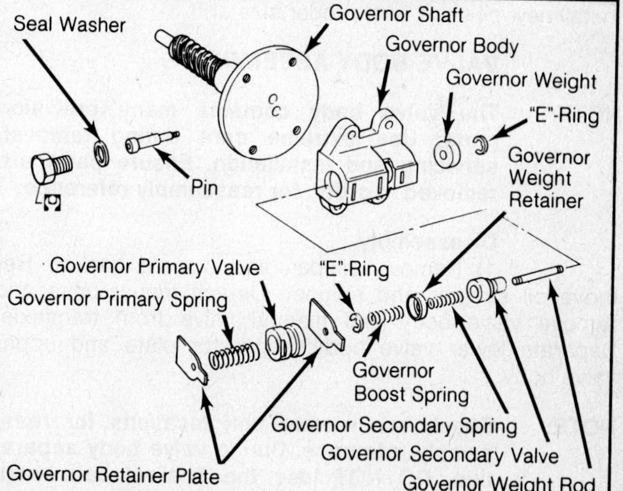

GOVERNOR ASSEMBLY

Disassembly

1) Remove governor cap, governor shaft securing bolt. Remove governor shaft assembly. Remove drive gear.

2) Disassemble governor valve body. Place components in order of disassembly. DO NOT interchange primary and secondary governor components. *See Fig. 8.*

Inspection

1) Check governor valves for burns and scratches. Inspect springs for weakness and burning. Check springs for proper installed length. See GOVERNOR SPRING chart

NISSAN MAXIMA TRANSAXLE (Cont.)

GOVERNOR VALVE SPRING CHART

Application	In. (mm)
Primary Governor	1.25 (31.7)
Secondary Governor	.99 (25.1)
Governor Boost	1.11 (28.2)

2) If any abnormalities are found, replace governor body, valves and springs as an assembly.

Reassembly

To reassemble, reverse disassembly procedure. Make sure governor boost, primary and secondary governor springs are properly installed.

CONVERTER HOUSING, TRANSMISSION CASE

Disassembly

Remove reduction pinion gear front outer race using Race Remover (J-34286). Using a drift, remove differential side bearing outer race. Using a drift, remove torque converter and differential oil seals.

Inspection

Thoroughly clean all parts and dry with compressed air. Inspect parst for wear, cracks, damage or scoring. Check converter housing for scratches or damage that may cause leaks or loose fit of seals or races.

Reassembly

Using appropriate size drifts, replace races into case. If races are hard to install, it may be necessary to warm case in oven, freeze race in freezer, or both. Install new oil seals with proper size drift.

VALVE BODY ASSEMBLY

NOTE: **The valve body contains many precision parts. Use extreme care during removal, servicing and installation. Ensure parts are removed in order, for reassembly reference.**

Disassembly

1) Remove oil pan and discard gasket. Remove oil strainer and magnet. Detach mount bolts and remove valve body and manual valve from transaxle. Separate lower valve body, separator plate and upper valve body.

NOTE: **Check two reamer bolt locations for reassembly reference. During valve body separation, DO NOT lose the 8 steel balls from upper valve body.**

2) Remove parallel pins from valve body by pushing out with a piece of wire. Remove valve body plugs. Extract 3-4 shift valve, spring and shift plug. Remove 2-3 shift valve and spring, 3-2 downshift valve and spring, 1-2 shift valve, 1-2 control valve and spring. Remove pressure regulator plug, spring seat, spring and pressure regulator. *See Fig. 9.*

3) Remove cutback sleeve, plug and valve, pressure modifier valve and spring. Remove manual valve, fail-safe valve, spring, detent valve, detent valve spring, snap ring and throttle valve. Place valves and springs in order of removal for reassembly reference.

4) Turn lower valve body over. Remove parallel pins by pushing out with wire. Remove valve body plugs. Remove 2-4 timing valve, 3-4 throttle plug, 4-2 accumulator plug, spring and piston. Remove 2-3 shift plug, 4-2 timing valve, spring and spacer. Remove torque regulator valve and spring. Remove 1st reducing valve, spring, low clutch timing valve, spring, back-up valve and spring.

5) Remove lock-up body. Disassemble lock-up body by removing 4 retaining clips one at a time and extracting separate springs and control valves. Remove lock-up accumulator piston and spring. Place valves and springs in order for reassembly reference. *See Fig. 9.*

Inspection

1) Clean valves in alcohol or lacquer thinner. Dip valve body in carburetor cleaner or lacquer thinner. DO NOT leave valve body in cleaner longer than 5 minutes. Rinse parts thoroughly and blow dry.

2) Use only crocus cloth to remove burns or heavy varnish deposits. DO NOT use emery cloth as it is too coarse and can scratch valves or valve bores. Replace valves if deposits cannot be removed.

NOTE: **If clearance between valves and valve bores exceeds .001" (.03 mm), replace entire valve body assembly.**

3) Check valves for rounded edges. If edges are not sharp, replace valve. Check oil strainer for general condition. Check separator plate for scratches or damage. Separator plate must not be scratched or damaged or oil will bypass correct oil passages and system malfunction will result. Replace components as needed.

VALVE BODY SPRING CHART

ValveSpring	Free Length In. (mm)
Pressure Regulator Valve	1.59 (40.3)
Pressure Modifier Valve	1.83 (46.4)
Throttle Valve	1.31 (33.3)
Detent Valve	1.31 (29.1)
Torque converter Regulator Valve	1.06 (27.0)
1st Reducing Valve	1.04 (26,4)
4-3 Timing Valve	1.17 (29.7)
3-2 Timing Valve	.92 (23.3)
2-4 Timing Valve	1.34 (34.0)
Low Clutch Timing Valve	1.17(29.7)
Lock-up Timing Valve	1.17 (29.7)
Back-up Valve	.74 (18.8)
3-2 Downshift Valve	1.65 (42.0)
1-2 Shift Valve	1.97 (50.1
2-3 Shift Valve	1.70 (43.1)
4-2 Accumulator	2.22 (56.5)
3-4 Shift Valve	2.77 (70.4)
3-4 Governor	.91 (23.0)
Lock-up Control Valve	1.50 (38.0)
3rd Speed Cut Valve	.88 (22.4)
4th Speed Cut Valve	.89 (22.6)
4-2 Timing Valve	.81 (20.6)
Lock-up Accumulator	1.65 (41.8)

NISSAN MAXIMA TRANSAXLE (Cont.)

Fig. 9: Exploded View of Control Valve Body

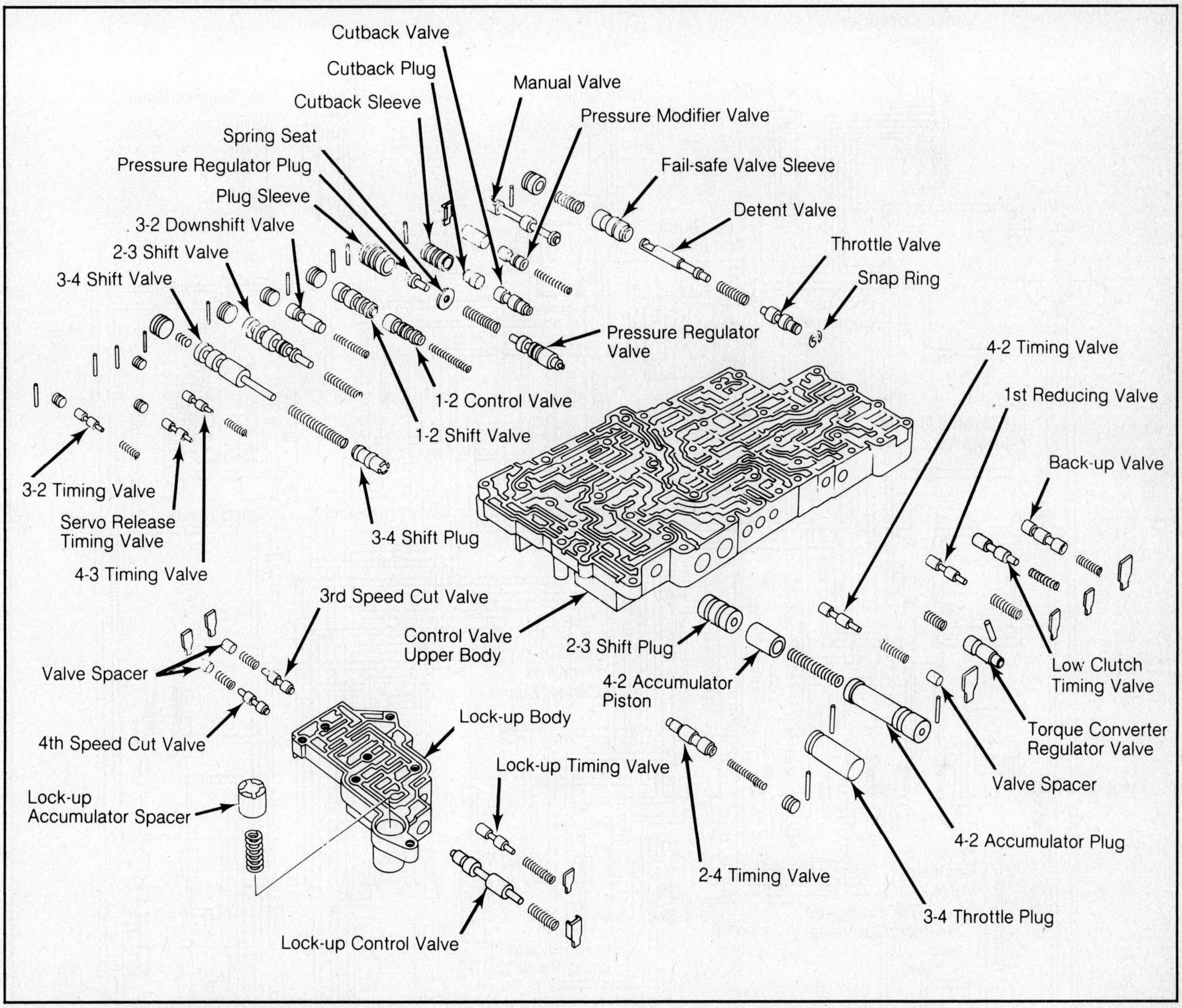

4) Inspect upper and lower valve body oil passages for varnish deposits, scratches or other damage that would impair valve movement. Check for stripped threads. Repair any damaged thread holes. Replace bolts and screws as needed. Test valve springs for weakness. Replace defective components as required.

NOTE: **If replacing pressure modifier valve spring, ensure new spring is the same type as the one which was removed.**

Reassembly

Install valves and springs in correct locations. Place 8 steel check balls in correct position in upper valve body. *See Fig. 10*. Assemble separator plate and valve bodies. Install 2 reamer bolts first, then install and tighten remaining bolts. Pay attention to position of harness clamps when installing control valve bolts.

Fig. 10: Locations of Check Balls

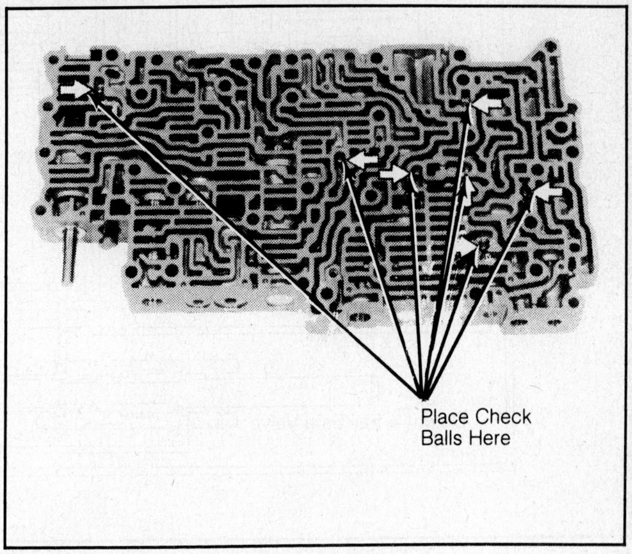

NISSAN MAXIMA TRANSAXLE (Cont.)

Fig. 11: RL4F02A Hydraulic Control Circuits

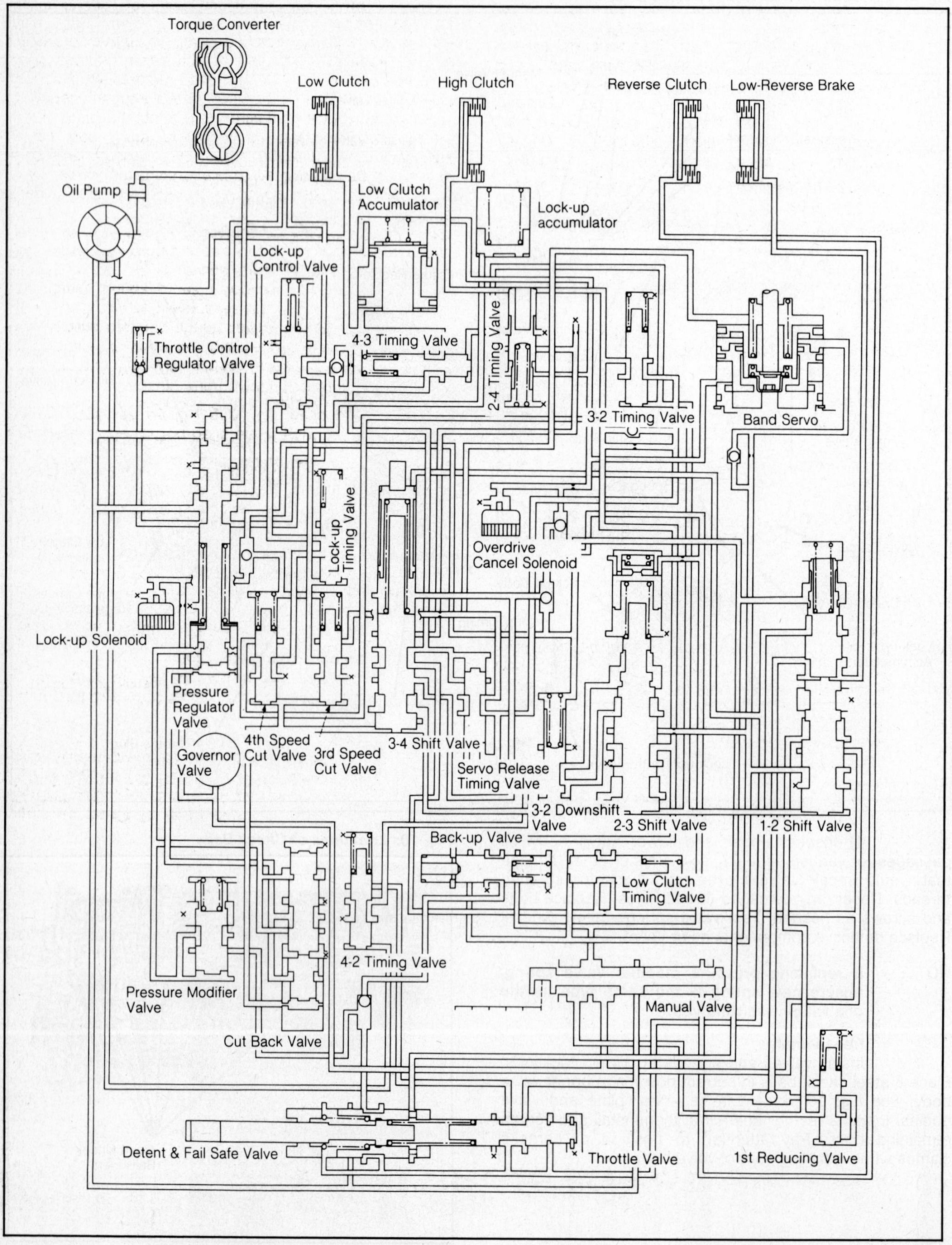

NISSAN MAXIMA TRANSAXLE (Cont.)

DIFFERENTIAL

Disassembly

1) Detach ring gear mount bolts. Separate ring gear from differential case. Using drift punch and hammer, drive out pinion shaft lock pin and remove pinion shaft.

2) Remove pinion gears and side gears from case. If bearings and races need replacement, remove races from converter housing and transmission case using bearing puller.

3) Using bearing puller and hydraulic press, pull side bearings off differential case. Ensure differential case does not drop during pressing operation. Mark left and right bearings for installation in original position. Remove governor drive gear and stopper.

Cleaning & Inspection

1) Clean all parts in solvent and blow dry. Inspect mating surfaces of differential case, side gears and pinion mating gears for chips, cracks and wear. Check bearings and races for scratches, flaking, pitting and excessive wear.

2) Check clearance between side gear and differential case. Place Bridge (J-34290-1) and Gauging Cylinder (J-34290-2) on machined gasket surface of transaxle. Allow gauging cylinder to rest on bearing mating surface. Lock cylinder in place and note measurement.

3) Place differential assembly into converter housing. Place side bearing inner cone on differential case. Seat bearings by holding cone in place and spinning differential case assembly. Insert Gauging Plunger (J-34290-3) into gauging cylinder. Place bridge, gauging cylinder, and gauging plunger onto machined surface of converter housing. Rest plunger on surface of bearing inner cone. Lock plunger in place.

4) Use feeler gauge to measure clearance between gauging cylinder and shoulder of gauging plunger. *See Fig. 12.* Measure other side gear in same manner. Clearance between side gear and differential case should be .008" (.2 mm) with washer in place.

5) Side bearing adjusting shims come in sizes ranging from .0173" (.44 mm) to .0362" (.92 mm) in .0016" (.04 mm) increments.

Reassembly

1) Install selected shim or shims and left side inner bearing cone. Placing transmission on wooden blocks, install reduction pinion gear and differential case assembly. Place gasket on transmission.

2) Install converter housing while assuring reduction pinion gear does not interfere with case.

OUTPUT SHAFT & IDLER GEAR

Disassembly & Inspection

1) Using bearing remover and hydraulic press, pull bearings off output shaft. Place idler gear on wooden blocks and drive out outer races. Thoroughly clean components in solvent and blow dry with compressed air.

2) Check and replace idler gear if chipped, cracked or worn. Replace output shaft if bent, cracked or splines are worn. Replace any bearing that is cracked, pitted, flaking or does not roll freely.

Reassembly

Using hydraulic press and drift, press bearing races into idler gear. Press bearings onto output shaft. Make sure bearings are properly seated and rotate without binding after installation.

Fig. 12: Measuring Differential Side Bearing Clearance

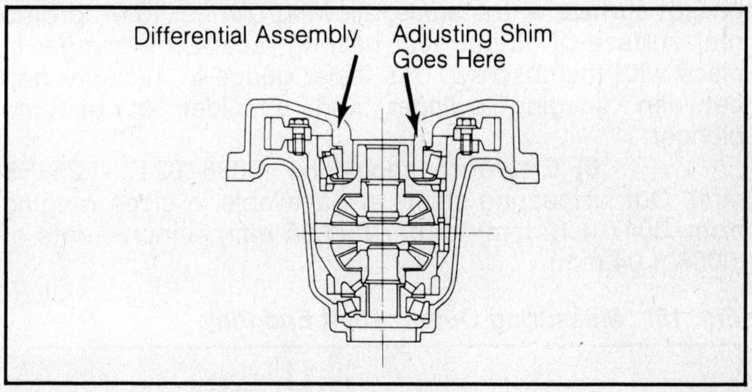

TRANSMISSION CASE

Disassembly & Reassembly

Remove bearing housing from transmission case. Press bearing off housing. Press out oil seal. Remove and discard "O" ring. Coat new seal and "O" ring with gear oil and press into position. Press bearing into housing. Install housing in transmission case.

TRANSAXLE ADJUSTMENTS

NOTE: If transmission case, bearing housing, tapered roller bearing, differential case or converter housing is replaced, final drive must be adjusted.

OUTPUT SHAFT BEARING

1) If transmission case, output shaft, bearing or front cover is replaced, adjust output shaft. Apply ATF to bearing. Press bearing into transmission case bore. Place 2 or 3 shims on front cover. Press bearing into front cover bore. Install output shaft in converter housing.

2) Install gasket and front cover on converter housing. Tighten bolts. Rotate output shaft at least 10 times to seat bearings. Shaft should rotate smoothly without binding. Mount an adapter and INCH lb. torque wrench to output shaft.

3) Measure rotational force of output shaft. If rotational force exceeds 3.1-4.2 INCH lbs. (.35-.47 N.m), remove front cover and output shaft. Remove or add shims as required to increase or decrease rotational force.

OUTPUT SHAFT END PLAY

1) After adjusting rotational force of output shaft bearing, measure output shaft end play. Install idler gear, with bearings on idler shaft. Install idler gear and output shaft assembly in converter housing.

2) Clean front cover bolt threads and converter housing with solvent. Install front cover gasket and front cover on converter housing. Install and tighten bolts to 10-13 ft. lbs. (14-18 N.m).

3) Install idler gear bolt and lock washer. Tighten idler gear bolt to 20-27 ft. lbs. (26-36 N.m). Ensure lock washer is aligned with groove on converter housing. *See Fig. 13.*

4) After tightening bolt, turn output shaft at least 5 complete revolutions. Loosen idler gear bolt, then retighten to specification. Bend lock washer. Install rear internal gear.

NISSAN MAXIMA TRANSAXLE (Cont.)

5) Place Output Gauging Cylinder (J-34290-4) into Bridge (J-34290-1). Place bridge onto machined gasket surface of transaxle, allowing plunger to drop onto rear surface of output gear bearing race. Lock plunger in place with thumbscrew. Use feeler gauge to measure gap between gauging cylinder and shoulder of gauging plunger.

6) Clearance should be .0098-.0217" (.25-.55 mm). Output bearing shims are available in sizes ranging from .0047" (.12 mm) to .0772" (1.96 mm) in increments of .0006" (.04 mm).

Fig. 13: Measuring Output Shaft End Play

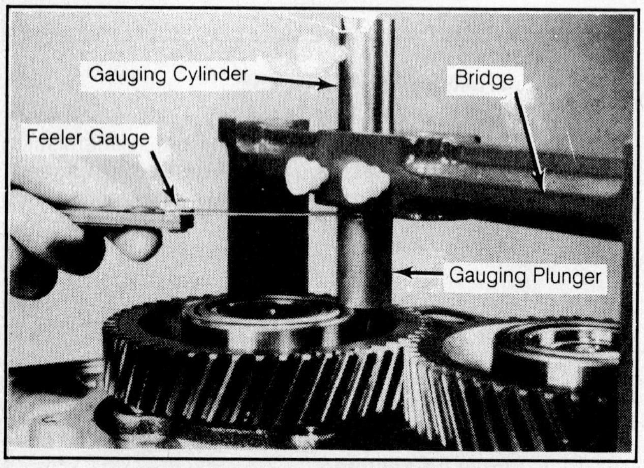

TRANSAXLE REASSEMBLY

1) All components must be clean before reassembly. Blow off parts with compressed air. New seals and "O" rings should be used during reassembly. Install differential lubrication tube and gutter to converter housing. *See Fig. 14.* Install oil strainer and detent spring assembly. Pass parking rod into hole in manual plate and install manual plate on manual shaft.

Fig. 14: Location of Differential Gutter and Lubrication Tube

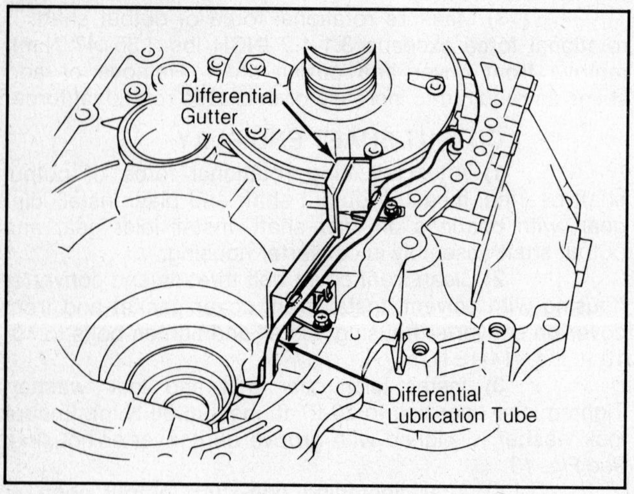

2) Install band brake servo, retainer, and return spring. Secure with snap ring. Lubricate low-reverse brake piston seal and install by tapping lightly using wooden block. Install low-reverse brake retainer and secure with snap ring. Install low-reverse brake driven and drive plates and retaining plate. Secure with snap ring.

3) Measure clearance between snap ring and retainer plate. Clearance is .087-.102" (2.2-2.6 mm). Maximum allowable limit is .157" (4 mm). If clearance exeeds allowable limit, replace retainer plate with appropriate sized replacement. Retainer plates are available in thickness ranging from .134" (3.4 mm) to. 197" (5 mm) in .008" (.2 mm).

4) Assemble front carrier, rear carrier and low clutch assemblies. *See Fig. 6.* Install carrier set. Install one way clutch assembly while rotating front carrier by high clutch hub. *See Fig. 15.* Remove high clutch hub. Install snap ring. Install seal rings onto bearing retainer with care. Clean grooves and apply petroleum jelly to hold rings in place. Install bearing retainer assembly.

Fig. 15: Installing One-way Clutch Assembly

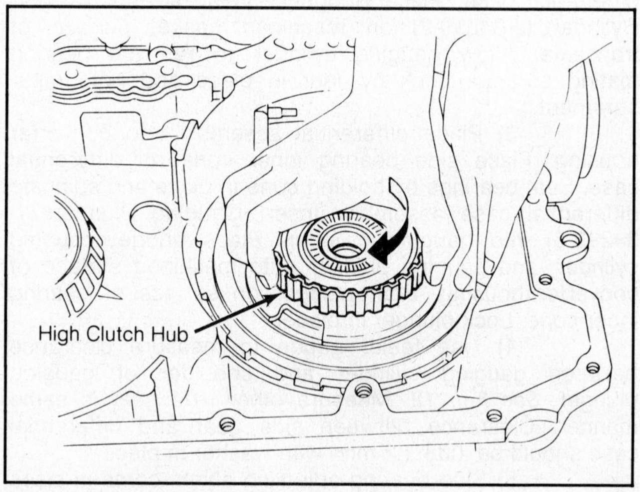

5) Assemble reverse clutch and high clutch. Install reverse and high clutch as a pack. Install brake band and brake band anchor bolt. *See Fig. 17.* Finger tighten anchor bolt. Adjust total end play and clutch pack end play. *See Fig. 16.* Remove thrust bearing race from high clutch drum. Install needle bearing on top of oil pump cover.

6) To measure total end play place Bridge (J-34290-1 and Gauging Cylinder (J-34290-2) on machined gasket surface of converter housing. Allow gauging cylinder to rest on needle bearings and lock in place with thumb screw. Insert Gauging Plunger (J-34290-7) into Gauging Cylinder (J-34290-2). Place bridge with legs facing up, onto machined gasket surface of transaxle case. Allow gauging plunger to rest on surface where bearing race was removed. Lock plunger in place.

7) Remove bridge and use feeler gauge to measure between gauging cylinder and shoulder of plunger. *See Fig. 18* Select appropriate oil pump bearing races. Bearing races are available from .031-.079" (.8-2.0 mm) in increments of .008" (.2 mm).

NISSAN MAXIMA TRANSAXLE (Cont.)

Fig. 16: Clutch Pack and Total End Play Adjustment Points

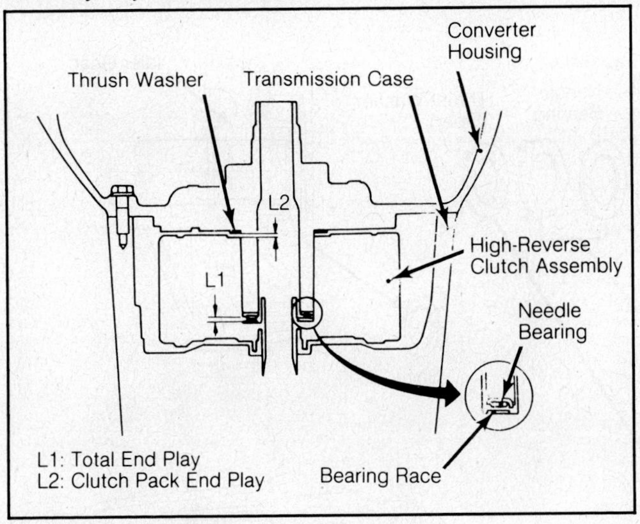

Fig 17: Installing Brake Band and Anchor Bolt

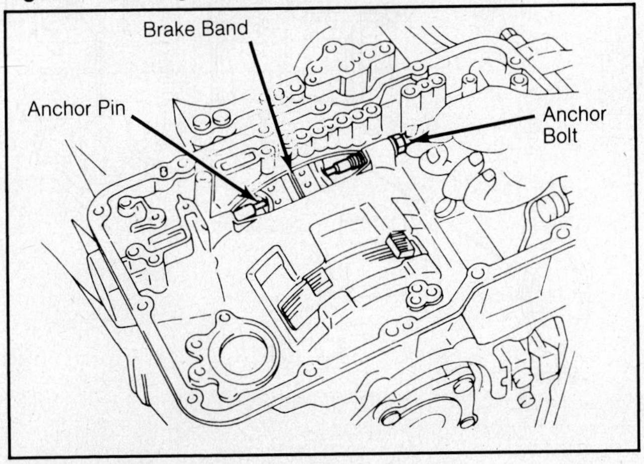

Temporarily tighten anchor bolt by hand.

Fig. 18: Measuring Total End Play with Feeler Gauge

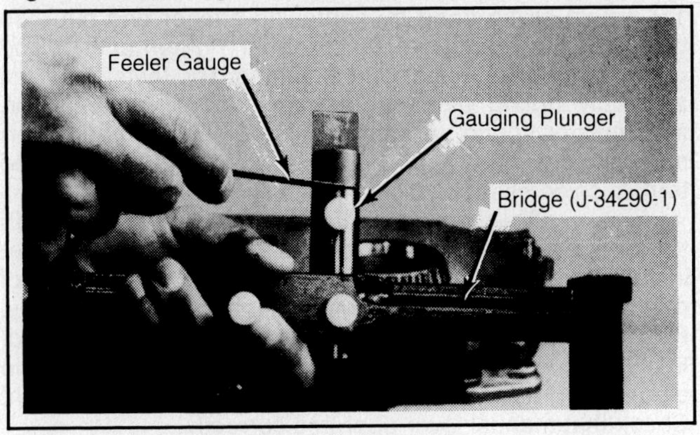

Remove bridge and measure gap between gauging cylinder and plunger.

Fig. 19: Removing Left Side Bearing Inner Cone and Shims

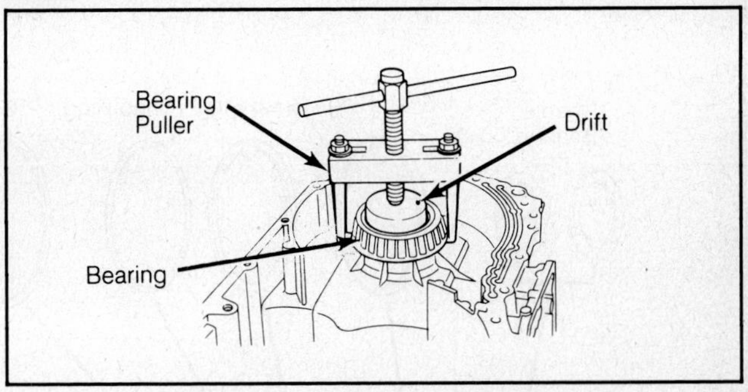

8) To measure clutch pack end play place Bridge (J-34290-1) and Gauging Cylinder (J-34290-2) onto machined gasket surface of transaxle case. Allow cylinder to rest on thrust washer surface of high clutch drum. Lock cylinder in place. Insert Gauging Cylinder (J-34290-6) into gauging cylinder.

9) Place bridge, gauging cylinder and plunger onto machined gasket surface of converter housing making sure thrust washer is removed. Lock plunger in place. Using a feeler gauge, measure gap between gauging cylinder and shoulder of gauging plunger. Total clutch pack end play should be .016-.031" (.4-.8 mm). Clutch pack thrust washers are available in thicknesses between .028-.075" (.7-1.9 mm) in increments of .008" (.2 mm).

10) To adjust differential side bearing preload, using proper size drift and bearing puller, remove left side bearing inner cone and shims from transaxle case. *See Fig. 19.* Place Bridge (J-34290-1 and Gauging Cylinder (J-34290-2) on machined gasket surface of transaxle case. Allow gauging cylinder to rest on bearing mating surface. Lock cylinder in place.

11) Place differential case assembly into converter housing. Place side bearing inner cone on differential case. Seat bearings by spinning differential case assembly while holding inner bearing cone. Insert Gauging Plunger (J-34290-3 into gauging cylinder. Place bridge, gauging cylinder and gauging plunger onto machined gasket surface of converter housing. Allow gauging plunger to rest on surface of bearing inner cone. Lock plunger in place.

12) Use feeler gauge to measure the clearance between gauging cylinder and shoulder of gauging plunger. Standard clearance should be .008" (.2 mm). Side bearing preload adjusting shims are available in from .017-.036" (.44-.92 mm) in increments of .0015" (.04 mm).

13) Using selected shims, install shims and left bearing cone into transaxle case. Placing transmission case on wooden blocks, install reduction pinion gear and differential case assembly. Place gasket on transmission case and install converter housing taking care that reduction pinion does not interfere with transmission case.

14) Install parking pawl, return spring, pawl shaft and spacer. Install idler gear. Install output gear taking care that output gear is well lubricated with petroleum jelly. Using a drift, install selected output shaft preload shims into side cover. Using a new gasket, install side cover. Move manual lever until parking pawl engages idler gear. Measure clearance between parking pawl and parking actuator.

NISSAN MAXIMA TRANSAXLE (Cont.)

Fig. 20: Locations of Shims, Snap Rings and Bearings

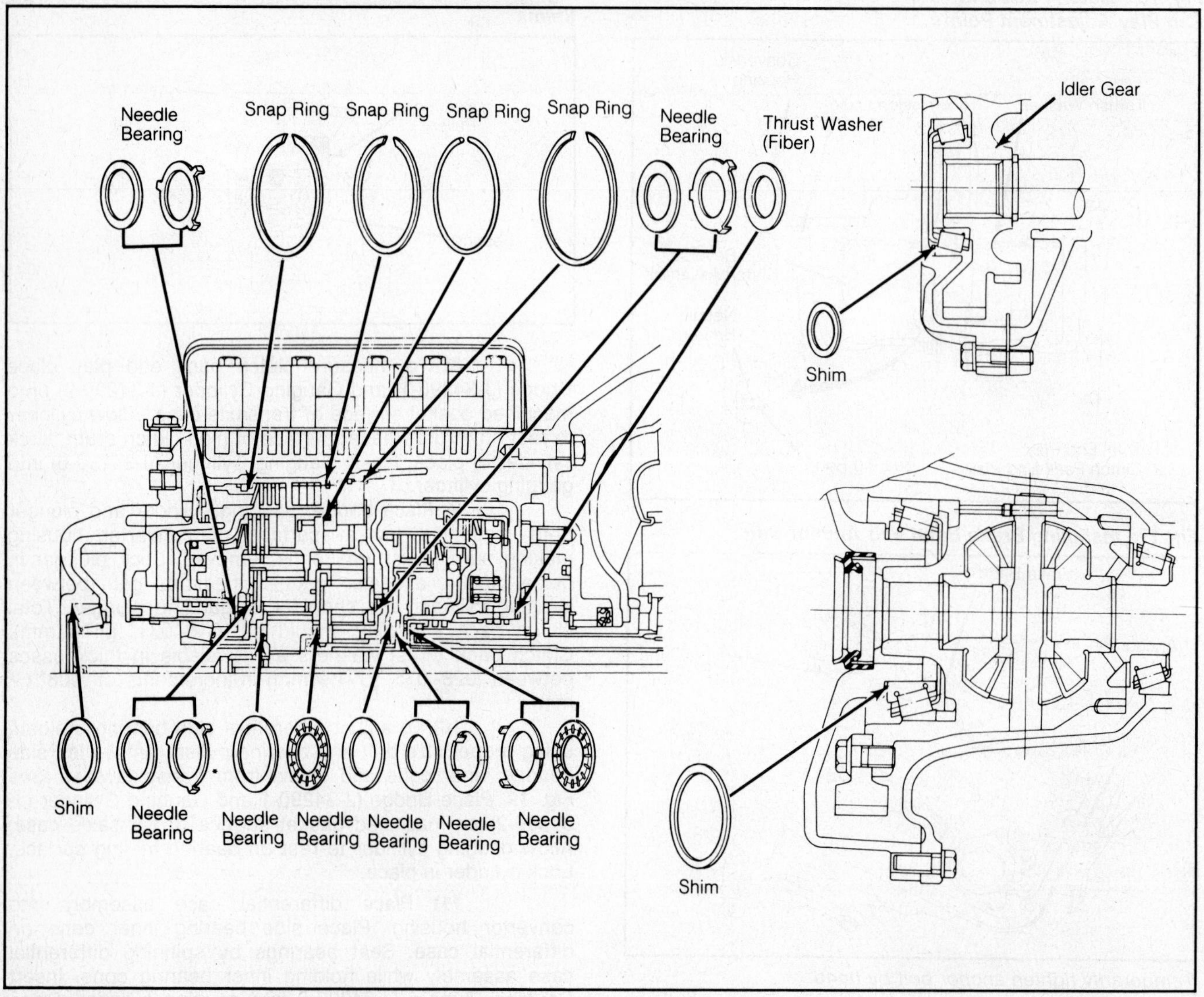

15) Standard clearance should be .01-.024" (.27-.61 mm). If clearance is outside specifications, replace parking pawl. Place input shaft into transaxle as far as possible. Measure distance between end of oil pump housing and tip of input shaft. Standard measurement should be 1.14-1.22" (29-31 mm). Check for smooth rotation of internal parts by placing Socket (J-34284) onto output shaft on torque converter side. Using a torque wrench with Socket (J-34284) it will be normal to find slightly more drag in a counter clockwise turning motion.

16) If any excessive drag or abnormal measurements of the input shaft are found, disassemble parts to see if they are properly assembled. Readjust bearing preloads of final drive, output shaft and idler gear as necessary.

17) Adjust brake band by tightening anchor end pin then backing anchor end pin off 4.5 turns. Tighten anchor end pin while holding anchor end pin stationary. Install terminal assembly noting direction of hook. Install accumulator, accumulator spring, throttle shaft and return spring. Insert manual valve into control valve body and install onto transmission case. Install throttle valve return spring.

18) Connect harness connectors between terminal assembly and solenoids. Using a new gasket install valve body cover and throttle lever. Install control cylinder, governor assembly and speedometer assembly. Fill torque converter with 2 1/8 quarts (2 liters) ATF fluid. Install torque converter to converter housing. Install drain plug using sealent on threads. Install inhibitor switch. Check that manual lever operates correctly.

NISSAN MAXIMA TRANSAXLE (Cont.)

TIGHTENING SPECIFICATIONS

Application	Ft. Lbs. (N.m)
Bearing Retainer	
to Transaxle Case	14-18 (19-25)
Converter-to-Drive Plate	36-51 (49-69)
Converter Housing-to-Engine	
8 mm Bolt	12-16 (16-22)
10 mm Bolt	29-36 (39-49)
Engine Gusset	
to Cylinder Block Bolt	22-30 (30-40)
to Converter Housing	12-15 (16-21)
Front Cover Mount Bolt	10-13 (14-18)
Oil Cooler Pipe	
to Transaxle Case	22-36 (29-49)
Piston Stem Lock Nut	12-16 (16-22)
Ring Gear Mount Bolt	51-58 (69-78)
Selector Shaft Nuts	19-23 (26-32)
Transaxle Case-to	
Converter Housing Mount Bolt	10-13 (14-18)
Transaxle Case to	
Front Cover	10-13 (14-18)
	INCH Lbs. (N.m)
Governor Valve Body	
to Governor Shaft	44-62 (5-7)
to Transaxle Case	62-80 (7-9)
Inhibitor Switch	
to Transaxle Case	18-22 (2.0-2.5)
Low-Reverse Brake	
Piston Retainer	62-80 (7-9)
Lower Body-to-Upper Body	62-80 (7-9)
Oil Pan-to-Transaxle Case	44-62 (5-7)
Oil Strainer-to-Lower Valve Body	44-62 (5-7)

Automatic Transmissions

NISSAN TRANSAXLES

Pulsar NX, Sentra, Stanza

DESCRIPTION

The Sentra (gas), Stanza and Pulsar transaxles (Model RL3F01A) consist primarily of a 3-element hydraulic lock-up torque converter, 2 planetary gear sets and final gear. Desired function of the 2 planetary gear sets is obtained by 2 multiple-disc clutches, a multiple-disc brake, brake band and 1-way clutch.

All models use a hydraulic control system to operate friction elements and automatic shift controls and are equipped with a non-serviceable torque converter. The Sentra diesel transaxle (Model RN3F01A) is the same as the gas models except for a non-lockup torque converter.

The lock-up torque convertor is attached to the crankshaft through a flexible drive plate. This serves to directly couple the turbine runner and pump impeller through the lock-up piston which is controlled by the speed cut valve and lock-up control valve. Heat generated in the torque converter is dissipated by circulating the transaxle fluid through an oil-to-water type cooler in the radiator lower tank.

LUBRICATION & ADJUSTMENT

See appropriate article in AUTOMATIC TRANSMISSION SERVICING article in IMPORT GENERAL SERVICING section.

SERVICE (IN VEHICLE)

NOTE: **The following units can be removed from transaxle without removing transaxle from vehicle: Oil Pan, Valve Body Assembly, Governor Shaft Assembly, Converter Housing Oil Seal and Governor Shaft Assembly. See procedures given in Transmission Disassembly and Transmission Reassembly.**

DRIVE SHAFTS

See SERVICE IN VEHICLE article in IMPORT GENERAL SERVICING section.

TROUBLE SHOOTING

NOTE: **The trouble shooting diagnosis steps are arranged in the order of probability.**

NO STARTER OPERATION IN "P" OR "N" RANGE

Check for faulty ignition switch or starter motor, control cable linkage out of adjustment or misadjusted, faulty inhibitor switch wiring and/or misadjusted inhibitor switch.

NO DRIVE IN "D" RANGE BUT RUNS IN "2", "1" AND "R" RANGE

Check for control cable linkage out of adjustment or misadjusted, line pressure too low and/or manual valve body malfunction. With transaxle out of vehicle, check for defective 1-way clutch.

NO DRIVE IN "R" RANGE BUT RUNS IN "D", "2" AND "1" RANGE

If transaxle clutch slips and/or vehicle has very poor acceleration, check for low transaxle oil level, control cable linkage is out of adjustment or misadjusted and/or line pressure too low. Check for burnt, dark, varnished or water contaminated fluid and/or manual valve body malfunction. If necessary, perform transaxle air pressure check.

With transaxle out of vehicle, check for faulty forward clutch (rear), faulty high-reverse clutch (front), faulty low-reverse brake, oil passage leak and/or faulty high-reverse clutch (front) check ball.

NO DRIVE IN ANY RANGE

Check for low transaxle oil level, control cable linkage out of adjustment or misadjusted, line pressure too low, fluid that is burnt, dark, varnished or water contaminated and/or manual valve body malfunction. If necessary, perform transaxle air pressure check.

With transaxle out of vehicle, check for faulty oil pump, leak in oil passage and/or park linkage out of adjustment or misadjusted.

HARSH ENGAGEMENT

From "N" to "D"

Check for engine idle speed that is too high, throttle control cable out of adjustment, line pressure too high and/or manual valve body malfunction. With transaxle out of vehicle, check for faulty forward clutch (rear).

From "1" to "2"

Check throttle control cable for out of adjustment, engine stall speed too high, burnt, dark, varnished or water contaminated fluid, manual valve body malfunction and/or faulty band servo. With transaxle out of vehicle, check for faulty brake band.

From "2" to "3"

Check for throttle control cable out of adjustment, faulty band servo, line pressure too high and/or manual valve body malfunction. If necessary, perform transaxle air pressure check. With transaxle out of vehicle, check for faulty high-reverse clutch (front).

POOR ACCELERATION

Check for low fluid level, control cable linkage out of adjustment or misadjusted, fluid that is burnt, dark, varnished or water contaminated, line pressure too low, engine stall speed too low, manual valve body malfunction and/or faulty band servo.

With transaxle out of vehicle, check for faulty forward clutch (rear), faulty high-reverse clutch (front), faulty brake band, faulty low-reverse brake and/or defective oil pump.

TRANSAXLE OVERHEATS

Check for low fluid level or poor lubrication, line pressure too low, engine stall speed too low, burnt, dark, varnished or water contaminated fluid, manual valve body malfunction and/or faulty band servo. If necessary, perform transaxle air pressure check.

With transaxle out of vehicle, check for faulty high-reverse clutch (front), faulty brake band, faulty low-reverse brake, faulty torque converter 1-way clutch, faulty planetary gear set, defective oil pump and/or oil passage leak.

TRANSAXLE SLIPS ON "1-2" UPSHIFT

Check for low fluid level, manual control cable linkage out of adjustment, throttle control cable out of adjustment, line pressure too low, burnt, dark, varnished or water contaminated fluid, manual valve body malfunction and/or faulty band servo. If necessary, perform transaxle air pressure check. With transaxle out of vehicle, check for faulty brake band or leak in oil passage.

TRANSAXLE SLIPS ON "2-3" UPSHIFT

Check for low fluid level, manual control cable linkage out of adjustment, throttle control cable out of adjustment, line pressure too low, burnt, dark, varnished or water contaminated fluid, manual valve body malfunction and/or faulty band servo. If necessary, perform transaxle air pressure test. With transaxle out of vehicle, check for faulty high-reverse clutch (front), leak in oil passage and/or faulty high-reverse clutch (front) check ball.

TRANSAXLE SLIPS ON STARTS

Check for low fluid level, manual control cable linkage out of adjustment, line pressure to low, burnt, dark, varnished or water contaminated fluid, throttle control cable out of adjustment and/or manual valve body malfunction. If necessary, perform transaxle air pressure check. With transaxle out of vehicle, check for defective oil pump or oil passage leak.

NO DOWNSHIFT FROM "2" TO "1" OR "3" TO "1"

Check for throttle control cable out of adjustment, burnt, dark, varnished or water contaminated fluid, manual valve body malfunction, faulty governor and/or faulty band servo. If necessary, perform transaxle air pressure check. With transaxle out of vehicle, check for faulty brake band or faulty transaxle 1-way clutch.

NO "1-2" UPSHIFT

Check for manual control cable linkage out of adjustment, throttle control cable out of adjustment, faulty detent valve, burnt, dark, varnished or water contaminated fluid, manual valve body malfunction, faulty governor and/or faulty band servo. If necessary, perform transaxle air pressure check. With transaxle out of vehicle, check for faulty brake band and leak in oil passage.

NO "2-3" UPSHIFT

Check for manual control cable linkage out of adjustment, throttle control cable out of adjustment, faulty detent valve, burnt, dark, varnished or water contaminated fluid, manual valve body malfunction, faulty governor and/or faulty band servo. If necessary, perform transaxle air pressure check. With transaxle out of vehicle, check for faulty high-reverse clutch (front), faulty high-reverse clutch (front) check ball and/or leak in oil passage.

TORQUE CONVERTER DIAGNOSIS (ALL EXCEPT SENTRA DIESEL)

Converter Not Locked-Up

Check for a faulty governor or line pressure that is too low. With transaxle out of vehicle, check for defective input shaft "O" ring, defective torque converter, faulty speed cut valve or lock-up control valve and/or defective oil pump.

Lock-Up Piston Slip

Check for line pressure that is too low. With transaxle out of vehicle, check for defective input shaft "O" ring, defective torque converter and/or oil pump.

Lock-Up Point Too High or Too Low

Check for a faulty governor. With transaxle removed from vehicle, check for faulty speed cut valve and/or lock-up control valve.

Engine Stops At "R", "D", "2" And "1" Ranges

With transaxle out of vehicle, check for faulty torque converter and/or faulty lock-up control valve.

Transaxle Overheats

Check for line pressure that is too low. With transaxle removed from vehicle, check for defective input shaft "O" ring, defective torque converter or oil pump.

TESTING

NOTE: The transaxle is provided with four pressure test ports. All are useful for transaxle trouble-shooting. Ports are; Line pressure, to high-reverse clutch (front). Line pressure, to forward clutch (rear). Governor pressure and Torque Converter lock-up pressure.

ROAD TEST

1) Before road testing, ensure fluid level, condition and control linkage adjustments have been checked and corrected as necessary. During test, transmission should upshift and downshift at approximately the same speeds as shown in SHIFT SPEEDS chart.

CAUTION: Do not shift transaxle into 1st gear from "D" range if car road speed is above 40 mph (65 km/h).

2) All shifts may vary slightly due to production tolerances or tire size. The important factor is the quality of the shifts. All shifts should be smooth and responsive with no slippage or engine speed runaway.

3) Slippage or engine runaway in any gear usually indicates clutch or band problems. The slipping clutch or band in a particular gear can usually be identified by noting transmission operation in other selector positions and comparing internal units which are applied in these positions. See CLUTCH AND BAND APPLICATION chart.

PULSAR & SENTRA SHIFT SPEEDS SPECIFICATIONS

Application	MPH
Minimum Throttle 1-2 Upshift	7-13
2-3 Upshift	14-20
3-2 Downshift	12-17
2-1 Downshift	7-12
Full Throttle	
1-2 Upshift	30-35
2-3 Upshift	59-65
3-2 Downshift	58-62
2-1 Downshift	18-27
Lock-Up Shift Points	
Engaged	38-45
Disengaged	36-43

Automatic Transmissions

NISSAN TRANSAXLES (Cont.)

CLUTCH AND BRAKE APPLICATION CHART (ELEMENTS IN USE)

Selector Lever Position	Clutch		Low-Reverse Brake	1-Way Clutch	Band Servo	
	High-Reverse (Front)	Forward (Rear)			Operation	Release
D - DRIVE						
Low		X	[1]	X		
Second		X			X	
Third [2]	X	X			X	X
2 - Second Gear						
Low		X		X		
Second		X			X	
1 - First Gear						
Low		X	X	X		
Second		X			X	
R - Reverse	X		X			

NEUTRAL OR PARK – All clutches and brakes released and/or ineffective.

[1] – Low & reverse brake applied to prevent free wheeling when coasting and to provide engine braking.
[2] – Lock-up converter engaged on all models except Sentra Diesel.

SENTRA DIESEL SHIFT SPEEDS SPECIFICATIONS

Application	MPH
Minimum Throttle 1-2 Upshift	8-14
2-3 Upshift	13-19
3-2 Downshift	11-16
2-1 Downshift	7-13
Full Throttle	
1-2 Upshift	27-32
2-3 Upshift	54-60
3-2 Downshift	53-57
2-1 Downshift	17-27

STANZA SHIFT SPEEDS SPECIFICATIONS

Application	MPH
Minimum Throttle 1-2 Upshift	8-14
2-3 Upshift	15-21
3-2 Downshift	13-18
2-1 Downshift	7-13
Full Throttle	
1-2 Upshift	32-37
2-3 Upshift	63-69
3-2 Downshift	62-66
2-1 Downshift	19-29
Lock-Up Shift Points	
Engaged	39-46
Disengaged	37-44

STALL SPEED TEST

Stall Test Precautions

A stall test should only be performed as a last resort due to the high temperature it generates and the excessive load it places on the engine and transaxle. DO NOT test more than two gear ranges without driving car to cool off drivetrain.

Before making a stall speed test, ensure that line pressure is correct. If line pressure is too low when performing a stall test, transmission can be damaged. During stall test, DO NOT hold throttle open for more than 5 seconds at a time.

Stall Test Procedure

1) Road test vehicle and warm transmission to normal operating temperature. Connect tachometer to engine. Position tachometer so that it can be read from driver's seat.

2) Set parking and service brakes. Start engine and place selector lever in "D". Depress accelerator pedal completely and note maximum RPM obtained. RPM should be approximately as shown in STALL SPEED chart.

3) Place selector lever in "N" and allow engine to idle to cool off transmission. Then, place selector lever in "R" and repeat stall test. Stall RPM should be approximately as shown in STALL SPEED chart.

NOTE: **If stall test indicates proper stall RPM in "D" range, no further testing is necessary.**

STALL SPEED SPECIFICATIONS

Application	Stall Speed (RPM)
Pulsar, Sentra	1800-2100
Sentra Diesel	1500-1800
Stanza	2000-2300

Stall Test Results

1) Satisfactory results in "D" range indicate forward clutch (rear), 1-way clutch of transaxle and sprag clutch of torque converter are functioning properly.

2) If the stall RPM in "D" range (1st gear) is above the specified vehicle RPM, the forward clutch (rear) is faulty. If the stall RPM in "R" range is above the specified vehicle RPM (for "D" range), the low and reverse brakes are faulty.

3) If the stall RPM in "D' range (1st gear) is below the specified vehicle RPM, the converter one-way clutch is faulty or the engine is not performing properly.

4) If the converter one-way clutch is frozen, vehicle will have poor high speed performance. If converter one-way clutch is slipping, vehicle will be sluggish up to 30-40 MPH (50-60 km/h).

LINE PRESSURE TEST

NOTE: **Measure line pressure at idling, at stall speed test and while road testing under different throttle conditions.**

1) Road test vehicle to bring transaxle to normal operating temperature of 109-135° F (43-57° C). Connect pressure gauge to appropriate test port. Place gauge so that it is visible from driver's seat.

2) To test all forward range line pressures, connect gauge to rear line pressure port (2). *See Fig. 1.* Connect tachometer to engine. Start engine and if necessary, adjust idle speed.

Fig. 1: Transaxle Case Pressure Test Port Locations

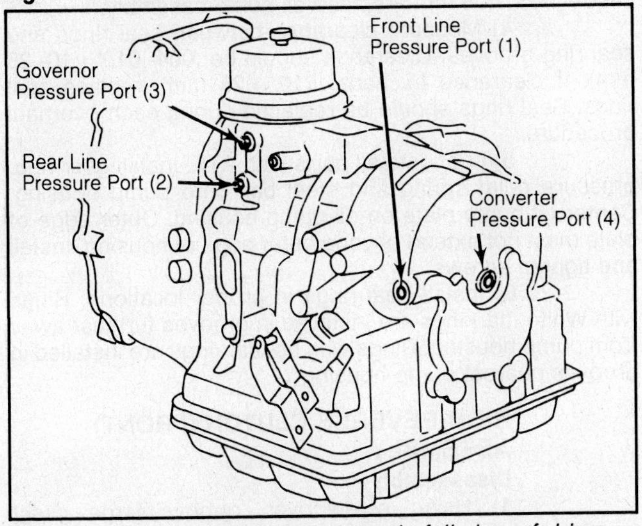

Connect pressure gauge at test port in full view of driver.

3) Depress brake pedal and place selector lever in "D". Note line pressure reading on gauge. Repeat procedure for each forward range. Pressure should be approximately as shown in LINE PRESSURE chart.

4) Connect gauge to front line pressure port (1) to test reverse range line pressure. *See Fig. 1.* Repeat line pressure test with selector lever in "R". Pressure should be approximately as shown in LINE PRESSURE chart.

5) After testing at idle and during stall speed test, road test vehicle and note readings at different throttle positions. Pressure should be approximately as shown in LINE PRESSURE chart.

LINE PRESSURE TEST RESULTS

Pressure Too High

If pressure is too high, check throttle cable adjustment. If cable is correctly adjusted and pressure is still high, regulator valve or throttle valve may be seized.

Pressure Too Low

If line pressure is too low, check for seizing of regulator valve or throttle valve in valve body. If valves are not seized, check pressure relief valve and oil pump assembly for damage. A defective oil pump assembly will usually make noise.

LINE PRESSURE SPECIFICATIONS

Application	psi (kg/cm²)
All Models	
Idle	
In All Forward Ranges	36-50 (2.5-3.5)
In "R" Range	91-112 (6.4-7.9)
At Half Throttle	
In All Forward Ranges	73-94 (5.1-6.6)
At Full Throttle	
In All Forward Ranges	80-101 (5.6-7.1)
At Stall Speed Test	
In All Forward Ranges	80-101 (5.6-7.1)
In "R" Range	185-213 (13-15)

GOVERNOR PRESSURE TEST

NOTE: **Line pressure MUST be correct before checking governor pressure.**

Testing Procedures

Road test vehicle to warm transmission to normal operating temperature. Connect pressure gauge to governor pressure port (3) on transmission case. *See Fig. 1.* Position gauge so it is visible from driver's seat. Test drive vehicle in "D" and note pressure readings. Governor pressure increases directly with road speed and should always be less than line pressure.

TORQUE CONVERTER LOCK-UP TEST (EXCEPT SENTRA DIESEL)

1) Road test vehicle to warm transmission to normal operating temperature. Connect pressure gauge to torque converter pressure port (4) on transmission case. *See Fig. 1.*

2) Position gauge so it is visible from driver's seat. Test drive vehicle in "D" and note pressure readings. Pressure should be approximately as shown in TORQUE CONVERTER LOCK-UP PRESSURE chart.

TORQUE CONVERTER LOCK-UP PRESSURE SPECIFICATIONS

Application	psi (kg/cm²)
Pulsar, Sentra (Gas) & Stanza	
Lock-Up Engaged	Less than 7.0 (0.5)
Lock-Up Disengaged	Greater than 28.0 (2.0)

3) The torque converter lock-up pressure at idle should show a steady rise in pressure as vehicle speed increases under light load.

4) The pressure drop between shift points should not exceed 14 psi (1.0 kg/cm²). Excessive pressure drop may indicate an internal leak at a servo or clutch seal.

REMOVAL & INSTALLATION

See appropriate article in AUTOMATIC TRANSMISSION REMOVAL article in IMPORT GENERAL SERVICING section.

TORQUE CONVERTER

Torque converter is a sealed unit and cannot be disassembled for service. Replace if defective.

11) Remove low-reverse brake retainer. Apply compressed air to oil passage to remove low-reverse brake piston. Place nylon cloth over piston to prevent it from jumping out. *See Fig. 4*. If compressed air is not available, use a screwdriver to carefully remove piston.

12) Remove oil pump assembly, nylon washer and thrust bearing by lifting straight out of case. Use care in lifting out oil pump; clearance is very close even though pump fits loosely. Remove inhibitor switch. Remove band servo piston and return spring. Remove transmission case as needed.

COMPONENT DISASSEMBLY & REASSEMBLY

OIL PUMP ASSEMBLY

Disassembly

1) Remove bearing and thrust washer. Remove oil pump plate. Mark pump drive and driven gears for reassembly in same position. DO NOT punch marks.

2) Remove gear hub and gears from pump housing. Remove steel ball and pressure relief spring from its bore. *See Fig. 5*.

Fig. 5: Exploded View of Oil Pump Assembly

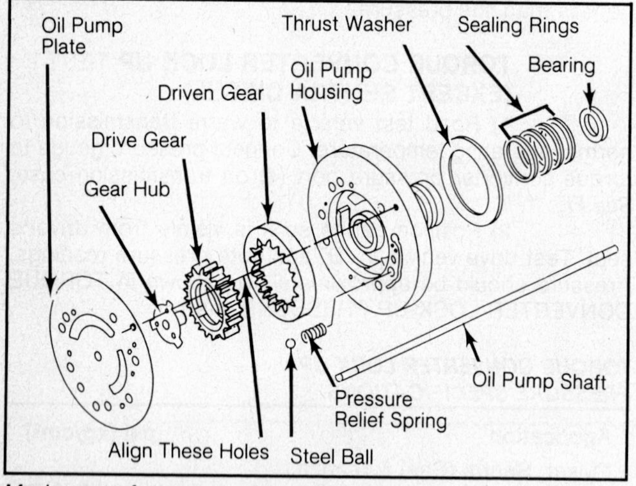

Mark gears for reassembly reference.

Cleaning & Inspection

1) Thoroughly clean all parts and dry with compressed air. Inspect parts for damage, wear, cracks, or scoring. Check oil pump shaft and ring groove areas of pump housing for wear.

2) If pump housing, cover plate, shaft, inner drive gear or outer driven gear requires replacement, complete oil pump assembly must be replaced as a matched set.

Reassembly

1) Install drive and driven gear into housing, aligning marks made at disassembly. Using a feeler gauge, measure clearance between pump driven gear and pump housing. *See Fig. 6*.

2) Clearance should be .008-.012" (.20-.30 mm). If clearance exceeds .014" (.35 mm), replace oil pump assembly. Check clearance between driven gear and crescent. Clearance should be .008-.012" (.20-.30 mm). If clearance exceeds .014" (.35 mm), replace oil pump.

Fig. 6: Measuring Housing-to-Gear Face Clearance

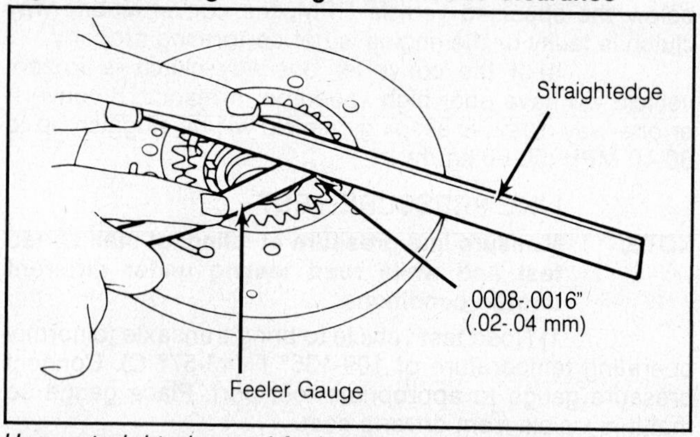

Use a straightedge and feeler gauge when measuring the gear-to-housing clearance.

3) Using a straightedge and feeler gauge, check pump housing face-to-gear face clearance. Clearance should be .0008-.0016" (.020-.040 mm). If clearance exceeds .003" (.08 mm), replace oil pump assembly.

4) Measure clearance between seal rings and seal ring grooves. Clearance should be .004-.010" (.10-.25 mm). If clearance exceeds .010" (.25 mm), replace seal rings. Seal rings should be replaced during each overhaul procedure.

5) Lubricate all parts with ATF. Install gear hub, pressure relief spring and steel ball onto pump housing. Center oil pump plate on oil pump housing. Outer edge of plate must not extend beyond outer edge of housing. Install and tighten screws.

6) Install seal rings in proper locations. Rings with White markings are installed in grooves furthest away from pump housing. Rings with no markings are installed in grooves nearest pump housing.

HIGH-REVERSE CLUTCH (FRONT) ASSEMBLY

Disassembly

1) Using screwdriver, remove large clutch retaining plate snap ring. Remove clutch plate assembly, noting number and arrangement of discs and plates.

2) Using Spring Compressor (ST25420001), compress clutch springs and remove snap ring from spring retainer. Remove spring retainer and lift out springs.

Fig. 7: Removing Front Clutch Piston

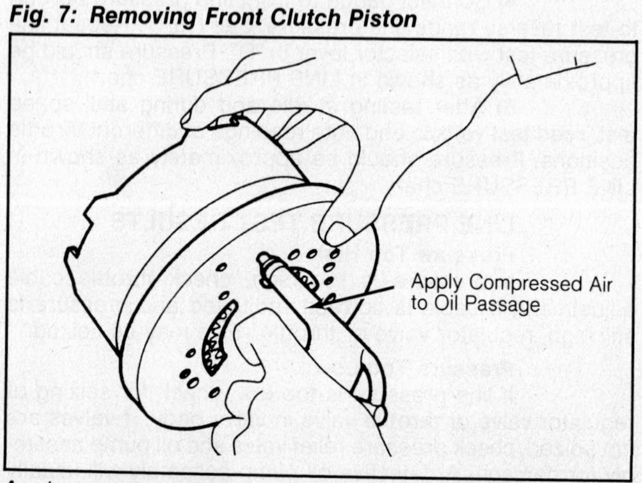

Apply compressed air to oil passage to remove the clutch piston from the drum.

TORQUE CONVERTER

Torque converter is a sealed unit and cannot be disassembled for service. Replace if defective.

TRANSAXLE DISASSEMBLY

1) With transaxle removed from vehicle, clean outside case thoroughly and disassemble in a clean area. When cleaning and wiping parts, use nylon cloth or paper towels. Common shop rags will leave lint that can interfere with transaxle's operation.

2) Remove hex plug and drain fluid. Remove torque converter. Remove oil pump shaft and input shaft. Remove snap ring, governor cap with breather hose (if equipped) and "O" ring. Remove oil pan guard and oil pan and inspect its contents.

NOTE: Inspection of foreign matter in pan may indicate area of problem in transaxle.

3) Remove valve body bolts and valve body. Remove particle magnet and manual valve. Remove gear selector shaft inside and outside retaining nuts. Pull out retaining pin. Remove throttle lever, selector plate, selector shaft, selector range lever and parking rod assembly.

4) Disconnect and remove throttle cable from throttle lever. Remove parking actuator support from case. Loosen brake band piston stem lock nut. Back off piston stem. Apply compressed air to oil supply hole to remove accumulator piston. Place rag over piston to prevent it from jumping out of bore. *See Fig. 2.*

Fig. 2: Removing Accumulator Piston

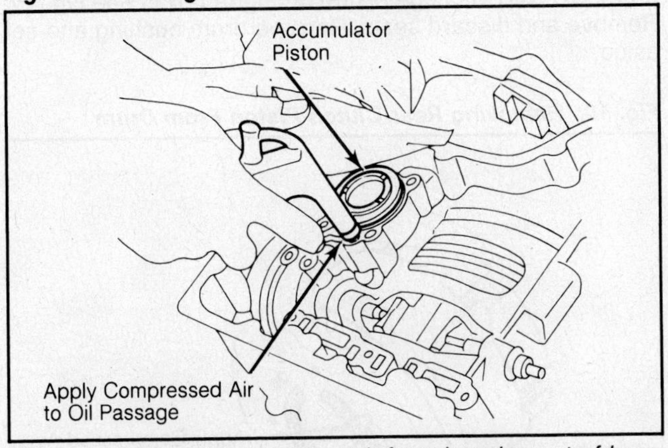

Place rag over piston to prevent it from jumping out of bore.

5) Remove converter housing mount bolts. Tap converter housing with plastic mallet to separate it from transaxle case. DO NOT drop final drive assembly. Remove final drive assembly and set aside. Pull out parking pawl shaft. Remove parking pawl and return spring.

6) With chisel and hammer, straighten tang on idler gear bolt lock washer. Remove idler gear bolt and lock washer. Turn transaxle case over. Remove front cover retaining bolts. Hold front cover and tap output shaft with plastic mallet to loosen. Remove output shaft and front cover as an assembly. DO NOT lose adjusting shim located on rear internal gear side of output shaft.

7) Remove front cover gasket. Tap out idler gear, idler gear shaft and bearings with drift and hammer. Remove planetary gear set seal bushing from case. Turn case so torque converter housing faces up. Remove governor shaft retaining bolt. Pull out governor shaft. Remove rear internal gear, bearing race and thrust washer.

8) Remove 1-way clutch snap ring. Lift out 1-way clutch assembly with rear carrier assembly. Remove bearing race and thrust washer. Remove low and reverse brake snap ring. Remove connecting shell, snap ring, thrust bearing and bearing race. Lift out planetary gear set (front carrier assembly and front internal gear), with thrust bearing and race, as an assembly.

9) Lift out forward clutch (rear) assembly and plastic thrust washer. Remove low-reverse brake retaining plate, driven plates and drive plates at the same time. Rotate and remove high-reverse clutch (front) assembly.

NOTE: If high-reverse clutch (front) seal rings have expanded, front clutch assembly will be difficult to remove. DO NOT force out clutch assembly as seal damage may occur.

10) To prevent brake linings from cracking or peeling, DO NOT stretch flexible band excessively. Before removing brake band, secure it with a clip placed into ends of band. Leave clip in position after removing brake band. Securing clip can be fabricated from .08" (2 mm) diameter wire stock. *See Fig. 3.*

Fig. 3: Brake Band Securing Clip Installation

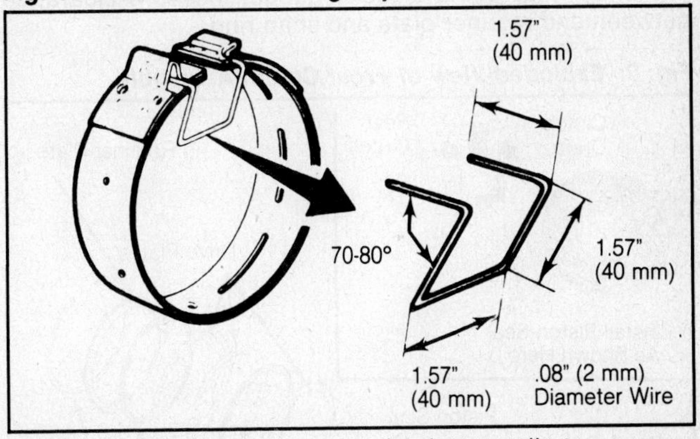

Use the specifications shown to fabricate a clip to secure the brake band.

Fig. 4: Low-Reverse Brake Piston Removal

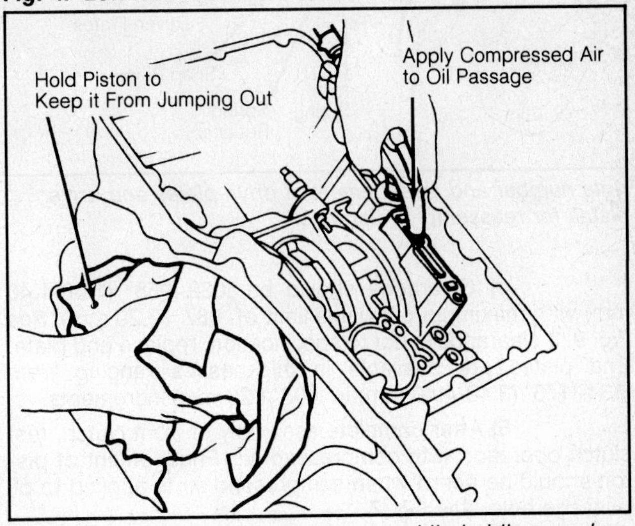

Apply compressed air to oil passage while holding a nylon cloth over piston.

3) Using rubber-tipped air blower, apply compressed air to oil passage hole to remove clutch piston from drum. DO NOT damage piston during removal. *See Fig. 7*. Remove and discard seals. Remove drum bushing and set aside.

Inspection

1) Check clutch discs for wear or damage. Measure plate thickness. Plate thickness should be .059-.065" (1.50-1.65 mm). Replace plate if any thickness measures less than .055" (1.40 mm).

2) Check snap ring for wear, springs for weakness or broken coils and spring retainer for warpage. Replace defective components as required.

Reassembly

1) Lubricate components with ATF. Install clutch drum bushing and seals. DO NOT stretch seals during installation. Ensure piston seal is installed in proper direction. *See Fig. 8*.

2) Install piston in drum without damaging or pinching seal. After installation, check for binding by rotating piston by hand. Place springs on top of piston. Install spring retainer. Compress spring retainer and install snap ring.

3) Assemble clutch discs and plates in proper sequence and install. *See Fig. 8*. Install end retainer plate and snap ring. Using a feeler gauge, measure clearance between end retainer plate and snap ring.

Fig. 8: Exploded View of Front Clutch Assembly

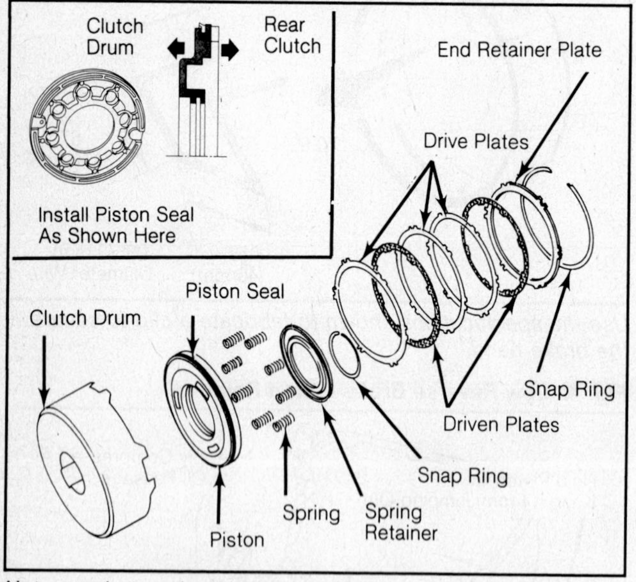

Note number and arrangement of drive plates and driven plates for reassembly reference.

4) Clearance should be .039-.055" (1.00-1.40 mm) with maximum allowable limit of .087" (2.20 mm). *See Fig. 9*. If clearance is not to specification, replace end plate. End plates are available in thicknesses ranging from .134-.173" (3.40-4.40 mm) in .008" (.20 mm) increments.

5) After complete assembly of front clutch, test clutch operation with compressed air. Engagement of piston should be heard when compressed air is applied to oil passage hole. *See Fig. 7*.

Fig. 9: Measuring End Plate-to-Snap Ring Clearance

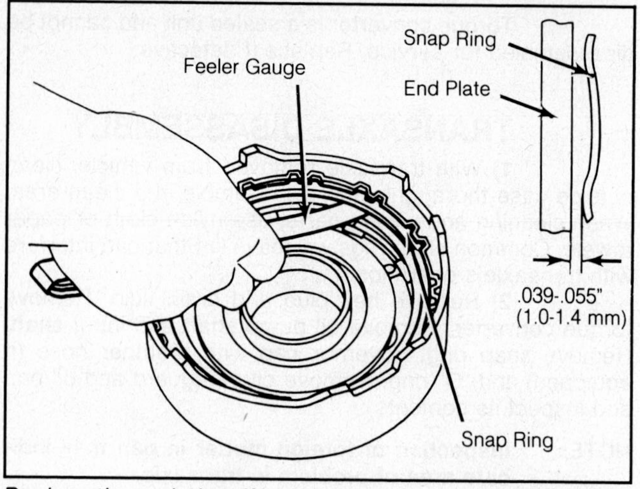

Replace the end plate if clearance is not to specification.

FORWARD CLUTCH (REAR) ASSEMBLY

Disassembly

1) Using a screwdriver, remove large clutch retaining snap ring. Remove clutch plates, noting number and arrangement of discs and plates.

2) Using a spring compressor, compress clutch springs and remove snap ring from spring retainer. Remove spring retainer and lift out springs.

3) Using a rubber-tipped air blower, apply compressed air to oil passage hole to remove clutch piston from drum. DO NOT damage piston during removal. *See Fig. 10*. Remove and discard seals. Remove drum bushing and set aside.

Fig. 10: Removing Rear Clutch Piston From Drum

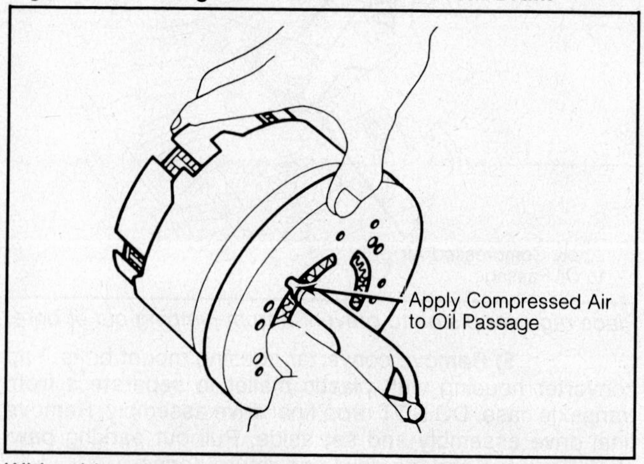

With rubber-tipped air blower, apply compressed air to oil passage to remove piston or to check piston operation.

Inspection

1) Check clutch discs for wear or damage. Measure fiber drive plate thickness. Plate thickness should be .059-.065" (1.50-1.65 mm). Minimum plate thickness is no less than .055" (1.40 mm).

2) Check snap ring for wear, springs for weakness or broken coils and spring retainer for warpage. Replace defective components as required.

NISSAN TRANSAXLES (Cont.)

Reassembly

1) Lubricate components with ATF. Install clutch drum bushing and seals. Ensure piston seal is properly installed. Install piston in drum without damaging or pinching seal.

2) After installation, check piston for binding by rotating piston by hand. Place springs on top of piston. Install and compress spring retainer. Install snap ring. Install dished plate with beveled end facing piston.

3) Assemble clutch discs and plates in proper sequence and install. *See Fig. 11*. Install end plate and large snap ring. Using a feeler gauge, measure clearance between end plate and snap ring.

Fig. 11: Exploded View of Rear Clutch Assembly

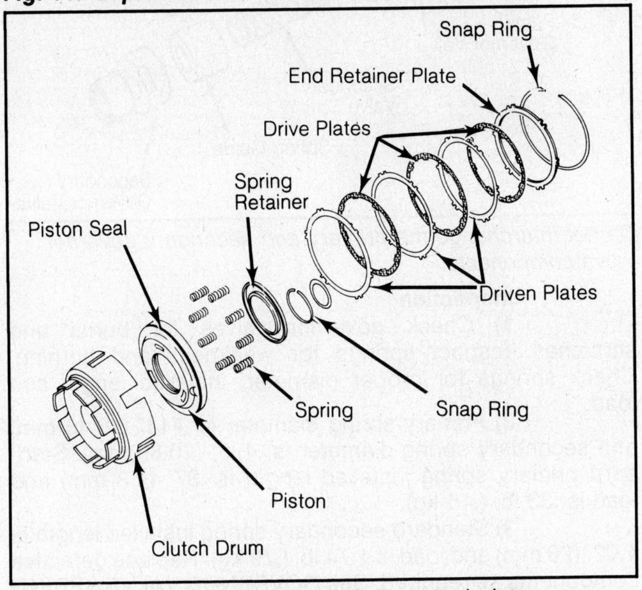

Note number and arrangement of discs and plates.

4) Clearance should be .031-.047" (.80-1.20 mm). Maximum allowable limit is .11" (2.8 mm). *See Fig. 12*. If clearance is not to specification, replace end plate. End plates are available in thicknesses ranging from .134-.173" (3.40-4.40 mm) in .008" (.20 mm) increments.

Fig. 12: Measuring End Plate-to-Snap Ring Clearance

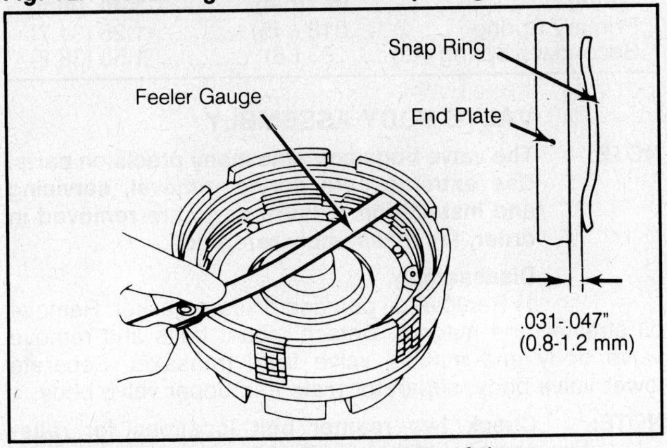

Replace the end retainer plate with one of the proper thickness if clearance is not to specification.

5) After complete assembly of rear clutch, test clutch operation with compressed air. Engagement of piston should be heard when compressed air is applied to oil passage hole. *See Fig. 10*.

LOW-REVERSE BRAKE ASSEMBLY

Disassembly

1) Using a screwdriver, remove large retaining snap ring. Remove driven and drive plates. Note number and arrangement of steel discs and fiber plates.

2) Using a spring compressor, compress springs and remove snap ring from spring retainer. Remove spring retainer and lift out springs.

NOTE: **Some models may use two plates instead of one rear end plate. Always install same configuration.**

Inspection

1) Check discs for wear or damage. Measure fiber plate thickness. Plate thickness should be .075-.081" (1.90-2.05 mm). Replace plate if any thickness measures less than .071" (1.80 mm).

2) Check snap ring for wear, springs for weakness or broken coils and spring retainer for warpage. Replace defective components as required.

Reassembly

1) Lubricate components with ATF. Place springs in piston and install spring retainer. Compress spring retainer and install snap ring. Install dished plate with beveled end facing piston. Assemble clutch discs and plates in proper sequence and install. *See Fig. 13*.

Fig. 13: Exploded View of Low-Reverse Brake Assembly

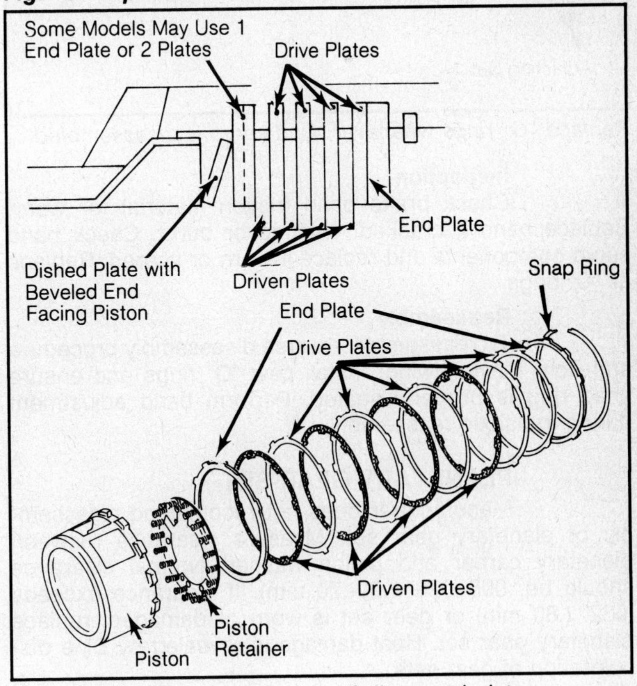

Note number and arrangement of discs and plates.

2) Install end retainer plate and large snap ring. Using a feeler gauge, measure clearance between end plate and snap ring. Clearance should be .075-.087" (1.90-2.20 mm) with maximum allowable limit of .15" (3.8 mm).

3) If clearance is not to specification, replace end retainer plate. End plates are available in thicknesses ranging from .142-.173" (3.60-4.40 mm) in .008" (.20 mm) increments.

BRAKE BAND & BAND SERVO

Disassembly

Remove adjusting nut and washer from anchor pin. Remove anchor pin. Pull off band servo assembly. Remove snap ring and separate servo piston retainer from piston. Disassemble piston assembly and discard "O" rings. *See Fig. 14*.

Fig. 14: Exploded View of Brake Band and Band Servo Assembly

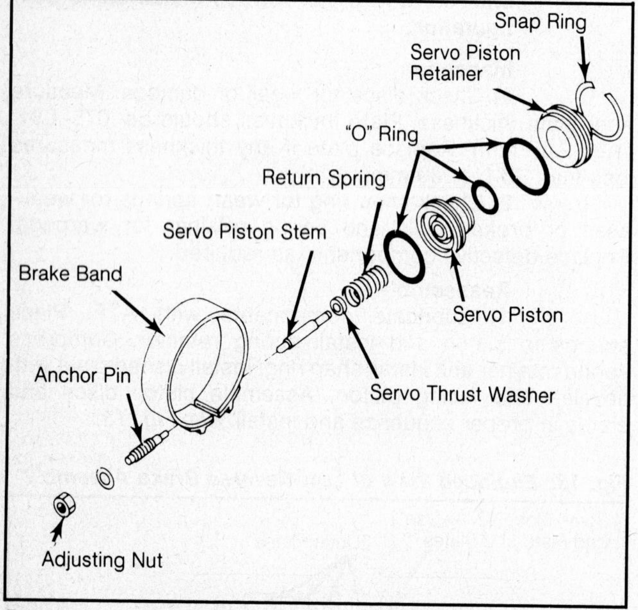

Replace "O" rings whenever band servo is disassembled.

Inspection

Check brake band friction material for wear. Replace band if cracked, chipped or burnt. Check band servo components and replace if worn or scored. Replace all "O" rings.

Reassembly

To reassemble, reverse disassembly procedure and note the following: Install new "O" rings and ensure snap ring is properly seated. Perform band adjustment during transaxle reassembly.

PLANETARY GEAR SET

Manufacturer does not recommend disassembly of planetary gear set. Measure clearance between planetary carrier and pinion washer. Normal clearance should be .008-.028" (.20-.70 mm). If clearance exceeds .032" (.80 mm) or gear set is worn or damaged, replace planetary gear set. Heat damage is revealed by Blue discoloration of gear sets.

GOVERNOR ASSEMBLY

Disassembly

1) Remove governor body-to-governor shaft bolts. Mount governor shaft in a soft-jawed vise and drive out gear retaining pin. Remove drive gear.

2) Disassemble governor valve body. Place components in order of disassembly. DO NOT interchange primary and secondary governor components. *See Fig. 15*.

Fig. 15: Exploded View of Governor Assembly

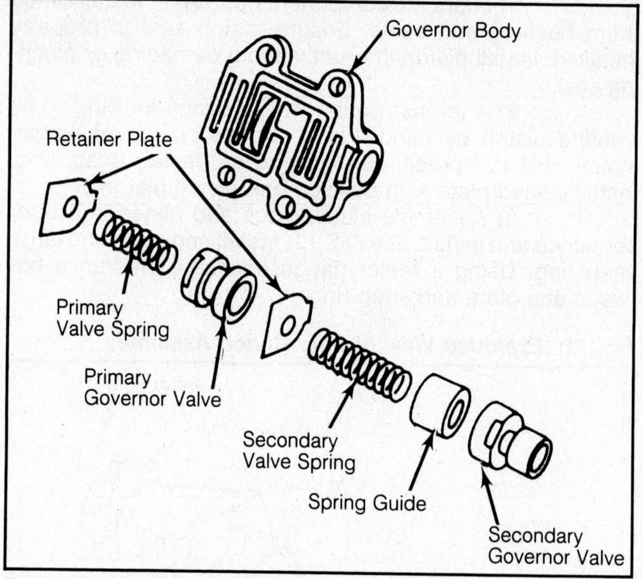

Do not interchange the primary and secondary governor valve components.

Inspection

1) Check governor valves for burns and scratches. Inspect springs for weakness and burning. Check springs for proper diameter, installed length and load.

2) Primary spring diameter is .411" (10.45 mm) and secondary spring diameter is .425" (10.80 mm). Standard primary spring installed length is .37" (9.3 mm) and load is .33 lb. (.15 kg).

3) Standard secondary spring installed length is 1.02" (26 mm) and load is 1.74 lb. (.79 kg). Replace defective components as required. See GOVERNOR VALVE SPRING chart.

Reassembly

To reassemble, reverse disassembly procedure and note the following: Make sure primary and secondary governor springs are properly installed.

GOVERNOR VALVE SPRING CHART

Governor Spring	Wire Dia. In. (mm)	Free Length In. (mm)
Primary Spring	.018 (.45)	1.25 (31.7)
Secondary Spring	.03 (.8)	1.50 (38.2)

VALVE BODY ASSEMBLY

NOTE: **The valve body contains many precision parts. Use extreme care during removal, servicing and installation. Ensure parts are removed in order, for reassembly reference.**

Disassembly

1) Remove oil pan and discard gasket. Remove oil strainer and magnet. Detach mount bolts and remove valve body and manual valve from transaxle. Separate lower valve body, separator plate and upper valve body.

NOTE: **Check two reamer bolt locations for reassembly reference. During valve body separation, DO NOT lose the 6 steel balls from upper valve body.**

2) Remove parallel pins from valve body by pushing out with a piece of wire. Remove valve body plugs.

Fig. 16: Upper Valve Body Check Ball Locations

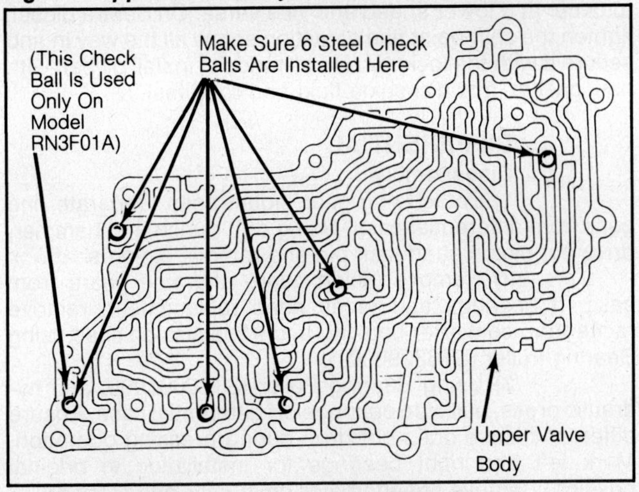

Ensure check balls are properly positioned.

Extract 3-2 downshift valve and spring, 2-3 shift valve and spring, 1-2 shift valve, 1-2 control valve and spring from lower valve body. Place valves and springs in order of removal for reassembly reference.

3) Turn lower valve body over. Remove parallel pins by pushing out with wire. Remove valve body plugs. Remove fail-safe valve, detent valve, throttle valve, throttle modulator valve and spring guide.

4) Remove pressure modifier valve, 1st reducing valve, top reducing valve and check ball, 3-2 timing valve and all springs. Place components in order of removal for reassembly reference. *See Fig. 17.*

5) Using a small screwdriver, depress spring under back-up valve retaining plate. Remove retaining pin. Remove plug, retaining plate, spring and back-up valve. Remove pressure regulator spring and valve.

6) Disassemble the lock-up valve body. Remove speed cut valve retainer, spring and valve. Remove lock-up control valve plate, spring and control valve.

Inspection

1) Clean valves in alcohol or lacquer thinner. Dip valve body in carburetor cleaner or lacquer thinner. DO NOT leave valve body in cleaner longer than 5 minutes. Rinse parts thoroughly and blow dry.

2) Use only crocus cloth to remove burns or heavy varnish deposits. DO NOT use emery cloth as it is too coarse and can scratch valves or valve bores. Replace valves if deposits cannot be removed.

NOTE: **If clearance between valves and valve bores exceeds .001" (.03 mm), replace entire valve body assembly.**

3) Check valves for rounded edges. If edges are not sharp, replace valve. Check oil strainer for general condition. Check separator plate for scratches or damage. Separator plate must not be scratched or damaged or oil will bypass correct oil passages and system malfunction will result. Replace components as needed.

4) Inspect upper and lower valve body oil passages for varnish deposits, scratches or other damage that would impair valve movement. Check for stripped threads. Repair any damaged thread holes. Replace bolts and

Fig. 17: Exploded View of Lower Control Valve Body Assembly

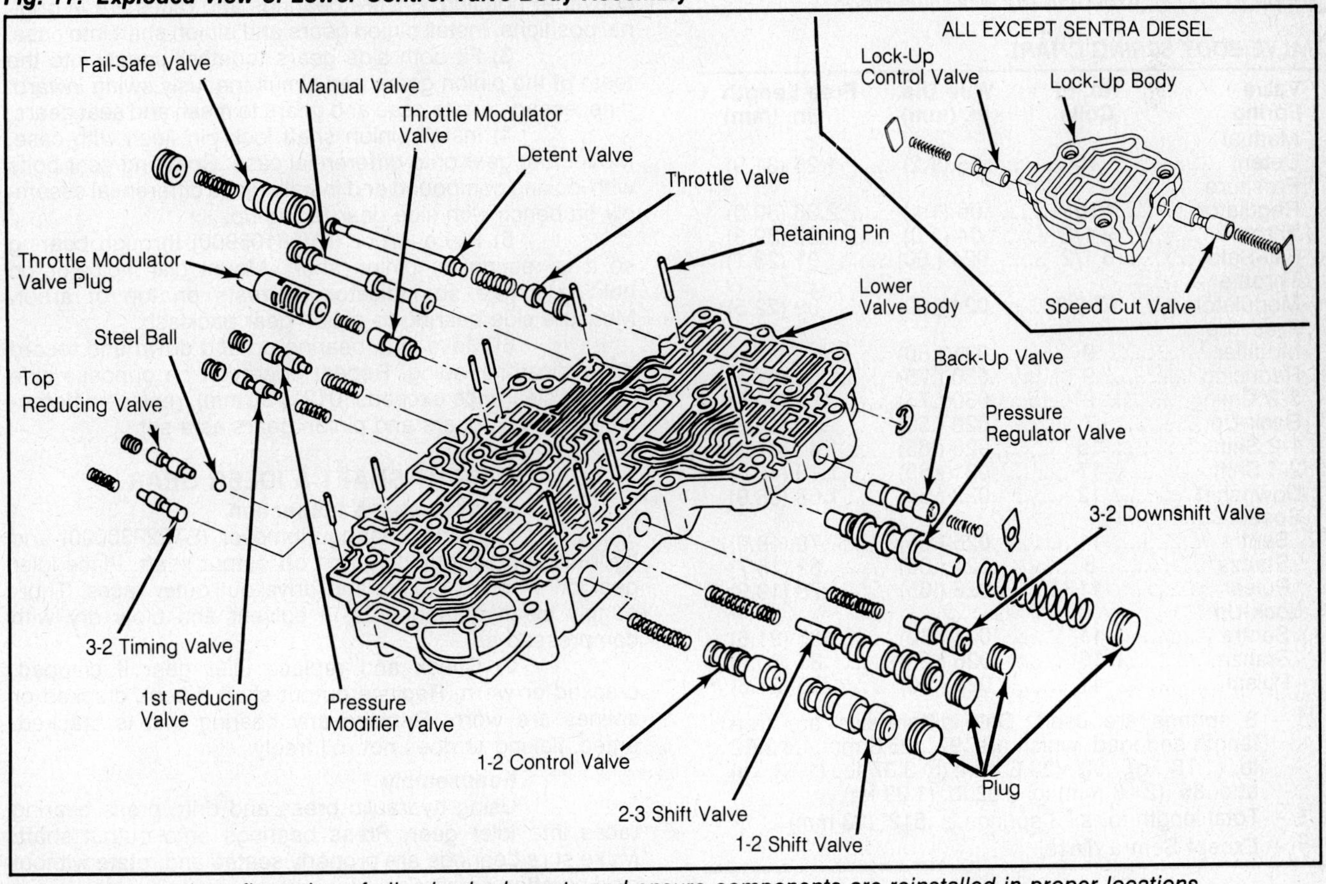

Note position and configuration of all valve body parts and ensure components are reinstalled in proper locations.

Automatic Transmissions

NISSAN TRANSAXLES (Cont.)

screws as needed. Test valve springs for weakness. Replace defective components as required.

NOTE: If replacing pressure modifier valve spring, ensure new spring is the same type as the one which was removed.

Reassembly

1) Install valves and springs in correct locations. Place 6 steel check balls in correct position in upper valve body. *See Fig. 16.* Assemble separator plate and valve bodies. Install reamer bolts first, then install and tighten remaining bolts. Install oil strainer and magnet.

2) Install manual valve after valve body is mounted on transaxle. On all models except Sentra diesel, shift point fine adjustment screw should be adjusted so that the distance from end of shaft to lock nut on valve body is .49-.51" (12.5-13.0 mm). *See Fig. 18.*

Fig. 18: Checking Shift Point Fine Adjusting Screw Position

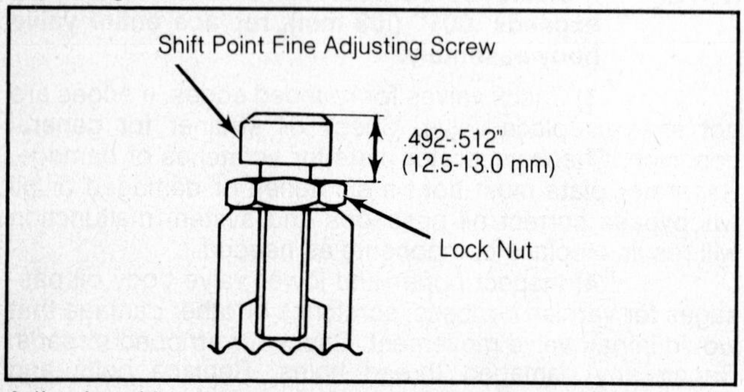

Adjusting this screw can change the shift points about 3 mph (5 km/h), except in the kickdown mode.

VALVE BODY SPRING CHART

Valve Spring	No. of Coils	Wire Dia. In. (mm)	Free Length In. (mm)
Manual Detent	16	.05 (1.2)	1.26 (31.9)
Pressure Regulator	10	.06 (1.4)	2.36 (60.0)
Throttle	9 1/2	.04 (1.0)	1.27 (32.3)
Fail-Safe	6 1/2	.024 (.60)	.91 (23.1)
Throttle Modulator	10 1/2	.024 (.60)	.89 (22.5)
Pressure Modifier [1]	9	.031 (.80)	[2]
Reducing	9	.030 (.75)	.84 (21.4)
3-2 Timing	9	.030 (.75)	.81 (20.6)
Back-Up	7	.020 (.50)	.74 (18.8)
1-2 Shift	16	.026 (.65)	1.47 (37.3)
2-3 Shift	17	.031 (.80)	1.79 (45.4)
Downshift	12	.022 (.55)	1.53 (38.9)
Speed Cut [3]			
Sentra	11	.026 (.65)	.78 (19.9)
Stanza	8	.024 (.60)	.62 (15.7)
Pulsar	11	.026 (.65)	.78 (19.9)
Lock-Up [3]			
Sentra	11	.024 (.60)	.85 (21.6)
Stanza	10	.026 (.65)	.81 (20.6)
Pulsar	11	.024 (.60)	.85 (21.6)

1 – 3 springs are used. Only differences are free length and load, which are .97" (25.3 mm) @ 3.92 lb. (1.78 kg), .93" (23.6 mm) @ 3.37 lb. (1.53 kg) and .86" (21.8 mm) @ 2.82 lb. (1.28 kg).

2 – Total length for all 3 springs is .512" (13 mm).

3 – Except Sentra diesel.

3) Tightening the screw will cause the shift point to occur at a lower speed and vice versa. On Sentra diesel, tighten the shift point fine adjusting screw all the way in and secure it with the lock nut. On all models, install oil pan with new gasket, add transaxle fluid and road test.

DIFFERENTIAL

Disassembly

1) Detach ring gear mount bolts. Separate ring gear from differential case. Using drift punch and hammer, drive out pinion shaft lock pin and remove pinion shaft.

2) Remove pinion gears and side gears from case. If bearings and races need replacement, remove races from converter housing and transmission case using Bearing Puller (ST33290001).

3) Using Bearing Puller (ST30031000) and hydraulic press, pull side bearings off differential case. Ensure differential case does not drop during pressing operation. Mark left and right bearings for installation in original position. Remove speedometer drive gear and stopper.

Cleaning & Inspection

Clean all parts in solvent and blow dry. Inspect mating surfaces of differential case, side gears and pinion mating gears for chips, cracks and wear. Check bearings and races for scratches, flaking, pitting and excessive wear. Replace defective components as required.

Reassembly

1) Install speedometer drive gear and stopper. Press side bearings onto differential case. Using Bearing Race Installers (ST30611000 and ST306621000), install bearing race into transaxle case.

2) Using race installers, install bearing race into converter housing. Ensure bearings and races are in original positions. Install pinion gears and pinion shaft into case.

3) Fit both side gears together snugly into the teeth of the pinion gears and simultaneously swing inward. If necessary, rotate case and gears to mesh and seat gears.

4) Install pinion shaft lock pin flush with case. Mount ring gear onto differential case. Coat ring gear bolts with locking compound and install. Place differential assembly on bench with side gear facing up.

5) Place Arbor (KV38105900) through bearing so it is resting on pinion shaft. Mount dial indicator on holding fixture so indicator tip rests on top of arbor. Measure side bearing-to-pinion gear backlash.

6) Move side bearing up and down and record dial indicator reading. Repeat operation on opposite side gear. If clearance exceeds .012" (.30 mm), replace differential case, side gears and pinion gears as a set.

OUTPUT SHAFT & IDLER GEAR

Disassembly & Inspection

1) Using Bearing Remover (ST22730000) and hydraulic press, pull bearings off output shaft. Place idler gear on wooden blocks and drive out outer races. Thoroughly clean components in solvent and blow dry with compressed air.

2) Check and replace idler gear if chipped, cracked or worn. Replace output shaft if bent, cracked or splines are worn. Replace any bearing that is cracked, pitted, flaking or does not roll freely.

Reassembly

Using hydraulic press and drift, press bearing races into idler gear. Press bearings onto output shaft. Make sure bearings are properly seated and rotate without binding after installation.

TRANSMISSION CASE

Disassembly & Reassembly

Remove bearing housing from transmission case. Press bearing off housing. Press out oil seal. Remove and discard "O" ring. Coat new seal and "O" ring with gear oil and press into position. Press bearing into housing. Install housing in transmission case.

TRANSAXLE ADJUSTMENTS

NOTE: **If transmission case, bearing housing, tapered roller bearing, differential case or converter housing is replaced, final drive must be adjusted.**

DIFFERENTIAL SIDE BEARING HEIGHT

1) Press differential side bearing outer race into converter housing bore. Place gasket on converter housing. Install differential assembly into converter housing.

2) Install tapered roller bearing on differential case. Turn differential assembly several times in each direction to properly seat bearings. Place counterweight on top of differential assembly. Mount Holding Bracket (KV381058S0) onto converter housing.

3) Tightening aligning bolts. Install micrometer to bracket. Measure distance from upper gasket surface of converter housing to upper surface of differential side bearing outer race. *See Fig. 19*. Record reading and subtract thickness of holding bracket to obtain actual measurement.

Fig. 19: Set-Up and Measuring Clearance Between Converter Housing and Differential Side Bearing

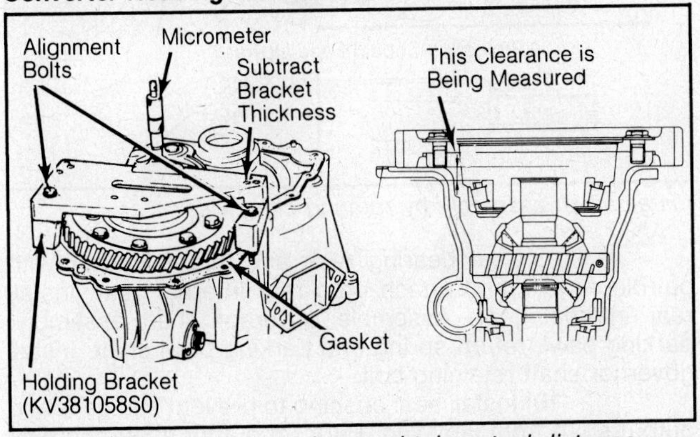

Subtract thickness of bracket to obtain actual distance.

4) Remove holding bracket and counterweight. With bearing housing installed in transmission case, rotate bearing several times in each direction to seat bearing.

5) Mount holding bracket on transmission case. Install micrometer to bracket and measure distance to bearing race. *See Fig. 20*. Record reading and subtract thickness of holding bracket to obtain actual measurement.

6) Subtract measurement obtained in step **3)** from reading obtained in step **5)**. Using this measurement, find proper shim (or shims) necessary to properly set differential side bearing height. See DIFFERENTIAL SIDE BEARING SHIM chart. **6)** Remove bearing housing from transmission case. Remove bearing and "O" ring. Install selected shim(s) on bearing housing and install bearing.

Fig. 20: Set-Up and Measuring Clearance to Bearing Race in Transmission Case

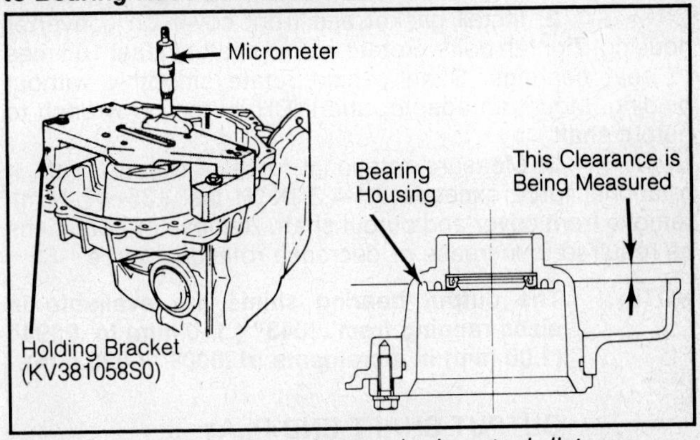

Subtract thickness of bracket to obtain actual distance.

Coat "O" ring with petroleum jelly and install. Install bearing housing to transmission case.

7) Install differential in transmission case. Place gasket on converter housing. Attach converter housing to transmission case. Install and tighten all bolts. Seat differential assembly by rotating it at least 10 times in each direction.

8) Insert Preload Adapter (KV38105900) into differential assembly. Using an INCH lb. torque wrench, measure rotational force of differential side bearings. If rotational force exceeds 52-65 INCH lbs. (5.7-7.2 N.m), disassemble transmission case and remove differential assembly.

NOTE: **If rotational force reading varies 8.7 INCH lbs. (1.0 N.m) or binds during any revolution, repeat adjustment procedure.**

9) Repeat adjustment procedures and recheck rotational force. Separate case and housing and remove differential assembly.

DIFFERENTIAL SIDE BEARING SHIM SPECIFICATIONS

Measured Distance In. (mm)	Required Shim In. (mm)
0-.0028 (0-.07)	.0150 (.38)
.0028-.0059 (.07-.15)	.0181 (.46)
.0059-.0091 (.15-.23)	.0213 (.54)
.0091-.0122 (.23-.31)	.0244 (.62)
.0122-.0154 (.31-.39)	.0276 (.70)
.0154-.0185 (.39-.47)	.0307 (.78)
.0185-.0217 (.47-.55)	.0339 (.86)
.0217-.0248 (.55-.63)	.0370 (.94)
.0248-.0280 (.63-.71)	.0402 (1.02)
.0280-.0311 (.71-.79)	.0433 (1.10)
.0311-.0343 (.79-.87)	.0465 (1.18)
.0343-.0374 (.87-.95)	.0496 (1.26)
.0374-.0406 (.95-1.03)	.0528 (1.34)
.0406-.0437 (1.03-1.11	.0559 (1.42)
.0437-.0469 (1.11-1.19)	.0591 (1.50)
.0469-.0500 (1.19-1.27)	.0622 (1.58)
.0500-.0531 (1.27-1.35)	.0654 (1.66)

OUTPUT SHAFT BEARING

1) If transmission case, output shaft, bearing or front cover is replaced, adjust output shaft. Apply ATF to bearing. Press bearing into transmission case bore. Place 2 or 3 shims on front cover. Press bearing into front cover bore. Install output shaft in converter housing.

2) Install gasket and front cover on converter housing. Tighten bolts. Rotate output shaft at least 10 times to seat bearings. Shaft should rotate smoothly without binding. Mount an adapter and INCH lb. torque wrench to output shaft.

3) Measure rotational force of output shaft. If rotational force exceeds 3.1-4.2 INCH lbs. (.35-.47 N.m), remove front cover and output shaft. Remove or add shims as required to increase or decrease rotational force.

NOTE: The output bearing shims are available in sizes ranging from .0043" (.110 mm) to .0394" (1.00 mm) in increments of .0008" (.020 mm).

OUTPUT SHAFT END PLAY

1) After adjusting rotational force of output shaft bearing, measure output shaft end play. Install idler gear, with bearings, on idler shaft. Install idler gear and output shaft assembly in converter housing.

2) Clean front cover bolt threads and converter housing with solvent. Install front cover gasket and front cover on converter housing. Install and tighten bolts to 10-13 ft. lbs. (14-18 N.m).

3) Install idler gear bolt and lock washer. Tighten idler gear bolt to 20-27 ft. lbs. (26-36 N.m). Ensure lock washer is aligned with groove on converter housing.

4) After tightening bolt, turn output shaft at least 5 complete revolutions. Loosen idler gear bolt, then retighten to specification. Bend lock washer. Install rear internal gear.

5) Assemble governor shaft assembly, parking pawl, return spring and parking pawl shaft. Install governor shaft retaining bolt. Place 2 beads of solder .098" (2.50 mm) in diameter on internal gear. *See Fig. 21.*

6) If necessary, a soldering plate that is .098" (2.50 mm) thick and .2" (5 mm) in length may be used as maximum gear clearance is .091" (2.30 mm). If diameter or thickness is smaller than .098" (2.50 mm), also use shim(s). Solder is used in the same manner as using Plastigage.

Fig. 21: Installing Solder on Internal Gear

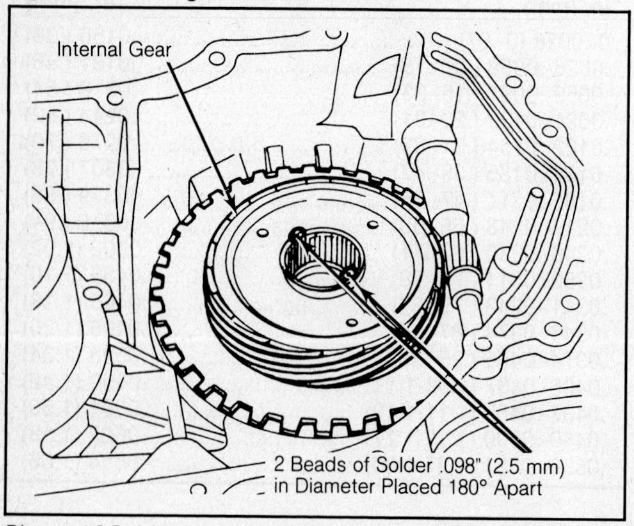

Pieces of Solder are used in same manner as Plastigage.

7) Install converter housing, with output shaft assembly installed, on transmission case. Install all converter housing-to-transmission case bolts and tighten.

8) Remove converter housing. Remove governor shaft retaining bolt. Remove parking pawl shaft, return spring, parking pawl and governor shaft assembly. Remove rear internal gear and dissamble output shaft. Measure thickness of solder or soldering plate. Select proper shim from OUTPUT SHAFT SHIM chart. End play should be between .0098-.0217" (.25-.55 mm).

OUTPUT SHAFT SHIM SPECIFICATIONS

Measured Thickness[1] In.(mm)	Required Shim In. (mm)
.0217-.0335 (.55-.85)	.012 (.3)
.0295-.0413 (.75-1.05)	.020 (.5)
.0374-.0492 (.95-1.25)	.028 (.7)
.0453-.0571 (1.15-1.45)	.035 (.9)
.0531-.0650 (1.35-1.65)	.043 (1.1)
.0610-.0728 (1.55-1.85)	.051 (1.3)
.0689-.0807 (1.75-2.05)	.059 (1.5)
.0768-.0886 (1.95-2.25)	.067 (1.7)

[1] - Measured thickness after subtracting .002" (.5 mm).

Fig. 22: Installing 1-Way Clutch & Rear Carrier

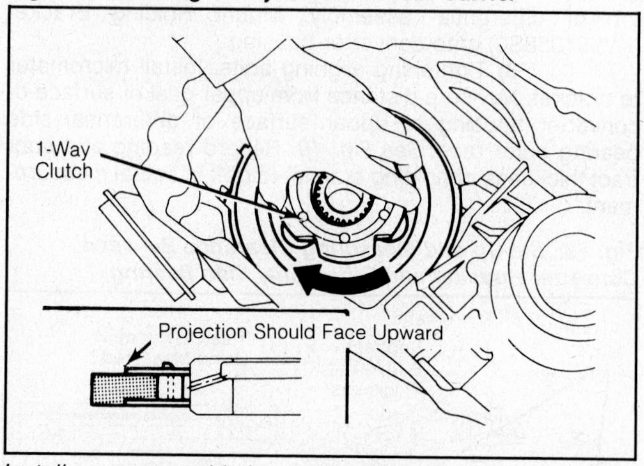

Install as an assembly by rotating clockwise.

9) Coat bearing race and thrust washer with petroleum jelly and attach onto rear internal gear. Install rear internal gear. Assemble governor shaft assembly, parking pawl, return spring and parking pawl shaft. Install governor shaft retaining bolt.

10) Install seal bushing to prevent sun gear and output shaft from jamming. Perform output shaft end play adjustment. Check rotary frictional force of output shaft and idler gear bearings. Check differential side bearing height adjustment and rotary friction force. See TRANSAXLE ADJUSTMENT section.

11) Install differential assembly on transmission case. Apply petroleum jelly to output shaft shim and attach onto output shaft. Place gasket on transmission case. Position converter housing assembly, with front cover assembly attached, in position over transmission case.

12) While supporting converter housing, turn rear internal gear clockwise with screwdriver to align output shaft splines, front carrier and rear internal gear. Install and tighten bolts.

13) Apply locking compound to 3 lower bolts before installation. *See Fig. 26.* Apply vaseline to accumulator piston rings. Install accumulator piston and return spring on transmission case.

Fig. 23: Sectional View of Transaxle Assembly

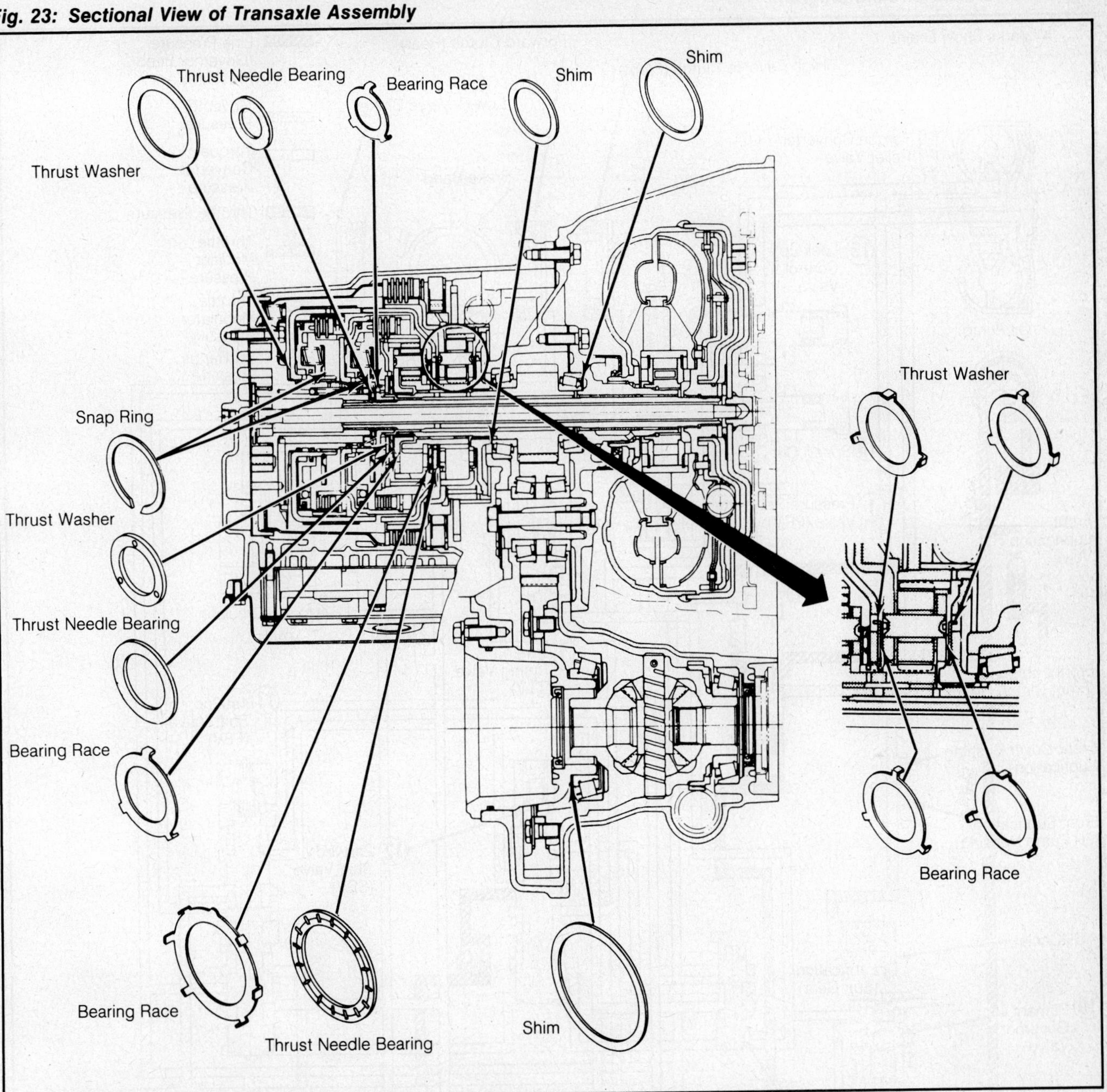

Use illustration as guide when installing/assembling the needle bearing/races, snap rings, shims and/or seal ring.

14) Loosen lock nut on brake band and perform band adjustment. Tighten anchor pin lock nut to 2.9-4.3 ft. lbs. (4-6 N.m). Back off nut 2 1/2 turns and retighten to 12-16 ft. lbs. (16-22 N.m) while holding anchor pin stationary. Tighten lock nut.

15) Assemble parking actuator support and throttle cable on transmission case, tighten nut and bend lock-plate to secure. Apply grease to outer end of selector shaft and vaseline to "O" ring and remaining portion of shaft.

16) Install throttle lever, selector plate, selector shaft, selector range lever and parking rod assembly. Secure with retaining pin. Pin should protrude from shaft about .12" (3 mm). Tighten selector shaft retaining nuts by tightening inner nut first, then tightening outer nut.

17) Install valve body on transmission case. Install particle magnet, if equipped. Install manual valve, manual plate, detent valve and throttle lever. *See Fig. 26.* Check alignment and operation of manual valve and parking pawl engagement. Ensure all bolts are installed in valve body.

18) Install new oil pan gasket, oil pan and pan guard. Install governor cap seal ring and governor cap. Secure assembly with snap ring, making sure cap recess fits over case protrusion.

19) Install oil pump shaft with concave portion of shaft facing outward. Install input shaft. Lubricate oil pump seal lip and converter neck. Install converter without scratching front cover oil seal.

Automatic Transmissions

NISSAN TRANSAXLES (Cont.)

Fig. 24: Hydraulic Circuits Diagram

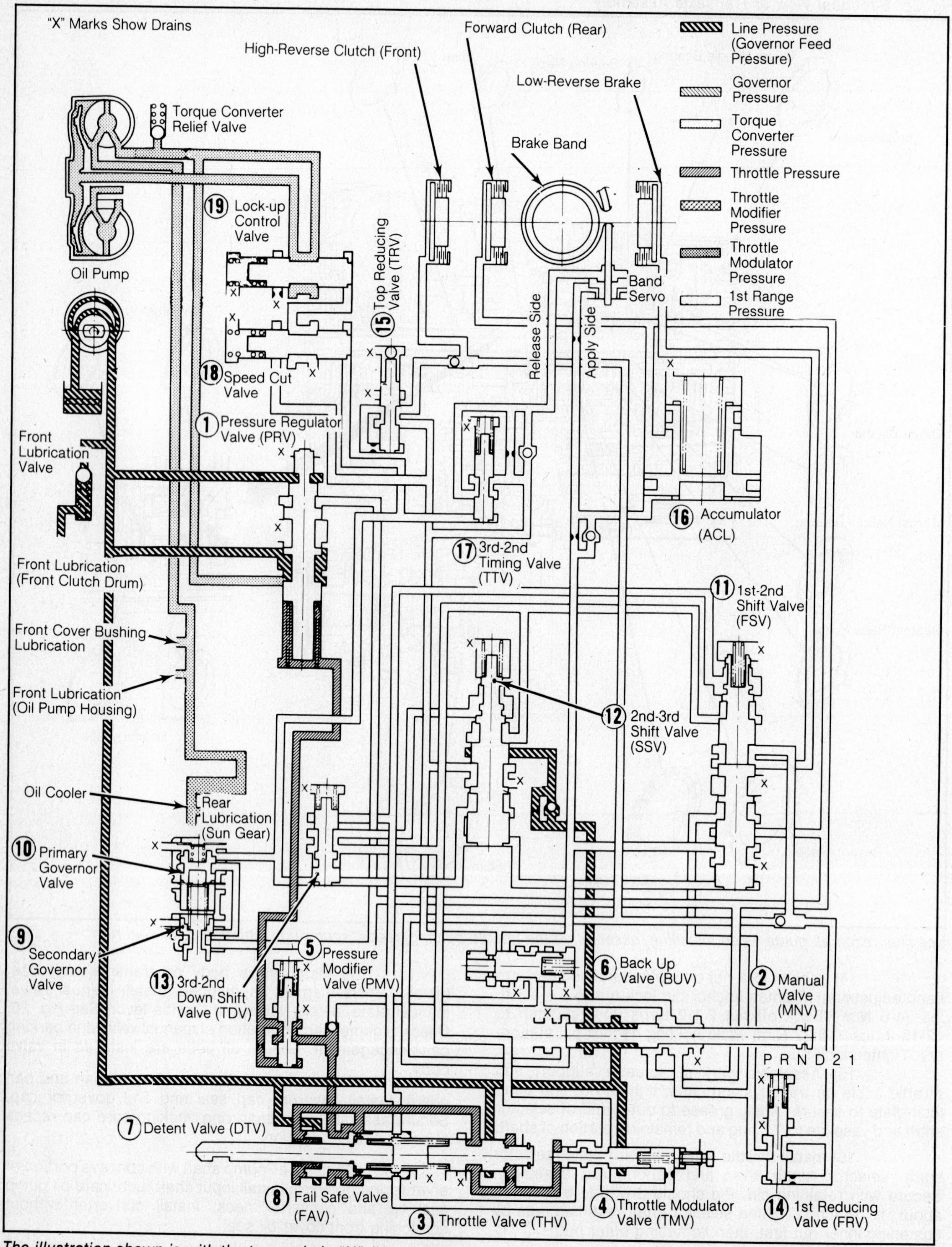

The illustration shown is with the transaxle in "N" (Neutral) range.

NISSAN TRANSAXLES (Cont.)

Fig. 25: Exploded View of Transaxle Assembly

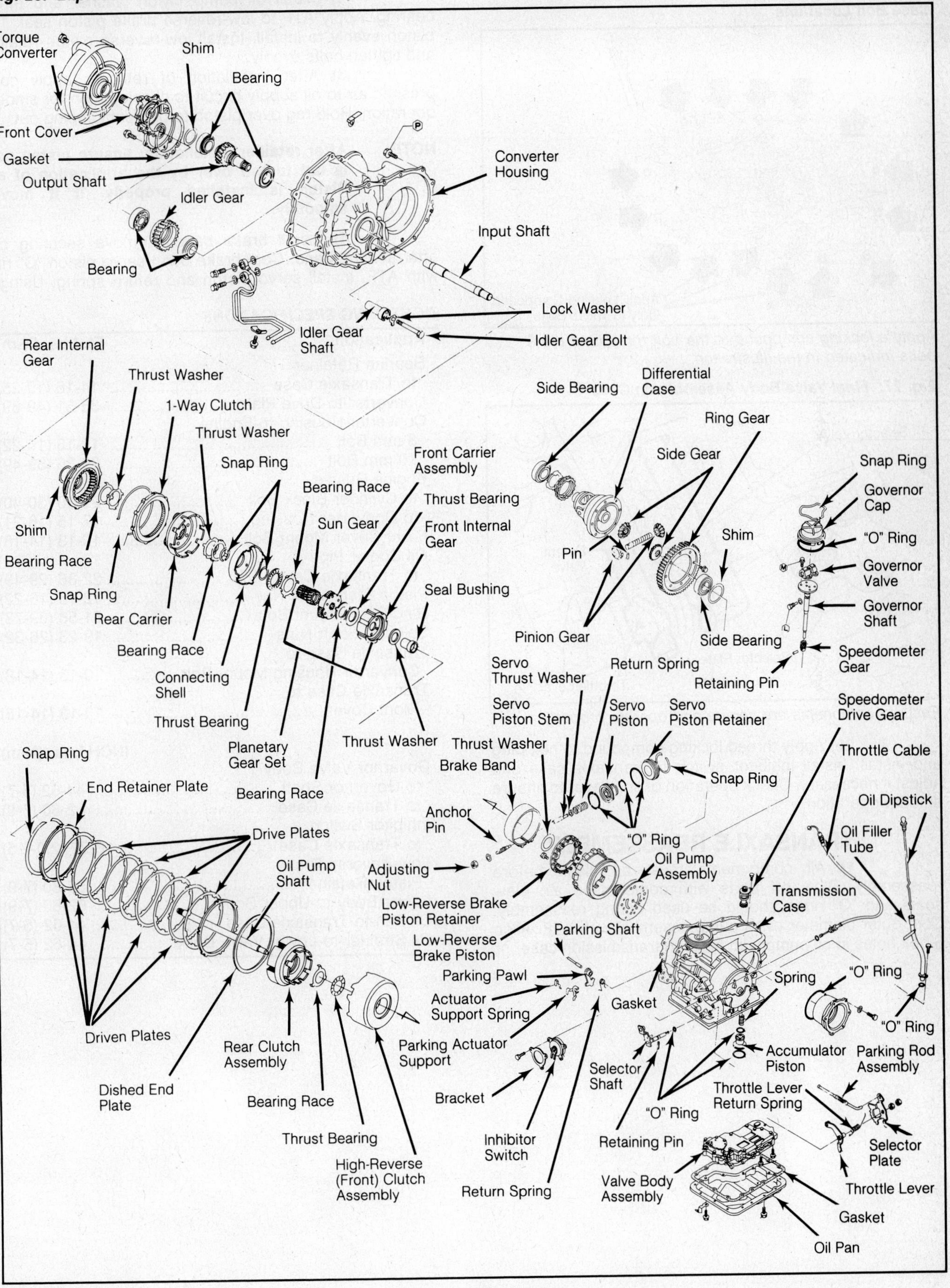

Fig. 26: Converter Housing-to-Transmission Case Bolt Locations

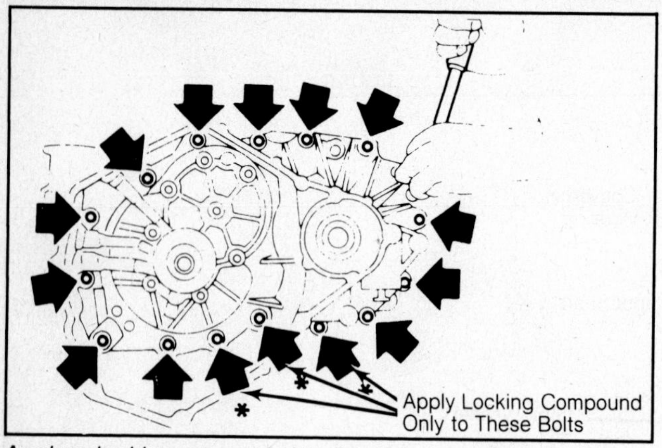

Apply a locking compound to the bolt threads of the 3 bolts indicated in the illustration.

Fig. 27: Final Valve Body Assembly on Case

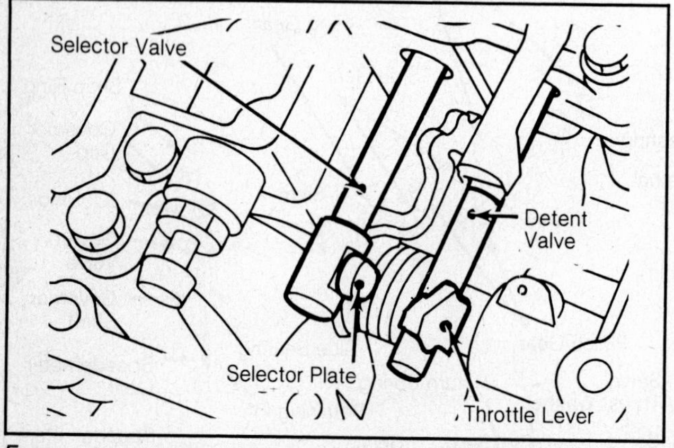

Ensure components are secure and operate properly.

20) Apply thread locking compound to hex plug and install. Install inhibitor switch to transaxle case and adjust if necessary. Check operation of shift lever to ensure smooth operation.

TRANSAXLE REASSEMBLY

1) All components must be clean before reassembly. Blow off parts with compressed air. New seals and "O" rings should be used during reassembly. Coat outer diameter of oil pump assembly with ATF. Align 5 bolt holes in oil pump with holes in transmission case.

2) Install oil pump, nylon washer and thrust bearing. Apply ATF to low-reverse brake piston seal. Tap piston evenly to install. Install low-reverse piston retainer and tighten bolts evenly.

3) After installation of retainer, apply compressed air to oil supply circuit to check piston for smooth operation. Hold rag over piston to prevent jumping out.

NOTE: **After retainer installation, ensure piston seal is not turned over by the application of air. Piston is installed properly, if it moves smoothly.**

4) Install brake band. Remove securing clip after seating band. Coat brake band servo piston "O" ring with ATF. Install servo piston and return spring. Using a

TIGHTENING SPECIFICATIONS

Application	Ft. Lbs. (N.m)
Bearing Retainer	
to Transaxle Case	14-18 (19-25)
Converter-to-Drive Plate	36-51 (49-69)
Converter Housing-to-Engine	
8 mm Bolt	12-16 (16-22)
10 mm Bolt	29-36 (39-49)
Engine Gusset	
to Cylinder Block Bolt	22-30 (30-40)
to Converter Housing	12-15 (16-21)
Front Cover Mount Bolt	10-13 (14-18)
Oil Cooler Pipe	
to Transaxle Case	22-36 (29-49)
Piston Stem Lock Nut	12-16 (16-22)
Ring Gear Mount Bolt	51-58 (69-78)
Selector Shaft Nuts	19-23 (26-32)
Transaxle Case-to	
Converter Housing Mount Bolt	10-13 (14-18)
Transaxle Case to	
Front Cover	10-13 (14-18)
	INCH Lbs. (N.m)
Governor Valve Body	
to Governor Shaft	44-62 (5-7)
to Transaxle Case	62-80 (7-9)
Inhibitor Switch	
to Transaxle Case	18-22 (2.0-2.5)
Low-Reverse Brake	
Piston Retainer	62-80 (7-9)
Lower Body-to-Upper Body	62-80 (7-9)
Oil Pan-to-Transaxle Case	44-62 (5-7)
Oil Strainer-to-Lower Valve Body	44-62 (5-7)

PORSCHE A28.04 TRANSAXLE

928S

DESCRIPTION

The model A28.04 is a 4-speed automatic, consisting of a Ravigneaux planetary gear set, 2 brake bands, 2 multiple-disc clutches, one disc-type brake, primary and secondary hydraulic pumps, valve body, input and output shafts.

Sealed torque converter, which cannot be serviced, is at front of transmission in 2-piece bellhousing. Final drive section, containing ring and pinion, side gears and pinion gears, is behind transmission. Differentials are either conventional or limited slip type.

OPERATION

Drive flange is bolted to torque converter and connected to central shaft via clamping sleeve. Hydraulic torque converter mutiplies engine torque 2.12 times. Stall speed is 2200-2600 RPM.

Turbine wheel of torque converter drives large planetary sun gear through input shaft. Primary pump supplies transmission and torque converter with ATF under pressure.

The one-way clutch locks in 1st and reverse gear. Shifting is controlled by valve body assembly. Governor pressure changes with road speed and influences upshifts and downshifts in valve body.

Governor also drives secondary pump, which will provide emergency hydraulic pressure whenever vehicle is moving. This pressure makes it possible to tow start vehicle at speeds between 19-31 MPH. Secondary pump will also lubricate critical parts of transmission if vehicle is towed with rear wheels on ground.

CAUTION: **If vehicle is towed with rear wheels on ground, maximum towing distance is 75 miles with maximum speed of 31 MPH. Secondary ATF pump will not provide lubrication beyond these limits and internal damage WILL occur.**

LUBRICATION & ADJUSTMENT

See appropriate AUTOMATIC TRANSMISSION SERVICING article in IMPORT GENERAL SERVICING section.

TROUBLE SHOOTING

SLIPS IN ALL SELECTOR POSITIONS

Incorrect modulating pressure. Modulating pressure control valve or pressure relief valve for modulating pressure dirty or sticking. Line to transmission vacuum unit clogged or leaking. Working pressure control valve dirty or sticking. Defective pump.

TRANSMISSION GRABS OR VEHICLE SHAKES WHEN STARTING OFF

Incorrect modulating pressure. Check transmission vacuum unit. If transmission fluid is found in vacuum unit, replace unit. If fuel is found in vacuum unit, check injection system and adjust.

TRANSMISSION SLIPS IN FIRST GEAR

Check for dirty or sticking valves in valve body. Defective center servo piston or piston sealing ring damaged. Defective center band or thrust body.

TRANSMISSION SLIPS ON UPSHIFT

Incorrect modulating pressure. Faulty valve body assembly (replace sealing bushings on plug pipes). Defective front or rear clutch. Oil distribution sleeve damaged.

TRANSMISSION SLIPS IN THIRD GEAR

Valve body seal bushings worn or damaged. Defective rear clutch assembly. Oil distributing sleeve damaged.

TRANSMISSION SLIPS IN FIRST AND SECOND GEARS

Rear band worn or damaged. Adjust brake band by installing a longer thrust pin.

TRANSMISSION SLIPS IN ALL GEARS

Incorrect modulating pressure. Defective modulating pressure relief valve or control valve.

TRANSMISSION WILL NOT ENGAGE PROPERLY

Torque converter not installed correctly. Driver not correctly engaging drive gear.

NO POSITIVE ENGAGEMENT IN REVERSE

Front band out of adjustment. Front servo piston sealing ring worn or damaged. Defective one-way clutch in gear unit assembly.

ROUGH JERK WHEN ENGAGING SELECTOR LEVER POSITION "D"

Adjust engine idle speed and emissions as specified. Incorrect modulating and/or working pressure. Vacuum leak. Defective pressure receiving piston in extension housing.

ROUGH JERK WHEN CHANGING GEARS

Check modulating pressure and working pressure and adjust modulating pressure if necessary. If working pressure is too high, replace valve body assembly. Vacuum lines or connections leaking. Control pressure linkage out of adjustment.

ROUGH JERK ON 3-2 DOWNSHIFT

Rear servo sealing ring worn or damaged. Defective rear servo piston.

NO UPSHIFTS

Incorrect governor pressure. Defective governor assembly.

UPSHIFTS ONLY IN UPPER SPEED RANGE OF GEARS

Control pressure linkage out of adjustment. Defective governor assembly.

Automatic Transmissions

PORSCHE A28.04 TRANSAXLE (Cont.)

UPSHIFTS ONLY IN LOWER SPEED RANGE OF GEARS

Control pressure linkage damaged or out of adjustment. Accelerator linkage out of adjustment. Defective governor assembly.

POOR ACCELERATION AT START

Check stalling speed. If speed drops 400/700 RPM, replace torque converter.

NO KICKDOWN SHIFTS

Fuse for power supply to solenoid valve blown. Defective solenoid valve. Control pressure linkage damaged or out of adjustment. Kickdown control valve in valve body sticking.

TRANSMISSION NOT UPSHIFTING

Governor or command valve in shift valve housing requires replacement.

NO ENGINE BRAKING ON DOWNSHIFTS

Control pressure linkage out of adjustment. Defective servo piston(s). Defective valve body assembly.

TESTING

STALL SPEED TEST

NOTE: **During this check all engine power is converted into heat in the converter, which is why this test must not last longer than 5 seconds.**

1) Rear must not be permitted to turn during this check. Also, engine must be at operating temperature and develop its full power. All equipment (A/C system) must be turned off. DO NOT use vehicle's tachometer for this test.

2) Connect tachometer so that it can be read from driver's seat. Run engine at about 2,000 RPM, 2 minutes prior to testing. Set parking brake and depress brake pedal with left foot.

3) Position selector lever to "D", floor accelerator with right foot and check whether specified stall speed is reached. Stall speed must be 2200-2600 RPM.

4) If stall speed drops about 400-700 RPM below specified value, one-way clutch in torque converter is slipping. Replace torque converter. If stall speed is faster than specified value, slip is in transmission.

5) If stall speed is correct and top speed is still not reached, one-way clutch is locking in both directions or has seized. This will usually be noticed during fast highway driving by ATF leaking through the vent.

6) The stall speed will drop about 125 RPM for each 1,000 ft. altitude above sea level because of a drop in engine power. Even excessively high outside temperatures could cause stall speed to drop slightly below the minimum value.

ROAD TESTING

1) Perform test drive, but only when transmission damage is not obvious. It is important that vehicle be driven in all driving conditions and all speed ranges of the automatic transmission, and be observed accurately during test drive. Observe in particular the shift points for up and down shifts as well as kickdown shift points in regards to speed and shift transitions.

2) All shifts must take place quickly and without interruption of power flow. Also check whether engine races suddenly while shifting. This would indicate that a brake or clutch is slipping. Check transmission for leaks after test driving vehicle.

HYDRAULIC PRESSURE TESTS

1) The transmission is fitted with 3 measuring connections, so that the 3 most important pressures (modulating pressure, operating pressure and governor pressure) can be measured with help of a tester.

2) Pressure gauges are connected so that they can be read by front passenger during test drive. Tester is set up in footwell in front of front passenger's seat. Pressure gauges are connected to their measuring points by way of hoses which are guided through window of right door. This requires disconnecting and pushing shield for rear muffler aside.

NOTE: **Disconnect and plug vacuum modulator line for tests.**

Modulation Pressure

Modulation pressure should be 63.09-64.54 psi (4.4-4.5 kg/cm^2) at road speed of 31 MPH. Specific adjustment procedure for modulation pressure is not available from manufacturer.

Operating Pressure

Operating pressure, which is not adjustable, should be 243.67-246.57 psi (17.1-17.3 kg/cm^2) with engine running at idle speed. Selector lever should be in "2", "3", or "D" positions.

Governor Pressure

1) Governor pressure, which is not adjustable, is checked with selector lever in "D" position and vehicle rolling with partial load. At 10 MPH, governor pressure reading should be .73-1.45 psi (.05-.10 kg/cm^2).

2) At 20 MPH, reading should be 13.78-15.23 psi (.97-1.07 kg/cm^2). At 55 MPH, reading should be 26.83-28.28 psi (1.89-1.99 kg/cm^2). At 80 MPH, reading should be 32.63-34.08 psi (2.29-2.40 kg/cm^2).

REMOVAL & INSTALLATION

NOTE: **During transmission repairs where the pinion head nut has to be removed, it is possible on some transmissions that the thread will be damaged. In these cases, the automatic section of the transmission should be replaced.**

SELECTOR LEVER CABLE

Removal

1) Remove battery ground strap from body. Remove selector lever grip and remove rubber boot. Remove cover frame. Pull light bulb holder out of retaining clips.

2) Mark location of selector lever base for reinstallation and remove mounting screws. Loosen intermediate muffler shield and push aside as far as possible. Disconnect selector lever cable on transmission lever and detach cable sleeve from brackets.

3) Remove ball head, nut and mounting parts. Attach tailing wire on cable and pull out of selector lever base with cable, by pulling forward at an angle. Remove

A28.04 SHIFT POINTS

Shift Conditions	MPH
928S	
Full Throttle	
1-2 Upshift	35-41
2-3 Upshift	70-81
3-4 Upshift	118-131
Partial Throttle	
1-2 Upshift	14-15
2-3 Upshift	16-21
3-4 Upshift	26-31
Kickdown	
1-2 Upshift	43-47
2-3 Upshift	79-82
3-4 Upshift	128-132
Full Throttle	
2-1 Downshift	18-15
3-2 Downshift	40-36
4-3 Downshift	95-84
Partial Throttle	
2-1 Downshift	11-10
3-2 Downshift	14-12
4-3 Downshift	21-17
Kickdown	
2-1 Downshift	28-24
3-2 Downshift	76-66
4-3 Downshift	126-114

cable clips on selector lever and detach cable sleeve on selector lever base.

Installation

1) Attach cable sleeve on selector lever base, tightening hexagon nut carefully. Push cable on to selector lever pin and install circlip.

2) Attach tailing wire, pulled forward during removal, on cable and pull cable toward rear. A person should guide in the selector lever base and a second person must pull wire and cable through.

3) Install selector lever base in correct position (watching mark) and tighten mounting screws to 132 INCH lbs. (15 N.m). Install cover frame and selector lever grip. Place selector lever at "N". *See Figs. 1 and 2.*

Fig. 1: Shift Selector Lever Installation

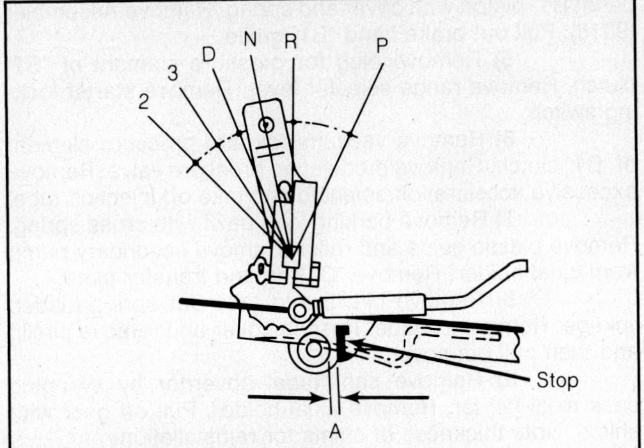

NOTE: **If light opening of gate and letter "N" are not exactly opposite each other in cover frame, remove cover frame again and reposition selector lever base in slots.**

4) Mount selector lever cable on transmission. Adjust selector lever cable.

STARTER SAFETY SWITCH & BACK-UP LIGHT SWITCH

Removal

1) Disconnect selector lever cable. Remove bolt for range selector lever and pull off lever. Unlock plug by turning White plastic ring upwards.

2) Pry off plug carefully with 2 screwdrivers applied on cable outlet and support bar. Remove switch mounting screws and take off switch.

Installation

1) Install switch with both mounting bolts, DO NOT tighten bolts. Install range selector lever so switch engages. Move range selector lever to position "N". *See Fig. 2.*

Fig. 2: View of Selector Cable Mounting

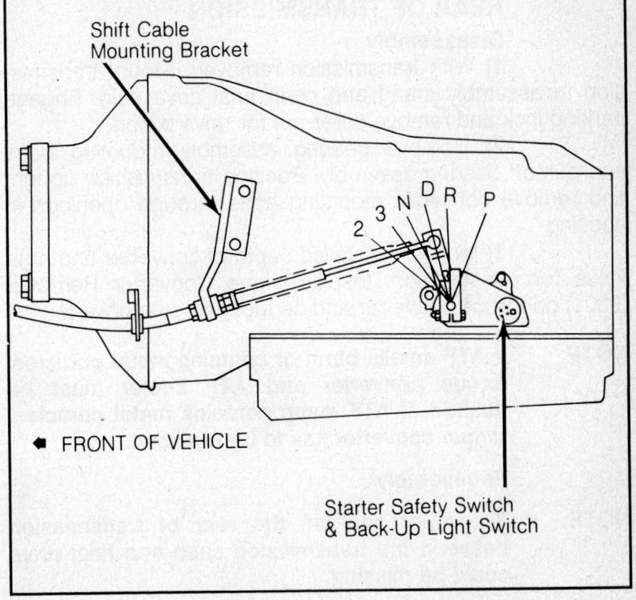

2) Install and tighten range selector lever bolts to 84 INCH lbs. (10 N.m). Adjust switch and connect plug. Attach selector lever cable on selector range lever.

REAR TRANSMISSION CASE

Removal & Installation

1) Remove final drive and bearing assembly and case mounting bolts. To install, drive in inner seal to correct position. Hold seal with a small amount of grease and drive in so that sealing lip faces transmission.

2) Drive in outer seal to correct position. Seal must be installed so that its sealing lip faces final drive.

TRANSMISSION DISASSEMBLY

NOTE: **To prevent drive flange from moving out while pressing in bearing, it must be supported from underneath with a suitable thrust pad.**

Automatic Transmissions

PORSCHE A28.04 TRANSAXLE (Cont.)

NOTE: **During transmission repairs where the pinion head nut has to be removed, it is possible on some transmissions that the thread will be damaged. In these cases, the automatic section of the transmission should be replaced.**

FRONT CONVERTER HOUSING

Disassembly

Remove circlip and press out drive flange. Press grooved ball bearing off of drive flange with a support rail.

Reassembly

1) Install both circlips in converter housing. Heat grooved ball bearing to 250°F (120°C). Press bearing on drive flange against shoulder with a suitable piece of pipe applied on bearing inner race.

2) Heat converter housing to about 250°F (120°C). Press in drive flange with grooved ball bearing against circlip. Install spacer and press in front grooved ball bearing against circlip with a suitable piece of pipe applied on inner race.

REAR OF TRANSMISSION

Disassembly

1) With transmission removed. Mount transmission in assembly stand and drain final drive fluid. Engage parking lock and remove collar nut for drive pinion.

2) Remove bearing assembly mounting bolts and pull off bearing assembly. Position transmission upright and remove converter mounting bolts through openings in housing.

3) Measure installed depth of converter and note value for reinstallation. Install Torque Converter Remover (9301) on torque converter and carefully lift out converter.

NOTE: **If ATF smells burnt or contains metal particles, torque converter and ATF cooler must be flushed. If ATF sump contains metal particles, torque converter has to be replaced.**

Reassembly

NOTE: **The outer seal on the rear of transmission between the transmission case and final drive could be missing.**

1) Drive outer seal to correct position. Outer seal must be installed so that sealing lip and spring supporting the sealing lip face the final drive.

2) Mount Torque Converter Holding Plate (9301) on torque converter. Coat drive flange and bearing journal of converter with a multi-purpose grease.

3) Set transmission upright and install converter carefully, while turning converter back and forth until splines mesh. Check installation depth of converter, approximately .62" (16 mm). *See Fig. 3.*

4) Determine thickness of shims for bearing assembly. Measure distance from tapered roller bearing surface to bearing flange surface with a depth gauge. Example - 1.36" (34.55 mm). Since the distance specified by design is only 1.34" (34 mm), shims having a total thickness of .002" (.55 mm) must be installed.

5) Install shims of determined thickness and install bearing assembly on output shaft. Tighten collar nut for drive pinion to 275 ft. lbs. (380 N.m). Lock by punching collar over onto nut.

Fig. 3: Measuring Installed Depth of Torque Converter

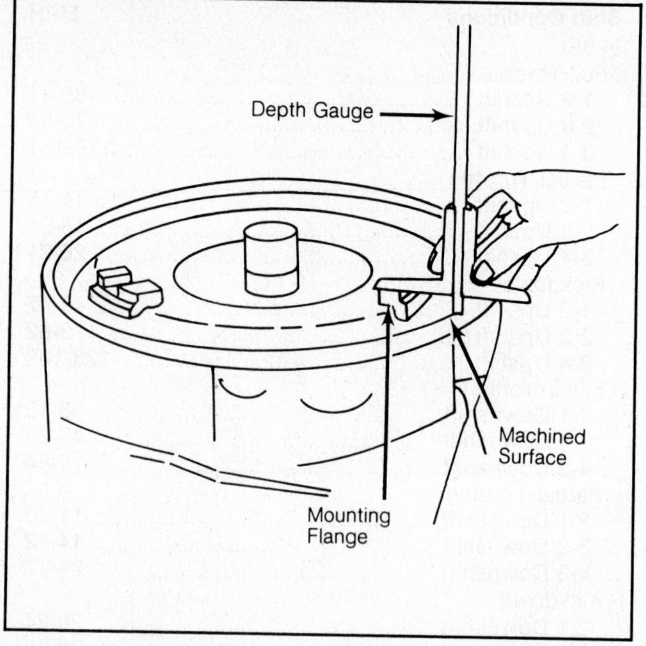

6) Adjust drive pinion and ring gear. See DRIVE PINION AND RING GEAR ADJUSTMENT. Install transmission and check adjustment of selector lever and control pressure cables.

MAIN TRANSMISSION CASE

1) Remove front converter housing and converter. Remove combination bolts and take off ATF sump with ATF reservoir. Remove ATF filter. Remove valve body. Remove bracket with leaf spring.

2) Remove combination bolts and lift off cover with transfer plate and oil plate. Remove lower cover. Remove one-way valve, brake band "B2" guide, filter and oil deflector. Reinstall lower cover.

3) Push in brake band "B2" piston cover. Remove circlip and take off cover. Pull out brake band "B2" piston. Install Assembler (9316) and remove circlip.

4) Release Assembler (9316). Remove brake band "B1" piston with cover and spring. Remove Assembler (9316). Pull out brake band "B1" guide.

5) Remove plug for pressure element of "B1" clutch. Remove range selector lever. Remove starter locking switch.

6) Remove vacuum box and pressure element of "B1" clutch. Remove modulating pressure valve. Remove excessive acceleration solenoid and take off injection tube.

7) Remove parking lock pawl with cross spring. Remove plastic guide and roller. Remove secondary pump from axial holder. Remove "O" ring and transfer plate.

8) Remove circlip and take out spring loaded linkage. Remove oil pipe. Push in cover and remove circlip and then pull out cover.

9) Remove centrifugal governor by swinging back axial holder. Remove axial holder. Pull off gear with shims. Note thickness of shims for reinstallation.

10) Remove circlip from output shaft. Remove front cover by removing combination bolts, then screw 2

Automatic Transmissions

PORSCHE A28.04 TRANSAXLE (Cont.)

bolts in tapped bores and pulling off cover onto bolts. Take hold of gear set on input shaft and carefully pull out toward front.

11) Pull clutch "K1" and brake band "B1" off of gear set. Remove "B3" plates , "K2" clutch and thrust pin. Set transmission case on incline and remove "B2" brake band. Remove bolt, pull out shaft and remove catch plate.

12) Remove thrust washer and pull out "B2" clutch presssure element. Remove case flange bolts and screw in two 3 1/16" (80 mm) long bolts opposite of each other. With light hammer knocks on both bolts, knock flange out of case. Remove seals and test connection plugs.

COMPONENT DISASSEMBLY & REASSEMBLY

SHIFT VALVE HOUSING

Disassembly

NOTE: **Absolute cleanliness is essential for any work on the shift valve housing. Work should be done on a plastic lined workbench. After disassembling, all parts must be washed and dried with compressed air.**

Remove plastic valve. Hold and turn shift valve housing and pick-up housing around. Lift off pick-up housing with transfer plate carefully. Remove valves and check balls, being careful not to lose any of the check balls.

Reassembly

1) Place all check balls and valves in shift valve housing. Install lubricating valve, modulating pressure valve and vent valve in pick-up housing. Hold shift valve housing and pick-up housing together and turn both around.

2) Screw in both bolts, DO NOT tighten. Tighten bolts only enough so that both housings can still be moved to align them. Install Green plastic valve in housing so that bore is in correct position. *See Fig. 4.*

PRIMARY PUMP

Removal

NOTE: **Primary pump can be removed and installed without disassembling transmission.**

1) Remove transmission. Remove front converter housing and converter. Remove mounting bolts for front transmission cover. Screw 2 bolts in tapped bores and pull out front cover.

2) Press in diaphragm spring and remove circlip. Unscrew mounting bolts and remove pump. This is done by screwing 2 bolts in tapped bores. Using a plastic hammer, carefully drive out primary pump. *See Fig. 5.*

Installation

1) Check bearing sleeve for traces of wear or damage. Replace primary pump, if damaged. Lubricate both pump gears with ATF and install in pump body. Large gear must be installed so that chamfer faces bearing sleeve.

Fig. 4: View of Shift Valve Housing & Check Ball Locations

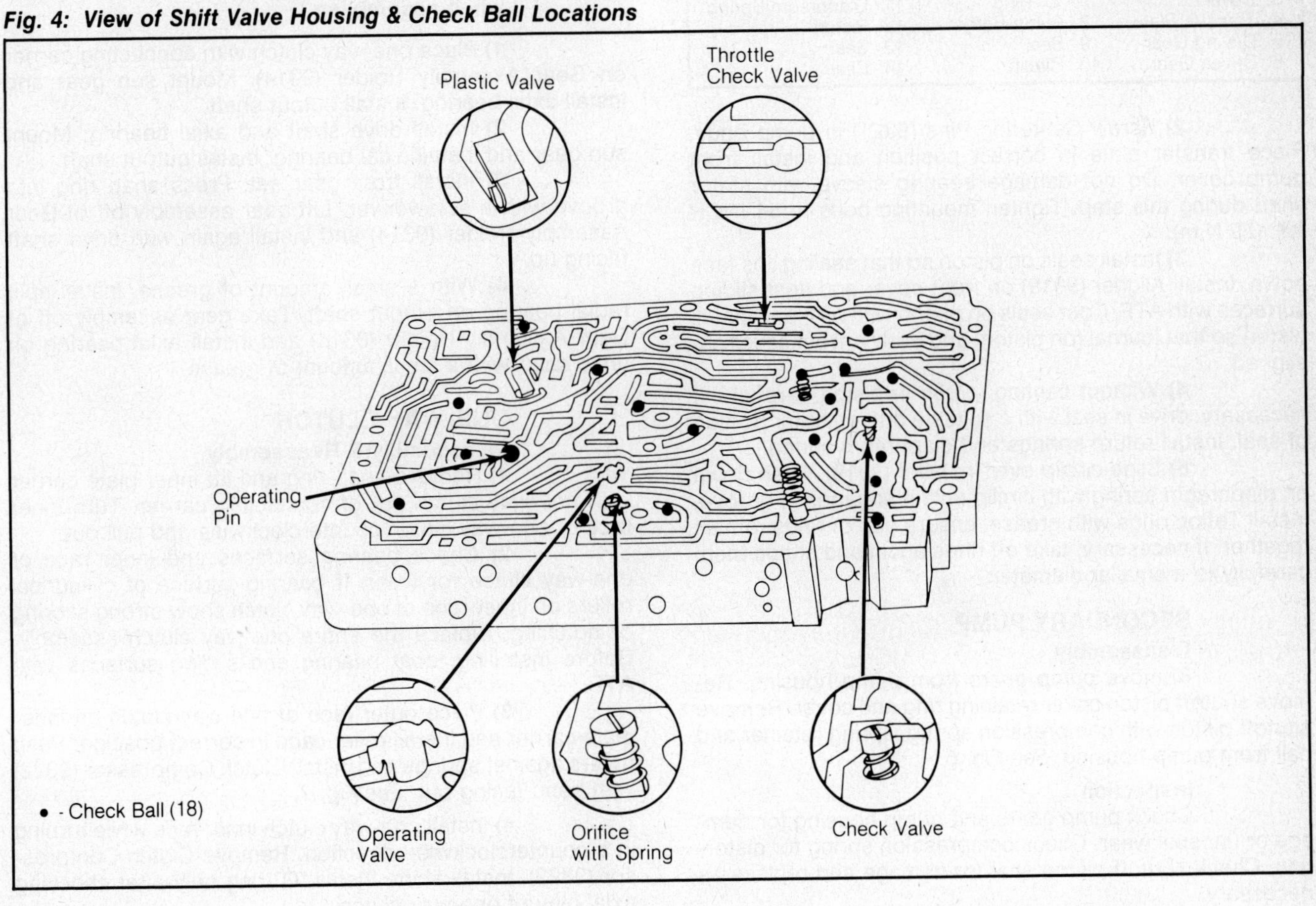

Fig. 5: Exploded View of Primary Pump

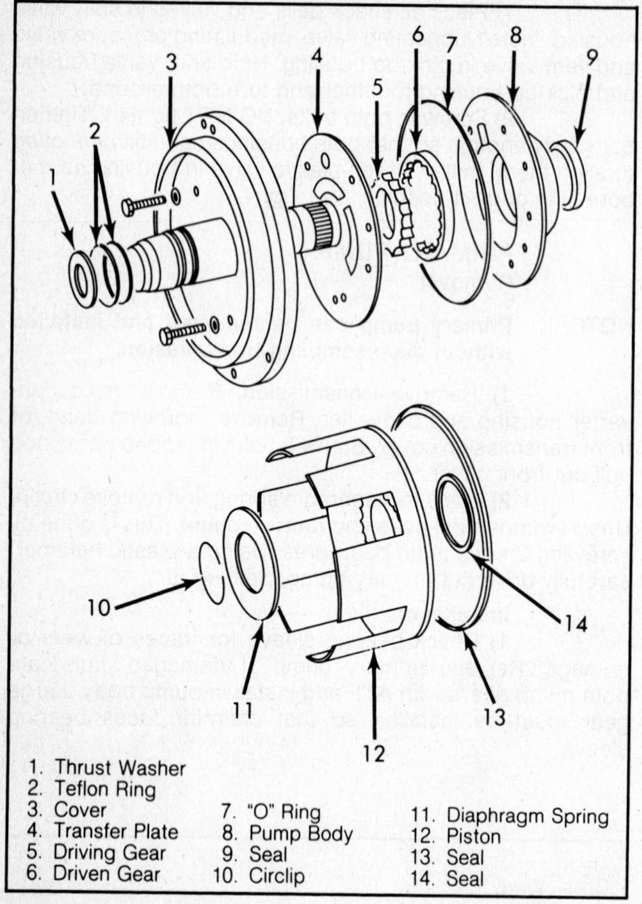

2) Screw Centering Pins (9321) in pump body. Place transfer plate in correct position and install front pump cover. Do not damage bearing sleeve with stator shaft during this step. Tighten mounting bolts to 54 INCH lbs. (20 N.m).

3) Install seals on piston so that sealing lips face down. Install Aligner (9319) on front cover and coat sliding surfaces with ATF. Coat seals on piston with ATF and install piston so that journal (on piston) and bore in front cover are aligned.

4) Without canting, press in piston carefully. If necessary, drive in seal with a suitable drift on outer portion of seal. Install return springs and diaphragm spring.

5) Slide circlip over Installer (9319). Push down on diaphragm spring with circlip until it engages in groove. Install Teflon rings with grease, ensure gap of rings remain together. If necessary, take off rings again and shape them carefully to a smaller diameter.

SECONDARY PUMP

Disassembly

Remove pump gears from pump housing. Remove shutoff piston cover retaining ring and cover. Remove shutoff piston with compression spring, spring retainer and ball from pump housing. *See Fig. 6.*

Inspection

Check pump gears and pump housing for damage or unusual wear. Check compression spring for distortion. Check shutoff piston seal for damage and replace as necessary.

Reassembly

Place "O" ring into pump housing. Install Teflon sealing ring on shutoff piston and install into pump housing. Install compression spring, spring retainer and ball into shutoff piston. Install piston cover and piston cover retaining ring. Lubricate pump gears and place in pump housing.

Fig. 6: Exploded View of Secondary Pump

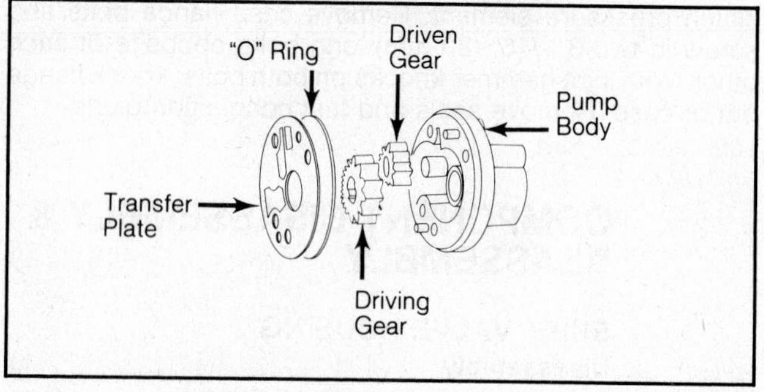

GEAR ASSEMBLY

Disassmbly

Clamp Gear Assembly Holder (9314) in a vise on both surfaces with plate facing up and mount gear assembly with drive shaft facing up. Remove snap ring and take inner plate carrier with one-way clutch out of connecting carrier. *See Fig. 8.*

Reassembly

NOTE: Coat all bearing sliding surfaces with ATF when assembling.

1) Place one-way clutch with connecting carrier on Gear Assembly Holder (9314). Mount sun gear and install axial bearing. Install output shaft.

2) Install drive shaft and axial bearing. Mount sun gear and install axial bearing. Install output shaft.

3) Install front gear set. Press snap ring into groove with a screwdriver. Lift gear assembly off of Gear Assembly Holder (9314) and install again with drive shaft facing up.

4) With a small amount of grease, install split radial bearing on output shaft. Take gear assembly off of Gear Assembly Holder (9314) and install axial bearing on drive shaft with a small amount of grease.

ONE-WAY CLUTCH

Disassembly & Reassembly

1) Remove snap ring and lift inner plate carrier with one-way clutch out of connecting carrier. Turn inner race of one-way clutch counterclockwise and pull out.

2) Check bearing surfaces and inner race of one-way clutch for wear. If bearing surface of cylindrical rollers on inner race of one-way clutch show strong scoring or notching, replace the entire one-way clutch assembly. Before installing, coat bearing and sliding surfaces with ATF.

3) Place outer race of one-way clutch on inner plate carrier and install roller cage in correct position. Push rollers against springs and install Clutch Compressor (9322) with bend facing out. *See Fig. 7.*

4) Install one-way clutch inner race while turning in a counterclockwise direction. Remove Clutch Compressor (9322). Install shim. Install "O" ring only after checking axial play of one-way clutch.

Fig. 7: Exploded View of One-Way Clutch

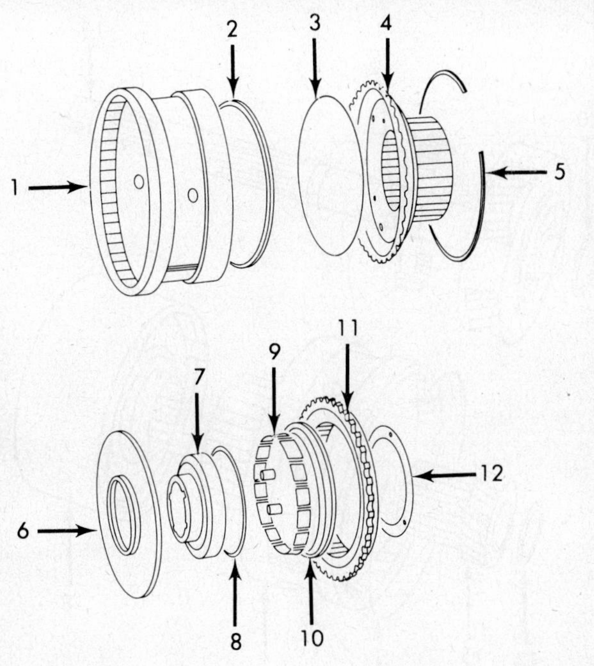

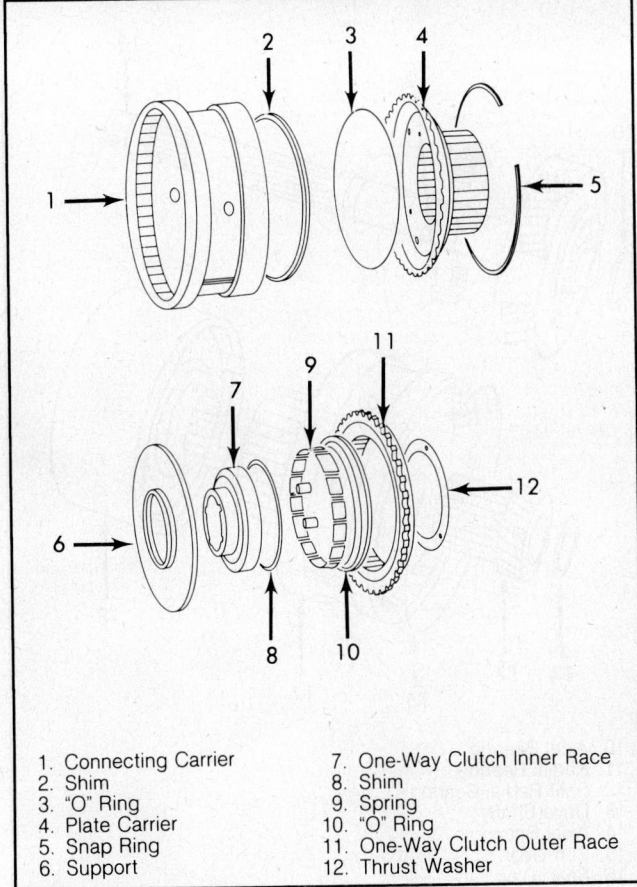

1. Connecting Carrier
2. Shim
3. "O" Ring
4. Plate Carrier
5. Snap Ring
6. Support
7. One-Way Clutch Inner Race
8. Shim
9. Spring
10. "O" Ring
11. One-Way Clutch Outer Race
12. Thrust Washer

5) Install support so that pin engages in bore of one-way clutch outer race. Place shims on outer race of one-way clutch and install connecting carrier on one-way clutch.

6) Install snap ring by pressing into groove with a screwdriver. Using a feeler gauge, check play between one-way clutch and connecting carrier. Adjust play to .0020-.008 (.05-.2 mm) with shims. Install "O" ring. *See Fig. 9.*

CLUTCH K-1

Disassembly

1) Install Assembler (9315) on diaphragm spring and tighten until snap ring can be removed. Remove diaphragm spring and springs.

2) The number of springs for clutch piston will vary. If new springs are required, the same number of springs must be installed. *See Fig. 10.*

Reassembly

1) Install seals in piston so that sealing lips face down. Install Assembler & Sleeve (9318 & 9317) in outer plate carrier. Without canting, carefully press piston into outer plate carrier.

2) Install spring in piston and place on diaphragm spring. When installing each spring, they must be centered by a guide pin.

3) Install snap ring and remove Assembler (9315). Check that snap ring fits properly. Install diaphragm spring with curved surface toward piston. Assemble set of plates and install plate carrier.

NOTE: **New inner plates must be placed in ATF for about one hour before installing.**

4) Push up snap ring around entire periphery with a suitable screwdriver. Using feeler gauge, check snap ring-to-plate clearance. Clearance should be .027-47" (.7-1.2 mm). *See Fig. 11.*

5) Snap ring clearance can be adjusted with snap rings that are available in 3 thicknesses (2.0, 2.5 and 3.0 mm). If specified play cannot be reached with snap rings, the center outer plates must also be used for adjusting. *See Fig. 12.*

CLUTCH K-2

Disassembly

Install Assembler (9315) on diaphragm spring and tighten until snap ring can be removed. Remove diaphragm spring and springs. *See Fig. 13.*

NOTE: **The number of springs for clutch piston will vary. If new springs are required, the number must not be changed.**

Reassembly

1) Install seal and ensure that seal does not turn on its own. Install seal in piston that sealing lip faces down. Install Assembler (9317) on plate carrier.

2) Install piston in plate carrier by turning slightly, DO NOT cant piston. Coat seals and sliding surfaces with ATF. Install springs in piston and mount diaphragm spring so that each spring is centered by a guide pin.

3) Install Assembler (9315) and install snap ring. Place new inner plates in ATF for approximately one hour before installing. Assemble set of plates and install in plate carrier.

4) Push up snap ring around entire periphery with a suitable screwdriver. Using feeler gauge, check snap ring-to-plate clearance. Clearance should be .027-47" (.7-1.2 mm). *See Fig. 14.*

5) Snap ring-to-plate clearance can be adjusted with a snap ring which is available in 3 thicknesses 2.0, 2.5 and 3.0 mm. If specified play cannot be reached with snap rings, the center outer plates must also be used for adjusting.

TRANSMISSION REASSEMBLY

NOTE: **Coat all bearing surfaces and sliding surfaces with ATF when assembling. Place new brake bands and lined plates in ATF for about one hour before installing.**

1) Install guide ring and drive in seal to correct position with Mandrel (9119), making sure sealing lip faces out toward brake band piston cover.

2) Install "O" ring and seal. Screw in plugs with new seals and tighten to 84 ft. lbs. (10 N.m). Place "O" ring in groove.

3) Coat grooves in support flange of clutch "K2" with grease. Install Teflon rings and press into gooves far enough so that gaps remain closed. Install support flange so that hole pattern matches. Tighten mounting bolt to 96 INCH lbs. (11 N.m).

4) Install thrust washer in correct position (locating tab engages in support flange). Install pressure element of clutch "B2" with support bar facing up. Recheck Teflon rings on support flange.

PORSCHE A28.04 TRANSAXLE (Cont.)

Fig. 8: Exploded View of Gear Train

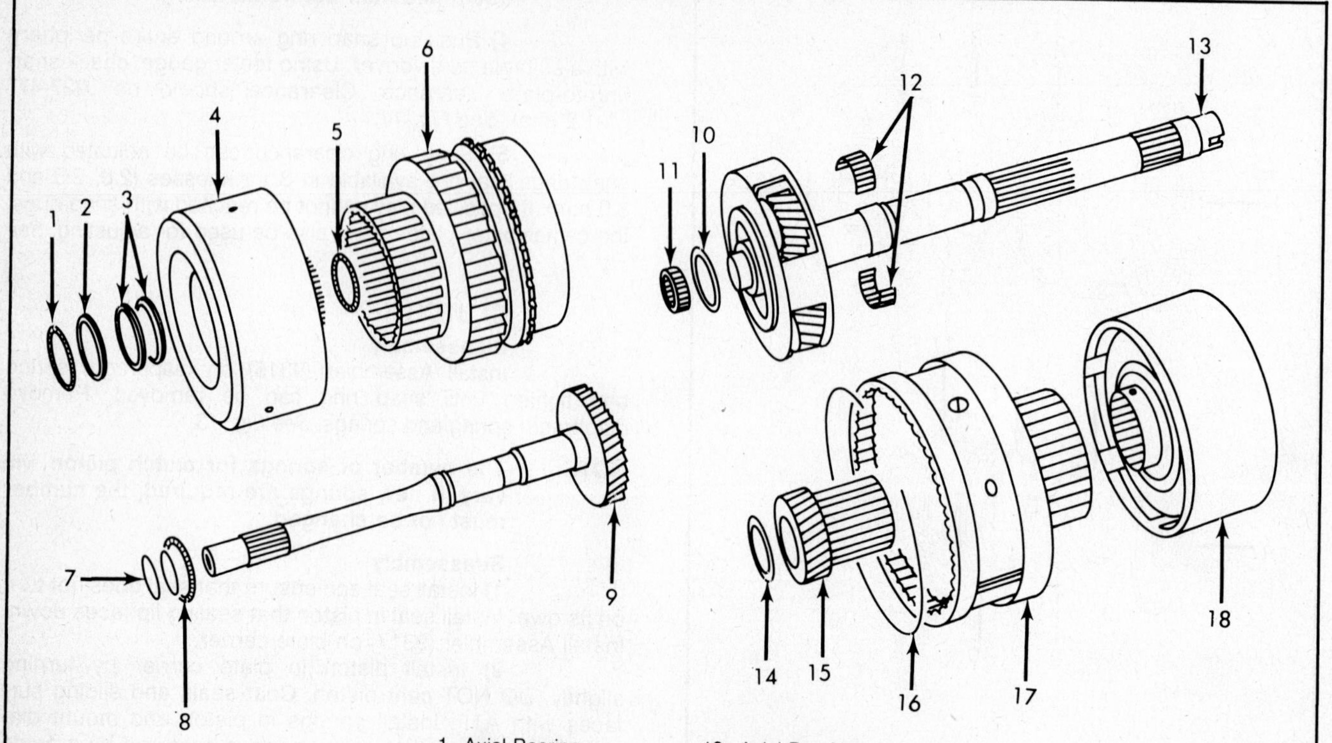

1. Axial Bearing
2. Thrust Washer
3. Shim
4. Clutch "K1"
5. Snap Ring
6. Front Gear Set
7. Lubricating Ring
8. Axial Bearing
9. Drive Shaft
10. Axial Bearing
11. Radial Bearing
12. Split Radial Bearing
13. Drive Shaft
14. Axial Bearing
15. Sun Gear
16. Snap Ring
17. Plate Carrier
18. Clutch "K2"

Fig. 9: Checking One-Way Clutch Axial Play

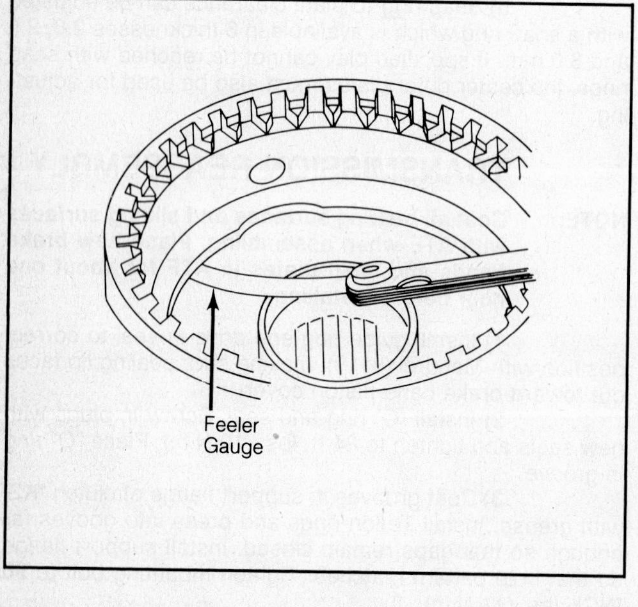

5) Compress brake band "B2" on supporting tabs as far as possible and install in case in correct position. Install split radial bearing on output shaft with grease.

6) Install split radial bearing on output shaft with grease. While turning input shaft, carefully install gear set in transmission case without clutch "K1". Position transmission with input shaft facing up upright.

7) Check installed position of gear set. Gear set is installed correctly when upper edge of connecting carrier is deeper than bearing surface of outer plate "LB 3". Install plates of brake plate "B3" in correct position.

8) Measure and eliminate play "L" of "B3". Determine distance "D". Place Gauge Bar (9313) on machined surface and measure distance to shim with a depth gauge. Determine distance "E". *See Fig. 15.*

9) Place Gauge Bar (9313) on piston of brake plate and measure distance to gasket with a depth gauge. The difference of both measured distances is play "L". Adjust play to specified value of .060-.078" (1.5 to 2.0 mm). Adjustment is made with different outer plate and shim thicknesses.

10) Place axial bearing in planet gear carrier. Check lubricating thrust rings for proper seating (install with grease). Attach brake band "B1" on assembly lock.

11) While turning, install clutch "K1" until splines mesh. Install brake band that pin faces from assembly lock to pressure element of "B1". Install axial bearing and shims only after measuring axial play of clutch "K1".

12) Install thrust pin in pressure element of "B1" (replace "O" rings). Install pressure element. Install and tighten plug to 51 ft. lbs. (70 N.m). Install brake band guide, letting locating pins engage in case bores.

PORSCHE A28.04 TRANSAXLE (Cont.)

Fig. 10: Exploded View of "K1" Clutch

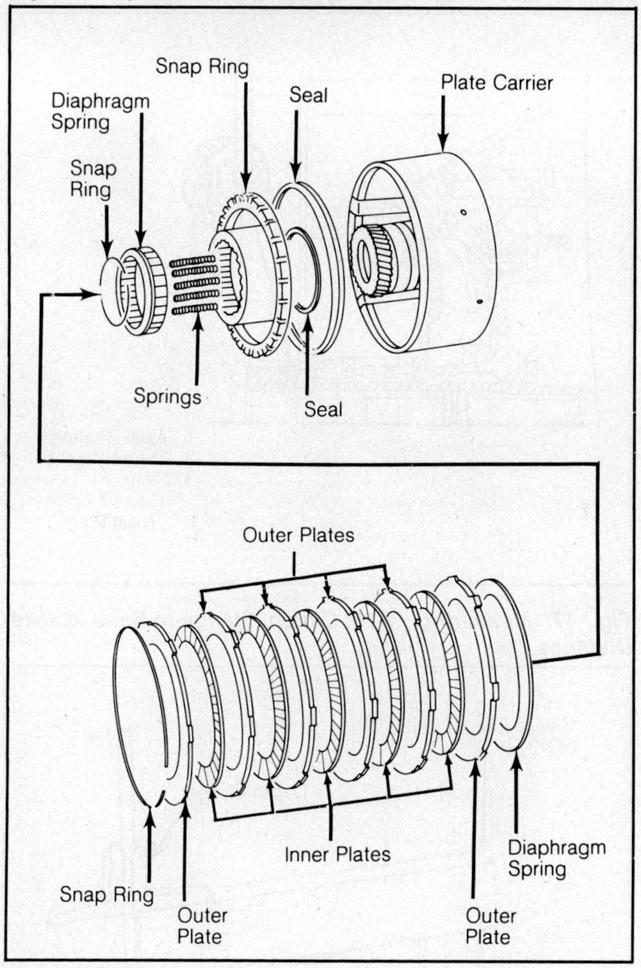

Fig. 11: Sectional View of "K1" Clutch

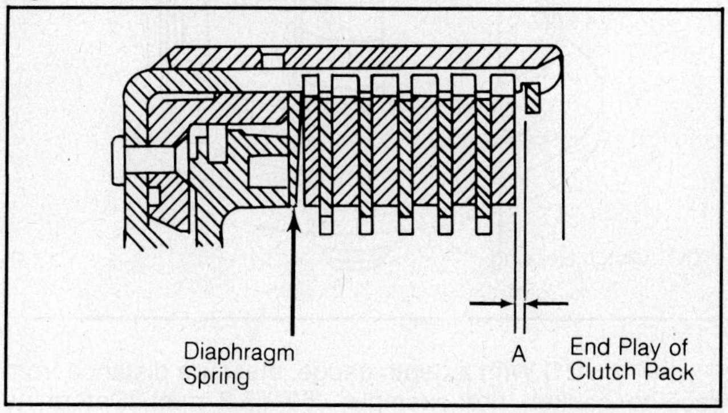

13) Measure and adjust axial play "B" for clutch "B1". To determine distance "A", place gasket on front cover. Place Gauge Bar (9313) on flange and measure distance to gasket using a depth gauge (for example 119.0 mm). *See Fig. 16.*

14) To determine distance "B", place Measuring Bar (9113) on machined surface and measure distance to clutch "K1" with a depth gauge (for example: 123.6 mm). Difference between both measured distances is axial play "B" (without axial bearing, thrust washer and shim). Adjust play to .003" (.8 mm) by installing axial bearing, thrust washer and shims of proper thickness. *See Fig. 17.*

Fig. 12: Checking Axial Play of "K1" Clutch

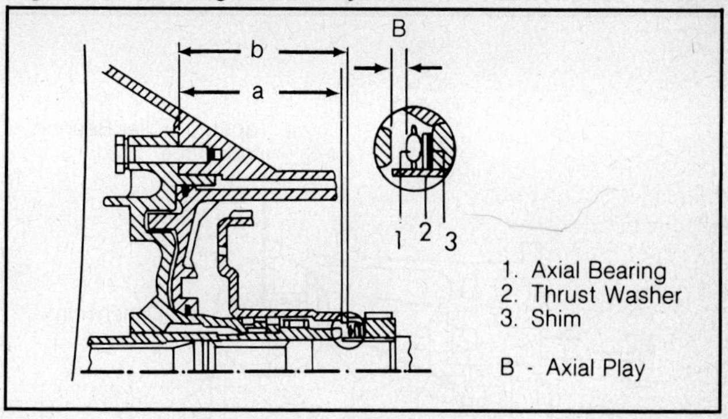

Fig. 13: Exploded View of "K2" Clutch Assembly

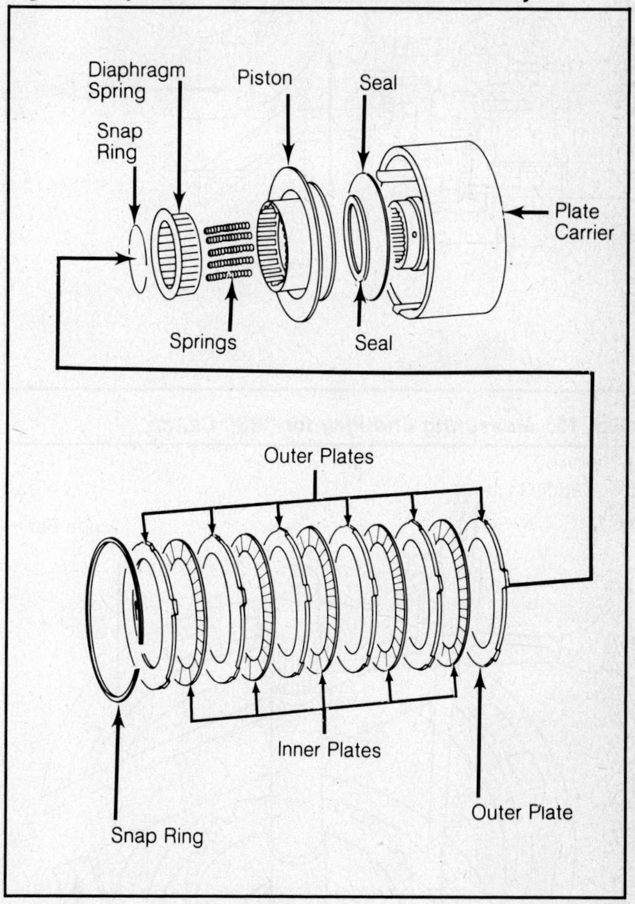

15) Check seating of Teflon rings on front cover and input shaft. Hold shim on support with grease and install front cover with gasket. Tighten mounting bolts to 108 INCH lbs. (13 N.m).

16) Turn assembly stand fixture so that output shaft faces up. Install circlip, gear and axial holder. Install "O" ring and insert centrifugal governor. Swing axial holder toward centrifugal governor so that it engages in groove of governor shaft. *See Fig. 18.*

17) Install cover and install circlip. Then pull cover toward outside so that it rests on circlip. Insert transfer plate and install "O" ring. Install secondary pump and tighten bolts to 72 INCH lbs. (8 N.m).

18) Install catch plate with shaft. Place spring loaded linkage on catch plate and install circlip. Place roller

PORSCHE A28.04 TRANSAXLE (Cont.)

Fig. 14: Sectional View of Output Shaft for "K2" Clutch

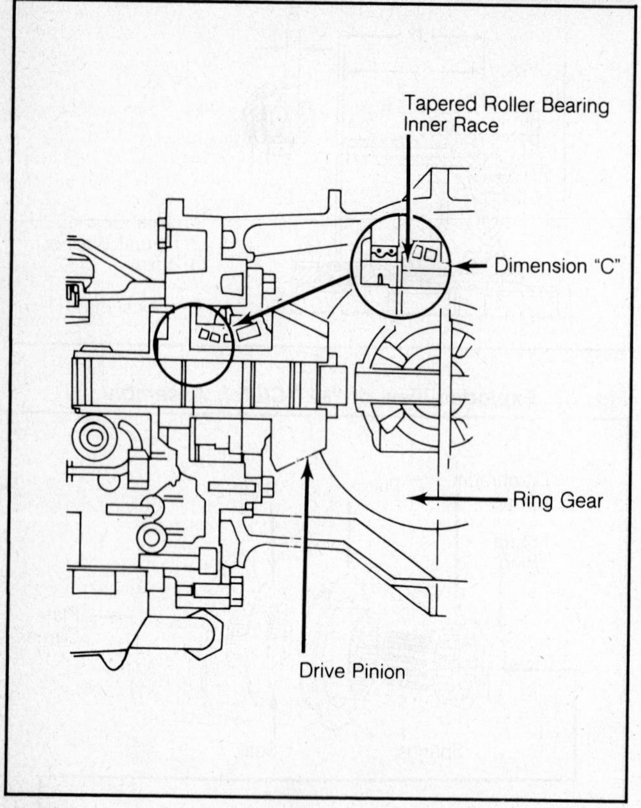

Fig. 15: Measuring End Play for "B3" Clutch

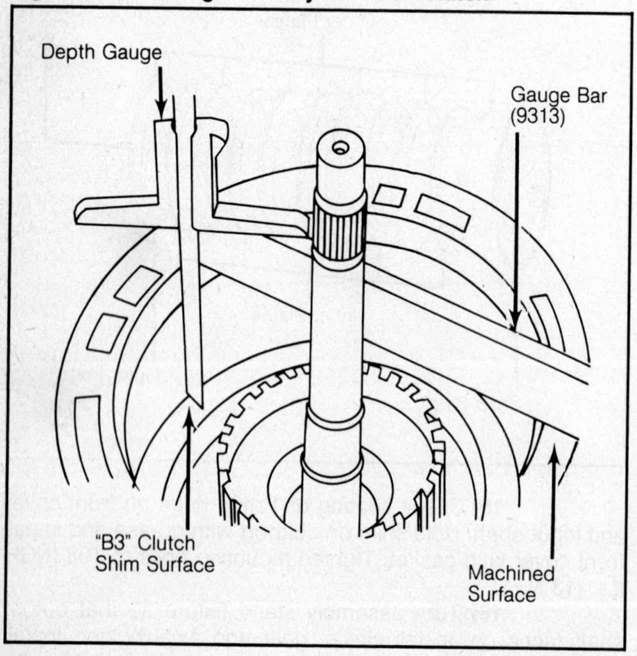

on spring-loaded linkage. Install plastic guide and press into locating bores.

19) Place old shims on gear. Install parking lock pawl, cross spring and parking lock gear. Measure and adjust axial play "C" of output shaft (clutch "K2").

20) Determine distance "B". Slide Spacer (9312) on to output shaft and tighten collar nut to 275 ft. lbs. (380 N.m). Engage parking lock pawl for this purpose. Install gasket.

Fig. 16: Checking Axial Play for "B1" Clutch

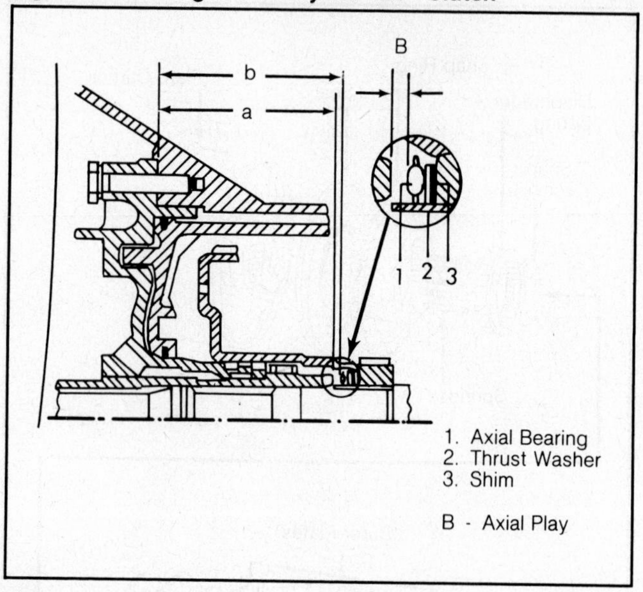

Fig. 17: Measuring "K1" Clutch Flange-to-Base Gasket Distance

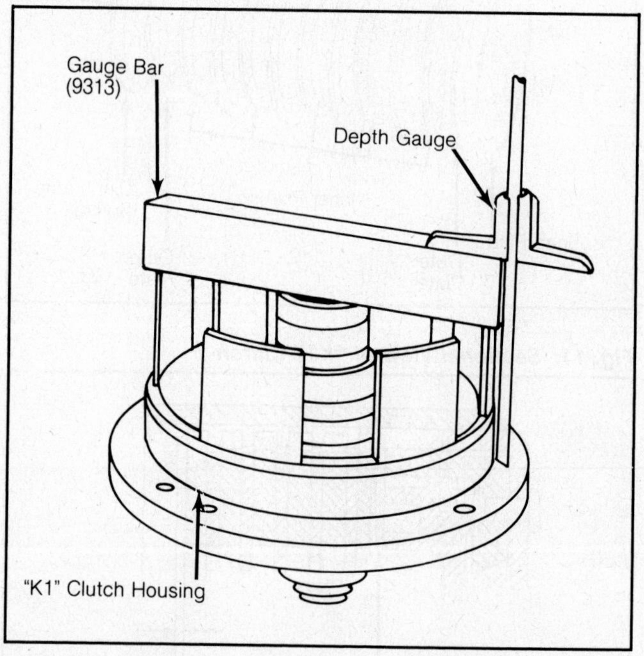

21) With a depth gauge, measure distance from race to gasket. For example: .60" (5.3 mm). Determine distance "A". Determine thickness of shims for bearing assembly.

22) Using a depth gauge, measure distance from tapered roller bearing surface to bearing assembly surface. Since distance specified by design is only 1.34" (34.55 mm), shims with a thickness of .021" (.55 mm) must be installed.

23) Install bearing assembly with shims of pertinent thickness in case and tighten all mounting bolts to 24 ft. lbs. (33 N.m). Using a depth gauge, measure distance from case bearing surface to inner race of cylinder roller bearing. For example: combined distance is .62" (15.9 mm).

24) Adjust axial play "C" to .015" (.4 mm) by installing or removing shims underneath the parking lock

PORSCHE A28.04 TRANSAXLE (Cont.)

Fig. 18: Sectional View of Centrifugal Governor

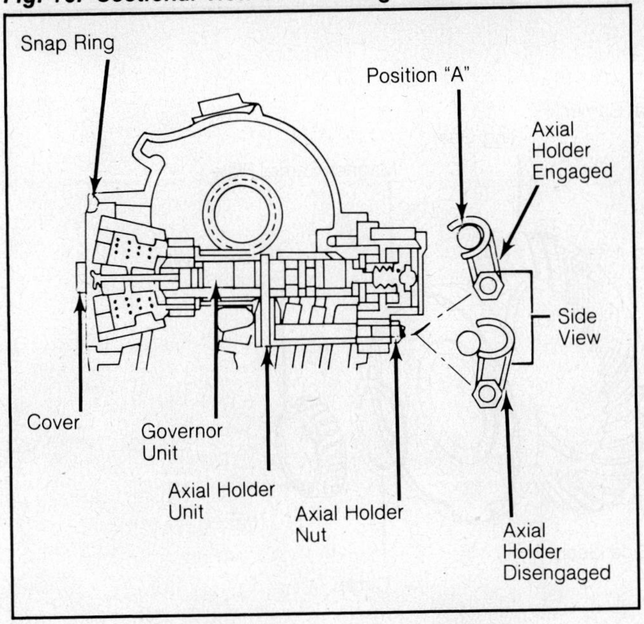

gear. Install injection tube. Screw in excessive acceleration solenoid and tighten to 168 INCH lbs. (20 N.m). Install modulating pressure valve and thrust pin.

25) Install vacuum box with holder and tighten bolts to 72 INCH lbs. (8 N.m). Install starter locking switch and bolt in mounting bracket, do not tighten. Mount range selector lever so that lug is positioned in lever.

26) Install seal on brake band "B1" piston so that its sealing lip faces toward the front.

NOTE: The brake band pistons have 5 different thrust pins, which are marked with grooves, for adjustment of play on brake band "B1". Brake band piston with shortest thrust pin has no groove, while brake band piston with longest thrust pin has 4 grooves.

27) Bolt Compressor (9316) on transmission case and install brake band "B1" piston with springs and Tester (9320). Screw in spindle-to-guide thrust pin of piston into brake band (be careful not to damage seal).

28) Install circlip and release Compressor (9316). Measure and adjust play "L" on brake band. Threads on Tester (9320) have a .039" (1 mm) pitch so that each turn is equal to .039" (1 mm) of travel.

29) Screw in bolt of Tester (9320) by hand until resistance is felt. Screw in bolt further with a torque wrench, counting number of turns. Tighten to 43 INCH lbs. (5 N.m).

30) Dead travel on brake band must be .12-.16" (3-4 mm). Tightening torque of 43.2 INCH lbs. (5 N.m) must be reached after 3 to 4 turns. If dead travel is excessive, install a brake band piston with a longer thrust pin. Install a brake band piston with shorter thrust pin when dead travel is insufficient.

31) Bolt Assembler (9316) to brake band "B1" piston and install brake band piston cover. Install thrust pin with large diameter facing brake band "B2". Install Teflon ring in groove with grease and insert thrust pin.

NOTE: Thrust pins are available in 4 different lengths for adjustment.

32) Guide in brake band "B2" piston, making sure that thrust pin engages in brake band. Press in brake band "B2" piston cover and install circlip. Measure and adjust play "L" on brake band "B2".

33) Press brake band "B2" on support bar toward brake band piston so that brake band piston touches cover of brake band piston. Measure distance "A" on brake band using sliding calipers.

34) Push brake band "B2" again on support bar toward pressure element. Measure distance "A" a second time. The difference of both measured distances is end play "L". Adjust end play "L" to .24-.28" (6-7 mm) by replacing thrust pin on brake band "B2" piston.

35) Install one-way valve and filter. Install brake band guide. Install temperature orifice. Push temperature orifice into oil bore far enough so that it is flush with case. Install oil deflector.

36) While guiding oil pipe into case bore, install lower cover. Install transfer plate and screw in combination bolts, do not tighten bolts. Attach return spring.

37) Install leaf spring with holder and screw in mounting bolts, do not tighten. Holder must be located accurately with pin. Install valve body so that range selector valve engages in lug on catch plate. Tighten combination bolts to 72 INCH lbs. (8 N.m).

NOTE: Check different length of bolts. The 3 bolts marked with arrows are 50 mm long, while remaining 12 bolts are 55 mm long.

38) Tighten combination bolts for transfer plate and leaf spring holder to 72 INCH lbs. (8 N.m). Check end play "A" between locking piston and stop in spring loaded linkage. Adjust end play, if necessary.

39) With selector at "N" position, end play is adjusted to .016-.039" (.4-1.0 mm). Plastic clips are available in 3 thicknesses. Mount ATF filter and tighten to 36 INCH lbs. (4 N.m). Mount oil sump with gasket and tighten mounting bolts to 72 INCH lbs. (8 N.m).

40) Move range selector lever to "N" position and guide locating pin made of .16" (4 mm) diameter welding rod through range selector lever locating bore for switch housing. Tighten mounting bolts to 72 INCH lbs. (8 N.m). Then pull out locating pin.

NOTE: Check modulating pressure after installation of transmission and adjust if necessary.

FINAL DRIVE

DISASSEMBLY

1) Place final drive housing in holding fixture. Remove axle flange bolts and remove axle flanges. Mark side covers for reassembly reference. Remove side cover bolts and side covers.

NOTE: Record number and thickness of shims for reassembly reference on each side.

2) Using a screwdriver, remove oil seals from side covers. Remove rear cover and pull differential assembly from case. Place differential assembly in vise fitted with jaw protectors. Remove ring gear bolts and drive ring gear from housing. Remove bearings (if required) using puller.

3) Drive differential shaft lock pin out, then remove differential shaft with a plastic mallet. Remove ring gear. *See Fig. 19.*

PORSCHE A28.04 TRANSAXLE (Cont.)

Fig. 19: Exploded View of Final Drive

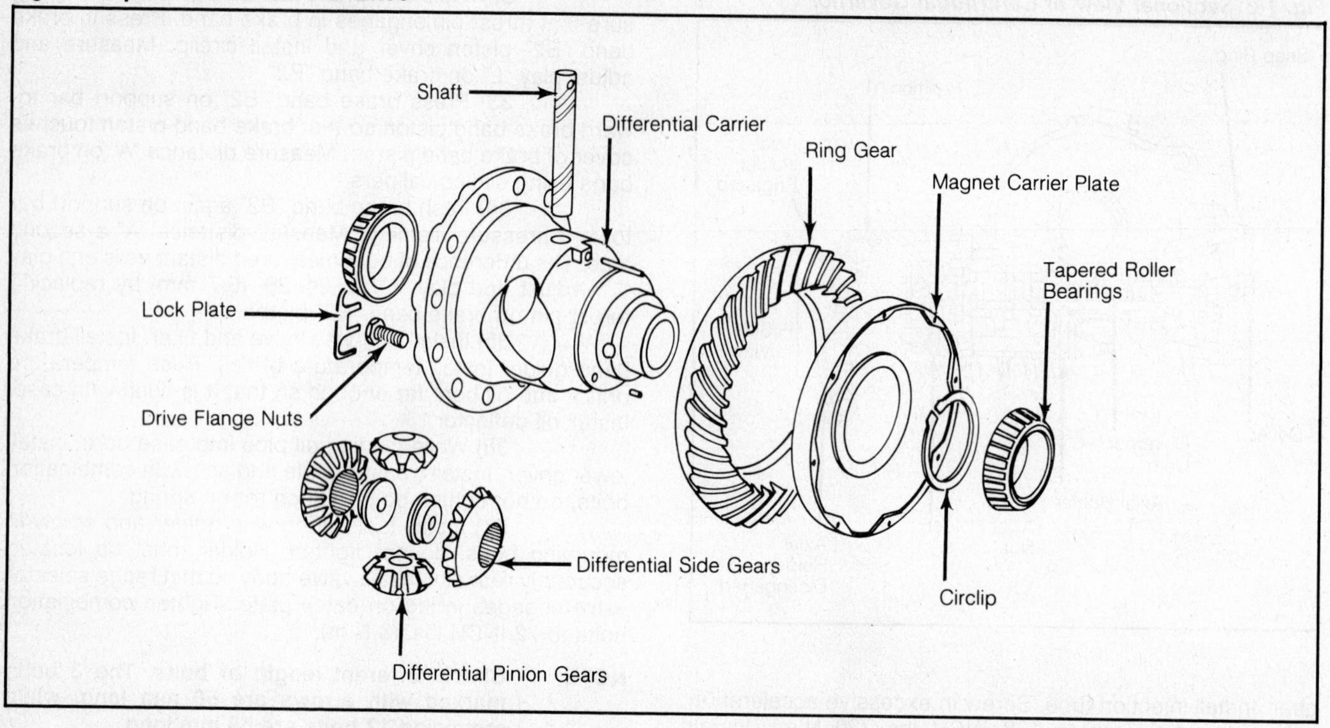

REASSEMBLY & ADJUSTMENTS

1) Heat ring gear to about 212°F (100°C) and place on case using centering pins to align bolt holes. Install new bolts and tighten crosswise to specifications. Bend lock plate ends over side of bolt heads.

2) Coat large gears with grease and install in differential carrier. Install small gears and align with bore, then insert shaft, position correctly and install locking pins. Drive tapered roller bearings on carrier with tool.

Pinion Gear Adjustment

The position of smoothest running is determined by moving the pinion in an axial direction. Then the ring gear is lifted out of the no-play meshing position far enough so that the backlash will be kept within specified tolerances. Deviation "r" is the adjusting distance called for by design (design distance "R"). This is measured and recorded on face of drive pinion. Ring and pinion gears are designed so that deviation "r" is always added to "R" and is proceeded by a "+" sign. *See Fig. 20.*

1) When adjusting pinion and ring gear, the following sequence should be used:

- Determine the total shim thickness ("S1" + "S2") for the specified preload of the tapered roller bearing differential.
- Determine shim thickness ("S3").
- Divide total shim thickness in "S1" and "S2" to provide correct backlash between the pinion and ring gear.

2) The adjustment distance "E" is calculated from known design distance "R" = 2.86" (72.20 mm) + deviation "r".

Fig. 20: Manufacturer's Codes Stamped in Pinion and Ring Gears

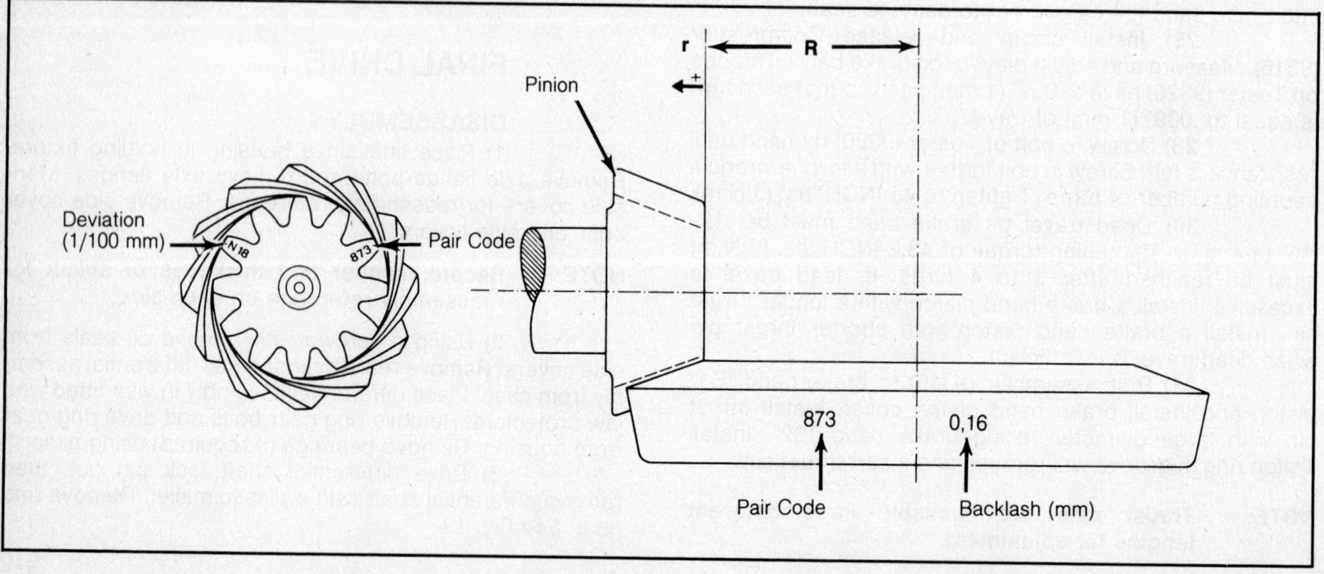

3) With pinion bearing adjusted and pinion nut tightened to proper specifications, install final drive housing (without shims) to transmission and tighten all nuts to specifications. Install one side cover (without "O" ring) secure with 2 bolts.

4) Set adjusting ring of Master Gauge (VW 385/1) at 1.61" (41 mm). Install Centering Discs (VW 385/4) on master gauge and attach Plunger (VW 385/14) with dial indicator extension. *See Fig. 21.*

Fig. 21: View of Master Measuring Gauge with Dial Indicator Attached

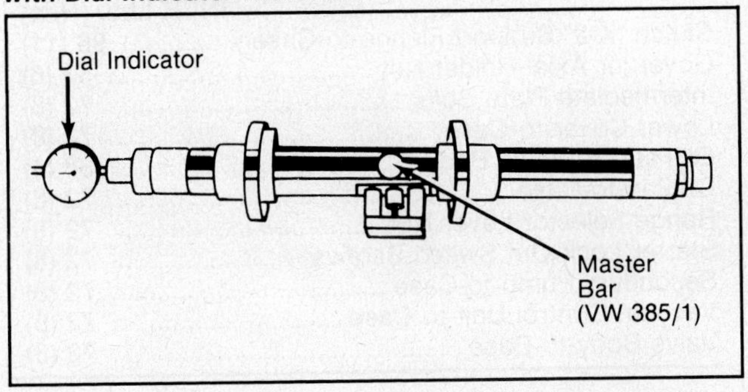

5) Install measuring gauge in case, install second side cover (without "O" ring) and secure with 2 bolts. Set dial indicator to distance "E" + .20" (5 mm). Install Measuring Bar (VW 385/1) and set at zero with .004" (1 mm) preload.

6) Turn measuring bar until dial gauge extension is vertical to face of pinion head. At this time, dial gauge needle will reach its point of reversal (highest point) and dial gauge should be read. Install determined shim thickness ("S3") between the transmission case and final drive housing. Recheck distance after installation of shims. A deviation of .0012" (.03 mm) is permissible.

Ring Gear Adjustment

1) Clamp final drive in a vise. Install differential with ring gear into final drive housing. Install side cover (without shims) and tighten all bolts to specifications.

2) Guide second cover (without shims) into place on the case and check gap between case and side cover. Then, determine shim thickness by subtracting bearing preload .012" (.30 mm) from gap measurement. Resulting shim thickness is "S" total.

Ring Gear Backlash Adjustment

1) Place shims determined for pinion adjustment between transmission case and final drive case. Install final drive to transmission and tighten all mounting bolts to specifications. Install differential assembly into case, install side covers with shims on ring gear side and tighten all bolts to specifications.

2) Turn differential in both directions several times to settle bearings. Install Dial Indicator (VW 388) and set to 3.1" (78.7 mm). Engage parking lock, turn ring gear by hand against stop and set dial indicator to zero.

3) Hold pinion with locally made tool and turn back ring gear and read amount of backlash. The measured backlash must be within specified tolerance:

- Getrag Pinion - .006-.008" (.15-.20 mm)
- Hurth Pinion - .008-.010" (.20-.25 mm)

4) The splitting and positioning of shims is determined by the following:

- Ring gear side - Take total shim thickness ("S total", then multiply by .026" (.66 mm). The result is the proper shim amount to be placed on ring gear side ("S1").
- Opposite ring gear side - Substract ring gear side ("S1") from total shim thickness ("S" total) the result is ("S2") which is the amount of shims placed opposite ring gear side.

5) Remove side covers and position shims as previously determined. Tighten side covers. Measure backlash. If not within specifications, change shim "S1" and "S2" until specified backlash is obtained. Check backlash at 4 places by turning ring gear 90° each time. The 4 measurements must not deviate from each other by more than .002" (.05 mm).

ADJUSTING DRIVE PLATE

NOTE: **To avoid axial presssure on crankshaft and crankshaft thrust bearings, the connection between flywheel and drive plate (distance "X") must be checked and adjusted after replacement of engine, flywheel or central tube. This adjustment is not necessary after replacement of transmission or transmission parts.**

Determining Distance "X"

1) Crankshaft must contact thrust bearing toward rear. Use a lever to press flywheel in direction of transmission, until axial play of crankshaft is eliminated.

2) Using Measuring Gauge (9211), determine distance "A" by measuring distance from engine flange to flywheel mating surface. Mark thickness of gauge when measuring.

3) If measured value is 2.067" (52.5 mm), subtract 1.57" (40 mm). Distance "A" will be .49" (12.5 mm). Mount transmission on central tube to specified torque. Screw in clamping sleeve mounting bolt by hand (do not tighten). *See Fig. 22.*

4) Push drive flange with bushing (without shims), on to central shaft and install circlip. Use a suitable lever and push central shaft on drive flange far enough forward, that central shaft rests on rear clamping screw in shaft groove.

5) Tighten rear mounting bolt for clamping sleeve 54-61 ft. lbs. (75-85 N.m). Push drive flange forward against stop on circlip and tighten bolt.

6) Determine distance "B". Using Measuring Bar (9211), measure distance from clutch housing to drive plate bearing surface (as far in as possible). Mark thickness of gauge used for measuring.

7) To determine shim thickness for shim "X" use the following formula: Distance "A" minus "B" plus preload of .012" (.3 mm) equals distance "X".

8) Install shim having thickness "X". Shims are available in thicknesses of .008" (.2 mm), .020" (.5 mm) and .039" (1.0 mm). Tighten mounting bolt for front drive flange only after central tube has been installed.

PORSCHE A28.04 TRANSAXLE (Cont.)

Fig. 22: Sectional View of Drive Plate

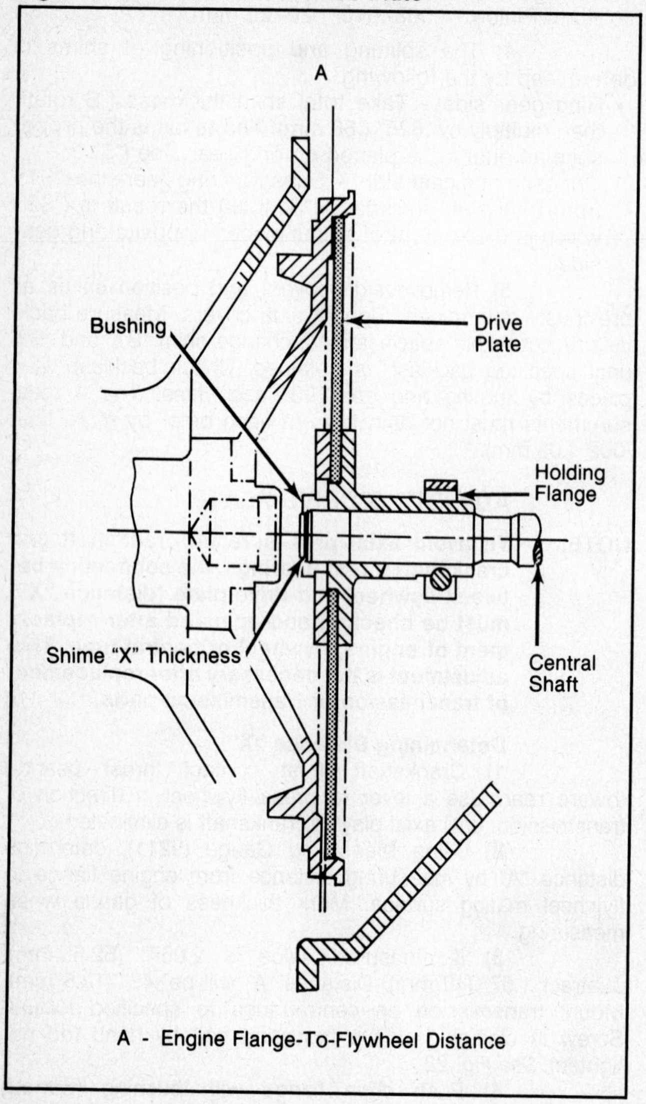

TIGHTENING SPECIFICATIONS

Application	Ft. Lbs. (N.m)
Converter Drain Plug	10 (14)
Front Cover-to-Case	10 (14)
Front Cover-to-Primary Pump	15 (21)
Kickdown Solenoid Valve	14 (20)
Propeller Shaft Clamping Nut	22 (30)
Rear Cover-to-Case	10 (14)
Thrust Body Plug	52 (70)
3-Arm Flange Slot Nut	89 (120)
	INCH Lbs. (N.m)
Clutch "K-2" Support Flange-to-Case	96 (11)
Governor Axial Holder Nut	53 (6)
Intermediate Plate Bolts	72 (8)
Lower Cover-to-Case	72 (8)
Oil Filter-to-Valve Body	36 (4)
Oil Pan-to-Case	72 (8)
Range Selector Lever Nut	72 (8)
Starter Lock-Out Switch Screws	72 (8)
Secondary Pump-to-Case	72 (8)
Vacuum Control Unit-to Case	72 (8)
Valve Body-to-Case	72 (8)

Automatic Transaxles

RENAULT FUEGO & SPORTWAGON

DESCRIPTION

The Fuego and Sportwagon transaxle is a 3-speed unit consisting basically of torque converter, differential assembly and transmission assembly. Differential consists of ring and pinion gear set, worm gear to drive governor, and step-down gears to change direction of drive centerline.

Transmission assembly consists of a planetary gear train, 2 clutches, 2 brakes and main control systems for transaxle. Mechanical, electrical and hydraulic control systems are used.

LUBRICATION & ADJUSTMENT

See appropriate MANUAL TRANSMISSION SERVICING article in IMPORT GENERAL SERVICING section.

TROUBLE SHOOTING

ENGINE IDLES ROUGH OR STALLS

Idle speed incorrect. Check ignition timing and spark plug condition. Throttle cable out of adjustment. Leak in vacuum circuit.

VEHICLE CREEPS IN "N"

Shift lever out of adjustment. Defective or damaged E1 clutch.

EXCESSIVE CREEPING IN "A"

Idle speed incorrect. Throttle cable out of adjustment. Torque converter faulty or damaged.

SLIPS IN FORWARD & REVERSE

Incorrect fluid level. Pressure regulator damaged or out of adjustment. Torque converter faulty or damaged.

NO MOVEMENT

In 3rd, OK in Other Gears

E1 clutch faulty or defective. One-way clutch damaged or faulty.

In 3rd, "1" or "R"

Fluid level incorrect. Pressure regulator or shift control mechanism out of adjustment. Oil pump shaft or turbine shaft bent or damaged. Defective oil pump. Torque converter drive plate warped or otherwise damaged. Final drive assembly faulty. Torque converter damaged.

Fig. 1: Cross Sectional View of Renault Fuego & Sportwagon Automatic Transaxle

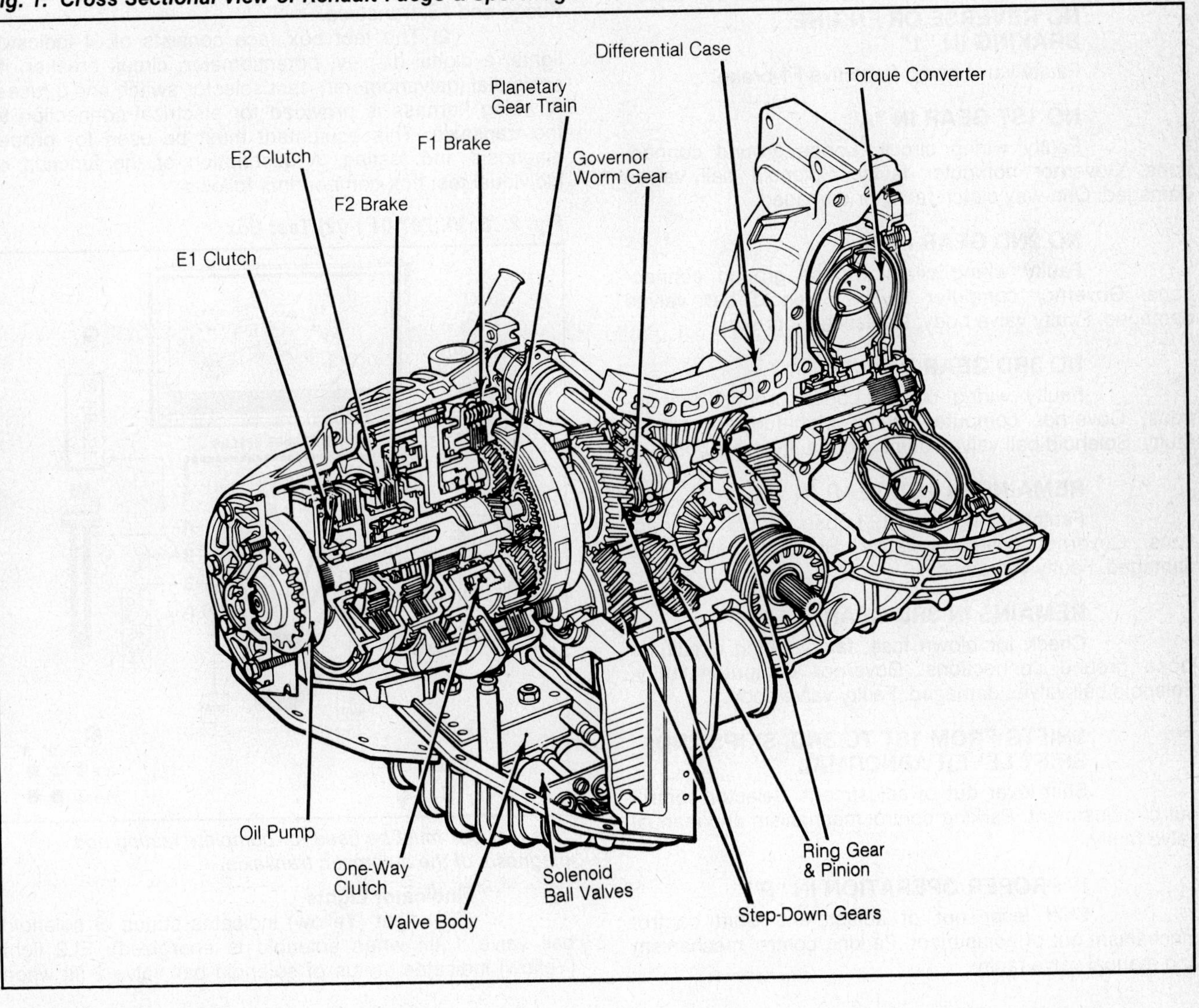

RENAULT FUEGO & SPORTWAGON (Cont.)

In 3rd or "1"
Defective E1 clutch.
In "R" or 3rd Gear
Faulty valve body. Defective E2 clutch.

SLIPPING ON SHIFTS

Incorrect fluid level. Fluid pressure regulator damaged or out of adjustment. Faulty valve body. Defective E1 or E2 clutch. Defective F1 or F2 brake.

ERRATIC STARTS

Idle speed incorrect. Throttle cable out of adjustment.

EXCESSIVE SHIFT SHOCK BETWEEN GEARS

Incorrect fluid level. Pressure regulator damaged or out of adjustment. Defective F1 brake. Leak in vacuum circuit. Faulty valve body.

SHIFT POINTS INCORRECT

Throttle cable, governor cable or kickdown switch out of adjustment. Governor cable faulty. Faulty wiring circuit. Loose ground connections. Governor computer faulty. Faulty valve body. Engine charging system.

NO REVERSE OR ENGINE BRAKING IN "1"

Faulty valve body. Defective F1 brake.

NO 1ST GEAR IN "A"

Faulty wiring circuit. Loose ground connections. Governor computer faulty. Solenoid ball valves damaged. One-way clutch faulty or damaged.

NO 2ND GEAR IN "A"

Faulty wiring circuit. Loose ground connections. Governor computer faulty. Solenoid ball valves damaged. Faulty valve body. Defective F2 brake.

NO 3RD GEAR IN "A"

Faulty wiring circuit. Loose ground connections. Governor computer faulty. Multi-function switch faulty. Solenoid ball valves damaged. Faulty valve body.

REMAINS IN 1ST GEAR IN "A"

Faulty wiring circuit. Loose ground connections. Governor computer faulty. Solenoid ball valves damaged. Faulty valve body.

REMAINS IN 3RD GEAR

Check for blown fuse, faulty wiring circuit, or loose ground connections. Governor computer faulty. Solenoid ball valves damaged. Faulty valve body.

SHIFTS FROM 1ST TO 3RD, SKIPS 2ND; SHIFT LEVER ABNORMAL

Shift lever out of adjustment. Selector control out of adjustment. Parking control mechanism and manual valve faulty.

IMPROPER OPERATION IN "P"

Shift lever out of adjustment. Shift control mechanism out of adjustment. Parking control mechanism and manual valve faulty.

STARTER NOT WORKING

Faulty wiring circuit. Loose ground connections. Shift lever out of adjustment. Multi-function switch faulty.

BACKUP LIGHTS NOT WORKING

Faulty wiring circuit. Loose ground connections. Multi-function switch faulty.

SLIPS WHEN STARTING OUT IN "A"

One-way clutch damaged or faulty.

TESTING

TESTING EQUIPMENT

1) No special equipment is needed for road testing. Hydraulic testing and transaxle diagnosis require the use of the following special test equipment: Test box (B. Vi. 797-01 or -02) and thermometer (B. Vi. 524-01). If test box (B. Vi. 797-01) is used, intermediate cable (B. Vi. 858) is required for hook-up to transaxle. In addition, hydraulic testing requires oil pressure switch (B. Vi. 466-04). The test box is equipped with indicator lights and gauges to diagnose various operating conditions of the Fuego and 18i transaxle.

2) The test box face consists of: 4 indicator lights, a digital display, potentiometer, circuit breaker, 4-scale dial (galvanometer), test selector switch and 3 fuses. A wiring harness is provided for electrical connection to the transaxle. This equipment must be used for proper diagnosis and testing. A description of the function of individual test box components follows.

Fig. 2: B. Vi. 797-01 (-02) Test Box

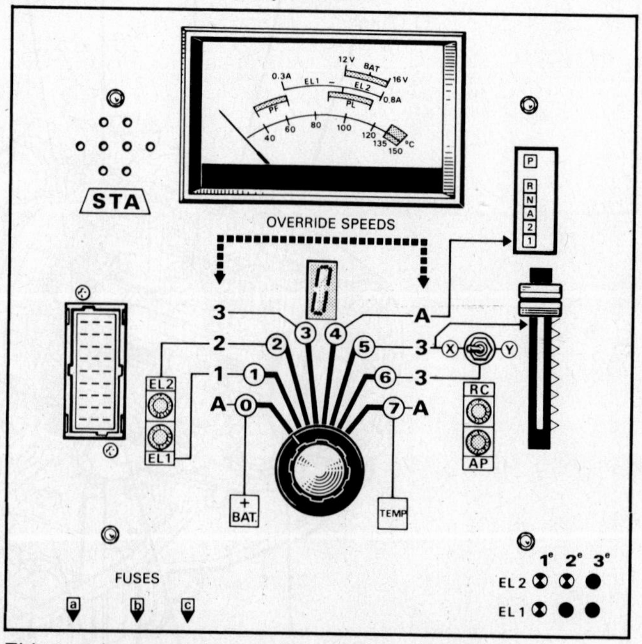

This test box must be used for complete testing and diagnosis of the automatic transaxle.

Indicator Lights

EL1 light (Yellow) indicates status of solenoid ball valve 1 (lit when solenoid is energized). EL2 light (Yellow) indicates status of solenoid ball valve 2 (lit when

RENAULT FUEGO & SPORTWAGON (Cont.)

energized). The AP indicator light (Red) indicates whether emission control system is operating (this system not used in these tests). RC light (Green) indicates whether the kickdown switch is operating.

Digital Display

Indicates multifunction switch operation and computer condition.

Potentiometer and Circuit Breaker

Systems not used in these tests.

Galvanometer

The galvanometer has 4 scales: BAT scale for reading of battery voltage, EL1-EL2 scale to measure current passing through solenoid ball valves, and temperature scale to measure transmission oil temperature (Red zone indicates maximum operating temperature). The PF and PL scales are not used.

Test Selector Switch

This switch is used to selected desired test made. Position "0" gives battery voltage; "1" measures current and input in EL1; "2" measures current and input in EL2; "3" places vehicle in 3rd gear with shift lever in "A" position (solenoid ball valves not activated); "4", "5" and "6" are not used; "7" measures transmission fluid temperature (with thermometer in place).

Fuses

All fuses are 1 amp capacity. Fuse "a" protects test box, fuse "b" protects EL1 and fuse "c" protects EL2.

ROAD TEST

1) Before road testing, make sure that fluid level and condition and control linkage adjustments have been checked and corrected as needed. During test, transmission should upshift and downshift at approximately the speeds shown in *Shift Speed Specifications* chart.

2) All shifts may vary somewhat due to production tolerances or tire size. What is important is the quality of the shifts. All shifts should be smooth, responsive and with no slippage or engine speed runaway.

3) Note any transmission malfunctions or faulty operating conditions. Slippage or engine runaway in any gear usually indicates clutch or brake problems. Compare noted malfunctions with *Trouble Shooting* section to determine probable cause.

SHIFT SPEED SPECIFICATIONS

Application	Shift Speed (MPH)
Part Throttle	
3-2 Downshift	17
2-1 Downshift	9
Full Throttle	
1-2 Upshift	44
2-3 Upshift	73
Kickdown	
3-2 Downshift	63
2-1 Downshift	39

4) This process should give a good indication of which units are faulty and/or out of adjustment. It will also give a reasonable indication of which units are operating properly; however, it is extremely difficult to determine the exact cause of any particular malfunction. Practically any condition can be caused by leaking hydraulic circuits or sticking valves. Therefore, unless an obvious condition exists, do not disassemble transmission until hydraulic pressure tests have been made.

HYDRAULIC PRESSURE TESTS

Perform tests with transmission fluid at normal operating temperature of about 175°F (80°C). Attach thermometer to test box, remove dipstick from tube and insert thermometer. Hydraulic pressures are checked in 2 steps, "Initial Adjustment" and "Full Throttle Road Test".

Initial Adjustment

1) Connect pressure gauge at rear of transaxle, but DO NOT disconnect the vacuum capsule. *See Fig. 3.* Check fluid level and top off if needed. With parking brake engaged, wheels blocked and tachometer attached, place shift lever in "P" and check fluid pressure.

2) With engine running at 800 RPM, pressure should be 58 psi (4.2 kg/cm²). As engine speed is increased, pressure should increase rapidly to a maximum pressure of 189-203 psi (13.3-14.3 kg/cm²).

Fig. 3: Pressure Test Port Location

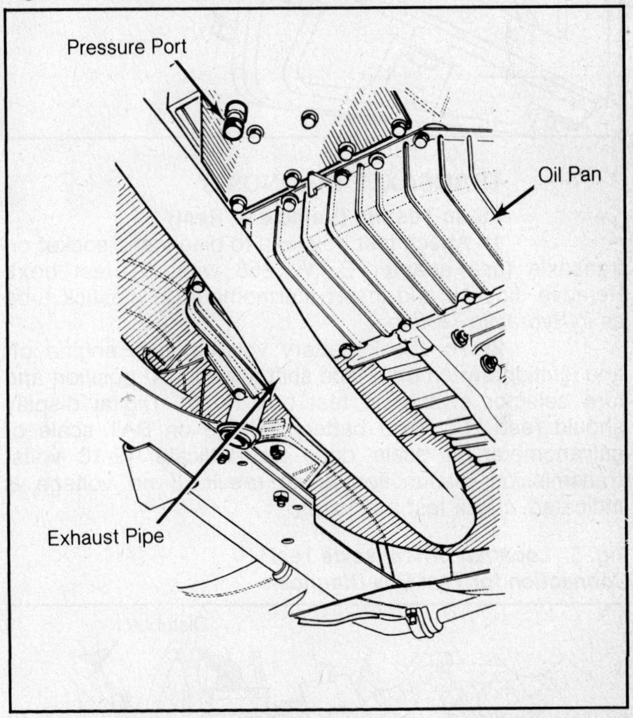

3) Move shift lever to "N", bring engine speed to 800 RPM, and read pressure at partial throttle. If pressure is not 36-39 psi (2.5-2.7 kg/cm²), adjust by turning the vacuum capsule one notch at a time. Changing capsule position by 1 notch will change pressure by about 1.5 psi (.11 kg/cm²). Pressure is increased as the vacuum capsule is screwed in.

Full Throttle Road Test

Reconnect vacuum capsule. Drive car to warm fluid. Place shift lever in "A". From standstill, press accelerator pedal to the floor. Read maximum fluid pressure obtained just before 1-2 upshift. If pressure is not about 58 psi (4.1 kg/cm²), check vacuum capsule and vacuum circuit. *See Service (In Vehicle)* in this article. Replace capsule if necessary and adjust full throttle pressure. If pressure will not adjust properly, check for faulty pressure regulator or transmission assembly.

RENAULT FUEGO & SPORTWAGON (Cont.)

Fig. 4: Vacuum Capsule Location

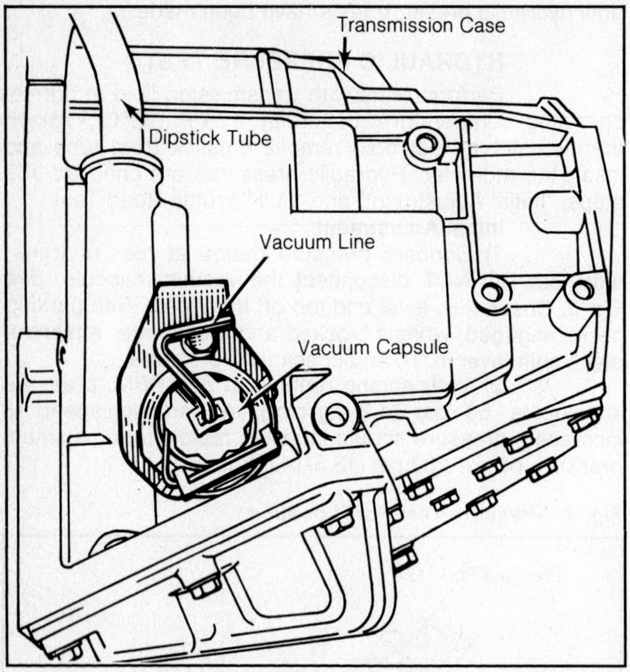

TRANSAXLE DIAGNOSIS

Static Testing (Vehicle at Rest)

1) Attach test box lead to diagnostic socket on transaxle (use adapter B. Vi. 858 with -01 test box). Remove dipstick and insert thermometer in dipstick tube as in *Hydraulic Testing*.

2) To check battery voltage, turn engine off and ignition switch on. Place shift lever in "A" position and turn selector switch on test box to "0". Digital display should read "1". Read battery voltage on BAT scale of galvanometer. If scale does not indicate 12-16 volts, transmission malfunction could result. If no voltage is indicated, check test box fuses.

Fig. 5: Location of Transaxle Test Connection for Test Box Diagnosis

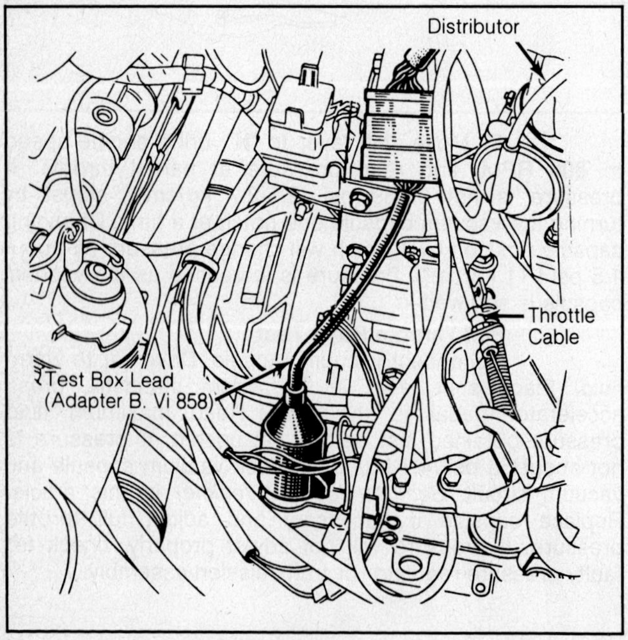

3) To check EL1 solenoid ball valve, move selector switch to "1". Digital display will read "3" and EL1 and EL2 indicator lights should light, indicating that solenoid ball valves are energized. Read current flow on EL1-EL2 scale of galvanometer. Current flow should be .3-.8 amps.

4) If current flow is correct, EL1 solenoid ball valve is in good electrical condition. Go to next step. If current is out of indicated range, check wiring and connecters. If wiring is good, solenoid ball valve is defective. If no current is indicated, check test box fuses.

5) EL2 solenoid ball valve is checked in the same manner as EL1, with the selector switch in the "2" position. If current is correct, go to next test.

6) Move selector switch to "3". Input current should still read .3-.8 amps. If current is incorrect, check test box leads and electrical controls. If input current is correct, transaxle malfunction is not in electrical system. Check hydraulic and mechanical systems.

Dynamic Testing (Vehicle in Motion)

1) With test equipment attached as before, position test box in vehicle so that it may be observed while vehicle is being driven. Start engine, place shift lever in "A" and begin driving with selector switch in "0". Digital display should show "1" and EL1 and EL2 lights should be on.

2) Continue driving. On 1-2 upshift, digital display should go to "2" and EL1 light should go out. Continue driving. On 2-3 upshift, digital display should go to "3" and both EL lights should be out.

3) Reduce speed to 40-45 MPH and move selector switch to "7". Press accelerator pedal to the floor to get 3-2 kickdown. RC light should come on. If it does not, check kickdown switch adjustment, ignition switch and the connecting wire.

SERVICE (IN VEHICLE)

DRIVE AXLE SHAFTS

See appropriate DRIVE AXLE SHAFT article in IMPORT AXLE SHAFTS, OVERDRIVES & TRANSFER CASES section.

SOLENOID BALL VALVES

Removal

Solenoid ball valves are located on the valve body. To remove, drain transmission fluid, remove inspection plate, oil pan and gasket. Remove solenoid ball valve clips and disconnect wiring. Note color of wire attached to each valve. Remove support plate retaining bolts (2) and remove valves from valve body. *See Fig. 38.*

Installation

Reverse removal procedure to install. Do not reverse valve positions. Be sure to install correct wire to correct valve as noted during removal.

VACUUM CAPSULE

Inspection

1) With test equipment connected as in *Hydraulic Pressure Tests*, connect vacuum pump to vacuum hose on capsule. Apply a vacuum of about 15.7 in. Hg. If needle on test box does not move, check pressure at full and part throttle.

2) If the needle falls, there is a leak in the vacuum circuit and the capsule or its hose must be replaced. Make sure that the vacuum hose connection on the intake manifold is in good condition.

RENAULT FUEGO & SPORTWAGON (Cont.)

3) Check to make sure that the hose connection to the capsule is tight. An air leak in the capsule or pipe causes a whistling sound, irregular idling, excessive light throttle pressure, and slightly harsh gear shifts under light load.

Removal

Drain transmission fluid. Disconnect vacuum hose from capsule. Move retaining clip out of way and unscrew the capsule, counting the number of turns.

Installation

The vacuum capsule cannot be disassembled and must therefore be replaced as a unit if faulty. Screw in capsule the same number of turns as needed to remove it. Install retaining clip and connect vacuum hose. Refill transmission. Adjust pressure.

KICKDOWN SWITCH

Removal & Installation

Remove accelerator cable. Disconnect wire from kickdown switch. Unscrew 2 retaining bolts and remove switch. Reverse removal procedure to install.

Fig. 6: Accelerator Cable Housing

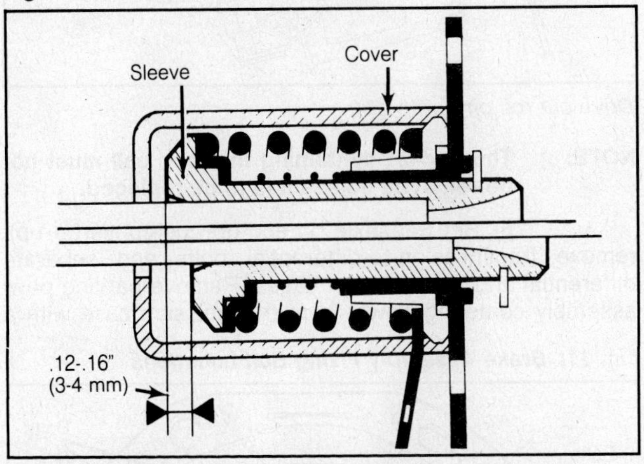

Adjust to allow .12-.16" (3-4 mm) free play in housing.

Adjustment

Adjustment is made with the accelerator cable. Make sure that the accelerator cable has enough play in it to allow .12-.16" (3-4 mm) movement in the sleeve when the accelerator pedal is depressed. Make sure that the cover is positioned correctly to prevent tarnishing of the contacts.

DIFFERENTIAL BEARING NUT & OIL SEAL

Removal

1) Raise and support vehicle. Disconnect battery. Drain transmission fluid. Disconnect vacuum capsule hose from intake manifold. Disconnect transaxle wiring connectors and remove support. Insert spacer tool (T. Av. 509-01) between lower shock mounting base and lower control arm pivot shaft on each side.

2) Remove drive shaft retaining roll pins with drift. Separate tie rod end ball joints and upper control arm ball joints from steering knuckle using puller. Tilt axle carriers away from transaxle to separate drive shafts from side gears.

3) Mark nut and housing for reassembly to same position. Remove lock nut. Remove nut with tool (B. Vi. 807). Count and record number of turns required to remove nut. Remove lip seal and "O" ring from nut. Remove "O" ring from side gear.

Fig. 7: Differential Bearing Nut Location

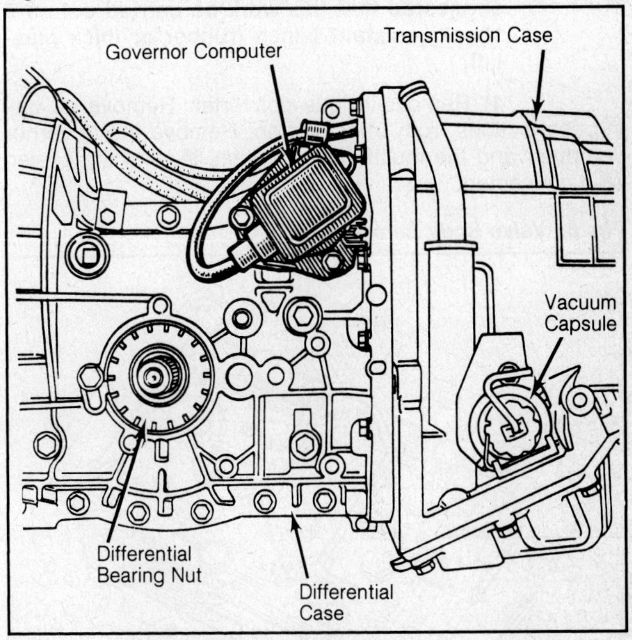

Installation

Install new lip seal and "O" ring on nut. Place tool (B. Vi. 813) around side gear to prevent damage to lip seal on installation. Install nut the same number of turns as was required to remove it. Align mark made during removal. Install nut lock. Remove tool from side gear and install new "O" ring. Reverse removal procedure to complete installation.

REMOVAL & INSTALLATION

TRANSAXLE

See appropriate MANUAL TRANSMISSION REMOVAL article in IMPORT GENERAL SERVICING section.

TORQUE CONVERTER

Removal

With transaxle removed from vehicle, pull converter straight out. Check general condition of converter components (i.e. input shaft, oil seal surface, converter sleeve, mounting bosses, etc.). If converter is damaged in any way, it must be replaced. Remove old oil seal from transmission case. Install new seal with tool (B. Vi. 465, Ref. A). Use of this tool automatically sets oil seal to correct depth.

Installation

1) Locate sharp-cornered edge on torque converter drive plate (marked with paint). There are 3 mounting bosses on the torque converter. Locate the boss which is directly opposite the hole in converter used as reference point for distributor timing.

2) When assembling torque converter to drive plate, align specified mounting boss with sharp-cornered edge on drive plate. Install new spring washers and tighten converter retaining bolts gradually and in rotation so that the converter is centered.

RENAULT FUEGO & SPORTWAGON (Cont.)

TRANSAXLE DISASSEMBLY

NOTE: It is very important that all components remain clean throughout operation. It is suggested that this work be carried out on a shock resistant bench (rubber or thick plastic).

1) Remove torque converter. Remove all wiring connections from transmission. Remove the governor computer and the multifunction switch, leaving the sealed plug connected.

Fig. 8: Valve Body Removal

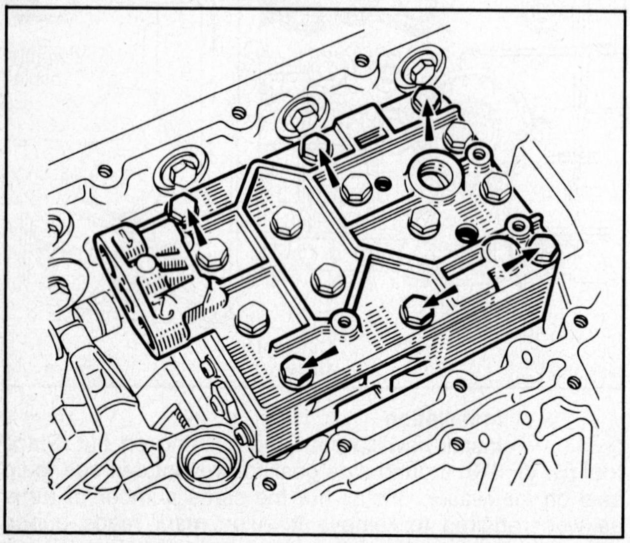

Remove only those bolts (6) indicated by arrows.

2) Remove vacuum capsule, oil pan, bottom cover and gasket. Remove filter and seal. Retain suction tube seal for reassembly. Disconnect sealed plug socket and remove wiring. Remove valve body retaining bolts indicated in *Fig. 8.* Remove valve body.

3) Remove the pump cover and shaft. If the oil pump driven gear is to be reused, mark upper face with felt pen or soft pencil so that it may be reinstalled in the same position. Remove drive gear. Remove 4 inner differential assembly bolts from transmission case. *See Fig. 9.*

Fig. 9: Inner Differential Assembly Bolts

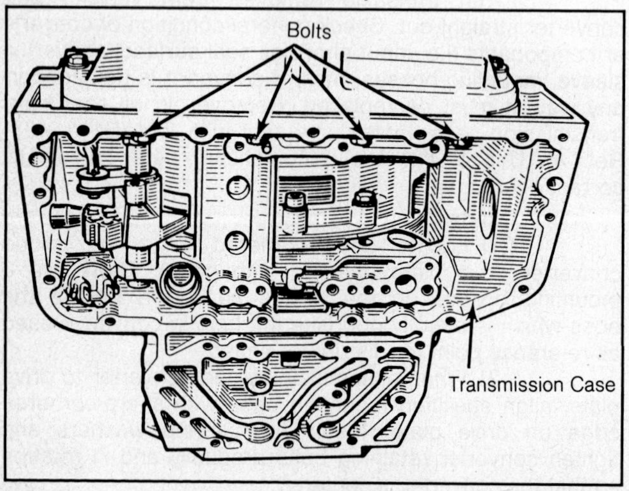

4) Drive out shift shaft roll pin(s) with drift. Remove bolt "A" in *Fig. 10.* Remove shift arm from shaft. Pull out shaft and save toothed wheel. Remove control linkage.

Fig. 10: Removing Shift Shaft Assembly

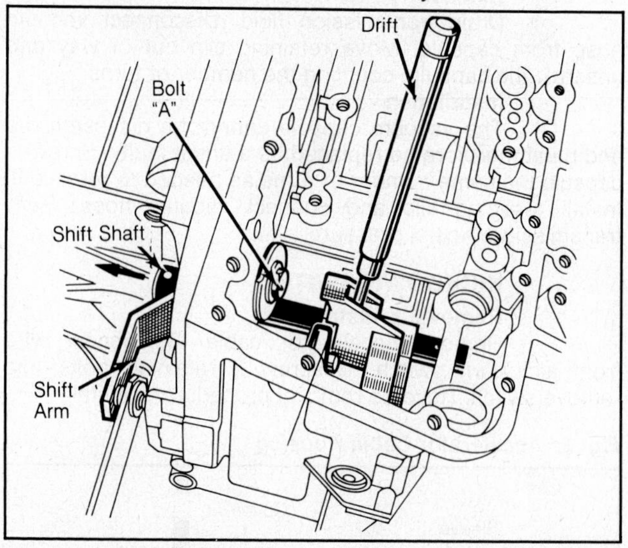

Drive out roll pins with drift.

NOTE: The socket containing the lock ball must not be removed unless it is to be replaced.

5) Set transaxle on end (torque converter up), remove transmission-to-differential bolts and separate differential and transmission cases. Remove parking pawl assembly centering dowel from transmission case with a

Fig. 11: Brake Assembly Fixing Bolt Locations

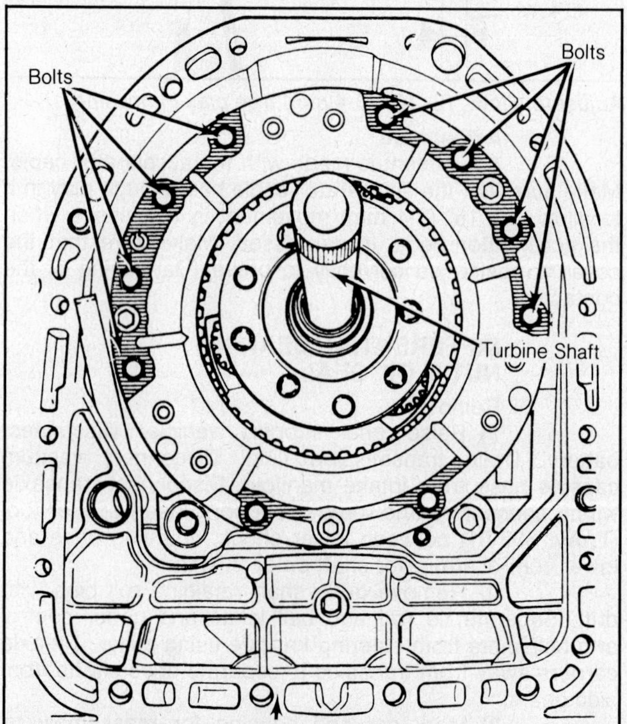

Remove bolts. Lift out drive train assembly by turbine shaft.

RENAULT FUEGO & SPORTWAGON (Cont.)

slide hammer. Remove pivot shaft, parking pawl and return spring.

6) Remove brake assembly fixing bolts. *See Fig. 11.* Grasp turbine shaft and lift out complete drive train assembly. Ensure that needle thrust bearing remains in case. Support assembly vertically on a 4" tube on bench and remove planetary gear assembly, sun gear and shaft, F1-F2 brake assembly and E2 clutch.

Fig. 12: Drive Train Assembly

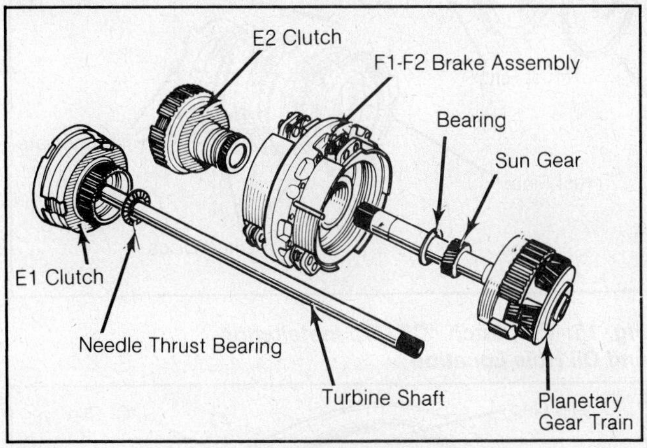

Separate components for disassembly.

COMPONENT DISASSEMBLY, REASSEMBLY & INSPECTION

INSPECTION

1) After disassembly and before reassembly, inspect condition of various components of transaxle. Check all machined surfaces for wear or scratches. Check oil seal and "O" ring surfaces and grooves for smoothness and uniformity of fit.

2) Check all white metal sleeves, as on transmission case, E2 clutch, planetary gear train, and other components. If excessively worn or damaged, replace part.

3) If any parts exhibit signs of excessive wear or damage, they must be replaced. For inspection procedures which apply to a particular component, see procedures below.

Transmission Case

Check condition of oil pump gears and housing, pump drive and cover. The transmission case and oil pump assembly are serviced as a complete unit only. If any one component requires replacement, the entire unit must be replaced.

Clutches & Brakes

1) Check all discs for damage, discoloration or separated linings. Replace as needed. All discs and plates should slide easily on hub splines or in their respective housings.

2) Check waved discs for proper bend. To do this, lay the disc on a flat surface and measure gap between waves and surface with a feeler gauge. Check wave height at all 3 positions on each disc. Do not apply pressure to the disc while making this measurement. Wave heights must be .010-.018" (.25-.45 mm). If disc is not to specification, it must be replaced.

3) Check all plates and thrust plates for signs of excessive wear, damage or overheating and replace as needed. Generally speaking, if one of the assemblies (E1, E2, F1, F2) has overheated, all intermediate discs and all with damaged linings must be replaced. All oil seals and "O" rings should be systematically replaced during any disassembly procedure.

4) E1 and E2 clutches utilize relief valve check balls which are crimped into place in the piston bodies (2 in E1 clutch, 1 in E2). Check that balls move freely in their sockets and do not stick to seat or crimped side. Total check ball travel should be about .04" (1 mm). If check ball operation is not satisfactory, the entire clutch piston assembly must be replaced.

5) On E1 clutch, check surface condition of piston bore. Check diaphragm spring for breakage, hub for disc marks on splines, fit of 2 sleeves in piston housing, and fit of the turbine shaft. On E2 clutch, check the piston bore and the return spring, spring retainer, and snap ring.

Planetary Gear Train

Check condition of planet gear teeth. Check one-way clutch. Ensure that one-way clutch hub plugs are securely in place. Check center bore and outer clutch track. Inspect needle thrust bearing and bearing plate for scoring or other damage. The one-way clutch or thrust plate may be replaced separately if damaged. If any other component of the gear train is damaged, the entire assembly must be replaced.

Valve Body

The valve body and regulator assembly must not be disassembled. Only the solenoid ball valves may be replaced. Whenever the automatic transmission is disassembled due to damaged clutches or brakes, or because of poor quality gear shifting, the valve body and its regulator must be replaced.

Fig. 13: Assembling Sun Gear Shaft & Planetary Gear Train

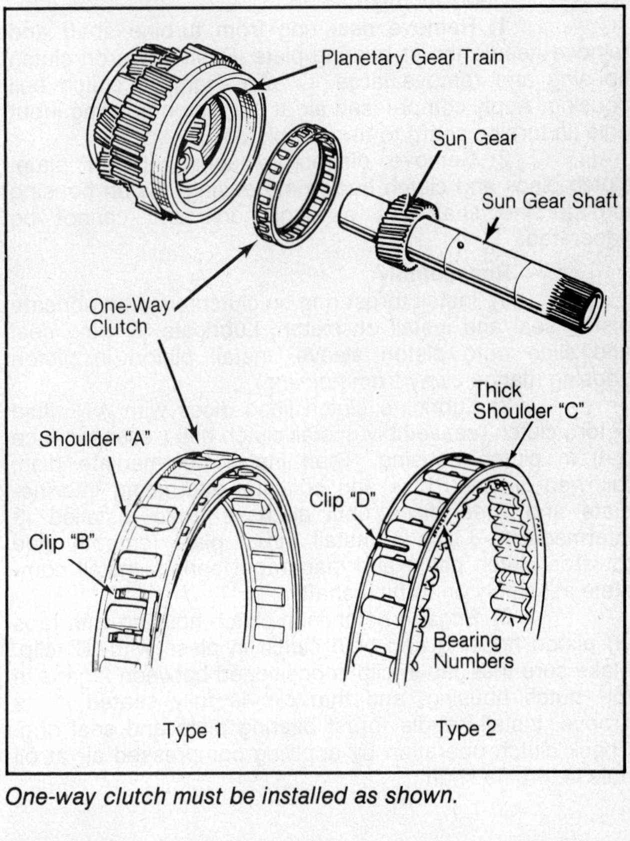

One-way clutch must be installed as shown.

RENAULT FUEGO & SPORTWAGON (Cont.)

Fig. 14: E1 Clutch and Turbine Shaft Assembly

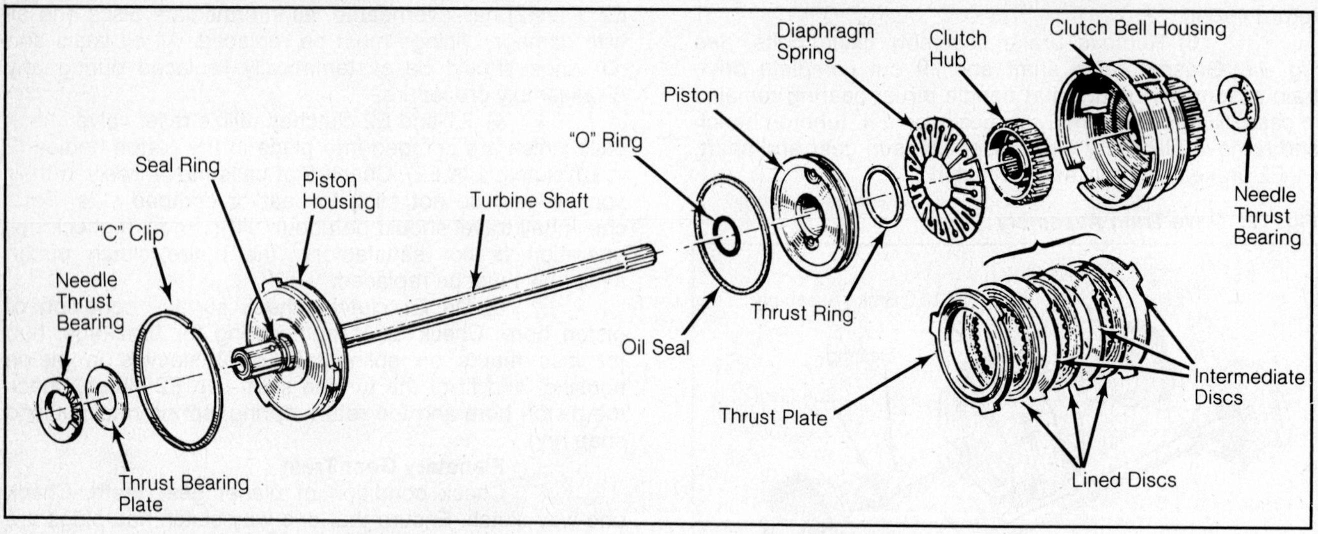

PLANETARY GEAR ASSEMBLY

Disassembly

Remove one-way clutch. Remove adjusting shim, needle bearing plate and needle thrust bearing. Remove remaining needle bearing plate. Leave inner needle thrust bearing in place.

Reassembly

Reverse disassembly procedure and note that there are 2 types of one-way clutch bearings. *See Fig. 13.* Be sure to install bearing correctly. Type 1 must be installed with shoulder "A" and clip "B" facing INWARD. Type 2 must be installed with thick shoulder "C", clip "D", and bearing numbers facing OUTWARD.

E1 CLUTCH

Disassembly

1) Remove seal ring from turbine shaft and remove needle thrust bearing plate. Push down on clutch housing and remove large "C" clip. Remove clutch bell housing. Apply compressed air at the piston housing input hole (in turbine shaft) to remove piston.

2) Remove diaphragm spring, thrust plate, clutch discs and clutch hub from housing. Piston housing and turbine shaft are a single unit and cannot be separated.

Reassembly

1) Install thrust ring on clutch piston. Lubricate piston seal and install on piston. Lubricate "O" ring seal and slide onto piston sleeve. Install piston in piston housing (flange away from housing).

2) Lubricate clutch lined discs with ATF fluid before clutch reassembly. Install clutch hub (recessed face out) in clutch housing. Then install intermediate disc, followed by lined disc and continue alternating intermediate and lined discs until all have been installed (3 intermediate, 3 lined). Install thrust plate (smooth side towards clutch pack) and diaphragm spring. Install complete assembly on turbine shaft.

3) Engage notches in clutch housing with tabs on piston housing and hold clutch in place with "C" clip. Make sure that gap in clip is positioned between 2 gaps in the clutch housing, and that clip is fully seated in its groove. Install needle thrust bearing plate and seal ring. Check clutch operation by applying compressed air at oil hole in turbine shaft.

Fig. 15: E1 Clutch "C" Clip Installation and Oil Hole Location

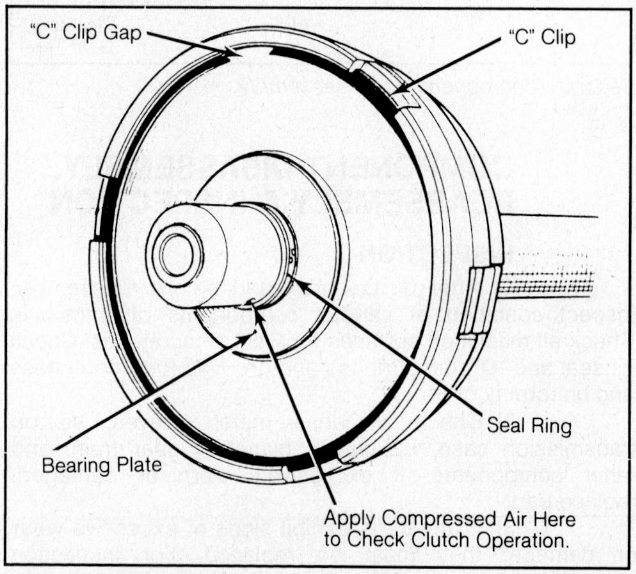

Install "C" clip with gap centered between housing notches.

E2 CLUTCH

Disassembly

Compress clutch return spring with press and tool (B. Vi. 489-14 or -19, Ref. 07) and remove snap ring. Lift out spring retainer and spring. Remove seal rings (3). Remove large "C" clip, thrust plate, clutch discs (3 lined, 2 waved) and flat disc from clutch housing. Remove piston by applying compressed air at oil hole in housing.

Reassembly

1) Install seal rings on clutch housing. Ensure that ring grooves are clean and square before installing rings. Lubricate piston seal and install on piston. Lubricate "O" ring seal and install on piston hub in clutch housing. Ensure that seals are firmly seated in their grooves.

2) Install piston in clutch housing so that slots in piston are aligned with slots in the housing. Install return spring and retainer. Compress spring and install

RENAULT FUEGO & SPORTWAGON (Cont.)

snap ring. Lubricate lined clutch discs with clean ATF. Install clutch components in housing in order: Thrust plate, lined disc, waved disc, lined disc, waved disc, lined disc, and thrust plate (with punch-marked side out).

Fig. 16: Installing E2 Clutch Piston

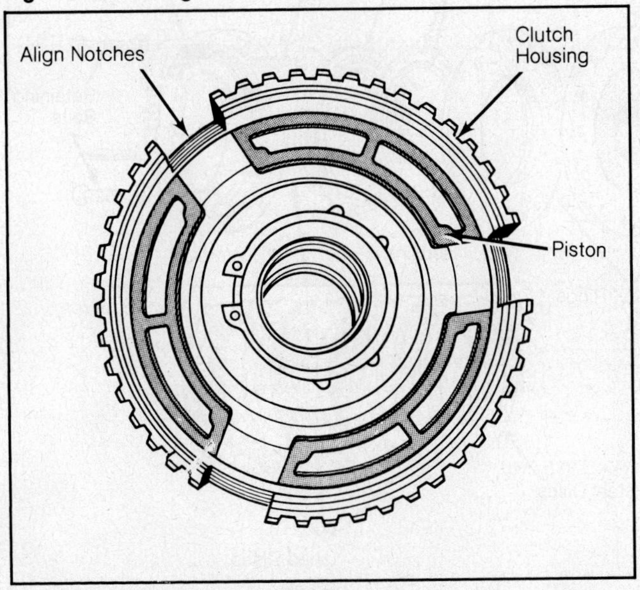

Align slots in piston and housing as shown.

3) Install "C" clip with gap centered between 2 slots in housing. Check clutch operation by applying compressed air at oil hole in housing. Place E2 clutch on a flat surface, large end up. Place flat metal disc (B. Vi. 489-14 or -19, Ref. 06) on top of clutch discs and position dial indicator with tip resting on disc. Zero indicator.

4) Raise clutch pack (at slots in housing) until "C" clip is against top of groove, without compressing waved discs. Read indicator dial. If end play is greater than .083" (2.1 mm), replace thrust plate with one .098" (2.5 mm) thick.

Fig. 18: Installing E2 Clutch "C" Clip

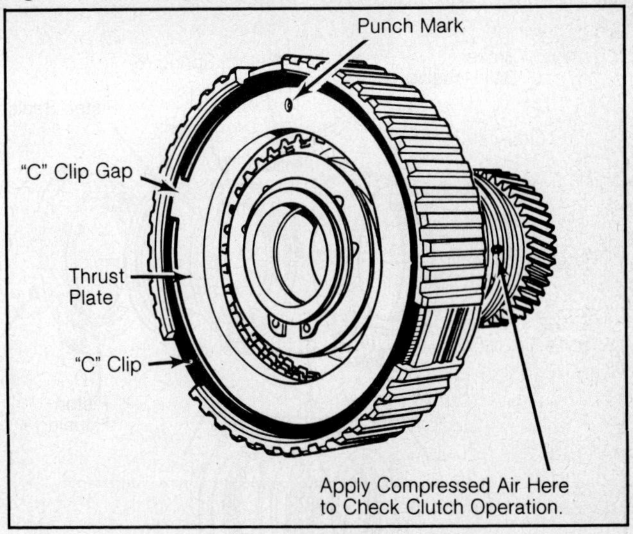

Install clip with gap located between notches in housing.

F1-F2 BRAKE ASSEMBLY

Disassembly

1) Remove 3 F1 brake bell housing retaining bolts. Remove housing and 6 piston return springs. Remove steel and lined discs, noting relative positions for reassembly reference. Note position of "O" ring between one-way clutch hub and F1 piston housing. Save "O" ring.

2) Remove 3 F2 brake bell housing retaining bolts. Remove housing and 6 piston return springs. Remove steel and lined discs, noting positions for reassembly reference. Note position of the "O" ring between one-way clutch hub and F1 piston housing. Save "O" ring. Apply compressed air at oil input holes to remove pistons. Remove piston seals (F1 and F2).

Reassembly

1) Check F2 brake operating play: Install F2 piston (without seal) in piston housing. Install flat disc

Fig. 17: Exploded View of E2 Clutch Assembly

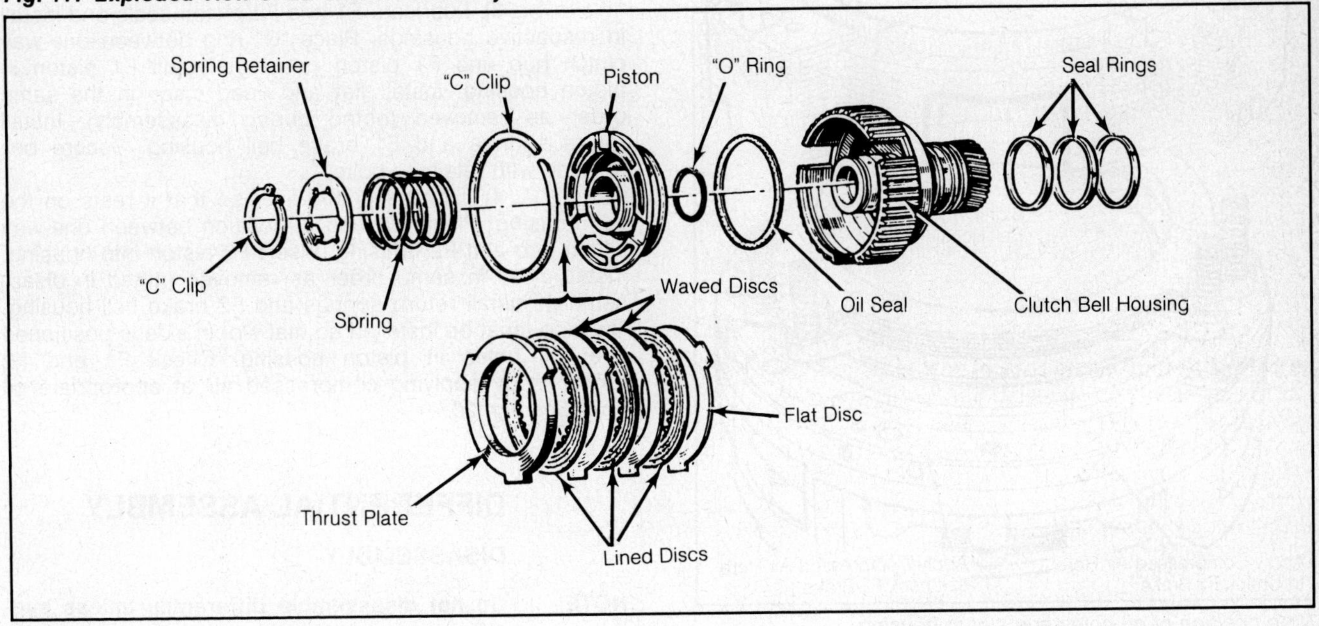

RENAULT FUEGO & SPORTWAGON (Cont.)

Fig. 19: Complete F1-F2 Brake Assembly

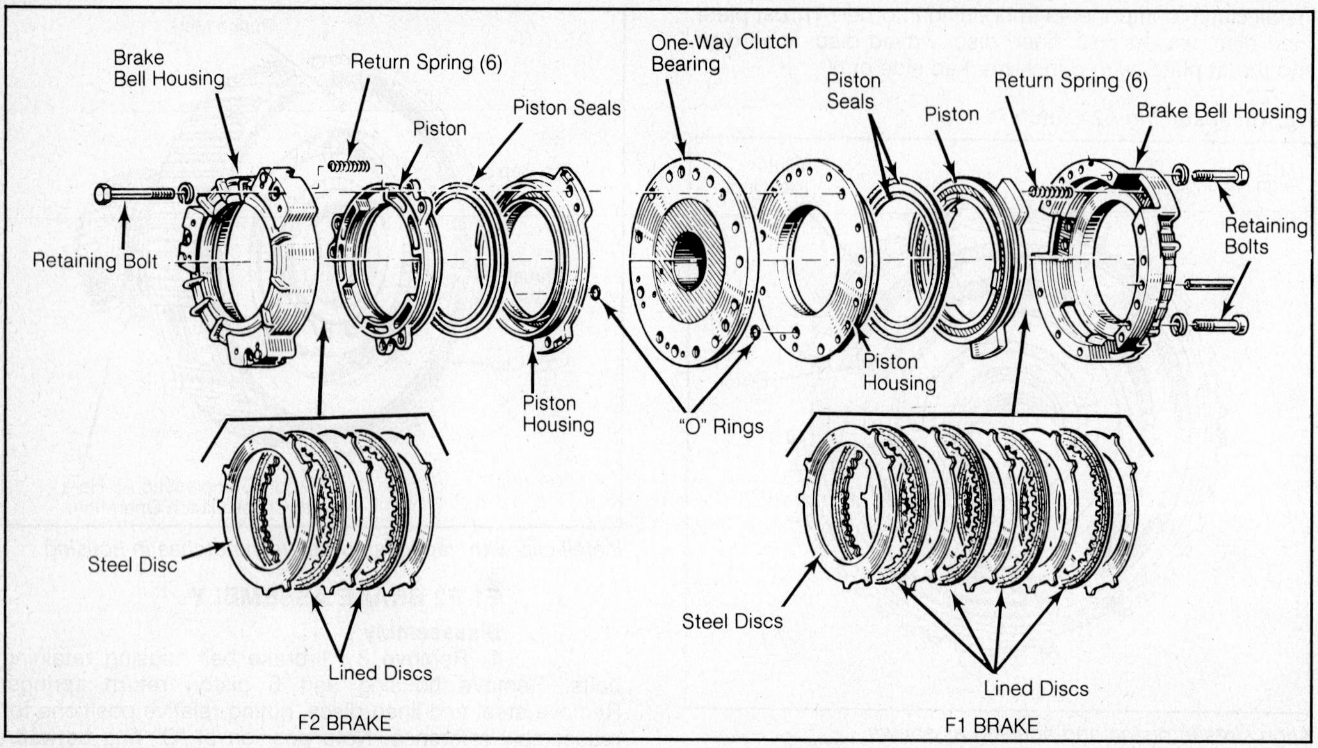

Fig. 20: Installing F2 Brake Bell Housing

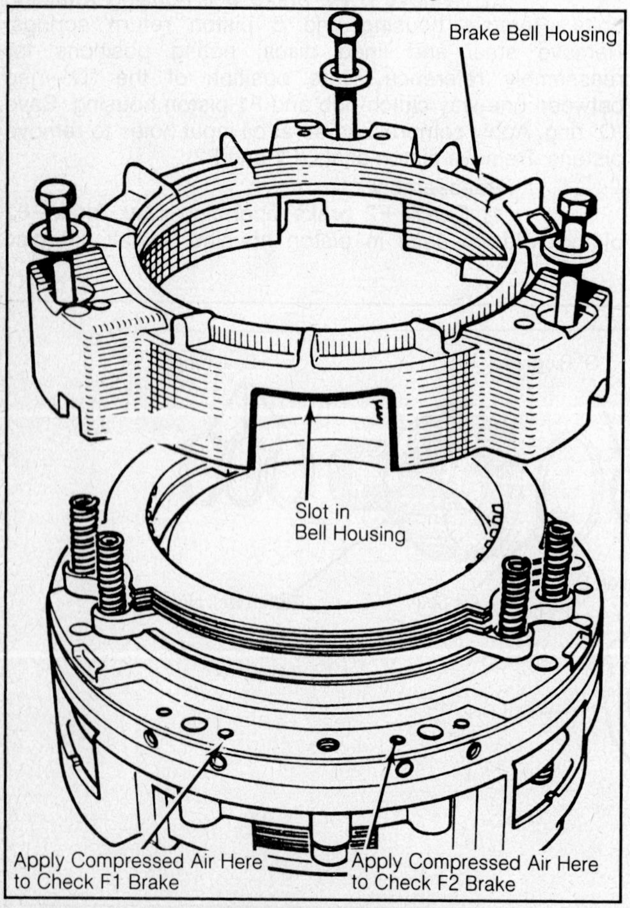

Note position of oil holes and slot in housing.

(.059", 1.5 mm thick), lined disc, waved disc (.079", 2 mm thick), lined disc and another flat disc in housing. Install brake bell housing and attach entire asembly to one-way clutch hub with bolts (3).

2) Position dial indicator with dial pin resting on a spline of the first lined disc. Zero indicator. Lift disc pack until it makes contact with bell housing. Read indicator dial. Take measurements at several points and average readings to obtain F2 operating play. If play is not .028-.067" (.70-1.70 mm), check piston and all discs for damage or distortion and replace as needed. Disassemble components.

3) Lubricate F1 and F2 piston seals and install in respective housings. Place "O" ring between one-way clutch hub and F1 piston housing. Install F1 piston in piston housing. Install flat and lined discs in the same order as removed (noted during disassembly). Install return springs and F1 brake bell housing. Secure bell housing with retaining bolts.

4) Turn assembly over so that it rests on the bell housing. Place "O" ring in position between one-way clutch hub and F2 housing. Insert F2 piston into housing. Install discs in same order as removed (noted in disassembly). Install return springs and F2 brake bell housing. Housing must be installed so that slot in side is positioned over oil holes in piston housing. Check F1 and F2 functions by applying compressed air at appropriate oil hole. *See Fig. 20.*

DIFFERENTIAL ASSEMBLY

DISASSEMBLY

NOTE: **Do not disassemble differential unless specific repairs are required.**

RENAULT FUEGO & SPORTWAGON (Cont.)

1) Place differential assembly on engine stand with adaptor (B. Vi. 16-01). Remove output shaft bearing lockplate retaining bolts. Using 2 slightly longer bolts, install fixing tool (B. Vi. 489-04) to lock output shaft in place. Remove drive pinion lock nut.

2) Remove torque converter (if still attached). Pry out converter oil seal with tool (B. Vi. 465, Ref. C). Remove stator support retaining bolts (4) and remove support. Remove side gear "O" rings.

Fig. 21: Complete Differential Assembly

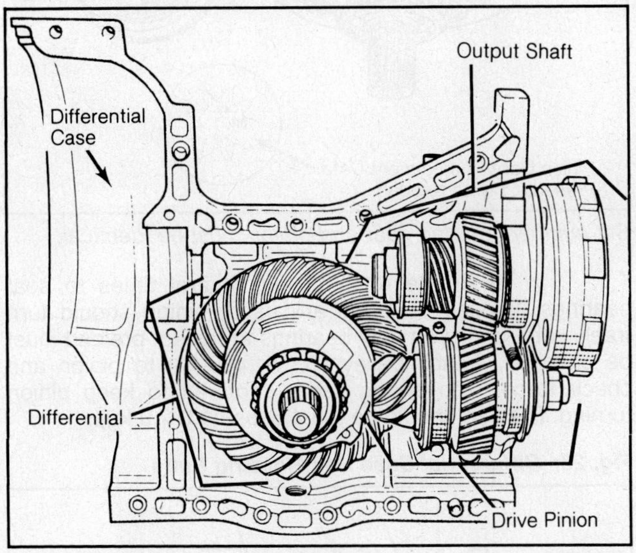

3) Remove bolts which secure the 2 differential half-housings together and separate half-housings (use a rubber mallet if needed). Remove output shaft, differential and drive pinion. Remove differential bearing adjusting nut lock washers, then remove adjusting nuts with tool (B. Vi. 807).

Differential

Remove 2 opposing ring gear-to-differential case retaining bolts. Support differential in soft-jawed vise and remove bearing from ring gear side with puller and clamp (T. Ar. 65 and B. Tr. 02). Turn differential over and remove bearing from opposite side. Remove remaining ring gear-to-case retaining bolts and discard all bolts.

Fig. 22: Exploded View of Differential

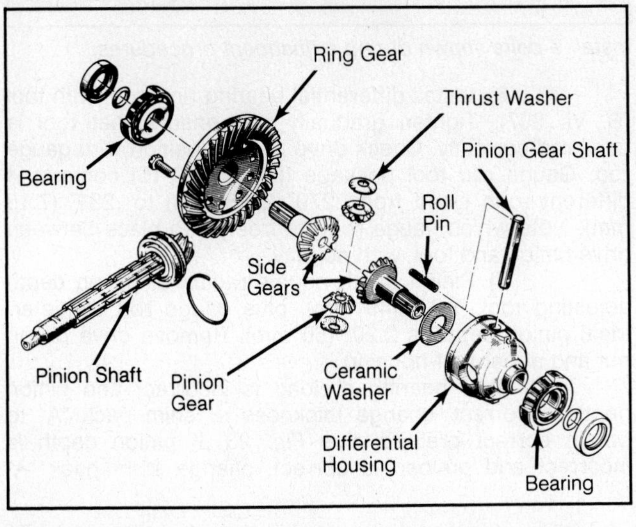

Drive out pinion gear shaft roll pin. Separate pinion gears, side gears and washers from differential housing.

Drive Pinion

Remove in order from pinion: Retaining nut, adjusting shims (note thickness for reassembly), spacer, stepdown gear, and adjusting shims (note thickness for reassembly). Remove bearing with puller and clamp. Check bearing condition.

Fig. 23: Exploded View of Drive Pinion

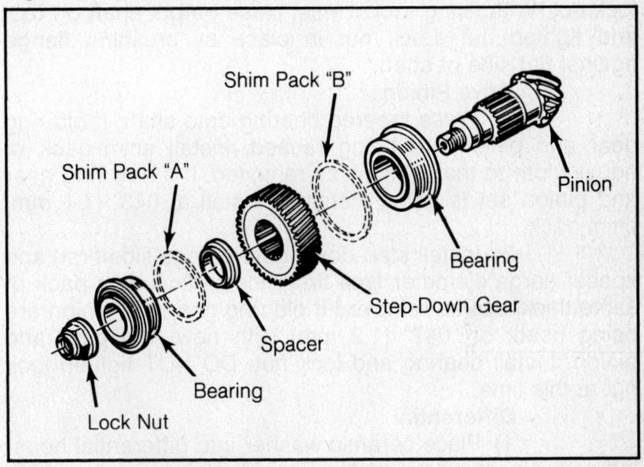

Output Shaft

Clamp fixing tool (B. Vi. 489-04) in vise and fit output shaft over it. Remove nut from end of shaft. Remove gear and bearings with puller, clamp and spacer (Rou. 15-01).

Fig. 24: Exploded View of Output Shaft

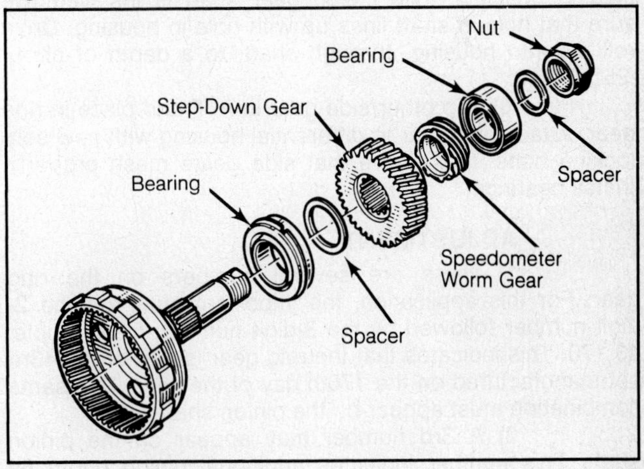

INSPECTION

1) Clean all parts thoroughly and blow dry with compressed air. Also blow out all oil holes and lubrication channels. Lubricate all parts with Dexron II ATF.

2) Check all gear teeth for wear or damage. Check all bearings and step-down gears for excessive wear or damage. Check condition of the 2 white metal bushings on the output shaft.

3) Check contact surfaces in both housings. Check stator support housing and breather. Check differential adjusting nut threads. Replace any damaged parts. The step-down gears are serviced as a complete set only. If either of the gears is damaged, both must be

RENAULT FUEGO & SPORTWAGON (Cont.)

replaced. Likewise, the ring gear and pinion are manufactured in matched pairs only and must always be replaced as a set.

REASSEMBLY

Output Shaft

Press bearing onto shaft, flange side first. Install parts in order: Spacer, step-down gear (flange towards speedometer worm gear), speedometer worm gear (large diameter bore end first), bearing, shim and lock nut. With fixing tool in vise, place output shaft on tool and tighten nut. Lock nut in place by crushing flange against flat side of shaft.

Drive Pinion

1) Press tapered bearing onto shaft. If old ring gear and pinion are being reused, install shim pack of equal width to that which was removed. If a new ring gear and pinion set is being installed, install a .043" (1.1 mm) shim pack.

2) Install step-down gear (flange side first) and spacer (large diameter face first). Install 2nd shim pack of same thickness as removed if old ring gear and pinion are being used, or .047" (1.2 mm) with new ring gear and pinion. Install bearing and lock nut. DO NOT tighten lock nut at this time.

Differential

1) Place ceramic washer into differential housing with oil groove toward side gear. Use a washer .077-.079" (1.96-2.0 mm) thick, unless side gear to pinion gear backlash is excessive. If so, use a washer .080-.081" (2.03-2.07 mm) thick. Dip side gear in ATF before installing.

2) Place pinion gears and thrust washers in housing (locking tabs on washers in holes in housing) and hold in position while pinion gear shaft is installed. Be sure that hole in shaft lines up with hole in housing. Drive roll pin into housing, through shaft, to a depth of about .25" (5 mm).

3) Dip other side gear in ATF and place in ring gear. Attach ring gear to differential housing with new self-locking bolts. Make sure that side gears mesh properly. Install bearings.

ADJUSTMENT

1) There are several numbers on the ring gear. For this application, the important ones are the 2-digit number followed by the 3-digit number, for example, 43 170. This indicates that the ring gear is part of the 43rd set manufactured on the 170th day of the year. This same combination must appear on the pinion shaft used.

2) A 3rd number may appear on the pinion shaft. This number indicates additional pinion depth (in hundredths of a millimeter) which must be set when the differential is assembled. For example, if the number is 20, pinion depth must be set at standard depth PLUS .20 mm (.008").

3) With governor side half-housing attached to engine stand, install differential bearing races and adjusting nuts on half-housing (make sure nuts are clean). Lubricate tapered faces of pinion depth adjusting tool (B. Vi. 489-12) and install in half-housing. Install drive pinion.

4) Install other half-housing and secure with bolts indicated in *Fig. 26.* Do not tighten bolts at this time. Hold drive pinion with tool (B. Vi. 489-04) and tighten lock nut. Now tighten half-housing bolts to specification.

Fig. 25: Ring Gear and Pinion Shaft ID Numbers

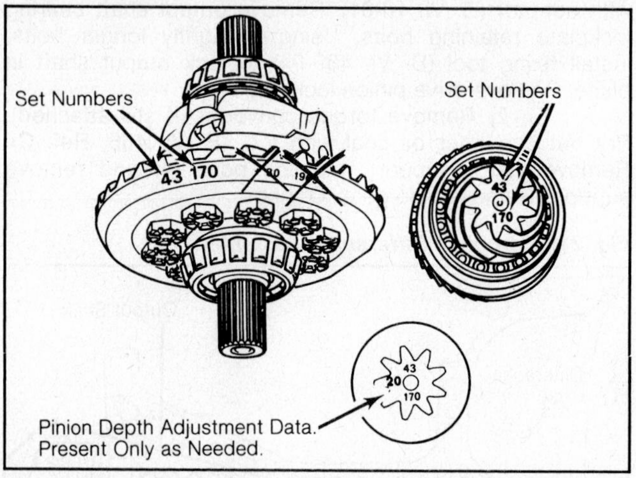

Set numbers on ring gear and pinion must be identical.

5) Rotate drive pinion several times to seat bearings. If used bearings are used, pinion should turn freely with no play. If new bearings are used, preload must be checked. Attach pulley (B. Vi. 489-13) to pinion and check force (with spring scale) required to keep pinion turning. Preload should be 2.3-4.5 lbs. (1.0-2.0 kg).

Fig. 26: Differential Case Half-Housing Bolts

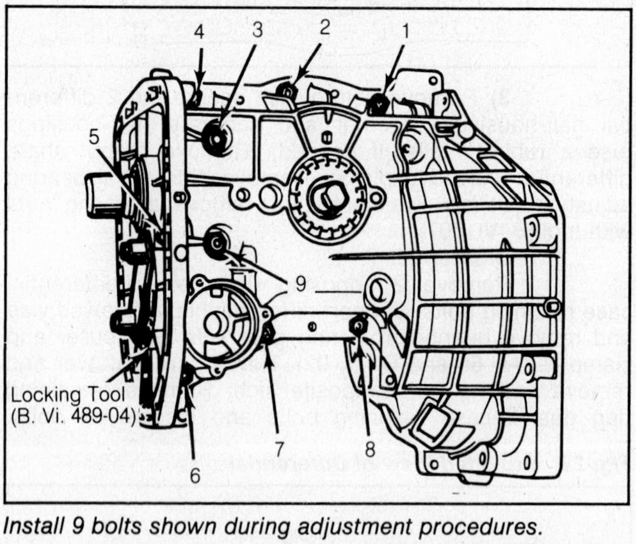

Install 9 bolts shown during adjustment procedures.

6) Install differential bearing ring nuts with tool (B. Vi. 807). Tighten gradually and ensure that tool is centered correctly. Check drive pinion position with gauge rod. Gauge rod tool package (B. Vi. 489-15) contains 4 different rods sized from .270" (6.85 mm) to .281" (7.15 mm). Note which gauge rod fits freely into place between drive pinion and tool, with no play.

7) Pinion depth equals radius of pinion depth adjusting tool, 1.93" (49 mm), plus gauge rod diameter. Ideal pinion depth is 2.20" (56 mm). Remove drive pinion nut and upper half-housing.

8) If bearing preload is incorrect and pinion depth is correct, change thickness of shim pack "A" to obtain correct preload. *See Fig. 23.* If pinion depth is incorrect and preload is correct, change shim pack "A"

RENAULT FUEGO & SPORTWAGON (Cont.)

Fig. 27: Checking Drive Pinion Preload

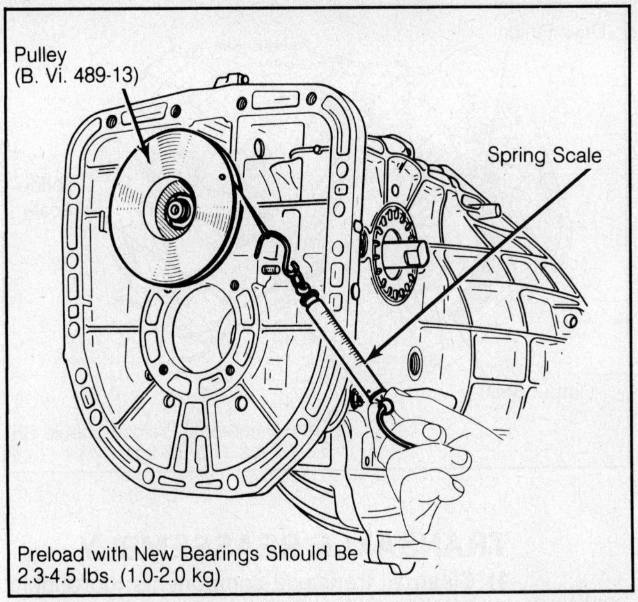

Preload must be checked when new bearings are installed.

and shim pack "B" by equal, but opposite, amounts: If pinion depth is too great, increase thickness of shim pack "B" and decrease thickness of shim pack "A"; if pinion depth is below specifications, increase "A" and decrease "B". The total combined thickness of shim packs "A" and "B" must remain the same. Change shim pack thickness by amount equal to the difference between measured pinion depth and ideal depth given in step **7)**.

Fig. 28: Checking Drive Pinion Depth

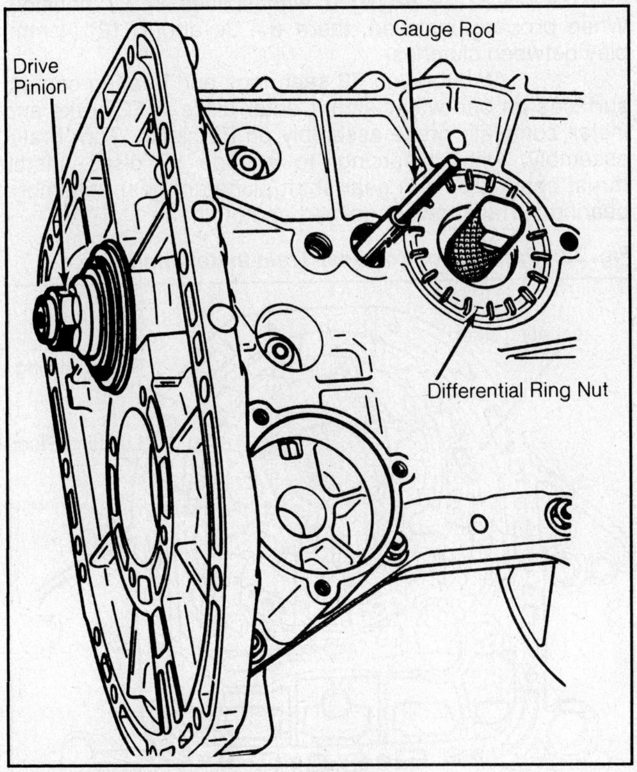

Check depth by placing tool between drive pinion and tapered face of adjusting tool.

9) If pinion depth and bearing preload are both incorrect, adjust preload by changing thickness of shim pack "A" or "B", approximating the pinion depth adjustment as closely as possible. Check new bearing preload. When preload is correct, adjust pinion depth as in step **8)**.

10) With half-housings separated, install differential without drive pinion or output shaft. Reassemble half-housings as before. Rotate ring gear several times to seat bearings. Tighten bearing ring nuts same number of turns as was required to remove them and line up match marks. Differential should turn freely with no play.

11) If new bearings are being used, preload must be checked. Run a hook and string through drive pinion hole and around the differential housing (several times) as close as possible to the ring gear. Attach a spring scale and measure the effort required to keep the differential housing turning.

12) Reading on scale should be 2.3-4.5 lbs. (1.0-2.0 kg). Adjust preload by tightening or loosening ring nuts as needed. When proper preload is obtained, mark new position of ring nuts.

Fig. 29: Checking Differential Bearing Preload

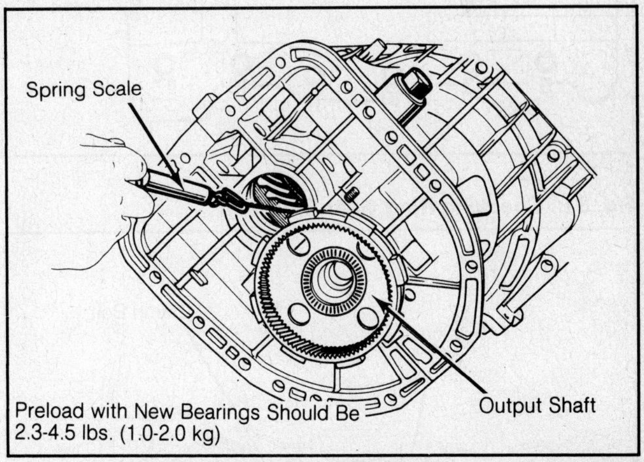

Preload must be checked when new bearings are installed.

13) Separate half-housings. Install drive pinion and output shaft. Reassemble differential assembly, aligning ring nuts with match marks. Apply a thick bead of sealer to mating surface of one half-housing before assembly. Tighten bolts in order indicated in *Fig. 30.* Lock output shaft with tool (B. Vi. 489-04) and tighten drive pinion nut. Rotate output shaft a few times to seat bearings.

14) Install dial indicator support (B. Vi. 489-16) in housing as shown in *Fig. 31.* Screw extension onto dial indicator tip (use extension B. Vi. 489-16 if indicator has a 3 mm diameter tip and .60 mm pitch, extension B. Vi. 489-17 for 2.5 mm diameter tip and .45 mm pitch).

15) Fit assembly into support and tighten clamp bolt until dial is snug. Place tip of extension against tooth of ring gear and zero indicator dial. Measure backlash at several places on ring gear. Backlash should be .005-.010" (.12-.25 mm).

16) If backlash is incorrect, adjust by tightening one ring nut and loosening the other the same amount. When final adjustments have been made and backlash is within specifications, mark new position of ring nuts.

17) Remove nuts, counting number of turns. Replace seals and "O" rings. Apply sealer to ring nut

RENAULT FUEGO & SPORTWAGON (Cont.)

Fig. 30: Differential Case Bolt Tightening Sequence

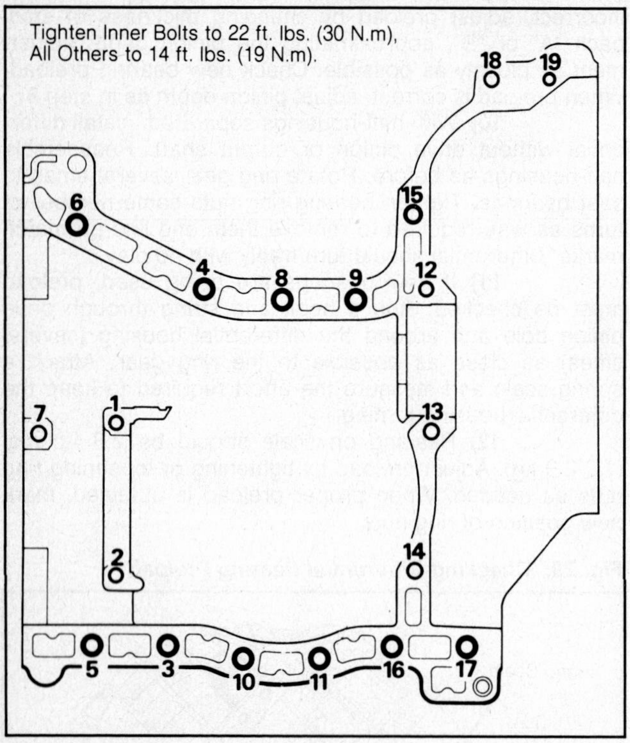

Fig. 31: Checking Ring Gear Backlash

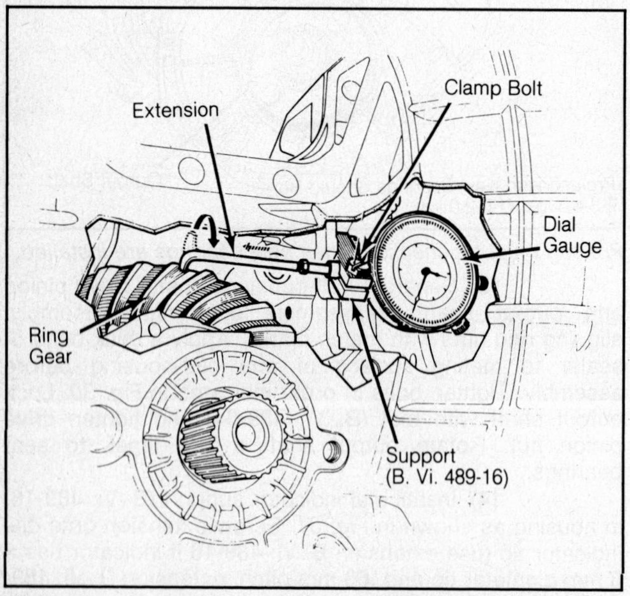

Check backlash at several points on gear.

threads and reinstall ring nuts same number of turns. Line up match marks. Install locks.

18) With adjustments correct and differential assembly assembled, check preload at output shaft. Starting force should be 3.3-7.7 lbs. (1.5-3.5 kg). Check condition of smooth part of stator support.

19) Lightly lubricate seal and tap gently into place with installer tool (B. Vi. 465, Ref. A). The tool will automatically position seal at the correct depth. Install torque converter and secure in place with retaining bracket.

Fig. 32: Checking Differential Assembly Total Preload

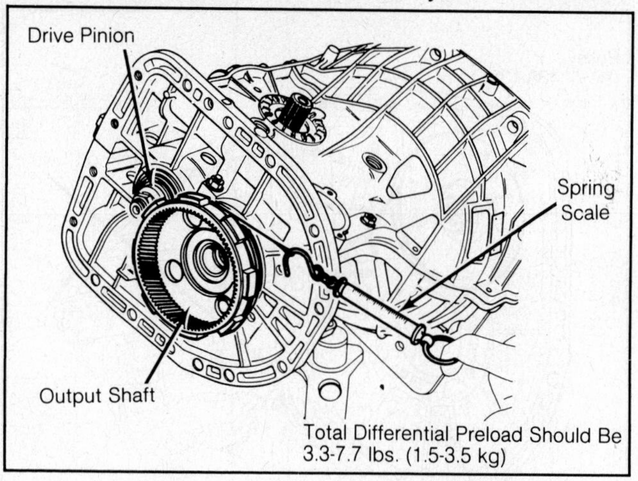

TRANSAXLE REASSEMBLY

1) Clean all transaxle components thoroughly. Blow out all oil holes and passages with compressed air. Lubricate all parts with clean ATF fluid before final assembly. Drain torque converter, pump out remaining fluid from center of turbine hub with a syringe and refill with clean fluid. Use Dexron II type transmission fluid only.

2) Support E1 clutch/turbine shaft assembly on a 4" diameter tube, clutch end down, during reassembly. Install needle thrust bearing on turbine shaft, bearing side up. Center clutch discs in E2 clutch and slide clutch assembly into position on turbine shaft.

3) Gently turn clutch assembly, do not force, until all discs are engaged with splines in E1 housing. When properly installed, there will be about .12" (4 mm) play between clutches.

4) Lubricate E2 seal rings and bearing contact surfaces on one-way clutch. Center discs in F2 brake and install complete brake assembly on E2 clutch. Turn brake assembly, without forcing, to engage all discs. Install thrust bearing on sun gear shaft/planetary gear assembly, bearing surface toward splined end of shaft.

Fig. 33: Preparation for Gear Train Installation

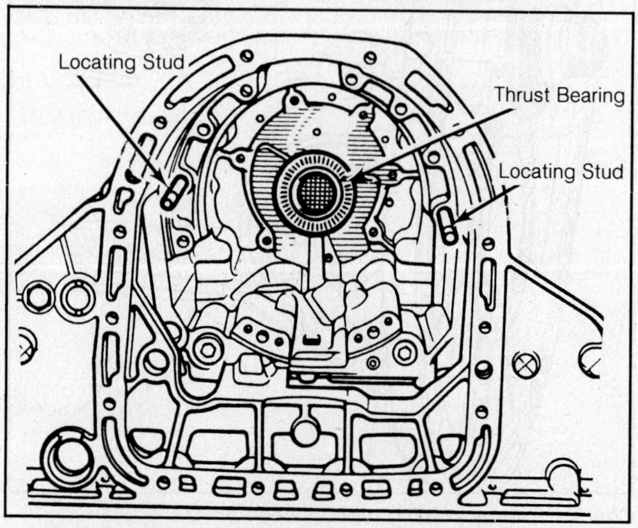

Install thrust bearing and locating studs as shown.

RENAULT FUEGO & SPORTWAGON (Cont.)

5) Center discs in F1 brake and lower sun gear shaft/planetary gear assembly into place. Turn gently, without forcing, to engage all discs. Install thrust bearing and two .275" (7 mm) diameter locating studs in transmission case. Lubricate seal ring housing and contact surface for one-way clutch hub.

6) Lift gear train assembly by turbine shaft and slowly lower into transmission case. Use locating studs to guide assembly into place. Ensure that one-way clutch hub is lined up properly and fits well up against the case.

7) Remove locating studs. Install retaining bolts removed in step **6)** of *Transaxle Disassembly*. Install parking pawl return spring on shaft. Install parking pawl. Install shaft (threaded hole up), centering dowel and retaining clip.

8) Install main shaft needle thrust bearing in differential housing. Lay a straightedge across output shaft and measure distance "A" from straightedge surface to housing mating surface. Then measure distance "B" from straightedge surface to needle bearing. Subtract "B" from "A" to get distance "C" and record. *See Fig. 34.*

Fig. 34: Measuring Output Shaft Clearances

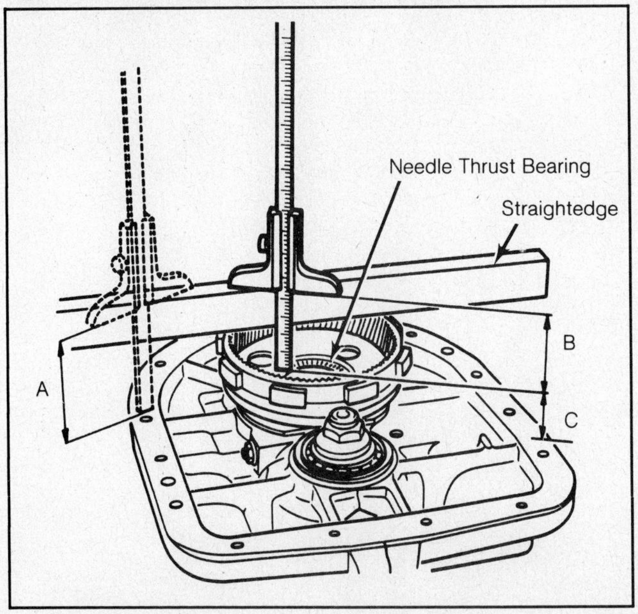

9) Install needle thrust bearing plate onto planetary gear carrier in transmission case. Lay a straightedge across transmission case mating surface and measure distance "E" from straightedge surface to bearing plate. *See Fig. 35.* Subtract straightedge width from "E" to get distance "D" and record. Subtract distance "C" from distance "D" to get total end play.

10) Desired end play is .024" (.6 mm). Subtract .024" (.6 mm) from total end play "D" to determine what thickness adjusting shim to install between needle thrust bearing plate and planetary gear carrier.

11) If end play "D" is less than .024" (.6 mm) or greater than .120" (3.1 mm), check that all needle thrust bearings are in position, sun gears are properly meshed and all discs are properly seated on their splines.

12) Install needle thrust bearing on output shaft in differential case. Install end-play adjusting shim (as determined in previous steps) and needle thrust bearing plate in transmission case. *See Fig. 36.*

Fig. 35: Measuring Gear Train Clearances

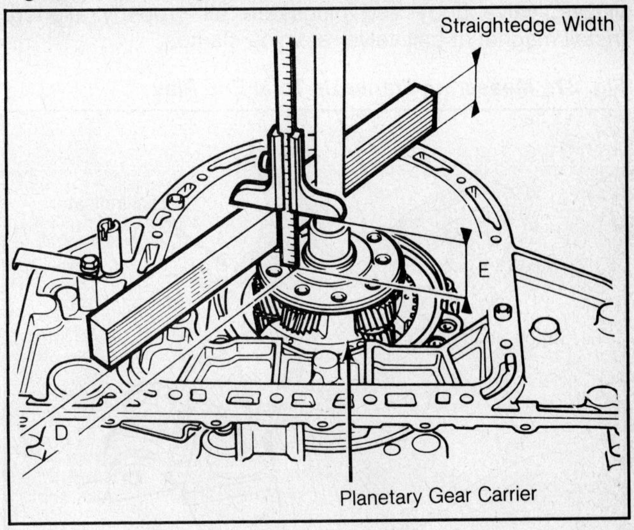

13) Install .28" (7 mm) studs and centering dowels on case. Smear gasket sealer (Perfect Seal) on case surface and install paper gasket (dry). Lubricate turbine shaft and slowly lower differential case onto transmission case.

Fig. 36: Location of Oil Seal Between Transmission and Differential Cases

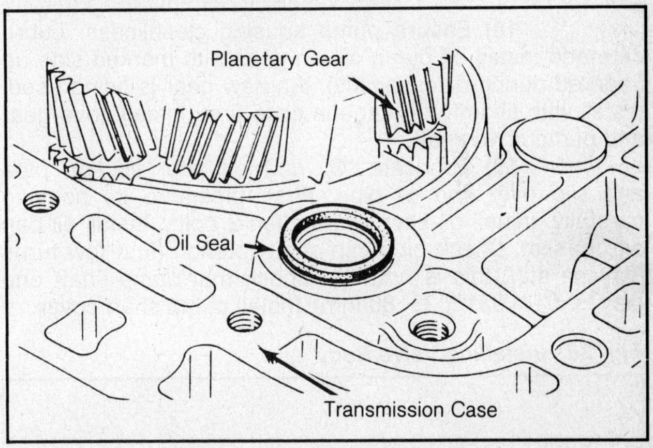

Install seal on transmission case before final assembly.

14) Install a few of the case-to-case retaining bolts and tighten. Install lower cover plate with new gasket (dry). Attach dial indicator to lower cover plate and set indicator tip on E1 clutch shaft. Pull turbine shaft out, zero gauge, push shaft back in and read gauge.

15) End play should be .016-.032" (.4-.8 mm). If play is not to specification, disassemble and replace end play adjusting shim as required. When correct play has been obtained, install remaining case-to-case bolts and tighten.

16) Reverse removal procedures to install shift control linkage and shift shaft. *See Transaxle Disassembly*. Check that valve body mounting surfaces and surfaces on case are clean and smooth. Make sure that centering dowels are in position on valve body and the 2 toothed wheels are properly meshed when in park.

17) Install valve body in housing, engaging the manual valve on shift lever. *See Fig. 38.* Tighten retaining screws in several steps. Install solenoid ball valves and

RENAULT FUEGO & SPORTWAGON (Cont.)

connect plug to sealed plug connector. Check that ball valves, valve body and plugs are all properly aligned. Install magnet at ball valve retaining clamp.

Fig. 37: Measuring Transaxle Total End Play

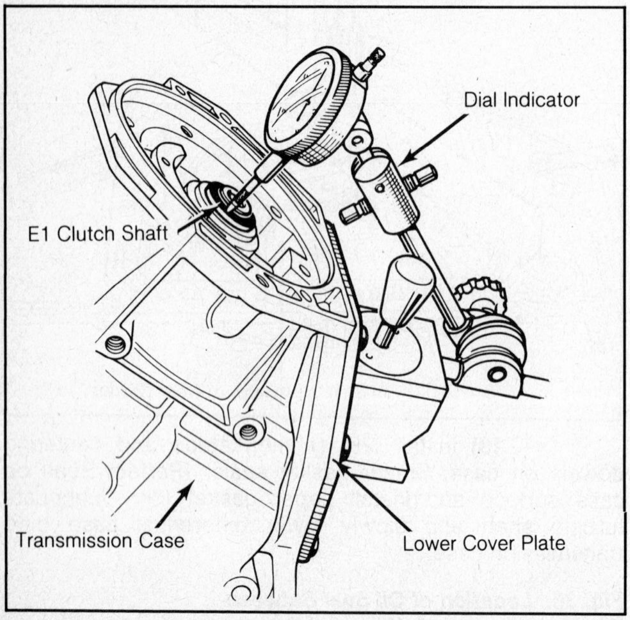

Total end play should be .016-.032" (.4-.8 mm)

18) Ensure pump housing cleanliness. Lubricate and install oil pump driven gear with marked side up (marked during disassembly). If a new gear is being used, install with chamfered edge in case first. Install drive gear and pump drive shaft.

19) Lubricate "O" ring on filter suction pipe and slip over end of pipe. Push pipe into its housing carefully. Install oil filter and tighten 2 bolts. Install oil pan and gasket. Check oil pump shaft rotation (first few turns may be stiff, this is normal). Check that pump shaft end play is .014-.031" (.35-.80 mm). Install pump shaft cover.

Fig. 38: Installing Valve Body

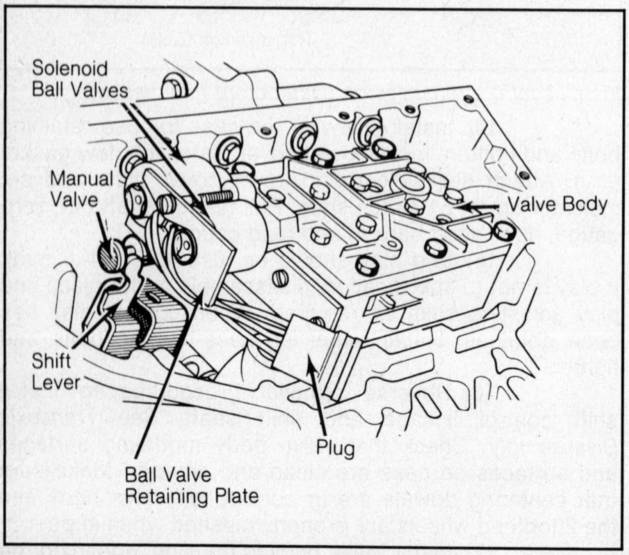

Make sure that shift lever and manual valve are properly engaged.

TIGHTENING SPECIFICATIONS

Application	Ft. Lbs. (N.m)
Torque Converter-to-Drive Plate	
Fuego	30 (42)
Sportwagon	24 (33)
Drive Plate-to-Crankshaft	50 (68)
Ring Gear-to-Differential Case	74 (101)
Drive Pinion Lock Nut	110 (150)
Half Housing-to-Half Housing	
Inner	22 (30)
Outer	14 (19)
	INCH Lbs. (N.m)
Transmission Housing-to-Differential Housing	180 (20)
Stator Support	180 (20)
Oil Pump Cover	96 (11)
Valve Body Bolts	60 (7)
Lower Cover Plate	72 (8)
Brake Retaining Bolts	96 (11)

SAAB – BORG-WARNER MODEL 37

900, 900 Turbo

IDENTIFICATION

All Saabs with A/T use the Borg-Warner model 37 transaxle. The transaxle identification number is stamped on a plate attached to torque converter housing near throttle cable.

DESCRIPTION

The transaxle assembly is a 3-speed unit mounted beneath engine. Transaxle assembly consists basically of a three-element torque converter, planetary gear set, two multi-disc clutches, a one-way clutch, two servos and brake bands, an oil pump, a hydraulic control system and a differential-type final drive assembly. Power is transmitted from turbine shaft of torque converter to input shaft of transmission via a sprocket/chain assembly.

LUBRICATION & ADJUSTMENTS

See appropriate AUTOMATIC TRANSMISSION SERVICING article in IMPORT GENERAL SERVICING section.

TROUBLE SHOOTING

NO DRIVE IN ANY LEVER POSITION

Check for low fluid level, manual linkage that is adjusted (or assembled) incorrectly, oil tubes that are missing or incorrectly installed, or missing/broken seals.

Ensure that valves operate properly. Clean strainer, magnet and valve housing. Check for broken pump drive tangs on converter hub, defective oil pump, or defective converter or one-way clutch.

NO DRIVE IN FORWARD GEARS

Check for manual linkage adjusted or assembled incorrectly, low fluid level, or missing/broken seals. Also check for dirty valve housing, defective front clutch, defective forward sun gear shaft seals, or a one-way clutch that is slipping (or incorrectly installed).

NO DRIVE IN REVERSE GEAR

Check for manual linkage that is adjusted (or assembled) incorrectly, rear band wear (or incorrect adjustment), or low fluid level. Also check for missing (or incorrectly installed) oil tubes, missing/broken seals, or dirty valve housing. Ensure that valves operate properly. Check for defective rear clutch or rear band.

Fig. 1: Cutaway View of Saab (Borg-Warner) Model 37 Automatic Transaxle Assembly

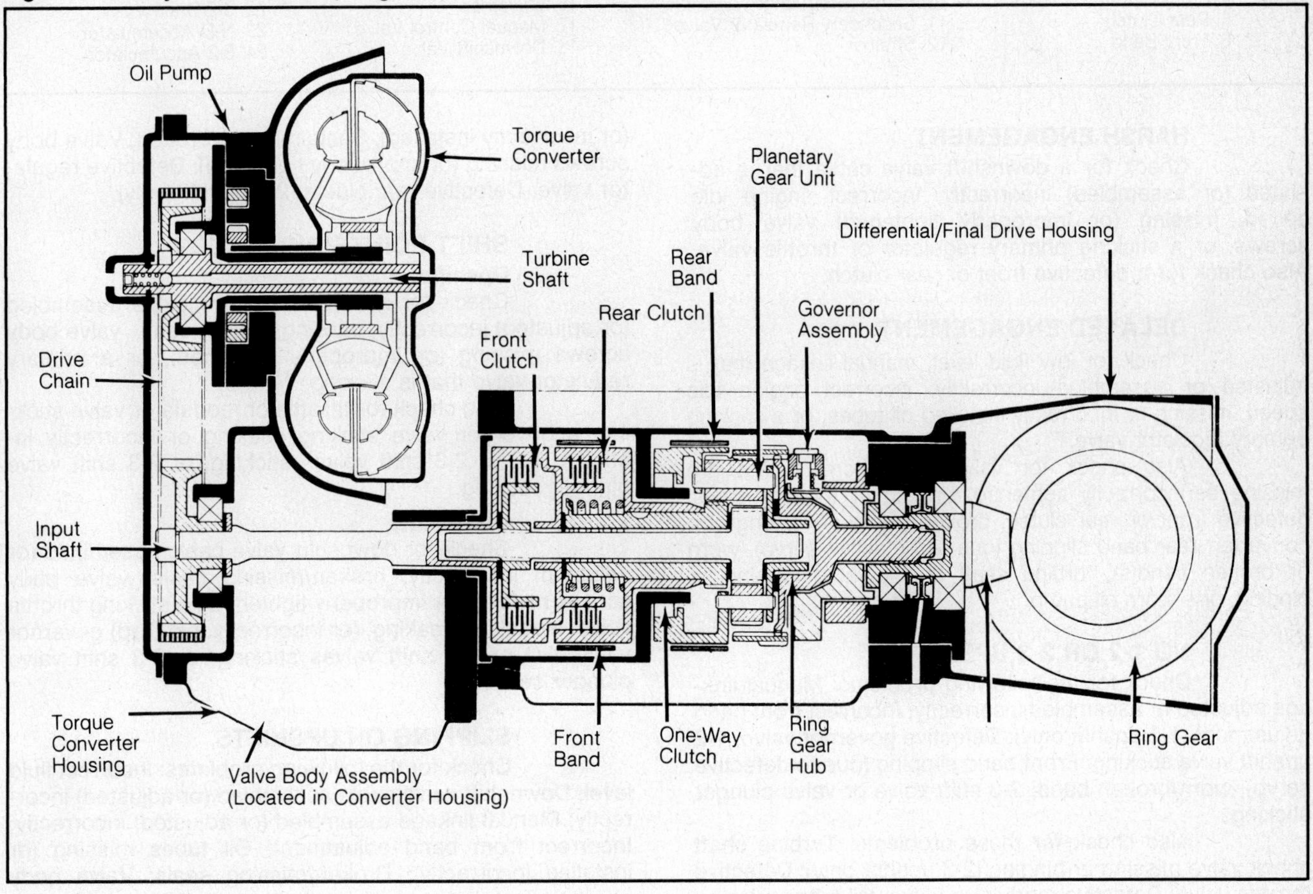

Automatic Transmissions

SAAB – BORG-WARNER MODEL 37 (Cont.)

Fig. 2: Saab (Borg-Warner) Model 37 Hydraulic Circuits Diagram

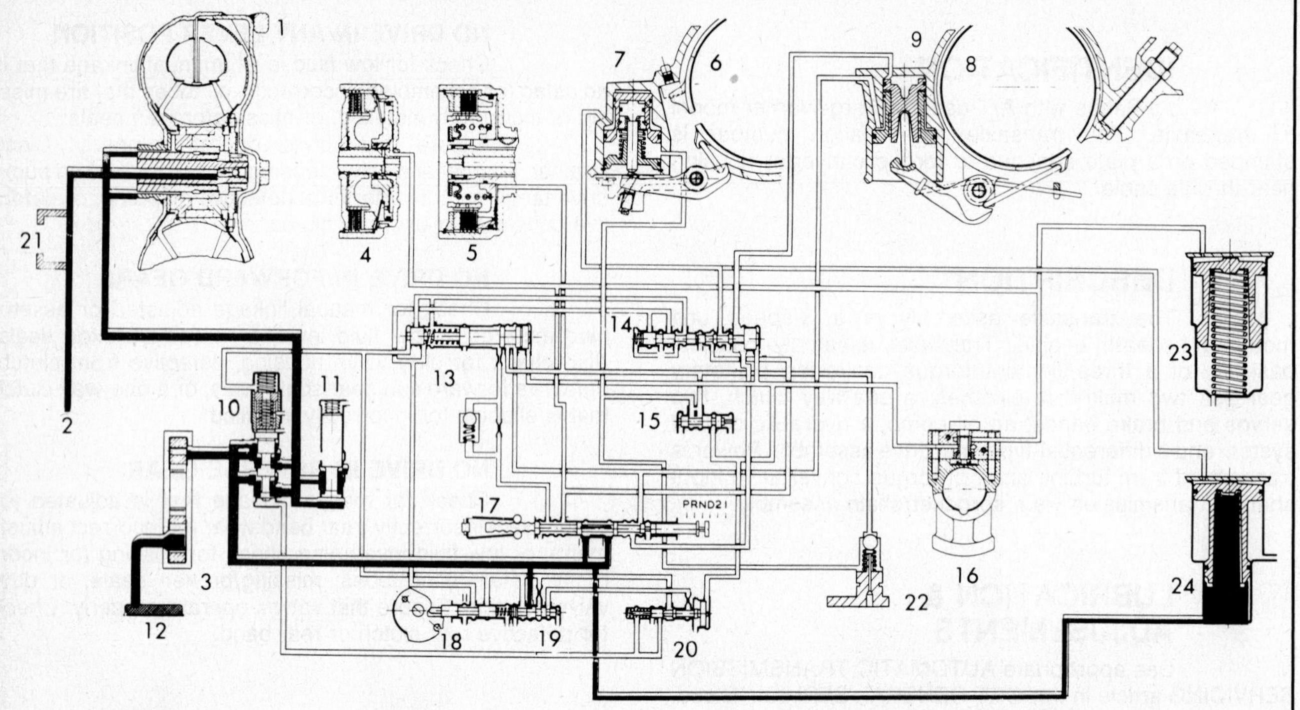

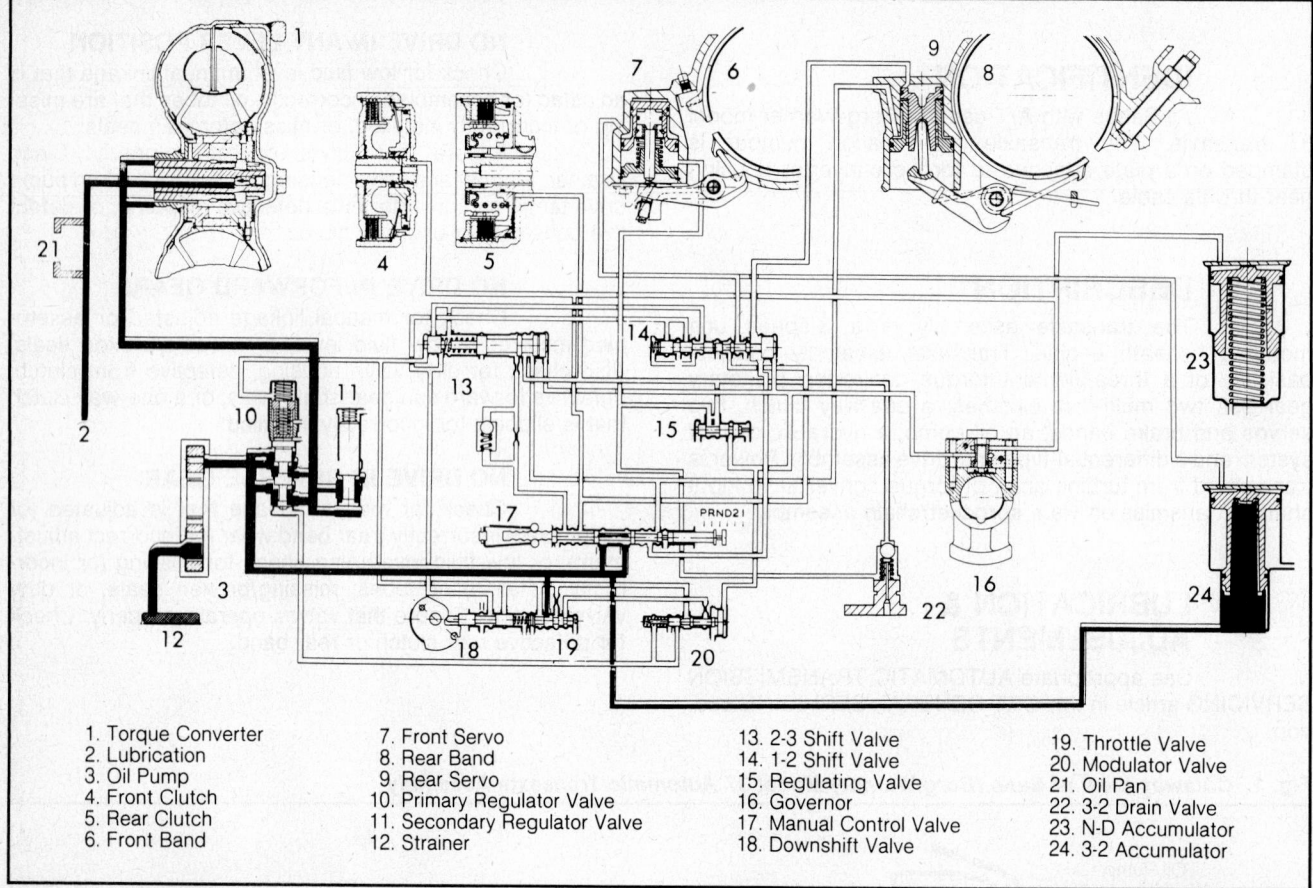

1. Torque Converter
2. Lubrication
3. Oil Pump
4. Front Clutch
5. Rear Clutch
6. Front Band
7. Front Servo
8. Rear Band
9. Rear Servo
10. Primary Regulator Valve
11. Secondary Regulator Valve
12. Strainer
13. 2-3 Shift Valve
14. 1-2 Shift Valve
15. Regulating Valve
16. Governor
17. Manual Control Valve
18. Downshift Valve
19. Throttle Valve
20. Modulator Valve
21. Oil Pan
22. 3-2 Drain Valve
23. N-D Accumulator
24. 3-2 Accumulator

HARSH ENGAGEMENT

Check for a downshift valve cable that is adjusted (or assembled) incorrectly, incorrect engine idle speed, missing (or improperly tightened) valve body screws, or a sticking primary regulator or throttle valve. Also check for a defective front or rear clutch.

DELAYED ENGAGEMENT

Check for low fluid level, manual linkage that is adjusted or assembled incorrectly, incorrect engine idle speed, missing or incorrectly installed oil tubes, or a sticking primary regulator valve.

Also check for valve body screws that are missing or incorrectly tightened, broken or missing seals, defective front or rear clutch, broken pump drive tangs on converter, rear band slipping (due to defective servo), worn or broken band(s), turbine shaft check valve missing or binding, or a worn oil pump.

NO 1-2 OR 2-3 UPSHIFT

Check for the following problems: Manual linkage adjusted or assembled incorrectly; Incorrect front band adjustment (1-2 upshift only); Defective governor valve; 1-2 upshift valve sticking; Front band slipping (due to defective servo), worn/broken band; 2-3 shift valve or valve plunger sticking.

Also check for these problems: Turbine shaft check valve missing or binding (2-3 upshift only); Defective throttle valve; Defective modulator valve; Oil tubes missing (or incorrectly installed); Seals missing/broken; Valve body screws missing (or improperly tightened); Defective regulator valve; Defective rear clutch (2-3 upshift only).

SHIFT POINTS INCORRECT

Upshifts

Check for a downshift valve cable assembled (or adjusted) incorrectly, missing/broken seals, valve body screws missing (or improperly tightened), or a primary regulator valve that is sticking.

Also check for throttle or modulator valve sticking, a governor valve sticking, leaking or incorrectly installed, 1-2 or 2-3 shift valves sticking, or 2-3 shift valve plunger sticking.

Downshifts

Check for downshift valve cable assembled (or adjusted) incorrectly, broken/missing seals, valve body screws missing (or improperly tightened), a sticking throttle valve, a sticking, leaking, (or incorrectly installed) governor valve, 1-2 or 2-3 shift valves sticking, or 2-3 shift valve plunger sticking.

SLIPPING ON UPSHIFTS

Check for the following problems: Incorrect fluid level; Downshift valve cable assembled (or adjusted) incorrectly; Manual linkage assembled (or adjusted) incorrectly; Incorrect front band adjustment; Oil tubes missing (or installed incorrectly); Broken/missing seals; Valve body screws missing (or improperly tightened); Primary regulator

CLUTCH & BAND APPLICATION CHART (ELEMENTS IN USE)

Selector Lever Position	Forward Clutch	Front Band	Rear Clutch	Rear Band	One-Way Clutch
"D" - DRIVE					
1st Gear	X				X
2nd Gear	X	X			
3rd Gear	X		X		
"2" - INTERMEDIATE					
1st Gear	X				X
2nd Gear	X	X			
"L1" - LOW 1	X			X	X
"R" - REVERSE			X	X	

NEUTRAL OR PARK – All clutches and bands released and/or ineffective.

valve sticking; Throttle valve sticking; Modulator valve sticking; Defective governor valve; 1-2 or 2-3 shift valves sticking; 2-3 shift valve plunger sticking; Defective rear clutch; Front band slipping (due to defective servo), or worn or broken band.

ROUGH UPSHIFTS

Check for a downshift valve cable that is assembled (or adjusted) incorrectly, incorrect front band adjustment, valve body screws missing (or improperly tightened), or a primary regulator valve that is sticking.

Also check for throttle or modulator valves that are sticking, a governor valve sticking, leaking or incorrectly installed, defective front or rear clutch, a one-way clutch that is slipping, incorrectly installed or seized.

NO 2-1 OR 3-2 DOWNSHIFT

Check for downshift valve cable that is assembled or adjusted incorrectly, a stiking, leaking, or incorrectly installed governor valve, or a sticking 1-2 shift valve. Also check for defective rear clutch, front or rear band slipping (due to defective servo), or worn/broken band.

SLIPPING ON DOWNSHIFTS

Check for incorrect front band adjustment, missing (or incorrectly installed) oil tubes, missing/broken seals, valve body screws that are missing (or improperly tightened), or a sticking primary regulator valve.

Also check for a sticking throttle valve, an orifice control valve that is sticking, a defective rear clutch, front clutch slipping (due to defective servo), a worn (or broken) band, or a one-way clutch slipping (or incorrectly installed).

ROUGH DOWNSHIFTS

Check for incorrect front band adjustment, broken/mising seals, valve body screws that are missing (or improperly tightened), a sticking primary regulator valve, or throttle valve.

Also check for an orifice control valve that is sticking, defective front (or rear) clutch, front band slipping (due to defective servo), a worn (or broken) band, or a one-way clutch that is slipping (or incorrectly installed).

TRANSMISSION OVERHEATING

Check for low fluid level, incorrect front or rear band adjustment, defective converter (or one-way clutch), or broken stator support.

TESTING

ROAD TEST

1) Before road test, ensure that fluid level/condition, and control linkage adjustments have been checked and corrected as necessary. During test, transmission should upshift and downshift at approximately same speed. See UPSHIFT & DOWNSHIFT SHIFT SPEEDS chart.

2) Shift speeds may vary slightly due to production tolerances or alternate tire size. All shifts should be smooth, responsive, and with no slippage or engine speed runaway.

3) Slippage or engine speed runaway in any gear usually indicates clutch or band problems. A slipping clutch or band in a particular gear can usually be identified by noting transmission operation in other selector positions and comparing internal units which are applied in these positions. See CLUTCH & BAND APPLICATION chart.

4) With vehicle at a standstill, accelerate both at minimum and full throttle and ensure that 1-2 and 2-3 shifts occur.

NOTE: **At minimum throttle opening, shifts may be difficult to detect. Confirmation that transmission is in 3rd gear may be obtained by shifting to "2" position when a 3-2 downshift should occur.**

5) With vehicle at 46-50 MPH in 3rd gear, depress accelerator to resistance point. Vehicle should accelerate without a downshift. With vehicle at 34-37 MPH in 3rd gear, depress accelerator beyond resistance point. Vehicle should downshift to 2nd gear, and then accelerate.

UPSHIFT & DOWNSHIFT SHIFT SPEEDS

Application	Shift Points (MPH) Minimum Throttle	Full Throttle
1-2 Upshift		
900	9-16	40-46
900 Turbo	9-17	40-48
2-3 Upshift		
900	12-19	67-75
900 Turbo	12-20	70-78
3-2 Downshift		
900		[1] 56-65
900 Turbo		[1] 62-72
2-1 Downshift		
900	1-11	27-36
900 Turbo	1-12	29-39

[1] – Kickdown.

6) With vehicle at 50 MPH, release accelerator and move selector lever to "2" position. Vehicle should downshift to 2nd gear and engine braking should be noticed.

7) Stop vehicle, put vehicle in Reverse. Check reverse operation by accelerating at full throttle and check for slipping and/or clutch break-away noise.

8) Stop vehicle on a hill facing downward. With vehicle in Park, release brakes and ensure parking pawl is operating. Repeat test with vehicle facing uphill.

STALL TEST

Precautions

When making test, do not hold throttle open any longer than 10 seconds. If engine speed exceeds limits, release accelerator immediately as clutch or band slippage is indicated. See STALL SPEED SPECIFICATIONS table.

Procedure

1) With engine at normal operating temperature, tachometer installed and parking and service brakes applied, perform transmission stall test in "D", "1" and "R" positions at full throttle, and note maximum RPM obtained. Engine speed should be within limits. See STALL SPEED SPECIFICATIONS table.

STALL SPEED SPECIFICATIONS

Application	Stall RPM
900	2150-2550
900 Turbo	2100-2600

2) If stall speed is about 300 RPM below specifications, engine is not operating at full power. If stall speed is about 800 RPM below specifications, torque converter assembly must be replaced.

3) A substantially higher stall speed than specifications indicates that converter is not receiving required oil supply, or that slippage is occurring in one of gearbox clutches.

SERVICE (IN VEHICLE)

WHEEL BEARINGS & DRIVE AXLE SHAFTS

NOTE: **Downward movement of control arms is limited by rubber buffer inside each shock absorber. Therefore, it will be necessary either to remove shock absorber, or to support lower control arm at outer end, before raising vehicle.**

Removal

1) Remove hub cap, loosen hub nut and wheel lugs. Raise and support vehicle. Remove wheels. Rotate brake disc to align recess along disc edge, with brake pads and caliper. Disconnect parking brake cable from each side. Remove caliper mounting bolts and hang caliper from coil spring using wire. DO NOT disconnect hydraulic line.

2) Remove hub and disc assembly using Extractor (89 96 084). Remove larger clamp on inner universal joint bellows. Remove steering arm and upper ball joint using Remover (89 95 409). Disconnect screws on lower control arm bracket. Separate inner CV joint from drive flange. Cover end of rubber bellows to prevent needle bearings from falling onto floor.

3) Pull axle assembly through wheel housing to remove. Thoroughly clean axle assembly. Place steering knuckle housing in a press and press out drive shaft. Remove snap ring from bearing housing. Press out and discard bearing.

Installation

1) Press bearing into steering knuckle housing, then install snap ring. Place axle shaft in press and press on knuckle housing and bearing. Install inner oil seal. Press wheel hub and brake disc onto axle splines and install washer. Install new lock nut, but do not tighten.

2) Install axle shaft through wheel housing. Install any needle bearings, which may have fallen out of inner CV joint, onto ends of "T" section. Attach inner CV joint to drive flange. Install upper ball joint to steering knuckle and reinstall lower control arm bracket. Install tie rod end on steering arm. Install brake caliper.

3) Reinstall front wheel and lower vehicle. Tighten hub lock nut, then secure in place by peening into locking groove. Pump brake pedal several times to seat brake pads.

CV JOINTS

NOTE: **Axle shafts cannot be disassembled. If damaged or defective, replace as complete assembly.**

VALVE BODY

NOTE: **Valve body cannot be serviced in vehicle. Removal and disasssembly of the transaxle is necessary to service valve body assembly.**

GOVERNOR ASSEMBLY

NOTE: **Governor assembly cannot be serviced in vehicle. Removal and disasssembly of the transaxle is necessary to service governor assembly.**

TRANSAXLE MOUNTS

Removal & Installation

1) Place transmission in Neutral. Unbolt exhaust pipe from manifold. Disconnect speedometer cable from transmission. Remove rear engine mounting bolt. Loosen front engine mounting bolt.

2) Attach hoist to 2 lifting rings, and raise engine and tranaxle assembly about 4". Remove bolts attaching front and rear mounts to frame, and remove mounts. To install, reverse removal procedure.

REMOVAL & INSTALLATION

TRANSAXLE

See appropriate AUTOMATIC TRANSMISSION REMOVAL article in IMPORT GENERAL SERVICING section.

TORQUE CONVERTER

NOTE: **Torque converter is a sealed unit and cannot be disassembled for service. If found defective, it must be replaced as a unit. Ventilation holes in torque converter housing must be kept free from dirt.**

TRANSAXLE DISASSEMBLY

1) Separate transaxle assembly from engine and mount on Transmission Stand (78 60 794). Attach Torque Converter Support (87 90 255). Drain fluid from transmission and final drive unit.

2) Remove all 5 covers from assembly. Remove sealing ring from turbine shaft. Hold drive chain sprockets stationary and remove sprocket attaching bolts. Remove drive chain and sprockets as an assembly. *See Fig. 3.*

Fig. 3: Removing Drive Chain and Sprockets

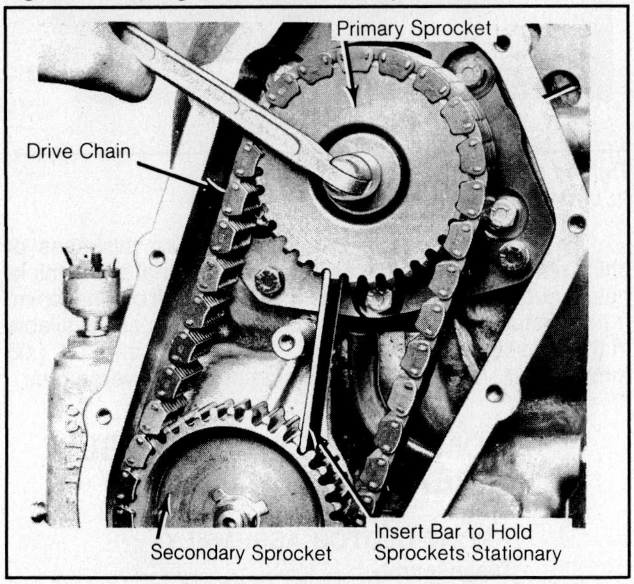

3) Turn transmission upside down. Remove oil screen and magnet. Remove oil tubes connecting front and rear sumps. Remove throttle valve cable. Remove oil pump strainer. Remove all oil tubes except 2 from drain valve to servo piston.

4) Remove valve body retaining bolts and lift out valve body. Remove accumulator piston (under valve body). Remove torque converter housing-to-transaxle housing attaching bolts. While holding parking pawl away from gear with screwdriver, remove torque converter housing and gasket. If necessary, tap housing with plastic hammer to separate.

5) Pry out front band pivot shaft with screwdriver. Remove band lever and strut. Remove self adjusting screw. Unhook rear band lever tension spring. Remove pivot shaft toward front of case. Use a strong screwdriver to push out shaft.

6) Remove band lever and strut. Remove 3 bolts securing center support to transaxle housing. Attach sprocket and nut to input shaft. Tap sprocket to loosen cover and remove front clutch.

7) Remove rear clutch assembly and sun gear shaft. Save shaft bearing and thrust washers for reassembly. Remove front and rear bands, planetary gear assembly and center support. Remove front servo snap ring. Using compressed air, remove front servo piston. *See Fig. 6.* Remove rear servo piston in same manner. *See Fig. 7.*

8) Install Hub Remover (87 90 958), or long bolt, through middle of ring gear hub. Pull hub, governor and pinion output shaft, by slowly tightening bolt. Use parking pawl to hold hub during removal. Do not remove parking pawl unless it is to be replaced. If necessary, remove snap ring from pivot shaft, push out shaft and remove pawl and spring. *See Fig. 8.*

Fig. 4: Bottom View of Torque Converter Case

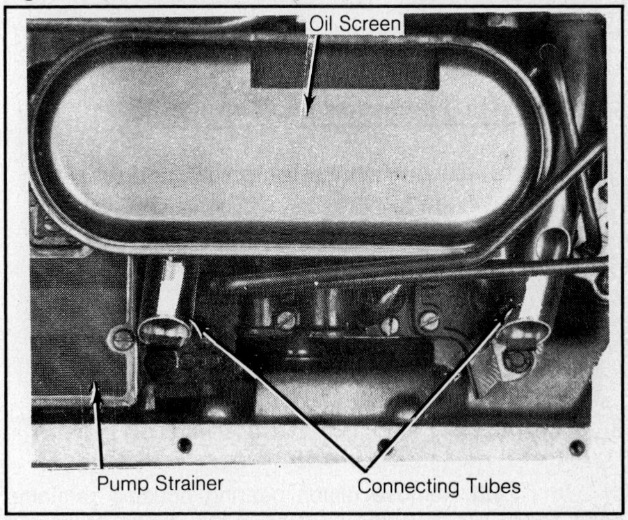

NOTE: **Before disassembling final drive unit, measure and record backlash and position of pinion for reassembly reference. See ADJUSTMENT procedures in TRANSAXLE REASSEMBLY. If ring and pinion gear assembly has been installed for less than 6000 miles, follow normal adjustment procedures on reassembly. If assembly has been installed for longer than 6000 miles, adjust to recorded measurements.**

9) Remove differential bearing housing retaining bolts (both sides). Using a puller and slide hammer, remove bearing housings and their axle shafts. Remove differential assembly from case.

SAAB – BORG-WARNER MODEL 37 (Cont.)

Fig. 5: Bottom View of Transaxle Case

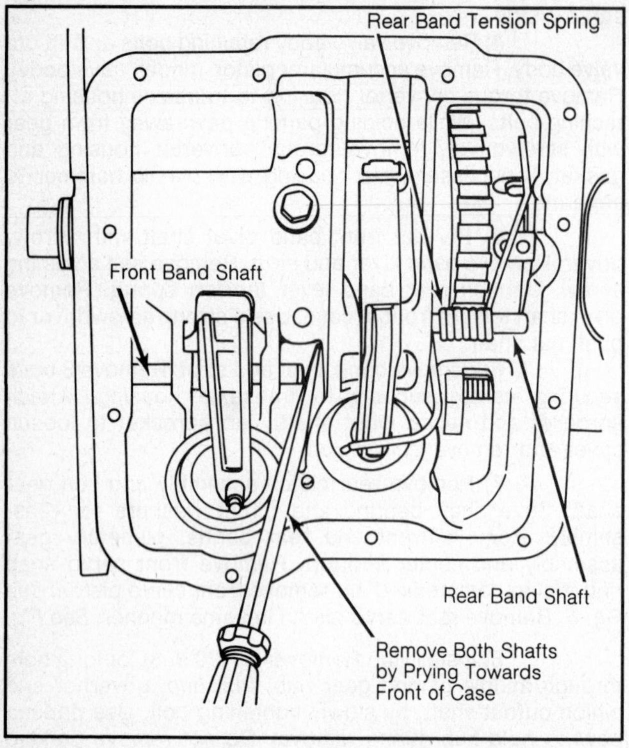

Fig. 6: Removing Front Servo Piston

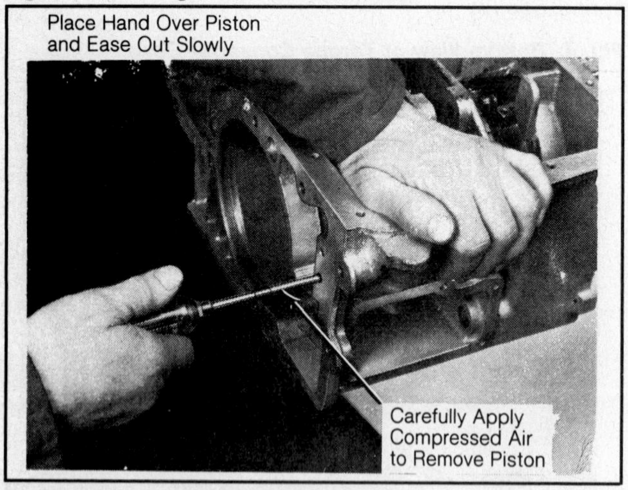

Place hand over piston to prevent possible damage.

10) Remove pinion bearing housing retaining bolts. Place transmission housing in press and press out pinion bearing housing and pinion seal housing (pressure applied at seal housing). *See Fig. 9.*

INPUT SHAFT END PLAY

NOTE: To obtain correct input shaft end play, retaining nut depth must be set correctly.

1) To accurately measure retaining nut depth, set depth gauge to 7.667" (195 mm) and install onto case. Measure distance between end of depth gauge and retaining nut using feeler gauge. Install shim of thickness equal to that of feeler gauge.

Fig. 7: Removing Rear Servo Piston

Place hand over piston and ease out gently.

Fig. 8: Removing Ring Gear Hub & Governor Assembly

Tighten bolt through center of assembly to press off components.

2) Using a micrometer, measure thickness of shim removed during disassembly. If original shim thickness equals required shim thickness, reinstall original shim. If not, install shim of proper thickness. Shims are available in thicknesses of .012" (.3 mm), .016" (.4 mm) and .02" (.05 mm). Install shim between retaining nut and reverse gear.

COMPONENT DISASSEMBLY & REASSEMBLY

FRONT CLUTCH ASSEMBLY

Disassembly

1) Slide clutch sealing plate from input shaft. Remove snap ring and lift input shaft and thrust washer from clutch drum. Lift out clutch hub and clutch plates from drum.

Fig. 9: Removing Differential Bearing Housing

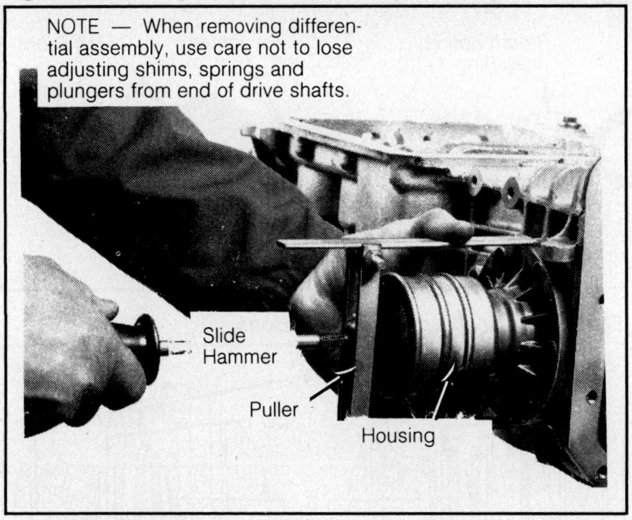

Use slide hammer and puller to detach bearing housing/axle shaft assembly.

NOTE: Record number of clutch plates used and order in which they are installed for reassembly reference.

2) Remove pressure plate from clutch drum. Remove piston return spring snap ring and remove spring from clutch drum. Remove clutch piston from drum with aid of compressed air. *See Fig. 10.* Inspect all seals and clutch plates for wear or damage and replace if necessary.

Fig. 10: Removing Front Clutch Piston

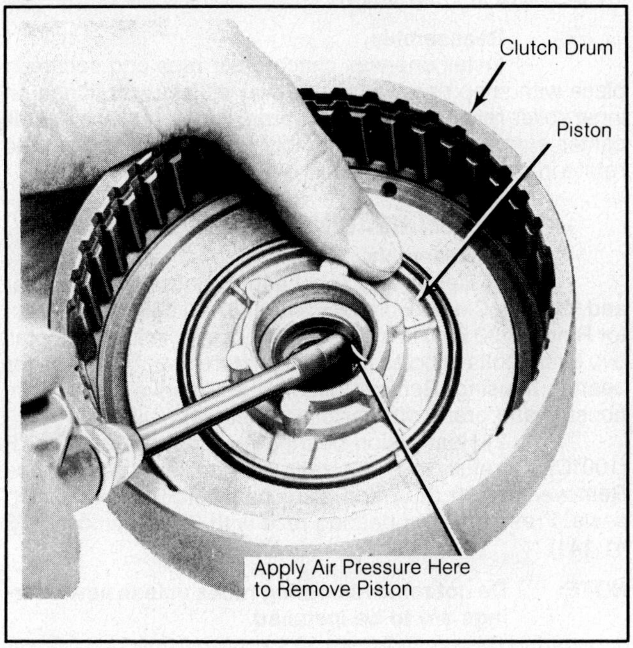

Hold piston as shown, while applying compressed air.

Reassembly

1) Prior to reassembly, lubricate all components with ATF. Install new "O" ring seal on clutch drum and in piston groove. Using seal protector, install piston into clutch drum until it is fully seated. Install clutch return spring into drum with convex side facing down, then install snap ring.

2) Install pressure plate with flat side up. Install clutch hub. Place clutch plates into drum in same order in which they were removed. Install thrust washer, then place input shaft into clutch drum and secure in place with snap ring.

NOTE: Ensure seal rings on input shaft rotate freely in their grooves.

Fig. 11: Installing Front Clutch Piston

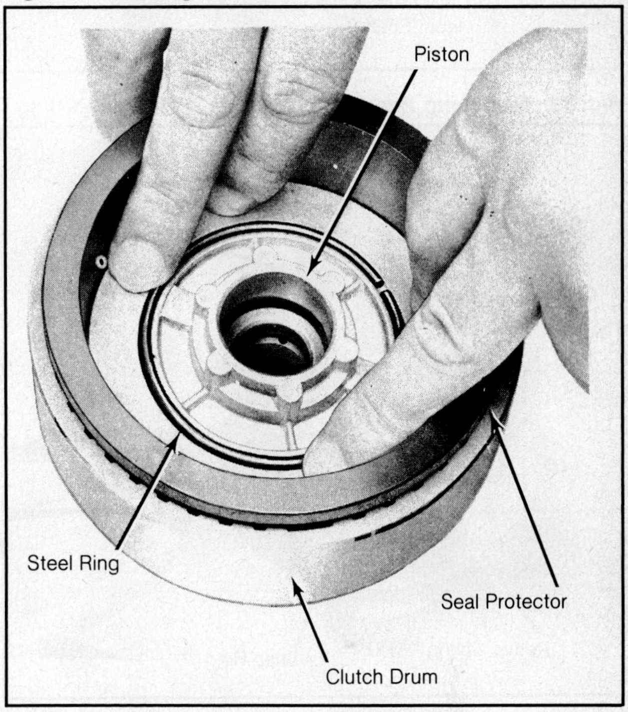

Ensure steel ring on piston is fully seated.

REAR CLUTCH ASSEMBLY

Disassembly

Remove clutch drum snap ring. Remove pressure plate and clutch plates, noting number of clutch plates used and order of installation for reassembly reference. Install Clutch Spring Compressor (87 90 018) and remove clutch return spring snap ring, spring seat and return spring. *See Fig. 13.* Use compressed air to remove piston. *See Fig. 14.*

Reassembly

NOTE: Lubricate all parts with ATF before reassembly. Inner clutch plates must be soaked in ATF before final installation.

1) Using Piston Installer (87 90 081) install piston (flat side down) until fully seated, then lubricate with petroleum jelly. Install return spring and spring seat. Compress return spring in a press, using Return Spring Installer (87 90 081) and install snap ring.

2) Assemble clutch plates, pressure plate and snap ring. Apply load to pressure plate, and measure clearance between pressure plate and snap ring. Clearance should be .025-.045" (.63-1.14 mm). If clearance is between .046-.064" (1.17-1.63 mm), install a thicker snap ring.

3) If clearance exceeds .064" (1.63 mm), install 2 thin snap rings. If clearance is below specification, replace

Fig. 12: Exploded View of Front Clutch Assembly and Input Shaft

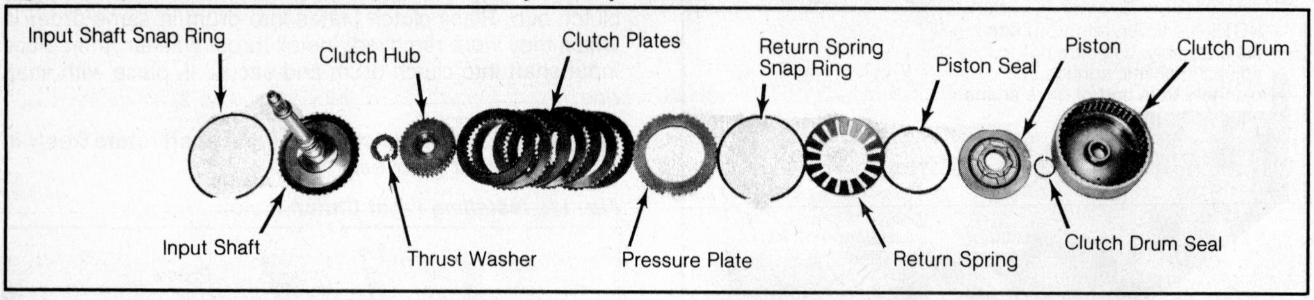

Fig. 13: Removing Rear Clutch Return Spring Snap Ring

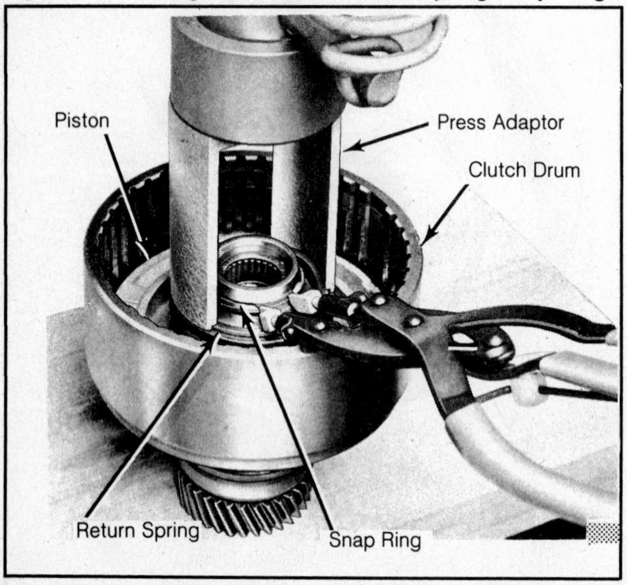

Fig. 14: Removing Rear Clutch Piston

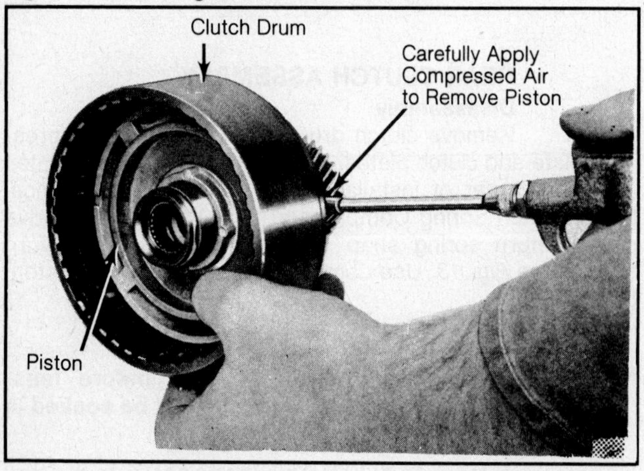

greatly concaved plates with slightly flatter plates (one at a time) until correct clearance is obtained. *See Fig. 15.*

PLANETARY GEAR ASSEMBLY

Disassembly

Remove center support from planetary gear assembly. Remove one-way clutch from outer race. Remove snap ring for one-way clutch outer race and remove race from planet carrier.

Fig. 15: Rear Clutch Plate Positions

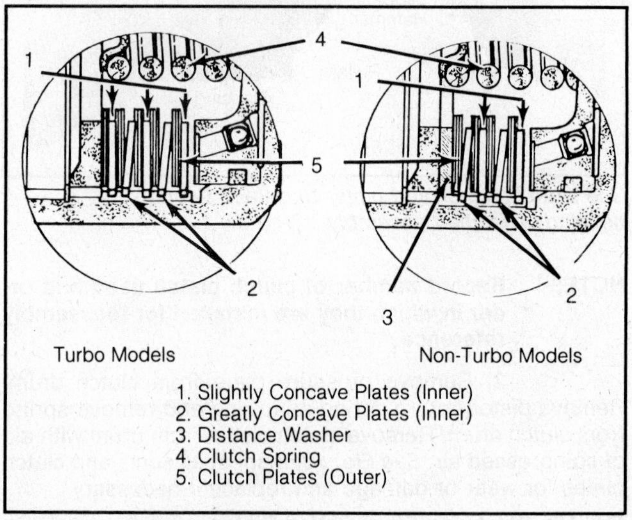

Install plates in order shown.

Reassembly

Install one-way clutch outer race and secure in place with snap ring. Install one-way clutch, with flange on inner roller retainer facing outwards, into outer race. Install center support. After reassembly, one-way clutch should rotate in a clockwise direction only.

PINION BEARING HOUSING

Disassembly

1) Remove pinion bearing housing seal cover and "O" ring. Clamp Holding Fixture (87 90 636) and Extractor Ring (87 90 651) in a vise and fit housing in fixture. Install two 8 mm bolts in holes in holding fixture to act as stops for bearing housing. Remove pinion nut. Remove pinion from housing and press off rear pinion bearing.

2) Heat pinion bearing housing to about 212°F (100°C). Carefully pull out rear bearing race using Race Remover (87 90 966) and slide hammer. Remove pinion seals. Press off front bearing race with Race Remover (78 41 141).

NOTE: **Do not remove bearing races unless new bearings are to be installed.**

Reassembly

1) Clean ventilation channel of housing thoroughly before beginning reassembly. Press in new front bearing race (if needed). Install pinion seals using Seal Installer (87 90 900). Press in new rear bearing race (if removed). Press rear bearing on to pinion shaft.

2) Install pinion shaft in bearing housing. Install spacer and front bearing. Oil threads of pinion shaft and install nut. Place complete assembly in tools as in disassembly and place in vise. Oil bearing and tighten nut to 160-195 ft. lbs. (215-264 N.m).

Fig. 16: Exploded View of Planetary Gear Assembly

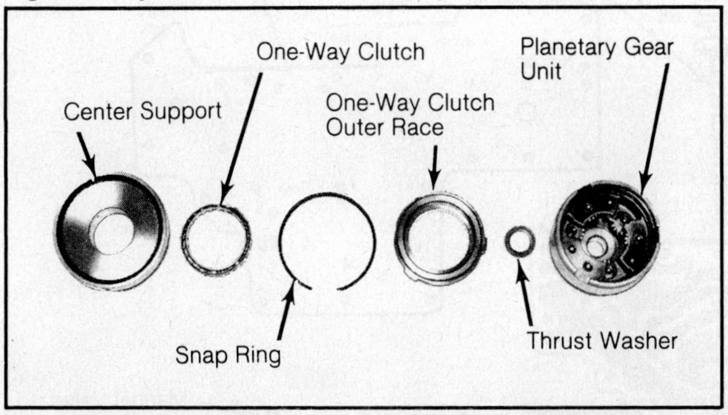

3) Check bearing preload. Preload for new bearings should be 19-24 INCH lbs. (2.2-2.7 N.m). For old bearings (with more than 1200 miles service), preload should be 8-13 INCH lbs. (.9-1.5 N.m). Preload can be adjusted by installing a new spacer of difference thickness. Spacers are available in thicknesses of .112 to .149" (2.85 to 3.78 mm).

GOVERNOR ASSEMBLY

Disassembly

Remove screws attaching governor body to housing. Remove cover plate. Remove retaining clip and weight from end of governor shaft. Separate governor body from housing. Remove governor shaft with valve and spring. Inspect all parts for wear or damage. Scratches on governor valve may be cleaned with fine emery cloth.

Reassembly

Before reassembly, lubricate all parts with ATF. To reassemble, reverse disassembly procedure. After reassembly, ensure governor valve moves freely.

VALVE BODY ASSEMBLY

NOTE: **As valve trains are removed from each valve body bore, place individual parts in correct order and in relative position to valve body to simplify reassembly.**

CAUTION: **Valves and springs are not interchangeable; all parts must be installed in correct order in proper valve body bore. See Fig. 20.**

Fig. 18: Exploded View of Pinion Bearing Assembly

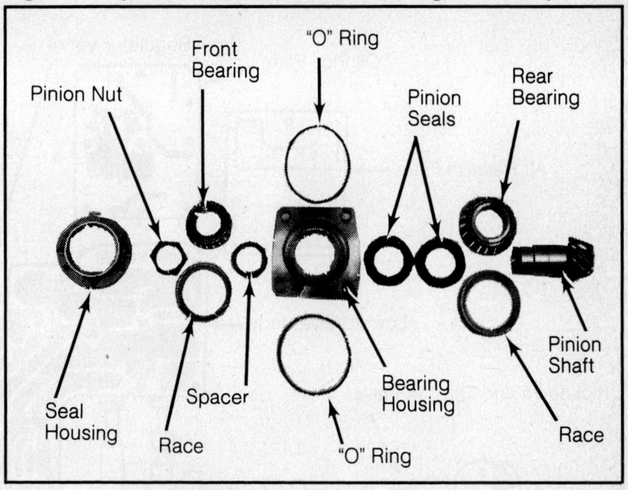

Disassembly

1) Remove retaining screws and lift off downshift valve carrier and cam assembly. Pull out manual valve. Remove kickdown valve and throttle valve and springs. Remove 6 upper-to-lower valve body retaining screws from top of assembly and 2 screws from bottom.

2) Separate upper and lower valve bodies. Remove 8 oil pipe plate-to-valve body retaining screws. Remove dividing plate, taking care not to lose check ball and spring from lower valve body.

Fig. 19: Exploded View of Governor Assembly

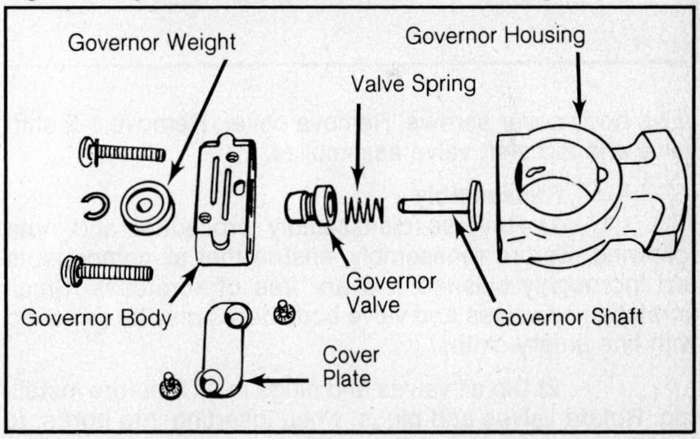

3) Remove orifice control valve stop and valve. Remove modulator valve plug retaining pin. Remove valves and springs. Remove 3 end plate retaining screws. Remove primary and secondary regulator valves. Remove upper

Fig. 17: Exploded View Showing Components of Rear Clutch Assembly

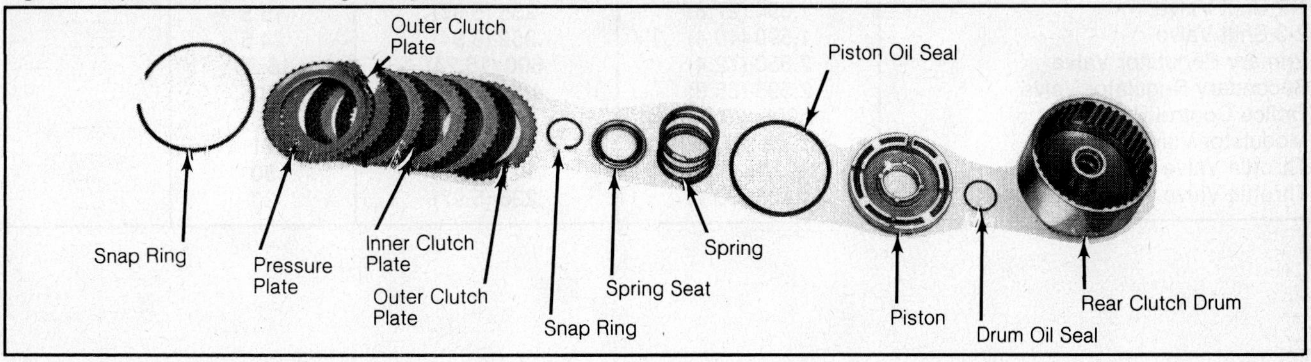

SAAB – BORG-WARNER MODEL 37 (Cont.)

Fig. 20: Exploded View of Upper and Lower Valve Body Assembly

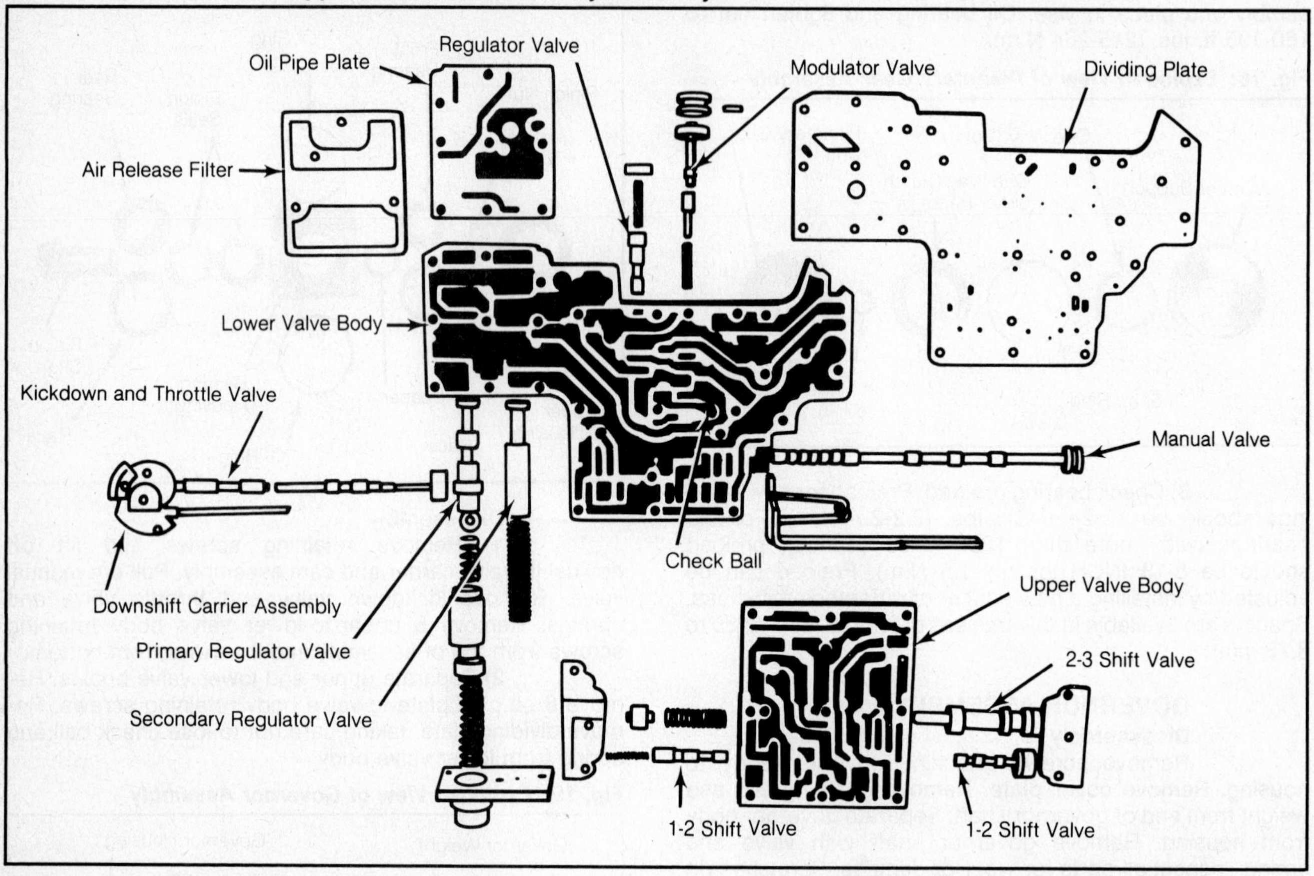

valve body cover screws. Remove cover. Remove 1-2 shift valve and 2-3 shift valve assemblies.

Reassembly

1) Reverse disassembly procedure and note following: Before reassembly, ensure that all components are thoroughly cleaned and are free of scratches. Small scratches on valves and valve body bores may be removed with fine emery cloth.

2) Dip all valves and plugs in ATF before installing. Rotate valves and plugs, when inserting into bores, to avoid shearing off soft body castings. Ensure all valves move freely and smoothly in their bores. Ensure check ball and spring are in correct position in lower valve body, before installing oil tube plate. *See Fig. 22.*

OIL PUMP

Disassembly

Remove 5 attaching screws and separate pump housings. Check back plate for scratches or other damage. Mark pump drive and driven gear for reassembly. DO NOT scribe mark on gears, use chalk or a soft pencil. Remove gears. Inspect gears for scratches or signs of other dam-

SAAB VALVE BODY SPRING IDENTIFICATION CHART

Valve Spring	Length In. (mm)	Diameter In. (mm)	Number Of Coils	Color
1-2 Shift Valve	1.094 (27.8)	.235 (5.97)	15.5	.....
2-3 Shift Valve	1.590 (40.4)	.352 (8.94)	24.5	.....
Primary Regulator Valve	2.850 (72.4)	.600 (15.24)	16.25	.....
Secondary Regulator Valve	2.593 (65.9)	.485 (12.24)	23.5	.....
Orifice Control Valve	1.005 (25.53)	.203 (5.16)	19	.....
Modulator Valve	1.069 (27.15)	.211 (5.36)	21	.....
Throttle Valve (Inner)	.807 (20.5)	.141 (3.58)	30	.....
Throttle Valve (Outer)	1.185 (30.1)	.236 (5.97)	20	.....

Fig. 21: Top View of Lower Valve Body

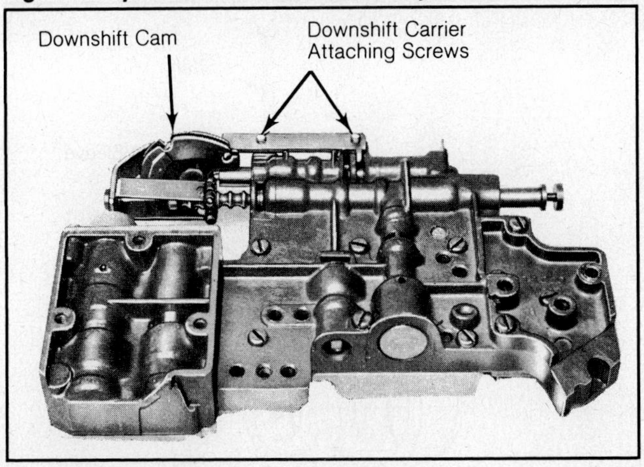

age. Inspect bearing and seals for wear, and replace if necessary.

Pump Bearing Replacement

Remove snap ring. Gently tap oil pump shaft with a plastic mallet to free shaft and bearing. Remove bearing. Reverse procedure to install new bearing.

Reassembly

Reverse disassembly procedure to reassemble. Use Centering Spacer (87 90 248) to center oil pump. Install a new "O" ring on outside of pump housing.

Fig. 22: Bottom View of Lower Valve Body

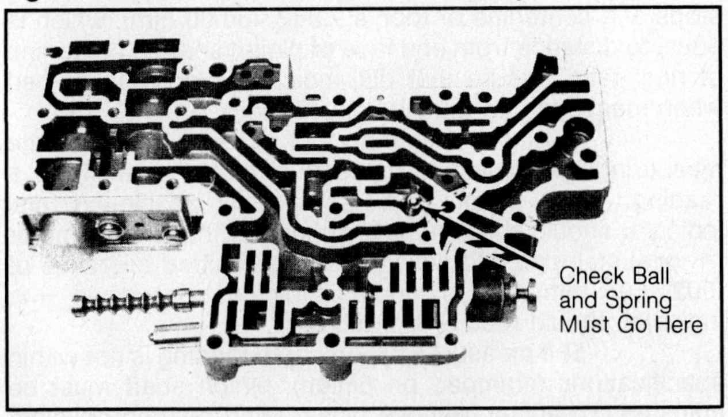

Fig. 23: Disassembled View of Oil Pump Assembly

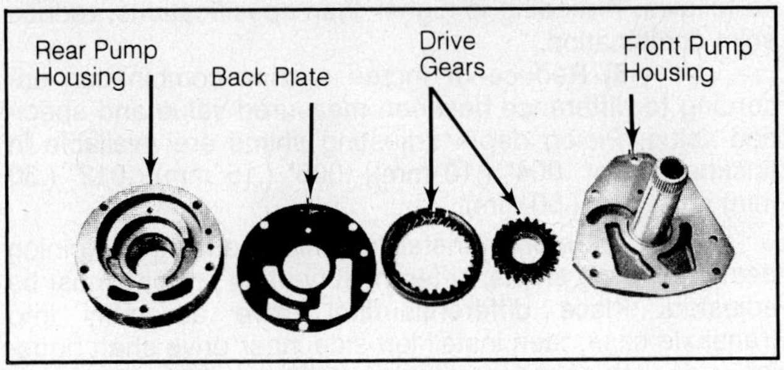

Use centering spacer when installing pump.

DIFFERENTIAL ASSEMBLY

Disassembly

1) Remove differential bearings only if they are to be replaced. Remove differential ring gear attaching bolts and separate ring gear from differential housing.

Fig. 24: Reassembling Oil Pump

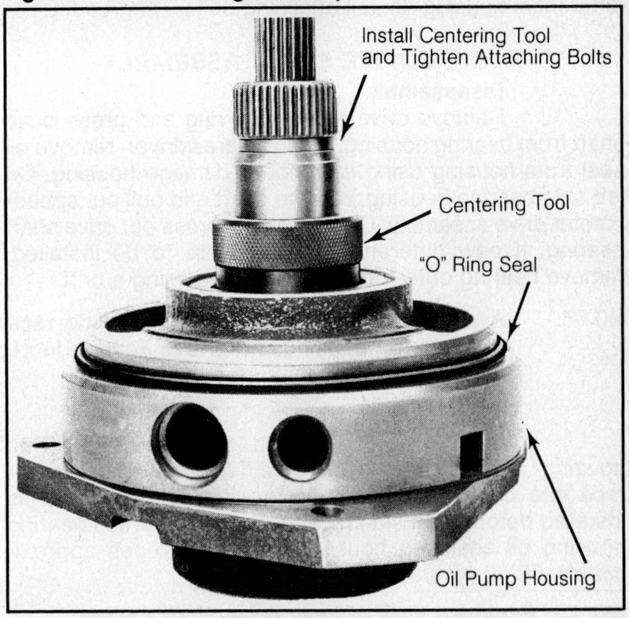

Tool must turn freely with attaching bolts tightened.

Fig. 25: Exploded View of Differential Assembly

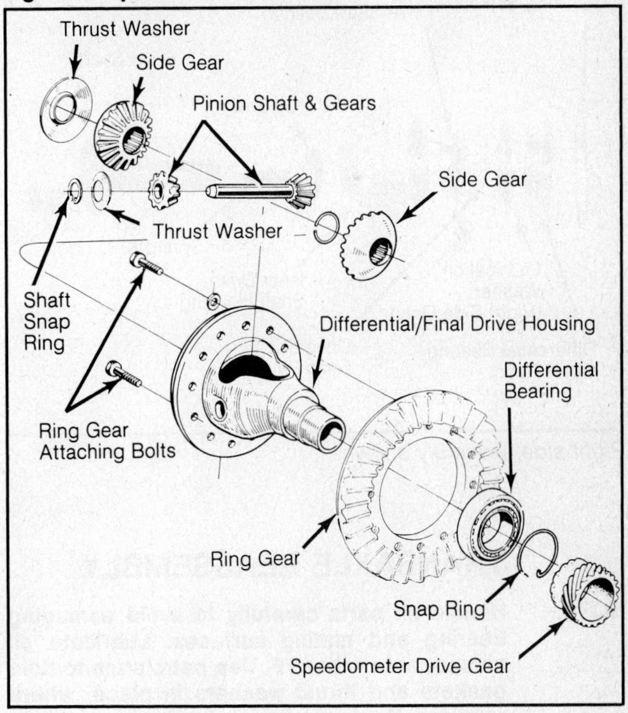

2) Remove snap ring, then push out differential pinion gear shaft. Remove pinion gears and side gears along with thrust washers from housing. If ring gear requires replacement, pinion shaft must also be replaced as they are serviced as a complete set.

NOTE: **Before left side bearing can be removed, speedometer drive gear must be pulled from housing.**

Reassembly

Install pinion gears and side gear along with thrust washers into differential housing, install pinion shaft

SAAB – BORG-WARNER MODEL 37 (Cont.)

and lock in place with snap ring. Mount ring gear on differential housing. Install attaching bolts using Loctite.

INNER DRIVE SHAFT ASSEMBLY

Disassembly

Remove drive shaft snap ring and press drive shaft from bearing housing. Using a screwdriver, remove oil seal from housing using care not to damage housing. On left side bearing housing, remove shaft and pull out speedometer drive assembly. On both sides, press out drive shaft bearing. If new differential bearings are to be installed, remove bearing outer race from housing using a drift.

NOTE: A washer is located between right side race and bearing housing to improve bearing lubrication.

Reassembly

Press new drive shaft bearing into bearing housing. If removed, press new differential bearing outer race into bearing housing. Ensure lubrication washer is installed before right side race. Using a drift, press bearing housing oil seal into housing until it protrudes approximately .08" (2 mm) above face of housing.

Fig. 26: Exploded View of Inner Drive Shaft Assembly

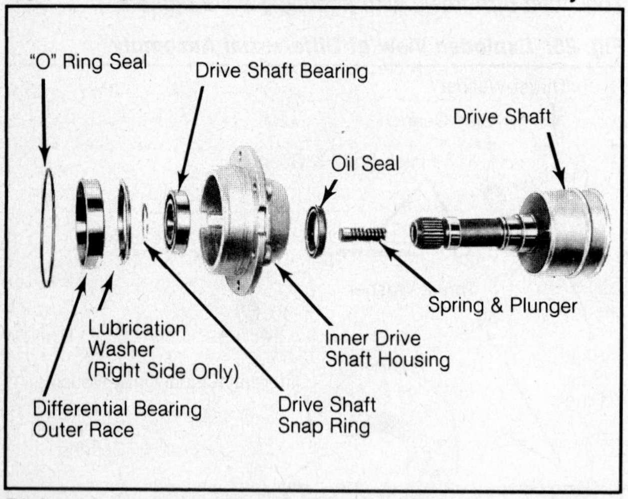

Right side assembly shown.

TRANSAXLE REASSEMBLY

NOTE: Handle all parts carefully to avoid damaging bearing and mating surfaces. Lubricate all components with ATF. Use petrolatum to hold gaskets and thrust washers in place, where required. Replace all worn or damaged parts. See Fig. 29 for thrust washer and bearing locations.

1) Blow out ventilation channels with compressed air. Install pinion bearing housing locating studs into case. Install pinion bearing shims. Lubricate bearing housing sealing rings.

2) Position complete pinion bearing housing assembly on locating stubs. Place case in press, and press in housing. Press bearing housing in as far as it can go. Remove locating studs and install retaining bolts. Check pinion clearance.

Fig. 27: Exploded View of Speedometer Drive Assembly

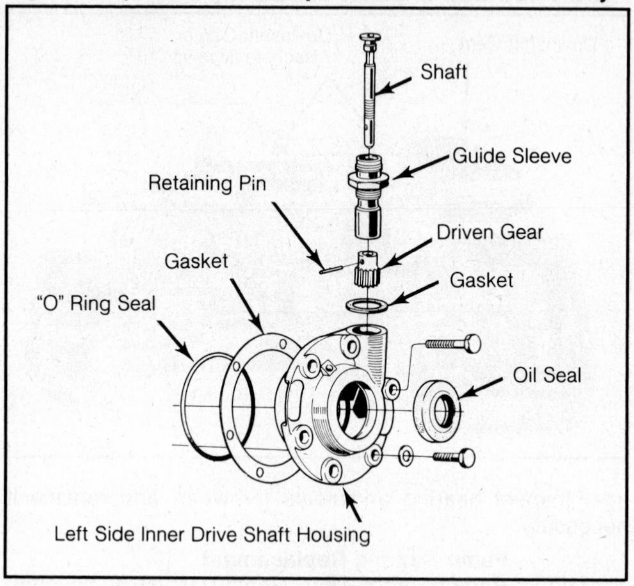

NOTE: Pinion depth must be measured using Saab Measuring Instrument (83 90 155), which consists of a measuring jig (with attached dial indicator) and a gauge block for calibrating dial indicator. See Fig. 30.

3) To calibrate indicator, place calibration stops of measuring tool against gauge block. Distance between stops and centerline of tool is 2.362" (60.00 mm), which is equal to distance from end face of pinion shaft to centerline of ring gear. Ensure that dial indicator pointer is zeroed when measuring tip touches gauge block.

4) Place measuring tool in transaxle case with measuring tip applied to flat end of pinion gear. Take a reading. When pinion gear is correctly positioned, dial indicator should show number of hundredths of a millimeter (+ or -) stamped into pinion, with a permitted tolerance of .002" (.05 mm). For example, if pinion is stamped +3, indicator should read +3 ± .05 mm.

5) If measured pinion depth reading is not within specifications (stamped on pinion), pinion shaft must be adjusted. To adjust, remove pinion shaft bearing housing. Add or remove shims between housing and transaxle case as follows: If reading is higher than specifications, reduce shim combination.

6) Reduce or increase shim combination according to difference between measured value and specified value. Pinion depth adjusting shims are available in thicknesses of .004" (.10 mm), .006" (.15 mm), .012" (.30 mm) and .020" (.50 mm).

7) Before reinstalling pinion housing and pinion depth adjusting shims, differential bearing preload must be adjusted. Place differential/final drive assembly into transaxle case, then install left side inner drive shaft housing (side with speedometer drive) without shims.

8) Install attaching bolts and tighten to 15-18 ft. lbs. (20-25 N.m). Oil differential bearing, and install right side drive shaft housing without shims. Tighten attaching bolts to 19 INCH lbs. (2.2 N.m) in 2 or 3 steps. Rotate differential assembly while tightening bolts.

SAAB – BORG-WARNER MODEL 37 (Cont.)

Fig. 28: View of Pinion Gear Showing Location of Adjustment Data

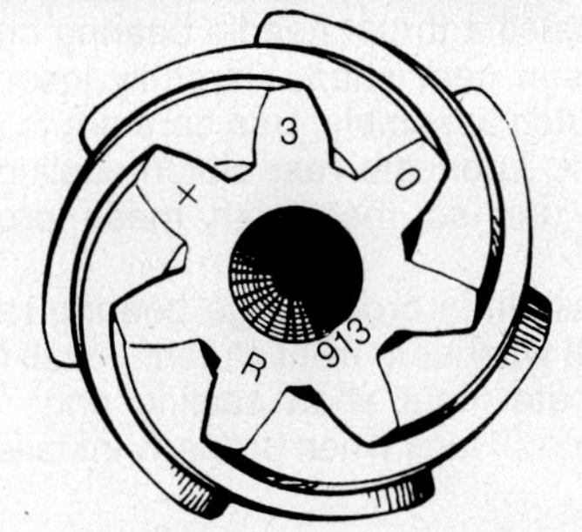

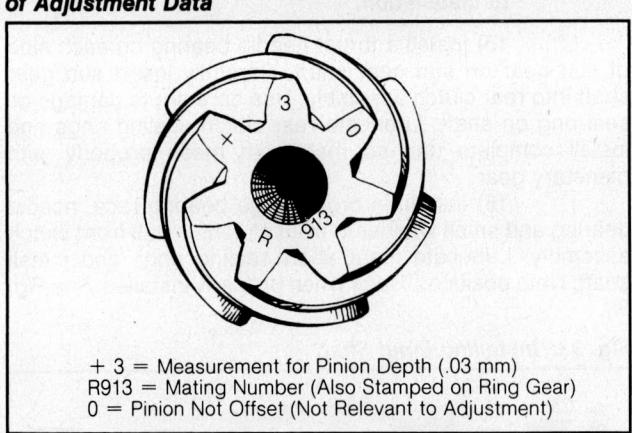

+ 3 = Measurement for Pinion Depth (.03 mm)
R913 = Mating Number (Also Stamped on Ring Gear)
0 = Pinion Not Offset (Not Relevant to Adjustment)

9) Using a feeler gauge, measure gap between right side drive shaft housing and transaxle case at 2 points opposite each other. Take average of 2 readings and select adjusting shims which will equal this value. Then add an additional .008" (.20 mm) in shim thickness to obtain correct bearing preload.

NOTE: Up to 4 shims may be used to obtain correct preload. Adjusting shims are available in thicknesses of .004" (.10 mm), .006" (.15 mm), .012" (.30 mm) and .020" (.50 mm).

Fig. 30: Using Special Tool to Measure Pinion Depth

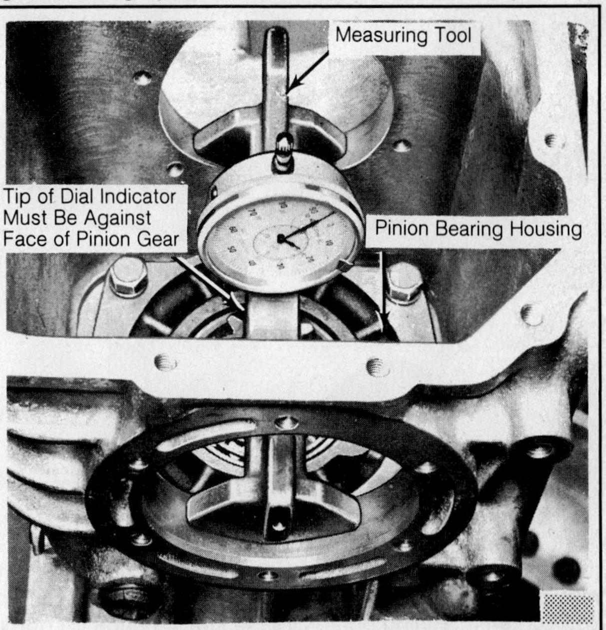

10) Remove right side drive shaft housing and lift out differential/final drive assembly. Reinstall pinion shaft housing along with pinion depth adjusting shims.

Fig. 29: Cutaway View of Transaxle Assembly Showing Location of Thrust Washers, Bearings and Shims

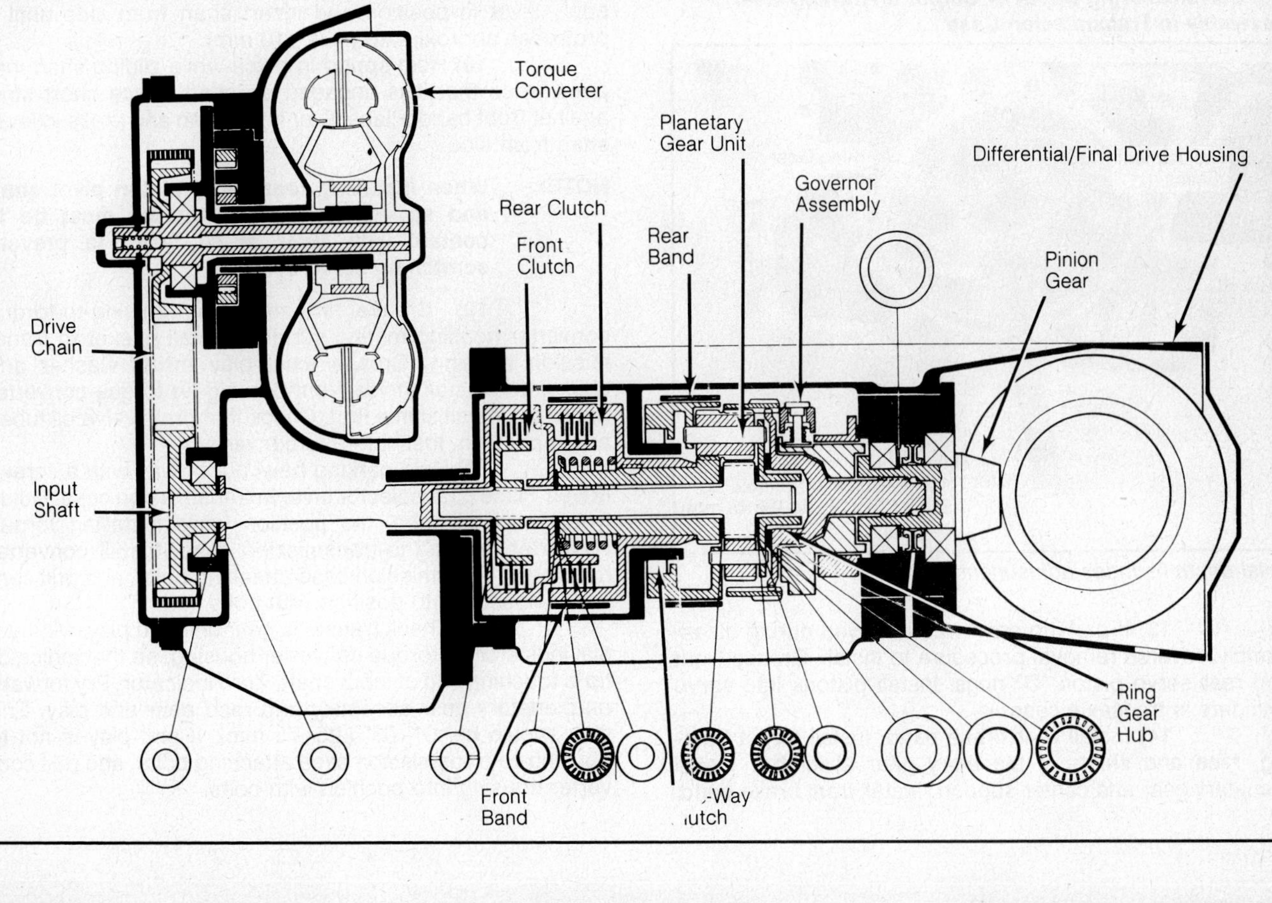

SAAB – BORG-WARNER MODEL 37 (Cont.)

Fig. 31: Measuring Differential Bearing Preload

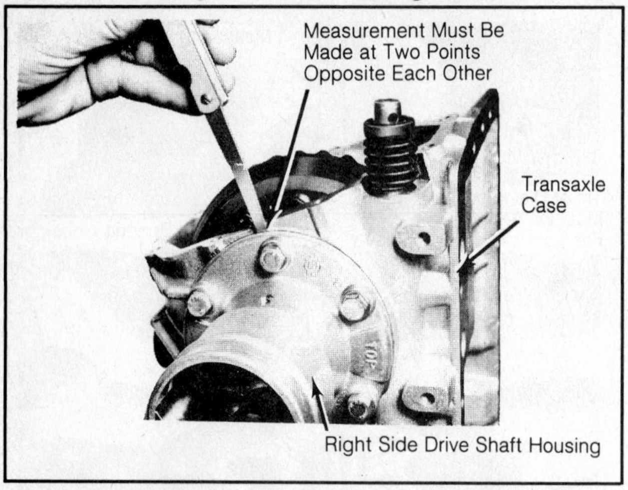

Recheck pinion depth adjustment. Reinstall differential/final drive assembly.

11) Reinstall right side drive shaft housing along with previously selected bearing preload adjusting shims and tighten attaching bolts. Grease sealing rings on output shaft. Place transmission housing in vise and support pinion with a drift.

12) Position output shaft on pinion, and carefully press on shaft. Be sure that shaft and pinion splines are properly aligned. Ensure that sealing rings on output shaft are located correctly in their grooves as they enter seal housing. Measure assembly depth in case with a large depth gauge. Total depth should be 7.561-7.578" (192.04-192.48 mm) including shims.

Fig. 32: Measuring Depth of Output Shaft/Ring Gear Assembly in Transmission Case

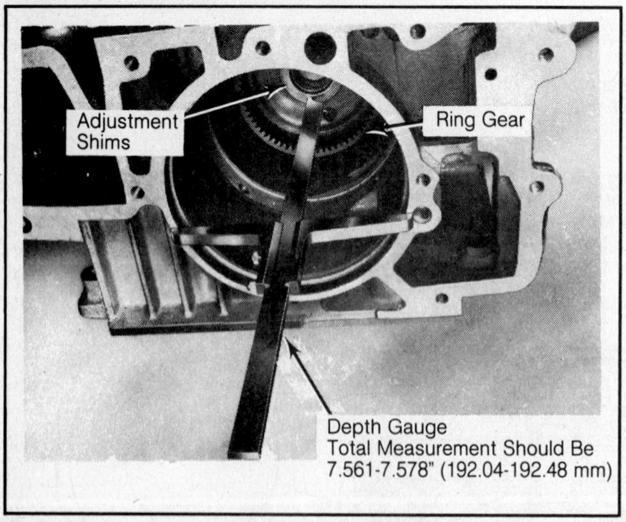

Total depth includes adjustment shims.

13) If parking pawl was removed during disassembly, reverse removal procedure to install. Grease front and rear servo piston "O" rings. Install pistons into servo cylinders in transaxle case.

14) Install rear brake band. Install thrust bearing, race and shims in planetary gear assembly. Install planetary gear and center support. Install front brake band.

NOTE: **Soak brake bands (front and rear) in ATF prior to installation.**

15) Install a thrust needle bearing on each side of sun gear on sun gear shaft. Carefully insert sun gear shaft into rear clutch assembly. Use care not to damage oil seal ring on shaft. Lubricate rear clutch sealing rings and install complete unit so that teeth mesh properly with planetary gear.

16) Install, in order, large bearing race, needle bearing and small washer in front clutch. Install front clutch assembly. Lubricate input shaft sealing rings and install shaft. Note position of lugs when properly installed. *See Fig. 33.*

Fig. 33: Installing Input Shaft

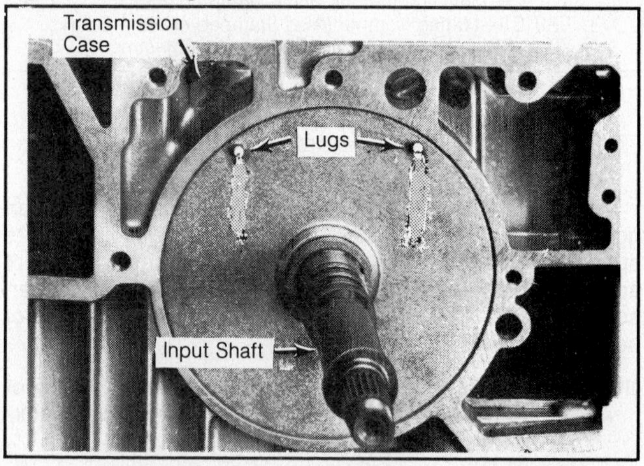

17) Place pin in rear servo piston. Place long band apply strut against rear band, then place rear band apply lever in position and insert shaft from side until it protrudes approximately .04" (10 mm).

18) Hold spring in place while sliding shaft into position so that it is engaged on shaft. Place short strut against front band. Place lever in position and press in lever shaft from side.

NOTE: **When installing rear servo piston pivot shaft and spring, one end of spring must be in contact with lever at all times to prevent scratching servo cylinder.**

19) Grease transmission housing-to-torque converter housing mating surface. Install gasket to transmission housing. Grease axial play thrust washer and shims, and install inside front bearing (in torque converter housing). Install shims first. Check that drain valve oil tubes are in position. Install torque converter.

20) Hold parking pawl out of way with a screwdriver. Place gear selector lever in transmission case. Guide front servo oil tube into position while installing torque converter housing-to-transmission case. Install converter housing-to-transmission case attaching bolts, and pull converter housing into position with bolts.

21) Check transaxle gear unit end play. Mount a dial indicator on torque converter housing, so that indicator tip is touching end of input shaft. Zero indicator. Pry forward on planetary gear assembly and read gear end play. End play should be .01-.03" (.25-.75 mm). If end play is not to housing-to-transmission case attaching bolts, and pull converter housing into position with bolts.

22) Check transaxle gear unit end play. Mount a dial indicator on torque converter housing, so that indicator tip is touching end of input shaft. Zero indicator. Pry forward on planetary gear assembly and read gear end play. End play should be .01-.03" (.25-.75 mm). If end play is not to specifications, adjust by adding or removing shims between thrust washer and front bearing.

Fig. 34: Measuring Gear Unit End Play

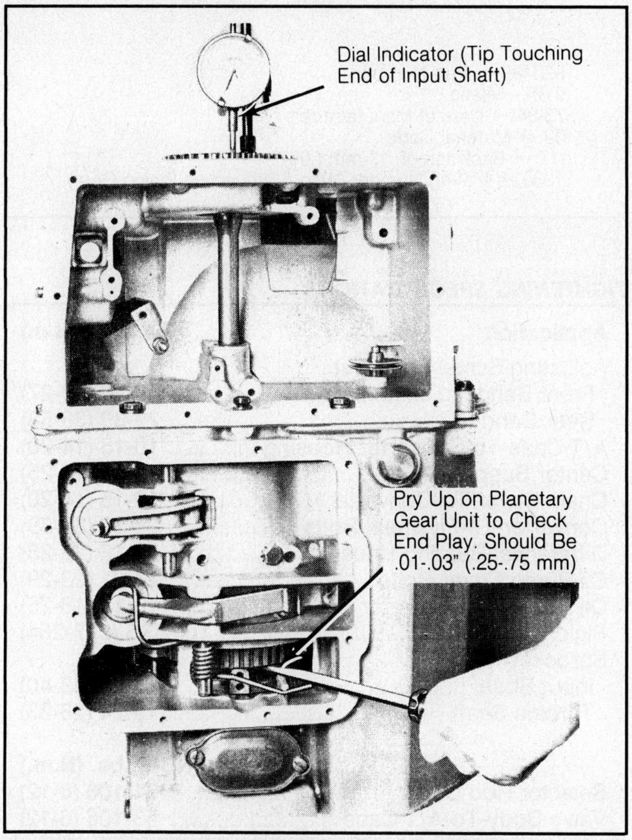

23) Install accumulator piston. Place valve body assembly into converter housing and ensure that manual gear selector is properly connected. Center valve body in position with 5 retaining bolts, tighten 2 and remove others. *See Fig. 35.* Attach cam disc cable to cam disc on valve body. Check that cable is positioned in pulley groove.

24) Install oil tubes in order. *See Fig. 36.* Tubes 16 and 17 should have been installed with drain valve. When installing tube 12, run it under tube 9 and install tube support (if equipped). Install oil strainer and magnet. Install connection pipes.

25) To adjust rear band, locate adjusting screw on outer left-hand side of transmission case. Loosen adjusting screw. Tighten screw to 10 ft. lbs. (14 N.m). Back adjusting screw off 1 turn, and tighten lock nut.

26) To adjust front band, loosen lock nut. Place Spacer (87 90 030), or 11/32" (8.9 mm) rod, between screw and piston pin. Tighten adjusting screw to 12 INCH lbs. (1.3 N.m). Remove spacer. Hold adjusting screw so it does not move, and tighten lock nut.

27) Install chain and sprockets. Place lock plate under retaining nuts and tighten nuts. Use a bar between sprockets to hold them in place while tightening bolts. Install turbine shaft seal. Install differential assembly and

Fig. 35: Positioning Valve Body in Case

Center with bolts 1-5 as shown. Tighten bolts 3 and 4. Remove bolts 1, 2 and 5 for installation with oil pump strainer and air escape pipe.

Fig. 36: Correct Routing of Oil Tubes

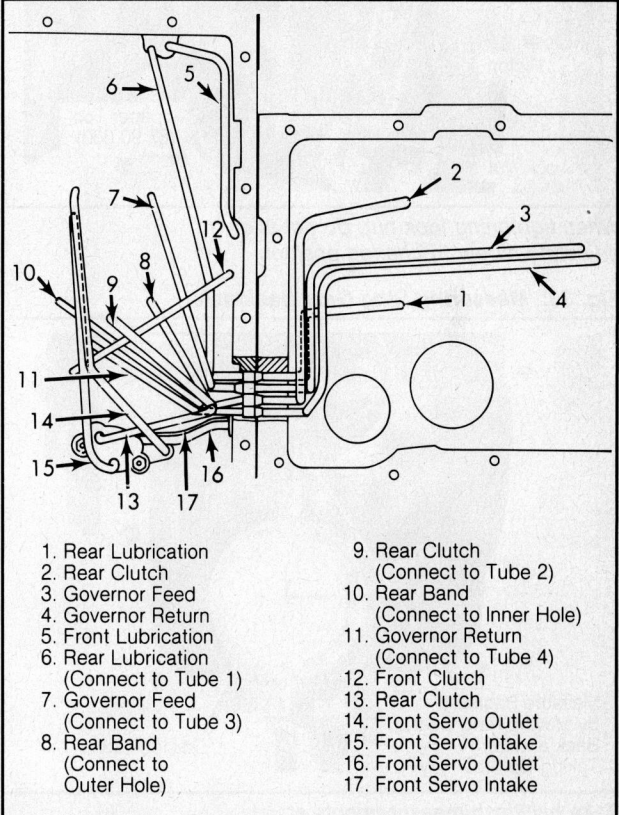

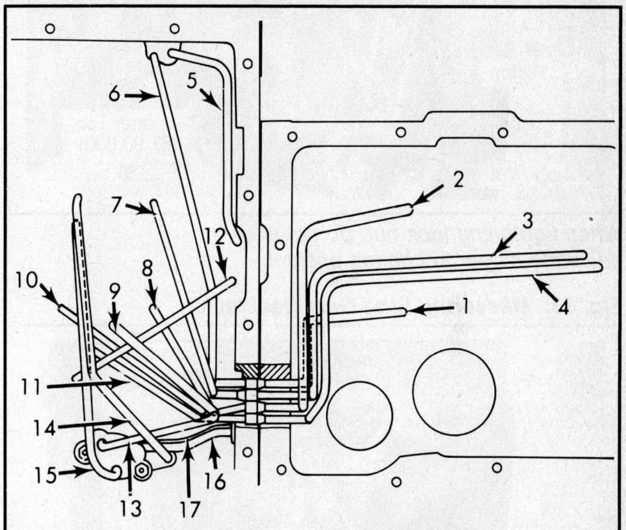

1. Rear Lubrication
2. Rear Clutch
3. Governor Feed
4. Governor Return
5. Front Lubrication
6. Rear Lubrication (Connect to Tube 1)
7. Governor Feed (Connect to Tube 3)
8. Rear Band (Connect to Outer Hole)
9. Rear Clutch (Connect to Tube 2)
10. Rear Band (Connect to Inner Hole)
11. Governor Return (Connect to Tube 4)
12. Front Clutch
13. Rear Clutch
14. Front Servo Outlet
15. Front Servo Intake
16. Front Servo Outlet
17. Front Servo Intake

Install tubes in proper order, as given in text.

bearing housing. Install complete shim pack under right bearing seat.

28) To check ring gear backlash, mount dial indicator on transaxle case so that indicator tip is touching ring gear teeth. Measure backlash. Check backlash at 4 different points around ring gear. Measurements must not vary by more than .002" (.05 mm) from specifications.

NOTE: **Backlash with a new ring and pinion set (or a used set with less than 6000 miles service)**

SAAB – BORG-WARNER MODEL 37 (Cont.)

should be to specification which appears on ring gear. See Fig. 39. If a used gear set with more than 6000 miles service is being re-installed, backlash should be same as was recorded during transaxle disassembly.

29) Calculate difference between measured backlash and backlash reading desired. Move shims of correct thickness from right bearing housing to left side housing. DO NOT add or remove any shims. Combination of shims installed has been preselected and must not be changed.

Fig. 37: Adjusting Front Band

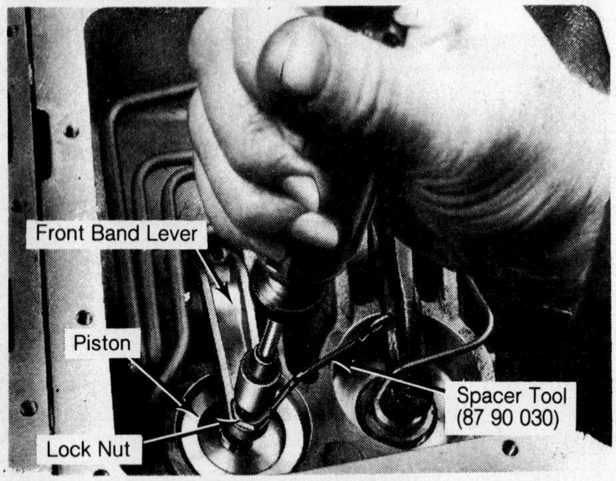

When tightening lock nut, do not allow adjusting screw to change position

Fig. 38: Measuring Ring Gear Backlash

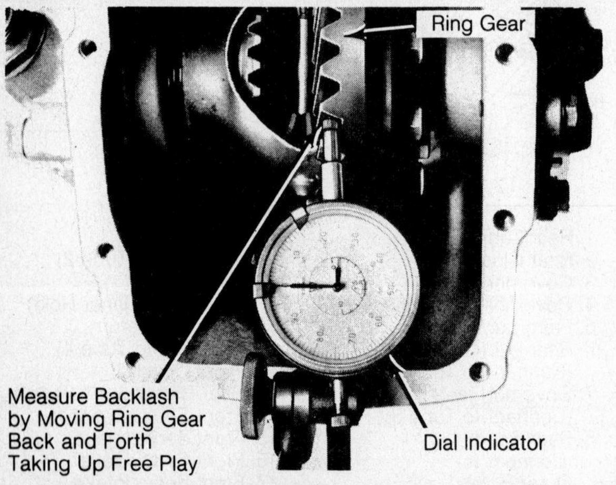

Take backlash measurements at 4 places around ring gear.

Fig. 39: View of Ring Gear Showing Adjustment Data

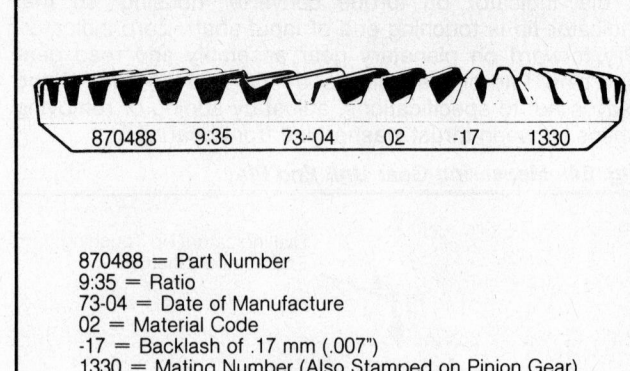

870488 = Part Number
9:35 = Ratio
73-04 = Date of Manufacture
02 = Material Code
-17 = Backlash of .17 mm (.007")
1330 = Mating Number (Also Stamped on Pinion Gear)

TIGHTENING SPECIFICATIONS

Application	Ft. Lbs. (N.m)
Adjusting Screw Lock Nut	
Front Band	15-20 (20-27)
Rear Band	29-39 (39-53)
A/T Case-To-Converter Housing	10-15 (14-20)
Center Support Bolts	10-18 (14-25)
Chain Cover-To-Converter	10-15 (14-20)
Converter-To-Flywheel Bolts	24-29 (33-39)
Differential Bearing Housing	16-18 (22-25)
Oil Pump Cover Bolts	17-21 (23-29)
Oil Pump-To-Converter Housing	13-18 (18-25)
Pinion Shaft Nut	160-195 (217-264)
Sprocket Wheel-To-	
Input Shaft	24-30 (33-40)
Turbine Shaft	19-24 (26-33)
	INCH Lbs. (N.m.)
Selector Rod Cover	71-106 (8-12)
Valve Body-To-A/T Case	53-106 (6-12)

SUBARU MODEL M41A

Brat, Hatchback, Sedan, Station Wagon, XT Coupe

DESCRIPTION

The transaxle assembly consists of 2 main units: automatic transmission and final drive assembly. The transmission housing contains a compound planetary gear unit and one-way clutch, 2 multi-disc clutches, a multi-disc brake, a servo and brake band, an oil pump, and a hydraulic control system. The final drive housing contains the torque converter, governor assembly, ring and pinion gears, and differential assembly.

The 4WD automatic transmission is similar to automatic transaxle in construction, the difference being the addition of a transfer case to rear of transmission housing. The rear transfer case consists of a hydraulic multi-disc clutch, transfer clucth valve and solenoid. These components are housed in the extension housing, along with a transfer gear. The transfer gear is connected to the final drive assembly through the transfer drive shaft.

Along with the adoption of a 4WD system, the final drive housing and transmission housing have been changed thoroughly. A new oil seal holder has been introduced in the reduction gear portion. The hydraulic clutch, planetary gear, control valve and other basic components are unchanged from those used in automatic transaxle.

LUBRICATION & ADJUSTMENTS

See appropriate AUTOMATIC TRANSMISSION SERVICING article in IMPORT GENERAL SERVICING section.

TROUBLE SHOOTING

NO DRIVE IN ANY RANGE

Check oil pressure, control valve and oil pump. Check for leaks in hydraulic circuit. Check parking linkage.

NO DRIVE IN FORWARD RANGES

Check oil pressure, control valve and forward clutch. Check for leaks in hydraulic circuit.

EXCESSIVE SLIP IN 4WD MODE VEHICLE O.K. IN FWD MODE

Check transfer valve. transfer pipe and rear shaft drive seal ring.

HARSH ENGAGEMENT

From "N" to "D"

Check oil pressure, control valve and forward clutch.

From 1st to 2nd Gear

Check brake band adjustment, oil pressure and control valve. Check brake band and band support.

From 2nd to 3rd Gear

Chack brake band adjustment, oil pressure and servo pipe. Check control valve, reverse clutch, brake band and band support.

POOR ACCELERATION & LOW TOP SPEED

Check stall speed, brake band adjustment and oil pressure. Check brake band and band support. Check low/reverse brake. Check torque converter one-way clutch.

VEHICLE BRAKED WHEN SHIFTED INTO "R"

Check brake band adjustment and forward clutch. Check brake band and band support. Check parking linkage.

VEHICLE MOVES IN "N"

Check control valve, forward clutch and reverse clutch.

NO SHIFT FROM 1ST TO 2ND GEAR

Check governor valve, servo pipe, control valve and nylon gear. Check brake band and band support. Check for leaks in hydraulic circuit.

NO SHIFT FROM 2ND TO 3RD GEAR

Check governor valve, brake band adjustment, servo pipe and control valve. Check reverse clutch. Check for leaks in hydraulic circuit.

SHIFT POINTS TOO HIGH FROM 1ST TO 2ND & 2ND TO 3RD GEARS

Check oil pressure and control valve. Check for leaks in hydraulic circuit.

SHIFTS FROM 1ST TO 3RD, SKIPPING 2ND

Check brake band adjustment, governor valve and oil pressure. Check servo pipe and control valve. Check brake band and band support. Check for leaks in hydraulic circuit.

LITTLE OR NO SHIFT SHOCK, EXCESSIVE SLIPPAGE FROM 1ST TO 2ND GEAR

Check brake band adjustment. Check for contaminated transmission fluid. Check servo pipe and control valve. Check brake band and band support.

LITTLE OR NO SHIFT SHOCK, EXCESSIVE SLIP & ENGINE RUNAWAY FROM 2ND TO 3RD GEARS

Check brake band adjustment, oil pressure, servo pipe and control valve. Check reverse clutch. Check for leaks in hydraulic circuit.

VEHICLE IS BRAKED WHEN SHIFTED FROM 1ST TO 2ND GEAR

Check control valve, low/reverse brake, reverse clutch and one-way clutch.

VEHICLE IS BRAKED WHEN SHIFTED FROM 2ND TO 3RD GEAR

Check brake band adjustment and control valve. Check brake band and band support.

SUBARU MODEL M41A (Cont.)

Fig. 1: Cross-Sectional View of Subaru Model M41A Automatic Transmission Assembly

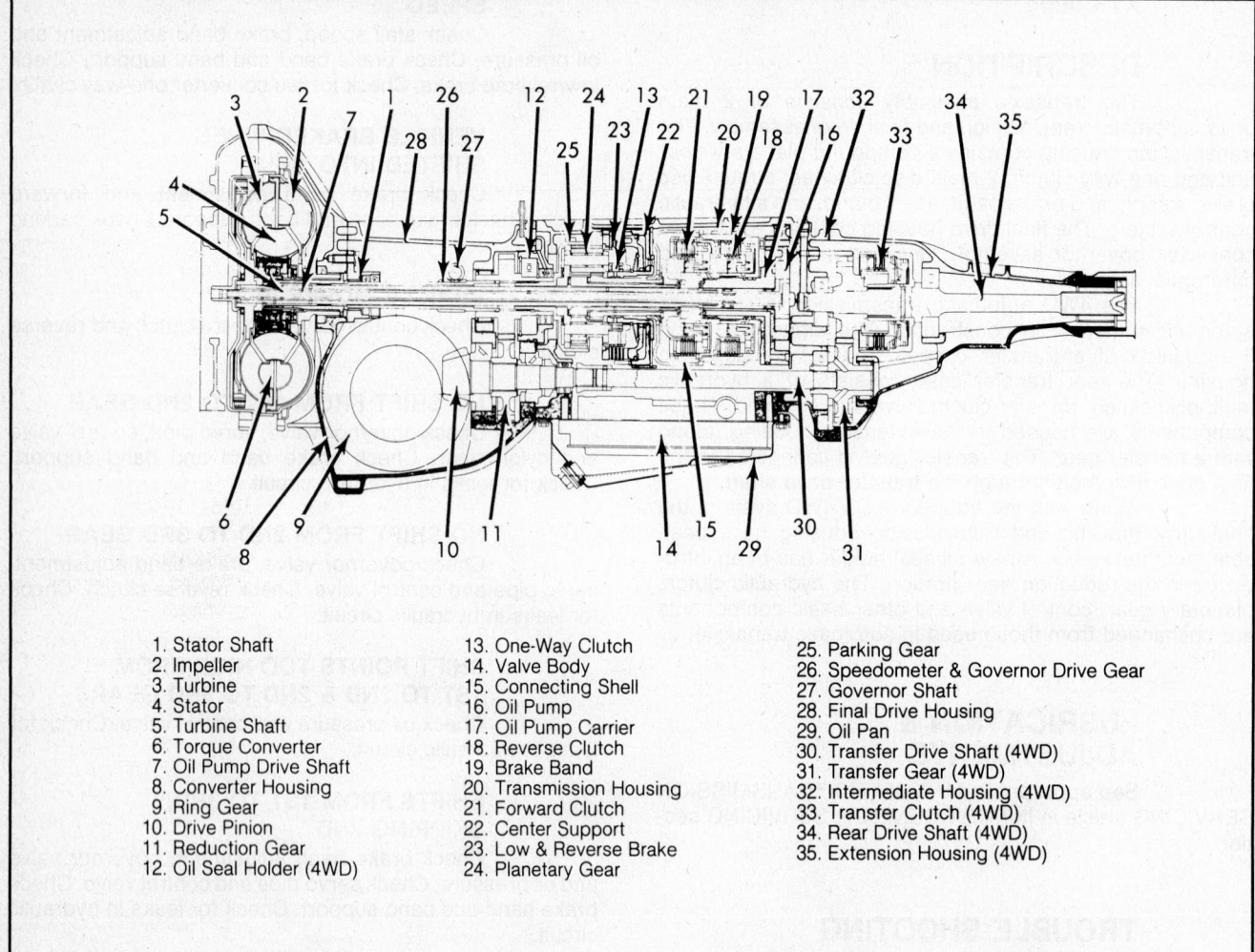

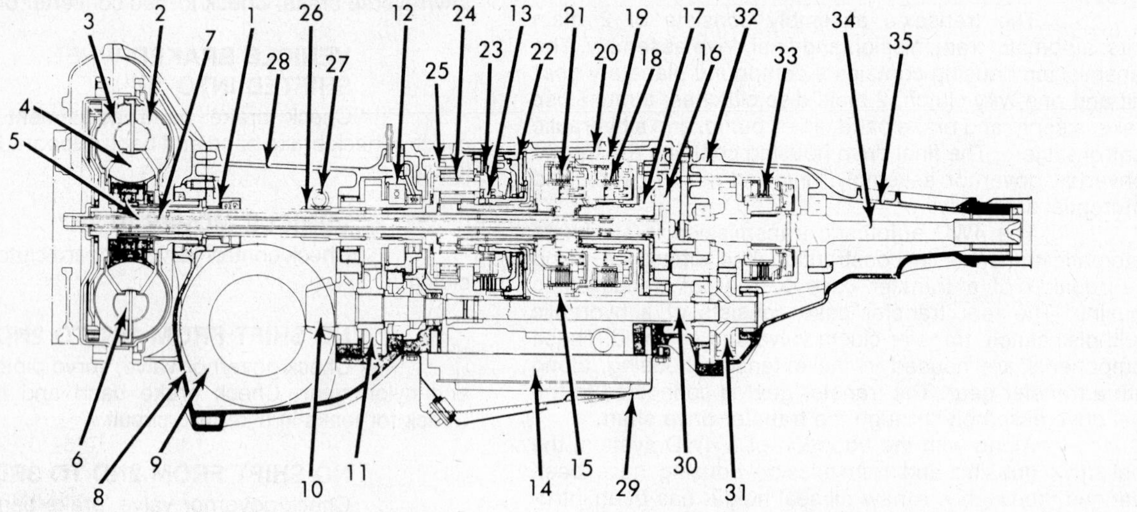

1. Stator Shaft
2. Impeller
3. Turbine
4. Stator
5. Turbine Shaft
6. Torque Converter
7. Oil Pump Drive Shaft
8. Converter Housing
9. Ring Gear
10. Drive Pinion
11. Reduction Gear
12. Oil Seal Holder (4WD)
13. One-Way Clutch
14. Valve Body
15. Connecting Shell
16. Oil Pump
17. Oil Pump Carrier
18. Reverse Clutch
19. Brake Band
20. Transmission Housing
21. Forward Clutch
22. Center Support
23. Low & Reverse Brake
24. Planetary Gear
25. Parking Gear
26. Speedometer & Governor Drive Gear
27. Governor Shaft
28. Final Drive Housing
29. Oil Pan
30. Transfer Drive Shaft (4WD)
31. Transfer Gear (4WD)
32. Intermediate Housing (4WD)
33. Transfer Clutch (4WD)
34. Rear Drive Shaft (4WD)
35. Extension Housing (4WD)

NO 3RD TO 2ND DOWNSHIFT

Check governor valve, oil pressure, servo pipe and control valve. Check reverse clutch, brake band and band support. Check for leaks in hydraulic circuit.

NO 2ND TO 1ST OR 3RD TO 1ST DOWNSHIFT

Check governor valve, brake band adjustment and control valve. Check brake band and band support. Check one-way clutch.

SHIFTING SHOCK FELT ON DECELERATION

Check governor valve, oil pressure and control valve. Check for leaks in hydraulic circuit.

SHIFT POINTS TOO HIGH FROM 3RD TO 2ND OR 2ND TO 1ST GEARS

Check governor valve, oil pressure and control valve. Check for leaks in hydraulic circuit.

NO KICKDOWN AT NORMAL SPEEDS IN 3RD GEAR

Check governor valve, servo pipe and control valve. Check brake band and band support. Check for leaks in hydraulic circuit.

EXCESSIVE ENGINE RPM WHEN ACCELERATING IN 3RD GEAR ABOVE KICKDOWN SPEED

Check oil pressure, governor valve, control valve and reverse clutch. Check for leaks in hydraulic circuit.

ENGINE RUNAWAY OR TRANSMISSION SLIPPAGE ON 3RD TO 2ND GEAR KICKDOWN

Check brake band adjustment, oil pressure, servo pipe and control valve. Check reverse clutch, brake band and band support. Check for leaks in hydraulic circuit.

NO ENGINE BRAKING IN 1ST GEAR

Check oil pressure and control valve. Check low/reverse brake. Check for leaks in hydraulic circuit.

SUBARU MODEL M41A (Cont.)

Fig. 2: Subaru Model M41A Automatic Transmission Hydraulic Circuits Diagram

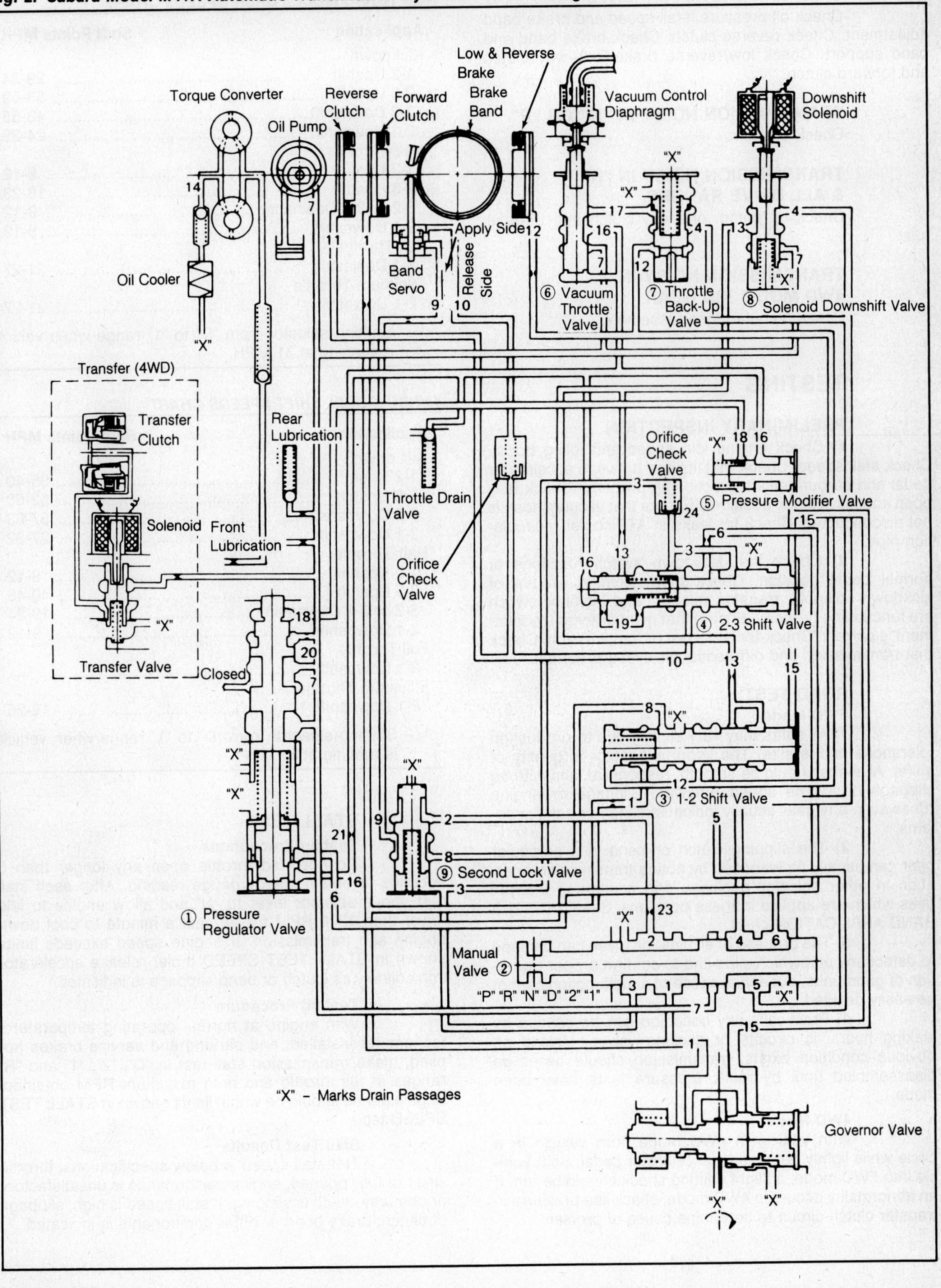

SUBARU MODEL M41A (Cont.)

TRANSMISSION OVERHEATS

Check oil pressure, stall speed and brake band adjustment. Check reverse clutch. Check brake band and band support. Check low/reverse brake, one-way clutch and forward clutch.

TRANSMISSION NOISY IN "N" OR "P"

Check oil pump.

TRANSMISSION NOISY IN "R" & ALL DRIVE RANGES

Check oil pump, one-way clutch and transfer gear.

TRANSMISSION NOISY IN 4WD MODE 3RD GEAR

Check planetary gear assembly.

TESTING

PRELIMINARY INSPECTION

1) Check engine idle speed and idling boost. Check stall speed. Check that linkage between accelerator pedal and carburetor are functioning properly. Check fully open and fully closed positions. Ensure that vacuum hose is not disconnected. Check for leaks at ATF cooler recirculation pipe.

2) Check that kickdown switch functions at normal pedal position. Check that electrical circuits of kickdown solenoid, transfer solenoid and inhibitor switch are functioning properly. Ensure that manual linkage adjustment is correct. Check for leaks out of transmission. Check that transmission and differential oil level are normal.

ROAD TEST

FWD Mode

1) All shifts may vary slightly due to production tolerances or tire size. The important factor is quality of shifts. All shifts should be smooth, responsive, and with no slippage or engine speed runaway. Slippage or engine runaway in any gear usually indicates clutch or band problems.

2) The slipping clutch or band in a particular gear can usually be identified by noting transmission operation in other selector positions and comparing internal units which are applied in these positions. See CLUTCH & BAND APPLICATION chart.

3) The process of elimination given can be used to detect any unit which slips and to confirm proper operation of good units, but actual cause of a malfunction cannot be easily decided.

4) Practically any condition can be caused by leaking hydraulic circuits or sticking valves. Unless an obvious condition exists, transmission should never be disassembled until hydraulic pressure tests have been made.

4WD Mode

With vehicle in 4WD mode, turn vehicle in a circle while lightly depressing accelerator pedal. Shift vehicle into FWD mode, a slight shifting shock should be felt. If an abnormality occurs in 4WD mode, check line pressure in transfer clutch circuit to determine cause of problem.

NON TURBO MODEL SHIFT SPEEDS CHART

Application	Shift Points MPH
Kickdown	
1-2 Upshift	29-34
2-3 Upshift	53-59
3-2 Downshift	48-55
2-1 Downshift	24-29
Half-Throttle	
1-2 Upshift	9-12
2-3 Upshift	18-23
3-2 or 3-1 Downshift	9-12
2-1 Downshift	9-12
Full Throttle	
2-1 Downshift [1]	21-27
Minimum Throttle	
2-1 Downshift [1]	21-27

[1] – Shifting selector from "D" to "1" range when vehicle is running at 31 MPH.

TURBO MODEL SHIFT SPEEDS CHART

Application	Shift Points MPH
Kickdown	
1-2 Upshift	35-40
2-3 Upshift	62-68
3-2 Downshift	57-63
2-1 Downshift	27-32
Half-Throttle	
1-2 Upshift	9-12
2-3 Upshift	40-45
3-2 or 3-1 Downshift	19-24
2-1 Downshift	9-12
Full Throttle	
2-1 Downshift [1]	.....
Minimum Throttle	
2-1 Downshift [1]	19-25

[1] – Shifting selector from "D" to "1" range when vehicle is running at 31 MPH.

STALL TEST

Testing Precautions

Do not hold throttle open any longer than 5 seconds to obtain steady gauge reading. After each stall test, move selector lever to "N" and allow engine to idle lower than 1200 RPM for at least a minute to cool down engine and transmission. If engine speed exceeds limits shown in STALL TEST SPEED table, release accelerator immediately as clutch or band slippage is indicated.

Testing Procedure

With engine at normal operating temperature, tachometer installed, and parking and service brakes applied, make transmission stall test in "D", "2", "1" and "R" ranges at full throttle and note maximum RPM obtained. Engine speed should be within limits shown in STALL TEST SPEED table.

Stall Test Results

1) If stall speed is below specifications, throttle was not fully opened, engine performance is unsatisfactory or one-way clutch is slipping. If stall speed is high, slippage of clutch, brake band or other components is indicated.

SUBARU MODEL M41A (Cont.)

CLUTCH AND BAND APPLICATION CHART (ELEMENTS IN USE)

Selector Lever Position	Foward Clutch	Reverse Clutch	Low-Reverse Band	Brake Band	One-Way Clutch
P - PARK			X		
R - REVERSE		X	X		
D - DRIVE					
First Gear	X				X
Second Gear	X				
Third Gear	X	X			
2 - SECOND	X			X	
1 - LOW					
First	X		X		
Second	X			X	
N - NEUTRAL - All clutches and bands released and/or ineffective.					

STALL TEST SPEED

Application	Stall RPM
Turbo Models	2700-2900
All Other Models	2300-2500

2) If stall speed is high in all drive ranges, check for low line pressure. If stall speed is high in "D" range only, one-way clutch is slipping. If stall speed is high in "2" range, brake band is slipping.

3) If stall speed is high in "R" range only, low/reverse brake or reverse clutch is slipping. Verify brake band slippage by road testing vehicle. If engine RPM is higher than specified, brake band is slipping.

4) Verify low/reverse brake or reverse clutch slippage by road testing vehicle. If engine can be used as a brake with selector lever in "1" range, reverse clutch is slipping. If engine cannot be used as a brake, low/reverse brake is slipping.

LINE PRESSURE TESTS

FWD Line Pressure

1) Connect a pressure gauge to line pressure checking plug on rear cover of transmission. *See Fig. 3.* Place gauge in position for viewing from driver's seat, route gauge hose through hole provided in floor-board (just left of steering column).

2) With engine at normal operating temperature and transmission fluid at correct level, perform line pressure test with transmission in Neutral and engine at idle (1500 RPM).

3) Perform line pressure test in "D", "2" and "R" ranges. Start vehicle from a standstill and slowly increase engine speed and note pressure in each range. Pressures should be approximately as shown in LINE PRESSURE table.

4WD Line Pressure

1) Connect a pressure gauge to line pressure checking plug located on transmission extension housing, behind oil pan. *See Fig. 4.* Place gauge in position for viewing from driver's seat.

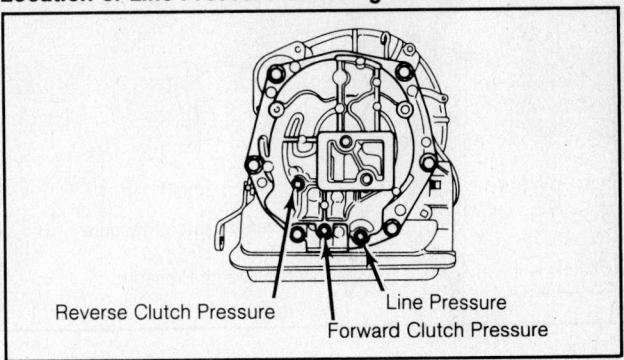

Fig. 3: Rear View of Transmission Housing Showing Location of Line Pressure Checking Points

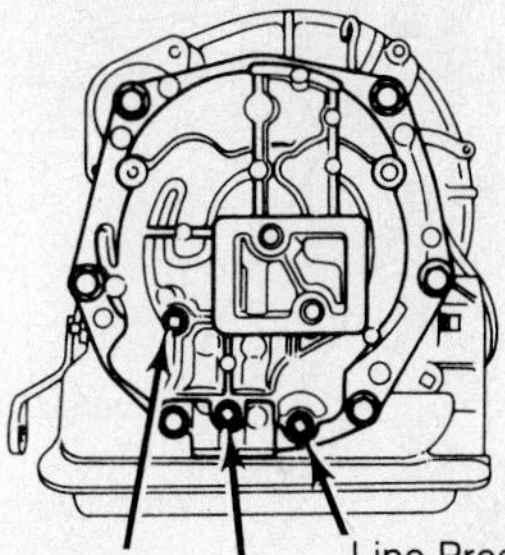

2) With engine at normal operating temperature and transmission fluid at correct level, perform line pressure test with transmission in Neutral and engine at idle (1500 RPM).

3) Perform line pressure test in "D", "2" and "R" ranges (FWD mode). Start vehicle from a standstill and slowly increase engine speed and note pressure in each range. Pressures should be approximately as shown in LINE PRESSURE table.

FWD Line Pressure Test Results

1) If line pressure in Neutral is low; oil pump is worn or improperly adjusted, oil pressure circuit is leaking or pressure regulator valve is inoperative. If oil pressure in Neutral is high, check for leaking vacuum hose or leaking diaphragm, or for long diaphragm rod.

2) If engine is at full throttle and pressure fails to rise even though vacuum pressure drops, check if diaphragm rod was installed. If pressure rises but does not enter specified range, check for sticking throttle valve, pressure regulator valve or pressure regulator plug.

4WD Line Pressure Test Results

If pressure difference between FWD and 4WD modes is more than 4 psi (0.3 kg/cm^2), transfer pipe is disconnected or rear shaft seal ring is not installed. If pressure difference between FWD and 4WD modes is less than 4 psi (0.3 kg/cm^2), solenoid transfer valve is inoperative.

SUBARU MODEL M41A (Cont.)

SUBARU LINE PRESSURE TABLE – psi (kg/cm ²)

Range	Throttle Opening	Before Cut-Back Point (Under 9.5 MPH)	After Cut-Back Point (Over 22 MPH)
"D"	Full Throttle	121-142 (8.5-10.0)	78-92 (5.5-6.4)
		188-202 (13.2-14.2) [1]	114-128 (8.0-9.0) [1]
	Minimum Throttle	43-57 (3.0-4.0)	43-57 (3.0-4.0)
		43-47 (3.0-4.0) [1]	43-57 (3.0-4.0) [1]
"2"	Full Throttle	145-168 (10.2-11.8)	84-98 (5.9-6.9)
		188-202 (13.2-14.2) [1]	114-128 (8.0-9.0) [1]
	Minimum Throttle	145-168 (10.2-11.8)	84-98 (5.9-6.9)
		97-114 (6.8-8.0) [1]	97-114 (6.8-9.0) [1]
"R"	Full Throttle	199-228 (14-16)	199-228 (14-16)
		284-313 (20.0-22.0) [1]	284-313 (20.0-22.0) [1]
	Minumum Throttle	67-81 (4.7-5.7)	67-81 (4.7-5.7)
		81-95 (5.7-7.6) [1]	81-95 (5.7-7.6) [1]

[1] – Applies to 4WD Turbo Models.

Fig. 4: Bottom View of Transmission Extension Housing Showing Location of Line Pressure Checking Points

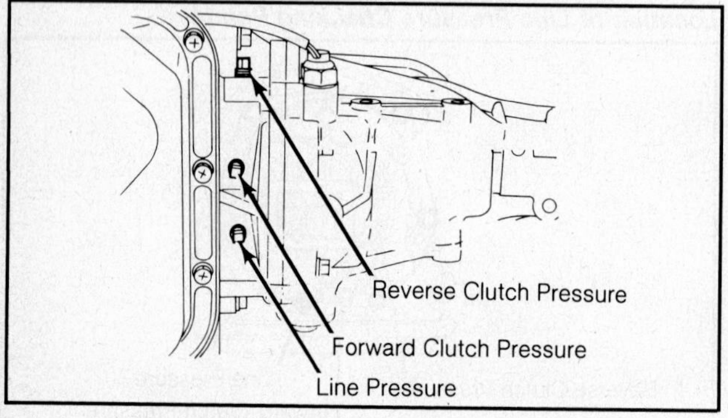

Fig. 5: View of Final Drive Housing Showing Location of Governor Pressure Checking Point

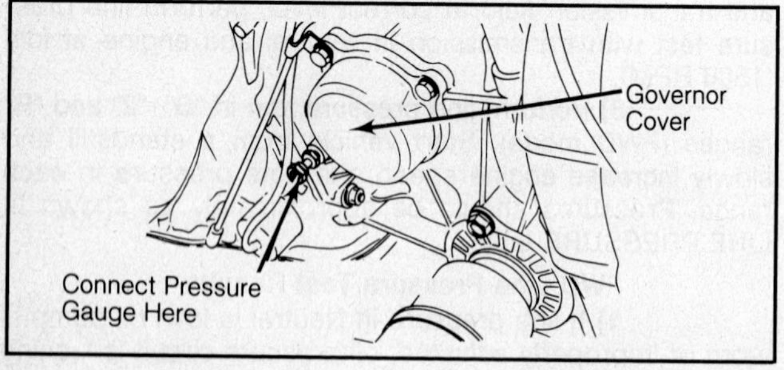

GOVERNOR PRESSURES

Vehicle Speed (MPH)	psi (kg/cm²)
9-12	
Turbo Models	0 (0)
Non-Turbo Models	0 (0)
25	
Turbo Models	24-27 (1.7-1.9)
Non-Turbo Models	21-24 (1.5-1.7)
50	
Turbo Models	63-65 (4.4-4.6)
Non-Turbo Models	60-63 (4.2-4.4)

Governor Pressure

1) Connect pressure gauge to governor pressure plug located on right side of final drive housing. *See Fig. 5.* Place gauge in driver's compartment as outlined in FWD line pressure test procedure.

2) With engine at normal operating temperature and transmission fluid level correct, check governor pressure at speeds shown in GOVERNOR PRESSURES chart with transmission in "2".

SERVICE (IN VEHICLE)

DRIVE AXLE SHAFTS

See appropriate DRIVE AXLE SHAFT article in IMPORT AXLE SHAFTS, OVERDRIVES & TRANSFER CASES section.

Fig. 6: View of Transfer Solenoid (4-WD)

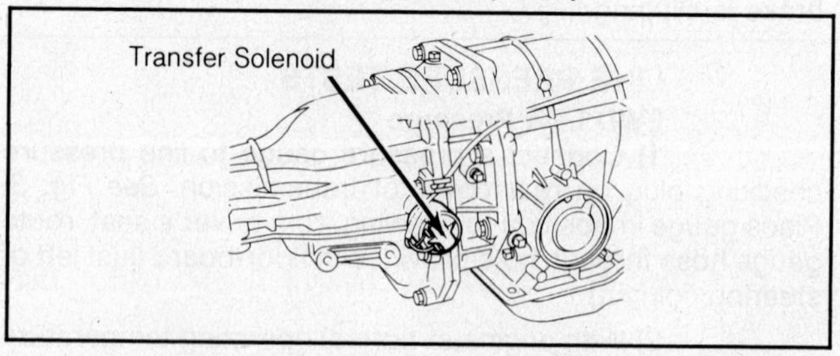

TRANSMISSION DISASSEMBLY

NOTE: Whenever working with transmission, it is important that normal standards of cleanliness be observed. Complete transmission assembly should be thoroughly steam cleaned before beginning any disassembly. Disassemble only those parts which require repair or replacement. Compressed air is preferred for drying components and oil passages, however, nylon cloth may be used. NEVER use fluffy rags or cloths to wipe parts dry.

SUBARU MODEL M41A (Cont.)

Fig. 7: Exploded View of Major Components of Subaru Automatic Transmission

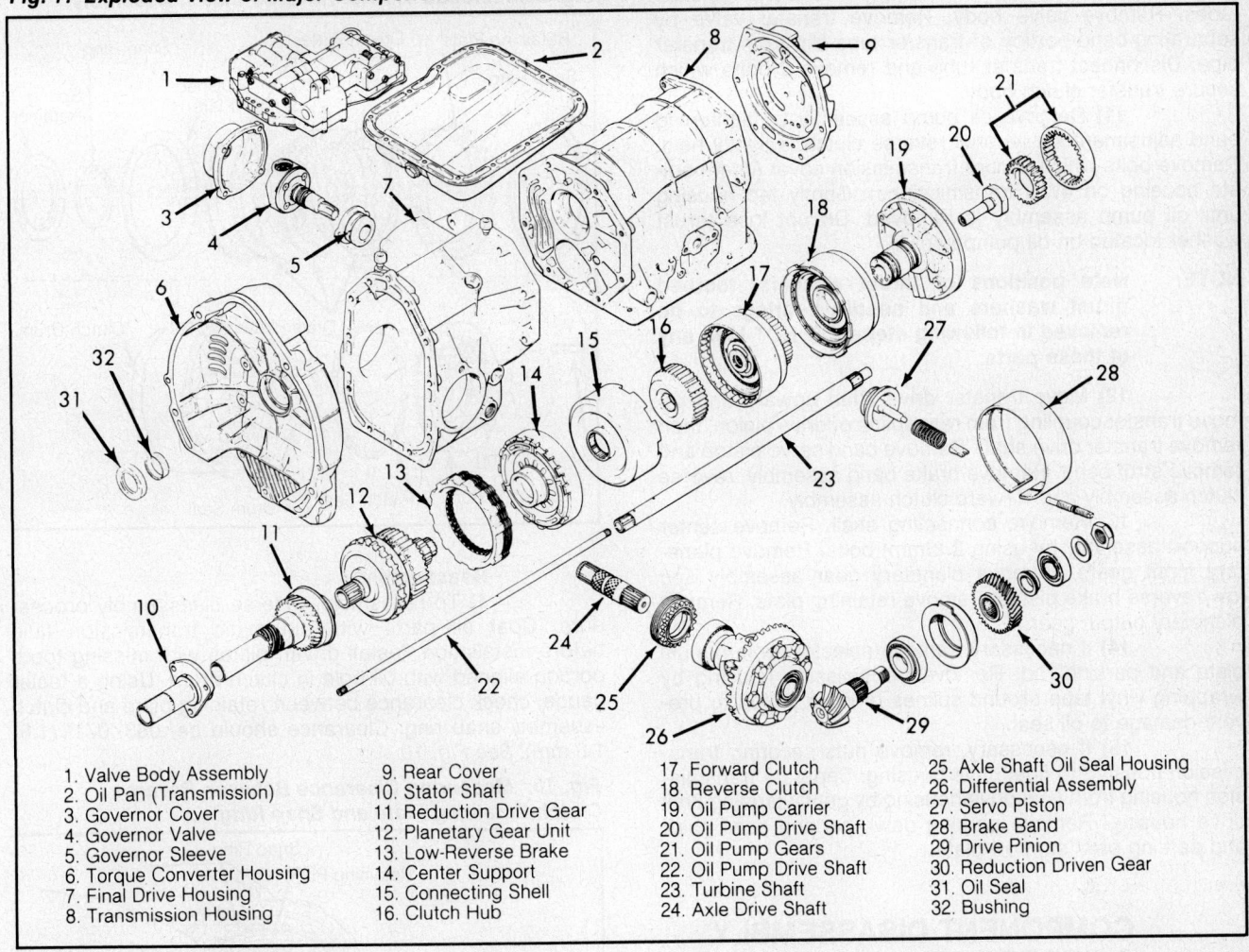

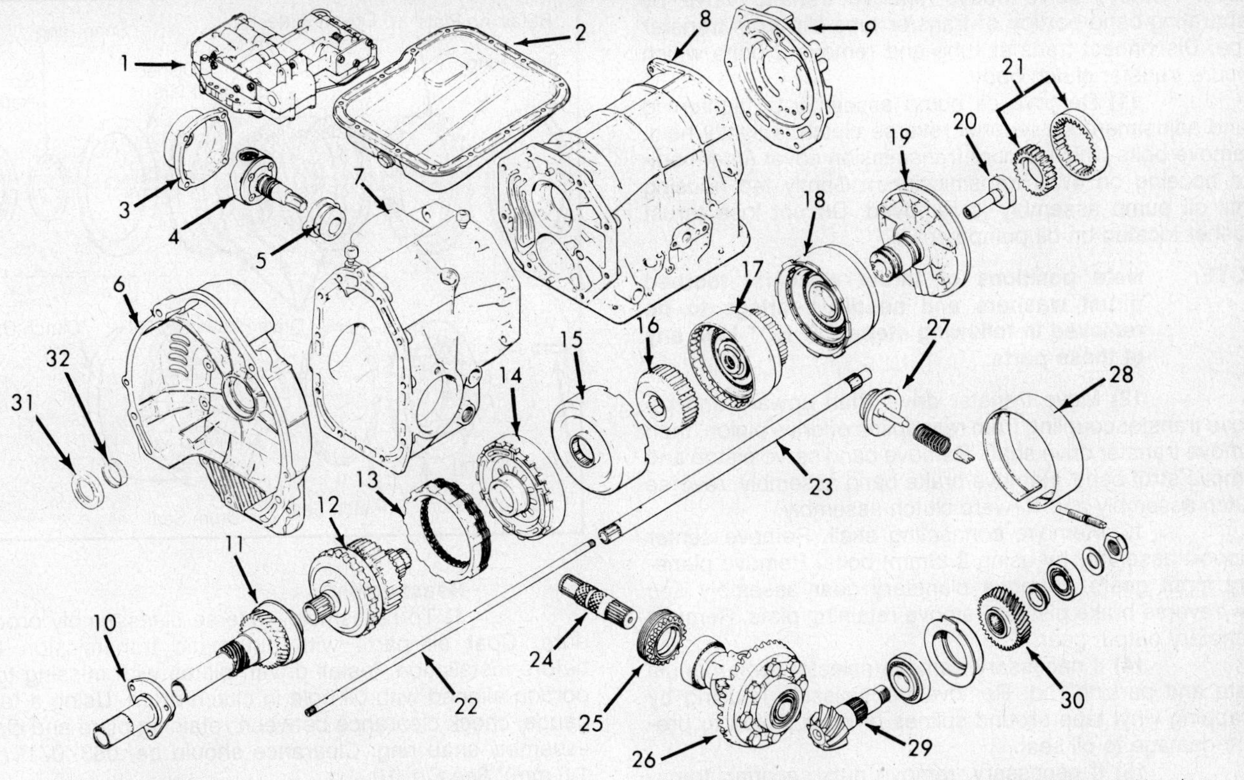

1. Valve Body Assembly
2. Oil Pan (Transmission)
3. Governor Cover
4. Governor Valve
5. Governor Sleeve
6. Torque Converter Housing
7. Final Drive Housing
8. Transmission Housing
9. Rear Cover
10. Stator Shaft
11. Reduction Drive Gear
12. Planetary Gear Unit
13. Low-Reverse Brake
14. Center Support
15. Connecting Shell
16. Clutch Hub
17. Forward Clutch
18. Reverse Clutch
19. Oil Pump Carrier
20. Oil Pump Drive Shaft
21. Oil Pump Gears
22. Oil Pump Drive Shaft
23. Turbine Shaft
24. Axle Drive Shaft
25. Axle Shaft Oil Seal Housing
26. Differential Assembly
27. Servo Piston
28. Brake Band
29. Drive Pinion
30. Reduction Driven Gear
31. Oil Seal
32. Bushing

1) On 4WD transmissions only, remove rear engine mount and place transmission on work bench with oil pan facing down. Remove solenoid from extension housing by turning it by hand. Disconnect temperature switch lead wire from clip and remove temperature switch from left side of extension housing.

2) On 4WD transmissions only, remove 8 (8 mm) bolts and remove extension housing. Drain automatic transmission fluid from extension housing, being careful not to drop rear drive gear thrust plate and transfer drive gear assembly. Remove washer from bearing bore on upper side of intermediate housing.

3) On 4WD transmissions only, remove rear shaft assembly from extension housing, being careful not to damage oil seal. Remove seal ring. Using Removal Plates (899864100 and 499717000), remove ball bearing, washer and transfer driven gear from shaft.

4) On 4WD transmissions only, remove drum and ball bearing. Disassemble transfer clutch assembly by removing snap ring and front pressure plate. Remove driven plates, drive plates and rear pressure plate.

NOTE: **Automatic transmission and differential sections are not normally separated. If they must be separated, place transmission section on stand (399933610).**

5) On all models, if transmission and differential sections are going to be separated, drain any remaining automatic transmission fluid by placing transmission on a work bench with converter housing facing down. Remove oil pan. Remove valve body on 4WD transmissions.

6) Wrap vinyl tape around spline portion of drive pinion rear end in order not to damage oil seal on 4WD transmissions. Separate transmission and differential sections.

7) If complete transmission is being disassembled: Remove turbine and oil pump drive shafts by pulling straight out with pliers (wrapped with vinyl tape), using care not to damage shafts. Disconnect oil cooler pipe from transmission housing.

8) Remove lead wire clips by removing nuts securing transmission housing to final drive housing. Remove downshift solenoid, transfer solenoid and temperature switch lead wire clips. Disconnect vacuum pipe and ground cable. Remove oil supply pipe from transmission after draining fluid. Do not lose "O" ring located at end of pipe.

9) Drain differential gear oil. Drain any remaining automatic transmission fluid by placing transmission on a work bench with converter housing facing down. Remove oil pan, downshift solenoid, vacuum diaphragm, diaphragm rod and "O" ring.

10) Remove servo apply and servo release tubes. Remove valve body. Remove transfer valve by separating bend portion of transfer tube clip from transfer pipe. Disconnect transfer tube and remove 2 bolts which secure transfer clutch body.

11) Remove oil pump assembly by tightening band adjustment screw until reverse clutch is lightly held. Remove bolts which secure transmission cover (intermediate housing on 4WD transmissions). Gently tap housing until oil pump assembly is removed. Do not lose thrust washer located on oil pump carrier.

NOTE: Note positions of thrust washers, toothed thrust washers and needle bearings to be removed in following steps. DO NOT lose any of these parts.

12) Move transfer drive shaft upward and remove transfer coupling from rear spline of drive pinion, then remove transfer drive shaft. Remove band servo piston and remove strut band. Remove brake band assembly, reverse clutch assembly and forward clutch assembly.

13) Remove connecting shell. Remove center support assembly by using 2 (6mm) bolts. Remove planetary input gears. Remove planetary gear assembly and low/reverse brake plates. Remove retaining plate. Remove planetary output gear.

14) If necessary, remove selector arm, manual plate and parking rod. Remove transmission housing by wrapping vinyl tape around splines of drive pinion to prevent damage to oil seal.

15) If necessary, remove nuts securing transmission housing to final drive housing. Separate transmission housing from final drive housing by gently tapping final drive housing. Remove parking pawl, parking pawl shaft and parking pawl support plate.

COMPONENT DISASSEMBLY & REASSEMBLY

REVERSE CLUTCH ASSEMBLY

Disassembly

1) Remove snap ring and lift out retaining plate, drive plates, driven plates and dished plate from clutch drum. Using a clutch spring compressor, compress clutch assembly return springs and remove retaining snap ring.

Fig. 8: Using Compressed Aid to Remove Reverse Clutch Piston

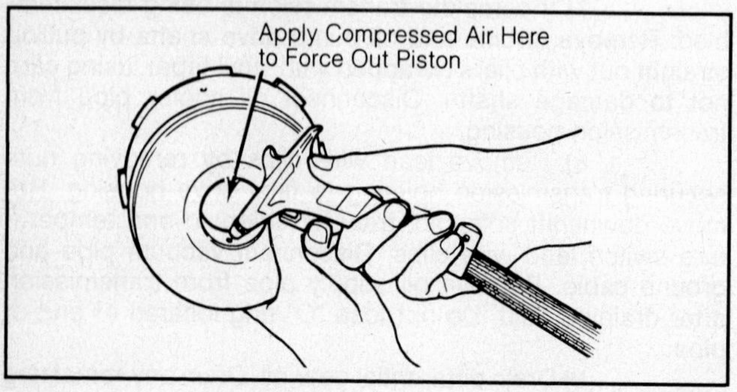

2) Remove return spring retainer and return springs. Apply compressed air to oil hole in clutch drum and remove clutch piston. *See Fig. 8.* Remove oil seal from clutch piston and drum.

Fig. 9: Exploded View of Reverse Clutch Assembly

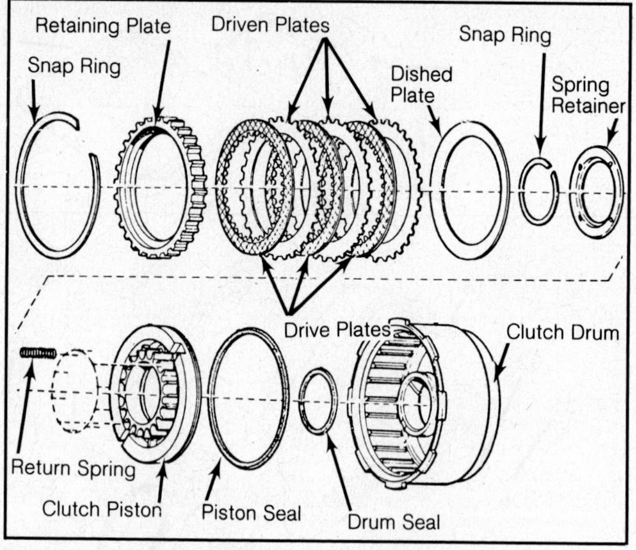

Reassembly

1) To reassmble, reverse disassembly procedure. Coat all parts with automatic transmission fluid before installation. Install driven plates with missing tooth portion aligned with oil hole in clutch drum. Using a feeler gauge, check clearance between retaining plate and clutch assembly snap ring. Clearance should be .063-.071" (1.6-1.8 mm). *See Fig. 10.*

Fig. 10: Measuring Clearance Between Reverse Clutch Retaining Plate and Snap Ring

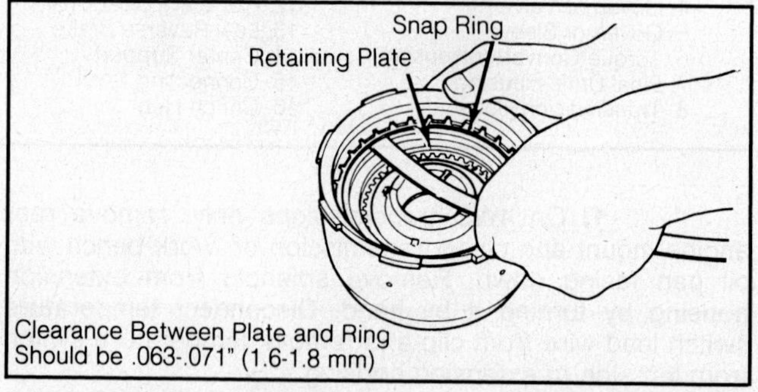

2) If clearance is not within specifications, correct by installing a retaining plate of different thickness. Reverse clutch retaining plates are available in thicknesses of 0.197" (5.0 mm) to 0.244" (6.2 mm) in .008" (0.2 mm) increments.

Fig. 11: Using Compressed Air to Check Operation of Reverse Clutch Assembly

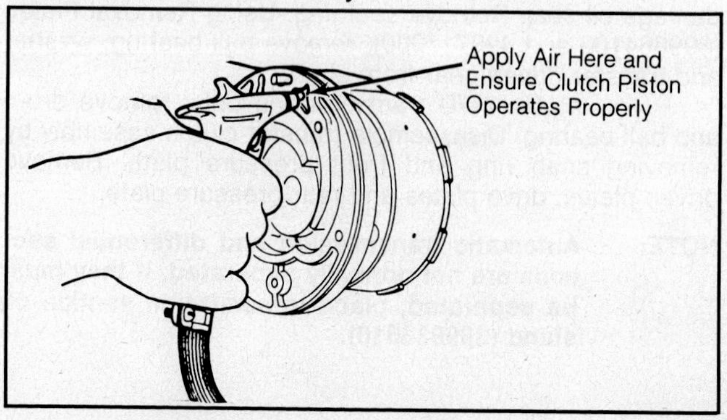

3) After clutch assembly is completed, check operation by installing clutch assembly on oil pump carrier and applying compressed air to oil hole in clutch drum to ensure clutch assembly moves properly. *See Fig. 12.*

FORWARD CLUTCH ASSEMBLY

Disassembly

1) Remove snap ring and lift out retaining plate, drive plates, driven plates and dished plate from clutch drum. Using a clutch spring compressor, compress clutch assembly return springs and remove retaining snap ring.

2) Remove return spring retainer and return springs. Apply compressed air to oil hole in clutch drum and remove clutch piston. Remove oil seal from clutch piston and drum.

Fig. 12: Using Compressed Air to Remove Forward Clutch Piston

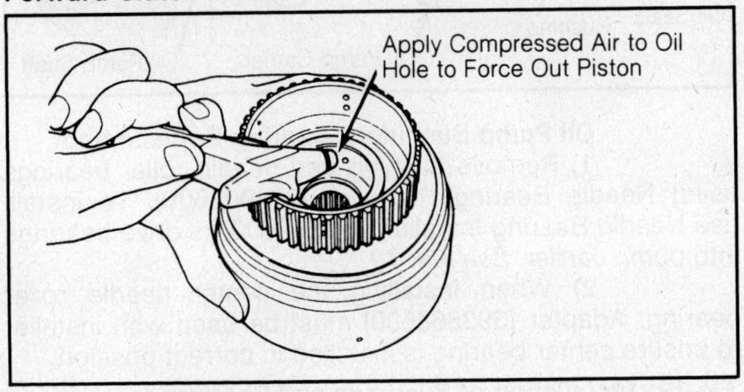

Reassembly

1) To reassemble, reverse disassembly procedure. Coat all parts with automatic transmission fluid before reassembly. Check clearance between retaining plate and clutch assembly snap ring using a feeler gauge. Clearance should be .040-.059" (1.0-1.5 mm).

Fig. 13: Exploded View of Forward Clutch Assembly

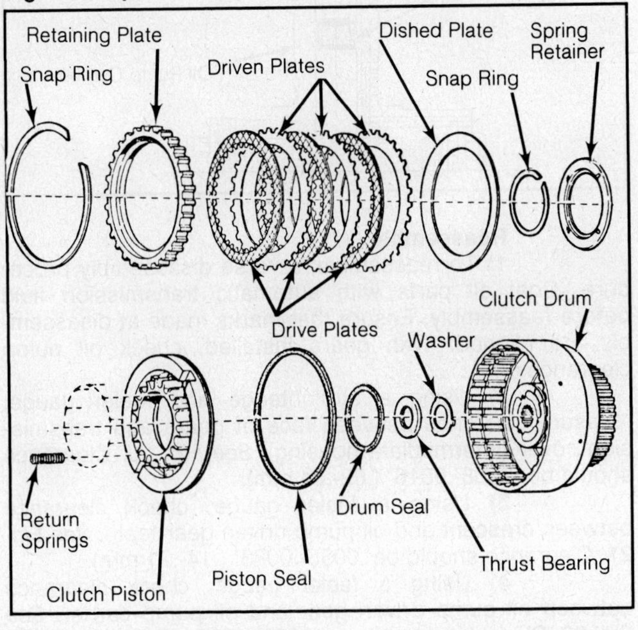

2) With reassembly completed, install forward and reverse clutches on oil pump carrier. Apply compressed air to oil hole in forward clutch drum to make sure clutch piston operates properly.

Fig. 14: Measuring Clearance Between Forward Clutch Retaining Plate and Snap Ring

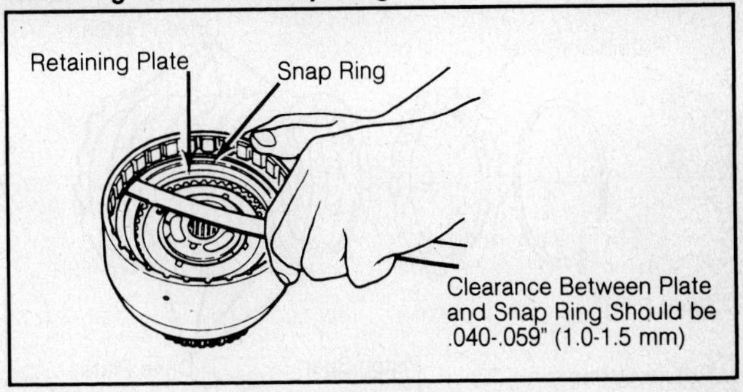

Fig. 15: Using Compressed Air to Check Operation of Forward Clutch Assembly

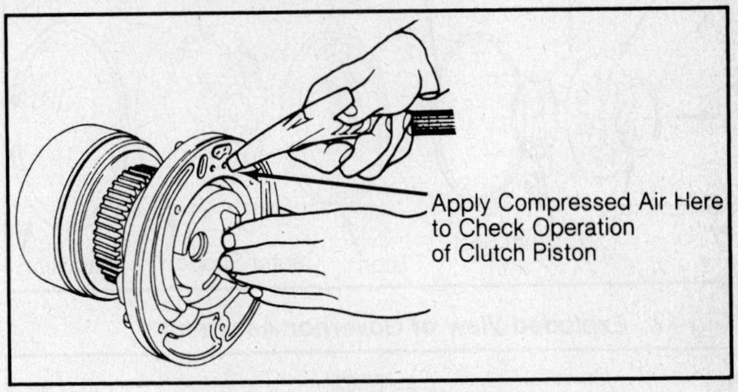

CENTER SUPPORT AND LOW-REVERSE BRAKE ASSEMBLY

NOTE: **Low-reverse brake plates were removed at TRANSMISSION DISASSEMBLY and will be installed at TRANSMISSION REASSEMBLY.**

Disassembly

Using a clutch spring compressor, compress low-reverse piston return spring and remove snap ring and lift out return spring and thrust ring. Apply compressed air to oil hole in center support and force low-reverse brake piston from center support. Remove oil seals from brake piston.

Reassembly

To reassemble, reverse disassembly procedure. Coat all parts with automatic transmission fluid before reassembly. When installing clutch piston to center support, use care not to damage piston oil seals.

GOVERNOR ASSEMBLY

NOTE: **Governor assembly is mounted on right side of final drive housing.**

Removal

Remove attaching bolts and lift off governor cover, then pull governor assembly while turning clockwise. Remove 2 attaching bolts and pull governor sleeve out of housing.

Disassembly

Remove "E" clip and snap ring from ends of valve body. Remove valve, springs and related components from valve body. Remove 2 governor shaft-to-valve body retaining bolts and separate valve body from shaft.

SUBARU MODEL M41A (Cont.)

Fig 16: Exploded View of Center Support and Low-Reverse Brake Assembly

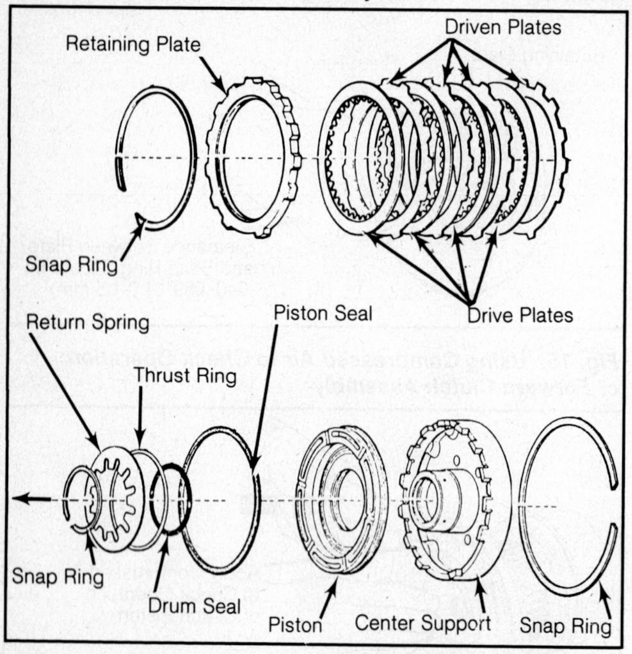

Fig 17: Exploded View of Governor Assembly

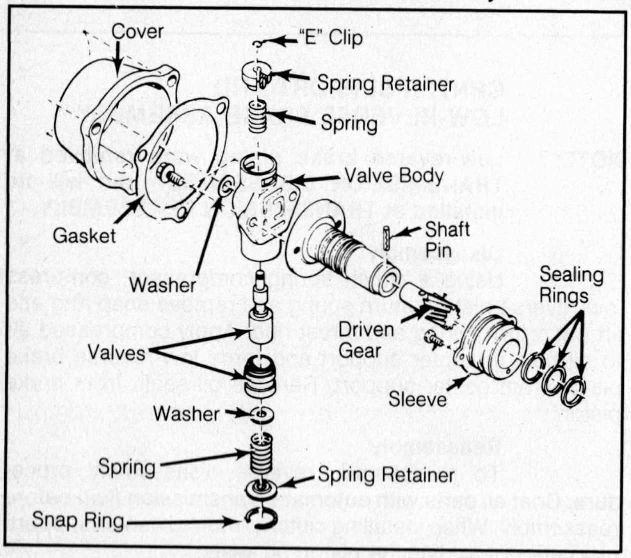

Reassembly

To reassemble, reverse disassembly procedure. Inspect all parts for wear or damage and replace as necessary. Ensure that parts move freely in governor bore when reassembly is completed. Inspect governor shaft oil seals and replace if worn or damaged.

Installation

To install, reverse removal procedure. Replace cover gasket and ensure that washer is installed. Use care to prevent damage to oil seals when installing governor assembly.

OIL PUMP

Disassembly

1) Remove bolts and disassemble oil pump carrier from transmission cover (intermediate housing on 4WD transmissions). Mark gears for reassembly in their original position and remove.

2) Inspect oil pump gears for wear or damage and replace as necessary. Inspect bushing and 2 needle roller bearings located in pump carrier and replace if necessary.

Fig. 18: Exploded View of Oil Pump and Transmission Cover Assembly

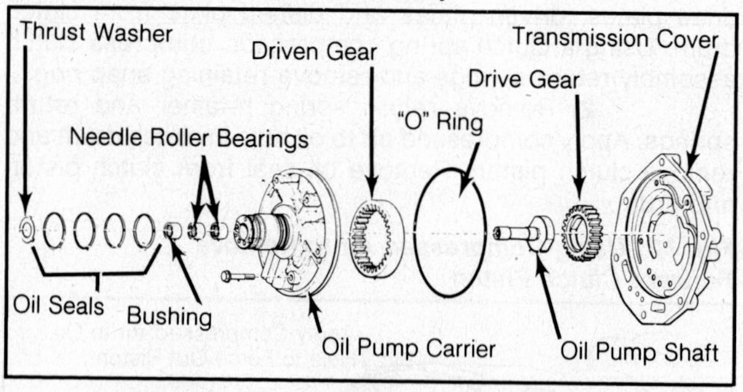

Oil Pump Bushing & Bearing Replacement

1) Remove bushing and needle roller bearings using Needle Bearing Remover (399903600). To install, use Needle Bearing Installer (399543600) to drive bearings into pump carrier. *See Fig. 19.*

2) When installing the center needle roller bearing, Adapter (398863600) must be used with installer to ensure center bearing is installed in correct position.

Fig 19: Installation of Bushings and Bearings into Oil Pump Carrier

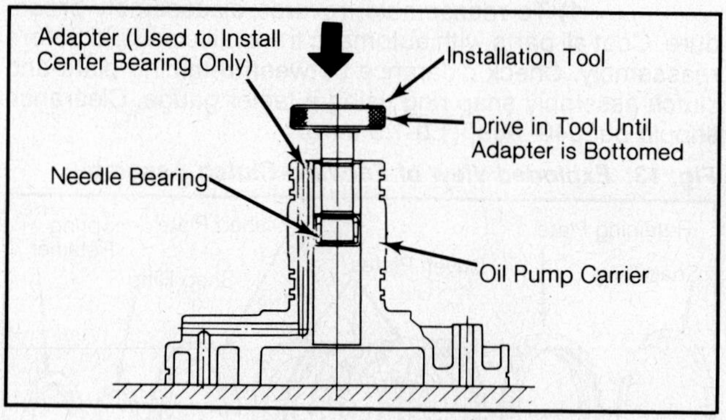

Reassembly

1) To reassemble, reverse disassembly procedure. Coat all parts with automatic transmission fluid before reassembly. Ensure that marks made at disassembly are aligned. With gears installed, check oil pump clearances.

2) Using a straightedge and feeler gauge, measure clearance between face of gears and transmission cover (intermediate housing). *See Fig. 20.* Clearance should be .0008-.0016" (.02-.04 mm).

3) Using a feeler gauge, check clearance between crescent and oil pump driven gear teeth. *See Fig. 21.* Clearance should be .0055-.0083" (.14-.21 mm).

4) Using a feeler gauge, check clearance between oil pump driven gear and oil pump carrier. *See Fig. 22.* Clearance should be .0020-.0079" (.05-.20 mm).

5) If clearance obtained in step **2)** exceeds .0031" (.08 mm), replace pump gears. If clearance obtained in step **3)** or **4)** exceeds .0098" (.25 mm), replace pump gears. Pump gears must always be replaced as a matched set.

Fig. 20: Checking Clearance Between Face of Gears and Rear Cover of Transmission

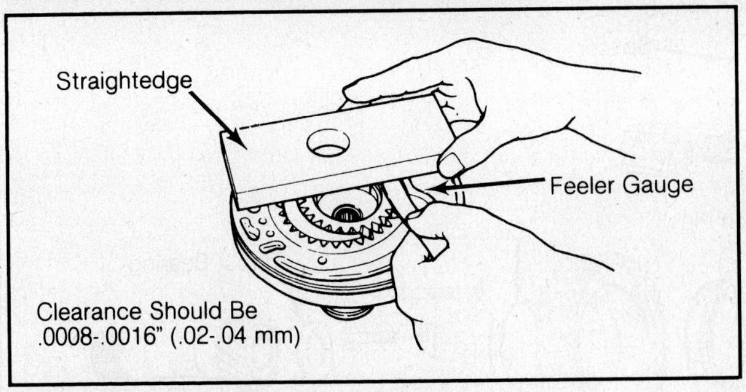

Limit of clearance is .0031" (.08 mm).

Fig. 21: Checking Clearance Between Crescent and Driven Gear Teeth

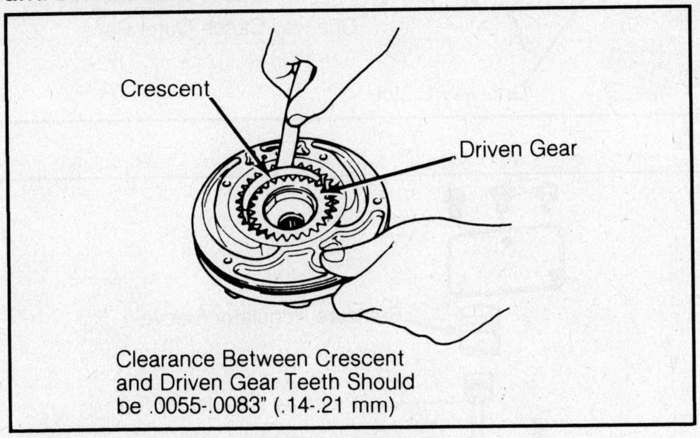

Limit of clearance is .0098" (.25 mm).

Fig. 22: Checking Clearance Between Driven Gear and Oil Pump Carrier

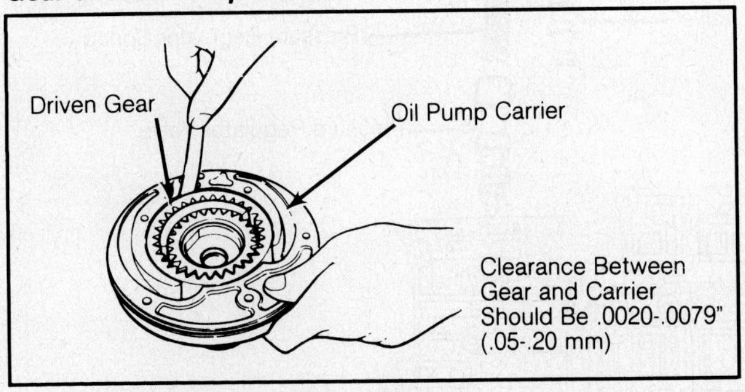

Limit of clearance is .0098" (.25 mm).

PLANETARY GEAR UNIT

Disassembly

Remove bolts securing one-way clutch outer race to planetary gear unit and separate one-way clutch from planetary gear unit. Push pinion pins out toward one-way clutch and remove short pinions, long pinions, thrust washers, needle roller bearings, spacers and thrust bearing. Separate one-way clutch from outer race.

Reassembly

1) To reassemble, reverse disassembly procedure. Use illustration as an assembly guide. *See Fig. 18.* Coat all parts with automatic transmission fluid. When installing one-way clutch on outer race, push "T" bar with finger to insert one-way clutch until a snap is felt, then secure retainer to outer race.

2) After reassembly, check planetary carrier-to-thrust washer clearance. Clearance should be .006-.024" (.15-.60 mm). If clearance exceeds .028" (.71 mm), replace parts as necessary.

VALVE BODY ASSEMBLY

NOTE: **As valve trains are removed from each valve body bore, place individual parts in correct order and in relative position to valve body to simplify reassembly. Spring loaded parts should be handled carefully, as springs may jump out of place when parts are disassembled or removed.**

Disassembly

1) Remove oil strainer bolts using a box-end wrench rather than a screwdriver and separate strainer from valve body. Remove bolts and detach lower valve body, separator plate and upper valve body. Pull manual valve out of valve body bore.

NOTE: **When removing separator plate, use care not to lose orifice check valve, spring, throttle relief spring and check ball.**

2) Remove side plate using a box-end wrench, then remove the 1-2 shift valve and spring, 2-3 shift valve and spring, 2-3 shift plug, pressure modifier valve and spring.

3) Remove side plate and lift out pressure regulator valve train assembly and second lock valve and spring. Remove plate and remove downshift valve and spring, throttle back-up valve and spring and vacuum throttle valve.

Reassembly

1) To reassemble, replace all parts in reverse order of disassembly procedure using illustrations as references. Coat all parts with ATF. When tightening parts, be sure to observe specified torque values.

2) DO NOT force valves into place, but lightly push them into place by hand. Make sure orifice check valves and springs, and throttle relief spring and check ball are in position before instaling separator plate to lower valve body.

TRANSMISSION REASSEMBLY

NOTE: **Handle all parts carefully to avoid damaging bearing and mating surfaces. Lubricate all components with automatic transmission fluid prior to reassembly. Gaskets and thrust washers may be held in place by using petroleum jelly. Use all new gaskets and oil seals, and tighten bolts evenly. See Fig. 35 for thrust washer and thrust bearing locations.**

1) If only transmission section and differential section were separated: Place final drive housing with converter housing facing downward. Install Guide (499257100) on spline portion of drive pinion rear end and join differential section with transmission section. Install transfer drive shaft at this time also (4WD transmissions only).

2) Ensure that parking rod and parking actuator engages properly and sealing lip is not damaged. Install valve body, vacuum diaphragm assembly and downshift solenoid. Install servo apply and servo release tubes and install oil pan.

SUBARU MODEL M41A (Cont.)

Fig. 23: Exploded View of Planetary Gear Assembly

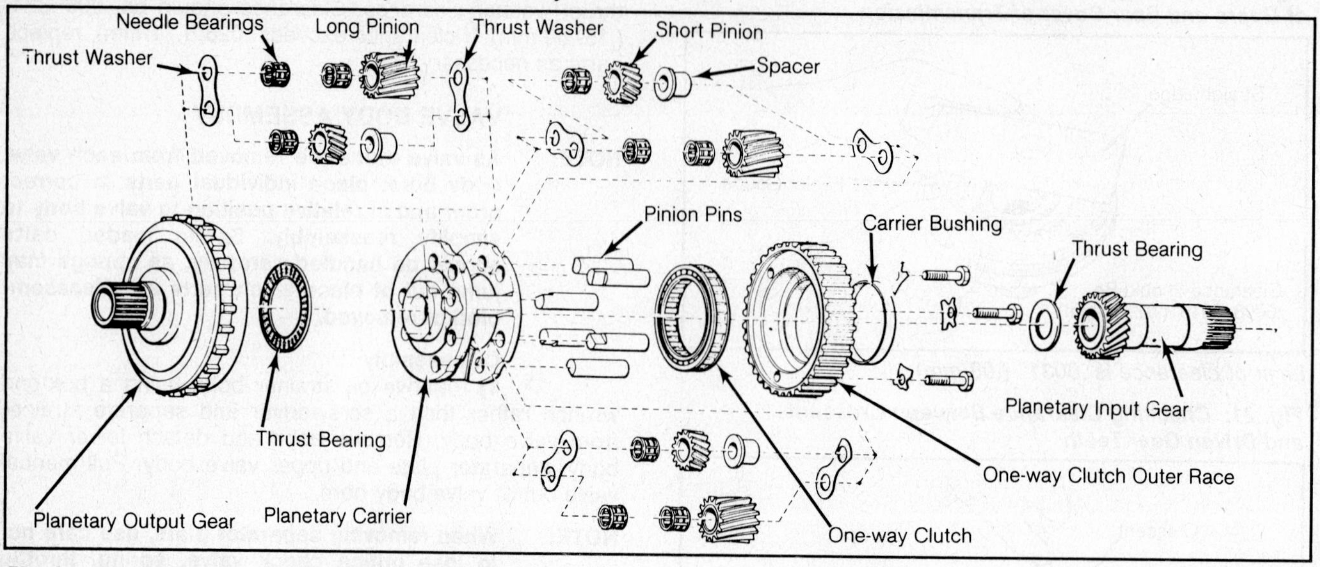

Fig. 24: Exploded View of Valve Body Assembly

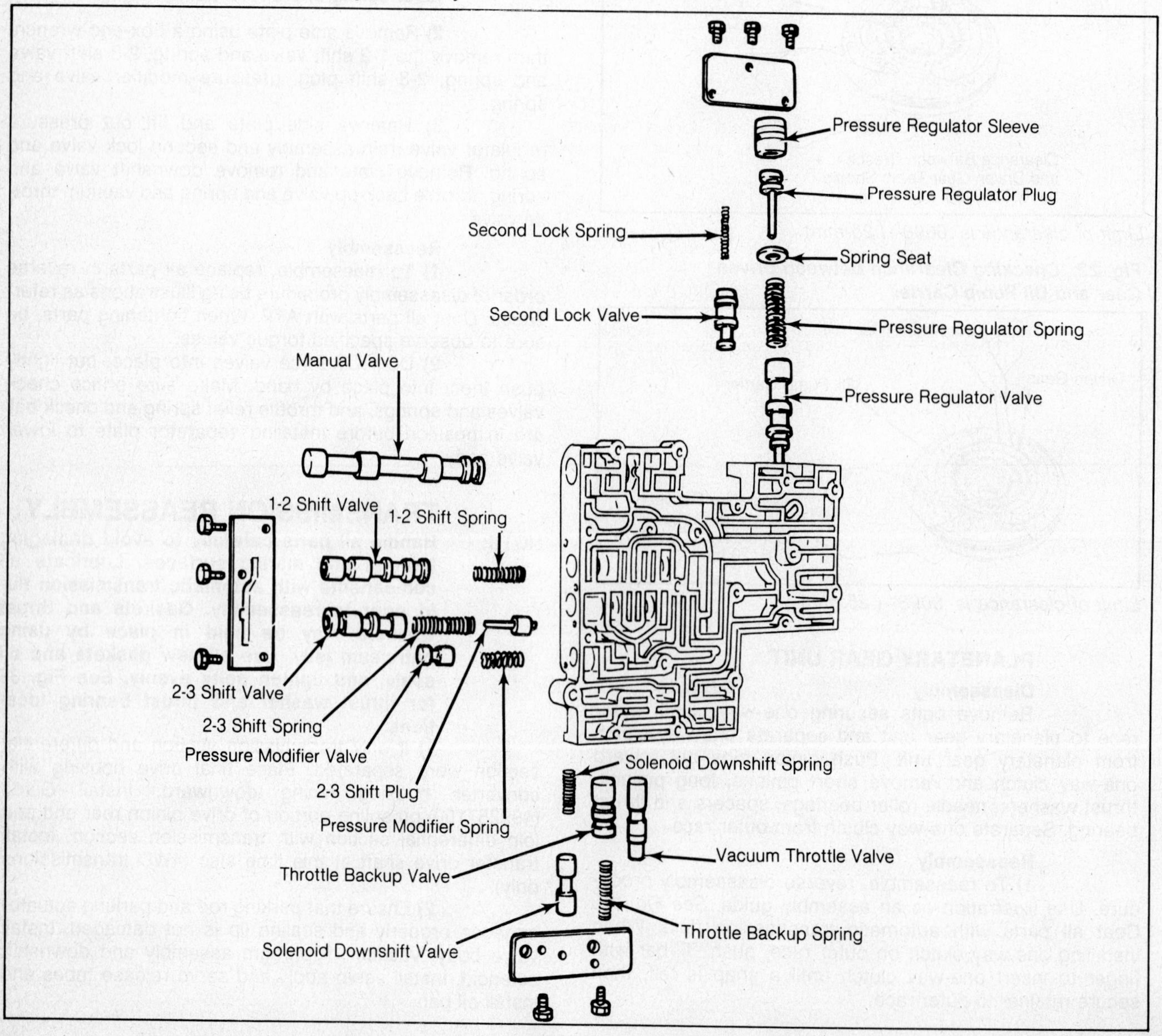

SUBARU MODEL M41A (Cont.)

Fig. 25: View of Lower Valve Body Showing Locations of Check Balls

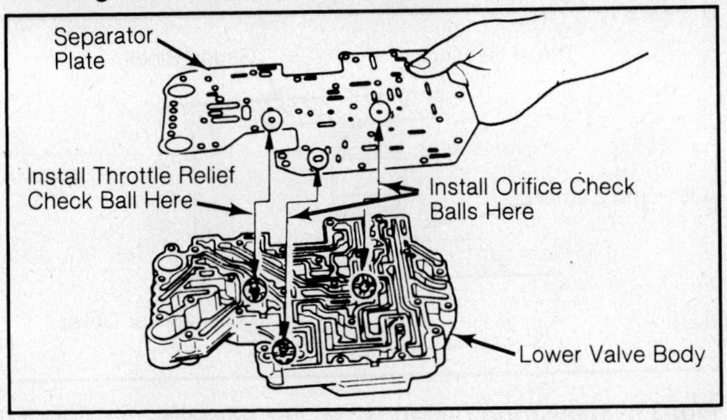

3) Place transmission on oil pan and install turbine shaft and oil pump drive shaft with single oil supply port positioned toward oil pump. Install torque converter onto stator shaft, turbine shaft and pump drive shaft taking care not to damage oil seal in converter housing.

Fig. 26: Oil Port Positioning

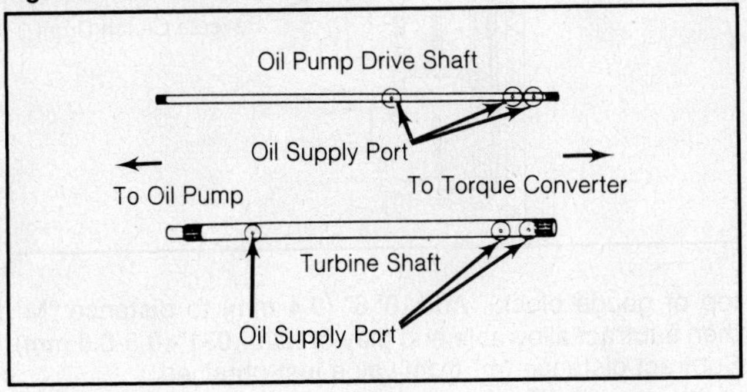

4) If complete transmission was disassembled, install parking pawl and parking pawl shaft. Install parking rod support plate, parking pawl return spring and parking pawl in housing and retain with spring after inserting shaft from front side. Connect parking rod, parking lever and retain with clip.

5) Install parking rod on notched portion of parking shaft support plate with cam portion positioned at back of parking pawl. Install parking lever to parking lever pin and retain with clip.

Fig. 27: View of Transmission Housing Showing Installation of Parking Pawl Assembly

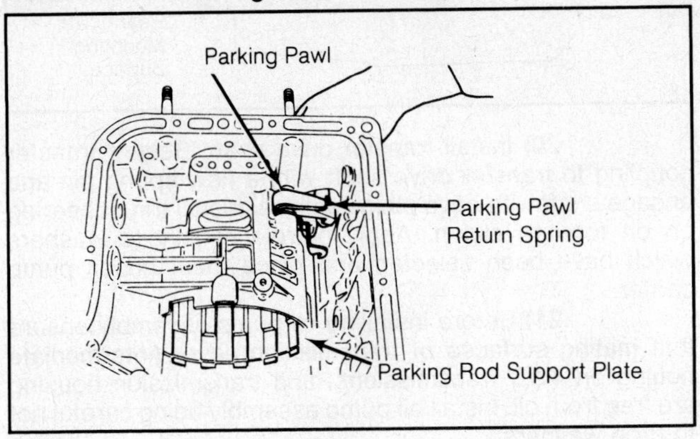

6) Install Drive Pinion Seal Guide (499257100) to splines of drive pinion rear end and connect transmission housing and final drive housing using 8 (8 mm) nuts being careful not to damage oil seal.

7) Engage planetary gear unit with center support assembly and check operation of one-way clutch. Check that one-way clutch in planetary gear unit rotates clockwise only, then separate assemblies.

8) Place center support and low-reverse brake assembly in Base (499687000) and select a retaining plate so that dimension "H" is 3.014-3.492" (77.25-77.45 mm). *See Fig. 28.*

Fig. 28: Retaining Plate Selection

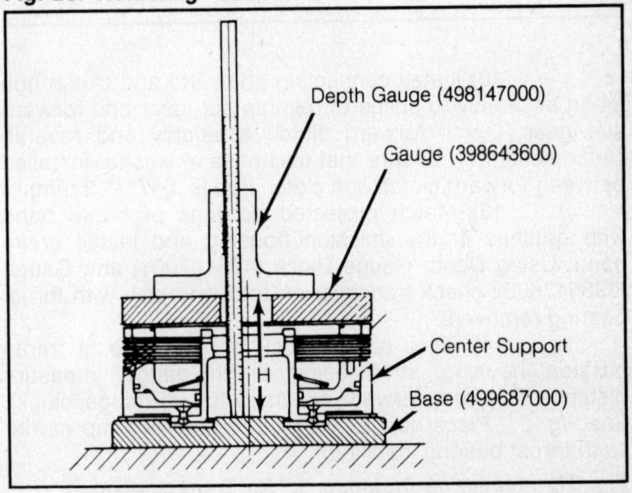

9) If clearance is not within specifications, correct by installing a retaining plate of different thickness. Center support and low-reverse brake assembly retaining plates are available in thicknesses of 0.268" (6.8 mm) to .323" (8.2 mm) in .008" (0.2 mm) increments.

10) Install snap ring, retaining plate, drive plates, driven plates, center support assembly and snap ring into transmission housing. When installing center support, install (6 mm) bolts in support while turning support gradually being careful not to damage one-way clutch or bushing.

11) After assembly, measure clearance between piston and driven plate. Clearance should be be .028-.039" (0.70-1.0 mm). With clearance correctly set, apply compressed air to oil hole in center support and check operation of low-reverse brake piston.

Fig. 29: Measuring Clearance Between Piston and Low-Reverse Driven Plate

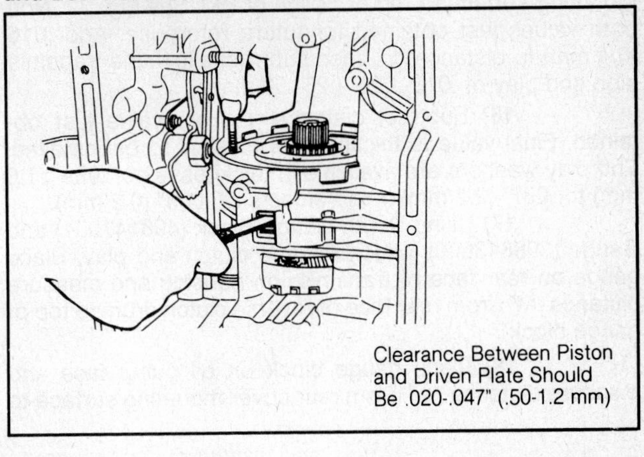

Clearance Between Piston and Driven Plate Should Be .020-.047" (.50-1.2 mm)

SUBARU MODEL M41A (Cont.)

Fig. 30: Using Compressed Air to Check Operation of Low-Reverse Brake Piston

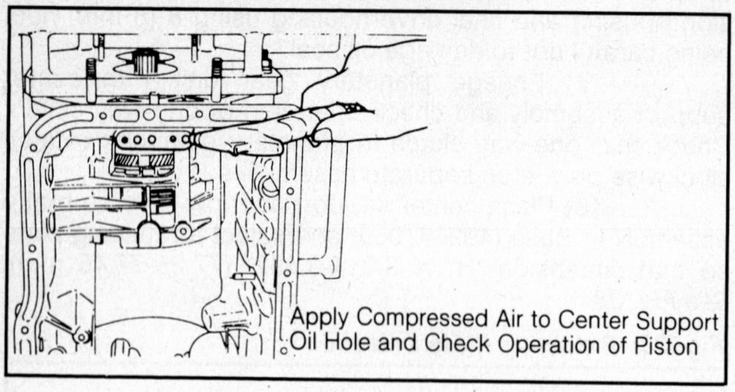

Apply Compressed Air to Center Support Oil Hole and Check Operation of Piston

12) Install connecting shell and and clutch hub as an assembly to spline of reverse sun gear and forward sun gear. Install forward clutch assembly and reverse clutch assembly. Ensure that thickness of washer installed between forward clutch and clutch hub is .047" (1.2 mm).

13) Match projected portions of brake band with notches in transmission housing and install brake band. Using Depth Gauge Block (498147001) and Gauge (398643600), check transmission total end play with thrust bearing removed.

14) Place gauge block on rear face of transmission housing, then using depth gauge, measure distance "L" (from forward clutch to top of gauge block). *See Fig. 31.* Place gauge block on top of oil pump carrier (with thrust bearing installed).

Fig. 31: Measuring Distance "L" for Transmission End Play Adjustment

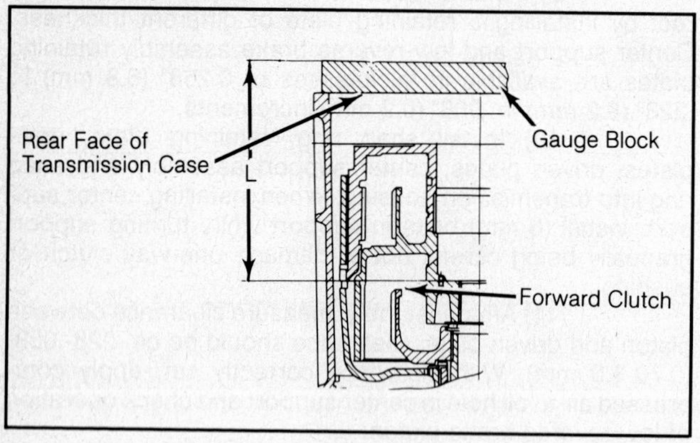

15) Measure distance "l" (from rear cover mounting surface to top of gauge block). *See Fig. 32.* Note both values just obtained for future reference. Add .016" (0.4 mm) to distance "L", then subtract allowable transmission end play of .010-.020" (.25-.50 mm).

16) Subtract distance "l" from value just obtained. Final value is thickness of washer to be installed. End play washers are available in thicknesses of .039" (1.0 mm) to .087" (2.2 mm) in increments of .008" (0.2 mm).

17) Using Depth Gauge Block (498147001) and Gauge (398643600), check reverse clutch end play. Place gauge on rear face of transmission housing and measure distance "M" (from rear face of reverse clutch drum to top of gauge block).

18) Place gauge block on oil pump face and measure distance "m" (from rear cover mounting surface to top of gauge block). Add .016" (0.4 mm) to distance "M", then subtract allowable end play of .020-.031" (0.5-0.8 mm). Subtract distance "m" from value just obtained.

Fig. 32: Measuring Distance "l" for Transmission End Play Adjustment

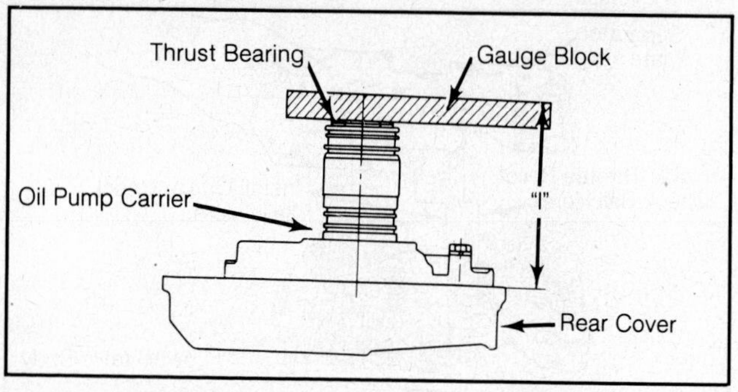

Fig. 33: Measuring Distance "M" for Reverse Clutch End Play Adjustment

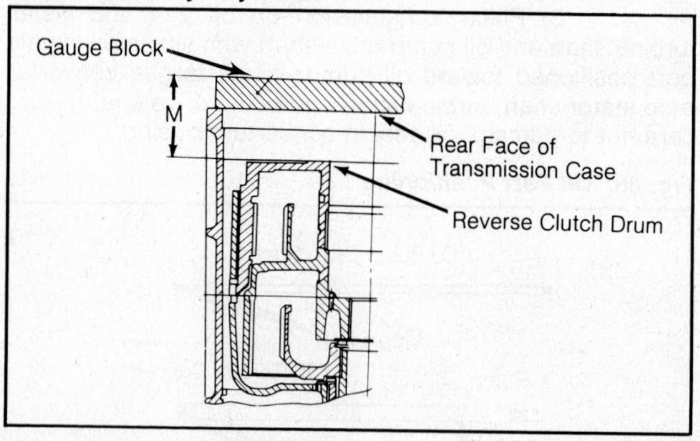

19) Final value is thickness of reverse clutch drum thrust washer to be installed. Reverse clutch drum thrust washers are available in thicknesses of .039" (1.0 mm) to .087" (2.2 mm) in increments of .008" (0.2 mm).

Fig. 34: Measuring Distance "m" for Reverse Clutch End Play Adjustment

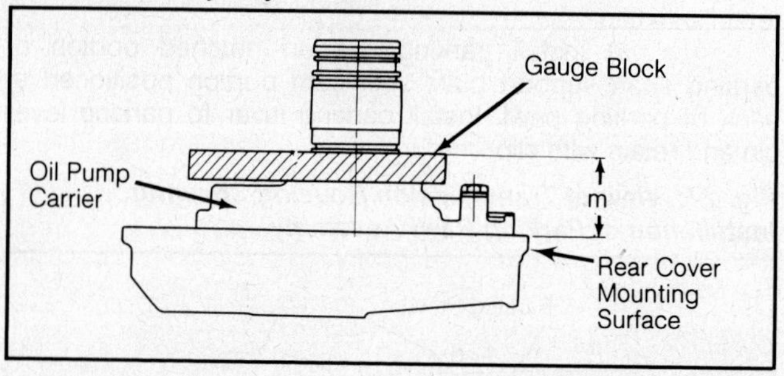

20) Install transfer drive shaft. Secure transfer coupling to transfer drive shaft with a new spring pin and engage shaft with drive pinion splines. Install thrust bearing on on forward clutch. Apply petroleum jelly to washers which have been selected and place them on oil pump carrier.

21) Before installing oil pump assembly ensure that mating surfaces of transmission cover (intermediate houing on 4WD transmissions) and transmission housing are free from oil. Install oil pump assembly being careful not to drop washers.

SUBARU MODEL M41A (Cont.)

Fig. 35: Cross Sectional View of Transmission Housing Showing Thrust Washer and Bearing Locations

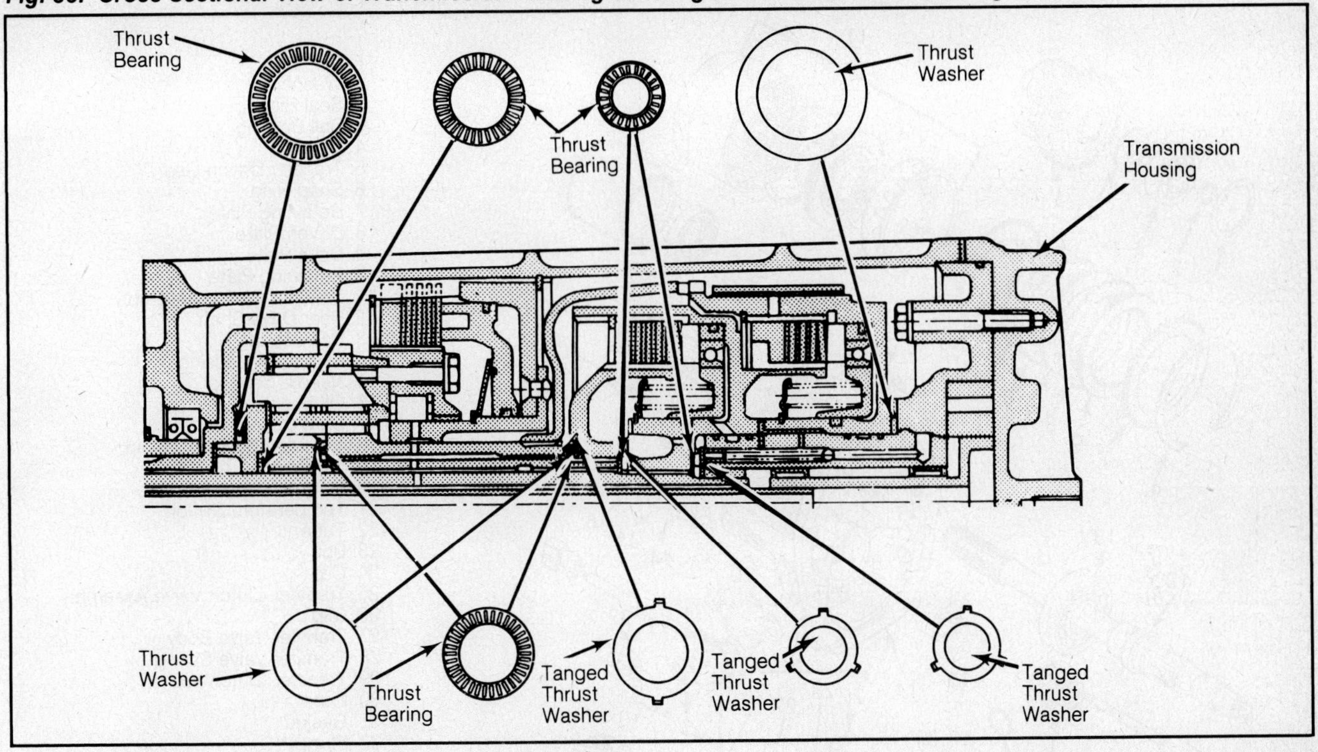

22) Install servo return spring on servo piston. Install band servo piston and piston cover into transmission housing by using piston rod as a guide. Ensure that "O" ring is not damaged. Secure piston with snap ring.

23) Install brake band apply strut and tighten band adjusting screw to 78 INCH lbs (9 N.m), then back screw off 2 complete turns and tighten lock nut to 20 ft. lbs. (27 N.m). Using shims, adjust clearance between manual plate and spacer to .012" (0.3 mm) and tighten nut to 25-33 ft. lbs. (33-44 N.m).

Fig. 36: Cross Sectional View Showing Manual Plate-to-Spacer Adjustment

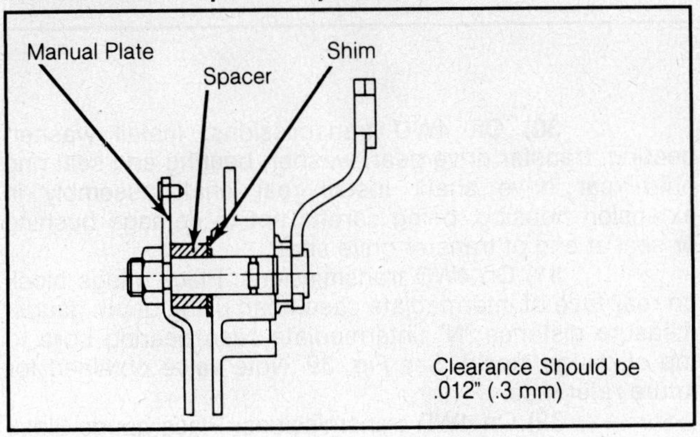

24) Install valve body into transmission housing, making sure that groove in manual valve engages pin in manual plate. Tighten valve body bolts to 52-70 INCH lbs (6-8 N.m). With valve body installed, fully compress vacuum throttle valve and measure distance from end of valve where modulator rod will seat to outside of transmission housing.

25) Resulting measurement will determine length of modulator rod to be installed. Select a rod from those listed in modulator rod selection table. Install "O" ring on vacuum diaphragm and install selected rod together with vacuum diaphragm.

Fig. 37: Measuring Throttle Valve Depth for Modulator Rod Selection

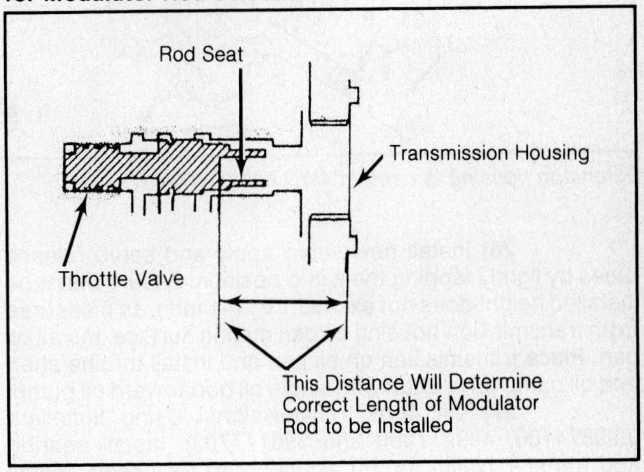

MODULATOR ROD SELECTION TABLE

Measurement In. (mm)	Rod to Use In. (mm)
1.201 (30.5) or Less	1.34 (34.0)
1.2067-1.2224 (30.65-31.05)	1.36 (34.5)
1.2264-1.2421 (31.15-31.55)	1.38 (35.0)
1.2461-1.2618 (31.65-32.05)	1.40 (35.5)
1.2618 (32.05) or More	1.42 (36.0)

SUBARU MODEL M41A (Cont.)

Fig. 38: Exploded View of Extension Housing Assembly

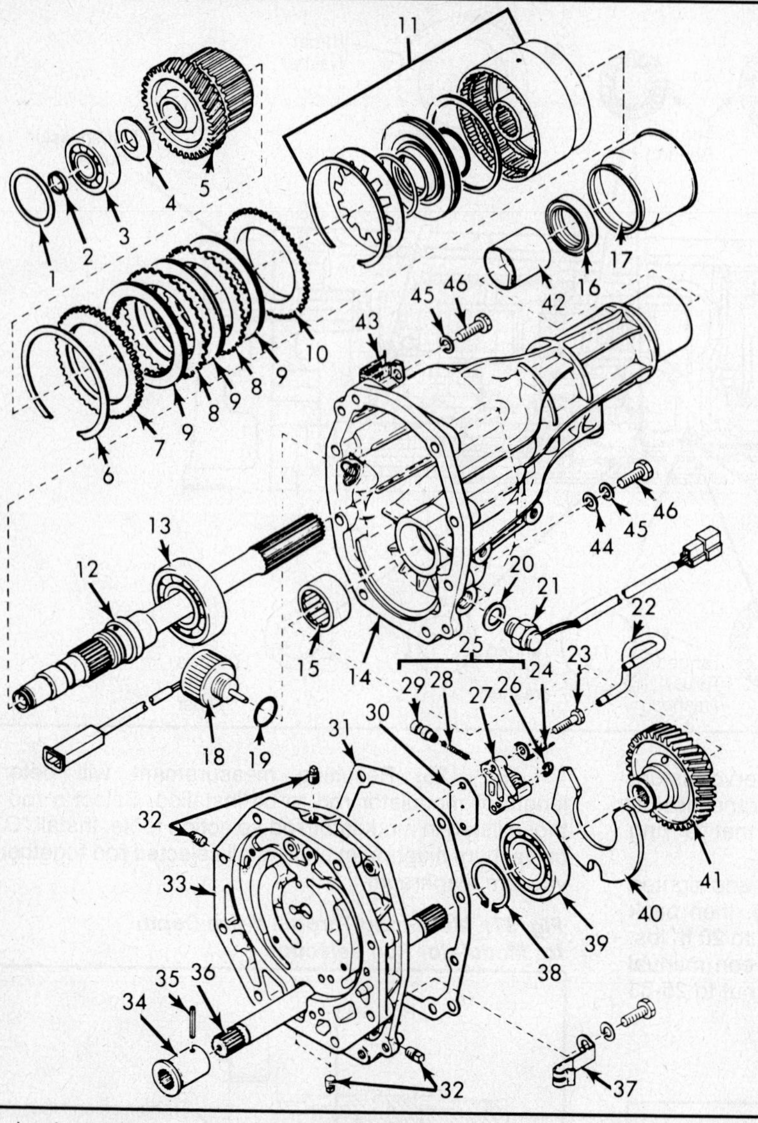

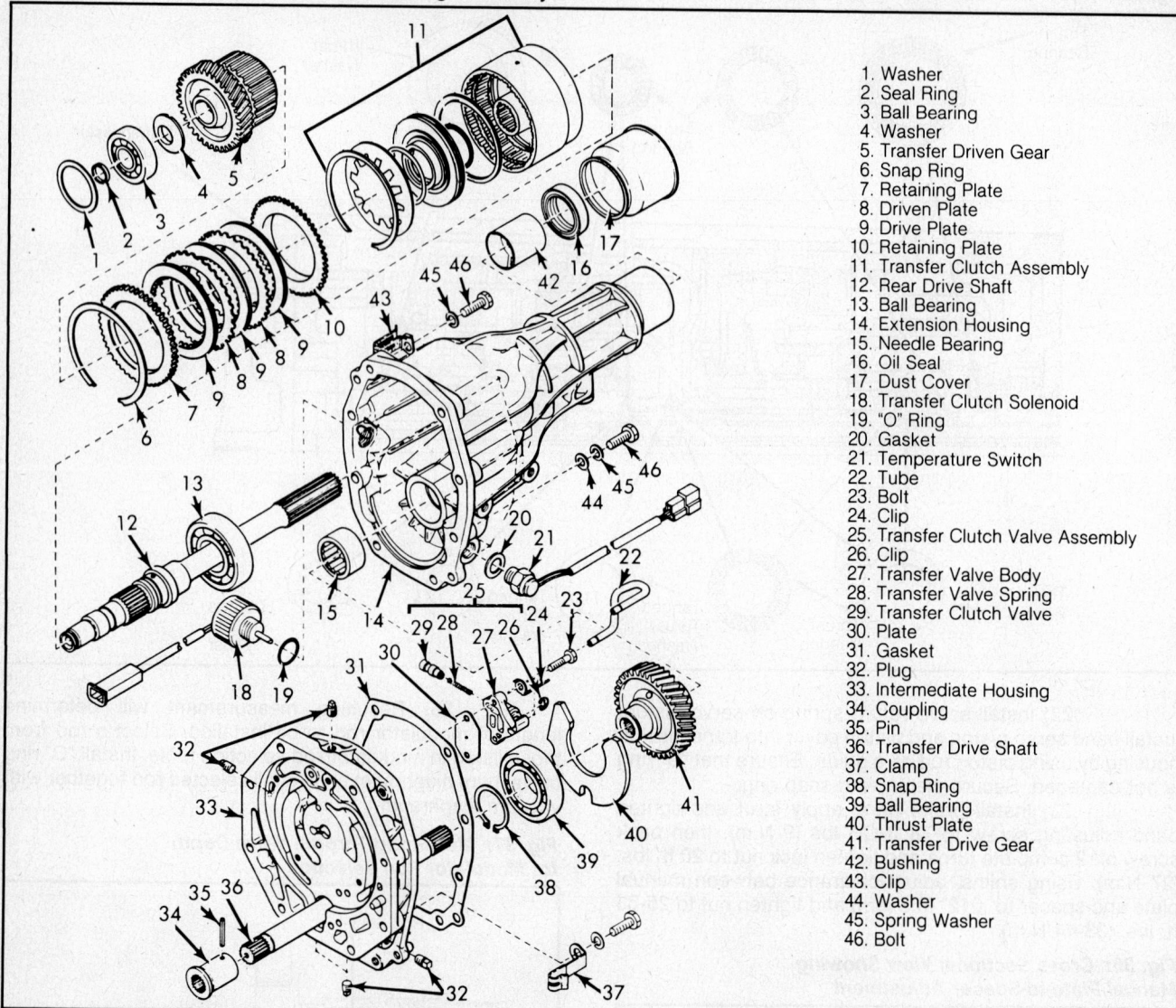

1. Washer
2. Seal Ring
3. Ball Bearing
4. Washer
5. Transfer Driven Gear
6. Snap Ring
7. Retaining Plate
8. Driven Plate
9. Drive Plate
10. Retaining Plate
11. Transfer Clutch Assembly
12. Rear Drive Shaft
13. Ball Bearing
14. Extension Housing
15. Needle Bearing
16. Oil Seal
17. Dust Cover
18. Transfer Clutch Solenoid
19. "O" Ring
20. Gasket
21. Temperature Switch
22. Tube
23. Bolt
24. Clip
25. Transfer Clutch Valve Assembly
26. Clip
27. Transfer Valve Body
28. Transfer Valve Spring
29. Transfer Clutch Valve
30. Plate
31. Gasket
32. Plug
33. Intermediate Housing
34. Coupling
35. Pin
36. Transfer Drive Shaft
37. Clamp
38. Snap Ring
39. Ball Bearing
40. Thrust Plate
41. Transfer Drive Gear
42. Bushing
43. Clip
44. Washer
45. Spring Washer
46. Bolt

Extension housing is used in 4WD vehicles only.

26) Install new servo apply and servo release tubes by lightly tapping them into position. Ensure that tube installed height does not exceed 1.61 (41 mm), as measured from transmission housing oil pan mating surface. Install oil pan. Place transmission on oil pan and install turbine shaft and oil pump drive shaft with single oil port toward oil pump.

27) On 4WD transmissions: Using Installers (899874100, 499277000 and 398177700), install bearing and transfer clutch (drum) assembly to rear shaft. Install rear pressure plate, plates and front pressure plate. Apply compressed air to oil hole located at end of rear shaft to ensure that piston moves freely.

28) On 4WD transmissions: Check clearance between retaining plate and clutch assembly snap ring using a feeler gauge. Clearance should be .016-.031" (0.4-0.8 mm) If clearance is not within specifications, correct by installing a retaining plate of different thickness.

29) On 4WD transmissions: Transfer clutch assembly retaining plates are available in thicknesses of .185" (4.7 mm) to .232" (5.9 mm) in .012" (0.3 mm) increments.

30) On 4WD transmissions: Install washer, bearing, transfer drive gear, washer, bearing and seal ring onto rear drive shaft. Install rear shaft assembly in extension housing, being careful not to damage bushing or seal at end of transfer drive shaft.

31) On 4WD transmissions: Place gauge block on rear face of intermediate case, then using depth gauge, measure distance "N" (intermediate case bearing bore to top of gauge block). *See Fig. 39.* Note value obtained for future reference.

32) On 4WD transmissions: Place gauge block on top of bearing, then using depth gauge, measure distance "n" (from extension housing to top of gauge block). *See Fig. 40.* Add .008" (0.2 mm) to distance "N", then subtract allowable end play of .012" (0.3 mm) from this value.

33) On 4WD transmissions: Subtract distance "n" from value just obtained. Resulting value is thickness of rear shaft thrust washers to be installed. Rear shaft thrust

Fig. 39: Measuring Distance "N" for Transfer Shaft Assembly End Play

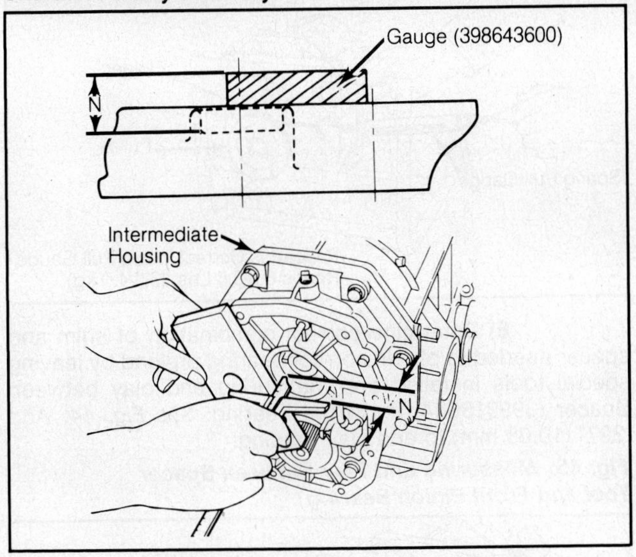

Fig. 40: Measuring Distance "n" for Transfer Shaft Assembly End Play

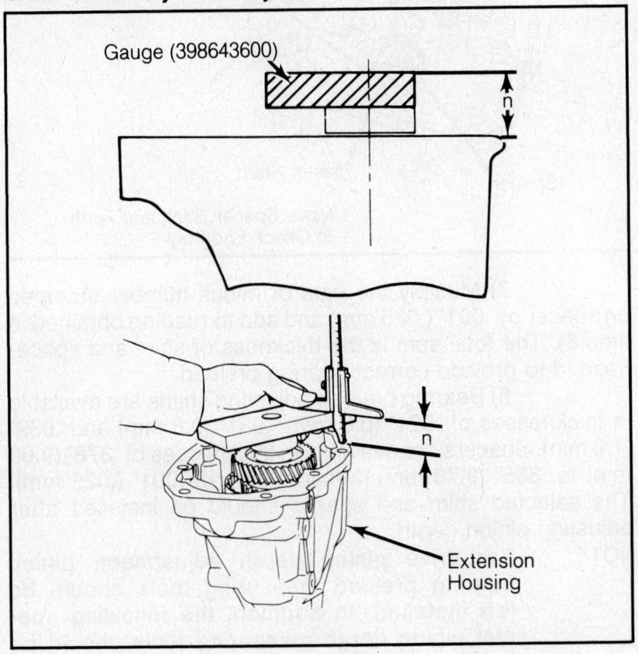

washers are available in thicknesses of .008" (0.2 mm) and .020" (0.5 mm). DO NOT install more than 3 thrust washers.

34) On 4WD transmissions: Install rear drive gear thrust plate and transfer drive gear in intermediate case. Ensure that thrust plate notch aligns with mounting bolt. Install selected washer in intermediate housing. Install extension assembly and tighten bolts to 18 ft. lbs. (24 N.m).

NOTE: Be sure to install transfer solenoid wire harness clip and seal ring.

35) Install "O" ring to bore in extension housing. Install transfer solenoid and tighten (hand tight). Install temperature switch and gasket. Tighten to 13 ft. lbs. (18 N.m). Fasten wire harnesses with clips and install rear engine mount.

FINAL DRIVE ASSEMBLY

DISASSEMBLY

1) Place final drive housing on Work Stand (499937000). Remove bolts attaching torque converter housing and separate torque converter housing. Remove governor cover and pull out governor assembly, then remove attaching bolts and pull out governor sleeve. Remove attaching bolts and lift out parking actuator assembly.

2) Remove bolts attaching reduction gear oil seal holders. Remove axle drive shaft snap rings from inside differential assembly. Wrap vinyl tape over axle shaft splines to protect oil seals. Remove lock plates and remove axle drive shaft oil seal holders and drive shafts as an assembly. Remove oil level gauge. Move differential assembly to one side and lift out of housing.

3) Install Shaft (398653600) on reduction drive gear and engage it with Holder (398781600). Remove drive pinion lock nut with Socket (499987100). Remove final drive housing from stand and press out drive pinion, paying close attention to reduction drive gear end.

4) Press out reduction driven gear and bearing retainer as an assembly. Remove snap ring from end of speedometer shaft, and detach driven gear and steel ball. Remove snap ring from speedometer shaft. Remove reduction drive gear and stator shaft.

Fig. 41: Exploded View of Drive Pinion and Reduction Drive Gear Assemblies

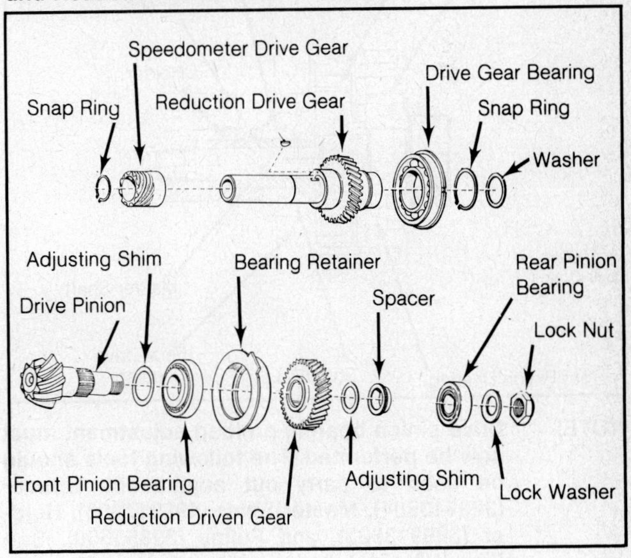

REASSEMBLY & ADJUSTMENT

1) Press thrust bearing retainer (with front bearing) and reduction driven gear into final drive housing. Be sure to align projection of retainer flange with groove of housing. Press retainer until retainer flage contacts housing.

2) Install transmission section front gasket and reduction drive gear on final drive housing. Install and snug down 3 bolts. Using Reduction Bearing Installer (499247200), press oil seal holder into bore of final drive housing being careful not to damage gasket.

SUBARU MODEL M41A (Cont.)

Fig. 42: Exploded View of Differential Assembly

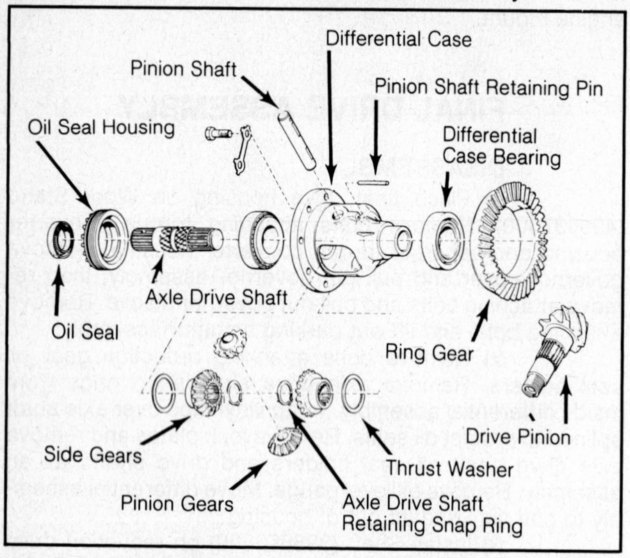

3) Attach final reduction housing to stand and tighten oil seal holder bolts to 18 ft. lbs. (24 N.m). Install speedometer driven gear. Ensure that runout at end of reduction drive gear shaft is within .003" (0.08 mm) by checking with Shaft (398653600) and Handle (899924100).

Fig. 43: Installation of Drive Pinion Bearing Preload Measuring Tools

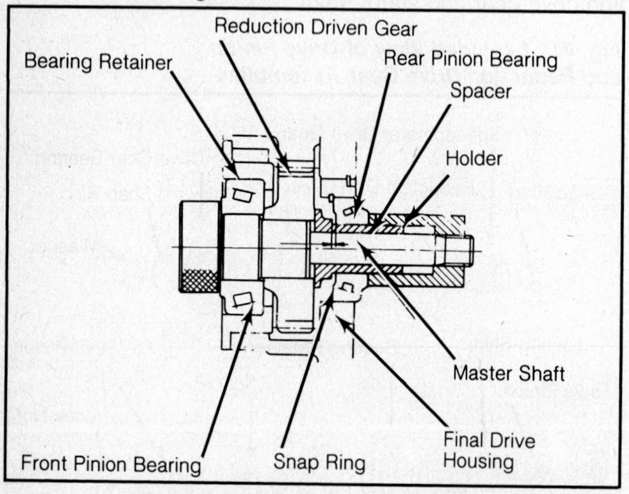

NOTE: Drive pinion bearing preload adjustment must now be performed. The following tools should be used to carry out adjustment: Spacer (399913604), Master Shaft (499917200), Holder (399913603), and Pulley (39853600). See Fig. 44 for installation of these special tools.

4) Install spacer, rear bearing, master shaft and holder in final drive housing. Using Socket (499987100) and an open end wrench (inside housing) to hold master shaft stationary, tighten holder to 84-108 INCH lbs. (9-11 N.m). DO NOT overtighten holder.

5) Attach pulley to hexagonal head of holder, then attach a spring pull gauge to pulley. Tighten holder until tension on pull gauge is 6.6-8.8 lbs. (3.0-4.0 kg), this will give the correct pinion bearing preload. With preload correctly set, starting torque of drive pinion will be 11-14 INCH lbs. (1.2-1.6 N.m).

Fig. 44: Measuring Pinion Bearing Preload

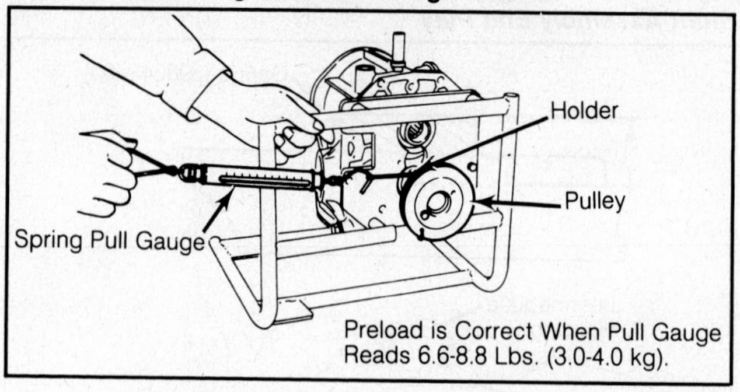

6) Determine correct combination of shim and spacer needed to obtain correct bearing preload by leaving special tools installed and measuring end play between Spacer (399913604) and front bearing. *See Fig. 44.* Add .397" (10.08 mm) to end play reading.

Fig. 45: Measuring End Play Between Spacer Tool and Front Pinion Bearing

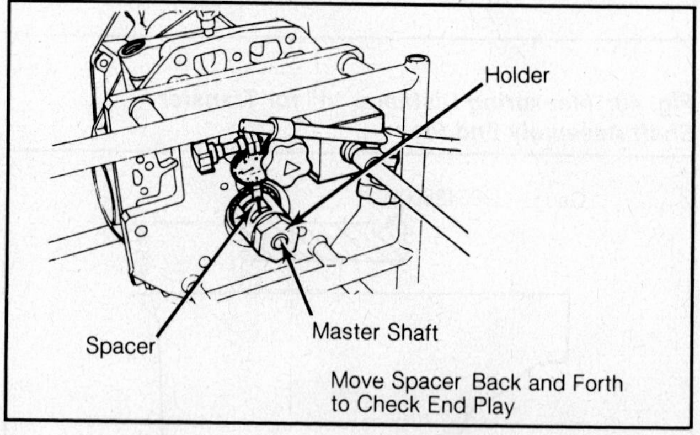

7) Multiply the plus or minus number stamped on spacer by .001" (.025 mm) and add to reading obtained in step **6)**. The total sum is the thickness of shim and spacer needed to provide correct bearing preload.

8) Bearing preload adjusting shims are available in thicknesses of .024" (0.6 mm), .031" (0.8 mm) and .039" (1.0 mm). Spacers are available in thicknesses of .378" (9.60 mm) to .385" (9.78 mm) in increments of .001" (.025 mm). The selected shim and spacer should be installed after adjusting pinion depth.

NOTE: For drive pinion depth adjustment, pinion bearing preload measuring tools should be left installed. In addition, the following special pinion depth measuring tools should be installed as shown in Fig. 46: Thickness Gauge (398643600) and Master Gauge (399913601).

9) Install thickness gauge and master gauge into final drive housing. Measure and record clearance between thickness gauge and master gauge. To determine thickness of pinion depth adjusting shim(s) to be installed, proceed as follows:

Step 1: Multiply the plus or minus figure on master gauge (499917002) by .001" (.025 mm) and record the result.

Step 2: Multiply the plus or minus figure on thickness gauge (39863600) by .001" (.025 mm) and record the result.

Step 3: Measure clearance between master gauge and thickness gauge and record the result. *See Fig. 47.*

SUBARU MODEL M41A (Cont.)

Fig. 46: Installation of Drive Pinion Depth Measuring Tools

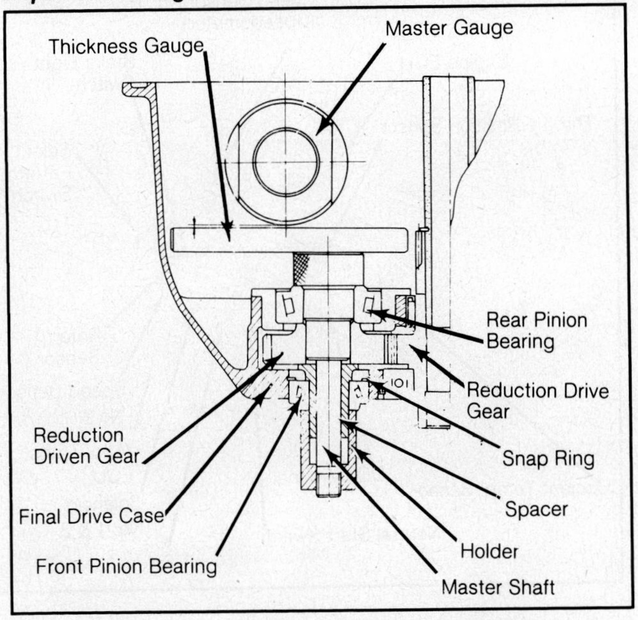

Fig. 47: Measuring Clearance Between Master Gauge and Thickness Gauge for Pinion Depth Adjustment

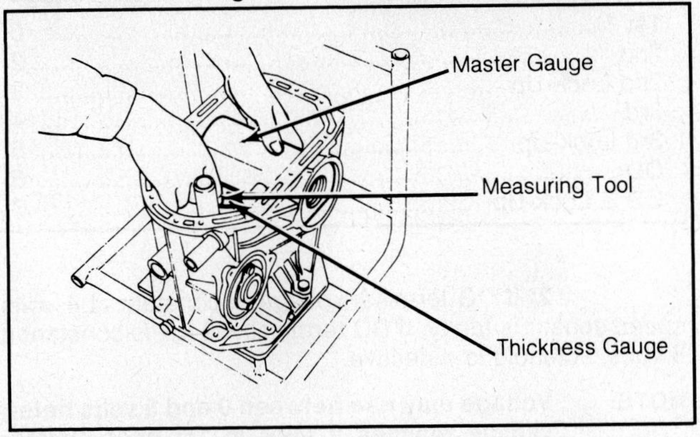

Step 4: Add totals of step 1, 2 and 3. The resulting sum is the shim thickness required for correct drive pinion depth.

10) Up to 3 adjusting shims may be installed to set pinion depth. Adjusting shims are available in thicknesses of .006" (.15 mm) to .020" (.50 mm) in increments of .001" (.025 mm). Remove and disassemble all measuring tools. Install selected pinion depth adjusting shim(s) onto drive pinion, then press on front bearing.

11) Install drive pinion into final drive housing. Install selected pinion bearing preload shim and spacer followed by rear bearing onto drive pinion. Install lock washer and nut. Tighten nut to 87 ft. lbs. (118 N.m). Install final drive housing on work stand and attach pulley and spring pull gauge to pinion lock nut.

12) Recheck pinion bearing preload and adjust as necessary. Stake lock nut at 2 places, if bearing preload is found to be okay. Install differential assembly without axle shaft in final drive housing, being careful not to damage oil seal holder bores. Install axle shafts and secure with snap rings.

13) Check clearance between differential pinion shaft and axle drive shafts using a feeler gauge. Clearance should be .008" (.2 mm) or less. If clearance is greater than specifications, install a snap ring of a different thickness. Axle drive shaft snap rings are available in thicknesses of .0394-.0433" (1.0-1.10 mm) and .0453-.0492" (1.15-1.25 mm).

14) Install axle shaft oil seal holders (without "O" rings) using Wrench (399780111), paying attention to left or right markings. Install Handle (899924100) and Shaft (398653600) to reduction drive gear and turn gear several times. Screw in holder on crown gear side until it lightly bottoms. Repeat procedure several times.

15) Screw in holder on opposite side of crown gear until it bottoms. Install oil seal holder lock plate and back of holder on crown gear side approximately 1 1/2 notches. Tighten holder on opposite side of crown gear. Temporarily tighten lock plate on crown gear side. Screw in holder on opposite side of crown gear 1/2 to 1 notch and temporarily tighten lock plate.

16) Mount a dial indicator on final drive housing with indicator tip touching ring gear teeth and check ring gear back lash. Ring gear backlash should be .004-.007" (.10-.18 mm). If backlash is not within specifications, recheck drive pinion depth adjustment and correct as necessary.

NOTE: **As an additional check, a Gear Tooth Pattern test may be performed. See GEAR TOOTH CONTACT PATTERN in GENERAL SERVICING section.**

17) Once correct adjustment has been made, loosen crown gear side holder until "O" ring groove appears. Install "O" ring and tighten holder to previous position. Place lock plate on holder and tighten to 20 ft. lbs. (27 N.m). Perform same procedure on opposite oil seal holder.

18) Apply a coating of petroleum jelly to governor assembly needle roller bearing and oil seal lips and install governor assembly. Install washer (with petroleum jelly) and new gasket to governor cover. Install governor cover assembly and tighten attaching bolts to 12 ft. lbs. (16 N.m).

19) Install stator shaft to torque converter housing with gasket in place and with flange of shaft facing upward. Tighten attaching bolts to 20 ft. lbs. (27 N.m). Coat reduction drive gear shaft with gear oil. Install a new gasket and attach converter housing to final drive housing. Tighten attaching bolts to 20 ft. lbs. (27 N.m). Install parking actuator assembly on final drive housing.

TIGHTENING SPECIFICATIONS

Application	Ft. Lbs. (N.m)
Band Adjust Screw Lock Nut	19-21 (26-28)
Converter Hsg.-to-Reduction Gear Housing	17-20 (23-27)
Drive Pinion Lock Nut	87 (118)
Manual Plate-to-Trans. Housing	25-33 (34-45)
Oil Pump Assembly	17-20 (23-27)
Stator Shaft Flange	17-20 (23-27)
Trans. Housing-to-Reduction Gear Housing	17-20 (23-27)
Transmission-to-Engine	34-40 (46-54)

TOYOTA A-40D, A-42DL, A-43D, A-43DE & A-44DL

A-40D 4-Speed
Celica
A-42DL
Corolla (RWD)
A-43D 4-Speed
Pickup, 4Runner
A-43DE 4-Speed
Cressida, Supra
A-44DL
Van

DESCRIPTION

All transmissions have 4 forward speeds (4th is overdrive) and reverse. Gear shifts on Cressida and Supra models are controlled by an electronic control unit (ECU) and actuated by solenoids in the valve body. Shift points are determined by engine temperature, road speed, throttle position and selector position.

On all models, the torque converter is a 3-element type. All transmission models except A-40D and A-43D have torque converters with lock-up clutches. Planetary gears are actuated by 3 multi-disc brakes and 2 clutches. Except for Cressida and Supra models, engine load and speed determine gear changes by use of throttle valve position and output shaft speed. These automatic transmissions have no bands, eliminating the need for internal adjustments. The only external adjustments are throttle cable position, shift linkage adjustment and neutral start switch.

LUBRICATION & ADJUSTMENT

See appropriate AUTOMATIC TRANSMISSION SERVICING article in IMPORT GENERAL SERVICING section.

TROUBLE SHOOTING (CRESSIDA & SUPRA)

PRELIMINARY CHECKS

Trouble shooting of the electrcal control system should begin with a voltage check at the DG terminal while driving and when vehicle is stopped. Solenoid valves and speed sensor system have the capability to retain malfunctions in memory. Malfunctions will be retained in memory until ignition switch is turned off, even after malfunction is repaired.

Malfunctions of the throttle position sensor or stop light switch are not retained in memory. Charge battery before testing to prevent false diagnosis.

NOTE: Use a circuit tester with an internal impedance of 10,000 ohms or more.

DG TERMINAL VOLTAGE

1) With engine at normal operating temperature, connect voltmeter to DG terminal. Place pattern selection switch in "NORMAL" and shift selector in "D" with "OD" switch on. Road test vehicle and ensure voltage at DG terminal for each upshift is correct. See DG TERMINAL VOLTAGE table.

Fig. 1: Cressida Transmission Electrical Components

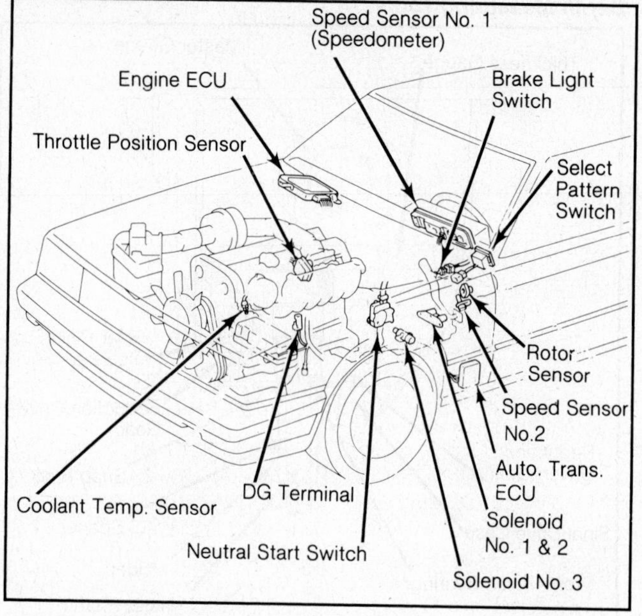

DG TERMINAL VOLTAGE

Gear Position	Voltage
1st	0
2nd	2
2nd Lock-Up	3
3rd	4
3rd Lock-Up	5
OD	6
OD & Lock-Up	7

2) If DG terminal voltage is constant at 4 volts, speed sensor is faulty. If DG terminal voltage is constant at 8 volts, solenoid is defective.

NOTE: Voltage may rise between 0 and 8 volts before vehicle reaches 6 MPH in 1st gear. Voltage jump is normal and depends how far throttle is open.

3) Stop vehicle, but DO NOT turn off engine or diagnostic codes in ECU memory will be erased. With engine running, recheck voltage at DG terminal. Zero volts indicates system is normal or defective brake system; 4 volts indicates faulty No. 2 speed sensor; 8 volts indicates faulty solenoid.

4) To check throttle position sensor system, turn off engine. While slowly depressing accelerator pedal, recheck voltage at DG terminal. Voltage should slowly rise to 8 volts.

5) To inspect brake signal, depress accelerator until DG terminal voltage is 8 volts. Depress brake pedal and check DG terminal voltage. With brake pedal released, there should be 8 volts. There should be 0 volts with brake pedal depressed.

MANUAL SHIFT TEST

To determine if transmissions problems are the result of electrical or mechanical/hydraulic malfunctions, unplug transmission ECU connector. Test drive vehicle

TOYOTA A-40D, A-42DL, A-43D, A-43DE & A-44DL (Cont.)

Fig. 2: Supra Transmission Electrical Components

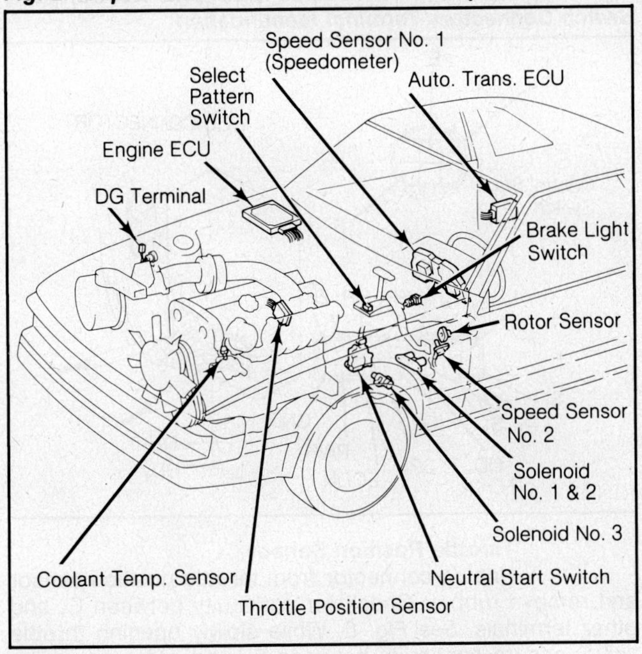

Fig. 3: Cressida Automatic Transmission ECU Wiring Diagram

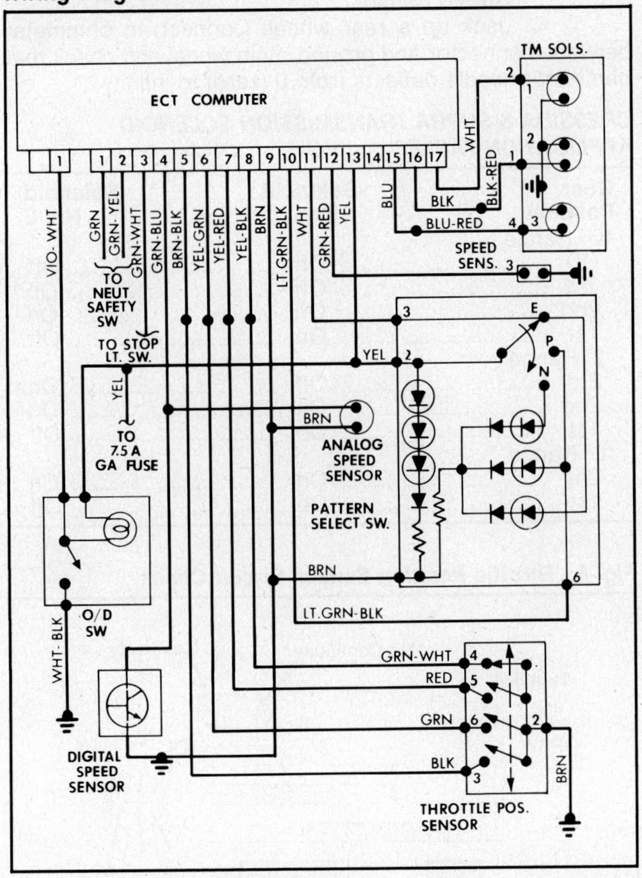

while manually shifting transmission through all forward gears. Also check if transmission performs correctly in "P", "N" and "R" range. If transmission will shift manually, problem is most likely in electrical system.

Fig. 4: Supra Automatic Transmission ECU Wiring Diagram

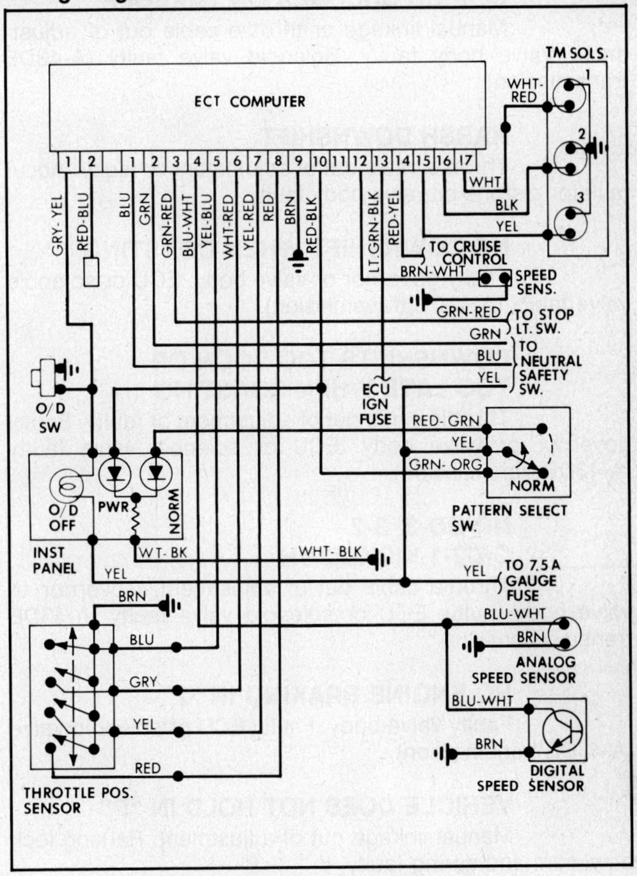

TROUBLE SHOOTING (ALL MODELS)

NO MOVEMENT IN ANY FORWARD GEAR OR REVERSE

Manual linkage out of adjustment. Faulty valve body or primary regulator. Park lock pawl faulty. Faulty torque converter. Converter drive plate damaged or broken. Oil pump intake screen blocked. ECU faulty (A-43DE transmission)

SHIFT LEVER POSITION INCORRECT

Manual linkage out of adjustment. Faulty manual valve and lever.

HARSH ENGAGEMENT INTO ANY DRIVE GEAR

Throttle cable out if adjustment. Faulty valve body, primary regulator or accumulator pistons.

DELAYED 1-2, 2-3, 3-OD UPSHIFTS, OR DOWNSHIFTS FROM OD-3 OR 3-2 THEN BACK TO OD OR 3

Faulty governor or valve body. ECU or solenoid valve faulty (A-43DE transmission).

TOYOTA A-40D, A-42DL, A-43D, A-43DE & A-44DL (Cont.)

SLIP ON ANY UPSHIFT OR SLIP OR SHUDDER ON TAKEOFF

Manual linkage or throttle cable out of adjustment. Valve body faulty. Solenoid valve faulty (A-43DE transmission).

HARSH DOWNSHIFT

Throttle cable out of adjustment or faulty. Accumulator pistons or valve body faulty.

NO DOWNSHIFT WHEN COASTING

Faulty governor or valve body. ECU or solenoid valve faulty (A-43DE transmission).

DOWNSHIFTS TOO SOON OR TOO LATE WHEN COASTING

Throttle cable out of adjustment or faulty. Faulty governor or valve body. ECU or solenoid valve faulty (A-43DE transmission).

NO OD-3, 3-2 OR 2-1 KICKDOWN

Throttle cable out of adjustment. Governor or valve body faulty. ECU or solenoid valve faulty (A-43DE transmission).

NO ENGINE BRAKING IN "2"

Faulty valve body. Faulty ECU or solenoid valve (A-43DE transmission).

VEHICLE DOES NOT HOLD IN "P"

Manual linkage out of adjustment. Parking lock pawl cam and spring faulty.

TESTING (CRESSIDA & SUPRA)

ECU CIRCUIT

Remove left kick panel (Cressida). Remove right pillar louver and arm rest (Supra). Turn ignition on. Measure voltage at each terminal of Auto. Trans. ECU connector. See *Fig. 5* and CRESSIDA & SUPRA ECU CONNECTOR VOLTAGE CHART.

COMPONENT TESTS

Transmission Solenoids

1) Unplug connector from Auto. Trans. ECU. Check resistance between S_1, S_2, S_3 and ground. Resistance should be 11-15 ohms. *See Fig. 5*.

2) Apply battery voltage to each solenoid to check operation. If there is foreign material in solenoid valve, there will be no fluid control even if solenoid operates.

3) Ensure No. 1 and No. 2 solenoids are applied in correct gear range. See CRESSIDA & SUPRA TRANSMISSION SOLENOID APPLICATION table.

Neutral Start Switch

Shift lever into "D" or "S". Unplug neutral start switch connector near starter motor. Check for continuity between L, S and ground. *See Fig. 5*.

Fig. 5: Automatic Transmission ECU and Neutral Start Switch Connectors Terminal Identification

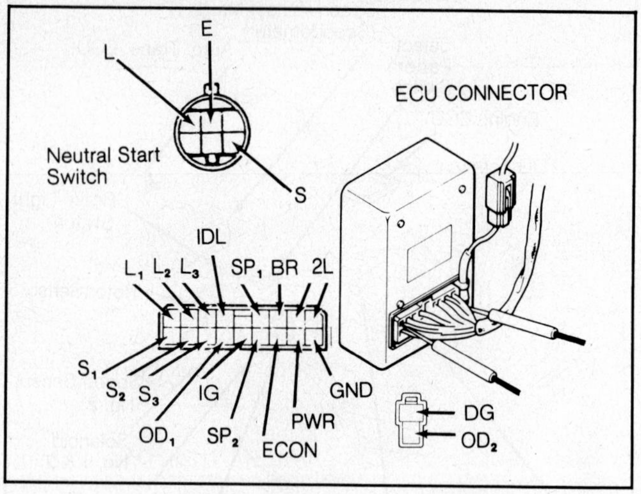

Throttle Position Sensor

Unplug connector from throttle position sensor and remove rubber. Check for continuity between E_1 and other terminals. *See Fig. 6*. While slowly opening throttle valve, ensure continuity between E_1 and each respective terminal is as specified.

Speed Sensor

Jack up a rear wheel. Connect an ohmmeter between connector and ground. Spin wheel and check that ohmmeter needle deflects from 0 (zero) to infinity.

CRESSIDA & SUPRA TRANSMISSION SOLENOID APPLICATION TABLE

Gear Position	Solenoid No. 1	Solenoid No. 2
"D" Range		
OD	Off	Off
3rd	Off	On
2nd	On	On
1st	On	Off
"2" Range		
3rd	Off	On
2nd	On	On
1st	On	Off
"L" Range		
2nd	On	On
1st	On	Off

Fig. 6: Throttle Position Sensor Circuit Check

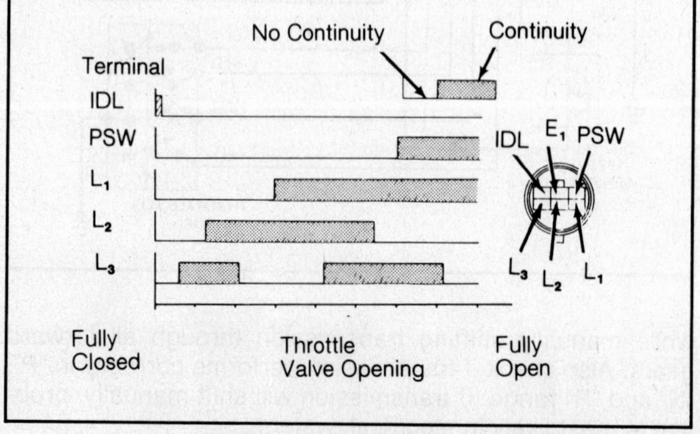

TOYOTA A-40D, A-42DL, A-43D, A-43DE & A-44DL (Cont.)

Speedometer
(Analog Type)

Remove speedometer from instrument panel. Connect ohmmeter between SP terminals. Rotate speedometer shaft and check that ohmmeter needle deflects from peg to peg.

Speedometer
(Digital Type)

Remove speedometer. Apply battery voltage between terminals IG(+) and IG(-). Connect voltmeter between terminal SP and GND. Rotate speedometer shaft and check that voltmeter needle deflects from 0 to 10 volts.

Pattern Selection Switch

On Cressida, check that there is continuity between terminal No. 2 and other terminals. On Supra, check that there is continuity between terminals No. 3 and 4. *See Fig. 7.*

Fig. 7: Pattern Select Switch Terminal Identification

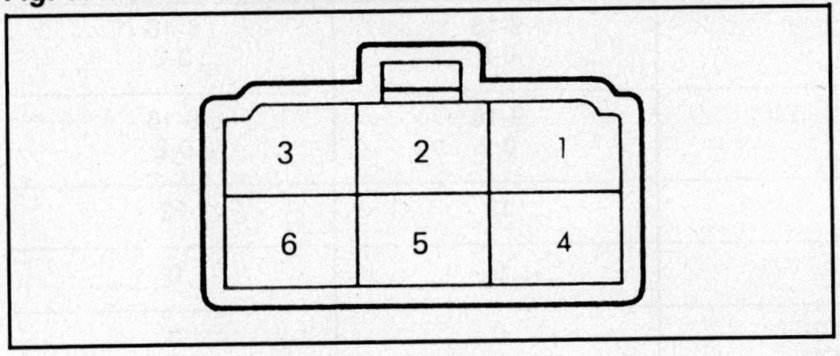

Lock-Up Mechanism

With engine and transmission at normal operating temperature, connect voltmeter to DG terminal. Select "Normal" pattern. Drive at about 30 MPH so voltmeter reads between 5 and 3 volts (lock-up range). Depress accelerator pedal and note tachometer. If RPM jumps considerably, there is no lock-up.

NOTE: **If torque converter lock-up clutch does not release when slowing to a stop, the cause may be a sticking lock-up relay valve in valve body.**

TESTING (ALL MODELS)

ROAD TEST

"D" Range Test

1) Engine must be at normal operating temperature. Shift into "D" range with "OD" switch on. Accelerate with throttle valve fully open and ensure all shifts occur at specified points. See SHIFT SPEED SPECIFCATIONS chart. Also check all downshift points.

NOTE: **On all models except Cressida and Supra, there is no 3-OD upshift with a throttle opening of more than 86% or coolant temperature below 122°F (50°C). On Cressida and Supra models, there is no 3-OD upshift or lock-up with vehicle speed below 37 MPH or coolant temperature below 140°F (60°C).**

2) While driving in "D" range, release foot from accelerator and shift into "2" and "L" ranges. Check engine braking effect in these ranges.

"D" Range Test Results

1) If there is no engine braking at "2" range, Brake No. 1 is defective. If no braking in "L" range, Brake No. 3 is defective.

NOTE: **On Cressida and Supra models, perform test in "NORM", "ECON", and "PWR" ranges.**

2) If there is no 1-2 upshift, 1-2 shift valve may be stuck. On Cressida and Supra models, check No. 2 solenoid. On all other models, check govenor valve. If there is no 2-3 upshift, check 2-3 shift valve. On Cressida and Supra models, check No. 1 solenoid.

3) On all models, check OD shift valve if there is no 3-OD upshift. If converter lock-up is defective, check lock-up relay valve in valve body. On Cressida and Supra models, also check No. 3 solenoid if lock-up is not correct.

"2" & "L" Range Test

1) Shift to "2" range and check for proper upshifts. Also, check engine braking effect with accelerator released.

2) Shift into "L" range. Ensure there is no upshift to "2" range. Check engine braking effect with accelerator released.

"P" & "R" Range Tests

Shift into "R" range. Check for slippage at full throttle. To check parking pawl, shift into "P" range while parked on a hill. Vehicle should not move.

HYDRAULIC PRESSURE TESTS

With transmission fluid at normal operating temperature, raise and support rear of vehicle so that rear wheels are free to turn. Connect pressure gauges to line pressure and governor pressure test ports on transmission. *See Fig. 8.*

Fig. 8: Transmission Hydraulic Pressure Test Ports

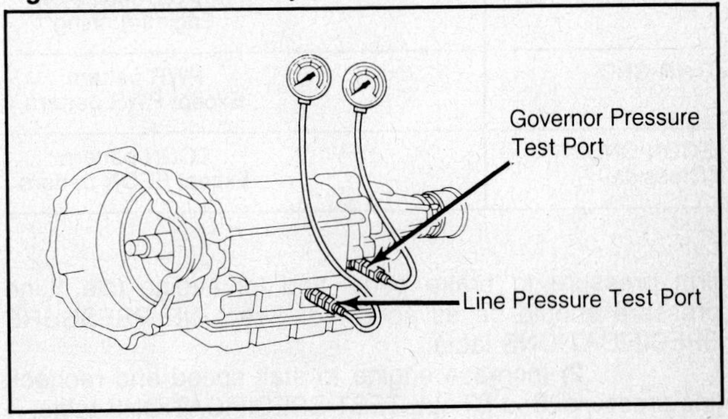

NOTE: **Pressures may also be tested on chassis dynamometer.**

Governor Pressure Test
(All Except Cressida & Supra)

1) Start engine and release parking brake. Slowly accelerate engine with transmission in "D" and check governor pressure at specified speed. See GOVERNOR PRESSURE SPECIFICATIONS table.

2) If governor pressures are incorrect, check for the following: incorrect line pressure, fluid leakage in governor pressure circuit, governor valve operation defective.

Line Pressure Test
(All Models)

1) Fully apply parking brake and block all 4 wheels. Start engine and shift transmission into "D". Apply

TOYOTA A-40D, A-42DL, A-43D, A-43DE & A-44DL (Cont.)

CRESSIDA AND SUPRA ECU CONNECTOR VOLTAGE CHART

Terminals	Conditions	Voltage (Denso Type)	Voltage (Aisin Type)
L_1-GND	Throttle valve fully closed Throttle valve fully open	5 0	12 0
L_2-GND	Throttle valve fully closed Throttle valve fully open	5 5	12 12
L_3-GND	Throttle valve fully closed Throttle valve fully open	5 5	12 12
IDL-GND	Throttle valve fully closed Throttle opening about 1.5°	0 4	0 4
SP_1-GND	Key on, engine off With engine running	12 or 0 6	12 or 0 6
BR-GND	Brake pedal depressed Brake pedal released	12 0	12 0
2-GND	"2" Range Except "2" Range	9-16 0-2	9-16 0-2
L-GND	"L" Range Except "L" Range	9-16 0-2	9-16 0-2
S_1-GND	.....	12	12
S_1, S_2-GND	.....	0	0
OD_1-GND	Coolant temperature below 150°F (70°C) Coolant temperature above 150°F (70°C)	0 5	0 12
OD_2-GND	OD switch "ON" OD switch "OFF"	12 0	12 0
IG-GND	Key on, engine off	12	12
SP_2-GND	Key on, engine off Engine running	5 or 0 4	12 or 0 10
PWR-GND	PWR pattern Except PWR pattern	12 1	12 1
ECON-GND (Cressida)	ECON pattern Except ECON pattern	12 1	12 1

firm pressure to brake pedal and let engine idle. Line pressure should be as specified. See LINE PRESSURE SPECIFICATIONS table.

2) Increase engine to stall speed and recheck line pressure. See STALL TEST SPECIFICATIONS table. If specified line pressures are not obtained, check throttle cable adjustment and repeat test. Repeat line pressure tests with transmission in "R".

Line Pressure Test Results

1) If line pressure in all ranges is higher than specified, check for the following: defective regulator valve, defective throttle valve, or throttle cable out of adjustment.

2) If line pressure is low in all ranges, check for the following: defective oil pump, defective regulator valve, defective throttle valve, throttle cable out of adjustment, or defective OD clutch.

3) If line pressure is low in "D" range only, check for the following: defective front clutch, fluid leak in "D" range circuit, or defective OD clutch.

GOVERNOR PRESSURE SPECIFICATIONS

Vehicle Speed (MPH)	Output Shaft (RPM)	Pressure psi (kg/cm²)
All Except A-44DL		
17-21	1000	13-21 (.9-1.5)
34-37	1800	23-31 (1.6-2.2)
58-71	3500	58-75 (4.1-5.3)
A-44DL		
17	1000	20-26 (1.4-1.8)
32	1800	34-40 (2.4-2.8)
62	3500	73-84 (5.1-5.9)

4) If line pressure is low in "R" range only, check for the following: defective rear clutch, defective No. 3 brake, fluid leak in "R" range circuit, or defective OD clutch.

TOYOTA A-40D, A-42DL, A-43D, A-43DE & A-44DL (Cont.)

SHIFT SPEED SPECIFICATIONS

Shift Condition [1]	Shift Point (MPH)
Celica	
1-2 Upshift in "D"	35-45
2-3 Upshift In "D"	65-76
3-OD Upshift In "D"	2
3-2 Downshift In "D"	57-67
2-1 Downshift In "D"	26-34
Corolla (RWD)	
1-2 Upshift In "D"	29-39
2-3 Upshift In "D"	54-63
3-OD Upshift In "D"	2
3-2 Downshift In "D"	52-61
2-1 Downshift In "D"	23-30
Cressida [3 4]	
1-2 Upshift In "D"	29-32
2-3 Upshift In "D"	59-63
3-OD Upshift in "D"	86-90
OD-3 Downshift In "D"	83-86
3-2 Downshift In "D"	56-59
2-1 Downshift In "D"	27-29
Pickup [5]	
22R Engine	
1-2 Upshift In "D"	35-45
2-3 Upshift In "D"	65-77
3-OD Upshift In "D"	2
3-2 Downshift in "D"	60-71
2-1 Downshift In "D"	24-34
22R-E Engine	
1-2 Upshift In "D"	37-47
2-3 Upshift In "D"	68-79
3-OD Upshift In "D"	2
3-2 Downshift in "D"	62-73
2-1 Downshift In "D"	25-35
Supra [3 4]	
1-2 Upshift In "D"	29-32
2-3 Upshift In "D"	57-63
3-OD Upshift In "D"	84-89
OD-3 Downshift In "D"	81-86
2-1 Downshift in "D"	55-60
2-1 Downshift In "D"	26-29
Van [3 6]	
1-2 Upshift In "D"	26-32
2-3 Upshift In "D"	51-61
3-OD Upshift In "D"	2
3-2 Downshift In "D"	50-58
2-1 Downshift in "D"	23-30

1 – All upshift points given at full throttle.
2 – No 3-OD upshifts occur at full throttle; 3-OD upshift occurs at closed throttle at 24-32 MPH.
3 – With throttle valve fully open and "Normal" range pattern.
4 – Lock-up "ON" point with closed throttle is 34-37 MPH; lock-up "OFF" with closed throttle is 31-34.
5 – Lock-up "ON" point with closed throttle is 39-43 MPH; lock-up "OFF" with closed throttle is 35-40.
6 – Lock-up "ON" point with closed throttle is 41-46 MPH; lock-up "OFF" with closed throttle is 39-43.

STALL TEST

1) With engine and transmission at normal operating temperature, connect a tachometer to engine. Apply parking brake and block front wheels.

LINE PRESSURE SPECIFICATIONS

Application	In "D" psi (kg/cm²)	In "R" psi (kg/cm²)
At Idle Speed		
Celica	63-68 (4.4-4.8)	74-88 (5.2-6.3)
Corolla & Pickup (22R)	50-63 (3.5-4.4)	71-91 (5.0-6.4)
Cressida & Supra	53-58 (3.7-4.1)	73-81 (5.1-5.7)
Pickup (22R-E)	65-77 (4.6-5.4)	100-117 (7.0-8.2)
Van	64-73 (4.5-5.1)	97-108 (6.8-7.6)
At Stall Speed		
Celica	139-154 (9.8-10.8)	164-205 (11.5.-14.4)
Corolla & Pickup (22R)	137-156 (9.6-11.0)	195-242 (13.7-17.0)
Cressida & Supra	151-185 (10.6-13.0)	203-270 (14.3-19.0)
Pickup (22R-E) & Van	144-169 (10.1-11.9)	213-270 (15.0-19.0)

NOTE: DO NOT maintain stall RPM for more than 5 seconds.

2) Start engine, apply brake pedal and place transmission in "D". Accelerate engine to full throttle and check maximum speed obtained. Repeat test in "R".

STALL TEST SPECIFICATIONS

Application	Stall RPM
Celica	1750-2050
Corolla, Cressida & Supra	1950-2250
Pickup	
22R Engine	1700-2000
22R-E Engine	1750-2050
Van	2050-2350

Stall Test Results

1) If stall speed is the same for both ranges but lower than specified , engine output may be insufficient, or stator one-way clutch may not be operating properly.

NOTE: If stall RPM is more than 600 RPM lower than specifications, torque converter may be faulty.

2) If stall speed is higher than specified in "D" range, front clutch may be slipping, one-way No. 2 clutch may not be operating, line pressure may be low, or OD one-way clutch may not be operating.

3) If stall speed in "R" is higher than specified, rear clutch and/or Brake No. 3 may be slipping, line pressure may be low, OD one-way clutch may not be operating.

4) If stall speed in "R" and "D" is higher than specified, line pressure may be too low, fluid level may be wrong, or OD one-way clutch is not operating properly.

TOYOTA A-40D, A-42DL, A-43D, A-43DE & A-44DL (Cont.)

CLUTCH AND BRAKE APPLICATION CHART (ELEMENTS IN USE – A-43DE ONLY)

Selector Lever Position	Overdrive Clutch	Front Clutch	Rear Clutch	Overdrive Brake	No.1 Brake	No.2 Brake	No.3 Brake
D – Drive							
First [1]	X	X					
Second [2]	X	X					
Third [3]	X	X	X [4]				
Overdrive		X	X [4]	X		X	
2 – Second [2]							
First [1]	X	X					
Second [2]	X	X			X	X	
Third [3]	X	X	X [4]			X	
L – LOW							
First [1]	X	X					
Second [2]	X	X			X	X	
R – REVERSE [3]	X		X				X
N – NEUTRAL	X						
P – PARK	X						

[1] – One-way clutch No. 0 and No. 2 applied. [2] – One-way clutch No. 0 and No. 1 applied. [3] – One-way clutch No. 0 applied.
[4] – Not applied in "POWER" mode.

OVERDRIVE CIRCUIT

NOTE: This section applies to all models except Cressida and Supra (A-43DE transmission).

Overdrive Circuit Test

1) Turn on ignition switch and overdrive switch. Unplug wire connector at thermo switch. Install jumper wire on connector. Repeatedly ground connector. A clicking sound from the overdrive solenoid and relay should be heard.

Fig. 9: Corolla & Van Overdrive Circuit Wiring Diagram

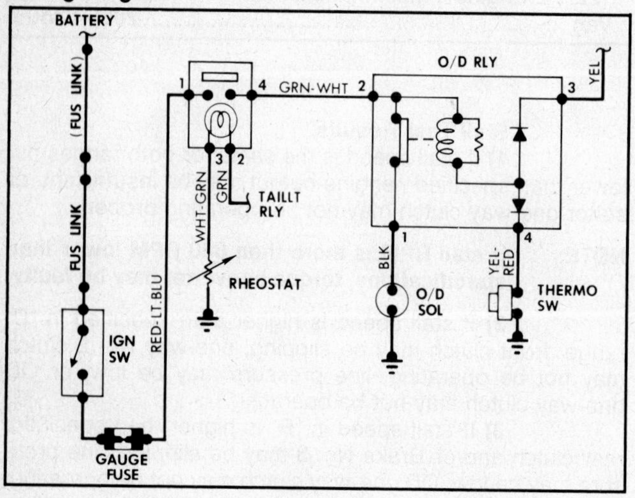

Fig. 10: Celica Overdrive Circuit Wiring Diagram

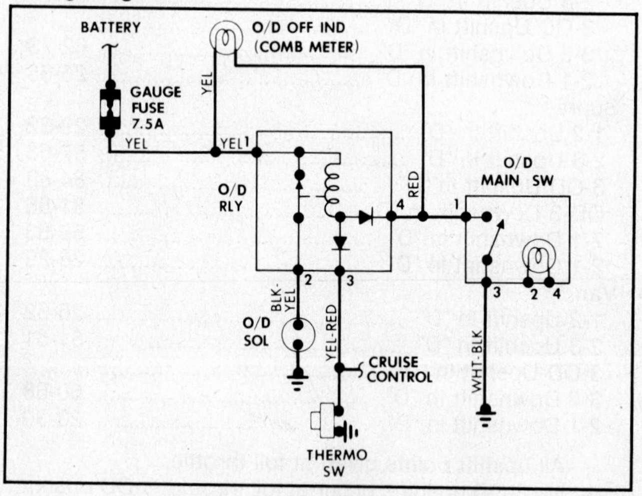

2) Overdrive solenoid is located on left side of transmission. Thermo switch is located on thermostat housing on pickup and Celica models. On Corolla models, thermo switch is located on water pump inlet pipe. The thermo switch on Van models is located on the engine block behind the distributor.

3) The OD relay is located on the steering column support on Celica models. The Van OD relay is under the center console next to the parking brake handle. Corolla OD relay is behind left side of instrument panel. OD relay is on brake pedal brake on pickup models.

TOYOTA A-40D, A-42DL, A-43D, A-43DE & A-44DL (Cont.)

Overdrive Relay Test

1) Using an ohmmeter, check that there is no continuity between terminals No. 1 and No. 2. *See Fig. 11*. Disconnect ohmmeter.

2) Apply 12 volts across terminals No. 2 and No. 4. Ensure there is no continuity between terminals No. 1 and No. 2. Replace relay if defective.

Fig. 11: Overdrive Relay Test Points

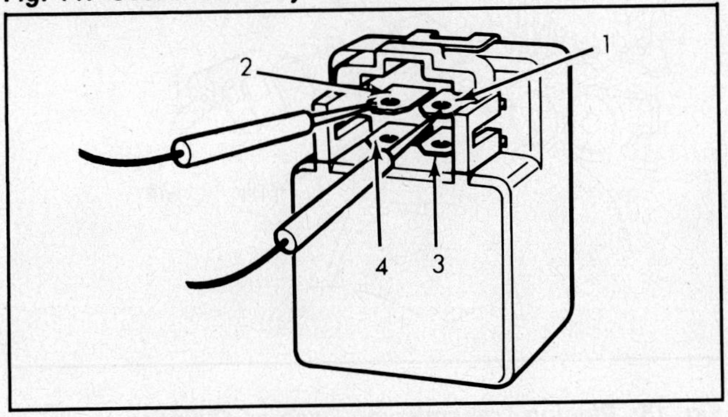

Overdrive Solenoid Test

Disconnect solenoid plug connector. Apply 12 volts to solenoid wire and listen for solenoid operation. Disconnect 12 volts source. Check solenoid resistance between terminal in plug connector and ground. Resistance should be 13 ohms.

Thermo Switch

Unplug thermo switch connector. Measure resistance between switch terminal and ground. There should be continuity below 109°F (43°C) and no continuity above 131°F (55°C).

Fig. 12: Pickup Overdrive Circuit Wiring Diagram

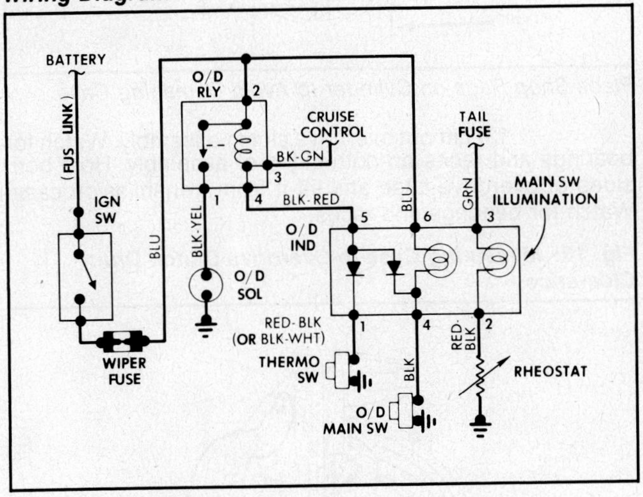

SERVICE (IN VEHICLE)

The following components can be removed from transmission with transmission installed in vehicle: oil pan, valve body assembly, throttle cable, parking pawl assembly, manual valve shaft oil seal, speedometer drive gear, rear oil seal, extension housing, speedometer driven gear, governor assembly, transmission solenoids, OD solenoid, speed sensor and rotor sensor. See TRANSMISSION DISASSEMBLY, COMPONENT DISASSEMBLY AND REASSEMBLY, AND TRANSMISSION REASSEMBLY in this article.

TRANSMISSION SOLENOIDS

Removal & Installation
(A-43DE Transmission Only)

Drain fluid. Remove oil pan, filler tube and gasket. Remove oil tubes. Unplug connectors from each solenoid. Remove solenoid (and gaskets from No. 1 and 2 solenoids). DO NOT remove the 2 valve springs. To install solenoids, reverse removal procedure.

EXTENSION HOUSING & GOVERNOR/ROTOR SENSOR

Removal

1) Remove propeller shaft. Support transmission with a jack and raise slightly to remove weight from rear support. Disconnect speedometer cable. Remove speedometer driven gear. Remove speed sensor (A-43DE only).

2) Remove ground strap, exhaust hanger and rear support member. Remove extension housing. Remove rotor sensor (A-43DE only) or governor (all other models) from output shaft.

Installation

On A-43DE transmissions, install rotor sensor on output shaft, making sure key is installed in groove. To complete installation on all models, reverse removal procedure.

TORQUE CONVERTER

Converter Flushing

If transmission appears contaminated, thoroughly flush converter with transmission cleaner before reassembly. Clean outside of converter and case.

One-Way Clutch Test

1) With converter placed on work surface, insert One-Way Clutch Tester (09350-20013). Kit consists of 2 pieces: a turning tool and a stopper. Insert turning tool in inner race of one-way clutch, insert stopper to fit in notch of converter hub and other race of one-way clutch.

2) Clutch should lock when turned counterclockwise, but should turn freely when rotated clockwise. Torque required to turn clutch clockwise should be less than 22 INCH lbs. (2.5 N.m). If necessary, clean converter and retest clutch. Replace converter if clutch still fails test.

Converter Runout

Torque converter runout should be less than .012" (.30 mm). Drive plate runout should be less than .008" (.20 mm).

TRANSMISSION DISASSEMBLY

INPUT SHAFT END PLAY

Mount dial indicator on front of transmission case. Measure input shaft end play. End play should be .012-.035" (.30-.90 mm).

DISASSEMBLY

1) Remove torque converter. Remove solenoid retaining bolts and solenoid (except A-43DE). On A-43DE only, remove speedometer driven gear and speed sensor.

2) On all models, remove shift handle and neutral start switch. Remove front pump housing bolts. Pull oil pump assembly from transmission case using Puller (SST 09610-20012).

CAUTION: Do not damage the shaft bushing surface.

3) Grab oil pump by stator shaft and pull pump out of case. Do not lose bearing race behind pump. Remove bellhousing retaining bolts (2 short, 4 long) and lift off bellhousing.

4) Remove speedometer driven gear housing (except A-43DE). On all models, remove extension housing and gasket. Remove speedometer drive gear and snap ring (except A-43DE).

5) On all except A-43DE, remove governor retaining bolt (if equipped). Pry up on governor retainer spring with a screwdriver and pull off governor assembly. Remove governor strainer if necessary.

6) On A-43DE only, remove rotor sensor and snap ring from output shaft.

7) On all models, remove oil pan retaining bolts. Remove pan by lifting case. DO NOT turn transmission over to remove pan as this will contaminate valve body with dirt. After removing oil pan, turn transmission over and remove oil tubes. Note installation position for reassembly reference.

8) On A-43DE only, unplug connector from No. 1, No. 2 and No. 3 solenoids. Remove grommet from transmission case. Pull solenoid wiring from case.

9) On all models, remove valve body attaching bolts. Valve body may have either 15 or 17 bolts. *See Fig. 13.* Carefully lift up valve body and disconnect throttle cable from throttle cam. Remove valve body from case. Hold throttle cable retainer with a 10 mm socket and pull cable from case.

Fig. 13: Removing Valve Body Bolts

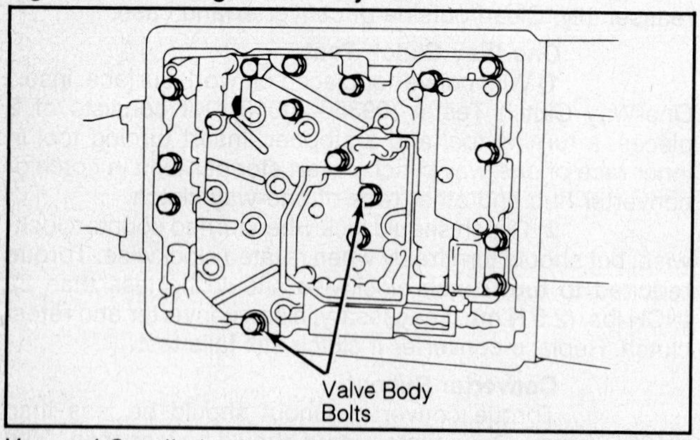

Van and Corolla is shown; other models are similar.

10) Remove accumulator pistons and springs from case by blowing compressed air through holes in case. *See Fig. 14.* Position a rag to catch piston when removing. Identify each accumulator piston and spring for reassembly reference.

11) Remove attaching bolts and parking lock pawl bracket. Remove lock rod after aligning lugs with manual valve lever. Remove parking pawl, pivot pin and spring. If necessary, pry manual shift lever shaft over to gain access to retaining pin. Drive out pin and remove shaft.

12) Stand transmission case upright with front of case facing up. Measure distance between top of case and clutch drum with Measuring Gauge (SST 09350-20013). Record reading for reassembly reference. *See Fig. 16.*

Fig. 14: Removing Accumulator Pistons and Springs

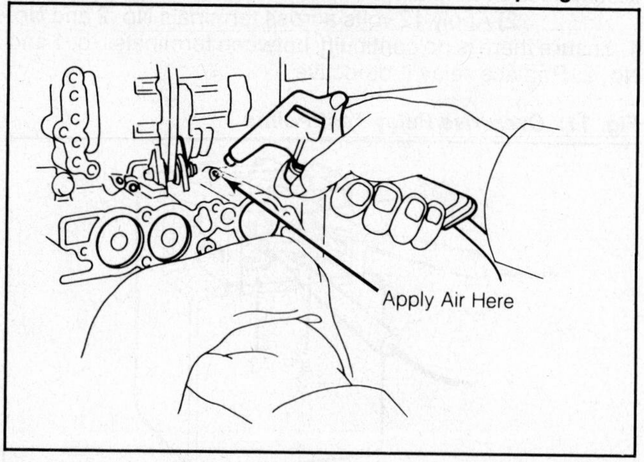

Fig. 15: Placing Transmission Case on Cylinder

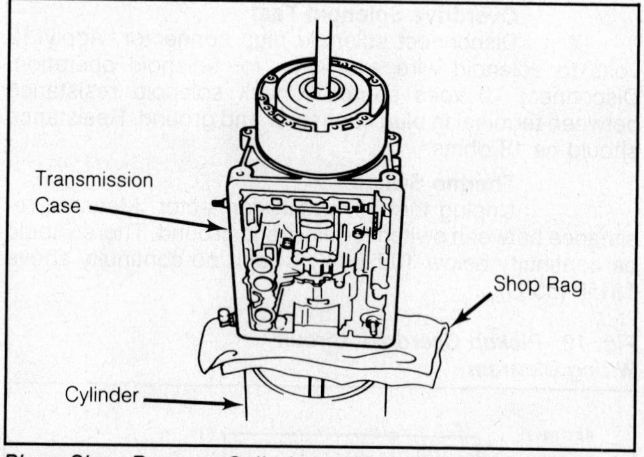

Place Shop Rags on Cylinder to Avoid Damaging Case.

13) Lift out overdrive clutch assembly. Watch for bearings and races on both sides of assembly. Hold both sides of overdrive case and lift it from transmission case. Watch for bearings and races.

Fig. 16: Measuring Case-to-Overdrive Clutch Drum Clearance

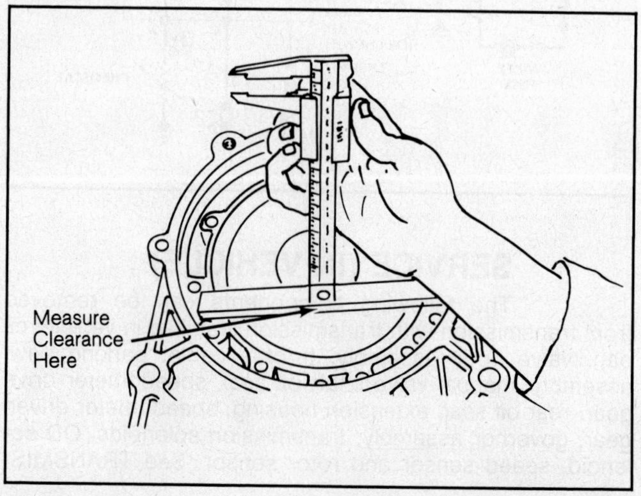

TOYOTA A-40D, A-42DL, A-43D, A-43DE & A-44DL (Cont.)

14) Grasp shaft and lift out front clutch assembly, bearings and races. Remove rear clutch from case. Remove 2 center support mounting bolts at valve body side of case.

15) Pull center support and sun gear shaft assembly from case. Watch for bearing race on end of sun gear. Using a long screwdriver, remove large snap ring from case groove.

16) Pull rear parts group from transmission case by intermediate shaft. If brake apply tube did not come out with rear parts group, remove it from case. Remove output shaft thrust bearing and race from inside of case.

COMPONENT DISASSEMBLY & REASSEMBLY

OIL PUMP & STATOR SHAFT

Disassembly

Set pump shaft in torque converter while working on pump. Remove 2 oil seals from pump cover and discard. Remove retaining bolts and washers and lift off pump cover. Remove large "O" ring from pump body. Mark drive and driven gears for reassembly reference and remove from pump body. Pry out front oil seal.

Fig. 17: Exploded View of Oil Pump and Stator Shaft Assembly

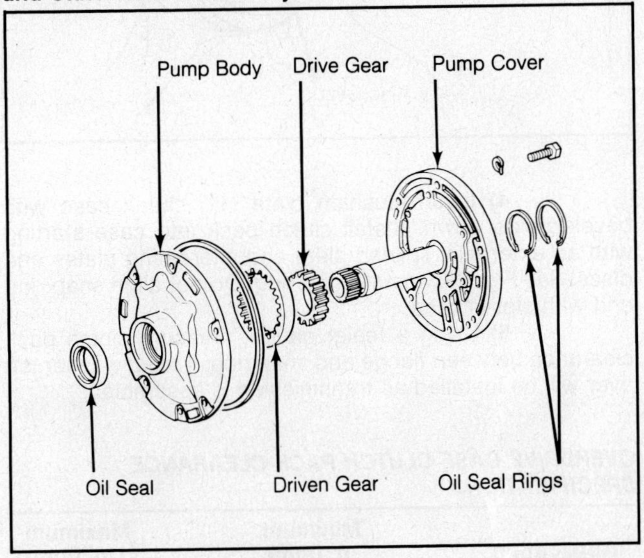

Cleaning & Inspection

1) Wash disassembled parts and blow dry with compressed air. Replace pump oil seal and transmission seal ring.

2) Inspect contacting surfaces between body and driven gear for ridged wear. Check gears for wear and body crescent for damage. Check pump gear contacting surface on stator shaft for damage and wear.

3) With a feeler gauge, measure clearance between driven gear and oil pump body with gear pushed over to other side. If clearance exceeds maximum, replace pump.

4) Measure clearance between crescent and driven gear. Using a feeler gauge and straightedge, measure clearance between pump body face and top of gears. If clearance exceeds maximum, replace oil pump.

OIL PUMP CLEARANCE SPECIFICATIONS

Application	Standard In. (mm)	Maximum In. (mm)
Cresent-to-Driven gear	.004-.006 (.11-.14)	.012 (.30)
Gear Side Clearance	.0008-.002 (.02-.05)	.004 (.10)
Oil Pump-to-Body	.003-.006 (.07-.15)	.012 (.30)

Fig. 18: Measuring Oil Pump Clearances

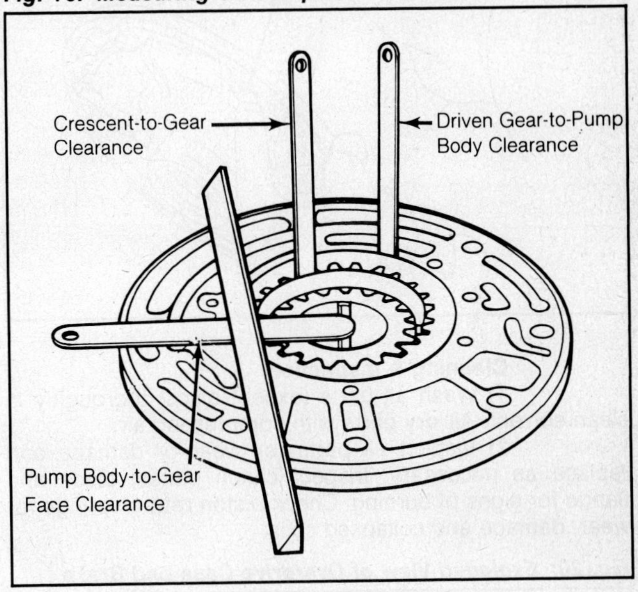

Reassembly

1) Coat all parts with ATF prior to reassembly. Use petroleum jelly to keep small parts in place. Install new oil seal in pump body. Coat drive and driven gears with automatic transmission fluid, then install them into pump body, aligning marks made at disassembly.

2) Align bolt holes and place pump cover onto body. Install, but do not tighten attaching bolts. Use Oil Pump Aligning Tool (SST 09350-20013) to align centers of stator shaft and oil pump body. Tighten attaching bolts. Install 2 new oil seal rings on pump cover.

CAUTION: Ensure oil seal ring ends are properly overlapped.

3) With pump body and cover assembled, check drive gear with a screwdriver to ensure it rotates freely. Lubricate and install "O" ring on pump body.

OVERDRIVE CASE & BRAKE

NOTE: New discs must be soaked in ATF at least 2 hours.

Disassembly

1) Remove thrust bearing and race from overdrive case. Pry large snap ring from case. Lift out clutch flange, clutch discs, plates and cushion plate. Retain in correct order for reassembly.

2) Remove ring gear. Pry thrust washer from ring gear. Remove thrust bearings and races from case and note order and position for reassembly. Compress piston and remove snap ring, spring retainer and return springs.

TOYOTA A-40D, A-42DL, A-43D, A-43DE & A-44DL (Cont.)

3) Remove brake piston from case by applying compressed air. *See Fig. 19.* Remove and discard oil seal rings from case and "O" rings from piston.

Fig. 19: Using Compressed Air to Remove Piston from Overdrive Clutch Case

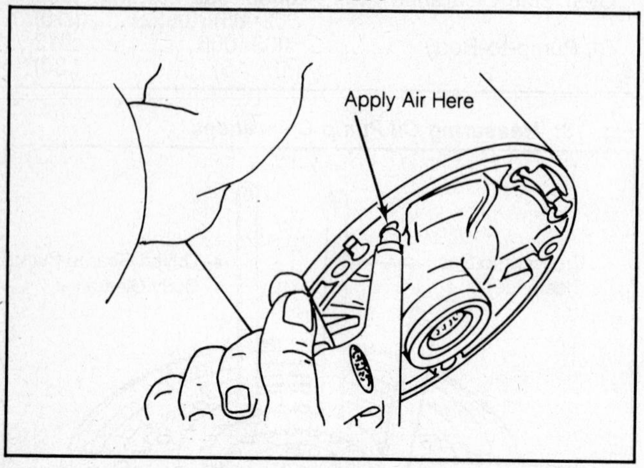

Cleaning & Inspection

1) Wash all parts (except discs) thoroughly in clean solvent. Air dry parts with compressed air.

2) Inspect all parts for wear or damage and replace as necessary. Inspect clutch plates, discs and flange for signs of burning. Check piston return springs for wear, damage and collapsed coils.

Fig. 20: Exploded View of Overdrive Case and Brake

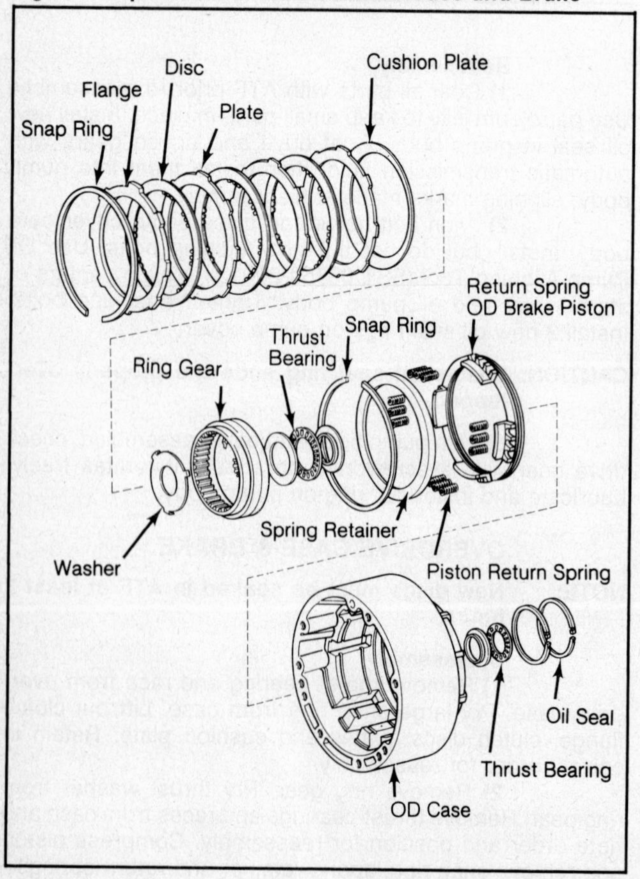

Reassembly

1) Coat all parts with ATF prior to reassembly. Use petroleum jelly to keep small parts in place. Lubricate and install oil seal rings on overdrive case ensure ring ends are properly overlapped. Install new "O" rings on brake piston. Carefully install piston (cup side up) into case. Save thrust washer for installation when transmission is reassembled.

2) Position return springs into pockets of clutch piston. Install spring retainer over springs. Compress return springs and install retaining snap ring, making sure snap ring gap is not aligned with a slot in housing.

3) Install bearing and races on ring gear in same positions as before disassembly. *See Fig. 21.* Install ring gear assembly into clutch case.

Fig. 21: View of Ring Gear Showing Correct Installation of Bearing and Races

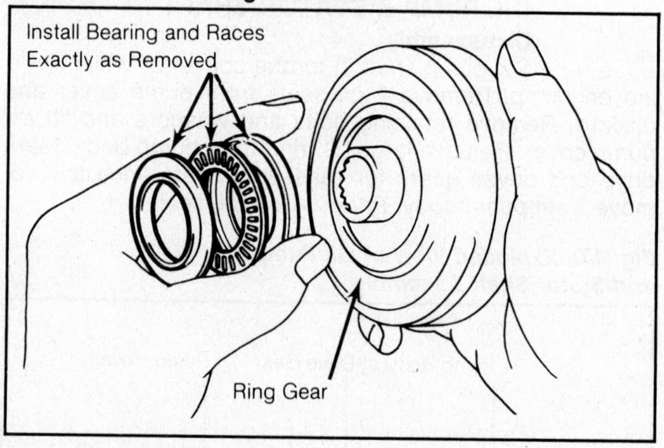

4) Install cushion plate into clutch case with beveled side down. Install clutch pack into case starting with an externally splined plate and alternating plates and discs. *See Fig. 20.*. Install snap ring. Do not align snap ring end with slot in case.

5) Using a feeler gauge, measure clutch pack clearance between flange and snap ring. Thrust washer left over will be installed as transmission is assembled.

OVERDRIVE CASE CLUTCH PACK CLEARANCE SPECIFICATIONS

Application	Minimum In. (mm)	Maximum In. (mm)
A-40D	.01 (.26)	.07 (1.8)
A-42DL	.02 (.56)	.08 (1.9)
A-43DE	.02 (.40)	.05 (1.4)
A-43D & A-44DL	.03 (.65)	.09 (2.2)

OVERDRIVE INPUT SHAFT & CLUTCH

Disassembly

1) Remove thrust bearings and races from clutch side by hand. Note position of races. *See Fig. 23.* Pry thrust washer from planetary gear side with a screwdriver. On A-40D, remove snap ring and hub from overdrive clutch assembly.

2) On all models, pull overdrive clutch assembly from input shaft. Remove thrust bearing and race (except

TOYOTA A-40D, A-42DL, A-43D, A-43DE & A-44DL (Cont.)

A-40D). Remove snap ring and hub from overdrive clutch assembly. Remove thin snap ring, flange disc and plate.

3) Compress piston return springs and remove snap ring. Remove spring retainer and 18 springs. Assemble overdrive clutch on oil pump and blow out piston with compressed air. *See Fig. 22.* Remove overdrive clutch from oil pump. Remove clutch piston "O" rings.

Fig. 22: Removing Overdrive Direct Clutch

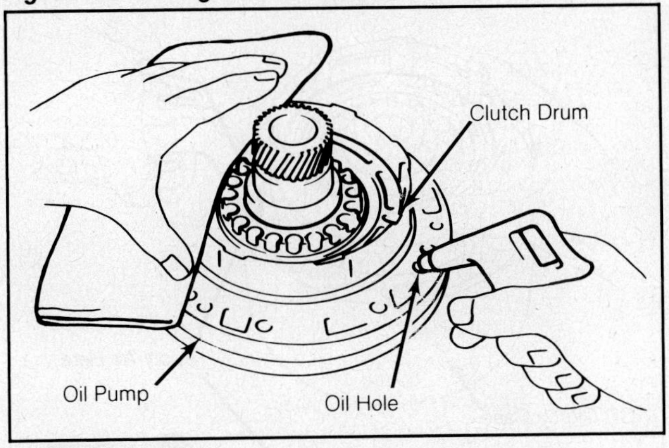

Apply air to oil hole.

4) Remove snap ring from overdrive planetary gear assembly. Remove thrust washers and one-way clutch from planetary gear assembly. Remove plugs (4) with a magnet. DO NOT lose plugs. Remove one-way clutch from outer race.

Cleaning & Inspection

Thoroughly clean all parts and inspect them for wear and damage. Check clutch plates for signs of burning. Shake piston to make sure check ball is free. Apply low-pressure compressed air to check that valve does not leak. Replace parts as necessary.

NOTE: Do not let discs dry out. Soak new clutch plates and discs in ATF for at least 2 hours before installation.

Reassembly

1) Coat all parts with ATF prior to reassembly. Use petroleum jelly to keep small parts in place. Install the 4 plugs. Except for A-40D, install thrust washer and bearing. Install thrust washer with lip facing outward.

2) On all models, assemble one-way clutch into outer race. Install a retainer on both sides of one-way clutch. Spring cage side of one-way clutch faces toward front of transmission. *See Fig. 24*. Install thrust washer in planetary carrier with oil grooves facing up.

3) Install one-way clutch assembly, thrust washer and snap ring. On all models, lubricate and install new "O" ring to piston. Press clutch piston into overdrive clutch drum with cup side up. Position return springs into pockets of piston. Install spring seat over springs.

4) Compress springs and seat and install retaining snap ring. Do not align snap ring gap with spring seat claw. Install clutch plates and discs into clutch drum in reverse order as removed. Do not install thin retaining snap

Fig. 24: View Showing Correct Installation of One-Way Clutch Assembly

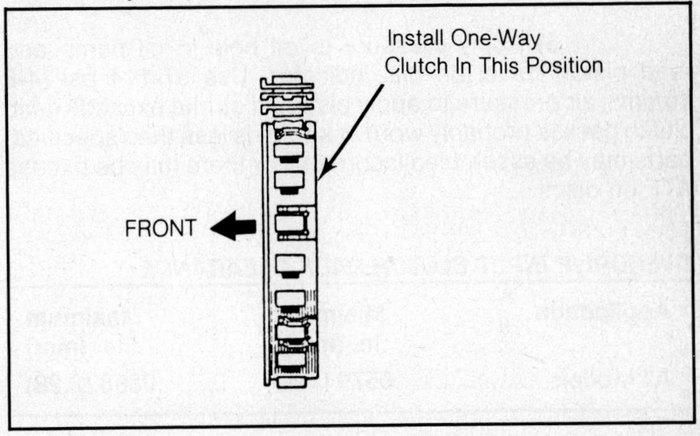

Fig. 23: Exploded View of Overdrive Input Shaft and Clutch

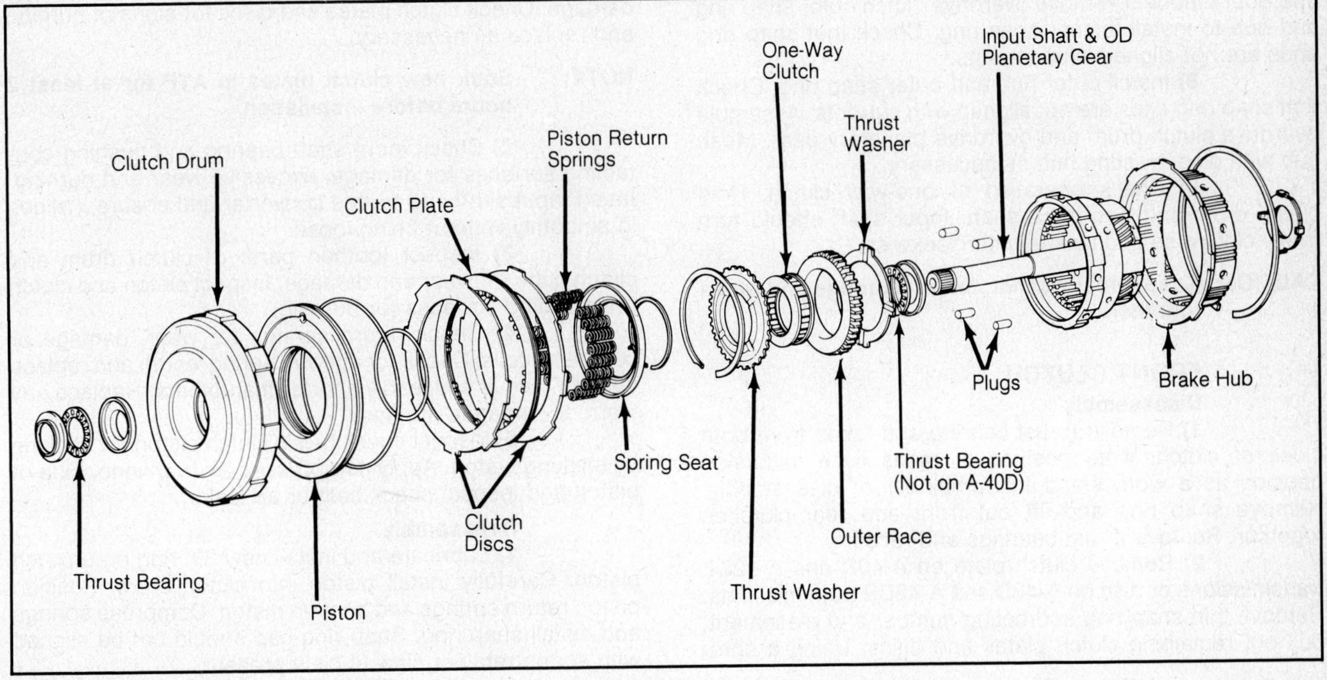

ring on A-40D and A-43DE. Install thinner snap ring before measuring piston travel on other models.

5) To check piston travel, temporarily install overdrive clutch hub and outer snap ring. Install front clutch drum on oil pump body. Mount a dial indicator so indicator tip touches top of clutch piston. *See Fig. 25.*

Fig. 25: Checking Clutch C0 Piston Travel

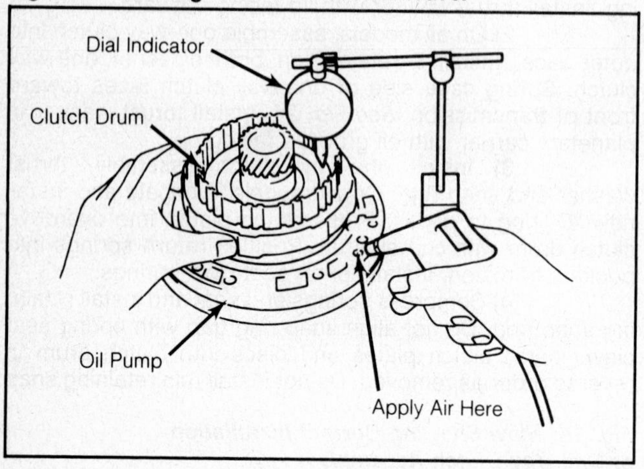

6) Apply pressure to oil hole in oil pump and read piston travel on dial indicator. Use 57-114 psi (4-8 kg/cm^2) air pressure to apply piston. If stroke exceeds limit, clutch pack is probably worn. If stroke is less than specified, parts may be assembled incorrectly or there may be excess ATF on discs.

OVERDRIVE INPUT CLUTCH PACK CLEARANCE

Application	Minimum In. (mm)	Maximum In. (mm)
All Models	.0579 (1.47)	.0898 (2.28)

7) Remove dial indicator. On Celica, Cressida and Supra models, remove overdrive clutch outer snap ring and hub to install thinner snap ring. Check that snap ring ends are not aligned with cut-outs.

8) Install outer hub and outer snap ring. Check that snap ring ends are not aligned with cut-outs. Assemble overdrive clutch drum and overdrive planetary gear. Mesh hub with disc, twisting hub as necessary.

9) Check operation of one-way clutch. Hold clutch drum and turn input shaft. Input shaft should turn freely clockwise and lock counterclockwise.

CAUTION: Keep thrust washer, thrust bearings and races together.

FRONT CLUTCH

Disassembly

1) Remove thrust bearing and races from both sides of clutch. Note position of races. Use extension housing as a work stand for remainder of disassembly. Remove snap ring and lift out front and rear clutches together. Remove thrust bearings and races.

2) Remove clutch plate on A-40D and A-42DL transmissions or disc on A-43D and A-43DE transmissions. Remove thin snap ring and noting number and placement, pull out remaining clutch plates and discs. Using a compressor tool, compress piston return spring and remove snap ring. Take out spring retainer and return springs (18).

3) Assemble clutch drum onto overdrive clutch case. Remove piston by applying compressed air to case oil hole. *See Fig. 26.* Remove "O" rings from clutch piston.

Fig. 26: Removing and Testing Front Clutch Piston Using Compressed Air

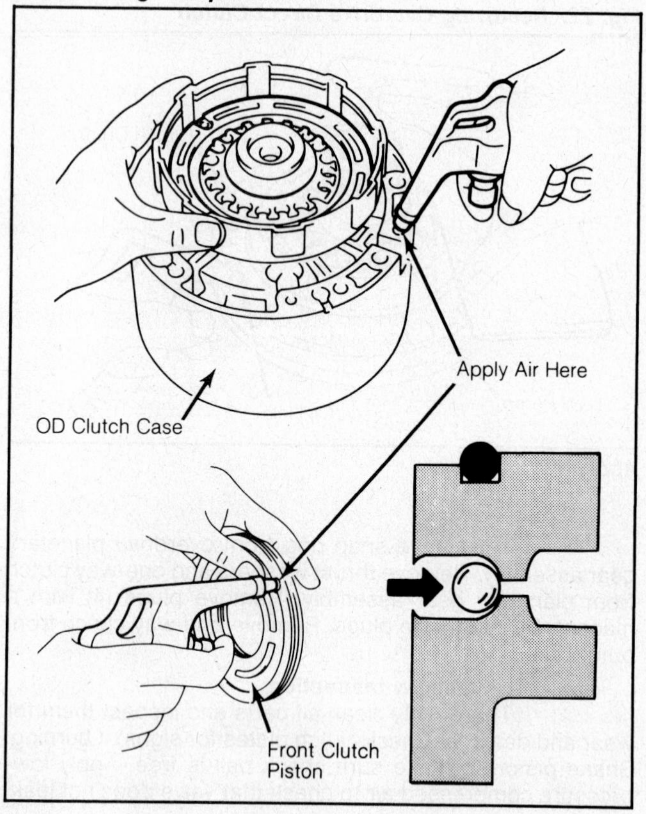

Cleaning & Inspection

1) Clean all parts and inspect for wear and damage. Check clutch plates and discs for signs of burning and replace as necessary.

NOTE: Soak new clutch plates in ATF for at least 2 hours before installation.

2) Check input shaft bearing and bushing contacting surfaces for damage, excessive wear and burning. Insert input shaft into torque converter and ensure it slides in smoothly without being loose.

3) Inspect toothed parts of clutch drum and clutch hubs for wear and damage. Inspect piston and clutch drum sliding surfaces for burning.

4) Check return springs for wear, damage or collapsed coils. Check for uniform spring length and replace spring if one is noticeably shorter than others. Replace any worn or damaged springs.

5) Inspect check ball in clutch piston for sticking by shaking piston. Apply compressed air from inner side of piston and inspect check ball for air leaks.

Reassembly

1) Lubricate and install new "O" ring onto clutch piston. Carefully install piston into clutch drum. Position piston return springs and seat on piston. Compress springs and install snap ring. Snap ring gap should not be aligned with spring retainer claw (if claw present).

TOYOTA A-40D, A-42DL, A-43D, A-43DE & A-44DL (Cont.)

Fig. 27: Exploded View of Pickup (A-43D) Front Clutch Assembly

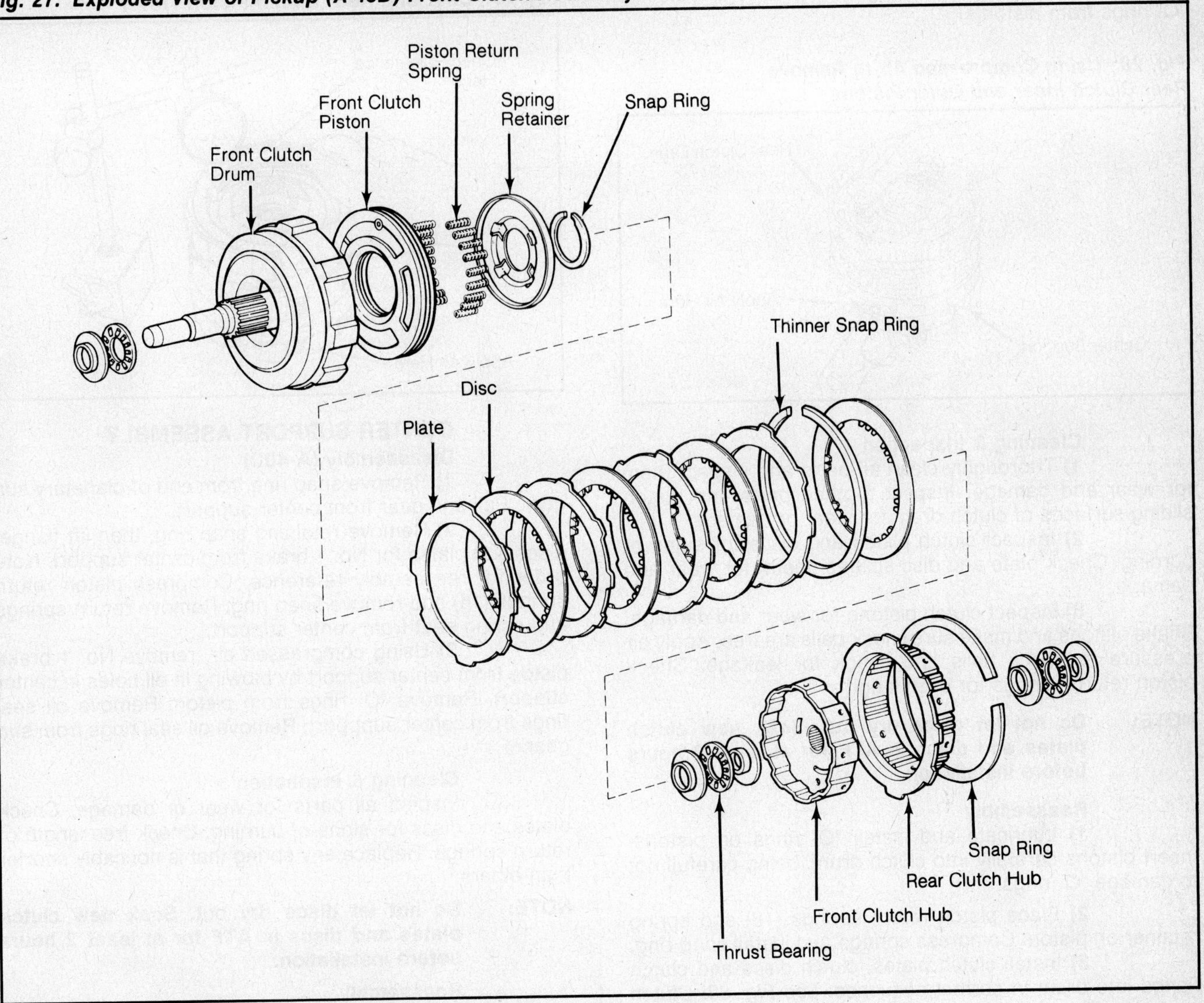

Number and spacing of clutch discs and plates will vary on other models

2) Blow excess ATF off of clutch discs and plates with LOW pressure compressed air. Install ALL clutch discs and plates into drum without thin (inner) snap ring. Assembly always starts with a plate. Install rear clutch hub and outer snap ring.

3) Make sure snap ring ends do not align with any slot in clutch drum. Install clutch on the overdrive case. Assemble a dial indicator with tip touching clutch piston. Apply 57-114 psi (4-8 kg/cm^2) air pressure to oil hole in pump body or overdrive case. Measure front clutch clearance.

FRONT CLUTCH PACK CLEARANCE SPECIFICATIONS

Application	In. (mm)
A-42DL	.0465-.0921 (1.18-2.34)
A-43DE	.0550-.0630 (1.40-1.60)
A-40D, A43D, A44DL	.0520-.1047 (1.32-2.34)

4) If clearance exceeds limit, clutch pack may be worn. If stroke is too short, component may be assembled improperly or there may be excess ATF on clutch discs. Remove dial indicator, snap ring and rear clutch hub.

5) For reassembly reference, front clutches are assembled as follows: On A-40D and A-44DL transmission, install 4 sets of plates and discs, 1 snap ring and a plate. On A-43D and A-43DE transmission, install 3 sets of plates and discs, a plate, snap ring and 1 disc. On A-42DL transmission, install 3 sets of plates and disc, snap ring and 1 plate.

6) Coat inner thrust bearing and races with petroleum jelly to hold them in place and install. Make sure lip of race faces toward front of clutch body. Install front clutch hub, rear clutch hub and snap ring. Check that snap ring ends do not align with slot in clutch drum.

7) Set remaining thrust bearings and races aside for installation when transmission is reassembled.

REAR CLUTCH

Disassembly

1) Remove snap ring and lift clutch flange, clutch discs and clutch plates from rear clutch drum. Compress piston return spring with compressor tool and remove snap ring. Lift out piston, springs and spring retainer.

2) Assemble clutch drum on center support. Apply compressed air to oil hole(s) in center support and remove rear clutch piston (inner and outer pistons on

TOYOTA A-40D, A-42DL, A-43D, A-43DE & A-44DL (Cont.)

A-40D) from clutch drum. *See Fig. 28.* Remove and discard "O" rings from piston(s).

Fig. 28: Using Compressed Air to Remove Rear Clutch Inner and Outer Pistons

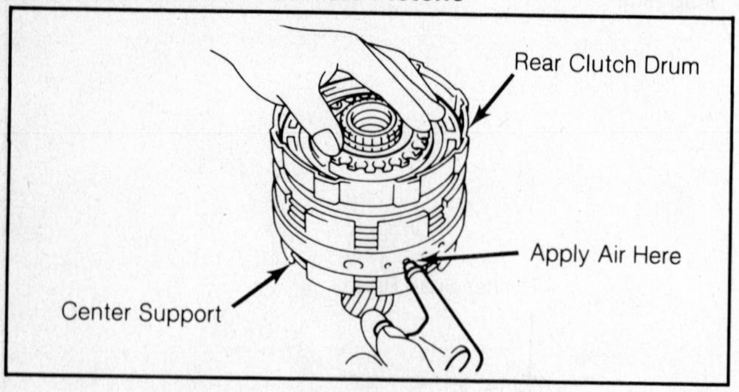

Cleaning & Inspection

1) Thoroughly clean all parts and inspect them for wear and damage. Inspect toothed parts and piston sliding surfaces of clutch drum for wear or damage.

2) Inspect clutch plates and discs for signs of burning. Check plate and disc splines (teeth) for wear and damage.

3) Inspect clutch pistons for wear and damage. Shake pistons and make sure check balls are free. Apply air pressure to check balls and check for leakage. Check piston return springs for even length.

NOTE: **Do not let discs dry out. Soak new clutch plates and discs in ATF for at least 2 hours before installation.**

Reassembly

1) Lubricate and install "O" rings on pistons. Insert pistons carefully into clutch drum, being carefull not to damage "O" rings.

2) Place piston return springs (18) and spring retainer on piston. Compress springs and install snap ring.

3) Install clutch plates, clutch discs and clutch flange into drum in correct sequence. *See Fig. 30.* Clutch packs on all models except Corolla are installed as shown in *Fig. 30*. Clutch pack on Corolla (A-42DL) are assembled as follows: plate, disc, plate, plate, disc and flange. Install clutch pack snap ring.

NOTE: **Install clutch flange with flat end facing down.**

4) Install rear clutch onto center support. Apply compressed air pressure of 57-114 psi (4-8 kg/cm^2) to oil hole in center support and measure travel with a dial indicator.

5) Excessive travel indicates worn clutch pack. If travel is below specifications, components may be misassembled or there may be excess ATF on clutch discs.

REAR CLUTCH PISTON STROKE SPECIFICATIONS

Application	In. (mm)
A-40D	.0433-.0512 (1.10-1.30)
A-42DL	.0366-.0717 (.93-1.82)
A-43DE	.0350-.0692 (.90-1.75)
A-43D	.0358-.0783 (0.91-1.99)
A-44DL	.0417-.0843 (1.06-2.14)

Fig. 29: Checking Rear Clutch Piston Travel

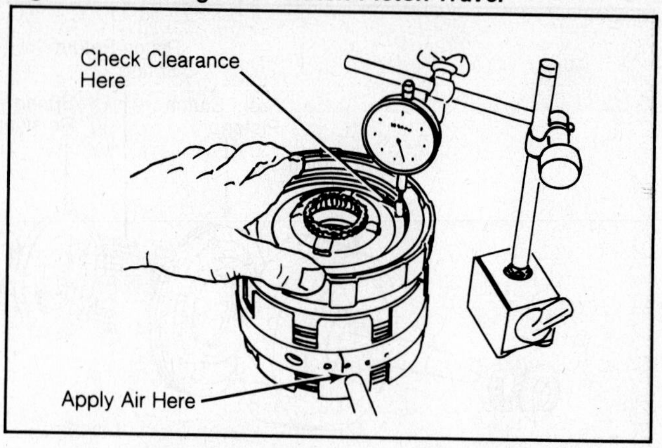

CENTER SUPPORT ASSEMBLY

Disassembly (A-40D)

1) Remove snap ring from end of planetary sun gear. Pull sun gear from center support.

2) Remove retaining snap ring, then lift flange, discs and plates for No. 1 brake from center support. Note order for reassembly reference. Compress piston return springs (16) and remove snap ring. Remove return springs and spring seat from center support.

3) Using compressed air, remove No. 1 brake piston from center support by blowing in oil holes in center support. Remove "O" rings from piston. Remove oil seal rings from center suppport. Remove oil seal rings from sun gear.

Cleaning & Inspection

Inspect all parts for wear or damage. Check plates and discs for signs of burning. Check free length of return springs. Replace any spring that is noticably shorter than others.

NOTE: **Do not let discs dry out. Soak new clutch plates and discs in ATF for at least 2 hours before installation.**

Reassembly

1) Install 2 oil seal rings on sun gear. Install 3 oil seal rings on center support. Lubricate and install new "O" rings on piston and center support. Press No. 1 brake piston into center support with cup side up. Install 16 piston return springs. Set spring seat with snap ring into place.

2) Compress springs. Install snap ring with screwdriver. Use low pressure compressed air to blow ATF from discs. Install No. 1 brake plates, discs and flange. Install in order noted during disassembly. *See Fig. 31*. Install flange with flat end down.

3) Install snap ring in center support. Check that snap ring ends are not aligned with a cut-out. Install dial indicator to measure piston stroke. Apply compressed air to piston oil hole at 57-114 psi (4-8 kg/cm^2) and measure stroke. Stroke should be .039-.047" (1.0-1.2 mm). Maximum stroke is .051" (1.3 mm).

4) Excessive travel indicates worn clutch pack. If travel is below specifications, components may be misassembled or there could be excess ATF on clutch discs. Assemble center support and sun gear shaft. Install snap ring on end of sun gear shaft.

Disassembly
(All Other Transmissions)

1) Remove snap ring from end of sun gear shaft. Pull center support assembly from shaft. Remove snap ring

TOYOTA A-40D, A-42DL, A-43D, A-43DE & A-44DL (Cont.)

Fig. 30: Exploded View of Rear Clutch Assembly

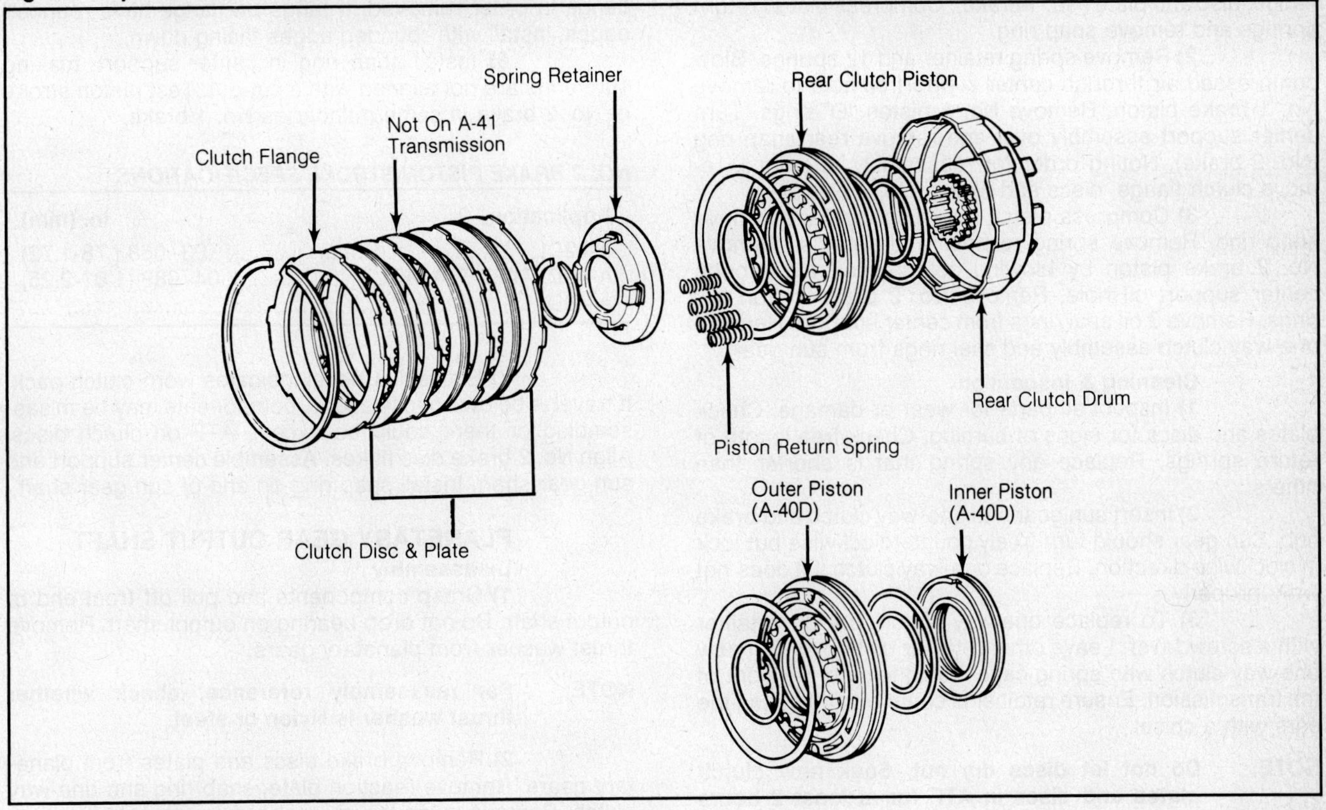

Fig. 31: Exploded View Of Center Support Assembly (A-40D Transmission)

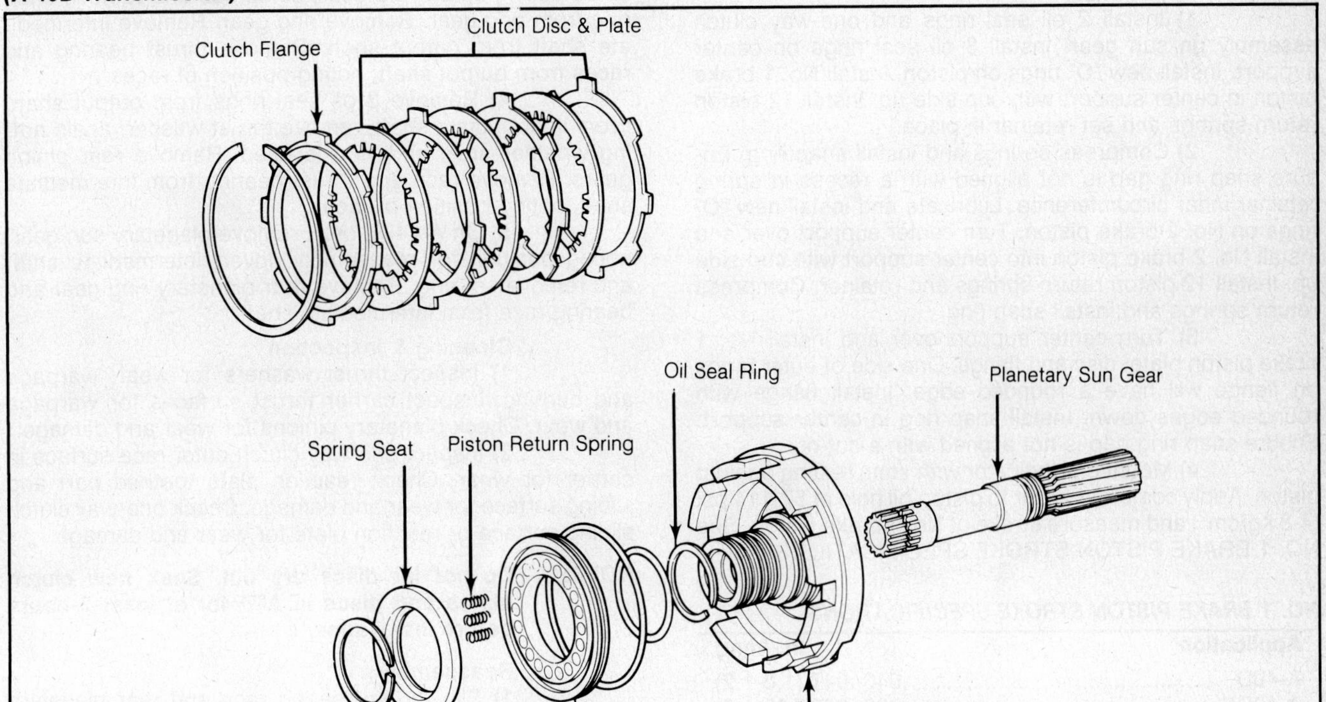

from front of center support assembly. Remove clutch flange, disc and plate (No. 1 brake). Compress piston return springs and remove snap ring.

2) Remove spring retainer and 12 springs. Blow compressed air through center support oil hole to remove No. 1 brake piston. Remove No. 1 piston "O" rings. Turn center support assembly over and remove rear snap ring (No. 2 brake). Noting order for reassembly reference, remove clutch flange, discs and plates (No. 2 brake).

3) Compress piston return springs and remove snap ring. Remove spring retainer and springs. Remove No. 2 brake piston by blowing compressed air through center support oil hole. Remove No. 2 brake piston "O" rings. Remove 3 oil seal rings from center support. Remove one-way clutch assembly and seal rings from sun gear.

Cleaning & Inspection

1) Inspect all parts for wear or damage. Check plates and discs for signs of burning. Check free length of return springs. Replace any spring that is shorter than others.

2) Insert sun gear into one-way clutch and brake hub. Sun gear should turn freely counterclockwise but lock in clockwise direction. Replace one-way clutch if it does not work properly.

3) To replace one-way clutch, pry off retainer with a screwdriver. Leave other retainer on hub. Install new one-way clutch with spring cage facing toward the front of the transmission. Ensure retainer is centered and flatten the ears with a chisel.

NOTE: **Do not let discs dry out. Soak new clutch plates and discs in ATF for at least 2 hours before installation.**

Reassembly

1) Install 2 oil seal rings and one-way clutch assembly on sun gear. Install 3 oil seal rings on center support. Install new "O" rings on piston. Install No. 1 brake piston in center support with cup side up. Install 12 piston return springs and set retainer in place.

2) Compress springs and install snap ring. Ensure snap ring gap is not aligned with a recess in spring retainer inner circumference. Lubricate and install new "O" rings on No. 2 brake piston. Turn center support over and install No. 2 brake piston into center support with cup side up. Install 12 piston return springs and retainer. Compress return springs and install snap ring.

3) Turn center support over and install No. 1 brake piston plate, disc and flange. One side of outer tangs on flange will have a rounded edge. Install flange with rounded edges down. Install snap ring in center support. Ensure snap ring gap is not aligned with a cut-out.

4) Mount dial indicator with stem resting against piston. Apply compressed air to piston oil hole at 57-114 psi (4-8 kg/cm^2) and measure stroke of No. 1 brake piston. See NO. 1 BRAKE PISTON STROKE SPECIFICATIONS table.

NO. 1 BRAKE PISTON STROKE SPECIFICATIONS

Application	In. (mm)
A-40D	.040-.047 (1.0-1.2)
A-43DE	.032-.068 (.80-1.7)
All Others	.023-.051 (.58-1.3)

5) Excessive travel indicates worn clutch pack. If travel is below specifications, components may be misassembled or there could be excess ATF on clutch discs. Turn center support over and install No. 2 brake plates, disc and flange in order removed. If tangs on flange have rounded edges, install with rounded edges facing down.

6) Install snap ring in center support, making sure ends are not aligned with a cut-out. Test piston stroke of No. 2 brake in same manner as No. 1 brake.

NO. 2 BRAKE PISTON STROKE SPECIFICATIONS

Application	In. (mm)
A-42DL	.03-.068 (.78-1.72)
A-43D, A43DE, A44DL	.04-.089 (1.01-2.25)
A-40D	.....

7) Excessive travel indicates worn clutch pack. If travel is below specifications, components may be misassembled or there could be excess ATF on clutch discs. Align No. 2 brake disc flukes. Assemble center support and sun gear shaft. Install snap ring on end of sun gear shaft.

PLANETARY GEAR OUTPUT SHAFT

Disassembly

1) Grasp components and pull off front end of output shaft. Do not drop bearing on output shaft. Remove thrust washer from planetary gears.

NOTE: **For reassembly reference, check whether thrust washer is Nylon or steel.**

2) Remove brake discs and plates from planetary gears. Remove reaction plate, snap ring and one-way clutch. Remove nylon thrust washer from planetary gears.

3) Remove apply tube and clutch pressure plate. While pulling up on ring gear, compress and remove snap ring from ring gear. Remove ring gear. Remove intermediate shaft from output shaft. Remove thrust bearing and races from output shaft, noting position of races.

4) Remove 3 oil seal rings from output shaft. From intermediate shaft, remove thrust washer, again noting whether steel or Nylon is used. Remove rear pinion gears. Remove race and thrust bearing from intermediate shaft, noting position of race.

5) On A-44DL only, remove planetary sun gear, noting position for reassembly. Invert intermediate shaft and remove set ring. Remove rear planetary ring gear and bearing race from intermediate shaft.

Cleaning & Inspection

1) Inspect thrust washers for wear, warpage and burning. Inspect carrier thrust surfaces for warpage and wear. Check planetary pinions for wear and damage.

2) Inspect one-way clutch outer race surface in carrier for wear. Check reaction plate toothed part and sliding surface for wear and damage. Check one-way clutch sliding surface or reaction plate for wear and damage.

NOTE: **Do not let discs dry out. Soak new clutch plates and discs in ATF for at least 2 hours before installation.**

Reassembly

1) Slip thrust bearing race and rear planetary ring gear onto shaft with exterior splines up. Install set ring on intermediate shaft. Turn over intermediate shaft and install thrust bearing and race.

2) Install pinion gear assembly thrust washer on rear planetary carrier (nylon washer on A-40D, A-42DL and A-44DL, steel on others). Install washer with lugs down,

Fig. 32: Exploded View of Center Support Assembly (A-42DL, A-43D, A-43DE & A-44DL Transmissions)

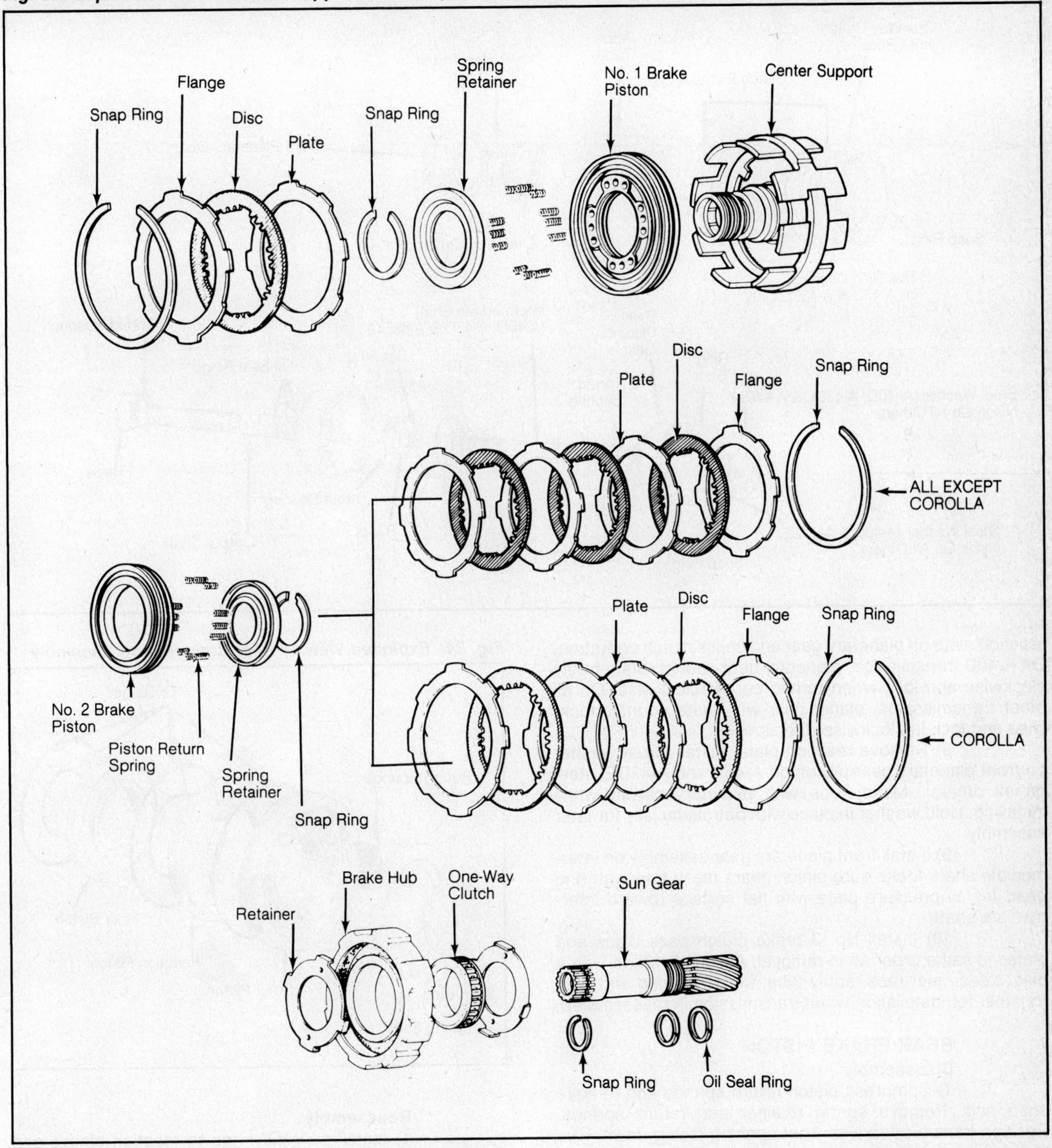

fitting into rear planetary carrier. Make sure lug shapes match opening on plate. Install 3 oil seal rings on output shaft.

3) Using extension housing as an assembly stand, install thrust bearing and race on output shaft. Hold race cup toward bearing. Install intermediate shaft assembly in output shaft. Install rear planetary carrier in output shaft. Slide into place and make sure lugs interlock.

4) On A-44DL only, install planetary sun gear. Install gear with non-splined portion of inner diameter facing up.

5) Install snap ring on front planetary ring gear. Align ends of snap ring with wide gap between teeth. Install ring gear on shaft and while pushing down on ring gear, squeeze ends of snap ring and install into groove. When snap ring is fully seated, gap is one lug wide.

6) Install nylon thrust washer in front planetary gear. Face lugs down and match them with slots in back of planetary gear. Install one-way clutch into outer race with spring cage toward front. Install snap ring.

7) Install one-way clutch into outer race, facing spring cage toward front. *See Fig. 24*. Temporarily install

TOYOTA A-40D, A-42DL, A-43D, A-43DE & A-44DL (Cont.)

Fig. 33: Exploded View of Output Shaft and Planetary Gears

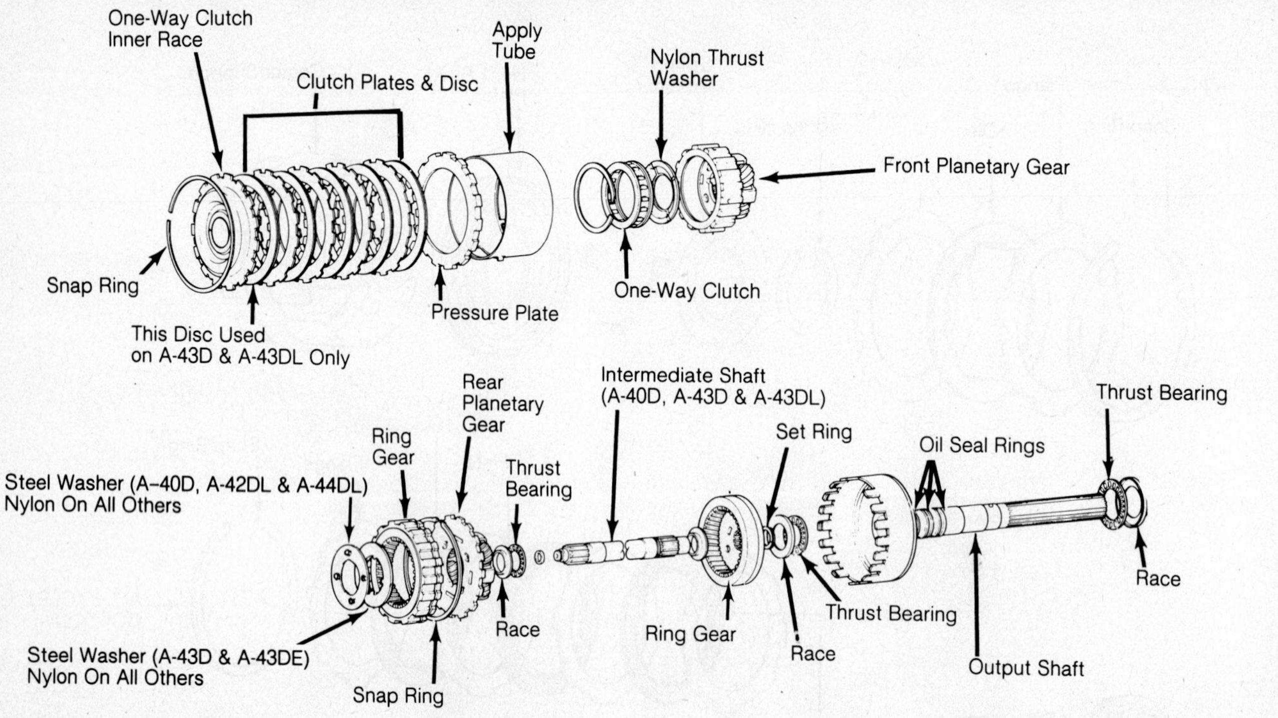

reaction plate on planetary gear and check clutch operation. On A-40D transmission, planetary gear should rotate freely clockwise and lock when turned counterclockwise. On all other transmissions, planet gear will rotate counterclockwise and lock in clockwise direction.

8) Remove reaction plate. Install thrust washer on front planetary gear (Nylon on A-43D and A-43DE, steel on all others). Match lugs with planetary carrier while installing. Hold washer in place with petroleum jelly for later assembly.

9) Install front planetary gear assembly on intermediate shaft. Make sure pinion gears mesh fully with ring gear. Install pressure plate with flat surface toward intermediate shaft.

10) Install No. 3 brake clutch pack discs and plates in same order as in removal. Assembly starts with a disc. Keep inner race, apply tube, thrust bearing and race together for installation when transmission is reassembled.

REAR BRAKE PISTON

Disassembly

1) Compress piston return springs and remove snap ring. Remove spring retainer and return springs. Position transmission with front opening facing down.

2) Place shop rags under rear brake piston. Using 2 air guns, blow SIMULTANEOUSLY through brake cylinder holes and remove inner piston, outer piston and brake reaction sleeve as a unit. *See Fig. 35.*

Cleaning & Inspection

Wash all parts in clean solvent and blow dry with compressed air. Inspect piston and reaction sleeve for scoring, wear or other damage. Check return springs for uniform height and cracked or broken coils. Replace all "O" rings and any damaged parts.

Fig. 34: Exploded View of Rear Brake Piston Assembly

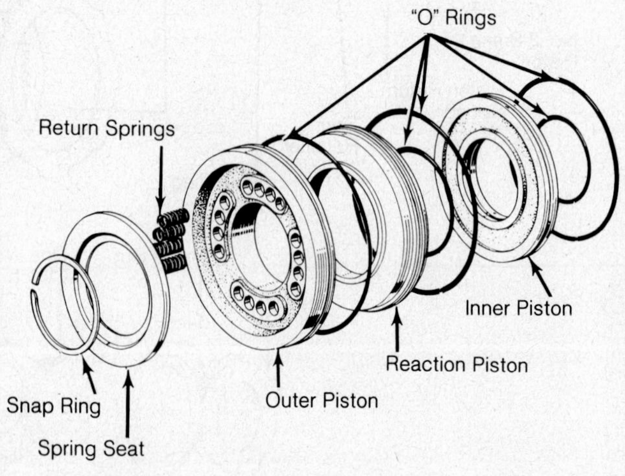

Reassembly

1) Install new "O" rings to reaction sleeve and pistons. Thin "O" ring goes on outside of reaction sleeve. Install inner and outer pistons on reaction sleeve. Push inner piston into cupped side of reaction sleeve. Push outer piston onto other side of reaction sleeve.

2) After cleaning and inspecting case, install pistons and sleeve. Hold assembly with outer piston up and push assembly into its bore in case. Install return springs and spring retainer. Compress springs and install snap ring. Snap ring gap should be centered between 2 of the 3 lugs of the spring retainer.

TOYOTA A-40D, A-42DL, A-43D, A-43DE & A-44DL (Cont.)

Fig. 35: Rear Brake Piston Removal

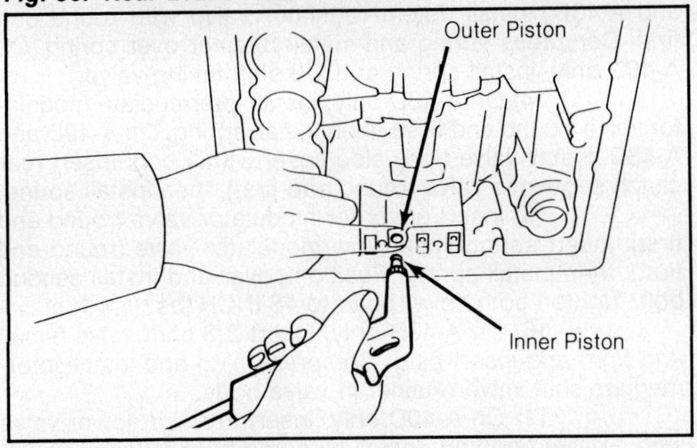

VALVE BODY

Disassembly

1) Disassembly procedures for all valve bodies are similar. Use appropriate valve body figure as a guide and note the following:

2) As valve trains are removed from each valve body bore, place individual parts in correct order in relative position to valve body in order to simplify reassembly.

3) When disassembling, use care not to damage valve surfaces or form burrs around valve body bores.

4) When separating upper valve bodies (front and rear) from lower valve body, be careful not to lose check balls and springs.

Cleaning & Inspection

1) Wash all disassembled parts and blow dry with compressed air. Inspect all valves for wear and damage, then insert them into valve body and check that they operate smoothly while being turned.

2) Inspect valve body bore sliding surfaces for damage and wear. Check all oil holes and oil passages for clogging.

3) Inspect all valve springs for wear, damage, excessive weakness and collapsed coils. Measure free length of all springs and replace if incorrect.

4) Inspect valve body cover plates and check balls for wear and damage. Check pressure relief valve for wear and damage. Inspect oil strainer for clogging and replace if necessary.

Reassembly (A-40D & A-43D)

1) To assemble lower valve body on A-40D and A-43D, install reverse brake plug. Carefully insert low-coast shift valve with small end first. Insert 3-4 shift control valve with cup side first. Insert 3rd-coast shift valve with small end first.

2) Insert inside plug with thick face first. Using tweezers, insert locating pin. Insert outside plug and locating pin. Install cover plate. Set valve body on edge, insert spring, 1-2 shift valve (small part first) and plug. Install 1-2 shift valve plug retainer.

3) Install spring, 3-4 shift valve (small end first) and plug. Install 3-4 shift valve plug retainer (A-40D) or locating pin (A-43D). On A-40D, insert overdrive clutch exhaust valve with round end first. Insert spring and retainer.

4) On both models, install manual down timing valve, small end first. Insert plug with large end first. Install manual down timing valve retainer.

VALVE BODY SPRING FREE LENGTH (A-42DL & A-44DL TRANSMISSIONS)

Application	A-42DL In. (mm)	A-44DL In. (mm)
Front Upper Body		
Throttle Valve	.864 (21.24)	.756 (19.24)
Downshift Plug	1.563 (39.71)	1.565 (39.76)
Sec. Reg. Valve	2.806 (71.27)	2.806 (71.27)
Rear Upper Body		
Low-Coast Mod. Valve	1.667 (42.35)	1.667 (42.35)
Intermediate Mod. Valve	1.073 (27.26)	1.073 (27.26)
Reverse Sequence Valve	1.478 (37.55)	.....
Gov. Mod. Valve	1.420 (36.07)	.....
2-3 Shift Valve	1.382 (35.10)	1.382 (35.10)
Det. Reg. Valve	1.236 (31.39)	1.263 (32.08)
Rear Clutch Sequence Valve	.....	1.478 (37.55)
Lower Body		
Reverse Sequence Valve	1.478 (37.55)	.....
1-2 Shift Valve	1.363 (34.62)	1.363 (34.62)
Pressure Relief Valve	1.265 (32.14)	1.265 (32.14)
Prim. Reg. Valve	2.887 (73.32)	.409 (61.20)
Damping Ball	.787 (20.00)	.787 (20.00)
3-4 Shift Valve	1.385 (35.18)	1.428 (36.28)
Oil Cooler By-Pass Valve	1.312 (33.32)	1.312 (33.32)
Lock-Up Relay Valve	.728 (18.50)	.728 (18.50)
Lock-Up Signal Valve	1.784 (45.31)	1.489 (37.83)

5) Insert primary regulator valve, large end first. Insert spring. Make sure primary regulator valve fits flush with valve body. Insert regulator valve plunger (rounded end first) into sleeve. Plunger should be recessed inside sleeve. Insert sleeve with plunger. Install regulator valve spring retainer.

6) Install pressure relief ball, spring and retainer. Install 4 check balls. *See Figs. 36 and 38.* Install gasket, plate, gasket and lower body cover. Install and tighten lower valve body bolts.

CAUTION: Lower valve body gaskets are NOT interchangeable.

7) Note different size of 2 rubber check balls. Spring goes with larger ball. Install smaller check ball, spring, larger check ball and oil cooler by-pass check valve. *See Figs. 39 and 40.*

8) Install lower valve body gasket, making sure new gasket matches old gasket. Install lower valve body plate. Temporarily install 2 bolts finger tight to compress plate against check valve.

9) To reassemble upper front valve body, insert throttle valve. Coat retainer with petroleum jelly and install. Install adjusting rings (same number as removed) on throttle valve shaft. Insert spring and downshift plug.

10) Temporarily install cut-back plug retainer to hold downshift plug in place. Assemble throttle cam assem-

TOYOTA A-40D, A-42DL, A-43D, A-43DE & A-44DL (Cont.)

Fig. 36: Installing Check Balls in Lower Valve Body (A-40D Transmission Only)

Install Balls Into Passages Indicated By Arrows

VALVE BODY SPRING FREE LENGTH (A-40D & A43D TRANSMISSIONS)

Application	A40D In. (mm)	A-43D In. (mm)
Front Upper Body		
Throttle Valve	.864 (21.94)	.864 (21.94)
Downshift Plug	1.693 (43.00)	1.563 (39.71)
Sec. Reg. Valve	2.806 (71.27)	2.806 (71.27)
Rear Upper Body		
Sequence Valve	1.478 (37.55)	1.478 (37.55)
Gov. Mod. Valve	1.420 (36.07)	1.420 (36.07)
2-3 Shift Valve	1.342 (34.09)	1.382 (35.10)
2-3 Shift Time Valve	1.174 (29.82)	......
Det. Reg. Valve	1.198 (30.43)	1.178 (29.93)
Low-Coast Mod. Valve	1.667 (42.35)	1.667 (42.35)
3-2 Kick-Down Valve	.991 (25.17)	......
Intermediate Modulator Valve	......	1.073 (27.26)
Lower Body		
1-2 Shift Valve	1.363 (34.62)	1.363 (34.62)
Pressure Relief Ball	1.265 (32.14)	1.265 (32.14)
Oil Cooler Check Valve	1.312 (33.32)	1.312 (33.32)
Prim. Reg. Valve	[1] 2.367 (60.13)	2.887 (73.32)
Damping Ball	.787 (20.00)	.787 (20.00)
3-4 Shift Valve	1.325 (33.65)	1.325 (33.65)
OD Clutch Exh. Valve	1.224 (31.09)	......

[1] – For 22R engine; 2.409 (61.20 mm) on 22R-E engine.

bly. Install throttle cam to upper front valve body, tightening to 65 INCH lbs. (7.4 N.m).

11) After throttle cam is installed, check to see that it turns smoothly and moves full stroke. Push in downshift valve and remove temporary retainer. Make sure roller or plug follows smaller portion of cam.

12) Partially install cover plate and insert spring and secondary regulator valve. Compress spring and swing cover plate into place. Install second bolt in cover plate and tighten both bolts. Insert cut-back valve and plug with smaller end of valve first. Install cut-back valve retainer. Install rubber check ball (except A-43DL). *See Fig. 41.*

13) To reassemble upper rear body on A-40D and A-43D, install detent regulator valve with round end first. Compress spring and install retainer over spring. On A-40D only, install spring and 2-3 shift timing valve.

14) On A-43D only, install intermediate modulator valve (round end first), then install spring. On A-40D and A-43D, install valve body side cover with 1 bolt. Insert rear clutch sequence valve (round end first), then install spring.

15) Insert governor modulator valve (round end first). Insert spring. Insert low modulator valve (round end first), then install spring. Position cover and install second bolt. Tighten both cover bolts to 48 INCH lbs. (5.4 N.m).

16) On A-43D only, insert 2-3 shift valve (small end first) and insert plug. Compress plug and install intermediate shift valve retainer in valve body.

17) On A-40D only, insert 2-3 shift lower valve with smaller end first. Install plug into bore hole facing up. Insert pin into hole (coat pin with petroleum jelly). Insert 2-3 shift valve with large end first.

18) On A-40D and A-43D, insert spring and intermediate shift valve (round end up) in bore. Insert plug and retainer.

19) Install check balls. A-40D has 1 steel and 4 rubber balls; A-43D has 1 steel and 3 rubber balls. *See Fig. 42.*

20) To reassemble valve body, make sure new gasket matches old and position on upper rear valve body. Align gasket at lower left corner. Place lower valve body with plate on top of upper rear valve body. Install and finger tighten 3 bolts in lower valve body to secure upper rear valve body.

21) Turn assembly over, check gasket alignment and finger tighten bolts in upper rear valve body. Remove temporary bolts from plate. Place lower and upper rear valve body assembly on upper front valve body. Install and finger tighten set bolts in lower valve body to secure upper front valve body.

22) Turn assembly over and finger tighten 5 bolts in upper front valve body. Recheck alignment of gaskets and tighten bolts in upper front and rear valve bodies. Turn assembly over and tighten bolts in lower valve body. Insert manual valve. Install detent spring and tighten bolts.

Reassembly (A-43DE)

1) Set valve body on edge. Drop in primary regulator valve (large end first) and spring. Ensure valve fits flush with valve body. Insert sleeve, plunger and regulator valve retainer.

2) Install lock-up relay valve, control valve, spring and retaining pin in valve body. Install No. 3 solenoid and temporarily tighten bolt. Install low-coast modulator valve and intermediate valve into bore. Install valve springs in bores. Short spring goes with low-coast modulator valve.

3) Install No. 1 and No. 2 solenoids with new gaskets. Install pressure relief ball, spring and retainer. Tighten bolt to 48 INCH lbs. (5.4 N.m). Install 2 valve body covers. Ensure retainers and locating pins are installed correctly.

NOTE: Use wave washer on smaller valve body cover.

4) Install damping ball, spring and cooler bypass check valve. *See Fig. 43.*

5) Install lower valve body gasket. Gasket is not interchangeable and must lay flat on valve body. Set lower valve body plate in place. Temporarily install 2 short oil strainer bolts finger tight to compress plate against spring loaded check valve.

TOYOTA A-40D, A-42DL, A-43D, A-43DE & A-44DL (Cont.)

Fig. 37: Exploded View of A-40D and A-43D Transmission Valve Body

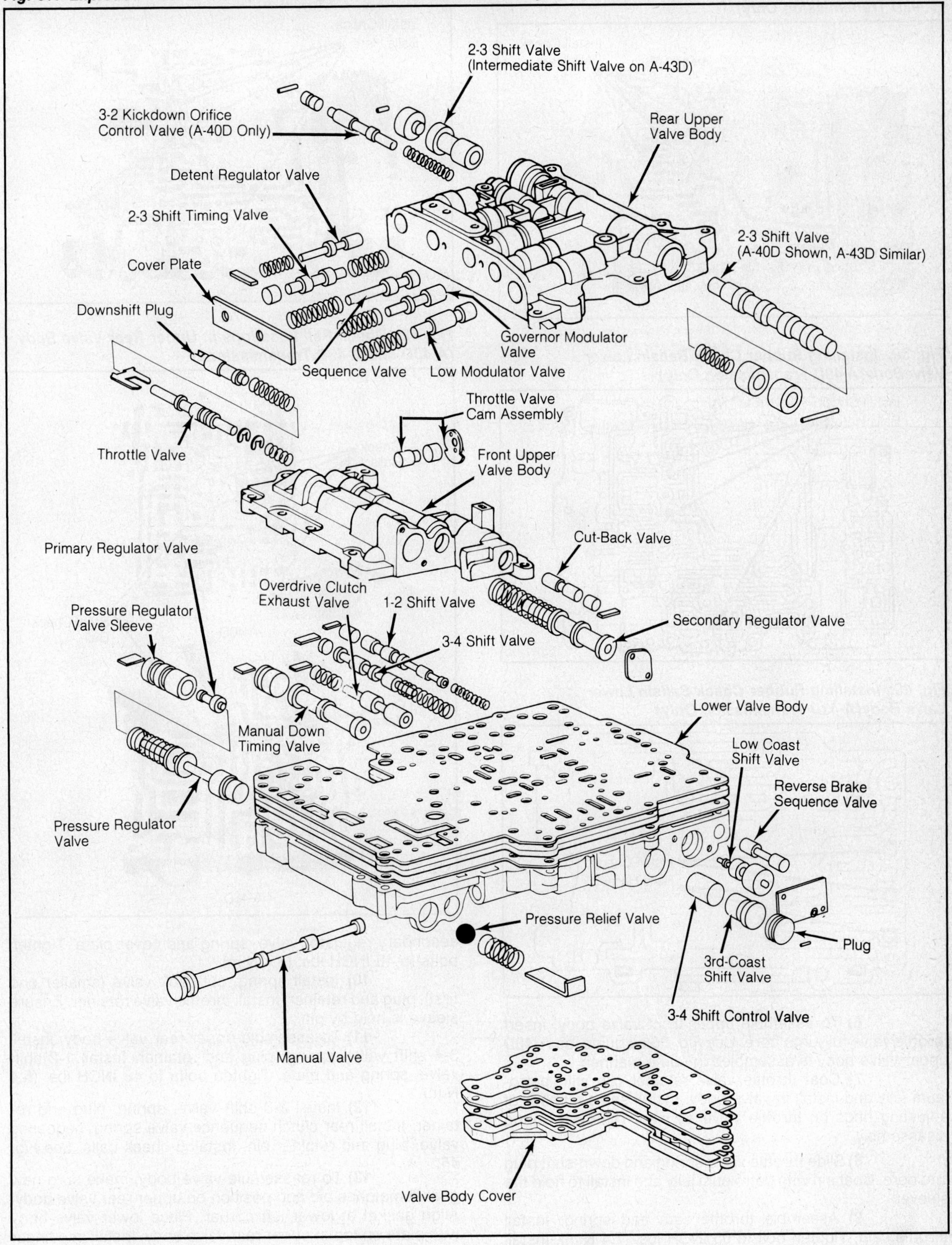

TOYOTA A-40D, A-42DL, A-43D, A-43DE & A-44DL (Cont.)

Fig. 38: Installing Check Balls in Lower Valve Body (A-43D Transmission Only)

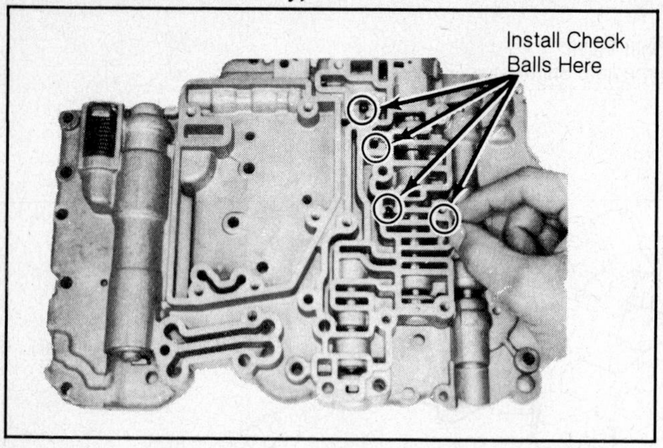

Fig. 39: Installing Rubber Check BallsIn Lower ValveBody(A-40D Transmission Only)

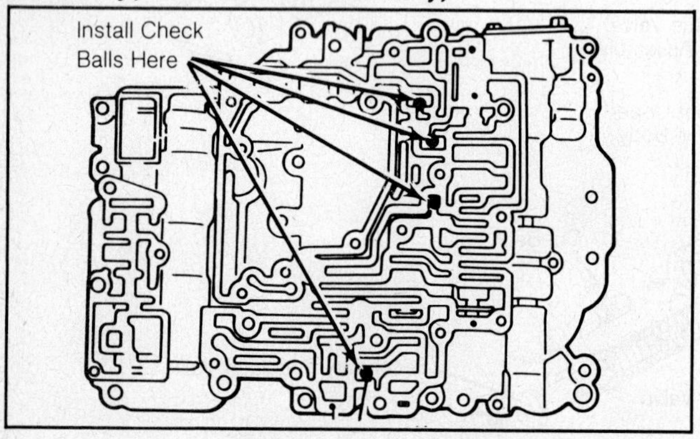

Fig. 40: Installing Rubber Check BallsIn Lower Valve Body(A-43D Transmission Only)

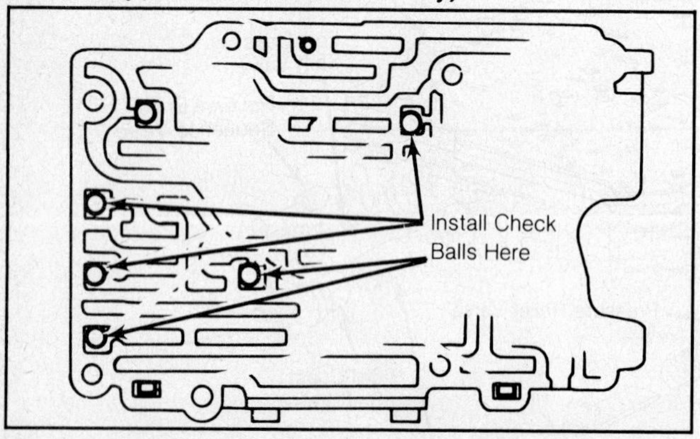

6) To assemble upper front valve body, insert throttle valve fully into bore. Use *Fig. 36* as guide, as A-40D upper valve body is assembled in same manner.

7) Coat throttle valve retainer clip with petroleum jelly and install in valve body. Install same number of adjusting rings on throttle valve as were removed during disassembly.

8) Slide throttle valve spring and down-shift plug into bore. Coat pin with petroleum jelly and install to hold the sleeve.

9) Assemble throttle cam and spring. Install throttle cam. Tighten bolt to 65 INCH lbs. (7.4 N.m). Install

Fig. 41: Installing Check Ball to Front Upper Valve Body

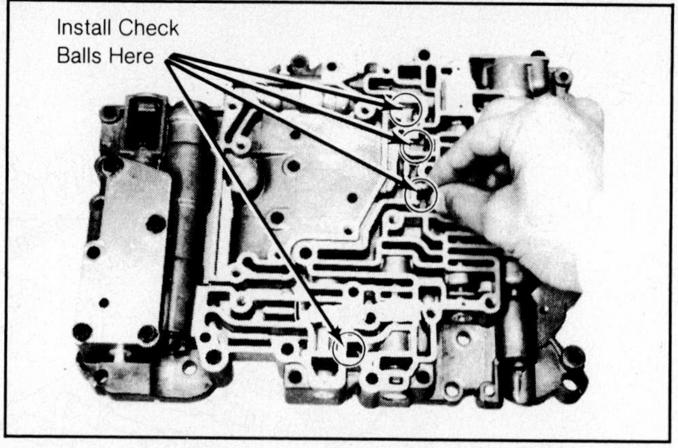

Fig. 42: Check Ball Locations in Upper Rear Valve Body (A-40D and A-43D Transmissions)

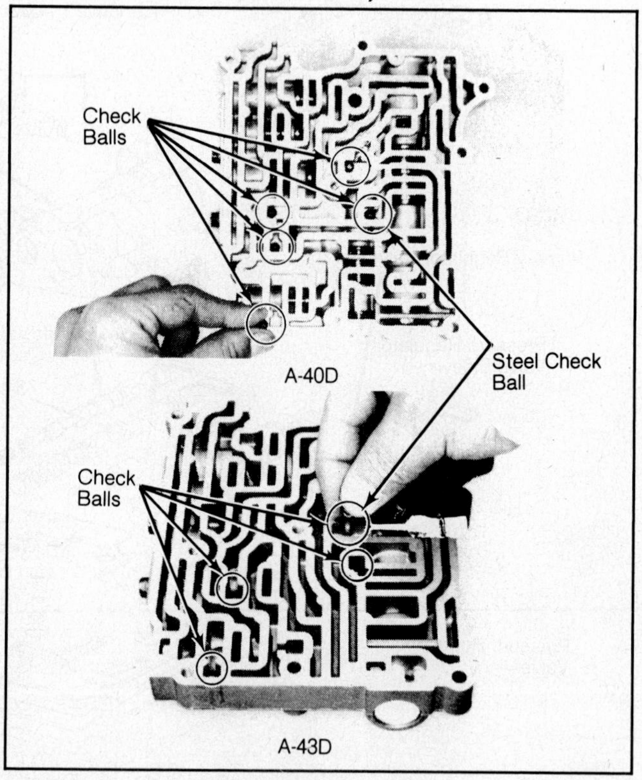

secondary regulator valve, spring and cover plate. Tighten bolts to 48 INCH lbs. (5.4 N.m).

10) Install spring, cut-back valve (smaller end first), plug and retainer. Install throttle valve retainer. Ensure sleeve is held by pin.

11) To assemble upper rear valve body, install 3-4 shift valve, spring, plug and retainer. Install 1-2 shift valve, spring and plate. Tighten bolts to 48 INCH lbs. (5.4 N.m).

12) Install 2-3 shift valve, spring, plug and retainer. Install rear clutch sequence valve spring, sequence valve, plug and retainer pin. Install 6 check balls. *See Fig. 45*.

13) To reassemble valve body, make sure new gasket matches old and position on upper rear valve body. Align gasket at lower left corner. Place lower valve body with plate on top of upper rear valve body. Install and finger

TOYOTA A-40D, A-42DL, A-43D, A-43DE & A-44DL (Cont.)

tighten 3 bolts in lower valve body to secure upper rear valve body.

Fig. 43: Exploded View of Upper Front Valve Body (All Models)

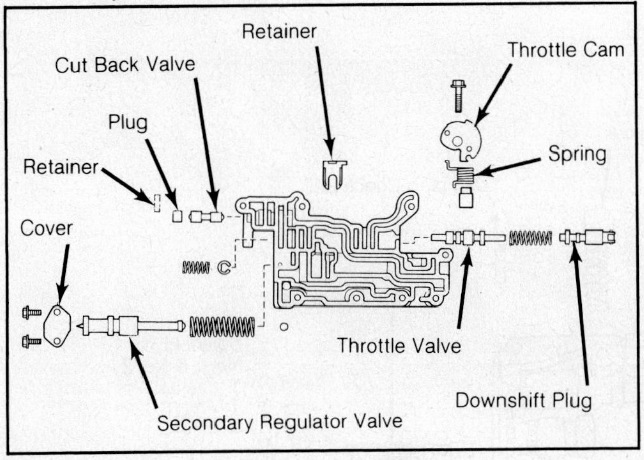

Fig. 44: Exploded View of Upper Rear Valve Body (A-43DE Transmission)

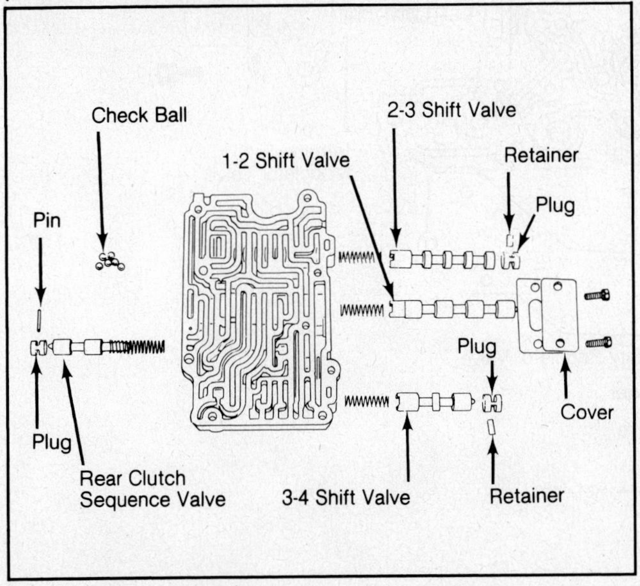

Fig. 45: Upper Rear Valve Body Check Ball Locations (A-43DE Transmission)

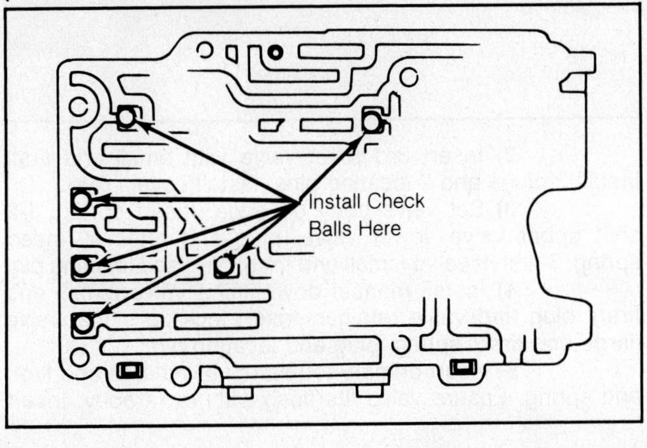

Fig. 46: Installing Lock-Up Relay Valve in Valve Body

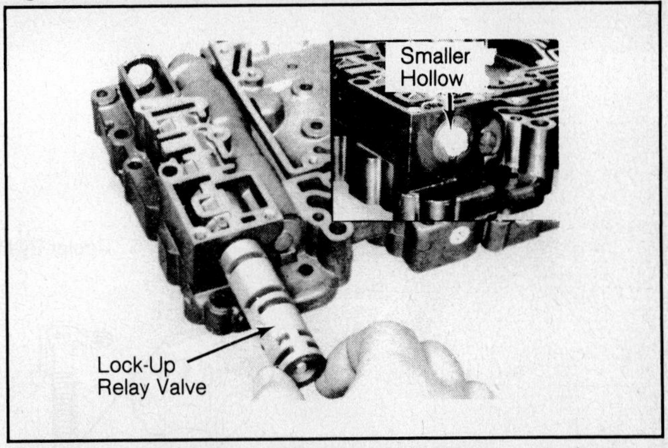

Illustration applies to A-42DL and A-44DL transmissions.

VALVE BODY SPRING FREE LENGTH (A-43DE TRANSMISSION)

Application	In. (mm)
Front Upper Body	
Secondary Regulator Valve	2.806 (71.27)
Down-Shift Plug	1.557 (39.55)
Throttle Valve	.758 (19.24)
Cut-Back Valve	.906 (23.00)
Rear Upper Body	
3-4 Shift Valve	1.148 (29.15)
3-2 Shift Valve	1.148 (29.15)
1-2 Shift Valve	1.148 (29.15)
Rear Clutch Sequence Valve	1.478 (37.55)
Lower Body	
Primary Regulator Valve	2.217 (56.30)
Low Coast Modulator	1.667 (42.35)
Intermediate Modulator	1.395 (35.43)
Lock-Up Relay Valve	1.362 (34.60)
Oil Cooler By-Pass Valve	1.312 (33.32)
Pressure Relief Valve	1.265 (32.14)
Damping Check Ball	.787 (20.00)

Fig. 47: Locations of Solenoids (A-43DE Transmissions)

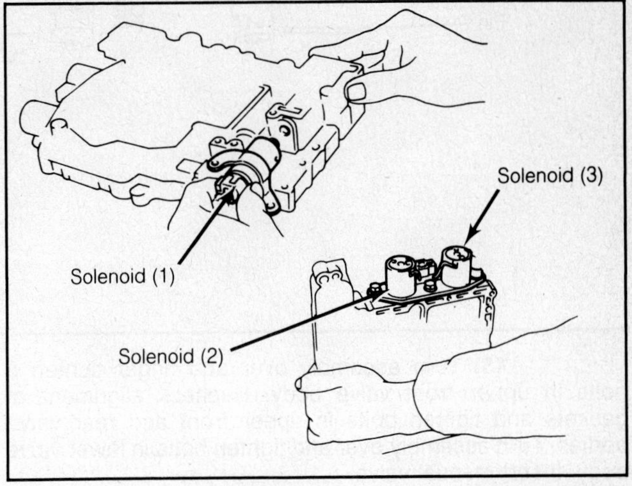

14) Turn assembly over, check gasket alignment and finger tighten bolts in upper rear valve body. Remove temporary bolts from plate. Place lower and upper rear valve body assembly on upper front valve body. Install and finger tighten set bolts in lower valve body to secure upper front valve body.

Fig. 48: Exploded View of A-43DE Transmission Lower Valve Body Assembly

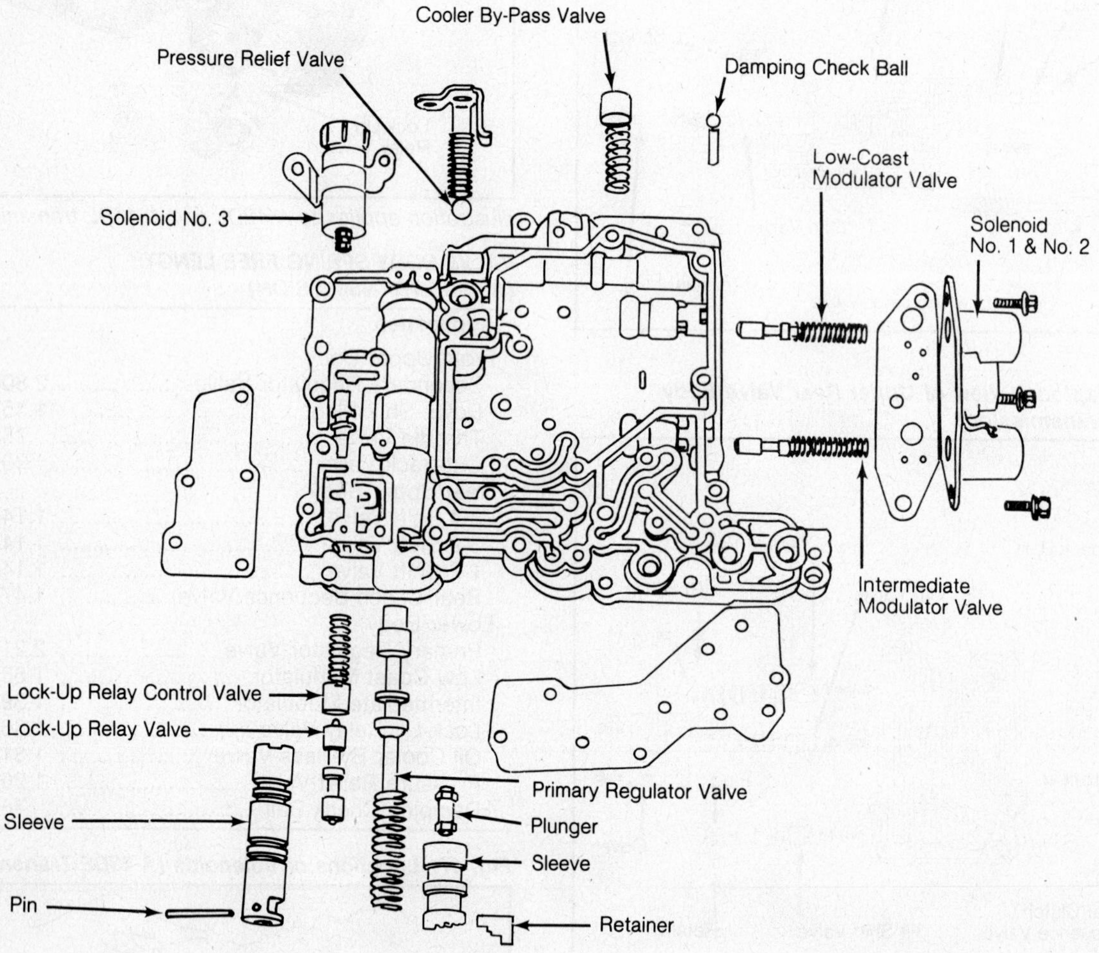

15) Turn assembly over and finger tighten 5 bolts in upper front valve body. Recheck alignment of gaskets and tighten bolts in upper front and rear valve bodies. Turn assembly over and tighten bolts in lower valve body. Insert manual valve.

Reassembly (A-42DL & A-44DL)

1) To reassemble lower valve body, install brake sequence plug. Install low-coast shift valve with small end first. Insert 3-4 coast shift valve with cup side first. *See Fig. 49.*

2) Insert 3rd-coast valve with small end first. Install 2 plugs and 2 locating pins. Install cover plate.

3) Set valve body on edge. Insert spring, 1-2 shift upper valve, lower valve, plug and retainer. Insert spring, 3-4 shift valve (small end first), plug and locating pin.

4) Install manual downtiming valve (small end first), plug and valve retainer. Insert lock-up signal valve (large end first), spring, plug and locating pin.

5) Insert primary regulator valve (large end first) and spring. Ensure valve fits flush with valve body. Insert

TOYOTA A-40D, A-42DL, A-43D, A-43DE & A-44DL (Cont.)

Fig. 49: Exploded View of A-42DL And A-44DL Transmission Valve Body

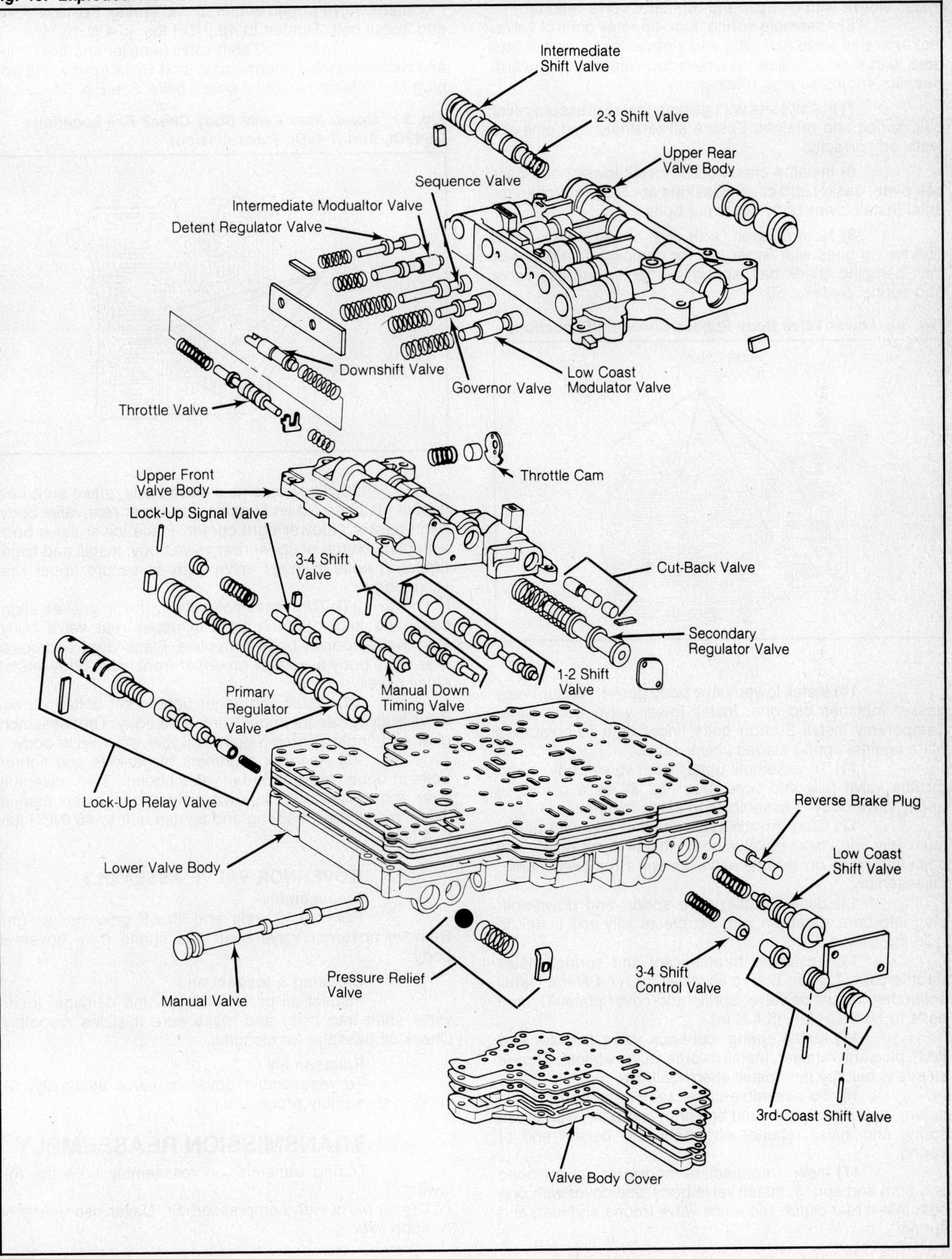

TOYOTA A-40D, A-42DL, A-43D, A-43DE & A-44DL (Cont.)

regulator valve plunger (rounded end first) into sleeve. Install sleeve with plunger and regulator valve retainer.

6) Assemble spring, lock-up relay control valve, lock-up relay valve and plug into sleeve. Insert sleeve into bore with smaller hollow on sleeve top side facing upward. *See Fig. 46*. Install plug retainer.

7) Install plate with gasket. Install pressure relief ball, spring and retainer. Ensure all retainers and pins are installed correctly.

8) Install 4 check balls. Install lower body gasket, plate, gasket and cover. Gaskets are NOT interchangeable. Install lower body cover set bolts.

9) Note different size of 2 rubber check balls. The spring goes with larger ball for damping. Install check ball, damping check ball, spring, oil cooler by-pass valve and spring. *See Fig. 50*.

Fig. 50: Lower Valve Body Rubber Check Ball Locations

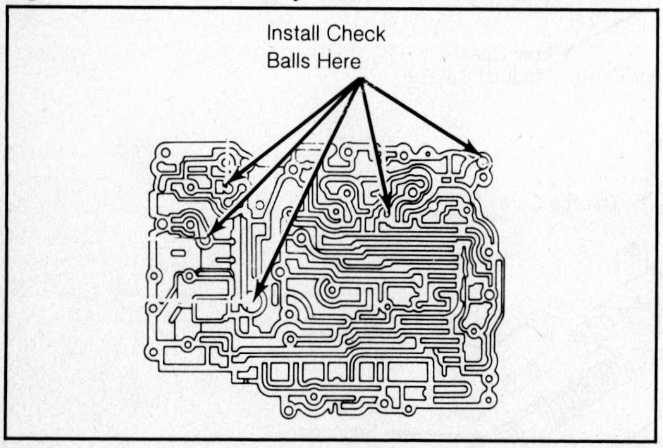

10) Install lower valve body gasket. Ensure new gasket matches old one. Install lower valve body plate. Temporarily install 2 short bolts finger tight to compress plate against spring loaded check valve.

11) To assemble upper front valve body, insert throttle valve fully into bore. Use *Fig. 36* as a guide, as upper valve body is assembled in same manner.

12) Coat throttle valve retainer clip with petroleum jelly and install in valve body. Install same number of adjusting rings on throttle valve as were removed during disassembly.

13) Slide throttle valve spring and down-shift plug into bore. Coat pin with petroleum jelly and install to hold the sleeve.

14) Assemble throttle cam and spring. Install throttle cam. Tighten bolt to 65 INCH lbs. (7.4 N.m). Install secondary regulator valve, spring and cover plate. Tighten bolts to 48 INCH lbs. (5.4 N.m).

15) Install spring, cut-back valve (smaller end first), plug and retainer. Install throttle valve retainer. Ensure sleeve is held by pin. Install check ball. *See Fig. 41*.

16) To assemble upper rear valve body, insert detent reguator valve (round end first) into bore. Compress spring and install retainer so that it fully covers end of spring.

17) Insert intermediate modulator valve (round end first) and spring. Install valve body side cover with one bolt. Insert rear clutch sequence valve (round end first) and spring.

18) Insert governor modulator plug. Insert low modulator valve (round end first) and spring. Position cover and install bolt. Tighten to 48 INCH lbs. (5.4 N.m).

19) Insert 2-3 shift valve (smaller end first), plug and retainer. Insert intermediate shift valve (round end up), plug and retainer. Install 4 check balls. *See Fig. 51*.

Fig. 51: Upper Rear Valve Body Check Ball Locations (A-42DL And A-44DL Transmission)

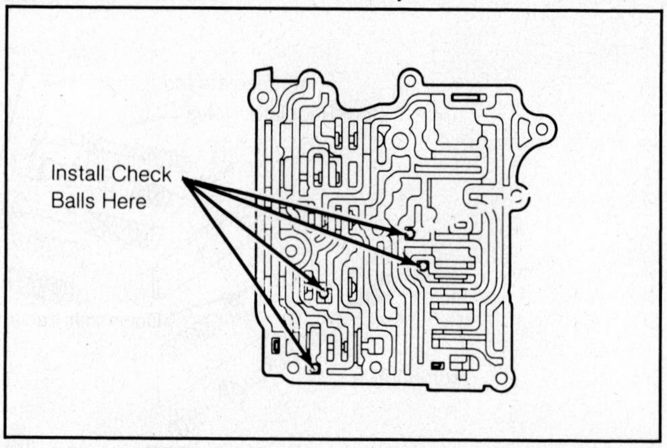

20) To reassemble valve body, make sure new gasket matches old and position on upper rear valve body. Align gasket at lower right corner. Place lower valve body with plate on top of upper rear valve body. Install and finger tighten 3 bolts in lower valve body to secure upper rear valve body.

21) Turn assembly over, check gasket alignment and finger tighten bolts in upper rear valve body. Remove temporary bolts from plate. Place lower and upper rear valve body assembly on upper front valve body. Install small cover.

22) Install and finger tighten set bolts in lower valve body to secure upper front valve body. Turn assembly over and finger tighten 5 bolts in upper front valve body.

23) Recheck alignment of gaskets and tighten bolts in upper front and rear valve bodies. Turn assembly over and tighten bolts in lower valve body. Insert manual valve. Install detent spring and tighten bolt to 48 INCH lbs. (5.4 N.m).

GOVERNOR VALVE ASSEMBLY

Disassembly

Remove "E" ring and lift off governor weight. Remove governor valve shaft and spring from governor body.

Cleaning & Inspection

Inspect all parts for wear and damage. Insert valve shaft into body and make sure it slides smoothly. Check oil passage for clogging.

Reassembly

To reassemble governor valve assembly, reverse disassembly procedure.

TRANSMISSION REASSEMBLY

During transmission reassembly note the following:

- Dry all parts with compressed air. Never use waste or shop towels.

TOYOTA A-40D, A-42DL, A-43D, A-43DE & A-44DL (Cont.)

Fig. 52: Exploded View of Governor Assembly

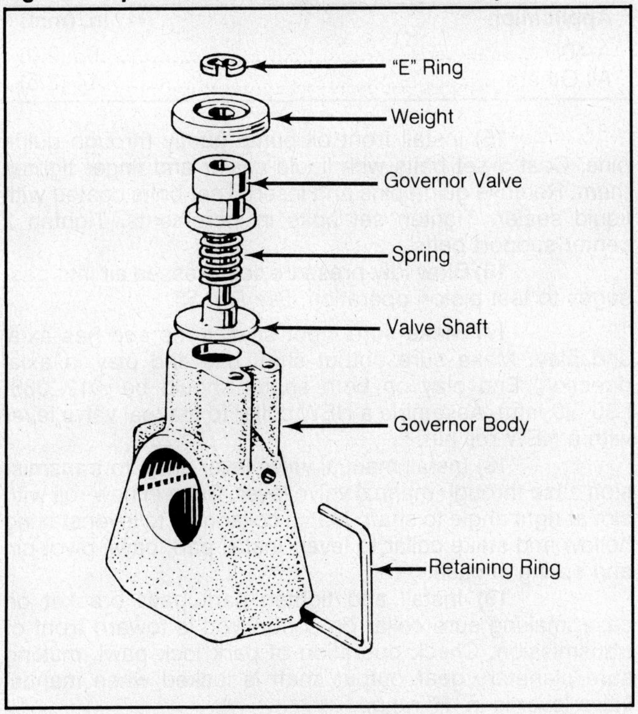

- Soak new clutch discs in automatic transmission fluid for at least 2 hours before installation.
- Apply ATF on all sliding and rotating surfaces before assembly.
- Do not use adhesive cements on gaskets and similar parts.
- Use all new "O" rings and gaskets.

1) Place transmission case on a cylindrical stand with front facing up. Install output shaft thrust bearing and race into case with race lip facing down over bearing.

2) Install brake apply tube into case. Ensure tube end lip are completely inserted into outer piston. Lip on outer circumference of brake apply tube must mate with recess in case.

3) Align clutch plates on output shaft. Partially insert output shaft assembly into case. On models with slot in case, align notch in clutch plates with slot in case.

4) Check clutch pack clearance. Measure depth of ledge below snap ring groove. *See Fig. 54.* If clutch pack is not lower than ledge, components may be assembled incorrectly or excess ATF may be on discs.

5) Position reaction plate notch tooth toward valve body side of case. Push plate into place. When correctly installed, snap ring groove is completely visible. Install snap ring. Work snap ring around case. Check that snap ring is seated and ends are between lugs. Push center support assembly into case.

6) Align oil hole and bolt hole of center support with those of body side. Align center support with holes in case and install support bolts with wave washers finger tight. Install rear clutch to case. Rotate clutch to mesh with center support.

7) When correctly installed, splined center of clutch will be flush with end of sun gear shaft. Install needle bearing race over splined end of rear clutch in case. Coat parts with petroleum jelly to hold in place. Place lip of race toward rear clutch.

Fig. 53: Toyota Automatic Transmission Thrust Bearing & Race Locations

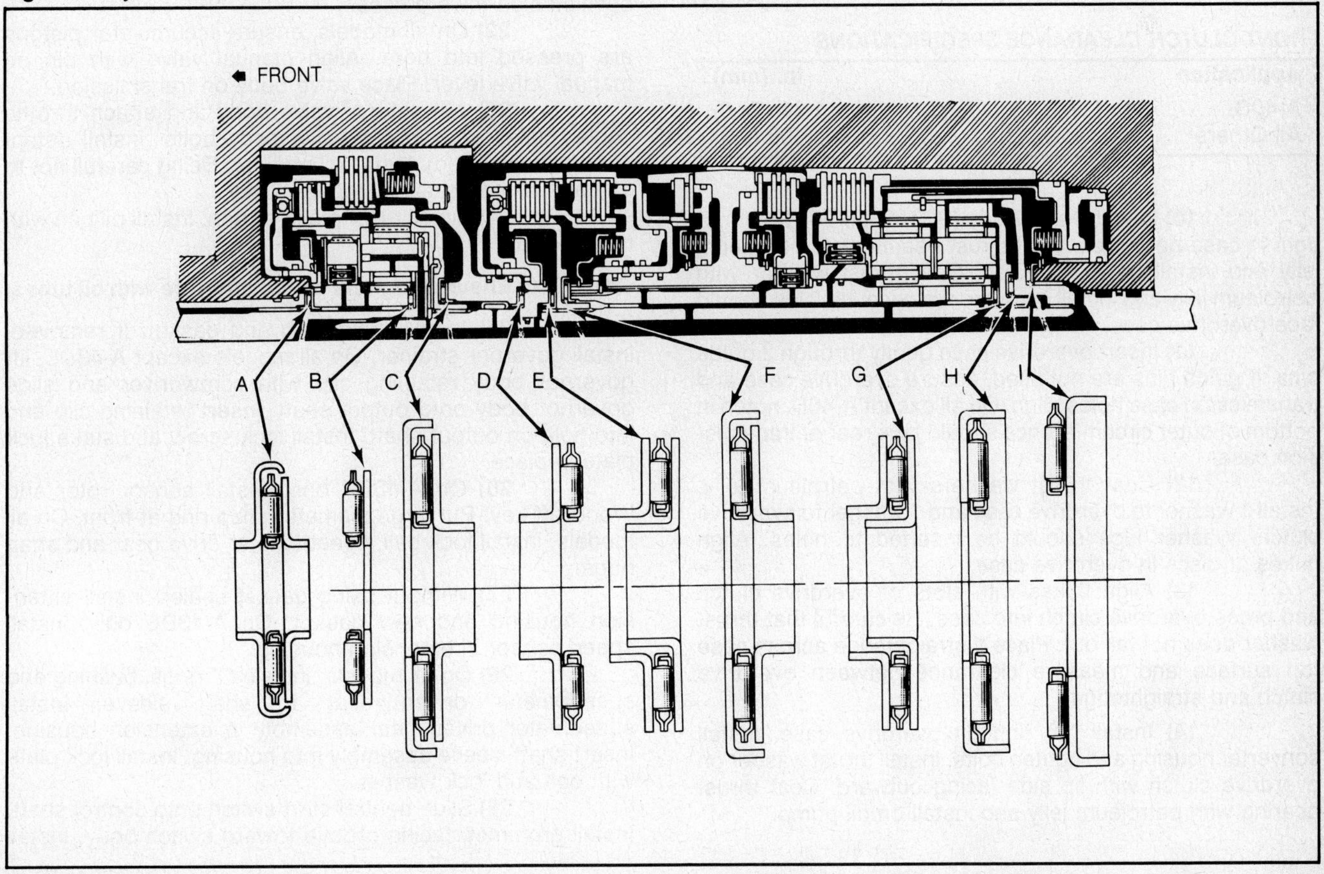

TOYOTA A-40D, A-42DL, A-43D, A-43DE & A-44DL (Cont.)

Fig. 54: Measuring Rear Brake Clutch Pack Clearance

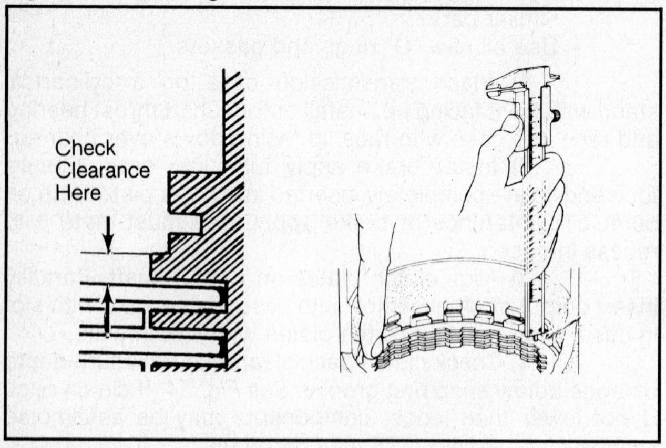

CLUTCH PACK CLEARANCE SPECIFICATIONS

Application	In. (mm)
A-42DL	.0220-.0902 (.56-2.29)
All Others	.0240-.1039 (.61-2.64)

8) Install thrust bearing and race on front clutch. Coat parts with petroleum jelly. Position lip of race outward. Align flukes of rear clutch discs and mesh with front clutch hub. Push front clutch assembly into case, being careful not to let thrust bearing fall out.

9) Place a straightedge across case top surface and measure clearance between clutch and straightedge. *See Fig. 16.* If value corresponds to distance recorded during disassembly, front clutch is installed correctly.

FRONT CLUTCH CLEARANCE SPECIFICATIONS

Application	In. (mm)
A-40D	1.34 (34.0)
All Others	.08 (2.0)

10) Install Guide Rods (SST09350-20013) finger tight in case bolt holes. Coat thrust bearing with petroleum jelly and install on front clutch. Coat thrust washer with petroleum jelly and install on overdrive case. Lip side should face overdrive case.

11) Insert overdrive case gently through 2 guide pins. If guide pins are not used, ensure overdrive case and transmission case holes align. On all except A-40D, notch in bottom of outer circumference should face rear of transmission case.

12) Coat thrust washers with petroleum jelly. Install 1 washer to overdrive case and 1 washer to overdrive clutch. Washer lugs should be inserted to holes. Align flukes of discs in overdrive case.

13) Align flukes with slots of overdrive clutch and press overdrive clutch into case. Be careful that thrust washer does not fall out. Place a straightedge across case top surface and measure clearance between overdrive clutch and straightedge.

14) Install "O" ring on overdrive case. Install converter housing and tighten bolts. Install thrust washer on overdrive clutch with lip side facing outward. Coat thrust bearing with petroleum jelly and install on oil pump.

OVERDRIVE CLUTCH CLEARANCE SPECIFICATIONS

Application	In. (mm)
A-40D	.08 (2.0)
All Others	.14 (3.5)

15) Install front oil pump gently through guide pins. Coat 5 set bolts with liquid sealer and finger tighten them. Remove guide pins and insert 2 set bolts coated with liquid sealer. Tighten set bolts in increments. Tighten 2 center support bolts.

16) Blow low-pressure compressed air into passages to test piston operation. *See Fig. 55.*

17) Make sure input shaft turns and has axial end play. Make sure output shaft has end play in axial direction. End play on both shafts should be .012-.035" (.30-.90 mm). Assemble a NEW collar to manual valve lever with a NEW roll pin.

18) Install manual valve lever shaft to transmission case through manual valve lever. Drive in new roll with slot at right angle to shaft. Match collar hole to lever staking hollow and stake collar to lever. Install park pawl, pivot pin and spring in case.

19) Install and tighten park pawl bracket on case, making sure collar on control rod is toward front of transmission. Check operation of park lock pawl, making sure planetary gear output shaft is locked when manual valve lever is in "P" range.

20) Install new "O" rings on throttle cable fitting. Install throttle cable in case, seating fully. Check accumulator spring free length. Replace as necessary. Install accumulator pistons and springs.

21) On A-40D only, install "O" rings on rear clutch and Brake No. 1 case holes. Install "O" rings with beveled side toward case.

22) On all models, ensure accumulator pistons are pressed into bore. Align manual valve with pin on manual valve lever. Place valve body on transmission.

23) Lift side of valve body and attach throttle cable. Install and tighten valve body bolts. Install detent spring (if equipped). Install oil strainer. Being carefull not to damage tubes, install oil tubes in case.

24) Install magnets in oil pan. Install oil pan with new gasket.

CAUTION: Ensure magnets do not interfere with oil tubes.

25) Install drain plug and gasket. If removed, install governor strainer. On all models except A-43DE, lift governor body retaining clip with screwdriver and slide governor body onto output shaft. Insert retaining clip end into hole on output shaft. Install lock screw and stake lock plate in place.

26) On A-43DE only, install sensor rotor and Woodruff key. Put large diameter snap ring at front. On all models, install lock ball, speedometer drive gear and snap rings.

27) Without using gasket sealer, install extension housing and new gasket. On A-43DE only, install speed sensor in extension housing.

28) On all models, install "O" rings, bushing and speedometer driven gear to shaft sleeve. Install speeometer driven gear assembly in extension housing. Insert shaft sleeve assembly into housing. Install lock plate with bolt and lock washer.

29) Slide neutral start switch onto control shaft. Install grommet, facing groove toward switch body. Install

TOYOTA A-40D, A-42DL, A-43D, A-43DE & A-44DL (Cont.)

washer and nut. Move switch so that slit in switch and neutral base line up. Tighten bolt and nut. Install shift handle. On all except A-43DE, install solenoid switch with 2 "O" rings.

Fig. 55: Testing Piston Operation

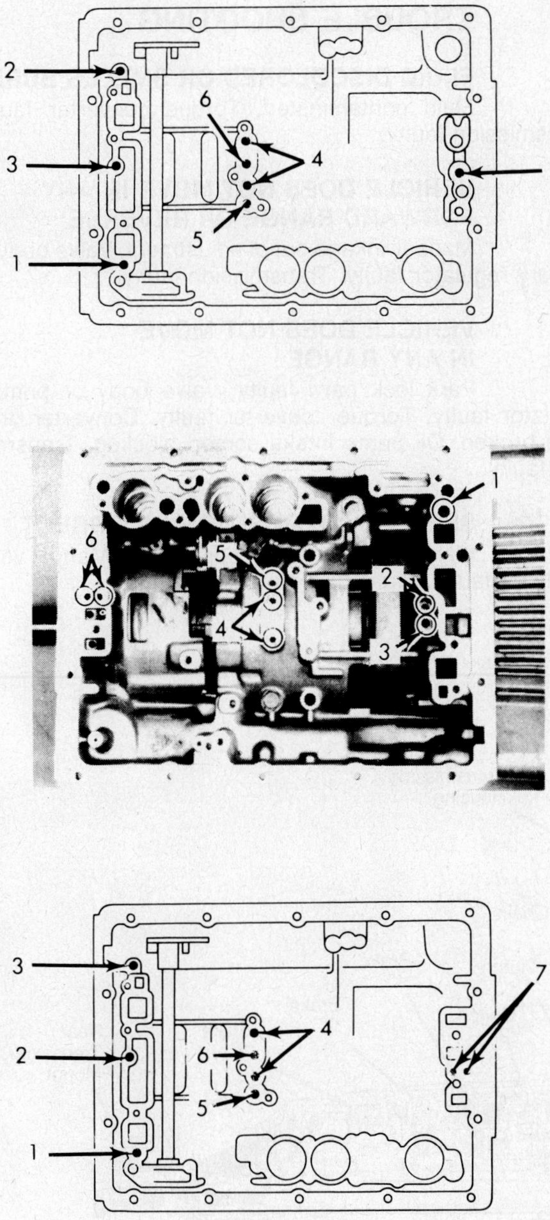

1. Overdrive Clutch
2. Overdrive Brake
3. Front Clutch
4. Rear Clutch
5. Brake No. 1.
6. Brake No. 2.
7. Brake No. 3.

Blow low pressure air into indicated passages.

ACCUMULATOR SPRING FREE LENGTH

Application	In. (mm)
A-40D	
B_1	2.625 (66.86)
C_2	2.410 (61.21)
C_1	2.699 (68.56)
A-43D	
B_2	[1] 2.618 (66.50)
C_2	2.172 (55.18)
C_1	[2] 2.699 (68.56)
A-42DL	
B_2	2.618 (66.50)
C_2	2.409 (61.21)
C_1	2.551 (64.80)
A-44DL	
B_2	
Upper	2.172 (55.18)
Lower	1.383 (35.13)
C_2	2.409 (61.21)
C_1	2.551 (64.80)
A-43DE	
B_2	
Upper	1.995 (50.68)
Lower	1.383 (35.13)
C_2	
Upper	1.715 (43.56)
Lower	1.289 (32.73)
C_1	2.551 (64.80)

[1] – For 22R engine; 2.625 (66.68) on 22R-E engine.
[2] – For 22R engine; 2.551 (64.80) on 22R-E engine.

TIGHTENING SPECIFICATIONS

Application	Ft. Lbs. (N.m)
Center Support-to-Case	19 (25)
Converter Housing-to-Case	
10 mm	25 (34)
12 mm	42 (57)
14 mm	42 (57)
17 mm	42 (57)
Converter-to-Drive Plate	13 (18)
Extension Housing-to-Case	25 (34)
Oil Pump-to-Case	16 (21)
Transmission-to-Engine	47 (64)
Cooler Pipe Union Bolt	25 (34)
	INCH Lbs. (N.m)
Oil Pan Cover	65 (7.4)
Oil Pan-to-Case	
A-42DL	48 (5.4)
A-44DL	36 (4.0)
All Others	39 (4.4)
Lock Pawl Bracket-to-Case	65 (7.4)
Strainer-to-Valve Body	48 (5.4)
Testing Plugs-to-Case	65 (7.4)
Upper-to-Lower Valve Body	48 (5.4)
Valve Body-to-Case	84 (10)
Neutral Start Switch (Bolt)	48 (5.4)
Neutral Start Switch (Nut)	61 (6.9)

TOYOTA A55 & A55F TRANSAXLE

Tercel, 2WD, 4WD

DESCRIPTION

The A55 transaxle assembly is a 3-speed unit consisting of an engine driven torque converter fitted to an oil pump which is coupled to the transaxle by a chain. The unit utilizes 2 clutches, 3 brakes, 2 planetary gear sets, a one-way clutch and a final drive assembly. Final drive assembly is directly below torque converter and connected to front of transmission. It consists of a housing, case, ring gear, pinion, side gears and pinion gears.

The A55F model transaxle is similar to the A55 model except with a different extension housing allowing for use of 4WD. The A55F also has slightly lower overall gear ratios. Except for the housing and 4WD associated linkage the service proceedures for the A55 and A55F are the same.

LUBRICATION & ADJUSTMENTS

See appropriate AUTOMATIC TRANSMISSION SERVICING article in IMPORT GENERAL SERVICING section.

SERVICE (IN VEHICLE)

DRIVE AXLE SHAFTS

See appropriate DRIVE AXLE SHAFT article in IMPORT AXLE SHAFTS, OVERDRIVES & TRANSFER CASES section.

TROUBLE SHOOTING

FLUID DISCOLORED OR SMELLS BURNT

Fluid contaminated. Torque converter faulty. Transmission faulty.

VEHICLE DOES NOT MOVE IN ANY FORWARD RANGE OR REVERSE

Manual linkage out of adjustment. Valve body or primary regulator faulty. Transmission faulty.

VEHICLE DOES NOT MOVE IN ANY RANGE

Park lock pawl faulty. Valve body or primary regulator faulty. Torque converter faulty. Converter drive plate broken. Oil pump intake screen blocked. Transmission faulty.

SHIFT LEVER POSITION INCORRECT

Manual linkage out of adjustment. Manual valve and lever faulty. Transmission faulty.

Fig. 1: Cross Sectional View of Toyota Tercel A55 Automatic Transaxle

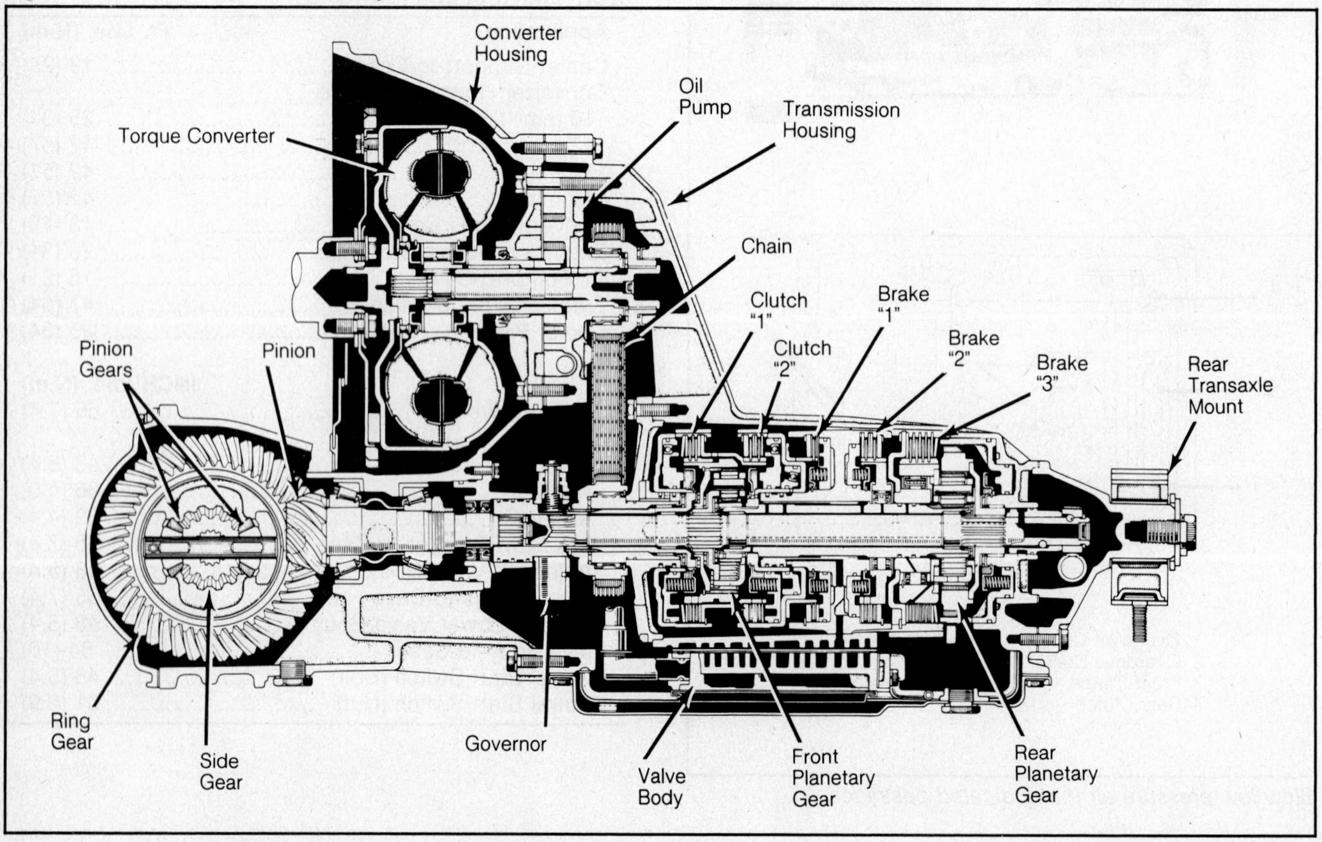

TOYOTA A55 & A55F TRANSAXLE (Cont.)

HARSH ENGAGEMENT INTO ANY DRIVE RANGE

Throttle linkage out of adjustment. Valve body or primary regulator faulty. Accumulator pistons faulty. Transmission faulty.

DELAYED 1-2 OR 2-3 UPSHIFT, OR DOWNSHIFTS FROM 3-2 THEN SHIFTS BACK TO 3

Throttle linkage out of adjustment. Governor faulty. Valve body faulty.

SLIPS ON 1-2 OR 2-3 UPSHIFT, OR SLIPS OR SHUDDERS ON TAKE-OFF

Manual linkage out of adjustment. Throttle linkage out of adjustment. Valve body faulty. Transmission faulty.

DRAG, BINDING OR TIE-UP ON 1-2 OR 2-3 UPSHIFTS

Manual linkage out of adjustment. Valve body faulty. Transmission faulty.

HARSH DOWNSHIFT

Throttle linkage out of adjustment. Accumulator pistons faulty. Valve body faulty. Transmission faulty.

NO DOWNSHIFT WHEN COASTING

Governor faulty. Valve body faulty.

DOWNSHIFT OCCURS TOO QUICK OR TOO LATE WHILE COASTING

Throttle linkage out of adjustment. Governor faulty. Valve body faulty. Transmission faulty.

NO 3-2 OR 2-1 KICKDOWN

Throttle linkage out of adjustment. Governor faulty. Valve body faulty.

NO ENGINE BRAKING IN "2" RANGE

Valve body faulty. Transmission faulty.

VEHICLE DOES NOT HOLD IN "P"

Manual linkage out of adjustment. Parking lock pawl cam and spring faulty.

TESTING

ROAD TEST

NOTE: Perform test with fluid at normal operating temperature.

"D" Range Test

1) Shift into "D" range and while driving with accelerator pedal held constant at a specified point (throttle valve opening 50% and 100%). At each throttle opening, check to see that 1-2 and 2-3 upshifts take place and that shift points conform with those in *Fig. 2.*

2) If there is no 1-2 upshift, governor valve may be defective or 1-2 shift valve may be stuck. If there is no 2-3 upshift, 2-3 shift valve may be stuck. If shift point is incorrect, throttle link may be out of adjustment, or throttle valve, 1-2 shift valve or 2-3 shift valve may be defective.

3) While performing step **1)** again, check for shock and slippage during 1-2 and 2-3 upshifts. If shock is severe, line pressure may be too high, accumulator may be defective or check ball may be defective. While in "D" range and in high gear, check for abnormal noise and vibration.

NOTE: Check for cause of abnormal noise and vibration must be made with extreme care as they could also be due to unbalance in differential, tires, torque converter, or bent power train components.

4) While in "D" and running in second or high gear, depress accelerator pedal fully to perform a kickdown and check to see that kick-down shift points, for 2-1, 3-1 and 3-2 kick-downs, conform to those in *Fig. 2.* Also check for abnormal shock and slip during kick-downs.

5) While running in high gear, move gear selector lever to "2" and "L" positions and check engine braking effect at each of these ranges. If there is no engine braking effect in "2" range, brake No. 1 is defective. If there is no engine braking effect in "L" range, brake No. 3 is defective.

6) While running in high gear, release foot from accelerator pedal and move gear selector lever into "L" range. Check to see if 3-2 and 2-1 downshift points conform to those in *Fig. 2.*

"2" Range Test

1) Shift to "2" range and run with throttle valve opening at 50% and 100% respectively. Then check 1-2 upshift points at each throttle valve opening to see that they conform to those in *Fig. 2.* While running in "2" range and in second gear, release accelerator pedal and check engine braking effect.

2) While running in "2" range and in second, depress accelerator fully to perform a 2-1 kickdown and check to see if speeds conform to those in *Fig. 2.* Check for abnormal noise at acceleration and deceleration and for shock during upshift and downshift.

"L" Range Test

While running in "L" range, check to see that there is no upshift to second gear. While running in "L" range, release accelerator pedal and check engine braking effect. Check for abnormal noise at acceleration and deceleration.

"R" Range Test

Shift into "R" range and while running at full throttle, check for slipping.

"P" Range Test

Stop vehicle on a gradient (more than 5°) and after shifting into "P" range, release parking brake. Then check to see that parking lock pawl keeps the vehicle from moving.

STALL TEST

NOTE: The object of this test is to check the overall performance of the transmission and engine by measuring the maximum engine speed at the "D" and "R" ranges.

1) Chock front wheels. Mount an engine tachometer. Fully apply parking brake. Step down strongly on brake pedal with left foot. Start engine. Shift into "D" range. Step down fully on accelerator pedal with right foot. Quickly read highest engine RPM at this time.

NOTE: Perform test with fluid at normal operating temperature.

TOYOTA A55 & A55F TRANSAXLE (Cont.)

Fig. 2: Shift Speeds Diagram

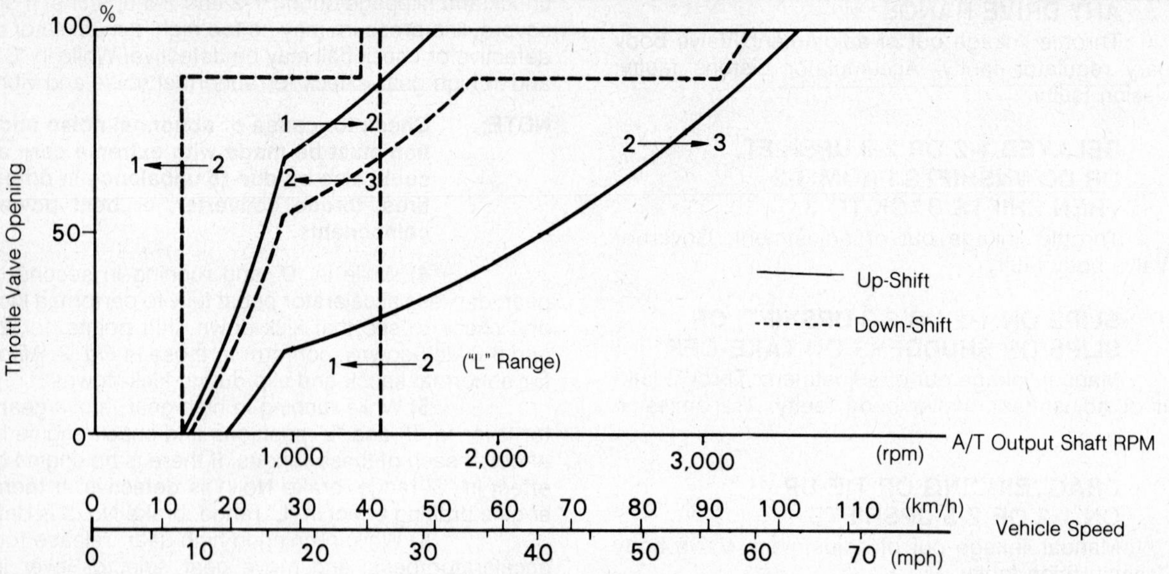

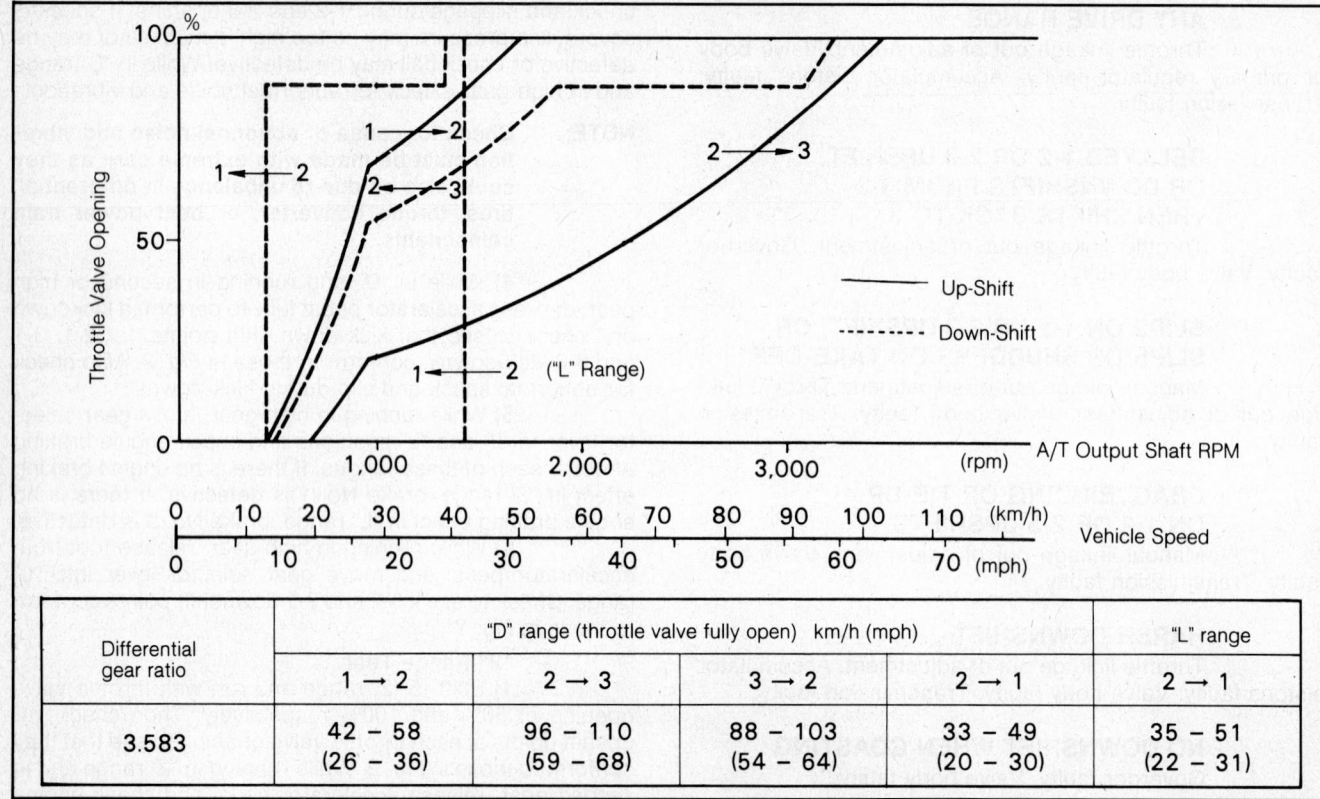

Differential gear ratio	"D" range (throttle valve fully open) km/h (mph)				"L" range
	1 → 2	2 → 3	3 → 2	2 → 1	2 → 1
3.583	42 – 58 (26 – 36)	96 – 110 (59 – 68)	88 – 103 (54 – 64)	33 – 49 (20 – 30)	35 – 51 (22 – 31)

CAUTION: Do not perform this test for longer than 5 seconds.

2) If engine speed is the same for both ranges but lower than specified value, then engine output may be insufficient or stator one-way clutch may not be operating properly.

NOTE: If more than 600 RPM below the specified value, the torque converter could be at fault.

3) If stall speed in "D" range is higher than specified, then front clutch may be slipping, one-way clutch No. 2 may not be operating properly or line pressure may be too low.

4) If stall speed in "R" range is higher than specified, rear clutch may be slipping, brake No. 3 may be slipping or line pressure may be too low.

STALL SPEED SPECIFICATIONS

Application	Stall RPM
All Models	2100-2400

TIME LAG TEST

NOTE: If shift lever is shifted while engine is idling, there will be a certain time elapse or lag before shock can be felt. This is used for checking the condition of front clutch, rear clutch and brake No. 3.

1) Fully apply parking brake. Start engine. Ensure proper idle speed. Move gear selector lever from "N" to "D" range. Using a stop watch, measure the time it takes from shifting lever until shock is felt. Then measure time lag for "N" to "R". Compare findings with those in the TIME LAG SPECIFICATIONS table.

2) If "N" to "D" time lag is longer than specifications, line pressure may be too low or front clutch may be worn. If "N" to "R" time lag is longer than specifications, rear clutch may be worn, brake No. 3 may be worn or line pressure may be too low.

TIME LAG SPECIFICATIONS

Application	Time Lag (Seconds)
"N" to "D"	Less Than 1.2
"N" to "R"	Less Than 1.5

HYDRAULIC PRESSURE TESTS

Governor Pressure

1) With transmission fluid warm and rear wheels chocked, raise and support front of vehicle. Remove transmission case test plugs and mount hydraulic pressure gauges.

CAUTION: Measurement can be made with 1000 RPM test, but if tests are to be made at 1800 and 3500 RPM, it would be safer to test on a road or chassis dynamometer because an on-stand test could be hazardous.

2) Fully apply parking brake and start engine. Shift into "D" range and measure governor pressure at speeds listed in HYDRAULIC PRESSURE SPECIFICATIONS table. If governor pressure is defective, then line pressure may be defective, there may be possible fluid leakage in governor pressure circuit or governor valve operation may be defective.

TOYOTA MODEL A55 & A55F (Cont.)

CLUTCH AND BRAKE APPLICATION CHART

Selector Lever Position	Clutch 1	Clutch 2 Inner Piston	Clutch 2 Outer Piston	Brake 1	Brake 2	Brake 3 Inner Piston	Brake 3 Outer Piston
D - DRIVE							
First Gear	X						
Second Gear	X				X		
Third Gear	X	X			X		
2 - INTERMEDIATE							
First Gear	X						
Second Gear	X			X	X		
1 - LOW	X					X	
R - REVERSE		X	X			X	X

NEUTRAL OR PARK - All clutches and brakes released and/or ineffective.

Fig. 3: Hydraulic Pressure Test Port Hookup Points

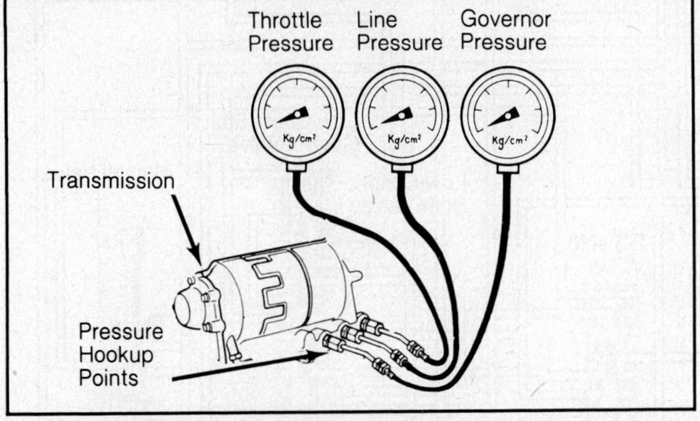

Line Pressure

1) Fully apply parking brake and chock all four wheels. Start engine and shift into "D" range.

2) Step down strongly on brake pedal with left foot and while manipulating accelerator pedal with right foot, measure line pressure at engine speeds listed in HYDRAULIC PRESSURE SPECIFICATIONS table.

3) Perform same procedure in "R" range. If measured pressures are not up to specifications, recheck throttle link adjustment and retest. If measured values at all ranges are higher than specifications, regulator valve may be defective, throttle valve may be defective or throttle link may be out of adjustment.

4) If measured values at all ranges are lower than specifications, oil pump may be defective, regulator valve may be defective, throttle valve may be defective or throttle link may be out of adjustment.

5) If pressure is low in "D" range only, front clutch may be defective or possible "D" range circuit fluid leakage may exist. When pressure is low in "R" range only, rear clutch may be defective, brake No. 3 may be defective or possible "R" range circuit fluid leakage may exist.

Throttle Pressure

1) Fully apply parking brake and chock all four wheels. Start engine and shift into "D" range.

2) Step down strongly on brake pedal with left foot and while manipulating accelerator pedal with right foot, measure throttle pressure at engine speeds listed in HYDRAULIC PRESSURE SPECIFICATIONS table.

3) In same manner, perform test for "R" range. If measured pressures are not up to specifications, recheck throttle link adjustment and retest.

4) If measured values are higher than specifications, throttle valve may be defective or throttle circuit orifice may be clogged.

5) If measured values are lower than specifications, oil pump may be defective, regulator valve may be defective or throttle valve may be defective.

HYDRAULIC PRESSURE SPECIFICATIONS

Application	psi (kg/cm^2) In "R"	psi (kg/cm^2) In "D"
Governor Pressure		
19 MPH	....	17-26 (1.2-1.8)
31 MPH	....	26-34 (1.8-2.4)
63 MPH	....	54-71 (3.8-5.0)
Line Pressure		
At Idle Speed	108-119 (7.6-8.4)	57-65 (4.0-4.6)
At Stall Speed	252-287 (17.7-20.2)	132-161 (9.3-11.3)
Throttle Pressure		
At Idle Speed	0-4.3 (0-.3)	0-4.3 (0-.3)
At Stall Speed	110-118 (7.7-8.3)	110-118 (7.7-8.3)

REMOVAL & INSTALLATION

TRANSMISSION

See appropriate AUTOMATIC TRANSMISSION REMOVAL article in IMPORT GENERAL SERVICING section.

TRANSMISSION DISASSEMBLY

1) Remove transmission from transaxle. Remove neutral start switch. Remove speedometer driven gear housing from extension housing. Remove extension housing and gasket. Remove speedometer drive gear. Remove output shaft sleeve.

TOYOTA A55 & A55F TRANSAXLE (Cont.)

Fig. 4: Toyota Tercel A-55 Automatic Transaxle Hydraulic Circuits Diagram

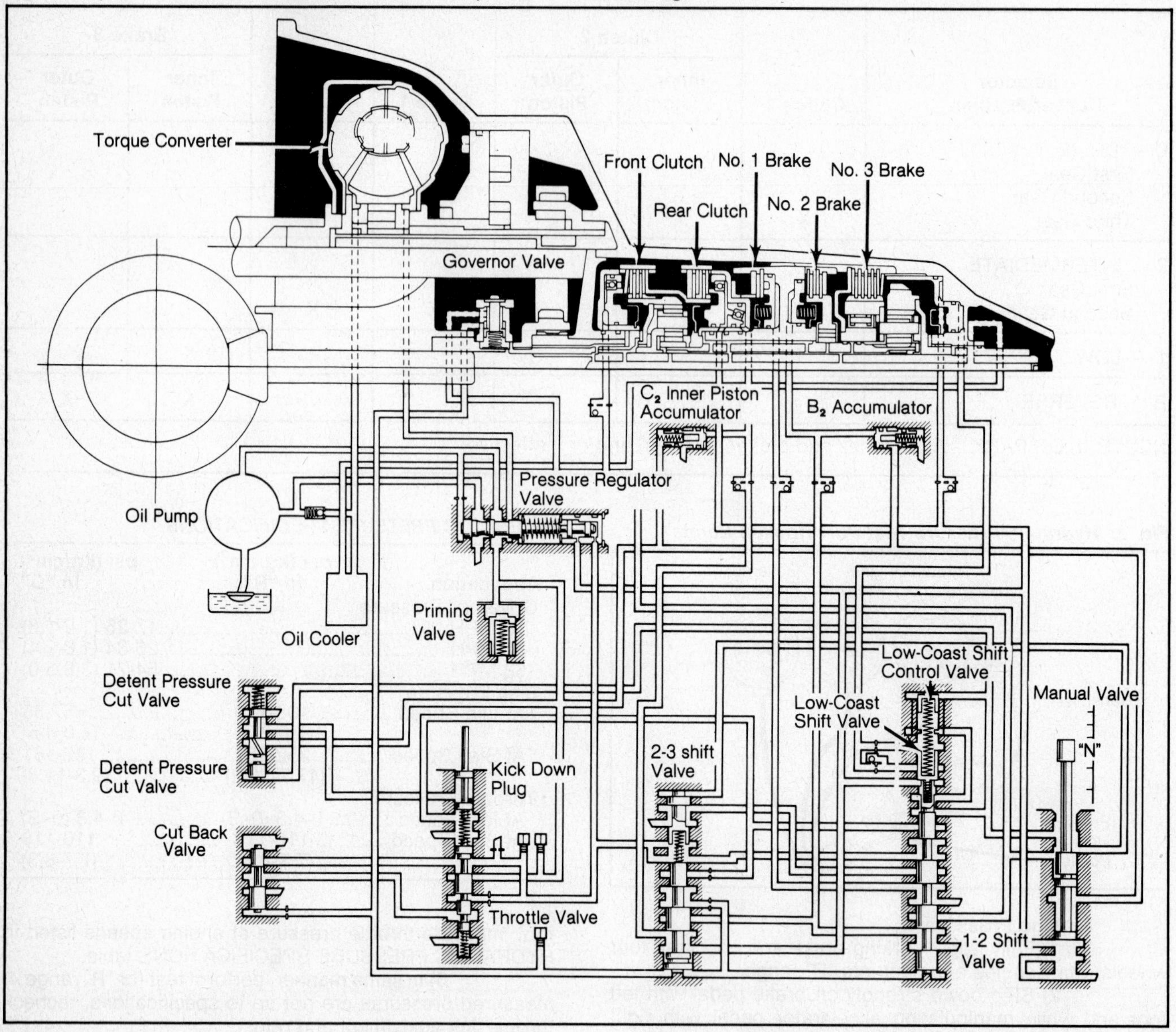

NOTE: Be careful not to lose locking balls.

CAUTION: Do not turn transmission over as this will contaminate valve body with foreign materials in bottom of pan.

2) Remove pan and gasket. Examine particles in pan. Remove magnet and use it to collect any steel chips. Look carefully at chips and particles in pan and on magnet to anticipate what type of wear may be found in transmission.

3) Steel (magnetic) means bearing, gear or clutch plate wear. Brass (nonmagnetic) means bushing wear. Turn transmission over and remove tubes by prying up both tube ends with a large screwdriver. Remove screen.

4) Remove valve body by removing 14 bolts, 6 steel balls and valve vibrating stopper. To remove accumulator pistons and springs, position a rag to catch each piston and using low pressure compressed air, 14 psi (1 kg/cm^2), pop each piston into rag. *See Fig. 5.*

CAUTION: Keep face away to avoid injury. Do not use regular high pressure air.

Fig. 5: Removing Accumulator Pistons With Compressed Air

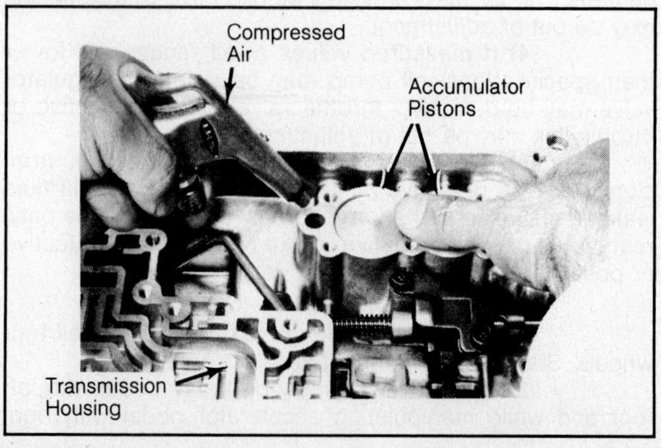

TOYOTA A55 & A55F TRANSAXLE (Cont.)

Fig. 6: Exploded View of Transmission Valve Body and Related Components

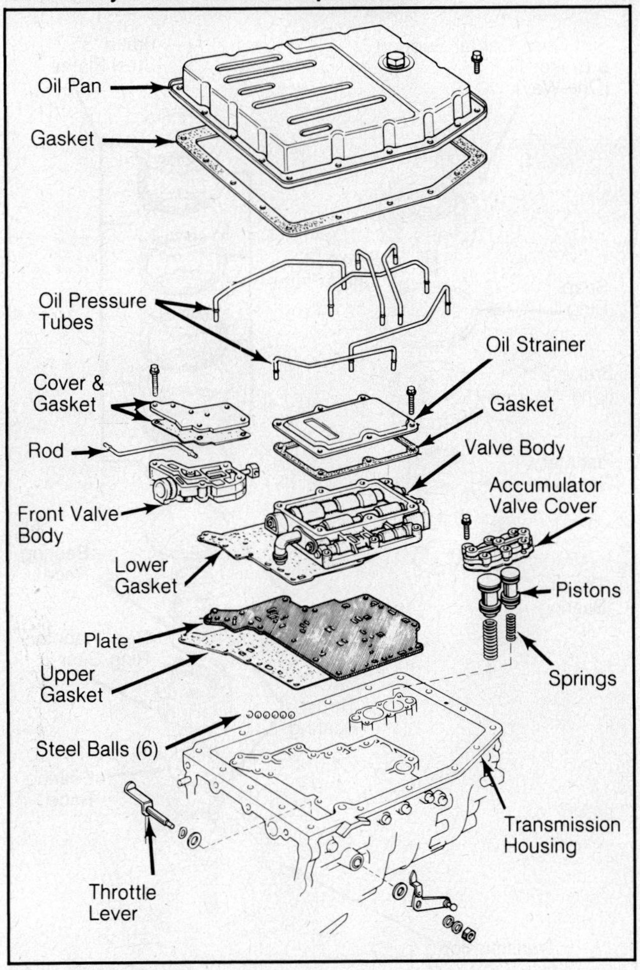

Fig. 7: Exploded View of Parking Lock Pawl and Manual Valve Shaft Components

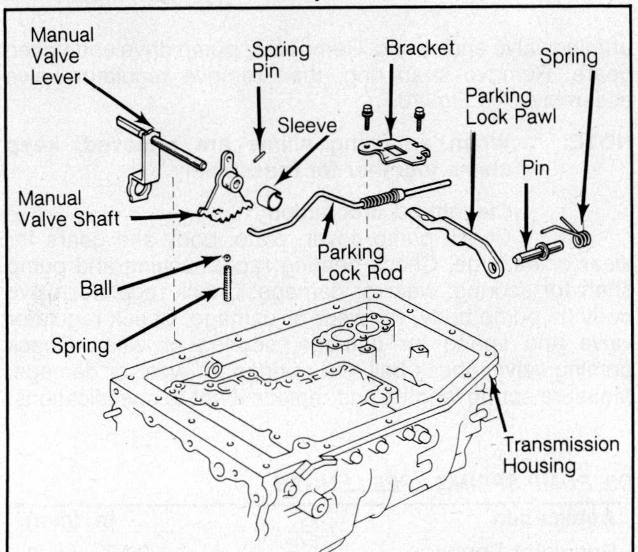

5) Remove park lock rod, spring, pivot pin and parking lock pawl. Remove spacer by unstaking spacer and turning ring 90°. Using a hammer and punch, drive out slotted spring pin and remove manual valve lever shaft.

6) After removing bracket bolt, remove pump suction tube. To remove oil pump delivery tube and pressure tube, pry up both tube ends with a large screwdriver and remove tubes. Remove oil pump by loosening 3 pump body-to-pump body (inner) bolts and removing 7 pump body-to-case (outer) bolts, then pull pump from case.

Fig. 8: Exploded View of Oil Pump and Components

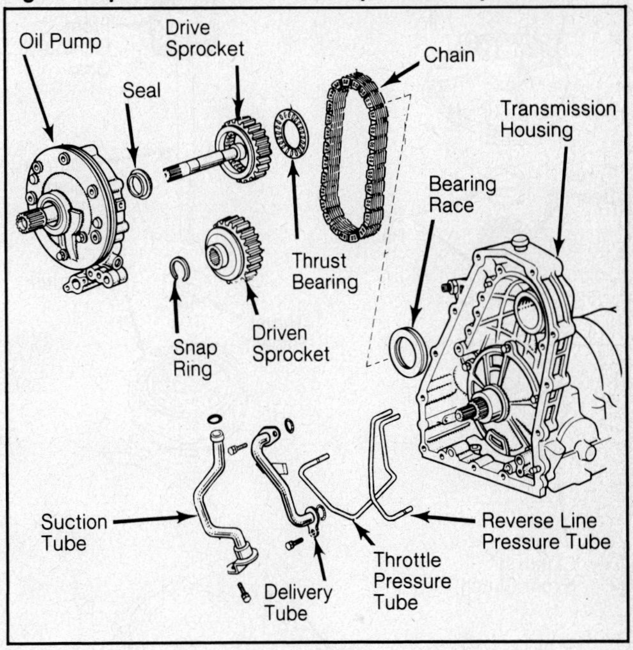

7) Remove input shaft, driven sprocket and chain by removing snap ring and pulling both sprockets out uniformly. Place case, facing up, on a wooden block and remove front support. Measure clearance between case tip and front clutch tip for reference at reassembly. Clearance should be .024-.063" (.6-1.6 mm). *See Fig. 9.*

8) Remove front clutch and bearings by grasping shaft and pulling out front clutch assembly. Be careful of bearings and races on both sides of assembly. Remove output shaft and front planetary gear. Grasp rear clutch hub and pull it from case. Remove two center support bolts.

Fig. 9: Measuring Front Clutch Clearance

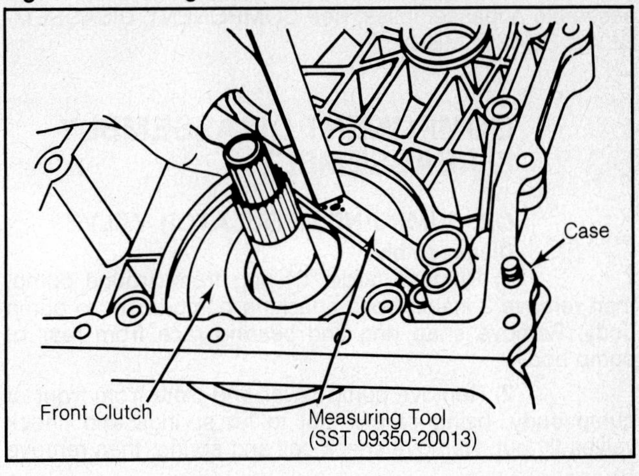

TOYOTA A55 & A55F TRANSAXLE (Cont.)

Fig. 10: Exploded View of Output Shaft & Components

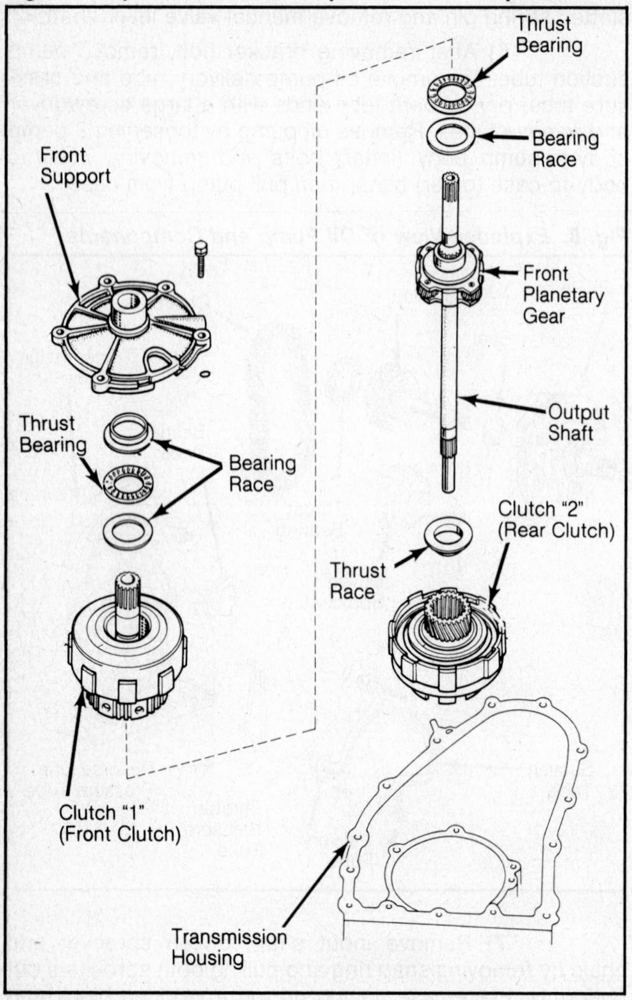

Fig. 11: Removing Center Support & Rear Clutch

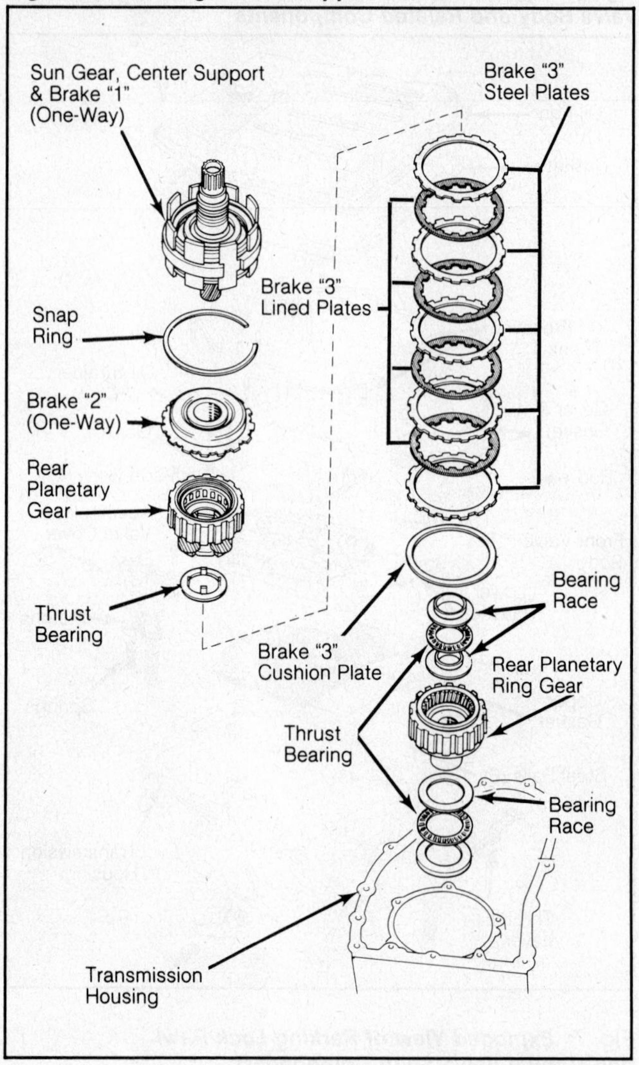

9) From front opening of case, grasp center support and sun gear assembly and pull it from case. Using a long screwdriver, compress reaction plate and lift retaining snap ring above groove with a wire hook and remove. Remove rear No. 2 one-way clutch and rear planetary gear.

10) Remove brake No. 3 disc, plate and cushion plate. Remove rear planetary ring gear. Basic disassembly is complete. Transmission is now in basic component subassemblies. To disassemble, clean, inspect, repair and assemble subassemblies, see COMPONENT DISASSEMBLY & REASSEMBLY.

COMPONENT DISASSEMBLY & REASSEMBLY

OIL PUMP AND REGULATOR VALVE

Disassembly

1) Remove large "O" ring from around pump, then remove 3 inside bolts attaching pump cover to pump body. Remove snap ring and bearing race from rear of pump body.

2) Remove pump cover and plate from front of pump body, being careful not to let springs and check valves fly out. Remove check ball and spring, then remove priming valve and spring. Remove oil pump drive and driven gears. Remove snap ring, then remove regulator valve assembly. *See Fig. 13*.

NOTE: **When adjusting shims are removed, keep shims together for reassembly.**

Cleaning & Inspection

Check pump cover, plate, body and gears for wear or damage. Check bearing race, bushing and pump shaft for scoring, wear or damage. Check regulator valve body (in pump body) for wear or damage. Check regulator valve and spring for damage, scoring or wear. Check priming valve, check ball and springs for wear or damage. Measure spring lengths and replace if not to specifications.

OIL PUMP SPRING FREE LENGTH

Application	In. (mm)
Regulator Spring	2.197 (55.8)
Check Ball Spring	1.032 (26.2)
Priming Valve	.756 (19.2)

Automatic Transmissions

TOYOTA A55 & A55F TRANSAXLE (Cont.)

Reassembly

1) Install oil pump driven and drive gears to pump body. Using a feeler gauge, measure clearance between a straightedge (layed across pump body) and pump gears. Clearance should be .008-.002" (.02-.05 mm). Measure clearance between driven gear and pump body.

2) Clearance should be .0028-.0060" (.07-.15 mm). Next, measure clearance between driven gear tooth and crescent in pump body. Clearance should be .0043-.0055" (.11-.14 mm). *See Fig. 12.* If clearances are not to specifications, replace oil pump.

3) Install check ball valve spring and check ball to pump body. Install priming valve spring and priming valve to pump body. Lubricate large "O" ring with ATF fluid, then install onto pump cover. Assemble pump cover plate to pump cover and install pump cover to pump body.

Fig. 12: Measuring Oil Pump Gear Clearance

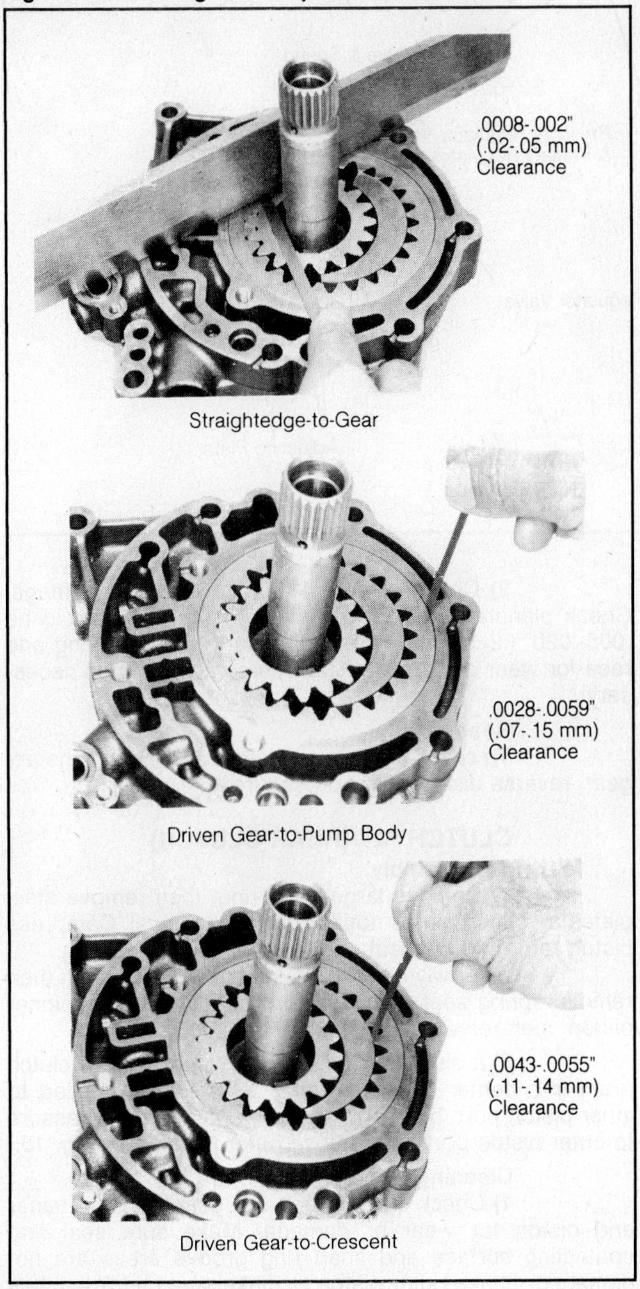

NOTE: **When installing pump cover, make sure check ball and priming valve seat into pump body correctly.**

4) Temporarily install and tighten (by hand) inside bolts to retain pump cover in place. Check rotation of pump drive gear. Install pressure regulator valve, washer and spring to pump body. Assemble same number of adjusting shims as removed to plunger, then install plunger to spring in pump body. Install sleeve and snap ring.

INPUT SHAFT, GEARS & CHAIN

Disassembly

Check input shaft, drive and driven gears for wear or damage. Remove snap ring, roller bearing and thrust bearing from input shaft driven gear. Check components for wear, scoring or damage. Check input shaft drive gear rear thrust bearing and race for wear or damage. Inspect chain for wear or damage. Check input shaft oil seal rings for wear or damage.

Reassembly

Replace any components found worn or damaged. Replace oil seal rings if worn or damaged. Install thrust bearing and roller bearing into input shaft driven gear and install snap ring. Install thrust bearing and roller bearing to input shaft drive gear and install snap ring. Place thrust bearing and race to rear of input shaft.

FRONT SUPPORT

Disassembly

Check mating surfaces of front support for wear or damage. Check oil seal rings on support shaft and replace if worn or damaged. Check front support shaft bushing for wear or damage.

Reassembly

Install new oil seal rings if they were worn or damaged. Install new small "O" ring to front support.

NOTE: **Oil seal ring ends are interlocking. Make sure rings fit together correctly.**

CLUTCH "1" (FRONT CLUTCH)

Disassembly

1) Remove thrust bearing and race from front side of race. Note position of races. Remove large snap ring from front clutch drum. Remove front and rear clutch hub by lifting out together. Remove thrust bearings and races. Note position of races.

2) Remove clutch plate and disc. Remove thin snap ring. Remove remaining clutch plates and discs. Place compressor tool (SST09350-20013) on spring retainer and compress springs with a press. Using a screwdriver, remove snap ring. Remove spring retainer and all springs.

3) Slide front clutch onto front support. Apply compressed air to front support to remove piston. Remove front clutch from front support. *See Fig. 14.*

NOTE: **Do NOT allow discs to dry out. Prepare new discs by soaking at least 2 hours in ATF.**

Cleaning & Inspection

Inspect front clutch piston. Check that check ball is free by shaking piston. Check that valve does not leak by applying low-pressure compressed air.

Reassembly

1) Install new "O" rings on piston. Install piston in front clutch drum. Press housing with cup side up (check ball down). Be careful not to damage "O" rings.

TOYOTA A55 & A55F TRANSAXLE (Cont.)

Fig. 13: Exploded View of Oil Pump and Regulator Valve Assembly

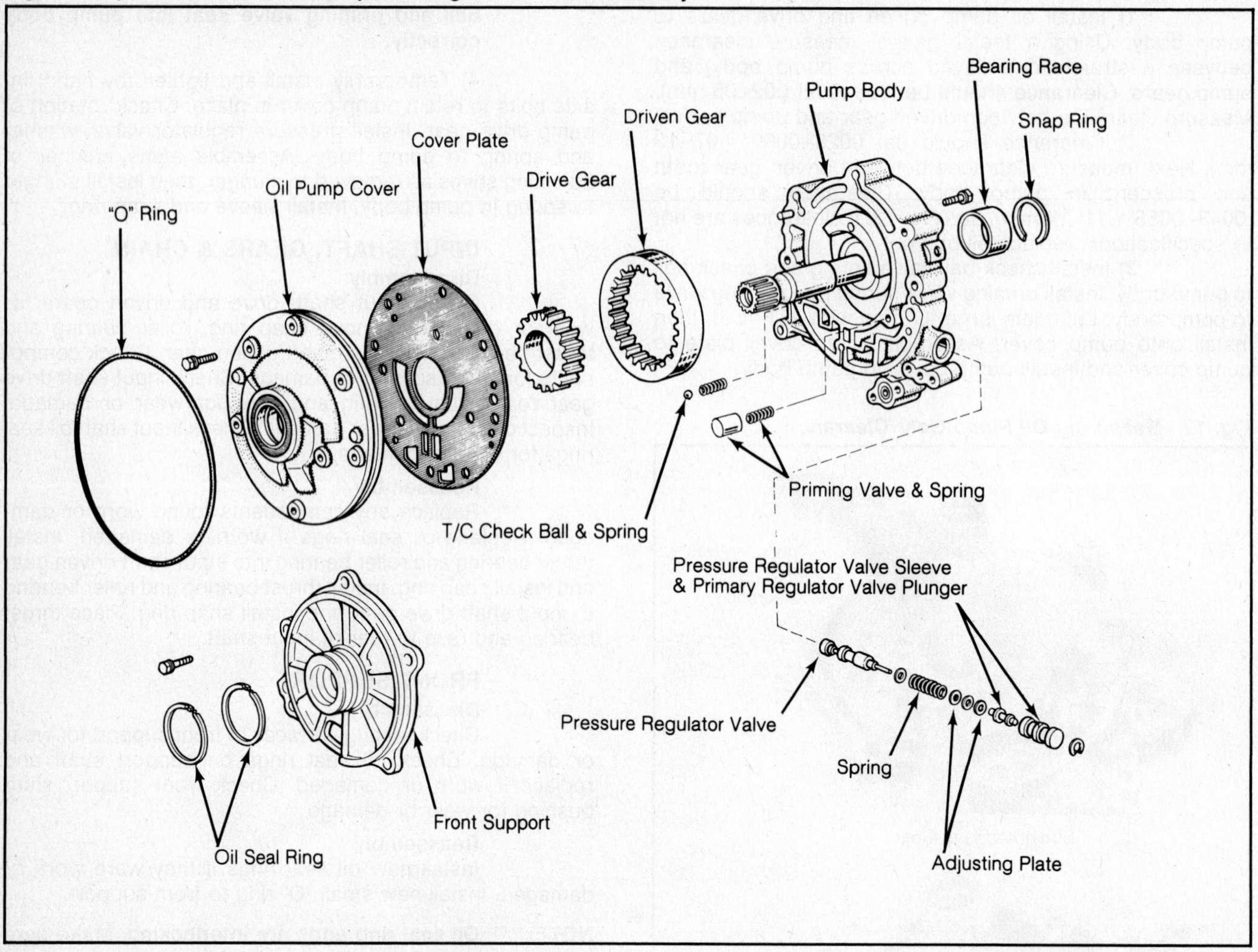

2) Install 20 piston return springs, spring retainer and snap ring into place. Compress return springs on spring retainer with Compressor (SST09350-20013) and arbor. Install snap ring with a screwdriver.

3) Using low-pressure compressed air, blow all excess ATF from discs. For measurement of clutch pack, install all plates and discs (temporarily without thinner snap ring). Install in following order: Cushion plate, plate, disc, plate, disc, plate, disc, plate.

4) Measure completely around circumference of front clutch. Standard clearance is .0118-.0587" (.30-1.49 mm). If not, use thicker snap ring. Remove snap ring, rear clutch hub and 1 plate and disc to allow installation of inner snap ring. Install inner race and needle bearing.

5) Press into place. Face lip of race toward front of clutch body. Install planetary ring gear, aligning disc lugs with hub teeth. Make sure hub meshes with all discs and is fully inserted. Install rear clutch drum and outer snap ring. Check that snap ring ends are not aligned with cut-outs.

OUTPUT SHAFT & FRONT PLANETARY GEAR

Disassembly

1) Remove thrust bearing and race from front side of planetary gear. Remove planetary gear snap ring. Pull planetary gear off output shaft. Check output shaft for wear or damage.

2) Check planetary gear for wear or damage. Check planetary gear thrust play. Thrust play should be .008-.020" (.2-.5 mm). Check planetary thrust bearing and race for wear or damage. Replace components as necessary.

Reassembly

To reassemble output shaft and front planetary gear, reverse disassembly procedure.

CLUTCH "2" (REAR CLUTCH)

Disassembly

1) Remove large snap ring, then remove steel plates and lined plates noting order of removal. Compress piston return spring seat and remove small snap ring.

2) Slowly remove pressure on spring seat, then remove spring seat with all return springs. Remove inner piston, then remove outer piston. *See Fig. 15*.

3) If pistons are difficult to remove, place clutch drum into center support. Using air pressure applied to inner piston port, blow out inner piston. Move air pressure to outer piston port and remove outer piston. *See Fig. 16*.

Cleaning & Inspection

1) Check clutch drum, sun gear, spring retainer and piston for wear or damage. Make sure seal ring contacting surface and snap ring groove areas are not damaged. Shake outer piston to make sure check ball has

TOYOTA A55 & A55F TRANSAXLE (Cont.)

Fig. 14: Exploded View of Clutch "1" (Front Clutch)

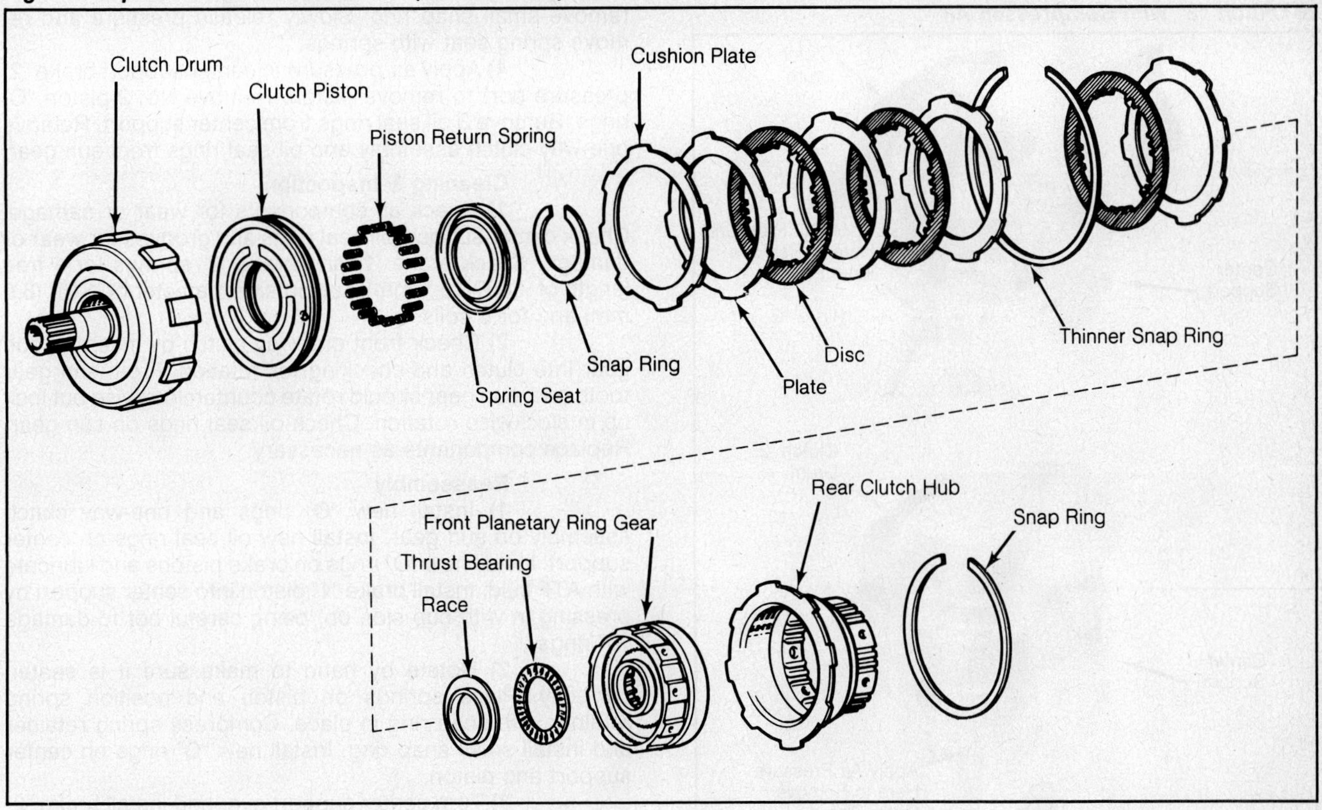

movement. Apply air to check ball orifice. No air should leak by.

2) Check inner piston in same manner as outer. Check return springs for a free length of 1.138" (28.9 mm), outside coil diameter of .315" (8.0 mm) and for 12 coils. Check steel plates and lined plates for burning, excessive wear or other damage.

Reassembly

1) Install new "O" rings to inner and outer pistons (lubricate "O" rings before installation). Lubricate pistons and install into clutch drum. Make sure spring seats in pistons are facing out of drum. With springs installed to pistons, install spring seat and compress to install snap ring. Make sure snap ring is seated properly before releasing spring compressor.

2) Install plates to clutch drum in this order: steel plate, lined plate, 2 steel plates, lined plate and cushion plate. Make sure round edge of cushion plate faces into drum. Install snap ring.

3) Install clutch "2" into center support and apply air pressure to center support. *See Fig. 18*. Measure piston stroke. Measurement should be .039.075" (.98-1.90 mm) with 56 psi (4 kg/cm^2) air pressure applied.

Fig. 15: Exploded View of Clutch "2" (Rear Clutch)

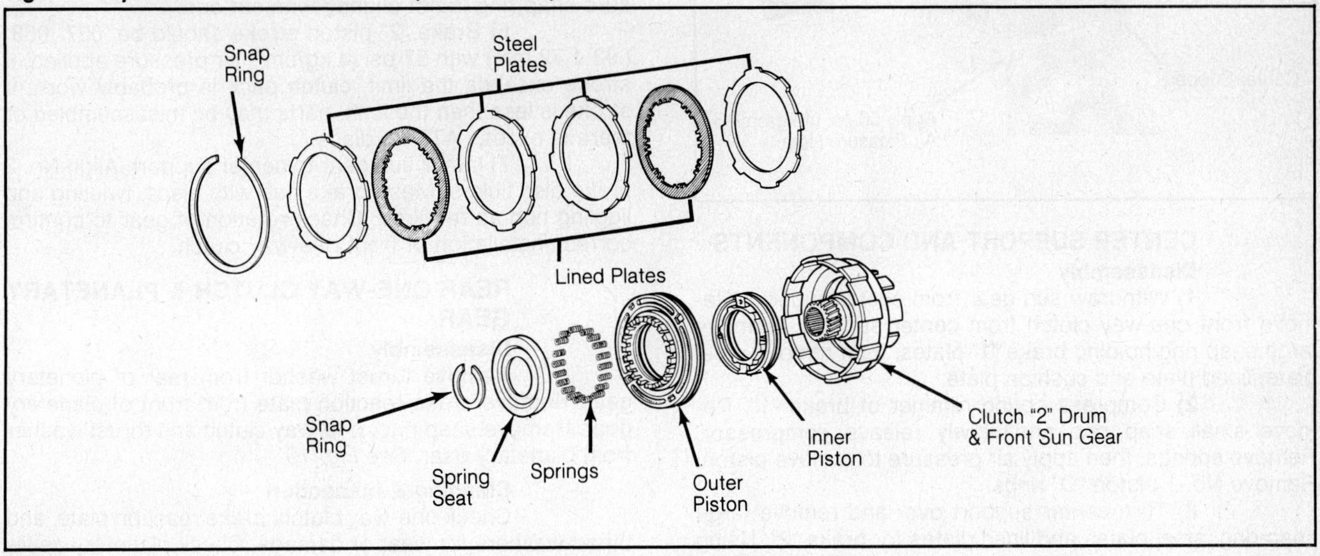

Automatic Transmissions

TOYOTA A55 & A55F TRANSAXLE (Cont.)

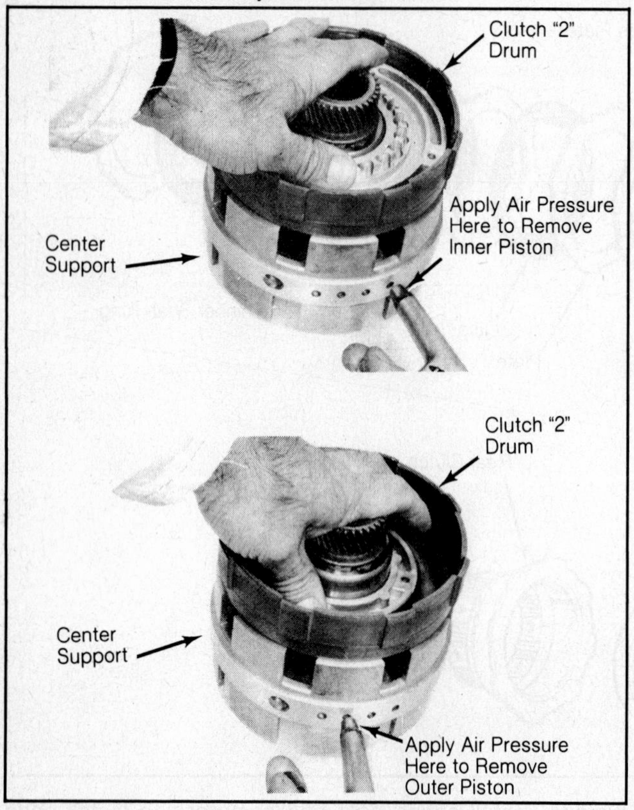

Fig. 16: Removing Inner and Outer Pistons of Clutch "2" with Compressed Air

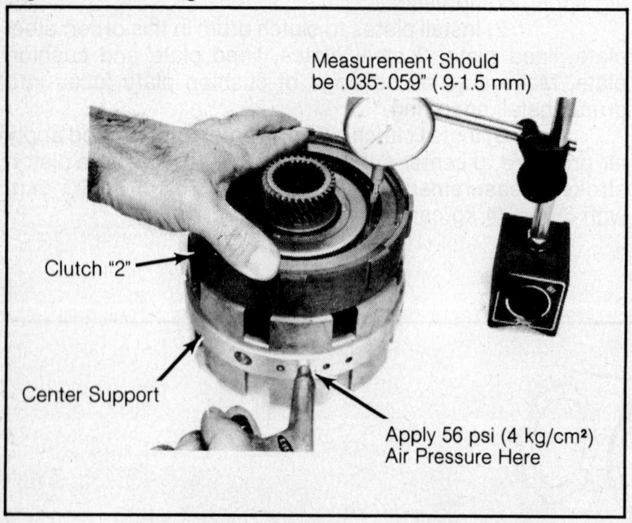

Fig. 17: Checking Clutch "2" Piston Stroke

CENTER SUPPORT AND COMPONENTS

Disassembly

1) Withdraw sun gear from center support. Remove front one-way clutch from center support. Remove large snap ring holding brake "1" plates, then remove steel plate, lined plate and cushion plate.

2) Compress spring retainer of brake "1". Remove small snap ring and slowly release compressor. Remove springs, then apply air pressure to remove piston. Remove No. 1 piston "O" rings.

3) Turn center support over and remove large snap ring, steel plates and lined plates for brake "2". Using a spring compressor, compress spring seat of brake "2" and remove small snap ring. Slowly release pressure and remove spring seat with springs.

4) Apply air pressure to center support brake "2" pressure port to remove piston. Remove No. 2 piston "O" rings. Remove 3 oil seal rings from center support. Remove one-way clutch assembly and oil seal rings from sun gear.

Cleaning & Inspection

1) Check all components for wear or damage. Check center support oil seal rings and grooves for wear or damage. Check brake "1" and brake "2" springs for a free length of .635" (16.1 mm), coil outside diameter of .315" (8.0 mm) and for 6 coils.

2) Check front one-way clutch by inserting sun gear into clutch and checking for rotation. From sun gear tooth end, sun gear should rotate counterclockwise but lock up in clockwise rotation. Check oil seal rings on sun gear. Replace components as necessary.

Reassembly

1) Install new "O" rings and one-way clutch assembly on sun gear. Install new oil seal rings on center support. Install new "O" rings on brake pistons and lubricate with ATF fluid. Install brake "1" piston into center support by pressing in with cup side up, being careful not to damage "O" rings.

2) Rotate by hand to make sure it is seated correctly. Place springs on piston and position spring retainer with snap ring in place. Compress spring retainer and install small snap ring. Install new "O" rings on center support and piston.

3) Turn center support over and install brake "2" piston, springs and retainer in the same manner as brake "1". Turn center support over and install No. 1 brake "1" plates, disc and flange. Use low pressue compressed air to blow all excess ATF from discs. *See Fig. 18* for steel plate and lined plate installation sequence.

4) With large snap rings installed to brake plates, measure piston stroke of brake piston. Make sure snap ring ends are not aligned with cut-outs. Brake "1" piston stroke should be .026-.051" (.65-1.3 mm) with 57 psi (4 kg/cm^2) air pressure applied.

5) Turn center support over and install No. 2 brake piston plate, discs and flange in the same manner as No. 1. Using low pressure compressed air, blow all excess ATF from discs. Install snap ring to center support. Make sure snap ring is not aligned with cut-outs.

6) Brake "2" piston stroke should be .037-.068" (.93-1.72 mm) with 57 psi (4 kg/cm^2) air pressure applied. If stroke exceeds the limit, clutch pack is probably worn. If stroke is less than the limit, parts may be misassembled or there is excess ATF on discs.

7) Install sun gear to center support. Align No. 2 brake disc flukes. Mesh brake hub with discs, twisting and jiggling hub as required. Check rotation of gear to confirm correct installation of front one-way clutch.

REAR ONE-WAY CLUTCH & PLANETARY GEAR

Disassembly

Remove thrust washer from rear of planetary gear. Remove brake reaction plate from front of planetary gear. Remove snap ring, one-way clutch and thrust washer from planetary gear. *See Fig. 19.*

Cleaning & Inspection

Check one-way clutch, brake reaction plate, and thrust washers for wear or damage. Check planetary gears

TOYOTA A55 & A55F TRANSAXLE (Cont.)

Fig. 18: Exploded View of Center Support, Brake "1", Brake "2", Sun Gear and Front One-Way Clutch

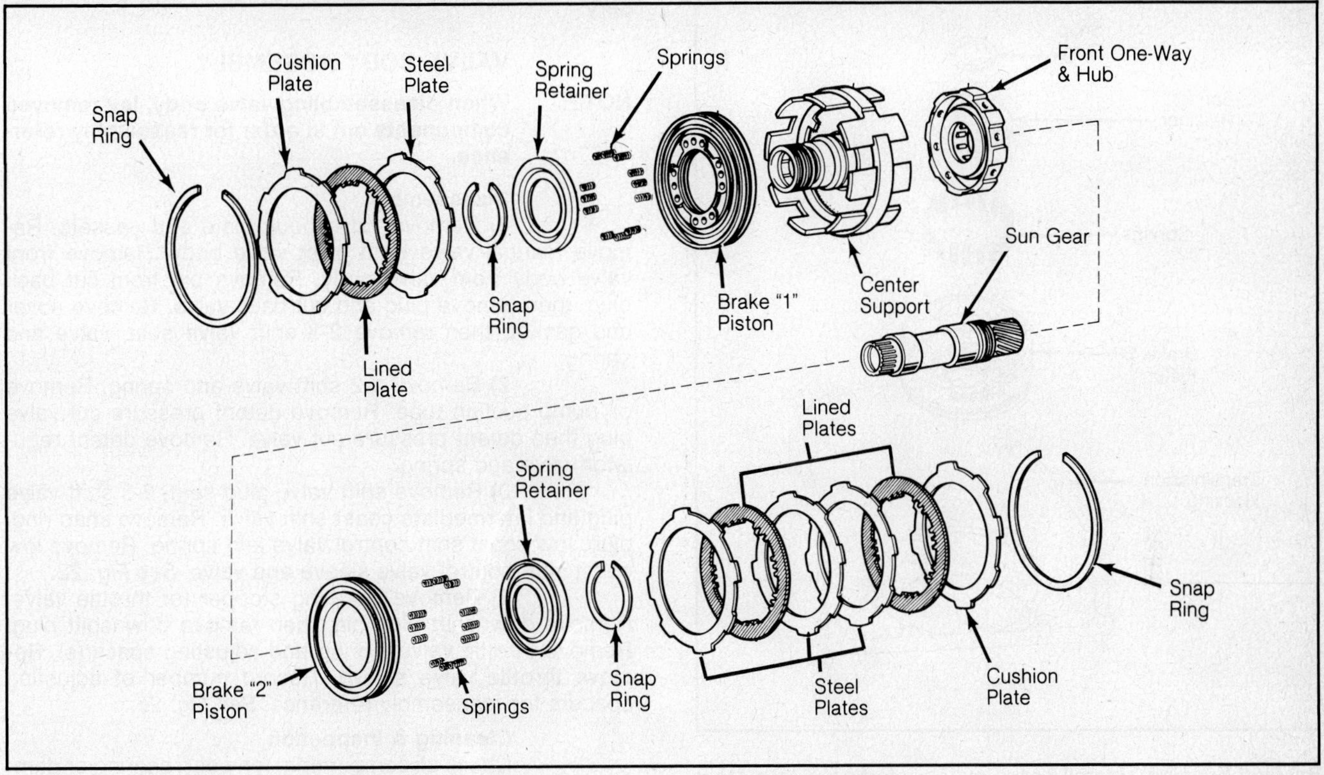

for smooth rotation and any damage to gear teeth. Check all thrust bearings for damage or wear.

Reassembly

1) Install thrust washer in planetary gear. Make sure thrust washer slot fits into slot in gear. Install one-way clutch into outer race with spring cage facing front. Rollers on clutch should be inclined in a counterclockwise direction.

2) Install snap ring. Install reaction plate to planetary gear to test. Planetary gear must rotate freely clockwise and lock counterclockwise. If clutch does not work correctly, it must be replaced.

BRAKE "3" PISTON

Disassembly

Compress spring retainer. Remove small snap ring. Slowly release spring compressor and remove spring retainer and springs. Place shop towels on top of piston and ease piston out slowly while applying air pressure to brake "3" pressure port. *See Fig. 20.*

Cleaning & Inspection

Check piston, spring retainer, snap ring and transmission housing (piston area) for wear or damage. Check bushing in transmission housing for wear or damage. Check piston springs for a free length of 1.03" (26.2 mm).

Reassembly

1) Install a new "O" ring to piston and reaction sleeve and install piston to transmission housing. Make sure lip on piston mates with notch in transmission housing (this notch is wider than other notches). Install springs and spring seat, then compress spring seat and install snap ring. *See Fig. 21.*

2) Check steel plates and lined plates of brake "3". Install cushion plate (concave side down toward trans-

Fig. 19: Exploded View of Rear One-Way Clutch and Planetary Gear

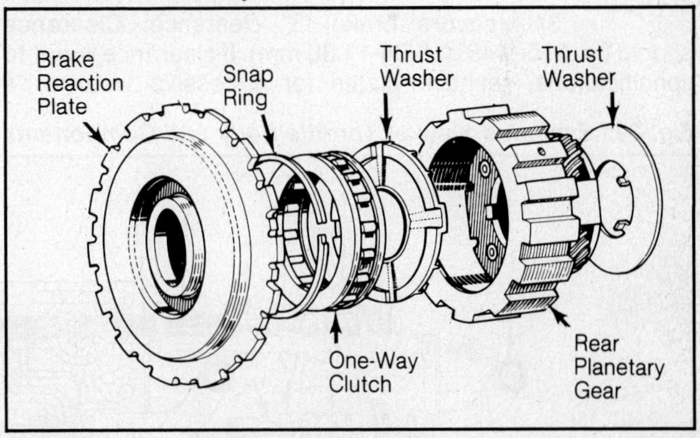

Fig. 20: Removing Brake "3" Piston with Air Pressure

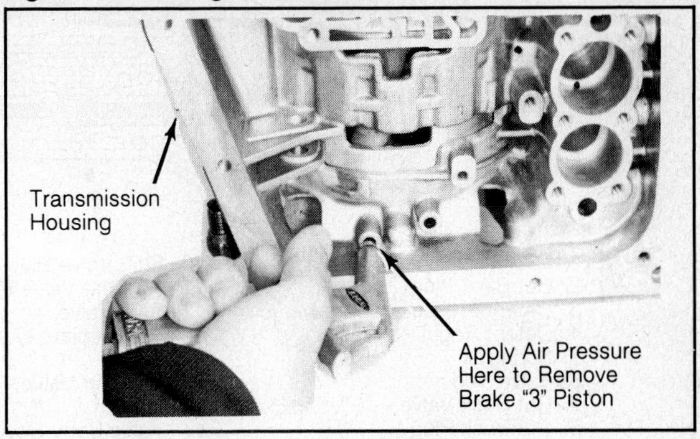

TOYOTA A55 & A55F TRANSAXLE (Cont.)

Fig. 21: Exploded View of Brake "3"

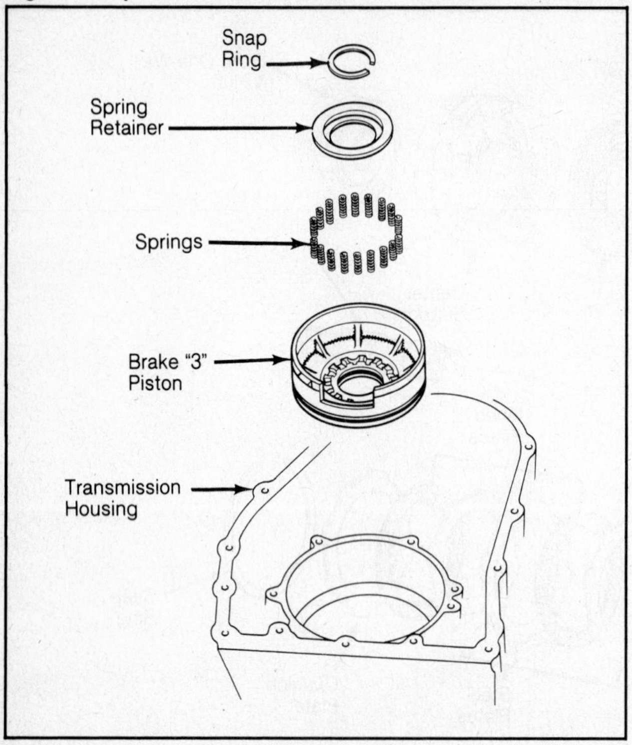

mission housing). Install brake plates, starting with a steel plate and alternating with lined plates until all plates are installed.

3) Measure brake "3" clearance. Clearance should be .395-.445" (10.04-11.30 mm). If clearance is not to specifications, recheck plates for excessive wear or a damaged cushion plate. Replace components as necessary.

VALVE BODY ASSEMBLY

NOTE: **When disassembling valve body, lay removed components out in order for reassembly reference.**

Disassembly

1) Remove valve body plate and gaskets. Remove manual valve from front valve body. Remove front valve body from valve body. Remove pin from cut back plug, then remove plug and cut back valve. Remove cover and gasket, then remove 2-3 shift valve seat, valve and spring.

2) Remove 1-2 shift valve and spring. Remove oil pump suction tube. Remove detent pressure cut valve plug then detent pressure cut valve. Remove detent regulator valve and spring.

3) Remove shift valve plug seat, 2-3 shift valve plug and intermediate coast shift valve. Remove snap ring, plug, low coast shift control valve and spring. Remove low coast shift control valve sleeve and valve. *See Fig. 22.*

4) Remove vibrating stopper for throttle valve. Remove downshift plug pin, then remove downshift plug. Remove throttle valve, spring and adjusting spacer(s). Remove throttle valve sleeve. Record number of adjusting spacers for reassembly reference. *See Fig. 26.*

Cleaning & Inspection

Check all components for wear, scoring or damage. Check springs for proper free length.

Reassembly

1) Install manual valve into front valve body. Insert low coast shift valve, low coast shift control valve sleeve, low coast shift control valve, 1-2 shift valve plug,

Fig. 22: Exploded View of Throttle Body and Components

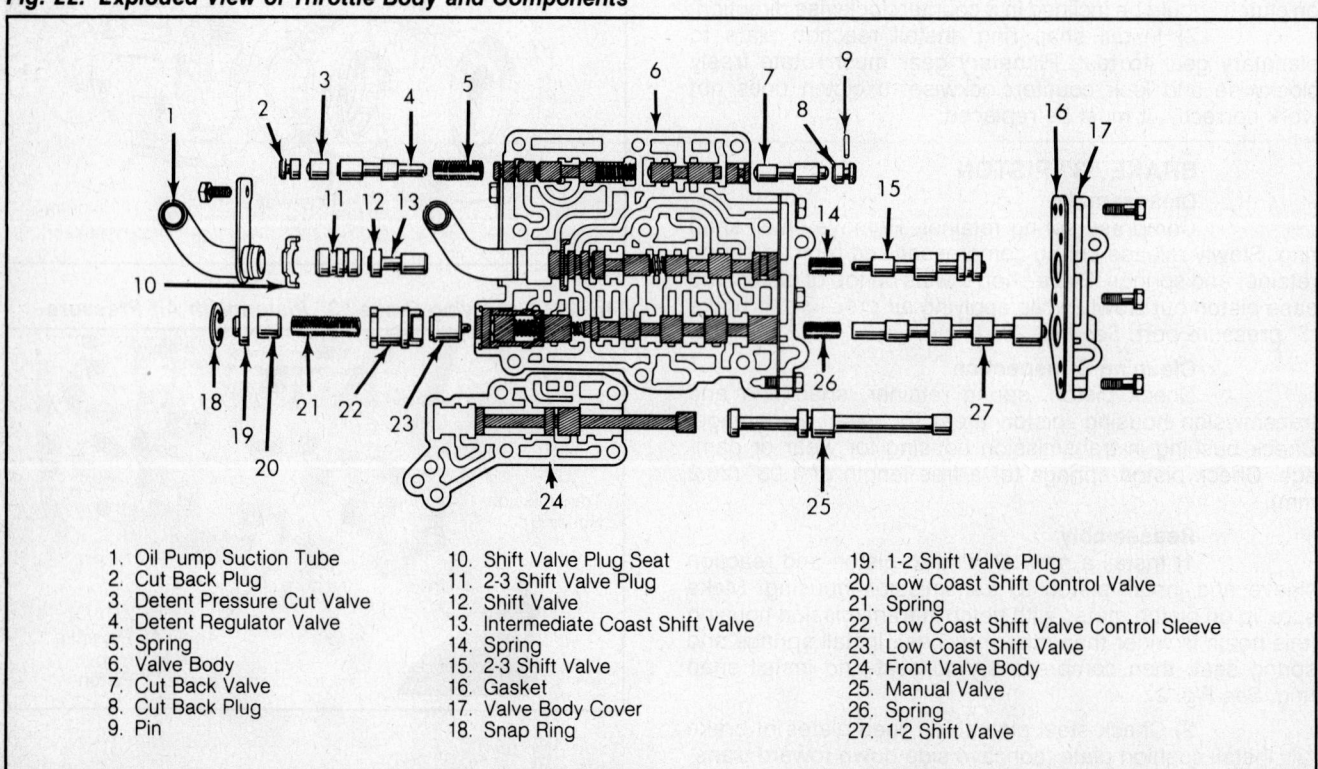

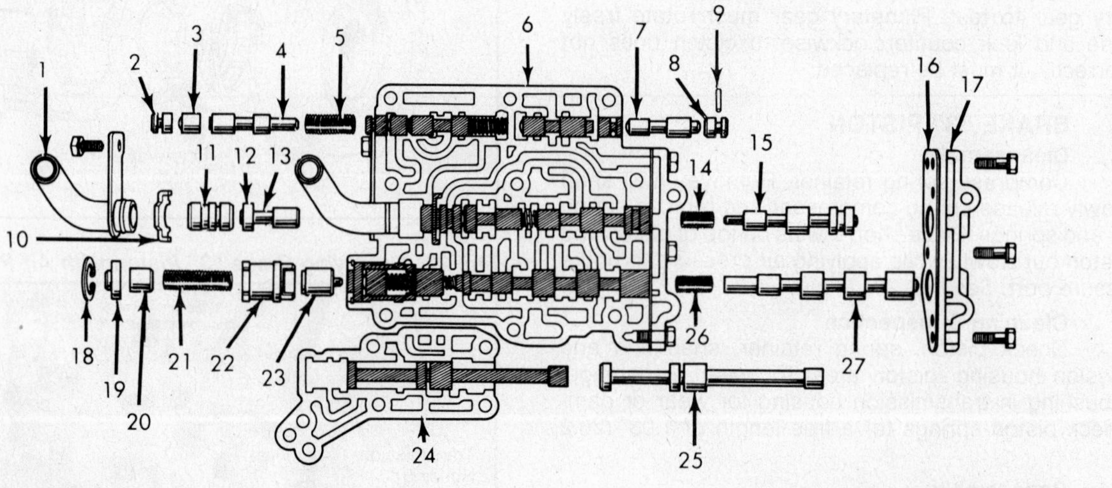

1. Oil Pump Suction Tube
2. Cut Back Plug
3. Detent Pressure Cut Valve
4. Detent Regulator Valve
5. Spring
6. Valve Body
7. Cut Back Valve
8. Cut Back Plug
9. Pin
10. Shift Valve Plug Seat
11. 2-3 Shift Valve Plug
12. Shift Valve
13. Intermediate Coast Shift Valve
14. Spring
15. 2-3 Shift Valve
16. Gasket
17. Valve Body Cover
18. Snap Ring
19. 1-2 Shift Valve Plug
20. Low Coast Shift Control Valve
21. Spring
22. Low Coast Shift Valve Control Sleeve
23. Low Coast Shift Valve
24. Front Valve Body
25. Manual Valve
26. Spring
27. 1-2 Shift Valve

TOYOTA A55 & A55F TRANSAXLE (Cont.)

and snap ring to valve body. *See Fig. 22.* Insert intermediate coast shift valve with small end down to valve body.

VALVE BODY SPRING FREE LENGTH

Application	In. (mm)
1-2 Shift Valve Spring	1.024 (26.0)
Low-Coast Valve Spring	1.437 (36.5)
2-3 Shift Valve Spring	.870 (22.1)
Detent Regulator Valve Spring	1.079 (27.4)
Throttle Valve Spring (Front)	1.193 (30.3)
Throttle Valve Spring (Rear)	1.083 (27.5)

2) Insert 2-3 shift valve plug into valve body and hold in place with shift valve plug seat (tangs on seat face into valve body). Place detent regulator valve spring, detent regulator valve, detent pressure cut valve and plug into valve body. Plug has a groove cut into it. Place edge of oil pump suction tube into this groove to hold components in place.

3) Attach suction tube to valve body with bolt. *See Fig. 22.* Insert 1-2 shift valve spring, 1-2 shift valve (small end down), 2-3 shift valve spring and 2-3 shift valve into valve body. Attach valve body cover, with gasket, to hold shift valves in position. Install cut back valve (small end down) and plug into valve body.

4) Insert pin into cut back valve plug. *See Fig. 22.* Install cut back valve retainer. Coat pin with petroleum jelly to keep it in place. Install same number of adjusting spacers into throttle valve sleeve as removed, then install sleeve into transmission housing. Insert spring, throttle valve, spring, down shift plug and pin into transmission housing.

5) Insert vibrating stopper into transmission housing. Apply petroleum jelly to hold it in place. *See Fig. 23.* Attach front valve body cover to valve body.

Fig. 23: Exploded View of Throttle Valve

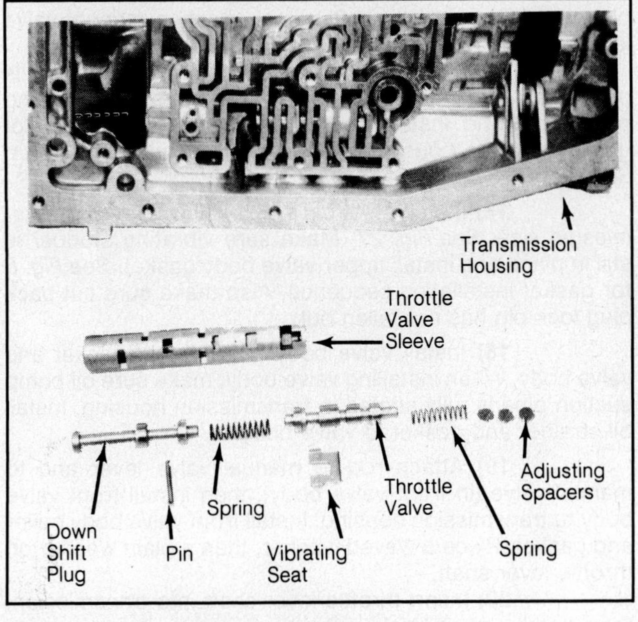

GOVERNOR VALVE

Disassembly

Remove snap ring and washer. Remove governor body support. Pry up retaining ring slightly with a screwdriver and pull out governor body with support. Compress spring by pushing up on the shaft and down on the weight. Remove "E" clip with screwdriver. Lift off governor weight. Remove governor valve by sliding it through bore. *See Fig. 24.*

Fig. 24: Exploded View of Governor Valve Assembly

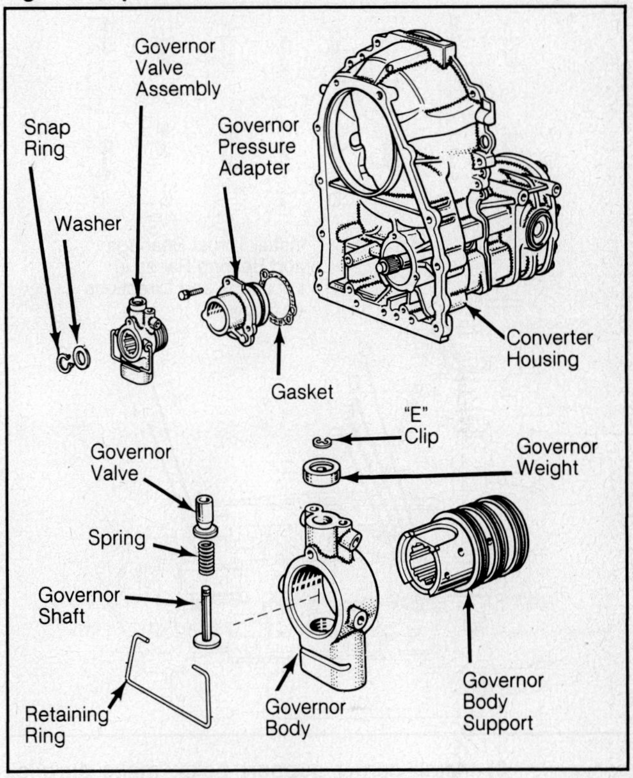

Cleaning & Inspection

Check all governor components for wear or damage. Check governor body support oil seal rings for wear or damage. Check governor spring for free length of .772" (19.6 mm). Clean oil strainer and check for wear or damage.

Reassembly

To reassemble governor, reverse disassembly procedure. Replace oil seal. Make sure retaining ring holes in governor body support are aligned with holes in governor body. When installing "O" ring and drive pinion, coat with multi-purpose grease.

TRANSMISSION REASSEMBLY

1) Install drive plate, with spacers, to crankshaft. Install front spacer, .127" (3.2 mm) thick, with beveled edge facing drive plate, then install drive plate. Install rear spacer, .056" (1.4 mm) thick, with cupped edge facing converter.

2) Install thrust bearing and races, then install rear planetary ring gear to transmission housing. Install cushion plate and steel and lined plates to transmission housing. Install thrust bearing by coating race with petroleum jelly and sticking to ring gear.

3) Align notch and tab of thrust washer and planetary gear, coat thrust washer with petroleum jelly and stick to planetary gear. Align disc flukes. Install rear planetary gear and thrust plate.

4) Make sure planetary ring gear is fully seated, then measure brake "3" clearance. Clearance should be .395-.445" (10.04-11.30 mm).

TOYOTA A55 & A55F TRANSAXLE (Cont.)

5) Install thrust washer, planetary gear, brake reaction plate, snap ring and center support to transmission housing. See *Fig. 11* for plate installation sequence and *Fig. 25* for thrust bearing and bearing race installation.

Fig. 25: Installation of Thrust Bearings and Bearing Races

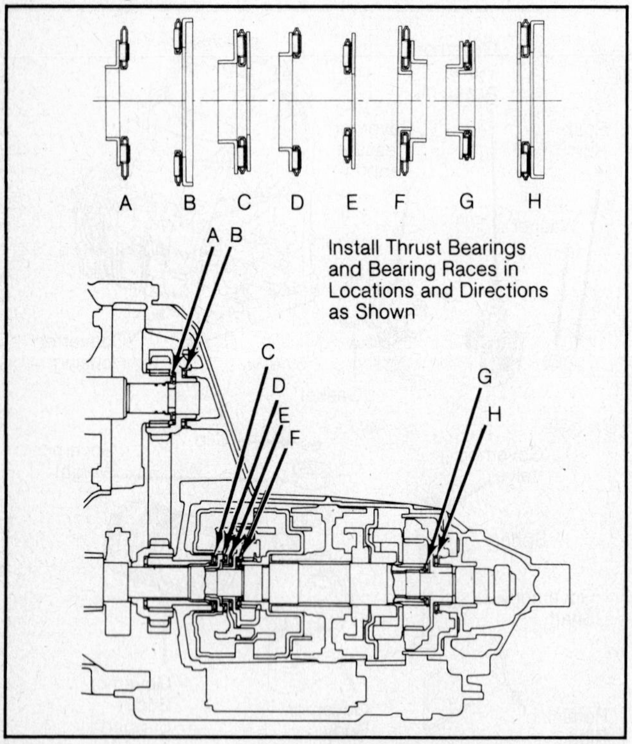

6) Install center support bolts, make sure oil holes in center support are aligned with oil holes in transmission housing and tighten center support bolts. After center support bolt installation, make sure planetary sun gear is easy to turn in a clockwise direction and hard to turn in a counterclockwise direction.

7) Install clutch "2", bearing race and output shaft to transmission housing. *See Fig. 10*. Install a thrust bearing and race over output shaft. Align the flukes of the rear clutch discs and mesh them with the front clutch hub. Install front clutch assembly into case (over output shaft).

8) After clutch "1" installation, lay a straightedge across clutch drum and transmission housing. Measure distance from straightedge to clutch drum. Distance should be the same as distance measured during disassembly. Standard distance is .024-.063" (.6-1.6 mm).

9) Install thrust bearing and race to clutch "1" shaft. Insert bearing race into front support. Install "O" ring to transmission housing. *See Fig. 26*. Coat thrust washer with petroleum jelly and set into front support with lip side to front support.

10) Install front support to transmission housing. Make sure there is no clearance between surfaces of support and case when pressing down. If there is clearance, front support is not correctly installed. Make sure there is thrust play on input shaft and tighten bolts diagonally a little at a time.

11) After front support installation, check clutch "1" shaft for ease of rotation and that end play is .0094-.0378" (.24-.96 mm). Check output shaft for ease of rotation and that end play is .012-.060" (.31-1.53 mm).

Fig. 26: Installation of "O" Ring in Transmission Housing Oil Passage

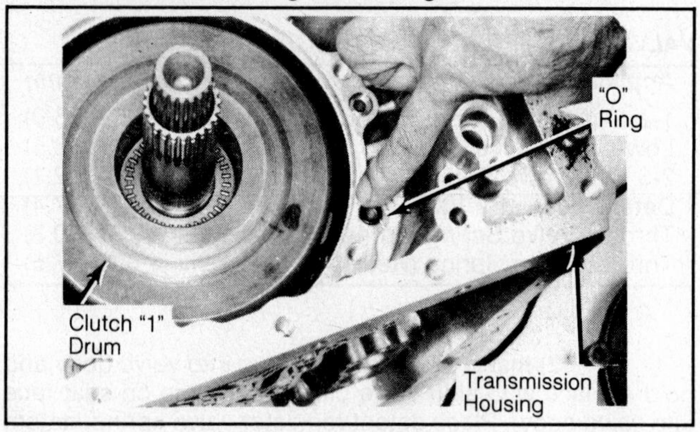

12) Place transmission so valve body side is down and install bearing race, thrust bearing, input shaft and drive sprocket to front of transmission housing. Install chain and driven sprocket, then secure driven sprocket with snap ring. Measure clearance between snap ring and driven sprocket. Clearance should be .0043-.027" (.11-.69 mm).

13) Install bearing race to input shaft, then install oil pump over input shaft. *See Fig. 13*. Install throttle pressure tube, then install reverse line pressure tube to front of transmission housing. Using new "O" rings, install oil pump delivery tube and oil pump suction to front of transmission housing. *See Fig. 29*.

14) Assemble new collar to manual valve lever. Install manual valve lever. While holding detent ball with plate, install manual valve shaft. Drive in slotted spring pin (always use new pin). After assembly, turn spacer 90° and stake.

15) Install park pawl, pivot pin and spring in case. Install park pawl bracket on case, making sure collar on control rod is toward front of transmission. Make sure planetary gear output shaft is locked when manual valve lever is in "P" range.

16) Turn transmission over so valve body side is up. Install accumulator springs and pistons, fully seating pistons by hand. Install accumulator gasket (straight side of gasket nearest housing), then install accumulator cover. *See Fig. 7*.

17) Install steel balls into valve body on transmission side. *See Fig. 27*. Make sure vibrating stopper is still in place and install upper valve body gasket. See *Fig. 6* for gasket installation sequence. Also make sure cut back plug lock pin has not fallen out.

18) Install valve body plate, lower gasket and valve body. When installing valve body, make sure oil pump suction pipe is fully seated in transmission housing. Install oil strainer and gasket to valve body.

19) Attach rod to manual valve lever and to manual valve (in front valve body), then install front valve body to transmission housing. Install front valve body cover and gasket. Place a waved washer, then a plain washer on throttle lever shaft.

20) Insert throttle lever shaft into transmission, then install a plain washer, throttle lever, washers and nut. Check throttle lever thrust clearance. If clearance is greater than .020" (.5 mm), install additional washers to outside of lever. Install oil pressure tubes. *See Fig. 28*. Install oil pan and gasket.

TOYOTA A55 & A55F TRANSAXLE (Cont.)

Fig. 27: Installation Locations of Valve Body Steel Balls

Fig. 28: Intallation of Oil Pressure Tubes

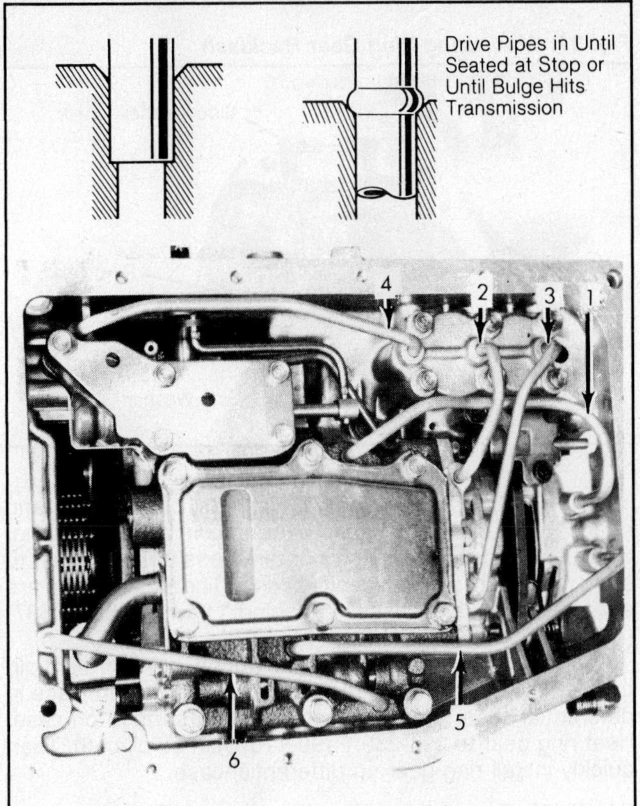

21) Place transmission housing-to-converter housing gasket on transmission housing (coated with sealant). Install new "O" rings into transmission housing-to-converter housing oil passages. Attach converter housing-to-transmission housing.

22) Install output shaft sleeve with speedometer drive gear and balls to transmission output shaft. Secure sleeve with snap ring. Install extension housing and gasket to transmission housing. Attach transmission rear mount to rear of transmission housing.

23) Install speedometer driven gear, neutral start switch, oil filler tube and control rod to transmission. When installing neutral start switch, align switch shaft groove to neutral base line. *See Fig. 30.* Install torque converter.

FINAL DRIVE

DIFFERENTIAL ASSEMBLY

Pre-Inspection

NOTE: **If the differential is noisy, perform the following pre-inspection before disassembly to determine the cause of the noise.**

1) Remove differential from transaxle. Install differential carrier on work stand with ring gear in horizontal position. Check ring gear backlash. *See Fig. 31.* If backlash in not within specification, adjust side bearing preload or repair as necessary. Backlash should be .0039-.0059" (.10-.15 mm).

2) Check ring gear runout. If runout is greater than maximum, install a new ring gear. Maximum runout is .0028" (.07 mm). Check teeth contact. Check total pinion preload with a torque wrench. Total preload (starting) should be 5.2-8.7 INCH lbs. (.6-1.0 N.m)

Disassembly

NOTE: **Before removing, tag bearing cap, outer race and side washer for reference at reassembly.**

1) Remove oil seals from differential carrier using a slide hammer. Remove side bearing caps. Remove side washer on ring gear teeth side using Side Washer Removal Tool (SST 09504-22010).

2) Remove differential case and bearing outer race. Remove side washer opposite ring gear. To remove governor body and governor pressure adaptor, use snap ring pliers to remove snap ring, then remove governor body. Wrap spline with tape and remove governor pressure adaptor.

3) Loosen staked part of drive pinion nut. Using drive pinion holding tool (SST 09564-16010 and SST 09556-16020) to loosen nut, turn drive pinion clockwise. Using a press, press drive pinion from housing.

Inspection

1) Inspect drive pinion bearings and outer races. If necessary, replace drive pinion bearing and outer race using a press to drive pinion from bearing.

NOTE: **If drive pinion or ring gear is damaged, replace both as a set.**

2) For drive pinion, select a plate washer of proper thickness, in accordance with teeth contact, inspected before disassembly. Install plate washer on drive pinion. Using a press, install new bearing on drive pinion.

3) Using a hammer and brass bar, remove pinion outer races by tapping on notched portions. Using a bearing race installer, install outer races.

TOYOTA A55 & A55F TRANSAXLE (Cont.)

Fig. 29: Installation of Oil Tubes and Pipes to Front of Transmission Housing

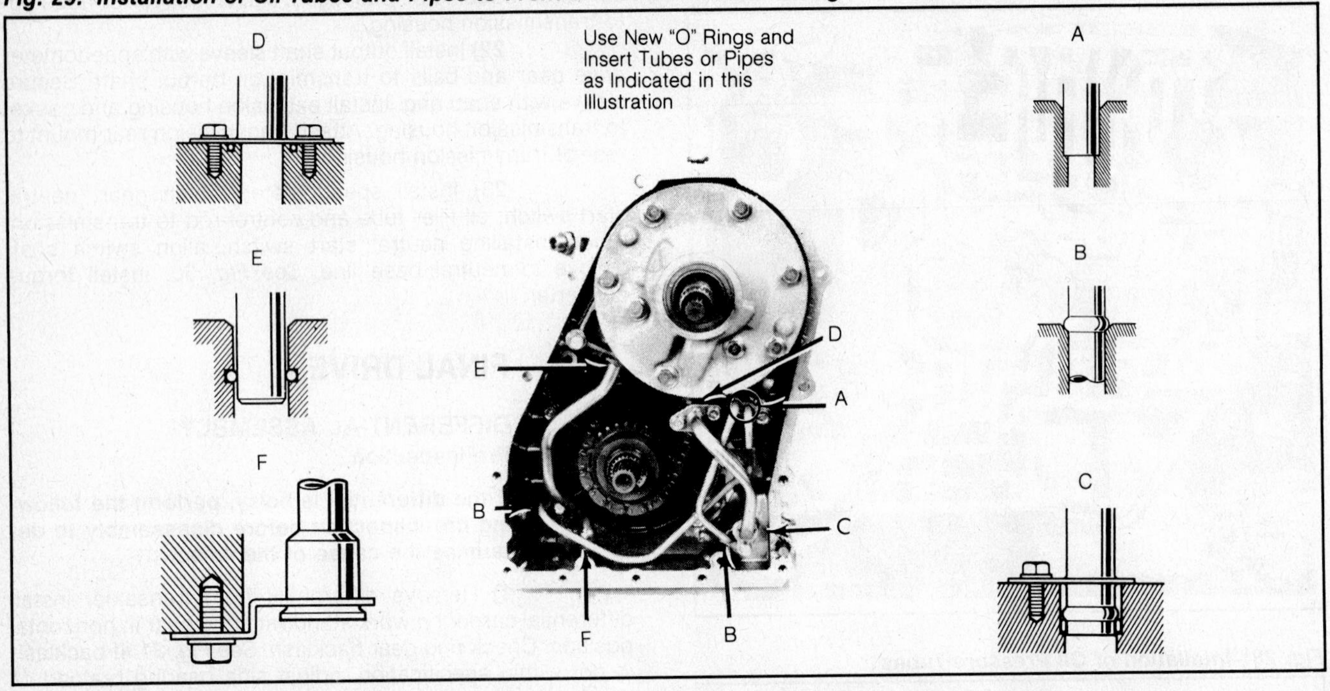

Fig. 30: Aligning Neutral Start Switch

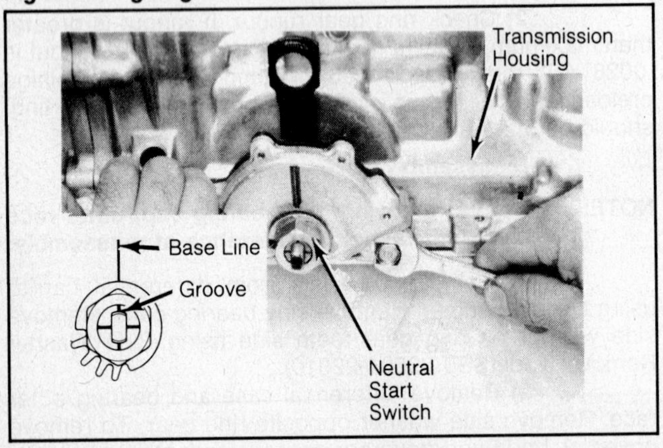

Fig. 31: Measuring Ring Gear Backlash

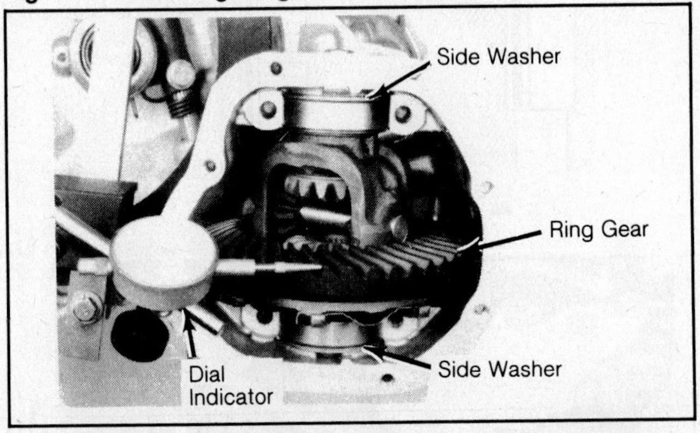

4) Inspect case side bearings and outer races. If necessary, replace side bearings and outer races by removing side bearings with a gear puller. The hooked ends of the puller fit into the indentations in the case. Install new bearings using a press.

5) Inspect pinion and side gears. Check side gear backlash by holding one side gear toward case and measuring backlash of the other. Backlash should be .0016-.0094" (.04-.24 mm).

6) If it becomes necessary to replace ring gear, differential pinions and side gears, then lift lock plates and remove set bolts. Using a brass bar and hammer, tap on ring gear to separate it from differential case.

NOTE: **If the ring gear is to be used again, before separating it, place marks on ring gear and case for reference at reassembly.**

7) Using a pin punch and hammer, tap out pinion shaft retaining pin toward ring gear mating surface. Remove pinion shaft, pinion gears, side gears and thrust washers. Check gears, shaft, case and washers.

8) Install side gears, washers, pinion gears and shaft. Remeasure side gear backlash. If backlash is not within specifications, use proper thickness thrust washer to bring backlash within specifications. Thrust washers are available in thicknesses ranging from .0583-.0697" (1.48-1.77 mm) in increments of .0015" (.04 mm).

9) Using a hammer and punch, drive straight pin through case and hole in pinion shaft. Stake pin in place in differential case. Clean ring gear mating surface on case. Heat ring gear to 194-230°F (90-110°C) in an oil bath. Then quickly install ring gear on differential case.

CAUTION: Do not heat ring gear above 230°F (110°C).

10) Coat ring gear bolts with gear oil. Install lock plates and bolts. Tighten bolts uniformly, in steps and to specifications. Stake lock plate.

NOTE: **Stake one claw flush with flat surface of nut. For claw contacting protruding portion of nut, stake (bend) only the half on the tightening side.**

TOYOTA A55 & A55F TRANSAXLE (Cont.)

11) Inspect governor pressure adaptor oil seal. If necessary, replace oil seals using a press and a 29 mm socket wrench. Press in oil seal on transmission side then press in oil seal on differential side. Be sure oil seal is positioned correctly.

Fig. 32: Exploded View of Final Drive

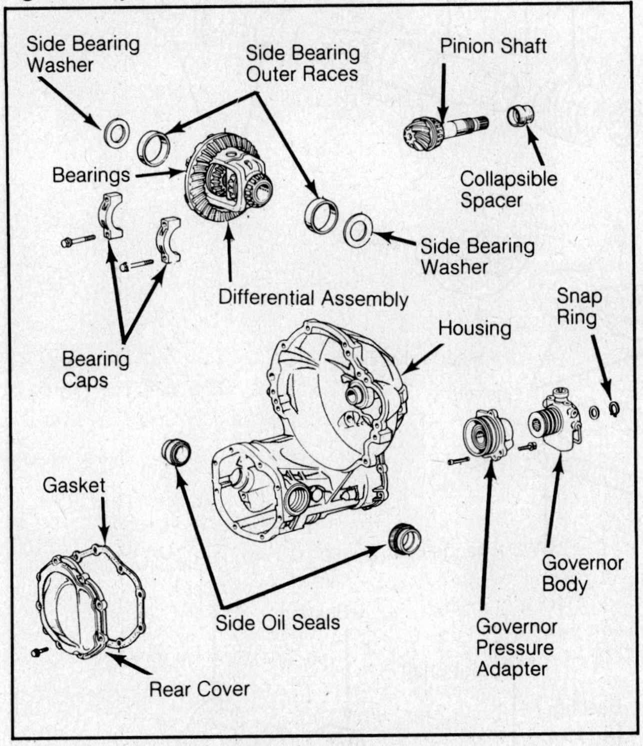

Reassembly

1) Install a new spacer on drive pinion. Install drive pinion into differential carrier. Using a press, temporarily press in bearing until threaded portion is protruding .12" (3 mm) without crushing spacer. Apply gear oil to the threaded portion of drive pinion.

2) Using Drive Pinion Holder (SST 09564-16010 and SST 09556-16020) install drive pinion nut. Apply gear oil to bearings. Snug down bearing by turning drive pinion several times. Using a torque wrench, check bearing preload. Preload should be 4.3-8.7 INCH lbs. (.5-1.0 mm) for new bearings and 2.6-4.3 INCH lbs. (.3-.5 mm) for used bearings.

3) If adjustment is needed, tighten drive pinion nut to 108 ft. lbs. (146 N.m). Measure preload. If preload is excessive, replace spacer and readjust. If preload is insufficient, increase torque in increments of 5-10 ft. lbs. (7-14 N.m) until proper preload is obtained, but do not exceed 268 ft. lbs. (363 N.m).

NOTE: **If preload in not within specification after tightening nut to maximum, a new spacer must be used.**

4) Install differential case, outer races and side washer on side nearest ring gear. Be sure ring gear has backlash. Snug down washer and bearing by tapping on ring gear with a plastic hammer. Push side bearing boss on teeth surface of ring gear and measure backlash. Backlash should be .0039" (.10 mm).

5) Select proper washer using backlash as reference. Side washers come in 23 different sizes ranging from .1028-.1295" (2.61-3.29 mm). After proper backlash side washer has been installed on side nearest ring gear, select a side washer for side farthest from ring gear, of a thickness which eliminates any clearance between outer race and housing.

6) Remove side washers and differential case. Install side washer into ring gear side of housing. Place other side washer on bearing race opposite ring gear and install differential case with outer race into housing. Using a plastic hammer, snug down washer and bearing by tapping on ring gear.

7) Using a dial indicator, measure ring gear backlash. It should be .0039-.0059" (.10-.15 mm). If not within specification, adjust by either increasing or decreasing number of washers on both sides by an equal amount. Insure that there is ring gear backlash and there should be no clearance between side washer and case.

8) After adjustment, using backlash as reference, remove ring gear side side washer and measure thickness. Install a new washer .0024-.0035" (.06-.09 mm) thicker than washer removed.

NOTE: **Select a washer which can be pressed in 2/3 of the way by finger.**

9) Use a plastic hammer to tap side washer in rest of the way. Recheck ring gear backlash. It should be .0039-.0059" (.10-.15 mm). If not within standard, adjust by either increasing and decreasing washers on both sides by an equal amount.

NOTE: **The backlash will change about .0008" (.02 mm) with a .0012" (.03 mm) variation of the side washer.**

10) Install side bearing caps and tighten bolts to specifications. To measure total preload, apply gear oil on bearings, turn drive pinion left and right several times and with a torque wrench measure total preload. Preload (starting) should be 2.6-4.3 INCH lbs. (.02-.03 N.m), in addition to drive pinion preload.

NOTE: **If preload is not within standard, readjust ring gear side washer.**

11) Measure ring gear backlash using a dial indicator. Measure at 3 places on outer edge of ring gear. Backlash should be .0039-.0059" (.10-.15 mm).

NOTE: **If not within standard, adjust by either increasing or decreasing washers on both sides by an equal amount. The backlash will change about .0008" (.02 mm) with a .0012" (.03 mm) variation of the side washer.**

12) To inspect teeth contact between ring gear and drive pinion, coat red lead on 3 or 4 teeth at 3 different positions of ring gear, rotate ring gear in both directions and inspect teeth pattern. If there is toe contact, replace pinion plate washer with a thinner one. If there is heel contact, replace pinion plate washer with a thicker one.

NOTE: **If the plate washer thickness is altered .0039" (.10 mm), the center of the teeth contact will change about 1/8 of the total teeth surface.**

13) If there is flank contact, increase backlash within standard specification. If there is face contact, decrease backlash within standard specification.

Automatic Transmissions

TOYOTA A55 & A55F TRANSAXLE (Cont.)

Fig. 33: Exploded View of 4WD Extension Housing Assembly

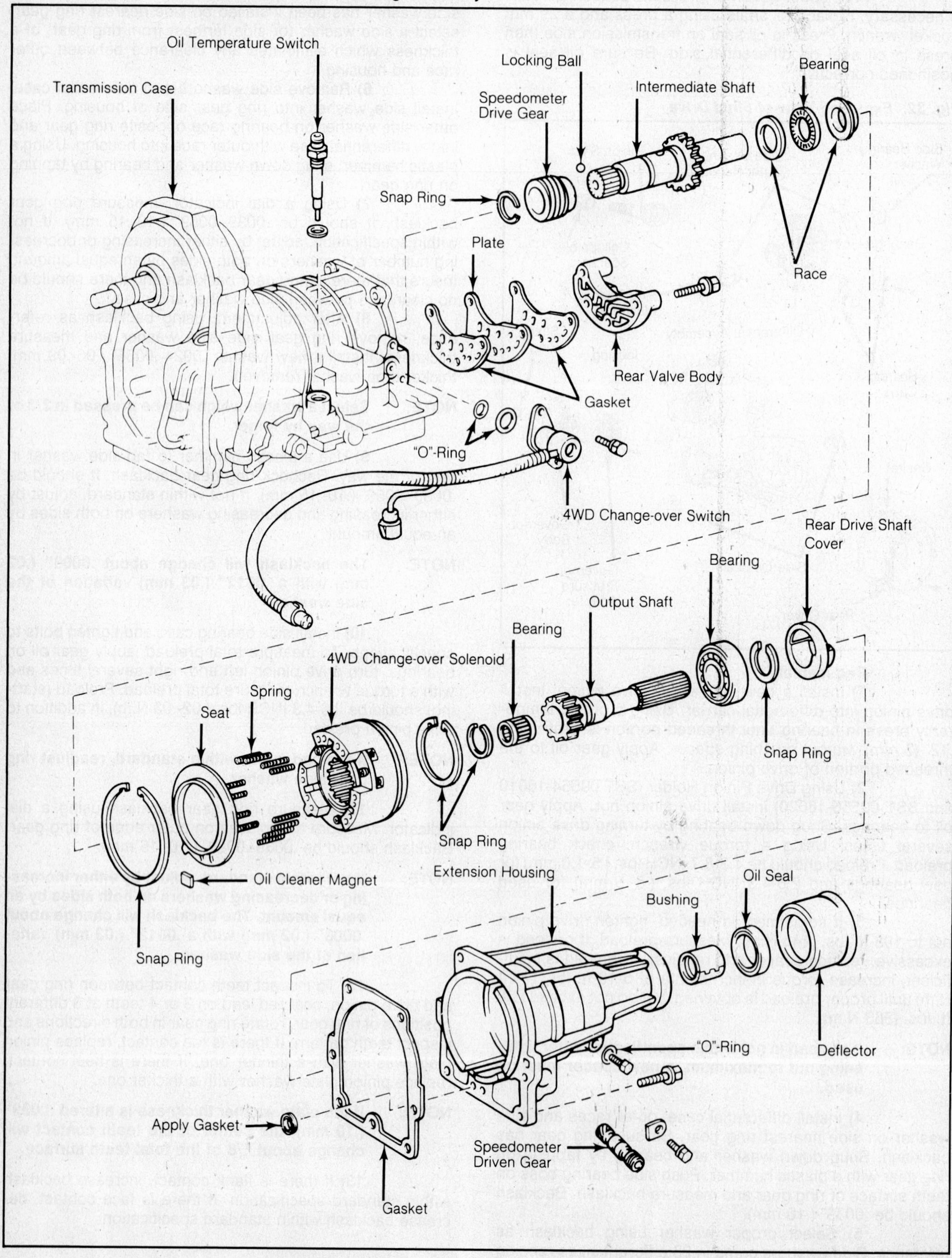

TOYOTA A55 & A55F TRANSAXLE (Cont.)

NOTE: Increase or decrease both side washers by an equal amount. The backlash will change about .0008" (.02 mm) with a .0012" (.03 mm) variation of the side washer.

14) Stake drive pinion nut using a chisel. Install differential carrier oil seal .331-.354" (8.4-9.0 mm) below surface using a hammer and seal installer. Install differential carrier cover and gasket and bolts.

15) After wrapping spline with tape, install governor pressure adaptor and governor body. Assemble with transmission.

TIGHTENING SPECIFICATIONS

Application	Ft. Lbs. (N.m)
Axle Shaft Nut	137 (186)
Ball Joint-to-Steering Knuckle	59 (80)
Center Support Bolts	19 (26)
Drive Plate	47 (64)
Engine Rear Mount-to-Body	67 (91)
Engine-to-Converter Housing	47 (64)
Lower Arm-to-Body	83 (113)
Lower Arm-to-Ball Joint	59 (80)
Pinion Nut	109-267 (148-362)
Ring Gear Bolts	71 (96)
Side Bearing Caps	36 (49)
Stabilizer Bracket	32 (43)
Stabilizer-to-Lower Arm	78 (106)
Strut-to-Steering Knuckle	105 (142)
Transmission-to-Converter Hsg.	14 (19)

Automatic Transmissions

TOYOTA A-130L, A-131L & A-240L TRANSAXLE

Corolla FWD

DESCRIPTION

Model A-130L and A-131L transaxles have 3 forward speeds and reverse. Transaxle assembly consists of a 3-element torque converter, a gear driven oil pump, a valve body, a differential, and 2 planetary gear sets actuated by 3 multi-disc brakes and 2 one-way clutches.

Model A-240L transaxles have 4 forward speeds and reverse. Transaxle has an electronically controlled overdrive. Transaxle assembly consists of a 3-element torque converter, gear driven oil pump, valve body, differential, and 3 planetary gear sets actuated by 3 multi-disc clutches, 1 brake band and 3 one-way clutches.

Engine load and speed determine gear changes by use of throttle valve position and output shaft speed.

LUBRICATION & ADJUSTMENT

See appropriate AUTOMATIC TRANSMISSION SERVICNG article in IMPORT GENERAL SERVICING section.

TROUBLE SHOOTING

PRELIMINARY CHECKS

Trouble occuring with the automatic transaxle can be caused by either the engine or the transaxle. Isolate trouble to engine or transaxle before proceeding with trouble shooting. Trouble shooting should begin with simplest test procedure, working up in order of difficulty, and in the following sequence:

- Check oil level.
- Check throttle cable.
- Check shift linkage.
- Check neutral safety switch.
- Check idle speed (cooling fan and A/C unit off).
- Check tire pressure.

CHECK ENGINE & TORQUE CONVERTER

Perform stall test and repair as necessary.

CHECK TRANSAXLE

Check each clutch, brake and gear for wear by performing time lag test. Confirm test results with road test. Repair as necessary.

CHECK LINE PRESSURE

Perform hydraulic test. Confirm shift point and extent of shock with road test. Repair as necessary.

ROAD TEST VEHICLE

Road test vehicle and confirm that trouble lies within transaxle. Perform on-vehicle service or overhaul transaxle.

TESTING

ROAD TEST

"D" Range Test

1) Allow ATF to reach a normal operating temperature of 122-176°F (50-80°C). Shift into "D" range, and while driving, hold throttle half open and then wide open.

2) Check that 1st-2nd upshift, 2nd-3rd and 3rd-overdrive (A-240L models) upshifts take place, and that upshift points conform to those indicated in diagrams. *See Figs. 1 and 2.*

3) If there is no 1st-2nd upshift, governor valve is defective or 1-2 shift valve is stuck. If there is no 2nd to 3rd upshift, 2-3 shift valve is stuck. If there is no 3rd-overdrive upshift (A-240L models), 3rd-overdrive shift valve is stuck.

4) If shift points are incorrect, throttle valve, 1-2, 2-3 or 3-overdrive (A-240L models) shift valves are stuck or defective. Repeat procedure and check shock and slip from 1st-2nd, from 2nd-3rd and 3rd-overdrive (A-240L models). If shock is severe, line pressure is too high, accumulator is defective or check ball is defective.

5) While driving in "D" range (3rd gear or overdrive), check for unusual noise and vibration. Abnormal noise and vibration may be due to an unbalanced propeller shaft, differential, tires, torque converter, or other drive train components.

6) With vehicle in "D" range, and while driving, hold throttle half open and then wide open. Check to see that 2nd-1st, 3rd-1st, 3rd-2nd, overdrive-3rd (A-240L models) and overdrive-2nd kickdown speeds conform to those indicated in diagram. *See Figs. 1 and 2.* Also check for abnormal shock and slip at kickdown.

7) While driving in "D" range, shift to "2" and "L" range and check engine braking power. If there is no engine braking at "2" range, 2nd coast brake is defective. If there is no engine braking at "L" range, 1st and reverse is defective.

8) While driving in "D" range, remove foot from accelerator pedal and shift into "L" range. Check to see that overdrive-3rd, 3rd-2nd and 2nd-1st downshift points conform to those indicated indicated in diagram. *See Figs. 1 and 2.*

Lock-Up Mechanism

With lock-up on, connect a tachometer to engine and drive vehicle at about 53 MPH for A-240L models and 40 MPH for all other models. Lightly depress accelelator pedal and read tachometer. If there is a large jump in engine RPM, lock-up mechanism is not working.

"2" Range Test

1) Shift into "2" range and drive with throttle half open and then wide open. Check 1st to 2nd upshift points at each of the throttle valve openings to see that they conform with those indicated in diagram. *See Figs. 1 and 2.*

2) While driving in "2" range, release accelerator pedal and check for engine braking. Perform a kickdown in "2" range and check 2nd to 1st kickdown speed. Kickdown speed must conform with that indicated in diagram. Check for abnormal noise at acceleration and deceleration, and for shock at upshift and downshift.

"L" Range Test

While driving in "L" range, check to see that there is no upshift to 2nd gear. Release accelerator pedal and check for engine braking. Also check for abnormal noise at acceleration and deceleration.

Automatic Transmissions

TOYOTA A-130L, A-131L & A-240L TRANSAXLE (Cont.)

Fig. 1: A-130L & A-131L Transaxle Downshift & Upshift Points

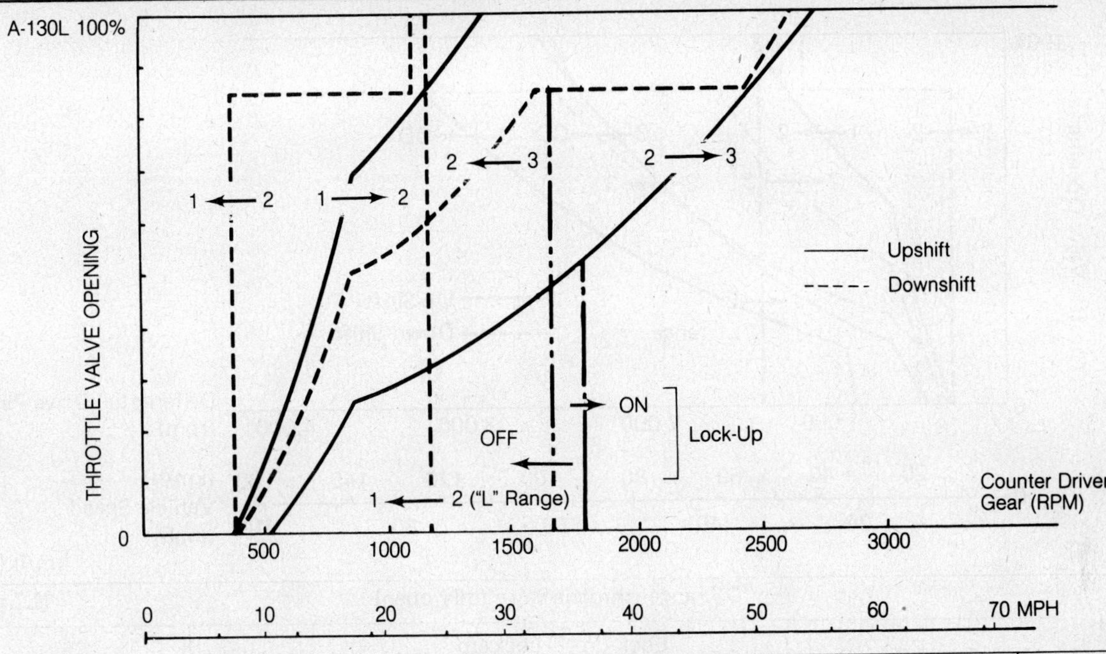

Differential Gear Ratio	"D" Range (Throttle Valve Fully Open)						"L" Range
	1 → 2	2 → 3	Lock-Up ON	Lock-Up OFF	3 → 2	2 → 1	2 → 1
3550	24-33 MPH	50-60 MPH	35-39 MPH	32-37 MPH	48-59 MPH	17-23 MPH	18-24 MPH

1 – Throttle valve is closed.

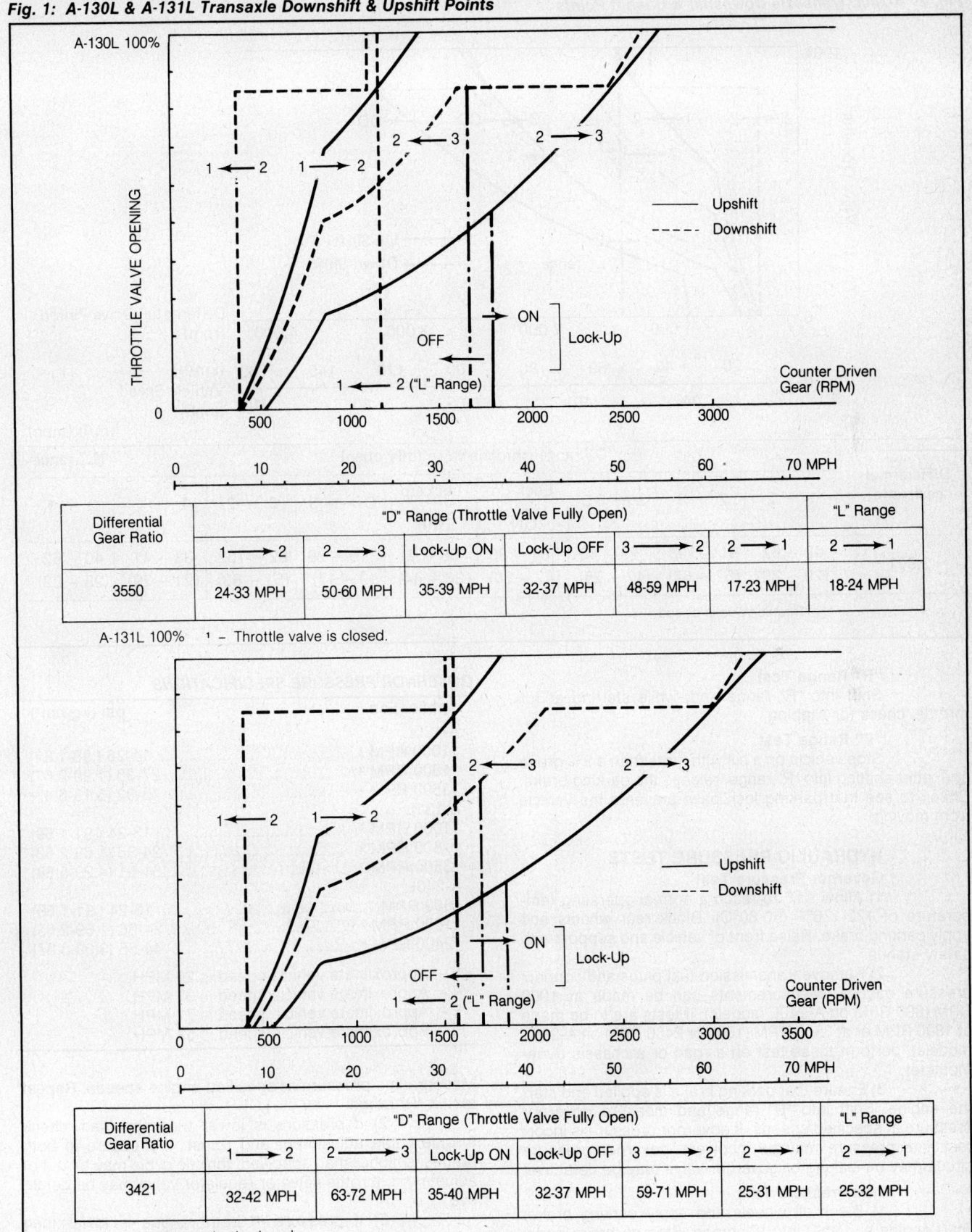

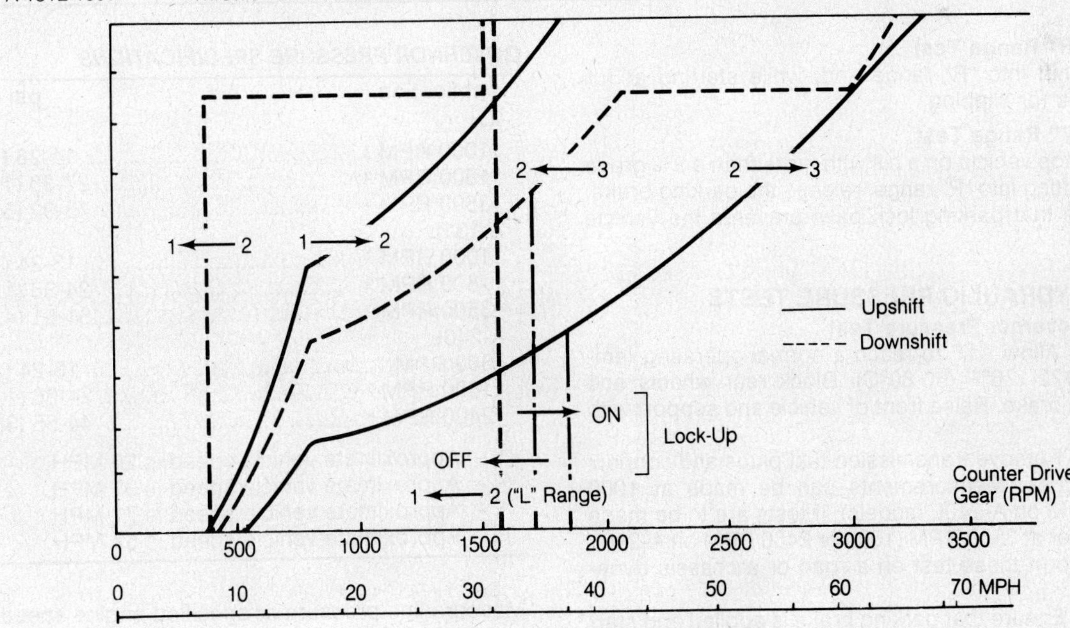

Differential Gear Ratio	"D" Range (Throttle Valve Fully Open)						"L" Range
	1 → 2	2 → 3	Lock-Up ON	Lock-Up OFF	3 → 2	2 → 1	2 → 1
3421	32-42 MPH	63-72 MPH	35-40 MPH	32-37 MPH	59-71 MPH	25-31 MPH	25-32 MPH

1 – Throttle valve is closed.

TOYOTA A-130L, A-131L & A-240L TRANSAXLE (Cont.)

Fig. 2: A-240L Transaxle Downshift & Upshift Points

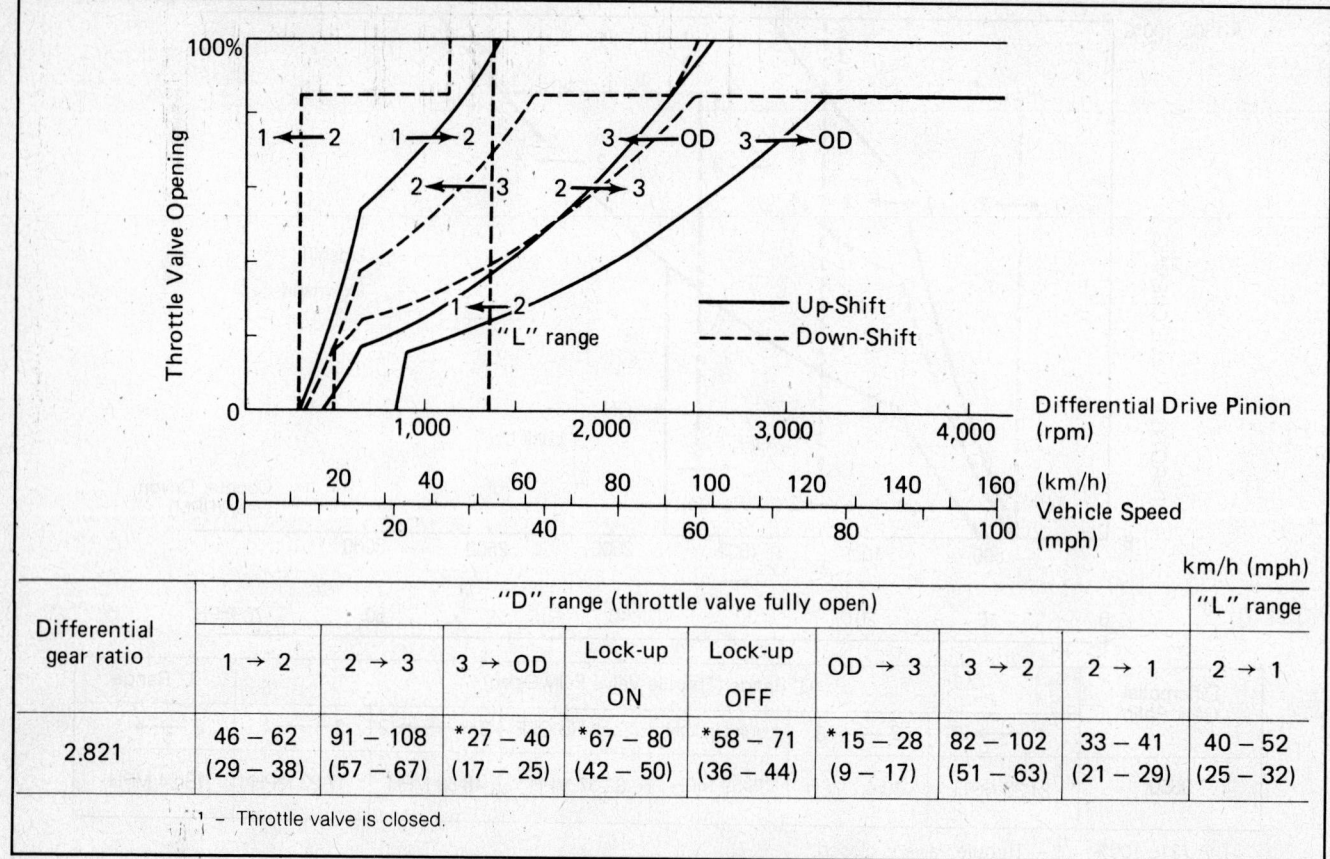

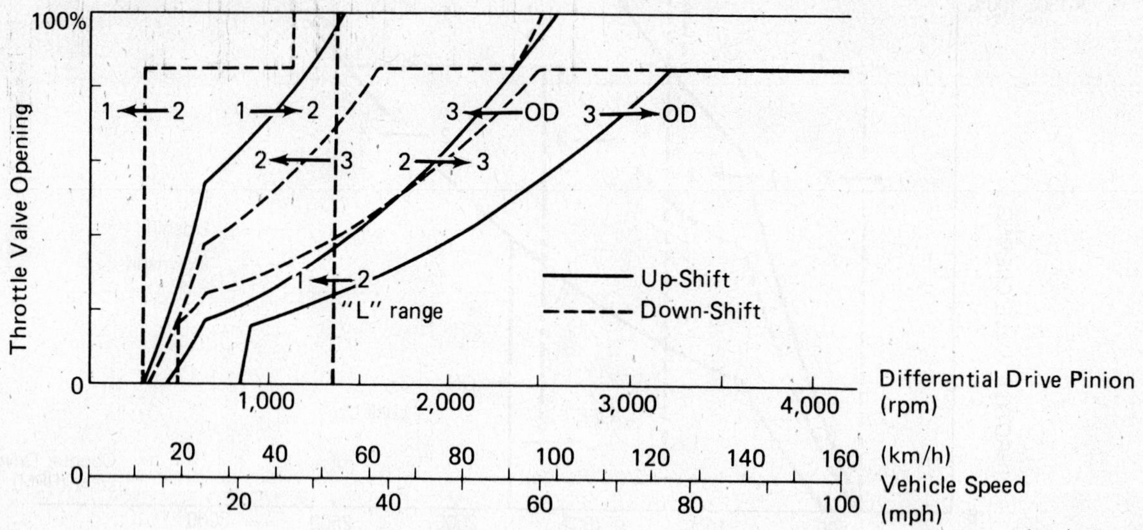

km/h (mph)

Differential gear ratio	"D" range (throttle valve fully open)								"L" range
	1 → 2	2 → 3	3 → OD	Lock-up ON	Lock-up OFF	OD → 3	3 → 2	2 → 1	2 → 1
2.821	46 – 62 (29 – 38)	91 – 108 (57 – 67)	*27 – 40 (17 – 25)	*67 – 80 (42 – 50)	*58 – 71 (36 – 44)	*15 – 28 (9 – 17)	82 – 102 (51 – 63)	33 – 41 (21 – 29)	40 – 52 (25 – 32)

*1 – Throttle valve is closed.

"R" Range Test

Shift into "R" range and, while starting at full throttle, check for slipping.

"P" Range Test

Stop vehicle on a hill with more than a 9% grade and, after shifting into "P" range, release the parking brake. Check to see that parking lock pawl prevents the vehicle from moving.

HYDRAULIC PRESSURE TESTS

Governor Pressure Test

1) Allow ATF to reach a normal operating temperature of 122-176°F (50-80°C). Block rear wheels and apply parking brake. Raise front of vehicle and support with safety stands.

2) Remove transmission test plugs and connect pressure gauges. Measurements can be made at 1000 RPM (800 RPM on A-240L models). If tests are to be made at 1800 RPM or at 3500 RPM (1600 or 2400 RPM on A-240L models), perform these test on a road or a chassis dynamometer.

3) Ensure that parking brake is applied and start the engine. Shift into "D" range and measure governor pressure at specified speeds. If governor pressure is incorrect, line pressure may be incorrect, governor pressure circuit may be leaking or governor valve may be defective.

Line Pressure Test

1) Block all wheels and apply parking brake. Start engine and shift into "D" range. Step on brake pedal with left foot and with right foot control accelerator pedal.

GOVERNOR PRESSURE SPECIFICATIONS

Application	psi (kg/cm^2)
A-130L	
1000 RPM [1]	14-26 (.98-1.82)
1800 RPM [2]	27-38 (1.90-2.67)
3500 RPM [3]	73-92 (5.13-6.47)
A-131L	
1000 RPM [1]	13-24 (.91-1.69)
1800 RPM [2]	24-36 (1.69-2.53)
3500 RPM [3]	61-81 (4.29-5.69)
A-240L	
800 RPM [1]	13-24 (.91-1.69)
1600 RPM [2]	24-36 (1.69-2.53)
2400 RPM [4]	44-55 (3.09-3.87)

[1] – Approximate vehicle speed is 20 MPH.
[2] – Approximate vehicle speed is 37 MPH.
[3] – Approximate vehicle speed is 71 MPH.
[4] – Approximate vehicle speed is 57 MPH.

Measure line pressure at specified engine speeds. Repeat test in "R" range.

2) If pressure is lower than specified, check throttle cable adjustment and retest. If pressure in both ranges is higher than specified, throttle cable may be out of adjustment, throttle valve or regulator valve may be defective.

3) If pressure in both ranges is lower than specified, throttle cable may be out of adjustment, oil pump may be defective, throttle valve or regulator valve may be defective, or underdrive one-way clutch may not be operating properly (A-240L models).

4) If pressure is low in "D" range only, "D" range circuit may be leaking, forward clutch may be defective, or underdrive one-way clutch may not be operating properly (A-240L models).

5) If pressure is low in "R" range only, "R" range circuit may be leaking, direct clutch may be defective, 1st and reverse brake may be defective, or underdrive one-way clutch may not be operating properly (A-240L models).

LINE PRESSURE SPECIFICATIONS IN "D" RANGE

Application	psi (kg/cm²)
At Idle Speed	53-61 (3.73-4.29)
At Stall Speed	
A-130L	121-142 (8.51-9.98)
A-131L & A-240L	131-152 (9.21-10.69)

LINE PRESSURE SPECIFICATIONS IN "R" RANGE

Application	psi (kg/cm²)
At Idle Speed	77-102 (5.41-7.17)
At Stall Speed	
A-130L	188-222 (13.22-15.61)
A-131L & A-240L	205-239 (14.41-16.80)

STALL TEST

NOTE: **The object of this test is to check the overall performance of the transaxle and engine by measuring maximum engine speeds in the "D" and "R" ranges. Perform this test with ATF at a normal operating temperature of 122-176°F (50-80°C). DO NOT continously run this test longer than 5 seconds.**

1) Block front and rear wheels and fully apply parking brake. Install tachometer. Step on brake pedal and start the engine. Shift into "D" range and fully depress accelerator pedal. Immediately read highest engine RPM.

2) Stall speed should be 1950-2250 RPM for gasoline engine equipped vehicles and 1600-1900 RPM for diesel engine equipped vehicles. Repeat test in "R" range.

3) If stall speed is the same for both ranges but lower than specified, then engine output may be insufficient or stator one-way clutch is not operating properly. If stall speed is more than 600 RPM below the specified value, the torque converter could be at fault.

4) If stall speed in "D" range is higher than specified, line pressure may be too low, forward clutch may be slipping, No. 2 one-way clutch may not be operating properly, or underdrive one-way clutch may not be operating properly (A-240L models).

5) If stall speed in "R" range is higher than specified, line pressure may be too low, direct clutch may be slipping, 1st and reverse brake may be slipping, or underdrive one-way clutch may not be operating properly (A-240L models).

6) If stall speed in "D" and "R" range is higher than specified, fluid level may be low, line pressure may be too low, or underdrive one-way clutch may not be operating properly (A-240L models).

TIME LAG TEST

NOTE: **If the shift lever is moved while the engine is idling, there will be a certain time lapse or lag before shock can be felt. This time lapse is used to check the condition of the forward clutch, direct clutch, and 1st and reverse brake. Allow a 1 minute interval between tests. Make 3 tests and take average value.**

1) With ATF at a normal operating temperature of 122-176°F (50-80°C), apply parking and check idle speed. Using a stop watch, measure the time that it takes for shock to be felt when moving shift lever from "N" to "D" range. Time lag must be less than 1.2 seconds.

2) Repeat procedure from "N" to "R" range, time lag must be less than 1.5 seconds. If "N" to "D" time lag is longer than specified, line pressure may be too low, forward clutch may be worn, or underdrive one-way clutch may not be operating properly (A-240L models).

3) If "N" to "R" time lag is longer than specified, line pressure may be too low, direct clutch may be worn, 1st and reverse brake may be worn, or underdrive one-way clutch may not be operating properly (A-240L models).

ENGINE IDLE SPEED

Application	Range	RPM
Gasoline Engine		
With P/S	"N"	800
Without P/S	"N"	900
Diesel Engine	"N"	700

OVERDRIVE SYSTEM TEST

NOTE: **These tests are used on A-240L model transaxles only.**

Coolant Temperature Switch

Disconnect coolant temperature switch connector. Connect ohmmeter between switch terminal and ground. Resistance should be zero ohms when coolant temperature is less than 109°F (43°C). Resistance should be infinity when coolant temperature is more than 131°F (55°C). Replace switch as necessary.

Overdrive Solenoid

1) Disconnect overdrive solenoid connector. Connect solenoid to battery voltage and ground. Solenoid should operate and a "click" should be heard. Disconnect solenoid. Connect ohmmeter between solenoid terminals. Resistance should be 11-15 ohms.

2) Reconnect solenoid connector to harness. Disconect coolant temperature switch. Turn ignition on. Turn overdrive system on and off using switch on gear selector. Solenoid should "click" when system is turned on and off. Turn ignition off. Reconnect coolant temperature switch. Replace solenoid as necessary.

Overdrive Main Switch

Remove console box. Check for continuity between switch terminals No. 1 and No. 3 with switch on and off. There should be continuity when switch is off and NO continuity when switch is on. Replace switch as necessary. Reinstall console box.

TOYOTA A-130L, A-131L & A-240L TRANSAXLE (Cont.)

CLUTCH AND BAND APPLICATION – A-240L (ELEMENTS IN USE)

Selector Lever Position	Direct (Front) Clutch	Forward (Rear) Clutch	Reduction Unit Clutch	2nd Coast Brake Band	2nd Gear Brake Drum	1st/Reverse Gear Brake (Piston)	Reduction Brake	No. 1 One-Way Clutch	No. 2 One-Way Clutch	Underdrive One-Way Clutch
P – PARK							X			
R – REVERSE		X				X	X			
N – NEUTRAL						X				
D – DRIVE										
First	X						X		X	X
Second	X				X		X	X		X
Third	X	X			X		X			X
OD	X	X	X		X					
2 – SECOND										
First	X						X		X	X
Second	X			X	X		X	X		X
1 – LOW	X					X	X		X	X

¹ – Downshift in "L" range, 2nd gear only; no upshift.

CLUTCH AND BAND APPLICATION – A-130L & A-131L (ELEMENTS IN USE)

Selector Lever Position	Direct (Front) Clutch	Forward (Rear) Clutch	2nd Coast Brake Band	2nd Gear Brake Drum	1st & Reverse Gear Brake (Piston)	No. 1 One-Way Clutch	No. 2 One-Way Clutch
P – PARK							
R – REVERSE		X			X		
N – NEUTRAL							
D – DRIVE							
First	X						X
Second	X			X		X	
Third	X	X		X			
2 – SECOND							
First	X						X
Second	X		X	X		X	
1 – LOW							
First	X				X		X
Second ¹	X		X	X			

¹ – Downshift in "L" range, 2nd gear only; no upshift.

SERVICE (IN VEHICLE)

DRIVE AXLE SHAFTS

See appropriate DRIVE AXLE SHAFT article in IMPORT AXLE SHAFTS, OVERDRIVES & TRANSFER CASES section.

GOVERNOR ASSEMBLY

Removal (A-130L & A-131L)

Remove transaxle dust cover. Remove left drive shaft. Remove bracket bolts, governor cover and "O" ring. Remove governor body, washer and thrust washer. Remove governor body adapter.

Removal (A-240L)

Disconnect speedometer cable. Remove governor cover and "O" ring. Remove governor body and thrust washer. Remove governor body adapter and gasket.

Installation
To install, reverse removal procedure.

THROTTLE CABLE
Removal
Disconnect throttle cable from throttle linkage. Disconnect transaxle control cable from manual shift lever and remove manual shift lever. Remove neutral safety switch. Remove valve body. Remove throttle cable bolt and retaining plate. Pull throttle cable out of transaxle.

Installation
1) Install throttle cable in transaxle and push it all the way in. Install retaining bolt and plate. If throttle cable is new, bend a 7.87" (200 mm) radius in cable.

2) Pull inner cable lightly, until a slight resistance is felt, and hold in place. Stake stopper on inner cable, leaving a .031-.059" (.8-1.5 mm) gap between cable housing and stopper. *See Fig. 3.*

3) Connect throttle cable to throttle linkage. Adjust throttle cable. See appropriate AUTOMATIC TRANSMISSION SERVICNG article in IMPORT GENERAL SERVICING section.

4) Install neutral safety switch and manual shift lever. Adjust neutral safety switch. See appropriate AUTOMATIC TRANSMISSION SERVICNG article in IMPORT GENERAL SERVICING section. Connect transaxle control cable. Test drive vehicle.

Fig. 3: Installing Throttle Cable Stopper

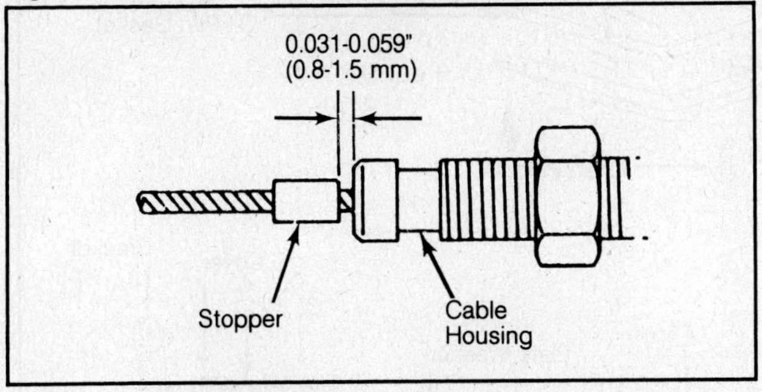

VALVE BODY
Removal
1) Clean exterior of transaxle to prevent contamination of valve body. Remove drain plug and drain ATF. Remove oil pan and gasket. Remove bolts and apply tube bracket. Remove 3 bolts and carefully remove oil strainer. Note position of oil tubes and, using a large screwdriver, remove oil tubes.

2) On A-130L and A-131L models, remove manual detent spring. Remove manual valve. Remove 4 manual valve body bolts and note their length. Remove valve body. On A-240L models, disconnect solenoid connector. On all models, remove 14 valve body bolts and note their length. Remove valve body. Remove throttle cable. Remove governor oil pressure line strainer. Remove governor apply gasket.

Installation
1) Install governor apply gasket. Install governor pressure line strainer. Hold valve body cam down, and slip cable into slot. Install valve body in transaxle. Do not entangle kickdown switch wire.

2) Install 14 valve body bolts finger tight, then tighten. On A-240L models, connect solenoid connector. On A-130L and A-131L models, align manual valve with pin on manual shift lever. Lower valve body into place. Install 4 valve body bolts finger tight, then tighten.

3) On all models, install detent spring and tighten bolts. Check that manual valve lever is in contact with center of roller at tip of detent spring. Using a plastic hammer, tap oil tubes into place.

4) On A-130L and A-131L models, install apply tube bracket. On all models, install oil strainer. Install magnet in oil pan. Ensure that magnet does not interfere with oil tubes. Install oil pan and drain plug. Fill transaxle with Dexron II ATF and check fluid level. Do not overfill.

REMOVAL & INSTALLATION

TRANSAXLE
See appropriate AUTOMATIC TRANSMISSION REMOVAL article in IMPORT GENERAL SERVICING section.

TORQUE CONVERTER

NOTE: **The torque converter is a sealed unit and cannot be disassembled for service. Make the following tests to be certain that converter is defective. If transaxle is contaminated, the torque converter and transaxle cooler must be thoroughly cleaned and flushed.**

ONE-WAY CLUTCH TEST
1) Insert "T" Handle (SST 09350-32011) in inner race of torque converter one-way clutch. Insert Locking Tab (SST 09350-32011) so that it fits into notch of converter hub and into one-way clutch.

2) With converter positioned upright, one-way clutch should lock when turned counterclockwise. Clutch should rotate freely and smoothly when turned clockwise.

3) Less than 22 INCH lbs. (2.5 N.m) should be required to rotate clutch. If necessary, clean converter and retest. If clutch still fails test, replace torque converter.

RUNOUT TEST
1) Mount dial indicator on engine and measure flex plate runout. If flex plate exceeds .008" (.20 mm) or if ring gear is damaged, replace flex plate. If installing a new flex plate, note orientation of spacers and tighten bolts.

2) Temporarily mount torque converter to engine flex plate. Place dial indicator tip on torque converter hub. Rotate converter and check runout. If runout exceeds .0118" (.30 mm), try to correct runout by changing position of converter on flex plate.

3) If excessive runout cannot be corrected, replace torque converter. If runout is okay, mark converter position to ensure correct installation. Remove converter from flex plate.

TRANSAXLE DISASSEMBLY

NOTE: **Several special service tools are contained in Toyota's Automatic Transaxle Tool Kit (SST 09350-32011).**

1) Remove oil cooler pipes, manual shift lever and neutral safety switch. Remove filler tube and dipstick.

TOYOTA A-130L, A-131L & A-240L TRANSAXLE (Cont.)

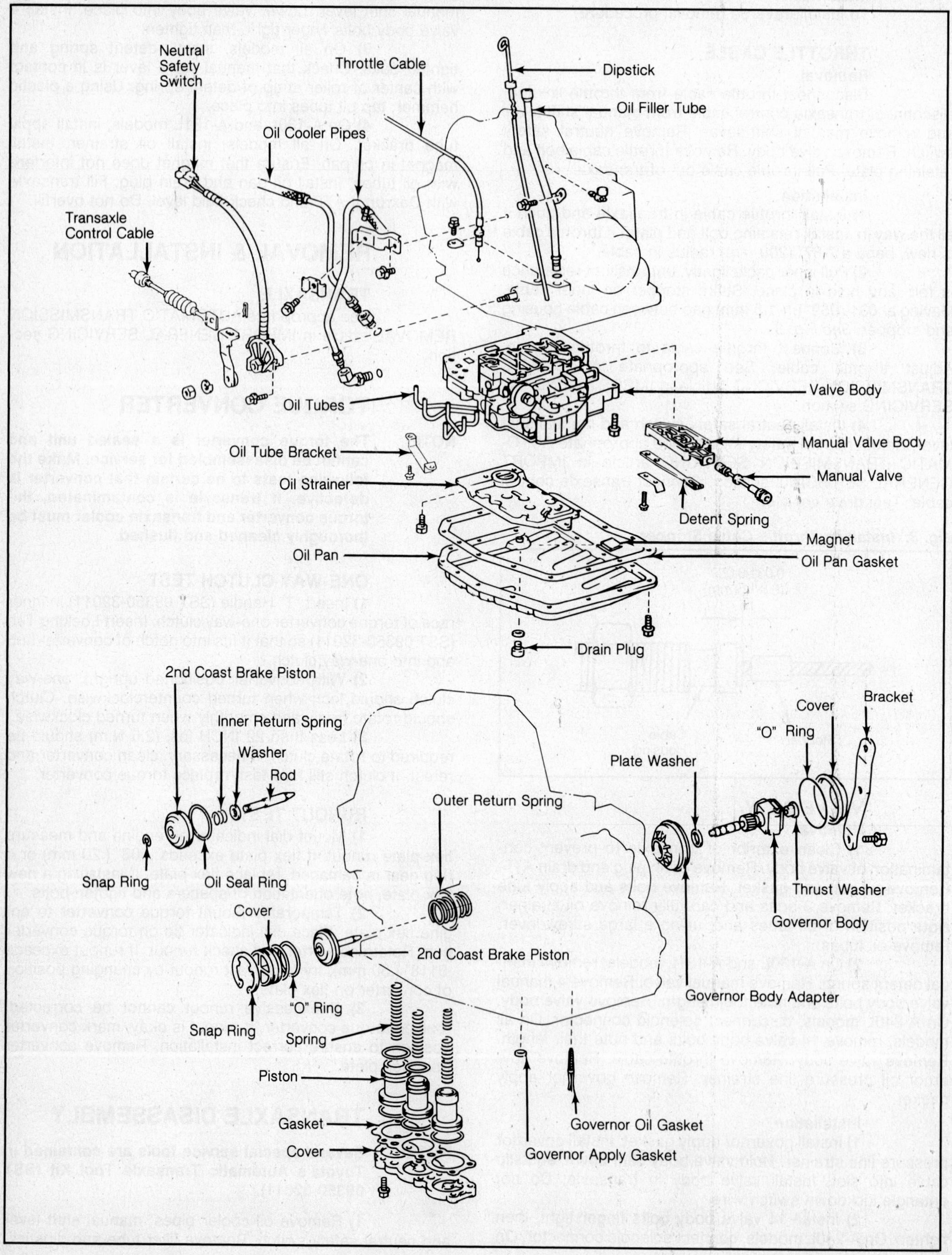

Fig. 4: Exploded View of A-130L & A-131L Automatic Transaxle

Fig. 5: Exploded View of A-130L & A-131L Automatic Transaxle

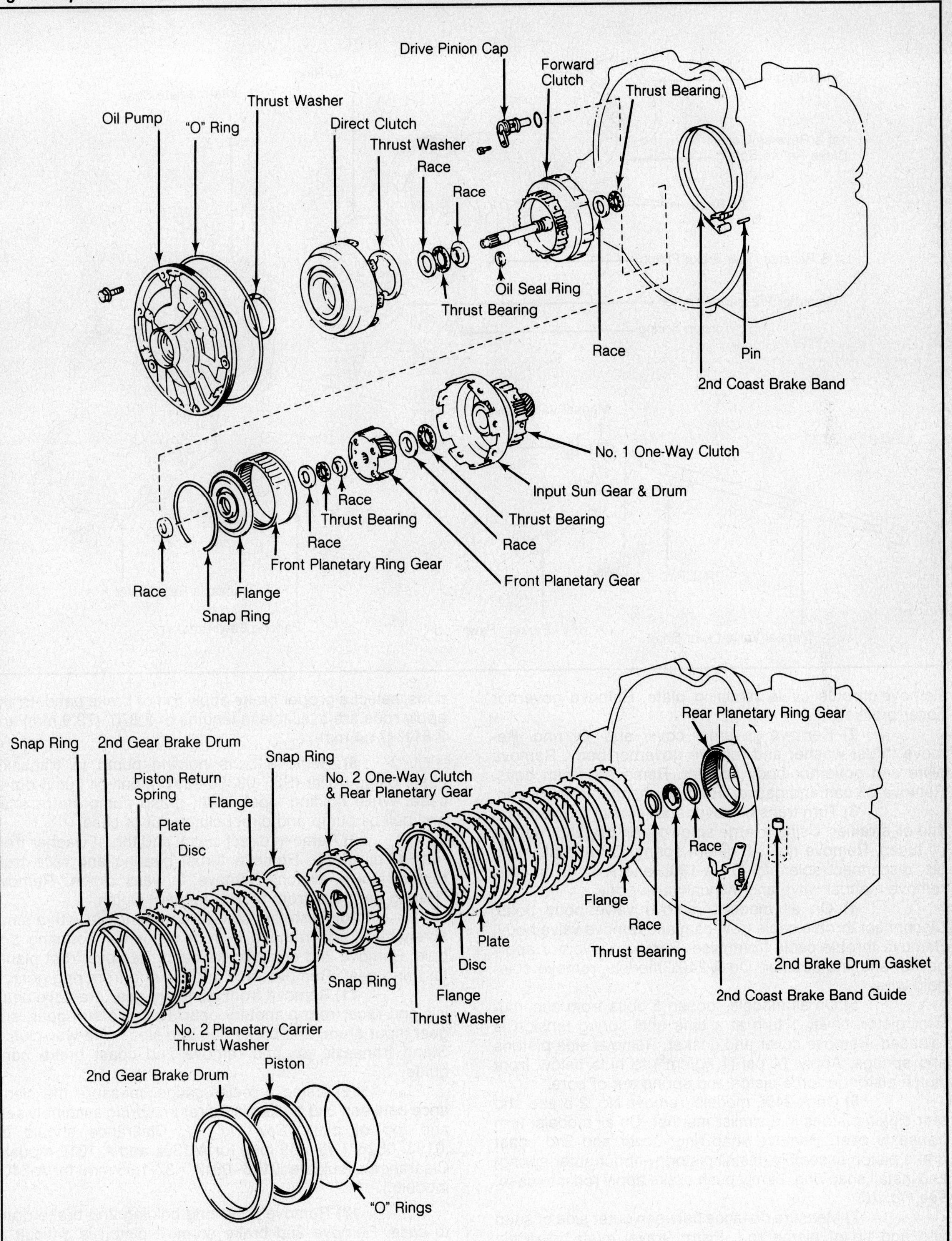

TOYOTA A-130L, A-131L & A-240L TRANSAXLE (Cont.)

Fig. 6: Exploded View of A-130L & A-131L Automatic Transaxle

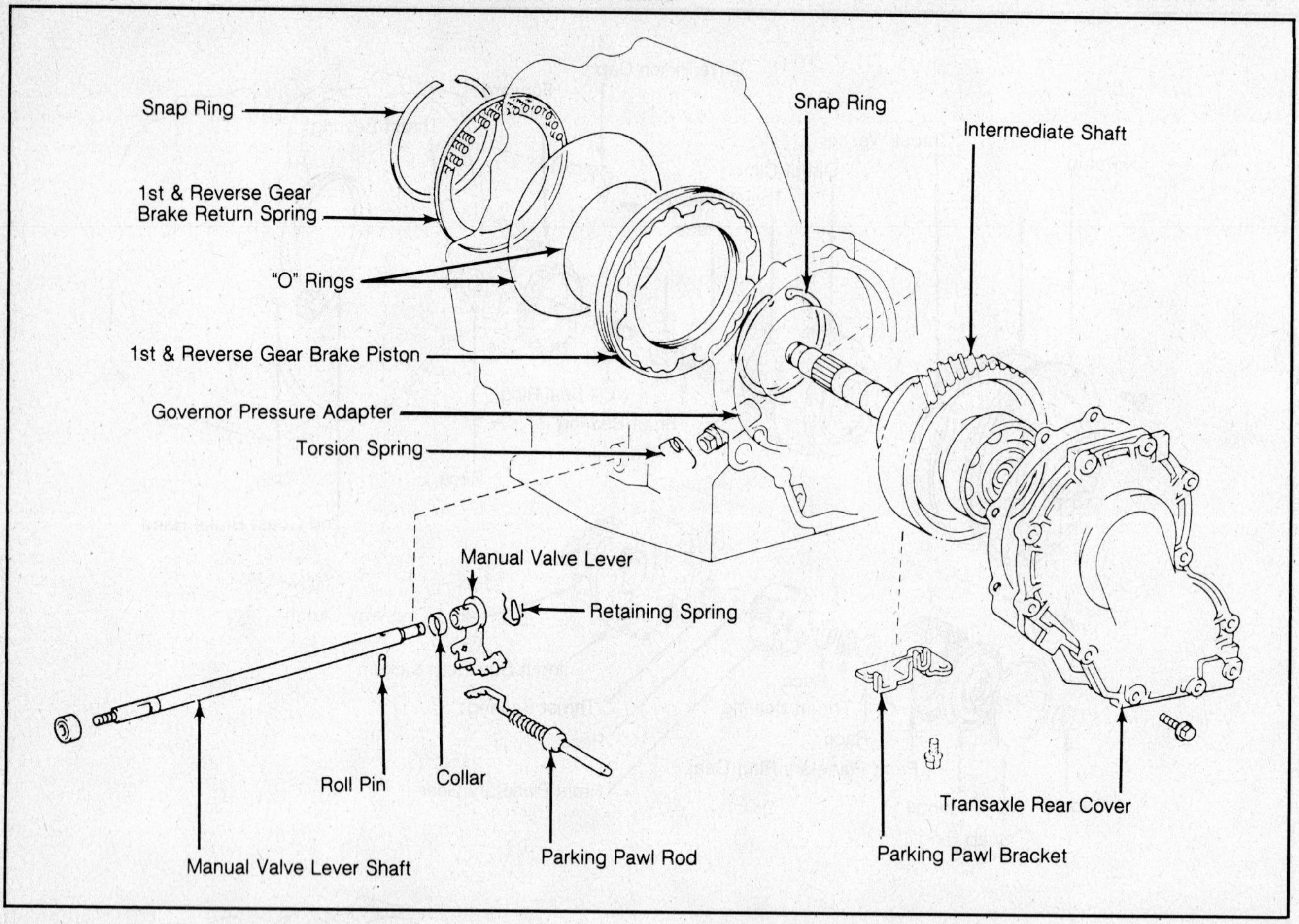

Remove throttle cable retaining plate. Remove governor cover bracket.

2) Remove governor cover and "O" ring. Remove thrust washer and remove governor body. Remove plate and governor body adapter. Remove oil pan bolts. Remove oil pan and gasket. Remove magnet from oil pan.

3) Turn transaxle over and remove tube bracket and oil strainer. Using a large screwdriver, pry and remove oil tubes. Remove manual detent spring. On A-240L models, disconnect solenoid. On A-130L and A-131L models, remove manual valve and manual valve body.

4) On all models, remove valve body bolts. Disconnect throttle cable from cam and remove valve body. Remove throttle cable from case. Remove governor apply gasket and line strainer. On A-240L models, remove solenoid wire.

5) On all models, loosen 5 bolts from accumulator piston cover 1 turn at a time until spring tension is released. Remove cover and gasket. Remove side pistons and springs. Apply 14 psi (1 kg/cm^2) to hole below front clutch piston to force piston and spring out of bore.

6) On A-240L models, remove No. 2 brake and rear clutch pistons in a similar manner. On all models, turn transaxle over. Remove snap ring, cover and 2nd coast brake piston assembly. Install piston (without outer spring) and install snap ring. Firmly push brake apply rod into case. *See Fig. 10.*

7) Measure distance between outer side of snap ring and tip of piston rod. Piston travel must be within .551-.610" (14.0-15.5 mm). If travel is not within specifications, select a proper brake apply rod or brake band. Brake apply rods are available in lengths of 2.870" (72.9 mm) and 2.811" (71.4 mm).

8) Remove bolts holding pump to transaxle case. Using Puller (SST 09350-32011), pull oil pump out of case. While holding input shaft, grasp pump stator shaft and pull oil pump and direct clutch out of case.

9) Remove direct clutch and thrust washer from rear of oil pump. Remove thrust bearing and race from forward (rear) clutch. Remove forward clutch. Remove bearing and race from rear of forward clutch.

10) Push 2nd coast brake band pin with a small screwdriver and remove it from oil pump mounting bolt hole. Remove 2nd coast brake band. Remove front planetary ring gear. Remove race and bearing from ring gear.

11) Remove front planetary gear. Remove bearing and race from planetary gear. Remove sun gear, sun gear input drum, 2nd brake hub and No. 1 one-way clutch. Stand transaxle up and remove 2nd coast brake band guide.

12) Using a feeler gauge, measure the clearance between 2nd brake piston return spring assembly seat and top of plate. *See Fig. 11.* Clearance should be .0193-.0626" (.49-1.59 mm) for A-130L and A-131L models. Clearance should be .0146-.0614" (.37-1.56 mm) for A-240L models.

13) Remove snap ring holding 2nd brake drum to case. Remove 2nd brake drum, if piston is difficult to remove, lightly tap drum with a wooden block. Using a pin punch and hammer, tap out 2nd brake drum seal.

TOYOTA A-130L, A-131L & A-240L TRANSAXLE (Cont.)

Fig. 7: Exploded View of A-240L Automatic Transaxle

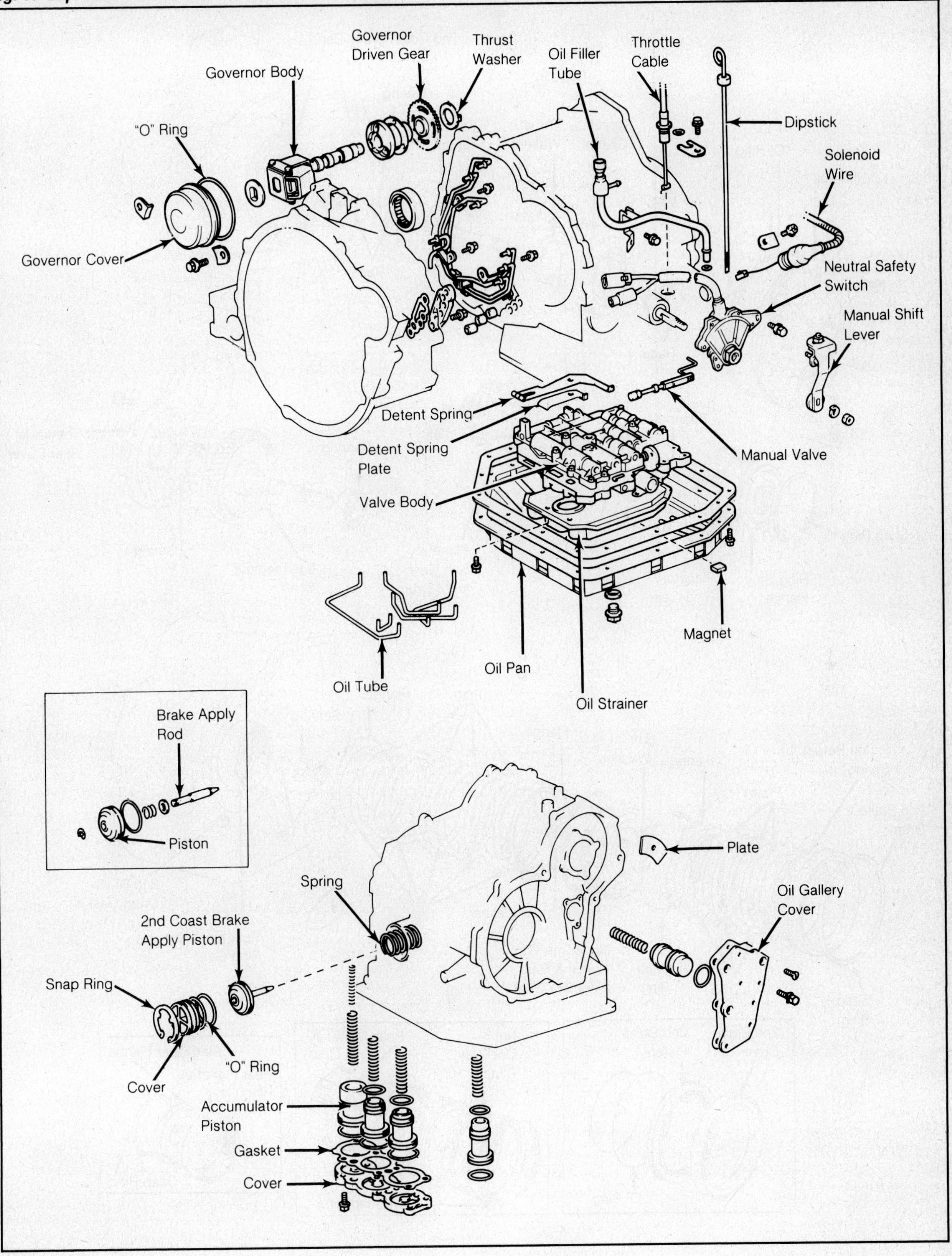

Automatic Transmissions

TOYOTA A-130L, A-131L & A-240L TRANSAXLE (Cont.)

Fig. 8: Exploded View of A-240L Automatic Transaxle

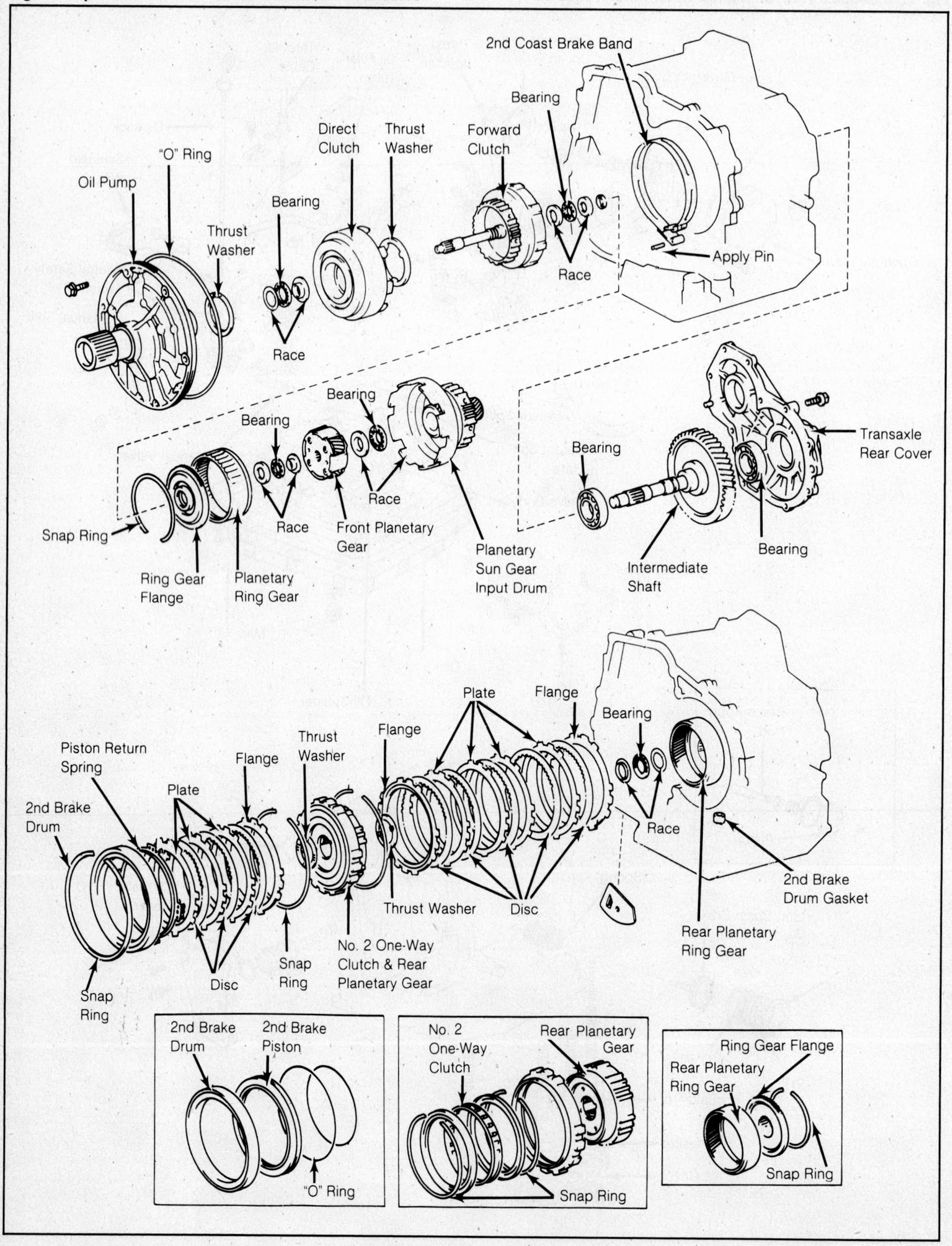

Fig. 9: Exploded View of A-240L Automatic Transaxle

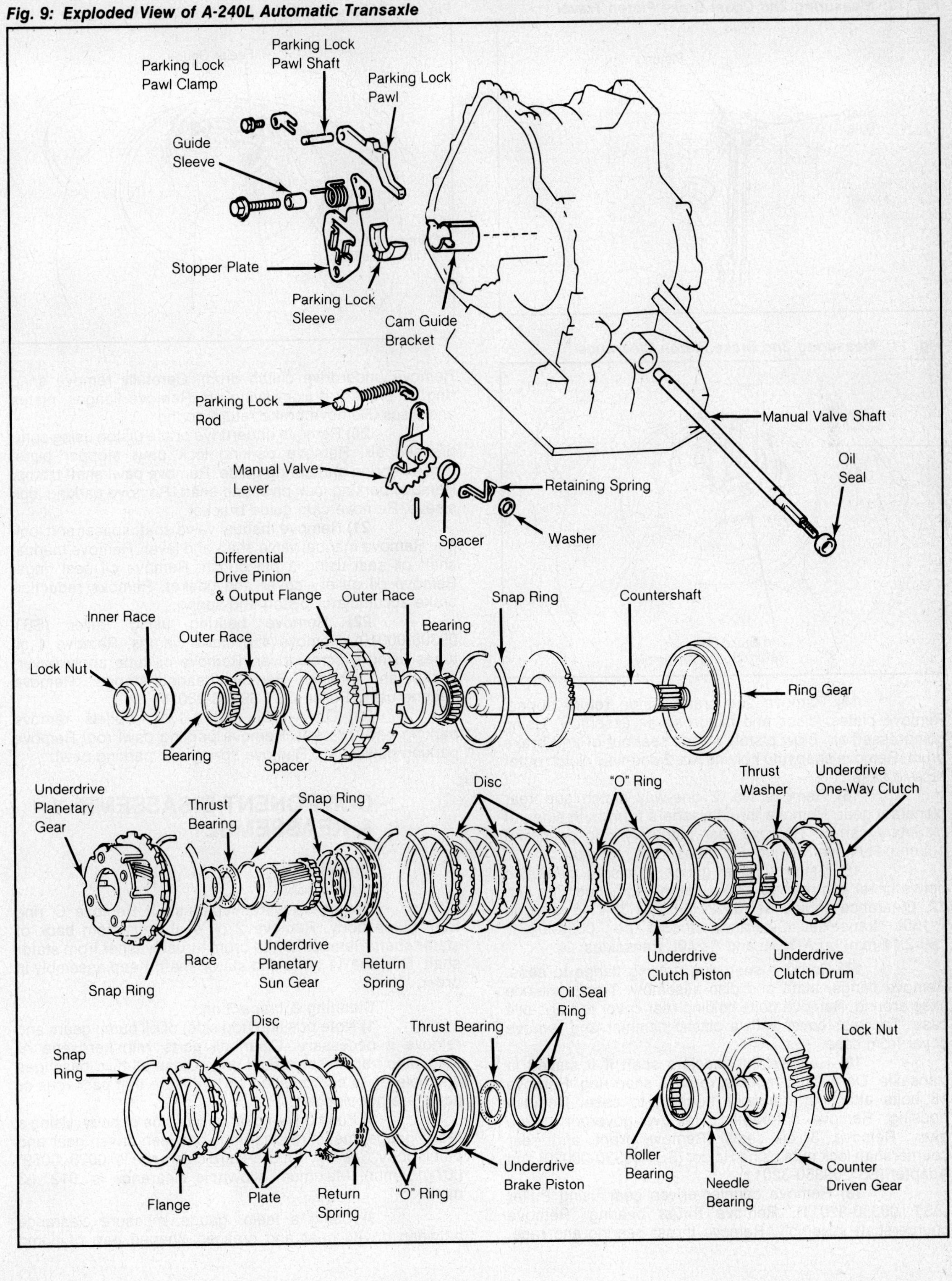

Automatic Transmissions

TOYOTA A-130L, A-131L & A-240L TRANSAXLE (Cont.)

Fig. 10: Measuring 2nd Coast Brake Piston Travel

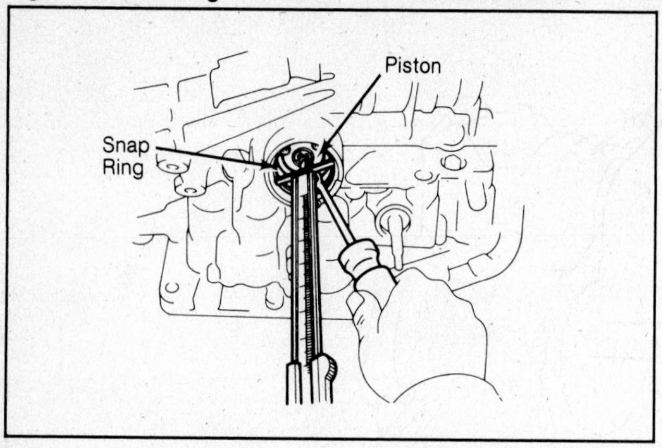

Fig. 11: Measuring 2nd Brake Piston Clearance

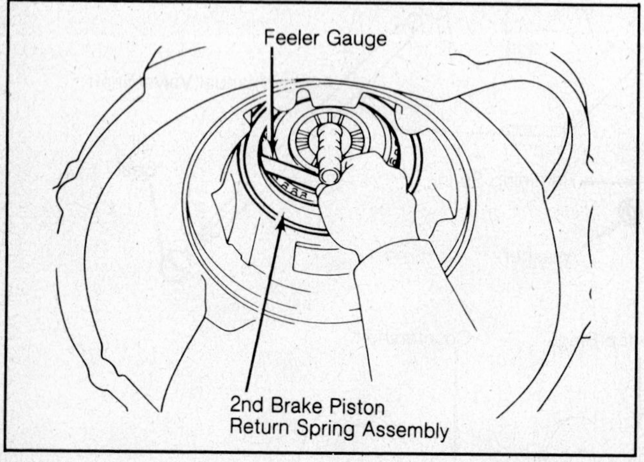

14) Remove 2nd brake piston return spring. Remove plates, discs and flange as an assembly. Using compressed air, blow piston and oil seal out of 2nd brake drum. Remove snap ring holding No. 2 one-way clutch outer race to case.

15) Remove No. 2 one-way clutch and rear planetary gear. Remove thrust washers from both sides of planetary carrier. Remove rear planetary ring gear and bearing. Remove bearing and races from ring gear.

16) Using a feeler gauge, measure clearance between 1st and reverse brake piston and flange. *See Fig. 12*. Clearance should be .0512-.0969" (1.30-2.46 mm) on A-130L transaxle. Clearance should be .0350-.0831" (.89-2.11 mm) on A-131L and A-240L transaxles.

17) Remove snap ring holding flange to case. Remove flange, plate and disc assembly. Turn transaxle case around. Remove bolts holding rear cover to transaxle case. Tap rear cover with a plastic hammer and remove cover from case.

18) Remove intermediate shaft if it stayed in transaxle. On A-240L models, remove snap ring. Remove 18 bolts attaching transaxle housing to case. Remove housing. Remove differential. Remove governor driven gear. Remove 3 oil seals. Remove front and rear countershaft lock nuts using Holder (SST 09330-00020) and Adapter (SST 09350-32011).

19) Remove counter driven gear using Puller (SST 09350-32011). Remove thrust bearing. Remove countershaft assembly. Remove thrust bearing and race.

Fig. 12: Measuring 1st & Reverse Brake Clearance

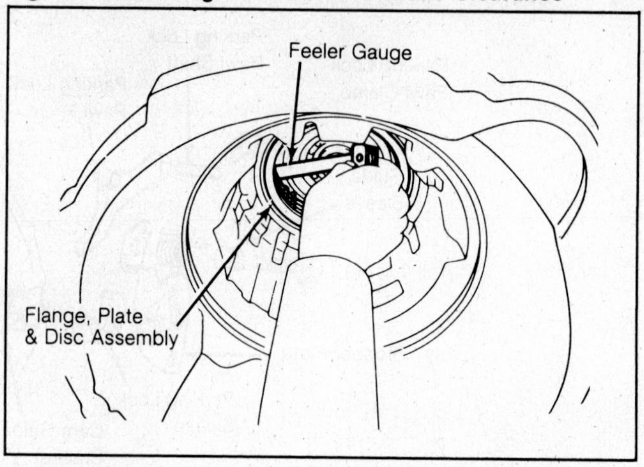

Remove underdrive clutch drum. Carefully remove snap ring, to prevent it from flying off. Remove flanges, plates and discs. Remove brake return spring.

20) Remove underdrive brake piston using compressed air. Remove parking lock pawl stopper plate, torsion spring and spring guide. Remove pawl shaft clamp. Remove parking lock pawl and shaft. Remove parking lock sleeve. Remove cam guide bracket.

21) Remove manual valve shaft spacer and lock pin. Remove manual valve shaft and lever. Remove manual shaft oil seal using a pin punch. Remove oil seal rings. Remove oil gallery cover and gasket. Remove reduction brake accumulator piston and spring.

22) Remove bearing using Puller (SST 09308-00010). Remove 4 oil tube clamps. Remove 4 oil tubes using a screwdriver. Remove oil tube apply cover, gasket and strainer. Remove bearing stopper. Remove bearing using Puller (SST 09308-00010).

23) On A-130L and A-131L models, remove parking pawl bracket. Remove parking pawl rod. Remove parking pawl shaft. Remove spring and parking pawl.

COMPONENT DISASSEMBLY & REASSEMBLY

OIL PUMP

Disassembly

Remove race from stator shaft. Remove "O" ring from pump body. Remove 2 oil seal rings from back of stator shaft. Remove clutch drum thrust washer from stator shaft. Remove 11 bolts and stator shaft. Keep assembly in order.

Cleaning & Inspection

1) Note position (top side) of oil pump gears and remove if necessary. Clean all parts with kerosene or automatic transmission fluid only. Clean all fluid passages and holes, use compressed air to ensure that passages or holes are not clogged.

2) Push driven gear to one side of body. Using a feeler gauge, measure clearance between driven gear and pump body. *See Fig. 13*. Standard clearance is .0028-.0059" (.07-.15 mm). Maximum allowable clearance is .012" (.3 mm).

3) Using a feeler gauge, measure clearance between driven gear and crescent-shaped part of pump

Fig. 13: Checking Driven Gear Clearance

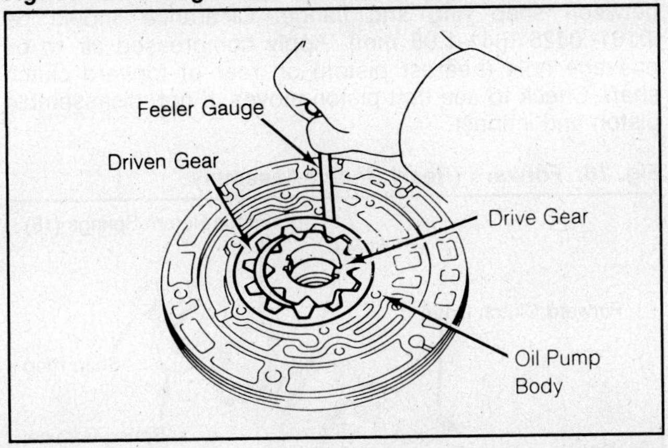

body. *See Fig. 14*. Standard clearance is .0043-.0055" (.11-.14 mm). Maximum allowable clearance is .012" (.3 mm).

Fig. 14: Checking Driven Gear Tip Clearance

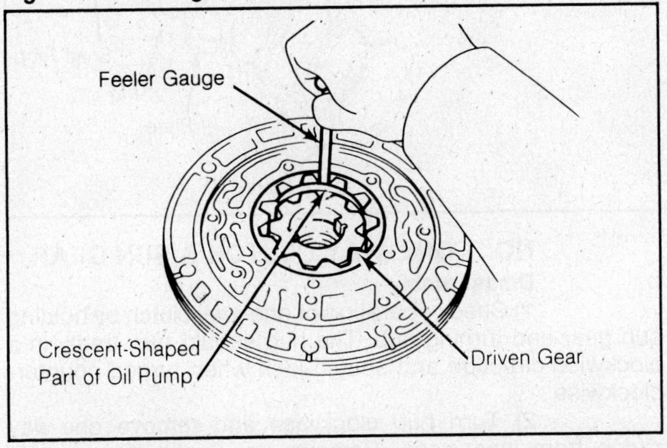

4) Using a feeler gauge and straightedge, measure oil pump gear side clearance. *See Fig. 15*. Standard clearance is .0008-.0020" (.02-.05 mm). Maximum allowable clearance is .004" (.1 mm).

5) Inspect front oil seal for wear, damage, or cracks. If necessary, replace oil seal. U using a screwdriver, pry off oil seal. Using Driver (SST 09350-32011), install new oil seal. Seal should be flush with outer edge of pump body.

Reassembly

1) Coat parts with ATF. Install oil pump gears with top side facing up. Align stator shaft with pump body, install bolts, and tighten. Coat thrust washer with petroleum jelly and align tab of washer with pump body.

2) Being careful not to spread seal rings too much, install rings on pump. Turn drive gear with 2 screwdrivers, ensure that drive gear rotates smoothly. Install "O" ring. Install race on stator shaft.

DIRECT CLUTCH

Disassembly

1) Using a feeler gauge, measure clearance between snap ring and flange. Clearance should be .0350-.0575" (.89-1.46 mm). Remove snap ring from clutch drum. Remove flange, disc, and plate assembly. Compress spring retainer and springs. Using a screwdriver, remove snap ring, spring retainer, and 18 springs.

Fig. 15: Checking Oil Pump Gear Side Clearance

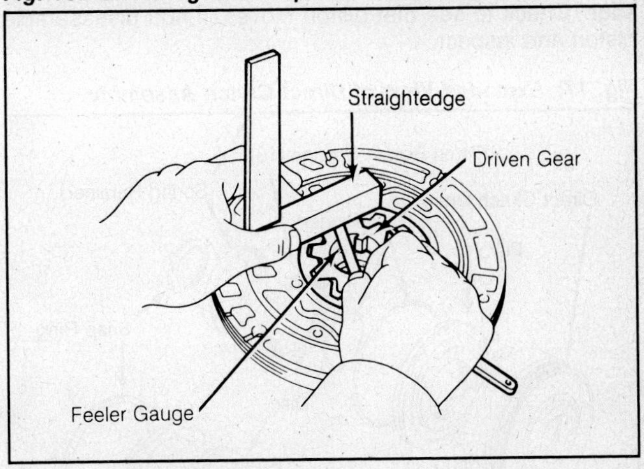

Fig. 16: Exploded View of Oil Pump Assembly

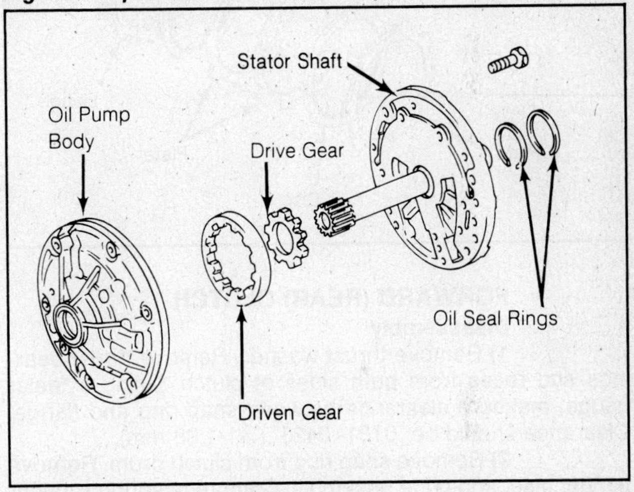

2) Install direct clutch on oil pump and apply compressed air to oil pump oval shaped passage to remove piston. If piston does not come out completely, use needle-nose pliers to remove it. Remove clutch piston "O" ring.

Cleaning & Inspection

Clean all parts with kerosene or automatic transmission fluid only. Use compressed air to dry all parts. Shake piston to ensure that check ball in piston is free. Check that valve does not leak by applying low pressure compressed air.

Reassembly

NOTE: **New discs or plates that are to be used for replacement must be soaked in transmission fluid for at least 2 hours before assembly.**

1) Coat new "O" rings with ATF and install on piston. Press piston into drum with cupped side up. Do not damage "O" rings. Install 18 piston return springs, retainer, and snap ring. Ensure that snap ring gap is not aligned with spring retainer claw.

2) Install 1 plate, 1 disc, 2 plates, and 1 disc. *See Fig. 17*. Install flange with flat side facing downward. Install outer snap ring and check that snap ring gap is not aligned with a cut-out.

3) Using a feeler gauge, measure clearance between snap ring and flange. Clearance should be .0350-.0575" (.89-1.46 mm). Install direct clutch on oil pump

TOYOTA A-130L, A-131L & A-240L TRANSAXLE (Cont.)

and apply compressed air to oil pump oval shaped passage. Check to see that piston moves, if not, disassemble piston and inspect.

Fig. 17: Exploded View of Direct Clutch Assembly

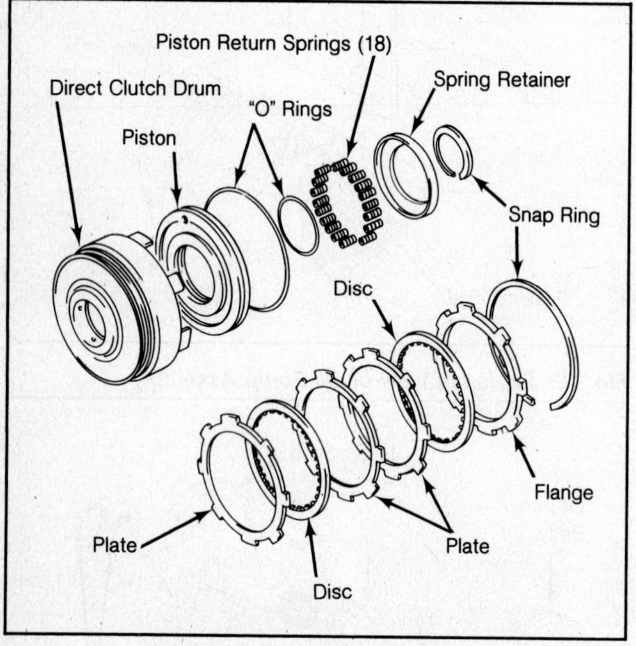

FORWARD (REAR) CLUTCH

Disassembly

1) Remove thrust washer. Remove thrust bearings and races from both sides of clutch. Using a feeler gauge, measure clearance between snap ring and flange. Clearance should be .0161-.0425" (.41-1.08 mm).

2) Remove snap ring from clutch drum. Remove flange, disc, and plate assembly. Compress spring retainer and return springs. Remove snap ring with snap ring pliers. Remove spring retainer and 18 springs.

3) Apply compressed air to oil passage hole (nearest piston) on rear of forward clutch shaft. If piston does not come out, use needle-nose pliers to remove it. Remove oil seal rings.

Cleaning & Inspection

Clean all parts with kerosene or automatic transmission fluid only. Use compressed air to dry all parts. Shake piston to ensure that check ball in piston is free. Check that valve does not leak by applying low pressure compressed air.

Reassembly

NOTE: New discs or plates that are to be used for replacement must be soaked in transmission fluid for at least 2 hours before assembly.

1) Being careful not to spread oil seal rings too much, install rings on shaft. Coat new "O" rings with ATF and install on piston. Press piston into drum with cupped side up. Do not damage "O" rings. Install 18 piston return springs, retainer, and snap ring.

2) Ensure that snap ring gap is not aligned with spring retainer claw. Install 1 plate, 1 disc, 1 plate, 1 disc, 1 plate, and 1 disc. *See Fig. 18*. Install flange with flat side facing downward. Install outer snap ring and check that snap ring gap is not aligned with a cut-out.

3) Using a feeler gauge, measure clearance between snap ring and flange. Clearance should be .0161-.0425" (.41-1.08 mm). Apply compressed air to oil passage hole (nearest piston) on rear of forward clutch shaft. Check to see that piston moves, if not, disassemble piston and inspect.

Fig. 18: Forward (Rear) Clutch Assembly

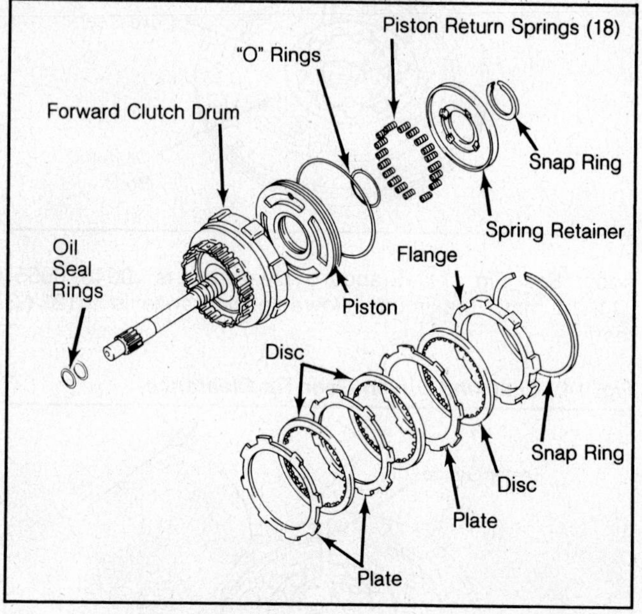

NO. 1 ONE-WAY CLUTCH & SUN GEAR

Disassembly

1) Check operation of one-way clutch by holding sun gear and turning hub. The hub should turn freely in a clockwise direction and should lock when turned counterclockwise.

2) Turn hub clockwise and remove one-way clutch from inner race. Remove No. 3 planetary carrier thrust washer from sun gear input drum. Remove shaft snap ring and remove sun gear input drum. Remove shaft snap ring. If necessary, pry off one-way clutch retainer and remove one-way clutch from hub.

Cleaning & Inspection

Clean all parts with kerosene or automatic transmission fluid only. Use compressed air to dry all parts. Check thrust bearings, races, and one-way clutch for wear or damage. Replace if necessary.

Reassembly

1) Coat parts with ATF. If one-way clutch was removed, install clutch on hub with spring cage toward rear cover. Hold brake hub in soft-jawed vise and flatten retainer ears. Ensure that retainer is centered. Check operation of one-way clutch.

2) Install shaft snap ring on sun gear. Install sun gear input drum on sun gear and install shaft snap ring. Install No. 3 planetary carrier thrust washer on sun gear input drum. Turn hub clockwise and install one-way clutch and 2nd brake hub on inner race. Check operation of one-way clutch.

NO. 2 ONE-WAY CLUTCH & REAR PLANETARY GEAR

Disassembly

1) Check operation of one-way clutch by holding outer race and turning hub. The hub should turn freely in a

Fig. 19: No. 1 One-Way Clutch & Sun Gear Assembly

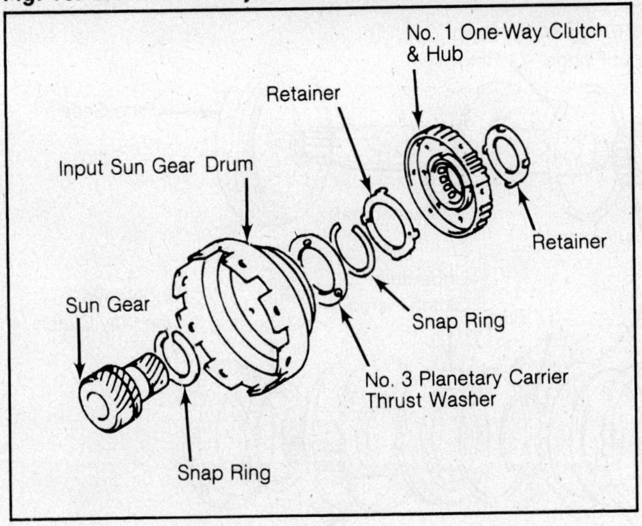

counterclockwise direction and should lock when turned clockwise.

2) Remove No. 2 planetary carrier thrust washer from both sides of carrier. Remove hub and planetary gear from one-way clutch. Remove snap rings and side retainers from sides of clutch. Note position of one-way clutch and remove from outer race.

Cleaning & Inspection

Clean all parts with kerosene or automatic transmission fluid only. Use compressed air to dry all parts. Check one-way clutch for wear or damage.

Reassembly

Coat all parts with ATF. Install one-way clutch into outer race with cage flange toward (front) oil pump. Reverse disassembly procedure to complete reassembly. Coat thrust washers with petroleum jelly. Check operation of one-way clutch.

Fig. 20: No. 2 One-Way Clutch & Rear Planetary Gear Assembly

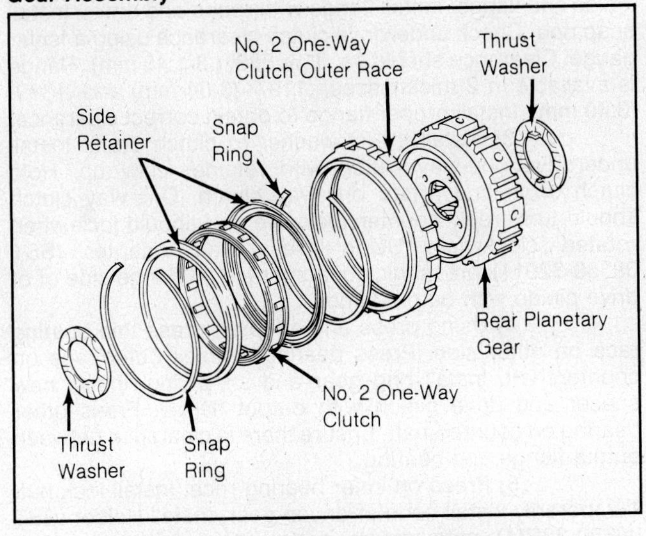

1ST & REVERSE BRAKE PISTON

Disassembly

1) Using 1st and Reverse Spring Compressor (SST 09350-32011), compress springs by tightening bolt gradually. Using snap ring pliers, remove snap ring. Remove compressor.

2) Remove snap ring and return spring assembly. Apply compressed air to case oil passage to remove piston from case. *See Fig. 21*. If piston does not pop out, remove piston with needle-nose pliers. Remove "O" rings from piston.

Fig. 21: Removing 1st & Reverse Brake Piston

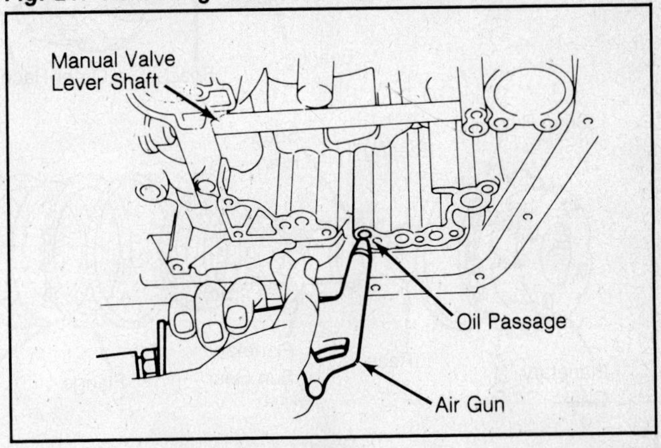

Cleaning & Inspection

Clean all parts with kerosene or automatic transmission fluid only. Use compressed air to dry all parts.

Reassembly

1) Coat new "O" rings with ATF and install on piston. Push piston into transaxle case with spring seats facing (up) forward. Install piston return spring assembly and snap ring in place.

2) Compress piston return springs to allow installation of snap ring. Avoid bending spring retainer or damaging case by overtightening compressor. Push snap ring into place with fingers.

3) Visually check snap ring to ensure that it is fully seated and centered by 3 lugs on spring retainer. Ensure that snap ring gap is not aligned with spring retainer claw. Remove compressor.

INTERMEDIATE SHAFT

Disassembly

Using Puller (SST 09950-00020) on A-130L and A-131L models and Puller (SST 09555-55010) on A-240L models, press intermediate shaft front and rear bearings from shaft.

Reassembly

Install new intermediate shaft front and rear bearings using Adapter (SST09350-32011) and a press. Ensure distance from gear flange end to intermediate shaft end is about .197" (5 mm) on A-130L and A-131L models and about .354" (9 mm) on A-240L models.

COUNTERSHAFT

Disassembly (A-240L Models Only)

1) Remove bearing from countershaft. Remove underdrive planetary sun gear from countershaft. Remove snap ring from sun gear. Remove snap ring from countershaft assembly. Remove underdrive planetary gear. Remove thrust bearing and race.

2) Remove drive pinion with output flange, bearing inner race and spacer using a press, Bearing Remover (SST 09555-55010) and Adapter (SST 09350-32011). Re-

TOYOTA A-130L, A-131L & A-240L TRANSAXLE (Cont.)

Fig. 22: Exploded View of Countershaft Assembly

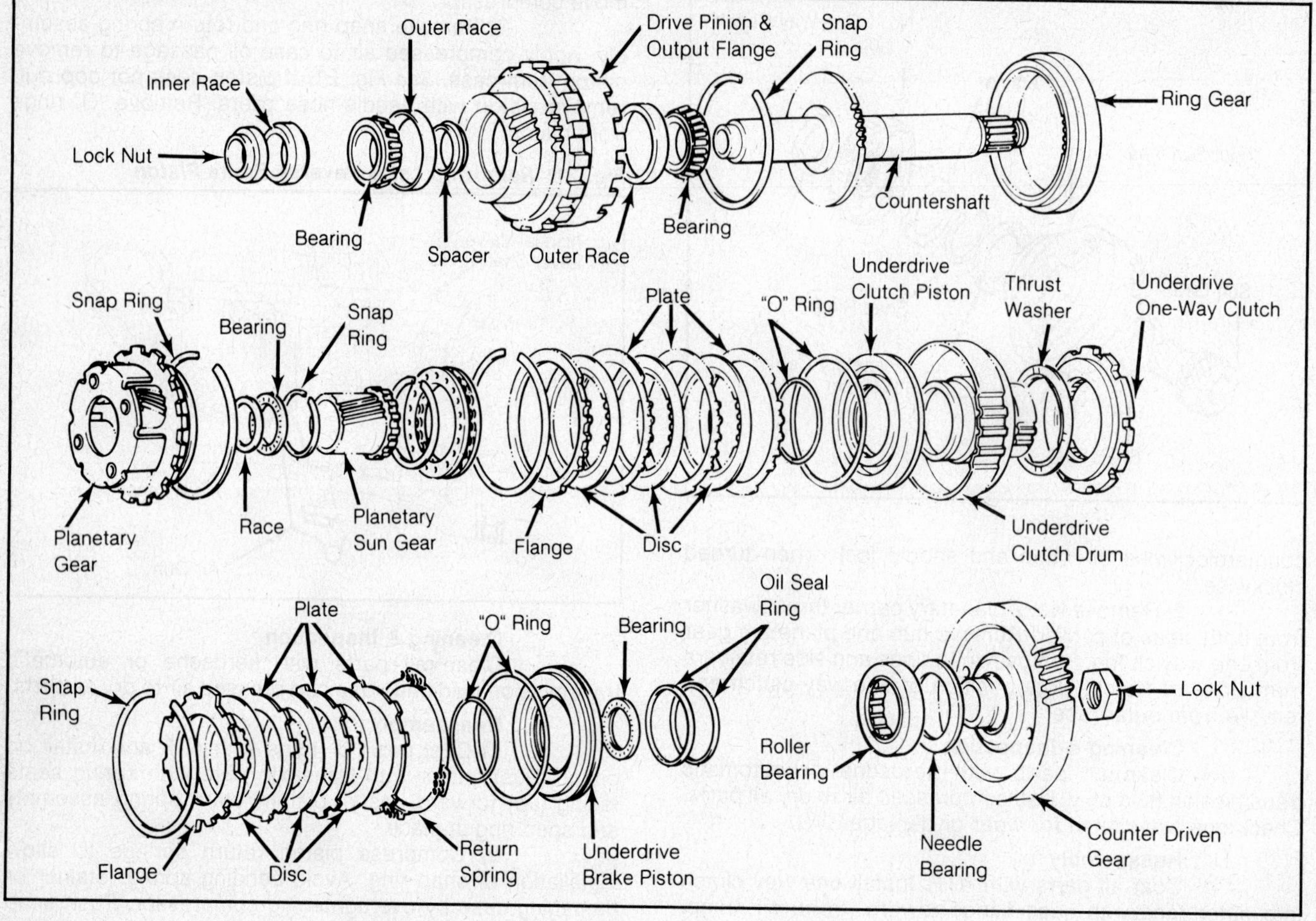

move snap ring and ring gear. Remove bearing using a press, Bearing Remover (SST 09550-00020) and Adapter (SST 09350-32011).

3) Remove bearing outer race using a brass punch and hammer. Remove underdrive one-way clutch from clutch drum. Remove thrust washer. Measure underdrive clutch clearance using a feeler gauge. Clearance should be .0315-.0583" (.80-1.48 mm). Remove snap ring. Remove flange, discs and plates.

4) Compress piston return spring using a press and Adapter (SST09350-32011). Remove snap ring. Remove return spring. Apply compressed air to oil passage to remove piston. If piston does not come out, remove piston using needle-nose pliers.

Cleaning & Inspection

Clean all parts with kerosene or automatic transmission fluid only. Use compressed air to dry all parts. Shake piston to ensure that check ball in piston is free. Check that valve does not leak by applying low pressure compressed air.

Reassembly

NOTE: New discs or plates that are to be used for replacement must be soaked in transmission fluid for at least 2 hours before assembly.

1) Coat new "O" rings with ATF and install "O" rings on piston. Install underdrive clutch piston in clutch drum. Be careful not to damage "O" rings. Position return spring on clucth piston. Compress return spring and install snap ring in groove. Ensure end of snap ring is not aligned with spring retainer claw.

2) Install 1 plate, 1 disc, 1 plate, 1 disc, 1 plate, 1 disc and flange. Install flange with round end down. Install snap ring. Check underdrive clutch clearance using a feeler gauge. Clearance should be .315-.583" (.8-1.48 mm). Flange is available in 2 thicknesses, .1197" (3.04 mm) and .1339" (3.40 mm). Install proper flange to obtain correct clearance.

3) Install thrust washer to clutch drum. Install underdrive one-way clutch with retainer claw up. Hold clutch drum and rotate one-way clutch. One-way clutch should turn freely counterclockwise and should lock when rotated clockwise. Using press and Adapter (SST 09350-32011), press thick bearing race on flange side of of drive pinion with output flange.

4) Using press and adapter, press thin bearing race on other side. Press bearing in thick outer race on countershaft. Install ring gear and snap ring. Install new spacer and drive pinion with output flange. Press other bearing on countershaft. Ensure there is clearance between output flange and bearing.

5) Press on inner bearing race. Install lock nut. Temporarily install counter driven gear. Install Holder (SST 09350-32011) onto driven gear. Install holder in vise. Tighten new lock nut using torque wrench and Adapter (SST 09350-32011). Tighten lock nut to 131-159 ft. lbs. (177-215 N.m).

Fig. 23: Exploded View of Upper Valve Body Assembly

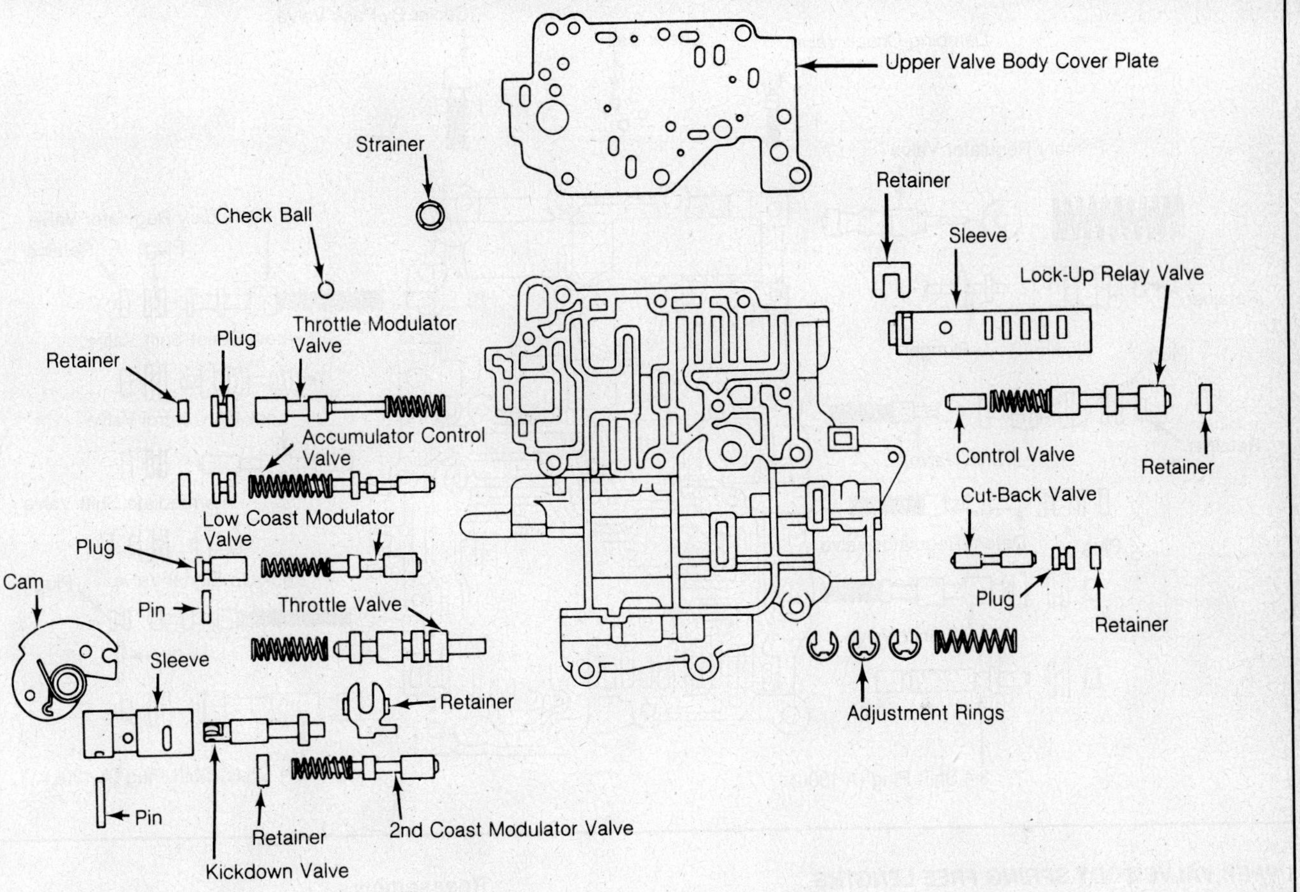

6) Measure rotating torque of countershaft using spring gauge and adapter. Starting torque should be 2.6-4.4 lbs. (1.2-2.0 kg). If starting torque exceeds specification, replace spacer and recheck rotating torque.

7) Remove counter driven gear. Install thrust bearing and race. Install underdrive planetary gear and snap ring. Install thrust bearing on counter driven gear.

VALVE BODY

Disassembly (A-130L & A-131L)

1) Remove 14 bolts. Remove lower valve body cover and gasket. Turn assembly over and remove 12 bolts from upper valve body and upper valve body cover. Remove upper valve body cover, strainer, and gasket.

2) Turn assembly over and remove 3 bolts from lower valve body. Hold valve body plate against lower valve body and carefully remove lower valve body. DO NOT allow check valve and ball to fall out. Note location of steel ball, retainers, and pins in valve body.

3) To disassemble upper valve body, remove throttle valve retainer and check ball. Remove plug retainer with a magnet and remove plug. Remove lock-up relay valve, control valve, and spring. Remove sleeve retainer with a magnet, then remove sleeve. *See Fig. 23.*

4) Remove retainer with a magnet and remove cut-back valve. Remove retainer with a magnet and remove plug, throttle modulator valve, and spring. Remove retainer with a magnet and remove plug, spring, and accumulator control valve.

5) Remove pin with a magnet and remove plug, spring, and low coast modulator valve. Remove retainer with a magnet and remove spring and 2nd coast modulator valve. Loosen throttle cam bolt. Remove bolt, throttle cam, spring, and collar.

6) Remove pin with a magnet and remove downshift plug, sleeve, and spring. Remove throttle valve. Remove springs and adjustment rings from upper valve body. Note and record number of adjustment rings.

7) To disassemble lower valve body, remove lower valve body plate and gaskets. Remove cooler by-pass valve and spring. *See Fig. 24.* Remove damping check valve and spring. Note position of 3 lower valve body check balls. Remove check balls.

8) Remove retainer with a magnet and remove plug, sleeve, and plunger. Remove spring and primary regulator valve. Note and record number of adjustment rings. Remove retainer with a magnet and remove plug, secondary regulator valve, and spring.

9) Remove retainer with a magnet and remove plug, 1-2 shift valve, and spring. Remove retainer with a magnet and remove plug and low coast shift valve. Remove retainer with a magnet and remove plug and lock-up control valve.

10) Remove retainer with a magnet and remove plug, detent regulator valve, and spring. Remove retainer with a magnet and remove plug, 2-3 shift valve, and spring. Remove retainer with a magnet and remove plug and intermediate shift valve.

TOYOTA A-130L, A-131L & A-240L TRANSAXLE (Cont.)

Fig. 24: Exploded View of Lower Valve Body Assembly

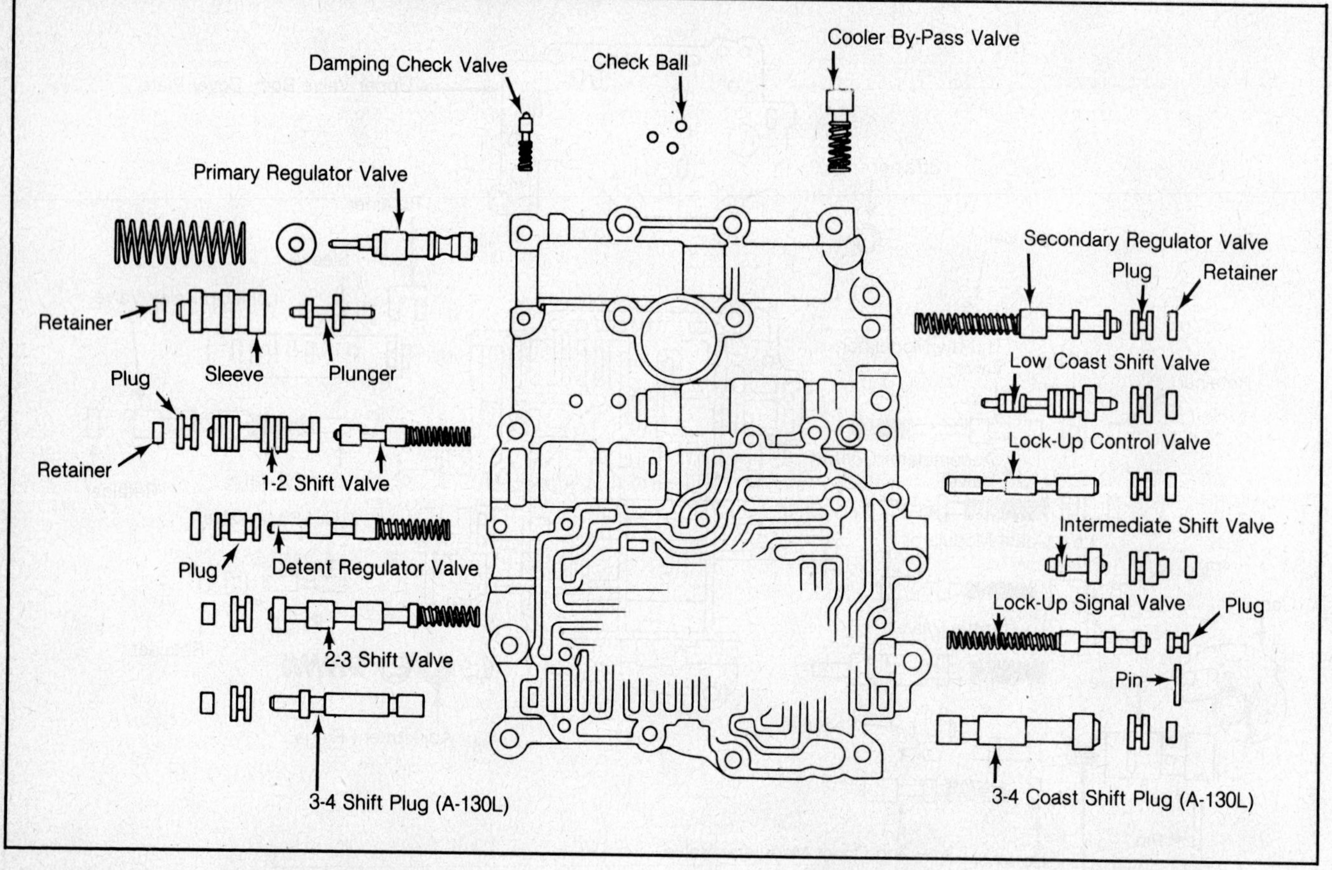

UPPER VALVE BODY SPRING FREE LENGTHS

Spring Application	Spring Color	Length In. (mm)
Accum. Control Valve		
A-130L	Lt. Blue	.9378 (23.82)
A-131L	None	1.3071 (33.20)
Downshift Plug		
A-130L	Gray	1.2205 (31.00)
A-131L	White	1.1717 (29.76)
Lock-Up Relay Valve	White	1.0457 (26.56)
Low Coast Mod. Valve	Red	.9213 (23.40)
Throttle Mod. Valve	None	.8543 (21.70)
Throttle Valve	None	1.2087 (30.70)
2nd Coast Mod. Valve	Yel/Grn	.8240 (20.93)

11) Remove retainer with a magnet and remove plug, lock-up signal valve, and spring. Remove retainer with a magnet and remove plug and 3-4 coast shift plug. Remove retainer with a magnet and remove plug and 3-4 shift plug.

Cleaning & Inspection

1) Clean all parts with kerosene or automatic transmission fluid only. Clean all fluid passages and holes, use compressed air to ensure that passages or holes are not clogged. After cleaning, arrange parts in proper order for inspection.

2) Inspect valve springs for damage, squareness, rust and collapsed coils. Measure spring free length and replace any spring whose length is less than specified. Keep valve body springs together with corresponding valve.

Reassembly

1) To reassemble upper valve body, coat parts with ATF before installing. With valve body in a horizontal position install sleeve into bore. Coat retainer with petroleum jelly and install it on end of sleeve.

2) Install control valve, spring, and lock-up relay valve. Push in on lock-up relay valve until control valve touches sleeve. Install plug and retainer. Install cut-back valve (flat end first) into bore. Install plug and retainer. Install throttle modulator valve into bore. Install plug and retainer.

3) Install accumulator control valve and spring into bore. Install plug and retainer. Install low coast modulator valve and spring into bore. Install plug and retainer. Install throttle valve into bore. Coat retainer with petroluem jelly and install it in valve body.

LOWER VALVE BODY SPRING FREE LENGTHS

Spring Application	Spring Color	Length In. (mm)
Detent Regulator Valve		
A-130L	Orange	1.1437 (29.05)
A-131L	Blue	1.2063 (30.64)
Cooler By-Pass Valve	None	.7835 (19.90)
Damping Check Valve	None	.4409 (11.20)
Lock-Up Signal Valve		
A-130L	Yellow	1.4528 (36.90)
A-131L	Red	1.6476 (41.85)
Pri. Regulator Valve	Purple	2.6240 (66.65)
Sec. Regulator Valve	None	1.7165 (43.60)
1-2 Shift Valve	Yellow	1.0697 (27.17)
2-3 Shift Valve	None	1.0921 (27.74)

Automatic Transmissions

TOYOTA A-130L, A-131L & A-240L TRANSAXLE (Cont.)

Fig. 25: Upper Valve Body Check Ball, Pin & Retainer Locations

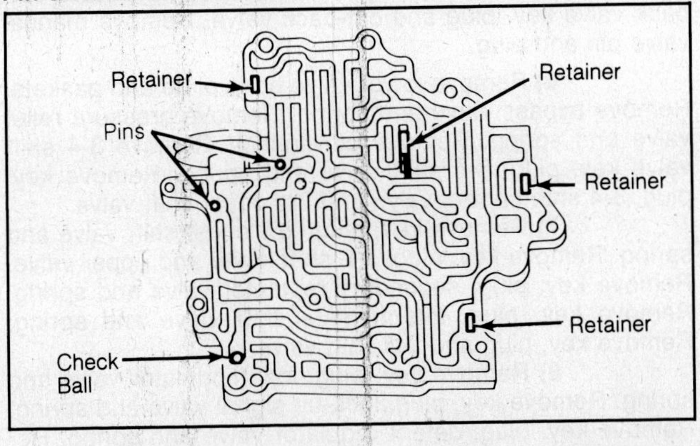

4) Install adjustment rings (number removed) on throttle valve shaft. Slip spring over end of valve shaft. Compress spring and slide it into place. Install spring on throttle valve. Install downshift plug and sleeve. Coat pin with petroluem jelly and install to hold sleeve in place.

5) Install 2nd coast modulator valve and spring into bore. Compress spring and allow retainer to fall into place. Ensure that retainer fully covers end of spring. Install hook of spring through hole in cam and install sleeve on side of cam.

6) Install cam assembly on upper valve body. Check position of spring ends. Tighten cam bolt. Ensure that cam moves on roller of downshift plug. Install check ball. Ensure that pins and retainers are correctly installed and in place. *See Fig. 25*.

7) To reassemble lower valve body, coat parts with ATF before installing. Place valve body in a horizontal position. Install adjustment rings (number removed) and spring seat on primary regulator valve. Place valve in bore. Stand valve body up and push valve in until it bottoms in bore. Install spring.

8) Insert plunger (short end first) into sleeve. Ensure that plunger is fully inserted in sleeve. Install sleeve and plunger in primary regulator valve bore. Install retainer.

9) Install spring and secondary regulator valve in bore. Install plug and retainer. Install spring and 1-2 shift valve in bore. Install plug and retainer. Install lock-up control valve in bore. Coat retainer with petroluem jelly and install plug and retainer.

10) Install spring and detent regulator valve (thin end first) into bore. Install plug and retainer. Install intermediate shift valve (small end first) into bore. Install plug and retainer. Install spring and 2-3 shift valve into bore. Install plug and retainer.

11) Install spring and lock-up signal valve in bore. Install plug and pin. Install 3-4 coast shift plug. Install plug and retainer. Install spring and cooler by-pass valve. Install spring and damping valve. Ensure that pin and retainers are correctly installed and in place. Install 3 check balls. *See Fig. 26*.

12) Place gasket having larger cooler by-pass valve hole against lower valve body. Place plate and second gasket on top of first gasket. Align bolt holes in valve body with gaskets and plate.

13) Tightly hold lower valve body, gaskets, and plate. Place lower valve body, gaskets, and plate on top of upper valve body. Align bolt holes in valve bodies, gaskets and plate. Install and finger tighten 3 bolts in lower valve body. *See Fig. 27*.

Fig. 26: Lower Valve Body Check Ball, Pin & Retainer Locations

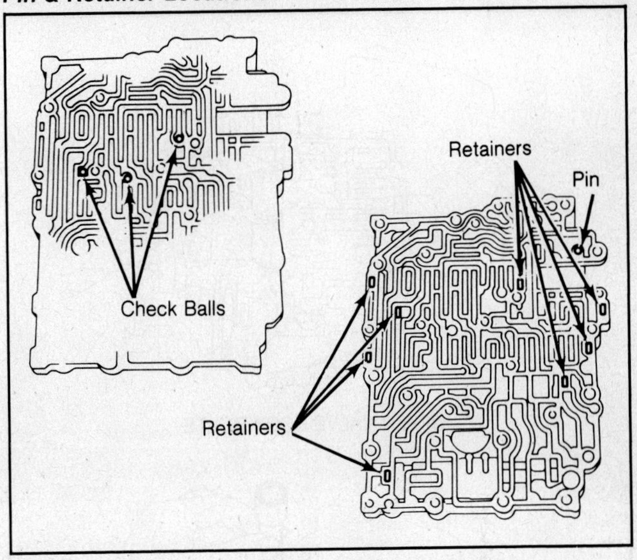

Fig. 27: Installing Lower Valve Body & Valve Body Cover Bolts

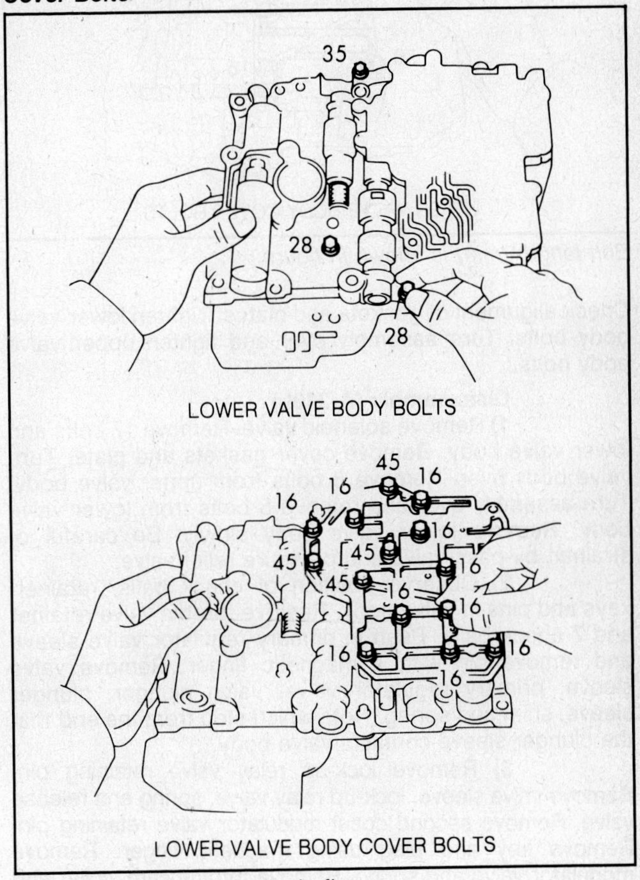

Bolt length (mm) is shown in figure.

14) Turn assembly over. Install and finger tighten 3 bolts in upper valve body. *See Fig. 28*. Install gasket, plate, and gasket on upper valve body. Install strainer on plate. Install upper valve body cover and finger tighten 9 bolts. *See Fig. 28*.

15) Turn assembly over. Install lower valve body gasket, cover, and finger tighten 14 bolts. *See Fig. 27*.

Fig. 28: Installing Upper Valve Body & Valve Body Cover Bolts

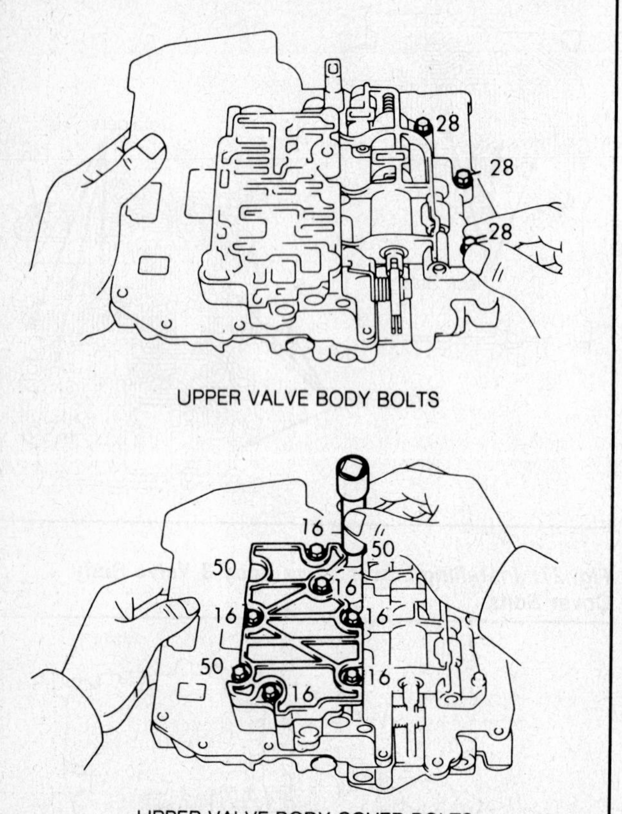

Bolt length (mm) is shown in figure.

Check alignment of gaskets and plates. Tighten lower valve body bolts. Turn assembly over and tighten upper valve body bolts.

Disassembly (A-240L)

1) Remove solenoid valve. Remove 17 bolts and lower valve body. Remove cover gaskets and plate. Turn valve body over. Remove 8 bolts from upper valve body. Turn assembly over and remove 5 bolts from lower valve body. Remove lower valve body slowly. Be careful of strainer, by-pass valve and pressure relief valve.

2) Observe position of check balls, retainer, keys and pins in valve body. Remove throttle valve retainer and 7 check balls. Push in primary regulator valve sleeve and remove pin with a magnetic finger. Remove valve sleeve, primary regulator valve, valve plunger, plunger sleeve, shim and spring. Note which step from the end that the plunger sleeve contacts valve body.

3) Remove lock-up relay valve retaining pin. Remove valve sleeve, lock-up relay valve, spring and release valve. Remove second coast modulator valve retaining pin. Remove key and plug using magnetic finger. Remove modulator valve and spring. Remove throttle cam, collar and spring.

4) Remove throttle valve retaining pin. Remove valve sleeve, kickdown valve, throttle valve and spring. Remove spring and adjusting shims. Note number of shims for reassembly reference. Remove throttle modulator valve retaining pin. Remove plug, throttle modulator valve and spring.

5) Remove accumulator valve retaining key and plug. Remove accumulator valve and spring. Remove cut-back valve key, plug and cut-back valve. Remove manual valve pin and plug.

6) Remove lower valve body plate and gaskets. Remove bypass valve and spring. Remove pressure relief valve and spring. Remove oil strainer. Remove 3-4 shift valve key, plug, 3-4 shift valve and spring. Remove key, plug, 3-4 shift control valve and 3rd coast shift valve.

7) Remove key, plug, low coast shift valve and spring. Remove key, plug, 1-2 shift lower and upper valve. Remove key, plug, secondary regulator valve and spring. Remove key, plug, intermediate shift valve and spring. Remove key, plug and 2-3 shift valve.

8) Remove key, plug, low modulator valve and spring. Remove key, plug, lock-up signal valve and spring. Remove key, plug, detent regulator valve and spring. Remove key, plug, 3-4 switch valve and spring.

Cleaning & Inspection

1) Clean all parts with kerosene or automatic transmission fluid only. Clean all fluid passages and holes, use compressed air to ensure that passages or holes are not clogged. After cleaning, arrange parts in proper order for inspection.

2) Inspect valve springs for damage, squareness, rust and collapsed coils. Measure spring free length and replace any spring whose length is less than specified. Keep valve body springs together with corresponding valve.

UPPER VALVE BODY SPRING FREE LENGTHS

Spring Application	Spring Color	Length In. (mm)
Accum. Control Valve	Yellow	1.5039 (38.20)
Kickdown Valve	White	1.1717 (29.76)
Lock-Up Relay Valve	None	.7402 (18.80)
Pri. Regulator Valve	Purple	2.6240 (66.65)
Throttle Mod. Valve	Green	1.1772 (29.90)
Throttle Valve	Yel/Grn	1.1488 (29.18)
2nd Coast Mod. Valve	Red	1.1665 (29.63)

LOWER VALVE BODY SPRING FREE LENGTHS

Spring Application	Spring Color	Length In. (mm)
Detent Reg. Valve	Pink	1.3126 (33.34)
Lock-up Signal Valve	White	1.6299 (41.40)
Low Coast Shift Valve	Yellow	1.0697 (27.17)
Low Modulator Valve	None	1.1476 (29.15)
Secondary Reg. Valve	Orange	1.2937 (32.86)
2-3 Shift Valve	None	1.0921 (27.74)
3-4 Shift Valve	None	1.3724 (34.86)
3-4 Switch Valve	None	1.2165 (30.90)

Reassembly

1) To assemble upper valve body, install cut-back valve with small end first. Install plug and key. Install accumulator control valve and spring. Install plug with thick end first and pin. Install spring and throttle modulator valve. Install plug with flat end first and pin.

2) Install kickdown valve into throttle valve sleeve. Install throttle valve with small end first and spring. Install same number of adjusting shims that were removed

TOYOTA A-130L, A-131L & A-240L TRANSAXLE (Cont.)

Fig. 29: Exploded View of Upper Valve Body Assembly

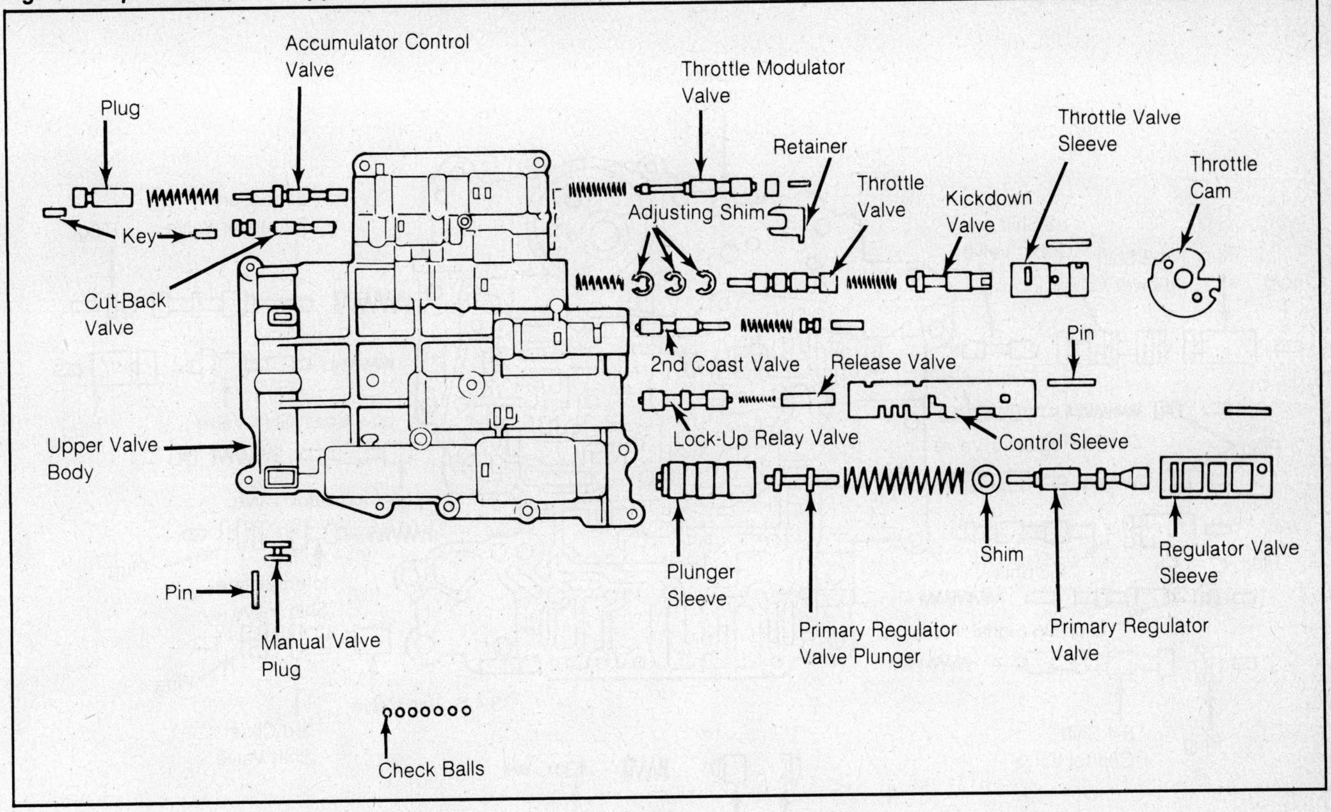

during disassembly. Install spring. Install kickdown valve and throttle valve sleeve. Install pin to hold sleeve in place.

3) Install collar through one side of throttle cam. Install spring with hook through hole in cam. Install throttle cam assembly to upper valve body. Ensure throttle cam moves on roller of kickdown valve. Install 2nd coast modulator valve and spring. Install plug and pin.

4) Install release valve into valve sleeve with flat end first. Install spring and relay valve to valve sleeve. Install lock-up relay valve sleeve assembly into upper valve body. Install pin to hold sleeve in place. Install primary regulator valve with small end first into plunger sleeve. Install regulator valve into valve sleeve.

5) Install primary regulator plunger sleeve assembly into upper valve body. Install spring, shim and regulator valve assembly. Install assembly so that end of plunger sleeve makes contact with valve body at same step as when it was disassembled. Install pin to hold valve sleeve.

6) Install manual valve plug and pin. Coat pin with petroleum jelly before installing. Coat valve retainer with petroleum jelly and install throttle valve retainer. Install 7 check balls.

7) To assemble lower valve body, install 3-4 switch valve and spring. Install plug and key. Install 2-3 shift valve with small end first. Install plug and key. Install low coast shift valve with small end first. Install plug with thin end first and key.

8) Install spring and intermediate shift valve. Coat key with petroleum jelly. Install key and plug. Turn assembly over and install 3-4 shift control valve with cup side first. Install 3rd coast shift valve with flat end first. Install plug and key.

Fig. 30: Installing Check Balls & Throttle Retainer

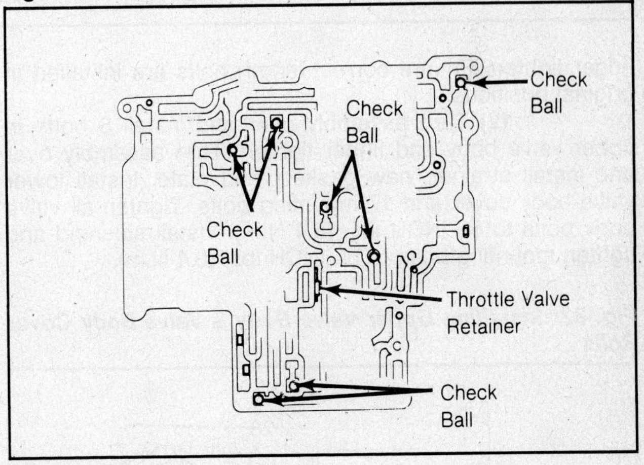

9) Install low modulator valve, spring, plug and key. Install spring, secondary regulator valve, plug and key. Install low coast shift valve spring and upper valve. Install lower valve with flat end first. Install plug with thin end first and key. Install detent regulator valve, spring, plug and key.

10) Install spring and lock-up signal valve. Install plug and key. Install spring and 3-4 shift valve. Install plug and key. Turn assembly over and install by-pass valve and spring. Install pressure relief valve and spring. Install oil strainer.

11) Position gaskets and plate on lower valve body. Align bolt holes in valve body with those in gaskets and plate. Place lower valve body, plate and gaskets on top of upper valve body. Install 5 bolts in lower valve body and

Fig. 31: Exploded View of Lower Valve Body Assembly

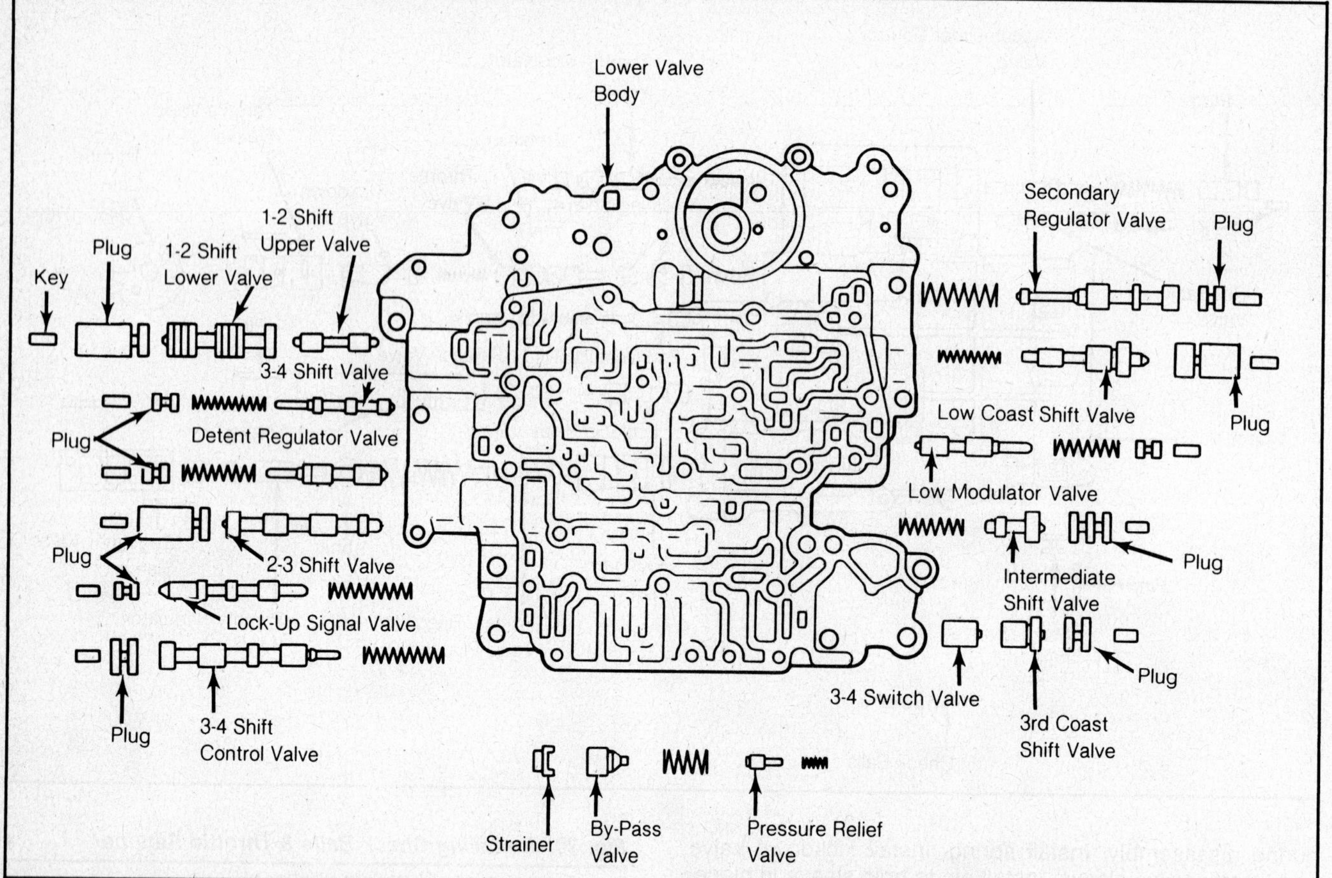

finger tighten. Ensure correct length bolts are installed in original positions.

12) Turn assembly over and install 8 bolts in upper valve body and finger tighten. Turn assembly over and install strainer, new gaskets and plate. Install lower valve body cover and 17 mounting bolts. Tighten all valve body bolts to 56 INCH lbs. (6.4 N.m). Install solenoid and tighten mounting bolts to 56 INCH lbs. (6.4 N.m).

Fig. 32: Installing Upper Valve Body & Valve Body Cover Bolts

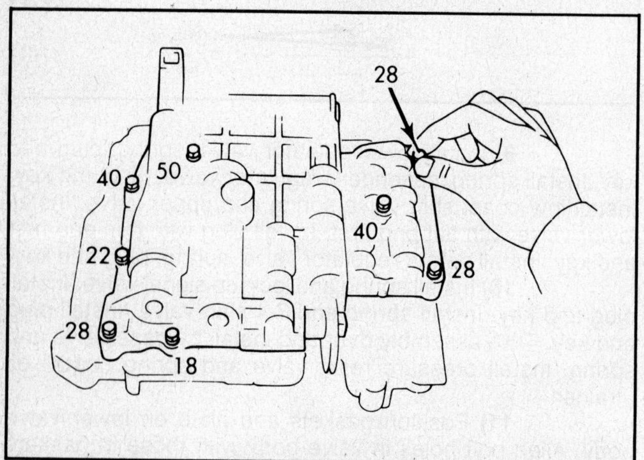

Bolt length (mm) is shown in figure.

DIFFERENTIAL

Disassembly

1) On A-130L & A-131L models, remove speedometer driven gear and neutral safety switch. Remove governor body. Remove oil pan and valve body. Remove 11 transaxle rear cover bolts. Using a plastic hammer, tap rear cover loose, and remove. Remove parking lock pawl assembly. Remove manual shaft and lever. Remove governor pressure adapter.

2) Remove carrier cover. Using an INCH lb. torque wrench, measure total preload. Note and record reading. Starting preload (with drive pinion preload added) should be 2.5-3.9 INCH lbs. (.3-.4 N.m) for a new bearing and 1.2-1.9 INCH lbs. (.1-.2 N.m) for a used bearing.

3) Measure side gear backlash while holding one pinion toward case. Backlash should be .0020-.0079" (.05-.20 mm). Remove 6 bolts from left bearing retainer. Tap retainer loose with a plastic hammer. Remove "O" ring from retainer. Remove 2 bolts and right side bearing cap. Remove differential, outer race and adjustment shim from transaxle case.

4) Using an INCH lb. torque wrench, measure drive pinion preload. Starting preload should be 8.7-13.9 INCH lbs. (1.0-1.6 N.m) for a new bearing and 4.3-6.9 INCH lbs. (.5-.8 N.m) for a used bearing. On A-240L models, remove speedometer driven gear and governor body. Remove oil pump. Remove transaxle housing. Remove differential.

5) On all models, remove bearings from differential case using Puller (SST 09502-10012). Remove speed-

Fig. 33: Installing Lower Valve Body & Valve Body Cover Bolts

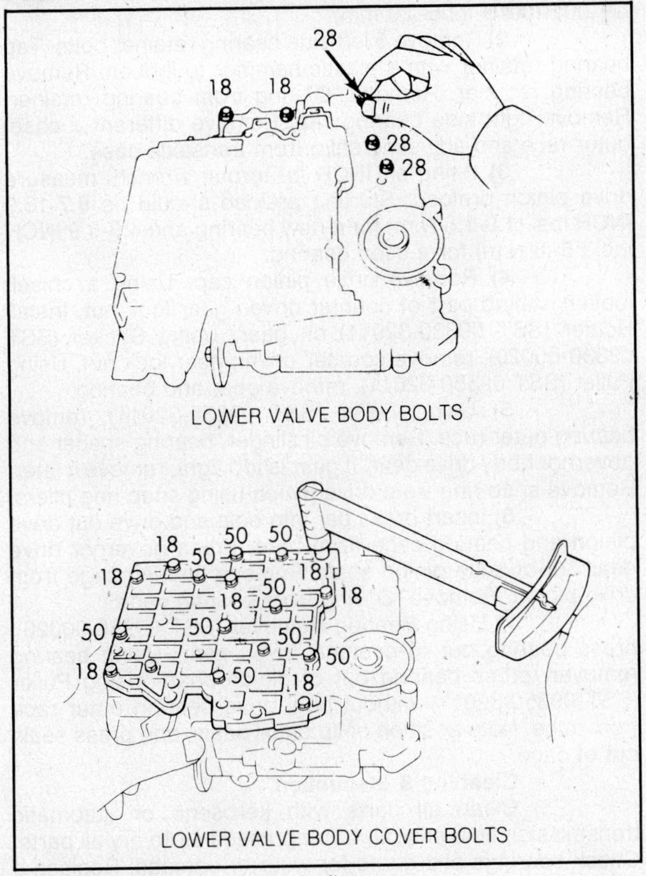

Bolt length (mm) is shown in figure.

ometer drive gear. Mark ring gear and case for reassembly reference. Spread locking tabs on ring gear bolts. Remove 8 bolts and locking tabs. Using a brass hammer, tap ring gear and remove from case.

6) While holding one pinion against case, measure side gear backlash. If backlash is incorrect, disassemble case and change thrust washer on side gears. Drive out pinion shaft lock pin and remove pinion shaft. Remove pinion gears, side gears, and thrust washers from each gear.

7) Remove oil seal from left bearing retainer. Press out of left bearing outer race and shim. Using a long screwdriver, remove right bearing oil seal from transfer case.

Cleaning & Inspection

Clean all parts with kerosene or automatic transmission fluid only. Use compressed air to dry all parts. Check bearings and gears for wear or damage. Replace if necessary.

Reassembly

1) Coat lip of oil seals with multipurpose grease and install oil seals. Install .0945" (2.40 mm) thick shim, in left bearing retainer. Using Driver (SST 09350-32011), press bearing outer race into left bearing retainer.

2) Select thrust washers that will ensure correct backlash. Install thrust washers and side gears in case. If possible, install same size washers on both sides of gears. Install pinions and pinion shaft.

3) While holding one pinion against case, check side gear backlash. Backlash should be .0020-.0079" (.05-.20 mm). If backlash is incorrect, disassemble case and change thrust washer on side gears.

NOTE: **Side gear thrust washers are available in the following thickness variations: .0374" (.95 mm), .0394" (1.00 mm), .0413" (1.05 mm), .0433" (1.10 mm), .0453" (1.15 mm) and .0472" (1.20 mm).**

4) Using a hammer and punch, drive lock pin through case and into pinion shaft. Stake differential case to hold pin in place. On A-240L models, install differential case into transaxle case. Install transaxle housing and tighten mounting bolts to 22 ft. lbs. (29 N.M).

5) On A-130L and A-131L models, clean ring gear contact surface of case. Heat ring gear to 212°F (100°C) in an oil bath. Clean contact surface of ring gear with cleaning solvent. Align ring gear with differential case, and quickly install ring gear on case.

6) Install locking tabs and bolts. Tighten bolts evenly and a little at a time. Using a hammer and punch, bend locking tabs. Stake 1st tab flush with flat surface of nut. Stake 2nd tab against corner of nut. Install speedometer drive gear.

7) Using Bearing Installer (SST 09350-32011), press bearings onto differential case. Install outer race and adjustment shim on right bearing. Install differential in transaxle case. Install left bearing retainer without "O" ring. Snug bolts evenly and gradually while turning ring gear, then tighten bolts.

8) Install right bearing cap. Snug bolts evenly and gradually while turning ring gear, then tighten bolts. On all models, measure differential bearing preload, using Differential Preload Adapter (SST 09564-32011) and an INCH lb. torque wrench.

Fig. 34: Measuring Differential Bearing Preload

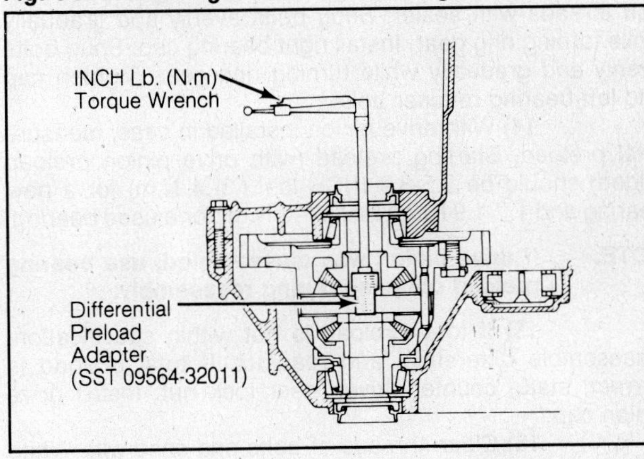

9) Starting preload should be 6.9-13.9 INCH lbs. (.8-1.6 N.m) on A-130L and A-131L models and 6.9-12.2 INCH lbs. (.8-1.4 N.m) on A-240L models using new bearings. Starting preload should be 4.3-6.9 INCH lbs. (.5-.8 N.m) on A-130L and A-131L models and 3.5-6.1 INCH lbs. (.4-.7 N.m) on A-240L models using used bearings.

10) If preload is incorrect, remove differential from case and change adjustment shim under right bearing (A-130L and A-131L models) and left bearing (A-240L models). Install ring gear on differential case (A-240L models). Install transaxle housing bolts in original locations and tighten to specification. *See Fig. 35.*

11) Differential bearing shims are available in various thicknesses, ranging from 1.90-2.80 mm, in .05 mm increments for A-130L models. On A-131L models, shims range in thickness from 1.60-2.65 mm, in .05 mm increments. On A-240L models, shims range in thickness from 2.00-2.90 mm, in .05 mm increments.

Fig. 35: Installing Transaxle Housing Mounting Bolts

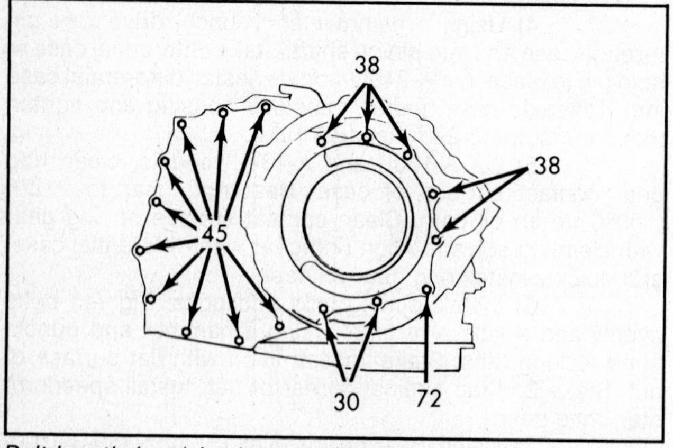

Bolt length (mm) is shown in figure.

NOTE: **Preload will change about 2.6-3.5 INCH lbs. (.3-.4 N.m) with each shim thickness.**

12) If preload is within specification, remove left bearing retainer, differential and shim. Do not lose selected adjustment shim. Reinstall outer race and adjustment shim on right bearing (A-130L and A-131L models) and left bearing (A-240L models). Install "O" ring on left bearing retainer.

13) Install differential and retainer on case. Clean threads of bolts and case with White gasoline. Coat bolt threads with sealer. Snug bolts evenly and gradually while turning ring gear. Install right bearing cap. Snug bolts evenly and gradually while turning ring gear. Tighten cap and left bearing retainer bolts.

14) With drive pinion installed in case, measure total preload. Starting preload (with drive pinion preload added) should be 2.5-3.9 INCH lbs. (.3-.4 N.m) for a new bearing and 1.2-1.9 INCH lbs. (.1-.2 N.m) for a used bearing.

NOTE: **If drive pinion was diassembled, use bearing preload obtained during reassembly.**

15) If total preload is not within specification, disassemble differential and readjust. If total preload is correct, stake counter driven gear lock nut. Install drive pinion cap.

16) Clean threads of bolts and case with White gasoline. Coat bolt threads with sealer. Install carrier cover over gasket. Install cover and tighten bolts.

17) Install intermediate shaft while turning counter driven gear. Do not damage bushing and oil seal. Install transaxle rear cover and tighten bolts. Install speedometer driven gear.

DIFFERENTIAL DRIVE PINION

Disassembly

1) Using an INCH lb. torque wrench, measure total preload. Total preload should be 2.5-3.9 INCH lbs. (.3-.4 N.m) for new bearings and 1.2-1.9 INCH lbs. (.1-.2 N.m) for used bearings. Measure each side gear backlash while holding one pinion gear toward case. Backlash should be .002-.0079" (.05-.20 mm).

2) Remove 6 left side bearing retainer bolts. Tap bearing retainer with a plastic hammer to loosen. Remove bearing retainer. Remove "O" ring from bearing retainer. Remove right side bearing cap. Remove differential case, outer race and adjusting shim from transaxle case.

3) Using an INCH lb. torque wrench, measure drive pinion preload. Starting preload should be 8.7-13.9 INCH lbs. (1.0-1.6 N.m) for a new bearing and 4.3-6.9 INCH lbs. (.5-.8 N.m) for a used bearing.

4) Remove drive pinion cap. Using a chisel, loosen staked part of counter driven gear lock nut. Install Holder (SST 09330-32011) on gear. Using Socket (SST 09330-00020), remove counter driven gear lock nut. Using Puller (SST 09350-32011), remove gear and bearing.

5) Using Puller (SST 09350-32011), remove bearing outer race. Remove oil slinger, bearing spacer and governor body drive gear. If gear is too tight, remove it later. Remove snap ring from drive pinion using snap ring pliers.

6) Insert brass bar into hole and drive out drive pinion and bearing cage from bore. Press governor drive gear out of drive pinion shaft. Remove bearing cage from drive pinion. Remove "O" ring from bearing cage.

7) Using Bearing Remover (SST 09950-00020), press bearing out of counter driven gear. Using bearing remover, press bearing out of pinion shaft. Using Puller (SST 09350-32011) without bolt, drive bearing outer race from cage. Note position of lip on oil seals, and press seals out of cage.

Cleaning & Inspection

Clean all parts with kerosene or automatic transmission fluid only. Use compressed air to dry all parts. Check bearings and gears for wear or damage. Replace if necessary.

Reassembly

1) Coat lip of cage oil seals with multipurpose grease. With lip of inner seal facing downward, press in oil seal until top of seal is at a depth of .43" (10 mm). With lip of outer seal facing upward, press in oil seal until it is flush with cage surface. Press outer bearing race into bearing cage.

2) Using Bearing Installer (SST 09350-32011), press bearing onto pinion shaft. Using bearing installer, press bearing onto counter driven gear. Install "O" ring on bearing cage. Install cage on drive pinion shaft. Do not damage oil seals with shaft splines.

3) Press governor drive gear onto drive pinion shaft. Install shaft assembly into case. Tap bearing cage into case. Ensure that cage is past snap ring groove in bore, and that groove can be seen.

4) Install snap ring using snap ring pliers. Insert brass bar into hole and tap drive pinion shaft against snap ring. Ensure that snap ring is properly installed. Install oil slinger with lip facing outward. Drive outer race into case.

5) Install new bearing spacer, small end first. Insert a bar into hole and position against drive pinion shaft. Position other end of bar against a solid object. Drive counter driven gear onto shaft until lock nut can be installed. Do not tap on transaxle case.

6) Coat threads and lock nut with multipurpose grease. Install nut on shaft. Install Holder (SST 09330-32011) on gear. Using Socket (SST 09330-00020), tighten counter driven gear lock nut. Turn gear counterclockwise and then clockwise several times.

Automatic Transmissions

TOYOTA A-130L, A-131L & A-240L TRANSAXLE (Cont.)

Fig. 36: Exploded View of A-130L & A-131L Transaxle Differential & Drive Pinion Assemblies

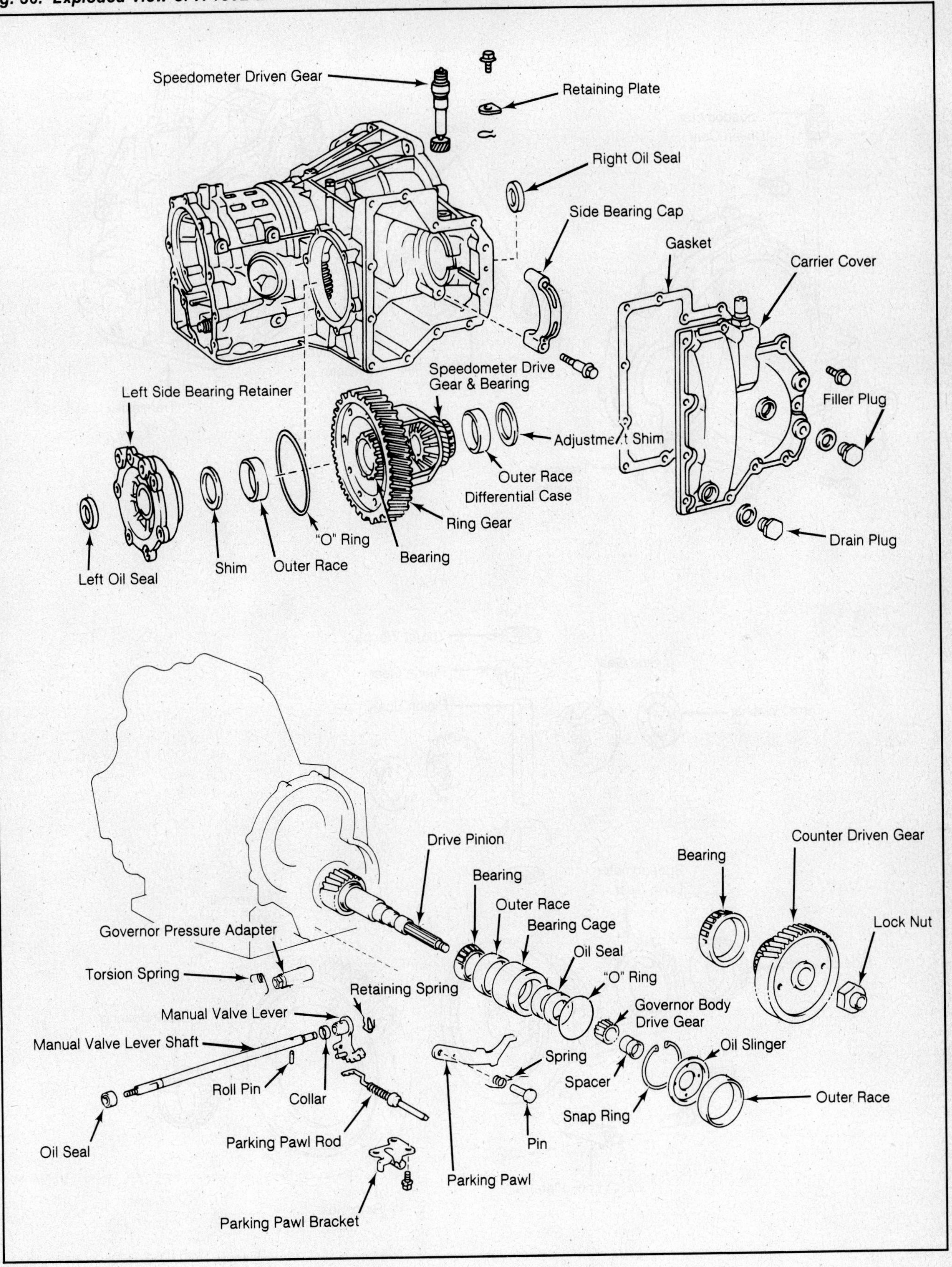

TOYOTA A-130L, A-131L & A-240L TRANSAXLE (Cont.)

Fig. 37: Exploded View of A-240L Transaxle Differential Assembly

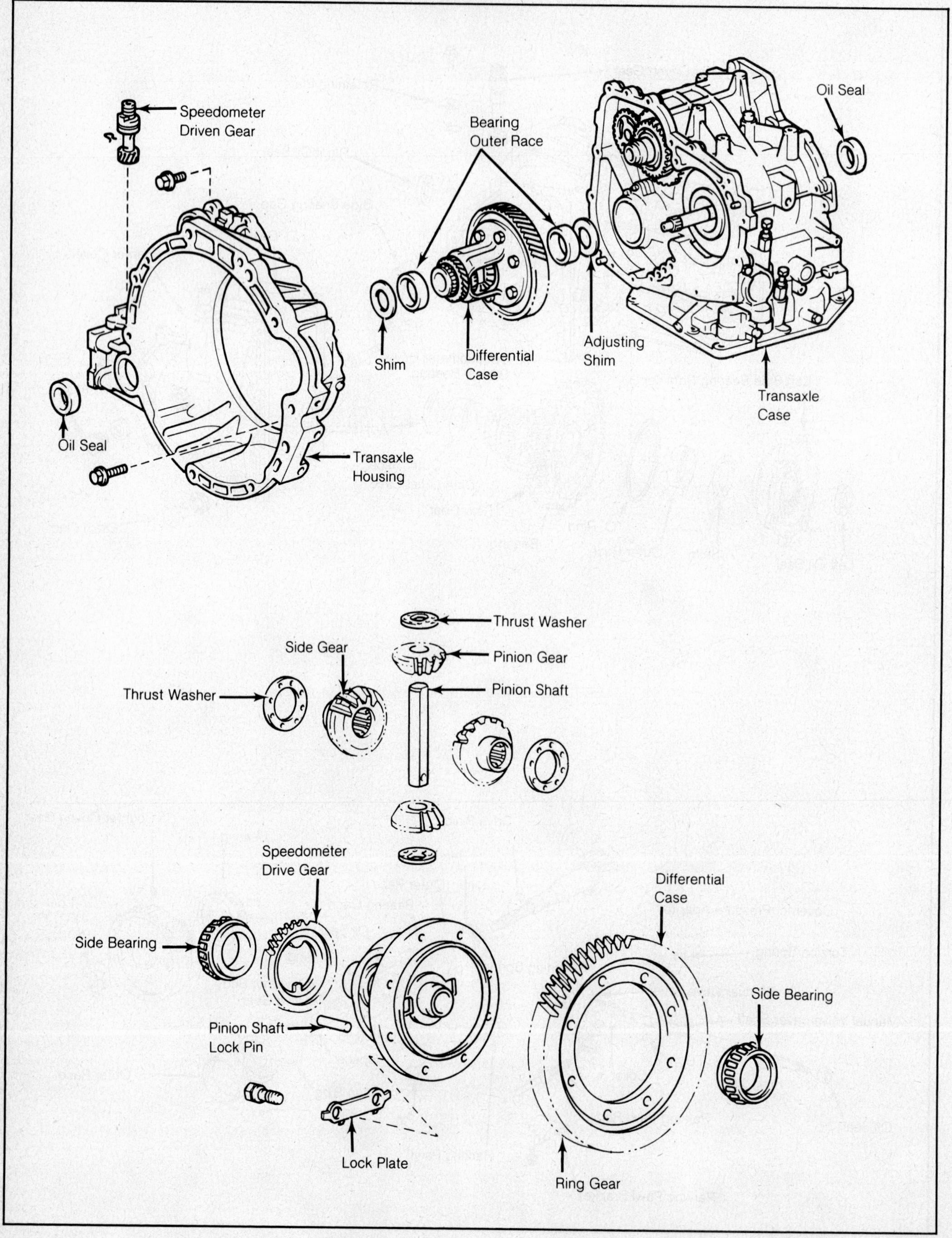

TOYOTA A-130L, A-131L & A-240L TRANSAXLE (Cont.)

7) Using an INCH lbs. torque wrench, measure drive pinion preload. Starting preload should be 8.7-13.9 INCH lbs. (1.0-1.6 N.m) for a new bearing and 4.3-6.9 INCH lbs. (.5-.8 N.m) for a used bearing. If preload is greater than specified, replace bearing spacer and repeat preload procedure.

8) If preload is less than specified, retighten lock nut 9 ft. lbs. (13 N.m) at a time until specified preload is obtained. If maximum torque of 213 ft. lbs. (289 N.m) is exceeded while retightening nut, replace bearing spacer and repeat procedure. DO NOT back off nut to reduce preload.

TRANSAXLE REASSEMBLY

A-130L & A-131L Models

1) Place parking pawl and manual valve lever shaft in transaxle case. Hook spring end on pawl and case. Install pin in case, through spring and pawl. Install parking lock rod.

2) Install parking pawl bracket and tighten bolt. Check operation of pawl to ensure that counter driven gear is locked when manual valve lever is in the "P" range.

3) Install intermediate shaft. Install transaxle rear cover over gasket. Install cover and tighten bolts. Ensure that intermediate shaft turns smoothly. Check intermediate shaft end play. End play should be .0193-.594" (.049-1.51 mm).

4) Install 1st and reverse inner flange with flat side facing (oil pump) forward. Install 1 disc, 1 plate, 1 disc, 2 plates, 1 disc, 1 plate, 2 plates, 1 disc, 1 plate, and 1 disc. Install outer flange with flat side toward piston. Install snap ring.

5) Using a feeler gauge, measure clearance between 1st and reverse brake piston and flange. *See Fig. 12*. Clearance should be .0953-.0465" (1.18-2.42 mm) on transaxle used with diesel engine. Clearance should be .0350-.0831" (.89-2.11 mm) on transaxle used with gasoline engine.

6) Apply compressed air to oil passage and check that piston moves. *See Fig. 21*. Coat No. 2 planetary carrier thrust washers with petroleum jelly and install them on carrier. Ensure that thrust washer lugs match openings in carrier.

7) Coat rear ring gear races and bearing with petroleum jelly and install them onto ring gear. Install planetary gear onto ring gear. Ensure that thrust bearing is installed in center of ring gear flange.

8) Align tabs of discs with 1st and reverse brake. Align splines of planetary carrier with tabs of discs and install rear planetary gear into 1st and reverse brake discs.

9) Place No. 2 one-way clutch in case. Install one-way clutch onto inner race while turning the planetary pinion counterclockwise with a screwdriver. Check operation on clutch by turning planetary carrier. The carrier should turn freely clockwise and should lock when turned counterclockwise. Install snap ring.

10) Install 2nd coast brake band guide and 2nd brake drum guide. Install band guide so that its tip touches case. Install 2nd brake flange with flat side toward 2nd brake piston. Install 1 disc, 1 plate, 1 disc, 1 plate, 1 disc, and 1 plate.

11) Install piston return spring assembly. Install each spring over protrusions in case. Align groove of 2nd brake drum with guide and install drum in case. Install snap ring so that end gap is installed in groove. Using 2 hammers, compress piston return springs with handles. Install snap ring into groove.

12) Using a feeler gauge, measure the clearance between 2nd brake piston return spring assembly seat and top of plate. *See Fig. 11*. Clearance should be .0193-.0626" (.49-1.59 mm). Apply compressed air to center oil passage (next to manual valve lever shaft) and ensure that piston moves.

13) Install 2nd brake drum seal in center oil passage until the distance between surface of case (passage) and top of seal is 1.140-1.144" (28.95-29.05 mm).

14) Align tabs of discs in 2nd brake. Align splines of 2nd brake hub and No. 1 one-way clutch with tabs of discs and install hub on 2nd brake discs. Install sun gear and sun gear input drum onto one-way clutch while turning sun gear clockwise.

NOTE: **Place sun gear in center of intermediate shaft to protect bushings from damage.**

15) Coat front ring gear races and bearing with petroleum jelly and install them onto ring gear. Coat race and bearing with petroluem jelly and install them onto carrier. Install front planetary gear onto ring gear. Install front planetary gear assembly onto sun gear.

16) If planetary gear and other parts are installed correctly in case, the bushing on the ring gear flange will be flush with shoulder of intermediate shaft. Coat race with petroluem jelly and install it onto tip of ring gear flange.

17) Install 2nd coast brake band in case. Install pin through oil pump mounting bolt hole. Coat forward (rear) clutch races and bearing with petroleum jelly and install them onto both sides of clutch drum. Align tabs of discs in forward clutch.

18) Install clutch on sun gear. Hold sun gear input drum and rotate input shaft to mesh hub with clutch discs of forward clutch. Align center of input shaft and intermediate shaft, and while pushing on input shaft, rotate it to mesh hub and disc.

19) If tabs of discs are correctly meshed with hub, the protrusion around clutch drum will be flush with tip of input sun gear drum. Coat direct clutch drum thrust washer with petroleum jelly and install it with oil groove facing upward onto drum.

20) Align tabs of discs in direct clutch. Hold input shaft, and install clutch drum through and into 2nd coast brake band. Mesh hub with tabs of direct clutch while turning clutch drum. If tabs of discs are correctly meshed with hub, the end of bushing on direct clutch drum will be flush with thrust bearing on forward clutch.

21) Coat oil pump race with petroleum jelly and install it onto stator shaft. Insert oil pump (without "O" ring) through input shaft, and align bolt holes with case. Hold input shaft and lightly press oil pump body to slide oil seal rings on stator shaft through direct clutch drum. Install and tighten bolts.

NOTE: **Do not push strongly on oil pump or the seal rings will stick to direct clutch drum.**

22) Ensure that input shaft rotates smoothly. Using a dial indicator, measure input shaft end play. End play should be .012-.035" (.3-.9 mm). If end play is incorrect, remove oil pump and install a new oil pump race. Oil pump races are available in thicknesses of .031" (.8 mm) and .055" (1.4 mm).

23) If input shaft end play is correct, remove oil pump. Install "O" ring around pump body. Insert oil pump through input shaft, and align bolt holes with case. Hold input shaft and lightly press oil pump body to slide oil seal rings on stator shaft through direct clutch drum. Install and tighten bolts.

24) Ensure that input shaft rotates smoothly and recheck input shaft end play. Install 2nd coast brake piston (without outer spring) and install snap ring. Firmly push brake apply rod into case. *See Fig. 10*.

25) Measure distance between outer side of snap ring and tip of piston rod. Piston travel must be within .551-.610" (14.0-15.5 mm). If travel is not within specifications, select a longer brake apply rod. Brake apply rods are available in 2.870" (72.9 mm) and 2.811" (71.4 mm) lengths.

26) Remeasure piston travel. If travel is still more than specified, replace 2nd coast brake band with a new one. If travel is correct, remove installed parts from bore. Install outer spring, piston and cover. Compress spring and install snap ring.

27) Apply compressed air to hole and check that piston rod moves. *See Fig. 38*. Install accumulator springs and pistons. Install cover, gasket and bolts. Tighten bolts a little at a time.

Fig. 38: Checking 2nd Coast Brake Band

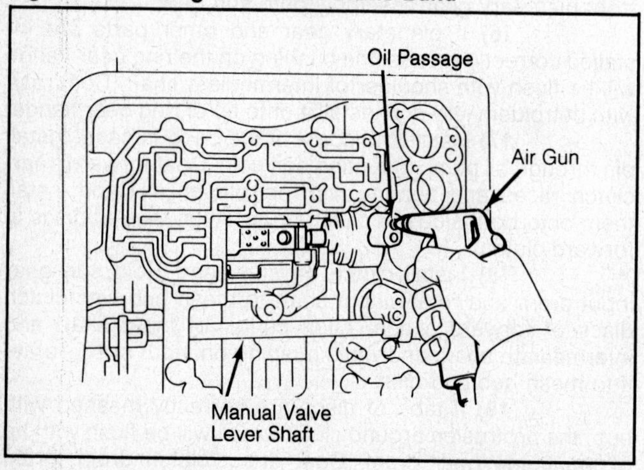

28) Install governor apply gasket and governor line strainer. Push throttle cable through case, being careful not to damage "O" ring. Ensure that cable is fully seated in case.

29) Place valve body in transaxle, and while holding cam down with your hand, slip cable end into slot in cam. Lower valve body into place. Install valve body bolts finger tight, and then tighten. *See Fig. 39*.

30) Align manual valve with pin on manual shaft lever. Lower valve body into place. Install detent spring. Check that manual valve lever is touching center of detent spring roller. Install valve body bolts finger tight, and then tighten. *See Fig. 40*.

31) Using a plastic hammer, install oil tubes. Be careful not to bend or damage tubes. Install tube bracket. Install oil strainer. Install (2) 45 mm bolts on top of strainer, install a 50 mm bolt on strainer tab.

32) Install magnet in oil pan. Ensure that magnet does not interfere with oil tubes. Install oil pan and gasket. Tighten bolts. Install governor body adapter. Install governor body with plate washer.

33) Install thrust washer onto governor body. Install cover over "O" ring. Install cover bracket with 2 bolts. Install throttle cable retaining plate. Install filler tube and

Fig. 39: Valve Body Bolt Installation

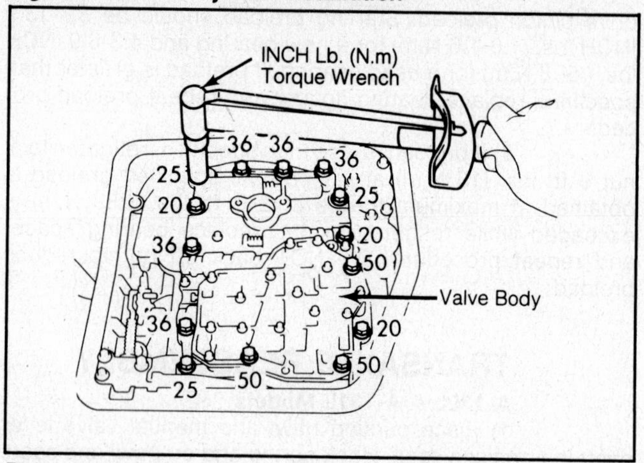

Bolt length (mm) is shown in figure.

Fig. 40: Installing Manual Valve Body Bolts

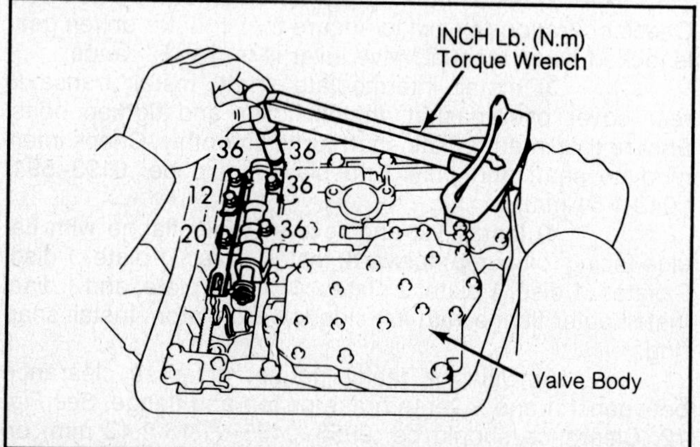

Bolt length (mm) is shown in figure.

dipstick. Install seal (lip facing inward) and neutral safety switch. Tighten nut and secure with lock washer. Install shift handle.

34) Connect an ohmmeter between neutral switch terminals. Shift lever into "N" position. Adjust switch so that there is continuity between terminals. Tighten neutral switch bolts. Install oil pipe bracket onto case. Connect pipes to union. Clamp pipes onto braket. Tighten union nuts.

A-240L Models

1) Install bearing into transaxle housing using a press. Install bearing stopper. Install oil tube apply cover, gasket and strainer. Install oil tubes using a plastic hammer. Install oil tube clamps. Press bearing into transaxle housing. Install reduction brake accumulator piston and spring.

2) Install oil gallery cover and gasket. Tighten mounting bolts. Apply Seal Packing (08833-00070) to 3 screws and install screws. Install oil seal rings to transmission case. Install manual shaft, washer and lever. Install retaining spring. Ensure washer is between retaining spring and case. Install pin.

3) Install and stake manual shaft spacer. Install cam guide bracket. Insert parking lock rod into guide bracket. Install parking lock sleeve with raised portion up. Position stopper plate on raised portion of lock sleeve. Install guide sleeve and spring. Install parking lock pawl, pawl shaft and shaft clamp.

4) Install new "O" rings on underdrive brake piston. Coat "O" rings with ATF. Install piston in case with cupped side up. Be careful not to damage "O" rings. Install brake piston return spring. Install 1 plate, 1 disc, 1 plate, 1 disc, 1 plate and 1 disc. Install flange with flat end up.

5) Compress return spring and install snap ring. Ensure snap ring end gap is not aligned with cut-out. Using a feeler gauge, check underdrive brake piston clearance between snap ring and flange. Clearance should be .0421-.0807" (1.07-2.05 mm).

6) Install underdrive clutch assembly. Check operation of underdrive one-way clutch. Check height of clutch assembly from sleeve to inner race. Height should be .681-.717" (17.3-18.2 mm). Install snap ring on sun gear. Install underdrive planetary sun gear to countershaft. Install thrust bearing and race.

7) Install countershaft assembly. Check height of countershaft, measuring distance between tip of countershaft and bolt seat of clutch support. Countershaft height should be 1.508-1.594" (38.3-40.5 mm). Install thrust bearing. Install counter driven gear using hammer and Installer (SST 09223-50010).

8) Install and tighten counter driven gear lock nut to 116 ft. lbs. (157 N.m). Hold counter driven gear with Flange Holder (SST 09330-00020) and adapter. Check countershaft end play. End play should be .0091-.0350" (.23-.89 mm). Stake lock nut. Install snap ring to transmission case.

9) Install intermediate shaft. Apply Sealer (Loctite No. 518) and install transaxle rear cover. Install and tighten 13 bolts to 22 ft. lbs. (29 N.m). Install thrust washer, governor driven gear and 3 oil seals. Check intermediate shaft. Ensure intermediate shaft rotates smoothly.

10) Install 1st and reverse brake in case. Install inner flange with flat end facing out. Install 1 disc, 1 plate, 1 disc, 1 plate, 1 disc, 1 plate, 1 disc, 1 plate and 1 disc. Install outer flange with flat end facing in. Install snap ring in groove. Check 1st and reverse brake clearance. Clearance should be .0350-.0831" (.89-2.11 mm).

11) Check operation of 1st and reverse brake. Apply compressed air into oil hole passage in case. Ensure piston moves. Coat No. 2 planetary carrier thrust washer with petroleum jelly and install on carrier. Ensure lugs fit into grooves in carrier. Coat thrust bearing races and bearing with petroleum jelly. Install races and bearing.

12) Install rear planetary ring gear into case. Install rear planetary gear. Install No. 2 one-way clutch into case with shiny side up. Rotate planetary gear clockwise while installing one-way clutch. Rotate planetary carrier. Carrier should rotate clockwise and lock counterclockwise. Install snap ring into groove.

13) Install 2nd coast brake band guide. Install 2nd brake into case with flat end facing up. Install 1 disc, 1 plate, 1 disc, 1 plate, 1 disc and 1 plate. Install piston return spring assembly. Install each spring over protrusion in case. Install 2nd brake drum into case. Align drum groove with bolt in case.

14) Install snap ring into groove while compressing piston return springs with hammer handles. Check clearance of 2nd brake using a feeler gauge. Clearance should be .0146-.0614" (.37-1.56 mm). Apply compressed air into 2nd brake oil passage in case. Ensure 2nd brake piston moves.

15) Install 2nd brake drum gasket. Drive in new gasket until distance between surface of case and top of gasket is .632-.636" (16.05-16.15 mm). Tap in drum gasket until it makes contact with 2nd brake drum. Install No. 1 one-way clutch and 2nd brake hub. Install sun gear and sun gear input drum. Rotate sun gear clockwise while rotating it into one-way clutch.

16) Coat thrust bearings and races with petroleum jelly and install them onto ring gear and planetary gear. Install front planetary gear, race and bearing, and intermediate shaft oil seal ring. Install front planetary ring gear. If planetary gear and other components are installed correctly in case, end of bushing with ring gear flange will be flush with intermediate shaft.

17) Coat thrust bearing and races with petroleum jelly and install on tip of ring gear flange. Install 2nd coast brake band into case. Install pin through oil pump mounting bolt hole.

18) Install forward clutch in case. Hold sun gear input drum and rotate input shaft to mesh hub with forward clutch discs. Align center of input shaft and intermediate shaft. While pushing on input shaft, rotate it to mesh with hub and disc. Install thrust bearing and races. Coat thrust bearing and races with petroleum jelly before installing.

19) Coat direct clutch drum thrust washer with petroleum jelly and install it with oil groove facing upward onto drum. Install direct clutch into case. Hold input shaft and place direct clutch drum in 2nd coast brake band. If direct clutch is installed correctly, end of bushing with direct clutch drum will be flush with thrust bearing on forward clutch.

20) Install differential. Apply Seal Packing (Loctite No. 518) to transaxle housing. Install transaxle housing. Install mounting bolts in original locations. Tighten mounting bolts to 22 ft. lbs. (29 N.m). Check differential side bearing preload. See DIFFERENTIAL REASSEMBLY in this article.

21) Coat oil pump "O" ring with ATF. Install "O" ring around oil pump body. Place oil pump through input shaft and align oil pump mounting bolt holes with transaxle case. Hold input shaft and lightly press oil pump body to slide oil seal rings on stator shaft through direct clutch drum. Install 6 oil pump mounting bolts and tighten to 18 ft. lbs. (25 N.m).

CAUTION: DO NOT push on oil pump strongly. Oil seal ring will stick to direct clutch drum.

22) Measure input shaft end play. End play should be .008-.035" (.2-.9 mm). If end play is not to specification, install new thrust bearing race as necessary. Thrust bearing race is available in .031" (.8 mm) and .055" (1.4 mm) thicknesses. Ensure input shaft rotates smoothly.

23) Check 2nd coast brake piston stroke. Install brake piston without outer spring in bore. Install snap ring. Push end of piston rod firmly. Measure distance between tip of piston rod and outside of snap ring. Distance should be .551-.610" (14.0-15.5 mm). If stroke is greater than specification, replace piston rod with a longer rod. If stroke is still not to specification, replace brake band.

24) Remove 2nd coast brake piston and outer spring. Place cover in bore. Install snap ring while depressing cover. Apply compressed air into oil hole in case and ensure piston rod moves. Coat accumulator piston "O" rings with ATF and install them onto pistons. Install pistons and springs. Install new gasket and accumulator cover. Install governor apply gasket.

25) Install throttle cable in case. Push cable through case, being careful not to damage "O" ring. Check for full seating. Install solenoid wire in case. Place valve

TOYOTA A-130L, A-131L & A-240L TRANSAXLE (Cont.)

body in transaxle. While holding cam down, slip cable end into slot. Attach connecting rod to manual lever and lower valve body into place.

26) Install 14 bolts into valve body. Ensure bolts are installed in original locations. Tighten bolts to 84 INCH lbs. (10 N.m). Connect solenoid and kickdown switch connector. Install detent spring. Ensure manual valve lever is in contact with center of roller, at tip of detent spring. Install oil tubes using a plastic hammer, being careful not to damage tubes.

27) Install oil strainer. Ensure mounting bolts are installed in original locations. Install magnet in oil pan. Install new gasket, oil pan and drain plug. Install gasket, governor body adapter with 3 bolts and governor body with thrust washer. Install cover over "O" ring. Install cover brackets with 2 bolts.

28) Install throttle cable retaining plate. Install solenoid retainer plate. Install and adjust neutral safety switch. Install manual shift lever. Install 2 oil cooler lines.

Fig. 41: A-240L Transaxle Overdrive Wiring Diagram

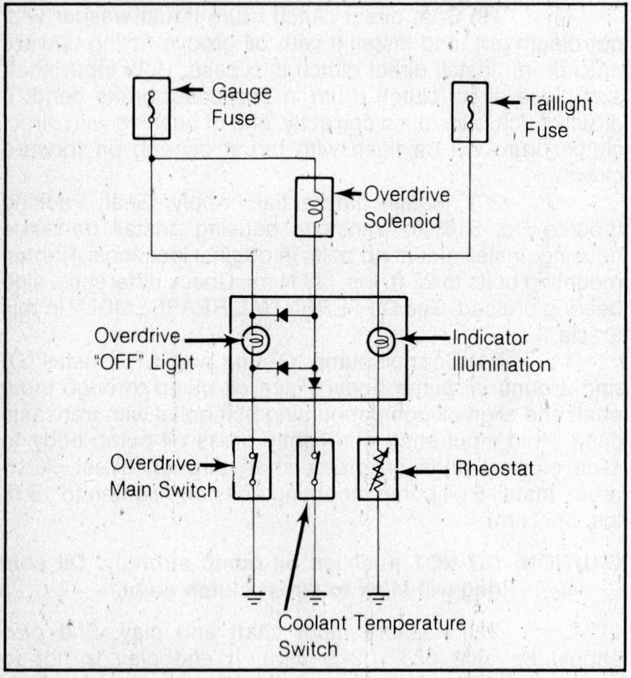

TIGHTENING SPECIFICATIONS

Application	Ft. Lbs (N.m)
Carrier Cover Bolts	18 (25)
Counter Driven Gear Lock Nut	127 (172)
Flex Plate Bolts	61 (83)
Left Bearing Retainer Bolts	14 (19)
Oil Cooler Pipes	25 (34)
Oil Pump Bolts	16 (22)
Right Bearing Cap Bolts	36 (49)
Ring Gear Bolts	71 (96)
Torque Converter Bolts	13 (18)
Transaxle Rear Cover Bolts	18 (25)
	INCH Lbs. (N.m)
Governor Bracket Bolts	108 (12)
Manual Valve Body-to-Transaxle Bolts	84 (10)
Oil Pan Bolts	43 (5.0)
Oil Pump Stator Shaft Bolts	84 (10)
Oil Strainer-to-Valve Body Bolts	84 (10)
Oil Tube Bracket Bolts	84 (10)
Parking Pawl Bracket Bolt	65 (7.0)
Upper Valve Body Cam Bolt	65 (7.0)
Valve Body Bolts	48 (5.4)
Valve Body-to-Transaxle Bolts	84 (10)

TOYOTA MODEL A140E & A140L

Camry

TRANSAXLE IDENTIFICATION

Toyota uses a Vehicle Indentification Number (VIN) for correct application of component parts and assemblies. This number is located at the top left of the instrument panel, and can be seen through the windshield from outside. The VIN is also stamped on the front cowl of the engine compartment and on the driver's door post. For ease when ordering parts, record VIN number.

DESCRIPTION

Transaxle combines a differential, 3-speed automatic transmission and an overdrive assembly. The A140E transaxle is used on gasoline powered Camrys. The A140L transaxle is used on diesel powered Camrys. The primary differences between the 2 transaxles are the main valve body, operating mechanism, and electronic control. The A140E transaxle, also called Electronic Controlled Transaxle (ECT), is different from the oil pressure control transaxle (A140L) in that it is controlled by a microcomputer located behind the glove box. Therefore, troubleshooting procedures are different.

NOTE: **All service which refers to computer and/or electronic controls applies to model A140E transmission only, unless otherwise specified.**

On A140E transaxles, the control module receives input signals from the water temperature sensing switch, throttle position switch and the shift pattern selection switch. The water temperature sensing switch does not allow transaxle to shift into overdrive until coolant has reached a minimum of 122°F (50°C). The throttle position switch is located at the throttle body of the E.F.I system. The shift pattern selection switch is located at the instrument panel and is used for various driving conditions. The module recieves signals from 2 speed sensors: 1 is located at the transaxle (refered to as speed sensor No. 2) and the other at the speedometer (refered to as speed sensor No. 1). Also, the back-up lamp/neutral safety switch signals the module for starting and back-up lamp circuits.

The module controls and sends output signals to the stop and back-up lamps. The module also controls shift control solenoids, located within transaxle.

LUBRICATION & ADJUSTMENTS

See appropriate article in AUTOMATIC TRANSMISSION SERVICING section.

TROUBLE SHOOTING

NOTE: **For A140L transmissions, go to STALL TEST section in this article.**

NO SHIFT

1) Road test vehicle. If slow acceleration from 0 to 37 MPH is not possible, transmission is faulty. If it is possible, check voltage at terminal DG while driving. If voltage rises from 0 to 7 volts in sequence, there is a stuck solenoid.

2) If not, stop vehicle and read voltage at terminal DG. If reading is 0 volts, check for 12 volts between terminals IG and GND (computer power source). If not, repair problem in computer power circuit.

3) If there is 12 volts, measure voltage between terminal IDL of throttle position sensor and GND. With throttle valve closed, reading should be 0 volts. With throttle valve just off idle, reading should be 4 volts. If not, throttle position sensor is bad, improperly adjusted or there is a wiring problem.

4) If readings are okay, check brake signal. Connect voltmeter between computer terminal BR and GND terminals. Reading should be 0 volts with brake pedal released, 12 volts when pedal is depressed. If readings are correct, there is a faulty computer. If voltage at BR remains on, brake switch is shorted or there is a wiring problem.

5) If voltage reading in step **2)** is 4 volts, check speed sensor No. 1. To do so, connect voltmeter between computer terminals SP and GND and check for a 6 volt reading. If 6 volts are obtained, proceed to step **7)**. If 6 volts are not obtained, there is a faulty speed sensor circuit.

6) To check speed sensor No. 1, remove instrument cluster from dash panel. Connect ohmmeter to the output leads of speed sensor. Using a short piece of speedometer cable, rotate speedometer and ensure there are 4 influctions of ohmmeter needle per revolution. If not, sensor is faulty.

7) To check speed sensor No. 2, connect voltmeter between computer terminals SP and GND. Check for a 3 volt reading. If 3 volts are not obtained, speed sensor circuit is faulty.

8) If voltage reading in step **2)** is 8 volts, check solenoid. To do so, disconnect computer connector and using an ohmmeter, check for 11 to 15 ohms of resistance between terminals S_1, S_2, S_3 and GND. If readings are correct, there is a faulty ECT computer. If not, there are faulty solenoids or problems in the wiring harness.

9) If any readings other than 0, 4 or 8 volts were obtained in step **2)**, check to see if voltage at terminal DG varies with changes in throttle opening. If not, check throttle position sensor. If it is okay, there is a faulty ECT computer. If it is bad, replacement is necessary.

10) If voltage does change after sensor replacement, check voltage between computer terminals L and GND. Shift transmission into "L" range. Voltage in "L" range should read 9 to 16 volts. Now shift transmission into "S" and "D" ranges. Voltage should be 0 to 2 volts.

11) If not, there is a faulty neutral safety switch or "L" terminal circuit is open. Check wiring. If readings in step **10)** are okay, pull out ECT computer connector and road test. Ensure when transmission is shifted into "D" range that OD is obtained and when transmission is shifted into "S" range that 3rd gear is obtained. And, when transmission is shifted to "L" range that it holds 1st gear only.

12) If transmission operates properly, there is a faulty computer. If not, there are problems within the transmission.

Automatic Transmissions

TOYOTA MODEL A140E & A140L (Cont.)

SHIFT POINTS TOO HIGH OR LOW

1) Bring engine coolant temperature and transmission fluid to normal operating temperatures. Connect voltmeter to terminal DG and perform road test. Confirm terminal voltage rises in sequence while accelerating from 0 to 37 MPH.

2) Stop vehicle and read terminal DG voltage. Check if voltage rises while throttle valve is opening. If not and/or there is a constant 0 or 8 volt reading, go back to NO SHIFT.

3) If reading is 4 volts, check speed sensor No. 2. To do so, check if it is okay when circuit between computer terminals SP_2 and GND are short circuited. If so, there is a faulty speed sensor No. 2.

4) If reading in step **2)** is correct, check pattern selection switch. To do so, connect a voltmeter between terminal "E" of switch and GND. When NORM or PWR button is actuated, reading should be 1 volt. When ECON button is actuated, a reading of 12 volts should be obtained.

5) Now, connect voltmeter between terminal "P" of switch and GND. When NORM or ECON button is actuated, reading should be 1 volt. When PWR button is actuated, reading should be 12 volts. If switch checks out okay, there is a fault with the ECT computer or transmission. If readings are incorrect, there is a fault within the selector switch. Replacement is necesary.

6) If selector switch checks out okay, check throttle position sensor. To do so, check voltage between terminals "L", "L_1", "L_2", IDL and GND. *See Fig. 3* for correct ranges.

7) If readings are correct, the ECT computer is at fault. If readings are incorrect, there is a fault in the throttle position sensor circuit.

NO UP-SHIFT TO OD

1) Perform a road test while shifting manually with computer connector pulled out. Check for up-shift in "D" range when shifting from "L" to "S" to "D". If there is no shift, there is a fault with transmission.

2) If shifting does occur, check OD cut-out signal. To do so, check for voltage between terminals ODC and GND. If equipped with Nippondenso, reading should be approximately 5 volts when coolant temperature is above 70°C. If equipped with Aisin Seiko, reading should be 12 volts when coolant temperature is above 70°C. (32°F.).

3) If voltage readings are correct in step **2)**, check "S" range signal. To do so, connect a voltmeter between computer terminals "S" and GND. Reading should be between 9 and 16 volts. If readings are correct, there is a fault with ECT computer. If readings are incorrect, check for a faulty "S" terminal at neutral safety switch or wiring harness.

4) If readings in step **2)** are incorrect, check OD cut-out signal. To do so, connect a voltmeter between computer terminals ODC and GND and check for normal voltage readings when cruise control computer connector is disconnected.

5) If readings do return to normal, there is a faulty cruise control computer. If readings still remain unchanged, there is a faulty engine control computer (short circuit in ECT wire harness or E.F.I. water temperature sensor is bad).

NO LOCK-UP (AFTER WARM-UP)

1) Start engine and bring engine and transmission to normal operating temperature. Connect a voltmeter to terminal DG. Perform a road test and check for 7, 5 or 3 volts in lock-up range while driving.

2) If so, there is a fault with transmission such as lock-up mechanism or stuck No. 3 solenoid. If readings are incorrect, stop vehicle and measure voltage at DG terminal.

3) If reading is 8 volts, there is a faulty No. 3 solenoid. If reading is 0 volts, check throttle position sensor and stop light switch. If switches are good, ECT computer is at fault. If switches are bad, replace faulty switch.

4) If reading is step **1)** is 4 volts, check and repair speed sensor. Then repeat procedure outlined in step **1)**.

TESTING

PRELIMINARY CHECK

Troubles occuring with the electronic controlled transaxle (ECT) can be caused by the engine, ECT electrical control or automatic transmission itself. It is necessary to isolate these 3 areas before proceeding with troubleshooting.

- Check transaxle oil level.
- Check throttle cable mark.
- Check shift linkage.
- Check neutral safety switch.
- Check idling speed.
- Check tire inflation pressure.

STALL TEST

A140E & A140L

CAUTION: Perform test at normal operating fluid temperature, 122-176°F. (50-80°C.). DO NOT continuously run this test longer than 5 seconds.

1) The object of test is to check overall performance of transmission and engine by measuring maximum engine speeds at "D" and "R" ranges.

2) Chock front and rear wheels. Hook up engine tachometer. Fully apply parking and service brakes. Start engine. Shift transmission into "D" range. Step all the way down on accelerator pedal.

3) Quickly read and record highest engine RPM at this time. Stall speed should be between 2150-2250 RPM. Perform same test in "R" range.

4) If engine speed is same for both ranges, but lower than specified RPM, engine output may be insufficient or stator one-way clutch is not operating properly.

5) If reading is more than 600 RPM lower than specified, torque converter could be at fault. If stall speed in "D" range is higher than specified, forward clutch may be slipping, one-way clutch No. 2 not operating properly, line pressure too low, or overdrive clutch slipping.

6) If stall speed in "R" range is higher than specified, direct clutch may be slipping, 1st and reverse brake could be slipping, line pressure is too low, or overdrive clutch is slipping.

TOYOTA MODEL A140E & A140L (Cont.)

TIME LAG TEST

A140E & A140L

CAUTION: Perform this test at normal operating fluid temperature 122°-176°F. (50-80°C.). Be sure to allow a 1 minute interval between tests. Make 3 measurements and take the average value.

1) If shift lever is shifted while engine is idling, there will be a time lapse before shock can be felt. This test is used for checking condition of overdrive clutch, forward clutch, direct clutch and 1st and reverse brake.

2) Fully apply parking brake. Start engine and ensure idle speed is correct. Shift tranmission from "N" into "D" range. Using a stop watch, measure time it takes from shifting the lever until shock is felt.

3) Standard measured value is less than 1.2 seconds. In the same manner, measure time lag for "N" to "R". Standard measured value is less than 1.5 seconds.

4) If "N" to "D" time lag is longer than specified, line pressure is too low, forward clutch may be worn, overdrive clutch may be worn, or overdrive clutch is not operating.

5) If "N" to "R" time lag is longer than specified, direct clutch may be worn, 1st and reverse brake may be worn, line pressure is too low, or overdrive clutch may be worn.

HYDRAULIC TEST

A140E & A140L

CAUTION: Perform test at normal operating fluid temperature of 122-176°F. (50-80°C.).

1) Warm up transmission fluid and chock wheels. Jack up vehicle and support it on safety stands. Remove transmission case test plugs and mount hydraulic pressure gauges.

2) Fully apply parking brake. Start engine and shift into "D" range. Step down strongly on brake pedal with left foot while depressing accelerator pedal with right foot.

3) Measure line pressure at engine speeds specified in LINE PRESSURE TABLE. In the same manner, perform test in "R" range.

LINE PRESSURE TABLE

Selector Position	Pressure PSI (kg/cm²)
At Idle	
"D" Range	53-61 (3.7-4.3)
"R" Range	77-102 (5.4-7.2)
At WOT Stall	
"D" Range	131-152 (9.2-10.7)
"R" Range	205-239 (14.4-16.8)

NOTE: If measured pressures are not up to specified values, check throttle cable adjustment and retest.

4) If measured values in all ranges are higher than specified, either regulator valve or throttle valve is defective or throttle cable out of adjustment.

5) If measured values in all ranges are lower than specified, either oil pump, regulator valve, throttle valve, or overdrive clutch is defective or throttle cable is out of adjustment.

6) If pressure is low in "D" range only, forward clutch is defective or "D" range circuit has a fluid leak.

7) If pressure is low in "R" range only, direct clutch is defective, 1st and reverse brake is defective, or "R" range circuit has a fluid leak.

ROAD TEST

CAUTION: Perform test at normal operating fluid temperature of 122-176°F. (50-80°C.).

"D" Range Test In NORM, ECON & PWR Pattern Ranges

1) Shift into "D" range and hold accelerator pedal constant at half and at full throttle positions. Push in 1 of pattern selection buttons and check 1st to 2nd, 2nd to 3rd and 3rd to OD lock-up and up-shift points.

NOTE: There is no overdrive up-shift when coolant temperature is below 122°F (50°C) and speed is under 12 MPH in ECON or 19 MPH in NORM or PWR selection modes. Also, there is no lock-up when vehicle speed is 6 MPH less than the set cruise control speed.

- If there is no 1st to 2nd gear upshift, 1st-2nd shift valve is stuck or No. 2 solenoid is stuck.
- If there is no 2nd to 3rd gear up-shift, 2-3 shift valve is stuck or No. 1 solenoid is stuck.
- If there is no 3rd to OD gear up-shift, (throttle valve opening at 50%), 3-OD shift valve is stuck.
- If all shift points are incorrect, throttle valve, 1-2 shift valve, 2-3 shift valve, 3-OD shift valve are defective.
- If all lock-up points are incorrect, lock-up relay valve is stuck or No. 3 solenoid is stuck.

2) In the same manner, check for shock and slip between 1st to 2nd gear, 2nd to 3rd gear and 3rd to OD gear up-shifts. If shock is harsh, line pressure is too high, accumulator is defective, or check ball is defective.

3) Run vehicle in "D" range lock-up or overdrive gear and check for abnormal noise and vibration.

NOTE: The check for cause of abnormal noise and vibration must be made with extreme care as problem could be due to an unbalanced drive shaft, differential, tire, torque converter or torquing of power train.

4) While running in "D" range, confirm proper kick-down vehicle speed limits for 2nd to 1st, 3rd to 1st, 3rd to 2nd, OD to 3rd and OD to 2nd gears. Also check for abnormal shock and slip at kick-down.

5) While running at about 50 MPH in "D" range OD gear or lock-up, shift to "2" and "L" ranges and check engine braking effect in all ranges. If there is no engine braking in "2" range in 3rd gear, brake is defective. If no braking effect is felt in 2nd gear, brake and coast brake are defective.

6) If there is no engine braking effect in "L" range in 2nd gear, brake and coast brake are defective. If no effect is felt in 1st gear, 1st and reverse brakes are defective.

7) While running in "D" range, release foot from accelerator and shift into "L" range. Check for proper down-shift points between OD to 3rd, 3rd to 2nd and 2nd to 1st gears.

Automatic Transmissions

TOYOTA MODEL A140E & A140L (Cont.)

8) On A140E transmissions, to inspect lock-up mechanism, connect voltmeter to the DG terminal of ECT. Set pattern selection switch in NORM mode. Accelerate vehicle to 50 MPH to where 7, 5 or 3 volts appear on voltmeter. This is lock-up range. Depress accelerator pedal and read tachometer. If there is big jump in engine RPM, there is no lock-up

9) On A140L transmissions, to inspect lock-up mechanism, connect tachometer to 11A terminal, Accelerate vehicle to 43 MPH. Depress accelerator pedal and read tachometer. If there is a big jump in engine RPM, there is no lock-up

"2" Range Test In
NORM, ECON & PWR Patterns
A140E Only

1) Shift into "2" range. Drive with accelerator pedal held constant at half or full throttle and push in 1 of the pattern selection buttons. Ensure that at each throttle position 1st to 2nd and 2nd to 3rd gear lock-up and up-shift take place and are operating properly.

NOTE: **There is no lock-up in PWR pattern mode.**

2) While running in "2" range, 3rd or 2nd gears, release accelerator pedal and check for engine braking effect. Also check for 3rd to 2nd down-shift and abnormal noise at acceleration and deceleration and for shock and up-shift and down-shift.

"2" Range Test
A140L Only

1) Shift to "2" range. Drive with accelerator pedal held constant at half or full throttle. Ensure 1st to 2nd up-shift points at each accelerator opening take place at and are operating properly.*See Fig. 1.*

2) While driving in "2" range, 2nd gear, release accelerator pedal and check engine breaking effect.

Fig. 1: A140L Automatic Shift Graph

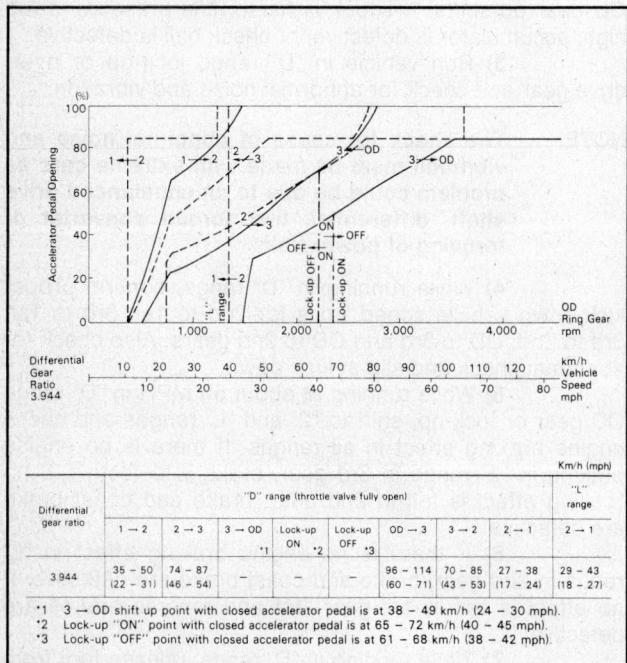

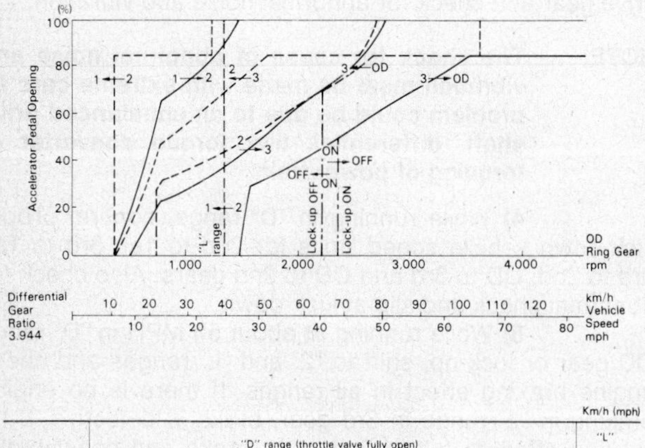

Km/h (mph)

Differential gear ratio	"D" range (throttle valve fully open)								"L" range
	1 → 2	2 → 3	3 → OD *1	Lock-up ON *2	Lock-up OFF *3	OD → 3	3 → 2	2 → 1	2 → 1
3.944	35 - 50 (22 - 31)	74 - 87 (46 - 54)	–	–	–	96 - 114 (60 - 71)	70 - 85 (43 - 53)	27 - 38 (17 - 24)	29 - 43 (18 - 27)

*1 3 → OD shift up point with closed accelerator pedal is at 38 - 49 km/h (24 - 30 mph).
*2 Lock-up "ON" point with closed accelerator pedal is at 65 - 72 km/h (40 - 45 mph).
*3 Lock-up "OFF" point with closed accelerator pedal is at 61 - 68 km/h (38 - 42 mph).

3) Perform kick-down from "2" range. Check possible 2nd to 1st kick-down vehicle speed. Check for abnormal noise and shock at acceleration and deceleration

"L" Range Test

1) On A140 E transmissions, operate vehicle above 50 MPH in "D" or "2" range, release accelerator pedal and shift into "L" range. Ensure that 2nd to 1st gear down-shift occurs at 31 MPH.

2) On both transmissions, operate vehicle in "L" range and ensure there is no up-shift to 2nd gear. Also check engine braking effect and abnormal noise at acceleration and deceleration.

"R" Range Test

Shift into "R" range. Accelerate vehicle from a stop at full throttle and check for slipping.

"P" Range Test

Stop vehicle on a slight grade. Shift transmission into "P". Release parking brake and check for proper parking pawl operation. Vehicle should not move.

A140E SHIFT SPEED SPECIFICATIONS [1]

Application	MPH
"D" Range	
ECON or NORM	
1st to 2nd	33-37
2nd to 3rd	63-70
3rd to OD	94-100
3rd to OD [2]	23-20
OD to 3rd [2]	11-14
OD to 3rd	88-94
3rd to 2nd	60-65
2nd to 1st	28-31
PWR	
1st to 2nd	35-42
2nd to 3rd	68-79
3rd to OD	96-103
3rd to OD [2]	28-31
OD to 3rd [2]	11-14
OD to 3rd	90-96
3rd to 2nd	65-70
2nd to 1st	28-31
"2" Range	
ECON or NORM	
1st to 2nd	33-37
2nd to 3rd	63-70
3rd to 2nd	60-65
2nd to 1st	28-31
PWR	
1st to 2nd	35-42
2nd to 3rd	68-79
3rd to 2nd	62-67
2nd to 1st	28-31
"L" Range	
ECON, NORM or PWR	
2nd to 1st	30-34

[1] – At Wide Open Throttle.
[2] – At Fully Closed Throttle.

TOYOTA MODEL A140E & A140L (Cont.)

A140E LOCK-UP SPEEDS [1]

Application	MPH
"D" Range	
NORM	
Lock-up ON in OD	40-44
Lock-up OFF in OD	39-42
ECON	
Lock-up ON in OD	35-39
Lock-up OFF in OD	34-37
PWR	
Lock-up ON in OD	43-47
Lock-up Off in OD	42-45
"2" Range	
NORM	
Lock-up ON in 3rd	52-55
Lock-up OFF in 3rd	47-52
ECON	
Lock-up ON in 3rd	32-35
Lock-up OFF in 3rd	30-33
PWR	[2]
"L" Range	[3]

1 – Throttle at 50%.
2 – There is no lock-up in PWR pattern.
3 – There is no lock-up in "L" range.

A140E NORMAL SOLENOID OPERATING PATTERN

Application	ON or OFF
Solenoid No. 1	
"D" Range	
1st	ON
2nd	ON
3rd	OFF
OD	OFF
"2" Range	
1st	ON
2nd	ON
3rd	OFF
"L" Range	
1st	ON
2nd	ON
Solenoid No. 2	
"D" Range	
1st	OFF
2nd	ON
3rd	ON
OD	OFF
"2" Range	
1st	OFF
2nd	ON
3rd	ON
"L" Range	
1st	OFF
2nd	ON

A140E ELECTRONIC CONTROL CIRCUIT

Precautions When Checking Voltage at Terminal DG

1) Diagnostic indications will be cancelled out if ignition switch is turned off.

2) All solenoid valves and speed sensor systems have the capability to retain malfunctions in memory and these will be retained in memory until ignition switch is turned off, even after problem has been repaired.

3) Malfunctions of throttle position sensor or stop lamp switch are not retained in memory. These should be checked by rotating throttle valve or by depressing brake pedal.

4) A low battery could result in a misdiagnosis. Always check battery voltage first.

5) Use a circuit tester with an internal impedance of 10,000 ohms or more.

Diagnosis

1) Troubles are diagnosed by voltage readings at terminal DG while driving vehicle and when vehicle is stopped.

2) If transmission indicates a NO SHIFT condition, and reading at terminal DG is a fixed 8 volts, check solenoids and ECT computer. If reading is 4 volts, check throttle position sensor. If reading is 0 volts, check throttle position sensor, ECT computer or brake signal. If reading is normal, check transmission, solenoids, neutral safety switch or pattern selection switch.

3) If transmission indicates an erratic shifting pattern, and reading at terminal DG is 8 volts, check solenoids and ECT computer. If reading is 4 volts, check speed sensors. If reading is 0 volts, check throttle position sensor, ECT computer or brake signal. If reading is normal, check transmission, throttle position sensor, ECT computer or pattern selection switch.

4) If transmission indicates no shift to overdrive (OD), check engine E.F.I. computer, cruise control computer and neutral safety switch.

5) If transmission fails to lock-up and voltage reading at terminal DG is 8 volts, check ECT computer. If reading is 4 volts, check speed sensor. If reading is 0 volts, check throttle position sensor, ECT computer and brake signal. If reading is normal, check transmission and ECT computer.

NOTE: With a 4 volt reading, even if speed sensor No. 2, located at transaxle, is malfunctioning, the ECT system is capable of functioning with speed sensor No. 1, located at speedometer. Be sure to inspect No. 2 sensor and recheck voltage at terminal DG.

NOTE: An 8 volt reading indicates a short or open circuit or continuity to solenoid. A separate check should be made for a sticking solenoid or presence of foreign material.

Testing

1) Warm up engine to normal operating temperature, 176°F. (80°C.). Ensure transmission fluid temperature is 122-140°F. (50-60°C.). Connect a voltmeter to terminal DG located in engine compartment.

DG TERMINAL VOLTAGE

Gear Position	Voltage
1st	0
2nd	2
2nd Lock-up	3
3rd	4
3rd Lock-up	5
OD	6
OD Lock-up	7

TOYOTA MODEL A140E & A140L (Cont.)

Fig. 2: Electronic Control Circuit

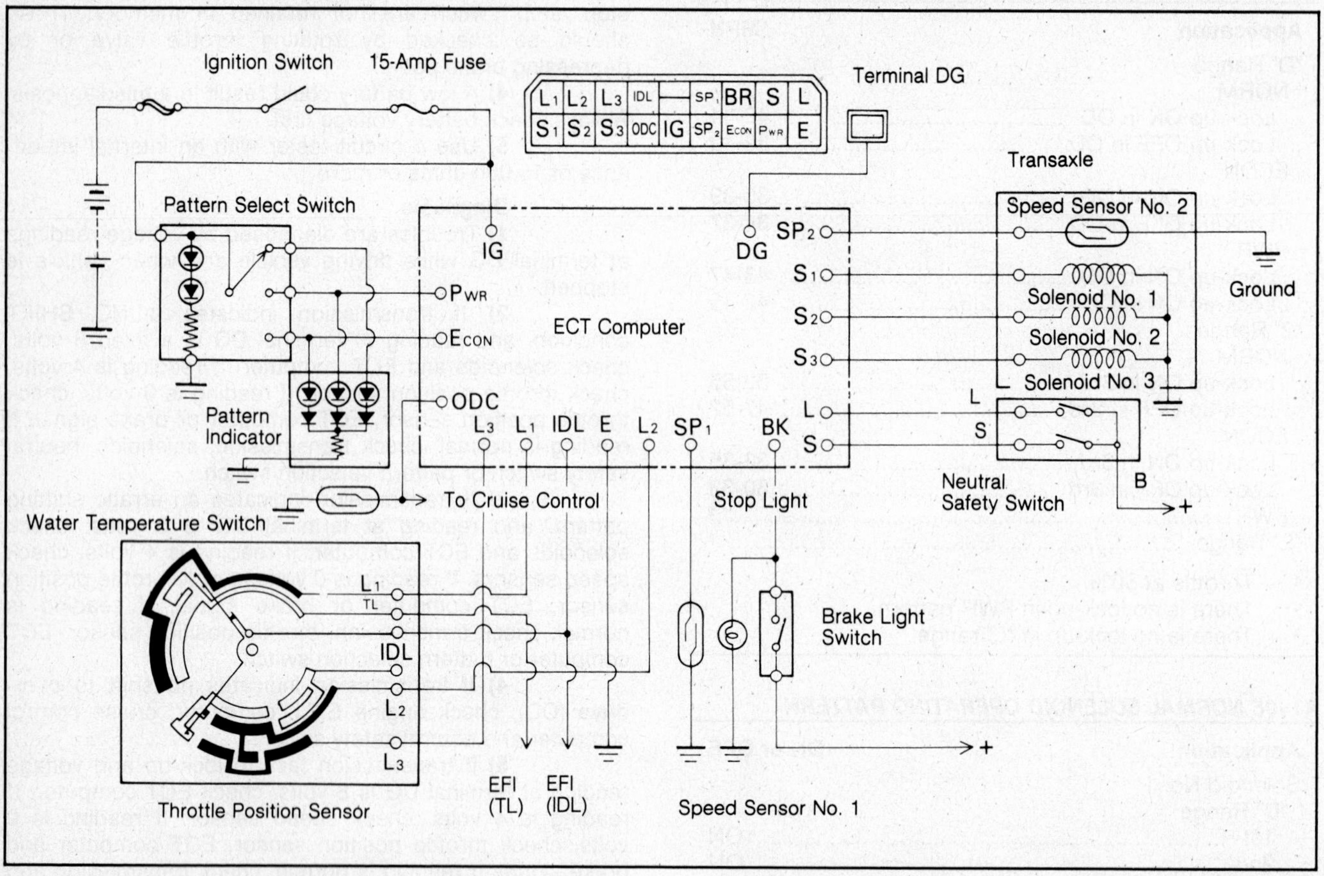

2) Place pattern selection switch in NORM position and shift transmission to "D". During road test, ensure that voltage is correct as indicated in DG TERMINAL VOLTAGE table. Check voltage for each up-shift position.

3) If voltage rises from 0 to 7 volts while shifting from 1st to OD lock-up, control system is okay. If there is a constant 4 volt reading, speed sensor No. 2 is faulty. If there is a constant 8 volt reading, solenoid is defective.

4) Stop vehicle. With engine at idle, check voltage at terminal DG. DO NOT turn ignition off as this will clear trouble memory. If voltage reading is 0, system is normal or there is a defective brake signal. If reading is 4 volts, there is a faulty speed sensor No. 2. If reading is 8 volts, there is a faulty solenoid.

5) To inspect throttle position sensor system, turn off engine and while depressing accelerator pedal ensure voltage at terminal DG rises as pedal is depressed.

6) To check brake signal system, depress accelerator pedal to where 8 volts is indicated at terminal DG. Then, depress brake pedal and check voltage at terminal DG. When brake pedal is depressed, voltage reading should be 0. When released, reading should be 8 volts.

COMPUTER CONNECTOR VOLTAGE

Remove glove box and right-hand speaker to gain access to ECT computer. Turn ignition switch on and measure voltage as follows:

- Connect voltmeter between terminals L_1 and GND. With throttle valve fully closed, voltage should be 5 volts (Nippondenso) or 12 volts (Aisin Seiko). With throttle valve fully closed and then moved to fully open position, voltage should read 5 to 0 volts (Nippondenso) or 12 to 0 volts (Aisin Seiko). With throttle valve open, voltage should read 0 for both models.
- Connect voltmeter between terminals L_2 and GND. With throttle valve fully closed voltage should read 5 volts (Nippondenso) or 12 volts (Aisin Seiko). With throttle valve fully closed and then moved to fully open position, voltage should read 5 to 0 to 5 volts (Nippondenso) or 12 to 0 to 12 volts (Aisin Seiko). With throttle valve open, voltage should read 5 volts (Nippondenso) or 12 volts (Aisin Seiko).
- Connect voltmeter between terminals L_3 and GND. With throttle valve closed, voltage reading should be 5 volts (Nippondenso) or 12 volts (Aisin Seiko). With throttle valve fully closed and then moved to fully open position, voltage should read 5 to 0 to 5 to 0 to 5 volts (Nippondenso) or 12 to 0 to 12 to 0 to 12 volts (Aisin Seiko). With throttle valve open, voltage should read 5 volts (Nippondenso) or 12 volts (Aisin Seiko).
- Connect voltmeter between terminals IDL and GND. With throttle valve closed, voltage should read 0 volts for both units. With throttle valve opened above idle, voltage reading should be 4 volts for both units.
- Connect a voltmeter between terminals SP_1 and GND. With engine off, voltage should read 12 or 0 volts for both units. With engine running, voltage should read 6 volts for both units.

TOYOTA MODEL A140E & A140L (Cont.)

- Connect voltmeter between terminals BR and GND. When brake pedal is depressed, voltage reading should be 12 volts for both units. When brake pedal is released, voltage reading should be 0 volts for both units.
- Connect voltmeter between terminals S and GND. With transmission shifter positioned in "2", voltage reading should be 9 to 16 volts for both units. In any other range, reading should be 0 to 2 volts.
- Connect voltmeter between terminals L and GND. With transmission shifter positioned in "L" range, voltage should read 9 to 16 volts for both units. In any other range, reading should be 0 to 2 volts.
- Connect voltmeter between terminals S_1 and GND. Voltage reading for both units should be 12 volts.
- Connect voltmeter between terminals S_2 , S_3 and GND. Voltage readings should be 0 volts for both units.
- Connect voltmeter between terminals ODC and GND. Voltage reading should be 12 volts for both units.
- Connect voltmeter between terminals IG and GND. When coolant temperature is below 158°F. (70°C.), voltage reading should be 0 for both units. When coolant temperature is above 158°F. (70°C.), reading should be 5 volts (Nippondenso) and 12 volts (Aisin Seiko).
- Connect voltmeter between terminals SP_2 and GND. With engine off, voltage reading should be 5 or 0 volts (Nippondenso) or 12 or 0 volts (Aisin Seiko). When engine is running, reading should be 4 volts (Nippondenso) or 10 volts (Aisin Seiko).
- Connect voltmeter between terminals PWR and GND. With PWR pattern button actuated, voltage should read 12 volts for both units. With any other pattern button actuated, reading should be 1 volt for both units.
- Connect voltmeter between terminals ECON and GND. With ECON pattern button actuated, voltage reading should be 12 volts for both units. With any other pattern button actuated, reading should be 1 volt for both units.

ELECTRIC COMPONENT TESTING

Solenoid

1) Disconnect wire harness from ECT computer. Using an ohmmeter, measure resistance between S_1, S_2, S_3 and GND. Standard resistance value is 11 to 15 ohms. *See Fig. 2*.

2) Apply battery voltage to solenoid. Solenoid should be heard operating at this time. If there is foreign material in solenoid valve, there will be no fluid control even with solenoid operation.

Neutral Safety Switch

Shift transmission into "D" or "2" range. Disconnect neutral safety switch connector. Using an ohmmeter, ensure continuity between L, S and ground. *See Fig. 3*.

Fig. 3: Neutral Safety Switch Connector

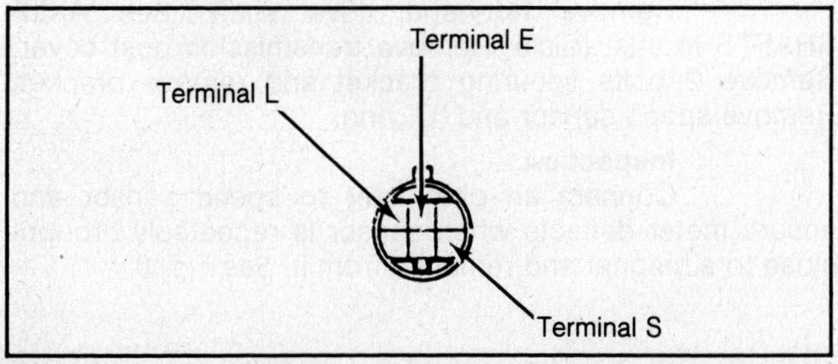

Throttle Position Sensor

Disconnect wire harness connector from throttle position sensor and remove rubber boot. Using an ohmmeter, ensure continuity between terminal E_1 and all other terminals. *See Fig. 4*.

NOTE: While slowly opening throttle valve, ensure continuity between E_1 and all other terminals.

Fig. 4: Throttle Position Sensor Switch Connector

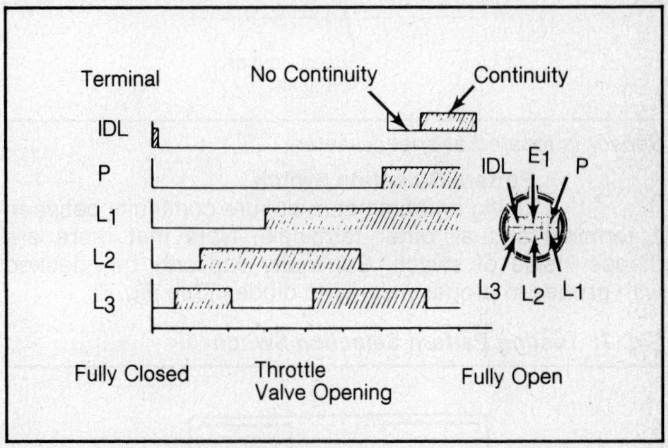

Brake Signal

Ensure brake lights come on when brake pedal is depressed.

Speed Sensor No. 2
(At Transaxle)

Jack up a front wheel on 1 side. Connect an ohmmeter between sensor terminals. Spin wheel and ensure meter needle deflects from 0 ohms to infinity. *See Fig. 5*.

Fig. 5: Testing Speed Sensor No. 2

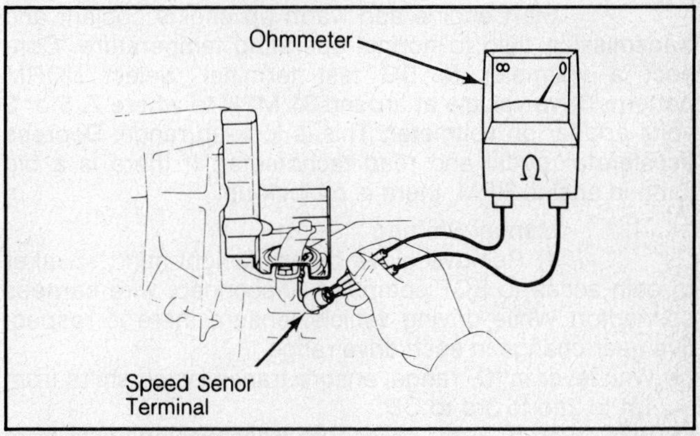

Sensor is located at transaxle.

Speed Sensor No. 1
(In Speedometer)

Remove instrument cluster. Connect an ohmmeter between sensor lead terminals. Revolve speedometer shaft and ensure meter needle deflects 4 times per revolution from 0 ohm to infinity. *See Fig. 6*.

Automatic Transmissions

TOYOTA MODEL A140E & A140L (Cont.)

Fig. 6: Testing Speed Sensor No. 1

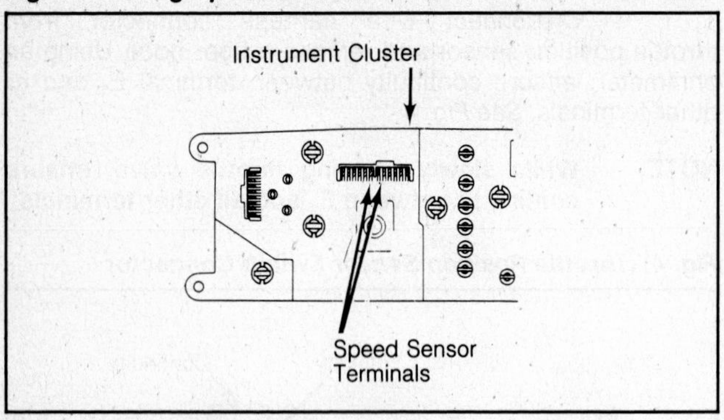

Sensor is located at speedometer.

Pattern Selection Switch

Using an ohmmeter, ensure continuity between 1 terminal and all other terminals. Note that there are diodes inside of switch. Continuity can only be checked with probes in proper polarity to diodes. *See Fig. 7.*

Fig. 7: Testing Pattern Selection Switch

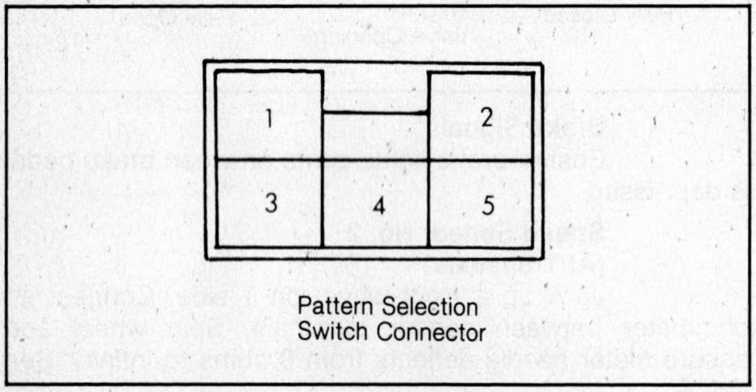

Switch is located in passenger compartment.

Lock-up Mechanism

Start engine and warm up engine coolant and transmission fluid to normal operating temperature. Connect a voltmeter to DG test terminal. Select NORM pattern. Drive vehicle at around 31 MPH to where 7, 5 or 3 volts appear on voltmeter. This is lock-up range. Depress accelerator pedal and read tachometer. If there is a big jump in engine RPM, there is no lock-up.

Manual Shifting

1) Remove glove box and right-hand speaker to gain acces to ECT computer. Disconnect wire harness connector. While driving vehicle, ensure there is respective gear change in each drive range.

- With lever in "D" range, ensure transmission shifts from 1st to 2nd to 3rd to OD.
- With lever in "2" range, ensure transmission shifts from 1st to 2nd to 3rd.
- With lever in "L" range, ensure transmission does not shift into any other gear.
- With lever in "R" range, ensure vehicle moves in reverse.
- With lever in "N" range, ensure vehicle does not move forward or backward.
- With lever in "P" range, ensure parking pawl locks.

2) If any range does not operated properly, check transmission.

A140L ELECTRIC CONTROL CIRCUIT

INSPECTION

NOTE: The following is the only electrical diagnosis required for the A140L transmission.

1) Disconnect solenoid connector and apply voltage between terminals 1 and 2. Confirm solenoid operation sound is heard. Using ohmmeter, measure resistance between terminals 1 and 2. Resistance should be approx. 17 ohms. Reconnect selenoid connector. *See Fig. 8.*

Fig. 8: A140L Electric Circut

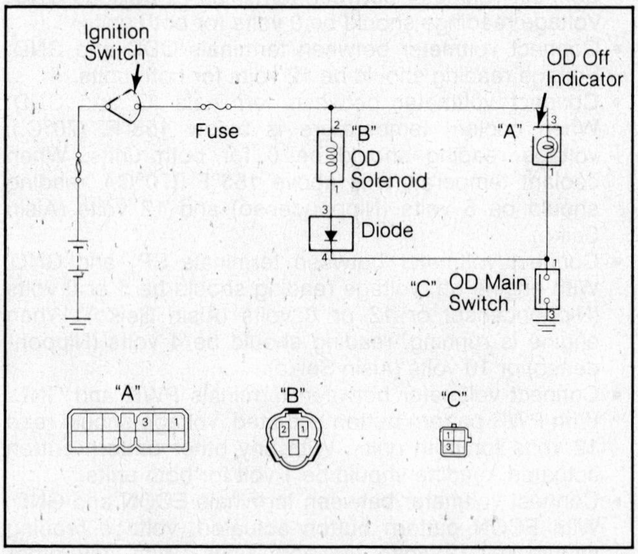

2) Turn ignition switch to ON position. Confirm operation sounds of solenoid can be heard when OD switch is turned off and on. Turn ignition switch off. Remove console box. Using ohmmeter, measure resistance between terminals 1 and 3 (on left side of box). With switch on, needle should move to infinity. With switch off, needle should not move.

3) Turn ignition switch to ON position. Turn OD main switch off. Check that OD OFF indicator lights.

SERVICE (IN VEHICLE)

DRIVE AXLE SHAFTS

See appropriate DRIVE AXLE SHAFT article in IMPORT AXLE SHAFTS, OVERDRIVES & TRANSFER CASES section.

A140E SPEED SENSOR

Removal

Remove left-hand drive shaft. See AXLE SHAFTS in this article. Remove transmission dust cover. Remove 2 bolts securing bracket and remove bracket. Remove speed sensor and "O" ring.

Inspection

Connect an ohmmeter to speed sensor and ensure meter deflects when sensor is repeatedly brought close to a magnet and removed from it. *See Fig. 9.*

TOYOTA MODEL A140E & A140L (Cont.)

Fig. 9: Testing Speed Sensor

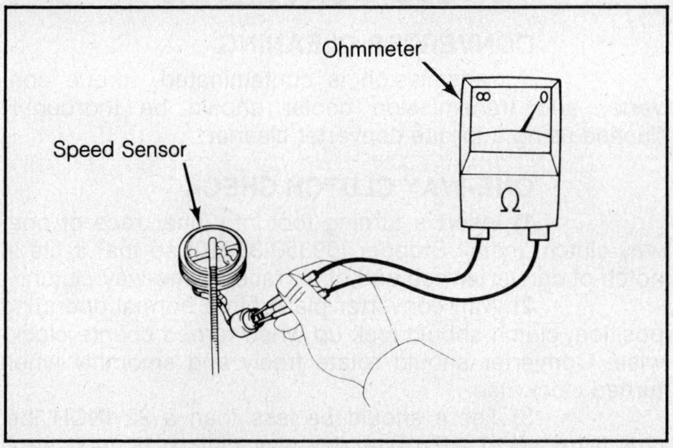

Installation

Reverse removal procedure. Replace "O" ring.

THROTTLE CABLE

Removal

1) Disconnect throttle cable housing from bracket at engine. Disconnect from throttle valve linkage. Remove clip and disconnect transmission control cable from manual shift lever.

2) Remove manual shift lever and neutral safety switch. Remove valve body. See VALVE BODY in this article. Remove bolt and retaining plate. Pull throttle cable out of transmission case.

Installation

1) To install, reverse removal procedure. New cables DO NOT have a cable stopper installed. To make adjustment possible, bend cable about 7.78" (200 mm) in radius, pull inner cable lightly until a slight resistance is felt, and hold it.

Fig. 10: Marking Replacement Throttle Cable

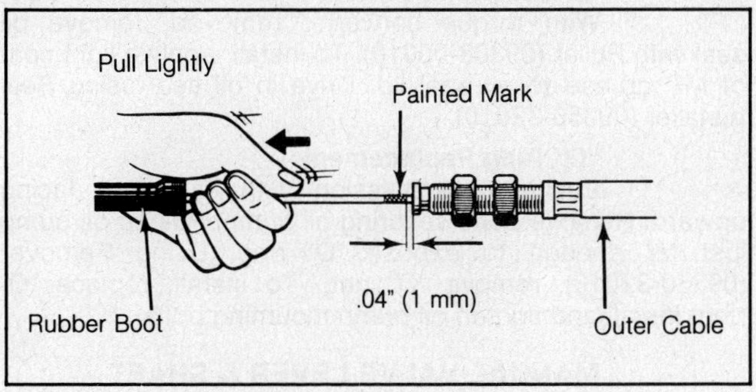

Fig. 11: Adjusting Neutral Safety Switch

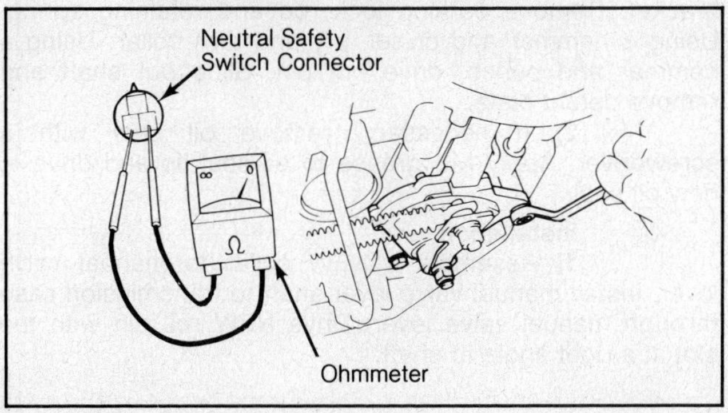

2) Pull rubber dust boot from end of cable sheathing. Paint a mark about .16" (4 mm) in width at .04" (1 mm) from end of cable sheathing. Connect cable and be sure to make necesary adjustments. *See Fig. 10*.

3) Install neutral saftey switch and manual shift lever. Adjust neutral safety switch. *See Fig. 11*. Connect transmission control cable and adjust transmission control cable. See appropriate article in AUTOMATIC TRANSMISSION SERVICING. Road test vehicle.

VALVE BODY ASSEMBLY

Removal

NOTE: Note bolt length and position during disassembly of valve body for ease in reassembly.

1) Clean exterior of transmission. Remove oil pan plug and drain transmission. Remove oil pan and gasket. Remove 2 bolts and apply tube bracket. Remove 3 bolts and oil filter.

2) Disconnect solenoid wiring lead connectors. Remove oil tubes. Remove manual detent spring. Remove manual valve and valve body. Remove 12 bolts (A140E), or 14 bolts (A140L). Disconnect throttle cable from cam and remove valve body. Remove governor apply gasket.

Installation

1) While holding cam down, slip cable end into slot. DO NOT tangle kick-down switch wire. Install valve body and tighten bolts to specifications. Connect solenoid lead wires. *See Fig. 12*.

Fig. 12: Valve Body Bolt Length & Location

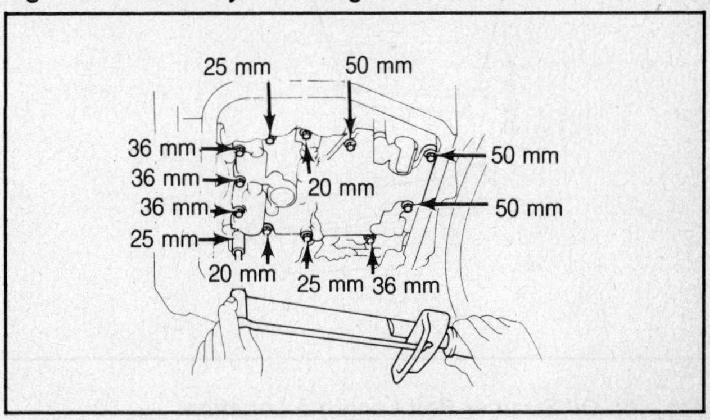

2) Align manual valve with pin on manual shift lever. Place lower valve body into position. Finger tighten 4 bolts first, then tighten to specifications. *See Fig. 13*.

Fig. 13: Manual Valve Body Bolt Length & Location

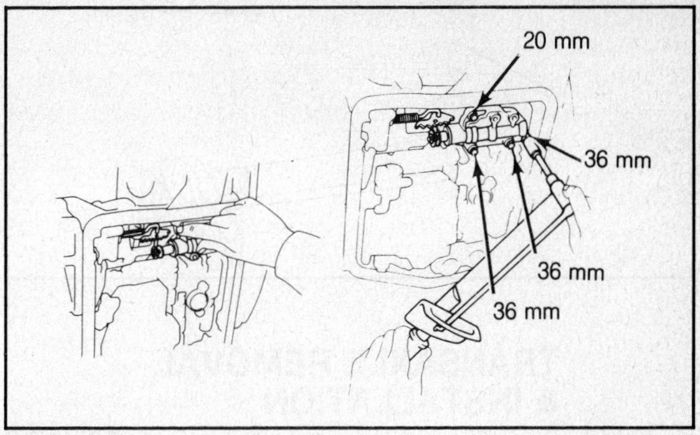

TOYOTA MODEL A140E & A140L (Cont.)

3) Install detent spring. *See Fig. 14*. Ensure manual valve lever is in contact with center of roller at tip of detent spring. Being careful not to bend or damage, tap oil tubes into proper positions. Install apply tube bracket. *See Fig. 15*.

Fig. 14: Detent Spring Bolt Length & Location

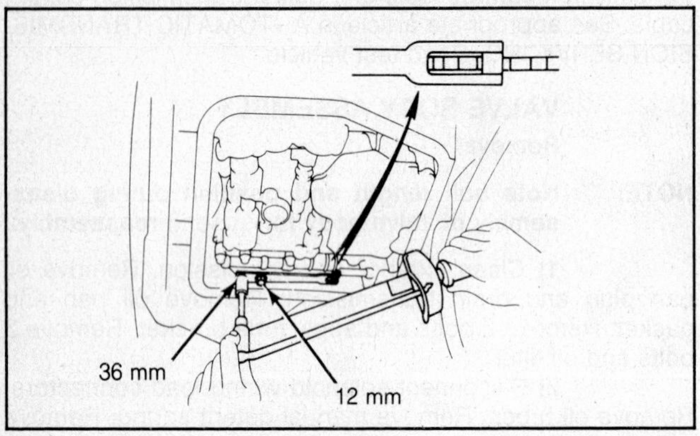

4) Install oil strainer. *See Fig. 16*. Install magnet in oil pan making sure magnet does not interfere with oil tubes. Install oil pan and tighten bolts to specifications. Install drain plug with new washer gasket. Fill transmission with oil.

Fig. 15: Apply Tube Bracket Bolt Length & Location

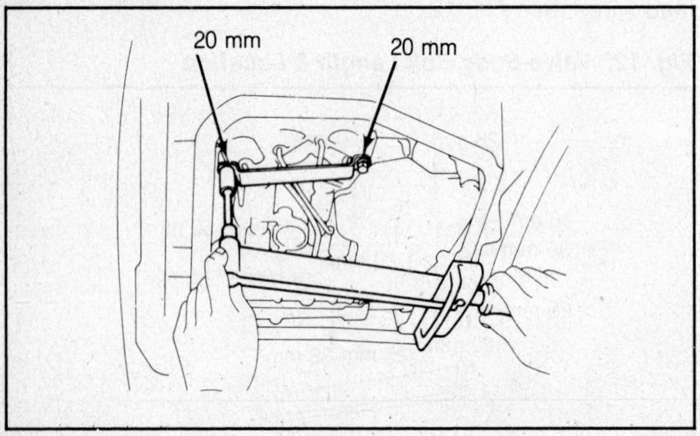

Fig. 16: Oil Strainer Bolt Length & Location

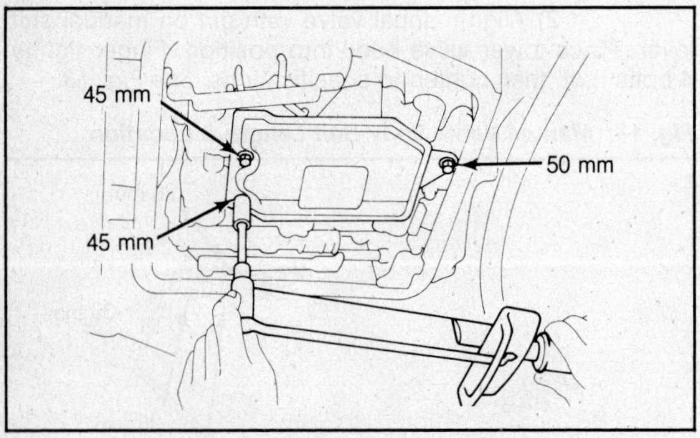

TRANSAXLE REMOVAL & INSTALLATION

See the appropriate article in AUTOMATIC TRANSMISSION REMOVAL section

TORQUE CONVERTER

CONVERTER CLEANING

If transmission is contaminated, torque converter and transmission cooler should be thoroughly flushed using a torque converter cleaner.

ONE-WAY CLUTCH CHECK

1) Insert a turning tool into inner race of one-way clutch. Install Stopper (09350-32010) so that it fits in notch of converter hub and other race of one-way clutch.

2) With converter placed in a normal operating position, clutch should lock up when turned counterclockwise. Converter should rotate freely and smoothly when turned clockwise.

3) There should be less than a 22 INCH lbs. (2.5 N.m) effort to rotate one-way clutch. If necessary, clean converter and retest clutch. Replace converter if clutch fails test.

CONVERTER SLEEVE RUNOUT CHECK

1) Temporarily mount torque converter to drive plate. Set up a dial indicator resting needle onto converter sleeve. Rotate converter. If runout exceeds .0118" (.30 mm), ensure converter is properly mounted to drive plate.

2) If converter is properly mounted and runout is still excessive, replace torque converter. Mark position of converter to ensure correct installation. Remove converter.

DRIVE PLATE RUNOUT CHECK

Set up a dial indicator. Measure drive plate runout. If runout exceeds .0079" (.20 mm), or if ring gear is damaged, replace drive plate. If installing a new drive plate, note position of spacers and tighten bolts.

OIL PUMP

Oil Seal Replacement

With torque converter removed, remove oil seal with Puller (09308-00010). To install, apply a light coat of MP grease to oil seal lip. Drive in oil seal using Seal Installer (09350-32010).

"O" Ring Replacement

Position transmission with oil pump facing upward. Remove bolts securing oil pump. Pull up oil pump just far enough to expose "O" ring. Using Remover (09350-32010), remove "O" ring. To install, replace "O" ring. Install and tighten oil pump mounting bolts.

MANUAL VALVE LEVER & SHAFT

Removal

1) Remove valve body. Remove parking pawl bracket. Remove parking lock rod and retaining spring. Using a hammer and chisel, pry and turn collar. Using a hammer and punch, drive out pin. Slide out shaft and remove detent plate.

2) If necessary, remove oil seal with a screwdriver. Apply MP grease to oil seal lip and drive in new oil seal.

Installation

1) Assemble a NEW collar to manual valve lever. Install manual valve lever shaft to transmission case through manual valve lever. Drive NEW roll pin with the slot at a right angle to shaft.

TOYOTA MODEL A140E & A140L (Cont.)

2) Match collar hole to lever calking hollow and press the collar to lever. Install retaining ring spring. Ensure that lever moves smoothly. Install parking lock rod and lock pawl bracket. Install valve body.

CLEANING, PARTS ARRANGEMENT & ASSEMBLY

CLEANING

All disassembled parts should be washed clean and fluid passages and holes blown through with compressed air to ensure they are not plugged. Recommended ATF (Dexron II) should be used for cleaning. When using compressed air to dry parts, keep face away to avoid spraying solvent in your face.

PARTS ARRANGEMENT

After cleaning, parts should be arranged in proper order to allow performing inspection, repairs, and reassembly with efficiency. New brakes and clutches that are to be used for replacement MUST be soaked in ATF for at least 2 hours before assembly. When valve body is disassembled, be sure to keep each valve together with corresponding spring.

ASSEMBLY

1) All oil seal rings, clutch discs, clutch plates, rotating parts, and sliding surfaces should be coated with ATF prior to reassembly. All gaskets and rubber "O" rings should be replaced. Make sure that ends of snap rings are not aligned with 1 of the cut-outs and are installed in the groove correctly.

2) If a worn bushing is to be replaced, replacement must be made with the subassembly containing that bushing. Check thrust bearings and races for wear or damage. Replace if necessary.

3) All gaskets and rubber "O" rings should be replaced. Make sure that ends of a snap ring are not aligned with cut-outs and are installed in groove correctly. Use petroleum jelly to hold parts in place.

TRANSMISSION DISASSEMBLY

1) Remove oil cooling tubes. Remove shift lever and neutral safety switch. Remove 2 bolts and remove solenoid. Remove oil filler tube. Remove throttle cable retaining plate and solenoid wire retaining bolt.

2) Remove 2 bolts and cover bracket. Remove speed sensor and "O" ring. Remove 15 bolts and oil pan by lifting transmission case. DO NOT turn transmission over as this will contaminate valve body with foreign material.

3) Place transmission on wooden blocks to prevent damage to pipe bracket. Examine particles found in oil pan. If particles are magnetic (steel), this indicates bearing, gear and clutch plate wear. If particles are non-magnetic (brass), this indicates bushing wear.

4) Turn transmission over and remove tube bracket, oil strainer and solenoid connectors. Using a screwdriver, remove 4 oil tubes. Remove manual detent spring. Remove manual valve and valve body.

5) Remove bolts, disconnect throttle cable from cam and remove valve body. Remove throttle cable and solenoid wiring from case. Remove 2nd brake apply gasket.

6) To remove accumulator piston and springs, loosen 5 bolts 1 turn at a time until spring tension is released. Remove cover and gasket. Remove piston and spring for C_1 and C_2. Pop out piston B_2 into a rag, using low pressure compressed air, 15 psi (1 kg/cm²). Force air into apply hole and remove piston and spring.

7) Turn transmission over and measure piston stroke of 2nd coast brake. To do so, remove snap ring and cover. Remove piston and outer spring. Install piston without outer spring. Install snap ring. Firmly push brake apply rod into case. Measure distance between outside of snap ring and tip of piston rod. Measurement should be .551-.610" (14-15.5 mm). There are 2 rods available to bring measurement into specifications.

8) Remove 7 bolts attaching oil pump to case. Pull oil pump free with Puller (09350-32010). Remove oil pump and direct clutch. To do so, hold input shaft, grasp stator shaft and pull oil pump and direct clutch together out of case.

NOTE: Push 2nd brake band into case, being careful not to catch it on direct clutch drum.

9) Remove direct clutch from oil pump. DO NOT lose race located behind oil pump. Remove clutch drum thrust washer. DO NOT lose bearing and race located on forward clutch.

10) Remove forward clutch. DO NOT lose bearing and race. Remove 2nd coast brake band. To do so, push pin with a small screwdriver and remove it from bolt hole of oil pump mounting. Remove brake band.

11) Remove front planetary ring gear. DO NOT lose race and bearing located on ring gear. Remove planetary gear. DO NOT lose race and bearing located on planetary gear.

12) Remove bearing from planetary sun gear. Remove sun gear, sun gear input drum, 2nd brake hub and No. 1 one-way clutch. Stand transmission case up and remove 2nd coast brake band guide.

13) Measure clearance of 2nd brake band. To do so, place a feeler gauge between the seat of return spring assembly and top of plate. Specified clearance is .0146-.0614" (.37-1.56 mm).

14) Remove snap ring holding 2nd brake drum to case. Remove 2nd brake drum. If piston is difficult to remove, lightly tap drum with a wooden block. Remove 2nd brake piston return spring.

15) Remove clutch plate, disc and flange. Hold piston straight and with air gun held slightly away from oil hole blow out piston with compressed air. Using a pin punch, drive out 2nd brake gasket.

16) Remove snap ring holding No. 2 one-way clutch outer race to case. Remove No. 2 one-way clutch and rear planetary gear. DO NOT lose planetary carrier thrust washers, located on both sides.

17) Remove rear planetary ring gear and bearing. DO NOT lose race and bearing located on ring gear. Measure clearance of 1st and reverse brake. To do so, place a feeler gauge between piston and flange end. Specified clearance is .0417-.0937" (1.06-2.38 mm).

18) Remove snap ring holding flange to case. Remove flanges, plates and discs. Turn transmission around. Remove 11 bolts attaching overdrive unit to transmission case.

TOYOTA MODEL A140E & A140L (Cont.)

19) To remove overdrive unit, tap on circumference of overdrive case with a plastic hammer. Remove overdrive planetary gear and counter gear if they remained in transmision. DO NOT DROP overdrive unit as it is heavy.

20) Remove case gasket. Remove governor apply gasket and overdrive brake apply gasket. Remove parking pawl bracket and lock rod. Remove lock pawl shaft. Remove spring and lock pawl.

COMPONENT DISASSEMBLY & REASSEMBLY

OIL PUMP

Disassembly

1) Remove race from stator shaft. Remove "O" ring from pump body. Remove 2 oil seals from back of stator shaft. Remove thrust washer of clutch drum from stator shaft.

2) Remove 11 bolts attaching oil pump body and stator shaft. Identify top and bottom and keep parts in order. *See Fig. 17.*

Fig. 17: Exploded View of Oil Pump

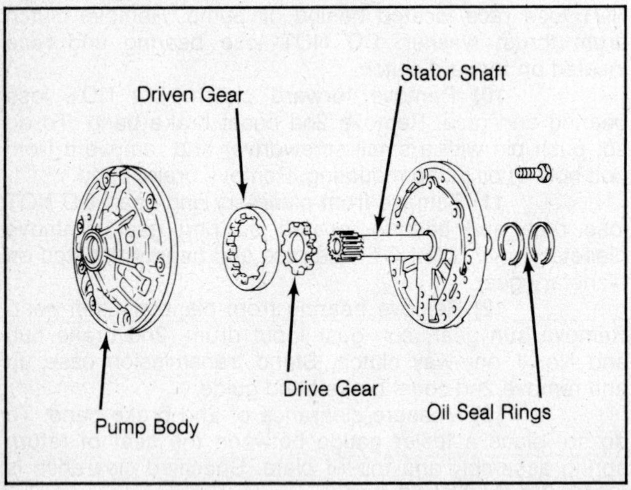

Inspection

1) Check body clearance of driven gear. To do so, push gear to one side of body. Using a feeler gauge, measure clearance. Standard specified body clearance is .0028-.0059" (.07-.15 mm). Maximum body clearance is .012" (.3 mm).

2) Check tip clearance of both gears. To do so, measure between gear teeth and cresent-shaped part of pump body. Standard specified clearance is .0043-.0055" (.11-.14 mm). Maximum clearance is .012 " (.3 mm).

3) Check side clearance of both gears. To do so, use a steel straightedge and a feeler gauge and measure side clearance of both gears. Standard specified clearance is .0008-.0020" (.02-.05 mm). Maximum clearance is .004" (.1 mm).

4) Inspect front oil seal for cracks, damage or wear. Replace oil seal if necesary. To do so, pry oil seal with screwdriver. Using Installer (09350-032010) and a hammer, install a NEW oil seal. Seal is properly installed when it is flush with the outer edge of pump body.

Reassembly

1) Install driven gear and drive gear. Ensure top of gears are facing upward. Install stator shaft onto pump body. Align bolt holes and install 11 bolts attaching stator shaft to oil pump body.

2) Coat thrust bearing with petroleum jelly. Align tab of washer with hollow of pump body and install thrust washer. Install 2 oil seal rings on oil pump. DO NOT spread ring lands too much.

3) Turn drive gear with screwdrivers to ensure a smooth rotation. DO NOT damage oil seal lip. Install race onto stator shaft.

DIRECT CLUTCH

Disassembly

1) Prior to disassembly, measure clearance of direct clutch. To do so, place a feeler gauge between snap ring and flange. Specified clearance is .0173-.0437" (.44-1.11 mm).

2) Remove snap ring from clutch drum. Remove flange, discs and plates. To compress piston return springs and remove snap ring, place Compressor Block (09350-32010) on spring retainer and compress springs with an arbor press.

3) Remove spring retainer and 18 springs. Slide direct clutch onto oil pump and remove piston by applying low pressure commpresed air. If piston does not completely come out, use needle-nose pliers to remove it. Remove direct clutch from oil pump. Remove "O" ring from clutch piston. *See Fig. 18.*

Fig. 18: Exploded View of Direct Clutch

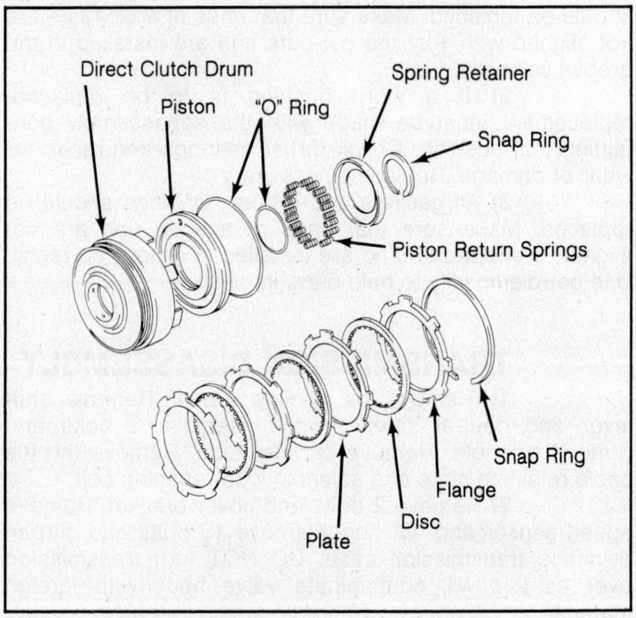

Inspection

Make sure that check ball is free by shaking piston. Make sure that valve does not leak by applying low pressure compressed air.

Reassembly

1) Install NEW "O" rings on piston. Coat rings with ATF. Press piston into drum with cup side up, being careful not to damage "O" ring. Install 18 piston return springs and set retainer and snap ring in position.

TOYOTA MODEL A140E & A140L (Cont.)

2) Compress return springs using Compressor Block (09350-32010) and an arbor press. Install snap ring in groove with a screwdriver. BE SURE end gap of spring is not aligned with spring retainer claw.

3) Install in order: plate, disc, plate, disc, plate, disc and flange. Install flange with flat end facing downward. Install outer snap ring. Ensure that end gap of snap ring is not aligned with any cut-outs.

4) Check clearance of direct clutch. To do so, place a feeler gauge between snap ring and flange. Specified clearance is .0173-.0437" (.44-1.11 mm). If incorrect, check order of assembly of plates and discs.

5) Check operation of direct clutch. To do so, install direct clutch onto oil pump. Apply compressed air into passage with oil pump body and ensure movement of piston. If piston does not move, disassemble and inspect.

FORWARD CLUTCH

Disassembly

1) Remove thrust bearings and races from both sides of clutch. Measure clearance of forward clutch. To do so, place a feeler gauge between snap ring and flange. Specified clearance is .0163-.0573" (.414-1.456 mm).

2) Remove snap ring from clutch drum and remove flange, discs and plates. Place Compressor Block (09350-32010) on spring retainer and compress springs with an arbor press. Remove retainer and 18 springs.

3) Apply compressed air into oil passage to remove piston. If piston does not come out, use needle-nose pliers to remove it. *See Fig. 19.*

Fig. 19: Exploded View of Forward Clutch

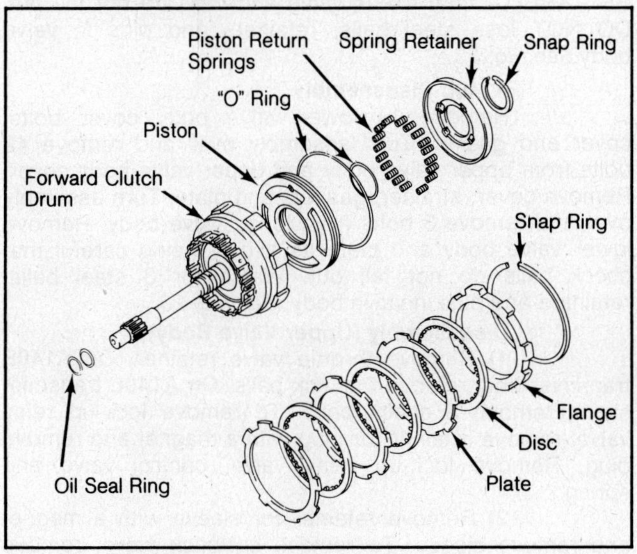

Inspection

Inspect clutch piston. Ensure that check ball is free by shaking piston. Ensure that valve does not leak by applying low pressure air. Replace oil seal rings. During installation, DO NOT spread ring ends too much.

Reassembly

1) Coat NEW "O" ring with ATF and install it onto piston. To install piston, press piston into drum with cup side up. Be careful not to damage "O" ring.

2) Set 18 piston return springs, retainer and snap ring into drum. Place compressor block onto top of retainer and compress using an arbor press. Install snap ring into groove with pliers. Be sure end gap of snap ring is not aligned with spring retainer claw.

3) Install in order: plate, disc, plate, disc, plate, disc and flange. Install flange with flat end facing downward. Install outer snap ring. Be sure not to align end gap of ring with any cut-outs.

4) Check clearance of forward clutch. To do so, place a feeler gauge between snap ring and flange. Specified clearance is .0163-.0573" (.414-1.456 mm).

5) To check operation of direct clutch, apply compressed air into oil passage of shaft. Ensure piston moves. If piston does not move, disassemble and inspect.

No. 1 ONE-WAY CLUTCH & SUN GEAR

Disassembly

1) Check operation of one-way clutch. Hold sun gear and turn hub. Hub should turn freely clockwise and should lock counterclockwise. While turning hub clockwise, remove one-way clutch from inner race.

2) Remove No. 3 planetary carrier thrust washer from sun gear input drum. Remove snap ring and remove sun gear input drum. Remove snap ring. *See Fig. 20.*

Fig. 20: Exploded View of No. 1 One-Way Clutch & Sun Gear

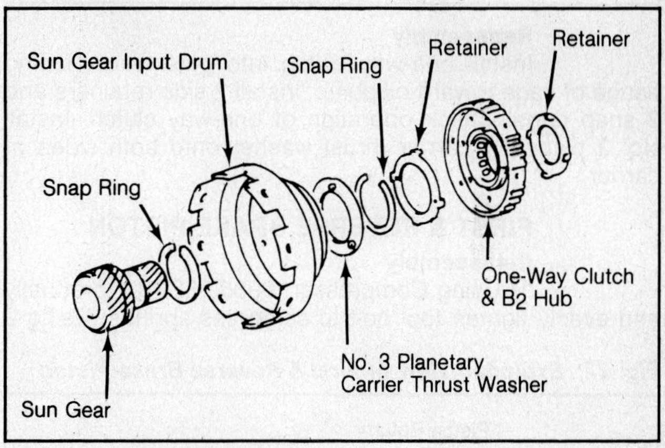

Inspection

If necessary, replace one-way clutch. To remove, pry off retainer with a screwdriver and remove clutch. To install, ensure spring cage is facing toward overdrive case. Hold brake hub in a vise and flatten ears with a chisel. Ensure retainer is centered. Check operation of one-way clutch.

Reassembly

1) Install shaft snap ring on sun gear. Install sun gear input drum on sun gear and install shaft snap ring. Install No. 3 planetary carrier thrust washer on sun gear input drum.

2) While turning hub clockwise, slide one-way clutch onto inner race. Recheck operation of No. 1 one-way clutch.

No. 2 ONE-WAY CLUTCH & REAR PLANETARY GEAR

Disassembly

1) Prior to disassembly, check operation of one-way clutch. To do so, hold outer race and turn hub. Hub should turn freely counterclockwise and should lock clockwise. *See Fig. 21.*

TOYOTA MODEL A140E & A140L (Cont.)

2) Remove No. 2 planetary carrier thrust washer from both sides of carrier. Remove hub and plentary gear from one-way clutch to disassemble one-way clutch.

3) Remove both side snap rings and 2 side retainers. Remove one-way clutch from outer race.

Fig. 21: Exploded View of No. 2 One-Way Clutch & Rear Planetary Gear

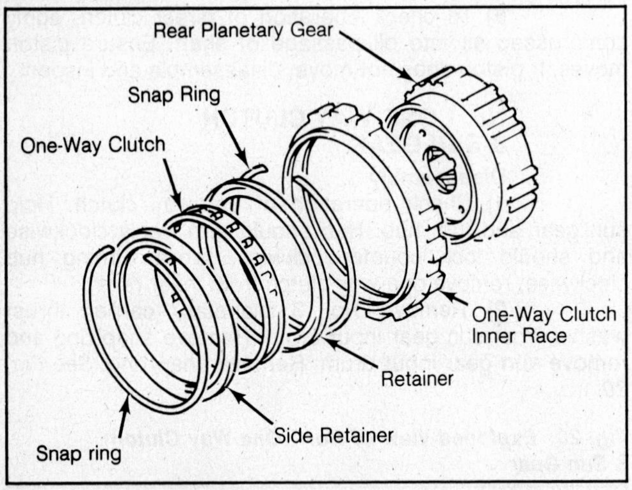

Reassembly

Install one-way clutch into outer race, facing flange of cage toward oil pump. Install 2 side retainers and 2 snap rings. Check operation of one-way clutch. Install No. 2 planetary carrier thrust washer onto both sides of carrier.

FIRST & REVERSE BRAKE PISTON

Disassembly

1) Using Compressor (09350-32010), gradually and evenly tighten tool bolt to compress springs. Using 2 screwdrivers, hook and remove snap ring. Remove piston return spring assembly and set snap ring in place.

Fig. 22: Exploded View of First & Reverse Brake Piston

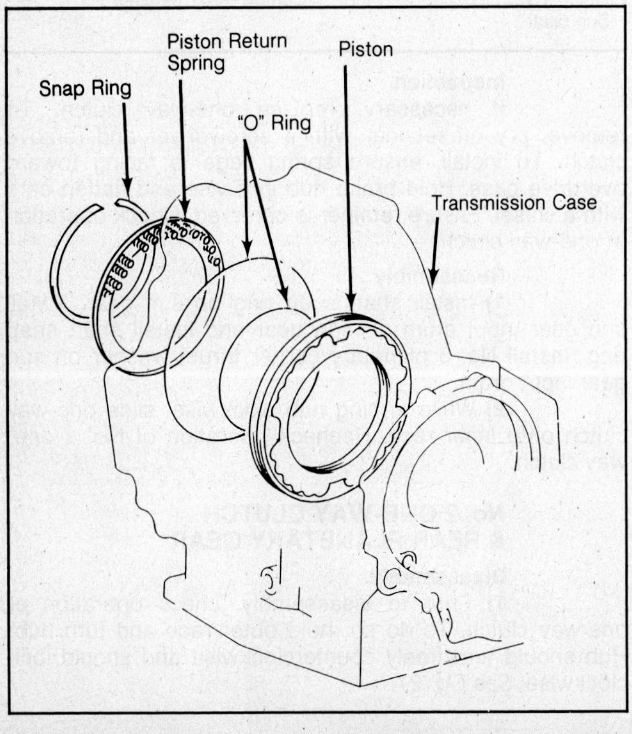

2) Apply compressed air into oil passage of case to remove piston. Hold air gun away from hole and be sure piston does not tilt during removal. Remove "O" rings from piston.

Reassembly

1) Install NEW "O" rings onto piston. Coat rings with ATF. Install piston into bore of case facing spring seats upward. Place base of spring compressor under case. Install piston return springs and retainer and set snap ring into place.

2) Compress piston return springs slowly and evenly to allow installation of snap ring. DO NOT overtighten bolt as it will cause spring retainer to bend.

3) Push snap ring into place with fingers and visually check to ensure its fully seated and centered on the 3 lugs on spring retainer. Be sure end gap of ring is not aligned with spring retainer claw. Remove compressor tool. *See Fig. 22.*

VALVE BODY ASSEMBLY

A140E Disassembly

1) Remove bolts attaching solenoids to valve body and remove solenoids. Remove 10 bolts, cover and gasket of lower valve body. Turn assembly over and remove 12 bolts from upper valve body and upper valve body cover.

2) Remove upper valve body cover, strainer, gasket and plate. Turn assembly over and remove 3 bolts from lower valve body. Hold valve body plate to lower valve body and lift off lower valve body and plate as a unit. BE CAREFUL that check valve and balls do not fall out. DO NOT lose steel balls, retainers and pins in valve body.*See Fig. 23.*

A140L Disassembly

Remove 14 lower valve body cover bolts, cover and gasket. Turn assembly over and remove 12 bolts from upper valve body and upper valve body cover. Remove cover, strainer, gaskets and plate. Turn assembly over and remove 3 bolts from lower valve body. Remove lower valve body and plate as a unit, being careful that check balls do not fall out. Watch for 3 steel balls, retainers and pins in valve body. *See Fig. 23.*

Disassembly (Upper Valve Body)

1) Remove throttle valve retainer. On A140E transmissions, remove 2 check balls. On A140L transmissions, remove 3 check balls. To remove lock-up relay valve, remove retainer for plug with a magnet and remove plug. Remove lock-up relay valve, control valve and spring.

2) Remove retainer for sleeve with a magnet and remove sleeve. To remove cut-back valve, remove retainer with a magnet and remove valve and spring. To remove throttle modulator valve, remove retainer with a magnet and remove plug, valve and spring.

3) To remove accumulator control valve, remove retainer with a magnet and remove plug, spring and control valve. To remove low coast modulator valve, remove pin with a magnet and remove plug, spring and valve. To remove 2nd coast modulator valve, remove retainer with a magnet and remove spring and valve.

4) To remove throttle cam, loosen bolt and remove cam, spring and collar. To remove down-shift plug and spring, remove pin with a magnet and remove plug

TOYOTA MODEL A140E & A140L (Cont.)

with sleeve and spring. Remove throttle valve. Remove spring and adjusting rings. Note number of adjusting rings installed. *See Fig. 23.*

Fig. 23: Exploded View of A140E & A140L Upper Valve Body

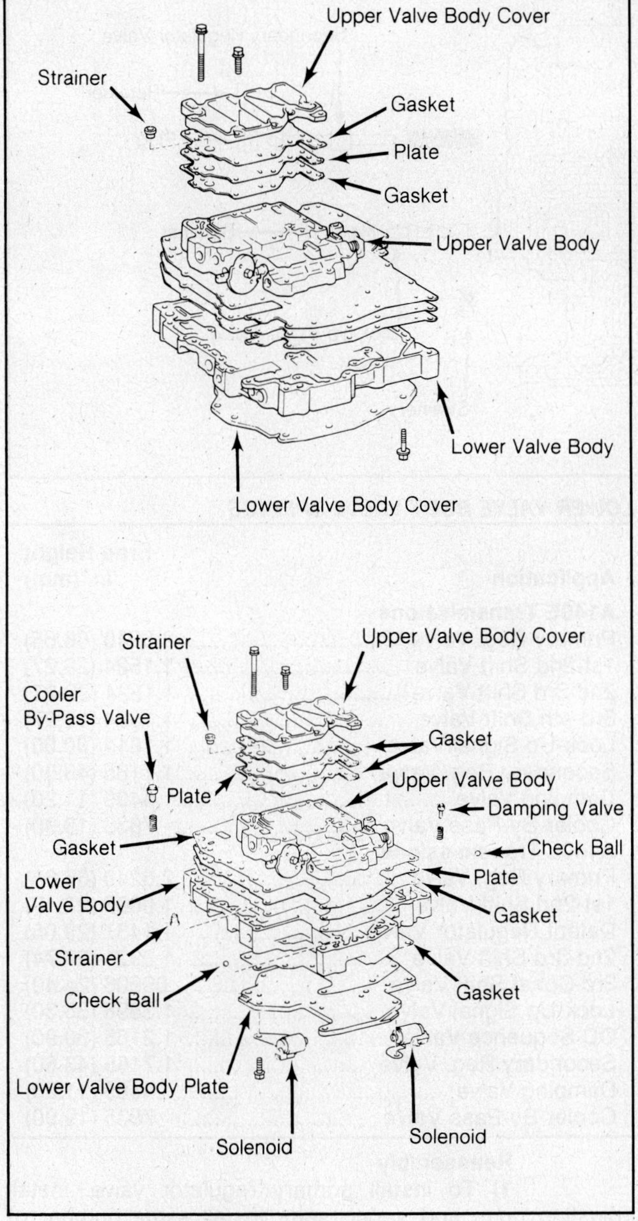

Inspection

Inspect valve springs for damage, squareness, rust and collapsed coils. Measure spring free height and replace if less than that shown in UPPER VALVE BODY VALVE SPRINGS table.

UPPER VALVE BODY VALVE SPRINGS

Application	Free Height In. (mm)
Throttle Mod. Valve	.8543 (21.70)
Accum. Control Valve	1.1047 (28.06)
A140L	.9378 (23.82)
Low Coast Mod. Valve	.8504 (21.60)
A140L	.9213 (23.40)
Down-Shift Plug	1.1717 (29.76)
A140L	1.2205 (31.00)
2nd Coast Mod. Valve	.8240 (20.93)
Throttle Valve	1.2087 (30.70)
Cut-Back Valve	.8587 (21.80)
Lock-Up Relay Valve	1.0457 (26.56)

Reassembly

1) Install lock-up relay sleeve into bore. Coat retainer with petroleum jelly and install it onto end of sleeve. Install control valve, spring and lock-up relay valve into bore in a horizontal position. Push in relay valve by hand until control valve touches end of sleeve. Install plug and retainer.

2) To install cut-back valve, install flat end first, then install plug and retainer. To install throttle modulator valve, install spring and valve, then install plug and retainer.

3) To install accumulator control valve, install valve and spring, then install plug and retainer. To install low coast modulator valve, install valve and spring, then install plug and pin.

4) To install 2nd coast modulator valve, install valve and spring, then compress spring and allow retainer to fall into place. Ensure retainer fully covers end of spring. To install throttle valve and retainer, install throttle valve, coat retainer with petroleum jelly and install it into place in valve body.

5) To install adjusting rings and spring on throttle valve shaft, install same number of rings as were removed during assembly. Slip spring over end of valve shaft. Compress and slide into place.

6) Install spring into throttle valve. Install down-shift plug with sleeve. Coat pin with petroleum jelly and install to hold sleeve in place. To assemble throttle cam, install spring with hood through hole in cam. Insert sleeve through 1 side of cam.

7) Install cam assembly on upper valve body. Check position of spring ends. Tighten bolt to specification. Ensure cam moves on roller of down-shift plug. Install check balls making sure that pins and retainer are installed correctly.

Disassembly (A140E Lower Valve Body)

1) Remove lower valve body plate and gaskets. Remove cooler by-pass valve and spring. Remove damping valve and spring. Remove 4 check balls and strainer.

2) To remove primary regulator valve, hold valve body face down, and press in on valve sleeve. Retainer will drop out. Remove sleeve and plunger. Remove spring and valve. Note number of adjusting rings.

3) To remove secondary regulator valve, remove retainer and plug. Then, remove valve and spring. To remove lock-up signal valve, compress spring with a screwdriver and remove retainer with a magnet. Remove valve and spring.

Automatic Transmissions

TOYOTA MODEL A140E & A140L (Cont.)

Fig. 24: Exploded View of A140E Lower Valve Body

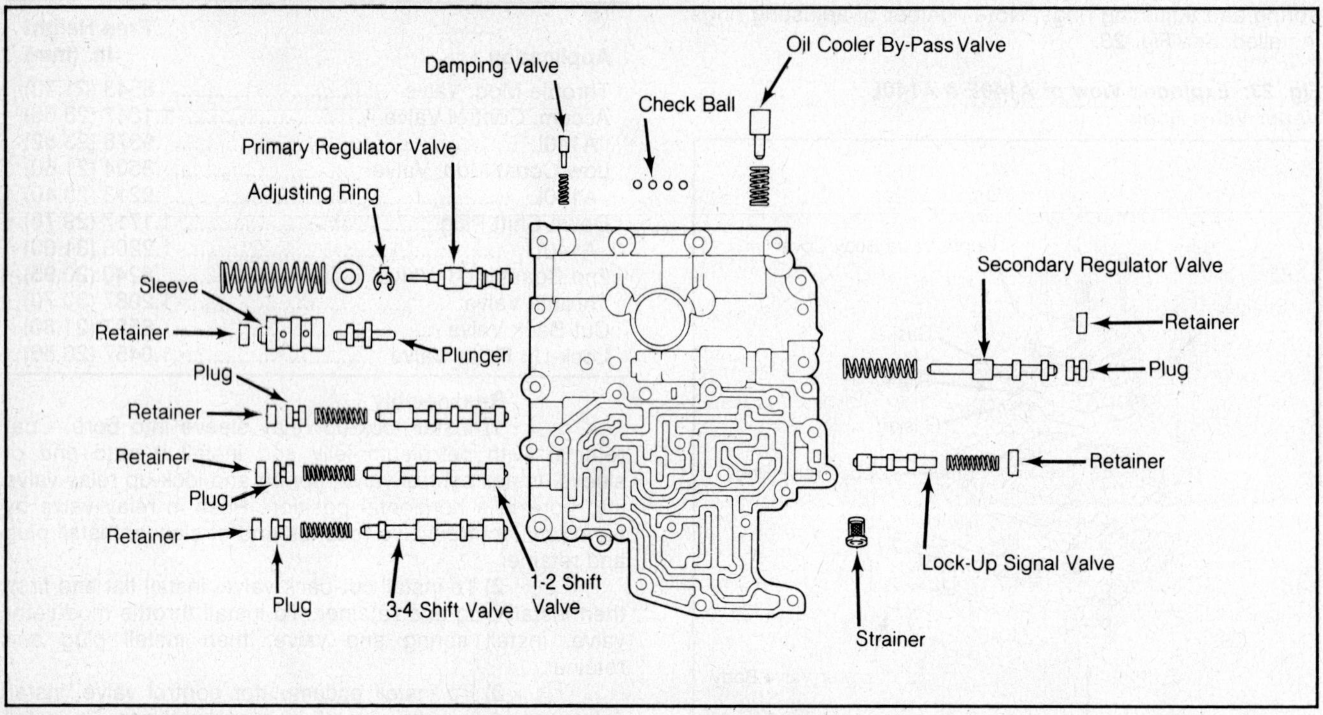

4) To remove 2nd-3rd shift valve, remove retainer and plug. Then, remove spring and valve. To remove 1st-2nd shift valve, remove retainer and plug, then, remove valve and spring.

5) To remove 3rd-4th shift valve, remove retainer with a magnet, remove plug, then remove 3rd-4th shift valve. *See Fig. 24*.

Inspection

Inspect valve spring for damage, squareness, rust and distorted coils. *See Fig. 25*. Measure spring free length and replace if less than that shown in LOWER VALVE BODY VALVE SPRINGS table.

Fig. 25: A140E Valve Body Springs

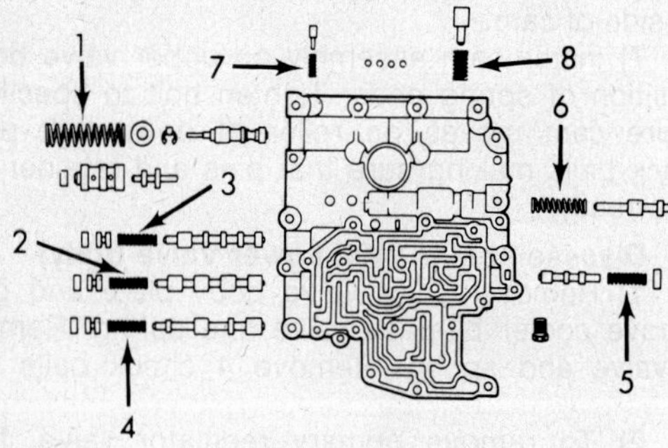

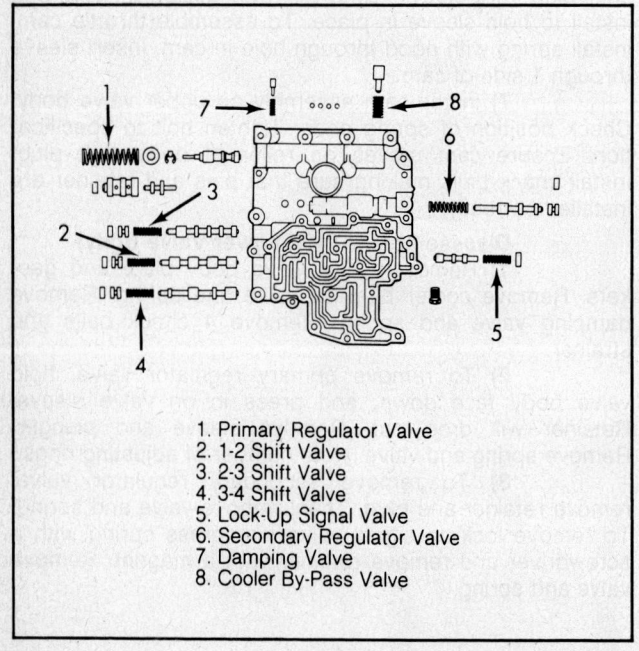

1. Primary Regulator Valve
2. 1-2 Shift Valve
3. 2-3 Shift Valve
4. 3-4 Shift Valve
5. Lock-Up Signal Valve
6. Secondary Regulator Valve
7. Damping Valve
8. Cooler By-Pass Valve

LOWER VALVE BODY VALVE SPRINGS

Application	Free Height In. (mm)
A140E Transmissions	
Primary Reg. Valve	2.6240 (66.65)
1st-2nd Shift Valve	1.1524 (29.27)
2nd-3rd Shift Valve	1.1524 (29-27)
3rd-4th Shift Valve	1.1524 (29.27)
Lock-Up Signal Valve	1.1811 (30.00)
Secondary Reg. Valve	1.7165 (43.60)
Damping Valve	.4409 (11.20)
Cooler By-Pass Valve	.7835 (19.90)
A140L Transmissions	
Primary Reg. Valve	2.6240 (66.65)
1st-2nd Shift Valve	1.0697 (27.17)
Detent Regulator Valve	1.1437 (29.05)
2nd-3rd Shift Valve	1.0921 (27.74)
3rd Coast Shift Valve	.09606 (24.40)
Lock-Up Signal Valve	1.3898 (35.30)
OD Sequence Valve	1.2165 (30.90)
Secondary Reg. Valve	1.7165 (43.60)
Damping Valve	.4409 (11.20)
Cooler By-Pass Valve	.7835 (19.90)

Reassembly

1) To install primary regulator valve, install adjusting rings and spring seat. Install same number of rings as were removed. Place valve into bore in horizontal position.

2) Stand valve body upward and push valve into bore until its tip touches bore. Install valve spring. Insert plunger with short end first. Ensure it is fully inserted. Plunger should be recesssed inside sleeve. Install sleeve with plunger. Ensure regulator valve fits with bore. Install retainer.

3) To install secondary regulator valve, install spring and valve, then install plug and retainer. To install

TOYOTA MODEL A140E & A140L (Cont.)

lock-up signal valve, install valve and spring, then compress spring with a screwdriver and install retainer.

4) To install 2nd-3rd shift valve, install valve and spring, then install plug and retainer. To install 1st-2nd shift valve, install valve and spring, then install plug and retainer. To install 3rd-4th shift valve, install valve flat and spring, then install plug and retainer.

5) Check retainers and locating pin. Ensure retainers and pin are installed correctly. Install spring and cooler by-pass valve. Install spring and damping valve. Install check balls as shown in *Fig. 26*. Install strainer onto lower valve body.

Fig. 26: Location of Check Balls in A140E Lower Valve Body

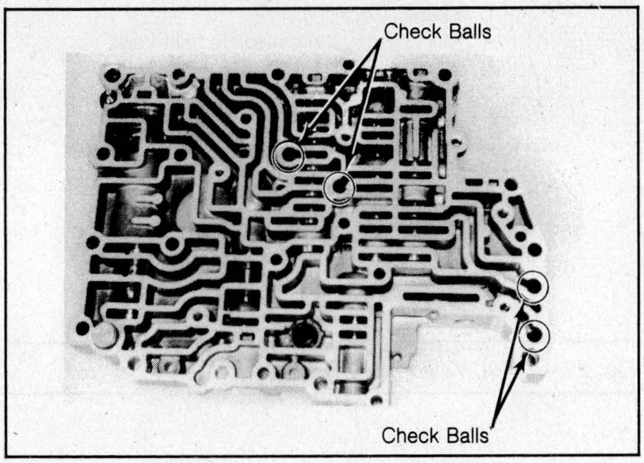

Reassembly
(Valve Body Assembly)

NOTE: Install lower valve body on upper valve body together with plate.

1) Position gasket with larger cooler by-pass valve hole to lower valve body. Place gasket and plate onto lower valve body. Align each bolt hole in valve with gasket and plate.

2) Position new gasket on upper valve body. Align gasket with each bolt hole. Place lower valve body with plate on top of upper valve body. Hold lower valve body and plate securely so they DO NOT separate. Align each bolt hole in valve bodies with gasket and plate.

3) Note length and location of bolts. Install and finger tighten 3 bolts in lower valve body to secure upper valve body. Turn valve body over. Install and finger tighten 3 bolts in upper valve body. Install upper valve body cover and strainer. To do so, install gasket, plate and gasket, then install strainer onto plate. *See Fig. 27.*

4) Install valve body cover and finger tighten 9 bolts in valve body cover. To install lower valve body cover, install cover over gasket and finger tighten 10 bolts.

5) Install Nos. 1 and 2 solenoids and tighten attaching bolts. Tighten bolts in upper valve body. Turn assembly over and tighten bolts in lower valve body.

Disassembly (A140L Lower Valve Body)

1) Remove lower valve body plate and gaskets. Remove cooler by-pass valve and spring, damping check valve and spring, and 4 check balls. Using magnet, remove retainer. Remove sleeve, plunger, spring and valve. Note number of adjusting rings. *See Fig. 28.*

Fig. 27: Noted Length & Location of A140E Valve Body Bolts

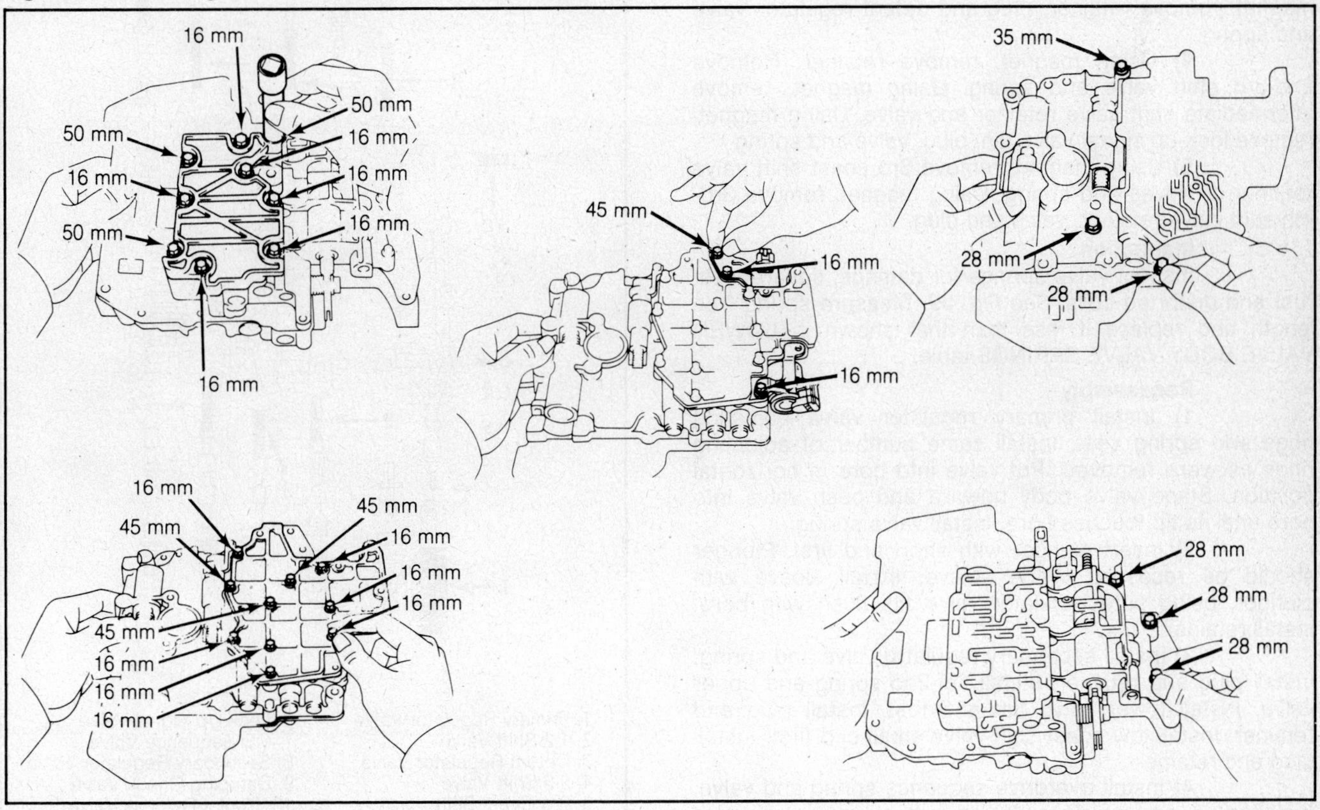

Automatic Transmissions

TOYOTA MODEL A140E & A140L (Cont.)

Fig. 28: Exploded View of A140L Lower Valve Body

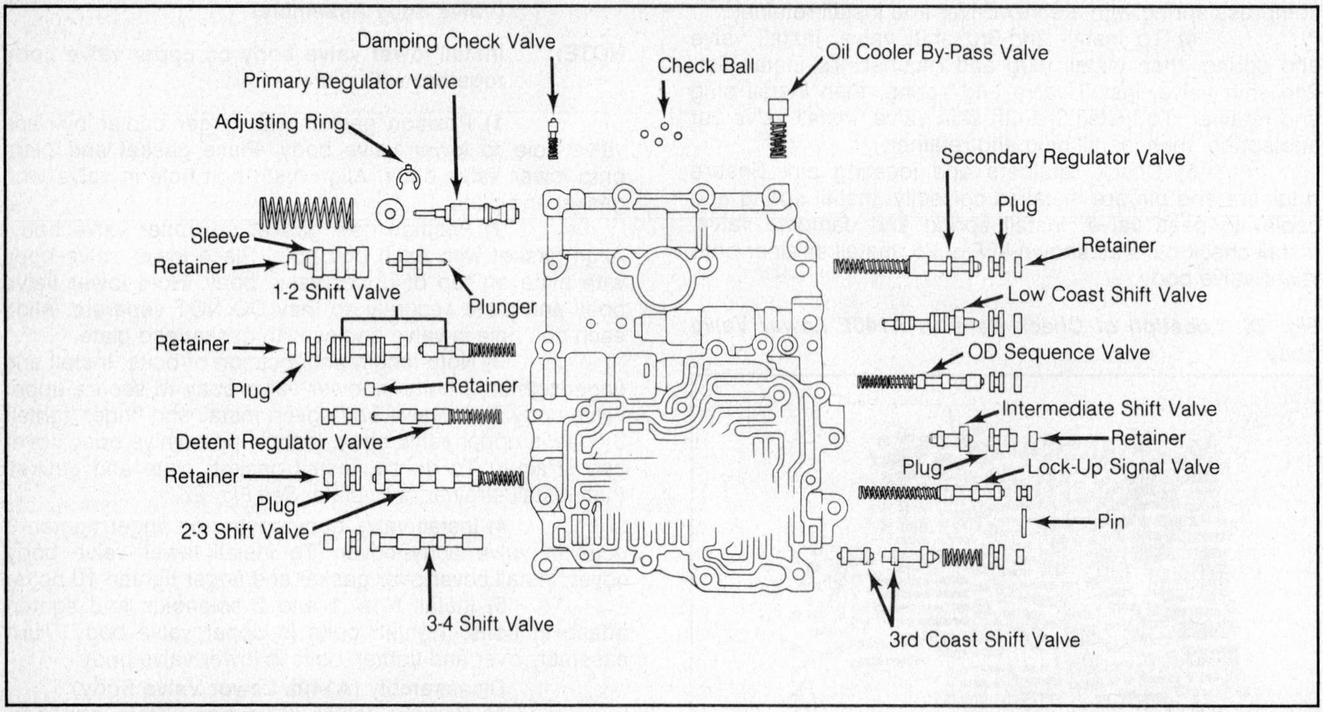

2) Remove retainer, plug, and secondary regulator valve. Remove valve, spring, retainer, and plug. Remove 1st-2nd shift lower valve and spring.

3) Remove retainer, plug, and low coast shift valve. Using magnet, remove retainer and overdrive sequence valve. Remove plug, valve and spring. Using magnet, remove retainer, plug and detent regulator valve and spring.

4) Using magnet, remove retainer. Remove 2nd-3rd shift valve and spring. Using magnet, remove intermediate shift valve retainer and valve. Using magnet, remove lock-up signal valve pin, plug, valve and spring.

5) Using magnet, remove 3rd coast shift valve retainer, 2 valves and spring. Using magnet, remove 3rd-4th shift valve retainer, valve and plug.

Inspection

Inspect valve springs for damage, squareness, rust and distorted coils. *See Fig. 29.* Measure spring free length and replace if less than that shown in LOWER VALVE BODY VALVE SPRINGS table.

Reassembly

1) Install primary regulator valve adjusting rings and spring seat. Install same number of adjusting rings as were removed. Put valve into bore in horizontal position. Stand valve body upward and push valve into bore until its tip touches bore. Install valve spring.

2) Insert plunger with short end first. Plunger should be recessed inside sleeve. Install sleeve with plunger, being sure regulator valve fits flush with bore. Install retainer.

3) Install secondary regulator valve and spring. Install plug and retainer. Install 1st-2nd spring and upper valve. Install lower valve flat end first. Install plug and retainer. Install low coast shift valve small end first. Install plug and retainer.

4) Install overdrive sequence spring and valve. Install plug and retainer. Install detent regulator valve spring and valve. Install valve with small end first. Install

Fig. 29: A140L Valve Body Springs

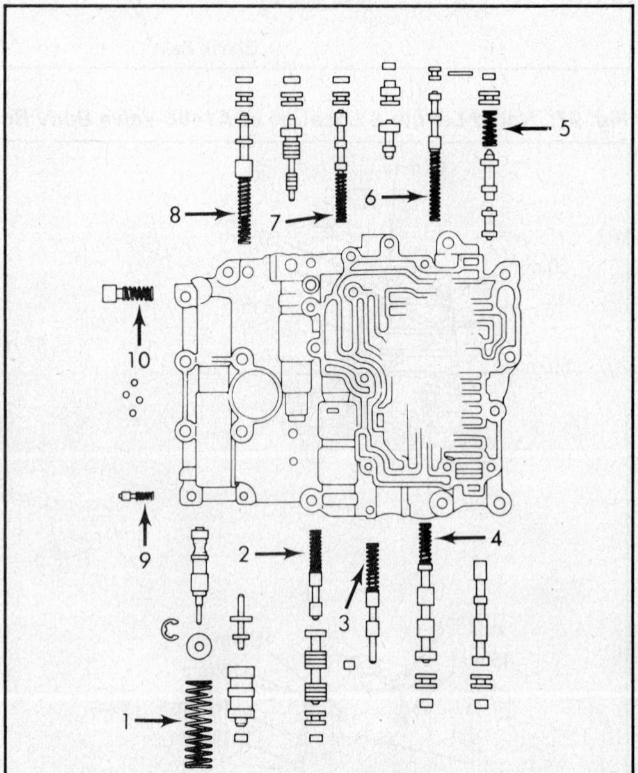

1. Primary Regulator Valve
2. 1-2 Shift Valve
3. Detent Regulator Valve
4. 2-3 Shift Valve
5. 3rd Coast Shift Valve
6. Lock-Up Signal Valve
7. OD Sequence Valve
8. Secondary Regulator Valve
9. Damping Check Valve
10. Cooler By-Pass Valve

TOYOTA MODEL A140E & A140L (Cont.)

retainer. Install intermediate shift valve small end first. Coat retainer with petroleum jelly. Install plug, flat end first, and install retainer.

5) Install 2nd-3rd shift valve spring and valve. Install plug and retainer. Install lock-up signal valve spring, valve, plug and pin. Install 3rd coast shift valves, spring, plug, and retainer. Install 3rd-4th shift valve flat end first. Install plug and retainer.

6) Be sure retainers and pin are installed correctly. Install spring, cooler by-pass valve, spring and damping check valve. Install 4 rubber check balls. *See Fig. 30.*

Fig. 30: A140L Check Ball Location

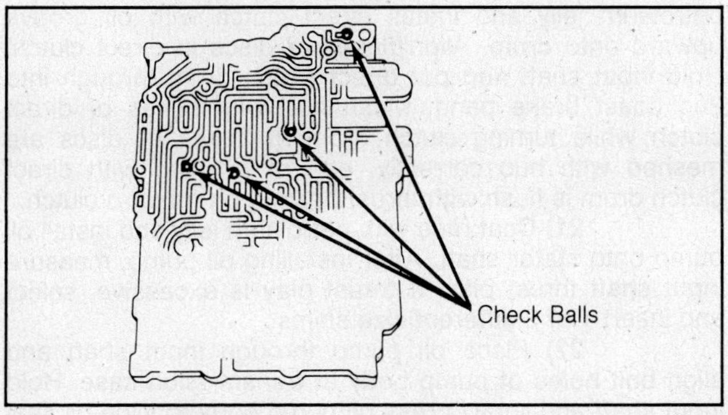

Reasembly
(Valve Body Assembly)

NOTE: **Install lower valve body on upper valve body together with plate.**

1) Position gasket with larger cooler by-pass valve hole to lower valve body. Place gasket and plate onto lower valve body. Align each bolt hole in valve with gasket and plate.

2) Position new gasket on upper valve body. Align gasket at each bolt hole. Place lower valve body with plate on top of upper valve body. Hold lower valve body and plate securely so they do not seperate. Align each bolt hole in valve bodies with gasket and plate. Note length and location of bolts. Install and finger tighten 3 bolts in lower valve body to secure upper valve body. *See Fig. 31.*

3) Turn assembly over and finger tighten 3 bolts in upper valve body. Install upper valve body cover and strainer. To do so, install gasket, plate and gasket, and strainer onto plate. Install valve body cover and finger tighten 9 bolts in valve body cover.

4) Install lower valve body cover over gasket. Finger tighten 14 bolts. Tighten bolts to 48 INCH lbs. (5.4 N.m). Turn assembly over and tighten upper valve body cover bolts to same specification.

TRANSMISSION REASSEMBLY

1) Place parking pawl onto case. Hook spring ends to case and pawl. Install pin into hole of case through spring and pawl. Install parking lock rod. Install parking lock pawl bracket and tighten bolts. Check operation of parking pawl and ensure counter driven gear is locked when manual lever in "P" range.

2) Coat gaskets with petroleum jelly to hold in place and install on transmission case. Install both overdrive brake and governor apply gaskets over appropriate case openting.

3) Align each bolt hole in gasket and case and install overdrive unit over gasket. Tighten fastening bolts.

Fig. 31: Notated Length & Location of A140L Valve Body Bolts

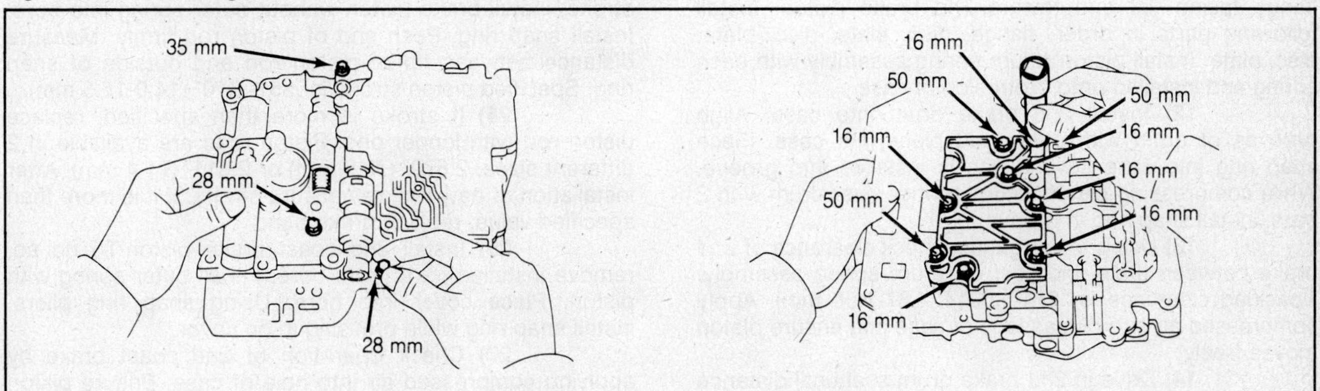

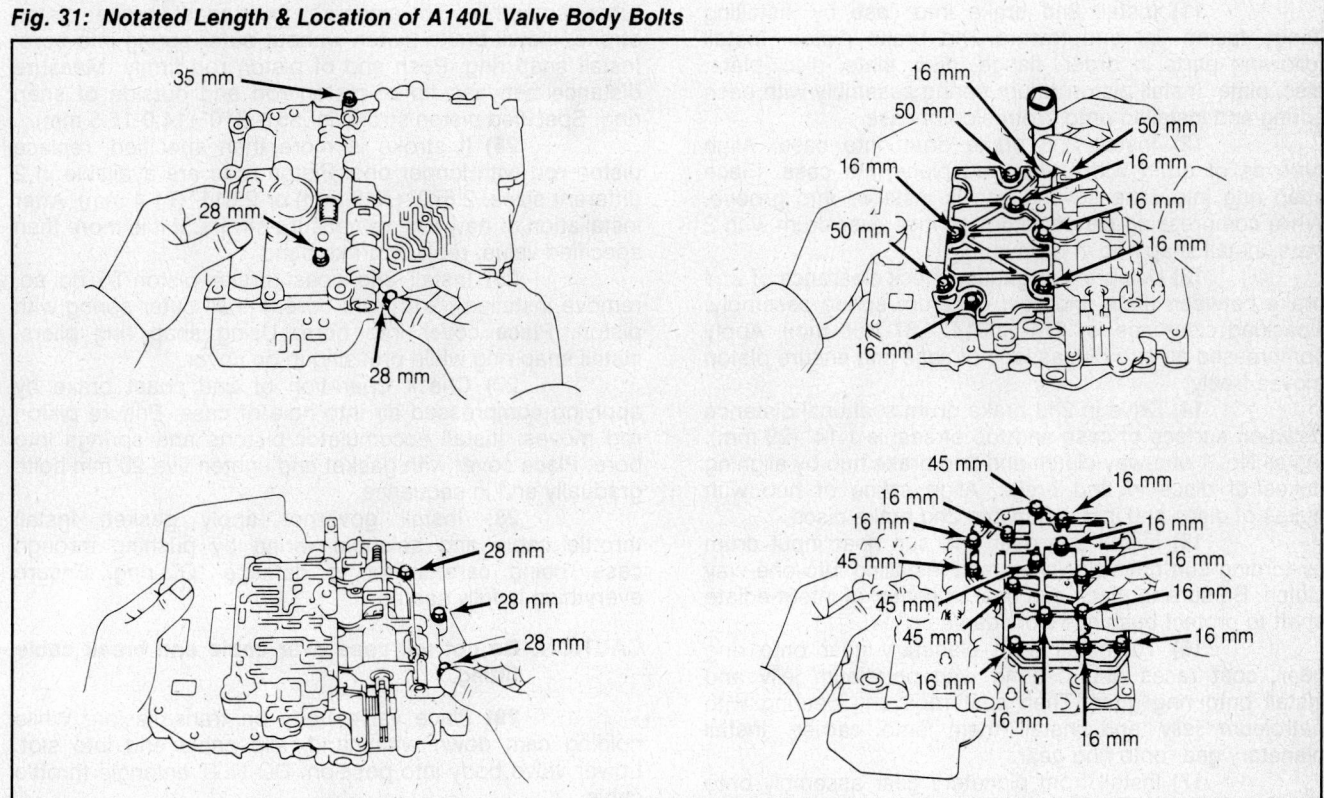

TOYOTA MODEL A140E & A140L (Cont.)

Check intermediate shaft end play. To do so, ensure shaft has thrust play in axial (in and out) direction. Standard specified thrust play is .0193-.0594" (.49-1.51 mm). Ensure shaft turns smoothly.

4) Install 1st and reverse brake in case by installing inner flange facing flat end toward oil pump side. Install following parts in order: flange, disc, plate, disc, plate, disc, plate, disc, plate, disc and flange. Install outer flange flat side facing toward piston side.

5) Install snap ring being sure ring end gap is installed into groove. Check clearance of 1st and reverse brake by placing feeler gauge between piston and flange. Specified clearance is .0465-.0953" (1.18-2.42 mm).

6) Check operation of 1st and reverse brake by applying compressed air into oil passage of transmission case and confirm piston movement. Coat No. 2 thrust washers with petroleum jelly and install onto planetary carrier.

7) Coat races and bearing with petroleum jelly and assemble rear planetary gear onto ring gear. Install planetary gear onto ring gear. Ensure thrust bearing is installed in center of ring gear flange.

8) Install rear planetary gear into case by aligning flukes of discs in 1st and reverse brake. Align spline of carrier with flukes of discs and install planetary gear into 1st and reverse brake discs.

9) Install No. 2 one-way clutch into case and install one-way onto inner race while turning planetary pinion counterclockwise with screwdriver. Check operation of No. 2 one-way clutch by turning planetary carrier. Carrier should turn freely clockwise and should lock counterclockwise.

10) Install snap ring and ensure end gap is installed into groove. Install 2nd coast brake band guide and 2nd brake drum guide. Install band guide so tip touches case.

11) Install 2nd brake into case by installing flange facing flat end toward 2nd brake piston. Install following parts in order: flange, disc, plate, disc, plate, disc, plate. Install piston return spring assembly with each spring end installed onto protrusion of case.

12) Install 2nd brake drum into case. Align grooves of drum with guide and place into case. Place snap ring into case so end gap is installed into groove. While compressing piston return springs over drum with 2 bars, install snap ring in groove.

13) Using feeler gauge, check clearance of 2nd brake between plate and seat of return spring assembly. Specified clearance is .0146-.0614" (.37-1.56 mm). Apply compressed air into oil passage of case and ensure piston moves freely.

14) Drive in 2nd brake drum seal until distance between surface of case and top of seal is 1.14" (29 mm). Install No. 1 one-way clutch and 2nd brake hub by aligning flukes of discs in 2nd brake. Align spline of hub with flukes of discs and install hub into 2nd brake discs

15) Install sun gear and sun gear input drum by turning sun gear clockwise and installing into one-way clutch. Be sure to place sun gear in center of intermediate shaft to protect bushings from damage.

16) To install front planetary gear onto ring gear, coat races and bearing with petroleum jelly and install onto ring gear. Then coat race and bearing with petroleum jelly and install them onto carrier. Install planetary gear onto ring gear.

17) Install front planetary gear assembly onto sun gear. If planetary gear and other parts are installed correctly into case, end of bushing with ring gear flange will be flush with intermediate shaft. Coat race with petroleum jelly and install onto tip of ring gear flange.

18) Install 2nd coast brake band by placing band into case and installing pin through oil pump mounting bolt hole. Install forward clutch into case by coating races and bearing with petroleum jelly and installing them onto both sides of clutch drum.

19) Align flukes of disc in forward clutch while holding sun gear input drum and rotating input shaft to mesh hub with clutch discs of forward clutch. Align center of input shaft and intermediate shaft. While pushing on the input shaft, rotate it to mesh hub and disc.

20) Coat clutch drum thrust washer with petroleum jelly and install direct clutch with oil groove upward onto drum. Align flukes of discs in direct clutch. Hold input shaft and put direct clutch drum through into 2nd coast brake band. Mesh hub with flukes of direct clutch while turning clutch drum. If flukes of discs are meshed with hub correctly, end of bushing with direct clutch drum is flush with thrust bearing on forward clutch.

21) Coat race with petroleum jelly and install oil pump onto stator shaft. After installing oil pump, measure input shaft thrust play. If thrust play is excessive, select and insert 1 of 2 different size shims.

22) Place oil pump through input shaft and align bolt holes of pump body at transmission case. Hold input shaft and lightly press oil pump body to slide oil seal rings on stator shaft thorugh direct clutch drum. DO NOT push on oil pump hard or oil seal ring will stick to direct clutch drum. Install and tighten oil pump mounting bolts.

23) Measure thrust play of input shaft in axial direction. Specified thrust play is .012-.035" (.30-.90 mm). There are 2 different thickness, .031" (.80 mm) or .055" (1.4 mm), of races for end of stator shaft.

24) Check input shaft rotation and ensure it turns smoothly. To measure 2nd coast brake piston stroke, install brake piston without outer spring into bore. Install snap ring. Push end of piston rod firmly. Measure distance between tip of piston rod and outside of snap ring. Specified piston stroke is .551-.610" (14.0-15.5 mm).

25) If stroke is more than specified, replace piston rod with longer one. Piston rods are available in 2 different sizes, 2.870" (72.9 mm) or 2.811" (71.4 mm). After installation of new rod, remeasure stroke. If it is more than specified value, replace brake band.

26) Install 2nd coast brake piston.To do so, remove installed parts from bore. Install outer spring with piston. Place cover into bore. Using snap ring pliers, install snap ring while pressing in on cover.

27) Check operation of 2nd coast brake by applying compressed air into hole of case. Ensure piston rod moves. Install accumulator pistons and springs into bore. Place cover with gasket and tighten five-20 mm bolts gradually and in sequence.

28) Install governor apply gasket. Install throttle cable and solenoid wiring by pushing through case, being careful not to damage "O" ring. Ensure everything is fully seated.

CAUTION: Do not roll case over cable and break cable fitting.

29) Place valve body on transmission. While holding cam down with hand, slip cable end into slot. Lower valve body into position. DO NOT entangle throttle cable.

TOYOTA MODEL A140E & A140L (Cont.)

30) Ensure proper length and location and finger tighten all bolts. Then tighten to specifications. Connect solenoid wire connectors. *See Fig. 32.*

Fig. 32: Valve Body Mounting Bolt Length & Location

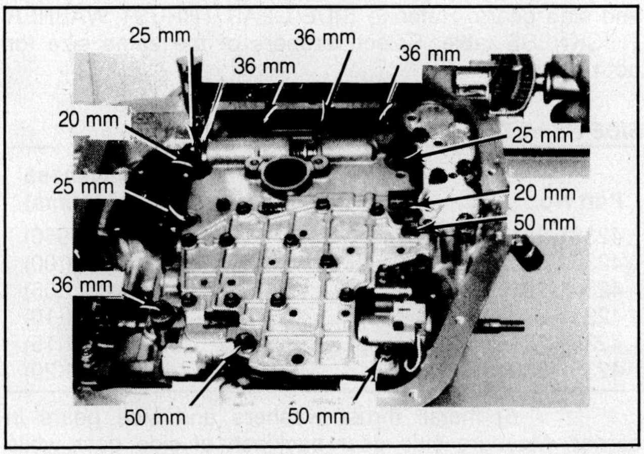

31) Place manual valve and body on transmission and align manual lever with pin of manual shaft lever. Lower valve body into positon. Ensure proper length and location and finger tighten bolts. Tighten bolts with torque wrench to specifications.

32) Install detent spring. To do so, ensure proper length and location of each bolt and finger tighten. Then tighten to specifications and check for proper operation of manual valve lever. Ensure lever is touching center of detent spring tip roller.

33) Install oil tubes using plastic hammer. DO NOT bend or damage tubes. Install tube bracket. Note length and proper location of bolts. Tighten bolts to specifications. Install oil strainer.

34) Install magnet on oil pan. Be sure magnet DOES NOT interfere with oil tubes. Install oil pan with gasket. Tighten pan bolts to specifications. Install speed sensor with "O" ring and install cover bracket with 2 bolts.

35) Install throttle and solenoid wiring retainers. Install filler tube and gauge. Install solenoid by coating "O" rings with ATF and pushing tip of solenoid into hole. Tighten pipes to union, clamping pipes onto bracket and tighten union nuts.

DIFFERENTIAL & DRIVE PINION

SERVICE (IN VEHICLE)

Left Output Shaft Seal Replacement

1) Remove dust cover and fender apron seal. Drain 1 qt. (1 L) of ATF. Remove axle shaft and speed sensor. Remove side gear shaft using Puller (09520-32010). Remove side bearing retainer.

2) Press out seal from retainer. Using Seal Installer (09350-32010) and arbor press, press in NEW oil seal. Seal should be recessed .106" (2.7 mm) when properly installed.

3) Coat lip of seal with MP grease. Coat threads with sealer (3 Bond 1324) and install side bearing retainer. Tighten retainer bolts to specifications. Using Slide Hammer (0950-32010), install side gear shaft until it contacts pinion shaft.

Fig. 33: Exploded View of Differential Unit

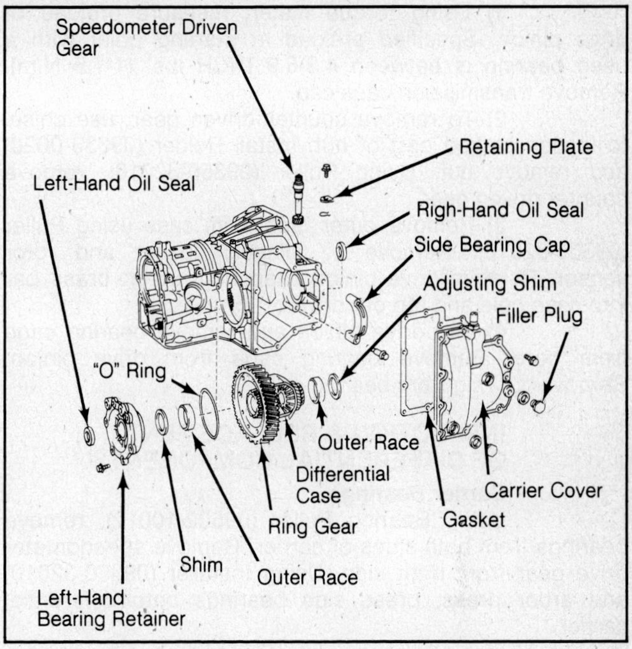

4) Install drive shaft and speed sensor. Fill differential with ATF. Install fender apron seal and dust seal.

Right Output Shaft Seal Replacement

1) Remove fender apron seal. Drain 1 qt. (1 L) of ATF from differential. Remove drive shaft and intermediate shaft. Remove universal joint using Slide Hammer and Adapter (09520-32010 and 09520-32030).

2) Remove oil seal using Inside Puller/Slide Hammer (09308-0010). Using Seal Installer (09350-32010), drive seal into case until surface is flush with surface of case. Coat lip of seal with MP grease.

3) Install universal joint using Slide Hammer and Adapter (09520-32010 and 09520-32030). Install intermediate shaft and drive shaft. Fill differential with ATF. Install fender apron seal.

DISASSEMBLY

1) Remove neutral safety switch, speedometer driven gear, speed sensor, oil pan and valve body. Remove 11 bolts and tap overdrive case with plastic hammer to remove. If intermediate shaft did not come out with overdrive case, remove from transmission case.

2) Remove overdrive clutch apply gasket and brake gasket. Remove parking pawl lock bracket and rod. Remove manual shaft and lever. Remove carrier cover.

3) Using torque wrench, measure total preload at starting point. Record measured value. Measure side gear backlash while holding 1 pinion against carrier casing. Standard specified backlash is .002-.0079" (.05-.20 mm).

4) Remove 6 bolts and tap left bearing retainer with plastic hammer to remove "O" ring from retainer. Remove 2 bolts and right bearing retainer. Remove differential carrier, outer race and adjusting shim from case.

TOYOTA MODEL A140E & A140L (Cont.)

Drive Pinion Shaft

1) Using torque meter, measure preload of drive pinion. Specified preload at starting point with a used bearing is between 4.3-6.9 INCH lbs. (1-1.5 N.m). Remove transmission case cap.

2) To remove counter driven gear, use chisel to loosen staked part of nut. Install Holder (09330-0020) and remove nut. Using Puller (09350-32010), remove counter driven gear.

3) Remove outer race from case using Puller (09350-32010). Remove oil slinger, spacer and rotor sensor. Remove drive pinion snap ring. Insert brass bar into case hole and tap out drive pinion.

4) Tap drive pinion and remove bearing cage from bore. Remove bearing cage from drive pinion. Remove "O" ring from bearing cage.

INSPECTION & REPLACEMENT OF DIFFERENTIAL COMPONENTS

Carrier Bearings

Using Bearing Puller (09502-10012), remove bearings from both sides of carrier. Remove speedometer drive gear from right side. Using Installer (09350-32010) and arbor press, press side bearings onto differential carrier.

Carrier Bearing Races

1) To replace left bearing race, remove oil seal. Using Remover/Installer (09350-32010) and arbor press, remove outer race and shim.

2) To replace, place shim onto retainer. Using Remover/Installer (09350-32010), press outer race into retainer. Use either same shim which was removed or one that is .0945" (2.40 mm).

3) Replace oil seal. Ensure seal is driven .106" (2.7 mm) below outer surface of retainer. Replace right output shaft oil seal. Install seal so it is flush with case.

Ring Gear

1) Loosen staked part of lock plate. Place alignment marks on ring gear and carrier. Remove 8 bolts and locking plates. Using hammer, tap on ring gear to remove from carrier.

2) Measure side gear backlash while holding 1 pinion toward carrier case. Specified standard backlash is .002-.0079" (.05-.20 mm). If backlash is out of specification, install correct thrust washer to side gears. *See Fig. 34.*

Fig. 34: Measuring Side Gear Backlash

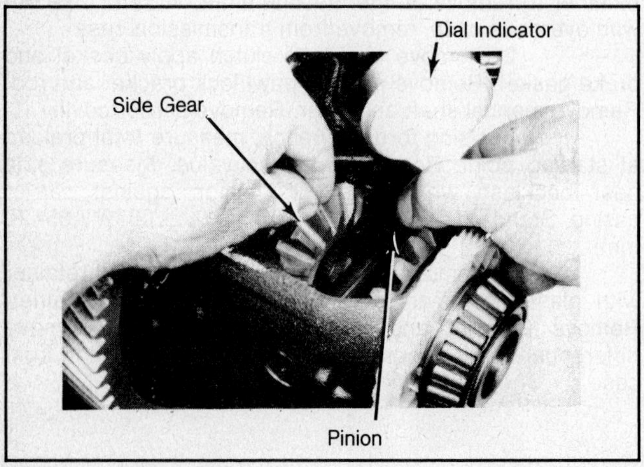

3) To remove pinion and side gears from differential carrier, drive out pinion shaft lock pin. Remove 2 pinion and 2 side gears with 4 thrust washers from each gear.

4) To assemble, install correct thrust washers and side gears. Refer to SIDE GEAR THRUST WASHER THICKNESS table. Select washers of the same size for both sides.

SIDE GEAR THRUST WASHER THICKNESS

Part No.	Thickness In. (mm)
42361-22140	.0374 (.950)
42361-22020	.0394 (1.00)
42361-22150	.0413 (1.05)
42361-22030	.0433 (1.10)
42361-22160	.0453 (1.15)
42361-22040	.0472 (1.20)

5) Install thrust washers and side gears in carrier. Measure side gear backlash of side gear while holding one pinion gear against carrier case. Standard specified backlash is .002-.0079" (.05-.20 mm). If backlash is not within specification, install thrust washer of different thickness.

6) Using hammer and punch, drive lock pin through carrier case and hole in pinion shaft. Stake differential carrier case to retain lock pin.

Counter Driven Gear Bearing

Using bearing puller and arbor press, press bearing off gear. Use Installer (09350-32010) and press to install bearing.

Drive Pinion Shaft Bearing & Outer Race

Using bearing puller and arbor press, press bearing from gear. Use Installer (09350-32010) and press to install bearing. Place bearing cage in Stand (09350-32010) and using driver handle and hammer drive out bearing race from cage. Use Bearing Race installer (09350-32010) and press to install race.

Cage Oil Seals

1) Using Remover/Installer (09350-32010) and press, press out 2 oil seals together. To install, position oil seal with lip facing downward. Place mark on tool marking 11 mm depth. *See Fig. 35.* Using arbor press and Remover/Installer (09350-32010), press in seal to depth of 11 mm below surface of flat end of cage.

Fig. 35: Marking Seal Installer

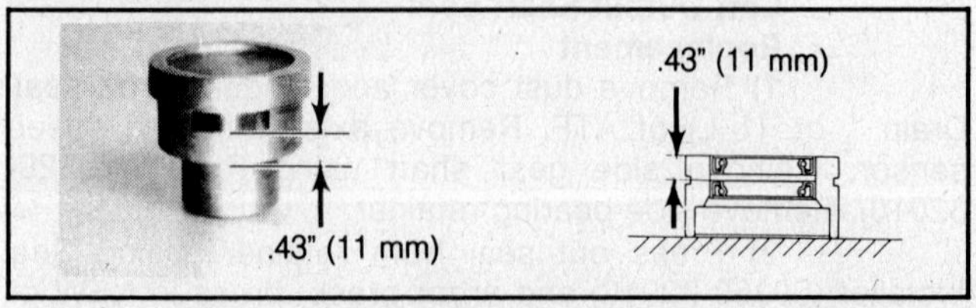

2) Position second seal, lip facing upward, into cage and press in seal until flush with case. Coat lip of both seals with MP grease.

TOYOTA MODEL A140E & A140L (Cont.)

ADJUSTMENTS

DIFFERENTIAL SIDE BEARING PRELOAD ADJUSTMENT

1) Place outer race and adjusting shim onto right side bearing. Place differential carrier with shim into case. Install left bearing retainer into case without "O" ring.

2) DO NOT coat threads with sealer. Temporarily tighten retainer bolts evenly and gradually while turning ring gear. Install right side bearing cap. Tighten bolts to specifications. Tighten left bearing retainer bolts to specifications.

3) To adjust ring gear preload, use torque meter and measure preload. Note and record torque required to turn ring gear at its starting point. Specified preload for a NEW bearing is 8.7-13.9 INCH lbs. (1-1.5 N.m). For a used bearing it is 4.3-6-9 INCH lbs. (.5-.8 N.m).

4) If preload is not within specifications, remove ring gear from case and select a shim from RIGHT ADJUSTING SHIM table.

NOTE: **Preload will change by about 2.6-3.5 INCH lbs. (.3-.4 N.m) with each increase or decrease of shim thickness.**

5) If preload is adjusted properly, remove bearing retainer, ring gear, right side bearing and shim. DO NOT lose shim.

RIGHT ADJUSTING SHIM

Part No.	Thickness In. (mm)
90564-45001	.0744-.0752 (1.89-1.91)
90564-45002	.0764-.0772 (1.94-1.96)
90564-45003	.0783-.0791 (1.99-2.01)
90564-45004	.0803-.0811 (2.04-2.06)
90564-45005	.0823-.0831 (2.09-2.11)
90564-45006	.0843-.0850 (2.14-2.16)
90564-45007	.0862-.0870 (2.19-2.21)
90564-45008	.0882-.0890 (2.24-2.26)
90564-45009	.0902-.0909 (2.29-2.31)
90564-45010	.0921-.0929 (2.34-2.36)
90564-45011	.0941-.0949 (2.39-2.41)
90564-45012	.0961-.0969 (2.44-2.46)
90564-45013	.0980-.0988 (2.49-2.51)
90564-45014	.1000-.1008 (2.54-2.56)
90564-45015	.1020-.1028 (2.59-2.61)
90564-45016	.1039-.1047 (2.64-2.66)
90564-45017	.1059-.1067 (2.69-2.71)
90564-45018	.1079-.1087 (2.74-2.76)
90564-45019	.1098-.1106 (2.79-2.81)

DRIVE PINION SHAFT PRELOAD

1) Install "O" ring onto bearing cage. Place bearing cage onto drive pinion shaft. Be careful not to damage oil seal on splines. Lightly tap cage into case until groove with bore can be seen.

2) Drive in bearing cage until surface of bearing cage passes through groove in bore. Install snap ring and lightly tap bearing cage to fit snap ring into groove. Install rotor sensor.

3) Install oil slinger with lip facing outward. Install outer face using Installer (09350-32010) and hammer. Install NEW spacer with small end first.

4) Install counter driven gear onto shaft by placing bar at the drive pinion side and position other end of bar against vise. Drive gear onto shaft until nut can be installed on thread of shaft. DO NOT cause shock to transmission case.

5) Adjust drive pinion preload by coating threads and surface of nut with MP grease. Use Socket and Holder (09350-32010 and 09330-00020) to hold gear and tighten nut. Tighten nut specifications.

6) Rotate gear counterclockwise and clockwise several times. Using torque meter, measure preload of drive pinion at starting point. Specified preload with NEW bearing is 8.7-13.9 INCH lbs. (1-1.5 N.m). If old bearing was reused, it should be 4.3-6.9 INCH lbs. (.5-,8 N.m).

7) If preload is greater than specified, replace bearing spacer. If preload is less than specified, retighten shaft nut 108 INCH lbs. (12 N.m) at a time until specified preload is reached.

8) If maximum torque is exceeded while retightening shaft nut, replace bearing spacer and repeat preload procedure. DO NOT back off nut to reduce preload. Maximum shaft nut torque is 213 ft. lbs. (288 N.m).

REASSEMBLY

1) Place outer race and selected adjusting shim onto right side carrier bearing. Place differential carrier into case. Ensure shim is properly installed.

2) Install "O" ring onto left bearing retainer. Install retainer by tapping while keeping carrier centered with retainer. Clean threads of bolts and case with White gas. Coat threads with sealer (3 Bond 1324).

Fig. 36: Exploded View of Overdrive Unit

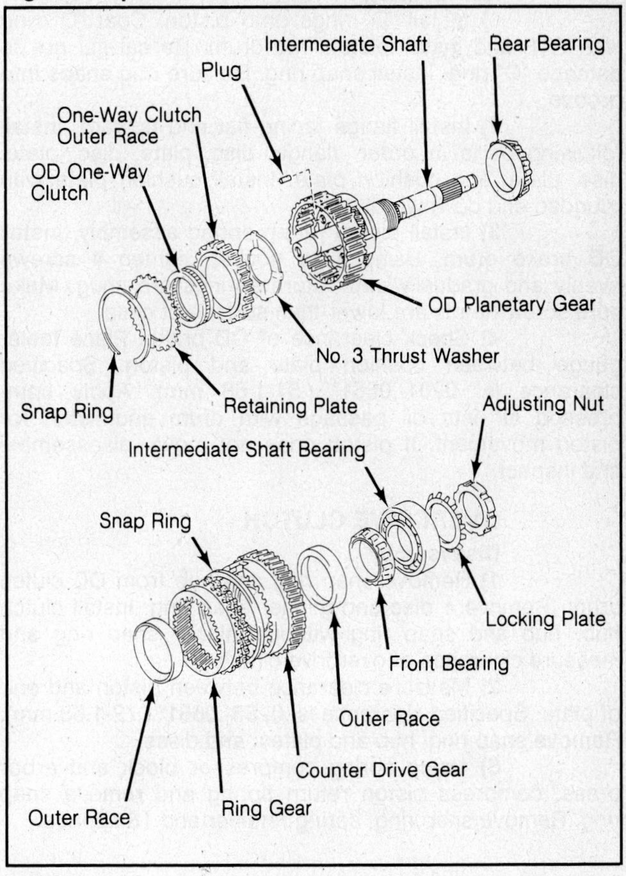

TOYOTA MODEL A140E & A140L (Cont.)

3) Finger tighten bolts evenly and gradually while turning ring gear. Install right side bearing cap and tighten bolts evenly and slowly while turning ring gear. Tighten bolts to specifications.

4) Tighten left carrier bearing retainer bolts to specifications. Using torque meter, measure total preload. Specified drive pinion preload at starting point with a NEW bearing is 2.2-4.1 INCH lbs. (.2-.5 N.m). If old bearing is reused, 1.1-2.0 INCH lbs. (.1-.2 N.m).

5) Stake counter driven gear nut. Install transmission case cap. Coat bolts with sealer (3 Bond 1324) and install carrier cover and gasket. Tighten bolts to specifications.

OVERDRIVE UNIT COMPONENT OVERHAUL

OVERDRIVE BRAKE

Disassembly

1) Pull up overdrive planetary gear and counter gear from transmission case. Measure clearance of overdrive brake. Place feeler gauge between piston and cushion plate. Specified clearance is .0201-.0661" (.51-1.68 mm).

2) Remove overdrive brake drum by using Torx socket to loosen 4 screws 1 turn at a time until spring tension is released. Remove overdrive brake drum with piston.

3) Remove snap ring and overdrive clutch from case. Remove bearing and race from clutch drum and case.

Reassembly

1) Install "O" rings onto piston. Coat "O" ring with ATF and install piston into drum. Be careful not to damage "O" ring. Install snap ring. Be sure ring snaps into groove.

2) Install flange facing flat end upward. Install following parts in order: flange, disc, plate, disc, plate, disc, plate, and cushion plate. Install cushion plate with rounded end downward.

3) Install piston return spring assembly. Install OD brake drum. Using Torx socket, tighten 4 screws evenly and gradually until return springs are snug. Make sure screw heads are lower than surface of case.

4) Check clearance of OD brake. Place feeler gauge between cushion plate and piston. Specified clearance is .0201-.0661" (.51-1.68 mm). Apply compressed air into oil passage with drum and listen for piston movement. If piston does not move, disassemble and inspect.

OVERDRIVE CLUTCH

Disassemby

1) Remove snap ring and hub from OD clutch drum. Remove 1 disc and thinner snap ring. Install clutch hub, hub and snap ring without thinner snap ring and measure clearance of overdrive clutch.

2) Measure clearance between piston and end of plate. Specified clearance is .0283-.0661" (.72-1.68 mm). Remove snap ring, hub and plates, and discs.

3) Using spring compressor block and arbor press, compress piston return spring and remove snap ring. Remove snap ring, spring retainer and 18 springs.

4) Install OD clutch drum on case. Apply compressed air to pressure apply passage of case. Remove OD clutch drum from case. If piston does not come out completely, use needle-nose pliers to remove. Remove "O" ring from piston.

Inspection

Inspect check ball of piston for free movement by shaking piston. Check that valve does not leak by applying low pressure compressed air.

Reassembly

1) Coat NEW "O" ring with ATF and install on piston. Press piston into drum with cup side up. DO NOT damage "O" ring. Install 18 springs. Set retainer and snap ring in place.

2) Set spring compressor block on spring retainer. Using arbor press, compress springs. Install snap ring by hand. Be sure end gap of ring is not aligned with spring retainer claw.

3) Install following parts in order: plate, disc, plate, disc and flange without installing thinner snap ring. Using low pressure compressed air, blow excessive ATF from discs. DO NOT use high pressure air as damage to discs could result.

4) Install hub and snap ring. Check clearance of OD clutch by placing feeler gauge between piston and end of plate. Specified clearance is .0283-.0661" (.72-1.68 mm).

5) If specified clearance is exceeded, clutch pack is probably worn. If clearance is less than specified, parts may be incorrectly assembled or excess amount of ATF may be on discs.

6) Remove OD clutch outer snap ring, hub and disc to allow installation of thinner snap ring. Compress and install snap ring into groove by hand. Be sure ends of snap ring are not alinged with cut-outs.

7) Install disc, hub and outer snap ring. Be sure ends of snap ring are not aligned with cut-outs. Install OD clutch into case. Apply compressed air into case passage and confirm piston moves. If piston does not move, disassemble and inspect. Remove OD clutch from case.

OVERDRIVE ONE-WAY CLUTCH

Disassembly

1) Install OD clutch into one-way clutch while turning OD gear clockwise. Hold OD clutch and turn intermediate shaft. Shaft should turn feeely clockwise and should lock counterclockwise.

2) Install No. 3 OD planetary thrust washer facing groove toward OD case. Install OD one-way clutch into hub. Be sure it is installed in correct direction. Install retaining plate and snap ring.

3) Install overdrive clutch into one-way clutch. Hold OD clutch and turn intermediate shaft. Shaft should turn freely clockwise and should lock counterclockwise. Remove OD clutch from one-way clutch.

OVERDRIVE CASE

Disassembly

1) To disassemble accumulator piston of OD clutch, remove snap ring, retaining plate and spring. Assemble OD clutch onto case and apply compressed air to oil passage to remove piston. Remove OD clutch.

2) Push 1 end of ring into groove and unhook both ends of ring by hand. Spread ring apart and remove.

TOYOTA MODEL A140E & A140L (Cont.)

Reassembly

Spread ring aprart and install ring into groove. Push 1 end of ring into groove and hook both ends by hand. Install piston spring, retainer plate and snap ring.

COUNTER DRIVE GEAR AND BEARING

Disassembly

1) Pry off locking washer with screwdriver. Hold shaft in soft-jawed vise and loosen adjusting nut. Remove nut and washer. Remove intermediate shaft bearing by using bearing puller and arbor press.

2) Using press, remove counter drive gear and front bearing together. Remove rear bearing using bearing puller and arbor press. To remove OD planetary ring gear from counter drive gear, pull up ring gear, compress snap ring with needle-nose pliers and remove from groove.

3) Remove ring gear from counter drive gear. Using brass bar and hammer, drive outer races from counter drive gear. Remove snap ring from counter drive gear.

Reassembly

1) Install snap ring into counter drive gear. Using a bearing race installer and arbor press, install 2 outer races into counter drive gear. Press in outer races until they touch snap ring.

2) While pushing down on ring gear, squeeze snap ring end with needle-nose pliers and install OD planetary ring gear into counter drive gear. When snap ring is fully seated, end is free.

3) Using plate and arbor press, install rear bearing into shaft. Press in bearing until side surface of inner race touches shaft. Install counter drive gear onto shaft and mesh ring gear with planetary pinions. Place front bearing onto shaft. Hold ring gear to prevent from falling.

4) Press in bearing until axial play between bearings is .020" (.50 mm). Using Bearing Collar (09350-32010) and arbor press, install intermediate shaft bearing. Press bearing until it just touches with front bearing of counter drive gear.

5) Place locking washer and adjusting nut onto intermediate shaft. Adjust preload of counter drive by placing Gauge (09350-32010) onto adjusting nut and hold shaft in a soft-jawed vise.

6) Rotate counter drive gear right and left several times before measuring preload. Then, tighten adjusting nut to the point where following gear starting load occours. Specified preload is 2.0-3.4 INCH lbs. (920-1520 G). Bend locking washer tab until even with adjusting nut groove.

COMPONENT INSTALLATION

OVERDRIVE CLUTCH

Install thrust bearing and races on case and OD clutch. Make sure races are installed in correct direction. Coat bearing and races with petroleum jelly to hold in place. Install OD clutch onto case.

OVERDRIVE BRAKE

1) Install "O" rings onto piston. Coat "O" ring with ATF and install piston into drum. Be careful not to damage "O" ring. Install snap ring, being sure it fits into groove.

2) Install flange facing flat end upward. Install following parts in order: flange, disc, plate, disc,plate, disc, plate, cushion plate. Install cushion plate facing rounded end downward.

3) Install piston return spring assembly. Install OD brake drum. Using Torx socket, tighten 4 screws evenly and gradually until return springs are snug. Make sure screw heads are lower than surface of case.

4) Check clearance of OD brake. Place feeler gauge between cushion plate and piston. Specified clearance is .0201-.0661" (.51-1.68 mm). Apply compressed air into oil passage with drum and listen for piston movement. If piston does not move, disassemble and inspect.

OVERDRIVE GEAR ASSEMBLY

1) Install OD gear assembly onto case and align center of shaft and bearing. Lock OD clutch drum with screwdriver and turn counter drive gear clockwise.

2) When meshing flukes of discs with hub, mesh one-way clutch with inner race. If OD gear assembly is properly installed to OD case, clearance between them will be about .138" (3.5 mm).

TIGHTENING SPECIFICATIONS

Application	Ft. Lbs (N.m)
Converter-to-Drive Plate Bolts	13 (18)
Converter Dust Cover Attaching Bolts	18 (24)
Drive Plate Mounting Bolts	61 (83)
Oil Pan Drain Plug	22 (30)
Oil Pump Mounting Bolts	16 (22)
Oil Cooler Tube Union Nuts	25 (34)
Overdrive Unit-to-Transmission Case Mounting Bolts	18 (24)
Stiffener Plate Mounting Bolts	27 (37)
Transmission Housing Mounting Bolts	27 (37)
12 mm Bolts	47 (51)
10 mm Bolts	25 (34)
Differential	
Carrier Bearing Cap Bolts	
Left	14 (19)
Right	53 (72)
Carrier Cover Bolts	18 (24)
Counter Driven Gear Mounting Nut	127 (172)
Maximum Torque (Preload Adj.)	213 (289)
Ring Gear Mounting Bolts	71 (96)
Side Bearing Retainer	14 (19)
	INCH Lbs. (N.m)
Cam Assembly Mounting Bolt	65 (7.2)
Detent Spring Mounting Bolts	89 (10)
Lower-to-Upper Valve Body Attaching Bolts	44-52 (4.9-5.8)
Manual Valve & Body Attaching Bolts	89 (10)
Oil Pan Attaching Bolts	43 (4.8)
Oil Strainer Attaching Bolts	89 (10)
Parking Pawl Mounting Bolt	165 (7.2)
Speed Sensor Bracket Bolt	108 (12)
Stator Shaft-to-Oil Pump Attaching Bolts	89 (10)
Tube Bracket Attaching Bolts	89 (10)
Upper-to-Lower Valve Body Attaching Bolts	44-52 (4.9-5.8)
Valve Body Mounting Bolts	89 (10)

Automatic Transmissions

VOLKSWAGEN TYPE 010 3-SPEED

Golf, Jetta, Scirocco

IDENTIFICATION

Number "010" denoting transmission type is cast into top of transaxle case over transmission portion. Code letters and date of manufacture is stamped into machined flat on bellhousing rim. Code letters "TJ" or "TNA" denote 1985 models. Valve body code letter is cast into valve body at end of 9-digit part number. Code letters "FG" denote 1985 valve bodies. Torque converter code letter is stamped on side of attaching lug. Code letter "K" denotes 1985 torque converter.

DESCRIPTION

Transaxle assembly consists of 2 main units: Automatic transmission and final drive assembly. The transmission housing contains 2 planetary gear sets, 2 multiple-disc clutches, 1 brake band and servo, 1 multiple-disc brake, a 1-way clutch and a hydraulic control system. The final drive housing contains torque converter, governor for transmission, three-gear type ring and pinion assembly and differential unit.

Transmissions with "E-Mode" operation are designed to improve fuel economy. The transmission valve body has redesigned ATF passages and some additional valves. The forward clutch is also redesigned. With selector lever in "E" position, transmission is disengaged from differential whenever accelerator pedal is released. In any other selector lever position, transmission operates the same as the conventional model.

CAUTION: Never tow a vehicle with this automatic transmission with the front wheels on the ground. Bearings can be damaged by lack of lubrication. If vehicle must be towed, place selector in "N" and lift front wheels. Do not tow vehicle backwards.

LUBRICATION & ADJUSTMENT

See appropriate AUTOMATIC TRANSMISSION SERVICING article in IMPORT GENERAL SERVICING section.

Fig. 1: Cross-Sectional View of Volkswagen Type 010 3-Speed Automatic Transmission Assembly

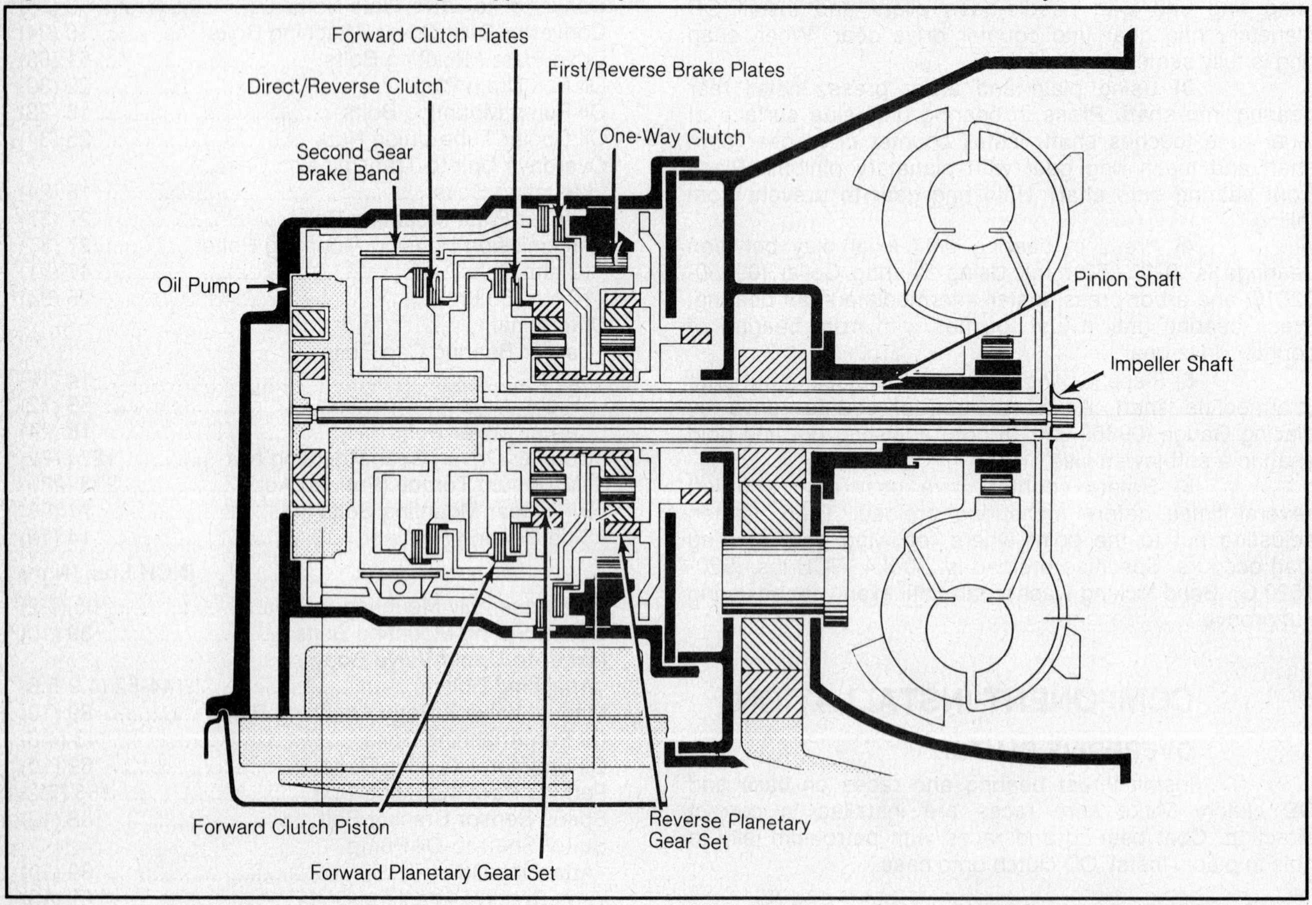

VOLKSWAGEN TYPE 010 3-SPEED (Cont.)

SERVICE (IN VEHICLE)

DRIVE AXLE SHAFTS

See appropriate DRIVE AXLE SHAFT article in IMPORT AXLE SHAFTS, OVERDRIVES & TRANSFER CASES section.

TROUBLE SHOOTING

NOTE: **The trouble shooting diagnosis steps are arranged in the order of probability.**

NO MOVEMENT

In Any Gear

Low ATF fluid level. Manual lever cable disconnected from manual valve. Drive plate broken or not bolted to torque converter. Main pressure valve sticking. Oil pump or pump drive faulty/no pressure. Broken gear or shaft, possibly in final drive.

In Forward Gears

Forward clutch internal damage (worn or burned plates, spring broken, seals leaking, etc.).

In 1st Gear (In "D" Or "2")

Check 1st gear 1-way clutch for slipping or forward clutch internal damage.

In 1st Gear (In "1")

Check transmission for worn and/or burnt 1st/Reverse brake plates.

In 2nd Gear

Check 2nd gear brake band for out of adjustment or burnt. Check for defective servo.

In 3rd Gear

Direct/Reverse clutch internal damage (worn and/or burnt plates, seals leaking, etc.).

In Reverse

Check 1st/Reverse brake plate for wear or burned linings. Direct/Reverse clutch internal damage. Forward clutch seized in applied position.

IRREGULAR MOVEMENT

In All Forward Gears

Check for low ATF fluid level and/or oil pump pick-up strainer partially clogged.

NO UPSHIFT

Into 2nd Gear

Governor drive defective. Governor dirty or improperly assembled during repair. Accumulator cover plate loose. Valve body assembly dirty. 1st/2nd gear shift valve sticking.

Into 3rd Gear

Governor dirty. Valve body assembly dirty. 2nd/3rd gear shift valve sticking. Sealing balls missing from transfer plate.

NO DOWNSHIFTS

Into 2nd And/Or 1st Gear

Governor or valve body dirty. Check 1st/2nd and/or 2nd/3rd gear shift valves for sticking, in valve body.

DELAYED ENGAGEMENT ON UPSHIFTS

1st-2nd

Fluid level too low. Valve body assembly dirty. 2nd gear brake band out of adjustment, worn or burnt. Incorrect piston installed in 2nd gear brake band servo during repair.

2nd-3rd

Fluid level too low. Valve body assembly dirty. 2nd gear brake band out of adjustment, worn or burnt. Incorrect piston installed in 2nd gear brake band servo during repair. Direct/Reverse clutch plates worn or burnt. Incorrect Direct/Reverse clutch installed during repair.

SHIFT SPEEDS ABOVE OR BELOW NORMAL

Governor or valve body assembly dirty, damaged or improperly installed. Paper gasket for transmission or intermediate plate damaged.

INCORRECT OPERATING PRESSURES

Check for defective oil pump, leakage in housing, oil leaks at oil seals and sealing surfaces. Check control valves for sticking.

CLUTCH AND BAND APPLICATION CHART (ELEMENTS IN USE)

Selector Lever Position	Forward Clutch	Direct-Reverse Clutch	First-Reverse Brake	Second Gear Band	One Way Clutch
D - DRIVE					
First Gear	X				X
Second Gear	X			X	
Third Gear	X	X			
2 - INTERMEDIATE					
First Gear	X				X
Second Gear	X			X	
1 - LOW	X		X		
R - REVERSE		X	X		

NEUTRAL OR PARK – All clutches, brake and band released and/or ineffective.

Automatic Transmissions

VOLKSWAGEN TYPE 010 3-SPEED (Cont.)

IMPROPER "E-MODE" OPERATION
Transmission Does Not Disengage From Engine At Closed Throttle With Shift Lever In "E"

Accelerator cable or shift lever cable incorrectly adjusted. Main pressure is to high. Declutching valve in valve body sticking.

TESTING

ROAD TEST

1) Before road testing, be certain that fluid level, condition and control linkage adjustments have been checked and corrected as necessary. During test, transmission should upshift and downshift at approximately the speeds shown in chart. See SHIFT SPEED SPECIFICATIONS.

2) All shifts may vary somewhat due to production tolerances or tire size. The important factor is the quality of the shifts. All shifts should be smooth, responsive and with no slippage or engine speed runaway.

3) Slippage or engine runaway in any gear usually indicates clutch, band or brake problems. The slipping unit in a particular gear can usually be identified by noting transmission operation in other selector positions and comparing which internal units are applied in those positions. See CLUTCH & BAND APPLICATION Chart.

4) This process of elimination can be used to detect any unit which slips and to confirm proper operation of good units. However, the actual cause of the malfunction usually cannot be easily decided.

5) Practically any condition can be caused by leaking hydraulic circuits or sticking valves. Therefore, unless an obvious condition exists, do not disassemble transmission until hydraulic pressure tests have been made.

NOTE: If shift points are incorrect or transmission does not kick down, check accelerator cable adjustments.

HYDRAULIC PRESSURE TEST

NOTE: To properly check hydraulic pressure, tests should be made on a dynamometer. If necessary, full throttle test may be made while driving vehicle on highway.

CAUTION: The engine idle speed must be adjusted to specification when performing pressure tests or readings will be inaccurate.

1) Connect 0-150 psi (0-10 kg/cm^2) pressure gauge to main pressure test point on case (adjacent to servo cover). *See Fig. 2.* Run engine until transmission is at normal operating temperature. Place selector lever in "D". Run engine to over 31 MPH, release throttle and read pressure on gauge (with engine idling).

2) With transmission in "D", run engine at full throttle (with vehicle speed above 31 MPH). Note pressure. With vehicle at rest, place selector lever in "R" position. Note reading on pressure gauge with engine idling.

3) Pressures in each part of test should be as shown in chart. See MAIN PRESSURES chart. If pressures obtained do not match those shown in chart, refer to INCORRECT OPERATING PRESSURES in TROUBLE SHOOTING section. Remove pressure gauge and install pressure tap plug.

SHIFT SPEED SPECIFICATIONS

Application	Shift Points (MPH)[1] Full Throttle	Kickdown
Transmission I.D. Codes "TF", "TK" & "TN"		
1st-2nd Upshift	21-33	37-39
2nd-3rd Upshift	50-61	64-66
3rd-2nd Downshift	36-48	61-63
2nd-1st Downshift	15-18	26-29
Transmission I.D. Code "TH"		
1st-2nd Upshift	23-27	34-37
2nd-3rd Upshift	49-61	58-60
3rd-2nd Downshift	32-45	53-55
2nd-1st Downshift	17-21	28-30
Transmission I.D. Code "TM"		
1st-2nd Upshift	21-24	35-37
2nd-3rd Upshift	50-61	61-62
3rd-2nd Downshift	33-45	56-58
2nd-1st Downshift	16-19	30-33

1 – When checking the shift points, the speedometer readings may vary within permissible manufacturing tolerances.

MAIN PRESSURES

Application	psi (kg/cm²)
"D" @ Idle [1]	42-44 (2.9-3.0)
"D" @ Full Throttle [2]	85-86 (5.85-5.95)
"R" @ Idle [1]	131-145 (9.0-10.0)

1 – Test should be performed on a dynamometer whenever possible. Perform idle test with vehicle stationary.
2 – Full throttle test up to more than 31 MPH.

Fig. 2: View of Transmission Case Showing Pressure Test Connection

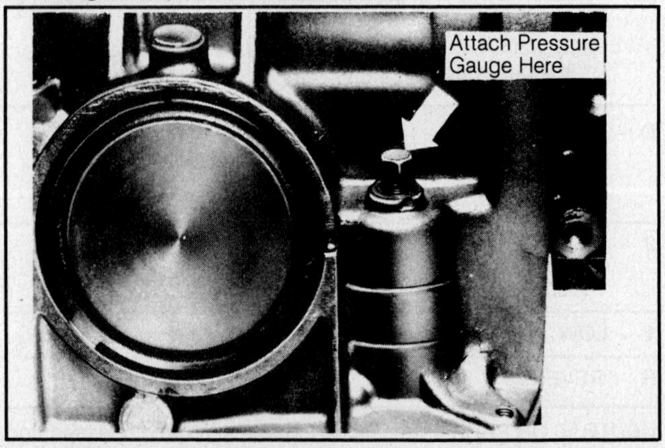

Only if defect cannot be found during other checks should a pressure check be carried out.

STALL SPEED TEST

Testing Precautions

Check stall speed only if vehicle shows poor performance or acceleration (despite properly tuned engine). When making test, do not hold throttle open any longer than the time it takes to read tachometer or torque converter will overheat. Maximum stall speed test time is 20 seconds (5 seconds with "E-Mode"). If test must be repeated, wait at least 20 seconds.

If engine speed exceeds limits shown, release accelerator immediately as clutch or band slippage is indicated. See STALL SPEED SPECIFICATIONS.

Testing Procedure

1) With engine at normal operating temperature, connect a tachometer to engine. Start engine and set parking and service brakes. Place selector lever in "D".

2) Depress accelerator briefly to full throttle and note maximum RPM obtained. Repeat test with selector lever in "1" position. Engine speed should be within limits shown in table.

NOTE: **Normal stall speed will drop about 125 RPM per 3200 feet altitude (4000 feet with "E-Mode"). Also, stall speed will drop slightly at high ambient temperature.**

STALL SPEED SPECIFICATIONS

Application	Stall RPM
Transmission Code Letters	
TF [1]	2300-2600
TH [2]	2500-2800
TM [3]	2555-2805
Engine Size	
1.5L	2250-2500
1.6L	2100-2350
1.7L	2200-2500

[1] – Torque convertor code letter "M".
[2] – Torque convertor code letter "X".
[3] – With "E-Mode".

Test Results

1) If stall speed is too high in "D", but OK in "1", 1-way clutch is defective. If stall speed is too high in both ranges, forward clutch is faulty.

2) If stall speed is about 200 RPM below normal, check engine operation (ignition timing, fuel injection, compression, pump timing).

3) If stall speed is about 400 RPM too low, stator 1-way clutch in torque converter is defective. Replace torque converter.

REMOVAL & INSTALLATION

TRANSAXLE ASSEMBLY

See appropriate AUTOMATIC TRANSMISSION REMOVAL article in IMPORT GENERAL SERVICING section.

TORQUE CONVERTER

NOTE: **The torque converter only requires removal when seal or bushing replacement is needed or to clean unit when transmission failure has contaminated ATF.**

CAUTION: **Do not rock or tilt converter during removal or installation. Damage to seal, stator one-way clutch or other components in converter hub can occur.**

Removal

Remove transaxle assembly. Remove wire or securing bar that was installed across mouth of bellhousing during transaxle removal. Holt torque conveter with both hands while pulling it (with a twisting motion) off its support tube on final drive housing.

Cleaning & Inspection

1) Torque converter is a sealed unit and cannot be disassembled for service. Replace the unit if leaky or noisy, loose welds are evident or if stall speed test shows unit to be faulty.

2) When charred material from a burned clutch disc or other pollutants have entered ATF, residual pollutants must be removed from torque converter. Attach a piece of plastic hose (with 5/16" I.D.) to a plastic squeeze bottle.

3) Ensure both hose connection and cap are an airtight fit on bottle. If necessary, cut free end of hose at an angle to allow it to lay nearly flat against lowest part of convertor interior.

4) Lay torque converter on work surface with one side elevated (low side toward hose and bottle). Place bottle lower than converter. Squeeze bottle and insert hose in converter. Release bottle and, as soon as ATF begins to flow, loosen cap to allow air to escape. Siphon out remaining ATF.

5) If torque converter requires replacement, inspect converter for identification code mark (stamped on boss on outside diameter of unit). Ensure the same code is stamped on replacement unit. See TORQUE CONVERTER CODE LETTER & APPLICATION table.

NOTE: **A leaking oil seal is often caused by a worn bushing in converter hub. Check bushing for excessive wear or out-of-round whenever seal is replaced.**

Oil Seal Replacement

1) Check converter hub seal seat for scoring, pitting or excessive wear. If seal seat on hub is rough, worn or damaged, replace converter. Do not attempt to smooth seal contact area of converter with emery cloth.

NOTE: **Ensure oil seal seat edge is chamfered. If not, round front edge with emery cloth to prevent seal damage during convertor installation.**

2) Remove any sharp edges and burrs with fine emery cloth. Do not damage surface where oil seal makes contact. If removal is necessary, note installed position, pry off oil seal and discard. Clean seal seat.

3) Dip new oil seal in clean ATF and drive into position using Oil Seal Installer (US4450). Do not allow gas or solvent to contact silicone-type seal or seal must be replaced.

NOTE: **Torque converter replacement bushings are manufactured to size and require no reaming or honing.**

VOLKSWAGEN TYPE 010 3-SPEED (Cont.)

TORQUE CONVERTER CODE LETTER & APPLICATION

Application	Code Letter
1.5L Engine (Gas)	U
1.6L Engine (Gas)	M
1.6L Engine (Diesel)	X
1.7L Engine (Gas)	K

Bushing Replacement

1) Check bushing I.D. for excessive wear and out-of-round using an inside micrometer. Bushing wear limit is 1.348" (34.25 mm) Maximum allowable out-of-round is .001" (.03 mm).

2) To replace bushing, assemble Bushing Pullers (VW201 and US691) and Adapter (US4452). Withdraw bushing from converter hub. *See Fig. 3.* Press new bushing into place using Bushing Drivers (VW412, VW420 and VW474) and Support (VW401).

Fig. 3: Removing Torque Converter Bushing

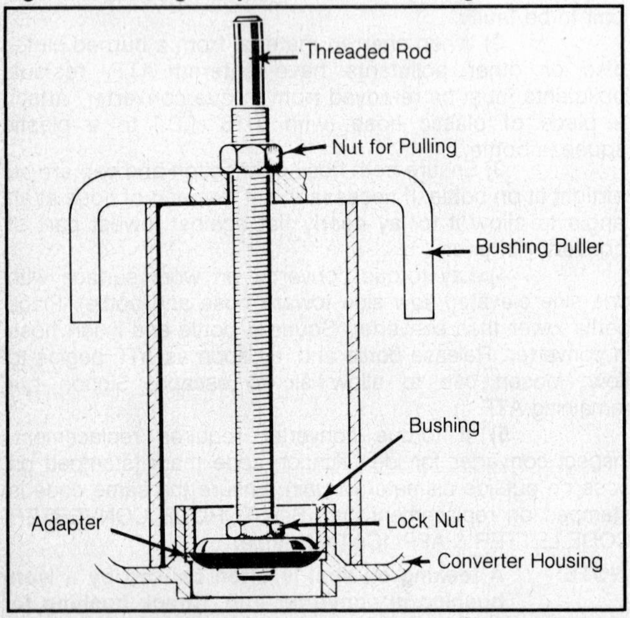

Ensure the converter housing is not damaged during bushing removal and installation.

Installation

1) Install torque converter in reverse of removal procedure. Ensure pump shaft is completely seated in pump (inside transmission) by checking splined ends for proper lenght.

2) Correct pump shaft lenght is 13 15/16" (354 mm), measured from tip-to-tip. Install converter by turning slowly clockwise and counterclockwise so turbine and pump shaft splines will engage.

TRANSMISSION INTERNAL LINKAGE (PARKING LOCK, KICKDOWN & MANUAL VALVE LINKAGE)

NOTE: **The kickdown valve operating lever and parking lock operating rod have been modified. With modified operating rod, parking lock engagement lever is secured with only 1 circlip. The kickdown valve operating lever has been flattened slightly at contact surface. The new-type kickdown valve operating lever can be used on earlier transmissions. Do not install earlier-type operating lever in transmissions with new kickdown valve.**

Removal & Disassembly

1) With ATF drained, oil pan detached and gasket discarded, remove valve body assembly from the transmission. Note linkage component locations for reassembly reference.

2) Remove "E" clip from parking lock operating lever pin. Detach parking lock pawl spring from under pawl. Detach "E" clip from operating rod guide pin. Pull operating rod assembly out of parking lever and detach from manual valve operating lever.

3) Slide parking lever off pin. From inside transmission case; detach small kickdown lever nut, with washer, from kickdown operating lever shaft. Remove kickdown valve operating lever.

4) Detach large manual lever retainer nut, with flat and lock washers, from cable lever. Slide manual lever off of cable lever. If necessary, pull cable lever from transmission case. Detach shaft and operating levers as needed. Discard "O" rings. *See Fig. 4.*

Inspection

1) Check parking lever roller and roller spring for excessive wear, damage and ease of movement. Inspect parking lock pawl, kickdown lever detent notches and manual lever detent notches for excessive wear or damage.

2) Check pin for parking lock pawl for location in case and straightness. If any linkage components are excessively worn or damaged, replace components as an assembly.

Reassembly & Installation

1) To complete installation, reverse removal procedures. To prevent ATF leaks when installing pin for parking lock pawl, ensure end of pin is flush with transmission case edge.

2) Install spring under parking lock pawl so that it will retract the pawl from engagement with notches in the periphery of the annular gear flange. Check the operation of the parking lock mechanism before installing valve body.

3) If cable lever was removed, install new "O" rings, lubricate with ATF and slide into transmission case. When installing operating lever for kickdown valve, ensure angled end of lever points toward center of transmission.

VALVE BODY ASSEMBLY

NOTE: **The valve body assembly may be removed with transaxle in the vehicle.**

Removal

1) Raise and support vehicle. Drain ATF. Detach oil pan mounting screws, remove oil pan and discard gasket. Detach mounting screws holding pump pick-up's ATF strainer to valve body assembly, then remove strainer.

2) Detach 10 (of 11) mounting bolts holding valve body assembly. Keep 1 bolt (near accumulator piston spring) installed so valve body does not fall.

3) While supporting valve body, remove remaining bolt. Remove valve body assembly. On transmissions through model No. 20 040, remove pump-to-valve body ATF strainer and discard. Do not replace this strainer.

4) If accumulator piston and spring require inspection, remove 3 galvanized screws from accumulator cover plate. Remove cover plate, spring and piston. If

Automatic Transmissions

VOLKSWAGEN TYPE 010 3-SPEED (Cont.)

Fig. 4: Bottom View of Transmission Case Showing Parking Lock, Kickdown & Manual Valve Linkage

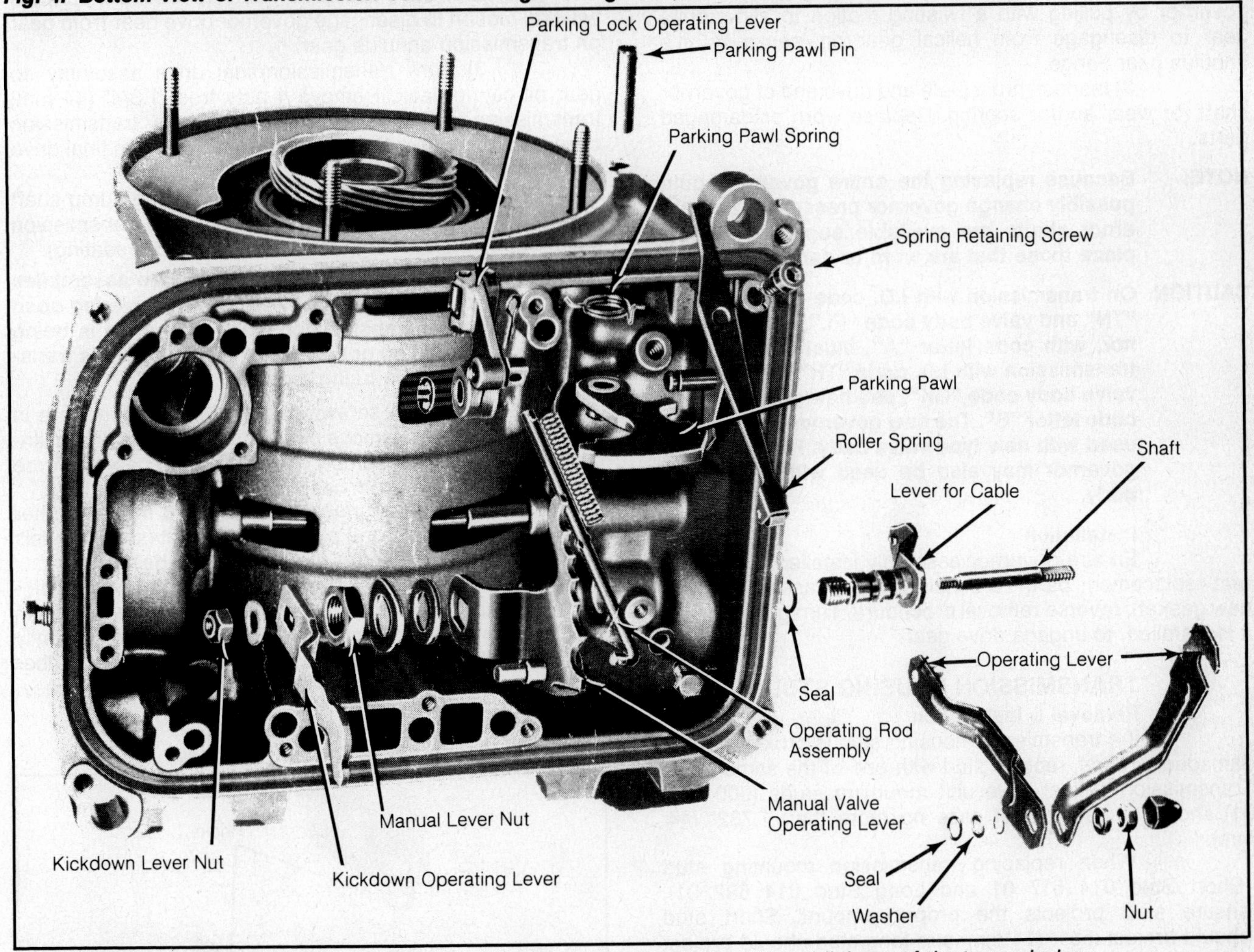

The oil pan and valve body assembly must be removed for access to the internal linkage of the transmission.

necessary, use circlip expanding pliers inserted into spring recess of piston to withdraw piston from transmission case. Inspect accumulator piston and note if sealing ring is separate or permanent type.

NOTE: On accumulator piston with separate sealing ring, install ring with lip toward pressure side of piston. Both separate and bonded sealing ring type pistons are interchangeable.

Installation

1) If accumulator piston was removed, lubricate sealing ring with ATF and install piston, spring and cover. Tighten mounting screws. If new valve body is being installed, ensure correct code letter of old valve body matches new valve body.

NOTE: The code letter is the only reliable indication that the valve body is suitable for the vehicle.

2) Position new valve body assembly on transmission with manual valve and kickdown valve correctly engaged with their operating levers. Attach valve body assembly to transmission case with 1 mounting bolt (near accumulator).

3) Install remaining bolts. Working in a diagonal patten, gradually tighten all mounting bolts. Install ATF strainer and tighten mounting bolts.

CAUTION: Do not use sealer on oil pan gasket. Any surplus may find its way into the ATF and cause control valve(s) to stick. Never tighten oil pan mounting bolts to more than 15 ft. lbs. (20 N.m) in an attempt to cure a leaking gasket. Overtightening will deform the pan and make it impossible to obtain a good seal. Always install a new gasket to correct leaks.

4) Install ATF oil pan (with new gasket) and tighten mounting bolts gradually, in a diagonal pattern. Refill transmission with new ATF, warm engine to operating temperature and recheck ATF level.

GOVERNOR

NOTE: Governor is located beneath a round, pressed steel cover on top of final drive housing, just right of transmission case. The cover is held in place with a spring wire clip. Governor may be removed with transaxle in vehicle.

1) Thoroughly clean governor housing and governor cover so that dirt cannot accidentally enter transaxle as cover is removed. Pry off spring wire clip that holds governor to transmission housing.

2) Remove cover and discard gasket. Withdraw governor by pulling with a twisting motion to allow drive gear to disengage from helical gear on transmission's annulus gear flange.

3) Inspect thrust plate and drive end of governor shaft for wear and/or scoring. Replace worn or damaged parts.

NOTE: **Because replacing the entire governor could possibly change governor pressure, new governor shafts are available separately to replace those that are worn or damaged.**

CAUTION: **On transmission with I.D. code "TF", "TK" or "TN" and valve body code "FL", a new governor, with code letter "A", must be used. On transmission with I.D. code "TH" or "TM" and valve body code "GK", use new governor with code letter "B". The new governor may only be used with new type valve body. Previous type governor may also be used with new valve body.**

Installation

Ensure governor assembly installed is the correct replacement part. To install governor assembly (with new gasket), reverse removal procedure. Turn governor, as it is installed, to engage drive gear.

TRANSMISSION HOUSING STUDS

Removal & Installation

If a transmission housing stud is broken or has damaged threads, replace stud with one of the same type. Transmission-to-final drive unit mounting studs (900 028 01) should project out of case no more than 1.732" (44 mm).

When replacing transmission mounting stud (Short Stud 014 517 01 and Long Stud 014 692 01), ensure stud projects the proper amount. Short stud should project .551" (14 mm) and long stud should project 1.339" (34 mm) from case.

TRANSAXLE DISASSEMBLY

NOTE: **Final drive disassembly and reassembly procedures are covered at end of this article.**

TRANSMISSION ASSEMBLY

Disassembly

1) With final drive housing/transmission assembly removed from vehicle, clean outside case thoroughly and disassemble in a clean area. When cleaning and wiping parts, use nylon cloth or paper towels. Common shop rags will leave lint that can interfere with transaxle's operation. Mount assembly on Repair Fixture (VW351 and VW309). Drain ATF from transmission.

CAUTION: **When removing/installing torque converter, do not rock or tilt converter. This could damage the converter oil seal, stator 1-way clutch or other components in torque converter hub.**

NOTE: **Remove governor before separating transmission from final drive unit.**

2) Withdraw torque converter from final drive housing using a twisting motion. Set converter aside and cover hub opening. Remove governor cover and gasket. Pull governor from final drive housing. Use a clockwise twisting motion to disengage governor drive gear from gear on transmission annulus gear.

3) Turn transmission/final drive assembly so gear oil cannot leak. Remove 4 nuts from 1 3/4" (44 mm) transmission-to-final drive studs. Separate transmission case from final drive housing. Drain gear oil from final drive if unit is to be repaired.

4) Withdraw 13.937" (354 mm) long pump shaft and 10.44" (265.1 mm) long turbine shaft from transmission (check turbine shaft rings for wear and proper seating).

NOTE: **Once transmission and final drive assemblies are separated, keep out dirt by covering open end of transmission when final drive is being worked on or both ends of final drive as transmission is being repaired.**

5) Detach screws retaining separation plate in transmission case. Remove plate and discard gasket. Withdraw annulus gear assembly (governor drive gear/Reverse planetary ring gear) from case. *See Fig. 6.*

6) Withdraw needle bearing and thrust washer from top of reverse (front) planetary gear set (some models may have thrust washer in place of needle bearing).

7) Using screwdriver, pry out large circlip retaining 1-way clutch assembly in case. Fabricate 2 hooks from 3/16" welding rod. Using hooks, lift 1-way clutch, internally and externally splined 1st/Reverse gear brake discs (3 fiber and 3 steel) and the reverse planetary gear set from case. *See Fig. 5.*

Fig. 5: Removing 1-Way Clutch from Case

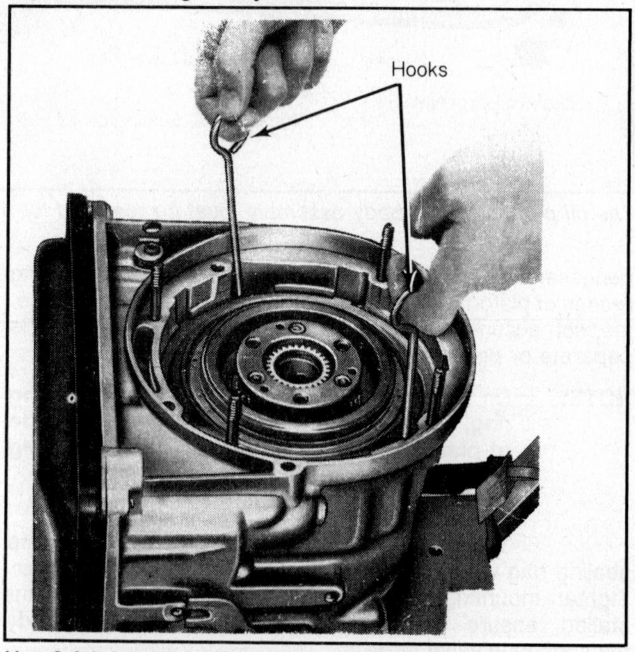

Use 2 fabricated hooks to lift assembly out of case.

8) Remove thrust washer(s). Withdraw apply shell (with internally splined washer), forward (rear) planetary gear set (with sun gear), needle bearing (some models may have thrust washer in place of needle bearing) and forward clutch as an assembly.

NOTE: **When removing forward clutch assembly, ensure thrust washers and/or thrust needle bearing (radial-roller type) which oil pump rides against are not lost or damaged.**

VOLKSWAGEN TYPE 010 3-SPEED (Cont.)

Fig. 6: Exploded View of Automatic Transmission Assembly

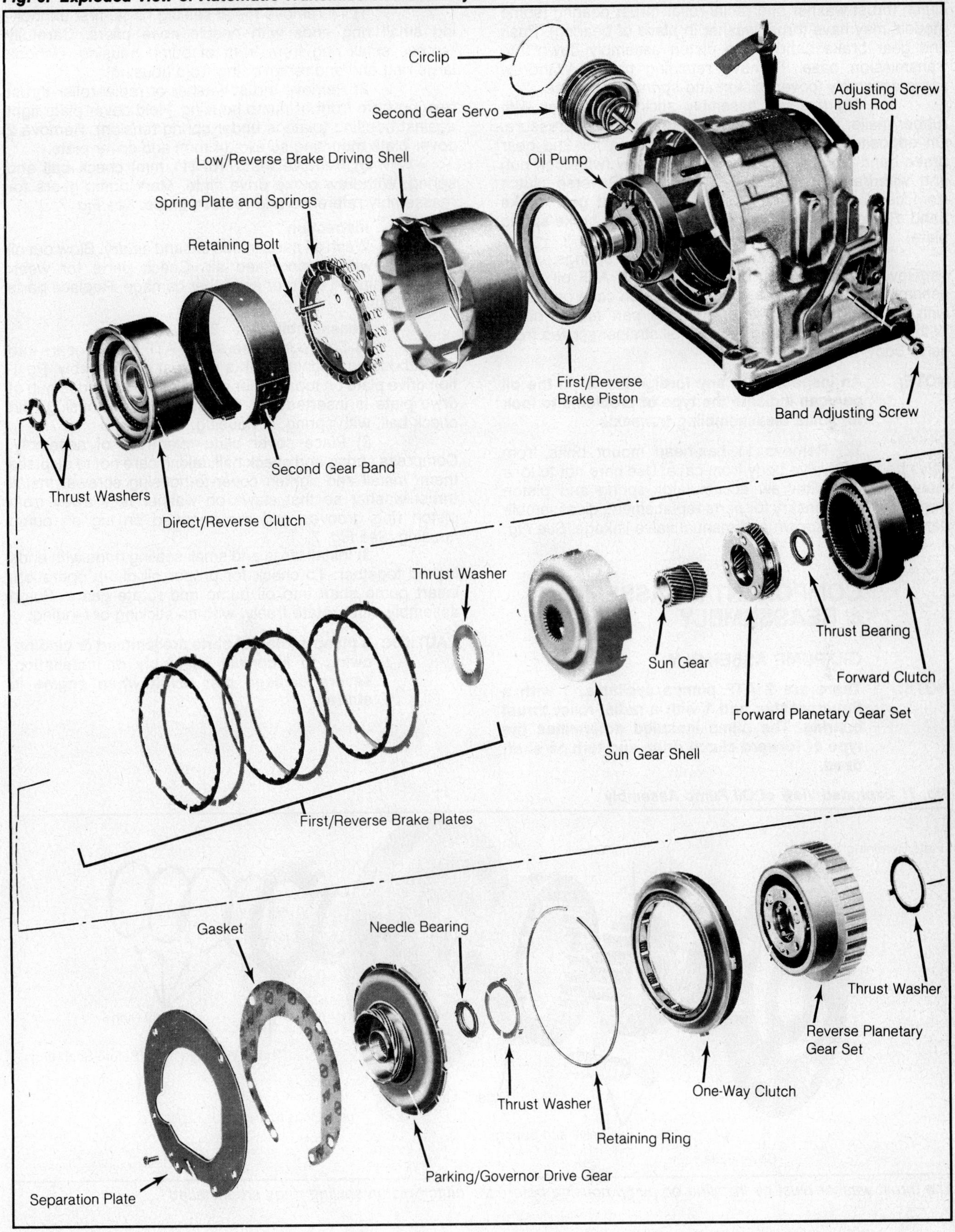

Automatic Transmissions

VOLKSWAGEN TYPE 010 3-SPEED (Cont.)

9) Remove forward clutch-to-Direct/Reverse clutch thrust washer and radial-roller thrust bearing (some models may have thrust washer in place of bearing). Push 2nd gear brake band servo piston assembly down into transmission case. Remove retaining circlip. Withdraw servo assembly (cover, piston and spring) from case.

10) If servo assembly sticks, tap cover with rubber mallet until piston pops out under spring pressure. On opposite side of case, loosen lock nut for 2nd gear brake band adjusting screw. Detach screw (with lock nut) and withdraw push rod. Remove Direct/Reverse clutch from case. From inside case, withdraw 2nd gear brake band. Remove 5 bolts from 1st/Reverse gear brake spring plate.

11) Withdraw plate and springs. Pull 1st/Reverse apply shell, brake piston and ATF oil pump assembly from case. Position transmission case on bench with oil pan facing upward. Remove pan mount bolts. Withdraw pan and gasket. Remove oil strainer screws from valve body.

NOTE: **An inspection of any foreign matter in the oil pan can indicate the type of problems to look for while disassembling transaxle.**

12) Remove 11 hex-head mount bolts from valve body. Lift valve body from case. Use care not to lose manual valve. Withdraw accumulator spring and piston from case. If necessary for parts replacement, disassemble parking lock, kickdown and manual valve linkage. *See Fig. 4.*

COMPONENT DISASSEMBLY & REASSEMBLY

OIL PUMP ASSEMBLY

NOTE: **There are 2 ATF pumps available, 1 with a thrust washer and 1 with a radial-roller thrust bearing. The pump installed determines the type of forward clutch drum and turbine shaft used.**

Disassembly

1) To remove metal sealing rings, first unhooking small ring ends with needle nose pliers. Carefully remove small ring from front of pump housing. Unhook large ring end and remove ring from housing.

2) Remove thrust washer or radial-roller thrust bearing from front of pump housing. Hold cover plate tight against housing (plate is under spring tension). Remove 2 cover plate mounting screws (4 mm) and cover plate.

3) Remove the 7/16" (11 mm) check ball and spring. Withdraw pump drive plate. Mark pump gears for reassembly reference and remove gears. *See Fig. 7.*

Inspection

Wash all parts in solvent and air dry. Blow out oil passages with compressed air. Check parts for wear, scoring, chipped teeth or any other damage. Replace parts as necessary.

Reassembly

1) Coat pump gears with ATF. Install gears into pump housing, aligning marks made at disassembly. Position drive plate on top of inner gear. Ensure extended hub of drive plate is inserted into shaft opening of housing. Set check ball, with spring, in housing.

2) Place cover plate over rear of assembly. Compress spring and check ball, taking care not to displace them. Install and tighten cover-to-housing screws. Install thrust washer so that claws on washer face away from piston ring grooves and are engaged on lug on pump housing. *See Fig. 7.*

3) Install large and small sealing rings with ends locked together. To check for proper oil pump operation, insert pump shaft into oil pump and rotate gears. Pump assembly must rotate freely, with no sticking or binding.

CAUTION: **If pump's internal parts are jammed or binding, owing to incorrect assembly or installation, severe damage can result when engine is started.**

Fig. 7: Exploded View of Oil Pump Assembly

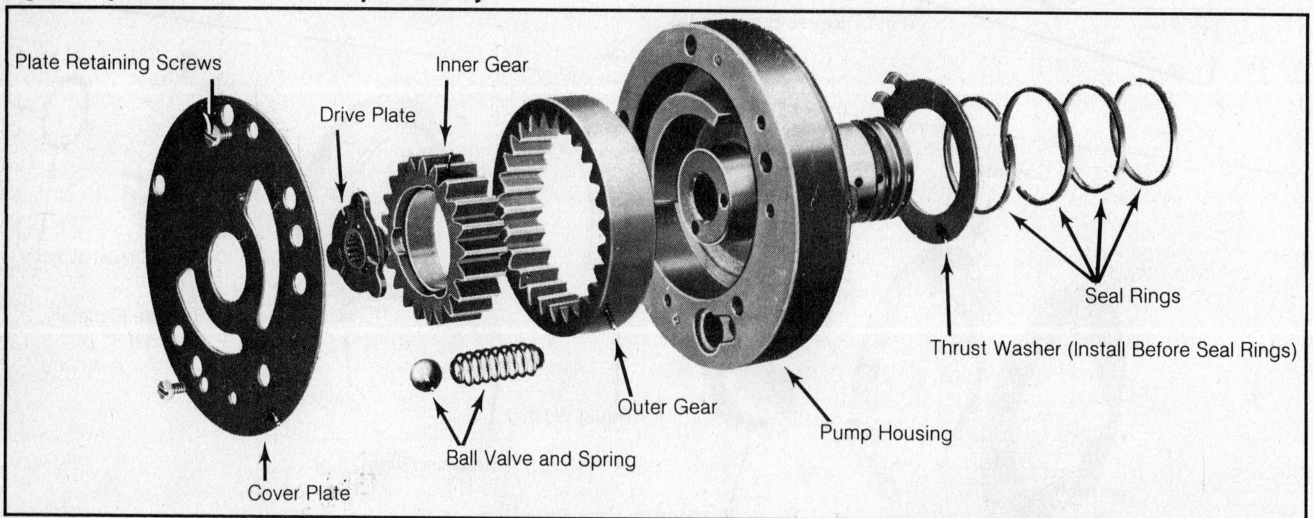

The thrust washer must be installed on pump housing before the clutch piston sealing rings are installed.

VOLKSWAGEN TYPE 010 3-SPEED (Cont.)

VALVE BODY ASSEMBLY

Disassembly Precautions

As a rule, valve body disassembly is necessary only for cleaning. Disassemble valve body if ATF is very dirty or contaminated by large solid particles. Otherwise, immerse complete valve body assembly in cleaning fluid and blow dry with compressed air. Do not hold air jet so close that it moves the valves violently or spring damage can occur.

Valve body components, especially the springs, are very similar in appearance. If removed, ensure all components are separated and marked for identification, for reassembly reference.

Spring washers are no longer used in the following locations:

- Detent spring-to-transmission housing.
- Oil pump-to-transmission housing.
- End (cover) plate-to-valve body assembly.
- Support plate-to-transfer plate.
- Transfer plate-to-valve body assembly.
- Oil strainer-to-transfer plate.
- Oil pan-to-transmission housing.
- Support tube-to-final drive.
- Speedometer drive-to-final drive.
- Oil filler pipe-to-transmission.

When disassembling late model transmission, check previously listed bolts and nuts for a spring washer. If equipped, reinstall bolts and nuts with new spring washers.

Disassembly

1) With ATF drained and oil pan and gasket detached, remove valve body assembly from transmission. Remove oil strainer-to-valve body mount screws. Remove strainer cover, strainer and gasket. *See Fig. 8*.

2) Note position of galvanized valve body (accumulator piston cover) mounting screws for reassembly reference. Remove 3 galvanized screws, then remove 19 transfer plate-to-main valve body mounting screws.

NOTE: **When removing and disassembling valve body components, ensure valve body I.D. tag remains on valve body assembly during repairs.**

3) Inspect valve body for proper identification by checking code letters stamped on I.D. tag (screwed to transfer plate). Gas engine vehicles have valve body code letters "FL" and diesel engine vehicles have valve body code letters "GK". Lift off transfer and separator plates from main body, as an assembly. *See Fig. 9 and 10*.

NOTE: **Lift off separator plate and transfer plate as a unit so that ball valves remain in valve body and any foreign matter in transfer plate will be kept there (for the time being) by separator plate.**

4) Check transfer plate identification. On transaxle with I.D. code "TF" (gas engine), transfer plate I.D. is part number 010 325 283 J. On transaxle with I.D. code "TH" (diesel engine), transfer plate I.D. is part number 010 325 283 K. Ensure only identical components are used for replacement.

5) Check separation plate identification. On transaxle with I.D. code "TF", separator plate I.D. is 2 notches at arrow 1, 1 notch at arrow 2 and 1 notch at arrow 3. *See Fig. 11*. On transaxle with I.D. code "TH", separator plate I.D. is 3 notches at arrow 1, 2 notches at arrow 2 and 1 notch at arrow 3. Ensure only identical components are used for replacement.

Fig. 8: Exploded View of Oil Pan, Oil Strainer Components, Valve Body Assembly & Transmission Case

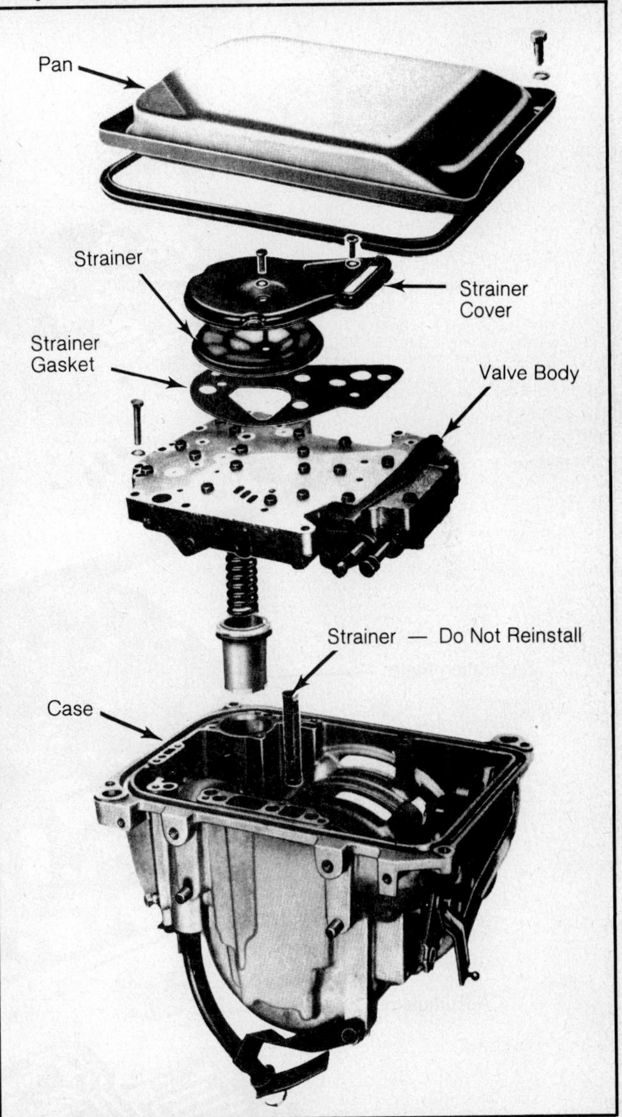

Checking the oil pan for foreign matter will help analysis of transmission problems during troubleshooting.

6) Note locations and sizes, then remove ball valves and springs from main valve body. *See Fig. 12*. There are five 6 mm ball valves in (early) valve body "AA" (transaxle code "EQ").

7) In valve body "FL" (transaxle code "TF"), valve body "GK" (transaxle code "TH") and in (early) valve body "BL" (transaxle code "TB"), there are five 6 mm ball valves and one 3 mm ball valve. *See Fig. 12*.

NOTE: **Do not alter settings of adjusting screws or interchange locations. Adjustments may only be set on a test stand.**

8) Detach mounting screws and remove large cover plate. Withdraw 1st/2nd governor plug, limiting and pressure valves, springs, adjusting screws and screw sleeves. Do not turn adjusting screws, they are factory set and can only be reset on a test stand.

9) Remove remaining cover plates one at a time and withdraw all valves, plugs, springs, spring seats and

VOLKSWAGEN TYPE 010 3-SPEED (Cont.)

Fig. 9: Exploded View Of Transfer Plate, Separation Plate & Valve Body Assembly (Gas Engine)

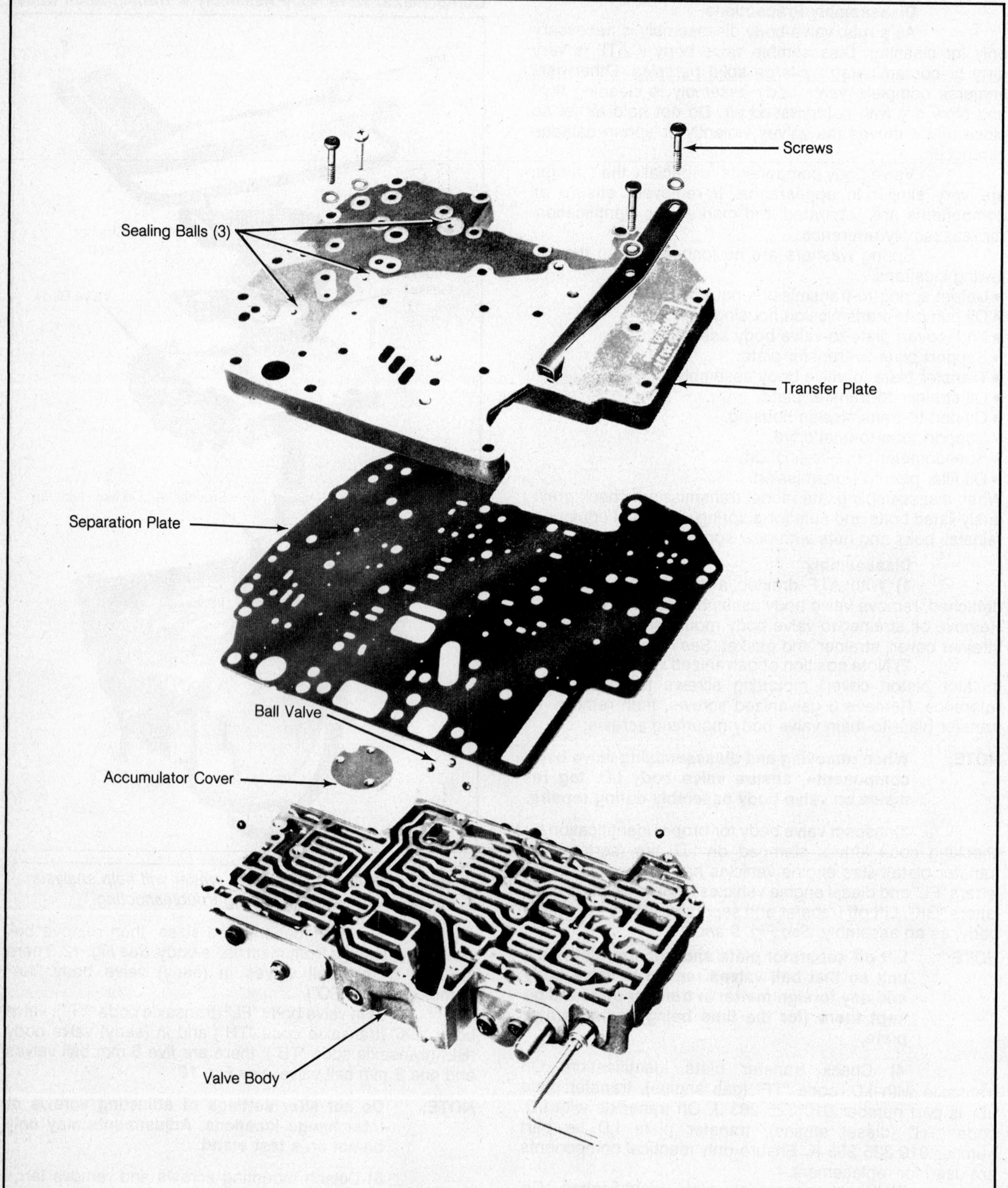

Transaxle (I.D. code "TF") components shown are transfer plate (010 325 283 J), separation plate (see step 5) and valve body (I.D. code "FL").

Automatic Transmissions

VOLKSWAGEN TYPE 010 3-SPEED (Cont.)

Fig. 10: Exploded View Of Transfer Plate, Separation Plate & Valve Body Assembly (Diesel Engine With "E-Mode")

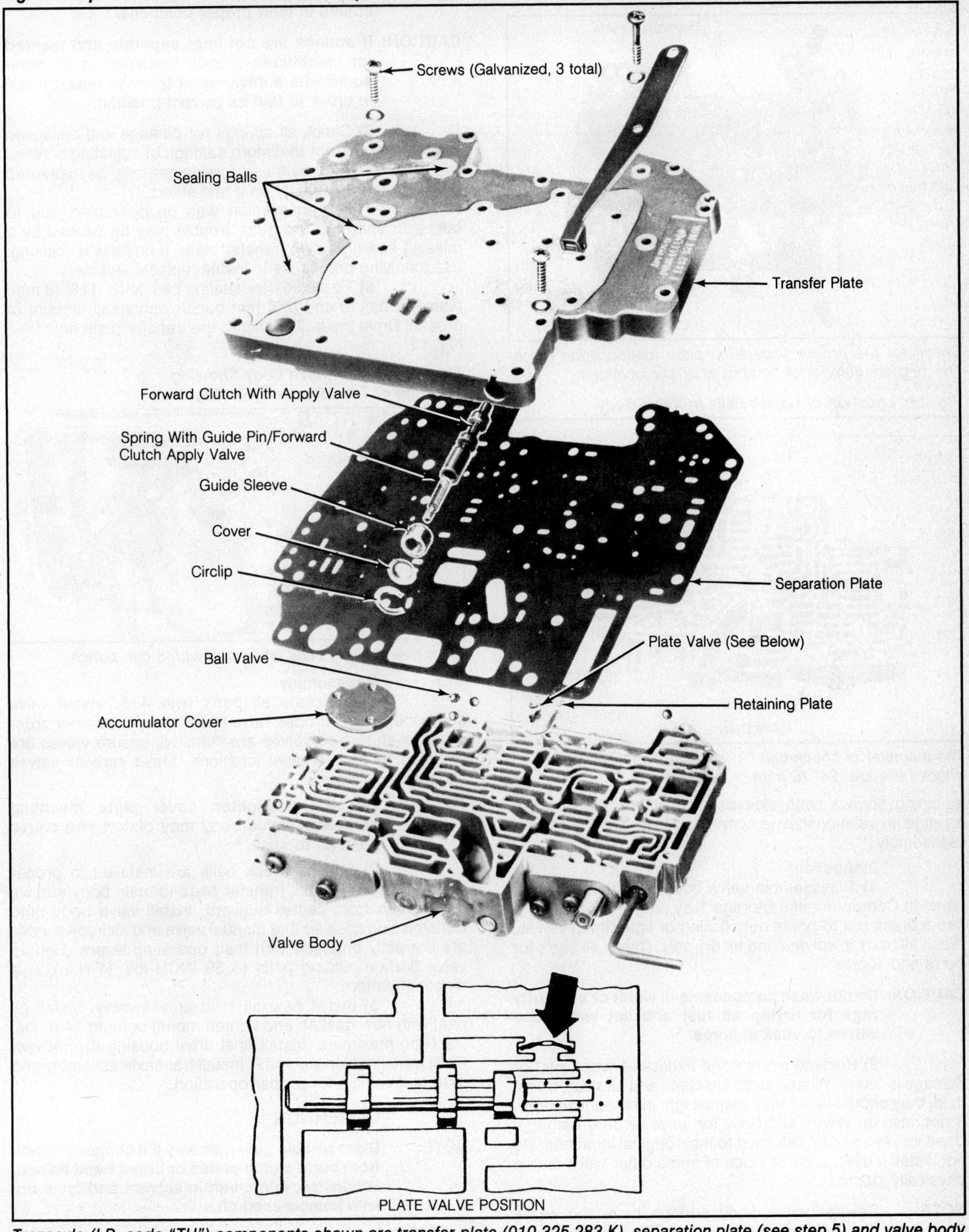

Transaxle (I.D. code "TH") components shown are transfer plate (010 325 283 K), separation plate (see step 5) and valve body (I.D. code "GK").

Automatic Transmissions

VOLKSWAGEN TYPE 010 3-SPEED (Cont.)

Fig. 11: Separation Plate Identification

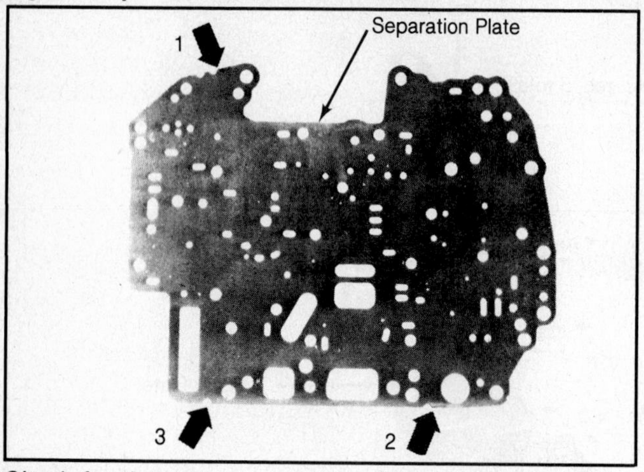

Check for the proper separation plate identification by inspecting the number of notches at arrow locations.

Fig. 12: Location of Check Balls in Valve Body

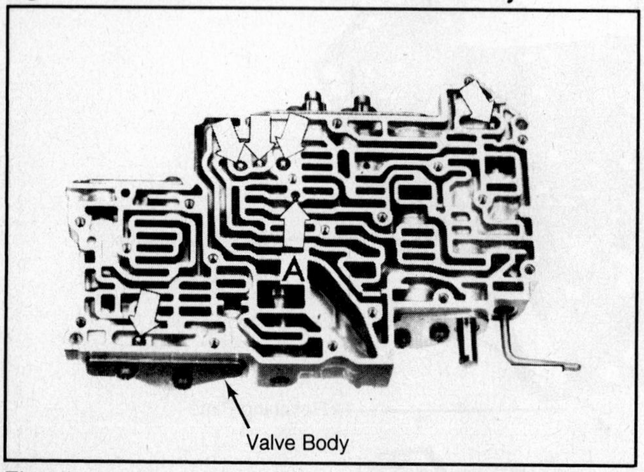

The diameter of check ball "A" is .12" (3 mm). All other check balls are .24" (6 mm).

adjusting screws (with sleeves). Tag all components, or arrange in relationship to valve body, to ensure correct reassembly.

Inspection

1) Disassemble valve body and place components in Compartmental Storage Tray (2008). If necessary, use a brass rod to press out sticking or tight-fitting valves. Wash all parts in solvent and air dry only. Check all parts for burrs and scores.

CAUTION: Do not wash components in water or use fluffy rags for drying as rust and lint will cause valves to stick in bores.

2) Replace assembly if excessive wear, rust or damage is found. When valves are clean and lubricated with fluid, they should fall of their own weight in respective bore. If not, inspect valves and body for valve or bore damage. Used valves must be returned to their original locations. Do not install a used valve in place of some other valve that is physically identical.

NOTE: Several valve body springs have the same dimensions but are not interchangeable due to different tolerances. Ensure all springs are the correct type for the application and are installed in their proper positions.

CAUTION: If springs are not kept separate and marked for identification, each spring must be measured with a micrometer (prior to reassembly) in order to find its correct position.

3) Check all springs for damage and collapsed coils. Take care not to disturb settings of adjusting screws; pressures affected by these screws can only be measured and adjusted accurately on a test stand.

4) If transmission was disassembled due to failure to shift into 3rd gear, trouble may be caused by a missing sealing ball in transfer plate. If any ball is missing, use following procedure to install replacement balls.

5) To install new sealing ball, stick .118" (3 mm) diameter ball to end of 8 mm punch with small amount of grease. Drive the ball flush into the transfer plate hole. *See Fig. 13.*

Fig. 13: View of Valve Body Showing Location of Transfer Plate Sealing Balls

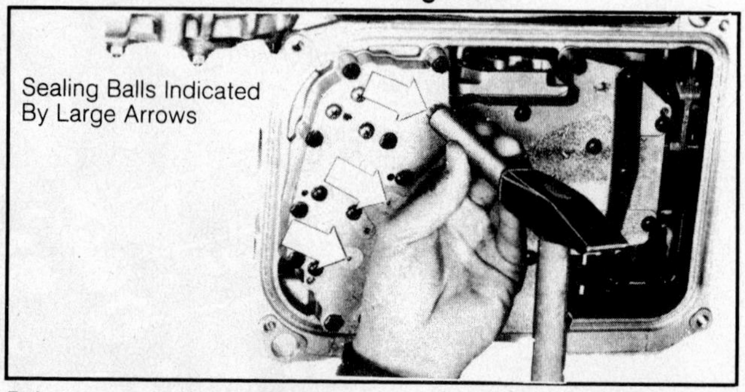

Drive new sealing balls into place with 8 mm punch.

Reassembly

1) Lubricate all parts with ATF. Install valve components into proper valve body bores in reverse order of removal. If used valves are installed, ensure valves are returned to their original locations. Make sure all valves slide freely in bores.

CAUTION: Do not overtighten cover plate mounting screws or valve body may distort and cause valve(s) to stick.

2) Ensure check balls are installed in proper body passages. Install transfer plate-to-main body screws and tighten from center outward. Install valve body onto transmission case so that manual valve and kickdown valve are correctly engaged with their operating levers. Tighten valve body mounting bolts to 35 INCH lbs. (4 N.m), in a diagonal pattern.

3) Install new oil strainer assembly. Install oil pan, with new gasket, and tighten mount bolts to 14 ft. lbs. (19 N.m) maximum. Install final drive housing if removed. Refill transmission with ATF, install transaxle assembly and road test vehicle for proper operation.

GOVERNOR

NOTE: Disassemble governor only if it contains debris from burnt clutch plates or brake band linings. Otherwise, just clean in solvent and blow dry with compressed air.

CAUTION: Ensure a new, matching governor is installed whenever a new valve body is installed, even if old governor is still serviceable.

VOLKSWAGEN TYPE 010 3-SPEED (Cont.)

Fig. 14: Exploded View of Main Valve Body Assembly

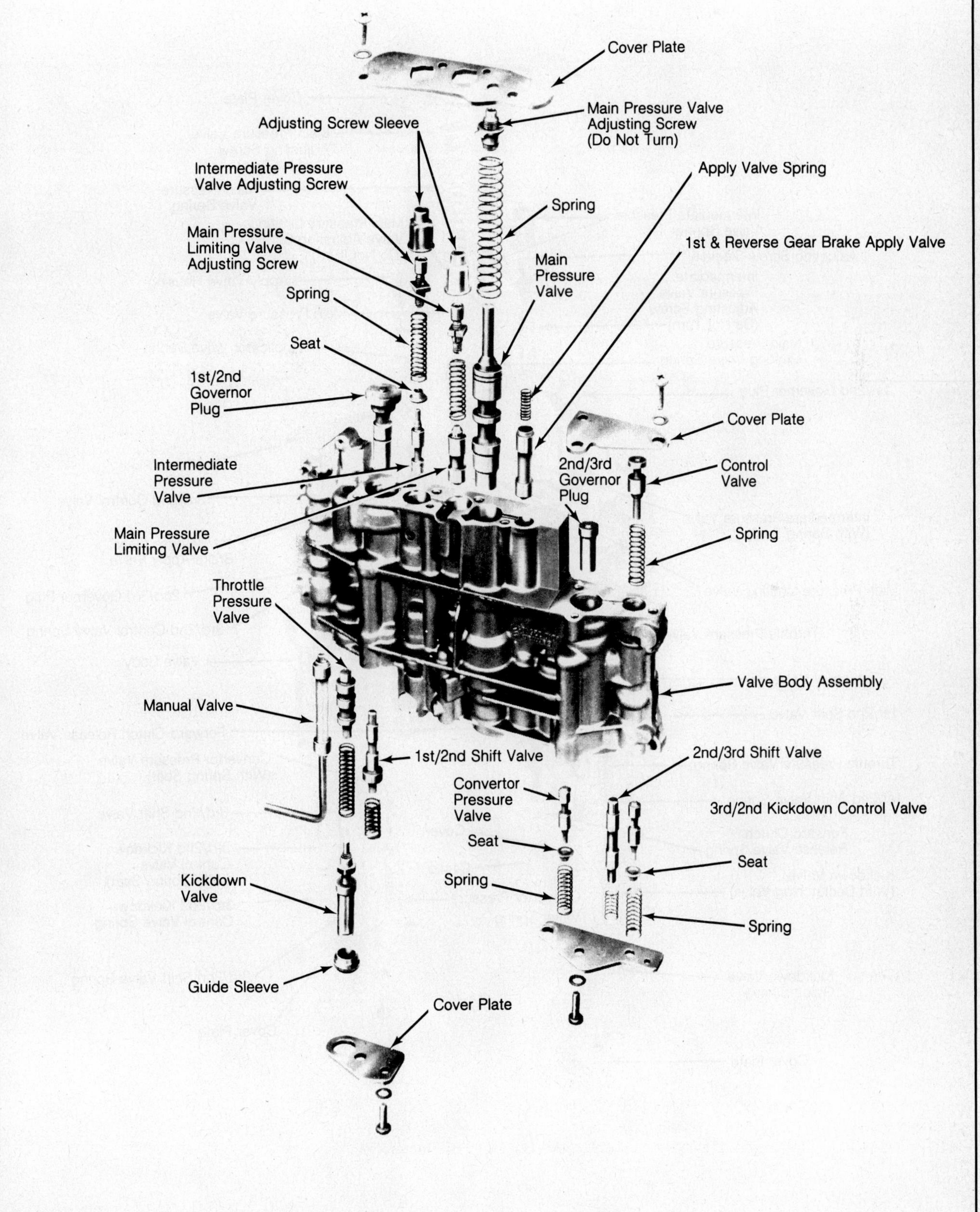

All transmission models except with "E-Mode".

VOLKSWAGEN TYPE 010 3-SPEED (Cont.)

Fig. 15: Exploded View of Main Valve Body Assembly

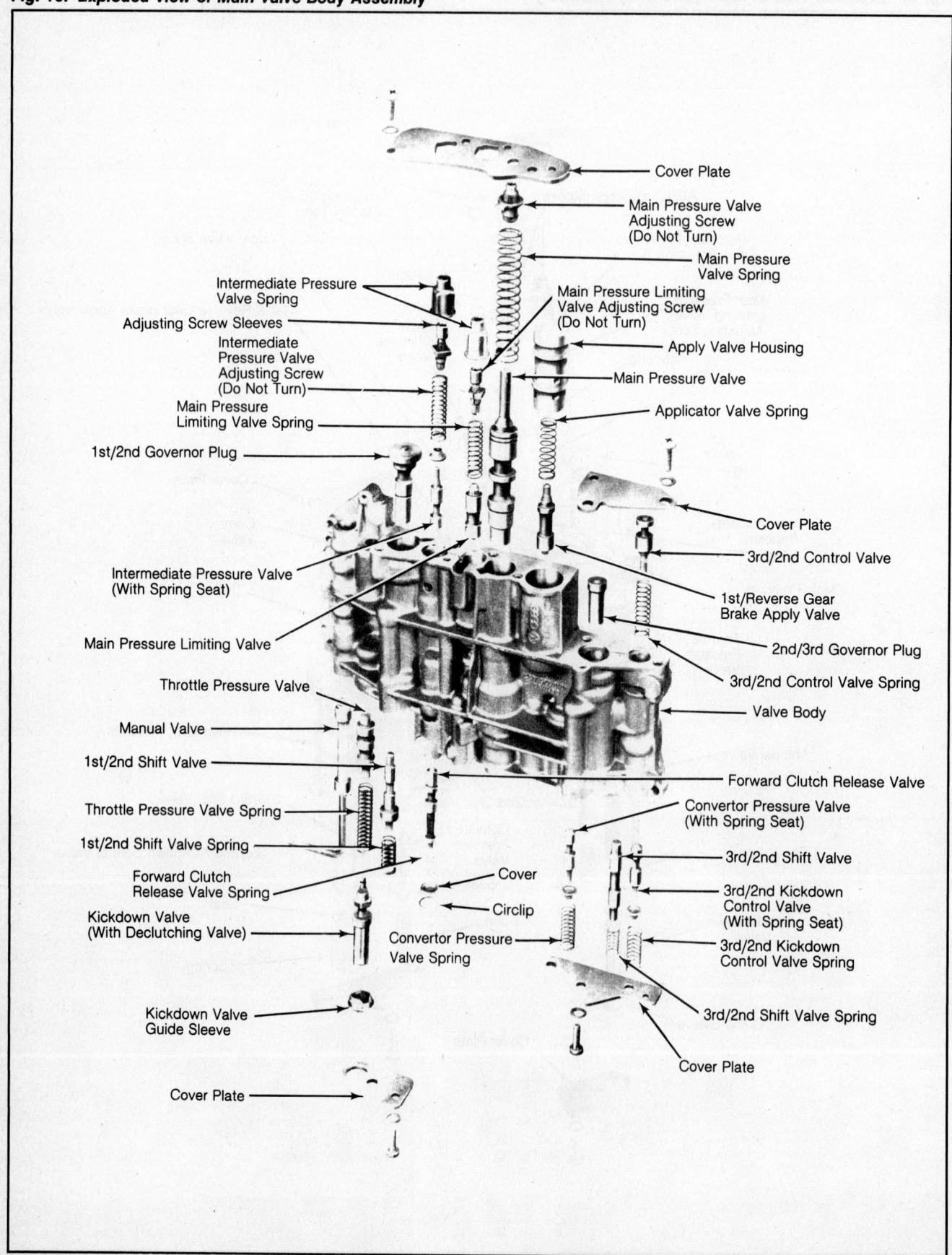

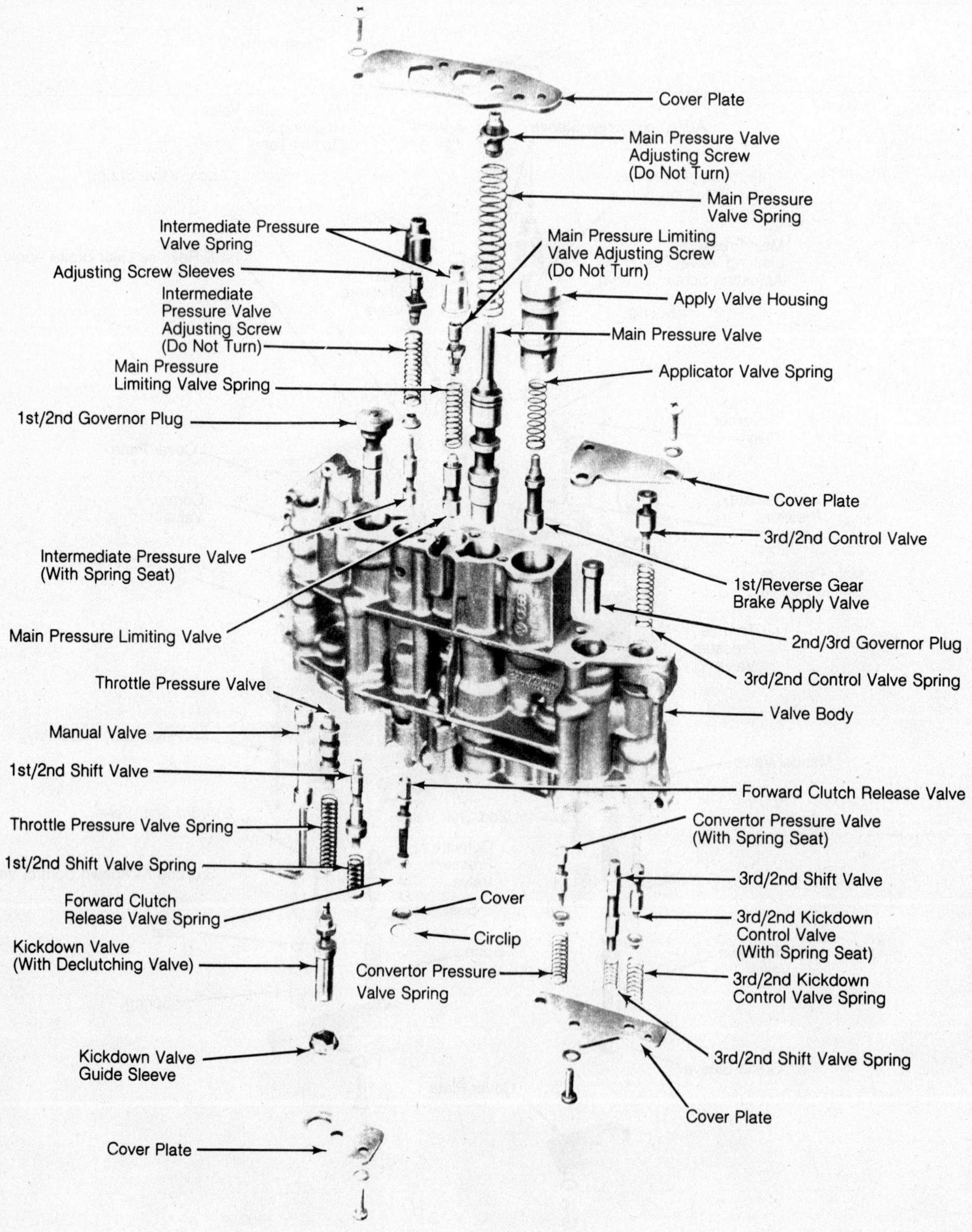
Cover Plate
Main Pressure Valve Adjusting Screw (Do Not Turn)
Main Pressure Valve Spring
Intermediate Pressure Valve Spring
Main Pressure Limiting Valve Adjusting Screw (Do Not Turn)
Adjusting Screw Sleeves
Apply Valve Housing
Intermediate Pressure Valve Adjusting Screw (Do Not Turn)
Main Pressure Valve
Main Pressure Limiting Valve Spring
Applicator Valve Spring
1st/2nd Governor Plug
Cover Plate
3rd/2nd Control Valve
Intermediate Pressure Valve (With Spring Seat)
1st/Reverse Gear Brake Apply Valve
Main Pressure Limiting Valve
2nd/3rd Governor Plug
3rd/2nd Control Valve Spring
Throttle Pressure Valve
Valve Body
Manual Valve
1st/2nd Shift Valve
Forward Clutch Release Valve
Convertor Pressure Valve (With Spring Seat)
Throttle Pressure Valve Spring
1st/2nd Shift Valve Spring
3rd/2nd Shift Valve
Forward Clutch Release Valve Spring
Cover
3rd/2nd Kickdown Control Valve (With Spring Seat)
Circlip
Kickdown Valve (With Declutching Valve)
Convertor Pressure Valve Spring
3rd/2nd Kickdown Control Valve Spring
Kickdown Valve Guide Sleeve
3rd/2nd Shift Valve Spring
Cover Plate
Cover Plate

All transmission models with "E-Mode".

VOLKSWAGEN TYPE 010 3-SPEED (Cont.)

VALVE BODY (GK) SPRING IDENTIFICATION CHART – TRANSAXLE MODELS (TH & TM) WITH E-MODE

Valve Spring	Free Length In. (mm)	Inner Diameter In. (mm) [1]	Number Of Coils	Wire Thickness In. (mm)
Throttle Pressure Limiting Valve	1.49 (37.9)	.303 (7.70)	14.5	.043 (1.10)
Main Pressure Valve	2.95 (75.0)	.468 (11.90)	16.5	.059 (1.50)
Main Pressure Limiting Valve	1.08 (27.5)	.299 (7.60)	12.5	.047 (1.20)
Throttle Pressure Valve	1.73 (44.0)	.305 (7.75)	16.5	.043 (1.10)
1st-2nd Shift Valve	1.13 (28.8)	.319 (8.10)	8.5	.035 (0.90)
Converter Pressure Valve	0.87 (22.2)	.303 (7.70)	8.5	.049 (1.30)
3rd-2nd Control Valve	1.28 (32.4)	.303 (7.70)	12.5	.039 (1.00)
2nd-3rd Shift Valve	0.69 (17.4)	.274 (6.95)	8.5	.031 (0.80)
3rd-2nd Kickdown Valve	1.12 (28.4)	.319 (8.10)	11.5	.035 (0.90)
Apply Valve				
Forward Clutch	0.68 (17.2)	.137 (3.50)	15.5	.019 (0.50)
Release Valve				
Forward Clutch	.578 (14.70)	.232 (5.90)	6.5	.015 (.40)
Apply Valve				
1st/Reverse Gear Brake	1.429 (36.30)	.354 (9.00)	10.5	.025 (.63)

[1] – Inner coil diameter is within a tolerance of ±.012" (.30 mm).

VALVE BODY (FG & FL) SPRING IDENTIFICATION CHART – TRANSAXLE MODELS (TK & TN)

Valve Spring	Free Length In. (mm)	Inner Diameter In. (mm) [1]	Number Of Coils	Wire Thickness In. (mm)
Throttle Pressure Limiting Valve	1.39 (35.3)	.302 (7.70)	14.5	.043 (1.10)
Main Pressure Valve				
Before Transaxle No. 23 07 9	2.82 (71.6)	.468 (11.90)	16.5	.059 (1.50)
As of Transaxle No. 23 07 9	3.03 (77.0)	.468 (11.90)	16.5	.059 (1.50)
Main Pressure Limiting Valve	1.28 (32.4)	.302 (7.70)	11.0	.047 (1.20)
Throttle Pressure Valve	1.71 (43.4)	.305 (7.75)	16.0	.049 (1.30)
1st-2nd Shift Valve	1.13 (28.8)	.319 (8.10)	8.5	.035 (0.90)
Converter Pressure Valve				
Gradual	1.28 (32.4)	.303 (7.70)	12.5	.039 (1.00)
Introduction	0.87 (22.2)	.303 (7.70)	8.5	.049 (1.30)
3rd-2nd Control Valve	1.28 (32.4)	.303 (7.70)	12.5	.039 (1.00)
2nd-3rd Shift Valve				
Standard	0.78 (19.9)	.319 (8.10)	6.5	.035 (0.90)
Alternative	1.02 (26.0)	.323 (8.20)	9.5	.031 (0.80)
3rd-2nd Kickdown Valve	1.12 (28.4)	.319 (8.10)	11.5	.035 (0.90)
Apply Valve	1.12 (28.4)	.319 (8.10)	11.5	.035 (0.90)

[1] – Inner coil diameter is within a tolerance of ±.012" (.3 mm).

Automatic Transmissions

VOLKSWAGEN TYPE 010 3-SPEED (Cont.)

Fig. 16: Exploded View of Governor Assembly

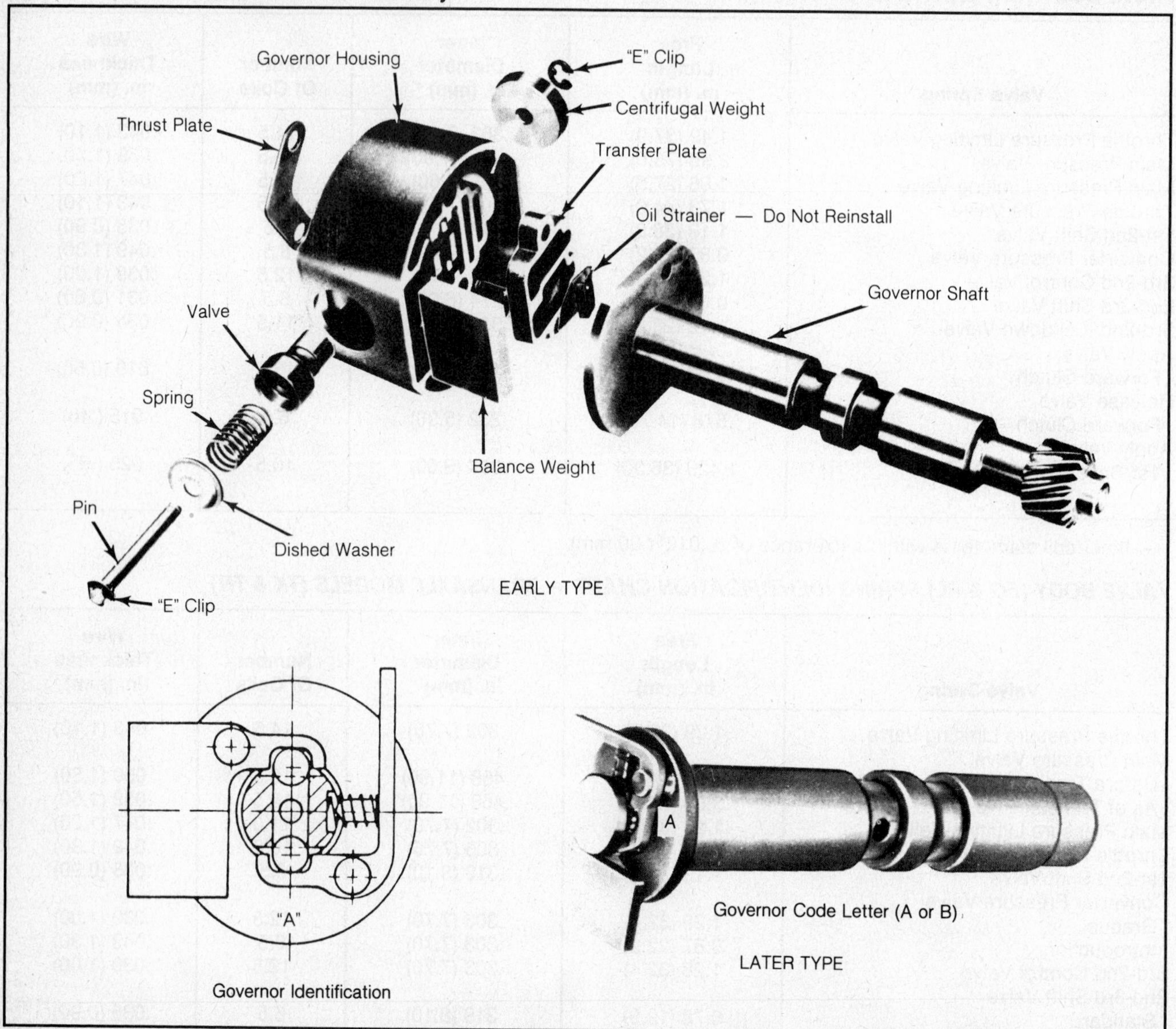

If present during disassembly, do not reinstall the oil strainer in governor assembly.

Disassembly

1) Detach 2 mounting screws (5 x 40 mm) and remove thrust plate and housing. Take out transfer plate, balance weight and oil strainer (if equipped).

2) If necessary, detach 1 "E" clip and withdraw centrifugal weight, valve, spring and dished washer from pin. *See Fig. 16.*

Inspection

Wash governor components in solvent and blow dry with compressed air. Inspect governor shaft for wear and thrust plate for scoring. Replace components as necessary.

NOTE: **Do not interchange balance weight in governor, unit is balanced by the manufacturer.**

Reassembly

To complete reassembly, reverse disassembly procedure and note the following: Lubricate all parts with ATF during assembly. Ensure angle in thrust plate is in center of housing so cover will bear against it. If strainer was present during disassembly, do not reinstall.

2nd GEAR BRAKE BAND SERVO PISTON ASSEMBLY

NOTE: **The 2nd gear brake band servo piston can be removed from vehicle with transmission installed.**

Disassembly

1) Apply inward pressure to servo piston using Lever (VW281a). Remove retaining circlip. Using a rubber mallet, tap piston cover until spring forces piston and cover out of case. Pull servo piston assembly out of cover.

2) Remove and discard "O" ring seals from cover O.D. Remove retaining clip. Separate piston pin, accumulator spring, spring seat and adjusting shim(s) from servo piston. *See Fig. 17.*

Inspection

Clean all parts and check for wear, scoring or other damage. Standard piston O.D. is 3.228" (82 mm). If piston is worn or damaged, replace piston, pin, spring retainer, accumulator spring and shim(s) as an assembly only.

Automatic Transmissions

VOLKSWAGEN TYPE 010 3-SPEED (Cont.)

Fig. 17: Exploded View of 2nd Gear Brake Band Servo Piston Assembly

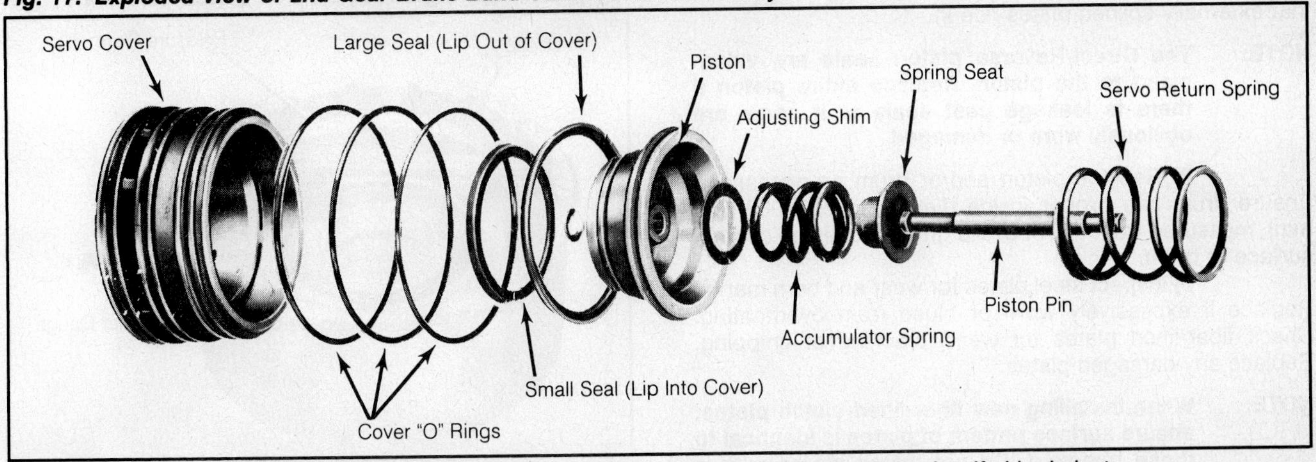

Do not interchange servo piston shim with shim from another piston or use ordinary washer if shim is lost.

NOTE: Piston assemblies supplied as replacement parts are already assembled and adjusted.

CAUTION: Never interchange shim (used in adjusting piston) with shim from another piston assembly or replace it with an ordinary washer.

Reassembly

1) Apply ATF to spring retainer, accumulator spring and shim(s), then position components on piston pin. Install assembly into servo piston and retain with "E" clip on pin.

2) Install new seals on piston with seal lips positioned as follows: Smaller (upper) seal is installed on piston with lip facing upward (into servo cover). Larger seal is installed on piston with lip pointed downward (out of servo cover).

3) Lubricate piston and cover assembly thoroughly with ATF. Install piston into cover using a twisting motion. Ensure piston seals are not damaged or forced out of position. Install new "O" rings on servo cover O.D.

4) When inserting piston assembly and cover into case, guide piston rod into engagement with 2nd gear brake band. Using Lever (VW281a), press cover and piston assembly into transmission case against spring pressure until circlip can be installed. Ensure circlip is completely seated in groove of case.

DIRECT/REVERSE CLUTCH ASSEMBLY

Disassembly

1) Place Direct/Reverse clutch assembly on clean, flat surface. Using large screwdriver, pry out large outer circlip. Remove pressure plate, 3 internally splined fiber plates and 3 externally splined steel plates.

2) Using hydraulic press with Adapters (VW411 and VW460/3) and Support Plate (VW401), press clutch pack into drum enough to remove small circlip that retains spring retainer plate.

3) Release press and remove spring retainer plate. Remove springs (24) and spring plate. With a twisting motion, remove clutch piston. *See Fig. 18.*

4) Check drum bushing for excessive wear or damage and replace if necessary. Place clutch drum in press. Using Bushing Extractor/Installer (VW408a), Support Plates (VW402 and VW401) and Receiver (US1099), drive bushing out of clutch drum.

Inspection

1) Clean all parts in solvent and dry with compressed air. Check for wear or damage on friction surfaces

Fig. 18: Exploded View of Direct/Reverse Clutch Assembly

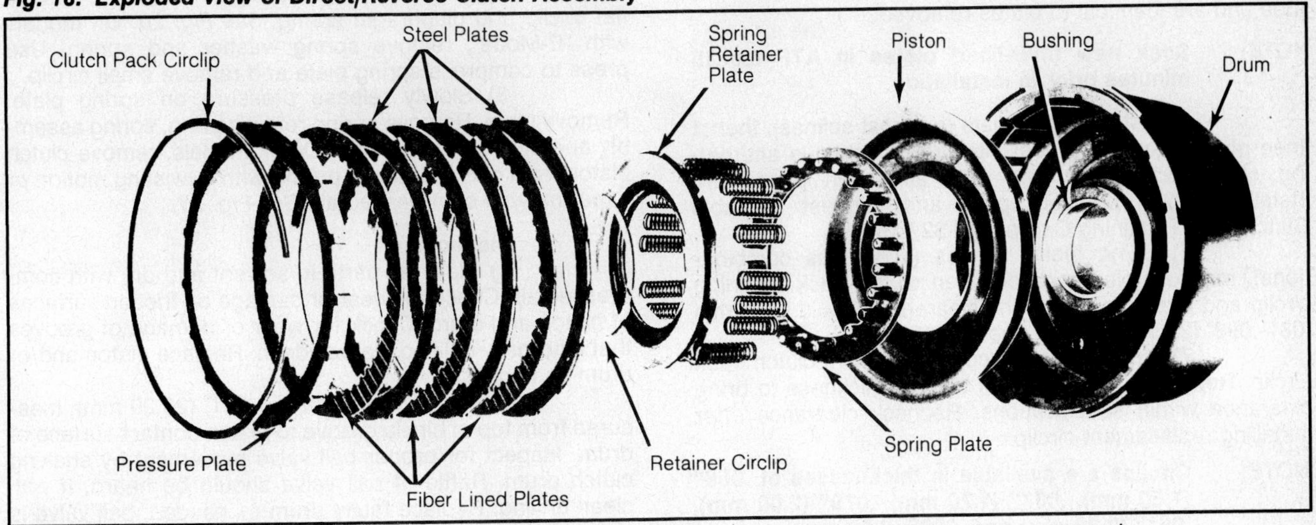

When installing new fiber-lined clutch plates, ensure surface pattern of plates is identical to those removed.

of piston and drum. Check for wear or damage of grooves that externally splined plates ride in.

NOTE: **The Direct/Reverse piston seals are vulcanized to the piston. Replace entire piston if there is leakage past seals or if seals are obviously worn or damaged.**

2) Replace piston and/or drum as necessary. Ensure drum has proper inside dimension of 1.063" (27 mm), measured from top of circlip groove to piston contact surface of drum.

3) Inspect steel plates for wear and burn marks. Replace if excessively worn or blued from overheating. Check fiber-lined plates for wear, cracking or chipping. Replace any damaged plates.

NOTE: **When installing new fiber-lined clutch plates, ensure surface pattern of plates is identical to those removed. Do not install plates with a different pattern of markings.**

4) Inspect ball valve in clutch drum for freedom of operation and proper sealing. Ensure clutch drum drilled passage for ball valve is clear. Check piston return springs for distortion, broken or collapsed coils. Replace any damaged parts.

Reassembly

1) If drum bushing is removed, install new bushing using hydraulic press with Bushing Driver (VW433), bushing extractor/installer and support plates. Install new clutch drum hub bushing flush with hub surface.

2) Using old bushing (between press tool and new bushing), press new bushing into hub until it is .067" (1.70 mm) below hub lip. Remove old bushing from hub bore with pliers.

3) Completely lubricate piston assembly with ATF. Insert a 1 1/2-2" (38-51 mm) wide, thin (but flexible) plastic sheet around inside diameter of drum to protect piston seals during installation. Lubricate seals with ATF, then install piston assembly into drum with a twisting motion. Remove plastic sheet.

4) Position spring plate on top of piston and springs on spring plate. Place retainer on top of springs. Compress drum assembly in press and install small circlip. Lubricate all clutch plates with ATF. Ensure new fiber-lined plates are marked with a pattern of vertical and horizontal lines and are identical to plates removed.

NOTE: **Soak new fiber-lined plates in ATF for 15 minutes prior to installation.**

5) Install 1 steel plate (external splines), then 1 lined plate (internal splines) into drum. Continue alternating steel and lined plates until all clutch plates are installed. Install pressure plate and thinnest available Clutch Pack Retaining Circlip (010 323 157 A).

6) Using feeler gauges (in various combinations), measure clearance between clutch pack retaining circlip and pressure plate. The clearance should be within .081-.098" (2.05-2.50 mm). *See Fig. 19.*

7) If clearance is incorrect, remove clutch pack circlip. Replace it with circlip of correct thickness to bring clearance within specifications. Recheck clearance after installing replacement circlip.

NOTE: **Circlips are available in thicknesses of .059" (1.50 mm), .067" (1.70 mm), .079" (2.00 mm), .091" (2.30 mm) and .098" (2.50 mm).**

Fig. 19: Measuring Direct/Reverse Clutch Clearance

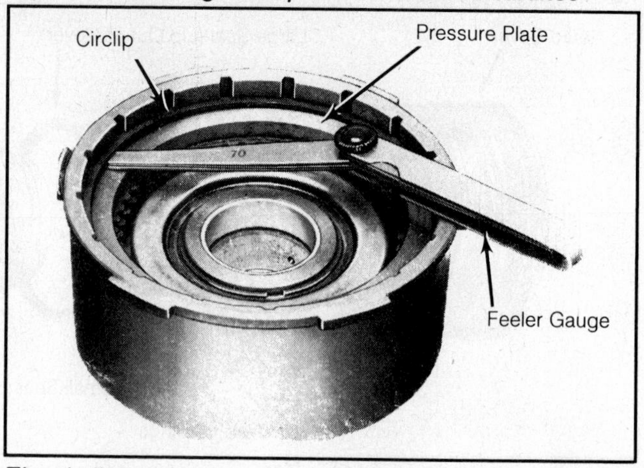

The circlip-to-pressure plate clearance should be within .081-.098" (2.05-2.50 mm).

8) To check operation of assembled Direct/Reverse clutch, lubricate sealing rings with ATF and temporarily install ATF pump in Direct/Reverse clutch assembly.

9) Blow compressed air into oil port and check that clutch piston audibly compresses clutch plates. When air pressure is released, ensure clutch plates release and piston returns to original position.

FORWARD CLUTCH ASSEMBLY

Disassembly

1) Using a screwdriver, pry out waved clutch plate circlip from clutch drum (flat circlip with "E-Mode"). Remove pressure plate, 3 fiber-lined clutch plates and 2 steel clutch plates, foreward planetary ring gear and thrust plate.

CAUTION: **Clutch piston sealing rings are vulcanized onto piston. Do not damage sealing rings during removal. If seal lips are obviously worn or damaged or leakage past rings is found, replace entire piston as an assembly.**

2) On all models (except with "E-Mode"), remove flat circlip and diaphragm spring. *See Fig. 20*. On models with "E-Mode", remove spring washer and spring. Use press to compress spring plate and remove small circlip.

3) Slowly release pressure on spring plate. Remove plate. Remove spring retaining ring, spring assembly and spring support ring. On all models, remove clutch piston from clutch drum by pulling with a twisting motion or expelling with compressed air. *See Fig. 21.*

Inspection

1) Clean all parts in solvent and dry with compressed air. Check for wear or damage on friction surfaces of piston and drum. Check for wear or damage of grooves that externally splined plates ride in. Replace piston and/or drum as necessary.

2) Ensure drum I.D. is 1.031" (26.20 mm), measured from top of circlip groove to piston contact surface of drum. Inspect for proper ball valve movement by shaking clutch drum. Rattle of ball valve should be heard. If not, clean drilling. Replace faulty drum as needed, ball valve is not replaceable separately.

Automatic Transmissions

VOLKSWAGEN TYPE 010 3-SPEED (Cont.)

Fig. 20: Exploded View of Forward Clutch Assembly

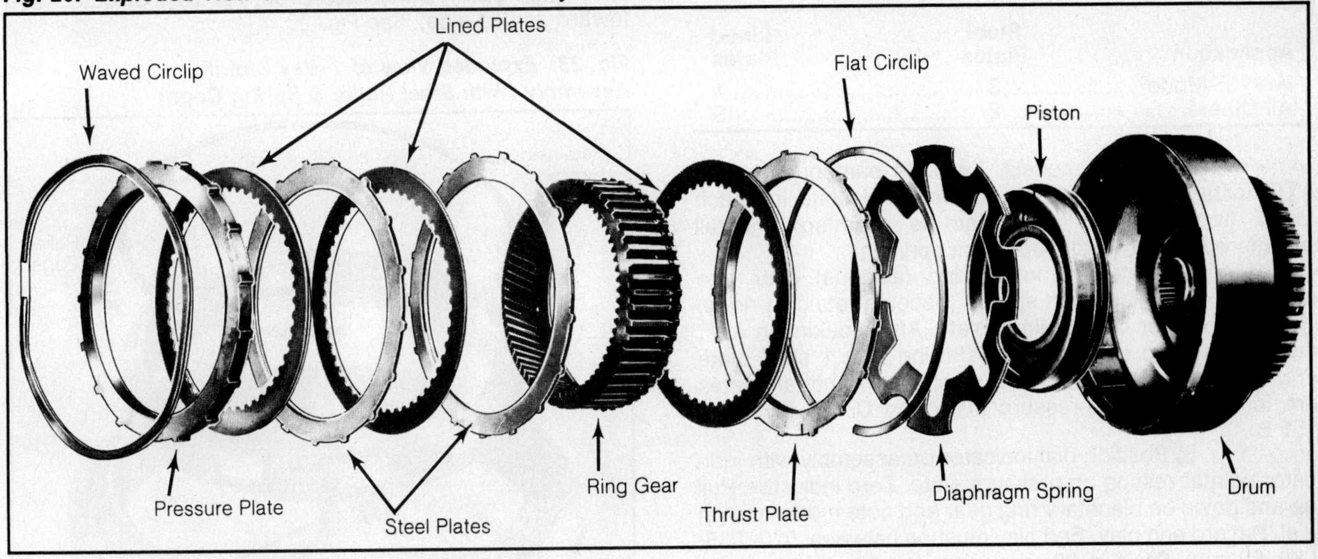

All models except with "E-Mode" transmission.

3) Inspect steel plates for wear and burn marks. Replace if excessively worn or blued from overheating. Check fiber-lined plates for wear, cracking or chipping. Replace any damaged plates.

NOTE: When installing new fiber-lined clutch plates, ensure surface pattern of plates is identical to those removed. Do not install plates with a different pattern of markings.

4) Check planetary ring gear inner and outer splines for wear, scoring or other damage. Replace as needed. Check diaphragm spring for settling by placing in drum. Spring should reach at least to the lower edge of circlip groove. Replace faulty spring as necessary.

CAUTION: Clutch drum with drillings must not be used in transmission with ATF pump that has radial-roller thrust bearing. Clutch drum without drillings must not be used in transmission with (early) ATF pump that has only a thrust washer.

NOTE: Soak new fiber-lined plates in ATF for 15 minutes prior to installation.

Reassembly

1) Coat clutch piston and sealing rings with ATF. Install piston assembly into drum using a twisting motion. On all models except with "E-Mode", position diaphragm spring in drum with convex side towards bottom of drum. Install flat 2.03 mm Retaining Circlip (010 323 157).

NOTE: With circlip installed, diaphragm spring should be under some tension and circlip should not be easily snapped into groove. If inserting circlip does not put spring under tension, replace spring.

2) On models with "E-Mode", install spring support ring, spring retaining ring and spring assembly and spring plate. Retaining ring and springs must be installed with small diameter end of springs up (towards spring plate).

3) Compress spring plate and install small circlip. Install spring and spring washer. Ensure that spring and washer are installed with convex side down (into drum).

Fig. 21: Exploded View of Forward Clutch Assembly

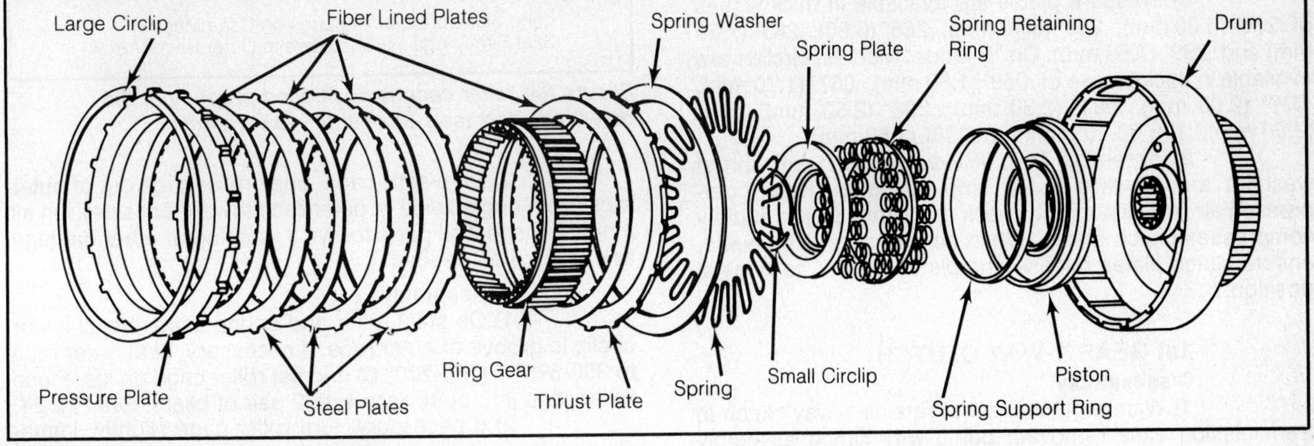

All models with "E-Mode" transmission.

Automatic Transmissions

VOLKSWAGEN TYPE 010 3-SPEED (Cont.)

FORWARD CLUTCH PLATE CHART

Application	Steel Plates	Lined Plates
With "E-Mode"	3	4
All Others	2	3

4) On all models, lubricate components with ATF. Install thrust plate and 1 fiber-lined plate in clutch drum. If 1 side of thrust plate is chamfered, install chamfered side toward diaphragm spring.

5) Install planetary ring (annulus) gear into assembly, engaging short splines (beneath retaining ridge) into inner splines of fiber-lined plate. After soaking in ATF, install remaining clutch plates, starting with 1 steel plate and alternating fiber-lined and steel plates until all plates are installed. Install pressure plate and Circlip (010 323 159 B).

6) Position dial indicator on assembly with indicator pointer resting on pressure plate. Zero indicator. Pull up and down on planetary ring gear and note movement on dial. Record end play. End play must be between .020-.035" (.50-.90 mm). *See Fig. 22.*

Fig. 22: Measuring Forward Clutch End Play

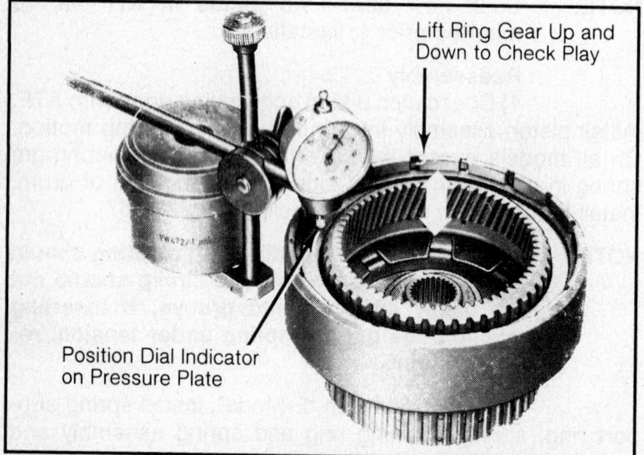

Lift Ring Gear Up and Down to Check Play

Check end play with feeler gauge, between circlip and pressure plate, if dial indicator is not available.

7) If end play is incorrect, replace pressure plate (large circlip on models with "E-Mode") with selective circlip of required thickness to bring play to proper specifications.

8) Pressure plates are available in thicknesses of .236" (6.00 mm), .252" (6.40 mm), .268" (6.80), .283" (7.20 mm) and .299" (7.60 mm). On "E-Mode" models, circlips are available in thicknesses of .059" (1.50 mm), .067" (1.70 mm), .079" (2.00 mm), .091" (2.30 mm), .098" (2.50 mm), .114" (2.90 mm), .126" (3.20 mm) and .138" (3.50 mm).

9) Assemble Direct/Reverse clutch with thrust washers and forward clutch onto oil pump. Blow compressed air into oil port and check that clutch piston audibly compresses clutch plates. When air pressure is released, ensure clutch plates release and piston returns to original position.

1st GEAR 1-WAY CLUTCH

Disassembly

1) With large circlip that retains 1-way clutch in transmission case removed, pull 1-way clutch assembly from case. Remove rollers and springs. On steel cage, detach upper and lower circlips. Using plastic hammer, drive cage out of outer race (from flat side of outer race toward angled side). *See Fig. 23.*

Fig. 23: Exploded View of 1-Way Clutch Assembly (With Steel Roller & Spring Cage)

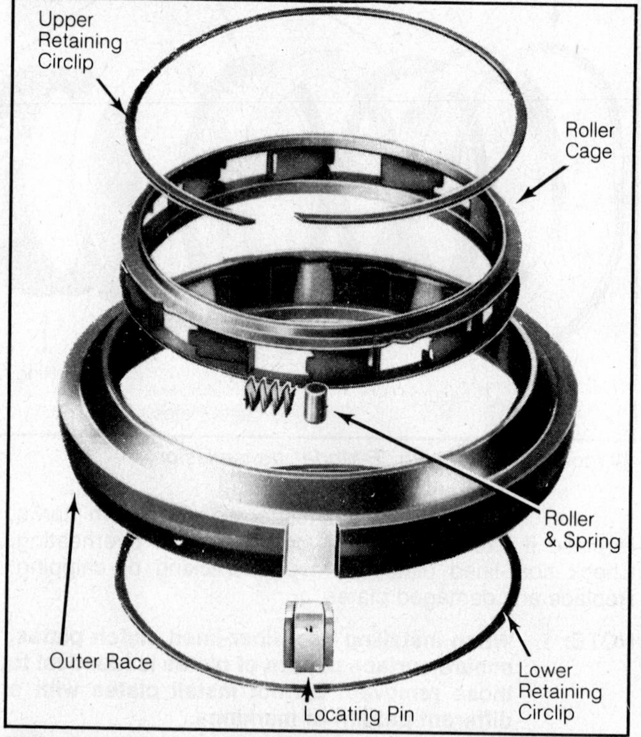

Before reassembly, ensure roller cage is marked with "B" and outer race has groove machined in angled outer face.

Fig. 24: Steel Roller Cage Installation In 1st Gear 1-Way Clutch Outer Race

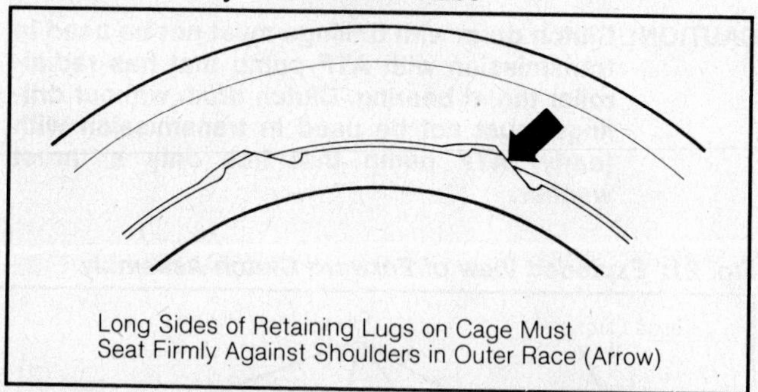

Long Sides of Retaining Lugs on Cage Must Seat Firmly Against Shoulders in Outer Race (Arrow)

Ensure the roller cage is positioned properly in the outer race and rests against the lower circlip.

2) On plastic cage, push roller cage out of outer race (from angled side of outer race toward flat side). On all models, Inspect all parts for wear, scoring or other damage and replace as needed.

Reassembly

1) On steel roller and spring cage, install lower circlip in groove of outer race. If necessary, heat outer race to 300-390° F (150-200° C) and set roller cage on ice. Place roller cage into outer race with 2 pair of pliers. *See Fig. 24.*

2) If necessary, turn roller cage slightly, immediately after installing, to locate it properly against the outer race.

NOTE: During installation, heat from outer race will transfer quickly to roller cage, causing cage to stick inside race. If cage is incorrectly posi tioned against lower circlip, do not attempt to press into position after cage has stuck. Carefully knock cage out. Repeat procedure again after race has cooled down.

3) Install upper circlip. Install rollers and springs into cage. Be sure that guide lug on springs (if so equipped) is pointed toward roller. *See Fig. 25.*

Fig. 25: Roller & Spring Installation in 1-Way Clutch Assembly (Steel Cage)

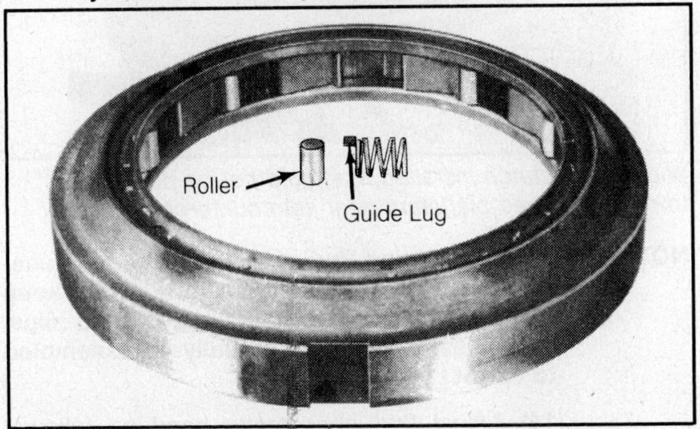

Assemble the guide lug on spring over roller as shown.

Fig. 26: Assembling & Installing 1-Way Clutch Plastic Roller Cage Into Outer Race

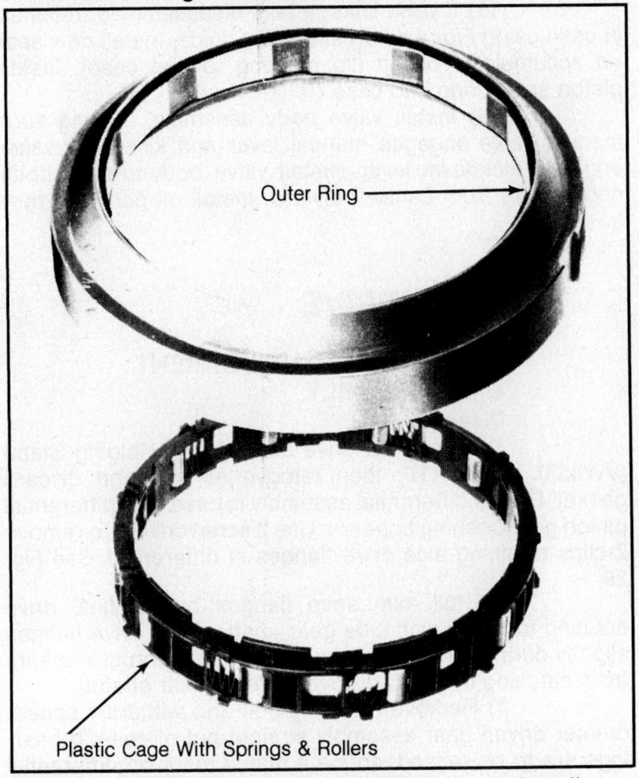

Assemble plastic cage segments to form a ring. Install (with springs and rollers) into outer race from flat side.

NOTE: Springs with and without tabs can be used together and are interchangeable. New plastic cage can be service installed in earlier transmissions. Do not use circlips with plastic cage.

4) On plastic roller and spring cage, assemble 10 segments of plastic cage to form a ring. Install all springs and rollers. Ensure each spring guide tab (lug) faces toward its roller.

5) Insert roller cage from flat side of outer race (small ledge toward tapered side and large ledge toward flat side). *See Fig. 26.* With outer race/roller cage assembled and laying on flat side, turn cage clockwise to secure. It should not be possible to turn assembly counterclockwise.

ANNULUS GEAR (2-PART) GOVERNOR DRIVE GEAR/PLANETARY RING GEAR

Disassembly & Reassembly

The annulus gear engages the planet gears of the reverse planetary gearset. The 2-part gear should be disassembled only if necessary to replace 1 of the components. To disassemble, detach circlip, then remove governor drive gear/hub from flanged annulus gear. Inspect for damage or excessive wear and replace components as necessary. If new circlip is needed, replace with proper Circlip (090 323 369).

TRANSAXLE REASSEMBLY

TRANSMISSION COMPONENT INITIAL ASSEMBLY

Reassembly

1) Coat 1st/Reverse brake piston with ATF and install on oil pump housing. Insert brake piston/oil pump assembly into transmission case. Ensure brake piston ball valve lines up with drilling in transmission housing and anti-rotation lug for thrust washer of oil pump is facing toward top of case.

NOTE: New 1st/Reverse brake piston with ball valve may be installed in previous transmissions if wave washer is not used and 3 inner and 3 outer splined plates are installed.

2) Before installing 1st/Reverse gear apply shell, measure overall length to ensure proper component is installed. Shell length is 3.957" (100.50 mm). Install apply shell into case so that tab of shell engages upper groove in transmission case. *See Fig. 27.*

Fig. 27: Installing 1st/Reverse Gear Apply Shell

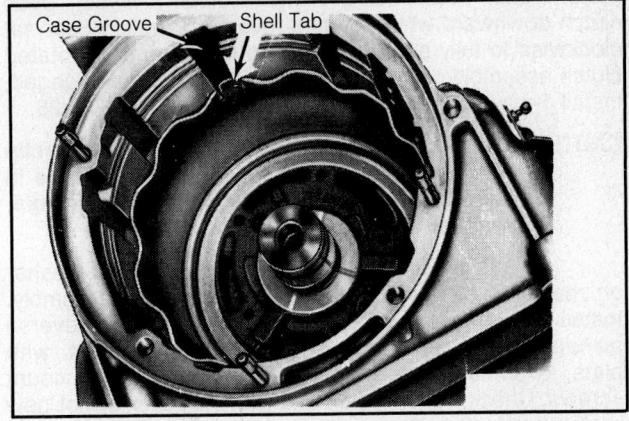

When installed, shell tab must engage with case groove.

VOLKSWAGEN TYPE 010 3-SPEED (Cont.)

3) Position 1st/Reverse brake piston return springs on spring plate. Ensure springs have a wire thickness of .039" (1 mm). If necessary, use petroleum jelly to adhere springs to plate. Insert assembly into case with springs downward and bolt holes in spring plate matching those in ATF pump.

4) Install spring plate mount bolts and gradually tighten, in a diagonal pattern, to 61 INCH lbs. (7 N.m). After installation, temporarily insert pump driveshaft into oil pump. Turn assembly by hand to ensure parts are not jammed and there is no binding.

5) Position 2nd gear brake band in transmission case. With new "O" rings installed on servo piston cover and coated with ATF, install 2nd gear servo piston in case. Ensure piston pin engages band end inside case. Using Lever (VW281a), push cover/piston assembly against spring pressure. Install circlip.

6) Turn transmission case horizontal (servo piston cover pointed down). On opposite side of case, install 2nd gear brake band adjusting screw push rod. Be sure rod engages band end inside case. Install adjusting screw just enough to hold band in place.

7) Lubricate Direct/Reverse clutch with ATF and insert unit into transmission case, sliding it onto neck of ATF pump and into 2nd gear brake band. Use care not to damage pump seal rings. Tighten 2nd gear brake band adjusting screw to 7.5 ft. lbs. (10 N.m) in order to prevent brake band from shifting its position. Turn transmission case upward.

8) Coat forward clutch-to-Direct/Reverse clutch thrust washers with petroleum jelly and position on rear end of forward clutch. Install forward clutch into Direct/Reverse clutch. Make sure that splines on forward clutch drum fully engage splines on Direct/Reverse clutch lined plates.

9) Ensure inner thrust washer, thrust bearing and outer thrust washer are between oil pump piston end and forward clutch. Install forward planetary gearset-to-forward clutch thrust bearing into forward clutch. Install forward planetary gearset into ring gear in forward clutch.

10) Install sun gear (short end first) into gear set. Install apply shell and thrust washer over sun gear. Position thrust washer on underside of reverse planetary gear set. Install gear set into case and onto sun gear.

11) Check for proper identification mark of "B1" on 1st gear inner splined plates. Install 3 fiber-lined and 3 steel plates in case alternately, starting with steel plate. If any new fiber-lined plates are used, soak plates in transmission fluid for 15 minutes prior to installation.

12) Install 1st gear 1-way clutch assembly into transmission case. Using Clutch Holder (VW458), push clutch downward while rotating reverse planetary gear set clockwise to fully engage parts. Do not attempt to rotated clutch assembly counterclockwise. With all parts engaged, install 1-way clutch-to-case retaining circlip. *See Fig. 28.*

CAUTION: With correctly installed components, circlip groove should be uncovered. Do not force in circlip on an incorrectly assembled transmission.

13) Position needle bearing and thrust washer on rear side of governor drive gear/ring gear assembly. Install unit into transmission case, fully engaging reverse planetary gear set. Install separation plate gasket, with plate, over case studs. Install and tighten plate mount screws. Check transmission end play (whether or not new parts were installed).

Fig. 28: Installing 1st Gear 1-Way Clutch Circlip

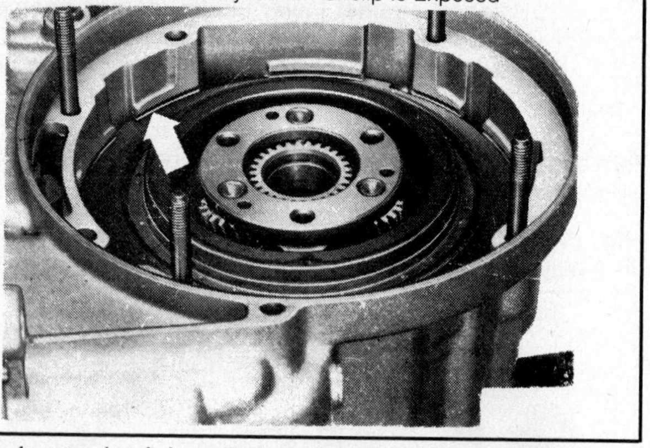

Parts Are Installed Properly if Groove
For One-Way Clutch Circlip is Exposed

With 1-way clutch installed, it should not be possible to rotate reverse planetary gear set counterclockwise.

NOTE: When adjusting 2nd gear brake band, transmission must be horizontal in order to keep band from slipping or jamming. If band slips, transmission must be partially disassembled to correct problem.

14) Adjust 2nd gear brake band as follows: Tighten band adjusting screw to 89 INCH lbs. (10 N.m). Loosen and retighten adjusting screw to 44 INCH lbs. (5 N.m). From this position, back off screw exactly 2 1/2 turns and tighten lock nut to 14 ft. lbs. (19 N.m).

15) If case linkage was disassembled, reinstall in case using *Fig. 4* as an assembly guide. Install new seal on accumulator piston (lip pointing toward case). Install piston and spring into case.

16) Install valve body assembly, making sure manual valve engages manual lever and kickdown valve engages kickdown lever. Install valve body-to-case bolts and tighten from center outward. Install oil pan with new gasket.

FINAL DRIVE

DISASSEMBLY, ADJUSTMENT & REASSEMBLY

Disassembly

1) Place final drive assembly in Holding Stand (VW353). Drain ATF, then remove oil pan and discard gasket. Rotate differential assembly in case until differential pinion gear opening appears. Use 2 screwdrivers to remove 2 clips retaining axle drive flanges in differential. *See Fig. 29.*

2) Pull axle drive flanges out of final drive housing together with side gear shafts. Turn drive flanges slightly during removal to prevent side gear thrust washers from catching in circlip grooves of side gear shafts.

3) Remove retaining bolt and withdraw speedometer driven gear assembly straight out of case. If bearings are to be reused, scribe a match mark on differential side bearing adjusting ring and case for reassembly reference.

4) Remove lock clip from adjusting ring. Using Spanner Wrench (VW182), screw ring out of case. *See Fig. 31.* On opposite side of case, remove nuts and withdraw the

Automatic Transmissions

VOLKSWAGEN TYPE 010 3-SPEED (Cont.)

Fig. 29: Location of Drive Flange Retaining Clips

Use 2 screwdrivers to press clips (ends are indicated by White arrows) off of shaft.

other differential side bearing retainer (cover). Grasp differential and ring gear assembly and remove from final drive case. *See Fig. 30.*

5) Inside converter housing area of final drive case, mark relationship of intermediate gear shaft and case

Fig. 31: Removing Differential Side Bearing Adjusting Ring

After index marking case and adjusting ring, screw ring out of case with spanner wrench.

Fig. 30: Exploded View of Differential & Related Parts in Final Drive Case

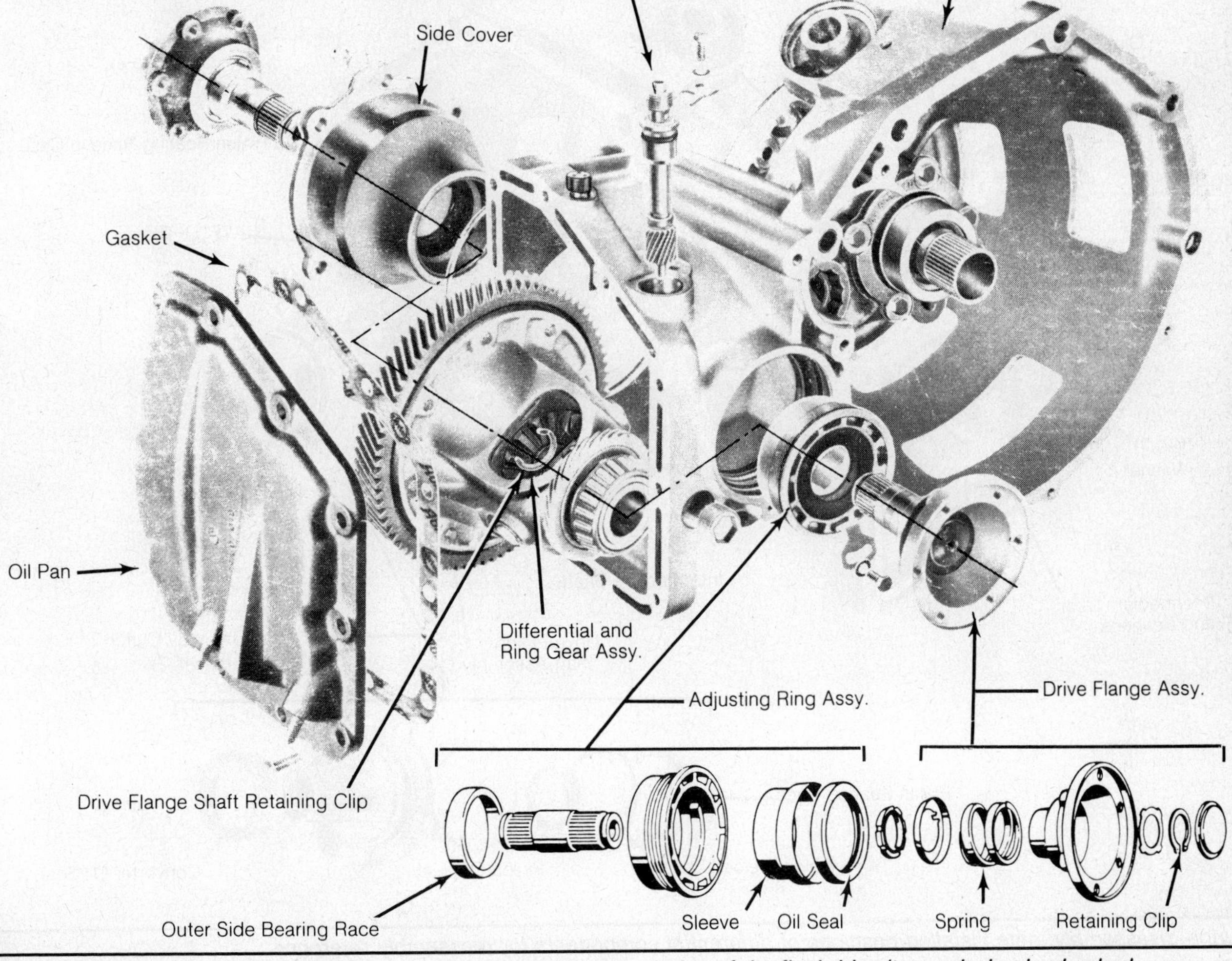

When final drive and/or transmission are repaired, ensure the end play of the final drive/transmission is checked.

with scribe. Remove lock clip from intermediate gear shaft. Using special tool, screw shaft out of case. *See Fig. 32.*

Fig. 32: Removing Intermediate Gear Shaft

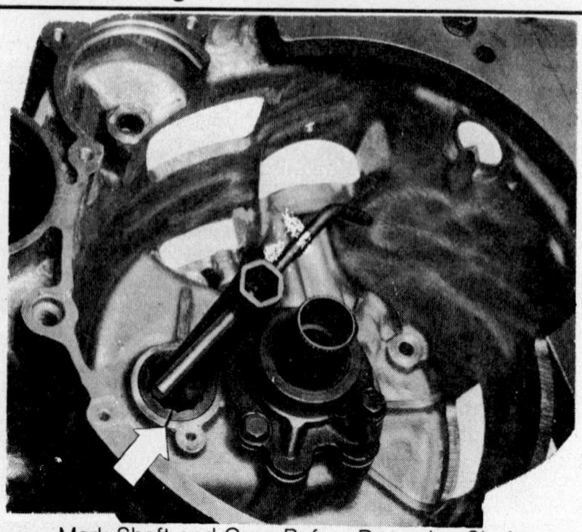

Mark Shaft and Case Before Removing Shaft

Use tool to remove the intermediate gear shaft from the final drive housing.

6) From inside case, remove intermediate gear, bearings and thrust washer. *See Fig. 33.* Remove bolts retaining 1-way clutch support to converter housing area of case. Withdraw support and drive pinion shaft assembly from case.

7) To disassemble differential assembly, remove 2 differential pinion shaft retaining snap rings. Remove drive shaft from case with drift. Move differential pinion gears around to case openings. Remove pinion gears and thrust washers. Remove differential side gears and thrust washers.

8) Remove ring gear-to-differential case mount bolts. Using hydraulic press, Adapters (VW411 and VW295a) with Support Plates (VW401 and VW402), separate ring gear from case. If required, withdraw differential side bearings and speedometer drive gear from case with press and Adapter (US1078).

9) Withdraw bearing races from adjusting ring and side cover. If replacement of pinion bearings or pinion shaft is required, proceed as follows: Place pinion assembly in press. With press plates positioned under bearings, drive bearings from pinion shaft.

10) Place stator support in press. Drive out pinion bearing race along with preload shim and pinion oil

Fig. 33: Exploded View of Intermediate Gear & Pinion Gear Assemblies in Final Drive Case

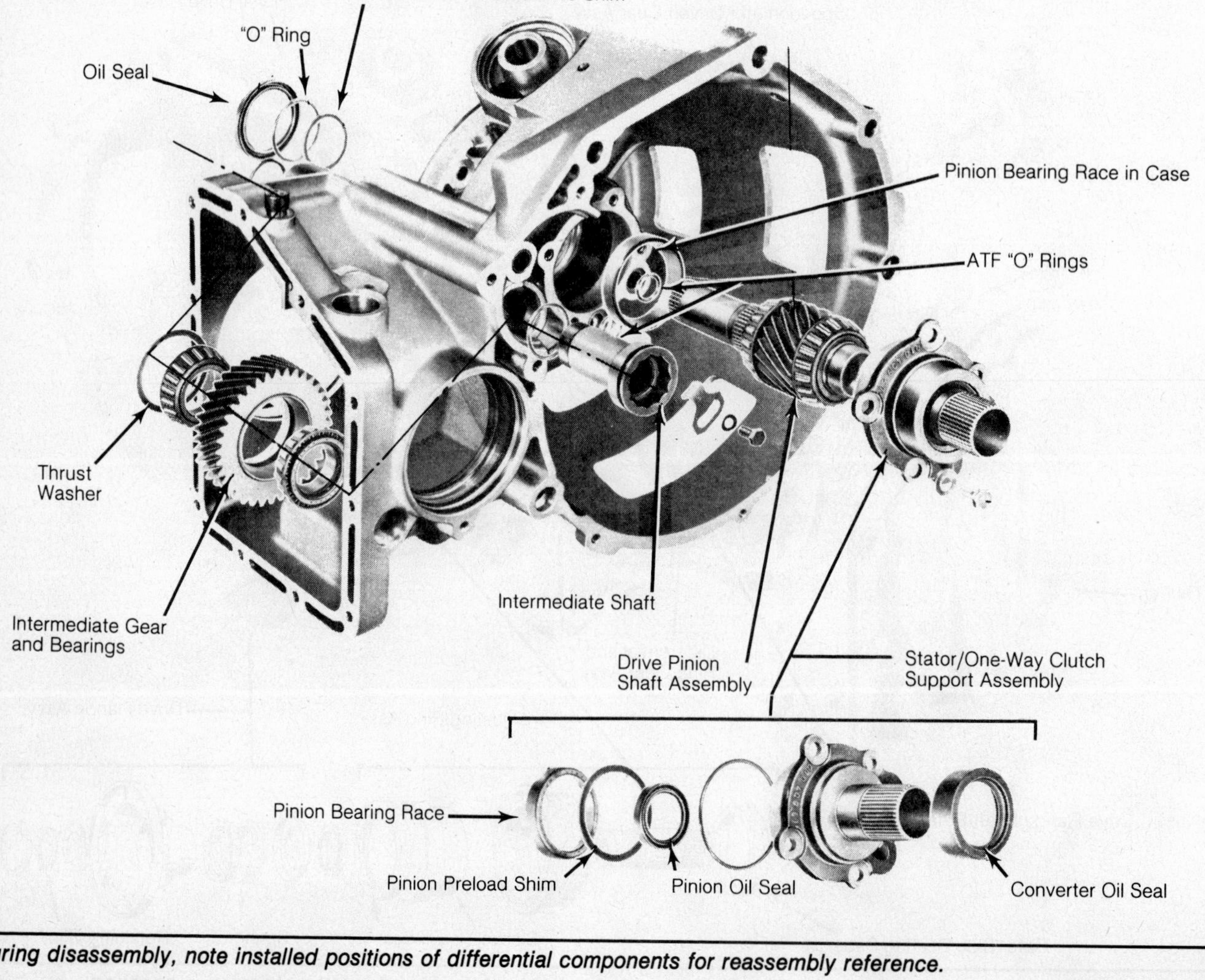

During disassembly, note installed positions of differential components for reassembly reference.

VOLKSWAGEN TYPE 010 3-SPEED (Cont.)

seal. Using hammer and drift, drive remaining pinion bearing race out of final drive case. Inspect ATF drillings in 1-way clutch/stator support assembly.

11) Check ball valve in support for proper action by installing a piece of tight fitting hose into ball valve hole. Apply suction. Ball valve must seal to prevent ATF from draining out of torque convertor when engine is not running. If ball does not seal, replace 1-way clutch support.

Pinion Reassembly & Preload Adjustment

1) If pinion gear and/or pinion bearings were replaced, lubricate bearings with gear oil. If preload check must be done, do not lubricate bearings until after check has been completed.

2) Press bearings onto pinion shaft. Using drift, install pinion bearing race into final drive housing. Temporarily install remaining pinion bearing race (without adjusting shim) into stator support.

NOTE: **When measuring end play of pinion shaft, do not lubricate bearings or turn drive pinion. If pinion is lubricated, turned when seating against outer race or when installing in final drive housing, measurement will be inaccurate.**

3) Install pinion assembly into final drive case, tightening stator support bolts securely. With transmission attaching face of final drive housing facing upward, position dial indicator on housing with button of indicator contacting pinion shaft.

4) Zero indicator. Move pinion shaft up and down (without turning) noting maximum end play reading on dial indicator. To determine proper pinion preload shim usage (to be installed under bearing race in stator support), add .008" (.20 mm) to end play reading.

5) Preload shim thickness should be equal to this amount. Pinion preload shims are available in thicknesses of .039" (1.00 mm) to .087" (2.20 mm) in increments of .002" (.05 mm). If exact size shim is not available, use shim size closest to ideal thickness.

Fig. 34: Using Dial Indicator to Determine Pinion Preload Shim Thickness

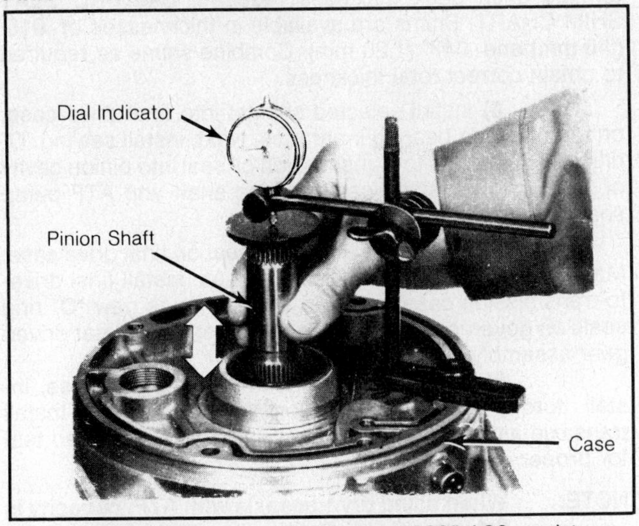

Move pinion shaft up and down. Add .008" (.20 mm) to highest value to determine preload shim thickness.

NOTE: **When installing used shim, measure shim in several places to ensure thickness accuracy. Do not use burred or damaged shims.**

6) Remove pinion assembly from final drive case. Press bearing race out of stator support. Install pinion oil seal into support. Install preload shim determined in steps **2)** and **3)**. Position bearing race in support and press into place.

7) Install converter oil seal on front side of support. Install sealing "O" ring on rear side. Install new transmission fluid passage "O" rings in final drive case, at stator support attaching face. Thoroughly coat pinion bearings with gear oil.

8) Position pinion assembly in final drive case. Install stator support and tighten mount bolts. Install Torque Gauge (VW249) and rapidly turn pinion shaft 15-20 times to settle bearings. Turn shaft with torque gauge and record turning torque reading for future reference.

Fig. 35: Checking Pinion Bearing Preload

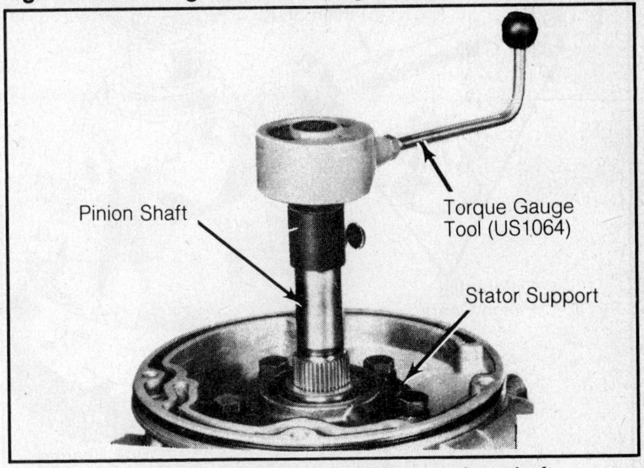

Check reading on torque gauge while rotating shaft.

NOTE: **Torque reading is basis for intermediate shaft and differential assembly preload adjustments. Reading must be noted before any further assembly steps are taken.**

Intermediate Gear Reassembly & Preload Adjustment

1) If intermediate gear and bearings were replaced, coat bearings with gear oil and install new "O" rings. Install bearings in intermediate gear. Position gear assembly into final drive case. Insert intermediate shaft and tighten shaft slightly. Attach torque gauge to pinion shaft. Rotate shaft and note preload reading on gauge.

2) While continuing to rotate pinion shaft, turn intermediate shaft left or right until preload reading on gauge is about 13 INCH lbs. (1.4 N.m) higher than reading obtained in step **6)** of PINION REASSEMBLY & PRELOAD ADJUSTMENT. With proper preload obtained, install and tighten shaft lock plate bolt.

Differential Reassembly & Preload Adjustment

1) Lubricate differential side gears and thrust washers with gear oil and position in differential case. Coat differential pinion gears and thrust washers with lubricant. Place gears and washers onto side gears through opening in differential case. Rotate gears into alignment with differential pinion shaft bores in case.

Automatic Transmissions

VOLKSWAGEN TYPE 010 3-SPEED (Cont.)

NOTE: **Pinion gears must be exactly opposite one another in order to install pinion shaft.**

2) Install differential pinion shaft into differential case and through pinion gears. Install pinion shaft retaining clips. If removed, press differential side bearings and speedometer drive gear onto differential case.

3) If ring gear is being replaced, install guide pins into differential case bolt hole. Heat ring gear in hot oil to about 212° F (100° C). Using pins to guide ring gear into place, install gear on case. Install and tighten mount bolts.

Fig. 36: Exploded View of Differential & Ring Gear Assembly

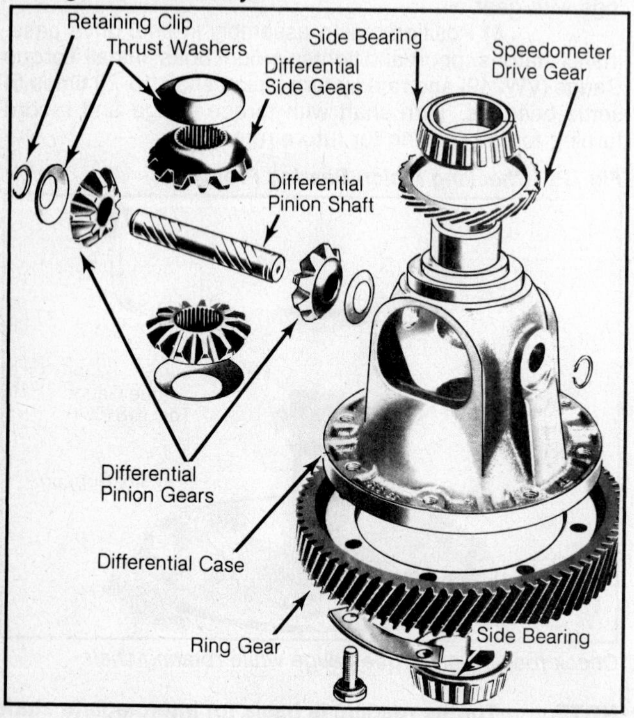

4) If differential case, pinion gears, side gears, thrust washers or axle drive flange shafts are replaced, drive flange shaft retaining rings must be selected. Two sizes of retaining rings are available. To determine which rings to use, go to step **5)**. If parts listed are being reused, go to step **6)**.

5) To select drive flange shaft retaining rings, install each flange shaft into differential case and bottom against differential pinion shaft. While holding side gear against differential case, attempt to install the thicker of the 2 available circlips. If ring jams at sides and cannot be installed, thinner retaining ring must be used when drive flanges are installed.

NOTE: **If differential must be adjusted, ensure old oil seals are removed. Do not install new oil seals until turning torque reading is recorded.**

6) Install side bearing races and new oil seals in adjusting ring and side cover (if removed). Install new sealing "O" rings on ring and cover. Thoroughly coat ring gear and side bearings with final drive lubricant.

7) Position differential assembly in final drive case and engage with intermediate gear. Install side cover to engage with side bearing, then install and tighten cover retaining nuts. Screw side bearing adjusting ring into case and over side bearing so differential is firmly supported.

8) With torque gauge attached to pinion shaft, rotate shaft and note torque reading. While continuing to rotate pinion shaft rapidly, gradually rotate side bearing adjuster left or right until preload reading is about 6 INCH lbs. (.7 N.m) greater than last reading obtained in INTERMEDIATE GEAR REASSEMBLY & PRELOAD ADJUSTMENT.

9) With proper preload obtained, install and tighten adjusting ring lock. If disassembled, install drive flanges onto flange shafts. Secure with spring rings and lock clips. Install end caps into flange shafts. Install shafts into final drive case, securing with retaining clips selected in step **5)**. Install oil pan with new gasket and fill final drive with proper amount of gear oil.

NOTE: **Final drive oil capacity is .8 qts. (.75L) of SAE 90W hypoid gear oil.**

TRANSAXLE REASSEMBLY

FINAL COMPONENT ASSEMBLY

End Play Checking & Adjustment

1) Measure end (axial) play between final drive and transmission: Place a straightedge on transmission attaching face of final drive housing. Using a depth gauge, measure distance from top surface of straightedge to surface of pinion bearing inner race. This is measurement "A".

2) Measure distance from top surface of straightedge to face of final drive housing. This is measurement "B". Subtract "B" from "A" to obtain "C". Record for future reference.

3) Place a new gasket on transmission separation plate. Position straightedge on transmission case and measure distance from top surface of straightedge to gasket surface. This is measurement "D".

4) Measure distance from top surface of straightedge down to inner shoulder of governor drive gear. This is measurement "E". Subtract "E" from "D" to obtain "F" and record.

5) Subtract "F" from "C". This amount is end play (without shims) between final drive and transmission. Determine shim pack thickness required. See END PLAY SHIM CHART. Shims are available in thicknesses of .016" (.40 mm) and .047" (1.20 mm). Combine shims as required to obtain correct total thickness.

6) Install selected shim(s) into final drive case, on top of pinion bearing inner race. Next, install sealing "O" ring and final drive-to-transmission oil seal into pinion cavity of final drive housing. Install turbine shaft and ATF pump shaft fully into transmission.

7) Position new "O" ring seal on final drive case. Mate final drive and transmission cases. Install final drive-to-transmission case nuts and tighten. Place new "O" ring seals on governor, governor cover and speedometer driven gear assembly.

8) Install components in transmission case. Install torque converter to complete assembly. Install transaxle assembly into vehicle, fill with ATF and road test for proper operation.

NOTE: **When filling dry transaxle with ATF, capacity is 6.4 qts. (6.1L). Refill capacity of transaxle is 3.2 qts. (3.0L). Use only DEXRON or DEXRON II type transmission fluid.**

Automatic Transmissions

VOLKSWAGEN TYPE 010 3-SPEED (Cont.)

Fig. 37: Measuring Transmission-to-Final Drive End Play

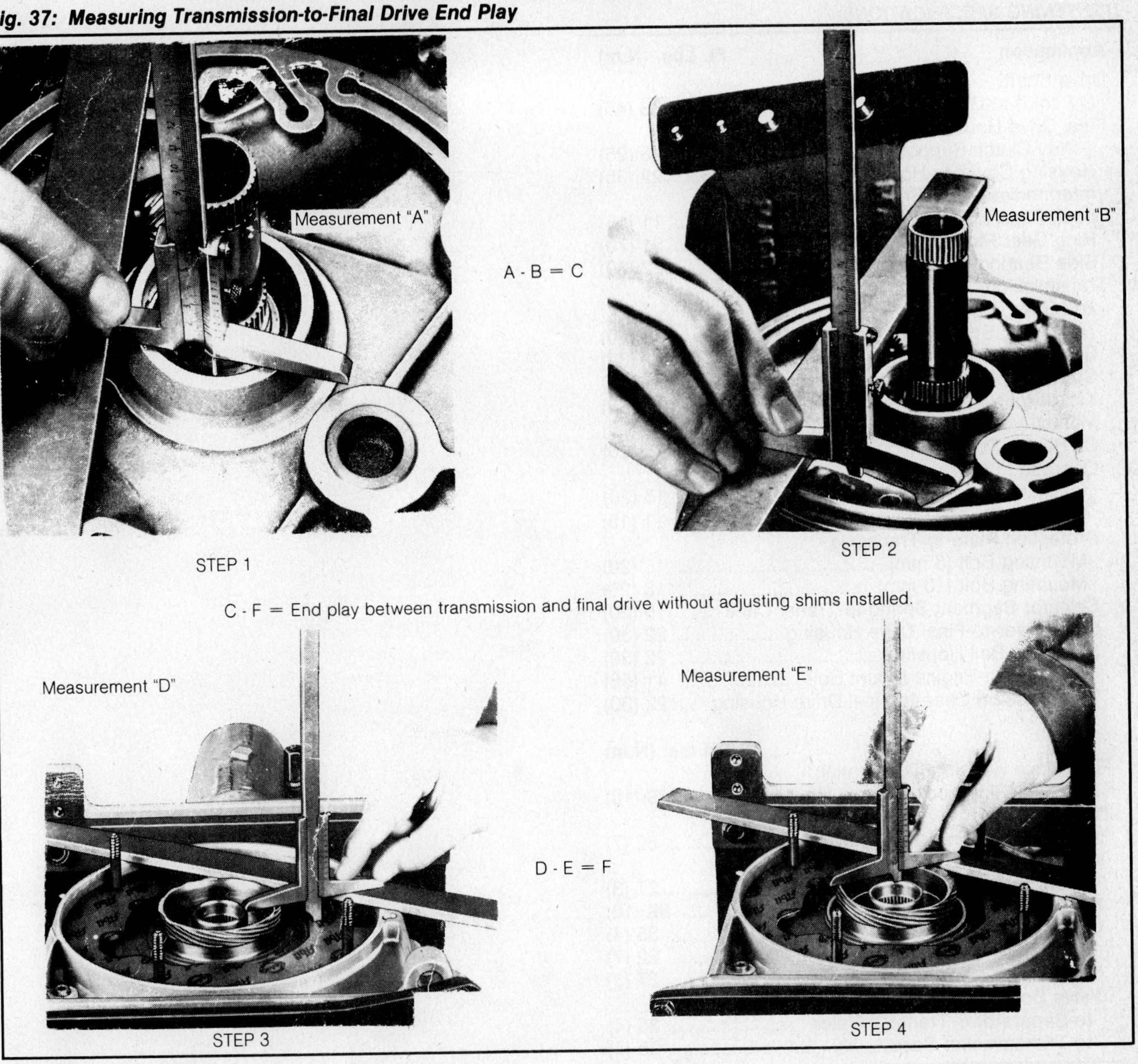

END PLAY SHIM CHART

If End Play Is In (mm)	Install Shim Pack In. (mm)
.009-.033 (0.23-0.84)	None
.034-.049 (0.85-1.24)	.016 (0.40)
.050-.065 (1.25-1.64)	.032 (0.80)
.066-.080 (1.65-2.04)	.048 (1.20)
.081-.096 (2.05-2.44)	.064 (1.60)
.097-.112 (2.45-2.84)	.080 (2.00)
.113-.128 (2.85-3.24)	.096 (2.40)
.129-.143 (3.25-3.64)	.112 (2.80)
.144-.153 (3.65-3.88)	.128 (3.20)

VOLKSWAGEN TYPE 010 3-SPEED (Cont.)

TIGHTENING SPECIFICATIONS

Application	Ft. Lbs. (N.m)
Drive Shaft	
CV Joint-to-Drive Flange	33 (45)
Final Drive Housing (Differential)	
1-Way Clutch Support Mounting Bolt	18 (25)
Housing Cover-to-Housing Mounting Bolt	22 (30)
Intermediate Gear Shaft	
Lock Plate-to-Housing	11 (15)
Ring Gear Mounting Bolt	51 (70)
Side Bearing Cover Mounting Nut	22 (30)
Transmission	
2nd Gear Brake Band	
Adjusting Screw Lock Nut	15 (20)
Converter-to-Drive Plate	22 (30)
Converter Cover Plate-to-Bell Housing	11 (15)
Kickdown Valve-to-Shaft Nut	11 (15)
Manual Valve-to-Shaft Nut	15 (20)
Oil Pan-to-Transmission Case	15 (20)
Operating Lever	
to-Shaft (New Type)	15 (20)
to-Shaft (For Kickdown Valve)	11 (15)
Protection Plate-to-Transaxle	
Mounting Bolt (8 mm)	15 (20)
Mounting Bolt (10 mm)	18 (25)
Selector Segment Spring-to-Trans. Case	15 (20)
Side Cover-to-Final Drive Housing	22 (30)
Starter-to-Bell Housing	22 (30)
Transaxle-to-Engine Mount Bolt	41 (56)
Transmission Case-to-Final Drive Housing	22 (30)
	INCH lbs. (N.m)
Final Drive Housing (Differential)	
Adjusting Ring Lock Plate-to-Housing	89 (10)
Transmission	
ATF Pump-to-Transmission Case	62 (7)
Accumulator Cover	
to-Transmission Case	27 (3)
Main Pressure Tap Plug	89 (10)
Operating Lever Shaft Lock Bolt	35 (4)
Separating Plate-to-Transmission Case	62 (7)
Strainer-to-Valve Body	27 (3)
Valve Body	
to-Separator & Transfer Plates	35 (4)
to-Transmission Case	35 (4)

VOLKSWAGEN VANAGON

TRANSAXLE IDENTIFICATION

Transmission portion of transaxle assembly may be identified by a group of numbers stamped into top of transmission case. One of the numbers is "090". This denotes the Volkswagen "2-planetary" type transmission. Final drive portion of transaxle assembly is identified by a group of figures stamped into final drive housing near governor assembly. These figures consist of a 2 letter model code and a build date code.

DESCRIPTION

Transaxle assembly consists of two main units: Automatic transmission and final drive assembly. The transmission housing contains two planetary gear sets, two multi-disc clutches, one brake band and servo, one multiple-disc brake, a one-way clutch, and a hydraulic control system. The final drive housing contains the torque converter, governor assembly for transmission, ring and pinion gear, and the differential assembly.

LUBRICATION & ADJUSTMENT

See the appropriate AUTOMATIC TRANSMISSION SERVICING article in IMPORT GENERAL SERVICING section.

SERVICE (IN VEHICLE)

DRIVE AXLE SHAFTS

See appropriate DRIVE AXLE SHAFT article in IMPORT AXLE SHAFTS, OVERDRIVES & TRANSFER CASES section.

TROUBLE SHOOTING

NO MOVEMENT

In Any Gear

Low fluid level. Manual lever not connected to manual valve. Torque converter disconnected from drive plate. Main pressure valve sticking. Oil pump drive plate and/or shaft defective.

In Forward Gears

Forward clutch internal damage (worn plates, broken diaphragm spring, seals leaking, etc.). Forward planetary gear set damaged.

In First Gear in "D" or "2"

One-way clutch not holding. Forward clutch internal damage.

In First Gear in "1"

1st/Reverse brake plates worn or burnt.

In Second Gear

2nd gear brake band out of adjustment, or burnt, or servo defective.

In Reverse

1st/Reverse brake plates damaged, worn or burnt. Direct/Reverse clutch internal damage. Forward clutch seized in applied position.

NO UPSHIFTS

Into Second Gear

Governor drive defective. Governor dirty or improperly assembled. Accumulator cover plate loose. Valve body dirty. 1-2 shift valve sticking. 2nd gear brake band burnt or worn.

Into Third Gear

Governor or valve body dirty. 2-3 shift valve sticking. Oil pump bolts loose.

Fig. 1: Volkswagen Vanagon Automatic Transaxle Assembly

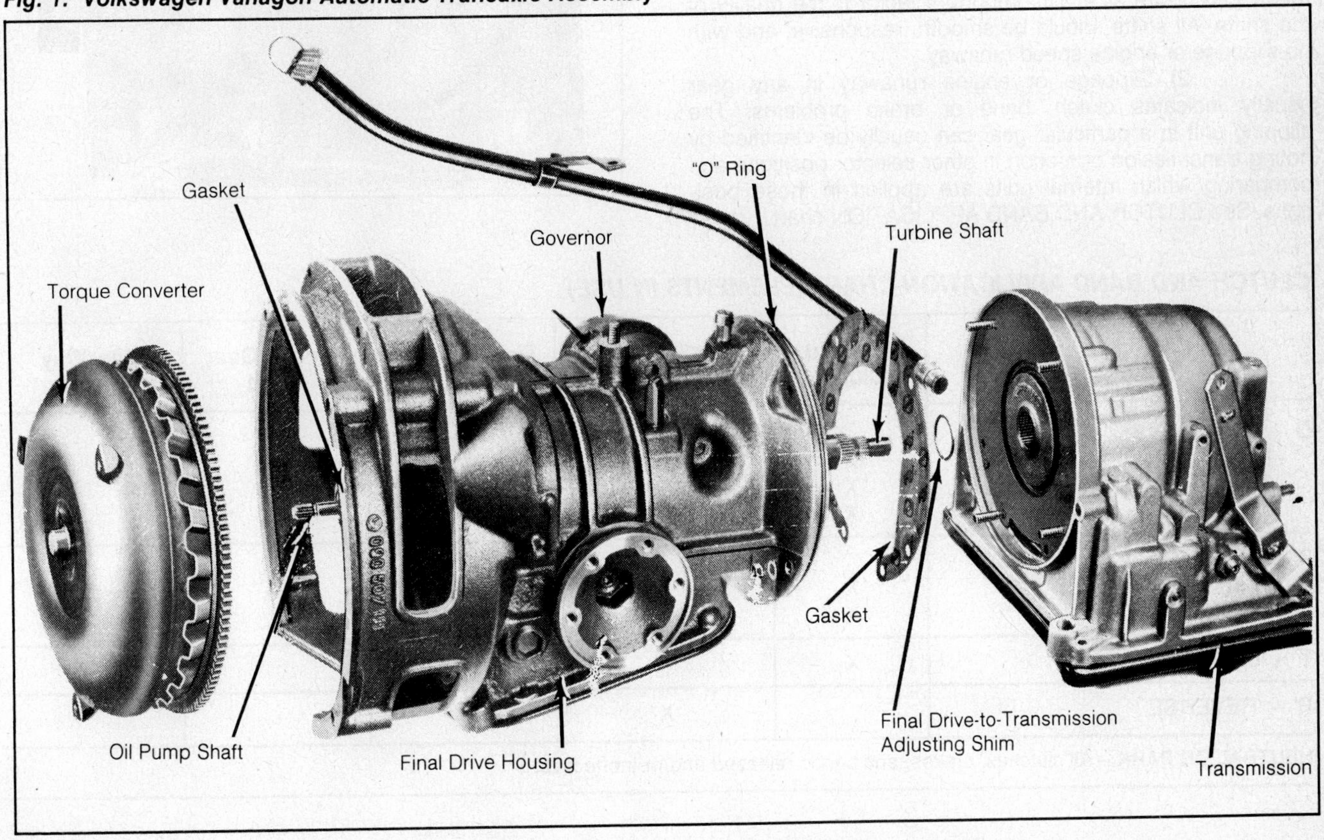

VOLKSWAGEN VANAGON (Cont.)

NO DOWNSHIFTS

Into Second Gear

Governor dirty. 2-3 shift valve sticking.

Into First Gear

Governor dirty. 1-2 shift valve sticking.

DELAYED ENGAGEMENT ON UPSHIFTS

1-2 Upshift

Low fluid level. Dirty valve body. 2nd gear brake band worn, burnt or out of adjustment. 2nd gear servo defective.

2-3 Upshift

Low fluid level. Dirty valve body. 2nd gear brake band worn, burnt or out of adjustment. 2nd gear servo defective. Direct/Reverse clutch plates worn or burnt. Wrong Direct/Reverse clutch installed.

ERRATIC DRIVE

Low fluid level. Bushing in one-way clutch support and turbine shaft worn. Oil filter dirty.

INCORRECT SHIFT SPEEDS

Governor dirty. Valve body dirty. Planetary gears or separation plate gasket damaged.

TESTING

ROAD TEST

1) Before road testing, be certain that fluid level and condition, and control linkage adjustments have been checked and corrected as necessary. During the test, transmission should upshift and downshift at approximately the speeds shown in SHIFT SPEED SPECIFICATIONS chart. All shifts may vary somewhat due to production tolerances or tire size. The important factor is the quality of the shifts. All shifts should be smooth, responsive, and with no slippage or engine speed runaway.

2) Slippage or engine runaway in any gear usually indicates clutch, band or brake problems. The slipping unit in a particular gear can usually be identified by noting transmission operation in other selector positions and comparing which internal units are applied in those positions. See CLUTCH AND BAND APPLICATION chart.

3) This process of elimination can be used to detect any unit which slips, and to confirm proper operation of good units. However, the actual cause of the malfunction usually cannot be easily determined. Most conditions can be caused by leaking hydraulic circuits or sticking valves. Therefore, unless an obvious condition exists, do not disassemble transmission until a hydraulic pressure test has been made.

SHIFT SPEED SPECIFICATIONS

Application	Shift Points (MPH) Full Throttle	Kickdown
1-2 Upshift	16-22	30-32
2-3 Upshift	37-47	55-56
3-2 Downshift	27-37	52-53
2-1 Downshift	11-12	27-29

HYDRAULIC PRESSURE TEST

1) Connect a pressure gauge to main pressure test point on case (adjacent to servo cover). Bring

Fig. 2: View of Transmission Case Showing Main Pressure Test Point

Arrow Indicates Pressure Connection

CLUTCH AND BAND APPLICATION CHART (ELEMENTS IN USE)

Selector Lever Position	Forward Clutch	Direct-Reverse Clutch	First-Reverse Brake	Second Gear Band	One-Way Clutch
D - DRIVE					
First Gear	X				X
Second Gear	X			X	
Third Gear	X	X			
2 - INTERMEDIATE					
First Gear	X				X
Second Gear	X			X	
1 - LOW (First)	X		X		
R - REVERSE		X	X		

NEUTRAL OR PARK – All clutches, brakes, and bands released and/or ineffective.

VOLKSWAGEN VANAGON (Cont.)

transmission to normal operating temperature and place selector lever in "D". Accelerate to about 30 MPH, release throttle completely and read pressure on gauge.

NOTE: **This test, as well as full throttle test performed next, should be carried out on a dynamometer when possible.**

2) Next, run engine at full throttle with vehicle speed about 30 MPH, and again note pressure reading in "D".

3) Finally, with vehicle at a standstill, place selector lever in "R" position, and note reading on pressure gauge.

4) Pressures obtained in each phase of test should be approximately as shown in MAIN PRESSURE SPECIFICATIONS chart. If not, disassemble and clean valve body and check especially for sticking valves.

MAIN PRESSURE SPECIFICATIONS

Application	psi (kg/cm²)
"D" at Idle [1]	41-43 (2.9-3.0)
"D" at Full Throttle	83-85 (5.9-6.0)
"R" at Idle [2]	129-138 (9.1-9.7)

[1] – Engine speed at about 30 MPH, throttle released.
[2] – With vehicle stationary.

STALL TEST

Testing Precautions

When making test, do not hold throttle open any longer than the time it takes to read tachometer. Maximum stall speed test time is 5 seconds. If repetition is necessary, wait at least 20 seconds between tests. If engine speed exceeds limits shown in STALL SPEED SPECIFICATIONS table, release accelerator immediately as clutch or band slippage is indicated.

Testing Procedure

With engine at normal operating temperature, connect a tachometer. Start engine and set parking and service brakes. Place selector lever in "D". Depress accelerator briefly to full throttle and note maximum RPM obtained. Engine speed should be within limits shown in STALL SPEED SPECIFICATIONS table.

NOTE: **Normal stall speed will drop approximately 125 RPM per 3200 feet altitude. Also, stall speed will drop slightly at high ambient temperatures.**

STALL SPEED SPECIFICATIONS

Application	Stall RPM
All Models	1950-2250

Stall Test Results

1) If stall speed is higher than specified, forward clutch or 1st gear one-way clutch is slipping. If stall speed in "D" is too high, repeat stall test in "1". If RPM is within specifications, one-way clutch for 1st gear is defective. If stall speed RPM is still too high, forward clutch is defective.

2) If stall speed is approximately 200 RPM below specifications, engine performance may be unsatisfactory. If stall speed is approximately 400 RPM below specifications, torque converter stator one-way clutch is defective and complete converter should be replaced.

REMOVAL & INSTALLATION

See appropriate AUTOMATIC TRANSMISSION REMOVAL article in IMPORT GENERAL SERVICING section.

TORQUE CONVERTER

NOTE: **The torque converter is a sealed unit and cannot be disassembled for service. However, the bushing in converter hub may be replaced as follows:**

BUSHING REPLACEMENT

1) Check bushing wear using an inside micrometer. Wear limit of bushing is 1.348" (34.25 mm), and maximum allowable out-of-round is .001" (.03 mm).

2) To replace bushing, use a bushing puller to withdraw bushing from converter hub. Press new bushing into place until it is fully seated in hub. Ensure that inside diameter of new bushing is 1.340-1.341" (34.03-34.05 mm).

TRANSMISSION DISASSEMBLY

NOTE: **To separate transaxle units, withdraw torque converter from final drive housing and remove oil pump shaft from center of turbine shaft. Disconnect oil filler pipe. Remove attaching nuts from transmission studs that attach final drive to transmission, then separate final drive unit from transmission case. Withdraw turbine shaft from final drive assembly pinion shaft. For final drive disassembly and reassembly, see Final Drive information at rear of this article.**

Fig. 3: Removing First Gear One-Way Clutch Assembly Retaining Snap Ring

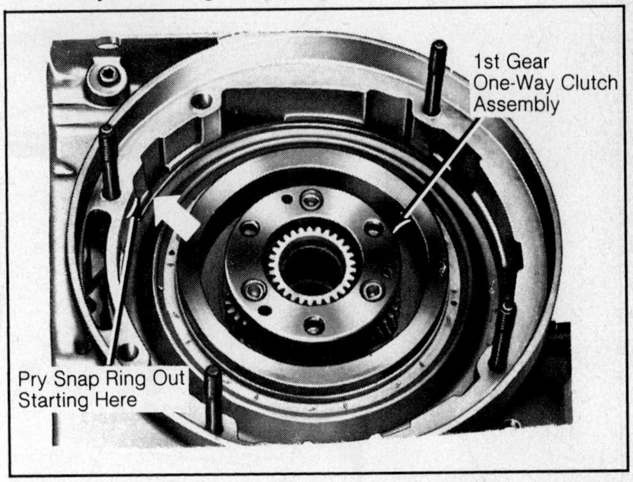

1) Mount transmission assembly in a work stand. Remove separation plate attaching screws and lift plate and gasket from transmission case. Remove forward annulus gear and 2 thrust washers behind it from case.

VOLKSWAGEN VANAGON (Cont.)

2) Using a screwdriver, carefully pry large snap ring retaining 1st gear one-way clutch assembly from case. Lift out one-way clutch, 1st/Reverse gear brake plates, and reverse planetary gear set as a unit.

3) Remove thrust washers, then lift the following components from case as an assembly: Sun gear, driving shell, forward planetary gear set, and forward clutch assembly.

Fig. 4: Removing Brake Band Servo Assembly

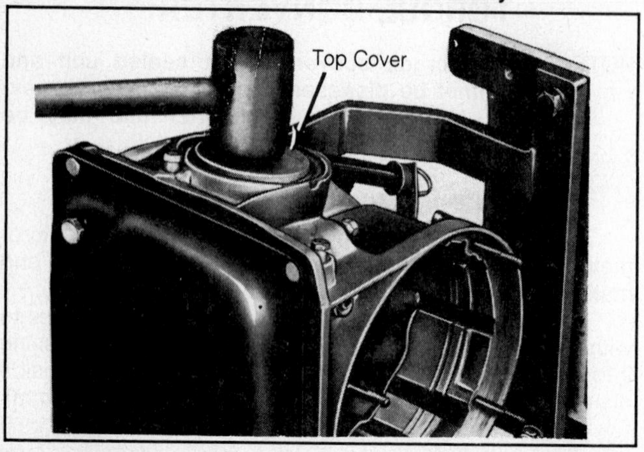

Tap cover until cover and piston pop out under spring pressure.

4) Remove 2nd gear brake band servo cover snap ring. Then using a rubber mallet, tap cover until cover and piston assembly pop out under spring tension.

5) Loosen 2nd gear brake band adjusting screw lock nut and remove lock nut and screw, then withdraw push rod for adjusting screw.

6) Lift out remaining planetary gear set components that are housed in 1st/Reverse gear brake shell. Remove bolt from 1st/Reverse brake spring plate, withdraw spring plate and springs, then pull driving shell, brake piston, and oil pump from case.

7) Invert transmission so that oil pan is facing up. Remove attaching bolts and lift off pan and gasket. Remove screws from oil strainer and separate strainer from valve body.

8) Remove the valve body attaching bolts and lift valve body assembly from case using care not to drop manual valve. Remove attaching screws from accumulator cover plate, then remove cover, spring and accumulator piston. If necessary for parts replacement, disassemble kickdown and selector linkage using *Fig. 5* as a disassembly guide.

COMPONENT DISASSEMBLY & REASSEMBLY

OIL PUMP ASSEMBLY

CAUTION: Oil pump cover is under spring tension.

Disassembly

1) Remove pump cover attaching screws and separate cover from housing. Remove check ball and

Fig. 5: Bottom View of Transmission Case Showing Kickdown and Selector Linkage

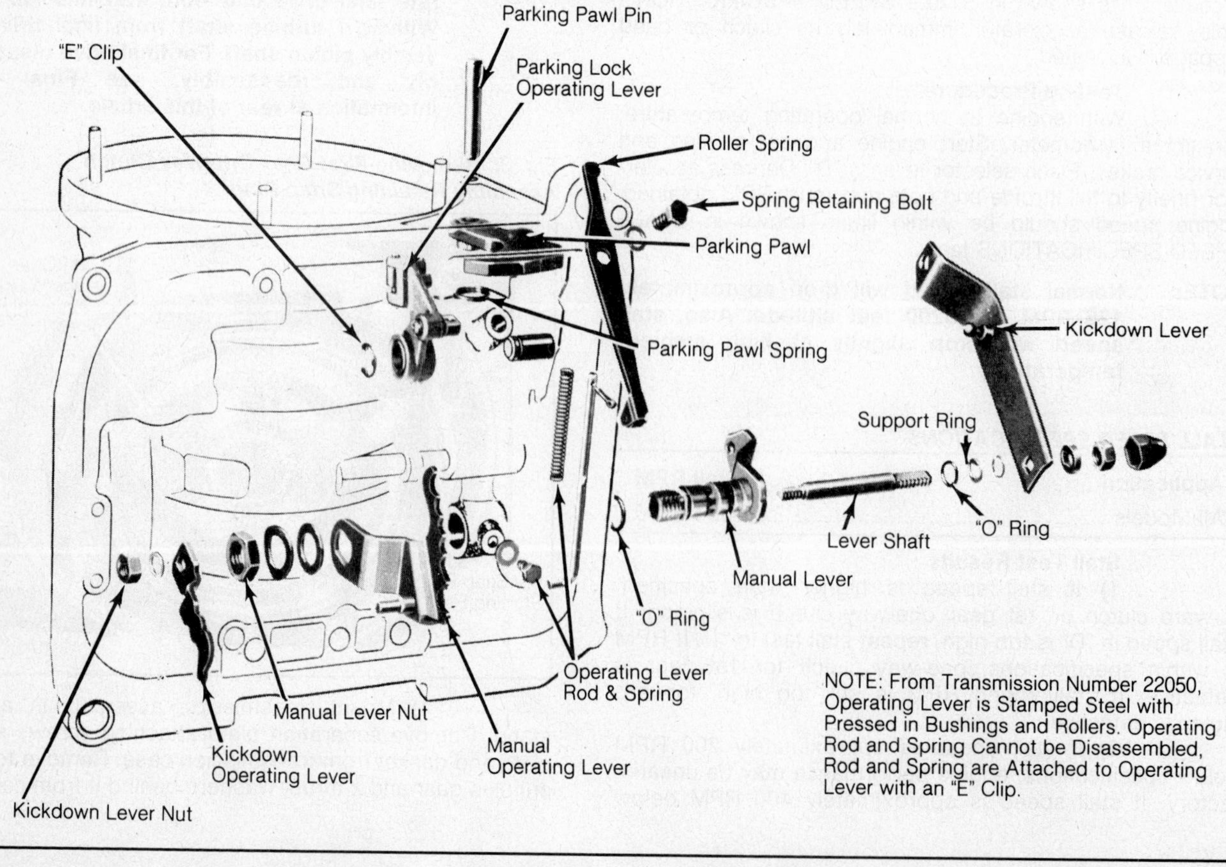

NOTE: From Transmission Number 22050, Operating Lever is Stamped Steel with Pressed in Bushings and Rollers. Operating Rod and Spring Cannot be Disassembled, Rod and Spring are Attached to Operating Lever with an "E" Clip.

VOLKSWAGEN VANAGON (Cont.)

Fig. 6: Exploded View Showing Major Components of Transmission Assembly

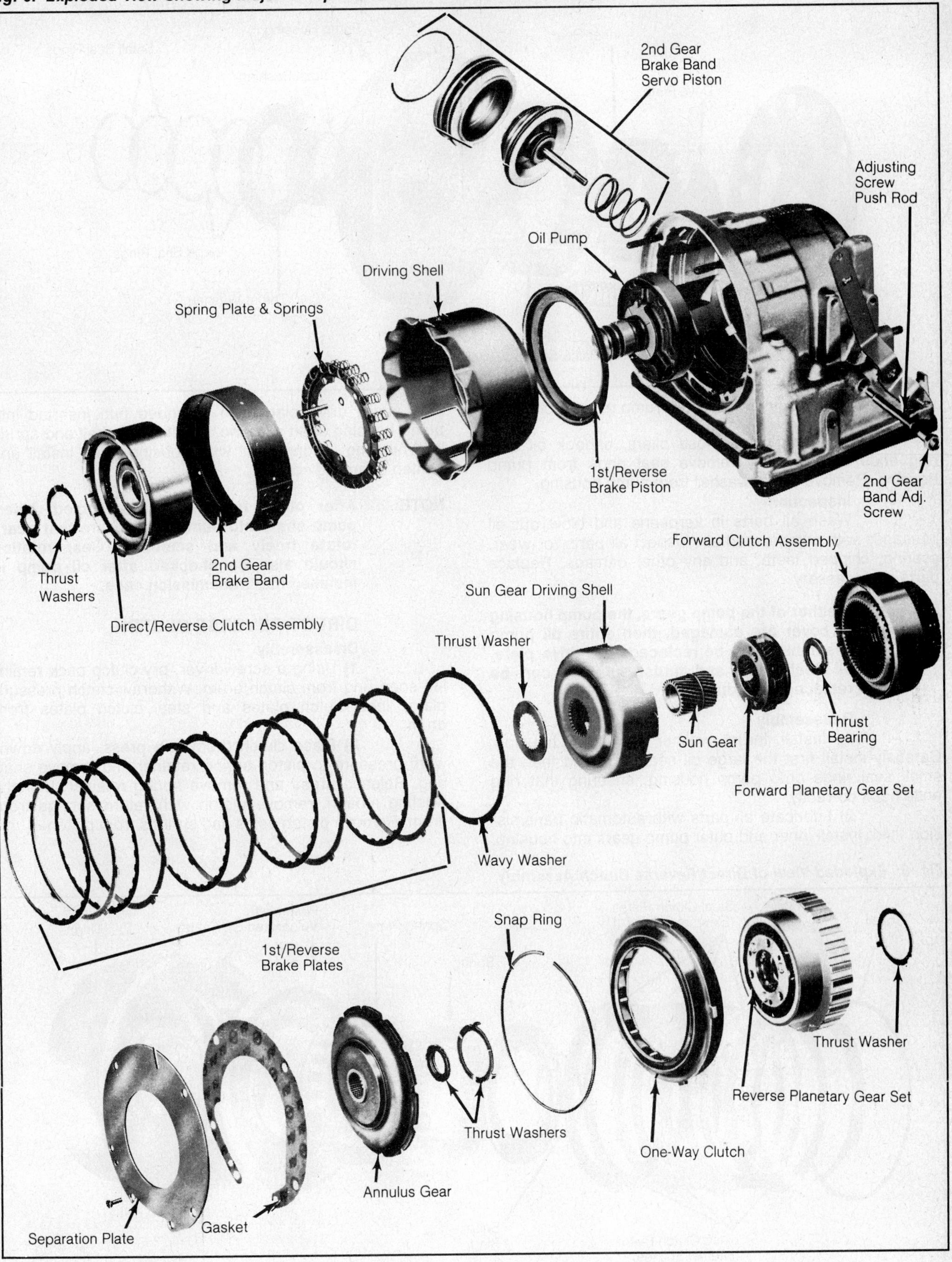

VOLKSWAGEN VANAGON (Cont.)

Fig. 7: Exploded View of Oil Pump Assembly

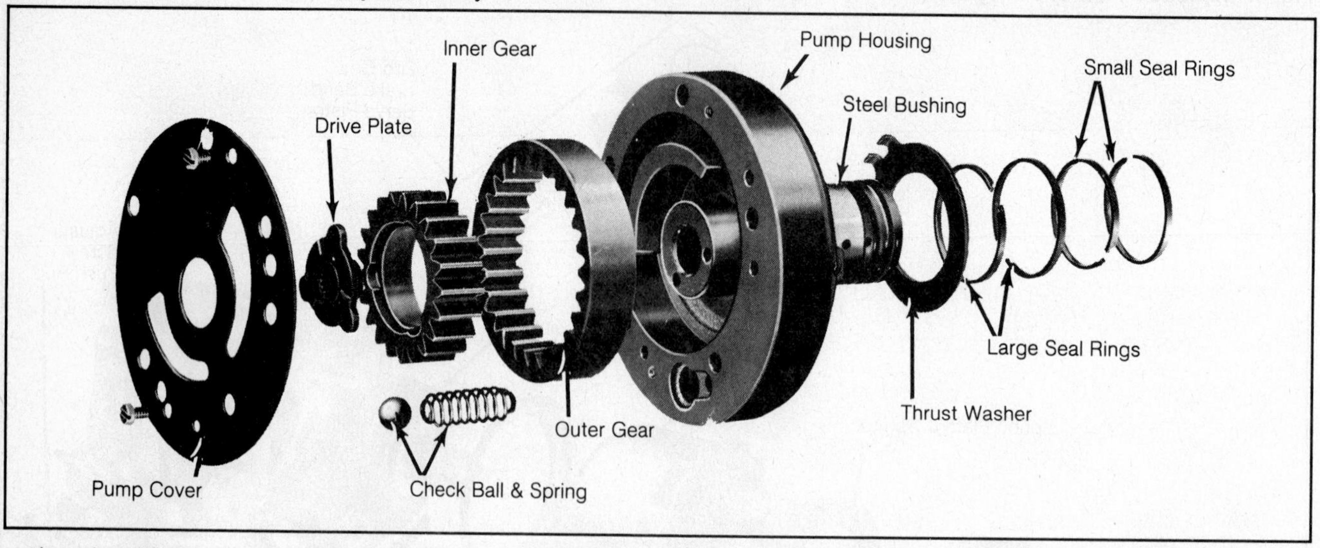

spring, then lift out inner and outer pump gears along with drive plate.

2) Using needle-nose pliers, unhook oil seal ring ends and carefully remove seal rings from pump housing. Remove thrust washer from pump housing.

Inspection

Wash all parts in kerosene and blow out oil passages with compressed air. Inspect all parts for wear, scoring, chipped teeth, and any other damage. Replace parts as necessary.

NOTE: **If either of the pump gears, the pump housing or cover are damaged, then entire oil pump assembly must be replaced. The drive plate, oil seal rings, and thrust washers can be replaced individually.**

Reassembly

1) Install thrust washer on pump housing. Carefully install first the large oil seal rings and then the small seal rings onto pump housing, ensuring that ring ends hook correctly.

2) Lubricate all parts with automatic transmission fluid. Install inner and outer pump gears into housing, then install drive plate with extended hub inserted into pump housing shaft opening. Install check ball and spring into housing. Align cover with housing, then install and tighten attaching screws.

NOTE: **After pump has been reassembled, insert pump shaft into pump and ensure that gears rotate freely and smoothly. Gear rotation should also be checked after oil pump is installed into transmission case.**

DIRECT/REVERSE CLUTCH

Disassembly

1) Using a screwdriver, pry clutch pack retaining snap ring from clutch drum. Withdraw clutch pressure plate, lined clutch plates and steel clutch plates from drum.

2) Place clutch drum in a press, apply downward pressure to piston spring retainer and remove snap ring. Release press and remove spring retainer. Using a twisting motion, remove piston with return springs from drum. Remove piston seals and springs from piston.

Fig. 8: Exploded View of Direct/Reverse Clutch Assembly

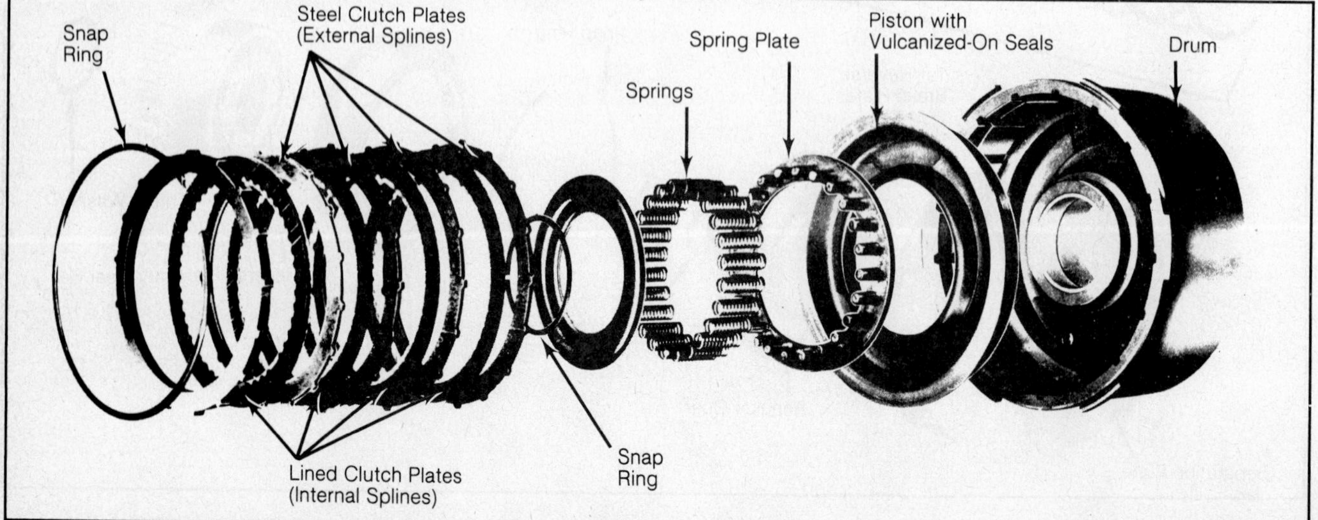

VOLKSWAGEN VANAGON (Cont.)

3) If necessary for replacement, place clutch drum in a press and drive bushing from drum hub using a driver.

Inspection

1) Inspect friction surfaces of piston and drum for wear or damage. Check clutch drum ball valve for free movement. Inspect piston springs for wear or collapsed coils and replace as necessary.

2) Inspect steel (external splines) clutch plates. If plates are scored or have radial grooves, they must be replaced. Plates that are only discolored can be reused.

3) Inspect lined (internal splines) clutch plates. Replace any plate that is worn, damaged or burnt.

NOTE: New lined clutch plates must be soaked in automatic transmission fluid for at least 15 minutes prior to installation.

Reassembly

1) If removed, press new clutch drum bushing into drum until it is flush with outer lip of hub.

2) Lubricate piston seals with automatic transmission fluid, then install them into clutch drum with lips facing into drum. Using a stiff plastic sheet to protect seals, install piston into drum using a twisting motion. Remove plastic sheet from drum.

3) Position piston return spring plate and springs on piston. Place spring retainer on springs, compress retainer and install snap ring. Install clutch plates into drum starting with a steel (external splines) plate and alternating lined and steel plates until all clutch plates are installed.

4) Install pressure plate and clutch pack retaining snap ring. Using a feeler gauge, measure clearance between pressure plate and retaining snap ring. Clearance should be .081-.098" (2.05-2.50 mm); if not, remove clutch pack snap ring and replace with a snap ring of sufficient thickness to bring clearance within specifications.

NOTE: Direct/Reverse clutch pack snap rings are available in various thicknesses from .059" (1.5 mm) to .098" (2.5 mm).

5) Install correct thickness snap ring. Recheck clutch pack clearance to ensure correct snap ring has been installed.

Fig. 10: Using a Feeler Gauge to Measure Direct/Reverse Clutch Pack Clearance

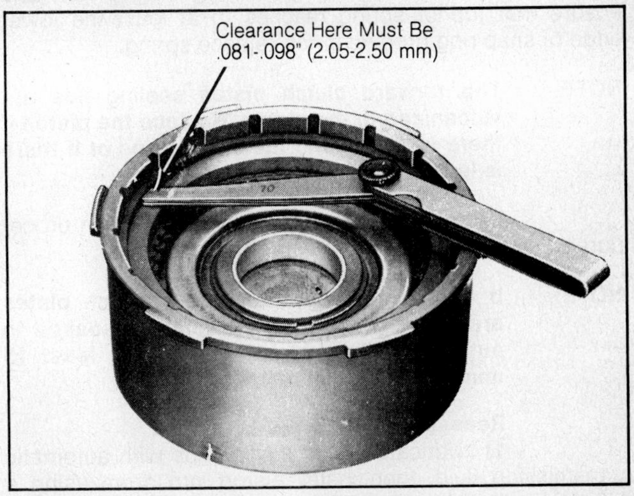

Insert feeler gauge between snap ring and pressure plate.

DIRECT/REVERSE CLUTCH PLATE CHART

Application	Steel Plates	Lined Plates
All Models	4	4

FORWARD CLUTCH

Disassembly

1) Using a screwdriver, pry clutch pack retaining snap ring from clutch drum. Then withdraw pressure plate, forward annulus gear, lined and steel clutch plates, and thrust plate.

2) Carefully pry out diaphragm spring snap ring. Remove diaphragm spring. Lift out piston.

NOTE: It may be necessary to force piston from clutch drum using compressed air.

Inspection

1) Inspect clutch drum for scoring, wear, or other damage. Check clutch drum ball valve for free movement and ensure that drilling is clear.

Fig. 9: Exploded View Showing Forward Clutch Assembly

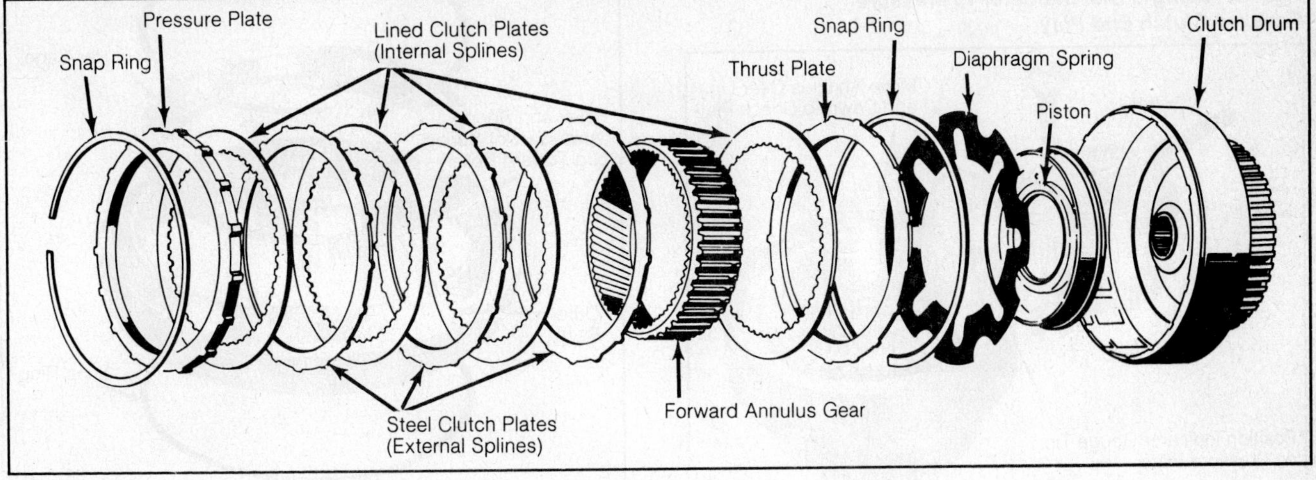

VOLKSWAGEN VANAGON (Cont.)

2) Inspect diaphragm spring and piston for damage. Also, place diaphragm spring onto piston and ensure that top of spring reaches to at least the lower edge of snap ring groove; if not, replace spring.

NOTE: **The forward clutch piston sealing lips are vulcanized to the piston. Replace the piston if there is damage to the sealing lips or if there is leakage past the sealing lips.**

3) Use Direct/Reverse clutch inspection procedures to inspect the lined and steel clutch plates.

NOTE: **If new lined (internal splines) clutch plates are to be installed, they must be soaked in automatic transmission fluid for at least 15 minutes prior to installation.**

Reassembly

1) Lubricate piston sealing lips with automatic transmission fluid, then install piston into drum using a twisting motion. Install diaphragm spring, with convex side toward piston, into clutch drum. Install retaining snap ring.

NOTE: **With snap ring installed, diaphragm spring should be lightly tensioned; if not, replace spring.**

2) Install thrust plate into drum. If one side of thrust plate is chamfered, install chamfered side toward diaphragm spring.

3) Install one lined (internal splines) clutch plate into drum, then install annulus gear so that short splines beneath its retaining ridge are engaged in the lined clutch plate. Install remaining clutch plates starting with a steel (external splines) plate and alternating lined and steel clutch plates until all plates have been installed.

FORWARD CLUTCH PLATE CHART

Application	Steel Plates	Lined Plates
All Models	3	4

4) Install pressure plate and retaining snap ring into clutch drum. Next, position a dial indicator on clutch assembly so that indicator tip contacts pressure plate, then zero dial face.

Fig. 11: Using a Dial Indicator to Measure Forward Clutch End Play

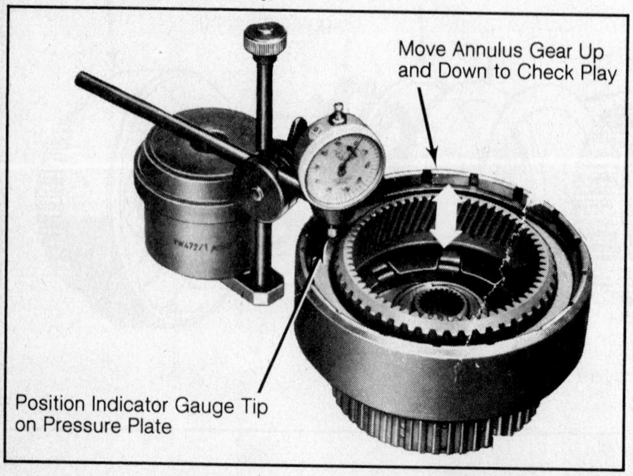

5) Measure forward clutch end play by moving annulus gear up and down so that dial indicator will show play between pressure plate and snap ring.

6) Forward clutch end play should be .020-.035" (.50-.90 mm). If not, replace pressure plate with one of sufficient thickness to bring end play within specifications. After correct pressure plate is installed, recheck end play.

NOTE: **Forward clutch pressure plates are available in thicknesses of .236" (6.0 mm) to .299" (7.6 mm) in increments of .016" (.4 mm).**

FIRST GEAR ONE-WAY CLUTCH

Disassembly

Remove one-way clutch rollers and springs. Remove snap rings. Using a plastic mallet, carefully drive roller cage out of outer race.

Fig. 12: Modified One-Way Clutch and Retaining Ring

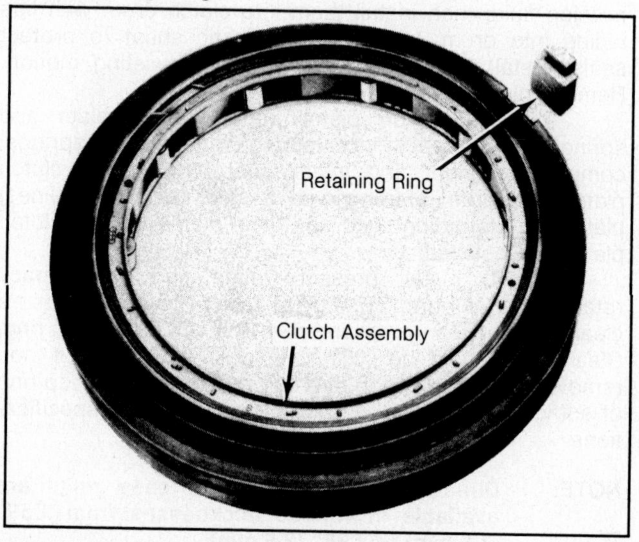

Fig. 13: Exploded View of First Gear One-Way Clutch Assembly

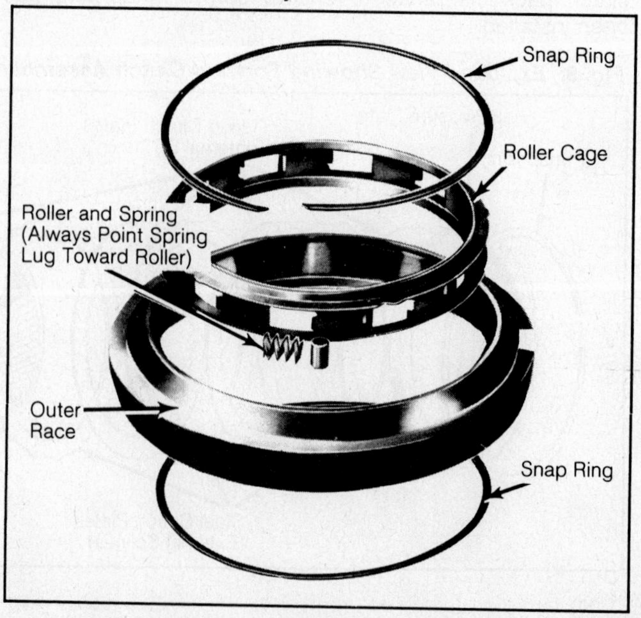

VOLKSWAGEN VANAGON (Cont.)

Inspection

Inspect all parts for wear scoring, or other damage and replace as necessary.

NOTE: One-way clutch has been modified and now has a retaining key to hold ring from turning in transmission housing. Previously, 5 protruding lugs served this purpose. New type clutch cannot be installed in transmission with old type clutch.

Reassembly

1) Install lower snap ring in groove of outer race. If necessary, heat outer race to 300°F (150°C), then place roller cage into race using 2 pair of pliers.

NOTE: The heat from outer race will transfer quickly to roller cage, causing cage to stick inside race. If cage is not correctly positioned against lower snap ring inside race, DO NOT attempt to press it into position after cage has stuck. Carefully knock cage out of outer race and repeat procedure again after race has cooled down.

2) Install upper snap ring. Install rollers and springs into cage as shown in *Fig. 14*.

Fig. 14: View of One-Way Clutch Assembly Showing Correct Roller and Spring Installation

Roller and spring must be installed as shown.

REVERSE ANNULUS GEAR

NOTE: Reverse annulus gear should be disassembled only if parts replacement is necessary.

Fig. 15: Disassembled View of Reverse Annulus Gear

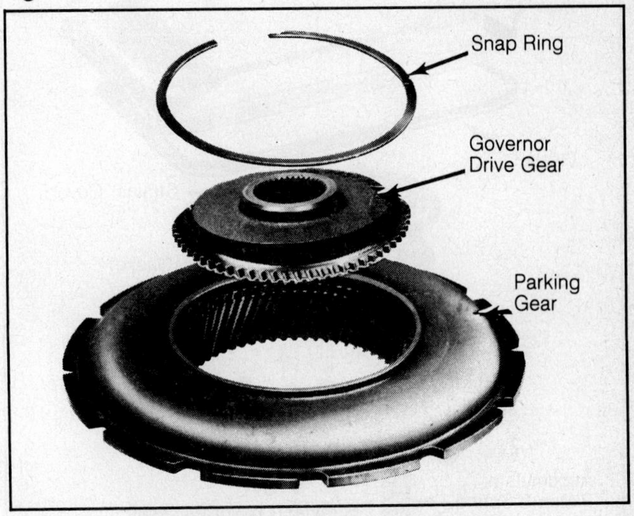

Disassembly & Reassembly

Remove snap ring and lift governor drive gear out of parking gear. Inspect parking lock notches on parking gear and replace worn part. To reassemble, reverse disassembly procedure.

VALVE BODY ASSEMBLY

NOTE: As valve body components are removed from each valve bore, place individual parts in correct order in relative position to valve body to simplify reassembly.

Disassembly

1) Remove transfer plate-to-valve body attaching screws. Lift transfer plate and separator plate from main valve body. Remove .24" (6 mm) check balls (5) and .12" (3 mm) check ball (1) from valve body. *See Fig. 17.*

VOLKSWAGEN VALVE BODY SPRING IDENTIFICATION CHART

Valve Spring	Length In. (mm)	Diameter In. (mm) [1]	Number Of Coils	Wire Thickness In. (mm)
Throttle Pressure Limiting Valve	1.389 (35.3)	.303 (7.7)	14.5	.043 (1.1)
Main Pressure Limiting Valve	1.275 (32.4)	.303 (7.7)	11	.047 (1.2)
Main Pressure Valve	3.031 (77.0)	.468 (11.9)	16.5	.059 (1.5)
3-2 Control Valve	1.275 (32.4)	.303 (7.7)	12.5	.039 (1.0)
Throttle Pressure Valve	1.708 (43.4)	.305 (7.75)	16	.049 (1.25)
1-2 Shift Valve	1.024 (26.0)	.323 (8.2)	9.5	.031 (0.8)
Converter Pressure Valve	0.874 (22.2)	.303 (7.7)	8.5	.049 (1.25)
Modulator Pressure Valve	1.126 (28.6)	.305 (7.75)	11.5	.031 (0.8)
2-3 Shift Valve	1.024 (26.0)	.323 (8.2)	9.5	.031 (0.8)
3-2 Kickdown Valve	1.118 (28.4)	.318 (8.1)	11.5	.035 (0.9)
1st/Reverse Apply Valve	1.118 (28.4)	.318 (8.1)	11.5	.035 (0.9)

[1] – Inner diameter of coils should be within a tolerance of ± .012" (.3 mm).

VOLKSWAGEN VANAGON (Cont.)

Fig. 16: Exploded View Showing Removal of Strainers and Valve Body Assembly

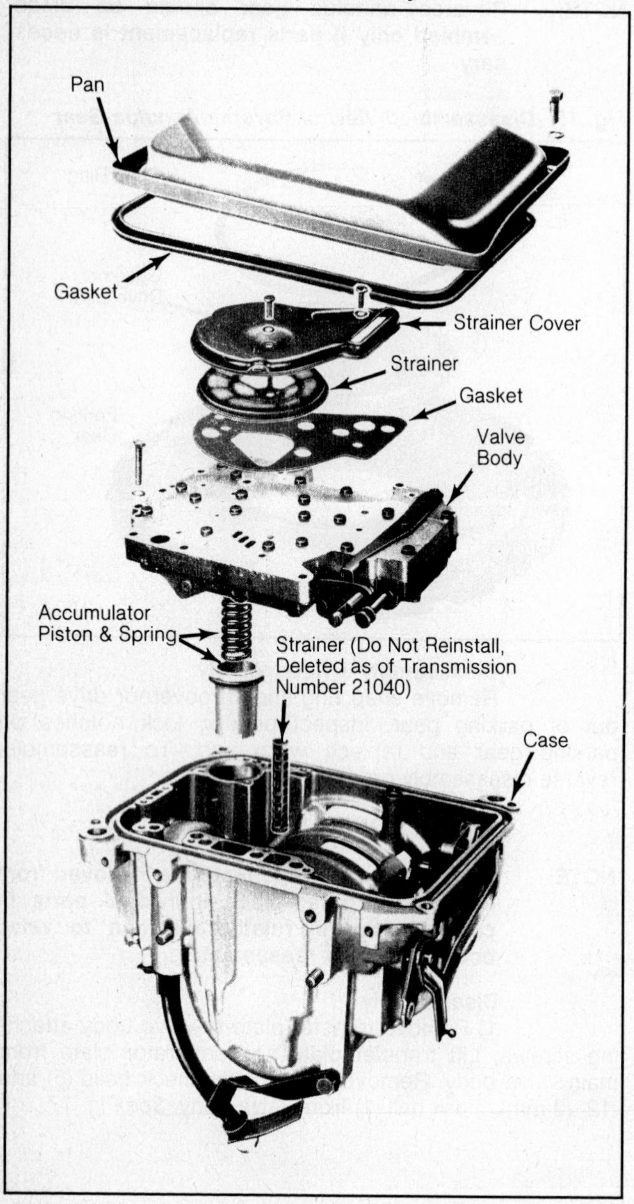

CAUTION: DO NOT alter setting of adjusting screws when removing from valve body.

2) Remove rear end cover plate and withdraw valves, springs and adjusting screws. Remove remaining end plates, one at a time, and withdraw all valves, plugs, springs and adjusting screws. Tag all parts for reassembly reference.

Inspection

1) Wash all parts in clean kerosene and dry them with compressed air only (do not use fluffy rags, etc.). Check all parts for burrs and scores; replace assembly if damage is found.

2) When valves are clean and lubricated with fluid, they should fall freely of their own weight in respective bore; if not, check for valve or bore damage.

3) Check all valve body springs for damage or collapsed coils.

CAUTION: Several valve body springs have similar dimensions; however, they must not be interchanged as they have different tolerances. See Valve Body Spring Identification table.

4) Take care not to disturb settings of adjusting screws; pressures affected by these screws can only be measured and adjusted accurately on a test stand.

Fig. 17: View of Main Valve Body Showing Check Ball Locations

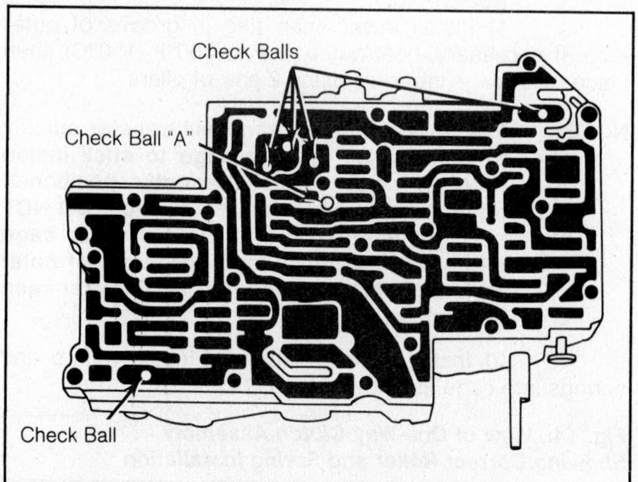

NOTE — Check ball "A" is .12" (3 mm) in diameter. All others are .24" (6 mm) in diameter.

Fig. 18: View of Valve Body Installed

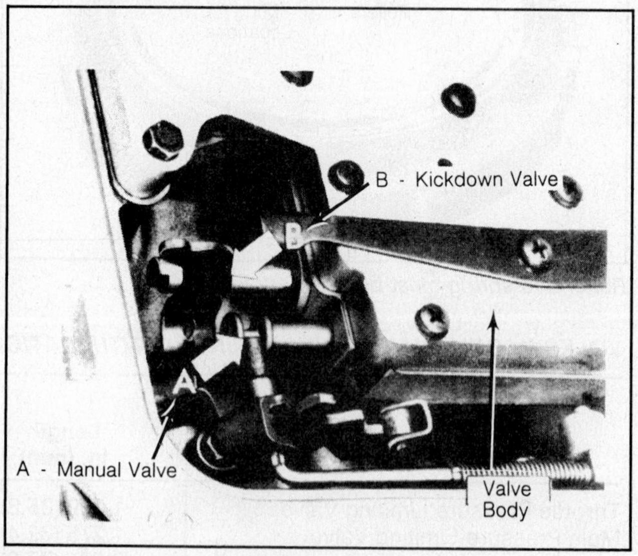

Arrows show relation of operating levers to manual control valves.

Reassembly

1) Lubricate all parts with automatic transmission fluid and install into proper valve body bores, in reverse order of disassembly. When tightening end plate attaching screws, be careful not to overtighten them as this could easily strip the threads or distort the valve body enough to cause a valve to stick.

VOLKSWAGEN VANAGON (Cont.)

Fig. 19: Exploded View Showing Main Body Assembly Valve Trains

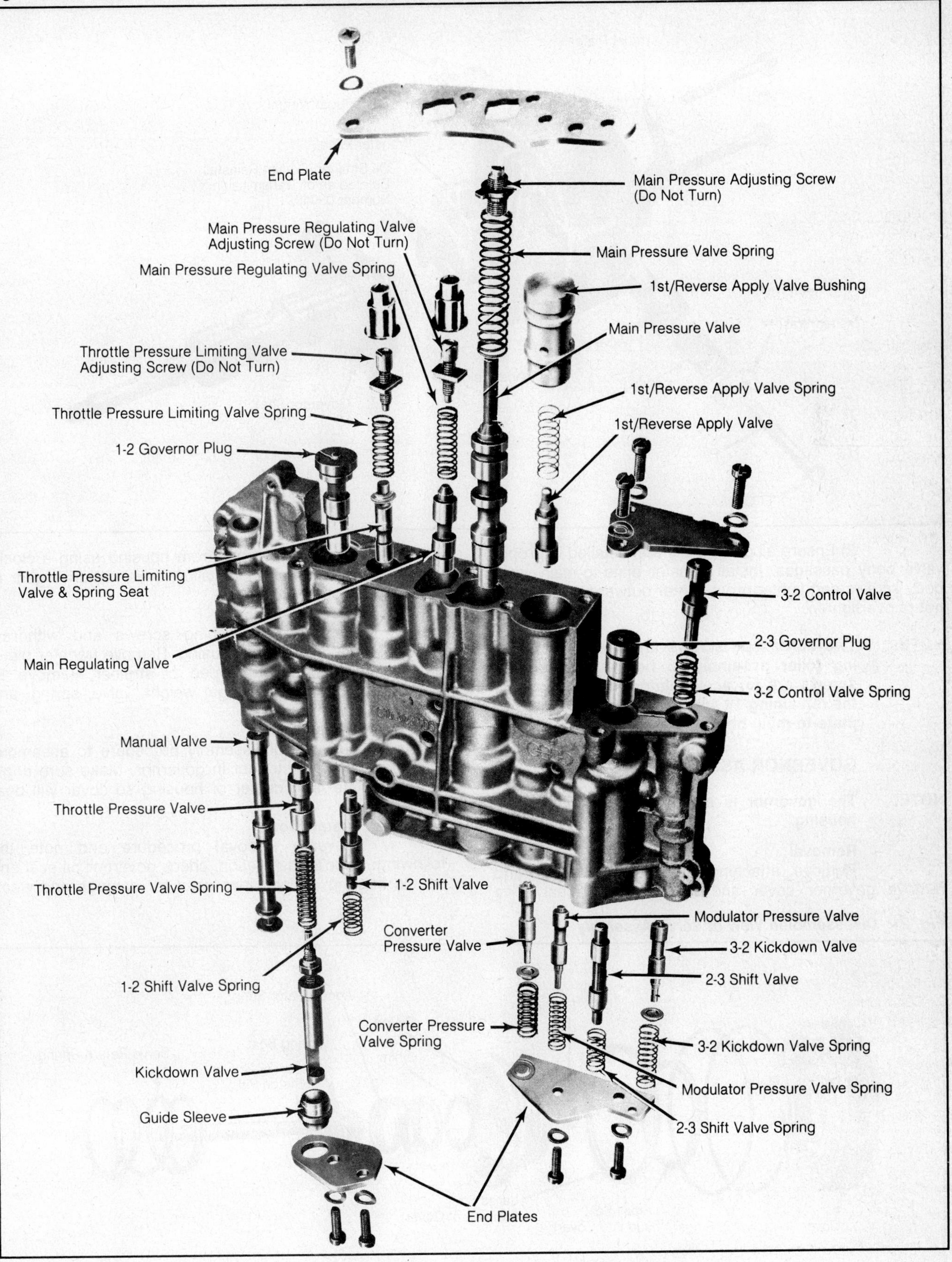
End Plate
Main Pressure Adjusting Screw (Do Not Turn)
Main Pressure Regulating Valve Adjusting Screw (Do Not Turn)
Main Pressure Valve Spring
Main Pressure Regulating Valve Spring
1st/Reverse Apply Valve Bushing
Main Pressure Valve
Throttle Pressure Limiting Valve Adjusting Screw (Do Not Turn)
1st/Reverse Apply Valve Spring
Throttle Pressure Limiting Valve Spring
1st/Reverse Apply Valve
1-2 Governor Plug
Throttle Pressure Limiting Valve & Spring Seat
3-2 Control Valve
2-3 Governor Plug
Main Regulating Valve
3-2 Control Valve Spring
Manual Valve
Throttle Pressure Valve
1-2 Shift Valve
Throttle Pressure Valve Spring
Modulator Pressure Valve
Converter Pressure Valve
3-2 Kickdown Valve
2-3 Shift Valve
1-2 Shift Valve Spring
Converter Pressure Valve Spring
3-2 Kickdown Valve Spring
Kickdown Valve
Modulator Pressure Valve Spring
Guide Sleeve
2-3 Shift Valve Spring
End Plates

VOLKSWAGEN VANAGON (Cont.)

Fig. 20: Exploded View Showing Components of Governor Assembly

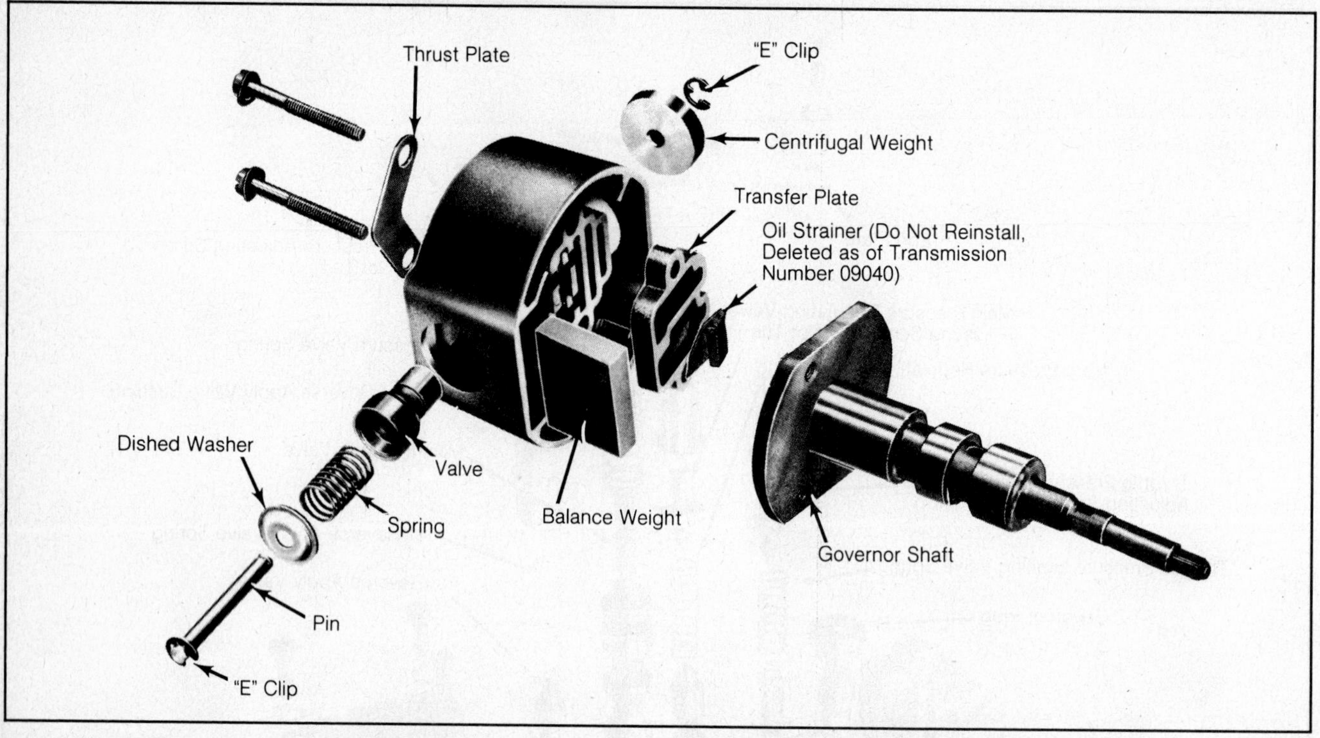

2) Ensure all check balls are installed in proper valve body passages. Install transfer plate-to-main valve body screws and tighten from center outward, taking care not to overtighten.

NOTE: Two collar-type screws are used for attaching roller assembly to body, 3 galvanized screws are for accumulator cover plate, and the remaining 19 screws are used for transfer plate-to-main body attachment.

GOVERNOR ASSEMBLY

NOTE: The governor is mounted in the final drive housing.

Removal

Remove attaching bolts and washers and remove governor cover and "O" ring from final drive housing. Withdraw governor from housing using a clockwise twisting motion that will allow governor drive gear to disengage drive pinion gear.

Disassembly

Remove 2 attaching screws and withdraw thrust plate and governor housing. Remove transfer plate, balance weight, and if equipped, oil strainer. Remove "E" clips and withdraw centrifugal weight, valve, spring, and dished washer from pin.

Reassembly

Reverse disassembly procedure to assemble. Do not reinstall oil strainer in governor. Make sure angle in thrust plate is in center of housing so cover will bear against it.

Installation

Reverse removal procedure and note the following: Prior to installation, check governor oil seal and needle bearing in final drive case for damage and wear,

Fig. 21: Disassembled View of Servo Assembly

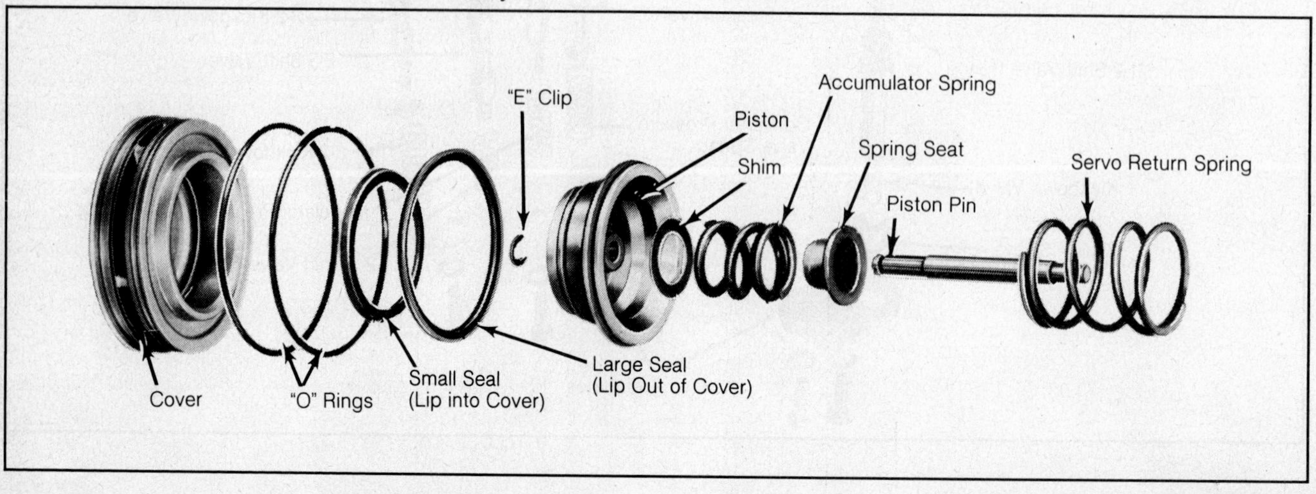

and replace if necessary. After installation, rotate governor to engage drive gear.

BAND SERVO

Disassembly

Pull servo piston assembly out of cover, then remove "O" ring seals from outside diameter of cover. Remove retaining "E" clip and separate piston pin, accumulator spring, spring seat, and adjusting shim from servo piston. Withdraw 2 lip seals from piston.

Inspection

Clean all parts and check for wear, scoring, or other damage. If replacement of piston is necessary, pin, spring, spring seat, and shim must also be replaced as this is serviced as an assembly only.

Reassembly

1) Position spring seat, accumulator spring, and shim on piston pin, install assembly into servo piston, and install "E" clip onto piston.

2) Install lip seals onto piston as follows: Smaller (upper) seal is installed onto piston with lip facing upward, or into servo cover. Larger seal is installed onto piston with lip pointed downward, or out of servo cover. Lubricate assembly thoroughly and install piston into cover. Install "O" rings onto servo cover.

TRANSMISSION REASSEMBLY

1) Lubricate 1st/Reverse gear brake piston with automatic transmission fluid. Install brake piston on oil pump. Install oil pump and piston assembly into transmission case, and position pump so that lug is toward top of case.

Fig. 22: Internal View of Transmission Case Showing Brake Shell Installation

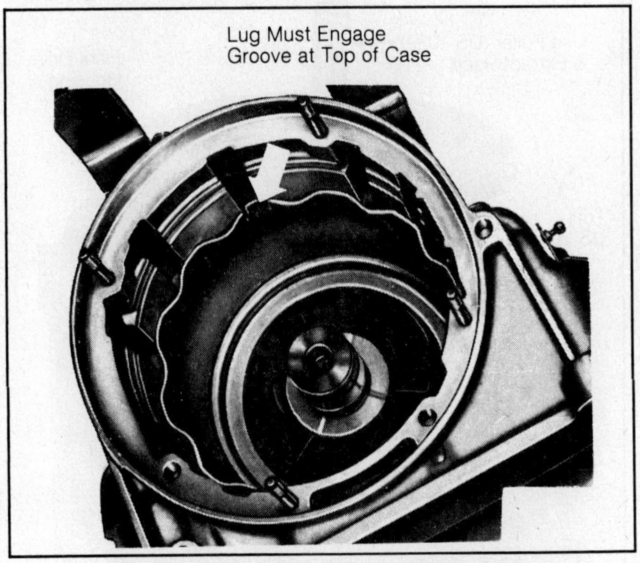

Lug Must Engage
Groove at Top of Case

2) Install 1st/Reverse gear brake shell into case so that lug engages in groove at top of case. Position 1st/Reverse brake piston return springs on spring plate, insert plate into case with springs downward, then install attaching bolts and tighten to specified torque in a diagonal pattern.

NOTE: **After spring plate installation, insert pump shaft into oil pump and ensure that pump gears rotate freely; if not, remove oil pump and ensure that it is assembled correctly.**

3) Lubricate servo cover "O" rings, then install servo assembly into case and install retaining snap ring. Rotate transmission on work stand so that servo cover points down.

4) Position 2nd gear brake band in case and ensure that it engages servo piston. Loosely install push rod for adjusting screw, then install adjusting screw and lock nut.

5) Lubricate Direct/Reverse clutch assembly, then install it into case, sliding it onto oil pump neck and into 2nd gear brake band.

6) Tighten brake band adjusting screw just enough to prevent band from shifting its position on Direct/Reverse clutch drum. Rotate transmission case so that open end is facing up.

7) Place thrust washer in position on forward clutch and use petrolatum to hold it in place. Install forward clutch assembly into Direct/Reverse clutch, making sure splines on forward clutch drum fully engage splines on Direct/Reverse clutch lined clutch plates.

8) Install forward planetary-to-forward clutch thrust washer into forward clutch. Install planetary gear set into forward annulus gear in forward clutch. Install sun gear (short end first) into gear set, then install driving shell and thrust washer over sun gear.

NOTE: **Ensure lugs of driving shell engage tabs of Direct/Reverse clutch drum.**

9) Install thrust washer on underside of reverse planetary gear set and use petrolatum to hold in place. Install gear set into case and onto sun gear.

NOTE: **Lined brake plates must be soaked in automatic transmission fluid for at least 15 minutes prior to installation**

10) Install 1st/Reverse brake waved washer into case. Install 1st/Reverse brake plates into case starting with a steel (external splines) plate and alternating lined (internal splines) plates and steel plates until all brake plates are installed.

FIRST/REVERSE BRAKE PLATE CHART

Application	Steel Plates	Lined Plates
All Models	5	5

11) Install 1st gear one-way clutch assembly into transmission case, then push clutch downward while rotating reverse planetary gear set to fully engage parts.

NOTE: **With one-way clutch installed, it should not be possible to rotate reverse planetary gear set counterclockwise due to the locking action of the one-way clutch.**

12) Install one-way clutch-to-case snap ring. If all parts are correctly installed, the one-way clutch snap ring groove will be exposed. Do not attempt to force snap ring into groove of an incorrectly assembled transmission.

13 Position both thrust washers on rear side of reverse planetary gear set annulus gear, then install gear into transmission case so that it fully engages planetary gear set.

VOLKSWAGEN VANAGON (Cont.)

Fig. 23: Checking for Correct Parts Installation

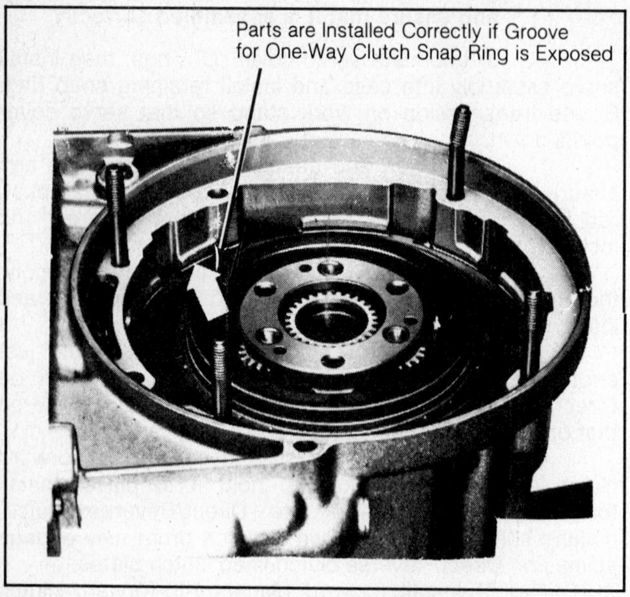

14) Install separation plate gasket over case studs, place separation plate on top of gasket, then install and tighten attaching screws.

NOTE: **At this time 2nd gear brake band must be adjusted. To adjust band, the transmission case must be horizontal to prevent band from jamming. Adjust band as follows:**

15) Loosen lock nut and tighten brake band adjusting screw to 87 INCH lbs. (10 N.m). Loosen screw. Retighten again to 43 INCH lbs. (5.0 N.m). Back off adjusting screw 2 1/2 turns and tighten adjusting screw lock nut.

16) If case linkage was disassembled, reassemble in case using *Fig. 5* as an assembly guide.

17) Install a new seal on accumulator piston (lip pointing toward case), and install piston and spring into case. Install valve body assembly into case, making sure manual valve engages manual lever, and that kickdown valve engages kickdown lever. Install valve body-to-case attaching bolts and tighten from center outward.

NOTE: **Do not use sealer on oil pan gasket, as any surplus sealer may find its way into transmission fluid and cause control valves to stick.**

18) Position a new oil pan gasket on transmission case. Install oil pan and tighten attaching bolts.

FINAL DRIVE

DISASSEMBLY

NOTE: **Measure pinion shaft turning torque BEFORE disassembly. See Pinion Depth and Bearing Preload adjustment for checking procedure.**

1) Remove retaining bolts from center of axle drive flange shafts and pull drive flanges from final drive housing. Mark position of each side bearing adjusting ring on ring and housing, then measure screw-in depth of each ring in housing using a micrometer. Record measurements for reassembly reference.

2) Remove final drive pan bolts and pan, then remove side bearing adjusting ring lock plates. While supporting differential, unscrew side bearing adjusting rings, move differential to right side of case, tilt upward, and remove from final drive housing.

3) If necessary for replacement, use a hook type puller and remove oil seal from each side bearing adjusting ring.

4) If differential side bearings are to be replaced, use a drift and drive bearing outer race from each adjusting ring.

5) Loosen ring gear attaching bolts, tap on bolts with a soft hammer to break loose ring gear, then remove ring gear from differential case.

6) If side bearings require replacement, pull from case using a puller. Using a screwdriver, pry differential housing cover from housing. Drive out pinion gear shaft, then withdraw differential pinion gears and thrust washers, side gears and thrust washers, and nuts for drive flange shaft retaining bolts.

7) Remove pinion shaft cover from final drive housing. Withdraw pinion shaft from final drive housing.

8) If necessary for replacement, use a press and press pinion oil seals out of pinion cover. If pinion shaft bearings are to be replaced, press bearing outer race from pinion cover.

9) Use a hook type puller and remove pinion oil seal from final drive housing. Remove other pinion shaft bearing outer race from final drive housing using a puller (US 1039 and US 1037) as shown in *Fig. 24*.

Fig. 24: Removing Pinion Bearing Outer Race from Final Drive Housing

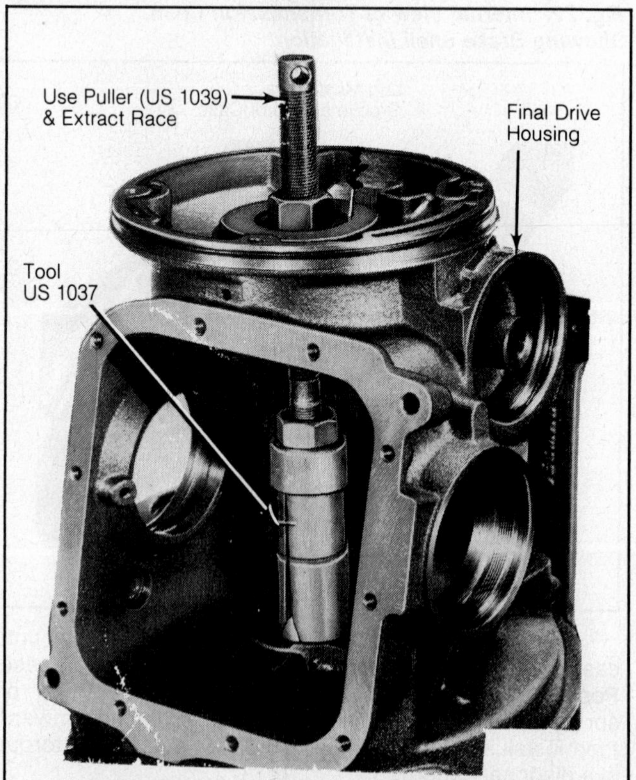

VOLKSWAGEN VANAGON (Cont.)

Fig. 25: Exploded View Showing Main Components of Final Drive Assembly

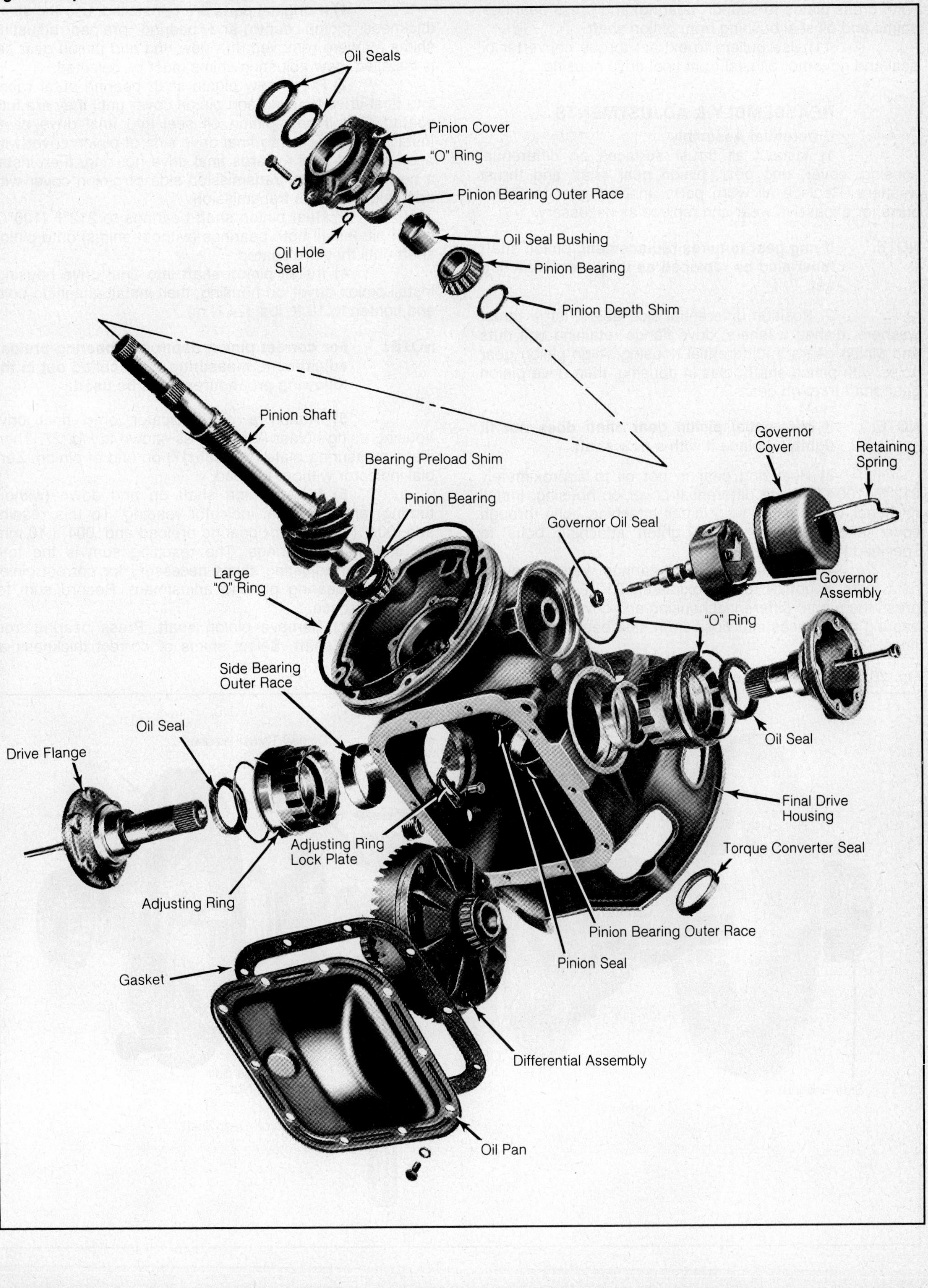

VOLKSWAGEN VANAGON (Cont.)

10) If necessary for replacement, use a press (with press plates to support bearing) and press bearings, shims and oil seal bushing from pinion shaft.

11) Use pullers to extract torque converter oil seal and governor oil seal from final drive housing.

REASSEMBLY & ADJUSTMENTS

Differential Assembly

1) Inspect all thrust surfaces on differential housing, cover, ring gear, pinion gear shaft and thrust washers. Replace all worn parts. Inspect gear teeth for burrs, or excessive wear and replace as necessary.

NOTE: **If ring gear requires replacement, pinion shaft must also be replaced as they are a matched set.**

2) Position differential side gears, large thrust washers, dished washers, drive flange retaining bolt nuts and pinion gears in differential housing. Align pinion gear holes with pinion shaft holes in housing, then drive pinion gear shaft through gears.

NOTE: **If differential pinion gear shaft does not fit tightly, replace it with a new shaft.**

3) Heat ring gear in hot oil to approximately 212°F (100°C). Place differential cover on housing. Install ring gear on housing, then install attaching bolts through cover and into ring gear. Tighten attaching bolts to specified torque.

4) If differential side bearings were removed, heat them in hot oil to approximately 212°F (100°C) and press them onto differential housing and cover. Press side bearing outer races into position in side bearing adjusting rings.

Pinion Depth and Bearing Preload

1) If original parts are reinstalled, use the same thickness pinion depth and bearing preload adjusting shims as were removed. If a new ring and pinion gear set is installed, new adjusting shims must be selected.

2) Press new pinion shaft bearing outer races into final drive housing and pinion cover until they are fully seated. Install new pinion oil seal into final drive case. Install new oil seal into final drive side of pinion cover with open side of seal towards final drive housing, then install a new oil seal into transmission side of pinion cover with open side towards transmission.

3) Heat pinion shaft bearings to 212°F (100°C) in hot oil. Install both bearings (without shims) onto pinion shaft until they are seated.

4) Install pinion shaft into final drive housing. Install pinion cover on housing, then install attaching bolts and tighten to 18 ft. lbs. (24 N.m).

NOTE: **For correct pinion depth and bearing preload adjustment, measuring tools called out in the following procedures must be used.**

5) Attach a dial indicator onto final drive housing using holder (VW 387) as shown in *Fig. 27.* Then, place measuring plate (VW 385/17) on end of pinion. Zero dial indicator without preload.

6) Move pinion shaft up and down (without turning) and note dial indicator reading. To this reading add .004" (.10 mm) for bearing preload and .004" (.10 mm) for settling of bearings. The resulting sum is the total thickness of adjusting shims necessary for correct pinion depth and bearing preload adjustment. Record sum for future reference.

7) Remove pinion shaft. Press bearing from gear end of shaft. Select shims of correct thickness as

Fig. 26: Exploded View of Differential Assembly

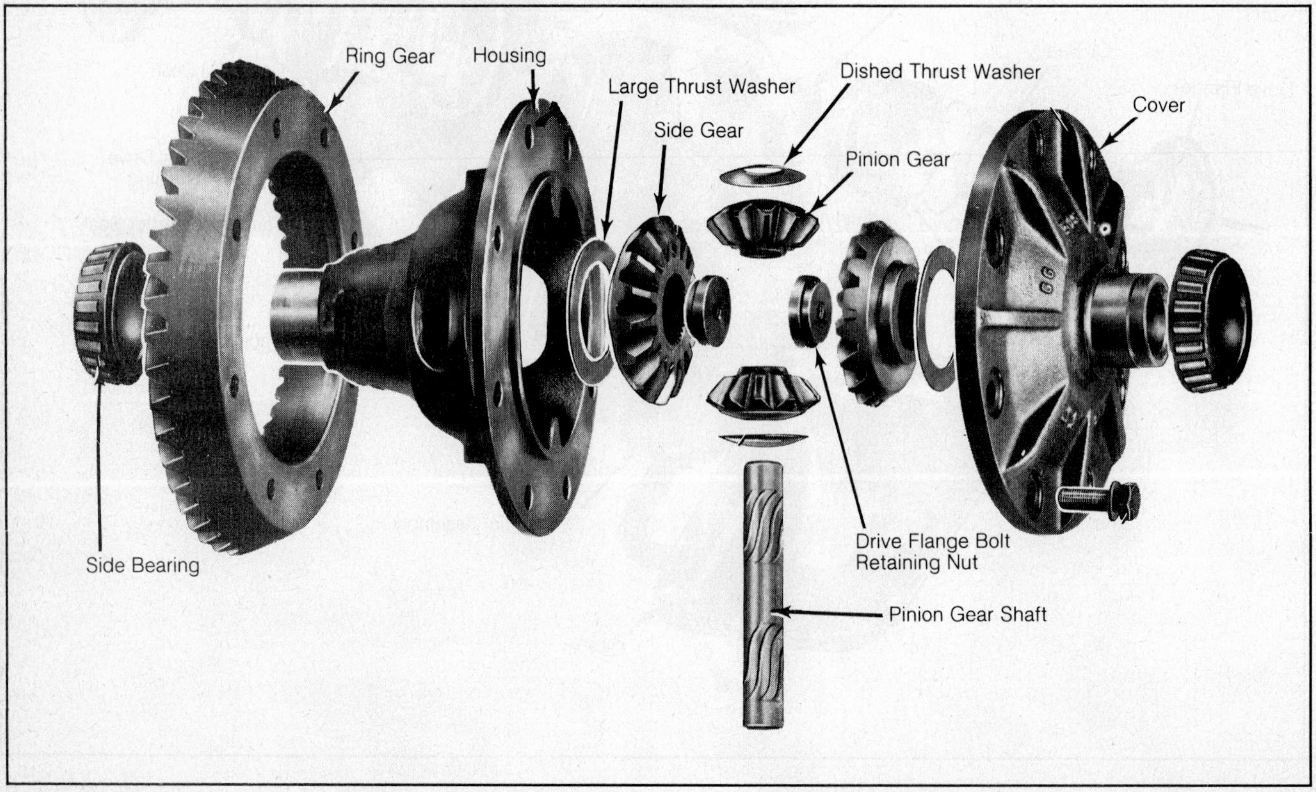

VOLKSWAGEN VANAGON (Cont.)

Fig. 27: Measuring Pinion Shaft Play to Determine Total Pinion Adjusting Shim Thickness

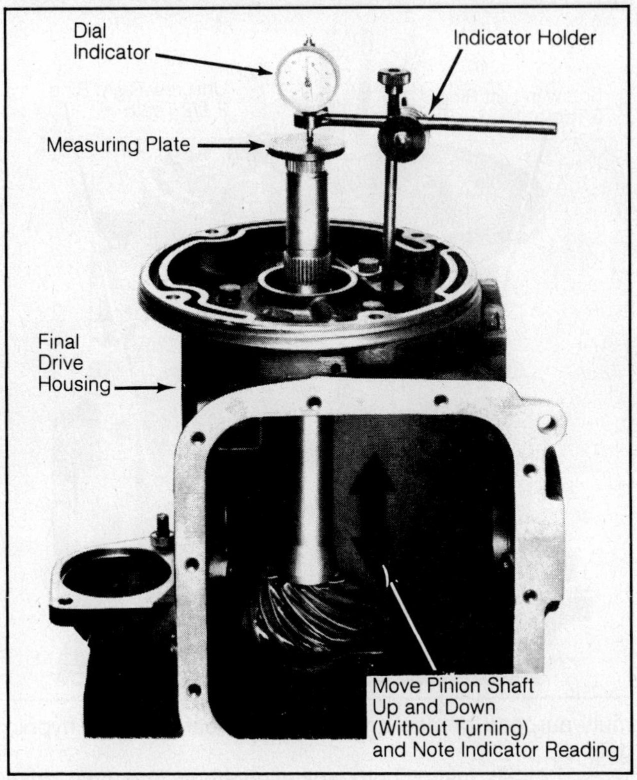

determined in step **6)**, and install them on gear end of shaft. Reinstall bearing onto shaft, then install shaft into final drive housing.

Fig. 28: Installation of Setting Gauge on Pinion Shaft

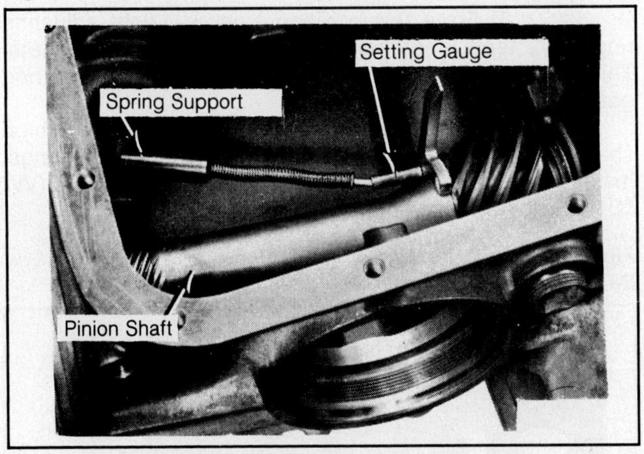

8) Install setting gauge (VW 385/22) on pinion as shown in *Fig. 28*, and hold in place with spring support (VW 385/19).

9) Adjust setting ring on measuring bar (VW 385/1), until distance from center of bar to outside of ring is approximately 2.9" (74 mm).

NOTE: **Refer to Fig. 29 for the assembling of tools to measuring bar.**

10) Slide centering discs (VW 385/2) on measuring bar. Screw measuring pin (VW 385/14) into bar with .118" (3 mm) extension (VW 385/20).

Fig. 29: Assembling Special Measuring Tools for Pinion Depth Shim Selection

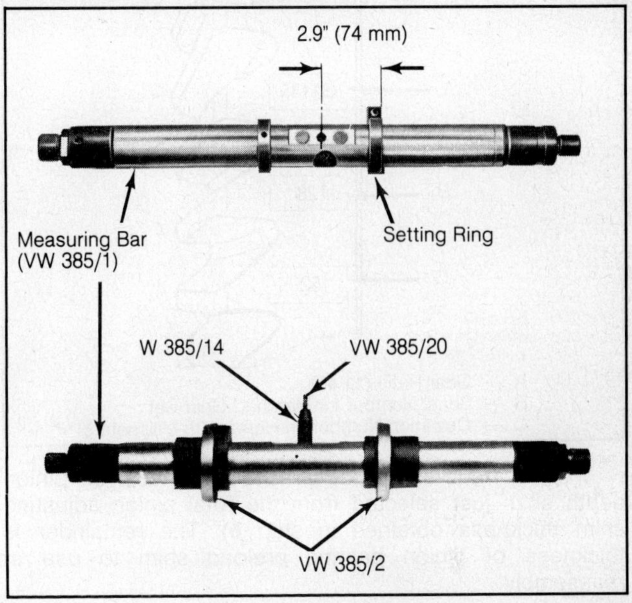

11) Screw left side differential side bearing adjusting ring into final drive housing until it is flush with housing. Place measuring bar assembly in final drive housing as shown in *Fig. 30.* Install right side bearing adjusting ring into final drive housing.

12) Turn knob on end of measuring bar to move centering discs outward until bar can just barely be turned by hand. Attach a dial indicator to measuring bar. Place setting block (VW 385/21) on measuring bar as shown in *Fig. 30,* then zero dial indicator without preload. Remove setting block.

Fig. 30: Positioning of Measuring Bar in Housing

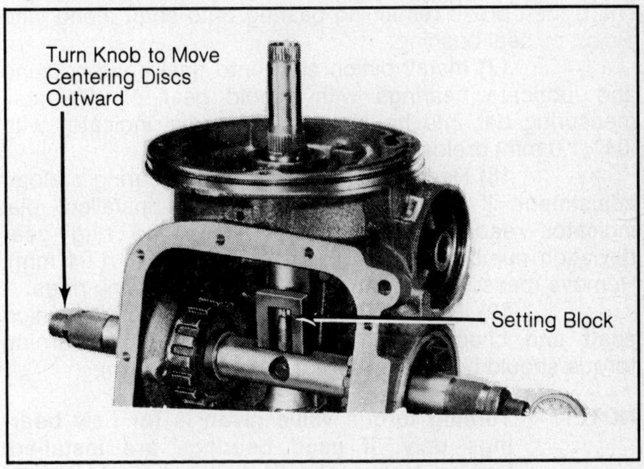

13) Rotate measuring bar until measuring pin rests against setting gauge on pinion face, then rotate bar back and forth over center. Read and record maximum dial indicator reading.

14) Add the dial indicator reading just obtained to the deviation number stamped in ring gear *(Fig. 31).* The resulting sum is thickness of pinion depth adjusting shim to use at reassembly.

NOTE: **The ring gear deviation number is in hundredth millimeters.**

VOLKSWAGEN VANAGON (Cont.)

Fig. 31: Location of Deviation Number on Ring Gear

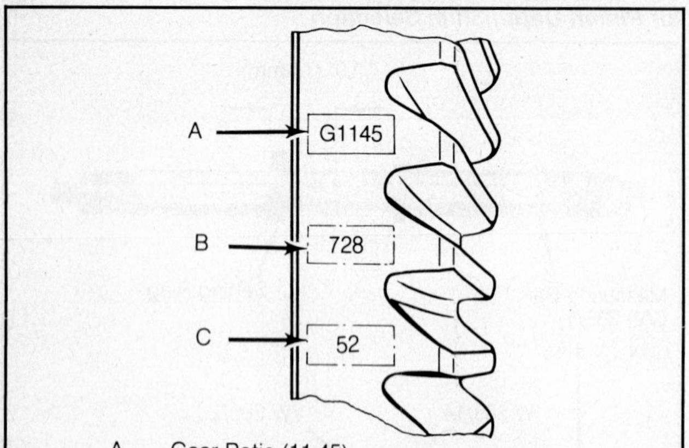

A — Gear Ratio (11:45)
B — Serial Number for Matched Gear Set
C — Deviation Number (In Hundredth-Millimeters)

15) Next, subtract the thickness of pinion depth shim just selected from the total pinion adjusting shim thickness obtained in step **6)**. The remainder is thickness of pinion bearing preload shim to use at reassembly.

NOTE: Pinion depth and bearing preload shims are available in thicknesses from .043" (1.1 mm) to .075" (1.9 mm) in increments of .001" (.025 mm). Also, shim thickness should be measured at several points on shim prior to installation to ensure correct thickness shims are being installed.

16) Remove measuring tools and pinion shaft from final drive housing. Press bearings from pinion shaft. Install the selected pinion bearing preload shim onto gear end of pinion shaft, then press bearing back onto shaft. Place the selected pinion depth shim on opposite end of shaft, then press remaining bearing onto shaft along with pinion oil seal bushing.

17) Install pinion shaft into final drive housing and lubricate bearings with hypoid gear oil. Reinstall measuring bar into housing and zero dial indicator with .04" (1.0 mm) preload.

18) Recheck pinion depth and bearing preload adjustment. If correct shims have been installed, dial indicator reading should be equal to the ring gear deviation number with a tolerance of ± .0016" (.04 mm). Remove measuring bar and side bearing adjusting rings.

19) Finally, attach a torque wrench to pinion shaft and check pinion shaft turning torque. Turning torque should be at least 12.4 INCH lbs. (1.4 N.m).

NOTE: Turning torque value given is for new bearings only. If used bearings are installed, turning torque should be measured piror to final drive disassembly. When assembled correctly, turning torque with used bearings should be approximately 1.7-3.5 INCH lbs. (.2-.4 N.m) greater than it was prior to disassembly.

Side Bearing Preload & Ring Gear Backlash

1) With pinion shaft correctly adjusted, install differential assembly into final drive housing. Coat "O" rings and threads of side bearing adjusting rings with multi-purpose grease and coat side bearings with hypoid gear oil.

Fig. 32: Adjusting Ring Settings for Side Bearing Preload Adjustment

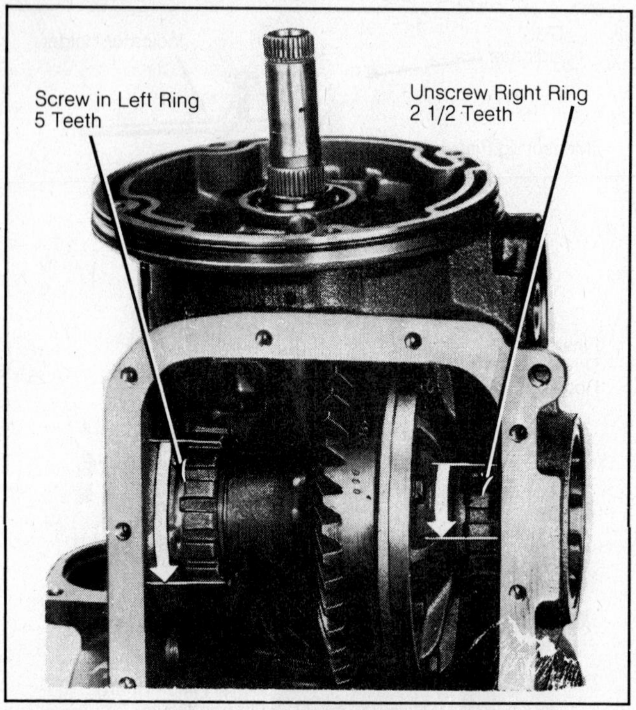

2) Install both adjusting rings into final drive housing until they are flush with housing. Next, adjust right side (ring gear end) adjusting ring in until ring gear meshes with pinion shaft gear with no backlash, then screw left ring in and preload slightly so that side bearings have no play.

3) From this position, unscrew right adjusting ring 2 1/2 teeth, then screw in left adjusting ring 5 teeth. This should correctly set side bearing preload and ring gear backlash.

4) To check ring gear backlash, rotate pinion shaft several times in both directions to settle bearings. Install locking sleeve (VW 521/4) with slotted sleeve (VW 521/7) in differential and secure with nut. *See Fig. 33.*

Fig. 33: Installation of Backlash Measuring Bar on Locking Sleeve

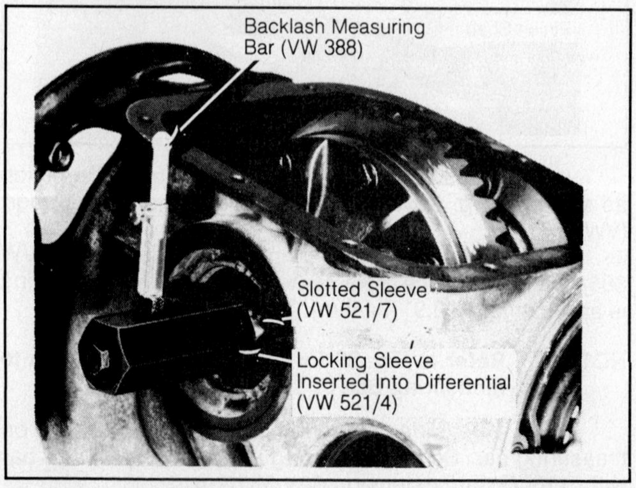

VOLKSWAGEN VANAGON (Cont.)

5) Adjust length of backlash measuring bar (VW 388) to 3.15" (80 mm). Attach correctly adjusted measuring bar to locking sleeve.

Fig. 34: Positioning of Ring Gear Backlash Measuring Tools

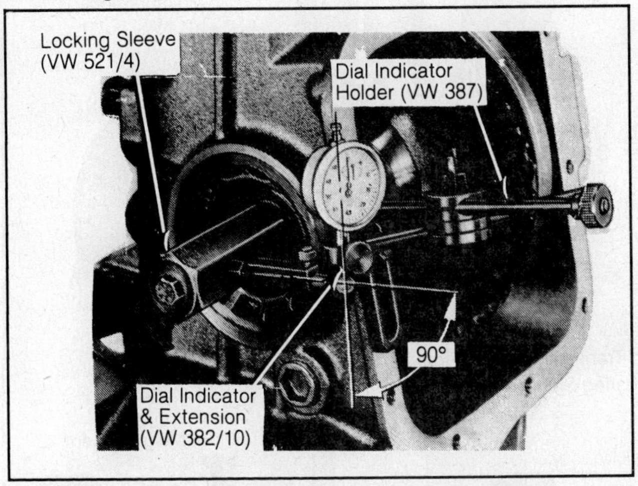

Indicator must be at right angle to measuring bar.

NOTE: **Refer to Fig. 34 for positioning of ring gear backlash measuring tools.**

6) Install dial indicator with .24" (6 mm) flat end extension (VW 382/10) in indicator holder (VW 387). Bolt holder to final drive housing so that indicator is located at a right angle to backlash measuring bar.

7) Turn ring gear (via pinion shaft) until measuring bar contacts dial indicator gauge pin, then turn ring gear further until indicator shows .04" (1 mm) preload. Attach locking clamp (VW 386) to pinion shaft as shown in *Fig. 35*, then tighten clamp screw to lock pinion shaft.

8) Turn ring gear away from dial indicator until it is stopped by the locked pinion shaft, then zero dial indicator. Next, turn ring gear towards indicator until it is again stopped by pinion shaft. Read and record indicator reading. This reading is the ring gear backlash.

Fig. 35: Attaching Locking Clamp to Pinion Shaft

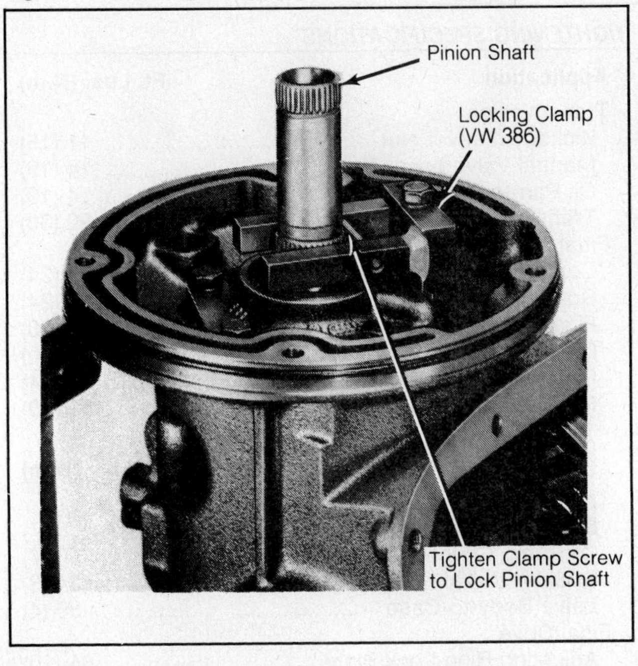

9) Repeat backlash measurement procedure at three other points 90° apart around ring gear. Add the four measurements together, then divide the total by four. The resulting sum is the average ring gear backlash, which should be .006-.010" (.15-.25 mm).

NOTE: **The individual backlash measurements should not vary from each other by more than .002" (.05 mm); if they do, ring gear or pinion shaft is worn or they have been improperly installed.**

10) If backlash is not within specifications, correct by turning both side bearing adjusting rings an equal amount in opposite directions so that bearing preload is not altered. Remove measuring tools.

11) With backlash correct, check pinion shaft turning torque. Total pinion shaft turning torque, with differential installed, should be 14.2 INCH lbs. (1.6 N.m).

12) Install side bearing adjusting ring lock plates and tighten bolts to specified torque. Install new oil seals in adjusting rings. Install final drive oil pan using a new gasket.

13) Install a new torque converter oil seal into final drive housing. Install a new governor oil seal into housing with lip pointing toward governor, then install governor assembly.

FINAL TRANSAXLE ASSEMBLY

1) To measure play between final drive and transmission, place a straightedge on transmission attaching face of final drive housing, and using a depth gauge, measure distance from top surface of straightedge down to edge of pinion shaft oil seal bushing.

2) Next, measure distance from top surface of straightedge to face of final drive housing. Subtract this second measurement from first measurement obtained in step **1)** and note for future reference.

3) Place a new gasket on transmission separation plate, position straightedge on transmission case, and measure distance from top surface of straightedge down to gasket surface. Next, measure distance from top of straightedge down to shim surface on shoulder of annulus gear flange. Subtract this measurement from first measurement obtained in this step and record for future reference.

4) Subtract the last measurement obtained in step **3)** from last measurement obtained in step **2)**. Remainder is end play (without shims) between final drive and transmission. Select proper end play shim(s) to use by finding applicable end play reading in first column of END PLAY SHIM SELECTION chart, and obtaining shim thickness noted in second column.

NOTE: **Transmission-to-final drive end play adjusting shims are available in thicknesses of .016" (.4 mm) and .047" (1.2 mm). Combine shim thicknesses to obtain total thickness required.**

5) Install selected shim(s) into final drive case, on top of pinion shaft oil seal bushing. Next, lubricate and

VOLKSWAGEN VANAGON (Cont.)

Fig. 36: Using a Depth Gauge to Determine Transmission-to-Final Drive End Play Shim

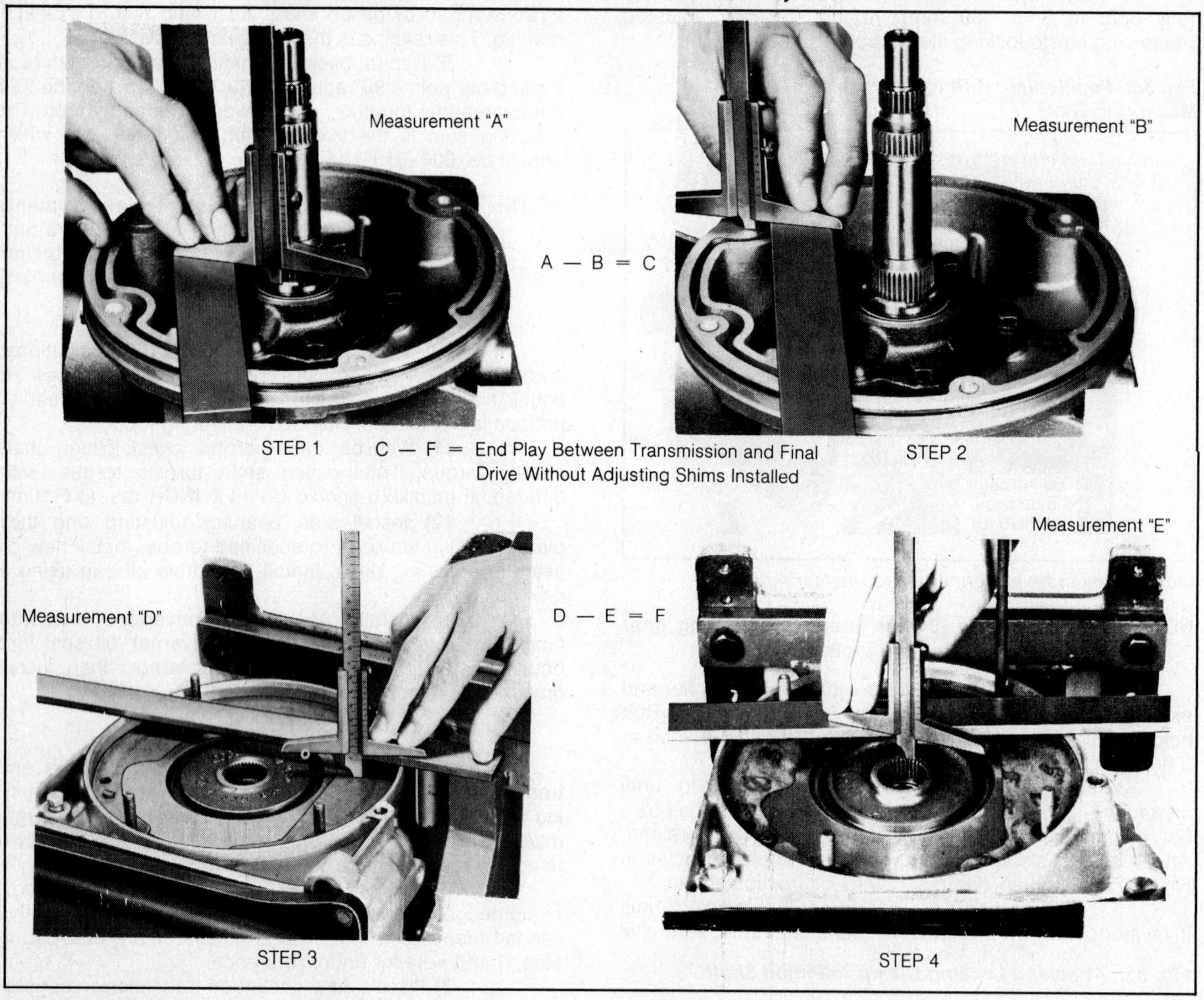

END PLAY SHIM SELECTION CHART

If End Play Is In. (mm)	Install This Shim In. (mm)
.009-.033 (.23-.84)	None
.034-.049 (.85-1.24)	.016 (.4)
.050-.065 (1.25-1.64)	.032 (.8)
.066-.080 (1.65-2.04)	.048 (1.2)
.081-.096 (2.05-2.44)	.064 (1.6)
.097-.112 (2.45-2.84)	.080 (2.0)
.113-.128 (2.85-3.24)	.096 (2.4)
.129-.143 (3.25-3.64)	.112 (2.8)
.144-.153 (3.65-3.88)	.128 (3.2)

install sealing "O" ring into groove on transmission end of final drive housing.

6) Install turbine shaft into final drive pinion shaft, then install oil pump shaft into turbine shaft. Position a new final drive-to-transmission gasket onto transmission case studs, then mate final drive to transmission. Install final drive-to-transmission case nuts and tighten to specified torque.

7) Set torque converter carefully on one-way support, then move converter back and forth and insert into splines ensuring that it does not jam.

TIGHTENING SPECIFICATIONS

Application	Ft. Lbs. (N.m)
Transmission	
Kickdown Lever Nut	11 (15)
Manual Valve Lever Nut	14 (19)
Oil Pan-to-Case	14 (19)
Transmission-to-Final Drive	22 (30)
Final Drive	
Converter-to-Drive Plate	18 (24)
Drive Flange Bolt	18 (24)
Final Drive-to-Engine	22 (30)
Oil Pan-to-Case	7 (10)
Pinion Cover-to-Case	18 (24)
Ring Gear Bolts	51 (70)
	INCH Lbs. (N.m)
Transmission	
Brake Spring Plate Bolts	60 (7)
Oil Pump Cover-to-Housing	60 (7)
Strainer-to-Valve Body	24 (3)
Valve Body-to-Case	36 (4)
Final Drive	
Adjusting Ring Lock Plate	84 (10)

ZF 3HP 22

Peugeot 505

TRANSMISSION IDENTIFICATION

Transmission identification is stamped on a metal tag fastened to the lower left of the center housing.

DESCRIPTION

Transmission is a fully automatic 3-speed unit. The transmission is equipped with a torque converter and Simpson planetary gear set.

LUBRICATION & ADJUSTMENT

See appropriate AUTOMATIC TRANSMISSION SERVICING article in IMPORT GENERAL SERVICING section.

TROUBLE SHOOTING

NO FORWARD OR REVERSE MOVEMENT

Oil level too low. Defective oil pump. Drive plate broken. Parking lock pawl stuck. Clutches "A" and "B" defective. Input or output shaft broken.

NO REVERSE

Selector linkage incorrectly adjusted. Clutch "B" or brake "D" defective. Oil leakage in clutch "B" or leak in brake "D" oil feed supply.

MOVES IN ONE GEAR ONLY

1st Gear Only

1st-2nd shift valve stuck. Governor bushing seized.

2nd Gear Only

1st-2nd and 2nd-3rd shift valve stuck.

1st & 2nd Gears Only

2nd-3rd shift valve stuck.

3rd Gear Only

1st-2nd and 2nd-3rd shift valve stuck. Governor bushing seized.

TRANSMISSION SLIPPAGE

In 3rd Gear

Clutch "B" slips. Accelerator cable disengaged or misadjusted. Oil level too low. Throttle pressure valve stuck.

In Reverse

Clutch "B" or brake "D" damaged. Loss of oil in supply line to clutch "B" or brake "D".

NO BRAKING EFFECT

In 1st Gear In "2" & "1"

Brake valve/damper "D" defective. Brake "D" defective.

Fig. 1: Sectional View of ZF 3HP-22 Transmission

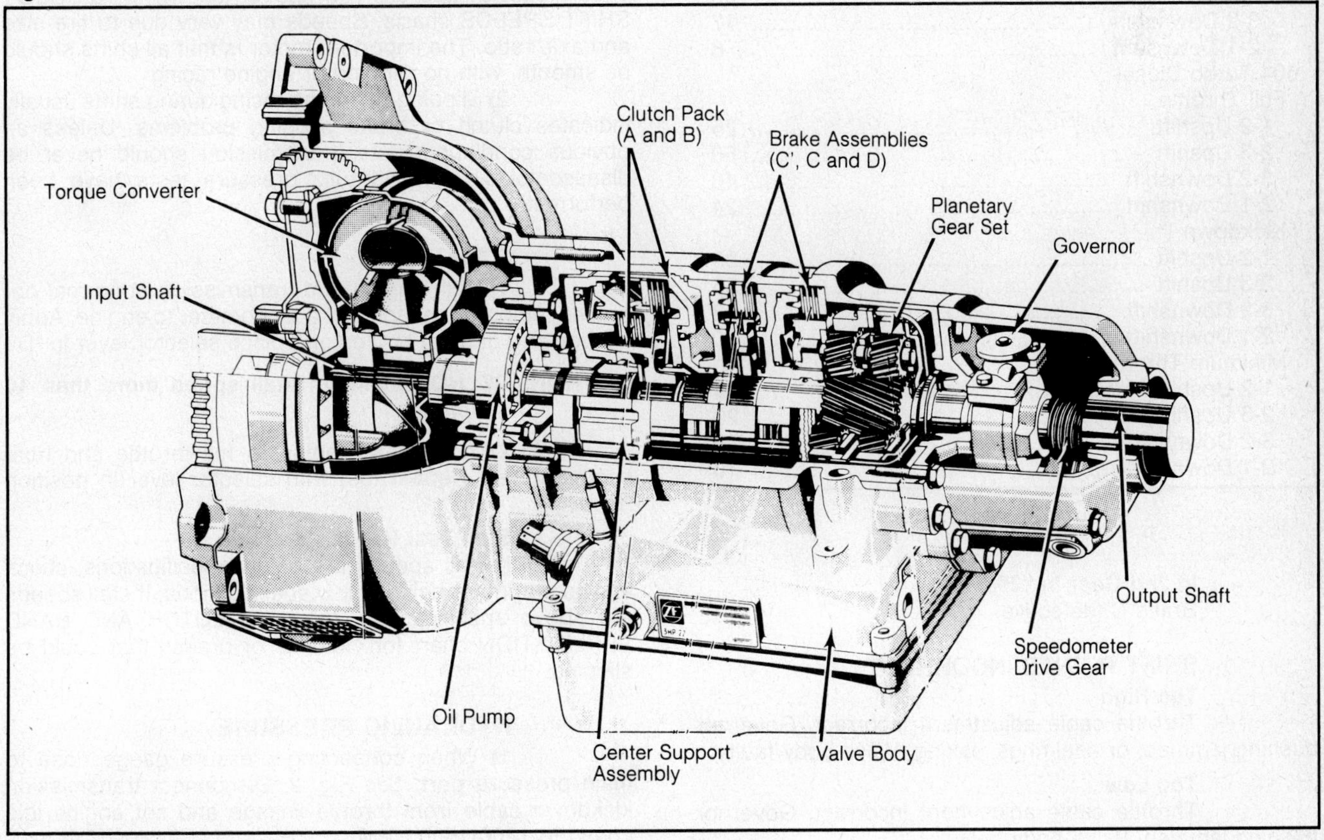

ZF 3HP 22 (Cont.)

PEUGEOT SHIFT SPEEDS

Shift Conditions	MPH
505	
Full Throttle	
Gasoline Models	
1-2 Upshift	25
2-3 Upshift	58
3-2 Downshift	46
2-1 Downshift	15
Diesel Models	
1-2 Upshift	22
2-3 Upshift	43
3-2 Downshift	35
2-1 Downshift	19
Kickdown	
Gasoline Models	
1-2 Upshift	39
2-3 Upshift	65
3-2 Downshift	63
2-1 Downshift	32
Diesel Models	
1-2 Upshift	29
2-3 Upshfit	50
3-2 Downshift	48
2-1 Downshift	28
Minimum Throttle	
Gasoline Models	
1-2 Upshift	9
2-3 Upshift	20
3-2 Downshift	14
2-1 Downshift	4
Diesel Models	
1-2 Upshift	12
2-3 Upshift	20
3-2 Downshift	17
2-1 Downshift	6
604 Turbo Diesel	
Full Throttle	
1-2 Upshift	25
2-3 Upshift	50
3-2 Downshift	40
2-1 Downshift	24
Kickdown	
1-2 Upshift	33
2-3 Upshift	55
3-2 Downshift	53
2-1 Downshift	30
Minimum Throttle	
1-2 Upshift	14
2-3 Upshift	23
3-2 Downshift	20
2-1 Downshift	10

In 2nd Gear In "2" & "1"

Brake C' defective.

SHIFT POINTS INCORRECT

Too High

Throttle cable adjustment incorrect. Governor bushing jammed, or seal rings leaking. Valve body faulty.

Too Low

Throttle cable adjustment incorrect. Governor bushing jammed. Valve body faulty.

NO KICKDOWN

In "1-2" & "2-3"

Throttle pressure too low. Accelerator cable not adjusted properly. Throttle pressure valve seized. Balls in valve body worn.

NO UPSHIFT

To 2nd Gear

Governor seized. 1-2 shift valve seized.

To 3rd Gear

Governor seized. Throttle pressure too high. Throttle pressure valve stuck. Clutch "B" damaged.

TRANSMISSION NOISES

In All Positions When Cold

Suction noise at oil pump due to loose valve body bolts. Defective valve body.

Noise in 1st Gear On Acceleration and Deceleration

Worn planetary gears.

Light Grinding Noise Which Is Speed Sensitive

Needle bearing in transmission extension housing defective.

TESTING

ROAD TEST

1) Before testing, make sure fluid level is correct and all linkage adjustments are correct. Transmission should shift at approximate speeds shown in PEUGEOT SHIFT SPEEDS charts. Speeds may vary due to tire size and axle ratio. The important factor is that all shifts should be smooth, with no slipping or engine racing.

2) Slipping or engine racing during shifts usually indicates clutch or brake slipping problems. Unless an obvious condition exists, transmission should never be disassembled until hydraulic pressure tests have been performed.

STALL TEST

1) With engine and transmission at normal operating temperature, connect a tachometer to engine. Apply service and parking brakes and place selector lever in "D".

CAUTION: **DO NOT maintain stall speed more than 10 seconds.**

2) Accelerate engine to full throttle and note engine speed. Repeat test with selector lever in position "R".

Stall Test Results

If stall speeds are below specifications, check engine output for being below specifications. If stall speeds are above specifications, refer to CLUTCH AND BAND APPLICATION chart for clutches or brakes that could be slipping.

HYDRAULIC PRESSURE

1) When connecting pressure gauge hose to main pressure port. *See Fig. 2.* Disconnect transmission kickdown cable from throttle linkage and set engine idle speed to 1200-1500 RPM.

STALL SPEED SPECIFICATIONS

Application	Stall RPM
Peugeot	
504	2150-2200
505 & 604	2050-2150

2) With rear wheels off the ground and transmission in "R", check main pressure. Pressure obtained should be within limits specified in HYDRAULIC PRESSURE charts. To check kickdown pressures, pull on kickdown cable.

3) Place transmission in Neutral and run engine at idle to cool transmission. With transmission in any position except "R", repeat check. Pressure obtained should be within limits specified in HYDRAULIC PRESSURE charts.

Fig. 2: Checking Hydraulic Pressure

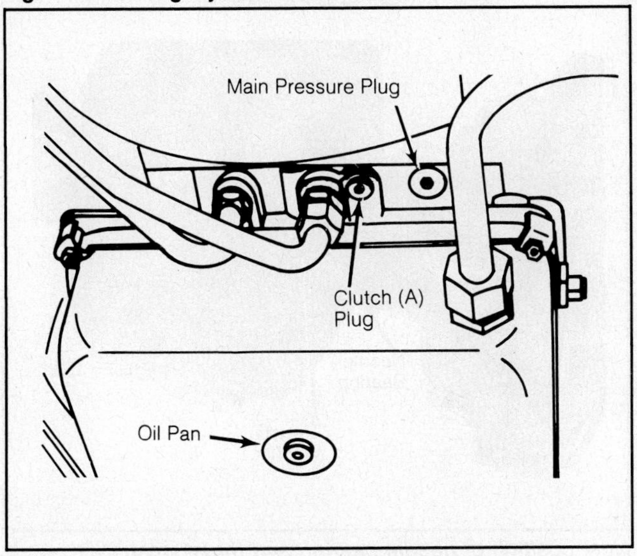

Allow transmission to cool between checks.

HYDRAULIC PRESSURES

Application	psi (kg/cm²)
In "R"	
Idle	178-206 (12.5-14.5)
Kickdown	234-260 (17.1-19.0)
All Other Positions	
Idle	78-91 (5.4-6.4)
Kickdown	102-113 (7.4-8.3)

REMOVAL & INSTALLATION

See the appropriate AUTOMATIC TRANSMISSION REMOVAL article in IMPORT GENERAL SERVICING section.

TRANSMISSION DISASSEMBLY

1) Place transmission in a holding fixture. Remove torque converter. Remove oil pan and gasket. Remove Torx bolts retaining valve body and remove valve body.

2) Remove retaining circlips from 4 oil supply bores in transmission case and withdraw compression springs. Using a puller that will thread into sleeves, remove sealing sleeves from oil bores. Screw tool into sleeve and pull out sharply.

3) Lock transmission output shaft by engaging parking gear. Hold output flange stationary. Remove retaining nut and flange. Remove extension housing. Using a puller, pull off speedometer drive gear. Remove washer and snap ring.

4) Loosen governor assembly retaining nut. Unscrew governor stud about 3 turns and pull governor off shaft. Remove torque converter housing with oil pump, seal, intermediate plate, thrust washer, needle bearing and angled disc. Remove and separate components. Remove input shaft and clutch "A".

5) Remove clutch "A" carrier plate, plastic thrust washer and metal thrust washer. Remove clutch "B" snap ring. Using 2 hooks, remove clutch "B". *See Fig. 3.* Catch washer and seal as they are pulled out with clutch "B".

Fig. 3: Removing Clutch "B"

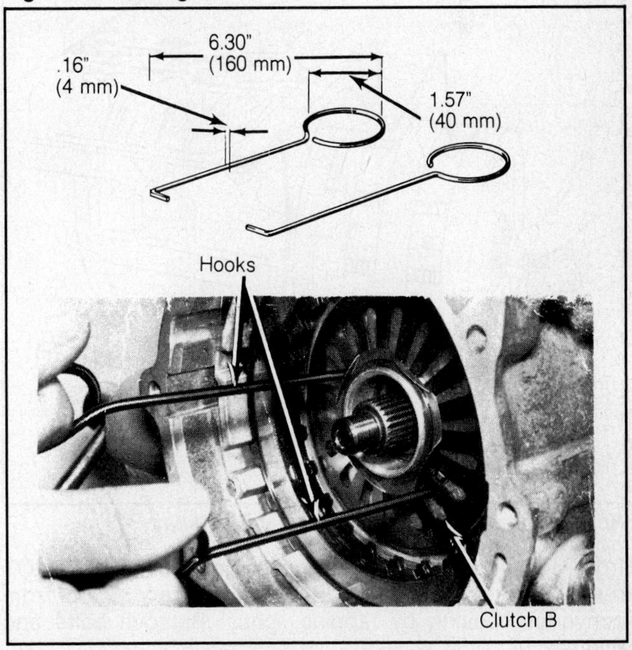

Fabricate hooks using dimensions shown.

6) Remove large snap ring and pull out center support and output shaft as an assembly. *See Fig. 4.* Remove thrust washer, needle bearing and angled disc from output shaft.

7) Remove center support assembly from output shaft. Remove planetary gears with sun gear shaft. Note position of needle bearing and thrust washer on end of sun gear shaft and remove. *See Fig. 5.*

COMPONENT DISASSEMBLY & REASSEMBLY

CONVERTER HOUSING & OIL PUMP ASSEMBLY

Disassembly

Remove torque converter. Remove converter housing with intermediate plate. Remove intermediate plate

Automatic Transmissions

ZF 3HP 22 (Cont.)

CLUTCH AND BAND APPLICATION CHART (ELEMENTS IN USE)

Selector Lever Position	Clutch A	Clutch B	Brake C'	Brake C	Brake D	Front Overrunning Clutch	Rear Overrunning Clutch
"1" - FIRST GEAR	X				X [1]		X
"2" - SECOND GEAR	X		X	X		X	
"3" - THIRD GEAR	X	X		X			
REVERSE		X			X		
PARK OR NEUTRAL - All bands and clutches released and/or ineffective.							

[1] - Applied in "1" and "2" selector positions only.

Fig. 4: Removing Center Support & Output Shaft Assembly

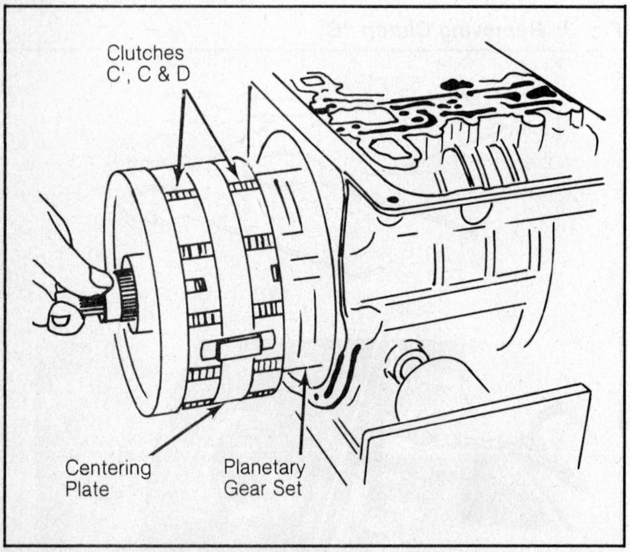

Note position of thrust washer on output shaft.

Fig. 5: Removing Planetary Gears & Sun Gear Shaft

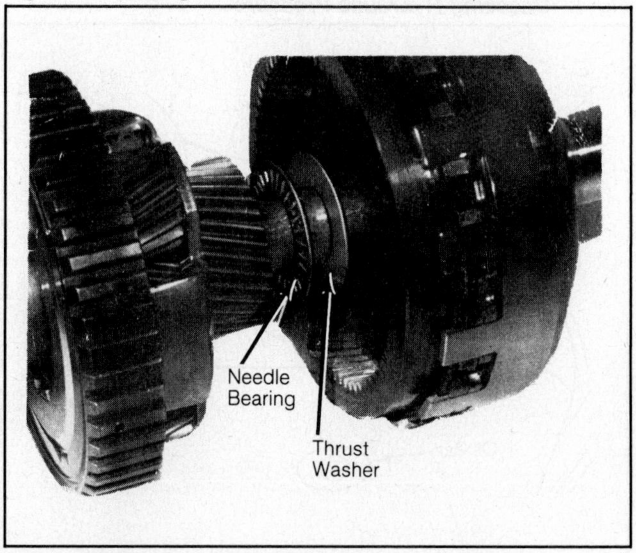

Note position of needle bearing and thrust washer.

from converter housing by loosening 2 bolts. DO NOT remove bolts. *See Fig. 6.* Separate primary pump from converter housing by tapping lightly. Remove bolts and pump.

Inspection

1) Clean all parts and check for signs of scoring or other wear. Check clearance between pump driven gear and pump housing; clearance must be .003-.006" (.07-.16 mm).

2) Check pump housing-to-gear face clearance; clearance must be .0008-.0015" (.02-.04 mm). Check the clearance between gear and crescent; the clearance must be .010-.015" (.250-.386 mm).

3) If any component is defective, complete pump assembly must be replaced. If any measurement is not within specifications, replace oil pump assembly.

Reassembly

Reassemble in reverse of disassembly, noting the following: Install drive and driven gears with punch marks up, if equipped. Replace all gaskets and seals. Install angled disc on input shaft, with collar facing needle bearing. Hold thrust washer on converter housing with grease.

Fig. 6: Intermediate Plate & Oil Pump Removal

Loosen bolts and tap pump lightly.

ZF 3HP 22 (Cont.)

CLUTCH "A"

Disassembly

1) Using a press, compress clutch assembly and remove large snap ring. *See Fig. 7.* Remove spacer plates, clutch plates, discs and diaphragm spring. Remove carrier plate. Note number and arrangement of plates and discs.

2) Remove snap ring from input shaft and separate input shaft from input hub. Remove piston from hub by applying compressed air to oil hole. Remove diaphragm spring and seals.

Fig. 7: Clutch "A" Snap Ring Removal

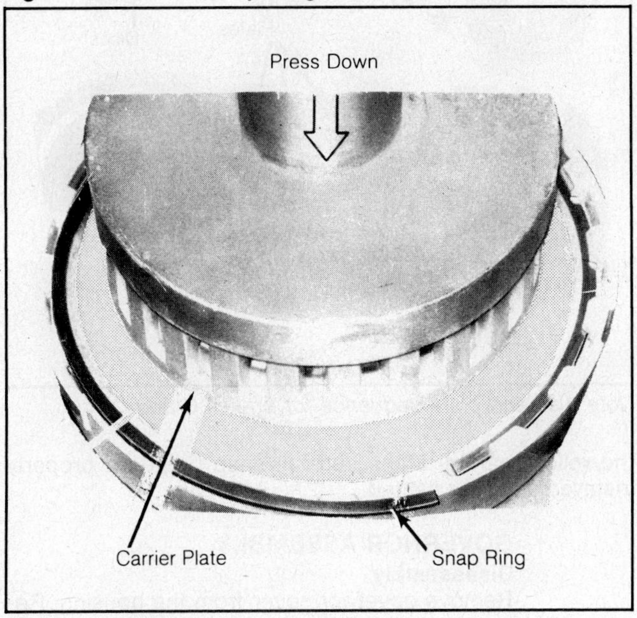

Compress clutch assembly and remove snap ring.

Reassembly

1) Coat all discs and plates with ATF. Insert input shaft into hub and retain with snap ring. Place diaphragm spring in hub with curved surface facing down. Replace all seals.

2) Alternate plates and discs until the number and position of plates and discs are installed as they were removed. *See Fig. 8.* There 5 clutch plates. Install spacer plates and carrier plate. Compress clutch assembly and install large snap ring.

Fig. 8: Clutch "A" Housing Assembly

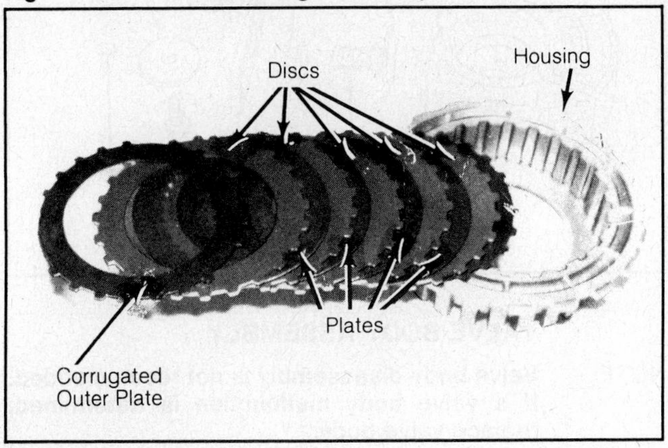

CLUTCH "B"

Disassembly

1) Remove washer and "O" ring from center of clutch "B" housing. Remove large snap ring. Remove end plate, clutch plates and discs, noting number and arrangement of plates and discs for reassembly reference.

2) Compress diaphragm spring and remove snap ring. Remove piston from housing by applying compressed air to oil feed hole. Remove and discard seals and "O" rings.

Reassembly

1) Coat discs and plates with ATF. Replace all seals and "O" rings. Position piston in housing and install diaphragm spring. Compress spring and install snap ring.

2) Alternate plates and discs until the number and position of plates and discs are installed as they were removed. *See Fig. 9.* Install end plate and large snap ring. Replace "O" ring and washer in center of housing.

Fig. 9: Clutch "B" Housing Assembly

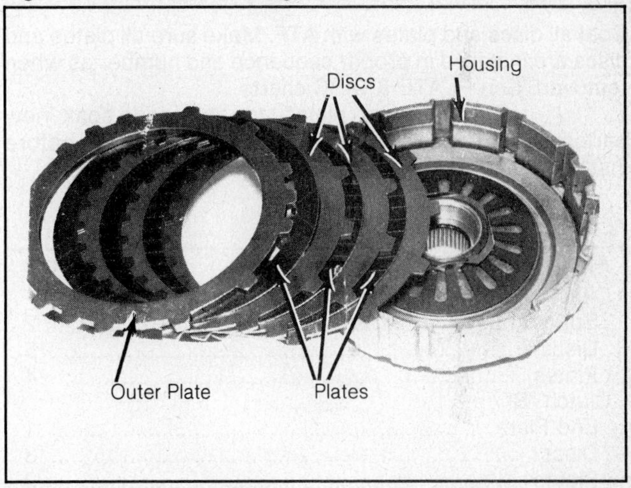

Note number and arrangement of plates and discs.

CENTER SUPPORT ASSEMBLY

Disassembly

1) Insert assembly into a pipe with an inside diameter of 1.142" (29 mm) and clamp assembly in a vise. Remove centering plate. Remove outer disc (2 on some models), plates and one-way clutch for brake C'. *See Fig. 10.*

2) Remove brake C' snap ring (if equipped). Remove end plate, discs and plates, noting number and arrangement for reassembly reference.

3) Lift center support assembly off output shaft. Remove brake "D" snap ring. Remove end plate, discs and plates, noting number and arrangement for reassembly reference.

4) Place center support assembly on work bench. Compress diaphragm spring and remove split retaining ring. Turn assembly over and remove large snap ring. Remove diaphragm springs. Place brake C' on bench and compress diaphragm. Remove split retaining ring.

5) Apply compressed air to respective oil input hole to remove brake pistons. Remove and discard piston "O" rings and seals. Replace with new "O" rings and seals.

Reassembly

1) To reassemble center support assembly, reverse disassembly procedure and note the following:

ZF 3HP 22 (Cont.)

Fig. 10: Brake C' One-Way Clutch & Plates

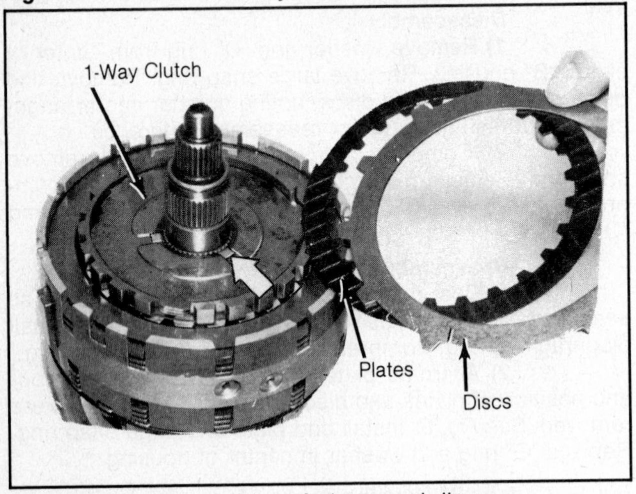

Note number and position of plates and discs.

Coat all discs and plates with ATF. Make sure all plates and discs are installed in proper sequence and number as when removed. See PLATE & DISC charts.

2) If discs or plates are replaced, soak new parts in warm ATF (160°F/70°C) for 20 minutes before installing.

PLATE & DISC USAGE CHART

Application	No. of Plates
Clutch "A"	
Spacer Plates	2
Discs	5
Plates	4
Clutch "B"	
End Plate	1
Discs	3
Plates	3
Brake C'	
Disc	1
Plate	1
Brake "C"	
Brake "D"	
End Plate	1
Discs	3
Plates	3

PLANETARY GEAR SET

Disassembly

1) Place output shaft in a support with output shaft facing down. Remove one-way clutch and front planetary gear set. Remove sun gear shaft. Remove large snap ring and lift off ring gear. Lift off rear planetary gear set.

2) Remove intermediate shaft from output shaft housing. Remove roller bearing and washer from output shaft housing and intermediate shaft. Remove large snap ring holding input ring gear to intermediate shaft. Remove washers and bearing. Remove other large snap ring.

Reassembly

To reassemble planetary gear set, reverse disassembly procedure and note the following: Make sure a large snap ring is on both sides of input ring gear when assembled to intermediate shaft. When installing mainshaft to output shaft, place washer onto output shaft first, then

Fig. 11: Center Support Housing

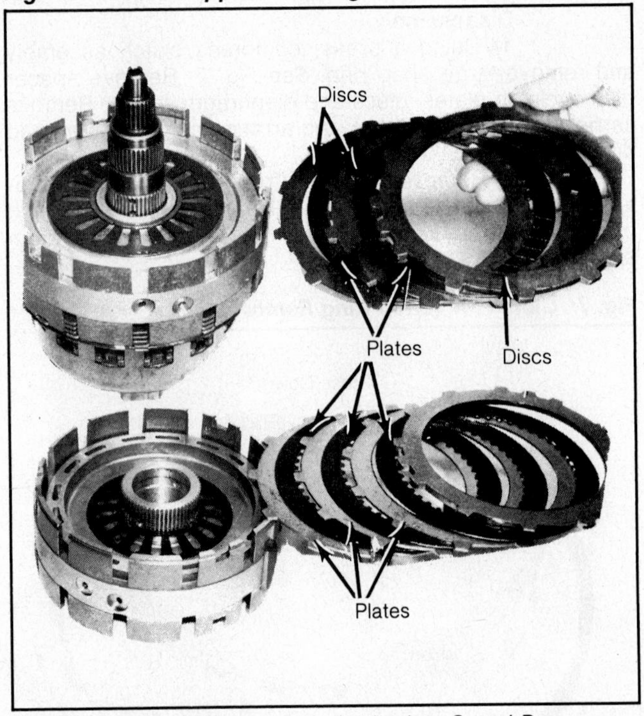

Note disc and plate sequence for brakes C and D.

the roller bearing. Make sure all snap rings are properly installed and fully seated.

GOVERNOR ASSEMBLY

Disassembly

Remove governor cover from the housing. Remove "E" clip, and the washer, piston, spring and bushing. *See Fig. 12.*

Reassembly

Assemble governor in reverse of disassembly procedure, ensuring that the piston slides into the bushing without restriction.

Fig. 12: Exploded View of Governor Assembly

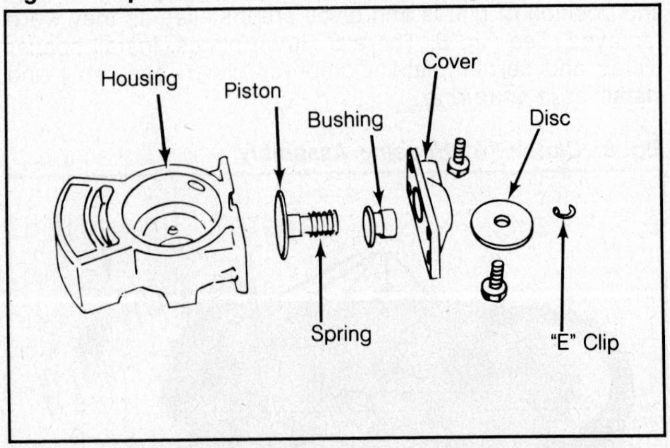

VALVE BODY ASSEMBLY

NOTE: **Valve body disassembly is not recommended. If a valve body malfunction is determined, replace valve body.**

TRANSMISSION REASSEMBLY

1) Install angled disc, needle bearing and thrust washer on output shaft. Install needle bearing and thrust washer on sun gear shaft and install planetary gear set onto output shaft. Assemble center support assembly to output shaft assembly.

2) Guide center support and output shaft assembly into transmission case, aligning keys in the center of cylinder groove. The 4 oil bores in the center support assembly must be aligned with bores in case. *See Fig. 13.* Retain in position with large snap ring.

Fig. 13: Installing Center Support & Output Shaft Assembly

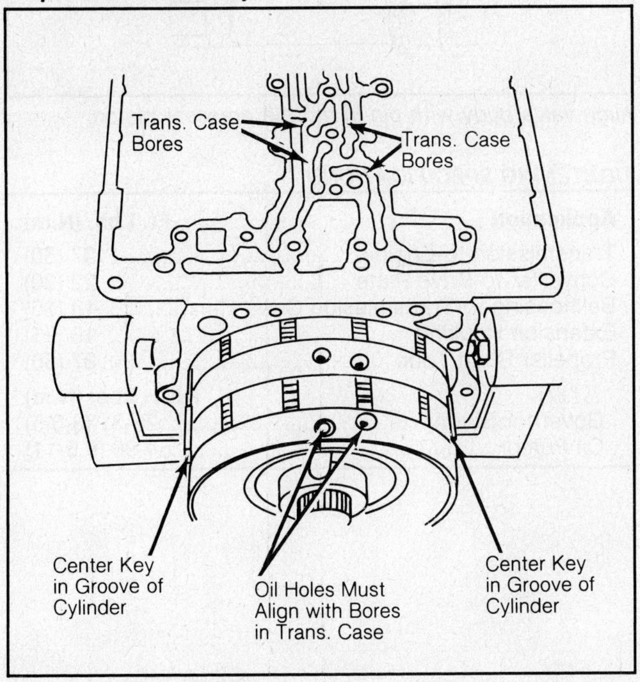

Align keys and oil holes.

3) Install clutch "B" and press in seal with washer. Retain clutch "B" in position with snap ring. Lubricate plastic thrust washer and metal thrust washer with grease. Install plastic thrust washer on carrier plate, aligning tabs with openings in carrier plate. *See Fig. 14.* Install metal thrust washer.

4) Install carrier plate in clutch "A" by turning back and forth slightly. Install clutch "A" into transmission case. Install angled disc on input shaft, with collar facing needle bearing. Install thrust washer and gasket on converter housing. Slide converter housing onto input shaft and secure.

5) Check input shaft end play. End play should be .012-.059" (.3-1.5 mm). *See Fig. 15.* Press piston rings together to slide governor assembly onto output shaft. Remove stud to help find the depression in the output shaft. Secure the governor by aligning the stud with the depression. Lock governor by counterpunching the stud.

6) Install washer and snapring on output shaft. Install speedometer drive gear. Install extension housing. Install seal and transmission output flange, securing with lock plate and nut.

Fig. 14: Plastic Thrust Washer Installation

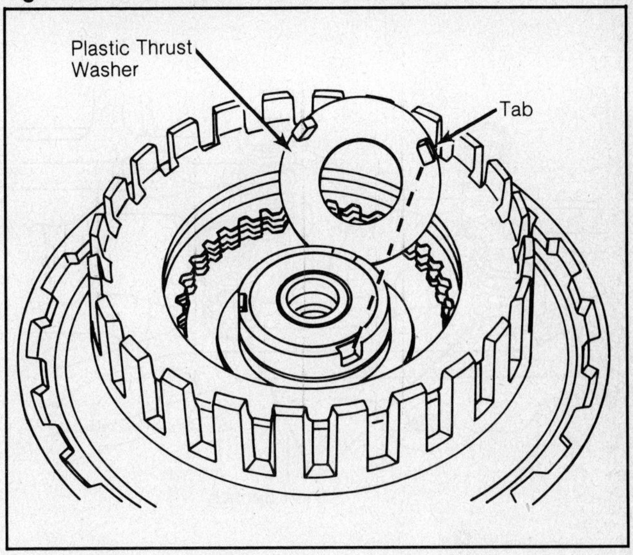

Align tabs on washer with carrier plate openings.

Fig. 15: Checking Input Shaft End Play

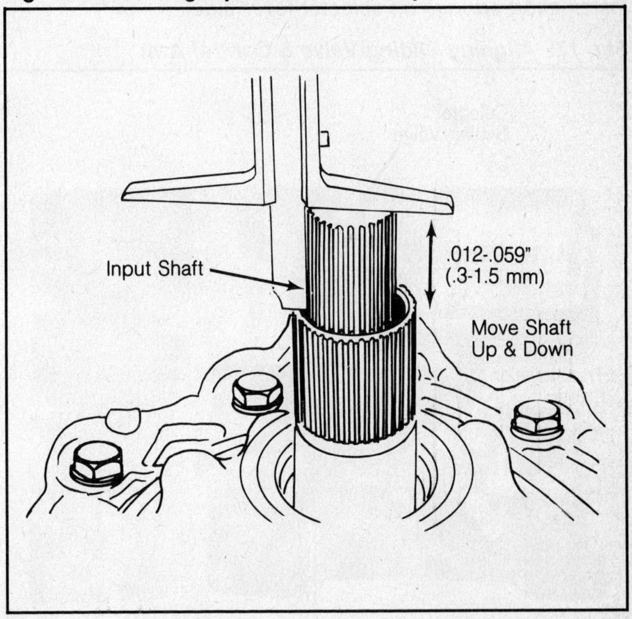

7) Using a punch, drive in the 4 sealing sleeves, up to the stop. Install and secure springs. Both of the short springs are installed on the selector lever side. *See Fig. 16.*

8) Install valve body so that the clamp on the selector sliding valve can be engaged in the opening arm of the pawl, by tightening the transmission cable slightly. *See Fig. 17.*

9) Align valve body with pin in the throttle pressure piston. Clearance must be .45" (11.5 mm). *See Fig. 18.* Tighten valve body screws. Install oil pan gasket and magnetic disc, next to oil filter screen. Install oil pan with short arm of retaining bracket pressing down on oil pan.

ZF 3HP 22 (Cont.)

Fig. 16: Installing Springs in Valve Body

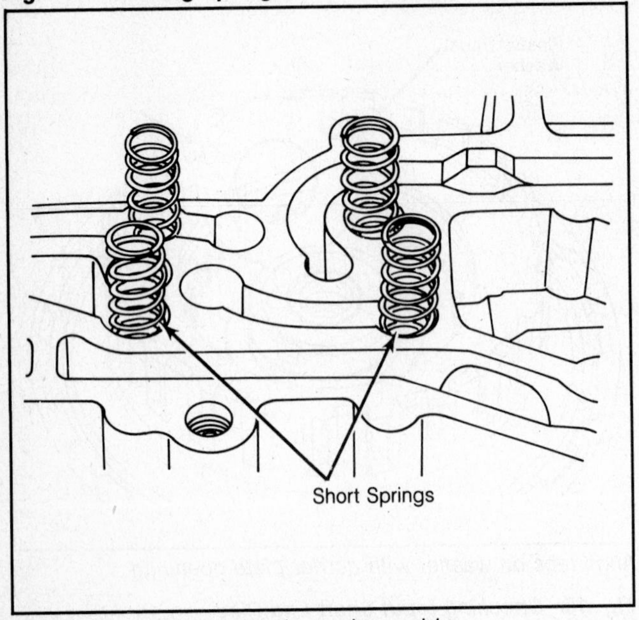

Install short springs on selector lever side.

Fig. 17: Aligning Sliding Valve & Control Arm

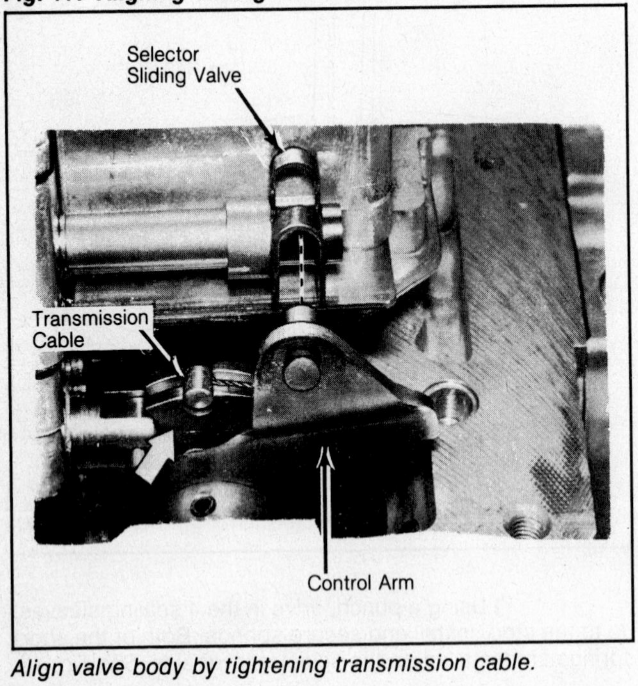

Align valve body by tightening transmission cable.

Fig. 18: Aligning Valve Body

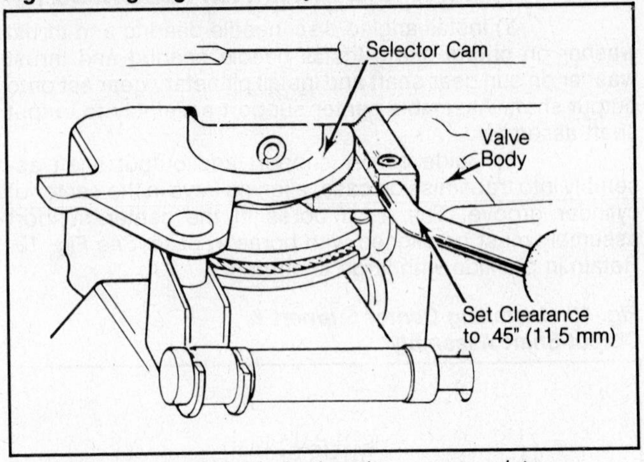

Align valve body with pin in throttle pressure piston.

TIGHTENING SPECIFICATIONS

Application	Ft. Lbs. (N.m)
Transmission-to-Engine	37 (50)
Converter-to-Drive Plate	22 (30)
Bellhousing-to-Transmission Case	18 (25)
Extension Housing	18 (25)
Propeller Shaft Tube	37 (50)
	INCH Lbs. (N.m)
Governor Studs	26-31 (3-3.5)
Oil Pump	84-96 (9.5-11)

ZF 4HP 22/EH

**BMW 325e, 528e,
535i, 635CSi, 735i
Volvo 760 GLE Turbo Diesel**

TRANSMISSION IDENTIFICATION

Transmission identification is stamped on a metal tag fastened to the lower left of the center housing.

BMW TRANSMISSION CODES

Model	Code
735i	TT
635CSi	UF
535i	UE
528e	UP
325e	TY

DESCRIPTION

Transmission is a fully automatic 4-speed unit, with 4th gear being an overdrive unit. The transmission is equipped with a torque converter incorporating a lock-up clutch and planetary gear set.

On BMW models, the "EH" transmission is equipped with electronic shift control. This system has 3 different shift programs: economy, sport and direct.

OPERATION

Starting off from a standstill is performed by the torque converter which acts as a fluid coupling and a torque multiplier. Once transmission input speed approaches that of the engine, torque converter acts only as fluid coupling. In 4th gear, torque converter lock-up clutch engages automatically, depending on road speed, so that there is a direct mechanical link between engine and transmission.

ELECTRONIC CONTROL SWITCH

"E" (Economy Mode)

This mode can be selected for normal driving conditions and low fuel consumption use. The converter lockup clutch engages automatically in 3rd and 4th gear.

"S" (Sports Mode)

This mode can be selected for higher shift points. The gear shift points are delayed to make full use of the vehicle's power range. The converter lockup clutch automatically locks out 3rd and 4th gears.

"3-2-1" (Direct Shift Mode)

This mode is for single gear driving (3rd gear if "D" is selected). The gear selected can also be used for passing. If shift selector lever is in "1" position, transmission will remain in that gear. This mode should be used only when extreme conditions require its use (road gradients or icy conditions).

CAUTION: Caution should be used with the shift mode selector the in "3-2-1" mode. The engine can be damaged if the rpm goes beyond its designed "Red" line.

Transmission Warning Light

The "EH" warning light is located on the main instrument panel. The warning light should go out after the engine is started. If the warning light does not go out, the electronic shift control circuit has a defect and the transmission will automatically select 3rd gear no matter what position the shift lever is in. See "EH" MODEL ELECTRONIC TESTING in this article.

LUBRICATION & ADJUSTMENT

See appropriate MANUAL TRANSMISSION SERVICING article in IMPORT GENERAL SERVICING section.

TROUBLE SHOOTING (4 HP 22 MODEL)

NO ENGAGEMENT OF DRIVE (FORWARD OR REVERSE MOVEMENT)

Oil level too low. Defective oil pump. Drive plate broken. Parking lock pawl stuck. Clutches "C-1" and No. 1 one-way clutch ("F-2") defective. Input or output shaft broken. Gear selector linkage broken or needs adjustment. On Volvo, if any internal components are defective, replace transmission.

NO REVERSE

Selector linkage cable incorrectly adjusted. Clutch "B", "E" or brake "D" defective. Oil leakage in clutch "B" or leak in brake "D" oil feed supply. Reverse gear arrest does not cancel.

MOVES IN ONE GEAR ONLY (SELECTOR IN "D" POSITION)

No Power Flow

Oil filter screen dirty. Clutch "A" defective. One-way clutch slips, 1st gear. Selector cable linkage broken or needs adjustment.

1st Gear Only

1st/2nd shift valve stuck. Governor bushing seized. Brake "C" defective.

2nd Gear Only

1st/2nd and 2nd/3rd shift valve stuck.

1st and 2nd Gears Only

2nd/3rd shift valve stuck.

3rd Gear Only

1st/2nd, 2nd/3rd or 3rd/4th shift valve stuck. Governor bushing seized.

4th Gear Only

Brake "F" defective

TRANSMISSION SLIPPAGE

In "D" Position

Clutch "A" slips. Oil level too low. Throttle pressure valve stuck.

In Reverse

Clutch "B" or brake "D" damaged. Loss of oil in supply line to clutch "B" or brake "D".

NO BRAKING EFFECT

In 3rd Gear Position

Clutch "E" damaged.

ZF 4HP 22/EH (Cont.)

Fig. 1: Sectional View of ZF 4 HP-22 Transmission

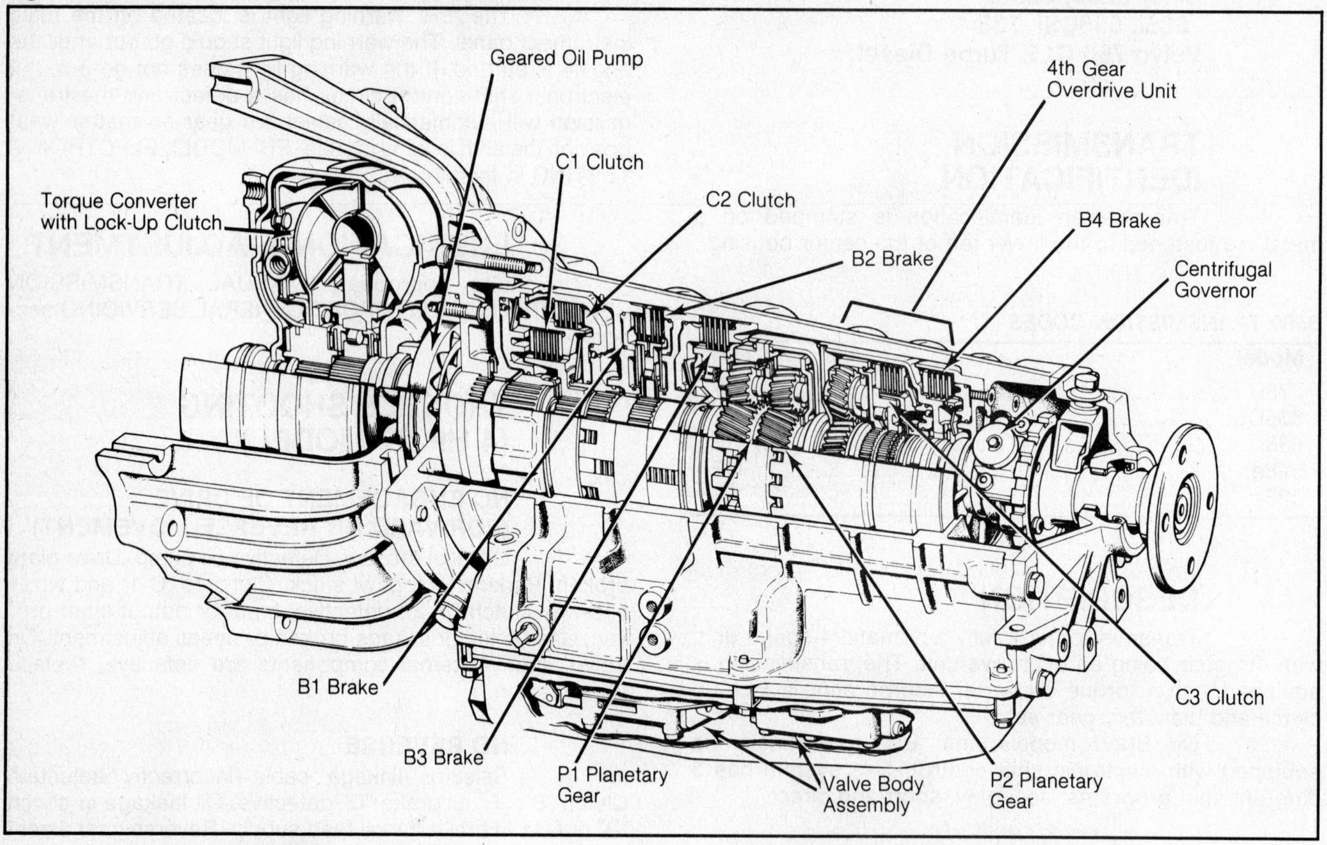

In 2nd Gear Position
Brake C' defective.

SHIFT POINTS INCORRECT

Too High
Throttle cable adjustment incorrect. Governor bushing jammed, or seal rings leaking. Valve body faulty.

Too Low
Throttle cable adjustment incorrect. Governor bushing jammed. Valve body faulty.

NO KICKDOWN

In "1-2" and "2-3"
Accelerator cable not adjusted properly. Throttle pressure valve seized. Balls in valve body worn.

NO UPSHIFT

To 2nd Gear
Governor seized. 1-2 shift valve seized.

To 3rd Gear
Governor seized. Throttle pressure too high. Throttle pressure valve stuck. Clutch "B" damaged.

To 4th Gear
Kickdown valve 4-3 seized.

TRANSMISSION NOISES

In All Positions When Cold
Suction noise at oil pump due to loose valve body bolts. Defective valve body. Low fluid level.

Noise in 1st Gear On Acceleration and Deceleration
Worn planetary gears.

Light Grinding Noise Which Is Speed Sensitive
Needle bearing in transmission extension housing defective.

Loud, Screeching Noise In All Positions
Oil level to low. Valve body leaks.

Loud Noise When Converter Closes
Torsion damper defective. Defective torque converter.

TROUBLE SHOOTING (4 HP 22/EH ELECTRONIC TRANSMISSION)

SHIFT SELECTOR IN "P" POSITION

Park Will Not Engage
Selector linkage between selector lever and transmission out of adjustment. Excessive friction in parking lock mechanism.

Park Does Not Hold (Slips Out)
Selector linkage between selector lever and transmission out of adjustment.

Engine Cannot Be Started In "N" or "P"
Transmission switch defective

SHIFT SELECTOR IN "R" POSITION

No Reverse Gear
Linkage between selector lever and transmission out of adjustment. Oil filter screen dirty. Clutch "B" defective (also no 3rd gear). Brake "D" defective (no engine

braking in 1st gear). Clutch "E" defective (no engine braking in 2nd or 3rd gear). Reverse gear lock does not cancel.

Slipping or Shaking When Moving Off
Clutch "B" or "E" damaged. Brake "D" defective.

Hard Engaging Jolt
Damper "B" defective (shift 2-3 not correct).

Backup Lights Do Not Come On
Transmission switch defective.

Vehicle Moves Or Crawls
Linkage between selector lever and transmission out of adjustment. Clutch "A" defective (bonded).

SHIFT SELECTOR IN "D" POSITION

No Power Flow
Oil filter screen dirty. Clutch "A" defective. 1st gear one-way clutch slips. Linkage between selector lever and transmission out of adjustment.

Slipping or Shaking When Starting Off
Clutch "A" is defective.

Hard Engagement Jolt
Clutch "A" or damper "A" is defective.

No Shift (Warm or Cold)
Kickdown switch defective (only kickdown shifts)

No 1-2 or 2-1 Shift
Transmission electronics defective. Shift solenoid defective. Control valve (shift 1-2/2-1) seized. Shift valve (1-2) seized.

No 1-2 Shift
Brake C' and/or "C" defective.

No 2-3 or 3-2 Shift
Shift solenoid defective. Shift valve 2-3 seized.

No 2-3 Shift
Clutch "B" defective.

No 3-4 or 4-3 Shift
Shift solenoid defective. Control valve 1-2 or 3-4 seized. Shift valve 3-4 seized.

No 3-4 Shift
Brake "F" defective. Program switch defective.

No 1-2 Shift (Engine Speed Does Not Go Beyond Stall Speed)
Pulse transmitter defective.

Vehicle Starts Off In 2nd Gear
Transmission electronics defective. Shift solenoid defective. Shift valve 1-2 seized.

Vehicle Starts Off In 3rd Gear
Transmission electronics defective. Shift solenoid defective. Shift valve 1-2 and 2-3 seized.

Vehicle Shifts From 1st to 3rd
Shift valve 2-3 seized. Transmission electronics defective. Shift solenoid defective.

SHIFT SPEEDS

Zero Load Shift Is Not Okay
Control unit defective.

Full Load Shift Points Not Okay
No full load signal being transmitted.

No Kickdown Shift
Kickdown switch defective.

Only Zero Load Shifts
Zero load Switch on engine defective.

Only Kickdown Shifts
Kickdown switch defective.

SHIFT TRANSITIONS

Zero Load Shifts Too Hard
Control unit or damper defective. Modulation pressure too high. Clutch plates damaged.

Full Load and Kickdown Shifts Too Long
Control or damper unit defective. Modulation pressure too high. Clutch plates damaged.

Full Load and Kickdown Shifts Too Hard
Modulation pressure not okay. Damper defective. Control unit defective.

SHIFT LEVER POSITION 3

No Engine Braking
Clutch "E" damaged.

SHIFT LEVER POSITION 2

Manual Downshift 3-2 Not Okay
Transmission electronics defective. Shift solenoid defective.

SHIFT LEVER POSITION 1

Manual Downshift 2-1 Not Okay
Transmission electronics defective. Shift solenoid defective.

No Engine Braking Effect
Brake C' or clutch "E" damaged.

CONVERTER CLUTCH

Shift Speed Not Okay
Control unit defective.

Shift Transition Too Hard
Converter clutch damper defective. Converter not okay.

No Shift
Transmission electronics defective. Shift solenoid defective. Converter defective.

Converter Clutch Always Locked (Engine Stops In Drive Position)
Transmission electronics defective. Shift solenoid defective.

GENERAL

Shifts Only As Positioned
Transmission electronics defective. Program switch defective.

Defect Indicator Lights Up
Transmission electronics defective. Shift solenoid defective.

Defect Indicator Lights Up While Driving
Transmission electronics defective. Poor contact of plug on transmission.

Noise and Power Loss After Long Drives
Oil filter screen on valve body dirty.

No power (Forward or Reverse) Loud Noise
Clutch drive plate between converter and engine torn off.

Automatic Transmissions

ZF 4HP 22/EH (Cont.)

TESTING

ROAD TEST

1) Before testing, make sure fluid level is correct and all linkage adjustments are correct. Transmission should shift at approximate speeds shown in SHIFT SPEED charts. Speeds may vary due to model, tire size and axle ratio. The important factor is that all shifts should be smooth, with no slipping or engine racing.

2) Slipping or engine racing during shifts usually indicates clutch or brake slipping problems. Unless an obvious condition exists, transmission should never be disassembled until hydraulic pressure tests have been performed.

STALL TEST

1) With engine and transmission at normal operating temperature, connect a tachometer to engine. Apply service and parking brakes and place selector lever in "D".

CAUTION: DO NOT maintain stall speed more than 10 seconds.

2) Accelerate engine to full throttle and note engine speed. Repeat test with selector lever in position "R".

Stall Test Results

If stall speeds are below specifications, check engine output for being below specifications. Check stall speeds for proper specifications, refer to STALL SPEED SPECIFICATIONS.

STALL SPEED SPECIFICATIONS

Application	Stall RPM
BMW	
325e & 528e	1900-2050
535i, 635CSi & 735i	1970-2120
Volvo	
760 GLE Turbo Diesel	1800-2000

VOLVO SHIFT SPEEDS

Shift Conditions	MPH
760 GLE Turbo Diesel	
Full Throttle (Kickdown Engaged)	
1-2 Upshift	29
2-3 Upshift	52
3-4 Upshift	61
4-3 Downshift	21
3-2 Downshift	49
2-1 Downshift	24

HYDRAULIC PRESSURE

NOTE: The following procedure applies to BMW models only. Information not available from Volvo.

1) Connect Pressure Gauge Hose (24 0 021) to Pressure Tester (13 3 061). Remove pertinent pressure plugs for pump pressure, clutch "A" and converter pressure.

2) To test pump pressure, install Adapter (24 0 070) with seal on transmission. Connect Elbow Pipe (24 0 023) in conjunction with Hose (24 0 021).

BMW SHIFT SPEEDS

Shift Conditions	RPM
325e & 528e	
Full Throttle	
1-2 Upshift	3370-3950
2-3 Upshift	4000-4320
3-4 Upshift	3740-3980
Kickdown	
1-2 Upshift	4410-4910
2-3 Upshift	4510-4810
4-3 Downshift	Immediately
3-2 Downshift	3030-3250
2-1 Downshift	2550-2790
Manual Downshift (Max.)	
4-3	Immediately
3-2	2890-3230
2-1	2020-2500
535i, 635CSi & 735i	
Full Throttle	
1-2 Upshift	4140-4790
2-3 Upshift	4960-5340
3-4 Upshift	4580-4880
Kickdown	
1-2 Upshift	5430-5970
2-3 Upshift	5570-5930
4-3 Downshift	Immediately
3-2 Downshift	3690-3940
2-1 Downshift	2920-3290
Manual Downshift	
4-3	Immediately
3-2	3620-4030
2-1	2570-3040

3) To test converter pressure, install Adapter (24 0 030) on transmission. Connect Elbow Pipe (24 0 023) in conjunction with Hose (24 0 021).

4) Connect main pressure port. *See Fig. 2.* Disconnect transmission kickdown cable from throttle linkage and set engine idle speed to 1200-1500 RPM.

5) With rear wheels off the ground and transmission in "R", check main pressure. Pressure obtained should be within limits specified in HYDRAULIC PRSSURE charts. To check kickdown pressures, pull on kickdown cable.

BMW HYDRAULIC PRESSURES

Application	psi (kg/cm²)
325e & 528e	
In "R"	
Idle	156-185 (11-13)
Kickdown	229-260 (16.3-19.0)
In "D" Position	
Idle	85-107 (6-7.5)
Kickdown	141-156 (9.9-10.9)
535i, 635CSi & 735i	
In "R"	
Idle	215-245 (15.5-17.1)
Kickdown	246-276 (17.3-19.4)
All Other Positions	
Idle	85-107 (6-7.5)
Kickdown	132-146 (7.9-10.2)

ZF 4HP 22/EH (Cont.)

Fig. 2: Hydraulic Pressure Connections

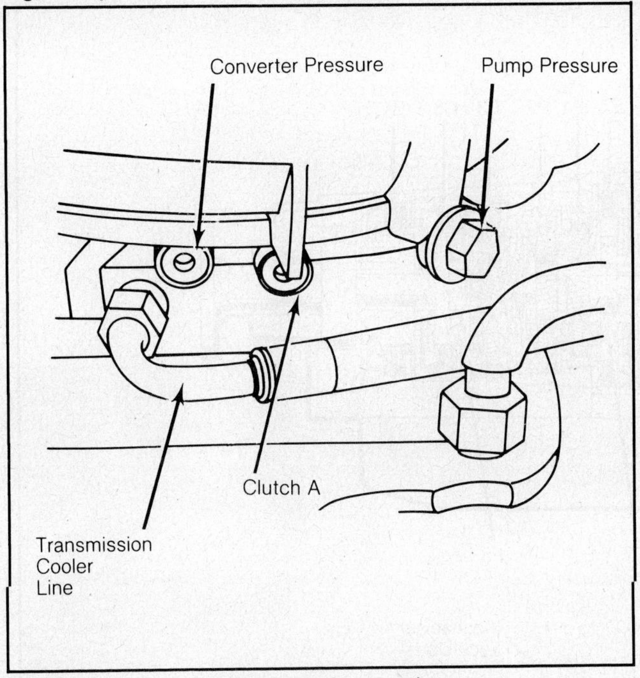

Be sure to check fluid level before testing.

6) Place transmission in Neutral and run engine at idle to cool transmission. With transmission in any position except "R", repeat check. Pressure obtained should be within limits specified in HYDRAULIC PRESSURE charts.

ELECTRONIC TESTING ("EH" MODEL)

CAUTION: NEVER disconnect the electronic control unit with the ignition switch on.

The control unit is located in the left front kick panel, behind the speaker. Connect Adapter (HWB 81 12 9 425 091) in conjunction with Connecting Lead (HWB 81 12 9 425 092) for all tests. Use only Bosch (AEGS) service tester to perform the following tests.

Test 1
(Warning Light)

1) If warning light on instrument panel does not come on when ignition switch is turned on, check voltage between wires 5/19 and 33. Voltage should be at least 10 volts. Check indicator light bulb for being defective. Check for break in wiring from instrument panel to indicator light. Repair or replace components as necessary. If no defect is found, replace printed circuit board for shift mode indicator.

2) If warning does not flash and remains on after engine is started, check for break in ground wire 5/19. Check voltage between wires 5/19 and 24 with ignition switch on. Voltage should be at least 5 volts. If voltage is not okay, repair defective wiring. If voltage is okay, replace transmission electronic control unit.

3) If warning light comes on while driving vehicle, check voltage between wires 5/19 and 35. Voltage should be at least 10 volts. If voltage is not okay, repair wiring. If voltage is okay, check wiring to valve body shift control solenoids for a break or grounded, go to **Test 2**.

4) If there's no "TD" signal from the control unit, check plug connection and power supply to control unit. If there's no "ti" signal from the control unit, check valve body shift control solenoids, go to **Test 2**.

Test 2
(Solenoid Valves)

NOTE: Specified resistance values for solenoid valves and pressure regulator should be measured with transmission fluid temperature above 68°F (20°C).

1) For 1st/2nd and 3rd/4th solenoid valve, check ohm resistance between wires 1 and 16. Nominal value should be 25-46 ohms. If ohm resistance is high, check wire to solenoid for being damaged or grounded. If ohm resistance is okay, replace solenoid valve.

2) For 2nd/3rd gear solenoid valve, check ohm resistance between wires 1 and 25. Nominal value should be 25-46 ohms. If ohm resistance is high, check wire to solenoid for being damaged or grounded. If ohm resistance is okay, replace solenoid valve.

3) For reverse gear lock solenoid valve, pull off control unit plug. Check resistance between wires 1 and 20. Nominal value should be 25-46 ohms. If ohm resistance is high, check wire to solenoid for being damaged or grounded. If ohm resistance is okay, replace solenoid valve.

4) For converter lockup clutch solenoid, check ohm resistance between wires 5/19 and 1/25. Nominal value should be 25-46 ohms. If ohm resistance is high, check wire to solenoid for being damaged or grounded. If ohm resistance is okay, replace solenoid valve.

Test 3

For pressure regulator, check ohm resistance between wires 1 and 22. Nominal value should be 1.8-4.6 ohms. If ohm resistance is high, check wire to pressure regulator for being damaged or grounded. If ohm resistance is okay, replace pressure regulator.

Test 4
(Mode Position Switch)

1) Switch mode switch to "S2". A magnet switch will return program switch to position "E" for each starting procedure. Check ohm resistance between wires 6 and 14. Resistance value should be infinity for switch positions "S", "3", "2" or "1". There should be zero ohms for switch position "E". If values are not as specified, check for wiring damage. If wiring is okay, replace program switch.

2) Measure direct voltage between Black and Brown wires, while starting vehicle. Nominal value should be at least 8 volts. If nominal value is not reached, check wiring for damage. Repair wiring as necessary.

Test 5
(Kickdown Switch)

1) With accelerator pedal at idle position, check resistance between wires 19 and 2. Nominal ohm value should be infinity. With accelerator pedal floored, nominal ohm value should be zero.

2) If nominal value is not reached, check wiring to kickdown switch for being damaged or shorted. If wiring is okay, replace kickdown switch

ZF 4HP 22/EH (Cont.)

Fig. 3: ZF 4HP 22 Power Flow Diagram and Clutch Component Applications.

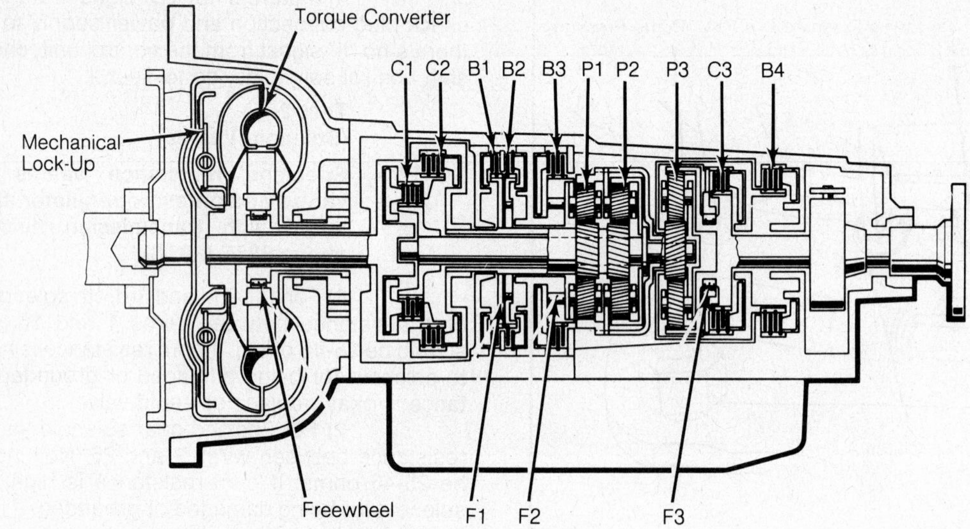

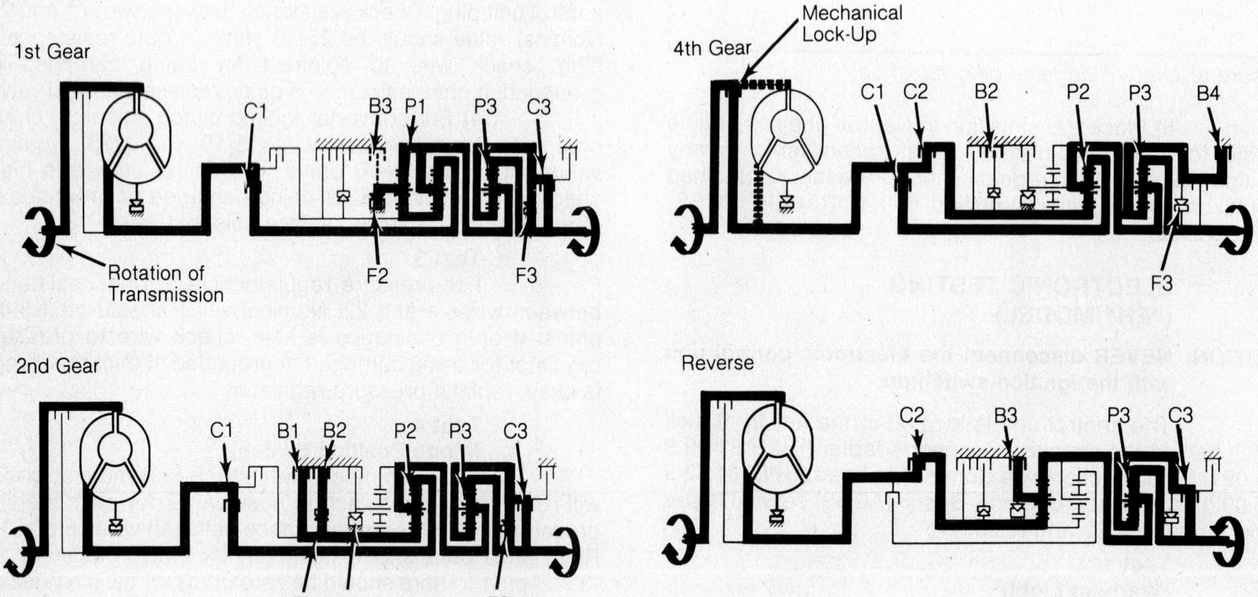

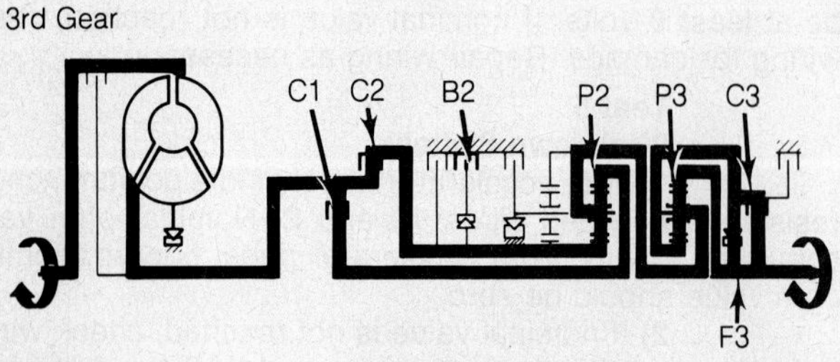

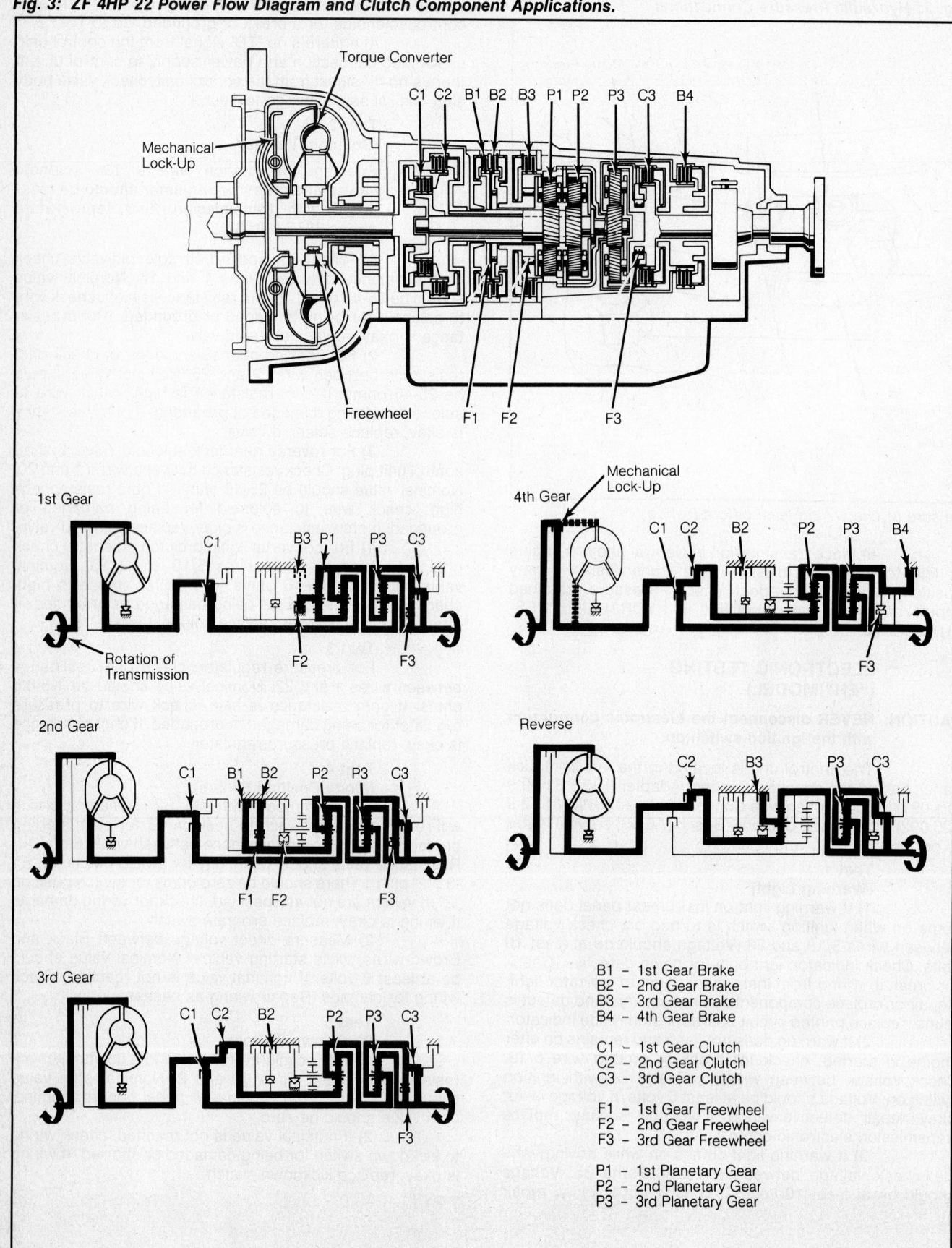

B1 – 1st Gear Brake
B2 – 2nd Gear Brake
B3 – 3rd Gear Brake
B4 – 4th Gear Brake

C1 – 1st Gear Clutch
C2 – 2nd Gear Clutch
C3 – 3rd Gear Clutch

F1 – 1st Gear Freewheel
F2 – 2nd Gear Freewheel
F3 – 3rd Gear Freewheel

P1 – 1st Planetary Gear
P2 – 2nd Planetary Gear
P3 – 3rd Planetary Gear

ZF 4HP 22/EH (Cont.)

Fig. 4: Valve Body for ZF 4 HP 22/EH Transmission

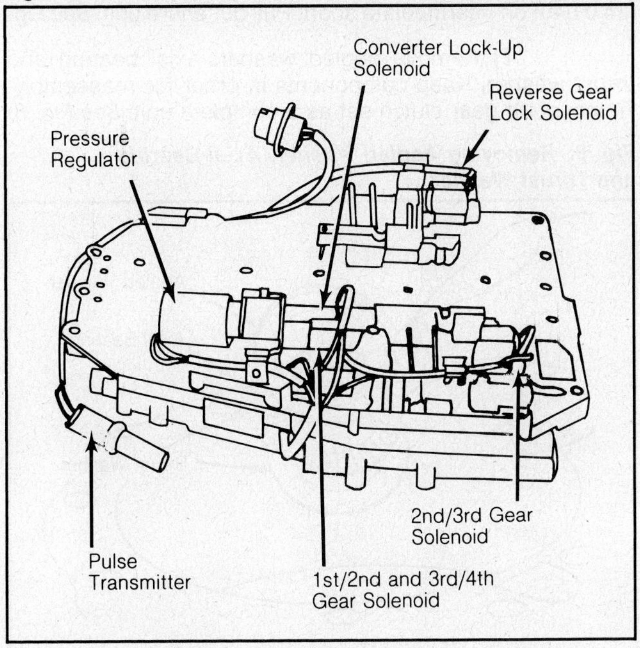

Test 6
(Mode Position Switch)

With ignition switch on and headlights off, shift mode position switch to "S1". Measure voltage between following wires:

- Wires 19 and 18, mode switch to position "1".
- Wires 19 and 28, mode switch to position "2".
- Wires 19 and 29, mode switch to position "3".
- Wires 19 and 30, mode switch to position "D".
- Wires 19 and 4, mode switch to position "N".

Nominal voltage should be at least 10 volts. If nominal voltage is low, check wires for being damaged or shorted. Check for defective mode position switch. Display unit is defective or battery voltage is too low. Repair or replace components as necessary.

Test 7
(Pulse Transmitter)

Check ohm resistance between wires 8 and 27. Nominal value should be between 800-1.6 k-ohms. If nominal value is not okay, check wire to pulse transmitter for being damaged or shorted. Repair wiring as necessary. If nomianl value is okay, replace pulse transmitter.

Test 8
(Dynamic Scope Test)

Connect test lead between wires 8 and 27. Lift vehicle on hoist. Rear wheels should turn easily. Start engine. Select position "D" on selector lever. Accelerate engine to about 25 mph. All "sine" curves on scope should be larger than 0-10. If nominal value is not okay, check wire to pulse transmitter. If nominal value is okay, replace pulse transmitter. End of test.

REMOVAL & INSTALLATION

See appropriate MANUAL TRANSMISSION REMOVAL article in IMPORT GENERAL SERVICING section.

SERVICE (IN VEHICLE)

The following units may be removed from transmission without removing transmission from vehicle: Oil Pan and Gasket, Shift Valve Body, Speedometer Driven Gear Assembly, Secondary Pump Assembly, Extension Housing, Pressure Receiving Piston, Modulating Pressure Housing, Speedometer Drive Gear, Secondary Pump Eccentric, Governor Assembly, Parking Pawl and Parking Linkage. See procedures given in TRANSMISSION DISASSEMBLY and TRANSMISSION REASSEMBLY.

TORQUE CONVERTER

NOTE: **Torque converter is a sealed unit and cannot be disassembled for service. If hub or torque converter is scored, or if metallic particles are found in transmission fluid, replace converter assembly.**

TRANSMISSION DISASSEMBLY

1) Place transmission in a holding fixture. Remove torque converter. Remove oil pan and gasket. Remove only 12mm Torx bolts using Torx Bolt Remover (00 2 100) and remove valve body.

2) Lift out 8 retaining circlips from 4 oil supply bores in transmission case and withdraw 8 compression springs. Using Puller (24 0 050) thread into sleeves, remove 8 sealing sleeves from oil bores. Screw tool into sleeve and pull out sharply.

3) Lock transmission output shaft by engaging parking gear. Hold output flange using Output Flange Holder (23 0 020) stationary. Remove lock ring, retaining nut using Collar Nut Wrench (23 1 210) and remove output flange. Remove extension housing. Using a puller, pull off speedometer drive gear. Remove washer and snap ring.

4) Pull off parking lock gear and governor. Remove parking lock pawl, spring and loosen governor assembly retaining nut. Unscrew governor stud about 3 turns and pull governor off shaft. Remove torque converter housing with oil pump, seal, intermediate plate, thrust washer, needle bearing and angled disc. Remove and separate components. Remove input shaft and clutch "A". *See Fig. 5.*

Fig. 5: Removing Lock Gear and Governor

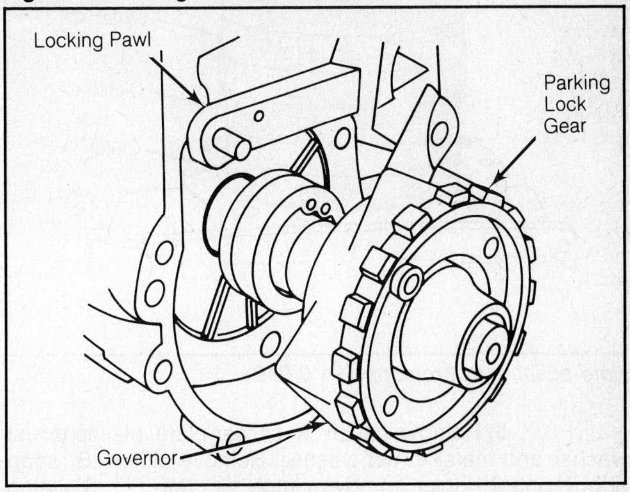

If necessary use tool (24 32 002) to remove pump.

ZF 4HP 22/EH (Cont.)

Fig. 6: Removing Clutches "A" and "B".

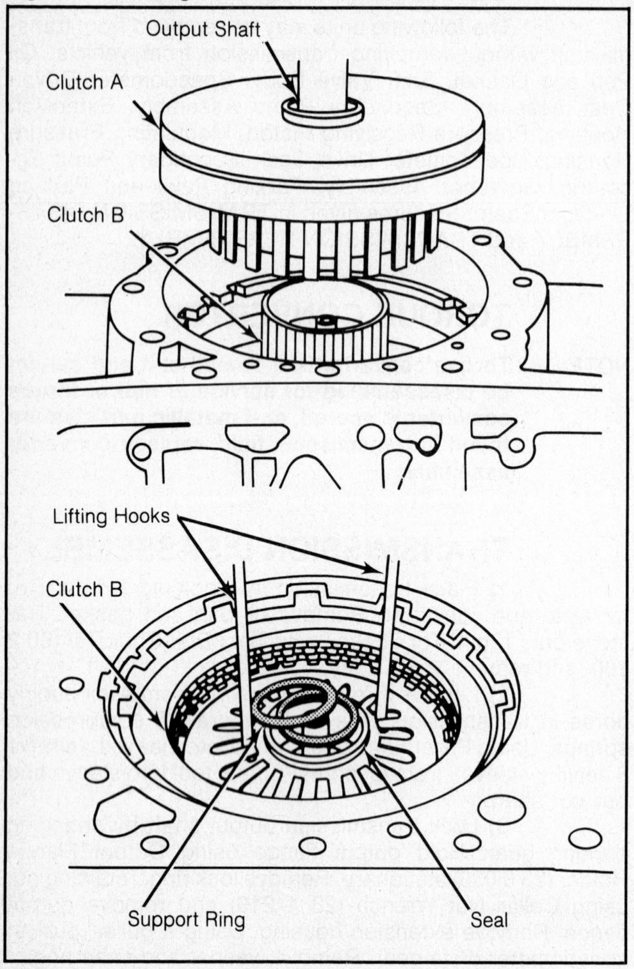

Remove clutch "A" with input shaft.

Fig. 7: Removing Intermediate Shaft and Gear Unit

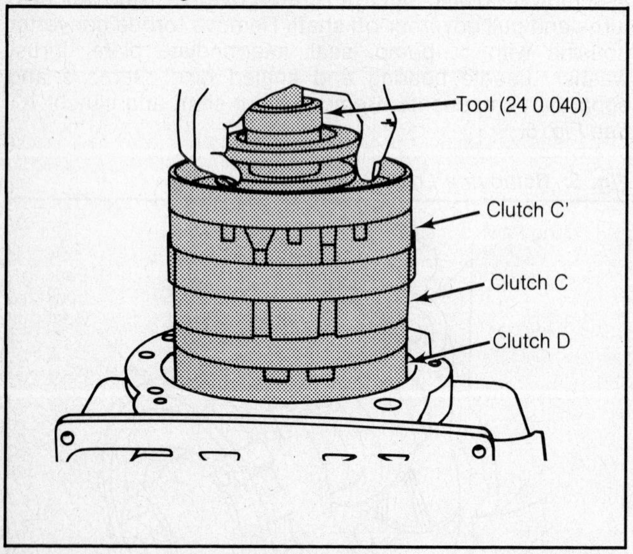

Note position of Protector (24 0 040).

5) Remove clutch "A" carrier plate, plastic thrust washer and metal thrust washer. Remove clutch "B" snap ring. Using 2 hooks, remove clutch "B". *See Fig. 6.* Catch washer and seal as they are pulled out with clutch "B".

6) Remove large snap ring and place Protector (24 0 040) on intermediate shaft. Pull out entire unit. *See Fig. 7.*

7) Remove angled washer, axial bearing and thrust washer. Keep components in order for reassembly. Remove 4th gear clutch set as a complete unit. *See Fig. 8.*

Fig. 8: Removing Angled Washer, Axial Bearing and Thrust Washer

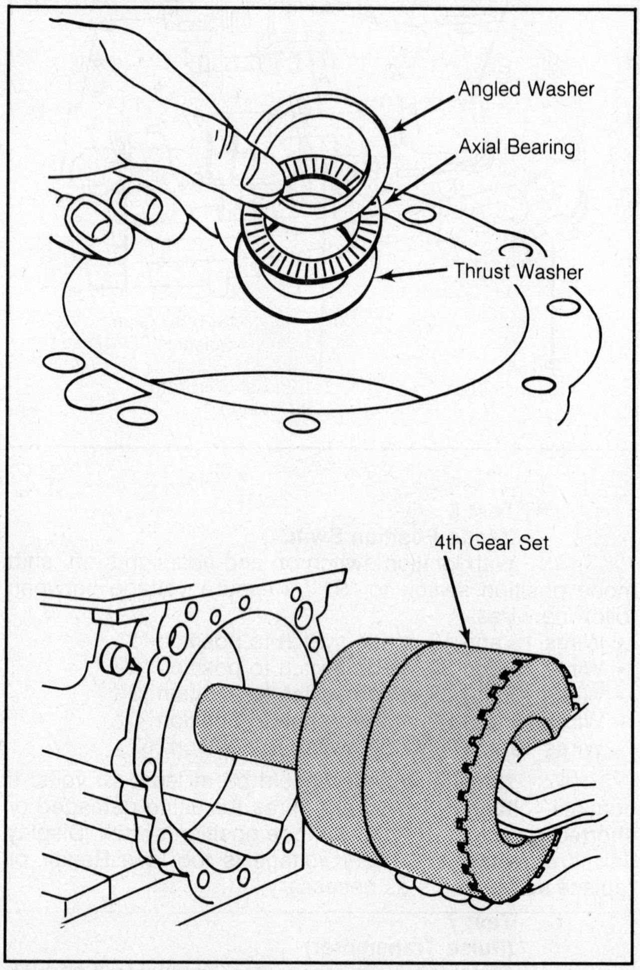

Note position of components for reassembly.

COMPONENT DISASSEMBLY & REASSEMBLY

PRIMARY PUMP ASSEMBLY

Disassembly

Remove torque converter. Remove converter housing with intermediate plate. Remove intermediate plate from converter housing by loosening 2 bolts. DO NOT remove bolts. Separate primary pump from converter housing by tapping lightly. Remove bolts and pump.

Inspection

1) Clean all parts and check for signs of scoring or other wear. Check clearance between pump driven gear and pump housing; clearance must be .003-.006" (.07-.16 mm).

2) Check pump housing-to-gear radial play while rotating gear 360°; clearance must be .0008-.0016" (.02-.04 mm).

ZF 4HP 22/EH (Cont.)

3) Check running clearance of primary pump with Measuring Tool (24 3 140).

4) Check axial play of both gears to face surface with a precision depth micrometer; axial play must be .008-.016" (.02-.04 mm). *See Fig. 9.*

5) If any component is defective, complete pump assembly must be replaced. If any measurement is not within specifications, replace oil pump assembly.

Fig. 9: Checking Primary Pump

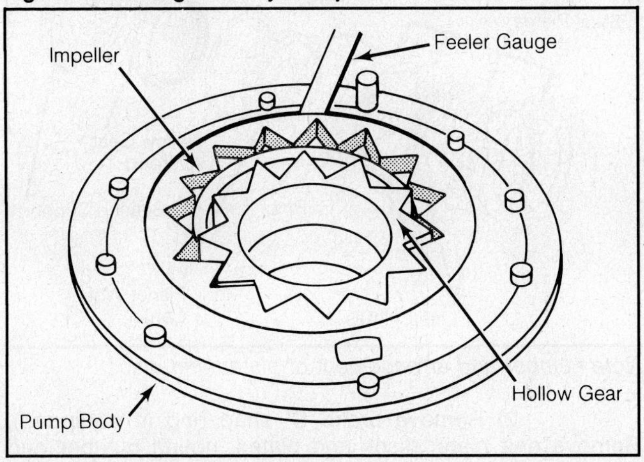

Measure while rotating pump 360°.

Reassembly

Install pump drive and gears with punch marks up (if equipped). Replace all gaskets and seals. Install angled disc on input shaft, with collar facing needle bearing. Hold thrust washer on converter housing with grease.

Fig. 10: Centrifugal Governor Assembly

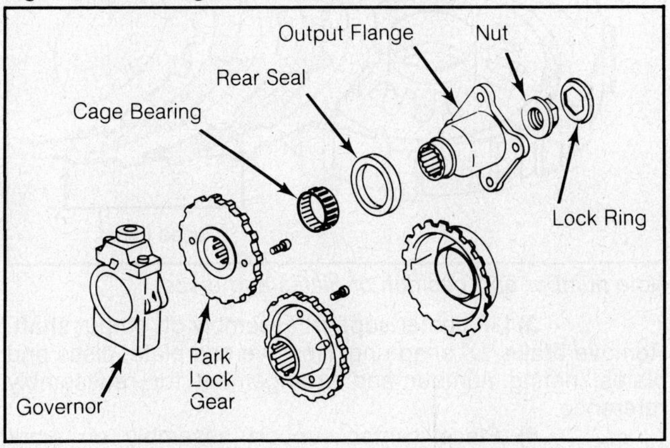

CENTRIFUGAL GOVERNOR

Disassembly

1) Remove transmission extension. Pull off parking lock gear with centrifugal governor. If equipped with bearing race, pull off parking lock gear with a Kukko puller. *See Fig. 10.*

2) Detach parking lock gear on centrifugal governor. Take off cover on case and lift out retainer and remove washer. Remove governor piston, spring and governor bushing. Remove spring clip and balance weight.

3) Clean all parts and check for signs of scoring or other wear. If any components show wear, replace complete governor assembly. *See Fig. 11.*

Fig. 11: Exploded View of Centrifugal Governor

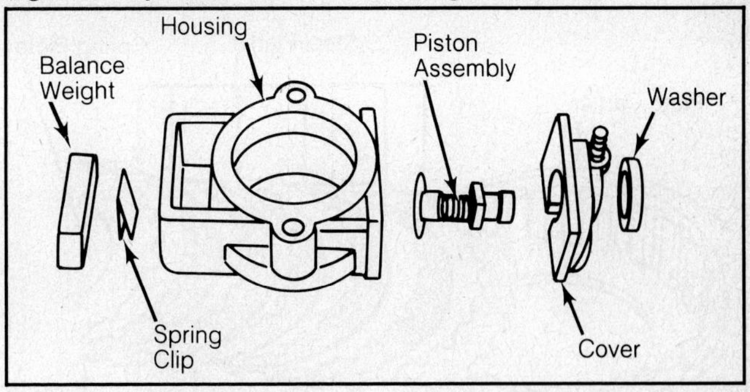

Reassembly

1) When installing governor piston make sure it slides easily into governor bushing. Remove spring clip and balance weight.

2) Slide parking lock gear with centifugal governor on to output shaft. Install centrifugal governor on parking lock gear and tighten to specification. Heat bearing race to about 175° F (80°C). and slide on to output shaft.

CLUTCH "A"

Disassembly

1) With transmission disassembled, press out input shaft. Using press, compress clutch assembly and remove large snap ring. *See Fig. 12.* Remove spacer plates, clutch plates, discs, diaphragm spring and carrier plate. Note number and arrangement of plates and discs.

2) Remove snap ring from input shaft and separate input shaft from input hub. Remove piston from hub by applying compressed air to oil hole. Remove diaphragm spring and seals.

Fig. 12: Clutch "A" Snap Ring Removal

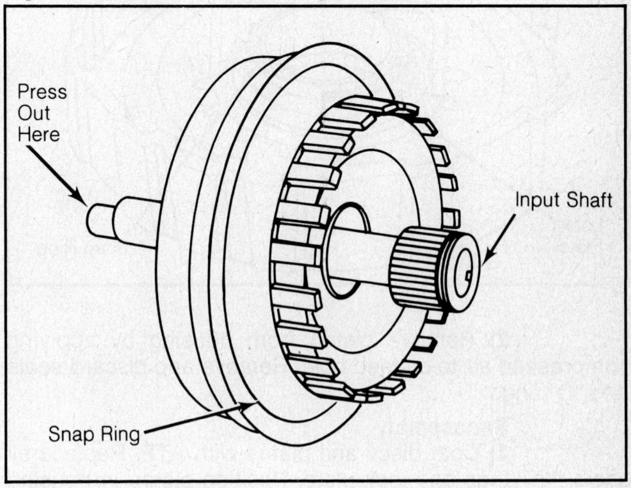

Compress clutch assembly and remove snap ring.

Reassembly

1) Coat all discs and plates with ATF. Insert input shaft into hub and retain with snap ring. Place diaphragm spring in hub with curved surface facing down. Replace all seals.

2) Alternate plates and discs until the number and position of plates and discs are installed as they were removed. *See Fig. 13.* Install spacer plates and carrier plate. Compress clutch assembly and install large snap ring.

ZF 4HP 22/EH (Cont.)

Fig. 13: Clutch "A" Disc and Plate Assembly

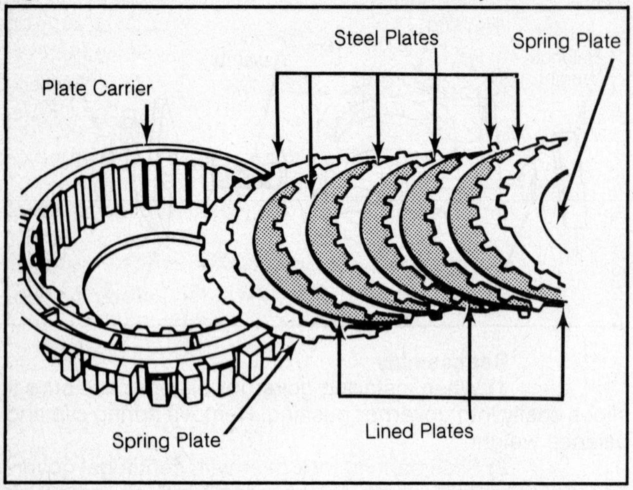

Be sure to install clutch "A" components in order.

CLUTCH "B"

Disassembly

1) Remove snap ring from center of clutch "B" housing. Remove steel and lined plates, noting number and arrangement of plates and discs for reassembly reference. Bend open lock plate and press down on diaphragm spring with Clutch Compressor (24 2 030) and remove snap ring. *See Fig. 14.*

Fig. 14: Removal of Clutch "B" Snap Ring

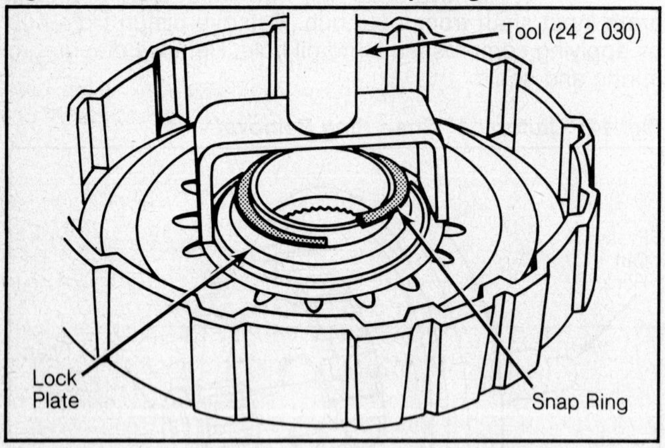

2) Remove piston from housing by applying compressed air to oil feed hole. Remove and discard seals and "O" rings.

Reassembly

1) Coat discs and plates with ATF. Replace all seals, "O" rings and lock plate. Position piston in housing and install diaphragm spring. Compress spring and install snap ring.

2) Alternate plates and discs until the number and position of plates and discs are installed as they were removed. *See Fig. 15.* Install end plate and large snap ring. Replace "O" ring and washer in center of housing.

CLUTCH C' & "C"

Disassembly

1) Insert assembly into a pipe with an inside diameter of 1.142" (29 mm) and clamp assembly in a vise. Remove centering plate. Remove outer disc (2 on some models), plates and 1-way clutch for brake C'. *See Fig. 16.*

Fig. 15: Exploded View of Clutch "B" Assembly

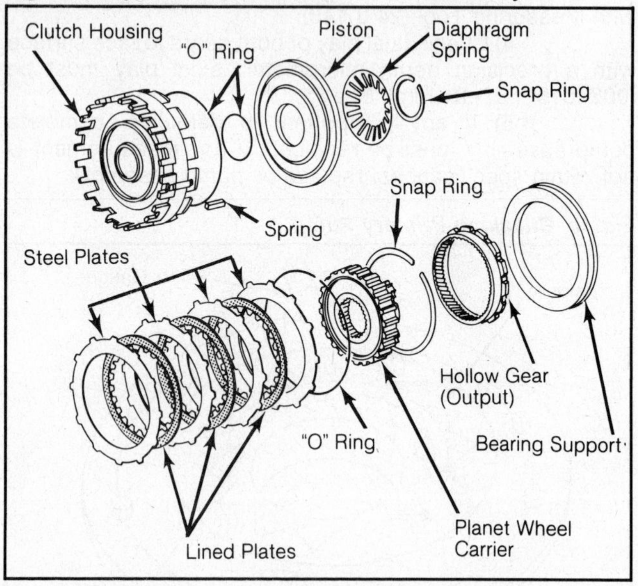

Note number and arrangement of plates and discs.

2) Remove brake C' snap ring (if equipped). Remove end plate, discs and plates, noting number and arrangement for reassembly reference.

Fig. 16: Brake C' One-Way Clutch and Plates

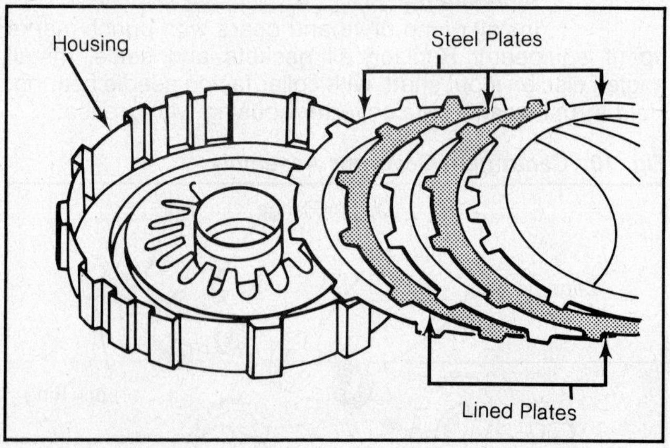

Note number and position of plates and discs.

3) Lift center support assembly off output shaft. Remove brake "D" snap ring. Remove end plate, discs and plates, noting number and arrangement for reassembly reference.

4) Place center support assembly on work bench. Using Clutch Compressor (24 2 030) compress diaphragm spring and remove split retaining ring. Turn assembly over and remove large snap ring. Remove diaphragm springs and place brake C' on bench and compress diaphragm. Remove split retaining ring.

5) Apply compressed air to respective oil input hole to remove brake pistons. Remove and discard piston "O" rings and seals. Replace with new "O" rings and seals.

Reassembly

1) Coat all discs and plates with ATF. Make sure all plates and discs are installed in proper sequence and number as when removed. See PLATE and DISC charts.

2) If discs or plates are replaced, soak new parts in warm ATF (160°F/70°C) for 20 minutes before installing.

Fig. 17: Exploded View of Clutch Plate "C" & "D"

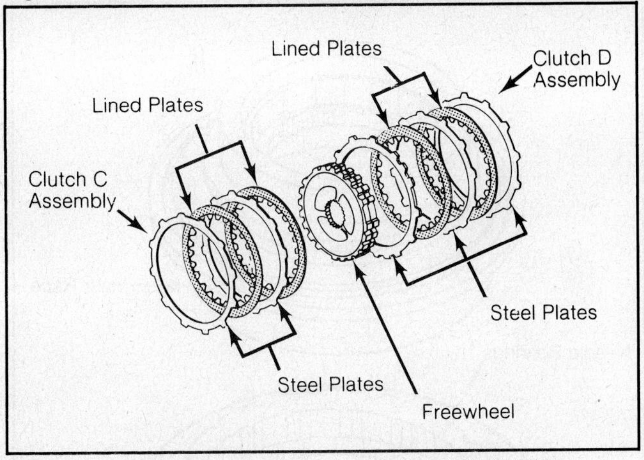

Note disc and plate sequence for brakes "C" & "D".

CLUTCH "D"

Disassembly

1) With clutches C' and "C" removed. Lift clutch member with "D" off of planet gear set. Remove snap ring and outer disc and lined plates. *See Fig. 18.*

2) Press down on diaphragm spring with Diaphragm Spring Compressor (24 2 030) and lift out snap ring. Press out clutch "D" piston with compressed air applied through oil bore. Discard "O" rings and seals.

Fig. 18: Exploded View of Clutch "D" Assembly

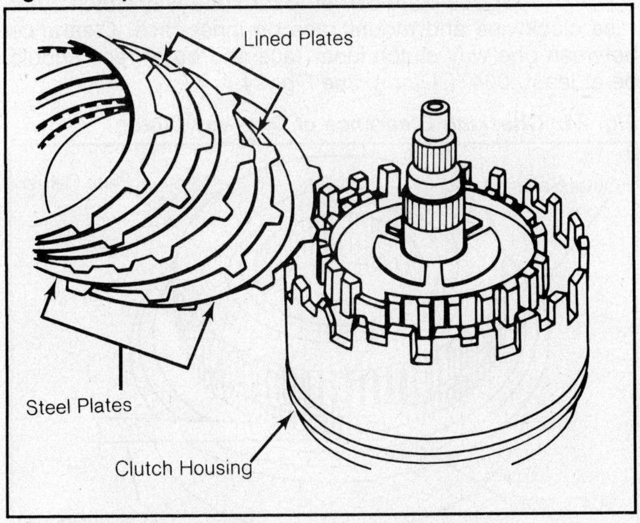

Note sequence of plates and disc for brake "D".

Reassembly

1) Insert diaphragm spring with curved surface facing up. Replace "O" rings and seals, lubricate "O" rings with a light coat of ATF.

2) Place planet plate with one-way clutch on hub of cylinder "D". If discs or plates are replaced, soak new parts in warm ATF (160°F/70°C) for 20 minutes before installing. *See Fig. 18.*

FRONT PLANETARY GEAR SET

Disassembly

1) Disassemble 1st planet gear assembly. Remove support ring for 2nd planet gear and remove 2nd planet gear assembly.

Fig. 19: Planet Gear Axial Bearing

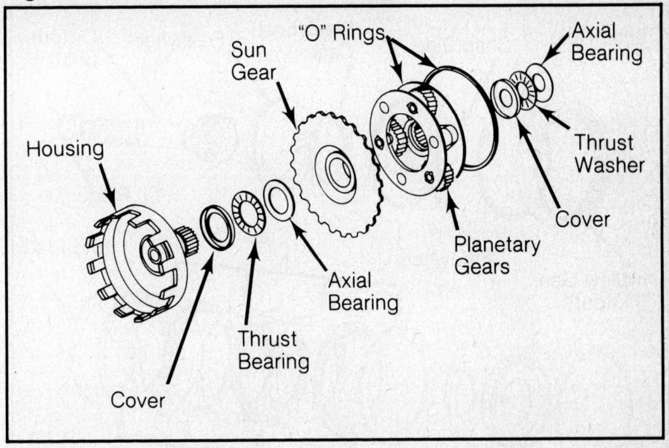

2) Pull out sun gear shaft. Remove axial bearing and input shaft thrust washer. Lift out input hollow gear snap ring. Remove input hollow gear and planet plate. *See Fig. 19.*

3) Remove output shaft thrust washer and axial bearing. Take off spacer and lift out snap ring. Take off output hollow gear. *See Fig. 20.*

Fig. 20: Output Shaft Thrust Washers

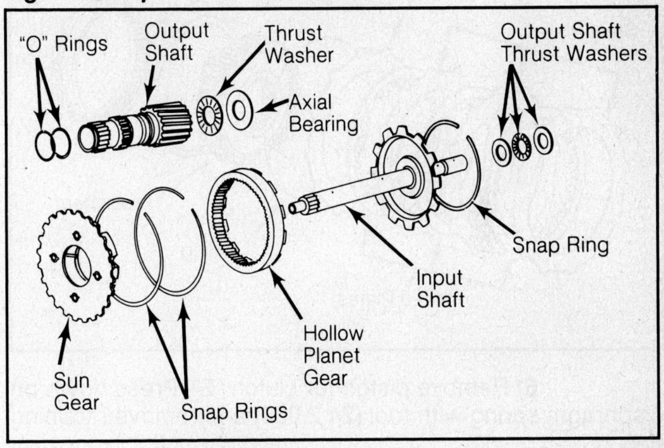

Reassembly

Replace any worn or scored parts. Mount support ring with fins facing down.

CLUTCHES "E" & "F"

Disassembly

1) Remove sun, planet and planet carrier. Remove angled washer, axial bearing and thrust washer. Lift clutch housing "F" off of clutch housing "E".

2) Lift off housing "E" on output shell. Take off thrust washer, axial bearing and steel/copper angled washer, keep components in order for reassembly. Remove snap ring out of clutch F housing. Remove clutch "F" plate set. *See Fig. 22.*

3) Remove piston for clutch "F". Press down on diaphragm spring with tool (24 2 020), and lift out split retaining ring.

4) Press out piston for clutch "F" with 2 mandrels. Remove clutch plates and discs in order for reassembly.

5) Remove snap ring from clutch "E" housing and remove clutch plate set. Keep components in order for reassembly. *See Fig. 21.*

ZF 4HP 22/EH (Cont.)

Fig. 21: Clutch "E" Assembly

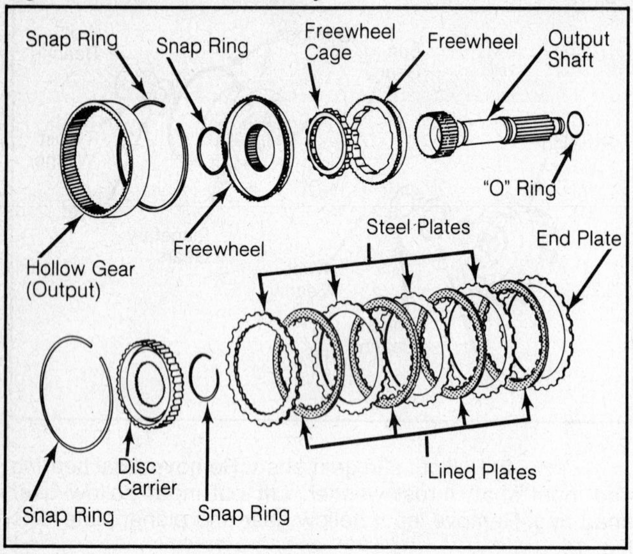

Fig. 22: Clutch "F" Assembly

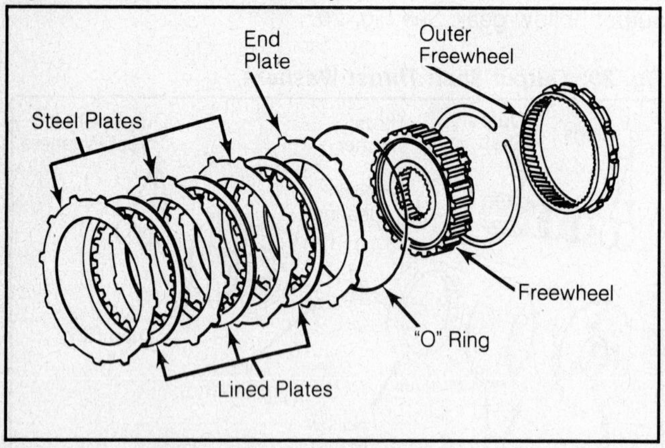

6) Remove piston for clutch "E". Press down on disphragm spring with tool (24 2 020) and remove retaining ring.

7) Lift off cover and press clutch "E" piston with compressed air applied through oil bore. Discard "O" rings and seal.

Reassembly

1) Replace all "O" rings and seals. Lubricate all components with ATF for ease of reassembly.

2) Insert diaphragm spring with curved surface facing up in clutch housing "E" and "F". Make sure all clutch plates and discs are installed in proper order.

3) Connect cylinders "E" and "F" by turning housing. Collar on output shaft must protrude by distance A = approx. .394" (10 mm).

ONE-WAY CLUCTCH

Disassembly & Reassembly

1) Lift out snap ring. Press output shaft from clutch unit. Lift off plate carrier. Carefully press one-way clutch cage out of outer race. Be careful, needle bearings can jump out of cage. *See Fig. 23.*

2) Place one-way clutch cage on outer race and align. Press in one-way clutch cage against stop and then turn until metal edge engages in holding groove of outer race.

Fig. 23: One-Way Clutch

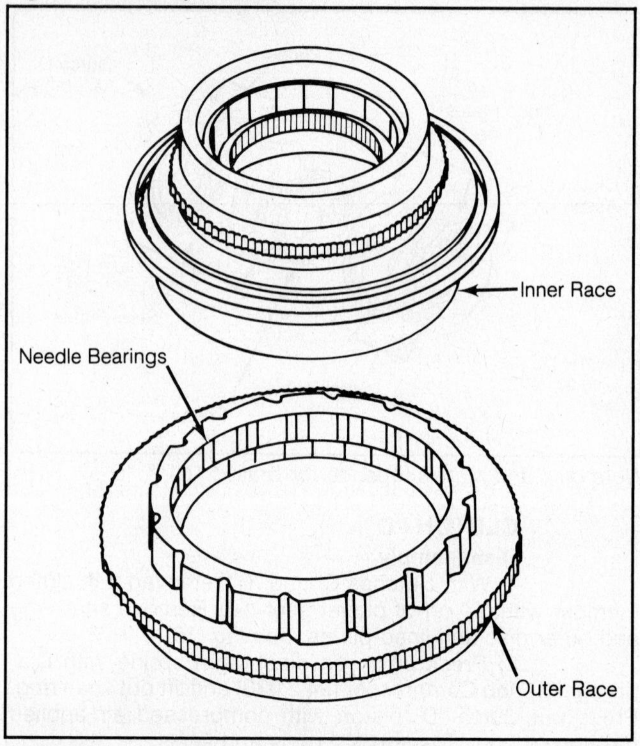

Be careful not to lose needle bearings.

3) Use plate carrier to turn one-way clutch outer race clockwise and mount race on inner race. Clearance between one-way clutch inner race and outer race should be at least .004" (.1 mm). *See Fig. 24.*

Fig. 24: Checking Clearance of One-Way Clutch

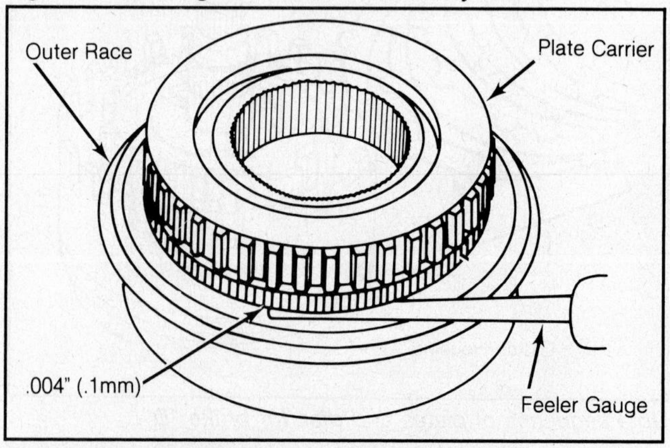

Check clearance between inner and outer race

REAR PLANETARY GEAR

Disassembly

1) Place output shaft in a support with output shaft facing down. Remove one-way clutch and front planetary gear set. Remove sun gear shaft. Remove large snap ring and lift off ring gear. Lift off rear planetary gear set.

2) Remove intermediate shaft from output shaft housing. Remove roller bearing and washer from output shaft housing and intermediate shaft. Remove large snap ring holding input ring gear to intermediate shaft. Remove washers and bearing. Remove other large snap ring.

ZF 4HP 22/EH (Cont.)

PLATE & DISC USAGE CHART

Application	No. of Plates
All BMW Models	
Clutch A	
Spacer Plates	2
Discs	6
Plates	5
Clutch B	
End Plate	1
Discs	4
Plates	4
Clutch C	
Discs	2
Plates	2
End Plate	1
Brake C'	
Discs	2
Plates	2
End Plate	1
Brake D	
End Plate	1
Discs	4
Plates	4
Brake E	
Discs	4
Plates	4
End Plate	1
Brake F	
Discs	4
Plates	4
End Plates	1

Fig. 25: Exploded Veiw of Rear Plantery Gear Assembly

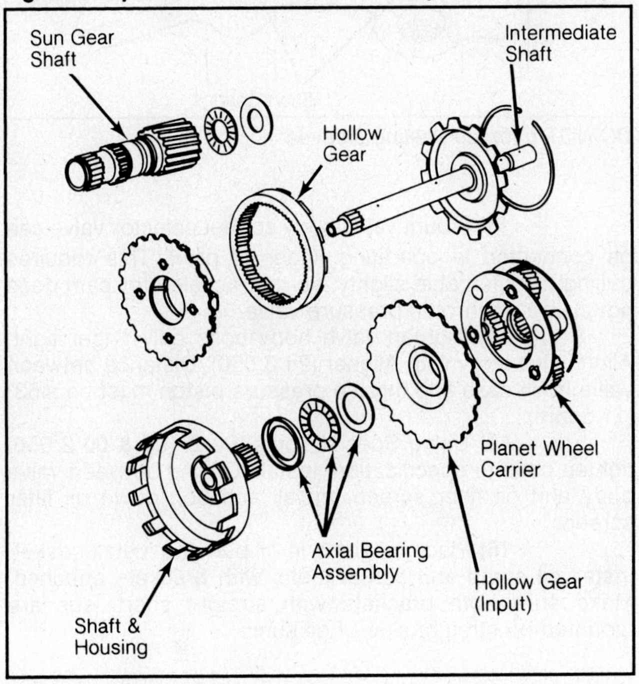

Reassembly

Ensure large snap rings are on both sides of input ring gear when assembled to intermediate shaft. When installing mainshaft to output shaft, place washer onto output shaft first, then the roller bearing. Make sure all snap rings are properly installed and fully seated.

VALVE BODY ASSEMBLY

NOTE: Valve body disassembly is not recommended. If a valve body malfunction is determined, replace valve body.

Fig. 26: Valve Body Assemblies

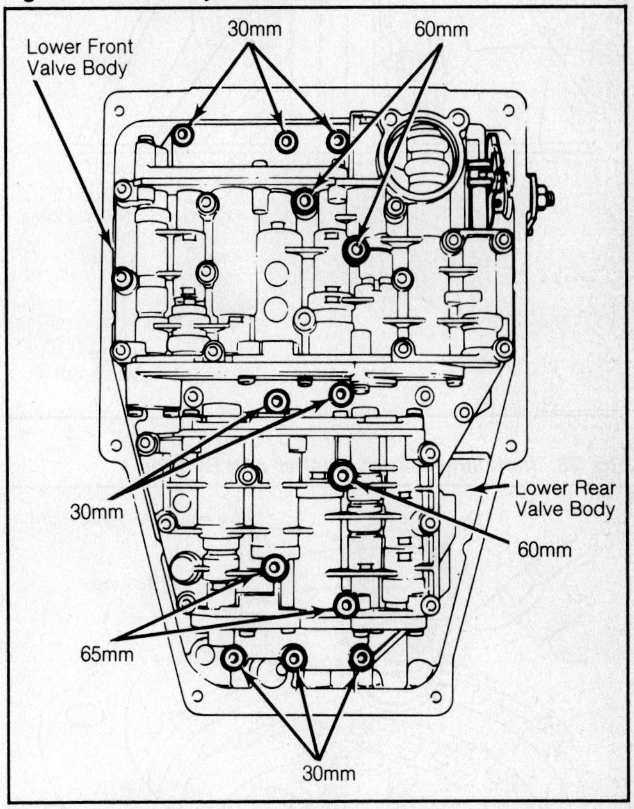

DO NOT disassemble valve bodies, replace as a unit

TRANSMISSION REASSEMBLY

1) Install 4th gear clutch set. Guide clutch set into transmission case so that 4 oil feed bores are aligned with bores in case. Bolt down clutch set with Clutch Assemblers (00 2 100 & 00 2 050). Tighten to specifications.

2) Set transmission upright. Insert thrust washer, axial bearing and angled washer with collar facing up.

3) Place entire gear set into case. Align 4 oil feed bores with bores in case. Springs must be in center of cylinder groove. *See Fig. 27.*

4) Insert clutch "B" snap ring into case. Insert and push clutch "B" against stop. Install seal, support and snap ring. Insert plate carrier and thrust washer and axial bearing. *See Fig. 28.*

5) Using white grease, paste angled washer on cylinder "A". Insert clutch A and move it back and forth until splines of plate carrier and plates mesh.

6) Install angled washer with collar facing up and install axial bearing. Using white grease, paste on gasket and thrust washer. Install converter bellhousing and tighten all bolts to specification.

7) Check axial play of input shaft. Mount Input Shaft Holder (24 0 010) to hold input shaft. Attach Dial

ZF 4HP 22/EH (Cont.)

Fig. 27: Aligning Oil Feed Holes

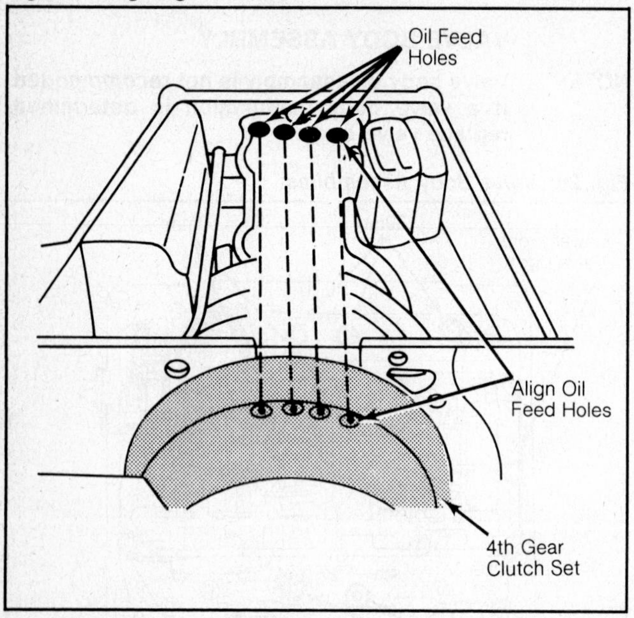

Fig. 28: Installing Thrust Washer and Bearing

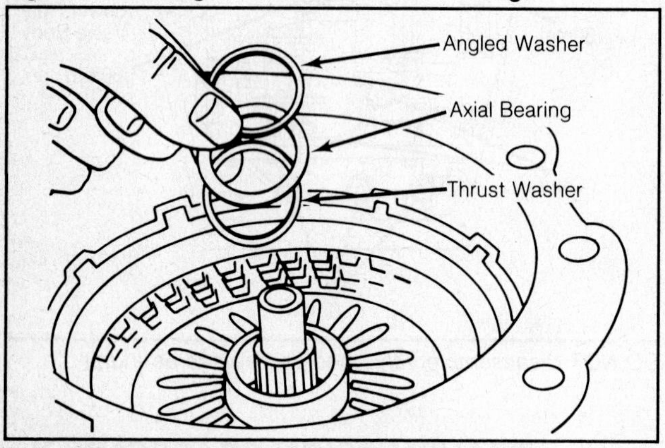

Be sure collar of angled washer faces up.

Fig. 29: Checking Axial Play of Input Shaft

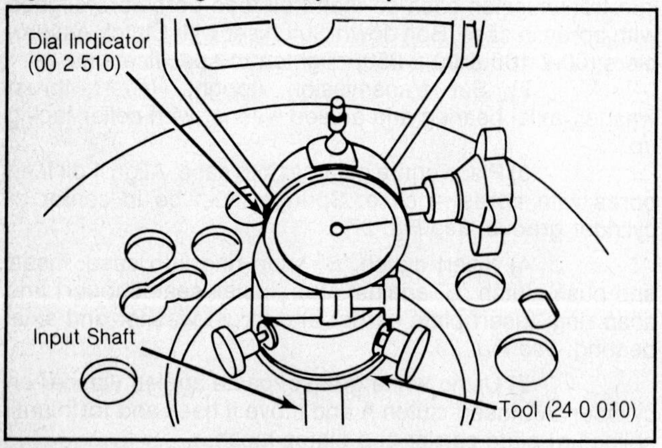

Check axial play by pulling on input shaft.

Indicator Gauge (00 2 510). Check axial play by pulling on input shaft. Clearance should be .008"-.016" (.2-.4 mm). *See Fig. 29.*

8) If play deviates, take off converter bell housing again and replace thrust washer with a thicker or thinner one. Recheck axial play. Tighten down converter bell housing to specification. Remove Input Shaft Holder (24 1 010).

9) Install parking lock pawl. Attach return spring in bore of pawl. Lubricate "O" ring with ATF. Push on parking lock gear and governor.

10) Using white grease, place gasket on transmission extension housing. Install housing to transmission and tighten to specification.

11) Install output flange. Install collar nut and using Output Flange Holder (23 0 020) hold output flange. Using Collar Nut Wrench (23 1 210), tighten collar nut. Install lock plate and lock in groove.

12) Install 8 sealing sleeves into valve body. Being careful not to damage sealing sleeves, press in sealing sleeves against stop. Install 8 springs and 8 circlips. Use longer springs to face cylinder "F". *See Fig. 30.*

Fig. 30: Sleeve & Spring Locations

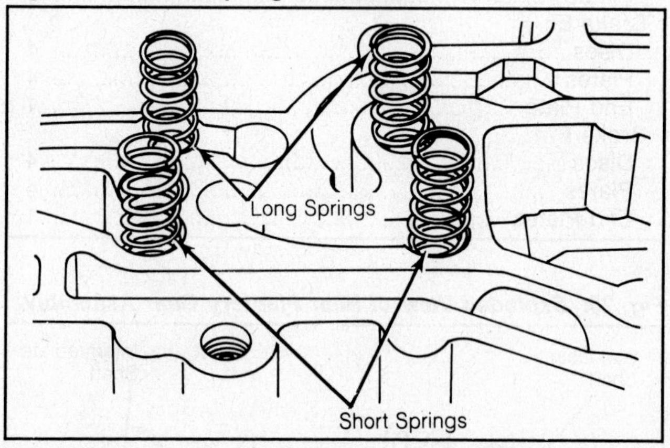

DO NOT damage sealing sleeves

13) Mount valve body so that selector valve can be connected in operating finger of pawl. This requires pulling throttle cable slighty, so that accelerator cam does not clamp on throttle pressure valve.

14) Tighten valve body bolts only finger tight. Align valve body with Aligner (24 3 050). Distance between valve body case and throttle pressure piston must be .453" (11.5 mm).

15) Using Special Tools (00 2 100 & 00 2 050) tighten bolts to specification. Install "O" ring between valve body and oil filter screen. Install and bolt down oil filter screen.

16) Place magnets in oil pan and install gasket. Install oil sump and tighten bolts with brackets attached. Make sure both brackets with straight short legs are mounted on straight side of oil sump.

ZF 4HP 22/EH (Cont.)

Fig. 31: Electrical Diagram For ZF 4 HP 22/EH Transmission

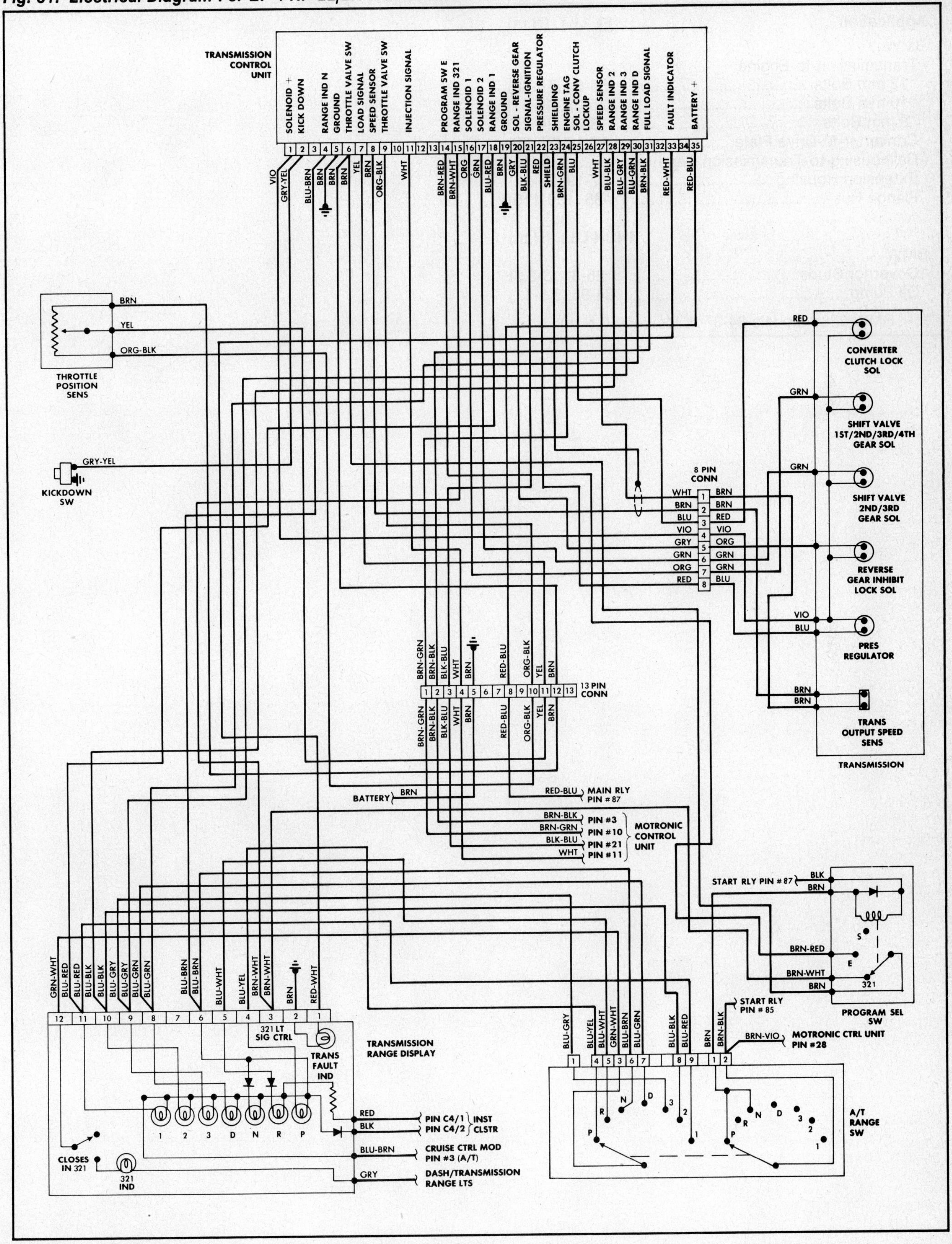

Automatic Transmissions

ZF 4HP 22/EH (Cont.)

TIGHTENING SPECIFICATIONS

Application	Ft. Lbs. (N.m)
BMW	
Transmission-to-Engine	
12 mm Bolts	56-64 (78-88)
10 mm Bolts	[1] 35-38 (48-51)
8 mm Bolts	18-20 (24-27)
Converter-to-Drive Plate	17-19 (23-26)
Bellhousing-to-Transmission Case	33 (46)
Extension Housing	17-19 (23-26)
Flange Nut	74-85 (100-115)
	INCH Lbs. (N.m)
BMW	
Governor Studs	26-31 (3-3.5)
Oil Pump	84-96 (9.5-11)

[1] – BMW 528e models 34-37 ft. lbs. (46-50 N.m).

SECTION 7

IMPORT MANUAL TRANSMISSIONS

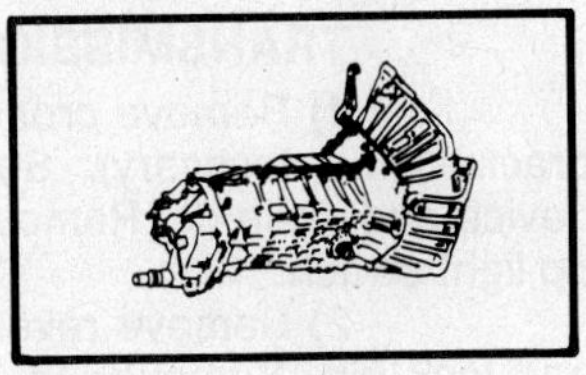

NOTE: ALSO SEE GENERAL INDEX.

Manual Transmission

BMW GETRAG 240 5-SPEED

318i

DESCRIPTION

The Getreg Model 240 5-speed transmission is fully synchronized, and uses constant mesh, helical-cut forward gears, and non-synchronized, helical-cut reverse gears. Shifting is accomplished through 3 shift rails and forks. Transmission case is of 2-piece design.

LUBRICATION & ADJUSTMENT

See appropriate MANUAL TRANSMISSION SERVICING article in IMPORT GENERAL SERVICING section.

TROUBLE SHOOTING

See MANUAL TRANSMISSION TROUBLE SHOOTING article in IMPORT GENERAL SERVICING section.

SERVICE (IN VEHICLE)

OUTPUT FLANGE & SELECTOR SHAFT SEALS

Removal

1) Disconnect propeller shaft from output flange and center support mount. Remove output flange lock plate. Install Special Tool (23 1 200) and hold output flange with Special Tool (23 0 020). Remove collar nut with Special Socket (23 1 210). Pull off output flange using Special Tool (33 1 150). Using a screwdriver, pry out output flange radial oil seal.

2) To remove shift selector shaft oil seal, remove shift selector shaft locking sleeve. Drive shift selector shaft retainer pin upwards and remove shift selector shaft. Using an ice pick, pry out shift selector shaft oil seal.

Installation

To install, reverse removal procedure. Lubricate lips of radial seals with grease. Install shift selector shaft oil seal using Special Tool (23 1 240). Install output flange radial oil seal using Special Tool (23 1 260).

REMOVAL & INSTALLATION

TRANSMISSION

See appropriate MANUAL TRANSMISSION REMOVAL article in IMPORT GENERAL SERVICING section.

TRANSMISSION DISASSEMBLY

TRANSMISSION CASE

1) Remove crossmember and exhaust support bracket (if necessary). Secure transmission in holding device and drain oil. Remove guide sleeve. Unscrew back up light switch.

2) Remove reverse lock-out detent cap, spring and lock pin. Remove input shaft snap ring and washer. Remove reverse gear selector arm retainer bolt.

Fig. 1: Exploded View of Getreg 240 5-Speed Transmission

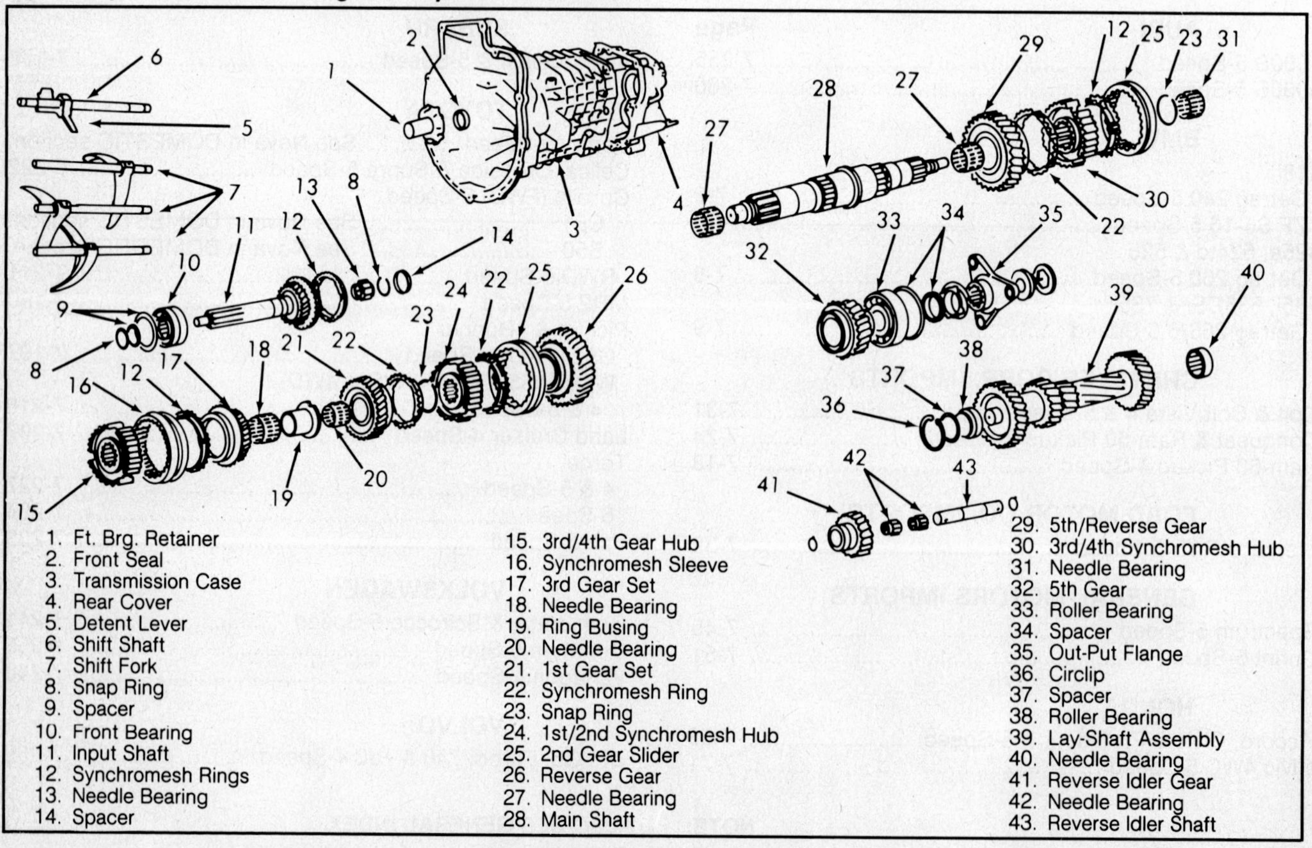

1. Ft. Brg. Retainer
2. Front Seal
3. Transmission Case
4. Rear Cover
5. Detent Lever
6. Shift Shaft
7. Shift Fork
8. Snap Ring
9. Spacer
10. Front Bearing
11. Input Shaft
12. Synchromesh Rings
13. Needle Bearing
14. Spacer
15. 3rd/4th Gear Hub
16. Synchromesh Sleeve
17. 3rd Gear Set
18. Needle Bearing
19. Ring Busing
20. Needle Bearing
21. 1st Gear Set
22. Synchromesh Ring
23. Snap Ring
24. 1st/2nd Synchromesh Hub
25. 2nd Gear Slider
26. Reverse Gear
27. Needle Bearing
28. Main Shaft
29. 5th/Reverse Gear
30. 3rd/4th Synchromesh Hub
31. Needle Bearing
32. 5th Gear
33. Roller Bearing
34. Spacer
35. Out-Put Flange
36. Circlip
37. Spacer
38. Roller Bearing
39. Lay-Shaft Assembly
40. Needle Bearing
41. Reverse Idler Gear
42. Needle Bearing
43. Reverse Idler Shaft

3) Drive forward the transmission rear housing locating pins. Remove transmission rear housing bolts. Pull off front transmission housing section.

Reassembly

1) To reassemble, reverse disassembly procedure. Install reverse gear roller bearing on layshaft so that small diameter end of bearing faces up.

2) Coat transmission front section in area of reverse gear shaft with Loctite (573). Surface must be thoroughly clean and dried of oil.

NOTE: **When installing reverse lock-out detent pin make sure that pin seats into the selector shaft groove.**

TRANSMISSION GEAR ASSEMBLIES

1) Remove transmission case front section. Remove output flange lock plate and collar nut using Special Tools (23 1 200, 23 0 020 and 23 1 210). Remove output flange using Special Tool (33 1 150).

2) Remove counter shaft gear bolt, holder and counter shaft retainer bolt. Remove countershaft with reverse gear and needle bearing. Remove operating lever retainer pin.

3) Pull out reverse gear selector rail. Engage 4th gear and drive in shift detent lever retainer pin.

NOTE: **Only drive in shift detent lever retainer pin far enough so that selector shaft can be pulled back and out.**

4) Pull out shift selector shaft, be careful not to loose rollers on shaft. Remove shift rail retainer plate. Carefully remove the shift rods 3 detent plugs and springs.

5) Drive out 3rd/4th shift fork retainer pin. Pull 3rd/4th shift rod forward. Engage 2nd/Reverse by pushing 1st/2nd and 5th/Reverse selector rods forward.

6) Using Special Tool (23 1 050), press out input shaft, output shaft and layshaft from rear case section. Be careful not to clamp selector rods and layshaft while pressing out components.

NOTE: **To avoid damage on sealing surface, use a piece of wood, aluminum or similar material between claws and sealing surface.**

CLEANING & INSPECTION

COUNTERSHAFT

Check shaft and gears for wear or damage. Lightly polish any scoring from shaft surfaces.

REVERSE IDLER GEAR & SHAFT

Inspect components for wear or damage and replace if necessary.

SYNCHROMESH ASSEMBLIES

Check all parts for wear or damage. Blocking rings must be replaced if tapered clutch surface is pitted or excessively worn. Place each synchromesh ring into position on its respective gear. Using a feeler gauge, measure clearance between ring and gear. If clearance is less than .040" (1 mm), replace synchromesh ring.

COMPONENT DISASSEMBLY & REASSEMBLY

MAINSHAFT

Disassembly

1) Remove input shaft, synchromesh blocking ring and needle bearing off mainshaft. Remove 5th gear, brass synchromesh ring and needle bearing. Remove circlip and spacer from inside of 5th gear operating sleeve.

2) Using Special Press Plate Tool (23 1 490), press off 3rd gear with guide, operating sleeve and needle bearing. Using Special Press Plate Tool (23 1 490), press off 2nd gear. Remove 2nd gear nickle-plated synchromesh ring and needle bearing.

3) Remove 1st gear circlip. Using Special Press Plate Tool (23 1 490), press off 1st gear, operating sleeve and needle bearing. Remove reverse gear circlip and press off reverse gear, guide, operating sleeve and needle bearing.

Reassembly

NOTE: **Allways replace circlips during reassembly.**

1) Install output shaft next to collar. Install needle bearing, reverse gear, brass synchromesh ring with coat of Molybdenum grease. Press on guide sleeve to fit tight with Special Tool (23 1 290). Make sure tabs on synchromesh ring are aligned with openings in guide sleeve while installing.

2) Move operating sleeve in direction of reverse gear. Adjust guide sleeve with circlip to take up all play. Adjust play between circlip and guide sleeve to .0035" (.09 mm). Install needle bearing, 1st gear and nickle-plated synchromesh ring.

NOTE: **Circlips are available in different thickness .067-.079" (1.7-2.0 mm).**

3) Install 2nd gear needle bearing and nickle-plated synchromesh ring. Collar for bearing sleeve on output shaft must protrude slightly, if necessary check circlip for proper fit.

4) Heat bearing sleeve to approximately 175°F (80°C) and install on output shaft. Install needle bearing, 3rd gear and nickle-plated synchromesh ring. Install guide and operating sleeve on spline with groove facing 4th gear. To complete reassembly, reverse disassembly procedure.

SYNCHROMESH ASSEMBLIES

Disassembly

Remove blocking ring, and push hub from sleeve. Separate inserts and insert springs from hub.

Inspection

Check all parts for wear or damage. Blocking rings must be replaced if tapered clutch surface is pitted or excessively worn. Place each synchromesh ring into position on its respective gear. Using a feeler gauge, measure clearance between ring and gear. If clearance is less than .040" (1 mm), replace synchromesh ring.

Reassembly

Evenly stagger hooks of insert springs in notches in hub. Install inserts and push sleeve over hub. Install blocking ring on hub and install synchromesh on mating gear.

Manual Transmission

BMW GETRAG 240 5-SPEED (Cont.)

COUNTERSHAFT

Disassembly

Pull bearing off front of countershaft, and press off 4th gear. Remove snap ring and press off 3rd gear. Remove rear snap rings, making note of shims. Pull outer bearing off rear of countershaft, and press off 5th gear. Pull off inner bearing.

Inspection

Check shaft and gears for wear or damage. Lightly polish any scoring from shaft surfaces.

Reassembly

To assemble, reverse disassembly procedure. Heat gears to 250-300°F (120-150°C) when installing gears on shaft.

REVERSE IDLER GEAR & SHAFT

Disassembly

Remove end plate. Unscrew hex bolt while holding shaft at front. Remove bolt and washers. Install a bolt in tapped bore and push out assembly towards rear. Separate needle bearing and gear from shaft.

Inspection

Inspect components for wear or damage and replace if necessary.

Reassembly

Reverse disassembly procedure using Loctite (or equivalent) on holding bolt.

TRANSMISSION REASSEMBLY

GEAR & SHAFT CONTROL ASSEMBLIES

1) Install mainshaft and countershaft assemblies in intermediate transmission case. Install appropriate shim, heat bearing race to about 175°F (80°C) and push onto mainshaft. Press needle bearing and reverse gear onto mainshaft. Slide 5th gear synchromesh assembly onto mainshaft.

2) Push 5th/Reverse shift rod up to spring in transmission case from input shaft end. Insert locking balls and press down, pushing rod on through to lock.

3) Insert 5th/Reverse shift fork in sliding sleeve. Install sleeve on mainshaft with pins facing out. Guide 5th/Reverse shift fork onto rod and drive in a .24 x .94" (6 x 24 mm) pin.

4) Drive sleeve against stop on mainshaft spline. Heat bearing race to about 175°F (80°C) and push on mainshaft to sleeve. Install synchromesh blocking ring, needle bearing and 5th gear onto mainshaft.

5) Install inner roller bearing and 5th countergear on countershaft. Using appropriate driver, drive bearing race onto countershaft.

6) Measure distance between spacer and bearing race and take up countershaft end play with appropriate shims. Install locking snap ring with .20 x 1" (5 x 26 mm) pin on countershaft.

7) Install washer with bevelled side out on mainshaft. Heat speedometer gear and push onto mainshaft. Install 1st/2nd and 3rd/4th shift forks. Push in 3rd/4th shift rod through shift fork to spring.

8) Insert locating ball and locking ball and press down. Push 3rd/4th shift rod on through to lock making sure that opening on shift rod faces 5th/Reverse shift rod. Drive in retainer pin.

9) Push in 1st/2nd shift rod through fork to spring in transmission case. Install driving dog. Install locating ball and locking ball and press down. Push 1st/2nd shift rod on through to lock and drive in retainer pin.

10) Push in upper selector rod with opening facing out. Install selector arm with long side facing 3rd/4th shift rod.

11) Install lower selector rod with opening facing up. Install operating lever with sharp edge facing up and push in rod.

12) Install bolt in top of transmission case with Loctite (or equivalent) making sure that center engages bore of operating lever. Test operating lever for ease of movement. Push clamp onto lower selector rod with bevelled side facing shift fork.

13) Install bolt in side of transmission case with Loctite (240) making sure that center engages groove in lower selector rod. Hold 4 rollers on selector rod with grease.

TIGHTENING SPECIFICATIONS

Application	Ft. Lbs. (N.m)
Crossmember	16-17 (22-23)
Propeller Shaft Flange Nut	72 (98)
Rear Seal Flange Bolts	7 (9.5)
Rubber Mount	32-35 (43-47)
Transmission Cover Plate Bolts	
Front & Rear	18 (24)
Trans. Rear Cover-to-Trans. Case	16-17 (22-23)
Transmission-to-Engine (or Clutch Hsg.)	
8 mm Bolts	18-19 (24-26)
10 mm Bolts	35-37 (47-50)
12 mm Bolts	54-60 (72-80)

Manual Transmissions

BMW 325e, 524td & 528e

DESCRIPTION

The Getrag Model 260 5-speed transmission is fully synchronized, and uses constant mesh, helical gears in forward speeds, and non-synchronized, helical reverse gears. Shifting is accomplished through 3 shift rails and forks. Transmission case is of 3-section design.

LUBRICATION & ADJUSTMENT

See appropriate MANUAL TRANSMISSION SERVICING article in IMPORT GENERAL SERVICING section.

TROUBLE SHOOTING

See MANUAL TRANSMISSION TROUBLE SHOOTING article in IMPORT GENERAL SERVICING section.

SERVICE (IN VEHICLE)

OUTPUT FLANGE & SECTOR SHAFT OIL SEAL

Removal

1) Remove complete exhaust system. Install Special Strap Tool (26 1 011) on the Guibo coupling. This strap is used for removal and installation of propeller shaft to prevent stress in the Guibo coupling.

Fig. 1: Exploded View of Getrag 260 5-Speed Transmission

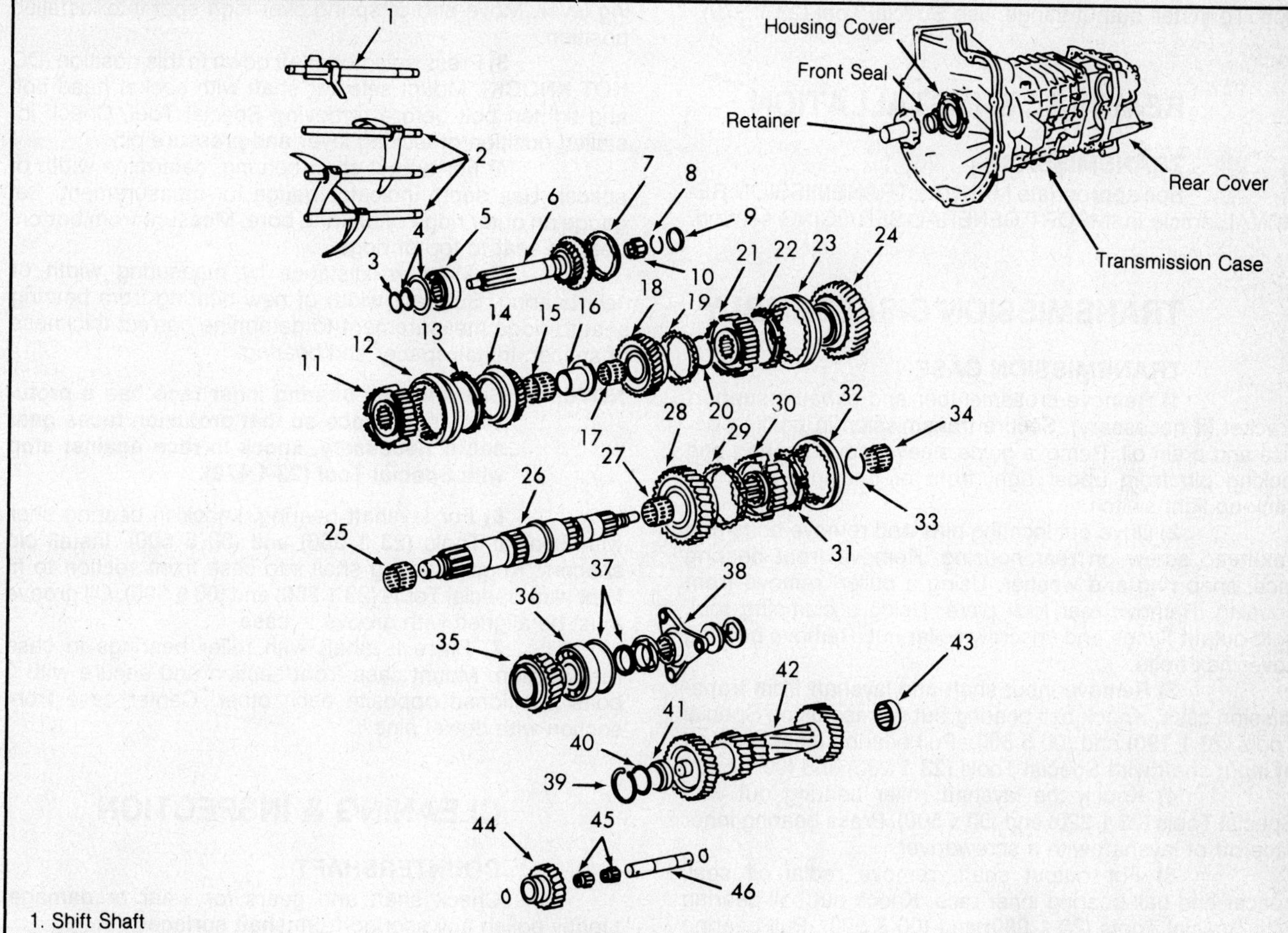

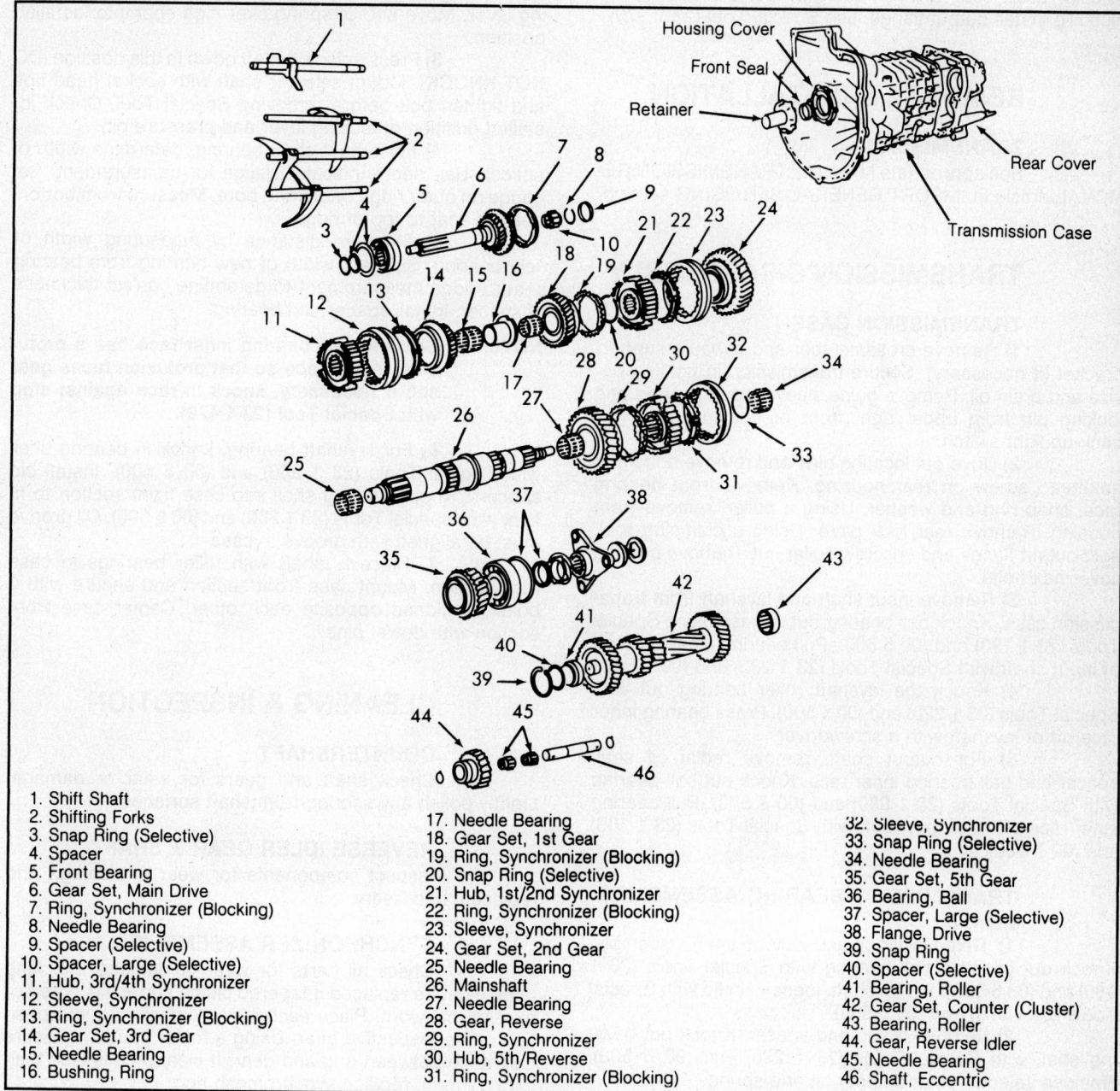

1. Shift Shaft
2. Shifting Forks
3. Snap Ring (Selective)
4. Spacer
5. Front Bearing
6. Gear Set, Main Drive
7. Ring, Synchronizer (Blocking)
8. Needle Bearing
9. Spacer (Selective)
10. Spacer, Large (Selective)
11. Hub, 3rd/4th Synchronizer
12. Sleeve, Synchronizer
13. Ring, Synchronizer (Blocking)
14. Gear Set, 3rd Gear
15. Needle Bearing
16. Bushing, Ring
17. Needle Bearing
18. Gear Set, 1st Gear
19. Ring, Synchronizer (Blocking)
20. Snap Ring (Selective)
21. Hub, 1st/2nd Synchronizer
22. Ring, Synchronizer (Blocking)
23. Sleeve, Synchronizer
24. Gear Set, 2nd Gear
25. Needle Bearing
26. Mainshaft
27. Needle Bearing
28. Gear, Reverse
29. Ring, Synchronizer
30. Hub, 5th/Reverse
31. Ring, Synchronizer (Blocking)
32. Sleeve, Synchronizer
33. Snap Ring (Selective)
34. Needle Bearing
35. Gear Set, 5th Gear
36. Bearing, Ball
37. Spacer, Large (Selective)
38. Flange, Drive
39. Snap Ring
40. Spacer (Selective)
41. Bearing, Roller
42. Gear Set, Counter (Cluster)
43. Bearing, Roller
44. Gear, Reverse Idler
45. Needle Bearing
46. Shaft, Eccentric

BMW 325e, 524td & 528e (Cont.)

2) Tighten Special Strap Tool (26 1 011) until bolts can be pulled out by hand. Remove strap. Remove lower heat shield attached to rear transmission mount bracket. Remove center bearing bracket. Pull propeller shaft down and out of the way.

3) Support rear of transmission and remove transmission mount bracket. Install Special Tool (23 1 200). Counterhold output flange with Special Tool (23 1 150). Unscrew collared nut with Special Tool (23 1 210). Remove output flange. Remove radial oil seal with Special Tool (00 5 000).

4) With output flange removed, engage 1st gear. Lift out selector shaft lock sleeve and drive out retaining pin (upward). Using an ice pick, pry out radial oil seal.

Installation

To install, reverse removal procedure. Fill output flange and selector shaft seals with grease. To install selector shaft seal, drive in using proper sized length of pipe. To install output flange, use Special Tool (23 1 370).

REMOVAL & INSTALLATION

TRANSMISSION

See appropriate MANUAL TRANSMISSION REMOVAL article in IMPORT GENERAL SERVICING section.

TRANSMISSION DISASSEMBLY

TRANSMISSION CASE

1) Remove crossmember and exhaust support bracket (if necessary). Secure transmission in holding device and drain oil. Remove guide sleeve, cover, spring and locking pin from upper right front of housing. Unscrew back-up light switch.

2) Drive out locating pins and remove bolts and hex-head screw on rear housing. Remove front bearing race, snap ring and washer. Using a puller, remove front housing. Remove rear lock plate. Using a clamping tool, hold output flange and unscrew collar nut. Remove bearing cover hex bolts.

3) Remove input shaft and layshaft from transmission case. Knock ball bearing out of case using Special Tools (23 1 190) and (00 5 500). Pull bearing inner race off of input shaft with Special Tools (23 1 230) and (00 7 500).

4) Knock the layshaft roller bearing out with Special Tools (23 1 220) and (00 5 500). Press bearing inner race off of layshaft with a screwdriver.

5) For output shaft, remove radial oil seal, spacer and ball bearing inner race. Knock out ball bearing with Special Tools (23 1 080) and (00 5 500). Pull bearing inner race off of output shaft with Special Tools (23 1 100) and (00 7 500).

TRANSMISSION BEARING ASSEMBLIES

Removal

1) Remove input and output shaft assembly. Knock out grooved ball bearing with Special Tools (23 1 480) and (00 5 500). For layshaft, loosen circlip with Special Tools (23 1 270) and (00 5 500).

2) Remove circlip and spacer. Knock out bearing shell with Special Tools (23 1 270) and (00 5 500). Remove selector shaft detent bolt and spring.

3) Install Special Tool (23 1 250) to remove the selector shaft. Remove socket head bolt. Remove selector shaft from above.

4) Remove output shaft bearing holder. Locking lever should remain on holder. Remove radial seal. Knock out grooved ball bearing with Special Tools (23 1 120) and (00 5 500).

5) To remove layshaft bearing, install Special Tool (23 1 280) with thickerend inserted in the bearing shell. Install Special Tool (33 4 020) and screw in Special Tool (23 1 300). Pull out bearing shell.

Installation

1) For layshaft, knock in bearing shell with Special Tools (23 1 260) and (00 5 500). Determine axial play by using a dial gauge and holder. Install dial gauge so that tip is on tooth of layshaft.

2) Insert selector shaft with Special Tool (23 1 250). Swing selector shaft outwards with roller above locking lever. Move end of spring over high spot into installed position.

3) Press selector shaft down in this position (DO NOT KNOCK). Mount selector shaft with socket head bolt and tighten bolt before removing Special Tool. Check installed position of locking lever and pressure pin.

4) For output shaft bearing, determine width of spacer. Use depth indicator gauge for measurement. Set gauge on outer ridge of bearing bore. Measure from bottom bearing seat to top of ridge.

5) Measure distance by measuring width of new bearing. Subtract width of new bearing from bearing seat-to-ridge measurement to determine correct thickness of spacer. Install spacer and bearing.

NOTE: Grooved ball bearing inner race has a protusion. Install race so that protusion faces gear set. If necessary, knock in race against stop with Special Tool (23 1 470).

6) For layshaft bearing, knock in bearing shell with Special Tools (23 1 260) and (00 5 500). Install old spacers. Knock bearing shell into case front section to fit tight with Special Tools (23 1 260) and (00 5 500). Oil groove must be aligned with groove in case.

7) Place layshaft with roller bearings in case rear section. Mount case front section and secure with 2 bolts positioned opposite each other. Center case front section with dowel pins.

CLEANING & INSPECTION

COUNTERSHAFT

Check shaft and gears for wear or damage. Lightly polish any scoring from shaft surfaces.

REVERSE IDLER GEAR & SHAFT

Inspect components for wear or damage and replace if necessary.

SYNCHRONIZER ASSEMBLIES

Check all parts for wear or damage. Blocking rings must be replaced if tapered clutch surface is pitted or excessively worn. Place each synchromesh ring into position on its respective gear. Using a feeler gauge, measure clearance between ring and gear. If clearance is less than .040" (1 mm), replace synchromesh ring.

BMW 325e, 524td & 528e (Cont.)

COMPONENT DISASSEMBLY & REASSEMBLY

MAINSHAFT

Disassembly

1) With gear assembly removed from transmission, pull off input shaft, synchromesh ring and needle bearing. Pull off thrust washer, 5th gear, synchromesh ring and needle bearing. Remove circlip and spacer.

2) Press off 3rd gear with guide sleeve and operating sleeve, using Special Tool (23 1 490). Remove needle bearing. Press off bearing bushing and 2nd gear with Special Tool (23 1 490).

3) Remove needle bearing and synchromesh ring (nickle plated). Remove circlip before pressing off the 1st gear. Press off 1st gear, guide sleeve and operating sleeve with Special Tool (23 1 490).

4) Remove needle bearing. Remove reverse gear circlip and press off reverse gear. Press guide sleeve, operating sleeve and reverse gear off of ouput shaft. Remove needle bearing.

Reassembly

1) Mount needle bearing, reverse gear and brass synchromesh ring. Slide guide sleeve and operating sleeve on spline of output shaft. Press on guide sleeve to fit tight with Special Tool (23 1 290).

NOTE: **When pressing on make sure tabs on synchromesh ring are aligned with openings in guide sleeve.**

2) Switch operating sleeve in direction of reverse gear. Adjust guide sleeve to be without play using circlip. Install circlip.

3) Mount needle bearing, 1st gear and nickel plated synchromesh ring. Slide guide sleeve and operating sleeve on spline of output shaft. Press on guide sleeve to fit tight with Special Tool (23 1 290). When pressing on make sure tabs on synchromesh ring are aligned with openings in guide sleeve.

4) Switch operating sleeve in direction of 1st gear. Adjust guide sleeve to be without play. Install circlip. Mount needle bearing, nickel plated synchromesh ring and 2nd gear. The collar for the bearing bushing on ouput shaft must project a little. Check circlip for proper seating.

5) Heat bearing bushing to about 175°F (80°C) and install on output shaft. Mount needle bearing, 3rd gear and brass synchromesh ring. Place guide sleeve and operating sleeve on spline with long collar facing 3rd gear.

6) Press guide sleeve to fit tight with Special Tool (23 1 290). When pressing on, make sure tabs on synchromesh ring are aligned with openings in guide sleeve. Install spacer and circlip.

SYNCHRONIZER ASSEMBLIES

Disassembly

Remove blocking ring, and push hub from sleeve. Separate inserts and insert springs from hub.

Inspection

Check all parts for wear or damage. Blocking rings must be replaced if tapered clutch surface is pitted or excessively worn. Place each synchromesh ring into position on its respective gear. Using a feeler gauge, measure clearance between ring and gear. If clearance is less than .040" (1 mm), replace synchromesh ring.

Reassembly

Evenly stagger hooks of insert springs in notches in hub. Install inserts and push sleeve over hub. Install blocking ring on hub and install synchromesh on mating gear.

COUNTERSHAFT

Disassembly

Pull bearing off front of countershaft, and press off 4th gear. Remove snap ring and press off 3rd gear. Remove rear snap rings, making note of shim positions. Pull outer bearing off rear of countershaft, and press off 5th gear. Pull off inner bearing.

Inspection

Check shaft and gears for wear or damage. Lightly polish any scoring from shaft surfaces.

Reassembly

To assemble, reverse disassembly procedure. Heat gears to 250-300°F (120-150°C) when installing gears on shaft.

REVERSE IDLER GEAR & SHAFT

Disassembly

Remove end plate. Unscrew hex bolt while holding shaft at front. Remove bolt and washers. Install a bolt in tapped bore and push assembly out towards rear. Separate needle bearing and gear from shaft.

Inspection

Inspect components for wear or damage and replace if necessary.

Reassembly

Reverse disassembly procedure using Loctite (or equivalent) on holding bolt.

TRANSMISSION REASSEMBLY

GEAR & SELECTOR SHAFT ASSEMBLIES

1) Install mainshaft and countershaft assemblies in intermediate transmission case. Install appropriate shim. Heat bearing race to about 175°F (80°C) and push onto mainshaft. Press needle bearing and reverse gear onto mainshaft. Slide 5th gear synchromesh assembly onto mainshaft.

2) Push 5th/Reverse shift rod up to spring in transmission case from input shaft end. Insert locking balls and press down, pushing rod on through to lock.

3) Insert 5th/Reverse shift fork in sliding sleeve. Install sleeve on mainshaft with pins facing out. Guide 5th/Reverse shift fork onto selector rod and drive in retainer pin (roll pin).

4) Drive sleeve against stop on mainshaft spline. Heat bearing race to about 175°F (80°C) and push mainshaft on to sleeve. Install synchromesh blocking ring, needle bearing and 5th gear onto mainshaft.

5) Install inner roller bearing and 5th countergear on countershaft. Using appropriate driver, drive bearing race onto countershaft. Measure distance between spacer and bearing race and take up countershaft end play with appropriate shims. Install washer with bevelled side out on mainshaft. Heat speedometer gear and push onto mainshaft.

Manual Transmissions

BMW 325e, 524td & 528e (Cont.)

6) Install 1st/2nd and 3rd/4th shift forks. Push in 3rd/4th shift rod through shift fork to spring. Insert locating ball and locking ball and press down. Push 3rd/4th shift rod on through to lock making sure that opening on shift rod faces 5th/Reverse shift rod. Drive in retainer pin (roll pin).

7) Push in 1st/2nd shift rod through fork to spring in transmission case. Install driving dog. Install locating ball and locking ball and press down. Push 1st/2nd shift rod on through to lock and drive in retainer pin (roll pin).

8) Push in upper selector rod with opening facing out. Install selector arm with long side facing 3rd/4th shift rod.

9) Install lower selector rod with opening facing up. Install operating lever with sharp edge facing up and push in selector rod.

10) Install bolt in top of transmission case with Loctite (or equivalent) making sure that center engages bore of operating lever. Test operating lever for ease of movement. Push clamp onto lower selector rod with bevelled side facing shift fork.

11) Install bolt in side of transmission case with Loctite (or equivalent) making sure that center engages groove in lower selector rod. Hold 4 rollers on selector rod with grease.

TRANSMISSION CASE

Thoroughly clean all sealing surfaces, coat with Loctite or equivalent and reverse disassembly procedure.

TIGHTENING SPECIFICATIONS

Application	Ft. Lbs. (N.m)
Crossmember	16-17 (22-23)
Propeller Shaft Flange Nut	72 (98)
Rear Seal Flange Bolts	7 (9.5)
Rubber Mount	32-35 (43-47)
Transmission Cover Plate Bolts	
Front & Rear	18 (24)
Transmission-to-Engine (or Clutch Hsg.)	
8 mm Bolts	18-19 (24-26)
10 mm Bolts	35-37 (47-50)
12 mm Bolts	54-60 (72-80)

Manual Transmission

BMW 265/6 5-SPEED

535i, 635CSi & 735i

DESCRIPTION

The Getrag Model 265/6 5-speed transmission is fully synchronized, and uses constant mesh, helical gears in forward speeds, and non-synchronized, helical gears in reverse gear. Shifting is accomplished through 3 shift rails and forks. Transmission is of a 3-section design, with a separate clutch housing bolted to the main transmission case.

NOTE: Complete repair information is not available from manufacturer.

LUBRICATION & ADJUSTMENT

See appropiate MANUAL TRANSMISSION SERVICING article in IMPORT GENERAL SERVICING section.

TROUBLE SHOOTING

OIL IN CLUTCH BELL HOUSING

Guide sleeve leaks. Radial oil seal for input shaft leaks. Gasket on end cover (crankcase) leaks. Radial oil seal for crankshaft leaks.

OIL ON OUTPUT FLANGE

Radial oil seal for output shaft leaks. Radial oil seal for selector shaft leaks.

TRANSMISSION CASE LEAKS BETWEEN FRONT AND REAR SECTIONS

Case gasket leaks.

OIL ON VENT

Oil level too high. Wrong oil (strong foaming).

GEAR DOES NOT HOLD (JUMPS OUT)

Worn sliding sleeve, defective sliding rails, broken springs. Shift console loose. Selector forks worn. Output flange loose.

HARD MOVING, HESITANT SHIFTS

Clutch doesn't disengage properly. Clutch pedal travel insufficient. Drive plate worn. Liner seized on flywheel. Drive plate seized on transmission input shaft. Bearing for transmission input shaft in crankshaft defective. Air in hydraulic system. Wrong transmission fluid. Sleeves of selector shaft damaged. Excessive play in selector lever bearings. Selector forks worn. Operating sleeve worn.

Fig. 1: Sectional View of Getrag 265/6 5-Speed Transmission

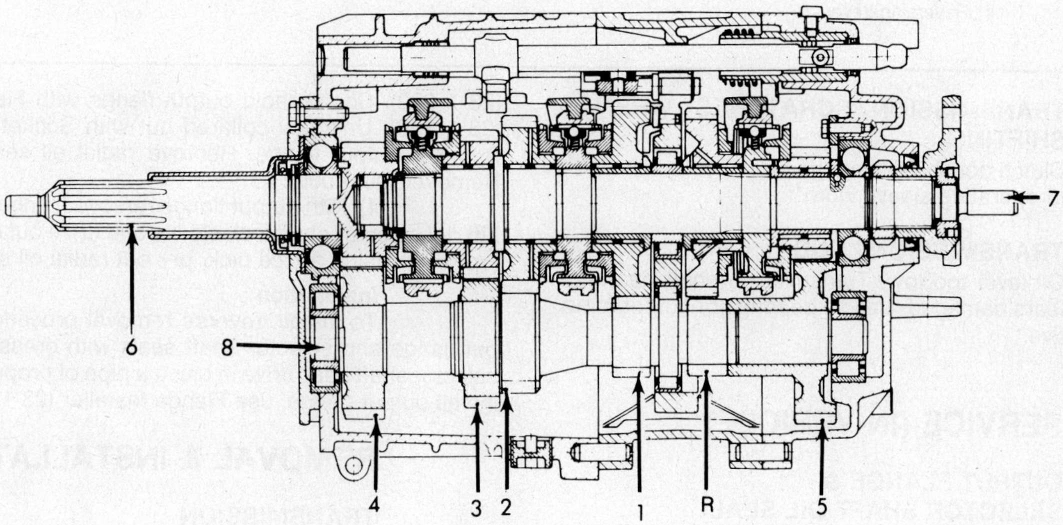

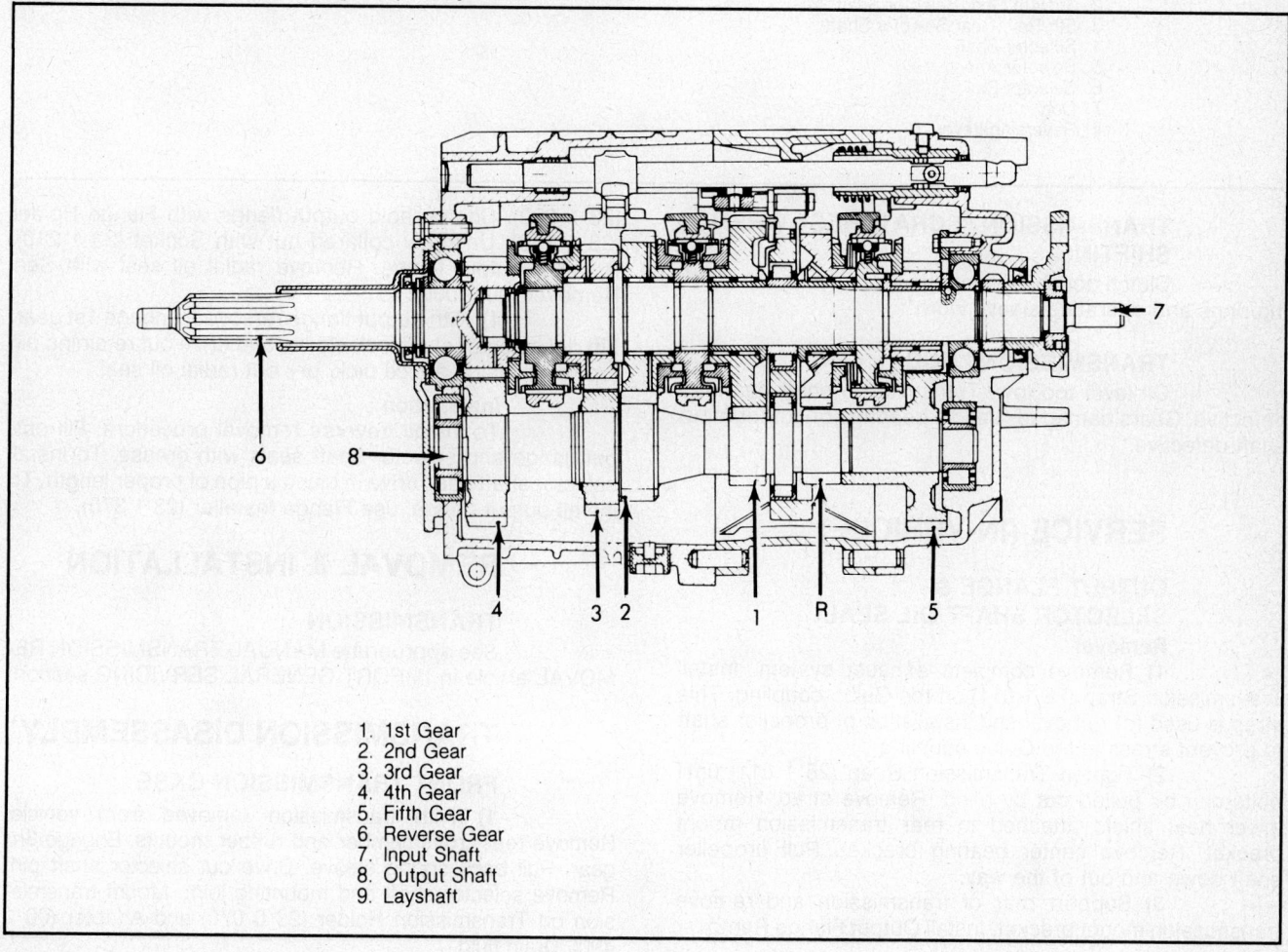

1. 1st Gear
2. 2nd Gear
3. 3rd Gear
4. 4th Gear
5. Fifth Gear
6. Reverse Gear
7. Input Shaft
8. Output Shaft
9. Layshaft

BMW 265/6 5-SPEED (Cont.)

Fig. 2: Sectional View of Getrag 265/6 Shift Components

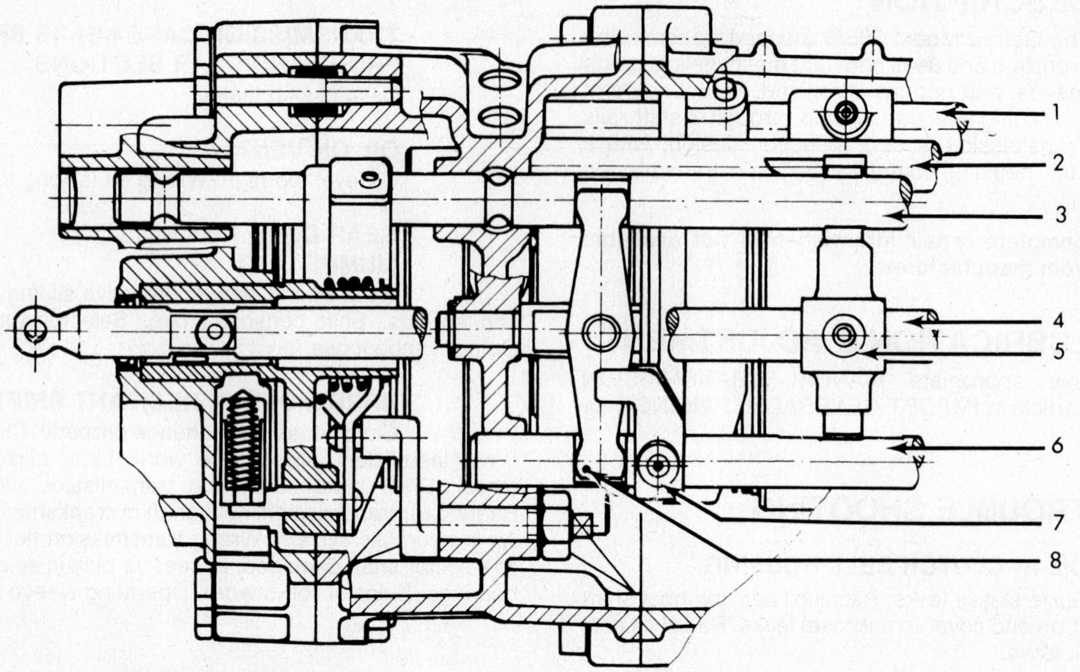

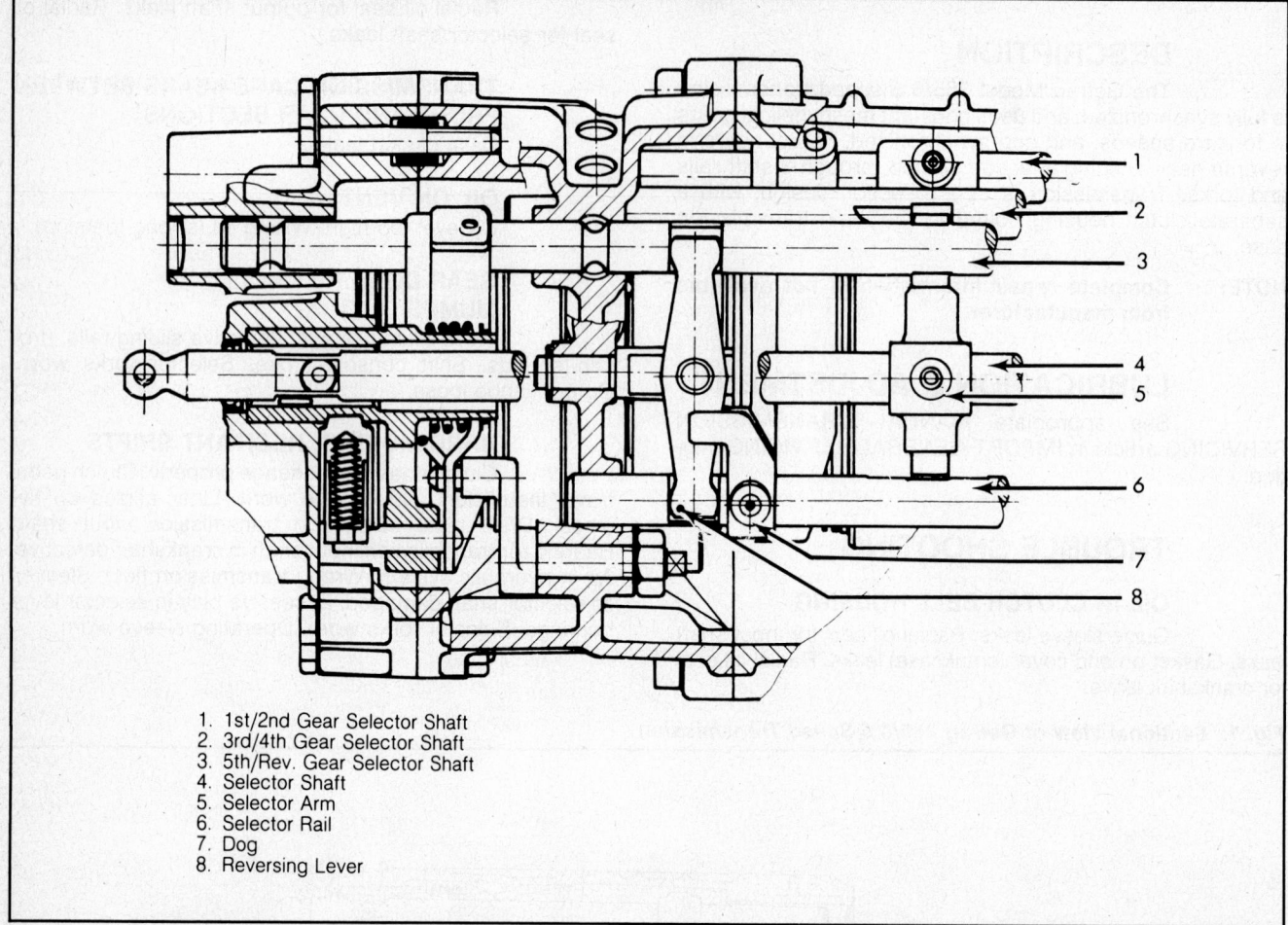

1. 1st/2nd Gear Selector Shaft
2. 3rd/4th Gear Selector Shaft
3. 5th/Rev. Gear Selector Shaft
4. Selector Shaft
5. Selector Arm
6. Selector Rail
7. Dog
8. Reversing Lever

TRANSMISSION "SCRATCHES" WHEN SHIFTING

Clutch doesn't disengage properly. Synchronizing rings and operating sleeve worn.

TRANSMISSION LOUD

Oil level too low. Transmission shaft bearings defective. Gears damaged. Needle bearings of output/input shaft defective.

SERVICE (IN-VEHICLE)

OUTPUT FLANGE & SELECTOR SHAFT OIL SEAL

Removal

1) Remove complete exhaust system. Install Transmission Strap (26 1 011) on the Guibo coupling. This strap is used for removal and installation of propeller shaft to prevent stress in the Guibo coupling.

2) Tighten Transmission Strap (26 1 011) until bolts can be pulled out by hand. Remove strap. Remove lower heat shield attached to rear transmission mount bracket. Remove center bearing bracket. Pull propeller shaft down and out of the way.

3) Support rear of transmission and remove transmission mount bracket. Install Output Flange Remover (23 1 200). Counterhold output flange with Flange Holder (23 1 150). Unscrew collared nut with Socket (23 1 210). Remove output flange. Remove radial oil seal with Seal Remover (00 5 000).

4) With output flange removed, engage 1st gear. Lift out selector shaft lock sleeve and drive out retaining pin (upward). Using an ice pick, pry out radial oil seal.

Installation

To install, reverse removal procedure. Fill output flange and selector shaft seals with grease. To install selector shaft seal, drive in using a pipe of proper length. To install output flange, use Flange Installer (23 1 370).

REMOVAL & INSTALLATION

TRANSMISSION

See appropriate MANUAL TRANSMISSION REMOVAL article in IMPORT GENERAL SERVICING section.

TRANSMISSION DISASSEMBLY

FRONT TRANSMISSION CASE

1) With transmission removed from vehicle. Remove rear crossmember and rubber mounts. Engage 3rd gear. Pull back spring sleeve. Drive out selector shaft pin. Remove selector shaft and mounting joint. Mount transmission on Transmission Holder (23 0 070) and Adapter (00 1 490). Drain fluid.

BMW 265/6 5-SPEED (Cont.)

2) Remove input shaft guide flange. Remove input shaft circlip and grooved washer. Lift out circlip and washer. Keep components in order for installation.

3) Remove shift lockpin detent cap. Pull out spring and lockpin. Drive out rear transmission case dowel pin. Using Bearing Pullers (23 1 170 & 33 1 301), pull front transmission case section off.

REAR TRANSMISSION CASE

1) Remove output flange nut lockplate. Install Output Flange Holder (23 0 020) and remove output flange nut using Flange Nut Socket (23 1 210). Using Puller (33 1 150), pull off output flange.

2) Engage 2nd gear before removing cover. To engage 2nd gear, swing selector shaft to the left against stop and slide forward. Remove rear transmission case mounting bolts.

3) Knock centering pin rearward. Using Case Puller's (23 1 350 & 33 1 301), remove rear case section. Using screwdriver, pry rear seal out. Remove spacer and inner bearing race.

INPUT & OUTPUT SHAFT ASSEMBLIES

Input Shaft

Disassembly

1) With front and rear transmission cases removed, swing down output shaft. Using Gear Puller (23 0 080), pull 5th gear wheel off of layshaft (this will also pull off the inner bearing race).

2) Using Puller's (23 1 100 and 00 7 500), pull off output shaft inner bearing race. Remove washer and shift ball. Pull off 5th gear wheel with sychronizing ring and split needle bearing. Remove needle rollers off selector shaft.

3) Drive out reverse/5th gear selector shaft-to-shift fork retainer pin. While counterholding, pull out selector shaft. Remove selector arm. Engage 2nd gear.

4) Drive out 3rd/4th gear selector shaft-to-shift fork retainer pin. Pull or take off turning lock and reversing lever. Pull selector shaft forward and out. Pull off operating sleeve and 5th gear selector fork.

5) Using Puller's (23 1 420 and 33 1 301), pull guide sleeve and inner bearing race off of output shaft. Pull off reverse gear and needle bearing.

6) Engage 3rd gear. Drive out shift fork-to-selector shaft pin. Pull output shaft toward rear far enough, so that inner bearing race can be pulled off with Puller (23 1 060). Remove shim "X".

7) Pull out input and output shaft assembly with layshaft and 1st/2nd gear selector shaft in intermediate case. Remove holder. While counterholding front of shaft, unscrew bolt. Remove 1st/2nd gear selector shaft.

Reassembly

1) Install selector shaft, while pushing on selector arm with long finger facing 3rd/4th gear selector shaft. Heat ball bearing inner races to about 175°F (80°C) and install on output shaft.

NOTE: **Opening in bearing inner race must engage in ball.**

2) Install split needle bearing, sychronizing ring and 5th gear. Place Shaft Aligner (23 1 450) in centering pin. Heat bearing sleeve to about 175°F (80°C) with a hot air blower and push on to output shaft.

3) Install reverse lever, smooth side face down. Insert selector rail. Push on turning lock. Install 6x26 mm lock pin. Push in selector shaft far enough so that 6x26 mm pin can be driven in, while counterholding selector shaft. Push in selector shaft and guide sleeve against arrest.

4) Install guide sleeve. Ensure centering pin faces 5th gear. Install 5th/reverse gear selector fork. Install detent ball.

5) Push in selector shaft up to spring. Insert locking balls and press down. Push in and turn selector shaft so that openings are always opposite lockings balls.

NOTE: **Stepped end of sliding sleeve must be opposite centering pin.**

6) Mount 1st/2nd gear selector fork. Push in 1st/2nd gear selector shaft up to spring. Insert locking balls and press down. Push in selector shaft against stop in this position.

7) Install 3rd/4th gear selector fork. Insert detent ball. Push in selector shaft up to spring. Insert locking balls and press down. Push in selector shaft against stop in this position.

8) While holding selector shaft, drive in roll pin for 3rd/4th gear selector fork. Install needle bearing and reverse gear. Install shim "X". Heat bearing sleeve to about 175°F (80°C) and install on output shaft.

9) Install and mount reverse idler gear. Stepped collar of reverse gear faces out.

Ouput Shaft

1) Pull off input shaft sychronizing rings and needle bearing. Remove snap ring and washer. Pull off guide sleeve, sychronizing ring, 3rd gear and needle bearing.

2) Press 2nd gear, needle bearing, sychronizing ring, guide sleeve and 1st gear needle bearing with bearing sleeve and bearing inner race off of output shaft. Check condition of all bearings, and replace as necessary.

CLEANING & INSPECTION

COUNTERSHAFT

Check shaft and gears for wear or damage. Lightly polish any scoring from shaft surfaces.

REVERSE IDLER GEAR & SHAFT

Inspect components for wear or damage and replace if necessary.

SYCHRONIZER ASSEMLBIES

Check all parts for wear or damage. Blocking rings must be replaced if tapered clutch surface is pitted or excessively worn. Place each synchronizing ring into position on its respective gear. Using a feeler gauge, measure clearance between ring and gear. If clearance is less than .039" (1 mm), replace synchronizing ring.

TRANSMISSION REASSEMBLY

GEAR & SELECTOR SHAFT

1) Install mainshaft and countershaft assemblies in intermediate transmission case. Install appropriate shim. Heat bearing race to about 175°F (80°C) and push onto mainshaft. Press needle bearing and reverse gear onto mainshaft. Slide 5th gear synchronizing ring assembly onto mainshaft.

2) Push 5th/reverse shift shaft up to spring in transmission case from input shaft end. Insert locking balls and press down, pushing shaft on through to lock.

Manual Transmission

BMW 265/6 5-SPEED (Cont.)

Fig. 3: Exploded View of Getrag 265/6 5-Speed Transmission

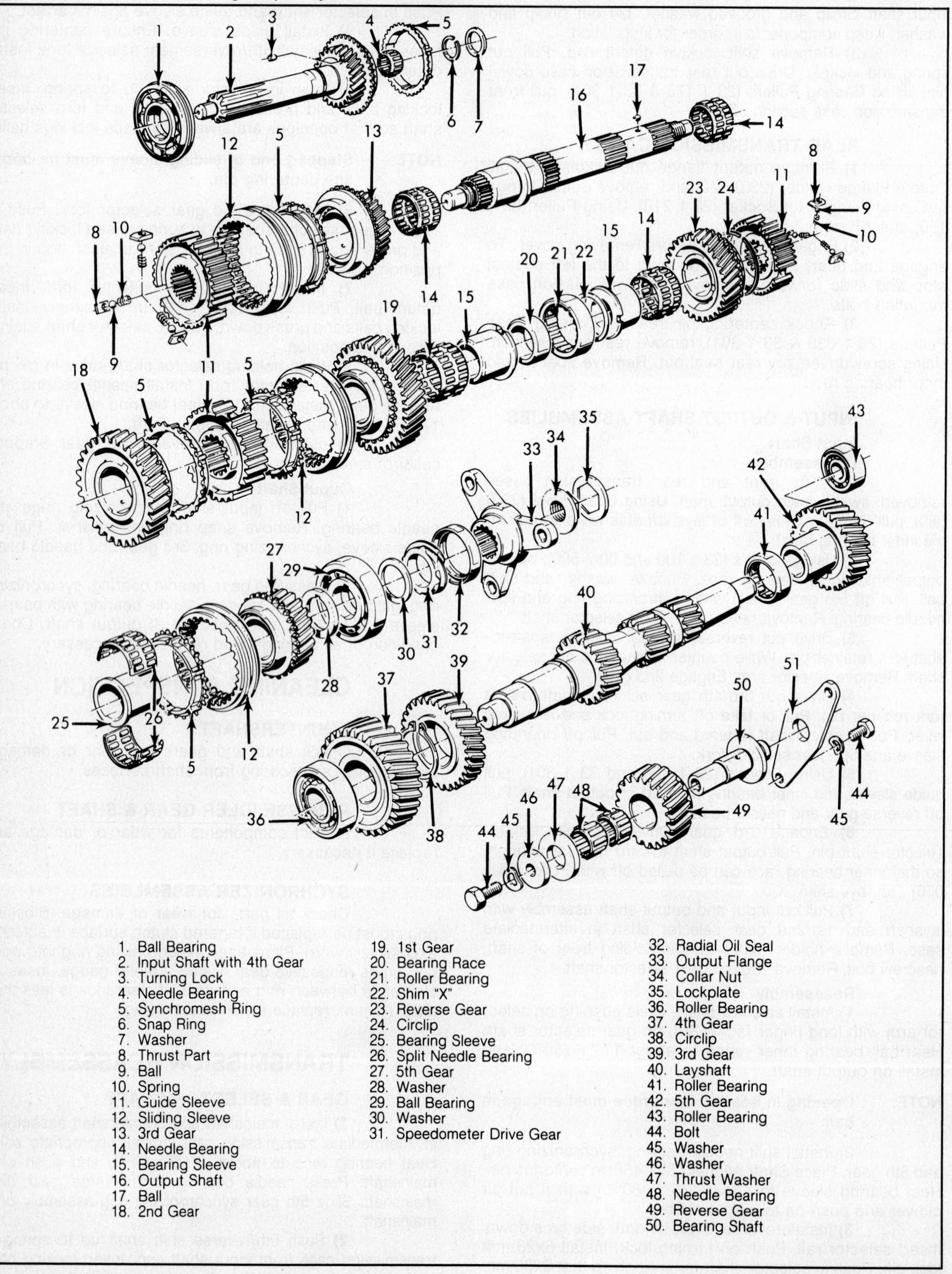

1. Ball Bearing
2. Input Shaft with 4th Gear
3. Turning Lock
4. Needle Bearing
5. Synchromesh Ring
6. Snap Ring
7. Washer
8. Thrust Part
9. Ball
10. Spring
11. Guide Sleeve
12. Sliding Sleeve
13. 3rd Gear
14. Needle Bearing
15. Bearing Sleeve
16. Output Shaft
17. Ball
18. 2nd Gear
19. 1st Gear
20. Bearing Race
21. Roller Bearing
22. Shim "X"
23. Reverse Gear
24. Circlip
25. Bearing Sleeve
26. Split Needle Bearing
27. 5th Gear
28. Washer
29. Ball Bearing
30. Washer
31. Speedometer Drive Gear
32. Radial Oil Seal
33. Output Flange
34. Collar Nut
35. Lockplate
36. Roller Bearing
37. 4th Gear
38. Circlip
39. 3rd Gear
40. Layshaft
41. Roller Bearing
42. 5th Gear
43. Roller Bearing
44. Bolt
45. Washer
46. Washer
47. Thrust Washer
48. Needle Bearing
49. Reverse Gear
50. Bearing Shaft

BMW 265/6 5-SPEED (Cont.)

3) Insert 5th/reverse shift fork in sliding sleeve. Install sleeve on mainshaft with pins facing out. Guide 5th/reverse shift fork onto selector shaft and drive in retainer pin (roll pin).

4) Drive sleeve against stop mainshaft spline. Heat bearing race to about 175°F (80°C) and push mainshaft on to sleeve. Install synchronizing blocking ring, needle bearing and 5th gear onto mainshaft.

5) Install inner roller bearing and 5th countergear on countershaft. Using appropriate driver, drive bearing race onto countershaft. Measure distance between spacer and bearing race and take up countershaft end play with appropriate shims. Install washer with bevelled side out on mainshaft. Heat speedometer gear and push onto mainshaft.

6) Install 1st/2nd and 3rd/4th shift forks. Push in 3rd/4th shift shaft through shift fork to spring. Insert locating ball and locking ball and press down. Push 3rd/4th shift shaft on through to lock ensuring that opening on shift shaft faces 5th/reverse shift shaft. Drive in retainer pin (roll pin).

7) Push in 1st/2nd shift shaft through fork to spring in transmission case. Install driving dog. Install locating ball and locking ball and press down. Push 1st/2nd shift shaft on through to lock and drive in retainer pin (roll pin).

8) Push in upper selector shaft with opening facing out. Install selector with long side facing 3rd/4th shift shaft.

9) Install lower selector shaft with opening facing up. Install operating lever with sharp edge facing up and push in selector shaft.

10) Install bolt in top of transmission with Loctite ensuring that center engages bore of operating lever. Test operating lever for ease of movement. Push clamp onto lower selector shaft with bevelled side facing shift fork.

11) Install bolt in side of transmission case with Loctite ensuring that center engages groove in lower selector shaft. Hold 4 rollers on selector shaft with grease.

12) To complete reassembly, reverse disassembly procedure. Fill transmission with proper fluid and reinstall in vehicle.

TIGHTENING SPECIFICATIONS

Application	Ft. Lbs. (N.m)
Crossmember	16-17 (22-23)
Propeller Shaft Flange Nut	72 (98)
Rear Seal Flange Bolts	7 (9.5)
Rubber Mount	32-35 (43-47)
Transmission Cover Plate Bolts	
Front & Rear	18 (24)
Transmission-to-Engine (or Clutch Hsg.)	
8 mm Bolts	18-19 (24-26)
10 mm Bolts	35-37 (47-50)
12 mm Bolts	54-60 (72-80)

BMW ZF S5-16 5-SPEED

318i

DESCRIPTION

The ZF Model S5-16 5-speed transmission is fully synchronized, and uses constant mesh, helical gears in forward speeds, and non-synchronized, helical reverse gears. Shifting is accomplished through 3 shift rails and forks. Transmission case is of 2-section design.

LUBRICATION & ADJUSTMENT

See appropriate MANUAL TRANSMISSION SERVICING article in IMPORT GENERAL SERVICING section.

TROUBLE SHOOTING

OIL ON CLUTCH BELL HOUSING

Check the following: "O" ring for guide flange, Radial oil seals for input shaft and crankshaft rear main bearing, end cover gasket.

OIL ON OUTPUT FLANGE

Check the following: Radial seals for output shaft and selector shaft.

OIL ON VENT

Oil level too high. Wrong type of oil grade (excessive foaming).

JUMPS OUT OF GEAR

Sliding sleeve worn, guide rail defective, springs broken. Sliding sleevers for 1st/2nd and 3rd/4th gear mixed up. Shift console loose. Selector forks worn. Output flange loose.

HARD SHIFTS

Check clutch release, pedal travel, clutch disc for wear, clutch disc seized on transmission input shaft, clutch pilot bearing seized, air in clutch hydraulic system, bushings for selector rod damaged, excessive play in shift lever mount, selector forks worn and sliding sleeve worn.

TRANSMISSION GRABS WHEN SHIFTING

Clutch release insufficient. Synchromesh rings or sliding sleeve worn. Improper shifting into reverse gear (3 second shift break).

TRANSMISSION LOUD

Oil level too low. Transmission shaft bearings defective. Gears are damaged. Needle bearing of input or output shaft defective. Pilot bearing for transmission input shaft defective.

SERVICE (IN VEHICLE)

OUTPUT SHAFT, FLANGE & OIL SEAL

Removal

1) Remove propeller shaft at front and center. Remove output shaft lockplate and nut. Install Special Tool (23 1 200) and hold output flange with Special Tool (23 0 020).

2) Unscrew collar nut with Special Tool (23 1 210). Remove output flange with Special Tool (33 1 150). Pry out oil seal.

Installation

To install, reverse removal procedure. Lubricate oil seal with transmission oil. Install oil seal with Special Tool (23 2 160).

REAR TRANSMISSION MOUNT

Removal & Installation

1) Remove exhaust assembly. Support rear of transmission. Remove bolts for rear crossmember and upper retaining nut for transmission mount.

2) To install, reverse removal procedure.

REMOVAL & INSTALLATION

TRANSMISSION

See appropriate MANUAL TRANSMISSION REMOVAL article in IMPORT GENERAL SERVICING section.

TRANSMISSION DISASSEMBLY

1) Remove transmission from vehicle. Install Special Tool (23 0 090) on Special Tool (00 1 490). Mount transmission on work stand. Drain oil.

2) Remove guide sleeve. Lift out circlip. Unscrew back-up light switch. Drive back locating pins. Remove all rear housing bolts.

3) Pull off front case section using Special Tool (23 1 460 and 33 1 301). Drive out end cap. Drive out grooved ball bearing in direction of clutch housing.

4) Remove output flange with Special Tool (33 1 150). Remove all end caps. Carefully remove end springs (under tension).

5) Pull out 3 stop pins with circlip pliers as far as possible (stem locks have to be taken off before stop pins can be pulled out completely). Drive pins (4 and 5) out of selector fork for 3rd/4th gear (counterhold).

6) Push back leaf spring for reverse gear far enough with Special Tool (23 2 170) until selector arm is accesible. It should be possible to move selector shaft back and forth easily. Swing selector arm out of groove in selector rod.

7) Pull out 3rd/4th gear selector rod. Remove lock in socket of bolt. Unscrew bolt. Remove reverse gear, reverse gear shaft, needle bearing and thrust washer.

8) Remove operating lever bolt. Engage reverse gear by moving sliding sleeve forward before pressing out gear set. Press input shaft, outshaft and layshaft out of case rear section with Special Tool (23 1 050). Remove reverse gear. Remove gear train.

BMW ZF S5-16 5-SPEED (Cont.)

Fig. 1: Exploded View Of ZF S5-16 5-Speed Transmission

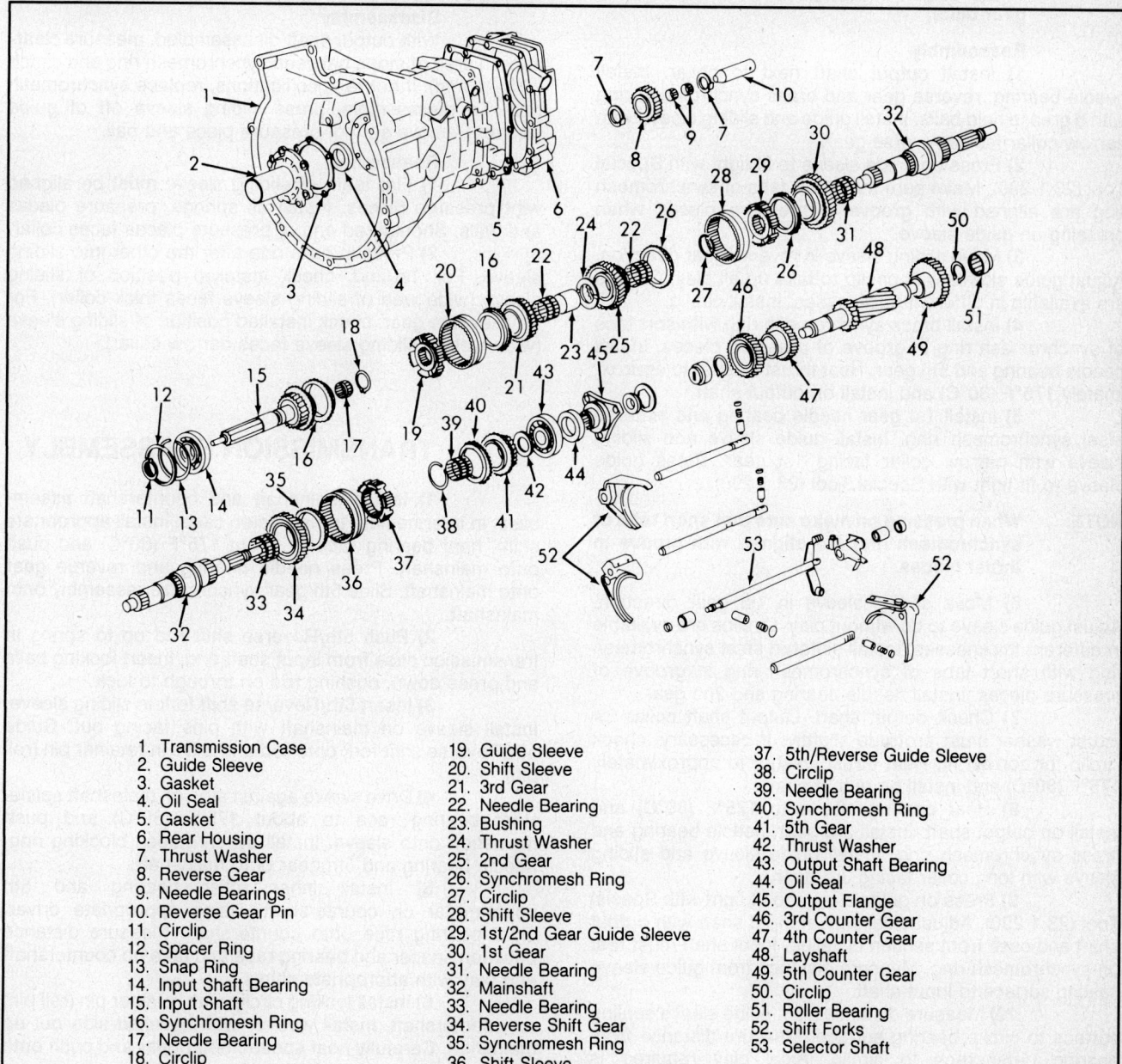

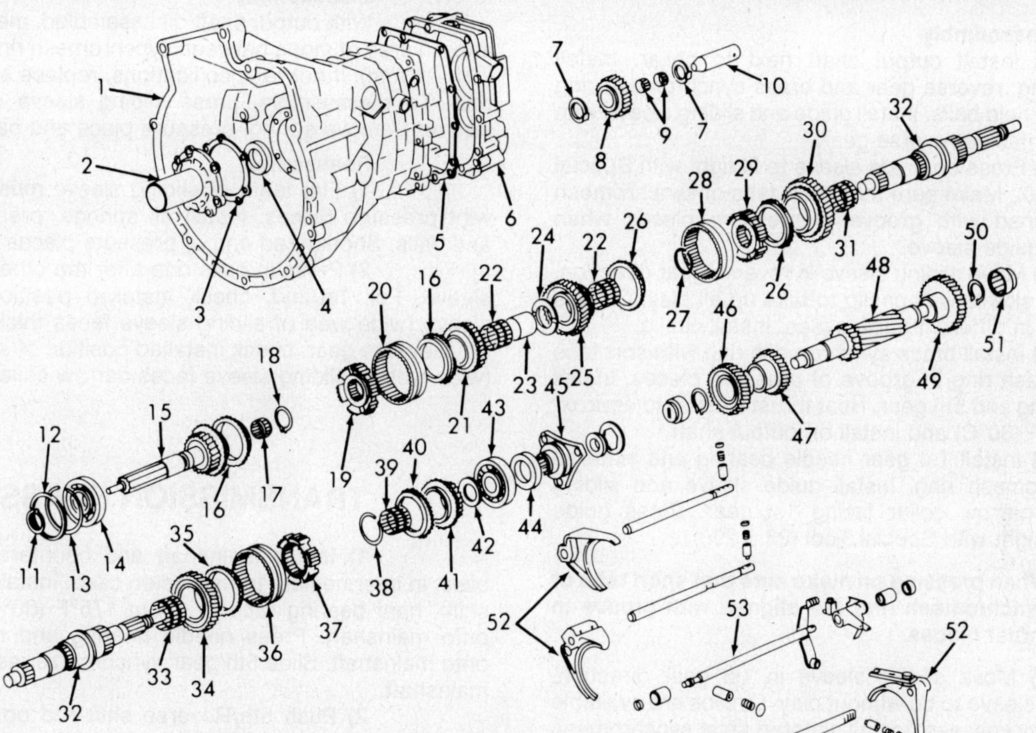

1. Transmission Case
2. Guide Sleeve
3. Gasket
4. Oil Seal
5. Gasket
6. Rear Housing
7. Thrust Washer
8. Reverse Gear
9. Needle Bearings
10. Reverse Gear Pin
11. Circlip
12. Spacer Ring
13. Snap Ring
14. Input Shaft Bearing
15. Input Shaft
16. Synchromesh Ring
17. Needle Bearing
18. Circlip
19. Guide Sleeve
20. Shift Sleeve
21. 3rd Gear
22. Needle Bearing
23. Bushing
24. Thrust Washer
25. 2nd Gear
26. Synchromesh Ring
27. Circlip
28. Shift Sleeve
29. 1st/2nd Gear Guide Sleeve
30. 1st Gear
31. Needle Bearing
32. Mainshaft
33. Needle Bearing
34. Reverse Shift Gear
35. Synchromesh Ring
36. Shift Sleeve
37. 5th/Reverse Guide Sleeve
38. Circlip
39. Needle Bearing
40. Synchromesh Ring
41. 5th Gear
42. Thrust Washer
43. Output Shaft Bearing
44. Oil Seal
45. Output Flange
46. 3rd Counter Gear
47. 4th Counter Gear
48. Layshaft
49. 5th Counter Gear
50. Circlip
51. Roller Bearing
52. Shift Forks
53. Selector Shaft

NOTE: Use a soft material (wood, aluminum or a similar material) between claws and sealing surface to avoid damage on sealing surface.

CLEANING & INSPECTION

Inspection

Check all parts for wear or damage. Blocking rings must be replaced if tapered clutch surface is pitted or excessively worn. Place each synchromesh ring into position on its respective gear. Using a feeler gauge, measure clearance between ring and gear. If clearance is less than .040" (1 mm), replace synchromesh ring.

COMPONENT DISASSEMBLY & REASSEMBLY

INPUT AND OUTPUT SHAFT ASSEMBLY

Disassembly

1) Pull off input shaft, synchromesh ring (made of brass) and needle bearing. Lift out circlip. Press 3rd gear with guide and sliding sleeve off of input shaft with Special Tool (23 1 490). Remove needle bearing.

2) Remove circlip for reverse gear. Press guide sleeve with sliding sleeve and reverse gear off of output shaft. Remove needle bearing. Press guide sleeve with sliding sleeve and reverse gear off of output shaft. Remove needle bearing.

Manual Transmissions

BMW ZF S5-16 5-SPEED (Cont.)

NOTE: **Always replace circlips when reassembling gear units.**

Reassembly

1) Install output shaft next to collar. Install needle bearing, reverse gear and brass synchromesh ring with 6 grease held balls. Install guide and sliding sleeve with narrow collar facing reverse gear.

2) Press on guide sleeve to fit tight with Special Tool (23 1 290). Make sure that short tabs of synchromesh ring are aligned with groove in pressure pieces when pressing on guide sleeve.

3) Move sliding sleeve in reverse gear direction. Adjust guide sleeve with circlip to take up all play. Circlips are available in different thicknesses. Install circlip.

4) Install brass synchromesh ring with sort tabs of synchromesh ring in groove of pressure pieces. Install needle bearing and 5th gear. Heat thrust washer to approximately 175°F (80°C) and install on output shaft.

5) Install 1st gear needle bearing and sintered steel synchromesh ring. Install guide sleeve and sliding sleeve with narrow collar facing 1st gear. Press guide sleeve to fit tight with Special Tool (23 1 290).

NOTE: **When pressing on make sure that short tabs of synchromesh ring are aligned with groove in thrust pieces.**

6) Move sliding sleeve in 1st gear direction. Adjust guide sleeve to be without play. Circlips are available in different thicknesses. Install sintered steel synchromesh ring with short tabs of synchromesh ring in groove of pressure pieces. Install needle bearing and 2nd gear.

7) Check output shaft. Output shaft collar for thrust washer must protrude slightly. If necessary, check circlip for correct fit. Heat thrust washer to approximately 175°F (80°C) and install on output shaft.

8) Heat bearing sleeve to 175°F (80°C) and install on output shaft. Install 3rd gear, needle bearing and brass synchromesh ring. Install guide sleeve and sliding sleeve with long collar facing 3rd gear.

9) Press on guide sleeve to fit tight with Special Tool (23 1 290). Adjust axial play of input shaft with output shaft and case front section installed. Input shaft must rest on synchromesh ring. Measure distance from guide sleeve sealing surface to input shaft.

10) Measure distance from guide sleeve sealing surface to circlip bearing surface. Measure distance from bearing outer race to circlip. Axial play required is .043-.051" (1.1-1.3 mm). Circlips are available in different thicknesses for making corrections. Install grooved ball bearing and circlip.

NOTE: **If a spacer is found between the circlip and case when removing the bearing, it must be installed again for measuring distance.**

11) Measure distance from bearing outer race to circlip. Heat grooved ball bearing inner race and case front section in area of bearing to 175°F (80°C). Push grooved ball bearing on to input shaft as far as possible.

12) Press grooved ball bearing on to input shaft and into case front section with Special Tools (23 1 007, 23 1 000 and 23 1 006). Insert Special Tools (23 1 006) that flat side faces input shaft.

13) Drive on grooved ball bearing further simultaneously with light hammer knocks. Install circlip and reverse gear switch.

SYNCHROMESH RINGS

Disassembly

With output shaft disassembled, measure clearance in area of stops between synchromesh ring and clutch (.040" 1 mm). If not to specifications, replace synchromesh ring. To disassemble, press sliding sleeve off of guide sleeve. Remove spring, pressure piece and ball.

Reassembly

1) Flat teeth of sliding sleeve must be aligned wiht pressure pieces. Install all springs, pressure pieces and balls. Shouldered end of pressure pieces faces collar.

2) Press in balls one after the other into sliding sleeve. For 1st/2nd, check installed position of sliding sleeve (wide web of sliding sleeve faces thick collar). For 5th/Reverse gear, check installed position of sliding sleeve (wide web of sliding sleeve faces narrow collar).

TRANSMISSION REASSEMBLY

1) Install mainshaft and countershaft assemblies, in intermediate transmission case. Install appropriate shim, heat bearing race to about 175°F (80°C) and push onto mainshaft. Press needle bearing and reverse gear onto mainshaft. Slide 5th gear synchronizer assembly onto mainshaft.

2) Push 5th/Reverse shift rod up to spring in transmission case from input shaft end. Insert locking balls and press down, pushing rod on through to lock.

3) Insert 5th/Reverse shift fork in sliding sleeve. Install sleeve on mainshaft with pins facing out. Guide 5th/Reverse shift fork onto rod and drive in retainer pin (roll pin).

4) Drive sleeve against stop on mainshaft spline. Heat bearing race to about 175°F (80°C) and push mainshaft onto sleeve. Install synchromesh blocking ring, needle bearing and 5th gear onto mainshaft.

5) Install inner roller bearing and 5th countergear on countershaft. Using appropriate driver, drive bearing race onto countershaft. Measure distance between spacer and bearing race and take up countershaft end play with appropriate shims.

6) Install locking circlip with retainer pin (roll pin) on countershaft. Install washer with bevelled side out on mainshaft. Carefully heat speedometer gear and push onto mainshaft.

7) Install 1st/2nd and 3rd/4th shift forks. Push in 3rd/4th shift rod through shift fork to spring. Insert locating ball and locking ball. Press down and push 3rd/4th shift rod through to lock. Make sure that opening on shift rod faces 5th/Reverse shift rod. Drive in retainer pin (roll pin).

8) Push in 1st/2nd shift rod through fork and up to spring in transmission case. Install driving dog, locating ball and locking ball. Press and hold down. Push 1st/2nd shift rod on through to lock and drive in retainer pin (roll pin).

9) Push in upper selector rod with opening facing out. Install selector arm with long side facing 3rd/4th shift rod.

10) Install lower selector rod with opening facing up. Install operating lever with sharp edge facing up and push in rod. Install bolt in top of transmission case with Loctite (573) making sure that center engages bore of operating lever.

BMW ZF S5-16 5-SPEED (Cont.)

11) Test operating lever for ease of movement. Push clamp onto lower selector rod with bevelled side facing shift fork. Using Loctite (573), install bolt in side of transmission. Make sure that center engages groove in lower selector rod.

12) Install output flange. Install collar nut using Loctite (573). Hold output flange using Special Tool (23 0 020) and tighten nut using Special Tool (23 1 210). Install lockplate.

13) Reassemble transmission front and rear cases.

TIGHTENING SPECIFICATIONS

Application	Ft. Lbs. (N.m)
Crossmember	16-17 (22-23)
Propeller Shaft Flange Nut	72 (98)
Rear Seal Flange Bolts	7 (9.5)
Rubber Mount	32-35 (43-47)
Transmission Cover Plate Bolts	
Front & Rear	18 (24)
Transmission-to-Engine (or Clutch Hsg.)	
8 mm Bolts	18-19 (24-26)
10 mm Bolts	35-37 (47-50)
12 mm Bolts	54-60 (72-80)

Manual Transmissions

CHRYSLER CORP. IMPORTS & MITSUBISHI KM130 4-SPEED

Chrysler Corp. 2WD Ram-50
Mitsubishi 2WD Pickup

IDENTIFICATION

Transmission may be identified by a serial number stamped on clutch housing.

DESCRIPTION

The KM 130 4-speed transmission is fully synchronized, constant mesh-type unit. All forward gears and countergear are located in transmission case. Reverse and idler gears are located in extension housing.

Access to transmission gears is obtained with bottom pan removed. Shift lever is mounted to extension housing and is connected to shift control rod which connects to shift rails located at rear of transmission case.

LUBRICATION & ADJUSTMENT

See appropriate MANUAL TRANSMISSION SERVICING article in IMPORT GENERAL SERVICING section.

TROUBLE SHOOTING

DIFFICULTY MESHING GEARS

Malfunction of gearshift lever or control shaft. Synchronizer rings or gear conical surfaces worn or excessive play. Synchronizer shift keys worn or damaged.

JUMPS OUT OF GEAR

Shifting forks worn or detent springs broken. Mainshaft or mainshaft support bearings worn or damaged. Clearance between synchronizer hub and sleeve excessive. Gears or gear bushings worn. Countergear worn.

NOISE IN TRANSMISSION

Lubrication oil incorrect or insufficient. Gears or bearings worn. Mainshaft spline worn or damaged.

REMOVAL & INSTALLATION

TRANSMISSION

See appropriate MANUAL TRANSMISSION REMOVAL article in IMPORT GENERAL SERVICING section.

TRANSMISSION DISASSEMBLY

NOTE: **Gasoline engine truck models use a mechanical cable-operated clutch. Diesel engine truck models use a hydraulic clutch.**

1) On gasoline engine truck models, remove return clip, clutch release bearing and carrier. Using a 3/16" (4.76 mm) punch, drive spring pin from clutch release shaft. *See Fig. 1*. Remove clutch shaft, felt packing, return springs and clutch release fork.

2) On diesel engine truck models, remove 2 return clips and remove throwout bearing. Remove clutch release cylinder. Remove boot from transmission case. Pull release fork to disengage it from pivot. Remove release fork.

Fig. 1: Removing Spring Pin From Clutch Release Shaft

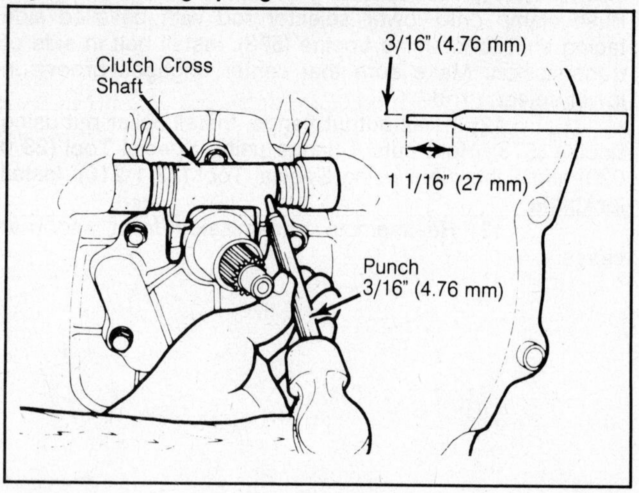

3) On all models, remove back-up light switch and ball. Remove speedometer driven gear assembly from extension housing. Remove extension housing attaching bolts. Rotate shifter to left, remove control finger from shift lug groove and remove extension housing.

4) Remove bottom pan from transmission case. Remove 3 detent plugs, springs and balls. Position all shift rails in Neutral position. Remove reverse shift rail and fork assembly together with reverse idler gear.

5) Using a 3/16" (4.76 mm) punch, remove 1st-2nd and 3rd-4th shift fork spring pins. Pull each shift rail and selector out toward rear of case. Remove shift fork. Keep shift rail and selector together as an assembly. Ensure interlock plungers are not lost when removing shafts.

6) Remove snap ring from rear of countergear. Remove counter reverse gear and spacer. Remove mainshaft lock nut and reverse gear from mainshaft. Lock nut can be loosened by double-engaging 3rd and 1st gears. Remove 5 retaining screws and rear bearing retainer. Remove front bearing retainer.

7) Remove snap rings from input shaft and input shaft bearing. Remove input shaft bearing, using Bearing Puller (MD998056). Remove mainshaft bearing snap ring and then bearing, using Bearing Puller (MD998056) and Adapter (MD998056-10). Press countergear rearward and remove rear bearing snap ring.

8) Using Bearing Puller (MD998192), remove countergear rear bearing. Remove snap ring from front countergear bearing. Remove bearing using Bearing Puller (MD998192). *See Fig. 2*. Remove countergear from transmission case.

9) Remove main drive gear from inside transmission case. Remove synchronizer ring and pilot bearing from end of mainshaft. Remove mainshaft assembly from transmission case. *See Fig. 3*.

CLEANING & INSPECTION

1) All parts should be thoroughly washed in cleaning solvent and air dried. Remove old gaskets with stiff brush or scraper. Rinse bearings in clean solvent and air dry. DO NOT spin bearings dry.

Fig. 2: Removing Countergear Rear Bearing From Transmission Case

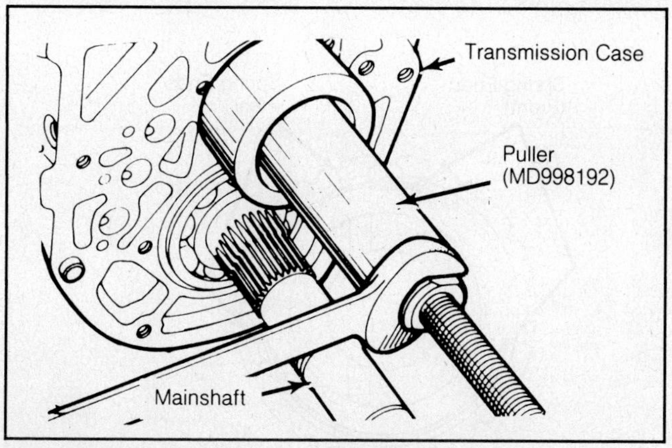

Fig. 3: Removing Mainshaft Assembly From Transmission Case

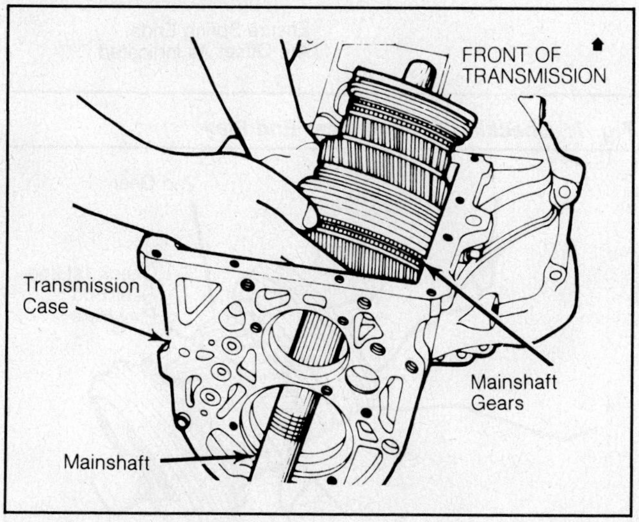

2) Lubricate bearings with light grade oil and wrap in clean paper until ready to install. Examine all gear teeth and splines for chips, wear, breaks or nicks. Check transmission case and extension housing for cracks and damage.

3) Check bearings and synchronizers for wear, damage and proper fit. Lubricate all moving parts before installation. Use new gaskets, seals and snap rings.

COMPONENT DISASSEMBLY & REASSEMBLY

MAINSHAFT

Disassembly

Pull spacer, 1st gear, 1st gear bearing and sleeve, 1st-2nd synchronizer assembly, 2nd gear and 2nd gear bearing, toward rear of mainshaft. Remove snap ring from forward end of mainshaft. Remove 3rd-4th synchronizer, 3rd gear and 3rd gear bearing.

Cleaning & Inspection

1) Check mainshaft for worn or damaged gear area, bearing surfaces and splines. Check spacers and bearings for wear or damage. Check all bearings for smooth rolling action. Replace parts as necessary.

2) Check all gears for damaged, worn or chipped teeth. Check gear inside diameter for wear or damage. Check all synchronizer assemblies for worn or damaged teeth, conical surface, internal surface and rings.

3) Check synchronizer ring-to-gear clearance on all synchronizer rings. *See Fig. 4.* If the clearance is not .032" (.80 mm) replace synchronizer ring. With hub and sleeve assembled, ensure sleeve slides smoothly and that it is not excessively loose. If either part is defective, replace synchronizer sleeve and hub as an assembly.

Fig. 4: Checking Synchronizer Ring-to-Gear Clearance

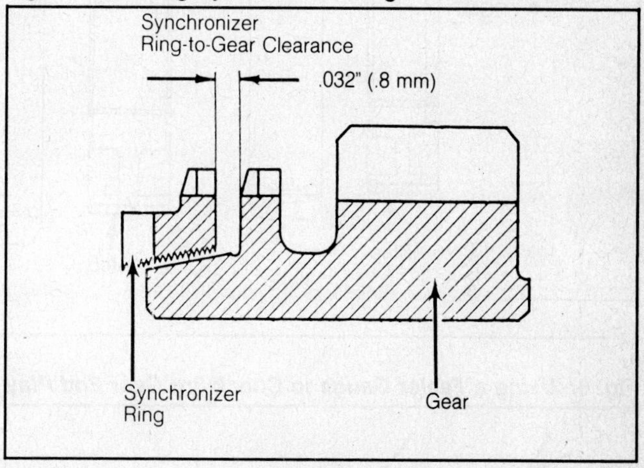

4) Check synchronizer components for wear and damage. Check synchronizer springs for deterioration and breakage. Check countergear for wear or chipped teeth.

5) Check reverse idler gear and shaft for wear or damage. Check shift forks, rail and selector for wear or damage. Check clearance between shift fork and fork groove on synchronizer sleeve and gear.

6) Clearance should be .006-.014" (.15-.35 mm) for reverse, .004-.012" (.10-.30 mm) for all others. Check detent ball slots for wear. Check clearance between selector and lever. Clearance should be .004-.012" (.10-.30 mm).

7) Check detent balls and springs for damage or breakage. Check shift rails, control lever and forks for wear, damage or breakage. Replace parts not within specifications.

Reassembly

1) Assemble both synchronizer assemblies. Ensure components are positioned correctly. *See Fig. 5.* Install needle bearing, 3rd gear, synchronizer ring and 3rd-4th synchronizer assembly on front of mainshaft.

NOTE: **Ensure synchronizer rings and assemblies are reinstalled in original position and location.**

2) Select snap ring of proper size so 3rd-4th synchronizer hub end play is 0-.003" (0-.08 mm). See 3RD-4TH SYNCHRONIZER HUB END PLAY table.

3RD-4TH SYNCHRONIZER HUB END PLAY

Application (Color)	Thickness In. (mm)
No Color	.085 (2.16)
Yellow	.087 (2.21)
Green	.090 (2.29)
White	.093 (2.36)

Manual Transmissions

CHRYSLER CORP. IMPORTS & MITSUBISHI KM130 4-SPEED (Cont.)

Fig. 5: Correct Position and Assembly of Synchronizer Assembly Components

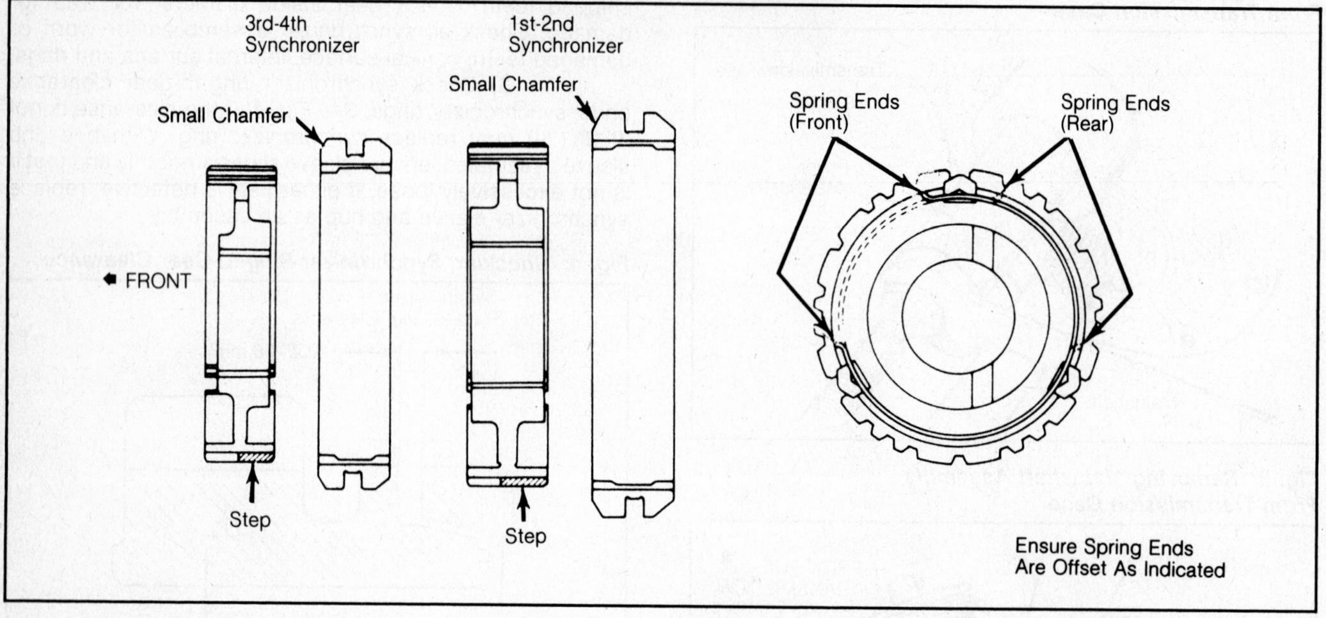

Fig. 6: Using a Feeler Gauge to Check 3rd Gear End Play

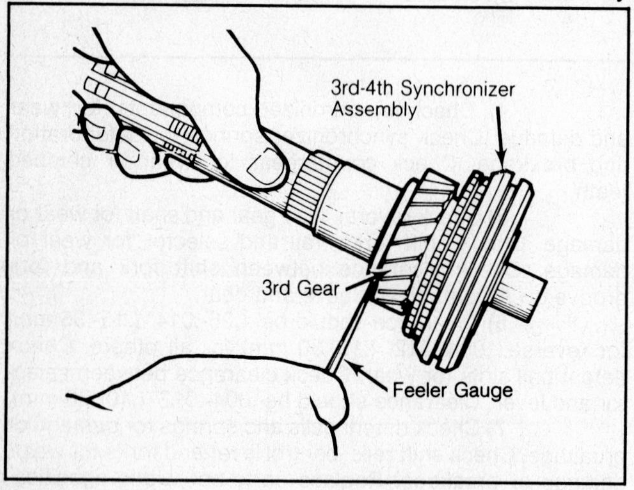

Fig. 7: Checking 1st-2nd Gear End Play

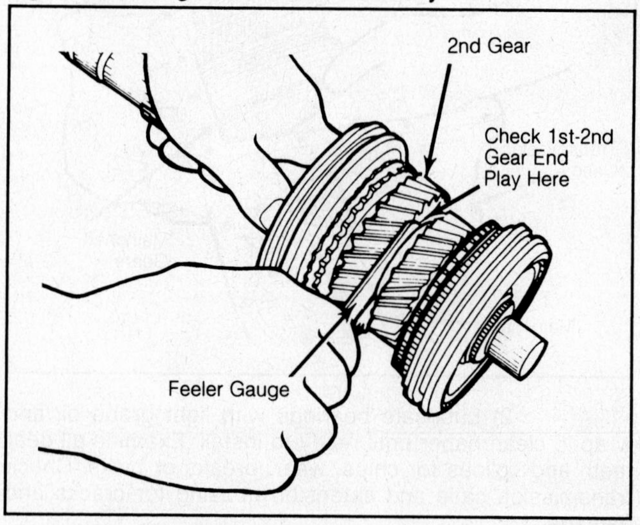

3) Check 3rd gear end play using a feeler gauge. Specified end play is .002-.008" (.05-.20 mm). *See Fig. 6*. If end play is not to specification, check conical part of 3rd gear and conical part of 3rd-4th synchronizer assembly for wear. Replace components as necessary.

4) Install needle bearing, 2nd gear, synchronizer assembly, bearing sleeve, needle bearing, 1st gear and bearing spacer onto rear of mainshaft. Press bearing spacer forward and check end play of 2nd and 1st gears. End play should be .002-.008" (.05-.20 mm). *See Fig. 7*.

INPUT SHAFT

Disassembly, Cleaning & Inspection

1) Check front end outside and inside diameter of needle bearing area for damage or wear. Check synchronizer conical surface for wear or damage. Check gear and splines for damage or wear.

2) Rotate input shaft ball bearing and check for noise or roughness. Replace bearing, if necessary, using Bearing Puller (MD998056). Check conical surface of gear for wear or damage.

Reassembly

To install input shaft ball bearing, use Bearing Installer (MD998029). Install selective fit snap ring to obtain clearance between snap ring and bearing of 0-.002" (0-.05 mm). See INPUT SHAFT SNAP RING table.

INPUT SHAFT SNAP RING

Application (Color)	Thickness In. (mm)
No Color	.091 (2.30)
Red	.092 (2.35)
White	.094 (2.40)
Blue	.096 (2.45)
Green	.098 (2.50)

COUNTERGEAR & REVERSE IDLER

Cleaning & Inspection

Check gears for wear, damage or tooth failure. Check bearings and thrust washers for wear or damage. Check shafts for scoring, wear or damage.

Manual Transmissions
CHRYSLER CORP. IMPORTS & MITSUBISHI KM130 4-SPEED (Cont.)

Fig. 8: Checking Input Shaft Bearing End Play

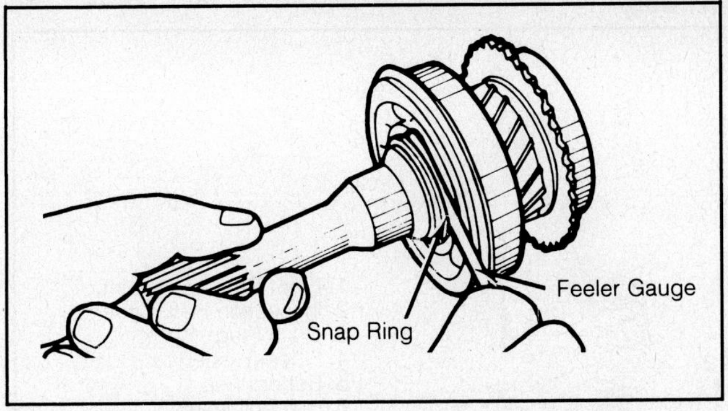

SHIFTING MECHANISM & COMPONENTS

Removal

Using a 3/16" (4.76 mm) punch, remove gear shifter locking pin. Remove control shaft assembly. Press gear shifter forward and pull lock pin off, being careful not to bend control shaft.

Cleaning & Inspection

Check shift rails and forks for smooth operation and excessive scoring. Check clearances as previously described. Check detent slots for wear. Check detent spring height. See DETENT SPRING SPECIFICATIONS table.

DETENT SPRING SPECIFICATIONS

Application	In. (mm)
Free Length	.744 (18.9)
Compressed Length @ 8.8 Lbs. (4 kg)	.598 (15.2)

TRANSMISSION REASSEMBLY

1) Insert mainshaft assembly into transmission case. Install needle bearing to front end of mainshaft. Install synchronizer ring to 3rd-4th synchronizer assembly. Install input shaft into front of transmission case. Install 1st-2nd and 3rd-4th shift forks to synchronizer sleeve groove.

2) Insert countergear into transmission case. Install snap ring to countergear front bearing. Install bearing into case by driving on outer race. Install snap ring to countergear rear bearing and install bearing and snap ring into place with Bearing Installer (MD998199).

3) Install input shaft bearing on input shaft, using Bearing Installer (MD998029). Install input shaft assembly into case using Bearing Installer (MD998067). Ensure synchronizer assembly is properly positioned while installing input shaft.

4) Install large snap ring on input shaft bearing. Select and install thickest input shaft snap ring that will fit in snap ring groove. See INPUT SHAFT SNAP RING table.

5) Install front bearing retainer with spacer to obtain clearance of 0-.004" (0-.1 mm). *See Fig. 9* and FRONT BEARING RETAINER SPACER table. Coat both sides of front bearing retainer packing with sealant. Apply gear oil to lip of seal. Install packing and oil seal. Apply Loctite to rear bearing retainer screws. Install rear bearing retainer and tighten screws.

INPUT SHAFT SNAP RING

Identification Color	Thickness Inches (mm)
White	.091 (2.30)
None	.092 (2.35)
Red	.094 (2.40)
Blue	.096 (2.45)
Yellow	.098 (2.50)

Fig. 9: Measuring Front Bearing-to-Retainer Clearance

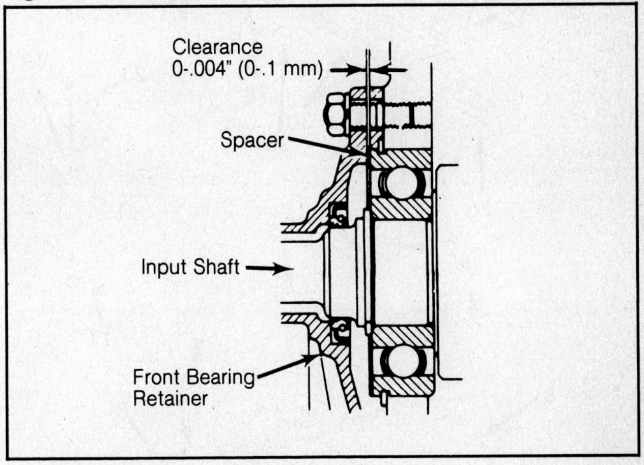

FRONT BEARING RETAINER SPACER

Application (Color)	Thickness In. (mm)
Black	.033 (.84)
No Color	.037 (.94)
Red	.040 (1.02)
White	.044 (1.12)
Yellow	.047 (1.19)
Blue	.051 (1.30)
Green	.054 (1.37)

6) Install reverse gear onto mainshaft and tighten lock nut. After tightening, lock the nut at notch on mainshaft. Install spacer and counter reverse gear to countergear rear end. Install snap ring so that counter reverse gear end play is 0-.003" (0-.08 mm). See COUNTER REVERSE GEAR SNAP RING table.

COUNTER REVERSE GEAR SNAP RING

Application (Color)	Thickness In. (mm)
Blue	.059 (1.5)
None	.063 (1.6)
None	.067 (1.7)
Blue	.071 (1.8)
Green	.075 (1.9)
Brown	.079 (2.0)

7) Install 3rd-4th and 1st-2nd shift forks onto synchronizer sleeves. Insert shift rails from rear of transmission case. Lock shift forks and rails with spring pins. Install interlock plungers between shift rails. Spring pins should have slits in axial direction of shift rail.

Manual Transmissions

CHRYSLER CORP. IMPORTS & MITSUBISHI KM130 4-SPEED (Cont.)

Fig. 10: Exploded View of Chrysler Corp. KM130 4-Speed Transmission

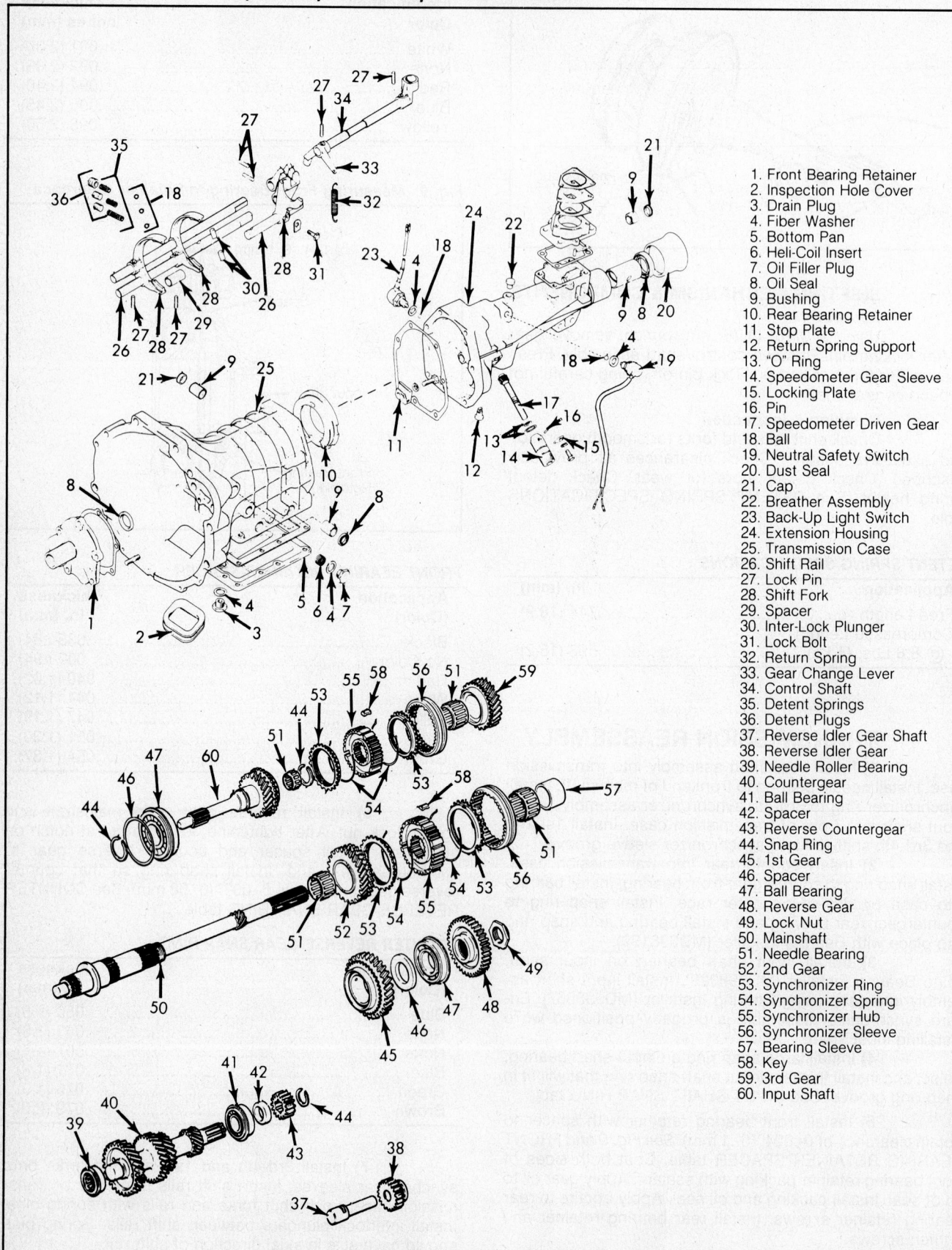

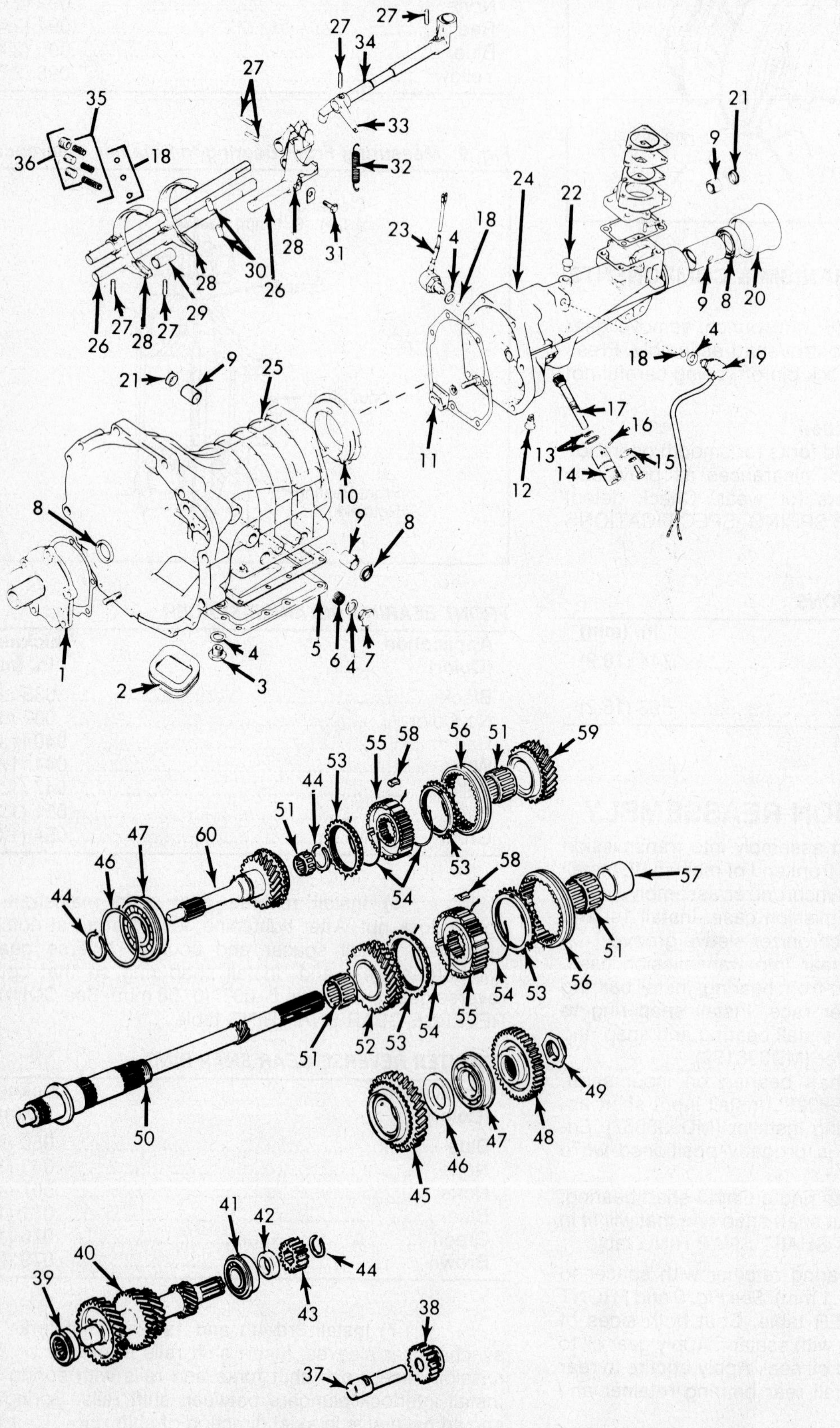

1. Front Bearing Retainer
2. Inspection Hole Cover
3. Drain Plug
4. Fiber Washer
5. Bottom Pan
6. Heli-Coil Insert
7. Oil Filler Plug
8. Oil Seal
9. Bushing
10. Rear Bearing Retainer
11. Stop Plate
12. Return Spring Support
13. "O" Ring
14. Speedometer Gear Sleeve
15. Locking Plate
16. Pin
17. Speedometer Driven Gear
18. Ball
19. Neutral Safety Switch
20. Dust Seal
21. Cap
22. Breather Assembly
23. Back-Up Light Switch
24. Extension Housing
25. Transmission Case
26. Shift Rail
27. Lock Pin
28. Shift Fork
29. Spacer
30. Inter-Lock Plunger
31. Lock Bolt
32. Return Spring
33. Gear Change Lever
34. Control Shaft
35. Detent Springs
36. Detent Plugs
37. Reverse Idler Gear Shaft
38. Reverse Idler Gear
39. Needle Roller Bearing
40. Countergear
41. Ball Bearing
42. Spacer
43. Reverse Countergear
44. Snap Ring
45. 1st Gear
46. Spacer
47. Ball Bearing
48. Reverse Gear
49. Lock Nut
50. Mainshaft
51. Needle Bearing
52. 2nd Gear
53. Synchronizer Ring
54. Synchronizer Spring
55. Synchronizer Hub
56. Synchronizer Sleeve
57. Bearing Sleeve
58. Key
59. 3rd Gear
60. Input Shaft

8) Install reverse shift rail and fork assembly together with reverse idler gear. Insert detent ball and spring (small end toward ball) into each shift rail. Tighten all plugs to a depth of .24" (6.1 mm) then apply sealant to fill plug holes.

9) Apply sealant to both sides of extension housing gasket. Install gasket and housing. When installing extension housing, rotate control lever to the left. Put sealant on extension housing bolts before installation.

10) Apply gear oil to speedometer driven gear and install with sleeve. Ensure number on sleeve (corresponding to number of teeth on gear) is aligned with mark on housing when gear and sleeve are installed. Install clamp and tighten bolt.

11) Install back-up light switch with steel ball. Install bottom pan. Fill gear shifter area with grease and install shifter lever. Fill transmission with SAE 80 gear oil.

TIGHTENING SPECIFICATIONS

Application	Ft. Lbs. (N.m)
Back-Up Light Switch	22 (30)
Drain Plug	43 (58)
Idler Shaft Set Screw	15-43 (20-58)
Mainshaft Lock Nut	72-94 (98-127)
Oil Filler Plug	22-25 (30-34)
Reverse Shaft Nut	15-43 (20-58)
Starter Mounting Bolts	16-23 (22-31)
Transmission Mounting Bolts	31-40 (42-54)
Transmission-to-Insulator Nut	15-17 (20-24)
	INCH Lbs.
Clutch Cable Bracket Bolts	84-108 (9.5-12)
Pan Attaching Bolts	72-84 (8-9.5)

Manual Transmissions

CHRYSLER CORP. IMPORTS & MITSUBISHI KM132/145 5-SPEED

Chrysler Corp. Conquest, Ram-50
Mitsubishi Montero, Pickup, Starion

IDENTIFICATION

Transmission may be identified by a serial number stamped on clutch housing.

DESCRIPTION

The KM 132 (2WD) and KM 145 (4WD) transmissions are 5-speed fully synchronized type with constant mesh in all forward gears. Forward gears are helical type. Reverse gear is a non-synchronized spur type. First through 3rd gears are located in transmission case, 4th gear is direct, 5th and reverse gears are located in the extension housing (2WD). Shift lever assembly is located on the top of extension housing or transfer case.

LUBRICATION & ADJUSTMENT

See appropriate MANUAL TRANSMISSION SERVICING article in IMPORT GENERAL SERVICING section.

TROUBLE SHOOTING

DIFFICULTY MESHING GEARS

Malfunction of gearshift lever or control shaft. Synchronizer rings or gear conical surfaces worn or excessive play. Synchronizer shift keys worn or damaged.

JUMPS OUT OF GEAR

Shifting forks worn or detent springs broken. Mainshaft or mainshaft support bearings worn or damaged. Clearance between synchronizer hub and sleeve excessive. Gears or gear bushings worn. Countergear worn.

NOISE IN TRANSMISSION

Lubricating oil incorrect or insufficient. Gears or bearings worn. Mainshaft spline worn or damaged.

REMOVAL & INSTALLATION

TRANSMISSION

See appropriate MANUAL TRANSMISSION REMOVAL article in IMPORT GENERAL SERVICING section. On 4WD models, transfer case may be removed with or without transmission assembly.

TRANSMISSION DISASSEMBLY

NOTE: **Gasoline engine truck models use a mechanical cable-operated clutch. Diesel engine truck and all car models use a hydraulic clutch.**

1) To remove transfer case assembly on 4WD models, remove back-up light switch and steel ball from lower right adapter. Remove plug from right side of transfer case. Remove select spring and select plunger. Remove 6 control lever assembly mounting bolts.

2) Remove control lever and gasket. Remove plugs from top of adapter. Remove detent spring and ball. Remove neutral return springs and plungers. Remove shifter spring pin using a pin punch.

3) Remove transfer case-to-adapter nuts and bolts. Remove transfer case and remove shifter from control shaft. To disassemble transfer case, see appropriate TRANSFER CASE article in IMPORT FWD AXLE SHAFTS, OVERDRIVES & TRANSFER CASES section.

4) On gasoline engine truck models, remove return clip, clutch release bearing and carrier. Using a 3/16" (4.76 mm) punch, drive spring pin from clutch release shaft. *See Fig. 1*. Remove shaft, felt packing, return spring(s) and clutch release fork.

Fig. 1: Removing Spring Pin From Clutch Release Shaft

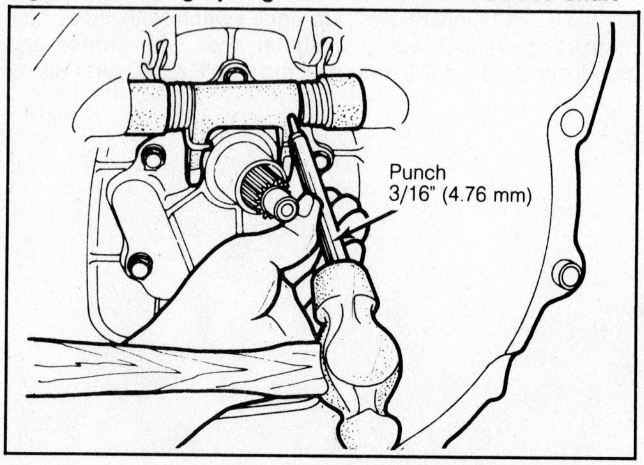

5) On diesel engine truck and all car models, remove 2 return clips and remove throwout bearing. Remove boot from transmission case. Pull release fork to disengage it from pivot. Remove release fork.

6) On Conquest and Starion models, remove control lever assembly. Remove extension housing cover and gasket. Remove resistance spring and ball from extension housing. Remove both neutral return plunger plugs, springs and plungers. *See Fig. 11*. Remove back-up light switch and steel ball.

7) Remove speedometer sleeve clamp. Remove speedometer sleeve assembly. Remove extension housing mounting bolts. Push shifter down to left side to move control finger from selector grooves.

8) On all other models, remove back-up light switch and steel ball. Remove extension housing bolts. Loosen neutral return plunger plug "B". Rotate shifter toward left side of housing. *See Fig. 2*.

9) On all models, slide extension housing from transmission case and mainshaft. Remove transmission lower cover. On Pickup and Montero models, remove snap ring and bearing from rear end of mainshaft. Remove 3 detent plugs, springs and balls.

10) On all models, using a 3/16" (4.76 mm) punch, drive 3rd-4th and 1st-2nd spring pins from shift forks. Remove 5th-reverse spring pin. On Pickup and Montero models, remove shift rails and forks. *See Fig. 3*.

11) On all models, place transmission with front side down. Remove mainshaft rear bearing and snap rings. Bend back mainshaft and countershaft lock washer tabs. Loosen mainshaft and countershaft nuts. Nuts can be loosened by double-engaging 2nd and reverse gears to lock mainshaft and countergear.

Manual Transmissions

CHRYSLER CORP. IMPORTS & MITSUBISHI KM132/145 5-SPEED (Cont.)

Fig. 2: Separating Extension Housing From Transmission

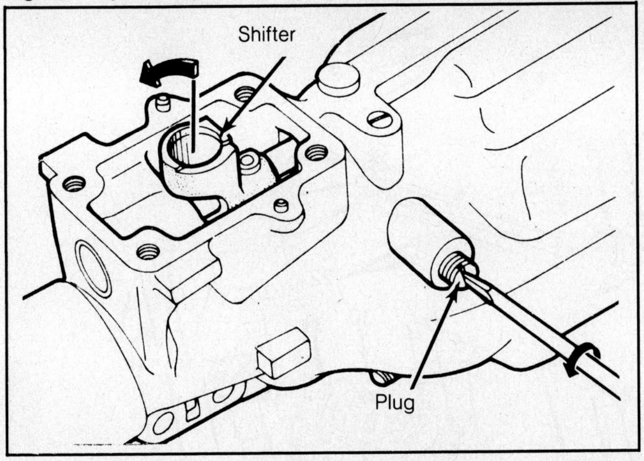

Fig. 3: Driving Out 5th-Reverse Spring Pin

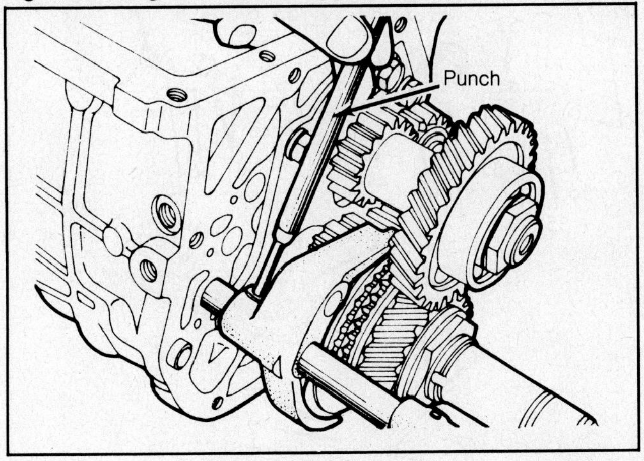

12) On Conquest and Starion models, remove detent plugs, springs and balls. On all models, remove counter 5th gear and bearing using a puller. *See Fig. 4.* Remove gear, bearing and 1-2 shift rail at same time. Remove spacers and reverse gear from countergear shaft.

Fig. 4: Removing 5th Gear and Bearing From Countergear

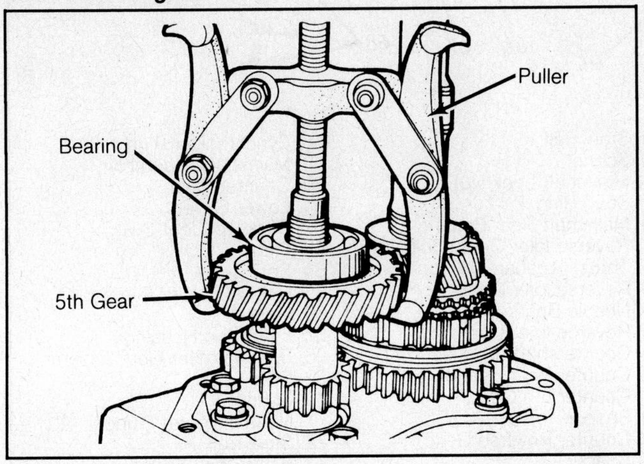

13) Remove 3-4 shift rail toward rear of case. Remove 5th-reverse shift rail and shift fork. Remove interlock plungers from case. Remove spacer, steel ball, 5th gear, needle bearing and bearing spacer from mainshaft. Remove bearing sleeve, 5th gear synchronizer assembly, stopper plate and spacer from mainshaft.

14) On Pickup and Montero models, remove synchronizer hub and 5th gear bearing sleeve using Bearing Puller (MD998056) and Adapter (MB998056-10). Remove synchronizer key, stop plate and distance spacer from mainshaft. Remove cotter pin from reverse idler gear shaft.

15) On all models, remove reverse idler gear shaft locking nut. Remove thrust washer, reverse idler gear and needle bearing. Remove reverse idler gear shaft retaining bolts. Working from inside case, use a punch to drive reverse idler shaft from case. *See Fig. 5.*

Fig. 5: Driving Reverse Idler Shaft From Transmission Case

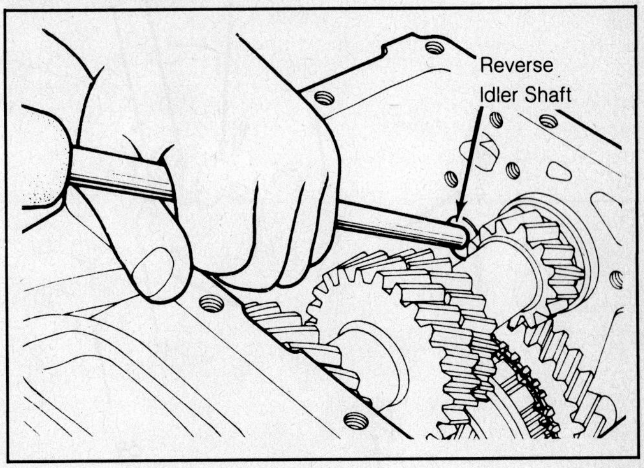

16) Remove front and rear bearing retainers from case. Remove main drive gear and main drive gear bearing snap rings. Remove main drive gear bearing using Bearing Puller (MB998056).

17) Remove mainshaft center bearing snap ring. Remove mainshaft center bearing using Bearing Puller (MB998020) and Adapter (MB998028). Remove snap ring from front countergear bearing. Remove rear countergear bearing snap ring. Remove rear countergear bearing using Bearing Puller (MD998192). Remove front countergear bearing using Bearing Puller (MD998192).

18) Pull countergear up in case and remove main drive gear with bearing toward front of case. Remove countergear from transmission case. Remove shift forks from mainshaft. Remove mainshaft bearing snap ring and pull bearing from case and shaft. Remove mainshaft assembly from case. *See Fig. 7.*

CLEANING & INSPECTION

1) All parts should be thoroughly washed in cleaning solvent and air dried. Remove old gaskets with stiff brush or scraper. Rinse bearings in clean solvent and air dry. DO NOT spin bearings dry.

2) Lubricate with light grade oil and wrap in clean paper until ready to install. Examine all gear teeth and splines for chips, wear, breaks or nicks. Check transmission case and extension housing for cracks and damage.

3) Check bearings and synchronizers for wear, damage and proper fit. Lubricate all moving parts before installation. Use new gaskets, seals and snap rings.

Manual Transmissions

CHRYSLER CORP. IMPORTS & MITSUBISHI KM132/145 5-SPEED (Cont.)

Fig. 6: Exploded View of Chrysler Corp. KM132 5-Speed Transmission Assembly

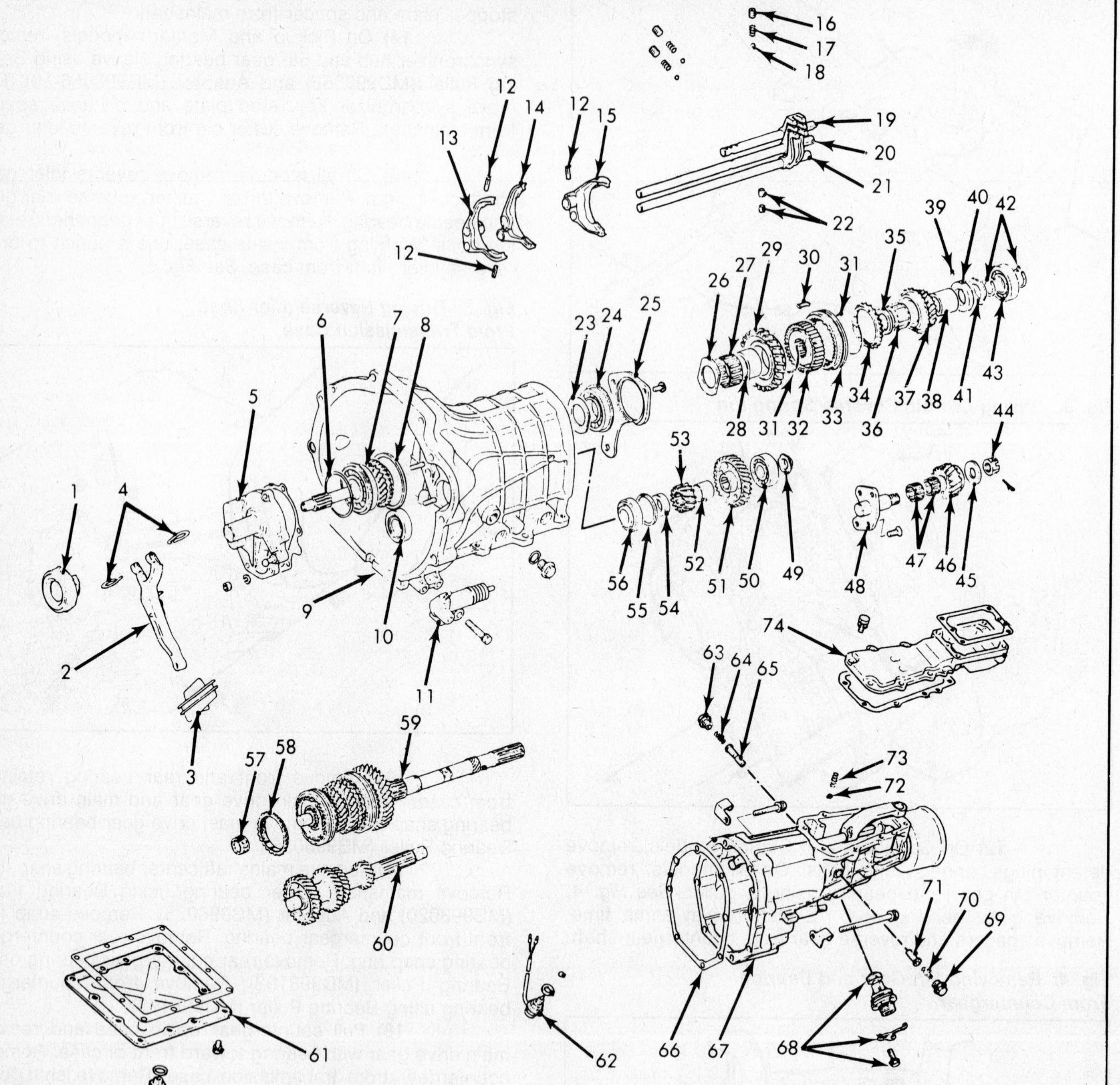

1. Throwout Bearing
2. Release Fork
3. Dust Boot
4. Clips
5. Front Bearing Retainer
6. Snap Ring
7. Input Shaft Assembly
8. Spacer
9. Transmission Case
10. Front Counter Gear Bearing
11. Clutch Release Cylinder
12. Spring Pin
13. 3rd-4th Shift Fork
14. 1st-2nd Shift Fork
15. 5th-Reverse Shift Fork
16. Detent Plug
17. Detent Spring
18. Detent Ball
19. 5th-Reverse Shift Rail
20. 3rd-4th Shift Rail
21. 1st-2nd Shift Rail
22. Interlock Plunger
23. Spacer
24. Mainshaft Center Bearing
25. Bearing Retainer
26. Spacer
27. Needle Bearing
28. Bearing Sleeve
29. Reverse Gear
30. Synchronizer Key
31. Synchronizer Spring
32. Synchronizer Hub
33. Synchronizer Sleeve
34. Synchronizer Ring
35. Spacer
36. Needle Bearing
37. 5th Gear
38. Bearing Sleeve
39. Steel Ball
40. Spacer
41. Mainshaft Lock Nut
42. Snap Ring
43. Mainshaft Rear Bearing
44. Reverse Idler Gear Lock Nut
45. Thrust Washer
46. Reverse Idler Gear
47. Needle Bearing
48. Reverse Idler Gear Shaft
49. Countershaft Lock Nut
50. Counter Rear Bearing
51. Counter 5th Gear
52. Spacer
53. Counter Reverse Gear
54. Spacer
55. Spacer
56. Counter Center Bearing
57. Needle Bearing
58. Synchronizer Ring
59. Mainshaft Assembly
60. Counter Gear
61. Lower Cover
62. Back-Up Light Switch
63. Plug
64. Spring
65. Neutral Return Plunger "B"
66. Gasket
67. Extension Housing
68. Speedometer Gear Assembly
69. Plug
70. Spring
71. Neutral Return Plunger "A"
72. Steel Ball
73. Resistance Spring
74. Extension Housing Cover

Hydraulic clutch models are shown.

Manual Transmissions

CHRYSLER CORP. IMPORTS & MITSUBISHI KM132/145 5-SPEED (Cont.)

Fig. 7: Removing Mainshaft Bearing From Transmission Case

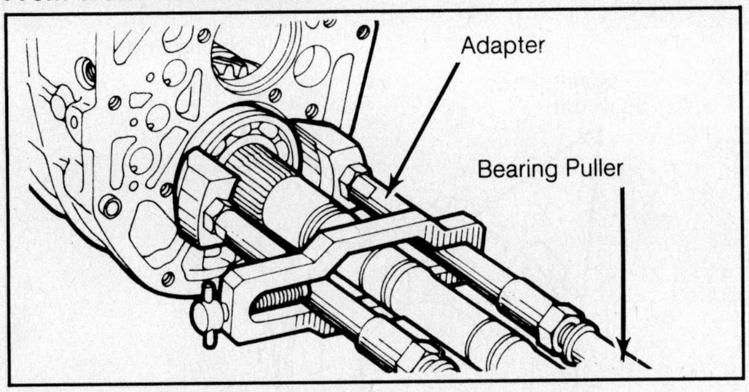

COMPONENT DISASSEMBLY & REASSEMBLY

MAINSHAFT

Disassembly

1) On Conquest and Starion models, support 2nd gear on press plate. Press bearing inner race, gear bearing sleeve, 1st gear, 1st-2nd synchronizer and 2nd gear from rear of mainshaft. Remove snap ring from front end of mainshaft. Remove 3rd-4th synchronizer, 3rd gear and needle bearing.

2) On Pickup and Montero models, remove 1st gear and inner race of bearing using bearing puller. Remove 1st-2nd synchronizer and 2nd gear off rear of mainshaft. Remove snap ring from front of mainshaft. Slide 3rd-4th synchronizer and 3rd gear from mainshaft.

Cleaning & Inspection

1) Clean and inspect mainshaft and gear assemblies. Check mainshaft O.D. and splines for wear or damage. Check gear teeth for wear or damage. Check I.D. of gear. Inspect synchronizer cone surface for wear or damage.

TRANSMISSION GEAR STANDARD DIMENSIONS

Application	Specification In. (mm)
1st & 2nd Gear I.D.	1.89 (48.0)
3rd & 5th Gear I.D.	1.58 (40.1)
Reverse Idler Gear I. D.	.79 (20.1)
Countergear Forward O.D.	.98 (25.0)

2) On synchronizer rings, check gear teeth and ring I.D. for wear and damage. Place ring on mating gear and measure dimension "A". *See Fig. 8.* Standard value is .031" (.80 mm). If clearance is considerably less, replace ring. With hub and sleeve assembled, check for excessive clearance and see if parts slide smoothly.

NOTE: If sleeve or hub need replacing, always replace them as an assembly. Check shift fork groove in sleeve for wear.

Reassembly

1) Assemble 1st-2nd and 3rd-4th synchronizers. *See Fig. 10.* Place needle bearing, 3rd gear, synchronizer ring and 3rd-4th synchronizer assembly on front of mainshaft.

2) Synchronizer sleeve has a tooth missing in 3 or 6 positions. Assemble hub to sleeve so that center tooth

Fig. 8: Measuring Synchronizer Ring-to-Gear Clearance

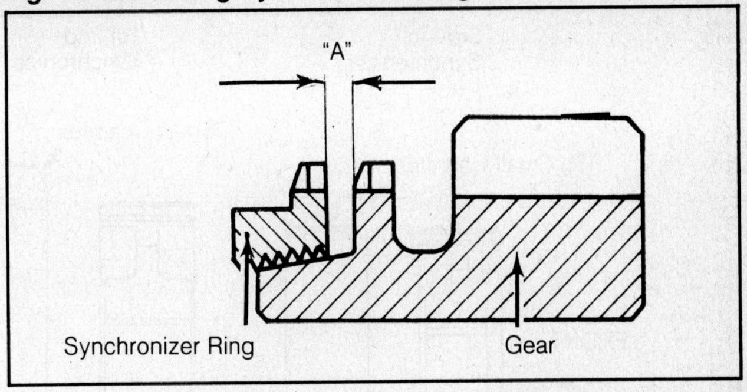

between 2 missing teeth will touch synchronizer key. Install 1st-2nd synchronizer hub and sleeve. Ensure synchronizer hub and sleeve are reinstalled in original directions.

3) Install thickest snap ring that will fit in snap ring groove on front of mainshaft. Ensure 3rd gear rotates smoothly. Install 1st-2nd synchronizer hub and sleeve. Ensure synchronizer hub and sleeve are reinstalled in original directions.

Fig. 9: Measuring Synchronizer Hub End Play

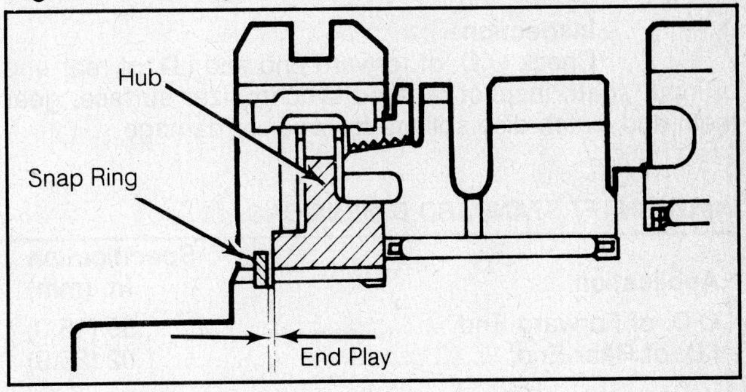

4) Place needle bearing, 2nd gear, synchronizer assembly, synchronizer ring, bearing sleeve, needle bearing, 1st gear and bearing spacer on mainshaft from rear. Pressing forward with bearing spacer, measure 1st and 2nd gear end play. End play should be as shown in SYNCHRONIZER SNAP RING END PLAY table.

SYNCHRONIZER SNAP RING END PLAY

Application	Clearance In. (mm)
1st & 2nd Gear End Play	.002-.008 (.05-.20)
3rd Gear End Play	.002-.008 (.05-.20)
3rd & 4th Synchronizer Hub End Play	0-.003 (0-.08)

NOTE: Synchronizer snap rings are available in different sizes, from .085" (2.15 mm) to .093" (2.36 mm).

INPUT SHAFT

Disassembly

Remove main drive gear and bearing snap rings. Remove bearing from main drive gear using Bearing Puller (MB998020).

Fig. 10: Synchronizer Assembly and Spring Location

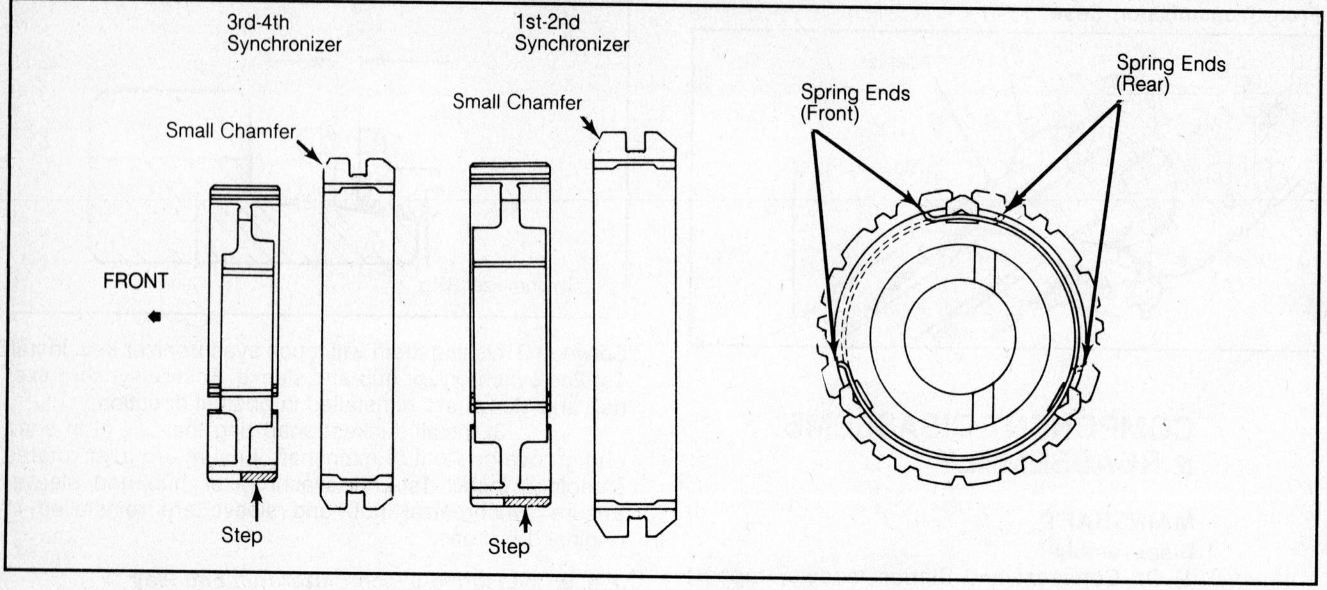

Inspection

Check O.D. of forward end and I.D. of rear end of input shaft. Inspect tapered synchronizer surface, gear teeth and clutch disc splines for wear or damage.

INPUT SHAFT STANDARD DIMENSIONS

Application	Specification In. (mm)
O.D. of Forward End	.59 (15.0)
I.D. of Rear End	1.02 (25.9)

Reassembly

Press ball bearing onto input shaft using Bearing Installer (MD998029). Install thickest main drive gear snap ring that will fit in snap ring groove.

REVERSE IDLER SHAFT

Disassembly

Remove reverse idler gear lock nut. Remove thrust washer, reverse idler gear and needle bearing from shaft. Remove reverse idler gear shaft retaining bolts. Working from inside case, use a punch to drive reverse idler shaft from case. *See Fig. 6.*

Inspection

Check shaft O.D. for wear or damage. O.D. should be .63" (16.0 mm).

Reassembly

Install reverse idler gear shaft, using retaining bolts as a guide. Install needle bearing, reverse idler gear and thrust washer. Ensure thrust washer is installed with rounded edge toward front of case. Install lock nut. Set reverse idler gear end play to .005-.011" (.13-.28 mm), using proper thickness thrust washer. Install lock nut and cotter pin.

SHIFTING MECHANISMS

Disassembly

See TRANSMISSION DISASSEMBLY in this article for shifting mechanism disassembly.

Inspection

Check shift fork ends for wear or damage. Check each shift rail for warpage and detent ball slot for wear. Check forward end of control finger and shift lug groove for wear. Replace any worn or damaged parts.

SHIFT MECHANISM STANDARD DIMENSIONS

Application	Specification In. (mm)
Shift Fork, Sleeve Groove	.197 (5.00)
Shift Fork-to-Sleeve	.004-.012 (.10-.30)
Shift Fork-to-Sleeve (5th Gear)	.006-.014 (.15-.36)
Warpage of Shift Rail	.0016 (.04) Max.
Control Finger-to-Shift Lug	.004-.012 (.10-.30)
Detent Spring Length	.744 (18.90)

Reassembly

See TRANSMISSION REASSEMBLY in this article for shift mechanism reassembly.

EXTENSION HOUSING

Disassembly

1) Remove locking plate and speedometer driven gear. Remove 3 screw plugs, springs, and detent balls. Remove neutral return plungers ("A" and "B") from housing. *See Fig. 11.*

2) Press gear shifter all the way forward in housing. Using a 3/16" (4.76 mm) punch, drive spring pins from shifter and neutral return finger. Separate shifter and control shaft by pulling shaft out front of housing.

Inspection

Inspect forward end of neutral return plunger and detent ball slot for wear. Check neutral return springs and detent spring for collapsing or beakage. Length of neutral return springs is 1.65" (42 mm) and detent spring is 1.10" (28 mm).

Reassembly

See TRANSMISSION REASSEMBLY in this article for extension housing reassembly.

Fig. 11: Removing Neutral Return Plungers From Extension Housing

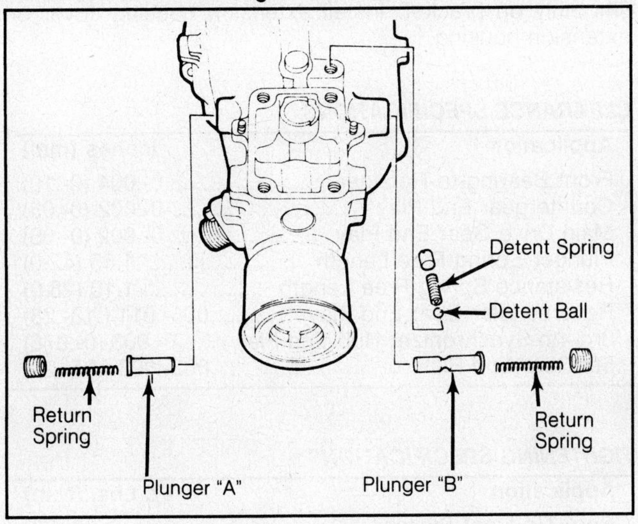

TRANSMISSION REASSEMBLY

NOTE: **Replace all gaskets, seals and spring pins with new ones. Oil all rolling or sliding parts and grease seal lips before reassembly.**

1) Place mainshaft assembly into transmission case. Install needle bearing on front end of mainshaft. Install synchronizer, then slide input shaft assembly into transmission case with needle bearing engaging end of mainshaft. Install 1st-2nd and 3rd-4th shift forks in synchronizer sleeve grooves.

2) Position countergear into case. Install respective snap rings on front needle bearing and rear ball bearing. Drive needle bearing and ball bearing into case. Install front bearing retainer with a bearing spacer which will give a clearance of 0-.004" (0-.1 mm) at dimension "C". *See Fig. 12*. Apply sealer to both sides of gasket.

FRONT BEARING RETAINER SPACER SIZES

Identification Color	Thickness In. (mm)
Black	.033 (.84)
None	.037 (.94)
Red	.040 (1.0)
White	.044 (1.1)
Yellow	.047 (1.2)
Blue	.051 (1.3)
Green	.054 (1.4)

3) Install rear bearing retainer. Place reverse idler shaft into position and install bolts to act as guides. Using a large drift, drive reverse idler shaft into case.

4) Install needle bearing, reverse idler gear and thrust washer with ground side facing gear. Install and tighten castle nut. Install cotter pin and check reverse idler gear end play. Ensure end play between washer and gear is .005-011" (.13-.28 mm). *See Fig. 13*.

5) Assemble 5th gear synchronizer. *See Fig. 14*. Install spacer, stop plate, synchronizer assembly, 5th gear bearing sleeve, needle bearing, synchronizer ring and 5th gear onto mainshaft from the rear end. Install and tighten lock nut, staking it at a notch in mainshaft.

Fig. 12: Retainer-to-Bearing Clearance Measurement

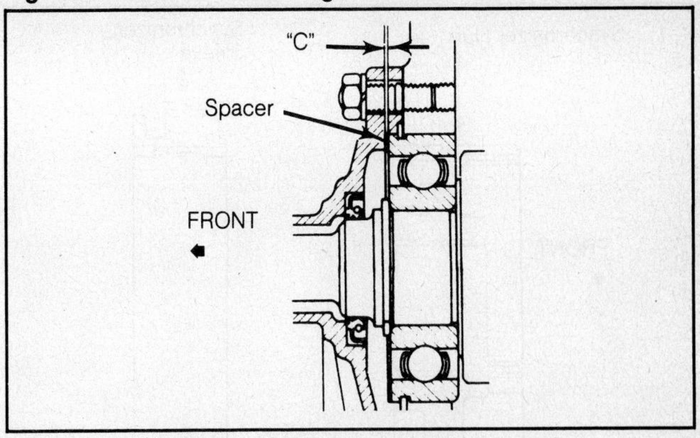

Fig. 13: Checking Reverse Idler Gear End Play

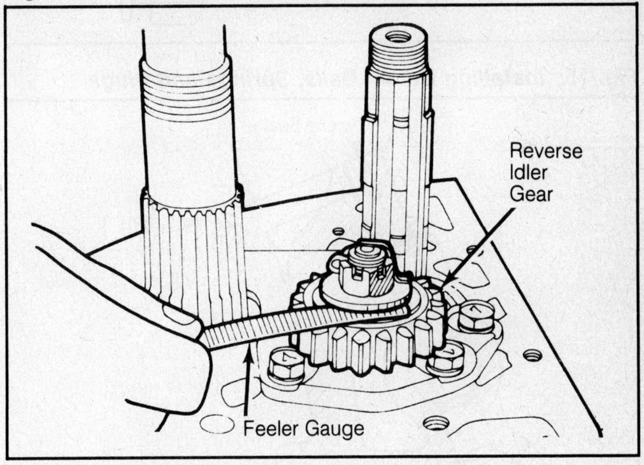

6) End play measured between 5th gear and lock nut should be .002-.008" (.05-.20 mm). Install spacer, counter reverse gear, spacer, 5th countergear and bearing onto countershaft gear from rear end. Tighten lock nut and stake into notch at rear end of countergear.

7) Insert 1st-2nd and 3rd-4th shift forks in their respective synchronizer sleeves. Slide shift rails into position and install shift fork spring pin. Install interlock plunger between shift rails.

8) Install all 3 detent balls and springs with small end of spring facing ball. Screw detent plugs, to a depth of approximately .24" (6.1 mm) into case, and apply sealer to head of plugs. *See Fig. 15*.

9) Install snap ring in forward groove of mainshaft. Install bearing retaining snap ring. Install speedometer gear snap ring and speedometer gear. Apply sealer to both sides of extension housing gasket and position on housing.

10) While holding shifter fully to the left, slide housing onto mainshaft. Ensure forward end of control finger is snugly fitted in slot of shift lug. Apply sealer to threads of attaching bolts and tighten bolts.

11) Install neutral return plungers "A" and "B", springs and plugs. Then install detent ball, spring and plug. Screw all plugs flush with housing and apply sealer to head of plugs. *See Fig. 16*.

12) Using sealer, install speedometer drive lock plate. Place steel ball in position and screw back-up light switch into housing. Install bottom pan and gasket.

Manual Transmissions

CHRYSLER CORP. IMPORTS & MITSUBISHI KM132/145 5-SPEED (Cont.)

Fig. 14: 5th Gear Synchronizer Assembly

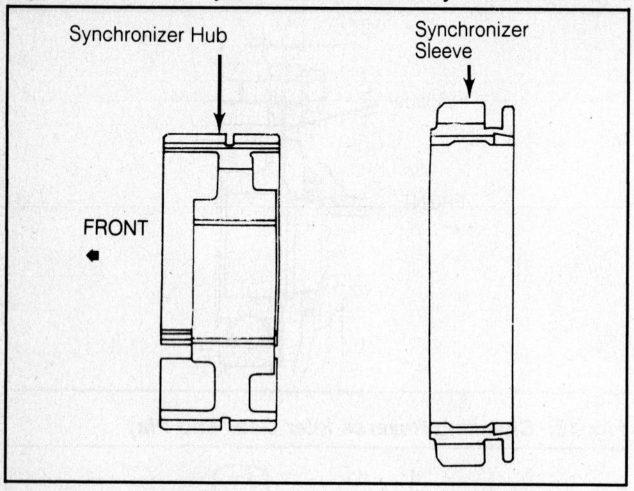

Fig. 15: Installing Detent Balls, Springs and Plugs

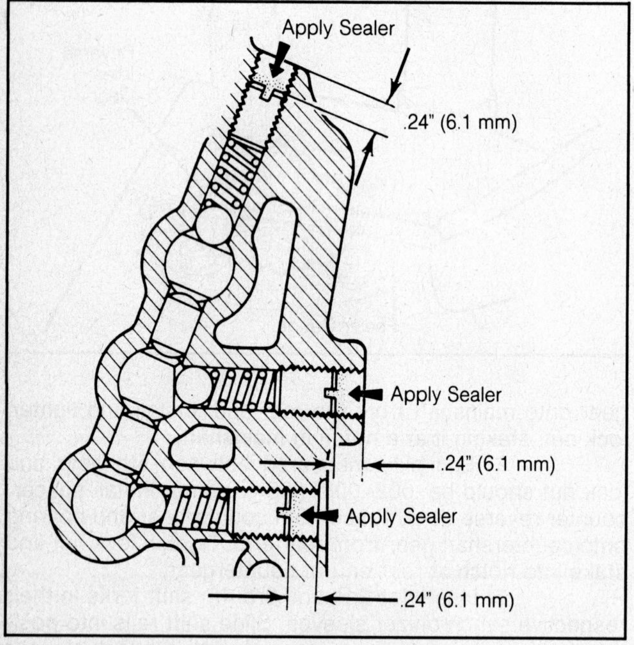

Fig. 16: Installing Neutral Return Plungers

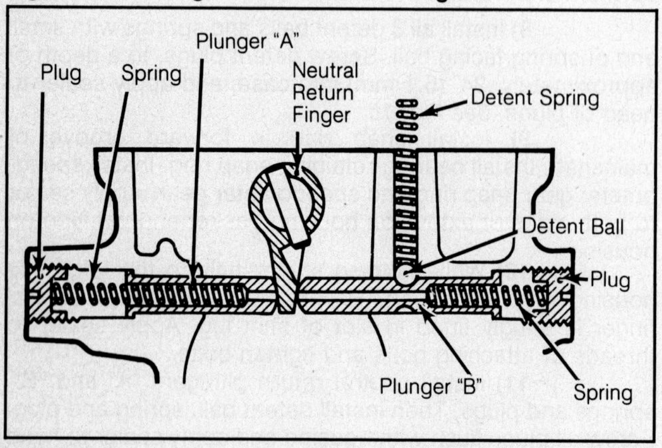

13) Install stopper bracket assembly to extension housing cover. Ensure reverse resistance plate moves smoothly on bracket. Install extension housing cover on extension housing.

CLEARANCE SPECIFICATIONS

Application	Inches (mm)
Front Bearing-to-Retainer	0-.004 (0-.10)
Countergear End Play	0-.002 (0-.05)
Main Drive Gear End Play	0-.002 (0-.05)
Plunger Spring Free Length	1.65 (42.0)
Resistance Spring Free Length	1.10 (28.0)
Reverse Idler Gear End Play	.005-.011 (.13-.28)
3rd-4th Synchronizer Hub End Play	0-.003 (0-.076)
5th Gear End Play	.002-.008 (.05-.20)

TIGHTENING SPECIFICATIONS

Application	Ft. Lbs. (N.m)
Back-Up Light Switch	22 (30)
Countershaft Lock Nut	116-137 (157-186)
Drain Plug	44 (60)
Idler Shaft Lock Nut	15-43 (20-58)
Mainshaft Lock Nut	196-216 (266-293)
Starter Mounting Bolt	16-23 (22-31)
Transmission Case-to-Engine Bolts	31-40 (42-54)
	INCH Lbs. (N.m)
Lower Cover	72-84 (8-9)

CHRYSLER CORP. IMPORTS & MITSUBISHI KM 161, 162 & 163 4 & 5-SPEED TRANSAXLES

Chrysler Corp. Colt, Colt Vista
Mitsubishi Cordia, Mirage, Tredia

IDENTIFICATION

Transmission may be identified by a serial number stamped on clutch housing.

DESCRIPTION

Colt models use KM 161 (4-speed) and KM 162 (5-speed) transaxles. Colt Turbo models use KM 163 (5-speed) transaxle. Colt Vista models use KM 163 (5-speed) transaxle. Cordia and Tredia models use KM 163 (5-speed) transaxle. Mirage models use KM 161 (4-speed) and KM 162 (5-speed) transaxles. Mirage Turbo models use KM 163 (5-speed) transaxle.

All transaxles are fully synchronized and incorporate an input shaft, intermediate shaft and output shaft. The differential assembly consists of a differential drive gear in mesh with output shaft gear, side gears and pinion gears.

LUBRICATION & ADJUSTMENT

See appropriate MANUAL TRANSMISSION SERVICING article in IMPORT GENERAL SERVICING section.

TROUBLE SHOOTING

DIFFICULTY MESHING GEARS

Malfunction of gearshift lever or control shaft. Synchro rings or gear conical surfaces worn or excessive play. Synchro shift keys worn or damaged.

JUMPS OUT OF GEAR

Shifting forks worn or detent springs broken. Mainshaft or mainshaft support bearings worn or damaged. Clearance between synchro hub and sleeve excessive. Gears or gear bushings worn. Countergear worn.

INTERNAL NOISES

Lubrication oil incorrect or insufficient. Gears or bearings worn. Mainshaft spline worn or damaged.

DRIVE AXLE SHAFTS

See appropriate DRIVE AXLE SHAFT article in IMPORT FWD AXLE SHAFTS, OVERDRIVES & TRANSFER CASES section.

SERVICE (IN VEHICLE)

TRANSAXLE MOUNTS

Removal & Installation

1) Support engine and transaxle assembly. Remove battery and battery tray. On turbocharged models, remove air cleaner assembly. On 5-speed models, remove select control valve. On all models, remove transaxle mount insulator bolts.

2) Remove cap from inside of right inner fender shield. Remove transaxle insulator bracket mounting bolts. Remove transaxle insulator bracket. To install, reverse removal procedure.

REMOVAL & INSTALLATION

TRANSAXLE

See appropriate MANUAL TRANSMISSION REMOVAL article in IMPORT GENERAL SERVICING section. Tighten engine-to-transaxle mounting bolts to specification. *See Fig. 1.*

Fig. 1: Engine-to-Transaxle Mounting Specifications

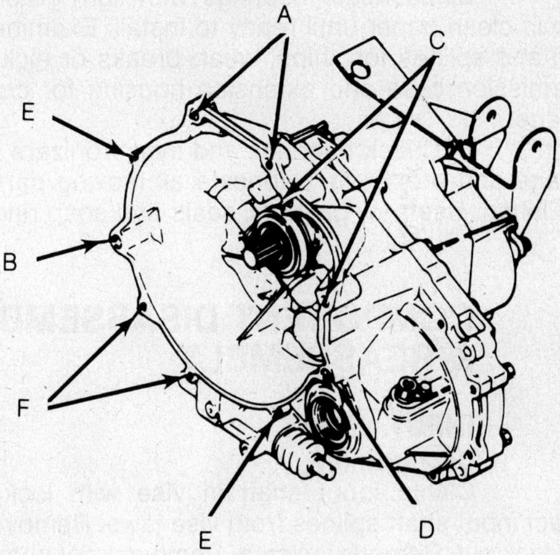

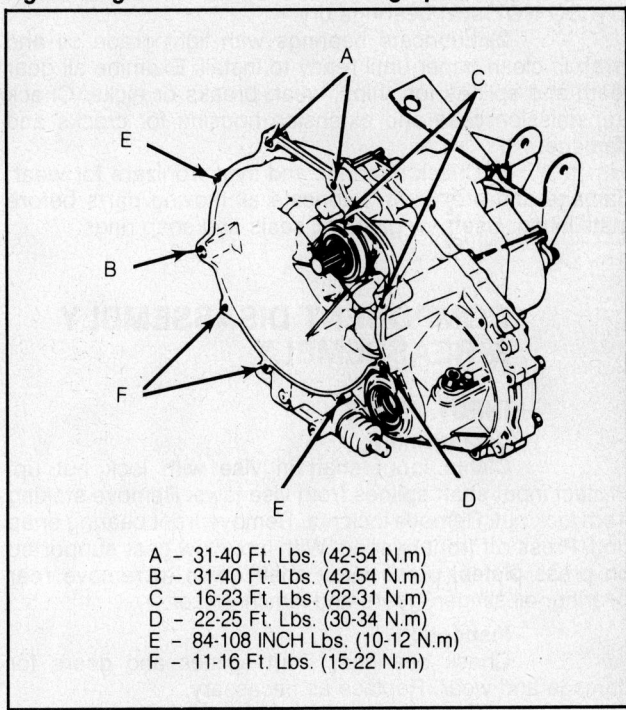

A - 31-40 Ft. Lbs. (42-54 N.m)
B - 31-40 Ft. Lbs. (42-54 N.m)
C - 16-23 Ft. Lbs. (22-31 N.m)
D - 22-25 Ft. Lbs. (30-34 N.m)
E - 84-108 INCH Lbs. (10-12 N.m)
F - 11-16 Ft. Lbs. (15-22 N.m)

TRANSAXLE DISASSEMBLY

1) Remove transaxle mounting bracket. On 5-speed models, remove 2 select actuator mounting bolts. Remove select switch wiring harness clamp. Remove select switch. On all models, remove back-up light switch and steel ball from case.

2) On 5-speed models, pull select actuator, to remove its shift rail connection from transaxle. Remove collar and pin. Remove select actuator. On all models, remove speedometer gear assembly. Remove transaxle case and gasket. Remove adapter and gasket.

3) Remove differential end play adjustment spacer. Remove 3 detent plugs, gaskets, springs and balls. Pull reverse idler gear shaft and remove reverse idler gear. Remove reverse shift lever from clutch housing. Remove spacer collar and reverse shift rail.

4) Using a pin punch, drive spring pins from shift forks and shift rails. On 5-speed models, remove select spacer. On all models, remove 1st-2nd shift rail from clutch housing and then remove 3rd-4th shift rail. Remove 1st-2nd shift rail and fork assembly with 3rd-4th shift rail and fork assembly.

CHRYSLER CORP. IMPORTS & MITSUBISHI KM 161, 162 & 163 4 & 5-SPEED TRANSAXLES (Cont.)

5) Remove 2 interlock plungers from clutch housing. On 5-speed models, remove 5th speed shift lug. On all models, remove output shaft assembly. Remove differential assembly from clutch housing.

6) Remove detent plug, spring and ball for select shift rail. Remove input shaft bearing retainer. Remove input shaft assembly, select shift rail and fork, and intermediate shaft.

CLEANING & INSPECTION

1) All parts should be thoroughly washed in cleaning solvent and air dried. Remove old gaskets with stiff brush or scraper. Rinse bearings in clean solvent and let air dry. DO NOT spin bearings dry.

2) Lubricate bearings with light grade oil and wrap in clean paper until ready to install. Examine all gear teeth and splines for chips, wear, breaks or nicks. Check transmission case and extension housing for cracks and damage.

3) Check bearings and synchronizers for wear, damage and proper fit. Lubricate all moving parts before installation. Use new gaskets, seals and snap rings.

COMPONENT DISASSEMBLY & REASSEMBLY

INPUT SHAFT

Disassembly

Clamp input shaft in vise with lock nut up. Protect input shaft splines from vise jaws. Remove staking from lock nut. Remove lock nut. Remove front bearing snap ring. Press off front bearing. With input low gear supported on press plates, press input shaft down to remove rear bearing, oil slinger, gears and synchronizer.

Inspection

Check bearings, shaft splines and gears for damage and wear. Replace as necessary.

Reassembly

1) Assemble synchronizer hub and sleeve. Ensure hub and sleeve slide smoothly. Insert 3 synchronizer keys into grooves in hub. Install 2 synchronizer springs. Ensure springs are installed in opposite directions.

2) Install sub-gear to input high gear. Apply gear oil to entire surface of gear. Install cone spring. Ensure cone spring is installed in proper direction. *See Fig. 2*. Install new snap ring. Ensure inner side of cone spring is not in snap ring groove.

Fig. 2: Installing Sub-Gear & Cone Spring

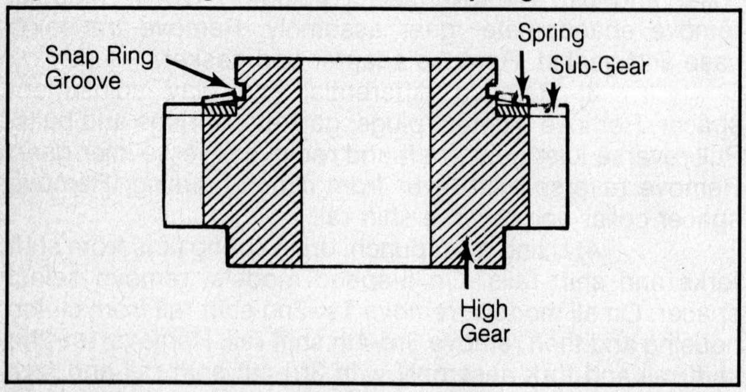

Ensure cone spring is installed correctly.

Fig. 3: Exploded View of Input Shaft

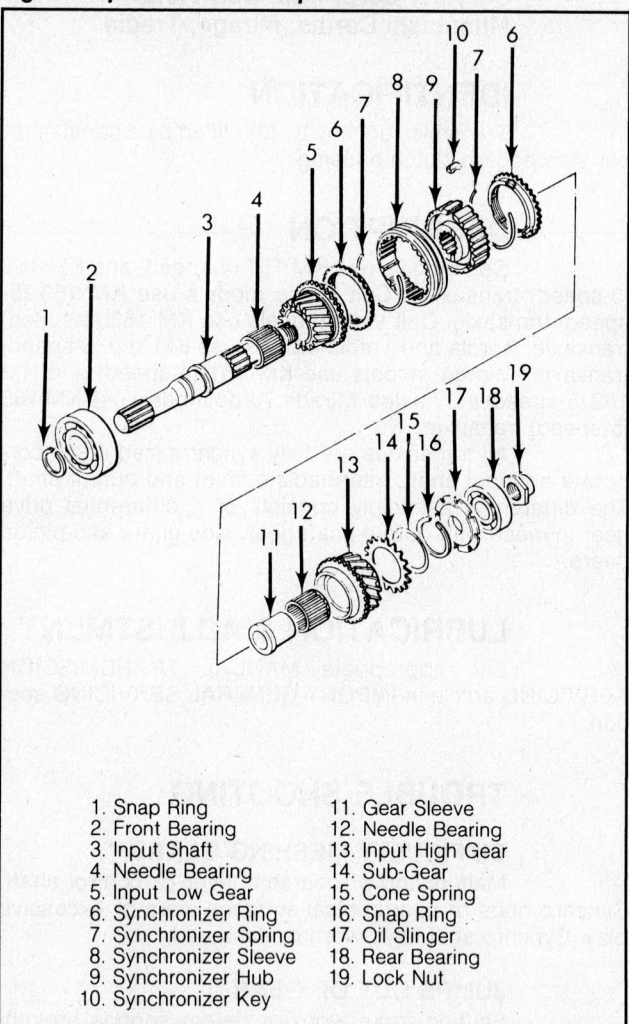

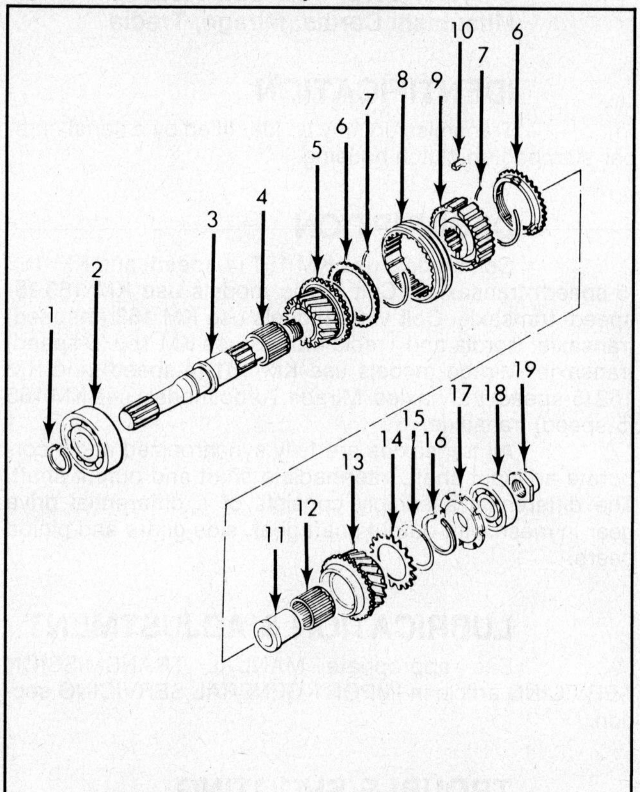

1. Snap Ring
2. Front Bearing
3. Input Shaft
4. Needle Bearing
5. Input Low Gear
6. Synchronizer Ring
7. Synchronizer Spring
8. Synchronizer Sleeve
9. Synchronizer Hub
10. Synchronizer Key
11. Gear Sleeve
12. Needle Bearing
13. Input High Gear
14. Sub-Gear
15. Cone Spring
16. Snap Ring
17. Oil Slinger
18. Rear Bearing
19. Lock Nut

3) Insert input low gear needle bearing on input shaft. Install input low gear on input shaft. Install synchronizer ring onto cone portion of input low gear. Install assembled synchronizer on input shaft. Using Driver (MD998322), press synchronizer assembly on shaft.

4) Press input high gear onto shaft using driver. Install needle bearing on sleeve. Install synchronizer ring. Install assembled input high gear on needle bearing. Install oil slinger on input shaft. Using driver, press rear bearing on rear of input shaft.

5) Tighten input shaft rear lock nut to specification. Carefully stake lock nut only at specific notch on shaft. *See Fig. 6*. Using Driver (MD998323), install front bearing on input shaft. Install front bearing snap ring.

6) Snap rings are available in 3 sizes; use thickest snap ring that will fit in groove. Do not reuse snap ring. When installing snap ring, be careful not to damage input shaft oil seal contacting surface.

FRONT BEARING SNAP RING THICKNESS

I. D. Color	Thickness In. (mm)	Part Number
None	.0882 (2.24)	MD706537
Blue	.0909 (2.31)	MD706538
Brown	.0937 (2.38)	MD706539

CHRYSLER CORP. IMPORTS & MITSUBISHI KM 161, 162 & 163 4 & 5-SPEED TRANSAXLES (Cont.)

Fig. 4: Exploded View of 4-Speed Transaxle

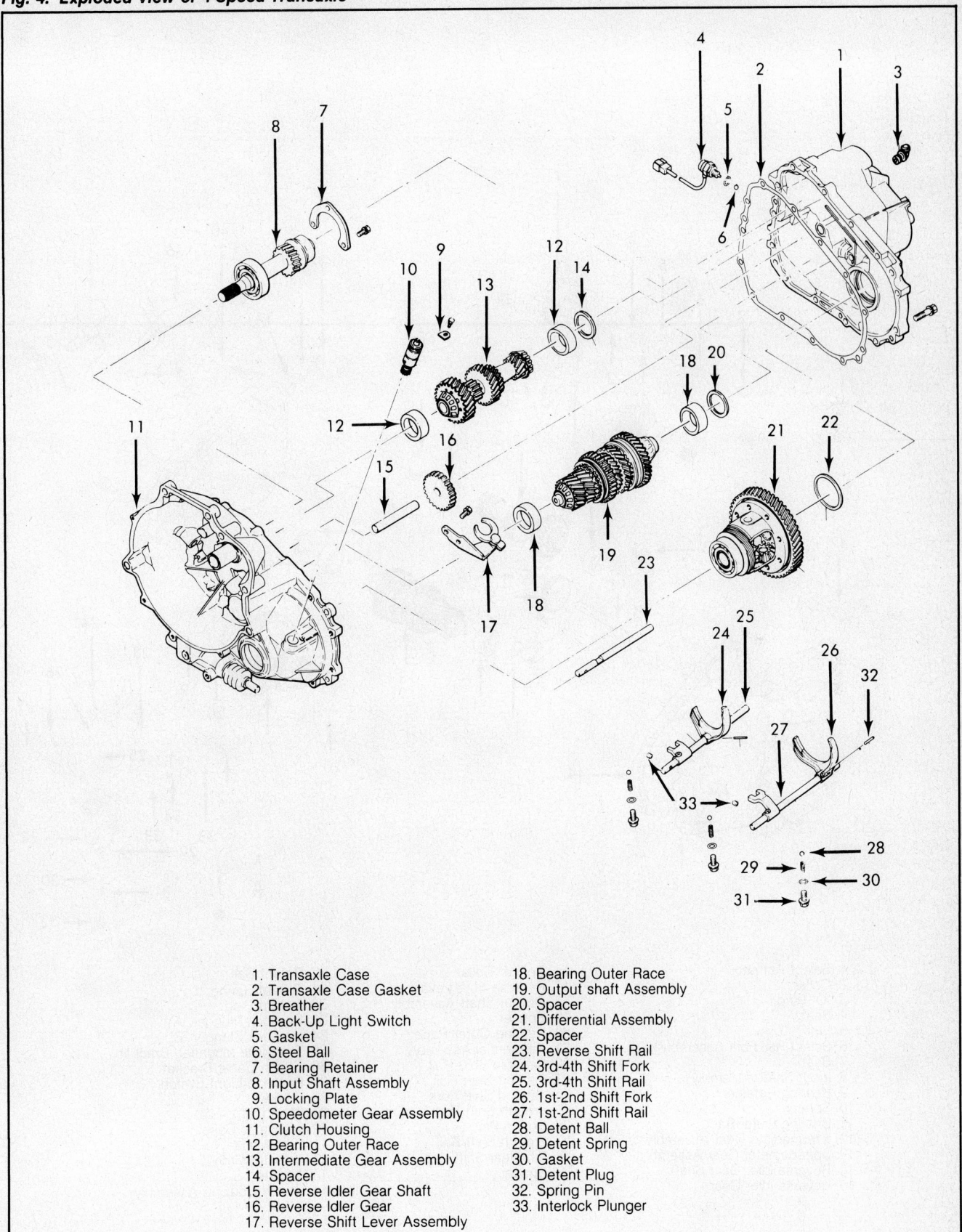

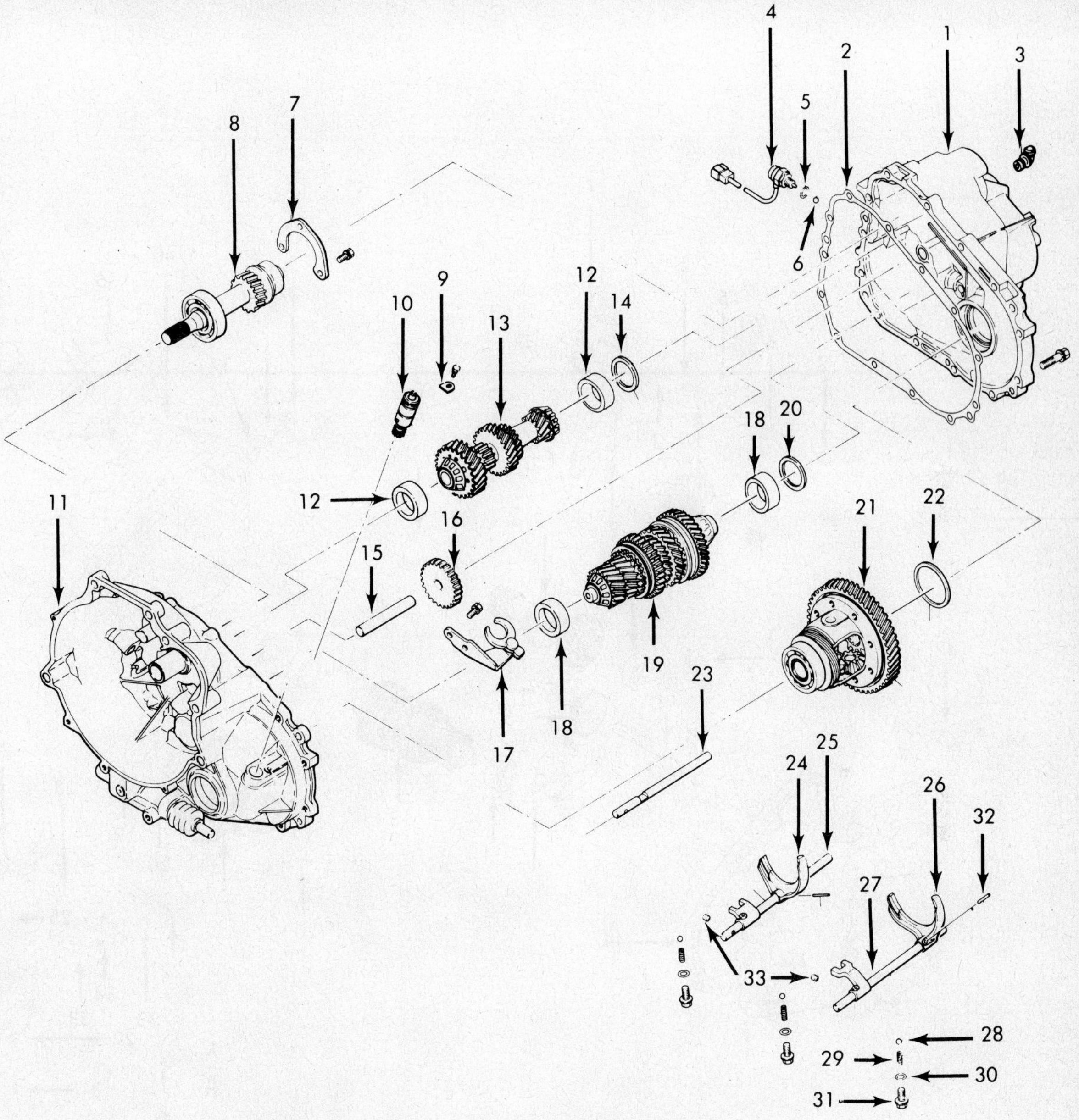

1. Transaxle Case
2. Transaxle Case Gasket
3. Breather
4. Back-Up Light Switch
5. Gasket
6. Steel Ball
7. Bearing Retainer
8. Input Shaft Assembly
9. Locking Plate
10. Speedometer Gear Assembly
11. Clutch Housing
12. Bearing Outer Race
13. Intermediate Gear Assembly
14. Spacer
15. Reverse Idler Gear Shaft
16. Reverse Idler Gear
17. Reverse Shift Lever Assembly
18. Bearing Outer Race
19. Output shaft Assembly
20. Spacer
21. Differential Assembly
22. Spacer
23. Reverse Shift Rail
24. 3rd-4th Shift Fork
25. 3rd-4th Shift Rail
26. 1st-2nd Shift Fork
27. 1st-2nd Shift Rail
28. Detent Ball
29. Detent Spring
30. Gasket
31. Detent Plug
32. Spring Pin
33. Interlock Plunger

CHRYSLER CORP. IMPORTS & MITSUBISHI KM 161, 162 & 163 4 & 5-SPEED TRANSAXLES (Cont.)

Fig. 5: Exploded View of 5-Speed Transaxle

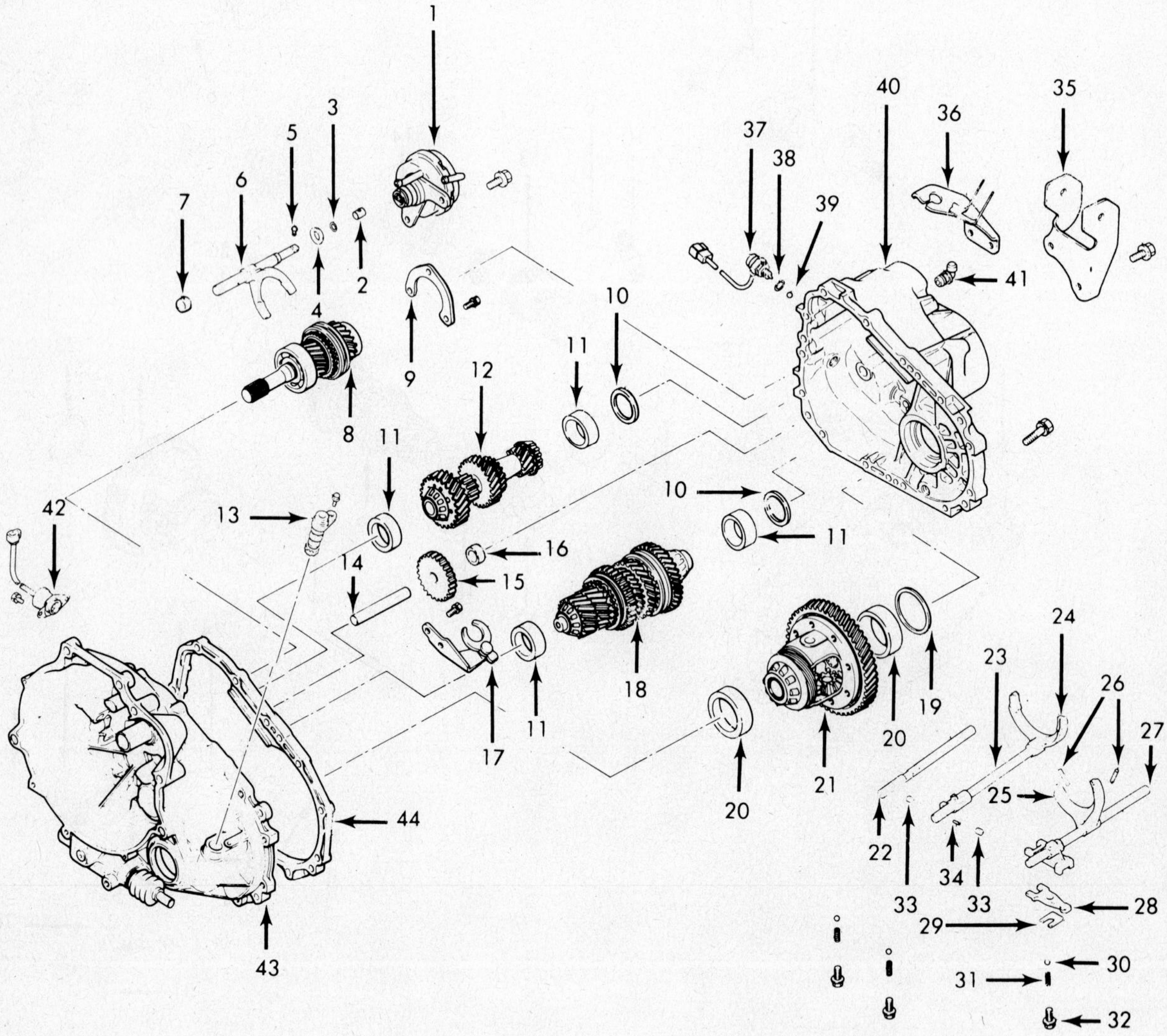

1. Select Actuator
2. Collar
3. "O" Ring
4. Seat
5. Pin
6. Select Rail Fork Assembly
7. Seat
8. Input Shaft Assembly
9. Bearing Retainer
10. Spacer
11. Bearing Outer Race
12. Intermediate Gear Assembly
13. Speedometer Gear Assembly
14. Reverse Idler Gear Shaft
15. Reverse Idler Gear
16. Spacer Collar
17. Reverse Shift Lever
18. Output Shaft Assembly
19. Spacer
20. Bearing Outer Race
21. Differential Assembly
22. Reverse Shift Rail
23. 1st-2nd Shift Rail
24. 1st-2nd Shift Fork
25. 3rd-4th Shift Fork
26. Spring Pin
27. 3rd-4th Shift Rail
28. 5th Gear Shift Lug
29. Spacer
30. Detent Ball
31. Detent Spring
32. Detent Plug
33. Interlock Plunger "A"
34. Interlock Plunger "B"
35. Transaxle Mounting Bracket
36. Clutch Cable Bracket
37. Back-Up Light Switch
38. Gasket
39. Steel Ball
40. Transaxle Case
41. Breather
42. Select Switch
43. Adapter
44. Clutch Housing Assembly

Manual Transmissions

CHRYSLER CORP. IMPORTS & MITSUBISHI KM 161, 162 & 163 4 & 5-SPEED TRANSAXLES (Cont.)

Fig. 6: Staking Input Shaft Lock Nut

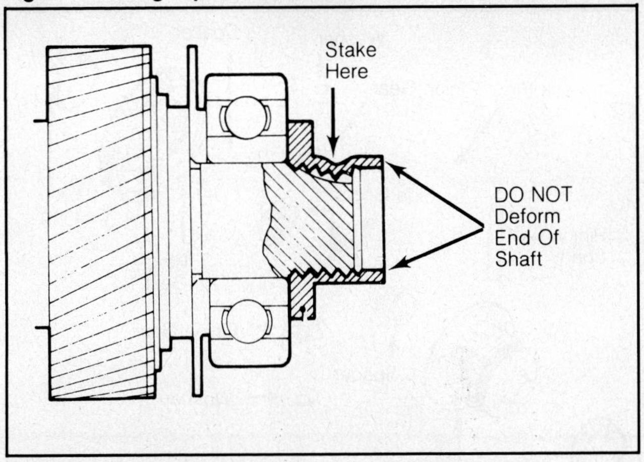

Carefully stake lock nut. If shaft is distorted, it will interfere with breather and result in breakage.

INTERMEDIATE SHAFT

Disassembly

Using Puller (MD998339-01) and Adapters (MIT45284 and MIT304325), remove bearing inner race from intermediate gear. Discard bearing. Remove spacer, sub-gear and spring.

Fig. 7: Exploded View of Intermediate Gear

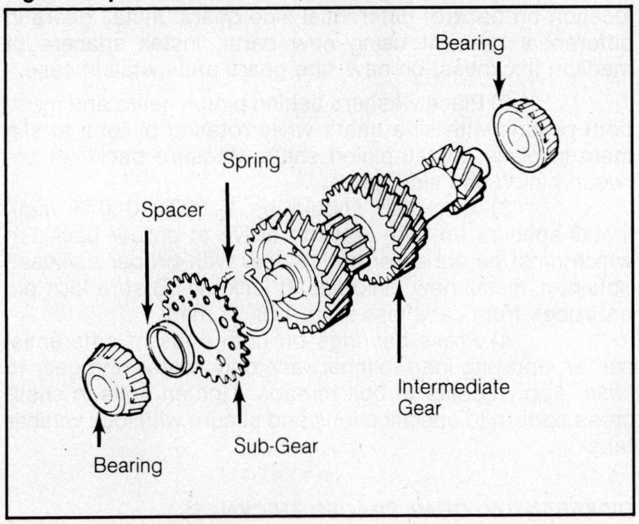

Inspection

Inspect gears for wear or damage. Replace defective intermediate gear as necessary.

Reassembly

Install sub-gear spring on intermediate shaft gear. Position longer leg of spring through .16" (4 mm) hole in gear. The 2 larger holes are for positioning gear during installation. Install sub-gear. Insert spring end through .16" (4 mm) hole in sub-gear. Install spacer. Using Installer (MD998322), press new inner bearings on gear. Replace outer bearing races.

OUTPUT SHAFT

Disassembly (4-Speed)

1) Using Puller (MD998339-01) and Adapters (MIT45284 and MIT304325), remove bearing inner race from output shaft. Using Bearing Separator (MD998327),

Fig. 8: Installing Sub-Gear

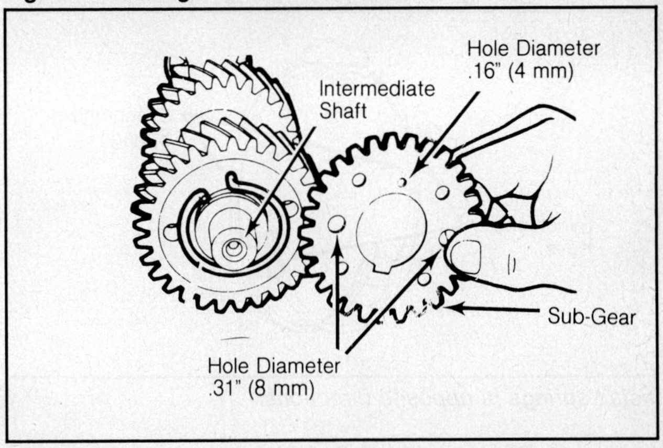

Install longer leg of sub-gear spring through .16" (4 mm) hole in intermediate gear.

remove 1st gear, gear sleeve, 1st-2nd synchronizer assembly and 2nd gear while holding 2nd gear.

2) While holding 4th gear with bearing separator, press rear of shaft to remove 2nd gear sleeve, 3rd gear sleeve, 3rd-4th synchronizer assembly and 4th gear.

Fig. 9: Exploded View of Output Shaft

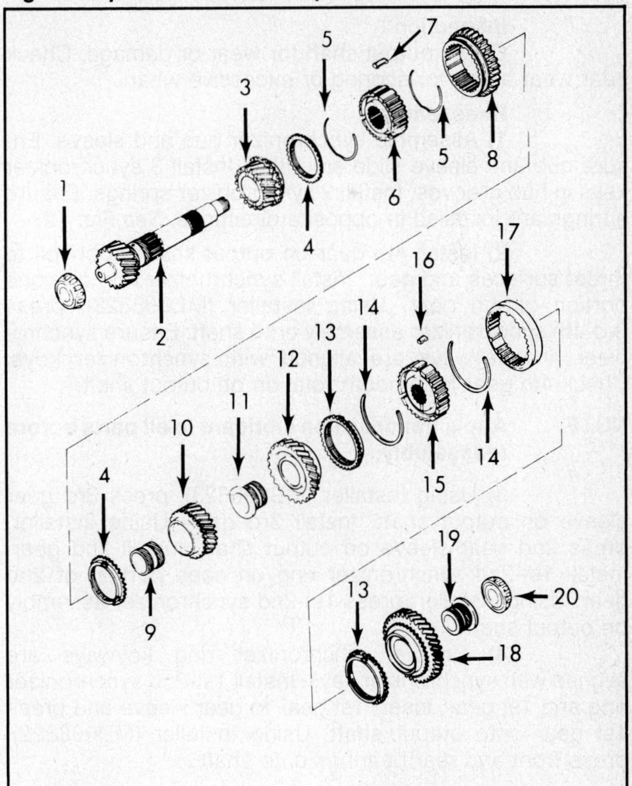

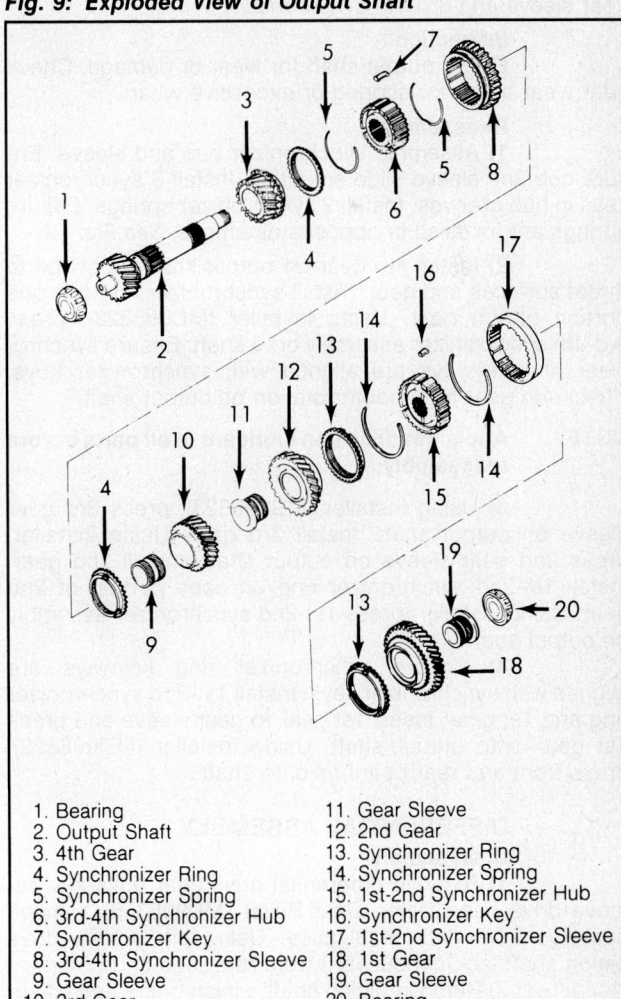

1. Bearing
2. Output Shaft
3. 4th Gear
4. Synchronizer Ring
5. Synchronizer Spring
6. 3rd-4th Synchronizer Hub
7. Synchronizer Key
8. 3rd-4th Synchronizer Sleeve
9. Gear Sleeve
10. 3rd Gear
11. Gear Sleeve
12. 2nd Gear
13. Synchronizer Ring
14. Synchronizer Spring
15. 1st-2nd Synchronizer Hub
16. Synchronizer Key
17. 1st-2nd Synchronizer Sleeve
18. 1st Gear
19. Gear Sleeve
20. Bearing

CHRYSLER CORP. IMPORTS & MITSUBISHI KM 161, 162 & 163 4 & 5-SPEED TRANSAXLES (Cont.)

Fig. 10: Installing Synchronizer Springs

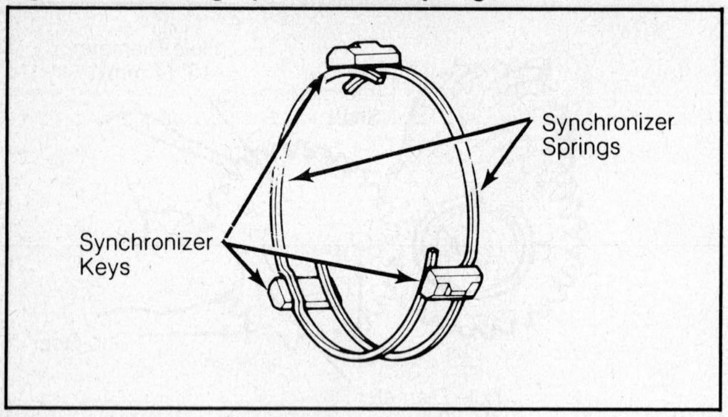

Install springs in opposite directions.

Disassembly (5-Speed)

1) Using Puller (MD998339-01) and Adapters (MIT45284 and MIT304325), remove bearing inner race from output shaft. Using Bearing Separator (MD998327), remove 1st gear, gear sleeve, 1st-2nd synchronizer assembly and 2nd gear while holding 2nd gear.

2) While holding 3rd gear with Gear Puller (MD998355), remove 2nd gear sleeve and 3rd gear. While holding 3rd-4th synchronizer ring in gear puller, remove 3rd gear sleeve and 3rd-4th synchronizer.

Inspection

Check output shaft for wear or damage. Check gear wear areas for scoring or excessive wear.

Reassembly

1) Assemble synchronizer hub and sleeve. Ensure hub and sleeve slide smoothly. Install 3 synchronizer keys in hub grooves. Install 2 synchronizer springs. Ensure springs are installed in opposite directions. *See Fig. 10.*

2) Install 4th gear on output shaft. Apply oil to thrust surfaces and gear. Install synchronizer ring on cone portion of 4th gear. Using Installer (MD998323), press 3rd-4th synchronizer assembly onto shaft. Ensure synchronizer ring keyways are aligned with synchronizer keys. Check 4th gear for smooth rotation on output shaft.

NOTE: Apply transmission lubricant to all parts before reassembly.

3) Using Installer (MB998323), press 3rd gear sleeve on output shaft. Install 3rd gear. Using installer, press 2nd gear sleeve on output shaft. Install 2nd gear. Install 1st-2nd synchronizer ring on cone portion of 2nd gear. Using installer, press 1st-2nd synchronizer assembly on output shaft.

4) Ensure synchronizer ring keyways are aligned with synchronizer keys. Install 1st-2nd synchronizer ring and 1st gear. Insert 1st gear to gear sleeve and press 1st gear onto output shaft. Using Installer (MD998322), press front and rear bearings onto shaft.

DIFFERENTIAL ASSEMBLY

Disassembly

1) Remove differential drive gear bolts and remove drive gear. Using Gear Puller (MD998355), remove bearings from differential case. Using pin punch, drive pinion shaft lock pin outward from recessed end of pin.

2) Remove pinion shaft, pinion gears and washers. Remove differential side gears and spacers. Keep spacers and gears separate and identified to ensure assembly in proper location.

Fig. 11: Exploded View of Differential Assembly

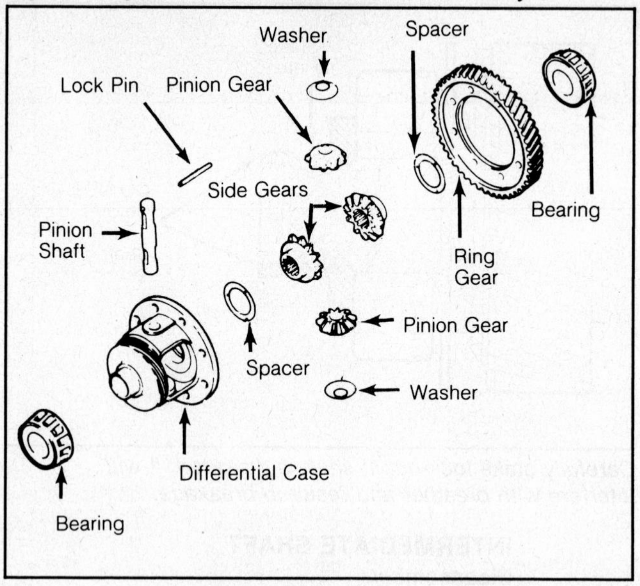

Inspection

Check splines for damage or wear. Check gears for chipped or worn teeth.

Reassembly

1) If reusing parts, position spacers in original location on back of differential side gears. Install gears in differential case. If using new parts, install spacers of medium thickness, on new side gears and install in case.

2) Place washers behind pinion gears and mesh both pinions with side gears while rotating pinions to slip them in place. Install pinion shaft. Measure backlash between pinion and side gears.

3) Backlash should be 0-.003" (0-.076 mm). Install spacers on both sides to arrive at proper backlash which must be equal for both sides. With proper backlash obtained, install new pinion shaft lock pin. Ensure lock pin protrudes from case less than .118" (3 mm).

4) Press bearings on both ends of differential carrier, applying load to inner race only. Install ring gear to case. Apply Loctite to bolt threads. Tighten bolts in crisscross pattern to specifications and secure with lock washer tabs.

DIFFERENTIAL GEAR SPACER THICKNESS

Part Number	Thickness In. (mm)
MA180862	.030-.032 (.76-.81)
MA180861	.033-.036 (.83-.92)
MA180860	.037-.039 (.93-1.0)
MA180875	.040-.043 (1.01-1.08)
MA180876	.043-.046 (1.09-1.16)

TRANSAXLE REASSEMBLY

NOTE: On 5-speed transaxles, 5th gear shift rail and fork are part of 3rd-4th shift rail and fork assemblies.

CHRYSLER CORP. IMPORTS & MITSUBISHI KM 161, 162 & 163 4 & 5-SPEED TRANSAXLES (Cont.)

1) Rotate sub-gear clockwise to align .31" (8 mm) hole in intermediate gear with hole in sub-gear. Insert a .31" (8 mm) diameter, 1.38" (35 mm) long, dummy pin through intermediate gear and into sub-gear.

2) Assemble select shift fork and rail assembly onto input shaft synchronizer sleeve. Install intermediate shaft, shift rail and shift fork as an assembly. Install front bearing retainer and tighten 3 retaining bolts to 11-15 ft. lbs. (15-20 N.m).

3) Install differential assembly to clutch housing. Install output shaft assembly. Ensure gears are properly meshed properly. Remove dummy pin from sub-gear and intermediate gear.

4) Install 5th gear shift lug on clutch housing pin (5-speed only). Ensure shift lug is installed properly. *See Fig. 12*. Insert 2 interlock plungers into holes in clutch housing. Install 1st-2nd shift rail assembly. Install 3rd-4th (3rd-4th-5th on 5-speed) shift rail assembly.

Fig. 12: Installing 5th Gear Shift Lug

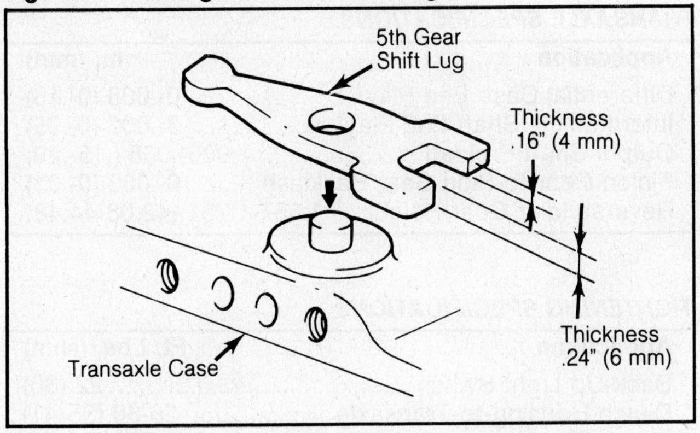

Hard shifting may result if lug is installed incorrectly.

5) Install roll pin on shift rail. Split on roll pin must be installed on shift rail centerline. Roll pin ends should protrude equally. Select and install spacer between 3rd-4th shift lug and 5th shift lug to adjust clearance to specification. Clearance should be .004-.020" (.1-.5 mm). See 5TH GEAR SELECT SPACER THICKNESS chart.

5TH GEAR SELECT SPACER THICKNESS

Thickness Inches (mm)	Mark	Part No.
.024 (.6)	G	MD712031
.035 (.9)	F	MD712032
.047 (1.2)	E	MD704819
.059 (1.5)	D	MD704820
.071 (1.8)	C	MD704821
.083 (2.1)	B	MD704822
.094 (2.4)	A	MD704823
.106 (2.7)	None	MD704824

6) Install reverse shift rail into clutch housing. Install reverse shift lever assembly and tighten 2 retaining bolts to 11-16 ft. lbs. (15-22 N.m).

7) Install reverse idler gear with chamfered side upward. Install idler gear shaft through gear into housing. Install spacer collar. Place reverse shift rail in neutral position. Measure dimension "A". *See Fig. 13*. If dimension "A" is not 1.657-1.751" (42.08-44.48 mm), replace reverse shift lever assembly.

Fig. 13: Measuring Reverse Idler Gear Height

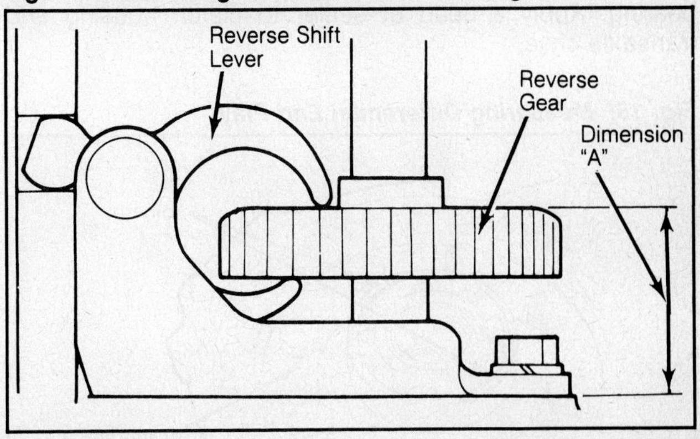

8) Adjust output shaft, intermediate shaft and differential case end play or preload as follows: Remove output shaft and intermediate shaft bearing outer race of transaxle case.

9) Place 2 pieces of solder, about .4" (10 mm) long, on outer races of transaxle case. *See Fig. 14*. Insert outer races in case and press firmly to hold solder in position.

Fig. 14: Determining Intermediate Gear End Play & Output Shaft Preload

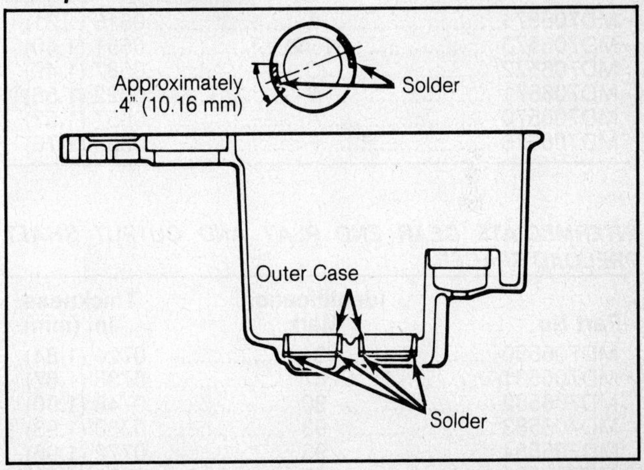

Place solder on shoulder of outer race hole in transmission case.

10) Place 2 pieces of solder, about .79" (20 mm) long, on bearing outer race. *See Fig. 15*. Install transaxle case with new gasket on clutch housing. Tighten 13 bolts to 26-30 ft. lbs. (35-41 N.m).

11) Remove bolts and transaxle case. Measure thickness of solder with micrometer. Select spacer of proper thickness to obtain correct end play. End play should be 0-.006" (0-.15 mm). See DIFFERENTIAL CASE END PLAY SPACER table.

12) Remove both bearing outer races from transaxle case. Measure solder and determine proper spacer to obtain proper intermediate gear end play and output shaft preload. End play should be 0-.002" (0-.05 mm). Preload should be .006-.008" (.15-.20 mm). See INTERMEDIATE GEAR END PLAY & OUTPUT SHAFT PRELOAD SPACER table.

13) Install intermediate gear end play spacers and taper roller bearing outer races into transaxle case.

CHRYSLER CORP. IMPORTS & MITSUBISHI KM 161, 162 & 163 4 & 5-SPEED TRANSAXLES (Cont.)

Install differential case end play spacer on differential ball bearing. Apply a bead of sealer to clutch housing and transaxle case.

Fig. 15: Measuring Differential End Play

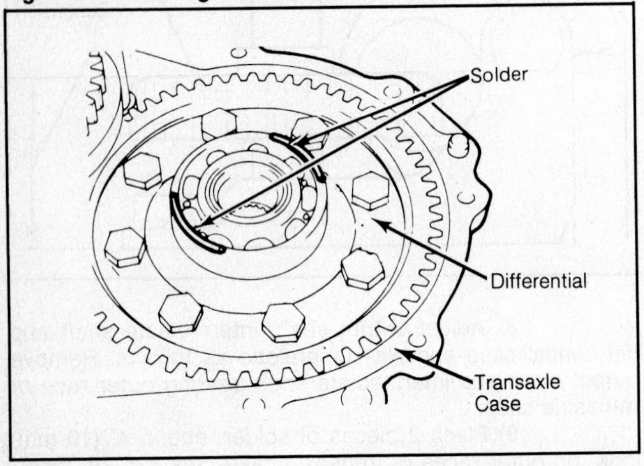

DIFFERENTIAL CASE END PLAY SPACER

Part No.	Identification Mark	Thickness In. (mm)
MD706574	E	.0516 (1.31)
MD706573	None	.0551 (1.40)
MD706572	C	.0587 (1.49)
MD706571	B	.0622 (1.58)
MD706570	A	.0657 (1.67)
MD706575	F	.0693 (1.76)

INTERMEDIATE GEAR END PLAY AND OUTPUT SHAFT PRELOAD SPACER

Part No.	Identification Mark	Thickness In. (mm)
MD706580	84	.0724 (1.84)
MD706581	87	.0736 (1.87)
MD706582	90	.0748 (1.90)
MD706583	93	.0760 (1.93)
MD706584	96	.0772 (1.96)
MD706585	99	.0783 (1.99)
MD706586	02	.0795 (2.02)
MD706587	05	.0807 (2.05)
MD706588	08	.0819 (2.08)
MD706589	11	.0831 (2.11)
MD706590	14	.0843 (2.14)
MD706591	17	.0854 (2.17)
MD706592	20	.0866 (2.20)
MD706593	23	.0878 (2.23)
MD706594	26	.0890 (2.26)
MD706595	29	.0902 (2.29)
MD706596	32	.0913 (2.32)
MD706597	35	.0925 (2.35)
MD706598	38	.0937 (2.38)
MD706599	41	.0949 (2.41)
MD706600	44	.0961 (2.44)
MD706601	47	.0972 (2.47)
MD706602	50	.0984 (2.50)
MD706603	53	.0996 (2.53)
MD706604	56	.1008 (2.56)
MD706605	59	.1020 (2.59)
MD706606	62	.1031 (2.62)
MD706607	65	.1043 (2.65)
MD706608	68	.1055 (2.68)

14) On 5-speed models, install adapter between transaxle case and clutch housing. Tighten mounting bolts to 26-30 ft. lbs. (35-41 N.m). On 4-speed models, apply a non-hardening sealer to case side of gasket and a hardening sealer to clutch housing side of gasket.

15) On all models, install transaxle case assembly on clutch housing and tighten 13 bolts to 26-30 ft. lbs. (35-41 N.m). With Control Shaft Seal Installer (MB998324) attached to control shaft, verify that control shifts smoothly.

16) Install speedometer gear assembly into clutch housing and tighten flange bolt. On 5-speed models, connect select actuator rod to select shift rail and insert pin. Install snap ring on pin. Tighten actuator mounting bolts to specification.

17) Place transaxle in Neutral. Install select switch and align mating marks. Tighten select switch mounting bolts. On all models, install steel ball and back-up light switch. On 5-speed models, install transaxle mounting and clutch cable brackets.

TRANSAXLE SPECIFICATIONS

Application	In. (mm)
Differential Case End Play	0-.006 (0-.15)
Intermediate Shaft End Play	0-.002 (0-.05)
Output Shaft Preload	.006-.008 (.15-.20)
Pinion Gear-to-Side Gear Backlash	0-.003 (0-.08)
Reverse Idler Gear Height	1.657-1.751 (42.08-44.48)

TIGHTENING SPECIFICATIONS

Application	Ft. Lbs. (N.m)
Back-Up Light Switch	22 (30)
Clutch Housing-to-Transaxle	26-30 (35-41)
Detent Plug	20-24 (27-33)
Engine-to-Transaxle Bolt	[1]
Front Retainer Bolt	11-15 (15-20)
Input Shaft Lock Nut	65-79 (88-107)
Oil Drain Plug	22-25 (30-34)
Oil Filler Plug	22-25 (30-34)
Output Shaft Lock Nut	65-79 (88-107)
Reverse Shift Lever Bracket Bolt	11-15 (15-20)
Ring Gear Bolts	94-101 (127-137)
Transaxle Mounting Bolt	
8 mm	22-25 (30-34)
10 mm	32-39 (43-53)
Transaxle Mounting Bracket Bolt	22-30 (30-41)
	INCH Lbs. (N.m)
Front Cover Bolt	84-96 (10-11)

[1] – See Fig. 1.

Manual Transmissions

FORD MOTOR CO. IMPORTS 5-SPEED

Merkur XR4Ti

DESCRIPTION

The Hummer 5-speed transmission, designed by Ford France, has 3 forward reduction gear ratios, a one-to-one (4th) gear ratio, and an overdrive (5th) gear ratio. These forward ratios are provided through helical-cut, constant-mesh gears.

Reverse gear is provided through an idle gear which slides along a shaft to engage spur gears on gear cluster and output shaft. All gears, except 5th gear (overdrive), are contained in transmission case. Overdrive gears are located in transmission extension housing.

OPERATION

Three synchronizers are used to lock driven gears on output shaft. Two synchronizers provided 1st gear through 4th speed gears, while the third synchronizer provides 5th gear.

Synchronizers are shifted by 3 forks attached to a common shift rail. A system of interlocks on shaft prevent engagement of more than one gear at any one time. The shift rail extends from shift lever, mounted on extension housing, to front of transmission case. A spring-loaded plunger contacts shift rail to provide shift detent.

Engagement of Reverse gear requires the use of an intermediate lever between shift rail and sliding gear. Intermediate lever is mounted on a pivot pin which is pressed into left side of case. A spring returns lever to released position when transmission is shifted out of Reverse.

LUBRICATION & ADJUSTMENT

See appropriate MANUAL TRANSMISSION SERVICING article in IMPORT GENERAL SERVICING section.

SERVICE (IN VEHICLE)

EXTENSION HOUSING SEAL

Removal & Installation

Remove driveshaft. Remove seal using Seal Remover (T71P-7657-A). Using Seal Installer (T71P-7095-A) and Extension Housing Bushing Replacer (T74P-7095-A), install new seal on extension housing. Install driveshaft.

EXTENSION HOUSING SEAL

Removal & Installation

1) Remove driveshaft. Remove extension housing seal. Using Bushing Remover (T77L-7697-E), remove extension housing bushing.

2) Install new bushing on Extension Housing Bushing Replacer (T77L-7697-F) and Replacer Adapter (T85M-7697-B). Install extension housing seal and driveshaft.

NOTE: **Adapter must be used to set bushing to correct depth in extension housing.**

SHIFT LEVER & BOOT

Removal

1) Remove shift knob. Remove console bezel attaching screws and bezel. If vehicle is equipped with power windows, raise bezel, disconnect wiring from switches and remove bezel.

Fig. 1: Hummer 5-Speed Gear Cluster Assembly

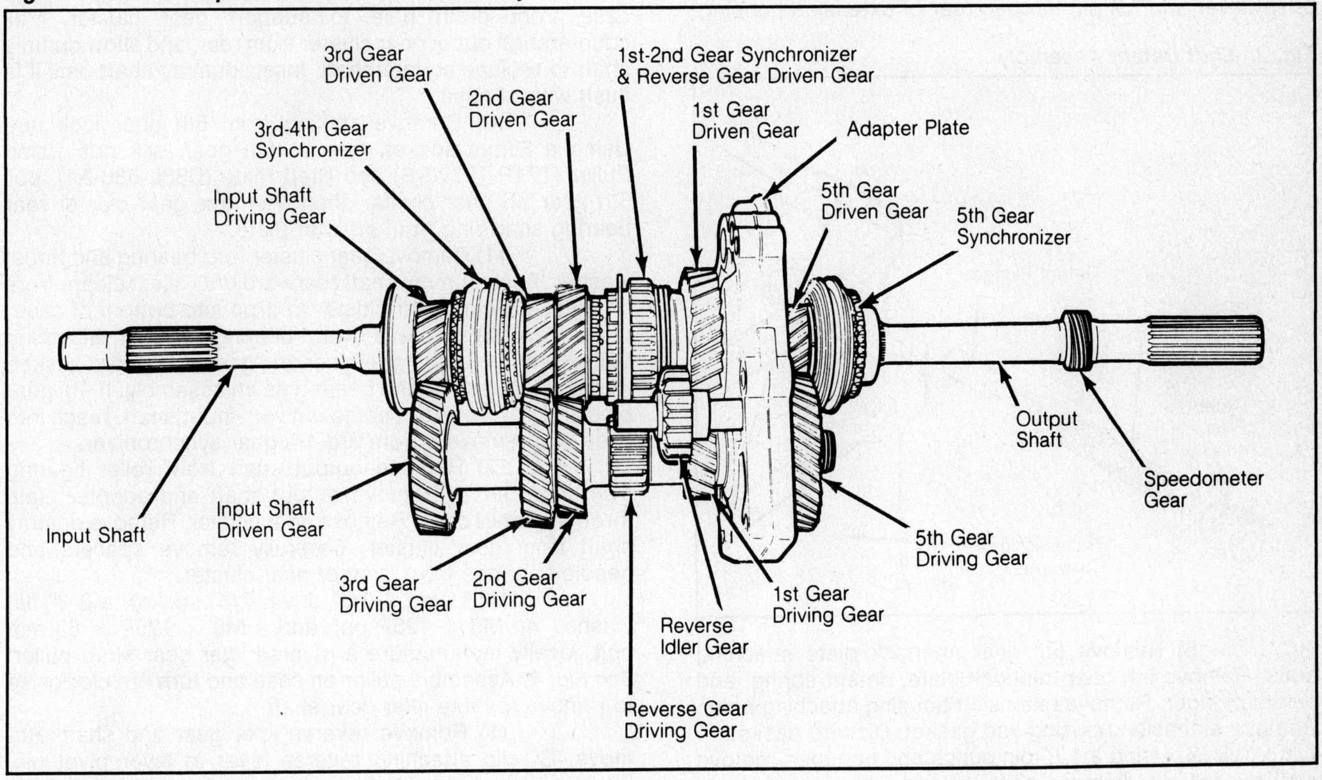

Manual Transmissions

FORD MOTOR CO. IMPORTS 5-SPEED (Cont.)

2) Remove shift boot and foam insulator. Remove screws attaching shift lever boot retainer to floor pan and remove retainer. Remove shift lever attaching bolts using a No. 40 Torx socket. Remove shift lever.

Installation

Install shift lever and install attaching bolts. Install boot retainer and attaching screws. Install shift lever boot and foam insulator. Install console bezel and attaching screws. Install shift knob.

REMOVAL & INSTALLATION

TRANSMISSION

See appropriate MANUAL TRANSMISSION REMOVAL article in IMPORT GENERAL SERVICING section.

TRANSMISSION DISASSEMBLY

1) Remove clutch release lever and release bearing from bellhousing. Remove bellhousing and install transmission in Holding Fixture (T57L-500-B). Remove speedometer driven gear from extension housing.

2) Remove back-up light switch and neutral/safety switch. Remove transmission cover attaching bolts, cover, and gasket. Discard gasket. Turn transmission over and allow fluid to drain from case.

3) Turn transmission until cover opening is up. Remove shift detent plug. Using a small magnet, remove detent spring and plunger. *See Fig. 2*. Using a drift and hammer, remove welsh plug from rear of extension housing.

4) Shift transmission into Reverse to gain access to offset lever roll pin. *See Fig. 13*. Using a 1/8" pin punch and hammer, remove offset lever roll pin. Remove offset lever and roll pin through rear of extension housing.

Fig. 2: Shift Detent Assembly

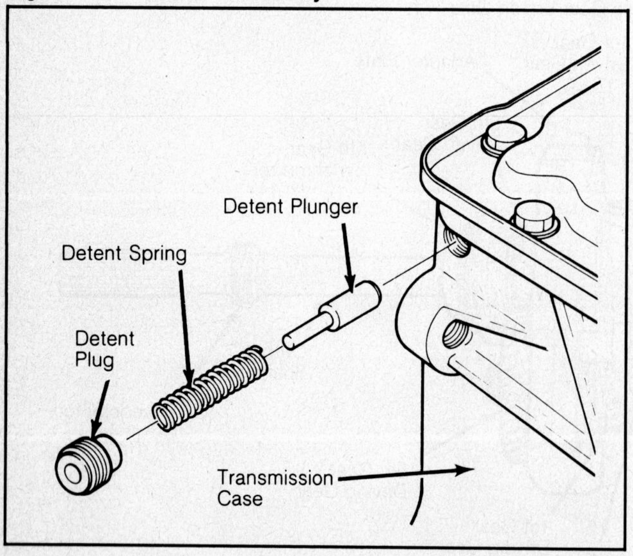

5) Remove 5th gear interlock plate attaching bolts. Remove 5th gear interlock plate, detent spring, and detent plunger. Remove extension housing attaching bolts. Remove extension housing and gasket. Discard gasket.

6) Using a 1/8" pin punch and hammer, remove shift rail roll pin. Remove shift rail and 5th gear interlock. Pull shift rail shaft out of transmission by using a twisting motion.

7) Remove shift interlock for 1st-2nd and 3rd-4th gear shift forks. Remove 1st-2nd and 3rd-4th gear shift forks. Remove 5th gear shift fork. Remove 5th gear synchronizer snap ring. Slide 5th gear and synchronizer assembly rearward until it stops against speedometer gear.

8) Shift transmission into 1st and Reverse to prevent rotation of mainshaft and gear cluster. To hold reverse idler gear in position, stretch a rubber band from reverse lever to a cover bolt screwed into transmission case. Leave cover bolt in place. *See Fig. 3*.

Fig. 3: Holding Reverse Gear Idler In Position

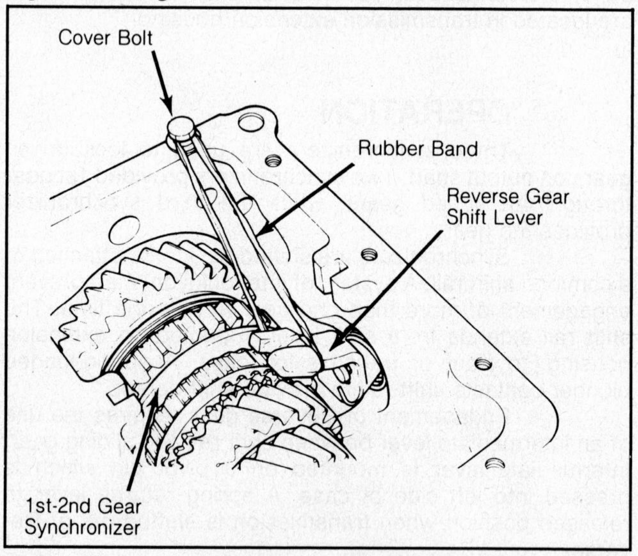

9) Install Dummy Shaft (T74P-7111-B) through case front drain hole to support gear cluster. Pull countershaft out of gear cluster from rear, and allow dummy shaft to replace countershaft. Insert dummy shaft until it is flush with of case.

10) Remove staking from 5th gear lock nut. Using a 36mm socket, remove 5th gear lock nut. Using Puller (T71P-19703-B) and Step Plate (D80L-630-A1), pull 5th gear off gear cluster shaft. Remove gear cluster rear bearing snap ring from adapter plate.

11) Remove gear cluster rear bearing and thrust washer. Push dummy shaft rearward until it just clears front of case, allowing gear cluster to drop into bottom of case.

12) Remove front bearing retainer attaching bolts. Remove bearing retainer and gasket. Discard gasket. Remove input shaft and bearing as an assembly. If 4th gear blocking ring does not come out with input shaft, reach into case and remove it from 3rd-4th gear synchronizer.

13) Remove output shaft front roller bearing from input shaft. Remove output shaft and adapter plate through rear of case. Remove gear cluster. Remove dummy shaft from gear cluster. Carefully remove spacers and needle bearings from front of gear cluster.

14) Using a 3/8" drive, 7/8" socket, a 3/8" flat washer, an M8 x 125P nut, and a M8 x 125P x 60 mm bolt, locally manufacture a reverse idler gear shaft puller. *See Fig. 4*. Assemble puller on case and turn nut clockwise to remove reverse idler gear shaft.

15) Remove reverse idler gear and shaft. Remove "C" clip attaching reverse lever to lever pivot pin. Remove reverse shift lever and return spring from pivot pin.

FORD MOTOR CO. IMPORTS 5-SPEED (Cont.)

Remove magnet from bottom of transmission case. DO NOT drop magnet, as it is easily broken.

Fig. 4: Removing Reverse Idler Gear Shaft

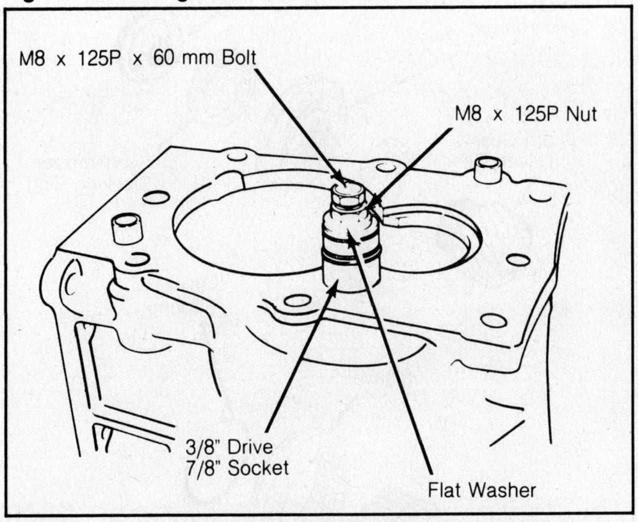

Locally manufacture a reverse idler gear shaft puller.

Fig. 5: Input Shaft & Bearing Disassembly

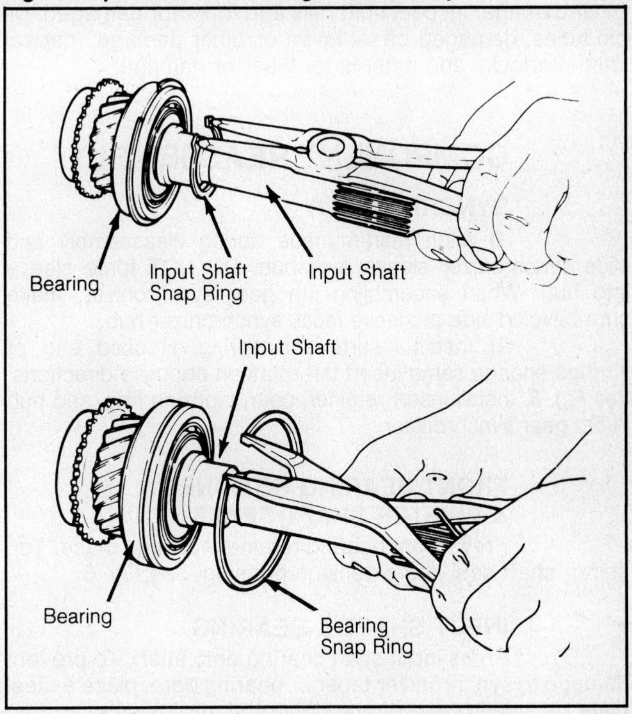

COMPONENT DISASSEMBLY

OUTPUT SHAFT & BEARING

1) Remove snap ring retaining 3rd-4th gear synchronizer. Remove 3rd-4th gear synchronizer, 3rd gear blocking ring, and 3rd gear as an assembly. Remove retaining ring and thrust washer halves.

2) Remove 2nd gear and 2nd gear blocking ring. A snap ring is installed on 2nd gear to prevent synchronizer overtravel. If necessary, remove snap ring from gear.

3) Using a center punch and hammer, make an alignment mark on 1st-2nd gear synchronizer sleeve and hub. Synchronizer sleeve and hub are a matched set, reference mark will provide correct alignment during reassembly.

4) Remove 1st-2nd synchronizer sleeve, inserts, and spring. Mark position of speedometer gear on output shaft. Using a bench press, remove speedometer gear from shaft.

NOTE: The 1st-2nd gear synchronizer hub cannot be removed from output shaft. If hub or sleeve are worn or damaged, the synchronizer and shaft have to be replaced as an assembly.

5) Remove 5th gear synchronizer snap ring from output shaft. Remove 5th gear and synchronizer. Remove output shaft bearing snap ring. Using a bench press, remove output shaft bearing. Make sure adapter plate and bearing are properly supported.

6) Remove oil slinger (located against 1st gear). Remove 1st gear synchronizer and blocking ring. Remove synchronizer insert spring. Remove snap ring from adapter plate. Using Bearing Replacer (T77F-4222-A), press output shaft bearing out of adapter plate.

INPUT SHAFT & BEARING

Remove input shaft snap ring and bearing snap ring. *See Fig. 5*. Using bench press, remove input shaft bearing. Make sure that bearing inner race is properly supported.

FRONT BEARING RETAINER & SHIFTER SHAFT SEALS

Using Inner Race Remover (T75P-3504-G) and a slide hammer, remove front bearing retainer seal. *See Fig. 6*. Using Puller (T58L-101-A) and slide hammer, remove shifter shaft seal from extension housing. If shifter shaft bushing is worn or damaged, replace extension housing.

SYNCHRONIZER

1) Remove hub, blocking ring, insert retainer, and 5th gear. Make an alignment mark on hub and sleeve. Synchronizer sleeve and hub are a matched set, reference mark will provide correct alignment during reassembly.

2) Using a small flat-bladed screwdriver, remove insert springs and inserts. Remove synchronizer hub from sleeve. *See Fig. 7*.

CLEANING & INSPECTION

1) Before inspecting transmission components, wash them throughly in cleaning solvent and dry parts with compressed air. Check transmission case, extension housing, and adapter plate for wear or damage.

2) Inspect input and output shafts for scoring, galling, or wear of bearing surfaces. Check for worn, nicked, or broken shaft splines. Check for worn, chipped, or broken synchronizer teeth. Check for bent or twisted shafts. Check snap ring grooves.

3) Check input shaft roller bearing for worn, bent, or broken roller cage. Inspect bearing retainer for cracks or damaged seal bore. Inspect countershaft needle bearings for scoring, galling, pitting, or other damage.

4) Check gears for worn, chipped, or broken teeth. Inspect gears for rough or scored thrust surfaces. Check synchronizers for worn hub splines, loose insert springs, or cracked blocking ring.

FORD MOTOR CO. IMPORTS 5-SPEED (Cont.)

5) Check snap rings for wear, loss of tension, or other damage. Inspect shift rails and forks for damaged roll pin holes, damaged offset lever, or other damage. Inspect shift interlocks and detents for wear or damage.

COMPONENT REASSEMBLY

SYNCHRONIZER

1) Align marks made during disassembly and slide synchronizer sleeve over hub. DO NOT force sleeve into hub. When assembling 5th gear synchronizer, make sure beveled side of sleeve faces synchronizer hub.

2) Install inserts and spring. Hooked end of springs engage same insert but rotate in opposite directions. *See Fig. 8*. Install insert retainer, gear, blocking ring, and hub in 5th gear synchronizer.

FRONT BEARING RETAINER & SHIFTER SHAFT SEALS

Press front bearing retainer seal into place. Tap shifter shaft seal into extension housing. *See Fig. 6*.

INPUT SHAFT & BEARING

Press input shaft bearing onto shaft. To prevent damage to synchronizer taper or bearing bore, place a steel plate between press ram and input shaft. Install snap ring on input shaft bearing. Install snap ring on input shaft.

Fig. 6: Front Bearing Retainer Seal & Shifter Shaft Seal Replacement

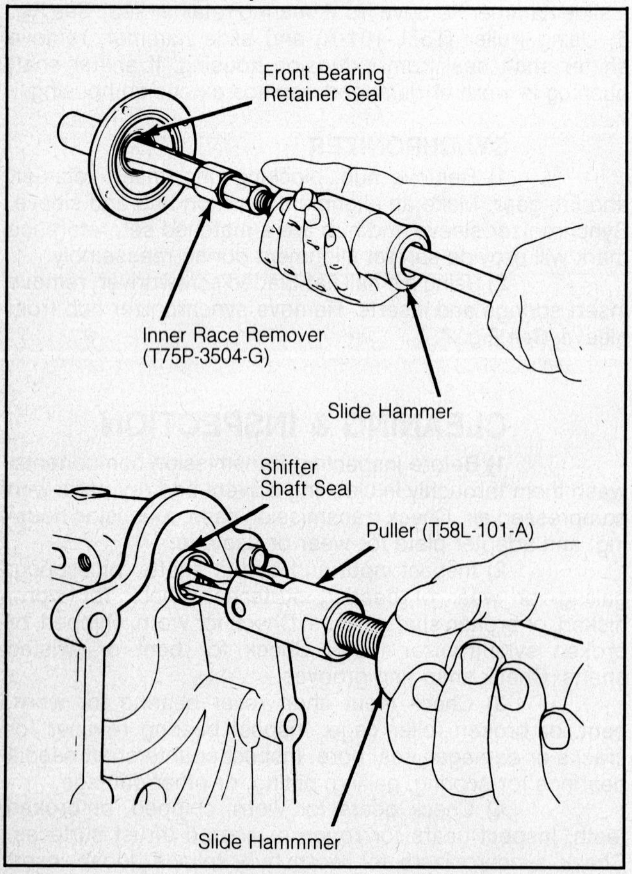

Fig. 7: Disassembling Synchronizer

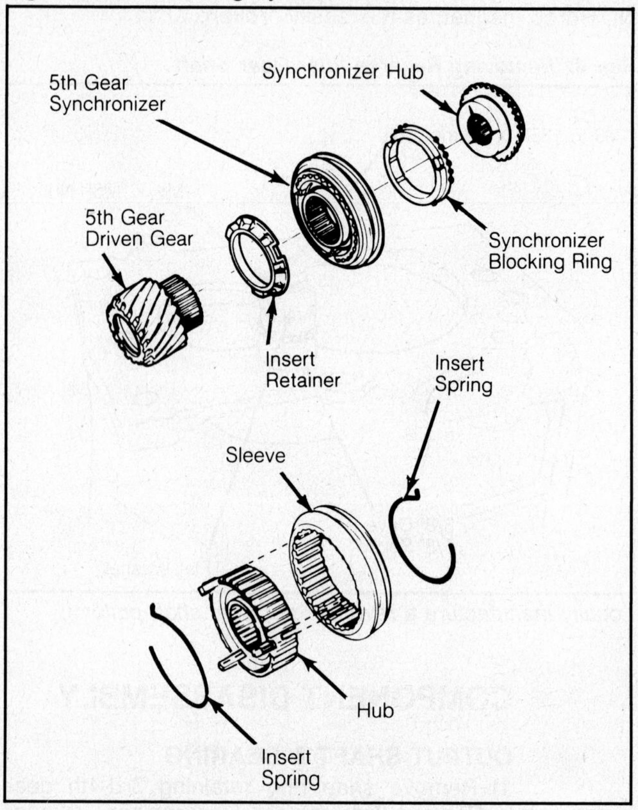

Fig. 8: Assembling Synchronizer

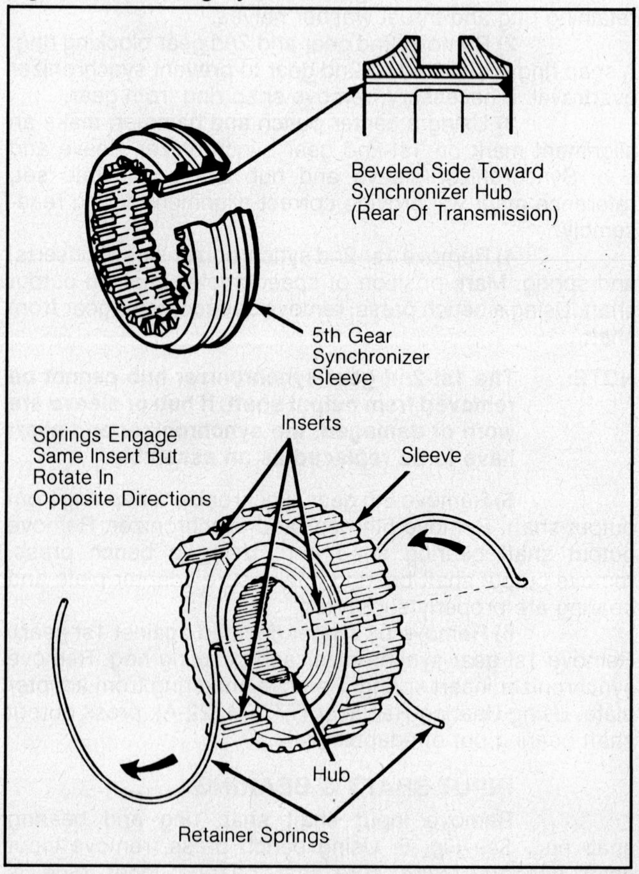

Fig. 9: Installing Bearing/Adapter Plate On Output Shaft

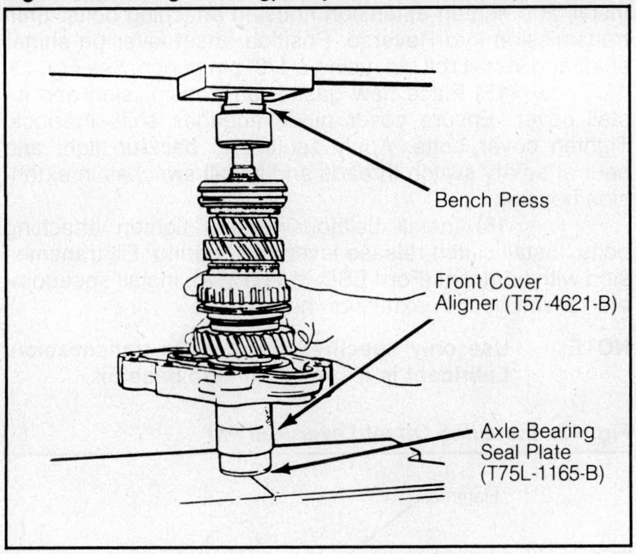

OUTPUT SHAFT & BEARING

1) Using bench press and Bearing Replacer (T77J-7025-K), install output shaft on adapter plate. Install bearing snap ring in adapter plate.

2) Assemble 1st-2nd gear synchronizer. Make sure shift fork groove faces front of output shaft as viewed in its assembled position in transmission. Install 2nd gear blocking ring and 2nd gear. Make sure 2nd gear snap ring is in position before installing gear.

3) Install thrust washer halves and retaining ring. Ensure thrust with tang engages hole in output shaft. Install 3rd gear and 3rd gear blocking ring. Install 3rd-4th gear synchronizer. Install 3rd-4th gear synchronizer snap ring.

4) Install 1st gear blocking ring and 1st gear. Install oil slinger with oil groove facing 1st gear. Using Front Cover Aligner (T57L-4621-B) and Axle Bearing Seal Plate (T75L-1165-B), press bearing/adapter plate assembly onto shaft. *See Fig. 9.*

5) Install snap ring on output shaft. Install 5th gear and 5th gear synchronizer. Make sure synchronizer is assembled with beveled side of sleeve facing end of shaft (speedometer gear).

6) Install 5th gear snap ring on output shaft. Press speedometer gear onto shaft until it aligns with mark made during removal. Replace gear if it fits loosely on shaft.

NOTE: **If output shaft is replaced, press speedometer gear onto shaft until distance from front face of gar to rear face of 5th gear synchronizer hub measures 4 27/32-4 7/8" (123-124 mm).**

TRANSMISSION REASSEMBLY

1) Install magnet in bottom of transmission case. Install return spring on reverse shift lever. Position return spring and reverse shift lever on pivot pin. Make sure spring is tensioned to return lever to released position. Install "C" clip.

2) Position reverse idler gear in case with shoulder facing rear of case and with gear engaged in reverse shift lever. Install reverse idler gear shaft. Gently tap shaft into case with plastic hammer.

3) Using a new gasket, install front bearing retainer. Position bearing retainer on case with groove in gasket and retainer alinging with oil drain hole at bottom of case. Install and tighten retainer bolts.

4) Rotate countershaft until flat spot on end of shaft is facing up. *See Fig. 10.* Position of flat spot is critical as it must fit into matching flat spot in extension housing. If flat spot is improperly positioned, extension housing will not be correctly installed.

Fig. 10: Positioning Countershaft Flat Spot

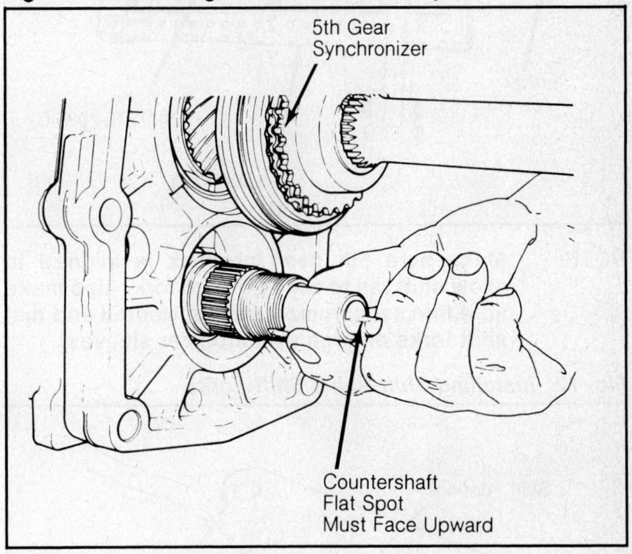

5) Raise front end of gear cluster to align countershaft with contershaft bore in case. With flat spot still up, tap counterchaft forward into case.

6) Remove 5th gear synchronizer snap rng from output shaft groove. Slide synchronizer and snap ring rearward against speedometer gear to make room for installation of 5th gear. Install gear cluster rear bearing. Install gear cluster bearing spacer.

7) Install gear cluster rear bearing snap ring. Using Screw (T75L-7025-J), Step Plate (D80L-630-3), Frame Press (T77L-7025-N), and Tube (T77L-7025-C), install 5th gear on countershaft. *See Fig. 11.* Position 5th gear and synchronizer. Install 5th gear synchronizer snap ring.

8) Shift transmission into 1st and Reverse to prevent rotation of mainshaft and gear cluster. To hold reverse idler gear in position, stretch a rubber band from reverse lever to cover bolt screwed into transmission case. *See Fig. 3.*

9) Install 5th gear washer and lock nut. Using a 36 mm socket, tighten 5th gear lock nut. Using a center punch and hammer, stake lock nut into place. Remove rubber band and cover bolt. Shift transmission out of 1st and Reverse.

10) Install 1st-2nd gear and 3rd-4th gear shift forks. Make sure 3rd-4th shift fork is on top of 1st-2nd shift fork. Position 5th gear shift fork and shift interlock on 5th gear synchronizer. Slide shift rail through interlock and shift fork until it enters case.

11) Position 1st-2nd shift fork, 2nd-3rd shift fork interlock and cam, and 3rd-4th shift fork. Slide shift rail through shift forks and shift interlock until shaft enters bore on front of case. *See Fig. 12.*

FORD MOTOR CO. IMPORTS 5-SPEED (Cont.)

Fig. 11: Installing 5th Gear On Gear Cluster

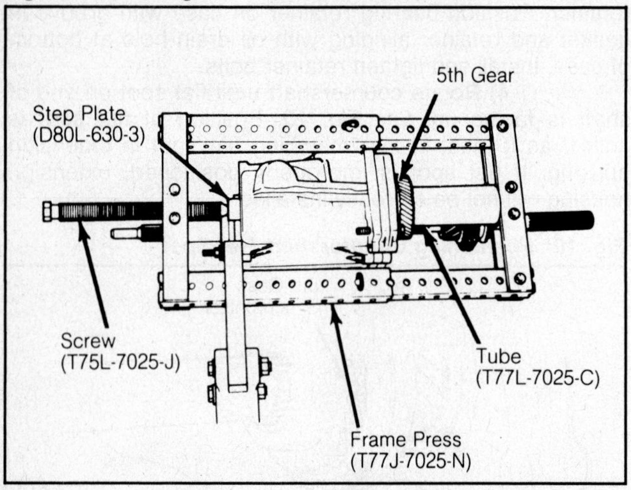

NOTE: **Make sure 5th gear interlock is aligned to allow shift rail to slide through fork. Also make sure that synchronizers are in Neutral and that shift forks engage synchronizer sleeves.**

Fig. 12: Installing Shift Rail & Shift Forks

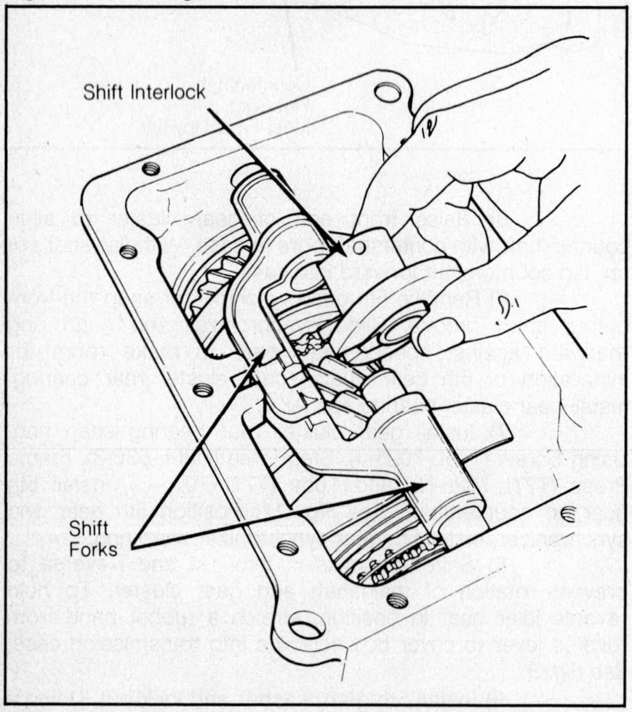

12) Align shift rail with shift interlock and install roll pin. To facilitate installation of pin, use center detent on shift rail as point of alignment.

13) Apply sealant to detent plug threads. Install shift detent plunger, spring, and plug. *See Fig. 2.* Tighten plug. Shift transmission into 4th gear. Place gasket on extension housing and install housing. Ensure that flat spots on countershaft and housing are properly aligned.

14) Apply sealant to extension housing bolts. Install and tighten extension housing attaching bolts. Shift transmission into Reverse. Position offset lever on shifter shaft and install roll pin, using a 1/8" pin punch. *See Fig. 13.*

15) Place new gasket on transmission and install cover. Ensure cover guide engages shift interlock. Tighten cover bolts. Apply sealant to back-up light and neutral safety switch threads and install switches in extension housing.

16) Install bellhousing and tighten attaching bolts. Install clutch release lever and bearing. Fill transmission with lubricant (Ford ESD-M-2C175A). Install speedometer driven gear in extension housing.

NOTE: **Use only specified lubricant in transmission. Lubricant is a semi-synthetic base oil.**

Fig. 13: Installing Offset Lever Roll Pin

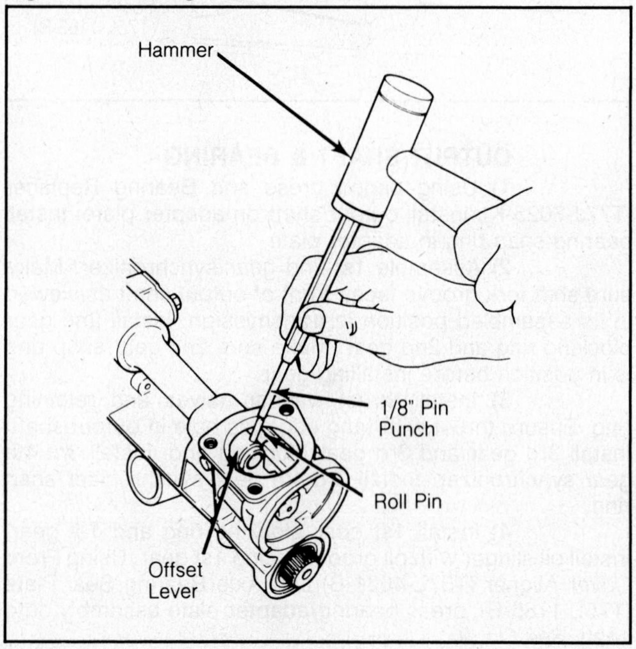

TIGHTENING SPECIFICATIONS

Application	Ft. Lbs. (N.m)
Bellhousing Bolts	52-67 (70-91)
Extension Housing Bolts	33-36 (45-49)
Shift Lever Bolts	16-19 (22-26)
5th Gear Lock Nut	89-111 (120-150)
	INCH Lbs. (N.m)
Front Bearing Retainer Bolts	84-96 (9-11)
Transmission Cover Retainer Bolt	84-96 (9-11)

GENERAL MOTORS IMPORTS & ISUZU 76MM 5-SPEED

I-Mark (FWD), Spectrum

DESCRIPTION

The 76mm 5-speed transaxle is a constant mesh, fully synchronized transaxle. All forward gears are in constant mesh, while reverse gear uses a sliding idler gear for engagement.

The unit consist of an aluminum case, aluminum rear cover, input shaft, output shaft, and a differential assembly. The input shaft, output shaft, and differential assembly are all supported by tapered roller bearings. The final output gear (an integral part of output shaft) turns ring gear and differential assembly, drive axles, and front wheels.

LUBRICATION & ADJUSTMENT

See appropriate MANUAL TRANSMISSION SERVICING article in IMPORT GENERAL SERVICING section.

REMOVAL & INSTALLATION

See appropriate MANUAL TRANSMISSION REMOVAL article in IMPORT GENERAL SERVICING section.

DISASSEMBLY

TRANSAXLE

1) Install transaxle on Holding Fixture (J-33366) and attach fixture to Base Plate (J-3389-20). Remove rear cover bolts and cover. Remove gearshift box assembly along with 4 bolts from transaxle case.

2) Using a screwdriver, shift transaxle into gear. Remove 5th gear drive and driven gear retaining nuts from input and output shafts. Discard retaining nuts.

3) Shift transaxle into Neutral. Remove detent spring retaining bolts for 1st-2nd gear, 3rd-4th gear, and 5th gear. Remove detent springs and balls. *See Fig. 1*.

4) Remove reverse detent spring retaining bolt from side of case. Remove detent spring and ball. Remove 1st-2nd gear, and 3rd-4th gear switches. Use a magnet to remove pins from 3rd-4th gear switch hole.

5) Place 5th gear synchronizer in Neutral. Remove roll pin at 5th gear shift fork. Remove 5th gear synchronizer hub, sleeve, roller bearing, gear, and shift fork from output shaft as an assembly.

6) Using Puller (J-35274), remove 5th gear from input shaft. Remove 7 screws Using a No. 45 Torx bit, remove 7 screws from bearing retainer. Remove bearing retainer and shims from input and output shafts.

7) Remove bolt retaining reverse idler shaft from side of case. Using Puller (J-22888 & J-22888-30), remove collar and thrust washer from output shaft. Remove transaxle case bolts and separate case from clutch housing.

8) Remove reverse idler gear and shaft. With shaft detents aligned and facing the same way, remove 5th and reverse shafts. *See Fig. 2*.

9) Using a punch and hammer, remove roll pin from 1st-2nd shift fork. Slide 1st-2nd shaft upward and remove fork and shaft from case. Remove roll pin and reverse shift lever. *See Fig. 3*.

10) Remove input shaft, output shaft, and 3rd-4th shift fork and shaft as an assembly. Remove differential assembly. Remove reverse shift bracket, and remove 3 interlock pins. Remove rear bearing outer races from transaxle case.

11) Remove outer races for input shaft front bearing, output shaft front and differential side bearings. Use Bearing Cup Remover (J-26941) with Puller (J-33367) for input, output, and differential bearing race removal. Use bearing cup remover and slide hammer to remove differential bearing race in housing.

12) Remove input shaft seals from housing. Remove clutch shaft seal only if replacement is required. Using Bushing Replacer (J-28412), drive out bushing toward inside of case. Remove fork assembly only if replacing clutch fork assembly.

Fig. 1: Removing Detent Bolts, Springs & Balls

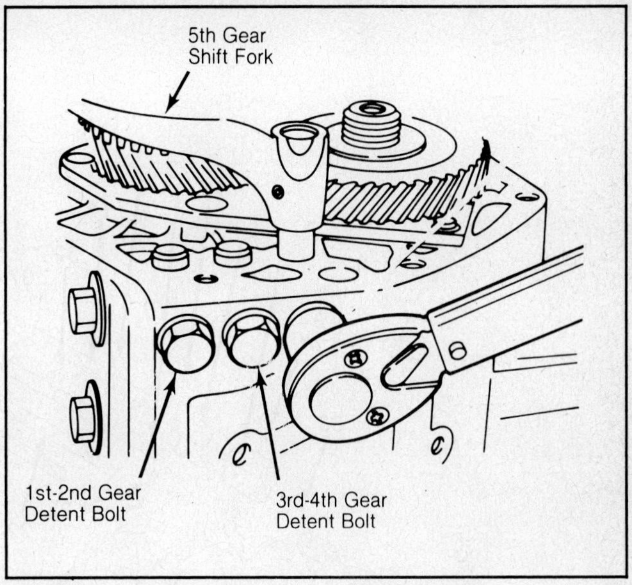

Fig. 2: Removing 5th & Reverse Shift Shafts

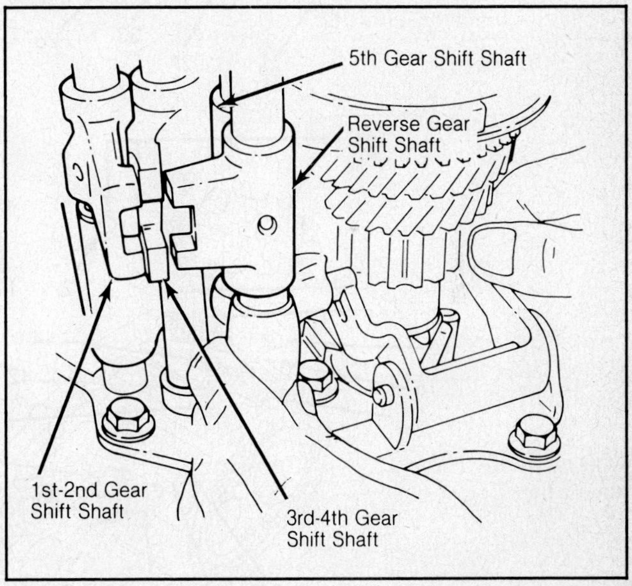

GENERAL MOTORS IMPORTS & ISUZU 76MM 5-SPEED (Cont.)

Fig. 3: Exploded View Of Transaxle Shift Lever & Shift Fork Assemblies

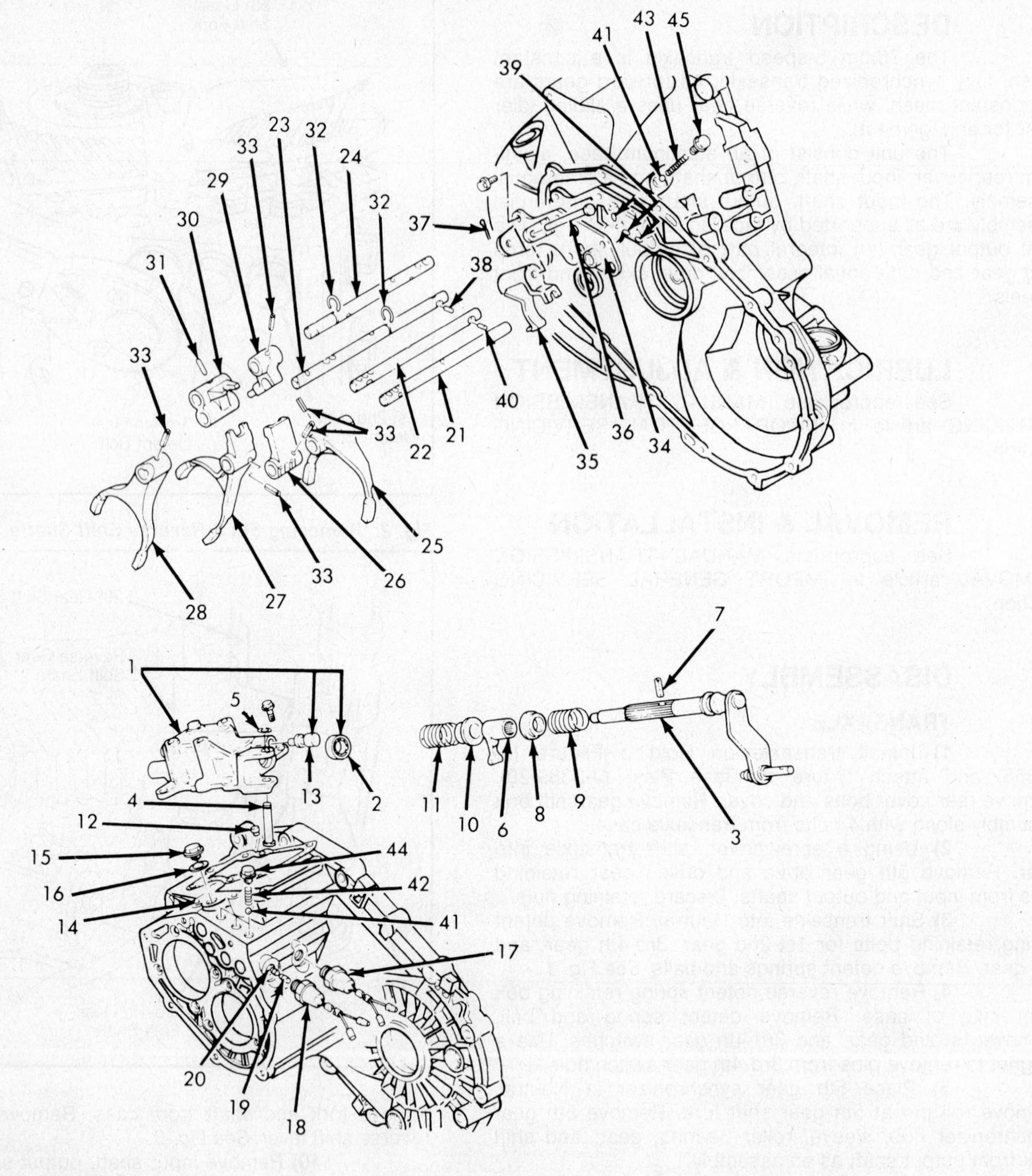

1. Gearshift Box
2. Gearshift Box Oil Seal
3. Shift Lever
4. Select Lever Pin
5. Snap Ring
6. Internal Shift Lever
7. Spring Pin
8. Spring Seat
9. Select Lever Spring
10. Spring Seat
11. Select Lever Spring
12. Pin
13. Breather
14. Gasket
15. Plug
16. Gasket
17. 1st-2nd Gear Switch
18. 3rd-4th Gear Switch
19. Pin, Short
20. Pin, Long
21. 1st-2nd Gear Shift Rod
22. 3rd-4th Gear Shift Rod
23. 5th Gear Shift Rod
24. Reverse Shift Rod
25. 1st-2nd Gear Shift Fork
26. 1st-2nd Gear Shift Block
27. 3rd-4th Gear Shift Fork
28. 5th Gear Shift Fork
29. Reverse Gear Shift Lever
30. Rev/5th Gear Shift Lever
31. Rev/5th Gear Lock Pin
32. Snap Ring
33. Spring Pin
34. Fulcrum Bracket
35. Reverse Gear Shift Lever
36. Reverse Gear Lever Pin
37. Split Pin
38. 5th Gear Lock Pin
39. Interlock Pin
40. 3rd-4th Gear Lock Pin
41. Detent Ball
42. Detent Spring
43. Reverse Gear Detent Spring
44. Detent Spring Screw
45. Detent Spring Screw

GENERAL MOTORS IMPORTS & ISUZU 76MM 5-SPEED (Cont.)

COMPONENT DISASSEMBLY

INPUT SHAFT

Using bench press and Bearing Remover (J-22912-01), remove front bearing. Using bench press and bearing remover, press out rear bearing, 4th gear, 3rd-4th synchronizer assembly, and 3rd gear as an assembly. Remove remaining parts from input shaft.

OUTPUT SHAFT

1) Using Bearing Remover (J-22227-A), Driver (J-33369), and bench press, remove front bearing. Using bench press and Bearing Remover (J-22912-01), remove rear bearing and 3rd-4th gear as an assembly.

2) Remove key, 2nd gear, needle bearing, and blocker ring. Using bench press, remove collar, reverse gear assembly, and 1st gear as an assembly. Remove thrust bearing and washer.

DIFFERENTIAL

1) Using bearing puller, remove differential case side bearings. Remove ring gear bolts and ring gear. Remove speedometer drive gear and discard.

2) Drive out lock pin, and pull out cross pin. Remove pinion gears and thrust washers. Remove side gears and thrust washers.

SYNCHRONIZER

Synchronizer hubs and sleeves are a matched set and should be kept together. Keys, springs, and rings may be replaced if worn or damaged. See SYNCHRONIZER in COMPONENT REASSEMBLY section.

CLEANING & INSPECTION

1) Thoroughly wash all parts in cleaning solvent. Make sure old lubricant, metallic particles, dirt, or foreign materials are removed from surface of parts. Dry parts with compressed air.

2) Inspect case halves for porosity, cracks, damaged mating surfaces, stripped threads, or distortion. Apply compressed air to each oil feed port or channel to remove obstructions.

3) Inspect all gears for wear or damage. Check splines for burrs, nicks, wear, or other damage. Remove minor nicks or scratches with an oil stone. Inspect thrust washers for wear, distortion, or damage.

4) Inspect condition of all needle, roller, and thrust bearings. Lubricate bearings with light oil and check them for roughness while slowly rotaing them by hand. Inspect shift forks and shafts for wear, distortion, or damage. Replace any part showing excessive wear or damage.

COMPONENT REASSEMBLY

SYNCHRONIZER

Install synchronizer springs on hubs. Each spring should support all 3 keys. Open portion of insert spring should face in opposite direction from the other so that load is evenly applied to synchronizer keys. *See Fig. 4*. Spring ends should not interfere with hub.

Fig. 4: 3rd Geat & 4th Gear Synchronizer Assemblies

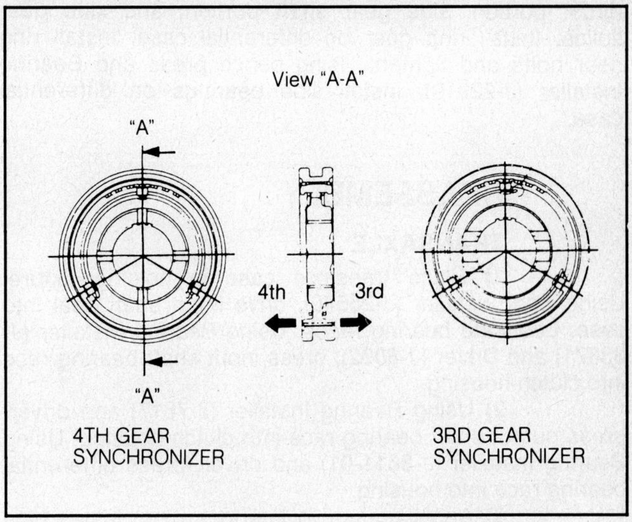

INPUT SHAFT

1) Lubricate input shaft thrust surfaces, gears and washers before assembly. Install needle bearing, 3rd gear, and block ring onto shaft. Match inserts of 3rd-4th sleeve and hub assembly with grooves of blocker ring.

2) Lubricate collar and hub interiors. Using bench press and Driver (J-33374), press on sleeve, hub assembly, and collar. After installation, apply oil to circumference of collar.

3) Install blocker ring and needle bearing. Install 4th gear and thrust washer. Install thrust washer with recessed area facing 4th gear. Lubricate front and rear bearings. Using bench press and Driver (J-33374), install front and rear bearings.

OUTPUT SHAFT

1) Lubricate output shaft thrust surfaces, gears and bearings before assembly. Install needle bearing and washer. Install needle bearing, 1st gear, and blocker ring. Match inserts of sleeve and hub assembly with grooves in blocker ring.

2) Lubricate collar and hub interiors. Using Support (J-8853-01) and Pilot (J-33369), press on sleeve, hub assembly, and collar. After installation, apply oil to circumference of collar.

3) Install blocker ring needle bearing, 2nd gear, and install key on groove. Apply oil to 3rd-4th gear interior, match key with groove, and fit key together with rear bearing. Using bench press and Driver (J-33374), press bearing assembly on shaft. Using Driver (J-33368), press front bearing onto shaft.

DIFFERENTIAL

1) Lubricate bearing races and bearing surfaces before assembly. Install side gears and thrust washers. Position thrust washers and pinion gears opposite each other, and install them into position by turning side gear.

2) Insert cross pin, and ensure backlash is within .0012-.0031" (.03-.08 mm). Install lock pin and stake in place. Using an oil bath heater, heat speedometer drive gear to 203°F (95°C). Install hot speedometer gear on differential.

GENERAL MOTORS IMPORTS & ISUZU 76MM 5-SPEED (Cont.)

3) Apply oil to cross pin, differential gears, thrust portion, side gear shaft portion, and side gear spline. Install ring gear on differential case. Install ring gear bolts and tighten. Using bench press and Bearing Installer (J-22919), install side bearings on differential case.

REASSEMBLY

TRANSAXLE

1) Place transaxle case in holding fixture. Using Seal Installer (J-26540), drive input shaft seal into case. Lubricate bearing races. Using Bearing Installer (J-33371) and Driver (J-8092), press input shaft bearing race into clutch housing.

2) Using Bearing Installer (J-7817) and driver, press output shaft bearing race into clutch housing. Using Bearing Installer (J-8611-01) and driver, press differential bearing race into housing.

3) Apply grease to interlock pins. Install pins on clutch housing. *See Fig. 5.* Install reverse shift bracket on clutch. Use 3rd-4th shaft rod to align bracket to housing. Install retaining bolts and tighten. Make sure rod operates smoothly.

4) Install differential assembly. Install input shaft, output shaft with 3rd-4th shift fork and shaft as an assembly. The 3rd-4th shift shaft is installed into raised collar of reverse shift lever bracket.

Fig. 5: Installing Interlock Pins

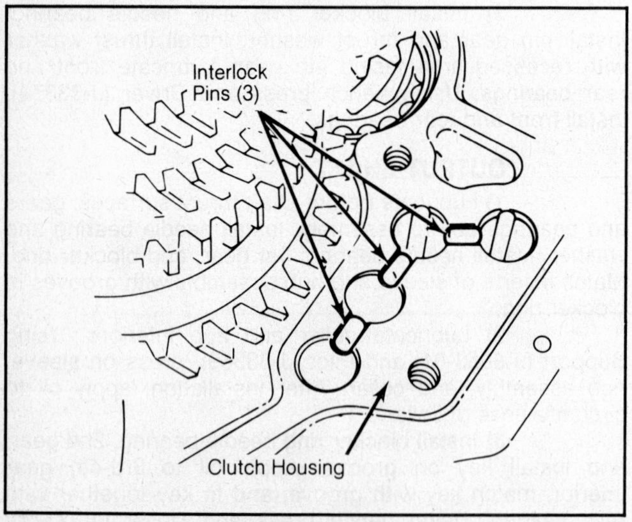

5) Install 1st-2nd shift fork onto synchronizer sleeve and insert shifter shaft into reverse shift lever bracket. Align hole in shift fork with shaft and install roll pin. Stake roll pin into place.

6) Install reverse lever on shift bracket. Ensure that interlock pin is installed in 5th gear shift shaft. Install reverse and 5th gear shift shaft and at same time, engage reverse shaft with reverse shift lever. Install reverse idler shaft and gear. Make sure reverse lever is engaged in gear collar.

7) Position outer bearing races on input shaft, output shaft, and differential bearings. Position Shim Selection Kit (J-33373) on bearing races. *See Fig. 6.* Kit gauges are marked "INPUT", "OUTPUT", and "DIFFERENTIAL".

8) Install 7 spacers, provided in kit, around perimeter of clutch housing. Install bearing and shim retainer on shafts. Tighten bolts to 11-16 ft. lbs. (15-22 N.m). Stake screws to retaining plate.

9) Carefully position transaxle case over gauges and on spacers. Install 7 bolts provided with kit and tighten bolts to 10 ft. lbs. (14 N.m). Ensure case is seated on spacers. *See Fig. 6.*

Fig. 6: Installing Shim Selection Kit

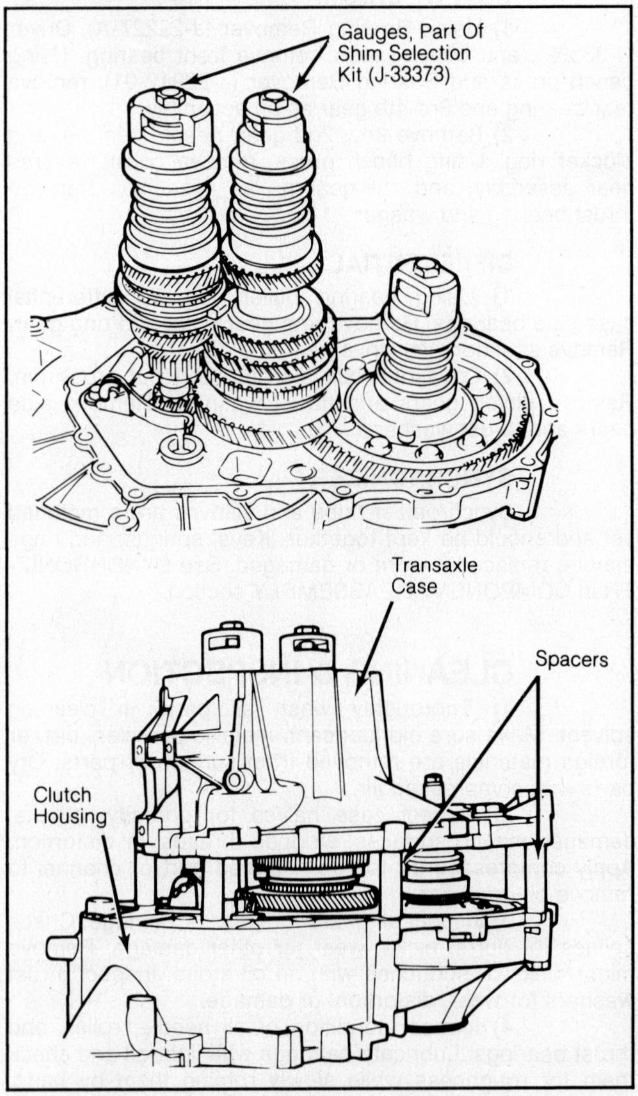

10) Rotate each gauge to seat bearings. Rotate differential case through 3 revolutions in each direction. With 3 gauges compressed, measure gap between outer sleeve and base pad using available shim sizes. Use the largest shim that can be placed in gap and drawn through without binding. *See Fig. 8.*

11) Input shaft shim should be one size smaller than the largest shim that will fit in gap. The differential should use a shim three sizes larger than that which will smoothly fit in gap. The output shaft should use the largest shim that can be placed in gap and drawn through without binding.

GENERAL MOTORS IMPORTS & ISUZU 76MM 5-SPEED (Cont.)

Fig. 7: Exploded View Of Transaxle Gear Assemblies

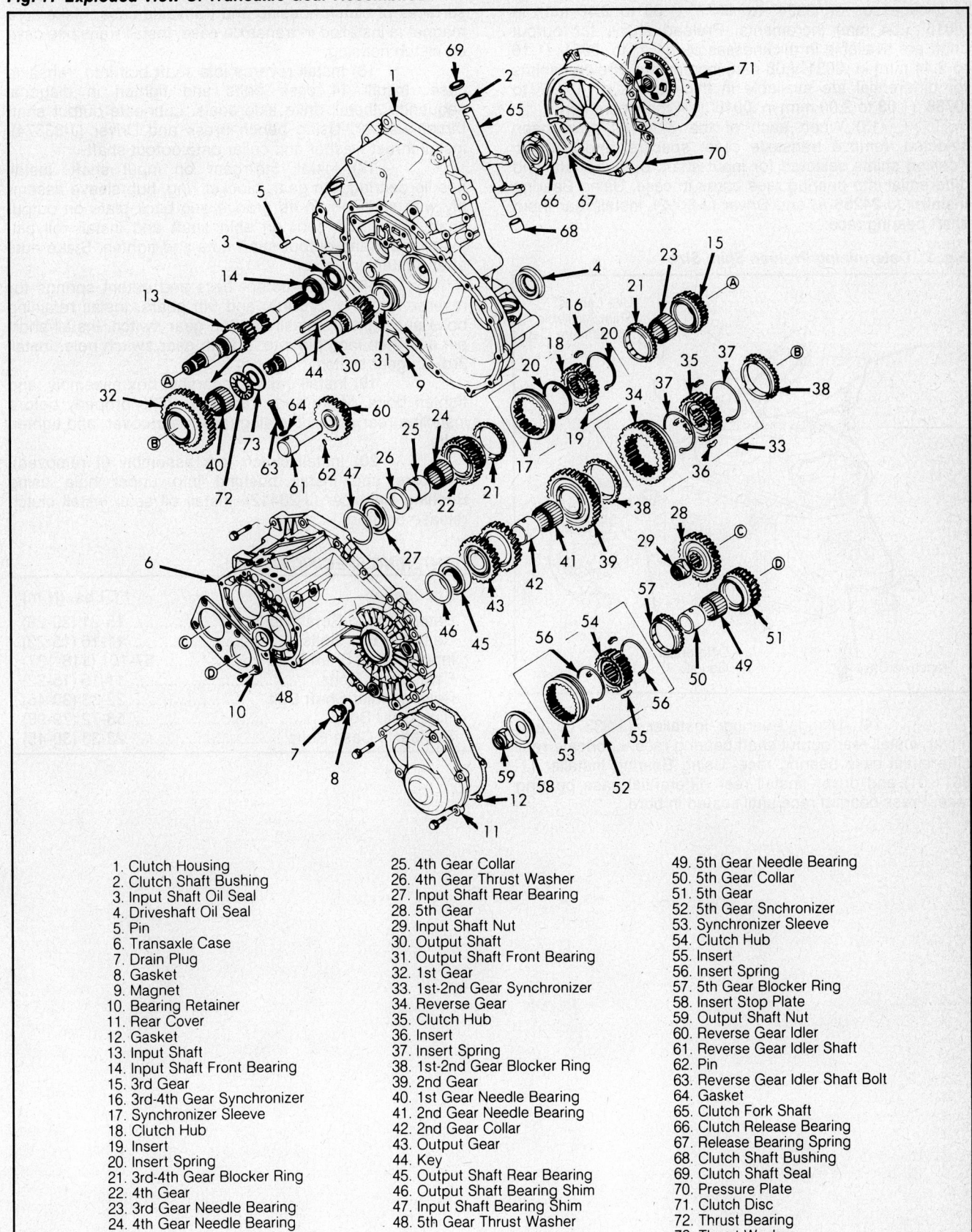

1. Clutch Housing
2. Clutch Shaft Bushing
3. Input Shaft Oil Seal
4. Driveshaft Oil Seal
5. Pin
6. Transaxle Case
7. Drain Plug
8. Gasket
9. Magnet
10. Bearing Retainer
11. Rear Cover
12. Gasket
13. Input Shaft
14. Input Shaft Front Bearing
15. 3rd Gear
16. 3rd-4th Gear Synchronizer
17. Synchronizer Sleeve
18. Clutch Hub
19. Insert
20. Insert Spring
21. 3rd-4th Gear Blocker Ring
22. 4th Gear
23. 3rd Gear Needle Bearing
24. 4th Gear Needle Bearing
25. 4th Gear Collar
26. 4th Gear Thrust Washer
27. Input Shaft Rear Bearing
28. 5th Gear
29. Input Shaft Nut
30. Output Shaft
31. Output Shaft Front Bearing
32. 1st Gear
33. 1st-2nd Gear Synchronizer
34. Reverse Gear
35. Clutch Hub
36. Insert
37. Insert Spring
38. 1st-2nd Gear Blocker Ring
39. 2nd Gear
40. 1st Gear Needle Bearing
41. 2nd Gear Needle Bearing
42. 2nd Gear Collar
43. Output Gear
44. Key
45. Output Shaft Rear Bearing
46. Output Shaft Bearing Shim
47. Input Shaft Bearing Shim
48. 5th Gear Thrust Washer
49. 5th Gear Needle Bearing
50. 5th Gear Collar
51. 5th Gear
52. 5th Gear Snchronizer
53. Synchronizer Sleeve
54. Clutch Hub
55. Insert
56. Insert Spring
57. 5th Gear Blocker Ring
58. Insert Stop Plate
59. Output Shaft Nut
60. Reverse Gear Idler
61. Reverse Gear Idler Shaft
62. Pin
63. Reverse Gear Idler Shaft Bolt
64. Gasket
65. Clutch Fork Shaft
66. Clutch Release Bearing
67. Release Bearing Spring
68. Clutch Shaft Bushing
69. Clutch Shaft Seal
70. Pressure Plate
71. Clutch Disc
72. Thrust Bearing
73. Thrust Washer

GENERAL MOTORS IMPORTS & ISUZU 76MM 5-SPEED (Cont.)

12) Preload shims for input shaft are available in thicknesses of .0394" to .0977" (1.00 to 2.48 mm) in .0016" (.04 mm) increments. Preload shims for output shaft are available in thicknesses of .0457" to .0961" (1.16 to 2.44 mm) in .0031" (.08 mm) increments. Preload shims for differential are available in thicknesses of .0426" to .0788" (1.08 to 2.00 mm) in .0016" (.04 mm) increments.

13) When each of the 3 shims have been selected, remove transaxle case, spacers, and gauges. Position shims selected for input shaft, output shaft, and differential into bearing race bores in case. Using Bearing Installer (J-24256-A) and Driver (J-8092), install rear input shaft bearing race.

Fig. 8: Determining Preload Shim Size

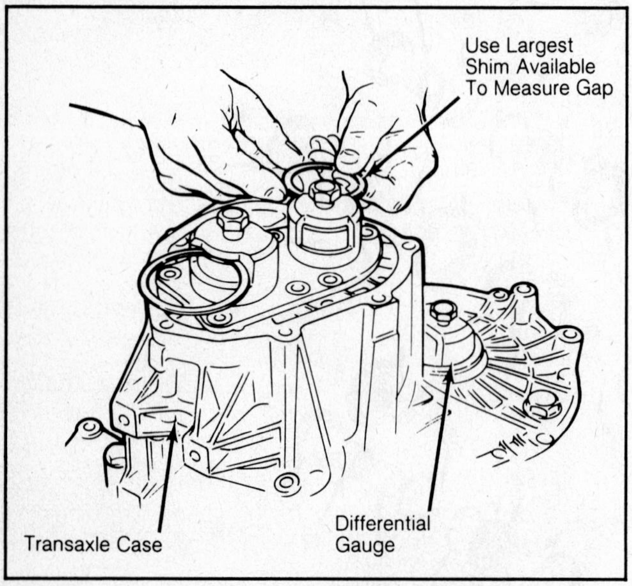

14) Using Bearing Installer (J-33370) and driver, install rear output shaft bearing race. Lubricate rear differential case bearing race. Using Bearing Installer (J-8611-01) and driver, install rear differential case bearing race. Press bearing race until seated in bore.

15) Apply a 1/8" bead of sealant to mating surfaces of clutch housing and transaxle case. Make sure magnet is installed in transaxle case. Install transaxle case on clutch housing.

16) Install reverse idle shaft bolt into transaxle case. Install 14 case bolts and tighten in diagonal sequence. Install drive axle seals. Lubricate output shaft thrust washer. Using bench press and Driver (J-33374), install thrust washer and collar onto output shaft.

17) Install 5th gear on input shaft. Install needle bearing, 5th gear, blocker ring, hub/sleeve assembly with shift fork in its groove and back plate on output shaft. Align shift fork on shift shaft and install roll pin. Install input and output shaft nuts and tighten. Stake nuts after tightening.

18) Install detent balls and detent springs for reverse, 1st-2nd, 3rd-4th, and 5th gears. Install retaining bolts and tighten. Install 1st-2nd gear switch. Install short pin and then long pin into 3rd-4th gear switch hole. Install 3rd-4th gear switch.

19) Install gasket, gearshift box assembly, and tighten bolts. Make sure transaxle shifts properly before installing rear cover. Install gasket, rear cover, and tighten bolts.

20) Install clutch fork assembly (if removed). Lubricate and install bushing into upper hole using Bushing Replacer (J-28412). Install oil seal. Install clutch release bearing.

TIGHTENING SPECIFICATIONS

Application	Ft. Lbs. (N.m)
Detent Spring Retaining Bolts	15-21 (20-28)
Gearshift Box Bolts	11-16 (15-22)
Input/Output Shaft Nuts	87-101 (118-137)
Rear Cover Bolts	11-16 (15-22)
Reverse Idler Shaft Bolt	22-33 (30-45)
Ring Gear Bolts	58-72 (79-98)
Transaxle Case Bolts	22-33 (30-45)

GENERAL MOTORS IMPORTS MV2 TRANSAXLE

Sprint

DESCRIPTION

The MV2 transaxle provides 5 forward drive speeds an one reverse speed by means of 3 synchronizers, input shaft, and countershaft. All forward speeds are in constant mesh, while reverse gear uses an idler gear for engagement.

The low-speed and high-speed synchronizers are mounted on countershaft. The low-speed synchronizer is engaged with countershaft in 1st or 2nd gear, while the high-speed synchronizer is engaged in 3rd and 4th gears only. The 5th gear synchronizer is mounted on input shaft.

OPERATION

Movement of gearshift lever is transmitted to gearshift select shaft through gearshift shaft. Gearshift select lever actuates each gear shift fork to shift transaxle into desired gear.

The gearshift interlock plate on select shaft prevents transaxle from engaging into more than one gear while shifting. The gearshift cam and gearshift cam guide prevent shifting from 5th gear directly into Reverse. Operation of cam and guide is as follows:

- When gearshift lever is in Neutral, the cam and guide are disengaged. *See Fig. 1*.
- When lever is shifted from Neutral into Reverse, the cam pushes up on guide and then turns clockwise. Guide is not turned but remains in Neutral position, as it is turned clockwise by a spring.
- When lever is shifted from Neutral into 5th gear, the cam pushes up on guide and then turns clockwise. At this time, cam is detached fron guide, the guide is pushed down by spring.
- The cam turns counterclockwise and interferes with guide preventing a direct shift from 5th gear into Reverse. As a result, the cam cannot be rotated further counterclockwise and a direct shift from 5th gear into Reverse is prevented.

LUBRICATION & ADJUSTMENT

See appropriate MANUAL TRANSMISSION SERVICING article in IMPORT GENERAL SERVICING section.

SERVICE (IN VEHICLE)

GEARSHIFT & SELECT SHAFT ASSEMBLY

Removal

1) Disconnect negative battery cable. Place transaxle in Neutral. Raise and support vehicle. Drain transaxle lubricant. Remove left transaxle case cap bolts, cap, and "O" ring.

2) Using pin punch and hammer, remove roll pin and gearshift yoke. DO NOT forget to remove roll pin from transaxle. Remove reverse check bolt, spring, and ball. It may be necessary to use a magnet to remove ball from hole.

3) Remove gearshift guide case by removing 4 retaining bolts. DO NOT loosen or remove nuts on guide case. Remove geashift locating bolt. Remove gearshift and select shaft assembly.

NOTE: **When shaft assembly is removed, the low-speed select spring may may drop into transaxle. Carefully take out spring together with shaft.**

Disassembly

Using pin punch and hammer, drive out 2 roll pins on gearshift and select shaft assembly. Remove gearshift cam, reverse select spring, interlock plate, gearshift/select lever, and low-speed select spring from shaft. *See Fig. 1*.

Reassembly

Install parts on shaft. Reverse select spring is shorter than low-speed select spring. Gearshift case plate should be installed as shown. *See Fig. 1*. Install gearshift guide case assembly and tighten.

Installation

1) Place transaxle into Neutral. Lubricate shaft assembly and install. Install gearshift locating bolt and washer. Install gearshift guide case. Install check ball, spring, washer, and bolt.

2) Install yoke on select shaft and gearshift arm. Install roll pin. Install "O" ring and left case cap. Fill transaxle with lubricant. Lower vehicle and install negative battery cable.

5TH GEAR ASSEMBLY

Removal

1) Disconnect negative battery cable. Raise and support vehicle. Drain transaxle lubricant. Remove transaxle side case. Remove snap ring and hub plate. Remove shift fork and shift guide ball.

2) Using pin punch and hammer, remove shift fork pin. Use care not to damage gear while removing pin. Shift transaxle into 1st gear and then slide 5th gear synchronizer down. This will lock input shaft and countershaft.

3) Using chisel and hammer, remove staked portion of countershaft nut. Remove nut. Remove 5th gear shift fork, sleeve, hub, synchronizer ring, and spring.

4) Shift transaxle into Neutral. Remove input and countershaft 5th gear, input shaft 5th gear bearing, washer and other parts (as required). *See Fig. 2*.

Installation

1) Install synchronizer to hub. To install spring, insert one end of spring in synchronizer hub, and install other spring in opposite direction so that load is evenly applied to synchronizer keys. *See Fig. 4*.

2) Install synchronizer keys and sleeve on hub. Install 5th gear washer, spacer, and bearing on input shaft. Install input shaft and countershaft 5th gears.

3) Install synchronizer ring, springs, sleeve, hub, and shift fork. When installing hub on input shaft, align oil groove in hub with oil hole in input shaft. Shift transaxle into 1st gear and then slide 5th gear synchronizer down. This will lock input shaft and countershaft.

4) Install and tighten countershaft nut. Stake nut into position. Shift transaxle into Neutral. Install shift guide ball and shift fork screw on shift fork. Tighten shift fork screw and stake bolt into place. Make sure bolt is securely staked.

Fig. 1: Gearshift/Select Shaft & Gearshift Shaft Assembly

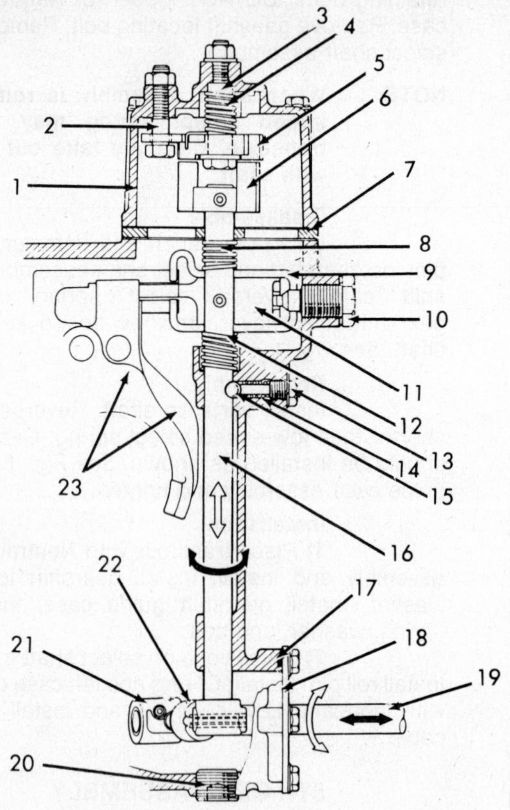

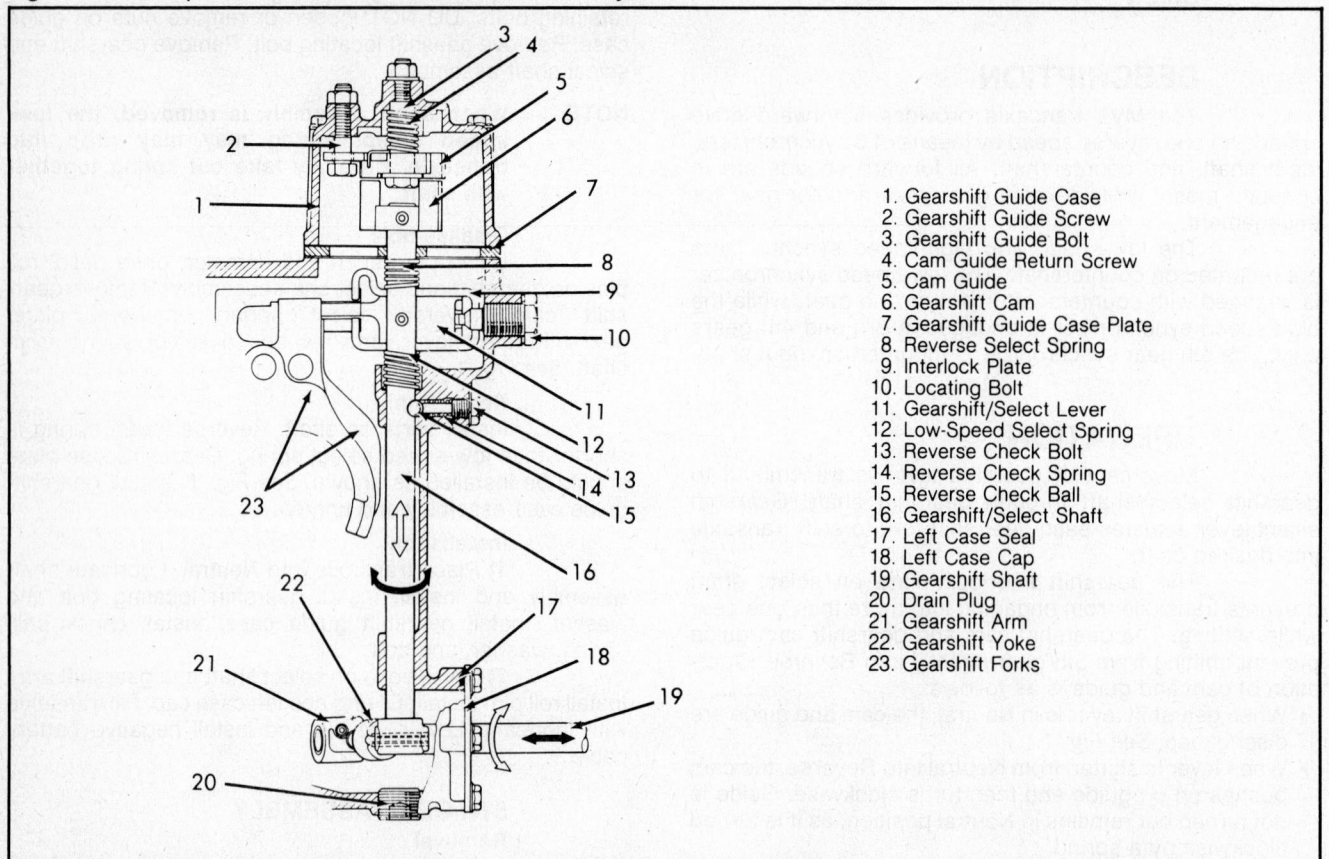

1. Gearshift Guide Case
2. Gearshift Guide Screw
3. Gearshift Guide Bolt
4. Cam Guide Return Screw
5. Cam Guide
6. Gearshift Cam
7. Gearshift Guide Case Plate
8. Reverse Select Spring
9. Interlock Plate
10. Locating Bolt
11. Gearshift/Select Lever
12. Low-Speed Select Spring
13. Reverse Check Bolt
14. Reverse Check Spring
15. Reverse Check Ball
16. Gearshift/Select Shaft
17. Left Case Seal
18. Left Case Cap
19. Gearshift Shaft
20. Drain Plug
21. Gearshift Arm
22. Gearshift Yoke
23. Gearshift Forks

5) Using pin punch and hammer, install new roll pin on 5th-Reverse gear shift shaft. Install synchronizer hub plate and new snap ring. Snap ring should be installed so that chamfered edge faces hub plate.

6) Apply sealant to side case. Align oil receiver cup in side case with hole of input shaft. Install side case and tighten bolts. Fill transaxle with lubricant. Lower vehicle and install negative battery cable.

NOTE: If oil receiver cup was removed for service, apply thread locking compound to threads of cup attaching screw before installing case.

REMOVAL & INSTALLATION

TRANSMISSION

See appropriate MANUAL TRANSMISSION REMOVAL article in IMPORT GENERAL SERVICING section.

TRANSMISSION DISASSEMBLY

1) Remove back-up light switch. Remove 7 bolts and side case. Remove snap ring and hub plate from input shaft. Remove shift fork screw and guide ball from 5th gear shift fork.

2) Place transaxle in Neutral. Remove roll pin from 5th gear shift fork. Push in on gearshift shaft to engage transaxle into 1st gear. Slide 5th gear synchronizer down to engage 5th gear. This will lock input shaft and countershaft.

3) Using chisel and hammer, remove staked portion of countershaft nut. Remove nut. Remove 5th gear shift fork, sleeve, hub, synchronizer ring, spring and keys as an assembly.

4) Remove 5th gear from countershaft. Remove 7 screws retaining bearing/shim retainer plate to left case. Remove plate and shims. Mark or tag shims for reassembly reference.

5) Remove bolts and left case. Remove roll pin retaining gearshift yoke to gearshift/select shaft. Install drift into roll pin hole and raise shaft for removal of yoke and roll pin.

6) Remove locating bolt for gearshift/select shaft. Remove 4 bolts and gearshift guide case. Remove gearshift/select shaft assembly along with low-speed select spring from case.

7) Remove 3 bolts retaining detent balls and springs on shift fork shafts. Remove 13 bolts retaining case halves. Insert a large flat-bladed screwdriver into case slots and pry case halves apart.

8) Remove left case. All internal parts should remain installed on right case. Raise 5th and reverse gear shift shafts to gain clearance for removal of reverse gear and shaft.

9) Remove bolts and reverse idler gear shift lever. Remove 5th and reverse gear shift shafts as an assembly. Remove input shaft, countershaft, 1st-2nd and 3rd-4th gear shift shaft as an assembly. It may be necessary to raise differential to gain clearance for removal of assembly.

GENERAL MOTORS IMPORTS MV2 TRANSAXLE (Cont.)

Fig. 2: Exploded View Of Transaxle Gear Assembly

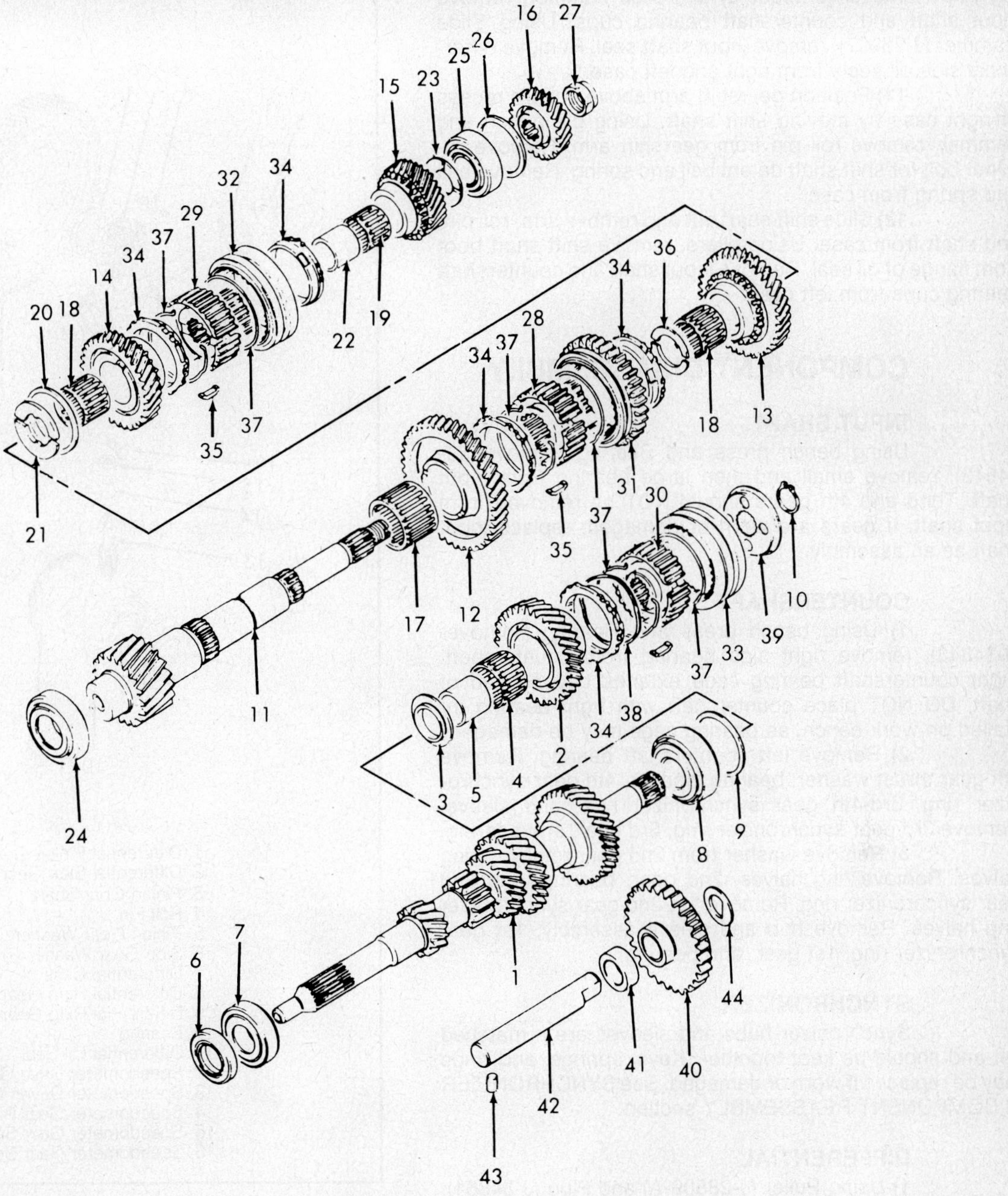

1. Input Shaft
2. Input Shaft 5th Gear
3. 5th Gear Washer
4. 5th Gear Bearing
5. 5th Gear Spacer
6. Input Shaft Oil Seal
7. Input Shaft Right Bearing
8. Input Shaft Left Bearing
9. Input Shaft Bearing Shim
10. Snap Ring
11. Countershaft
12. Countershaft Low Gear
13. Countershaft 2nd Gear
14. Countershaft 3rd Gear
15. Countershaft 4th Gear
16. Countershaft 5th Gear
17. 1st Gear Bearing
18. 2nd-3rd Gear Bearing
19. 4th Gear Bearing
20. 2nd-3rd Gear Ring Washer
21. 2nd-3rd Gear Ring
22. 4th Gear Spacer
23. 4th Gear Thrust Washer
24. Countershaft Right Bearing
25. Countershaft Left Bearing
26. Countershaft Bearing Shim
27. Countershaft Nut
28. 1st-2nd Gear Synchronizer Hub
29. 3rd-4th Gear
30. Synchronizer Hub
31. 1st-2nd Gear
32. 3rd-4th Gear Synchronizer Sleeve
33. 5th Gear Synchronizer Sleeve
33. Synchronizer Ring
34. Synchronizer Ring
35. Synchronizer Shifting Key
36. 1st-2nd Gear Synchronizer Hub Ring
37. Synchronizer Spring
38. Synchronizer Ring Spring
39. 5th Gear Synchronizer Hub Plate
40. Reverse Idler Gear
41. Idler Gear Spacer
42. Reverse Gear Shaft
43. Roll Pin
44. Washer

GENERAL MOTORS IMPORTS MV2 TRANSAXLE (Cont.)

10) Remove differential assembly. Using Bearing Cup Remover (J-29369-2) and slide hammer, remove input shaft and countershaft bearing cups. Using Slide Hammer (J-23907), remove input shaft seal. Remove differential side oil seals from right and left case.

11) Position gearshift arm above square recess of right case by moving shift shaft. Using pin punch and hammer, remove roll pin from gearshift arm. Remove retainer bolt for shift shaft detent ball and spring. Remove ball and spring from case.

12) Slide shift shaft out and remove arm, roll pin, and shaft from case. Using pliers, remove shift shaft boot from flange of oil seal. Remove input shaft and countershaft bearing cups from left case.

COMPONENT DISASSEMBLY

INPUT SHAFT

Using bench press and Bearing Remover (J-34843), remove small and then large bearing from input shaft. Third and 4th gears should NOT be removed from input shaft. If gears are worn or damaged, replace input shaft as an assembly.

COUNTERSHAFT

1) Using bench press and Bearing Remover (J-34843), remove right side bearing from countershaft. Right countershaft bearing cage extends beyond end of shaft. DO NOT place countershaft with right bearing installed on work bench, as bearing cage may be damaged.

2) Remove left countershaft bearing. Remove 4th gear thrust washer, bearing, spacer, 4th gear synchronizer ring, 3rd-4th gear synchronizer hub, and sleeve. Remove 3rd gear synchronizer ring, 3rd gear, and bearing.

3) Remove washer from 2nd gear retaining ring halves. Remove ring halves, 2nd gear, bearing, and 2nd gear synchronizer ring. Remove 1st-2nd gear synchronizer ring halves. Remove hub and sleeve assembly, 1st gear synchronizer ring, 1st gear, and bearing.

SYNCHRONIZER

Synchronizer hubs and sleeves are a matched set and should be kept together. Keys, springs, and rings may be replaced if worn or damaged. See SYNCHRONIZER in COMPONENT REASSEMBLY section.

DIFFERENTIAL

1) Using Puller (J-28509-A) and Plug (J-34851), remove differential case side bearings. Using Puller (J-28509-A), remove speedometer drive gear. *See Fig. 3.*

2) Remove roll pin securing pinion shaft. Remove pinion shaft, pinion gears, and side gears from case. Remove ring gear bolts and then remove ring gear.

CLEANING & INSPECTION

1) Thoroughly wash all parts in cleaning solvent. Make sure old lubricant, metallic particles, dirt, or foreign materials are removed from surface of parts. Dry parts with compressed air.

2) Inspect case halves for porosity, cracks, damaged mating surfaces, stripped threads, or distortion. Apply compressed air to each oil feed port or channel to remove obstructions.

Fig. 3: Differential Assembly

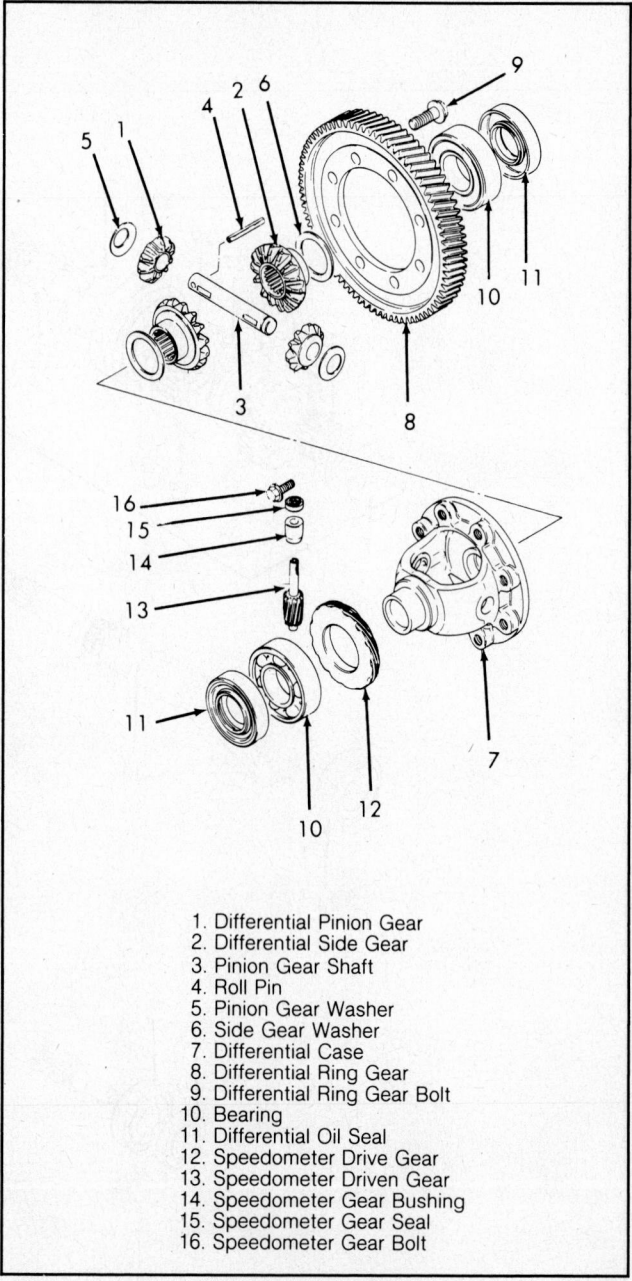

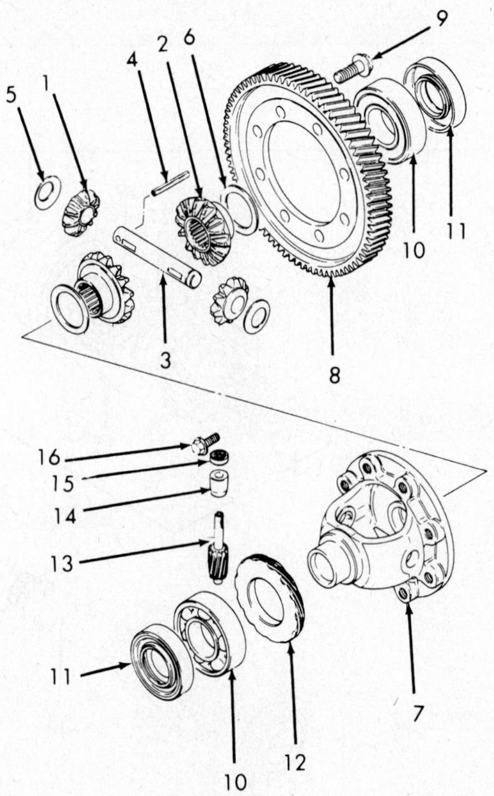

1. Differential Pinion Gear
2. Differential Side Gear
3. Pinion Gear Shaft
4. Roll Pin
5. Pinion Gear Washer
6. Side Gear Washer
7. Differential Case
8. Differential Ring Gear
9. Differential Ring Gear Bolt
10. Bearing
11. Differential Oil Seal
12. Speedometer Drive Gear
13. Speedometer Driven Gear
14. Speedometer Gear Bushing
15. Speedometer Gear Seal
16. Speedometer Gear Bolt

3) Inspect all gears for wear or damage. Check splines for burrs, nicks, wear, or other damage. Remove minor nicks or scratches with an oil stone. Inspect thrust washers for wear, distortion, or damage.

4) Inspect condition of all needle, roller, and thrust bearings. Lubricate bearings with light oil and check them for roughness while slowly rotaing them by hand. Inspect shift forks and shafts for wear, distortion, or damage. Replace any part showing excessive wear or damage.

COMPONENT REASSEMBLY

SYNCHRONIZER

Install low and high-speed synchronizer springs on hubs. To install spring(s), insert one end of spring in

Fig. 4: Synchronizer Assemblies

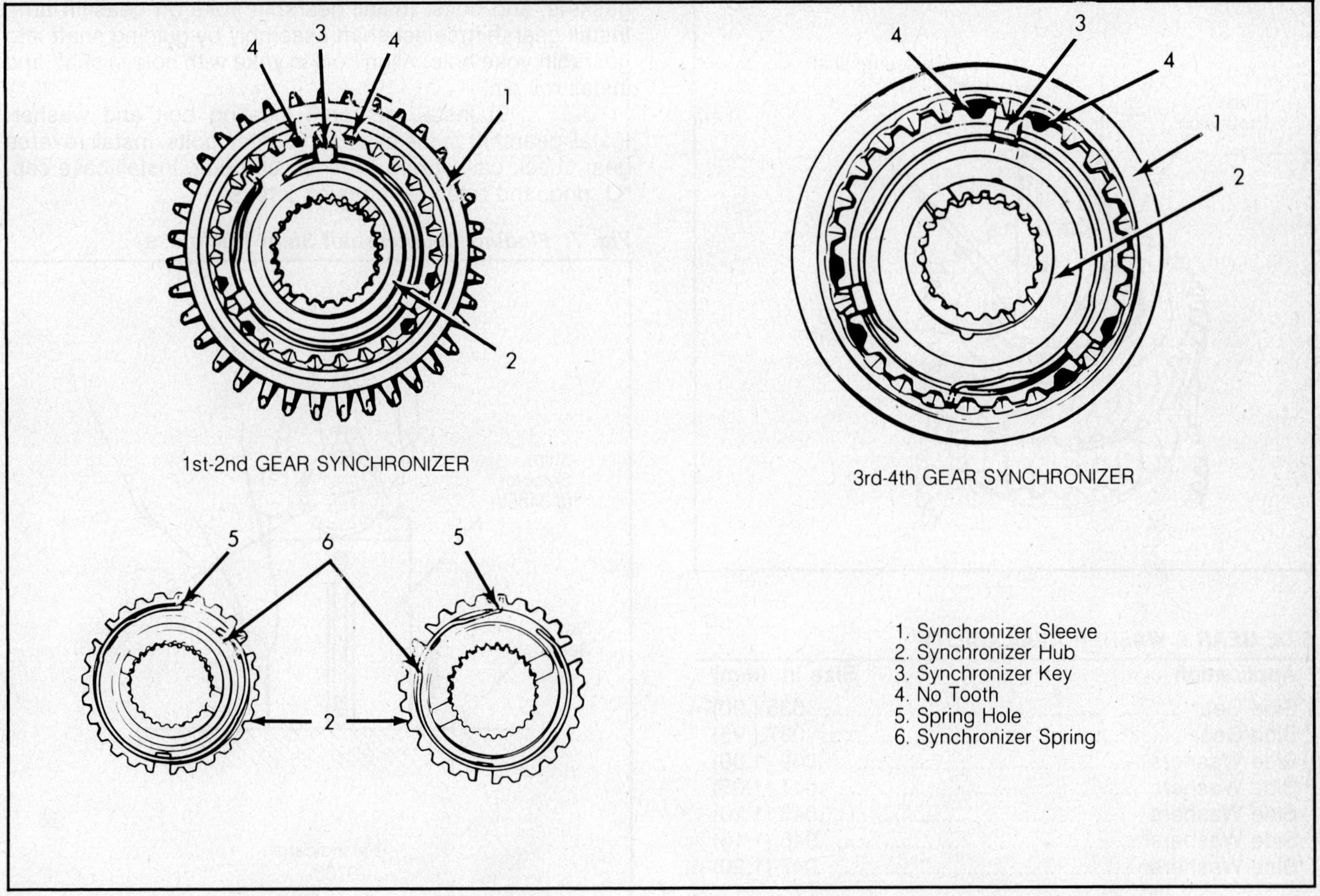

synchronizer hub, and install other spring in opposite direction so that load is evenly applied to synchronizer keys. *See Fig. 4*.

INPUT SHAFT

Using bench press and Bearing Installer (J-34844), press right and left bearings onto input shaft.

COUNTERSHAFT

1) Lubricate countershaft sliding surfaces before assembly. Install low gear bearing and gear on shaft. Install 1st-2nd gear synchronizer assembly on shaft. Align oil groove on hub with oil hole on shaft. *See Fig. 5*.

2) Install low-speed synchronizer hub rings. Fit rings into groove of countershaft. Install 2nd gear bearing and gear on shaft. Install ring washer and rings with ring protrusion in countershaft hole. *See Fig. 6*. Install 3rd gear bearing and 3rd gear on shaft.

3) Install 3rd-4th gear synchronizer assembly. Install hub so that oil groove aligns with oil hole on shaft. Install 3th gear and thrust washer. Oil grooves on washer go against 4th gear. Using bench press and Bearing Installer (J-34844), install bearings on shaft.

DIFFERENTIAL

1) Lubricate differential components before assembly. Install side washers and side gears. Install pinion washers an pinion gears. Install pinion gear shaft.

Fig. 5: Installing 1st-2nd Gear Synchronizer

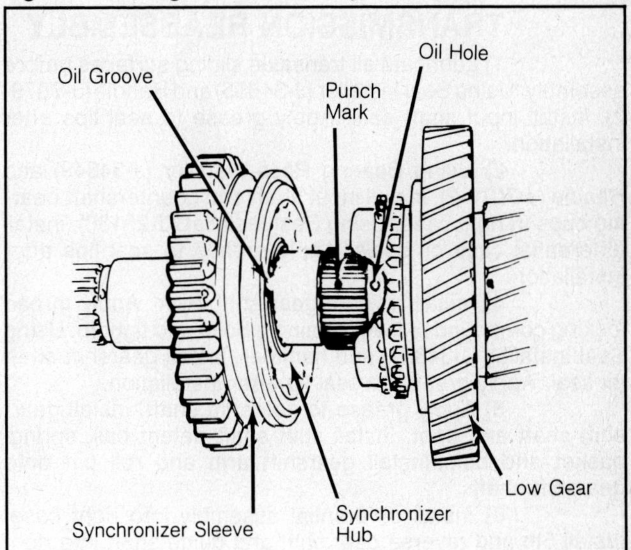

2) Using a feeler gauge, measure backlash between pinions and side gears. If backlash is not 0.004-.009" (.01-.25 mm), adjust backlash by changing thickness of side gear washers. Install pinion shaft roll pin.

3) Install ring gear and tighten retaining bolts. Using bench press, install speedometer gear. Install differential bearings with bearing seal toward differential case.

GENERAL MOTORS IMPORTS MV2 TRANSAXLE (Cont.)

Fig. 6: Installing 2nd Gear Rings & Washer

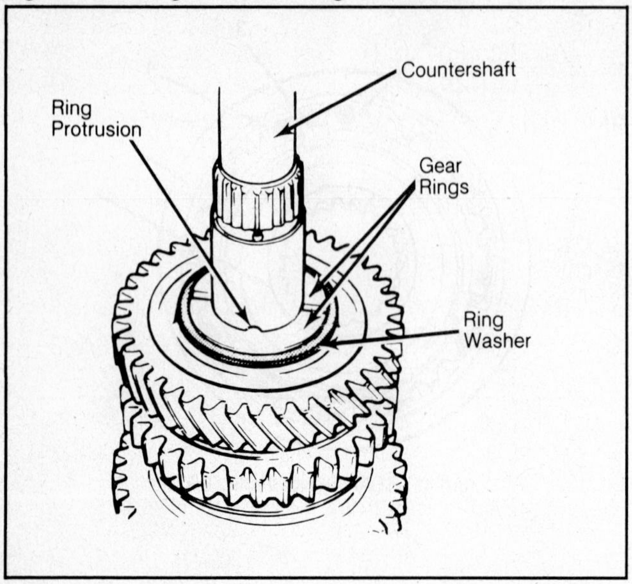

SIDE GEAR & WASHER AVAILABILITY

Application	Size In. (mm)
Side Gear	.035 (.90)
Side Gear	.037 (.95)
Side Washers	.039 (1.00)
Side Washers	.041 (1.05)
Side Washers	.043 (1.10)
Side Washers	.045 (1.15)
Side Washers	.047 (1.20)

TRANSMISSION REASSEMBLY

1) Lubricate all transaxle sliding surfaces before assembly. Using Seal Installer (J-34855) and Handle (J-7079-2), install input shaft seal. Apply grease to seal lips after installation.

2) Using Bearing Race Installer (J-34849) and Handle (J-7079-2), install input shaft and countershaft bearing cups in right case. Using Seal Installer (J-29130), install differential case oil seals. Apply grease to seal lips after installation.

4) Install reverse gear shift lever. Apply thread locking compound to lever retaining bolts and tighten. Using Seal Installer (J-34857) and hammer, install gearshift shaft oil seal. Apply grease to seal lip after installation.

5) Apply grease to gearshift shaft. Install gearshift shaft and boot. Install shift shaft detent ball, spring, gasket and bolt. Install gearshift arm and roll pin onto gearshift shaft.

6) Install differential assembly into right case. Install 5th and reverse gear shift and guide shaft into right case. Install input shaft, countershaft, 1st/2nd and 3rd/4th gear shift shafts into right case.

7) Install idler gear, shaft, pin, spacer, and washer into right case. Install magnet into right case. Apply sealant to left case mating surface. Install left case on right case. Install and tighten bolts.

NOTE: **After tightening case bolts, check input shaft and countershaft for smooth rotation by turning shafts by hand.**

8) Install shift fork shaft detent balls, spring, gaskets, and bolts. Install gearshift yoke on geashift arm. Install gearshift/select shaft assembly by guiding shaft into gearshift yoke hole. Align hole in yoke with hole in shaft and install roll pin.

9) Install gearshift locating bolt and washer. Install gearshift guide case and tighten bolts. Install reverse gear check ball, spring, washer, and bolt. Install case cap, "O" ring, and retaining bolts on left case.

Fig. 7: Finding Countershaft Shim Thickness

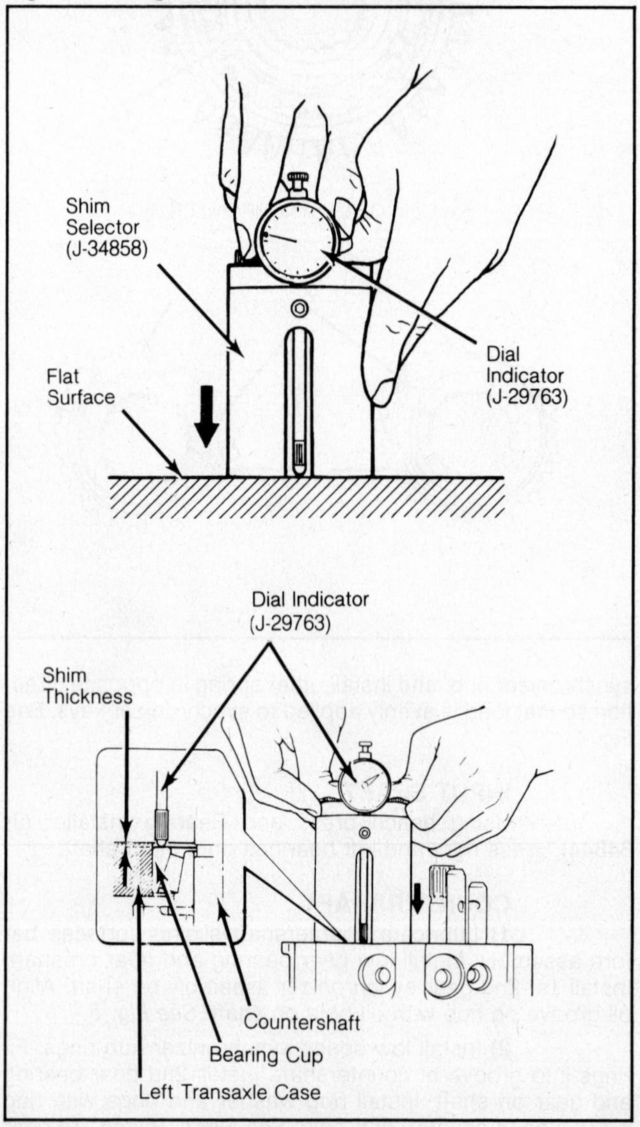

10) Install left bearing cups for input shaft and countershaft. Using finger pressure, press countershaft bearing cup against bearing rollers. Rotate countershaft 3-4 times to seat bearing.

11) Install Nut (Part of J-34858) on shaft an then install used countershaft nut. Tighten nut to 44-58 ft. lbs (60-79 N.m). Install Shim Selector (J-34858) on flat surface and zero Dial Indicator (J-29763). *See Fig. 7.*

12) Place shim selector over countershaft and left case. Press down on shim selector and read dial indicator. Reading equals size of shim required. Select shim and install it on back of left countershaft bearing cup.

GENERAL MOTORS IMPORTS MV2 TRANSAXLE (Cont.)

COUNTERSHAFT SHIM AVAILABILITY

Reading On Dial Indicator (mm)	Thickness Of Shim To Be Installed (mm)
.42-.47	.60
.48-.52	.65
.53-.57	.70
.58-.62	.75
.63-.67	.80
.68-.72	.85
.73-.77	.90
.78-.82	.95
.83-.87	1.00
.88-.92	1.05
.93-.97	1.10
.98-1.02	1.15

13) Repeat steps **10)** through **12)** to find shim thickness for input shaft. Select shim and install it on back of left input shaft bearing cup. *See Fig. 8.*

Fig. 8: Finding Input Shaft Shim Thickness

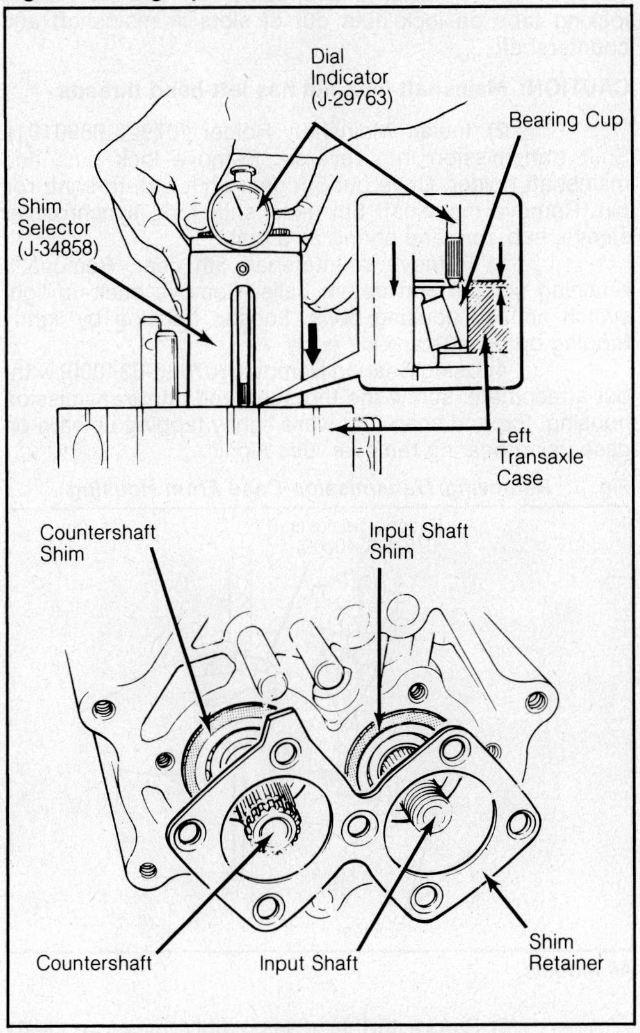

14) Install shim/bearing retainer plate. Fit protrusion of plate into groove of gearshift guide shaft. Apply thread locking compound to plate screws and install.

15) Install Preload Wheel (J-34852) on input shaft. *See Fig. 9.* Connect spring scale to wire and pull on scale. Check input shaft preload in Neutral and in 4th gear.

INPUT SHAFT SHIM SELECTION

Reading On Dial Indicator (mm)	Thickness Of Shim To Be Installed (mm)
.48-.52	.60
.53-.57	.65
.58-.62	.70
.63-.67	.75
.68-.72	.80
.73-.77	.85
.78-.82	.90
.83-.87	.95
.88-.92	1.00
.93-.97	1.05
.98-1.02	1.10
1.03-1.07	1.15

16) If preload is out of specification, shims in input shaft and/or countershaft will have to changed. If preload is 26-132 INCH lbs. (3-15 N.m), remove countershaft nut and special nut.

17) With transaxle in 4th gear, install 5th gear on input shaft and countershaft. Engage synchronizer so transaxle will lock in 2 gears. Install new countershaft nut and tighten. Stake nut into place.

18) Disengage 5th gear synchronizer and shift transaxle into Neutral. Install shift guide ball and shift fork screw on shift fork. After tightening screw, stake screw into place.

19) Install new roll pin to 5th and reverse gear shift shaft. Install synchronizer hub plate and new snap ring. Apply sealant to side case mating surface. Install side case. Fit oil receiver cup on side case into input shaft hole. Install side case bolts and tighten. Install back-up light switch.

Fig. 9: Checking Input Shaft Preload

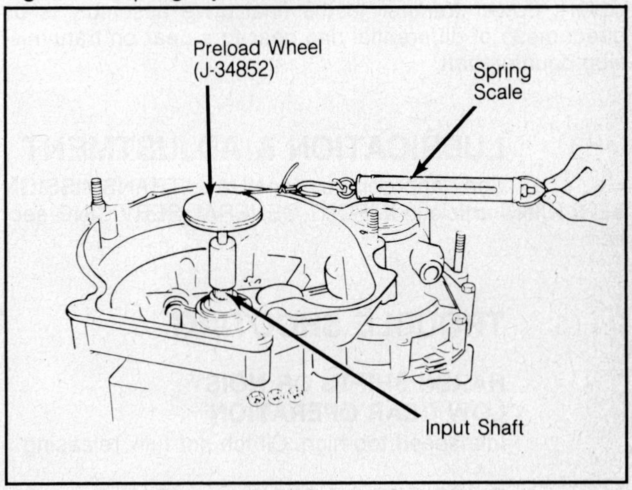

TIGHTENING SPECIFICATIONS

Application	Ft. Lbs. (N.m)
Countershaft Nut	44-58 (60-79)
Differential Ring Gear Bolts	58-72 (79-98)
Locating Bolt	30-43 (41-58)
Reverse Lever Bolts	14-20 (19-27)
Transaxle Case Bolts	14-20 (19-27)
	INCH Lbs. (N.m)
Guide Case Bolts	72-84 (8-9)
Left Case Cap Bolts	36-60 (4-7)
Shift Fork Screw	72-96 (8-11)
Shim Retainer Plate Screws	60 (7)

HONDA 2WD 4 & 5-SPEED TRANSAXLE

Accord, Civic 2WD, Prelude

TRANSAXLE IDENTIFICATION

Transaxle identification number is stamped into top of transaxle case flange near transaxle-to-engine union.

MANUAL TRANSAXLE CODES

Application	Code
Accord 5-Speed	
California & High Altitude	GS
Federal	GY
Civic	
4-Speed	GV
5-Speed	GW
Prelude 5-Speed	GM

DESCRIPTION

Transmission and final drive are mounted in a common 2-piece case. Accord and Prelude models use a 5-speed unit exclusively, while Civic models offer both a 4 and 5-speed.

The transaxle is fully synchronized in all forward gears. All forward gears are helically cut and are in constant mesh. Reverse gears are spur cut and are engaged by a sliding reverse idler gear.

On 5-speed transmissions, 5th gear is mounted on mainshaft on rear side of transaxle case (inside end cover). Power transfer to the final drive assembly is by direct mesh of differential ring gear to a gear on transmission countershaft.

LUBRICATION & ADJUSTMENT

See appropriate MANUAL TRANSMISSION SERVICING article in IMPORT GENERAL SERVICING section.

TROUBLE SHOOTING

HARSH SHIFTS OR NOISY LOW GEAR OPERATION

Idle speed too high. Clutch not fully releasing.

SLIPS OUT OF GEAR

Synchronizer teeth worn. Interlock mechanism damaged. Weak interlock spring. Shift linkage out of adjustment.

TRANSMISSION NOISY

Worn or damaged gear teeth or bearings. Improperly adjusted clutch. Oil soaked or damaged clutch.

REVERSE GEAR ENGAGEMENT DURING FORWARD GEAR CHANGE

Check for a weak or damaged reverse interlock mechanism.

SERVICE (IN VEHICLE)

DRIVE AXLE SHAFTS

See appropriate DRIVE AXLE SHAFT article in IMPORT AXLE SHAFTS, OVERDRIVES & TRANSFER CASES section.

REMOVAL & INSTALLATION

TRANSAXLE

See appropriate MANUAL TRANSMISSION REMOVAL article in IMPORT GENERAL SERVICING section.

TRANSAXLE DISASSEMBLY

ACCORD & PRELUDE

1) Remove transaxle from vehicle and install on work stand. *See Fig. 5.* Remove transmission end cover. Before removing lock nuts, measure clearance between spacer collar and shoulder on 5th gear. Bend locking tabs on lock nuts out of slots in mainshaft and countershaft.

CAUTION: Mainshaft lock nut has left-hand threads.

2) Install Mainshaft Holder (07923-6890101). Shift transmission into reverse. Remove lock nuts and mainshaft holder. Drive out 5th gear shift fork-to-shaft roll pin. Remove mainshaft 5th gear, shift fork, synchronizer sleeve, hub, ring and spring as a unit.

3) Remove countershaft 5th gear. Remove 3 retaining screws and detent balls. Remove back-up light switch and 13 housing bolts. Loosen housing by lightly tapping on bosses around edge.

4) Using Bearing Remover (07936-634000) without attachment, screw the threaded end into transmission housing. Expand snap ring while lightly tapping upward on case using bearing remover. *See Fig. 1.*

Fig. 1: Removing Transmission Case From Housing

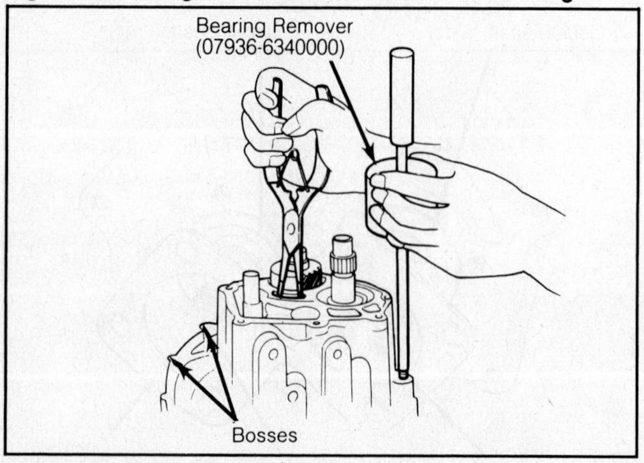

All models.

5) Before further disassembly, measure clearance between 5th-reverse shift shaft pin and reverse shift fork. Standard (new) clearance is .002-.014" (.05-.35 mm). Service limit is .02" (.5 mm).

6) If clearance is out of limit, measure width of slot in reverse shift fork. Standard (new) slot width is .278-.285" (7.05-7.25 mm). Check reverse idler gear-to-shift

HONDA 2WD 4 & 5-SPEED TRANSAXLE (Cont.)

fork clearance. Standard (new) gear-to-fork clearance is .008-.040" (.20-1.00 mm). Service limit is .07" (1.7 mm).

7) Pull out reverse idler shaft and remove gear. If gear-to-fork clearance is beyond limit, measure gap between ends of shift fork fingers. Standard (new) clearance is .46-.48" (11.8-12.1 mm). Shift transaxle into neutral. Detach three 8 mm mount bolts and remove mainshaft bearing retainer plate.

8) Pull out shift guide shaft and reverse idler shaft. Remove gear. Pull 3rd-4th and 1st-2nd shift shafts up, to shift into 4th and 2nd. Remove the 5th-reverse shift shaft by pulling it up while lifting the reverse shift fork.

9) Tilt interlock and shift guide to the side, then lift them out. Remove countershaft and mainshaft as an assembly, with 1st-2nd and 3rd-4th shift shafts. If seals are to be replaced or the differential needs repair, use Driver (07749-0010000) and Driver Attachment (07947-6340500) to remove differential assembly.

10) Drive out differential oil seal from clutch housing. Remove 80 mm snap ring in transmission housing. Drive out differential oil seal from transmission housing.

NOTE: **Replace the differential oil seal in the transmission housing whenever disassembled.**

11) On clutch housing, remove countershaft bearing retaining plate. Remove breather chamber plate. Remove countershaft bearing with Bearing Remover (07936-6340000) and Attachment (07936-6890101).

12) Remove mainshaft oil seal from clutch housing. Replace bearings and mainshaft oil seal whenever removed. Install oil seal with sealing lips facing mainshaft bearing. Install countershaft oil barrier plate.

13) With the driver and Attachment (07746-0010400), drive in countershaft bearing with support block under case to support bearing boss. Install bearing retainer plate, tighten screws with impact driver and stake screw heads. Reinstall breather chamber plate.

14) To replace countershaft and mainshaft bearings on transmission housing, expand snap rings (68 mm countershaft, 52 mm mainshaft), on transmission housing and remove bearings. To replace, reverse removal procedure ensuring part numbers are facing up.

15) When bearings and snap rings are securely seated, ensure snap ring gap is within specification; .118-.314" (3.0-8.0 mm) for mainshaft snap ring and .276-.279" (7.0-7.1 mm) for countershaft snap ring. Reseat or replace if not within specification.

CIVIC

Speedometer Driven Gear Replacement

1) If necessary to remove speedometer gear assembly from 4 or 5-speed transmissions, remove bolt and pull speedometer holder out. *See Fig. 2.*

2) Remove speedometer driven gear from gear holder. Remove driven gear clip and speedometer driven gear. Check gear assembly for wear. If excessively worn, replace gear holder assembly including "O" ring.

3) Ensure proper speedometer driven gear is identified by type of transmission and tire size. See CIVIC SPEEDOMETER DRIVEN GEAR IDENTIFICATION table. Align slot in gear holder with lock plate. Set holder in clutch housing and tighten lock plate.

Snap Ring Inspection

1) To inspect the end cover snap ring on 4-speed models, remove bolts from end cover and remove end cover. Remove ball bearing from mainshaft. Inspect bearing for wear.

Fig. 2: Removing Speedometer Driven Gear Assembly

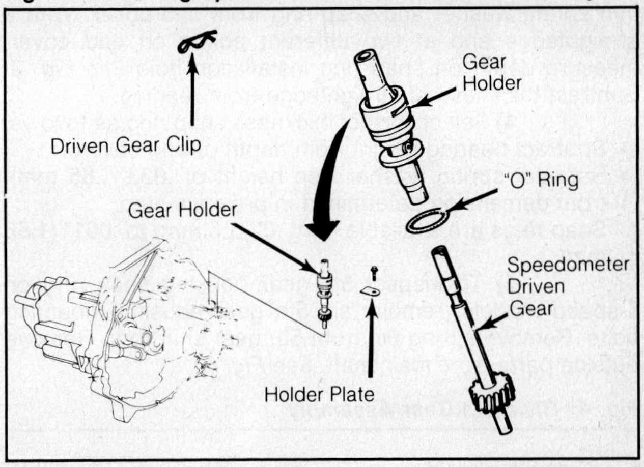

Civic only.

CIVIC SPEEDOMETER DRIVEN GEAR IDENTIFICATION

Application	No. of Gear Teeth
4-Speed	
1300 Hatchback	
P165/70 R 13 Tires	21
5-Speed	
CRX/Si	
P165/70 R 13 Tires	21
1500 Hatchback DX	
P175/70 R 13 Tires	20
1500 Hatchback S	
175/SR 13 Tires	20
1500 Sedan	
R175/70 R 13 Tires	20
1500 Wagon	
175/70 R 13 Tires	20

2) Clean sealant residue from transmission housing. Replace bearing and at two different points measure distance from top of bearing's outer race to mounting flange for end cover.

Fig. 3: Measuring Civic End Cover Snap Ring

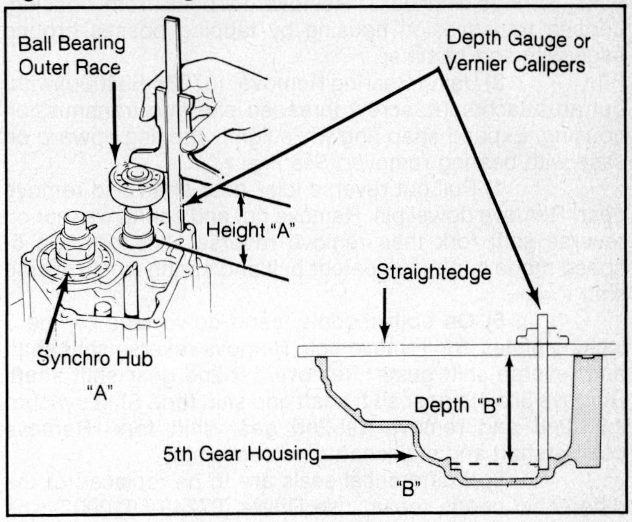

HONDA 2WD 4 & 5-SPEED TRANSAXLE (Cont.)

3) To measure end cover snap ring, remove 52 mm spring washer and snap ring from end cover. With a straightedge and at two different points on end cover, measure depth on snap ring installation hole *See Fig. 3*. Subtract thickness of straightedge from reading.

4) Select correct thickness snap ring as follows:

- Subtract bearing height from depth of end cover.
- Subtract spring washer free height of .033" (.85 mm), from demension determined in previous step.
  Snap rings are available from .02" (.5 mm) to .061" (1.55 mm).

5) To inspect 5th gear housing snap ring on 5-speed models, remove six 5th gear housing mounting bolts. Remove spring pin from 5th gear shift fork. Remove outside parts from mainshaft. *See Fig. 4*.

Fig. 4: Civic 5th Gear Assembly

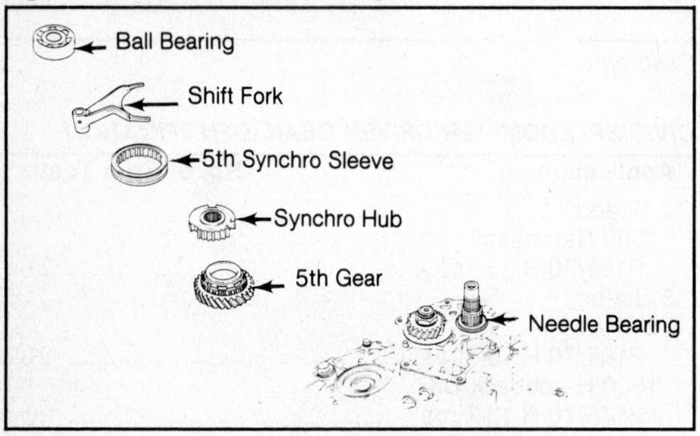

6) Inspect parts for wear. Reinstall synchro hub and ball bearing onto mainshaft. Use cleaning and measuring procedures from steps **2)**, **3)** and **4)**.

Transaxle Disassembly

1) Disassembly procedures for Civic 4 and 5-speed transaxles are similar. *See Figs. 6 and 7*. Remove transaxle from vehicle and install on work stand. For 5-speed housing disassembly, drive out spring securing 5th gear shift fork to shaft. Remove ball bearing. Remove shift fork and synchro-hub as a unit. Remove synchro-ring, spring and mainshaft 5th gear.

2) On both models, remove detent ball retaining bolts, springs and balls. Remove 11 bolts from housing. Loosen transmission housing by tapping bosses around edge with soft hammer.

3) Using Bearing Remover (07936-634000) without an attachment, screw threaded end into transmission housing. Expand snap ring while lightly tapping upward on case with bearing remover. *See Fig. 1*.

4) Pull out reverse idler gear shaft and remove gear. Remove dowel pin. Remove nut and spring washer on reverse shift fork then remove reverse shift fork. On 5-speed models, remove detent ball and spring from reverse shift fork.

5) On both models, bend down tabs on the 3 locking plates and remove bolt. Remove reverse shift shaft and reverse shift guide. Remove 1st-2nd gear shift shaft. Remove 3rd-4th gear shift shaft and shift fork. Shift synchro into 2nd and remove 1st-2nd gear shift fork. Remove countershaft and mainshaft as an assembly.

6) If differential seals are to be replaced or the differential needs repair, use Driver (07749-0010000) and Driver Attachment (07947-6340500) to remove differential assembly. Remove 72 mm snap ring in transmission housing. Drive out seal from clutch housing. Drive out seal from transmission housing.

NOTE: Replace the differential oil seal in the transmission housing whenever disassembled.

7) On clutch housing, remove countershaft bearing retaining plate. Remove countershaft bearing using Bearing Remover (07936-6340000) and Attachment (07936-6340101).

8) Remove and clean oil barrier plate, then reinstall plate. With driver and Attachment (07746-0010300), drive in countershaft bearing with support block under case to support bearing boss. Install bearing retainer plate, tighten screws with impact driver and stake screw heads.

9) On clutch housing, remove mainshaft bearing and seal by driving out with a drift. Always install a new bearing and seal. With driver and Attachment (00746-0010100), drive in mainshaft oil seal. Drive in mainshaft bearing with a support block placed under case to support bearing boss.

10) To replace countershaft and mainshaft bearings on transmission housing, expand snap rings and push bearing out by hand. Do not remove snap rings unless it is necessary to clean grooves in the housing.

11) To install, reverse removal procedure ensuring part numbers are facing up. When bearings and snap rings are securely seated, ensure snap ring gap is within specification; .14-.19" (3.5-4.7 mm) for mainshaft snap ring and .22-.35" (5.7-8.8 mm) for countershaft snap ring. Reseat or replace if not within specification.

COMPONENT DISASSEMBLY & REASSEMBLY

NOTE: When checking clearances, countershaft and mainshaft bearings must be removed from transaxle housing.

Before disassembling mainshaft and countershaft, measure and record clearances listed in appropriate COUNTERSHAFT/MAINSHAFT CLEARANCES tables. If clearances are within specifications and no parts are defective, disassembly of shafts is unnecessary.

The mainshaft and countershaft, (including bearings and, if equipped, 5th gear components) must be assembled and installed in clutch housing. Install mainshaft holder to prevent shafts from turning and shift transmission into gear. Tighten countershaft and mainshaft lock nuts to 65 ft. lbs. (90 N.m). Remove shafts from housing and check clearances.

CAUTION: Incorrect gear clearances can be caused by overtightening the mainshaft or countershaft lock nuts. Ensure torque wrench used is correctly calibrated.

COUNTERSHAFT

Disassembly

1) If disassembly is required after checking clearances, remove countershaft and mainshaft bearings as described in the TRANSAXLE DISASSEMBLY section of this article.

2) To disassemble countershaft, raise tab on countershaft lock nut. Remove lock nut. Remove 5th gear and spring washer if equipped and disassemble countershaft. *See Figs. 8 and 9*.

HONDA 2WD 4 & 5-SPEED TRANSAXLE (Cont.)

Fig. 5: Exploded View of Accord and Prelude 5-Speed Manual Transaxle Assembly

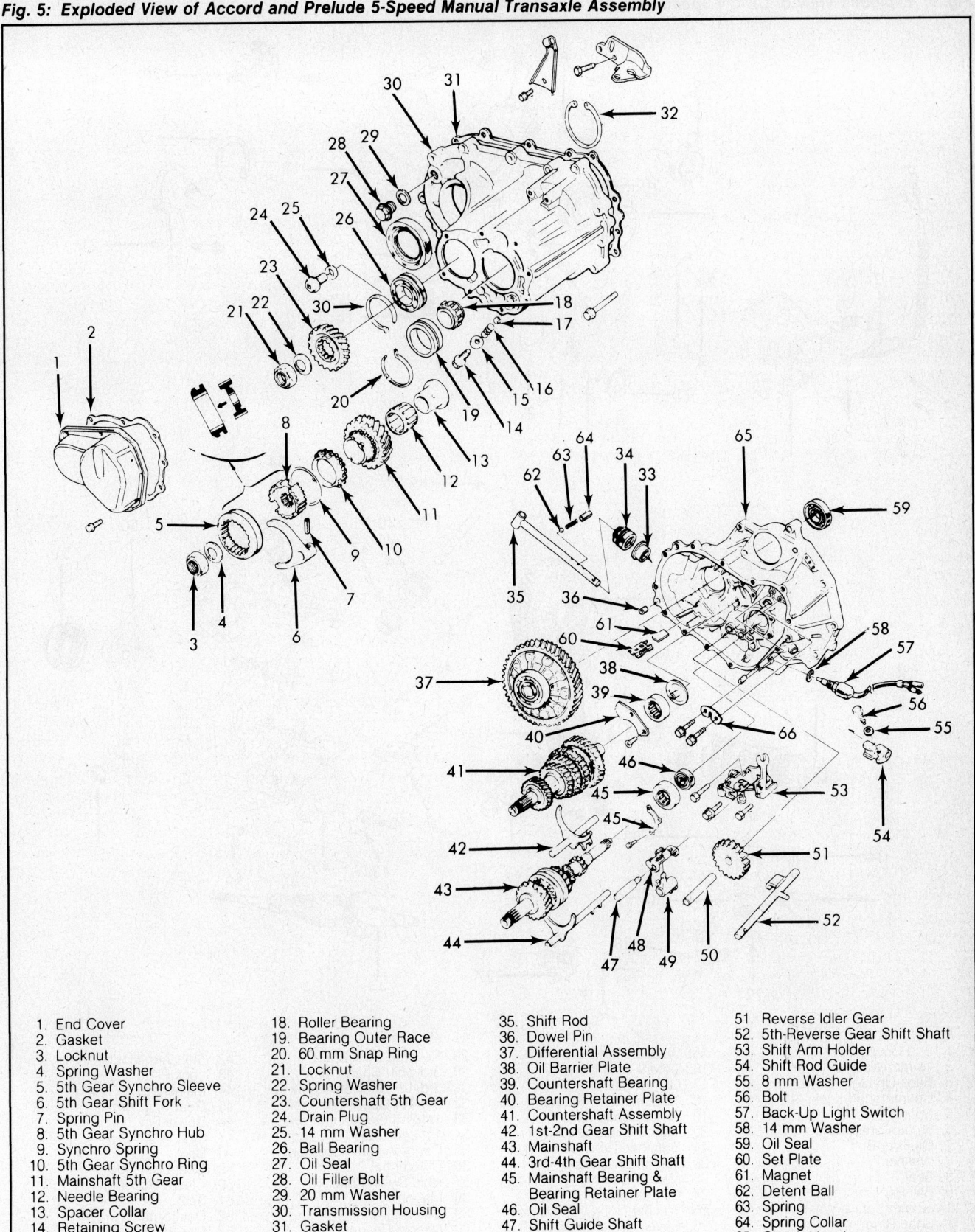

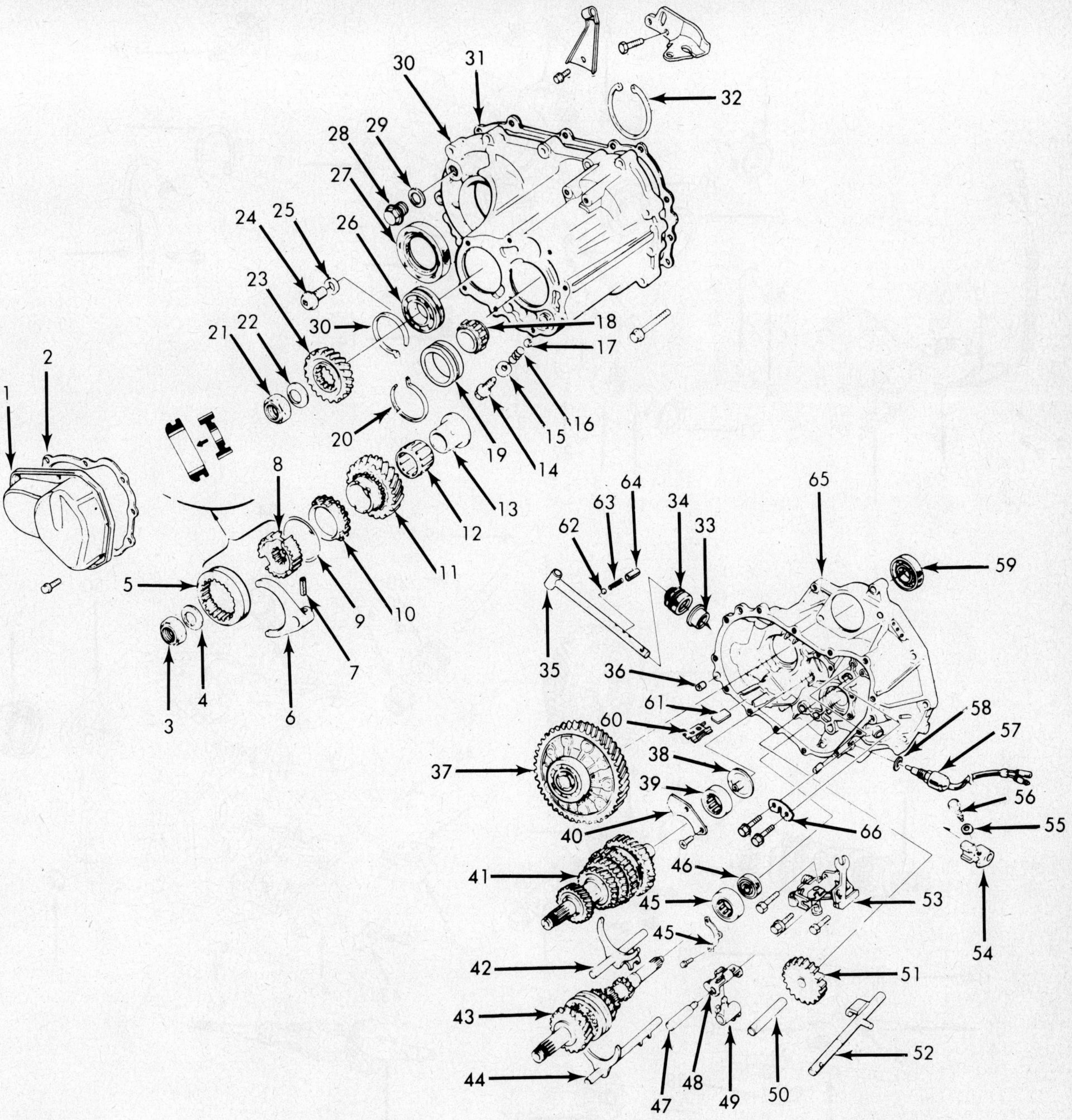

1. End Cover
2. Gasket
3. Locknut
4. Spring Washer
5. 5th Gear Synchro Sleeve
6. 5th Gear Shift Fork
7. Spring Pin
8. 5th Gear Synchro Hub
9. Synchro Spring
10. 5th Gear Synchro Ring
11. Mainshaft 5th Gear
12. Needle Bearing
13. Spacer Collar
14. Retaining Screw
15. 12 mm Washer
16. Spring
17. Detent Ball
18. Roller Bearing
19. Bearing Outer Race
20. 60 mm Snap Ring
21. Locknut
22. Spring Washer
23. Countershaft 5th Gear
24. Drain Plug
25. 14 mm Washer
26. Ball Bearing
27. Oil Seal
28. Oil Filler Bolt
29. 20 mm Washer
30. Transmission Housing
31. Gasket
32. 80 mm Snap Ring
33. Oil Seal
34. Boot
35. Shift Rod
36. Dowel Pin
37. Differential Assembly
38. Oil Barrier Plate
39. Countershaft Bearing
40. Bearing Retainer Plate
41. Countershaft Assembly
42. 1st-2nd Gear Shift Shaft
43. Mainshaft
44. 3rd-4th Gear Shift Shaft
45. Mainshaft Bearing & Bearing Retainer Plate
46. Oil Seal
47. Shift Guide Shaft
48. Interlock
49. Shift Guide
50. Reverse Idler Gear Shaft
51. Reverse Idler Gear
52. 5th-Reverse Gear Shift Shaft
53. Shift Arm Holder
54. Shift Rod Guide
55. 8 mm Washer
56. Bolt
57. Back-Up Light Switch
58. 14 mm Washer
59. Oil Seal
60. Set Plate
61. Magnet
62. Detent Ball
63. Spring
64. Spring Collar
65. Clutch Housing
66. Breather Chamber Plate

Manual Transmissions

HONDA 2WD 4 & 5-SPEED TRANSAXLE (Cont.)

Fig. 6: Exploded View of Civic 4-Speed Manual Transaxle Assembly

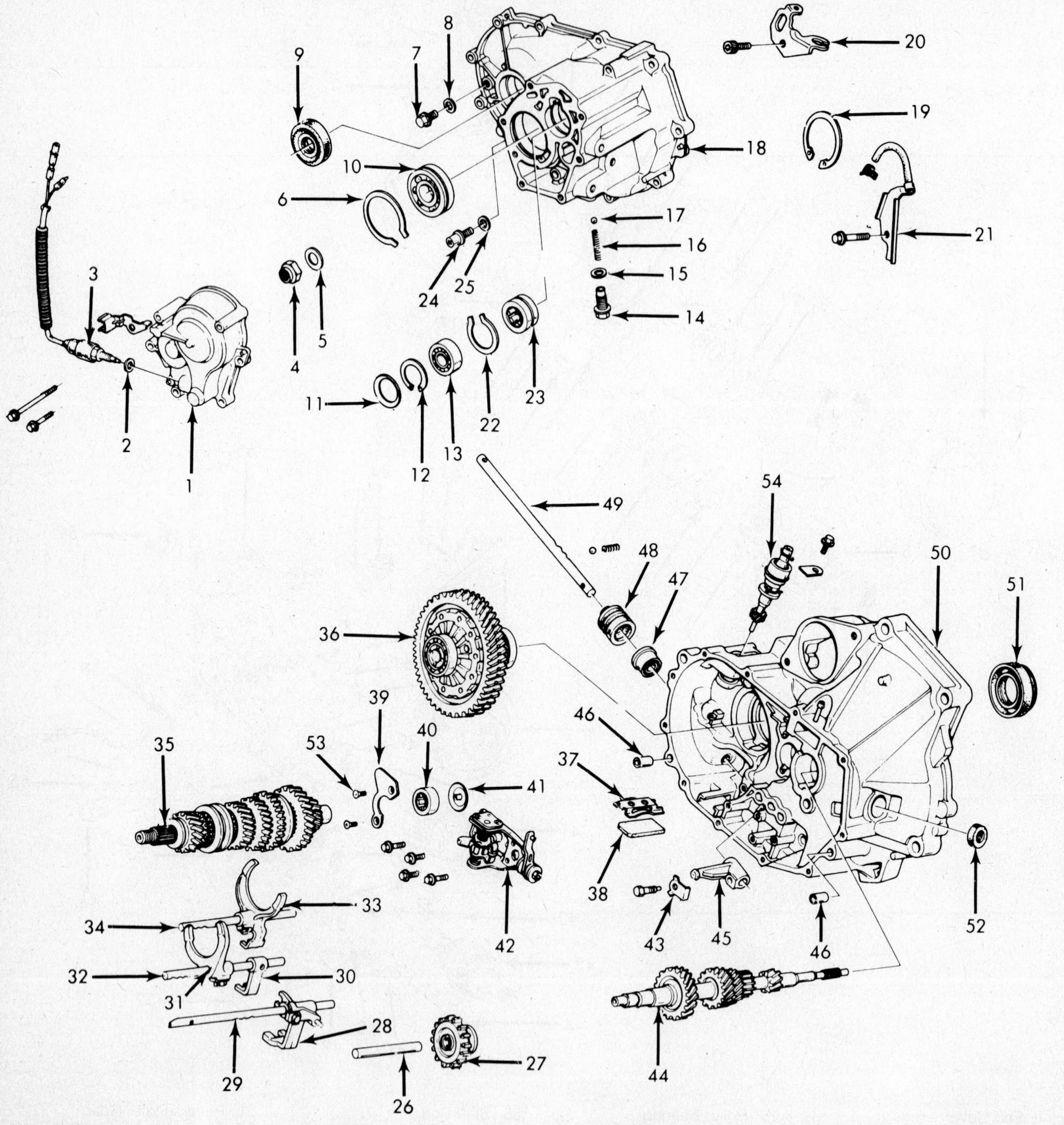

1. End Cover
2. 14 mm Washer
3. Back-Up Light Switch
4. Countershaft Locknut
5. Spring Washer
6. 65 mm Snap Ring
7. Oil Filler Bolt
8. Washer
9. Seal
10. Ball Bearing
11. 52 mm Spring Washer
12. Snap Ring
13. Ball Bearing
14. Detent Ball Retaining Screw
15. Washer
16. Detent Spring
17. Detent Ball
18. Transmission Housing
19. 72 mm Snap Ring
20. Clutch Cable Bracket
21. Breather Tube Assembly
22. 45 mm Snap Ring
23. Needle Bearing
24. Oil Drain Plug
25. Washer
26. Reverse Idler Gear Shaft
27. Reverse Idler Gear
28. Reverse Shift Guide
29. Reverse Shift Shaft
30. 3rd Shift Shaft Guide
31. 3rd-4th Gear Shift Fork
32. 3rd-4th Gear Fork Shaft
33. 1st-2nd Gear Shift Fork
34. 1st-2nd Gear Fork Shaft
35. Countershaft Assembly
36. Differential
37. Hold-Down Plate
38. Magnet
39. Bearing Retainer Plate
40. Needle Bearing
41. Oil Barrier Plate
42. Shift Arm Holder
43. Lock Plate
44. Mainshaft
45. Gear Shift Arm
46. Dowel Pin
47. Seal
48. Boot
49. Gear Shift Rod
50. Clutch Housing
51. Seal
52. Dust Seal
53. Flat Screw
54. Speedometer Driven Gear

Manual Transmissions

HONDA 2WD 4 & 5-SPEED TRANSAXLE (Cont.)

Fig. 7: Exploded View of Civic 5-Speed Manual Transaxle Assembly

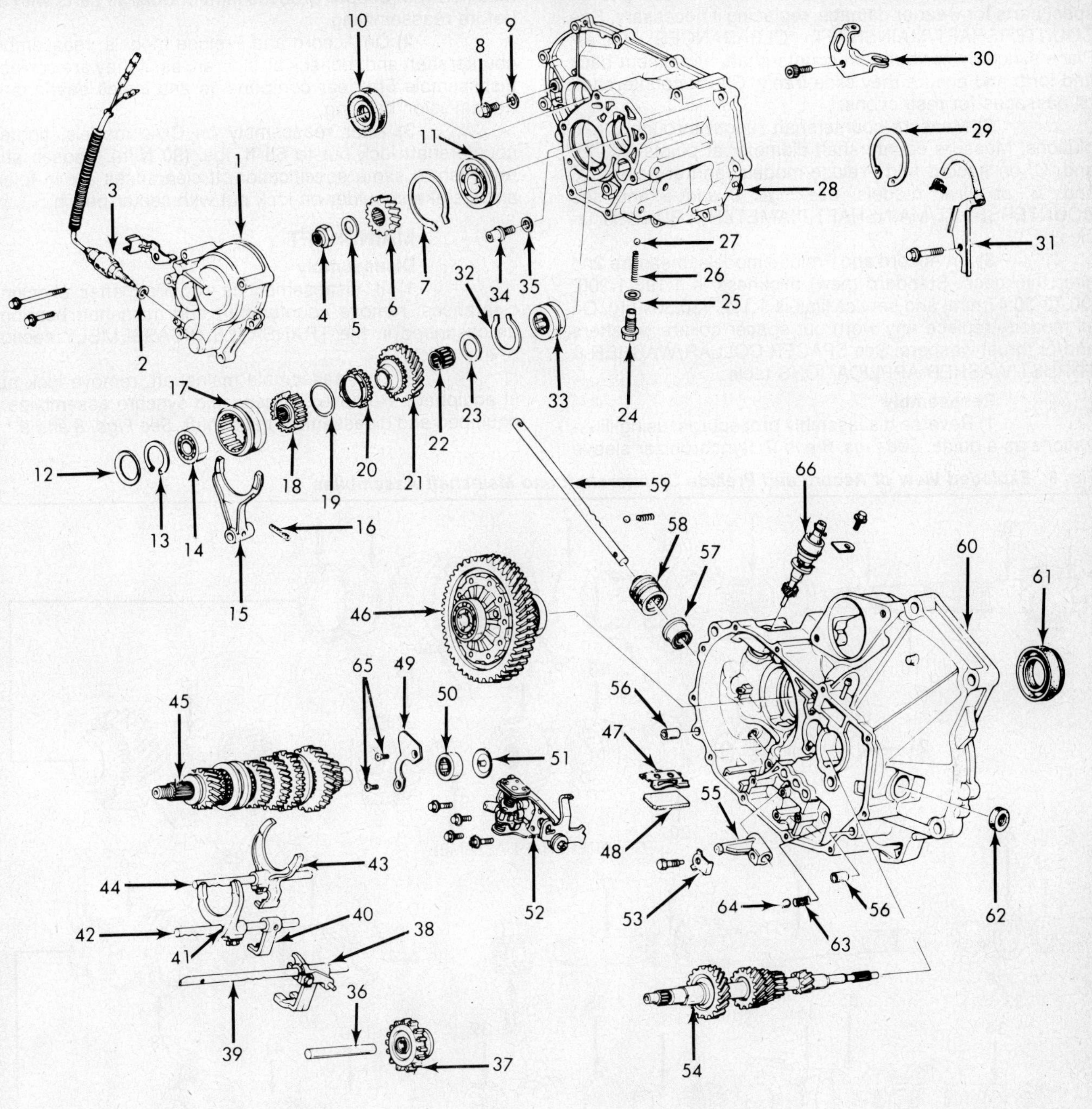

1. 5th Gear Housing
2. 14 mm Washer
3. Back-Up Light Switch
4. Countershaft Locknut
5. Spring Washer
6. Countershaft 5th Gear
7. 65 mm Snap Ring
8. Oil Filler Bolt
9. Sealing Washer
10. Seal
11. Countershaft Ball Bearing
12. 52 mm Spring Washer
13. Snap Ring
14. Mainshaft Ball Bearing
15. 5th Gear Shift Fork
16. Spring Pin
17. 5th Gear Synchro Sleeve
18. 5th Gear Synchro Hub
19. Synchro Spring
20. 5th Gear Synchro Ring
21. 5th Gear
22. Needle Bearing
23. Thrust Washer
24. Detent Ball Retainer Screw
25. Sealing Washer
26. Detent Spring
27. Detent Ball
28. Transmission Housing
29. 72 mm Snap Ring
30. Clutch Cable Bracket
31. Breather Tube Assembly
32. 45 mm Snap Ring
33. Needle Bearing
34. Oil Drain Plug
35. Sealing Washer
36. Reverse Idler Gear Shaft
37. Reverse Idler Gear
38. Reverse Shift Guide
39. Reverse Shift Shaft
40. 3rd Gear Shaft Guide
41. 3rd Gear Shift Fork
42. 3rd Gear Fork Shaft
43. 1st Gear Shift Fork
44. 1st Gear Fork Shaft
45. Countershaft Assembly
46. Differential
47. Hold-Down Plate
48. Magnet
49. Bearing Retainer Plate
50. Needle Bearing
51. Oil Barrier Plate
52. Shift Arm Holder
53. Lock Plate
54. Mainshaft
55. Gear Shift Arm
56. Dowel Pin
57. Seal
58. Boot
59. Gear Shift Rod
60. Clutch Housing
61. Seal
62. Dust Seal
63. Detent Spring
64. Detent Ball
65. Detent Flat Screw
66. Speedometer Driven Gear

HONDA 2WD 4 & 5-SPEED TRANSAXLE (Cont.)

Inspection

1) On all models, measure clearances and inspect parts for wear or damage, replacing if necessary. See COUNTERSHAFT/MAINSHAFT CLEARANCES tables. Place synchronizer hubs on countershaft, slide them back and forth and ensure they slide freely. Check countershaft oil passages for restrictions.

2) Measure countershaft runout through 2 revolutions. Measure countershaft diameter at points "A", "B" and "C" on Accord and Prelude models, and at points "A" and "B" on Civic models. *See Figs. 8 and 9* and see COUNTERSHAFT/MAINSHAFT DIAMETER & RUNOUT tables.

3) On Accord and Prelude models, measure 2nd gear thickness. Standard (new) thickness is 1.198-1.200" (30.42-30.47 mm) and service limit is 1.192" (30.30 mm). On all models, replace any worn out spacer collars, washers and/or thrust washers. See SPACER COLLAR/WASHER & THRUST WASHER APPLICATIONS table.

Reassembly

1) Reverse disassembly procedures, using illustrations as a guide. *See Figs. 8 and 9*. Synchronizer sleeve has 3 sets of longer teeth spaced 120° apart that must be matched with deeper grooves in hub. Coat all parts with oil before reassembling.

2) On Accord and Prelude models, reassemble countershaft and recheck all clearances. If they are correct, disassemble 5th gear components and install bearings in transmission housing.

3) After reassembly on Civic models, tighten countershaft lock nut to 65 ft. lbs. (90 N.m). Loosen and retighten to same specification. If clearances are in tolerance, stake shoulder on lock nut with center punch.

MAINSHAFT

Disassembly

1) If disassembly is required after checking clearances, remove countershaft and mainshaft bearings as described in the TRANSAXLE DISASSEMBLY section of this article.

2) To disassemble mainshaft, remove lock nut (if equipped). Remove 5th gear and synchro assemblies if equipped and disassemble mainshaft. *See Figs. 8 and 9*.

Fig. 8: Exploded View of Accord and Prelude Countershaft and Mainshaft Assemblies

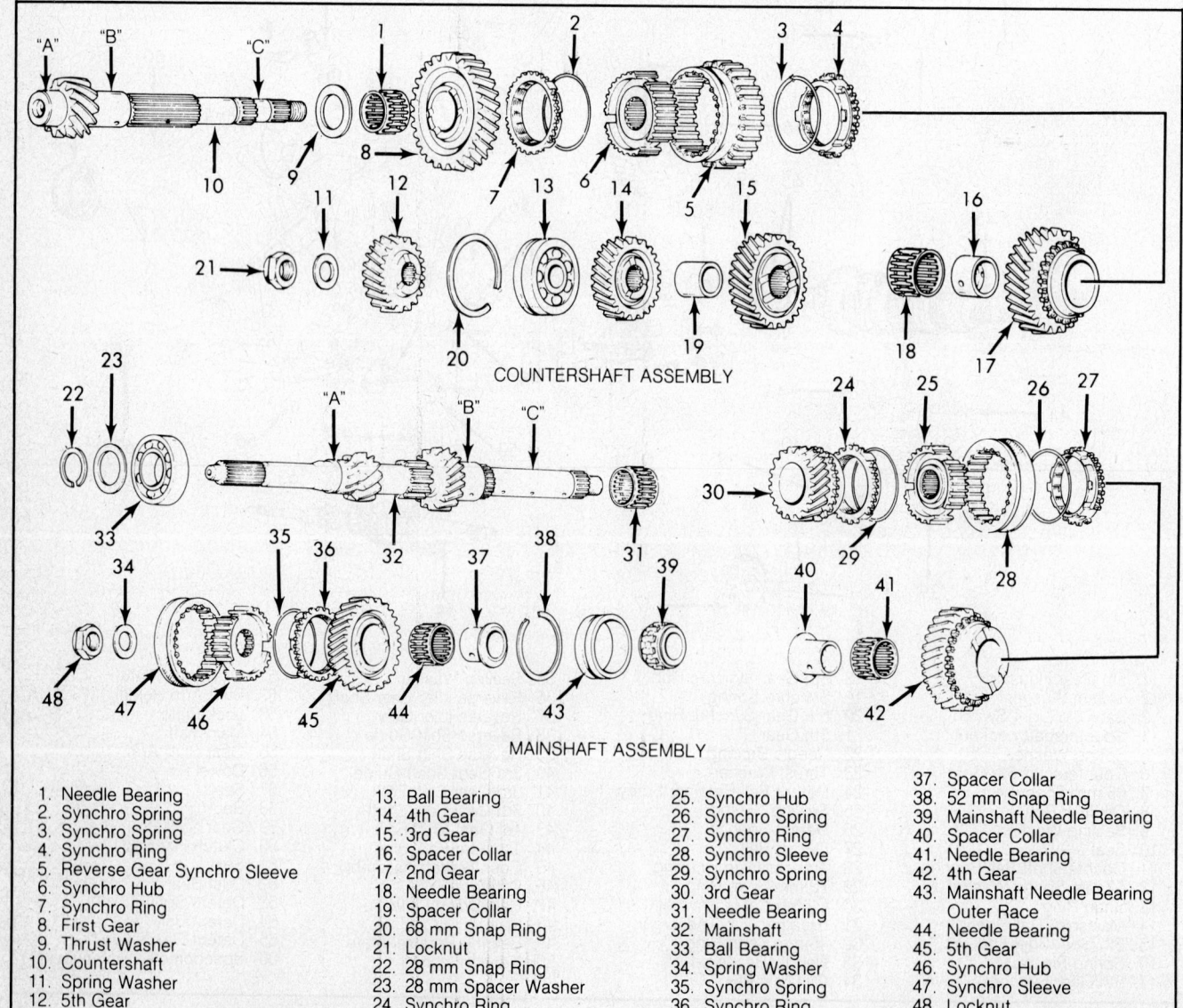

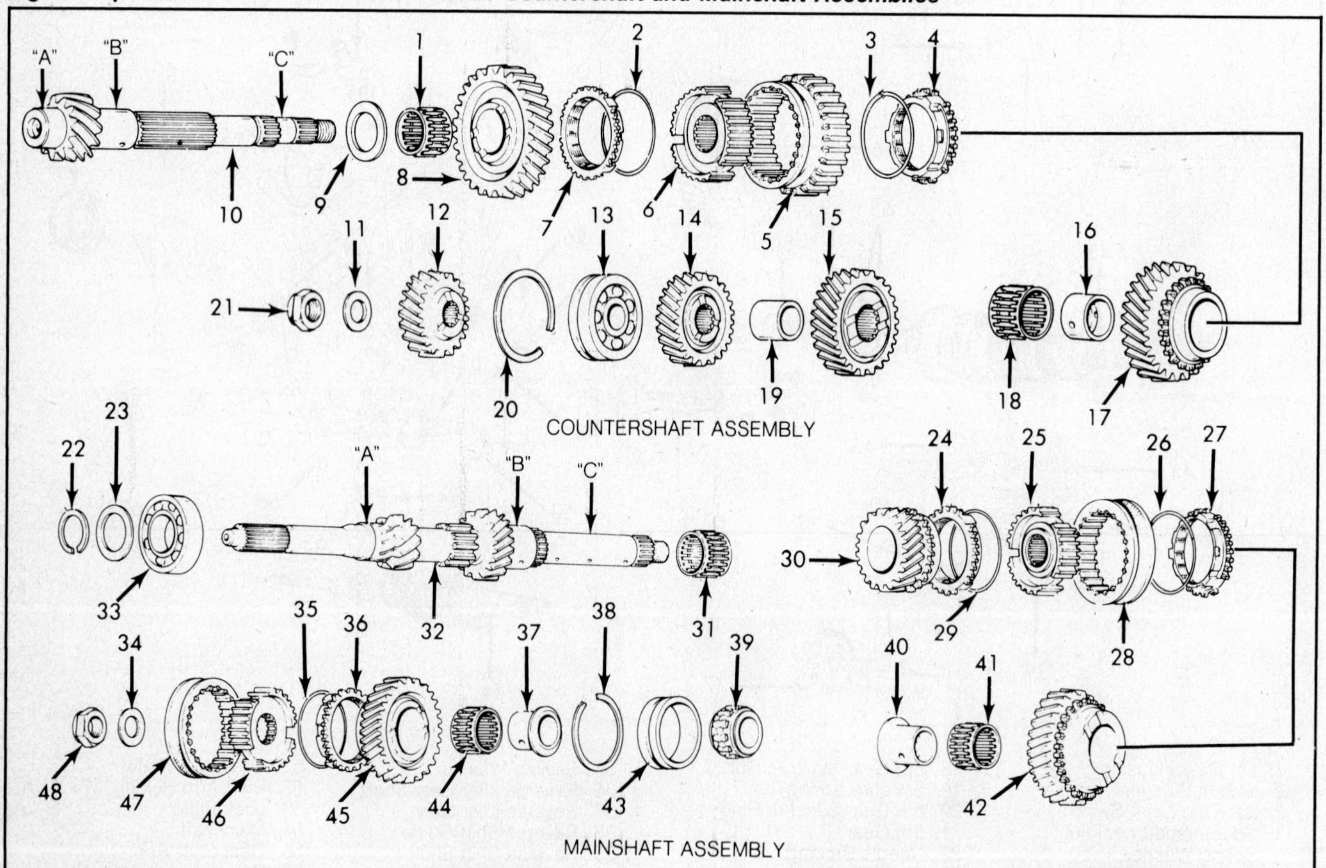

1. Needle Bearing
2. Synchro Spring
3. Synchro Spring
4. Synchro Ring
5. Reverse Gear Synchro Sleeve
6. Synchro Hub
7. Synchro Ring
8. First Gear
9. Thrust Washer
10. Countershaft
11. Spring Washer
12. 5th Gear
13. Ball Bearing
14. 4th Gear
15. 3rd Gear
16. Spacer Collar
17. 2nd Gear
18. Needle Bearing
19. Spacer Collar
20. 68 mm Snap Ring
21. Locknut
22. 28 mm Snap Ring
23. 28 mm Spacer Washer
24. Synchro Ring
25. Synchro Hub
26. Synchro Spring
27. Synchro Ring
28. Synchro Sleeve
29. Synchro Spring
30. 3rd Gear
31. Needle Bearing
32. Mainshaft
33. Ball Bearing
34. Spring Washer
35. Synchro Spring
36. Synchro Ring
37. Spacer Collar
38. 52 mm Snap Ring
39. Mainshaft Needle Bearing
40. Spacer Collar
41. Needle Bearing
42. 4th Gear
43. Mainshaft Needle Bearing Outer Race
44. Needle Bearing
45. 5th Gear
46. Synchro Hub
47. Synchro Sleeve
48. Locknut

HONDA 2WD 4 & 5-SPEED TRANSAXLE (Cont.)

Fig. 9: Exploded View of Civic Countershaft and Mainshaft Assemblies

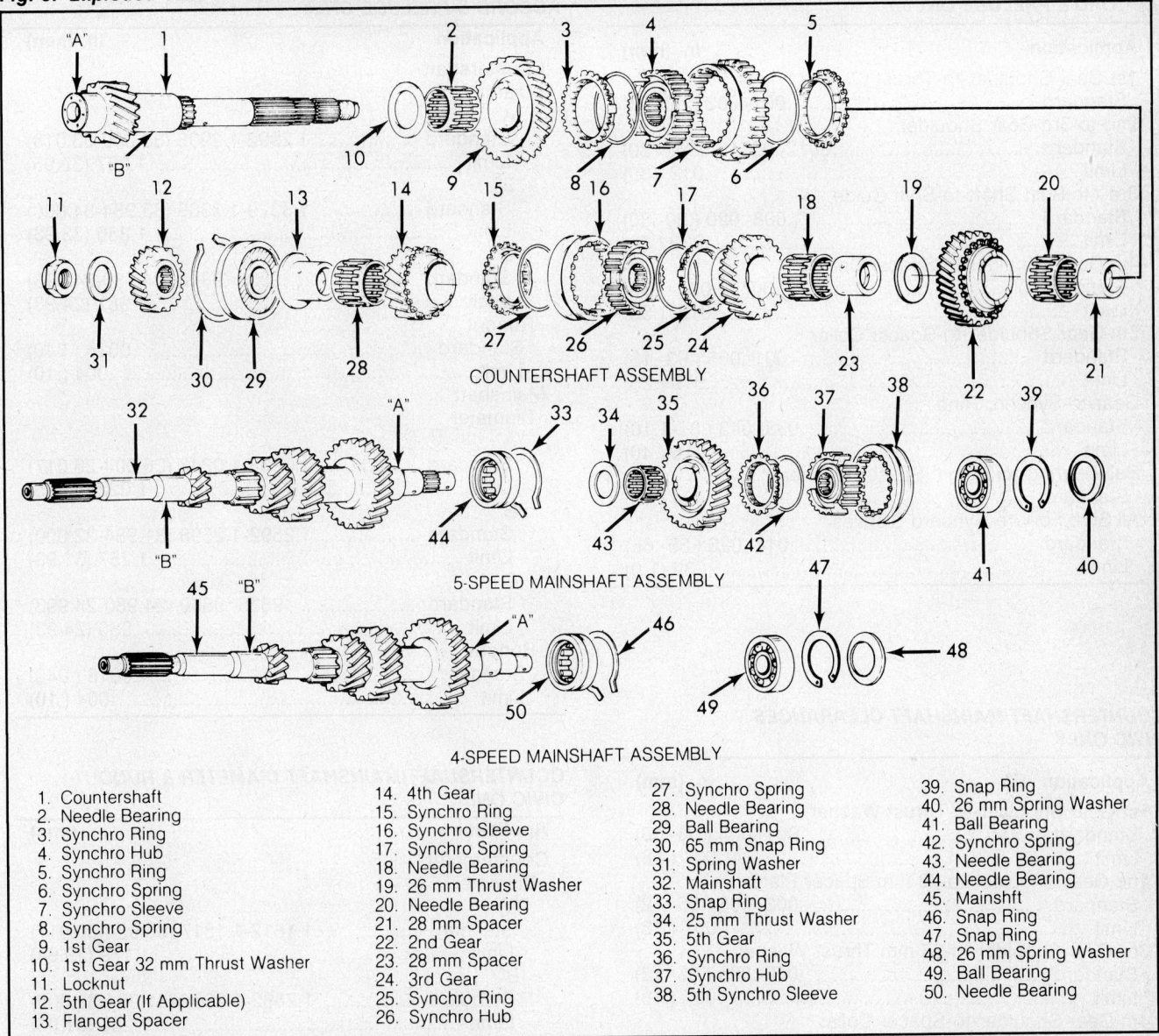

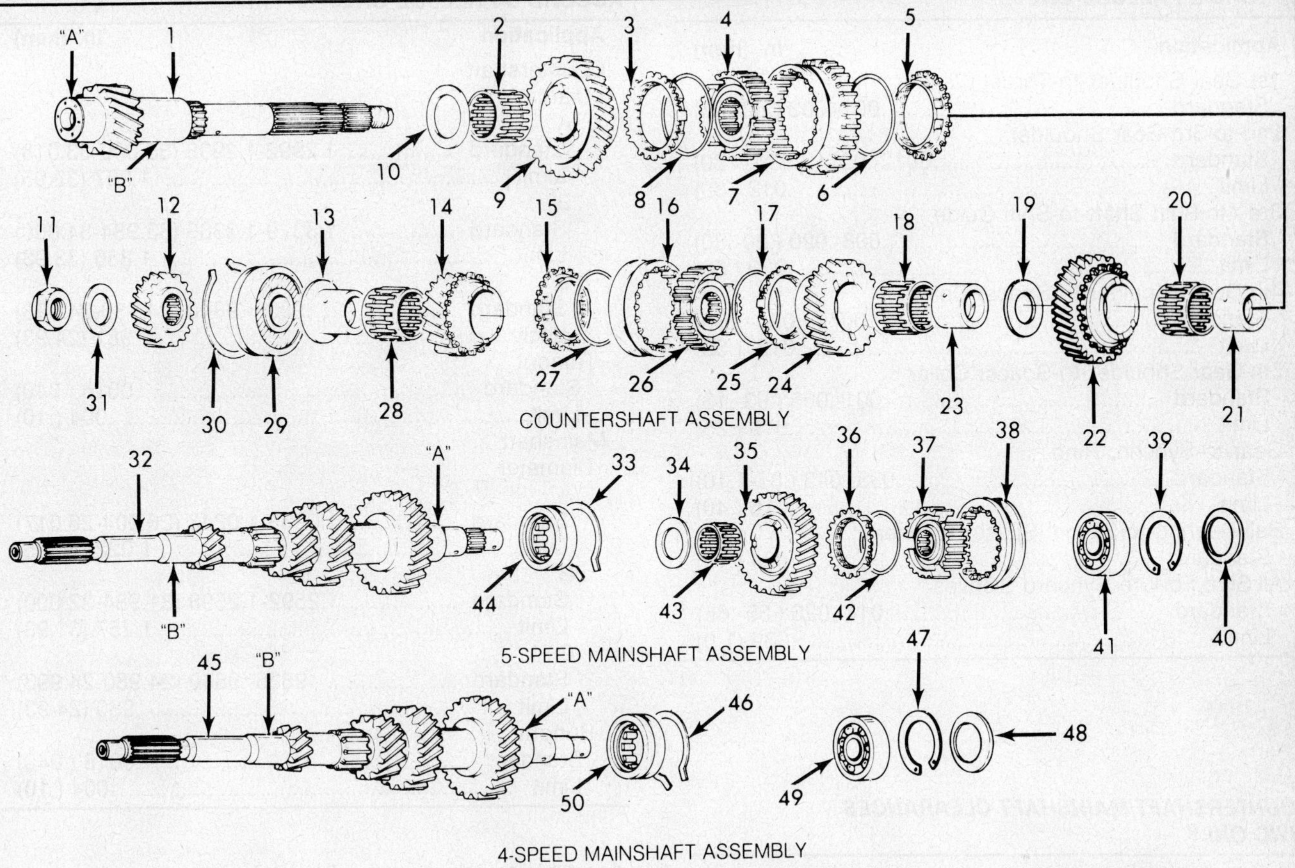

1. Countershaft
2. Needle Bearing
3. Synchro Ring
4. Synchro Hub
5. Synchro Ring
6. Synchro Spring
7. Synchro Sleeve
8. Synchro Spring
9. 1st Gear
10. 1st Gear 32 mm Thrust Washer
11. Locknut
12. 5th Gear (If Applicable)
13. Flanged Spacer
14. 4th Gear
15. Synchro Ring
16. Synchro Sleeve
17. Synchro Spring
18. Needle Bearing
19. 26 mm Thrust Washer
20. Needle Bearing
21. 28 mm Spacer
22. 2nd Gear
23. 28 mm Spacer
24. 3rd Gear
25. Synchro Ring
26. Synchro Hub
27. Synchro Spring
28. Needle Bearing
29. Ball Bearing
30. 65 mm Snap Ring
31. Spring Washer
32. Mainshaft
33. Snap Ring
34. 25 mm Thrust Washer
35. 5th Gear
36. Synchro Ring
37. Synchro Hub
38. 5th Synchro Sleeve
39. Snap Ring
40. 26 mm Spring Washer
41. Ball Bearing
42. Synchro Spring
43. Needle Bearing
44. Needle Bearing
45. Mainshft
46. Snap Ring
47. Snap Ring
48. 26 mm Spring Washer
49. Ball Bearing
50. Needle Bearing

Inspection

1) On all models, measure clearances and inspect parts for wear or damage and replace as necessary. See COUNTERSHAFT/MAINSHAFT CLEARANCES tables. Place synchronizer hubs on mainshaft, slide them back and forth and ensure they slide freely. Check mainshaft oil passages for restrictions.

2) Measure mainshaft runout through 2 revolutions. On Accord and Prelude models, measure mainshaft diameter at points "A", "B" and "C". On Civic models, measure mainshaft diameter at points "A" and "B". *See Figs. 8 and 9* and see COUNTERSHAFT/MAINSHAFT DIAMETER & RUNOUT tables.

3) On Accord and Prelude models, measure 3rd and 4th gear thicknesses. Standard 3rd and 4th gear thickness is 1.158-1.160" (29.42-29.47 mm). Service limit thickness is 1.15" (29.3 mm). Measure 5th gear thickness. Standard 5th gear thickness is 1.060-1.062" (26.92-26.97 mm). Service limit thickness is 1.055" (26.80 mm).

Reassembly

1) Reverse disassembly procedure. Coat all parts with oil before reassembly. Ensure correct thickness spacer collars/washers and thrust washers are installed.

2) On all mainshafts, clearances must be rechecked after assembly. Make sure lock nut is tightened to specification (if equipped).

SHIFT ARM HOLDER ASSEMBLY

Disassembly (Accord & Prelude)

Remove 3 bolts from shift arm holder. Remove shift rod by removing shoulder bolt. To remove selector arm from holder for shimming or replacement, drive out spring pin with driver. *See Fig. 10.*

HONDA 2WD 4 & 5-SPEED TRANSAXLE (Cont.)

COUNTERSHAFT/MAINSHAFT CLEARANCES ACCORD & PRELUDE ONLY

Application	In. (mm)
1st Gear Shoulder-to-Thrust Washer	
Standard	.001-.003 (.03-.08)
2nd-to-3rd Gear Shoulder	
Standard	.0012-.0071 (.030-.180)
Limit	.012 (.30)
3rd-4th Shift Shaft-to-Shift Guide	
Standard	.008-.020 (.20-.50)
Limit	.030 (.80)
4th Gear Shoulder-to-Spacer Collar	
Standard	.0012-.0071 (.030-.180)
Limit	.012" (.30)
5th Gear Shoulder-to-Spacer Collar	
Standard	.001-.005 (.03-.13)
Limit	.010 (.25)
Gear-to-Synchro Ring	
Standard	.033-.043 (.85-1.10)
Limit	.016 (.40)
Ball Bearing-to-25 mm Spacer Washer	
Standard	.004 (.10)
All Shift Fork-to-Synchro Sleeves	
Standard	.014-.026 (.35-.65)
Limit	.039 (1.0)

COUNTERSHAFT/MAINSHAFT CLEARANCES CIVIC ONLY

Application	In. (mm)
1st Gear Shoulder-to-Thrust Washer	
Standard	.001-.003 (.03-.08)
Limit	.007 (.18)
2nd Gear Shoulder-to-28 mm Spacer Plate	
Standard	.002-.005 (.05-.12)
Limit	.007 (.18)
3rd Gear Shoulder-to-26 mm Thrust Washer	
Standard	.002-.005 (.05-.12)
Limit	.007 (.18)
4th Gear Shoulder-to-Spacer Collar	
Standard	.002-.005 (.05-.12)
Limit	.007 (.18)
5th Gear Shoulder-to-Thrust Washer	
Standard	.002-.015 (.05-.38)
Limit	.016 (.40)
Gear-to-Synchro Ring	
Standard	.033-.043 (.85-1.10)
Limit	.016 (.40)
All Shift Forks-to-Synchro Sleeve	
Standard	..018-.026 (.45-.65)
Limit	.039 (1.0)
All Shift Fork Finger Thickness	
Standard	.252-.256 (6.4-6.5)
Limit	.236 (6.0)

COUNTERSHAFT/MAINSHAFT DIAMETER & RUNOUT ACCORD & PRELUDE ONLY

Application	In. (mm)
Countershaft	
Diameter	
"A"	
Standard	1.2992-1.2998 (33.000-33.015)
Limit	1.297 (32.95)
"B"	
Standard	1.3379-1.3386 (33.984-34.000)
Limit	1.336 (33.93)
"C"	
Standard	.9835-.9840 (24.980-24.993)
Limit	.981 (24.93)
Runout	
Standard	.0016 (.040)
Limit	.004 (.10)
Mainshaft	
Diameter	
"A"	
Standard	1.0238-1.0243 (26.004-26.017)
Limit	1.022 (25.95)
"B"	
Standard	1.2592-1.2598 (31.984-32.000)
Limit	1.257 (31.93)
"C"	
Standard	.9835-.9840 (24.980-24.993)
Limit	.980 (24.93)
Runout	
Standard	.0016 (.040)
Limit	.004 (.10)

COUNTERSHAFT/MAINSHAFT DIAMETER & RUNOUT CIVIC ONLY

Application	In. (mm)
Countershaft	
Diameter	
"A"	
Standard	1.1812-1.1817 (30.004-30.017)
Limit	1.179 (29.94)
"B"	
Standard	1.2592-1.2598 (31.984-32.000)
Limit	1.257 (31.93)
Runout	
Standard	.0008 (.020)
Limit	.0019 (.050)
Mainshaft	
Diameter	
"A"	
Standard	1.1022-1.1027 (27.997-28.010)
Limit	1.100 (27.94)
"B"	
Standard	.8656-.8661 (21.987-22.000)
Limit	.863 (21.93)
Runout	
Standard	.0008 (.020)
Limit	.0019 (.050)

HONDA 2WD 4 & 5-SPEED TRANSAXLE (Cont.)

SPACER COLLAR/WASHER & THRUST WASHER APPLICATIONS – ALL MODELS

Application	In. (mm)
Spacer Collars [1]	
Civic Only	
1	1.103-1.104 (28.01-28.04)
2	1.104-1.105 (28.04-28.07)
3	1.105-1.106 (28.07-28.10)
4	1.106-1.107 (28.10-28.13)
Spacer Washers	
Accord & Prelude Only	
A	.074-.075 (1.88-1.92)
B	.076-.078 (1.94-1.98)
C	.079-.080 (2.00-2.04)
D	.081-.082 (2.06-2.10)
E	.083-.085 (2.12-2.16)
Thrust Washers	
Accord & Prelude	
A	.080-.081 (2.02-2.04)
B	.079-.080 (2.00-2.02)
C	.078-.079 (1.98-2.00)
D	.077-.078 (1.96-1.98)
Civic	
A	.077-.078 (1.95-1.98)
B	.076-.077 (1.92-1.95)
C	.074-.076 (1.89-1.92)

[1] – No letter designation available for Civic spacer collars.

Inspection (Accord & Prelude)

1) Check clearances against SHIFT ARM HOLDER ASSEMBLY CLEARANCES table. Replace shift guide, selector arm, shift rod guide and/or gear selector arm if not within specification.

2) If clearance between collar and shim on selector arm shaft is out of specification, see SHIFT ARM HOLDER SHIM THICKNESS table to select a new shim.

Reassembly (Accord & Prelude)

1) To install shift rod, ensure detent notches face downward. Install spring and detent ball. Lubricate spring with molylube. Install shift rod while pushing detent ball in. Install shift rod guide on shift rod.

2) To install shift arm holder assembly, hook selector arm into shaft rod guide. Reinstall 3 bolts in shift arm holder.

SHIFT ARM HOLDER SHIM THICKNESS ACCORD & PRELUDE ONLY

Application	In. (mm)
A	.031 (.80)
B	.039 (1.00)
C	.047 (1.20)
D	.055 (1.40)
E	.063 (1.60)

Disassembly (Civic)

Using an impact driver, remove retainer plate screws and retainer plate. Pull out shift arm shaft and interlock shaft. Remove detent ball and spring. Remove shift arm, shift springs and spring retainers. *See Fig. 11.*

SHIFT ARM HOLDER ASSEMBLY CLEARANCES ACCORD & PRELUDE ONLY

Application	In. (mm)
Selector Arm Collar-to-Shim	
Standard	.0004-.0008 (.01-.20)
Shift Arm-to-Shift Guide	
Standard	.004-.012 (.10-.30)
Limit	.024 (.60)
Shift Guide Slot Width	.311-.315 (7.90-8.00)
Selector Arm-to-Interlock	
Standard	.002-.010 (.05-.25)
Limit	.03 (.8)
Selector Arm Finger Gap	.396-.400 (10.05-10.15)
Shift Arm-to-Shift Rod Guide	
Standard	.002-.010 (.05-.25)
Limit	.03 (.8)
Shift Rod Guide Slot Width	.46-.47 (11.8-12.0)
Selector Arm-to-Shift Rod Guide	
Standard	.002-.010 (.05-.25)
Limit	.02 (.5)
Selector Arm Tab Width	.469-.472 (11.90-12.00)

Fig. 10: Exploded View of Accord & Prelude Shift Arm Holder Assembly

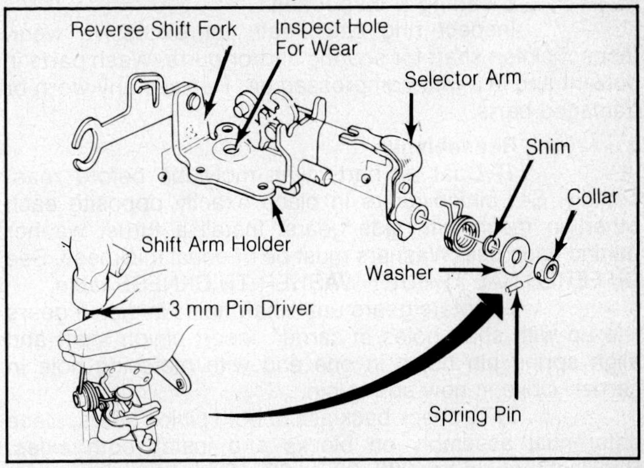

Reassembly (Civic)

1) Install shift arm, shift springs and spring retainers in shift arm holder. Invert shift arm holder and place detent ball and spring in shift arm. Hold detent ball in place and align groove in shift arm shaft with detent ball.

2) Insert shaft through shift arm holder and shift arm. Insert interlock shaft and install retainer plate. Tighten retainer plate screws with impact driver and stake screw heads. After reassembly, check gear shift arm for free movement.

DIFFERENTIAL

CAUTION: Ring gear bolts have LEFT HAND threads.

Disassembly

1) On all models, check bearings for for wear and rough rotation. If bearings need replacing, use a bearing puller and remove bearings from differential housing. To install bearings, use Bearing Driver (07746-003000) and Attachment (07746-0030400).

2) Detach mount bolts and lift ring gear from differential. Drive out spring pin with pin punch. Remove pinion shaft, pinion gears and thrust washers. *See Fig. 12.*

HONDA 2WD 4 & 5-SPEED TRANSAXLE (Cont.)

Fig. 11: Exploded View of Civic Shift Arm Holder

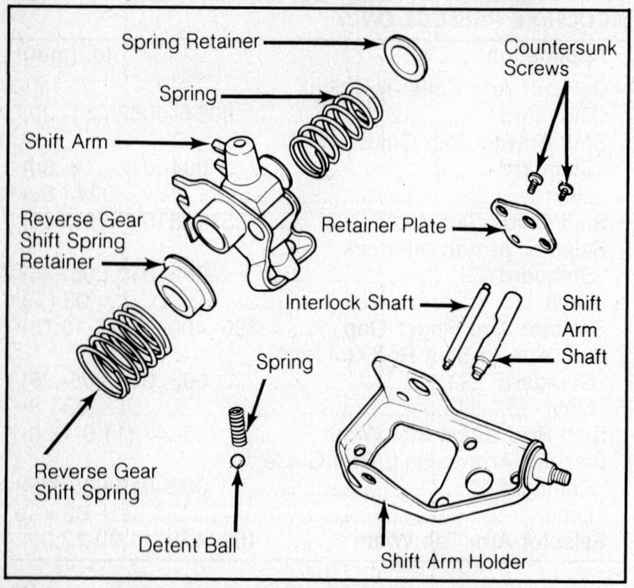

After assembly, check shift arm for free movement.

Fig. 12: Exploded View of Differential Assembly

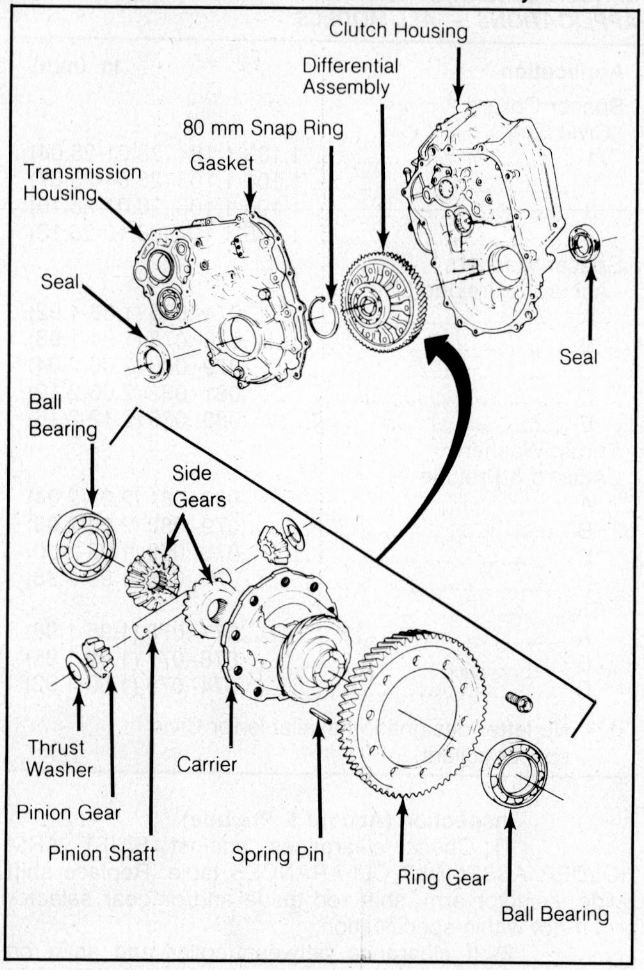

Cleaning & Inspection

Inspect ring gear teeth for excessive wear. Inspect pinion shaft for scoring and/or burrs. Wash parts in solvent and dry with compressed air. Replace any worn or damaged parts.

Reassembly

1) Coat all parts with molylube before reassembly. Set pinion gears in place exactly opposite each other, in mesh with side gears. Install a thrust washer behind each one. Washers must be of equal thickness. See DIFFERENTIAL THRUST WASHER THICKNESS table.

2) Rotate gears until shaft holes in pinion gears line up with shaft holes in carrier. Insert pinion shaft and align spring pin holes in one end with matching hole in carrier. Drive in new spring pin.

3) To check backlash of both pinion gears, place differential assembly on blocks and install both axles. Backlash should be .002-.006" (.05-.15 mm) for all models.

4) If backlash exceeds limit, disassemble differential and select new thrust washers according to DIFFERENTIAL THRUST WASHER THICKNESS table. Check backlash again. If still out of tolerance, replace both pinion gears and recheck backlash. If still out of tolerance, replace side gears and recheck backlash. If still out of tolerance, replace carrier assembly.

5) After final backlash check and with all tolerances correct, install ring gear. Ensure chamfer on inside diameter of ring gear is facing the carrier.

DIFFERENTIAL THRUST WASHER THICKNESS ALL MODELS

Part No.	In. (mm)
41351-689-0000	.028 (.70)
41355-PC8-0000	.030 (.75)
41352-689-0000	.031 (.80)
41356-PC8-0000	.033 (.85)
41353-689-0000	.035 (.90)
41357-PC8-0000	.037 (.95)
41354-689-0000	.039 (1.00)

TRANSAXLE REASSEMBLY & ADJUSTMENT

NOTE: **Civic 4 and 5-speed transaxles use no gaskets between major housings. Use Honda Sealant (08740-99986) and assemble housings within 20 minutes after applying sealant. Allow sealant to cure at least 30 minutes after assembly before filling with oil.**

DIFFERENTIAL ASSEMBLY

NOTE: **If transaxle housing, differential carrier or differential bearings were replaced, the differential side clearance must be measured.**

Accord & Prelude

1) Install differential assembly and transmission gear assemblies in clutch housing using Driver (07749-0010000). Tap on differential using driver and Attachment (07947-6340500) to seat snap ring in clutch housing.

2) Install transmission gear assemblies in clutch housing. See TRANSAXLE REASSEMBLY in this article. Shift transmission into 3rd gear to position shift shaft guide for reassembly. Install new gasket and dowel pins on clutch housing and carefully lower transmission housing into place.

3) Bolt housings together and tighten the 13 bolts to 21 Ft. Lbs. (28 N.m) in sequence, to specification. *See Fig. 13.*

4) Install 80 mm snap ring in transmission housing. Use driver and attachment to secure differential assembly in transmission housing. Measure clearance between snap ring and outer bearing race in transmission housing. Clearance is .006" (.15 mm), maximum.

5) If out of specification, select a new snap ring. Snap rings are available in thicknesses from .098" (2.50 mm), to .114" (2.90 mm), in increments of .004" (.10 mm). Seat snap ring against clutch housing.

6) Reseat differential and recheck bearing-to-snap ring clearance. Apply oil to differential seals. Using driver and Attachment (07947-6110500), install seals to clutch and transmission housings.

Fig. 13: Tightening Transaxle Housing Bolts

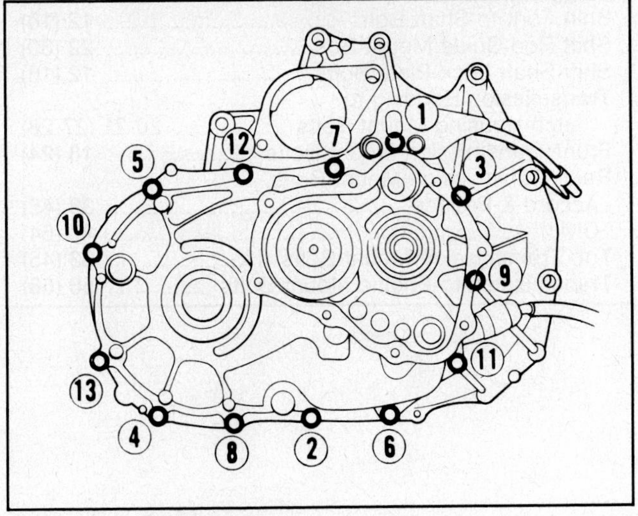

Accord and Prelude only.

Civic

1) Install differential assembly and transmission gear assemblies in clutch housing. Install sealant and dowel pins in clutch housing and lower transmission housing into place. Install 72 mm snap ring in transmission housing.

2) Using Driver (07749-0010000) and Attachment (07947-6340500), seat snap ring. Seat differential assembly in clutch housing. Measure clearance between snap ring and outer bearing race of in transmission housing. Clearance is .006" (.15 mm), maximum.

3) If out of specification, select a new snap ring. Snap rings are available in thicknesses from .096" (2.45 mm), to .116" (2.95 mm), in increments of .004" (.10 mm). Seat snap ring against clutch housing.

4) Apply oil to differential seals. Using driver and Attachment (07947-6110500), install seals to clutch and transmission housings.

TRANSAXLE ASSEMBLY

Accord & Prelude

1) Install differential assembly into clutch housing. Install mainshaft, countershaft, 1st-2nd gear shift shaft and 3rd-4th gear shift shaft together as an assembly. Ensure forks are in 4th and 2nd gear positions to make installation easier.

2) Lift mainshaft and install interlock into selector arm. Place shift rod in neutral. Hook interlock into selector arm, 1st-2nd gearshift shaft and 3rd-4th gearshift shaft. Hook shift guide into shift arm.

3) Install 5th-reverse shift shaft and hook pin into reverse shift fork slot. Install shift guide so that it bottoms in clutch housing hole. Ensure guide shaft does not protrude more than .5" (12 mm) above interlock.

4) Install mainshaft bearing retainer plate. Install reverse idler gear and shaft. Install back-up light switch with new washer. Place new gasket on clutch housing and install dowel pins. Shift transmission into 3rd gear to position shift guide shaft for reassembly.

5) Install transmission housing, being sure to line up shafts. Shift guide shaft must seat in blind hole in transaxle housing. Tighten 13 bolts to 21 Ft. Lbs. (28 N.m) in sequence, to specification. *See Fig. 13.*

6) Install 3 detent balls, washers and retaining screws. Install countershaft 5th gear with high side facing down. Install spring washer with dished side facing 5th gear.

7) Install spacer collar and needle bearing onto mainshaft. Install mainshaft 5th gear. Install synchro ring, synchro spring, synchro hub and synchro sleeve onto mainshaft. Install 5th gear shift fork on synchro sleeve.

8) Install spring washer with spring washer with dished side facing synchro hub. With a 5 mm pin punch, drive spring pin into 5th gear shift fork. Install Mainshaft Holder (07923-6890101) to prevent shaft from turning. Shift transmission into reverse.

9) Tighten mainshaft and countershaft lock nuts to specification. Loosen and retighten to same specification. Stake shoulders on lock nuts into slots in mainshaft and countershaft. Install end cover on transmission housing with new gasket and tighten mount bolts.

Civic

1) Clean all liquid gasket residue from surfaces of transmission and clutch housings. Install shift rod, selector arm, new lock plate and bolt. Bend lock tab on lock plate over against bolt head. Ensure 72 mm snap ring is installed in clutch housing and install differential assembly.

2) Align shift arm with selector arm and install shift arm holder. Install bolts, using correct bolt in each hole. Tighten to specification. Install mainshaft and countershaft as an assembly.

3) Lift countershaft 1st-2nd synchro sleeve to shift transmission into 2nd gear. Install 1st-2nd gear shift fork on synchronizer sleeve. Rotate into place so that lugs on back of fork fit over shift arm. Insert 3rd-4th shift fork shaft into 3rd-4th shift guide and install spring pin.

4) Insert 3rd-4th shift fork shaft into 3rd-4th shift fork. Install shift fork and hook shift guide to shift arm. Install 1st-2nd shift shaft.

5) On 4-Speed models, hook reverse shift guide to shift arm and install shift shaft. On 5-Speed models, hook 5th-reverse shift guide to shift arm and install shift shaft. Install spring and detent ball in hole in clutch housing.

6) On both models, install reverse shift fork with special washer and nut. Install reverse idler gear and shaft. Install 3 bolts and lock plates on shift shafts then bend tab on each lock plate against bolt head.

7) Apply liquid gasket to clutch housing. Install dowel pins. Install transmission housing being careful to line up shafts. Ensure countershaft bearing is seated properly. Tighten 11 bolts to 20 Ft. Lbs. (27 N.m) in sequence, to specification. *See Fig. 14.* Install 3 detent balls, washers, springs and retaining screws.

Manual Transmissions

HONDA 2WD 4 & 5-SPEED TRANSAXLE (Cont.)

8) On 5-Speed models, install thrust washer and needle bearing. Install synchro ring and spring. Install synchro hub (with raised inner shoulder facing down), and sleeve onto shift fork. Install assembly onto mainshaft.

9) On both models, install bearing onto mainshaft. On 5-Speed models, drive spring into shift fork, apply liquid gasket to transmission housing and install 5th gear housing. On 4-Speed models, apply liquid gasket to end cover and install end cover. On both models, tighten bolts to specification.

Fig. 14: Tightening Transaxle Housing Bolts

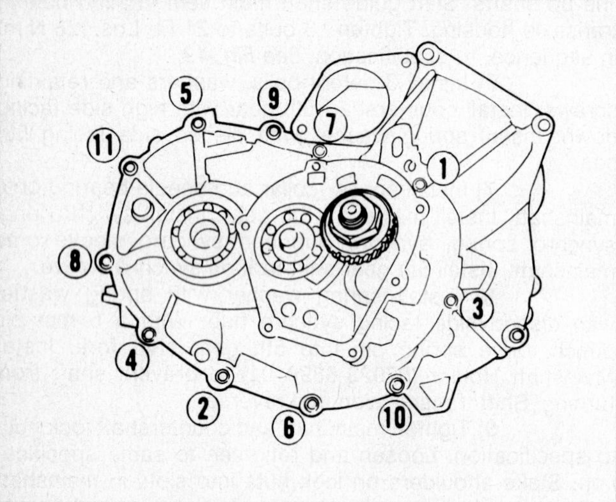

Civic only.

TIGHTENING SPECIFICATIONS

Application	Ft. Lbs. (N.m)
Back-up Light Switch	18 (24)
Countershaft Lock Nut	65 (88)
Cover-to-Transaxle Bolts	10 (14)
Damper Fork Bolt	47 (64)
Detent Ball Retainer Screw	16 (22)
End Cover Mount Bolt	7 (10)
Gear Holder Lock Plate Bolts	9 (12)
Mainshaft Bearing Retainer	
Plate Mount Bolt	21 (28)
Mainshaft Lock Nut	65 (88)
Oil Filler Bolt	33 (45)
Reverse Shift Fork Nut	17 (23)
Ring Gear Attaching Bolts	74 (101)
Shift Arm Holder Bolts	
Accord & Prelude	9-11 (12-15)
Civic	13 (18)
Shift Fork-to-Shaft Bolts	12 (16)
Shift Rod Guide Mount Bolt	22 (30)
Shift Shaft Lock Plate Bolts	12 (16)
Transmission Housing-to	
Clutch Housing Mount Bolts	20-21 (27-28)
Front Transmission Mount Bolts	18 (24)
Rear Transmission Mount Bolts	
Accord & Prelude	33 (45)
Civic	47 (64)
Top Transmission Mount Bolts	33 (45)
Transmission-to-Engine Mount Bolts	50 (68)

HONDA 4WD 5-SPEED TRANSAXLE WITH INTEGRAL TRANSFER CASE

Civic 4WD

TRANSAXLE IDENTIFICATION

Transaxle identification number is stamped into top of transaxle case flange near transaxle-to-engine union.

MANUAL TRANSAXLE CODE

Application	Code
Civic 4WD 5-Speed	[1] GW/SL

[1] - SL pertains to the Super-Low gear.

DESCRIPTION

The Transmission, final drive and transfer case are mounted in a 3-piece case. The transaxle is fully synchronized in all forward gears. All forward gears are helically cut and are in constant mesh. Reverse gears are spur cut and are engaged by a sliding reverse idler gear.

5th gear is mounted on mainshaft on rear side of transaxle case. Power transfer to the final drive assembly is by direct mesh of differential ring gear to a gear on transmission countershaft. *See Fig. 1.*

In 4WD, power from front differential is transmitted 90° through transfer to provide additional power to the rear wheels. The transmission, clutch and transfer cases are sealed with a liquid sealant. Shims are used to position mainshaft in its axial direction.

OPERATION

Since transfer case gear has more teeth than the driven gear, a speed increase occurs in the transfer. The power is then conveyed through the propeller shaft to the rear differential where a gear reduction takes place to match the speed of the front and rear wheels.

For 4WD applications, the transmission includes a Super-Low gear in addition to the normal five forward ratios. An interlock mechanism prevents shifting to Super-

Fig. 1: Transaxle/Transfer Case Components

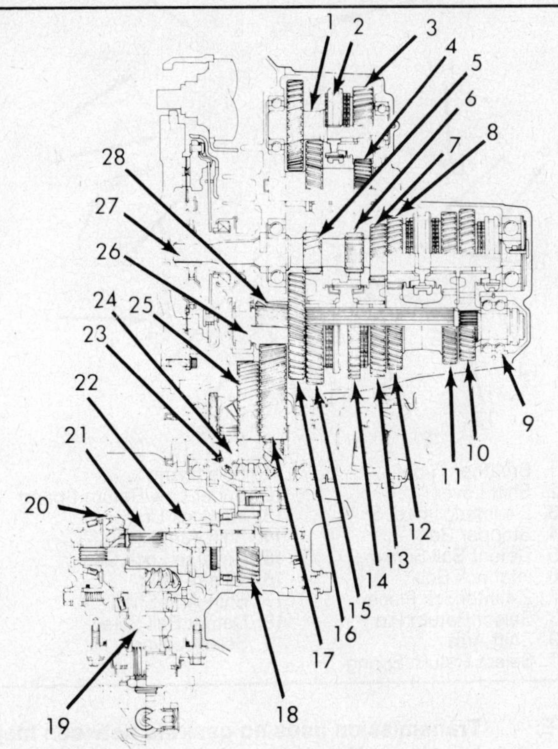

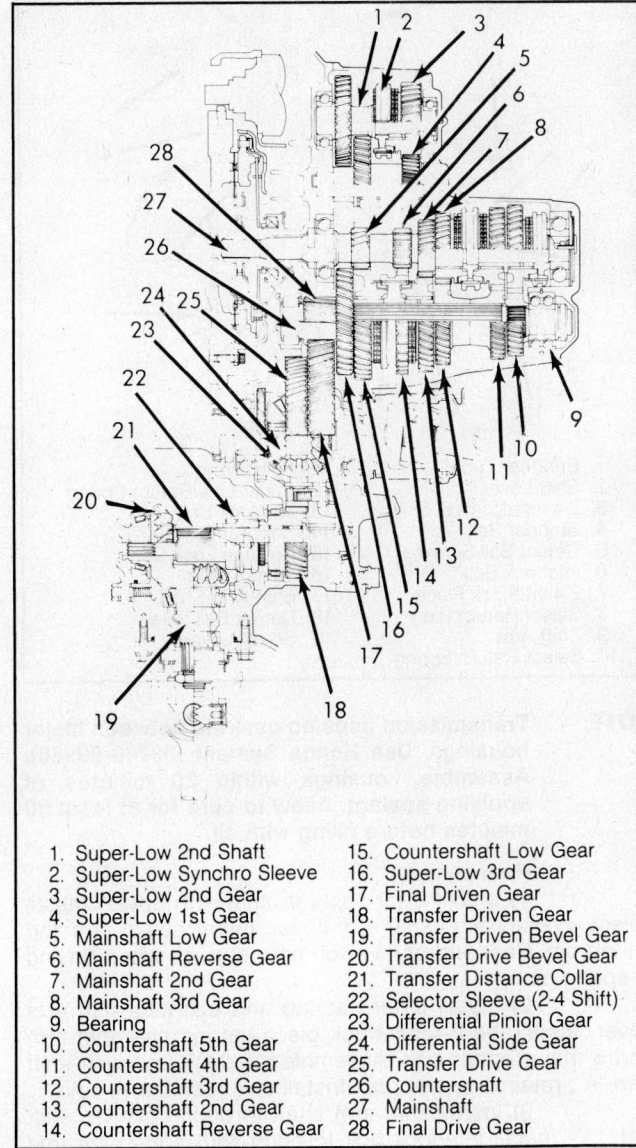

1. Super-Low 2nd Shaft
2. Super-Low Synchro Sleeve
3. Super-Low 2nd Gear
4. Super-Low 1st Gear
5. Mainshaft Low Gear
6. Mainshaft Reverse Gear
7. Mainshaft 2nd Gear
8. Mainshaft 3rd Gear
9. Bearing
10. Countershaft 5th Gear
11. Countershaft 4th Gear
12. Countershaft 3rd Gear
13. Countershaft 2nd Gear
14. Countershaft Reverse Gear
15. Countershaft Low Gear
16. Super-Low 3rd Gear
17. Final Driven Gear
18. Transfer Driven Gear
19. Transfer Driven Bevel Gear
20. Transfer Drive Bevel Gear
21. Transfer Distance Collar
22. Selector Sleeve (2-4 Shift)
23. Differential Pinion Gear
24. Differential Side Gear
25. Transfer Drive Gear
26. Countershaft
27. Mainshaft
28. Final Drive Gear

Fig. 2: Shift Mechanism Cable Assemblies

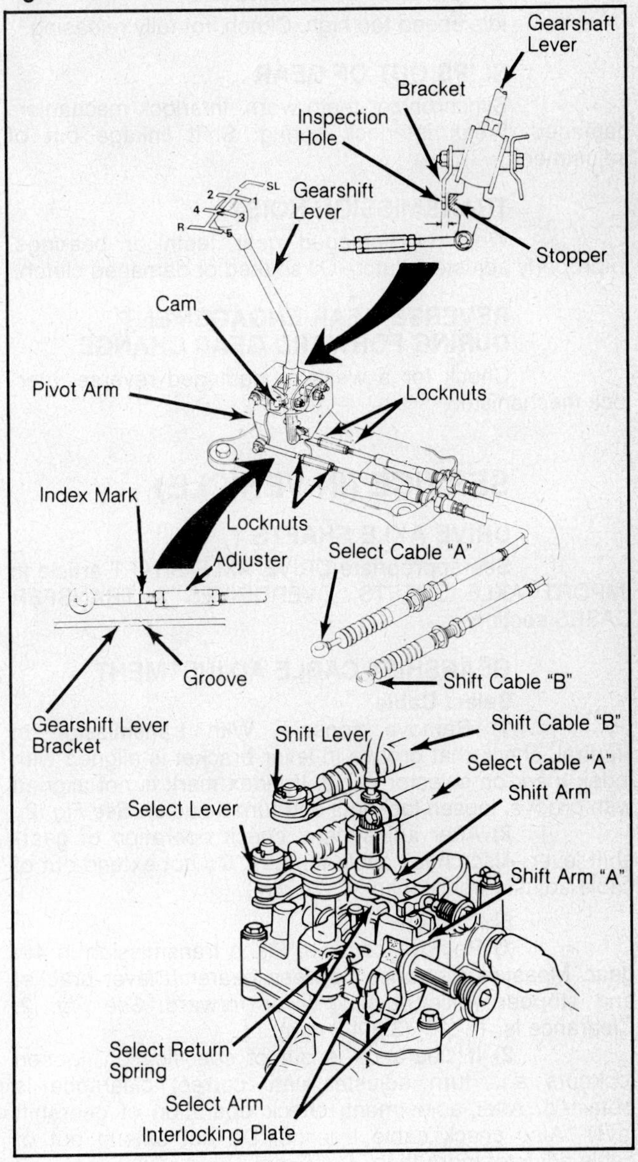

HONDA 4WD 5-SPEED TRANSAXLE WITH INTEGRAL TRANSFER CASE (Cont.)

Low when engaged in 2WD and also prevents disengagement of 4WD.

Shifting to and from 4WD is possible when vehicle is moving or stationary, as long as the engine is running. When select switch is pressed, manifold vacuum is applied to the actuator diaphram through a solenoid valve.

Transmission shifting is controlled by a pair of push-pull cables; shift and select. Right and left movements of shift lever are controlled by select cable "A". Forward and rearward movements are controlled by shift cable "B". *See Fig. 2.*

LUBRICATION & ADJUSTMENT

See appropriate MANUAL TRANSMISSION SERVICING article in IMPORT GENERAL SERVICING section.

TROUBLE SHOOTING

HARSH SHIFTS OR NOISY LOW GEAR OPERATION

Idle speed too high. Clutch not fully releasing.

SLIPS OUT OF GEAR

Synchronizer teeth worn. Interlock mechanism damaged. Weak interlock spring. Shift linkage out of adjustment.

TRANSMISSION NOISY

Worn or damaged gear teeth or bearings. Improperly adjusted clutch. Oil soaked or damaged clutch.

REVERSE GEAR ENGAGEMENT DURING FORWARD GEAR CHANGE

Check for a weak or damaged reverse interlock mechanism.

SERVICE (IN VEHICLE)

DRIVE AXLE SHAFTS

See appropriate DRIVE AXLE SHAFT article in IMPORT AXLE SHAFTS, OVERDRIVES & TRANSFER CASES section.

GEARSHIFT CABLE ADJUSTMENT

Select Cable

1) Remove console. With transmission in Neutral, check that groove in lever bracket is aligned with index mark on selector cable. If index mark is not aligned with groove, loosen locknuts and turn adjuster. *See Fig. 2.*

2) After adjustment, check operation of gearshift lever. Also check cable threads. Do not extend out of cable adjuster more than .4" (10 mm).

Shift Cable

1) Remove console. Place transmission in 4th gear. Measure clearance between gearshift lever bracket and stopper while pushing lever forward. *See Fig. 2.* Clearance is .15-.19" (3.8-4.8 mm).

2) If clearance is out of specification, loosen locknuts and turn adjuster until correct clearance is obtained. After adjustment, check operation of gearshift lever. Also check cable threads. Do not extend out of cable adjuster more than .4" (10 mm).

SELECTOR ARM COVER ASSEMBLY

Disassembly

1) Remove 4 attaching bolts and dowel pins. Remove shift arm cover assembly. Remove breather tube and remove shift lever from shift arm "A". Remove detent screws and back-up light switch from cover. *See Figs. 3 and 4.*

2) Remove reverse lock cam from cover. Remove 18 mm plug, shift arm shaft from shift arm "A". Remove interlock bolt and unit, retainer and return spring from selector arm cover assembly. Remove 16 mm stopper bolt.

3) Remove spring pin holding 2-4 interlock piece to interlock lever. Remove detent ball and spring, piece and lever. Remove spring pin holding select lever to select arm. Remove select lever and select arm. Remove 3 oil seals from shift arm cover.

Fig. 3: Exploded View of Shift Arm Cover Assembly

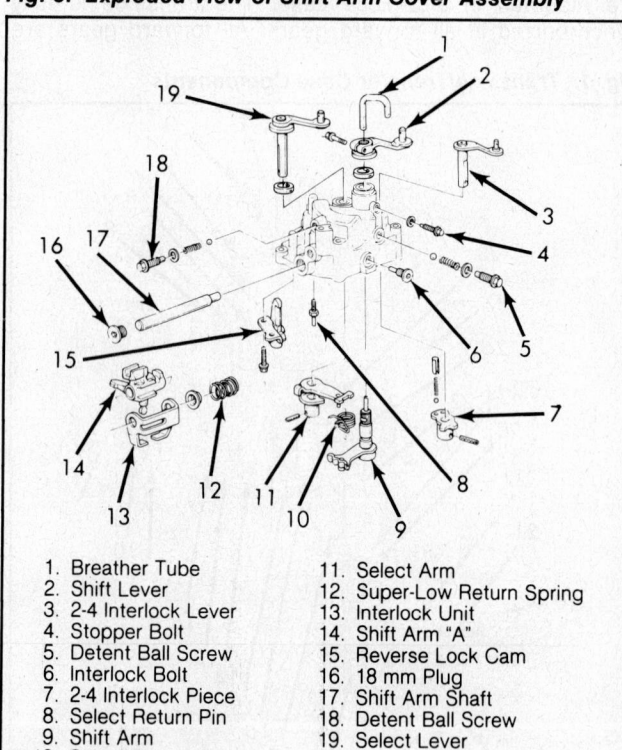

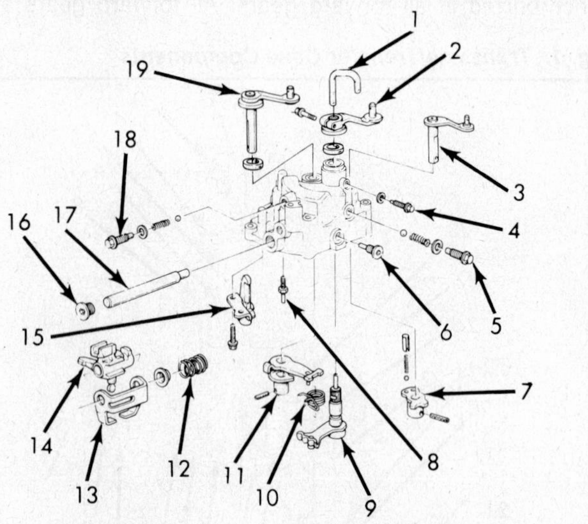

1. Breather Tube
2. Shift Lever
3. 2-4 Interlock Lever
4. Stopper Bolt
5. Detent Ball Screw
6. Interlock Bolt
7. 2-4 Interlock Piece
8. Select Return Pin
9. Shift Arm
10. Select Return Spring
11. Select Arm
12. Super-Low Return Spring
13. Interlock Unit
14. Shift Arm "A"
15. Reverse Lock Cam
16. 18 mm Plug
17. Shift Arm Shaft
18. Detent Ball Screw
19. Select Lever

NOTE: **Transmission uses no gaskets between major housings. Use Honda Sealant (08740-99986). Assemble housings within 20 minutes of applying sealant. Allow to cure for at least 30 minutes before filling with oil.**

Reassembly

1) Install 3 oil seals in shift arm cover. Install select lever through shift arm cover. Install select arm and spring pin. Rest end of lever on hard surface when driving in spring pin.

2) Install detent spring and ball into shift arm cover. Install the 2-4 interlock piece, spring pin, shift arm and 6 mm stopper bolt. Assemble interlock unit with shift arm "A", retainer and spring. Install unit in shift arm cover.

3) Install shift arm shaft through cover to shift arm "A". Install interlock bolt through shift arm cover and align bolt with groove in interlock unit. Install 18 mm plug.

HONDA 4WD 5-SPEED TRANSAXLE WITH INTEGRAL TRANSFER CASE (Cont.)

Fig. 4: Exploded View of Civic 4WD 5-Speed Transaxle/Transfer Case Assembly

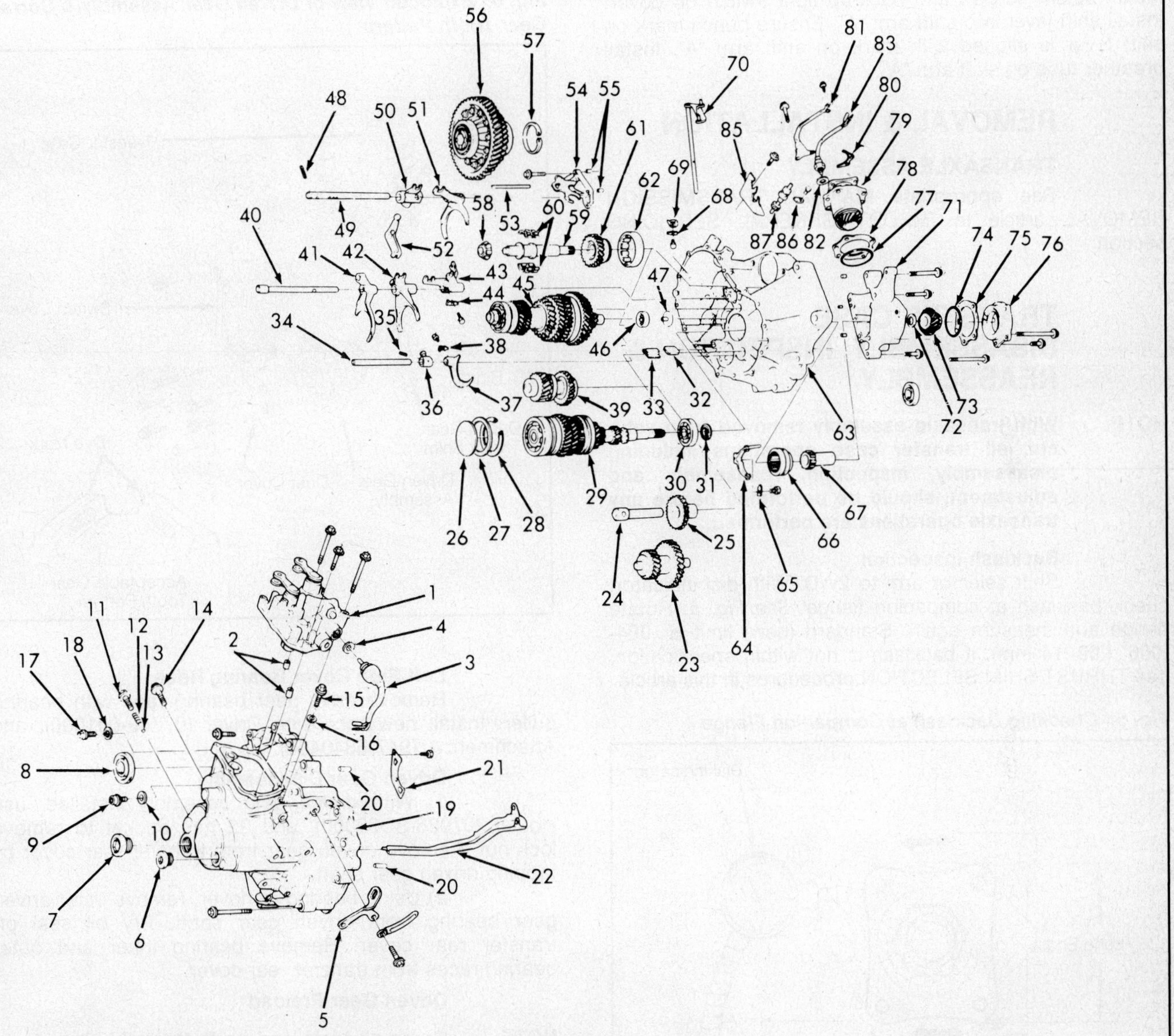

1. Shift Arm Cover
2. Dowel Pin
3. Back-Up Light
4. 14 mm Aluminum Washer
5. Transmission Hanger
6. 18 mm Sealing Bolt
7. 32 mm Sealing Bolt
8. Oil Seal
9. 14 mm Drain Bolt
10. 14 mm Aluminum Washer
11. Super-Low Shift Set Bolt
12. Spring
13. Detent Ball
14. Super-Low Shift Lever Bolt
15. Reverse Idler Shaft Bolt
16. 14 mm Aluminum Washer
17. 14 mm Drain Plug
18. Washer
19. Transmission Housing
20. Dowel Pin
21. Oil Collect Plate
22. Oil Gutter Plate
23. Super-Low 1st Gear Assembly
24. Reverse Idler Gear Shaft
25. Reverse Idler Gear
26. Oil Guide Plate
27. 75 mm Dished Spring
28. 75 mm Thrust Shim
29. Mainshaft Assembly
30. Mainshaft Bearing
31. Mainshaft Oil Seal
32. Magnet
33. Magnet Spring Holder
34. Super-Low Shift Fork Shaft
35. 5 mm Spring Pin
36. Super-Low Shift Piece "B"
37. Super-Low Shift Fork
38. Lock Washer
39. Super-Low 2nd Gear Assembly
40. 5th-Reverse Fork Shaft
41. 5th Shift Fork
42. 3rd-4th Shift Fork
43. 5th-Reverse Shift Piece
44. Lock Plate
45. Countershaft Assembly
46. Countershaft Needle Bearing
47. Oil Guide Plate
48. 5 mm Spring Pin
49. 1st-2nd Shift Fork Shaft
50. Super-Low Shift Piece "A"
51. 1st-2nd Shift Fork
52. Super-Low Shift Lever
53. Super-Low Shift Piece Bar
54. Reverse Shift Holder Assembly
55. Dowel Pin
56. Differential
57. 80 mm Set Ring
58. Transfer Shaft Bearing
59. Transfer Shaft
60. Needle Bearing
61. Transfer Driven Gear
62. Needle Bearing
63. Clutch Case
64. Selector Fork
65. Lock Washer
66. Sleeve Selector
67. Transfer Specer Collar
68. Lock Washer
69. 2-4 Indicator Arm
70. Selector Rod
71. Transfer Case
72. Drive Gear Thrust Washer
73. Transfer Drive Gear
74. "O" Ring
75. Transfer Thrust Shim
76. Transfer Left Side Cover
77. "O" Ring
78. Driven Gear Thrust Shim
79. Driven Gear Assembly
80. Dust Cover
81. 2WD-4WD Switch Protector
82. Aluminum Washer
83. 2WD-4WD Switch
84. Differential Oil Seal
85. Gearshift Cable Stay
86. Lock Plate
87. Speedometer Gear

HONDA 4WD 5-SPEED TRANSAXLE WITH INTEGRAL TRANSFER CASE (Cont.)

Seal threads of interlock bolt and 18 mm plug with Honda Sealant (08740-99986).

4) Install reverse lock cam on shift arm cover. Install detent screws and back-up light switch on cover. Install shift lever into shift arm "A". Ensure punch mark on shift lever is aligned with mark on shift arm "A". Install breather tube on shift arm "A".

REMOVAL & INSTALLATION

TRANSAXLE ASSEMBLY

See appropriate MANUAL TRANSMISSION REMOVAL article in IMPORT GENERAL SERVICING section.

TRANSFER CASE DISASSEMBLY, INSPECTION & REASSEMBLY

NOTE: **With transaxle assembly removed from vehicle, all transfer case operations including disassembly, inspection, reassembly and adjustment, should be performed before any transaxle operations are performed.**

Backlash Inspection

Shift selector arm to 2WD. With dial indicator, check backlash at companion flange. *See Fig. 5.* Rotate flange and measure again. Standard (new) limit is .004-.006" (.09-.14 mm). If backlash is not within specification, see THRUST SHIM SELECTION procedures in this article.

Fig. 5: Checking Backlash at Companion Flange

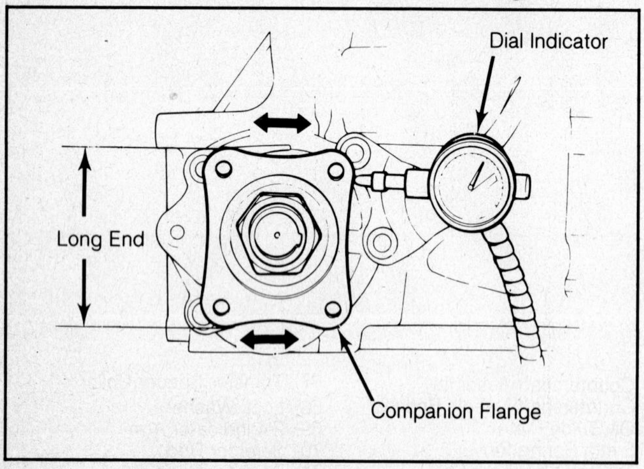

Gear Tooth Contact

1) Shift selector lever to 2WD. Remove bolt holding 2WD-4WD switch cover to clutch case. Remove 6 mounting bolts and remove dust cover, 2WD-4WD switch cover, driven gear assembly, thrust shim and "O" ring from clutch and transfer case housings. *See Fig. 6.*

2) Apply blue dye evenly to driven gear teeth. Reinstall gear and tighten mounting bolts to 20 Ft. Lbs. (26 N.m). Turn companion flange back and forth several times to spread dye. Remove driven gear assembly and inspect teeth. *See Fig. 6.*

3) If correct pattern is not as shown, see TRANSFER CASE DISASSEMBLY, REMOVEL & REASSEMBLY procedures, steps **7)** through **10)**, in this section.

If tooth contact is correct, reinstall driven gear assembly and components by reversing removal procedure.

Fig. 6: Exploded View of Driven Gear Assembly & Correct Gear Tooth Pattern

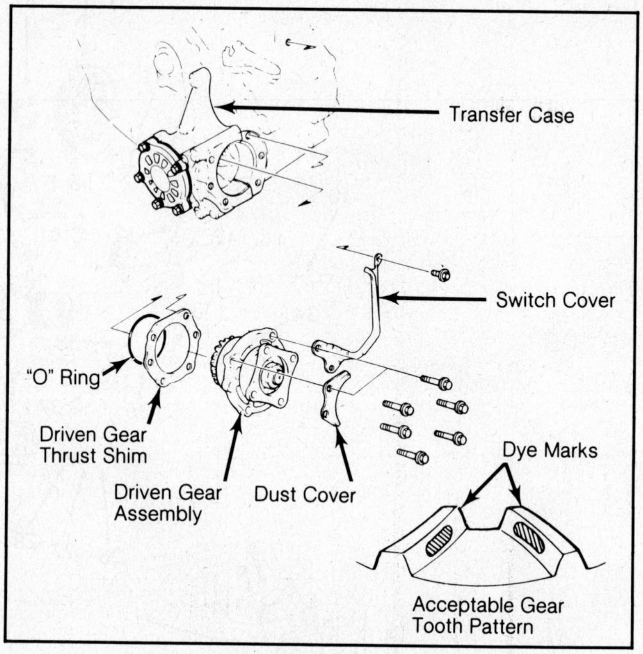

Left Side Cover Bearing Race

Remove drive gear bearing race with bearing puller. Install new race with Driver (07749-001000), and Attachment (07947-6340400).

Driven Gear Disassembly

1) With driven gear assembly installed, use Holder (07926-SD90000), and 22 mm socket to remove lock nut. Remove driven gear from transfer rear cover by tapping driven gear shaft.

2) Using bearing remover, remove inner driven gear bearing from driven gear shaft. Pry oil seal off transfer rear cover. Remove bearing inner and outer bearing races from transfer rear cover.

Driven Gear Preload

NOTE: **Clean all tools and parts throughly in solvent and dry with compressed air.**

1) Using Driver (07749-0010000), and Attachment (07746-0010500), press inner driven gear bearing into transfer rear cover. Using driver and Attachment (07746-0010400), press outer driven gear bearing race into transfer rear cover.

2) Coat races with clean oil. Slide inner driven gear bearing onto Dummy Driven Gear Shaft (07973-SD90400), and install dummy shaft into rear cover. *See Fig. 7.*

3) Slide outer driven gear bearing onto dummy driven gear shaft. Install companion flange, lock washer and a new 22 mm lock nut. Install lock washer with dished side toward rear cover. Do not install oil seal at this time.

4) Hold dummy shaft by inserting end of a screwdriver into hole in shaft. Tighten 22 mm locknut to about 7 Ft. Lbs. (10 N.m). Turn companion flange several times to ensure proper bearing contact.

HONDA 4WD 5-SPEED TRANSAXLE WITH INTEGRAL TRANSFER CASE (Cont.)

5) Using torque wrench, measure preload. Standard (new) preload limit is 36-58 Ft. Lbs. (50-80 N.m). If preload is out of specification, readjust by turning locknut.

Fig. 7: Installing Driven Gear Bearings & Dummy Shaft

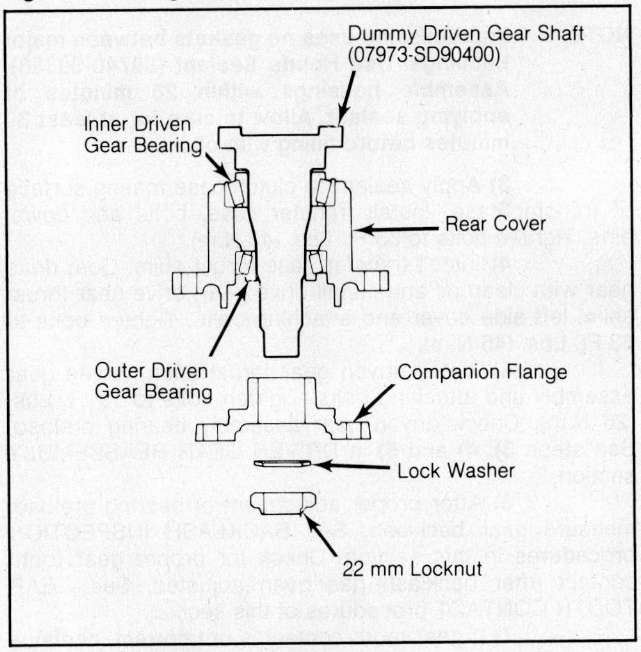

Thrust Shim Selection

1) Insert dummy shaft/driven gear assembly into transfer housing. Remove the 5 attaching bolts holding left side cover. Using bearing puller and Spring Compressor Attachment (07960-1870100), remove drive gear bearing. *See Fig. 8.*

Fig. 8: Installing Drive Gear Gauge & Components

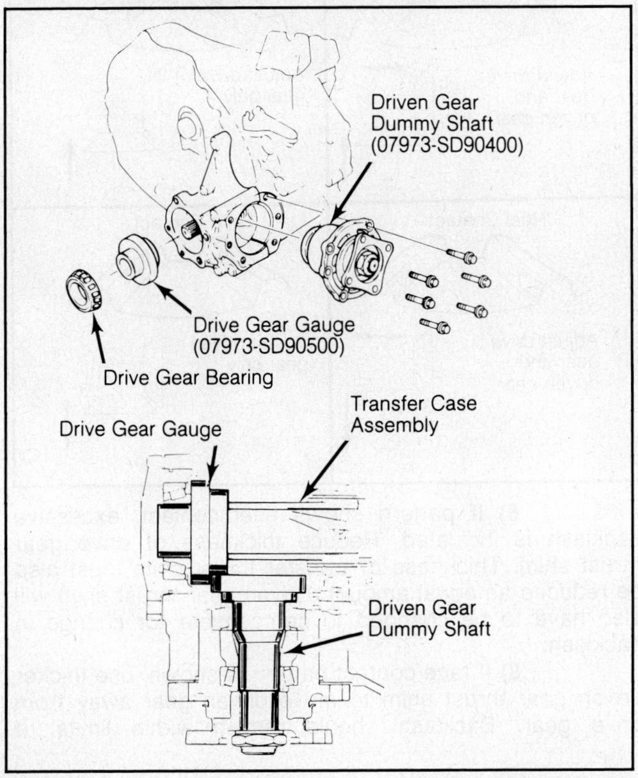

2) Lubricate drive gear bearing with clean oil and install it on Drive Gear Gauge (07973-SD90500). Slide bearing and gauge onto transfer shaft. Do not install drive gear thrust washer, Pull dummy shaft/driven gear assembly out slightly to allow drive gear gauge to seat properly.

3) Install left side cover without the bolts. To determine driven gear thrust shim thickness, rotate companion flange several times to seat bearings. With feeler gauge, measure clearance between transfer rear cover and transfer case in several locations. Note average clearance.

NOTE: Clearance should be measured while pushing dummy shaft all the way in.

4) Correct shim thickness is determined by adding to or subtracting from average measured clearance, the machined tolerance which is etched into the driven gear. The plus (+) or minus (-) number etched on driven gear represents hundredths of a millimeter. For example:

- Measured average clearance is 1.07 mm.
- Machined tolarence etched in driven (or drive) gear is (+3).

Correct shim thickness would be 1.10 mm.

DRIVEN GEAR THRUST SHIM THICKNESS

Part Number	In. (mm)
29481-PH8-000	.020 (.50)
29482-PH8-000	.033 (.85)
29483-PH8-000	.035 (.90)
29484-PH8-000	.037 (.95)
29485-PH8-000	.039 (1.00)
29486-PH8-000	.041 (1.05)
29487-PH8-000	.043 (1.10)
29488-PH8-000	.045 (1.15)
29489-PH8-000	.047 (1.20)
29491-PH8-000	.049 (1.24)
29492-PH8-000	.051 (1.30)

5) With feeler gauge, measure clearance between transfer left side cover and transfer case in several locations. Note average clearance. Clearance should be measured while pressing left side cover all the way against transfer case.

6) Correct dummy shim thickness is determined by adding to or subtracting from average measured clearance, the machined tolerance which is etched into the drive gear. Follow measurement procedures from step **4)**.

DRIVE GEAR DUMMY THRUST SHIM THICKNESS

Part Number	In. (mm)
29461-PH8-000	.012 (.30)
29462-PH8-000	.039 (1.00)
29463-PH8-000	.041 (1.03)
29464-PH8-000	.042 (1.06)
29465-PH8-000	.043 (1.09)
29466-PH8-000	.044 (1.12)
29467-PH8-000	.045 (1.15)
29468-PH8-000	.046 (1.18)
29469-PH8-000	.048 (1.21)
29471-PH8-000	.049 (1.24)
29472-PH8-000	.050 (1.27)
29473-PH8-000	.051 (1.30)
29474-PH8-000	.052 (1.33)

HONDA 4WD 5-SPEED TRANSAXLE WITH INTEGRAL TRANSFER CASE (Cont.)

7) Install two 1.75 mm Dummy Washers (29415-PH8-000), on transfer shaft. Using press, Hub Base "A" (07965-6340301), and Driver Attachment (07746-0030400), press drive gear bearing onto drive gear.

8) Slide drive gear onto transfer shaft. Place dummy shim selected from step **6)** on left side cover and install cover on transfer case. Rotate companion flange several times to seat bearings.

9) With feeler gauge, measure clearance between left side cover and trensfer case at several locations while pushing against left side cover. Note average clearance.

10) Correct shim thickness is determined subtracting average measured clearance from 3.5 mm. For example:

- Measured average clearance is 1.57 mm.
- Thickness of dummy washers is 3.5 mm.

Corrected drive gear thrust shim thickness would 1.93 mm, (3.5 mm minus (-) 1.57 mm).

DRIVE GEAR THRUST SHIM THICKNESS

Part Number	In. (mm)
29411-PH8-000	.019 (.48)
29412-PH8-000	.062 (1.57)
29413-PH8-000	.064 (1.63)
29414-PH8-000	.067 (1.69)
29415-PH8-000	.069 (1.75)
29416-PH8-000	.071 (1.81)
29417-PH8-000	.074 (1.87)
29418-PH8-000	.076 (1.93)
29419-PH8-000	.078 (1.99)

Driven Gear Reassembly

1) Remove Driven Gear Dummy Shaft (07973-SD90400), from transfer rear cover. Install outer driven gear bearing into transfer rear cover. Using Driver (07749-0010000), and Oil Seal Attachment (07965-SA00600). Press oil seal into transfer rear cover.

2) Coat main and side sealing lips of oil seal with grease. Using press, Hub Base "A" (07965-6340301), and Driver Attachment (07746-0030400), press inner driven gear bearing onto drive gear. Install new transfer spacer, drive gear, companion flange, lock washer and 22 mm locknut. Install lock washer with dished side toward companion flange.

3) Temporarily install driven gear assembly and mounting bolts in transfer case. To measure preload, tighten locknut to 87 Ft. Lbs. Remove driven gear assembly from transfer case and measure preload.

4) Before measuring preload, rotate companion flange several times to ensure normal bearing contact. Preload should be 7.0-9.5 INCH Lbs. If preload exceeds specification, replace transfer spacer and readjust. Do not try and adjust preload by loosening locknut.

5) If preload is less than specification, adjust by turning locknut in a bit at a time. Replace transfer spacer if preload is still out of specification when locknut is tightened to 166 Ft. Lbs. (230 N.m).

Transfer Case Disassembly, Inspection & Reassembly

1) Shift select lever to 2WD. Remove 5 attaching bolts holding left side cover to clutch case. Remove left side cover, transfer thrust shim, "O" ring, drive gear and drive gear thrust shim. Remove 2WD-4WD switch from clutch housing.

2) Remove 6 attaching bolts holding driven gear assembly to clutch and transfer case housings. Remove 2WD-4WD drive switch protector and dust cover. Remove driven gear assembly, thrust shim and "O" ring. Remove 5 transfer cover attaching bolts and dowel pins and remove transfer case assembly.

NOTE: Transmission uses no gaskets between major housings. Use Honda Sealant (08740-99986). Assemble housings within 20 minutes of applying sealant. Allow to cure for at least 30 minutes before filling with oil.

3) Apply sealant to clutch case mating surface of transfer case. Install transfer case, bolts and dowel pins. Tighten bolts to 33 Ft. Lbs. (45 N.m).

4) Install transfer case thrust shim. Coat drive gear with clean oil and install drive gear, drive gear thrust shim, left side cover and attaching bolts. Tighten bolts to 33 Ft. Lbs. (45 N.m).

5) Install driven gear thrust shim, driven gear assembly and attaching bolts. Tighten bolts to 19 Ft. Lbs. (26 N.m). Check driven gear assembly bearing preload. See steps **3)**, **4)** and **5)** in DRIVEN GEAR REASSEMBLY section.

6) After proper adjustment of bearing preload, measure gear backlash. See BACKLASH INSPECTION procedures in this section. Check for proper gear tooth contact after backlash has been adjusted. See GEAR TOOTH CONTACT procedures of this section.

7) If gear tooth contact is not correct, continue checking and adjusting procedures. *See Fig. 9.* If pattern shows toe contact, use a thicker drive gear thrust shim and increase thrust shim thickness an equal amount.

Fig. 9: Gear Tooth Contact Patterns

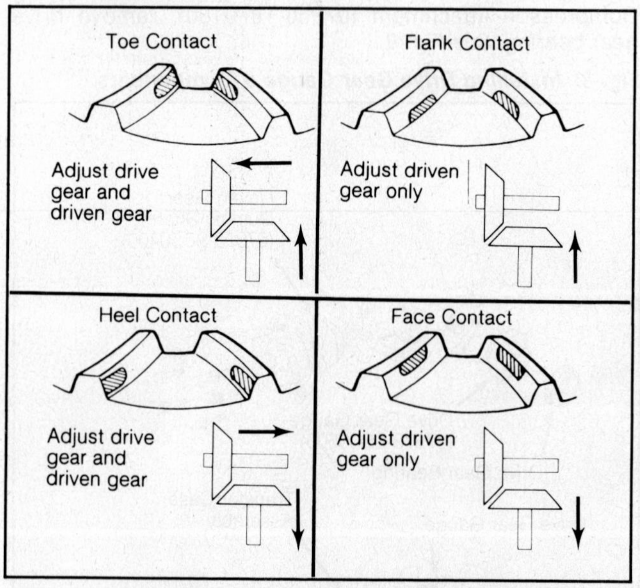

8) If pattern shows heel contact, excessive backlash is indicated. Reduce thickness of drive gear thrust shim. Thickness of transfer thrust shim must also be reduced an equal amount. Driven gear thrust shim will also have to be changed to compensate for change in backlash.

9) If face contact pattern is shown, use thicker driven gear thrust shim to move driven gear away from drive gear. Backlash should remain within limits. If

HONDA 4WD 5-SPEED TRANSAXLE WITH INTEGRAL TRANSFER CASE (Cont.)

backlash becomes out of specification after adjustment, make correction in same manner as HEEL CONTACT in step **8**).

10) If flank contact pattern is shown, move driven gear in toward drive gear by using thinner shim for driven gear. Backlash should remain within limits. If backlash becomes out of specification after adjustment, make correction in same manner as TOE CONTACT in step **7**).

11) When gear tooth pattern is correct, apply sealant to mating surfaces of clutch and transfer cases. Install thrust shim and "O" ring on driven gear assembly and install assembly in transfer case. *See Fig. 10*. Tighten bolts to 33 Ft. Lbs. (45 N.m).

12) Slide drive gear thrust shim and drive gear onto transfer shaft. Place transfer thrust shim and "O" ring on left side cover. Coat "O" ring with clean oil. Apply Honda Sealant to 2 bolts closest to driven gear assembly side. Install cover on transfer case. Tighten all bolts to 33 Ft. Lbs. (45 N.m).

13) After all components are installed, check driven gear assembly bearing preload. See steps **3)**, **4)** and **5)** in DRIVEN GEAR REASSEMBLY section.

Fig. 10: Installing Transfer Case Components

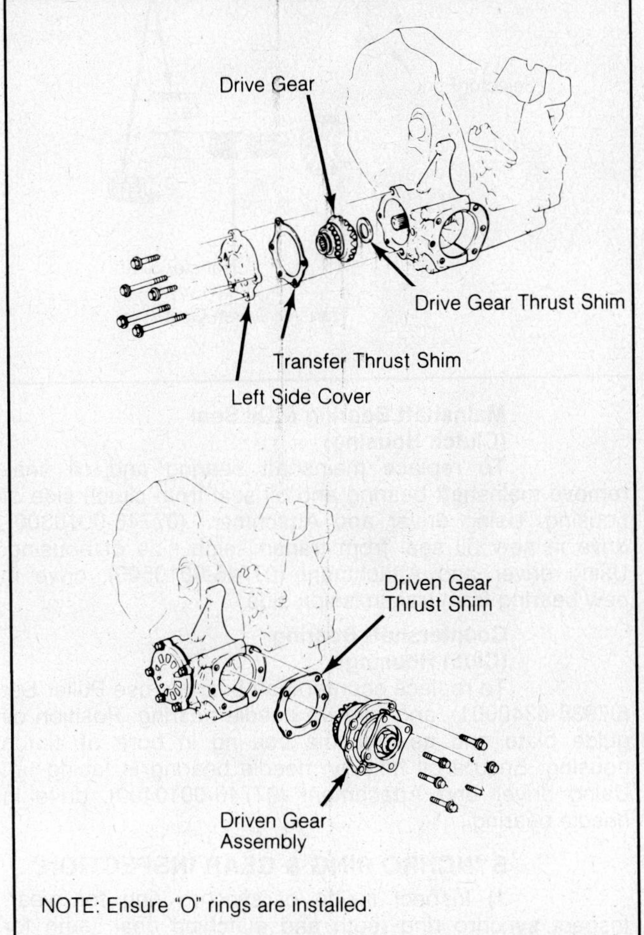

NOTE: Ensure "O" rings are installed.

TRANSAXLE DISASSEMBLY

1) Remove transaxle from vehicle and install on work stand. *See Fig. 4*. Remove reverse idle shaft bolt and washer, super-low shift set ball screw and washer, and super-low shift lever bolt from transmission housing. Remove 8 mm bolts attaching clutch case to transmission housing.

2) Remove 32 mm sealing bolt and circlip holding countershaft ball bearing. Seperate clutch housing from transmission housing. Clean mating surfaces. Remove thrust shim, dish spring and oil guide plate from transmission housing.

3) Before further disassembly, measure clearance between reverse shift fork and 5th-reverse shift piece pin. Standard (new) clearance is .002-.014" (.05-.35 mm). Service limit is .071" (1.8 mm).

4) If clearance exceeds service limit, measure width of reverse fork pawl groove. Standard (new) width is .512-.524" (13.0-13.3 mm). If width is out of specification, replace shift fork.

5) To remove countershaft and mainshaft assemblies, remove reverse idler gear from clutch housing. Remove 1st-2nd shift fork shaft, super-low shift piece

Fig. 11: Exploded View of Super-Low 2nd Shaft & Clutch Housing Assembly

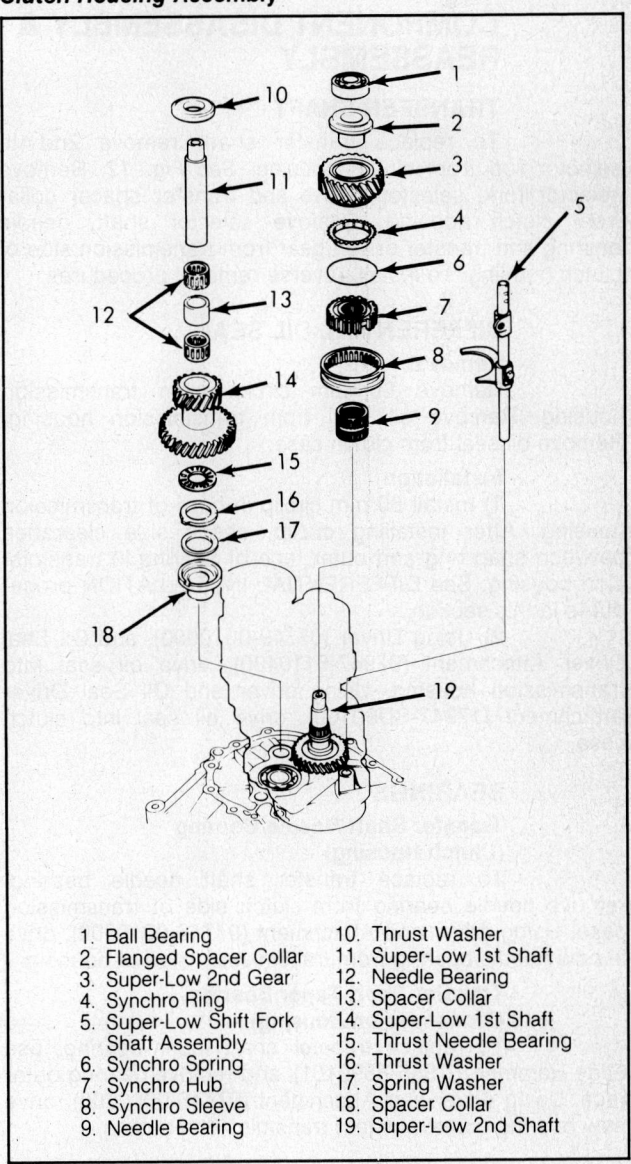

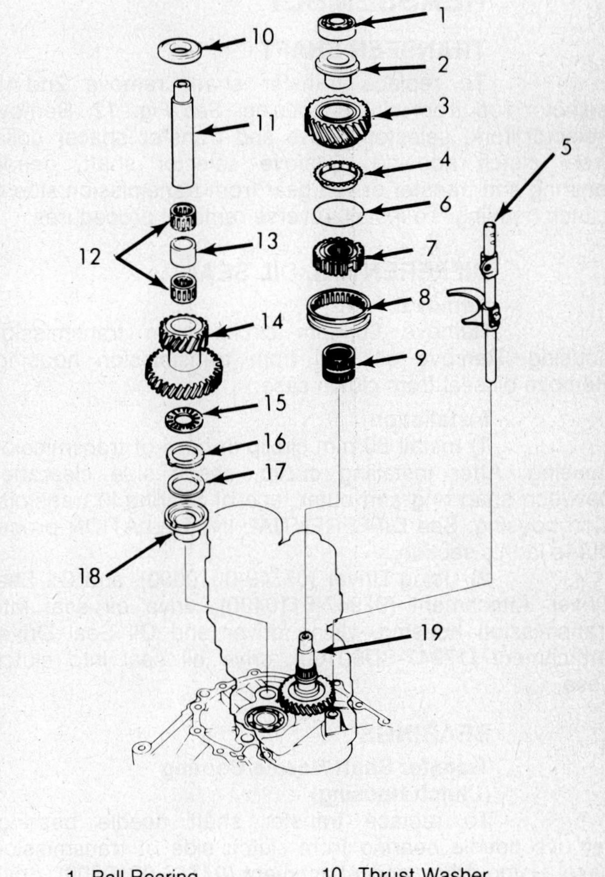

1. Ball Bearing
2. Flanged Spacer Collar
3. Super-Low 2nd Gear
4. Synchro Ring
5. Super-Low Shift Fork Shaft Assembly
6. Synchro Spring
7. Synchro Hub
8. Synchro Sleeve
9. Needle Bearing
10. Thrust Washer
11. Super-Low 1st Shaft
12. Needle Bearing
13. Spacer Collar
14. Super-Low 1st Shaft
15. Thrust Needle Bearing
16. Thrust Washer
17. Spring Washer
18. Spacer Collar
19. Super-Low 2nd Shaft

HONDA 4WD 5-SPEED TRANSAXLE WITH INTEGRAL TRANSFER CASE (Cont.)

bar, super-low shift lever, super-low shift piece "A" and 1st-2nd shift fork from reverse shift holder assembly.

6) Remove 6 mm bolt, lock plate, 5th-reverse shift fork shaft, 5th shift fork, 3rd-4th shift fork, and reverse shift fork from cluch housing. Remove bolts and dowel pins and remove reverse shift arm holder assembly from clutch housing.

7) Remove ball bearing, flanged spacer collar, super-low 2nd gear, synchro ring and super-low shift fork shaft assembly from clutch housing and super-low 2nd shaft assembly. *See Fig. 11*

8) Remove synchro spring, synchro hub and synchro sleeve. Remove needle bearing, thrust washer, super-low 1st shaft, needle bearing, spacer collar and super low 1st gear. Remove thrust needle bearing, thrust washer spring washer and spacer collar from clutch housing and super-low 2nd shaft assembly.

9) Remove mainshaft assembly, countershaft assembly and super-low 2nd shaft from clutch housing. Remove bearing from transfer shaft. Remove differential assembly from clutch housing.

COMPONENT DISASSEMBLY & REASSEMBLY

TRANSFER SHAFT

To replace transfer shaft, remove 2nd-4th selector rod from clutch housing. *See Fig. 12*. Remove selector fork, selector sleeve and transfer spacer collar from clutch housing. Remove selector shaft, needle bearing and transfer driven gear from transmission side of clutch housing. To install, reverse removal procedures.

DIFFERENTIAL OIL SEAL

Removal

Remove 80 mm circlip from transmission housing. Remove oil seal from transmission housing. Remove oil seal from clutch case.

Installation

1) Install 80 mm circlip in bore of transmission housing. After installing circlip, check side clearance between snap ring and outer race of bearing in transmission housing. See DIFFERENTIAL INSTALLATION procedures in this section.

2) Using Driver (07749-0010000), and Oil Seal Driver Attachment (07947-6110400), drive oil seal into transmission housing. Using driver and Oil Seal Driver Attachment (17947-SD90100), drive oil seal into clutch case.

BEARINGS

Transfer Shaft Needle Bearing (Clutch Housing)

To replace transfer shaft needle bearing, remove needle bearing from clutch side of transmission case. Using driver and Attachment (07746-0010600), drive in new needle bearing from transmission side of housing.

Transfer Shaft Taper Bearing (Transmission Housing)

To raplace transfer shaft taper bearing, use Slide Hammer (07936-8890101), and remove bearing outer race. Using driver and Attachment (07746-0010200), drive new bearing outer race into transmission housing.

Fig. 12: Replacing Transfer Shaft

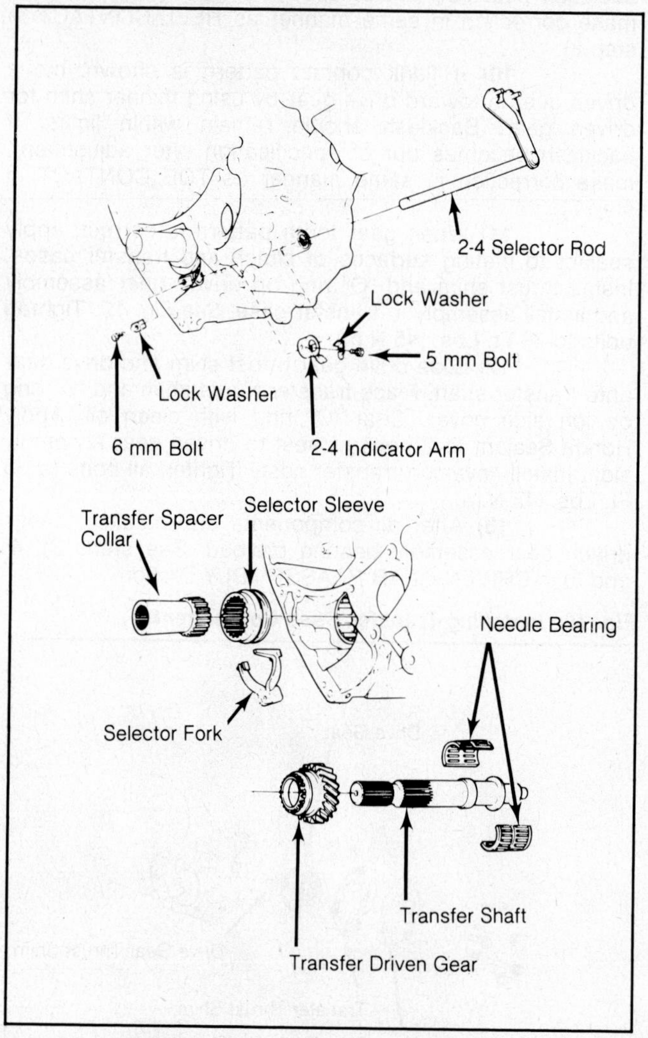

Mainshaft Bearing & Oil Seal (Clutch Housing)

To replace mainshaft bearing and oil seal, remove mainshaft bearing and oil seal from clutch side of housing. Using driver and Attachment (07746-0010300), drive in new oil seal from transmission side of housing. Using driver and Attachment (07746-0010500), drive in new bearing from transmission side.

Countershaft Bearing (Cluth Housing)

To replace countershaft bearing, use Puller Set (07936-6340001), and remove needle bearing. Position oil guide plate and new needle bearing in bore of clutch housing. Ensure oil hole on needle bearing is facing up. Using driver and Attachment (07746-0010400), drive in needle bearing.

SYNCHRO RING & GEAR INSPECTION

1) Inspect inside of synchro ring for wear. Inspect synchro ring teeth and matching gear teeth for wear. Inspect gear hub thrust surface and cone surface for wear and/or roughness. Inspect all gear teeth for uneven wear, scoring, galling and/or cracking.

2) Coat cone surface of gear with oil and place synchro ring on matching gear. Rotate ring, ensuring it

HONDA 4WD 5-SPEED TRANSAXLE WITH INTEGRAL TRANSFER CASE (Cont.)

does not slip. Measure clearance between ring and gear. Standard (new) clearance is .033-.043" (.85-1.10 mm). Service limit is .016" (.40 mm).

3) Seperate synchro ring and gear, and coat them with oil. Install synchro spring on synchro ring and set synchro assembly aside for later reassembly.

COUNTERSHAFT

NOTE: When checking clearances, countershaft and mainshaft bearings must be removed from transaxle housing.

CAUTION: Before disassembling countershaft and/or mainshaft, measure and record clearances listed in the appropriate COUNTERSHAFT CLEARANCES table and/or MAINSHAFT CLEARANCES & THICKNESSES table. If clearances are within specification and no parts are defective, disassembly of shafts is unnecessary.

Disassembly

If disassembly is required after checking clearances, remove locknut and disassemble countershaft. *See Fig. 13.*

Inspection

1) Measure clearances and inspect all parts for wear or damage, replacing if necessary. Place synchronizer hubs on countershaft and slide them back and forth to ensure they slide freely. Check countershaft oil passages for restrictions.

Fig. 13: Exploded View of Countershaft & Mainshaft Assemblies

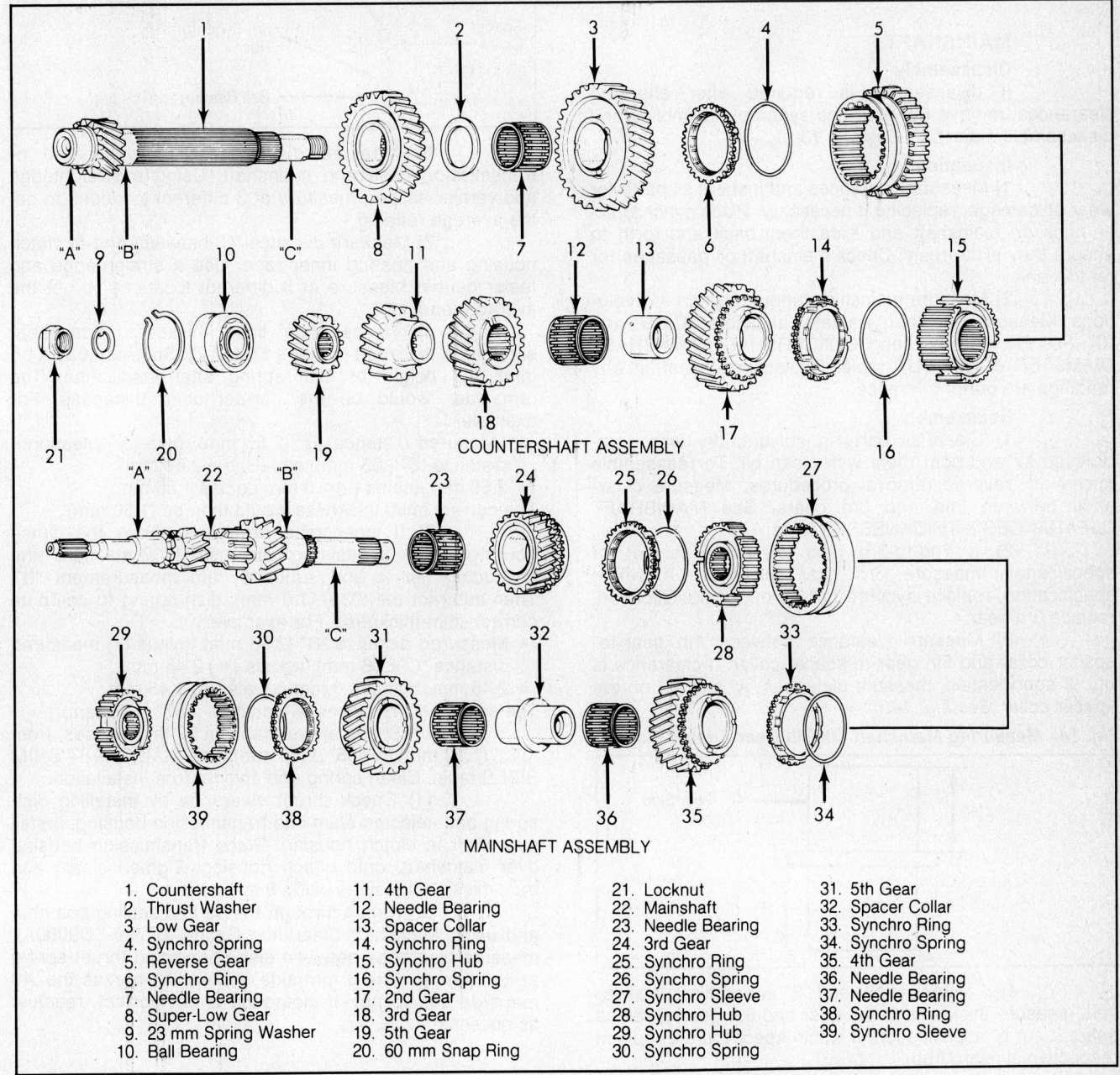

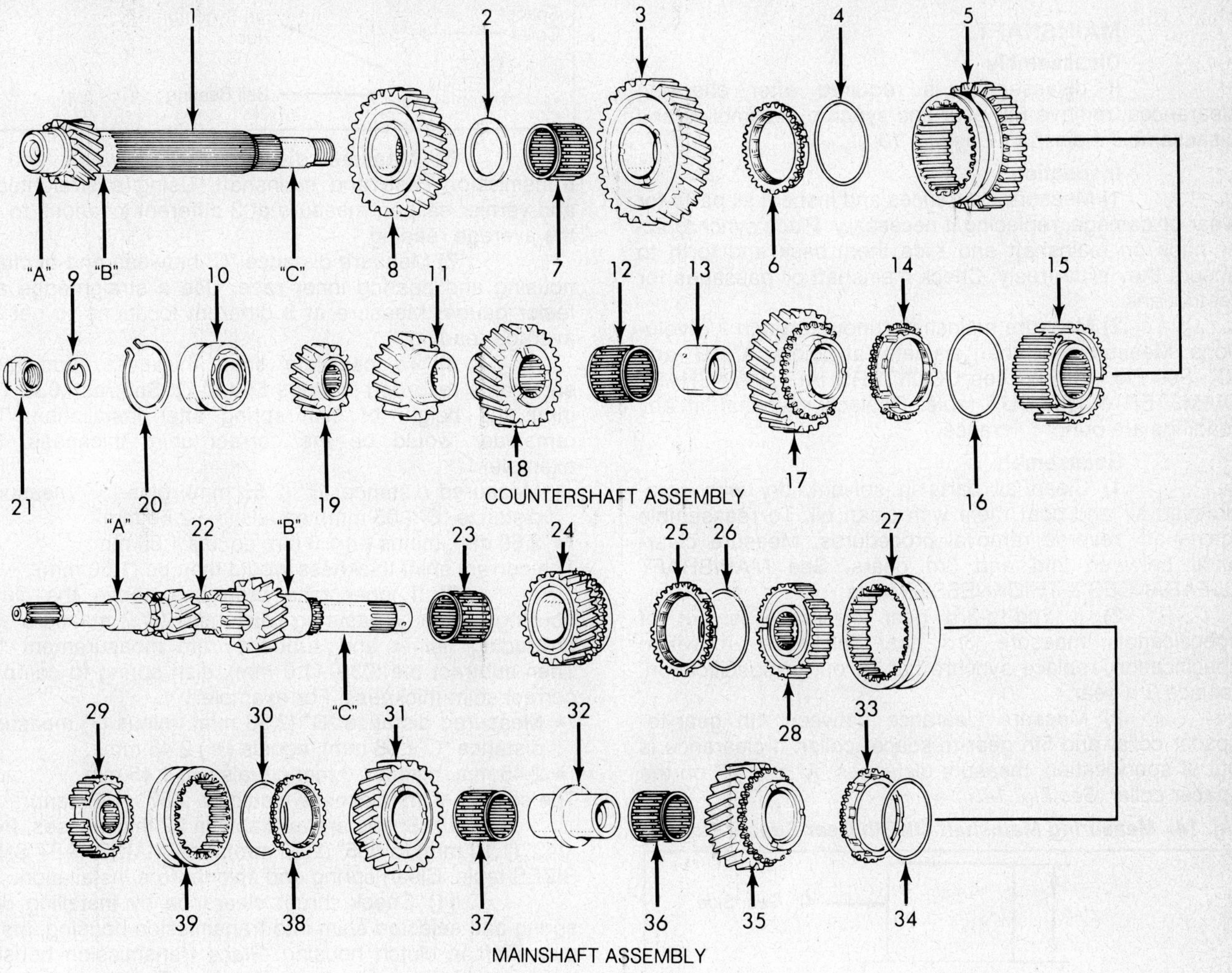

1. Countershaft
2. Thrust Washer
3. Low Gear
4. Synchro Spring
5. Reverse Gear
6. Synchro Ring
7. Needle Bearing
8. Super-Low Gear
9. 23 mm Spring Washer
10. Ball Bearing
11. 4th Gear
12. Needle Bearing
13. Spacer Collar
14. Synchro Ring
15. Synchro Hub
16. Synchro Spring
17. 2nd Gear
18. 3rd Gear
19. 5th Gear
20. 60 mm Snap Ring
21. Locknut
22. Mainshaft
23. Needle Bearing
24. 3rd Gear
25. Synchro Ring
26. Synchro Spring
27. Synchro Sleeve
28. Synchro Hub
29. Synchro Hub
30. Synchro Spring
31. 5th Gear
32. Spacer Collar
33. Synchro Ring
34. Synchro Spring
35. 4th Gear
36. Needle Bearing
37. Needle Bearing
38. Synchro Ring
39. Synchro Sleeve

Manual Transmissions

HONDA 4WD 5-SPEED TRANSAXLE WITH INTEGRAL TRANSFER CASE (Cont.)

2) Measure countershaft runout through 2 revolutions. Measure countershaft diameter at points "A", "B" and "C". *See Fig. 13*, and see COUNTERSHAFT/MAINSHAFT DIAMETER & RUNOUT table. Replace countershaft if any readings are out of tolerance.

Reassembly

1) Clean all parts in solvent, dry with compressed air and coat them with clean oil. To reassemble countershaft, reverse removal procedures. Tighten countershaft locknut 80 Ft. Lbs. (110 N.m). Place assembled countershaft in a soft-jawed vice.

2) Measure clearances between super-low gear and thrust washer, then between 2nd gear and 3rd gear. See COUNTERSHAFT CLEARANCES table. If either is out of specification, select appropriate spacer collar or thrust washer for correct clearance. See COUNTERSHAFT SPACER COLLARS & THRUST WASHERS table. Recheck clearances.

MAINSHAFT

Disassembly

If disassembly is required after checking clearances, remove 5th gear and synchro assemblies and disassemble mainshaft. *See Fig. 13*.

Inspection

1) Measure clearances and inspect all parts for wear or damage, replacing if necessary. Place synchronizer hubs on mainshaft and slide them back and forth to ensure they slide freely. Check mainshaft oil passages for restrictions.

2) Measure mainshaft runout through 2 revolutions. Measure mainshaft diameter at points "A", "B" and "C". *See Fig. 13*, and see COUNTERSHAFT/MAINSHAFT DIAMETER & RUNOUT table. Replace mainshaft if any readings are out of tolerance.

Reassembly

1) Clean all parts in solvent, dry with compressed air and coat them with clean oil. To reassemble mainshaft, reverse removal procedures. Measure clearance between 2nd and 3rd gears. See MAINSHAFT CLEARANCES & THICKNESSES table.

2) If 2nd-to-3rd gear clearance is out of specification, measure 3rd gear thickness. If within specification, replace synchro hub. If out of specification, replace 3rd gear.

3) Measure clearance between 4th gear-to-spacer collar and 5th gear-to-spacer collar. If clearance is out of specification, measure distances "A" and "B" on the spacer collar. *See Fig. 14*.

Fig. 14: Measuring Mainshaft 4th-5th Gear Spacer Collar

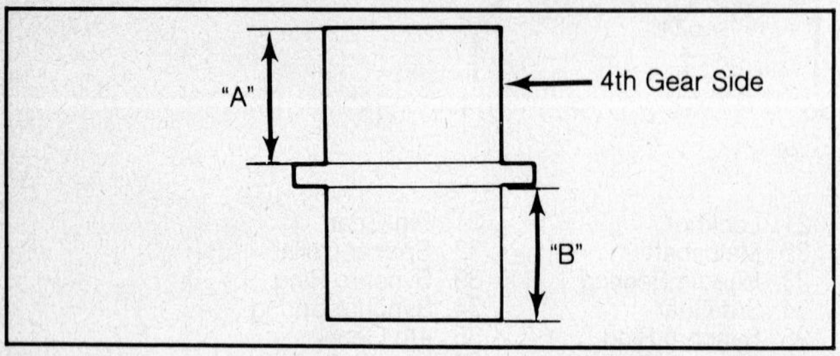

4) If distances "A" and "B" are within specification, measure thickness of 4th gear and 5th gear. Replace gears if out of specification. If within specification, replace respective synchro hub.

5) To select proper mainshaft shim, remove thrust shim, dish spring and oil guide plate from transmission housing. Install 3rd-4th synchro hub, spacer collar, 5th synchro hub and ball bearing on mainshaft. Install into transmission case. *See Fig. 15*.

Fig. 15: Measuring Mainshaft for Shim Selection

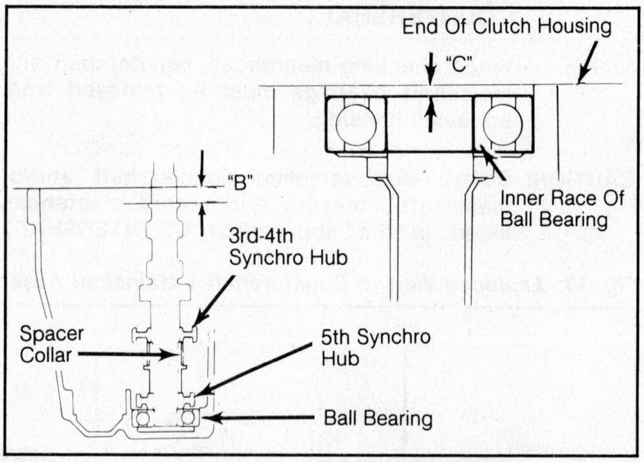

6) Measure distance "B" between end of transmission case and mainshaft. Using a straightedge and vernier caliper, measure at 3 different locations to get the average reading.

7) Measure distance "C" between end of clutch housing and bearing inner race. Use a straightedge and feeler gauge. Measure at 3 different locations to get the average reading.

8) To calculate shim thickness, add measurements recorded in steps **6)** and **7)**. Subtract .039" (1.0 mm); the height of dish spring after installation. The remainder would be the correct shim thickness. For example:

- Measured distance "B" (2.55 mm), plus (+) measured distance "C" (.05 mm), equals (=) 2.60 mm.
- 2.60 mm, minus (-) 1.0 mm equals 1.60 mm.

The correct shim thickness would then be (1.60 mm).

9) If inner race protrudes above the clutch housing when measuring distance "C", measure the protruding height and subtract from measurement "B". Then subtract the .039" (1.0 mm), dish spring to compute correct shim thickness. For example:

- Measured distance "B" (2.53 mm), minus (-) measured distance "C" (.08 mm), equals (=) 2.45 mm.
- 2.45 mm, minus 1.0 mm equals (=) 1.45 mm.

The correct shim thickness would be .057" (1.45 mm).

10) Shims are available in 22 thicknesses, from .043" (1.10 mm) to 085" (2.15 mm). See MAINSHAFT SHIM SIZES table. Clean spring and shim before installation.

11) Check thrust clearance by installing dish spring and selected shim into transmission housing. Install mainshaft in clutch housing. Place transmission housing over mainshaft, onto clutch housing. Tighten clutch and transmission housings using 8 mm bolts.

12) Reach through the 18 mm sealing bolt hole and using Mainshaft Clearance Gauge (07798-SD9000A), measure clearance between dish spring and thrust spring at its opening. The 3 mm side should fit whereas the .49 mm side should not. If clearance is not correct, readjust as necessary.

HONDA 4WD 5-SPEED TRANSAXLE WITH INTEGRAL TRANSFER CASE (Cont.)

COUNTERSHAFT CLEARANCES

Application	In. (mm)
Super-Low Gear-to-Thrust Washer	
Standard	.001-.003 (.03-.08)
Limit	.007 (.18)
2nd Gear-to-3rd Gear	
Standard	.0004-.0010 (.010-.030)
Limit	.007 (.18)

MAINSHAFT CLEARANCES & THICKNESSES

Application	In. (mm)
2nd Gear-to-3rd Gear Clearance	
Standard	.002-.008 (.06-.21)
Limit	.012 (.30)
3rd Gear Thickness	
Standard	1.276-1.278 (32.42-32.47)
Limit	1.272 (32.30)
4th Gear-to-5th Gear Spacer Collar Clearance	
Standard	.002-.008 (.06-.21)
Limit	.012 (.30)
Spacer Collar Distances "A" and "B"	
Standard	1.025-1.027 (26.03-26.08)
Limit	1.024 (26.01)
4th Gear Thickness	
Standard	1.217-1.220 (30.92-30.97)
Limit	1.213 (30.80)
5th Gear Thickness	
Standard	1.198-1.200 (30.42-30.47)
Limit	1.193 (30.30)

COUNTERSHAFT/MAINSHAFT DIAMETER & RUNOUT

Application	In. (mm)
Countershaft	
Diameter	
"A"	
Standard	1.1420-1.4230 (29.000-29.015)
Limit	1.139 (28.94)
"B"	
Standard	1.1990-1.2000 (30.464-30.480)
Limit	1.197 (30.41)
"C"	
Standard	.9830-.9840 (24.987-25.000)
Limit	.981 (24.93)
Runout	
Standard	.0008 (.020)
Limit	.0019 (.050)
Mainshaft	
Diameter	
"A"	
Standard	1.1018-1.1020 (27.987-28.000)
Limit	1.100 (27.93)
"B"	
Standard	1.3770-1.3780 (34.984-35.000)
Limit	1.375 (34.93)
"C"	
Standard	.9830-.9840 (24.987-25.000)
Limit	.981 (24.93)
Runout	
Standard	.0008 (.020)
Limit	.0019 (.050)

COUNTERSHAFT SPACER COLLARS & THRUST WASHERS

Application	In. (mm)
Spacer Collars	
"A"	1.143-1.144 (29.03-29.05)
"B"	1.141-1.142 (28.98-29.00)
Thrust Washers	
"A"	.078 (1.98)
"B"	.079 (2.00)
"C"	.080 (2.02)
"D"	.081 (2.04)

MAINSHAFT SHIM SIZES

Application	In. (mm)
23931-PH8-0000	.043 (1.10)
23932-PH8-0000	.045 (1.15)
23933-PH8-0000	.047 (1.20)
23934-PH8-0000	.049 (1.25)
23935-PH8-0000	.051 (1.30)
23936-PH8-0000	.053 (1.35)
23937-PH8-0000	.055 (1.40)
23938-PH8-0000	.057 (1.45)
23939-PH8-0000	.059 (1.50)
23940-PH8-0000	.061 (1.55)
23941-PH8-0000	.063 (1.60)
23942-PH8-0000	.065 (1.65)
23943-PH8-0000	.067 (1.70)
23944-PH8-0000	.069 (1.75)
23945-PH8-0000	.071 (1.80)
23946-PH8-0000	.073 (1.85)
23947-PH8-0000	.075 (1.90)
23948-PH8-0000	.077 (1.95)
23949-PH8-0000	.079 (2.00)
23950-PH8-0000	.081 (2.05)
23951-PH8-0000	.083 (2.10)
23952-PH8-0000	.085 (2.15)

DIFFERENTIAL

Backlash Inspection

Place differential on workstand and install both axles. Check backlash of both pinion gears. Standard (new) clearance is .002-.006" (.05-.15 mm). If out of specification, install new thrust washer. See DIFFERENTIAL THRUST WASHER SIZES table.

Bearing Replacement

NOTE: Check bearings for wear and rough rotation. If bearings are OK, removal is not necessary.

Remove bearings using standard bearing puller. Install new bearings using Bearing Driver "C" (07746-0030100), and Attachment (07746-0030400).

Differential Disassembly, Inspection & Reassembly

CAUTION: Ring gear bolts have left hand threads.

1) To disassemble, remove final drive and transfer gears and inspect teeth for excessive wear. *See Fig. 16.* Drive out spring pin with pin punch.

2) Remove pinion shaft, pinion gears and thrust washers. Wash all parts in solvent and dry with compressed air. Inspect all parts for damage, replacing any that are defective.

HONDA 4WD 5-SPEED TRANSAXLE WITH INTEGRAL TRANSFER CASE (Cont.)

Fig. 16: Exploded View of Differential Assembly

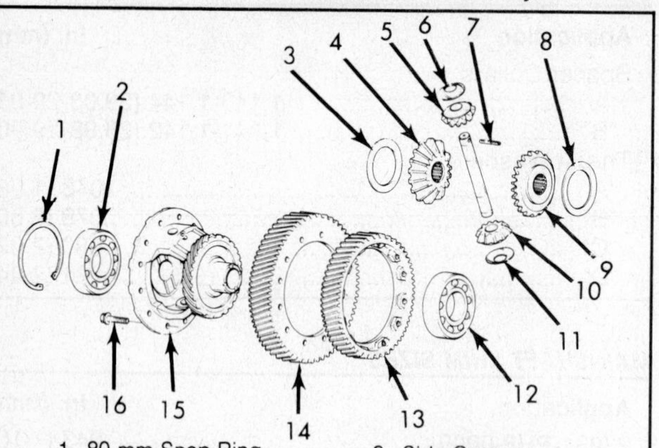

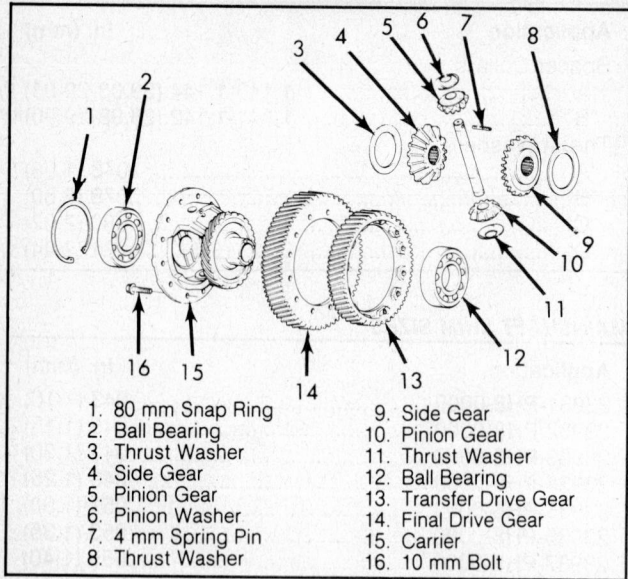

1. 80 mm Snap Ring
2. Ball Bearing
3. Thrust Washer
4. Side Gear
5. Pinion Gear
6. Pinion Washer
7. 4 mm Spring Pin
8. Thrust Washer
9. Side Gear
10. Pinion Gear
11. Thrust Washer
12. Ball Bearing
13. Transfer Drive Gear
14. Final Drive Gear
15. Carrier
16. 10 mm Bolt

3) To reassemble, install side gears in differential carrier. Coat gears on all sides with molylube. Set pinion gears in place exactly opposite each other, mesh with side gears.

4) Install a thrust washer behind each pinion gear. Washers must be of equal thickness. See DIFFERENTIAL PINION GEAR THRUST WASHER SIZES table.

DIFFERENTIAL PINION GEAR THRUST WASHER SIZES

Part Number	In (mm)
41351-689-000	.028 (.70)
41355-PC8-000	.030 (.75)
41352-689-000	.031 (.80)
41356-PC8-000	.033 (.85)
41353-689-000	.035 (.90)
41357-PC8-000	.037 (.95)
41354-689-000	.039 (1.00)

5) Rotate gears until shaft holes in pinion gears line up with shaft holes in carrier. Insert pinion shaft and align spring pin holes in one end with matching hole in carrier.

6) Drive in new spring pin with pin punch. Recheck backlash of both pinion gears. See BACKLASH INSPECTION procedures in this section. If still out of specification, replace both pinion gears and recheck backlash.

7) If still out of specification, replace side gears and recheck backlash. If still out of specification, replace carrier assembly. Install final drive and transfer drive gears with camfer on inside diameter facing carrier. Tighten 10 mm bolts to 76 Ft. Lbs. (103 N.m).

8) Install differential assembly in clutch housing, and install 80 mm snap ring in transmission housing. See TRANSAXLE REASSEMBLY section of this article. If clutch housing, transmission housing, differential carrier or differential bearings were replaced, side clearance must be measured.

9) Seat snap ring by tapping on clutch housing side of differential assembly with Driver (07749-0010000), and Attachment (07947-6340500). Turn transmission over and seat differential assembly by tapping on transmission housing side of differential assembly with driver and attachment.

10) Measure clearance between snap ring and outer bearing race in transmission housing. Side clearance is .006 (.15 mm), maximum. If out of specification, select snap ring from 80 MM SNAP RING THICKNESSES table.

11) After selecting new snap ring, repeat 2nd part of step **9)** and step **10)**. Apply oil to new differential oil seals and install in clutch and transmission housings using Driver (07749-0010000), and Attachments (07947-6110400, 07947-SD90100).

80 MM SNAP RING THICKNESSES

Part Number	In. (mm)
90414-689-000	.098 (2.50)
90415-689-000	.102 (2.60)
90416-689-000	.106 (2.70)
90417-689-000	.110 (2.80)
90418-689-000	.114 (2.90)

TRANSAXLE REASSEMBLY

NOTE: **Ensure correct mainshaft thrust shim is used for proper mainshaft thrust clearance. See MAINSHAFT REASSEMBLY section of this article.**

1) Install oil guide plate, dish spring and mainshaft thrust shim in transmission housing. Install oil gutter and collect plates in transmission housing. Install transfer shaft assembly and 2-4 selector rod. See TRANSFER SHAFT section of this article.

2) Install differential assembly in clutch housing. See DIFFERENTIAL DISASSEMBLY, INSPECTION &

Fig. 17 Installing Super-Low 2nd Shaft Components

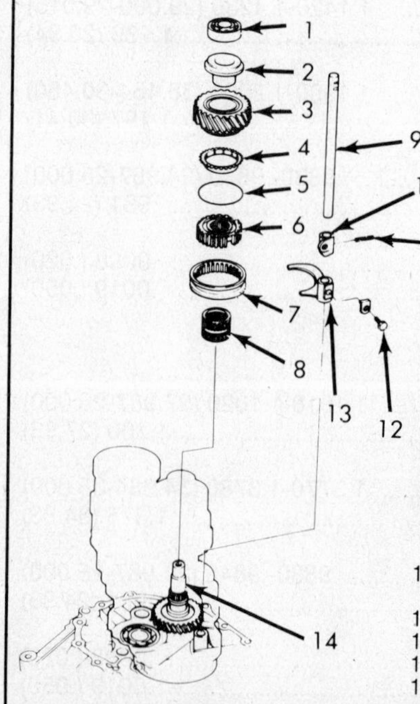

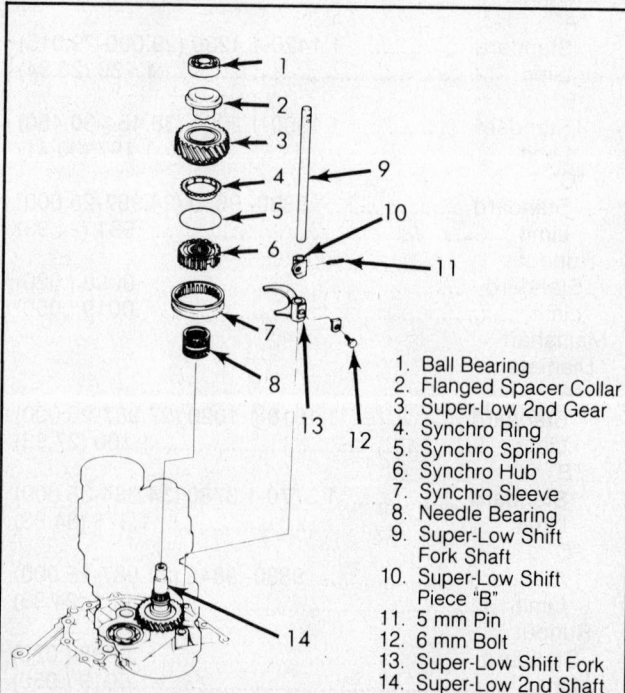

1. Ball Bearing
2. Flanged Spacer Collar
3. Super-Low 2nd Gear
4. Synchro Ring
5. Synchro Spring
6. Synchro Hub
7. Synchro Sleeve
8. Needle Bearing
9. Super-Low Shift Fork Shaft
10. Super-Low Shift Piece "B"
11. 5 mm Pin
12. 6 mm Bolt
13. Super-Low Shift Fork
14. Super-Low 2nd Shaft

HONDA 4WD 5-SPEED TRANSAXLE WITH INTEGRAL TRANSFER CASE (Cont.)

REASSEMBLY section of this article. Place bearing on transfer shaft. Install super-low 2nd shaft, countershaft and mainshaft assemblies in clutch housing.

3) Install super-low piece "B" and shift fork on super-low shift fork shaft. *See Fig. 17*. Install needle bearing, synchro sleeve, hub, spring, super-low fork shaft assembly, ring, super-low 2nd gear, flanged spacer collar and ball bearing onto super-low 2nd shaft.

4) Install super-low 1st shaft, spacer collar, lock washer, thrust washer, thrust needle bearing, super-low 1st gear, needle bearing, spacer collar, needle bearing and thrust washer in clutch housing.

5) Ensure lug on end of super-low 1st shaft is aligned with groove in clutch case. Install 62 mm lock washer with dished side facing up. *See Fig. 11*.

6) Install reverse shift holder assembly in clutch housing. Install reverse shift fork, 3rd-4th shift fork and 5th shift fork on mainshaft. Slide 5th-reverse shift fork shaft down through each shift fork. *See Fig. 18*. Ensure detent hole in shift shaft is facing countershaft.

Fig. 18 Installing Mainshaft Components & 5th-Reverse Shift Fork Shaft

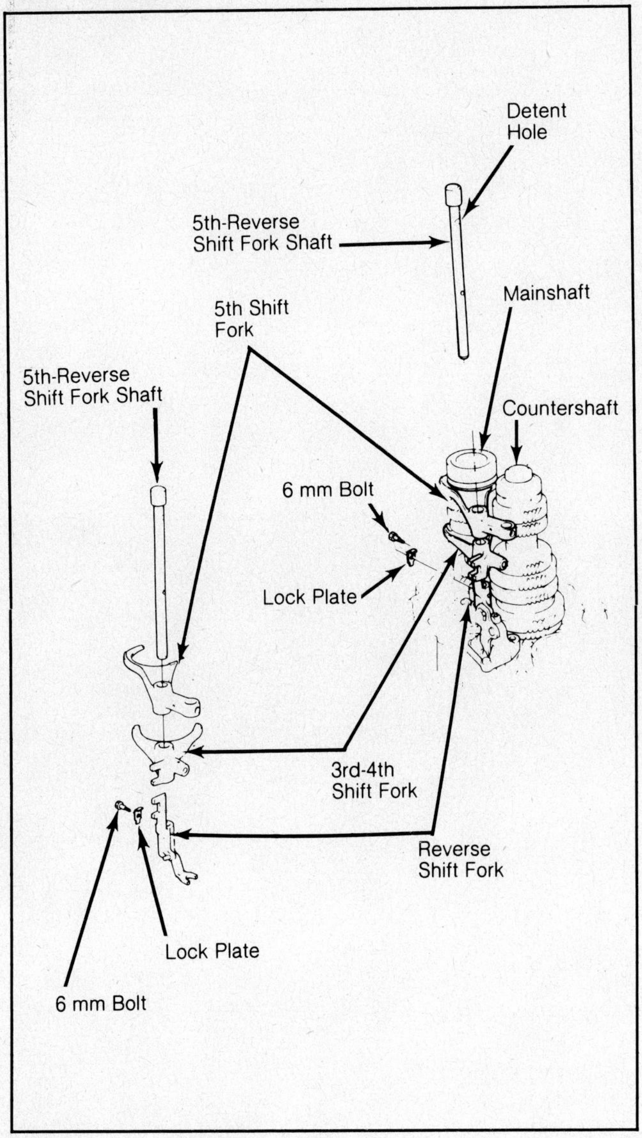

7) Install 1st-2nd shift fork, super-low shift piece "A" and super-low shift lever on countershaft. Slide 1st-2nd shift fork shaft through each shift piece and shift lever. *See Fig. 19*. Ensure detent hole in shift shaft is facing mainshaft.

8) Install super-low shift piece bar in reverse shift holder assembly. Install reverse idler gear and idler gear shaft in clutch case. Install idler shaft with threads facing outward.

NOTE: **Transmission uses no gaskets between major housings. Use Honda Sealant (08740-99986). Assemble housings within 20 minutes of applying sealant. Allow to cure for at least 30 minutes before filling with oil.**

9) Apply sealant to transmission mating surface of clutch housing. Install dowel pins and place transmission housing over clutch housing being careful to line up shafts. Tighten Bolts in sequence to 19 Ft. Lbs. (26 N.m). *See Fig. 20*.

10) Install reverse idler shaft bolt and washer, super-low detent ball screw, washer, spring and detent ball. Using Honda Sealant, install super-low shift lever bolt. To install differential oil seal, see DIFFERENTIAL OIL SEAL section of this article.

Fig. 19 Installing Countershaft Components & 1st-2nd Shift Fork Shaft

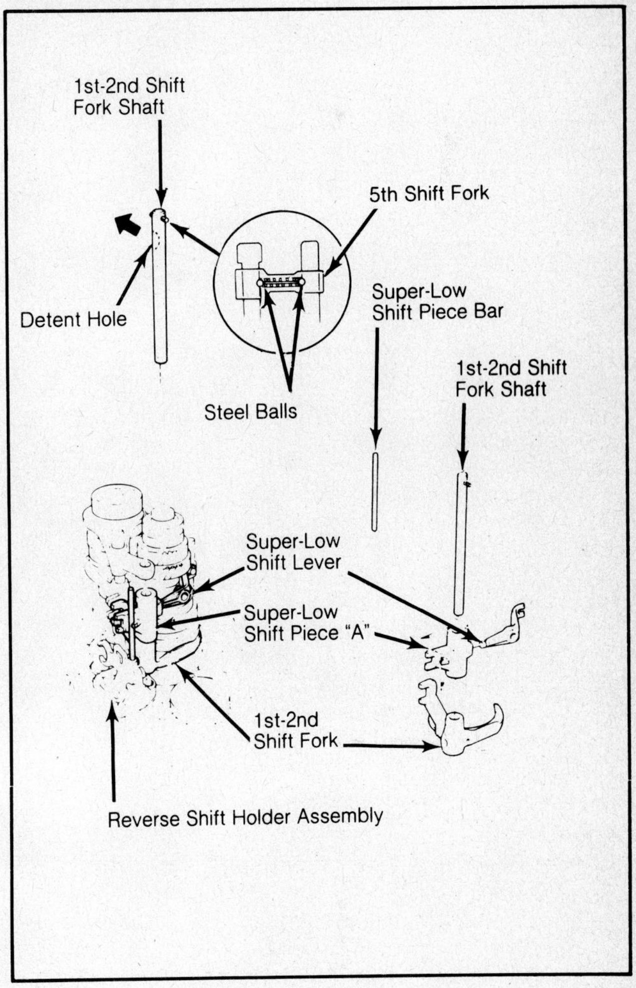

HONDA 4WD 5-SPEED TRANSAXLE WITH INTEGRAL TRANSFER CASE (Cont.)

Fig. 20 Transmission-to-Clutch Housing Bolt Tightening Sequence

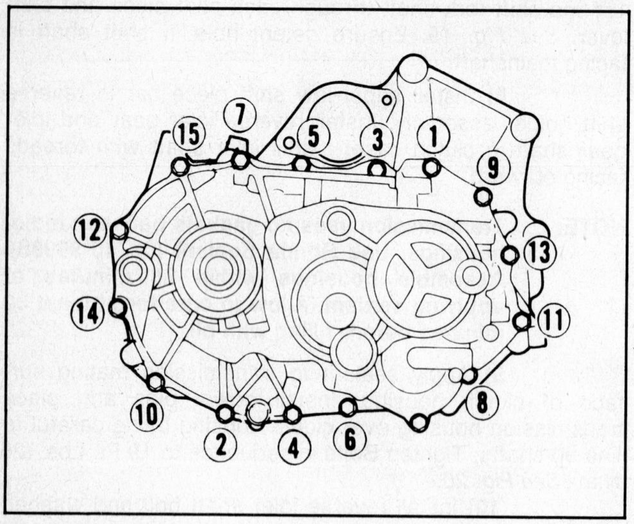

TIGHTENING SPECIFICATIONS

Application	Ft. Lbs. (N.m)
Back-Up Light Switch	18 (25)
Countershaft Locknut	80 (110)
Drain Bolt	22 (30)
Driven Gear Assembly Attaching Bolts	45 (33)
Left Side Cover Attaching Bolts	33 (45)
Oil Collect Plate Bolt	9 (12)
Oil Filler Bolt	33 (45)
Reverse Idle Shaft Bolt	40 (55)
Reverse Shift Holder Bolts	9 (12)
Shift Arm Cover Bolts	9 (12)
Shift Arm Cover Detent Screws	16 (22)
Shift Arm Cover Interlock Bolt	30 (40)
Super-Low Shift Lever Bolt	30 (40)
Super-Low Shift Screw	16 (22)
Shift/Select Cables	22 (30)
Transfer Case Attaching Bolts	33 (45)
Transmission-to-Engine Mount Bolts	33 (45)
6 mm Shift Arm Cover Stopper Bolt	9 (12)
18 mm Shift Arm Shaft Plug	30 (40)

ISUZU 4-SPEED

Isuzu I-Mark, P'UP

DESCRIPTION

Transmission is a floor shifted, fully synchronized 4-speed unit with block ring type synchronizers and a sliding mesh type reverse. The unit consists of a case with integral clutch housing, center support, rear extension, and gears. A shifter cover, located on top of rear extension housing, contains the transmission control mechanism. The case, center support and rear extension case are aluminum alloy to reduce weight.

LUBRICATION & ADJUSTMENT

See appropriate MANUAL TRANSMISSION SERVICING article in IMPORT GENERAL SERVICING section.

TROUBLE SHOOTING

HARD SHIFTING

Improperly adjusted clutch. Weakened insert spring. Face of blocker ring, in contact with insert, worn. Cones on blocker ring and gear worn or not in proper contact.

SLIPS OUT OF GEAR

Bearings worn or defective. Excessive play between gears and collars. Play in clutch hub and sliding sleeve. Shift arm worn. Lock ball spring weak or broken.

TRANSMISSION NOISY

Low or incorrect lubricant. Gears or bearings worn or damaged. Worn collars. Worn clutch hub or mainshaft splines. Incorrectly meshed gears.

REMOVAL & INSTALLATION

See appropriate MANUAL TRANSMISSION REMOVAL article in IMPORT GENERAL SERVICING section.

Fig. 1: Removing Throw-Out Bearing & Clutch Fork

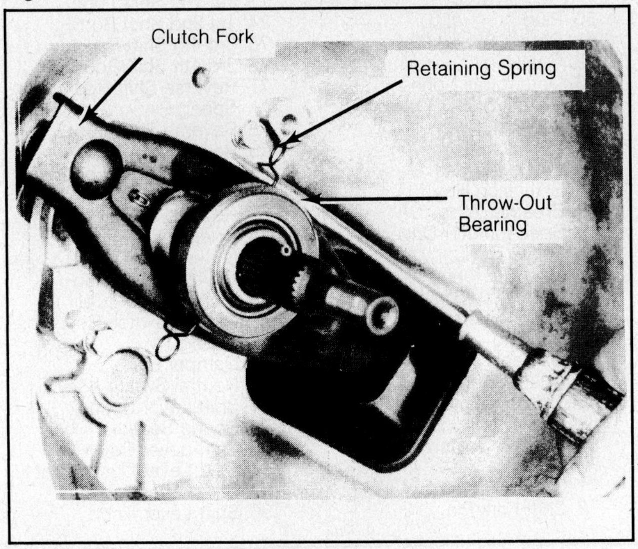

TRANSMISSION DISASSEMBLY

1) Disconnect retaining springs from throw-out bearing and remove bearing, dust cover and clutch fork. Remove 4 front bearing retainer bolts and remove retainer, gasket and spring washer.

2) Remove speedometer gear attaching bolt and take out speedometer driven gear assembly. Unscrew shifter cover bolts and remove cover and gasket.

3) Remove back-up light switch and CRS switch (if equipped). Remove rear extension attaching bolts, then remove extension and gasket.

4) Remove thrust washers and reverse idler gear from reverse idler gear shaft, then remove snap rings, speedometer drive gear and key from mainshaft.

5) Drive out roll pin from reverse shifter fork and remove shifter fork and reverse gear. Remove snap ring from outer edge of input shaft bearing. Slide off center support assembly from transmission case. Drive out roll pins from 3rd-4th and 1st-2nd shift forks.

Fig. 2: Removing Reverse Gear

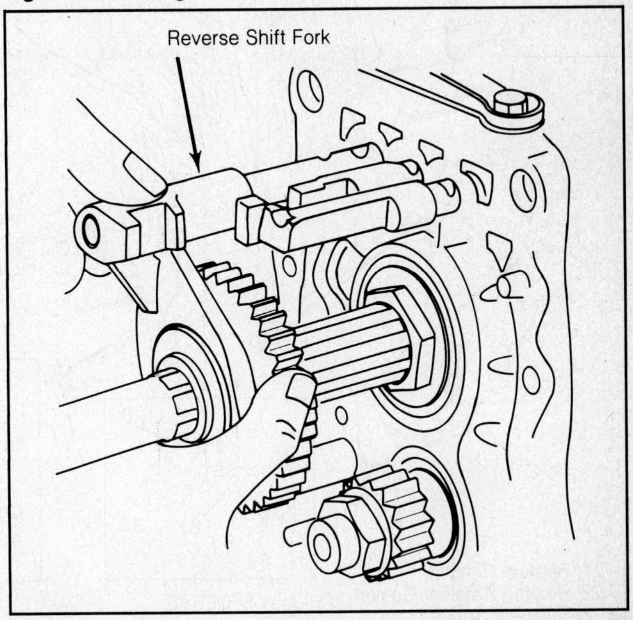

NOTE: **Be careful not to damage shift forks when removing roll pins.**

6) Remove detent spring plate, springs and balls from center support. Slide out 1st-2nd and 3rd-4th shift rods and remove shift forks. Remove reverse shift rod through front of case as it is fitted with detent interlock pins located between shifter rods in center support.

7) Move both synchros rearward to lock mainshaft. It may be necessary to tap synchros with hammer handle to engage them both. Straighten tab on lock washer and remove lock nut and washer from mainshaft.

8) Remove locking nut, washer, countergear reverse gear and collar from rear of countergear. Remove countergear bearing snap ring by expanding snap ring and tapping on front face of center support. Remove mainshaft rear bearing snap ring and remove center support.

ISUZU 4-SPEED (Cont.)

Fig. 3: Exploded View of Isuzu 4-Speed Transmission Assembly

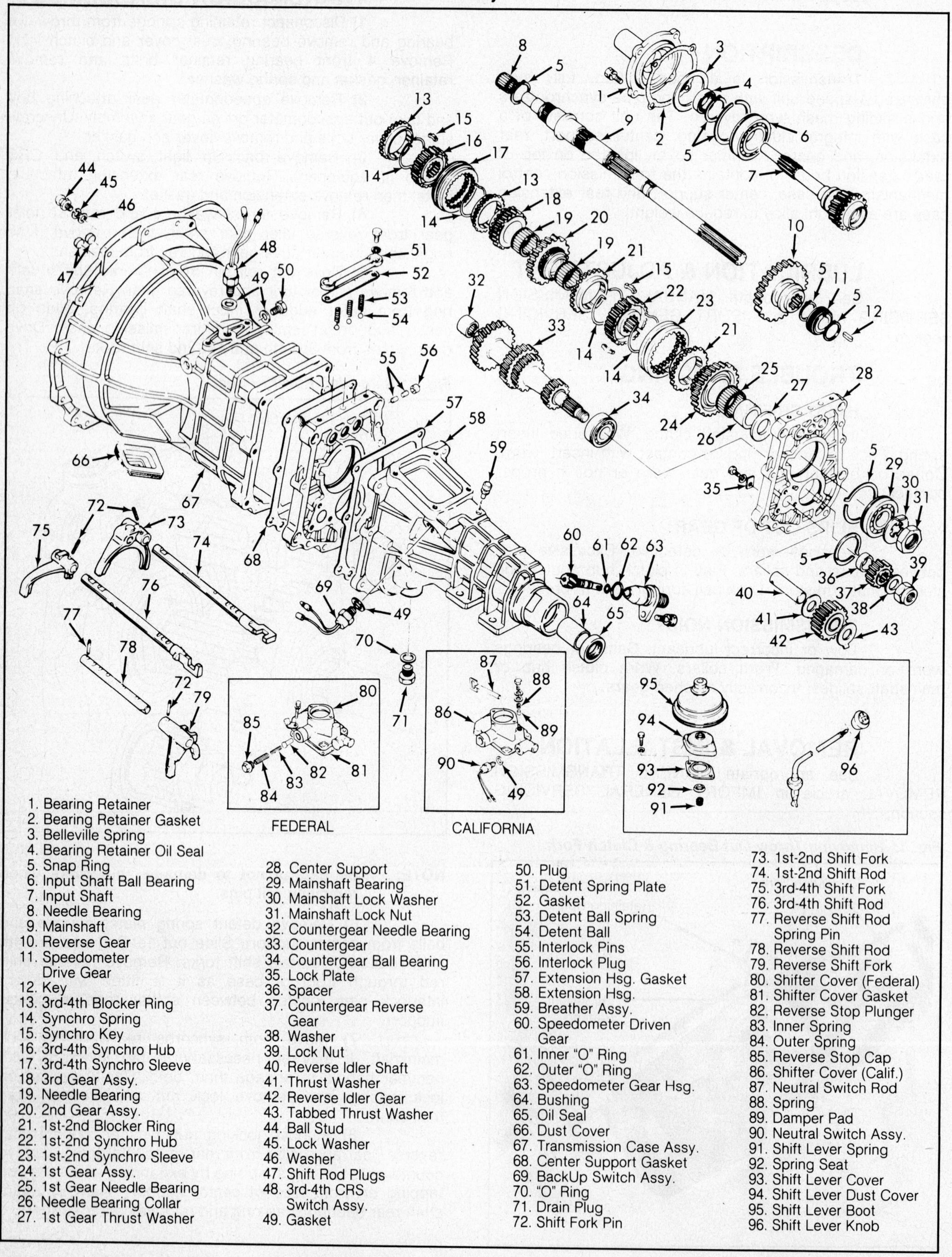

1. Bearing Retainer
2. Bearing Retainer Gasket
3. Belleville Spring
4. Bearing Retainer Oil Seal
5. Snap Ring
6. Input Shaft Ball Bearing
7. Input Shaft
8. Needle Bearing
9. Mainshaft
10. Reverse Gear
11. Speedometer Drive Gear
12. Key
13. 3rd-4th Blocker Ring
14. Synchro Spring
15. Synchro Key
16. 3rd-4th Synchro Hub
17. 3rd-4th Synchro Sleeve
18. 3rd Gear Assy.
19. Needle Bearing
20. 2nd Gear Assy.
21. 1st-2nd Blocker Ring
22. 1st-2nd Synchro Hub
23. 1st-2nd Synchro Sleeve
24. 1st Gear Assy.
25. 1st Gear Needle Bearing
26. Needle Bearing Collar
27. 1st Gear Thrust Washer
28. Center Support
29. Mainshaft Bearing
30. Mainshaft Lock Washer
31. Mainshaft Lock Nut
32. Countergear Needle Bearing
33. Countergear
34. Countergear Ball Bearing
35. Lock Plate
36. Spacer
37. Countergear Reverse Gear
38. Washer
39. Lock Nut
40. Reverse Idler Shaft
41. Thrust Washer
42. Reverse Idler Gear
43. Tabbed Thrust Washer
44. Ball Stud
45. Lock Washer
46. Washer
47. Shift Rod Plugs
48. 3rd-4th CRS Switch Assy.
49. Gasket
50. Plug
51. Detent Spring Plate
52. Gasket
53. Detent Ball Spring
54. Detent Ball
55. Interlock Pins
56. Interlock Plug
57. Extension Hsg. Gasket
58. Extension Hsg.
59. Breather Assy.
60. Speedometer Driven Gear
61. Inner "O" Ring
62. Outer "O" Ring
63. Speedometer Gear Hsg.
64. Bushing
65. Oil Seal
66. Dust Cover
67. Transmission Case Assy.
68. Center Support Gasket
69. BackUp Switch Assy.
70. "O" Ring
71. Drain Plug
72. Shift Fork Pin
73. 1st-2nd Shift Fork
74. 1st-2nd Shift Rod
75. 3rd-4th Shift Fork
76. 3rd-4th Shift Rod
77. Reverse Shift Rod Spring Pin
78. Reverse Shift Rod
79. Reverse Shift Fork
80. Shifter Cover (Federal)
81. Shifter Cover Gasket
82. Reverse Stop Plunger
83. Inner Spring
84. Outer Spring
85. Reverse Stop Cap
86. Shifter Cover (Calif.)
87. Neutral Switch Rod
88. Spring
89. Damper Pad
90. Neutral Switch Assy.
91. Shift Lever Spring
92. Spring Seat
93. Shift Lever Cover
94. Shift Lever Dust Cover
95. Shift Lever Boot
96. Shift Lever Knob

ISUZU 4-SPEED (Cont.)

Fig. 4: Removing Center Support from Transmission Case

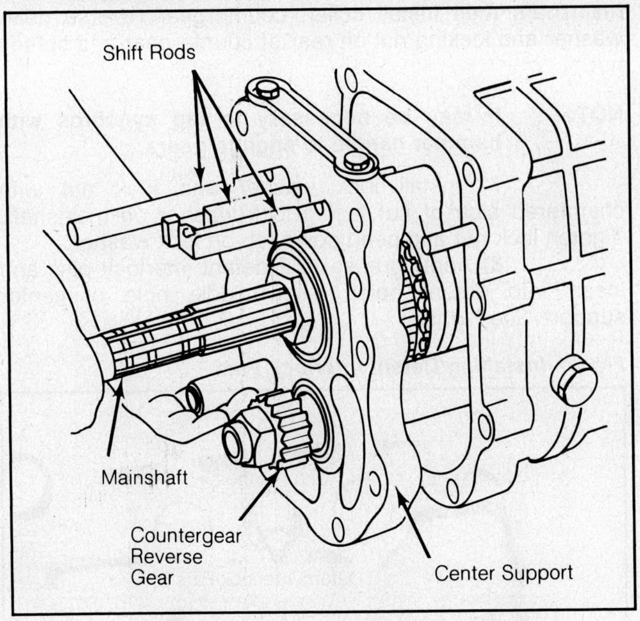

COMPONENT DISASSEMBLY & REASSEMBLY

MAINSHAFT

Disassembly

1) Separate input shaft, needle bearing and blocker ring from mainshaft. Using adapter plate tool (J-22912) and an arbor press, remove rear bearing from mainshaft. Remove thrust washer, 1st gear, needle bearing, collar and blocker ring.

2) Remove 1st-2nd synchro assembly. Remove 2nd gear, blocker ring and needle bearing. Remove snap ring, 3rd-4th synchro assembly and blocker ring. Remove 3rd gear and needle bearings. Remove snap ring from input shaft and press bearing off shaft. Using adapter plate tool (J-22912) and an arbor press, remove countergear bearing from countergear.

Fig. 5: Mainshaft Components

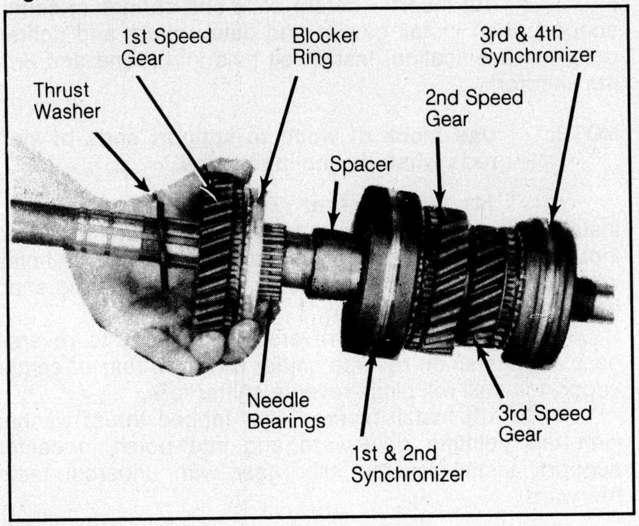

Inspection

1) Check mainshaft for wear, scoring or excessive runout. Maximum mainshaft runout is .002" (.05 mm). Check all gear teeth and splines for wear and/or damage. Check all bearings for smooth operation.

2) Check synchronizer assemblies for wear by holding blocker ring against cone section of gear and measuring clearance. If clearance exceeds .032" (.8 mm), replace blocker ring. Measure inside diameter of 1st, 2nd and 3rd gears. Measurements should be 1.773-1.776" (45.0-45.1 mm) for 1st gear; 1.615-1.619" (41.0-41.1 mm) for 2nd and 3rd gear.

3) Measure inside diameter of 1st gear and outside diameter of collar. If clearance exceeds .0197" (.5 mm), replace gear. Measure outside diameter of reverse idler gear shaft and inside diameter of gear bushing. Shaft diameter should be .866" (22 mm). If clearance between shaft and bushing exceeds .006" (.15 mm), replace bushing. Measure clearance between synchronizer hub splines and mainshaft splines in normal direction of rotation.

4) If clearance exceeds .008" (.2 mm), replace synchro-clutch hub. Check grooves in shift arms and blocks for wear and/or distortion. If thickness of shift arm pad is less than .256" (6.5 mm) for 3rd-4th shift arm and .276" (7.0 mm) for all other shift arms, replace as required.

Fig. 6: Measuring Blocker Ring Clearance

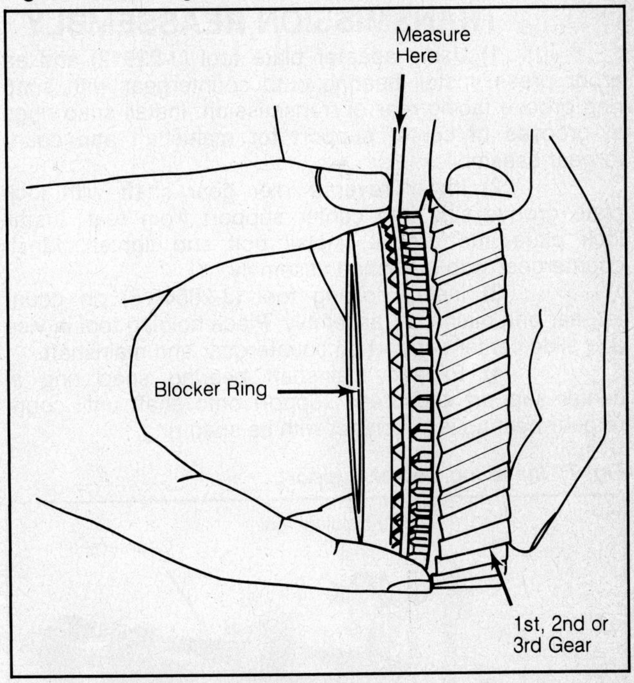

5) Check shift rod detent springs for weakening and/or damage. Measure spring free length. If less than 1.083" (27.5 mm) for all forward gears, or 1.051" (26.7 mm) for reverse gear, replace springs as required.

Reassembly

1) Hold front of mainshaft upward. Install 3rd gear with tapered side facing front of mainshaft and install needle bearing. Install blocker ring with teeth upward. Install synchro hub with heavy boss toward face of sleeve with small chamfer on outer edge.

2) Place keys into key grooves and position synchro springs into hole inside face of hub. Make sure

ISUZU 4-SPEED (Cont.)

hub and sleeve slide smoothly. Install 3rd-4th synchro assembly on mainshaft with face of sleeve with small chamfer on outer edge facing rearward. Install snap ring.

3) Hold rear of mainshaft upward. Install 2nd gear and needle bearing with taper surface of gear facing rearward on mainshaft. Install blocker ring with teeth downward. Install 1st-2nd synchro assembly with small chamfer on sleeve facing front of mainshaft. Install synchro hub with chamfer on inner edge toward face of sleeve with large chamfer on outer edge.

4) Place keys into key grooves and position synchro springs into hole in either side face of hub. Make sure hub and sleeve slide smoothly. Install blocker ring with teeth rearward. Install collar, needle bearing and 1st gear with tapered side of gear facing front of mainshaft.

5) Install 1st gear thrust washer with grooved side facing 1st gear on mainshaft. Place rear bearing on mainshaft with snap ring groove facing front of mainshaft. Press bearing onto shaft using adapter plate tool (J-22912) and an arbor press. Place input shaft bearing on input shaft with snap ring groove facing front of input shaft.

6) Press bearing onto shaft using adapter plate tool (J-22912) and an arbor press. Install snap ring on input shaft bearing and install needle bearing, blocker ring and input shaft assembly to front of mainshaft.

TRANSMISSION REASSEMBLY

1) Using adapter plate tool (J-22912) and an arbor press, install bearing onto countergear with snap ring groove facing rear of transmission. Install snap rings in grooves of center support for mainshaft and countergear assemblies.

2) Install reverse idler gear shaft with lock plate groove side into center support from rear. Install lock plate into groove, install bolt and tighten. Mesh countergear with mainshaft assembly.

3) Install holding tool (J-26545-5) on countergear and mainshaft assembly. Place holding tool in vise and slide center support on countergear and mainshaft.

4) Expand mainshaft bearing snap ring in center support and press support onto shaft until countergear bearing is in contact with its snap ring.

Fig. 7: Installing Center Support

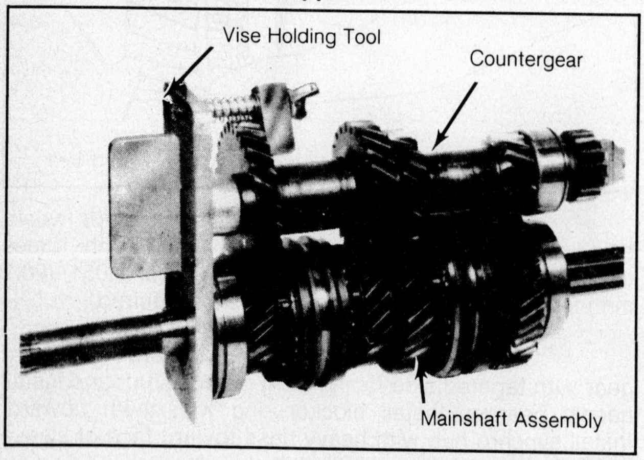

5) Expand countergear bearing snap ring and press center support further until the mainshaft and countergear snap rings snap into their grooves.

6) Remove holding tool from countergear and mainshaft assembly. Slide both synchros rearward to lock mainshaft, then install collar, countergear reverse gear, washer and locking nut on rear of countergear and tighten nut.

NOTE: **It may be necessary to tap synchros with hammer handle to engage gears.**

7) Install lock washer and lock nut with chamfered side of nut facing lock washer on mainshaft. Tighten lock nut and bend down tab on lock washer.

8) Apply grease to 2 detent interlock pins and insert into detent holes from middle hole of center support. *See Fig. 8.*

Fig. 8: Installing Detent Interlock Pins

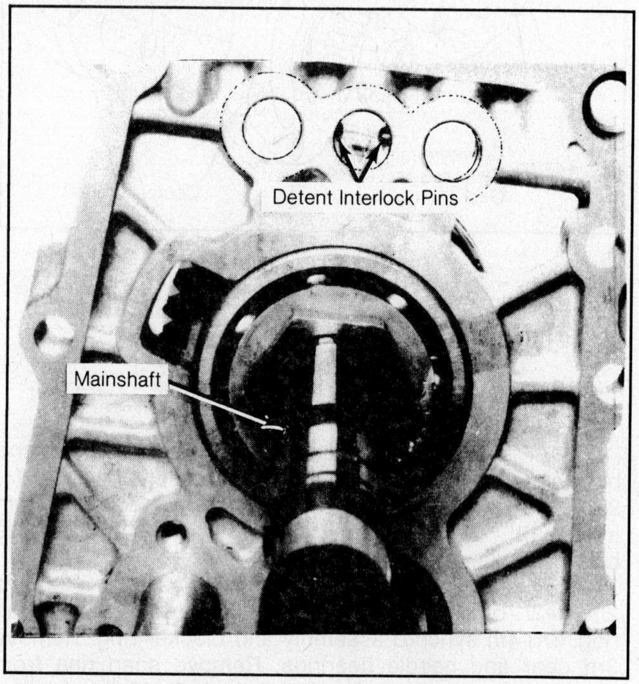

9) Place shift forks into position on synchronizer grooves then install 1st-2nd and 3rd-4th shifter rods through holes in center support and shift forks from front side of center support.

10) Insert 3 detent balls and springs in center support, then install gasket and detent plate and tighten bolts to specification. Install roll pins in 1st-2nd and 3rd-4th shift fork.

NOTE: **Use block of wood to support ends of shift rods when driving in roll pins.**

11) Place gasket on transmission case and install center support with mainshaft, countergear and input shaft assembly, making sure to align dowel pin holes with dowel pins correctly. Install input shaft bearing snap ring.

12) Assemble reverse shifter fork to reverse gear and install on reverse shifter rod from rear of center support. Install roll pin in reverse shifter fork.

13) Install reverse idler tabbed thrust washer with tab pointing downward and into notch in center support. Install reverse idler gear with undercut teeth rearward.

ISUZU 4-SPEED (Cont.)

Fig. 9: Installing Reverse Idler Gear

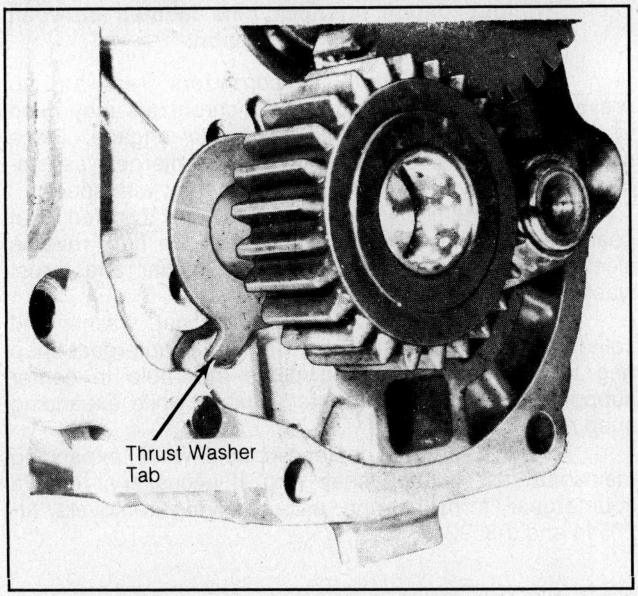

14) Install speedometer drive gear snap ring and Woodruff key on mainshaft, then install speedometer drive gear on shaft, aligning gear with key. Install snap ring.

15) Coat outer reverse idler thrust washer with grease and install in extension housing with tab pointing downward into notch in housing. Check gear backlash. It should not exceed .016" (.4 mm) for all gears. If not, replace gears as required.

16) Place gasket on center support and install extension housing. Make sure to align dowel pin correctly. Install and tighten bolts. Install back-up light and CRS (Federal models) switches.

17) Install gasket and gear shift cover on extension housing and tighten bolts to specification, then install speedometer driven gear to rear extension and tighten bolt.

18) Install spring washer on shaft, with dished face toward input shaft gear bearing. Install input shaft bearing retainer gasket and retainer. Tighten bolts.

NOTE: The 2 shorter bolts are used on countergear front bearing side of bearing retainer.

19) Install dust cover, clutch fork and throw-out bearing with retaining springs. Install drain plug and refill transmission with correct fluid.

TIGHTENING SPECIFICATIONS

Application	Ft. Lbs. (N.m)
Countergear Lock Nut	108 (146)
Mainshaft Lock Nut	94 (127)
Detent Plate Bolts	14 (19)
Extension Housing-to-Center Support Bolts	27 (37)
Shift Cover Bolts	14 (19)
Input Shaft Bearing Retainer	14 (19)

ISUZU 4-SPEED WITH INTEGRAL TRANSFER CASE

Isuzu P'UP (4WD), Trooper II

DESCRIPTION

Transmission is a floor shifted, fully synchronized 4-speed unit with block ring type synchronizers and a sliding mesh type reverse. This unit consists of a transmission case with integral clutch housing, center support, transfer case with transfer side case and gears. A shifter cover, located on top of transfer case, contains the transmission control mechanism. Another shifter cover located on the transfer side case contains the range and four wheel drive shifting mechanism.

LUBRICATION & ADJUSTMENT

See appropriate MANUAL TRANSMISSION SERVICING article in IMPORT GENERAL SERVICING section.

REMOVAL & INSTALLATION

See appropriate MANUAL TRANSMISSION REMOVAL article in IMPORT GENERAL SERVICING section.

TROUBLE SHOOTING

HARD SHIFTING

Improperly adjusted clutch. Weakened insert spring. Face of blocker ring, in contact with insert, worn. Cones on blocker ring and gear worn or not in proper contact.

SLIPS OUT OF GEAR

Bearings worn or defective. Excessive play between gears and collars. Play in clutch hub and sliding sleeve. Shift arm worn. Lock ball spring weak or broken.

TRANSMISSION NOISY

Low or incorrect lubricant. Gears or bearings worn or damaged. Worn gears or collars. Worn clutch hub or mainshaft splines. Incorrectly meshed gears.

TRANSMISSION DISASSEMBLY

1) Remove retainer springs, throw-out bearing, clutch fork and boot. Remove 4 bolts holding bearing retainer-to-transmission case. Remove bearing retainer, gasket and spring washer. Remove speedometer gear mount bolt, bushing and driven gear assembly.

2) Remove back-up light and coasting richer switch (Federal models) switches. Remove snap ring from input shaft bearing. Remove 8 bolts holding transfer case, center support and transmission case together. Separate transmission case and gasket from center support and transfer case.

3) Remove 4 bolts attaching transfer countershaft lock plate. Remove lock plate and shim. Remove center support assembly from transfer case. Drive spring pins out from 3rd-4th and 1st-2nd shift forks. Remove spring pin from reverse shifter fork.

4) Remove detent spring plate from center support, then remove detent springs and balls. Remove 1st-2nd and 3rd-4th shift rods from center support. Remove shift forks. Remove reverse shifter rod forward to avoid losing the detent interlock pins.

CAUTION: **Remove shifter rods carefully so as not to lose detent interlock pins located between shifter rods in center support.**

5) Move both synchronizers rearward to prevent mainshaft from turning. Synchronizers may need to be tapped with hammer handle to engage. Place support tool (J-26545), with mainshaft countergear assembled, into a vise. Remove mainshaft lock nut with spacer.

6) Remove transfer clutch hub, transfer input gear, needle bearing, collar, reverse clutch hub, reverse sleeve, reverse gear, needle bearing, collar and thrust washer from rear of mainshaft.

7) Remove countergear lock nut, washer and collar from rear of countergear. Remove countergear snap ring by inserting snap ring pliers into hole in center support. Tap on front of center support while expanding snap ring.

8) Remove center support while expanding mainshaft rear bearing snap ring. If necessary, remove countergear front bearing using bearing removers (J-26544 and J-8092).

COMPONENT DISASSEMBLY & REASSEMBLY

MAINSHAFT

Disassembly

1) Separate input shaft gear, needle bearing and blocker ring from mainshaft assembly. Using bearing removal tool (J-22912) and an arbor press, remove rear bearing from mainshaft.

2) Remove thrust washer, 1st gear, needle bearing, collar and blocker ring. Remove 1st-2nd gear synchronizer assembly. Remove 2nd gear, blocker ring and needle bearing.

3) Remove snap ring, 3rd-4th synchronizer assembly and blocker ring. Remove 3rd gear and needle bearings.

4) Remove snap ring from input shaft gear. Remove bearing using an arbor press and bearing removal tool. Remove countershaft reverse gear and countergear bearing using bearing removal tool (J-22912) and an arbor press.

Inspection

1) Check mainshaft outer face, needle bearing fitting faces and splined portion of shaft for wear, scoring or warpage. Maximum permissable runout of mainshaft is .002" (.05 mm). Check all gear teeth for wear or damage. Inspect all bearings for smooth operation.

2) Check synchronizer assemblies for wear by holding blocker ring against cone section of gear and measure clearance. If clearance is less than .032" (.80 mm), replace blocker ring. Measure clearance between synchronizer clutch hub splines and mainshaft splines in normal direction of rotation.

3) If clearance exceeds .008" (.20 mm), replace synchronizer clutch hub. Check grooves in shift arms and blocks for wear and/or damage. If thickness of shift arm pads is less than .256" (6.50 mm) for 3rd-4th shift arm, .276" (7 mm) for 1st-2nd, .256" (6.50 mm) for reverse shift arm and .236" (6 mm) for transfer range and 4WD shift arms, replace shift arms.

4) Inspect shift rods for bending or wear and replace as needed. Check shift rod detent springs for weakening and/or distortion. Measure spring free length.

ISUZU 4-SPEED WITH INTEGRAL TRANSFER CASE (Cont.)

Fig. 1: Exploded View Showing 4-Speed Transmission Case & Transfer Case with Shifting Mechanism

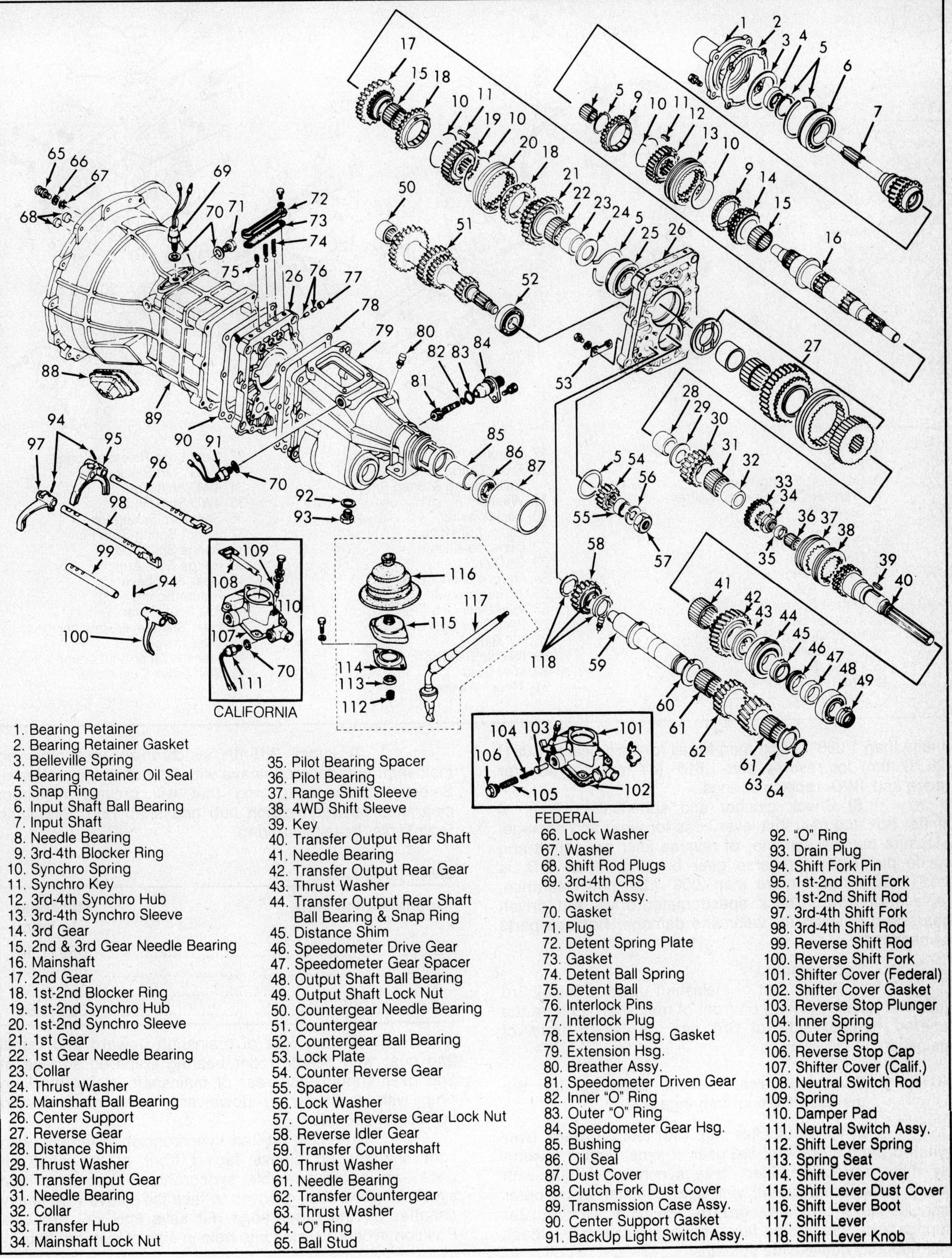

1. Bearing Retainer
2. Bearing Retainer Gasket
3. Belleville Spring
4. Bearing Retainer Oil Seal
5. Snap Ring
6. Input Shaft Ball Bearing
7. Input Shaft
8. Needle Bearing
9. 3rd-4th Blocker Ring
10. Synchro Spring
11. Synchro Key
12. 3rd-4th Synchro Hub
13. 3rd-4th Synchro Sleeve
14. 3rd Gear
15. 2nd & 3rd Gear Needle Bearing
16. Mainshaft
17. 2nd Gear
18. 1st-2nd Blocker Ring
19. 1st-2nd Synchro Hub
20. 1st-2nd Synchro Sleeve
21. 1st Gear
22. 1st Gear Needle Bearing
23. Collar
24. Thrust Washer
25. Mainshaft Ball Bearing
26. Center Support
27. Reverse Gear
28. Distance Shim
29. Thrust Washer
30. Transfer Input Gear
31. Needle Bearing
32. Collar
33. Transfer Hub
34. Mainshaft Lock Nut
35. Pilot Bearing Spacer
36. Pilot Bearing
37. Range Shift Sleeve
38. 4WD Shift Sleeve
39. Key
40. Transfer Output Rear Shaft
41. Needle Bearing
42. Transfer Output Rear Gear
43. Thrust Washer
44. Transfer Output Rear Shaft Ball Bearing & Snap Ring
45. Distance Shim
46. Speedometer Drive Gear
47. Speedometer Gear Spacer
48. Output Shaft Ball Bearing
49. Output Shaft Lock Nut
50. Countergear Needle Bearing
51. Countergear
52. Countergear Ball Bearing
53. Lock Plate
54. Counter Reverse Gear
55. Spacer
56. Lock Washer
57. Counter Reverse Gear Lock Nut
58. Reverse Idler Gear
59. Transfer Countershaft
60. Thrust Washer
61. Needle Bearing
62. Transfer Countergear
63. Thrust Washer
64. "O" Ring
65. Ball Stud
66. Lock Washer
67. Washer
68. Shift Rod Plugs
69. 3rd-4th CRS Switch Assy.
70. Gasket
71. Plug
72. Detent Spring Plate
73. Gasket
74. Detent Ball Spring
75. Detent Ball
76. Interlock Pins
77. Interlock Plug
78. Extension Hsg. Gasket
79. Extension Hsg.
80. Breather Assy.
81. Speedometer Driven Gear
82. Inner "O" Ring
83. Outer "O" Ring
84. Speedometer Gear Hsg.
85. Bushing
86. Oil Seal
87. Dust Cover
88. Clutch Fork Dust Cover
89. Transmission Case Assy.
90. Center Support Gasket
91. BackUp Light Switch Assy.
92. "O" Ring
93. Drain Plug
94. Shift Fork Pin
95. 1st-2nd Shift Fork
96. 1st-2nd Shift Rod
97. 3rd-4th Shift Fork
98. 3rd-4th Shift Rod
99. Reverse Shift Rod
100. Reverse Shift Fork
101. Shifter Cover (Federal)
102. Shifter Cover Gasket
103. Reverse Stop Plunger
104. Inner Spring
105. Outer Spring
106. Reverse Stop Cap
107. Shifter Cover (Calif.)
108. Neutral Switch Rod
109. Spring
110. Damper Pad
111. Neutral Switch Assy.
112. Shift Lever Spring
113. Spring Seat
114. Shift Lever Cover
115. Shift Lever Dust Cover
116. Shift Lever Boot
117. Shift Lever
118. Shift Lever Knob

ISUZU 4-SPEED WITH INTEGRAL TRANSFER CASE (Cont.)

Fig. 2: Exploded View Showing 4-Speed Transmission Side Case Gears and Shift Mechanism

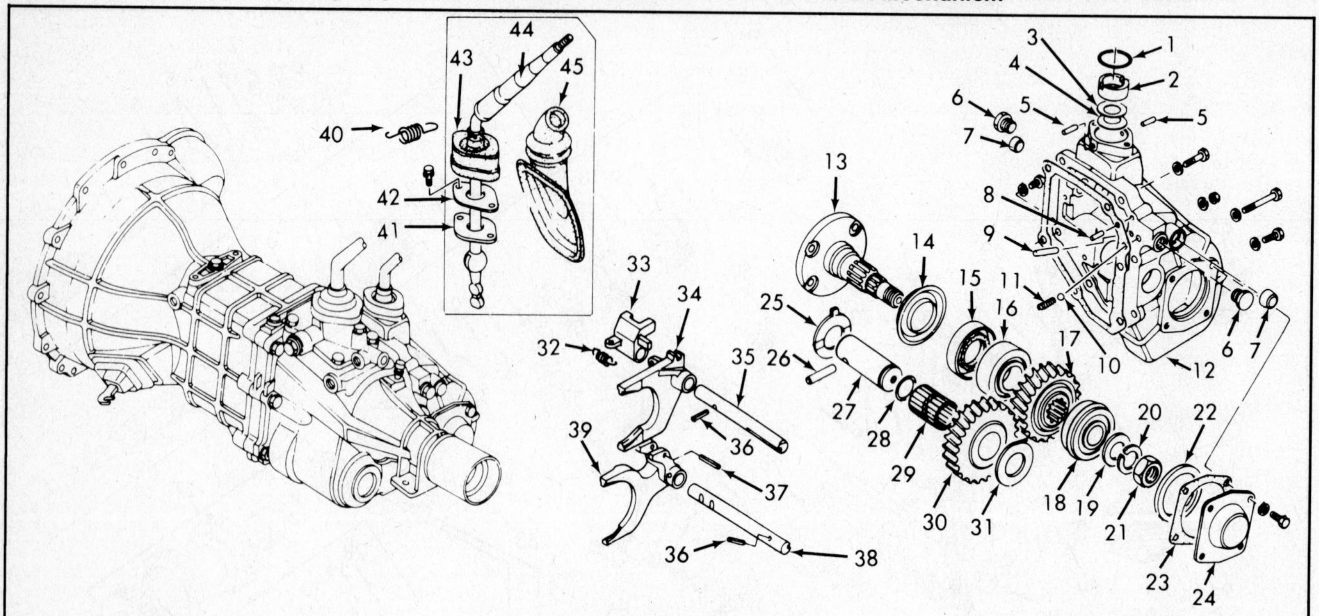

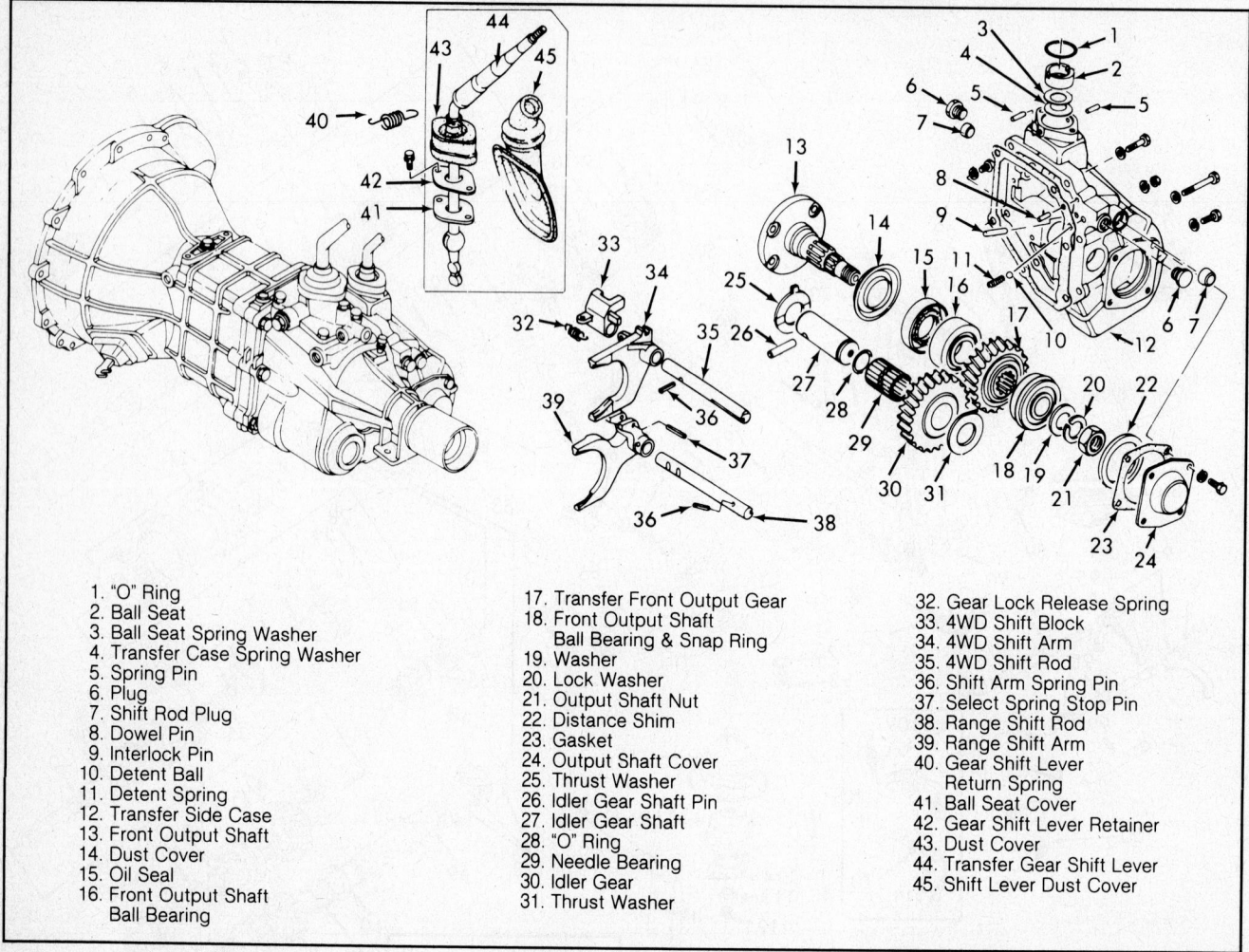

1. "O" Ring
2. Ball Seat
3. Ball Seat Spring Washer
4. Transfer Case Spring Washer
5. Spring Pin
6. Plug
7. Shift Rod Plug
8. Dowel Pin
9. Interlock Pin
10. Detent Ball
11. Detent Spring
12. Transfer Side Case
13. Front Output Shaft
14. Dust Cover
15. Oil Seal
16. Front Output Shaft Ball Bearing
17. Transfer Front Output Gear
18. Front Output Shaft Ball Bearing & Snap Ring
19. Washer
20. Lock Washer
21. Output Shaft Nut
22. Distance Shim
23. Gasket
24. Output Shaft Cover
25. Thrust Washer
26. Idler Gear Shaft Pin
27. Idler Gear Shaft
28. "O" Ring
29. Needle Bearing
30. Idler Gear
31. Thrust Washer
32. Gear Lock Release Spring
33. 4WD Shift Block
34. 4WD Shift Arm
35. 4WD Shift Rod
36. Shift Arm Spring Pin
37. Select Spring Stop Pin
38. Range Shift Rod
39. Range Shift Arm
40. Gear Shift Lever Return Spring
41. Ball Seat Cover
42. Gear Shift Lever Retainer
43. Dust Cover
44. Transfer Gear Shift Lever
45. Shift Lever Dust Cover

If less than 1.083" (27.50 mm) for all forward gears, 1.051" (26.70 mm) for reverse and 1.615" (41 mm) for transfer range and 4WD, replace springs.

5) Check plunger and spherical portions of shifter box and gearshift lever boss for wear and damage. Measure outside diameter of reverse idler gear shaft and inside diameter of reverse gear bushing. Shaft O.D. is 1.181" (30 mm). If more than .008" (.20 mm) clearance, replace bushing. Check speedometer drive and driven gears and bushing for wear and damage. Replace parts as necessary.

Reassembly

1) Place front of mainshaft upward. Install 3rd gear and needle bearing on front of mainshaft. Ensure the tapered (coned) side of 3rd gear is facing front of mainshaft.

NOTE: **Front and rear needle bearings for the mainshaft are interchangeable.**

2) Install blocker ring, with teeth upward, over synchronizing surface of 3rd gear. If synchronizer assembly must be reassembled, face synchronizer hub with heavy boss facing sleeve with light chamfering on outer rim. Fit keys into key groove. Position synchronizer springs into hole in side face of synchronizer hub. Check that hub and sleeve slide smoothly.

3) Install 3rd-4th synchronizer assembly on mainshaft with face of sleeve with light chamfer rearward. Select thickest snap ring that will provide minimum clearance between clutch hub and snap ring. *See Snap Ring Table*. Install snap ring.

SNAP RING TABLE

Identification Mark	Thickness In. (mm)
1	.059 (1.50)
2	.061 (1.55)
3	.063 (1.60)
4	.065 (1.65)

4) Turn rear of mainshaft upward and install 2nd gear with needle roller bearing. Tapered surface of 2nd gear should face rear of mainshaft. Install blocking ring, with teeth facing downward, over synchronizing surface of 2nd gear.

5) Install 1st-2nd synchronizer assembly, with light chamfer on sleeve facing front of mainshaft. If necessary to reassemble synchronizer assembly, face synchro hub with oil grooves to face the sleeve with heavy chamfer on the outer edge. Fit keys into key grooves. Position synchro spring into hole in side of synchro hub.

ISUZU 4-SPEED WITH INTEGRAL TRANSFER CASE (Cont.)

6) Install blocker ring with teeth facing rearward. Install collar, needle bearing and 1st gear on mainshaft. Tapered side of gear should face front of mainshaft. Install 1st gear thrust washer on mainshaft with grooved side facing 1st gear.

7) Install rear bearing onto mainshaft using bearing removal tool (J-22912) and an arbor press. Ensure snap ring groove in bearing is facing front of mainshaft.

8) If removed, install ball bearing onto input shaft, using bearing removal tool (J-22912) and an arbor press. Ensure snap ring groove on bearing is facing front of transmission. Install snap ring on input shaft. Install needle bearing, blocker ring and input shaft assembly onto front of mainshaft.

TRANSFER CASE

Disassembly

1) Remove thrust washer, reverse idler gear and thrust washer with ball (pin). Remove range shift sleeve and pilot needle bearing from rear of output shaft.

2) Lightly tap transfer countershaft assembly out through shaft hole in transfer case. Expand rear output shaft front bearing snap ring and remove output shaft assembly.

3) Remove "O" ring, thrust washer, countergear, needle bearings and thrust washer from transfer countershaft. Remove rear output shaft nut. Press rear bearing off output shaft using press. Remove spacer, speedometer drive gear and key distance piece from output shaft.

4) Press output shaft front bearing, with thrust washer and rear output gear, from output shaft. Remove output gear needle bearing and 4WD shift sleeve from output shaft.

Inspection

1) Check the outer face and needle bearing fitting faces of rear output shaft for wear or scoring. Check splines for damage. Light scoring or damage can be corrected with an oil stone, otherwise replace shaft.

2) Inspect bearings for smoothness of rotation, abnormal noises, play in direction of thrust and cracking, wear or corrosion on needle rollers. Check gears for step wear or roughness. Replace components that are worn or damaged beyond correction.

Reassembly

1) Install new oil seal into transfer case using seal installer (J-29769). If removed, install output shaft front bearing snap ring to transfer case. Install 4WD shift sleeve, with heavy chamfered side toward output gear, on rear of output shaft.

2) Install needle bearing, output gear and thrust washer on output shaft. Ensure oil grooved side of thrust washer faces output gear. Press output shaft front bearing onto output shaft. Ensure snap ring groove on bearing is turned rearward.

3) Install shim (with oil grooved side toward front bearing), speedometer drive gear key, drive gear and spacer to output shaft. Press output shaft rear bearing, with sealed face toward the rear, onto output shaft. Install output shaft nut and tighten. Stake nut to groove in shaft.

4) Apply grease to needle bearings and both faces of thrust washers. Install thrust washer on countershaft (with oil groove facing countergear) by aligning finger on washer with cutaway portion of shaft. Install needle bearing, countergear, needle bearing, thrust washer and new "O" ring onto transfer countergear.

5) Install output shaft assembly into transfer case by expanding front bearing snap ring into transfer case groove far enough so front bearing can be inserted. Allow snap ring to engage bearing groove.

6) Install transfer countershaft assembly into transfer case. Ensure cutaway portion at front end of countershaft is positioned correctly. The finger on thrust washer, on rear of shaft, should be aligned with groove in transfer case. *See Fig. 3 and Fig. 4.*

Fig. 3: Alignment of Transfer Countershaft in Transfer Case

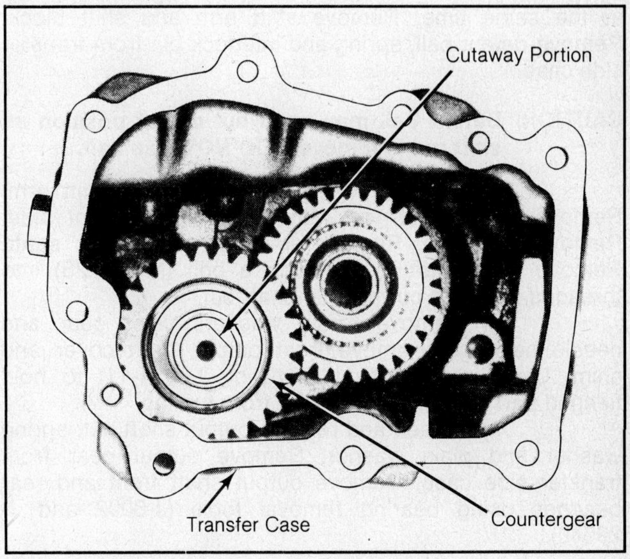

Ensure that the cutaway portion at front end of the countershaft is positioned as shown.

Fig. 4: Alignment of Thrust Washer on Transfer Countershaft in Transfer Case

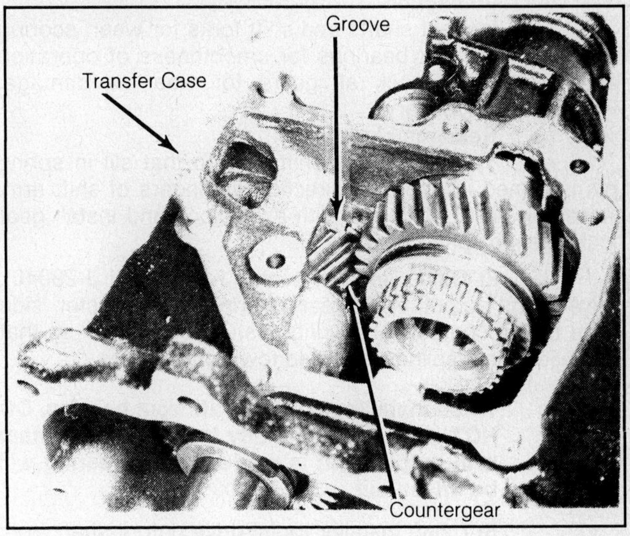

Ensure that finger on thrust washer fitted to rear of shaft is aligned with groove in case.

7) Grease output shaft pilot bearing. Install bearing and range shift sleeve on output shaft. Ensure end of sleeve with heavy chamfering is toward front of transfer case.

ISUZU 4-SPEED WITH INTEGRAL TRANSFER CASE (Cont.)

8) Install thrust washer with ball (pin), reverse idler gear (with shift arm) and thrust washer (with oil groove side toward reverse idler gear).

TRANSFER SIDE CASE

Disassembly

1) Remove range shift rod detent spring and ball. Remove 4WD indicator light switch (if equipped). Remove screw plug from each shift rod. Remove spring pin from 4WD shift arm.

2) Hold range shift rod in high range position. Drive out 4WD shift rod from rear side. Plug will come out at the same time. Remove shift arm and shift block. Remove detent ball, spring and interlock pin from transfer side case.

CAUTION: Detent ball may snap out out of position as shift rod is removed. DO NOT lose ball.

3) Remove spring pin from range shift arm. Remove range shift rod with plug through front side. Remove shift arm. Remove dowel pin from idler shaft. Remove idler shaft by inserting a bolt (M8 x 1.25) into threaded hole and pulling idler shaft out.

4) Remove thrust washers, idler gear and needle bearings. Remove front output shaft cover and shim. Use pin wrench (J-29042 or J-8614-11) to hold flanged part of front output shaft from turning.

5) Loosen and remove output shaft nut, spring washer and plain washer. Remove output gear from transfer side case. Remove output shaft front and rear bearings using bearing removal tools (J-8092 and J-29040).

NOTE: Remove front bearing with oil seal.

6) Remove gear lock release spring from 4WD shift arm, then disconnect shift arm and shift block. Remove spring pin from range shift arm.

Inspection

Inspect shafts and shift forks for wear, scoring or damage. Check bearings for smoothness of operation and for wear. Check all gears for wear or damage. Replace as necessary.

Reassembly

1) Install range shift arm so that slit in spring pin is turned in opposite direction as fingers of shift arm. Assemble 4WD shift arm with shift block and install gear lock release spring. *See Fig. 5*.

2) Using installer tools (J-8092 and J-29040), drive front output shaft rear bearing into transfer side case until it contacts snap ring. Install output gear so that end with uncut splines is turned toward front side.

NOTE: When installing output shaft front bearing, DO NOT drive bearing in any farther once contact with output gear is made or rear bearing will be driven out.

3) Using installer tools, drive output shaft front bearing into transfer side case until it contacts output gear. After installing front bearing, check rear bearing snap ring for proper contact with case. Install output shaft oil seal using seal installer (J-29037).

4) Install output shaft, plain washer, spring washer and output shaft nut. Use pin wrench to hold shaft from turning and tighten output shaft nut. Install shim in transfer side case. Install output shaft cover and tighten bolts.

Fig. 5: Assembling 4WD Shift Arm with Shift Block

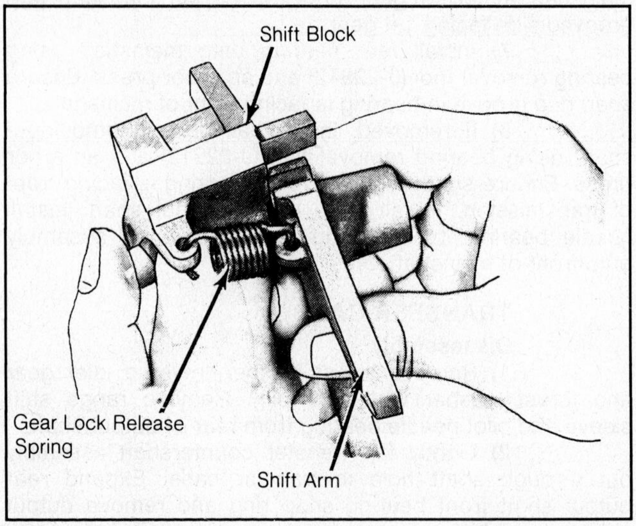

5) Apply grease to both sides of idler gear thrust washer and install with oil grooved face toward gear. Ensure tab on washer aligns with notch in case. Grease idler gear needle bearing and install bearings on gear. Ensure heavier bossed end is turned toward front.

6) Apply grease to new "O" ring on idler shaft. Install idler shaft, with dowel pin groove turned downward, into case until groove lines up with dowel pin fitting hole. Install dowel pin into transfer side case. Dowel should protrude .355-.433" (9-11 mm).

7) Install range shift arm and shift rod, then install spring pin to hold parts in place. Install interlock pin, 4WD shift rod detent spring and detent ball into case. Hold range shift rod in high range and install 4WD shift arm and shift block (with shift rod) into transfer side case.

8) Insert spring pin to secure parts. Install shift rod plugs and screw plugs. Install range shift rod detent ball and spring into position. Install 4WD indicator light switch. *See Fig. 6*.

TRANSMISSION REASSEMBLY

1) If removed, install countershaft reverse gear and countergear ball bearing with snap ring groove facing rear of transmission. Use adapter (J-22912) and press to install bearing. If removed, install snap rings in grooves in inner circumference of countergear and mainshaft bores of center support.

2) If removed, install countergear front bearing using bearing installer tools (J-26544 and J-8092). Mesh gears of mainshaft and countergear together and install on a holding fixture (J-26545). Install holding fixture in a vise, then install center support.

3) While installing center support, expand mainshaft snap ring and press center support onto mainshaft and countergear until countergear bearing hits its snap ring. Expand countergear snap ring and press center support further until both snap rings fit into grooves.

4) Move both synchronizers rearward to prevent mainshaft from turning. If necessary, tap synchronizers with hammer handle to engage them. Install

ISUZU 4-SPEED WITH INTEGRAL TRANSFER CASE (Cont.)

washers and lock nut on rear of countergear. Tighten nut to 80 ft. lbs. (110 N.m.).

Fig. 6: Installation of 4WD Shift Rod, Fork, Range Shift Rod, Range Shift Fork and Detent Spring

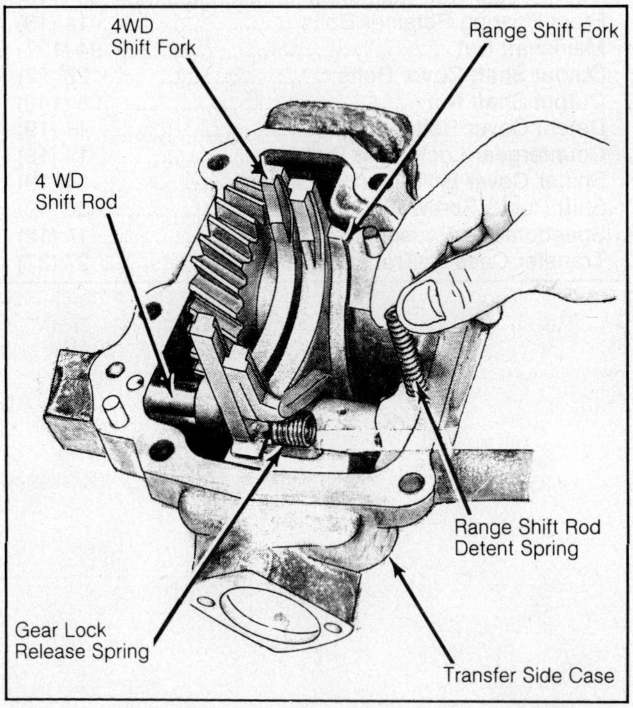

5) Install reverse gear thrust washer on mainshaft with grooved side facing reverse gear. Install collar, needle bearing and reverse gear on mainshaft. The clutch teeth side of reverse gear should be facing rear of mainshaft.

6) Assemble sleeve with reverse clutch hub. Ensure stepped face of hub is on chamfered side of sleeve. Install reverse clutch hub and sleeve. Ensure chamfered face of sleeve is turned to front side of mainshaft.

7) Install collar, needle bearing and input gear onto mainshaft. Ensure input gear is installed with clutching teeth rearward. Install transfer clutch hub on mainshaft with chamfering on outer edge facing rear of mainshaft. Install lock nut on mainshaft and tighten. Caulk lock nut to prevent loosening. Install spacer to mainshaft.

8) Remove holding fixture from mainshaft and countergear and remove assembly from vise. Apply grease to 2 interlock pins. Insert pins into detent holes from middle hole of center support. Install 1st and 2nd shifter forks and 3rd and 4th shifter forks into their grooves in synchronizer assembly.

NOTE: The 3rd-4th shifter rod can be identified by 2 detent grooves on side of rod.

9) Install 3rd-4th shifter rod from rear of center support through middle hole. Then install into 1st-2nd and 3rd-4th shifter forks. Align spring pin hole in shifter fork with hole in shifter rod.

10) Install 1st-2nd shifter rod from rear of center support, through 1st-2nd shifter fork. Align hole in rod to hole in shifter fork. The reverse detent spring is identified as the shorter of the 3 springs. Install reverse shifter fork into its groove in reverse sliding sleeve.

11) Install reverse shifter rod from the front of center support through the reverse shifter fork. Align hole in rod with hole in shifter fork. Install 3 spring pins in 1st-2nd, 3rd-4th and reverse shifter forks.

NOTE: When installing spring pins, ensure shifter rod is supported, by round bar against end of shifter rod, to prevent damage.

12) Install detent balls, detent spring, gasket and retainer on top of center support. Tighten cover bolts to 14 ft. lbs. (19 N.m). Place transfer case upright on wooden blocks. Apply thin coat of grease to end of reverse shift rod, mainshaft and transfer countershaft. Install center support assembly and new gasket into transfer case.

13) Ensure the following parts are installed together in the following order: reverse shift rod-to-reverse shift rod hole fitting, mainshaft-to-output shaft fitting, transfer countershaft-to-countershaft hole fitting, countershaft reverse gear-to-reverse idler gear engaged, input gear-to-transfer countergear engaged, range shift sleeve-to-clutch hub is engaged and dowel pins fit into dowel pin holes. *See Fig. 7*.

Fig. 7: Installation of Center Support to Transfer Case

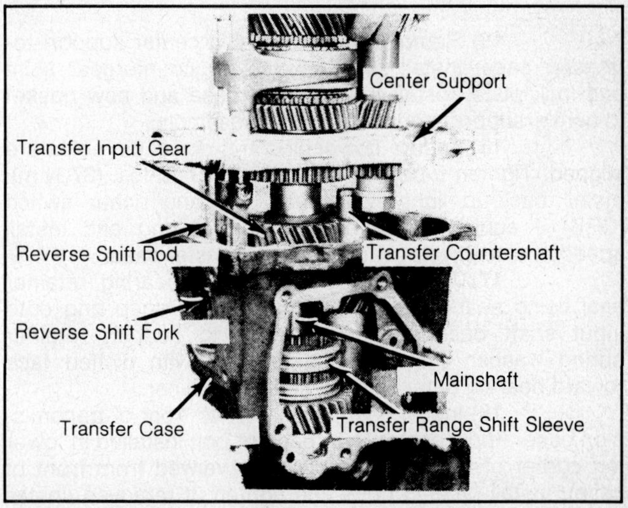

When installing center support, ensure components are installed in the proper sequence.

14) Tighten 4 bolts attaching center support-to-transfer case evenly. Measure how much transfer countershaft protrudes from center support. Select distance shim so thrust clearance will be .004-.014" (.10-.35 mm). *See Fig. 8*.

TRANSFER COUNTERGEAR DISTANCE SHIMS

Countergear Measurement	Shim Thickness	Color Code
.106-.114" (2.70-2.90 mm)	.118" (3.00 mm)	Red
.114-.122" (2.90-3.10 mm)	.126" (3.20 mm)	Orange
.122-.130" (3.10-3.30 mm)	.134" (3.40 mm)	No Color
.130-.138" (3.30-3.50 mm)	.142" (3.60 mm)	Green
.138-.142" (3.50-3.60 mm)	.150" (3.80 mm)	Blue

ISUZU 4-SPEED WITH INTEGRAL TRANSFER CASE (Cont.)

Fig. 8: Measuring Transfer Countershaft for Distance Shim Selection

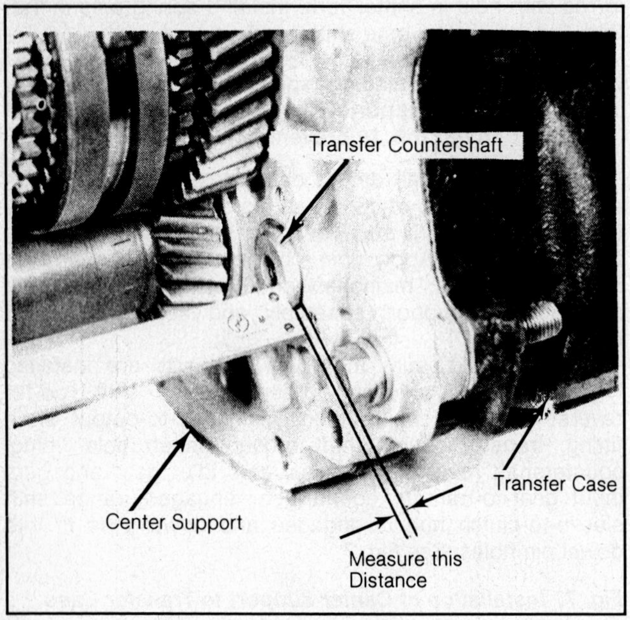

15) Remove bolts attaching center support-to-transfer case. Install selected transfer countergear shim and lock plate. Install transmission case and new gasket to center support and tranfer case assembly.

16) Ensure dowel pins and dowel pin holes are aligned. Tighten 6 bolts and 8 nuts to 27 ft. lbs. (37 N.m). Install back-up light switch and coasting richer switch (CRS) if equipped. Lubricate new "O" ring and install speedometer driven gear to rear of transfer case.

17) If removed, install front bearing retainer seal using seal installer (J-26540). Install snap ring onto input shaft bearing. Apply grease to bearing retainer spring washer. Install spring washer, with dished face toward bearing outer race, in bearing retainer.

18) Install bearing retainer to front of transmission case. Apply sealer to threads of bolt installed in lower left corner of transmission case (as veiwed from front of case). Install other 3 bolts and tighten. If removed, install ball stud to transmission case.

19) Install dust boot, clutch fork and throw-out bearing. Install retaining springs. Apply molybdenum grease to input shaft splines and shift fork support. Apply regular grease to shift block. Ensure hook on clutch fork is installed on support correctly. Install drain plug on transfer case.

20) If removed, install transfer side case studs to transmission. Position transmission, with transfer side case fitting face down, in vehicle. Slide forward guiding clutch gear into pilot bearing. Install transmission-to-engine mount bolts. Install shifter cover with new gasket and tighten mount bolts.

21) Install transfer side case-to-transfer case by aligning grooves in shift arms and sleeve. Install components with shift arms and shift sleeves held in the 4H position. Complete transmission installation by reversing removal procedure. After installation, fill transmission with 2.37 qts. (2.5L) of gear oil.

TIGHTENING SPECIFICATIONS

Application	Ft. Lbs. (N.m)
Clutch Ball Stud-to-Case	30 (41)
Countergear Nut	80 (110)
Front Bearing Retainer Bolts	14 (19)
Mainshaft Nut	94 (127)
Output Shaft Cover Bolts	20 (27)
Output Shaft Nut	108 (146)
Detent Cover Bolts	14 (19)
Countergear Lock Plate Bolts	14 (19)
Shifter Cover Bolts	14 (19)
Shift Rod & Screw Plugs	36 (49)
Speedometer Housing Retainer Bolt	14 (19)
Transfer Case-to-Transmission Case Bolts	27 (37)

ISUZU 5-SPEED

Isuzu I-Mark, Impulse, P'UP

DESCRIPTION

Five speed fully synchronized unit with blocker ring synchronizers and a constant mesh reverse gear. First through fourth gears are housed within the case. Reverse and fifth gears are contained in the extension housing. The input/output shaft and the countershaft are supported by 3 ball bearings. The bearings are located in the front wall of the case, the center support and the extension housing. All gear teeth are helical cut.

LUBRICATION & ADJUSTMENT

See appropriate MANUAL TRANSMISSION SERVICING article in IMPORT GENERAL SERVICING section.

TROUBLE SHOOTING

HARD SHIFTING

Improperly adjusted clutch. Synchronizers worn or broken. Shift shafts or forks worn.

SLIPS OUT OF GEAR

Shift shafts and/or bearings worn. Drive gear retainer broken or loose. Excessive play in synchronizers.

TRANSMISSION NOISY

Low or incorrect lubricant. Gears or bearings worn or damaged. Worn clutch hub or mainshaft splines. Incorrectly meshed gears.

REMOVAL & INSTALLATION

See appropriate MANUAL TRANSMISSION REMOVAL article in IMPORT GENERAL SERVICING section.

TRANSMISSION DISASSEMBLY

1) Remove plug and drain transmission. Remove release bearing and fork assembly. Remove input shaft bearing retainer and Belleville spring. *See Fig. 3.*

2) Remove speedometer driven gear, retainer and back-up light switch. Remove shift lever quadrant and coasting fuel cut switch. Remove extension housing from transmission case.

Fig. 1: Cutaway View of Isuzu 5-Speed Transmission

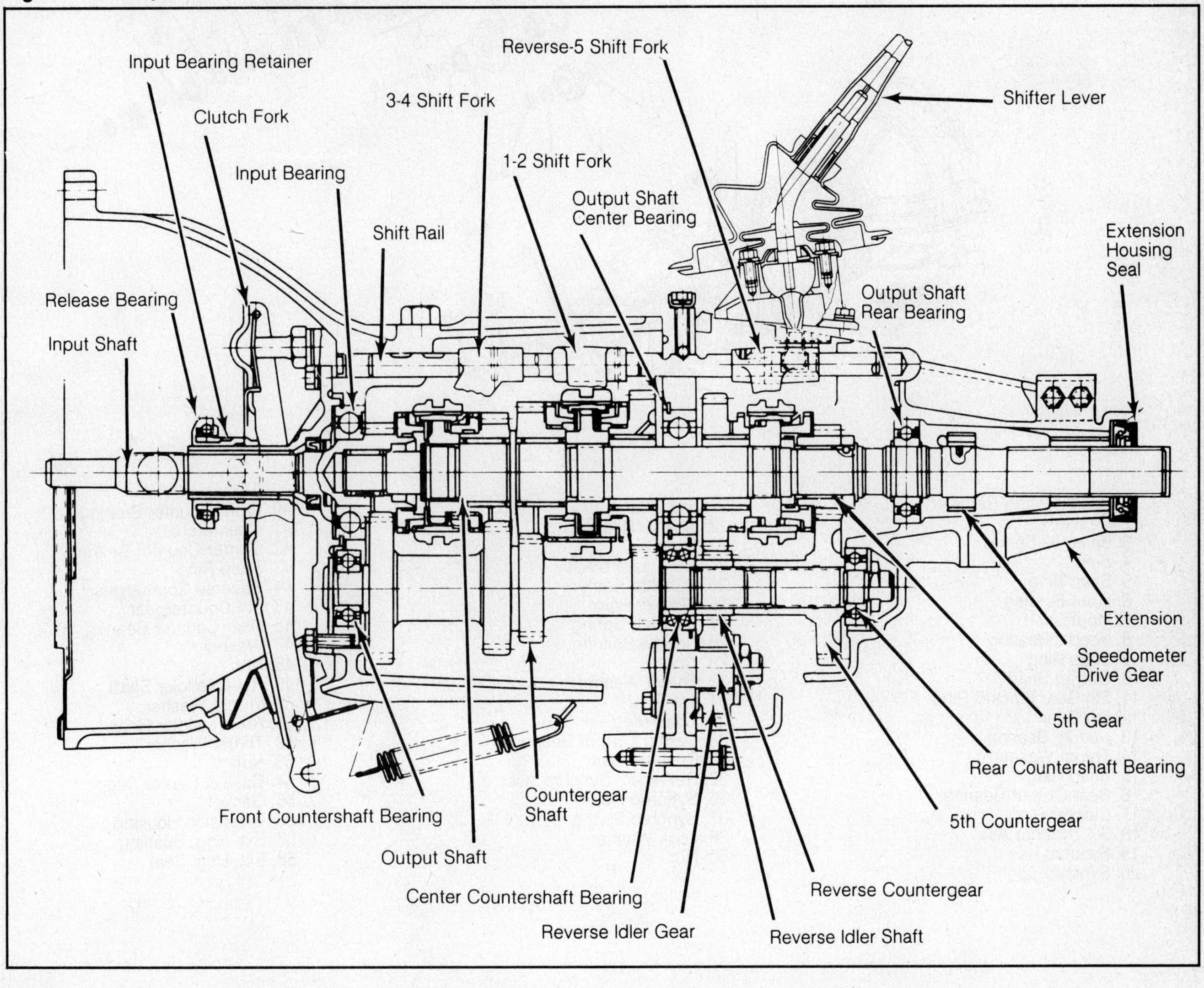

ISUZU 5-SPEED (Cont.)

Fig. 2: Exploded View of Isuzu 5-Speed Transmission

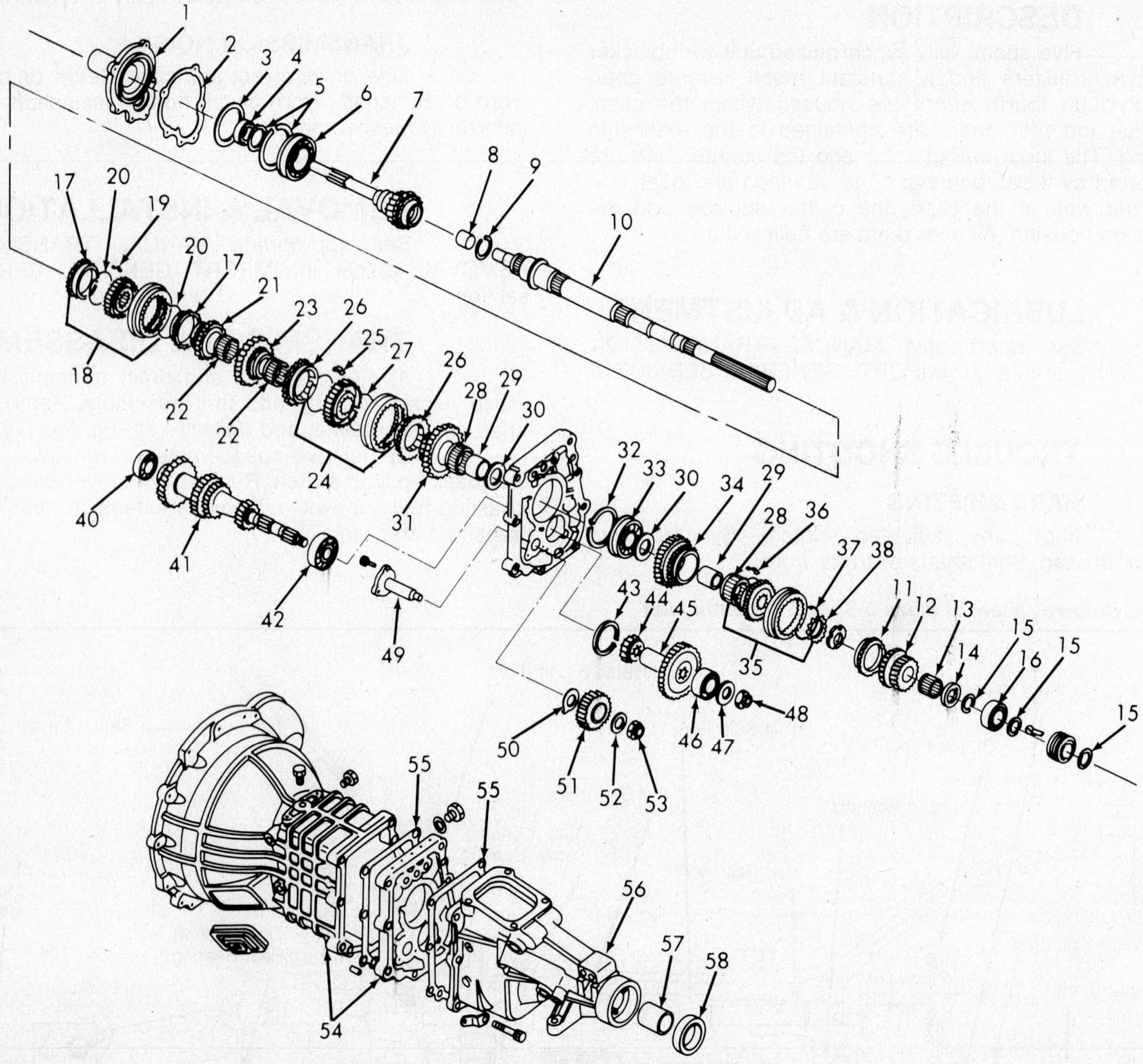

1. Input Bearing Retainer
2. Gasket
3. Belleville Spring
4. Seal
5. Snap Ring
6. Input Bearing
7. Input Shaft
8. Needle Bearing
9. Snap Ring
10. Output Shaft
11. 5th Gear Blocker Ring
12. 5th Gear
13. Needle Bearing
14. Thrust Washer
15. Snap Ring
16. Rear Output Bearing
17. Blocker Ring
18. 3-4 Synchro Assy.
19. Synchro Key
20. Synchro Spring
21. 3rd Gear
22. Needle Bearing
23. 2nd Gear
24. 1-2 Synchro Assy.
25. Synchro Key
26. Blocker Ring
27. Synchro Spring
28. Needle Bearing
29. Collar
30. Thrust Washer
31. 1st Gear
32. Snap Ring
33. Center Output Bearing
34. Reverse Gear
35. Reverse-5 Synchro Assy.
36. Synchro Key
37. Synchro Spring
38. Lock Washer
39. Nut
40. Front Counter Bearing
41. Countershaft
42. Center Counter Bearing
43. Snap Ring
44. Reverse Countergear
45. 5th Countergear
46. Rear Counter Bearing
47. Washer
48. Nut
49. Reverse Idler Shaft
50. Thrust Washer
51. Reverse Idler Gear
52. Thrust Washer
53. Nut
54. Case & Center Support
55. Gasket
56. Extension Housing
57. Ext. Hsg. Bushing
58. Ext. Hsg. Seal

ISUZU 5-SPEED (Cont.)

3) Remove speedometer drive gear, snap rings, spacer and bearing. Remove snap ring from main shaft, thrust washer and lock ball. Remove outer snap ring from input shaft bearing. Remove center support from case with all gears attached.

4) Using a punch, drive pins out of shift forks, making sure to support ends of shift shafts. Remove detent spring plate, springs and detent balls. Remove shift shafts from center support. Remove shift forks from synchronizer sleeves. Remove interlock pins. *See Fig. 4.*

Fig. 3: Input Bearing Retainer Assembly

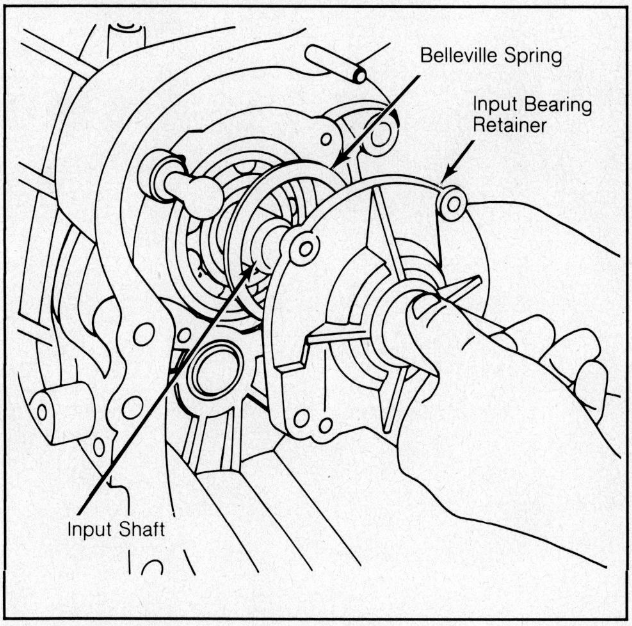

Dished side of spring faces rearward.

5) Engage 1st and 3rd gears to prevent rotation of countershaft. Install holding fixture (J-29768) onto front of gear assembly. Remove nut from rear of countershaft. Using a puller, remove rear countershaft bearing and 5th gear.

Fig. 4: Exploded View of Shift Shaft Assembly

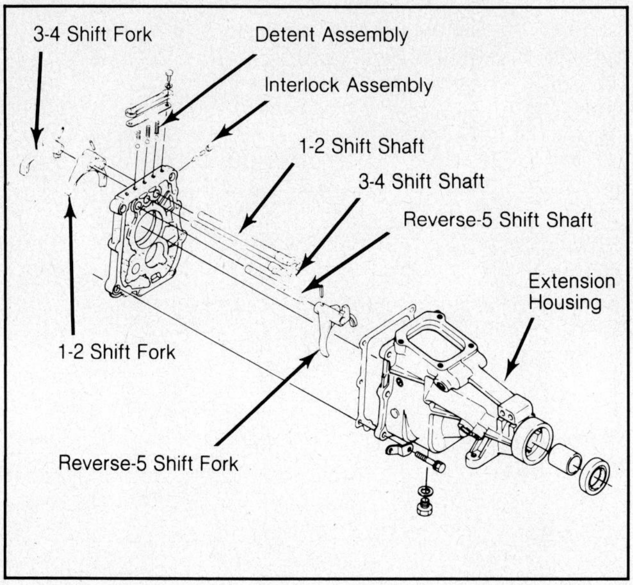

6) Remove 5th gear, needle bearings and blocker ring from output shaft. Remove thrust washers, reverse idler gear and retaining nut from reverse idler shaft.

7) Bend locking retainer back and remove mainshaft nut. Remove retainer and reverse-5th synchronizer assembly. Remove reverse gear, collar, needle bearings and thrust washer from rear of output shaft. Remove reverse gear from countershaft. Remove holding fixture.

8) Return synchronizers to neutral position. Expand countergear center bearing snap ring. Gently tap on front of center support to remove countershaft. Expand output shaft center bearing snap ring. Remove output shaft from center support. Remove input shaft, needle bearings and 4th gear blocker ring from output shaft.

COMPONENT DISASSEMBLY & REASSEMBLY

OUTPUT SHAFT

Disassembly

1) Using a press, remove output shaft center bearing. Remove thrust washer, 1st gear, needle bearings and spacer. Remove 1-2 synchronizer, 2nd gear and needle bearings.

2) Remove snap ring from front of output shaft. Remove 3-4 synchronizer and 3rd gear blocker ring. Remove 3rd gear and needle bearings.

Inspection

Check all parts for excessive wear or damage. Check bearings and synchronizers for rough operation. Replace damaged parts as necessary.

Reassembly

1) Install 3rd gear onto front of output shaft. Synchronizer cone faces forward. Install 3rd needle bearings. Install 3-4 synchronizer with chamfered end forward. Retain synchronizer with selective fit snap ring. Snap ring size should be selected to minimize end play.

2) Install 2nd gear and needle bearings on rear of shaft. Coned end of 2nd gear faces rearward. Install 1-2 synchronizer on rear of shaft with chamfered end facing rearward.

3) Install spacer, needle bearings and 1st gear on rear of shaft. Coned end of 1st gear faces forward. Install 1st gear thrust washer with slots facing gear. Press center bearing onto shaft. Groove on bearing faces front of transmission.

INPUT SHAFT

Disassembly

Remove snap ring from front of shaft. Press bearing off of shaft.

Reassembly

Press bearing onto shaft, so bearing groove faces toward front of transmission. Install snap ring.

COUNTERSHAFT

Disassembly & Reassembly

Countershaft bearings are removed and installed using a bearing separator and press. Groove on center bearing faces rearward.

ISUZU 5-SPEED (Cont.)

OIL SEALS

Removal & Installation

Remove seals by prying with a screwdriver or small chisel. Coat outside of new extension housing seal with sealer (Permatex No. 2 or equivalent). Install seals with seal driver (Ext. Hsg. J-26508; Input J-26540).

TRANSMISSION REASSEMBLY

1) If removed, install center support snap rings and reverse idler shaft. Install input shaft onto front of output shaft. Engage countershaft with input and output shaft gears. Install gear assembly into holding fixture (J-29768).

2) Install center support onto gear assembly. Expand center support snap rings. Position center support and seat snap rings into bearing grooves. Engage 1st and 3rd gears to prevent countershaft rotation.

3) Install reverse countergear. Install reverse thrust washer with oil groove facing rearward. Install reverse gear with needle bearing and collar assembly onto rear of output shaft. Install reverse-5th synchronizer. Recessed side of synchronizer hub faces rearward.

4) Install locking retainer and nut onto rear of output shaft. Chamfered side of nut faces forward. Tighten to 94 ft. lbs. (127 N.m), then bend down retainer to lock nut in place.

5) Install reverse idler gear and thrust washers onto idler shaft. Flange on side thrust washer is fitted to stopper on center support. Install new self-locking nut on idler shaft.

6) Install 5th gear with blocker ring and needle bearing onto output shaft. Install 5th countergear, bearing and new self-locking nut onto countershaft. Remove assembly from holding fixture. Shift synchronizers to neutral position.

7) Grease interlock pins and install in center support. Install shift forks onto synchronizer sleeves. Insert shift shafts through center support and shift forks. Install detent balls and springs in center support, then install gasket and detent plate.

8) Support shift shafts and replace shift fork retaining pins. Place a new gasket on rear of transmission case. Install center support and gear assembly into case. Do not apply load to mainshaft rear end.

9) Install outer snap ring on input shaft bearing. Install lock ball, thrust washer and snap ring onto rear of output shaft. Check clearance between 5th gear and thrust washer with a feeler gauge. Clearance should be .004-.012" (.10-.30 mm). Adjust clearance as necessary with selective thickness thrust washers. Do not bend or distort thrust washer snap ring.

10) Install speedometer drive gear front snap ring, ball bearing and spacer. Align lug in speedometer drive gear with groove and install on shaft, then install rear snap ring.

11) Install gasket on rear of center support. Install extension housing. Install gasket and shift lever quadrant on extension housing. Install speedometer driven gear and back-up light switch.

12) Install belleville washer with dished side to drive gear bearing. Install gasket and input bearing retainer into front of transmission. Seal lower 3 retainer bolts with sealer (Permatex No. 2 or equivalent). Install release bearing and fork assembly.

TIGHTENING SPECIFICATIONS

Application	Ft. Lbs. (N.m)
Input Shaft Bearing Retainer Bolts	14 (19)
Shift Box Bolts	14 (19)
Reverse Idler Shaft Bolts	14 (19)
Extension Housing Bolts	27 (37)
Countergear Nut	80 (108)
Reverse Idler Gear-to-Shaft	80 (108)
Output Shaft Nut	94 (127)

MAZDA FWD 4 & 5-SPEED TRANSAXLE

GLC, 626

DESCRIPTION

Transaxle combines a 4 or 5-speed transmission, a differential and a clutch housing into an integral drivetrain. This unit is designed for a transverse engine, front wheel drive vehicle. All gear assemblies are supported by tapered roller bearings with preload being adjusted by shims. Helical cut gears are used throughout, so adjustment of gear tooth contact is not necessary.

LUBRICATION & ADJUSTMENT

See appropriate MANUAL TRANSMISSION SERVICING article in the IMPORT GENERAL SERVICING section.

SERVICE (IN VEHICLE)

DRIVE AXLE SHAFTS

See appropriate DRIVE AXLE SHAFT article in IMPORT AXLE SHAFTS, OVERDRIVES & TRANSFER CASES section.

REMOVAL & INSTALLATION

See appropriate MANUAL TRANSMISSION REMOVAL article in IMPORT GENERAL SERVICING section.

TRANSAXLE DISASSEMBLY

1) Mount transaxle in a support fixture. Engage any gear and lock mainshaft with Holder (49 F401 440). On 5-speed models, remove rear cover. Check end clearance between 5th gear and gear sleeve. Clearance should be .006-.020" (.14-.5 mm). Remove 5th gear retaining nut and stop plate from output shaft.

2) Remove 5th gear shift fork and synchronizer. Remove blocker ring, 5th gear and gear sleeve from output

Fig. 1: Exploded View of Mazda GLC Transaxle Assembly

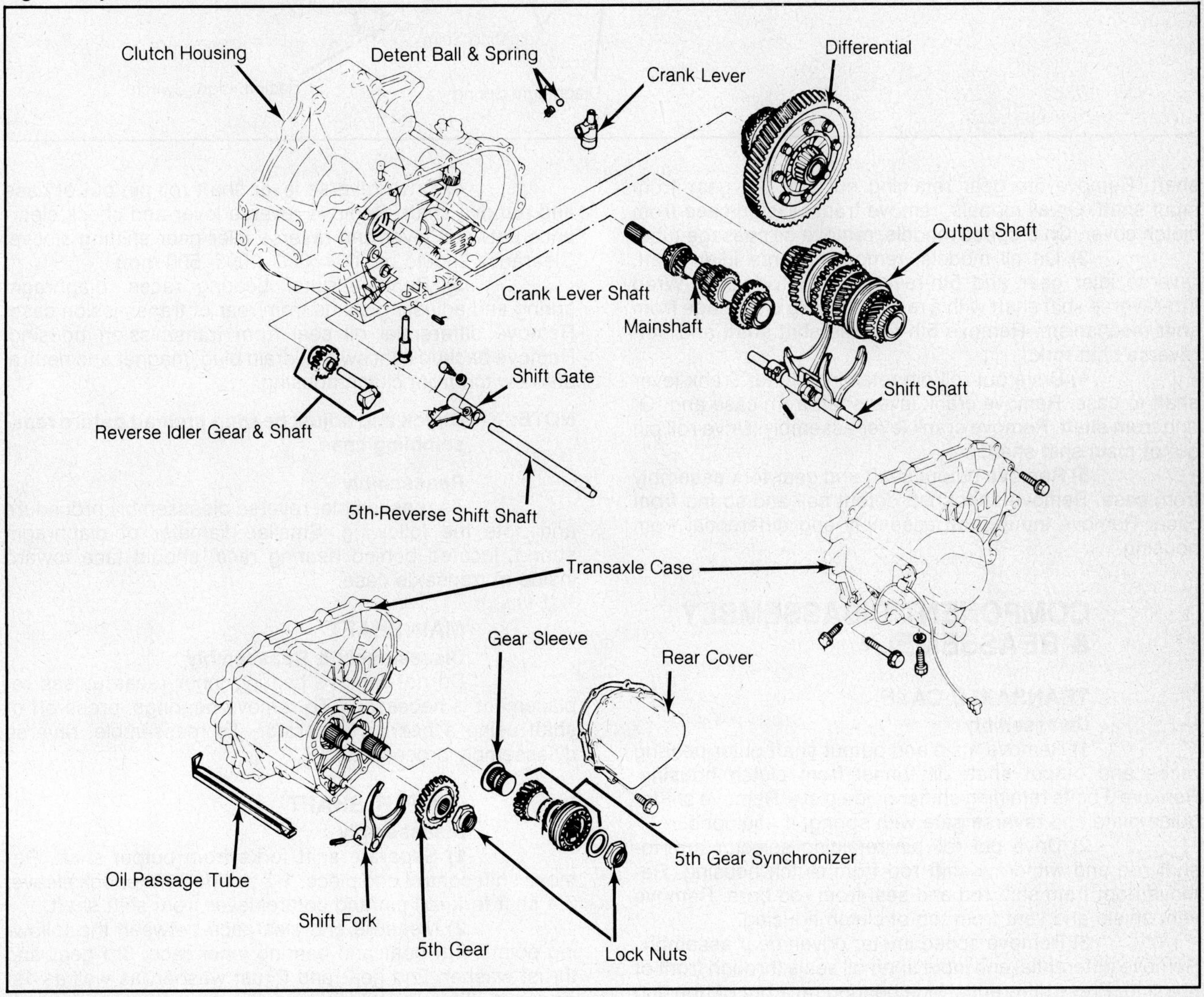

MAZDA FWD 4 & 5-SPEED TRANSAXLE (Cont.)

Fig. 2: Exploded View of Transaxle Case and Related Components

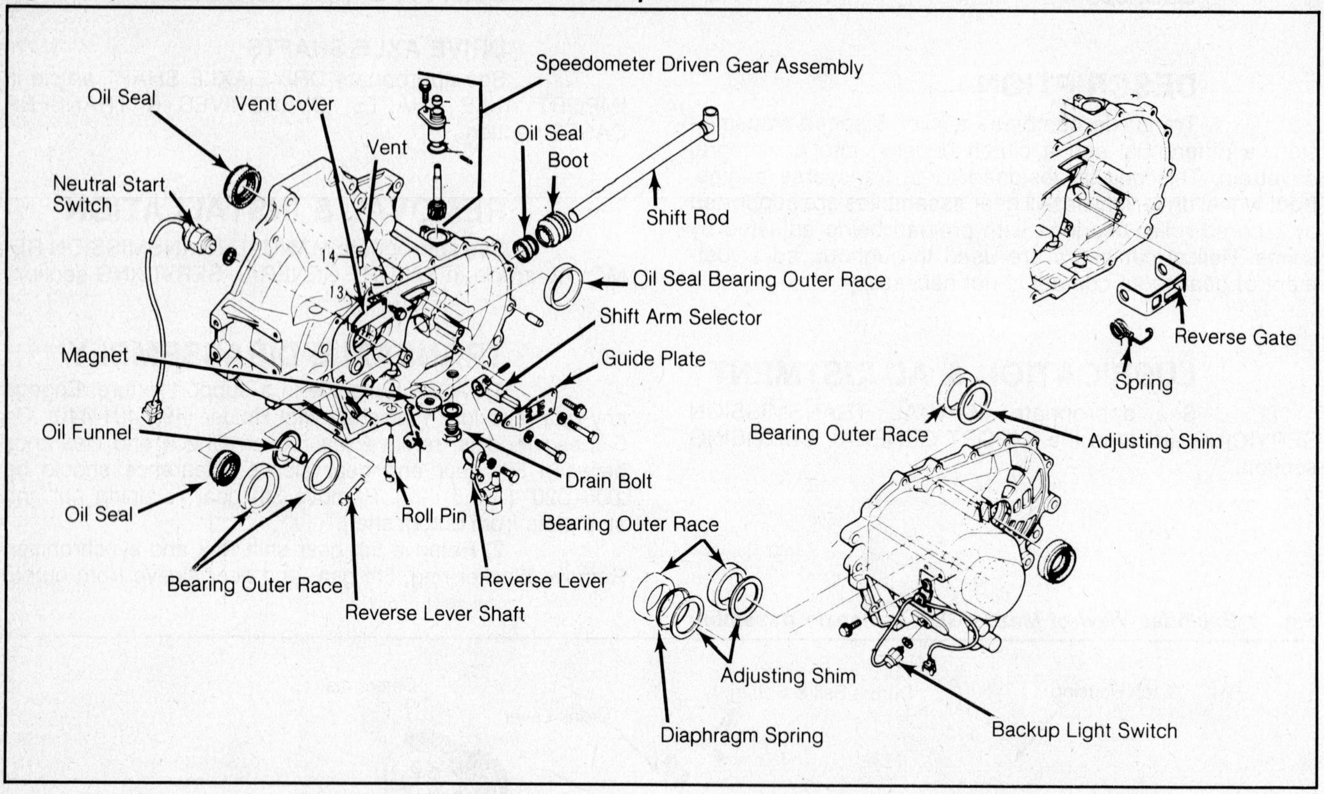

shaft. Remove 5th gear retaining nut and 5th gear from input shaft. On all models, remove transmission case from clutch cover. On 5-speed models, remove oil passage tube.

3) On all models, remove reverse idler shaft, reverse idler gear and 5th-reverse shift fork bolt. Wrap 5th-reverse shift shaft with a rag and turn to disengage from shift mechanism. Remove 5th-reverse shift shaft and 5th-reverse shift fork.

4) Drive out roll pin retaining shifter crank lever shaft to case. Remove crank lever shaft from case and "O" ring from shaft. Remove crank lever assembly. Drive roll pin out of main shift shaft.

5) Remove output shaft and gear fork assembly from case. Remove shift shaft detent ball and spring from case. Remove input shaft assembly and differential from housing.

COMPONENT DISASSEMBLY & REASSEMBLY

TRANSAXLE CASE

Disassembly

1) Remove main and output shaft outer bearing races and output shaft oil funnel from clutch housing. Remove 3 bolts retaining shifter guide plate. Remove shifter guide plate and reverse gate with spring, if equipped.

2) Drive out roll pin retaining selector arm-to-shift rod and withdraw shift rod from clutch housing. Remove boot from shift rod and seal from rod bore. Remove vent shield and vent from top of clutch housing.

3) Remove speedometer driven gear assembly. Remove differential and input shaft oil seals through front of housing. Press differential side bearing race out of housing with a drift punch.

4) Drive reverse lever shaft roll pin out of case and remove shaft. Remove reverse lever and check clearance between lever and reverse idler gear shifting sleeve. Clearance should be .004-.020" (.095-.500 mm).

5) Remove outer bearing races, diaphragm spring and adjusting shims from rear of transmission case. Remove differential oil seal from transmission housing. Remove backup light switch, drain plug, magnet and neutral start switch from clutch housing.

NOTE: Check and adjust bearing preload before reassembling case.

Reassembly

To reassemble, reverse disassembly procedure and note the following: Smaller diameter of diaphragm spring, located behind bearing race, should face toward inside of transaxle case.

MAINSHAFT

Disassembly & Reassembly

Do not remove bearing inner races unless replacement is necessary. To remove bearings, press off of shaft using a bearing separator. To reassemble, reverse disassembly procedure.

OUTPUT SHAFT

Disassembly

1) Separate shift forks from output shaft. Remove shift control end piece, 1-2 shift fork, interlock sleeve, 3-4 shift fork roll pin and control lever from shift shaft.

2) Measure end clearance between the following points: 4th gear and bearing inner race, 3rd gear and thrust washer, 2nd gear and thrust washer, as well as 1st gear and differential drive gear.

Fig. 3: Exploded View of Transaxle Gear Shafts

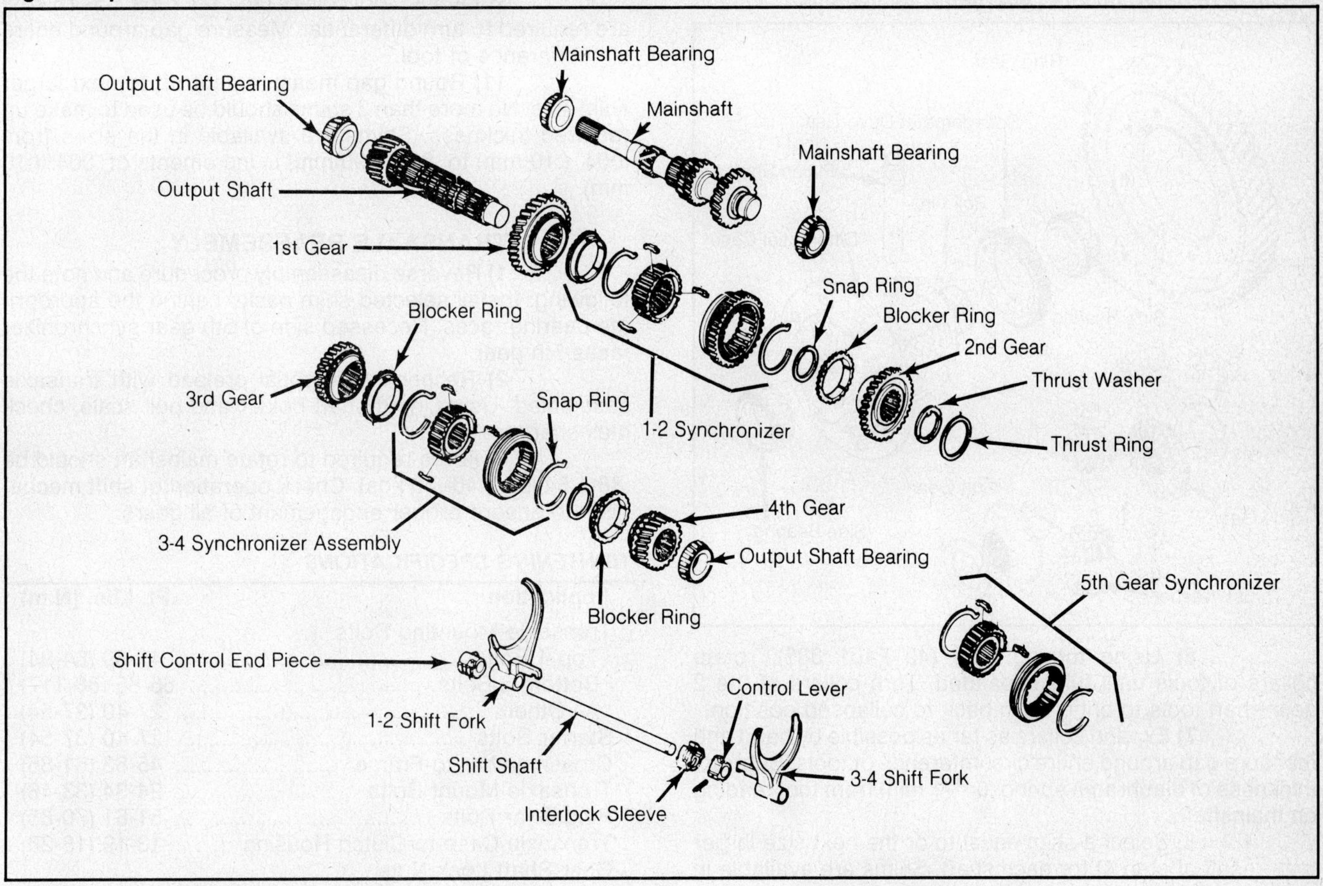

3) Clearance should be .004-.020" (.095-.5 mm) on 4th and 3rd gears, .010-.020 (.245-.5 mm) on 2nd gear and .006-.020" (.14-.5 mm) on 1st gear.

4) Press inner bearing race and 4th gear off rear of output shaft. Remove blocker ring and synchronizer retaining ring from shaft.

5) Press 3-4 synchronizer assembly and 3rd gear off shaft with a bearing separator. Remove thrust ring, thrust washer, 2nd gear, blocker ring and synchronizer retaining ring from shaft.

6) Press 1st gear and 1-2 synchronizer assembly off of shaft. Do not remove front bearing inner race unless replacement is necessary. To remove bearing, press off using bearing separator.

7) Slide synchronizer sleeves off of their hubs and remove all keys and springs. Check end clearance between blocker ring matching teeth and gear matching teeth. Clearance should be .031-.059" (.79-1.5 mm). Check to make sure that blocker ring grips gear cone properly.

Reassembly

To reassemble, reverse disassembly procedure and note the following: Ensure that interlock sleeve engages shift forks properly.

DIFFERENTIAL

Disassembly

1) Remove ring gear bolts and ring gear. Drive roll pin retaining pinion shaft out of differential case. Press pinion shaft out of case.

2) Rotate side gears to bring pinion gears and thrust washers to an opening in case. Remove pinion gears, side gears and thrust washers from case. Press differential side bearings and speedometer drive gear off of case.

Reassembly

To reassemble, reverse removal procedure and note the following: Pinion gear to side gear backlash must be checked using a dial indicator. Backlash should be 0-.004" (0-.1 mm). Adjust backlash by changing the thickness of the side gear thrust washer.

REASSEMBLY & ADJUSTMENT

BEARING PRELOAD

1) Remove differential side oil seals and rear side bearing outer race. Remove side bearing adjusting shim. Remove outer races of both shaft bearings from transaxle housing.

2) Remove adjusting shims and diaphragm spring. Reinstall shaft bearing races without shims or spring. Remove outer races of both shaft gears from clutch housing.

3) Insert rear differential race and front shaft races into Shim Selectors (49 401 383 for mainshaft, 49 F401 382 for output shaft and 49 F401 381 for differential).

4) Adjust all 3 shim selectors to minimum height. Place clutch housing on bench or support fixture with clutch housing flange facing down. Install differential in case.

5) Place shim selectors for mainshaft and output shaft into proper bearing bore and install both gear shafts. Install differential shim selector on top of differential. Install transaxle case and secure with 10 Spacers and Bolts (49 F401 384 and 49 F401 386). Tighten bolts.

MAZDA FWD 4 & 5-SPEED TRANSAXLE (Cont.)

Fig. 4: Exploded View of Differential Assembly

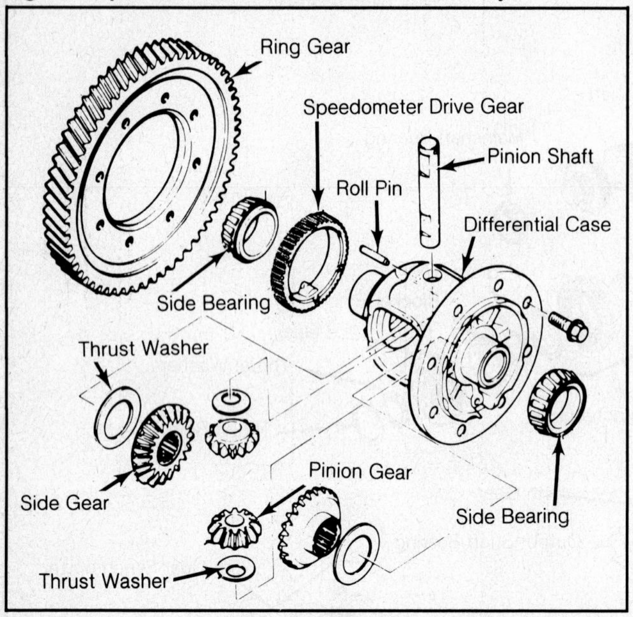

6) Using turning bars (49 F401 385), rotate collars of tools until fully expanded. Turn collars of the 2 gear shaft tools to bring them back to collapsed position.

7) Expand collars as far as possible by hand and measure gap around entire circumference of tools. Subtract thickness of diaphragm spring .04" (1 mm) from tool reading on mainshaft.

8) Select a shim equal to or the next size larger than result of step **4)** for each shaft. Shims are available in sizes from .008" (.2 mm) to .022" (.55 mm) in increments of .002" (.05 mm).

9) Install preload adapter shaft and attachment arm (49 FT01 515 & 49 01080 510A) into the differential. Attach a pull scale to hole in end of arm.

10) Adjust tool collars until 1-1.7 lbs. (.5-.76 kgs) are required to turn differential. Measure gap around entire circumference of tool.

11) Round gap measurement off to next larger shim size. No more than 3 shims should be used to make up required thickness. Shims are available in the sizes from .004" (.10 mm) to .036" (.90 mm) in increments of .004" (.10 mm).

TRANSAXLE REASSEMBLY

1) Reverse disassembly procedure and note the following: Install selected shim packs behind the appropriate bearing races. Recessed side of 5th gear synchronizer faces 5th gear.

2) Recheck differential preload with transaxle assembled. Using input shaft holder and pull scale, check mainshaft preload.

3) Force required to rotate mainshaft should be .88-1.54 lbs. (.40-.70 kgs). Check operation of shift mechanism to ensure proper engagement of all gears.

TIGHTENING SPECIFICATIONS

Application	Ft. Lbs. (N.m)
Transaxle Mounting Bolts	
Top 4 Bolts	47-69 (64-94)
Bottom 2 Bolts	65-86 (88-117)
All Others	27-40 (37-54)
Starter Bolts	27-40 (37-54)
Crossmember-to-Frame	45-63 (61-85)
Transaxle Mount Bolts	24-34 (33-46)
Ring Gear Bolts	51-61 (70-85)
Transaxle Case-to-Clutch Housing	13-19 (18-26)
Gear Shaft Lock Nuts	
(5-Speed Only)	94-152 (127-206)
	INCH Lbs. (N.m)
Rear Cover Bolts	
(5-Speed Only)	72-96 (8-11)

Fig. 5: Bearing Preload Adjustment Procedure

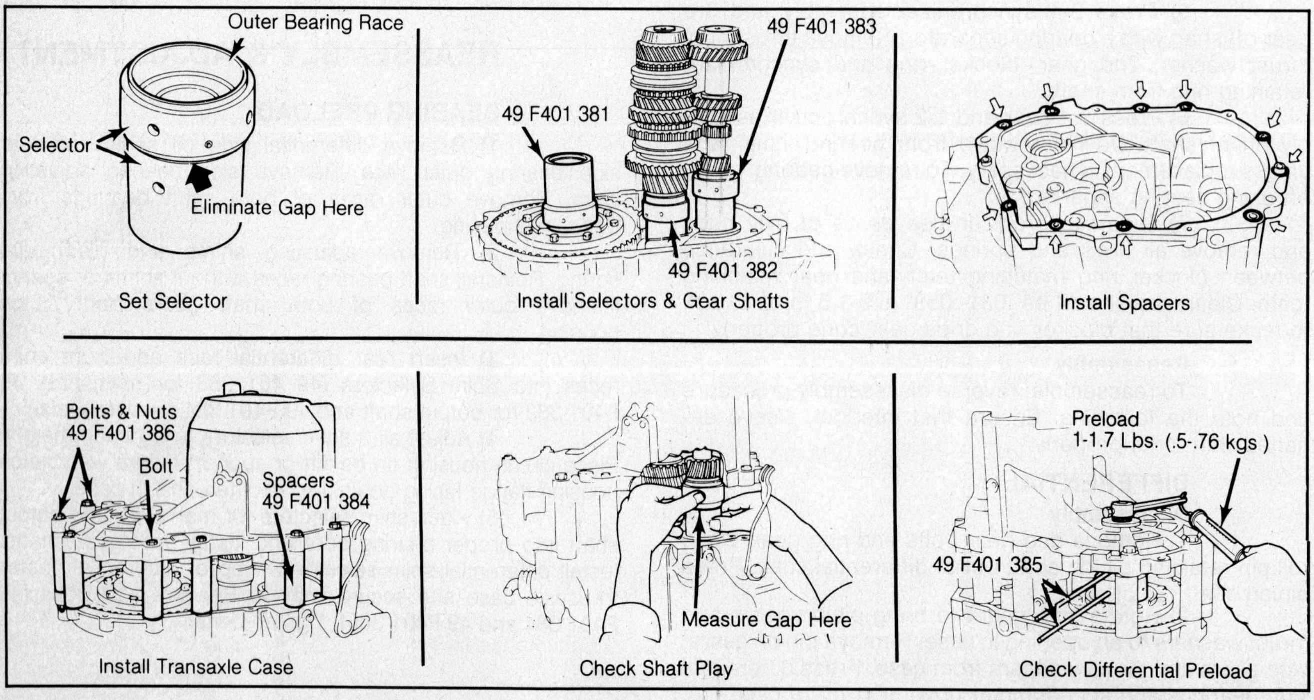

MAZDA REAR WHEEL DRIVE 4 & 5-SPEED

B2000 Pickup, RX7

DESCRIPTION

The 4 and 5-speed transmissions are fully synchronized in all forward gears. Synchronizers are of blocker type and provide for smooth gear engagement. Gear selection is accomplished by direct control from floor mounted shift lever. On all models, clutch housing is integral with transmission case. The center support plate is mounted between transmission case and extension housing on 4-speed models, and between transmission case and intermediate housing on 5-speed models and is also the main gear support.

LUBRICATION & ADJUSTMENT

See the appropriate article in MANUAL TRANSMISSION SERVICING section.

TROUBLE SHOOTING

HARD SHIFTING

Improperly adjusted clutch. Wear or play of shift fork or shift rod. Weakened synchronizer insert spring. Face of synchronizer ring, in contact with insert, worn. Excessive wear of synchronizer key spring. Cones on synchronizer ring and gear worn or not in proper contact. Excessive bearing wear.

SLIPS OUT OF GEAR

Bearings worn or defective. Excessive play between gears and collars. Play in clutch hub and sliding sleeve. Shift arm worn. Lock ball spring weak or broken. Loose or incorrect installation of engine mounts or transmission mounts

TRANSMISSION NOISY

Low or incorrect lubricant. Gears or bearings worn or damaged. Worn gears or collars. Worn clutch hub or mainshaft splines. Incorrectly meshed gears.

REMOVAL & INSTALLATION

See the appropriate article in MANUAL TRANSMISSION REMOVAL section.

TRANSMISSION DISASSEMBLY

1) Clean exterior of transmission assembly. Remove throw-out bearing and clutch release fork. Remove front cover bolts (or nuts) and remove front cover, shims, gasket and oil seal.

2) Remove gearshift lever retainer and gasket from extension housing. Remove extension housing bolts and slide extension housing off mainshaft with control lever positioned to the left as far as possible. Remove control lever end attaching bolt and remove control lever end and control rod from housing.

3) Remove speedometer driven gear assembly, back-up light switch and overdrive switch from extension housing. Remove top switch from transmission case. On 4-speed models, remove speedometer drive gear snap ring from mainshaft and slide drive gear off mainshaft. Remove lock ball.

Fig. 1: Exploded View of Front Bearing Cover and Input Shaft Assembly

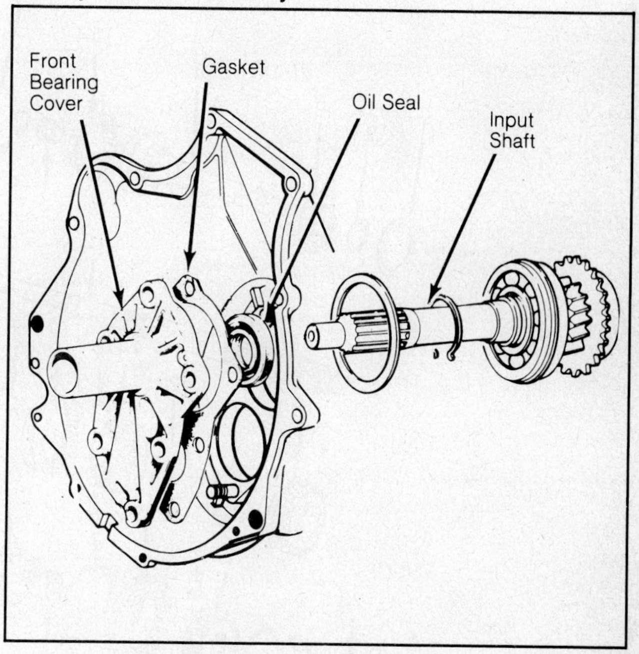

4) On all models, remove snap ring from input shaft and countershaft. Separate transmission case from bearing plate/intermediate housing using Pusher (49 0305 430) or by tapping input shaft with plastic faced hammer. Remove input shaft bearing from transmission case. Using Bearing Puller (49 0710 520), remove countershaft front bearing from countershaft.

5) On 5-speed models, remove speedometer drive gear snap ring from mainshaft and slide drive gear off mainshaft. Remove lock ball and drive gear positioning snap ring. On 4-speed models, remove 3 spring cap bolts and remove springs and shift locking balls.

6) On 5-speed models, remove shift rod end attaching bolts and remove shift rod ends. Separate bearing plate from intermediate housing by lightly tapping housing with plastic faced hammer.

7) On 4-speed models, remove reverse shift rod, shift fork assembly and reverse gear from bearing plate. Remove shift fork set screws. Remove shift rods and forks by pushing shift rods rearward through shift forks and bearing plate. Remove reverse shift rod locking ball, spring and interlock pins from bearing plate.

8) On 5-speed models, remove 3 spring cap bolts and remove springs and shift locking balls. Remove 3 shift rod snap rings. Remove shift fork attaching bolts, shift fork rods and shift forks. Remove lock ball, spring and interlock pins.

NOTE: **On 5-speed, be careful not to lose lock ball when removing 5th-Reverse shift rod.**

9) On 4-speed models, straighten lock washer tab and secure mainshaft with Holder (49 0259 440) and loosen lock nut using wrench. Remove reverse gear and key from mainshaft. Remove countershaft snap ring and counter reverse gear.

MAZDA REAR WHEEL DRIVE 4 & 5-SPEED (Cont.)

Fig. 2: Exploded View of Mazda 4 and 5-Speed Transmission Gears and Shafts

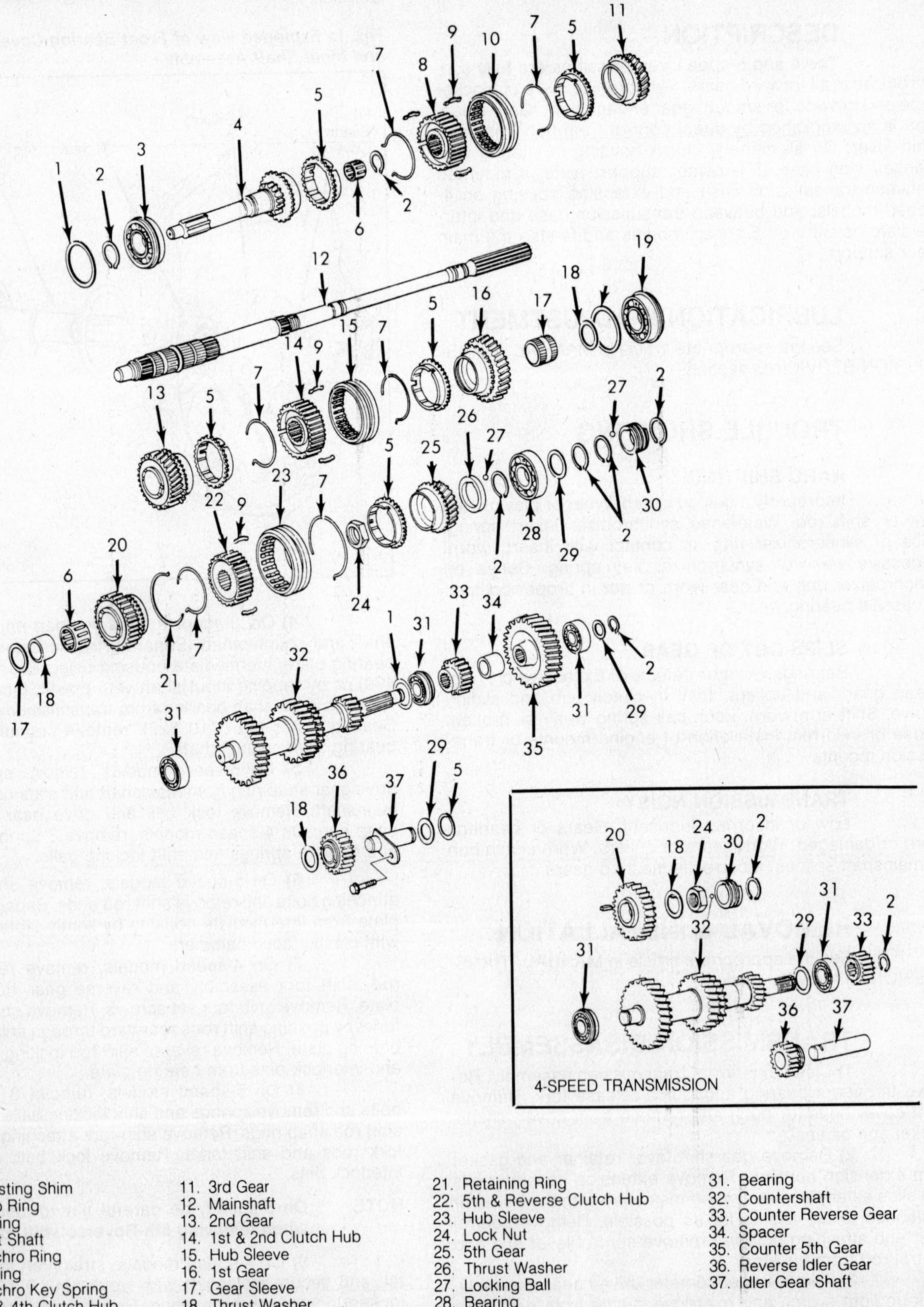

1. Adjusting Shim
2. Snap Ring
3. Bearing
4. Input Shaft
5. Synchro Ring
6. Bearing
7. Synchro Key Spring
8. 3rd & 4th Clutch Hub
9. Synchro Key
10. Hub Sleeve
11. 3rd Gear
12. Mainshaft
13. 2nd Gear
14. 1st & 2nd Clutch Hub
15. Hub Sleeve
16. 1st Gear
17. Gear Sleeve
18. Thrust Washer
19. Bearing
20. Reverse Gear
21. Retaining Ring
22. 5th & Reverse Clutch Hub
23. Hub Sleeve
24. Lock Nut
25. 5th Gear
26. Thrust Washer
27. Locking Ball
28. Bearing
29. Adjusting Washer
30. Speedometer Drive Gear
31. Bearing
32. Countershaft
33. Counter Reverse Gear
34. Spacer
35. Counter 5th Gear
36. Reverse Idler Gear
37. Idler Gear Shaft

10) Remove bearing cover and reverse idler gear shaft from bearing plate. Using plastic faced hammer, tap rear end of mainshaft and countershaft assemblies and remove from bearing plate, being careful not to damage shafts. Remove bearings from bearing plate.

11) On 5-speed models, remove mainshaft and countershaft snap rings and adjusting washers. Remove rear bearings using Bearing Remover (49 0839 425C).

12) From rear of mainshaft, remove snap ring, thrust washer, lock ball, 5th gear, synchronizer ring, counter 5th gear and spacer. Engage clutch sleeves into 1st and reverse gear to lock mainshaft assembly. Mount bearing plate in vise. Remove lock nut caulking using a chisel.

13) Remove and discard lock nut using wrench. Remove 5th-Reverse clutch hub assembly, reverse gear, needle bearing, inner race, thrust washer, counter reverse gear, snap ring, thrust washers and reverse idler gear.

14) Using plastic faced hammer, tap rear end of mainshaft and countershaft assemblies and remove from bearing plate. Remove bearing cover and bearings from bearing plate.

Fig. 3: Removing Reverse and Counter Reverse Gear Assemblies

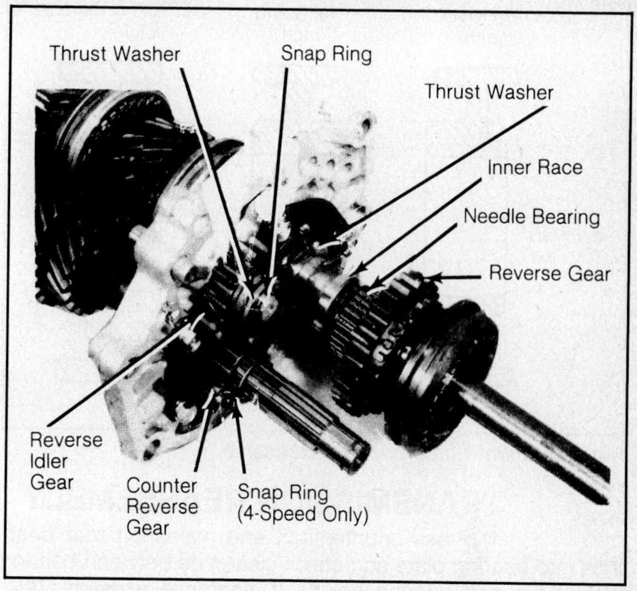

COMPONENT DISASSEMBLY & REASSEMBLY

MAINSHAFT

Disassembly

1) On 4-speed models, remove thrust washer, 1st gear, sleeve and synchronizer ring from mainshaft. Remove snap ring from front of mainshaft. Using arbor press and Pulley-Boss Puller (49 0636 145), remove 3rd-4th clutch hub and sleeve assembly, synchronizer ring and 3rd gear from front of mainshaft.

2) Reposition mainshaft in press and remove 1st-2nd clutch hub and sleeve assembly, synchronizer ring and 2nd gear from rear of mainshaft.

3) On 5-speed models, remove snap ring from front of mainshaft. Remove 3rd-4th synchronizer hub assembly, synchronizer ring, 3rd gear, thrust washer and synchronizer ring. Remove 1st gear, needle bearing, inner race, 1st-2nd synchronizer hub assembly, synchronizer ring and 2nd gear.

Mainshaft Inspection

Inspect mainshaft for runout by positioning a dial indicator along the shaft in several places. If runout exceeds .0002" (.03 mm), replace mainshaft. Inspect all other surfaces and splines for wear and/or damage.

Synchronizer Inspection

1) Inspect unit for worn or damaged parts. Install synchronizer ring evenly to gear cone and measure clearance between side faces of ring and gear with feeler gauge. If clearance is less than .031" (0.8 mm), replace synchronizer ring or gear. *See Fig. 4.*

2) Inspect contact between ring and gear using machinist blue on cone surface of gear. If contact pattern is poor, correct by lapping surfaces together or by replacing ring or gear. Check synchronizer key spring for tension. Ensure that clutch sleeve slides easily on clutch hub. Check clearance between shift fork and clutch using feeler gauge. Clearance limit is .031" (0.8 mm). *See Fig. 5.*

Fig. 4: Checking Synchronizer Ring Clearance with Feeler Gauge

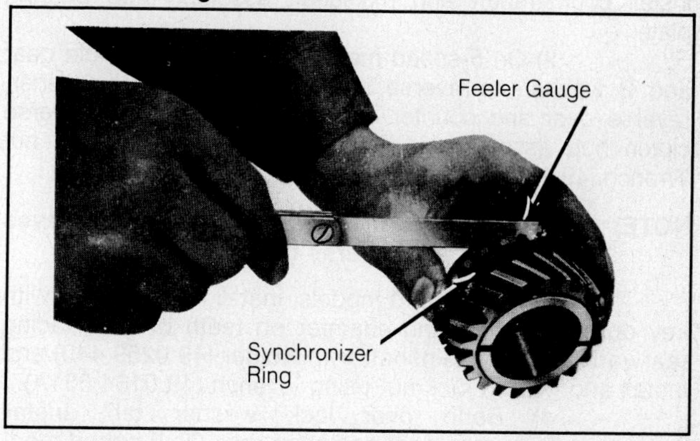

Fig. 5: Checking Clutch Hub Sleeve and Release Fork Clearance with Feeler Gauge

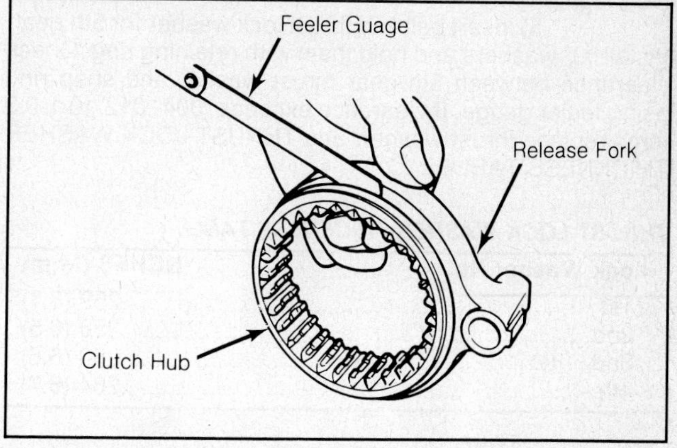

Reassembly Mainshaft

Place 3rd gear and synchronizer ring on mainshaft. Press 3rd and 4th clutch hub assembly using arbor press and Puller-Boss Puller (49 0636 145). Install 2nd gear, synchronizer ring, 1st-2nd clutch hub and sleeve assembly on mainshaft using arbor press. Install gear sleeve, 1st gear and washer to mainshaft. Install needle bearing, synchronizer ring and input shaft.

MAZDA REAR WHEEL DRIVE 4 & 5-SPEED (Cont.)

Fig. 6: Checking Bearing Housing Clearances

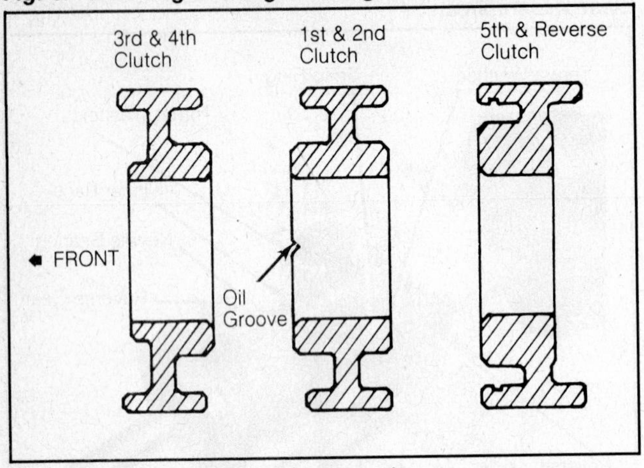

Replace shim if clearance is excessive.

TRANSMISSION REASSEMBLY

1) Press countershaft and mainshaft rear bearings into bearing plate and check clearance between bearing plate bore and bearing height. If clearance exceeds .004" (0.1 mm), replace adjusting shim. *See Fig. 6.* Install and tighten bearing cover-to-bearing housing. Using arbor press, install countershaft and mainshaft assembly into bearing plate.

2) On 5-speed models, secure reverse idle gear and 2 washers-to-reverse idle gear shaft. Install washer, reverse gear and counter reverse gear. Install 5th reverse clutch hub assembly and tighten lock nut with Lock nut Wrench (49 1243 465A).

NOTE: **Tighten after first sliding clutch hub sleeves onto 1st and reverse gears to lock shaft.**

3) On 4-speed models, install reverse gear with key onto mainshaft and chamfer on teeth of gear facing rearward. Secure mainshaft with Holder (49 0259 440) and install and tighten lock nut using Wrench (49 0164 631A).

4) Bend over lock washer tab. Install countershaft reverse gear and snap ring. On 5-speed models, bend lock washer tab. Install 5th gear and synchronizer ring on mainshaft. Install spacer, counter gear, lock nut and hand tighten.

5) Insert ball and thrust lock washer for 5th gear. Install "C" washers and hold them with retaining ring. Check clearance between 5th gear thrust washer and snap ring using feeler gauge. If clearance exceeds .004-.012" (0.1-0.3 mm), replace thrust washer. See THRUST LOCK WASHER THICKNESS TABLE.

THRUST LOCK WASHER THICKNESS TABLE

Lock Washer No.	INCHES (M m)
1st	.252 (6.4)
2nd	.256 (6.5)
3nd	.260 (6.6)
4th	..264 (6.7)

6) Press mainshaft side bearing on using Lock Nut Wrench (49 1243 465A). Install "C" washers, retaining ring, washer and snap ring. Check clearance between mainshaft "C" washers and wash using feeler gauge. If clearance exceeds .012" (0.3 mm), replace "C" washer. See "C" WASHER THICKNESS TABLE.

"C" WASHER THICKNESS TABLE

"C" Washer No	INCHES (M m)
1st	.114 (2.9)
2nd	.118 (3.0)
3nd	.122 (3.1)
4th	.126 (3.2)

CAUTION: **Insure that there is no clearance between mainshaft side bearing and "C" washers**

7) Install countershaft rear bearing using Bearing Installer (49 0500 330). Shift clutch hubs sleeves to first gear and reverse to put gears in double-engaged condition. Install Mainshaft Holder (49 0259 440) on mainshaft and install and tighten lock nut.

NOTE: **There are 2 types of springs; be sure to install them correctly.**

Fig. 7: Shift Rod Spring (5th and Reverse)

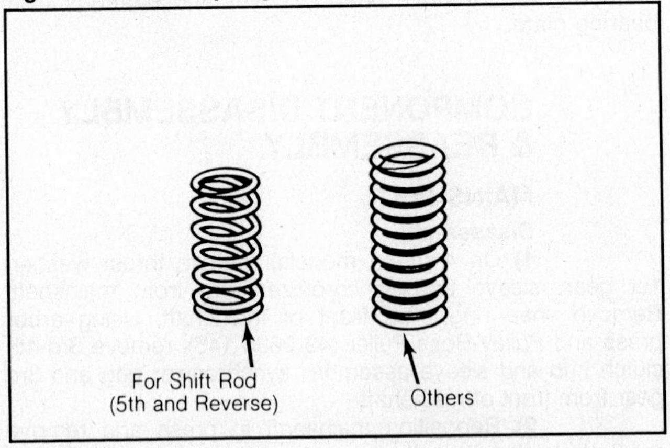

8) On all models, install reverse shift spring and locking ball into bearing plate. *See Fig. 7.* Push ball down using screwdriver and Interlock Pin Guide (49 0187 451A) and install reverse shift rod, shift fork and reverse idler gear (4-speed only) at same time. Install 5th and reverse shift rod, washer and snap ring (5-speed only).

9) Install 1st-2nd and 3rd-4th shift forks onto clutch sleeves. Using Guides (49 0862 350 & 49 0187 451A), install each shift fork rod and interlock pin. Align bolt holes in both shift forks and rods. Install and tighten lock bolts. Install snap rings onto shift rods (5-speed only). *See Fig. 8.*

NOTE: **On 4-speed, make sure that spacer is installed in position on reverse shift fork rod.**

10) Install shift locking balls and springs into respective bores in bearing plate. Install and tighten spring cap bolts. On 4-speed models, apply thin coat of sealer on contact surfaces of bearing plate and transmission case and assemble.

11) On 5-speed models, apply thin coat of sealer on contact surfaces of bearing plate and intermediate housing and assemble. Install shift rod ends to shift rods and install and tighten bolts. On all models, install speedometer drive gear, lock ball and snap ring on mainshaft.

12) On 5-speed models, apply thin coat of sealer on contact surfaces of bearing plate and transmission case, and assemble. On all models, install input shaft bearing, using bearing Installer (49 0500 330), and install snap ring. Install countershaft front bearing, using bearing Installer (49 0180 321A).

MAZDA REAR WHEEL DRIVE 4 & 5-SPEED (Cont.)

Fig. 8: Assembled View of Reverse Shift Fork and Shift Rod Assemblies

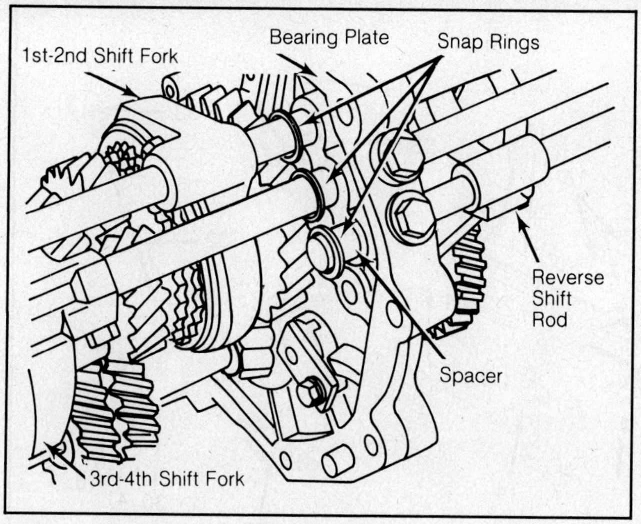

Fig. 9: View of Front Case Showing Front Bearing End Play Shim Location

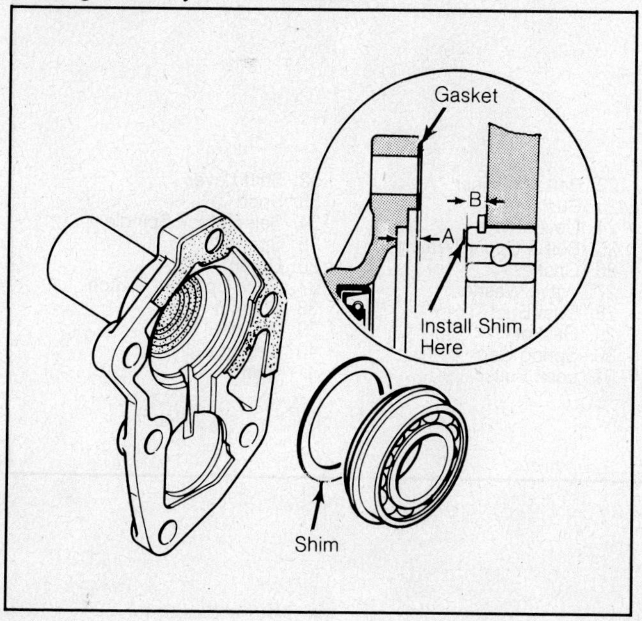

13) Install speedometer driven gear assembly, lock plate and bolt into extension housing and tighten bolt. Install control lever through holes from front side of extension housing. Install control lever end, control lever and tighten bolt. Install back-up light switch, top switch and overdrive switch.

14) Apply thin coat of sealer on contact surfaces of bearing plate/intermediate housing and extension housing and assemble with control lever positioned to the left as far as possible. Install and tighten bolts, making sure control rod operates properly. Install gearshift lever retainer and gasket to extension housing.

15) Lubricate lip of oil seal inside front cover and install front cover to transmission case. Check clearance between bearing outer race and front cover using feeler gauge. *See Fig. 10*. If clearance exceeds .004" (0.1 mm), replace adjusting shim. See ADJUSTING SHIM TABLE.

16) On all models, install throw-out bearing, clutch release fork and dust cover.

ADJUSTING SHIM TABLE

Washer No.	INCH (mm)
1st	.006 (.15)
2nd	.012 (.30)

TIGHTENING SPECIFICATIONS

Application	Ft. Lbs. (N.m)
Bearing Cover	13-20 (18-26)
Countershaft Lock Nut	94-145 (127-196)
Extension Housing	12-17 (16-23)
Front Cover	14-19 (19-26)
Mainshaft Lock Nut	
4-Speed	116-174 (157-237)
5-Speed	94-152 (128-207)
	INCH Lbs. (N.m)
Shift Fork Bolts	108-144 (12-16)
Spring Cap Bolts	84-132 (10-15)
Interlock Pin Plug	84-132 (10-15)
Shift Rod End Bolts	72-108 (8-12)

MAZDA REAR WHEEL DRIVE 4 & 5-SPEED (Cont.)

Fig. 10: Exploded View of 4-Speed Transmission Shift Control Linkage

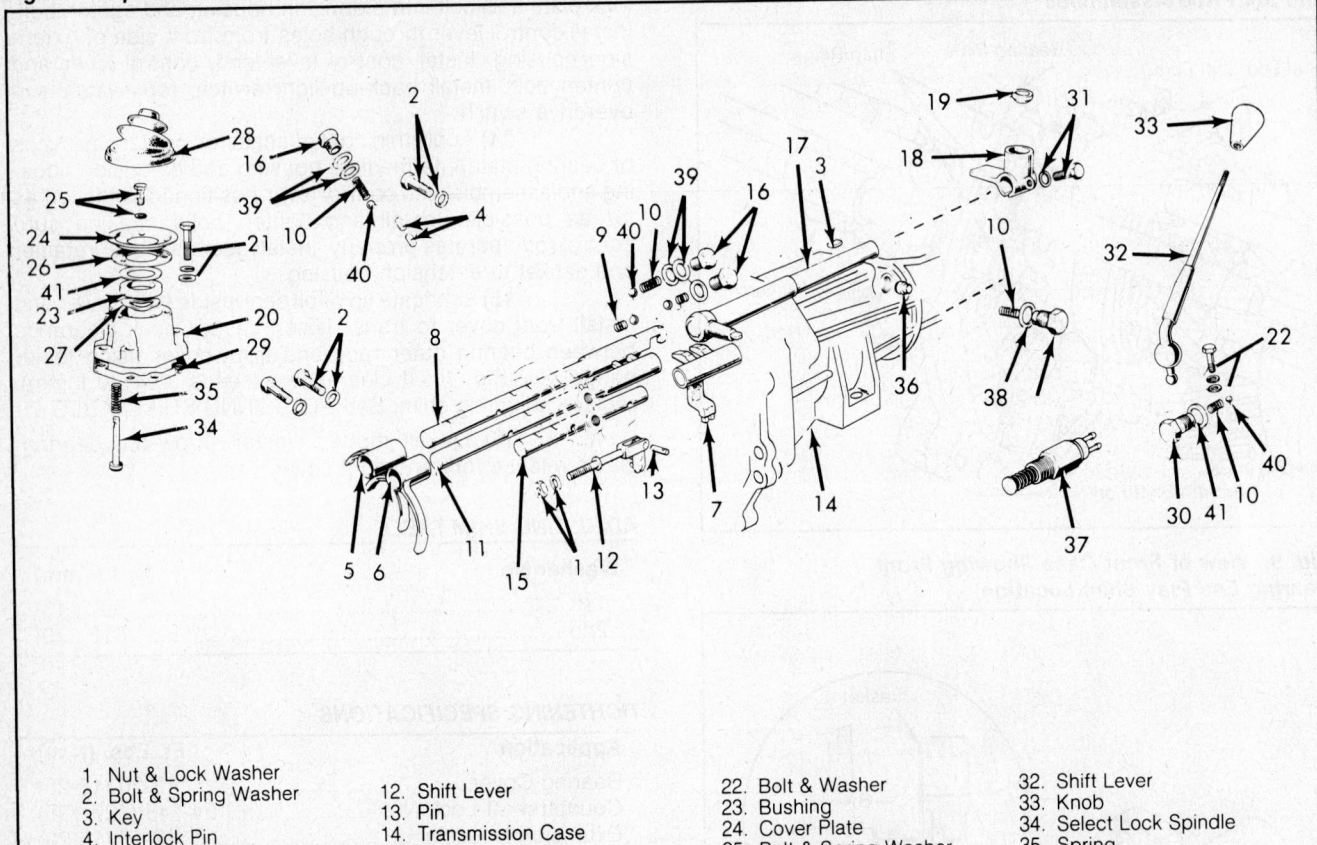

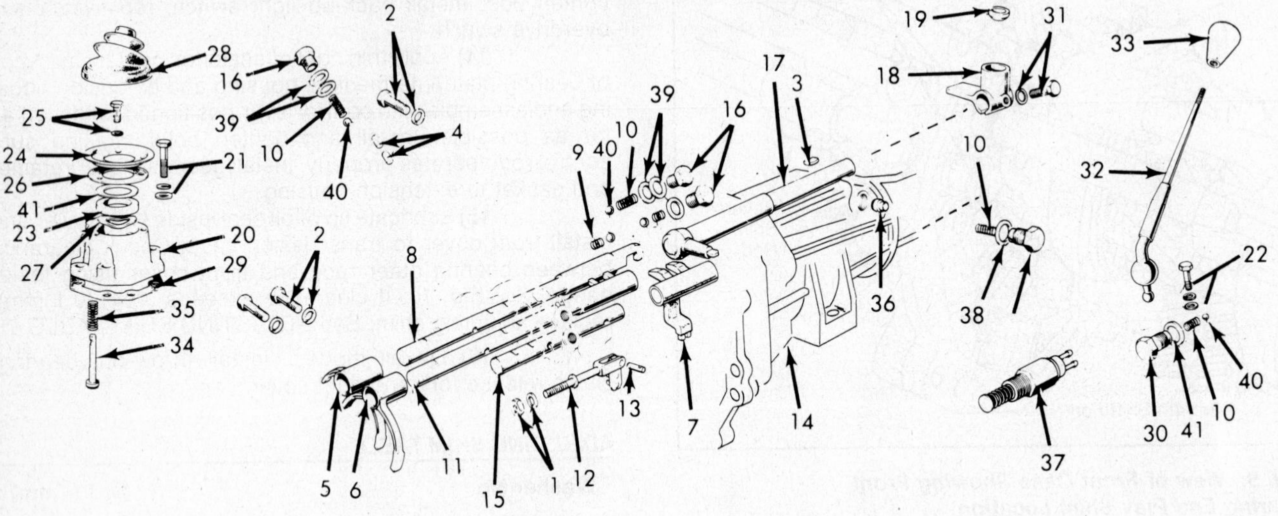

1. Nut & Lock Washer
2. Bolt & Spring Washer
3. Key
4. Interlock Pin
5. 1st-2nd Shift Fork
6. 3rd-4th Shift Fork
7. Reverse Shift Fork
8. Shift Rod
9. Spring
10. Spring
11. Shift Rod
12. Shift Lever
13. Pin
14. Transmission Case
15. Reverse Shift Rod
16. Plug
17. Control Lever
18. Control Rod End
19. Spring Seat
20. Shifter Housing
21. Retaining Bolt & Washer
22. Bolt & Washer
23. Bushing
24. Cover Plate
25. Bolt & Spring Washer
26. Gasket
27. Wave Washer
28. Dust Boot
29. Gasket
30. Spring Cap
31. Lock Bolt
32. Shift Lever
33. Knob
34. Select Lock Spindle
35. Spring
36. Detent
37. Back-Up Light Switch
38. Washer
39. Washer
40. Detent Ball
41. Shim

5-speed shift control linkage similar.

MERCEDES BENZ GL 68/20 5-SPEED

190D, 190E

DESCRIPTION

Transmission model 717.4 (GL 68/20) is a countershaft type with 5 synchromesh forward gears and one synchronized reverse gear. The reverse gear is located between the intermediate plate and the rear transmission cover. The 5th gear, is designed as an overdrive and is located at the rear of the transmission.

The reverse gear is a standstill synchronizing system. The reverse gear can only be engaged on a stopped vehicle. When reverse gear is engaged, the synchronization of the 5th gear is deactivated by a slotted lever and the input shaft.

The mainshaft and countershaft are mounted in 2 tapered roller bearings each, the countershaft has an additional needle bearing. All transmission housing components and rear cover are light alloy die castings. The clutch housing is part of the main transmission housing.

REMOVAL & INSTALLATION

See appropriate article in MANUAL TRANSMISSION REMOVAL section.

LUBRICATION & ADJUSTMENT

See appropriate article in MANUAL TRANSMISSION SERVICING section

TROUBLE SHOOTING

GEAR SELECTING

Transmission Can Be Shifted Only From 1st to 2nd Gear

Roughness of sliding sleeve too high or friction value too low. Replace sliding sleeve and synchronizing rings as necessary.

Shift Throw Too Long

Shift lever on transmission loose. Unscrew bolt on shift lever. Clean and lubricate threads and sealing surface with Loctite (242) and tighten shift lever to 67 INCH lbs. (25 N.m).

Movement Of Shift In 3rd Gear On Acceleration And Deacceleration

End play of 3rd and 4th sychronizing rings too high or locking ring not seated in groove. Reduce end play of sychronizing rings by using locking of different thickness.

Gear Hop In Forward Speeds Under No-Load Conditions

Check engine mounts and replace as necessary. Adjust gear shift. Replace shif rocker with detent contour for 1st and 2nd gear or 3rd and 4th gear. Replace leaf spring.

Gear Hop In Forward Gears During Acceleration or Deacceleration

Backing of stub teeth of gear wheel or sliding sleeve defective. Replace sliding sleeve and gear wheel for appropriate gear.

Fig. 1: Sectional View of Mercedes-Benz GL 68/20 5-Speed Transmission

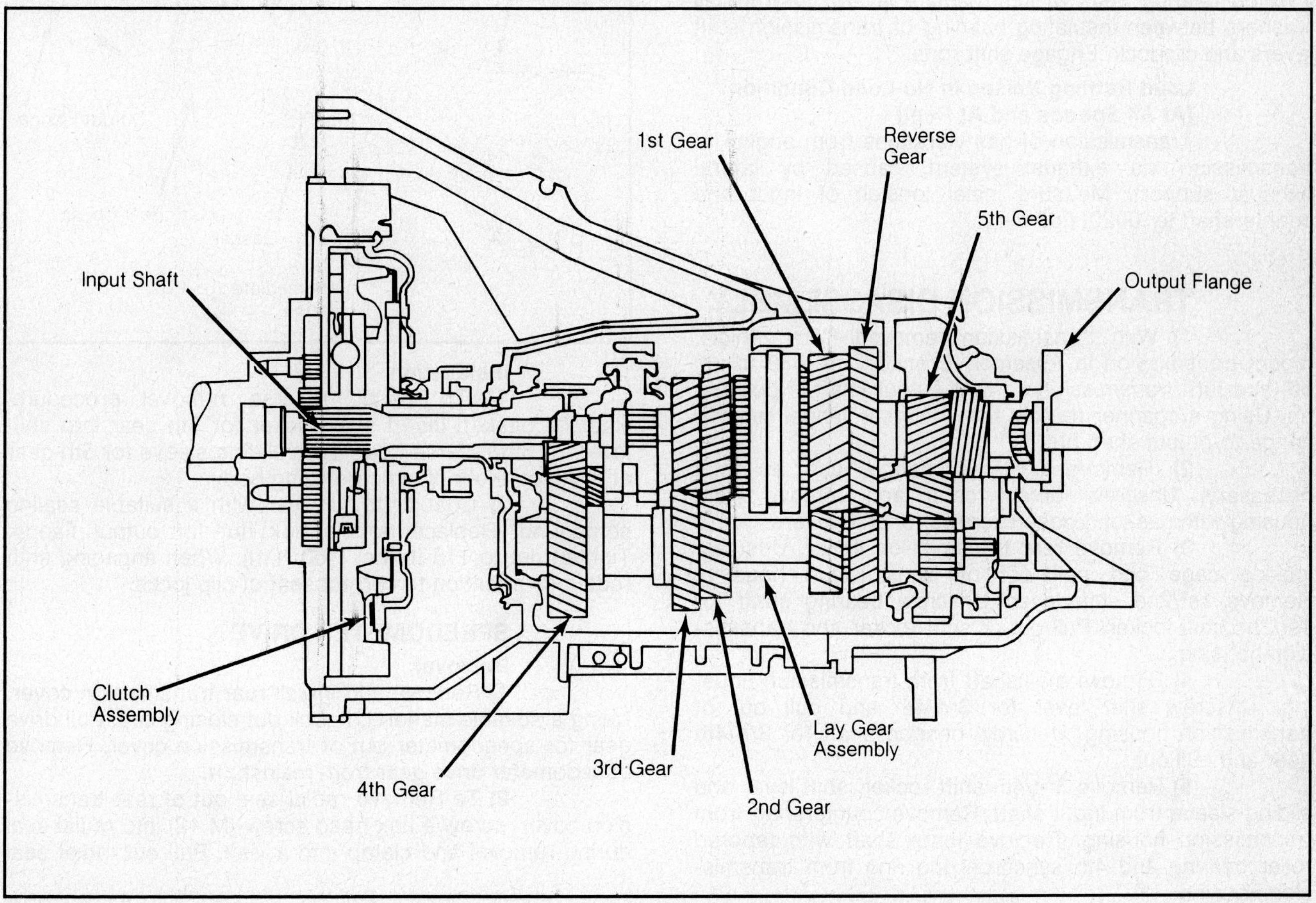

MERCEDES BENZ GL 68/20 5-SPEED (Cont.)

Forward Gears Hard To Shift

1) Measure path for clutch pedal (limiting stop for clutch pedal must be adjusted. Bleed clutch hydraulic system. Check clutch master cylinder for leaks.

2) With clutch pedal depressed, check whether fluid in supply tank is agitated with air. Check slave cylinder for leaks. Check clutch disc for proper runout. Maximum runout is .020" (.5 mm).

Hard Shifting Into 2nd Gear (Cold Condition)

Friction torque between synchronizing ring and sliding sleeve is either too low or internal friction looses of transmission. Replace synchronizing rings and sliding sleeve.

Clicking Noise When Starting Off

Loose tolerances between teeth of main shaft and teeth of universal joint flange. Install Washer (116 272 00 76) between speedometer gear and output flange.

Loud Rattling Noises In Forward Gear and Reverse

Teeth of countershaft and input shaft damaged by fractured tooth flanks on reverse slide gear and reverse gear of main shaft. Change transmission. Install oil drain plug with a magnet.

Rattling Noise In Reverse Gear Only

Damage on tooth tips of main shat reverse gear and reverse slide gear. Install oil drain plug with a magnet.

Humming Noises Of Shift Rods

Disengage all shift rods on intermediate levers of gear shift bracket. Install convex spring (10 N a DIN 137) on bearing bolts of intermediate levers. Also install washers between insulating bushing of transmission shift levers and clip lock. Engage shift rods.

Loud Rattling Noises In No-Load Condition (At All Speeds and At Rest)

Transmission of gas vibrations from engine to transmission via exhaust system, caused by lateral exhaust support. Measure initial tension of input and countershaft to .0020" (.05 mm).

TRANSMISSION DISASSEMBLY

1) With transmission removed from vehicle, mount transmission in Assembly Bracket (116 589 05 59 00) and turn transmission so that output shaft is pointing up. Using a spanner to hold the universal flange, remove flange-to-output shaft nut.

2) Remove universal flange, use puller if necessary. Unscrew detent cage and remove from housing with gasket. Loosen screws for shift levers.

3) Remove rear transmission cover. Unscrew locking cage and pull out of transmission housing. Remove 1st/2nd shift lever. Unscrew bearing shaft for 1st/2nd shift locker. Pull out of shift rocker and transmission housing.

4) Remove mainshaft from transmission housing. Unscrew shift lever for 3rd/4th and pull out of transmission housing. Unscrew bearing shaft for 3rd/4th gear and pull out.

5) Remove 3rd/4th shift rocker, shift lever and sliding sleeve from input shaft. Remove countershaft from transmission housing. Remove input shaft with tapered roller bearing and 4th synchronizing ring from transmission housing.

6) Remove front transmission cover, DO NOT lose washers. Using a suitable mandrel, knock out bearing race for input and countershaft. Remove collar nut, bearing bolt with detent leaf spring, locking lever, bearing bushing and spacing washer.

COMPONENT DISASSEMBLY & REASSEMBLY

REAR COVER

Removal

1) Drain transmission fluid. Install an engine support. Disconnect shift rods. Using Torque Wrench (001 589 66 21 00) and Open-End Wrench (201 589 00 01 00), loosen clamping nut of propeller shaft.

2) Disconnect exhaust system at rear suspension, carefully lower and suspend with wire. Remove propeller shaft. Remove speedometer cable.

3) Using Socket (126 589 02 09 00) and Allen Wrench (116 589 10 07 00), remove nut from output flange. Remove output flange. Remove bolts for rear transmission cover and remove cover. *See Fig. 2.*

Fig. 2: Exploded View of Rear Cover Assembly

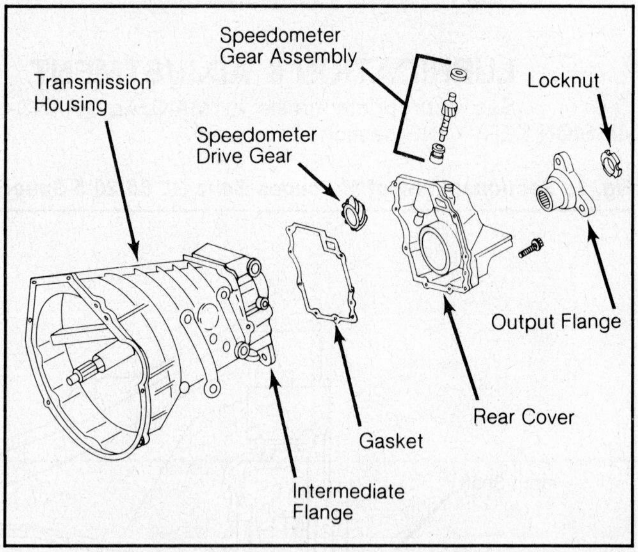

Installation

1) To install, reverse removal procedure. Replace gasket. Insert shift rocker for 5th gear into shift lever for 5th/reverse gear. Turn sliding sleeve for 5th gear and slip on teeth of synchronizing body.

2) Coat bolts for rear with a suitable sealing compound. Replace double hex nut for output flange. Tighten nut to 118 ft. lbs. (160 N.m). When engaging shift rods, pay attention to correct seat of clip locks.

SPEEDOMETER DRIVE

Removal

1) Remove and install rear transmission cover. Using a suitable mandrel, knock out closing cap. Pull drive gear for speedometer out of transmission cover. Remove speedometer drive gear from mainshaft.

2) To Remove radial seal out of rear transmission cover, screw a hex head screw (M 12) into radial seal during removal and clamp into a vise. Pull out radial seal

MERCEDES BENZ GL 68/20 5-SPEED (Cont.)

while applying light blows with a plastic hammer against transmission cover. *See Fig. 3.*

Fig. 3: View of Locking Cap for Reverse Gear

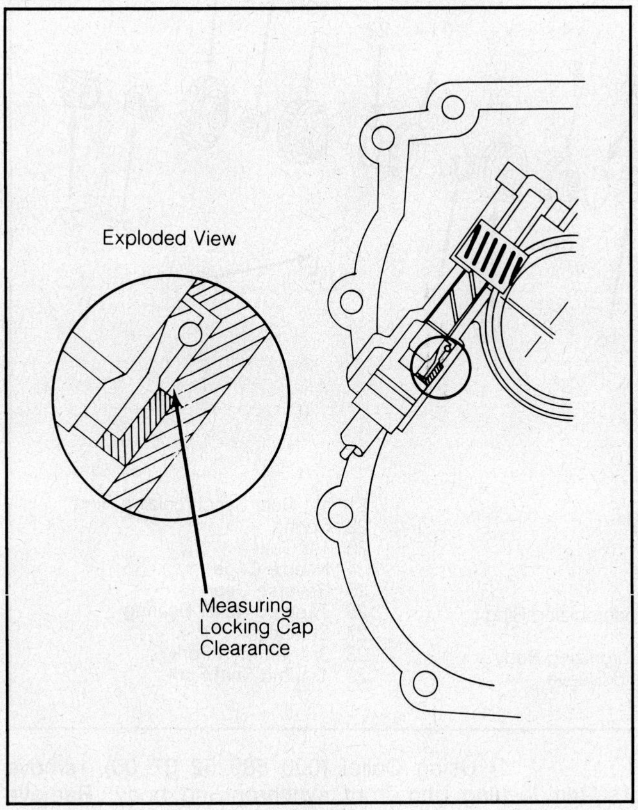

Installation

Using a press, carefully press in radial seal up to stop. Using a suitable mandrel, knock closing cap into rear transmission cover until clearance of .020" (.5 mm) is attained between drive gear and transmission cover. Slip helical gear on mainshaft so that flat side faces toward the rear.

INTERMEDIATE COVER

Removal

1) Remove rear transmision cover and speedometer drive gear. Remove 5th gear locking ring.

2) Remove 5th/reverse sychronizing body and gear with sychronizing ring from countershaft (remove needle cage bearing with gear). Remove thrust washer from countershaft.

3) Remove bolt for reverse shaft and remove intermediate plate from transmission. Remove shift lever for 5th/reverse gear from inside of housing. Force out cover for "O" ring. Remove cover from intermediate plate.

4) Remove pin for reverse idler gear and remove idler gear. Using a press, remove shaft for reverse idler gear. Using a suitable mandrel, knock outer bearing races for main and countershaft out of intermediate plate. *See Fig. 4.*

Inspection

1) Measure distance between parting surface and recess for mainshaft bearing in old and new intermediate plate. If dimension of new intermediate plate is not similar to dimension of old intermediate plate, add required number of compensating washers.

2) Compensating washers are available in .1, .3 and .5 mm thickness. Insert compensating washers into intermediate plate and press in outer bearing race.

Fig. 4: Exploded View of Intermediate Plate Assembly

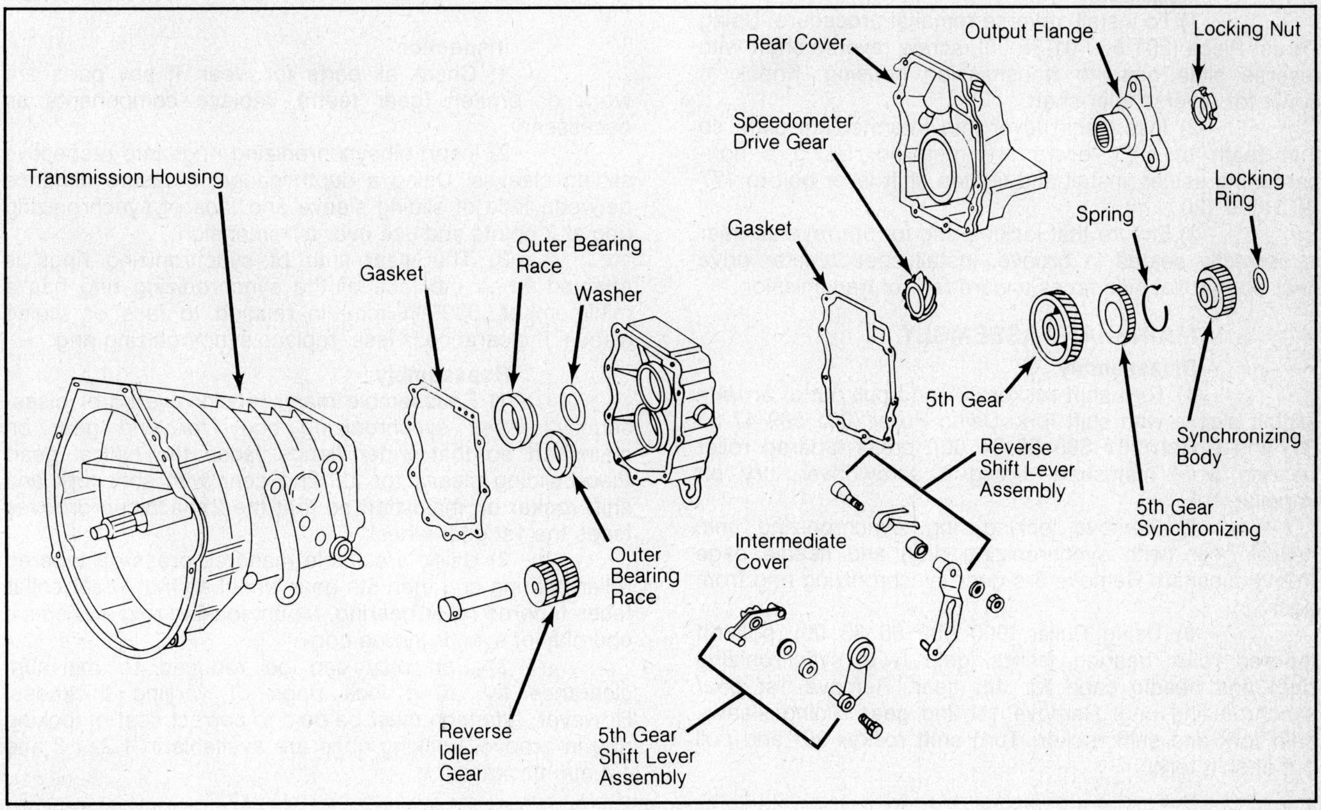

MERCEDES BENZ GL 68/20 5-SPEED (Cont.)

Fig. 5: Exploded View of Main Shaft Assembly

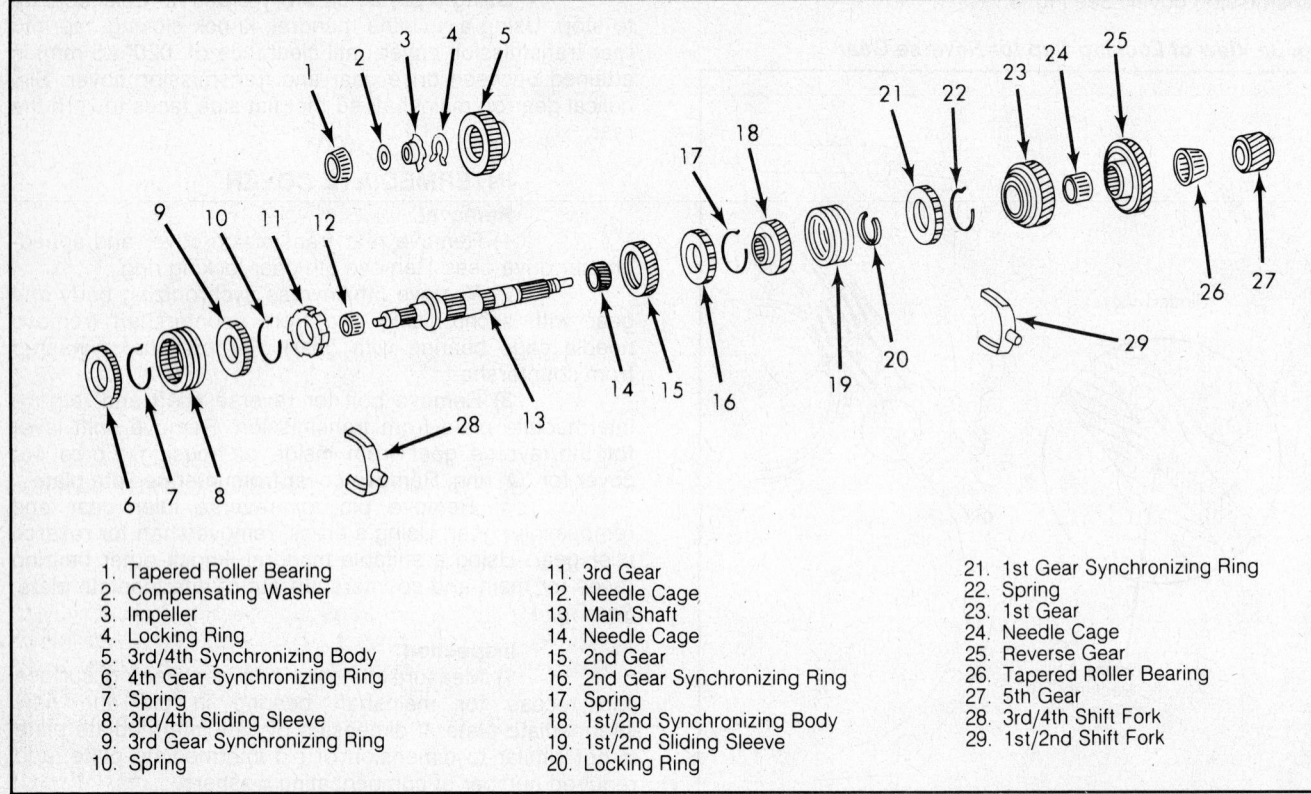

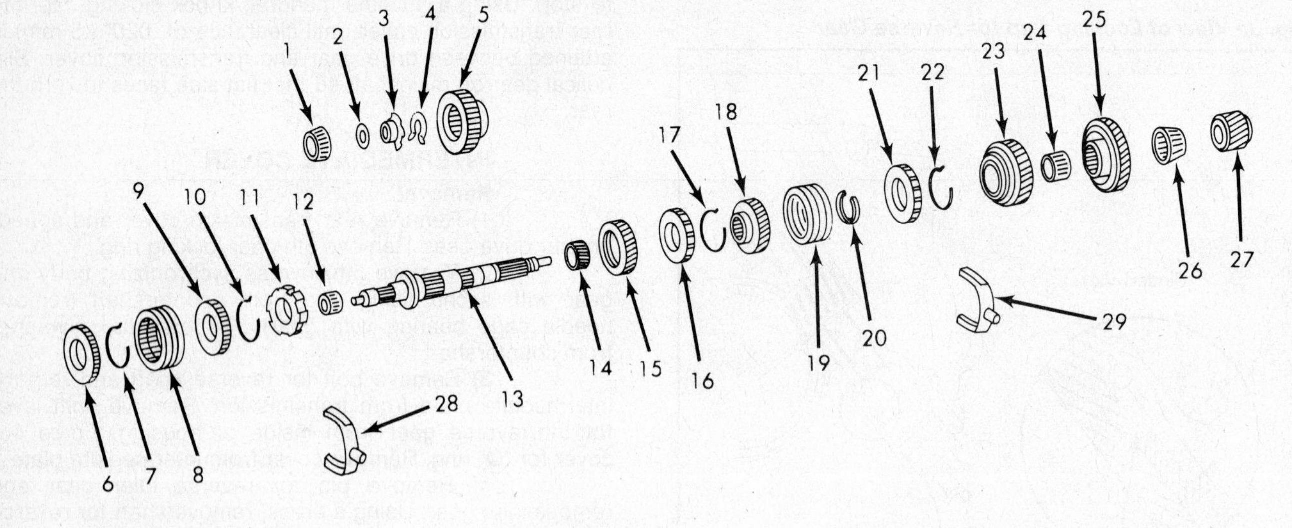

1. Tapered Roller Bearing
2. Compensating Washer
3. Impeller
4. Locking Ring
5. 3rd/4th Synchronizing Body
6. 4th Gear Synchronizing Ring
7. Spring
8. 3rd/4th Sliding Sleeve
9. 3rd Gear Synchronizing Ring
10. Spring
11. 3rd Gear
12. Needle Cage
13. Main Shaft
14. Needle Cage
15. 2nd Gear
16. 2nd Gear Synchronizing Ring
17. Spring
18. 1st/2nd Synchronizing Body
19. 1st/2nd Sliding Sleeve
20. Locking Ring
21. 1st Gear Synchronizing Ring
22. Spring
23. 1st Gear
24. Needle Cage
25. Reverse Gear
26. Tapered Roller Bearing
27. 5th Gear
28. 3rd/4th Shift Fork
29. 1st/2nd Shift Fork

3) Measure preload of tapered roller bearing for input shaft and countershaft. Measured preload should be .020" (.05 mm).

Installation

1) To install, reverse removal procedure. Using Thrust Piece (201 589 01 35 00), screw reverse shaft with reverse slide gear to transmission housing. Knock in cover for reverse idler shaft.

2) Insert shift lever into intermediate plate so that teeth of shift levers are meshing. Using a non-hardening sealer, install and tighten shift lever bolt to 177 INCH lbs. (20 N.m).

3) Ensure that locking ring for 5th/reverse gear is correctly seated in groove. Install speedometer drive gear so that flat side faces toward rear of transmission.

MAINSHAFT ASSEMBLY

Disassembly

1) Turn shift rocker 90° and pull out of 3rd/4th sliding sleeve with shift fork. Using Puller (001 589 47 33 00) and Collet (201 589 06 34 00), press tapered roller bearing from mainshaft. Using a screwdriver, pry off impeller.

2) Remove locking ring, synchronizing unit, helical gear (with synchronizing ring) and needle cage from mainshaft. Remove 3rd gear synchronizing ring from gear.

3) Using Puller (000 589 65 33 00), pull off tapered roller bearing, helical gear (with synchronizing ring) and needle cage for 4th gear. Remove 1st gear synchronizing ring. Remove 1st/2nd gear sliding sleeve, shift fork and shift rocker. Turn shift rocker 90° and pull out of shift fork.

4) Using Collet (000 589 52 37 00), remove 1st/2nd locking ring from synchronizing body. Remove 1st/2nd gear synchronizing body, helical gear (with synchronizing ring) and needle cage from mainshaft. *See Fig. 5.*

Inspection

1) Check all parts for wear. If any parts are worn or broken (gear teeth), replace components as necesssary.

2) Insert all synchronizing rings into respective sliding sleeves. Using a depth gauge, measure distance between face of sliding sleeve and face of synchronizing ring at 3 points and use over all dimension.

3) The wear limit of synchronizing rings is attained when the face of the synchronizing ring has a minimum of .039" (1 mm) in relation to face of sliding sleeve. If clearance is less, replace synchronizing ring.

Reassembly

1) Reassemble mainshaft in reverse of disassemlby. Press synchronizing body for 2nd gear on mainshaft so that wider flange faces the helical gear. Place sliding sleeve for 1st/2nd gear with shift fork and shift rocker on mainshaft so that the 2 machined grooves faces the 1st gear wheel.

2) Using a suitable mandrel, press on tapered roller bearing and then 5th gear wheel so that wider collar faces tapered roller bearing. Mount locking ring and check end play of synchronizing body.

3) End play can be reduced to minimum clearance by using lock rings of varying thickness. However, attention must be paid to correct seat of locking ring in groove. Locking rings are available in 1.2, 1.3 and 1.4 mm thickness.

MERCEDES BENZ GL 68/20 5-SPEED (Cont.)

4) Push synchronizing ring for 3rd gear onto helical gear until annular spring is engaged in groove of helical gear. Assemble shift rocker with shift fork and sliding sleeve so that detent of shift rocker and groove in sliding sleeve are pointing toward 3rd gear.

5) Shift rocker, shift fork and sliding sleeve must be separately installed into transmission housing.

MEASURING TRANSMISSION

MAINSHAFT MEASUREMENT (GEARS ASSEMBLED)

1) Clamp input shaft (without synchronizing rings) into vise and place main shaft with tapered roller bearing on input shaft. Turn main shaft for correct seat of tapered roller bearing.

2) Using a feeler gauge, measure distance between face of locking sleeve on input shaft and face of 3rd/4th synchronizing body. For example: Nominal dimension is .060" (1.5 mm) and measured distance is .051" (1.3 mm), thickness of compensating washer is .0079" (.2 mm).

3) Compensating washers come in thickness from .0020" (.05 mm) to .048" (1.2 mm). Using Collet (201 589 06 34 00) and Puller (001 589 47 33 00), pull tapered roller bearing from mainshaft.

4) Place calculated compensating washers on mainshaft so that thin compensating washers are placed on first. Ensure that compensating washers are not slipping when tapered roller bearing is pressed on, hold down with grease.

5) Using a suitable mandrel, press tapered roller bearing on mainshaft. Check measurement of assembled gear train.

6) Place intermediate plate in vise and insert mainshaft with tapered roller bearing into intermediate plate. Turn mainshaft so that tapered roller bearing is correctly seated.

7) Using a depth gauge, measure from face of synchronizing body for 3rd/4th gear to parting surface of intermediate plate with gasket. Nominal dimension is 5.448" (138.4 mm) and measured distance is 5.440" (138.2), thickness of washers is .008" (.2 mm).

8) Compensating washers are available in thickness from .004" (.1 mm) to .020" (.5 mm). Using a suitable mandrel, knock outer bearing race for mainshaft bearing out of intermediate plate. Place calculated compensating washers into intermediate plate.

INPUT SHAFT MEASUREMENT (IN TRANSMISSION HOUSING)

1) Measure preload of input shaft to .0020" (.05 mm). Knock outer bearing race uniformly down by means of a suitable mandrel. Input shaft must be rotated to obtain a correct seat for tapered roller bearing.

2) Measure depth from parting surface of front transmission cover to 4 flat surfaces of bearing tube (smallest dimension is okay). Using a depth micrometer, measure distance from face of outer bearing race to parting surface of transmission housing.

3) Thickness of compensating washers required for adjustment is determined as follows. For example: If depth is .2303" (5.85 mm) and measured distance is .2086" (5.30 mm), the difference is .022" (.55 mm), add preload of .0020" (.05 mm) and the difference is .024" (.60 mm). Use a washer of proper thickness for compensation (or as close as possible). Compensating washers come in varying thickness from .0020" (.05 mm) to .012" (.3 mm) thickness.

COUNTERSHAFT MEASUREMENT

1) Using a depth micormeter from parting surface of front transmission cover to recess, measure preload of countershaft to .0020" (.05 mm). Using a suitable mandrel, knock outer bearing race of countershaft down, while rotating transmission to obtain correct seat for tapered roller bearing.

2) Measure distance from face of outer bearing race up to parting surface of transmission housing. Thickness of compensating washers required for adjustment is determined as follows. For example: If depth is .090" (2.28 mm) and measured distance is .072" (1.83 mm), the difference is .018" (.45 mm), add preload of .0020" (.05 mm) and the difference is .020" (.50 mm). Use a washer of proper thickness for compensation (or as close as possible). Compensating washers come in varying thickness from .020" (.50 mm) to .008" (.2 mm).

3) Insert compensating washers into front transmision cover and glue down with grease. Coat parting surface of front transmission cover with sealing compound Loctite (573) and slip front transmission cover over input shaft.

NOTE: **There should be no clearance if the input shaft is correctly measured.**

TRANSMISSION REASSEMBLY

1) Install locking lever for reverse gear with bolt, bushing, leaf spring and spacing washer. Tighten new flange nut. Before inserting input shaft into transmission housing, screw down front transmission cover with 2 screws, so that input shaft and outer bearing race cannot be pushed out of transmission housing when installing mainshaft.

2) Using a suitable mandrel, knock input shaft with bearing and compensating washers into transmission housing. Insert needle cage into input shaft. Press 4th gear synchronizing ring on input shaft until annular spring enters groove of input shaft.

3) Position sliding sleeve for 3rd/4th gear with fork and shift rocker onto synchronizing ring and input shaft. Ensure that groove on sliding sleeve points toward 3rd gear.

4) Install bearing shaft for 3rd/4th gear shift rocker and tighten. Use care when mounting new "O" ring in housing around shaft. Install shift lever for 3rd/4th gear. Teeth on shift lever must engage teeth on shift rocker. Coat shift lever bolt with Loctite (242) and tighten.

5) Carefully insert countershaft into transmission housing. Tension leaf spring with Locking Lever (201 265 01 08). Pull countershaft toward bottom of case. Carefully install main and input shaft with shift rocker for 1st/2nd gear in case.

6) Install bearing shaft for 1st/2nd gear shift rocker and tighten, when mounting new "O" ring in housing around shaft. Install shift lever for 1st/2nd gear. Teeth on shift lever must engage teeth on shift rocker. Coat shift lever bolt with Loctite (242) and tighten.

7) Remove locking lever from leaf spring. Remove hose from mainshaft. Place new gasket on

MERCEDES BENZ GL 68/20 5-SPEED (Cont.)

parting surface at rear of transmission case. Place Assembly Sleeve (201 589 00 14 00) on countershaft. Let locking lever for reverse gear rest against case.

8) With bearings installed in intermediate plate, install plate on rear of transmission and press it onto mainshaft with Press Mandrel (201 589 03 43 00). Ensure to fit reverse gear lever through plate. To prevent plate from canting during assembly, tap it with a plastic hammer while using press.

9) Remove Press Mandrel (201 589 03 43 00) and Assembly Sleeve (201 589 00 14 00). Install Holder (2011 589 05 31 00) for countershaft and screw knob all the way in. Place front ball bearing on countershaft. Ensure that ball side of bearing is facing out.

10) Using 2-piece Mandrel (201 589 02 15 00) drive front countershaft bearing in until groove on mandrel handle lines up with top edge of mandrel. Loosen knurled screw of holding fixture and drive bearing in until it seats in case. Install snap ring to front of countershaft.

11) Adjust end play of input shaft. See INPUT SHAFT MEASUREMENT in this article. Place Assembly Sleeve (201 589 01 14 00). Place front cover over input shaft and tighten bolts. Remove assembly sleeve from input shaft. Remove holding fixture from counter shaft.

12) Slide reverse gear onto mainshaft. Install speedometer drive gear behind reverse gear with recess pointing out. Install reverse gear on countershaft and secure with snap ring.

13) Insert 5th/reverse slide gear into transmission rear cover. Ensure that shift bolt enters ring gear on groove. Insert 5th/reverse shaft into slide gear in such a manner that cut on shaft is in alignment with locating bore in cover. Check shaft for anti-torsion lock.

14) Set locking lever for reverse gear so that it comes to rest at lower end of recess. *See Fig. 6.* Mount rear cover on transmission. Ensure reverse gear shaft does not fall out. Install cover screws and tighten.

15) Grease universal flange on running surface of seal and mount flange on mainshaft. Install new nut, tighten and stake in place. Insert detent cage with gasket into transmission case. Ensure that one ball is pointing downward. Tighten detent cage screws. Reinstall transmission and fill with proper lubricate. Road test vehicle.

Fig. 6: View of Reverse Shift Lever

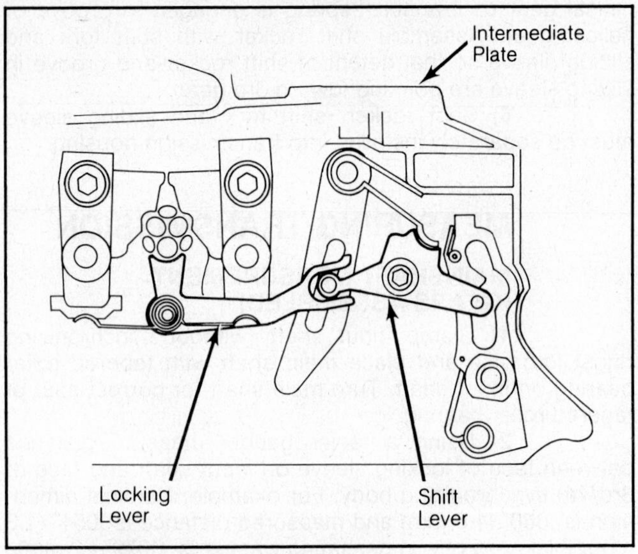

Ensure locking lever enter's shift lever

TIGHTENING SPECIFICATIONS

Application	Ft. Lbs. (N.m)
Clamping Nut on Driveshaft	2-30 (30-40)
Drain & Fill Plug	52 (70)
Driveshaft Intermediate Bearing Bolts	18 (25)
Slot Nut for Universal Flange	118 (160)
	INCH lbs.
Front Cover Bolts	180 (20)
Shift Lever Nut	216 (25)
Holding Ring Bolts	132 (15)
Reverse Flange Locking Nut	180 (20)
Reverse Gear Shift Lever Bolts	216 (25)
Rear Cover Bolts	144 (16)
Shift Rocker Shaft Bolts	72 (8)
Detent Cage Bolts	72 (8)
Shift Bracket-to-Tunnel Bolts	53 (6)
Guide Pin-to-Shift Bracket Bolts	84 (10)

NISSAN MAXIMA 5-SPEED TRANSAXLE

DESCRIPTION

The manual transaxle assembly contains the clutch, transmission and final drive (differential). Transmission is a 5-speed unit (Model RS5F50A), fully sychronized in all forward gears. All forward gears are helically cut and in constant mesh.

Final drive is directly coupled to transmission and housed in transmission case. Transmission and final drive are lubricated from a common oil supply. Constant velocity (CV) joints are used on both ends of drive axle shafts.

LUBRICATION & ADJUSTMENT

See appropriate MANUAL TRANSMISSION SERVICING article in IMPORT GENERAL SERVICING section.

REMOVAL & INSTALLATION

See appropriate MANUAL TRANSMISSION REMOVAL article in IMPORT GENERAL SERVICING section.

SERVICE (IN VEHICLE)

DRIVE AXLE SHAFTS

See appropriate DRIVE AXLE SHAFT article in IMPORT AXLE SHAFTS, OVERDRIVES & TRANSFER CASES section.

TRANSAXLE DISASSEMBLY & REASSEMBLY

TRANSAXLE CASE

Disassembly

1) Wipe dirt and grease off of transaxle. Drain oil from transaxle case. Remove transmission case to clutch housing bolts. Remove check plugs, springs and check balls from case. *See Fig. 2.* Using a plastic hammer, tap transmission case to dislodge it from clutch housing.

2) Remove transmission case by lifting and tilting away from clutch housing. Remove back-up light switch and oil gutter from case. Remove mainshaft rear bearing outer race and differential side bearing outer race.

Reassembly

1) Press differential side bearing and mainshaft rear bearing outer races into transmission case. Install oil gutter and back-up light switch. If a new case is being installed, adjust differential side bearing and mainshaft rotational force by selecting proper shims. See ADJUSTMENTS in this article.

2) Install transmission case using new sealant. To aid in installing transmission case, place shift selector in 1-2 shift bracket or between 1-2 and 3-4 shift bracket. Apply sealant to check plugs. Install balls, springs and plugs.

CLUTCH HOUSING

Disassembly

1) Clean dirt and grease off of outside of transaxle. Drain oil. Remove transmission case. Mesh 4th gear and remove reverse idler shaft and reverse idler gear. Pull out retaining pin and remove reverse arm shaft. Tap

Fig. 1: Exploded View of Maxima Transaxle Case Assembly

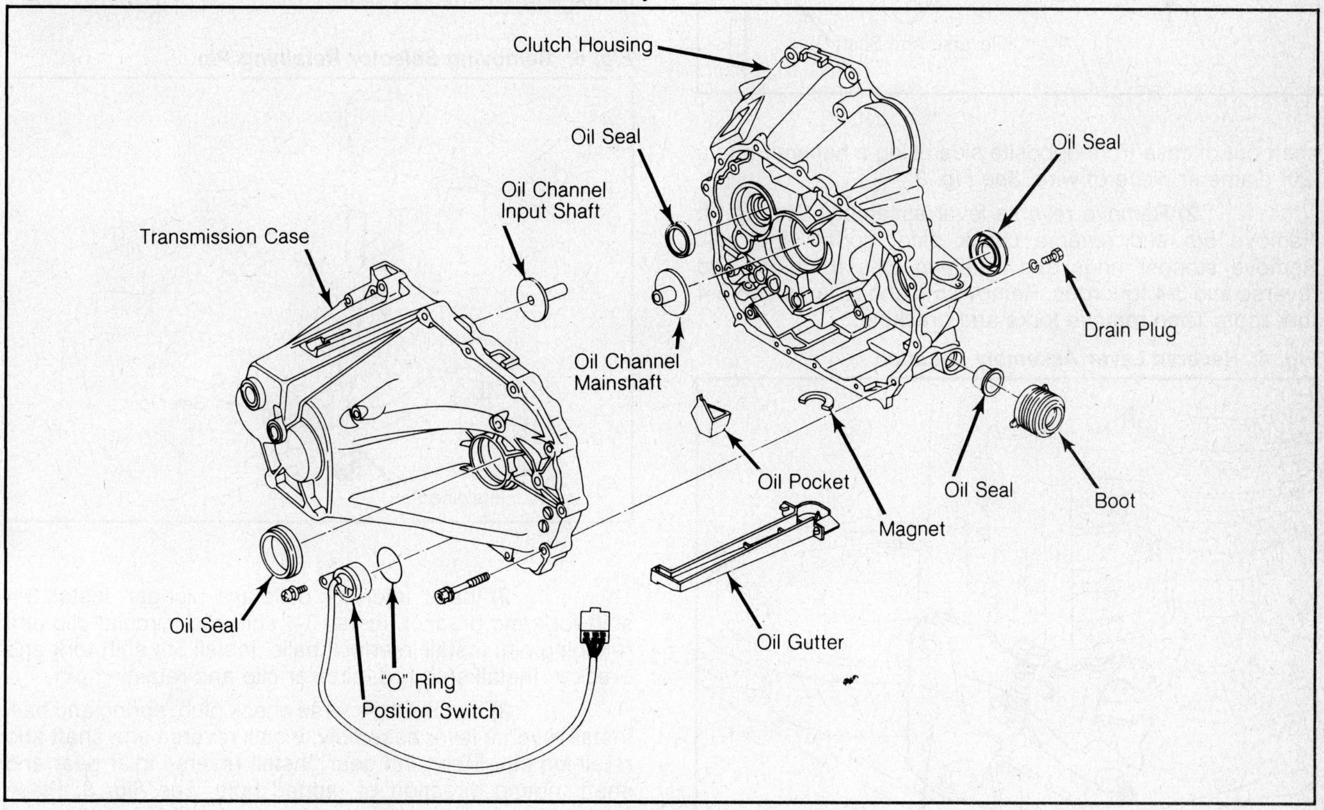

NISSAN MAXIMA 5-SPEED TRANSAXLE (Cont.)

Fig. 2: Removing Check Plugs

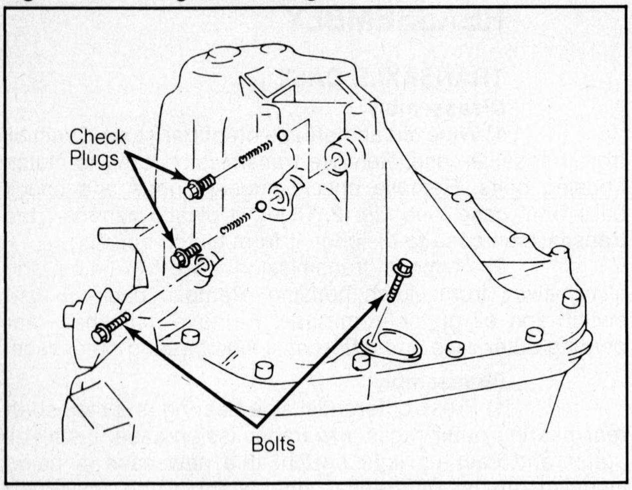

Fig. 3: Removing Reverse Arm Shaft

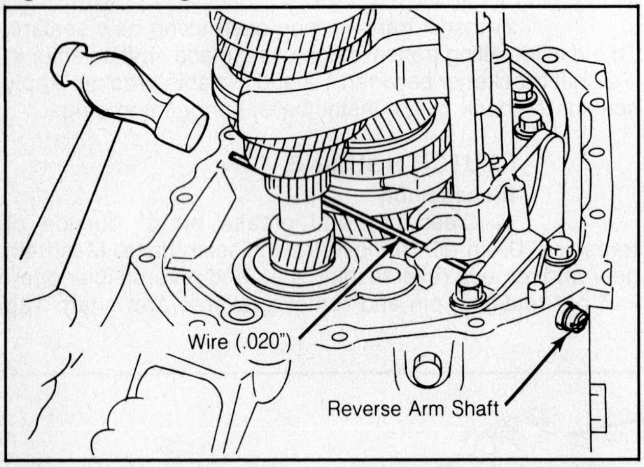

shaft out of case from opposite side using a hammer and a .20" diameter piece of wire. *See Fig. 3*.

2) Remove reverse lever assembly. *See Fig. 4*. Remove 5th and reverse check plug, spring and ball. Remove stopper rings and retaining pins from 5th and reverse and 3-4 fork rods. Remove 5th and reverse and 3-4 fork rods. Then remove forks and brackets.

Fig. 4: Reverse Lever Assembly Location

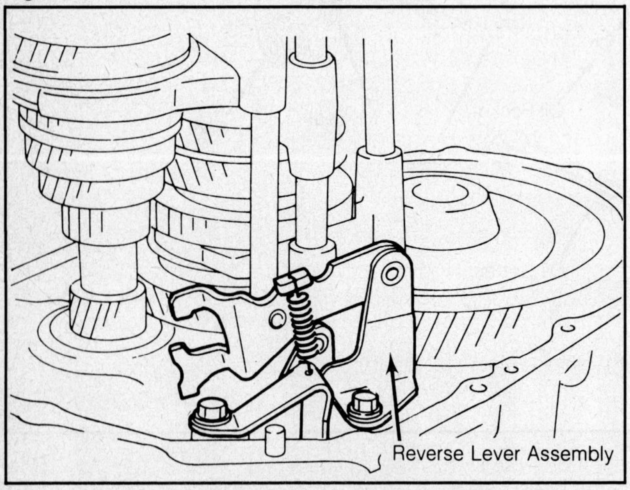

3) Remove both input and mainshafts with 1-2 fork and fork rod as a set. Remove final drive (differential). Remove reverse check assembly. *See Fig. 5*. Remove retaining pin and detach selector. *See Fig. 6*. Remove retaining pin which holds shifting lever to shifting rod. *See Fig. 7*. Remove shifting lever and shifting rod. Remove oil pocket.

Fig. 5: Reverse Check Assembly Location

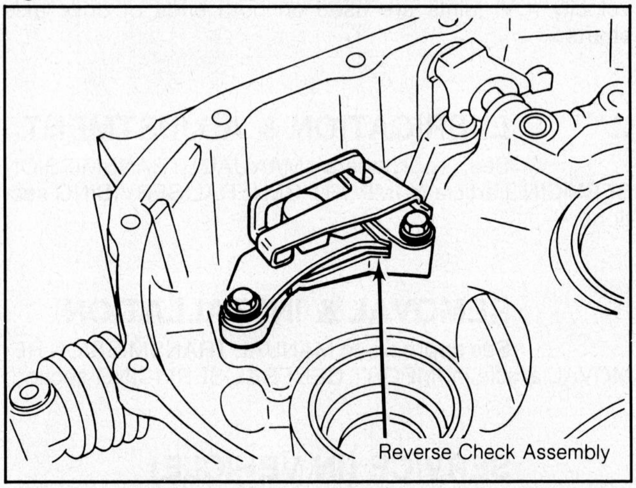

Reassembly

1) Install oil pocket and make sure oil flows from oil pocket to oil channel. Install shifting lever and shifting rod. Install selector and retaining pin. Install reverse check assembly. Install final drive assembly. Install input shaft and mainshaft with 1-2 shift fork assembly. Be careful not to damage input shaft oil seal.

Fig. 6: Removing Selector Retaining Pin

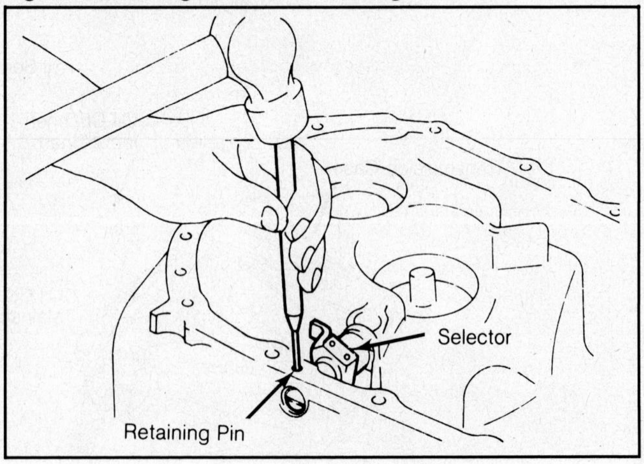

2) Install interlock balls and plunger. Install 3-4 shift fork and bracket. Install 3-4 shift rod, circular clip and retaining pin. Install interlock balls. Install 5th shift fork and bracket. Install shift rod, circular clip and retaining pin.

3) Install 5th reverse check plug, spring and ball. Install reverse lever assembly. Install reverse arm shaft and retaining pin. Mesh 4th gear. Install reverse idler gear and shaft, noting direction of tapped hole. *See Fig. 8*. Place magnet on clutch housing.

NISSAN MAXIMA 5-SPEED TRANSAXLE (Cont.)

Fig. 7: Removing Shifting Rod & Lever Retaining Pin

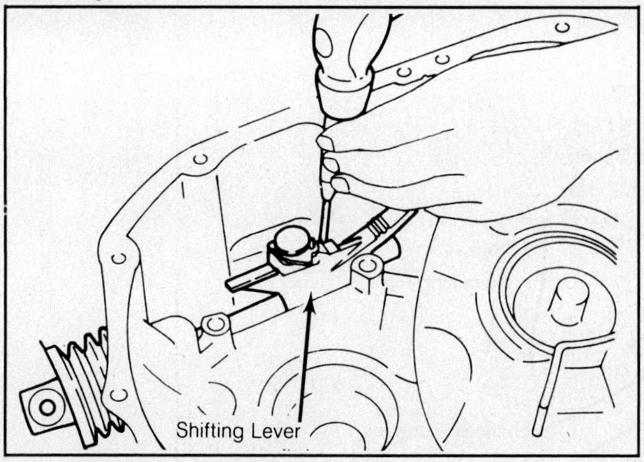

Fig. 8: Installing Reverse Idler Gear & Shaft

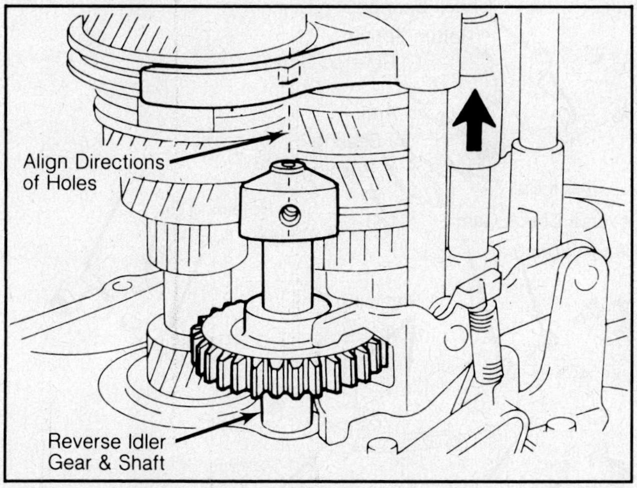

Note Direction of Tapped Hole

4) Install shims if bearing preload was adjusted. Install transmission case. Measure gear rotory frictional force and ensure that gears move smoothly and without binding. Use Adapter (KV38106500) and torque wrench to check rotary frictional force. Required force with a new bearing should be 78-191 INCH lbs. (9-22 N.m). *See Fig. 9.*

Fig. 9: Checking Turning Torque

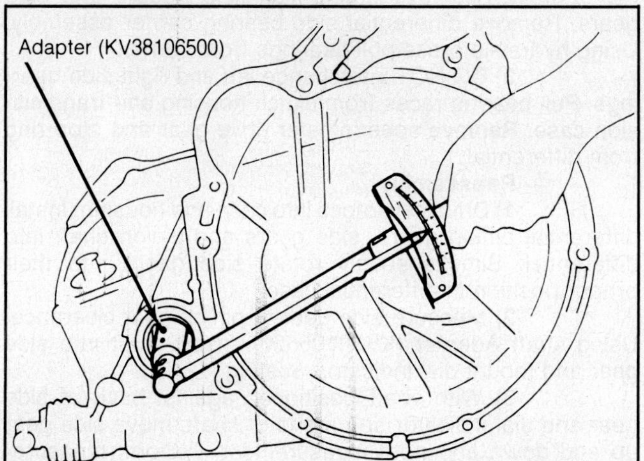

COMPONENT DISASSEMBLY & REASSEMBLY

INPUT SHAFT

Disassembly

1) Before disassembly, measure gear end play. Input 3rd gear end play should be .0091-.0169" (.23-.43 mm). Input 4th gear end play should be .0098-.0217" (.25-.55 mm). Input 5th gear end play should be .0091-.0189" (.23-.48 mm).

2) Remove input shaft rear bearing. Remove 5th sychro and gear. Remove thrust washer ring, thrust washers and 4th gear. Remove snap ring. Remove 3-4 synchro and 3rd gear. Remove input shaft front bearing.

Reassembly

1) Apply gear oil to 3rd gear inner surface and install 3rd gear and blocker ring. Press on 3-4 synchro hub with shallow side of hub facing toward 4th gear. Install proper thickness snap ring to obtain snap ring groove clearance of 0-.004" (0-.10 mm). The 3-4 synchro hub snap rings are available in sizes .0768" (1.95 mm), .0787" (2.0 mm), .0807" (2.05 mm), and .0827" (2.10 mm).

2) Apply gear oil to 4th gear surface and install 4th gear, thrust washers (selective) and thrust washer ring. Install proper selective input shaft thrust washers to obtain groove clearance of 0-.0024" (0-.06 mm). Input shaft thrust washers are available in sizes .1772" (4.50 mm), .1781" (4.525 mm), .1791" (4.55 mm) and .1801" (4.575 mm).

3) Apply gear oil to 5th gear and install. Press on 5th gear synchro. Install front and rear bearings. Check gear end play.

MAINSHAFT

Disassembly

1) Before disassembly, measure 1st and 2nd gear end play. Main 1st gear end play should be .0091-.0169" (.23-.43 mm). Main 2nd gear end play should be .0091-.0228" (.23-.58 mm).

2) Remove mainshaft rear bearing. Remove thrust washer and snap ring. Remove 5th main gear and 4th main gear. Remove 3rd and 2nd main gears. Remove snap ring. Remove 1-2 synchro and 1st main gear. Remove mainshaft front bearing.

Reassembly

1) Apply gear oil to 1st gear and install 1st gear and blocker ring. Press on 1-2 synchro with shallow side of hub facing toward 1st gear. Install 2nd blocker ring.

2) Install proper thickness snap ring to obtain snap ring groove clearance of 0-.004" (0-.10 mm). The 1-2 synchro hub snap rings are available in sizes of .0768" (1.95 mm), .0787" (2.0 mm), .0807" (2.05 mm) and .0827" (2.10 mm). Apply gear oil to 2nd gear and install. Press on 3rd gear, 4th gear and 5th gear.

3) Install proper thickness snap ring to obtain snap ring groove clearance of 0-.006" (0-.15 mm). The 5th gear snap rings are available in sizes of .0768" 1.95 mm), .0807" (2.05 mm), .0846" (2.15 mm) and .0886" (2.25 mm). Install thrust washer and press on rear bearing. Press on front bearing. Check gear end play.

SYCHRONIZERS

Disassembly

Remove springs and inserts from synchro assembly. Note component positions and locations for reassembly reference. Slide coupling sleeve off of synchro hub.

NISSAN MAXIMA 5-SPEED TRANSAXLE (Cont.)

Fig. 10: Exploded View of Shift Mechanism

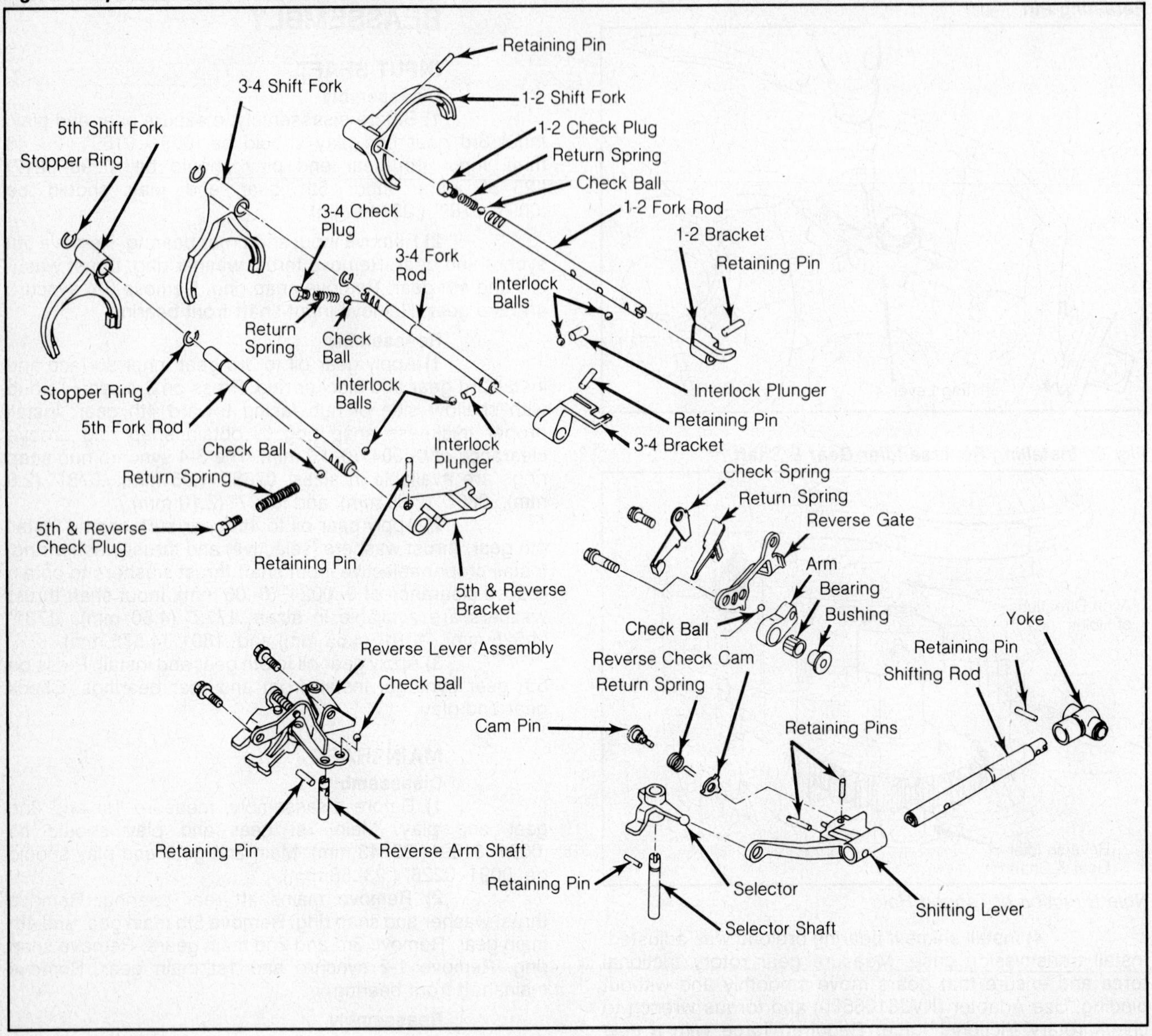

Inspection

Check blocker ring for deformation, cracking or excessive wear. Check clearance by placing blocker ring in position on gauge cone. While holding ring against gear as far as it will go, measure gap between synchro ring and outer gear. Standard blocker ring to gear clearance is .039-.053" (1.00-1.35 mm). Service limit is .028" (.70 mm).

Reassembly

1) To reassemble, reverse disassembly procedure. Fit shifting inserts in 3 grooves in synchro hub. Insert protrusion of spread spring into groove so that insert is securely attached to inner side of coupling sleeve.

2) Install other spread spring on opposite side of synchro hub. Be careful not to hook front and rear ends of spread springs to the same synchro insert. Ensure that open portion of springs are offset.

DIFFERENTIAL

Disassembly

1) With differential removed from transaxle, detach ring gear mount bolts. Remove ring gear from differential. Using a punch, drive out pinion shaft retaining lock pin. Remove pinion shaft from differential.

2) Remove differential pinion gears and side gears. Remove differential side bearing carrier assembly. Using hydraulic press pull bearings from carrier.

3) DO NOT interchange left and right side bearings. Pull bearing races from clutch housing and transmission case. Remove speedometer drive gear and stop ring from differential.

Reassembly

1) Drive new races into case and housing. Install differential pinion gears, side gears and pinion shaft into differential. Simultaneously rotate side gears into their proper position in differential case.

2) Measure side gear-to-pinion gear clearance. Using shaft Adapter (KV38106500), insert shaft into side gear and mount dial indicator. *See Fig. 12.*

3) With shaft positioned against back of side gear and dial indicator tip on end of shaft, move side gear up and down and note measurement. Perform measure-

Manual Transmissions

NISSAN MAXIMA 5-SPEED TRANSAXLE (Cont.)

Fig. 11: Exploded View of Transaxle Gears & Differential

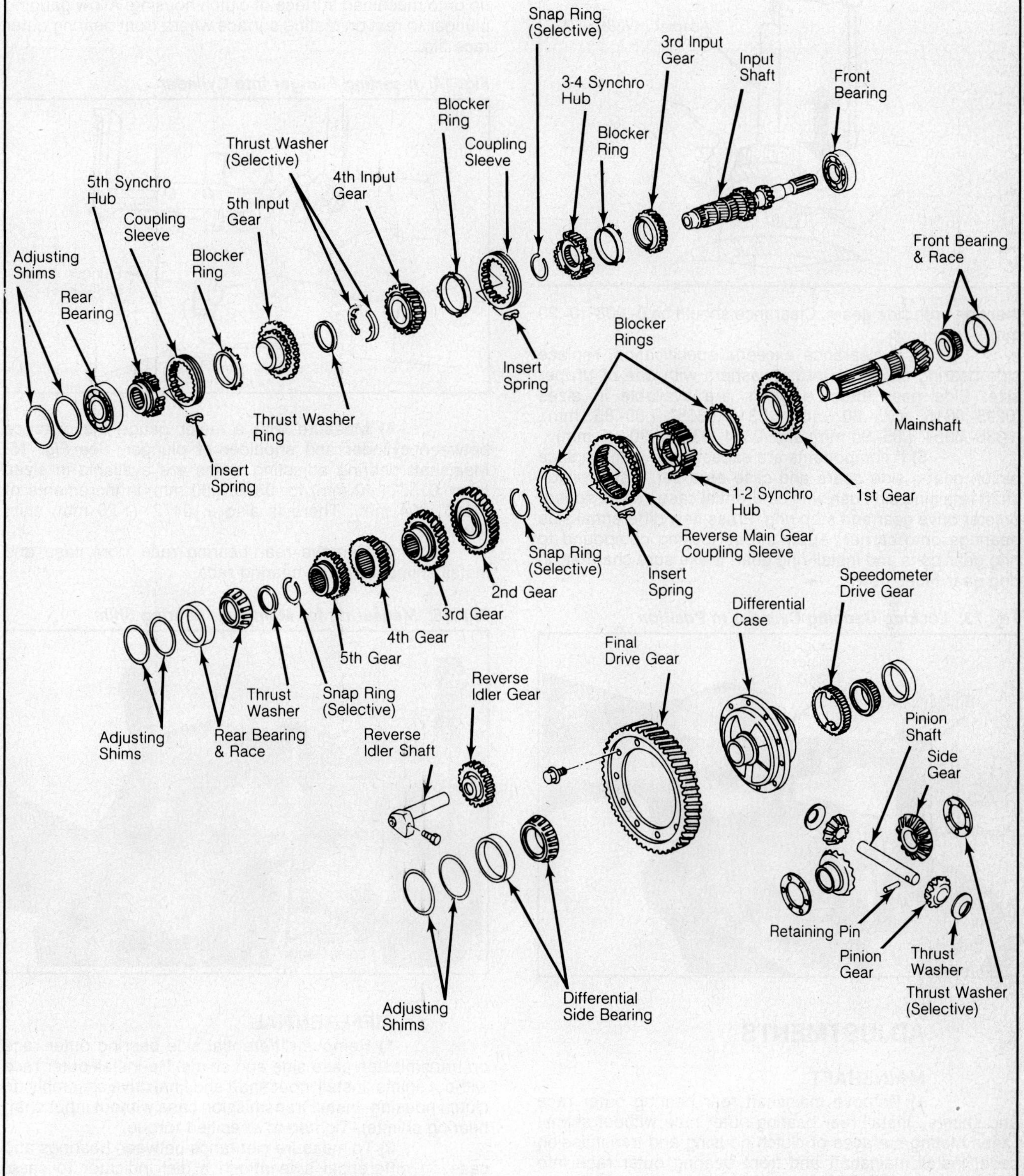

Fig. 12: Checking Side Gear Clearance

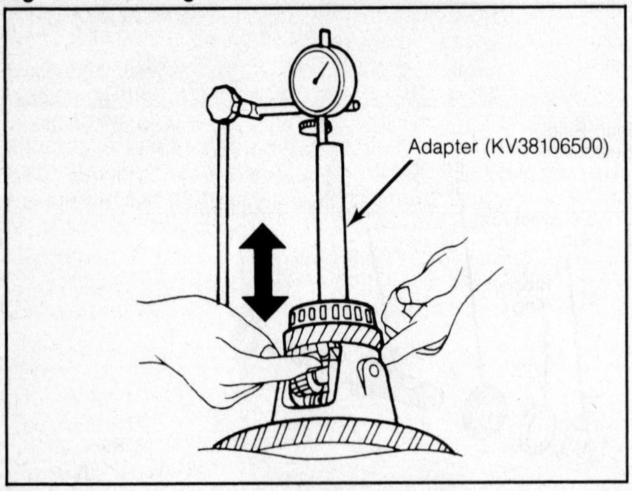

ment on both side gears. Clearance should be 0-.008" (0-.20 mm).

4) If clearance exceeds specification, replace side bearing adjusting thrust washers with one of proper size. Side gear thrust washers are available in sizes .0295-.0315" (.75-.80 mm), .0315-.0335" (.80-.85 mm), .0335-.0354" (.85-.90 mm) and .0354-.0374" (.90-.95 mm).

5) If components are excessively worn, replace pinion gears, side gears and case as a set. Install pinion shaft retaining pin flush with differential case. Install speedometer drive gear and stop ring. Press new differential side bearings onto carrier. Apply thread locking compound to ring gear bolts and install ring gear. Make sure chamfer on ring gear faces down.

Fig. 13: Locking Gauging Cylinder in Position

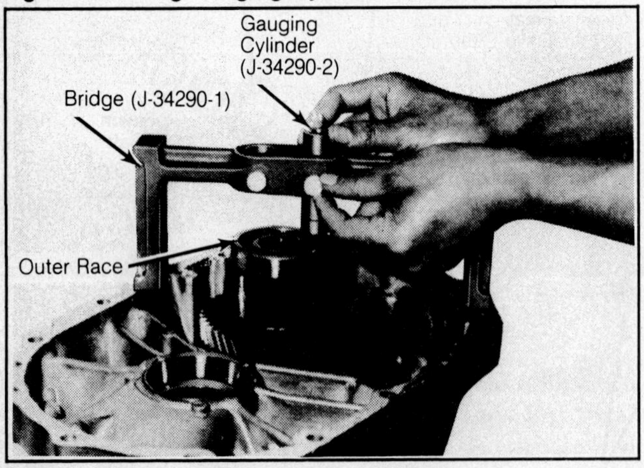

ADJUSTMENTS

MAINSHAFT

1) Remove mainshaft rear bearing outer race and shim(s). Install rear bearing outer race without shims. Clean mating surfaces of clutch housing and transmission case. Install mainshaft and front bearing outer race into case. Turn mainshaft while holding bearing race to seat bearings.

2) Place Bridge (J-34290-1) with Gauging Cylinder (J-34290-2) onto machined surface of transmission case. Gauging cylinder should rest on front bearing outer race surface. Turn screw in bridge to lock cylinder in place. *See Fig. 13.*

3) Turn bridge over and insert Plunger (J-34290-8) into gauging cylinder. *See Fig. 14.* Place bridge with legs up onto machined surface of clutch housing. Allow gauging plunger to rest on mating surface where front bearing outer race fits.

Fig. 14: Inserting Plunger into Cylinder

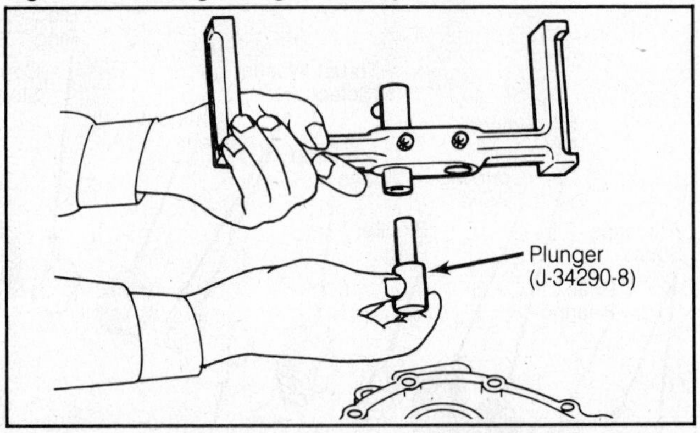

4) Measure with a feeler gauge the distance between cylinder and shoulder of plunger. *See Fig. 15.* Mainshaft bearing adjusting shims are available in sizes from .0157" (.40 mm) to .0315" (.80 mm) in increments of .0016" (.04 mm). There is also a .0472" (1.20 mm) shim available.

5) Remove rear bearing race from case and install shims. Replace bearing race.

Fig. 15: Measuring for Mainshaft Bearing Shim

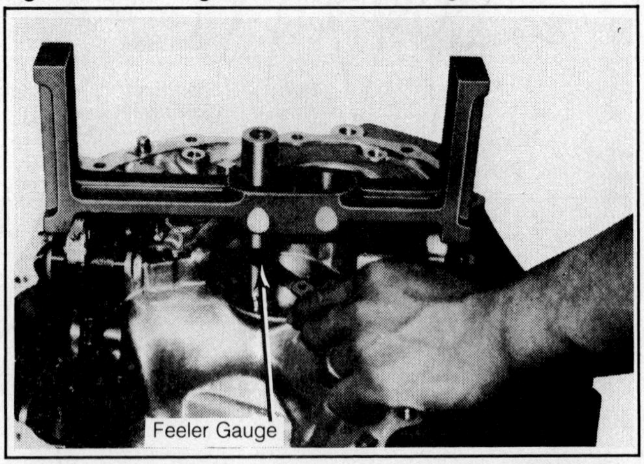

DIFFERENTIAL

1) Remove differential side bearing outer race on transmission case side and shims. Re-install outer race without shims. Install input shaft and final drive assembly on clutch housing. Install transmission case without input shaft bearing shim(s). Tighten to specified torque.

2) To measure clearance between bearings and case on differential side attach a dial indicator to case. Insert Preload Adapter (KV38106500) all the way into side gear. Move tool up and down and measure gauge deflection. *See Fig. 16.*

NISSAN MAXIMA 5-SPEED TRANSAXLE (Cont.)

Fig. 16: Checking Side Gear Preload

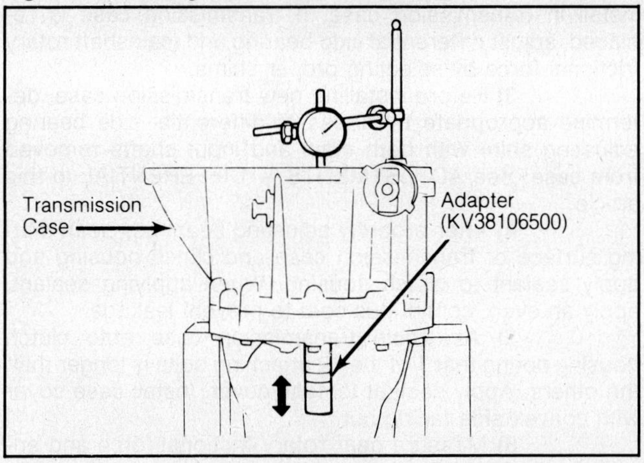

3) To calculate proper shim size take measured distance and add .0169" (.43 mm). Then add AND subtract .0008" (.02 mm) to this total to determine minimum and maximum shim thickness range. Choose 2 shims that when combined fall within this range. DO NOT combine more than 2 shims. Differential side bearing adjusting shims are available in sizes from .0157" (.40 mm) to .0315" (.80 mm) in increments of .0016" (.04mm). There is also a .0472" (1.20 mm) shim available.

INPUT SHAFT

1) Swing dial indicator around and set on rear end of input shaft. Move input shaft up and down and measure gauge deflection. *See Fig. 17*.

2) To calculate proper shim thickness needed take measured distance and subtract .0012" (.03 mm). Then add AND subtract .0008" (.02 mm) to this total to determine minimum and maximum shim thickness range. Choose a shim that falls within the range. Input shaft side adjusting shims are available in sizes from .0157" (.40 mm) to .0315" (.80 mm) in increments of .0016" (.04 mm). There is also a .0472" (1.20 mm) shim available. It may be necessary to use 2 shims to achieve proper thickness. DO NOT combine more than 2 shims.

Fig. 17: Checking Input Shaft Clearance

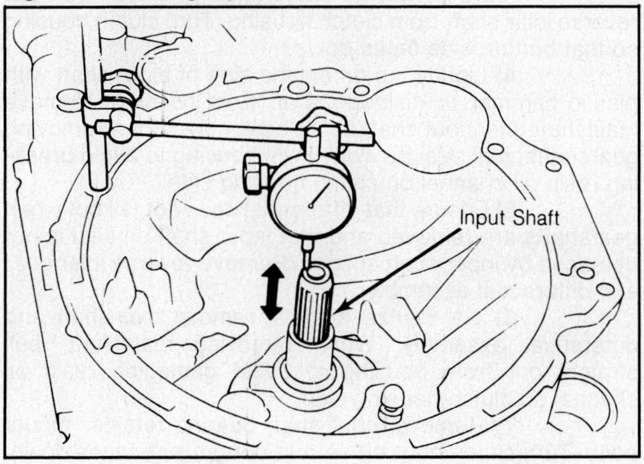

BEARING PRELOAD

Bearing	Inch (N.m)
Mainshaft	.0098-.0122 (.25-.31)
Input Shaft	-.0024 to 0 (-.06 to 0)
Differential Side	.0157-.0181 (.40-.46)

TIGHTENING SPECIFICATIONS

Application	Ft. Lbs. (N.m)
Back-Up Light Switch	14-22 (19-30)
Clutch Housing-to Transmission Case	12-15 (16-20)
Drain Plug	18-25 (24-34)
Filler Plug	18-25 (24-34)
Ring Gear Mount Bolts	54-65 (73-88)
Transaxle-to-Engine Mount Bolts	29-40 (39-54)
5th/Reverse Check Plug	14-18 (19-24)
1-2 Check Plug	12-16 (16-21)
3-4 Check Plug	12-16 (16-21)
	INCH Lbs. (N.m)
Position Switch Bolt	36-48 (4-5)
Speedometer Gear Assembly Mount Bolt	36-48 (4-5)

NISSAN 4 & 5-SPEED TRANSAXLE

Pulsar, Sentra, Stanza

DESCRIPTION

The Nissan manual transaxle assembly contains the clutch, transmission and final drive (differential). Transmission is a 4-speed (Sentra model RN4F30A) or 5-speed (Pulsar and Sentra model RS5F30A, Stanza model RS5F31A) unit, fully synchronized in all forward gears. All forward gears are helically cut and in constant mesh.

Final drive is directly coupled to transmission and housed in transmission case. Transmission and final drive are lubricated from a common oil supply. Constant velocity (CV) joints are used on both ends of drive axle shafts.

LUBRICATION & ADJUSTMENT

See appropriate MANUAL TRANSMISSION SERVICING article in IMPORT GENERAL SERVICING section.

REMOVAL & INSTALLATION

See appropriate MANUAL TRANSMISSION REMOVAL article in IMPORT GENERAL SERVICING section.

SERVICE (IN VEHICLE)

DRIVE AXLE SHAFTS

See appropriate DRIVE AXLE SHAFT article in IMPORT AXLE SHAFTS, OVERDRIVES & TRANSFER CASES section.

TRANSAXLE DISASSEMBLY & REASSEMBLY

TRANSAXLE CASE

Disassembly

1) Wipe dirt and grease off of transaxle. Drain oil from transaxle case. Remove transmission case to clutch housing bolts. Note location of long mount bolt for reassembly reference. Using a plastic hammer, tap transmission case to dislodge it from clutch housing.

2) Remove transmission case from clutch housing by lifting (and slightly tilting on 5-speed models, to prevent 5th shift fork from interfering with case) away from clutch housing. Remove back-up light switch and oil gutter from transmission case.

3) Remove input shaft rear bearing. Remove case cover and mainshaft bearing adjusting shim and spacer. Remove mainshaft rear bearing outer race and differential side bearing outer race.

4) Clean transmission case and inspect for cracks or cavities. Check all gasket surfaces for nicks, projections or excess sealant. Replace any seals suspected of leakage.

Reassembly

1) Press differential side bearing and mainshaft rear bearing outer races into transmission case. Install input shaft rear bearing. Apply sealer to input shaft access welch plug and install plug into case. Install oil gutter.

2) Apply sealer to back-up light switch and install in transmission case. If transmission case is replaced, adjust differential side bearing and mainshaft rotary frictional force by selecting proper shims.

3) Before installing new transmission case, determine appropriate thickness of differential side bearing adjusting shim with both main and input shafts removed from case. See ADJUSTMENTS - DIFFERENTIAL in this article.

4) After properly adjusting bearings, clean mating surface of transmission case and clutch housing and apply sealant to clutch housing. When applying sealant, apply an even, continuous coat to prevent leakage.

5) Assemble transmission case onto clutch housing noting that 1 of the 12 attaching bolts is longer than the others. Apply sealant to case cover. Install case cover with convex side facing out.

6) Measure gear rotary frictional force and ensure that gear moves smoothly and without binding. See ADJUSTMENTS - MAINSHAFT in this article. Make sure that gears shift smoothly. Apply sealant to drain plug and install in transmission case.

CLUTCH HOUSING

Disassembly

1) Clean dirt and grease off outside of transaxle. Drain oil. Remove transmission case. Remove reverse idler spacer and shift fork shaft. Remove 5th shift fork (if equipped) and 3-4 shift forks, without dropping shifter caps.

2) Remove control bracket with 1st and 2nd shift fork. Be careful not lose shifter caps. On Stanza 5-speed transaxle, be careful not to lose detent ball, spring or shift cap.

3) On Sentra and Pulsar models, remove 3 screws securing bearing retainer to clutch housing. One of the screws is a Torx-head screw and requires use of an offset Torx-bit screwdriver for removal. DO NOT remove reverse idler shaft from clutch housing. Turn clutch housing so that bottom side faces down.

4) Lightly tap on engine side of input shaft with plastic hammer to dislodge shaft from housing. Remove mainshaft and input shaft as an assembly. When removing gearshafts, pull straight away from housing to avoid breaking resin oil channel on clutch housing side.

5) Ensure that differential does not fall out when gearshafts are removed and that input shaft oil seal is not damaged by input shaft splines. Remove reverse idler gear and differential assembly.

6) On Stanza models, remove mainshaft and differential assembly. When removing mainshaft, pull straight out from housing to avoid damaging resin oil channel on clutch housing side.

7) Remove input shaft bearing retainer mount bolts. Turn clutch housing so that bottom side faces down. Lightly tap on engine side of input shaft with a plastic hammer to dislodge shaft from housing.

8) Remove input shaft together with bearing retainer and reverse idler gear. Make sure that input shaft oil seal is not damaged by input shaft splines. DO NOT remove reverse idler shaft from housing.

9) On all models, remove oil pocket, shift check ball, check springs and check ball plug. Drive roll pin out of shifting rod. Remove shifting rod, shifting lever and shifting interlock. Tape edges of shifting rod to prevent seal from being damaged when rod is removed.

NISSAN 4 & 5-SPEED TRANSAXLE (Cont.)

Fig. 1: Exploded View of Pulsar, Sentra and Stanza Transaxle Case Assembly

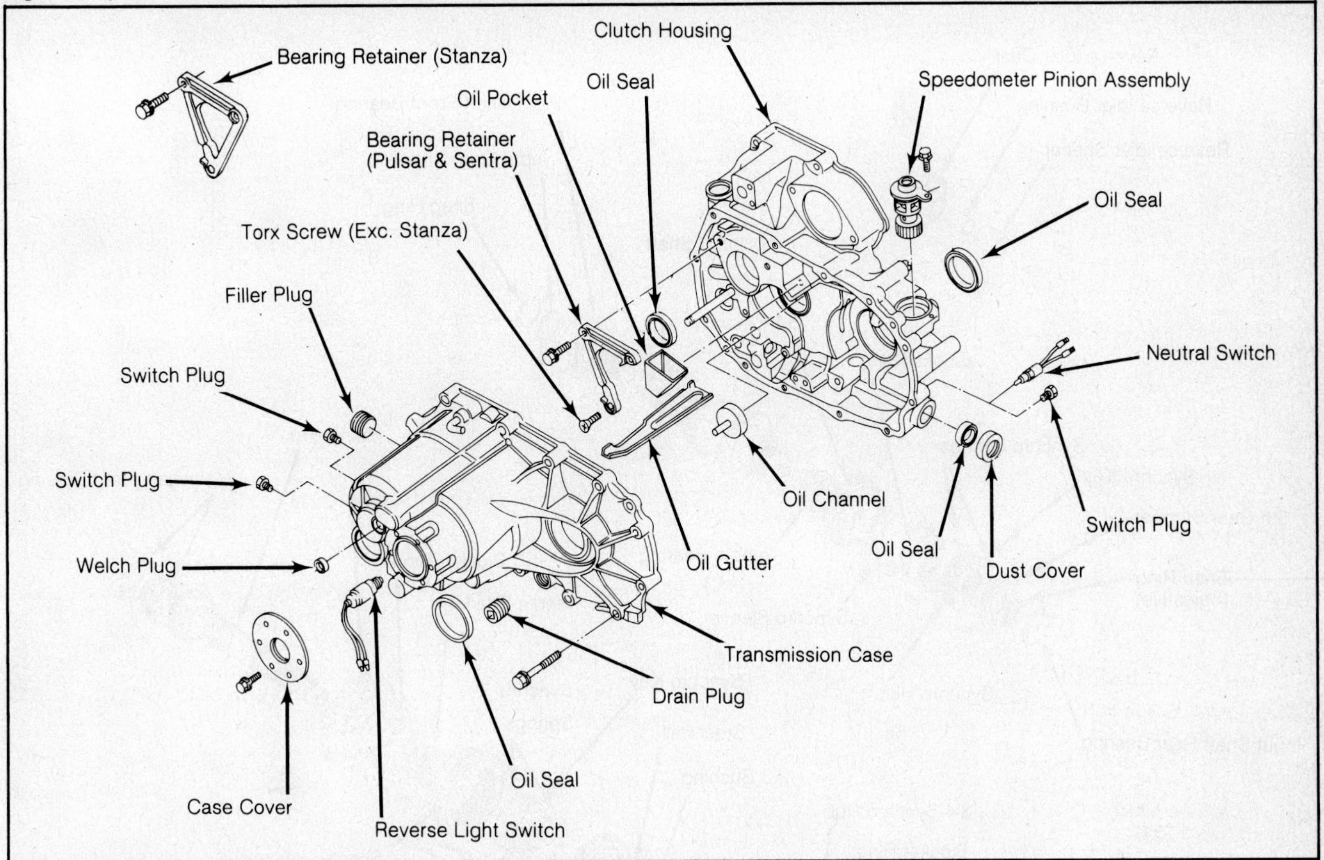

The transaxle case assemblies are the same for these models except for the Stanza bearing retainer.

Fig. 2: Exploded View of Stanza Shift Mechanism

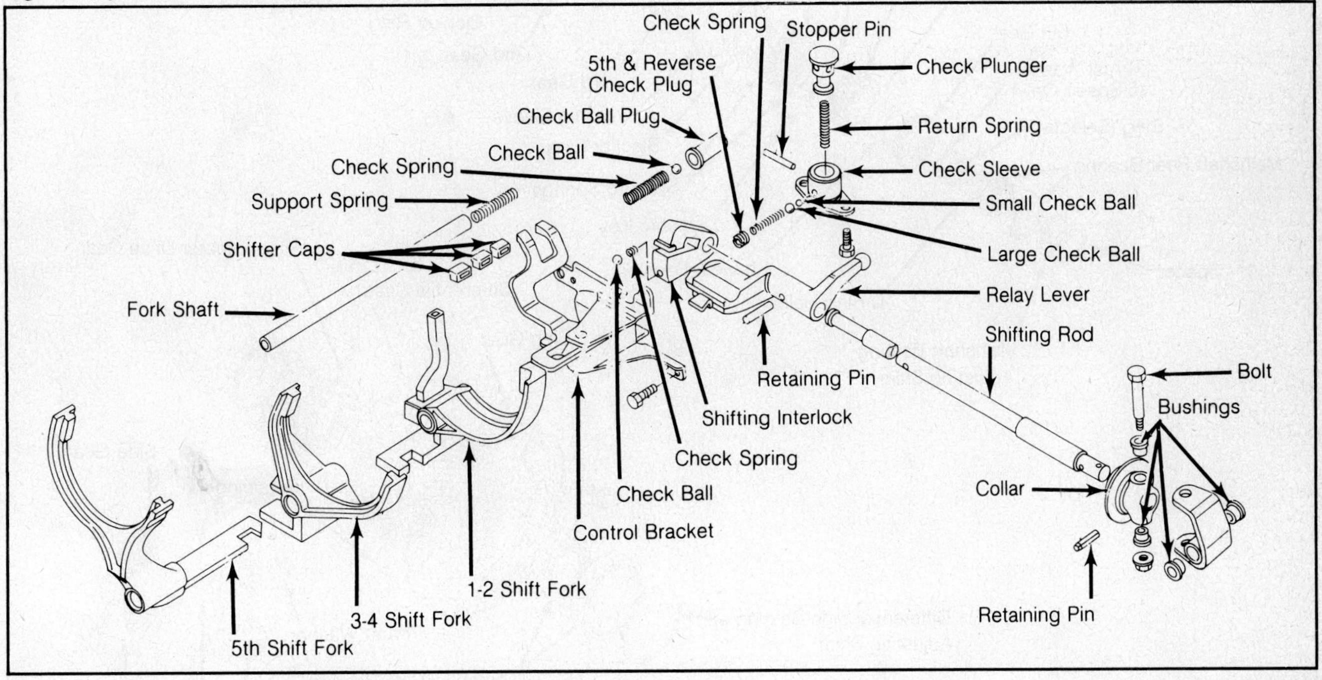

NISSAN 4 & 5-SPEED TRANSAXLE (Cont.)

Fig. 3: Exploded View of 4 and 5-Speed Transaxle Gears & Differentials

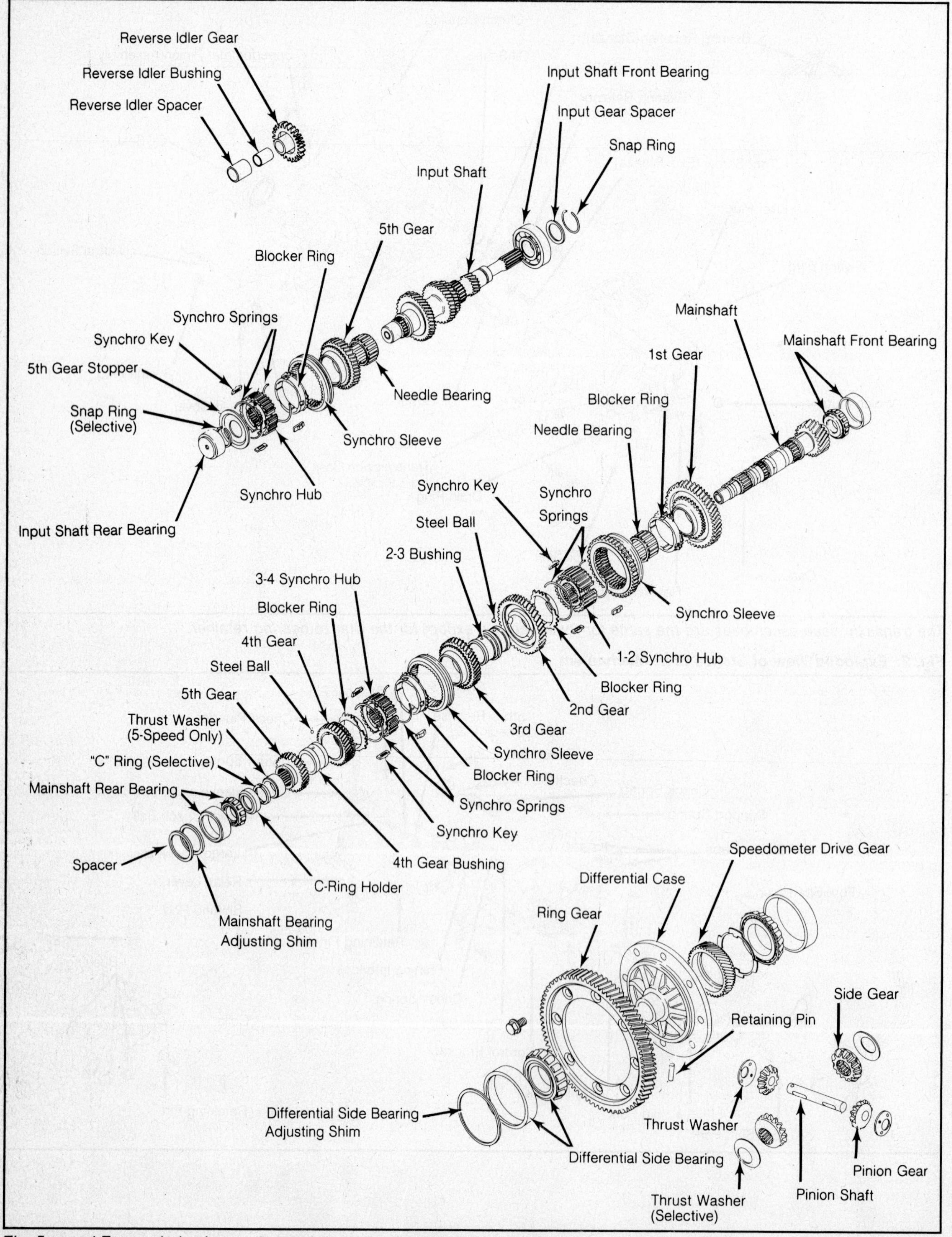

The 5-speed Transaxle is shown; 4-speed does not use 5th gear or related components.

NISSAN 4 & 5-SPEED TRANSAXLE (Cont.)

Fig. 4: Exploded View of Pulsar & Sentra Shift Mechanism

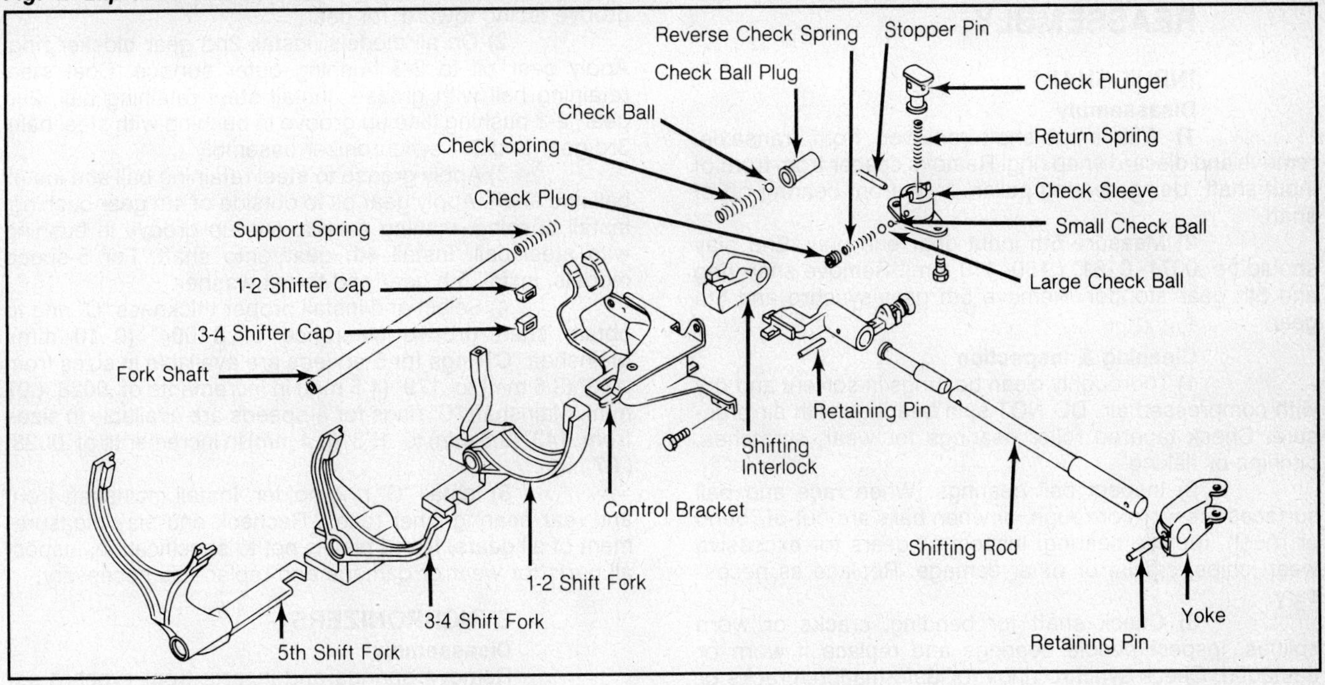

10) Remove reverse and 5th check plug, check balls and check spring. Remove 5th and reverse check assembly. Remove clutch control shaft, release bearing and clutch lever.

11) Remove mainshaft bearing outer race and differential side bearing outer race. Remove oil channel. Clean clutch housing and check for cracks or cavities. Check mating surfaces of clutch housing for nicks, projections or excess sealer. Replace any seals suspected of leakage.

Reassembly

1) Install a new oil channel making sure that channel oil groove faces housing oil pocket. Install mainshaft bearing outer race and differential side bearing outer race.

2) Install clutch control shaft, clutch release bearing and clutch lever. Install oil pocket and make sure that oil flows from oil pocket to oil channel. *See Fig. 5.*

Fig. 5: Checking Lubrication Passage

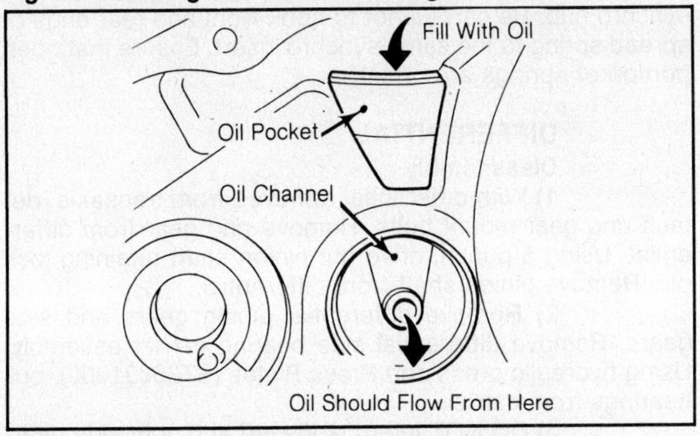

When oil pocket is installed, ensure oil flows from pocket to oil channel.

3) Reverse remainder of disassembly procedure to complete reassembly, and note the following: When replacing any part that affects reverse and 5th check assembly, reverse check force must be checked at shift lever.

NOTE: **When installing reverse/5th check assembly, install smaller check ball first, then install larger check ball, spring and reverse/5th check plug.**

4) On Sentra 4-speed models, required force should be 139-200 INCH lbs. (16-23 N.m). On Stanza 5-speed models, required force should be 195-239 INCH lbs. (22-27 N.m). On Sentra and Pulsar 5-speed models, required force should be 91-113 INCH lbs. (10-12 N.m). If force is not as specified, replace reverse check plug with a shorter or longer plug. Apply locking sealer to threads of check plug and install.

NOTE: **The reverse check plug is available in standard size of .327" (8.30 mm), shorter lengths of .28" (7.1 mm) or .303" (7.70 mm) and longer length of .35" (8.9 mm) for replacement.**

5) On bearing retainer of Sentra and Pulsar models, use thread locking compound on threads of Torx-head screw and stake head of screw in 2 places after installation. On Stanza 5-speed model, apply grease to check ball, then install check ball and spring in shifting interlock hole.

6) Apply grease onto shifter caps prior to installing control bracket. Install control bracket with 1-2 shift fork. Install 3-4 and, if equipped, 5th shift fork. Apply grease to support spring to prevent it from falling into hole for fork shaft on clutch housing.

7) Install spring and fork shaft into housing. Install reverse idler spacer. Install transmission case. Measure gear rotary frictional force and ensure that gears move smoothly and without binding. See ADJUSTMENTS in this article. Apply sealer to drain plug and install into case.

COMPONENT DISASSEMBLY & REASSEMBLY

INPUT SHAFT

Disassembly

1) With input shaft removed from transaxle, remove and discard snap ring. Remove spacer from front of input shaft. Using bearing puller, draw front bearing off of shaft.

2) Measure 5th input gear end play. End play should be .0071-.0161" (.180-.410 mm). Remove snap ring and 5th gear stopper. Remove 5th gear synchro and 5th gear.

Cleaning & Inspection

1) Thoroughly clean bearings in solvent and dry with compressed air. DO NOT spin bearings with air pressure. Check tapered roller bearings for wear, scratches, pitching or flaking.

2) Inspect ball bearings. When race and ball surfaces are worn or rough, or when balls are out-of-round or rough, replace bearing. Inspect all gears for excessive wear, chips, cracks or other damage. Replace as necessary.

3) Check shaft for bending, cracks or worn splines. Inspect needle bearings and replace if worn or damaged. Check synchro rings for deformation, cracks or excessive damage. Replace components as necessary.

Reassembly

1) Install 5th gear and 5th gear synchronizer onto shaft. Install 5th gear stopper onto shaft. Select and install proper thickness snap ring to obtain snap ring groove clearance of 0-.004" (0-.10 mm). Shims for input shaft 5th gear at available in sizes from .0787" (2 mm) to .0906" (2.3 mm) in increments of .002" (.05 mm).

2) Recheck 5th gear end play. If end play is not within specification, inspect all parts for wear or damage and replace as necessary. Install bearing retainer on Stanza models only. Install input shaft front bearing with a press.

3) Install input shaft spacer. Select and install proper thickness snap ring to obtain snap ring groove clearance of 0-.004" (0-.1 mm). Snap rings for input shaft front bearing are available in sizes of .050" (1.27 mm), .052" (1.33 mm), .055" (1.39 mm) and .057" (1.45 mm).

MAINSHAFT

Disassembly

1) With mainshaft removed from transaxle, measure end play of gears. End play at 1st gear should be .007-.012" (.18-.31 mm). End play at 2nd, 3rd and 4th gears should be .008-.016" (.20-.40 mm).

2) Remove mainshaft front and rear bearing inner races. Remove "C" rings and "C" ring holder. On 5-speed models only, remove thrust washer. Using Press Plates (ST22730000) and press, hook tool under flange and remove 5th gear.

3) Remove 4th gear, 4th gear bushing and steel retaining ball. DO NOT lose steel ball. Remove 3-4 synchro, 3rd gear, 2-3 bushing, steel ball and 2nd gear.

4) Remove 1-2 synchro and 1st gear as an assembly. Remove 1st gear needle bearing. Inspect all parts for wear or damage and replace as necessary.

Reassembly

1) Apply gear oil to 1st gear needle bearing. Install needle bearing, 1st gear and 1st gear blocker ring onto shaft. On Sentra and Pulsar models, install 1-2 synchro onto shaft with shallow side of hub and shift fork groove facing toward 1st gear.

2) On all models, install 2nd gear blocker ring. Apply gear oil to 2-3 bushing outer surface. Coat steel retaining ball with grease. Install steel retaining ball, 2nd gear, 2-3 bushing (line up groove in bushing with steel ball), 3rd gear and 3-4 synchronizer assembly.

3) Apply grease to steel retaining ball and install ball into shaft. Apply gear oil to outside of 4th gear bushing. Install bushing, making sure to line up groove in bushing with steel ball. Install 4th gear onto shaft. For 5-speed models, install 5th gear and thrust washer.

4) Select and install proper thickness "C" ring to obtain shaft groove clearance of 0-.004" (0-.10 mm). Mainshaft "C" rings for 5-speeds are available in sizes from .143" (3.6 mm) to .179" (4.5 mm) in increments of .0028" (.07 mm). Mainshaft "C" rings for 4-speeds are available in sizes from .143" (3.6 mm) to .173" (4.4 mm) in increments of .0028" (.07 mm).

5) Install "C" ring holder. Install mainshaft front and rear bearing inner races. Recheck end play measurement of all gears. If end play is not to specification, inspect all parts for wear or damage and replace as necessary.

SYNCHRONIZERS

Disassembly

Remove springs and inserts from synchro assembly. Note component positions and locations for reassembly reference. Slide coupling sleeve off of synchro hub.

Cleaning & Inspection

1) Wash all parts in solvent and blow dry with compressed air. Check blocker ring for deformation, cracking or excessive wear. Check clearance by placing blocker ring in position on gauge cone.

2) While holding ring against gear as far as it will go, measure gap between synchro ring and outer gear. Standard blocker ring-to-gear clearance is .039-.053" (1.00-1.35 mm). Service limit is .028" (.70 mm) or less.

3) Inspect synchro insert for wear at shoulders. Check synchro hub and sleeve for smooth movement. Inspect remaining parts for damage or wear. Replace components as necessary.

Reassembly

1) To reassemble, reverse disassembly procedure. Fit shifting inserts in three grooves in synchro hub. Insert protrusion of spread spring into groove so that insert is securely attached to inner side of coupling sleeve.

2) Install other spread spring on opposite side of synchro hub. Be careful not to hook front and rear ends of spread spring to the same synchro insert. Ensure that open portion of springs are offset.

DIFFERENTIAL

Disassembly

1) With differential removed from transaxle, detach ring gear mount bolts. Remove ring gear from differential. Using a punch, drive out pinion shaft retaining lock pin. Remove pinion shaft from differential.

2) Remove differential pinion gears and side gears. Remove differential side bearing carrier assembly. Using hydraulic press and Press Plates (ST30031000), pull bearings from carrier.

3) DO NOT interchange left and right side bearings. Using Bearing Remover (ST33290001), pull bearing races from clutch housing and transmission case. Remove speedometer drive gear and stop ring from differential.

NISSAN 4 & 5-SPEED TRANSAXLE (Cont.)

Cleaning & Inspection

Wash all parts in solvent and blow dry with compressed air. Inspect mating surfaces of differential case, side gears and pinion gears. Check all parts for excessive wear or damage. Replace components as necessary.

Reassembly

1) Using hammer and Bearing Race Installers (ST30611000 and ST30621000), drive new races into case and housing.

2) Install differential pinion gears, side gears and pinion shaft into differential. Simultaneously rotate side gears into their proper position in differential case.

3) Measure side gear-to-pinion gear clearance. Using shaft Adapter (KV38105900), insert shaft into side gear and mount dial indicator.

4) With shaft positioned against back of side gear and dial indicator tip on end of shaft, move side gear up and down and note measurement. Perform measurement on both side gears. Clearance should be no more than .012" (.30 mm).

5) If clearance exceeds specification, replace side bearing adjusting thrust washers with one of proper size. Thrust washers are available in sizes .030-.032" (.76-.81 mm), .032-.034" (.81-.86 mm), .034-.036" (.86-.91 mm), and .036-.038" (.91-.96 mm).

6) If components are excessively worn, replace pinion gears, side gears and case as a set. Install pinion shaft retaining pin flush with differential case. Install speedometer drive gear and stop ring. Press new differential side bearings onto carrier. Apply thread locking compound to ring gear bolts and install ring gear.

ADJUSTMENTS

DIFFERENTIAL

Side Bearing Shim

1) Remove side bearing outer race from transmission case. Place differential assembly, side bearing outer race and Selector (J-33200) in clutch housing. *See Fig. 6.*

Fig. 6: Installing Side Bearing Shim Selector

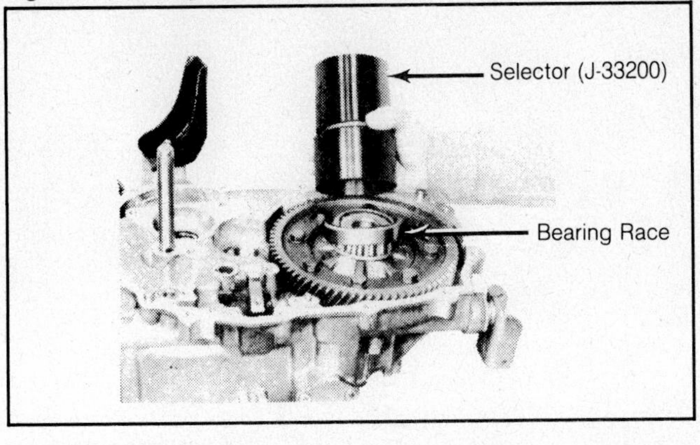

2) Position 4 Spacers (J-33200) evenly around clutch housing and tighten alternately to 12-15 ft. lbs. (16-21 N.m). Rotate differential a few times to seat bearing. Using a feeler gauge measure the widest gap around selector. *See Fig. 7.*

Fig. 7: Measuring for Side Bearing Shim

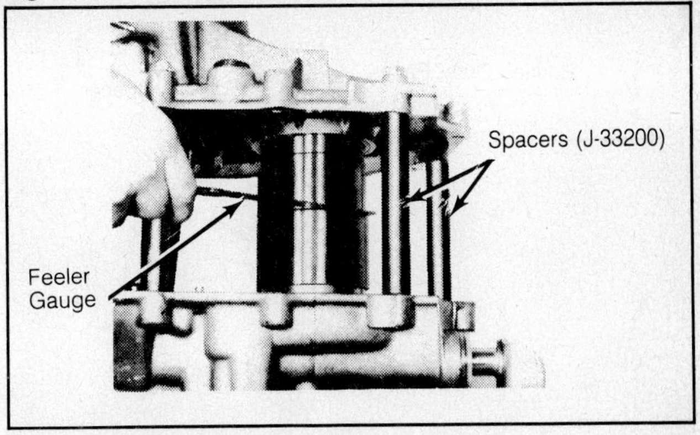

3) Shims are available in thicknesses from .0173" (.440 mm) to .0346" (.880 mm) in increments of .0016" (.040 mm). Select proper thickness shim by first adding .0016" (.04 mm) to measured distance. Then determine minimum and maximum shim thickness range by adding AND subtracting .0008" (.020 mm). Choose a shim that matches or falls within the range. It may be necessary to use 2 shims to achieve proper thickness. Install proper size shim(s) and side bearing outer race.

4) With differential in position, assemble transmission case to clutch housing. Insert torque wrench Adapter (KV38105900) into differential through axle shaft hole. Connect torque wrench to adapter. Rotate differential at least 10 times to seat bearings.

5) Measure force required to rotate differential assembly. With input shaft and mainshaft removed, required force should be 43-65 INCH lbs. (5.0-7.5 N.m). Fluctuations in required force should be no more than 9 INCH lbs. (1 N.m).

6) If specifications are not met, change differential side bearing shim thickness to obtain desired result. After obtaining correct preload, separate transmission case from clutch housing and install remainder of transaxle components.

MAINSHAFT

Mainshaft Bearing

1) If the mainshaft, mainshaft front and/or rear bearings, clutch housing or transmission case were replaced, mainshaft bearing rotary frictional force should be checked and, if necessary, adjusted.

2) To properly adjust rotary force, apply gear oil to mainshaft rear bearing outer race. Install outer race. Using a depth gauge, measure distance from case surface to outer race. *See Fig. 8.*

3) Select proper thickness of shim by first subtracting .0896" (2.27 mm) from measured distance. Then determine minimum and maximum shim thickness range by adding AND subtracting .0010" (.025 mm). Choose a shim that matches or falls within the range. Mainshaft shims are available in sizes from .004" (.10 mm) to .040" (1 mm) in increments of .002" (.05 mm). Install proper shim between bearing outer race and spacer. Temporarily install case cover.

4) Ensure that differential side bearing rotary frictional force is within specifications. Shift into 4th gear and turn input shaft at least 10 times to seat bearings. Insert torque wrench Adapter (KV38105900) into differential through axle shaft hole. *See Fig. 9.*

NISSAN 4 & 5-SPEED TRANSAXLE (Cont.)

Fig. 8: Mainshaft Bearing Preload Adjustment

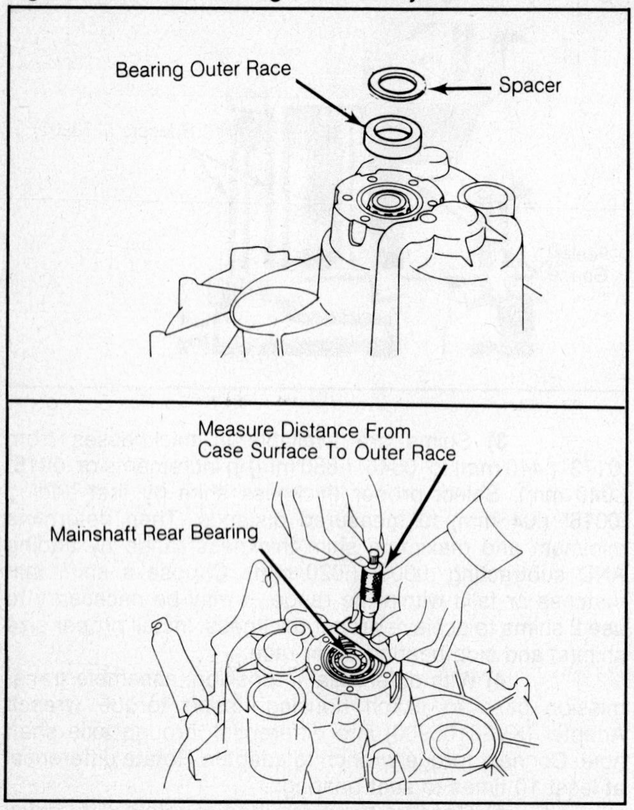

5) Connect torque wrench to adapter. Measure force required to rotate differential assembly. Required force should be 65-95 INCH lbs. (7.5-11 N.m). Fluctuations in required force should be no more 9 INCH lbs. (1 N.m). Apply sealant to case cover and tighten to specification.

Fig. 9: Measuring Rotational Drag

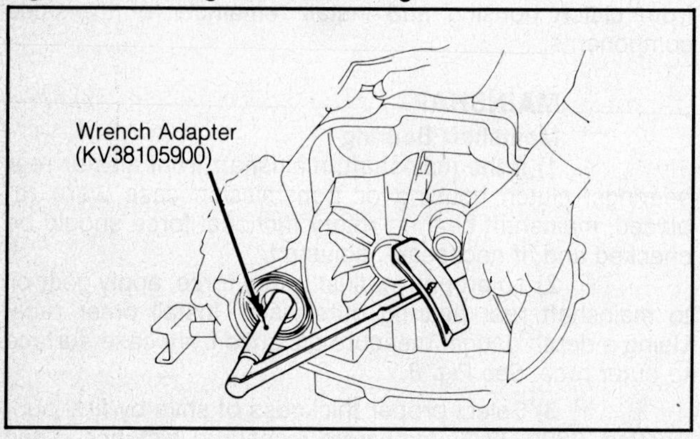

TIGHTENING SPECIFICATIONS

Application	Ft. Lbs. (N.m)
Back-Up Light Switch	14-22 (19-30)
Bearing Retainer-to Clutch Housing	12-15 (16-20)
Clutch Housing-to Transmission Case	12-15 (16-20)
Drain Plug	18-25 (24-34)
Filler Plug	18-25 (24-34)
Neutral Switch	14-22 (19-29)
Ring Gear Mount Bolts	54-65 (73-88)
Switch Plug	11-14 (15-19)
Transaxle-to-Engine Mount Bolt (E-16 Engine)	12-15 (16-20)
Transaxle-to-Engine Mount Bolt (CD-17 7T Engine)	22-30 (30-40)
Transaxle-to-Engine Mount Bolt (Stanza only)	22-30 (30-40)
Transaxle-to-Engine Mount Bolt (CD-17 9T Engine)	32-43 (43-58)
Transaxle-to-Engine Gusset Bolt (All Models)	12-15 (16-20)
5th/Reverse Check Plug	14-18 (19-24)
	INCH Lbs. (N.m)
Control Bracket-to Clutch Housing Mount Bolt	55-73 (6.2-8.2)
Shift Rod Yoke Mount Bolt (Stanza)	55-73 (6.2-8.2)
Speedometer Gear Assembly Mount Bolt	32-44 (2.7-3.7)
Transmission Case Cover Mount Bolt	55-73 (6.2-8.2)
5th/Reverse Detent Assembly	55-73 (6.2-8.2)

NISSAN PICKUP, 200SX, 300ZX 5-SPEED

DESCRIPTION

The FS5W71B and C transmissions are fully synchronized with constant mesh gears. All forward gears are helical type. The 5th overdrive (O.D.) gear rides freely on mainshaft. The countershaft 5th gear is fitted to countershaft by splines. The 5th gear synchronizer system is also on rear of mainshaft.

Placing control lever in 5th gear position will bring reverse and 5th gear coupling sleeve on mainshaft into mesh with countershaft gear. The main components of transmission are: Transmission case, adapter plate and rear extension housing.

LUBRICATION & ADJUSTMENT

See appropriate MANUAL TRANSMISSION SERVICING article in IMPORT GENERAL SERVICING section.

REMOVAL & INSTALLATION

See appropriate MANUAL TRANSMISSION REMOVAL article in IMPORT GENERAL SERVICING section.

TRANSMISSION DISASSEMBLY

1) Clean transmission case before disassembly. Drain gear oil. If equipped, remove O.D. gear switch. Remove "E" clip and stopper guide pin. Remove shifter return spring plug, spring and plunger from extension housing.

2) Remove rear extension housing by turning shifter control fully to the left while lightly tapping housing. Use standard puller to help remove housing, if necessary. Remove lock pin and striking rod.

3) Remove Reverse check sleeve. Remove dust cover, release bearing and withdrawal lever. Remove back-up light switch, speedometer driven gear and front cover with gasket.

4) Detach countershaft front bearing shim. Remove input shaft bearing snap ring. Separate transmission case from adapter plate, using a soft hammer.

COMPONENT DISASSEMBLY & REASSEMBLY

GEAR ASSEMBLY

Disassembly

1) Install gear and fork assembly onto adapter setting plate (ST23810001) and install assembly in vise. Remove 3 check ball plugs and check springs. Drive out retaining pins from fork rods with pin punch. *See Fig. 1*.

2) Drive out fork rods from adapter plate, by tapping lightly on front of rods. Remove 4 interlock balls and 3 check balls. Before disassembling mainshaft, measure gear backlash.

3) *Refer to Gear End Play Chart for measurement limits*. Record gear end play measurements for reassembly reference.

4) With 2nd and Reverse gears engaged, remove countershaft front bearing, using a puller. Remove countergear snap ring. Remove counterdrive gear and input shaft assembly.

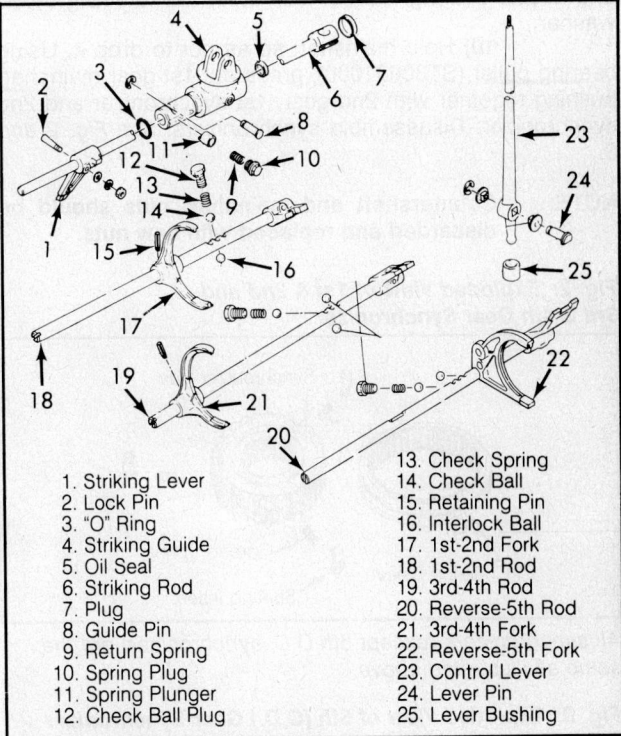

Fig. 1: Exploded View of Shift Control Components

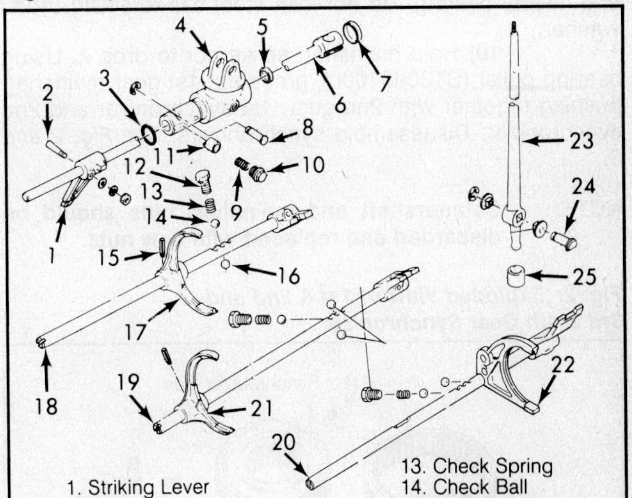

1. Striking Lever
2. Lock Pin
3. "O" Ring
4. Striking Guide
5. Oil Seal
6. Striking Rod
7. Plug
8. Guide Pin
9. Return Spring
10. Spring Plug
11. Spring Plunger
12. Check Ball Plug
13. Check Spring
14. Check Ball
15. Retaining Pin
16. Interlock Ball
17. 1st-2nd Fork
18. 1st-2nd Rod
19. 3rd-4th Rod
20. Reverse-5th Rod
21. 3rd-4th Fork
22. Reverse-5th Fork
23. Control Lever
24. Lever Pin
25. Lever Bushing

Model C is similar.

GEAR END PLAY MEASUREMENTS

Application	In. (mm)
1st Gear	.011-.013 (.27-.34)
2nd Gear	.005-.008 (.12-.19)
3rd Gear	.005-.015 (.13-.37)
5th Gear (O.D.)	.012-.014 (.31-.35)
Reverse Gear	.002-.020 (.05-.50)

NOTE: **When drawing out main drive gear assembly, do not drop pilot needle bearing and synchro ring.**

5) Remove snap ring and thrust washer from mainshaft. Remove 3rd and 4th synchronizer assembly. Remove 3rd gear. Engage 2nd and Reverse gears. Release staking on countershaft and mainshaft nuts. Remove and discard countershaft nut.

6) Using puller, remove countershaft 5th gear and bearing. Remove counter reverse idler gear and spacer. Remove countershaft by tapping lightly at the rear end. Remove reverse idler gear snap ring and reverse idler gear.

7) Remove snap rings, steel ball, speedometer gear and bearing from rear of mainshaft. Remove snap ring on mainshaft bearing. Remove mainshaft end bearing with puller (KV32101330).

8) Remove mainshaft nut, thrust washer, steel roller, needle bearing, O.D. gear and baulk ring. Remove mainshaft reverse gear, overdrive synchronizer, insert retainer and overdrive gear bushing.

9) Remove components by tapping rear end of mainshaft gear assembly and countershaft. While tapping, hold front of mainshaft assembly to prevent dropping

NISSAN PICKUP, 200SX, 300ZX 5-SPEED (Cont.)

counter gear. Remove thrust washer, steel ball, 1st gear and needle bearing. Do not lose steel ball retaining thrust washer.

10) Hold mainshaft so as not to drop it. Using bearing puller (ST30031000), press out 1st gear mainshaft bushing together with 2nd gear, 1st synchronizer and 2nd synchronizer. Disassemble synchronizers. *See Fig. 2 and 3.*

NOTE: Countershaft and mainshaft nuts should be discarded and replaced with new nuts.

Fig. 2: Exploded View of 1st & 2nd and 3rd & 4th Gear Synchronizer

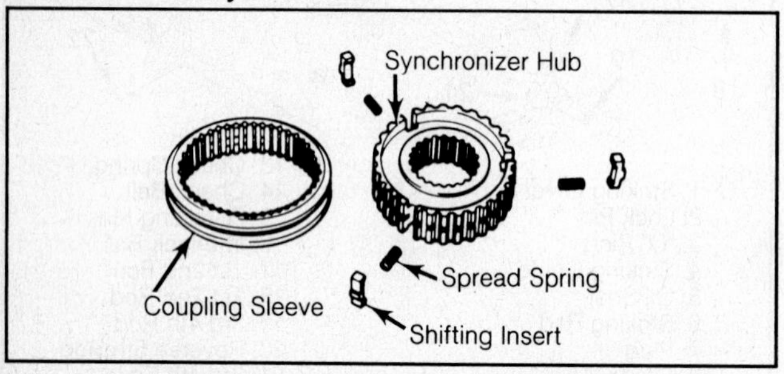

All synchronizers (except 5th O.D. synchronizer) are the same as illustrated above.

Fig. 3: Exploded View of 5th (O.D.) Gear Synchronizer & Reverse Main Gear

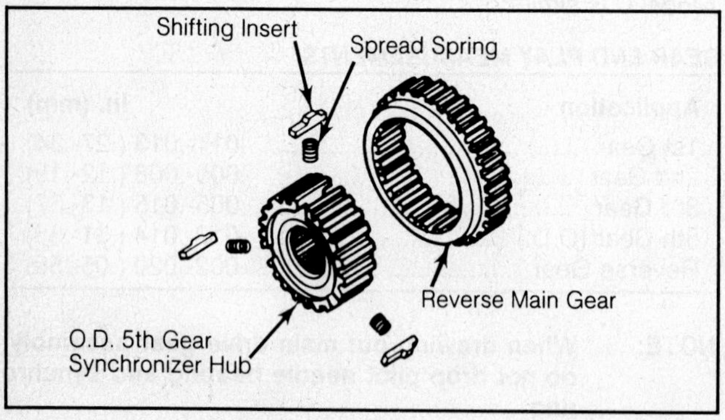

Inspection

1) Wash all parts in a cleaning solvent and check for wear, damage or other faulty conditions. Inspect bearing race and ball surfaces for rough or worn condition. Check balls for rough or out of round. Replace as necessary.

2) Check transmission case and extension housing for cracks, damage or other faulty conditions. If rear extension housing bushing is worn or cracked, replace extension housing and bushing as an assembly.

3) Check synchro assemblies (baulk rings) for wear. Place synchro ring on gear cone as far as it will go. Measure gap between gear and synchro ring. Standard clearance for 1st-4th gears is .047-.063" (1.20-1.60 mm) and .039-.055" (1.00-1.40 mm) for 5th O.D. gear.

4) If clearance is less than .031" (.80 mm) on 1st-4th gears or .020" (.50 mm) on 5th gear, replace synchro ring. Check oil seal for spring out of position and cracked or deformed sealing lip. Check oil seal lip contact with shaft. If necessary, replace oil seal and shaft as an assembly.

Reassembly

1) Place new dowel pins (2) and mainshaft bearing on adapter plate and tap into position. Install oil gutter on adapter plate, bending it on front side and expanding it on rear side.

2) Install Reverse idle shaft and bearing retainer. Tighten two screws and stake at two points. Install rear countershaft bearing with soft face hammer. Assembly coupling sleeve and hub. Position spread springs and shifting inserts in three slots in synchronizer hub.

3) Place coupling sleeve (Reverse main gear) on synchronizer hub. Install 2nd gear needle bearing, 2nd gear, 2nd gear synchro ring, 1st and 2nd gear synchro assembly, 1st gear synchro ring, 1st gear bushing, needle bearing, 1st gear, steel ball and thrust washer on mainshaft. *See Fig. 5.*

4) Place adapter plate on transmission press stand (KV31100401). *See Fig. 6.* Press mainshaft assembly onto adapter plate. Ensure bearing is placed squarely against shaft when pressed into place.

5) Install new Woodruff keys in grooves in countershaft and tap lightly until seated. Place adapter plate assembly and mainshaft assembly so that countershaft rear bearing rests on transmission press stand. Install countershaft into adapter plate.

6) Install 3rd gear needle bearing, mainshaft 3rd gear, synchro ring and 3rd and 4th gear synchro assembly on front of mainshaft. Ensure 3rd and 4th gear synchronizers are facing in the proper direction. Install thrust washer and secure with a snap ring of the proper thickness to minimize clearance of groove in mainshaft.

NOTE: Snap rings are available in the following thicknesses: .055" (1.40 mm), .059" (1.50 mm) and .063" (1.60 mm).

7) Using transmission adapter plate (ST23860000) and press stand (KV31100401), press input shaft bearing onto input shaft, making sure that snap ring groove on shaft clears bearing. Place input bearing spacer on input shaft bearing and secure bearing with a snap ring that will eliminate end play. *See Main Drive Bearing Snap Ring Chart.*

MAIN DRIVE BEARING SNAP RINGS

No.	Thickness In. (mm)
1	.0681 (1.730)
2	.0709 (1.800)
3	.0736 (1.870)
4	.0764 (1.940)
5	.0791 (2.010)
6	.0819 (2.080)

8) On Maxima Diesel vehicles only, install washer on countershaft. Install torsional damper-to-counter drive gear. Insert coil spring end in .2" (5 mm) hole in sub gear. Insert other spring end into .2" (5 mm) hole in counter drive gear. Rotate sub gear 2 teeth counterclockwise and engage with input shaft gear.

9) On all models, mesh and install countershaft gear and input shaft, onto transmission shaft assemblies. *See Fig. 8.* Press countershaft front bearing onto countershaft.

NISSAN PICKUP, 200SX, 300ZX 5-SPEED (Cont.)

Fig. 4: Exploded View of FS5W71B 5-Speed Transmission Assembly

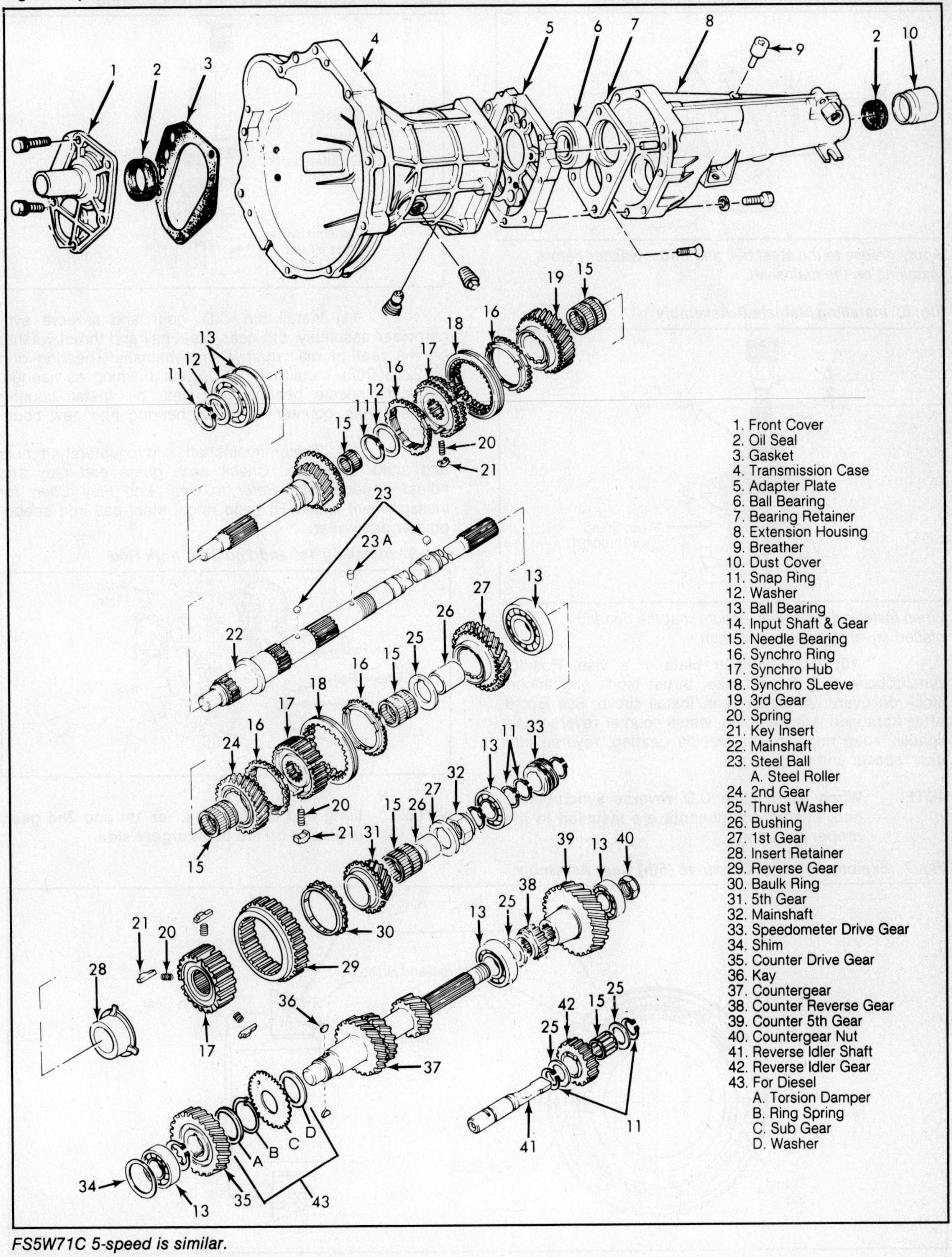

FS5W71C 5-speed is similar.

NISSAN PICKUP, 200SX, 300ZX 5-SPEED (Cont.)

Fig. 5: Component Installation (on Mainshaft)

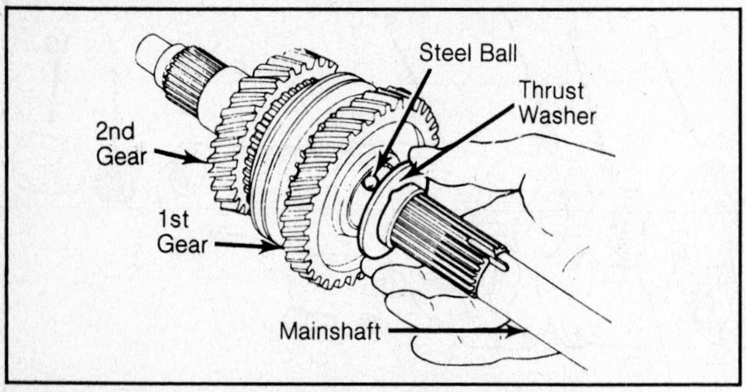

Apply grease to the steel ball and thrust washer before installing on the mainshaft.

Fig. 6: Installing Mainshaft Assembly

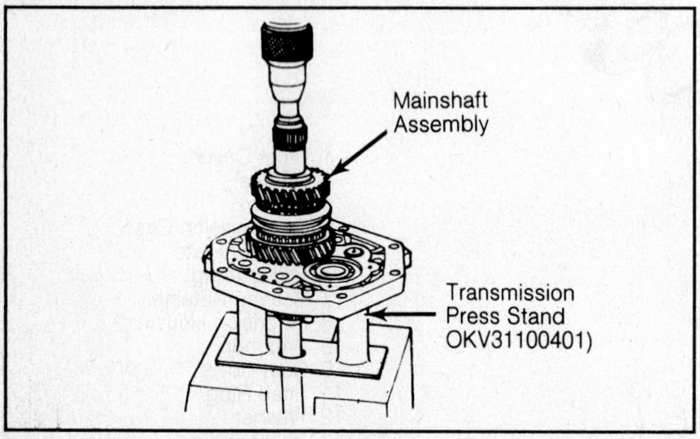

When installing assembly, ensure that the bearing is placed squarely against the shaft.

10) Place adapter plate in a vise. Position synchronizer ring, band brake, thrust block and anchor block on overdrive clutch gear. Install circlip. *See Fig. 8*. After front side is assembled, install counter reverse gear spacer, snap ring, spacer, needle bearing, reverse idler gear, spacer and snap ring.

NOTE: When assembling O.D.-reverse synchronizer hub, ensure components are installed in the proper direction.

Fig. 7: Exploded View of Overdrive (5th) Gear Assembly

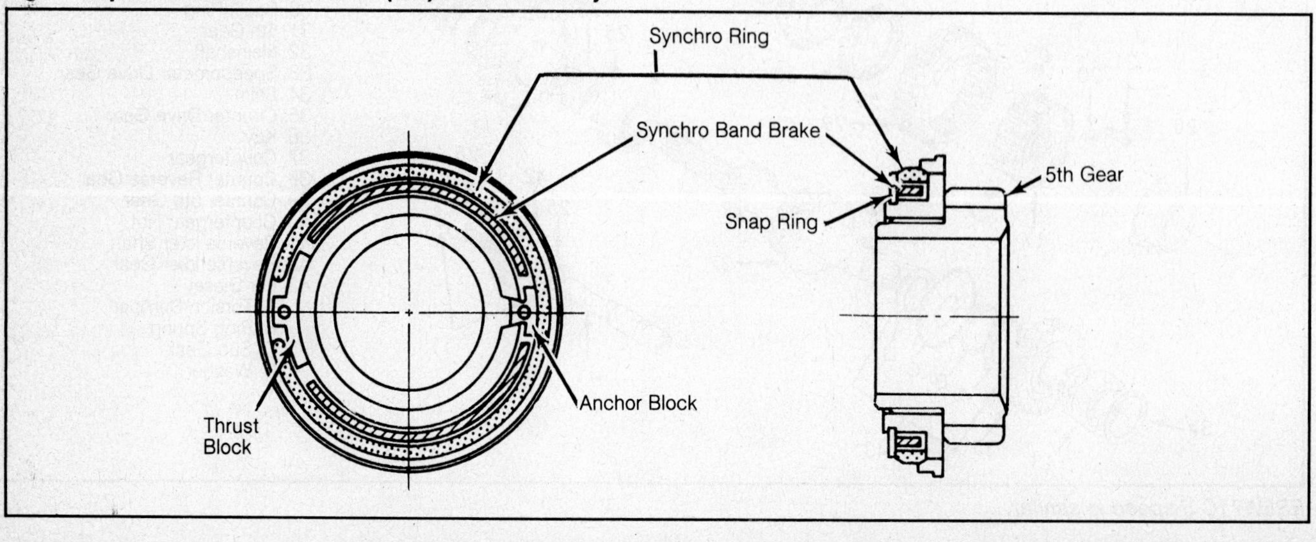

Fig. 8: Installing Countershaft Front Bearing

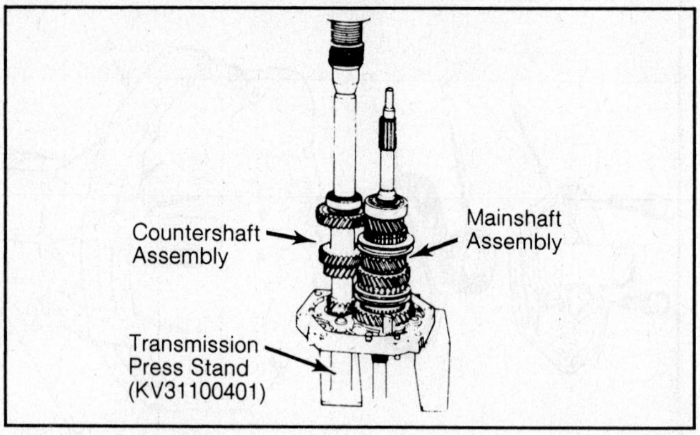

11) Install 5th O.D. gear and reverse synchronizer assembly, 5th gear, steel ball and thrust washer on the rear of mainshaft. Using mainshaft bearing drift (ST22350000), install new O.D. gear bushing as needed. Lubricate needle bearing with gear oil. Install counter reverse gear, counter 5th gear, bearing and new countershaft nut.

12) Tighten mainshaft and countershaft nuts and stake to shafts. Check each gears end play and adjust if necessery. *Refer to Gear End Play Chart for measurement limits*. Fit snap rings, steel ball and speedometer drive gear.

Fig. 9: Installing 1st and 2nd Shift Fork Rod

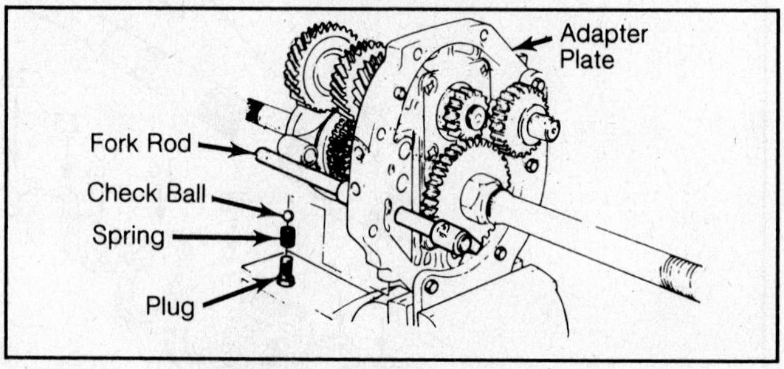

NOTE: Long end of shift fork, for 1st and 2nd gear, is placed on the countergear side.

NISSAN PICKUP, 200SX, 300ZX 5-SPEED (Cont.)

13) Install 1st/2nd and 3rd/4th shift forks into grooves on coupling sleeves. Slide 1st/2nd fork rod through adapter plate and 1st/2nd shifter fork. *See Fig. 9.* Secure rod to shift fork with a new retaining pin. Install check ball, check spring and plug. Apply sealant to plug before installing. Align notch in 1st/2nd fork rod with check ball.

14) Slide 3rd/4th fork rod through adapter plate and 3rd/4th shift fork. Secure with a new retaining pin. Install check ball, spring and plug. Apply sealant to plug before installing. Align notch in 3rd/4th fork rod with check ball. *See Fig. 10.*

Fig. 10: Installing 3rd and 4th Shift Fork Rod

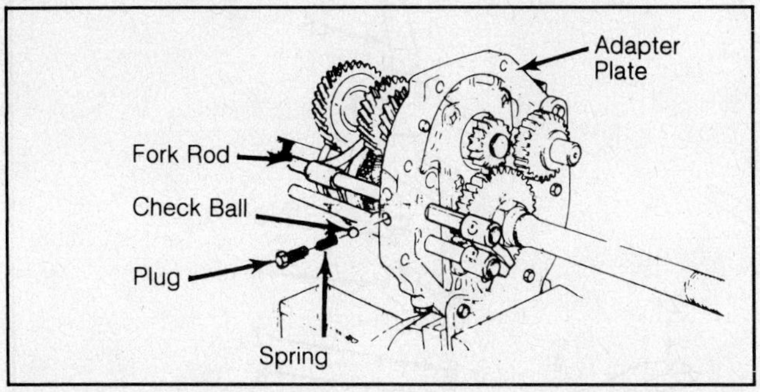

15) Place reverse shift fork in reverse idler gear. Slide reverse fork rod through reverse shift fork and adapter plate and secure with a new retaining pin. Install check ball, spring and plug. Apply sealant to plug before installing. Align notch in reverse fork rod with check ball. *See Fig. 11.*

Fig. 11: Installing Reverse Shift Fork Rod

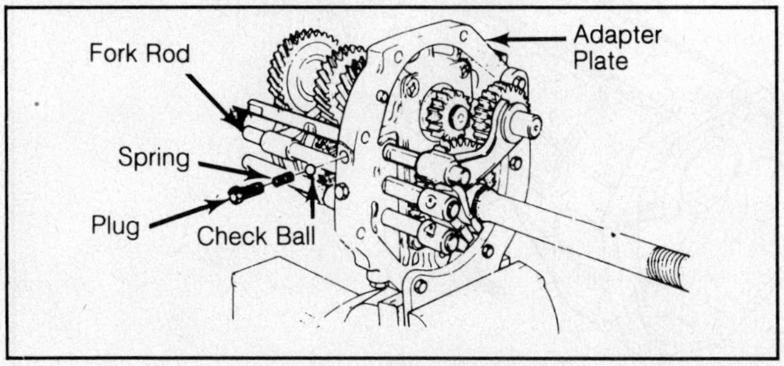

TRANSMISSION REASSEMBLY

1) Clean mating surfaces of extension and adapter plate. Apply sealant to mating surfaces. With fork rods in neutral position and shifter control fully to the left, gradually slide extension onto adapter plate. Ensure gear change cross lever engages with fork rod bracket.

2) Clean mating surfaces of adapter plate and transmission case. Apply sealant to mating surfaces. Slide transmission case onto adapter plate. Install main drive bearing and countershaft front bearing. Ensure mainshaft rotates freely. Install bolts and torque to specifications.

Fig. 12: Countershaft Front Bearing Shim

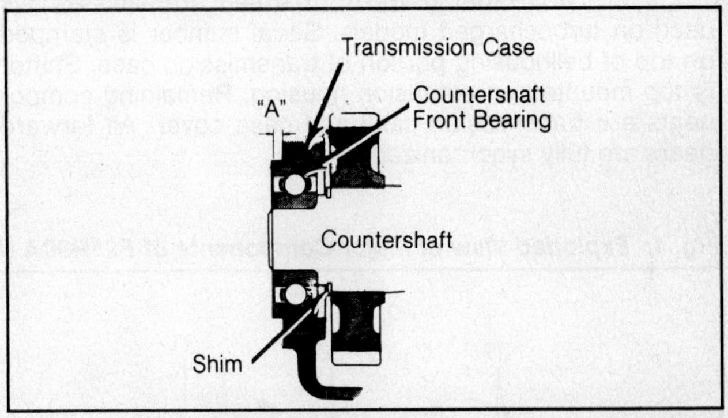

3) Measure depth "A" from front end of transmission case-to-countershaft front bearing. *See Fig. 12.* Select a countershaft front bearing shim from *Countershaft Front Bearing Shims Chart*.

COUNTERSHAFT FRONT BEARING SHIMS

"A" Measurement In. (mm)	Shims In. (mm)
.1150-.1185 (2.910-3.010)	.024 (.60)
.1189-.1224 (3.020-3.110)	.020 (.50)
.1228-.1264 (3.120-3.210)	.016 (.40)
.1268-.1303 (3.220-3.310)	.012 (.30)
.1307-.1343 (3.320-3.410)	.008 (.20)
.1346-.1382 (3.420-3.510)	.004 (.10)

4) Apply grease to shim to retain it on countershaft front bearing. Install front cover to transmission case. Apply grease to reverse select return plunger and install in rear extension.

5) Install speedometer pinion assembly on rear extension. Apply grease to release bearing. Temporarily install control lever and shift control lever. Shift transmission through all gears to ensure correct operation.

TIGHTENING SPECIFICATIONS

Application	Ft. Lbs. (N.m)
Backup Lamp Switch	14-22 (20-29)
Ball Pin	14-25 (20-34)
Bearing Retainer-to-Adapter	12-17 (16-25)
Check Ball Plug	14-18 (20-25)
Counter Gear Lock Nut	72-94 (98-128)
Drain/Filler Plugs	18-25 (25-34)
Front Cover-to Transmission Case	12-15 (16-21)
Mainshaft Lock Nut	101-123 (137-167)
Rear Extension-to Transmission Case	12-15 (16-21)

NISSAN 300ZX 5-SPEED

IDENTIFICATION

FS5R90A (BW-T5) 5-speed transmission is used on turbocharged models. Serial number is stamped on top of bellhousing portion of transmission case. Shifter is top mounted on extension housing. Remaining components are transmission case and case cover. All forward gears are fully synchronized.

LUBRICATION & ADJUSTMENT

See appropriate MANUAL TRANSMISSION SERVICING article in IMPORT GENERAL SERVICING section.

REMOVAL & INSTALLATION

See appropriate MANUAL TRANSMISSION REMOVAL article in IMPORT GENERAL SERVICING section.

Fig. 1: Exploded View of Major Components of FS5R90A (BW-T5) Transmission

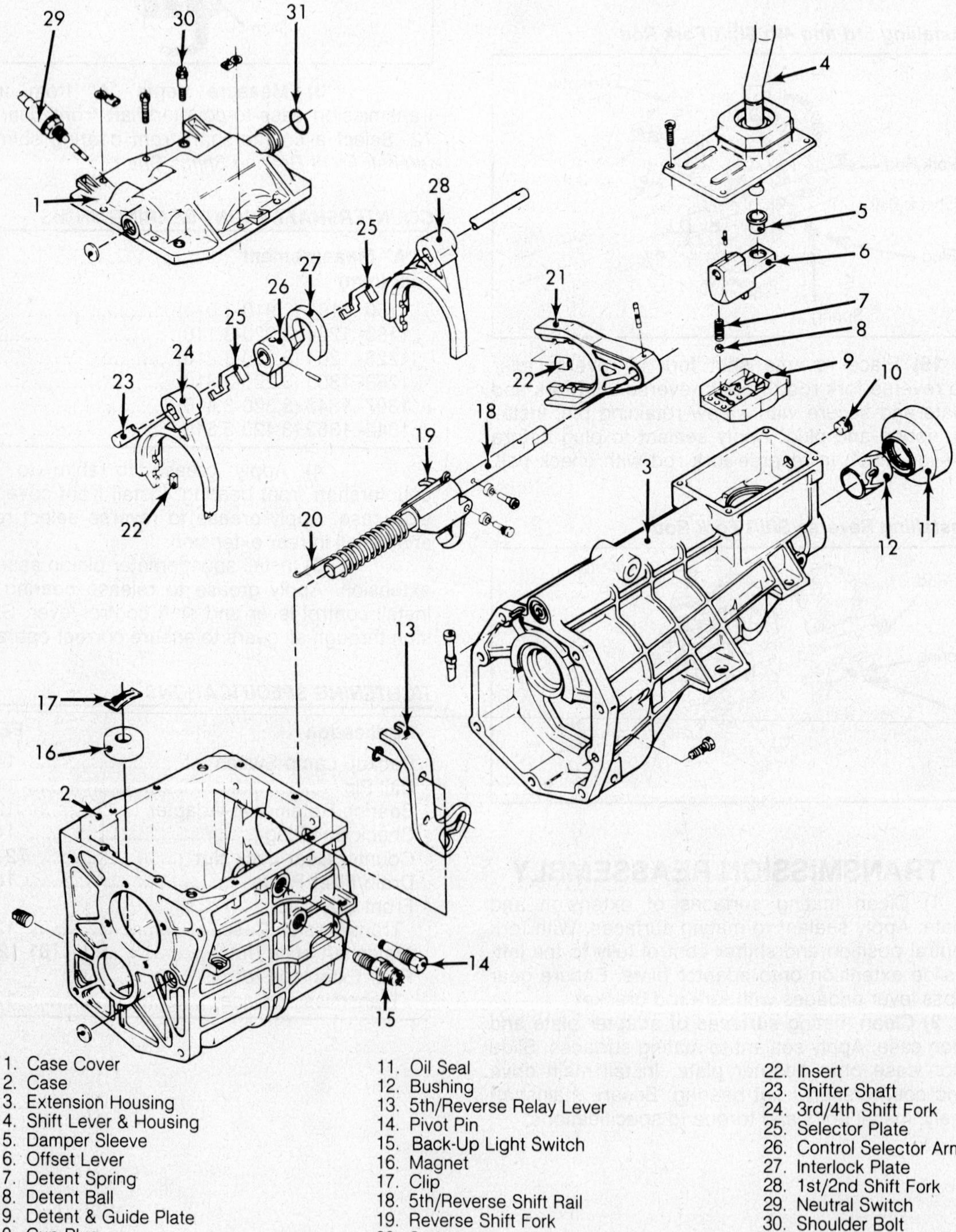

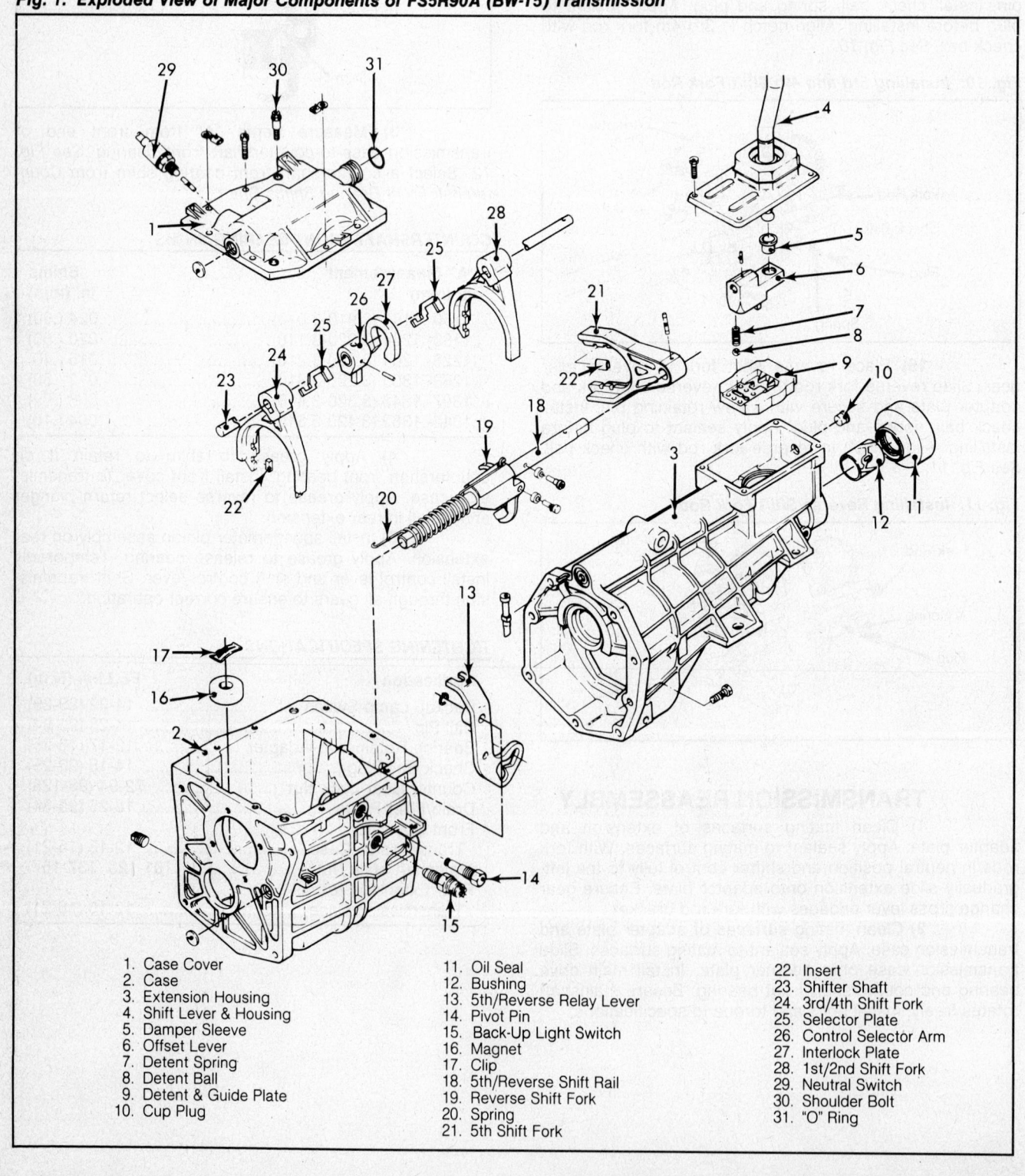

1. Case Cover
2. Case
3. Extension Housing
4. Shift Lever & Housing
5. Damper Sleeve
6. Offset Lever
7. Detent Spring
8. Detent Ball
9. Detent & Guide Plate
10. Cup Plug
11. Oil Seal
12. Bushing
13. 5th/Reverse Relay Lever
14. Pivot Pin
15. Back-Up Light Switch
16. Magnet
17. Clip
18. 5th/Reverse Shift Rail
19. Reverse Shift Fork
20. Spring
21. 5th Shift Fork
22. Insert
23. Shifter Shaft
24. 3rd/4th Shift Fork
25. Selector Plate
26. Control Selector Arm
27. Interlock Plate
28. 1st/2nd Shift Fork
29. Neutral Switch
30. Shoulder Bolt
31. "O" Ring

NISSAN 300ZX 5-SPEED (Cont.)

TRANSMISSION DISASSEMBLY

NOTE: **Before beginning disassembly of transmission, clean all external parts thoroughly to remove dirt and grease.**

REAR EXTENSION

1) Drain oil. Select neutral position with shift lever. Remove shift lever assembly and damper sleeve. Drive roll pin from offset lever. Unbolt rear extension housing from transmission case. Remove rear extension housing with offset lever, detent spring and ball.

2) Tap extension with plastic mallet to loosen if necessary. When removing extension housing, do not lose funnel and thrust race from rear of countershaft. Clean complete extension housing with solvent. Check for cracks.

3) Check sealing surface for nicks, projections, or sealant. If rear bushing or guide plate are worn or damaged, extension housing, guide plate, and bushing must be replaced as assembly.

CASE COVER

1) Remove cover-to-case bolts and tap cover to loosen it. Slide cover to right and lift to remove. Pull shifter shaft to rear of cover. Drive out striking lever-to-shifter shaft roll pin. Remove shifter shaft through rear of cover. Remove selector plates from shift fork assemblies.

2) Clean all parts with solvent. Check for wear, scratches, or other damage. Check shift fork inserts for wear. Replace worn or damaged parts as necessary.

TRANSMISSION CASE

1) Remove back-up light switch. Remove "E" clip and pivot pin, leaving 5th/reverse relay lever in place. If not removed with extension housing, remove countershaft funnel, thrust ring, and needle thrust bearing. Remove 5th synchro snap ring and thrust race. Drive roll pin from 5th shift fork, supporting shaft with wood block.

Fig. 2: Removing 5th Gear Shift Fork Roll Pin

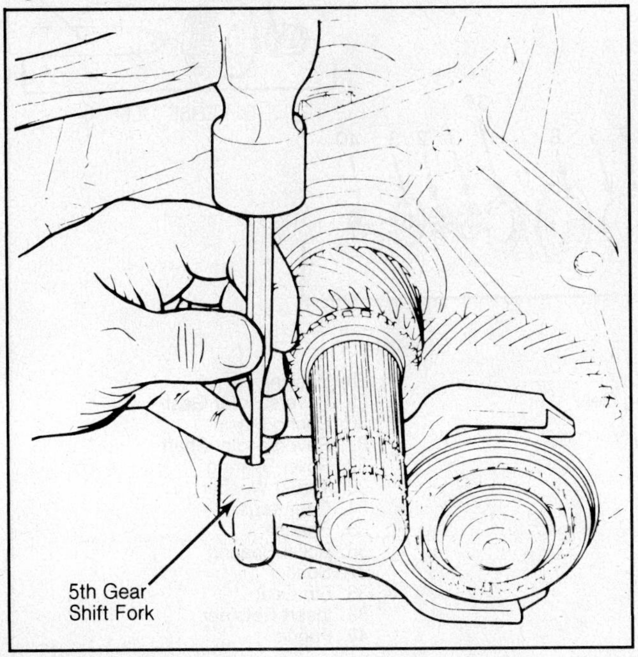

Support shift shaft when driving roll pin in or out.

2) Remove 5th shift fork, synchro, and counter gear. Mark synchro hub-to-sleeve position for reassembly procedure. Unbolt and remove input shaft bearing retainer. Rotate input shaft and main drive gear assembly until flat on main drive gear faces countershaft. Remove input shaft assembly through front of case.

3) Remove rear output shaft bearing outer race. Remove output shaft assembly through top of case. Remove 5th shift rail. Remove reverse fork with spring. Remove 5th/reverse relay lever. Drive roll pin from reverse idler shaft. Remove reverse idler shaft and gear. Remove snap ring and outer bearing spacer from rear of countershaft.

CAUTION: **When pressing rear countershaft bearing from case, do not allow bearing or countergear to drop. Press front countershaft bearing from case only if replacement is necessary.**

4) Press countershaft toward rear of case until rear bearing is out of case. Remove rear bearing and inner spacer from countershaft. Remove countershaft and front thrust washer through top of case.

5) Press front countershaft bearing from case ONLY if necessary for replacement. Clean case with solvent. Check for cracks or pitting. DO NOT remove magnet from bottom of case. Magnet is held in place with clip and special glue.

COMPONENT DISASSEMBLY & REASSEMBLY

GEARS & SHAFTS

NOTE: **It is necessary to measure gear end play on output shaft both before disassembly and after reassembly. Excessive end play before disassembly will indicate worn or damaged parts.**

Disassembly

1) Remove output shaft rear snap ring. Remove speedometer drive gear and retaining ball from rear of output shaft. Press 3rd/4th synchro assembly from front of output shaft. Note relation of hub and sleeve for reassembly. Remove 3rd gear and synchro ring from output shaft.

2) Remove snap ring and press 5th gear off output shaft. Slide rear bearing off output shaft and remove thrust washer. Pull retaining pin from output shaft behind 1st gear. Remove 1st gear.

3) Remove snap ring and thrust washer in front of 2nd gear. Remove 2nd gear. Remove 1st/2nd synchro sleeve, inserts, and insert retaining springs. Note position of sleeve in relation to hub for correct reassembly. Hub is not to be removed from shaft. Shaft and synchro assembly must be replaced as unit if any part needs replacement.

Inspection

1) Clean and dry bearings. If races or rollers are rough, replace bearing. Replace worn or damaged needle bearings. Check gears for wear or damage. Check shafts for bending, cracks, or worn splines. Measure gear end play. *See Gear End Play* table. Replace worn or damaged parts.

NISSAN 300ZX 5-SPEED (Cont.)

Fig. 3: Exploded View of Gears and Shafts

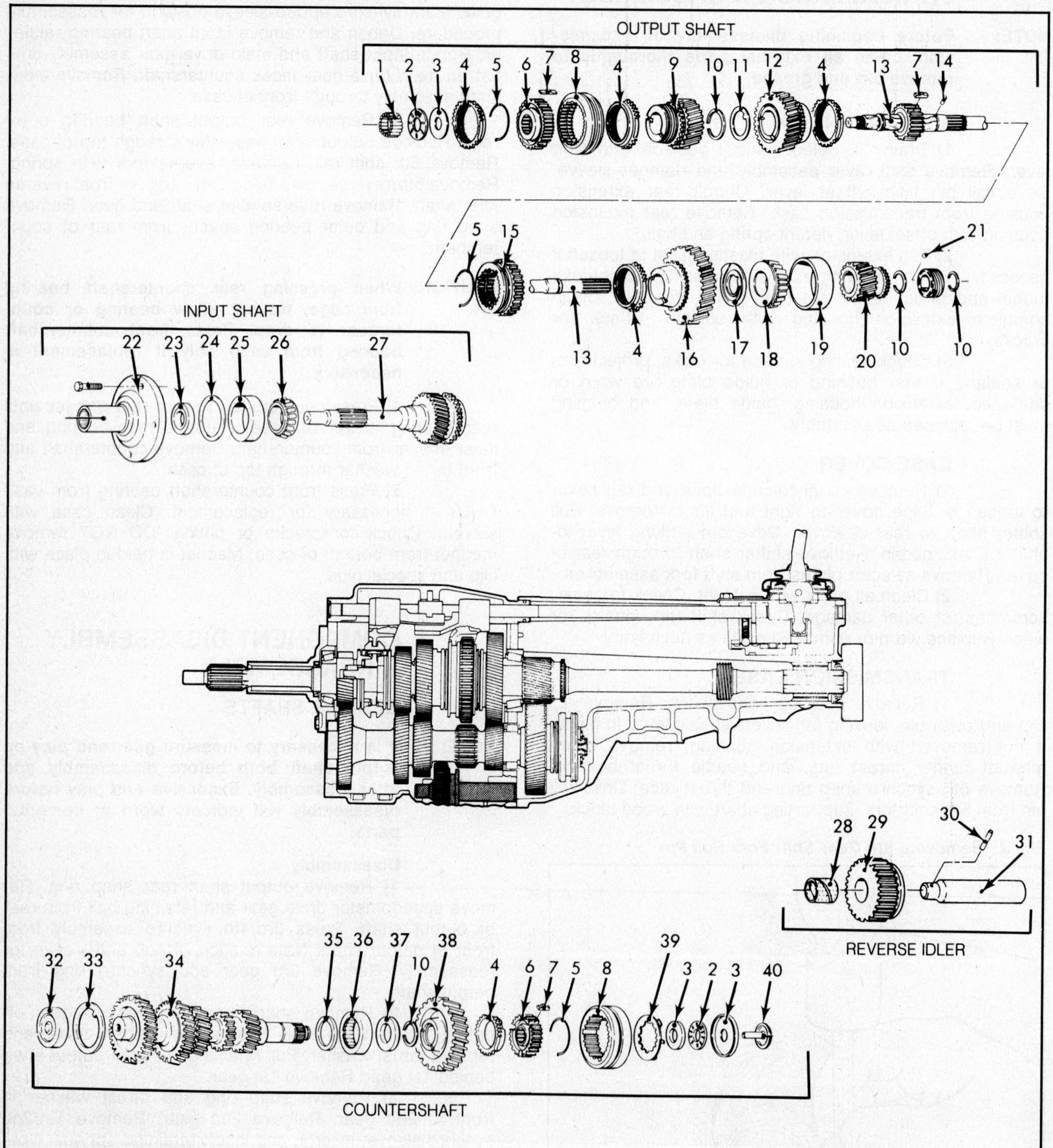

1. Needle Rollers
2. Thrust Needle Bearing
3. Thrust Race
4. Synchro Ring
5. Spring
6. Synchro Hub
7. Synchro Insert
8. Synchro Sleeve
9. 3rd Gear
10. Snap Ring
11. 2nd Gear Thrust
12. 2nd Gear
13. Output Shaft & Hub
14. Pin
15. Reverse Sliding Gear
16. 1st Gear
17. Thrust Washer
18. Rear Bearing
19. Bearing Race
20. 5th Gear
21. Ball
22. Front Retainer
23. Seal
24. Shim
25. Bearing Race
26. Roller Bearing
27. Input Shaft
28. Bushing
29. Reverse Idler Gear
30. Spring Pin
31. Reverse Idler Shaft
32. Roller Bearing
33. Thrust Washer
34. Countergear
35. Spacer
36. Roller Bearing
37. Spacer
38. 5th Gear
39. Insert Retainer
40. Funnel

NISSAN 300ZX 5-SPEED (Cont.)

GEAR END PLAY

Application	In. (mm)
Output Shaft	
1st Gear	.004-.010 (.10-.25)
2nd Gear	.004-.010 (.10-.25)
3rd Gear	.006-.016 (.15-.40)
Countershaft	
5th Drive Gear	.003-.019 (.10-.48)
Countergear	.010-.020 (.25-.50)

2) Check synchro rings for cracks or wear. Make sure edges of teeth and notches are proper size and well defined. Check taper surface. Machine grooves must be evident on inner surface of taper. Measure synchro ring clearance with ring firmly pressed against taper of gear.

3) Clearance should be minimum of .020" (.51 mm) between back of synchro ring and face of gear. Shift fork inserts should be replaced if worn unevenly or damaged. Check oil seal contact surface on shafts. If seal has worn shaft, shaft must be replaced.

Reassembly

1) Assemble synchro sleeves to hubs. Make sure marks made on disassembly are aligned. Sleeve must slide smoothly on hub. Position 3 inserts into slots with raised portion facing out. Install insert spring with hooked end inside insert. Slide spring under lip of other 2 inserts.

Fig. 4: Installing Synchro Insert Spring

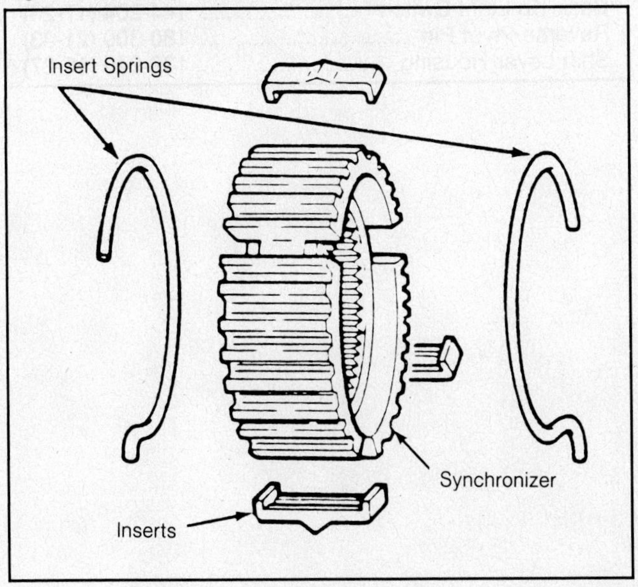

2) Turn synchro assembly over. Install other insert spring with hooked end inside same insert. Spring must run in opposite direction to that of spring on other side of assembly.

3) With 1st/2nd synchro assembly mounted on output shaft, install 2nd gear with thrust washer and snap ring. Install 1st gear. Install thrust washer locating pin into output shaft. Pin must project .12" (3.0 mm) above bearing surface when installed.

4) Install thrust washer against 1st gear, making sure slot in washer aligns with pin. Install rear bearing. Press 5th gear onto output shaft using installer (J 26010 01). Install 3rd gear.

5) Press 3rd/4th synchro assembly onto front of output shaft, using installer (J 25863 01). Extended nose of hub must face forward. Install locking ball for speedometer drive gear. Install gear and snap ring. Measure end play of output shaft gears. *See Gear End Play* table.

TRANSMISSION REASSEMBLY

NOTE: **During reassembly procedure, replace any "O" rings, roll pins, and seals with new parts.**

1) Apply thin bead of sealer to outside diameter of front countershaft bearing. Press bearing into case until front edge of bearing is flush with front edge of case. Lightly coat countershaft thrust washer with petroleum jelly and install washer in case. Make sure to align tang on washer with notch in case.

2) Place countergear in case with front journal riding in front bearing. Install rear countershaft spacer on rear of countergear. Install bearing protector (9J 33032) over countergear. Install bearing over protector. Drive bearing into case with installer (J 29895).

3) Bearing is properly installed when outer race protrudes from case by distance of .123-.127" (3.12-3.22 mm). Remove bearing protector. Install spacer and snap ring at rear of bearing. Put reverse idler gear into case. Shift fork groove should be toward rear. Install reverse idler shaft, new "O" ring, and retaining pin.

4) Install reverse fork with 5th/reverse relay lever, 5th speed shift rail and spring. Install back-up light switch. Install output shaft assembly into case. Install output shaft rear bearing outer race. Install roller bearings into rear of main drive gear on input shaft. Retain rollers in place with petroleum jelly.

5) Mount 4th gear synchro ring, thrust bearing race and needle thrust bearing onto main drive gear assembly. Install input shaft and main drive gear assembly into case.

NOTE: **Be sure needle roller bearings stay in place when installing input shaft. Flat area on main drive gear must be aligned with countergear in order to install input shaft and main drive gear into case.**

6) Remove minimum of .006" (.15 mm) in shims from under front bearing race in bearing retainer. Install remaining shims and race into retainer. Mount front bearing retainer on case. Make sure that oil collector groove faces upward.

7) Install 5th gear shift fork, 5th countergear and synchro as unit. Align pin holes in shift fork and shift rail. Install new roll pin. Put thrust race and snap ring on at rear of 5th synchro hub.

8) Assemble selector plates with shift fork assemblies. Install shifter shaft through rear opening of case cover. Slide shaft through 1st/2nd shift fork, interlock plate, striking lever, and 3rd/4th shift fork. Install new shifter shaft-to-striking lever roll pin.

9) Apply continuous bead of RTV sealer on case cover-to-case surface. Place cover on case. After putting sealant on threads, install 2 shouldered aligning bolts. Put sealer on threads and install case cover bolts.

10) Apply continuous bead of RTV sealer on extension housing-to-transmission case surface. Put

NISSAN 300ZX 5-SPEED (Cont.)

needle thrust bearing, race and funnel on rear of countershaft. Retain in place with coating of petroleum jelly. Place detent ball, spring and offset lever in place on guide plate. *See Fig. 5.*

Fig. 5: Offset Lever, Ball & Spring Location

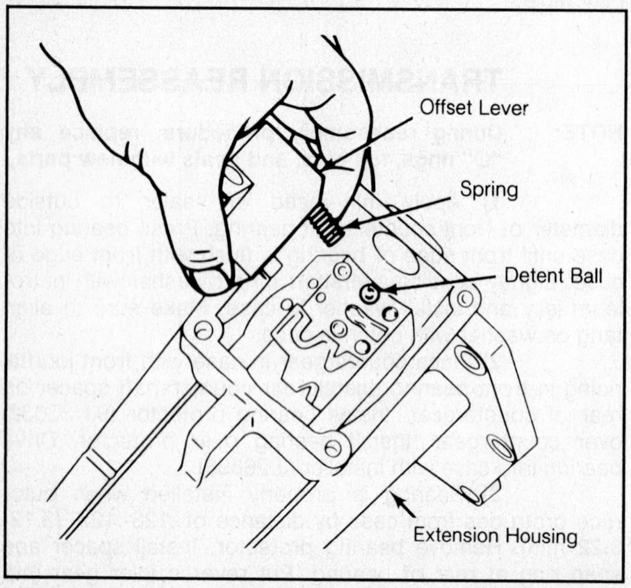

11) Install extension housing onto transmission case. Align hole in offset lever with hole in shifter shaft. Drive in roll pin. Install and tighten extension housing-to-transmission case bolts. Apply continuous bead of RTV sealer to control lever housing opening on extension housing.

12) Put damper sleeve into offset lever. Install shift lever and tighten shifter housing-to-extension housing bolts. Operate shift lever through entire shift pattern. Make sure gear changes occur smoothly. Install drain plug with sealant on threads.

13) Remove extension housing oil seal. Lightly coat oil seal surface with transmission oil. Drive seal into housing with installer (J 28894). Push input shaft to rear. Mount dial indicator so tip touches front end of input shaft. Zero indicator dial.

14) Push output shaft forward. Record dial indicator reading as "A". Remove indicator. Remove bearing retainer. Remove bearing race from retainer. Select proper thickness of shim to give preload "B" of .0051-.0098" (.129-.248 mm) on bearing race.

15) To determine preload shim thickness; add value "A", which is dial indicator reading from step **14)**, to value "B", which is desired preload amount. If dial indicator reading "A" is .10 mm (end play clearance) and preload desired "B" is .20 mm, shim thickness needed would be .30 mm.

16) Install selected shims and bearing race into front bearing retainer. Install new oil seal into bearing retainer, using driver (J 23096). Apply continuous bead of RTV sealant to bearing retainer sealing surface. Install bearing retainer with oil collector groove up.

TIGHTENING SPECIFICATIONS

Application	Ft. Lbs. (N.m)
Clutch Housing-to-Case	30-51 (41-69)
Extension-to-Case	20-46 (27-62)

	INCH Lbs. (N.m)
Cover-to-Case	72-132 (8-14)
Bearing Retainer-to-Case	132-240 (15-27)
Back-Up Light Switch	144-204 (17-24)
Reverse Pivot Pin	180-300 (21-33)
Shift Lever Housing	132-240 (15-27)

PEUGEOT 5-SPEED

DESCRIPTION

The 5-speed transmission has a split aluminum case. Gear assembly can be accessed after one half of case is removed. All forward gears are helical-type, and are synchronized for smooth gear engagement. Shift linkage is floor mounted with external linkage. Reverse and 5th gears are located in extension housing.

LUBRICATION & ADJUSTMENT

See appropriate MANUAL TRANSMISSION SERVICING article in IMPORT GENERAL SERVICING section.

TROUBLE SHOOTING

HARD SHIFTING

Improperly adjusted clutch. Excessive input shaft end play. Face of syncro hub in contact with cone, worn. Syncro cones worn, damaged, distorted or not in proper contact.

SLIPS OUT OF GEAR

Bearings worn or defective. Excessive play between gears and syncro cage. Play in syncro hub. Shift arm worn. Lock ball spring weak or broken. Lock ball missing.

TRANSMISSION NOISY

Low or incorrect lubricant. Gears or bearing worn or damaged. Worn syncro gears and/or cage. Excessive input shaft end play. Worn syncro hub or splines. Incorrectly meshed gears.

SERVICE (IN VEHICLE)

GEAR SHIFT LEVER

Removal & Installation

1) Remove emergency brake handle cover, rear section of center console, gearshift knob and front section of center console. Remove air ducting. Remove transmission top cover plate (with rubber boot).

2) Disconnect gearshift linkage and remove gearshift lever. If transmission is to be removed, remove engine/transmission rear mount bolt. The bolt is located just ahead of the gearshift. To install, reverse removal procedure.

EXTENSION HOUSING SEAL

Removal & Installation

Remove 4 attaching screws from driveshaft at extention housing. Pull driveshaft rearward and clear of transmission. Support driveshaft with a wire. Using a puller, remove extension housing seal. To install, reverse removal procedure. Ensure seal is installed straight in housing.

REMOVAL & INSTALLATION

TRANSMISSION

See appropriate MANUAL TRANSMISSION REMOVAL article in IMPORT GENERAL SERVICING section.

TRANSMISSION DISASSEMBLY

1) Place transmission on holding fixture with right side facing away from fixture. From extension housing,

Fig. 1: Sectional View of Peugeot 5-Speed Transmission

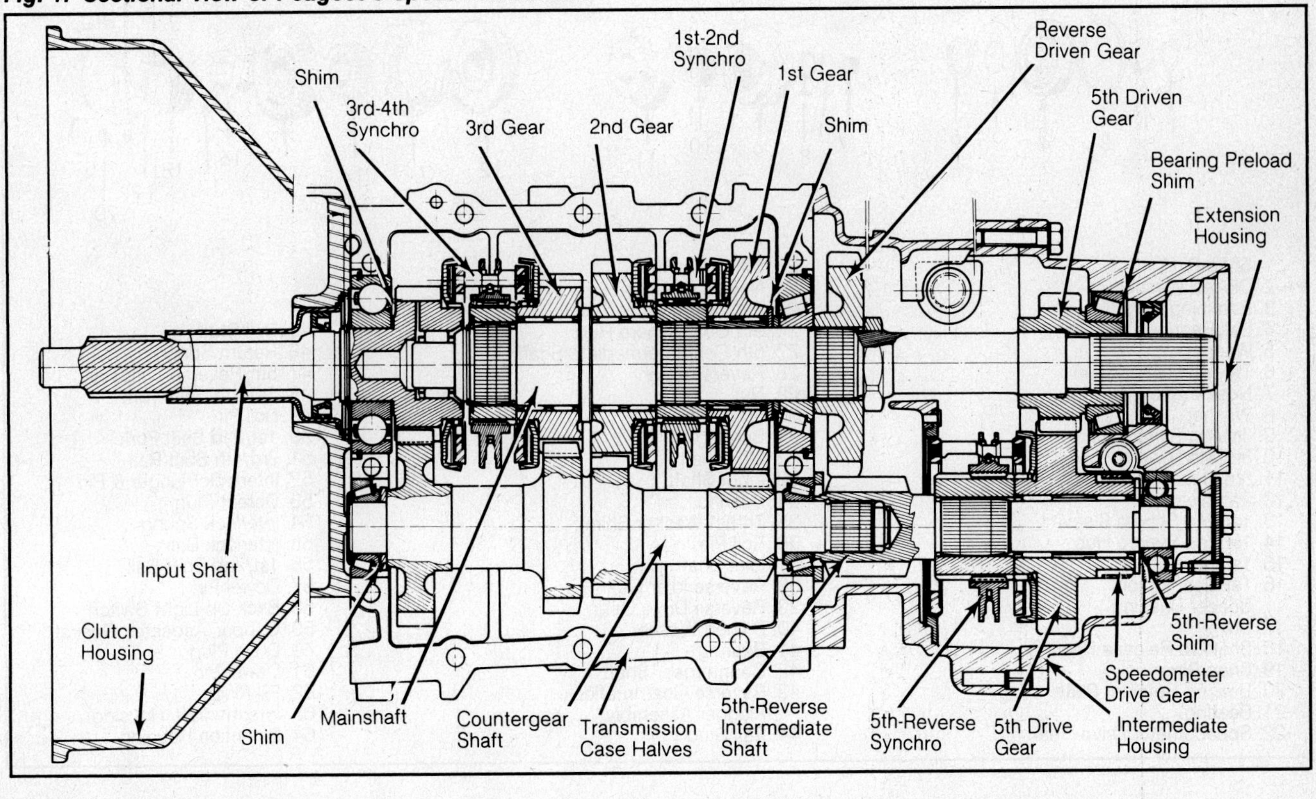

PEUGEOT 5-SPEED (Cont.)

Fig. 2: Exploded View of Peugeot 5-Speed Transmission

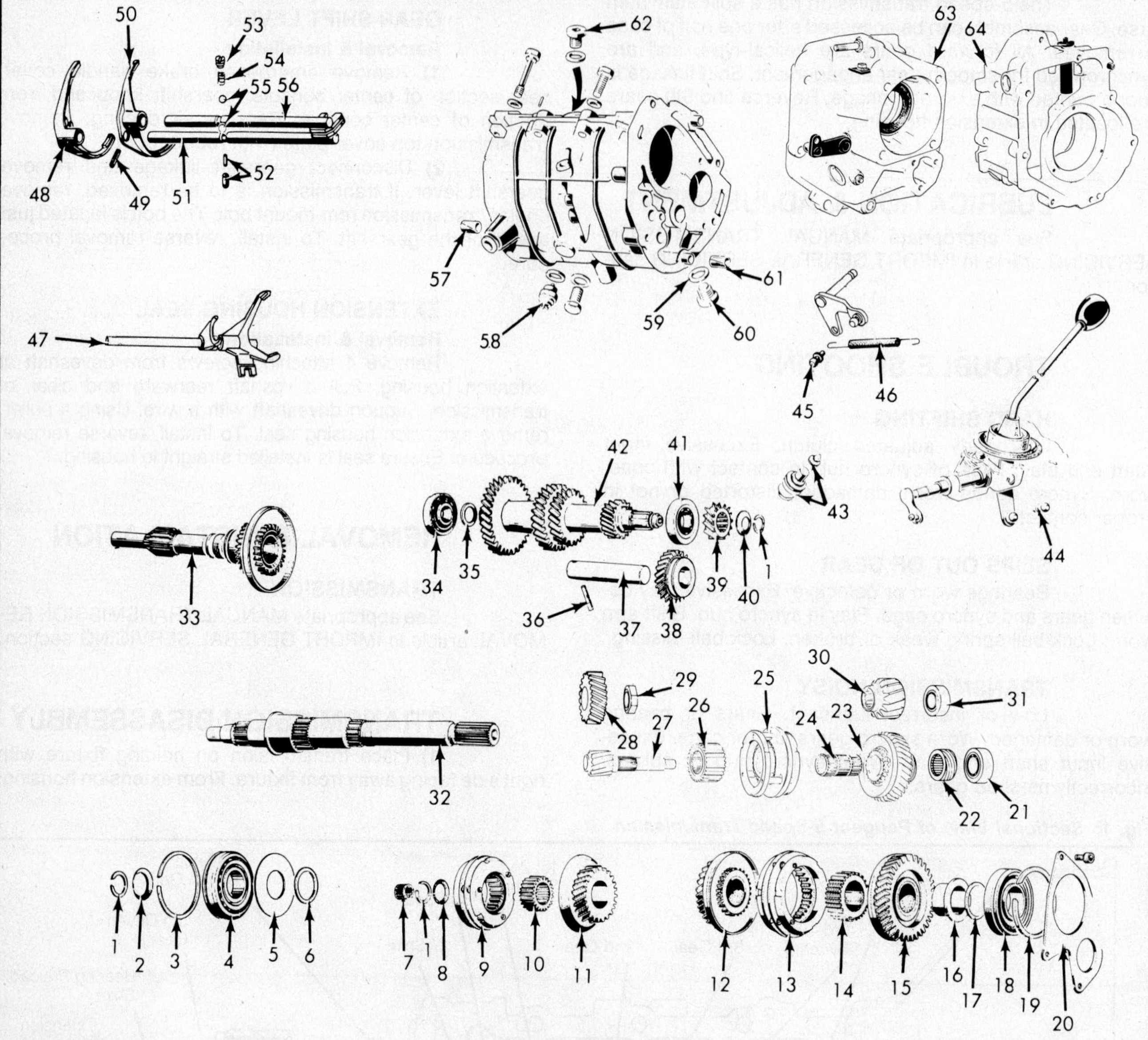

1. Snap Ring
2. Dished Washer
3. Retaining Ring
4. Ball Bearing
5. Washer
6. Thrust Washer Shim
7. Needle Bearing
8. Washer
9. 3rd/4th Syncro Ring
10. 3rd/4th Syncro Hub
11. 3rd Gear
12. 2nd Gear
13. 1st/2nd Syncro Sleeve
14. 1st/2nd Syncro Hub
15. 1st Gear
16. 1st Gear Pinion Spacer Bushing
17. Shim
18. Shaft-To-Release Bearing
19. Snap Ring
20. Bearing Retainer Plate
21. Bearing
22. Speedometer Drive Gear
23. 5th Drive Gear
24. Needle Bearing
25. 5th Gear Syncro Sleeve
26. 5th Gear Syncro Hub
27. 5th Gear Intermediate Shaft
28. Reverse Gear
29. Nut
30. 5th Driven Gear
31. Bearing
32. Mainshaft
33. Input Shaft
34. Bearing
35. Thrust Washer Shim
36. Roll Pin
37. Idler Shaft
38. Reverse Idler Gear
39. Reverse Drive Gear
40. Dished Washer
41. Bearing
42. Countergear Shaft
43. Reverse Gear Interlock Plunger Assembly
44. Ball Stud
45. Ball Stud
46. Return Spring
47. 5th/Reverse Shift Rail
48. 3rd/4th Shift Fork
49. Roll Pin
50. 1st/2nd Shift Fork
51. 3rd/4th Shift Rail
52. Interlock Plunger & Pin
53. Detent Plug
54. Interlock Spring
55. Interlock Ball
56. 1st/2nd Shift Rail
57. Dowel Pin
58. Back-Up Light Switch
59. Copper/Asbestos Gasket
60. Drain Plug
61. Dowel Pin
62. Fill Plug
63. Intermediate Housing
64. Extention Housing

remove speedometer driven gear set screw and gear. Place shift control levers in neutral position.

2) Turn transmission so extension housing is facing up. Remove extension housing bolts. Remove large plug on rear of housing and replace with Extractor Body (V1 of tool set 8.0314).

3) Insert Extractor Bolt (V2 of tool set 8.0314) into extractor body. To remove extension housing, turn bolt and tap sides of housing with plastic mallet.

4) Remove snap ring from mainshaft. Using a puller, remove 5th driven gear and speedometer drive gear. Remove 5th-reverse countergear shaft adjusting shim and washer. Lift off 5th drive gear. Remove snap ring from mainshaft.

Fig. 3: Bearing Retainer Plate Screw Removal

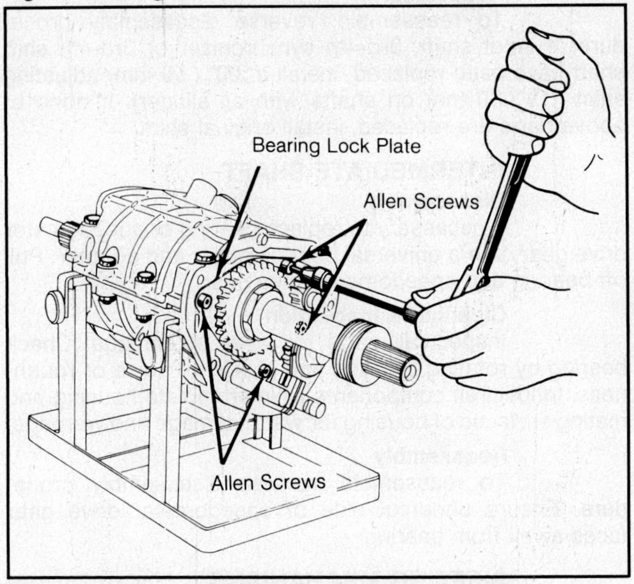

Remove Allen screws before removing case bolts.

5) Index mark position of 5th-reverse synchronizer sleeve to its hub for reassembly reference. Engage 5th gear and mount Holding Plate (8.0314W) over 5th gear selector fork shaft. Attach plate to housing with 2 bolts. Drive out 5th-reverse fork roll pin without damaging face of housing. Remove holding plate.

6) Return transmission to neutral position. Remove 5th-reverse selector fork and collar and synchronizer hub. Lift 5th-reverse intermediate shaft from housing. Disengage selector fork fingers from shift rail. Remove intermediate housing bolts and housing.

Fig. 4: Separating Input Shaft from Mainshaft

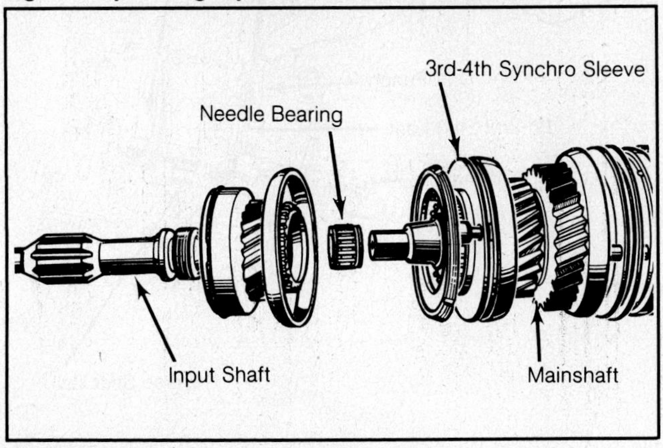

Remove needle bearing and place aside.

7) Remove clutch release fork, release bearing and back-up light switch. Remove clutch housing bolts and clutch housing. Remove 4 bearing retainer plate Allen screws. *See Fig. 3.*

8) Turn holding fixture until right side of case is facing up. Remove right side transmission case bolts and case half. Lift and remove entire gear assembly. Mark and remove countergear shaft end bearings. Slide synchronizer sleeve on mainshaft into 3rd gear position. Separate input shaft from mainshaft and place needle bearing aside. *See Fig. 4.*

COMPONENT DISASSEMBLY & REASSEMBLY

COUNTERSHAFT

Disassembly

Use a press and adapter plates to remove front and rear bearings. Set adjusting shim (located under rear bearing) aside.

Reassembly

Clean all parts in solvent and blow dry with compressed air. To reassemble, reverse disassembly procedure. DO NOT install adjusting shim at this time.

Fig. 5: Removing 3rd-4th Synchronizer Hub and Nut from Mainshaft

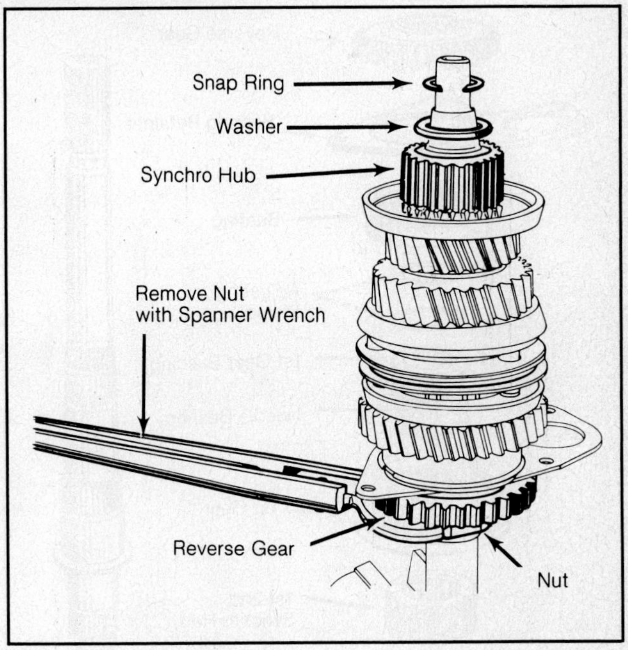

Hold mainshaft reverse gear and remove lock nut.

MAINSHAFT

Disassembly

1) Mark position of 3rd-4th speed synchronizer sleeve to its hub for reassembly reference. Remove synchronizer sleeve. Place mainshaft in vise, rear end down. Remove snap ring and washer from 3rd-4th synchronizer hub. While holding mainshaft reverse gear, use Spanner Wrench (8.0310P) to loosen mainshaft rear lock nut.

PEUGEOT 5-SPEED (Cont.)

2) Using a press with adapter plates placed beneath outer edge of 3rd gear, press off synchronizer hub and 3rd gear. Position mainshaft upside down with input shaft end facing down.

3) Place Safety Plate (8.0310K) between press and mainshaft. Press on mainshaft until bearing is released. Remove safety plate and press.

4) Remove following components from mainshaft and arrange in order of removal (facing correct direction): lock nut, reverse gear, retainer plate, bearing, adjusting shim, 1st gear, bushing, needle bearings, 1st-2nd synchronizer (without separating hub from sleeve), needle bearings and 2nd gear.

Cleaning & Inspection

Inspect all parts for wear or damage and replace necessary components.

Reassembly

Clean all parts in solvent and blow dry with compressed air. To reassemble, reverse disassembly procedure and align marks scribed during disassembly. If mainshaft, gears or synchronizers are replaced, install a new .13" (3.3 mm) adjusting shim. If none of above parts are replaced, install original shim.

Fig. 6: Mainshaft Rear Components

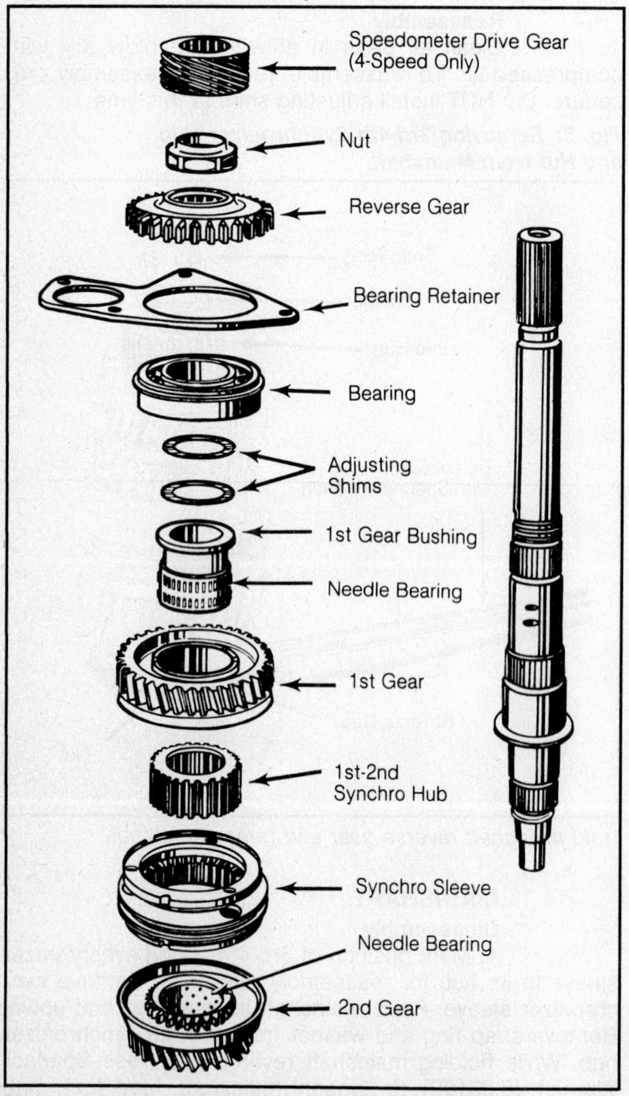

Note position and direction of components.

INPUT SHAFT

NOTE: Shafts which have oil slingers are identified by grooves in front of bearing.

Disassembly

If necessary to replace bearing, remove snap ring and press off old bearing. When bearing is removed, pay particular attention to thickness of shims for reassembly reference. Also note position of oil slinger, if equipped.

Cleaning & Inspection

Inspect all parts for wear or damage. Check bearing by rotating by hand and check for noise or roughness.

Reassembly

To reassemble, reverse disassembly procedure. If input shaft, 3rd-4th synchronizer or 3rd-4th shift shaft have been replaced, install a .20" (.50 mm) adjusting shim (.14"/.50 mm on shafts with oil slinger). If none of above parts are replaced, install original shim.

INTERMEDIATE SHAFT

Disassembly

If necessary to replace bearing or speedometer drive gear, use a universal bearing puller and adapter. Pull off bearing and speedometer drive gear.

Cleaning & Inspection

Inspect all parts for wear or damage. Check bearing by rotating by hand and check for noise or roughness. Inspect all components of intermediate housing and mating surfaces of housing for wear, damage and warpage.

Reassembly

To reassemble, reverse disassembly procedure. Ensure undercut side of speedometer drive gear faces away from bearing.

SHIFTING MECHANISMS

Disassembly

1) Place 1st-2nd shift rail in 2nd gear position and remove pin in 1st-2nd gear shift fork. With pin removed,

Fig. 7: Removing Pins from Shift Forks

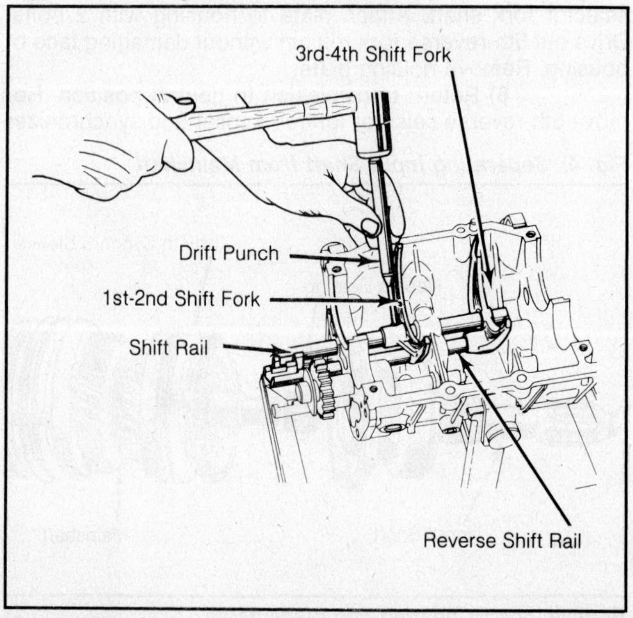

Use a drift punch to drive out roll pins.

PEUGEOT 5-SPEED (Cont.)

Fig. 8: Removing Detent Plug

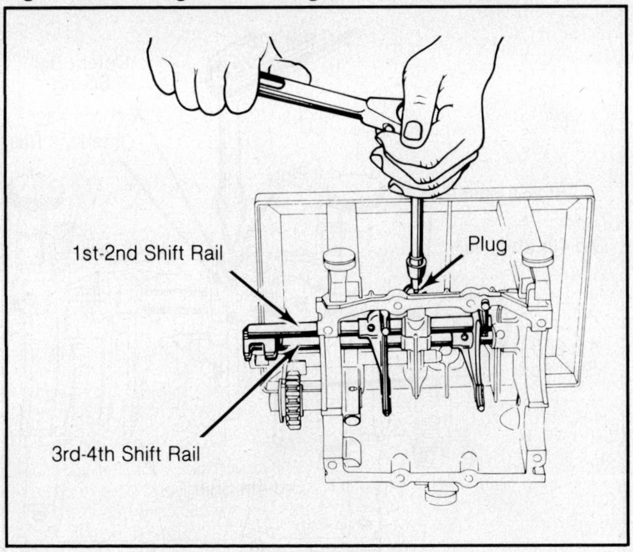

Catch detent ball and spring if they pop out.

move shift rail back to neutral position. Shift 3rd-4th shift rail into 4th gear position and remove pin in shift fork. Return shift rail to neutral position.

2) Turn transmission case so it is on its side and remove detent plug. *See Fig. 8.* Remove shift rail for 1st-2nd gear and 3rd-4th gears. As shift rails are removed, catch detent ball and spring. Remove and set aside lock-out needle for 3rd-4th shift rail.

3) Remove 5th-reverse detent plug, spring and ball from side of case. Remove reverse shift fork with idler gear. Using a punch, drive out reverse idler shaft pin. Remove shaft by pushing it toward outside of case. Using a long punch, push interlock balls and plunger out of case.

Fig. 9: Removing Interlock Balls and Plunger

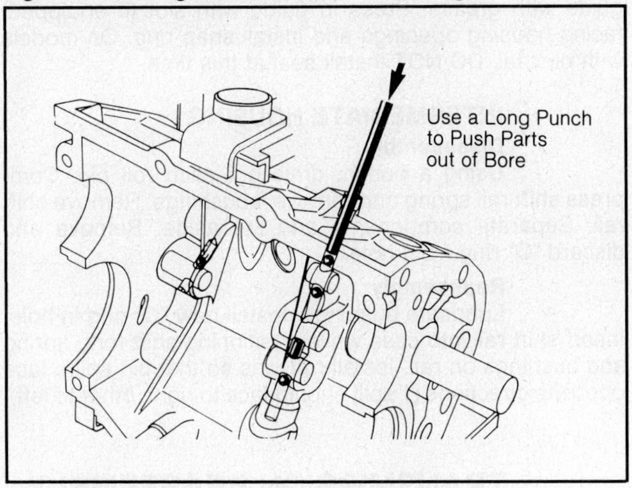

Ensure all balls and plungers are removed.

Cleaning & Inspection

Check neutral ball lock for positive locking action by moving selector lever in both directions. Also check that neutral ball lock plug is flush with case. If ball lock is inoperative, remove plug and inspect ball and spring. Clean all parts in solvent and blow dry with compressed air. Inspect all parts for wear or damage and replace necessary components.

Fig. 10: Detent and Interlock Positions

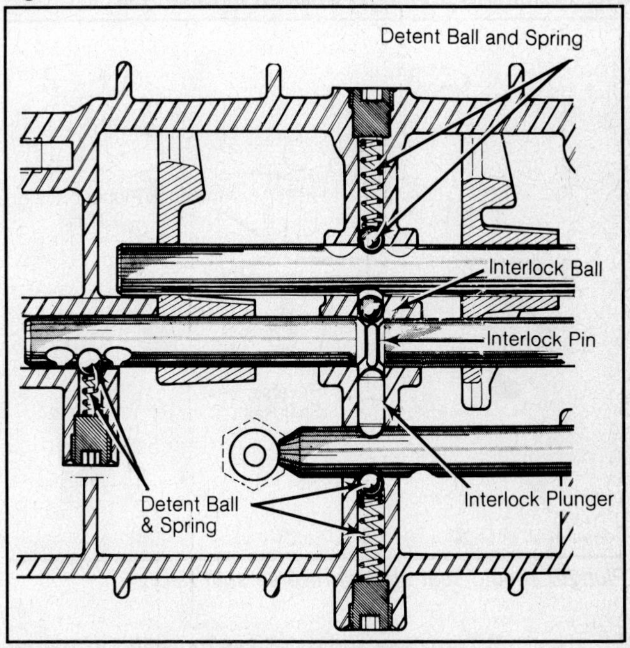

Use illustration as a guide during reassembly.

Reassembly

1) Install reverse idler gear shaft and use new straight pin to hold shaft in position. Position shift fork on reverse idler gear with beveled edge of gear facing transmission case. Install reverse shift rail into hole while positioning reverse idler gear on its shaft. Insert detent ball and spring. Use sealer on detent plug threads and install plug into reverse detent hole.

Fig. 11: Installing Reverse Idler Gear & Detent Assembly

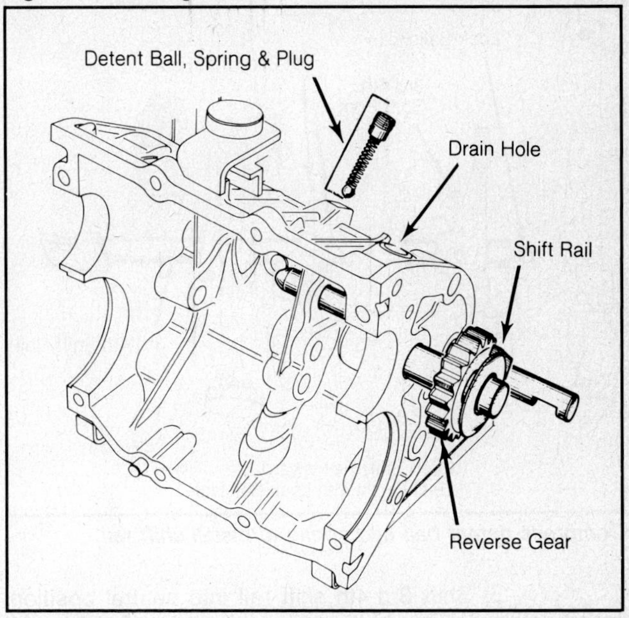

Install shift rail and gear at the same time.

2) Position reverse shift rail in neutral position. Flip case over to other side. Install 3rd-4th-reverse interlock plunger in case and seat it against reverse shift rail. Grease and install interlock pin into 3rd-4th shift rail.

Fig. 12: Interlock Plunger Position in Case Half

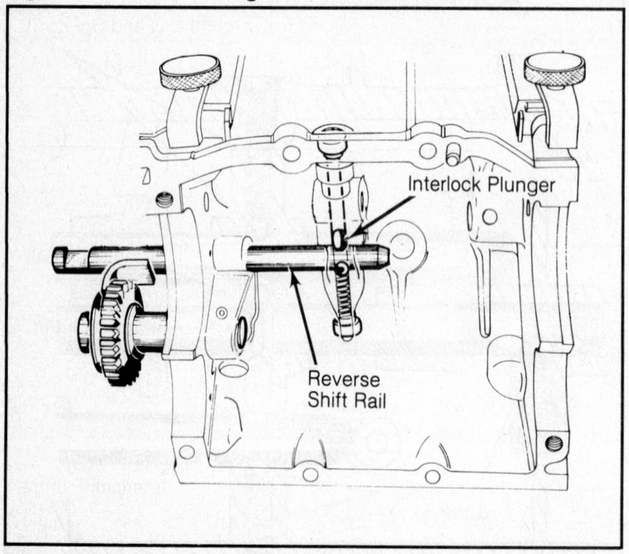

Plunger should seat against reverse shift rail.

3) Turn case and install 1st-2nd shift fork (larger of 2) and 3rd-4th shift fork in transmission case. Insert 3rd-4th shift rail into case, through both shift forks, until shaft is flush with edge of detent hole.

4) Insert 1 detent spring and ball into detent hole. Use drift punch to compress spring and ball assembly. Slide shift rail forward until punch can be released and ball will not jump out of hole.

Fig. 13: Installing 3rd-4th Shift Rail and Fork

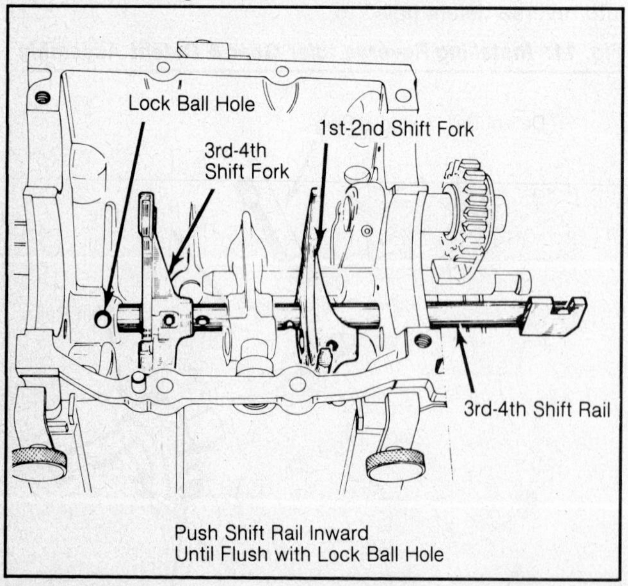

Compress detent ball and spring to install shift rail.

5) Shift 3rd-4th shift rail into neutral position. Insert detent ball into hole and push it against 3rd-4th shift rail. Engage 1st-2nd shift rail and insert detent ball and spring into hole. Coat threads of detent plug with sealant and install. Place 1st-2nd shift rail in neutral position. Lock shift forks onto shift rails with new pins.

Fig. 14: Completed Shifting Mechanism Installation

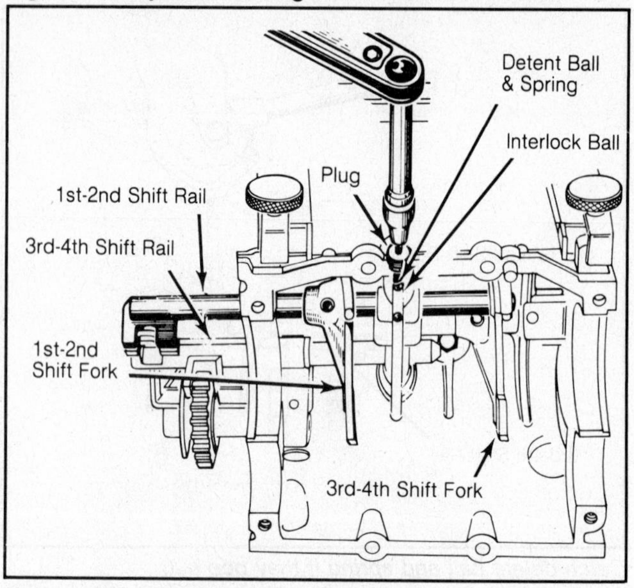

Note position of shift rails, forks and lock-out components.

CLUTCH HOUSING

Disassembly

If equipped with oil seal, carefully pry out seal without damaging case. Remove release bearing guide snap ring and press out guide. Transmissions which use an oil slinger on input shaft do not use an oil seal.

Cleaning & Inspection

Mount a dial indicator and measure runout of front and rear mating surfaces of housing. If runout exceeds .004" (.10 mm), replace clutch housing. Inspect all mating surfaces for wear or damage.

Reassembly

Lightly coat bearing face of release bearing guide with grease. Press in guide with slot (if equipped) facing housing openings and install snap ring. On models with oil seal, DO NOT install seal at this time.

INTERMEDIATE HOUSING

Disassembly

Using a punch, drive out each roll pin. Compress shift rail spring and remove 4 bushings. Remove shift rail. Separate components and set aside. Remove and discard "O" ring from hole.

Reassembly

Lubricate bushings. Install new "O" ring in hole. Insert shift rail into case while positioning shift fork, spring and bushings on rail. Install roll pins so that pin splits face opposite directions (1 split should face to right; other to left).

TRANSMISSION REASSEMBLY & ADJUSTMENTS

ADJUSTMENTS

Centering 1st, 2nd, 3rd & 5th Gear Synchronizers

NOTE: **This adjustment is made by changing size of shim located under mainshaft bearing.**

PEUGEOT 5-SPEED (Cont.)

1) Install needle bearing inside input shaft. Assemble input shaft to mainshaft (without reverse driven gear and nut). Install mainshaft assembly in transmission case. Install clutch housing. Install and tighten Allen screws in retainer plate. Place all synchronizers in neutral position.

2) Spread synchronizers apart between sleeve and hub. Insert Gauge (8.0314X) between each synchronizer sleeve and hub without forcing. *See Fig. 15.* If gauge fits easily between all 3 points, retain original shim. If gauge does not easily fit between all 3 points, perform following adjustments to determine new shim size.

Fig. 15: Synchronizer Centering Adjustment (Except 4th Gear)

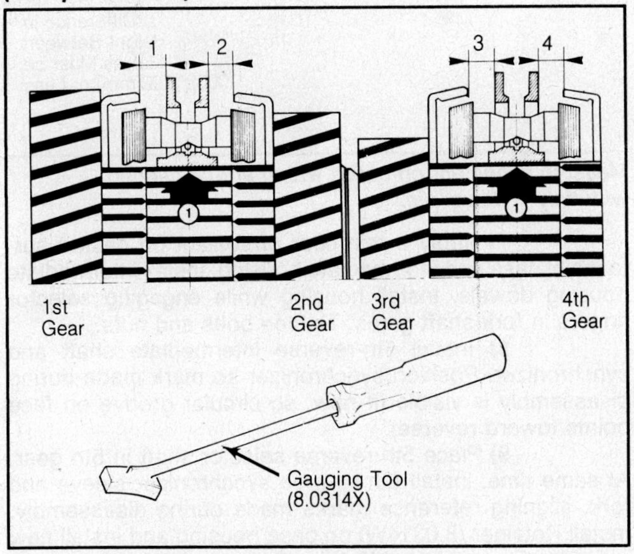

Do not force gauge between synchronizers.

3) If gauge does not easily fit between points 1 and/or 3 of *Fig. 15*, insert gauge and feeler gauge at point 2. Insert feeler gauge of various thicknesses to determine amount of change. Reduce shim thickness by this amount.

4) If gauge does not easily fit at point 2 of *Fig. 15*, measure clearance at points 1 and 3. Increase shim thickness by smaller of readings.

NOTE: **Shims are available in sizes .094-.134" (2.4-3.4 mm) for transmissions without shouldered 1st gear spacer. Shims for shouldered applications are .0098", .0118", .0138", .0157" and .0236" (.25, .30, .35, .40 and .60 mm).**

Centering 4th Gear Synchronizer

NOTE: **This adjustment is made by changing size of shims located under input shaft bearing.**

1) Spread 4th gear synchronizer apart and insert gauge without forcing. If gauge slides in freely, measure excess clearance. If clearance is .039" (1 mm) or less, retain original shims. If clearance exceeds .039" (1 mm), increase shims to equal thickness of original shim plus measured excess.

2) If gauge does not fit, remove mainshaft, input shaft and clutch housing. Separate input shaft from mainshaft and remove shims. Reinstall components and measure and record clearance at 4th gear synchronizer. On transmissions equipped with an oil slinger, leave slinger on shaft at all times.

3) Remove components, disassemble input shaft and install shims of thickness equal to measured clearance. Reinstall all components and recheck clearance. Remove all components after final check.

NOTE: **Shims are available from .006-.020" (.15-.50 mm) in .002" (.05 mm) increments. Use as few shims as possible to reach desired thickness.**

Bearing Preload (Countergear Shaft)

1) Remove clutch housing and install countergear shaft in transmission case. Install right half of transmission case and retain in position with 4 bolts (1 at each corner). Install bearing retainer and hold in position with Allen screws. Hand tighten all retaining bolts and screws.

2) With case securely attached to transmission stand, turn case so front of transmission is facing up. Place Adapter (8.0310S) on top of shaft. Press on adapter by hand while rotating shaft to seat bearings.

3) On transmission cases which use 2 split pins to position case halves, tighten following bolts in sequence: 4 case bolts and 4 retainer plate bolts.

4) On transmission cases which use 1 pin to position case halves, install clutch housing. Retain housing to case by using 4 bolts, 2 on each half of case. Tighten clutch housing bolts, case bolts and retainer plate bolts. Remove clutch housing. Check offset between case halves with Gauge Block (8.0310FZ) and dial indicator. If offset exceeds .0008" (.02 mm), remove all components and repeat procedure.

5) On all models, center hole in gauge block on countergear shaft. Install dial indicator so indicator tip rests against bearing outer race surface. Rotate indicator through 1 complete revolution. Warpage between case halves must not exceed .0008" (.02 mm).

6) If specification is exceeded, align bearing race by inserting Arbor (8.0310S) and tapping with a plastic mallet. After aligning outer bearing race, check that drag is not added to shaft and recheck warpage. To reduce drag, loosen and retighten 2 front case bolts.

7) With dial indicator in place on countergear shaft bore (tip resting on outer race), zero dial indicator at "5" and "0" with .20" (5 mm) preload. Move indicator so tip is resting on front face of case. *See Fig. 16.*

Fig. 16: Measuring Countergear Shaft Bearing Preload

Zero dial indicator with .20" (5 mm) preload.

PEUGEOT 5-SPEED (Cont.)

8) Note dial indicator reading. Add .004" (.10 mm) to reading. Subtract bearing preload of .20" (5 mm) to calculate thickness of shim to be installed between bearing and countergear shaft. Round result to nearest .002" (.05 mm). Remove countergear shaft. Remove front bearing and insert shim of determined thickness with inside chamfer facing gear. Reinstall bearing.

NOTE: Shims are available from .089-.134" (2.25-3.40 mm) in .002" (.05 mm) increments.

REASSEMBLY

1) Install retaining plate with machined surface toward bearing. Install reverse driven gear on mainshaft with teeth chamfer facing rearward. Install new nut and stake in position.

2) Install needle bearing inside input shaft and assemble input shaft and mainshaft. Place 3rd-4th synchronizer in neutral position. Install outer races onto outer bearings of countergear shaft. Mesh countergear shaft with mainshaft and input shaft.

3) With teeth of shaft assemblies meshed and while holding assembly together in this manner, install assembly into transmission case. *See Fig. 17.* Ensure shift forks engage with synchronizer sleeves. Apply a thin coat of sealer to faces of case halves.

Fig. 17: Installing Shafts into Transmission Case

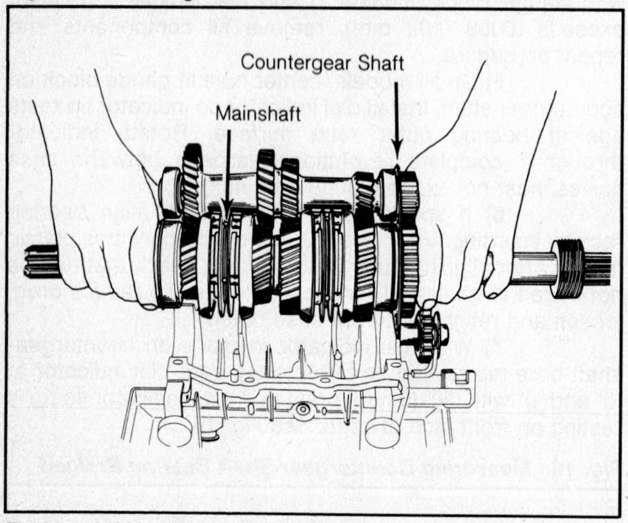

Ensure shift forks engage synchronizer sleeves.

4) With countergear and mainshaft installed, assemble 2 halves of transmission case together. Ensure positioning dowels are in place. Install new prelubricated input shaft oil seal. Using a seal protector, install clutch housing with small amount of sealant on rear face of clutch housing.

5) Tighten case half bolts. Rotate input shaft to seat bearings. Tighten retainer plate bolts. Loosen 4 bearing bolts and tap case half while turning input shaft. Tighten 4 bearing bolts.

6) On transmissions which use 1 dowel pin for positioning, rotate case so clutch housing faces down. Using a dial indicator, measure to determine if case halves are aligned with one another. If case half alignment varies more than .0008" (.02 mm), loosen case half bolts and try to align case halves. Retighten bolts.

Fig. 18: Measuring Case Half Alignment

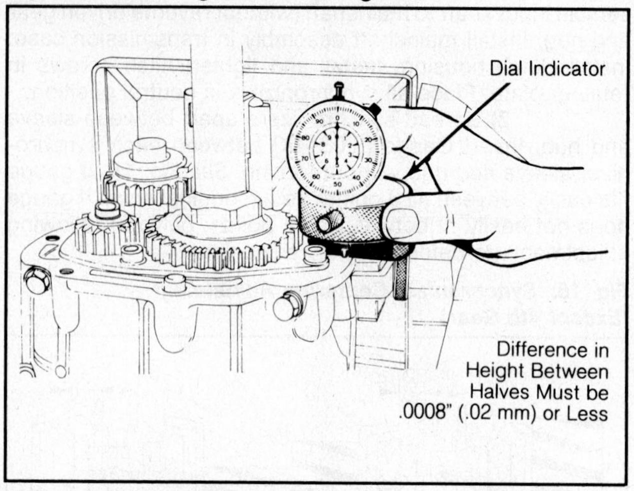

Measure alignment on cases which are positioned with only 1 dowel pin.

7) Apply a thin coat of sealant on gasket surfaces of case and intermediate housing. Install intermediate housing dowels. Install housing while engaging selector fingers in fork shaft gates. Tighten bolts and nuts.

8) Install 5th-reverse intermediate shaft and synchronizer. Position synchronizer so mark made during disassembly is visible (if new, so circular groove on face points toward reverse).

9) Place 5th-reverse selector shaft in 5th gear. At same time, install 5th-reverse synchronizer sleeve and fork, aligning reference marks made during disassembly. Install Retainer (8.0314W) on case housing and install new roll pin in 5th-reverse shift fork. Remove retainer and place assembly in neutral.

10) Install 5th drive gear, needle bearing and spacer. Ensure lugs on spacer are properly aligned. Install extension housing without bearing. Mount dial indicator and holder on extension housing with indicator tip resting on countergear shaft shoulder (not on spacer). Zero dial indicator with .236" (6 mm) preload.

11) Remove extension housing and press bearings into housing. Place Gauge Block (8.0314G) under countergear shaft bearing. Mount dial indicator on extension housing with indicator tip resting on gauge block and note reading.

12) Subtract preload amount of .236" (6 mm). From difference, subtract .002" (.05 mm). Round off reading to nearest .002" (.05 mm) and install this size shim on 5th-reverse shaft. Remove dial indicator and gauge block.

13) Install snap ring in mainshaft groove. Lubricate machined surface of mainshaft and press 5th driven gear and speedometer drive onto mainshaft using Bushing (8.0310Y) and Installers (8.0310P and 8.0314).

14) Install new snap ring to retain 5th driven gear and speedometer drive gear. Using Bearing Driver (8.0314Y), install lubricated extension housing seal until driver contacts housing surface.

15) Install 2 locating dowel pins in extension housing and coat housing mating surfaces with sealant. Install extension housing while engaging selector finger with selector fork shaft gate. Tap housing just above 5th-reverse intermediate shaft with a mallet and tighten bolts.

PEUGEOT 5-SPEED (Cont.)

Fig. 19: Countergear Shaft Shim Measurement

Place indicator tip on gauge block.

16) Install plug and new "O" ring in extension housing. Install speedometer driven gear with 2 new "O" rings. Retain speedometer driven gear with set screw.

17) Pack dust boot in clutch housing with grease. Apply grease to release bearing guide. Install clutch fork with retaining spring behind dust boot. Place push rod inside rubber protector on outside of clutch housing and install release bearing. Install back-up light switch.

TIGHTENING SPECIFICATIONS

Application	Ft. Lbs. (N.m)
Case Half	
4 Bearing Bolts	11 (15)
Clutch Housing-To-Trans. Case	20 (27)
Extension Housing-To-Trans. Case	11 (15)
Intermediate Hsg.-To-Trans.	
Nuts	13 (18)
Bolts	11 (15)
Mainshaft Lock Nut	40 (54)
Propeller Shaft Hsg.-To-Extension Hsg.	44 (60)
	INCH Lbs. (N.m)
Case Half Bolts	7.25 (9.8)
Retainer Plate	7.25 (9.8)

Manual Transmissions

PORSCHE G28.11 5-SPEED

928S

DESCRIPTION

The Porsche 928S is equipped with a manual transmission (type G28.11) which has 5 speeds. Engine and transaxle are connected by a rigid central tube which also houses the propeller shaft and supports the gearshift lever. Bellhousings on each end of this tube attach to the engine and transaxle.

The propeller shaft is splined to the clutch disc at the front and is connected to the transmission mainshaft at the rear by a coupling. Access to this coupling is through an inspection hole in the rear bellhousing.

A hypoid ring and pinion differential assembly drives joint rear axle drive shafts. The whole assembly is mounted to the unitized body by 2 front engine mounts and 2 rear transmission mounts.

NOTE: **The term "Transaxle" in this article refers to the rear axle transmission/differential assembly. The central tube and bellhousing may be referred to as the "transaxle tube". Axle drive shafts include the flexible couplings. Rear wheel axle shaft indicates the driven axle shaft mounted in the trailing arms of the rear wheel suspension.**

LUBRICATION & ADJUSTMENT

See appropriate MANUAL TRANSMISSION SERVICING article in IMPORT GENERAL SERVICING section.

REMOVAL & INSTALLATION

TRANSAXLE

See appropriate MANUAL TRANSMISSION REMOVAL article in IMPORT GENERAL SERVICING section.

SERVICE (IN VEHICLE)

FLANGED SHAFT SEAL

NOTE: **Complete transaxle information is not available from manufacturer.**

Removal

Remove socket head screws at inner end of shaft, then disconnect and support axle drive shaft. Remove inner flange bolt while holding flange from turning by inserting punch in drive flange bolt hole. Remove flange and pull out seal with Seal Removal Tool (VW 681).

Fig. 1: Cross-Section of Porsche 928S Manual Transaxle Assembly

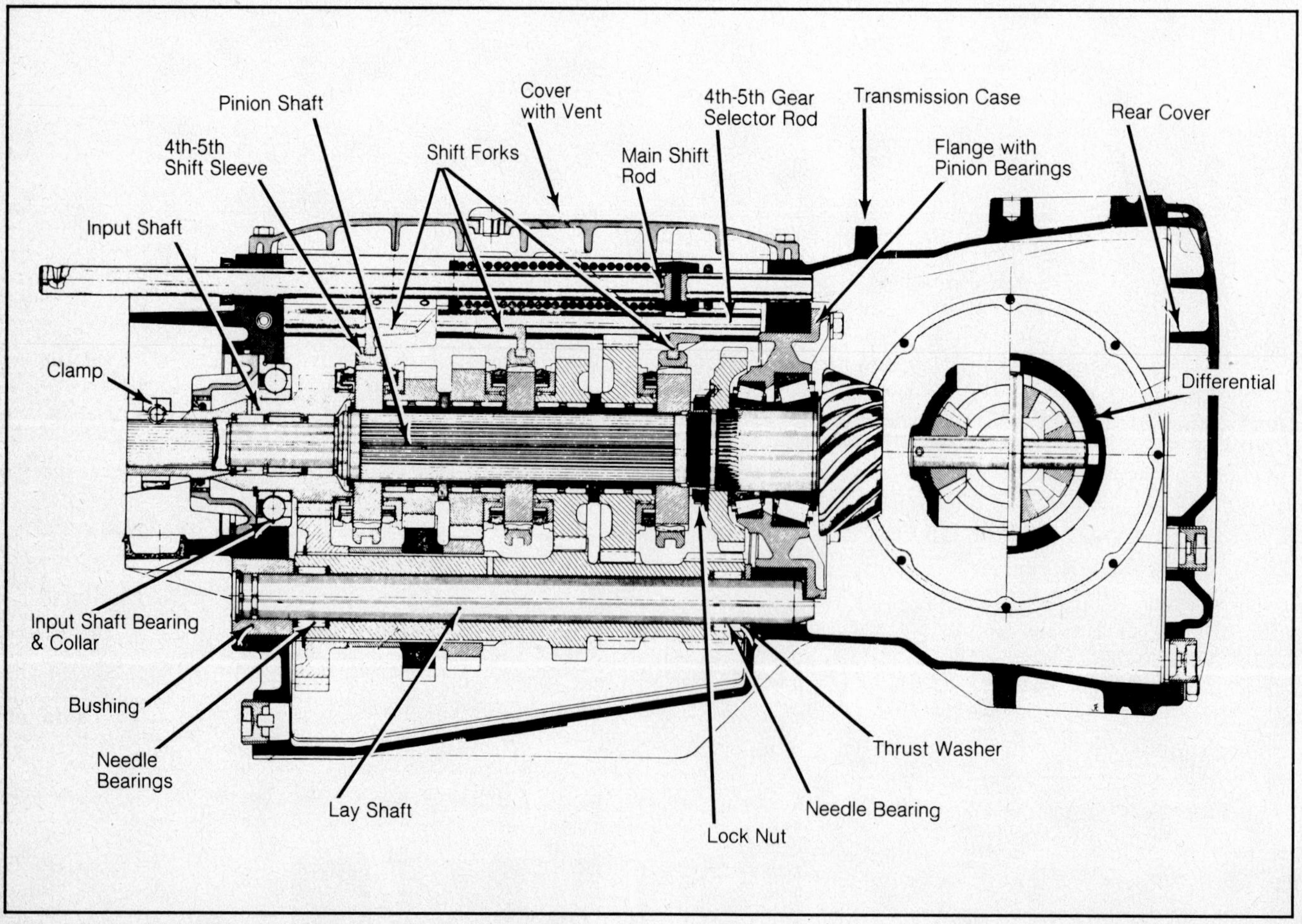

Transmission G28/08 model is shown, G28/11 is similar.

PORSCHE G28.11 5-SPEED (Cont.)

Installation

Fill cavity between sealing and dust lips with multi-purpose grease and drive seal in place with Seal Installer Tool (VW 195). Replace flange and drive shaft and tighten to specifications.

TRANSAXLE DISASSEMBLY

Disassembly

1) Mount transmission on Assembly Stand (9149) and drain oil. Remove differential unit. Remove shift rod, shift forks and locks.

NOTE: Always counterhold on interior shift rod with a suitable tool when driving out pins and keys.

2) Using a pair of suitable pliers, pull out clamp for reverse gear. Unscrew drive pinion mounting bolts, mount Slide Hammer (VW 771). Remove circlip for input shaft.

NOTE: Always remove countershaft and lower countershaft to bottom of transmission first.

COMPONENT DISASSEMBLY & REASSEMBLY

DRIVE PINION

Disassembly

1) Using Pinion Nut Removers (9216 and 9218), remove lock nut for drive pinion. Using Press Tool (VW 457), press off gear wheels and bearing cap.

2) Press off bearing cap with a pertinent pressure pad. Press off large taper roller bearing inner race using a separator.

Reassembly

NOTE: If drive pinion has to be adjusted, it must only be assembled after completion of adjustments. See ADJUSTMENTS in this article.

1) Inner races of needle bearings as well as bearing surfaces on guiding sleeves and thrust washers must be cleaned of oil. Lubricate needle cages, bores and bearing surfaces on both sides of gear wheels with oil thoroughly.

2) Mount bearing assembly on drive pinion and apply initial pressure of 4000 lbs. (2 tons). Mount drives for synchronization in correct position (domed side facing sliding sleeve).

3) Check synchronizing rings by pressing rings against tapers of gear wheels and measuring gaps with a feeler gauge. Installed distance (new) should be .035-.060" (.9-1.5 mm). The wear limit is .024-.028" (.6-.7 mm).

4) Press assembled drive pinion over hub of guiding sleeve with an initial pressure of 12,000 lbs. (6 tons). Tighten lock nut to 217 ft. lbs. (300 N.m).

SYNCHRONIZER ASSEMBLIES

NOTE: Synchronizers MUST be replaced in pairs only.

Disassembly

Transmission is equipped with modified synchronization for all forward speeds. Each synchronizer is different, therefore no parts are interchangeable between synchronizers. Mark synchronizers before disassembly to facilitate reassembly. Axial movement is eliminated by using a shift band with beveled flanks.

Fig. 2: Selecting Gear Set End Shim

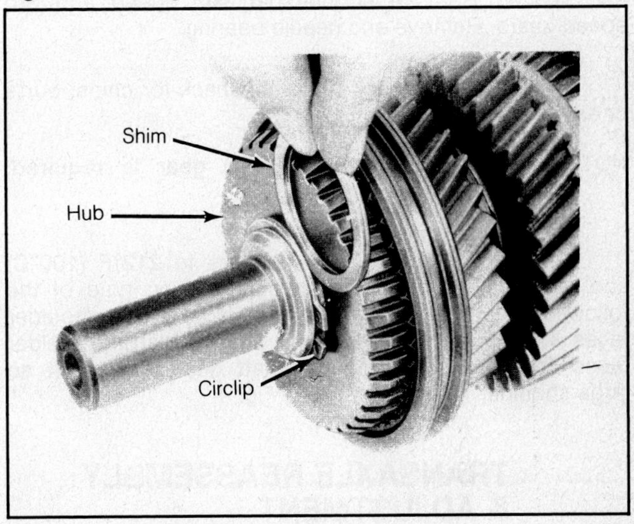

Inspection

Clean and dry all parts. Check for chipped teeth or any other irregularity. Using a micrometer, check all synchronizer rings at the thickest point. Measurement should read 3.38-3.40" (85.76-86.24 mm).

Fig. 3: Correct Position for Measuring Synchronizer Ring at Thickest Location

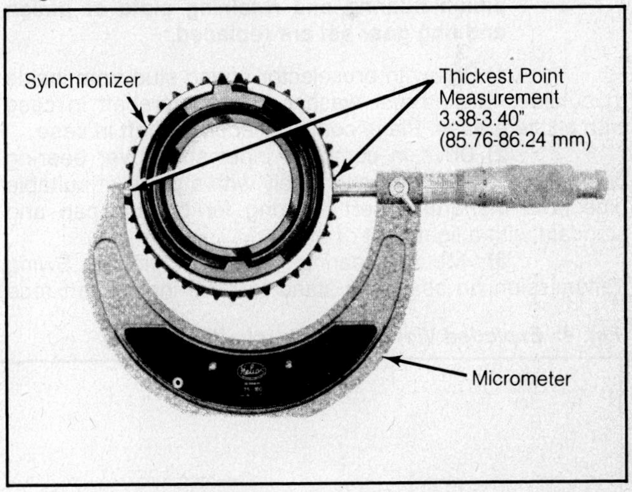

Reassembly

To reassemble, reverse disassembly procedure, insuring that correct parts for particular synchronizer are used.

NOTE: When reassembling 1st gear, short side of shift band must be to right of thrust block. When reassembling 2nd gear, bevelled side of stop must face to right as seen from top view.

PORSCHE G28.11 5-SPEED (Cont.)

COUNTERSHAFT

Disassembly

Remove circlip and needle bearing. Place countershaft assembly in a press. Using Support Rail (VW 457) and Arbor (VW 407), press off countershaft drive gear and spacer. Remove countershaft 4th speed and 3rd speed gears. Remove end needle bearing.

Inspection

Clean and dry all parts. Check for chips, burrs or any irregularities.

NOTE: **When replacement of a gear is required, replace in pairs only.**

Reassembly

To reassemble, heat gears to 212°F (100°C) and reverse disassembly procedure making note of the following: Place 3rd gear onto shaft so small shoulder faces stop. Place 4th gear onto shaft so large shoulder faces 3rd gear. Place countershaft gear onto shaft so large shoulder faces spacer. *See Fig. 4.*

TRANSAXLE REASSEMBLY & ADJUSTMENT

NOTE: **Differential assembly must be adjusted ONLY when repairs to assembly require replacement parts. Adjust ring gear if transmission case, side cover, pinion bearing and retaining plate, pinion and ring gear set, differential housing or differential bearings are replaced. Adjust pinion gear if transmission case, pinion bearing and retaining plate or pinion and ring gear set are replaced.**

1) Screw in preselector spring stud from inside to outside. Stick thrust washer for countershaft in case with a little grease. Place complete countershaft in case.

2) Drive in complete input shaft over bearing outer race against stop alternately with a piece of suitable pipe or a mandrel. Insert "O" ring for bearing cap and lubricate with a light coat of oil.

3) Mount bearing cap and circlip. Swing transmission on assembly stand to have input shaft face down. Install needle cages and thrust ring in input shaft. Place synchronizing ring for 5th gear on clutch body.

4) Place reverse gear and needle cages in case. Angle reverse gear upward at front, to mesh gears and then lower into position. Screw Centering Pins (9321), in case for installation of drive pinion and install shims.

5) Mount Pinion Drive Installer (9144) on drive pinion bearing cap and move in drive pinion carefully (with 4th gear engaged). Check that reverse gear is positioned correctly.

NOTE: **When installing drive pinion ensure that pins of 5th gear synchronizing ring engage in openings of guide sleeve.**

6) Move reverse gear to correct installed position. Remove Centering Pins (9321) for bearing assembly and turn together with shims until reverse gear shaft can be mounted.

7) Drive in reverse gear shaft only far enough so that thrust washer can be installed. Then drive in reverse gear shaft to correct installed position and install clamp.

8) Turn bearing assembly and shims to installed position, tighten mounting bolts to 265 INCH lbs. (30 N.m) and remove Pinion Drive Installer (9144). Move countershaft to correct installed position and install shaft with "O" ring.

NOTE: **To ease installation, turn transmission on assembly stand until countershaft falls into correct installed position on its own weight.**

9) Install countershaft circlip. Turn gears in neutral and install shift rods, shift forks and locks in following order: lock (short), 1st/reverse shift rods, locking sleeve (long), spring (long), plug, 2nd/3rd shift rod, locking sleeve (short), spring, lock (long), 4th/5th shift rod, locking sleeve (short), spring and plug.

10) Mount interior shift rod with preselector lever and shift arm, counter holding on shift rod. Cavity for pointed screw in interior shift rod must face left (in forward direction).

11) Install lock pin in correct position. Adjust preselector spring and shift forks.

Fig. 4: Exploded View of Countershaft Assembly

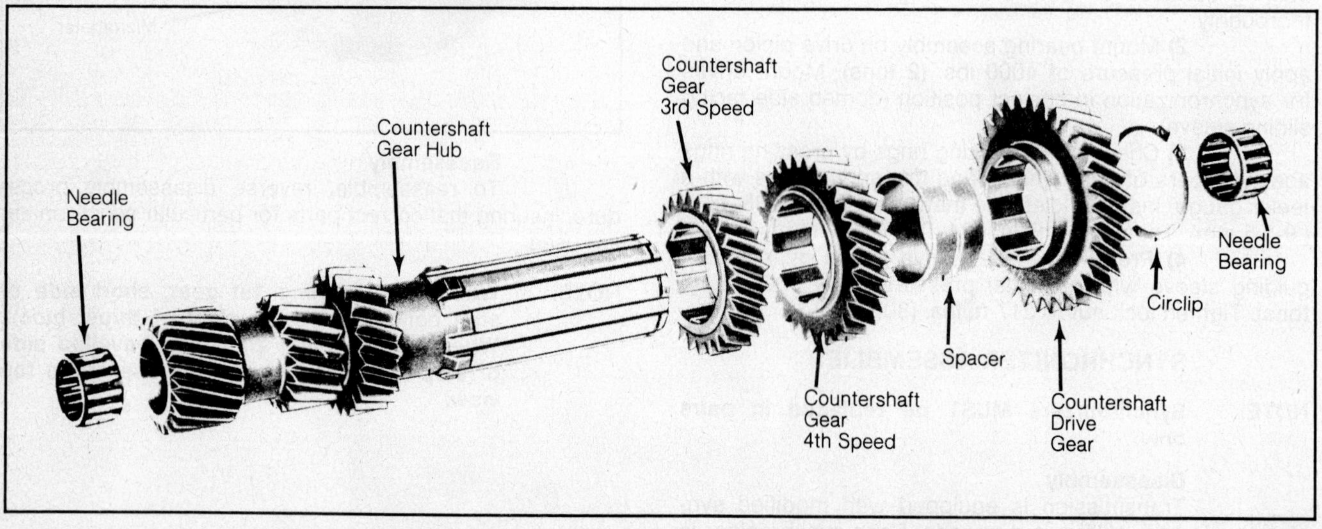

PORSCHE G28.11 5-SPEED (Cont.)

DIFFERENTIAL

Disassembly

1) Place differential assembly in vise fitted with jaw protectors. Remove ring gear bolts and drive ring gear off housing. Remove bearings (if required) using a double arm puller.

2) Remove pinion shaft lock pin, then remove pinion shaft, pinion gears, side gear drive flange nuts and side gears. Note location and thickness of any shims removed from side gears.

Reassembly

1) Heat ring gear to about 212°F (100°C) and place on differential using centering pins to align bolt holes. Install new retaining bolts and tighten to specifications in an alternating sequence. Slide lock plate into bolt head groove, bend ends together, then bend lock plate ends down over side of bolt head.

2) Place correct shims under large gears and insert in case. Hold small gear thrust washers in place with grease and install small gears. Align gear and washer holes with bore and insert shaft. Position correctly and lock in position with lock pin.

3) If bearings were removed, heat inner bearing race to 212°F (100°C) and press on case.

PINION GEAR ADJUSTMENT

1) Pinion depth adjustment is calculated by adding design specification "R", which equals 2.78" (70.7 mm), to deviation "r" stamped on pinion gear face. *See Fig. 5.* Pinion depth is adjusted by shims "S3".

Fig. 5: Location of Stamped Codes and Specifications of Pinion and Ring Gears

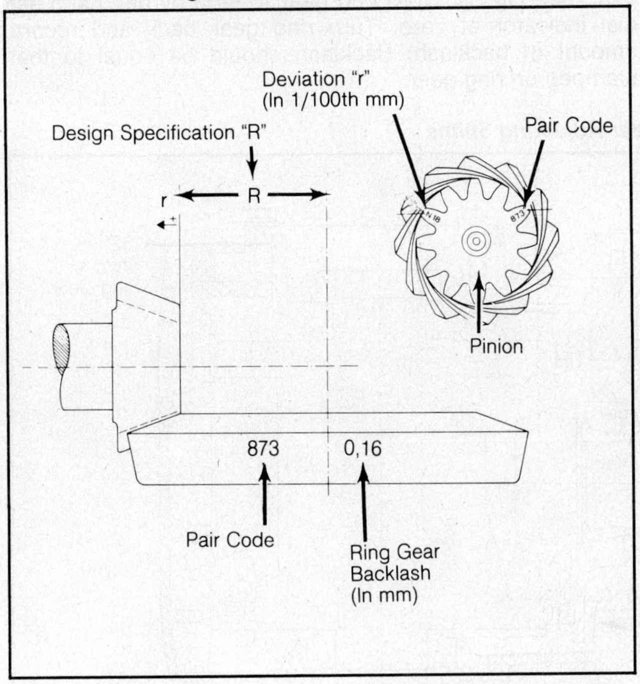

2) Install input shaft. Install pinion without shim(s) and tighten bearing retaining plate bolts. Install one side cover without "O" ring and secure with 2 bolts. Set adjusting ring of Universal Master Gauge (VW 385/1) at 2.36" (60 mm) from gauge center point. *See Fig. 6.*

Fig. 6: Universal Master Measuring Gauge

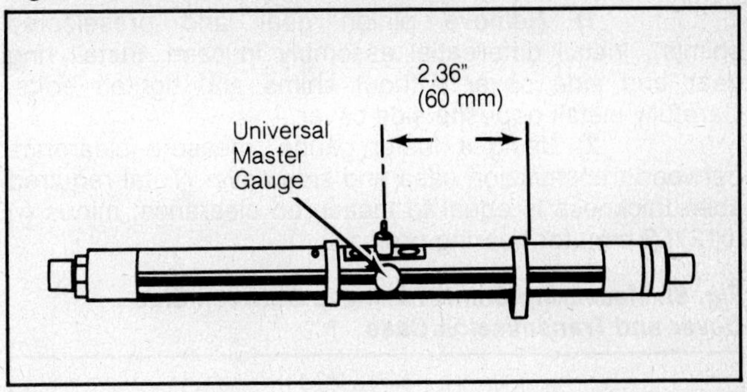

3) Install Centering Discs (VW 385/4) onto master gauge and attach Gauge Plunger (VW 385/14) with dial indicator extension. *See Fig. 7.* Install opposite side cover without "O" ring and secure with 2 bolts.

Fig. 7: Universal Master Measuring Gauge with Dial Indicator Attached

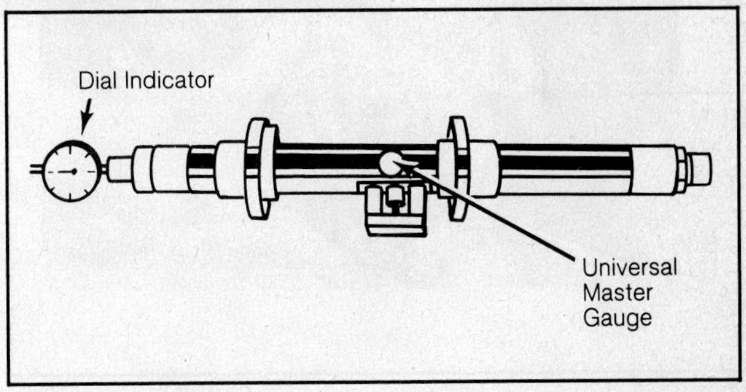

4) Install master gauge and set dial indicator at zero with .004" (1 mm) preload. Install gauge plate on pinion head. Carefully turn universal gauge until dial gauge extension is perpendicular to face of pinion head. At this time dial gauge needle will reach reversal point (highest point). Read and record dial gauge. *See Fig. 8.*

5) Remove master gauge and pinion shaft. Install calculated shim rounded off to nearest .002" (.05 mm) and pinion shaft. Recheck pinion depth adjustment. Adjustment should be 2.78" (70.7 mm) with variation of ±.001" (.03 mm).

Fig. 8: Measuring Pinion Depth with Master Gauge

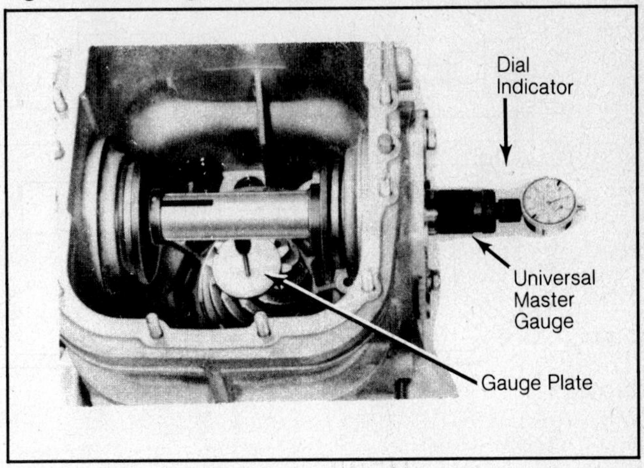

Manual Transmissions

PORSCHE G28.11 5-SPEED (Cont.)

RING GEAR ADJUSTMENT

1) Remove pinion gear and preselected shim(s). Install differential assembly in case. Install ring gear end side cover without shims and tighten bolts. Carefully install opposite side cover.

2) Using a feeler gauge, measure clearance between transmission case and side cover. Total required shim thickness is equal to measured clearance, minus (-) .012" (.3 mm) for bearing preload.

Fig. 9: Measuring Shim Thickness Between Side Cover and Transmission Case

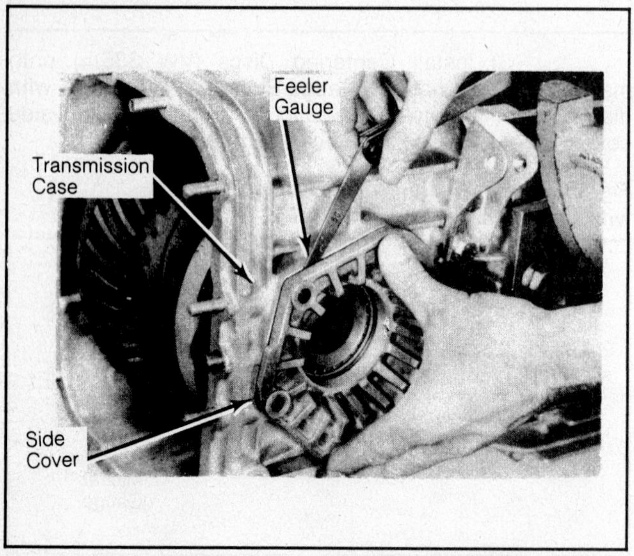

RING GEAR BACKLASH ADJUSTMENT

1) Install countershaft assembly into transmission case. Install pinion shaft with preselected shim ("S3") and tighten bearing retainer bolts. Install differential assembly in case. Install ring gear end side cover with preselected shim pack and tighten bolts. Install opposite side cover and tighten bolts.

2) Turn differential in both directions several times to seat bearings. Mount Dial Indicator with Support (VW 388) and set adjustable lever at 3.15" (80 mm). *See Fig. 11.*

Fig. 11: Gauge Installation for Measuring Backlash

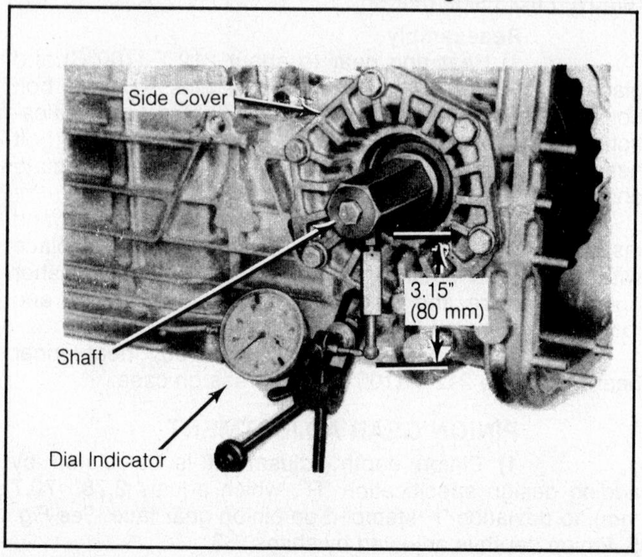

3) Engage 5th and reverse gears. Hold pinion gear assembly with a locally fabricated tool on reverse gear. *See Fig. 12.* Turn ring gear to stop by hand and set dial indicator at zero. Turn ring gear back and record amount of backlash. Backlash should be equal to that stamped on ring gear.

Fig. 10: Sectional View Showing Location of Pinion and Ring Gear Adjusting Shims

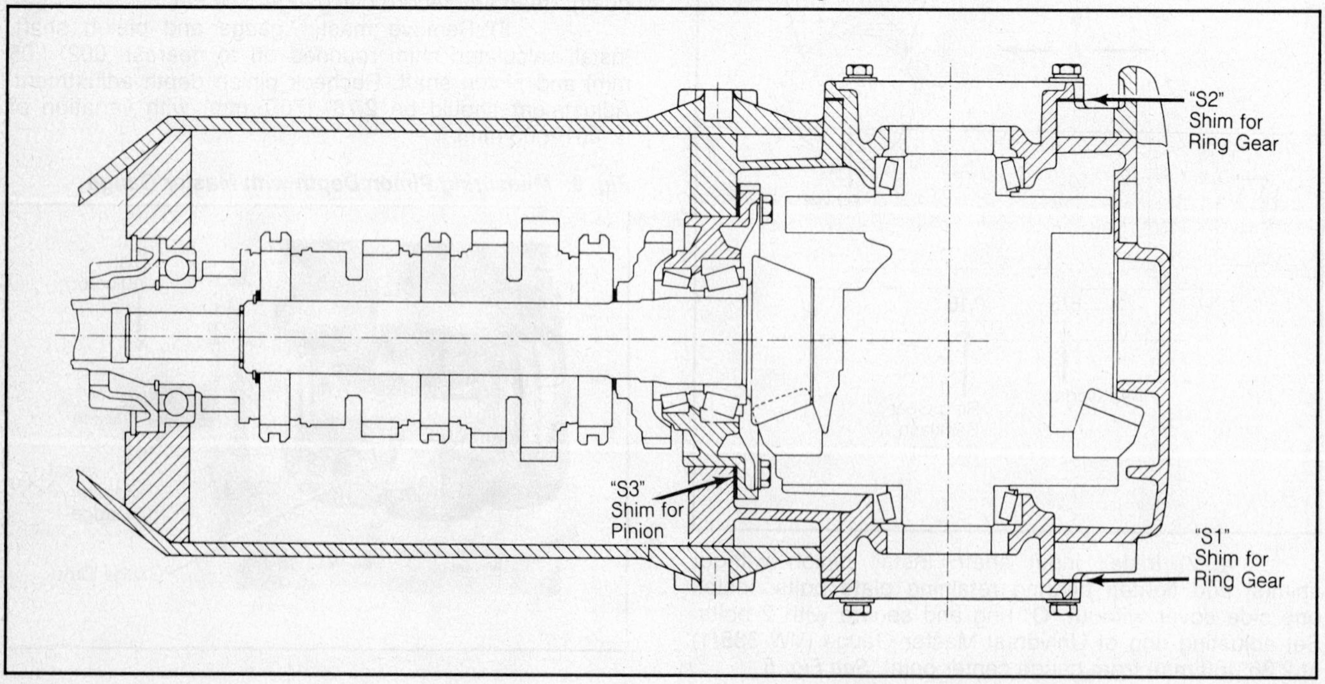

PORSCHE G28.11 5-SPEED (Cont.)

Fig. 12: Installation of Fabricated Tool on Reverse Gear to Hold Pinion Gear Assembly in Position

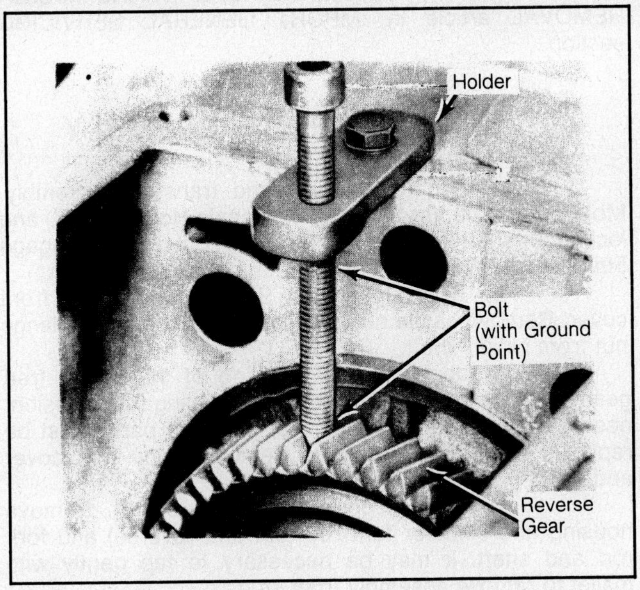

NOTE: **When shift rods are installed, the engagement of 2 gears will require removal of detent plunger for 1st and reverse gear shift rod.**

4) To determine thickness of shim "S1", subtract measured backlash from shim total, then add specified backlash (stamped on ring gear). Multiply results by .66 (lift constant).

5) Final figure equals thickness of shim "S1" (ring gear side shim). Calculate thickness of shim "S2" by subtracting shim "S1" thickness from total shim thickness.

6) Remove side covers and divide shims to give correct shim "S1" and "S2" thicknesses. Install shift rods and forks into case. Install side covers and shims and tighten bolts.

7) Measure backlash again. If not within specifications, change shims "S1" and "S2" until specified backlash is obtained. Check backlash 4 times by turning ring gear 90° each time. The 4 measurements must not deviate from each other by more than .002" (.05 mm).

TIGHTENING SPECIFICATIONS

Application	Ft. Lbs. (N.m)
Central Tube-to-Transaxle	40 (54)
Pinion Retaining Nut	202 (280)
Pinion Retaining Plate-to-Case	25 (34)
Ring Gear Retaining Bolts	120 (163)
Side Cover Bolts	17 (23)
Rear Cover Bolts	17 (23)
Drive Shaft-to-Input Shaft Coupling	35 (47)
Axle Shaft Flange Bolts	30 (41)

PORSCHE 911 CARRERA 5-SPEED TRANSAXLE

DESCRIPTION

The 5-speed transaxle (code 915/73) combines both transmission and differential into a single assembly consisting of 3 subassemblies: front cover, gear housing and transmission/clutch housing.

In all gears, power flows from input shaft to pinion shaft through respective gear pairs. Torque is transferred to pinion gear, ring gear and drive axles. Reverse gear power flows from input shaft through reverse idler gear, sliding gear and pinion shaft.

The 915 transaxle is also equipped with a oil pump driven by the input shaft. Oil is drawn from the transmission oil sump through a pickup tube and forced through passages in the pump cover and pressure lines.

A "12" between the type and transmission numbers means the transmission has 40% limited slip differential.

LUBRICATION & ADJUSTMENT

See appropriate MANUAL TRANSMISSION SERVICING article in IMPORT GENERAL SERVICING section.

SERVICE (IN VEHICLE)

DRIVE AXLE SHAFTS

See appropriate DRIVE AXLE SHAFT article in IMPORT AXLE SHAFTS, OVERDRIVES & TRANSFER CASES section

REMOVAL & INSTALLATION

See appropriate MANUAL TRANSMISSION REMOVAL article in IMPORT GENERAL SERVICING section.

TRANSAXLE DISASSEMBLY

GEAR HOUSING

1) Separate engine and transaxle assembly. Mount transaxle assembly on Transaxle Holder (9106) and lock input shaft in place with Special Tool (P 37a). Engage 5th gear.

2) Drain lubricant. Remove transaxle front cover. Remove castle nut from input shaft. Remove flange nut from pinion shaft.

3) Identify needle bearing of 5th speed free gear to aid in reassembly. When assembling transmission, needle bearings, gears and other matched parts must be replaced in original positions. Remove guide fork cover and gasket.

4) Remove gear housing nuts (12). Remove housing and selector fork rod (5th and reverse) and fork rod and shaft. It may be necessary to tap gently with mallet to remove assembly from studs.

NOTE: **Shift fork rod for 5th and reverse must be in Neutral position. If not, housing will jam.**

5) Remove reverse gear lock plug on left lower side of transaxle. Remove 3rd-4th gear detent plug. Take out spring and detent. Remove bolt from 1st-2nd gear selector fork. Spread clamp with screwdriver. Remove input and pinion shaft retaining plates.

Fig. 1: Exploded View of 911 5-Speed Transaxle

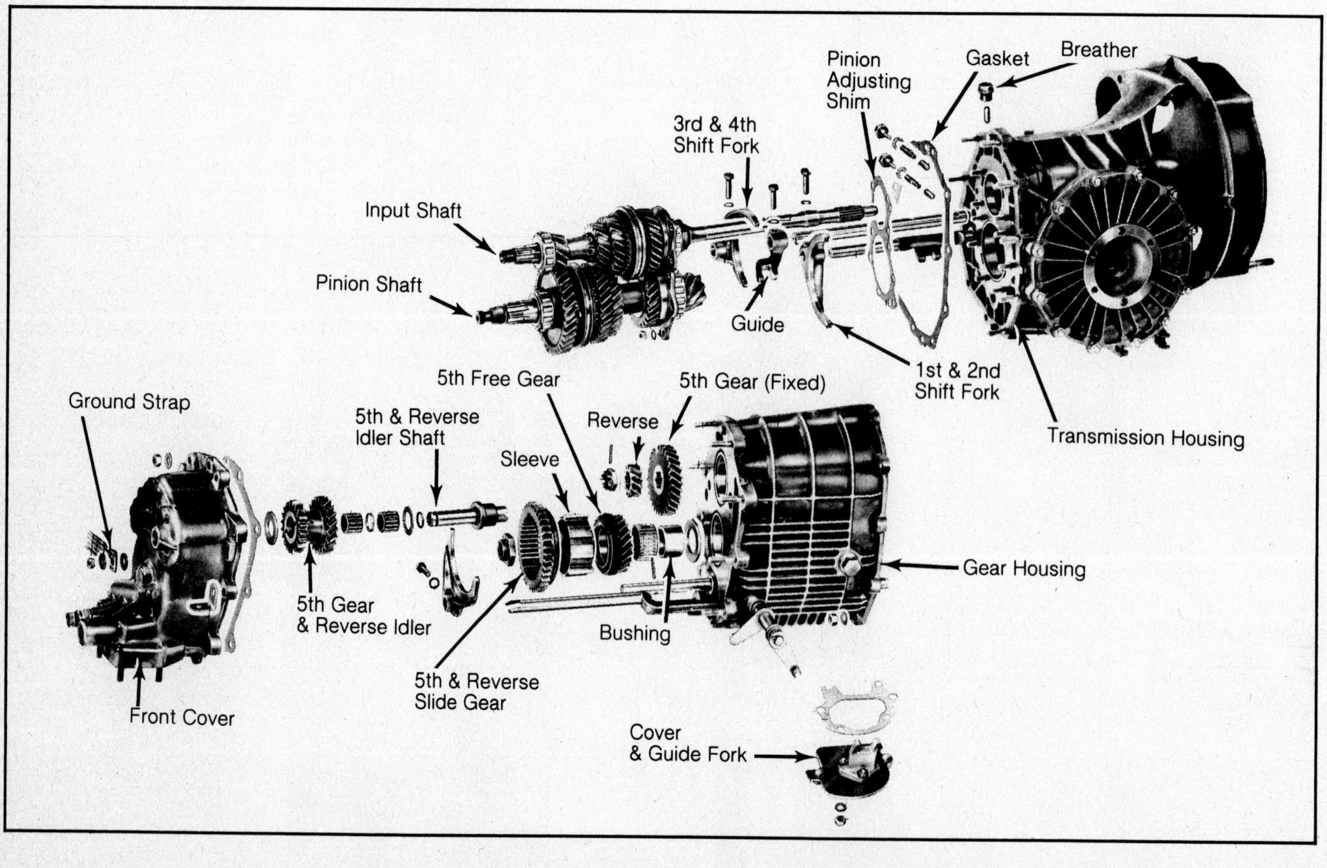

PORSCHE 911 CARRERA 5-SPEED TRANSAXLE (Cont.)

Fig. 2: Exploded View of Gear Housing

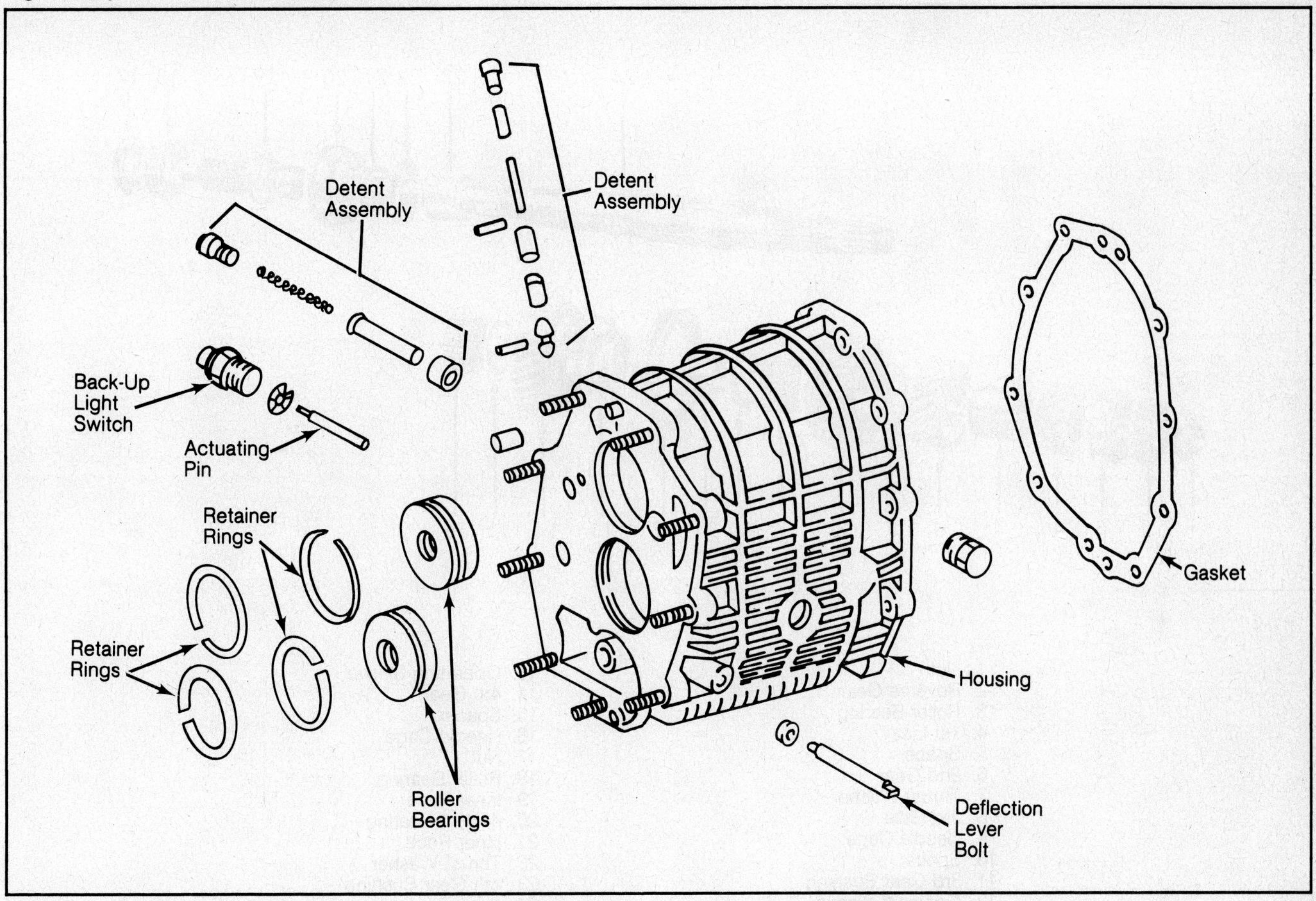

6) Remove input and pinion shaft assemblies from case. Shift fork rod for 3rd and 4th gear and shift fork for 1st and 2nd gear should come out with assembly. Remove selector shaft detent.

7) Remove 1st-2nd shift detent plug and take out spring and detent. Pull out 1st-2nd shift fork rod.

NOTE: **Be sure to note the number and thickness of shims between transaxle housing and retaining plates for reassembly.**

8) To disassemble gear housing, drive shift detents securing roll pins out of respective seats. Drive out half-round dowel pin.

9) If bearing outer races are to be removed, use Special Tool (US 8050). Gear housing must be heated to about 250°F (120°C) to drive out races.

INPUT SHAFT

1) Place Support Plate (P 355a) in a vise and insert input shaft assembly. Remove flange nut with Special Tool (P 252a). Press roller bearing off shaft using Thrust Plates (VW 401 and 402) and Thrust Disc (VW 412).

2) Remove remaining parts in order shown in *Fig. 3.* Keep respective gear and needle bearing assemblies together for assembly in original locations.

3) Press roller bearing off input shaft with Thrust Tube (VW 415a) and Press Punch (VW 407).

PINION SHAFT

Carefully press roller bearing off pinion shaft using Thrust Plate (VW 401), Disc (VW 412) and Tube (P 255a). Remove pinion shaft components. Keep needle bearings and gear pairs together; these parts MUST be installed in original position. Remove speedometer drive gear.

SYNCHRONIZERS

Remove clip from gear. Disassemble as shown in *Figs. 4 and 5.* Check all parts for wear or damage and replace as necessary.

FRONT COVER

Remove parts as shown in *Fig. 6.* If speedometer gear shaft bushing is to be removed, heat front cover to about 250°F (120°C). Pull out bushing. If necessary, bushing may be carefully drilled out. Clean cover and check for cracks or damage. Replace parts as necessary.

FINAL DRIVE (DIFFERENTIAL)

1) Remove expansion bolt from center of flange. Withdraw flange shaft. Drive seals and outer bearing races out of final drive housing and side cover with drift.

2) Drive roll pin from differential pinion shaft, then drive pinion shaft out and remove anchor piece. Remove tapered roller bearing with puller and Thrust

PORSCHE 911 CARRERA 5-SPEED TRANSAXLE (Cont.)

Fig. 3: Exploded View of Input Shaft Assembly

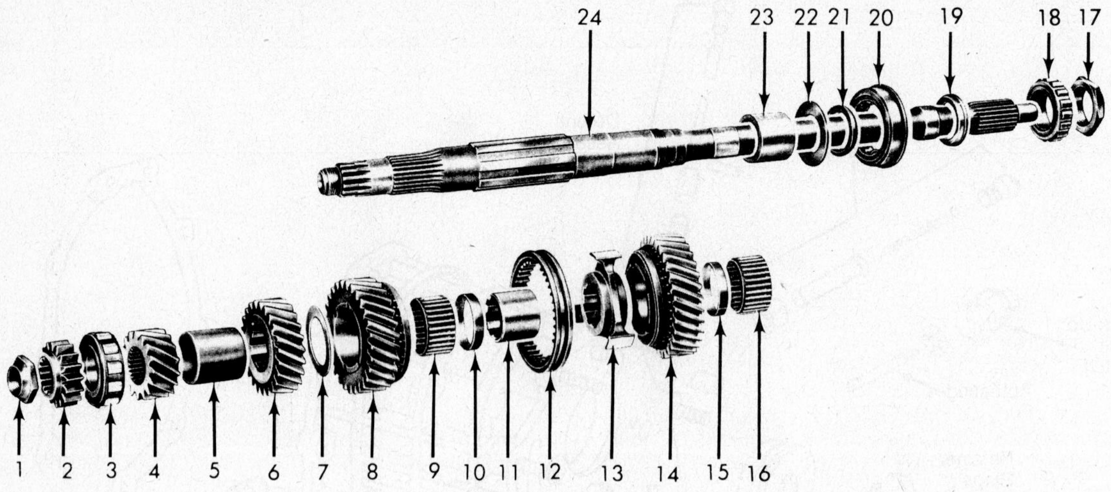

1. Nut
2. Reverse Gear
3. Roller Bearing
4. 1st Gear
5. Spacer
6. 2nd Gear
7. Thrust Washer
8. 3rd Gear
9. Needle Cage
10. Spacer
11. 3rd Gear Bushing
12. Gearshift Sleeve
13. Operating Sleeve
14. 4th Gear
15. Spacer
16. Needle Cage
17. Nut
18. Roller Bearing
19. Inner Race
20. 4-Point Bearing
21. Inner Race
22. Thrust Washer
23. 4th Gear Bushing
24. Drive Shaft

Fig. 4: Exploded View of 1st Gear Synchronizer

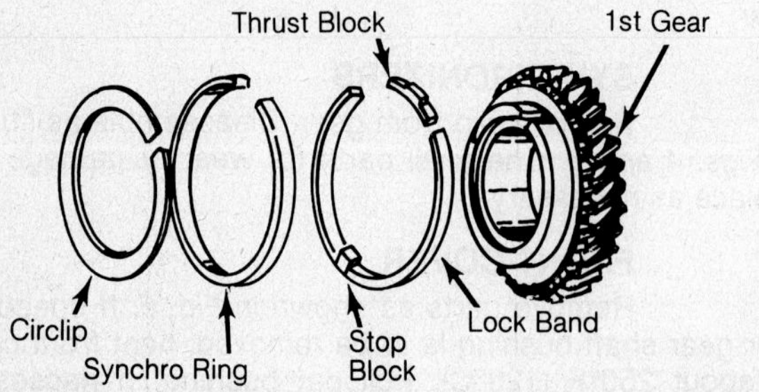

Piece (P 263). Puller arms must fit through openings in magnetic carrier disc to remove bearing from side opposite ring gear.

3) Do not interchange spacer washers and shims. Right and left side must be kept separate and installed in original positions. Remove lock plates from ring gear retaining bolts. Remove bolts and ring gear.

FINAL DRIVE HOUSING

1) Remove adjusting lever spring and circlip. Pull adjusting lever off shaft and disengage auxiliary spring while pressing clutch release lever toward front transmission cover. Drive release lever shaft and bushings from housing.

2) Remove snap ring from input shaft bearing race. Bearing must first be driven slightly away from snap ring with soft punch.

3) Heat differential housing to about 250°F (120°C), and drive out both bearing races using Thrust Blocks (US 8050 and P 254d).

INPUT SHAFT SEAL

Remove both countersunk Phillips head bolts on guide tube. Pull out drive shaft seal guide tube with hook and bar without bending tube lip. Remove seal from tube with Remover (P 381).

PORSCHE 911 CARRERA 5-SPEED TRANSAXLE (Cont.)

Fig. 5: Exploded View of Pinion Shaft Assembly

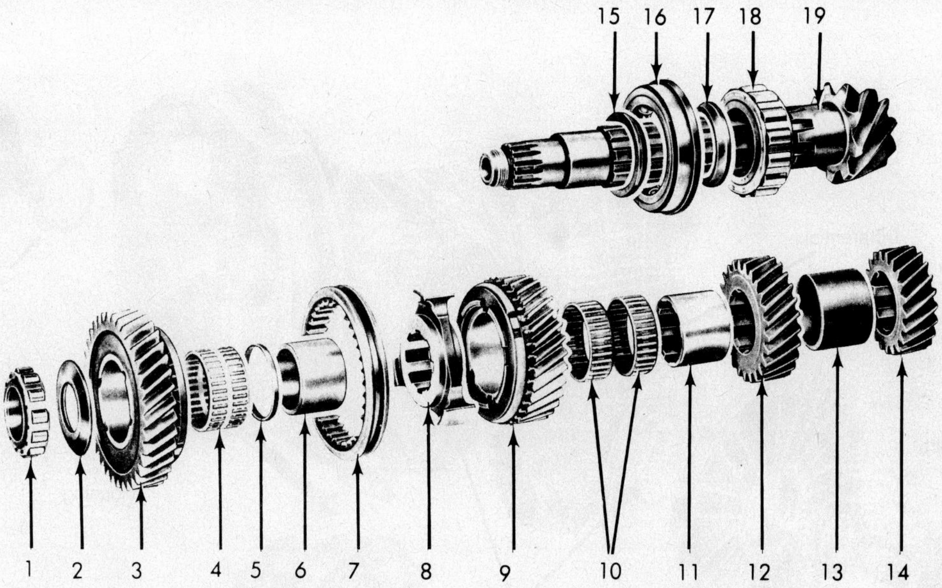

1. Roller Bearing
2. Thrust Washer
3. 1st Gear
4. Needle Cage
5. Spacer
6. 1st Gear Sleeve
7. Operating Sleeve
8. Guide Sleeve
9. 2nd Gear
10. Needle Cage
11. 2nd Gear Sleeve
12. 3rd Gear
13. Spacer
14. 4th Gear
15. Bearing Inner Race
16. 4-Point Bearing
17. Bearing Inner Race
18. Roller Bearing
19. Drive Pinion

Fig. 6: Exploded View of Front Cover Assembly

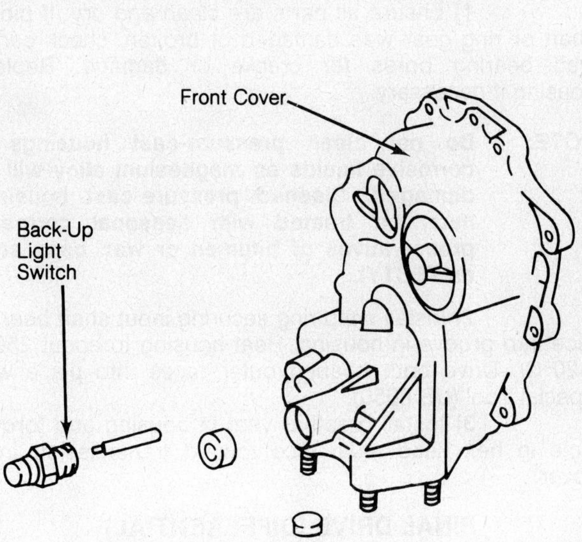

TRANSAXLE REASSEMBLY & ADJUSTMENT

INPUT SHAFT SEAL

Drive in seal to stop with piece of pipe. Install rubber seal. Lubricate rubber seal and sealing lip. Insert tube with rubber seal. Install guide sleeve for release bearing and coat with White grease.

CLUTCH RELEASE LEVER AND SHAFT

1) Install bushings with Driver (P 375). *See Fig. 8.* Lubricate and install operating shaft, release fork and roll pin.

2) Install release lever on shaft along with spring and adjusting screw. Secure in place with pin. Snap auxiliary spring past dead point to stop pin in order to pretension against lever.

NOTE: **Do not install adjusting lever until after transaxle assembly has been installed in vehicle.**

PORSCHE 911 CARRERA 5-SPEED TRANSAXLE (Cont.)

Fig. 7: Exploded View of Final Drive and Housing

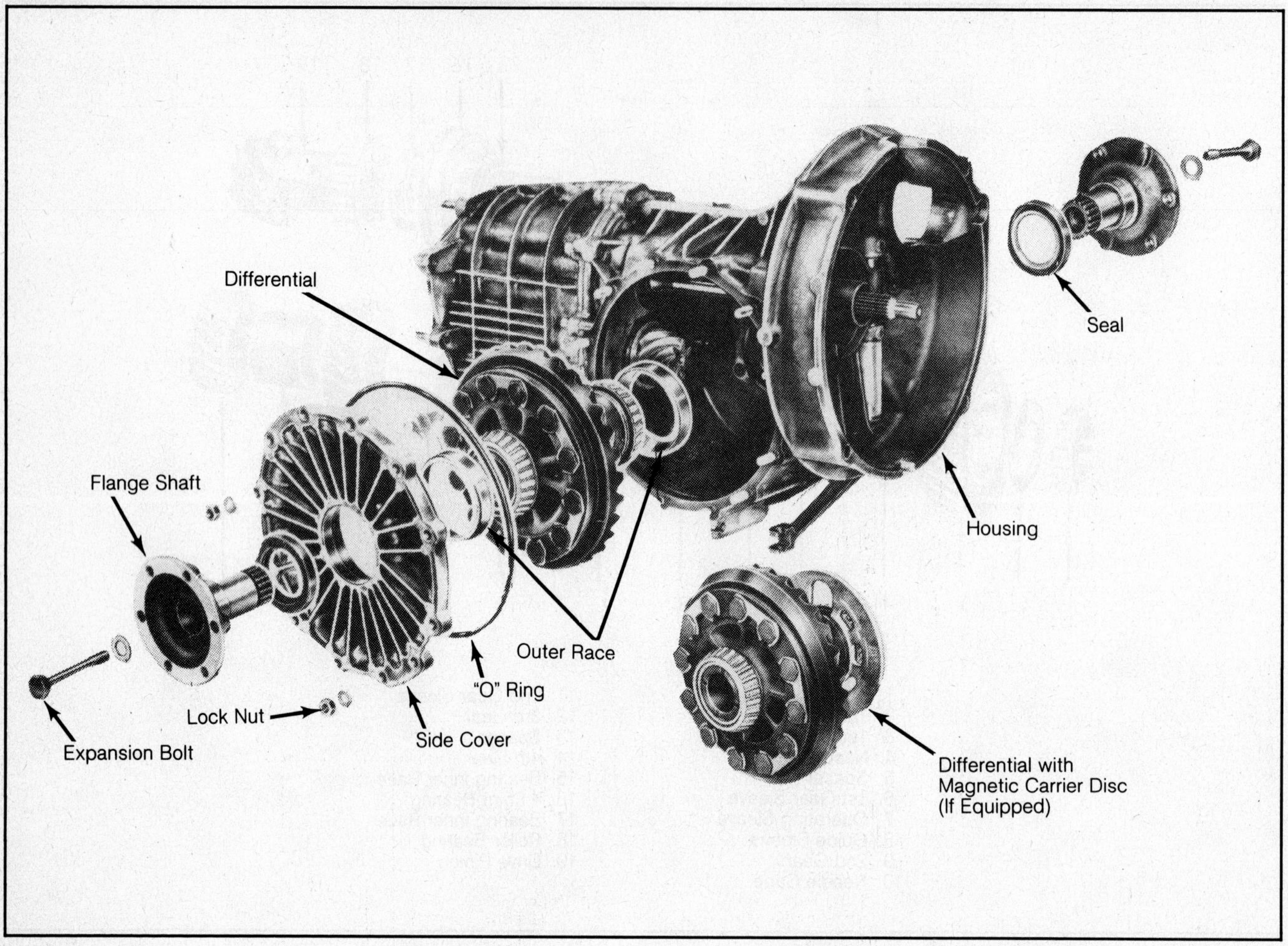

Fig. 8: Clutch Lever Shaft Bushing Installation and Location

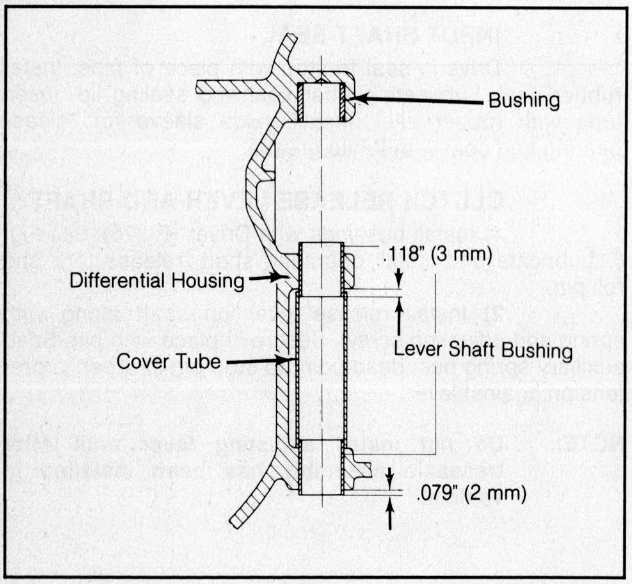

FINAL DRIVE HOUSING

1) Ensure all parts are clean and dry. If pinion shaft or ring gear was damaged or broken, check center web bearing bores for cracks or damage. Replace housing if necessary.

NOTE: **Do not clean pressure-cast housings in corrosive liquids as magnesium alloy will be damaged. Cleaned pressure-cast housings must be treated with seasonal corrosion preservatives of bitumen or wax base such as TECTYL.**

2) Install snap ring securing input shaft bearing race into groove in housing. Heat housing to about 250°F (120°C). Drive both bearing outer races into place with Special Tool (US 8050).

3) Install breather vent in housing and torque. Hole in hex head must face toward transmission front cover.

FINAL DRIVE (DIFFERENTIAL)

1) Slide lock plates into bolt head grooves. Pinch open ends together with pliers to firmly hold plates to bolts. Bolt ring gear to carrier. Secure bolts by bending plate tab down over corner of bolt head.

PORSCHE 911 CARRERA 5-SPEED TRANSAXLE (Cont.)

Fig. 9: Exploded View of Ring Gear and Carrier Assembly

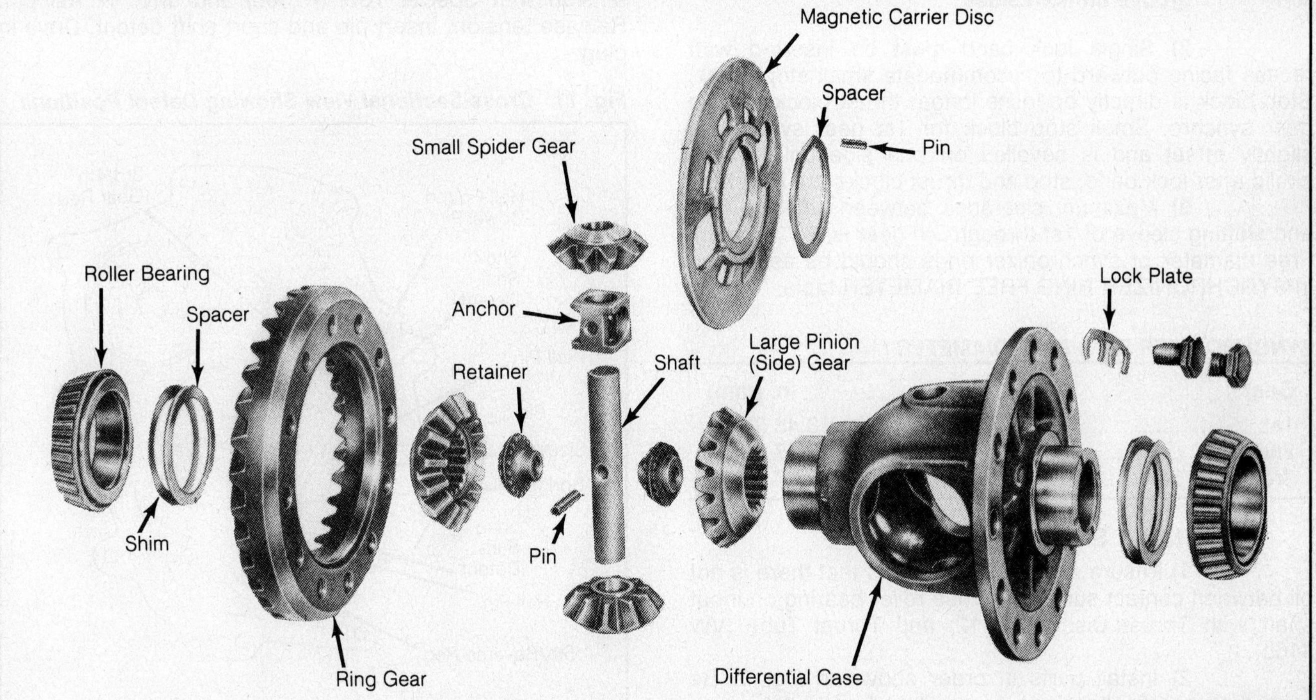

2) Coat thrust surfaces of differential pinion and spider gear with Molykote or other lubricant. Insert large pinion side gears through oval shaped opening in housing.

3) Insert flange shafts to center pinions. Insert small spider gears through housing opening and position opposite each other so that bores align with bores in housing.

4) Install threaded retainers with lock rings into large side gears. Slide anchor between threaded retainers.

CAUTION: Differential pinion shaft must be positioned so pinion shaft hole aligns with hole in anchor.

5) Hold anchor in place and drive in pinion shaft. Install bearing shims and spacer washers in CORRECT ORIGINAL locations on differential housing. Install anchor pin.

6) Install tapered roller bearing using Thrust Plate (P 264). When replacing magnetic carrier disc, tapered roller preload does not have to be checked if same shims are reused.

NOTE: If only differential has been replaced, proceed to RING GEAR & PINION ADJUSTMENT. If transmission gears have been removed and disassembled, proceed to correct assembly steps for remainder of transmission, then proceed to adjustment.

SYNCHRONIZERS

1) Place synchro ring on clutch carrier; rough ring surfaces face shift sleeve. Insert thrust block, stop block and lock band(s).

Fig. 10: Second Gear Synchronizer

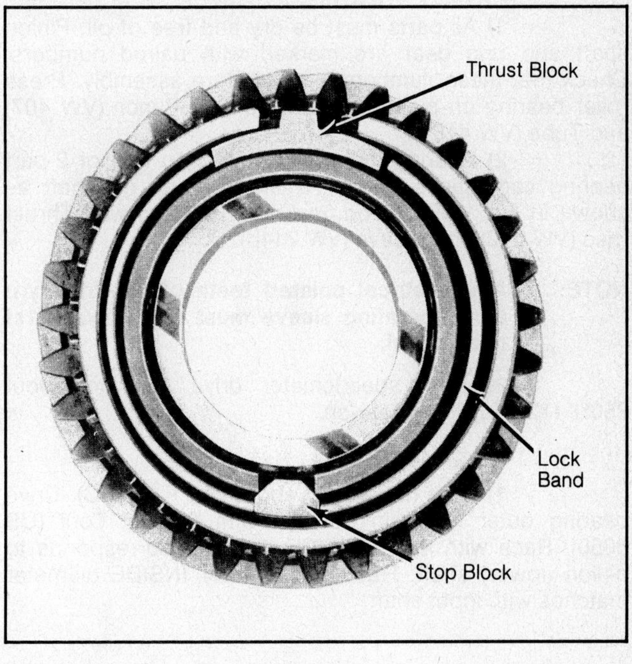

PORSCHE 911 CARRERA 5-SPEED TRANSAXLE (Cont.)

NOTE: First gear synchro ring has only 1 lock band. Also, 1st gear synchro ring is identified by a groove on both sides.

2) Single lock band must be inserted with recess facing outward to accommodate small stop block. Stop block is directly opposite longer thrust block on 2nd gear synchro. Small stop block for 1st gear synchro is slightly offset and is bevelled on one side only. Install circlip after lock band, stop and thrust blocks are installed.

3) Maximum clearance between selector fork and shifting sleeve of 1st through 5th gear is .02" (.5 mm). Free diameter of synchronizer rings should be as shown in SYNCHRONIZER RING FREE DIAMETER table.

SYNCHRONIZER RING FREE DIAMETER

Gear	In. (mm)
1st	3.43 (87.1)
2nd	3.47 (88.1)
3rd, 4th & 5th	3.07 (78.0)

INPUT SHAFT

1) Ensure all parts are dry and that there is not oil between contact surfaces. Press roller bearing on input shaft with Thrust Disc (VW 412) and Thrust Tube (VW 416b).

2) Install parts in order shown in *Fig. 3.* Be sure that needle bearings are installed with the same gears they were removed with.

3) Press roller bearing on end of input shaft with Thrust Plate (VW 401) and Punch (VW 407). Torque flange nut to correct specification. Peen flange nut in place with punch.

4) Measure input shaft runout. Maximum allowable runout is .004" (.1 mm). If runout does not exceed .012" (.3 mm), it is possible to carefully straighten shaft with press and "V" blocks.

PINION SHAFT

1) All parts must be dry and free of oil. Pinion shaft and ring gear are marked with paired numbers. Check that these numbers match before assembly. Press roller bearing on pinion shaft with Press Punch (VW 407) and Tube (VW 415a).

2) Bearing must be installed so ring of 2-part bearing cage faces gears. Assemble parts on shaft as shown in *Fig. 4.* Press on final roller bearing with Thrust Disc (VW 412) and Sleeve (VW 244b).

NOTE: Asymmetrical pointed teeth of 1st-2nd synchro operating sleeve must face toward 1st gear wheel.

3) Heat speedometer drive gear to about 250°F (120°C). Drive gear on.

GEAR HOUSING

1) Heat housing to about 250°F (120°C). Drive bearing outer races in position with Special Tool (US 8050). Race with larger INSIDE diameter corresponds to pinion (lower) shaft. Race with smaller INSIDE diameter matches with input shaft.

2) Install 5th-reverse shift rod. Insert long shift detent. Drive in roll pin. Install spring and sleeve. Apply tension with Special Tool (P 366) and drive in roll pin. Release tension. Insert pin and short shift detent. Drive in plug.

Fig. 11: Cross-Sectional View Showing Detent Positions

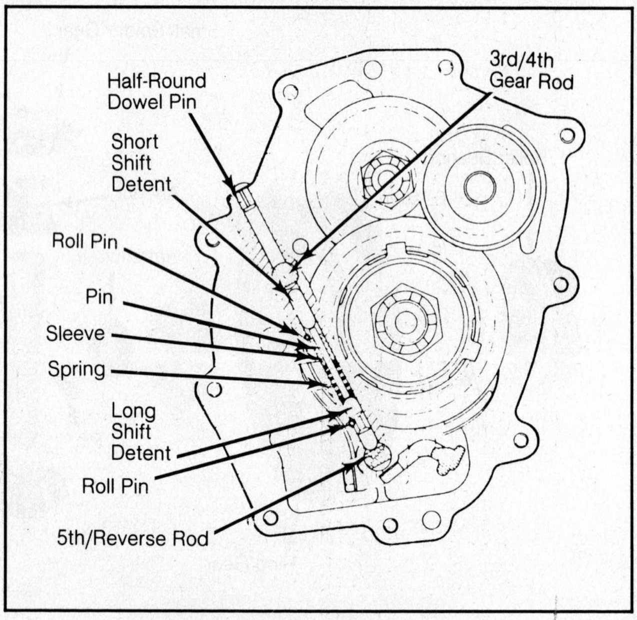

INPUT & PINION ASSEMBLY-TO-HOUSING

1) Install same number and thickness of shims on transmission housing studs as noted during disassembly. Also determined by adjusting the pinion. Insert 1st-2nd gear selector fork rod.

2) If removed, insert 1st-2nd gearshift detent and spring. Tighten bolt. Install pinion shaft with 1st-2nd gear selector fork so that pinion rests lightly in bearing race of transmission/differential housing. Slightly open selector fork clamping piece to prevent fork from binding on fork rod.

3) Insert input shaft and press into place with pinion shaft assembly. Tighten clamping plate nuts to specification.

4) Lightly tighten 1st-2nd gear selector fork bolt. Insert detent from top. Unscrew 3rd-4th gear selector fork and clamping piece bolts. Push fork and clamping piece back. Install selector fork and rod.

5) Lightly tighten fork and clamp bolts. If not already done, insert detent with spring and tighten plug. Adjust selector forks at this time. See SELECTOR (SHIFTING) FORK ADJUSTMENT in this article.

6) Install housing gasket on studs. Install gear housing with 5th/reverse gear selector fork rod and shaft. Tighten correctly. Push fork rod in ball sleeve and selector shaft into shift pawl guides. Install guide fork cover, gasket and tighten.

7) Install idler gear shaft turning shaft until pin in housing stops rotation. Install reverse gear and start castle nut on threads. Install thrust washer for 5th (free) gear. Install 5th (free) gear needle bearing.

PORSCHE 911 CARRERA 5-SPEED TRANSAXLE (Cont.)

8) Install guide sleeve for 5th-reverse gear and start flange nut on threads. Install thrust needle bearing cage, idler gear with needle bearing cages, intermediate piece and thrust washer on idler shaft.

9) Slide 5th gear and reverse sliding gear with fork onto guide sleeve and selector fork rod. Open clamping piece on fork slightly for easier assembly. Lightly tighten selector fork bolt.

10) Apply light coat of oil to "O" ring and install. Use tool (P 37a) to block input shaft and engage 5th gear. Tighten input and pinion shaft nuts to specification.

11) Adjust 5th/reverse gear selector fork. See SELECTOR (SHIFTING) FORK ADJUSTMENT in this article. Secure castle nut with roll pin. Secure flange nut by peening. Install back-up light switch actuator pin with recessed end facing switch.

ADJUSTMENTS

GEARSHIFT ADJUSTMENT

1) Loosen selector rod clamp. Turn selector rod for transmission's inner selector lever left in neutral to stop.

2) Move selector lever in neutral position so that the lower part of the selector lever is vertical and on right stop (3rd and 4th gear). Tighten selector rod clamp slightly.

3) Check shift travel is just as much in 1st through 4th gears and if reverse is easy to engage. Correct adjustments if necessary.

CAUTION: Unit must be assembled correctly. Front cover should not be installed at this time. Parts should be clean and dry.

Fig. 12: Ring and Pinion Identification

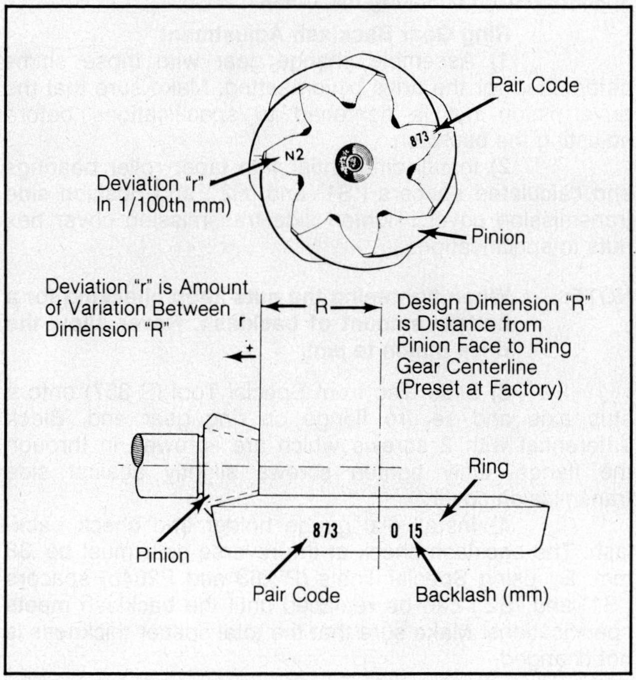

DRIVE PINION

1) Distance "E" is calculated by adding together design distance "R" and deviation "r" as indicated on face of drive pinion. Install preassembled drive pinion and drive shaft without shims and tighten to specifications.

2) Install 4th gear with operating and guide sleeve, and shift into 4th gear. Slide a 1.92 X .16 X 5.92" (48 X 4 X 148 mm) piece of pipe onto drive pinion.

3) Install thrust washer and cylindrical roller bearing. Mount gear housing and secure with 2 nuts. Install reverse gears. Place appropriate pin or reverse gear shaft in bore of transmission case and slide in reverse gear.

4) Tighten drive pinion nut to specifications. Make sure that the taper roller bearing outer races fit tight in transmission case and side cover. Set adjusting ring of Universal Gauge (VW 385/1) to distance "A" (2.32" 58 mm).

5) Slide Centering Discs (9109) on gauge. Screw in Gauge Plunger (VW 385/14) with 1.2" (30 mm) Dial Gauge Extension (VW 385/56). Install taper roller bearing from differential, or spare taper roller bearing on centering discs.

6) Install Master Gauge (VW 385/55), and set dial gauge (3 mm) range at zero with .040" (1 mm) preload (small indicator faces 1, large 0). Remove master gauge after setting dial gauge.

7) Place Gauge Plate (VW 385/17) on head of drive pinion. Place gauge mandrel in transmission case. The dial gauge extention is near the gauge plate. Install side transmission cover without seal and tighten the 4 nuts crosswise.

NOTE: DO NOT use a hammer to set up the side transmission cover (this could cause the gauge plate, held by a magnet, to fall down). Position the cover by tightening the nuts evenly.

8) Pull second centering disc so far out with the spindle that the gauge mandrel can just barely be turned by hand. Turn gauge mandrel carefully until the dial gauge extension is vertical to the face of the drive pinion head. At this moment the dial gauge needle will be at its point of inflection, so that it can be read.

9) Check the following when reading the dial gauge: Design distance "R"= 3.29" (82.29 mm) has been set with Master Gauge (VW 385/55). If the dial gauge reading differs from the design distance in clockwise direction, the distance is smaller than the design distance, so that the amount from "0" has to be substracted from the design distance.

10) The small dial gauge indicator needle is between 1 and 2, the large needle points to 0.10 mm. For an example, see the following:

- Design distance: 3.29" (82.29 mm).
  Less dial gauge reading: -.004" (.10 mm).
  Drive pinion face distance:=3.28" (82.19 mm).
- Distance "E": 3.30" (82.41 mm).
  Drive pinion face distance: -3.28" (82.19 mm).
- Thickness of shims: .008" (.22 mm).

The drive pinion must therefore be moved .008" (.20 mm) away from the center of the ring gear. This is accomplished by inserting a .008" (.20 mm) thick shim.

11) Recheck distance "E" after installing the shims. A deviation of .013" (.33 mm) is permissable. It is not necessary to check the surface appearance.

PORSCHE 911 CARRERA 5-SPEED TRANSAXLE (Cont.)

NOTE: **If the correct size shims have been chosen, the dial gauge will show deviation "r" (.004" .12 mm or .007" .18 mm) with a tolerance of .001" (.03 mm).**

12) The small dial gauge needle with .040" (1 mm), the large needle points to deviation "r" with a tolerance of .001" (.03 mm).

NOTE: **In order to check backlash correctly, spacer (S1) should be .004" (.1 mm) thinner than 1/2 the sum of spacers (S1) and (S2). Spacer (S2) should be .004" (.1 mm) thicker than 1/2 the total thickness of (S1) and (S2).**

RING GEAR BACKLASH ADJUSTMENT

Determining Total Thickness of Spacers For Ring Gear Adjustment

1) Install gear cluster with shims determined during pinion shaft adjustment. Be sure to tighten pinion shaft flange nut if not already done.

2) Make sure that the taper roller bearing outer races fit tight in the transmission case or side cover. Place a .14" (3.5 mm) thick spacer on the ring gear end of the differential housing in question and a .12" (3.0 mm) thick spacer underneath the taper roller bearing or magnetic support disc on the opposite end.

3) Insert differential with taper roller bearing into transmission case and install side transmission cover without rubber seal. Press side transmission cover against the taper roller bearing by slightly tightening 2 nuts located opposite each other.

NOTE: **Reference data for pressing taper roller bearing is .06" (.15 mm).**

4) If the reference data of .06" (.15 mm) is not given, replace spacer. See the following example:

- Distance measure with feeler gauge: = .016" (.40 mm)
  Less axial pressure reference data: = .006" (.15 mm)
- The .14" (3.5 mm) thick spacer "S1" installed is .01" (.25 mm) too thick. Install a .13" (3.25 mm).
  Tighten side transmission cover.

NOTE: **All nuts must be installed and tightened to specifications to assure correct results.**

5) Slide disc from Special Tool (P 357) onto flange and install flange. Tighten stretch bolt with washer. Using a torque gauge, check rotational torque of assembled differential. The following data is required:

- SKF bearings = 22-31 INCH lbs. (2.5-3.5 N.m)
- FAG bearings = 35-57.5 INCH lbs. (4-6.5 N.m)

6) The drive pinion may not engage when checking the rotational torque and the seal on the side transmission cover must be removed to avoid any additional friction. The specified torque must be given to assure correct axial pressure on the taper roller bearings. If necessary, replace the spacer again until the torque meets specifications.

7) Remove differential, pull off both taper roller bearings and check thickness of spacers with a micrometer at 4 positions around the circumference. The thickness of both spacers together is the total thickness of spacers for ring gear adjustments.

8) Spacer "S1" is chosen 008" (.2 mm) thinner than spacer "S2" as a starting point for later adjustments of the backlash (ring gear to drive pinion). *See Fig. 13.*

Fig. 13: Backlash Adjustment Formula

$$\frac{6.25\text{ mm}}{2} = 3.125$$
$$3.125 - 0.10 = 3.025$$

Thickness of spacer "S2"

$$\frac{6.25\text{ mm}}{2} = 3.125$$
$$3.125 + 0.10 = 3.225$$

NOTE: **Spacers with thicknesses from 2.4 to 3.7 mm are available in steps of .10 mm.**

9) A .25 mm thick shim allows spacers in steps of .05 mm. Round off the calculated spacer thicknesses so that the total thickness of spacers "S1" and "S2" is not changed. See the following example:

- Calculated spacer thickness.
  "S1" + "S2" = 3.025 + 3.225 = 6.25 mm.
- Rounded off spacer thickness.
  "S1" + "S2" = 3.0 + 3.25 = 6.25 mm.

10) Check thickness of spacers with a micrometer at 4 locations around circumference. Maximum deviation is .02 mm. Remove any burrs along edges of spacers before checking thickness.

Ring Gear Backlash Adjustment

1) Assemble change gear with those shims determined for the drive pinion settng. Make sure that the drive pinion nut is tightened to specifications before adjusting the backlash.

2) Install differential with taper roller bearings and calculated spacers ("S1" and "S2") and position side transmission cover. Tighten side transmission cover hex nuts to specifications.

NOTE: **When tightening the nuts keep checking for a certain amount of backlash. Never allow the drive pinion to jam.**

3) Slide disc from Special Tool (P 357) onto a stub axle and secure flange on ring gear end. Block differential with 2 screws which are screwed in through the flange. Only tighten screws slightly against side transmission cover.

4) Install dial gauge holder and check backlash. The backlash check at the reverse gear must be .38 mm. By using Special Tools (P 263 and P264b) spacers ("S1" and "S2") can be replaced until the backlash meets specifications. Make sure that the total spacer thickness is not changed.

PORSCHE 911 CARRERA 5-SPEED TRANSAXLE (Cont.)

SELECTOR (SHIFTING) FORK ADJUSTMENT

1) Input shaft flange nut must be correctly tightened. Install mounting plate (P 260a). Install 5th gear synchro hub and reverse sliding gear.

2) Block input shaft with tool (P 37a). Engage 5th gear. Tighten input shaft flange nut. Turn 1st-2nd gear selector fork rod LEFT (in driving direction) to stop.

3) Turn fork rod slightly back until unmachined flat inner surface is nearly vertical. Do not turn past middle point or back to right stop.

4) Position 1st-2nd gear selector fork so that shift sleeve is exactly in middle between synchronizing rings. Tighten bolt to proper specification. Adjust 3rd-4th gear fork in same way.

5) Position 3rd-4th gear shift guide even with selector fork. Be sure there is .08-.12" (2-3 mm) clearance between 3rd-4th shift guide and 1st-2nd shift guide. They must not touch. Check ease of shifting and readjust as necessary.

6) Adjust 5th/reverse gear fork as follows: Push idler gear on shaft against 5th (fixed) gear. Adjust idler gear and sliding gear to obtain a clearance of .040" (1 mm) in NEUTRAL position.

7) Press idler gear gently in direction of travel. There should be no play between shift fork and sliding gear groove.

FRONT COVER

Heat cover to about 250°F (120°C) and drive gearshift bushing in place. Drive shift rod seal on with mandrel (P 369). Install new gasket and tighten front cover nuts to specification.

TIGHTENING SPECIFICATIONS

Application	Ft. Lbs. (N.m)
Front & Side Cover Nuts	18 (24)
Guide Fork Cover Nuts	18 (24)
Input Shaft Flange Nut	120 (163)
Input Shaft Castle Nut	95 (129)
Pinion Shaft Flange Nut	180 (244)
Ring Gear Bolts	
Standard Differential	84 (115)
Positive Traction Differentials	
Grade 11.9 Bolts	105 (142)
Grade 12.9 Bolts	112 (152)
Retaining Plate & Trans.	
Support Attachment	15 (20)
Starter Nut	35 (47)

Manual Transmissions

RENAULT NG1 5-SPEED TRANSAXLE

Fuego, Sportwagon

DESCRIPTION

Transaxle consists of a removable clutch housing, a split gear case and a rear cover. The rear cover houses the shift mechanism as well as 5th gear. All forward gears are in constant mesh and are fully synchronized. Final drive is located in front of transmission section of transaxle.

LUBRICATION & ADJUSTMENT

See appropriate MANUAL TRANSMISSION SERVICING article in the IMPORT GENERAL SERVICING section.

SERVICE (IN VEHICLE)

DRIVE AXLE SHAFTS

See appropriate DRIVE AXLE SHAFT article in IMPORT AXLE SHAFTS, OVERDRIVES & TRANSFER CASES section.

Fig. 1: Cutaway View of Renault Manual Transaxle

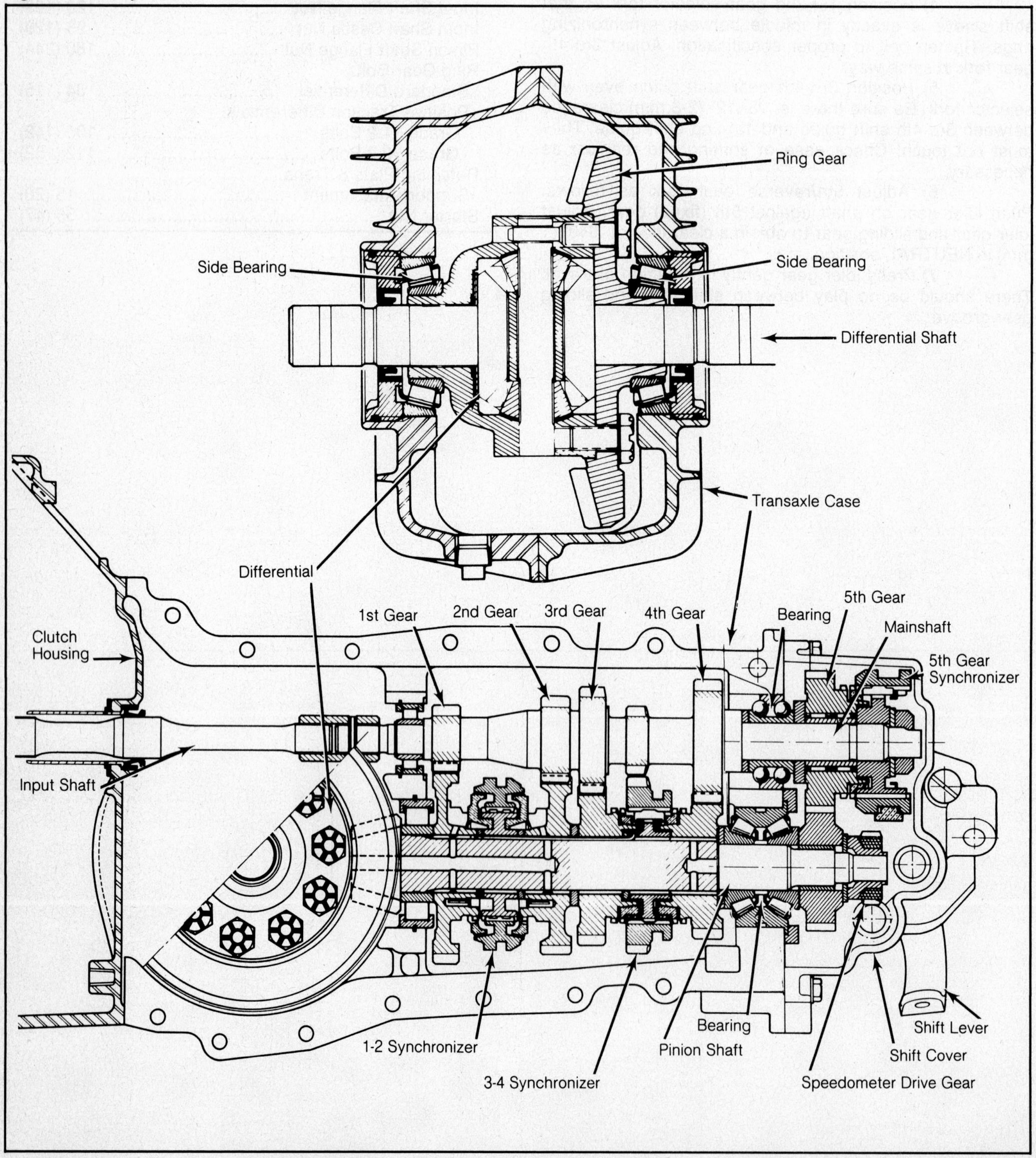

RENAULT NG1 5-SPEED TRANSAXLE (Cont.)

REMOVAL & INSTALLATION

See appropriate MANUAL TRANSMISSION REMOVAL article in IMPORT GENERAL SERVICING section.

TRANSAXLE DISASSEMBLY

1) Drain transaxle, remove backup light switch and mount transaxle in a support fixture. Remove bell housing attaching bolts. Remove 5th gear detent screw, spring, and ball.

2) Shift transaxle into neutral and remove rear cover while turning selector lever to disengage. Engage 5th and 2nd gear. Remove 5th gear synchronizer nut and washer. Remove speedometer drive gear nut. Return shift forks to neutral.

3) Engage 3rd gear and drive roll pin out of 5th gear shift fork. Mark 5th gear synchronizer hub and sleeve for reassembly reference. Remove 5th gear synchronizer assembly and shift fork.

4) Remove 5th gear from mainshaft with needle bearing and ring. Remove speedometer drive gear, nut and washer. Remove 5th gear and bearing thrust washer from pinion shaft.

5) Remove differential nut lock stops. Remove differential nuts. Remove housing-half bolts and separate halves. Remove differential assembly. Secure outer race of pinion bearing to inner race and remove pinion shaft. Remove mainshaft.

COMPONENT DISASSEMBLY & REASSEMBLY

TRANSAXLE CASE

Disassembly

1) Return all shift forks to neutral and remove 5th gear shift shaft. Drive roll pin out of 3-4 shift fork, then remove fork and shaft. Remove detent ball, spring and interlock disc.

2) Remove reverse gear selector and shaft. Drive roll pin out of 1-2 shift fork, then remove fork and shaft. Remove detent ball and spring.

3) Remove circlip retaining reverse idler gear to shaft. Remove reverse idler gear, shaft, thrust washer, guide, detent ball and spring. Drive side bearing outer races out of case and remove adjusting nut seals.

NOTE: DO NOT reassemble case until the various adjustments of gear position and preload have been made.

Reassembly

To reassemble, reverse disassembly procedure and note the following: Bronze side of reverse idler gear thrust washer faces gear. Check to make sure that all detents and interlocks operate properly. Roll pin gaps face rear of transaxle.

REAR COVER

Disassembly

1) Remove roll pins securing selector lever to shaft. Slide out selector lever shaft. Remove bushings, spring, selector lever and bellows. Remove cover seal.

2) Remove snap ring and plastic bushing from holding shaft. Press holding shaft out of rear cover. Pry open catches holding speedometer drive gear onto shaft. Remove shaft. Remove and discard speedometer gear. Remove seals from housing.

Reassembly

To reassemble rear cover, reverse disassembly procedures.

MAINSHAFT

Disassembly & Reassembly

Drive roll pin out of coupling and separate input shaft from mainshaft. Remove bearing retaining ring and outer bearing race from front of mainshaft. Press inner race off front of shaft. Using a bearing separator, press bearing assembly off rear of mainshaft. To reassemble, reverse disassembly procedure.

PINION SHAFT

Disassembly

1) Support shaft in a vise by clamping onto 1st gear. Remove double taper bearing, 4th gear, 4th gear blocker ring and 3-4 synchronizer sleeve with keys and springs (scribe a reference mark on hub and sleeve for reassembly).

NOTE: Observe position of synchro springs and hub offset during disassembly. Differences in pinion shaft design require that the synchronizer be assembled and installed exactly as it was removed. Also, location of 3-4 synchro snap ring and lock washer can be on either side of

Fig. 2: Exploded View of Mainshaft Assembly

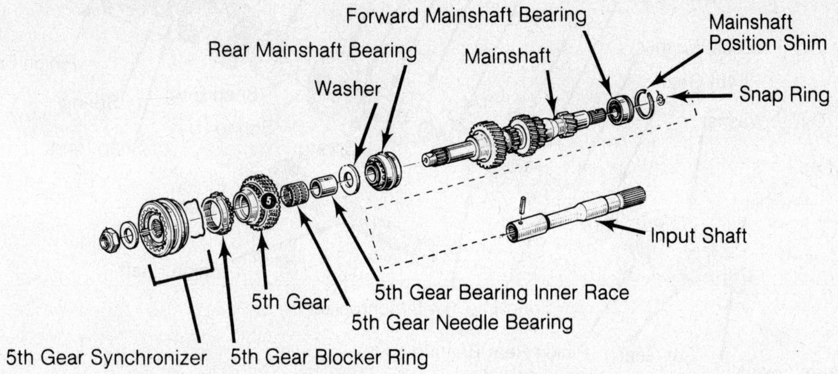

3-4 synchro hub depending on snap ring groove location. Snap ring and lock washer must be installed in same position that they were removed from. The only exception is when pinion shaft is replaced with one of different design. If this is the case, reverse orientation of 3-4 synchro hub, springs, keys, lock washer and snap ring. Do not reverse orientation of 3-4 synchro sleeve.

2) Remove snap ring and lock washer (if installed). Using a bearing separator, press 3-4 synchronizer hub off of shaft. Remove snap ring and lock washer (if installed). Remove 3rd gear and 3rd gear blocker ring.

3) Remove 2nd gear lock washers, snap ring, 2nd gear, 2nd gear blocker ring, 1-2 synchronizer sleeve (scribe a reference mark on hub and sleeve for reassembly) with keys and springs, and 1-2 synchronizer hub lock washer.

4) Using a bearing separator, press 1-2 synchronizer hub off of shaft. Remove 1st gear blocker ring, lock washer, snap ring and 1st gear. Remove front bearing from pinion shaft.

Reassembly

To reassemble, reverse disassembly procedure. Snap rings and speedometer drive gear cannot be reused. Orientation of components related to the 3-4 synchro depends on snap ring groove location. After tightening the speedometer drive gear to specifications, stake the gear to the shaft.

DIFFERENTIAL

Disassembly

Remove and discard all ring gear bolts except for 2 directly opposite each other. Remove side bearings with puller. Remove and discard remainder of ring gear bolts. Drive roll pin out of pinion shaft. Remove pinion shaft, pinion gears and side gears.

Reassembly

To reassemble, reverse disassembly procedure and note the following: Lubrication groove on side gear thrust washer must face gear. Use oversize thrust washer if excessive end play exists. Locking pin of pinion thrust washers should engage hole in case.

TRANSAXLE REASSEMBLY & ADJUSTMENT

DIFFERENTIAL PRELOAD

1) Differential preload is adjusted with ring adjusting nuts on either side of the differential housing. Install proper outer bearing race into each housing half so that it is just below the inner surface.

2) Place differential, with inner bearing races installed, in the right half of housing. Install left housing half onto right half. Install and tighten all case bolts. Do not install drive shaft seals at this time.

3) Using Wrench Adapter (B. Vi. 807), tighten adjusting nuts until they make contact with bearing races. Tighten nut on side facing ring gear more than other side to allow backlash adjustment at a later time. For used side bearings, tighten nuts down until differential can be turned without any play.

4) If new side bearings are used, preload must be set using a pull scale. Wrap a string around differential case and attach loose end to pull scale. Tighten nuts until a force of 2-7 lbs. (1-3 kgs) is required to rotate differential. Mark position of both differential adjusting nuts on case. Remove nuts from case, separate case halves and remove differential.

Fig. 3: Exploded View of Pinion Shaft Assembly

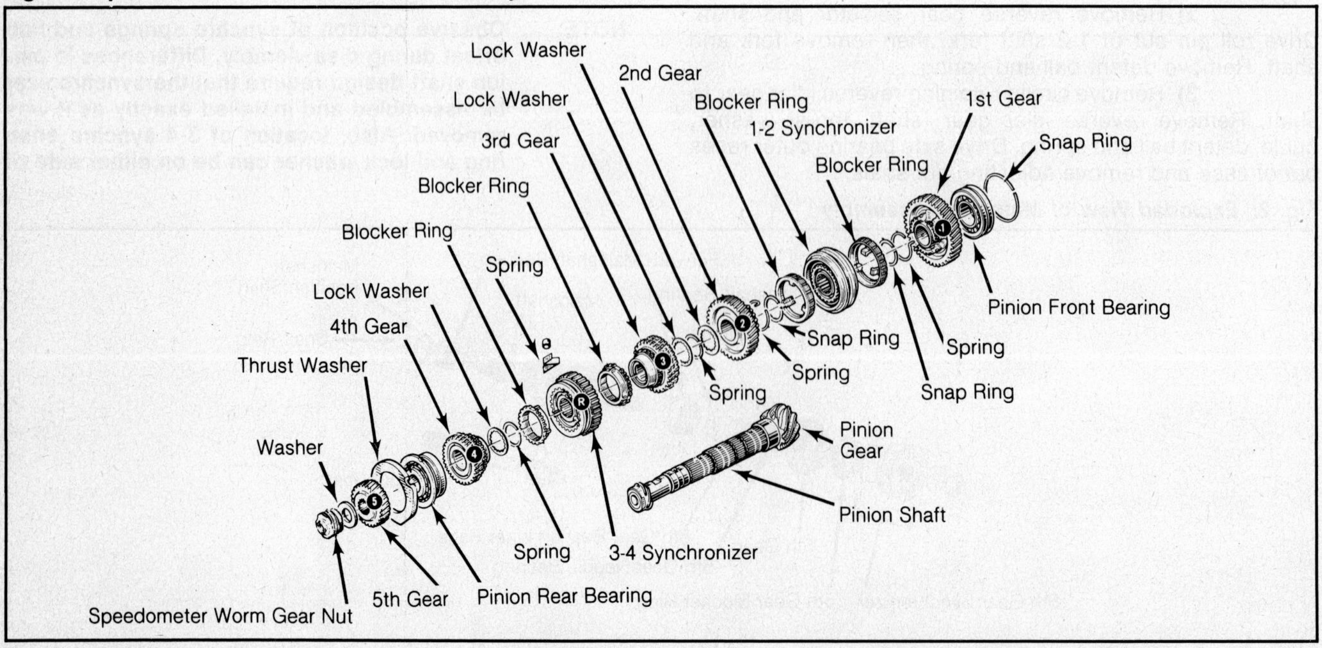

RENAULT NG1 5-SPEED TRANSAXLE (Cont.)

Fig. 4: Exploded View of Differential Assembly

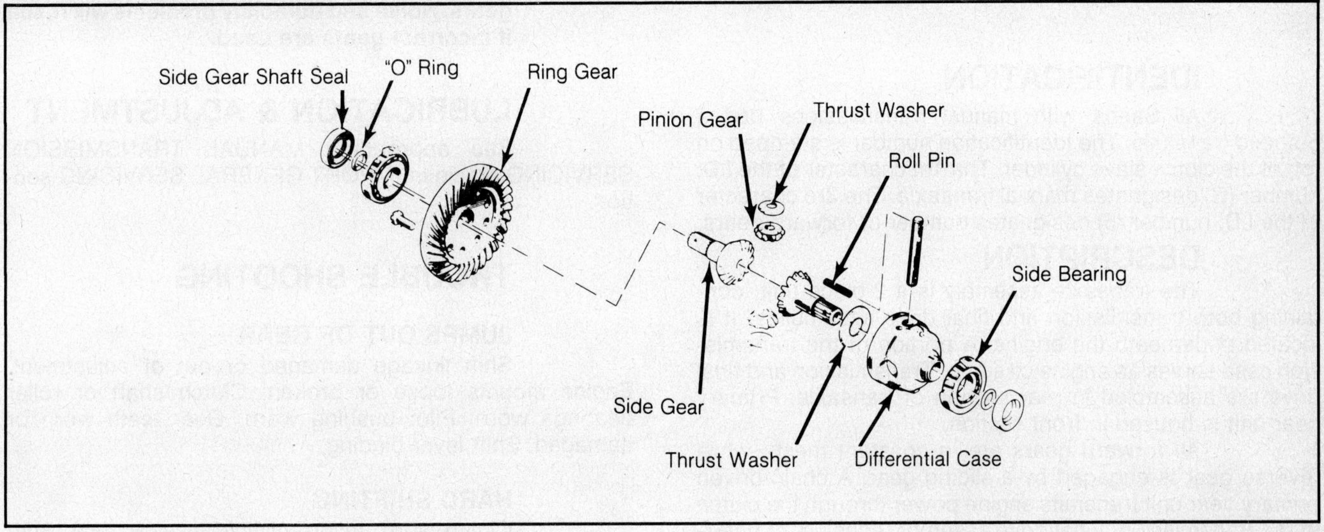

TRANSAXLE REASSEMBLY

1) To reassemble, reverse disassembly procedure and note the following: Align differential adjusting nuts with reference marks made during preload adjustment procedure.

2) Before installing clutch housing, ring gear backlash must be checked and adjusted if necessary. Mount dial indicator on front of transaxle housing so that plunger squarely contacts a ring gear tooth. Lock pinion shaft in place and check backlash by rotating differential.

3) Adjust backlash, if necessary, by turning 1 adjusting nut in and the other adjusting nut out an equal number of turns (to maintain preload setting) to move differential in required direction. Backlash should be .005-.010" (.12-.25 mm).

Fig. 5: Case Bolt Tightening Sequence

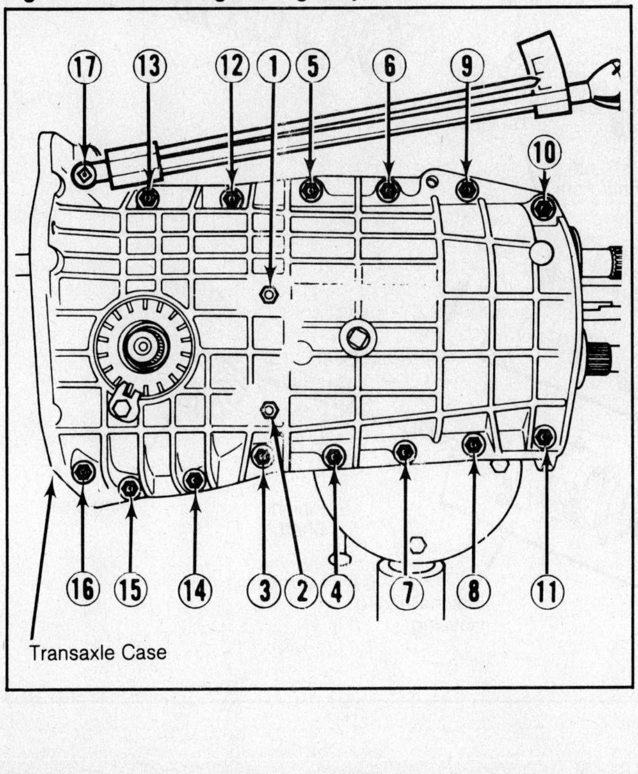

4) Recheck backlash at 4 equally spaced points around ring gear. Variation between points should be minimal. If variation exceeds specification range, disassemble case and check for proper installation of bearings.

TIGHTENING SPECIFICATIONS

Application	Ft. Lbs. (N.m)
Clutch Housing-to-Transaxle	
8 mm Bolts	18 (24)
10 mm Bolts	26 (35)
Speedometer Worm Gear Nut	74-89 (100-121)
Input Shaft Nut (5-Speed Only)	74-89 (100-121)
Ring Gear Bolts	92 (125)
Wheel Hub Nut	185 (251)
	INCH Lbs. (N.m)
Case Half Bolts	
7 mm Bolts	180-228 (20-26)
8 mm Bolts	240-288 (27-33)
Rear Cover Bolts	120 (14)
Reverse Relay Lever Bolt	228 (26)
Differential Adjusting Nut Lock Bolt	216 (24)
Wheel Bearing Retaining Bolts	132 (15)

Manual Transmissions

SAAB 5-SPEED TRANSAXLE

Turbo, 900

IDENTIFICATION

All Saabs with manual transmissions use a 5-speed transaxle. The Identification number is stamped on top of the clutch slave cylinder. The 1st character of the I.D. number (G) designates manual transaxle. The 3rd character of the I.D. number (5) designates number of forward gears.

DESCRIPTION

The transaxle assembly is a 2-piece unit, containing both transmission and final drive assemblies. It is located underneath the engine. A portion of the transmission case serves as engine oil sump. Transmission and final drive are assembled in rear section of transaxle. Primary gear unit is housed in front section.

All forward gears are in constant mesh, while reverse gear is engaged by a sliding gear. A chain-driven primary gear unit transmits engine power through the clutch to the transmission. Final drive assembly consists of differential assembly, pinion shaft, and drive axle shaft housings.

NOTE: **Ensure any gears being replaced match old gears. Noise and durability problems will result if incorrect gears are used.**

LUBRICATION & ADJUSTMENT

See appropriate MANUAL TRANSMISSION SERVICING article in IMPORT GENERAL SERVICING section.

TROUBLE SHOOTING

JUMPS OUT OF GEAR

Shift linkage damaged or out of adjustment. Engine mounts loose or broken. Clutch shaft or roller bearings worn. Pilot bushing worn. Gear teeth worn or damaged. Shift lever binding.

HARD SHIFTING

Clutch worn. Incorrect fluid level or type. Shift rail binding or bent. Clutch disc warped or deformed. Shift linkage binding.

Fig. 1: Exploded View of Transaxle Assembly

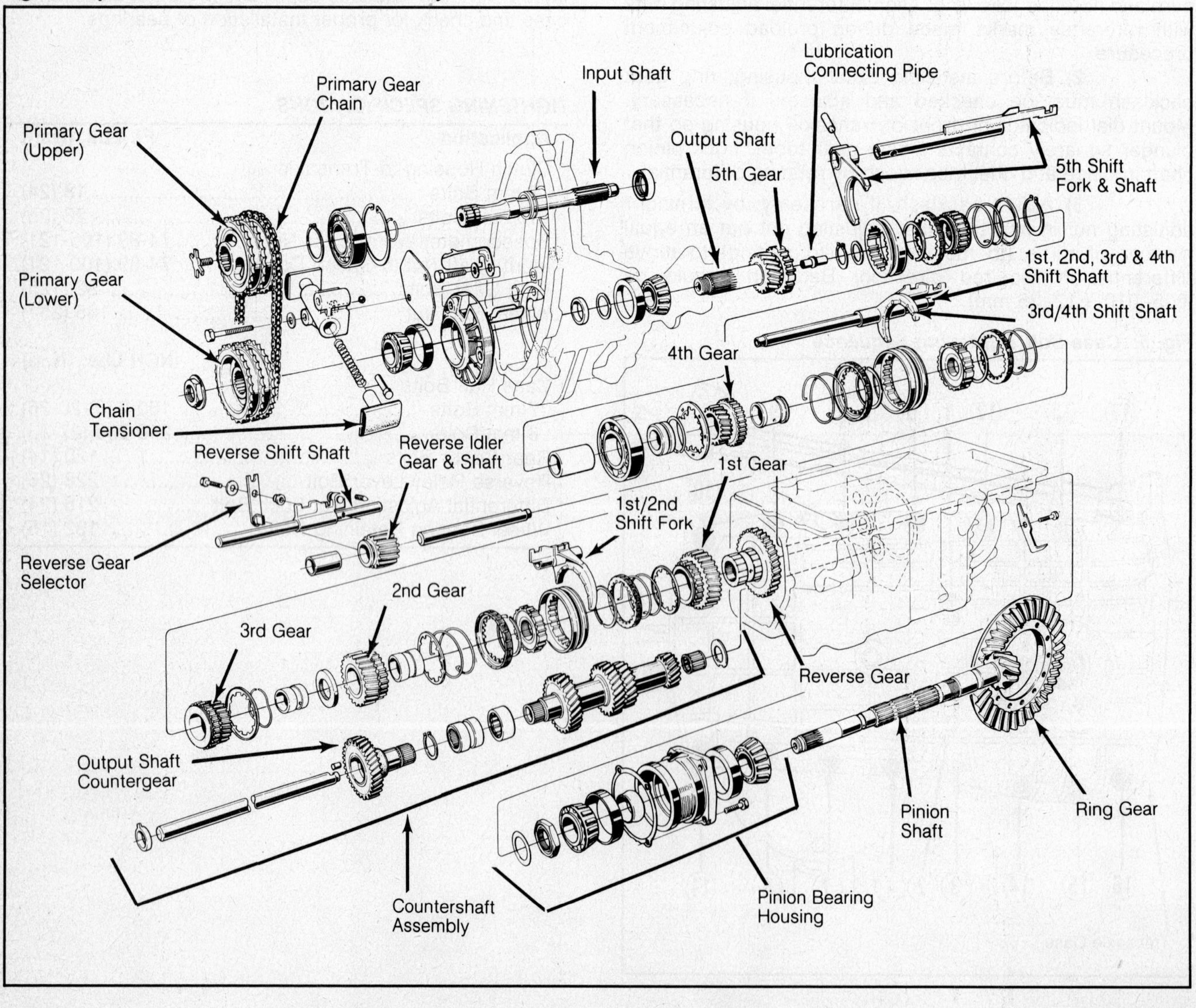

NOISY IN FORWARD GEARS

Incorrect fluid level or type. Clutch housing bolts loose. Worn bearing or gears. Speedometer gears worn or damaged.

LOCKED IN GEAR

Damaged or incorrectly positioned shift linkage. Shift fork loose on shift rail. Broken gear teeth on clutch shaft.

SERVICE (IN VEHICLE)

DRIVE AXLE SHAFTS

See appropriate DRIVE AXLE SHAFT article in IMPORT AXLE SHAFTS, OVERDRIVES & TRANSFER CASES section.

TRANSAXLE MOUNTS

Removal & Installation

1) Place transmission in Neutral. Unbolt exhaust pipe from manifold. Disconnect speedometer cable from transmission. Remove rear engine mounting bolt. Loosen front engine mounting bolt.

2) Attach hoist to 2 lifting rings. Raise engine and transaxle assembly about 4". Remove bolts attaching front and rear mounts to frame. Remove mounts. To install mounts, reverse removal procedure.

REMOVAL & INSTALLATION

TRANSAXLE

See appropriate MANUAL TRANSMISSION REMOVAL article in IMPORT GENERAL SERVICING section.

TRANSAXLE DISASSEMBLY

NOTE: Prior to disassembly of transmission gears, measure and record ring-to-pinion gear backlash and pinion depth. See PINION DEPTH ADJUSTMENT.

1) Place transaxle assembly on work stand and drain fluid. Remove primary gear housing front and side covers. Remove oil filler plug cover and final drive cover. Measure and record ring-to-pinion gear backlash and pinion depth. Remove axle shaft housing attaching bolts. Using puller, remove housings.

NOTE: When removing axle housings, do not lose spring and plunger located in end of inner shaft. Also, note number and thickness of adjusting shims installed with housings.

2) Tilt differential assembly to one side and remove assembly from case. Remove reverse gear operating lever retaining bolt and lever. Engage reverse gear and 5th gear to lock transmission. Unstake output shaft tab washer (lower primary gear), and remove unit. Remove chain tensioner.

3) Remove snap ring (located behind upper primary gear). Using slide hammer and Puller (87 90 891), remove primary gears and chains simultaneously. Free countershaft gear from output shaft countergear by loosening snap ring and pushing sleeve against countershaft. *See Fig. 2.*

Fig. 2: Disconnecting Mainshaft Countergear

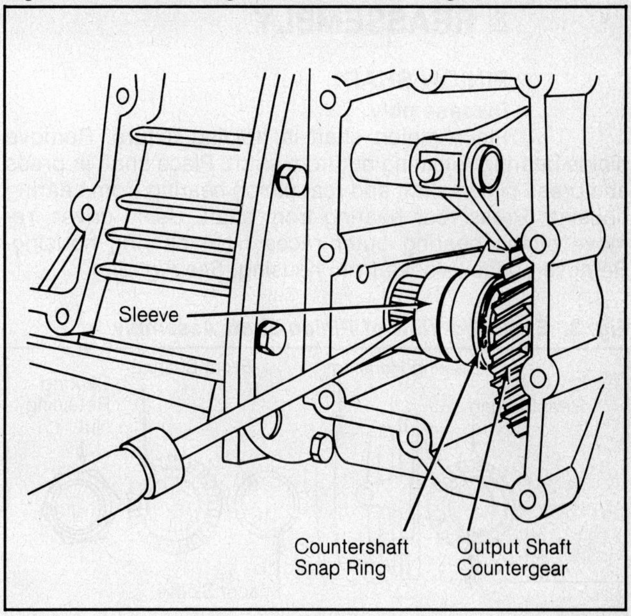

4) Remove countershaft and reverse idler shaft retaining plate. Using Extractor (83 90 049), remove countershaft. Remove countershaft gear (with sleeve) and snap ring through side cover.

5) Remove input shaft bearing housing oil catcher bolts and oil catcher. Remove bearing housing bolts. Using slide hammer and Adapter (87 90 917), remove bearing housing.

6) Remove 5th gear selector fork locking stud. Push gear selector toward housing until it stops. Remove fork and slider. Remove 5th gear synchro hub snap ring and shim(s). Remove synchro hub and spacer from pinion shaft.

7) Remove all primary gear housing retaining bolts. Drive dowels into case to separate primary gear housing from transmission housing. The 5th gear selector will remain in housing and may be removed later.

8) Remove countershaft assembly with needle bearings and thrust washer identified for installation in original position. Remove selector shafts (from front) and selectors. Remove 1st and 2nd gear selectors together with respective synchro unit.

9) Reverse selector should be removed while still attached to selector shaft. Remove selector ball, guide pin, reverse idler shaft and reverse idler gear. Remove 4 pinion shaft bearing housing retaining screws. Using Remover (87 90 909), press out pinion.

CLEANING & INSPECTION

Clean all gasket material from covers and flanges. After washing parts, inspect for unusual wear and discoloration. Check for knicks or chips of mating surfaces. Ensure mating surfaces are flat and smooth.

COMPONENT DISASSEMBLY & REASSEMBLY

PINION SHAFT

Disassembly

Place pinion shaft in holding fixture. Remove pinion bearing retaining nut from shaft. Place shaft in press and press pinion shaft and rear pinion bearing from bearing housing. Press rear bearing from shaft. Using driver, remove pinion bearing outer races from bearing housing. Remove spacer sleeve from housing. *See Fig. 3.*

Fig. 3: Exploded View of Pinion Shaft Assembly

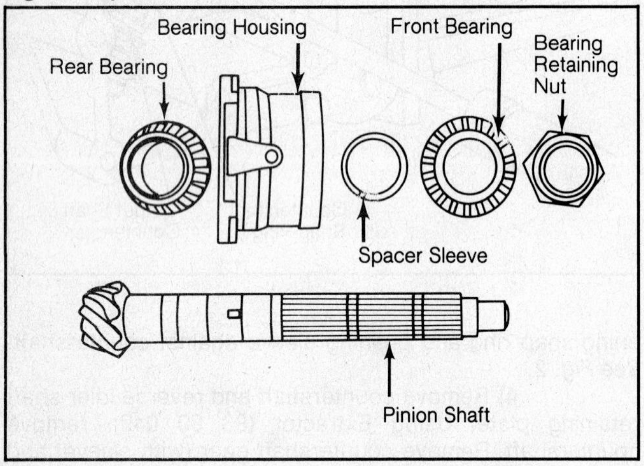

Reassembly

1) Lubricate bearings with ATF. Press bearing outer races into bearing housing. Press rear pinion bearing onto pinion shaft until it butts against stop. Place spacer sleeve onto shaft. Install housing over sleeve.

2) Place front bearing on shaft and position shaft in press. Turn housing by hand. Slowly press bearing into housing until resistance is felt. Remove shaft from press.

3) Coat bearing retaining nut threads with Loctite and install nuts, but do not tighten. Install pinion shaft assembly in holding fixture and place in vise. Attach spring pull gauge to housing. *See Fig. 4.*

4) Tighten retaining nut until force required to rotate housing is 10-15 lbs. (4.5-6.8 kg) for new bearings or 4.2-9.2 lbs. (1.9-4.2 kg) for used bearings (1200 miles or more). When correct value is obtained, stake retaining nut.

NOTE: **Pinion bearing preload is set to correct specification with retaining nut correctly tightened.**

PRIMARY GEAR HOUSING

Disassembly

Remove 4 Allen head screws from input shaft bearing retainer and remove retainer. Drive out bearing using Drift (83 90 106) and Sleeve (83 90 148). Remove needle bearing from primary gear case using a drift. Pry out input shaft oil seal. Remove upper primary gear snap ring. Using Sleeve (87 90 842), press bearing out of upper primary gear.

NOTE: **DO NOT remove lever control ball valve. Check that ball moves freely and securely sets on seat. Ball acts at low speeds while going down hills to prevent oil from running from gear case into primary gear housing.**

Fig. 4: Checking Pinion Bearing Preload

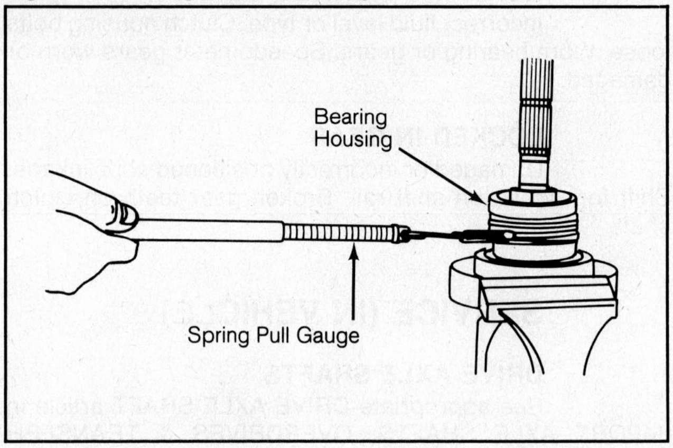

Reassembly

Inspect all parts for wear or damage and replace as necessary. Press in new input shaft oil seal and needle bearing (mark facing outward in housing). Press input shaft bearing into housing. Install bearing retainer. Apply Loctite to Allen head screw threads. Install and tighten screws.

OUTPUT SHAFT BEARING HOUSING

Disassembly

Remove oil catcher from bearing housing. Being careful not to damage lubrication connection pipe, use Support (83 90 098) and press output shaft from bearing housing. Retain front bearing, spacer and shims. Using Support (87 90 636) and Ring (87 90 933), press rear bearing off output shaft. Using drift, remove bearing outer races from bearing housing.

Reassembly

1) Press rear bearing onto output shaft. Press outer races into bearing housing. Install output shaft, shims, spacer and bearing into bearing housing. Shims must be installed between rear bearing and spacer.

2) Lubricate bearings and press together using Support (83 90 098) and Drift (78 41 075). While pressing, use 3 tons (2722 kg) pressure. Rotate bearing housing against upper and lower bearings 40 times in each direction to seat ball bearings.

3) Install dial indicator. *See Fig. 5.* Maintain installation pressure and check axial play of bearing housing. Adjust axial play to 0 by inserting correct shim.

4) After installing correct shim, recheck axial play. If axial play cannot be removed with shims, replace spacer. Bearings should have no resistance to movement or play. Install oil catcher in bearing housing.

NOTE: **Shims are available in .004" (.10 mm), .006" (.15 mm), .010" (.25 mm) and .020" (.50 mm) thicknesses. Spacers are available in .3181" (8.08 mm), .3185" (8.09 mm), .3189" (8.10 mm) and .3192" (8.11 mm) lengths.**

SYNCHRO ASSEMBLIES

Disassembly

Synchro rings are removed by removing snap ring which attaches ring to gear. Fifth gear synchro ring is removed by removing snap ring in front of guide ring. DO NOT remove synchro ring snap ring.

Manual Transmissions

SAAB 5-SPEED TRANSAXLE (Cont.)

Reassembly

1) Install guide ring for retaining ring. On 3rd and 4th gears only, lock guide rings in place on gears with snap rings.

2) Install retaining spring on gear with long wire end nearest guide ring. Position other end on gear so there are 11 teeth between spring ends (5 teeth on 5th gear). Retaining spring for 1st gear is shorter and softer.

NOTE: **Guide rings for 3rd and 4th gears are assembled during production and are peened into position. DO NOT peen replacement guide rings.**

3) Install synchro ring onto gear so ends of spring fit into spaces between teeth. Install snap ring.

Fig. 5: Checking Axial Play of Output Shaft Bearing Housing

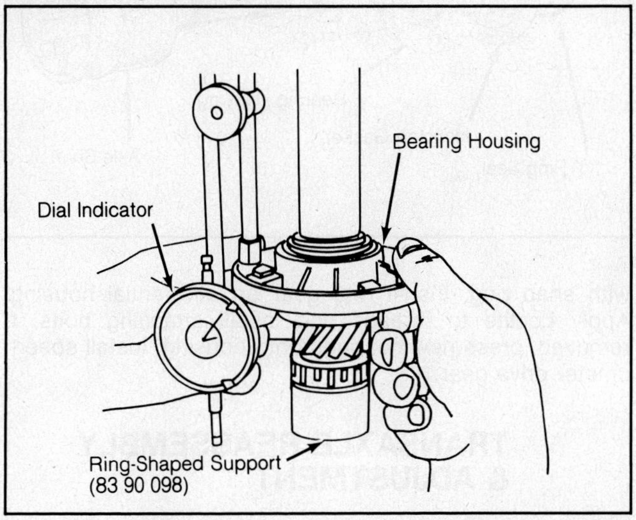

NOTE: **Synchro ring for 2nd gear has molybdenum-coated synchronizing surface for identification.**

Fig. 6: Separating Synchro Ring from 1st-4th Gears

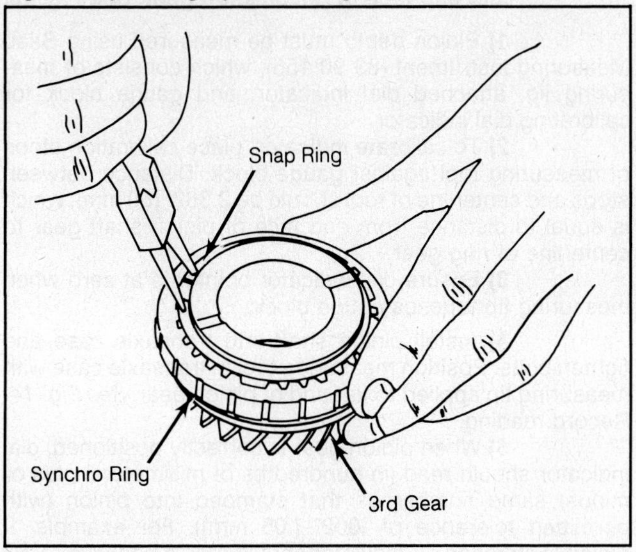

Fig. 7: Exploded View of 1st-2nd Gear Synchro

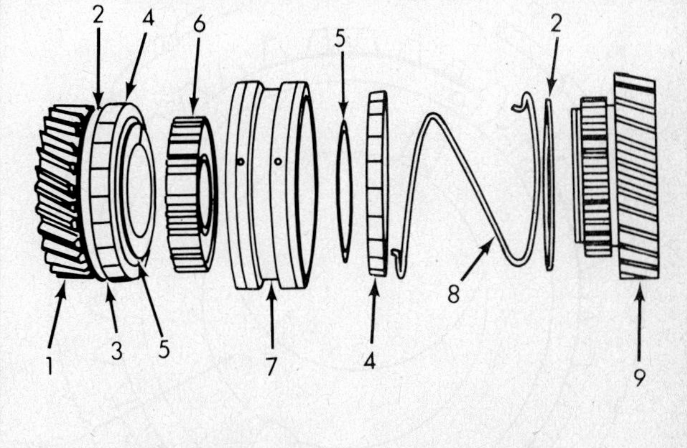

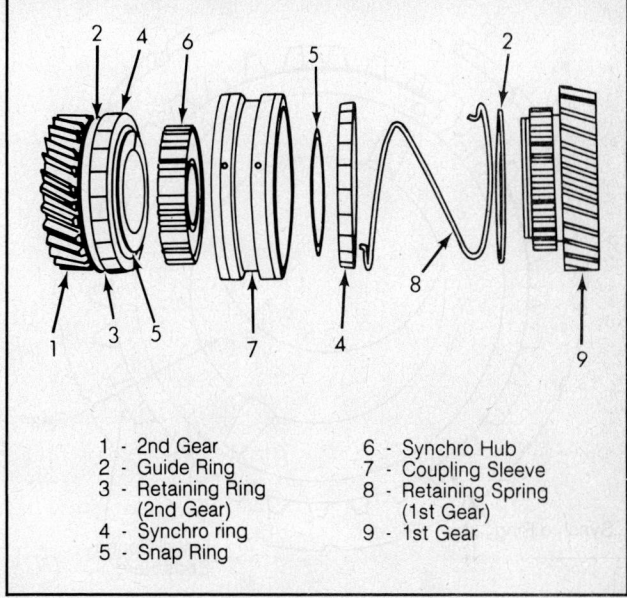

1 - 2nd Gear
2 - Guide Ring
3 - Retaining Ring (2nd Gear)
4 - Synchro ring
5 - Snap Ring
6 - Synchro Hub
7 - Coupling Sleeve
8 - Retaining Spring (1st Gear)
9 - 1st Gear

Fig. 8: Exploded View of 3rd Gear Synchro

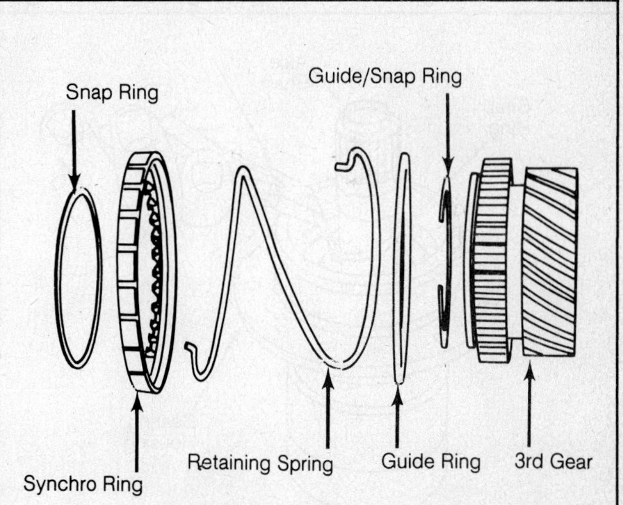

INNER AXLE SHAFT & BEARING HOUSING

Disassembly

1) Remove axle shaft snap ring and press axle shaft out of bearing housing. Using screwdriver, remove oil seal from housing taking care not to damage housing. On left side bearing housing, remove shaft and lift out speedometer drive assembly.

2) On both sides, press axle shaft roller bearings from housing. If new differential bearings are to be installed, remove bearing outer races from bearing housing using drift.

NOTE: **A washer is located between race and housing on right side to improve lubrication.**

Reassembly

Press new axle shaft bearing into housing. Install lubrication washer on right side. Press new differential bearing outer races into bearing housing. Using drift, press

Manual Transmissions

SAAB 5-SPEED TRANSAXLE (Cont.)

Fig. 9: Installing Synchro Retaining Spring

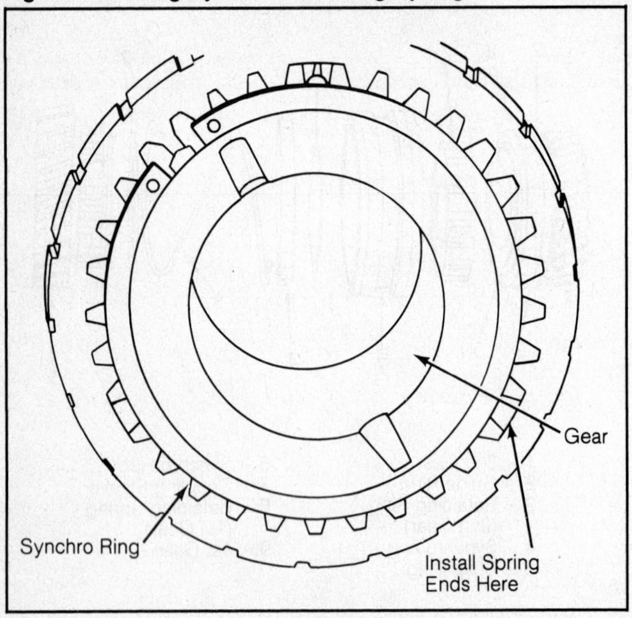

Fig. 10: Removing Axle Shaft Snap Ring From Housing

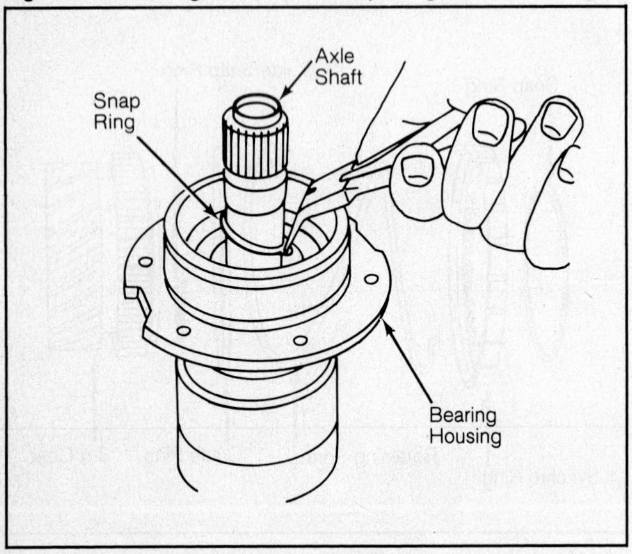

bearing housing oil seal into housing until it protrudes .08" (2 mm) above face of housing.

NOTE: **Axle shafts will be installed during Transaxle Reassembly.**

DIFFERENTIAL ASSEMBLY

Disassembly

1) If differential bearings require replacement, remove speedometer drive gear from left side. Use puller to remove bearings from differential housing.

2) Remove ring gear bolts and separate ring gear from differential. Remove snap ring and press out pinion shaft. Remove pinion gears, side gears, thrust washers and gear springs from housing.

Reassembly

Install pinion gears and side gears, thrust washers and springs into housing. Install pinion shaft and secure

Fig. 11: Exploded View of Left Side Inner Axle Shaft and Differential Bearing Housing

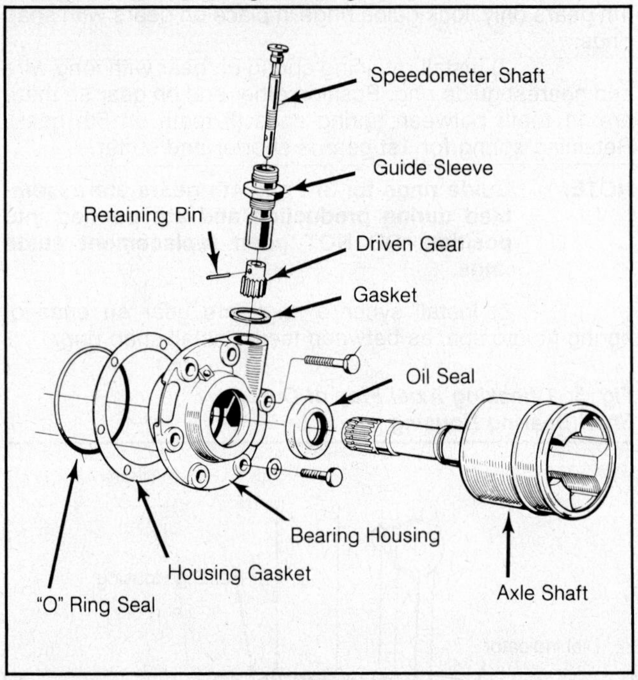

with snap ring. Install ring gear on differential housing. Apply Loctite to threads and install attaching bolts. If removed, press new bearings onto housing. Install speedometer drive gear.

TRANSAXLE REASSEMBLY & ADJUSTMENT

PINION DEPTH ADJUSTMENT

NOTE: **Pinion bearing preload must be correctly adjusted before adjusting pinion depth. See PINION SHAFT REASSEMBLY. Metric Pinion Depth Adjustment specifications are stamped into end face of pinion shaft gear. See Fig. 13.**

1) Pinion depth must be measured using Saab Measuring Instrument (83 90 155), which consists of measuring jig, attached dial indicator, and gauge block for calibrating dial indicator.

2) To calibrate indicator, place calibration stops of measuring tool against gauge block. Distance between stops and centerline of tool should be 2.362" (60 mm), which is equal to distance from end face of pinion shaft gear to centerline of ring gear.

3) Ensure dial indicator pointer is at zero when measuring tip touches gauge block.

4) Install pinion shaft into transaxle case and tighten bolts. Position measuring tool in transaxle case with measuring tip applied to flat end of pinion gear. *See Fig. 14.* Record reading.

5) When pinion gear is correctly positioned, dial indicator should read (in hundredths of millimeters; plus or minus) same number as that stamped into pinion (with permitted tolerance of .002" (.05 mm)). For example, if pinion is stamped -7, indicator should read a negative (-) .07 mm with a tolerance of ±.05 mm.

SAAB 5-SPEED TRANSAXLE (Cont.)

Fig. 12: Exploded View of Differential Assembly

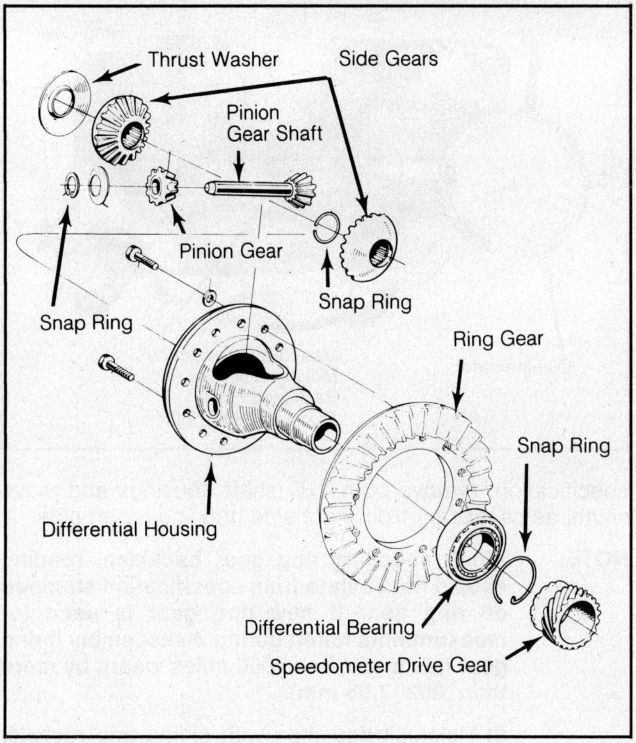

Fig. 13: Pinion Shaft Gear Depth Adjustment Specifications

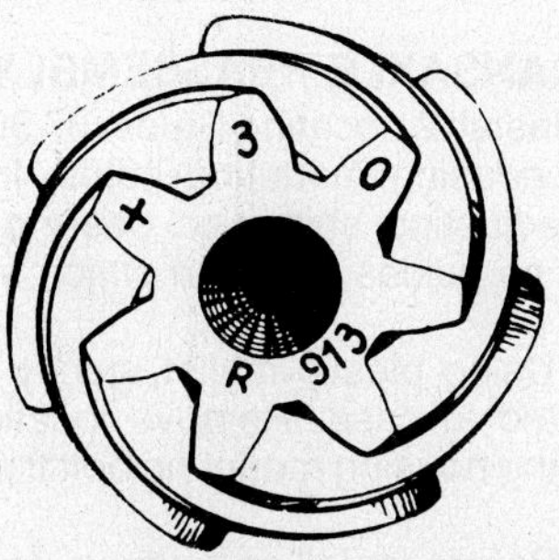

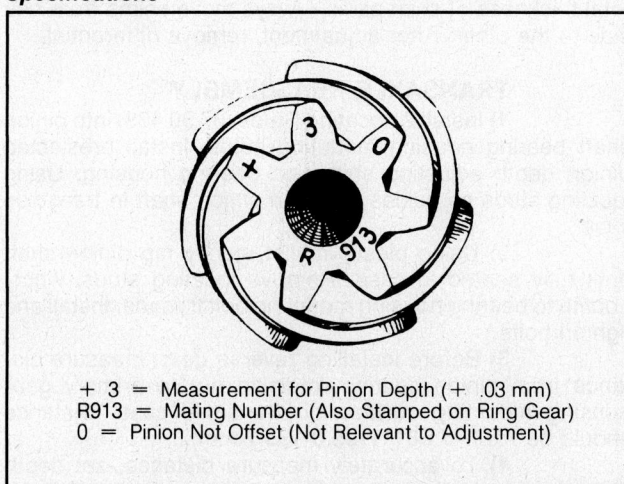

+ 3 = Measurement for Pinion Depth (+ .03 mm)
R913 = Mating Number (Also Stamped on Ring Gear)
0 = Pinion Not Offset (Not Relevant to Adjustment)

NOTE: **On dial indicator, clockwise movement of needle is positive.**

NOTE: **If ring and pinion gear set have been in use for over 6000 miles, reassemble pinion shaft to specifications recorded during disassembly.**

6) If measured pinion depth is not within specification stamped on pinion gear, pinion shaft must be adjusted. Remove pinion shaft from case and add thicker shim if reading is higher than specifications, reduce shim thickness if reading is lower than specification.

NOTE: **Pinion depth adjusting shims are available in following thicknesses: .004" (.10 mm), .006" (.15 mm), .012" (.30 mm), and .020" (.50 mm).**

Fig. 14: Measuring Transaxle Case

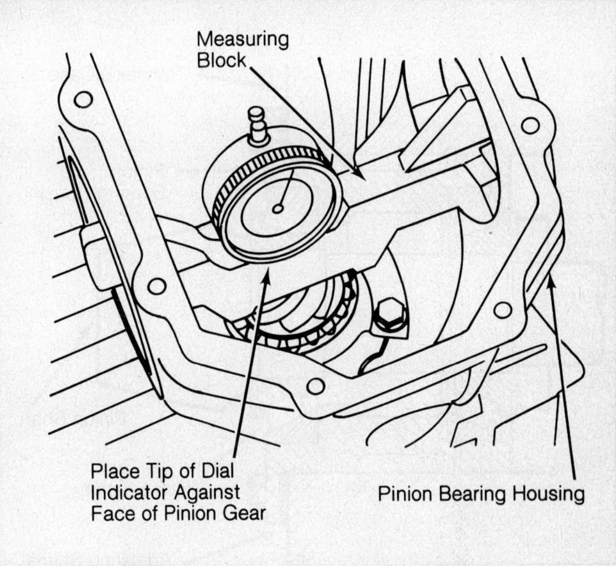

7) Reduce or increase shim thickness according to difference between measured value and specified value. Before reinstalling pinion shaft assembly, adjust differential bearing preload. See DIFFERENTIAL BEARING PRELOAD ADJUSTMENT.

DIFFERENTIAL BEARING PRELOAD ADJUSTMENT

NOTE: **Differential bearing preload must be adjusted prior to installation of pinion shaft.**

1) Position differential assembly in transaxle case. Install left axle (side with speedometer drive gear) shaft bearing housing without shims and tighten bolts to 14-18 ft. lbs. (19-24 N.m). Oil differential bearings. Install right side axle shaft bearing housing and tighten attaching bolts to 19 ft. lbs. (26 N.m) while rotating differential assembly.

NOTE: **If inner axle shaft is installed in right axle shaft housing, remove spring and plunger before mounting axle shaft housing.**

2) Using feeler gauge, measure clearance between right axle housing and transaxle case at 2 points opposite each other. Compute average of 2 measurements, and select adjusting shims which equal the average. Add an additional .008" (.2 mm) in shim thickness to obtain correct bearing preload.

3) Measure bearing preload using an INCH lb. torque wrench. Preload for new, slightly oiled bearings should be 16-24 INCH lbs. (1.8-2.7 N.m). Preload for used bearings (1200 miles or more) should be 7-11 INCH lbs. (.79-1.24 N.m).

NOTE: **Right-to-left distribution of shims will be determined during RING GEAR BACKLASH ADJUSTMENT. Up to 4 shims may be combined to obtain correct preload. Shims are available in the following thicknesses: .004" (.10 mm), .006" (.15 mm), .012" (.30 mm) and .020" (.50 mm).**

Manual Transmissions

SAAB 5-SPEED TRANSAXLE (Cont.)

Fig. 15: Pinion Depth Adjusting Shims Location

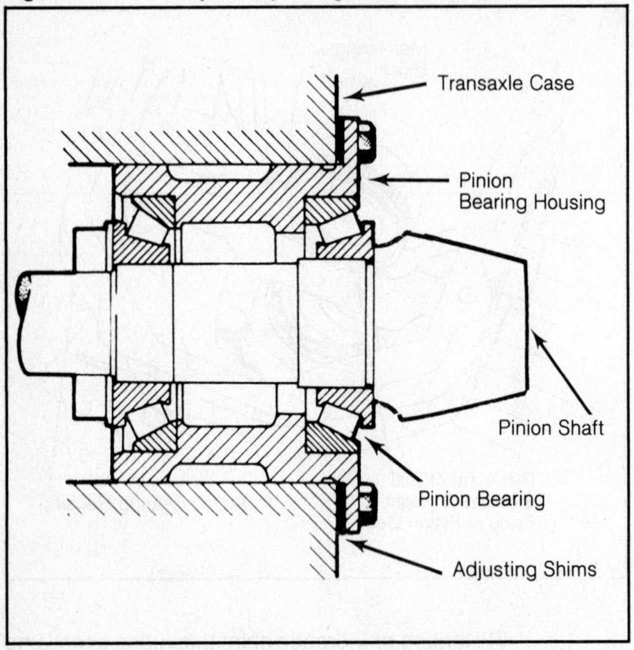

RING GEAR BACKLASH ADJUSTMENT

NOTE: **Ring gear adjustment specifications (in metric) are stamped onto ring gear. See Fig. 16. If ring and pinion gear set have been in use for over 6000 miles, reassemble differential according to specifications recorded during disassembly. Install pinion shaft with shims in housing.**

1) Place differential assembly into transaxle case. Install left side (speedometer drive gear side) axle shaft bearing housing to transaxle case without adjusting shims and tighten attaching bolts to 14-18 ft. lbs. (19-24 N.m). Install right side axle shaft bearing housing along with selected bearing preload adjusting shims. Tighten attaching bolts.

Fig. 16: Ring Gear Backlash Adjustment Specifications

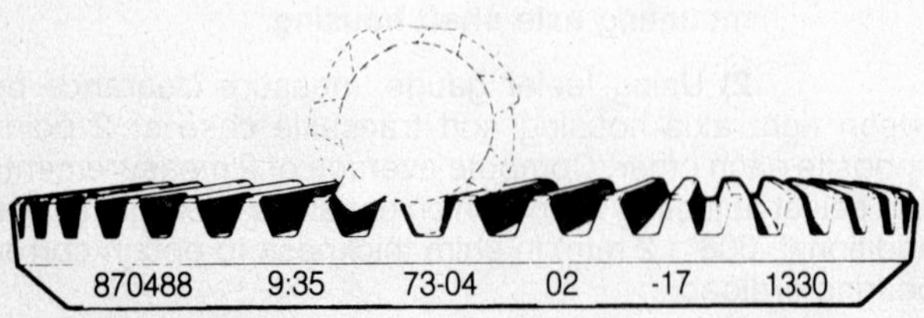

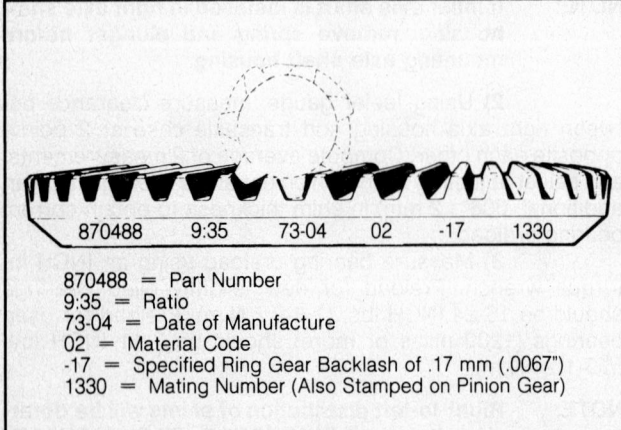

870488 = Part Number
9:35 = Ratio
73-04 = Date of Manufacture
02 = Material Code
-17 = Specified Ring Gear Backlash of .17 mm (.0067")
1330 = Mating Number (Also Stamped on Pinion Gear)

2) Place dial indicator on transaxle case so indicator tip is touching ring gear teeth. Move ring gear back and forth and measure backlash between ring gear and pinion gear in 4 different locations. If backlash is not to

Fig. 17: Measuring Ring Gear Backlash

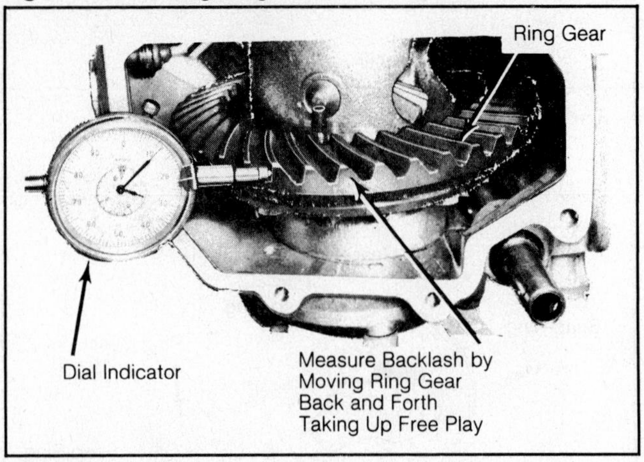

specification, remove both axle shaft housings and move shims as necessary from right side housing to left side.

NOTE: **When checking ring gear backlash, reading should not deviate from specification stamped on ring gear if new ring gear is used (or measurments taken during disassembly if ring gear has more than 6000 miles wear), by more than .002" (.05 mm).**

3) Reinstall housings with shims and recheck backlash. If not to specifications, repeat adjustment procedure until correct backlash is obtained. DO NOT reduce total thickness of shim pack. Always move shims from one side to the other. After adjustment, remove differential.

TRANSAXLE REASSEMBLY

1) Install 2 Locating Studs (87 90 438) into pinion shaft bearing housing mounting holes. Install preselected pinion depth adjusting shims on bearing housing. Using locating studs as guides, position pinion shaft in transaxle case.

2) Using plastic mallet, gently tap pinion shaft until fully seated in case. Remove locating studs. Apply Loctite to bearing housing mounting bolt threads. Install and tighten bolts.

3) Before installing reverse gear, measure distance from pinion bearing retaining nut to primary gear housing mounting surface on transaxle case. Distance should be 7.677-7.681" (195.0-195.1 mm).

4) To accurately measure distance, set depth gauge to proper distance and install onto case. *See Fig. 18.* Measure distance between end of depth gauge and retaining nut using feeler gauge. Install shim of thickness equal to that of feeler gauge.

5) Using micrometer, measure thickness of shim removed during disassembly. If original shim thickness equals required shim thickness, reinstall original shim. If not, install shim of proper thickness. Shims are available in thicknesses of .012" (.3 mm), .016" (.4 mm) and .02" (.05 mm). Install shim between retaining nut and reverse gear.

6) Install reverse gear on pinion shaft. Fit 1st gear on bearing sleeve of reverse gear. Install 1st-2nd synchro hub onto pinion shaft. Insert 1st-2nd gear shift fork into 1st-2nd coupling sleeve and install onto synchro hub.

7) Install 2nd gear sleeve using Installer (83 90 148). Install 2nd gear onto sleeve. Install 3rd gear spacer and sleeve on pinion shaft. Install 3rd gear on sleeve.

SAAB 5-SPEED TRANSAXLE (Cont.)

Fig. 18: Measuring Retaining Nut Depth

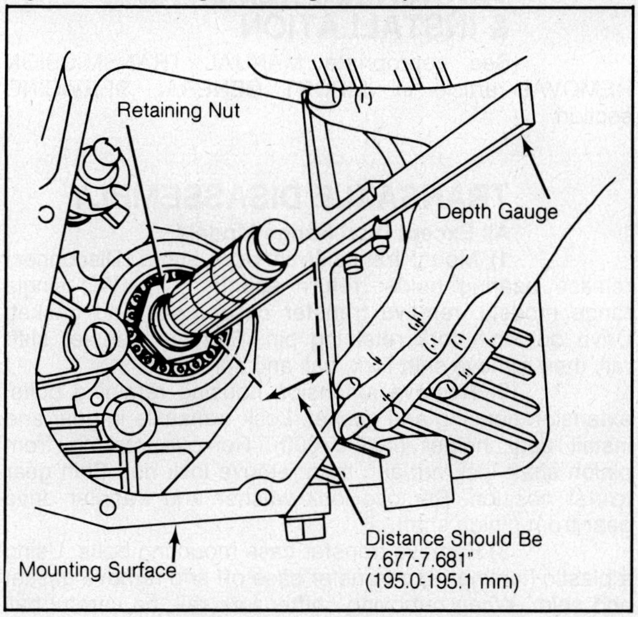

8) Install 3rd-4th synchro hub onto pinion shaft. Install 3rd-4th gear shift fork into 3rd-4th gear coupling sleeve and install on synchro hub. Install 4th gear bushing onto pinion shaft. Install 4th gear onto bushing. Install selector shaft with double lock out guide pin.

9) Place transmission gears in Neutral. Install gear shift rail for 1st-2nd and 3rd-4th gearshift forks. Install reverse operating lever onto reverse selector shaft. Apply Loctite to shaft stop bolt. Install and tighten stop bolt. Install 5th gear selector onto reverse selector shaft.

10) Install countershaft gear needle bearing into countershaft gear. Install countershaft gear into housing. While alinging countershaft, install countershaft gear shaft just enough to hold gears in position. Thrust washer will be installed later.

11) Install 5th gear spacer, 5th gear synchro hub and snap ring onto pinion shaft. Measure distance between coupling sleeve and hub using feeler gauge so there is no play between parts on pinion shaft. Shims are available in .012" (.3 mm) and .016" (.4 mm) thicknesses.

12) Remove snap ring, hub and spacer. Apply sealing compound to gasket surfaces of primary gear housing. Install gasket and housing to transmission housing.

13) Install spacer and 5th gear synchro hub on output shaft. Install shims selected to provide zero play between parts on shaft. Install snap ring, 5th gear operating sleeve and selector fork.

14) Install 3 Output Shaft Guide Pins (87 90 438) into lower primary gear bearing housing mounting bolt holes. Insert output shaft with bearing housing, oil catcher and oil connecting pipe installed on Adapter (87 90 917). Install lower primary gear socket between adapter and bearing housing.

15) Using slide hammer, insert bearing housing and output shaft assembly so bearing housing is seated and output shaft meets operating sleeve. Install output shaft countershaft thrust washer, coated with grease, so tab fits into recess of case.

16) Slide output shaft countergear onto shaft and install sleeve, bearings and snap ring. Install countershaft in case and slide gear toward thrust washer to allow alignment of gear for final installation.

17) Install operating sleeve onto countershaft and insert snap ring into recess. Install countergear thrust washer. Using Installer (83 90 049), insert countergear shaft so it locks in position. Install reverse idler gear and spindle. Using installer, insert reverse idler gear shaft until it locks in position.

18) Install locking plate into primary gear cover. Seal locking plate and threads with Loctite. Install and tighten bolts. Install upper primary gear and chain assembly. Ensure hole for lower primary gear tab washer is facing outward. Install chain tensioner. Coat threads of chain tensioner bolts with Loctite. Install and tighten bolts.

19) Lock pinion shaft by engaging reverse gear and 5th gear. Install pinion shaft nut and tighten. Bend 1 nut tab into hole provided in lower primary gear. Install reverse gear operating lever and tighten bolt.

20) Seal bolt with Loctite. Install differential unit. Install selector ball and gearbox top cover gasket and cover. Install primary gear housing gasket and cover.

FINAL ASSEMBLY

1) Remove axle shaft housing from transaxle. Press axle housings onto axle shaft, then install snap rings to secure shafts in place. Install speedometer drive assembly into left axle shaft housing.

2) Install "O" rings onto both housings. Install spring and plunger in end of axle shaft. Install axle shaft housings onto transaxle case, making sure correct adjusting shims are in place on each housing. Install and tighten bolts.

3) Recheck backlash adjustment and readjust if necessary. Install rear cover on transaxle case and tighten attaching bolts. Fill transaxle to correct fluid level.

TIGHTENING SPECIFICATIONS

Application	Ft. Lbs. (N.m)
Hub-To-Rotor Bolts	22-36 (30-49)
Front Hub Nut	251-266 (340-361)
Input Shaft Nut	67-81 (91-110)
Pinion Shaft Retaining Nut	30-45 (41-61)
All 8 mm Bolts	14-18 (19-24)
Speedometer Drive Shaft	21-36 (28-49)
Ring Gear Attaching Bolts	30-45 (41-61)
Axle Shaft Housing Bolts	14-18 (19-24)

SUBARU 4 & 5-SPEED TRANSAXLE

Brat, Hatchback, Sedan, Station Wagon, XT Coupe

DESCRIPTION

Transmission has 4 or 5 speeds with synchromesh in all forward gears. Both transmission and differential are mounted in the same 2-piece aluminum housing. A hypoid-type gear is used for the final drive. Gear shift linkage is incorporated in transmission cover.

Transmission and differential are lubricated from a common oil supply. Front axle drive shafts employ constant velocity joints at transaxle drive flange and axle shaft.

Four-wheel drive models have rear drive shaft which rotates with drive pinion at gear ratio of 1 to 1. Rear drive shaft is equipped with a claw clutch for 4-wheel drive shifting. Claw clutch has conventional type synchromesh system to ensure no damage to gears when shifting to 4-wheel drive while vehicle is in motion.

LUBRICATION & ADJUSTMENT

See appropriate MANUAL TRANSMISSION SERVICING article in IMPORT GENERAL SERVICING section.

TROUBLE SHOOTING

TRANSMISSION NOISE

Lubricant insufficient. Worn or chipped gears or bearings. If gear tooth surface is excessively worn, a growling sound should be apparent at high speed. When teeth are chipped, periodic knocking is audible at both high and low speeds.

DIFFERENTIAL NOISE

Lubricant insufficient. Tapered roller bearings out of adjustment. Ring and/or pinion gear out of adjustment, ring gear loose. Worn differential side gears, washers or pinion.

NOTE: Noise from exhaust system, tires, wheel bearings etc. is easily mistaken for differential noise. Eliminate these noises prior to disassembling differential.

HARD SHIFTING

Clutch not properly adjusted or hanging up when released. Worn, damaged or burred sleeve on gear spline or chamfered parts. Scratched bushings. Defective contact or worn synchro ring and gear cone.

SLIPS OUT OF GEAR

Loose engine mounts. Worn shifter fork or broken shifter fork rail spring. Damaged ball bearing. Excessive clearance between synchro hub and sleeve splines. Worn gears or bushings.

SERVICE (IN VEHICLE)

DRIVE AXLE SHAFTS

See appropriate DRIVE AXLE SHAFT article in IMPORT AXLE SHAFTS, OVERDRIVES & TRANSFER CASES section.

TRANSAXLE REMOVAL & INSTALLATION

See appropriate MANUAL TRANSMISSION REMOVAL article in IMPORT GENERAL SERVICING section.

TRANSAXLE DISASSEMBLY

All Except Dual Range Models

1) Mount transaxle in work stand. Disconnect release bearing holder return springs. On 4WD single range models, remove transfer case cover and gasket. Drive out shift fork retaining pin. Remove transfer shift rail, then remove shift fork, ball and spring.

2) Remove extension housing retaining bolts, extension housing and gasket. Lock transaxle in gear and install gear holder (498787000). Remove staking from pinion shaft lock nut and then remove lock nut. Shift gear to 1st position. Remove lock washer and transfer drive gear from pinion shaft.

3) Remove transfer case mounting bolts. Using a plastic hammer, tap transfer case off and remove gasket and shim. When removing shifter fork rail, be careful ball does not pop out of transmission case.

4) On all models, remove clutch release fork and release bearing holder. Remove transmission rear case, main case rear gasket, main shaft rear plate and back-up light clip. Remove drive pinion attaching bolts.

5) Clean spline portion of the axle drive shafts on right and left sides and wrap with vinyl tape. Separate transmission main case into right and left halves. Remove clutch cable bracket, back-up light cord clip, radio ground and oxygen sensor harness clip.

6) Remove drive pinion as shown in *Fig. 1.* Remove transmission main shaft. Remove differential. On 5-speed models, remove spring pin and 5th shifter fork. Do not mix right and left roller bearing outer races.

7) On all models, remove plugs, gaskets, springs and balls from case. Unscrew shifter fork set screws, and remove 3rd-4th and 1st-2nd shifter forks as well as shifter rails. Remove shifter set screw, reverse shifter rail arm and reverse shifter rail.

8) Remove oil seal holder lock plates, axle shaft oil seal holders and "O" rings. Remove snap ring and speedometer driven gear. Remove knock pins, reverse idler gear shaft, reverse idler gear and shifter lever.

Fig. 1: Prying Pinion Shaft Out of Case

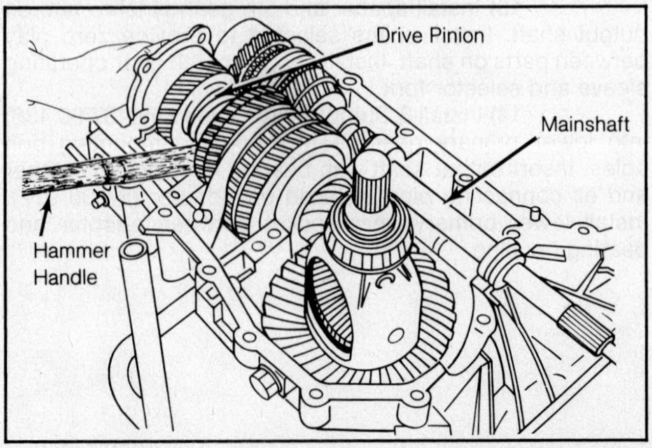

SUBARU 4 & 5-SPEED TRANSAXLE (Cont.)

9) On 5-speed, use a punch to drive out 5th gear shift fork lock pin and remove fork. On all models, remove 3 shift rail plugs, springs and balls. Unscrew shift fork set screws and remove shift forks and fork rails.

NOTE: When pulling out a rail, keep other rails in neutral position. To remove 3rd-4th rail, rotate it 90°. Take care not to drop shifter rail plungers.

10) On 4-speed, remove reverse shift fork set screw and remove reverse shift rail arm and reverse shift rail. Remove transaxle case bolts and remove output shaft oil seal holder lock plates. Using remover (399780111), remove drive axle shaft oil seal holder and "O" ring.

11) Remove speedometer driven gear snap ring and gear. Lightly tap speedometer shaft out of case. Oil seal should come out with shaft. Remove reverse idler gear shaft retaining pins. Remove reverse idler gear shaft, idler gear and shift lever.

12) On 5-speed, remove reverse idler gear shaft retaining pins. Remove reverse idler gear shaft, idler gear and shift lever. Remove reverse shift rail outer snap ring, then remove shift rail arm and shift rail. Remove reverse shift ball, spring and plunger.

13) Remove output shaft oil seal holder. Using remover (399780111), remove drive axle shaft oil seal holder and "O" ring. Remove speedometer driven gear snap ring and gear. Lightly tap speedometer shaft out of case. Oil seal should come out with shaft.

NOTE: When removing reverse shift rail arm, ensure ball does not pop out of case.

Fig. 2: Removing Mainshaft and Differential Assembly from Transaxle Case

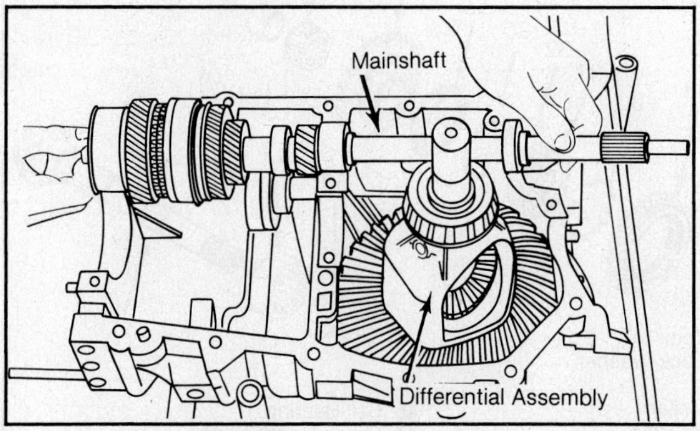

Dual Range 4WD Models

1) Set transmission in stand. Remove clutch release fork and release bearing holder complete. Remove transfer case cover. Punch out the spring pin connecting high-low shifter rod to rod arm. Remove clip on transfer shifter rail with screwdriver after shifting transfer shifter rail into "4WD LO" position.

2) Pull out transfer shifter rail after shifting into "4WD HI" position. When pulling out, fix both high-low shifter arm and transfer shifter fork into "4WD HI" position in order not to interlock plunger. Be careful that ball does not fly out and drop into transfer case. Remove pin and clip on interlock rail with pliers.

3) Pull out interlock rail by turning 90°. Be careful that pin and clip on interlock rail do not fly out. Remove transfer shifter fork from transfer case, turning it in order not to interfere with high-low shifter rail. Be carefull not to loose ball and spring. Remove extension assembly.

4) Loosen front nut of rod adjusting screw connecting high-low shifter rod with ball joint assembly, and loosen rear nut (nut is left-hand threaded). Disconnect high-low shifter rod from rod arm by turning rod adjust arm screw clockwise. Disconnect rod ball joint assembly from high-low shifter center pivot by removing nut.

5) Punch out spring pin connecting high-low shifter rail to rod arm and remove rod arm. Punch out spring pin connecting high-low shifter rail to high-low shifter arm and remove high-low shifter rail and arm. Be careful not to lose ball and plunger. Lock transmission main shaft with stopper (498787000). Release staking and remove lock nut.

6) Shift gear to 1st position to prevent shaft from turning. Remove transfer case attaching bolts. Pull out transfer case by about .040" (10 mm). Separate transfer case from main case by tapping with plastic hammer. Remove ball bearing attaching bolts at the drive pinion gear.

7) Remove input shaft holder attaching bolts. Wrap spline portions of axle shafts with vinyl tape. Separate transmission main case into left and right halves. Remove clutch cable bracket, oxygen sensor harness clip, radio ground, back-up light clips, clutch cable clamp, and stopper plate.

8) Punch out spring pin and remove high-low shift lever center pivot. Turn 90° and remove high-low shift fork. Pull countergear shaft forward until it hits on transmission main case and remove clip with screwdriver. Slide countergear washer to the rear and remove knock pin from countergear shaft.

9) Remove countergear shaft from main case being careful not to drop countergear and washers. Remove countergear from main case. Remove drive pinion as shown in *Fig. 1.* Remove transmission main shaft. Remove differential. *See Fig. 2.* Do not mix right and left roller bearing outer races.

10) Remove plugs, gaskets, springs and balls from case. Unscrew shifter fork set screws, and remove 3rd-4th and 1st-2nd shifter forks as well as shifter rails. Remove shifter set screw, reverse shifter rail arm and reverse shifter rail.

11) Remove oil seal holder lock plates, axle shaft oil seal holders and "O" rings. Remove snap ring and speedometer driven gear. Remove knock pins, reverse idler gear shaft, reverse idler gear and shifter lever.

12) Remove 3 shift rail plugs, springs and balls. Unscrew shift fork set screws and remove shift forks and fork rails. When pulling out a rail, keep other rails in neutral position. To remove 3rd-4th rail, rotate it 90°. Take care not to drop shifter rail plungers.

13) Remove reverse shift fork set screw and remove reverse shift rail arm and reverse shift rail. Remove transaxle case bolts and remove output shaft oil seal holder lock plates. Using remover (399780111), remove drive axle shaft oil seal holder and "O" ring.

14) Remove speedometer driven gear snap ring and gear. Lightly tap speedometer shaft out of case. Oil seal should come out with shaft. Remove reverse idler gear shaft retaining pins. Remove reverse idler gear shaft, idler gear and shift lever.

NOTE: When removing reverse shift rail arm, ensure ball does not pop out of case.

SUBARU 4 & 5-SPEED TRANSAXLE (Cont.)

Fig. 3: Exploded View of Transaxle Assembly Components

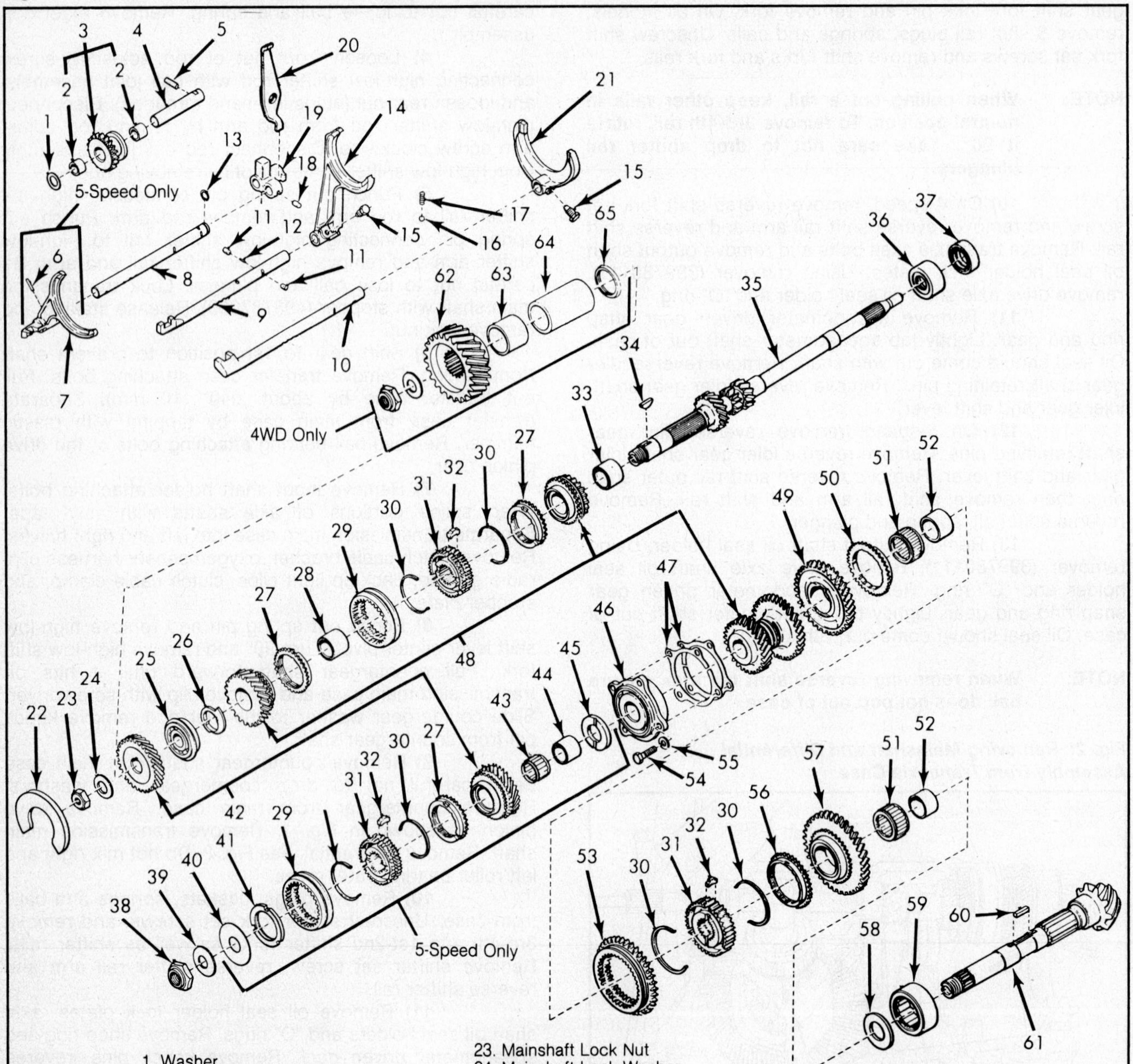

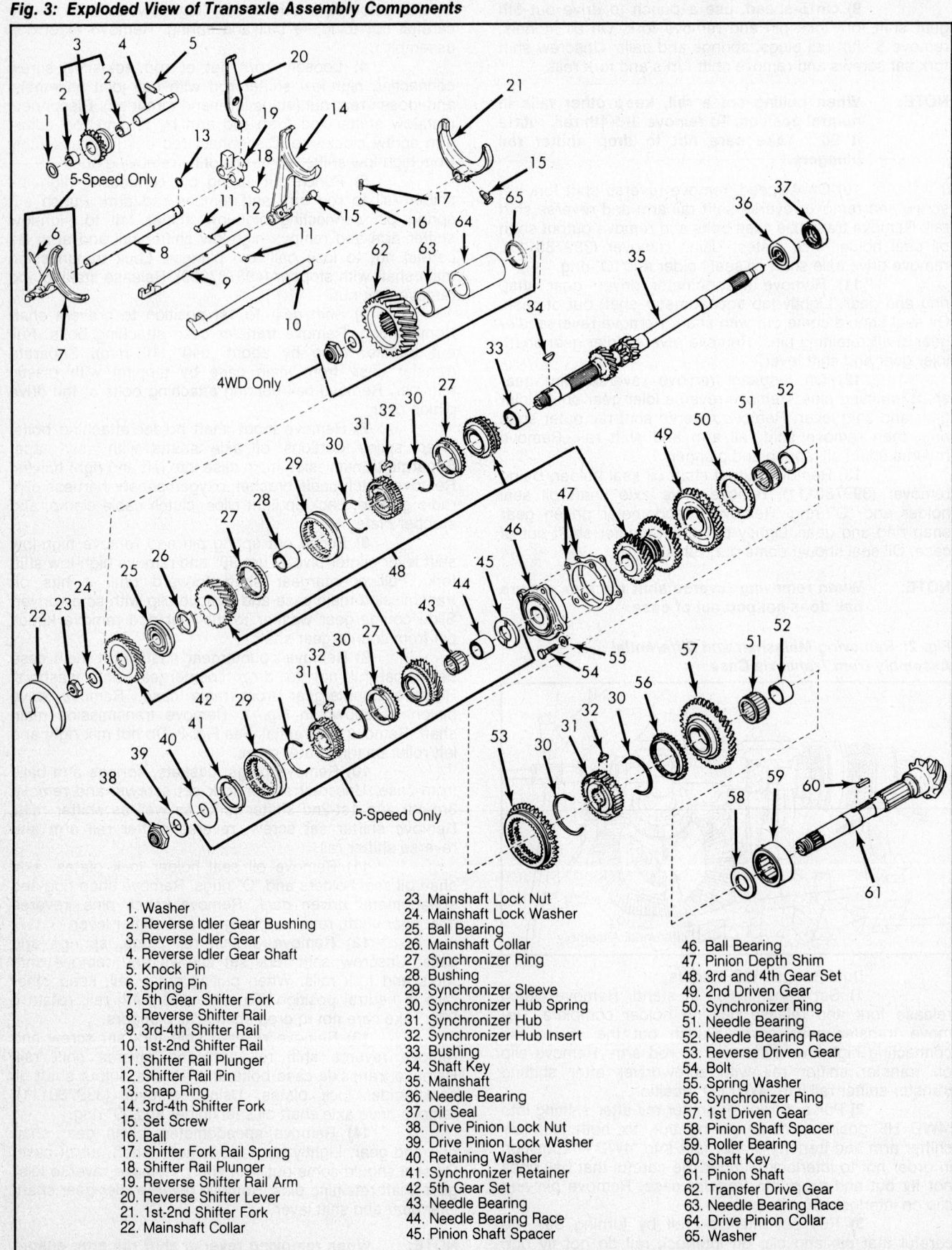

1. Washer
2. Reverse Idler Gear Bushing
3. Reverse Idler Gear
4. Reverse Idler Gear Shaft
5. Knock Pin
6. Spring Pin
7. 5th Gear Shifter Fork
8. Reverse Shifter Rail
9. 3rd-4th Shifter Rail
10. 1st-2nd Shifter Rail
11. Shifter Rail Plunger
12. Shifter Rail Pin
13. Snap Ring
14. 3rd-4th Shifter Fork
15. Set Screw
16. Ball
17. Shifter Fork Rail Spring
18. Shifter Rail Plunger
19. Reverse Shifter Rail Arm
20. Reverse Shifter Lever
21. 1st-2nd Shifter Fork
22. Mainshaft Collar
23. Mainshaft Lock Nut
24. Mainshaft Lock Washer
25. Ball Bearing
26. Mainshaft Collar
27. Synchronizer Ring
28. Bushing
29. Synchronizer Sleeve
30. Synchronizer Hub Spring
31. Synchronizer Hub
32. Synchronizer Hub Insert
33. Bushing
34. Shaft Key
35. Mainshaft
36. Needle Bearing
37. Oil Seal
38. Drive Pinion Lock Nut
39. Drive Pinion Lock Washer
40. Retaining Washer
41. Synchronizer Retainer
42. 5th Gear Set
43. Needle Bearing
44. Needle Bearing Race
45. Pinion Shaft Spacer
46. Ball Bearing
47. Pinion Depth Shim
48. 3rd and 4th Gear Set
49. 2nd Driven Gear
50. Synchronizer Ring
51. Needle Bearing
52. Needle Bearing Race
53. Reverse Driven Gear
54. Bolt
55. Spring Washer
56. Synchronizer Ring
57. 1st Driven Gear
58. Pinion Shaft Spacer
59. Roller Bearing
60. Shaft Key
61. Pinion Shaft
62. Transfer Drive Gear
63. Needle Bearing Race
64. Drive Pinion Collar
65. Washer

SUBARU 4 & 5-SPEED TRANSAXLE (Cont.)

COMPONENT DISASSEMBLY & REASSEMBLY

MAINSHAFT

Disassembly

1) On 4WD dual range models, separate mainshaft assembly from input shaft, and remove high-low synchronizer ring. Be careful not to drop needle bearing in input shaft. Remove snap ring with expander (899474100).

2) Remove the following parts by hand: High-low synchronizer hub with inserts, springs and sleeve, high-low synchronizer ring, input low gear, input low gear collar, needle bearing, input low gear spacer, ball and needle bearing.

3) On 5-speed models, remove lock nut staking, then remove lock nut. Using a press, remove 5th gear from shaft. Remove shaft key. On 4-speed models, remove snap ring from end of mainshaft.

NOTE: Snap ring should not be reused.

4) On all models, use press to remove ball bearing, 4th drive gear thrust plate, 4th drive gear, synchronizer hub, 4th drive gear bushing and 3rd drive gear.

NOTE: Do not remove 3rd drive gear bushing unless it is defective. If replacement is necessary, cut a groove in bushing, then press from mainshaft.

Fig. 4: Pressing Gears Off of Mainshaft

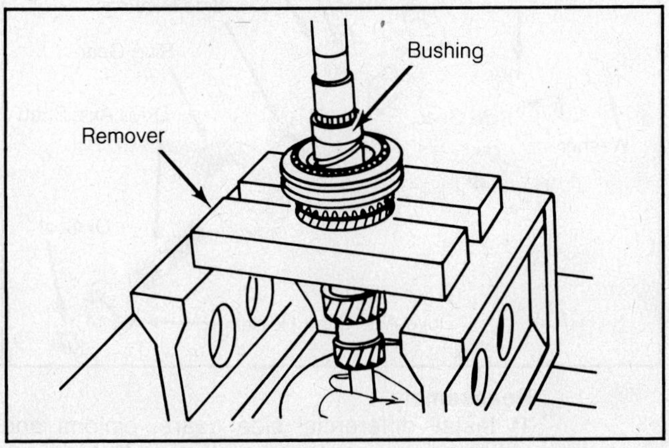

Cleaning & Inspection

Clean all parts and inspect carefully. Replace any parts which are worn or damaged. Lubricate all bearings with gear oil and spin to check for smooth and quiet operation. Replace synchro ring if ring gap is reduced to below limit .020" (.50 mm) when ring is pressed against cone. Standard clearance is .06" (1.5 mm).

Reassembly

1) If removed, install new 3rd gear bushing using press and installer (899580100) and retainer (899714110). Assemble synchro assemblies ensuring that hub spring ends are 120° apart. Note also that the shorter inserts are installed in 3rd-4th synchro and longer inserts in the 1st-2nd synchro.

2) Install 3rd drive gear and synchro assembly on mainshaft ensuring that narrower tooth width of synchro spline is on 3rd gear side. Press synchro assembly on mainshaft, if necessary.

Fig. 5: Exploded View of Synchro Hub Assembly

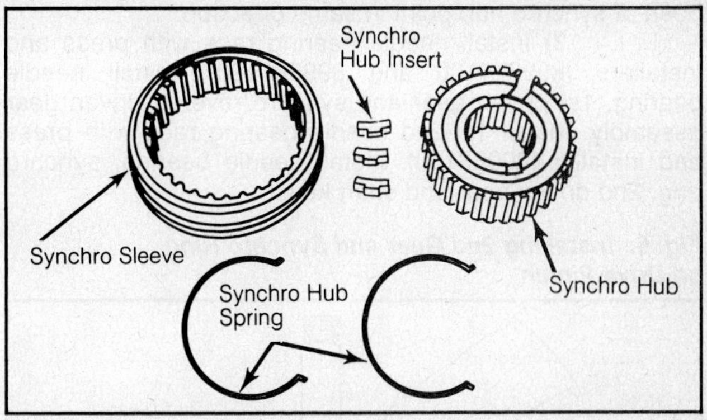

3) Press 4th drive gear bushing onto mainshaft. Install 4th drive gear and thrust plate. Press bearing onto shaft. On 4-speed models, install 1 of 12 available snap rings on shaft to obtain 0-.002" (0-.05 mm) end play. On 5-speed models, install shaft key and press 5th drive gear onto shaft. Install lock nut, tighten and restake.

4) On 4WD single range models, install washer, drive pinion collar, transfer needle bearing race and transfer drive gear to drive pinion with press and installer (899580100). Tighten lock washer and nut. Do not stake at this time.

5) On 4WD dual range models, install 3 high-low synchronizer inserts, sleeve and 2 springs on synchronizer hub. Install springs so that relative positions of cut ends are 120° apart.

6) Install needle bearing, ball, input low gear spacer, needle bearing, input low gear collar, input low gear, high-low synchronizer ring and hub assembly previously assembled.

PINION SHAFT

Disassembly

1) Remove pinion shaft lock nut if still installed. On 5-speed models, remove lock washer, insert stopper plate, insert guide, synchro hub, 5th driven gear and needle bearing. Press 5th needle bearing race, 5th driven gear thrust plate and bearing from shaft.

2) On all models, use a press to remove 3rd-4th driven gear, rear bearing and any components between bearing and end of shaft. Remove 2nd driven gear and needle bearing.

3) Using a press, remove 1st driven gear, synchro/reverse driven gear assembly and needle bearing race. Remove shaft key and needle bearing. Use a press to remove pinion spacer and needle bearing race. Remove roller bearing.

Cleaning & Inspection

Clean all parts and inspect carefully. Replace any parts which are worn or damaged. Lubricate all bearings with engine oil and spin to check for smooth and quiet operation. Replace synchro ring if ring gap is reduced to below limit of .020" (.50 mm) when ring is pressed against cone. Standard clearance is .06" (1.5 mm).

Reassembly

1) Install roller bearing on drive pinion and install drive pinion thrust plate with a press and drive pinion installers (899278600, 899874100 and 899580100).

2) Install three 1st-2nd synchro inserts, reverse driven gear and 2 synchro springs on 1st-2nd synchro hub. Ensure synchro spring cut ends are 120° apart. Also

SUBARU 4 & 5-SPEED TRANSAXLE (Cont.)

check that toothed side of reverse driven gear and lower boss of synchro hub point in same direction.

3) Install needle bearing race with press and installers (899874100 and 899580100). Install needle bearing, 1st driven gear and synchro/reverse driven gear assembly. Install 1st-2nd needle bearing race with press and installer (89958100). Install needle bearing, synchro ring, 2nd driven gear and shaft key.

Fig. 6: Installing 2nd Gear and Synchro Ring on Drive Pinion

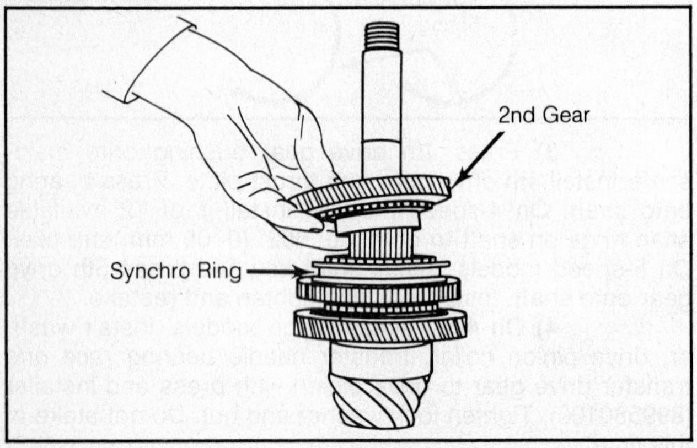

4) Install 3rd-4th driven gear using a press and installer (899580100). Install rear bearing using press and installer tool (899874100).

NOTE: If bearing slides onto shaft without being pressed on, no problem is indicated.

Fig. 7: Installing 3rd-4th Driven Gear on Drive Pinion

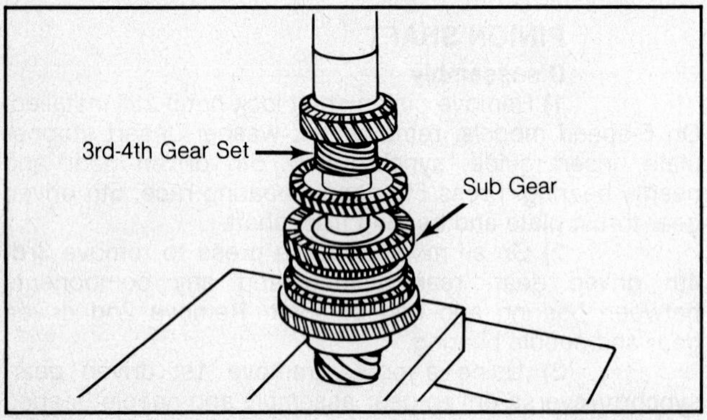

5) On 4-speed, install lock washer and tighten lock nut. On 5-speed, install thrust plate, then press needle bearing race onto shaft. Install needle bearing, 5th driven gear, synchro hub, insert guide, insert stopper plate, lock washer and lock nut. On 4WD, install washer, pinion shaft collar, rear shaft drive gear, lock washer and lock nut.

NOTE: On all models except 4WD, stake pinion shaft lock nut at this time.

DIFFERENTIAL ASSEMBLY

Disassembly

1) Remove snap rings securing drive axle shafts to differential assembly and remove shafts. Right and left shafts are not interchangeable; mark for reassembly reference. Bend back ring gear bolt locking tabs. Remove ring gear bolts and lift off ring gear.

2) Using a drift, remove pinion shaft retaining pin and pull out pinion shaft. Remove side gears, pinion gears and thrust washers. Remove side bearings with a puller.

Cleaning & Inspection

Wash and carefully inspect all parts. Replace all worn or damaged parts.

Fig. 8: Removing or Installing Pinion Shaft in Differential Case

Fig. 9: Exploded View of Differential Assembly

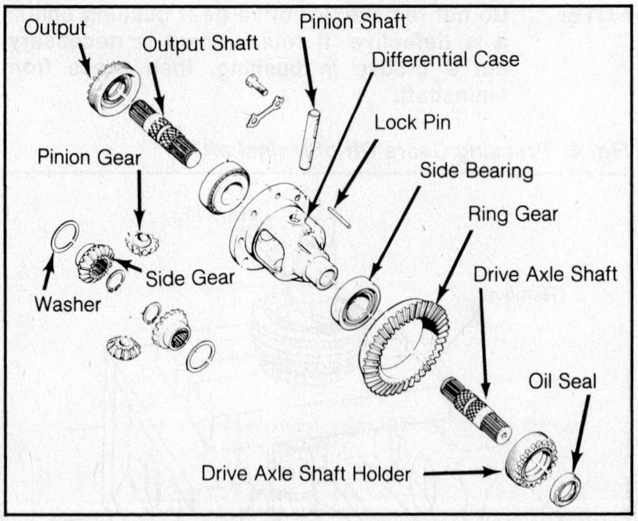

Reassembly

1) Install differential side gears, pinions and washers in differential case. Insert pinion shaft. Measure side gear and pinion backlash. Backlash should be .005-.007" (.13-.18 mm). If backlash is not correct, make adjustments by selecting a different thickness of washer.

2) Align pinion shaft with holes in case and drive lock pin from ring gear side until pin falls about .039" (1 mm) below surface. Lock pin in position by peening hole. Press side bearings onto case. Install ring gear. Install and tighten ring gear bolts, then bend locking tabs to hold bolts.

3) Install drive axle shafts and secure with snap rings. Measure clearance between pinion shaft and tip of drive axle shaft. Adjust clearance to less than .008" (.2 mm) by using thicker snap ring.

NOTE: Snap rings are available in 2 thicknesses: .039-.043" (1.0-1.1 mm) and .045-.049" (1.15-1.25 mm).

SUBARU 4 & 5-SPEED TRANSAXLE (Cont.)

Fig. 10: Pressing Differential Bearings onto Case

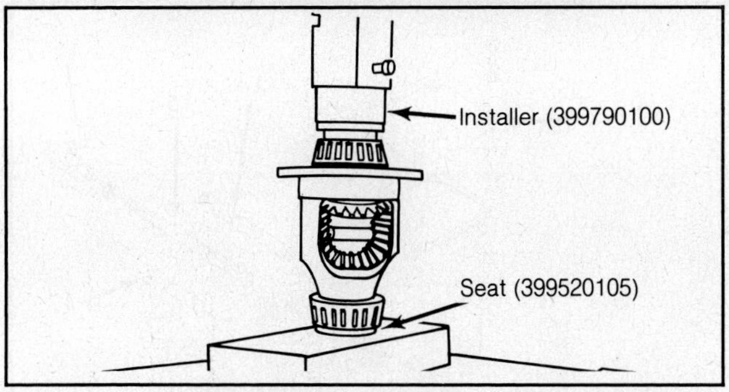

TRANSFER CASE (4WD MODELS ONLY)

Disassembly

Remove "O" ring from shifter arm and remove arm. Remove filler plug and gasket from transfer case. Remove reverse accent spring and ball. Remove back-up light switch and gasket. Remove plug, gasket, reverse accent shaft and spring. Using a hammer and aluminum rod, drive needle bearing out of case.

Cleaning & Inspection

Wash and carefully inspect all parts. Replace all worn or damaged parts.

Reassembly

1) Place needle bearing in bore of case with marked side toward front of case and press in until marked side is flush with case. Install snap ring to transfer case with fingers. Insert reverse return spring and reverse accent shaft, fit an aluminum adjusting gasket on plug and tighten plug.

2) Place an aluminum gasket on back-up light switch and install switch. Install ball and shifter fork rail spring in case, place aluminum washer on filler plug and tighten plug. Slide shifter arm into case and install "O" ring on arm.

EXTENSION HOUSING (4WD MODELS ONLY)

Disassembly

1) Remove snap ring from extension housing, then drive rear drive shaft from housing using a hammer and aluminum rod. Remove oil seal from rear of housing. Shift synchro into drive position. Install holder (899884100) on shaft and mount assembly in a vise.

2) Unstake lock nut and remove lock nut and lock washer. Mount shaft assembly on retainer (899714110) and press out shaft. Remove bearing, spacer collar, rear driven gear, bushing, synchro hub and spacer.

Cleaning & Inspection

Wash and carefully inspect all parts. Replace all worn or damaged parts. Pay particular attention to extension housing rear bushing. If it is excessively worn or scratched, replace it.

Reassembly

1) Assemble synchronizer sleeve on the synchronizer hub. Be sure to use sleeve without reverse taper. Press rear bearing onto shaft. Install new oil seal in rear of extension housing. Using a plastic hammer, tap rear drive shaft into extension housing. Install snap ring in groove in extension housing. Install rear drive spacer, synchro hub and sleeve assembly to rear drive shaft.

2) Using a press, install driven gear bushing to rear drive shaft. Fit transfer driven gear and 4th drive gear thrust plate to rear drive shaft. Press fit front bearing on shaft. Shift synchro sleeve into drive position, install holder on driven gear, install lock washer and tighten lock nut. Stake nut.

Fig. 11: Removing Snap Ring from Extension Housing

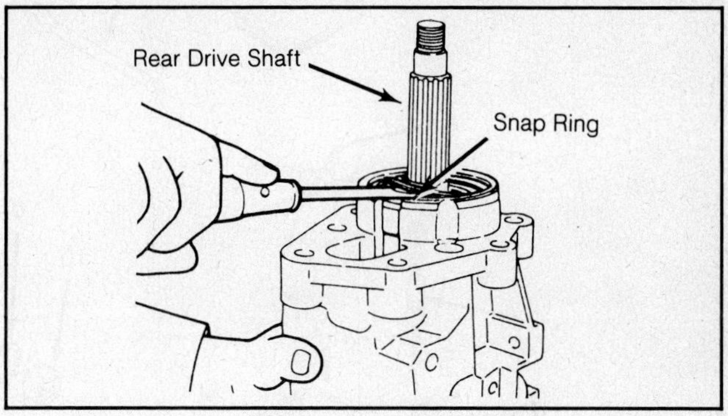

TRANSAXLE REASSEMBLY & ADJUSTMENT

PINION SHAFT DEPTH ADJUSTMENT

NOTE: **This adjustment must be performed using Subaru Pinion Gauge (899914100).**

1) Install pinion shaft assembly in transaxle case half (right half) with no shims between rear bearing and case. Install and tighten 2 pinion shaft retaining bolts to 22 ft. lbs. (30 N.m).

2) Place pinion gauge on its edge on a level surface, then loosen 2 setting bolts on gauge plate. Adjust gauge plate so scale indicates 0.5 when edges of plate and scale are even. Tighten bolts. Place calibrated gauge into case as shown in *Fig. 12*.

NOTE: **Ensure dowel pins of gauge are installed in dowel holes of transaxle case.**

3) Slide gauge scale along plate until it comes in contact with drive pinion, then read and record value shown on scale. The thickness of shim(s) required to obtain correct drive pinion depth is determined by adding or subtracting value stamped on end of pinion to or from gauge scale value.

Fig. 12: Measuring Pinion Shaft Depth Using Special Gauge

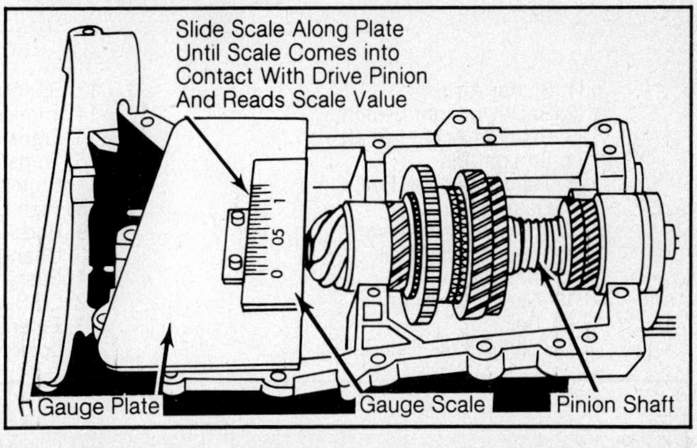

Manual Transmissions

SUBARU 4 & 5-SPEED TRANSAXLE (Cont.)

Fig. 13: Exploded View of 4WD Transfer Case, Extension Housing and Related Components

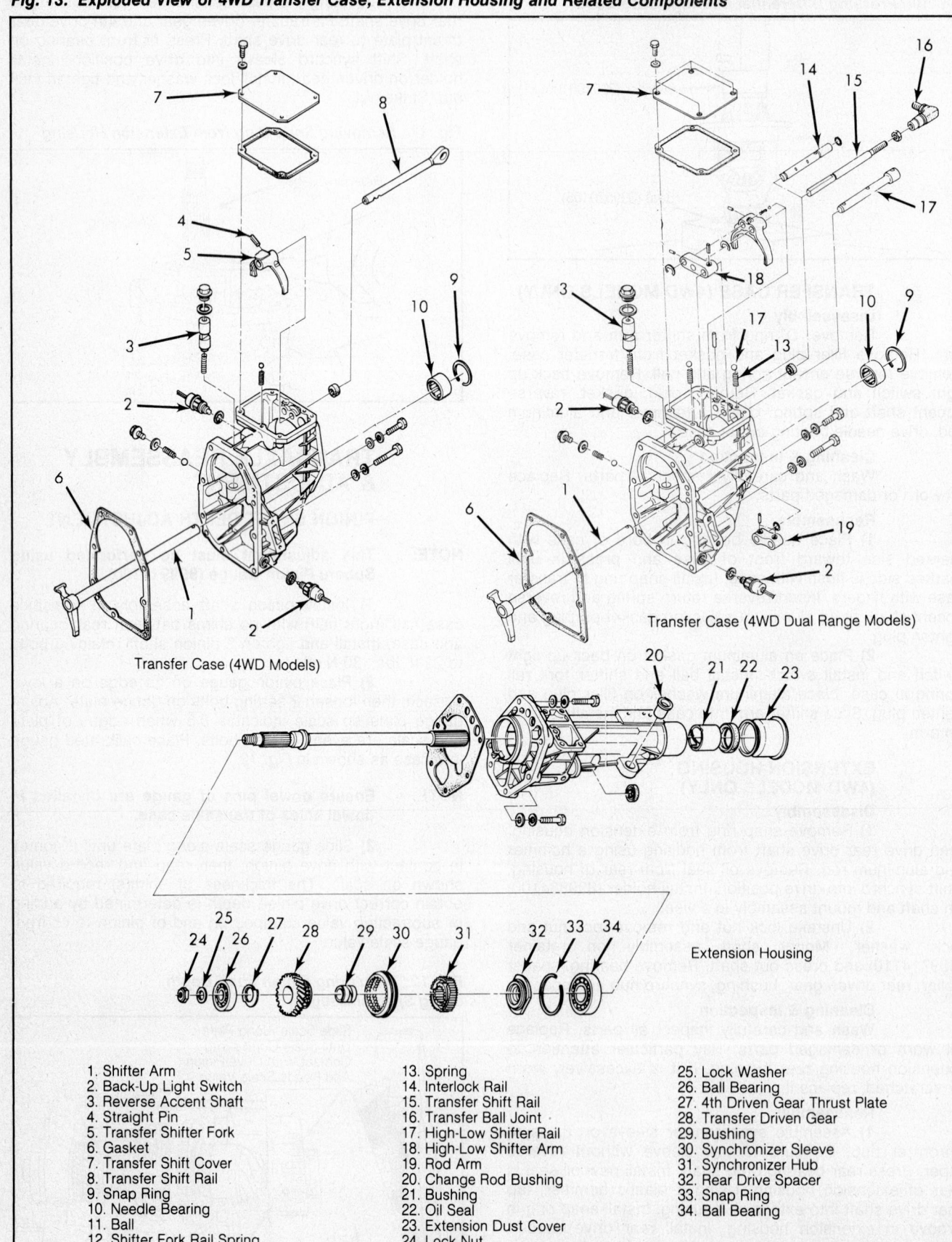

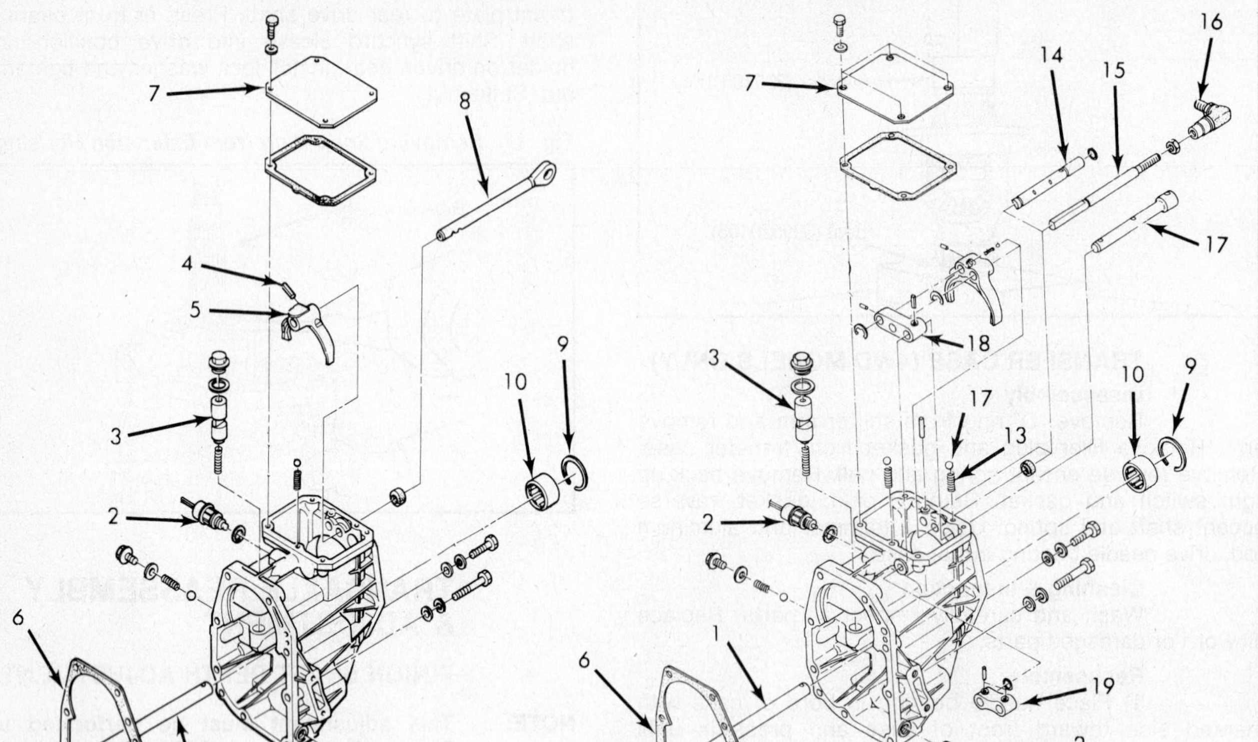

1. Shifter Arm
2. Back-Up Light Switch
3. Reverse Accent Shaft
4. Straight Pin
5. Transfer Shifter Fork
6. Gasket
7. Transfer Shift Cover
8. Transfer Shift Rail
9. Snap Ring
10. Needle Bearing
11. Ball
12. Shifter Fork Rail Spring
13. Spring
14. Interlock Rail
15. Transfer Shift Rail
16. Transfer Ball Joint
17. High-Low Shifter Rail
18. High-Low Shifter Arm
19. Rod Arm
20. Change Rod Bushing
21. Bushing
22. Oil Seal
23. Extension Dust Cover
24. Lock Nut
25. Lock Washer
26. Ball Bearing
27. 4th Driven Gear Thrust Plate
28. Transfer Driven Gear
29. Bushing
30. Synchronizer Sleeve
31. Synchronizer Hub
32. Rear Drive Spacer
33. Snap Ring
34. Ball Bearing

SUBARU 4 & 5-SPEED TRANSAXLE (Cont.)

4) Add if value stamped on pinion is prefixed by a "+"; subtract if value is prefixed by a "-". Select from 1 to 3 adjusting shims which will equal value just obtained. Remove gauge and pinion shaft from case.

NOTE: **If no value is stamped on pinion, value is zero. Adjusting shim(s) will be installed during Transaxle Reassembly.**

TRANSAXLE REASSEMBLY

All Except 4WD Dual Range Models

1) Press new oil seals into axle drive shaft holders. Place speedometer shaft side of transmission case in a work stand, then screw axle shaft holder (without "O" ring) into case until threads are embedded completely in case.

2) Install speedometer shaft outer snap ring and washer on shaft, then install assembly in case. Install speedometer driven gear on shaft and retain with outer snap ring. Press in new speedometer shaft oil seal.

NOTE: **Install speedometer driven gear snap ring from driven gear side to avoid damaging oil seal.**

3) On 5-speed, insert reverse shift arm spring and ball into reverse shift rail arm. Install reverse shift rail into case, then fit shift rail arm onto shift rail and install snap ring. Install shift fork rail spring, ball and gasket into case and tighten shift rail spring plug.

4) Install reverse idler gear and shaft. Select shift lever that will provide .06-.12" (1.5-3.0 mm) clearance between reverse idler gear and case wall when shifting reverse shift rail. Remove reverse idler gear and shaft. Install and tighten correct shift lever. Shift lever to neutral position and reinstall reverse idler gear and shaft.

5) Select washer that will provide a clearance of less than .02" (.5 mm) between washer and case wall. Remove reverse idler gear and shaft. Install washer and reinstall reverse idler assembly. Install retaining pins. Install 5th shift fork onto reverse shift rail and secure with spring pin.

6) On all other models, install reverse shift lever into case. Install reverse idler gear and shaft into case and retain with pin. Install reverse shift rail arm to end of reverse shift lever, then install reverse shift rail and tighten set screw. Install reverse shift fork rail spring, ball and gasket into case. Tighten spring plug.

7) Move reverse shift rail to reverse position and measure clearance between reverse idler gear and case. Install shift rail arm which will provide .06-.12" (1.5-3.0 mm) clearance between gear and case. Install shift rail arm and secure with retaining pin.

8) On all models, wrap vinyl tape around splines of drive axle shafts to protect seals, then install differential in case. Install mainshaft in case, ensuring that dowel pin on case is fitted into hole in needle bearing outer race. Install shift rail pin in 3rd-4th shift rail, then install rail and 3rd-4th shift fork. Tighten set screw.

9) Install previously selected pinion depth adjusting shim(s) on pinion shaft rear bearing. If more than 1 shim is used, do not place slit ends of shims on same side. Install pinion shaft in case, ensuring that dowel pin on case is fitted into hole in rear bearing outer race.

10) Place shift rail plunger into hole in case. Install 1st-2nd shift rail and shift fork, then tighten set screw. Install shift rail balls, springs and plugs. Force mainshaft and pinion shaft toward front of case until there is no clearance between shafts and case.

11) Check that synchro sleeves (with rails in neutral) are centered between respective gears. Check that clearance between 5th driven gear and synchro sleeve is .41" (10.5 mm). If not, select correct shift forks (5 available) to provide this alignment.

RAIL CLEARANCE VALUES

Application	In. (mm)
1600 cc Models	
"A"	.012-.063 (0.3-1.6)
"B"	.012-.063 (0.3-1.6)
1800 cc Models	
"A"	.012-.063 (0.3-1.6)
"B"	.071-.122 (1.8-3.1)

Fig. 14: Clearances Between Rails

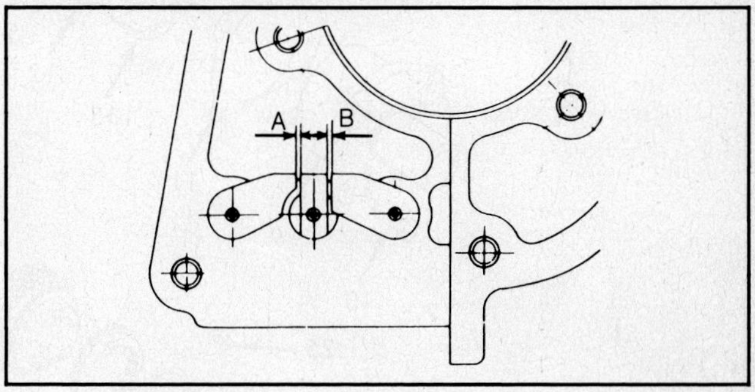

Fig. 15: Transaxle Case Tightening Sequence

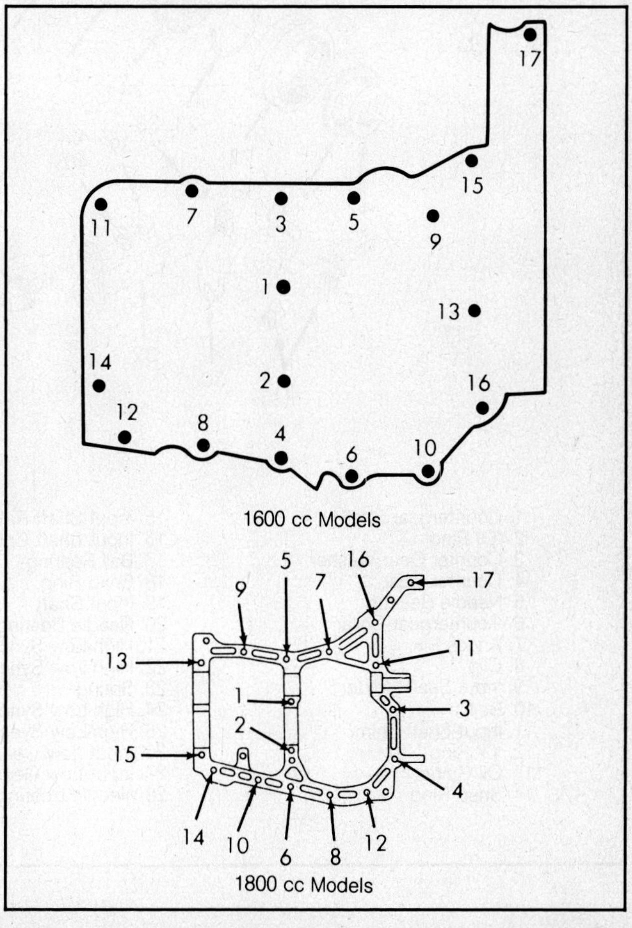

SUBARU 4 & 5-SPEED TRANSAXLE (Cont.)

Fig. 16: Auxiliary Transmission and High-Low Shift Linkage (4WD Dual Range Models)

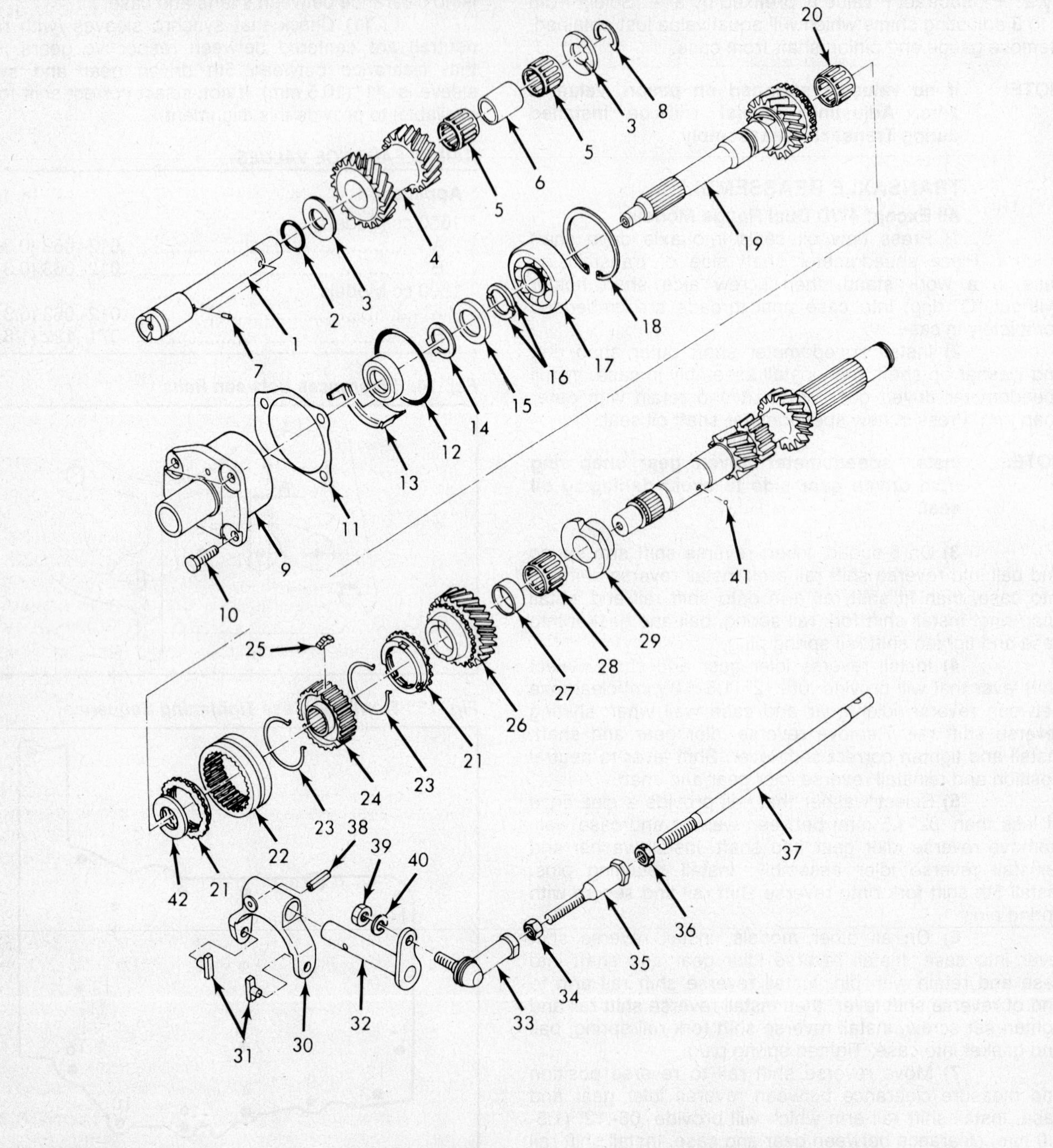

1. Countergear Shaft
2. "O" Ring
3. Counter Gear Washer
4. Counter Gear
5. Needle Bearing
6. Countergear Collar
7. Knock Pin
8. Clip
9. Input Shaft Holder
10. Bolt
11. Input Shaft Shim
12. "O" Ring
13. Oil Guide
14. Snap Ring
15. Input Shaft Retainer
16. Input Shaft Cotter
17. Ball Bearing
18. Snap Ring
19. Input Shaft
20. Needle Bearing
21. High-Low Synchronizer Ring
22. High-Low Synchronizer Sleeve
23. Spring
24. High-Low Synchronizer Hub
25. High-Low Synchronizer Insert
26. Input Low Gear
27. Input Low Gear Collar
28. Needle Bearing
29. Input Low Gear Spacer
30. High-Low Shifter Fork
31. Shift Fork Piece
32. High-Low Shifter Lever Center Pivot
33. Rod Ball Joint Assembly
34. Nut
35. Rod Adjust
36. Nut
37. High-Low Shifter Rod
38. Spring Pin
39. Nut
40. Spring Washer
41. Ball
42. Snap Ring

SUBARU 4 & 5-SPEED TRANSAXLE (Cont.)

12) Check clearance between edges of each shift rail. *See Fig. 14.* If clearance is not as listed in table, replace rail, fork and set screw. Install mainshaft oil seal. Clean mating surfaces of transaxle case halves, then apply sealant to all mating surfaces.

13) Align case halves while slightly shifting case so pinion depth shim(s) is not caught between case halves, then install and tighten attaching bolts. *See Fig. 15.* Install clutch cable bracket, back-up light cord clip, radio ground cord and oxygen sensor harness clip. Install and tighten pinion shaft retaining bolts.

Dual Range 4WD Models

1) Press new oil seals into axle drive shaft holders. Place speedometer shaft side of transmission case in a work stand, then screw axle shaft holder (without "O" ring) into case until threads are embedded completely in case.

2) Install speedometer shaft outer snap ring and washer on shaft, then install assembly in case. Install speedometer driven gear on shaft and retain with outer snap ring. Press in new speedometer shaft oil seal.

NOTE: **Install speedometer driven gear snap ring from driven gear side to avoid damaging oil seal.**

3) Install reverse shift lever into case. Install reverse idler gear and shaft into case and retain with pin. Install reverse shift rail arm to end of reverse shift lever, then install reverse shift rail and tighten set screw.

4) Install reverse shift fork rail spring, ball and gasket into case. Tighten spring plug. Move reverse shift rail to reverse position and measure clearance between reverse idler gear and case. Install shift rail arm which will provide .06-.12" (1.5-3.0 mm) clearance between gear and case.

5) Install shift rail arm and secure with retaining pin. Wrap vinyl tape around splines of drive axle shafts to protect seals, then install differential in case. Install "O" ring and knock pin at front side onto countergear shaft.

6) Install the following parts onto the countergear shaft when installing it into main case: 2 countergear washers, 2 needle bearings, countergear collar, knock pin and clip. Make sure the cut-out end surface of the countergear shaft does not protrude above the end surfaces of the case. *See Fig. 17.*

Fig. 17: Countergear Shaft Positioning

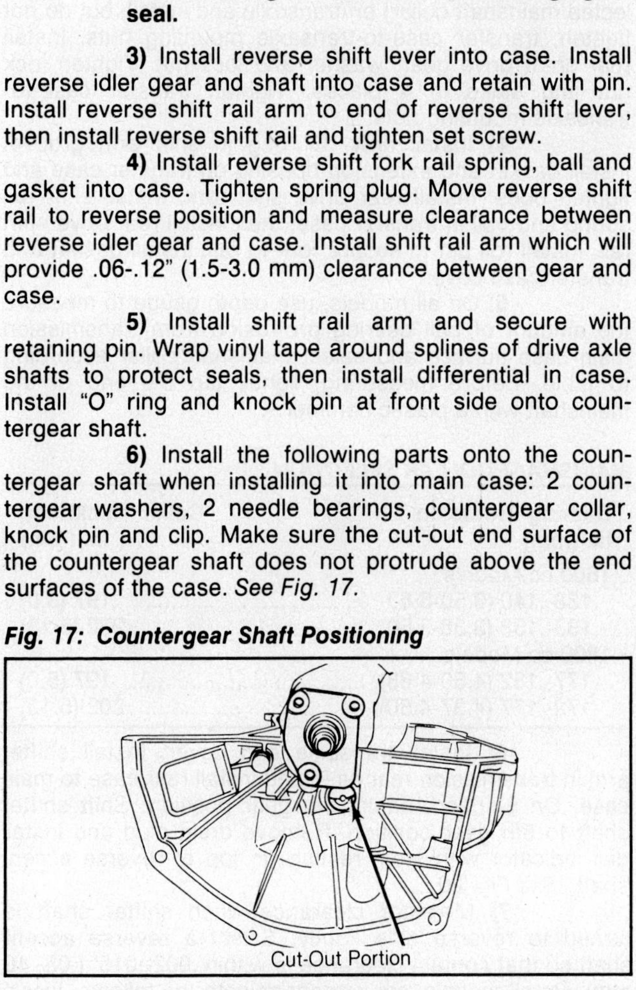

7) Put mainshaft assembly, needle bearing, high-low synchronizing ring and input shaft together. Shim input shaft with shim number determined by calculating measurement "D" shown in *Fig. 18.*.

SHIM DETERMINATION ("D" Distance)

Shim Used	In. (mm)
No Shim	More than 1.984 (50.39)
No. 1	1.983-1.964 (50.38-49.89)
No. 2	Less than 1.96 (49.88)

Fig. 18: Adjustment of Input Shaft

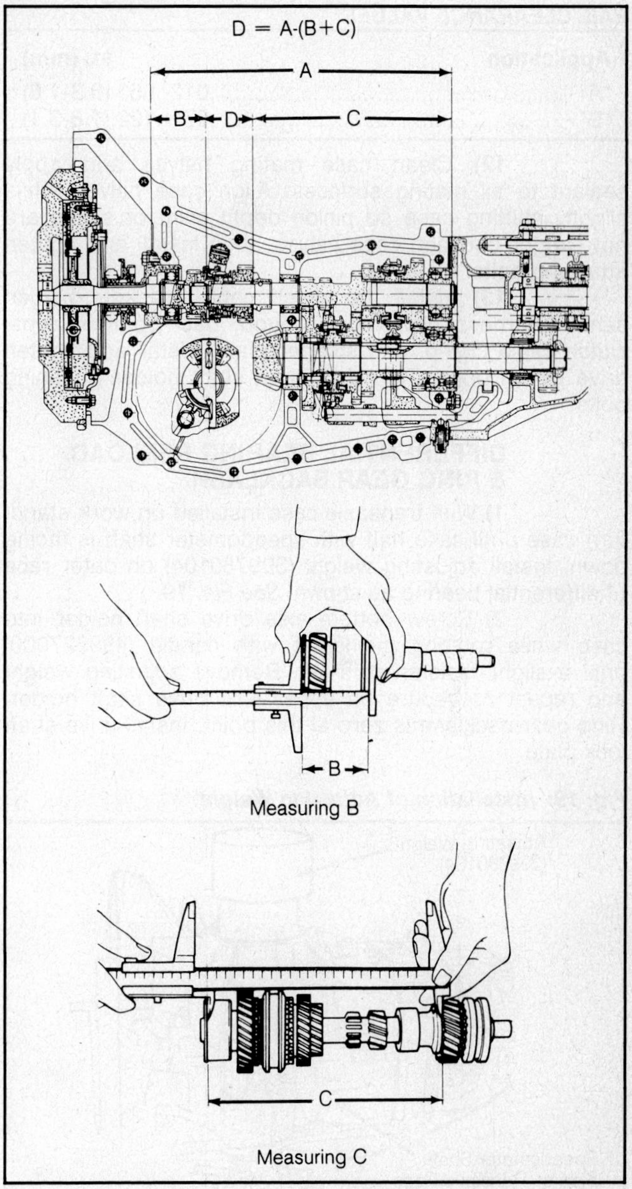

8) Install transmission mainshaft into case. Install high-low shifter fork with 2 high-low shifter pieces into high-low shifter sleeve. Install high-low shift lever into high-low shift fork through the case and install the pin.

9) Install the 3rd-4th shifter fork and rail with plunger and tighten set screw. Install previously selected shims and drive pinion assembly into case. Make sure the knock pin is fit to roller bearing outer race. Fit plunger to case and install 1st-2nd shifter fork and rail. Tighten set screw.

10) Fit 3rd-4th and 1st-2nd shifter fork rail springs, balls, and gaskets into the case. Tighten the shifter rail spring plugs. Force mainshaft and pinion shaft

SUBARU 4 & 5-SPEED TRANSAXLE (Cont.)

toward front of case until there is no clearance between shafts and case.

11) Check that synchro sleeves (with rails in neutral) are centered between respective gears. Check clearance between edges of each shift rail. If clearance is not as shown in table, replace rail, fork and set screw. *See Fig. 14.*

RAIL CLEARANCE VALUES

Application	In. (mm)
"A"	.012-.063 (0.3-1.6)
"B"	.071-.122 (1.8-3.1)

12) Clean case mating halves and apply sealant to all mating surfaces. Align case halves while slightly shifting case so pinion depth shim or shims are not caught between case halves, then install and tighten attaching bolts.

13) Install the clutch cable bracket, oxygen sensor harness clip, radio ground, back-up light clips, clutch cable clamp, and stopper plate. Install and tighten drive pinion bolts. Tighten 3 input shaft holder attaching bolts.

DIFFERENTIAL BEARING PRELOAD & RING GEAR BACKLASH

1) With transaxle case installed on work stand, turn case until case half with speedometer shaft is facing down. Install adjusting weight (399780104) on outer race of differential bearing as shown. *See Fig. 19.*

2) Screw bottom axle drive shaft holder into case while rotating mainshaft with handle (499927000) until a slight resistance is felt. Remove adjusting weight and repeat procedure on upper axle drive shaft holder. Ring gear backlash is zero at this point. Install drive shaft lock plate.

Fig. 19: Installation of Adjusting Weight

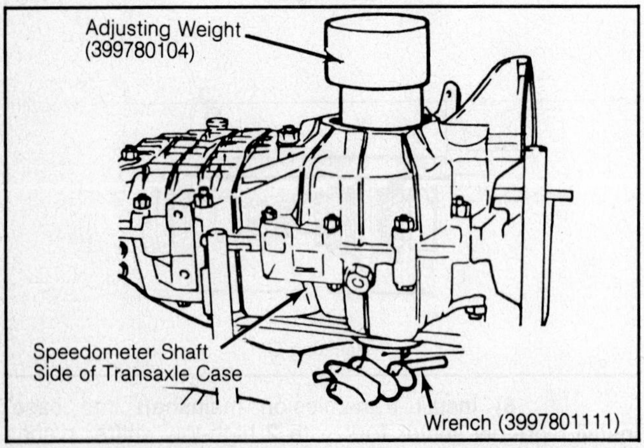

3) Loosen bottom drive shaft holder 1 1/2 notches, then screw in upper holder by the same amount to obtain ring gear backlash. Turn upper holder in an additional 1/2 to 1 notch to obtain differential bearing preload.

4) Tighten holder lock plates, then mark position of both holders for later readjustment. Turn mainshaft many times while tapping around axle shaft bearing holder lightly with a plastic hammer.

5) Install a dial indicator to transaxle case with tip of indicator inserted through transaxle drain hole and touching ring gear teeth. Measure ring gear backlash by rotating drive shafts back and forth taking up free play. If backlash does not match specification in table, repeat adjustment procedure.

RING GEAR BACKLASH

Application	In. (mm)
1600 cc Models	.004-.007 (.10-.18)
1800 cc Models	.005-.007 (.13-.18)

FINAL ASSEMBLY

All Except 4WD Dual Range

1) With differential bearing preload and ring gear backlash correctly adjusted, remove both axle drive shaft holders. Install "O" ring seal on each holder. Reinstall holders into transaxle case, making sure alignment marks on holders and case are aligned.

2) Remove tape from around axle drive shaft splines. On 4WD models, remove pinion shaft lock nut, washer and rear shaft drive gear. Elect a mainshaft collar which will provide 0-.012" (0-.30 mm) clearance between mainshaft bearing and transfer case.

3) Install gasketand transfer case (with selected mainshaft collar) on transaxle and install, but do not tighten, transfer case-to-transaxle mounting nuts. Install rear shaft drive gear, washer and lock nut. Tighten lock nut and stake in 4 places. Tighten transfer case-to-transaxle mounting nuts.

4) Install new "O" ring in shift arm groove. Install gasket and extension housing on transfer case and tighten bolts. Install rear drive shift fork. Install shift rail spring and ball in transfer case, then install rear drive shift rail. Install roll pin to secure fork to rail. Install gasket and transfer case cover.

5) On all models, use depth gauge to measure the amount of ball bearing protrusion from transmission main case surface and select mainshaft collar according to table. Before measuring, lightly tap the end of the mainshaft with a plastic hammer.

MAINSHAFT COLLAR SELECTION

Bearing Protusion In. (mm)	Collar Thickness In. (mm)
1600 cc Models	
.138-.140 (3.50-3.63)	.197 (5.0)
.133-.138 (3.38-3.50)	.202 (5.13)
1800 cc Models	
.177-.182 (4.50-4.63)	.197 (5.0)
.172-.177 (4.37-4.50)	.202 (5.13)

6) Install transaxle end cover. Install shifter arm in transmission rear case and install rear case to main case. On 5-speed, adjust 5th gear position. Shift shifter shaft to 5th gear position. Remove drain plug and install dial indicator with stem resting on top of reverse accent shaft. *See Fig. 20*

7) Measure clearance when shifter shaft is turned to reverse side lightly. Select a reverse accent shaft so that contact clearance is within .002-.015" (.05-.40 mm). On all models, adjust gear selector as follows: Insert a rod through hole in shift arm and shift into 3rd gear.

8) Arm should move easily toward 1st-2nd gear side, but harder toward reverse side because of return spring action. Next, make adjustment to effort

SUBARU 4 & 5-SPEED TRANSAXLE (Cont.)

Fig. 20: Measuring Contact Clearance for 5th Gear Positioning

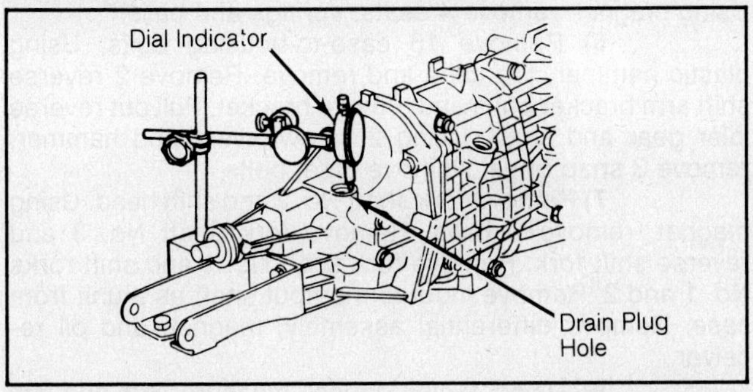

required to move lever to either position. Adjusment is performed by removing plug on cover and changing thickness of aluminum gasket.

9) On all except 4WD models, make adjustment so the heavy stroke (reverse side) is a little more than light side. On 4WD models, adjust strokes to take equal effort. On all models, install release bearing guide on case together with 2 release spring brackets.

10) Install clutch release fork and release bearing holder. Secure with release bearing holder spring. Install clutch release fork seal ring and spring. Fill internal groove of release bearing holder with grease.

4WD Dual Range

1) Remove lock plate, lock washer and transfer drive gear from drive pinion. Measure bearing protrusion and select proper bearing plate. Fit transfer case assembly with gasket and plate on main case and tighten bolts.

2) Transfer drive gear should be installed when clearance between main case and transfer case becomes approximately .394" (10 mm). Install lock washer and lock nut on drive pinion. When tightening, the gear should be shifted to the 1st position.

3) High-low shifter lever should be shifted to "HI" or "LO" position. After tightening nut, stake it. Install "O" ring in the side of high-low shifter rail bushing. Apply grease to plunger and fit into high-low shifter arm. Fit shifter fork rail spring and ball in transfer case, and install high-low shifter rail with high-low shifter arm.

4) Punch in straight pin into high-low shifter rail. Install extension assembly with transfer rear gasket and tighten. Before tightening, ensure that shifter arm center pivot can be shifted to any selected direction. Apply gear oil on shifter arm center pivot, and ensure oil seal fits.

5) Transfer drive and transfer driven gears should engage each other. Fit plunger, shifter fork rail spring and ball into transfer shifter fork, and install it to synchronizer sleeve. Apply gear oil to interlock rail, fit "O" ring to rail and insert rail into transfer case.

6) Punch in clip onto interlock rail groove, and insert knock pin into interlock rail hole. Install transfer ball joint assembly to transfer shifter rail. Adjust to 6.7-7.2" (171-185 mm) and tighten nut. Fit shifter fork rail spring and ball in transfer case, and install transfer shifter rail center pivot with transfer case in "4WD HI" so interlock mechanism does not operate.

7) Fit clip onto transfer shifter rail groove. Fit nut, rod adjusting screw, nut and ball joint assembly to high-low shifter rod. Shorten linkage length by turning turnbuckle clockwise.

8) Insert rod arm into rear portion of high-low shifter rod, and punch in straight pin. Connect rod ball joint assembly with high-low shifter lever center pivot and tighten nut to the specified torque. Confirm operation by moving rod back and forth.

9) Shift transfer shifter rail into "4WD LO" position and fix high-low shifter rail by inserting stopper pin into its hole. Shift high-low shifter lever into LO position and lengthen linkage by turning turnbuckle counterclockwise while holding high-low shifter rod. Align holes of rod arm and high-low shifter rod, and punch in straight pin.

10) While holding rod ball joint assembly, turn rod adjusting screw counterclockwise and then turn back 90° clockwise at the point where ball joint movement becomes tight. Tighten rear nut, and then tighten front nut while holding rod ball joint assembly. Pull out stopper pin and confirm shift operation.

11) Install transfer case cover with gasket and tighten bolts. Insert a bar through shifter arm hole and shift gear to 3rd gear position. Shifter arm should turn lightly toward the 1st-2nd gear side and heavily toward the reverse side.

12) Remove plug on the transfer case and change the thickness of the aluminum gasket to adjust the heavy stroke (reverse side) to be the same as the light stroke. Install clutch release fork and release bearing holder by installing retainer spring into fork.

13) While pushing fork to pivot and twisting it to fit both sides, fit retainer spring onto constricted portion of pivot. Install holder and fasten with 2 clips. Install release fork seal ring.

TIGHTENING SPECIFICATIONS

Application	Ft.Lbs.(N.m)
Ball Joint Nut	25 (34)
Tie Rod Nut	22 (30)
Axle Shaft Nut	145 (197)
Drive Pinion-to-Case	22 (30)
Ring Gear-to-Differential	42-50 (57-68)
Transaxle Case Bolts	
8 mm Bolts	18 (24)
10 mm Bolts	29 (39)
Axle Shaft Holder Lock Plate	18 (24)
Drive Pinion Lock Nut	58 (79)
Transaxle Cover Bolts	16 (22)

TOYOTA MR2 5-SPEED

MR2

DESCRIPTION

The Toyota C52 transaxle assembly consists of transaxle, differential and case cover with common oil supply. Transaxle is fully synchronized in all forward gears.

LUBRICATION & ADJUSTMENT

See appropriate MANUAL TRANSMISSION SERVICING article in INPORT GENERAL SERVICING section.

SERVICE (IN VEHICLE)

See appropriate DRIVE AXLE SHAFT article in IMPORT AXLE SHAFTS, OVERDRIVES & TRANSFER CASES section.

TRANSAXLE REMOVAL & INSTALLATION

See appropriate MANUAL TRANSMISSION REMOVAL article in IMPORT GENERAL SERVICING section.

TRANSAXLE DISASSEMBLY

1) Remove release fork, bearing, speedometer driven gear, back-up light switch, and front bearing retainer. Remove transaxle case cover. Using dial indicator, measure 5th gear thrust clearance. Standard clearance is .0040-.0224" (.100-.570 mm). Maximum clearance is .0256" (.650 mm). Record reference for installation.

2) Remove selector bellcrank. Remove shift lever set nut. Using pin punch and hammer, remove lock pin and shift lever. Remove 4 control shaft retainer bolts. Remove lock bolt from retainer case and remove shift and select lever shaft assembly.

3) Looking inside control shaft retainer case, engage gear meshing. Remove lock nut from 5th gear shaft. Disengage meshing. *See Fig. 1.*

Fig. 1: Engaging Gear Meshing

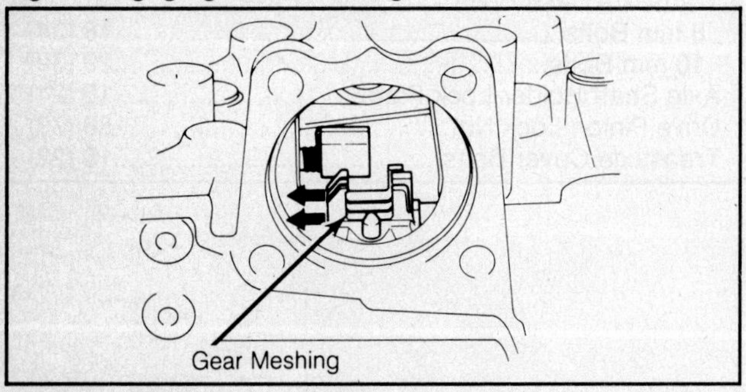

4) Using 2 screwdrivers and hammer, remove snap ring from end of shaft. Remove No. 3 shift fork bolt, hub sleeve, and shift fork. Using Puller (SST09213-36020), remove 5th gear, No. 3 hub and synchro ring. Remove needle roller bearing and spacer. Using Puller (SST09950-20016), remove 5th driven gear. Remove bearing retainer and 2 bearing snap rings

5) Remove reverse idler gear shaft lock bolt. Using 2 screwdrivers and hammer, remove snap ring from No. 2 shift fork shaft. Using Detent Ball Plug Socket (SST09313-30021), remove 3 plugs and lock ball assembly. Using magnet, remove 4 seats, springs and balls.

6) Remove 16 case-to-housing bolts. Using plastic hammer, tap case and remove. Remove 2 reverse shift arm bracket bolts and remove bracket. Pull out reverse idler gear and shaft. Using 2 screwdrivers and hammer, remove 3 snap rings. Remove 3 set bolts.

7) Remove fork shaft No. 2 and shift head. Using magnet, remove 2 balls. Remove fork shaft No. 3 and reverse shift fork. Remove fork shaft No. 1 and shift forks No. 1 and 2. Remove input and output shaft as a unit from case. Remove differential assembly, magnet, and oil receiver.

8) Using feeler gauge, measure 3rd and 4th gear bearing thrust clearance. *See Fig. 2.* Using 2 screwdrivers and hammer, remove input shaft snap ring. Using Bearing Remover (SST09950-00020) and press, remove bearing. Remove 4th gear, needle roller bearings, and synchro ring. Using 2 screwdrivers and hammer, remove snap ring. Using Bearing Remover and press, remove hub sleeve No. 2, 3rd gear, synchro ring and needle roller bearings. Using feeler gauge, measure 1st and 2nd gear thrust clearance.

Fig. 2: Measuring Thrust Gear Clearance

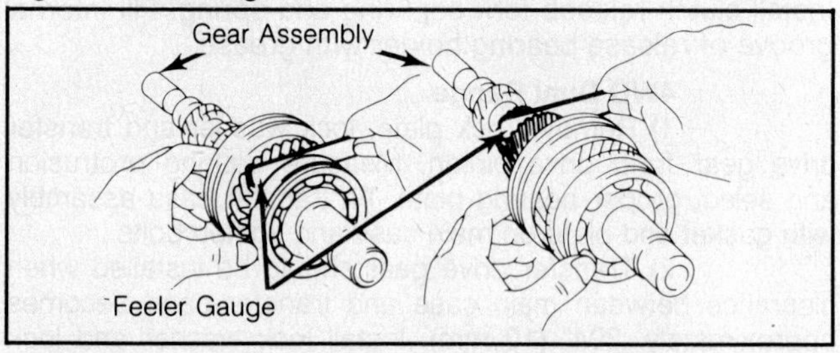

GEAR THRUST CLEARANCE

Application	In. (mm)
Standard Clearance	
1st Gear	.0039-.0157 (.10-.40)
2nd Gear	.0039-.0177 (.10-.45)
3rd Gear	.0039-.0138 (.10-.35)
4th Gear	.0039-.0217 (.10-.55)
Maximum Clearance	
1st Gear	.0177 (.45 mm)
2nd Gear	.0197 (.50 mm)
3rd Gear	.0157 (.40 mm)
4th Gear	.0236 (.60 mm)

9) Using Bearing Remover (SST09950-00020) and press, remove bearing and 4th driven gear. Remove spacer. Shift hub sleeve No. 1 into 1st gear. Using same tools, remove 3rd driven gear and 2nd gear. Remove needle roller bearing, spacer, and synchro ring.

10) Using 2 screwdrivers and hammer, remove snap ring. Using Bearing Remover (SST09950-00020) and press, remove hub sleeve No. 1, 1st gear and synchro ring. Remove needle roller bearing, thrust washer, and locking ball. Remove "E" ring and compression spring. Using pin punch and hammer, remove 3 slotted spring pins from shift inner levers and select inner lever. Remove No. 1 and No. 2 shift inner levers, shift interlock plate, select inner lever, compression spring and spring seat. Using 2 screwdrivers and hammer, remove snap ring from lever shaft.

Fig. 3: Exploded View of Transaxle Assembly

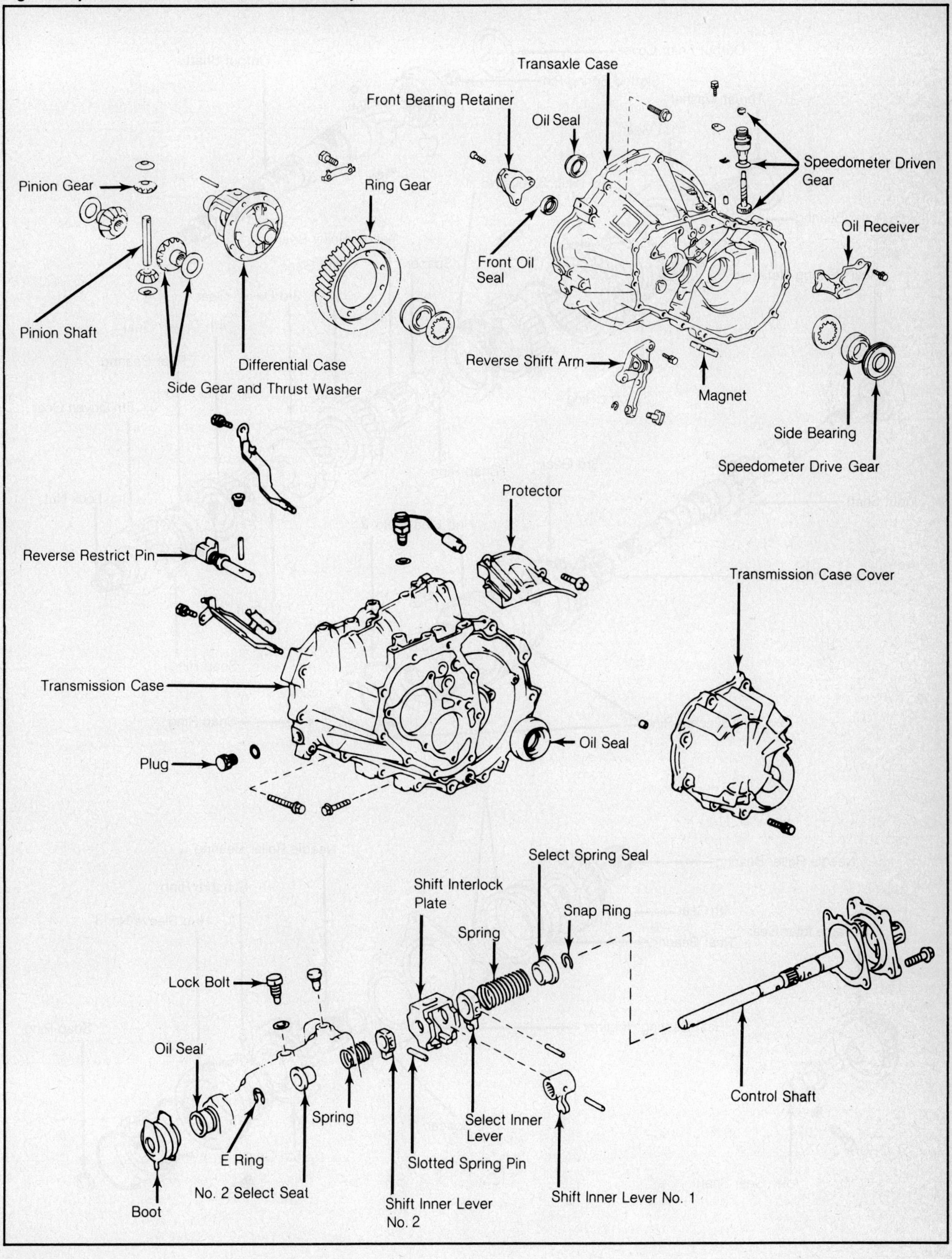

Manual Transmissions

TOYOTA MR2 5-SPEED (Cont.)

Fig. 4: Exploded View of Transmission Gear Assemblies

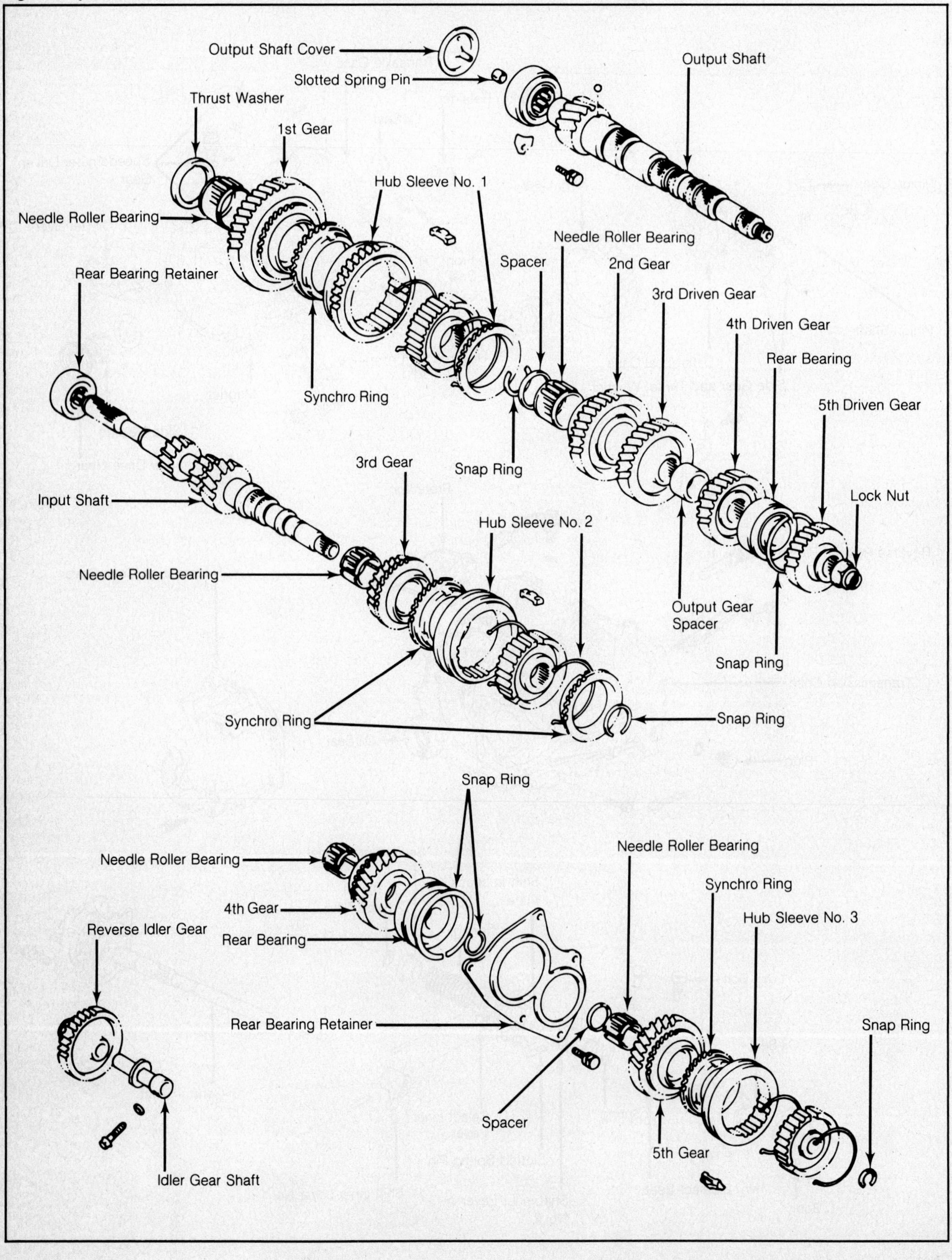

TOYOTA MR2 5-SPEED (Cont.)

COMPONENT INSPECTION & REPAIR

INPUT SHAFT

Inspect shaft for wear or damage. Using micrometer, measure outer diameter of shaft journal surface. *See Fig. 5.* Using dial indicator, measure shaft runout.

INPUT SHAFT SPECIFICATIONS

Section [1]	Minimum Diameter In. (mm)
A	.9791 (24.87)
B	1.0421 (26.47)
C	1.2193 (30.97)
D	.9831 (24.97)
Maximum Runout	.0020 (.05)

[1] – See Fig. 5 for input shaft section applications.

Fig 5: Input Shaft Measurement Points

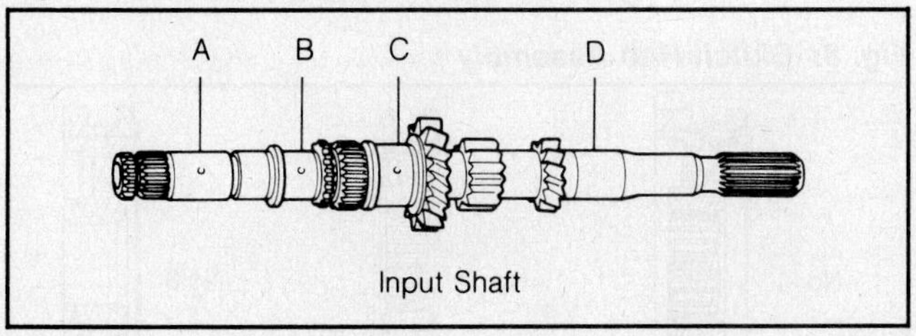

OUTPUT SHAFT

Inspect shaft for wear or damage. Using micrometer, measure outer diameter of output shaft journal surface. *See Fig. 6.* Using dial indicator, measure shaft runout.

OUTPUT SHAFT SPECIFICATIONS

Section [1]	Minimum Diameter In. (mm)
A	1.2980 (32.97)
B	1.4949 (37.97)
C	1.2587 (31.97)
Maximum Runout	.0020 (.05)

[1] – See Fig. 6 for input shaft section applications.

Fig. 6: Output Shaft Measurement Points

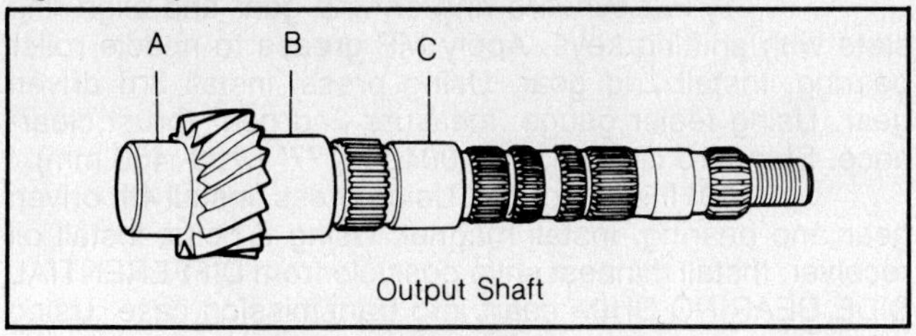

GEARS, SYNCHRO RINGS, SHIFT FORKS & HUB SLEEVES

1) Using dial indicator, measure oil clearance between gear and input or output shaft with needle roller bearings installed. Standard clearance is .0008-.0020" (.020-.050 mm). Maximum clearance is .0028 (.070 mm).

2) Check synchro rings for wear or damage and replace as necessary. Turn ring and push in to check braking action. Using feeler gauge, measure clearance between synchro ring back and gear spline end. Minimum clearance is .024" (.60 mm). *See Fig. 7.*

3) Using feeler gauge, measure clearance between hub sleeve and shift fork. Maximum clearance is .039" (1.0 mm).

Fig. 7: Checking Synchro Rings

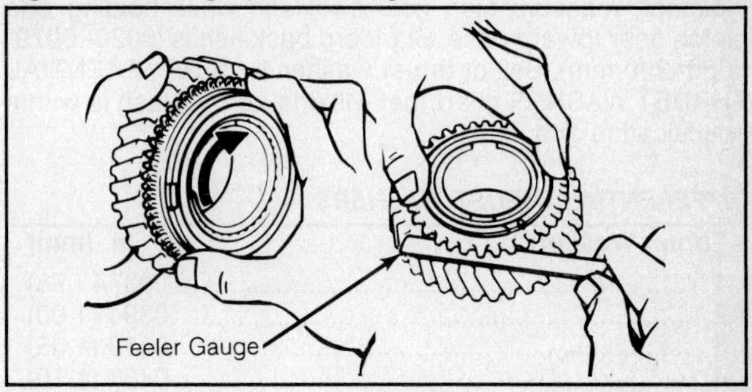

TRANSMISSION BEARINGS & OIL SEALS

Inspect all bearings and oil seals for wear or damage and replace as necessary. Use standard pullers and drivers to remove and install all bearings and seals. If replacing output shaft front bearing, tighten bearing lock plate bolts to 8 ft. lbs. (11 N.m). If replacing speedometer driven gear oil seal, install to a depth of .98" (25 mm).

REVERSE RESTRICT PIN

Check action of reverse restrict pin. If replacement is necessary, use Detent Ball Plug Socket (SST09313-30021) and remove reverse restrict holder. Using pin punch and hammer, remove slotted spring pin. To install reverse restrict pin, reverse removal procedure.

DIFFERENTIAL SIDE BEARINGS & RING GEAR

1) Using Puller (SST09502-10012), remove bearings from both sides of case. Using Installer (SST09350-32011) and press, press side bearings onto differential case.

2) Loosen staked part of ring gear lock plate. Place alignment marks on ring gear and case. Remove 8 bolts and locking plates. Using copper hammer, tap ring gear and remove from case. Clean contact surface of differential case.

3) Heat ring gear to about 212° (100°C) in an oil bath. Do not heat ring gear above 230° (110°C). Clean contact surface of ring gear with solvent. Quickly install ring gear on differential case. Align marks on ring gear and differential case. Install new locking plates and bolts. Tighten set bolts evenly to 71 ft. lbs. (97 N.m). Using hammer and punch, install locking plates by staking one claw flush with flat surface of nut. For claw contacting protruding portion of nut, stake only the half on the tightened side.

4) Using dial indicator, stand ring gear up and measure gear backlash on one side while holding one pinion toward case. Standard backlash is .0020-.0079" (.050-.200 mm).

Manual Transmissions

TOYOTA MR2 5-SPEED (Cont.)

DIFFERENTIAL CASE

Disassembly

Using pin punch and hammer, remove pinion shaft lock pin from side on which ring gear is installed. Remove pinion shaft from case. Remove 2 pinion gears, 2 side gears, and 4 thrust washers from case.

Reassembly

1) Install thrust washers, side gears and pinion gears in differential case. Install pinion shaft. Using dial indicator, measure side gear backlash while holding one pinion gear toward case. Standard backlash is .0020-.0079" (.050-.200 mm). Select thrust washer from DIFFERENTIAL THRUST WASHER chart that will ensure backlash is within specification and install.

DIFFERENTIAL THRUST WASHERS

Thrust Washer	In. (mm)
1	.0374 (.96)
2	.0394 (1.00)
3	.0413 (1.05)
4	.0433 (1.10)
5	.0453 (1.15)
6	.0472 (1.20)

2) Using hammer and pin punch, install lock pin through case and hole in pinion shaft. Stake differential case.

TRANSAXLE REASSEMBLY & ADJUSTMENT

1) Install clutch No. 2 and shifting keys to hub sleeve. Install shifting key springs under shifting keys. Be sure key spring end gaps are not in line. Apply MP grease to needle roller bearings. Put synchro ring on 3rd gear and align ring slots with shifting keys. Using press, install 3rd gear and hub sleeve No. 2. Select snap ring from 3RD GEAR BEARING SNAP RING chart and install.

3RD GEAR BEARING SNAP RINGS

Mark on Ring	Thickness In. (mm)
0	.0906 (2.30)
1	.0929 (2.36)
2	.0953 (2.42)
3	.0976 (2.48)
4	.1000 (2.54)
5	.1024 (2.60)

2) Using feeler gauge, measure 3rd gear thrust clearance. Standard clearance is .0040-.0138" (.100-.350 mm).

3) Apply MP grease to needle roller bearing. Put synchro ring on gear and align ring slots with shifting keys. Using press, install bearing. Select snap ring from 4TH GEAR SNAP RING chart that will allow minimum axial play and install.

4) Using feeler gauge, measure 4th gear thrust clearance. Standard clearance is .0040-.0217" (.100-.550 mm).

5) If installing new output shaft, install slotted spring pin in output shaft to a depth of .236" (6.0 mm).

4TH GEAR SNAP RINGS

Mark on Ring	Thickness In. (mm)
A	.0902 (2.29)
B	.0925 (2.35)
C	.0949 (2.41)
D	.0972 (2.47)
E	.0996 (2.53)
F	.1020 (2.59)

6) Install cutch hub No. 1 and shifting keys to hub sleeve. Install shifting key springs under shifting keys. Be sure key spring end gaps are not in line. *See Fig. 8* Install locking ball on shaft. Fit thrust washer groove securely over locking ball when installing thrust washer on shaft.

7) Apply MP grease to needle roller bearing. Put synchro ring on gear and align ring slots with shifting keys. Using press, install 1st gear and hub sleeve No. 1. Select snap ring from 1ST GEAR SNAP RING chart that will allow minimum axial play and install.

Fig. 8: Clutch Hub Assembly

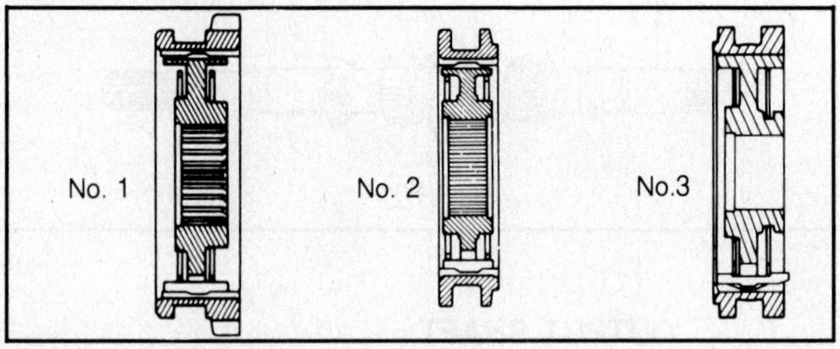

1ST GEAR SNAP RINGS

Mark on Ring	Thickness In. (mm)
A	.0984 (2.50)
B	.1008 (2.56)
C	.1031 (2.62)
D	.1055 (2.68)
E	.1079 (2.74)
F	.1102 (2.80)

8) Using feeler gauge, measure 1st gear thrust clearance. Standard clearance is .0039-.0157" (.100-.400 mm).

9) Put synchro ring on 2nd gear and align ring slots with shifting keys. Apply MP grease to needle roller bearing. Install 2nd gear. Using press, install 3rd driven gear. Using feeler gauge, measure 2nd gear thrust clearance. Standard clearance is .0040-.0177" (.100-.450 mm).

10) Install spacer. Using press, install 4th driven gear and bearing. Install magnet. Using 2 bolts, install oil receiver. Install thinnest shim possible from DIFFERENTIAL SIDE BEARING SHIM chart into transmission case. Using driver, install outer race of the side bearing. Install differential to transmission. Install transmission case. Tighten case bolts to 22 ft. lbs. (29 N.m).

11) Using Differential Preload Adapter (SST09564-32011) and torque wrench, measure bearing preload. New bearing preload is 6.9-13.9 INCH lbs. (.8-1.6 N.m). Reused bearing preload is 4.3-8.7 INCH lbs. (.5-1.0

DIFFERENTIAL SIDE BEARING SHIMS

Mark on Shim	Thickness In. (mm)
A	.0827 (2.10)
B	.0846 (2.15)
C	.0866 (2.20)
D	.0886 (2.25)
E	.0906 (2.30)
F	.0925 (2.35)
G	.0945 (2.40)
H	.0965 (2.45)
J	.0984 (2.50)
K	.1004 (2.55)
L	.1024 (2.60)
M	.1043 (2.65)
N	.1063 (2.70)
P	.1083 (2.75)
Q	.1102 (2.80)
R	.1122 (2.85)
S	.1142 (2.90)
T	.1161 (2.95)
U	.1181 (3.00)

N.m). If preload is not within specification, remove transmission case side outer race of the side bearing with above tool and reselect adjusting shim. Preload will differ approx. 2.6-3.5 INCH lbs (.30-.40 N.m) with each shim thickness.

12) Remove transmission case and install input and output shafts as a unit. Put shift forks No. 1 and No. 2 into No. 1 and No. 2 hub sleeve grooves. Insert fork shaft No. 1 into fork shaft No. 1 hole. Insert 2 interlock balls into reverse shift fork hole. Install fork shaft No. 3 and reverse shift fork. Install fork shaft No. 2 and shift head. Install 3 bolts and tighten to 12 ft. lbs. (16 N.m). Install 3 snap rings. *See Fig. 9.*

Fig. 9: Shift Fork & Shaft Assembly

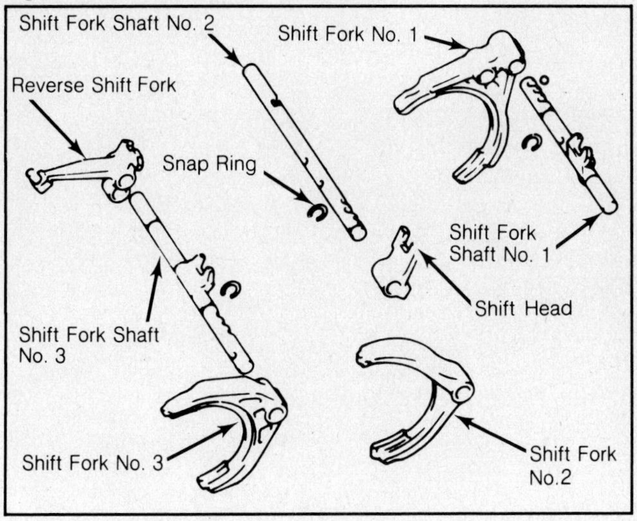

13) Install reverse shift fork pivot into reverse shift arm. Install reverse shift arm to transmission case. Tighten bolts to 13 ft. lbs. (17 N.m). Align mark on reverse idler gear with mark on case and install gear and shaft. *See Fig. 10.*

14) Making sure mounting surfaces of transmission case and transaxle case are clean and free of oil, apply

Fig. 10: Aligning Marks on Shaft & Case

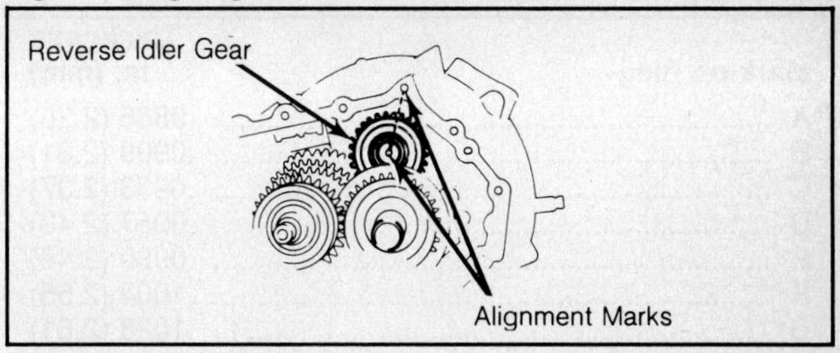

seal packing to transmission case. See Fig. 11. Use Toyota Packing 08826-00090 or Three Bond TB1281. Install transmission case as soon as seal packing is applied. Install and tighten 16 bolts to 22 ft. lbs. (29 N.m).

Fig. 11: Applying Sealer to Case

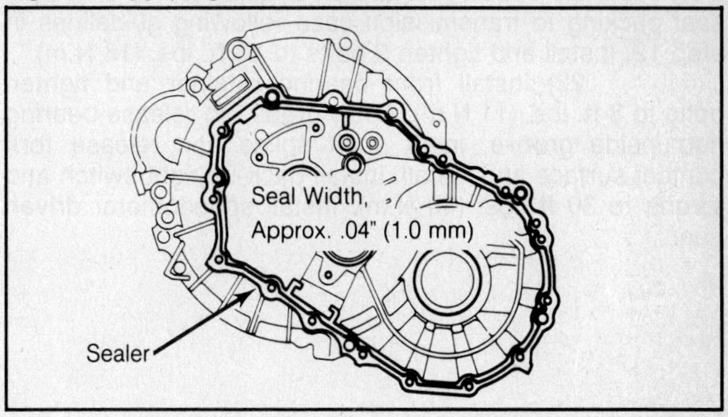

15) Install balls, springs and seats into holes. Apply sealer to plugs and lock ball assembly. Using Detent Ball Plug Socket (SST09313-30021), tighten 3 plugs to 18 ft. lbs. (25 N.m). Tighten lock ball assembly to 29 ft. lbs. (39 N.m). Install and tighten reverse idler gear shaft bolt to 29 ft. lbs. (39 N.m).

16) Install 2 bearing snap rings. Install snap ring to fork shaft No. 2. Install rear bearing retainer and tighten 5 bolts to 14 ft. lbs. (19 N.m). Using press, install 5th driven gear. Install spacer. Apply MP grease to needle roller bearings and install. Install 5th gear with needle roller bearing and synchro ring.

17) Install clutch hub No. 3 and shifting keys to hub sleeve. Install shifting key springs under shifting keys, being sure end gaps are not in line. Using driver, install hub sleeve No. 3 with No. 3 shift fork. Be sure to align synchro ring slots with shifting keys. Measure 5th gear thrust clearance. Standard clearance is .0040-.0224" (.100-.570 N.m). Select snap ring from 5TH GEAR SNAP RING chart that will allow minimum axial play and install.

18) Engage gear double meshing. Install and tighten shaft lock nut to 87 ft. lbs. (118 N.m). Disengage gear double meshing. Stake lock nut. Install 5th gear shift fork bolt and tighten to 12 ft. lbs. (16 N.m).

19) Apply MP grease to shift and select lever shaft. Install snap ring, spring seat, compression spring and select inner lever. Using pin punch and hammer, install slotted spring pin. Align interlock plate with shift inner lever No. 1 and install. Install shift inner lever No. 2. Using pin punch and hammer, install slotted spring pin. Install compression spring, spring seat and "E" ring. Install shift and select lever shaft assembly and lock bolt.

20) Using new gasket, install control shaft retainer. With air bleed of boot facing downward, install boot

TOYOTA MR2 5-SPEED (Cont.)

5TH GEAR SNAP RINGS

Mark on Ring	Thickness In. (mm)
A	.0886 (2.25)
B	.0909 (2.31)
C	.0933 (2.37)
D	.0957 (2.43)
E	.0980 (2.49)
F	.1004 (2.55)
G	.1028 (2.61)

to control shaft oil seal. Fit groove on pin with notch on shaft and tap with hammer. Install nut and tighten to 9 ft. lbs. (12 N.m). Install selecting bellcrank.

21) Make sure mounting surfaces of transmission case and case cover are clean and free of oil. Apply seal packing to transmission case following guidelines in step 12. Install and tighten 9 bolts to 13 ft. lbs. (18 N.m).

22) Install front bearing retainer and tighten bolts to 8 ft. lbs. (11 N.m). Apply grease to release bearing hub inside groove, input shaft spline and release fork contact surface and install. Install back-up light switch and torque to 30 ft. lbs. (40 N.m). Install speedometer driven gear.

TIGHTENING SPECIFICATIONS

Application	Ft. Lbs. (N.m)
Back-Up Light Switch	29-31 (39-41)
Differential Ring Gear	70-72 (96-98)
Front Bearing Retainer	7-9 (10-12)
Locking Ball Plug	28-30 (38-40)
Output Shaft Front Bearing Retainer	7-9 (10-12)
Rear Bearing Retainer	13-15 (18-20)
Reverse Idler Gear	28-30 (38-40)
Reverse Shift Arm	12-14 (16-18)
Shift Fork Shaft Bolts	11-13 (15-17)
Straight Screw Plug	17-19 (24-26)
Transaxle-to-Transmission	21-23 (28-30)
Transmission Case-to-Transmission	12-14 (17-19)
Transaxle-to-Engine	
12 mm Bolt	46-48 (63-65)
10 mm Bolt	33-35 (45-47)

TOYOTA G52 5-SPEED

4WD Pickup, 4Runner

DESCRIPTION

The Toyota G52 5-speed transmission is a fully synchronized unit. All forward gears are helical cut and in constant mesh. Reverse gear is spur cut. Reverse and 5th gears are mounted on the rear side of the intermediate plate. The floor shifter actuates a single control rod in the transfer adapter which operates 3 shift rails mounted in the intermediate plate and the main case.

Fig. 1: Toyota G52 Transmission

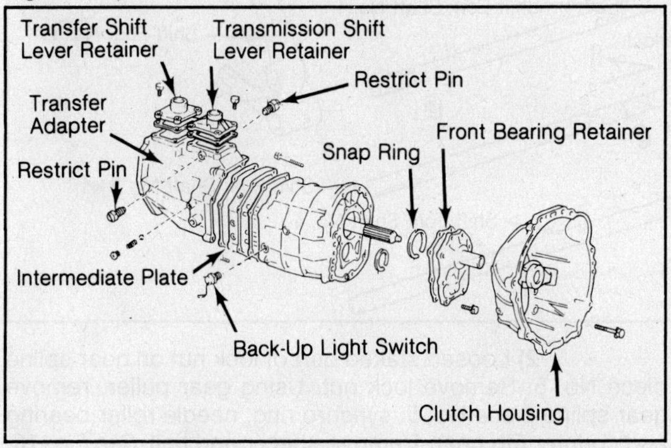

LUBRICATION & ADJUSTMENT

See appropriate MANUAL TRANSMISSION SERVICING article in IMPORT GENERAL SERVICING section.

REMOVAL & INSTALLATION

See appropriate MANUAL TRANSMISSION REMOVAL article in IMPORT GENERAL SERVICING section.

TRANSMISSION DISASSEMBLY

TRANSFER ADAPTER

1) Remove back-up light switch, shift lever retainer and restrict pins. Remove 9 clutch housing bolts. Using plastic hammer, remove clutch housing from transmission case.

2) Using Torx head socket, remove screw plug from transfer adapter. Remove Allen head plug from rear face of transfer adapter. Remove shift lever housing set bolt and lock washer. *See Fig. 2.*

3) Remove shift lever shaft and housing. Remove 8 transfer adapter bolts. Using plastic hammer, remove transfer adapter. Leave gasket attached to intermediate plate.

INTERMEDIATE PLATE

Shift Fork Shafts

1) Remove front bearing retainer and 2 bearing snap rings from front of transmission case. Using plastic hammer, carefully separate transmission case from intermediate plate.

Fig. 2: Removing Screw Plug, Spring & Ball

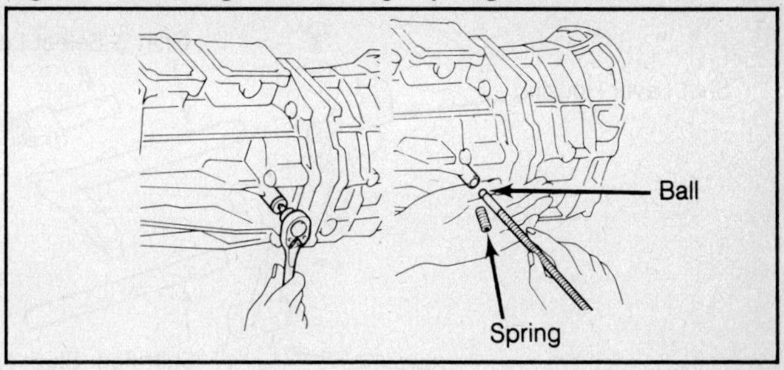

2) Install bolts, flat washers and nuts through lower 2 holes of intermediate plate. Mount intermediate plate in vise. *See Fig. 3.*

Fig. 3: Mounting Intermediate Plate in Vise

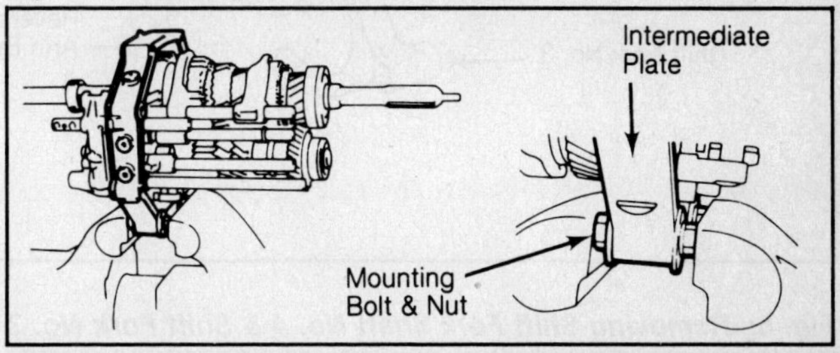

Fig. 4: Removing Intermediate Plate Plugs, Springs & Locking Balls

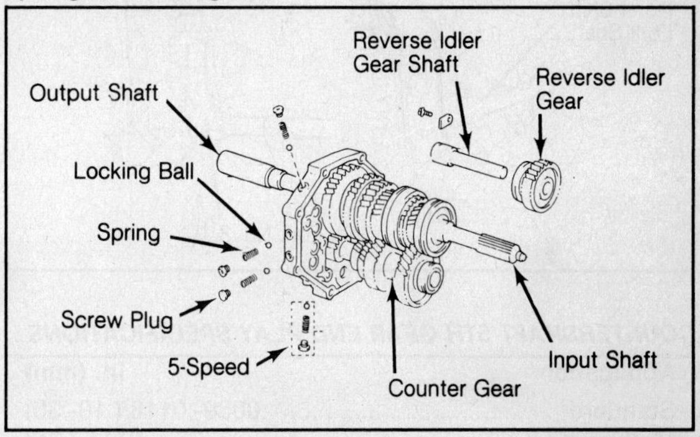

3) Using Torx head socket, remove 4 screw plugs, locking balls and springs from intermediate plate. *See Fig. 4.* Using hammer and pin punch, drive out 5 shift fork-to-shift rail pins. Remove 2 shift rail "E" rings.

4) Pull out shift fork shaft No. 4 from intermediate plate catching 2 interlock balls and pin. If they do not fall out, remove with magnet. Remove shift fork shaft No. 4 and shift fork No. 3. *See Fig. 6.*

5) Pull out shift fork shaft No. 5 from intermediate plate, and remove with reverse shift head. Pull out shift fork shaft No. 3 from intermediate plate catching 2 interlock pins as they fall out. If they do not come out, remove with magnet.

6) Remove shift fork shaft No. 1 and interlock pin from intermediate plate. Pull out shift fork shaft No. 2 and remove shift fork No. 2 and No. 1.

Input, Output & Countershafts

1) Remove reverse idler gear shaft stopper. Remove reverse idler gear and shaft. Remove reverse shift arm from reverse shift arm bracket. Measure countershaft 5th gear end play. *See Fig. 7.*

Manual Transmissions

TOYOTA G52 5-SPEED (Cont.)

Fig. 5: Exploded View of Shift Forks & Shafts

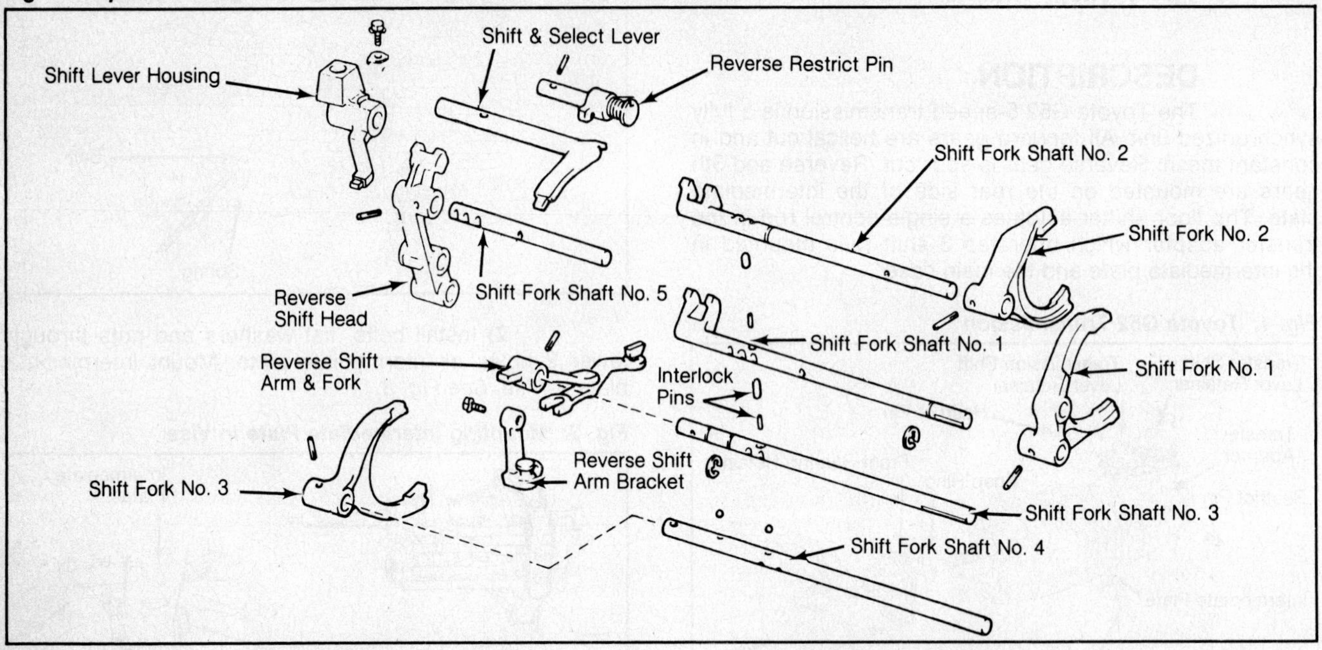

Fig. 6: Removing Shift Fork Shaft No. 4 & Shift Fork No. 3

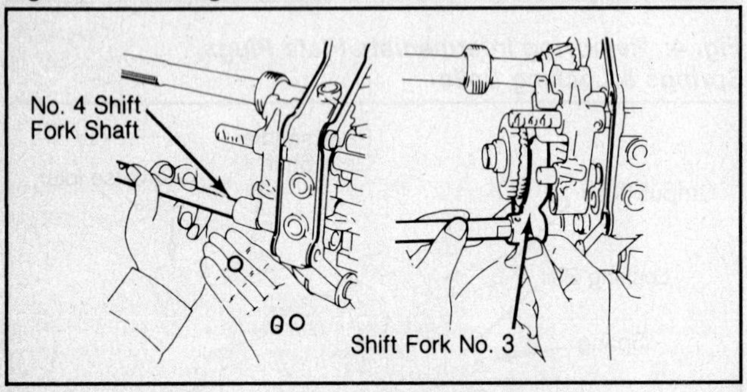

COUNTERSHAFT 5TH GEAR END PLAY SPECIFICATIONS

Application	In. (mm)
Standard	.0039-.0118 (.10-.30)
Maximum	.0118 (.30)

Fig. 7: Measuring Point For Countershaft 5th Gear End Play

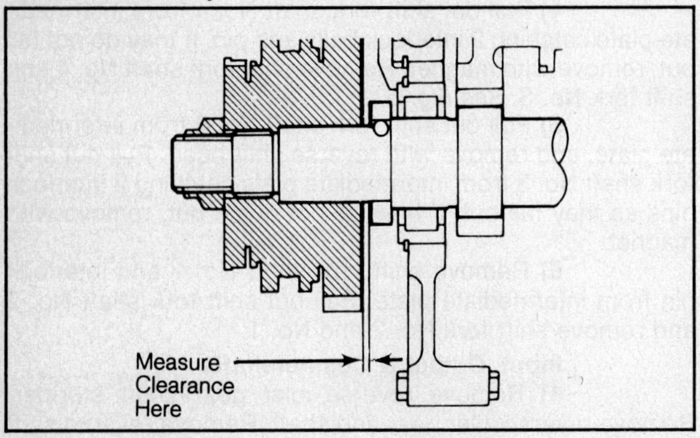

2) Loosen staked part of lock nut on gear spline piece No. 5. Remove lock nut. Using gear puller, remove gear spline piece No. 5, synchro ring, needle roller bearing and counter 5th gear. Remove spacer and ball. *See Fig. 10*.

3) Remove 2 bolts and reverse shift arm bracket. Using Torx head socket, remove 4 rear bearing retainer bolts. Remove rear bearing snap ring.

4) Remove output shaft, countershaft and input shaft as a unit from intermediate plate by pulling on countergear and tapping intermediate plate with plastic hammer. Remove input shaft and needle roller bearings from output shaft. Remove countershaft rear bearing from intermediate plate. Remove sleeve from output shaft using gear puller.

COMPONENT DISASSEMBLY & REASSEMBLY

OUTPUT SHAFT

Disassembly

1) Measure end play of each gear on output shaft. *See Fig. 8*. Remove snap ring and press 5th gear, rear bearing, 1st gear and inner race from output shaft. Remove needle roller bearing.

OUTPUT SHAFT END PLAY SPECIFICATIONS

Application	In. (mm)
1st, 2nd & 3rd Gear	
Standard	.0039-.0098 (.10-.25)
Maximum	.0098 (.25)

2) Remove synchro ring. Remove locking ball using magnet. Press hub sleeve No. 1, synchro ring and 2nd gear off output shaft. *See Fig. 9*. Remove needle roller bearing.

3) Remove snap ring and press hub sleeve No. 2, synchro ring and 3rd gear off output shaft. Remove needle roller bearing.

Manual Transmissions

TOYOTA G52 5-SPEED (Cont.)

Fig. 8: Measuring Output Shaft Gear End Play

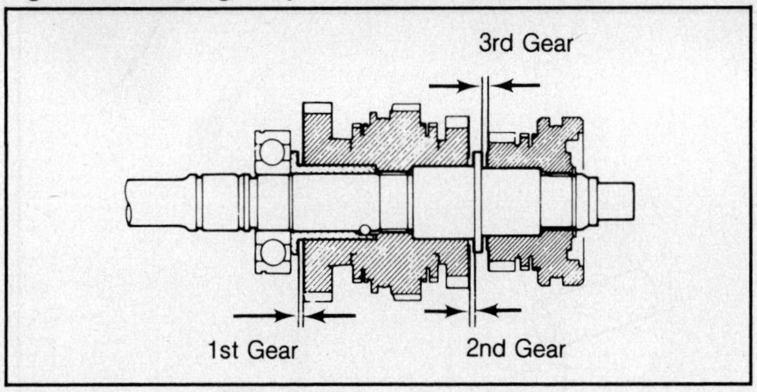

Fig. 9: Removing Locking Ball, Hub Sleeve No. 1 & 2nd Gear

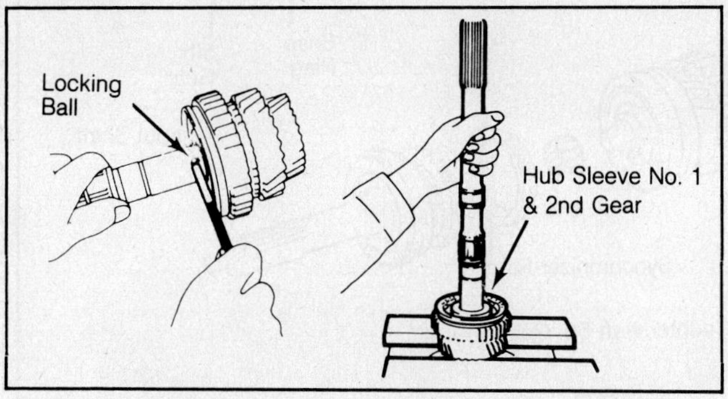

Cleaning & Inspection

1) Clean all parts in solvent. Inspect output shaft and inner race for wear or damage. Using Vernier caliper, measure output shaft flange thickness and inner race flange thickness.

2) Using micrometer, measure outer diameter of output shaft journal surface and outer diameter of inner race. Mount output shaft between 2 "V" blocks and measure shaft runout at center of shaft.

OUTPUT SHAFT SPECIFICATIONS

Application	In. (mm)
Output Shaft Flange	
Minimum Thickness	.1890 (4.80)
Inner Race Flange	
Minimum Thickness	.1571 (3.99)
Inner Race Outer Diameter	
Minimum Thickness	1.5348 (38.985)
Output Shaft Journal (Outer Diameter)	
Minimum Thickness	
2nd Gear	1.495 (37.984)
3rd Gear	1.3773 (34.984)
Maximum Runout	.002 (.05)

3) Using dial indicator, measure oil clearance between 1st gear and inner race with needle roller bearing installed. Measure oil clearance between output shaft and 2nd gear between shaft and 3rd gear. Measure oil clearance between countershaft and 5th gear.

4) Check all synchro rings for wear or damage. Turn ring and push in to check braking action. Measure clearance between synchro ring back and gear spline end. *See Fig. 11*.

5) Measure clearance between shift forks and hubs. Maximum clearance is .039" (1.0 mm).

GEAR-TO-SHAFT OIL CLEARANCE SPECIFICATIONS

Application	Standard In. (mm)	Maximum In. (mm)
1st Gear-to-Inner Race	.00035-.00126 (.009.-032)	.0126 (.032)
2nd Gear-to-Shaft	.00035-.00130 (.009-.033)	.00130 (.033)
3rd Gear-to-Shaft	.00035-.00130 (.009-.033)	.00130 (.033)
5th Gear-to-Countershaft	.00035-.00126 (.009-.032)	.00126 (.032)

SYNCHRO RING CLEARANCE SPECIFICATIONS

Application	In. (mm)
Standard	.039-.079 (1.0-2.0)
Maximum	.031 (.80)

Reassembly

1) Install clutch hub and shifting keys in hub sleeve. *See Fig. 12*. Install shifting key springs under shifting keys. Install key springs so end gaps are not in line.

2) Apply gear oil to shaft and needle roller bearing. Place synchro ring on gear and align ring slots with shifting keys. Install needle roller bearing in 3rd gear.

3) Press 3rd gear and No. 2 hub sleeve on output shaft. Select snap ring from NO. 2 HUB SLEEVE SNAP RING chart that will allow minimum axial end play and install. Using feeler gauge, measure 3rd gear end play to ensure it is correct.

NO. 2 HUB SLEEVE SNAP RING SIZES

Mark	Thickness In. (mm)
C-1	.0689-.0709 (1.75-1.80)
D	.0709-.0728 (1.80-1.85)
D-1	.0728-.0748 (1.85-1.90)
E	.0748-.0768 (1.90-1.95)
E-1	.0768-.0787 (1.95-2.00)
F	.0787-.0807 (2.00-2.05)
F-1	.0807-.0827 (2.05-2.10)

4) Install synchro ring on 2nd gear and align ring slots with shifting keys. Install needle roller bearing in 2nd gear. Press 2nd gear and No. 1 hub sleeve onto shaft.

5) Install interlocking ball in output shaft. Apply gear oil to needle roller bearing and assemble 1st gear, synchro ring, needle roller bearing and bearing inner race.

6) Install assembly on output shaft with synchro ring slots aligned with shifting keys. Turn inner race to align with locking ball.

7) Press bearing on output shaft with outer snap ring groove toward rear. Using feeler gauge, measure 1st, 2nd and 3rd gear end play to ensure it is correct. *See Fig. 8*.

8) Press 5th gear on end of output shaft. Install snap ring from OUTPUT SHAFT SNAP RING chart that will allow minimum axial end play and install.

Manual Transmissions

TOYOTA G52 5-SPEED (Cont.)

Fig. 10: Exploded View of Toyota G52 Transmission Gears

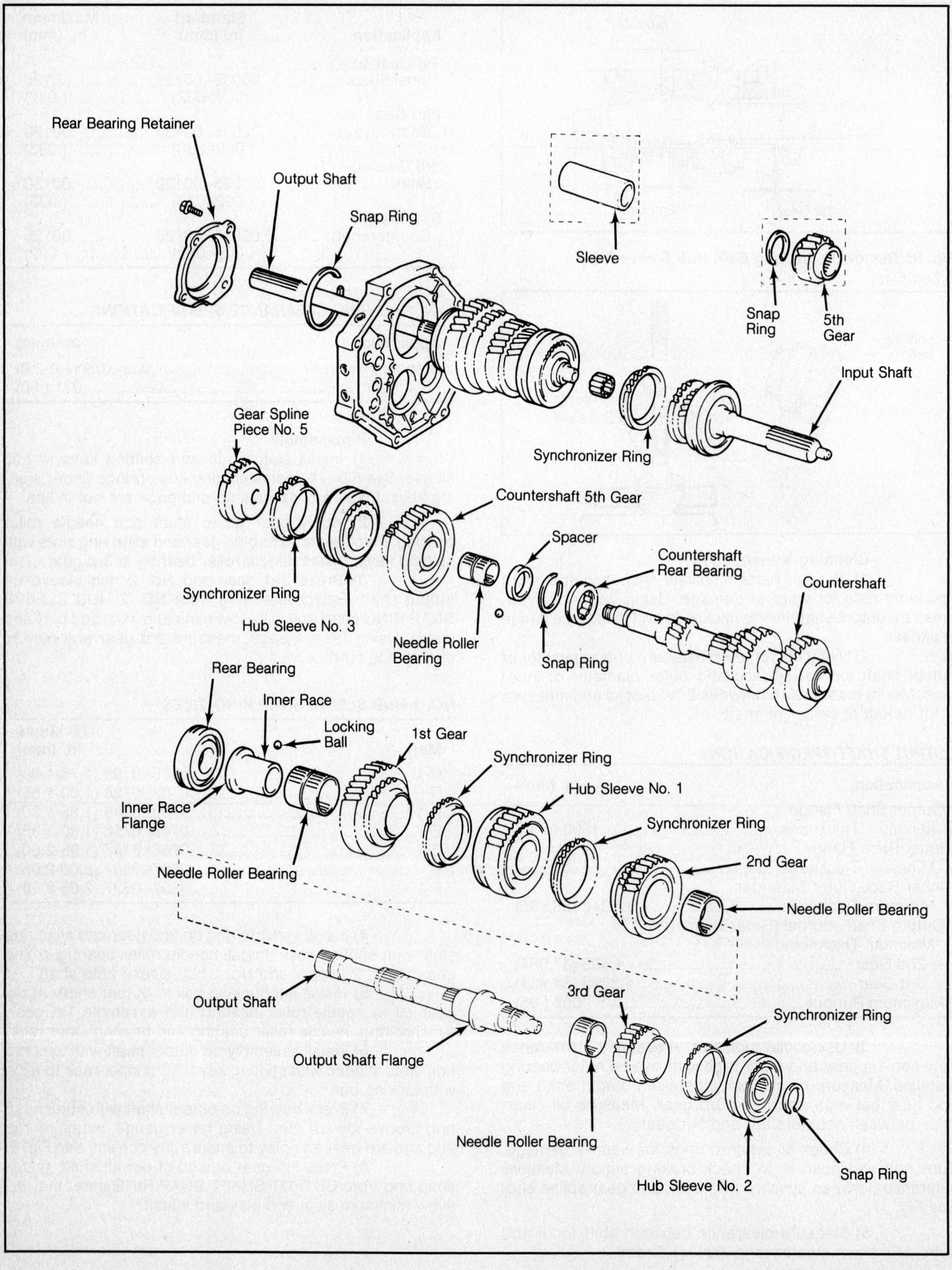

Fig. 11: Checking Synchro Rings

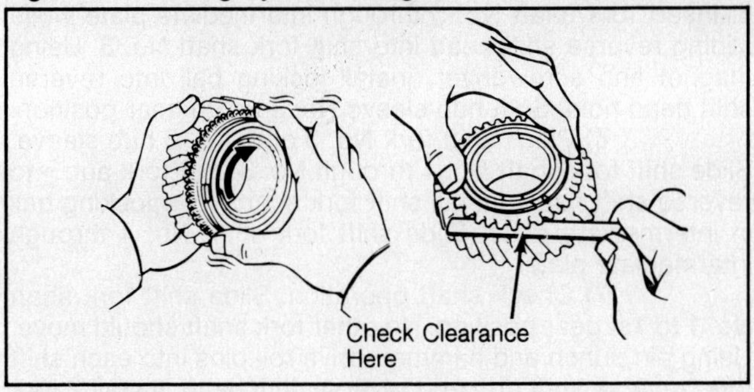

Fig. 12: Sectional View of Clutch Hubs

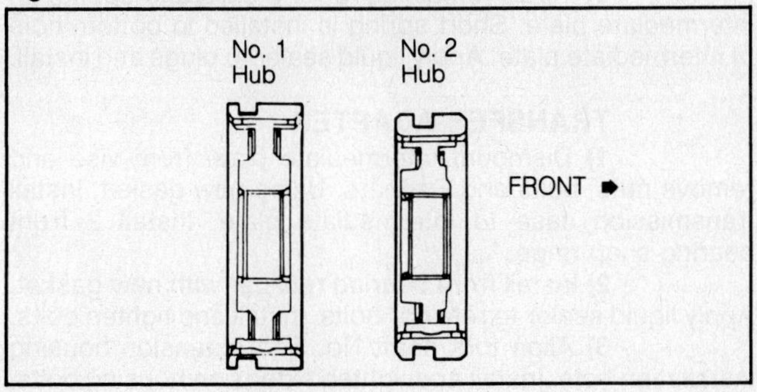

OUTPUT SHAFT SNAP RING

Mark	Thickness In. (mm)
A	.1051-.1071 (2.67-2.72)
B	.1075-.1094 (2.73-2.78)
C	.1098-.1118 (2.79-2.84)
D	.1122-.1142 (2.85-2.90)
E	.1146-.1165 (2.91-2.96)
F	.1169-.1189 (2.97-3.02)
G	.1193-.1213 (3.03-3.08)
H	.1217-.1236 (3.09-3.14)
J	.1240-.1260 (3.15-3.20)
K	.1264-.1283 (3.21-3.26)
L	.1287-.1307 (3.27-3.32)

INPUT SHAFT & FRONT BEARING RETAINER

1) Inspect input shaft and bearing for wear or damage. If necessary, press new bearing on input shaft. Select snap ring from COUNTERSHAFT AND INPUT SHAFT SNAP RING chart that will allow minimum axial end play and install.

COUNTERSHAFT & INPUT SHAFT SNAP RING

Mark	Thickness In. (mm)
0	.0807-.0827 (2.05-2.10)
1	.0827-.0846 (2.10-2.15)
2	.0846-.0866 (2.15-2.20)
3	.0866-.0886 (2.20-2.25)
4	.0886-.0906 (2.25-2.30)
5	.0906-.0925 (2.30-2.35)

2) Inspect front input shaft bearing retainer for damage. Replace oil seal. Install oil seal .441-.480" (11.2-12.2 mm) below transmission case surface.

COUNTERSHAFT

1) Inspect countershaft gear teeth for wear or damage. Check front bearing for wear or damage. Replace worn parts if necessary.

2) Bearing may be pressed off shaft after removing snap ring. When pressing new front bearing on countershaft, select snap ring from COUNTERSHAFT AND INPUT SHAFT SNAP RING chart that will allow minimum axial end play and install.

REVERSE RESTRICT PIN

1) Check reverse restrict pin for wear or damage. To replace restrict pin, remove screw plug using Torx head socket. Drive out slotted spring pin with punch and hammer.

2) Pull off lever housing and slide out shaft. To install reverse restrict pin, reverse removal procedure.

TRANSMISSION REASSEMBLY

INTERMEDIATE PLATE

Input, Output & Countershafts

1) Place intermediate plate in vise. Apply grease to needle roller bearings and install in input shaft. Install output shaft in intermediate plate by pulling on output shaft and tapping on plate. Install input shaft on output shaft with synchro ring slots aligned with shifting keys. Install countershaft on intermediate plate.

2) Install countershaft rear bearing using hammer and Installer (09316-60010). Install output shaft rear bearing snap ring. Ensure snap ring is flush with intermediate plate surface. Install rear bearing retainer.

3) Install reverse shift arm bracket. Install ball and spacer. Install shifting keys and hub sleeve No. 3 onto the countershaft 5th gear. *See Fig. 13*. Install shifting key springs under shifting keys, being sure end gaps are not in line.

Fig. 13: Sectional View of 5th Countershaft Gear & No. 3 Hub Sleeve

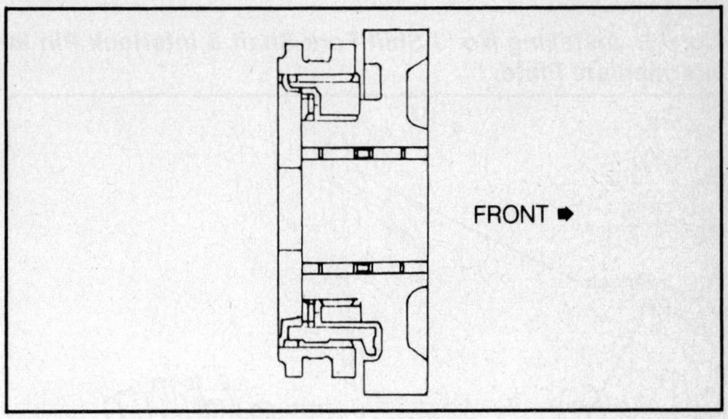

4) Install countershaft 5th gear, hub sleeve No. 3 and bearings onto countershaft. Install synchro ring on gear spline piece No. 5. Using Installer (09316-60010), support front of countershaft with 5 lb. hammer and drive in gear spline piece No. 5 with synchro ring slots aligned with shifting keys.

TOYOTA G52 5-SPEED (Cont.)

5) Install and tighten lock nut on rear of countershaft. Stake nut after installation. Measure countershaft 5th gear end play to ensure it is correct. *See Fig. 7.*

6) Connect reverse shift arm to reverse shift arm bracket. Install reverse idler gear on countershaft. Align reverse shift arm shoe to reverse idler gear groove. Insert reverse idler gear shaft in intermediate plate. Install reverse idler gear shaft stopper and tighten bolt.

Shift Fork Shafts

1) Place shift forks No. 1 and 2 in groove of hub sleeves No. 1 and 2. Install fork shaft No. 2 through intermediate plate and in shift forks No. 1 and 2.

2) Apply grease to interlock pins. Using magnet and screwdriver, install No. 1 shift fork shaft interlock pin in intermediate plate. *See Fig. 14.*

Fig. 14: Installing No. 1 Shift Fork Shaft & Interlock Pin in Intermediate Plate

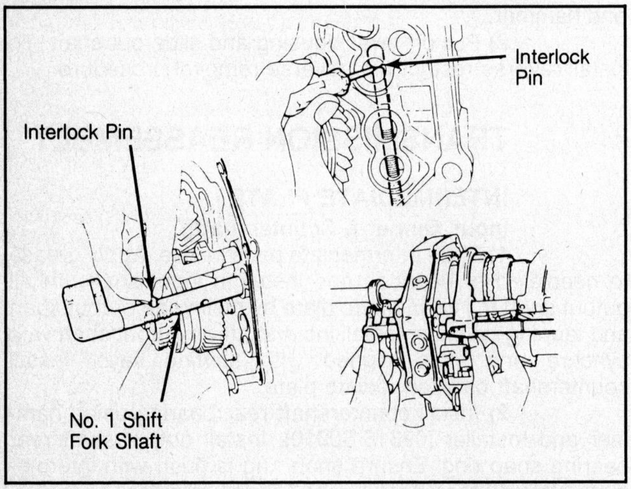

3) Place interlock pin in hole in No. 1 shift fork shaft. Install No. 1 shift fork shaft through intermediate plate and into shift fork No. 1.

4) Install No. 3 shift fork shaft interlock pin in intermediate plate. Install interlock pin in No. 3 shift fork shaft hole. Install No. 3 shift fork shaft through intermediate plate and into reverse shift arm. *See Fig. 15.*

Fig. 15: Installing No. 3 Shift Fork Shaft & Interlock Pin in Intermediate Plate

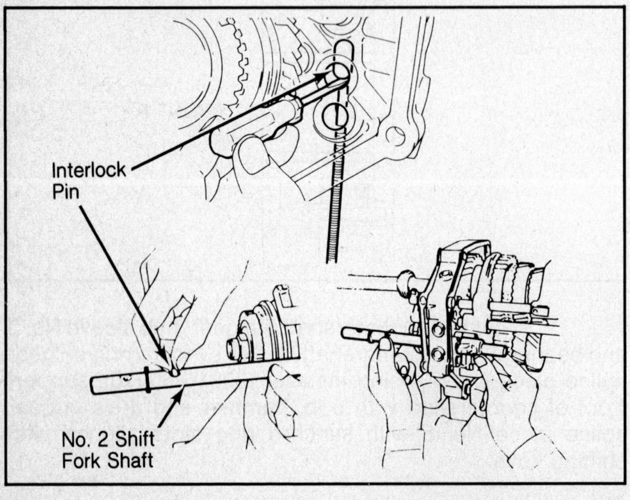

5) Install reverse shift head onto fork shaft No. 5. Insert fork shaft No. 5 through intermediate plate while sliding reverse shift head into shift fork shaft No. 3. Using magnet and screwdriver, install locking ball into reverse shift head hole. Shift hub sleeve No. 3 to 5th gear position.

6) Place shift fork No. 3 onto No. 3 hub sleeve. Slide shift fork shaft No. 4 through No. 3 shift fork and into reverse shift head. Install shift fork shaft No. 4 locking ball in intermediate plate. Slide shift fork shaft No. 4 through intermediate plate.

7) Check shaft operation. Slide shift fork shaft No. 1 to 1st gear position. No other fork shaft should move. Using pin punch and hammer, drive roll pins into each shift fork, reverse shift arm and reverse shift head. Install 2 fork shaft "E" rings.

8) Install remaining locking balls and springs in intermediate plate. Short spring is installed in bottom hole of intermediate plate. Apply liquid sealer to plugs and install.

TRANSFER ADAPTER

1) Dismount intermediate plate from vise and remove nuts, bolts and washers. Using new gasket, install transmission case to intermediate plate. Install 2 front bearing snap rings.

2) Install front bearing retainer with new gasket. Apply liquid sealer to retainer bolts. Install and tighten bolts.

3) Align fork shaft No. 5 to extension housing installation hole. Install and tighten extension housing bolts. Install and tighten shift lever housing bolt and new lock washer. Install new gasket on intermediate plate. Install transfer adapter with 8 attaching bolts

4) Insert shift lever housing to transfer adapter and connect fork shafts. Insert shift lever shaft to transfer adapter and shift lever housing. Install and tighten shift lever housing bolt and lock washer. Stake lock washer. Install and tighten plug on rear of transfer adapter. Apply liquid sealer to locking ball plug. Install locking ball, spring and plug.

5) Ensure input and output shaft rotate smoothly. Ensure transmission shifts easily into all gear positions.

6) Install and tighten restrict pins in extension housing/transfer adapter. Install clutch housing and attaching bolts. Install shift lever retainer. Install back-up light switch.

TIGHTENING SPECIFICATIONS

Application	Ft. Lbs. (N.m)
Back-Up Light Switch	27 (37)
Clutch Housing Bolts	27 (37)
Countershaft Rear Nut [1]	87 (118)
Extension Housing & Transfer Adapter Bolts	27 (37)
Front Bearing Retainer Bolts	12 (17)
Locking Ball Screw Plugs	14 (19)
Rear Bearing Retainer	13 (18)
Restrict Pins	20 (27)
Reverse Idler Gear Shaft Stopper Bolt	13 (18)
Reverse Restrict Pin Plug	14 (19)
Reverse Shift Arm Bracket Bolts	13 (18)
Shift Lever Housing Bolt	28 (38)
Shift Lever Retainer Bolts	13 (18)

[1] – Stake nut after installation.

Manual Transmissions

TOYOTA G53 5-SPEED

Van

DESCRIPTION

The Toyota G53 5-speed transmission is fully synchronized in all forward gears. Synchronizers are of the blocker type. Gear selection is accomplished by direct control through a floor mounted shift lever.

LUBRICATION & ADJUSTMENT

See appropriate MANUAL TRANSMISSION SERVICING article in IMPORT GENERAL SERVICING section.

TROUBLE SHOOTING

If transmission is hard to shift or will not shift, splines on input shaft may be dirty or burred, or transmission may be faulty. Disassemble, inspect and repair as necessary.

REMOVAL & INSTALLATION

See appropriate MANUAL TRANSMISSION REMOVAL article in IMPORT GENERAL SERVICING section.

TRANSMISSION DISASSEMBLY

1) Remove release fork and bearing. Remove back-up light switch and speedometer driven gear. Remove clutch housing from transmission. Remove shift lever housing assembly. Remove 8 extension housing bolts. Using plastic hammer, tap extension housing and remove. Remove shift lever housing and shift and select lever. Leave gasket attached to intermediate plate.

2) Remove front bearing retainer and 2 snap rings. Using plastic hammer, carefully tap transmission case and separate from intermediate plate. Install 2 clutch bolts, washers and nuts in 2 bottom holes of intermediate plate. Increase or decrease plate washers so bolt tip and front surface of nut are aligned. Mount intermediate plate in vise with pressure on nuts and bolts, NOT intermediate plate.

3) Using Torx socket, remove 4 plugs. Using care, remove 4 springs and balls, catching them by hand as they fall out. If they do not fall out, use magnet to remove. Using pin punch and hammer, drive out 4 pins. Remove 3 "E" clips and No. 1 shift fork bolt. Pull out shift fork shaft No. 3 from intermediate plate.

4) Remove shift fork and shaft No. 3. Remove locking ball and reverse shift head. Pull out shift fork shaft No. 4 from intermediate plate, catching pins as they fall out. If they do not fall out, remove with magnet.

5) Remove shift fork shaft No. 4. Remove shift fork shaft No. 2 from intermediate plate. Catch pin by hand when it falls from hole. If it does not fall out, remove with magnet.

6) Remove shift fork shaft No. 2 and shift fork No. 2. Pull out shift fork shaft No. 1 and remove shift fork No. 2, No. 1 and 1st and 2nd shift head. Remove reverse idler gear shaft stopper. Remove reverse idler gear and shaft.

7) Remove reverse shift arm from reverse shift arm bracket. Using feeler gauge, measure counter 5th gear thrust clearance. Standard clearance is .004-.012" (.10-.30 mm). Maximum clearance is .012" (.30 mm).

8) Slide synchros to engage 2nd and 3rd gears. Using hammer and chisel, loosen staked part of nut. Remove lock nut and disengage synchros. Using gear puller, remove gear spline piece No. 5 synchro ring, needle roller bearing and counter 5th gear.

9) Remove spacer and ball using magnet. Remove 2 bolts and reverse shift arm bracket. Using Torx socket, remove 4 rear bearing retainer bolts and snap ring. Remove output shaft, counter gear and input shaft as a unit from intermediate plate by pulling counter gear and tapping intermediate plate with plastic hammer.

10) Remove input shaft with 13 needle roller bearings from output shaft. Remove counter rear bearing from intermediate plate. Remove speedometer drive gear snap ring, speedometer drive gear and ball. Using magnet, remove steel ball. Using snap ring pliers, remove snap ring.

11) Measure thrust clearance of each gear. Standard clearance is .004-.010" (.10-.25 mm); maximum clearance is .010" (.25 mm). Using 2 screwdrivers and hammer, tap out 5th gear retaining snap ring. Using press, remove 5th gear, rear bearing, 1st gear and inner race. Remove needle roller bearing.

12) Remove synchro ring. Using magnet, remove locking ball. Using press, remove hub sleeve No. 1, synchro ring and 2nd gear. Remove needle roller bearing. Using snap ring pliers, remove snap ring. Using press, remove hub sleeve No. 2, synchro ring and 3rd gear. Remove needle roller bearing.

13) Remove lever lock pin and nut. Remove select outer lever and lever shaft from shift lever housing. Remove lever lock pin and pull out shift outer lever and boot. Using pin punch and hammer, drive out slotted spring pin.

14) Remove shift and select lever and shaft. Remove seat and compression spring. Remove tight plug. Using pliers, remove slotted spring pin, reverse restrict pin and compression spring.

INSPECTION

1) Check output shaft and inner race for wear or damage. Using caliper, measure thickness of output shaft flange. Minimun thickness is .1890" (4.80 mm). Measure thickness of inner race flange. Minimum thickness is .1571" (3.99 mm).

2) Using micrometer, measure outer diameter of output shaft journal surface. Minimum thickness for 2nd gear is 1.4954" (37.984 mm); 3rd gear, 1.3773" (34. 984 mm).

3) Using micrometer, measure outer diameter of inner race. Minimum diameter is 1.5348" (38.985 mm). Using dial indicator, measure shaft runout. Maximum runout is .0020" (.050 mm).

4) Using dial indicator, measure oil clearance between gear and inner race with needle roller bearing installed. Standard clearance is .00035-.00126" (.0090-.0320 mm); maximum clearance, .00126" (.032 mm).

5) Using dial indicator, measure oil clearance between 2nd, 3rd and counter 5th gear and shaft with needle roller bearing installed. Maximum clearance for 2nd and 3rd gears is .00130" (.033 mm); counter 5th gear is .00126" (.032 mm).

6) Check synchro rings for wear or damage. Turn ring and push in to check braking action. Measure clearance between synchro ring back and gear spline end.

TOYOTA G53 5-SPEED (Cont.)

Fig. 1: Exploded View of Case & Shifter Fork Assemblies

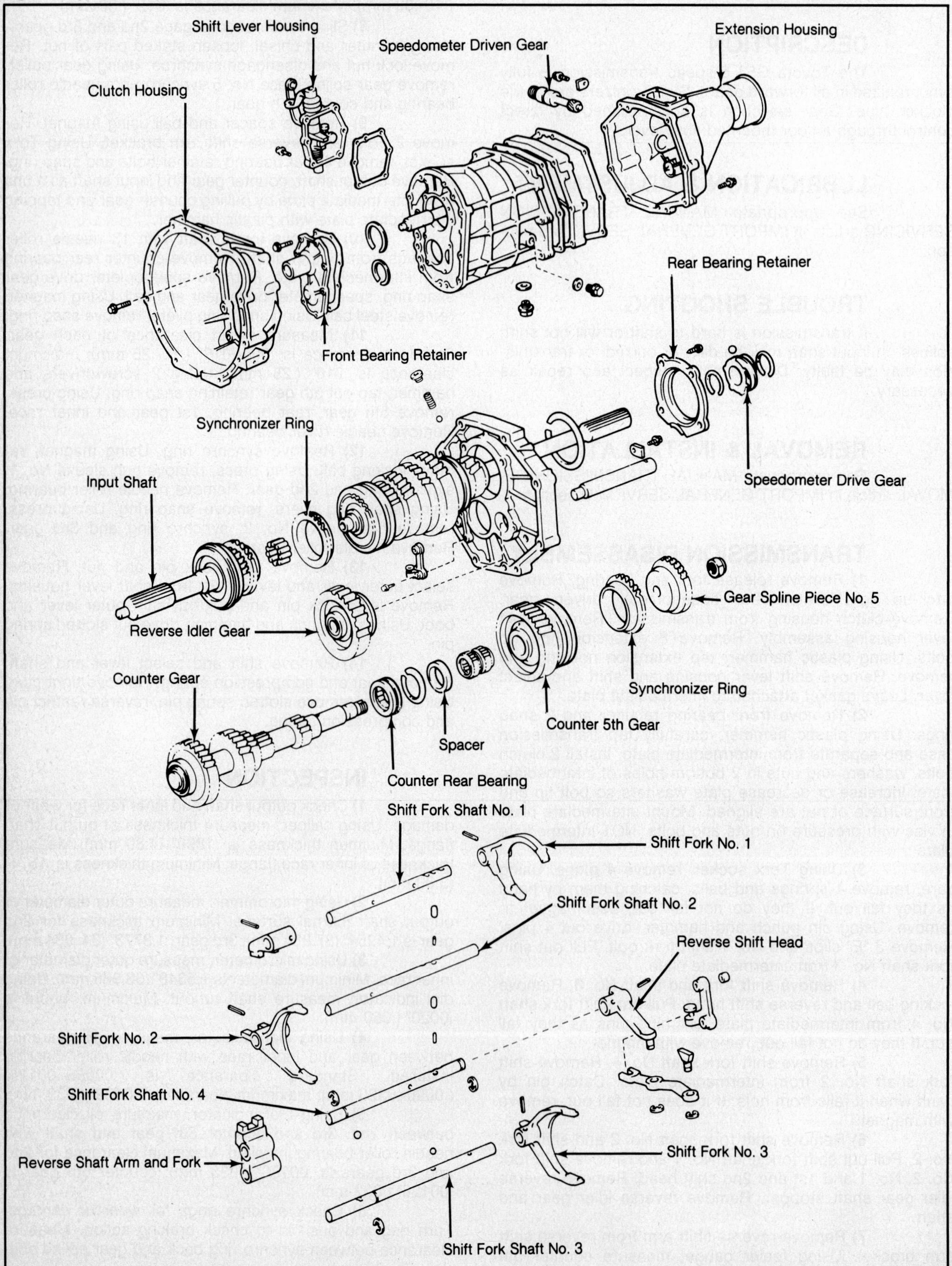

TOYOTA G53 5-SPEED (Cont.)

Fig. 2: Exploded View of Gear Assemblies

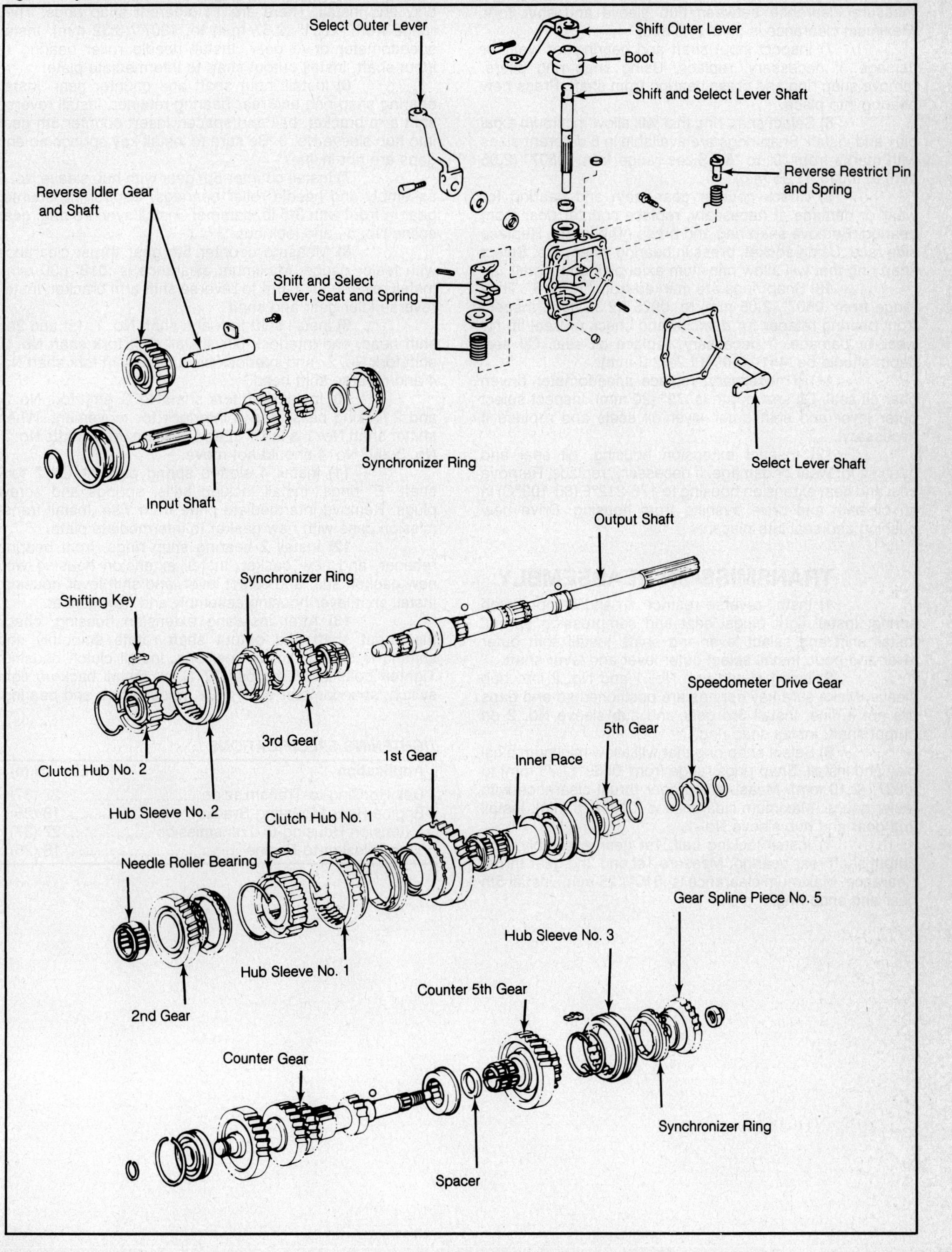

Manual Transmissions

TOYOTA G53 5-SPEED (Cont.)

Maximum clearance is .031" (.80 mm) Using feeler gauge, measure clearance between hub sleeve and shift fork. Maximum clearance is .040" (1.0 mm).

7) Inspect input shaft and bearing for wear or damage. If necessary, replace. Using snap ring pliers, remove snap ring and press bearing from shaft. Press new bearing into place.

8) Select snap ring that will allow minimum axial play and install. Snap rings are available in 6 different sizes with marks from "0" to "5". Sizes range from .0807" (2.05 mm) to .0925" (2.35 mm).

9) Check counter gear teeth and bearing for wear or damage. If necessary, replace counter gear front bearing. Remove snap ring and press off bearing. Replace side race. Using socket, press in bearing inner race. Select snap ring that will allow minimum axial play and install.

10) Snap rings are marked from "1" to "6". They range from .0807" (2.05 mm) to .0925" (2.35 mm). Inspect front bearing retaner for damage and check oil seal lip for wear or damage. If necessary, replace oil seal. Oil seal depth should be .441-.480" (11.2-12.2 mm).

11) If necessary, replace speedometer driven gear oil seal. Oil seal depth is .79" (20 mm). Inspect select outer lever and shift outer lever oil seals and replace if necessary.

12) Inspect extension housing, oil seal and bushing for wear or damage. If necessary, replace. Remove seal and heat extension housing to 176-212°F (80-100°C) in an oil bath and drive bushing from housing. Drive new bushing and seal into place.

TRANSMISSION REASSEMBLY

1) Install reverse restrict pin and compression spring. Install tight plugs, seat and compression spring. Install shift and select lever and shaft. Install shift outer lever and boot. Install select outer lever and lever shaft.

2) Insert clutch hub No. 1 and No. 2 into hub sleeve. Make sure key springs are positioned so end gaps are not in line. Install 3rd gear and hub sleeve No. 2 on output shaft. Install snap ring.

3) Select snap ring that will allow minimum axial play and install. Snap rings range from .0689" (1.75 mm) to .0827" (2.10 mm). Measure 3rd gear thrust clearance with feeler gauge. Maximum clearance is .010" (.25 mm). Install 2nd gear and hub sleeve No. 1.

4) Install locking ball, 1st gear assembly, and output shaft rear bearing. Measure 1st and 2nd gear thrust clearance. Maximum clearance is .010" (.25 mm). Install 5th gear and snap ring.

5) Install snap ring that will allow minimum axial play and install. There are 11 different snap rings. They range from .1051" (2.67 mm) to .1307" (3.32 mm). Install speedometer drive gear. Install needle roller bearing to input shaft. Install output shaft to intermediate plate.

6) Install input shaft and counter gear. Install bearing snap ring and rear bearing retainer. Install reverse shift arm bracket, ball and spacer. Insert counter 5th gear into hub sleeve No. 3. Be sure to install key springs so end gaps are not in line.

7) Install counter 5th gear with hub sleeve No. 3 assembly and needle roller bearings. Supporting counter gear in front with 3-5 lb. hammer, install synchro ring, gear spline No. 5 and lock nut.

8) Measure counter 5th gear thrust clearance with feeler gauge. Maximum clearance is .012" (.30 mm). Install reverse shift arm to reverse shift arm bracket. Install reverse idler gear and shaft.

9) Install shift fork and shaft No. 1, 1st and 2nd shift head, and interlock pin. Install shift fork shaft No. 2, shift fork No. 2 and interlock pin. Install shift fork shaft No. 4 and reverse shift head.

10) Install shift fork shaft No. 3, shift fork No. 3, and 2 locking balls. Check interlock for movement. When shifter shaft No. 1 is in 1st speed position, fork shafts No. 2, No. 3 and No. 4 should not move.

11) Install 4 slotted spring pins. Install 2 fork shaft "E" rings. Install locking balls, springs and screw plugs. Remove intermediate plate from vise. Install transmission case with new gasket to intermediate plate.

12) Install 2 bearing snap rings, front bearing retainer, and new gasket. Install extension housing with new gasket, shift and select lever, and shift lever housing. Install shift lever housing assembly and new gasket.

13) After installing extension housing, check that input shaft and output shaft rotate smoothly and shifting is smooth to all positions. Install clutch housing. Tighten bolts to 27 ft. lbs. (37 N.m). Install back-up light switch, speedometer drive gear, release fork and bearing.

TIGHTENING SPECIFICATIONS

Application	Ft. Lbs. (N.m)
Bell Housing-to-Transmission	27 (37)
Engine Rear Mounting Bracket	18 (25)
Extension Housing-to-Transmission	27 (37)
Transmission-to-Engine	18 (25)

TOYOTA H42 4-SPEED

Land Cruiser

DESCRIPTION

The Toyota model H42 manual transmission is a 4-speed unit, synchronized in all forward gears due to the use of blocker type synchro assemblies. All forward gears are helical cut and in constant mesh. Reverse gears are spur cut and are engaged by a sliding reverse idler gear.

NOTE: **For Transfer Case service and repair procedures see appropriate article in OVERDRIVES & TRANSFER CASE section.**

LUBRICATION & ADJUSTMENT

See appropriate MANUAL TRANSMISSION SERVICING article in IMPORT GENERAL SERVICING section.

TROUBLE SHOOTING

HARD SHIFTING

Clutch not releasing. Check for proper adjustment, deformed clutch disc, seized or damaged pilot bearing. Incorrect or insufficient lubricant. Gearshift lever retainer binding or improperly lubricated. Shift forks worn or damaged. Shift shafts bent.

JUMPS OUT OF GEAR

Worn or damaged shift forks. Detent balls and springs worn or broken. Worn or damaged synchro assemblies. Improper thrust clearance between gears.

NOISY OPERATION

Improper or insufficient lubricant. Worn or damaged bushings, bearings and/or gears. Worn splines.

NOTE: **When checking transmission for noise, ensure that it is not coming from other parts of drive line.**

REMOVAL & INSTALLATION

See appropriate MANUAL TRANSMISSION REMOVAL article in IMPORT GENERAL SERVICING section.

TRANSMISSION DISASSEMBLY

1) Remove transmission rear bearing retainer and spacer. Remove transmission shift cover assembly and side cover. Remove front bearing retainer from transmission case.

Fig. 2: Lifting Output Shaft Assembly from Transmission Case

2) Remove inner and outer front bearing retaining snap rings from countershaft. Remove bearing from transmission case using puller. Using same procedure, remove countershaft rear bearing and thrust washer.

3) Drive input shaft assembly and bearing from case. Remove output shaft bearing snap ring. Pull bearing from transmission case with puller.

Fig. 1: Disassembled View of Land Cruiser 4-Speed Transmission Assembly

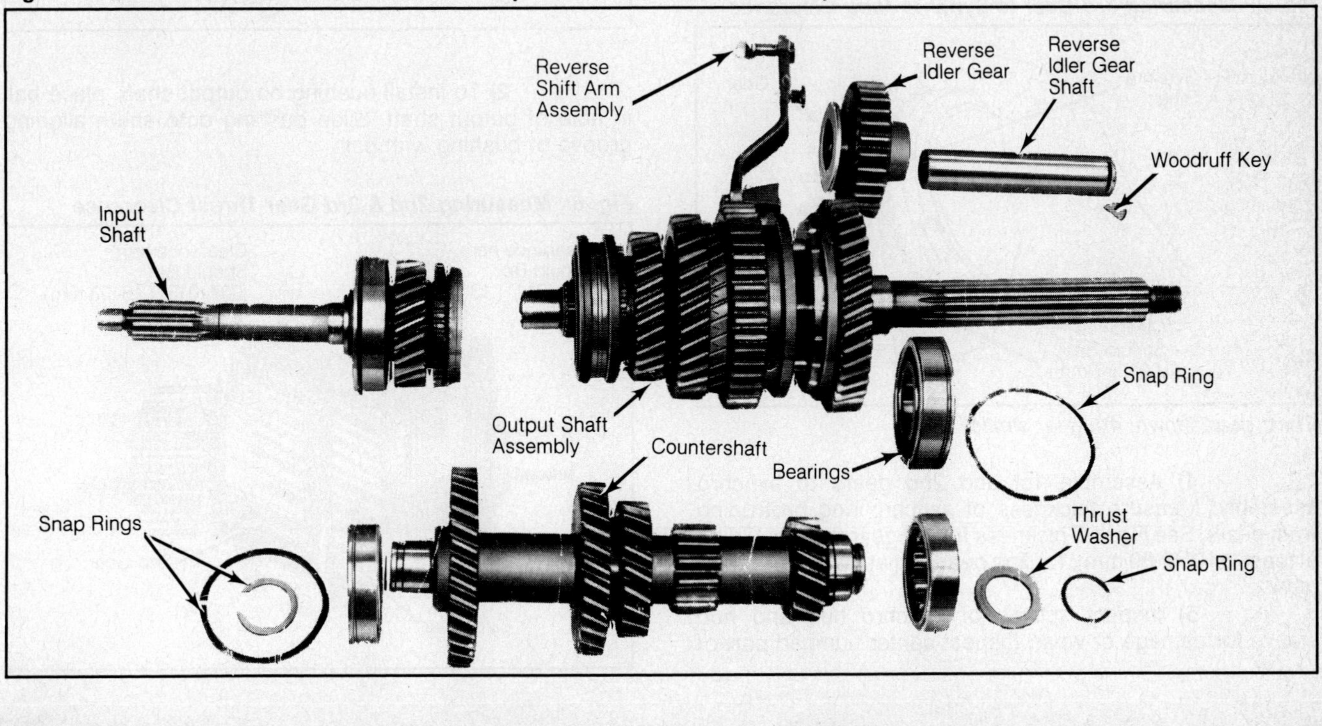

TOYOTA H42 4-SPEED (Cont.)

4) Hold 1st gear tightly against other gears to prevent from sliding off. Lift output shaft assembly from transmission case. *See Fig. 2.* Remove countershaft from case.

5) Drive reverse idler gear shaft out rear of case using care not to lose Woodruff key. Lift reverse idler gear from bottom of transmission case. Remove reverse shift arm assembly from case.

COMPONENT DISASSEMBLY & REASSEMBLY

OUTPUT SHAFT ASSEMBLY

Disassembly

1) From rear of output shaft, remove 1st gear thrust washer. Slide off 1st gear and needle bearing using care not to lose pin. Slide 1st-2nd synchro assembly from output shaft.

2) Remove snap ring from front of output shaft. Slide off 3rd-4th synchro hub. Pull 3rd gear and bushing off shaft using care not to lose ball. Slide 2nd gear and needle bearing off output shaft.

3) To disassemble synchro assembly, slide synchro hub sleeve from hub. Remove key springs and keys.

Inspection

1) Check output shaft surfaces and bushing for wear or damage. Check bushing-to-3rd gear oil clearance (clearance between outer diameter of bushing and inner diameter of gear). Clearance should be .003-.005" (.07-.12 mm).

2) Inspect gears for wear or damage to teeth, thrust faces, inside diameter, and coned surfaces. Inspect output shaft ball bearing and needle bearings for wear or damage.

3) Assemble synchro ring on 3rd gear and check ring-to-gear clearance. *See Fig. 3.* Clearance should be .031" (.80 mm). Repeat measurement for 4th gear ring.

Fig. 3: Measuring 3rd Gear-to-Synchro Ring Clearance

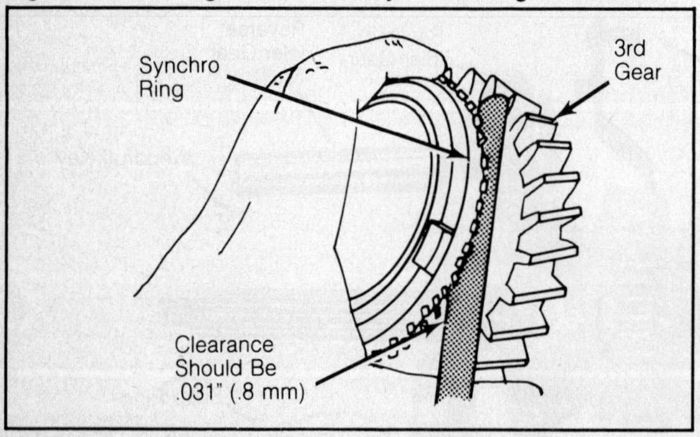

Third gear shown; 4th gear similar.

4) Assemble 1st and 2nd gears to synchro assembly. Measure thickness of synchro ring protruding from gears. *See Fig. 4.* Thickness for 1st gear ring should be at least .110" (2.80 mm); for 2nd gear ring at least .071" (1.80 mm).

5) Inspect splines of synchro hub and hub sleeve for damage or wear. Inspect center humped part of keys for damage and wear. Inspect key springs for weakening and damage.

6) Insert shift forks into their respective synchro hub sleeve and measure clearance between shift fork and sleeve. Clearance should be less than .032" (.80 mm).

Fig. 4: Checking 1st & 2nd Gear Synchronizer Ring Wear

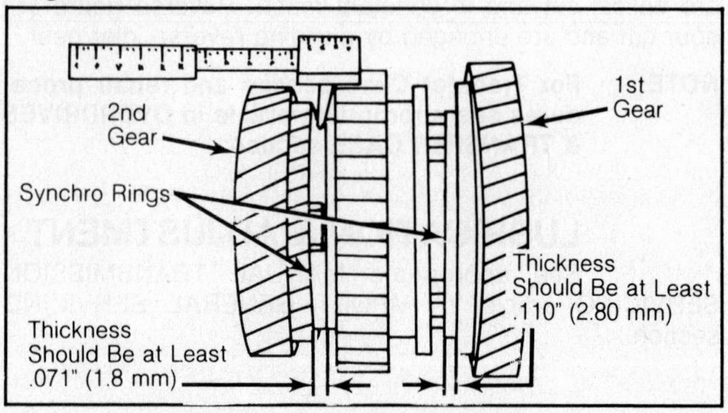

Reassembly

1) To reassemble component, reverse disassembly procedure. Reassemble synchro assembly. *See Fig. 5.* Ensure key springs are positioned so end gaps will not be in line.

Fig. 5: Cross-Section View of Synchro Assembly

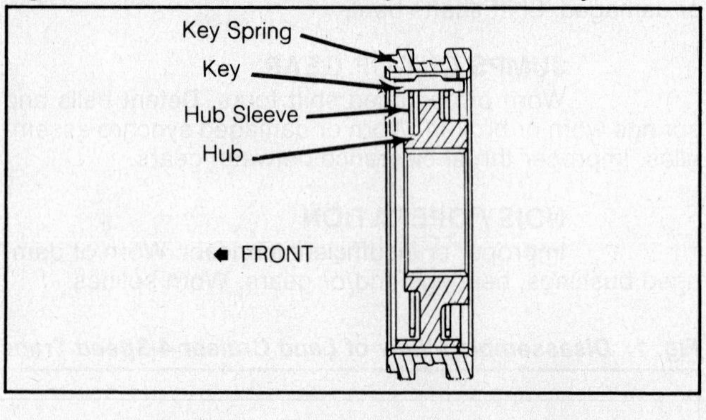

2) To install bushing on output shaft, place ball in hole of output shaft. Slide bushing onto shaft, aligning groove of bushing with ball.

Fig. 6: Measuring 2nd & 3rd Gear Thrust Clearance

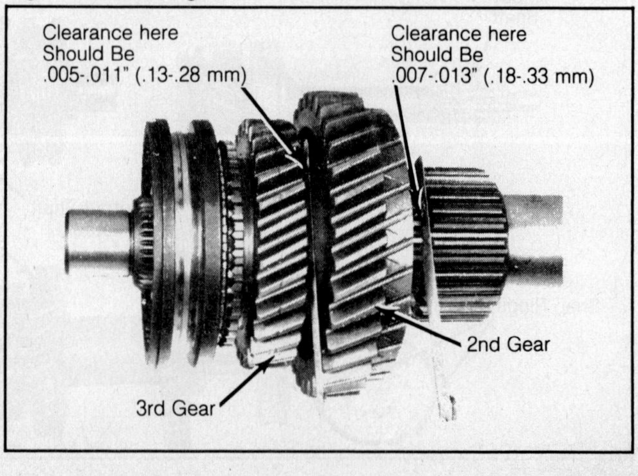

TOYOTA H42 4-SPEED (Cont.)

3) Install thickest possible snap ring on front of output shaft that will provide a gear thrust clearance of .007-.013" (.18-.33 mm) for 2nd gear and .005-.011" (.13-.28 mm) for 3rd gear. *See Fig. 6.*

SHIFT COVER ASSEMBLY

Disassembly

1) Remove attaching bolts and lift off shift lever retainer and gasket. Move shift forks and shafts into neutral position. Invert shift cover assembly and drive out spring pin retaining 3rd-4th shift fork-to-shift fork shaft.

2) Drive out shift fork shaft with expansion plug using brass drift. Cover service hole with hand to prevent locking ball from flying out. Remove 3rd-4th shift fork and interlock pin. Remove locking ball and spring with magnet.

3) Drive out spring pin retaining reverse shift head. Drive out shift fork shaft together with expansion plug. Cover service hole with hand. Remove 2nd locking ball and spring with magnet.

4) Drive out slotted spring pin to remove 1st-2nd shift fork. Drive out fork shaft together with expansion plug. Cover service hole with hand. Remove interlock pin from shaft using magnet. Remove 3rd locking ball and spring with magnet. Remove lock pins from case.

5) If necessary to disassemble reverse shift head, remove cotter pin and remove spring and lock ball from bore in shift head. Remove "C" washer and pull out reverse shift return plunger and spring.

Inspection

Inspect shift fork shafts and heads for bending, wear, or damage at sliding surfaces. Check shift cover bores for wear or damage. Inspect detent balls and springs for wear or damage. *See Fig. 8.*

Reassembly

Reverse disassembly procedure ensuring shift forks and heads are correctly positioned before installing shift forks. Coat expansion plugs with sealer and install in shift cover. Plugs must not be driven more than .10" (2.5 mm) below cover surface.

INPUT SHAFT

Inspection

Inspect input shaft gear teeth, splines, coned surfaces, and bearing for damage or wear. Check inner surface of input shaft for damage or wear. Inspect needle bearings for wear. If necessary, replace needle bearings as a set.

Fig. 8: Exploded View of Shift Cover Assembly

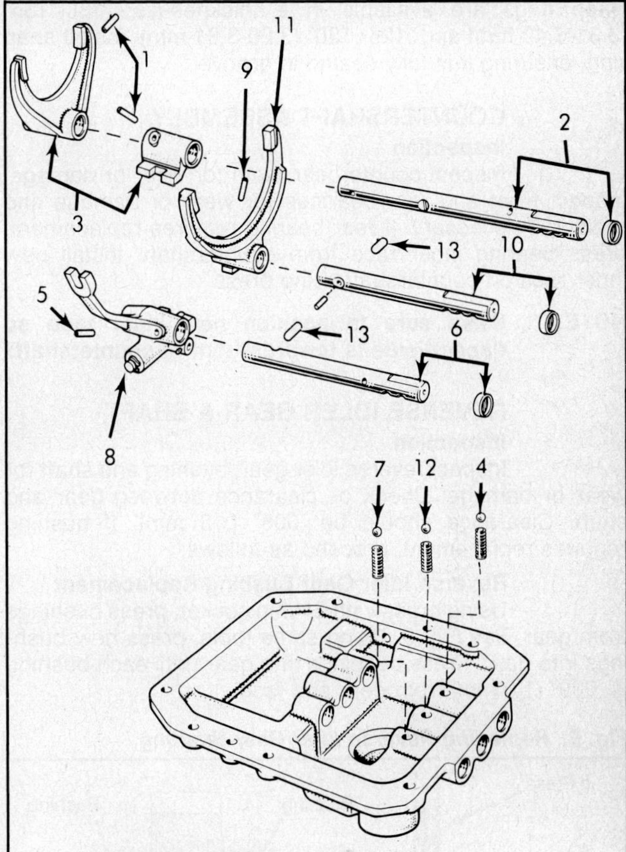

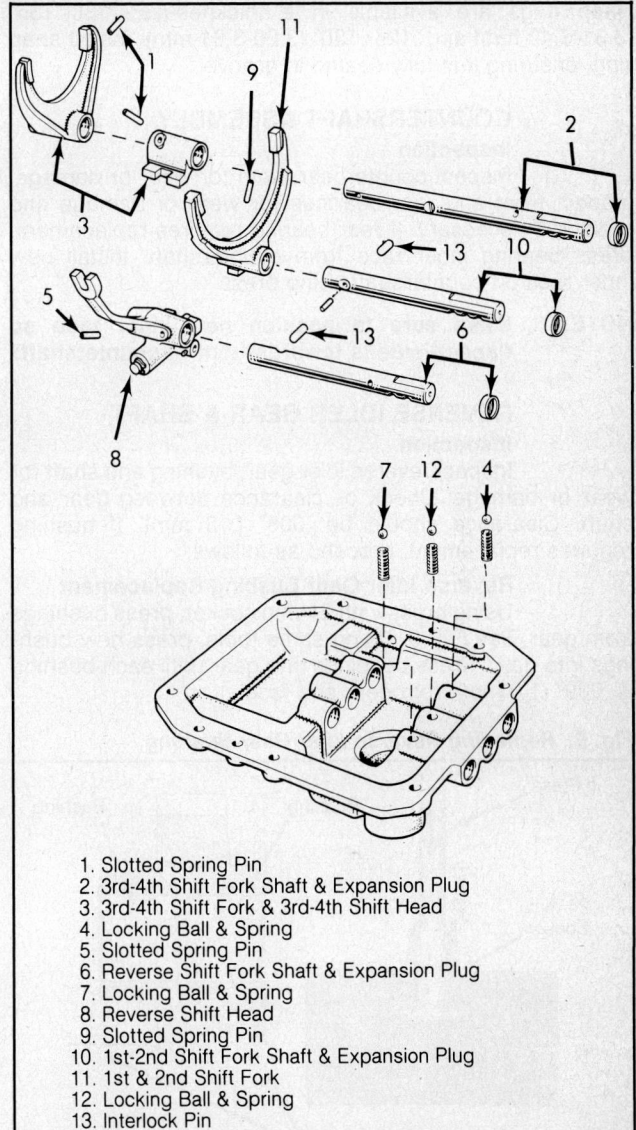

1. Slotted Spring Pin
2. 3rd-4th Shift Fork Shaft & Expansion Plug
3. 3rd-4th Shift Fork & 3rd-4th Shift Head
4. Locking Ball & Spring
5. Slotted Spring Pin
6. Reverse Shift Fork Shaft & Expansion Plug
7. Locking Ball & Spring
8. Reverse Shift Head
9. Slotted Spring Pin
10. 1st-2nd Shift Fork Shaft & Expansion Plug
11. 1st & 2nd Shift Fork
12. Locking Ball & Spring
13. Interlock Pin

Input Shaft Bearing Replacement

Remove snap ring and press off old bearing. Press new bearing in position and select a snap ring of

Fig. 7: Exploded View Showing Output Shaft Components

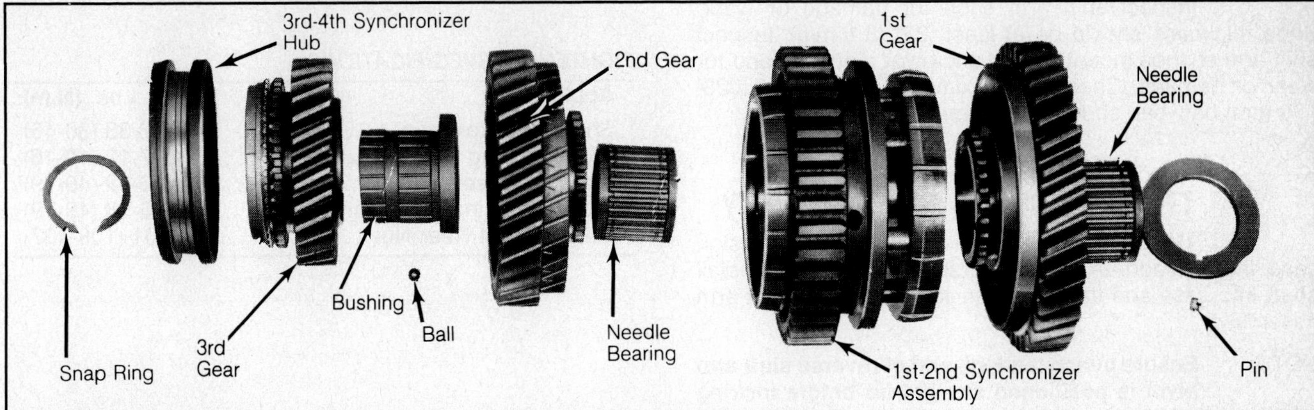

Manual Transmissions

TOYOTA H42 4-SPEED (Cont.)

proper thickness to provide minimum amount of axial play. Snap rings are available in 2 thicknesses: .130-.135" (3.31-3.42 mm) and .126-.130" (3.20-3.31 mm). Install snap ring, ensuring it is fully seated in groove.

COUNTERSHAFT ASSEMBLY

Inspection

Inspect countergear teeth for wear or damage. Inspect front and rear bearings for wear or damage and replace if necessary. If rear bearing requires replacement, press bearing inner race from countershaft. Install new inner race on countershaft using press.

NOTE: **Make sure to position new inner race so flanged side is towards front of countershaft.**

REVERSE IDLER GEAR & SHAFT

Inspection

Inspect reverse idler gear, bushing and shaft for wear or damage. Check oil clearance between gear and shaft. Clearance should be .006" (.16 mm). If bushing requires replacement, proceed as follows:

Reverse Idler Gear Bushing Replacement

Using press with 24 mm socket, press bushings from gear. *See Fig. 9.* Using same tools, press new bushings into gear. Press bushings into gear until each bushing is .039" (1.0 mm) from gear end face.

Fig. 9: Replacing Reverse Idler Gear Bushing

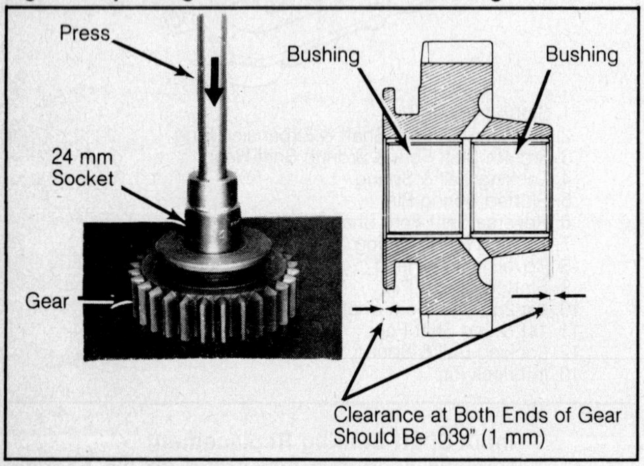

REVERSE SHIFT ARM

Inspection

Inspect shift arm shoe for damage or wear. Shoe thickness should be at least .32" (8.1 mm). Inspect shift arm at shoe mounting end and pivot mounting end for wear or damage. Check for maximum clearance of .028" (.70 mm) between shoe and reverse idler gear slot.

TRANSMISSION REASSEMBLY

1) Position reverse idler gear in transmission case. Install Woodruff key in reverse idler gear shaft. Install shaft into case and through gear. Install reverse shift arm assembly.

NOTE: **Ensure punch mark on end of reverse shift arm pivot is positioned straight up before locking pivot nut.**

2) Lay countershaft in bottom of transmission case. Install output shaft assembly into transmission case. Drive output shaft rear bearing onto shaft and into case bore until it is fully seated.

3) Using grease to hold in place, install the 17 needle bearings into input shaft bore. Assemble synchro ring to synchro hub on input shaft. Drive input shaft into transmission case with plastic hammer.

4) Align countershaft with bores in case. Start rear bearing onto shaft and into case bore. Position front bearing on countershaft. Drive bearings onto shaft and into case bores by alternately tapping with plastic hammer.

5) Install thrust washer and snap ring on rear of countershaft. Install large (outer) snap ring on countershaft front bearing. Install thickest snap ring that will properly fit groove on front of countershaft.

NOTE: **Countershaft selective fit snap rings are available in following thicknesses: .0807-.0827" (2.05-2.10 mm), .0846-.0866" (2.15-2.20 mm) and .0886-.0906" (2.25-2.30 mm).**

6) Install front bearing retainer and tighten attaching bolts. Install transmission side cover. Install rear bearing retainer and spacer.

7) Place shift cover assembly and all gears in neutral position. Position shift cover assembly on transmission case. Install and tighten attaching bolts.

8) Temporarily install transmission shift lever into shift cover assembly. While rotating input shaft check shifting and output shaft rotational relationship.

9) If abnormal noise develops while turning input shaft, correct by adjusting reverse shift arm pivot within range of 0° to 45° of marker point (punch mark). *See Fig. 10.*

Fig. 10: Reverse Shift Arm Pivot Adjustment

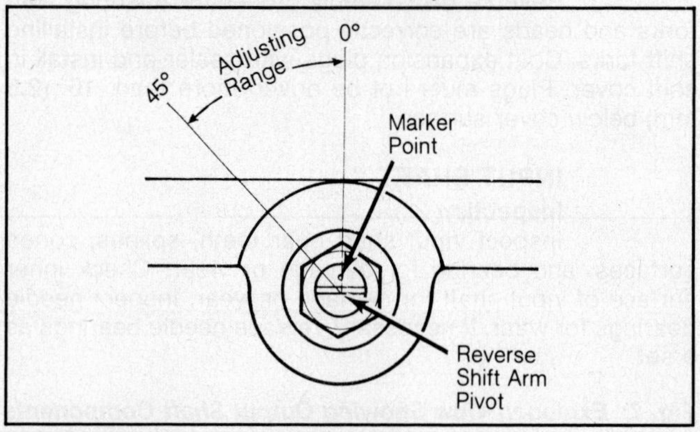

TIGHTENING SPECIFICATIONS

Application	Ft. Lbs. (N.m)
Shift Cover-to-Case	22-33 (30-45)
Front Bearing Retainer-to-Case	7-12 (10-16)
Transfer Case-to-Transmission	36-58 (49-79)
Clutch Housing-to-Transmission	36-58 (49-79)
Output Shaft Rear Nut	80-101 (108-137)

TOYOTA T50 5-SPEED

Corolla RWD

IDENTIFICATION

The T50 transmission can be identified from other Toyota transmissions by its 2-piece ribbed aluminum case.

Fig. 1: Exterior View of Transmission Case

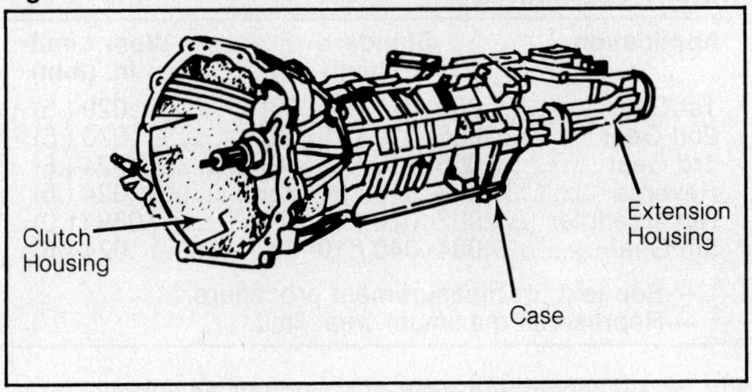

DESCRIPTION

Transmission is a 5-speed, fully synchronized unit, in which all gears are helical cut and in constant mesh. Gear engagement is accomplished through use of 3 blocker-type synchro assemblies. Floor shift lever operates a single control rod in extension housing, which in turn is connected to shifting rails in rear of transmission case. To access internal parts it is necessary to separate transmission case halves.

LUBRICATION & ADJUSTMENT

See appropriate MANUAL TRANSMISSION SERVICING article in IMPORT GENERAL SERVICING section.

SERVICE (IN VEHICLE)

GEAR SHIFT LEVER

Removal & Installation

Pull up rubber shift lever boot. Remove 4 bolts holding shift lever to transmission. Pull shift lever out of transmission. To install gear shift lever, reverse removal procedure.

EXTENSION HOUSING SEAL

Removal & Installation

Remove center driveshaft support bearing and heat insulating shield. Remove drive shaft. Use puller to remove seal. To install extension housing, reverse removal procedure. Ensure seal is installed straight and even in bore. Apply multipurpose grease to oil seal.

REMOVAL & INSTALLATION

TRANSMISSION

See appropriate MANUAL TRANSMISSION REMOVAL article in IMPORT GENERAL SERVICING section.

TRANSMISSION DISASSEMBLY

CLUTCH HOUSING

Remove four bolts, front bearing retainer, and spacer. Ensure oil seal lip is not damaged.

EXTENSION HOUSING

Remove speedometer driven gear retainer bolt. Remove shaft sleeve and driven gear. Remove back-up light switch. Remove 6 housing bolts. When removing extension housing, ensure output spline does not damage rear oil seal.

TRANSMISSION CASE

1) Remove plate holding shift fork rail locking balls and springs. Remove balls and springs with magnet. Remove bolts holding case halves together and separate by tapping protrusion on right case with plastic hammer. *See Fig. 2.* Be sure to retain locking balls between cases and countergear bearing.

Fig. 2: Using Hammer to Separate Case Halves

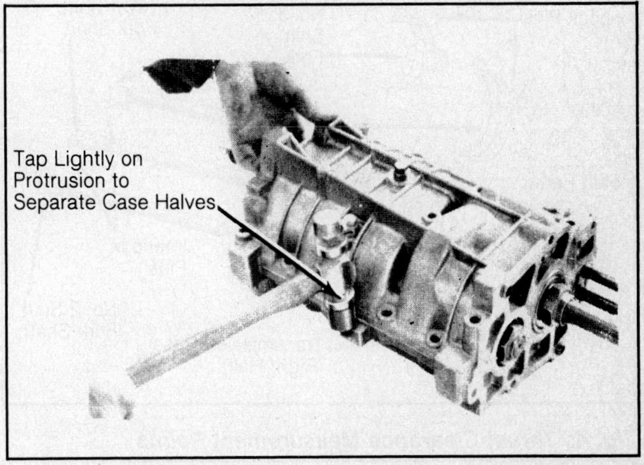

2) With left case removed, lift mainshaft from right case. Lift out countergear assembly. Using pin punch, drive out pins holding shift forks to rails. Note pin holding No. 1 fork is driven out through hole in case. Drive out pin in No. 2 and No. 3 shift forks. Place all shift rails in neutral position and pull individually from rear of case.

CLEANING & INSPECTION

Clean all mating surfaces and check for warpage. Check all components for abnormal wear or discoloration from overheating. Verify components are not cracked or chipped.

COMPONENT DISASSEMBLY, INSPECTION & REASSEMBLY

MAINSHAFT

Disassembly

1) Measure thrust clearance of each gear and record for reassembly reference. *See Fig. 4.* Remove snap rings holding speedometer drive gear and remove drive gear.

TOYOTA T50 5-SPEED (Cont.)

Fig. 3: Exploded View of T50 Transmission

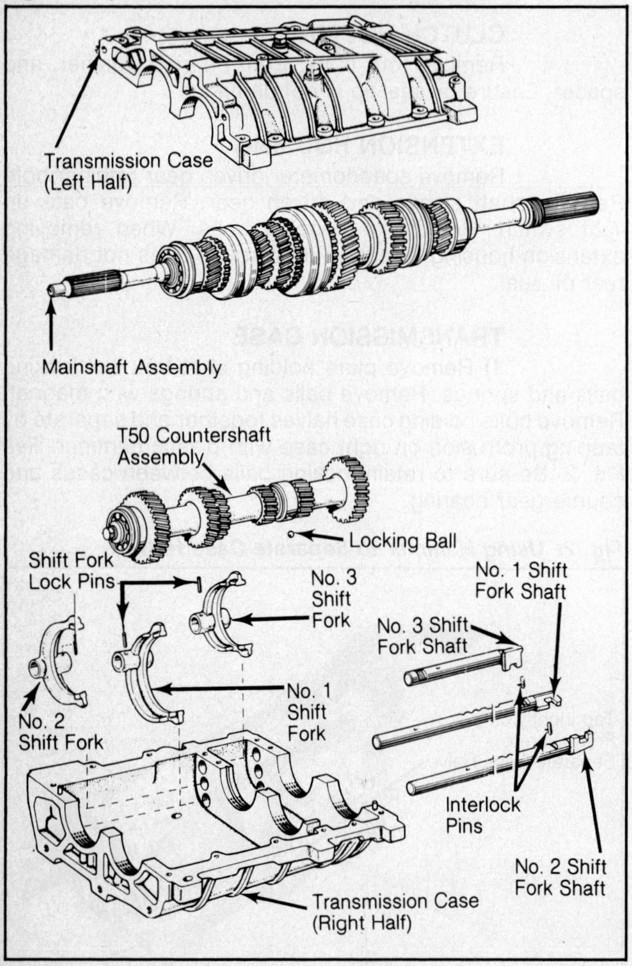

Fig. 4: Thrust Clearance Measurement Points

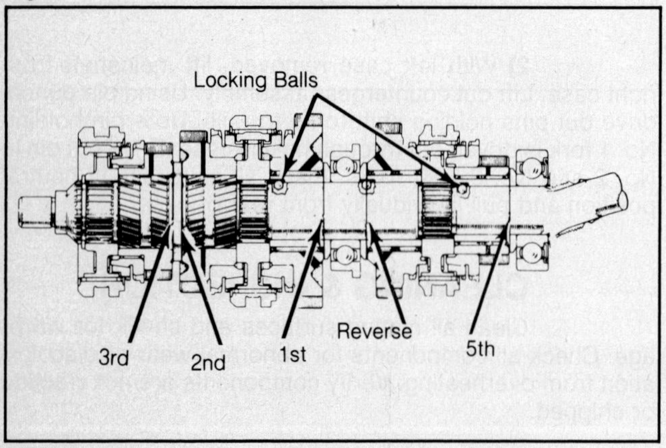

2) Remove snap ring from rear bearing. Remove rear bearing using Puller (SST 09950-20014). Remove spacer, 5th gear, synchro ring, needle roller bearings, spacer and steel ball. Remove snap ring, No. 3 clutch hub and sleeve. Support reverse gear with vise jaws. Press down on output shaft. Remove reverse gear, needle bearing and bushing.

3) Remove center bearing, bushing, needle bearing, 1st gear, and synchro ring. Remove and retain locking ball. Press output shaft from 1st gear assembly using same procedure as for reverse gear. Remove snap ring from front of shaft. Press No. 2 clutch hub and sleeve with 3rd gear and synchro ring from shaft.

NOTE: When pressing gear assemblies from mainshaft, support shaft with hand to prevent from dropping when it clears hub splines. Retain all locking balls.

THRUST CLEARANCE

Application [1]	Standard In. (mm)	[2] Wear Limit In. (mm)
1st Gear	.006-.011 (.15-.28)	.020 (.5)
2nd Gear	.006-.010 (.15-.25)	.020 (.5)
3rd Gear	.006-.012 (.15-.30)	.024 (.6)
Reverse	.008-.013 (.20-.32)	.024 (.6)
Reverse Idler	.002-.020 (.05-.50)	.039 (1.0)
5th Gear	.004-.040 (.10-.93)	.024 (.6)

[1] – See text for measurement procedure.
[2] – Represents maximum wear limit.

Fig. 5: Disassembled View of Mainshaft Assembly

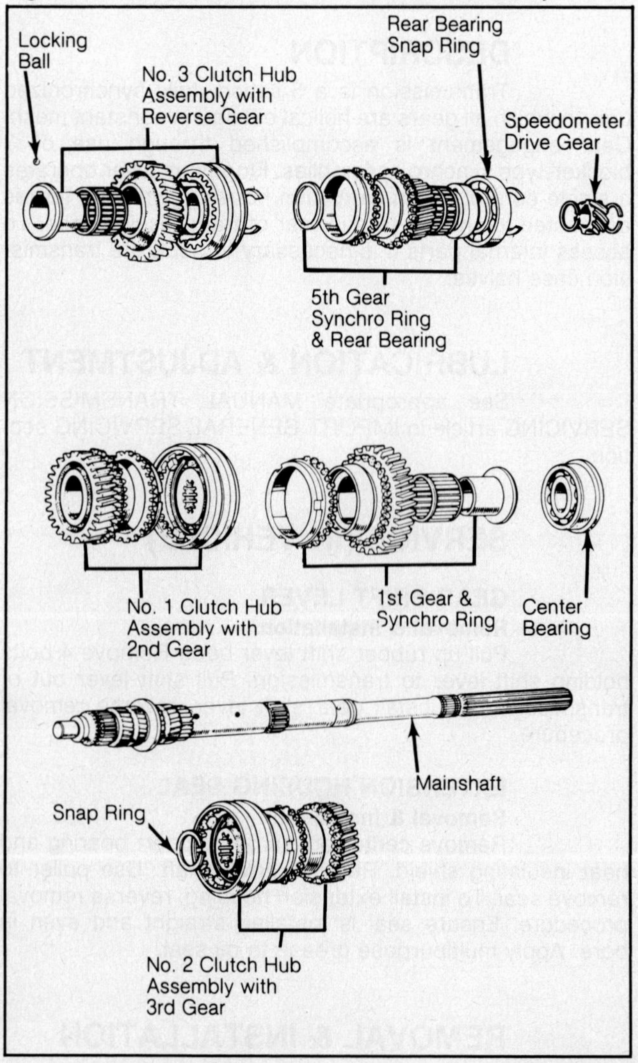

Inspection

1) Inspect output shaft for wear, damage or distortion. Minimum thickness of flange between 2nd and

3rd gear is .157" (4.0 mm). Minimum diameter of 2nd gear journal is 1.44" (36.8 mm); 3rd gear 1.48" (37.8 mm). Check shaft deflection at speedometer drive gear journal while rotating shaft. Maximum deflection is .002" (.06 mm).

2) Check each gear, bushing and bearing surface for wear or damage. Check inside gear limits. See BEARING SURFACE INSIDE DIAMETER WEAR LIMIT table. Note oil clearance for 1st and 2nd gear is .0004-.0024" (.01-.06 mm); 3rd gear is .0024-.0040" (.06-.101 mm); 5th gear is .0004-.002" (.01-.05 mm).

BEARING SURFACE INSIDE DIAMETER WEAR LIMIT

Application	Specification In. (mm)
1st	1.66 (42.15)
2nd	1.50 (38.15)
3rd	1.50 (38.15)
5th	1.42 (36.15)
Reverse	1.66 (42.15)

Fig. 6: Mainshaft Inspection Points

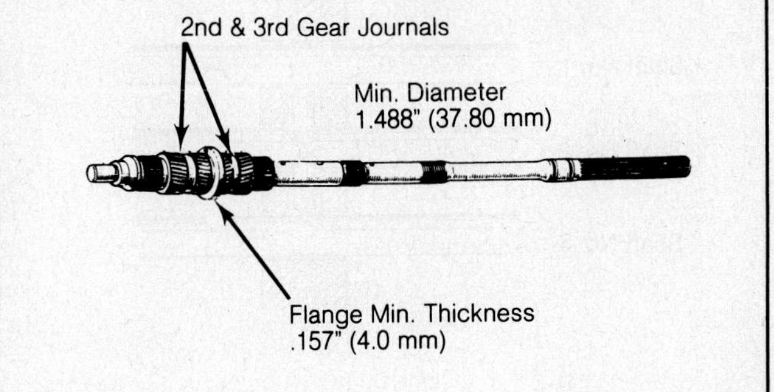

3) Disassemble clutch hubs using care not to mix parts. Inspect for wear or damage. Check clearance limit of .039" (1.0 mm) between shift fork and sleeve grooves. Groove width is .335" (8.5 mm). *See Fig. 7.*

Fig. 7: Checking Shift Fork Groove Clearance

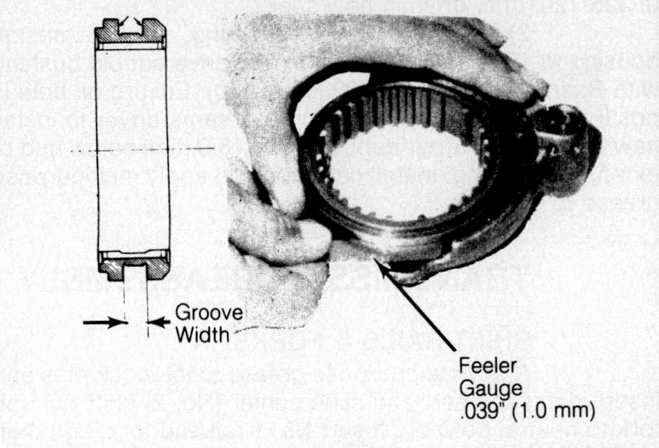

4) Check synchro rings for wear, damage, and braking effect. Ring should stick to gear cone when turned and pressed against cone. Standard clearance between synchro ring and gear is .039-.079" (1.0-2.0 mm). *See Fig. 8.* Minimum clearance is .031" (.8 mm). Replace ring and/or gear as required. Inspect shift keys and springs for wear or damage. Replace if necessary.

Fig. 8: Synchro Ring Braking Check

Reassembly

1) Assemble synchro assemblies individually, ensuring key spring ends are staggered. Note location and identification of each synchro assembly.

Fig. 9: View Showing Synchro Identification

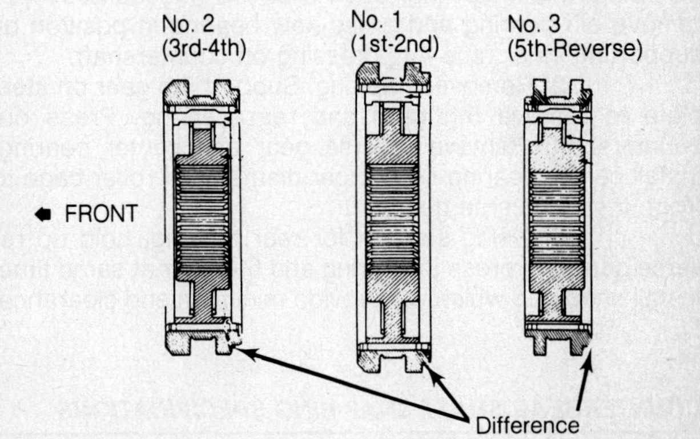

2) From rear of mainshaft, slide 2nd gear on shaft. With synchro No. 2 assembled, including synchro rings, slide assembly on shaft from rear. Slide on 1st gear, with coned surface facing front of shaft. Install bearing sleeve lock ball in mainshaft. Slide 1st gear roller bearing and sleeve on from rear of shaft and install inside 1st gear.

3) Slide center support radial ball bearing directly behind 1st gear. Install bearing sleeve lock ball in shaft. Install bearing and sleeve. Install reverse gear and reverse synchro hub No. 3. Install 5th gear, bushing, bearing, sleeve lock ball and rear bearing.

INPUT SHAFT, BEARING & RETAINER

Inspection

1) Check input shaft spline by placing input shaft into clutch disc and checking that shaft slides smoothly. Ensure there is no excessive play.

TOYOTA T50 5-SPEED (Cont.)

2) Check input shaft bearing by pressing on front of bearing and rotating input shaft. If there is abnormal resistance or noise, it will be necessary to replace bearing.

3) To replace bearing, use snap ring pliers and remove front snap ring. Use press and Adapter (SST 09506-10010) to press off old bearing. Use Adapter (SST 09316-60010) to press on new bearing. Choose a selective snap ring which will engage securely in groove and eliminate play between bearing and shaft.

INPUT SHAFT SNAP RING SPECIFICATIONS

Application	In. (mm)
T50	.100-.102 (2.55-2.60)
	.098-.100 (2.50-2.55)
	.097-.098 (2.45-2.50)
	.095-.097 (2.40-2.45)
	.093-.096 (2.35-2.40)

4) Check front bearing retainer and oil seal for wear or damage. If seal shows evidence of leakage, it must be replaced. Also check mating surfaces of transmission case and clutch housing.

COUNTERGEAR, REVERSE IDLER GEAR & SHAFT

Inspection

1) Check countergear faces and bearings for wear or damage. To replace front bearing, remove bearing lock plate and snap ring. Use Puller (SST 09950-20014) to remove old bearing and press new bearing in position by supporting inner race and pressing on countershaft.

2) Remove snap ring. Support 5th gear on steel plate to remove 5th gear and rear bearing. Press out countershaft. Remove reverse gear and center bearing. Install center bearing with larger diameter of roller cage to front. Install reverse gear.

3) Using support for rear bearing, hold up reverse gear and press in bearing and 5th gear at same time. Install snap ring which will provide minimum end clearance.

COUNTERGEAR SHAFT SNAP RING SPECIFICATIONS

Application	In. (mm)
T50	.063-.065 (1.60-1.65)
	.071-.073 (1.80-1.85)
	.079-.081 (2.00-2.05)

4) Measure reverse idler thrust clearance between case and gear. *See Fig. 10.* Standard clearance is .002-.020" (.05-.50 mm) with a maximum limit of .039" (1.0 mm).

5) Remove shaft and gear with thrust washers. Bushing bore wear limit is .634" (16.1 mm) and shaft diameter wear limit is .626" (15.9 mm). If installing new bushing, ensure oil holes in bushing and gear line up.

SHIFT FORK RAILS & SELECTOR SHAFT

Inspection

Check sliding action of shift fork rails and selector shaft. Rails and shaft should move freely without binding or excessive play. Check springs, balls and interlock pins for wear and damage

Fig. 10: Measuring Reverse Idler Gear Thrust Clearance

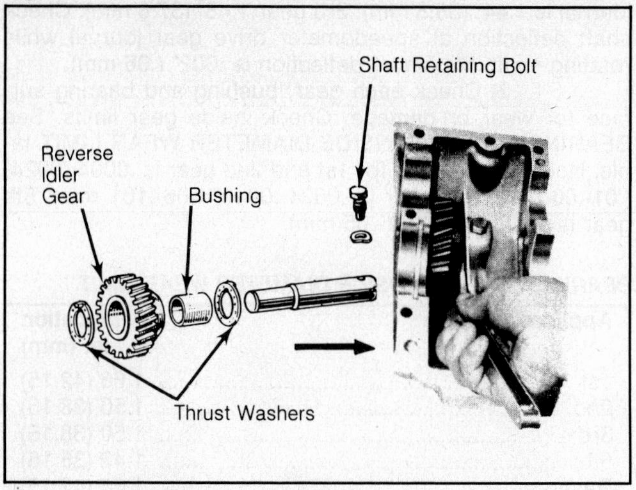

Fig. 11: Cutaway View of Case Showing Locking Pins & Fork Rail Installation

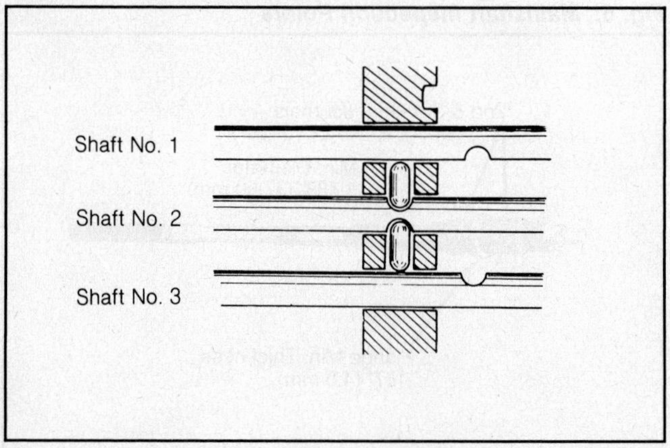

EXTENSION HOUSING

Inspection

1) Inspect speedometer gear and oil seal for wear or damage. Replace inner seal and outer "O" ring as necessary. Inspect rear oil seal and bushing for wear or damage. If seal replacement is required, use Puller (SST 09308-00010) to remove old oil seal and Installer (SST 09325-12010) to drive in new seal.

2) To replace rear bushing, heat extension housing to 176-212°F (80-100°C) and drive out old bushing with Bushing Driver (SST 09307-12010). Ensure oil hole is positioned at top of housing and use same driver to install new bushing to proper depth of .59" (15.0 mm) below end of extension housing. Install new seal and apply multipurpose grease to seal lips.

TRANSMISSION REASSEMBLY

SHIFT RAILS & FORKS

Apply multipurpose grease to interlock pins and insert in case. Insert and slide center (No. 2) shift rail and fork to neutral position. Insert No. 1 rail and fork, and then No. 3 rail and fork (short rail) to neutral position. Install all 3 shift fork pins. Pull center rail out to 3rd speed position. No. 1 and No. 3 rail should not move. *See Fig. 11.*

TOYOTA T50 5-SPEED (Cont.)

Fig. 12: Transmission Case Bolt Tightening Sequence

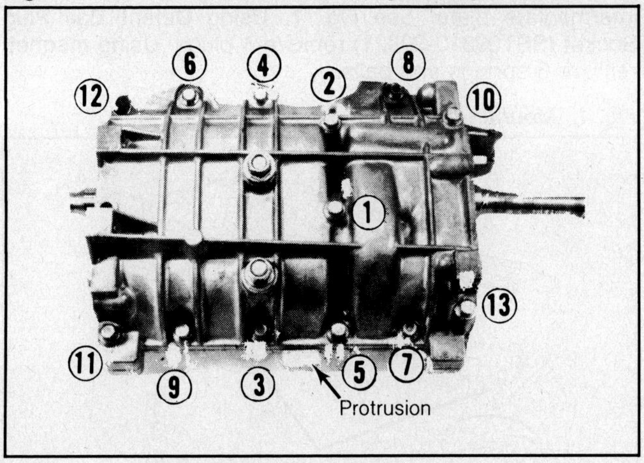

TRANSMISSION CASE

1) Apply multipurpose grease to input shaft needle bearings and assemble input shaft to output shaft. Line up synchro grooves and shift forks to neutral position. Ensure shifting keys are lined up with key slots in synchro rings. Install mainshaft assembly in right transmission case.

2) Install countergear assembly in case and insert locking ball in case groove. Clean case joining surfaces and bearing recesses. Apply liquid sealer to case joining faces and bolt threads. Install left half of case to right half and tighten bolts gradually in sequence. *See Fig. 12.*

3) Check front end of input shaft for about .012" (.3 mm) play radially. Be sure shift rods move smoothly to all gear selections.

EXTENSION HOUSING & CLUTCH HOUSING

1) Apply liquid sealer to both sides of gasket. Place gasket on rear of transmission housing and carefully install extension housing. Shift selector shaft should engage in No. 2 fork rail. Install and tighten extension housing bolts.

2) Install restricting pins and tighten. Install shift lever retainer on extension housing. Install speedometer drive gear. Install shift rail detent balls, springs and retainer plate. Install back-up light switch.

3) Apply multipurpose grease to oil seal lip in clutch housing. Apply liquid sealer to joining surfaces and install clutch housing on transmission.

NOTE: **When installing transmission on clutch housing, ensure pilot shaft splines do not damage lip of oil seal.**

4) Using a criss-cross pattern, tighten housing bolts in 3 or 4 steps. Apply multipurpose grease to sliding surfaces and install clutch release fork and bearing.

TIGHTENING SPECIFICATIONS

Application	Ft. Lbs. (N.m)
Reverse Idler Shaft Retaining Bolt	10-13 (14-18)
Case Half Bolts	14-15 (19-20)
Extension Housing-to-Case Bolts	22-33 (30-45)
Clutch Housing-to-Case Bolts	22-33 (30-45)
Clutch Housing-to-Engine	37-50 (50-70)
Restricting Pins	27-32 (37-45)

TOYOTA 4 & 5 SPEED W46, W55 & W56

Pickup 2WD & 4WD

DESCRIPTION

This Toyota transmission comes in 3 different versions: 4-speed (W46), 5-speed (W52), and 4WD (W56). All forward gears are helical cut and in constant mesh. Reverse gear is spur cut. Reverse and 5th gears are in constant mesh and are mounted on rear side of intermediate plate inside extension housing. The floor shifter actuates a single control rod which operates 3 shift rails mounted in the intermediate plate and main case. The transmission consists of 4 main sections: clutch housing, main case, intermediate plate, and extension housing (2WD) or transfer adapter (4WD).

LUBRICATION & ADJUSTMENT

See appropriate MANUAL TRANSMISSION SERVICING article in IMPORT GENERAL SERVICING section.

TROUBLE SHOOTING

HARD SHIFTING

Clutch not disengaging properly. Bushings in cross shaft worn or damaged. Synchro rings making faulty contact with gear cone. Synchro worn or pitted.

SLIPS OUT OF GEAR

Improper meshing of gears due to shift rails being out of adjustment. Shift forks worn or ball locks broken. Excessive play in synchro hub No. 2, output shaft or drive gear worn. Reverse idler gear or bushing worn. Countergear, bushing or shaft worn.

TRANSMISSION NOISY

Gears or bearings worn or damaged. Insufficient lubricant. Output splines worn or damaged. Reverse idler gear bushing worn.

REMOVAL & INSTALLATION

See appropriate MANUAL TRANSMISSION REMOVAL article in IMPORT GENERAL SERVICING section.

TRANSMISSION DISASSEMBLY

1) Remove back-up light switch, shift lever retainer and restrict pins. On 2WD models, remove speedometer driven gear. Remove clutch housing from transmission case.

2) Remove shift lever housing set bolt. Remove 9 extension housing/transfer adapter-to-case bolts. Using plastic hammer, tap housing/adapter. Disengage shift and select lever from shift head. Remove housing/adapter. Leave gasket attached to intermediate plate. Remove front bearing retainer and bearing snap rings. Using plastic hammer, tap transmission case and remove from intermediate plate.

3) Install 2 long clutch housing bolts, plate washers and nuts in 2 bottom holes of intermediate plate. Increase or decrease plate washers so bolt tips and front tip surface of nuts are aligned. Mount intermediate plate in vise, with pressure on nuts and bolts just installed, NOT intermediate plate. *See Fig. 1.* Using Detent Ball Plug Socket (SST09313-30021) remove 4 plugs. Using magnet, remove 3 springs and balls.

Fig. 1: Mounting Intermediate Plate in Vise

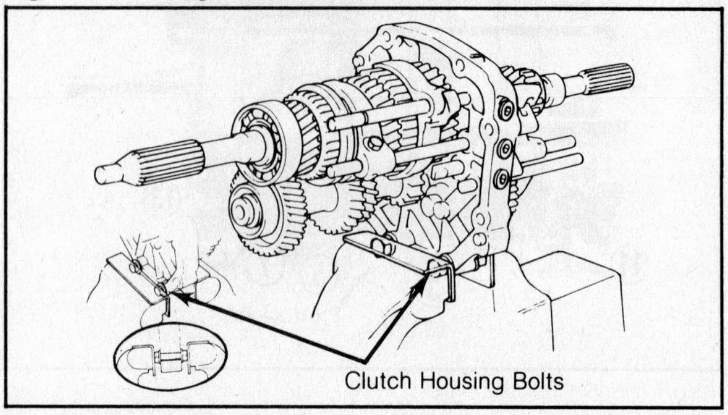

4) Remove No. 1 and No. 2 shift fork lock washers and set bolts. Using 2 screwdrivers and hammer, remove both fork shaft snap rings. Remove reverse idler gear shaft stopper, reverse idler gear, and shaft. Pull out No. 1 shift fork and shaft. Using magnet, remove 2 interlock pins. Remove No. 2 shift fork and shaft. Using magnet, remove No. 3 interlock pin. On 4-speed transmissions, remove No. 3 fork shaft with reverse shift arm.

5) On 5-speed transmissions, use pin punch and hammer and drive out No. 3 fork shaft pin. Remove No. 4 shift fork shaft. Remove No. 3 shift fork, fork shaft and reverse shift arm with pin. On 2WD models, remove speedometer drive gear from shaft. Using feeler gauge, measure counter 5th gear thrust clearance. Standard clearance is .004-.016" (.10-.41 mm); maximum is .018" (.46 mm).

6) On 5-speed transmissions, use snap ring pliers and remove 5th gear snap ring. Using puller, remove rear bearing, spacer, 5th gear, bearing and spacer. Use care not to catch output shaft rear bearing roller on counter 5th gear.

7) On 5-speed transmissions, use 2 screwdrivers and hammer and remove snap ring. *See Fig. 2.* Using puller, remove No. 3 clutch hub, being careful not to latch puller on shifting key retainer. Using two screwdrivers and hammer, remove output shaft snap ring. Remove rear bearing and 5th gear.

Fig. 2: Removing Output Shaft Snap Rings

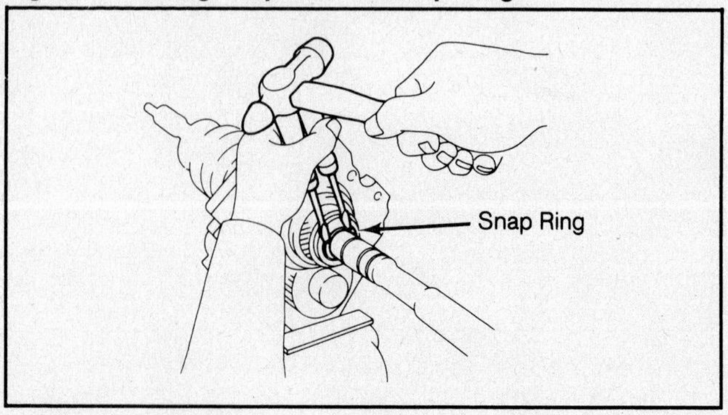

8) On all transmissions, use snap ring pliers and remove reverse gear snap ring. Using puller, remove reverse gear. Using snap ring pliers, remove reverse gear

TOYOTA 4 & 5 SPEED W46, W55 & W56 (Cont.)

Fig. 3: Measuring Counter 5th Gear Thrust Clearance

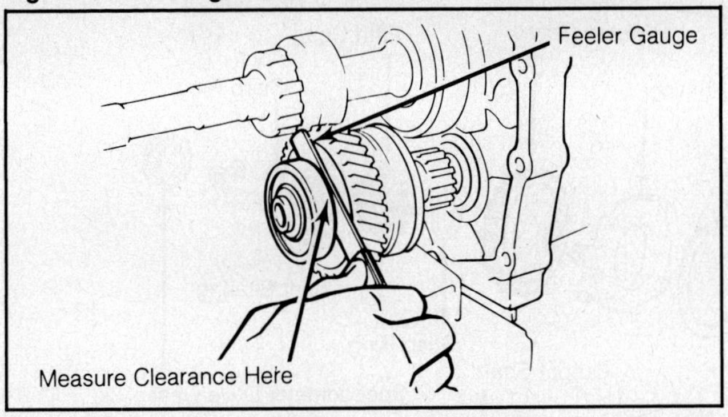

snap ring and reverse gear. Using Torx socket, remove 4 center bearing retainer screws. Remove snap ring. Using plastic hammer, tap intermediate plate and remove output shaft, input shaft, and counter gear as a unit. Remove input shaft from output shaft.

9) Using feeler gauge, measure thrust clearance of each gear. *See Fig. 3.* Standard clearance is .004-.010" (.10-.25 mm); maximum clearance is .012" (.30 mm). Shift hub sleeve No. 1 onto 2nd gear. Using press, remove center bearing, 1st gear, needle roller bearing, inner race and synchro ring. Using magnet, remove locking ball. Using press, remove hub sleeve No. 1, 2nd gear and needle roller bearing as a unit.

10) Using snap ring pliers, remove hub sleeve No. 2 and 3rd gear snap ring. Using press, remove hub sleeve, synchro ring, and 3rd gear as a unit.

COMPONENT INSPECTION & REASSEMBLY

OUTPUT SHAFT

1) Use "V" block or shaft holding fixture to measure output shaft runout. Runout should not exceed .0024" (.06 mm). Measure output shaft, 1st gear inner race, and 5th gear inner race flange minimum thicknesses. Replace worn parts as necessary. *See Fig. 4.*

Fig. 4: Measuring Output Shaft & Inner Race Flanges

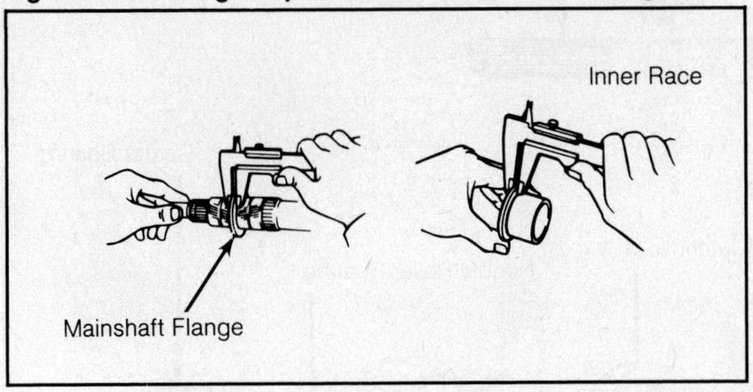

2) Measure output shaft journal diameter and outer diameter of both inner races. See OUTPUT SHAFT SPECIFICATIONS chart.

3) Inspect all gear surfaces, thrust faces, inside diameter surfaces and coned parts for wear or damage. Inspect output shaft rear bearing and needle roller bearing surfaces for wear or damage.

OUTPUT SHAFT SPECIFICATIONS

Application	In. (mm)
Output Shaft	
Flange Minimum Thickness	.185 (4.70)
Journal Minimum Diameter	
2nd Gear	1.687 (42.80)
3rd Gear	1.488 (37.80)
Inner Race	
Flange Minimum Thickness	.185 (4.70)
Minumum O.D.	1.687 (42.85)

GEAR OIL CLEARANCE

Using dial indicator, measure oil clearance between 1st gear and inner race, 2nd and counter 5th gear and shaft, and 3rd gear and output shaft. Needle roller bearings must be installed during inspection. See GEAR OIL CLEARANCE SPECIFICATIONS chart.

GEAR OIL CLEARANCE SPECIFICATIONS

Application	Standard In. (mm)	Maximum In. (mm)
1st & 2nd	.0004-.0024	.006
	(.009-.060)	(.15)
Counter 5th	.0004-.0024	.006
	(.009-.060)	(.15)
3rd Gear	.0024-.0041	.008
	(.060-.103)	(.20)

SYNCHRO RINGS

Turn synchro rings clockwise and push in to check braking action. Using feeler gauge, measure clearance between synchro ring back and gear spline end. Standard clearance is .028-.067" (.70-1.7 mm); minimum clearance is .020" (.50 mm). *See Fig. 5.*

Fig. 5: Checking Synchro Ring-to-Gear Clearance

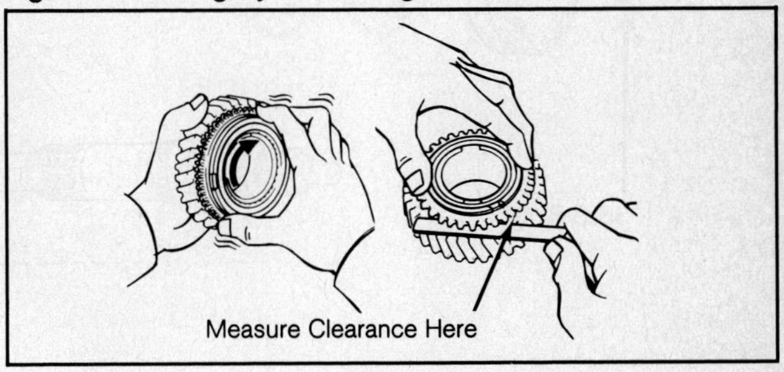

SHIFT FORKS & HUB SLEEVES

Using feeler gauge, measure clearance between hub sleeve and shift fork. Maximum clearance is .04" (1.0 mm).

INPUT SHAFT

1) Inspect input shaft inner surface and gear teeth for wear or damage. Check input shaft bearing for wear by rotating bearing and listening for noise.

TOYOTA 4 & 5 SPEED W46, W55 & W56 (Cont.)

Fig. 6: Exploded View of Transmission Gear Assemblies

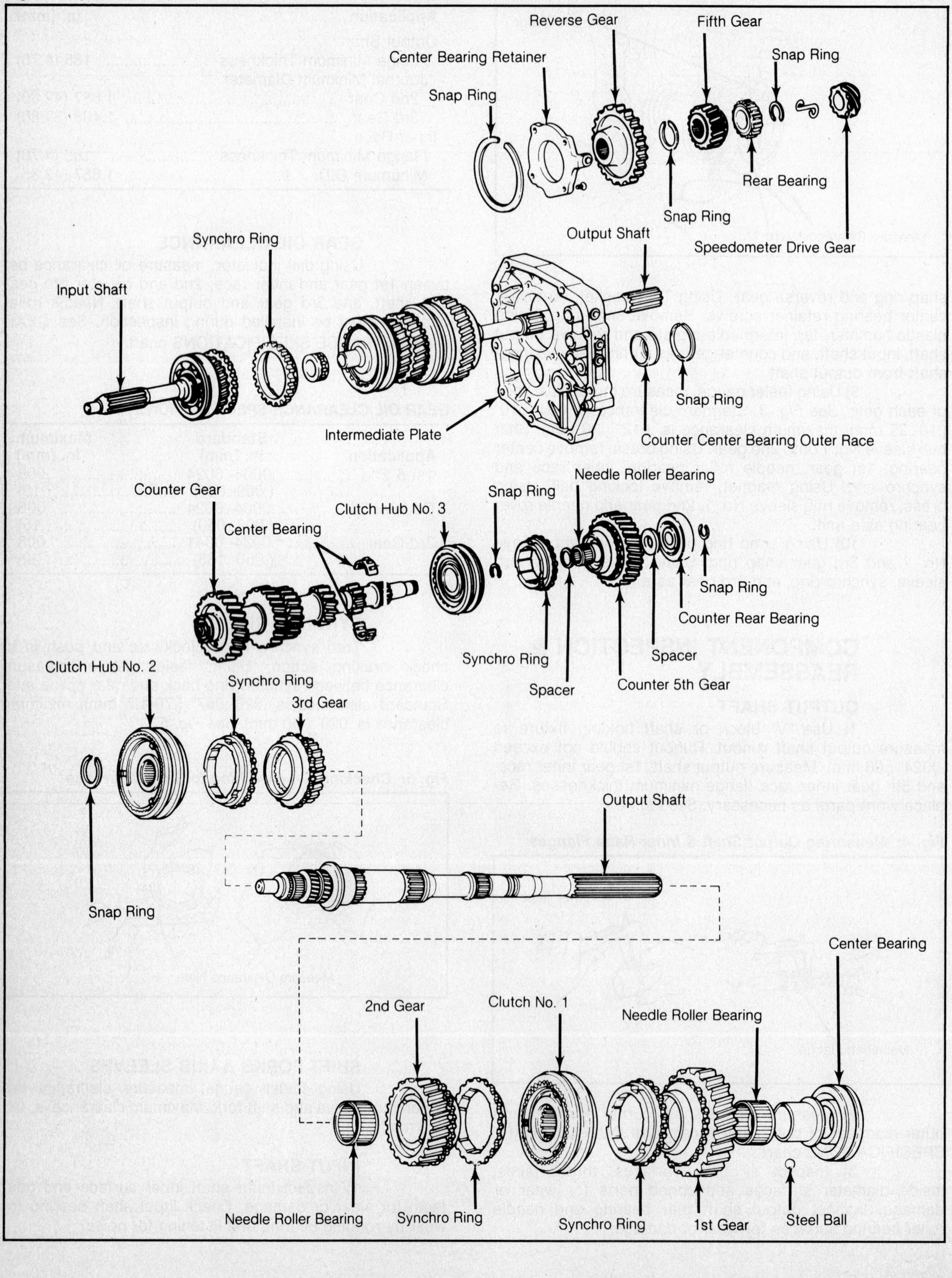

TOYOTA 4 & 5 SPEED W46, W55 & W56 (Cont.)

2) If necessary to replace input shaft bearing, remove snap ring and press off shaft. When installing new bearing, select snap ring which will allow minimum axial play. See INPUT SHAFT SNAP RING chart.

INPUT SHAFT SNAP RINGS

Snap Ring Mark	Thickness In. (mm)
1	.0807-.0827 (2.05-2.10)
2	.0827-.0846 (2.10-2.15)
3	.0846-.0866 (2.15-2.20)
4	.0866-.0886 (2.20-2.25)
5	.0886-.0906 (2.25-2.30)
11	.0906-.0925 (2.20-2.35)
12	.0925-.0945 (2.35-2.40)

FRONT BEARING OIL SEAL

Inspect seal for wear or damage and replace as necessary. When installing new seal be sure depth is .449-.472" (11.4-12.0 mm) from retainer end.

COUNTERGEAR FRONT BEARING & SIDE RACE

1) Inspect bearing and race for wear or damage and replace as necessary. To install new bearing, remove snap ring. Using press and Holder, (SST09950-00020) remove bearing. Using Puller, (SST09950-20016) remove side race. Using socket, press in new bearing and side race. Select snap ring from COUNTERGEAR SNAP RING chart that will allow minimum axial play and install.

COUNTERGEAR SNAP RINGS

Snap Ring Mark	Thickness In. (mm)
1	.0807-.0827 (2.05-2.10)
2	.0827-.0846 (2.10-2.15)
3	.0846-.0866 (2.15-2.20)
4	.0866-.0886 (2.20-2.25)
5	.0886-.0906 (2.25-2.30)
6	.0906-.0925 (2.30-2.35)
7	.0925-.0945 (2.35-2.40)

2) Inspect countergear center bearing for wear or damage and replace as necessary. To install new bearing, remove bearing from countergear. Install new bearing being sure to engage roller cages. Using driver, remove bearing outer race.

REVERSE RESTRICT PIN

Check reverse restrict pin for proper operation and replace as necessary. To install new pin, remove screw plug. Using pin punch and hammer, remove slotted spring pin. Pull out lever housing and slide shaft out. Install lever housing. Using pin punch and hammer, install slotted spring pin. Apply seal to plug and tighten to 18 ft. lbs. (25 N.m).

REAR BEARING OUTER RACE

5-Speed Only

Inspect rear bearing outer race for wear or damage and replace as necessary. To install new bearing, use 2 screwdrivers and hammer and remove snap ring. Using brass drift, tap out outer race. Using same tool, install new race. Install snap ring.

OIL SEALS

Inspect all oil seals for wear or damage and replace as necessary. On 2WD models the extension housing oil seal and bushing are replaced as a unit. Use Puller (SST09308-10010) and remove seal. Heat extension housing end to 176-212° (80-100°C) in an oil bath. Using Puller/Installer (SST09307-30010) remove bushing. Install new seal using Driver (SST09325-20010).

TRANSMISSION REASSEMBLY

CLUTCH HUBS & GEARS

1) Install No. 1 and No. 2 clutch hubs and shifting keys to hub sleeve. Install shifting key springs under shifting keys, being sure key spring end gaps are not in line. *See Fig. 7.* Apply oil to output shaft. Put synchro ring on gear and align ring slots with shifting keys. Using press, install 3rd gear and No. 2 clutch hub to shaft. Select snap ring from OUTPUT SHAFT SNAP RING chart that will allow minimum axial play and install.

Fig. 7: Sectional View of No. 1 & No. 2 Clutch Hubs

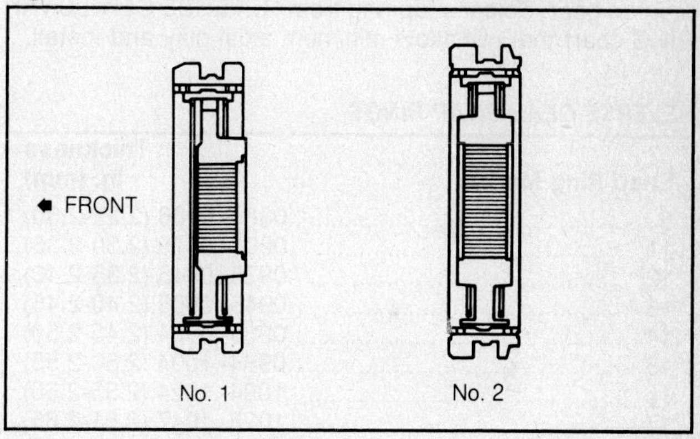

OUTPUT SHAFT SNAP RINGS

Snap Ring Mark	Thickness In. (mm)
D	.0709-.0728 (1.80-1.85)
11	.0732-.0752 (1.86-1.91)
12	.0756-.0776 (1.92-1.97)
13	.0780-.0799 (1.98-2.03)
14	.0803-.0823 (2.04-2.09)
15	.0827-.0846 (2.10-2.15)

2) Using feeler gauge, measure 3rd gear thrust clearance. Standard clearance is .004-.010" (.10-.25 mm). Apply oil to shaft and 2nd gear needle roller bearing. Put synchro ring on gear and align ring slots with shifting keys. Install needle roller bearing in 2nd gear. Using press, install 2nd gear and No. 1 clutch hub.

3) Install locking ball in shaft. Apply oil to 1st gear needle roller bearing. Assemble 1st gear, synchro ring, needle roller bearing and bearing inner race. Install assembly on output shaft with synchro ring slots aligned with shifting keys. Turn inner race and align with locking ball.

4) Using press, install output shaft center bearing with snap ring groove toward rear. Hold 1st gear inner race to prevent from falling. Using feeler gauge, measure 1st and 2nd gear thrust clearance. Standard clearance is .004-.010" (.10-.25 mm).

Manual Transmissions

TOYOTA 4 & 5 SPEED W46, W55 & W56 (Cont.)

COUNTER 5TH GEAR SHAFT SNAP RINGS

Snap Ring Mark	Thickness In. (mm)
1	.0748-.0768 (1.90-1.95)
2	.0772-.0791 (1.96-2.01)
3	.0795-.0815 (2.02-2.07)
4	.0819-.0839 (2.08-2.13)
5	.0843-.0862 (2.14-2.19)
6	.0866-.0886 (2.20-2.25)
7	.0890-.0909 (2.26-2.31)

5) With intermediate plate in vise, use Driver (SST09608-35014) to remove counter gear center bearing outer race. Install output shaft into intermediate plate by pulling on shaft and tapping intermediate plate with plastic hammer. Install input shaft and counter gear as a unit. Using care not to damage bearing rollers, install counter gear center bearing outer race.

6) Using snap ring pliers, install bearing snap ring. Using Torx socket, tighten bearing retainer screws to 9 ft. lbs. (13 N.m). Using Installer, (SST09312-20011) install reverse gear. Select snap ring from REVERSE GEAR SNAP RING chart that will allow minimum axial play and install.

REVERSE GEAR SNAP RINGS

Snap Ring Mark	Thickness In. (mm)
5	.0886-.0906 (2.25-2.30)
11	.0906-.0925 (2.30-2.35)
12	.0925-.0945 (2.35-2.40)
13	.0945-.0965 (2.40-2.45)
14	.0965-.0984 (2.45-2.50)
15	.0984-.1004 (2.50-2.55)
16	.1004-.1024 (2.55-2.60)
17	.1028-.1047 (2.61-2.66)
18	.1051-.1071 (2.67-2.72)
19	.1075-.1094 (2.73-2.78)
20	.1098-.1118 (2.79-2.84)
21	.1122-.1142 (2.85-2.90)
22	.1146-.1165 (2.91-2.96)
23	.1169-.1189 (2.97-3.02)

7) On 5-speed transmissions, use Installer (SST09312-20011) and install 5th gear and rear bushing. Select snap ring from 5TH GEAR REAR BEARING SNAP RING chart that will allow minimum axial play and install.

5TH GEAR REAR BEARING SNAP RINGS

Snap Ring Mark	Thickness In. (mm)
8	.0909-.0929 (2.31-2.36)
9	.0933-.0953 (2.37-2.42)
10	.0957-.0976 (2.43-2.48)
11	.0980-.1000 (2.49-2.54)
12	.1004-.1024 (2.55-2.60)
13	.1028-.1047 (2.61-2.66)
14	.1055-.1075 (2.68-2.73)
15	.1079-.1098 (2.74-2.79)

8) On 5-speed transmissions, install No. 3 clutch hub and shifting keys to hub sleeve. Install shifting key springs under shifting keys, being sure end gaps are not in line. Using Installer (SST09238-47012), install shifting key retainer. Support front of countershaft with 3-5 lb. hammer. Using Driver (SST09316-60010), install No. 3 clutch hub. Select snap ring from NO. 3 CLUTCH HUB SNAP RING chart that will allow minimum axial play and install.

NO. 3 CLUTCH HUB SNAP RINGS

Snap Ring Mark	Thickness In. (mm)
2	.0811-.0831 (2.06-2.11)
3	.0835-.0854 (2.12-2.17)
4	.0858-.0878 (2.18-2.23)
5	.0882-.0902 (2.24-2.29)

9) On 5-speed transmissions, install bearing spacer. Apply oil to shaft and install needle roller bearings. Assemble counter 5th gear, synchro ring and needle roller bearings. Install 5th gear assembly as a unit with synchro ring slots aligned with shifting keys. Install spacer and bearing with ball shield toward rear. Support front of countershaft with 3-5 lb. hammer and drive in bearing. Select snap ring from COUNTER 5TH GEAR SHAFT SNAP RING chart that will allow minimum axial play and install.

10) On 5-speed transmissions, install speedometer drive gear clip on output shaft. Install drive gear clip into slot. Slide drive gear with clip and fit clip into holes.

SHIFT FORKS & SHAFTS

4-Speed

1) Install reverse shift arm into pivot of bearing retainer. *See Fig. 8.* Install shift fork shaft No. 3 to intermediate plate. Apply MP grease to interlock pin No. 3. Install pin into intermediate plate hole. Align reverse idler gear groove to reverse shift arm shoe. Install reverse idler gear shaft to intermediate plate.

2) Apply MP grease to interlock pin No. 2 and install. Put shift fork No. 2 into hub sleeve No. 2 groove. Install fork shaft No. 2 to shift fork through intermediate case. Install snap ring.

3) Apply MP grease to interlock pin No. 1 and install in intermediate plate. Install shift fork No. 1 into groove of hub sleeve No. 1. Insert fork shaft No. 1 to shift fork through intermediate plate. Install snap ring. Install shift fork set bolts with lock washers and tighten to 8-10 ft. lbs. (10-14 N.m). Using pliers, stake bolts.

5-Speed

1) Coat reverse shift head pin with MP grease and insert into reverse shift head hole. *See Fig. 8.* Insert shift fork shaft No. 3 through shift fork No. 3 and reverse shift arm. Align shift fork No. 3 with hub sleeve No. 3 groove. Put reverse shift arm into pivot of bearing retainer and align reverse shift arm shoe with reverse idler gear groove. Install shift fork shaft No. 3 to intermediate plate.

2) Push reverse shift head pin into groove of shift fork shaft No. 3. Install shift fork shaft No. 4 to intermediate plate over reverse shift arm. Using pin punch and hammer, install slotted spring pin until flush with fork.

3) Apply MP grease to interlock pin No. 3. Install pin into intermediate plate hole. Apply MP grease to interlock pin No. 2 and install into shaft hole. Put shift fork No. 2 into groove of hub sleeve No. 2. Install fork shaft No. 2 to shift fork through intermediate plate. Install snap ring.

4) Apply MP grease to interlock pin No. 1. Install pin into intermediate plate. Install shift fork No. 1 into groove of hub sleeve No. 1. Insert fork shaft No. 1 to shift

TOYOTA 4 & 5 SPEED W46, W55 & W56 (Cont.)

Fig. 8: Exploded View of Shift Fork Assemblies

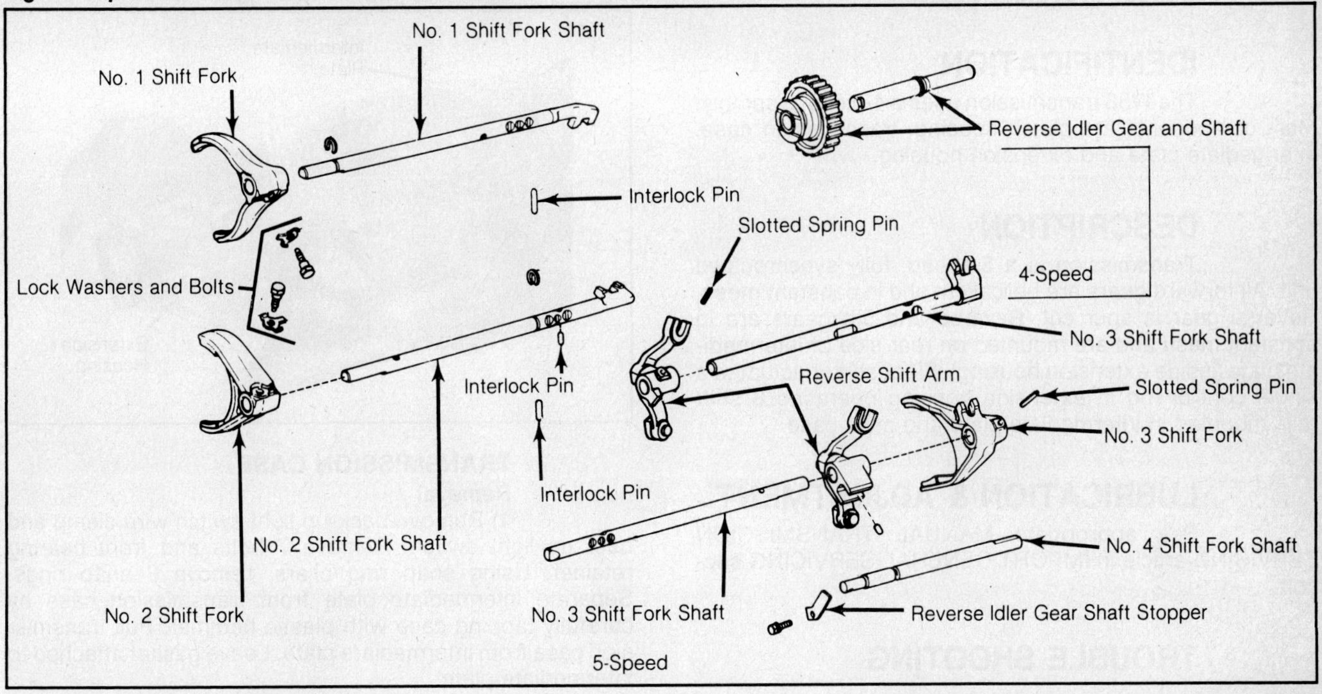

fork through intermediate plate. Install snap ring. Install shift fork set bolts with lock washers and tighten to 9 ft. lbs. (12 N.m). Using pliers, stake bolts.

TRANSMISSION CASE

1) Install locking balls and springs into holes. Apply sealer to plugs and tighten to 18 ft. lbs. (25 N.m). Install reverse idler gear shaft stopper and tighten bolt to 18 ft. lbs. (25 N.m). Remove intermediate plate from vise.

2) Align each bearing outer race and shift fork shaft with case holes. Using plastic hammer, tap case to install. Using snap ring pliers, install 2 bearing snap rings. Place new gasket on front bearing retainer. Apply sealer to bolts and tighten to 18 ft. lbs. (25 N.m).

3) With new gasket on intermediate plate, insert shift and select lever into extension housing/transfer adapter. Install shift and select lever to shift fork shaft. Install shift lever housing to shift and select lever shaft.

4) Push in extension housing/transfer adapter. Install and tighten shift lever bolt to 29 ft. lbs. (39 N.m). Install and tighten extension housing/transfer adapter bolts to 27 ft. lbs. (36 N.m). Check that input and output shafts rotate smoothly and shifting is smooth in all positions.

5) Install restrict pins with gasket. On 4-speed transmissions, install screw plug on reverse gear side. On 5-speed transmissions, install Black pin on reverse gear/5th gear side. Tighten pins to 30 ft. lbs. (40 N.m). Install clutch housing, release fork and bearing. Using new gasket, install shift lever retainer. On 2WD models, install speedometer driven gear, back-up light switch and wire clamp.

TIGHTENING SPECIFICATIONS

Application	Ft. Lbs. (N.m)
Clutch Housing-to-Case Bolts	25-30 (35-40)
Extension Housing Bolts	25-30 (35-40)
Lock Ball Plugs	14-22 (19-30)
Restrict Pin Plugs	27-33 (37-45)
Reverse Pivot Lock Nut	11-15 (15-20)
Reverse Shift Arm Bracket	11-15 (15-20)
Shift Lever Housing Bolts	11-15 (15-20)
Front Bearing Retainer Bolts	15-20 (23-27)
Output Shaft Bearing Retainer	9-11 (11-15)

TOYOTA W58 5-SPEED

Celica, Cressida, Supra

IDENTIFICATION

The W58 transmission uses a 4-piece assembly. Main components are clutch housing, transmission case, intermediate plate and extension housing.

DESCRIPTION

Transmission is a 5-speed, fully synchronized unit. All forward gears are helical cut and in constant mesh. Reverse gear is spur cut. Reverse and 5th gears are in constant mesh and are mounted on rear side of intermediate plate (inside extension housing). Floor shifter actuates a single control rod in extension housing operating 3 shift rails mounted in intermediate plate and main case.

LUBRICATION & ADJUSTMENT

See appropriate MANUAL TRANSMISSION SERVICING article in IMPORT GENERAL SERVICING section.

TROUBLE SHOOTING

HARD SHIFTING

Clutch not disengaging properly. Bushings in cross shaft worn or damaged. Synchro rings making faulty contact with gear cone. Synchro worn or pitted.

SLIPS OUT OF GEAR

Improper meshing of gears due to shift rails being out of adjustment. Shift forks worn or ball locks broken. Excessive play in synchro hub No. 2. Output shaft of drive gear worn. Reverse idler gear or its bushing is worn. Countergear or its bushing or shaft is worn.

NOISE IN TRANSMISSION

Gears or bearings worn or damaged. Insufficient or incorrect lubricant. Input shaft splines worn or damaged. Reverse idler gear bushing worn.

REMOVAL & INSTALLATION

See appropriate MANUAL TRANSMISSION REMOVAL article in IMPORT GENERAL SERVICING section.

TRANSMISSION DISASSEMBLY

CLUTCH HOUSING

Removal

Release spring clips and remove clutch release fork and bearing. Loosen 9 bolts evenly and remove housing.

EXTENSION HOUSING

Removal

Remove speedometer driven gear retainer bolt and take out shaft sleeve and driven gear. Remove 9 housing bolts. Disengage shift lever and select lever from shift head. Take care when removing extension housing so output spline does not damage rear oil seal. *See Fig. 1.*

Fig. 1: Removing Extension Housing

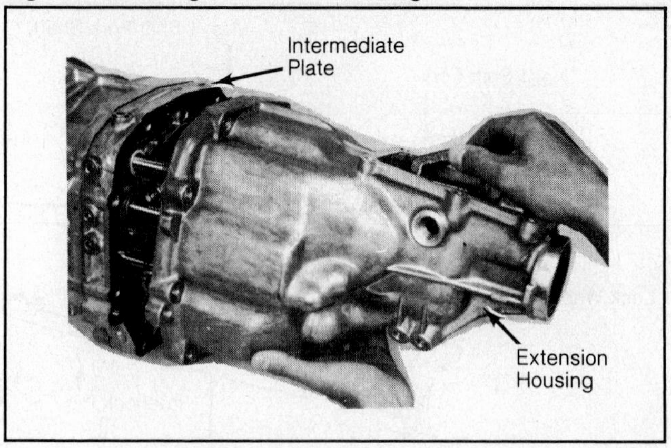

TRANSMISSION CASE

Removal

1) Remove back-up light switch wire clamp and back-up light switch. Remove 7 bolts and front bearing retainer. Using snap ring pliers, remove 2 snap rings. Separate intermediate plate from transmission case by carefully tapping case with plastic hammer. Pull transmission case from intermediate plate. Leave gasket attached to intermediate plate.

2) Install 2 long clutch housing bolts, plate washers and nuts in 2 bottom holes of intermediate plate. Install plate washers in reverse of normal. Mount intermediate plate in vise, with vise jaw pressure on bolts. Increase or decrease plate washers so bolt tip and front tip surface of nut are aligned and mounted evenly.

3) Remove 4 straight screw plugs with Detent Ball Plug Socket (SST 09313-30021). Using magnet, remove 3 springs and balls. Remove shift forks, shafts, and reverse idler gear by prying out lock washers of shift fork No. 1 and No. 2. Remove 2 set bolts. Using 2 screwdrivers and hammer, tap out 2 snap rings of No. 1 and No. 2 fork shafts. Remove reverse idler gear shaft stopper, reverse idler gear, and shaft.

4) Remove shift fork and shaft No. 1. Using magnet, remove interlock pin No. 1 and No. 2. Remove shift fork and shaft No. 2. Using magnet, remove interlock pin No. 3. Using pin punch and hammer, drive out No. 3 fork shaft pin. Pull out shaft fork No. 4. Remove shift fork No. 3 and reverse shift arm with pin.

5) Remove speedometer drive gear by prying both ends of clip. Using feeler gauge, measure counter 5th gear thrust clearance. Standard clearance is .004-.016" (.10-.41 mm). Maximum clearance is .018" (.46 mm). Remove snap ring. Using Puller (SST 09213-36010) remove counter rear bearing, spacer, 5th gear and needle bearing. Remove spacer.

NOTE: Be careful not to catch output shaft rear bearing roller on counter 5th gear.

6) Using 2 screwdrivers and hammer, tap out snap ring. Use Sleeve Remover (SST 09950-20014) to remove hub sleeve No. 3 assembly. Be sure to latch claw of tool onto clutch hub, not shifting key retainer. Tap out snap ring from output shaft. Remove output shaft rear bearing and 5th gear with Puller (SST 09312-20010). Remove snap ring and reverse gear using Puller (SST 09950-20014).

7) Remove center bearing retainer using Torx-type socket. Unscrew Torx screw and remove retainer. Remove bearing snap ring.

TOYOTA W58 5-SPEED (Cont.)

Fig. 2: Exploded View of W58 5-Speed Transmission

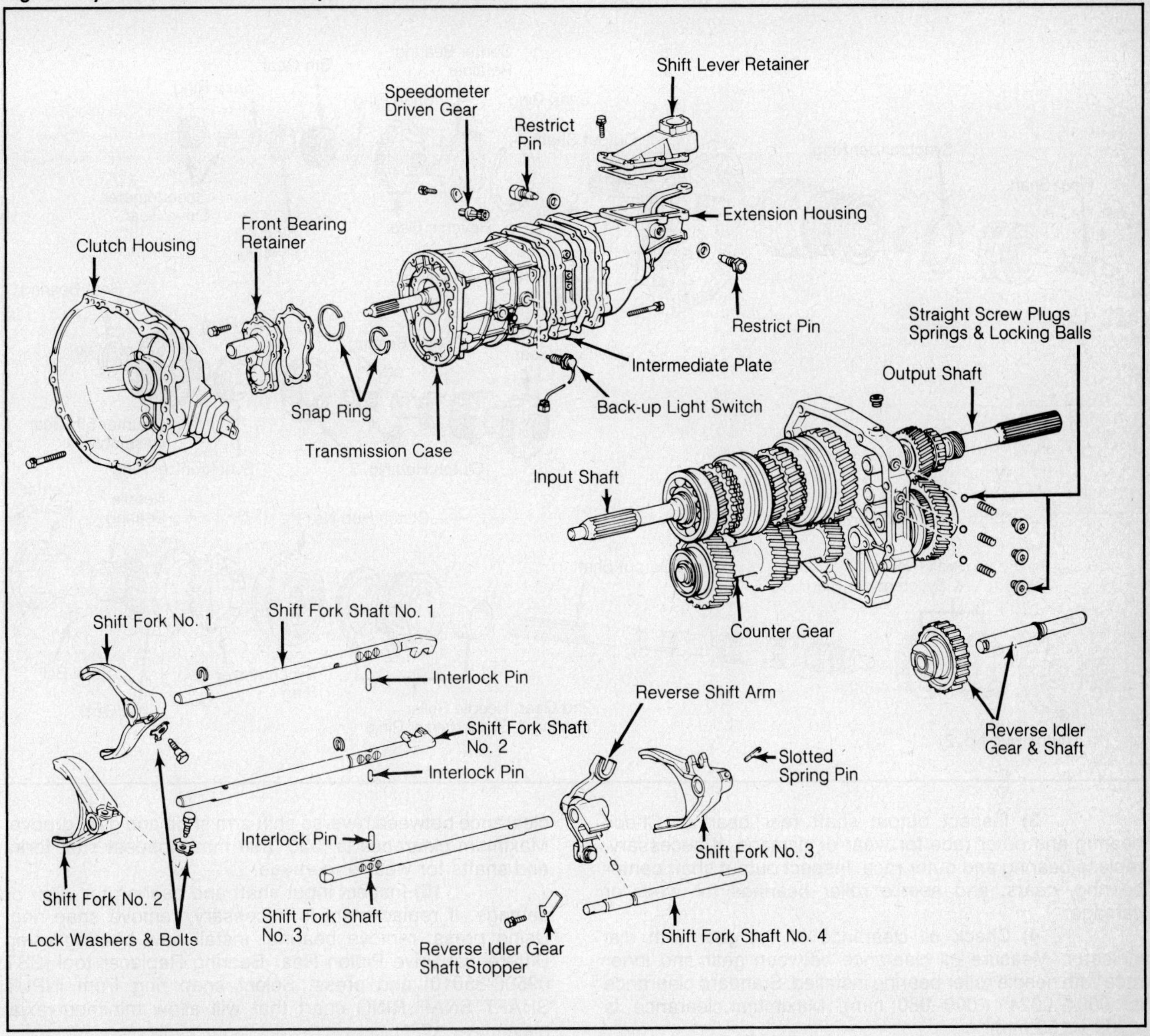

COMPONENT DISASSEMBLY, INSPECTION & REASSEMBLY

NOTE: **See TRANSMISSION REASSEMBLY in this article for COMPONENT REASSEMBLY.**

INPUT & OUTPUT SHAFTS

Disassembly

1) Remove output shaft, input shaft and countergear as a unit from intermediate plate by pulling on countergear and tapping intermediate plate with plastic hammer. Using feeler gauge, measure each gear thrust clearance. Standard clearance between each gear is .004-.010" (.10-.25 mm). Maximum clearance is .012" (.30 mm).

2) Remove input shaft from output shaft. Shift hub sleeve No. 1 onto 2nd gear. Remove center bearing with press. Pull off 1st gear, needle roller bearing, inner race, and synchro ring.

3) Remove locking ball. Using press, remove hub sleeve No. 1 assembly, 2nd gear and needle roller bearing. Remove parts as an assembly. Using snap ring pliers, remove snap ring. Remove hub sleeve No. 2, synchro ring, and 3rd gear with press.

Inspection

1) Inspect output shaft and inner race for wear or damage. Using caliper, measure output shaft flange thickness. Minimum thickness is .221" (5.60 mm). Using caliper, measure inner race flange thickness. Minimum thickness is .185" (4.70 mm).

2) Measure 2nd gear with micrometer; minimum is 1.69" (42.85 mm). Measure 3rd gear; minimum is 1.49" (37.80 mm). Using micrometer, measure outer diameter of inner race. Minimum diameter is 1.69" (42.85 mm). Use dial indicator to check runout. Maximum measurement should be .0024" (.060 mm).

Manual Transmissions

TOYOTA W58 5-SPEED (Cont.)

Fig. 3: Exploded View of W58 5-Speed Transmission

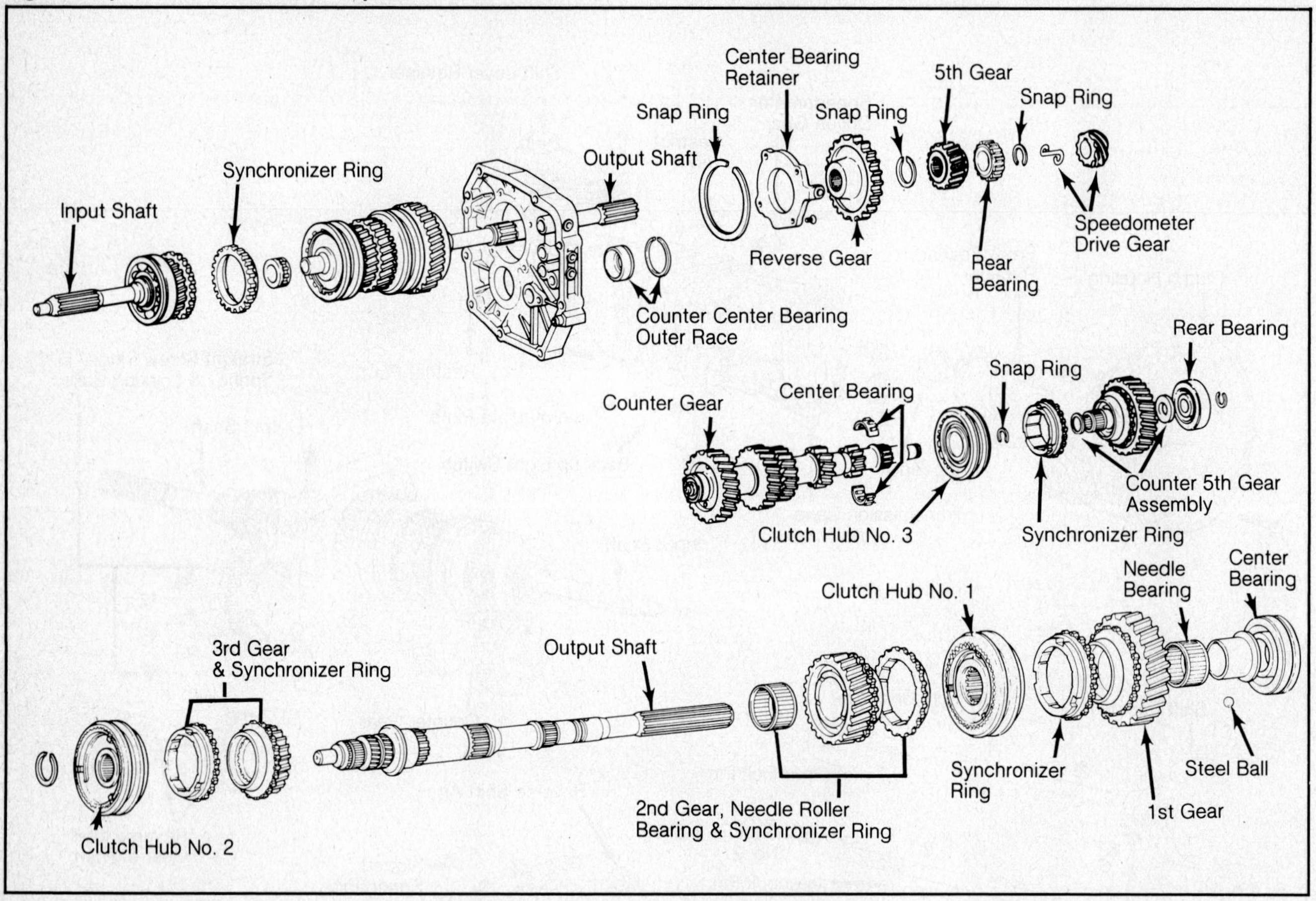

3) Inspect output shaft rear bearing. Check bearing and outer race for wear or damage. If necessary, replace bearing and outer race. Inspect output shaft center bearing, gears, and needle roller bearings for wear or damage.

4) Check oil clearance of 1st gear with dial indicator. Measure oil clearance between gear and inner race with needle roller bearing installed. Standard clearance is .0004-.0024" (.009-.060 mm). Maximum clearance is .0059" (.150 mm).

5) Check oil clearance of 2nd gear and counter 5th gear with dial indicator. Measure oil clearance between gear and output shaft with needle roller bearing installed. Standard clearance for 2nd gear is .0004-.0024" (.009-.060 mm). Standard clearance for 5th gear is .0004-.0024" (.009-.062 mm). Maximum clearance is .0059" (.15 mm).

6) Check oil clearance of 3rd gear using dial indicator. Measure oil clearance between gear and output shaft. Standard clearance is .0024-.0040" (.060-.103 mm). Maximum clearance is .008" (.20 mm).

7) Inspect synchro rings for wear or damage. Turn ring and push in to check braking action. Measure clearance between synchro ring back and gear spline end. Standard clearance is .028-.067" (.70-1.70 mm). Minimum clearance is .020" (.50 mm).

8) Inspect clutch hubs, sleeve keys and key springs for wear or damage. Using feeler gauge, measure clearance between shift forks and hub sleeves. Maximum clearance is .039" (1.0 mm).

9) Using feeler gauge, inspect clearance of reverse shift arm shoe and reverse idler gear. Measure clearance between reverse shift arm shoe and gear groove. Maximum clearance is .035" (.90 mm). Inspect shift forks and shafts for wear or damage.

10) Inspect input shaft and bearing for wear or damage. If replacement is necessary, remove snap ring. Using press, remove bearing. Install new bearing using Differential Drive Pinion Rear Bearing Replacer tool (SST 09506-35010) and press. Select snap ring from INPUT SHAFT SNAP RING chart that will allow minimum axial play.

INPUT SHAFT SNAP RING

Mark On Ring	Thickness In. (mm)
1	.0807-.0827 (2.05-2.10)
2	.0827-.0846 (2.10-2.15)
3	.0846-.0866 (2.15-2.20)
4	.0866-.0886 (2.20-2.25)
5	.0886-.0906 (2.25-2.30)
11	.0906-.0925 (2.30-2.35)
12	.0925-.0945 (2.35-2.40)

11) Inspect countergear and bearing for wear or damage. If replacement of bearing is necessary, remove snap ring and press out bearing. Check side of race for wear or damage. If replacement of side race is necessary, use Puller (SST 09950-20014).

12) If side race cannot be removed with puller, grind part of side race and cut off with chisel. Using socket, press in bearing, side race, and inner race. Install snap ring from COUNTERGEAR SNAP RING chart that will allow minimum axial play.

COUNTERGEAR SNAP RING

Mark On Ring	Thickness In. (mm)
1	.0807-.0827 (2.05-2.10)
2	.0827-.0846 (2.10-2.15)
3	.0846-.0866 (2.15-2.20)
4	.0866-.0886 (2.20-2.25)
5	.0886-.0906 (2.25-2.30)
6	.0906-.0925 (2.30-2.35)
7	.0925-.0945 (2.35-2.40)

13) Inspect countergear rear bearing, idler gear and shaft, and front bearing retainer for wear or damage. If oil seal is worn or damaged, pry out with screwdriver and install with Driver (SST 09608-35013).

EXTENSION HOUSING

Inspection

Inspect housing, rear oil seal and bushing for wear or damage. If oil seal replacement is necessary, use Puller (SST 09308-00010 or SST 09308-10010) with output shaft installed. If rear bushing replacement is necessary, heat extension housing end to 176-212°F (80-100°C). Use Transmission Extension Housing Metal Replacer tool (SST 09307-30010) to remove. Use same tool to install new bushing. To drive in new oil seal, use Installer (SST 09325-20010).

CLUTCH HOUSING

Inspection

Inspect release fork, bearing, clips and clutch housing for wear or damage. Replace if necessary.

TRANSMISSION REASSEMBLY

TRANSMISSION CASE

1) Install No. 1 and No. 2 clutch hub and shifting keys to hub sleeve. Install shifting key springs under shifting keys. Install key springs so end gaps are not in line.

2) Install 3rd gear and clutch hub No. 2 on output shaft. Apply oil to shaft. Place synchro ring on gear and align ring slots with shifting keys. Using press, install 3rd gear and clutch hub No. 2. Select snap ring from OUTPUT SHAFT SNAP RING chart that will allow minimum axial play.

OUTPUT SHAFT SNAP RING

Mark On Ring	Thickness In. (mm)
D	.0709-.0728 (1.80-1.85)
11	.0732-.0752 (1.86-1.91)
12	.0756-.0776 (1.92-1.97)
13	.0780-.0799 (1.98-2.03)
14	.0803-.0823 (2.04-2.09)
15	.0827-.0846 (2.04-2.15)

3) Using feeler gauge, measure 3rd gear thrust clearance. Standard clearance is .004-.010" (.10-.25 mm). Maximum clearance is .012" (.30 mm). Install clutch hub No. 1 into hub sleeve and install shifting keys. Place key springs under shifting keys. Be sure end gaps do not line up on key springs.

4) Install 2nd gear and clutch hub No. 1. Place synchro ring on gear and align ring slots with shifting keys. Install lubricated needle roller bearing in 2nd gear. Using press, install 2nd gear and clutch hub No. 1. Install locking ball and 1st gear assembly. Using press, install bearing on output shaft with outer race snap ring groove toward rear.

5) Using feeler gauge, measure 1st and 2nd gear thrust clearance. Standard clearance is .004-.010" (.10-.25 mm). Maximum clearance is .012" (.30 mm). Install output shaft into intermediate plate. Before installing shaft, use Driver (SST 0908-35013) to remove countergear center bearing outer race. Install output shaft into intermediate plate by pulling output shaft and tapping plate.

6) Install input shaft and countergear as a unit. Using Driver (SST 09316-60010), install countergear center bearing outer race. Install bearing snap ring. Be sure snap ring is flush with intermediate plate surface. Install bearing retainer with Torx-type socket. Install reverse gear using Installer (SST 09312-20010). Select snap ring from REVERSE GEAR SNAP RING chart and install.

REVERSE GEAR SNAP RING

Mark On Ring	Thickness In. (mm)
5	.0886-.0906 (2.25-2.30)
11	.0906-.0925 (2.30-2.35)
12	.0925-.0945 (2.35-2.40)
13	.0945-.0965 (2.40-2.45)
14	.0965-.0984 (2.45-2.50)
15	.0984-.1004 (2.50-2.55)
16	.1004-.1024 (2.55-2.60)
17	.1028-.1047 (2.61-2.66)
18	.1051-.1071 (2.67-2.72)
19	.1075-.1094 (2.73-2.78)
20	.1098-.1118 (2.79-2.84)
21	.1122-.1142 (2.85-2.90)
22	.1146-.1165 (2.91-2.96)
23	.1169-.1189 (2.97-3.02)

7) Install 5th gear and output shaft rear bearing using Installer (SST 09312-20010). Select snap ring from OUTPUT SHAFT REAR BEARING SNAP RING chart that will allow minimum axial play and install.

OUTPUT SHAFT REAR BEARING SNAP RING

Mark On Ring	Thickness In. (mm)
8	.0909-.0929 (2.31-2.36)
9	.0933-.0953 (2.37-2.42)
10	.0957-.0976 (2.43-2.48)
11	.0980-.1000 (2.49-2.54)
12	.1004-.1024 (2.55-2.60)
13	.1028-.1047 (2.61-2.66)
14	.1055-.1075 (2.68-2.73)
15	.1079-.1098 (2.74-2.79)

8) Install clutch hub No. 3 and shifting key to hub sleeve. Install shifting key springs under shifting keys. Install key springs so end gaps are not in line. Install shifting key retainer using Installer (SST 09238-47012).

TOYOTA W58 5-SPEED (Cont.)

9) Install clutch hub No. 3 using driver (SST 09316-60010) while supporting countershaft in front with 3-5 lb. hammer. Select snap ring from CLUTCH HUB NO. 3 SNAP RING chart that will allow minimum axial play and install.

CLUTCH HUB NO. 3 SNAP RING

Mark On Ring	Thickness In. (mm)
2	.0811-.0831 (2.06-2.11)
3	.0835-.0854 (2.12-2.17)
4	.0858-.0878 (2.18-2.23)
5	.0882-.0902 (2.24-2.29)

10) Install bearing spacer. Apply counter 5th gear, synchro ring, and lubricated needle roller bearings. Install 5th gear assembly with synchro ring slots aligned with shifting keys.

11) Using hammer and socket, drive in spacer and bearing. Support countershaft in front with 3-5 lb. hammer. Select snap ring from 5TH GEAR ASSEMBLY SNAP RING chart that will allow minimum axial play and install.

5TH GEAR ASSEMBLY SNAP RING

Mark On Ring	Thickness In. (mm)
1	.0748-.0768 (1.90-1.95)
2	.0772-.0791 (1.96-2.01)
3	.0795-.0815 (2.02-2.07)
4	.0819-.0839 (2.08-2.13)
5	.0843-.0862 (2.14-2.19)
6	.0866-.0886 (2.20-2.25)
7	.0890-.0909 (2.26-2.31)

12) Put clip on output shaft and install speedometer drive gear slot to clip. Slide drive gear with clip into hole. Install reverse idler gear and shaft. Insert lubricated pin into reverse shift fork No. 3 and reverse shift arm. Align shift fork No. 3 to hub sleeve No. 3 groove. Put reverse shift arm into pivot of bearing retainer and install shift fork shaft No. 3 to intermediate plate.

13) Install shift fork shaft No. 4 by pushing pin which was inserted into reverse shift arm hole into groove of shift fork shaft No. 3. Install shift fork shaft No. 4 to intermediate plate. Install shift fork shaft No. 4 by aligning pin hole in fork with hole in shaft. Using pin punch, drive in slotted spring pin until flush with fork. Install lubricated interlock pin No. 3 into intermediate plate hole.

14) Install lubricated interlock pin No. 2 to shaft hole. Install shift fork No. 2 into groove of hub sleeve No. 2. Install fork shaft No. 2 to shift fork shaft No. 2 through intermediate plate. Install No. 2 fork shaft snap ring.

15) Install lubricated interlock pin No. 1 into intermediate plate. Install shift fork No. 1 into groove of hub sleeve No. 2. Install fork shaft No. 1 to shift fork shaft No. 1 through intermediate plate. Install No. 1 fork shaft snap ring.

16) Install shift fork set bolts with lock washers. Install 3 springs and 3 locking balls. Using Detent Ball Plug Socket (SST 09313-30021), install 4 straight screw plugs. Install reverse idler gear shaft stopper and tighten bolt.

17) Remove intermediate plate from vise. Remove nuts, bolts, plate washers and gaskets. Install transmission case to intermediate plate. Using plastic hammer, tap case to install plate.

18) Install 2 bearing snap rings. Install bearing retainer with new gasket. Install and tighten bolts. Install shift lever retainer together with new gasket and tighten bolt. Install back-up light switch wire clamp. Install speedometer driven gear, lock plate and bolt.

EXTENSION HOUSING

1) Put new gasket in position on intermediate plate before installing extension housing. Push shift lever housing forward, turn clockwise, and push in extension housing so it is positioned 1.57-1.97" (40-50 mm) from intermediate plate. Slighty revolve extension housing clockwise and connect select lever to shift fork shaft.

2) With shift lever housing fully turned clockwise, push in extension housing. Install restrict pins (Black pin at reverse gear/5th gear side, Silver on opposite side) together with gasket and tighten pins.

CLUTCH HOUSING

Install clutch housing and tighten bolts. Install release fork and bearing. Bearing is held in place by 2 clips.

TIGHTENING SPECIFICATIONS

Application	Ft. Lbs. (N.m)
Clutch Housing Bolts	27 (37)
Extension Housing Bolts	22-32 (30-44)
Front Bearing Retainer	15-21 (20-29)
Idler Gear Shaft Stopper	14-22 (19-30)
Restrict Pins	27-32 (37-44)
Shift Lever Retainer	11-15 (15-20)
Starter Bolts	37-57 (50-78)
Straight Screw Plugs	14-22 (19-30)
Transmission-to-Engine Bolts	37-57 (50-78)
	INCH Lbs. (N.m)
Release Cylinder Bolts	96-132 (11-15)
Shift Fork Set Bolt	96-120 (11-14)
Speedometer Driven Gear Bolt	96-132 (11-15)

TOYOTA Z45, Z46 & Z53 TRANSAXLE

Tercel 2WD

DESCRIPTION

Transaxle assembly consists of transmission case, transfer case adapter, and extension housing with common oil supply. Transmission is fully synchronized in all forward gears.

LUBRICATION & ADJUSTMENT

See appropriate MANUAL TRANSMISSION SERVICING article in IMPORT GENERAL SERVICING section.

SERVICE (IN VEHICLE)

DRIVE AXLE SHAFTS

See appropriate DRIVE AXLE SHAFT article in IMPORT AXLE SHAFTS, OVERDRIVES & TRANSFER CASES section.

TRANSAXLE REMOVAL & INSTALLATION

See appropriate MANUAL TRANSMISSION REMOVAL article in IMPORT GENERAL SERVICING section.

TRANSAXLE DISASSEMBLY

1) Remove mounting insulator, speedometer driven gear and back-up light switch. Remove 2 plugs, springs and reverse restrict pins from extension housing. Remove 9 bolts holding extension housing to case. Turn select lever and disconnect tip from shift head groove. Using plastic hammer, tap extension housing and remove.

2) Remove snap ring and speedometer drive gear. Using magnet, remove locking ball. Remove 2 input shaft bolts, transmission case cover, and input shaft. Remove reverse shift arm pivot.

3) Using Detent Ball Plug Socket (SST 09313-30021), remove 3 screw plugs from side of case. Using magnet, remove 3 springs and detent balls. Remove bearing snap ring. Using plastic hammer, tap case protrusion and remove from intermediate plate.

4) Secure protrusion on lower part of intermediate plate in vise. Using Detent Ball Plug Socket (SST 09313-30021), remove screw plug. Using magnet, remove spring and detent ball. Use punch and hammer to drive out slotted spring pins. Remove gear shift head.

5) Position each fork shaft in Neutral position. Hold shift fork, pull out fork shaft and remove shift fork. Remove interlock pins from fork shaft and intermediate plate.

6) Using feeler gauge, measure counter 5th gear thrust clearance. Standard clearance is .006-.013" (.15-.33 mm). Maximum clearance is .016" (.40 mm).

7) On 5-speed transmissions, use screwdriver to remove hole snap ring and shifting key retainer. Remove snap ring. Use Puller (SST 09950-20014) to remove clutch hub No. 3, synchro ring, and counter 5th gear as a unit. Remove needle roller bearing.

8) Remove spacer and steel ball. On 4-speed transmissions, remove counter gear plate. On all transmissions, remove bearing retainer and 2 bearing snap rings. Using plastic hammer, tap reverse gear shaft, idler gear and output shaft halfway from intermediate plate while supporting gear shaft by hand.

9) Remove idler gear and reverse gear shaft as a unit. Using plastic hammer, tap out counter gear and output shaft together while supporting gear and shaft by hand.

10) Measure each gear thrust clearance. Using dial indicator, measure 1st and 4th gear thrust clearance. Using feeler gauge, measure 2nd and 3rd gear thrust clearance.

GEAR THRUST CLEARANCE

Application	In. (mm)
Standard Clearance	
1st Gear	.006-.011 (.15-.27)
2nd Gear	.006-.010 (.15-.25)
3rd Gear	.006-.010 (.15-.25)
4th Gear	.001-.009 (.02-.24)
Maximum Clearance	.012 (.30)

11) Using Remover (SST09950-00020), press out sleeve yoke, remove snap ring and press out 5th gear. Remove snap ring and press out bearing, spacer and thrust bearing.

12) Remove 4th gear, synchro ring and needle roller bearing. Using 2 screwdrivers and hammer, tap out snap ring. Remove spacer and thrust bearing. Press out clutch hub No. 2, synchro ring and 3rd gear using Remover (SST09950-00020).

13) Remove 1st gear snap ring, synchro ring, needle roller bearing, and inner race. Using magnet, remove steel ball. Using Remover (SST09950-00020), press out clutch hub No. 1, synchro and 2nd gear.

14) Remove 9 bolts from transmission. From transaxle side, install 4 bolts an equal distance apart. Separate transaxle from differential by turning 4 bolts a little at a time on transmision case side. *See Fig. 1.*

Fig. 1: Position of Bolts to Separate Housings

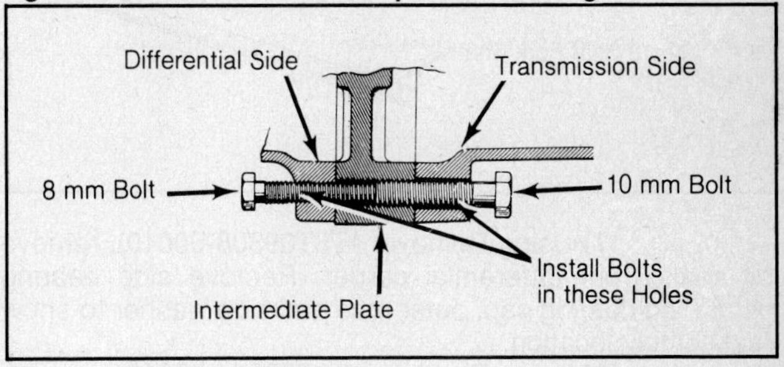

15) Install differential carrier to work stand with ring gear in horizontal position. Remove 8 bolts, differential carrier cover, and gasket. Measure and record ring gear backlash. If backlash is not .004-.006" (.10-.15 mm), adjust side bearing preload or repair as necessary.

16) Check ring gear runout. If maximum runout is greater than .003" (.07 mm), install new ring gear. Inspect teeth pattern for proper wear. Using Adaptor (SST09556-16010) and torque meter, measure preload. Total preload should be 5.2-8.7 INCH Lbs. (.59-.98 N.m).

TOYOTA Z45, Z46 & Z53 TRANSAXLE (Cont.)

Fig. 2: Exploded View of Transaxle Components

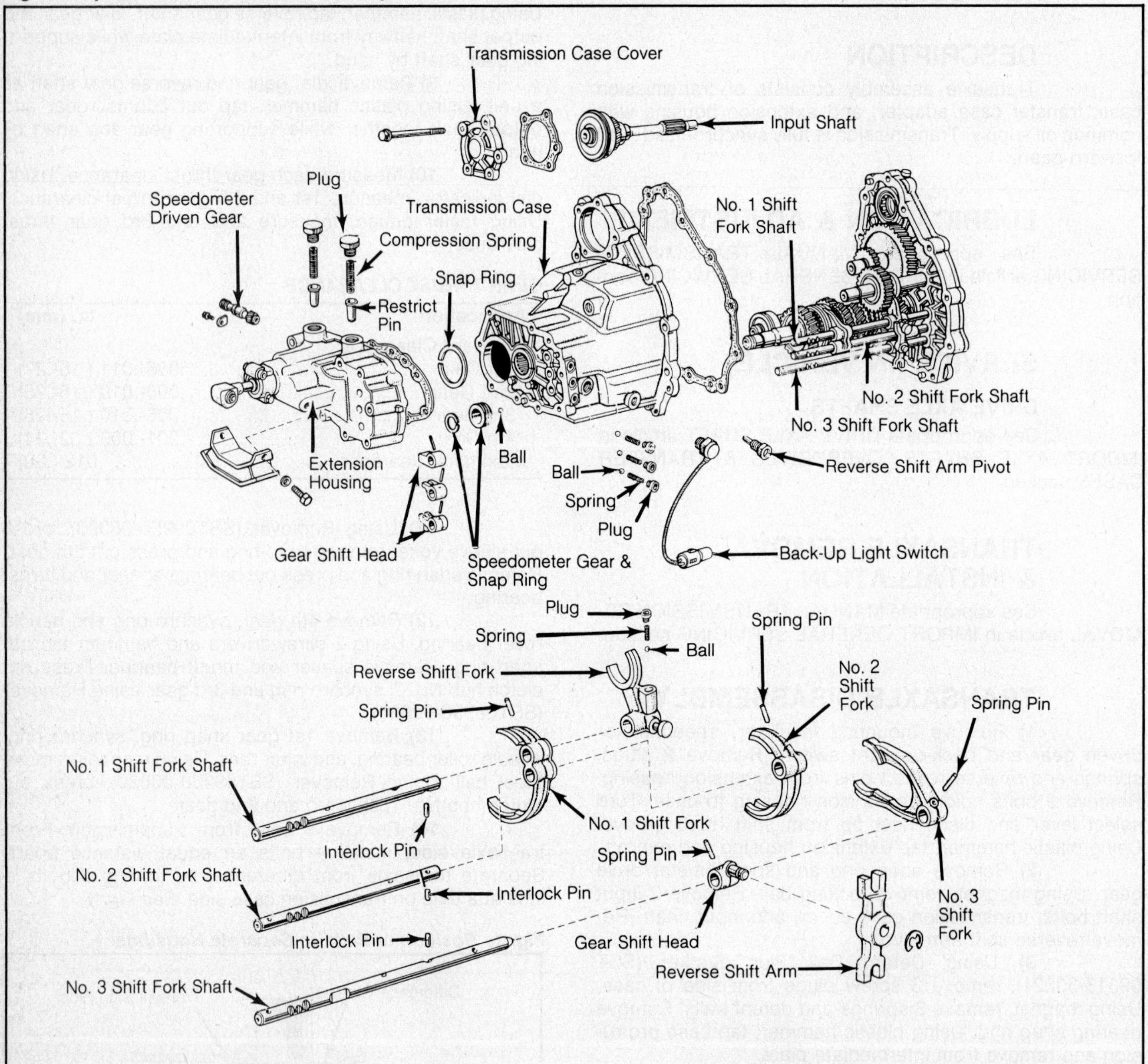

17) Using Remover (SST09308-00010), remove oil seals from differential carrier. Remove side bearing caps. Tag bearing cap, outer race and side washer to show reassembly location.

18) Using Remover (SST09504-22010), remove washer on ring gear teeth side. Remove differential case, bearing outer race, side washer and oil reservoir.

19) Loosen staked part of drive pinion nut. Using Remover (SST09556-16010), loosen nut and turn drive pinion clockwise. Using press, remove drive pinion.

COMPONENT INSPECTION & REPAIR

DIFFERENTIAL DRIVE PINION BEARINGS & OUTER RACES

1) If bearings or races are worn or damaged, use Remover (SST09950-00020) to press out rear bearing from drive pinion. Install plate washer with one of same thickness as was assembled.

2) Using Installer (SST09608-2011) and press, install bearing. Using hammer and brass bar, remove outer race by tapping on notched portion. Using Installer (SST09608-30011 for front and SST09608-30021 for rear) and hammer, install new outer race.

TOYOTA Z45, Z46 & Z53 TRANSAXLE (Cont.)

Fig. 3: Exploded View of Transaxle Gears

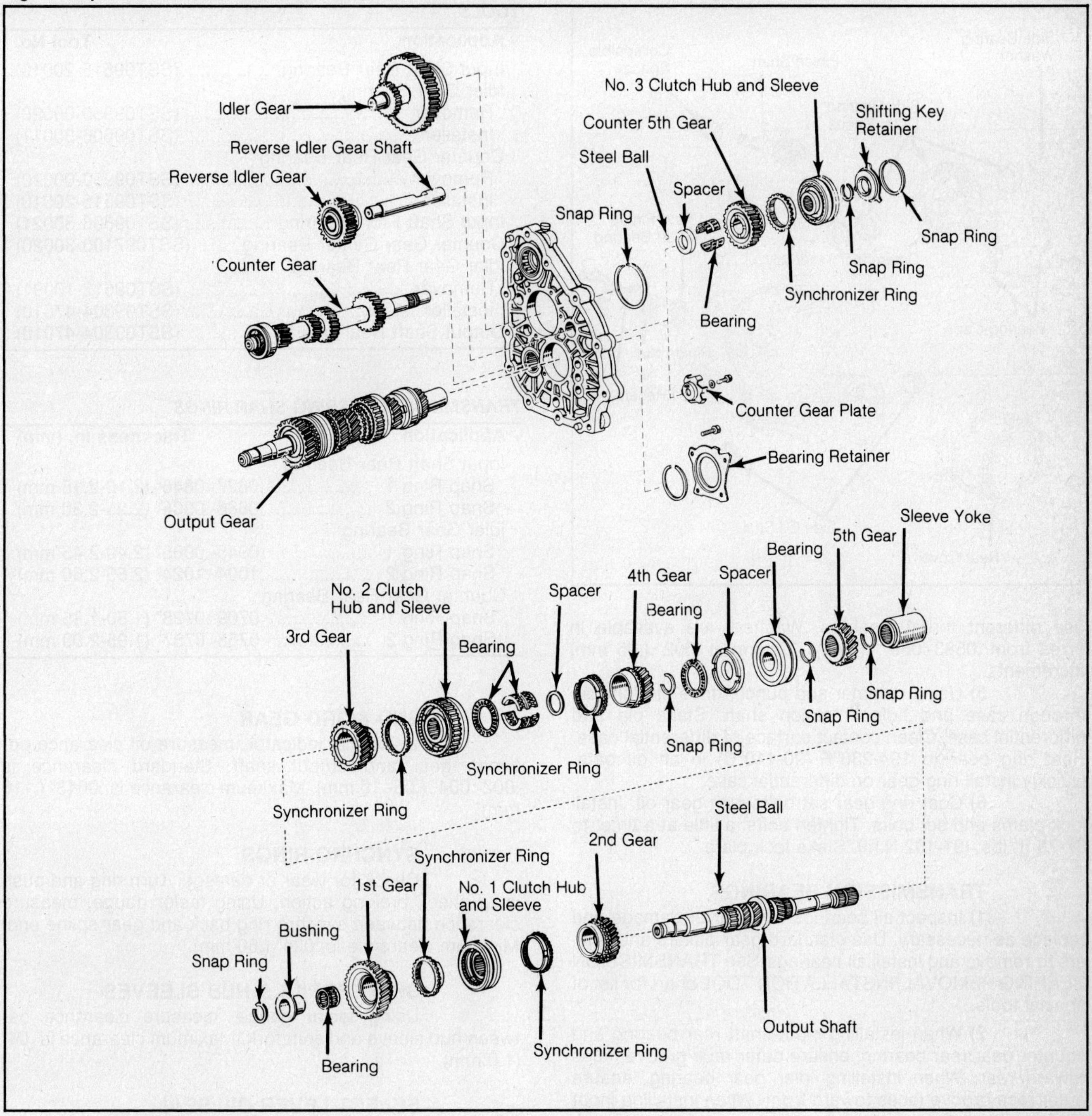

DIFFERENTIAL SIDE BEARINGS & OUTER RACES

Using Remover (SST09502-10012), remove side bearing from differential case. Using Installer (SST09608-20011) and press, install new bearing.

DIFFERENTIAL PINION & SIDE GEARS

1) Measure side gear backlash while holding another side gear toward case. Standard backlash is .002-.010" (.04-.24 mm). If necessary, replace ring gear, differential pinions and side gears.

2) Lift lock plates and remove set bolts. Using brass drift and hammer, tap ring gear to separate from differential case. If ring gear is to be reused, place alignment marks before separating. If ring gear or drive pinion are damaged, replace as a set.

3) Using pin punch and hammer, tap out straight pin toward ring gear installation surface. Remove pinion shaft, pinion gears, side gears and thrust washers. Check gears, shaft, case and washers. Install side gears, washers, pinion gears and shaft.

4) Measure side gear backlash while holding another side gear toward case. Standard backlash is .002-.010" (.04-.24 mm). If backlash is not within specifications,

Fig. 4: View of Clutch/Differential Housing

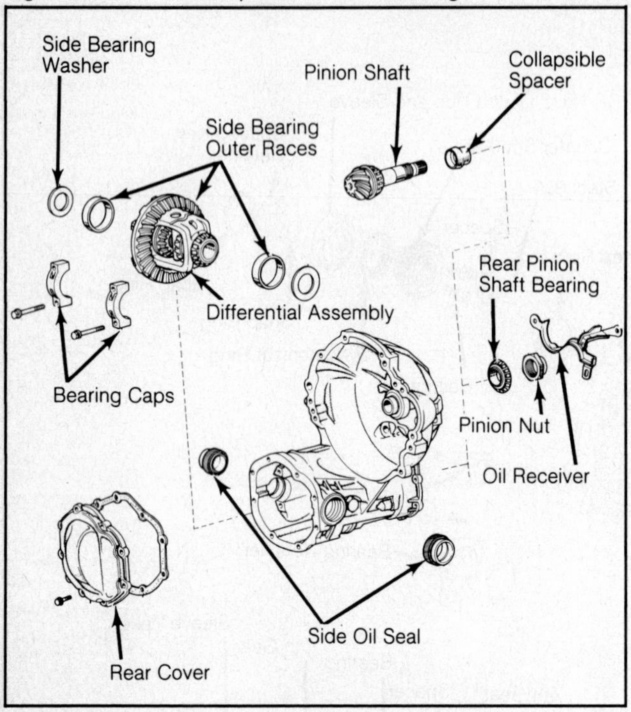

use different thrust washers. Washers are available in sizes from .0583-.0697" (1.48-1.77 mm) in .002" (.05 mm) increments.

5) Using hammer and punch, drive straight pin through case and hole in pinion shaft. Stake pin and differential case. Clean contact surface of differential case. Heat ring gear to 194-230°F (90-110°C) in an oil bath. Quickly install ring gear on differential case.

6) Coat ring gear set bolts with gear oil. Install lock plates and set bolts. Tighten bolts, a little at a time, to 67-75 ft. lbs. (91-102 N.m). Stake lock plate.

TRANSMISSION BEARINGS

1) Inspect all bearings for wear or damage and replace as necessary. Use standard gear pullers and drivers to remove and install all bearings. See TRANSMISSION BEARING REMOVAL/INSTALLATION TOOL chart for list of special tools.

2) When installing input shaft rear bearing and counter gear rear bearing, ensure outer race groove faces toward rear. When installing idler gear bearing, ensure outer race groove faces toward front. When installing input shaft front bearing, ensure outer race groove faces upward.

3) Several bearings utilize snap rings of various thickness to ensure minimum axial play. See TRANSMISSION BEARING SNAP RING chart for proper application.

1ST GEAR

Using dial indicator, measure oil clearance between gear and inner race with needle roller bearing installed. Standard clearance is .0004-.0024" (.009-.060 mm).

TRANSMISSION BEARING REMOVAL/INSTALLATION TOOLS

Application	Tool No.
Input Shaft Rear Bearing	(SST09515-20010)
Idler Gear Bearing	
Remover	(SST09950-00020)
Installer	(SST09506-30011)
Counter Gear Rear Bearing	
Remover	(SST09950-00020)
Installer	(SST09515-20010)
Input Shaft Front Bearing	(SST09608-30021)
Counter Gear Center Bearing	(SST097100-30020)
Idler Gear Rear Bearing	
Remover	(SST09612-10091)
Installer	(SST09304-47010)
Output Shaft Rear Bearing	(SST09304-47010)

TRANSMISSION BEARING SNAP RINGS

Application	Thickness In. (mm)
Input Shaft Rear Bearing	
Snap Ring 1	.0827-.0846" (2.10-2.15 mm)
Snap Ring 2	.0886-.0906" (2.25-2.30 mm)
Idler Gear Bearing	
Snap Ring 1	.0945-.0965" (2.40-2.45 mm)
Snap Ring 2	.1004-.1024" (2.55-2.60 mm)
Counter Gear Rear Bearing	
Snap Ring 1	.0709-.0728" (1.80-1.85 mm)
Snap Ring 2	.0768-.0787" (1.95-2.00 mm)

2ND & 3RD GEAR

Using dial indicator, measure oil clearance between gear and output shaft. Standard clearance is .002-.004" (.06-.10 mm). Maximum clearance is .0043" (.110 mm).

SYNCHRO RINGS

Check for wear or damage. Turn ring and push in to check braking action. Using feeler gauge, measure clearance between synchro ring back and gear spline end. Minimum clearance is .024" (.60 mm).

SHIFT FORKS & HUB SLEEVES

Using feeler gauge, measure clearance between hub sleeve and shift fork. Maximum clearance is .04" (1.0 mm).

SELECT LEVER OIL SEAL

Check oil seal for wear or damage and replace as necessary. Using Installer (SST09304-30012), drive in new oil seal.

EXTENSION HOUSING OIL SEAL & BUSHING

1) Check for wear or damage and replace as necessary. Check sliding action of lever. Using plastic hammer, lightly tap in lever lock pin.

2) Remove oil seal. Using Seal Installer (SST09304-12012), drive in new oil seal. Install lever lock pin, aligning notch with groove of shift lever shaft.

Manual Transmissions

TOYOTA Z45, Z46 & Z53 TRANSAXLE (Cont.)

SPEEDOMETER GEAR OIL SEAL

Check for wear or damage and replace as necessary. Using Remover (SST09921-00010), remove oil seal. Using Installer (SST09201-60011), install new oil seal.

TRANSAXLE REASSEMBLY & ADJUSTMENT

1) Install new spacer to differential drive pinion. Install drive pinion to differential carrier. Using Installer (SST09612-22010) and press, temporarily press in bearing until threaded portion is protruding .12" (3.0 mm) from carrier.

2) Apply gear oil onto threaded portion of drive pinion. Using Drive Pinion Lock Nut Wrench and Differential Drive Pinion Holding Tool (SST09564-16010) and 09556-16010), tighten nut to 108 ft. lbs. (147 N.m). Apply gear oil on bearings.

3) Using Adapter (SST09556-16010), snug down bearing by turning drive pinion. Using adapter and torque meter, measure differential drive pinion preload. Preload for new bearing is 4.3-8.7 INCH Lbs. (.49-.99 N.m).

4) If preload is not correct, tighten nut to 108 ft. lbs. (147 N.m). Remeasure preload. If excessive, replace spacer. If insufficient, increase tightening 5-10° at a time and remeasure.

5) If preload is insufficient even after specified torque range is exceeded, loosen nut and tighten to 268 ft. lbs. (364 N.m). If preload is still not correct, replace spacer.

6) Set transaxle case with back side of ring gear facing down. Install differential case. Install only side washer on ring gear back side. Ensure ring gear has backlash. Snug down washer and bearings by tapping ring gear with plastic hammer.

7) Push side bearing boss on teeth surface of ring gear and measure backlash. If backlash is not .004" (.10 mm), select a ring gear back side washer from DIFFERENTIAL RING GEAR BACK SIDE WASHER chart using backlash as reference.

8) Select ring gear teeth side washer of a thickness which eliminates any clearance between outer race and case. Remove side washers and differential case. Install side washer into lower part of case.

9) Place other side washer onto differential case. Install differential case with outer race into transaxle case. Using plastic hammer, snug down washer and bearing by tapping ring gear.

10) Using dial indicator, measure ring gear backlash. If backlash is not .004-.006" (.10-.15 mm), adjust by increasing or decreasing number of washers on both sides by an equal amount. There should be no clearance between side washer and case. There should be ring gear backlash. *See Fig. 5.*

11) After adjustment, using backlash as reference, remove ring gear teeth side washer and measure thickness. Install a new washer .002-.004" (.06-.09 mm) thicker than washer removed. Select a washer that can be pressed 2/3 of the way in by finger.

12) Using plastic hammer, tap in side washer. Recheck ring gear backlash. If still not correct, adjust by increasing or decreasing washers on both sides by an equal amount. Install side bearing caps and tighten bolts to 33-39 ft. lbs. (45-53 N.m).

13) Apply gear oil on bearings. Using Adapter (SST09556-16010), turn drive pinion left and right several times. Using adapter and torque meter, measure total

DIFFERENTIAL RING GEAR BACK SIDE WASHERS

I.D. No.	Thickness In. (mm)
1	.1028-.1035 (2.61-2.63)
2	.1039-.1047 (2.64-2.66)
3	.1051-.1059 (2.67-2.69)
4	.1063-.1071 (2.70-2.72)
5	.1075-.1083 (2.73-2.75)
6	.1087-.1094 (2.76-2.78)
7	.1098-.1106 (2.79-2.81)
8	.1110-.1118 (2.82-2.84)
9	.1122-.1130 (2.85-2.87)
10	.1134-.1142 (2.88-2.90)
11	.1146-.1154 (2.91-2.93)
12	.1157-.1165 (2.94-2.96)
13	.1169-.1177 (2.97-2.99)
14	.1181-.1189 (3.00-3.02)
15	.1193-.1201 (3.03-3.05)
16	.1205-.1213 (3.06-3.08)
17	.1217-.1224 (3.09-3.11)
18	.1228-.1236 (3.12-3.14)
19	.1240-.1248 (3.15-3.17)
20	.1252-.1260 (3.18-3.20)
21	.1264-.1272 (3.21-3.23)
22	.1276-.1283 (3.24-3.26)
23	.1287-.1295 (3.27-3.29)

Fig. 5: Measuring Ring Gear Backlash

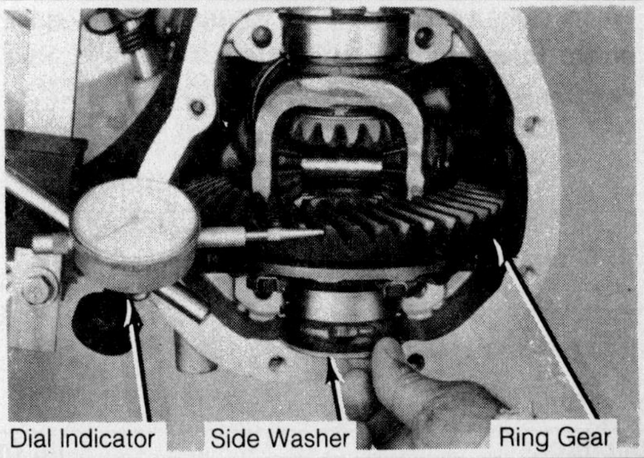

preload. Preload should be 2.6-4.3 INCH Lbs. (.29-.49 N.m) in addition to drive pinion preload. If not, readjust ring gear teeth side washer.

14) Using dial indicator, measure ring gear backlash at 3 places on outer circumference of ring gear. Backlash should be .004-.006" (.10-.15 mm). If not, adjust by either increasing or decreasing washers on both sides by equal amount.

15) Using chisel, stake drive pinion lock nut. Using Installer (SST09223-46011) and hammer, install new differential carrier oil seal. Ensure distance "A" is .331-.354" (8.4-9.0 mm). *See Fig. 6.*

16) Install differential carrier cover and gasket. Tighten set bolts to 96-132 INCH Lbs. (11-15 N.m). Install oil reservoir.

17) Install clutch hub and shifting keys to hub sleeve. Install shifting key springs under shifting keys. Ensure key springs are positioned so end gaps are not in line.

18) Apply gear oil to output shaft. Place synchro ring on 2nd gear and align ring slots with shifting keys. Using Installer (SST09515-30010) and press, install 2nd gear and clutch hub No. 1.

Manual Transmissions

TOYOTA Z45, Z46 & Z53 TRANSAXLE (Cont.)

Fig. 6: Installing Differential Carrier Oil Seal

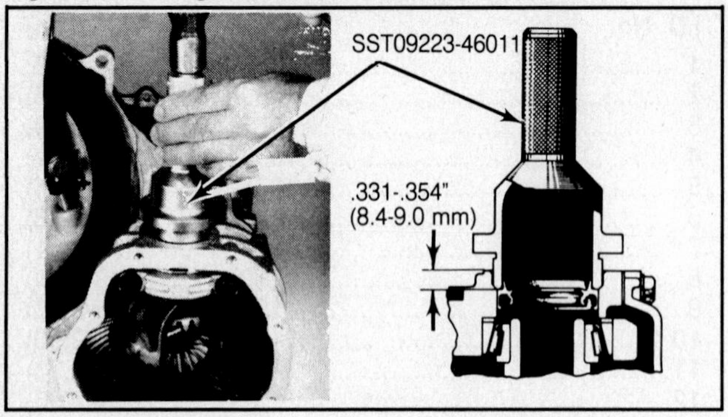

19) Install locking ball in shaft. Apply gear oil to needle roller bearing. Assemble 1st gear, synchro ring, needle roller bearing and inner race.

20) Place synchro ring on 1st gear and align ring slots with shifting keys. Fit inner race groove securely over locking ball. Select snap ring from OUTPUT SHAFT SNAP RING chart that allows minimum axial play and install.

OUTPUT SHAFT SNAP RING

I.D. Mark	Thickness In. (mm)
1	.0846-.0866 (2.15-2.20)
2	.0866-.0886 (2.20-2.25)
3	.0886-.0906 (2.25-2.30)
4	.0906-.0925 (2.30-2.35)
5	.0925-.0945 (2.35-2.40)
6	.0945-.0965 (2.40-2.45)
7	.0965-.0984 (2.45-2.50)
8	.0984-.1004 (2.50-2.55)
9	.1004-.1024 (2.55-2.60)

21) Using dial indicator, measure 1st gear thrust clearance. Using feeler gauge, measure 2nd gear thrust clearance.

1ST & 2ND GEAR THRUST CLEARANCE

Application	In. (mm)
Standard Clearance	
1st Gear	.0059-.0108 (.15-.27)
2nd Gear	.0059-.0098 (.15-.25)
Maximum Clearance	.0118 (.30)

22) Install shifting keys and key springs to No. 2 clutch hub. Install clutch hub to hub sleeve. Apply gear oil to output shaft. Place synchro on 3rd gear and align ring slots with shifting keys.

23) Using Installer (SST09515-30010) and press, install 3rd gear and clutch hub No. 2. Assemble widest thrust bearing to No. 2 clutch hub.

24) Apply gear oil and install 4th gear needle roller bearing and synchro. Line shifting keys with key slots in synchro ring. Install spacer and tap in snap ring.

25) Stick thrust bearing onto spacer with MP grease. Using Installer (SST09612-22010) and press, install spacer. Using installer and press, install output shaft front bearing. Ensure outer race groove is facing toward front. Select snap ring from OUTPUT SHAFT SNAP RING chart that allows minimum axial play and install.

OUTPUT SHAFT SNAP RING

I.D. Mark	Thickness In. (mm)
2	.0827-.0846 (2.10-2.15)
3	.0846-.0866 (2.15-2.20)
4	.0866-.0886 (2.20-2.25)
5	.0886-.0906 (2.25-2.30)
6	.0906-.0925 (2.30-2.35)
7	.0925-.0945 (2.35-2.40)
8	.0945-.0965 (2.40-2.45)
9	.0965-.0984 (2.45-2.50)
10	.0984-.1004 (2.50-2.55)

26) Using feeler gauge, measure 3rd gear thrust clearance. Using dial indicator, measure 4th gear thrust clearance. Go to step **28)** on 4 speed transmissions.

3RD & 4TH GEAR THRUST CLEARANCE

Application	In. (mm)
Standard Clearance	
3rd Gear	.0059-.0098 (.15-.25)
4th Gear	.0008-.0094 (.02-.24)
Maximum Clearance	.0118 (.30)

27) Using Installer (SST09612-22010) and press, install 5th gear. Select and install snap ring from 5TH GEAR SNAP RING chart that allows minimum axial play and install. Using press, install sleeve yoke.

5TH GEAR SNAP RING SELECTION

I.D. Mark	In. (mm)
2	.0827-.0846 (2.10-2.15)
3	.0846-.0866 (2.15-2.20)
4	.0866-.0886 (2.20-2.25)
5	.0886-.0906 (2.25-2.30)
6	.0906-.0925 (2.30-2.35)
7	.0925-.0945 (2.35-2.40)

28) Mount intermediate plate in vise by securing lower protrusion. Using plastic hammer, tap output shaft and counter gear together about halfway. Align idler with notched portion of reverse idler gear shaft.

29) Using plastic hammer, tap idler gear shaft bearing about halfway. Ensure idler gear and output shaft spacer are not contacting each other. Using plastic hammer, tap each gear shaft until bearing is in as far as possible.

30) Using snap ring pliers, install 2 snap rings. Install bearing retainer and tighten bolts to 108 INCH Lbs. (12 N.m). On 4-speed transmissions, install counter gear plate and tighten bolt to 108 INCH Lbs. (12 N.m). On 5-speed transmissions, install steel ball in shaft. Align spacer groove with steel ball and install spacer.

31) Install clutch hub No. 3 and shifting keys to hub sleeve. Install shifting key springs under shifting keys with key end gaps not in line.

32) Apply gear oil to 5th gear needle roller bearing. Install counter 5th gear, needle roller bearing and synchro ring on shaft. Using Installer (SST09612-222010) and press, install clutch hub. Line up shifting keys with key slots in synchro ring.

Manual Transmissions

TOYOTA Z45, Z46 & Z53 TRANSAXLE (Cont.)

33) Select a snap ring that allows minimum axial play and install on shaft. Snap rings are available in sizes from .0709-.0846" (1.80-2.15 mm) in .002" (.05 mm) increments. Using feeler gauge, measure 5th counter gear thrust clearance.

5TH COUNTER GEAR THRUST CLEARANCE

Application	In. (mm)
Standard Clearance	.0059-.0128 (.15-.32)
Maximum Clearance	.0157 (.40)

34) Install shifting key retainer and hole snap ring. On all transmissions, insert shift fork shaft No. 1 through shift fork No. 1 and reverse shift fork. Align reverse shift fork into reverse gear groove, align shift fork No. 1 with hub sleeve No. 1 groove and install shift fork shaft No. 1 through intermediate plate.

35) Align shift fork No. 2 into hub sleeve No. 2 groove. Install shift fork shaft No. 2 to intermediate plate through shift forks No. 1 and No. 2. Insert shift fork shaft No. 3 to gear shift head and install so pin hole of shift fork shaft No. 3 aligns with interlock pin hole.

36) Insert piece of wire into interlock pin hole and confirm it goes in about 4.72" (120 mm) from intermediate plate circumference. Coat interlock pins with MP grease and push in with a piece of wire. After inserting 3 interlock pins, insert a piece of wire and ensure it goes in about 3.15" (80 mm) from intermediate plate circumference.

37) Align shift fork No. 3 into hub sleeve No. 3 groove and insert shift fork shaft No. 3 into shift fork No. 3. Apply sealer to straight screw plug and install.

38) Align pin hole in fork with hole in shaft. Using pin punch, drive in slotted spring pins until flush with fork. Apply sealer to straight screw plug and install with spring and ball.

39) Apply sealer to gasket and install transmission case to intermediate plate. Using snap ring pliers, install snap ring. Install 3 locking balls and springs. Apply sealer to straight screw plugs and install.

40) Insert reverse shift arm pivot through reverse shift arm. Install "C" washer to No. 1 and No. 2 shift fork shafts. Install gear shift head to fork shaft and drive in slotted spring pin with pin punch and hammer.

41) Install speedometer drive gear, steel ball and snap ring. Align end of shift lever shaft and gear shift head No. 2 and install extension housing. Tighten bolts to 19 ft. lbs. (26 N.m).

42) Install locking ball and spring. Install transmission case cover and shift lever retainer and tighten bolts.

43) Install restrict pins to extension housing. Note Green pin is located on 1st and 2nd gear and Yellow pin is located on 5th and reverse gear. Install speedometer driven gear, extension housing mount stay and back-up light switch. Install transmission case cover.

TIGHTENING SPECIFICATIONS

Application	Ft. Lbs. (N.m)
Counter Gear Plate (4-Speed)	9 (12)
Differential Cover	8-11 (11-15)
Differential Ring Gear	67-75 (91-102)
Differential Side Bearing Cap	33-39 (45-53)
Extension Hsg.-to-Transaxle Case	19 (26)
Front Wheel Bearing Lock Nut	137 (186)
Input Shaft Bearing Retainer	15-21 (20-28)
Locking Ball Plug	16 (22)
Output Shaft Rear Bearing Retainer	9 (12)
Pinion Rear Bearing Lock Nut	109-267 (148-362)
Restrict Pin Plug	27-32 (37-43)
Stabilizer Bar-to-Lower Arm	66-90 (89-122)
Stabilizer Bracket	32 (43)
Steering Knuckle-to-Brake Caliper	57-83 (77-113)
Steering Knuckle-to-Lower Arm	59 (80)
Steering Knuckle-to-Shock Absorber	105 (142)
Steering Knuckle-to-Tie Rod End	29-43 (39-58)
Transaxle-to-Transmission	18 (24)
Transaxle-to-Engine	37-57 (50-77)

TOYOTA Z54F TRANSAXLE

4WD Tercel

DESCRIPTION

Transaxle assembly consists of transmission case, transfer case adapter and extension housing with common oil supply. Transmission is fully synchronized in all forward gears.

LUBRICATION & ADJUSTMENT

See appropriate MANUAL TRANSMISSION SERVICING article in IMPORT GENERAL SERVICING section.

SERVICE (IN VEHICLE)

AXLE DRIVE SHAFTS

See appropriate DRIVE AXLE SHAFT article in IMPORT AXLE SHAFTS, OVERDRIVES & TRANSFER CASES section.

TRANSAXLE REMOVAL & INSTALLATION

See appropriate MANUAL TRANSMISSION REMOVAL article in IMPORT GENERAL SERVICING section.

TRANSAXLE DISASSEMBLY

1) Remove mounting insulator, speedometer driven gear, and reverse restrict pin. Remove back-up light, extra low gear, and 4WD indicator switches. Remove 6 bolts, shift lever retainer, and gasket. Unstake shift lever housing mount bolt lock washer and remove bolt.

2) Remove 9 extension housing bolts, extension housing, shift lever housing and gasket. Remove 3 oil pump cover bolts and oil pump cover. Remove oil pump rotors, transfer output shaft, and oil baffle.

3) Using Plug Remover (SST09313-30021), remove straight screw plug. Using magnet, remove spring seat, spring and ball. Remove shift fork, shift shaft and hub sleeve as a unit.

4) Temporarily install input shaft. Cover input shaft tip with shop cloth and secure with pliers. Remove oil pump drive shaft by turning clockwise.

5) Remove snap ring, clutch hub, and No. 4 synchro ring. Remove 4 transfer case cover bolts, transfer case cover, and gasket. Remove spring seat and spring. Using magnet, remove detent ball. Unstake No. 4 shift head mount bolt lock plate and bolt. Using Detent Ball Plug Socket (SST 09313-30021), remove screw plug. Using pin punch and hammer, tap out slotted spring pin. Remove No. 4 shift fork with shift fork shaft. Using magnet, remove interlock pin.

6) Remove transfer adaptor plug, spring, and reverse restrict pin. Remove 9 bolts attaching transfer adaptor to case. Using plastic hammer, tap transfer adaptor. Turn select lever and remove tip from shift head groove. Remove transfer adaptor with select lever and extra low gear from transmission case.

7) Install needle roller bearing, extra low gear, and transfer clutch hub with snap ring. Using feeler gauge, measure and record extra low gear thrust clearance. Remove snap ring, transfer clutch hub, extra low gear and needle roller bearing.

EXTRA LOW GEAR THRUST CLEARANCE

Application	In. (mm.)
Standard	.0070-.0169" (.180-.430 mm)
Maximum	.0197" (.50 mm)

8) Remove extra low gear thrust washer. Using magnet, remove locking ball. Using 2 screwdrivers and hammer, remove snap ring. Remove drive gear and locking ball. Using pin punch and hammer, drive out slotted spring pins and remove gear shift heads. Using 2 screwdrivers and hammer, remove snap ring from No. 1 and No. 2 shift fork shafts.

9) Using hexagon wrench, remove straight screw plugs. Using magnet, remove springs and balls. Using snap ring pliers, remove bearing snap ring. Remove transmission case cover and input shaft.

10) Using plastic hammer, tap case protrusion and separate case from intermediate plate. Mount intermediate plate in vise by securing protrusion on lower part of plate.

11) Remove straight screw plug, spring and ball. Remove shift fork mount bolts. Using pin punch and hammer, drive out 4 slotted spring pins. Remove gear shift heads. Set each fork shaft to neutral positon.

12) Holding shift fork, pull out fork shaft and remove fork. Remove interlock pins from fork shaft and intermediate plate. Using feeler gauge, measure counter 5th gear thrust clearance.

COUNTER 5TH GEAR THRUST CLEARANCE

Application	In. (mm)
Standard	.0059-.0128 (.15-.32)
Maximum	.0157 (.40)

13) Using 2 screwdrivers and hammer, remove snap ring. Remove shifting key retainer. Using snap ring pliers, remove snap ring. Using Hub Remover (SST09950-20014), remove clutch hub No. 3, synchro ring and counter 5th gear as a unit. Carefully remove needle roller bearing.

14) Remove spacer, steel ball and bearing retainer. Using snap ring pliers, remove 2 snap rings. Using plastic hammer, tap reverse gear shaft, idler gear and output shaft halfway from intermediate plate. Support gear shaft by hand.

15) Remove idler gear and reverse gear shaft together. Using plastic hammer, tap out counter gear and output shaft together. Support gear and shaft by hand. Using dial indicator, measure 1st and 4th gear thrust clearance.

GEAR THRUST CLEARANCE

Application	In. (mm)
Standard Clearance	
1st Gear	.0059-.0108 (.15-.27)
2nd & 3rd Gear	.0059-.0098 (.15-.25)
4th Gear	.0008-.0094 (.02-.24)
Maximum Clearance	.0118 (.30)

16) Using Remover (SST09950-00020), press out sleeve yoke. Using snap ring pliers, remove snap ring. Using Remover (SST09950-00020), press out 5th gear.

TOYOTA Z54F TRANSAXLE (Cont.)

Fig. 1: Exploded View of Toyota 6-Speed Transaxle

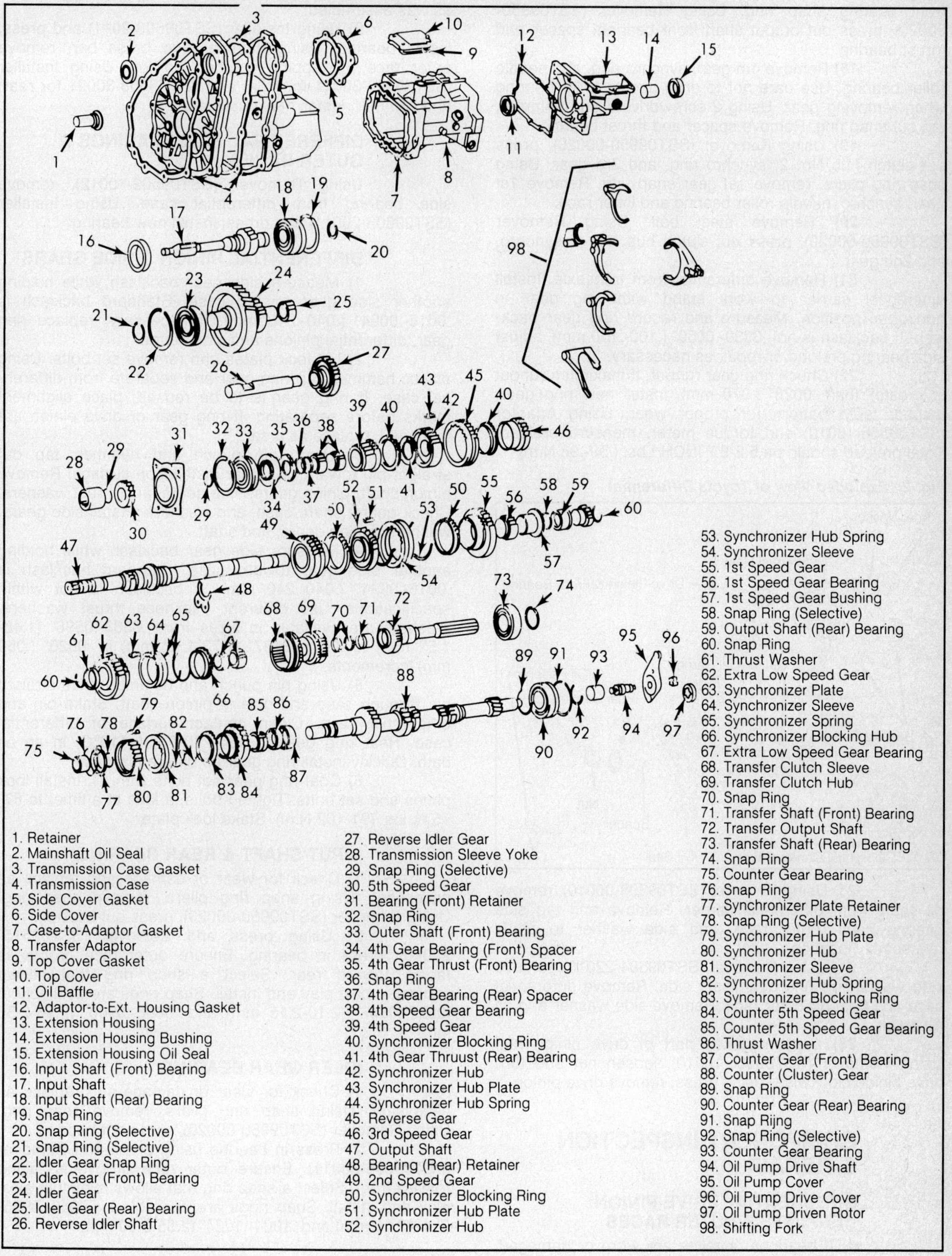

1. Retainer
2. Mainshaft Oil Seal
3. Transmission Case Gasket
4. Transmission Case
5. Side Cover Gasket
6. Side Cover
7. Case-to-Adaptor Gasket
8. Transfer Adaptor
9. Top Cover Gasket
10. Top Cover
11. Oil Baffle
12. Adaptor-to-Ext. Housing Gasket
13. Extension Housing
14. Extension Housing Bushing
15. Extension Housing Oil Seal
16. Input Shaft (Front) Bearing
17. Input Shaft
18. Input Shaft (Rear) Bearing
19. Snap Ring
20. Snap Ring (Selective)
21. Snap Ring (Selective)
22. Idler Gear Snap Ring
23. Idler Gear (Front) Bearing
24. Idler Gear
25. Idler Gear (Rear) Bearing
26. Reverse Idler Shaft
27. Reverse Idler Gear
28. Transmission Sleeve Yoke
29. Snap Ring (Selective)
30. 5th Speed Gear
31. Bearing (Front) Retainer
32. Snap Ring
33. Outer Shaft (Front) Bearing
34. 4th Gear Bearing (Front) Spacer
35. 4th Gear Thrust (Front) Bearing
36. Snap Ring
37. 4th Gear Bearing (Rear) Spacer
38. 4th Speed Gear Bearing
39. 4th Speed Gear
40. Synchronizer Blocking Ring
41. 4th Gear Thruust (Rear) Bearing
42. Synchronizer Hub
43. Synchronizer Hub Plate
44. Synchronizer Hub Spring
45. Reverse Gear
46. 3rd Speed Gear
47. Output Shaft
48. Bearing (Rear) Retainer
49. 2nd Speed Gear
50. Synchronizer Blocking Ring
51. Synchronizer Hub Plate
52. Synchronizer Hub
53. Synchronizer Hub Spring
54. Synchronizer Sleeve
55. 1st Speed Gear
56. 1st Speed Gear Bearing
57. 1st Speed Gear Bushing
58. Snap Ring (Selective)
59. Output Shaft (Rear) Bearing
60. Snap Ring
61. Thrust Washer
62. Extra Low Speed Gear
63. Synchronizer Plate
64. Synchronizer Sleeve
65. Synchronizer Spring
66. Synchronizer Blocking Hub
67. Extra Low Speed Gear Bearing
68. Transfer Clutch Sleeve
69. Transfer Clutch Hub
70. Snap Ring
71. Transfer Shaft (Front) Bearing
72. Transfer Output Shaft
73. Transfer Shaft (Rear) Bearing
74. Snap Ring
75. Counter Gear Bearing
76. Snap Ring
77. Synchronizer Plate Retainer
78. Snap Ring (Selective)
79. Synchronizer Hub Plate
80. Synchronizer Hub
81. Synchronizer Sleeve
82. Synchronizer Hub Spring
83. Synchronizer Blocking Ring
84. Counter 5th Speed Gear
85. Counter 5th Speed Gear Bearing
86. Thrust Washer
87. Counter Gear (Front) Bearing
88. Counter (Cluster) Gear
89. Snap Ring
90. Counter Gear (Rear) Bearing
91. Snap Rijng
92. Snap Ring (Selective)
93. Counter Gear Bearing
94. Oil Pump Drive Shaft
95. Oil Pump Cover
96. Oil Pump Drive Cover
97. Oil Pump Driven Rotor
98. Shifting Fork

Manual Transmissions

TOYOTA Z54F TRANSAXLE (Cont.)

17) Using snap ring pliers, remove output shaft front bearing snap ring. Using Remover (SST09950-00020), press out output shaft front bearing, spacer and thrust bearing.

18) Remove 4th gear, synchro ring, and needle roller bearing. Use care not to drop needle roller bearing when removing gear. Using 2 screwdrivers and hammer, tap out snap ring. Remove spacer and thrust bearing.

19) Using Remover (SST09950-00020), press out clutch hub No. 2, synchro ring, and 3rd gear. Using snap ring pliers, remove 1st gear snap ring. Remove 1st gear, synchro, needle roller bearing and inner race.

20) Remove steel ball. Using Remover (SST09950-00020), press out clutch hub No. 1, synchro, and 2nd gear.

21) Remove differential from transaxle. Install differential carrier to work stand with ring gear in horizontal position. Measure and record ring gear backlash. If backlash is not .0039-.0059" (.100-.150 mm), adjust side bearing preload or repair as necessary.

22) Check ring gear runout. If maximum runout is greater than .0028" (.070 mm), install new ring gear. Inspect teeth pattern for proper wear. Using Adaptor (SST09556-16010) and torque meter, measure preload. Total preload should be 5.2-8.7 INCH Lbs. (.59-.98 N.m)

Fig. 2: Exploded View of Toyota Differential

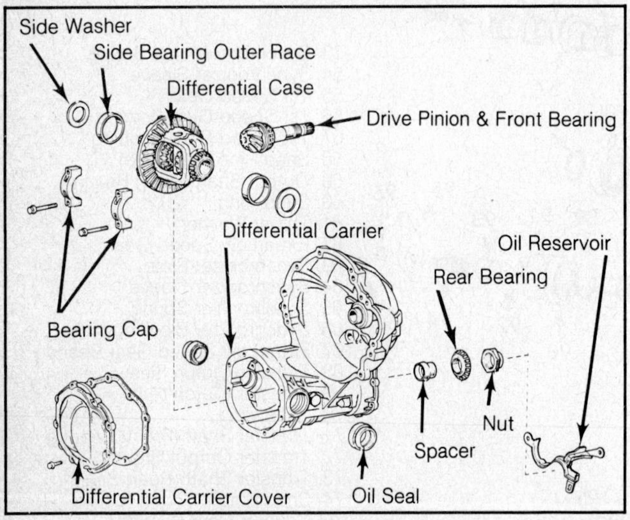

23) Using Remover (SST09308-00010), remove oil seals from differential carrier. Remove and tag side bearing caps, outer race, and side washer to show reassembly location.

24) Using Remover (SST09504-22010), remove side washer on ring gear teeth side. Remove differential case and bearing outer race. Remove side washer and oil reservoir.

25) Loosen staked part of drive pinion nut. Using Remover (SST09556-16010), loosen nut and turn drive pinion clockwise. Using press, remove drive pinion.

COMPONENT INSPECTION & REPAIR

DIFFERENTIAL DRIVE PINION BEARINGS & OUTER RACES

1) If bearings or races are worn or damaged, use Remover (SST09950-00020) to press out rear bearing from drive pinion. Install plate washer of same thickness as was assembled.

2) Using Installer (SST09608-2011) and press, install bearing. Using hammer and brass bar, remove outer race by tapping notched portion. Using Installer (SST09608-30011 for front and SST09608-30021 for rear) and hammer, install new outer race.

DIFFERENTIAL SIDE BEARINGS & OUTER RACES

Using Remover (SST09502-10012), remove side bearing from differential case. Using Installer (SST09608-20011) and press, install new bearing.

DIFFERENTIAL PINION & SIDE GEARS

1) Measure side gear backlash while holding another side gear toward case. Standard backlash is .0016-.0094" (.040-.240 mm). If necessary, replace ring gear, differential pinions and side gears.

2) Lift lock plates and remove set bolts. Using plastic hammer, tap ring gear and separate from differential case. If ring gear is to be reused, place alignment marks before separating. If ring gear or drive pinion are damaged, replace as a set.

3) Using pin punch and hammer, tap out straight pin toward ring gear installation surface. Remove pinion shaft, pinion gears, side gears, and thrust washers. Check gears, shaft, case, and washers. Install side gears, washers, pinion gears, and shaft.

4) Measure side gear backlash while holding another side gear toward case. Standard backlash is .0016-.0094" (.040-.240 mm). If backlash is not within specifications, use different thickness thrust washers. Washers are available in sizes from .0583-.0598" (1.48-1.52 mm) to .0681-.0697" (1.73-1.77 mm) in .0020" (.050 mm) increments.

5) Using pin punch and hammer, drive straight pin through case and hole in pinion shaft. Stake pin and differential case. Clean contact surface of differential case. Heat ring gear to 194-230°F (90-110°C) in an oil bath. Quickly install ring gear on differential case.

6) Coat ring gear set bolts with oil. Install lock plates and set bolts. Tighten bolts, a little at a time, to 67-75 ft. lbs. (91-102 N.m). Stake lock plate.

INPUT SHAFT & REAR BEARING

1) Check for wear or damage and replace as necessary. Using snap ring pliers, remove snap ring. Using Remover (SST09950-00020), press out bearing.

2) Using press and Remover (SST09515-20010), press in bearing. Ensure outer race groove is facing toward rear. Select a snap ring that allows minimum axial play and install. Snap rings are available in .0827-.0846" (2.10-2.15 mm) and .0886-.0906" (2.25-2.30 mm).

IDLER GEAR BEARING

1) Check for wear or damage and replace as necessary. Using snap ring pliers, remove snap ring. Using Remover (SST09950-00020), press out bearing.

2) Press in bearing using press and Remover (SST09506-30011). Ensure outer race groove is facing toward front. Select a snap ring that allows minimum axial play and install. Snap rings are available in .0945-.0965" (2.40-2.45 mm) and .1004-.1024" (2.55-2.60 mm).

TOYOTA Z54F TRANSAXLE (Cont.)

1ST GEAR

Using dial indicator, measure oil clearance between gear and inner race with needle roller bearing installed. Standard clearance is .0004-.0024" (.009-.060 mm).

2ND & 3RD GEAR

Using dial indicator, measure oil clearance between gear and output shaft. Standard clearance is .0024-.0039" (.06-.10 mm). Maximum clearance is .0043" (.110 mm).

SYNCHRO RINGS

Check for wear or damage. Turn ring and push in to check braking action. Using feeler gauge, measure clearance between synchro ring back and gear spline end. Minimum clearance is .024" (.60 mm).

SHIFT FORKS & HUB SLEEVES

Using feeler gauge, measure clearance between hub sleeve and shift fork. Maximum clearance is .039" (1.0 mm).

COUNTER GEAR & REAR BEARING

1) Check gear teeth and bearing for wear or damage and replace as necessary. Using 2 screwdrivers and hammer, tap out snap ring. Using press and Remover (SST09950-00020), press out bearing.

2) Install front snap ring. Using press and Remover (SST09608-20011 No. 11), press in bearing. Select snap ring from COUNTER GEAR REAR BEARING SNAP RING chart that will allow minimum axial play and install.

COUNTER GEAR REAR BEARING SNAP RING SELECTION

I.D. Mark	Thickness In. (mm)
A	1.925-1.975 (.0758-.0778)
B	1.975-2.025 (.0778-.0797)
C	2.025-2.075 (.0797-.0817)
D	2.075-2.125 (.0817-.0837)
E	2.125-2.175 (.0837-.0856)
F	2.175-2.225 (.0856-.0876)

OIL PUMP DRIVE SHAFT

Check that left hand threads are not damaged. Check that pump drive shaft slides smoothly in axial direction.

SELECT LEVER OIL SEAL

Check oil seal for wear or damage. If oil seal is worn or damaged, use screwdriver to pry out. Using Installer (SST09304-30012), drive in new oil seal.

INPUT SHAFT FRONT BEARING & OIL SEAL

1) Check for wear or damage and replace as necessary. Using screwdriver and hammer, drive out oil seal. Remove lock plate.

2) Using Remover/Installer (SST09608-30021), drive out old bearing and drive in new bearing. Ensure outer race groove is facing upward. Install lock plate. Using remover/installer, drive in oil seal.

COUNTER GEAR CENTER BEARING

Check for wear or damage and replace as necessary. Using Remover/Installer (SST097100-30020) and press, press out old bearing and press in new bearing.

IDLER GEAR REAR BEARING

Check for wear or damage and replace as necessary. Remove oil receiver. Using Remover (SST09612-10091), remove bearing. Using Installer (SST09304-47010) and hammer, drive in bearing. Install oil receiver.

OUTPUT SHAFT REAR BEARING

Check for wear or damage and replace as necessary. Remove oil receiver. Using Remover/Installer (SST09304-47010) and hammer, drive out old bearing and drive in new bearing. Install oil receiver.

COUNTER GEAR FRONT BEARING

Check for wear or damage and replace as necessary. Using Removers (SST09310-36021 and 09612-10091), remove bearing. Using Installer (SST09304-47010) and hammer, drive in bearing until level with end surface of transaxle case.

COUNTER SHAFT BEARING

Check for wear or damage and replace as necessary. Using socket and press, press out old bearing. Using Installer (SST09304-12012) and press, press in bearing.

OUTPUT SHAFT BEARINGS

1) Check for wear or damage and replace as necessary. To replace outer bearing, use snap ring pliers and remove snap ring. Using press and Remover (SST09950-00020), press out bearing.

2) Using press and Installer (SST09608-20011 No. 11), press in bearing. Install snap ring. To install inner bearing, use screwdriver to remove snap ring and bearing. Install new bearing and snap ring.

EXTENSION HOUSING OIL SEAL & BUSHING

1) Check for wear or damage and replace as necessary. Using Remover (SST09308-00010 or, with output shaft installed, SST09308-10010), remove oil seal.

2) Heat end of extension housing to 176-212°F (80-100°C) in an oil bath. Using Remover/Installer (SST09307-12010), remove bushing and install new bushing. Using Driver (SST09325-12010), drive in new oil seal.

SPEEDOMETER GEAR OIL SEAL

Check for wear or damage and replace as necessary. Using Remover (SST09921-00019), remove oil seal. Using Installer (SST09201-60011), install new oil seal.

TRANSAXLE REASSEMBLY & ADJUSTMENT

1) Install new spacer to differential drive pinion. Install drive pinion to differential carrier. Using

TOYOTA Z54F TRANSAXLE (Cont.)

Installer (SST09612-22010) and press, temporarily press in bearing until threaded portion is protruding .12" (3 mm) from carrier.

2) Apply gear oil to threaded portion of drive pinion. Using Drive Pinion Lock Nut Wrench (SST09564-16010) and Differential Drive Pinion Holding Tool (SST09556-16010), tighten nut to 108 ft. lbs. (147 N.m). Apply gear oil to bearings.

3) Using Adaptor (SST09556-16010), snug down bearing by turning drive pinion several times. Using adaptor and torque meter, measure differential drive pinion preload. Preload for new bearing is 4.3-8.7 INCH Lbs. (.49-.99 N.m).

4) If preload is not correct, tighten nut to 108 ft. lbs. (147 N.m). Remeasure preload. If excessive, replace spacer. If insufficient, increase tightening 5-10° at a time and remeasure each time.

5) If preload is insufficient even after specified torque range is exceeded, loosen nut and tighten to 268 ft. lbs. (364 N.m). If preload is still not correct, replace spacer.

6) Set transaxle case with back of ring gear facing down. Install differential case. Install only side washer on ring gear back side. Ensure ring gear has backlash. Snug down washer and bearings by tapping on ring gear with plastic hammer.

7) Push side bearing boss on teeth surface of ring gear and measure backlash. If backlash is not .0039" (.100 mm), select a ring gear back side washer from DIFFFERENTIAL RING GEAR BACK SIDE chart using backlash as reference.

DIFFERENTIAL RING GEAR BACK SIDE WASHER SELECTION

I.D. No.	Thickness In. (mm)
1	.1028-.1035 (2.61-2.63)
2	.1039-.1047 (2.64-2.66)
3	.1051-.1059 (2.67-2.69)
4	.1063-.1071 (2.70-2.72)
5	.1075-.1083 (2.73-2.75)
6	.1087-.1094 (2.76-2.78)
7	.1098-.1106 (2.79-2.81)
8	.1110-.1118 (2.82-2.84)
9	.1122-.1130 (2.85-2.87)
10	.1134-.1142 (2.88-2.90)
11	.1146-.1154 (2.91-2.93)
12	.1157-.1165 (2.94-2.96)
13	.1169-.1177 (2.97-2.99)
14	.1181-.1189 (3.00-3.02)
15	.1193-.1201 (3.03-3.05)
16	.1205-.1213 (3.06-3.08)
17	.1217-.1224 (3.09-3.11)
18	.1228-.1236 (3.12-3.14)
19	.1240-.1248 (3.15-3.17)
20	.1252-.1260 (3.18-3.20)
21	.1264-.1272 (3.21-3.23)
22	.1276-.1283 (3.24-3.26)
23	.1287-.1295 (3.27-3.29)

8) Select ring gear teeth side washer of a thickness which eliminates any clearance between outer race and case. Remove side washers and differential case. Install side washer into lower part of case.

9) Place other side washer onto differential case. Install differential case with outer race into transaxle case. Using plastic hammer, snug down washer and bearing by tapping ring gear.

10) Using dial indicator, measure ring gear backlash. If backlash is not .0039-.0059" (.100-.150 mm), adjust by either increasing or decreasing number of washers on both sides by an equal amount. There should be no clearance between side washer and case. There should be ring gear backlash.

11) After adjustment, using backlash as reference, remove ring gear teeth side washer and measure thickness. Install a new washer .0024-.0035" (.060-.090 mm) thicker than washer removed. Select washer that can be pressed 2/3 of the way in by finger.

12) Using plastic hammer, tap in side washer. Recheck ring gear backlash. If still not correct, adjust by either increasing or decreasing the washers on both sides by an equal amount. Install side bearing caps and tighten bolts to 33-39 ft. lbs. (45-53 N.m).

13) Apply gear oil on bearings. Using Adaptor (SST09556-16010), turn drive pinion left and right several times. Using adaptor and torque meter, measure total preload. Preload should be 2.6-4.3 INCH Lbs. (.29-.49 N.m) in addition to drive pinion preload. If not, readjust ring gear teeth side washer.

14) Using dial indicator, measure ring gear backlash at 3 places on outer circumference of ring gear. Backlash should be .0039-.0059" (.100-.150 mm). If not, adjust by either increasing or decreasing washers on both sides by equal amount.

15) Using chisel, stake drive pinion lock nut. Using Installer (SST09223-46011) and hammer, install new differential carrier oil seal. Ensure distance "A" is .331-.354" (8.4-9.0 mm). *See Fig. 3.*

Fig. 3: Installing Differential Carrier Oil Seal

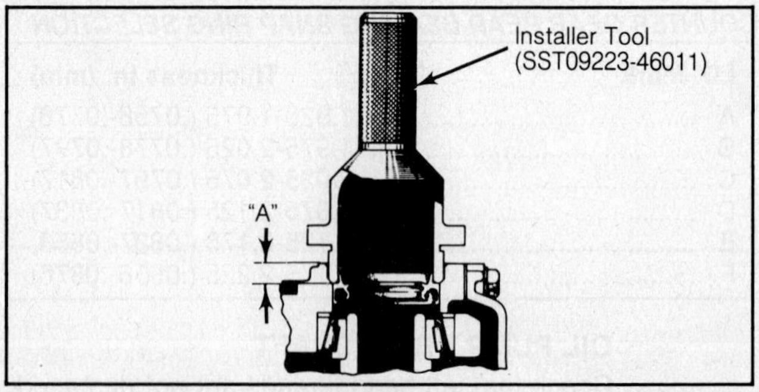

16) Install differential carrier cover and gasket. Tighten set bolts to 96-132 INCH Lbs. (11-15 N.m). Install oil reservoir.

17) Install clutch hub and shifting keys to hub sleeve. Install shifting key springs under shifting keys. Ensure key springs are positioned so end gaps are not in line.

18) Apply gear oil to output shaft. Place synchro ring on 2nd gear and align ring slots with shifting keys. Using Installer (SST09515-30010) and press, install 2nd gear and clutch hub No. 1.

19) Install locking ball in shaft. Apply gear oil to needle roller bearing. Assemble 1st gear, synchro ring, needle roller bearing and inner race.

20) Place synchro ring on 1st gear and align ring slots with shifting keys. Fit inner race groove securely over locking ball. Select snap ring from OUTPUT SHAFT SNAP RING chart that allows minimum axial play and install.

TOYOTA Z54F TRANSAXLE (Cont.)

OUTPUT SHAFT SNAP RING SELECTION

I.D. Mark	Thickness In. (mm)
1	.0846-.0866 (2.15-2.20)
2	.0866-.0886 (2.20-2.25)
3	.0886-.0906 (2.25-2.30)
4	.0906-.0925 (2.30-2.35)
5	.0925-.0945 (2.35-2.40)
6	.0945-.0965 (2.40-2.45)
7	.0965-.0984 (2.45-2.50)
8	.0984-.1004 (2.50-2.55)
9	.1004-.1024 (2.55-2.60)

21) Using dial indicator, measure 1st gear thrust clearance. Using feeler gauge, measure 2nd gear thrust clearance.

1ST & 2ND GEAR THRUST CLEARANCE

Application	In. (mm)
Standard Clearance	
1st Gear	.0059-.0108 (.15-.27)
2nd Gear	.0059-.0098 (.15-.25)
Maximum Clearance	.0118 (.30)

22) Install shifting keys and key springs to No. 2 clutch hub. Install clutch hub to hub sleeve. Apply gear oil to output shaft. Place synchro on 3rd gear and align ring slots with shifting keys.

23) Using Installer (SST09515-30010) and press, install 3rd gear and clutch hub No. 2. Assemble widest thrust bearing to No. 2 clutch hub.

24) Apply gear oil and install 4th gear needle roller bearing and synchro. Line shifting keys with key slots in synchro ring. Install spacer and tap in snap ring.

25) Stick thrust bearing onto spacer with MP grease. Using Installer (SST09612-22010) and press, install spacer and output shaft front bearing. Ensure outer race groove is facing toward front. Select snap ring from OUTPUT SHAFT SNAP RING chart that allows minimum axial play and install.

OUTPUT SHAFT SNAP RING SELECTION

I.D. Mark	Thickness In. (mm)
2	.0827-.0846 (2.10-2.15)
3	.0846-.0866 (2.15-2.20)
4	.0866-.0886 (2.20-2.25)
5	.0886-.0906 (2.25-2.30)
6	.0906-.0925 (2.30-2.35)
7	.0925-.0945 (2.35-2.40)
8	.0945-.0965 (2.40-2.45)
9	.0965-.0984 (2.45-2.50)
10	.0984-.1004 (2.50-2.55)

26) Using feeler gauge, measure 3rd gear thrust clearance. Using dial indicator, measure 4th gear thrust clearance.

3RD & 4TH GEAR THRUST CLEARANCE

Application	In. (mm)
Standard Clearance	
3rd Gear	.0059-.0098 (.15-.25)
4th Gear	.0008-.0094 (.02-.24)
Maximum Clearance	.0118 (.30)

27) Using Installer (SST09612-22010) and press, install 5th gear. Select snap ring from 5TH GEAR SNAP RING chart that allows minimum axial play and install. Using press, install sleeve yoke.

5TH GEAR SNAP RING SELECTION

I.D. Mark	In. (mm)
2	.0827-.0846 (2.10-2.15)
3	.0846-.0866 (2.15-2.20)
4	.0866-.0886 (2.20-2.25)
5	.0886-.0906 (2.25-2.30)
6	.0906-.0925 (2.30-2.35)
7	.0925-.0945 (2.35-2.40)

28) Mount intermediate plate in vise by securing lower protrusion. Using plastic hammer, tap output shaft and counter gear together about halfway. Align idler with notched portion of reverse idler gear shaft.

29) Using plastic hammer, tap idler gear shaft bearing in about halfway. Ensure idler gear and output shaft spacer are not contacting each other. Using plastic hammer, tap each gear shaft until bearing is in as far as possible.

30) Using snap ring pliers, install 2 snap rings. Install bearing retainer and tighten bolts to 108 INCH Lbs. (12 N.m). Install steel ball in shaft. Align spacer groove with steel ball and install spacer.

31) Install clutch hub No. 3 and shifting keys to hub sleeve. Install shifting key springs under shifting keys with key end gaps not in line. Apply gear oil to 5th gear needle roller bearing.

32) Apply oil to counter gear shaft. Install locking ball, thrust washer, needle roller bearing, counter 5th gear, and No. 3 synchro ring. Using Installer (SST09612-22011) and press, install clutch hub. Install shifting keys to hub sleeve. Install shifting key springs under shifting keys so end gaps are not in line.

33) Select snap ring that allows minimum axial play and install on shaft. Snap rings are available in sizes from .0709-.0728" (1.80-1.85 mm) to .0827-.0846" (2.10-2.15 mm) with .0020" (.050 mm) increments. Using feeler gauge, measure 5th counter gear thrust clearance.

5TH COUNTER GEAR THRUST CLEARANCE

Application	In. (mm)
Standard Clearance	.0059-.0128 (.15-.32)
Maximum Clearance	.0157 (.40)

34) Align claws of key retainer with key groove of clutch hub. Install shifting key retainer snap ring. Assemble reverse shift arm and shift head with "E" clip. Install No. 3 shift fork guide bushing, compression spring, and spacer.

35) Using 2 screwdrivers and hammer, install snap ring. Insert shift fork shaft No. 1 through shift fork No. 1 and reverse shift fork. Align reverse shift fork into reverse gear groove. Align shift fork No. 1 with hub sleeve No. 1 groove. Install shift fork shaft No. 1 through intermediate plate.

36) Align shift fork No. 2 into hub sleeve No. 2 groove. Install shift fork shaft No. 2 to intermediate plate through shift forks No. 1 and No. 2. Insert shift fork shaft No. 3 to gear shift head and install so pin hole of shift fork shaft No. 3 aligns with interlock pin hole.

TOYOTA Z54F TRANSAXLE (Cont.)

37) Insert piece of wire into interlock pin hole and confirm it goes in about 4.72" (120 mm) from intermediate plate circumference. Coat MP grease to interlock pins and push in with a piece of wire. After inserting the 3 interlock pins, insert a piece of wire and ensure it goes in about 3.15" (80 mm) from intermediate plate circumference.

38) Align shift fork No. 3 into hub sleeve No. 3 groove. Insert shift fork shaft No. 3 into shift fork No. 3. Apply sealer to straight screw plug and install.

39) Apply sealer to gasket and install transmission case to intermediate plate. Using snap ring pliers, install snap ring. Install 3 locking balls and springs. Apply sealer to straight screw plugs and tighten to 16 ft. lbs. (22 N.m.).

40) Insert reverse shift arm pivot through reverse shift arm. Install snap rings on No. 1 and No. 2 shift fork shafts. Install gear shift head to fork shaft and drive in slotted spring pin with pin punch and hammer.

41) Install speedometer drive gear locking ball, drive gear, and snap ring. Using plastic hammer, tap in snap ring. Install locking ball in output shaft. Install and align groove of thrust washer with locking ball. Install extra low gear and shifting keys to hub sleeve. Install shifting key springs under shifting keys so end gaps are not in line.

42) Install reverse restrict pin to transfer adaptor. Using pin punch and hammer, tap in slotted spring pin by aligning pin holes of reverse restrict pin and transfer adaptor. Apply sealer and install screw plug. Tighten to 16 ft. lbs (22 N.m.). Install shift lever shaft and shift link lever as a unit with plate washer. Align cutouts of lever lock pin and shift lever shaft. Install pin, spring washer and nut.

43) Apply oil to output shaft. Install 2 needle roller bearings on output shaft. Install new gasket on transmission case. Install No. 4 shift fork to No. 4 hub sleeve. Install extra low gear assembly and No. 4 sleeve in transfer adaptor. Install select lever on transfer adaptor. Install transfer adaptor. Turn select lever and insert tip into shift head groove. Tighten 9 bolts to 19 ft. lbs. (26 N.m.). Install reverse restrict pin and spring. Tighten plug to 30 ft. lbs. (40 N.m.).

44) Using magnet, install interlock pin. Using plastic hammer, install snap ring on No. 4 shift fork shaft and install shift fork. Install No. 4 shift head. Using pin punch and hammer, tap slotted spring pin until flush. Apply sealer to screw plug threads and install. Install gear shift head No. 4 set bolt and tighten to 108 INCH Lbs. (12 N.m). Stake one lock plate claw flush with flat surface of nut. For claw contacting protruding portion of nut, stake only half on tightening side.

45) Install detent ball, spring and spring seat. Install transfer case cover with new gasket and tighten 4 bolts to 14 ft. lbs. (19 N.m.). Install No. 4 synchro ring and transfer clutch hub by aligning slots with shifter keys. Install snap ring. Temporarily install input shaft. Cover tip of input shaft with shop cloth, secure with pliers and install oil pump drive shaft by turning clockwise.

46) Assemble transfer shift fork and transfer shift fork shaft. Using pin punch and hammer, align pin holes and install slotted pin. Put transfer shift fork on transfer hub sleeve. Install transfer shift fork assembly and transfer hub sleeve as a unit. Install transfer shift lever shaft into transfer shift fork groove. Install locking ball and spring. Using Installer (SST09313-300021), install straight screw plug.

47) Install oil baffle, transfer output shaft, oil pump rotors, and oil pump cover. Tighten bolts to 14 ft. lbs. (19 N.m.). Insert lever housing into select lever and install extension housing to transfer adaptor. Tighten bolts to 19 ft. lbs. (26 N.m.). Install lock plate and set bolt to lever housing. Tighten bolts to 25 ft. lbs. (34 N.m.). Stake one lock plate claw flush with flat surface of nut. For claw contacting protruding portion of nut, stake only half on tightening side.

48) Align end of shift lever shaft and gear shift head No. 2 and install extension housing. Tighten bolts to 19 ft. lbs. (26 N.m.).

49) Install shift lever retainer and tighten bolts to 14 ft. lbs. (19 N.m.). Install reverse restrict pin and tighten to 30 ft. lbs. (40 N.m.). Install back-up light, 4WD indicator, and extra low gear switches. Install spedometer driven gear and mounting insulator.

TIGHTENING SPECIFICATIONS

Application	Ft. Lbs. (N.m)
Brake Caliper-to-Steering Knuckle	57-83 (78-113)
Shift Lever Retainer Bolt	14 (19)
Tie Rod End-to-Steering Knuckle Nut	29-43 (39-58)
Transmission Case Cover Bolts	14 (19)

Manual Transmissions
VOLKSWAGEN GOLF, JETTA & SCIROCCO 5-SPEED

DESCRIPTION

Transaxles 5-speed, fully synchronized units, mounted transversely at the front of vehicle. Transmission gears are all helical cut and are in constant mesh with mating gears on countershaft.

Forward gear engagement is accomplished through blocker ring type synchronizer assemblies. Reverse gears are spur type and are not in constant mesh, and are engaged by a sliding type reverse idler gear.

Final drive portion of transaxle consists of a drive pinion shaft (which also carries some of the transmission gears), and a differential and ring gear assembly. The 5th gear assembly is located on the end of the pinion and mainshaft in a separate housing.

Transaxle code (020F) is stamped on lower side of transaxle case, adjacent to left axle drive flange.

LUBRICATION & ADJUSTMENT

See appropriate MANUAL TRANSMISSION SERVICING article in the IMPORT GENERAL SERVICING section.

SERVICE (IN VEHICLE)

DRIVE AXLE SHAFTS

See appropriate DRIVE AXLE SHAFT article in IMPORT AXLE SHAFTS, OVERDRIVES & TRANSFER CASES section.

REMOVAL & INSTALLATION

See appropriate MANUAL TRANSMISSION REMOVAL article in IMPORT GENERAL SERVICING section.

TRANSAXLE DISASSEMBLY

NOTE: Before disassembly, measure and record pinion depth and ring gear backlash.

Fig. 1: Installation of Mainshaft Support Fixture

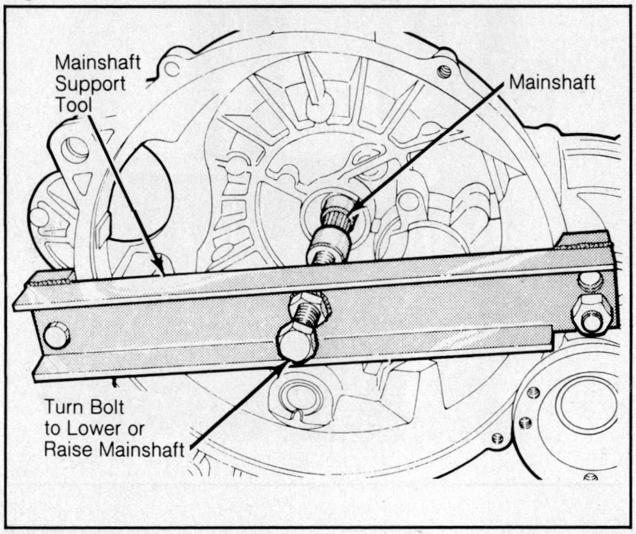

Fig. 2: View of Transaxle Assembly

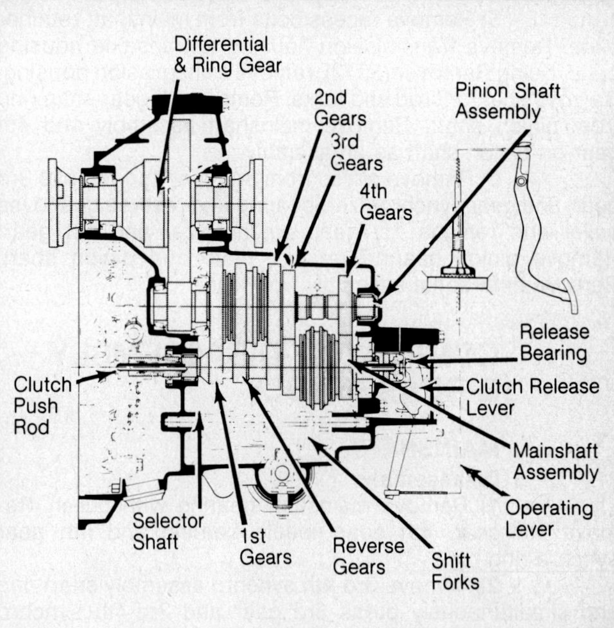

1) Mount transaxle in holding fixture and drain fluid. Remove clutch release push rod from center of mainshaft and withdraw from bell housing end. Install Support Bar (30-211) across mouth of bell housing and install Support Block (VW295a) between support bar and mainshaft. Tighten bolt of bar to take up clearance between bar and mainshaft. *See Fig. 1.*

2) Remove rear housing bolts and rear housing. Remove backup light switch, 5th gear lock out and selector shaft detent. Remove selector shaft cover. Set gears in neutral position and remove selector shaft and spring. Remove cap, snap ring and spring washer from drive shaft flange. Remove both drive shaft flanges with Remover (VW391).

3) Lock transmission in 5th and reverse gears and remove 5th gear synchronizer hub retaining bolt. Pry locking plate loose until tube can be turned and screw tube out of shift fork in a counterclockwise rotation with Remover (3059).

4) Remove tube with Remover (3038). Remove 5th gear synchronizer, 5th gear and shift fork from transmission case. Remove circlip and thrust washer from 5th gear and pull 5th gear off pinion shaft with a puller.

Fig. 3: Removing 5th Gear Synchronizer Assembly

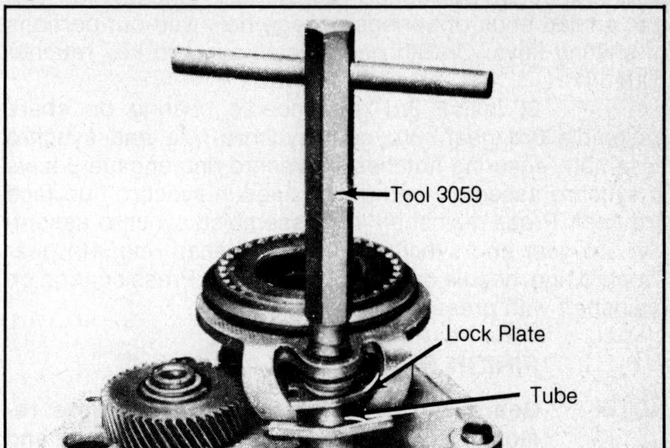

NOTE: Do not pull selector rod out of tube.

5) Remove recess bolts from mainshaft retainer plate. Remove transmission housing-to-transaxle housing bolts. Using Remover (3042), remove transmission housing. Remove shift fork rod and forks. Remove 4th gear snap ring from pinion shaft. Remove mainshaft assembly and 4th gear on pinion shaft as an asembly.

6) Remove circlip from 3rd gear and remove 3rd gear, 2nd gear synchronizer, bearing and reverse gear. Use puller and remove 1st gear synchronizer and 1st gear. Remove pinion bearing retainer plate and pinion shaft. Remove differential assembly from case.

COMPONENT DISASSEMBLY & REASSEMBLY

MAINSHAFT

Disassembly

1) Remove mainshaft bearing with puller. Remove 4th gear, 4th gear needle bearing and 4th gear synchro ring.

2) Remove 3rd-4th synchro assembly snap ring and simultaneously press 3rd gear and 3rd-4th synchro assembly off shaft. Remove 3rd gear needle bearing. Place reference marks on synchro hub and sleeve for reassembly reference, then push hub, shifting keys and spring out of sleeve.

Inspection

1) Check all shaft surfaces, splines, and gear teeth for wear, chipping, scoring, or other damage. Check clutch push rod bushing in mainshaft for wear or damage, and if replacement is necessary, drive out push rod bushing using a 3/8" (10 mm) rod inserted through rear of shaft.

2) Position a new bushing and oil seal on front of mainshaft, and press into shaft until flush. Assemble synchro rings on gears and check ring-to-gear clearance. Clearance for new parts should be .044-.069" (1.12-1.75 mm) for 3rd gear, .051-.075" (1.3-1.9 mm) for 4th gear. Wear limit for used parts is .020" (.5 mm).

NOTE: Replacement of any gear necessitates replacement of meshing gear, as gears are available as matched pairs only.

Reassembly

1) Position shifting keys in slots of synchronizer hub, then install hub into synchronizer sleeve, after aligning reference marks. Install key springs into assembly, making sure springs are positioned 120° offset of one another and that angled ends of springs engage hollowed-out portions of shifting keys. On 5th gear, install synchro key retainer plate.

2) Install 3rd gear needle bearing on shaft. Assemble 3rd gear, 3rd gear synchro ring and synchro assembly, ensuring notches in synchro ring engage 3 keys in synchro assembly and that splines in synchro hub face 3rd gear. Press mainshaft into assembled synchro assembly, 3rd gear and synchro ring. Install snap ring, 4th gear synchro ring, needle bearing and 4th gear. Press bearing on mainshaft with press.

PINION SHAFT

NOTE: Gears and synchronizer assembly were removed during Transmission Disassembly, and will be installed during Transmission Reassembly. Synchronizer overhaul and bearing replacement are covered below.

Disassembly

Bearings cannot be reused after removal from pinion shaft. If bearing replacement is required, use press to remove large and small bearings from shaft. Use puller to remove small bearing outer race from case. For reassembly reference, scribe reference marks on synchro hub and operating sleeve. Then, push hub, shifting keys and springs out of sleeve.

Inspection

Check all shaft surfaces, splines and gear teeth for wear, chipping, scoring or other damage. Assemble synchro rings on gears and check ring-to-gear clearance. Clearance for new parts should be .043-.067" (1.1-1.7 mm). Wear limit for used parts is .020" (.5 mm).

NOTE: Replacement of any gear necessitates replacement of meshing gear, as gears are available as matched pairs only.

Reassembly

If bearings were removed from pinion shaft, heat new bearings to approximately 212°F (100°C) and install on pinion shaft with press. Install shifting keys into synchronizer hub, then install hub into synchronizer sleeve, making sure reference marks are aligned. Install shifting key springs into assembly with springs offset 120° from each other. Angled ends of springs must engage hollowed out portions of shifting keys.

NOTE: DO NOT install pinion bearing race into case half at this time; adjustment of pinion is required and will be covered in Transmission Reassembly.

REVERSE IDLER GEAR & SHAFT

The stop sleeve is no longer installed on idler gear shaft. Gear end movement is limited by the stop on drive pinion shaft bearing retainer. To install, loosely install idler gear support bolt in idler gear shaft. Align shaft as shown in *Fig. 9*. Bolt in shaft should be an equal distance from each bolt hole in flange of case.

Fig. 4: Reverse Idler Gear Stop on Pinion Cover Plate

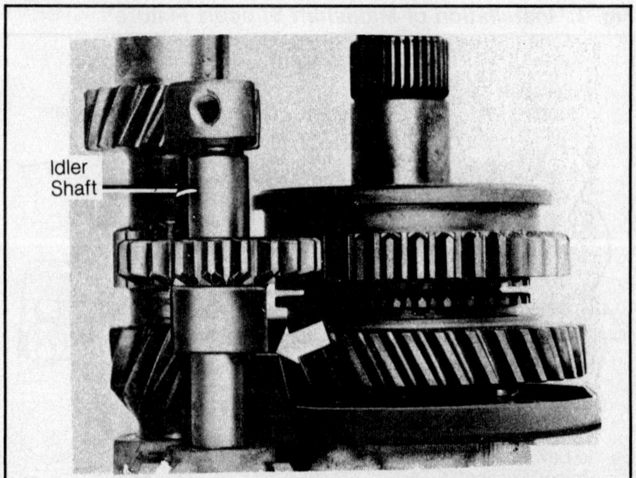

DIFFERENTIAL

Disassembly

1) Ring gear is attached to differential housing by rivets. Drill out rivet heads with a 15/32" (12 mm) drill bit, then knock out rivets with a drift. Place assembly in a press and press off differential ring gear.

NOTE: **Ring gear is reinstalled with special bolts, washers and nuts. Serrations on shank of bolts lock bolt in housing.**

2) Remove snap rings from differential pinion shaft, and drive shaft out of housing. Remove snap rings securing side gears to axle drive flange shafts, and remove shafts from housing. Remove pinions and side gears. Rotate thrust cage and remove from housing.

Reassembly

1) Insert thrust cage into differential housing. Insert pinion gears into housing and drive in pinion shaft. Install pinion shaft snap rings. Rotate thrust cage to align side gear shaft holes with side gear shaft holes of housing.

NOTE: **If bearings were removed from case, heat bearings to approximately 212°F (100°C) and use a press to drive bearings into place.**

2) Insert and position side gears so they mesh with pinion gears and are 180° apart. Rotate side gears into position inside housing. Install axle drive flange shafts, and push each shaft firmly against differential pinion shaft and install thickest snap ring possible. *See Fig. 5.*

Fig. 5: Cutaway View of Differential Showing Flange Shaft Snap Ring Installation

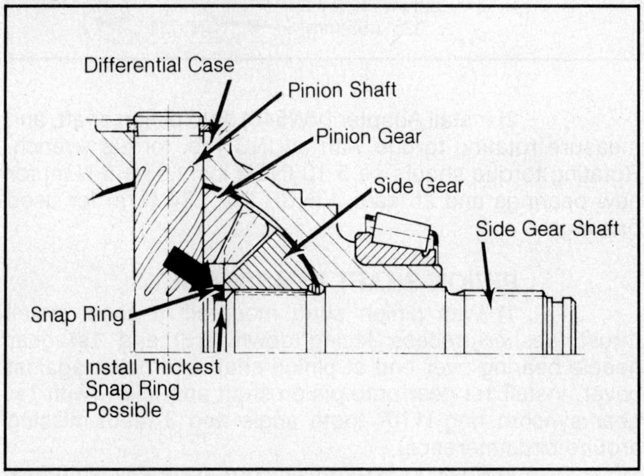

NOTE: **There are two available snap rings. One is .079" (2.0 mm) thick, and the other is .091" (2.3 mm). If thicker snap ring jams sideways, install thinner snap ring.**

3) Heat ring gear to about 212°F (100°C). Drive bolts into differential housing and place heated ring gear onto housing. Install washers and nuts onto ring gear bolts and tighten to 50 ft. lbs. (68 N.m).

TRANSAXLE REASSEMBLY & ADJUSTMENT

NOTE: **During reassembly of transaxle, it is not always necessary to perform all adjustments**

Fig. 6: Exploded View of Differential Assembly

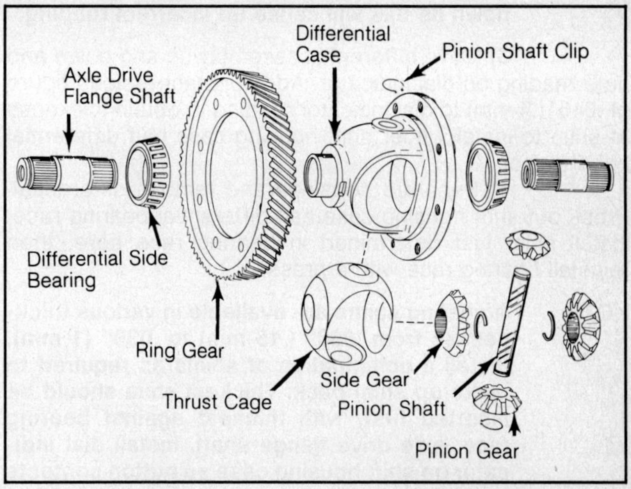

described in the following procedures. If transaxle case or mainshaft have been replaced, check mainshaft adjustment. If transaxle case, pinion bearings or ring and pinion set have been replaced, adjust drive pinion. If transaxle case, differential side bearings or differential have been replaced, adjust differential. If no components were replaced during reassembly, make corresponding adjustments to conform to specifications taken prior to disassembly.

DIFFERENTIAL BEARING PRELOAD

1) If differential bearing race and shim were removed from final drive housing case half, position a .039" (1 mm) shim in bearing race bore and press in bearing race. Remove bearing race and shim from shift housing case half (if not already removed), and reinstall bearing race into housing without shims.

Fig. 7: Using a Dial Indicator to Measure Differential Side Play in Case

2) Install differential assembly into final drive housing case half. Position shift housing case half with gasket onto final drive housing case half and install and tighten attaching bolts. Place gauge block (VW385/17) onto

Manual Transmissions

VOLKSWAGEN GOLF, JETTA & SCIROCCO 5-SPEED (Cont.)

CAUTION: Do not rotate differential when moving up and down as this will cause an incorrect reading.

3) Move differential assembly up and down and note reading on dial indicator. Add constant preload figure of .016" (.4 mm) to dial indicator reading to obtain thickness of shim to install under shift housing case half differential bearing race.

4) Separate housings and remove differential. Press out shift housing case half differential bearing race, install shim just determined in bearing race bore, then reinstall bearing race with a press.

NOTE: Adjusting shims are available in various thicknesses from .006" (.15 mm) to .039" (1 mm). Install a combination of shims as required to make up shim pack. Thickest shim should be inserted first, with thinnest against bearing race. axle drive flange shaft. Install dial indicator on shift housing case so button contacts gauge block. Zero dial indicator with .039" (1 mm) preload.

5) Lubricate bearings with hypoid oil and reinstall in transaxle case. Install adapter and INCH lb. torque wrench to drive axle flange shaft and check rotating torque.

6) Rotating torque should be 11-31 INCH lbs. (1.2-3.5 N.m) for new bearings and 3 INCH lbs. (.34 N.m) for used bearings. If not within specifications, recheck bearing condition and verify proper shim thickness.

PINION BEARING PRELOAD

1) If not already removed, use a puller to withdraw pinion bearing race from final drive housing case half. Temporarily install a .025" (.65 mm) shim into bearing race bore of case half, then reinstall race using a press. Install pinion shaft into bearing race, then install pinion bearing cover, tightening cover-to-case half bolts securely.

CAUTION: Do not rotate pinion when moving up and down as this will cause an incorrect reading.

2) Install surface plate on top of pinion shaft. Install dial indicator and support on case half so button of indicator contacts surface plate. *See Fig. 8.* Preload dial indicator with .039" (1 mm) and zero dial face. Move pinion up and down and note maximum dial indicator reading.

3) To dial indicator reading, add thickness of shim temporarily installed under bearing race (.025" - .65 mm), plus a constant preload figure of .008" (.2 mm). Total of 3 figures equals thickness of shims to install under pinion bearing race in case half. Remove pinion and bearing race, replace .025" (.65 mm) shim with shim pack just determined, then reinstall bearing race.

NOTE: Adjusting shims are available in thicknesses ranging from .026" (.65 mm) to .055" (1.4 mm) in increments of .002" (.5 mm). Install a combination of shims as required to make up shim pack.

DIFFERENTIAL & PINION INSTALLATION

1) Place final drive housing on work bench and lubricate differential bearings with gear oil. Install differential assembly into transaxle case. Lubricate pinion bearings with gear oil and install pinion shaft. Install pinion bearing cover and tighten bearing retainer plate and transmission case-to-transaxle case attaching bolts.

Fig. 8: Method Used to Measure Pinion Shaft End Play

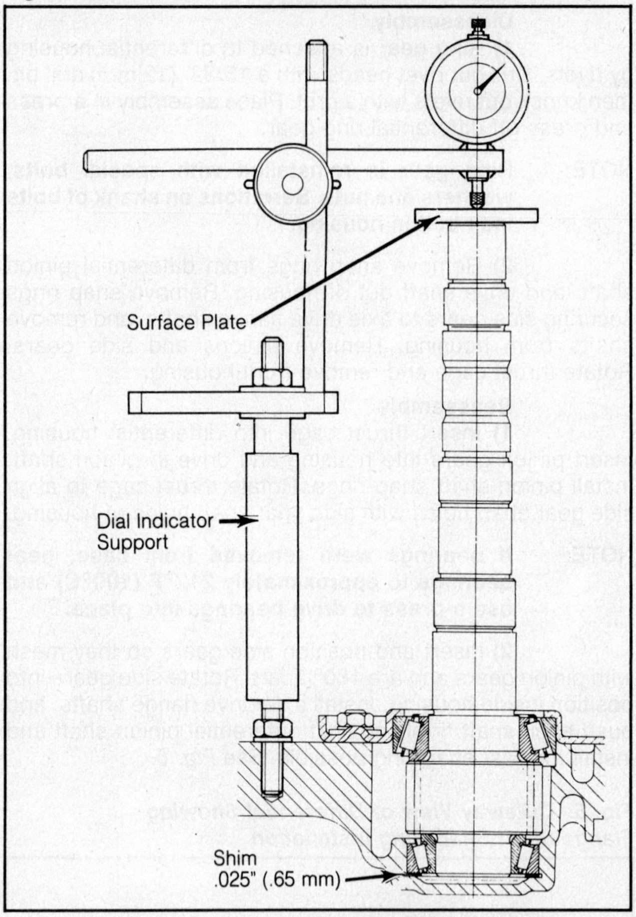

2) Install Adapter (VW548) onto pinion shaft, and measure rotating torque with an INCH lb. torque wrench. Rotating torque should be 5-13 INCH lbs. (.56-1.5 N.m) for new bearings and at least 3 INCH lbs. (.34 N.m) for used bearings.

PINION SHAFT REASSEMBLY

1) With pinion shaft mounted in case, install thrust washer (recess facing downward) and 1st gear needle bearing over end of pinion shaft and down against cover. Install 1st gear onto pinion shaft and follow with 1st gear synchro ring (110° tooth angle and 3 teeth missing around circumference).

2) Position 1st-2nd synchro assembly (shift fork slot facing upward) onto shaft. While ensuring correct engagement of synchro assembly, press synchro onto shaft.

NOTE: Special 1st gear synchro ring (110° tooth angle) is not available as replacement part. If defective, replace with standard synchro ring used for 2nd, 3rd or 4th gear.

3) Install 2nd synchro ring into 1st-2nd synchronizer. Position 2nd gear needle bearing inner race over pinion shaft and press into place against synchro hub. Install 2nd gear needle bearing and 2nd gear, then follow with 3rd gear. Install selective snap ring that will provide clearance of 0-.008" (0-.2 mm) between snap ring and 3rd gear.

NOTE: Always use a new snap ring when reassembling. Final installation of 4th gear and snap ring will be performed after mainshaft installation.

MAINSHAFT INSTALLATION & ADJUSTMENT

1) Install mainshaft without shims into case. Hold mainshaft in place with Special Tool (30-211) and Adapter (VW295a). Install 4th gear on pinion shaft and install circlip. Press mainshaft bearing with old shim into case. Install clamping plate and insert lower spring for selector rod into gear carrier housing.

Fig. 9: Centering 4-Speed Reverse Idler Shaft in Case

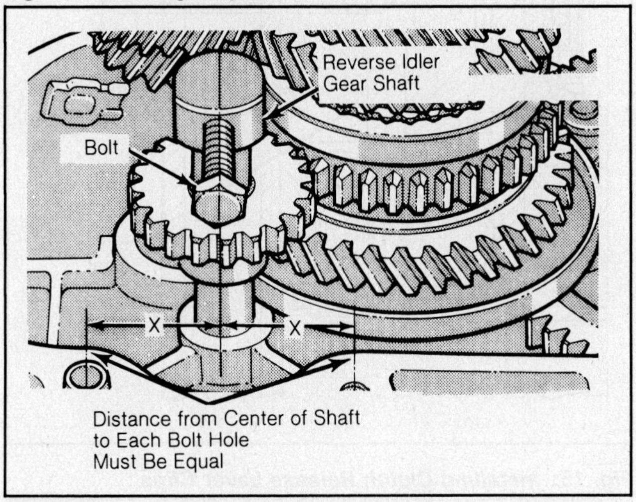

2) Insert 1st-2nd gear shift fork into operating sleeve. Lift selector rod slightly and swing shift fork around pinion shaft, guiding 3rd-4th shift fork into synchronizer sleeve and reverse shift fork into relay lever. Push selector rod in and align shift forks.

REVERSE IDLER INSTALLATION

Temporarily install reverse idler shaft retaining bolt into idler shaft, then position shaft into case bore. Center reverse idler bolt so center of shaft is equal from each bolt hole of case. Remove bolt without disturbing shaft alignment.

SHIFT FORKS & SHIFT HOUSING INSTALLATION

1) Install Special Tool (VW295a) on mainshaft, install transmission case onto gear carrier. Install reverse gear shaft lock bolt and tighten. Install transmission case-to-gear case bolts and tighten.

2) Install backup light switch. Tighten mainshaft bearing clamping plate bolts. Install drive shaft flange, install spring washer and circlip, press circlip into place and check for proper setting.

3) Heat 5th gear to 212°F (100°C) and install. Install thrust washer and circlip. Install synchronizer with 5th gear onto mainshaft. Screw selector tube clockwise into shift fork, then screw tube out until it projects above shift fork by .19" (5 mm). *See Fig. 13.*

CAUTION: Do not pull selector rod out of tube because shift forks in transmission will fall apart and transmission will have to be disassembled again.

Fig. 10: Installing 5-Speed Shift Forks

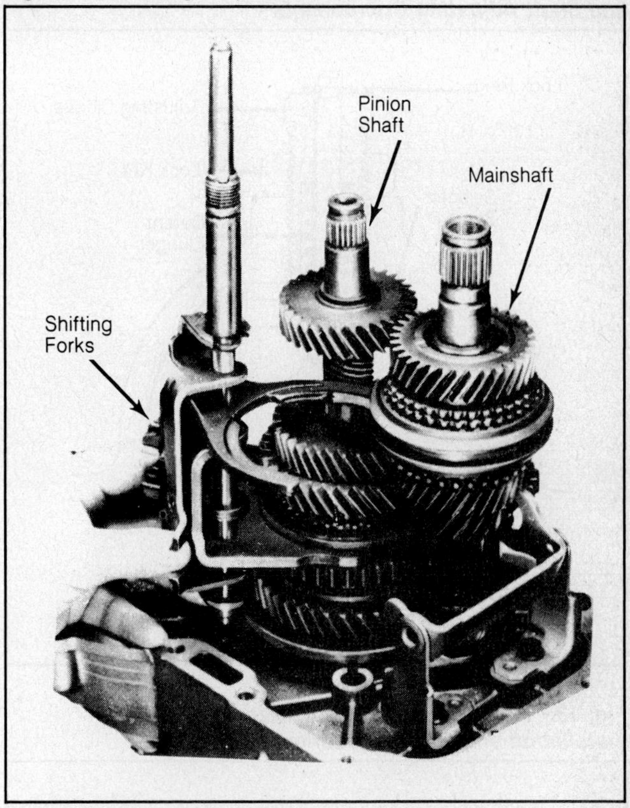

Fig. 11: Shift Fork Retaining Clip Locations

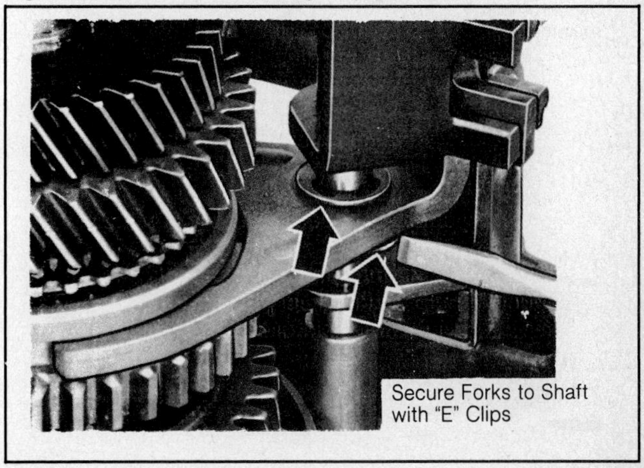

4) Coat synchronizer hub bolt with locking compound and tighten. Place transmission in neutral and install selector shaft. Install spring and cover for selector shaft. Install lock out plunger for 5th gear and detent plunger for selector shaft.

5) To adjust detent plunger, loosen lock nut and turn adjusting sleeve in until lock ring lifts off sleeve. Turn adjusting sleeve back until lock ring just contacts sleeve, tighten lock nut. Turn selector shaft slightly and check that lock ring lifts as soon as shaft is turned.

6) To adjust 5th gear lock out plunger, set transmission in neutral. Remove adjusting sleeve cap and loosen lock nut. Tighten adjusting sleeve until detent plunger just starts to move up. Loosen adjusting sleeve 1/3 turn and tighten lock nut.

VOLKSWAGEN GOLF, JETTA & SCIROCCO 5-SPEED (Cont.)

Fig. 12: Cutaway View of Case Showing Selector Shaft and Shaft Adjusting Components

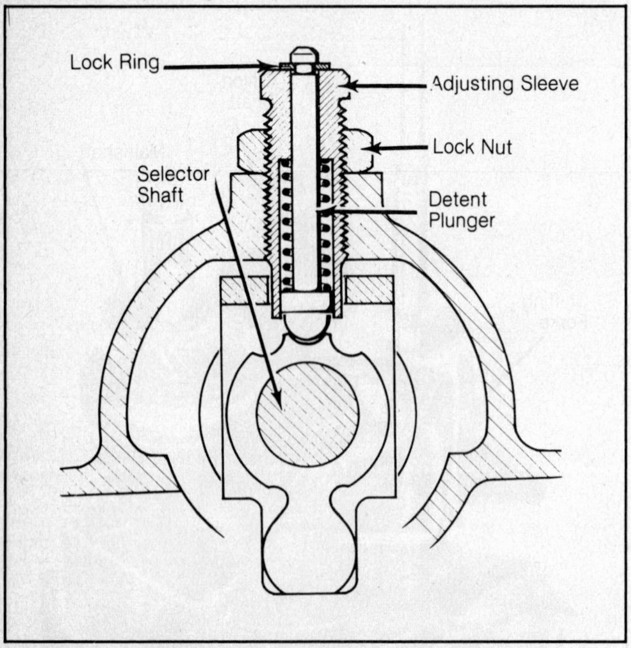

Fig. 13: View Showing Synchronizer with 5th Gear Installation and Tube Adjustment

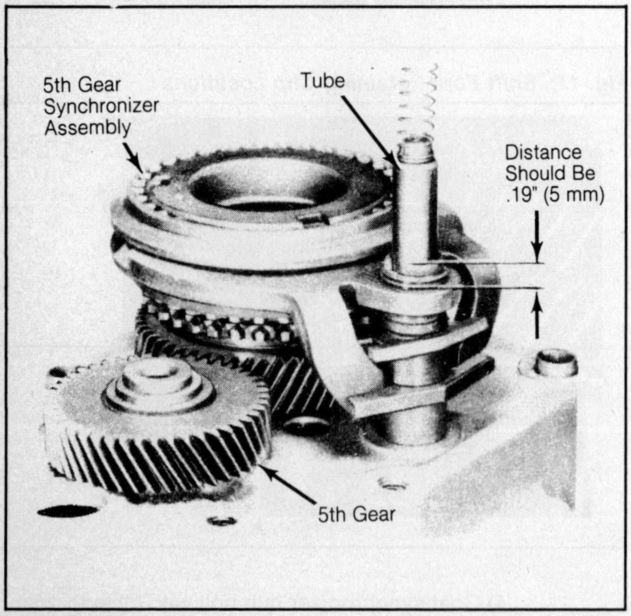

7) To adjust 5th gear shift fork, shift selector lever in 5th gear position, lift 5th gear synchronizer sleeve slightly to eliminate play. Check engagement of sleeve coupling teeth on 5th gear for proper engagement. Overlap should be .039" (1 mm). Adjust by turning selector tube. *See Fig. 14.*

FINAL ASSEMBLY

1) Install speedometer drive gear assembly, being careful to mesh drive gear with teeth on drive pinion shaft. Apply grease to clutch push rod and insert into mainshaft. Install release bearing and sleeve into rear end of shift housing.

Fig. 14: Adjusting 5th Gear Shift Fork Position

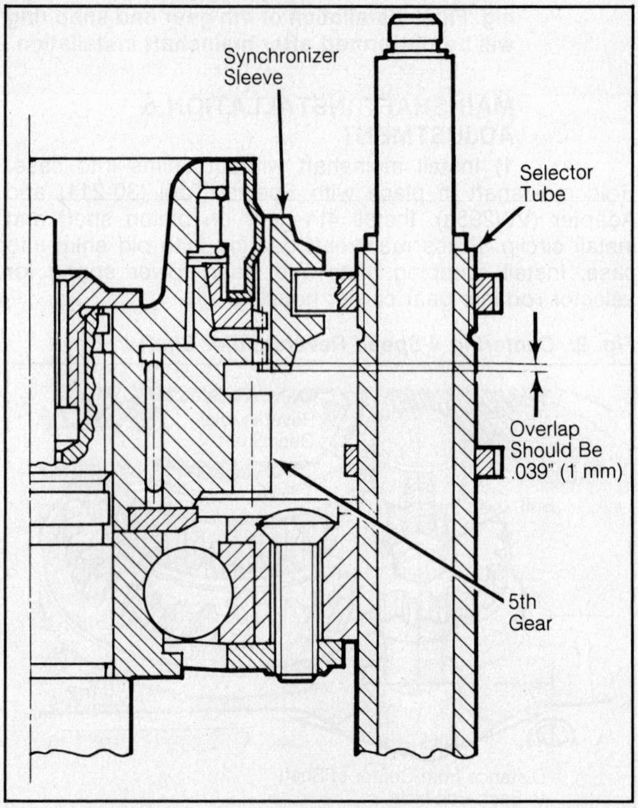

Fig. 15: Installing Clutch Release Lever Clips

2) Position clutch release lever and return spring in rear of shift housing, then install clutch operating lever through release lever and spring.

NOTE: Bent ends of spring must contact housing, and center part of spring hooks over release lever. Install 2 snap rings to secure assembly.

3) Apply grease to selector shaft and install into shift housing, engaging shift forks. Install 2 springs, spring seat and cover into case. Install selector shaft locking bolt into case and tighten. To adjust interlock plunger, loosen lock nut and turn adjusting sleeve in until lock ring lifts off sleeve.

4) Back off adjusting sleeve until lock ring just touches sleeve and tighten lock nut. Turn selector shaft slightly and check that lock ring lifts as soon as shaft is turned.

NOTE: Transmission must be in neutral with linkage disconnected when adjusting selector shaft.

5) Install rear cover with a new gasket onto shift housing. If removed, install a new seal into selector shaft bore (shift lever end).

6) Install new drive flange oil seals into housing, position drive flange onto shafts and retain with washers and snap rings. Install new plastic caps into flanges. If removed, install backup light switch, drain and fill plugs into case.

TIGHTENING SPECIFICATIONS

Application	Ft. Lbs. (N.m)
Axle Shaft Nut	173 (235)
Case Half Bolts	18 (24)
Drive Shaft-to-Flange	32 (43)
Fifth Gear Synchro Assembly	50 (68)
Mainshaft Bearing Retaining Nuts	14 (19)
Pinion Bearing Cover	29 (39)
Release Bearing Cover Bolts	11 (15)
Reverse Fork Support Bolts	11 (15)
Reverse Idler Bolt	14 (19)
Reverse Shaft Bolt	22 (30)
Ring Gear Nuts	50 (68)
Selector Shaft Cover	32 (43)
Selector Shaft Lock Nut	14 (19)
Transaxle-to-Engine Bolts	40 (54)

VOLKSWAGEN VANAGON 4-SPEED

TRANSMISSION IDENTIFICATION

The Volkswagen Vanagon uses a Type 091 manual transmission. First 3 digits of transmission part number cast in right side of transmission case indicate transmission model. Transmission code letters (DK) and date of manufacture are stamped on bottom of transmission case.

DESCRIPTION

The transaxle assembly is a 2-piece unit containing both the transmission and final drive. The transmission and final drive are asembled in one section and clutch is housed in second section.

The transaxle is mounted at rear of vehicle and engine is mounted to rear of transaxle. The transmission is a 4-speed manual type. Gears are in constant mesh in all forward gears. The final drive, mounted between transmission and engine, uses a hypoid ring gear and pinion.

The rear axle unit is a double joint type, using constant velocity (CV) joints on both ends of axle drive shafts. Outer wheel bearings are mounted in a housing connected to control arm.

LUBRICATION & ADJUSTMENT

See appropriate MANUAL TRANSMISSION SERVICING article in the IMPORT GENERAL SERVICING section.

SERVICE (IN VEHICLE)

DRIVE AXLE SHAFTS

See appropriate DRIVE AXLE SHAFT article in IMPORT AXLE SHAFTS, OVERDRIVES & TRANSFER CASES section.

REMOVAL & INSTALLATION

See appropriate MANUAL TRANSMISSION REMOVAL article in IMPORT GENERAL SERVICING section.

TRANSMISSION DISASSEMBLY

1) Before attempting to remove clutch housing, loosen left differential adjusting ring to relieve tension in housing. Mark position of ring before loosening for ease of assembly. Remove (10) housing nuts from studs.

2) Separate housing from transmission case. Remove circlip from input shaft. Pull reverse drive gear forward and unscrew input shaft from stud in end of mainshaft. Pry out drive flange center caps.

3) Remove circlips and wavy spacers from center of flanges. Use 2 levers to pry drive flanges off of output shafts.

4) Remove screws from adjusting ring lock plates and remove lock plates. Measure depth of adjusting ring or mark position in case. Remove adjusting rings.

5) Making sure ring gear teeth stay in mesh with pinion gear, rotate differential toward rear of transmission case and pull out through rear of case.

6) Remove attaching nuts and lift shift housing from gear carrier. Remove pinion bearing retaining ring from bearing race on differential end of case. Remove selector link, shaft and bracket from face of gear carrier.

7) Remove (9) nuts from gear carrier mounting studs on transmission case. Apply leverage to end of pinion gear and press gear train and carrier out of case.

8) Loosen nut on reverse lever support clamp sleeve. Turn shaft far enough to remove reverse slider and shift fork. Slide shift forks off shift rods. Remove circlip from end of mainshaft.

9) Press out mainshaft and drive pinion at the same time by applying pressure to end of mainshaft. Care must be taken not to damage any gear train components.

COMPONENT DISASSEMBLY & REASSEMBLY

CLUTCH HOUSING

Disassembly

1) Pry retaining springs off spring clips and remove clutch release bearing. Remove release bearing guide sleeve. Remove circlip from end of clutch shaft. Pry off lever and remove return spring and spring collar.

2) Remove clutch shaft lock bolt. Slide shaft outward, pressing out bushing and rubber seals. Remove bushing, seals and flat washer from shaft. Pull shaft inward and out of housing to remove. Pry oil seal out of input shaft hole in housing.

Reassembly

Coat outside of new seal with a sealing compound. Position in hole with lip toward transmission side of housing and drive squarely into place. To complete clutch housing reassembly, reverse disassembly procedure. Tighten shaft lock bolt to specifications.

DIFFERENTIAL

Disassembly

1) Remove ring gear bolts and drive ring gear off differential housing with a punch. Remove differential cover with a slide hammer. Remove side gears and thrust washers from housing and cover.

2) If necessary, remove roller bearing using a press and supports. Drive out pinion shaft lock pin. Drive pinion shaft out of differential housing. Remove pinion gears, spacer and thrust washer.

Reassembly

1) Inspect all components for wear or damage and replace as necessary. If roller bearings were removed, heat to 212°F (100°C), and press into position using a press and supports.

NOTE: **If unit is not equipped with spacer sleeve, or if components other than pinion shaft or roller bearings have been replaced, axial play must be checked and adjusted.**

2) To check axial play, install side gear with short shaft and both large thrust washers in differential cover. Place assembly in a vise and clamp gear tight against cover.

3) Install side gear with long shaft in housing. Place sleeve on machined surface of side gear with short shaft. Position differential housing on cover. Install and tighten 4 bolts pulling housing into place on cover.

4) Install a gauge bar with a dial indicator to end of drive gear shaft in housing. Dial indicator plunger must

Manual Transmissions

VOLKSWAGEN VANAGON 4-SPEED (Cont.)

Fig. 1: Exploded View of Clutch Housing

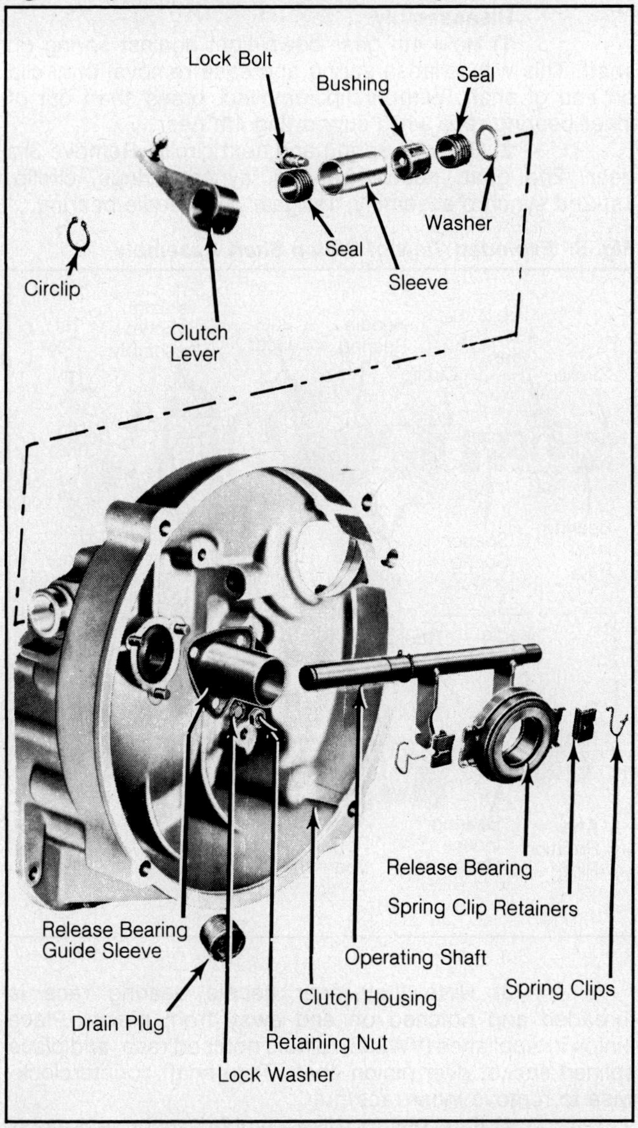

contact differential housing neck. Press down on side gear shaft and zero dial indicator with .080" (2 mm) preload.

5) Move side gear up and down to determine axial play. Play should be .001-.004" (.03-.11 mm). If not to specifications, install a spacer of correct size to obtain specified play.

6) Recheck play after installing correct spacer. Spacers are available in the following lengths: 1.253" (31.84 mm), 1.257" (31.93 mm), 1.261" (32.02 mm), 1.264" (32.11 mm), and 1.268" (32.20 mm).

Fig. 3: Measuring Differential Gear Axial Play

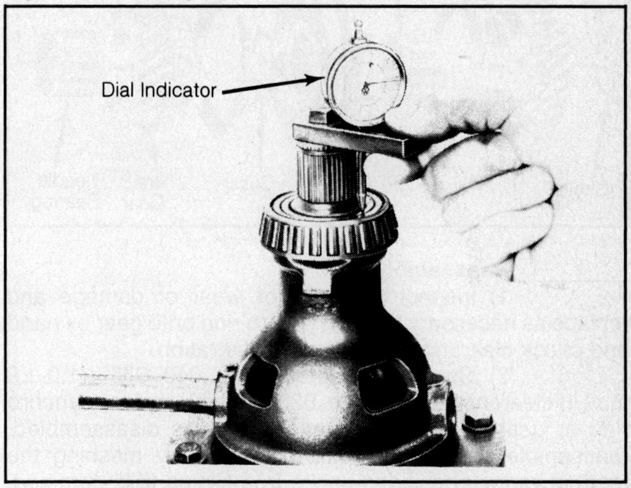

MAINSHAFT

Disassembly

1) With mainshaft removed from gear carrier, remove 4th gear, needle bearing and synchro ring. Remove circlip and slide off clutch gear assembly. Remove remaining circlip and slide off 3rd gear.

2) Open split in needle bearing cage just enough to slide over mainshaft splines and remove bearing. If necessary, remove spring rings from clutch gear assembly. Then separate synchronizer hub from sleeve.

Fig. 2: Exploded View of Differential Assembly

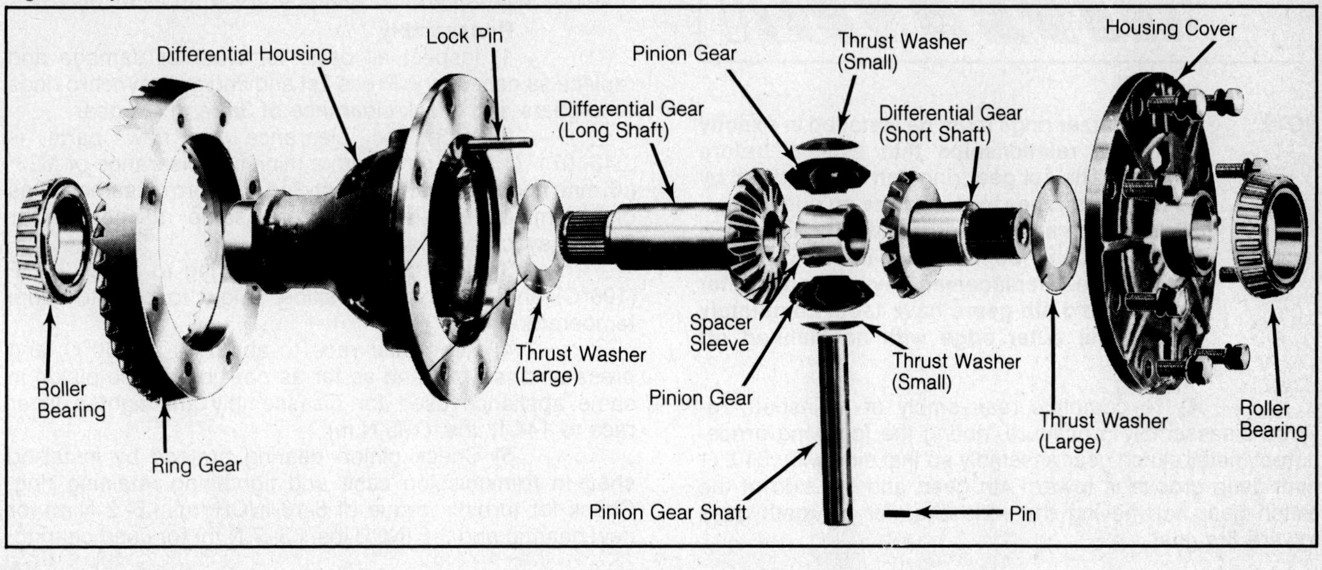

VOLKSWAGEN VANAGON 4-SPEED (Cont.)

Fig. 4: Exploded View of Mainshaft Assembly

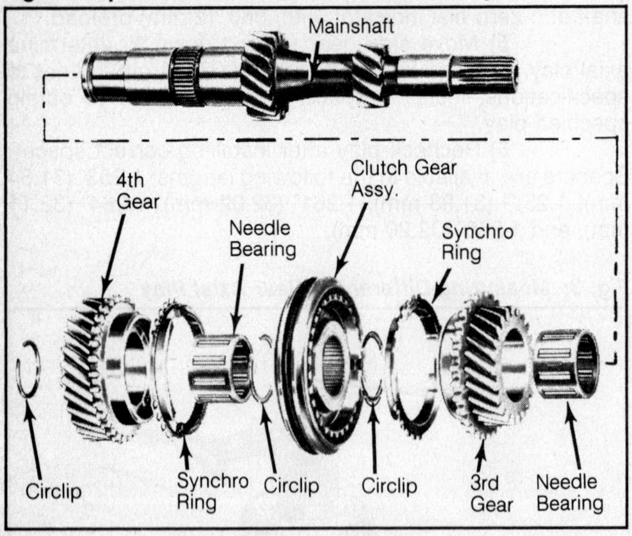

Reassembly

1) Inspect all parts for wear or damage and replace as necessary. Press synchro ring onto gear by hand and check clearance as shown in illustration.

2) Specified clearance is .040-.075" (1.0-1.9 mm). If clearance is less than .023" (.6 mm), replace synchro ring or gear. If clutch gear assembly was disassembled, reassemble synchronizer hub to sleeve by meshing the teeth in various positions until a free sliding fit is obtained.

3) Spring ring diameter for 3rd-4th gear clutch hub is 2.91" (74 mm) while larger ring for 1st-2nd clutch gear should be 3.07" (78 mm). Open ends of springs on opposite sides of assembly must be installed 120° apart with angled ends over the keys.

Fig. 5: Measuring Synchro Ring-to-Gear Clearance

NOTE: **Synchronizer rings must be installed in exactly the same relationships that existed before removal. The 1st gear ring can be identified by having no notches in blank area on outer edge. Synchronizers for 2nd, 3rd and 4th gears each have 3 notches (depressions) in blank area on outer edge. Replacement synchronizers for 2nd, 3rd and 4th gears have teeth completely around the outer edge with no blanked off areas.**

4) To complete reassembly of mainshaft, reverse disassembly procedure, noting the following procedures: Install clutch gear assembly so that side with .040" (1 mm) deep groove is toward 4th gear, and the side of the clutch gear hub having the wide chamfer on teeth goes toward 3rd gear.

DRIVE PINION SHAFT

Disassembly

1) Hold 4th gear down tight against spring on shaft. This will collapse spring and ease removal of circlip on end of shaft. With circlip removed, press shaft out of inner bearing race while supporting 4th gear.

2) Remove spring and next circlip. Remove 3rd gear, 2nd gear, needle bearing, synchro rings, circlip, 1st-2nd synchro assembly, 1st gear and needle bearing.

Fig. 6: Exploded View of Pinion Shaft Assembly

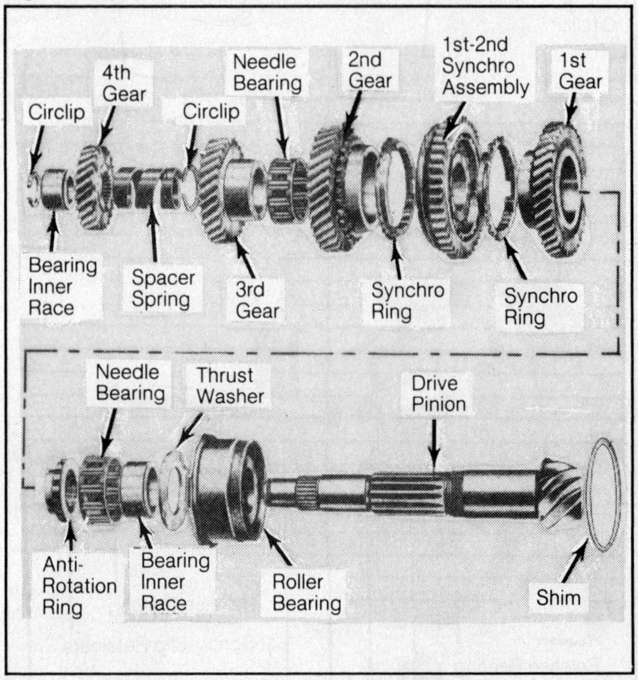

3) Note that inner needle bearing race is threaded and notched on end away from pinion. Place pinion in Appliance (VW293) to hold notched race, and place splined socket over pinion shaft. Turn shaft counterclockwise to remove inner race/nut.

4) If necessary, disassemble synchro assembly hub. Press off tapered roller bearing with outer race. If required, use separating tool and press off inner race.

Reassembly

1) Inspect all parts for wear or damage and replace as necessary. Press 1st and 2nd gear synchro rings onto gears and check clearance of 3rd and 4th gear.

2) Specified clearance for new parts is .043-.071" (1.1-1.8 mm), with a minimum clearance of .023" (.6 mm) for used parts. If 1st-2nd synchro assembly was disassembled, reassemble in the same manner as for 3rd-4th synchro assembly.

3) Heat tapered roller bearing to about 212°F (100°C) and press into position. Allow to cool to room temperature.

4) Heat inner race to about 140°F (60°C) and press on shaft by hand as far as possible. Place pinion in same appliance used for disassembly and tighten inner race to 144 ft. lbs. (195 N.m).

5) Check pinion bearing preload by installing shaft in transmission case and tightening retaining ring. Check for turning torque of 5-18 INCH lbs. (.6-.2 N.m) for new bearing and 3-6 INCH lbs. (.3-.7 N.m) for used bearing.

VOLKSWAGEN VANAGON 4-SPEED (Cont.)

6) Install needle bearing, 1st gear, 1st-2nd synchro assembly with synchro rings, and install circlip. Synchro ring grooves must align with keys when pressing on. Assemble needle bearing, 2nd gear and 3rd gear on shaft, then fit circlip properly in groove.

7) Check axial play between circlip and 3rd gear. Correct play is .004-.010" (.10-.25 mm), with the lower limit preferred. Install proper circlip to obtain specified clearance.

NOTE: 3rd gear circlips are available in thicknesses of .057" (1.45 mm) to .087" (2.2 mm) in increments of .006" (.15 mm).

Fig. 7: Checking Pinion Bearing Preload

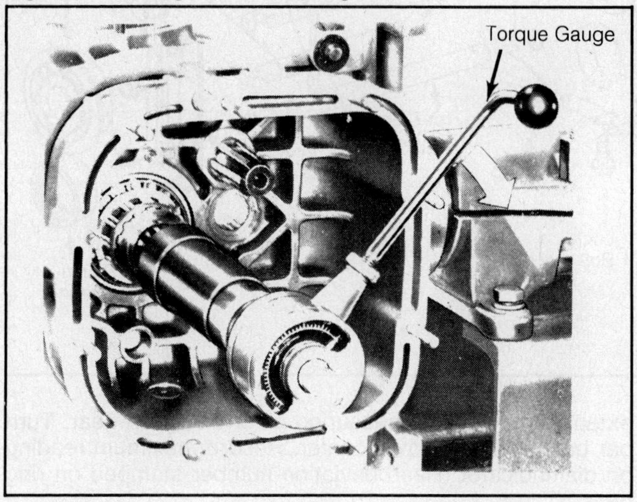

8) Install spacer spring and 4th speed gear with shoulder toward spring. Press on 4th gear and install circlip.

TRANSMISSION CASE

Disassembly

Remove reverse gear shaft circlip from inside gear case. Remove reverse drive gear, shaft and needle bearing as a unit with a plastic hammer. Remove lock rings from mainshaft needle bearing and drive bearing out.

Reassembly

Insert shaft, bearing and reverse drive gear as a unit. Drive mainshaft needle bearing in case with lettered side of bearing towards the driver. Install lock rings.

GEAR CARRIER

Disassembly

1) Remove selector link shaft and selector link. Remove 2 bolts and then remove link bracket. Remove drive pinion bearing lock bolt.

2) Using a mandrel, press out mainshaft bearing and pinion shaft bearing. Loosen clamp sleeve and remove with reverse lever support and union nut from carrier.

3) Remove (4) relay shaft bracket bolts, brackets and relay shaft. Detent plugs and shift rails should only be removed if necessary. To remove, drill out detent plugs and thread a self-tapping bolt into plug until plug is pulled out.

4) Remove circlips and pull shift rails out of carrier. Remove detent springs, balls and interlock, and intermediate pins.

NOTE: Removal of selector shafts and detents should not be necessary unless shifting is either too stiff or too easy. Check movement effort by attaching spring scale under hook in end of selector shaft. Pull of 33 to 44 lbs. (15 to 20 kg) should be required to overcome detent springs.

Reassembly

Check all components for wear or damage and replace as necessary. Detent spring length should be .906-.984" (23-25 mm). To reassemble, reverse disassembly procedure and ensure that interlock and intermediate pins are installed properly so that it is not possible to engage 2 gears at the same time.

SHIFT HOUSING

Disassembly

1) Drill and tap plugs for rocker lever shaft. Remove rocker lever shaft, rocker lever and thrust washer. Remove backup light switch plug and seal. Remove selector shaft oil seal and bushing.

Fig. 8: Vanagon Shift Housing Assembly

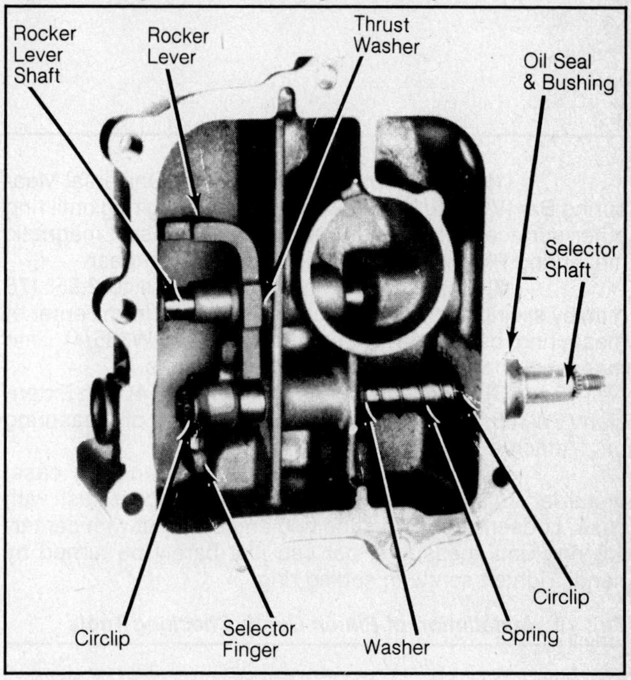

2) Remove circlips from selector shaft. Push selector shaft out of shift housing. As selector shaft slides out, remove selector finger, washer and spring.

Reassembly

To reassemble shift housing, reverse disassembly procedures and install new seals.

TRANSMISSION REASSEMBLY & ADJUSTMENT

PINION DEPTH

NOTE: Pinion bearing preload must be correctly adjusted before adjusting pinion depth; see Drive Pinion Shaft Reassembly.

VOLKSWAGEN VANAGON 4-SPEED (Cont.)

Fig. 9: Exploded View of Gear Carrier Assembly

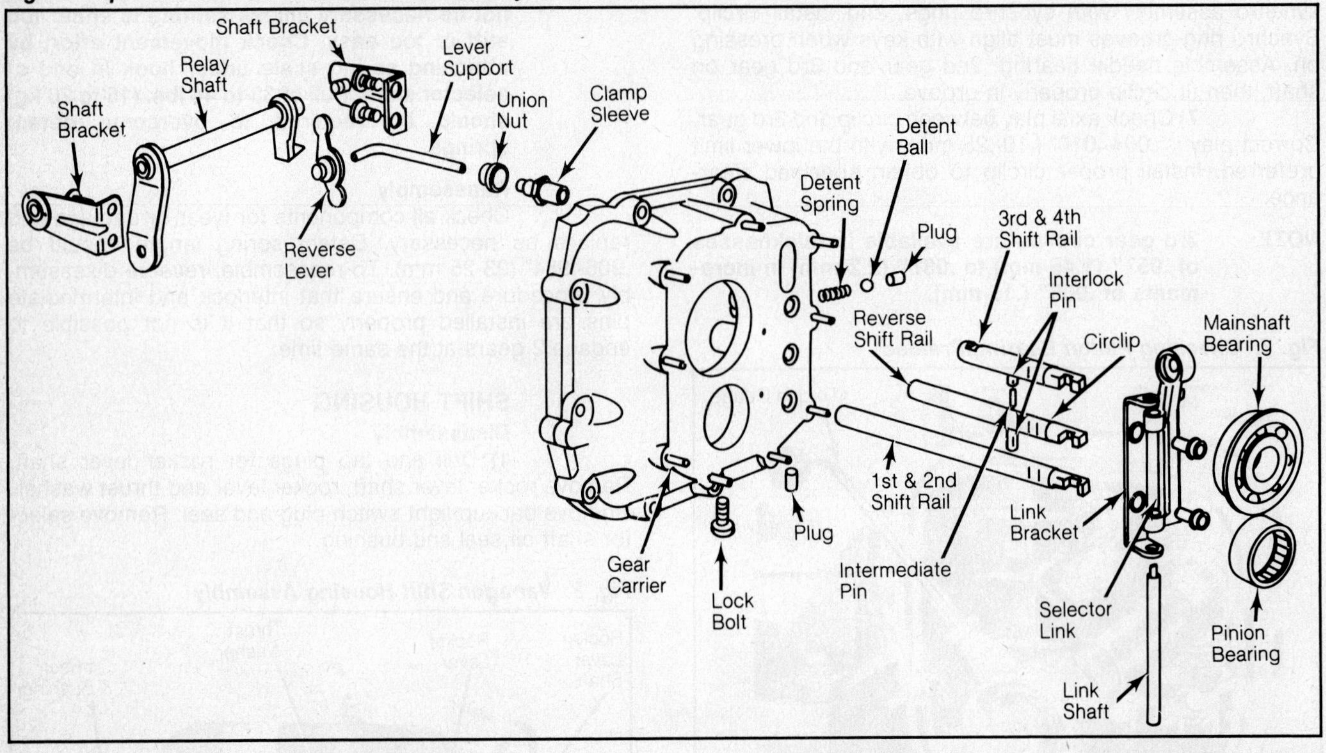

1) Pinion depth is checked using Universal Measuring Bar (VW385/1). Screw in right adjusting ring until ring outer surface is flush with transaxle case. Install magnetic measuring Plate (VW385/17) on end of pinion gear.

2) Set dimension "A" *(see Fig. 10)* to 2.95" (75 mm) by sliding setting ring to correct distance from center of measuring bar. Slide 2 Centering Discs (VW385/4) onto measuring bar until they contact setting rings.

3) Attach measuring Pin (VW385/14) with Extension (VW385/16) to gauge pin hole in center of measuring bar. Attach a dial indicator to end of bar.

4) Position measuring bar in transaxle case. Install left adjusting ring in case until outer edge is flush with case. Loosen second setting ring and slide out with centering ring until measuring bar can just barely be turned by hand. Tighten screw in setting ring.

Fig. 10: Installation of Pinion Depth Checking Tools

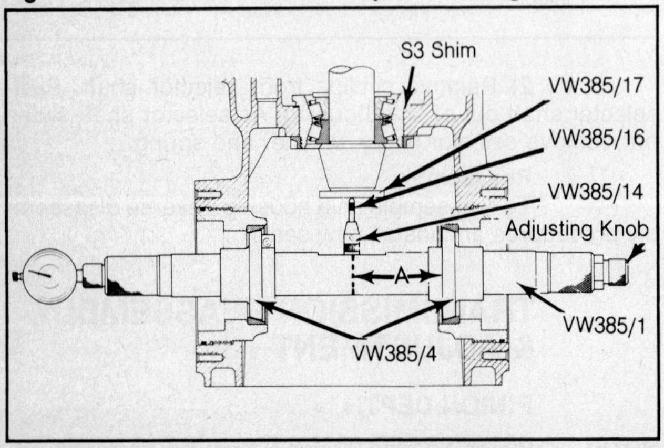

5) Using setting Block (VW385/1), zero dial indicator. Turn measuring bar by hand until measuring pin extension is against measuring plate on pinion gear. Turn bar back and forth over center. Record maximum reading on dial indicator. Read deviation number stamped on ring gear.

NOTE: **Although production gears are no longer marked with deviation "r" in .01 mm readings, replacement gear sets will have this number. Shims (S3) must be installed between pinion bearing shoulder and gear case to correct axial placement of pinion gear for proper meshing with ring gear teeth.**

6) To find correct shim thickness (S3), add dial indicator deflection to "r" number stamped on gear. Shims are available in thicknesses of .006" (.15 mm), .008" (.20 mm), .012" (.30 mm), .016" (.40 mm), .020" (.50 mm), and .024" (.60 mm). Install shim or combination of shims required to obtain correct pinion depth.

TRANSMISSION REASSEMBLY

1) Mesh mainshaft and drive pinion and support as shown in *Fig. 11.* Place in a press and, using a sleeve type driver that applies pressure only to mainshaft bearing inner race, press gear carrier down onto gear train.

2) With pressure from press still applied, install new circlip on mainshaft. Using same tool in press, push circlip down until it snaps into groove. Release press and squeeze circlip into bottom groove with a pair of pliers.

NOTE: **Shift forks must now be adjusted. See Shift Fork Adjustment.**

3) With shift forks correctly adjusted, tighten shift fork set screws and reverse lever support union nut. Install original shims on pinion bearing or new shims if pinion depth has been adjusted.

VOLKSWAGEN VANAGON 4-SPEED (Cont.)

4) Position new carrier gasket on transaxle case studs. Position gear train in case. Install a new shim and retaining ring onto pinion (large threaded roller bearing). Tighten ring to 160 ft. lbs. (217 N.m), back off, then retighten to same specification.

5) Install and tighten gear carrier nuts in a diagonal pattern. Install selector link, bracket and link shaft. Tighten bolts. Install shift housing using new gasket. Make sure rocker lever and selector finger engages selector shafts correctly. Tighten shift housing bolts.

Fig. 11: Pressing Mainshaft and Pinion Shaft into Gear Carrier

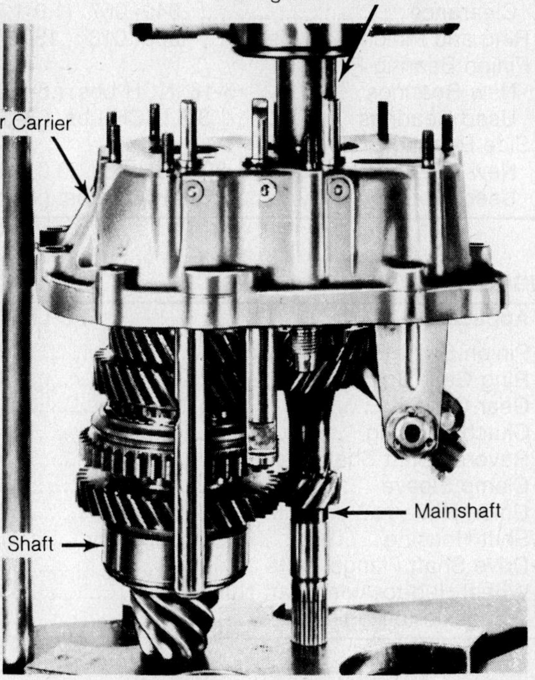

SHIFT FORK ADJUSTMENT

NOTE: Shift fork adjustment is made with Special Tool (VW294b). Tool consists of the following: Mounting Plate (VW294b/2); mounting plate-to-gear carrier Spacer (VW294b/4); pinion Retaining Ring (VW294b/7); reverse gear Spacer (VW294b/10); and 2 bolts to hold gear carrier to mounting plate.

1) Attach assembled gear carrier, with pinion shim S3, to Adjuster (VW294b). *See Fig. 12.* Tighten Retaining Ring (VW294b/7) by hand. Install shift forks for 1st-2nd and 3rd-4th gears.

NOTE: Install flat side of 1st-2nd shift fork away from gear carrier. Install flat side of 3rd-4th shift fork toward gear carrier.

2) Install relay lever support and relay lever. Place 1st-2nd gear selector in 2nd gear position. Slide operating sleeve, with fork, over synchro teeth until it is against 2nd gear. Center shift fork in groove of operating sleeve and tighten clamp screw.

CAUTION: Shift fork must not rub or press against sides of groove in operating sleeve when in neutral position. Clearance must exist.

Fig. 12: Assembled View of Shift Fork Adjustment Tools

3) Select 1st and 2nd gear position several times while turning mainshaft. Check clearance of shift fork in operating sleeve in each position. If necessary, reposition shift fork until there is same amount of clearance on selector shaft in both end positions, then tighten clamp screw.

4) Place 3rd-4th gear selector shaft in 3rd gear position and adjust 3rd-4th gear shift fork in same manner as 1st-2nd.

CAUTION: For correct adjustment of 3rd-4th gears, mainshaft bearing must be pressed fully into gear carrier housing.

5) Place reverse gear selector shaft into reverse gear position. Adjust reverse gear so that sliding gear is fully in mesh with teeth on operating sleeve for 1st-2nd gear. Tighten union nut on relay lever support.

6) Shift out of reverse gear and press sliding gear lightly toward gear carrier. Clearance between reverse gear and 2nd gear on mainshaft must be a minimum of .020" (.5 mm).

7) Engage 2nd gear and check clearance between operating sleeve and reverse sliding gear. Adjust if necessary. Check interlock mechanism. When gear is engaged, it must not be possible to engage any other gear.

SIDE BEARING PRELOAD & RING GEAR BACKLASH

1) Remove oil seals from side bearing adjusting rings. Install adjusting ring on ring gear side of case and screw in until ring is approximately .004-.008" (.1-.2 mm) below measuring surface of case.

VOLKSWAGEN VANAGON 4-SPEED (Cont.)

2) Install differential in case, with ring gear on left side. Install opposite adjusting ring and tighten until differential is supported without preload.

3) Turn transaxle so that differential is at top and install Spacer Bridge (VW381/8) on dowel pins to prevent case spreading. Install a torque wrench on ring gear side of differential.

4) Spin differential 15-20 turns in each direction while lubricating the side bearings with hypoid oil. While turning, screw in adjusting ring on side opposite ring gear until preload measured on torque wrench is 26-30 INCH lbs. (3.0-3.4 N.m) for new bearings and 3-6 INCH lbs. (.3-.7 N.m) for used bearings.

5) Measure and record depth to which adjusting rings are screwed in. Mark position of adjusting rings in case. Remove adjusting rings and differential. Rings must be installed on the same side from which they are removed.

6) Install transmission gear train. See TRANSMISSION REASSEMBLY. Install differential and adjusting rings. Turn adjusting rings until marks made during side bearing preload are aligned. Install a Measuring Bracket (VW381/7) on ring gear bolts.

7) Mount a spacer bar and dial indicator across ring gear end of case. Turn mainshaft until dial indicator stem contacts measuring bracket on ring gear. Continue turning mainshaft until dial indicator shows .060" (1.5 mm) preload. Lock pinion shaft with a clamping bar bolted on gear carrier.

8) Turn ring gear by hand away from dial indicator until it is stopped by locked pinion. Now zero dial indicator. Again turn ring gear by hand toward dial indicator until it is stopped by locked pinion. The reading on dial indicator is ring gear backlash.

9) Backlash should be .006-.010" (.15-.25 mm). If backlash not to specifications, screw one adjusting ring inward and the other ring outward by exactly the same amount until backlash is within specification.

10) Recheck backlash measuring procedure at three other points on ring gear, 90° apart. All measurements must be within specification and not vary more than .002" (.06 mm).

11) Install new oil seals and "O" rings in adjusting rings if not previously done. Coat outer surface of adjusting rings with an anti-rust preventative sealer. Install new adjusting ring lock plates and tighten screws evenly.

NOTE: **Do not tighten left hand adjusting ring until the clutch housing has been fitted and the nuts tightened.**

FINAL ASSEMBLY

Install clutch housing and tighten nuts to specification. Install thrust rings, axle drive shaft flanges and new circlips. It may be necessary to lift differential pinion gear shaft slightly to gain clearance for installation of circlips. Install new plastic caps in center of axle drive shaft flanges.

TRANSAXLE SPECIFICATIONS

Application	Measurement
Synchro Ring-to-Gear	
Clearance	.040-.067" (1.0-1.7 mm)
Ring and Pinion Backlash	.006-.010" (.15-.25 mm)
Pinion Bearing Preload	
New Bearings	5-18 INCH Lbs. (.6-2.0 N.m)
Used Bearings	3-6 INCH Lbs. (.3-.7 N.m)
Side Bearing Preload	
New Bearings	26-30 INCH Lbs. (3.0-3.4 N.m)
Used Bearings	3-6 INCH Lbs. (.3-.7 N.m)

TIGHTENING SPECIFICATIONS

Application	Ft. Lbs. (N.m)
Pinion Shaft Retainer Ring	160 (217)
Ring Gear Bolts	36 (49)
Gear Carrier	14 (19)
Clutch Housing	14 (19)
Reverse Shift Shaft Bracket	18 (24)
Clamp Sleeve	32 (43)
Union Nut	21 (28)
Shift Housing	14 (19)
Drive Shaft Flange Bolts	32 (43)
Wheel Hub-to-Axle Shaft Nut	253 (343)
Transaxle-to-Engine	22 (30)

VOLKSWAGEN 013 & 093 5-SPEED TRANSAXLE

Audi 4000S, Volkswagen Quantum

DESCRIPTION

This 5-speed transaxle is fully synchronized in all forward gears. The mainshaft and pinion shaft are supported by roller bearings housed in the gear carrier. The final drive housing contains the clutch housing, clutch release mechanism as well as a ring and pinion gear differential.

The differential drive pinion shaft also serves as the countershaft for the transmission. Fifth gear is housed in the rear cover and all others are contained in the gear carrier.

LUBRICATION & ADJUSTMENT

See appropriate MANUAL TRANSMISSION SERVICING article in IMPORT GENERAL SERVICING section.

SERVICE (IN VEHICLE)

DRIVE AXLE SHAFTS

See appropriate DRIVE AXLE SHAFT article in IMPORT AXLE SHAFTS, OVERDRIVES & TRANSFER CASES section.

REMOVAL & INSTALLATION

TRANSAXLE

See appropriate MANUAL TRANSMISSION REMOVAL article in IMPORT GENERAL SERVICING section.

TRANSAXLE DISASSEMBLY

NOTE: **If any components affecting pinion position are to be replaced, it will be necessary to measure pinion depth prior to disassembly of gear carrier and final drive housing. For measuring procedure, see Pinion Depth Measurement.**

1) Mount transaxle in holding fixture and drain fluid. Remove mainshaft rear cover by driving a screwdriver or punch through center of cover and then prying out. Lock front of mainshaft with holding tool (VW294b/1). Remove bolt on mainshaft and all bolts from shift housing.

2) Pull shift housing off using puller tool (30-207). Drive roll pin out of 1-2 shift fork. Turn selector dog to the left. Engage 3rd gear and pull out center selector shaft. Turn inner shift lever counterclockwise and then pull out on shaft. *See Fig. 2.* Remove 1-2 selector dog.

Fig. 2: Inner Shift Lever Removal

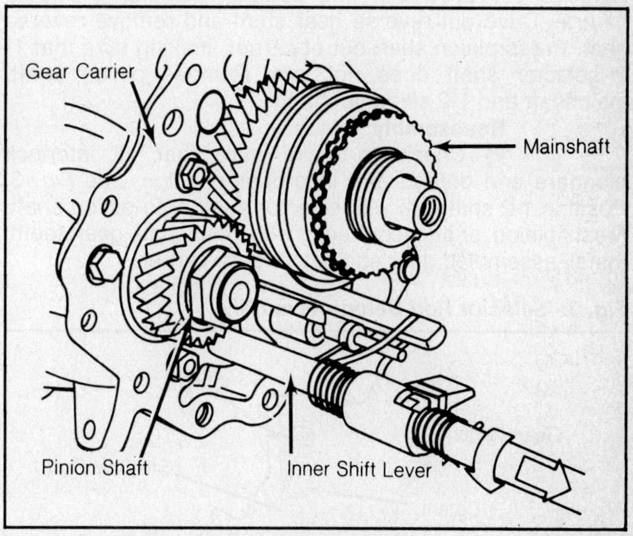

3) Drive roll pin out of 5th gear selector fork. Using a puller, remove 5th gear with synchronizer, blocker ring and selector fork from rear of gear carrier.

4) Remove drive flange retaining bolts and drive flanges. Remove final drive cover. Remove differential from housing. Measure pinion depth at this point if necessary. Remove 5th gear bearing inner race and thrust washer from mainshaft using a puller. Engage any gear and lock mainshaft with holding tool (VW294b/1). Remove pinion nut.

5) Remove 5th gear from pinion shaft. Shift gear train into neutral. Remove gear carrier-to-final drive housing bolts and dowel pins. Pull complete gear carrier assembly off of final drive housing.

Fig. 1: Exploded View of Transaxle

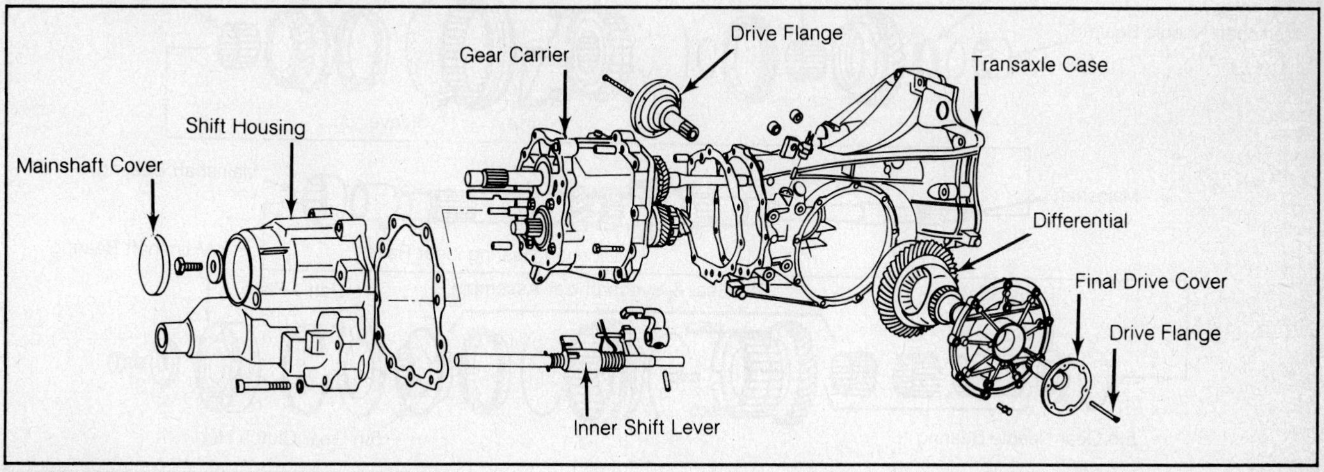

VOLKSWAGEN 013 & 093 5-SPEED TRANSAXLE (Cont.)

COMPONENT DISASSEMBLY & REASSEMBLY

GEAR CARRIER

Disassembly

1) Place gear carrier assembly in a soft-jawed vise. Drive roll pin out of 3-4 shift fork and pull back 3-4 selector shaft so that shift fork is clear of gears. If pinion shaft is to be removed, 3-4 selector shaft must be removed.

2) Press pinion shaft down 1/4-5/16" (6-8 mm). Remove 3-4 shift fork and position selector shafts in neutral. Drive out reverse gear shaft and remove reverse gear. Press pinion shaft out of carrier, making sure that 1-2 selector shaft does not jam. Remove pinion shaft, mainshaft and 1-2 selector shaft.

Reassembly

1) Check to make sure that all interlock plungers and detents are in proper position. *See Fig. 3.* Position 1-2 shift fork with selector shaft onto pinion shaft. Mesh pinion shaft gear teeth with mainshaft gear teeth. Install assembled gear shafts into gear carrier.

Fig. 3: Selector Rod Detent Assembly

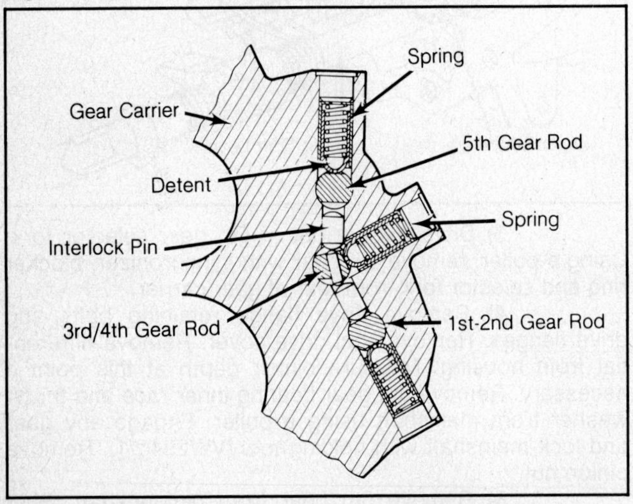

2) Install reverse gear and shaft. Position selector shafts in neutral. Install 3-4 selector shaft with small interlock pin and secure with roll pin at 3-4 shift fork.

3) Press inner bearing race onto pinion shaft. Install mainshaft thrust washer. Heat 5th gear inner bearing race to 250°F (121°C) and install onto mainshaft. Heat 5th gear to 250°F (121°C) and install onto mainshaft.

4) Install 5th gear and synchronizer assembly with blocker ring onto mainshaft. Heat synchronizer clutch hub to 250°F (121°C) and install on to mainshaft.

MAINSHAFT

Disassembly

1) Remove circlip from end of mainshaft. Remove shim, 4th gear, needle bearing and blocker ring. Remove and discard circlip holding 3-4 synchronizer onto shaft. Press 3-4 synchronizer hub and sleeve off of shaft.

2) Remove 3rd gear and needle bearing. Press mainshaft bearing inner race off rear of mainshaft. Remove circlip retaining mainshaft bearing outer race to gear carrier. Press outer race out of carrier. Drive mainshaft needle bearing out of final drive housing.

Reassembly

Check all bearings for damage or excessive wear. To reassemble, reverse disassembly procedure and note the following: End play measured between 4th gear and shim should be .004-.016" (.10-.40 mm). If end play is not within specifications, adjust by changing shim thickness. Shims are available in the following sizes: .137" (3.47 mm), .141" (3.57 mm) and .145" (3.67 mm).

PINION SHAFT

Disassembly

Engage 2nd gear. Press pinion rear bearing inner race and 1st gear off of shaft. Press 1-2 synchronizer hub with sleeve and 2nd gear off of pinion shaft. Press 3rd gear off shaft and then remove circlip retaining 4th gear. Press 4th gear off of shaft and then remove pinion front bearing inner race.

Reassembly

1) Ensure that pinion shaft is free of all traces of grease and oil. Reinstall front bearing onto pinion shaft.

Fig. 4: Exploded View of Mainshaft Assembly

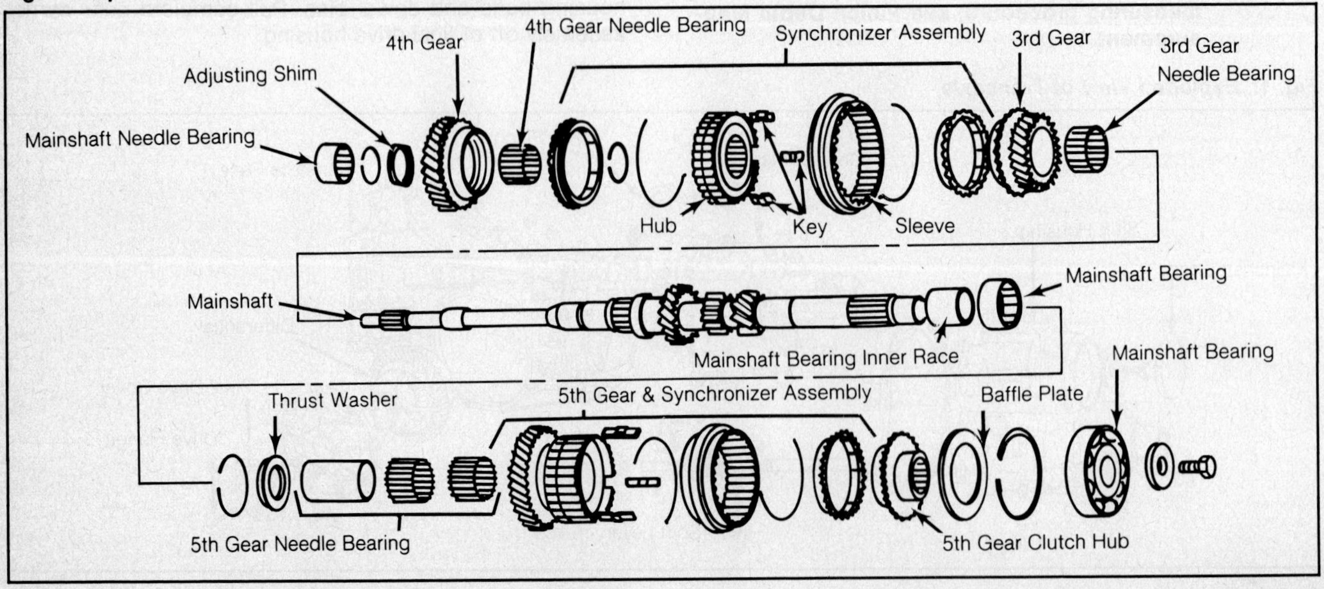

VOLKSWAGEN 013 & 093 5-SPEED TRANSAXLE (Cont.)

Fig. 5: Exploded View of Pinion Shaft Assembly

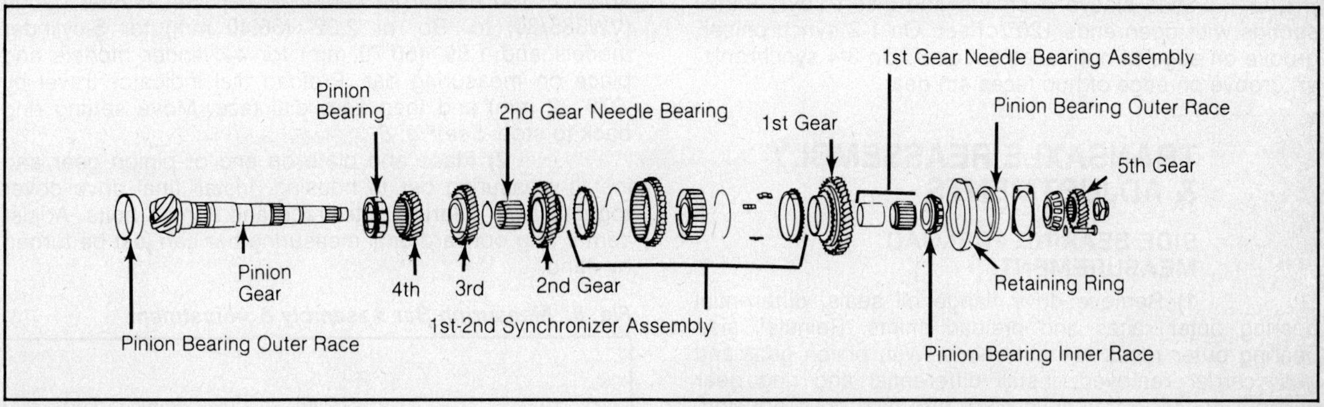

Heat 4th gear to 250°F (121°C) and install onto pinion shaft until fully seated.

2) Press 3rd gear onto shaft and retain with a selective fit snap ring. Snap rings are available in thicknesses of .060-.063" (1.5-1.6 mm). Install 2nd gear, blocker ring and 1-2 synchronizer onto shaft. Groove on edge of synchronizer hub faces 1st gear. Press 1st gear bearing inner race and 1st gear onto shaft. Press pinion rear bearing inner race onto pinion shaft.

SHIFT HOUSING

Disassembly

Pry out baffle plate and remove circlip holding rear mainshaft in place. Press out rear mainshaft bearing. Pry or drive out shift lever oil seal and bushing.

Reassembly

Press seal and bushing into shift lever bore. Press rear mainshaft into bore and retain with circlip. Reinstall baffle plate.

FINAL DRIVE HOUSING

Disassembly

1) Remove and discard "O" ring from final drive cover. Using a puller, remove outer bearing races and shims from drive flange bores. Remove drive flange oil seals as previously described. Remove bearing race lock bolt and pinion bearing outer race from rear of final drive housing.

2) Remove speedometer drive gear and adapter from housing. Remove clutch release bearing, clutch release shaft with bushings and clutch release bearing guide sleeve with mainshaft oil seal from front of housing.

Reassembly

1) Inspect all bearings for damage or excessive wear. Replace seals as necessary. Reinstall new mainshaft oil seal after filling lips of seal with multi-purpose grease. Reinstall clutch release bearing guide sleeve, but do not lubricate.

2) Coat moving parts of clutch release shaft with molybdenum disulphide grease and reinstall along with release bearing. Replace mainshaft needle bearing and pinion bearing outer race into rear of housing. Secure pinion bearing outer race with lock bolt.

DIFFERENTIAL

Disassembly

1) Place differential, with ring gear facing down, in a soft-jawed vise. Remove ring gear bolts and drive ring gear off of differential with a drift punch. Using a puller, remove speedometer drive gear and differential side bearings.

2) Drive roll pin securing differential pinion shaft out of case. Drive shaft out of case with a drift punch. Remove drive flange nuts and rotate side gears to bring pinion gears to an opening in case. Remove pinion gears, thrust washers and side gears.

Reassembly

To reassemble, reverse disassembly procedure and note the following: Differential side gear shim must be selected so that gears turn freely by hand with a maximum of .004" (.10 mm) of play. Shims are available in thicknesses of .02-.03" (.5-.8 mm).

SYNCHRONIZERS

Disassembly

1) Remove springs and keys. Slide sleeve off of hub. Inspect all parts for damage or wear. Check blocker rings for wear by placing on appropriate gear and checking clearance between gear and synchronizer matching teeth with a feeler gauge.

2) Clearance should be at least .020" (.5 mm). If clearance is not within specifications, replace blocker ring.

Fig. 6: Exploded View of Differential Assembly

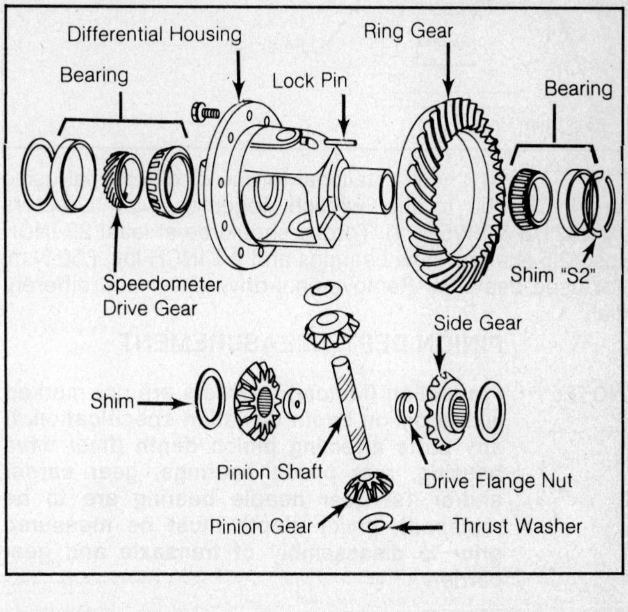

Manual Transmissions

VOLKSWAGEN 013 & 093 5-SPEED TRANSAXLE (Cont.)

Reassembly

Slide sleeve over hub and insert keys. Install springs with open ends 120° offset. On 1-2 synchronizer, groove on edge of hub faces 1st gear. On 3-4 synchronizer, groove on edge of hub faces 4th gear.

TRANSAXLE REASSEMBLY & ADJUSTMENTS

SIDE BEARING PRELOAD MEASUREMENT

1) Remove drive flange oil seals, differential bearing outer races and preload shims. Reinstall side bearing outer races without shims. With pinion gear and gear carrier removed, install differential and ring gear (without speedometer drive gear) into final drive housing. Install final drive cover and tighten bolts in a diagonal sequence.

2) Place an end plate (VW385/17) on cover end of differential. Assemble a dial indicator to read differential end play. Move differential up and down. Note dial indicator reading.

3) Add dial indicator reading to a preload constant of .0197" (.50 mm) on 5-cylinder models and .0157" (.40 mm) on 4-cylinder models to obtain total differential side bearing shim thickness. Temporarily install entire shim pack behind side bearing outer race on "S2" side of differential. *See Fig. 7.*

Fig. 7: Final Drive Adjustment Locations

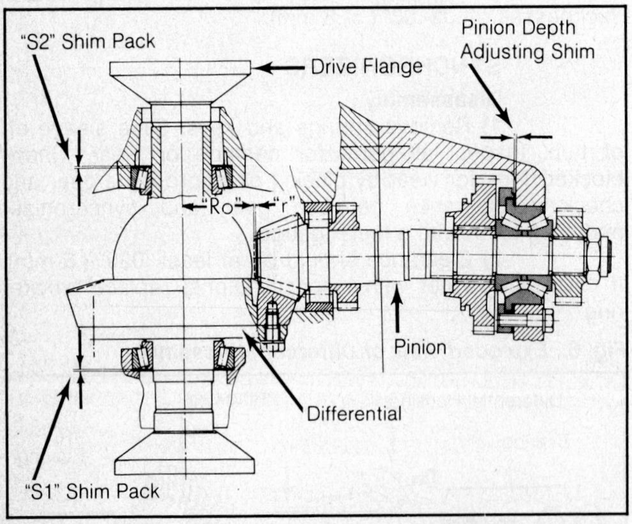

4) Check rotational torque of differential using an INCH lb. torque wrench together with adapters (VW521/8 & VW521/4). Torque should be at least 23 INCH lbs. (2.5 N.m) for new bearings and 2.7 INCH lbs. (.30 N.m) for used bearings. Remove final drive cover and differential.

PINION DEPTH MEASUREMENT

NOTE: Production (factory) gearsets are not marked with a pinion depth deviation specification. If any parts affecting pinion depth (final drive housing, rear pinion bearings, gear carrier and/or 1st gear needle bearing are to be replaced), pinion depth must be measured prior to disassembly of transaxle and gear carrier.

1) Assemble measuring bar. Slide setting ring about 2" (50 mm) from center of bar. Set master gauge (VW385/30) to "Ro" or 2.22" (56.40 mm) for 5-cylinder models and 1.99" (50.70 mm) for 4-cylinder models and place on measuring bar. Preload dial indicator travel by .079" (2 mm) and then zero dial face. Move setting ring back to stop. *See Fig. 8.*

2) Place end plate on end of pinion gear and install measuring bar in housing. Install final drive cover together with bearing outer race and tighten bolts. Adjust center ring outward until measuring bar can just be turned by hand.

Fig. 8: Measuring Bar Assembly & Adjustment

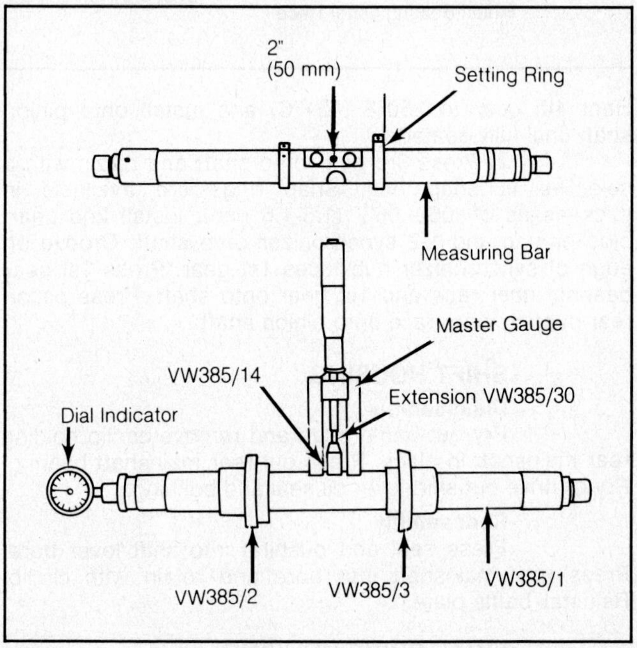

CAUTION: Dial indicator extension must contact pinion measuring plate and remain in contact with plate until measurement is completed. Otherwise dial indicator extension may push measuring plate off of pinion face when measuring bar is turned. Do not strike final drive cover when installing, as this may upset dial indicator reading.

3) Turn measuring bar back and forth slightly until maximum dial indicator reading is reached. This reading, when taken prior to gear carrier removal, is "r" or deviation from nominal pinion depth. Pinion depth deviation, when added to nominal pinion depth ("Ro") included in gauge travel in step **1)**, results in actual pinion depth ("R").

4) When this reading is taken during reassembly, pinion depth shim(s) should not be in place. Deviation from nominal pinion depth ("r"), whether marked on side of new service gear or measured at disassembly, should be subtracted from dial indicator reading to provide shim thickness necessary for reassembly. Remove final drive cover and measuring bar.

PINION DEPTH ADJUSTMENT

NOTE: This procedure may be carried out by installing mainshaft together with shift forks and

VOLKSWAGEN 013 & 093 5-SPEED TRANSAXLE (Cont.)

selector shafts at the same time as pinion shaft as described in Gear Carrier Reassembly. However, if it becomes necessary to remove pinion shaft to add or subtract shim thickness, the extra components involved will complicate the procedure.

1) Press pinion rear bearing outer race into gear carrier together with correct pinion depth shim selected previously. Install race retaining ring and bolts. Install preassembled pinion shaft into gear carrier. Press pinion rear bearing inner race onto rear of pinion shaft.

2) Place gear carrier assembly in soft-jawed vise. Install spacer (VW472/2) in place of pinion shaft 5th gear. Install and tighten pinion nut to specifications. Install gear carrier onto final drive housing and secure with 4 bolts. Recheck pinion depth measurement and correct as necessary.

RING GEAR BACKLASH ADJUSTMENT

1) With entire side bearing shim pack installed behind outer bearing race of "S2" side of differential, install differential and side cover into housing. Install fully assembled gear carrier with correct pinion depth shim onto final drive housing. Lock pinion shaft with holding tool (VW381/11). Attach dial indicator to differential. *See Fig. 9.*

Fig. 9: Backlash Measurement

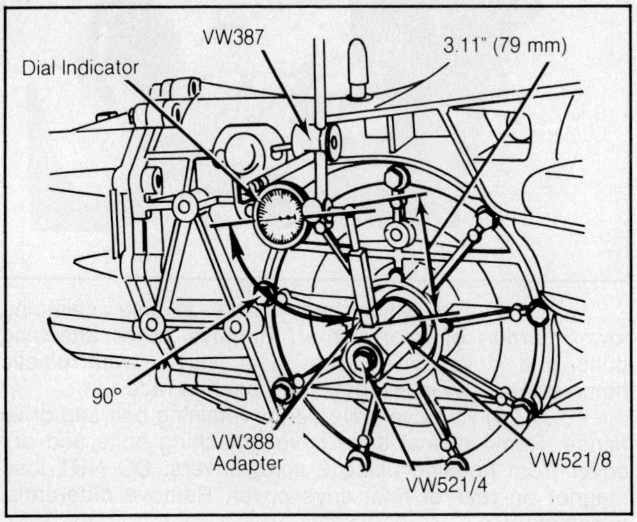

2) Turn ring gear to stop and zero dial indicator. Turn ring gear back and note backlash. Loosen locking bolts and rotate ring gear 90°. Retighten locking bolts and repeat procedure 3 more times at equally spaced points around the ring gear. Add all 4 dial indicator readings together and divide total by 4 to obtain average backlash.

3) Subtract average backlash from total side bearing shim pack thickness determined during SIDE BESRING PRELOAD MEASUREMENT and add .006" (.15 mm) to the result to obtain "S2" shim pack thickness. Subtract "S2" shim pack thickness from total thickness to obtain "S1" thickness. Install shims in appropriate location. *See Fig. 7.* Recheck backlash and correct as necessary.

TRANSAXLE REASSEMBLY

1) Lightly coat sealing face on final drive housing with sealing compound. Install new gasket and dowel pins. Attach gear carrier housing to final drive housing and install bolts. Engage any gear and lock mainshaft with holding tool (VW294b/1). Install and tighten pinion nut to specifications.

2) Install selector dog for 1st-2nd gear and shift transaxle into 3rd gear (pull out selector shaft). Install inner shift lever selector, placing ends of spring on 3-4 gear shaft and supporting selector dog against selector shaft. Position all selector shafts in neutral.

3) Align selector dog for 1st-2nd gear selector shaft and drive in roll pin. Install new gasket between gear carrier and shift housings. Press on shift housing and install bolts. Install new mainshaft cover.

TIGHTENING SPECIFICATIONS

Application	Ft. Lbs. (N.m)
Axle Shaft Hub Nut	167 (226)
Inner CV Joint Bolts	25 (34)
Drive Flange Retaining Bolt	18 (24)
Transaxle-to-Engine Bolts	40 (54)
Shift Housing-to-Gear Carrier Bolts	18 (24)
Gear Carrier-to-Final Drive Housing Bolts	18 (24)
Final Drive Cover Bolts	18 (24)
Mainshaft Bearing Retainer Bolt	33 (45)
Pinion Nut	72 (98)
Pinion Bearing Outer Race Retainer	18 (24)
Reverse Lever Bolt	25 (34)
Ring Gear Bolts	51 (69)

VOLKSWAGEN 016 5-SPEED TRANSAXLE

Audi 5000S, Porsche 944

DESCRIPTION

The 5-speed transaxle 016K (code QM) combines both transmission and differential into a single assembly consisting of 3 subassemblies: Front cover, gear housing and transmission/clutch housing.

In all gears, power flows from input shaft to pinion shaft through respective gear pairs. Torque is transferred to pinion gear, ring gear and drive axles. Reverse gear power flows from input shaft through reverse idler gear, sliding gear and then to pinion shaft.

LUBRICATION & ADJUSTMENT

See appropriate MANUAL TRANSMISSION SERVICING article in IMPORT GENERAL SERVICING section.

SERVICE (IN VEHICLE)

DRIVE AXLE SHAFTS

See appropriate DRIVE AXLE SHAFT article in IMPORT AXLE SHAFTS, OVERDRIVES & TRANSFER CASES section.

Fig. 1: Exploded View of Transaxle Assembly

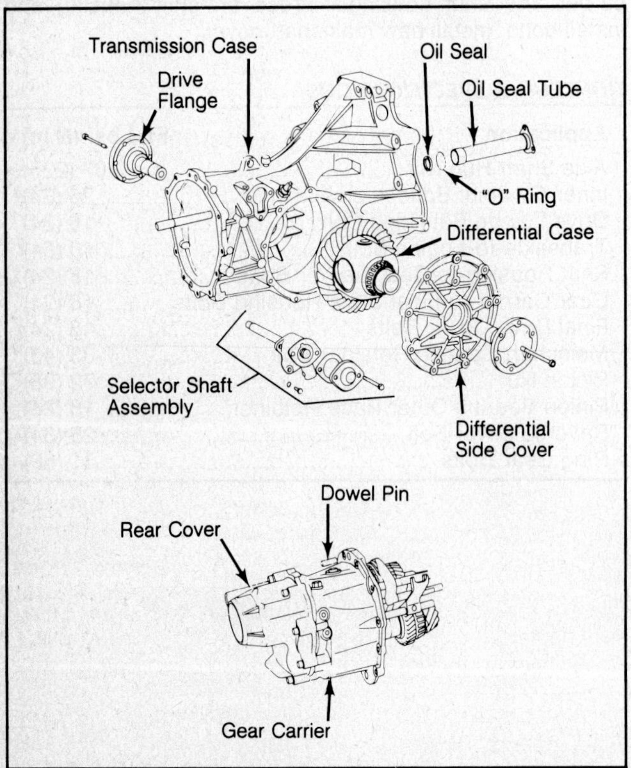

REMOVAL & INSTALLATION

TRANSAXLE

See appropriate MANUAL TRANSMISSION REMOVAL article in IMPORT GENERAL SERVICING section.

TRANSAXLE DISASSEMBLY

1) Mount transaxle in Holding Fixture (VW 540) and drain oil. Remove selector shaft. On 944 models, loosen bolts securing mainshaft oil seal tube. Place Seal Protector (9113) over mainshaft splines. Pry tube loose with an offset screwdriver. Remove tube and remove seal from tube.

2) On all models, remove transaxle case-to-gear carrier bolts, drive out dowel pins and separate gear carrier from transaxle case. On all models, remove input shaft front oil seal. On 944 models, remove input shaft front needle bearing from transmission case using a puller.

3) Mount gear carrier in soft-jawed vise with rear cover facing up. Remove cap from end of rear cover by driving a screwdriver into center of cap and prying up. Remove bolt from end of mainshaft.

Fig. 2: Removing Rear Cover from Gear Carrier

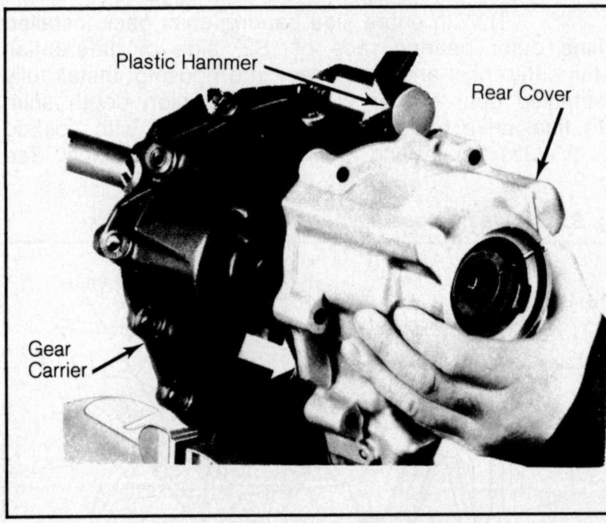

4) Reposition gear carrier in vise, clamping lower portion of gear carrier. Remove cover attaching bolts and drive cover from gear carrier with plastic hammer. Remove mainshaft inner bearing race.

5) Remove drive flange retaining bolt and drive flange. Remove final drive cover attaching bolts and pry cover from housing using 2 screwdrivers. DO NOT lose magnet on rear of final drive cover. Remove differential assembly.

COMPONENT DISASSEMBLY & REASSEMBLY

GEAR CARRIER ASSEMBLY

Disassembly

1) Remove 5th gear clutch hub and mainshaft bearing with Puller and Adapter (US1078 & VW431). Remove 5th gear synchronizer ring. Support selector rod with a hammer to prevent damage to selector rod bore, then drive out 5th gear shift fork roll pin.

2) Remove snap ring from mainshaft, then remove 5th gear with synchro hub, needle bearing and 5th gear shift fork (5th gear/reverse selector rod remains in housing). Remove 5th gear/reverse selector rod stop screws from side of housing.

VOLKSWAGEN 016 5-SPEED TRANSAXLE (Cont.)

Fig. 3: Removing Snap Ring Retaining 5th Gear Components to Mainshaft

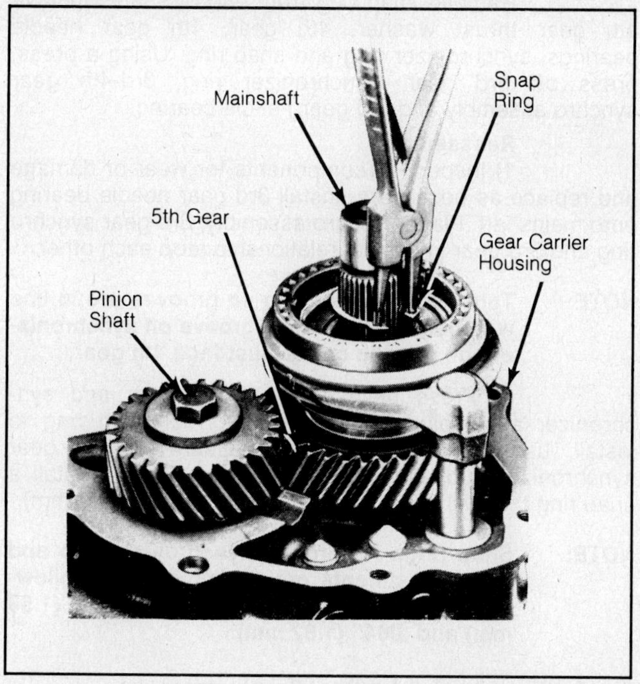

3) Clamp 4th gear/pinion shaft in soft-jaw vise and remove bolt from pinion shaft. Remove 5th gear from pinion shaft with puller, then remove adjusting shim.

Fig. 4: Removing Shift Fork Roll Pins

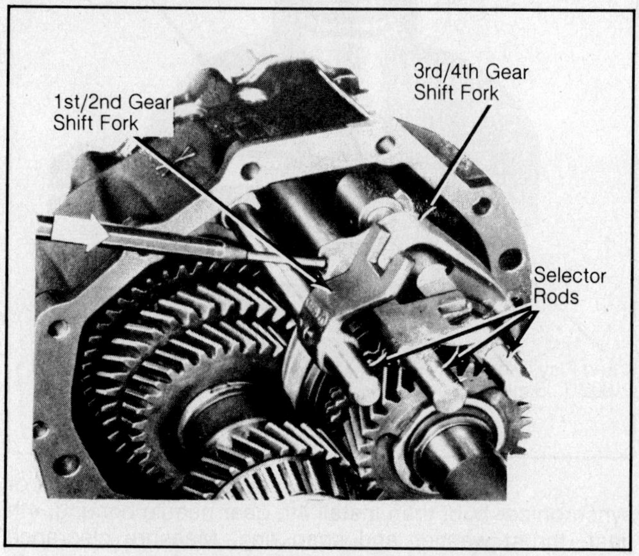

4) Reposition gear carrier in vise by clamping carrier housing. Drive out 1st-2nd gear selector fork roll pin, while supporting with hammer. Turn 3rd-4th selector fork up and drive out roll pin, while supporting with hammer. Pull out 3rd-4th selector rod (shift fork remains in synchro hub) without losing small interlock pin. Remove reverse relay lever boot.

5) Partially pull out pinion shaft and mainshaft and remove mainshaft assembly with 3rd-4th gear shift fork attached. Unhook reverse gear spring clip and move it out of the way. Lift up pinion shaft just enough to remove 1st-2nd gear selector rod and shift fork. Remove pinion shaft from gear carrier.

Reassembly

1) Insert interlock pins in correct position in carrier case bore. Insert springs and plungers for 1st through 4th gear detents. Insert reverse gear detent plunger and spring. Install 5th-reverse selector rod and relay lever. Press relay lever until lever rests on selector rod and in groove of reverse gear. *See Fig. 5.*

Fig. 5: Reverse Relay Lever Adjustment

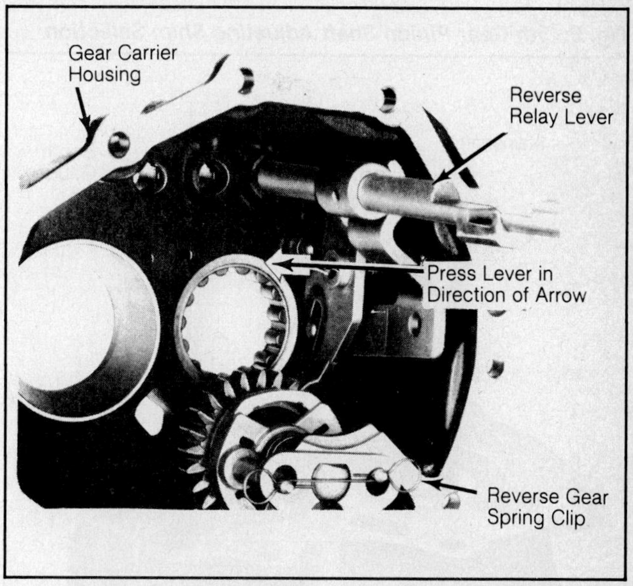

NOTE: Reverse relay lever bolt and threaded bushing of lever must be in line.

2) Tighten adjusting screw against stop on threaded bushing. Press relay lever against screw and loosen screw until tip of threads can be heard to engage in threaded bushing. Tighten screw to 25 ft. lbs. (34 N.m). Engage reverse gear several times and check that relay lever moves easily in all positions. Relay lever should be centered over reverse gear detent.

3) Engage pinion shaft with reverse gear and partially insert pinion shaft into gear carrier. Install 1st-2nd gear shift fork and selector rod, then press pinion shaft into housing. Push 3rd-4th gear shift fork onto 5th-reverse gear selector rod.

4) Press off mainshaft inner bearing race, then partially install mainshaft into housing. Insert 3rd-4th gear shift fork into clutch sleeve and press mainshaft into housing until fully seated. Move selector rods into neutral position and check for proper position of interlock pins.

5) Install 3rd-4th gear shift rod and insert small interlock pin (coated with grease). Secure 3rd-4th and 1st-2nd gear shift forks and selector rods with roll pins. Install selector rod stop screws into carrier housing using new gaskets.

6) Position gear carrier assembly in a soft-jawed vise, with jaws clamped on 4th gear of pinion shaft. Using a depth gauge, measure dimension "A" as shown in *Fig. 6* to determine correct 5th gear adjusting shim to install. Select correct 5th gear adjusting shim using the following table:

NOTE: See Fig. 6 for Dimension "A" measurement.

VOLKSWAGEN 016 5-SPEED TRANSAXLE (Cont.)

PINION SHAFT 5TH GEAR ADJUSTING SHIM CHART

If "A" Is In. (mm)	Use this Shim In. (mm)
.331-.339 (8.4-8.6)	.043 (1.1)
.343-.350 (8.7-8.9)	.055 (1.4)
.354-.362 (9.0-9.2)	.067 (1.7)
.366-.374 (9.3-9.5)	.079 (2.0)
.378-.386 (9.6-9.8)	.091 (2.3)

Fig. 6: 5th Gear Pinion Shaft Adjusting Shim Selection

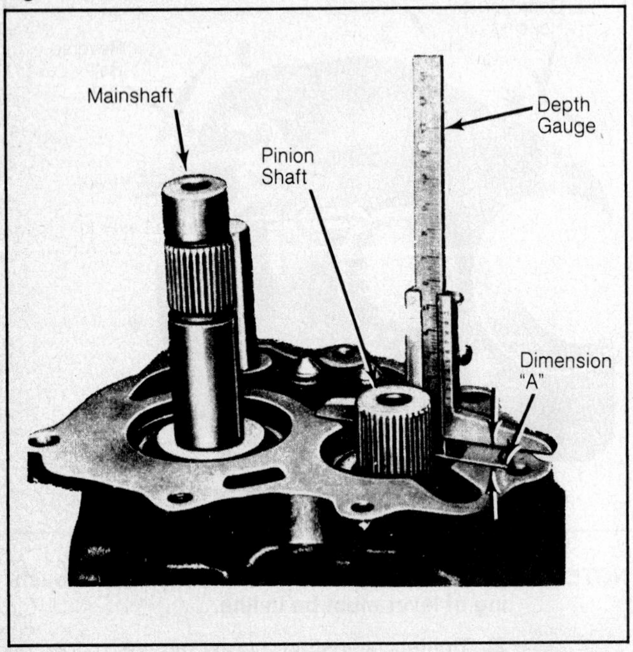

Measure depth at "A" and convert to shim size using chart.

7) Install selected 5th gear adjusting shim, then heat 5th gear to 250°F (120°C) and slide onto pinion shaft until seated. Install washer and bolt on end of pinion shaft and tighten bolt. Collar of washer must face pinion head.

8) Clamp mainshaft in soft-jawed vise so that mainshaft and pinion shaft are vertical. Heat mainshaft bearing inner race to 250°F (120°C) and slide it onto mainshaft until seated.

9) Install 5th gear with synchronizer hub, needle bearing and shift rod onto mainshaft. Install shift fork roll pin into fork and selector rod. Select a snap ring that will provide a maximum mainshaft end play of .002" (.05 mm), then install snap ring into mainshaft groove.

NOTE: **Mainshaft snap rings are available in following thicknesses: .050" (1.35 mm), .055" (1.40 mm) and .060" (1.45 mm).**

10) Install 5th gear synchronizer ring. Heat 5th gear clutch hub to 250°F (120°C) and install it on mainshaft until fully seated. Drive on mainshaft bearing inner race, then install guide sleeve and new gasket on gear carrier housing. Install rear cover on carrier housing.

11) Heat other half of mainshaft bearing inner race and drive onto mainshaft. Install washer and bolt on end of mainshaft and tighten bolt. Install and tighten rear cover mounting bolts. Install new rear cover cap.

MAINSHAFT ASSEMBLY

Disassembly

Remove snap ring from end of shaft. Remove 4th gear thrust washer, 4th gear, 4th gear needle bearings, synchronizer ring and snap ring. Using a press, press off 3rd gear, synchronizer ring, 3rd-4th gear synchro assembly and 3rd gear needle bearing.

Reassembly

1) Inspect all components for wear or damage and replace as necessary. Install 3rd gear needle bearing onto mainshaft. Place synchro assembly, 3rd gear synchro ring and 3rd gear in correct relationship atop each other.

NOTE: **Turn synchronizer ring so grooves are in line with hollow keys. Also, groove on synchronizer hub or wide collar must face 4th gear.**

2) Press mainshaft into 3rd gear and synchronizer assembly. To determine correct snap ring to install, use a feeler gauge to measure 3rd/4th gear synchronizer hub end play as shown in *Fig. 7.* Install a snap ring that will allow an end play of 0-.002" (0-0.5 mm).

NOTE: **Snap rings for 3rd-4th synchronizer hub end play adjustments are available in the following thicknesses: .059" (1.59 mm), .061" (1.56 mm) and .064" (1.62 mm).**

Fig. 7: Checking 3rd-4th Gear Synchronizer Hub End Play

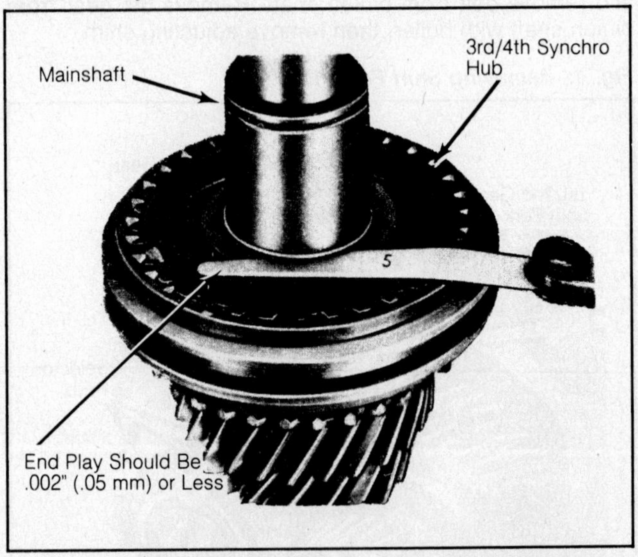

3) Install synchronizer ring on 4th gear side of synchronizer hub, then install 4th gear needle bearing, 4th gear, thrust washer and snap ring. Measure clearance between thrust washer and snap ring. Clearance should be .008-.013" (.20-.35 mm). If not, correct by installing a different thickness snap ring.

NOTE: **Snap rings for 4th gear end play adjustment are available in the following thicknesses: .065" (1.65 mm), .067" (1.70 mm) and .069" (1.75 mm).**

VOLKSWAGEN 016 5-SPEED TRANSAXLE (Cont.)

PINION SHAFT

Disassembly

1) Mount pinion shaft assembly into a holding fixture. Using a press, remove small inner bearing and 1st gear by pressing from shaft.

2) Remove 1st gear needle bearing and synchro ring. Remove snap ring, then press off 1st-2nd gear synchro hub assembly, 2nd gear synchro ring and 2nd gear.

Fig. 8: Exploded View of Mainshaft Assembly

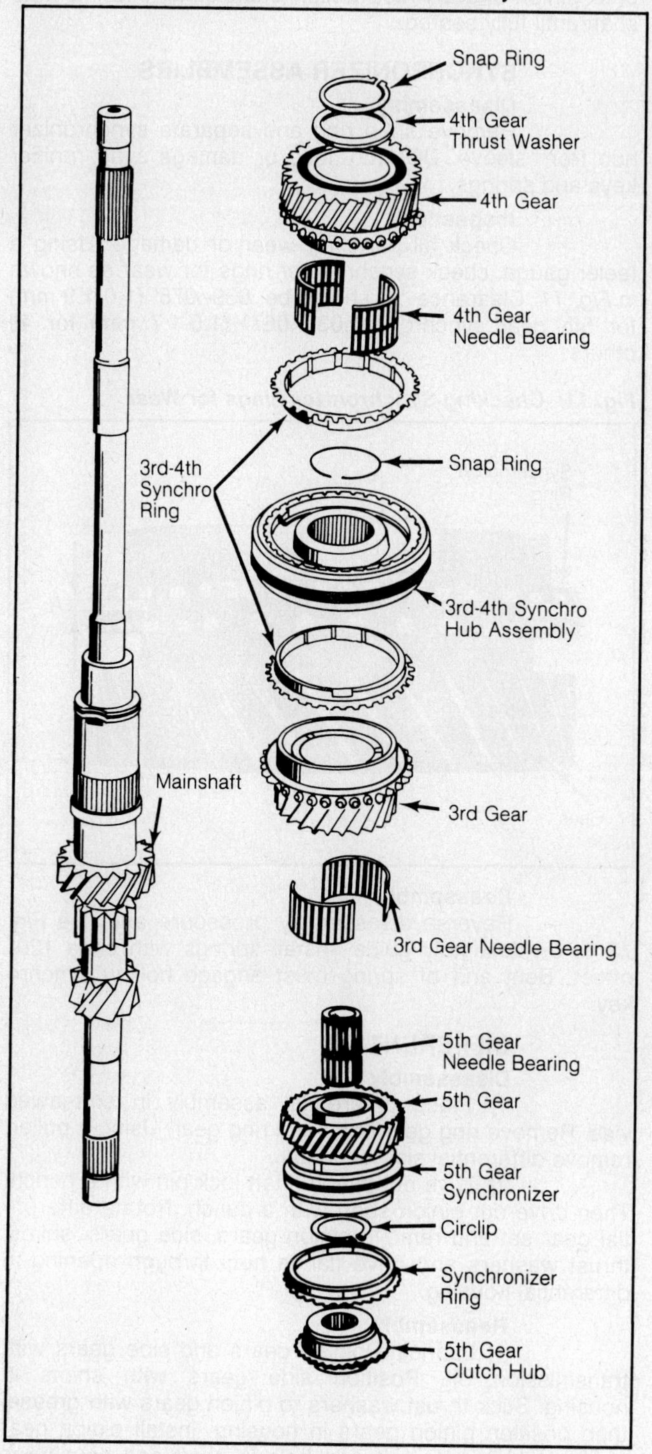

Fig. 9: Exploded View of Pinion Shaft Assembly

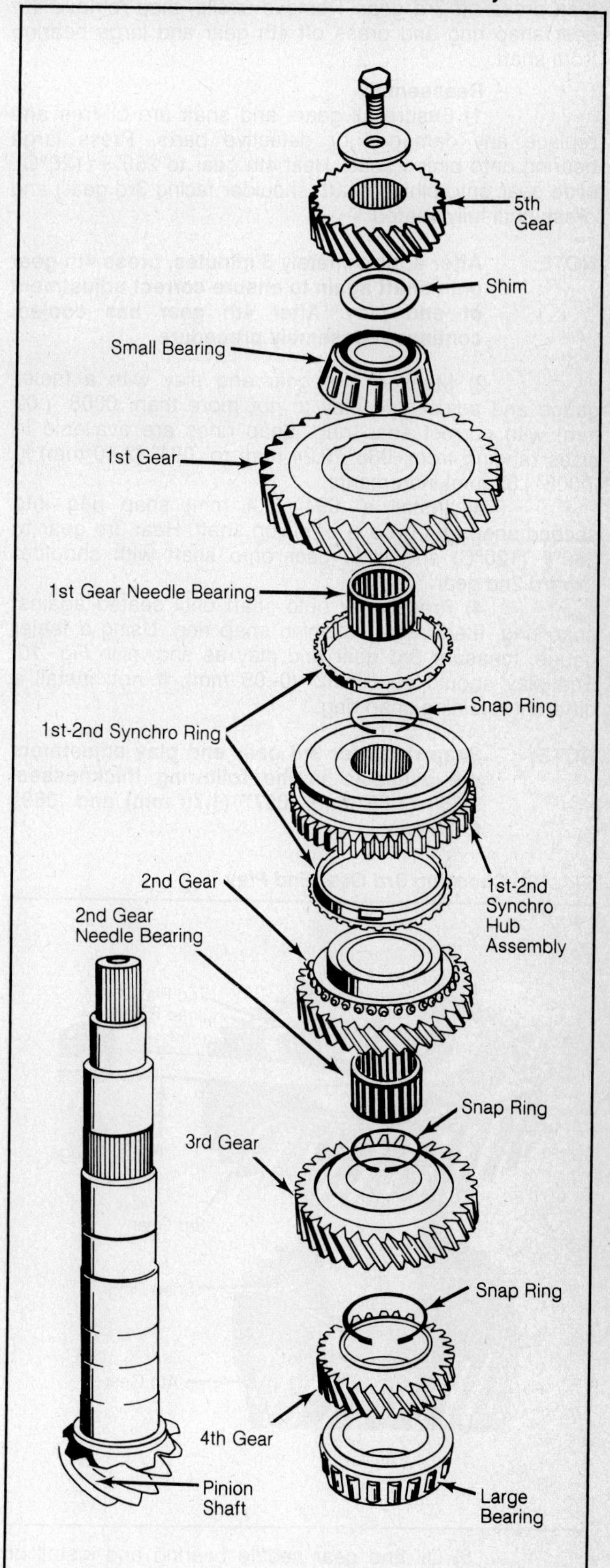

VOLKSWAGEN 016 5-SPEED TRANSAXLE (Cont.)

3) Remove 2nd gear needle bearing, snap ring, then press off 3rd gear. Remove circlip, then remove 4th gear snap ring and press off 4th gear and large bearing from shaft.

Reassembly

1) Ensure all gears and shaft are oil-free and replace any damaged or defective parts. Press large bearing onto pinion shaft. Heat 4th gear to 250°F (120°C), slide gear onto pinion shaft (shoulder facing 3rd gear) and press until fully seated.

NOTE: **After approximately 3 minutes, press 4th gear onto shaft again to ensure correct adjustment of end play. After 4th gear has cooled, continue reassembly procedure.**

2) Measure 4th gear end play with a feeler gauge and adjust end play to not more than .0008" (.02 mm) with correct snap ring. Snap rings are available in sizes ranging from .088" (2.24 mm) to .094" (2.40 mm) in .0008" (.02 mm) increments.

3) Install a .094" (2.4 mm) snap ring into second snap ring groove of pinion shaft. Heat 3rd gear to 250°F (120°C) and slide gear onto shaft with shoulder toward 2nd gear.

4) Press gear onto shaft until seated against snap ring, then install retaining snap ring. Using a feeler gauge, measure 3rd gear end play as shown in *Fig. 10.* End play should be 0-.002" (0-.05 mm). If not, install a different retaining snap ring.

NOTE: **Snap rings for 3rd gear end play adjustment are available in the following thicknesses: .065" (1.65 mm), .067" (1.70 mm) and .069" (1.75 mm).**

Fig. 10: Checking 3rd Gear End Play

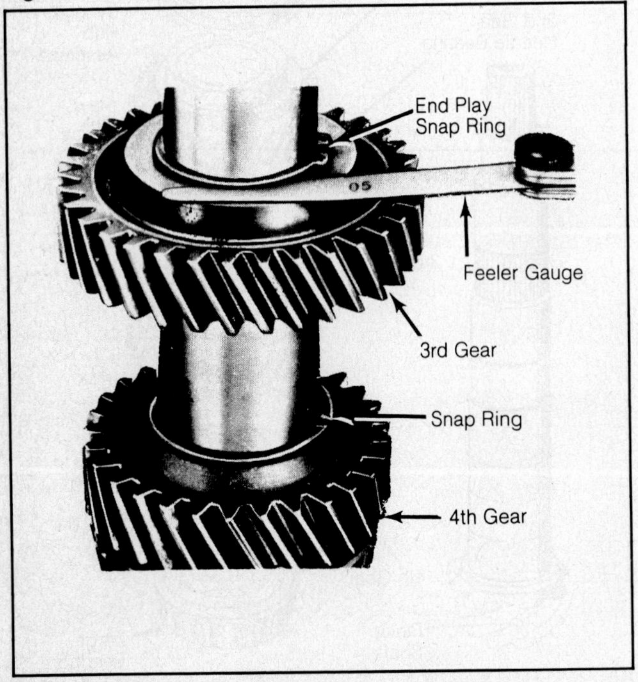

5) Oil 2nd gear needle bearing and install on shaft. Place 2nd gear, 2nd gear synchro ring and synchro hub assembly atop one another. Press all components onto pinion shaft. Measure synchronizer hub assembly end play with a feeler gauge. End play should be 0-.0016" (0-.04 mm). Adjust end play with a snap ring.

NOTE: **Snap rings for 1st-2nd synchronizer hub adjustment are available in the following thicknesses: .059" (1.50 mm), .061" (1.55 mm) and .063" (1.60 mm).**

6) Install remaining synchronizer ring onto hub. Oil and install 1st gear needle bearing, then slide 1st gear onto pinion shaft. Press pinion shaft small bearing onto shaft until fully seated.

SYNCHRONIZER ASSEMBLIES

Disassembly

Remove snap ring and separate synchronizer hub from sleeve. DO NOT lose or damage synchronizer keys and springs.

Inspection

Check all parts for wear or damage. Using a feeler gauge, check synchronizer rings for wear as shown in *Fig. 11.* Clearance "A" should be .039-.075" (1.0-1.9 mm) for 5th gear synchro or .039-.067" (1.0-1.7 mm) for all others.

Fig. 11: Checking Synchronizer Rings for Wear

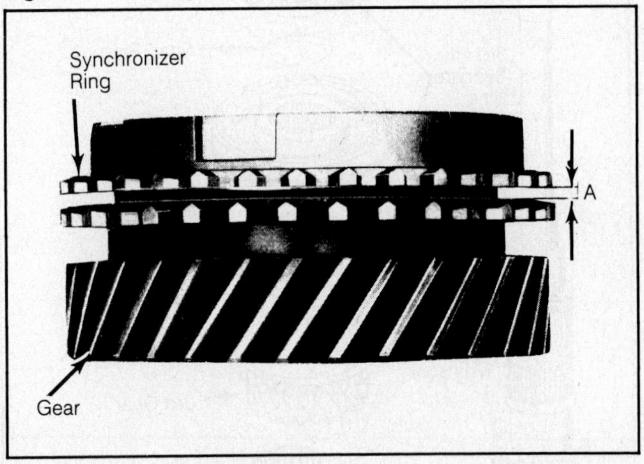

Reassembly

Reverse disassembly procedure and use *Fig. 12* as an assembly guide. Install springs with ends 120° offset. Bent end of spring must engage hollow synchro key.

DIFFERENTIAL

Disassembly

1) Place differential assembly in soft-jawed vise. Remove ring gear bolts and ring gear. Using a puller, remove differential side bearings.

2) Drive out pinion shaft lock pin with a punch. Then drive out pinion shaft with a punch. Rotate differential gear set and remove pinion gears, side gears, shims, thrust washers and drive flange nuts through opening in differential housing.

Reassembly

1) Lubricate pinion gears and side gears with transmission oil. Position side gears with shims in housing. Stick thrust washers to pinion gears with grease, then position pinion gears in housing. Install pinion gear shaft, making sure lock pin hole in shaft and housing is aligned.

VOLKSWAGEN 016 5-SPEED TRANSAXLE (Cont.)

Fig. 12: Assembled View of Synchronizer Assembly

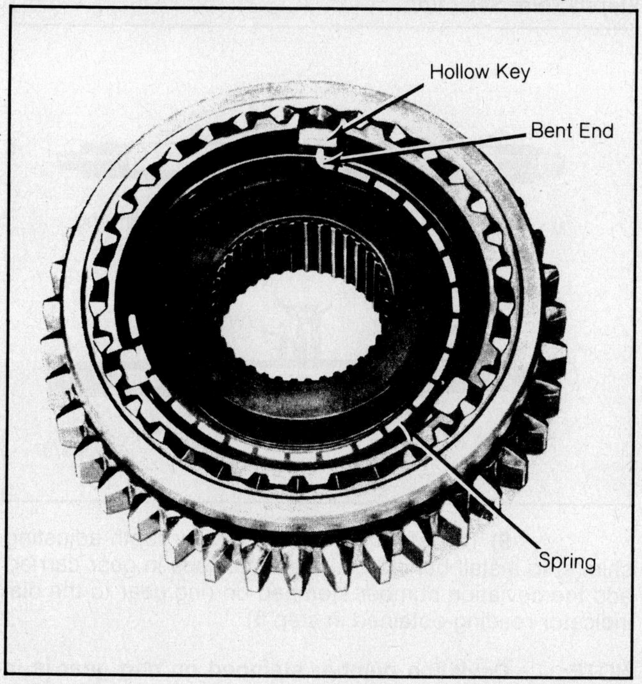

CAUTION: Side gears, pinion gears, shims and thrust washers must not be interchanged.

2) Check pinion and side gear adjustment by pushing pinion gears outward and check play of side gears. Adjustment is correct if no play can be felt by hand, but differential gears can be turned easily without binding. If not to specification outlined, correct by installing thicker or thinner side gear shims.

NOTE: Side gear shims are available in the following thicknesses: .020" (.5 mm), .024" (.6 mm), .028" (.7 mm) and .032" (.8 mm).

3) Install correct side gear adjusting shims, then install pinion gear shaft lock pin. Heat ring gear to approximately 250°F (120°C), then position ring gear in place on differential housing. Pull ring gear into place with new attaching bolts, then tighten bolts in crosswise manner.

4) Heat differential side bearings to approximately 212°F (100°C), then press them onto each end of differential housing.

TRANSAXLE REASSEMBLY & ADJUSTMENTS

PINION SHAFT ADJUSTMENTS

1) Install pinion shaft bearing outer races into final drive housing and gear carrier WITHOUT shims. Install assembled gear carrier to final drive housing and tighten attaching bolts.

2) Place Magnetic Measuring Plate (VW385/17) onto rear end of pinion shaft, then mount a dial indicator to gear carrier as shown in *Fig. 14.* Zero dial indicator with .039" (1 mm) preload. Move pinion shaft up and down (without turning shaft) and record indicator reading.

CAUTION: Turning pinion shaft during measurement will cause bearings to settle, giving an inaccurate reading.

3) Remove gear carrier from final drive housing. To determine total thickness of shims necessary to obtain correct pinion depth and bearing preload, add constant preload value of .012" (.30 mm) to dial indicator reading just obtained. Resulting sum is total thickness of required shims.

4) Remove pinion shaft bearing outer race from gear carrier, then install a shim of total shim thickness determined in step **3)** behind outer race and reinstall race into gear carrier. Install gear carrier to final drive housing and tighten attaching bolts. Turn pinion shaft several times in each direction to settle bearings.

5) Adjust clamping ring on Measuring Bar (VW385/1) so dimension "a" in *Fig. 15* is 2" (50 mm). Next, assemble the following measuring tools onto measuring bar as shown in *Fig. 15:* Dial Indicator, Centering Discs (VW385/2 and 3), Measuring Pin (VW385/14), Measuring Pin Extension (VW385/15), and Setting Gauge

Fig. 13: Exploded View of Differential Assembly

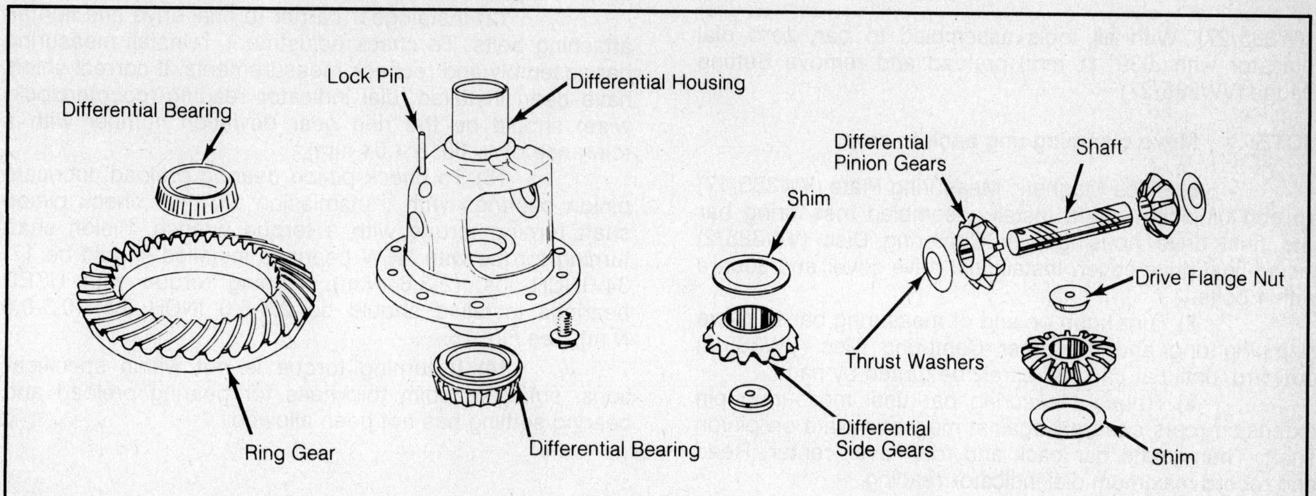

VOLKSWAGEN 016 5-SPEED TRANSAXLE (Cont.)

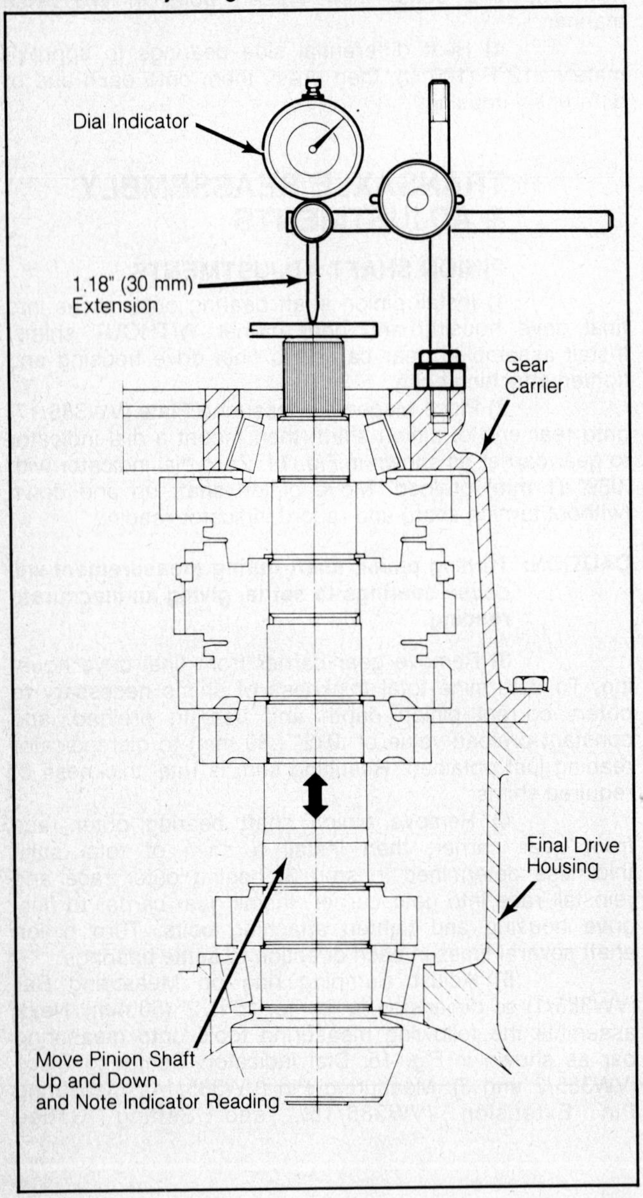

Fig. 14: Measuring Pinion Shaft End Play to Determine Total Pinion Adjusting Shim Thickness

(VW385/27). With all tools assembled to bar, zero dial indicator with .039" (1 mm) preload and remove Setting Gauge (VW385/27).

NOTE: Move clamping ring back to stop.

6) Place Magnetic Measuring Plate (VW385/17) on end of pinion shaft. Install assembled measuring bar into final drive housing with Centering Disc (VW385/2) facing final drive cover. Install final drive cover and secure with 4 bolts.

7) Turn knob on end of measuring bar to move clamping ring and the other Centering Disc (VW385/3) outward, until bar can just barely be turned by hand.

8) Rotate measuring bar until measuring pin extension rests squarely against magnetic plate on pinion shaft. Then rotate bar back and forth over center. Read and record maximum dial indicator reading.

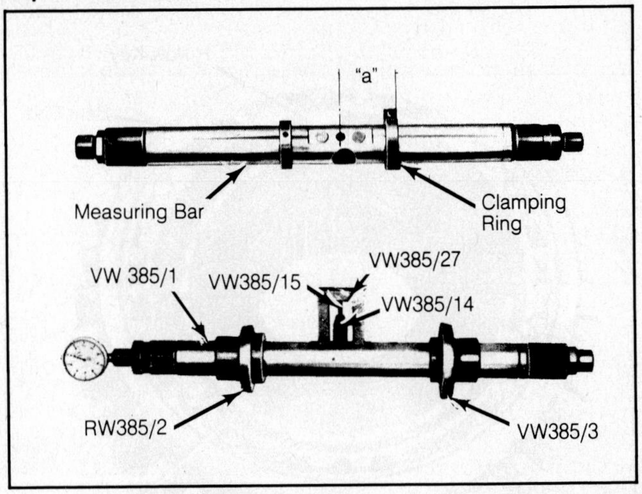

Fig. 15: Assembling Measuring Tools for Pinion Depth Shim Selection

9) To determine correct pinion depth adjusting shim(s) to install behind bearing outer race in gear carrier, add the deviation number stamped on ring gear to the dial indicator reading obtained in step **8)**.

NOTE: Deviation number stamped on ring gear is in hundredth millimeters. A marking of 25 would be .25 mm.

10) To determine thickness of shim to install under pinion bearing outer race in final drive housing, subtract thickness of pinion depth shim determined in step **9)** from total pinion shim thickness obtained in step **3)**.

NOTE: Shims for outer race installed in gear carrier are available in thicknesses of .008" (.20 mm) to .045" (1.15 mm) in various increments. Shims for outer bearing race in final drive housing are available in thicknesses of .009" (.24 mm) to .056" (1.41 mm) in various increments.

11) Remove measuring bar assembly from final drive housing. Separate gear carrier from final drive housing. Remove pinion shaft bearing outer race from gear carrier and final drive housing, then install selected shims with outer race back into carrier and housing.

12) Install gear carrier to final drive and tighten attaching bolts. To check adjustment, reinstall measuring bar assembly and recheck measurements. If correct shims have been installed, dial indicator reading (counterclockwise) should be the ring gear deviation number with a tolerance of ±.0016" (.04 mm).

13) To check pinion bearing preload, lubricate pinion bearings with transmission oil, then check pinion shaft turning torque with a torque wrench. Pinion shaft turning torque with NEW bearings installed should be 17-34 INCH lbs. (2-3.8 N.m). Turning torque with USED bearings installed should be 2.5-5.0 INCH lbs. (0.3-0.6 N.m). *See Fig. 16.*

14) If turning torque is not within specifications, sufficient shim thickness for bearing preload and bearing settling has not been allowed.

VOLKSWAGEN 016 5-SPEED TRANSAXLE (Cont.)

Fig. 16: Checking Pinion Shaft Turning Torque

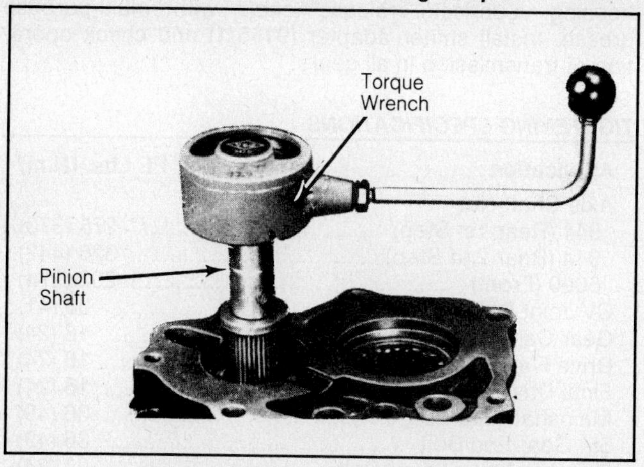

RING GEAR ADJUSTMENTS

1) Remove gear carrier from final drive housing. Remove differential oil seals and side bearing outer races from final drive housing and take out shims. Reinstall side bearing outer races WITHOUT shims. Install differential assembly into final drive housing. Install final drive cover and tighten attaching bolts in a diagonal pattern to 18 ft. lbs. (24 N.m).

NOTE: Differential assembly is installed with ring gear side facing final drive cover.

Fig. 17: Measuring Differential Bearing Preload

2) Position Magnetic Measuring Plate (VW385/17) and dial indicator as shown in *Fig. 17*, then zero dial indicator with .039" (1 mm) preload. Move differential assembly up and down and note dial indicator reading.

CAUTION: DO NOT rotate differential while taking measurement as bearings will settle and make measurement inaccurate.

3) To the dial indicator reading obtained in step **2)**, add the constant preload value of .020" (.50 mm). Resulting sum is thickness of shims necessary for correct differential bearing preload.

4) Remove measuring tools and final drive housing cover. Remove differential side bearing outer race from cover, then reinstall race with a shim of the thickness obtained in step **3)** behind it. Reinstall final drive housing cover.

5) Lubricate differential side bearings with transmission oil, then connect an INCH lb. torque wrench to differential and check turning torque. Differential turning torque with new side bearings should be 22 INCH lbs. (2.5 N.m).

NOTE: It is not necessary to measure differential turning torque when used bearings are reinstalled.

6) Insert Clamping Sleeve (VW521/4) with Slotted Sleeve (VW521/8) into differential and secure with nut. Adjust length of Backlash Measuring Bar (VW388) until dimension "A" in *Fig. 18* in 3.11" (79 mm).

Fig. 18: Position of Ring Gear Backlash Measuring Tools

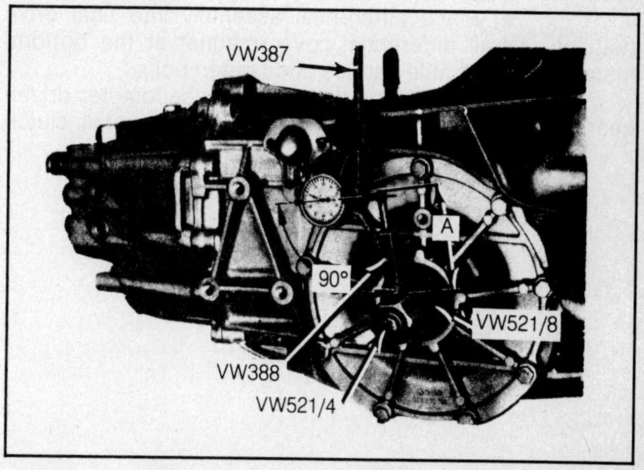

7) Attach measuring bar to clamping sleeve. Install dial indicator in Holder (VW387) and bolt holder to final drive housing as shown in *Fig. 18*.

NOTE: Dial indicator must be installed so foot will contact end of measuring bar at a 90° angle.

8) Turn ring gear to take up backlash. Zero dial indicator and clamp in holder. Turn ring gear in opposite direction until it is stopped and note indicator reading. This reading is ring gear backlash.

9) Check ring gear at 4 locations (90° apart) around circumference of ring gear. Add the 4 measurements together, then divide by 4 to find the average ring gear backlash. Ring gear backlash should be .004-.008" (.10-.20 mm).

NOTE: Difference between the 4 ring gear backlash measurements must not exceed .002" (.06 mm). If measurements differ more than this, ring gear is incorrectly installed or final drive housing is damaged.

10) To determine thickness of shim to install behind differential bearing outer race in final drive housing cover (opposite ring gear side), subtract the average ring gear backlash from the total shim thickness obtained in

VOLKSWAGEN 016 5-SPEED TRANSAXLE (Cont.)

step **3)**. To this value add the constant preload value of .006" (.15 mm). Resulting sum is the thickness of ring gear adjusting shim to install in final drive housing cover.

NOTE: Ring gear adjusting shims for final drive housing cover are available in thicknesses from .006" (.15 mm) to .047" (1.2 mm) in various increments.

11) To determine thickness of ring gear adjusting shim to install behind differential side bearing outer race in final drive housing (ring gear side), subtract thickness of shim determined in step **10)** from the total ring gear adjusting shim thickness determined in step **3)**.

FINAL ASSEMBLY

1) On 944 models, install input shaft front needle bearing and input shaft seal. On all models, lightly coat joints of gear carrier and final drive housings with sealing compound. Mate units together and tighten bolts. Coat selector shaft with sealing compound and install into case. Tighten bolts.

2) Place differential assembly into final drive housing. Install differential cover magnet at the bottom. Install both drive axle flanges and tighten bolts.

3) On 5000 models, install speedometer driven gear and adapter. Install input shaft seal. Install clutch release shaft, spring and bearing assembly into clutch housing. Lubricate release shaft with multi-purpose grease. Install shifter adapter (9155/1) and check operation of transmission in all gears.

TIGHTENING SPECIFICATIONS

Application	Ft. Lbs. (N.m)
Axle Shaft Nut	
944 (Rear 1st Step)	275 (373)
944 (Rear 2nd Step)	326 (442)
5000 (Front)	202 (274)
CV Joint Bolts	30 (41)
Gear Carrier-to-Final Drive Housing	18 (24)
Drive Flange Bolts	18 (24)
Final Drive Cover	18 (24)
Mainshaft End Bolt	36 (49)
5th Gear End Bolt	36 (49)
Reverse Relay Lever Bolt	25 (34)
Ring Gear Bolts	72 (98)
Upper Strut Retaining Nuts (5000)	18 (24)
Transaxle-to-Engine (5000)	40 (54)
Central Tube-to-Transaxle (944)	
10 mm Bolts	30 (41)
12 mm Bolts	61 (83)
Central Tube-to-Clutch Housing (944)	30 (41)

VOLVO 4-SPEED – MODEL M46

DL, GL, Turbo, 740, 760

DESCRIPTION

Transmission is fully synchronized 4-speed unit with all gears in constant mesh except reverse gear. Gears on mainshaft are carried by bronze or needle bearings. Input shaft and mainshaft rotate on ball bearings. Countershaft rotates on roller bearings.

In Neutral position, the mainshaft gears rotate freely. An overdrive unit is bolted to rear of transmission and can only be engaged in 4th gear. Engagement of gears is accomplished by means of a synchronizer sleeve working together with a synchronizer ring. The synchronizer sleeve moves sideways on synchronizer hub splines.

LUBRICATION & ADJUSTMENT

See appropriate MANUAL TRANSMISSION SERVICING article in IMPORT GENERAL SERVICING section.

TROUBLE SHOOTING

HARD SHIFTING

Clutch may not release fully due to deformed clutch disc or being out of adjustment. Pilot bearing seized, damaged or dry. Selector plate damaged. Shift forks bent.

SLIPS OUT OF GEAR

Selector plate damaged or worn. Detent balls and springs worn or broken. Shift forks bent or worn. Transmission and clutch housing misaligned.

NOISY OPERATION

Insufficient or wrong type lubricant. Worn or damaged bushings and/or gears. Worn splines.

NOTE: **When checking transmission for noise, ensure that it is not coming from other parts of drive line.**

SERVICE (IN VEHICLE)

REAR OIL SEAL

Removal

Raise and support vehicle. Disconnect propeller shaft from overdrive unit. Using Wrench (5149) and a 1 1/6" (27 mm) socket, remove drive flange nut. Using Puller (2261), remove flange from mainshaft. Using Rear Seal Puller (5069), remove oil seal.

Installation

Using Drift (5064) and hammer, install new oil seal. Using Wrench (5149) and a 1 1/6" (27 mm) socket, install drive flange and nut. Reverse removal procedure to complete installation.

REMOVAL & INSTALLATION

TRANSMISSION

See appropriate MANUAL TRANSMISSION REMOVAL article in IMPORT GENERAL SERVICING section.

TRANSMISSION DISASSEMBLY

1) Install transmission in work stand and drain lubricant. Disconnect wires at overdrive solenoid. Remove back-up light switch and overdrive switch. Remove transmission top cover.

2) Lift out detent spring and ball. Remove selector plate assembly, return spring, gasket, glide washers, and shifter lock pin. *See Fig. 1.* Remove overdrive retaining nuts from intermediate flange and remove overdrive.

Fig. 1: Removing Selector Plate Assembly

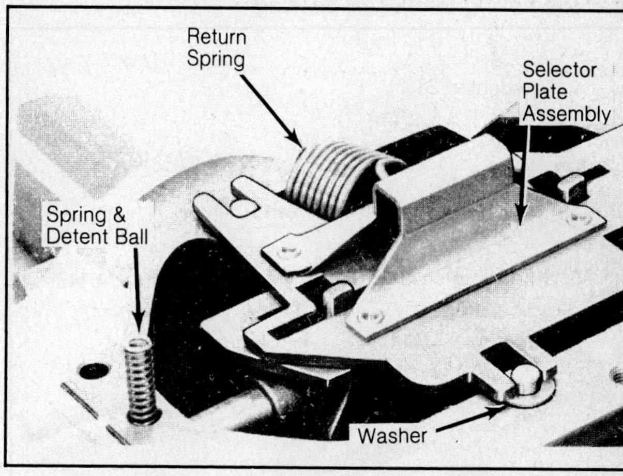

3) Remove gearshift carrier assembly. *See Fig. 2.* Remove sleeve for gearshift rod joint and knock out rear pin. Turn rod, knock out front pin and remove rod. Unbolt intermediate housing from transmission and remove with gasket and shims.

4) Remove selector rail, shifter and shift forks. Remove lock ring and pull off overdrive oil pump eccentric. *See Fig. 2.* Catch and retain drive key. Remove lock ring and spacer ring for main shaft bearing.

5) Place Adapter (2985) between input shaft and front synchronizer ring. Using Puller (5147) and Adapters (5085 and 5148), pull off mainshaft bearing and remove thrust washer. *See Fig. 3.* Leave Adapter (2985) in place.

6) Remove clutch fork, clutch housing, gasket and shims. On cast iron housings, remove intermediate shaft rear bearing race by tapping shaft back until race is free, then tap forward until front race can be removed. On aluminum housings, tap shaft back only enough to install Puller (5177), and remove races.

7) On all transmissions, pull out input shaft, then remove 4th gear synchronizer ring. Lift out mainshaft, intermediate shaft, reverse gear and shaft. It may be necessary to tap reverse gear shaft back for removal.

8) Remove reverse gear shift fork and seal for selector rail. Using Puller (5131), remove intermediate shaft bearings. Remove rubber ring from gearshift rod joint and gearshift rod bushings. Remove clutch housing seal.

VOLVO 4-SPEED – MODEL M46 (Cont.)

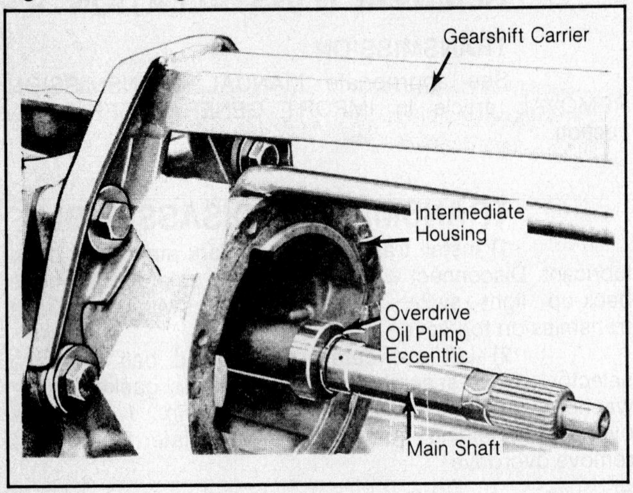

Fig. 2: Removing Gearshift Carrier Assembly

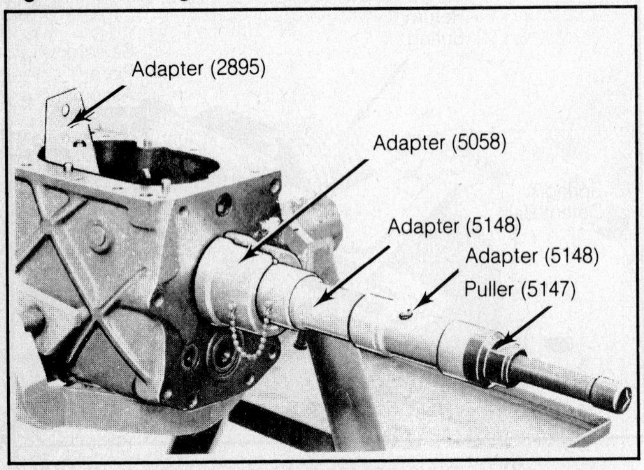

Fig. 3: Removing Mainshaft Bearing

COMPONENT DISASSEMBLY & REASSEMBLY

OVERDRIVE

See appropriate article in IMPORT AXLE SHAFTS, OVERDRIVES & TRANSFER CASES section.

MAINSHAFT

Disassembly

1) Remove 1st gear and synchronizer ring from mainshaft. Remove snap ring retaining 1st-2nd gear synchronizer hub and 2nd gear. Using bench press and Adapter (2853), press off 1st-2nd gear synchronizer hub.

2) Remove snap ring retaining 3rd-4th gear synchronizer hub. Using bench press and Adapter (2853), press off 3rd-4th gear synchronizer hub and 3rd gear. Push hubs out of synchronizer sleeves. Clean and inspect parts for wear or damage, replace if necessary.

Reassembly

1) Assemble 1st-2nd and 3rd-4th synchronizer hubs. Position hub in sleeve so that hub slots align chamfered teeth in sleeve. Insert keys and lock them with springs. With curved lock ring, align springs to let free ends press against synchronizer ring. *See Fig. 4*.

2) Using Drift (2867) and Handle (1801), install clutch housing seal. Install rubber ring in gearshift rod joint. Install gearshift rod bushings, use grease to retain right ring. Use Drift (5065) to install selector rail seal.

3) Using bench press and Adapter (2852), press 3rd gear, synchronizer ring, and 3rd-4th synchronizer hubs onto mainshaft. Install lock ring. Using same adapter, press 2nd gear, synchronizer ring, and 1st-2nd synchronizer hub onto mainshaft. Install lock ring. Install 1st gear and synchronizer ring.

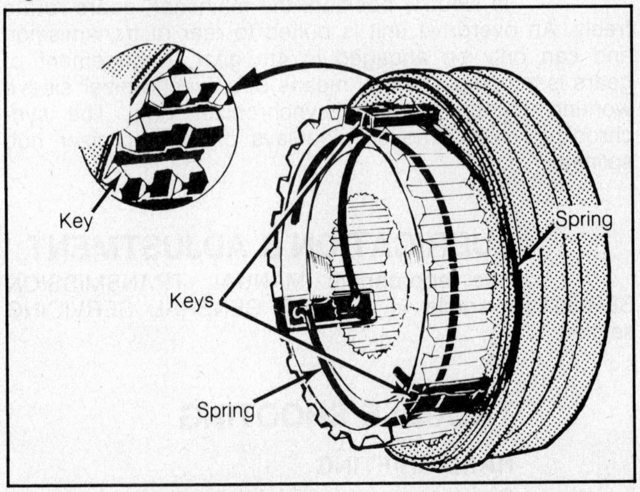

Fig. 4: Synchronizer Hub Assembly

INPUT SHAFT

Disassembly

Remove snap ring from input shaft and spacer ring on input shaft bearing. Using bench press and Adapter (2853), press off input shaft bearing.

Reassembly

Using bench press and Drift (2412), install input shaft bearing. Install inout shaft snap ring. DO NOT install spacer ring on bearing at this time, spacer ring will be installed during transmission reassembly.

TRANSMISSION REASSEMBLY

1) Using bench press and Drift (2986), install intermediate shaft bearings. Intermediate shaft small end bearing is different for Diesel engine applications. Place intermediate shaft in transmission case and use Drift (5180) to install bearing front bearing race.

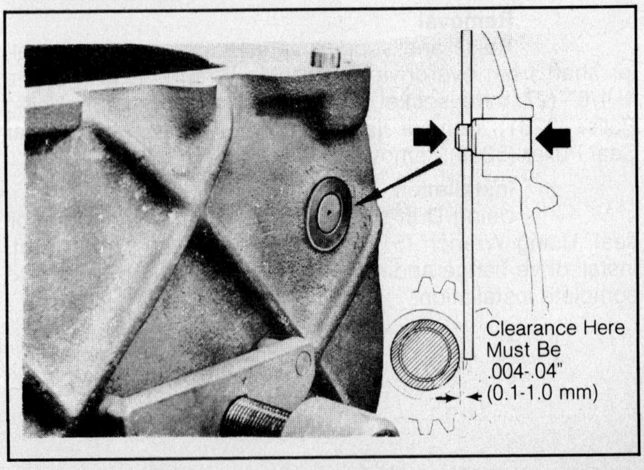

Fig. 5: Adjusting Clearance Between Reverse Gear and Shift Fork

VOLVO 4-SPEED – MODEL M46 (Cont.)

NOTE: Use steps 2) through 5) to determine intermediate shaft shim thickness for transmission with aluminum housing.

2) On aluminum housing transmissions, install clutch housing with gasket and tighten bolts. Turn transmission so clutch housing is down. Use Drift (5180) to tap rear race until intermediate shaft free play is eliminated and shaft turns in a slightly sluggish manner.

3) Using depth gauge, measure distance between intermediate shaft bearing outer race and housing surface. Add .010" (.25 mm), plus bearing preload of .001-.003" (.03-.08 mm) to measurement. Total measurement is required shim size.

4) Select shim within this range and set aside for reassembly. Intermediate shaft shims are available in .002" (.05 mm), .004" (.10 mm), .006" (.15 mm), .014" (.35 mm), .020" (.50 mm), .027" (.70 mm) and .039" (1.0 mm) thicknesses.

5) Remove clutch housing and gasket. Remove intermediate shaft bearings and intermediate shaft. See TRANSMISSION DISASSEMBLY.

6) On all transmissions, install reverse gear shifter and lock ring. Install reverse gear and shaft. Shaft end should be at least .002" (.05 mm) below housing surface.

7) Adjust clearance between reverse gear and shift fork to .004-.040" (.10-1.0 mm). Tap shift fork pivot pin in or out with a punch to adjust clearance. *See Fig. 5*.

8) Place intermediate shaft in bottom of housing, then position mainshaft in housing. With positioning ring fitted to bearing, fit thrust washer and bearing on mainshaft.

9) Ensure that gears do not interfere with each other and use Press (2831) to press mainshaft bearing into position. *See Fig. 6*. If bearing does not align correctly, use a spacer between press spindle and front of housing. Press bearing in until positioning ring is flush with housing.

10) Install lock ring on mainshaft bearing. Insert key in mainshaft keyway. Install oil pump eccentric cam and lock ring. Grease and install input shaft roller bearings.

11) Install 4th gear synchronizer ring in synchronizer hub. Push input shaft onto mainshaft, while lifting intermediate shaft so that bearings are correctly positioned in housing.

Fig. 6: Installing Mainshaft Bearing

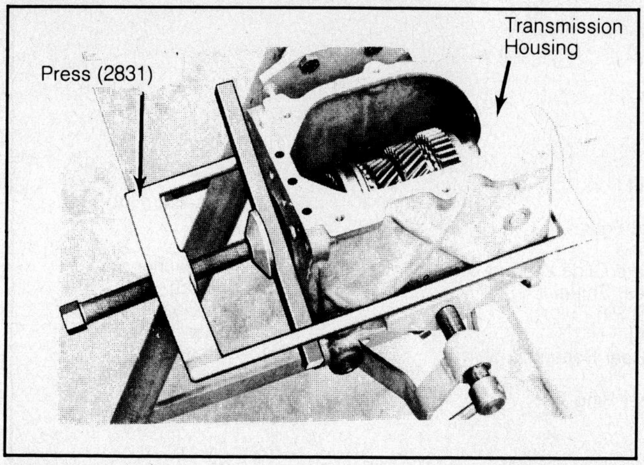

12) Pull out input shaft slightly, and install spacer ring on bearing. Push shaft in until ring is against housing. Install outer bearing races for intermediate shaft bearings. Use Drift (5180) to install bearing races on aluminum housing.

13) Using depth gauge, measure distance between input shaft bearing and front transmision housing surface. Measure distance from clutch housing surface to bottom of bearing seat. *See Fig. 8*.

14) Add .010" (.25 mm) to clutch housing measurement. Subtract input shaft bearing measurement and .0004-.008" (.01-.20 mm) axial clearance from clutch housing measurement. Total measurement is required shim size.

15) Select shim within this range and set aside for reassembly. Input shaft shims are available in .024" (.60 mm), .029" (.75 mm), .035" (.90 mm) and .039" (1.0 mm) thicknesses.

Fig. 7: Measuring Clutch Housing Surface to Bearing Seat

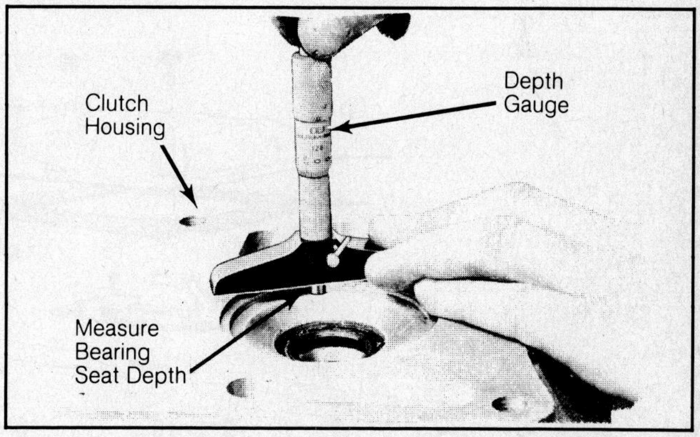

16) Install clutch housing, gasket, and input shaft shim. On aluminum housing transmission, install clutch fork and spacer. On all transmissions, install throw-out bearing.

17) On aluminum housing transmission, turn transmission so clutch housing is down. Using Drift (5180) and hammer, tap intermediate bearing race in until clearance is gone and slight drag is felt on shaft when rotated.

NOTE: Use steps 18) and 19) to determine intermediate shaft shim thickness for transmission with cast iron housing.

18) On cast iron housing transmission, turn transmission so clutch housing is down. Using depth gauge, measure distance between intermediate shaft bearing outer race and rear housing surface. Add gasket thickness of .010" (.25 mm), then subtract axial clearance of .001-.004" (.025-.10 mm) from measurement. Total measurement is required shim size.

19) Select shim within this range and set aside for reassembly. Intermediate shaft shims are available in .002" (.05 mm), .004" (.10 mm), .006" (.15 mm), .014" (.35 mm), .020" (.50 mm), .027" (.70 mm) and .039" (1.0 mm) thicknesses.

20) On all transmissions, measure distance between mainshaft bearing and rear housing surface. Measure distance from rear cover surface to bottom of rear bearing seat. *See Fig. 9*.

VOLVO 4-SPEED – MODEL M46 (Cont.)

Fig. 8: Exploded View of M46 4-Speed Transmission Assembly

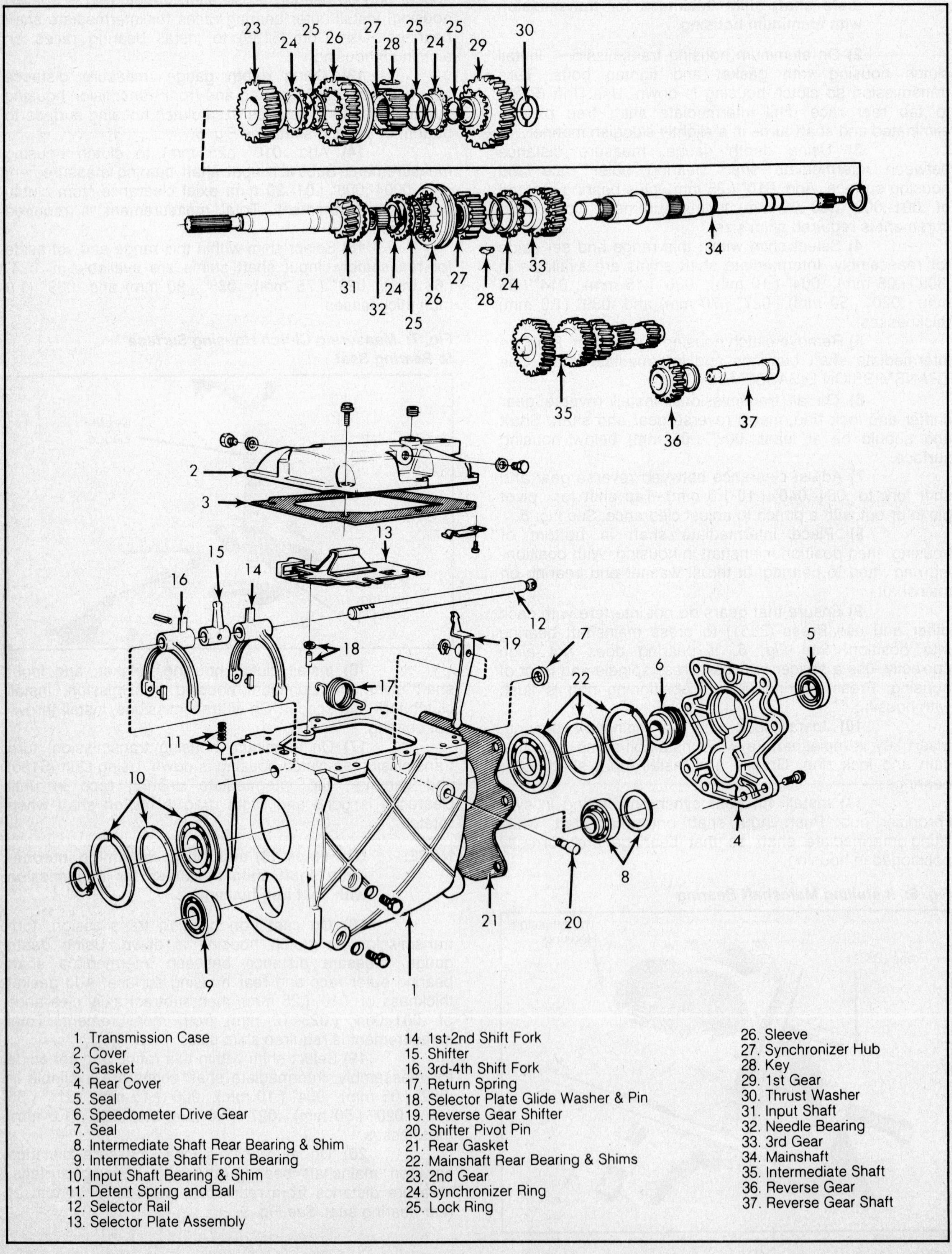

1. Transmission Case
2. Cover
3. Gasket
4. Rear Cover
5. Seal
6. Speedometer Drive Gear
7. Seal
8. Intermediate Shaft Rear Bearing & Shim
9. Intermediate Shaft Front Bearing
10. Input Shaft Bearing & Shim
11. Detent Spring and Ball
12. Selector Rail
13. Selector Plate Assembly
14. 1st-2nd Shift Fork
15. Shifter
16. 3rd-4th Shift Fork
17. Return Spring
18. Selector Plate Glide Washer & Pin
19. Reverse Gear Shifter
20. Shifter Pivot Pin
21. Rear Gasket
22. Mainshaft Rear Bearing & Shims
23. 2nd Gear
24. Synchronizer Ring
25. Lock Ring
26. Sleeve
27. Synchronizer Hub
28. Key
29. 1st Gear
30. Thrust Washer
31. Input Shaft
32. Needle Bearing
33. 3rd Gear
34. Mainshaft
35. Intermediate Shaft
36. Reverse Gear
37. Reverse Gear Shaft

VOLVO 4-SPEED – MODEL M46 (Cont.)

21) Add .010" (.25 mm) to rear cover measurement. Subtract mainshaft bearing measurement and .0004-.008" (.01-.20 mm) axial clearance from rear cover measurement. Total measurement is required shim size.

Fig. 9: Measuring Rear Cover Surface to Bearing Seat

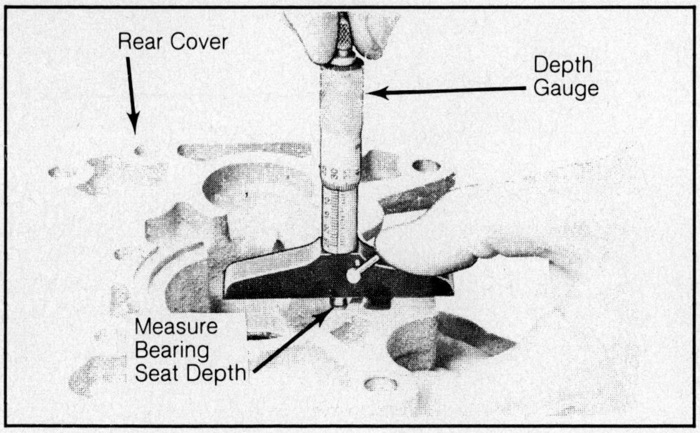

22) Select shim within this range and set aside for reassembly. Shims are available in .024" (.60 mm), .029" (.75 mm), .035" (.90 mm) and .039" (1.0 mm) thicknesses.

23) Install shift forks and gear selector rail with shift boss forward. Position gasket and shim for intermediate shaft on transmission housing. Use grease to keep mainshaft shim in place and install intermediate housing. Install 2 outer (lower) bolts finger tight. Install gearshift rod and sleeve on joint.

Fig. 10: Installing Shift Forks & Shifter

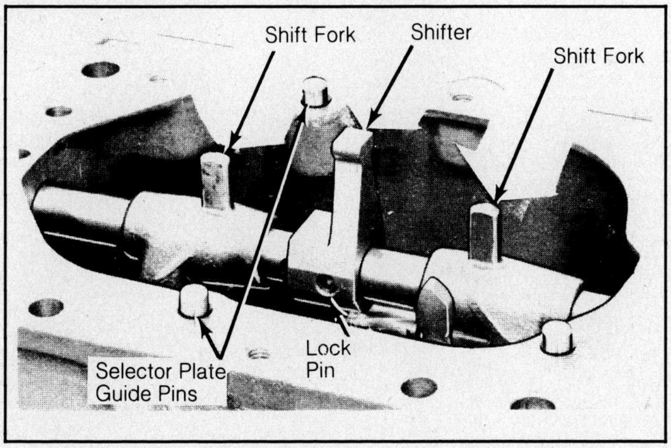

24) Install gearshift rod and carrier. Install bolt, washer, spacer, washer. Tighten rear cover bolts. Install 2 inner (lower) intermediate housing bolts. Tighten intermediate housing bolts (2 inner and 2 outer).

25) Install overdrive. Install lock pin for shifter and glide washers for selector plate assembly. Install selector plate assembly and return spring. Install gearshift lever without lock screw and lock ring. Hold selector plate down with palm of hand and check gearshift operation. Correct as necessary, then remove gearshift lever.

26) Install detent ball and spring. Install top cover with new gasket. Install overdrive switch, back-up light switch and wires at overdrive solenoid. Lower transmission rear and fill with transmission fluid. Install fill plug.

Fig. 11: Checking Gearshift Operation

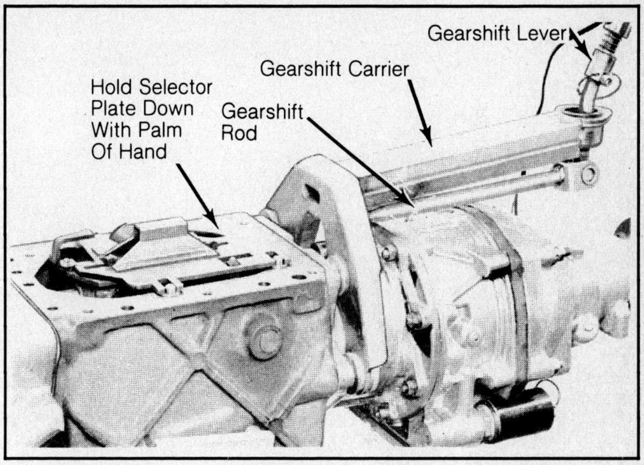

TIGHTENING SPECIFICATIONS

Application	Ft. Lbs. (N.m)
Clutch Housing-to-Transmission	25-35 (34-48)
Rear Cover Attaching Bolts	25-35 (34-48)
Drive Flange Nut	65-80 (88-109)
Intermediate Housing	25-35 (34-48)
Shift Cover Bolts	11-18 (15-24)

SECTION 8

IMPORT AXLE SHAFTS OVERDRIVES & TRANSFER CASES

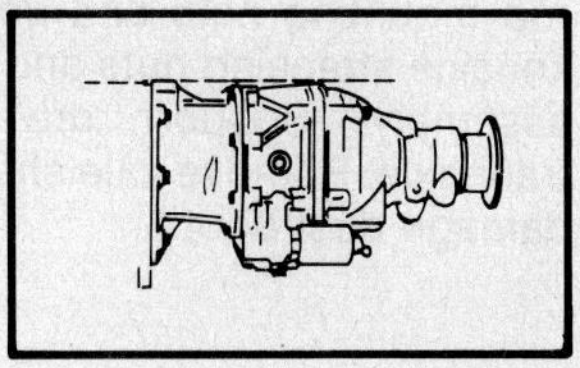

NOTE: ALSO SEE GENERAL INDEX.

Axle Shafts

ALL MODELS

Audi, Chrysler Corp. Imports, FoMoCo Imports, GM Imports, Honda, Isuzu, Mazda, Mitsubishi, Nissan, Renault, Saab, Subaru, Toyota, Volkswagen, Porsche (At end of article.)

DESCRIPTION

Axle shafts transfer power from transaxle to driving wheels. All axle shafts consist of a shaft and flexible Constant Velocity (CV) joints at each end. Inner CV joint is splined or bolted to transaxle. Outer CV joint is splined to wheel bearing hub and secured by a nut.

There are 3 design types of CV joints. The Double Offset Joint (DOJ), Birfield Joint (BJ) or Tripot-Rzeppa Joint (TJ) design type. DOJ joint consists of equally spaced balls between an inner and outer race. TJ joint consists of a triangle yoke within a housing.

On Audi, Ford Motor Co. Imports, Toyota Camry and Corolla, and Volkswagen models, inner CV joint is bolted to differential case drive flanges. On Renault and Subaru models, inner CV joint is splined onto differential output shafts and secured with a pin. On Saab models, inner CV joint housing is pressed into differential side gear and secured with a snap ring. On all other models, inner CV joint is splined into differential side gear and held with a spring clip.

TROUBLE SHOOTING

TROUBLE SHOOTING CHART

Condition	Possible Cause
Grease Leaks	CV boot torn or cracked
Clicking Noise on Cornering	Damaged outer CV
Clunk Noise on Acceleration	Damaged inner CV
Vibration or Shudder on Acceleration	Sticking, damaged or worn CV Misalignment or spring height

REMOVAL & INSTALLATION

AXLE SHAFTS

CAUTION: Vehicle weight must not be allowed to rest on wheel bearings and hub, without axle shaft installed and axle shaft nut tightened to specification.

Removal (Audi & Volkswagen)

1) Remove hub cap. Loosen axle shaft nut. Raise and support vehicle. Remove axle nut and wheel. Disconnect and remove exhaust pipe from exhaust manifold and transaxle as required. Remove Allen bolts connecting inner CV joint to differential case drive flange.

2) On 5000S models with automatic transaxle, remove sway bar brackets. On all other models, mark position of both ball joint flanges on control arms. Remove ball joint from control arm and pull pivot mounting outward while removing axle shaft. Press axle shaft out of hub and guide past transaxle.

NOTE: Axle shafts should be disassembled ONLY to replace defective rubber boots. If boots are replaced, check all components for wear or damage and replace as complete assembly.

Removal (Chevrolet Spectrum & Isuzu I-Mark)

1) Raise and support vehicle. Remove tire and wheel. Remove cotter pin and drive axle nut. Drain transaxle fluid. Pry inner CV joint from transaxle using a large screwdriver to detach snap ring.

2) Remove brake hose retaining clip at strut. Disconnect flex hose from caliper. Remove and support caliper aside. Remove brake rotor. Remove splash shield from vehicle. Disconnect tie rod end.

3) Remove 2 ball joint-to-control arm and strut rod mounting nuts and bolts. Remove 2 strut-to-steering knuckle attaching nuts and bolts. Remove hub and knuckle assembly. Support drive axle. Remove shaft from transaxle. Remove axle shaft from vehicle. Be careful not to damage dust boots.

Fig. 1: Exploded View of Typical Audi & Volkswagen Axle Shaft Assembly

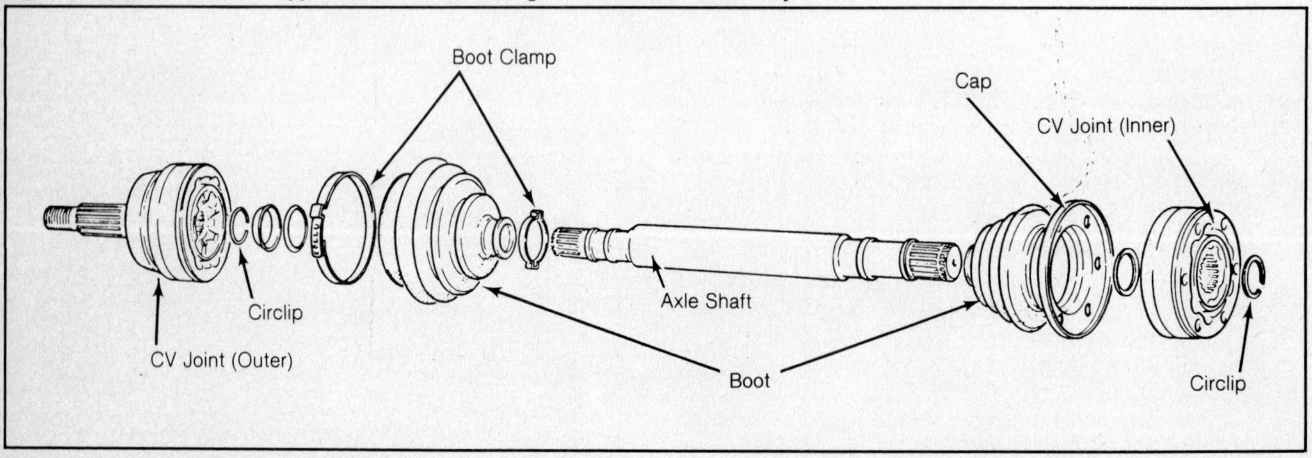

ALL MODELS (Cont.)

Removal (Chevrolet Sprint)

1) Raise and support vehicle. Remove front wheels. Remove cotter pin and axle shaft nut. Drain transaxle oil. Disconnect lower ball joint from steering knuckle by pulling down on stabilizer bar and lower control arm. Remove stabilizer bar.

2) Pry axle shaft from transaxle case using a large screwdriver. Remove axle shaft from hub. Remove drive axle, being careful not to damage CV joint boots.

Removal (Chrysler Corp. Imports & Mitsubishi)

1) Remove front wheel dust cap and loosen lock nut. Raise vehicle and remove front wheels and undercover panel. Remove lower ball joint and strut from lower control arm. Drain transaxle fluid.

2) Remove spring strut-to-support and support-to-spindle bolts. Separate lower ball joint.

3) On all models, insert pry bar between transaxle case and BJ or TJ type CV joint. Apply pressure on pry bar and force axle shaft from transaxle.

NOTE: Replace side retainer ring each time the axle shaft is removed from transaxle case.

Fig. 2: Removing Axle Shaft/BJ & TJ Type CV Joints

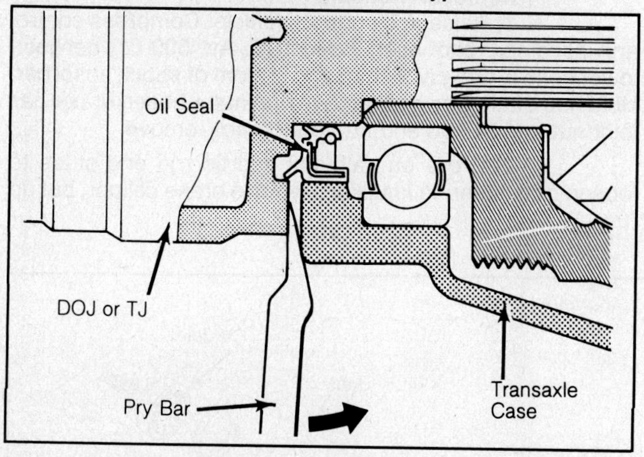

4) On Chrysler Corp. Imports, force axle shaft out of hub with Axle Puller (CT-1003). When axle shaft is forced out, do not let spacer fall out of hub (inner side).

Removal (Ford Motor Co. Imports)

1) Place transaxle in Neutral. Release parking brake. Raise and support vehicle with rear wheels hanging free. Remove 6 bolts attaching drive axle to stub axle shaft. Rotate drive axle as necessary to access bolts.

2) Support outer end of drive axle to prevent damage to outer CV joint. Remove bolts attaching drive axle to drive axle flange. Remove drive axle from vehicle.

NOTE: Drive axles are different lengths and MUST BE installed on correct side of vehicle. Longer drive axle is installed on right side of vehicle.

Removal (Honda)

1) Raise and support vehicle. Remove front wheels and tires. Drain transaxle oil. Spread locking tab on spindle nut. Remove nut using 32 mm socket. Support lower control arm with a floor jack.

2) On Prelude models, remove damper fork-to-strut and damper fork-to-lower control arm attaching bolts. On all models, remove ball joint bolt. Separate ball joint from knuckle. Disconnect tie rod ends from steering knuckles.

3) Remove stabilizer bar bolts. Slowly lower floor jack to allow lower control arm to lower. Use a plastic hammer to tap lower control arm free from knuckle.

4) Pull front hub outward, clear of drive axle. Pry inboard CV joint out approximately .5" (12 mm) to force spring clip past groove in differential side gear splines. Remove drive axle from transaxle.

NOTE: DO NOT pull on inner CV joint. CV joint may come apart.

Removal (Isuzu P'UP & Trooper II)

1) Raise and support vehicle. Remove tire and wheel. Remove brake caliper and support. Remove hub and rotor assembly. Remove backing plate, steering knuckle and steering knuckle arm.

2) Remove inner CV joint boot band. Remove boot and circlip. Remove inner CV joint from housing. Remove drive axle.

Removal (Mazda)

1) On GLC models, raise and support vehicle. Drain transaxle fluid. Remove wheels and axle hub cap. Apply brakes. Loosen axle shaft lock nut. Remove sway bar and supports as required. Remove lower ball joint nut and swing lower control arm away from steering knuckle.

Fig. 3: View of Mazda 626 Axle Shafts & Intermediate Shaft

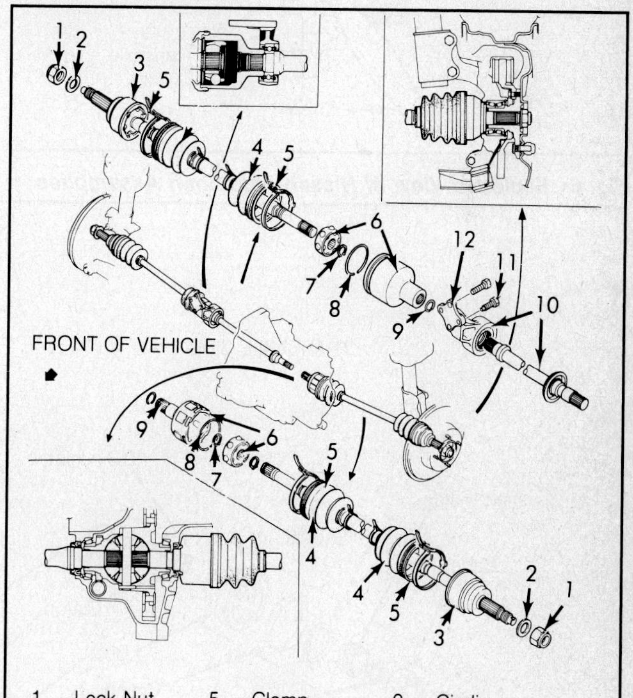

1 - Lock Nut	5 - Clamp	9 - Circlip
2 - Washer	6 - CV Joint	10 - Intermediate Shaft
3 - CV Joint	7 - Snap Ring	11 - Bolt
4 - Boot	8 - Clip	12 - Mounting Bracket

2) Separate axle shaft from the transaxle by pulling out firmly but slowly on steering knuckle. Pull axle shaft out of steering knuckle and lower away from vehicle.

3) On 626 models, raise and support vehicle. Drain transaxle fluid. Remove wheels and axle hub cap. Apply brakes. Loosen axle shaft lock nut. Remove sway bar and supports as required. Remove lower ball joint nut and swing lower control arm away from steering knuckle.

Axle Shafts

ALL MODELS (Cont.)

Fig. 4: Removing Mazda 626 Axle Shaft With Manual Transaxle

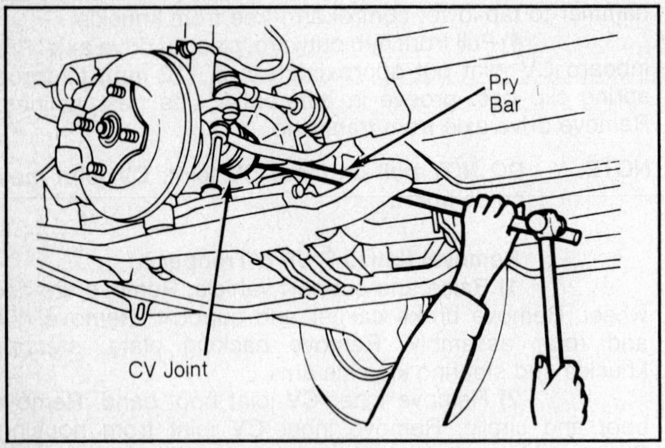

Fig. 5: Removing Mazda 626 Axle Shaft With Automatic Transaxle

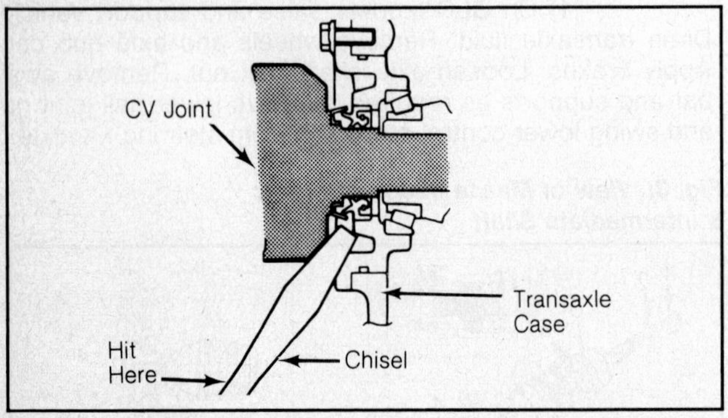

4) On manual transaxle models, insert pry bar between left inner CV joint and transaxle. Hit pry bar to remove shaft. *See Fig. 4*. On automatic transaxle models, insert chisel between left inner CV joint and transaxle. Hit chisel to remove shaft. *See Fig. 5*.

5) Use pry bar on right inner CV joint to uncouple axle shaft from intermediate shaft. Pull axle shaft out of wheel hub. If required, unbolt intermediate shaft mounting bracket and remove from vehicle.

Removal (Nissan)

1) Raise and support vehicle. Remove wheel and tire. Remove brake caliper and pry cotter pin out of hub. Loosen, do not remove, wheel hub nut from drive axle while preventing hub from turning. Remove tie rod end from steering knuckle.

2) Remove lower ball joint and discard nut. Drain gear oil from transaxle case. Pry axle shaft from transaxle and discard axle shaft snap ring. Do not damage oil seal during axle shaft removal. Insert a bar into each side of differential case to prevent dropping of side gear.

3) Remove knuckle attaching bolts and remove hub, knuckle and axle shaft as an assembly. Remove hub nut and pull hub off shaft. Using a ball joint remover, separate lower ball joint from knuckle, if necessary.

Removal (Renault)

1) Raise and support vehicle. Compress control arm assembly and insert Spacer (T. Av. 509-01) between lower control arm pivot shaft and bottom of shock absorber. Hold hub stationary and remove hub nut. Loosen upper ball joint nut and tie rod end nut, but do not remove.

2) Press on ball joint and tie rod end studs to loosen from steering knuckle. Remove brake caliper, but do

Fig. 6: Exploded View of Nissan Axle Shaft Assemblies

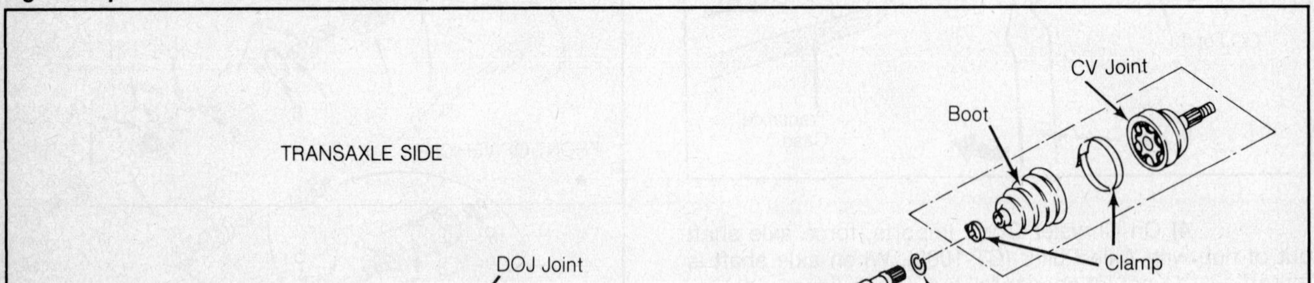

Pulsar NX models are shown. Other models are similar.

Axle Shafts

ALL MODELS (Cont.)

Fig. 7: Cutaway View of Renault Outer CV Joint

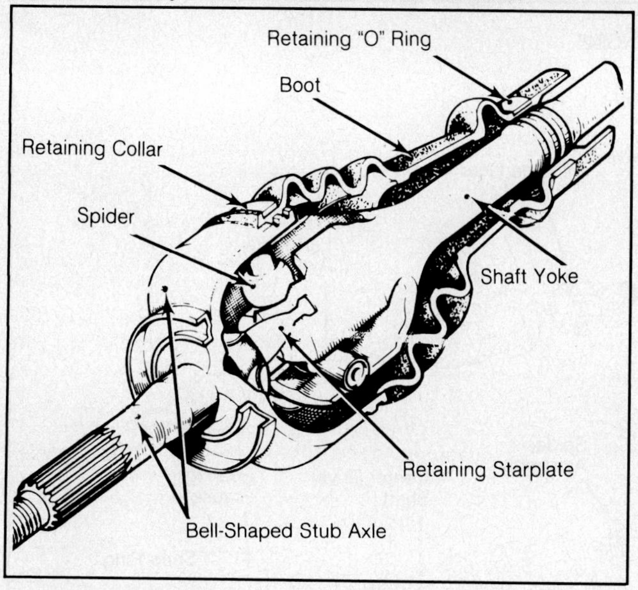

not disconnect hydraulic line. Remove ball joint and tie rod end nuts.

3) Tilt steering knuckle outward to allow removal of axle shaft. Separate axle shaft from hub. Drive roll pin out of inner CV joint and separate axle shaft from transaxle. If components show excessive or abnormal wear, complete axle shaft must be replaced.

Removal (Saab)

NOTE: **Downward movement of Saab control arms is limited by rubber buffer inside of shock absorber. Therefore, it will be necessary either to remove shock absorber before raising vehicle or to support outer end of lower control arm with a jack.**

1) Remove hub cap, loosen hub nut and loosen wheel lugs. Raise and support vehicle. Remove wheels. Rotate brake disc to align recess in disc edge with brake pads. Disconnect parking brake cable. Remove caliper mounting bolts and hang caliper out of way with wire. DO NOT disconnect hydraulic line.

2) Remove hub and disc assembly with Extractor (8996084). Remove larger clamp on inner universal joint bellows. Remove steering arm and upper ball joint with Remover (8995409). Disconnect screws on lower control arm bracket. Separate inner CV joint from axle flange. Cover end of rubber bellows to prevent needle bearings from falling onto floor.

3) Grasp wheel splash guard and pull axle assembly through wheel housing to remove. Thoroughly clean axle assembly. Place steering knuckle housing in a press and press out axle shaft. Remove snap ring from bearing housing. Press out and discard bearing.

NOTE: **Axle shafts cannot be disassembled. If damaged or defective, replace as complete assembly.**

Removal (Subaru)

1) Disconnect negative battery cable. Apply parking brake. Remove front wheel cap and cotter pin, and loosen castle nut and wheel nuts. Raise and support vehicle and remove front tires and wheels. Release parking brake. Remove parking brake cable bracket from transverse link.

2) Drive out spring pin of DOJ. Remove disc brake assembly. Disconnect tie rod end, transverse link and damper strut. Remove axle shaft from differential spindle along with housing. Remove housing from axle shaft by using Puller (926470000).

Removal (Toyota)

1) Raise and support vehicle. Remove wheel assembly. Depress brake pedal and remove axle shaft nut. Remove brake caliper and suspend caliper from frame. DO NOT remove hydraulic line. Remove brake rotor.

2) On Camry models, remove transaxle case protector, if equipped. Remove 6 bolts holding axle shaft-to-differential side gear flange. Separate steering knuckle from lower control arm.

3) Remove drive axle using Puller (SST09950-20015). Drain transaxle fluid. Unbolt bearing bracket. Remove snap ring and pull out center drive axle. *See Fig. 8*.

4) On Corolla models, remove 6 bolts holding axle shaft-to-differential side gear flange. Separate steering knuckle from lower control arm. Remove drive axle using Puller (SST09950-20015).

5) On MR2 models, remove transaxle case protector. Remove 6 nuts holding axle shaft-to-differential side gear flange. Drive rear axle shaft from hub assembly using a plastic hammer.

6) On Tercel models, check bearing axial play. Maximum axial bearing play is .002" (.05 mm). Disconnect tie rod end from steering knuckle. Place alignment marks on steering knuckle-to-suspension strut for reassembly reference. Remove 2 upper steering knuckle-to-suspension strut bolts.

7) Separate steering knuckle from strut and lower control arm. Remove hub from axle shaft using Puller (SST09950-20015). Remove stiffener plate (left side only).

8) Tap shaft out from differential with Remover (SST09648-16010) and hammer. Install Stopper (SST09563-16010) in differential case to prevent oil leakage.

NOTE: **Do not damage rubber boots of axle shaft. Always carry and store shaft in level position.**

Installation (Saab)

1) Press bearing into steering knuckle housing, then install snap ring. Mount axle shaft in a press and press on knuckle housing and bearing. Install inner oil seal. Press wheel hub and brake disc onto axle splines and install washer and new lock nut.

NOTE: **Do not tighten lock nut at this time.**

2) Install axle shaft through wheel housing. Mount any needle bearings which may have fallen out of inner CV joint on ends of "T" piece. Attach inner CV joint to axle flange. Install upper ball joint to steering knuckle and reinstall lower control arm bracket. Mount tie rod end to steering arm. Mount brake caliper.

3) Reinstall front wheel and lower vehicle. Tighten hub lock nut. Secure in place by peening into locking groove. Pump brake pedal several times to seat brake pads.

Installation (All Other Models)

1) To install, reverse removal procedure and note the following: Install a new side retainer ring. Check seals at both ends of axle shaft and replace prior to installation if necessary. Lubricate transaxle seal lip with transaxle oil.

Axle Shafts

ALL MODELS (Cont.)

Fig. 8: Exploded View of Camry Axle Shaft Assembly

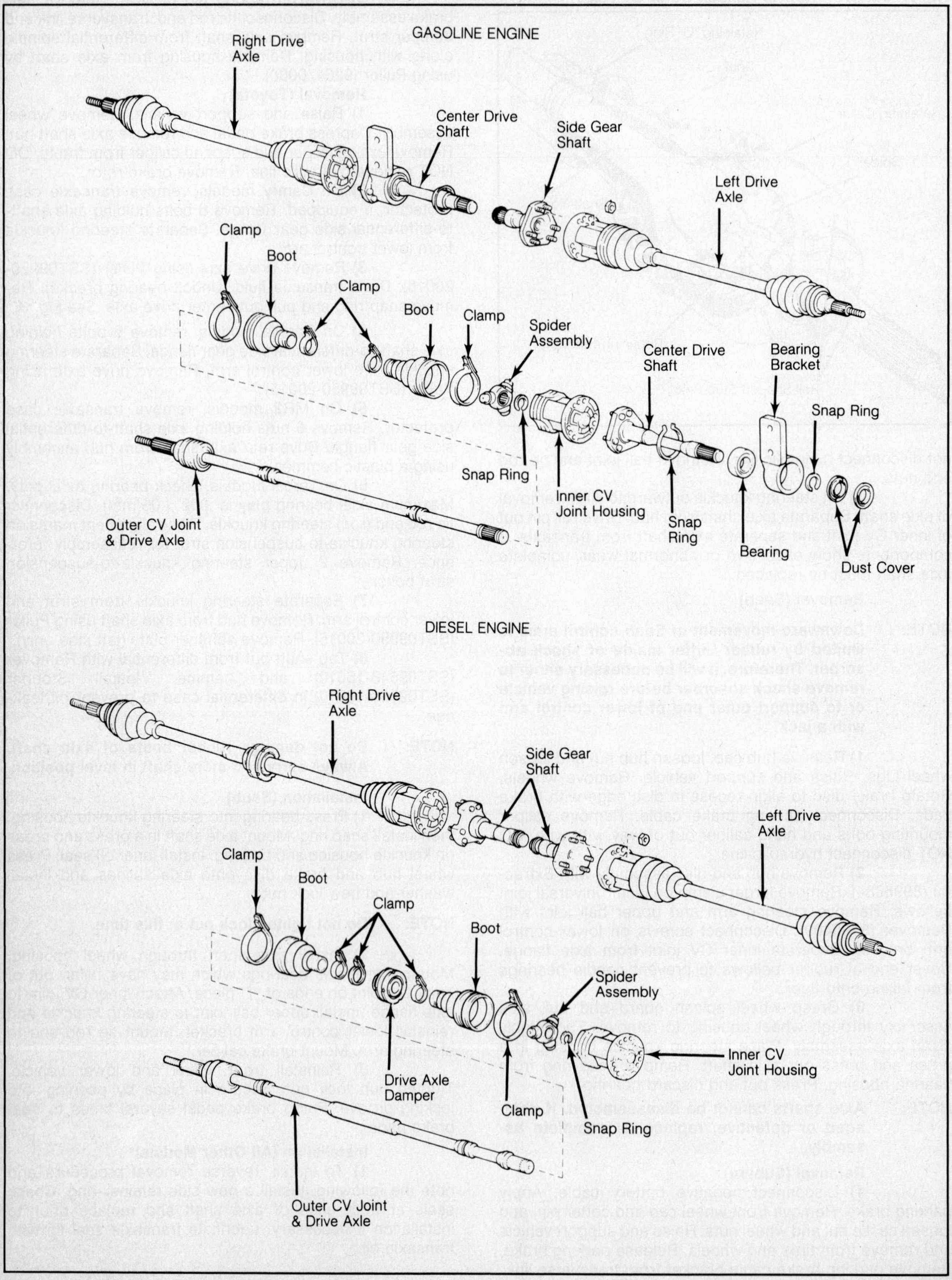

Axle Shafts

ALL MODELS (Cont.)

NOTE: **Always install new cotter pins, washers and suspension nuts.**

2) Install axle shaft into transaxle case. On all models with snap ring retained axle shafts, try to pull axle shaft out of differential by hand to ensure proper engagement of snap ring. On Renault models, apply locking compound to axle shaft roll pins before installing.

3) On Audi Coupe models, apply (D6) locking compound to splines. On all models, install axle shafts into wheel hub. Align suspension marks made at removal and tighten nuts. Check camber setting and adjust if necessary. Stake axle shaft nut in place with a punch or install new cotter pin after tightening.

4) Bleed brake system and replace transaxle fluid, if required. On Tercel models, measure the distance between drive shafts at transaxle. Distance should be less than 7.6" (194 mm).

OVERHAUL

DISASSEMBLY & REASSEMBLY

Disassembly (Audi & Volkswagen)

1) On inner CV joint, remove circlip from axle shaft and drive protective cap from CV joint. Place axle shaft in Holder (VW402) and press CV joint from shaft with Adapter (VW408a), supporting hub to prevent damage. Pivot hub and cage assembly out of inner joint. Push out and remove balls. Align ball hub grooves with cage and remove hub.

NOTE: **Inner CV joint and ball hub are matched sets. DO NOT interchange with outer joint. Also, balls of CV joints cannot be interchanged between CV joints.**

Fig. 9: Removing Audi & Volkswagen Inner CV Joint Ball Hub

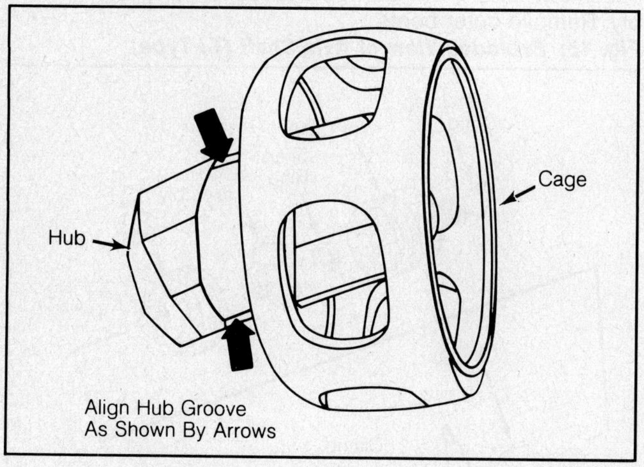

2) Remove and discard inner boot clamp and boot. On outer CV joint, spread circlip inside ball hub and drive CV joint off axle shaft with brass drift by tapping on hub. Mark position of ball hub and outer joint. Tilt cage and remove each ball.

3) Align cage perpendicular to joint. Align 2 large openings of cage with raised portions of joint and remove cage and hub. Position 1 retainer of hub in large opening and remove hub by tilting outward. Remove and discard outer boot and clamp.

Reassembly

1) To reassemble CV joints, reverse disassembly procedure and note the following: Lubricate joints with 3 ozs. of molybdenum disulphide grease. After inserting balls into inner CV joint hub and cage, insert hub and cage into joint perpendicularly.

2) Chamfer of ball hub splines must face larger diameter of joint. Rotate ball and cage into position and ensure CV joint wide ball groove and narrow hub groove are on same side of joint. *See Fig. 10.* Joint is correctly assembled if hub can move over shaft splines by hand.

Fig. 10: Installing Audi & Volkswagen Ball Hub and Cage in Inner CV Joint

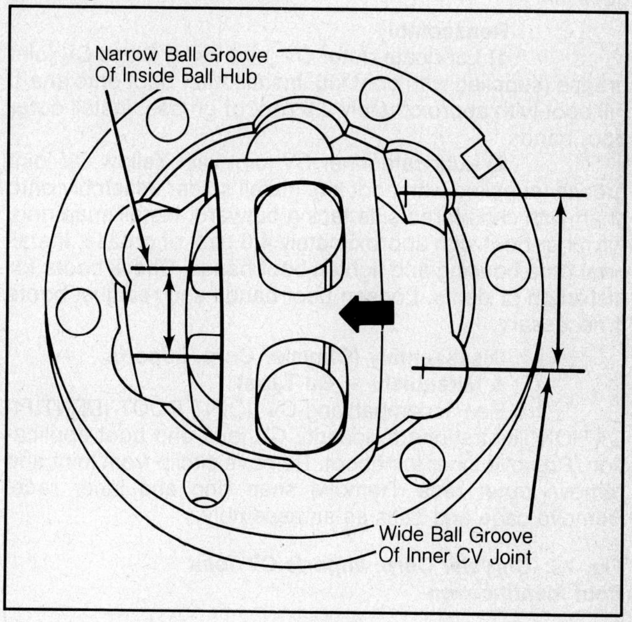

3) Outer CV joint alignment marks must match after reassembly. Replace dust boots and clamps. Install CV joints onto axle shaft with inside ball hub chamfer facing shaft.

4) Outer CV joint must be assembled with dished washer concave side facing thrust washer and convex side of thrust washer facing CV joint. *See Fig. 11.*

5) Inner CV joint must be assembled with dished washer concave side facing CV joint when installed on shaft. Install boot clamps with open end facing opposite direction of normal rotation. Always use new circlips to retain CV joints on shafts.

Fig. 11: Cutaway View of Audi & Volkswagen Outer CV Joint Showing Installation of Dished and Thrust Washers

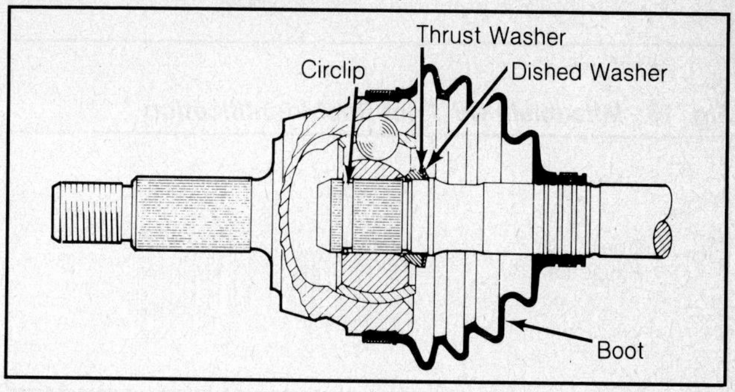

Axle Shafts

ALL MODELS (Cont.)

Disassembly (Chevrolet Sprint)

NOTE: DO NOT disassemble outer CV joint or spider assembly of inner CV joint. If worn or damaged, replace CV joint as an assembly.

1) Remove CV joint boot bands. Remove housing from inner joint. Remove snap ring and spider from shaft. Remove inner and outer CV joint boots. Clean boots and spider assembly with a clean rag. DO NOT clean in solvent.

2) Clean all other parts in solvent. Dry with compressed air. Inspect boots for cracks and tears. Check circlip, snap ring and boot bands for wear. Replace as necessary.

Reassembly

1) Lubricate outer CV joint using Black CV joint grease (supplied with boot kit). Install outer boot onto shaft. Fill boot with approximately 2.8 ozs. of grease. Install outer boot bands.

2) Lubricate inner CV joint with Yellow CV joint grease (supplied with boot kit). Install spider assembly onto shaft with chamfered side facing outward. Install snap ring. Fill inner boot with approximately 4.6 ozs. of grease. Install boot onto housing and tighten boot bands. Check boots for distortion or dents. Loosen boot bands and readjust boots if necessary.

Disassembly (Chrysler Corp. Imports & Mitsubishi – BJ Type)

See accompanying CV JOINT BOOT IDENTIFICATION illustrations to identify CV joint and boot application. Remove inner joint boot. Remove circlip from joint and remove outer race. Remove snap ring and inner race. Remove cage and balls as an assembly.

Fig. 12: Chrysler Corp. Imports CV Joint Boot Identification

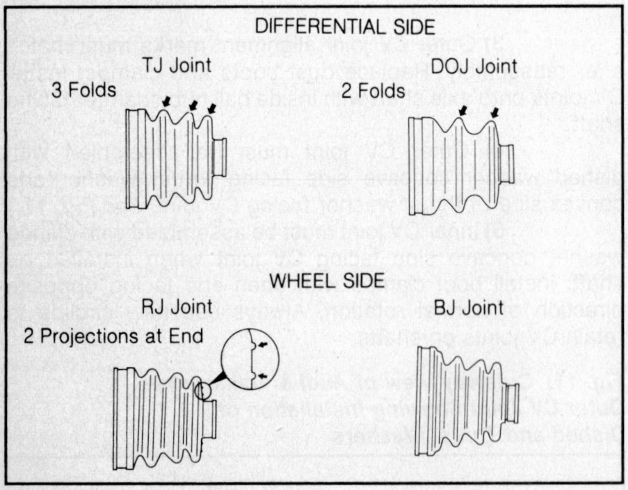

Fig. 13: Mitsubishi CV Joint Boot Identification

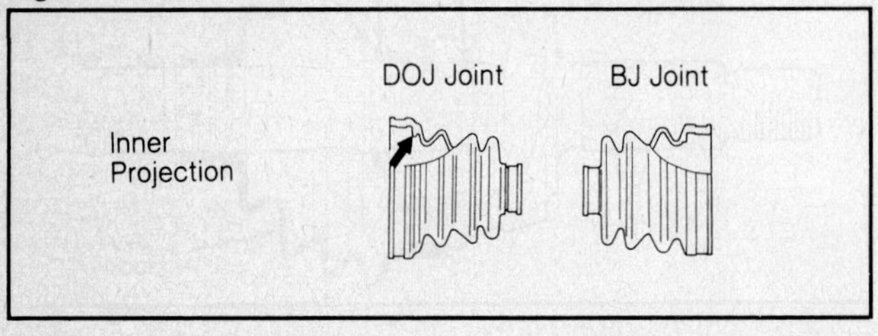

NOTE: Do not disassemble inner bearing assembly as they are matched parts and should not be disturbed.

Fig. 14: Exploded View of Axle Shaft (BJ Type)

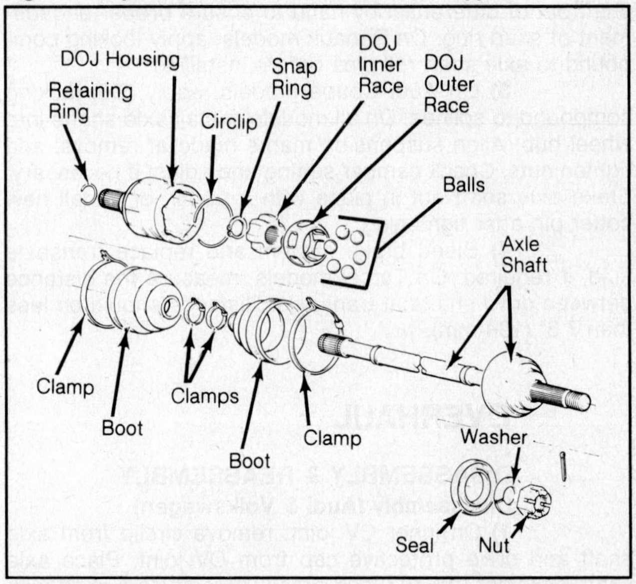

Reassembly

To assemble, reverse disassembly procedure and note the following: Apply grease to inner and outer races. Install CV joint assembly on shaft with chamfered edge of inner race facing outer edge of shaft. Install new boots and place boot clamps 3.5" (90 mm) apart.

Disassembly (Chrysler Corp. Imports & Mitsubishi – TJ Type)

Remove nner joint boots. Pull axle shaft out from inner case. Remove snap ring and take out spider assembly. Clean, but do not disassemble, spider assembly. Remove outer boots.

Fig. 15: Exploded View of Axle Shaft (TJ Type)

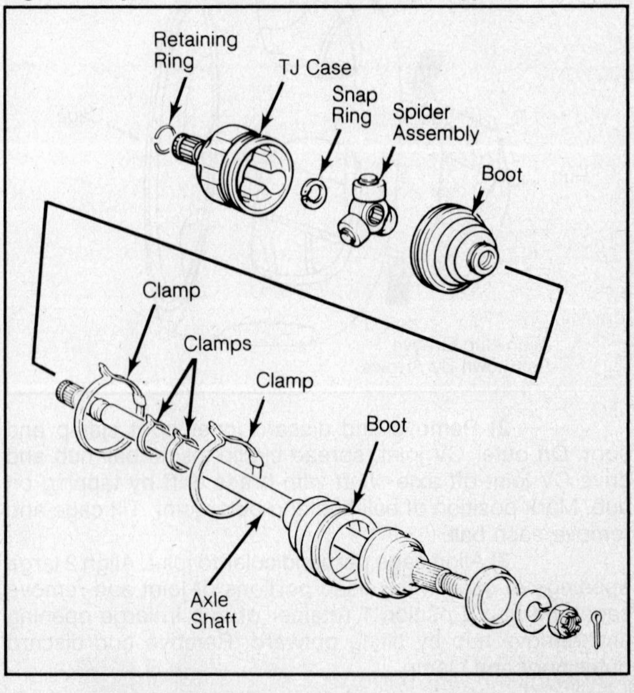

ALL MODELS (Cont.)

Reassembly

To assemble, reverse disassembly procedure. Apply grease to the inner and outer races. Install new boots and place boot clamps 3.0" (75 mm) apart.

CAUTION: Outer CV joint on all models cannot be serviced. If joint is found to be worn or damaged, complete axle shaft assembly must be replaced. Always replace inboard housing spring clip when axle shafts are removed.

Disassembly (Ford Motor Co. Imports)

1) Clamp axle shaft assembly in a vise using protective jaw covers. Remove boot clamps. Slide boot up shaft to access CV joint. Remove snap ring from end of shaft. Remove CV joint from axle shaft using Puller (D81L-1002-A).

2) Clamp CV joint in vise using protective covers. Using a large screwdriver, roll inner race and ball cage out of outer race. Pry balls from cage using a small screwdriver. Clean and inspect CV joints, boots and axle shafts for damage or wear. Replace components as necessary.

Reassembly

1) Assemble inner race, cage and ball bearings. Install assembly in housing with 2 balls entering 2 races. *See Fig. 16*. Pull upward on inner race and rotate assembly into position.

NOTE: Narrow ends of inner races must be aligned with wide ends of housing races before race, cage and ball assembly can enter housing.

2) Pack CV joints with lubricant. Tap CV joint on shaft using a socket and hammer. Install snap ring. Position dust boot and install new boot clamps using Keystone Clamp Pliers (T63P-9171-A).

Fig. 16: Installing Inner Race & Bearing Assembly Into Housing

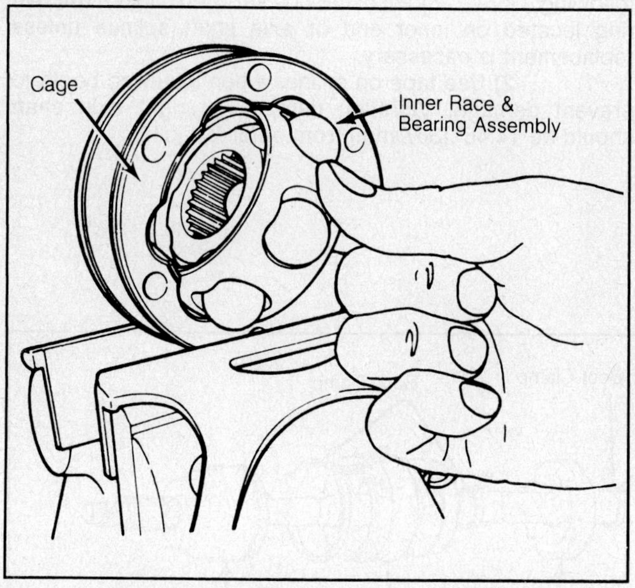

Disassembly (Honda - DOJ Type)

1) Remove boot bands from CV joints. Slide inner boot up drive axle to access inner CV joint. Wipe grease from joint. Remove large retaining ring and separate shaft with ball bearing from housing. Remove and discard spring clip. Remove dust boot from shaft.

2) Remove snap rings and ball bearing assembly from shaft. Remove outer dust boot from shaft. Pry balls from cage using a screwdriver. Remove race from cage. Clean and inspect all components.

Reassembly

To assemble, reverse disassembly procedure. Apply grease to the inner and outer races. Install new boots and boot clamps.

CAUTION: Outer CV joint on all models cannot be serviced. If joint is found to be worn or damaged, complete axle shaft assembly must be replaced. Always replace inboard housing spring clip when axle shafts are removed.

Fig. 17: Exploded View of Honda Civic Axle Shaft Assembly

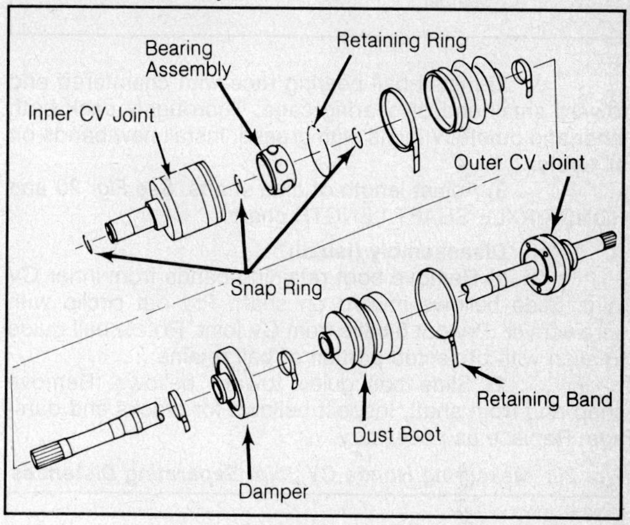

Disassembly (Honda - TJ Type)

Remove inner joint boots. Pull axle shaft out from inner case. Remove snap ring and take out spider assembly. Remove and discard inner CV joint spring clip. Separate joint housing from axle shaft. Clean, but do not disassemble, spider assembly. Remove outer boots.

Fig. 18: Honda Accord & Prelude Axle Shaft Assembly

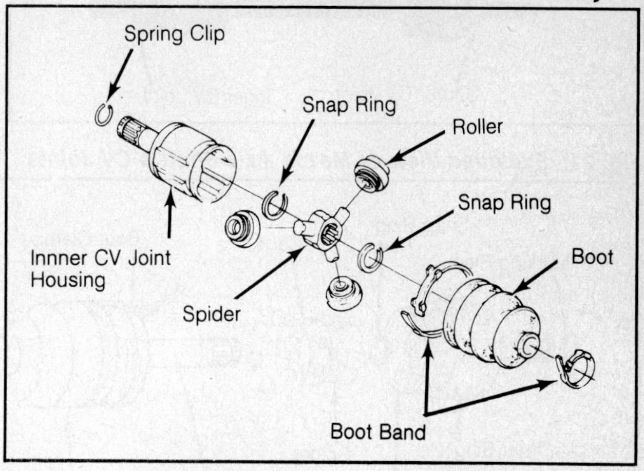

Reassembly

1) To reassemble, reverse disassembly procedure. For Civic models, vibration damper must be installed .08" (2 mm) from start of taper on outer axle shaft end. *See Fig. 19*. Press ball bearings into race until firmly seated.

Axle Shafts

ALL MODELS (Cont.)

Fig. 19: Adjusting Damper Position on Honda Civic Axle Shaft

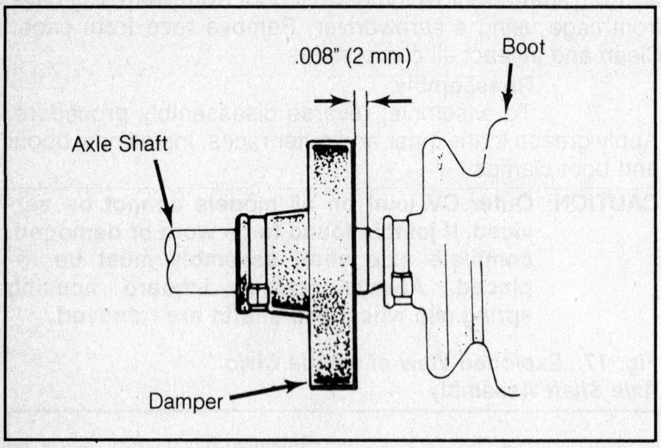

2) Install ball bearing race with chamfered end toward small end of bearing cage. Thoroughly pack both inner and outer CV joints with grease. Install new bands on all boots.

3) Adjust length of axle shafts. *See Fig. 20* and HONDA AXLE SHAFT LENGTH chart.

Disassembly (Isuzu)

1) Remove boot retaining bands from inner CV joint. Slide bellows inward on shaft. Pry out circlip with screwdriver. Pry out 6 balls from CV joint. Rotate ball guide to align with projected portion of ball retainer.

2) Slide ball guide toward bellows. Remove snap ring from shaft. Inspect bellows for cracks and damage. Replace as necessary.

Fig. 20: Measuring Honda CV Joint Separating Distances

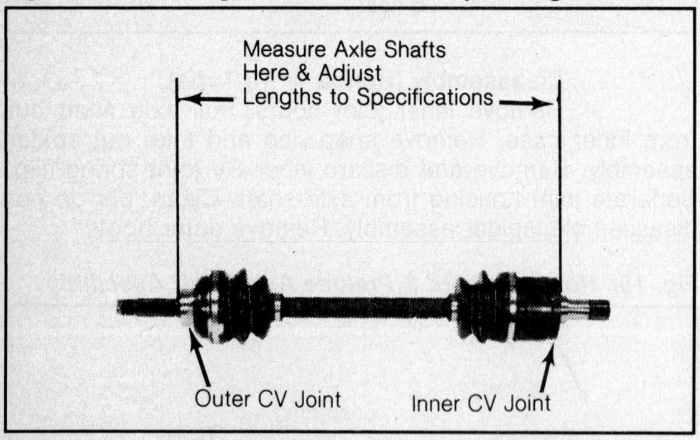

HONDA AXLE SHAFT LENGTH

Application	Length In. (mm)
Accord	
Right Axle Shaft	19.53-19.70 (496.0-500.5)
Left Axle Shaft	
Man. Trans.	30.67-30.85 (779.0-783.5)
Auto. Trans.	30.98-31.16 (787-791.5)
Civic	
Right Axle Shaft	18.54-18.74 (471.0-476.0)
Left Axle Shaft	30.35-30.55 (771.0-776.0)
Prelude	
Right Axle Shaft	20.2-20.4 (514-518.5)
Left Axle Shaft	
Man. Trans.	31.50-31.67 (800.0-804.5)
Auto. Trans.	31.80-32.03 (809.0-813.5)

Reasssembly

1) Reverse disassembly procedure and note the following: Apply a light coat of grease to axle shaft before installing bellows. Fill bellows 1/2 full with grease. Ensure ball retainer is installed with smaller diameter toward the inside.

2) Install circlip so that end gap is positioned away from ball groove. Ensure bellows is not collapsed after installation.

Disassembly (Mazda)

1) Remove boot retaining band from inner CV joint. Remove circlip from outer ring of inner CV joint. Separate housing from race and axle shaft.

2) Remove snap ring retaining race-to-axle shaft. Slide race off shaft and pry balls out of cage with screwdriver. Turn race slightly and remove from inner race.

Reassembly

1) Reverse disassembly procedure and note the following: Outer CV joint cannot be serviced. Do not remove ring located on inner end of axle shaft splines unless replacement is necessary.

2) Use tape on splines when installing boots to prevent damage. Vibration damper on right axle shaft should be 14.45" (367 mm) from outer CV joint.

Fig. 21: Exploded View of Mazda Axle Shaft & CV Joints

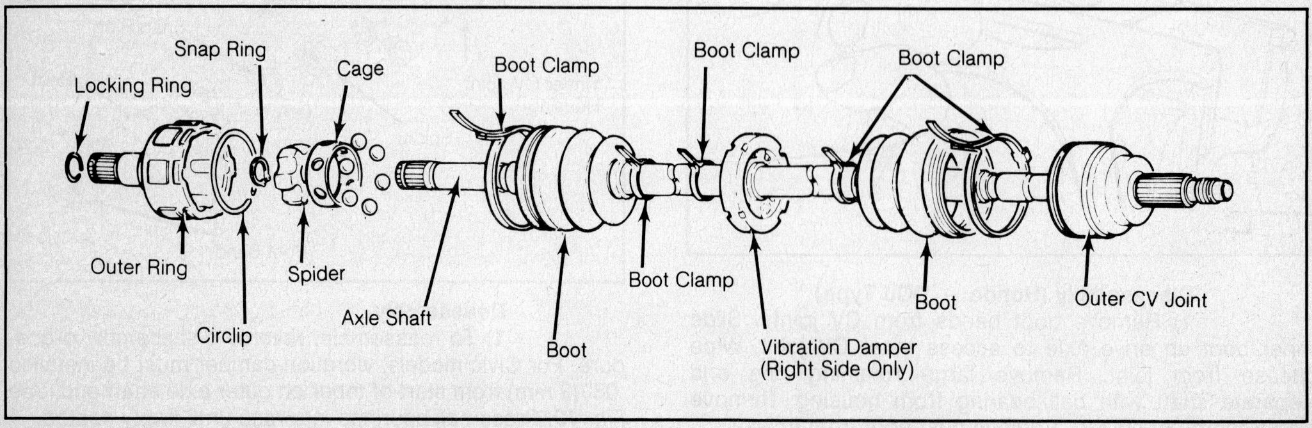

Axle Shafts

ALL MODELS (Cont.)

Disassembly (Nissan - BJ Type)

NOTE: Nissan does not recommend disassembly of inner CV joints. If defective, replace CV joint assemblies as complete components.

1) Mark drive axle and CV joint assembly for reassembly reference. Separate inner CV joint from axle shaft by tapping it lightly with a plastic mallet. DO NOT disassemble inner CV joint. Replace if damaged. Remove dust boot.

2) On outer CV joint, remove and discard boot bands. Mark outer CV joint-to-shaft position for reassembly reference. Remove and discard snap ring. Remove slide joint housing. Remove snap ring.

3) Remove ball cage, inner race and balls as a unit. Remove snap ring and dust boot. Inspect parts for wear or damage. Replace any damaged or defective parts as necessary.

Fig. 22: Exploded View of Nissan Drive Axle (DOJ Type)

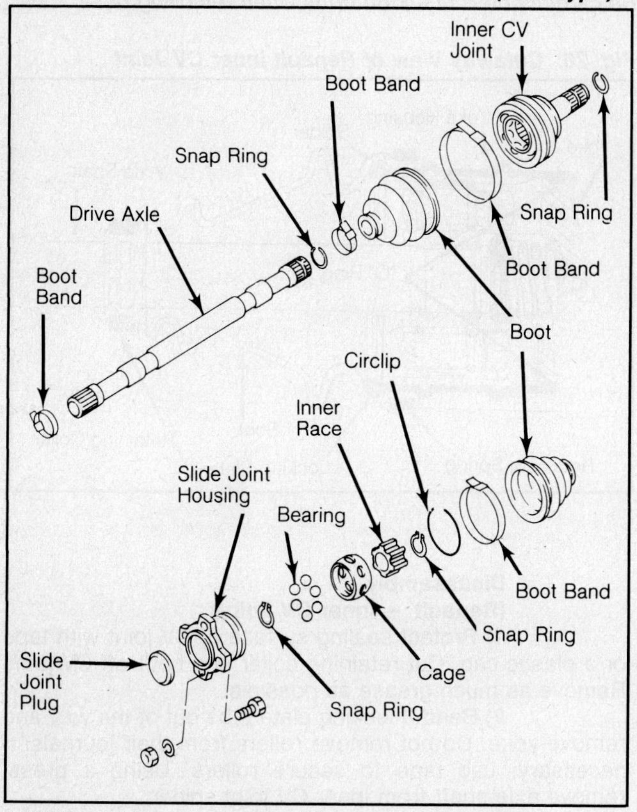

300ZX models are shown. Other models are similar.

Reassembly

1) Install boot and new boot band on drive axle. Ensure boot is not damaged by end of axle. Install CV joint on shaft with new circlip, aligning mating marks. Seat CV joint lightly with a plastic hammer.

2) Pack CV joint with 5 ozs. of grease. Install and tighten new large boot band. Position dust boot on shaft so its length is 3.58" (91 mm). Secure small band in position without deforming or buckling dust boot. Turn axle shaft in vise so inner end faces up.

3) On outer CV joints, pack joint with 5 ozs. of grease. Install boot and secure as for inner CV joint. Position boot on shaft so its length is 3.70" (94 mm).

Disassembly (Nissan - TJ Type)

1) Place axle shaft in soft-jawed vise with inner CV joint facing up. Remove and discard boot bands from inner boot. Remove inner CV joint housing and stub axle from axle shaft.

2) Cut off boot assembly using a hacksaw. When cutting, ensure drive axle is pushed into sub-assembly to prevent spider assembly from being scratched. Mark spider assembly-to-shaft position for reassembly reference. *See Fig. 23.*

Fig. 23: Removing Nissan Inner CV Joint (TJ Type)

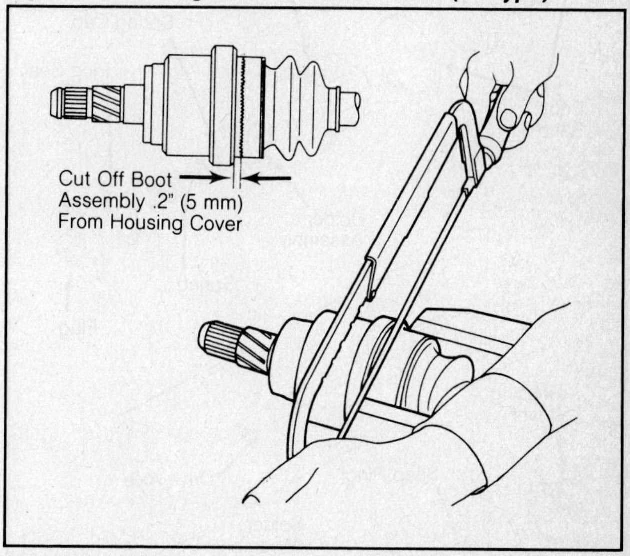

300ZX models are shown. Other models are similar.

3) Remove and discard snap ring and press off spider assembly without dropping axle shaft. Using a saw blade, cut off remaining part of boot housing and remove housing ring. Be careful not to scratch housing sub-assembly and housing ring.

4) On wheel side, remove plug and boot bands. Remove spider assembly as outlined in steps **2)** and **3)**. Inspect drive axles and CV joints for wear and damage. Replace as necessary.

Reassembly

1) Mount axle shaft in soft-jawed vise with outer end facing out. Position dust boot and new small boot band on shaft without tearing boot on shaft splines. Slide outer CV joint spider assembly onto shaft, aligning marks made during disassembly. Seat joint by lightly tapping with plastic mallet.

2) Stake drive axle to retain spider assembly in position. Pack joint assembly with 6.5 ozs. of grease. Install new large boot band. Using a punch, lock band in position. Cut off excess band, leaving amount equal to band width. Bend excess back over itself.

3) Position dust boot on shaft so its length is 4.40" (111.5 mm). On inner CV joint, coat new "O" ring with grease and install on CV joint housing. Install new cover on housing and bend outer edge at 2 points (180° apart) using block of wood to prevent damage. Housing cover should not rattle. Apply sealant at outer edge of housing and cover.

4) Position boot and new small band on axle shaft. Slide spider assembly onto shaft, aligning marks made during disassembly. Press spider assembly into position with splined chamfer facing axle shaft. Retain in position with new snap ring (round surface facing spider assembly).

Axle Shafts

ALL MODELS (Cont.)

5) Pack CV joint assembly with 5.5 ozs. of grease. Install new large boot band and secure in same manner as for inner CV joint. Position dust boot on shaft so its length is 3.64" (92.5 mm). Secure small band in position without deforming or buckling dust boot.

Fig. 24: Exploded View of Nissan Drive Axle (TJ Type)

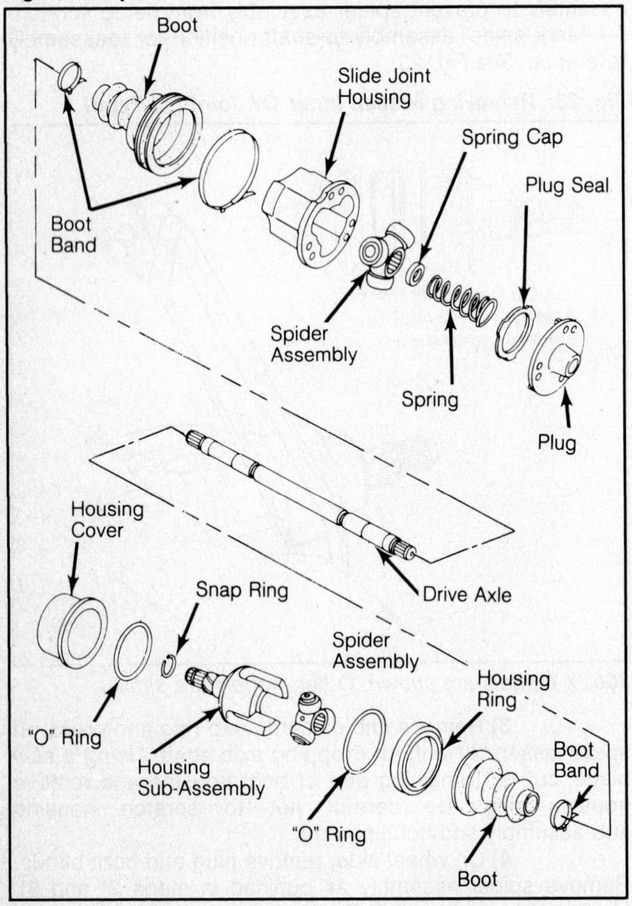

Disassembly
(Renault - Outer CV Joint)

Remove boot retaining collar from CV joint. Remove as much grease as possible from joint. Remove bell-shaped stub axle from axle shaft by lifting arms of retaining starplate one at a time. Do not twist arms off of starplate. Separate stub axle from axle shaft and remove boot if necessary.

Reassembly

1) Install Seal Expander (T. Av. 537-02) over outer end of axle shaft. Place axle shaft in soft-jawed vise. Using motor oil, lubricate entire surface of seal expander and inside of boot. Slide boot onto end of seal expander and smooth out first fold of boot.

2) Move boot as close as possible toward axle shaft, then let it slide back on installer. Repeat 4 to 5 times to stretch boot, adding oil as necessary. When boot becomes easier to slide back and forth, slide it all the way into position on axle shaft. Remove seal expander.

3) Install spring and thrust ball joint into spider. Position roller cages in center of joint. Align retaining starplate so that each arm is between 2 roller cages. Reinstall axle shaft into bell-shaped stub axle. Fill boot and spider with about 5.3 ozs. of grease. Secure boot with retaining rings.

Fig. 25: Separating Retaining Starplate From Outer End of Renault Axle Shaft

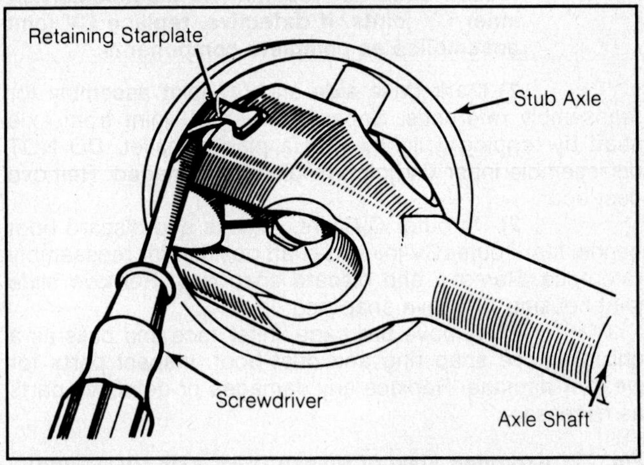

Be careful not to break off arms when removing plate.

Fig. 26: Cutaway View of Renault Inner CV Joint

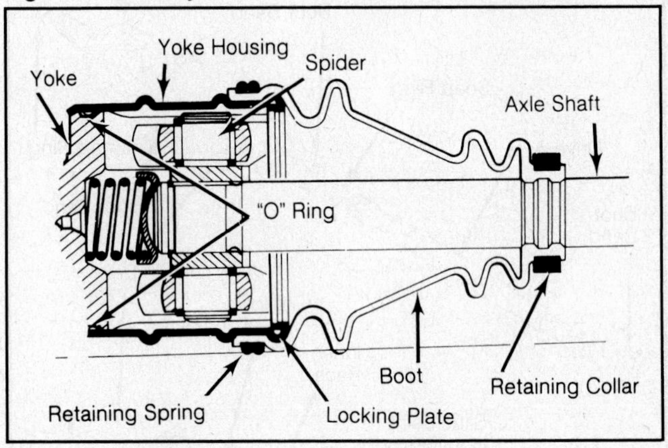

Disassembly
(Renault - Inner CV Joint)

1) Protect sealing surface of CV joint with tape or a plastic cap. Cut retaining collar and boot off CV joint. Remove as much grease as possible.

2) Bend 3 locking plate tabs out of the way and remove yoke. Do not remove rollers from their journals. If necessary, use tape to secure rollers. Using a press, remove axle shaft from inner CV joint spider.

Reassembly

NOTE: Boot, spider or yoke may be replaced. Disassembly procedures are same for all 3 operations. Only reassembly procedure for replacement of yoke is different.

1) If yoke is being replaced, lubricate drive shaft and slide new boot and retaining collar on shaft. Install spider onto axle shaft splines and stake in place at 3 equally spaced locations around shaft.

2) Install new "O" ring onto yoke perforation. Install yoke into metal housing by tapping in until fully seated and hold with a press. Crimp end of housing that faces transaxle. Proceed to step **5)**.

3) If boot or spider is being replaced, lubricate axle shaft and slide on boot with new retaining collar.

Axle Shafts

ALL MODELS (Cont.)

Install spider onto axle shaft splines and stake in place at 3 equally spaced points around shaft. Remove plastic collar or tape and engage spider with yoke.

4) Fabricate a shim from .098" (2.5 mm) flat stock measuring 1.575" (40 mm) long, .236" (6 mm) at each end and having a 1.772" (45 mm) radius across one of the long sides. Insert this shim between locking plate and yoke. Carefully bend back locking plate tabs to their original position. Remove shim.

5) Fill yoke and boot with about 5.25 ozs. of grease. Position lips of boot in grooves of axle shaft and yoke housing. Place retaining collar on axle shaft end of boot. Insert a smooth round-ended rod under yoke end of boot to allow air to escape.

6) Extend or compress joint until distance from back of yoke housing (not splined coupling) to axle shaft end of boot is to specification. See RENAULT AXLE BOOT SPECIFICATIONS chart. Remove rod from boot. Place retaining spring around yoke end of boot being careful not to stretch spring.

RENAULT AXLE BOOT SPECIFICATIONS

Application	Length In. (mm)
Fuego & Sportwagon	
GI 76	6.14 (156)
GI 82	6.34-6.42 (161-163)

Disassembly
(Saab - Outer CV Joint)

Install wheel assembly in a press to remove axle shaft with outer CV joint. Peel the boot back. Wipe grease from inner race. Use circlip pliers to open snap ring and remove axle shaft.

Disassembly
(Saab - Inner CV Joint)

Remove snap ring. Remove TJ joint and boot. The differential side cover must be removed to service inner CV joint housing.

Reassembly (Inner & Outer CV Joints)

Pack CV joints with Lithium-Lead based EP grease. To reassemble, reverse disassembly procedure.

Disassembly (Subaru)

1) Straighten bent claw of larger end of boot on DOJ side. Loosen band by means of screwdriver or pliers, taking care not to damage boot. Remove boot band from small end of DOJ boot in same manner.

2) Remove larger end of boot on DOJ side. Pry and remove round circlip located at neck of outer race on DOJ side with a screwdriver. Remove outer race on DOJ side from shaft assembly.

3) Wipe off grease and remove balls. Move cage to boot side. Remove snap ring with snap ring pliers. Remove inner race of DOJ. Remove cage of DOJ from shaft and remove boot from DOJ. Pull out boot on CV joint side.

Inspection

Examine CV joint for corrosion, damage or wear. Ensure axle shaft does not have excessive deflection, twist or wear. Replace components as necessary.

Reassembly

To reassemble, reverse disassembly procedure. Grease CV joint and DOJ with Molylex No. 2 grease.

Fig. 27: Sectional View of Saab Steering Knuckle

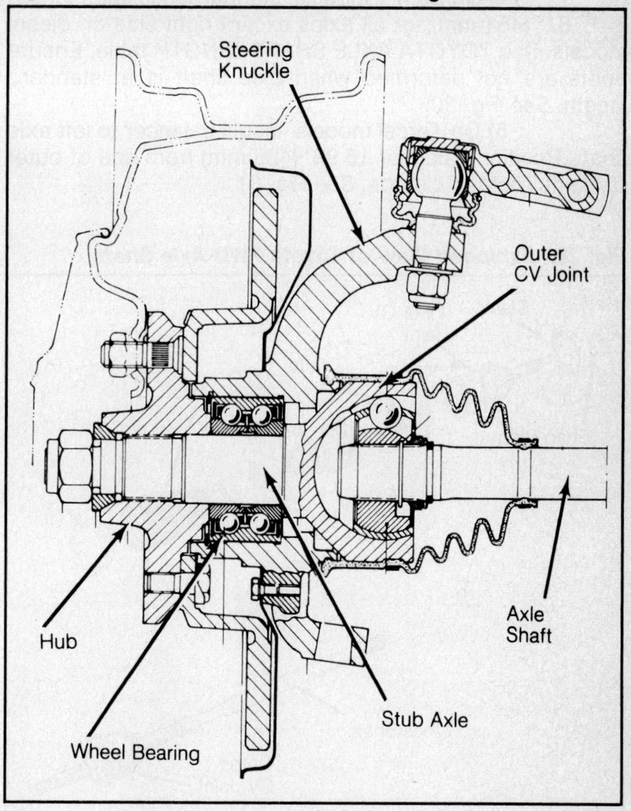

Disassembly (Toyota)

NOTE: Before disassembling Toyota axle shaft, check outer CV joint for any play. If play exists at outer CV joint, replace complete axle shaft assembly. Outer CV joint cannot be disassembled.

1) Draw alignment marks on inner CV joint and shaft with paint. Remove snap ring and boot clamps. Remove inner joint from shaft. Place index marks on tripod and axle shaft. Remove snap ring and tap body of tripod to drive tripod off shaft.

2) Remove inner CV joint boot. Remove damper clamp and damper, if equipped. On all models, remove outer CV joint boot clamps and slide boot off axle shaft. Inspect boots for cracks and tears. Clean all parts. Replace damaged parts as necessary.

Reassembly

1) Wrap axle shaft splines with vinyl tape. Slide new boots onto axle shaft. Place clamping rings loosely over boots with open end of clamp away from direction of rotation. Do not tighten clamps at this time. Place beveled side of tripod onto shaft with beveled splines facing outer joint and align reference marks.

2) Before tapping tripod into final position, align centers of inner and outer joints. *See Fig. 29*. Tap tripod into position and install new snap ring. Pack outer CV joint with 8 ozs. of grease (supplied with boot kit). Install outer boot and tighten clamps.

3) Pack inner CV joint with 5 ozs. of grease (supplied with boot kit). Align reference marks made at disassembly and install inner CV joint. Install inner CV joint boot and tighten clamps. Install new snap ring on axle shaft.

Axle Shafts

ALL MODELS (Cont.)

4) On Camry models, standard axle shaft length is 17.87" (454 mm) for all axles except right side on diesel models. See TOYOTA AXLE SHAFT LENGTH table. Ensure boots are not deformed when axle shaft is at standard length. *See Fig. 30.*

5) On Tercel models, install balancer to left axle shaft. Position balancer 15.98" (406 mm) from end of outer CV joint. Tighten clamps. *See Fig. 31.*

Fig. 28: Exploded View of Toyota FWD Axle Shaft

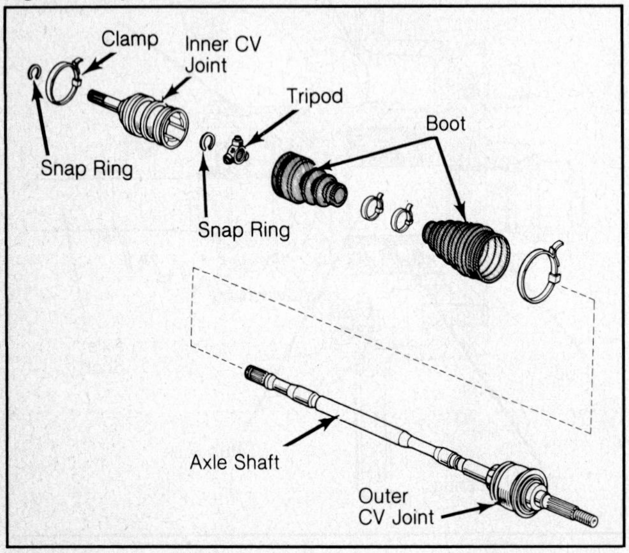

Fig. 29: Cutaway View Showing Alignment of Toyota Inner & Outer CV Joint Centers

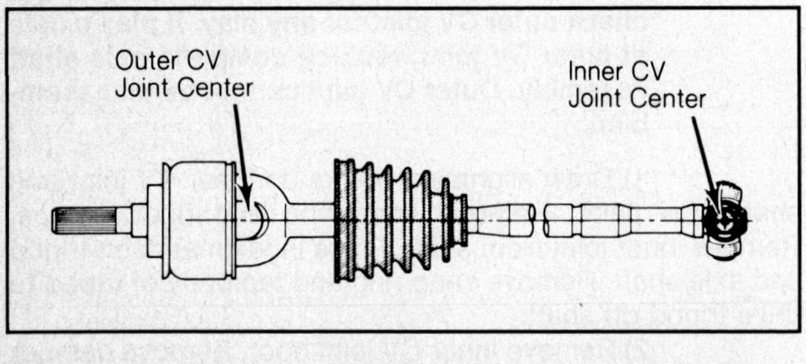

Fig. 30: Standard Length of Toyota Camry Axle Shaft

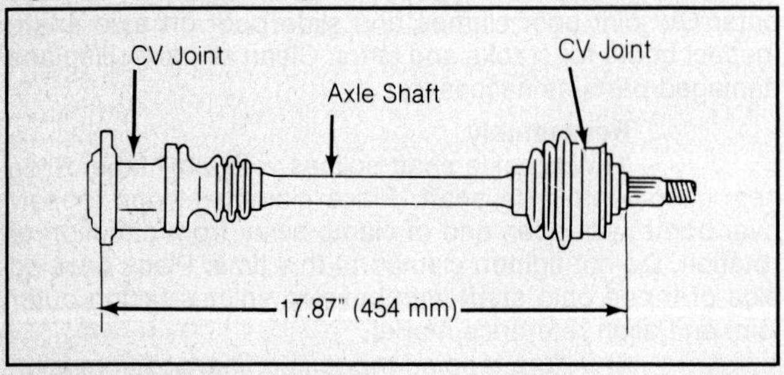

Length is for all axle shafts except right side on diesel models.

Fig. 31: Locating Toyota Tercel Damper on Axle Shaft

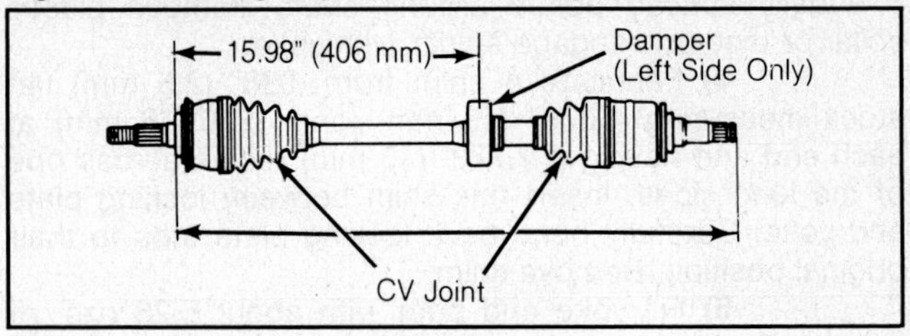

Damper is on left axle shaft only.

TOYOTA AXLE SHAFT LENGTH

Application	Length In. (mm)
Camry	
Gas	
Right Side	17.67-18.07 (449-459)
Left Side	17.67-18.07 (449-459)
Diesel	
Right Side	27.99-28.39 (711-721)
Left Side	17.67-18.07 (449-459)
Corolla	
Gas	
Right Side	27.2-27.6 (693-703)
Left Side	16.34-16.74 (415-425)
Diesel	
Right Side	27.56-27.96 (700-710)
Left Side	16.26-16.66 (413-423)
MR2	
Right Side	[1] 26.97 (685)
Left Side	17.28 (439)
Tercel	
Right Side	24.41 (620)
Left Side	28.43 (722)

[1] – Position damper 7.95" (202 mm) in from outer edge of outer CV joint.

Axle Shafts

ALL MODELS (Cont.)

TIGHTENING SPECIFICATIONS

Application	Ft. Lbs. (N.m)
Audi & Volkswagen	
All Models Except 5000S	
Axle Shaft Nut	167 (230)
Ball Joints	47 (64)
CV Joint Bolts	32 (43)
5000S	
Axle Shaft Nut	200 (274)
CV Joint Bolts	32 (43)
Chevrolet Spectrum & Isuzu I-Mark (FWD)	
Axle Shaft Nut	137 (186)
Wheel Lug Nuts	65 (88)
Chevrolet Sprint	
Axle Shaft Nut	109-195 (150-270)
Ball Joint	37-51 (50-70)
Brake Caliper	18-26 (24-36)
Spring Strut-to-Knuckle	51-65 (70-90)
Tie Rod End	22-40 (30-55)
Chrysler Corp. Imports	
Axle Shaft Nut	167 (230)
Ball Joints	78 (105)
Honda	
Axle Shaft Nut	137 (185)
Ball Joints	40 (54)
Support-To-Strut	32 (43)
Support-to-Spindle	47 (64)
Isuzu P'UP & Trooper II	
Ball Joint-to-Lower Control Arm	51 (69)
Ball Joint-to-Knuckle	75 (102)
Brake Caliper-to-Support	22-25 (30-34)
Hub-to-Rotor	33-40 (45-54)
Support-to-Steering Knuckle	62-65 (84-88)
Strut Rod	41-61 (56-83)

TIGHTENING SPECIFICATIONS (Cont.)

Application	Ft. Lbs. (N.m)
Mazda	
Axle Shaft Nut	140 (200)
Ball Joints	36 (48)
Sway Bar Link	11 (15)
Mitsubishi	
Axle Shaft Nut	167 (230)
Ball Joints	47 (64)
Nissan	
Axle Shaft Nut	115 (157)
Ball Joint Nuts	44 (58)
Renault	
Axle Shaft Nut	185 (250)
Ball Joints	48 (65)
Tie Rod Ends	30 (40)
Saab	
Axle Shaft Nut	260 (350)
Subaru	
Axle Shaft Nut	145 (197)
Ball Joint Nut	25 (34)
Tie Rod Ends	22 (30)
Toyota	
Camry	
Axle Shaft Nut	137 (185)
Brake Caliper	70 (96)
CV Joint Bolts	25 (34)
Intermediate Shaft Mount	40 (54)
Tercel	
Axle Shaft Nut	137 (185)
Brake Caliper	70 (96)
Spring Strut-to-Knuckle	105 (142)
Sway Bar	35 (47)
Tie Rod End	32 (43)

Axle Shafts

PORSCHE MODELS

DESCRIPTION

Axle shafts transfer power from transaxle to driving wheels. All axle shafts consist of a shaft and flexible Constant Velocity (CV) joints at each end. Inner CV joint is splined or bolted to transaxle. Outer CV joint is splined to wheel bearing hub and secured by a nut.

TROUBLE SHOOTING

See AXLE SHAFTS article at beginning of IMPORT AXLE SHAFTS, OVERDRIVES & TRANSFER CASES section.

REMOVAL & INSTALLATION

DRIVE FLANGE OIL SEALS

NOTE: **Removal of certain guards may be necessary to provide access to oil seals.**

Removal (911 & 928S)

Remove socket head screws at inner end of shaft, then disconnect and support drive axle shaft. Remove inner flange bolt while holding flange from turning by inserting punch in drive flange bolt hole. Remove flange and pull out seal with Seal Remover (VW 681).

Installation

Fill cavity between sealing and dust lips with multi-purpose grease and drive seal in place with Seal Installer (VW 195). Install flange and drive axle shaft and tighten to specifications.

Removal (944)

Disconnect inner CV joint from drive flange and support drive axle out of the way. Insert a long drift punch in 1 drive flange hole to prevent drive flange movement, then remove drive flange retaining bolt. Place a drip pan under transmission housing and pull out drive flange. Pry out oil seal.

Installation

Lightly lubricate seal lips and fully seat seal with a seal installer. Install drive flange and tighten drive flange retaining bolt. Install axle drive shafts and tighten bolts. Check and add lubricant to transaxle as necessary.

REAR WHEEL BEARINGS

Removal (911 & 928S)

With brake calipers off and drive shaft disconnected at axle flange, press shaft from housing, remove circlip and drive grooved ball bearing and roller bearing out with soft drift.

Installation

Press grooved ball bearing in inner end of housing and replace circlip. Put spacer in housing and drive roller bearing in place (flanged side facing out). Install seal in inboard side of housing. Put outer spacer in shaft and press in along with bearing inner race using castellated nut and driver.

Removal (944)

Remove brake drum and wheel. Disconnect drive shaft from axle flange. Press shaft from housing with double arm puller. Pry seal out of housing, remove circlip and drive grooved ball bearing and roller bearing out with soft drift.

Installation

Press grooved ball bearing in inner end of housing and replace circlip. Put spacer in housing and drive roller bearing in place (flanged side facing out). Install seal in inboard side of housing. Place outer spacer on shaft and press in along with inner bearing race, using castellated nut and driver.

DRIVE AXLE SHAFTS

NOTE: **Drive axle shafts should only be disassembled to replace defective rubber boots. If boots are being replaced, inspect all parts for damage or wear and replace as a complete assembly if necessary.**

Removal & Installation (911 & 928S)

Raise vehicle on hoist. Remove bolts from constant velocity joint-to-mating flange and remove drive axle from vehicle. To install, reverse removal procedure and tighten mounting bolts to specification.

Removal (944)

Raise and support vehicle. Remove bolts attaching inner CV joint to transaxle drive flange. Remove bolts attaching outer CV joint to wheel shaft. Remove axle drive shaft from vehicle.

Fig. 1: Exploded View of Rear Axle Shaft Assembly

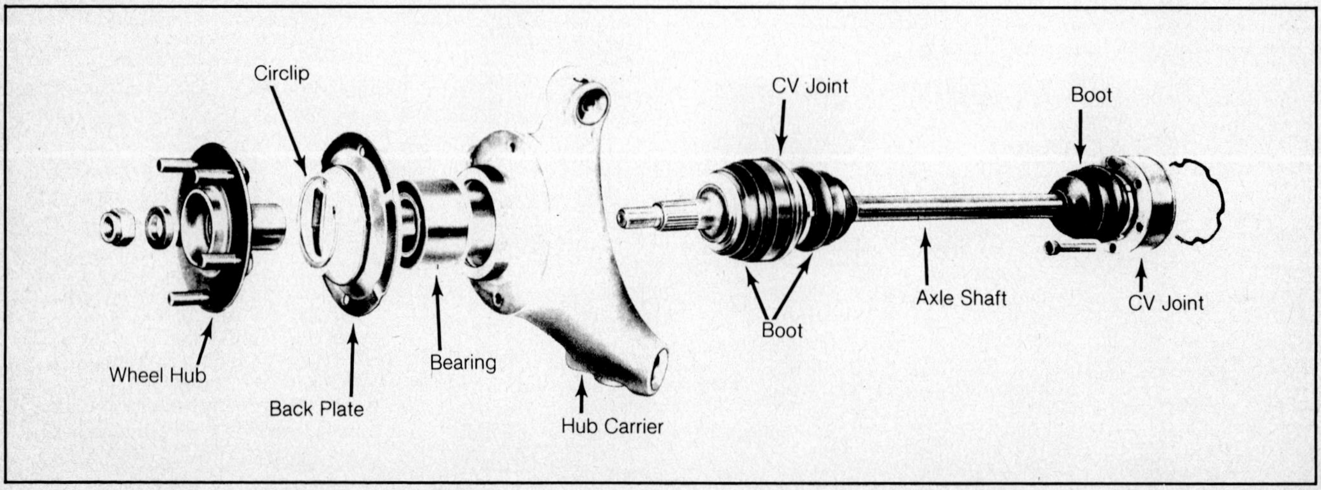

PORSCHE MODELS (Cont.)

Installation

To install, reverse removal procedure. Splines on shaft and in hub must be free of oil, grease and old locking compound prior to installation of shaft.

CONSTANT VELOCITY JOINTS

NOTE: Axle shafts must be removed from vehicle before servicing.

Disassembly (911 & 928S)

1) Clamp axle shaft in a vise with soft jaws. Remove boot clamp and push boot to center of axle. Remove circlip from axle shaft, press joint from axle shaft using CV Joint Removers (VW 401 and VW 408).

2) Swing ball and ball cage from joint and press out in direction of arrow. *See Fig. 2.* Tilt ball hub out of ball cage via ball groove. *See Fig. 3.* Clean all parts in a cleaning solvent and blow dry. Inspect for wear and damage.

NOTE: Ball hub and joint are a matched pair. DO NOT mix parts. The 6 balls are also mated together and cannot be mixed with others.

Fig. 2: Ball Hub & Ball Cage Removal

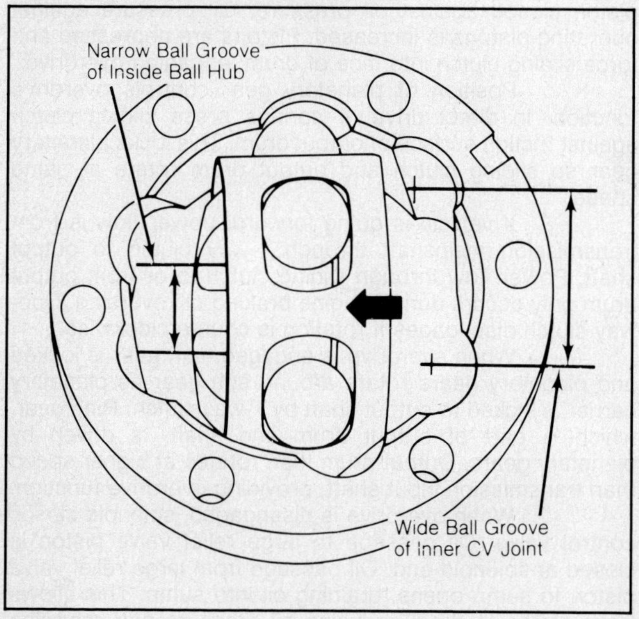

Reassembly

Place ball hub in ball cage. Press balls into cage. Install hub with cage and balls into joint and swing into assembled position. Check for smooth operation. To reinstall CV joint on axle shaft, reverse removal procedure. Install a new gasket on flange cover. Pack joint with molybdenum grease.

Fig. 3: Removal of Ball Hub from Cage

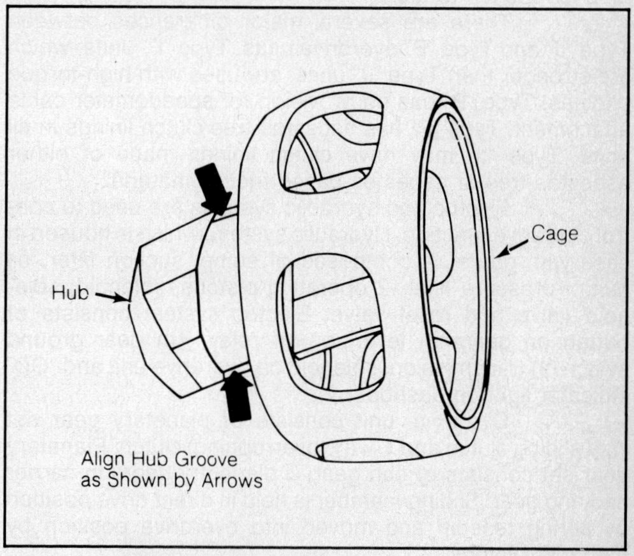

Disassembly (944)

1) On inner CV joint, remove circlip and drive protective cap off of CV joint. Press drive shaft out of inner CV joint. To remove outer CV joints, repeat procedure used for inner CV joints.

2) Tilt cage and hub out of CV joint to remove balls and disassemble joint. Inspect parts for abnormal wear or damage. Parts cannot be interchanged between joints. DO NOT mix parts. If any part of joint is damaged, replacement of entire CV joint is necessary.

Reassembly

To reassemble, reverse disassembly procedure. Pack each side of CV joints with 1.6 oz. of molybdenum disulfide grease.

Overdrives

LAYCOCK "J" & "P" TYPES

Volvo

DESCRIPTION

Overdrive is mounted on rear of transmission housing. When overdrive is engaged, propeller shaft will rotate faster than transmission output shaft. Final output ratio is reduced to .79:1.

There are several major differences between Type "J" and Type "P" overdrive units. Type "P" units, which are stronger than Type "J" units, are used with high-torque engines. Type "P" has no provision for speedometer cable attachment. Type "P" has asbestos-free clutch linings in all units. Type "J" may have clutch linings made of either asbestos-free or asbestos-based friction material.

Electric and hydraulic systems are used to control overdrive function. Hydraulic system, which is housed in case with gears, is composed of sump, suction filter, oil pump, pressure filter, 2 operating pistons, solenoid, solenoid valve and relief valve. Electric system consists of button on gearshift lever, on/off relay, 4th gear ground switch on transmission, solenoid on overdrive unit and "OD" indicator light on dashboard.

Overdrive unit consists of planetary gear set with sliding clutch and 1-way (overrunning) clutch. Planetary gear set consists of sun gear, 3 planetary gears in carrier and ring gear. Sliding member is held in direct drive position by spring tension and moved into overdrive position by hydraulic pistons.

OPERATION

CAUTION: NEVER try to operate transmission in Reverse when overdrive is engaged. Severe internal damage will occur to transmission and/or overdrive units.

Push button on lever signals relay to activate or deactivate solenoid on overdrive unit. "OD" light on dashboard should come on whenever overdrive is engaged. Relay is also controlled by switch on transmission, which will provide ground for relay only when transmission is in 4th gear. Overdrive can be disengaged by driver at push button or automatically by shifting out of 4th gear.

Piston-type hydraulic pump is powered by eccentric cam which is keyed to overdrive input shaft. In direct drive, low-pressure lubricating oil drawn from sump is constantly being pushed past oil pump check valve into hydraulic circuit. Oil passes through pressure filter and past 2 operating pistons. Low-pressure oil does not affect rest position of operating pistons. Oil travels to relief and solenoid valves. *See Fig. 1.*

When solenoid valve is disengaged (closed), oil cannot pass this point in circuit. Large (outer) piston in relief valve remains at lowest position and only minor spring pressure is exerted upon small (inner) piston by outer spring.

Lubricating oil depresses small piston and passes through galley to overdrive mainshaft. This oil lubricates mainshaft and passes on to 1-way clutch and shaft bushing. Baffle catches oil, which is delivered to sump by planetary gears. Ball-type check valve, mounted in front housing galley pressure relief valve, maintains constant lubricating oil pressure.

Fig. 1: Schematic of Overdrive Hydraulic Circuit

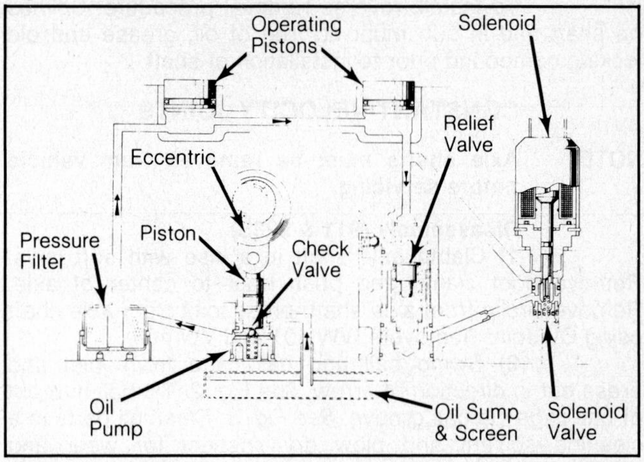

Direct drive function is shown as solenoid is disengaged.

When solenoid control valve is activated by selecting overdrive mode in 4th gear, pressurized oil passes through valve and pushes upward against bottom of large relief valve piston. This raises large piston in bore of relief valve, compressing inner spring and keeping small piston closed against oil pressure. Oil pressure against operating pistons is increased. Pistons are depressed and force sliding clutch into face of drum, engaging overdrive.

Position of planetary gear controls overdrive function. In direct drive, 4 springs press sliding clutch against friction surface of output drum. This locks planetary gear so sliding clutch and output drum rotate at same speed.

If vehicle is going forward, power flow is from transmission mainshaft through 1-way clutch to output shaft. Power flow through sliding clutch to or from output drum only occurs during engine braking or reversing. One-way clutch disengages if rotation is counterclockwise.

When overdrive is engaged, sun gear is locked and planetary gears rotate around sun gear as planetary carrier is locked to output shaft by 1-way clutch. Ring gear, which is part of output drum and shaft, is driven by planetary gears. Output drum then rotates at higher speed than transmission input shaft, providing overdrive function.

When overdrive is disengaged, solenoid closes control valve. Oil passage to large relief valve piston is closed at solenoid end. Oil passage from large relief valve piston to sump opens, draining oil into sump. This allows large piston to drop, reducing oil pressure and returning pistons to rest position.

TESTING

OVERDRIVE MALFUNCTIONS

Check that oil level is up to plug opening. Low oil level can cause both lubrication problems and/or hydraulic pressure problems. Check if solenoid is being energized. Working solenoid will make clicking noise when engaging. Always apply power and ground connections directly to solenoid before replacing solenoid.

If overdrive does not engage and indicator light does not work, check fuses and wiring for power supply. Check 4th gear switch operation. If solenoid does not engage but indicator light is on, check 4th gear switch, solenoid ground circuit and solenoid itself.

Overdrives

LAYCOCK "J" & "P" TYPES (Cont.)

Fig. 2: Exploded Views of Type "J" And "P" Overdrives

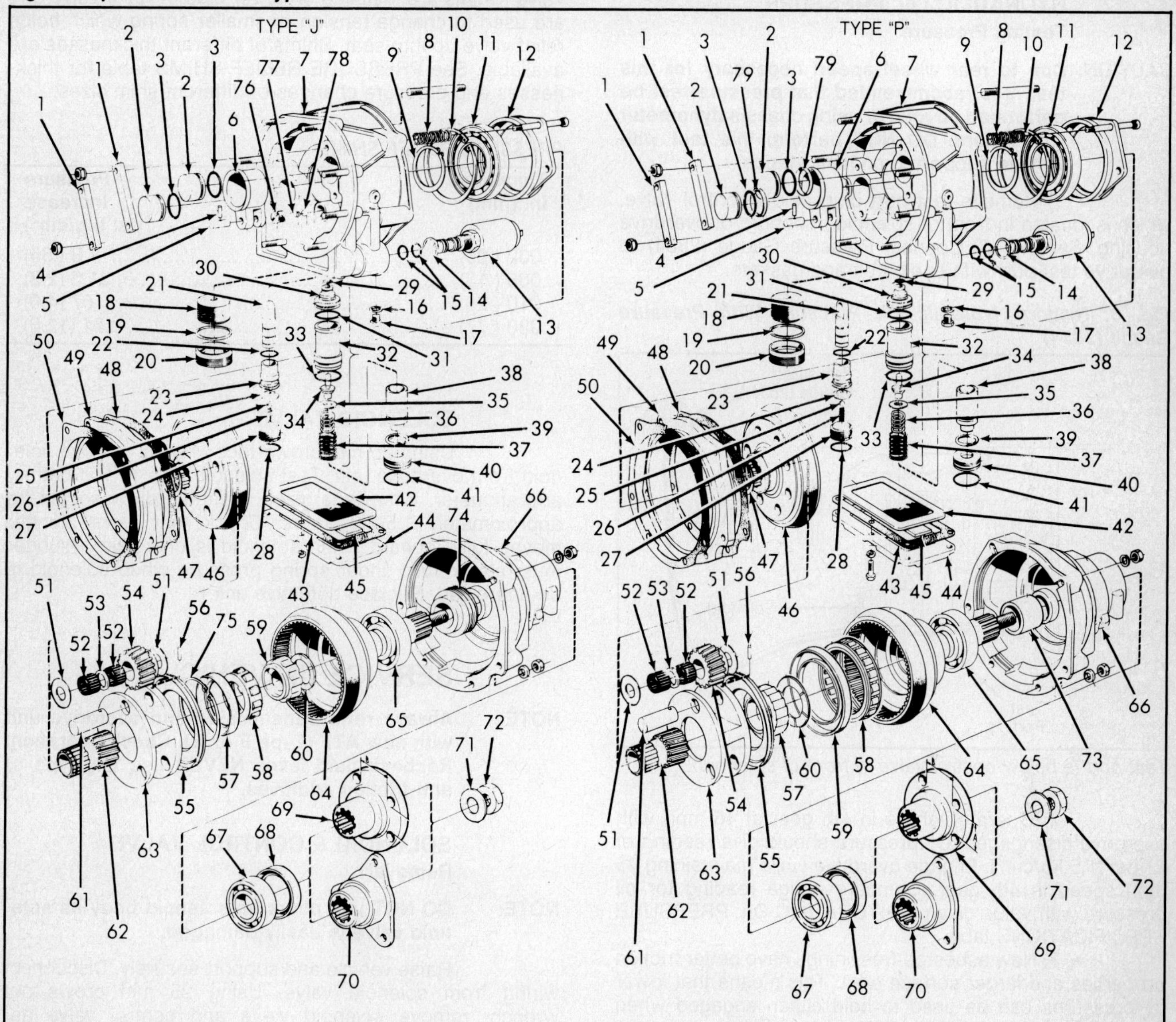

1. Piston Bridge
2. Operating Piston
3. "O" Ring
4. Pin
5. Guide Pin
6. Pump Link
7. Front Housing
8. Spring
9. Lock Ring
10. Lock Ring
11. Clutch Bearing
12. Bearing Holder
13. Solenoid Valve
14. Seal
15. "O" Ring
16. Seal
17. Plug
18. Pressure Filter
19. Washer
20. Plug
21. Piston
22. "O" Ring
23. Pump Cylinder
24. Seat
25. Check Ball
26. Spring
27. Plug
28. "O" Ring
29. "O" Ring
30. Seat
31. "O" Ring
32. Cylinder
33. "O" Ring
34. Piston
35. Pressure Adjusting Shim
36. Spring
37. Spring
38. Piston
39. "O" Ring
40. Plug
41. "O" Ring
42. Strainer
43. Gasket
44. Oil Pan
45. Magnet
46. Clutch
47. Lock Ring
48. Gasket
49. Brake Drum
50. Gasket
51. Thrust Washer
52. Needle Bearing
53. Spacer Washer
54. Pinion Gear
55. Oil Slinger
56. Lock Pin
57. Race
58. Roller Cage
59. 1-Way Clutch Hub
60. Thrust Washer
61. Pinion Shaft
62. Sun Gear
63. Planetary Gear Carrier
64. Output Shaft
65. Ball Bearing
66. Rear Housing
67. Ball Bearing
68. Seal
69. Round Drive Flange
70. 3-Arm Drive Flange
71. Washer
72. Nut
73. Spacer
74. Speedometer Drive Gear
75. Lock Ring
76. Relief Valve
77. Spring
78. Ball
79. Teflon Washer

HYDRAULIC OIL PRESSURE
Testing Pressure

CAUTION: Due to rear wheel speed necessary for this test, it is recommended that pressure test be performed on road or using chassis dynometer with rollers. DO NOT perform this test with vehicle supported on jack stands.

1) Remove test port plug below control valve, which is located in front of solenoid in bottom of overdrive housing. *See Fig. 3.* Connect Pressure Gauge (2834) to overdrive test port with banjo bolt and gaskets.

Fig. 3: Testing Hydraulic Oil Pressure With Pressure Gauge (2834)

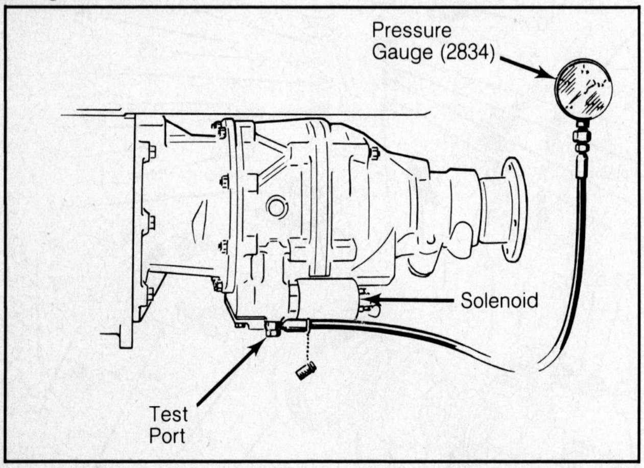

Test port is below control valve in front of solenoid.

2) Operate vehicle in 4th gear at 45 mph with overdrive disengaged. Oil pressure should give reading of 21 psi (1.5 kg/cm^2). Engage overdrive while maintaining 45 mph speed in 4th gear. Compare gauge reading for oil pressure with value given in HYDRAULIC OIL PRESSURE SPECIFICATIONS table.

3) New asbestos-free linings have better friction properties and larger surface area. This means that lower oil pressures can be used to hold clutch engaged when overdrive is operating. When overdrive is disengaged, oil pressure must return to 21 psi (1.5 kg/cm^2) in less than 3 seconds.

HYDRAULIC OIL PRESSURE SPECIFICATIONS

Application	psi (kg/cm^2)
Overdrive Disengaged	
All Models	21 (1.5)
Overdrive Engaged	
Type "J"	
D24T	
Original/Asbestos-Free Lining	400-440 (28-31)
Rebuilt/Asbestos-Free Lining	440-483 (31-34)
Gas Turbo	
Original/Asbestos Lining	554-596 (39-42)
Rebuilt/Asbestos-Free Lining	440-483 (31-34)
All Other Models	
Original/Asbestos Lining	525-568 (37-40)

Adjusting Pressure

If hydraulic oil pressures are not correct, adjustments can be made by changing shims in pressure relief valve. Shims are installed on lower side of relief valve and are used to change tension of smaller spring which holds relief valve up into seat. Shims of different thicknesses are available. See PRESSURE RELIEF SHIMS table for thicknesses and pressure changes of different shim sizes.

PRESSURE RELIEF SHIMS

Thickness In. (mm)	Pressure Increase psi (kg/cm^2)
.002 (.05)	7.8 (.55)
.005 (.13)	31.3 (2.2)
.010 (.25)	57 (4.0)
.030 (.77)	171 (12.0)

SOLENOID VALVE

Using 25 mm crows-foot wrench, remove solenoid from overdrive unit. Test solenoid with 12 volt battery and ammeter. When energized, solenoid draw should be approximately 1.5-2.0 amps. Check that valve plunger moves fully forward when solenoid is energized. Plunger must also return under spring pressure when solenoid is de-energized. Replace defective unit.

SERVICE (IN VEHICLE)

NOTE: Always refill transmission and overdrive unit with new ATF (Type F or G). Check operation. Recheck fluid level. NEVER use any type of anti-friction additives.

SOLENOID & CONTROL VALVE
Removal

NOTE: DO NOT use pliers on solenoid body as solenoid valve is easily damaged.

Raise vehicle and support securely. Disconnect wiring from solenoid valve. Using 25 mm crows-foot wrench, remove solenoid valve and control valve assemblys.

Installation

Lubricate new "O" ring seal on solenoid with ATF. Install solenoid into overdrive unit. Tighten solenoid to 30-40 ft. lbs. (41-54 N.m). Connect wiring to solenoid and check operation.

STRAINER & PRESSURE FILTER
Removal

Remove oil pan, magnet and strainer. Using Plug Socket (2836), remove pressure filter base plug (largest plug under sump cover). Aluminum gasket and pressure filter will come out with plug.

Cleaning & Inspection

Clean parts in solvent. Use compressed air to dry filters lightly or allow them to air dry. If either filter is damaged or too plugged for cleaning, replace filter.

Installation

Install pressure filter and plug with new gasket. Install screen, magnet and oil pan with new pan gasket. Fill oil to proper level.

LAYCOCK "J" & "P" TYPES (Cont.)

RELIEF VALVE ASSEMBLY

Removal

1) Remove oil pan, magnet and screen. Using plug socket, remove relief valve plug from bore farthest from pressure filter bore. Remove relief valve and spring assembly. DO NOT lose pressure adjustment shim.

Fig. 4: Exploded View of Relief Valve Assembly

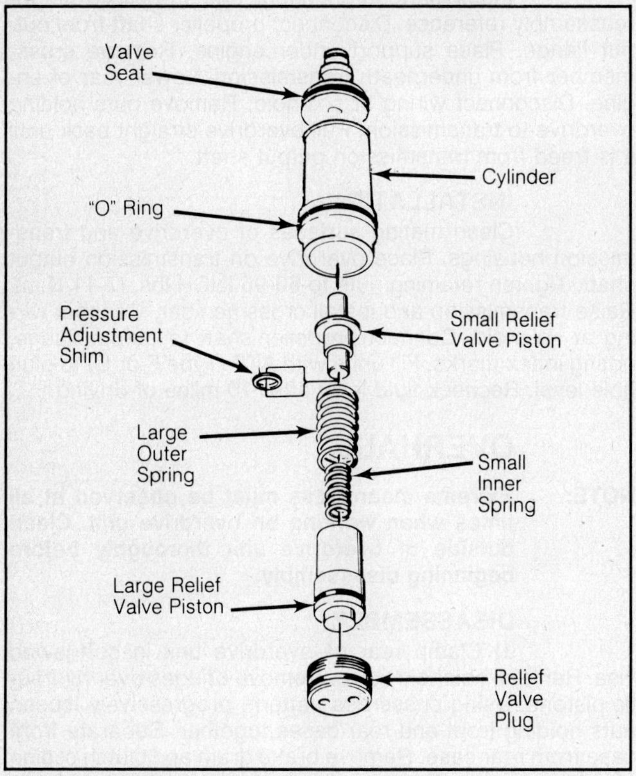

"O" ring on valve body cylinder MUST be at outer (lower) end.

2) Install Relief Valve Cylinder/Seat Puller (5183) by turning center screw out until slotted end can be inserted into seat. Turn center screw in until tight. Turn large collar nut in until seat and cylinder are pulled from overdrive housing. *See Fig. 5.*

Cleaning & Inspection

1) Wash parts in solvent. Blow dry with compressed air. Inspect cylinder for burrs, cracks, corrosion or excessive wear. Make sure pistons move freely in bores. Check springs for damage or wear. Discard old "O" rings.

2) Check relief valve piston carefully as any scoring will cause "O" ring damage. Check valve seat closely if overdrive engaged slowly or slipped during engagement. If there are ANY signs of wear on valve seat, replace relief valve assembly.

NOTE: ALWAYS use new style relief valve piston if relief valve is replaced.

Installation

1) Remove solenoid valve assembly. Use compressed air to clean control orifice, which is located in relief valve bore inside case. Install solenoid valve assembly. Install new "O" rings on relief valve seat, cylinder and plug. Use ATF to oil all components lightly.

2) Using cylinder to press seat into proper position, install seat in bore. Make sure that cylinder end with "O" ring is closest to plug end of bore. Position small piston and springs in large piston. *See Fig. 4.*

Fig. 5: Removing Relief Valve Cylinder And Seat

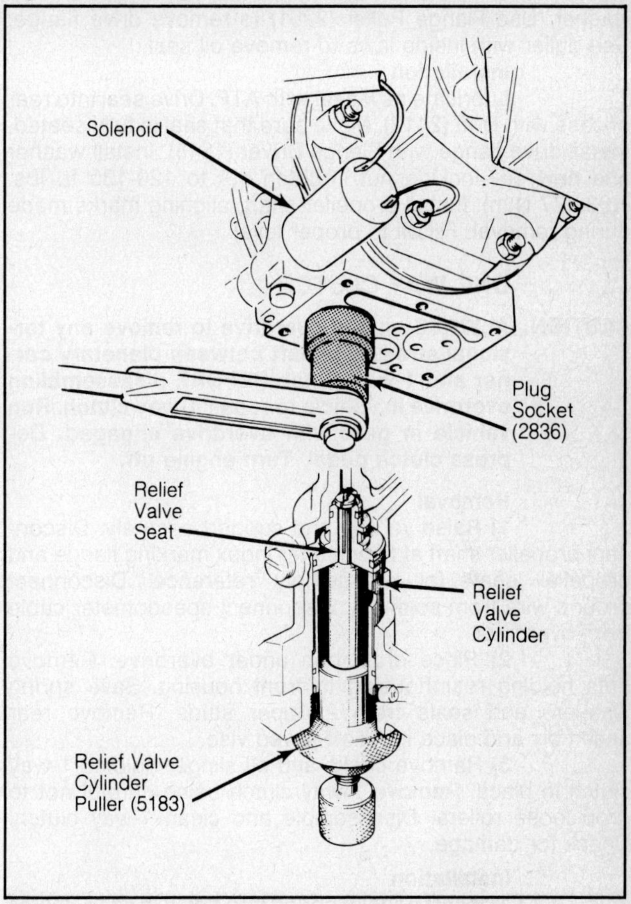

Slotted end of puller must be inserted into seat.

3) Place assembly in cylinder while making sure that small piston slips into seat properly. Install base plug and tighten to 14-18 ft. lbs. (19-24 N.m). Install screen, magnet and oil pan with new pan gasket. Fill oil to proper level.

PUMP CHECK VALVE

Removal

Remove oil pan, magnet and screen. Remove center plug with plug socket. Do not let ball and spring fall out as plug is removed. Remove spring, check ball and valve seat. Use magnet to remove valve seat.

Cleaning & Inspection

Clean all parts in solvent. Use compressed air to dry parts. Check valve seat and ball for corrosion, wear or burrs. Inspect spring for cracks, distortion or loss of tension.

Installation

Install new "O" ring on plug. Place spring in plug with check ball on top of spring. Put valve seat on check ball. Carefully set assembly into case. Tighten plug to 14-18 ft. lbs. (19-24 N.m). Install screen, magnet and oil pan with new pan gasket. Fill oil to proper level.

REAR OIL SEAL

Removal

Raise vehicle and support securely. Mark rear universal joint and pinion yoke for reassembly reference.

LAYCOCK "J" & "P" TYPES (Cont.)

Disconnect propeller shaft. Remove drive flange nut and washer. Use Flange Puller (2261) to remove drive flange. Use puller with inside jaws to remove oil seal.

Installation

Lubricate new seal with ATF. Drive seal into rear of case with Drift (2412). Make sure that seal is fully seated. Install drive flange with Flange Driver (1845). Install washer and new self-locking nut. Tighten nut to 120-130 ft. lbs. (163-177 N.m). Install propeller shaft, aligning marks made during removal. Fill oil to proper level.

ONE-WAY CLUTCH

CAUTION: **ALWAYS unload overdrive to remove any torsional stress on shaft between planetary carrier and 1-way clutch BEFORE disassembling overdrive in vehicle to repair 1-way clutch. Run vehicle in gear with overdrive engaged. Depress clutch pedal. Turn engine off.**

Removal

1) Raise vehicle and support securely. Disconnect propeller shaft at flange after index marking flange and propeller shaft for reassembly reference. Disconnect ground wire from solenoid. Disconnect speedometer cable from overdrive.

2) Place drain pan under overdrive. Remove nuts holding rear housing to front housing. Save spring washers and seals from 2 upper studs. Remove rear assembly and place it in soft-jawed vise.

3) Remove circlip and oil slinger holding 1-way clutch in place. Remove 1-way clutch being careful not to drop loose rollers. Disassemble and clean 1-way clutch. Check for damage.

Installation

1) Insert ends of spring into holes in cage. Install hub with cams facing in correct direction. Rotate cage clockwise to end and lock in place with key. Insert rollers, holding them in place with rubber band.

2) Ensure that thrust washer is properly located in ring gear. Thrust washer and output shaft MUST be mating parts. Install 1-way clutch. Remove rubber band. Install oil slinger and circlip.

3) Ensure that gasket in front of brake has not been damaged during removal of clutch. Clean housing mating surfaces and fit new gasket. Install rear housing. Install seals and spring washers on 2 upper studs. Tighten mounting nuts to 60-144 INCH lbs. (7-16 N.m).

4) Connect ground wire at solenoid. Install speedometer cable and drive shaft. Fill transmission and overdrive with correct oil. Engage overdrive while driving vehicle. Recheck oil level after test drive.

REMOVAL & INSTALLATION

CAUTION: **ALWAYS unload overdrive to relieve any torsional stress on shaft BEFORE removing overdrive from transmission.**

REMOVAL

Relieving Torsional Stress

1) During operation of overdrive, torsional stress can build up in shaft between planetary carrier and 1-way clutch. To "unload" overdrive stresses, drive vehicle with overdrive engaged. Depress clutch and then disengage overdrive. This will unload torsional stress from shaft.

2) If vehicle cannot be driven before work begins, unload stress by engaging and disengaging overdrive in vehicle. To do this, connect shop oil line to pressure test port and apply oil at pressure of 280-350 psi (20-25 kg/cm^2). Turn ignition and overdrive switches to "ON" and then "OFF" positions.

Removal

Index mark output flange and propeller shaft for reassembly reference. Disconnect propeller shaft from output flange. Place support under engine. Remove crossmember from underneath transmission. Lower rear of engine. Disconnect wiring at solenoid. Remove nuts holding overdrive to transmission. Pull overdrive straight back until it is freed from transmission output shaft.

INSTALLATION

Clean mating surfaces of overdrive and transmission housings. Place overdrive on transmission output shaft. Tighten retaining nuts to 60-96 INCH lbs. (7-11 N.m). Raise transmission and install crossmember. Connect wiring at solenoid. Connect propeller shaft to output flange, noting index marks. Fill units with ATF (Type F or G) to plug hole level. Recheck fluid level after 10 miles of driving.

OVERHAUL

NOTE: **Extreme cleanliness must be observed at all times when working on overdrive unit. Clean outside of overdrive unit thoroughly before beginning disassembly.**

DISASSEMBLY

1) Clamp rear of overdrive unit in soft-jawed vise. Remove solenoid valve. Remove bridges over hydraulic pistons. Using crisscross pattern, progressively loosen nuts holding front and rear cases together. Separate front case from rear case. Remove brake drum and clutch sliding member springs. Remove clutch, thrust bearing and sun gear assembly.

2) On Type "J" units, remove planetary gear assembly. On Type "P" units, remove planetary gear carrier and thrust washer. If either carrier or 1-way clutch is to be replaced, use 2-jaw puller and bearing plate to remove 1-way clutch from planetary carrier. Use locally supplied thrust washer to protect carrier from force of puller screw.

3) On both models, use pliers to remove operating pistons from front case. Identify pistons as to respective bores for reassembly reference. Remove oil pan, gasket and screen. Using plug socket, remove threaded plugs in housing under pressure filter, check valve and relief valve.

4) If plugs do not move easily, tap them with soft mallet to ease removal. Remove pressure filter, oil pump check valve with spring, ball and seat and relief valve assembly. Using puller, remove relief valve cylinder and seat. Remove oil pump body and plunger.

5) Remove locking ring. Pull sun gear and clutch disc from bearing carrier. Remove locking ring. Using Bearing Driver (5103), tap bearing out of carrier. On Type "J", clamp overdrive unit into soft-jawed vise. Remove lock ring and 1-way clutch oil slinger.

6) Test 1-way clutch by turning it in locking direction. Make sure outer ring does not slip on input shaft. Using Roller Ring (5210), remove 1-way clutch by turning ring clockwise. Turn roller ring over while keeping bearings in place. Check roller cage. If cage is oval, replace it with newer type.

Overdrives

LAYCOCK "J" & "P" TYPES (Cont.)

Fig. 6: Pressure Filter, Check and Relief Valve Assemblies

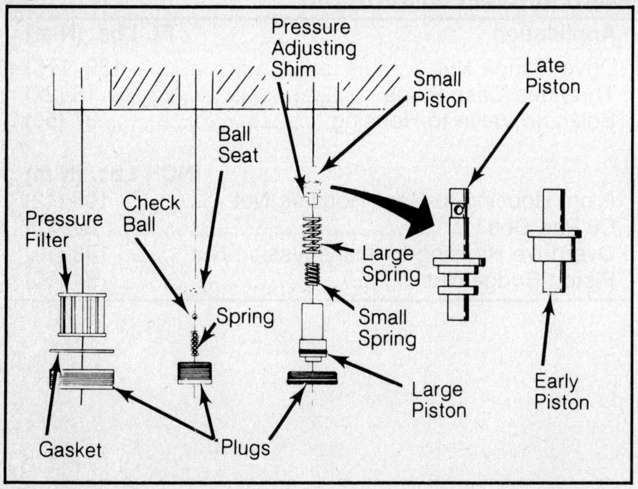

Replace relief valve if ANY damage or wear is evident.

7) On Type "P", disassemble 1-way clutch and check cage, rollers and rachet, replacing any damaged parts. If early type clutch is being used, replace it with newer type which has lock spring hole moved further away from step in gear. Clamp Type "P" overdrive rear housing in soft-jawed vise.

8) Move oil slinger back in 2 places to mount modified 2-jawed puller opposite one another. Puller is modified by installing 40 mm Center Bolt which is threaded along its full length. Place Thrust Collet (5103) in base of housing. Using 2-jaw puller, remove oil slinger from housing. Remove roller cage.

9) On all models, remove output flange. Using Spanner (5149), hold round flange while loosening nut. If flange is 3-arm type, use vise to hold output drive flange while removing nut. Pull flange off driveshaft. Remove oil seal from rear housing. If rear housing bearing is bad, remove it by tapping bearing out of housing. Press output shaft out of housing on type "P", using tool.

INSPECTION

1) Thoroughly wash all parts except friction linings in clean solvent. After cleaning, dry all parts with compressed air. Make sure control orifice between relief valve and solenoid is clean. If compressed air will not clean orifice, use pointed matchstick. DO NOT clean orifice with wire as calibration could be damaged.

2) Make sure output shaft groove in front of ring gear is clean. Check all parts for cracks or wear. Closely inspect pressure filter, gear wheels and bearings, operating pistons and valves for wear or cracks. Measure clutch return springs for distortion or cracking.

3) Make sure clutch return spring is 2.13-2.24" (54-57 mm) in length. Brake ring must be free of cracks and scores. Check cone clutch for burns or wear. Using 12-volt battery and ammeter, check that solenoid draws 1.5-2.0 amps and that plunger extends properly.

REASSEMBLY

NOTE: **Always use new gaskets, "O" rings, lock washers and seals for overhaul. Maintain extemely clean conditions during assembly procedure.**

1) Using Drift (2412), press bearing into rear case until seated. Using drift, press bearing onto output shaft. Install spacer (Type "P") or speedometer gear (Type "J") onto output shaft. Using drift, press output shaft into rear housing. Using Driver (5308), install oil seal into rear housing.

2) On Type "J", install correct thrust washer. Make sure that washer extends .024" (.6 mm) above edge of recess in case. Make sure that thrust washer is .1" (2.5 mm) (Part. No. 380 715-3) thick if early output shaft (Part No. 380 679-1 or 1 232 105-5) is used. If late output shaft (Part No. 1 232 646-3) is used, thrust washer must be .15" (3.8 mm) thick (Part No. 1 232 644-4).

3) Install 1-way clutch hub and roller cage with rollers. Install oil slinger and lock ring. Make sure that 1-way clutch rotates counterclockwise only. Using Press Tube (2835), install output flange with locking compound on splines. Do not get any locking compound on seal.

4) Tighten retaining nut to 130 ft. lbs. (175 N.m) while holding flange with either spanner or vise. Using Centering Drift (2835), install planetary gear carrier on output shaft.

5) On Type "P", put locking compound on splines of output shaft. Do not get any locking compound on seal. Using press tube, install output flange. Tighten retaining nut to 130 ft. lbs. (175 N.m) while holding flange with spanner or vise. Place cage of 1-way clutch in housing with groove on cage facing upward.

6) Using drift, tap oil slinger into place. Using Press Ring (5210), install 1-way clutch hub on planetary carrier with bevel on edge of hub facing downward. Wipe off splines and install brass thrust washer and planetary carrier in housing.

7) On all models, press sliding clutch bearing into holder, using Press Drift (2806). On Type "J" installed in Diesel Turbo models, use asbestos-free clutch linings and brake drum if not already used. Most units have asbestos-free linings as original equipment except for those with Volvo Part No. 1 208 282 (Laycock No. 115 925) used on transmissions from Serial No. 1 208 438/108 306 and higher.

8) On all models, clutch and brake linings MUST be dried in warm area to remove all moisture from linings. After drying, oil linings with ATF (Type F or G). Assemble sun gear and sliding clutch with lock rings. Install clutch and sun gear assembly on planetary carrier. Place clutch return springs on studs. Place gasket for brake drum on rear housing. Install brake drum.

9) Inspect front housing to make certain it is completely clean as hydraulic system is extremely sensitive to dirt. Lubricate oil pump with ATF. Install pump in housing with groove and bevel on plunger aligned with recess of pressure filter. If plunger is not aligned correctly, pump will make knocking noise.

10) Using compressed air, test check valve for leakage. If slight leakage occurs, try to correct seating of ball by placing valve seat and ball on flat surface and tapping ball with soft mallet. This will reform seat to ball and should allow proper 1-way action to occur. If leakage is heavy, valve seat is usually too deformed to repair and should be replaced.

11) Make sure ball is located properly in seat when installing check valve. Install pressure filter and relief valve. Always use new gaskets and late style relief valve piston if piston is to be replaced. Install pressure adjusting shims with relief valve assembly if used. See ADJUSTMENTS in this article for checking and adjusting procedure of relief valve.

Overdrives

LAYCOCK "J" & "P" TYPES (Cont.)

NOTE: Do not use any shims in pressure relief valve if new asbestos-free linings have been installed in clutch assembly.

12) Using plug socket, tighten all plugs in housing to 16 ft. lbs. (22 N.m). Install strainer, gasket and oil pan. Magnet must be clean. Install operating pistons in housing. Always replace earlier style pistons, which are sealed with "O" rings, using newer style pistons which are 4 mm longer and sealed with Teflon rings. Install new nylon washers on 2 upper bolts of rear housing with small end of washers facing rear housing.

13) Make sure gasket between brake drum and rear housing is installed. Assemble front and rear housings. Tighten retaining nuts to 108 INCH lbs. (12 N.m) in increments. Install bridges for operating pistons and tighten nuts to 84 INCH lbs. (10 N.m). Using crows-foot wrench, tighten solenoid to 37 ft. lbs. (50 N.m). Install solenoid ground wire.

TIGHTENING SPECIFICATIONS

Application	Ft. Lbs. (N.m)
Drive Flange Nut	130 (175)
Threaded Case Plugs	16 (22)
Solenoid Valve-to-Housing	37 (50)
	INCH Lbs. (N.m)
Front Housing-to-Rear Housing Nut	108 (12)
Oil Pan Bolt	84 (10)
Overdrive Housing-to-Transmission Nut	108 (12)
Piston Bridge Nut	84 (10)

Transfer Cases

CHRYSLER CORP. IMPORTS & MITSUBISHI

Chrysler Corp. Imports – Ram 50 Pickup
Mitsubishi – Montero, Pickup

DESCRIPTION

Two-speed transfer case is mounted on rear of transmission. KM145 is model number for manual transmission/transfer case combination, which uses KM132 5-speed manual transmission. KM146 is model number for automatic transmission/transfer case combination, which uses MA904 3-speed automatic transmission. There are only minor differences between transfer cases and these are due to difference in attachment to manual or automatic transmissions.

OPERATION

Shifting procedures vary between vehicles equipped with manual or automatic transmissions. Shifting procedures also differ between models equipped with either automatic or manual free-wheeling hubs. Hubs must always be in "LOCK" position for 4WD operation. Both hubs should be in same position.

On models with manual free-wheeling hubs, hubs must be in "LOCK" position before shifting into 4WD from 2WD. On models with automatic free-wheeling hubs, hubs are locked or unlocked depending upon position of transfer case lever.

Vehicles equipped with M/T and manual hubs may be shifted in either direction between "2H" and "4H" without stopping vehicle or depressing clutch pedal if hubs are in "LOCK" position. These models must be at full stop with clutch pedal depressed before shifting in either direction between "4H" and "4L".

Vehicles equipped with M/T and automatic hubs must be at full stop with clutch pedal depressed when shifting from "2H" to "4H". Shift from "4H" to "2H" can be made while moving although hubs will not unlock until vehicle moves 3-7 feet in direction opposite to most recent travel in "4H" position. These models must be at full stop with clutch pedal depressed before shifting in either direction between "4H" and "4L".

Vehicles equipped with A/T must be at full stop before shifting from "2H" to "4H". Shift from "4H" to "2H" can be made while moving although hubs will not unlock until vehicle moves 3-7 feet in direction opposite to most recent travel in "4H" position. These models must be at full stop with transmission selector lever in "N" or "P" position before shifting in either direction between "4H" and "4L".

If transfer case is difficult to shift between "4H" and "4L" positions, apply parking brake or step on brake pedal. Move transmission selector lever to either "P" or "N" position (depending upon initial position) after pausing at "R" position for short time. Try to move transfer case lever again. If it is possible to safely do so, coasting vehicle at speed of less than 3 mph with transmission selector lever in "N" position may also ease shifting of transfer case between "4H" and "4L" positions.

LUBRICATION

SERVICE INTERVAL

Under normal operating conditions, check oil levels in KM145 models at every 30,000 mile service interval. Change ATF in KM146 models at every 30,000 mile service interval. Under severe usage conditions, change gear oil in KM145 models and both ATF and gear oil in KM146 models at every 30,000 mile interval.

FLUID TYPE

Automatic transmissions use Dexron or Dexron II type ATF. Manual transmission and both transfer cases use hypoid gear oil with API classification of GL-4 and viscosity of SAE 80W or SAE 75W-85W.

CAPACITY

Model KM145 uses 2.3 qts. (2.2L) of gear oil in both transmission and transfer case sections for total of 4.6 qts. (4.4L). Model KM146 uses 7.2 qts. (6.8L) of ATF in transmission section and 2.3 qts. (2.2L) of gear oil in transfer case section.

REMOVAL & INSTALLATION

REMOVAL

Model KM145 (M/T)

1) Remove transfer case skid plate (if equipped). Disconnect both propeller shafts. Drain oil from transfer case. Disconnect wiring harness from backup light switch and both 4WD switches.

2) Disconnect speedometer cable from drive and unclip cable from case. Remove back-up light switch and take out steel ball under switch. Remove select plunger bore plug at right side of case. Remove select spring and plunger. Remove 6 bolts holding control lever assembly.

3) Remove control lever assembly and gasket. Remove plugs at top of adapter. Remove detent spring, steel ball, neutral return springs and plungers. Using .22" (5.8 mm) pin punch, drive roll pin out of change shifter. Remove change shifter from control shaft. Remove 4 bolts and 2 nuts holding transfer case to adapter. Remove transfer case from vehicle.

Model KM146 (A/T)

1) Remove transfer case skid plate (if equipped). Disconnect both propeller shafts. Drain oil from transfer case. Disconnect wiring harness from backup light switch and both 4WD switches. Disconnect speedometer cable from drive and unclip cable from case.

2) Remove bolts holding transfer case and adapter to transmission case. Remove bolts holding transfer case to support bracket. Remove transfer case assembly from transmission. Remove 4 bolts and 2 nuts holding transfer case to adapter. Remove adapter from transfer case.

INSTALLATION

Model KM145 (M/T)

1) Position transmission shifter in neutral position and transfer case lever in "4H" position. Mount neutral return plungers and springs in holes on top of adapter. Tighten plug until it is flush with adapter surface. Cover plug with sealant.

2) Coat inside of change shifter with grease. Mount detent plunger, spring and install plug (if equipped). Install back-up light switch and steel ball. To complete installation, reverse remainder of removal procedure. Fill transfer case with oil.

Model KM146 (A/T)

To install, reverse removal procedure. Fill transfer case with oil.

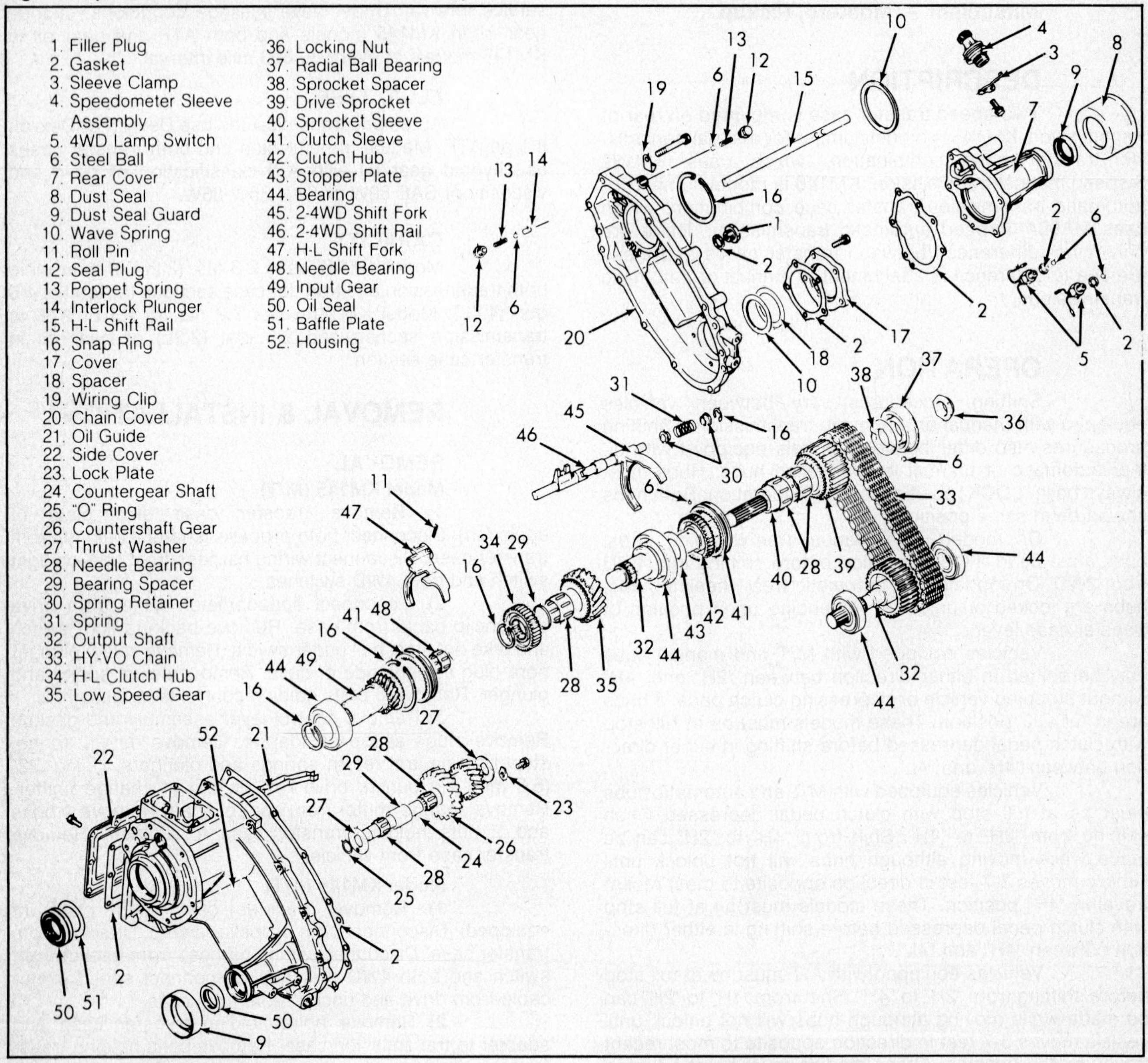

Fig. 1: Exploded View of Transfer Case Assembly

DISASSEMBLY

1) Remove both 4WD switches and steel balls. Remove speedometer sleeve assembly. Remove cover, gasket, wave spring and spacer. Drive roll pin out of H-L shift fork with 3/16" (4.8 mm) punch.

2) Remove 2 seal plugs. Remove 2 poppet springs and steel balls. Pull H-L shift rail out backward. Remove interlock plunger. Remove snap ring from rear bearing on output shaft. Remove chain cover, oil guide and side cover. Remove countershaft locking plate. Pull countershaft out.

3) Remove countergear, 2 thrust washers, 2 needle bearings and spacer through side cover opening. Remove snap ring, spring retainers and spring from 2-4WD shift rail. Remove front output shaft, rear output shaft and chain as assembly.

4) Remove 2-4WD shift rail. Remove H-L shift fork and clutch sleeve. Remove needle bearing and snap ring from input gear. Remove input gear assembly. Remove snap ring from front of rear output shaft. Remove H-L clutch hub, low speed gear thrust washer and needle bearing.

5) Remove detent from lock nut of rear output shaft. Remove lock nut. Using bearing puller, remove ball bearing from rear with bearing puller. Remove sprocket spacer and steel balls. Remove drive sprocket, 2 needle bearings, sprocket sleeve and steel ball.

6) Remove 2-4WD clutch sleeve, hub and stop plate. Using puller or press, remove ball bearing. Remove snap ring from input gear. Support bearing with press base. Push on front of input gear to remove bearing. Using puller, remove 2 bearings from front output shaft.

7) If either control shaft or input gear oil seals are to be replaced, drive out roll pin from transmission control change shifter. Separate transfer case from adapter.

CHRYSLER CORP. IMPORTS & MITSUBISHI (Cont.)

Fig. 2: Shift Rods And Levers Of Model KM145 (M/T)

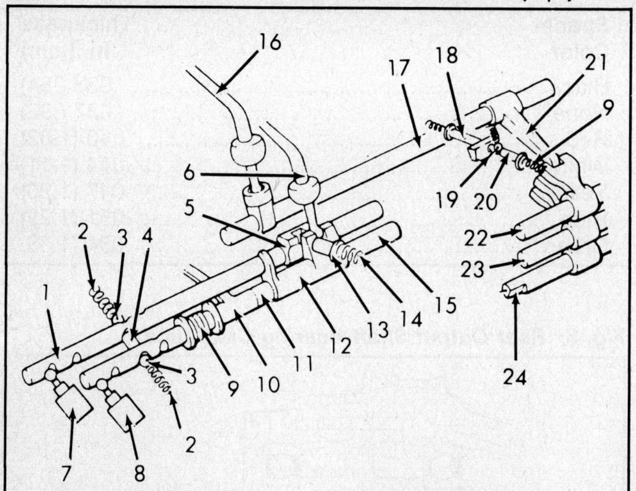

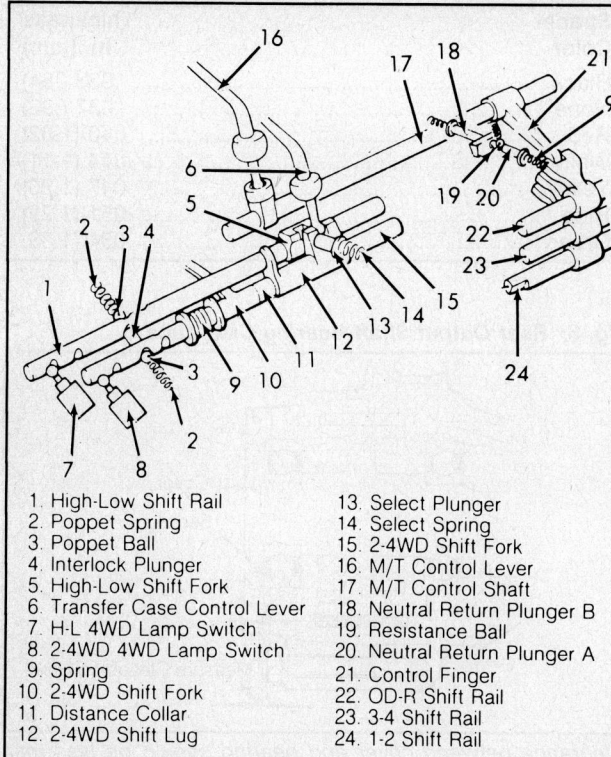

1. High-Low Shift Rail
2. Poppet Spring
3. Poppet Ball
4. Interlock Plunger
5. High-Low Shift Fork
6. Transfer Case Control Lever
7. H-L 4WD Lamp Switch
8. 2-4WD 4WD Lamp Switch
9. Spring
10. 2-4WD Shift Fork
11. Distance Collar
12. 2-4WD Shift Lug
13. Select Plunger
14. Select Spring
15. 2-4WD Shift Fork
16. M/T Control Lever
17. M/T Control Shaft
18. Neutral Return Plunger B
19. Resistance Ball
20. Neutral Return Plunger A
21. Control Finger
22. OD-R Shift Rail
23. 3-4 Shift Rail
24. 1-2 Shift Rail

Fig. 3: Cross Sectional View Of Rear Output Shaft

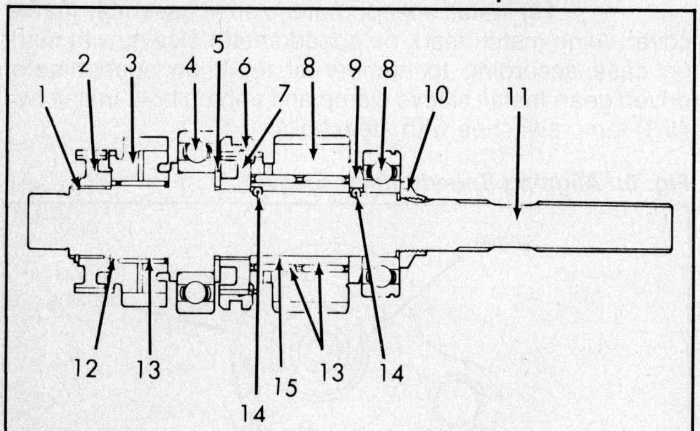

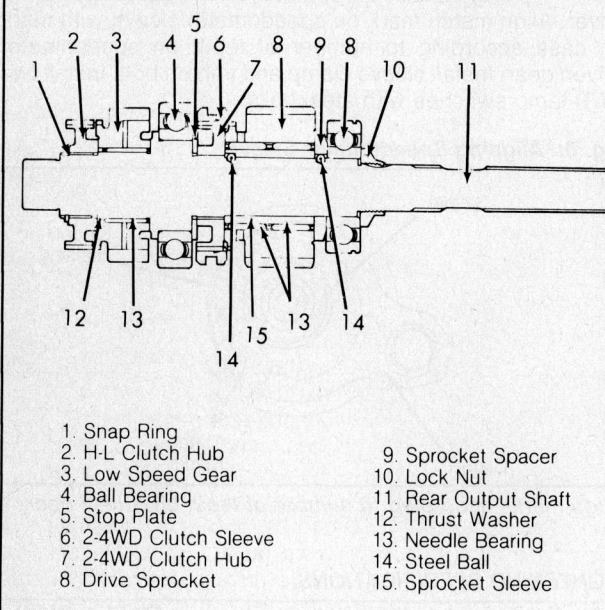

1. Snap Ring
2. H-L Clutch Hub
3. Low Speed Gear
4. Ball Bearing
5. Stop Plate
6. 2-4WD Clutch Sleeve
7. 2-4WD Clutch Hub
8. Drive Sprocket
9. Sprocket Spacer
10. Lock Nut
11. Rear Output Shaft
12. Thrust Washer
13. Needle Bearing
14. Steel Ball
15. Sprocket Sleeve

REASSEMBLY

NOTE: **ALWAYS replace all gaskets, oil seals and roll pins with new parts. Coat gaskets and threads with sealant. Lubricate all sliding and rotating parts with transmission oil before assembling. Never reuse roll pins.**

1) Press control shaft, input gear and front output shaft oil seals into transfer case housing. When fitting seals, press circumference uniformly. Pack grease between lips of installed seals.

2) Join adapter and transfer case with new gasket. Be sure to install change shifter over control shaft before tightening nuts and bolts. Make sure to remove burrs from change shifter. Tighten bolts and nuts.

3) Press bearing into input gear, pushing against inner race. After fitting, make sure that bearing rotates smoothly. Fit selective fit snap ring over front end of input gear. Snap rings are available in 5 thicknesses. Select thickest snap ring that will fit in groove. See INPUT GEAR BEARING SNAP RING table.

INPUT GEAR BEARING SNAP RING

Ring Color	Thickness In. (mm)
None	.091 (2.30)
Red	.093 (2.35)
White	.094 (2.40)
Blue	.096 (2.45)
Green	.098 (2.50)

4) Press 2 ball bearings on front output shaft, pushing against inner race. After fitting, make sure bearings rotate smoothly. Install ball bearing over rear output shaft from rear. Press into place, pushing against inner race. Check for smooth rotation.

5) Install stop plate. Install 2-4WD clutch hub and sleeve. Make sure hub and sleeve face correct direction. *See Fig. 4.* Install steel ball (for sprocket sleeve positioning) on rear output shaft. Install sprocket sleeve.

Fig. 4: Installation Of Clutch Hubs And Sleeve

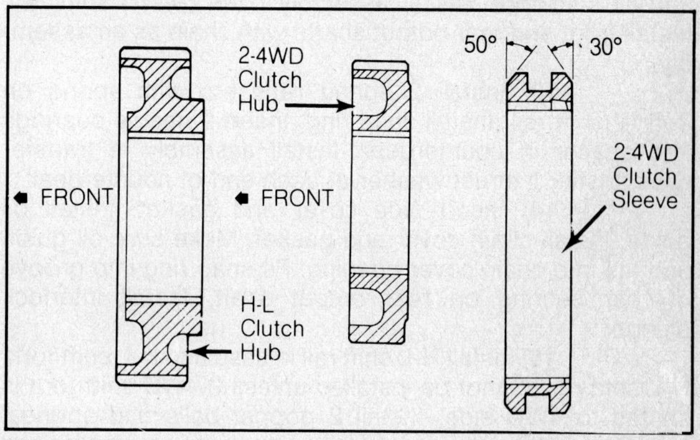

Clutch hubs and sleeve must face direction shown for proper operation.

6) Install 2 needle bearings on outer circumference of sprocket sleeve. Install drive sprocket. Install steel balls and sprocket spacer. Press ball bearing onto inner race. Check for smooth rotation.

7) Tighten mainshaft lock nut. Lock detent with punch. After lock nut is tightened, make sure that drive sprocket rotates smoothly. Install needle bearing, thrust washer and low speed gear on front of rear output shaft.

8) Install needle bearing, thrust washer and low speed gear on front of rear output shaft. Mount H-L clutch hub. Make sure hub faces correct direction. *See Fig. 4.*

Transfer Cases

CHRYSLER CORP. IMPORTS & MITSUBISHI (Cont.)

H-L CLUTCH HUB SNAP RING

Ring Color	Thickness In. (mm)
None	.084 (2.14)
Yellow	.087 (2.21)
White	.090 (2.28)
Blue	.093 (2.35)
Red	.095 (2.42)

INPUT GEAR RETAINER SNAP RING

Ring Color	Thickness In. (mm)
Purple	.106 (2.70)
Pink	.108 (2.75)
Yellow	.110 (2.80)
White	.112 (2.85)
Blue	.114 (2.90)

9) Mount H-L clutch hub snap ring on front end of rear output shaft. Selective fit snap rings are available in 5 thicknesses. Use thickest snap ring that will fit in output shaft groove. See H-L CLUTCH HUB SNAP RING table.

10) Install input gear assembly in transfer case. Input gear retaining snap rings are available in 5 thicknesses. Use thickest snap ring that will fit in input gear groove. See INPUT GEAR RETAINER SNAP RING table.

11) Insert needle bearing in input gear. Install H-L clutch sleeve and shift fork. Clutch sleeve must face same direction as 2-4WD clutch sleeve. Install 2-4WD shift rail. *See Fig. 4.*

12) Engage chain securely on front and rear output shaft sprockets. Assemble 2-4WD clutch sleeve with 2-4WD shift fork. Install assembly over 2-4WD shift rail. Install front and rear output shafts with chain as an assembly.

13) Install 2 spring retainers with spring on 2-4WD shift rail. Install snap ring. Insert 2 needle bearings and spacer in countergear. Install assembly in transfer case. Install 1 thrust washer at each end of countergear.

14) Insert side cover and gasket. Install oil guide. Install chain cover and gasket. Make sure oil guide end fits into chain cover opening. Fit snap ring into groove of rear bearing on rear output shaft. Install interlock plunger.

15) Install H-L shift rail in case and H-L shift fork. H-L shift rail cannot be installed unless 2-4WD shift fork is shifted to 4WD side. Install 2 poppet balls and springs. Install seal plug. When installing poppet spring, smaller end must be toward ball.

16) With H-L shift fork and shift rail spring holes aligned, drive in roll pin with punch. Roll pin should be installed with slit on center line of shift rail.

17) Install wave spring on rear of rear output shaft bearing. Install rear cover and gasket. Install wave spring on back of rear bearing on front output shaft. Install cover and gasket.

18) Check clearance between rear end of bearing and cover. *See Fig. 5.* Clearance should be .079" (2 mm). If clearance is excessive, change spacer to reduce clearance to less than .079" (2 mm). See OUTPUT SHAFT BEARING CLEARANCE SPACER table.

OUTPUT SHAFT BEARING CLEARANCE SPACER

Spacer Color	Thickness In. (mm)
Black	.033 (.84)
None	.037 (.93)
Red	.040 (1.02)
White	.044 (1.11)
Yellow	.047 (1.20)
Blue	.051 (1.29)
Green	.054 (1.38)

Fig. 5: Rear Output Shaft Bearing Clearance

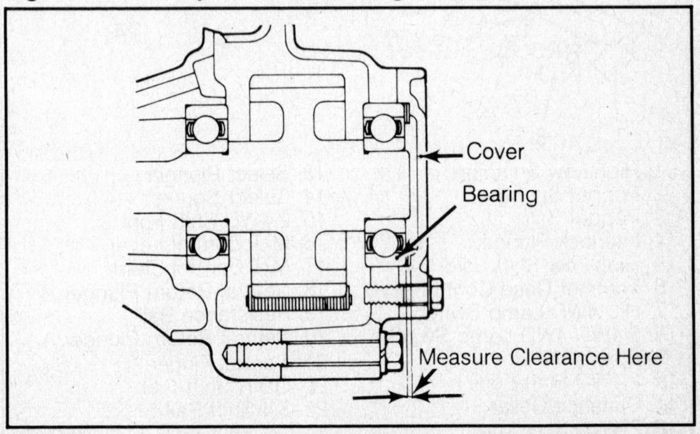

Clearance between cover and bearing should be less than .079" (2 mm).

19) Install speedometer sleeve assembly in rear cover. Align match mark on speedometer sleeve with mark on case according to number of teeth on speedometer driven gear. Install sleeve clamp and tighten bolt. Install two 4WD lamp switches with steel balls.

Fig. 6: Aligning Speedometer Sleeve

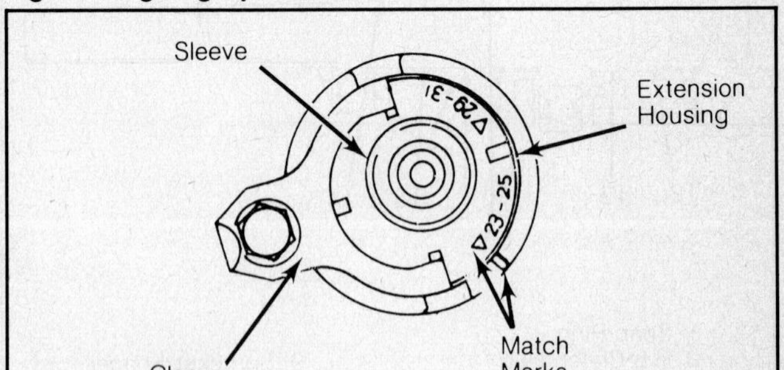

Align marks according to number of teeth on driven gear.

TIGHTENING SPECIFICATIONS

Application	Ft. Lbs. (N.m)
Chain & Side Cover Bolts	22-30 (30-41)
Cover Bolts	11-15 (15-21)
Drain, Fill & Select Plugs	22-25 (30-34)
Rear Output Shaft Lock Nut	73-94 (98-127)
Speedometer Sleeve Clamp Bolt	11-15 (15-21)
Transfer Case Mounting Nuts & Bolts	22-30 (30-41)
4WD Switch	22 (30)

NISSAN

4WD Pickup

DESCRIPTION

Two-speed transfer case is bolted to frame. Short propeller shaft connects transmission to transfer case. Transfer case is connected to drive axles by propeller shafts. Transfer case can be shifted into "4H" range at any speed, if locking hubs are set in "LOCK" position. Vehicle must be stopped before shifting into "4L" range. Transfer case is provided with indicator switch and light. Indicator light should be on whenever transfer lever is in "4H", "N" or "4L" positions.

LUBRICATION

SERVICE INTERVAL

Under normal operating conditions, check gear oil every 15,000 miles or 12 months (whichever comes first). Under severe operating conditions, change fluid every 30,000 miles or 24 months (whichever comes first).

FLUID TYPE

Use hypoid gear oil with API classification of GL-4 and viscosity of SAE 80W-90 or SAE 75W-90.

CAPACITY

3.0 pts (1.4L).

REMOVAL & INSTALLATION

TRANSFER CASE ASSEMBLY

Removal

1) Disconnect negative battery cable. Remove shift lever boot from floor pan. Raise vehicle and support securely. Remove transfer case protector pan.

2) Disconnect short input propeller shaft at transmission. Remove front and rear propeller shafts. Disconnect wiring at 4WD indicator switch. Disconnect speedometer cable and remove exhaust pipe. Support transfer case with transmission jack.

3) Loosen transfer case insulator bolts. Make sure transfer case shift lever boot is free of floor pan. Lower transfer case with input propeller shaft. Remove insulators from transfer case.

Installation

Install transfer case in reverse order of removal. Make sure transfer case is filled with proper amount and type of lubricant after installation.

OVERHAUL

DISASSEMBLY

1) Make sure transfer case is clean of dirt and grease. Drain gear oil. Place control lever in "4L" and "2H" positions to aid in removing output flange lock nuts.

Fig. 1: Exploded View of Transfer Case Housings and Shift Linkage

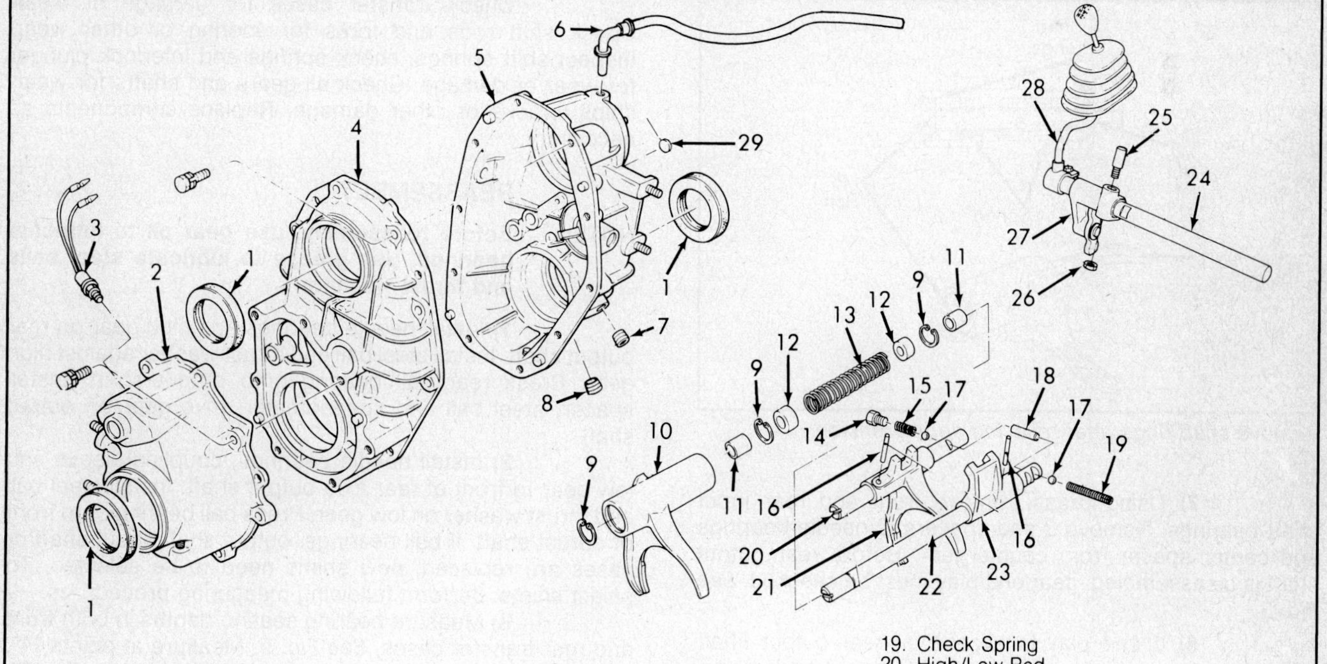

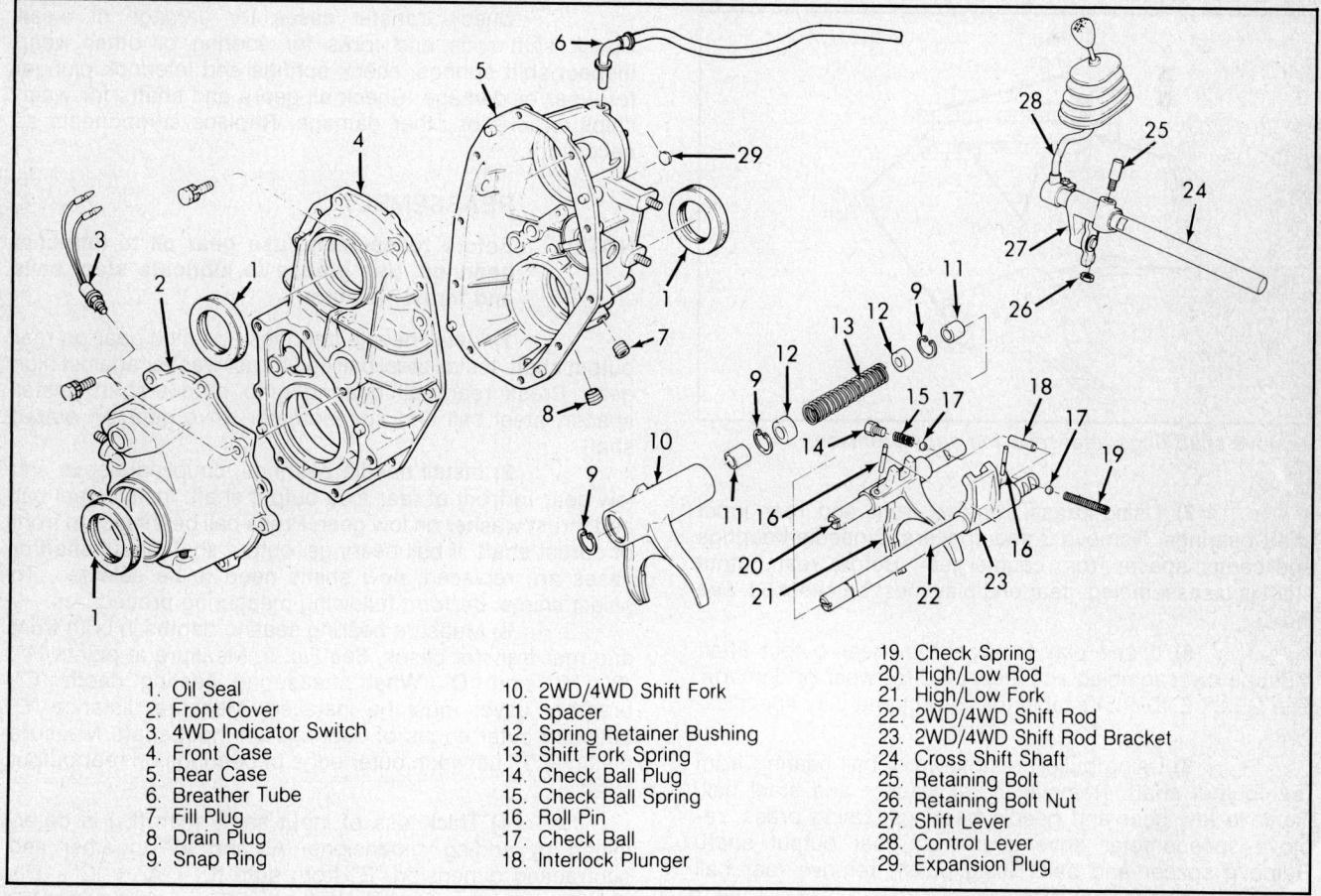

1. Oil Seal
2. Front Cover
3. 4WD Indicator Switch
4. Front Case
5. Rear Case
6. Breather Tube
7. Fill Plug
8. Drain Plug
9. Snap Ring
10. 2WD/4WD Shift Fork
11. Spacer
12. Spring Retainer Bushing
13. Shift Fork Spring
14. Check Ball Plug
15. Check Ball Spring
16. Roll Pin
17. Check Ball
18. Interlock Plunger
19. Check Spring
20. High/Low Rod
21. High/Low Fork
22. 2WD/4WD Shift Rod
23. 2WD/4WD Shift Rod Bracket
24. Cross Shift Shaft
25. Retaining Bolt
26. Retaining Bolt Nut
27. Shift Lever
28. Control Lever
29. Expansion Plug

2) Using Flange Spanner (ST31530000), hold output flanges while removing lock nuts. Remove flanges. Remove 4WD indicator switch. Remove transfer case front cover. Using soft mallet, tap cover to aid removal.

3) Remove front output shaft and needle bearing. Remove snap ring holding 2WD/4WD shift fork on shift rod. Remove shift fork assembly with spacer and coupling sleeve. *See Figs. 1 and 4.* Remove coupling hub snap ring and coupling hub. Remove front transfer case retaining bolts. Tap front case with soft mallet to aid removal. DO NOT pry case halves apart with screwdriver as machined surfaces could be damaged.

4) Remove retaining bolt and nut from cross shift shaft. Remove cross shift shaft. Remove shift lever with differential lever. Remove check ball plug, spring and ball. Drive roll pin out of High/Low shift fork. Tap rear output shaft assembly with soft mallet.

5) Remove output shaft with High/Low shift fork and countergear assembly. Remove input shaft assembly. Be careful when removing countergear assembly so needle bearings do not drop. Remove transfer case front shim. Make sure to save shim in safe location for reassembly. Remove shift rods, interlock plunger, steel ball and check spring.

6) Drive roll pin out of 2WD/4WD shift fork. Remove fork shaft. Insert 8 mm bolt with nut into shift fork. Tighten 8 mm nut to relieve spring tension in shift fork. *See Fig. 2.* Remove snap ring. Remove 8 mm nut and bolt slowly. Remove spring retainer bushings and shift fork spring.

Fig. 2: Compressing Spring in 2WD/4WD Shift Fork

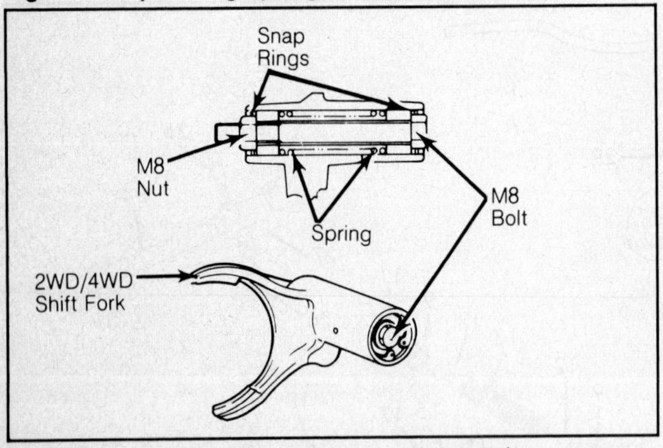

Remove snap rings after relieving spring tension.

7) Using press, remove front and rear input shaft bearings. Remove 2 end spacers, 2 needle bearings and center spacer from countergear. Before rear output shaft is disassembled, gear end play must be checked. *See Fig. 3.*

8) If end play is excessive, rear output shaft must be disassembled and inspected for wear or damage. See GEAR END PLAY table for correct end play specifications.

9) Using puller, remove front ball bearing from rear output shaft. Remove thrust washer and steel ball. Remove low gear and needle bearings. Using press, remove speedometer drive gear from rear output shaft. Remove spacer and ball. Using puller, remove rear ball bearing from rear output shaft.

Fig. 3: Checking Gear End Play on Rear Output Shaft

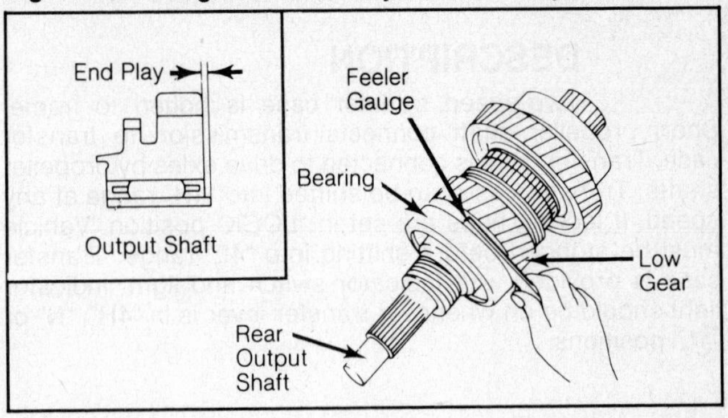

GEAR END PLAY

Application	In. (mm)
High Gear	.004-.008 (.10-.20)
Low Gear	.004-.008 (.10-.20)
Coupling Hub	0-.008 (0-.20)

10) Remove thrust washer, steel ball, high gear, needle bearings and coupling sleeve. Check transfer case, bearings and oil seals for damage. If components are damaged, pry out all oil seals. On front cover, remove snap ring and press bearing out.

INSPECTION

Check transfer cases for damage or wear. Check shift rods and forks for scoring or other wear. Inspect shift springs, check springs and interlock plunger for wear or damage. Check all gears and shafts for wear, chips, cracks or other damage. Replace components as necessary.

REASSEMBLY

NOTE: Before reassembly, use gear oil to lubricate bearings. Use grease to lubricate steel balls and thrust washers.

1) Install needle bearings and high gear on rear output shaft. Install steel ball and thrust washer against high gear. Press rear ball bearing onto output shaft. Install spacer, steel ball and speedometer drive gear on output shaft.

2) Install needle bearings, coupling sleeve and low gear to front of rear axle output shaft. Install steel ball and thrust washer on low gear. Press ball bearing onto front of output shaft. If ball bearings, output shaft, input shaft or cases are replaced, new shims need to be selected. To select shims, perform following measuring procedures.

3) Measure bearing seating depths in both front and rear transfer cases. *See Fig. 5.* Measure at points "A", "B", "C" and "D". When measuring seating depth "C", breather cover must be installed. Measure distance "E" between outer edges of bearings on input shaft. Measure distance "F" between outer edge of bearings on rear output shaft.

4) Thickness of input shaft shim (L_1) is determined by adding dimensions "A" and "C" together and subtracting dimension "E" from sum (L_1="A" + "C" - "E"). Thickness of rear output shaft shim (L_2) is determined by

Fig. 4: Exploded View of Gears And Shafts

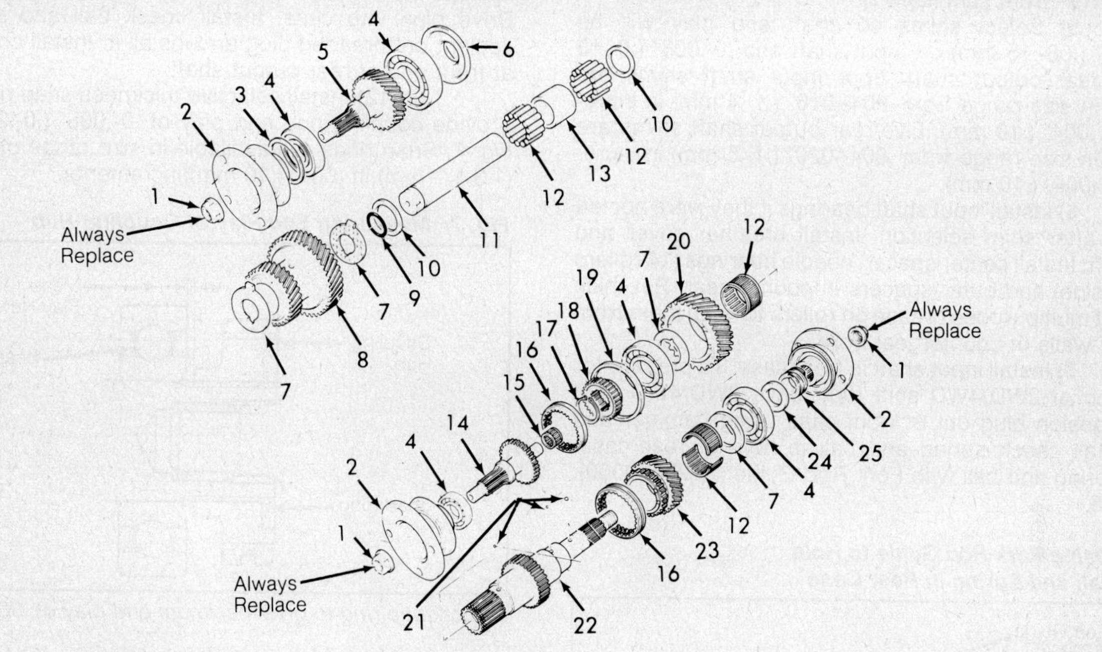

1. Output Flange Nut
2. Output Flange
3. Shim
4. Ball Bearing
5. Input Shaft
6. Breather Cover
7. Thrust Washer
8. Countergear
9. "O" Ring
10. Spacer
11. Countershaft
12. Needle Bearings
13. Front Output Shaft
14. Pilot Bearing
15. Coupling Sleeve
16. Snap Ring
17. Coupling Hub
18. Shim
19. Low Gear
20. Steel Ball
21. Rear Output Shaft
22. High Gear
23. Speedometer Drive Gear

Fig. 5: Measuring Bearing Seating Depths and Gearset Lengths

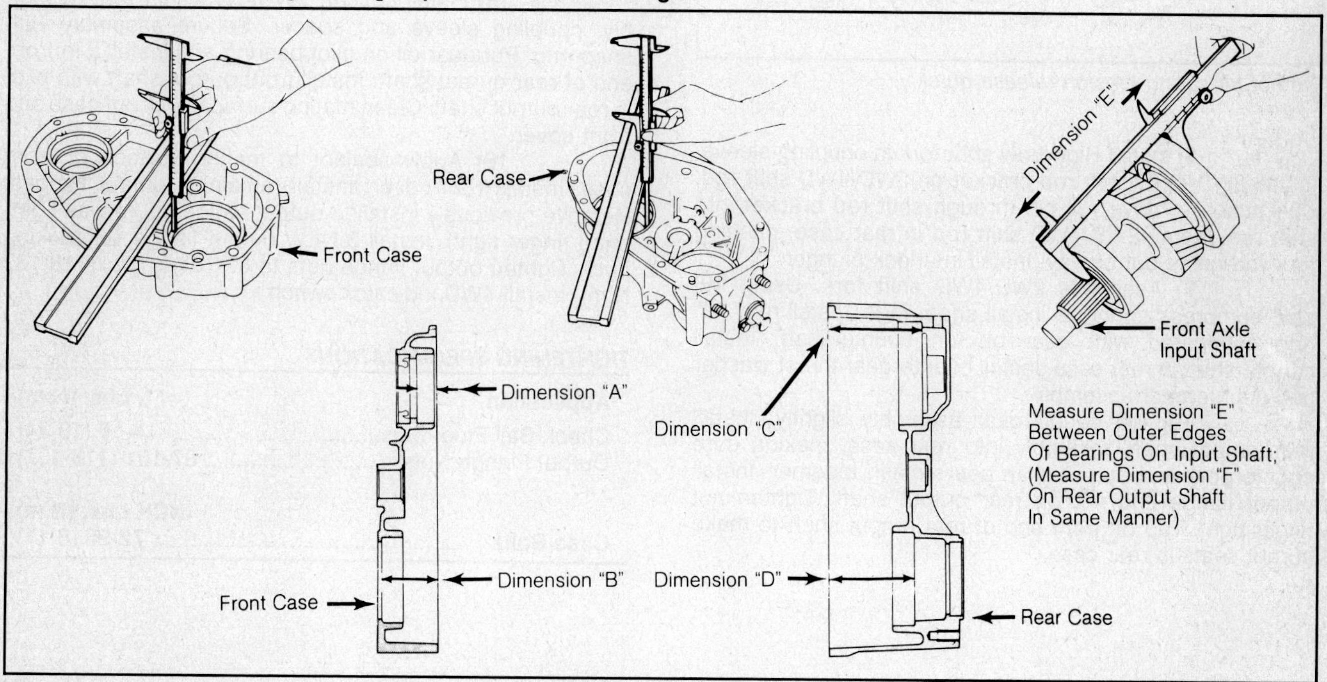

Measure at these points to determine correct shim thickness.

Transfer Cases

NISSAN (Cont.)

adding dimensions "B" and "D" together and subtracting dimension "F" from sum (L_2="B" + "D" - "F").

5) Select shims so shaft end play will be .002-.006" (.06-.15 mm) on input shaft and .0-.005" (.0-.13 mm) on rear output shaft. Four input shaft shims are available in size range from .004-.016" (.1-.4 mm) in increments of .004" (.10 mm). Five rear output shaft shims are available in size range from .004-.020" (.1-.5 mm) in increments of .004" (.10 mm).

6) Install input shaft bearings if they were not left on shaft after shim selection. Install breather cover and input shaft. Install center spacer, needle bearings (14 rollers on each side) and outer spacers in countergear. Put thick coating of multipurpose grease on rollers to keep them from falling off walls of countergear bore.

7) Install input shaft in front case. To prepare for installation of 2WD/4WD shift fork, drive 2WD/4WD shift fork expansion plug out of front case using hammer and drift. Install check spring and ball in hole of rear case. Retain spring and ball with Fork Rod Guide (ST23620000). *See Fig. 6.*

Fig. 6: Using Fork Rod Guide to Hold Check Ball and Spring in Rear Case

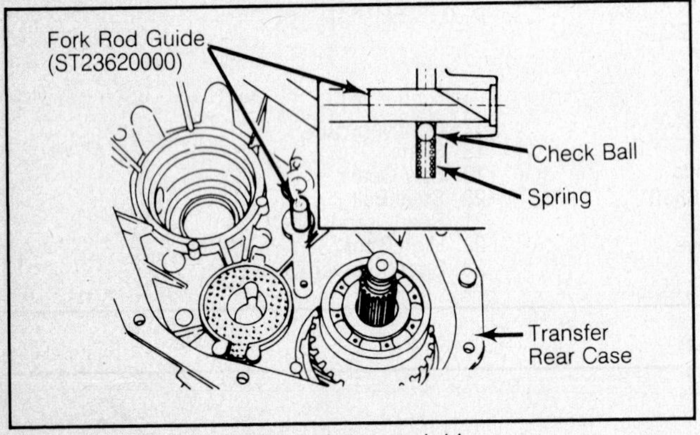

Do not let spring tension release quickly.

8) Install High/Low shift fork in coupling sleeve. Install 2WD/4WD shift rod bracket on 2WD/4WD shift rod. Use punch to drive roll pin through shift rod bracket into shift rod. Install 2WD/4WD shift rod in rear case, pushing fork rod guide out of way. Install interlock plunger.

9) Assemble 2WD/4WD shift fork. Using M8 bolt, compress spring to install snap rings. Install new "O" ring, lubricated with gear oil, on countershaft. Install countershaft in rear case. Install countergear thrust washer and countergear assembly.

10) Lift countergear assembly slightly. Install rear output shaft assembly into rear case, making sure countergear and output shaft gears mesh together. Install output flange and nut on rear output shaft. Tighten nut finger tight. Tap on front end of rear output shaft to make sure it seats in rear case.

11) Install High/Low rod. Secure fork to rod with roll pin. Apply sealant to 2WD/4WD shift fork plug hole. Drive plug into case. Install check ball and spring. Put sealant on threaded plug and install it. Install coupling hub at front end of rear output shaft.

12) Install selective thickness snap ring that will provide coupling hub end play of .0-.008" (.0-.2 mm). *See Fig. 7.* Snap rings are available in size range of .051-.067" (1.3-1.7 mm) in .004" (.10 mm) increments.

Fig. 7: Measuring End Play of Coupling Hub

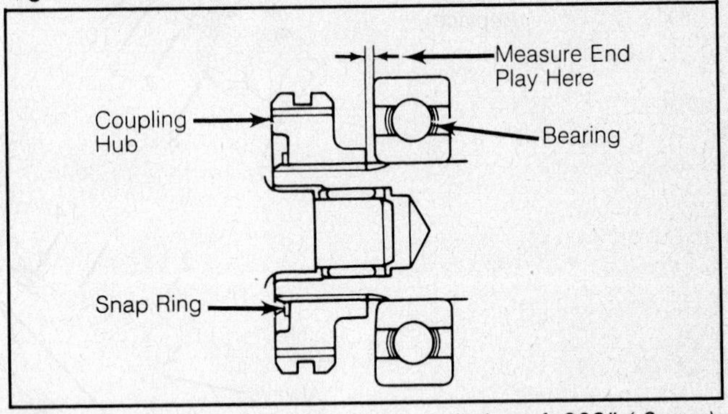

Select snap ring to give maximum end play of .008" (.2 mm).

13) Install shift lever with differential lever. Install cross shift shaft. Apply grease to thrust washer and both shims selected in steps **4)** and **5)**. Install washers and shims in front case. Clean mating surfaces of front case. Apply sealant to mating surface of front case.

14) Install front case on rear case. Make sure gear assemblies, shift forks, shift rods, shims and thrust washer remain in correct positions. Tapping case with soft mallet will aid in installation.

15) Install spacer, 2WD/4WD shift fork assembly, coupling sleeve and spacer. Secure assembly with snap ring. Put gear oil on pilot bearing and install it in front end of rear output shaft. Install front output shaft with pilot in rear output shaft. Clean mating surfaces of front case and front cover.

16) Apply sealant to mating surface of front case. Install front cover. Install remaining output flanges. Remove previously installed output flange nut (it was tightened finger tight). Install 3 NEW output flange self-locking nuts. Tighten output flange nuts to 87-101 ft. lbs. (118-137 N.m). Install 4WD indicator switch.

TIGHTENING SPECIFICATIONS

Application	Ft. Lbs. (N.m)
Check Ball Plug	14-18 (19-24)
Output Flange Nuts	87-101 (118-137)
	INCH Lbs. (N.m)
Case Bolts	72-96 (8-11)

Transfer Cases

TOYOTA

Land Cruiser

DESCRIPTION

Two-speed transfer case is mounted on back of transmission. Transfer case provides direct drive high speed and underdrive low speed to rear axle and to front axle when 4WD is selected. High and low speeds as well as 4WD are selected through auxiliary shifter.

LUBRICATION

Under normal operating conditions, check fluid level every 15,000 miles or 12 months (whichever comes first). Under severe operating conditions, drain and refill transfer case every 15,000 miles or 12 months (whichever comes first).

FLUID TYPE

Transfer case uses hypoid gear oil with API classification of GL-4 or GL-5 and viscosity of SAE 90.

CAPACITY

Transfer case requires 2.3 qts. (2.2L) for refill.

REMOVAL & INSTALLATION

TRANSFER CASE ASSEMBLY

Removal

Remove PTO (if equipped) from transfer case and hang from frame with wire. Remove transmission and transfer case assembly from vehicle. See TOYOTA MANUAL TRANSMISSION REMOVAL article in IMPORT GENERAL SERVICING section.

Installation

Reverse removal procedure and refill gear cases with lubricant.

OVERHAUL

DISASSEMBLY & INSPECTION

Disassembly

1) Remove speedometer driven gear, bolt and retainer. Remove transfer shift lever assembly. Check rear output shaft bearing preload. Preload should be 15-25 INCH lbs. (1.7-2.8 N.m) for new bearings and 6-10 INCH lbs. (.68-1.1 N.m) for used bearings. Remove detent balls, springs and output shaft cover.

Fig. 1: Exploded View Of Toyota Land Cruiser Transfer Case

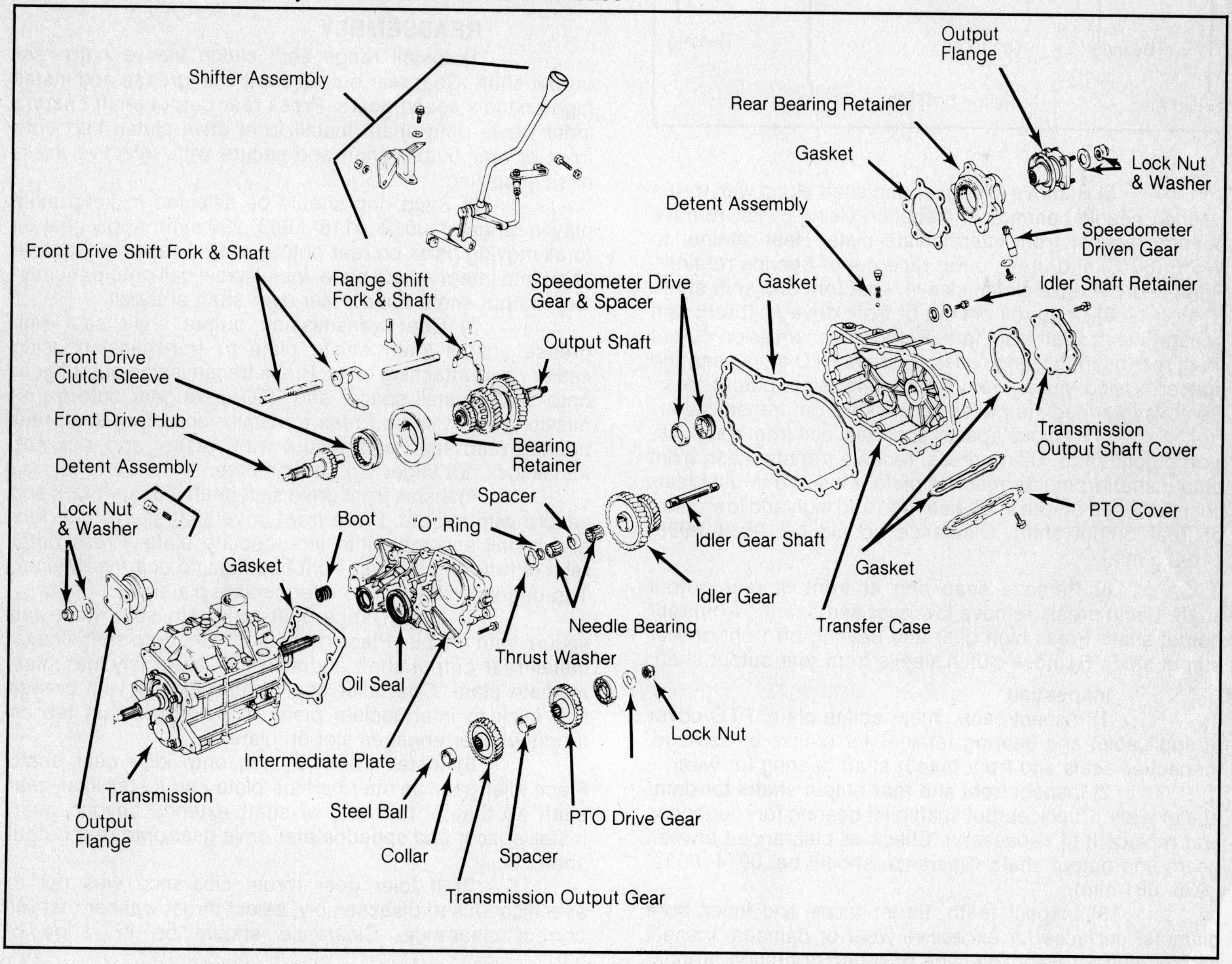

Transfer Cases

TOYOTA (Cont.)

2) Shift transfer case into 4WD Low range. Remove transmission output shaft nut and transfer case output flange nuts. Remove both output flanges. Remove rear output shaft bearing retainer and gasket. Remove idler gear shaft lock plate. Remove PTO cover if vehicle is not equipped with PTO.

3) Measure idler gear thrust clearance through PTO opening. Clearance should be .0108-.0246" (.274-.625 mm). If clearance exceeds specifications, idler gear thrust washer will need to be replaced at reassembly. Remove transfer case-to-intermediate plate attaching bolts.

4) Separate transfer case from intermediate plate. Remove speedometer drive gear and spacer from rear output shaft. Remove rear output shaft together with range shift fork and shift shaft. Drive roll pin out of range shift fork and separate fork from shaft.

Fig. 2: Exploded View Of Rear Output Shaft

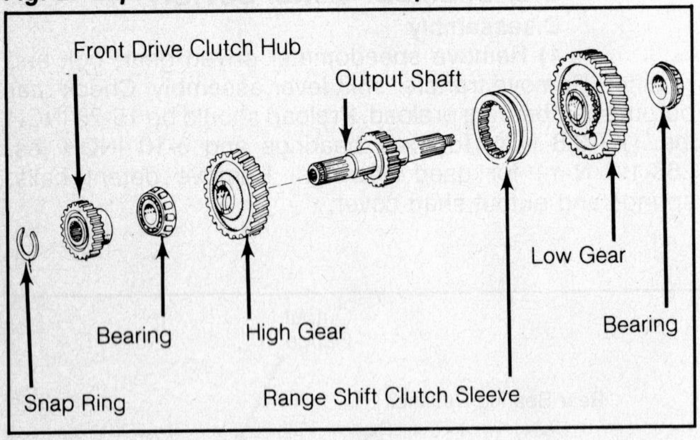

5) Remove idler gear and shaft along with thrust washer, needle bearings and spacer. Using puller, remove bearing retainer from intermediate plate. Heat retainer to 175°F (80°C) and press outer race out of bearing retainer. Remove front drive clutch sleeve, shift fork and shift shaft.

6) Drive roll pin out of front drive shift fork and separate shift shaft from fork. Remove transmission output shaft rear bearing using puller. Remove PTO drive gear and spacer. Using puller, remove transmission output gear. Remove intermediate plate and gasket from transmission.

7) Remove spacer and steel ball from transmission output shaft. Using press, remove transfer case front output shaft from intermediate plate. Measure thrust clearance between output shaft bearings and high and low gears on rear output shaft. Clearance should be .0039-.0098" (.10-.25 mm).

8) Remove snap ring at front of rear output shaft. Using press, remove low gear and bearing from rear output shaft. Press high gear and bearing off front of rear output shaft. Remove clutch sleeve from rear output shaft.

Inspection

1) Inspect case, intermediate plate, PTO cover (if applicable) and bearing retainer for cracks or damage. Inspect oil seals and front output shaft bearing for wear.

2) Inspect front and rear output shafts for damage or wear. Check output shaft pilot bearing for roughness and replace it (if necessary). Check oil clearance between gears and output shaft. Clearance should be .0014-.0032" (.035-.081 mm).

3) Inspect teeth, thrust faces and inner bore diameter surfaces for excessive wear or damage. Inspect all bearings for wear, damage or rough operation. If inner

Fig. 3: Thrust Measurement On Output Shaft

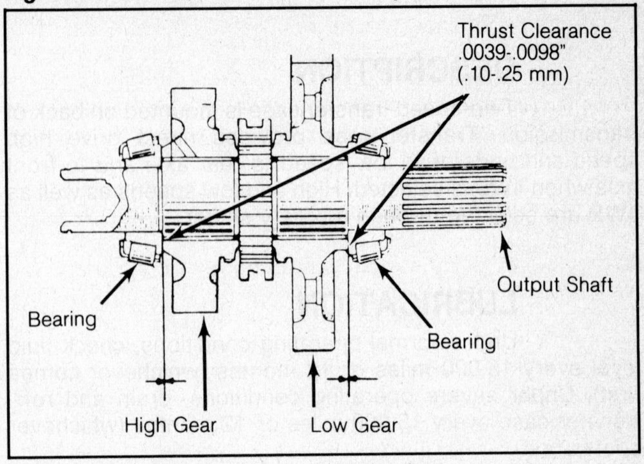

Measure between bearings and gear faces.

bearing race requires replacement, outer race should be replaced at same time.

4) Insert shift forks into clutch sleeves and measure clearance between fork and sleeve. Clearance should be .004-.016" (.1-.4 mm). Inspect idler gear for chipped teeth or excessive wear. Check idler gear shaft and bearings for wear or damage.

REASSEMBLY

1) Install range shift clutch sleeve onto rear output shaft. Coat rear output shaft with grease and install high and low speed gears. Press rear output shaft bearing inner races onto shaft. Install front drive clutch hub onto front of rear output shaft and secure with selective thickness snap ring.

2) Snap ring should be selected to keep axial play in range of .0012-.0118" (.003-.299 mm). Apply gear oil to all moving parts on rear output shaft. Press front output shaft into intermediate plate. Install steel ball onto transmission output shaft. Slide collar over shaft and ball.

3) Coat transmission output shaft seal with grease. Install intermediate plate to transmission using sealer on all attaching bolts. Press transmission output gear onto shaft. Install spacer and PTO drive gear onto transmission output shaft. Press transmission output shaft rear bearing onto shaft and secure with washer and lock nut. Install lock nut finger tight at this time.

4) Install front drive shift shaft into shift fork and secure with roll pin. Place front drive shift sleeve into fork and install assembly into intermediate plate. Press outer race of rear output shaft front bearing into bearing retainer. Tap bearing retainer into intermediate plate.

5) Install range shift fork onto shift shaft and secure with roll pin. Place range shift fork onto shift sleeve. Install rear output shaft and shift fork assembly into intermediate plate. Coat idler gear thrust washer with grease and stick to intermediate plate, making sure that tab on thrust washer engages slot on plate.

6) Install front "O" ring onto idler gear shaft. Place idler gear on intermediate plate and install idler gear shaft so that 2" (50 mm) of shaft extends beyond gear. Install spacer and speedometer drive gear onto rear output shaft.

7) If idler gear thrust clearance was not to specifications at disassembly, select thrust washer that will correct clearance. Clearance should be in range of

.0108-.0246" (.275-.625 mm). Coat idler gear thrust washer with grease and place on transfer case. Make sure that tab on thrust washer engages slot in case.

8) Install transfer case onto intermediate plate, taking care to engage range selector lever tip with groove in range shift shaft. Install transfer case attaching bolts using liquid sealer.

9) Rotate idler gear shaft so that locking groove aligns with bolt hole. Install rear "O" ring on idler shaft. Tap shaft into place. Secure shaft with locking plate and bolt. Check operation of range shift lever to ensure smooth operation and proper engagement.

10) Recheck idler gear thrust clearance. Install rear bearing retainer, making sure that rib on case and retainer line up. Shift transfer case to 4WD Low range. Install front and rear output flanges and secure with washers and lock nuts. Hold output shaft stationary and tighten output flange nuts and transmission output shaft nut.

11) Disengage front drive and check rear output shaft bearing preload. Rotational torque should be 13-24 INCH lbs. (1.47-2.71 N.m) for new bearings and 6-10 INCH lbs. (.678-1.13 N.m) for used bearings.

12) If preload is not within specifications, preload shims must be changed. Preload shims are located between rear bearing retainer and rear output shaft bearing outer race.

13) Install PTO and transmission output shaft covers. Use liquid sealer on all bolts. Install shifter assembly. Check for smooth operation and proper engagement of all gear ranges.

TIGHTENING SPECIFICATIONS

Application	Ft. Lbs. (N.m)
Intermediate Plate Bolts	37-57 (50-77)
Transfer Case-to-Intermediate Plate Bolts	
10 mm Bolts	26-32 (35-43)
12 mm Bolts	37-57 (50-77)
Rear Bearing Retainer Bolt	22-33 (30-45)
Output Flange Nuts	102-122 (138-165)

Transfer Cases

TOYOTA

4Runner, 4WD Pickup

DESCRIPTION

Two-speed transfer case is connected to rear of transmission by adapter housing. High range is used in both 2WD and 4WD modes depending upon traction needs. Low range is used only in 4WD mode when maximum power and traction is required. Neutral range is to be used only when vehicle is stopped and winch or other optional equipment is being used.

Either manual or automatic locking front hubs are available. These hubs are set to "FREE" position in 2WD mode so that front drive axle shafts and front propeller shaft are disengaged from front wheels. As shafts do not turn, wear and noise are reduced. Disengaging front drive train usually also results in more economical operation. Both front hubs must be in same position for proper operation.

OPERATION

NOTE: **When operating in 2WD in cold climates, noise may be heard until transfer case reaches normal operating temperature. Always operate in 4WD in cold climates until transfer case is warmed up.**

Manual Locking Hubs

Transfer case control lever is set in "H2" position for normal 2WD operation in good driving conditions. Front hubs should be in "FREE" position. BOTH front hubs must be set to "LOCK" position before shifting to any 4WD mode.

Whenever transfer case control lever is in "H4", "N" or "L4" positions, switch on transfer case will close causing "4WD" indicator light to come on. When returning to 2WD ("H2") mode, both front hubs should be returned to "FREE" positon.

If front hubs are in "LOCK" position, shift from "H2" to "H4" may be made at any speed without using clutch. If shifting is difficult, depress or release gas pedal momentarily while pushing against transfer shift lever. Maximum operating speed in "H4" mode should be no greater than 50 MPH.

Before shifting into "4L" position from "4H" position, vehicle must be completely stopped. Move transfer case shift lever to "4L" position. If shifting is difficult, drive vehicle short distance in either direction and try to complete shift again. Maximum operating speed in "4L" should be no greater than 25 MPH.

Automatic Locking Hubs

"H2" operation is same in vehicles with manual or automatic front hubs. Whenever transfer case control lever is in "H4", "N" or "L4" positions, switch on transfer case will close causing "4WD" indicator light to come on. Shifting from 2WD to 4WD while moving, quick starts or spinning wheels on wet surfaces may cause both noise and excessive wear in automatic locking hubs.

When shifting to "H4" position from "H2" position or between "H4" and "L4" positions, vehicle must be brought to complete stop. After shift is completed, start out slowly from stop to allow hubs to engage automatically. If shifting is difficult, drive vehicle in either direction for short distance. Try shift again.

Shift from "H4" position to "H2" position may be made with vehicle moving at any speed without using clutch. If shifting is difficult, depress or release gas pedal momentarily while pushing against transfer shift lever. Automatic front hubs will remain locked until vehicle is driven slowly in Reverse for distance of 10 feet.

NOTE: **In order to assure proper lubrication of all front end components, vehicle should be operated with hubs in "LOCK" position for minimum of 10 miles per month.**

LUBRICATION

SERVICE INTERVAL

Under normal operating conditions, check fluid level every 15,000 miles or 18 months (whichever comes first). Under severe operating conditions, drain and refill transfer case every 15,000 miles or 18 months (whichever comes first).

FLUID TYPE

Transfer case uses hypoid gear oil with API classification of GL-4 or GL-5 and viscosity of SAE 75W-90.

CAPACITY

1.7 qts. (1.6L).

REMOVAL & INSTALLATION

TRANSFER CASE ASSEMBLY

Removal

1) Transmission and transfer case are removed and installed as complete assembly. See TOYOTA MANUAL TRANSMISSION REMOVAL article in IMPORT GENERAL SERVICING section for removal procedure.

2) Place transmission and transfer assembly in upright position with transfer case at top. Rest bellhousing on 2 wooden blocks to avoid possible damage to transmission input shaft. Remove rear engine mount from reduction gear case.

3) Remove front propeller shaft upper dust cover from bracket. Remove bolts holding transfer reduction gear case to adapter. Pull transfer case straight up to remove assembly from adapter. Be careful to avoid damaging rear oil seal in adapter with splines of transfer input gear.

Installation

1) Stand transmission on end with bellhousing resting on wooden blocks to avoid possible damage to input shaft. Set transfer shift fork shafts in positions for "H4" operation. Put some multipurpose grease on adapter oil seal. Place new gasket on transfer adapter. Lower transfer case onto transmission. Do not let transfer input splines damage adapter oil seal.

2) Install bolts holding transfer to adapter. Install bolts holding front propeller shaft upper dust cover to bracket. Make sure that bolts holding dust cover are 1.7" (43 mm) in length and bolts holding transfer case to adapter are 1.5" (39 mm) in length.

3) Complete transmission installation as described in TOYOTA MANUAL TRANSMISSION REMOVAL article in IMPORT GENERAL SERVICING section. Be sure to fill both transmission and transfer case assemblies with correct type of gear oil.

Transfer Cases

TOYOTA (Cont.)

Fig. 1: Exploded View Of Transfer Case Components

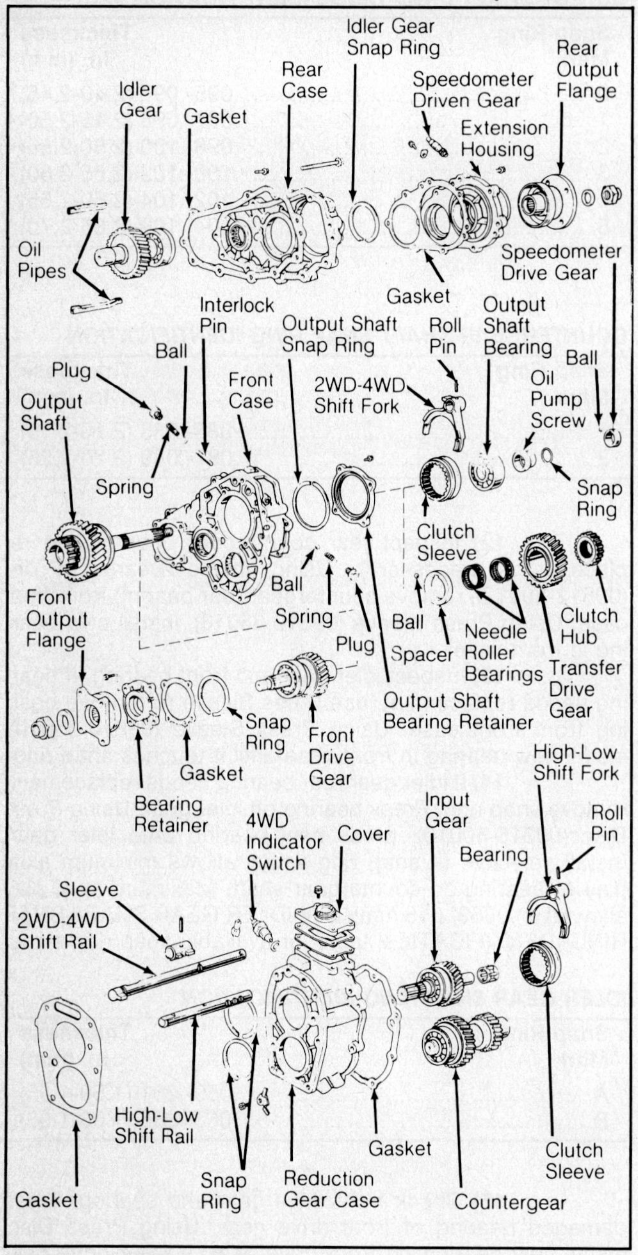

OVERHAUL

DISASSEMBLY & INSPECTION

Disassembly

1) Remove speedometer driven gear and transfer indicator switch. Loosen staked portion of both output flange nuts. Remove flanges. Remove extension housing. Remove speedometer drive gear, steel ball, oil pump screw and bearing.

2) Remove rear case with idler gear. Do not let case fall as clutch hub and steel ball could fall and be damaged. Remove idler gear snap ring. With case supported on wooden blocks, use soft mallet to drive idler gear from rear case. Remove bearing retainer. Remove snap ring from front output gear. Using soft mallet, drive gear out of case.

3) Remove 2 oil pipes. Using pin punch, drive out roll pin in No. 1 shift fork. Remove shift fork and clutch sleeve. Remove clutch hub and transfer drive gear. Remove needle roller bearing, No. 2 spacer and steel ball. On models with 22R-EC and diesel engines, remove shift lever retainer. On models with 22R engine, remove transfer case cover. Remove detent plugs, springs and steel balls.

4) Using pin punch, drive out roll pins in shift fork shaft. Remove front drive shift fork shaft. Remove interlock pin. Remove high-low shift fork shaft. Remove bolts holding front case to reduction case. Using soft mallet, remove front case with output shaft. Remove No. 2 fork together with clutch sleeve and needle bearing.

5) Remove 2 snap rings from input gear and countergear. Place reduction gear case on blocks of wood. Using soft mallet, tap input gear and countergear out of reduction gear case. Remove output shaft bearing retainer. Remove snap ring from output shaft bearing. Place front case on wooden blocks. Using soft mallet, tap output shaft from front case.

Inspection

1) Use dial indicator to check oil and thrust clearances between transfer low gear and output shaft. Measure oil clearance between low gear and output shaft with needle roller bearing installed. Standard range of clearance is .0004-.0022" (.010-.055 mm) with wear limit (maximum clearance) of .003" (.075 mm).

2) Measure thrust clearance of transfer low gear on output shaft with spacer and bearing installed on shaft. Do not allow shaft of dial indicator to touch sub-gear while measuring thrust. Standard range of clearance is .0039-.0098" (.10-.25 mm) with wear limit of .0118" (.30 mm).

3) Use dial indicator to check oil and thrust clearances between transfer drive gear and output shaft. Measure oil clearance between low gear and output shaft with needle roller bearing installed. Standard range of clearance is .0004-.0020" (.009-.051 mm) with wear limit of .0028" (.071 mm).

4) Measure thrust clearance of transfer drive gear on output shaft with spacer and clutch hub installed on shaft. Standard range of clearance is .0035-.0106" (.09-.27 mm) with wear limit of .0126" (.32 mm).

5) Using feeler gauge, measure clearance between shifting forks and clutch hub sleeves. Wear limit allowed is .039" (1.0 mm). Check input gear and bearing for damage or excessive wear. If bearing needs replacing, remove snap ring.

6) Using Bearing Puller (09950-20015), remove bearing from input gear. Using Press Disc (09316-60010), press new bearing onto shaft. Pick selective retaining snap ring that allows minimum axial play of bearing. Maximum axial play allowed is .0059" (.15 mm). See INPUT GEAR SNAP RING IDENTIFICATION table for available snap ring sizes.

INPUT GEAR SNAP RING IDENTIFICATION

Snap Ring Mark	Thickness In. (mm)
1	.081-.083 (2.05-2.10)
3	.085-.087 (2.15-2.20)
5	.089-.091 (2.25-2.30)

7) Check output shaft and bearing for damage or excessive wear. If output shaft front bearing, low gear or

Transfer Cases

TOYOTA (Cont.)

Fig. 2: Exploded View of Transfer Case Gears And Shafts

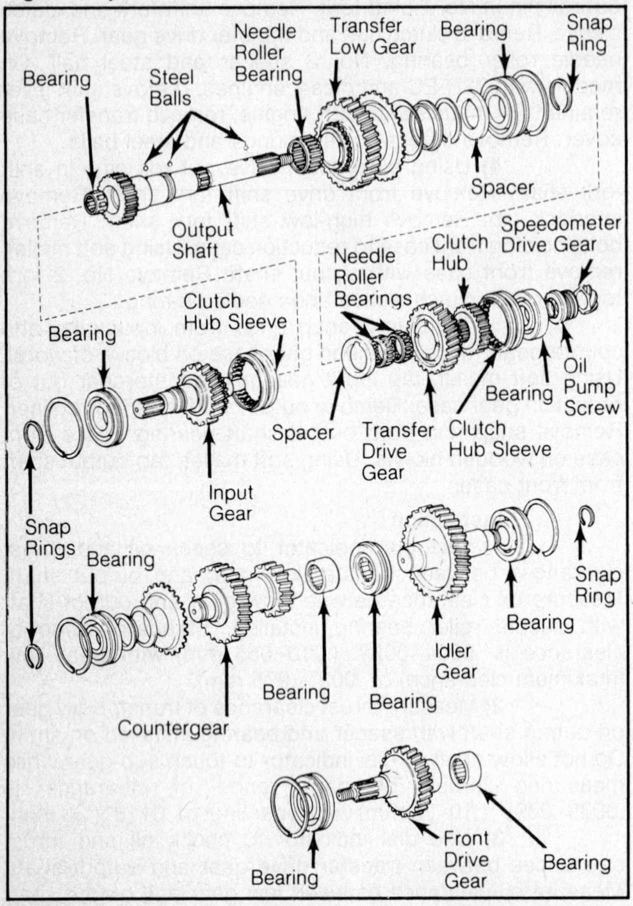

Always use new snap rings during reassembly.

sub-gear need replacing, remove snap ring. Using press and bearing puller, remove output shaft front bearing, No. 1 spacer and low gear. Remove steel ball and needle roller bearing. Using dial indicator, measure shaft runout. Maximum runout allowed for output shaft is .0012" (.03 mm).

8) Remove low gear snap ring. Remove and inspect spacer, thrust spring and sub-gear. Install good sub-gear, thrust spring and spacer. Install snap ring. Coat needle roller bearing with multipurpose grease. Install low gear and needle roller bearing on output shaft. Install steel ball and No. 1 spacer.

9) Using press and Press Sleeve (09316-60010), install new bearing on output shaft. Pick selective fit snap ring which allows minimum axial play of bearing on shaft. Maximum axial play allowed is .0039" (.10 mm). See OUTPUT GEAR SNAP RING IDENTIFICATION table for available snap ring sizes.

10) Check countergear and bearing. Remove snap ring if countergear front bearing or sub-gear need replacement. Using press and bearing puller, remove countergear front bearing. Remove spacer, thrust spring and sub-gear. Install good sub-gear, thrust spring and spacer.

11) Using press and 32 mm socket for press sleeve, press bearing onto countergear shaft. Install selective fit snap ring which allows minimum axial play of bearing on countergear shaft. Maximum axial play allowed is .0059" (.15 mm). See COUNTERGEAR SHAFT SNAP RING IDENTIFICATION table for available snap ring sizes.

OUTPUT SHAFT SNAP RINGS IDENTIFICATION

Snap Ring Mark	Thickness In. (mm)
0	.095-.097 (2.40-2.45)
1	.097-.098 (2.45-2.50)
2	.098-.100 (2.50-2.55)
3	.100-.102 (2.55-2.60)
4	.102-.104 (2.60-2.65)
5	.104-.106 (2.65-2.70)

COUNTERGEAR SHAFT SNAP RING IDENTIFICATION

Snap Ring Mark	Thickness In. (mm)
1	.083-.085 (2.10-2.15)
3	.087-.089 (2.20-2.25)

12) Inspect rear countergear bearing and replace it (if necessary). Using Inside Bearing Puller (09612-30012), remove countergear rear bearing from front case. Using Press Sleeve (09310-35010), install new bearing in front case.

13) Inspect idler gear and front bearing. If bearing needs replacement, use Press Sleeve to remove bearing from front case. Using Press Sleeve (09310-35010), install new bearing in front case until it touches snap ring.

14) If idler gear rear bearing needs replacement, remove snap ring. Press bearing off idler gear. Using Press Disc (09316-60010), press new bearing onto idler gear. Install selective fit snap ring which allows minimum axial play of bearing on countergear shaft. Maximum axial play allowed is .0059" (.15 mm). See IDLER GEAR SHAFT SNAP RING IDENTIFICATION table for available snap ring sizes.

IDLER GEAR SNAP RING IDENTIFICATION

Snap Ring Mark	Thickness In. (mm)
A	.059-.061 (1.50-1.55)
B	.063-.065 (1.60-1.65)

15) Check front drive gear and bearing. Press damaged bearing of front drive gear. Using Press Disc, install new bearing on front drive gear. If front drive gear rear bearing is bad, use Inside Bearing Puller (09612-30012) to remove bearing from rear case. Using Press Sleeve (09310-35010), press new bearing into rear case.

16) Check oil seal at speedometer driven gear for wear or damage to sealing lips. If seal is damaged, use seal puller to remove oil seal. Using Seal Driver (09201-60011), install seal in sleeve so that face of seal is .79" (20 mm) below top edge of bore.

17) Check oil seals in extension housing for wear or damage to sealing lips. If either seal is damaged, use slide hammer with inside jaws to remove 2 seals. Using Seal Driver (09310-35010), install new seal for oil pump screw. Flat surface of this seal must face upward. Second seal in extension housing is output shaft oil seal.

18) Output shaft and front drive gear oil seals are identical except for certain markings. *See Fig. 3.* Identify output shaft oil seal by grooves which lean to right (clockwise) and by single arrow pointing in counterclockwise direction on this seal. Using Seal Driver (09325-20010), install output shaft oil seal in extension housing.

Fig. 3: Identifying Output Shaft And Front Drive Gear Oil Seals

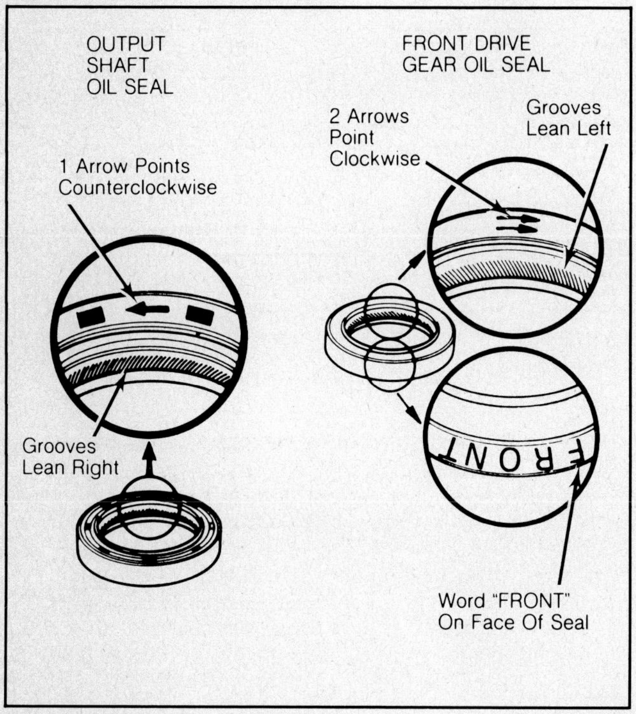

Check for different markings as shown.

19) Check oil seal at front drive gear for wear or damage to sealing lips. If seal is damaged, use Seal Driver (09325-20010) to drive seal and dust cover out of front bearing retainer. Be sure to place retainer on wooden blocks to avoid damage to retainer surface while driving seal out.

20) Identify front drive gear oil seal by grooves which lean to left (counterclockwise), by double arrows pointing in clockwise direction and word "FRONT" on face of front drive gear oil seal. *See Fig. 3.* Using seal driver, install new oil seal with face at depth of .28" (7 mm) from front end of retainer. Install new dust cover using seal driver.

21) Using ohmmeter, check transfer position indicator switch. When plunger is out, switch should be open and show no continuity (infinity). When plunger is in, switch should be closed and show continuity (0 ohms).

REASSEMBLY

1) Place front case on wooden blocks. Using soft mallet, drive output shaft into place in case. Install rear output shaft into front case. Install retaining snap ring on roller bearing. Install bearing retainer on front case and tighten bolts.

2) Place reduction gear case on wooden blocks. Using plastic hammer, install input gear and countergear in reduction gear case. Install input gear and countergear retaining snap rings. Install roller bearing on input shaft. Install high-low hub sleeve on input shaft. Install high-low (No. 2) shift fork on input shaft.

3) Place new gasket on front case. Install reduction gear case, with input gear and countergear, on front case. Install and tighten bolts. Using plastic hammer, install front drive gear in front case. Install front drive gear retaining snap ring. Place new gasket on front case. Lubricate oil seal lip with multipurpose grease. Install front drive gear bearing retainer.

4) Insert high-low shift fork shaft into No. 2 shift fork. Install interlock pin. Install 2WD-4WD shift fork shaft with 2 grooves facing outward. Align holes in shift shafts with holes in shift forks. Drive roll pins through forks into shafts. Coat 1 detent plug with sealer. Install either detent ball with spring and plug. Repeat procedure with opposite detent ball, spring and plug.

5) Install steel locking ball and No. 2 spacer on output shaft. Install needle roller bearings, transfer lower gear and clutch hub. Install No. 1 shift fork and hub sleeve on front drive shift fork shaft. Align pin hole in fork with hole in shaft. Using pin punch, drive roll pin through fork and shaft. Install 2 oil pipes, positioned so that cutout side faces upward.

6) Place rear case on wooden blocks. Using soft mallet, drive idler gear into rear case. Install idler gear retaining snap ring. Place new gasket on front case. Install rear case, together with idler gear, on front case. Install bearing, oil pump screw, locking bolt and speedometer drive gear. Using new gasket, install extension housing on rear case.

7) On vehicles with 22R engine, install transfer case cover. On vehicles with 22R-EC engine, install shift lever retainer. Place rear companion flange on output shaft. Tighten retaining nut while holding flange with Spanner (09330-00020). After nut is tightened, it must be staked into flange. Install transfer indicator switch with washer. Install speedometer driven gear. Secure gear with lock plate.

TIGHTENING SPECIFICATIONS

Application	Ft. Lbs. (N.m)
Adapter Housing Bolts	29 (39)
Bearing Retainer Bolts	
Front Output Shaft	14 (19)
Rear Output Shaft	9 (13)
Crossmember-to-Frame	70 (95)
Crossmember-to-Transfer Case	9 (13)
Engine Rear Mounting	19 (25)
Output Shaft Nut	90 (123)
Propeller Shaft-to-Flange	54 (74)
Rear Case-to-Front Case	29 (39)
Rear Case-to-Extension Hsg.	29 (39)
Reduction Gear Housing Bolts	29 (39)
Stiffener Plate Bolt	27 (37)
Transmission-to-Engine Bolts	53 (72)

Latest Changes & Corrections

FOR 1985 & EARLIER IMPORT MODELS

NOTE: The Latest Changes and Corrections represent a collection of the last minute 1985 information which arrived to late to be included into the regular data pages. In addition, we have included information on prior year models which we have received since last year's edition.
This information is numbered to assist you in relating them to the regular data pages. To correctly use them, simply write the corresponding number within the arrow and the year of the edition on the appropriate page(s) of the text.

AUTOMATIC TRANSMISSIONS

1 *1985 PORSCHE 928S WITH 4-SPEED AUTOMATIC TRANSAXLE: PINION HEAD NUT DAMAGED DURING REPAIRS* - Before performing repairs that require removal of the pinion head nut, identify the transaxle production number. The production number is on the right side, above the oil pan.

On transaxles built between production No. 525772-640351, it is possible that the pinion shaft threads will be damaged. If damaged, the automatic section of the transaxle should be replaced.

2 *1984-85 TOYOTA CAMRY AND COROLLA MODELS USING A-130 AND A-140 TRANSMISSIONS: INPUT SHAFT OIL SEAL GROOVE DEFORMED* - When repairing these transmissions for stator shaft bushing wear, the groove for the oil seal on the input shaft should be checked for deformation. Replace input shaft if the oil seal groove width is less than .0925" (2.35 mm).

This inspection and measurement is important. If the input shaft support bushing wears to the point that the shaft is allowed to wobble in its bore on the stator shaft, the corners of the seal groove bend over, reducing the width of the groove.

View of Input Shaft Oil Seal Groove

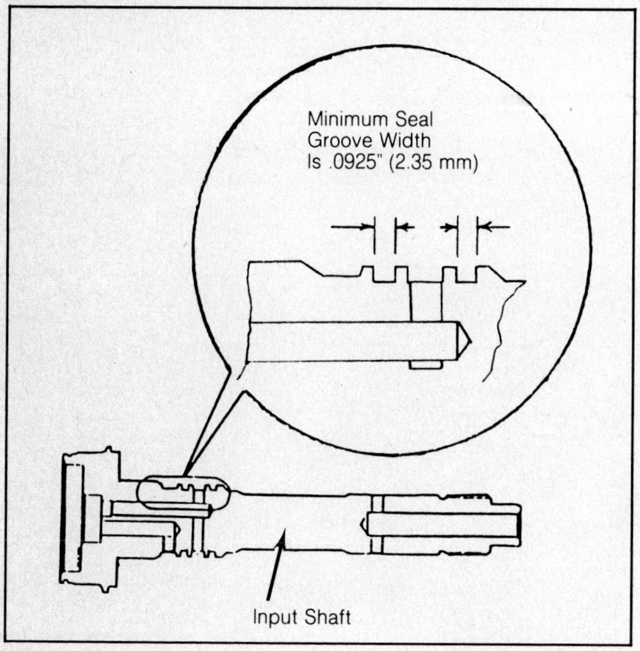

3 *1984-85 VOLVO MODELS WITH M46 OVERDRIVE: REVISED OVERDRIVE MAIN HOUSING* - The overdrive relief valve has been deleted from the overdrive main housing in M46 model overdrive. This new housing has been in production since December 1983.

View of M46 Overdrive Main Housing

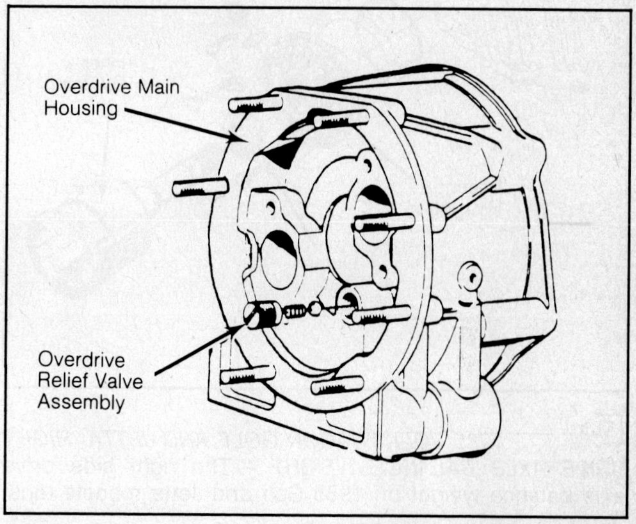

MANUAL TRANSMISSIONS

4 *1980-85 BMW MODELS WITH 4-SPEED OR 5-SPEED TRANSMISSIONS: HARD SHIFTING IN COLD WEATHER* - The synthetic gear oil (SAE 80W GL-4) that is used in 4-speed and 5-speed transmissions is very viscous. This may cause hard shifting at cold temperatures.

If hard shifting persists, drain transmission fluid. Refill transmission with a straight-weight engine oil (SAE 30W) or automatic transmission fluid (ATF) during the winter months. Drain and refill transmission with synthetic gear oil (SAE 80W GL-4) during the summer months. Shift effort will be reduced at temperatures less than 59°F (15°C) when using engine oil or ATF.

5 *1985-86 VOLKSWAGON VANAGON WITH 4-SPEED OR 5-SPEED TRANSAXLES: GEARSHIFT LINKAGE LUBRICATION* - 1985-86 Volkswagon Vanagon models equipped with 4-speed or 5-speed transaxles are now using Moly grease (Part No. G 000 602) instead of White grease (Part No. 126 000 05) to lubricate the gearshift linkage. Linkages already lubricated with White grease must be thoroughly cleaned before applying moly grease.

DRIVE AXLES

6 *1985 SAAB 900 TURBO MODELS WITH 5-SPEED MANUAL TRANSAXLE: REVISED DRIVE AXLE INNER CV JOINT* - The 1985 Saab 900 Turbo drive axle inner CV joint used on 5-speed manual transaxle has been revised to handle the increased engine output. If any repair is required, ensure the correct parts are used, as the previous inner CV joint and related parts will not interchange with the new design components.

Latest Changes & Corrections

FOR 1985 & EARLIER IMPORT MODELS (Cont.)

Revised Inner CV Joint & Related Components

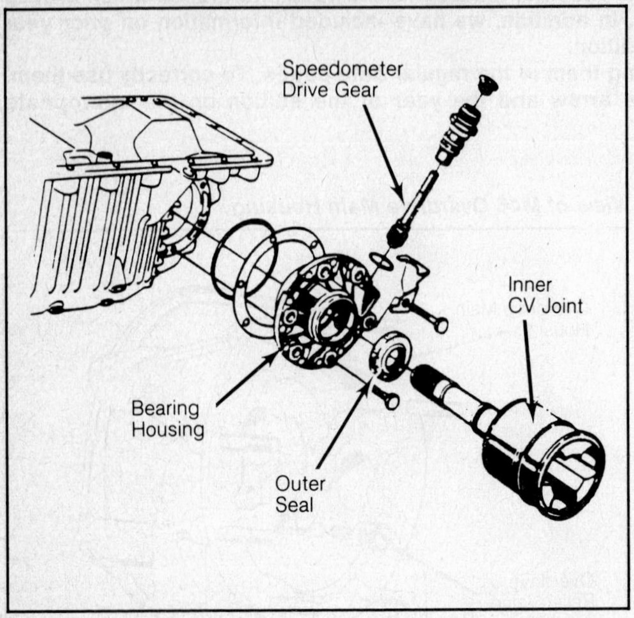

7 *1985 VOLKSWAGON GOLF AND JETTA: RIGHT DRIVE AXLE BALANCE WEIGHT* - The right side drive axle balance weight on 1985 Golf and Jetta models must be located precisely to function properly. To determine if weight is positioned properly, measure distance between edge of weight and the point where the conical section of the shaft begins. The edge of the weight should be .157"(4.0 mm) from the conical section of the shaft.

Installing Drive Axle Balance Weight

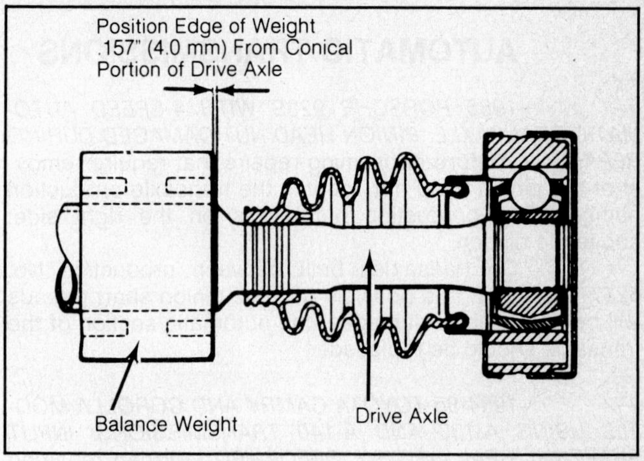

"WE LISTEN"

Do you have any comments or recommended changes to this book?
We will appreciate receiving them so that we may continue to publish the world's best Service & Repair manuals. **Mail this card today. We'd like to hear from you!**

□ Domestic Cars □ Imported Cars & Trucks □ Domestic Light Trucks & Vans □ Medium & Heavy Duty Trucks
□ Tune-Up □ Mechanical □ Transmission □ Emission □ Air Conditioning □ Electrical

Section No.________ Page No. ________ Vehicle Model & Year ________________

Comments: ________________________________

Name ________________ Company ________________

Address ________________ City ________ State ______ Zip ______

Phone ( ) ____________ Date ____________ THANK YOU

Please be sure to fill out this form completely.

"WE LISTEN"

Do you have any comments or recommended changes to this book?
We will appreciate receiving them so that we may continue to publish the world's best Service & Repair manuals. **Mail this card today. We'd like to hear from you!**

□ Domestic Cars □ Imported Cars & Trucks □ Domestic Light Trucks & Vans □ Medium & Heavy Duty Trucks
□ Tune-Up □ Mechanical □ Transmission □ Emission □ Air Conditioning □ Electrical

Section No.________ Page No. ________ Vehicle Model & Year ________________

Comments: ________________________________

Name ________________ Company ________________

Address ________________ City ________ State ______ Zip ______

Phone ( ) ____________ Date ____________ THANK YOU

Please be sure to fill out this form completely.

"WE LISTEN"

Do you have any comments or recommended changes to this book?
We will appreciate receiving them so that we may continue to publish the world's best Service & Repair manuals. **Mail this card today. We'd like to hear from you!**

□ Domestic Cars □ Imported Cars & Trucks □ Domestic Light Trucks & Vans □ Medium & Heavy Duty Trucks
□ Tune-Up □ Mechanical □ Transmission □ Emission □ Air Conditioning □ Electrical

Section No.________ Page No. ________ Vehicle Model & Year ________________

Comments: ________________________________

Name ________________ Company ________________

Address ________________ City ________ State ______ Zip ______

Phone ( ) ____________ Date ____________ THANK YOU

Please be sure to fill out this form completely.

Name
Address
City State Zip

BUSINESS REPLY MAIL

FIRST CLASS PERMIT NO. 3701 SAN DIEGO, CA

POSTAGE WILL BE PAID BY ADDRESSEE

MITCHELL INFORMATION SERVICES, INC.
P.O. Box 26260
San Diego, California 92126

NO POSTAGE NECESSARY IF MAILED IN THE UNITED STATES

Name
Address
City State Zip

BUSINESS REPLY MAIL

FIRST CLASS PERMIT NO. 3701 SAN DIEGO, CA

POSTAGE WILL BE PAID BY ADDRESSEE

MITCHELL INFORMATION SERVICES, INC.
P.O. Box 26260
San Diego, California 92126

NO POSTAGE NECESSARY IF MAILED IN THE UNITED STATES

Name
Address
City State Zip

BUSINESS REPLY MAIL

FIRST CLASS PERMIT NO. 3701 SAN DIEGO, CA

POSTAGE WILL BE PAID BY ADDRESSEE

MITCHELL INFORMATION SERVICES, INC.
P.O. Box 26260
San Diego, California 92126

NO POSTAGE NECESSARY IF MAILED IN THE UNITED STATES

DOMESTIC CAR: THROUGH 1986 (Cont)

Mechanical Manual

Get 10 years of complete mechanical information for 35 domestic car models. You'll receive three volumes, over 5,800 pages, of up-to-date repair data. Two volumes cover engines, cooling systems, clutches, drive axles and transmission servicing. The other volume covers brakes, steering, front and rear suspension, and wheel alignment.

Transmission Manual

Covers all domestic automatics and manual transmission and transaxles, as well as overdrives produced from 1977-86. You'll receive trouble-shooting and diagnosis information, testing procedures, step-by-step disassembly, overhaul and reassembly procedures, R&R instructions, torque specifications, information on throttle-linkage adjustment and valve-body illustrations.

Air Conditioning and Heating Service Manual

This two-volume set covers all domestic factory-installed systems since 1977. You'll get in-depth trouble-shooting and diagnosis information; servicing, repair and overhaul data; hundreds of specification tables; and a section on labor estimates.

Emission Control Service Manual

Get the most current data available on emission control servicing. You'll find descriptions and information on operation, trouble-shooting, maintenance, repair and overhaul for all domestic car emission systems produced since 1977. Plus, you'll get a complete fuel-system section, computerized engine control articles, engine I.D., emission-system wiring and vacuum diagrams.

DOMESTIC LIGHT TRUCK: THROUGH 1986

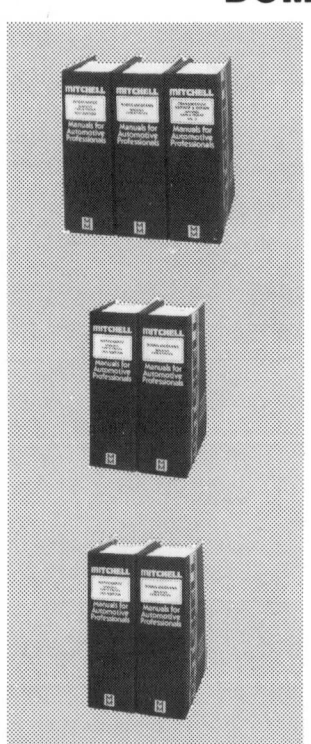

Tune-Up and Electrical Manual

Now you can service all domestic light trucks and vans, up to one ton, manufactured during the last 10 years. You'll receive complete information on service and repair, trouble-shooting, and adjustment. Two volumes cover tune-ups, computerized engine controls, carburetion, fuel systems (including diesel-fuel injection), distributors, ignition systems and emission control. The third volume covers alternators, starters, regulators, switches, accessories and equipment, fuses and circuit breakers, plus a complete section on wiring and printed circuit diagrams.

Mechanical Manual

Get 10 years of accurate mechanical data on domestic light trucks and vans. One volume covers engines (both gas and diesel), cooling systems, clutches, and drive axles (including 4-wheel drives). The other volume includes brakes, suspension, steering, plus a complete alignment section. Each volume has complete information on repair and overhaul procedures, R&R, trouble-shooting, and adjustment.

Transmission Manual

Now you can have 10 years of complete servicing and repair data for all light truck and van transmissions and transfer cases. You'll receive information on testing, trouble-shooting, in-vehicle repair, R&R and overhaul for 3, 4 and 5-speed manuals, automatics, overdrives, and 4-wheel drive transfer cases.

To order, or for more information, contact your local Mitchell representative or call (800) 854-7030, or (800) 421-0159 in California.